SCOTT®

2024
STANDARD POSTAGE
STAMP CATALOGUE

ONE HUNDRED AND EIGHTIETH EDITION IN SIX VOLUMES

Volume 5A
N-PHIL

EDITOR-IN-CHIEF	Jay Bigalke
EDITOR-AT-LARGE	Donna Houseman
CONTRIBUTING EDITOR	Charles Snee
EDITOR EMERITUS	James E. Kloetzel
SENIOR EDITOR /NEW ISSUES AND VALUING	Martin J. Frankevicz
ADMINISTRATIVE ASSISTANT/CATALOGUE LAYOUT	Eric Wiessinger
SENIOR GRAPHIC DESIGNER	Cinda McAlexander
SALES DIRECTOR	David Pistello
SALES DIRECTOR	Eric Roth
SALES DIRECTOR	Brenda Wyen
SALES REPRESENTATIVE	Julie Dahlstrom

Released August 2023
Includes New Stamp Listings through the June 2023 *Scott Stamp Monthly* Catalogue Update

Copyright© 2023 by
AMOS MEDIA

1660 Campbell Road, Suite A, Sidney, OH 45365
Publishers of *Linn's Stamp News, Scott Stamp Monthly, Coin World* and *Coin World Monthly.*

Table of contents

See the following volumes for other country listings:
Volume 1A: United States, United Nations, Abu Dhabi-Australia; Volume 1B: Austria-B
Volume 2A: C-Cur; Volume 2B: Cyp-F
Volume 3A: G; Volume 3B: H-I
Volume 4A: J-L; Volume 4B: M
Volume 5B: Pit-San
Volume 6A: San-Tete; Volume 6B: Thai-Z

Scott Catalogue Mission Statement

The Scott Catalogue Team exists to serve the recreational,
educational and commercial hobby needs of stamp collectors and dealers.
We strive to set the industry standard for philatelic information and products by developing and
providing goods that help collectors identify, value, organize and present their collections.
Quality customer service is, and will continue to be, our highest priority.
We aspire toward achieving total customer satisfaction.

What's new for 2024 Scott Standard Volume 5?

Another catalog season is upon us as we continue the journey of the 155-year history of the Scott catalogs. The 2024 volumes are the 180th edition of the Scott *Standard Postage Stamp Catalogue.*

Volume 5A includes listings for the countries of the world Namibia through Philippines.

Listings for Pitcairn Islands through Samoa can be found in Volume 5B.

Because Vol. 5B is a continuation of the first part of the Vol. 5 catalog, the introduction pages are not repeated in each volume.

This year's Vol. 5A cover features a Nevis 1981 50¢ Pinney's Beach stamp (Scott 129) from a set of 14 Island Landmarks stamps.

And the Vol. 5B cover features a 1965 St. Vincent 1¢ Boat Building Bequia stamp (Scott 226) from a set of 16 stamps showing highlights of the island.

For the 2024 Scott catalog season, we continue a review of Portuguese areas, which for Vol. 5 include Kionga, Nyassa, Ponta Delgada, Portuguese Africa, Portuguese Congo, Portuguese Guinea, Portuguese India and Quelimane. Numerous value changes were made for each location with a mix of increases and slight decreases noted.

The first set of 12 Ponta Delgada stamps of 1892-93 showing King Carlos (Scott 1-12) moved from $312.75 in unused condition to $394.25 and from $202.30 to $291.25 used.

With a review of these areas in play, it is no surprise that Portugal was also reviewed. It was an extensive review that netted approximately 2,000 value changes. Of those changes, only a handful were decreases. One notable change was for the 1926 Ceres definitive set (Scott 398-421). In unused condition, the set went from $129.50 to $199.85; it jumped from $19.80 to $28.75 in used condition.

For Portugal, condition is key to value. Stamps with original gum and no toning, staining or disturbances do quite well. A legible cancellation on a stamp in used condition is also helpful. Deviations from those conditions will result in significant reductions in actual market value, especially in the classic period.

Modern Azores and modern Madeira were reviewed with a handful of changes made for each, mostly increases for Europa theme issues. This was somewhat of a surprise to the Scott editors because the Europa market has been soft for the most part.

For those only interested in Portugal and colonies, there is a Scott Digital Catalogue Subscription option that includes only those 25 areas in one volume.

Panama was reviewed for the 2024 catalog season, and approximately 1,900 value changes were made. There appears to be additional interest in Latin American countries, and some of the increases reflect that. One example is the 1956 10-centesimo President Carlos A. Mendoza birth centennial stamp (Scott 405), which went from 35¢ in unused condition to 65¢, and from 25¢ to 40¢ used.

Paraguay was reviewed, and approximately 250 value changes, a mix of increases and decreases, were made. One increase was for the 2-real Vigilant Lion Supporting Liberty Cap stamp (Scott 2), which went from $120 to $150 in used condition. The value is in italics to indicate an item that trades infrequently in the marketplace.

Lastly, Nicaragua received a detailed review. More than 4,000 value changes were made; most were slight increases. For example, the set of four 1983 Visit of Pope John Paul II stamps (Scott 1225-1228) went from $5.60 in unused condition to $6.45, and the souvenir sheet (1229) advanced from $6.50 to $6.75 unused.

Other reviewed countries include Oman and Qatar.

Many other countries received less extensive reviews that are not noted in this letter. We encourage you to pay special attention to the Number Additions, Deletions and Changes listing in this volume. We also suggest reading the catalog introduction, which includes an abundance of useful information.

A digital subscription is also available for the Scott catalogs, and information about the subscription can be found online at www.amosadvantage.com.

Approximately 500 images of stamps not pictured in the Vol. 5 print edition were added to this year's Vol. 5 digital catalog.

Best wishes in your collecting pursuits!

Jay Bigalke, Scott catalog editor-in-chief

Acknowledgments

Our appreciation and gratitude go to the following individuals who have assisted us in preparing information included in this year's Scott catalogues. Some helpers prefer anonymity. These individuals have generously shared their stamp knowledge with others through the medium of the Scott catalogue.

Those who follow provided information that is in addition to the hundreds of dealer price lists and advertisements and scores of auction catalogues and realizations that were used in producing the catalogue values. It is from those noted here that we have been able to obtain information on items not normally seen in published lists and advertisements. Support from these people goes beyond data leading to catalogue values, for they also are key to editorial changes.

> A special acknowledgment to Liane and Sergio Sismondo of The Classic Collector for their assistance and knowledge sharing that have aided in the preparation of this year's Standard and Classic Specialized Catalogues.

Clifford J. Alexander
 (Carriers and Locals Society)
Roland Austin
Michael & Cecilia Ball (A To Z Stamps)
Jim Bardo (Bardo Stamps)
Brian M. Bleckwenn
 (The Philatelic Foundation)
James Booth
Les Bootman
Roger S. Brody
Tom Brougham
 (Canal Zone Study Group)
Paul and Josh Buchsbayew
 (Cherrystone Auctions, Inc.)
Timothy Bryan Burgess
Tina and John Carlson (JET Stamps)
Jay T. Carrigan
Carlson Chambliss
Bob Coale
Tony L. Crumbley
 (Carolina Coin and Stamp, Inc.)
Christopher Dahle
Charles Deaton
Bob and Rita Dumaine
 (Sam Houston Duck Co.)
Charles Epting (H.R. Harmer)
Mike Farrell
David Feldman International Auctioneers
Robert A. Fisher
Jeffrey M. Forster

Robert S. Freeman
Henry L. Gitner
 (Henry Gitner Philatelists, Inc.)
Stan Goldfarb
Marc E. Gonzales
Daniel E. Grau
Bruce Hecht (Bruce L. Hecht Co.)
Eric Jackson
Michael Jaffe (Michael Jaffe Stamps, Inc.)
William A. (Bill) Jones
Allan Katz (Ventura Stamp Co.)
Patricia A. Kaufmann
 (Civil War Philatelic Society)
Jon Kawaguchi
 (Ryukyu Philatelic Specialist Society)
Han Ki Kim
Ingert Kuzych
Ulf Lindahl (Ethiopian Philatelic Society)
Ignacio Llach (Filatelia Llach, S.L.)
William K. McDaniel
Pat McElroy
Brian Metz
Mark S. Miller (India Study Circle)
Gary Morris (Pacific Midwest Co.)
Peter Mosiondz Jr.
Bruce M. Moyer
 (Moyer Stamps & Collectables)
Scott Murphy
 (Professional Stamp Experts)
Dr. Tiong Tak Ngo

Nik and Lisa Oquist
Don Peterson
 (International Philippine Philatelic
 Society)
Todor Drumev Popov
Dr. Charles Posner
Peter W. W. Powell
Ed Reiser (Century Stamp Co.)
Ghassan D. Riachi
Robert G. Rufe
Theodosios D. Sampson Ph.D.
Dennis W. Schmidt
Joyce and Chuck Schmidt
Guy Shaw
 (Mexico-Elmhurst Philatelic Society
 International)
J. Randall Shoemaker
 (Philatelic Stamp Authentication and
 Grading, Inc.)
Sergio and Liane Sismondo
 (The Classic Collector)
Jay Smith
Telah Smith
Mark Stelmacovich
Scott R. Trepel
 (Robert A. Siegel Auction Galleries)
Dan Undersander
Steven Unkrich
Herbert R. Volin
Val Zabijaka (Zabijaka Auctions)

Addresses, telephone numbers, web sites, email addresses of general and specialized philatelic societies

Collectors can contact the following groups for information about the philately of the areas within the scope of these societies, or inquire about membership in these groups. Aside from the general societies, we limit this list to groups that specialize in particular fields of philately, particular areas covered by the Scott *Standard Postage Stamp Catalogue*, and topical groups. Many more specialized philatelic society exist than those listed below. These addresses are updated yearly, and they are, to the best of our knowledge, correct and current. Groups should inform the editors of address changes whenever they occur. The editors also want to hear from other such specialized groups not listed.

Unless otherwise noted all website addresses begin with http://

General Societies

American Philatelic Society, 100 Match Factory Place, Bellefonte, PA 16823-1367; (814) 933-3803; https://stamps.org; apsinfo@stamps.org

International Society of Worldwide Stamp Collectors, Joanne Murphy, M.D., P.O. Box 19006, Sacramento, CA 95819; www.iswsc.org; executivedirector@iswsc.org

Royal Philatelic Society of Canada, P.O. Box 69080, St. Clair Post Office, Toronto, ON M4T 3A1 Canada; (888) 285-4143; www.rpsc.org; info@rpsc.org

Royal Philatelic Society London, 15 Abchurch Lane, London EX4N 7BW, United Kingdom; +44 (0) 20 7486 1044; www.rpsl.org.uk; secretary@rpsl.org.uk

Libraries, Museums, and Research Groups

American Philatelic Research Library, 100 Match Factory Place, Bellefonte, PA 16823; (814) 933-3803; www.stamplibrary.org; library@stamps.org.

V. G. Greene Philatelic Research Foundation, P.O. Box 69100, St. Clair Post Office, Toronto, ON M4T 3A1, Canada; (416) 921-2073; info@greenefoundation.ca

Aero/Astro Philately

American Air Mail Society, Stephen Reinhard, P.O. Box 110, Mineola, NY 11501; www.americanairmailsociety.org; sreinhard1@optonline.net

Postal History

Auxiliary Markings Club, Jerry Johnson, 6621 W. Victoria Ave., Kennewick, WA 99336; www.postal-markings.org; membership-2010@postal-markings.org

Postage Due Mail Study Group, Bob Medland, Camway Cottage, Nanny Hurn's Lane, Cameley, Bristol BS39 5AJ, United Kingdom; 01761 45959; www.postageduemail.org.uk; secretary.pdmsg@gmail.com

Postal History Society, Yamil Kouri, 405 Waltham St. #347, Lexington, MA 02421; www.postalhistorysociety.org; yhkouri@massmed.org

Post Mark Collectors Club, Bob Milligan, 7014 Woodland Oaks Drive, Magnolia, TX 77354; (281) 259-2735; www.postmarks.org; bob.milligan0@gmail.com

U.S. Cancellation Club, Roger Curran, 18 Tressler Blvd., Lewisburg, PA 17837; rdcnrc@ptd.net

Revenues and Cinderellas

American Revenue Association, Lyman Hensley, 473 E. Elm St., Sycamore, IL 60178-1934; www.revenuer.org; ilrno2@netzero.net

Christmas Seal and Charity Stamp Society, John Denune Jr., 234 E. Broadway, Granville, OH 43023; (740) 814-6031; www.seal-society.org

National Duck Stamp Collectors Society, Anthony J. Monico, P.O. Box 43, Harleysville, PA 19438-0043; www.ndscs.org; ndscs@ndscs.org

State Revenue Society, Kent Gray, P.O. Box 67842, Albuquerque, NM 87193; www.staterevenue.org; srssecretary@comcast.net

Thematic Philately

Americana Unit, Dennis Dengel, 17 Peckham Road, Poughkeepsie, NY 12603-2018; www.americanaunit.org; ddengel@americanaunit.org

American Topical Association, Jennifer Miller, P.O. Box 2143, Greer, SC 29652-2143; (618) 985-5100; americantopical.org; ata@americantopical.org

Astronomy Study Unit, Leonard Zehr, 1411 Chateau Ave., Windsor, ON N8P 1M2, Canada; (416) 833-9317; www.astronomystudyunit.net; lenzehr@gmail.com

Bicycle Stamps Club, Corey Hjalseth, 1102 Broadway, Suite 200, Tacoma, WA 98402; (253) 318-6222; www.bicyclestampsclub.org; coreyh@evergreenhomeloans.com

Biology Unit, Chris Dahle, 1401 Linmar Drive NE, Cedar Rapids, IA 52402-3724; www.biophilately.org; chris-dahle@biophilately.org

Bird Stamp Society, Mr. S. A. H. (Tony) Statham, Ashlyns Lodge, Chesham Road, Berkhamsted, Herts HP4 2ST United Kingdom; www.bird-stamps.org/bss; tony.statham@sky.com

Captain Cook Society, Jerry Yucht, 8427 Leale Ave., Stockton, CA 95212, www.captaincooksociety.com; us@captaincooksociety.com

The CartoPhilatelic Society, Marybeth Sulkowski, 2885 Sanford Ave., SW, #32361, Grandville, MI 49418-1342; www.mapsonstamps.org; secretary@mapsonstamps.org

Casey Jones Railroad Unit, Jeff Lough, 2612 Redbud Land, Apt. C, Lawrence, KS 66046; www.uqp.de/cjr; jeffydplaugh@gmail.com

Cats on Stamps Study Unit, Robert D. Jarvis, 2731 Teton Lane, Fairfield, CA 94533; www.catstamps.info; catmews1@yahoo.com

Chemistry and Physics on Stamps Study Unit, Dr. Roland Hirsch, 13830 Metcalf Ave., Apt. 15218, Overland Park, KS 66223-8017; (301) 792-6296; www.cpossu.org; rfhirsch@cpossu.org

Chess on Stamps Study Unit, Barry Keith, 511 First St. N., Apt. 106; Charlottesville, VA 22902; www.chessonstamps.org; keithfam@embarqmail.com

Cricket Philatelic Society, A. Melville-Brown, 11 Weppons, Ravens Road, Shoram-by-Sea, West Sussex BN43 5AW, United Kingdom; www.cricketstamp.net; mel.cricket.100@googlemail.com

Earth's Physical Features Study Group, Fred Klein, 515 Magdalena Ave., Los Altos, CA 94024; http://epfsu.jeffhayward.com; epfsu@jeffhayward.com

Ebony Society of Philatelic Events and Reflections (ESPER), Don Neal, P.O. Box 5245, Somerset, NJ 08875-5245; www.esperstamps.org; esperdon@verizon.net

Europa Study Unit, Tonny E. Van Loij, 3002 S. Xanthia St.; Denver, CO 80231-4237; (303) 752-0189; www.europastudyunit.org; tvanloij@gmail.com

Fire Service in Philately, John Zaranek, 81 Hillpine Road, Cheektowaga, NY 14227-2259; (716) 668-3352; jczaranek@roadrunner.com

Gastronomy on Stamps Study Unit, David Wolfersburger, 5062 NW 35th Lane Road, Ocala, FL 34482; (314) 494-3795; www.gastronomystamps.org

Gay and Lesbian History on Stamps Club, Joe Petronie, P.O. Box 190842, Dallas, TX 75219-0842; www.glhsonline.org; glhsc@aol.com

Gems, Minerals and Jewelry Study Unit, Fred Haynes, 10 Country Club Drive, Rochester, NY 14618-3720; fredmhaynes55@gmail.com

Graphics Philately Association, Larry Rosenblum, 1030 E. El Camino Real, PMB 107, Sunnyvale, CA 94087-3759; www.graphics-stamps.org; larry@graphics-stamps.org

Journalists, Authors and Poets on Stamps, Christopher D. Cook, 7222 Hollywood Road, Berrien Springs, MI 49103; cdcook2@gmail.com

Lighthouse Stamp Society, www.lighthousestampsociety.org

Lions International Stamp Club, David McKirdy, s-Gravenwetering 248, 3062 SJ Rotterdam, Netherlands; 31(0) 10 212 0313; www.lisc.nl; davidmckirdy@aol.com

Masonic Study Unit, Gene Fricks, 25 Murray Way, Blackwood, NJ 08012-4400; genefricks@comcast.net

Medical Subjects Unit, Dr. Frederick C. Skvara, P.O. Box 6228, Bridgewater, NJ 08807; fcskvara@optonline.net

Napoleonic Age Philatelists, Ken Berry, 4117 NW 146th St., Oklahoma City, OK 73134-1746; (405) 748-8646; www.nap-stamps.org; krb4117@att.net

Old World Archaeological Study Unit, Caroline Scannell, 14 Dawn Drive, Smithtown, NY 11787-176; www.owasu.org; editor@owasu.org

Petroleum Philatelic Society International, Feitze Papa, 922 Meander Drive, Walnut Creek, CA 94598-4239; www.ppsi.org.uk; oildad@astound.net

Rotary on Stamps Fellowship, Gerald L. Fitzsimmons, 105 Calle Ricardo, Victoria, TX 77904; www.rotaryonstamps.org; glfitz@suddenlink.net

Scouts on Stamps Society International, Woodrow (Woody) Brooks, 498 Baldwin Road, Akron, OH 44312; (330) 612-1294; www.sossi.org; secretary@sossi.org

Ships on Stamps Unit, Erik Th. Matzinger, Voorste Havervelden 30, 4822 AL Breda, Netherlands; www.shipsonstamps.org; erikships@gmail.com

Space Topic Study Unit, David Blog, P.O. Box 174, Bergenfield, NJ 07621; www.space-unit.com; davidblognj@gmail.com

Stamps on Stamps Collectors Club, Michael Merritt, 73 Mountainside Road, Mendham, NJ 07945; www.stampsonstamps.org; michael@mischu.me

Windmill Study Unit, Walter J. Hallien, 607 N. Porter St., Watkins Glenn, NY 14891-1345; (607) 229-3541; www.windmillworld.com

Wine On Stamps Study Unit, David Wolfersburger, 5062 NW 35th Lane Road, Ocala, FL 34482; (314) 494-3795; www.wine-on-stamps.org;

United States

American Air Mail Society, Stephen

Reinhard, P.O. Box 110, Mineola, NY 11501; www.americanairmailsociety.org; sreinhard1@optonline.net

American First Day Cover Society, P.O. Box 246, Colonial Beach VA 22443-0246; (520) 321-0880; www.afdcs.org; afdcs@afdcs.org

Auxiliary Markings Club, Jerry Johnson, 6621 W. Victoria Ave., Kennewick, WA 99336; www.postal-markings.org; membership-2010@postal-markings.org

American Plate Number Single Society, Rick Burdsall, APNSS Secretary, P.O. BOX 1023, Palatine, IL 60078-1023; www.apnss.org; apnss.sec@gmail.com

American Revenue Association, Lyman Hensley, 473 E. Elm St., Sycamore, IL 60178-1934; www.revenuer.org; ilrno2@netzero.net

American Society for Philatelic Pages and Panels, Ron Walenciak, P.O. Box 1042, Washington Township, NJ 07676; www.asppp.org; ron.walenciak@asppp.org

Canal Zone Study Group, Mike Drabik, P.O. Box 281, Bolton, MA 01740, www.canalzonestudygroup.com; czsgsecretary@gmail.com

Carriers and Locals Society, John Bowman, 14409 Pentridge Drive, Corpus Christi, TX 78410; (361) 933-0757; www.pennypost.org; jbowman@stx.rr.com

Christmas Seal & Charity Stamp Society, John Denune Jr., 234 E. Broadway, Granville, OH 43023; (740) 814-6031; www.seal-society.org; john@christmasseals.net

Civil War Philatelic Society, Patricia A. Kaufmann, 10194 N. Old State Road, Lincoln, DE 19960-3644; (302) 422-2656; www.civilwarphilatelicsociety.org; trishkauf@comcast.net

Error, Freaks, and Oddities Collectors Club, Scott Shaulis, P.O. Box 549, Murrysville, PA 15668-0549; (724) 733-4134; www.efocc.org; scott@shaulisstamps.com

National Duck Stamp Collectors Society, Anthony J. Monico, P.O. Box 43, Harleysville, PA 19438-0043; www.ndscs.org; ndscs@ndscs.org

Plate Number Coil Collectors Club (PNC3), Gene Trinks, 16415 W. Desert Wren Court, Surprise, AZ 85374; (623) 322-4619; www.pnc3.org; gctrinks@cox.net

Post Mark Collectors Club, Bob Milligan, 7014 Woodland Oaks Drive, Magnolia, TX 77354; (281) 259-2735; www.postmarks.org; bob.milligan0@gmail.com

Souvenir Card Collectors Society, William V. Kriebel, www.souvenircards.org; kriebewv@drexel.edu

United Postal Stationery Society, Dave Kandziolka, 404 Sundown Drive, Knoxville, TN 37934; www.upss.org;

membership@upss.org

U.S. Cancellation Club, Roger Curran, 18 Tressler Blvd., Lewisburg, PA 17837; rdcnrc@ptd.net

U.S. Philatelic Classics Society, Rob Lund, 2913 Fulton St., Everett, WA 98201-3733; www.uspcs.org; membershipchairman@uspcs.org

US Possessions Philatelic Society, Daniel F. Ring, P.O. Box 113, Woodstock, IL 60098; http://uspps.tripod.com; danielfring@hotmail.com

United States Stamp Society, Rod Juell, P.O. Box 3508, Joliet, IL 60434-3508; www.usstamps.org; execsecretary@usstamps.org

Africa

Bechuanalands and Botswana Society, Otto Peetoom, Roos, East Yorkshire HU12 0LD, United Kingdom; 44(0)1964 670239; www.bechuanalandphilately.com; info@bechuanalandphilately.com

Egypt Study Circle, Mike Murphy, 11 Waterbank Road, Bellingham, London SE6 3DJ United Kingdom; (44) 0203 6737051; www.egyptstudycircle.org.uk; secretary@egyptstudycircle.org.uk

Ethiopian Philatelic Society, Ulf Lindahl, 21 Westview Place, Riverside, CT 06878; (203) 722-0769; https://ethiopianphilatelicsociety.weebly.com; ulindahl@optonline.net

Liberian Philatelic Society, P.O. Box 1570, Parker, CO 80134; www.liberiastamps.org; liberiastamps@comcast.net

Orange Free State Study Circle, J. R. Stroud, RDPSA, 24 Hooper Close, Burnham-on-sea, Somerset TA8 1JQ United Kingdom; 44 1278 782235; www.orangefreestatephilately.org.uk; richard@richardstroud.plus.com

Philatelic Society for Greater Southern Africa, David McNamee, 15 Woodland Drive, Alamo, CA 94507; www.psgsa.org; alan.hanks@sympatico.ca

Rhodesian Study Circle, William R. Wallace, P.O. Box 16381, San Francisco, CA 94116; (415) 564-6069; www.rhodesianstudycircle.org.uk; bwall8rscr@earthlink.net

Society for Moroccan and Tunisian Philately, S.P.L.M., 206, Bld Pereire, 75017 Paris, France; http://splm-philatelie.org; splm206@aol.com

South Sudan Philatelic Society, William Barclay, 1370 Spring Hill Road, South Londonderry, VT 05155; barclayphilatelics@gmail.com

Sudan Study Group, Andy Neal, Bank House, Coedway, Shrewsbury SY5 9AR United Kingdom; www.sudanstamps.org; andywneal@gmail.com

Transvaal Study Circle, c/o 9 Meadow Road, Gravesend, Kent DA11 7LR United Kingdom; www.transvaalstamps.org.uk; transvaalstudycircle@aol.co.uk

West Africa Study Circle, Martin Bratzel, 1233 Virginia Ave., Windsor, ON N8S 2Z1 Canada; www.wasc.org.uk; marty_bratzel@yahoo.ca

Asia

Aden & Somaliland Study Group, Malcom Lacey, 108 Dalestorth Road, Sutton-in-Ashfield, Nottinghamshire NG17 3AA, United Kingdom; www.stampdomain.com/aden; neil53williams@yahoo.co.uk

Burma (Myanmar) Philatelic Study Circle, Michael Whittaker, 1, Ecton Leys, Hillside, Rugby, Warwickshire CV22 5SL United Kingdom; https://burmamyanmarphilately.wordpress.com/burma-myanmar-philatelic-study-circle; manningham8@mypostoffice.co.uk

Ceylon Study Circle, Rodney W. P. Frost, 42 Lonsdale Road, Cannington, Bridgwater, Somerset TA5 2JS United Kingdom; 01278 652592; www.ceylonsc.org; rodney.frost@tiscali.co.uk

China Stamp Society, H. James Maxwell, 1050 W. Blue Ridge Blvd., Kansas City, MO 64145-1216; www.chinastampsociety.org; president@chinastampsociety.org

Hong Kong Philatelic Society, John Tang, G.P.O. Box 446, Hong Kong; www.hkpsociety.com; hkpsociety@outlook.com

Hong Kong Study Circle, Robert Newton, www.hongkongstudycircle.com/index.html; newtons100@gmail.com

India Study Circle, John Warren, P.O. Box 7326, Washington, DC 20044; (202) 488-7443; https://indiastudycircle.org; jw-kbw@earthlink.net

International Philippine Philatelic Society, James R. Larot, Jr., 4990 Bayleaf Court, Martinez, CA 94553; (925) 260-5425; www.theipps.info; jlarot@ccwater.com

International Society for Japanese Philately, P.O. Box 1283, Haddonfield NJ 08033; www.isjp.org; secretary@isjp.org

Iran Philatelic Study Circle, Nigel Gooch, Marchwood, 56, Wickham Ave., Bexhill-on-Sea, East Sussex TN39 3ER United Kingdom; www.iranphilately.org; nigelmgooch@gmail.com

Korea Stamp Society, Peter Corson, 1109 Gunnison Place, Raleigh, NC 27609; (919) 787-7611; koreastampsociety.org; pbcorson@aol.com

Nepal & Tibet Philatelic Study Circle, Colin Hepper, 12 Charnwood Close, Peterborough, Cambs PE2 9BZ United Kingdom; http://fuchs-online.com/ntpsc; ntpsc@fuchs-online.com

Pakistan Philatelic Study Circle, Jeff Siddiqui, P.O. Box 7002, Lynnwood, WA 98046; jeffsiddiqui@msn.com

Society of Indo-China Philatelists, Ron Bentley, 2600 N. 24th St., Arlington, VA 22207; (703) 524-1652; www.sicp-online.org; ron.bentley@verizon.net

Society of Israel Philatelists, Inc.,

Sarah Berezenko, 100 Match Factory Place, Bellefonte, PA 16823-1367; (814) 933-3803 ext. 212; www.israelstamps.com; israelstamps@gmail.com

Australasia and Oceania

Australian States Study Circle of the Royal Sydney Philatelic Club, Ben Palmer, G.P.O. 1751, Sydney, NSW 2001 Australia; http://club.philas.org.au/states

Fellowship of Samoa Specialists, Trevor Shimell, 18 Aspen Drive, Newton Abbot, Devon TQ12 4TN United Kingdom; www.samoaexpress.org; trevor.shimell@gmail.com

Malaya Study Group, Michael Waugh, 151 Roker Lane, Pudsey, Leeds LS28 9ND United Kingdom; http://malayastudygroup.com; mawpud43@gmail.com

New Zealand Society of Great Britain, Michael Wilkinson, 121 London Road, Sevenoaks, Kent TN13 1BH United Kingdom; 01732 456997; www.nzsgb.org.uk; mwilkin799@aol.com

Pacific Islands Study Circle, John Ray, 24 Woodvale Ave., London SE25 4AE United Kingdom; www.pisc.org.uk; secretary@pisc.org.uk

Papuan Philatelic Society, Steven Zirinsky, P.O. Box 49, Ansonia Station, New York, NY 10023; (718) 706-0616; www.papuanphilatelicsociety.com; szirinsky@cs.com

Pitcairn Islands Study Group, Dr. Everett L. Parker, 207 Corinth Road, Hudson, ME 04449-3057; (207) 573-1686; www.pisg.net; eparker@hughes.net

Ryukyu Philatelic Specialist Society, Laura Edmonds, P.O. Box 240177, Charlotte, NC 28224-0177; (336) 509-3739; www.ryukyustamps.org; secretary@ryukyustamps.org

Society of Australasian Specialists / Oceania, Steve Zirinsky, P.O. Box 230049, New York, NY 10023-0049; www.sasoceania.org; president@sosoceania.org

Sarawak Specialists' Society, Stephen Schumann, 2417 Caballo Drive, Hayward, CA 94545; (510) 785-4794; www.britborneostamps.org.uk; vpnam@s-s-s.org.uk

Western Australia Study Group, Brian Pope, P.O. Box 423, Claremont, WA 6910 Australia; (61) 419 843 943; www.wastudygroup.com; wastudygroup@hotmail.com

Europe

American Helvetia Philatelic Society, Richard T. Hall, P.O. Box 15053, Asheville, NC 28813-0053; www.swiss-stamps.org; secretary2@swiss-stamps.org

American Society for Netherlands Philately, Hans Kremer, 50 Rockport Court, Danville, CA 94526; (925) 820-5841; www.asnp1975.com; hkremer@usa.net

Andorran Philatelic Study Circle, David Hope, 17 Hawthorn Drive, Stalybridge, Cheshire SK15 1UE United Kingdom; www.andorranpsc.org.uk; andorranpsc@btinternet.com

Austria Philatelic Society, Ralph Schneider, P.O. Box 978, Iowa Park, TX 76376; (940) 213-5004; www.austriaphilatelicsociety.com; rschneiderstamps@gmail.com

Channel Islands Specialists Society, Richard Flemming, Burbage, 64 Falconers Green, Hinckley, Leicestershire, LE102SX, United Kingdom; www.ciss.uk; secretary@ciss.uk

Cyprus Study Circle, Rob Wheeler, 47 Drayton Ave., London W13 OLE United Kingdom; www.cyprusstudycircle.org; robwheeler47@aol.com

Danish West Indies Study Unit of Scandinavian Collectors Club, Arnold Sorensen, 7666 Edgedale Drive, Newburgh, IN 47630; (812) 480-6532; www.scc-online.org; valbydwi@hotmail.com

Eire Philatelic Association, John B. Sharkey, 1559 Grouse Lane, Mountainside, NJ 07092-1340; www.eirephilatelicassoc.org; jsharkeyepa@me.com

Faroe Islands Study Circle, Norman Hudson, 40 Queen's Road, Vicar's Cross, Chester CH3 5HB United Kingdom; www.faroeislandssc.org; jntropics@hotmail.com

France & Colonies Philatelic Society, Edward Grabowski, 111 Prospect St., 4C, Westfield, NJ 07090; (908) 233-9318; www.franceandcolsps.org; edjjg@alum.mit.edu

Germany Philatelic Society, P.O. Box 6547, Chesterfield, MO 63006-6547; www.germanyphilatelicusa.org; info@germanyphilatelicsocietyusa.org

Gibraltar Study Circle, Susan Dare, 22, Byways Park, Strode Road, Clevedon, North Somerset BS21 6UR United Kingdom; www.gibraltarstudycircle.wordpress.com; smldare@yahoo.co.uk

International Society for Portuguese Philately, Clyde Homen, 1491 Bonnie View Road, Hollister, CA 95023-5117; www.portugalstamps.com; ispp1962@sbcglobal.net

Italy and Colonies Study Circle, Richard Harlow, 7 Manor Road, Teddington, Middlesex TW118BE United Kingdom; 44 208 977 8737; www.icsc-uk.com; richardharlow@outlook.com

Liechtenstudy USA, Paul Tremaine, 410 SW Ninth St., Dundee, OR 97115-9731; (503) 538-4500; www.liechtenstudy.org; tremaine@liechtenstudy.org

Lithuania Philatelic Society, Audrius Brazdeikis, 9915 Murray Landing, Missouri City, TX 77459; (281) 450-6224; www.lithuanianphilately.com/lps; audrius@lithuanianphilately.com

Luxembourg Collectors Club, Gary B. Little, 7319 Beau Road, Sechelt, BC V0N 3A8 Canada; (604) 885-7241; http://lcc.luxcentral.com; gary@luxcentral.com

Plebiscite-Memel-Saar Study Group of the German Philatelic Society, Clayton Wallace, 100 Lark Court, Alamo, CA 94507; claytonwallace@comcast.net

Polonus Polish Philatelic Society, Daniel Lubelski, P.O. Box 2212, Benicia, CA 94510; (419) 410-9115; www.polonus.org; info@polonus.org

Rossica Society of Russian Philately, Alexander Kolchinsky, 1506 Country Lake Drive, Champaign, IL 61821-6428; www.rossica.org; alexander.kolchinsky@rossica.org

Scandinavian Collectors Club, Alan Warren, Scandinavian Collectors Club, P.O. Box 39, Exton PA 19341-0039; (612) 810-8640; www.scc-online.org; alanwar@att.net

Society for Czechoslovak Philately, Tom Cossaboom, P.O. Box 4124, Prescott, AZ 86302; (928) 771-9097; www.csphilately.org; klfck1@aol.com

Society for Hungarian Philately, Alan Bauer, P.O. Box 4028, Vineyard Haven, MA 02568; (617) 645-4045; www.hungarianphilately.org; alan@hungarianstamps.com

Spanish Study Circle, Edith Knight, www.spaincircle.wixsite.com/spainstudycircle; spaincircle@gmail.com

Ukrainian Philatelic & Numismatic Society, Martin B. Tatuch, 5117 8th Road N., Arlington, VA 22205-1201; www.upns.org; treasurer@upns.org

Vatican Philatelic Society, Dennis Brady, 4897 Ledyard Drive, Manlius NY 13104-1514; www.vaticanphilately.org; dbrady7534@gmail.com

Yugoslavia Study Group, Michael Chant, 1514 N. Third Ave., Wausau, WI 54401; 208-748-9919; www.yugosg.org; membership@yugosg.org

Interregional Societies

American Society of Polar Philatelists, Alan Warren, P.O. Box 39, Exton, PA 19341-0039; (610) 321-0740; www.polarphilatelists.org; alanwar@att.net

First Issues Collector's Club, Kurt Streepy, 3128 E. Mattatha Drive, Bloomington, IN 47401; www.firstissues.org; secretary@firstissues.org

Former French Colonies Specialist Society, Col.fra, BP 628, 75367 Paris, France; www.colfra.org; postmaster@colfra.org

France & Colonies Philatelic Society, Edward Grabowski, 111 Prospect St., 4C, Westfield, NJ 07090; (908) 233-9318, www.franceandcolsps.org; edjjg@alum.mit.edu

Joint Stamp Issues Society, Richard Zimmermann, 29A, Rue Des Eviats, 67220 Lalaye, France; www.philarz.net; richard.zimmermann@club-internet.fr

The King George VI Collectors Society, Brian Livingstone, 21 York Mansions, Prince of Wales Drive, London SW11 4DL United Kingdom; www.kg6.info; livingstone484@btinternet.com

International Society of Reply Coupon Collectors, Peter Robin, P.O. Box 353, Bala Cynwyd, PA 19004; peterrobin@verizon.net

Italy and Colonies Study Circle, Richard Harlow, 7 Duncombe House, 8 Manor Road, Teddington, Middlesex TW118BE United Kingdom; 44 208 977 8737; www.icsc-uk.com; richardharlow@outlook.com

St. Helena, Ascension & Tristan Da Cunha Philatelic Society, Dr. Everett L. Parker, 207 Corinth Road, Hudson, ME 04449-3057; (207) 573-1686; www.shatps.org; eparker@hughes.net

United Nations Philatelists, Blanton Clement, Jr., P.O. Box 146, Morrisville, PA 19067-0146; www.unpi.org; bclemjunior@gmail.com

Latin America

Asociación Filatélica de Panamá, Edward D. Vianna B. ASOFILPA, 0819-03400, El Dorado, Panama; http://asociacionfilatelicadepanama.blogspot.com; asofilpa@gmail.com

Asociacion Mexicana de Filatelia (AMEXFIL), Alejandro Grossmann, Jose Maria Rico, 129, Col. Del Valle, 3100 Mexico City, DF Mexico; www.amexfil.mx; amexfil@gmail.com

Associated Collectors of El Salvador, Pierre Cahen, Vipsal 1342, P.O. Box 02-5364, Miami FL 33102; www.elsalvadorphilately.org; sfes-aces@elsalvadorphilately.org

Association Filatelic de Costa Rica, Giana Wayman (McCarty), #SJO 4935, P.O. Box 025723, Miami, FL 33102-5723; 011-506-2-228-1947; scotland@racsa.co.cr

Brazil Philatelic Association, William V. Kriebel, www.brazilphilatelic.org, info@brazilphilatelic.org

Canal Zone Study Group, Mike Drabik, P.O. Box 281, Bolton, MA 01740; www.canalzonestudygroup.com; czsgsecretary@gmail.com

Colombia-Panama Philatelic Study Group, Allan Harris, 26997 Hemmingway Ct, Hayward CA 94542-2349; www.copaphil.org; copaphilusa@aol.com

Falkland Islands Philatelic Study Groups, Morva White, 42 Colton Road, Shrivenham, Swindon SN6 8AZ United Kingdom; 44(0) 1793 783245; www.fipsg.org.uk; morawhite@supanet.com

Federacion Filatelica de la Republica de Honduras, Mauricio Mejia, Apartado Postal 1465, Tegucigalpa, D.C. Honduras; 504 3399-7227; www.facebook.com/filateliadehonduras; ffrh@hotmail.com

International Cuban Philatelic Society (ICPS), Ernesto Cuesta, P.O. Box 34434, Bethesda, MD 20827; (301) 564-3099; www.cubafil.org; ecuesta@philat.com

International Society of Guatemala Collectors, Jaime Marckwordt, 449 St. Francis Blvd., Daly City, CA 94015-2136; (415) 997-0295; www.guatemalastamps.com; president@guatamalastamps.com

Mexico-Elmhurst Philatelic Society International, Eric Stovner, P.O. Box 10097, Santa Ana, CA 92711-0097; www.mepsi; treasurer@mepsi.org

Nicaragua Study Group, Erick Rodriguez, 11817 S. W. 11th St., Miami, FL 33184-2501; nsgsec@yahoo.com

North America (excluding United States)

British Caribbean Philatelic Study Group, Bob Stewart, 7 West Dune Lane, Long Beach Township, NJ 08008; (941) 379-4108; www.bcpsg.com; bcpsg@comcast.net

British North America Philatelic Society, Andy Ellwood, 10 Doris Ave., Gloucester, ON K1T 3W8 Canada; www.bnaps.org; secretary@bnaps.org

British West Indies Study Circle, Steve Jarvis, 5 Redbridge Drive, Andover, Hants SP10 2LF United Kingdom; 01264 358065; www.bwisc.org; info@bwisc.org

Bermuda Collectors Society, John Pare, 405 Perimeter St., Mount Horeb, WI 53572; (608) 852-7358; www.bermudacollectorssociety.com; pare16@mhtc.net

Haiti Philatelic Society, Ubaldo Del Toro, 5709 Marble Archway, Alexandria, VA 22315; www.haitiphilately.org; u007ubi@aol.com

Hawaiian Philatelic Society, Gannon Sugimura, P.O. Box 10115, Honolulu, HI 96816-0115; www.hpshawaii.com; hiphilsoc@gmail.com

Stamp Dealer Associations

American Stamp Dealers Association, Inc., P.O. Box 513, Centre Hall PA 16828; (800) 369-8207; www.americanstampdealer.com; asda@americanstampdealer.com

National Stamp Dealers Association, Sheldon Ruckens, President, 3643 Private Road 18, Pinckneyville, IL 62274-3426; (618) 357-5497; www.nsdainc.org; nsda@nsdainc.org

Youth Philately

Young Stamp Collectors of America, 100 Match Factory Place, Bellefonte, PA 16823; (814) 933-3803; https://stamps.org/learn/youth-in-philately; ysca@stamps.org

Expertizing services

The following organizations will, for a fee, provide expert opinions about stamps submitted to them. Collectors should contact these organizations to find out about their fees and requirements before submitting philatelic material to them. The listing of these groups here is not intended as an endorsement by Amos Media Co.

General Expertizing Services

American Philatelic Expertizing Service (a service of the American Philatelic Society)
100 Match Factory Place
Bellefonte PA 16823-1367
(814) 237-3803
www.stamps.org/stamp-authentication
apex@stamps.org
Areas of Expertise: Worldwide

BPA Expertising, Ltd.
P.O. Box 1141
Guildford, Surrey, GU5 0WR
United Kingdom
www.bpaexpertising.com
sec@bpaexpertising.org
Areas of Expertise: British Commonwealth, Great Britain, Classics of Europe, South America and the Far East

Philatelic Foundation
353 Lexington Avenue, Suite 804
New York NY 10016
(212) 221-6555
www.philatelicfoundation.org
philatelicfoundation@verizon.net
Areas of Expertise: U.S. & Worldwide

Philatelic Stamp Authentication and Grading, Inc.
P.O. Box 41-0880
Melbourne FL 32941-0880
(305) 345-9864
www.psaginc.com
info@psaginc.com
Areas of Expertise: U.S., Canal Zone, Hawaii, Philippines, Canada & Provinces

Professional Stamp Experts
P.O. Box 539309
Henderson NV 89053-9309
(702) 776-6522
www.gradingmatters.com
www.psestamp.com
info@gradingmatters.com
Areas of Expertise: Stamps and Covers of U.S., U.S. Possessions, British Commonwealth

Royal Philatelic Society London Expert Committee
15 Abchurch Lane
London, EX4N 7BW
United Kingdom
www.rpsl.limited/experts.aspx
experts@rpsl.limited
Areas of Expertise: Worldwide

Expertizing Services Covering Specific Fields or Countries

China Stamp Society Expertizing Service
1050 W. Blue Ridge Blvd.
Kansas City MO 64145
(816) 942-6300
hjmesq@aol.com
Areas of Expertise: China

Civil War Philatelic Society Authentication Service
C/O Stefan T. Jaronski
P.O. Box 232
Sidney, MT 59270-0232
www.civilwarphilatelicsociety.org/authentication/
authentication@civilwarphilatelicsociety.org
Areas of Expertise: Confederate stamps and postal history

Errors, Freaks and Oddities Collectors Club Expertizing Service
138 East Lakemont Drive
Kingsland GA 31548
(912) 729-1573
Areas of Expertise: U.S. errors, freaks and oddities

Hawaiian Philatelic Society Expertizing Service
P.O. Box 10115
Honolulu HI 96816-0115
www.stampshows.com/hps.html
hiphilsoc@gmail.com
Areas of Expertise: Hawaii

Hong Kong Stamp Society Expertizing Service
P.O. Box 206
Glenside PA 19038
Areas of Expertise: Hong Kong

International Association of Philatelic Experts United States Associate members:
Paul Buchsbayew
300 Frank W. Burr Blvd. - Second Floor
Box 35
Teaneck, NJ 07666.
(212) 977-7734
Areas of Expertise: Russia, Soviet Union

William T. Crowe
P.O. Box 2090
Danbury CT 06813-2090
wtcrowe@aol.com
Areas of Expertise: United States

International Society for Japanese Philately Expertizing Committee
132 North Pine Terrace
Staten Island NY 10312-4052
(718) 227-5229
Areas of Expertise: Japan and related areas, except WWII Japanese Occupation issues

International Society for Portuguese Philately Expertizing Service
P.O. Box 43146
Philadelphia PA 19129-3146
(215) 843-2106
s.s.washburne@worldnet.att.net
Areas of Expertise: Portugal and Colonies

Mexico-Elmhurst Philatelic Society International Expert Committee
Expert Committee Administrator
Marc E. Gonzales
P.O. Box 29040
Denver CO 80229-0040
www.mepsi.org/expert_committeee.htm
expertizations@mepsi.org
Areas of Expertise: Mexico

Ukrainian Philatelic & Numismatic Society Expertizing Service
30552 Dell Lane
Warren MI 48092-1862
Areas of Expertise: Ukraine, Western Ukraine

V. G. Greene Philatelic Research Foundation
P.O. Box 69100
St. Clair Post Office
Toronto, ON M4T 3A1
Canada
(416) 921-2073
www.greenefoundation.ca
info@greenefoundation.ca
Areas of Expertise: British North America

Vario Stocksheets

Vario stock sheets offer unparalleled quality and versatility.

They're a convenient and easy way to store and organize stamps. Vario stock sheets are carefully manufactured to be free of harmful plasticized PVC, and softeners. Vario stock will fit all standard 3-ring binders and are available in a variety of sizes.

NOTE: Black sheets have pockets on both sides. Clear sheets have pockets on one side only. "S" in item number denotes black page. "C" in item number denotes clear page.

Sold in packages of 5.

Item#			Retail	AA
V1S	1 Pocket 258mm	Black (Double-Sided)	$6.75	$5.25
V1C	1 Pocket 258mm	Clear (Single-Sided)	$6.75	$5.25
V2S	2 Pockets 128mm	Black (Double-Sided)	$6.75	$5.25
V2C	2 Pockets 128mm	Clear (Single-Sided)	$6.75	$5.25
V3S	3 Pockets 84mm	Black (Double-Sided)	$6.75	$5.25
V3C	3 Pockets 84mm	Clear (Single-Sided)	$6.75	$5.25
V4S	4 Pockets 63mm	Black (Double-Sided)	$6.75	$5.25
V4C	4 Pockets 63mm	Clear (Single-Sided)	$6.75	$5.25
V5S	5 Pockets 48mm	Black (Double-Sided)	$6.75	$5.25
V5C	5 Pockets 48mm	Clear (Single-Sided)	$6.75	$5.25
V6S	6 Pockets 39mm	Black (Double-Sided)	$6.75	$5.25
V7S	7 Pockets 33mm	Black (Double-Sided)	$6.75	$5.25
V8S	8 Pockets 29mm	Black (Double-Sided)	$6.75	$5.25
VIB	Interleaving Sheets Black		$4.95	$3.75

LIGHTHOUSE VARIO BINDER & SLIPCASE

The Lighthouse Vario Red Binder & Slipcase combo is our most popular Stamp Binder for collectors! This high quality, durable 3-ring Vario Binder features 2 sheet-lifters as well as a matching leatherette cover slipcase. Available in multiple colors with matching slipcase. Customize your Lighthouse Vario album binder with stock pages, cover pages, mint sheet pages and more!

Binder Dimensions: 12 1/2"(H) x 10 (W) x 2 1/4" (D)
Hinge Type: 3-Ring. Capacity: 50 Pages

Item		Retail	AA
LHVBNDRD	Red Slipcase	$39.95	$33.96
LHVBNDBR	Brown Slipcase	$39.95	$33.96
LHVBNDBL	Blue Slipcase	$39.95	$33.96
LHVBNDBK	Black Slipcase	$39.95	$33.96

Prices and availability are subject to change

AmosAdvantage.com | 1-800-572-6885

Information on catalogue values, grade and condition

Catalogue value

The Scott Catalogue value is a retail value; that is, an amount you could expect to pay for a stamp in the grade of Very Fine with no faults. Any exceptions to the grade valued will be noted in the text. The general introduction on the following pages and the individual section introductions further explain the type of material that is valued. The value listed for any given stamp is a reference that reflects recent actual dealer selling prices for that item.

Dealer retail price lists, public auction results, published prices in advertising and individual solicitation of retail prices from dealers, collectors and specialty organizations have been used in establishing the values found in this catalogue. Amos Media Co. values stamps, but Amos Media is not a company engaged in the business of buying and selling stamps as a dealer.

Use this catalogue as a guide for buying and selling. The actual price you pay for a stamp may be higher or lower than the catalogue value because of many different factors, including the amount of personal service a dealer offers, or increased or decreased interest in the country or topic represented by a stamp or set. An item may occasionally be offered at a lower price as a "loss leader," or as part of a special sale. You also may obtain an item inexpensively at public auction because of little interest at that time or as part of a large lot.

Stamps that are of a lesser grade than Very Fine, or those with condition problems, generally trade at lower prices than those given in this catalogue. Stamps of exceptional quality in both grade and condition often command higher prices than those listed.

Values for pre-1900 unused issues are for stamps with approximately half or more of their original gum. Stamps with most or all of their original gum may be expected to sell for more, and stamps with less than half of their original gum may be expected to sell for somewhat less than the values listed. On rarer stamps, it may be expected that the original gum will be somewhat more disturbed than it will be on more common issues. Post-1900 unused issues are assumed to have full original gum. From breakpoints in most countries' listings, stamps are valued as never hinged, due to the wide availability of stamps in that condition. These notations are prominently placed in the listings and in the country information preceding the listings. Some countries also feature listings with dual values for hinged and never-hinged stamps.

Grade

A stamp's grade and condition are crucial to its value. The accompanying illustrations show examples of Very Fine stamps from different time periods, along with examples of stamps in Fine to Very Fine and Extremely Fine grades as points of reference. When a stamp seller offers a stamp in any grade from fine to superb without further qualifying statements, that stamp should not only have the centering grade as defined, but it also should be free of faults or other condition problems.

FINE stamps (illustrations not shown) have designs that are quite off center, with the perforations on one or two sides very close to the design but not quite touching it. There is white space between the perforations and the design that is minimal but evident to the unaided eye. Imperforate stamps may have small margins, and earlier issues may show the design just touching one edge of the stamp design. Very early perforated issues normally will have the perforations slightly cutting into the design. Used stamps may have heavier than usual cancellations.

FINE-VERY FINE stamps will be somewhat off center on one side, or slightly off center on two sides. Imperforate stamps will have two margins of at least normal size, and the design will not touch any edge. For perforated stamps, the perfs are well clear of the design, but are still noticeably off center. *However, early issues of a country may be printed in such a way that the design naturally is very close to the edges. In these cases, the perforations may cut into the design very slightly.* Used stamps will not have a cancellation that detracts from the design.

VERY FINE stamps will be just slightly off center on one or two sides, but the design will be well clear of the edge. The stamp will present a nice, balanced appearance. Imperforate stamps will be well centered within normal-sized margins. *However, early issues of*

many countries may be printed in such a way that the perforations may touch the design on one or more sides. Where this is the case, a boxed note will be found defining the centering and margins of the stamps being valued. Used stamps will have light or otherwise neat cancellations. This is the grade used to establish Scott Catalogue values.

EXTREMELY FINE stamps are close to being perfectly centered. Imperforate stamps will have even margins that are slightly larger than normal. Even the earliest perforated issues will have perforations clear of the design on all sides.

Amos Media Co. recognizes that there is no formally enforced grading scheme for postage stamps, and that the final price you pay or obtain for a stamp will be determined by individual agreement at the time of transaction.

Condition

Grade addresses only centering and (for used stamps) cancellation. *Condition* refers to factors other than grade that affect a stamp's desirability.

Factors that can increase the value of a stamp include exceptionally wide margins, particularly fresh color, the presence of selvage, and plate or die varieties. Unusual cancels on used stamps (particularly those of the 19th century) can greatly enhance their value as well.

Factors other than faults that decrease the value of a stamp include loss of original gum, regumming, a hinge remnant or foreign object adhering to the gum, natural inclusions, straight edges, and markings or notations applied by collectors or dealers.

Faults include missing pieces, tears, pin or other holes, surface scuffs, thin spots, creases, toning, short or pulled perforations, clipped perforations, oxidation or other forms of color changelings, soiling, stains, and such man-made changes as reperforations or the chemical removal or lightening of a cancellation.

Grading illustrations

On the following two pages are illustrations of various stamps from countries appearing in this volume. These stamps are arranged by country, and they represent early or important issues that are often found in widely different grades in the marketplace. The editors believe the illustrations will prove useful in showing the margin size and centering that will be seen on the various issues.

In addition to the matters of margin size and centering, collectors are reminded that the very fine stamps valued in the Scott catalogues also will possess fresh color and intact perforations, and they will be free from defects.

Examples shown are computer-manipulated images made from single digitized master illustrations.

Stamp illustrations used in the catalogue

It is important to note that the stamp images used for identification purposes in this catalogue may not be indicative of the grade of stamp being valued. Refer to the written discussion of grades on this page and to the grading illustrations on the following two pages for grading information.

Fine-Very Fine →

**SCOTT
CATALOGUES
VALUE
STAMPS IN
THIS GRADE**

Very Fine →

Extremely Fine →

Fine-Very Fine →

**SCOTT
CATALOGUES
VALUE
STAMPS IN
THIS GRADE**

Very Fine →

Extremely Fine →

Fine-Very Fine →

SCOTT CATALOGUES VALUE STAMPS IN THIS GRADE

Very Fine →

Extremely Fine →

Fine-Very Fine →

SCOTT CATALOGUES VALUE STAMPS IN THIS GRADE

Very Fine →

Extremely Fine →

Gum Conditions

For purposes of helping to determine the gum condition and value of an unused stamp, Scott presents the following chart which details different gum conditions and indicates how the conditions correlate with the Scott values for unused stamps. Used together, the Illustrated Grading Chart on the previous pages and this Illustrated Gum Chart should allow catalogue users to better understand the grade and gum condition of stamps valued in the Scott catalogues.

Never Hinged (NH; ★★): A never-hinged stamp will have full original gum that will have no hinge mark or disturbance. The presence of an expertizer's mark does not disqualify a stamp from this designation.

Original Gum (OG; ★): Pre-1900 stamps should have approximately half or more of their original gum. On rarer stamps, it may be expected that the original gum will be somewhat more disturbed than it will be on more common issues. Post-1900 stamps should have full original gum. Original gum will show some disturbance caused by a previous hinge(s) which may be present or entirely removed. The actual value of a post-1900 stamp will be affected by the degree of hinging of the full original gum.

Disturbed Original Gum: Gum showing noticeable effects of humidity, climate or hinging over more than half of the gum. The significance of gum disturbance in valuing a stamp in any of the Original Gum categories depends on the degree of disturbance, the rarity and normal gum condition of the issue and other variables affecting quality.

Regummed (RG; (★)): A regummed stamp is a stamp without gum that has had some type of gum privately applied at a time after it was issued. This normally is done to deceive collectors and/or dealers into thinking that the stamp has original gum and therefore has a higher value. A regummed stamp is considered the same as a stamp with none of its original gum for purposes of grading.

Gum Categories:	MINT N.H.	ORIGINAL GUM (O.G.)				NO GUM
	Mint Never Hinged *Free from any disturbance*	**Lightly Hinged** *Faint impression of a removed hinge over a small area*	**Hinge Mark or Remnant** *Prominent hinged spot with part or all of the hinge remaining*	**Large part o.g.** *Approximately half or more of the gum intact*	**Small part o.g.** *Approximately less than half of the gum intact*	**No gum** *Only if issued with gum*
Commonly Used Symbol:	★★	★	★	★	★	(★)
Pre-1900 Issues (Pre-1881 for U.S.)	*Very fine pre-1900 stamps in these categories trade at a premium over Scott value*			Scott Value for "Unused"		Scott "No Gum" listings for selected unused classic stamps
From 1900 to breakpoints for listings of never-hinged stamps	Scott "Never Hinged" listings for selected unused stamps	Scott Value for "Unused" (Actual value will be affected by the degree of hinging of the full o.g.)				
From breakpoints noted for many countries	Scott Value for "Unused"					

Understanding the listings

On the opposite page is an enlarged "typical" listing from this catalogue. Below are detailed explanations of each of the highlighted parts of the listing.

1 Scott number — Scott catalogue numbers are used to identify specific items when buying, selling or trading stamps. Each listed postage stamp from every country has a unique Scott catalogue number. Therefore, Germany Scott 99, for example, can only refer to a single stamp. Although the Scott catalogue usually lists stamps in chronological order by date of issue, there are exceptions. When a country has issued a set of stamps over a period of time, those stamps within the set are kept together without regard to date of issue. This follows the normal collecting approach of keeping stamps in their natural sets.

When a country issues a set of stamps over a period of time, a group of consecutive catalogue numbers is reserved for the stamps in that set, as issued. If that group of numbers proves to be too few, capital-letter suffixes, such as "A" or "B," may be added to existing numbers to create enough catalogue numbers to cover all items in the set. A capital-letter suffix indicates a major Scott catalogue number listing. Scott generally uses a suffix letter only once. Therefore, a catalogue number listing with a capital-letter suffix will seldom be found with the same letter (lower case) used as a minor-letter listing. If there is a Scott 16A in a set, for example, there will seldom be a Scott 16a. However, a minor-letter "a" listing may be added to a major number containing an "A" suffix (Scott 16Aa, for example).

Suffix letters are cumulative. A minor "b" variety of Scott 16A would be Scott 16Ab, not Scott 16b.

There are times when a reserved block of Scott catalogue numbers is too large for a set, leaving some numbers unused. Such gaps in the numbering sequence also occur when the catalogue editors move an item's listing elsewhere or have removed it entirely from the catalogue. Scott does not attempt to account for every possible number, but rather attempts to assure that each stamp is assigned its own number.

Scott numbers designating regular postage normally are only numerals. Scott numbers for other types of stamps, such as air post, semi-postal, postal tax, postage due, occupation and others have a prefix consisting of one or more capital letters or a combination of numerals and capital letters.

2 Illustration number — Illustration or design-type numbers are used to identify each catalogue illustration. For most sets, the lowest face-value stamp is shown. It then serves as an example of the basic design approach for other stamps not illustrated. Where more than one stamp use the same illustration number, but have differences in design, the design paragraph or the description line clearly indicates the design on each stamp not illustrated. Where there are both vertical and horizontal designs in a set, a single illustration may be used, with the exceptions noted in the design paragraph or description line. When an illustration is followed by a lower-case letter in parentheses, such as "A2(b)," the trailing letter indicates which overprint or surcharge illustration applies.

Illustrations normally are 70 percent of the original size of the stamp. Oversized stamps, blocks and souvenir sheets are reduced even more. Overprints and surcharges are shown at 100 percent of their original size if shown alone, but are 70 percent of original size if shown on stamps. In some cases, the illustration will be placed above the set, between listings or omitted completely. Overprint and surcharge illustrations are not placed in this catalogue for purposes of expertizing stamps.

3 Paper color — The color of a stamp's paper is noted in italic type when the paper used is not white.

4 Listing styles — There are two principal types of catalogue listings: major and minor.

Major listings are in a larger type style than minor listings. The catalogue number is a numeral that can be found with or without a capital-letter suffix, and with or without a prefix.

Minor listings are in a smaller type style and have a small-letter suffix or (if the listing immediately follows that of the major number) may show only the letter. These listings identify a variety of the major item. Examples include perforation and shade differences, multiples (some souvenir sheets, booklet panes and se-tenant combinations), and singles of multiples.

Examples of major number listings include 16, 28A, B97, C13A, 10N5, and 10N6A. Examples of minor numbers are 16a and C13Ab.

5 Basic information about a stamp or set — Introducing each stamp issue is a small section (usually a line listing) of basic information about a stamp or set. This section normally includes the date of issue, method of printing, perforation, watermark and, sometimes, some additional information of note. *Printing method, perforation and watermark apply to the following sets until a change is noted.* Stamps created by overprinting or surcharging previous issues are assumed to have the same perforation, watermark, printing method and other production characteristics as the original. Dates of issue are as precise as Scott is able to confirm and often reflect the dates on first-day covers, rather than the actual date of release.

6 Denomination — This normally refers to the face value of the stamp; that is, the cost of the unused stamp at the post office at the time of issue. When a denomination is shown in parentheses, it does not appear on the stamp. This includes the nondenominated stamps of the United States, Brazil and Great Britain, for example.

7 Color or other description — This area provides information to solidify identification of a stamp. In many recent cases, a description of the stamp design appears in this space, rather than a listing of colors.

8 Year of issue — In stamp sets that have been released in a period that spans more than a year, the number shown in parentheses is the year that stamp first appeared. Stamps without a date appeared during the first year of the issue.

Dates are not always given for minor varieties.

9 Value unused and Value used — The Scott catalogue values are based on stamps that are in a grade of Very Fine unless stated otherwise. Unused values refer to items that have not seen postal, revenue or any other duty for which they were intended. Pre-1900 unused stamps that were issued with gum must have at least most of their original gum. Later issues are assumed to have full original gum. From breakpoints specified in most countries' listings, stamps are valued as never hinged. Stamps issued without gum are noted. Modern issues with PVA or other synthetic adhesives may appear ungummed. Unused self-adhesive stamps are valued as appearing undisturbed on their original backing paper. Values for used self-adhesive stamps are for examples either on piece or off piece. For a more detailed explanation of these values, please see the "Catalogue Value," "Condition" and "Understanding Valuing Notations" sections elsewhere in this introduction.

In some cases, where used stamps are more valuable than unused stamps, the value is for an example with a contemporaneous cancel, rather than a modern cancel or a smudge or other unclear marking. For those stamps that were released for postal and fiscal purposes, the used value represents a postally used stamp. Stamps with revenue cancels generally sell for less.

Stamps separated from a complete se-tenant multiple usually will be worth less than a pro-rated portion of the se-tenant multiple, and stamps lacking the attached labels that are noted in the listings will be worth less than the values shown.

10 Changes in basic set information — Bold type is used to show any changes in the basic data given for a set of stamps. These basic data categories include perforation gauge measurement, paper type, printing method and watermark.

11 Total value of a set — The total value of sets of three or more stamps issued after 1900 are shown. The set line also notes the range of Scott numbers and total number of stamps included in the grouping. The actual value of a set consisting predominantly of stamps having the minimum value of 25 cents may be less than the total value shown. Similarly, the actual value or catalogue value of se-tenant pairs or of blocks consisting of stamps having the minimum value of 25 cents may be less than the catalogue values of the component parts.

A6

King George VI
A7

SCOTT NUMBER 1

ILLUS. NUMBER 2

5 BASIC INFORMATION ON STAMP OR SET

6 DENOMINATION

7 COLOR OR OTHER DESCRIPTION

8 YEAR OF ISSUE

9 CATALOGUE VALUES

1938-44			Engr.	Perf. 12½	
54	A6	½p	green	.25	2.00
54A	A6	½p	dk brown ('42)	.25	2.25
55	A6	1p	dark brown	2.50	.35
55A	A6	1p	green ('42)	.25	1.75
56	A6	1½p	dark carmine	5.00	6.00
56A	A6	1½p	gray ('42)	.25	5.75
57	A6	2p	gray	5.00	1.25
57A	A6	2p	dark car ('42)	.25	2.00
58	A6	3p	blue	.60	1.00
59	A6	4p	rose lilac	1.75	2.00
60	A6	6p	dark violet	2.00	2.00
61	A6	9p	olive bister	2.00	5.25
62	A6	1sh	orange & blk	2.10	3.25

UNUSED   USED

PAPER COLOR 3

LISTING STYLES 4   MAJORS
MINORS

Typo.
Perf. 14
Chalky Paper

63	A7	2sh	ultra & dl vio, *bl*	7.00	17.50
64	A7	2sh6p	red & blk, *bl*	9.00	24.00
65	A7	5sh	red & grn, *yel*	35.00	30.00
a.		5sh dk red & dp grn, *yel* ('44)		55.00	140.00
66	A7	10sh	red & grn, *grn*	35.00	70.00

10 CHANGES IN BASIC SET INFORMATION

Wmk. 3

67	A7	£1	blk & vio, *red*	30.00	52.50
		Nos. 54-67 (18)		138.20	228.85
		Set, never hinged		220.00	

11 TOTAL VALUE OF SET

Catalogue listing policy

It is the intent of Amos Media Co. to list all postage stamps of the world in the Scott *Standard Postage Stamp Catalogue*. The only strict criteria for listing is that stamps be decreed legal for postage by the issuing country and that the issuing country actually have an operating postal system. Whether the primary intent of issuing a given stamp or set was for sale to postal patrons or to stamp collectors is not part of our listing criteria. Scott's role is to provide basic comprehensive postage stamp information. It is up to each stamp collector to choose which items to include in a collection.

It is Scott's objective to seek reasons why a stamp should be listed, rather than why it should not. Nevertheless, there are certain types of items that will not be listed. These include the following:

1. Unissued items that are not officially distributed or released by the issuing postal authority. If such items are officially issued at a later date by the country, they will be listed. Unissued items consist of those that have been printed and then held from sale for reasons such as change in government, errors found on stamps or something deemed objectionable about a stamp subject or design.

2. Stamps "issued" by non-existent postal entities or fantasy countries, such as Nagaland, Occusi-Ambeno, Staffa, Sedang, Torres Straits and others. Also, stamps "issued" in the names of legitimate, stamp-issuing countries that are not authorized by those countries.

3. Semi-official or unofficial items not required for postage. Examples include items issued by private agencies for their own express services. When such items are required for delivery, or are valid as prepayment of postage, they are listed.

4. Local stamps issued for local use only. Postage stamps issued by governments specifically for "domestic" use, such as Haiti Scott 219-228, or the United States nondenominated stamps, are not considered to be locals, since they are valid for postage throughout the country of origin.

5. Items not valid for postal use. For example, a few countries have issued souvenir sheets that are not valid for postage. This area also includes a number of worldwide charity labels (some denominated) that do not pay postage.

6. Egregiously exploitative issues such as stamps sold for far more than face value, stamps purposely issued in artificially small quantities or only against advance orders, stamps awarded only to a selected audience such as a philatelic bureau's standing order customers, or stamps sold only in conjunction with other products. All of these kinds of items are usually controlled issues and/or are intended for speculation. These items normally will be included in a footnote.

7. Items distributed by the issuing government only to a limited group, club, philatelic exhibition or a single stamp dealer or other private company. These items normally will be included in a footnote.

8. Stamps not available to collectors. These generally are rare items, all of which are held by public institutions such as museums. The existence of such items often will be cited in footnotes.

The fact that a stamp has been used successfully as postage, even on international mail, is not in itself sufficient proof that it was legitimately issued. Numerous examples of so-called stamps from non-existent countries are known to have been used to post letters that have successfully passed through the international mail system.

There are certain items that are subject to interpretation. When a stamp falls outside our specifications, it may be listed along with a cautionary footnote.

A number of factors are considered in our approach to analyzing how a stamp is listed. The following list of factors is presented to share with you, the catalogue user, the complexity of the listing process.

Additional printings — "Additional printings" of a previously issued stamp may range from an item that is totally different to cases where it is impossible to differentiate from the original. At least a minor number (a small-letter suffix) is assigned if there is a distinct change in stamp shade, noticeably redrawn design, or a significantly different perforation measurement. A major number (numeral or numeral and capital-letter combination) is assigned if the editors feel the "additional printing" is sufficiently different from the original that it constitutes a different issue.

Commemoratives — Where practical, commemoratives with the same theme are placed in a set. For example, the U.S. Civil War Centennial set of 1961-65 and the Constitution Bicentennial series of 1989-90 appear as sets. Countries such as Japan and Korea issue such material on a regular basis, with an announced, or at least predictable, number of stamps known in advance. Occasionally, however, stamp sets that were released over a period of years have been separated. Appropriately placed footnotes will guide you to each set's continuation.

Definitive sets — Blocks of numbers generally have been reserved for definitive sets, based on previous experience with any given country. If a few more stamps were issued in a set than originally expected, they often have been inserted into the original set with a capital-letter suffix, such as U.S. Scott 1059A. If it appears that many more stamps than the originally allotted block will be released before the set is completed, a new block of numbers will be reserved, with the original one being closed off. In some cases, such as the U.S. Transportation and Great Americans series, several blocks of numbers exist. Appropriately placed footnotes will guide you to each set's continuation.

New country — Membership in the Universal Postal Union is not a consideration for listing status or order of placement within the catalogue. The index will tell you in what volume or page number the listings begin.

"No release date" items — The amount of information available for any given stamp issue varies greatly from country to country and even from time to time. Extremely comprehensive information about new stamps is available from some countries well before the stamps are released. By contrast some countries do not provide information about stamps or release dates. Most countries, however, fall between these extremes. A country may provide denominations or subjects of stamps from upcoming issues that are not issued as planned. Sometimes, philatelic agencies, those private firms hired to represent countries, add these later-issued items to sets well after the formal release date. This time period can range from weeks to years. If these items were officially released by the country, they will be added to the appropriate spot in the set. In many cases, the specific release date of a stamp or set of stamps may never be known.

Overprints — The color of an overprint is always noted if it is other than black. Where more than one color of ink has been used on overprints of a single set, the color used is noted. Early overprint and surcharge illustrations were altered to prevent their use by forgers.

Personalized Stamps — Since 1999, the special service of personalizing stamp vignettes, or labels attached to stamps, has been offered to customers by postal administrations of many countries. Sheets of these stamps are sold, singly or in quantity, only through special orders made by mail, in person, or through a sale on a computer website with the postal administrations or their agents for which an extra fee is charged, though some countries offer to collectors at face value personalized stamps having generic images in the vignettes or on the attached labels. It is impossible for any catalogue to know what images have been chosen by customers. Images can be 1) owned or created by the customer, 2) a generic image, or 3) an image pulled from a library of stock images on the stamp creation website. It is also impossible to know the quantity printed for any stamp having a particular image. So from a valuing standpoint, any image is equivalent to any other image for any personalized stamp having the same catalogue number. Illustrations of personalized stamps in the catalogue are not always those of stamps having generic images.

Personalized items are listed with some exceptions. These include:

1. Stamps or sheets that have attached labels that the customer cannot personalize, but which are nonetheless marketed as "personalized," and are sold for far more than the franking value.

2. Stamps or sheets that can be personalized by the customer, but where a portion of the print run must be ceded to the issuing country for sale to other customers.

3. Stamps or sheets that are created exclusively for a particular commercial client, or clients, including stamps that differ from any similar stamp that has been made available to the public.

4. Stamps or sheets that are deliberately conceived by the issuing authority that have been, or are likely to be, created with an excessive number of different face values, sizes, or other features that are changeable.

5. Stamps or sheets that are created by postal administrations using the same system of stamp personalization that has been put in place for use by the public that are printed in limited quantities and sold above face value.

6. Stamps or sheets that are created by licensees not directly affiliated or controlled by a postal administration.

Excluded items may or may not be footnoted.

Se-tenants — Connected stamps of differing features (se-tenants) will be listed in the format most commonly collected. This includes pairs, blocks or larger multiples. Se-tenant units are not always symmetrical. An example is Australia Scott 508, which is a block of seven stamps. If the stamps are primarily collected as a unit, the major number may be assigned to the multiple, with minors going to each component stamp. In cases where continuous-design or other unit se-tenants will receive significant postal use, each stamp is given a major Scott number listing. This includes issues from the United States, Canada, Germany and Great Britain, for example.

Special notices

Classification of stamps

The Scott Standard Postage Stamp Catalogue lists stamps by country of issue. The next level of organization is a listing by section on the basis of the function of the stamps. The principal sections cover regular postage, semi-postal, air post, special delivery, registration, postage due and other categories. Except for regular postage, catalogue numbers for all sections include a prefix letter (or number-letter combination) denoting the class to which a given stamp belongs. When some countries issue sets containing stamps from more than one category, the catalogue will at times list all of the stamps in one category (such as air post stamps listed as part of a postage set).

The following is a listing of the most commonly used catalogue prefixes.

Prefix.......Category
C..........Air Post
M.........Military
P..........Newspaper
N..........Occupation - Regular Issues
O..........Official
Q..........Parcel Post
J..........Postage Due
RA.......Postal Tax
B..........Semi-Postal
E..........Special Delivery
MR.......War Tax

Other prefixes used by more than one country include the following:
H..........Acknowledgment of Receipt
I...........Late Fee
CO.......Air Post Official
CQ.......Air Post Parcel Post
RAC.....Air Post Postal Tax
CF........Air Post Registration
CB.......Air Post Semi-Postal
CBO ....Air Post Semi-Postal Official
CE ....Air Post Special Delivery
EY........Authorized Delivery
S..........Franchise
G..........Insured Letter
GY ....Marine Insurance
MC.......Military Air Post
MQ ......Military Parcel Post
NC ....Occupation - Air Post
NO ....Occupation - Official
NJ........Occupation - Postage Due
NRA.....Occupation - Postal Tax
NB ....Occupation - Semi-Postal
NE ....Occupation - Special Delivery
QY ....Parcel Post Authorized Delivery
AR ....Postal-fiscal
RAJ......Postal Tax Due
RAB .....Postal Tax Semi-Postal
F ....Registration
EB........Semi-Postal Special Delivery
EO ....Special Delivery Official
QE ....Special Handling

New issue listings

Updates to this catalogue appear each month in the *Linn's Stamp News* monthly magazine. Included in this update are additions to the listings of countries found in the Scott *Standard Postage Stamp Catalogue* and the *Specialized Catalogue of United States Stamps and Covers,* as well as corrections and updates to current editions of this catalogue.

From time to time there will be changes in the final listings of stamps from the *Linn's Stamp News* magazine to the next edition of the catalogue. This occurs as more information about certain stamps or sets becomes available.

The catalogue update section of the *Linn's Stamp News* magazine is the most timely presentation of this material available. Annual subscriptions to *Linn's Stamp News* are available from Linn's Stamp News, Box 4129, Sidney, OH 45365-4129.

Number additions, deletions and changes

A listing of catalogue number additions, deletions and changes from the previous edition of the catalogue appears in each volume. See Catalogue Number Additions, Deletions & Changes in the table of contents for the location of this list.

Understanding valuing notations

The *minimum catalogue value* of an individual stamp or set is 25 cents. This represents a portion of the cost incurred by a dealer when he prepares an individual stamp for resale. As a point of philatelic-economic fact, the lower the value shown for an item in this catalogue, the greater the percentage of that value is attributed to dealer mark up and profit margin. In many cases, such as the 25-cent minimum value, that price does not cover the labor or other costs involved with stocking it as an individual stamp. The sum of minimum values in a set does not properly represent the value of a complete set primarily composed of a number of minimum-value stamps, nor does the sum represent the actual value of a packet made up of minimum-value stamps. Thus a packet of 1,000 different common stamps — each of which has a catalogue value of 25 cents — normally sells for considerably less than $250!

The *absence of a retail value* for a stamp does not necessarily suggest that a stamp is scarce or rare. A dash in the value column means that the stamp is known in a stated form or variety, but information is either lacking or insufficient for purposes of establishing a usable catalogue value.

Stamp values in *italics* generally refer to items that are difficult to value accurately. For expensive items, such as those priced at $1,000 or higher, a value in italics indicates that the affected item trades very seldom. For inexpensive items, a value in italics represents a warning. One example is a "blocked" issue where the issuing postal administration may have controlled one stamp in a set in an attempt to make the whole set more valuable. Another example is an item that sold at an extreme multiple of face value in the marketplace at the time of its issue.

One type of warning to collectors that appears in the catalogue is illustrated by a stamp that is valued considerably higher in used condition than it is as unused. In this case, collectors are cautioned to be certain the used version has a genuine and contemporaneous cancellation. The type of cancellation on a stamp can be an important factor in determining its sale price. Catalogue values do not apply to fiscal, telegraph or non-contemporaneous postal cancels, unless otherwise noted.

Some countries have released back issues of stamps in canceled-to-order form, sometimes covering as much as a 10-year period. The Scott Catalogue values for used stamps reflect canceled-to-order material when such stamps are found to predominate in the marketplace for the issue involved. Notes frequently appear in the stamp listings to specify which items are valued as canceled-to-order, or if there is a premium for postally used examples.

Many countries sell canceled-to-order stamps at a marked reduction of face value. Countries that sell or have sold canceled-to-order stamps at *full* face value include United Nations, Australia, Netherlands, France and Switzerland. It may be almost impossible to identify such stamps if the gum has been removed, because official government canceling devices are used. Postally used examples of these items on cover, however, are usually worth more than the canceled-to-order stamps with original gum.

Abbreviations

Scott uses a consistent set of abbreviations throughout this catalogue to conserve space, while still providing necessary information.

Color Abbreviations

amb	amber	crim	crimson	ol	olive
anil	aniline	cr	cream	olvn	olivine
ap	apple	dk	dark	org	orange
aqua	aquamarine	dl	dull	pck	peacock
az	azure	dp	deep	pnksh	pinkish
bis	bister	db	drab	Prus	Prussian
bl	blue	emer	emerald	pur	purple
bld	blood	gldn	golden	redsh	reddish
blk	black	grysh	grayish	res	reseda
bril	brilliant	grn	green	ros	rosine
brn	brown	grnsh	greenish	ryl	royal
brnsh	brownish	hel	heliotrope	sal	salmon
brnz	bronze	hn	henna	saph	sapphire
brt	bright	ind	indigo	scar	scarlet
brnt	burnt	int	intense	sep	sepia
car	carmine	lav	lavender	sien	sienna
cer	cerise	lem	lemon	sil	silver
chlky	chalky	lil	lilac	sl	slate
cham	chamois	lt	light	stl	steel
chnt	chestnut	mag	magenta	turq	turquoise
choc	chocolate	man	manila	ultra	ultramarine
chr	chrome	mar	maroon	Ven	Venetian
cit	citron	mv	mauve	ver	vermilion
cl	claret	multi	multicolored	vio	violet
cob	cobalt	mlky	milky	yel	yellow
cop	copper	myr	myrtle	yelsh	yellowish

When no color is given for an overprint or surcharge, black is the color used. Abbreviations for colors used for overprints and surcharges include: "(B)" or "(Blk)," black; "(Bl)," blue; "(R)," red; and "(G)," green.

Additional abbreviations in this catalogue are shown below:

Adm.	Administration
AFL	American Federation of Labor
Anniv.	Anniversary
APS	American Philatelic Society
Assoc.	Association
ASSR.	Autonomous Soviet Socialist Republic
b	Born
BEP	Bureau of Engraving and Printing
Bicent.	Bicentennial
Bklt.	Booklet
Brit.	British
btwn	Between
Bur.	Bureau
c. or ca.	Circa
Cat.	Catalogue
Cent.	Centennial, century, centenary
CIO	Congress of Industrial Organizations
Conf.	Conference
Cong.	Congress
Cpl.	Corporal
CTO	Canceled to order
d	Died
Dbl.	Double
EDU	Earliest documented use
Engr	Engraved
Exhib	Exhibition
Expo.	Exposition
Fed	Federation
GB	Great Britain
Gen.	General
GPO	General post office
Horiz.	Horizontal
Imperf.	Imperforate
Impt.	Imprint
Intl.	International
Invtd	Inverted
L	Left
Lieut., lt.	Lieutenant
Litho.	Lithographed

LL	Lower left
LR	Lower right
mm	Millimeter
Ms.	Manuscript
Natl.	National
No.	Number
NY	New York
NYC	New York City
Ovpt.	Overprint
Ovptd.	Overprinted
P	Plate number
Perf.	Perforated, perforation
Phil.	Philatelic
Photo.	Photogravure
PO	Post office
Pr.	Pair
P.R.	Puerto Rico
Prec.	Precancel, precanceled
Pres.	President
PTT	Post, Telephone and Telegraph
R	Right
Rio	Rio de Janeiro
Sgt.	Sergeant
Soc.	Society
Souv.	Souvenir
SSR	Soviet Socialist Republic, see ASSR
St.	Saint, street
Surch.	Surcharge
Typo.	Typographed
UL	Upper left
Unwmkd.	Unwatermarked
UPU	Universal Postal Union
UR	Upper Right
US	United States
USPOD	United States Post Office Department
USSR	Union of Soviet Socialist Republics
Vert.	Vertical
VP	Vice president
Wmk.	Watermark
Wmkd.	Watermarked
WWI	World War I
WWII	World War II

Examination

Amos Media Co. will not comment upon the genuineness, grade or condition of stamps, because of the time and responsibility involved. Rather, there are several expertizing groups that undertake this work for both collectors and dealers. Neither will Amos Media Co. appraise or identify philatelic material. The company cannot take responsibility for unsolicited stamps or covers sent by individuals.

All letters, emails, etc. are read attentively, but they are not always answered because of time considerations.

How to order from your dealer

When ordering stamps from a dealer, it is not necessary to write the full description of a stamp as listed in this catalogue. All you need is the name of the country, the Scott catalogue number and whether the desired item is unused or used. For example, "Japan Scott 422 unused" is sufficient to identify the unused stamp of Japan listed as "422 A206 5y brown."

Basic stamp information

A stamp collector's knowledge of the combined elements that make a given stamp issue unique determines his or her ability to identify stamps. These elements include paper, watermark, method of separation, printing, design and gum. On the following pages each of these important areas is briefly described.

Paper

Paper is an organic material composed of a compacted weave of cellulose fibers and generally formed into sheets. Paper used to print stamps may be manufactured in sheets, or it may have been part of a large roll (called a web) before being cut to size. The fibers most often used to create paper on which stamps are printed include bark, wood, straw and certain grasses. In many cases, linen or cotton rags have been added for greater strength and durability. Grinding, bleaching, cooking and rinsing these raw fibers reduces them to a slushy pulp, referred to by paper makers as "stuff." Sizing and, sometimes, coloring matter is added to the pulp to make different types of finished paper.

After the stuff is prepared, it is poured onto sieve-like frames that allow the water to run off, while retaining the matted pulp. As fibers fall onto the screen and are held by gravity, they form a natural weave that will later hold the paper together. If the screen has metal bits that are formed into letters or images attached, it leaves slightly thinned areas on the paper. These are called watermarks.

When the stuff is almost dry, it is passed under pressure through smooth or engraved rollers — dandy rolls — or placed between cloth in a press to be flattened and dried.

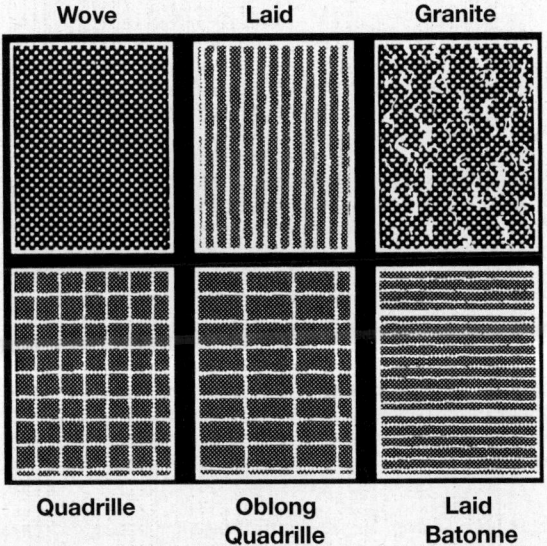

Wove   **Laid**   **Granite**

Quadrille   **Oblong Quadrille**   **Laid Batonne**

Stamp paper falls broadly into two types: wove and laid. The nature of the surface of the frame onto which the pulp is first deposited causes the differences in appearance between the two. If the surface is smooth and even, the paper will be of fairly uniform texture throughout. This is known as wove paper. Early papermaking machines poured the pulp onto a continuously circulating web of felt, but modern machines feed the pulp onto a cloth-like screen made of closely interwoven fine wires. This paper, when held to a light, will show little dots or points very close together. The proper name for this is "wire wove," but the type is still considered wove. Any U.S. or British stamp printed after 1880 will serve as an example of wire wove paper.

Closely spaced parallel wires, with cross wires at wider intervals, make up the frames used for what is known as laid paper. A greater thickness of the pulp will settle between the wires. The paper, when held to a light, will show alternate light and dark lines. The spacing and the thickness of the lines may vary, but on any one sheet of paper they are all alike. See Russia Scott 31-38 for examples of laid paper.

Batonne, from the French word meaning "a staff," is a term used if the lines in the paper are spaced quite far apart, like the printed ruling on a writing tablet. Batonne paper may be either wove or laid. If laid, fine laid lines can be seen between the batons.

Quadrille is the term used when the lines in the paper form little squares. Oblong quadrille is the term used when rectangles,

rather than squares, are formed. Grid patterns vary from distinct to extremely faint. See Mexico-Guadalajara Scott 35-37 for examples of oblong quadrille paper.

Paper also is classified as thick or thin, hard or soft, and by color. Such colors may include yellowish, greenish, bluish and reddish.

Brief explanations of other types of paper used for printing stamps, as well as examples, follow.

Colored — Colored paper is created by the addition of dye in the paper-making process. Such colors may include shades of yellow, green, blue and red. Surface-colored papers, most commonly used for British colonial issues in 1913-14, are created when coloring is added only to the surface during the finishing process. Stamps printed on surface-colored paper have white or uncolored backs, while true colored papers are colored through. See Jamaica Scott 71-73.

Pelure — Pelure paper is a very thin, hard and often brittle paper that is sometimes bluish or grayish in appearance. See Serbia Scott 169-170.

Native — This is a term applied to handmade papers used to produce some of the early stamps of the Indian states. Stamps printed on native paper may be expected to display various natural inclusions that are normal and do not negatively affect value. Japanese paper, originally made of mulberry fibers and rice flour, is part of this group. See Japan Scott 1-18.

Manila — This type of paper is often used to make stamped envelopes and wrappers. It is a coarse-textured stock, usually smooth on one side and rough on the other. A variety of colors of manila paper exist, but the most common range is yellowish-brown.

Silk — Introduced by the British in 1847 as a safeguard against counterfeiting, silk paper contains bits of colored silk thread scattered throughout. The density of these fibers varies greatly and can include as few as one fiber per stamp or hundreds. U.S. revenue Scott R152 is a good example of an easy-to-identify silk paper stamp.

Silk-thread paper has uninterrupted threads of colored silk arranged so that one or more threads run through the stamp or postal stationery. See Great Britain Scott 5-6 and Switzerland Scott 14-19.

Granite — Filled with minute cloth or colored paper fibers of various colors and lengths, granite paper should not be confused with either type of silk paper. Austria Scott 172-175 and a number of Swiss stamps are examples of granite paper.

Chalky — A chalk-like substance coats the surface of chalky paper to discourage the cleaning and reuse of canceled stamps, as well as to provide a smoother, more acceptable printing surface. Because the designs of stamps printed on chalky paper are imprinted on what is often a water-soluble coating, any attempt to remove a cancellation will destroy the stamp. Do not soak these stamps in any fluid. To remove a stamp printed on chalky paper from an envelope, wet the paper from underneath the stamp until the gum dissolves enough to release the stamp from the paper. See St. Kitts-Nevis Scott 89-90 for examples of stamps printed on this type of chalky paper.

India — Another name for this paper, originally introduced from China about 1750, is "China Paper." It is a thin, opaque paper often used for plate and die proofs by many countries.

Double — In philately, the term double paper has two distinct meanings. The first is a two-ply paper, usually a combination of a thick and a thin sheet, joined during manufacture. This type was used experimentally as a means to discourage the reuse of stamps.

The design is printed on the thin paper. Any attempt to remove a cancellation would destroy the design. U.S. Scott 158 and other Banknote-era stamps exist on this form of double paper.

The second type of double paper occurs on a rotary press, when the end of one paper roll, or web, is affixed to the next roll to save time feeding the paper through the press. Stamp designs are printed over the joined paper and, if overlooked by inspectors, may get into post office stocks.

Goldbeater's Skin — This type of paper was used for the 1866 issue of Prussia, and was a tough, translucent paper. The design was printed in reverse on the back of the stamp, and the gum applied over the printing. It is impossible to remove stamps printed on this type of paper from the paper to which they are affixed without destroying the design.

Ribbed — Ribbed paper has an uneven, corrugated surface made by passing the paper through ridged rollers. This type exists on some copies of U.S. Scott 156-165.

Various other substances, or substrates, have been used for stamp manufacture, including wood, aluminum, copper, silver and gold foil, plastic, and silk and cotton fabrics.

Watermarks

Watermarks are an integral part of some papers. They are formed in the process of paper manufacture. Watermarks consist of small designs, formed of wire or cut from metal and soldered to the surface of the mold or, sometimes, on the dandy roll. The designs may be in the form of crowns, stars, anchors, letters or other characters or symbols. These pieces of metal — known in the paper-making industry as "bits" — impress a design into the paper. The design sometimes may be seen by holding the stamp to the light. Some are more easily seen with a watermark detector. This important tool is a small black tray into which a stamp is placed face down and dampened with a fast-evaporating watermark detection fluid that brings up the watermark image in the form of dark lines against a lighter background. These dark lines are the thinner areas of the paper known as the watermark. Some watermarks are extremely difficult to locate, due to either a faint impression, watermark location or the color of the stamp. There also are electric watermark detectors that come with plastic filter disks of various colors. The disks neutralize the color of the stamp, permitting the watermark to be seen more easily.

Multiple watermarks of Crown Agents and Burma

Watermarks of Uruguay, Vatican City and Jamaica

WARNING: Some inks used in the photogravure process dissolve in watermark fluids (Please see the section on Soluble Printing Inks). Also, see "chalky paper."

Watermarks may be found normal, reversed, inverted, reversed and inverted, sideways or diagonal, as seen from the back of the stamp. The relationship of watermark to stamp design depends on the position of the printing plates or how paper is fed through the press. On machine-made paper, watermarks normally are read from right to left. The design is repeated closely throughout the sheet in a "multiple-watermark design." In a "sheet watermark," the design appears only once on the sheet, but extends over many stamps. Individual stamps may carry only a small fraction or none of the watermark.

"Marginal watermarks" occur in the margins of sheets or panes of stamps. They occur on the outside border of paper (ostensibly outside the area where stamps are to be printed). A large row of letters may spell the name of the country or the manufacturer of the paper, or a border of lines may appear. Careless press feeding may cause parts of these letters and/or lines to show on stamps of the outer row of a pane.

Soluble printing inks

WARNING: Most stamp colors are permanent; that is, they are not seriously affected by short-term exposure to light or water. Many colors, especially of modern inks, fade from excessive exposure to light. There are stamps printed with inks that dissolve easily in water or in fluids used to detect watermarks. Use of these inks was intentional to prevent the removal of cancellations. Water affects all aniline inks, those on so-called safety paper and some photogravure printings - all such inks are known as fugitive colors. Removal from paper of such stamps requires care and alternatives to traditional soaking.

Separation

"Separation" is the general term used to describe methods used to separate stamps. The three standard forms currently in use are perforating, rouletting and die-cutting. These methods are done during the stamp production process, after printing. Sometimes these methods are done on-press or sometimes as a separate step. The earliest issues, such as the 1840 Penny Black of Great Britain (Scott 1), did not have any means provided for separation. It was expected the stamps would be cut apart with scissors or folded and torn. These are examples of imperforate stamps. Many stamps were first issued in imperforate formats and were later issued with perforations. Therefore, care must be observed in buying single imperforate stamps to be certain they were issued imperforate and are not perforated copies that have been altered by having the perforations trimmed away. Stamps issued imperforate usually are valued as singles. However, imperforate varieties of normally perforated stamps should be collected in pairs or larger pieces as indisputable evidence of their imperforate character.

PERFORATION

The chief style of separation of stamps, and the one that is in almost universal use today, is perforating. By this process, paper between the stamps is cut away in a line of holes, usually round, leaving little bridges of paper between the stamps to hold them together. Some types of perforation, such as hyphen-hole perfs, can be confused with roulettes, but a close visual inspection reveals that paper has been removed. The little perforation bridges, which project from the stamp when it is torn from the pane, are called the teeth of the perforation.

As the size of the perforation is sometimes the only way to differentiate between two otherwise identical stamps, it is necessary to be able to accurately measure and describe them. This is done with a perforation gauge, usually a ruler-like device that has dots or graduated lines to show how many perforations may be counted in the space of two centimeters. Two centimeters is the space universally adopted in which to measure perforations.

Perforation gauge

To measure a stamp, run it along the gauge until the dots on it fit exactly into the perforations of the stamp. If you are using a graduated-line perforation gauge, simply slide the stamp along the surface until the lines on the gauge perfectly project from the center of the bridges or holes. The number to the side of the line of dots or lines that fit the stamp's perforation is the measurement. For example, an "11" means that 11 perforations fit between two centimeters. The description of the stamp therefore is "perf. 11." If the gauge of the perforations on the top and bottom of a stamp differs from that on the sides, the result is what is known as compound perforations. In measuring compound perforations, the gauge at top and bottom is always given first, then the sides. Thus, a stamp that measures 11 at top and bottom and 10½ at the sides is "perf. 11 x 10½." See U.S. Scott 632-642 for examples of compound perforations.

Stamps also are known with perforations different on three or all four sides. Descriptions of such items are clockwise, beginning with the top of the stamp.

A perforation with small holes and teeth close together is a "fine perforation." One with large holes and teeth far apart is a "coarse perforation." Holes that are jagged, rather than clean-cut, are "rough perforations." *Blind perforations* are the slight impressions left by the perforating pins if they fail to puncture the paper. Multiples of stamps showing blind perforations may command a slight premium over normally perforated stamps.

The term *syncopated perfs* describes intentional irregularities in the perforations. The earliest form was used by the Netherlands from 1925-33, where holes were omitted to create distinctive patterns. Beginning in 1992, Great Britain has used an oval perforation to help prevent counterfeiting. Several other countries have started using the oval perfs or other syncopated perf patterns.

A new type of perforation, still primarily used for postal stationery, is known as microperfs. Microperfs are tiny perforations (in some cases hundreds of holes per two centimeters) that allows items to be intentionally separated very easily, while not accidentally breaking apart as easily as standard perforations. These are not currently measured or differentiated by size, as are standard perforations.

perce en arc

perce en lignes

perce en points

oblique roulette

perce en scie

perce serpentin

ROULETTING

In rouletting, the stamp paper is cut partly or wholly through, with no paper removed. In perforating, some paper is removed. Rouletting derives its name from the French *roulette*, a spur-like wheel. As the wheel is rolled over the paper, each point makes a small cut. The number of cuts made in a two-centimeter space determines the gauge of the roulette, just as the number of perforations in two centimeters determines the gauge of the perforation.

The shape and arrangement of the teeth on the wheels varies. Various roulette types generally carry French names:

Perce en lignes — rouletted in lines. The paper receives short, straight cuts in lines. This is the most common type of rouletting. See Mexico Scott 500.

Perce en points — pin-rouletted or pin-perfed. This differs from a small perforation because no paper is removed, although round, equidistant holes are pricked through the paper. See Mexico Scott 242-256.

Perce en arc and perce en scie — pierced in an arc or saw-toothed designs, forming half circles or small triangles. See Hanover (German States) Scott 25-29.

Perce en serpentin — serpentine roulettes. The cuts form a serpentine or wavy line. See Brunswick (German States) Scott 13-18.

Once again, no paper is removed by these processes, leaving the stamps easily separated, but closely attached.

DIE-CUTTING

The third major form of stamp separation is die-cutting. This is a method where a die in the pattern of separation is created that later cuts the stamp paper in a stroke motion. Although some standard stamps bear die-cut perforations, this process is primarily used for self-adhesive postage stamps. Die-cutting can appear in straight lines, such as U.S. Scott 2522, shapes, such as U.S. Scott 1551, or imitating the appearance of perforations, such as New Zealand Scott 935A and 935B.

Printing processes

ENGRAVING (Intaglio, Line-engraving, Etching)

Master die — The initial operation in the process of line engraving is making the master die. The die is a small, flat block of softened steel upon which the stamp design is recess engraved in reverse.

Photographic reduction of the original art is made to the appropriate size. It then serves as a tracing guide for the initial outline of the design. The engraver lightly traces the design on the steel with his graver, then slowly works the design until it is completed. At various points during the engraving process, the engraver hand-inks the die and makes an impression to check his progress. These are known as progressive die proofs. After completion of the engraving, the die is hardened to withstand the stress and pressures of later transfer operations.

Transfer roll

Transfer roll — Next is production of the transfer roll that, as the name implies, is the medium used to transfer the subject from the master die to the printing plate. A blank roll of soft steel, mounted on a mandrel, is placed under the bearers of the transfer press to allow it to roll freely on its axis. The hardened die is placed on the bed of the press and the face of the transfer roll is applied to the die, under pressure. The bed or the roll is then rocked back and forth under increasing pressure, until the soft steel of the roll is forced into every engraved line of the die. The resulting impression on the roll is known as a "relief" or a "relief transfer." The engraved image is now positive in appearance and stands out from the steel. After the required number of reliefs are "rocked in," the soft steel transfer roll is hardened.

Different flaws may occur during the relief process. A defective relief may occur during the rocking in process because of a minute piece of foreign material lodging on the die, or some other cause. Imperfections in the steel of the transfer roll may result in a breaking away of parts of the design. This is known as a relief break, which will show up on finished stamps as small, unprinted areas. If a damaged relief remains in use, it will transfer a repeating defect to the plate. Deliberate alterations of reliefs sometimes occur. "Altered reliefs" designate these changed conditions.

Plate — The final step in pre-printing production is the making of the printing plate. A flat piece of soft steel replaces the die on the bed of the transfer press. One of the reliefs on the transfer roll is positioned over this soft steel. Position, or layout, dots determine the correct position on the plate. The dots have been lightly marked on the plate in advance. After the correct position of the relief is determined, the design is rocked in by following the same method used in making the transfer roll. The difference is that this time the image is being transferred from the transfer roll, rather than to it. Once the design is entered on the plate, it appears in reverse and is recessed. There are as many transfers entered on the plate as there are subjects printed on the sheet of stamps. It is during this process that double and shifted transfers occur, as well as re-entries. These are the result of improperly entered images that have not been properly burnished out prior to rocking in a new image.

Modern siderography processes, such as those used by the U.S. Bureau of Engraving and Printing, involve an automated form of rocking designs in on preformed cylindrical printing sleeves. The same process also allows for easier removal and re-entry of worn images right on the sleeve.

Transferring the design to the plate

Following the entering of the required transfers on the plate, the position dots, layout dots and lines, scratches and other markings generally are burnished out. Added at this time by the siderographer are any required guide lines, plate numbers or other marginal markings. The plate is then hand-inked and a proof impression is taken. This is known as a plate proof. If the impression is approved, the plate is machined for fitting onto the press, is hardened and sent to the plate vault ready for use.

On press, the plate is inked and the surface is automatically wiped clean, leaving ink only in the recessed lines. Paper is then forced under pressure into the engraved recessed lines, thereby receiving the ink. Thus, the ink lines on engraved stamps are slightly raised, and slight depressions (debossing) occur on the back of the stamp. Prior to the advent of modern high-speed presses and more advanced ink formulations, paper had to be dampened before receiving the ink. This sometimes led to uneven shrinkage by the time the stamps were perforated, resulting in improperly perforated stamps, or misperfs. Newer presses use drier paper, thus both *wet and dry printings* exist on some stamps.

Rotary Press — Until 1914, only flat plates were used to print engraved stamps. Rotary press printing was introduced in 1914, and slowly spread. Some countries still use flat-plate printing.

After approval of the plate proof, older rotary press plates require additional machining. They are curved to fit the press cylinder. "Gripper slots" are cut into the back of each plate to receive the "grippers," which hold the plate securely on the press. The plate is then hardened. Stamps printed from these bent rotary press plates are longer or wider than the same stamps printed from flat-plate presses. The stretching of the plate during the curving process is what causes this distortion.

Re-entry — To execute a re-entry on a flat plate, the transfer roll is re-applied to the plate, often at some time after its first use on the press. Worn-out designs can be resharpened by carefully burnishing out the original image and re-entering it from the transfer roll. If the original impression has not been sufficiently removed and the transfer roll is not precisely in line with the remaining impression, the resulting double transfer will make the re-entry obvious. If the registration is true, a re-entry may be difficult or impossible to distinguish. Sometimes a stamp printed from a successful re-entry is identified by having a much sharper and clearer impression than its neighbors. With the advent of rotary presses, post-press re-entries were not possible. After a plate was curved for the rotary press, it was impossible to make a re-entry. This is because the plate had already been bent once (with the design distorted).

However, with the introduction of the previously mentioned modern-style siderography machines, entries are made to the preformed cylindrical printing sleeve. Such sleeves are dechromed and softened. This allows individual images to be burnished out and re-entered on the curved sleeve. The sleeve is then rechromed, resulting in longer press life.

Double Transfer — This is a description of the condition of a transfer on a plate that shows evidence of a duplication of all, or a portion of the design. It usually is the result of the changing of the registration between the transfer roll and the plate during the rocking in of the original entry. Double transfers also occur when only a portion of the design has been rocked in and improper positioning is noted. If the worker elected not to burnish out the partial or completed design, a strong double transfer will occur for part or all of the design.

It sometimes is necessary to remove the original transfer from a plate and repeat the process a second time. If the finished re-worked image shows traces of the original impression, attributable to incomplete burnishing, the result is a partial double transfer.

With the modern automatic machines mentioned previously, double transfers are all but impossible to create. Those partially doubled images on stamps printed from such sleeves are more than likely re-entries, rather than true double transfers.

Re-engraved — Alterations to a stamp design are sometimes necessary after some stamps have been printed. In some cases, either the original die or the actual printing plate may have its "temper" drawn (softened), and the design will be re-cut. The resulting impressions from such a re-engraved die or plate may differ slightly from the original issue, and are known as "re-engraved." If the alteration was made to the master die, all future printings will be consistently different from the original. If alterations were made to the printing plate, each altered stamp on the plate will be slightly different from each other, allowing specialists to reconstruct a complete printing plate.

Dropped Transfers — If an impression from the transfer roll has not been properly placed, a dropped transfer may occur. The final stamp image will appear obviously out of line with its neighbors.

Short Transfer — Sometimes a transfer roll is not rocked its entire length when entering a transfer onto a plate. As a result, the finished transfer on the plate fails to show the complete design, and the finished stamp will have an incomplete design printed. This is known as a "short transfer." U.S. Scott No. 8 is a good example of a short transfer.

TYPOGRAPHY (Letterpress, Surface Printing, Flexography, Dry Offset, High Etch)

Although the word "Typography" is obsolete as a term describing a printing method, it was the accepted term throughout the first century of postage stamps. Therefore, appropriate Scott listings in this catalogue refer to typographed stamps. The current term for this form of printing, however, is "letterpress."

As it relates to the production of postage stamps, letterpress printing is the reverse of engraving. Rather than having recessed areas trap the ink and deposit it on paper, only the raised areas of the design are inked. This is comparable to the type of printing seen by inking and using an ordinary rubber stamp. Letterpress includes all printing where the design is above the surface area, whether it is wood, metal or, in some instances, hardened rubber or polymer plastic.

For most letterpress-printed stamps, the engraved master is made in much the same manner as for engraved stamps. In this instance, however, an additional step is needed. The design is transferred to another surface before being transferred to the transfer roll. In this way, the transfer roll has a recessed stamp design, rather than one done in relief. This makes the printing areas on the final plate raised, or relief areas.

For less-detailed stamps of the 19th century, the area on the die not used as a printing surface was cut away, leaving the surface area raised. The original die was then reproduced by stereotyping or electrotyping. The resulting electrotypes were assembled in the required number and format of the desired sheet of stamps. The plate used in printing the stamps was an electroplate of these assembled electrotypes.

Once the final letterpress plates are created, ink is applied to the raised surface and the pressure of the press transfers the ink impression to the paper. In contrast to engraving, the fine lines of letterpress are impressed on the surface of the stamp, leaving a debossed surface. When viewed from the back (as on a typewritten page), the corresponding line work on the stamp will be raised slightly (embossed) above the surface.

PHOTOGRAVURE (Gravure, Rotogravure, Heliogravure)

In this process, the basic principles of photography are applied to a chemically sensitized metal plate, rather than photographic paper. The design is transferred photographically to the plate through a halftone, or dot-matrix screen, breaking the reproduction into tiny dots. The plate is treated chemically and the dots form depressions, called cells, of varying depths and diameters, depending on the degrees of shade in the design. Then, like engraving, ink is applied to the plate and the surface is wiped clean. This leaves ink in the tiny cells that is lifted out and deposited on the paper when it is pressed against the plate.

Gravure is most often used for multicolored stamps, generally using the three primary colors (red, yellow and blue) and black. By varying the dot matrix pattern and density of these colors, virtually any color can be reproduced. A typical full-color gravure stamp will be created from four printing cylinders (one for each color). The original multicolored image will have been photographically separated into its component colors.

Modern gravure printing may use computer-generated dot-matrix screens, and modern plates may be of various types including metal-coated plastic. The catalogue designation of Photogravure (or "Photo") covers any of these older and more modern gravure methods of printing.

For examples of the first photogravure stamps printed (1914), see Bavaria Scott 94-114.

LITHOGRAPHY (Offset Lithography, Stone Lithography, Dilitho, Planography, Collotype)

The principle that oil and water do not mix is the basis for lithography. The stamp design is drawn by hand or transferred from engraving to the surface of a lithographic stone or metal plate in a greasy (oily) substance. This oily substance holds the ink, which will later be transferred to the paper. The stone (or plate) is wet with an acid fluid, causing it to repel the printing ink in all areas not covered by the greasy substance.

Transfer paper is used to transfer the design from the original stone or plate. A series of duplicate transfers are grouped and, in turn, transferred to the final printing plate.

Photolithography — The application of photographic processes to lithography. This process allows greater flexibility of design, related to use of halftone screens combined with line work. Unlike photogravure or engraving, this process can allow large, solid areas to be printed.

Offset — A refinement of the lithographic process. A rubber-covered blanket cylinder takes the impression from the inked lithographic plate. From the "blanket" the impression is offset or transferred to the paper. Greater flexibility and speed are the principal reasons offset printing has largely displaced lithography. The term "lithography" covers both processes, and results are almost identical.

EMBOSSED (Relief) Printing

Embossing, not considered one of the four main printing types, is a method in which the design first is sunk into the metal of the die. Printing is done against a yielding platen, such as leather or linoleum. The platen is forced into the depression of the die, thus forming the design on the paper in relief. This process is often used for metallic inks.

Embossing may be done without color (see Sardinia Scott 4-6); with color printed around the embossed area (see Great Britain Scott 5 and most U.S. envelopes); and with color in exact registration with the embossed subject (see Canada Scott 656-657).

HOLOGRAMS

For objects to appear as holograms on stamps, a model exactly the same size as it is to appear on the hologram must be created. Rather than using photographic film to capture the image, holography records an image on a photoresist material. In processing, chemicals eat away at certain exposed areas, leaving a pattern of constructive and destructive interference. When the photoresist is developed, the result is a pattern of uneven ridges that acts as a mold. This mold is then coated with metal, and the resulting form is used to press copies in much the same way phonograph records are produced.

A typical reflective hologram used for stamps consists of a reproduction of the uneven patterns on a plastic film that is applied to a reflective background, usually a silver or gold foil. Light is reflected off the background through the film, making the pattern present on the film visible. Because of the uneven pattern of the film, the viewer will perceive the objects in their proper three-dimensional relationships with appropriate brightness. The first hologram on a stamp was produced by Austria in 1988 (Scott 1441).

FOIL APPLICATION

A modern technique of applying color to stamps involves the application of metallic foil to the stamp paper. A pattern of foil is applied to the stamp paper by use of a stamping die. The foil usually is flat, but it may be textured. Canada Scott 1735 has three different foil applications in pearl, bronze and gold. The gold foil was textured using

a chemical-etch copper embossing die. The printing of this stamp also involved two-color offset lithography plus embossing.

THERMOGRAPHY

In the 1990s stamps began to be enhanced with thermographic printing. In this process, a powdered polymer is applied over a sheet that has just been printed. The powder adheres to ink that lacks drying or hardening agents and does not adhere to areas where the ink has these agents. The excess powder is removed and the sheet is briefly heated to melt the powder. The melted powder solidifies after cooling, producing a raised, shiny effect on the stamps. See Scott New Caledonia C239-C240.

COMBINATION PRINTINGS

Sometimes two or even three printing methods are combined in producing stamps. In these cases, such as Austria Scott 933 or Canada 1735 (described in the preceding paragraph), the multiple-printing technique can be determined by studying the individual characteristics of each printing type. A few stamps, such as Singapore Scott 684-684A, combine as many as three of the four major printing types (lithography, engraving and typography). When this is done it often indicates the incorporation of security devices against counterfeiting.

INK COLORS

Inks or colored papers used in stamp printing often are of mineral origin, although there are numerous examples of organic-based pigments. As a general rule, organic-based pigments are far more subject to varieties and change than those of mineral-based origin.

The appearance of any given color on a stamp may be affected by many aspects, including printing variations, light, color of paper, aging and chemical alterations.

Numerous printing variations may be observed. Heavier pressure or inking will cause a more intense color, while slight interruptions in the ink feed or lighter impressions will cause a lighter appearance. Stamps printed in the same color by water-based and solvent-based inks can differ significantly in appearance. This affects several stamps in the U.S. Prominent Americans series. Hand-mixed ink formulas (primarily from the 19th century) produced under different conditions (humidity and temperature) account for notable color variations in early printings of the same stamp (see U.S. Scott 248-250, 279B, for example). Different sources of pigment can also result in significant differences in color.

Light exposure and aging are closely related in the way they affect stamp color. Both eventually break down the ink and fade colors, so that a carefully kept stamp may differ significantly in color from an identical copy that has been exposed to light. If stamps are exposed to light either intentionally or accidentally, their colors can be faded or completely changed in some cases.

Papers of different quality and consistency used for the same stamp printing may affect color appearance. Most pelure papers, for example, show a richer color when compared with wove or laid papers. See Russia Scott 181a, for an example of this effect.

The very nature of the printing processes can cause a variety of differences in shades or hues of the same stamp. Some of these shades are scarcer than others, and are of particular interest to the advanced collector.

Luminescence

All forms of tagged stamps fall under the general category of luminescence. Within this broad category is fluorescence, dealing with forms of tagging visible under longwave ultraviolet light, and phosphorescence, which deals with tagging visible only under shortwave light. Phosphorescence leaves an afterglow and fluorescence does not. These treated stamps show up in a range of different colors when exposed to UV light. The differing wavelengths of the light activates the tagging material, making it glow in various colors that usually serve different mail processing purposes.

Intentional tagging is a post-World War II phenomenon, brought about by the increased literacy rate and rapidly growing mail volume. It was one of several answers to the problem of the need for more automated mail processes. Early tagged stamps served the purpose of triggering machines to separate different types of mail. A natural outgrowth was to also use the signal to trigger machines that faced all envelopes the same way and canceled them.

Tagged stamps come in many different forms. Some tagged stamps have luminescent shapes or images imprinted on them as a form of security device. Others have blocks (United States), stripes, frames (South Africa and Canada), overall coatings (United States), bars (Great Britain and Canada) and many other types. Some types of tagging are even mixed in with the pigmented printing ink (Australia Scott 366, Netherlands Scott 478 and U.S. Scott 1359 and 2443).

The means of applying taggant to stamps differs as much as the intended purposes for the stamps. The most common form of tagging is a coating applied to the surface of the printed stamp. Since the taggant ink is frequently invisible except under UV light, it does not interfere with the appearance of the stamp. Another common application is the use of phosphored papers. In this case the paper itself either has a coating of taggant applied before the stamp is printed, has taggant applied during the papermaking process (incorporating it into the fibers), or has the taggant mixed into the coating of the paper. The latter method, among others, is currently in use in the United States.

Many countries now use tagging in various forms to either expedite mail handling or to serve as a printing security device against counterfeiting. Following the introduction of tagged stamps for public use in 1959 by Great Britain, other countries have steadily joined the parade. Among those are Germany (1961); Canada and Denmark (1962); United States, Australia, France and Switzerland (1963); Belgium and Japan (1966); Sweden and Norway (1967); Italy (1968); and Russia (1969). Since then, many other countries have begun using forms of tagging, including Brazil, China, Czechoslovakia, Hong Kong, Guatemala, Indonesia, Israel, Lithuania, Luxembourg, Netherlands, Penrhyn Islands, Portugal, St. Vincent, Singapore, South Africa, Spain and Sweden to name a few.

In some cases, including United States, Canada, Great Britain and Switzerland, stamps were released both with and without tagging. Many of these were released during each country's experimental period. Tagged and untagged versions are listed for the aforementioned countries and are noted in some other countries' listings. For at least a few stamps, the experimentally tagged version is worth far more than its untagged counterpart, such as the 1963 experimental tagged version of France Scott 1024.

In some cases, luminescent varieties of stamps were inadvertently created. Several Russian stamps, for example, sport highly fluorescent ink that was not intended as a form of tagging. Older stamps, such as early U.S. postage dues, can be positively identified by the use of UV light, since the organic ink used has become slightly fluorescent over time. Other stamps, such as Austria Scott 70a-82a (varnish bars) and Obock Scott 46-64 (printed quadrille lines), have become fluorescent over time.

Various fluorescent substances have been added to paper to make it appear brighter. These optical brightners, as they are known, greatly affect the appearance of the stamp under UV light. The brightest of these is known as Hi-Brite paper. These paper varieties are beyond the scope of the Scott Catalogue.

Shortwave UV light also is used extensively in expertizing, since each form of paper has its own fluorescent characteristics that are impossible to perfectly match. It is therefore a simple matter to detect filled thins, added perforation teeth and other alterations that involve the addition of paper. UV light also is used to examine stamps that have had cancels chemically removed and for other purposes as well.

Gum

The Illustrated Gum Chart in the first part of this introduction shows and defines various types of gum condition. Because gum condition has an important impact on the value of unused stamps, we recommend studying this chart and the accompanying text carefully.

The gum on the back of a stamp may be shiny, dull, smooth, rough, dark, white, colored or tinted. Most stamp gumming adhesives use gum arabic or dextrine as a base. Certain polymers such as polyvinyl alcohol (PVA) have been used extensively since World War II.

The Scott Standard Postage Stamp Catalogue does not list items by types of gum. The Scott Specialized Catalogue of United States Stamps and Covers does differentiate among some types of gum for certain issues.

Reprints of stamps may have gum differing from the original issues. In addition, some countries have used different gum formulas for different seasons. These adhesives have different properties that may become more apparent over time.

Many stamps have been issued without gum, and the catalogue will note this fact. See, for example, United States Scott 40-47. Sometimes, gum may have been removed to preserve the stamp. Germany Scott B68, for example, has a highly acidic gum that eventually destroys the stamps. This item is valued in the catalogue with gum removed.

Reprints and reissues

These are impressions of stamps (usually obsolete) made from the original plates or stones. If they are valid for postage and reproduce obsolete issues (such as U.S. Scott 102-111), the stamps are reissues. If they are from current issues, they are designated as second, third,

etc., printing. If designated for a particular purpose, they are called special printings.

When special printings are not valid for postage, but are made from original dies and plates by authorized persons, they are official reprints. Private reprints are made from the original plates and dies by private hands. An example of a private reprint is that of the 1871-1932 reprints made from the original die of the 1845 New Haven, Conn., postmaster's provisional. Official reproductions or imitations are made from new dies and plates by government authorization. Scott will list those reissues that are valid for postage if they differ significantly from the original printing.

The U.S. government made special printings of its first postage stamps in 1875. Produced were official imitations of the first two stamps (listed as Scott 3-4), reprints of the demonetized pre-1861 issues (Scott 40-47) and reissues of the 1861 stamps, the 1869 stamps and the then-current 1875 denominations. Even though the official imitations and the reprints were not valid for postage, Scott lists all of these U.S. special printings.

Most reprints or reissues differ slightly from the original stamp in some characteristic, such as gum, paper, perforation, color or watermark. Sometimes the details are followed so meticulously that only a student of that specific stamp is able to distinguish the reprint or reissue from the original.

Remainders and canceled to order

Some countries sell their stock of old stamps when a new issue replaces them. To avoid postal use, the remainders usually are canceled with a punch hole, a heavy line or bar, or a more-or-less regular-looking cancellation. The most famous merchant of remainders was Nicholas F. Seebeck. In the 1880s and 1890s, he arranged printing contracts between the Hamilton Bank Note Co., of which he was a director, and several Central and South American countries. The contracts provided that the plates and all remainders of the yearly issues became the property of Hamilton. Seebeck saw to it that ample stock remained. The "Seebecks," both remainders and reprints, were standard packet fillers for decades.

Some countries also issue stamps canceled-to-order (CTO), either in sheets with original gum or stuck onto pieces of paper or envelopes and canceled. Such CTO items generally are worth less than postally used stamps. In cases where the CTO material is far more prevalent in the marketplace than postally used examples, the catalogue value relates to the CTO examples, with postally used examples noted as premium items. Most CTOs can be detected by the presence of gum. However, as the CTO practice goes back at least to 1885, the gum inevitably has been soaked off some stamps so they could pass as postally used. The normally applied postmarks usually differ slightly from standard postmarks, and specialists are able to tell the difference. When applied individually to envelopes by philatelically minded persons, CTO material is known as favor canceled and generally sells at large discounts.

Cinderellas and facsimiles

Cinderella is a catch-all term used by stamp collectors to describe phantoms, fantasies, bogus items, municipal issues, exhibition seals, local revenues, transportation stamps, labels, poster stamps and many other types of items. Some cinderella collectors include in their collections local postage issues, telegraph stamps, essays and proofs, forgeries and counterfeits.

A fantasy is an adhesive created for a nonexistent stamp-issuing authority. Fantasy items range from imaginary countries (Occusi-Ambeno, Kingdom of Sedang, Principality of Trinidad or Torres Straits), to non-existent locals (Winans City Post), or nonexistent transportation lines (McRobish & Co.'s Acapulco-San Francisco Line).

On the other hand, if the entity exists and could have issued stamps (but did not) or was known to have issued other stamps, the items are considered bogus stamps. These would include the Mormon postage stamps of Utah, S. Allan Taylor's Guatemala and Paraguay inventions, the propaganda issues for the South Moluccas and the adhesives of the Page & Keyes local post of Boston. Phantoms is another term for both fantasy and bogus issues.

Facsimiles are copies or imitations made to represent original stamps, but which do not pretend to be originals. A catalogue illustration is such a facsimile. Illustrations from the Moens catalogue of the last century were occasionally colored and passed off as stamps. Since the beginning of stamp collecting, facsimiles have been made for collectors as space fillers or for reference. They often carry the word "facsimile," "falsch" (German), "sanko" or "mozo" (Japanese), or "faux" (French) overprinted on the face or stamped on the back. Unfortunately, over the years a number of these items have had fake cancels applied over the facsimile notation and have been passed off as genuine.

Forgeries and counterfeits

Forgeries and counterfeits have been with philately virtually from the beginning of stamp production. Over time, the terminology for the two has been used interchangeably. Although both forgeries and counterfeits are reproductions of stamps, the purposes behind their creation differ considerably.

Among specialists there is an increasing movement to more specifically define such items. Although there is no universally accepted terminology, we feel the following definitions most closely mirror the items and their purposes as they are currently defined.

Forgeries (also often referred to as Counterfeits) are reproductions of genuine stamps that have been created to defraud collectors. Such spurious items first appeared on the market around 1860, and most old-time collections contain one or more. Many are crude and easily spotted, but some can deceive experts.

An important supplier of these early philatelic forgeries was the Hamburg printer Gebruder Spiro. Many others with reputations in this craft included S. Allan Taylor, George Hussey, James Chute, George Forune, Benjamin & Sarpy, Julius Goldner, E. Oneglia and L.H. Mercier. Among the noted 20th-century forgers were Francois Fournier, Jean Sperati and the prolific Raoul DeThuin.

Forgeries may be complete replications, or they may be genuine stamps altered to resemble a scarcer (and more valuable) type. Most forgeries, particularly those of rare stamps, are worth only a small fraction of the value of a genuine example, but a few types, created by some of the most notable forgers, such as Sperati, can be worth as much or more than the genuine. Fraudulently produced copies are known of most classic rarities and many medium-priced stamps.

In addition to rare stamps, large numbers of common 19th- and early 20th-century stamps were forged to supply stamps to the early packet trade. Many can still be easily found. Few new philatelic forgeries have appeared in recent decades. Successful imitation of well-engraved work is virtually impossible. It has proven far easier to produce a fake by altering a genuine stamp than to duplicate a stamp completely.

Counterfeit (also often referred to as Postal Counterfeit or Postal Forgery) is the term generally applied to reproductions of stamps that have been created to defraud the government of revenue. Such items usually are created at the time a stamp is current and, in some cases, are hard to detect. Because most counterfeits are seized when the perpetrator is captured, postal counterfeits, particularly used on cover, are usually worth much more than a genuine example to specialists. The first postal counterfeit was of Spain's 4-cuarto carmine of 1854 (the real one is Scott 25). Apparently, the counterfeiters were not satisfied with their first version, which is now very scarce, and they soon created an engraved counterfeit, which is common. Postal counterfeits quickly followed in Austria, Naples, Sardinia and the Roman States. They have since been created in many other countries as well, including the United States.

An infamous counterfeit to defraud the government is the 1-shilling Great Britain "Stock Exchange" forgery of 1872, used on telegraph forms at the exchange that year. The stamp escaped detection until a stamp dealer noticed it in 1898.

Fakes

Fakes are genuine stamps altered in some way to make them more desirable. One student of this part of stamp collecting has estimated that by the 1950s more than 30,000 varieties of fakes were known. That number has grown greatly since then. The widespread existence of fakes makes it important for stamp collectors to study their philatelic holdings and use relevant literature. Likewise, collectors should buy from reputable dealers who guarantee their stamps and make full and prompt refunds should a purchased item be declared faked or altered by some mutually agreed-upon authority. Because fakes always have some genuine characteristics, it is not always possible to obtain unanimous agreement among experts regarding specific items. These students may change their opinions as philatelic knowledge increases. More than 80 percent of all fakes on the philatelic market today are regummed, reperforated (or perforated for the first time), or bear forged overprints, surcharges or cancellations.

Stamps can be chemically treated to alter or eliminate colors. For example, a pale rose stamp can be re-colored to resemble a blue shade of high market value. In other cases, treated stamps can be made to resemble missing color varieties. Designs may be changed by painting, or a stroke or a dot added or bleached out to turn an ordinary variety into a seemingly scarcer stamp. Part of a stamp can be bleached and reprinted in a different version, achieving an inverted center or frame. Margins can be added or repairs done so deceptively that the stamps move from the "repaired" into the "fake" category.

Fakers have not left the backs of the stamps untouched either. They may create false watermarks, add fake grills or press out genuine grills.

A thin India paper proof may be glued onto a thicker backing to create the appearance an issued stamp, or a proof printed on cardboard may be shaved down and perforated to resemble a stamp. Silk threads are impressed into paper and stamps have been split so that a rare paper variety is added to an otherwise inexpensive stamp. The most common treatment to the back of a stamp, however, is regumming.

Some in the business of faking stamps have openly advertised fool-proof application of "original gum" to stamps that lack it, although most publications now ban such ads from their pages. It is believed that very few early stamps have survived without being hinged. The large number of never-hinged examples of such earlier material offered for sale thus suggests the widespread extent of regumming activity. Regumming also may be used to hide repairs or thin spots. Dipping the stamp into watermark fluid, or examining it under longwave ultraviolet light often will reveal these flaws.

Fakers also tamper with separations. Ingenious ways to add margins are known. Perforated wide-margin stamps may be falsely represented as imperforate when trimmed. Reperforating is commonly done to create scarce coil or perforation varieties, and to eliminate the naturally occurring straight-edge stamps found in sheet margin positions of many earlier issues. Custom has made straight-edged stamps less desirable. Fakers have obliged by perforating straight-edged stamps so that many are now uncommon, if not rare.

Another fertile field for the faker is that of overprints, surcharges and cancellations. The forging of rare surcharges or overprints began in the 1880s or 1890s. These forgeries are sometimes difficult to detect, but experts have identified almost all. Occasionally, overprints or cancellations are removed to create non-overprinted stamps or seemingly unused items. This is most commonly done by removing a manuscript cancel to make a stamp resemble an unused example. "SPECIMEN" overprints may be removed by scraping and repainting to create non-overprinted varieties. Fakers use inexpensive revenues or pen-canceled stamps to generate unused stamps for further faking by adding other markings. The quartz lamp or UV lamp and a high-powered magnifying glass help to easily detect removed cancellations.

The bigger problem, however, is the addition of overprints, surcharges or cancellations — many with such precision that they are very difficult to ascertain. Plating of the stamps or the overprint can be an important method of detection.

Fake postmarks may range from many spurious fancy cancellations to a host of markings applied to transatlantic covers, to adding normally appearing postmarks to definitives of some countries with stamps that are valued far higher used than unused. With the increased popularity of cover collecting, and the widespread interest in postal history, a fertile new field for fakers has come about. Some have tried to create entire covers. Others specialize in adding stamps, tied by fake cancellations, to genuine stampless covers, or replacing less expensive or damaged stamps with more valuable ones. Detailed study of postal rates in effect at the time a cover in question was mailed, including the analysis of each handstamp used during the period, ink analysis and similar techniques, usually will unmask the fraud.

Restoration and repairs

Scott bases its catalogue values on stamps that are free of defects and otherwise meet the standards set forth earlier in this introduction. Most stamp collectors desire to have the finest copy of an item possible. Even within given grading categories there are variances. This leads to a controversial practice that is not defined in any universal manner: stamp *restoration*.

There are broad differences of opinion about what is permissible when it comes to restoration. Carefully applying a soft eraser to a stamp or cover to remove light soiling is one form of restoration, as is washing a stamp in mild soap and water to clean it. These are fairly accepted forms of restoration. More severe forms of restoration include pressing out creases or removing stains caused by tape. To what degree each of these is acceptable is dependent upon the individual situation. Further along the spectrum is the freshening of a stamp's color by removing oxide build-up or the effects of wax paper left next to stamps shipped to the tropics.

At some point in this spectrum the concept of *repair* replaces that of restoration. Repairs include filling thin spots, mending tears by reweaving or adding a missing perforation tooth. Regumming stamps may have been acceptable as a restoration or repair technique many decades ago, but today it is considered a form of fakery.

Restored stamps may or may not sell at a discount, and it is possible that the value of individual restored items may be enhanced over that of their pre-restoration state. Specific situations dictate the resultant value of such an item. Repaired stamps sell at substantial discounts from the value of sound stamps.

Terminology

Booklets — Many countries have issued stamps in small booklets for the convenience of users. This idea continues to become increasingly popular in many countries. Booklets have been issued in many sizes and forms, often with advertising on the covers, the panes of stamps or on the interleaving.

The panes used in booklets may be printed from special plates or made from regular sheets. All panes from booklets issued by the United States and many from those of other countries contain stamps that are straight edged on the sides, but perforated between. Others are distinguished by orientation of watermark or other identifying features. Any stamp-like unit in the pane, either printed or blank, that is not a postage stamp, is considered to be a *label* in the catalogue listings.

Scott lists and values booklet panes. Modern complete booklets also are listed and valued. Individual booklet panes are listed only when they are not fashioned from existing sheet stamps and, therefore, are identifiable from their sheet stamp counterparts.

Panes usually do not have a used value assigned to them because there is little market activity for used booklet panes, even though many exist used and there is some demand for them.

Cancellations — The marks or obliterations put on stamps by postal authorities to show that they have performed service and to prevent their reuse are known as cancellations. If the marking is made with a pen, it is considered a "pen cancel." When the location of the post office appears in the marking, it is a "town cancellation." A "postmark" is technically any postal marking, but in practice the term generally is applied to a town cancellation with a date. When calling attention to a cause or celebration, the marking is known as a "slogan cancellation." Many other types and styles of cancellations exist, such as duplex, numerals, targets, fancy and others. See also "precancels," below.

Coil Stamps — These are stamps that are issued in rolls for use in dispensers, affixing and vending machines. Those coils of the United States, Canada, Sweden and some other countries are perforated horizontally or vertically only, with the outer edges imperforate. Coil stamps of some countries, such as Great Britain and Germany, are perforated on all four sides and may in some cases be distinguished from their sheet stamp counterparts by watermarks, counting numbers on the reverse or other means.

Covers — Entire envelopes, with or without adhesive postage stamps, that have passed through the mail and bear postal or other markings of philatelic interest are known as covers. Before the introduction of envelopes in about 1840, people folded letters and wrote the address on the outside. Some people covered their letters with an extra sheet of paper on the outside for the address, producing the term "cover." Used airletter sheets, stamped envelopes and other items of postal stationery also are considered covers.

Errors — Stamps that have some major, consistent, unintentional deviation from the normal are considered errors. Errors include, but are not limited to, missing or wrong colors, wrong paper, wrong watermarks, inverted centers or frames on multicolor printing, inverted or missing surcharges or overprints, double impressions, missing perforations, unintentionally omitted tagging and others. Factually wrong or misspelled information, if it appears on all examples of a stamp, are not considered errors in the true sense of the word. They are errors of design. Inconsistent or randomly appearing items, such as misperfs or color shifts, are classified as freaks.

Color-Omitted Errors — This term refers to stamps where a missing color is caused by the complete failure of the printing plate to deliver ink to the stamp paper or any other paper. Generally, this is caused by the printing plate not being engaged on the press or the ink station running dry of ink during printing.

Color-Missing Errors — This term refers to stamps where a color or colors were printed somewhere but do not appear on the finished stamp. There are four different classes of color-missing errors, and the catalog indicates with a two-letter code appended to each such listing what caused the color to be missing. These codes are used only for the United States' color-missing error listings.

FO = A *foldover* of the stamp sheet during printing may block ink from appearing on the face of a stamp. Instead, the color will appear on the back of the foldover (where it might fall on the back of the selvage or perhaps a bit on the back of the stamp or on the back of another stamp. FO also will be used in the case of foldunders, where the paper may fold underneath the other stamp paper and the color will print on the platen.

EP = When the extraneous paper is removed, an unprinted area of stamp paper remains and may show a color or colors to be totally missing on the finished stamp.

CM = A misregistration of the printing plates during printing will result in a *color misregistration*, and such a misregistraion may result in a color not appearing on the finished stamp.

PS = A *perforation shift* after printing may remove a color from the finished stamp. Normally, this will occur on a row of stamps at the edge of the stamp pane.

Measurements – When measurements are given in the Scott catalogues for stamp size, grill size or any other reason, the first measurement given is always for the top and bottom dimension, while the second measurement will be for the sides (just as perforation gauges are measured). Thus, a stamp size of 15mm x 21mm will indicate a vertically oriented stamp 15mm wide at top and bottom, and 21mm tall at the sides. The same principle holds for measuring or counting items such as U.S. grills. A grill count of 22x18 points (B grill) indicates that there are 22 grill points across by 18 grill points down.

Overprints and Surcharges — Overprinting involves applying wording or design elements over an already existing stamp. Overprints can be used to alter the place of use (such as "Canal Zone" on U.S. stamps), to adapt them for a special purpose ("Porto" on Denmark's 1913-20 regular issues for use as postage due stamps, Scott J1-J7) or to commemorate a special occasion (United States Scott 647-648).

A *surcharge* is a form of overprint that changes or restates the face value of a stamp or piece of postal stationery.

Surcharges and overprints may be handstamped, typeset or, occasionally, lithographed or engraved. A few hand-written overprints and surcharges are known.

Personalized Stamps — In 1999, Australia issued stamps with se-tenant labels that could be personalized with pictures of the customer's choice. Other countries quickly followed suit, with some offering to print the selected picture on the stamp itself within a frame that was used exclusively for personalized issues. As the picture used on these stamps or labels vary, listings for such stamps are for any picture within the common frame (or any picture on a se-tenant label), be it a "generic" image or one produced especially for a customer, almost invariably at a premium price.

Precancels — Stamps that are canceled before they are placed in the mail are known as precancels. Precanceling usually is done to expedite the handling of large mailings and generally allow the affected mail pieces to skip certain phases of mail handling.

In the United States, precancellations generally identified the point of origin; that is, the city and state. This information appeared across the face of the stamp, usually centered between parallel lines. More recently, bureau precancels retained the parallel lines, but the city and state designations were dropped. Recent coils have a service inscription that is present on the original printing plate. These show the mail service paid for by the stamp. Since these stamps are not intended to receive further cancellations when used as intended, they are considered precancels. Such items often do not have parallel lines as part of the precancellation.

In France, the abbreviation *Affranchts* in a semicircle together with the word *Postes* is the general form of precancel in use. Belgian precancellations usually appear in a box in which the name of the city appears. Netherlands precancels have the name of the city enclosed between concentric circles, sometimes called a "lifesaver." Precancellations of other countries usually follow these patterns, but may be any arrangement of bars, boxes and city names.

Precancels are listed in the Scott catalogues only if the precancel changes the denomination (Belgium Scott 477-478); if the precanceled stamp is different from the non-precanceled version (such as untagged U.S. precancels); or if the stamp exists only precanceled (France Scott 1096-1099, U.S. Scott 2265).

Proofs and Essays — Proofs are impressions taken from an approved die, plate or stone in which the design and color are the same as the stamp issued to the public. Trial color proofs are impressions taken from approved dies, plates or stones in colors that vary from the final version. An essay is the impression of a design that differs in some way from the issued stamp. "Progressive die proofs" generally are considered to be essays.

Provisionals — These are stamps that are issued on short notice and intended for temporary use pending the arrival of regular issues. They usually are issued to meet such contingencies as changes in government or currency, shortage of necessary postage values or military occupation.

During the 1840s, postmasters in certain American cities issued stamps that were valid only at specific post offices. In 1861, postmasters of the Confederate States also issued stamps with limited validity. Both of these examples are known as "postmaster's provisionals."

Se-tenant — This term refers to an unsevered pair, strip or block of stamps that differ in design, denomination or overprint.

Unless the se-tenant item has a continuous design (see U.S. Scott 1451a, 1694a) the stamps do not have to be in the same order as shown in the catalogue (see U.S. Scott 2158a).

Specimens — The Universal Postal Union required member nations to send samples of all stamps they released into service to the International Bureau in Switzerland. Member nations of the UPU received these specimens as samples of what stamps were valid for postage. Many are overprinted, handstamped or initial-perforated "Specimen," "Canceled" or "Muestra." Some are marked with bars across the denominations (China-Taiwan), punched holes (Czechoslovakia) or back inscriptions (Mongolia).

Stamps distributed to government officials or for publicity purposes, and stamps submitted by private security printers for official approval, also may receive such defacements.

The previously described defacement markings prevent postal use, and all such items generally are known as "specimens."

Tete-Beche — This term describes a pair of stamps in which one is upside down in relation to the other. Some of these are the result of intentional sheet arrangements, such as Morocco Scott B10-B11. Others occurred when one or more electrotypes accidentally were placed upside down on the plate, such as Colombia Scott 57a. Separation of the tete-beche stamps, of course, destroys the tete beche variety.

Scott International Album Series

The Ultimate Album for Worldwide Collectors! Pick a period in history and embark on a philatelic adventure. With the International Album, the whole world is divided chronologically into 40 parts. From the classic era of philately to present day, the International is one of the broadest and far reaching worldwide albums available. Binders are sold separately.

- More than 16,000 pages with spaces for over 220,000 stamps.
- Pages printed on 2 sides.

Prices and availability are subject to change

SCOTT INTERNATIONAL SET

Item				Retail	AA
INTLALBSET 1840-2015 w/53 binders and slipcases				$18,999.99	$16,149.99
INTL1940 1840-1940 w/4 binders and slipcases				$822.20	$698.87

Item	Part		Binder	Retail	AA
801A140	1A1	1840-1940 US, Aden-Ethiopia	Regular	$173.41	$147.40
801A240	1A2	1840-1940 F-Latvia	Regular	$173.41	$147.40
801B140	1B1	1840-1940 Lebanon Quelimane	Regular	$173.41	$147.40
801B240	1B2	1840-1940 Reunion-Zululand	Regular	$173.41	$147.40
802P149	2A	1940-49 US, Aden-Jamaica	Jumbo	$173.41	$147.40
802P249	2B	1940-49 Japan-Zanzibar	Jumbo	$173.41	$147.40
803P155	3A	1949-55 US, Aden-Jugoslavia	Regular	$173.41	$147.40
803P255	3B	1949-55 Kenya-Zanzibar	Regular	$173.41	$147.40
804P159	4A	1956-60	Regular	$173.41	$147.40
804P259	4B	1956-60	Regular	$173.41	$147.40
805P063	5	1960-63	Jumbo	$173.41	$147.40
805P165	5A	1963-65	Jumbo	$173.41	$147.40
806P066	6	1965-66	Jumbo	$173.41	$147.40
806P168	6A	1966-68	Jumbo	$173.41	$147.40
807P171	7A	1968-71	Jumbo	$173.41	$147.40
807P271	7B	1968-71	Jumbo	$173.41	$147.40
808P173	8A	1971-73	Regular	$173.41	$147.40
808P273	8B	1971-73	Regular	$173.41	$147.40
809P074	9	1973-74	Regular	$173.41	$147.40
810P075	10	1974-75	Jumbo	$194.61	$165.42
811P076	11	1975-76	Jumbo	$173.41	$147.40
812P077	12	1976-77	Jumbo	$173.41	$147.40
813P078	13	1977-78	Jumbo	$194.61	$165.42
814P078	14	1978	Regular	$173.41	$147.40
815P079	15	1979	Regular	$173.41	$147.40
816P080	16	1980	Jumbo	$173.41	$147.40

Item	Part		Binder	Retail	AA
817P081	17	1981	Regular	$173.41	$147.40
818P082	18	1982	Regular	$173.41	$147.40
819P083	19	1983	Regular	$173.41	$147.40
820P084	20	1984	Jumbo	$173.41	$147.40
821P085	21	1985	Jumbo	$194.61	$165.42
822P186	22A	1986	Regular	$173.41	$147.40
822P286	22B	1986	Regular	$173.41	$147.40
823P187	23A	1987	Regular	$173.41	$147.40
823P287	23B	1987	Regular	$173.41	$147.40
824P188	24A	1988	Regular	$173.41	$147.40
824P288	24B	1988	Regular	$173.41	$147.40
825P189	25A	1989	Regular	$173.41	$147.40
825P289	25B	1989	Regular	$173.41	$147.40
826P190	26A	1990	Regular	$173.41	$147.40
826P290	26B	1990	Regular	$173.41	$147.40
827P191	27A	1991	Regular	$173.41	$147.40
827P291	27B	1991	Regular	$173.41	$147.40
828P192	28A	1992	Regular	$173.41	$147.40
828P292	28B	1992	Regular	$173.41	$147.40
829P193	29A	1993	Regular	$173.41	$147.40
829P293	29B	1993	Regular	$173.41	$147.40
830P194	30A	1994	Regular	$173.41	$147.40
830P294	30B	1994	Regular	$173.41	$147.40
831P195	31A	1995	Regular	$173.41	$147.40
831P295	31B	1995	Regular	$173.41	$147.40
832P196	32A	1996	Regular	$173.41	$147.40
832P296	32B	1996	Regular	$173.41	$147.40
833P197	33A	1997	Regular	$173.41	$147.40
833P297	33B	1997	Regular	$173.41	$147.40
834P198	34A	1998	Regular	$173.41	$147.40
834P298	34B	1998	Regular	$173.41	$147.40
835P199	35A	1999	Regular	$173.41	$147.40
835P299	35B	1999	Regular	$173.41	$147.40
836P100	36A	2000	Regular	$173.41	$147.40
836P200	36B	2000	Regular	$173.41	$147.40
837P101	37A	2001	Regular	$173.41	$147.40
837P201	37B	2001	Regular	$173.41	$147.40
838P102	38A	2002	Regular	$173.41	$147.40
838P202	38B	2002	Regular	$173.41	$147.40
839P103	39A	2003	Regular	$173.41	$147.40
839P203	39B	2003	Regular	$173.41	$147.40

Item	Part		Binder	Retail	AA
840P104	40A	2004	Regular	$173.41	$147.40
840P204	40B	2004	Regular	$173.41	$147.40
841P105	41A	2005	Regular	$173.41	$147.40
841P205	41B	2005	Regular	$173.41	$147.40
842P106	42A	2006	Jumbo	$173.41	$147.40
842P206	42B	2006	Jumbo	$173.41	$147.40
843P107	43A	2007	Jumbo	$173.41	$147.40
843P207	43B	2007	Jumbo	$173.41	$147.40
844P108	44A	2008	Jumbo	$173.41	$147.40
844P208	44B	2008	Jumbo	$173.41	$147.40
845P109	45A	2009	Regular	$173.41	$147.40
845P209	45B	2009	Regular	$173.41	$147.40
846P110	46A	2010	Jumbo	$173.41	$147.40
846P210	46B	2010	Jumbo	$173.41	$147.40
847P111	47A	2011	Jumbo	$173.41	$147.40
847P211	47B	2011	Jumbo	$173.41	$147.40
848P112	48A	2012	Jumbo	$173.41	$147.40
848P212	48B	2012	Jumbo	$173.41	$147.40
849P113	49A	2013	Jumbo	$173.41	$147.40
849P213	49B	2013	Jumbo	$173.41	$147.40
850P114	50A	2014	Jumbo	$173.41	$147.40
850P214	50B	2014	Regular	$173.41	$147.40
851P115	51A	2015	Regular	$173.41	$147.40
851P215	51B	2015	Regular	$173.41	$147.40
852P116	52A	2016	Regular	$185.07	$157.31
852P216	52B	2016	Regular	$185.07	$157.31
853P117	53A	2017	Regular	$185.07	$157.31
853P217	53B	2017	Regular	$185.07	$157.31
854P118	54A	2018	Regular	$185.07	$157.31
854P218	54B	2018	Regular	$185.07	$157.31
855P119	55A	2019	Regular	$185.07	$157.31
855P219	55B	2019	Regular	$185.07	$157.31
856P120	56A	2020	Regular	$177.65	$151.00
856P220	56B	2020	Regular	$177.65	$151.00
857P121	57A	2021	Regular	$177.65	$151.00
857P221	57B	2021	Regular	$177.65	$151.00
858P122	58A	2022	Regular	$177.65	$151.00
858P222	58B	2022	Regular	$177.65	$151.00
800BOH	Bosnia & Herzegovina Addendum			$58.64	$49.84
800PC72	People's Republic of China			$58.64	$49.84
800LBLANK	International Blank Label			$5.99	$4.99

SCOTT INTERNATIONAL SERIES BINDERS & SLIPCASES

This attractive, blue two-post binder is available in two sizes. Features distinctive silver embossed spine. Matching slipcases are available. Binder will hold International pages only.

Item		Retail	AA
800B001	Regular Size Binder (Holds 300 Pages)	$55.99	$44.79
800B001SET	Scott Intl Blue Binder & Slipcase Set-Small	$89.98	$71.98
800BC01	Regular Size Slipcase	$33.99	$27.19
800B002	Jumbo Size Binder (Holds 400 Pages)	$55.99	$44.79
800B002SET	Scott Intl Blue Binder & Slipcase Set-Large	$89.98	$71.98
800BC02	Jumbo Size Slipcase	$33.99	$27.19

SCOTT INTERNATIONAL SERIES ACCESSORIES

Protect the pages inside your album with these accessories.

Item		Retail	AA
ACC104	Black Protector Flysheets (2 Per Pack)	$65.99	$5.82
ACC108	Glassine Interleaving (100 Per Pack)	$14.99	$12.85
ACC106	Round Hole Reinforcement	$8.99	$6.74

SCOTT INTERNATIONAL SERIES BLANK PAGES

Perfect for those stamps not illustrated in the International album. Match regular album pages in every respect. Sold in packs of 20.

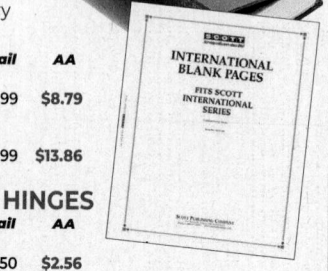

Item		Retail	AA
ACC130	International Blank Pages (2-Sided)	$10.99	$8.79
ACC131	International Quadrille Blank Pages (2-Sided)	$15.99	$13.86

SUPERSAFE PRE-FOLDED HINGES

Item		Retail	AA
SSHI	SuperSafe Hinges - Pack of 1,000	$3.50	$2.56

AmosAdvantage.com | 1-800-572-6885

Pronunciation Symbols

ə .... banana, collide, abut

'ə, ˌə .... humdrum, abut

ə .... immediately preceding \l\, \n\, \m\, \ŋ\, as in battle, mitten, eaten, and sometimes open \'ō-pᵊm\, lock and key \-ᵊŋ-\; immediately following \l\, \m\, \r\, as often in French table, prisme, titre

ər .... further, merger, bird

'ər-
'ə-r } .... as in two different pronunciations of hurry \'hər-ē, 'hə-rē\

a .... mat, map, mad, gag, snap, patch

ā .... day, fade, date, aorta, drape, cape

ä .... bother, cot, and, with most American speakers, father, cart

ȧ .... father as pronounced by speakers who do not rhyme it with bother; French patte

au̇ .... now, loud, out

b .... baby, rib

ch .... chin, nature \'nā-chər\

d .... did, adder

e .... bet, bed, peck

'ē, ˌē .... beat, nosebleed, evenly, easy

ē .... easy, mealy

f .... fifty, cuff

g .... go, big, gift

h .... hat, ahead

hw .... whale as pronounced by those who do not have the same pronunciation for both whale and wail

i .... tip, banish, active

ī .... site, side, buy, tripe

j .... job, gem, edge, join, judge

k .... kin, cook, ache

ḵ .... German ich, Buch; one pronunciation of loch

l .... lily, pool

m .... murmur, dim, nymph

n .... no, own

ⁿ .... indicates that a preceding vowel or diphthong is pronounced with the nasal passages open, as in French un bon vin blanc \œ̃ⁿ -bōⁿ -vaⁿ -bläⁿ\

ŋ .... sing \'siŋ\, singer \'siŋ-ər\, finger \'fiŋ-gər\, ink \'iŋk\

ō .... bone, know, beau

ȯ .... saw, all, gnaw, caught

œ .... French boeuf, German Hölle

œ̄ .... French feu, German Höhle

ȯi .... coin, destroy

p .... pepper, lip

r .... red, car, rarity

s .... source, less

sh .... as in shy, mission, machine, special (actually, this is a single sound, not two); with a hyphen between, two sounds as in grasshopper \'gras-ˌhä-pər\

t .... tie, attack, late, later, latter

th .... as in thin, ether (actually, this is a single sound, not two); with a hyphen between, two sounds as in knighthood \'nīt-ˌhu̇d\

th .... then, either, this (actually, this is a single sound, not two)

ü .... rule, youth, union \'yün-yən\, few \'fyü\

u̇ .... pull, wood, book, curable \'kyu̇r-ə-bəl\, fury \'fyu̇r-ē\

ue .... German füllen, hübsch

ue̅ .... French rue, German fühlen

v .... vivid, give

w .... we, away

y .... yard, young, cue \'kyü\, mute \'myüt\, union \'yün-yən\

ʸ .... indicates that during the articulation of the sound represented by the preceding character the front of the tongue has substantially the position it has for the articulation of the first sound of yard, as in French digne \dēnʸ\

z .... zone, raise

zh .... as in vision, azure \'a-zhər\ (actually, this is a single sound, not two); with a hyphen between, two sounds as in hogshead \'hȯgz-ˌhed, 'hägz-\

\ .... slant line used in pairs to mark the beginning and end of a transcription: \'pen\

' .... mark preceding a syllable with primary (strongest) stress: \'pen-mən-ˌship\

ˌ .... mark preceding a syllable with secondary (medium) stress: \'pen-mən-ˌship\

- .... mark of syllable division

( ) .... indicate that what is symbolized between is present in some utterances but not in others: factory \'fak-t(ə-)rē\

÷ .... indicates that many regard as unacceptable the pronunciation variant immediately following: cupola \'kyü-pə-lə, ÷-ˌlō\

Currency conversion

Country	Dollar	Pound	S Franc	Yen	HK $	Euro	Cdn $	Aus $
Australia	1.4787	1.8317	1.6154	0.0111	0.1884	1.6069	1.0978	—
Canada	1.3470	1.6685	1.4715	0.0101	0.1716	1.4638	—	0.9109
European Union	0.9202	1.1399	1.0052	0.0069	0.1172	—	0.6831	0.6223
Hong Kong	7.8500	9.7240	8.5755	0.0590	—	8.5308	5.8278	5.3087
Japan	133.10	164.87	145.40	—	16.955	144.64	98.812	90.011
Switzerland	0.9154	1.1339	—	0.0069	0.1166	0.9948	0.6796	0.6191
United Kingdom	0.8073	—	0.8819	0.0061	0.1028	0.8773	0.5993	0.5460
United States	—	1.2387	1.0924	0.0075	0.1274	1.0867	0.7424	0.6763

Country	Currency	U.S. $ Equiv.
Namibia	dollar	.0559
Nauru	Australian dollar	.6763
Nepal	rupee	.0076
Netherlands	euro	1.0867
Nevis	East Caribbean dollar	.3704
New Caledonia	Community of French Pacific (CFP) franc	.0091
New Zealand	dollar	.6290
Nicaragua	cordoba	.0273
Niger	CFA franc	.0017
Nigeria	naira	.0022
Niue	New Zealand dollar	.6290
Norfolk Island	Australian dollar	.6763
Norway	krone	.0966
Oman	rial	2.5974
Pakistan	rupee	.0035
Palau	U.S. dollar	1.0000
Palestinian Authority	Jordanian dinar	1.4104
Panama	balboa	1.0000
Papua New Guinea	kina	.2843
Paraguay	guarani	.0001
Penrhyn Island	New Zealand dollar	.6290
Peru	new sol	.2658
Philippines	peso	.0183
Pitcairn Islands	New Zealand dollar	.6290
Poland	zloty	.2326
Portugal	euro	1.0867
Azores	euro	1.0867
Maderia	euro	1.0867
Qatar	riyal	.2747
Romania	leu	.2201
Russia	ruble	.0127
Rwanda	franc	.0009
St. Helena	British pound	1.2387
St. Kitts	East Caribbean dollar	.3704
St. Lucia	East Caribbean dollar	.3704
St. Martin	guilder	.5587
St. Pierre & Miquelon	euro	1.0867
St. Thomas & Prince	dobra	.0440
St. Vincent	East Caribbean dollar	.3704
St. Vincent Grenadines	East Caribbean dollar	.3704
El Salvador	U.S. dollar	1.0000
Samoa	tala (dollar)	.3679

Source: xe.com Apr. 3, 2023. Figures reflect values as of Apr. 3, 2023.

Vols. 5A-5B number additions, deletions and changes

Number in 2023 Catalogue	Number in 2024 Catalogue

Nauru
new	4c

New Republic
new	57C

Nigeria
8a	8g
8b	8e
8c	8f
new	8a
new	8b
new	8c
new	8d
11	11a
11a	11e
11b	11c
11c	11d
new	11b

Niue
new	8b
9	deleted
9a	deleted
9b	deleted

Panama
new	C342a
new	C348a
new	C348b

Pakistan - Bahawalpur
new	A1-A23
new	A24
new	A34
new	A35-A57
new	A58-A69
new	A70-A84
new	A85-A88
new	A89-A107
new	A94a
new	A108-A110
A1	A111
A2	A112
A3	A113
A4	A114
A5	A115
A6	A116
A6a	A116a
A7	A117
A8	A118
A9	A119
A10	A120
A10a	A120a
A11	A121
A12	A122
A13	A123
A14	A124
A14a	A124a
A15	A125
A16	A126
A17	A127
new	26a
new	27a
new	28a
new	29a
new	1L1
new	1L2
new	1L3
new	1L4
new	1L5
new	1L6
new	1L7
new	O2b
new	O4a
new	O5a
O7	O8
O10	O7

Pakistan - Bahawalpur
Number in 2023 Catalogue	Number in 2024 Catalogue
O8	O9
new	O9a
O9	O10
new	O25a
New	O26a
new	O27a
new	O28a

St. Kitts-Nevis
new	79a
new	80a
new	80b
new	80c
new	82a
new	86a
new	86b
new	87a
new	87b
new	88a

COMMON DESIGN TYPES

Pictured in this section are issues where one illustration has been used for a number of countries in the Catalogue. Not included in this section are overprinted stamps or those issues which are illustrated in each country. Because the location of Never Hinged breakpoints varies from country to country, some of the values in the listings below will be for unused stamps that were previously hinged.

EUROPA
Europa, 1956

The design symbolizing the cooperation among the six countries comprising the Coal and Steel Community is illustrated in each country.

Belgium		496-497
France		805-806
Germany		748-749
Italy		715-716
Luxembourg		318-320
Netherlands		368-369

Nos. 496-497 (2)	9.00	.50
Nos. 805-806 (2)	5.25	1.00
Nos. 748-749 (2)	7.40	1.10
Nos. 715-716 (2)	9.25	1.25
Nos. 318-320 (3)	65.50	42.00
Nos. 368-369 (2)	25.75	1.50
Set total (13) Stamps	122.15	47.35

Europa, 1958

"E" and Dove — CD1

European Postal Union at the service of European integration.

1958, Sept. 13

Belgium		527-528
France		889-890
Germany		790-791
Italy		750-751
Luxembourg		341-343
Netherlands		375-376
Saar		317-318

Nos. 527-528 (2)	3.75	.60
Nos. 889-890 (2)	1.65	.55
Nos. 790-791 (2)	2.95	.60
Nos. 750-751 (2)	1.05	.60
Nos. 341-343 (3)	1.35	.90
Nos. 375-376 (2)	1.25	.75
Nos. 317-318 (2)	1.05	2.30
Set total (15) Stamps	13.05	6.30

Europa, 1959

6-Link Enless Chain — CD2

1959, Sept. 19

Belgium		536-537
France		929-930
Germany		805-806
Italy		791-792
Luxembourg		354-355
Netherlands		379-380

Nos. 536-537 (2)	1.55	.60
Nos. 929-930 (2)	1.40	.80
Nos. 805-806 (2)	1.35	.60
Nos. 791-792 (2)	.80	.50
Nos. 354-355 (2)	2.65	1.00
Nos. 379-380 (2)	2.10	1.85
Set total (12) Stamps	9.85	5.35

Europa, 1960

19-Spoke Wheel CD3

First anniverary of the establishment of C.E.P.T. (Conference Europeenne des Administration des Postes et des Telecommunicas.) The spokes symbolize the 19 founding members of the Conference.

1960, Sept.

Belgium		553-554
Denmark		379
Finland		376-377
France		970-971
Germany		818-820
Great Britain		377-378
Greece		688
Iceland		327-328
Ireland		175-176
Italy		809-810
Luxembourg		374-375
Netherlands		385-386
Norway		387
Portugal		866-867
Spain		941-942
Sweden		562-563
Switzerland		400-401
Turkey		1493-1494

Nos. 553-554 (2)	1.25	.55
No. 379 (1)	.55	.50
Nos. 376-377 (2)	1.80	1.40
Nos. 970-971 (2)	.50	.50
Nos. 818-820 (3)	1.90	1.35
Nos. 377-378 (2)	7.00	2.75
No. 688 (1)	4.25	1.75
Nos. 327-328 (2)	1.30	1.85
Nos. 175-176 (2)	47.50	27.50
Nos. 809-810 (2)	.50	.50
Nos. 374-375 (2)	1.00	.80
Nos. 385-386 (2)	2.00	2.00
No. 387 (1)	1.00	.80
Nos. 866-867 (2)	3.05	1.75
Nos. 941-942 (2)	1.50	.75
Nos. 562-563 (2)	1.05	.55
Nos. 400-401 (2)	1.75	.75
Nos. 1493-1494 (2)	2.10	1.35
Set total (34) Stamps	80.00	47.40

Europa, 1961

19 Doves Flying as One — CD4

The 19 doves represent the 19 members of the Conference of European Postal and Telecommunications Administrations C.E.P.T.

1961-62

Belgium		572-573
Cyprus		201-203
France		1005-1006
Germany		844-845
Great Britain		382-384
Greece		718-719
Iceland		340-341
Italy		845-846
Luxembourg		382-383
Netherlands		387-388
Spain		1010-1011
Switzerland		410-411
Turkey		1518-1520

Nos. 572-573 (2)	.75	.50
Nos. 201-203 (3)	2.10	1.20
Nos. 1005-1006 (2)	.50	.50
Nos. 844-845 (2)	.60	.75
Nos. 382-384 (3)	.75	.75
Nos. 718-719 (2)	.80	.50
Nos. 340-341 (2)	1.10	1.60
Nos. 845-846 (2)	.50	.50
Nos. 382-383 (2)	.55	.55
Nos. 387-388 (2)	.50	.50
Nos. 1010-1011 (2)	.60	.50
Nos. 410-411 (2)	1.90	.60
Nos. 1518-1520 (3)	1.55	.90
Set total (29) Stamps	12.20	9.35

Europa, 1962

Young Tree with 19 Leaves CD5

The 19 leaves represent the 19 original members of C.E.P.T.

1962-63

Belgium		582-583
Cyprus		219-221
France		1045-1046
Germany		852-853
Greece		739-740
Iceland		348-349
Ireland		184-185
Italy		860-861
Luxembourg		386-387
Netherlands		394-395
Norway		414-415
Switzerland		416-417
Turkey		1553-1555

Nos. 582-583 (2)	.65	.65
Nos. 219-221 (3)	76.25	6.75
Nos. 1045-1046 (2)	.60	.50
Nos. 852-853 (2)	.65	.75
Nos. 739-740 (2)	2.00	1.15
Nos. 348-349 (2)	.85	.85
Nos. 184-185 (2)	2.00	.50
Nos. 860-861 (2)	1.00	.55
Nos. 386-387 (2)	.75	.55
Nos. 394-395 (2)	1.35	.90
Nos. 414-415 (2)	1.75	1.70
Nos. 416-417 (2)	1.65	1.00
Nos. 1553-1555 (3)	2.05	1.10
Set total (28) Stamps	91.55	16.95

Europa, 1963

Stylized Links, Symbolizing Unity — CD6

1963, Sept.

Belgium		598-599
Cyprus		229-231
Finland		419
France		1074-1075
Germany		867-868
Greece		768-769
Iceland		357-358
Ireland		188-189
Italy		880-881
Luxembourg		403-404
Netherlands		416-417
Norway		441-442
Switzerland		429
Turkey		1602-1603

Nos. 598-599 (2)	1.60	.55
Nos. 229-231 (3)	64.00	9.40
No. 419 (1)	1.25	.55
Nos. 1074-1075 (2)	.60	.50
Nos. 867-868 (2)	.50	.55
Nos. 768-769 (2)	4.65	1.65
Nos. 357-358 (2)	1.20	1.20
Nos. 188-189 (2)	4.75	3.25
Nos. 880-881 (2)	.50	.50
Nos. 403-404 (2)	.75	.55
Nos. 416-417 (2)	1.30	1.00
Nos. 441-442 (2)	2.60	2.40
No. 429 (1)	.90	.60
Nos. 1602-1603 (2)	1.20	.50
Set total (27) Stamps	85.80	23.20

Europa, 1964

Symbolic Daisy — CD7

5th anniversary of the establishment of C.E.P.T. The 22 petals of the flower symbolize the 22 members of the Conference.

1964, Sept.

Austria		738
Belgium		614-615
Cyprus		244-246
France		1109-1110
Germany		897-898
Greece		801-802
Iceland		367-368
Ireland		196-197
Italy		894-895
Luxembourg		411-412
Monaco		590-591
Netherlands		428-429
Norway		458
Portugal		931-933
Spain		1262-1263
Switzerland		438-439
Turkey		1628-1629

No. 738 (1)	1.10	.25
Nos. 614-615 (2)	1.40	.60
Nos. 244-246 (3)	32.25	5.10
Nos. 1109-1110 (2)	.50	.50
Nos. 897-898 (2)	.50	.50
Nos. 801-802 (2)	4.15	1.55
Nos. 367-368 (2)	1.40	1.15
Nos. 196-197 (2)	17.00	4.25
Nos. 894-895 (2)	.50	.50
Nos. 411-412 (2)	.75	.55
Nos. 590-591 (2)	2.50	.70
Nos. 428-429 (2)	.75	.60
No. 458 (1)	3.50	3.50
Nos. 931-933 (3)	10.00	2.00
Nos. 1262-1263 (2)	1.15	.80
Nos. 438-439 (2)	1.65	.50
Nos. 1628-1629 (2)	2.00	.80
Set total (34) Stamps	81.10	23.85

Europa, 1965

Leaves and "Fruit" CD8

1965

Belgium		636-637
Cyprus		262-264
Finland		437
France		1131-1132
Germany		934-935
Greece		833-834
Iceland		375-376
Ireland		204-205
Italy		915-916
Luxembourg		432-433
Monaco		616-617
Netherlands		438-439
Norway		475-476
Portugal		958-960
Switzerland		469
Turkey		1665-1666

Nos. 636-637 (2)	.50	.50
Nos. 262-264 (3)	25.35	6.00
No. 437 (1)	1.25	.55
Nos. 1131-1132 (2)	.70	.55
Nos. 934-935 (2)	.50	.50
Nos. 833-834 (2)	2.25	1.15
Nos. 375-376 (2)	2.50	1.15
Nos. 204-205 (2)	16.00	3.35
Nos. 915-916 (2)	.50	.50
Nos. 432-433 (2)	.75	.55
Nos. 616-617 (2)	3.25	1.65
Nos. 438-439 (2)	.55	.50
Nos. 475-476 (2)	2.40	1.90
Nos. 958-960 (3)	16.00	2.75
No. 469 (1)	1.15	.50
Nos. 1665-1666 (2)	2.00	1.25
Set total (32) Stamps	75.65	23.95

Europa, 1966

Symbolic Sailboat — CD9

1966, Sept.

Andorra, French		172
Belgium		675-676
Cyprus		275-277
France		1163-1164
Germany		963-964

Greece		862-863
Iceland		384-385
Ireland		216-217
Italy		942-943
Liechtenstein		415
Luxembourg		440-441
Monaco		639-640
Netherlands		441-442
Norway		496-497
Portugal		980-982
Switzerland		477-478
Turkey		1718-1719

No. 172 (1)	3.00	3.00
Nos. 675-676 (2)	.80	.50
Nos. 275-277 (3)	4.75	2.75
Nos. 1163-1164 (2)	.55	.50
Nos. 963-964 (2)	.50	.55
Nos. 862-863 (2)	2.10	1.05
Nos. 384-385 (2)	4.50	3.50
Nos. 216-217 (2)	6.75	2.00
Nos. 942-943 (2)	.50	.50
No. 415 (1)	.40	.35
Nos. 440-441 (2)	.70	.55
Nos. 639-640 (2)	2.00	.65
Nos. 441-442 (2)	.85	.50
Nos. 496-497 (2)	2.35	2.15
Nos. 980-982 (3)	15.90	2.25
Nos. 477-478 (2)	1.40	.60
Nos. 1718-1719 (2)	3.35	1.75
Set total (34) Stamps	50.40	23.15

Europa, 1967

Cogwheels
CD10

1967

Andorra, French		174-175
Belgium		688-689
Cyprus		297-299
France		1178-1179
Germany		969-970
Greece		891-892
Iceland		389-390
Ireland		232-233
Italy		951-952
Liechtenstein		420
Luxembourg		449-450
Monaco		669-670
Netherlands		444-447
Norway		504-505
Portugal		994-996
Spain		1465-1466
Switzerland		482
Turkey		B120-B121

Nos. 174-175 (2)	10.75	6.25
Nos. 688-689 (2)	1.05	.55
Nos. 297-299 (3)	4.25	2.50
Nos. 1178-1179 (2)	.55	.50
Nos. 969-970 (2)	.55	.55
Nos. 891-892 (2)	3.05	.85
Nos. 389-390 (2)	3.00	2.00
Nos. 232-233 (2)	5.90	2.30
Nos. 951-952 (2)	.60	.50
No. 420 (1)	.45	.40
Nos. 449-450 (2)	1.00	.70
Nos. 669-670 (2)	2.75	.70
Nos. 444-447 (4)	2.70	2.05
Nos. 504-505 (2)	2.00	1.80
Nos. 994-996 (3)	16.10	1.85
Nos. 1465-1466 (2)	.50	.50
No. 482 (1)	.60	.30
Nos. B120-B121 (2)	2.50	2.00
Set total (38) Stamps	58.30	26.30

Europa, 1968

Golden Key
with
C.E.P.T.
Emblem
CD11

1968

Andorra, French		182-183
Belgium		705-706
Cyprus		314-316
France		1209-1210
Germany		983-984
Greece		916-917
Iceland		395-396
Ireland		242-243
Italy		979-980

Liechtenstein		442
Luxembourg		466-467
Monaco		689-691
Netherlands		452-453
Portugal		1019-1021
San Marino		687
Spain		1526
Switzerland		488
Turkey		1775-1776

Nos. 182-183 (2)	16.50	10.00
Nos. 705-706 (2)	1.25	.50
Nos. 314-316 (3)	2.90	2.50
Nos. 1209-1210 (2)	.85	.55
Nos. 983-984 (2)	.50	.55
Nos. 916-917 (2)	3.10	1.45
Nos. 395-396 (2)	3.00	2.20
Nos. 242-243 (2)	3.30	2.25
Nos. 979-980 (2)	.50	.50
No. 442 (1)	.45	.40
Nos. 466-467 (2)	.80	.70
Nos. 689-691 (3)	5.40	.95
Nos. 452-453 (2)	1.05	.70
Nos. 1019-1021 (3)	15.90	2.10
No. 687 (1)	.55	.35
No. 1526 (1)	.25	.25
No. 488 (1)	.40	.25
Nos. 1775-1776 (2)	2.50	1.25
Set total (35) Stamps	59.20	27.45

Europa, 1969

"EUROPA"
and "CEPT"
CD12

Tenth anniversary of C.E.P.T.

1969

Andorra, French		188-189
Austria		837
Belgium		718-719
Cyprus		326-328
Denmark		458
Finland		483
France		1245-1246
Germany		996-997
Great Britain		585
Greece		947-948
Iceland		406-407
Ireland		270-271
Italy		1000-1001
Liechtenstein		453
Luxembourg		475-476
Monaco		722-724
Netherlands		475-476
Norway		533-534
Portugal		1038-1040
San Marino		701-702
Spain		1567
Sweden		814-816
Switzerland		500-501
Turkey		1799-1800
Vatican		470-472
Yugoslavia		1003-1004

Nos. 188-189 (2)	18.50	12.00
No. 837 (1)	.55	.25
Nos. 718-719 (2)	.75	.50
Nos. 326-328 (3)	3.00	2.25
No. 458 (1)	.75	.75
No. 483 (1)	2.50	.60
Nos. 1245-1246 (2)	.55	.50
Nos. 996-997 (2)	.70	.50
No. 585 (1)	.25	.25
Nos. 947-948 (2)	4.00	1.25
Nos. 406-407 (2)	4.20	2.40
Nos. 270-271 (2)	3.50	2.00
Nos. 1000-1001 (2)	.50	.50
No. 453 (1)	.45	.45
Nos. 475-476 (2)	.95	.50
Nos. 722-724 (3)	10.50	2.00
Nos. 475-476 (2)	1.35	1.00
Nos. 533-534 (2)	2.20	1.95
Nos. 1038-1040 (3)	17.75	2.40
Nos. 701-702 (2)	.90	.90
No. 1567 (1)	.25	.25
Nos. 814-816 (3)	4.00	2.85
Nos. 500-501 (2)	1.85	1.00
Nos. 1799-1800 (2)	2.50	1.65
Nos. 470-472 (3)	.75	.75
Nos. 1003-1004 (2)	4.00	4.00
Set total (51) Stamps	87.20	43.45

Europa, 1970

Interwoven
Threads
CD13

1970

Andorra, French		196-197
Belgium		741-742
Cyprus		340-342
France		1271-1272
Germany		1018-1019
Greece		985, 987
Iceland		420-421
Ireland		279-281
Italy		1013-1014
Liechtenstein		470
Luxembourg		489-490
Monaco		768-770
Netherlands		483-484
Portugal		1060-1062
San Marino		729-730
Spain		1607
Switzerland		515-516
Turkey		1848-1849
Yugoslavia		1024-1025

Nos. 196-197 (2)	20.00	8.50
Nos. 741-742 (2)	1.10	.55
Nos. 340-342 (3)	2.70	2.75
Nos. 1271-1272 (2)	.65	.50
Nos. 1018-1019 (2)	.60	.50
Nos. 985,987 (2)	6.35	1.60
Nos. 420-421 (2)	6.00	4.00
Nos. 279-281 (3)	7.50	2.50
Nos. 1013-1014 (2)	.50	.50
No. 470 (1)	.45	.45
Nos. 489-490 (2)	.80	.55
Nos. 768-770 (3)	6.35	2.10
Nos. 483-484 (2)	1.30	1.15
Nos. 1060-1062 (3)	18.95	2.35
Nos. 729-730 (2)	.90	.55
No. 1607 (1)	.25	.25
Nos. 515-516 (2)	1.85	.70
Nos. 1848-1849 (2)	2.50	1.50
Nos. 1024-1025 (2)	.80	.80
Set total (40) Stamps	79.55	31.80

Europa, 1971

"Fraternity,
Cooperation,
Common
Effort"
CD14

1971

Andorra, French		205-206
Belgium		803-804
Cyprus		365-367
Finland		504
France		1304
Germany		1064-1065
Greece		1029-1030
Iceland		429-430
Ireland		305-306
Italy		1038-1039
Liechtenstein		485
Luxembourg		500-501
Malta		425-427
Monaco		797-799
Netherlands		488-489
Portugal		1094-1096
San Marino		749-750
Spain		1675-1676
Switzerland		531-532
Turkey		1876-1877
Yugoslavia		1052-1053

Nos. 205-206 (2)	20.00	7.75
Nos. 803-804 (2)	1.30	.55
Nos. 365-367 (3)	2.60	3.25
No. 504 (1)	2.50	.50
No. 1304 (1)	.45	.40
Nos. 1064-1065 (2)	.60	.50
Nos. 1029-1030 (2)	4.00	1.80
Nos. 429-430 (2)	5.00	3.75
Nos. 305-306 (2)	4.50	1.50
Nos. 1038-1039 (2)	.65	.50
No. 485 (1)	.45	.45
Nos. 500-501 (2)	1.00	.65
Nos. 425-427 (3)	.80	.80
Nos. 797-799 (3)	15.00	2.80
Nos. 488-489 (2)	1.20	.95
Nos. 1094-1096 (3)	16.15	1.75
Nos. 749-750 (2)	.65	.55
Nos. 1675-1676 (2)	.75	.55
Nos. 531-532 (2)	1.85	.65
Nos. 1876-1877 (2)	2.50	1.25
Nos. 1052-1053 (2)	.50	.50
Set total (43) Stamps	82.45	31.40

Europa, 1972

Sparkles, Symbolic
of Communications
CD15

1972

Andorra, French		210-211
Andorra, Spanish		62
Belgium		825-826
Cyprus		380-382
Finland		512-513
France		1341
Germany		1089-1090
Greece		1049-1050
Iceland		439-440
Ireland		316-317
Italy		1065-1066
Liechtenstein		504
Luxembourg		512-513
Malta		450-453
Monaco		831-832
Netherlands		494-495
Portugal		1141-1143
San Marino		771-772
Spain		1718
Switzerland		544-545
Turkey		1907-1908
Yugoslavia		1100-1101

Nos. 210-211 (2)	21.00	7.00
No. 62 (1)	60.00	60.00
Nos. 825-826 (2)	.95	.55
Nos. 380-382 (3)	5.95	4.25
Nos. 512-513 (2)	4.00	1.00
No. 1341 (1)	.50	.35
Nos. 1089-1090 (2)	1.10	.50
Nos. 1049-1050 (2)	2.00	1.55
Nos. 439-440 (2)	2.90	2.65
Nos. 316-317 (2)	13.00	4.50
Nos. 1065-1066 (2)	.55	.50
No. 504 (1)	.45	.45
Nos. 512-513 (2)	.95	.65
Nos. 450-453 (4)	1.05	1.40
Nos. 831-832 (2)	5.00	1.40
Nos. 494-495 (2)	1.20	.90
Nos. 1141-1143 (3)	15.85	1.50
Nos. 771-772 (2)	.70	.50
No. 1718 (1)	.50	.40
Nos. 544-545 (2)	1.65	.60
Nos. 1907-1908 (2)	4.00	2.00
Nos. 1100-1101 (2)	1.20	1.20
Set total (44) Stamps	144.50	93.85

Europa, 1973

Post Horn
and Arrows
CD16

1973

Andorra, French		219-220
Andorra, Spanish		76
Belgium		839-840
Cyprus		396-398
Finland		526
France		1367
Germany		1114-1115
Greece		1090-1092
Iceland		447-448
Ireland		329-330
Italy		1108-1109
Liechtenstein		528-529
Luxembourg		523-524
Malta		469-471
Monaco		866-867
Netherlands		504-505
Norway		604-605
Portugal		1170-1172
San Marino		802-803
Spain		1753
Switzerland		580-581
Turkey		1935-1936
Yugoslavia		1138-1139

Nos. 219-220 (2)	20.00	11.00
No. 76 (1)	1.25	.85
Nos. 839-840 (2)	1.00	.65
Nos. 396-398 (3)	4.25	3.85
No. 526 (1)	1.25	.55
No. 1367 (1)	1.25	.75
Nos. 1114-1115 (2)	.85	.50
Nos. 1090-1092 (3)	2.10	1.40
Nos. 447-448 (2)	6.65	3.35

Nos. 329-330 (2)	5.25	2.00
Nos. 1108-1109 (2)	.50	.50
Nos. 528-529 (2)	.60	.60
Nos. 523-524 (2)	.90	.75
Nos. 469-471 (3)	.90	1.20
Nos. 866-867 (2)	15.00	2.40
Nos. 504-505 (2)	1.20	.95
Nos. 604-605 (2)	4.00	1.80
Nos. 1170-1172 (3)	24.95	2.15
Nos. 802-803 (2)	1.00	.60
No. 1753 (1)	.35	.25
Nos. 580-581 (2)	1.55	.60
Nos. 1935-1936 (2)	4.15	2.25
Nos. 1138-1139 (2)	1.15	1.10
Set total (46) Stamps	100.10	40.05

Europa, 2000

CD17

2000

Albania	2621-2622
Andorra, French	522
Andorra, Spanish	262
Armenia	610-611
Austria	1814
Azerbaijan	698-699
Belarus	350
Belgium	1818
Bosnia & Herzegovina (Moslem)	358
Bosnia & Herzegovina (Serb)	111-112
Croatia	428-429
Cyprus	959
Czech Republic	3120
Denmark	1189
Estonia	394
Faroe Islands	376
Finland	1129
Aland Islands	166
France	2771
Georgia	228-229
Germany	2086-2087
Gibraltar	837-840
Great Britain (Jersey)	935-936
Great Britain (Isle of Man)	883
Greece	1959
Greenland	363
Hungary	3699-3700
Iceland	910
Ireland	1230-1231
Italy	2349
Latvia	504
Liechtenstein	1178
Lithuania	668
Luxembourg	1035
Macedonia	187
Malta	1011-1012
Moldova	355
Monaco	2161-2162
Poland	3519
Portugal	2358
Portugal (Azores)	455
Portugal (Madeira)	208
Romania	4370
Russia	6589
San Marino	1480
Slovakia	355
Slovenia	424
Spain	3036
Sweden	2394
Switzerland	1074
Turkey	2762
Turkish Rep. of Northern Cyprus	500
Ukraine	379
Vatican City	1152

Nos. 2621-2622 (2)	9.50	9.50
No. 522 (1)	2.00	1.00
No. 262 (1)	1.75	.80
Nos. 610-611 (2)	4.75	4.75
No. 1814 (1)	1.25	1.25
Nos. 698-699 (2)	6.00	6.00
No. 350 (1)	1.75	1.75
No. 1818 (1)	1.40	.60
No. 358 (1)	4.75	4.75
Nos. 111-112 (2)	110.00	110.00
Nos. 428-429 (2)	6.25	6.25
No. 959 (1)	2.10	1.40
No. 3120 (1)	1.20	.40
No. 1189 (1)	3.50	2.25
No. 394 (1)	1.25	1.25
No. 376 (1)	2.40	2.40
No. 1129 (1)	2.00	.60
No. 166 (1)	1.10	1.20
No. 2771 (1)	1.25	.40
Nos. 228-229 (2)	9.00	9.00
Nos. 2086-2087 (2)	4.35	2.10
Nos. 837-840 (4)	5.50	5.30

Nos. 935-936 (2)	2.40	2.40
No. 883 (1)	1.75	1.75
No. 363 (1)	1.90	1.90
Nos. 3699-3700 (2)	6.50	2.50
No. 910 (1)	1.60	1.60
Nos. 1230-1231 (2)	4.35	4.35
No. 2349 (1)	1.50	.40
No. 504 (1)	5.00	2.40
No. 1178 (1)	2.25	1.75
No. 668 (1)	1.50	1.50
No. 1035 (1)	1.40	.85
No. 187 (1)	3.00	3.00
Nos. 1011-1012 (2)	4.35	4.35
No. 355 (1)	3.50	3.50
Nos. 2161-2162 (2)	2.80	1.40
No. 3519 (1)	1.25	.75
No. 2358 (1)	1.95	.65
No. 455 (1)	2.00	.50
No. 208 (1)	2.25	.50
No. 4370 (1)	2.50	1.25
No. 6589 (1)	4.00	.85
No. 1480 (1)	1.00	1.00
No. 355 (1)	1.60	.80
No. 424 (1)	3.25	3.25
No. 3036 (1)	1.00	.40
No. 2394 (1)	3.00	1.50
No. 1074 (1)	2.10	1.05
No. 2762 (1)	2.75	2.00
No. 500 (1)	2.50	2.50
No. 379 (1)	4.50	3.00
No. 1152 (1)	1.75	1.75
Set total (68) Stamps	264.25	228.35

The Gibraltar stamps are similar to the stamp illustrated, but none have the design shown above. All other sets listed above include at least one stamp with the design shown, but some include stamps with entirely different designs. Bulgaria Nos. 4131-4132, Guernsey Nos. 802-803 and Yugoslavia Nos. 2485-2486 are Europa stamps with completely different designs.

PORTUGAL & COLONIES
Vasco da Gama

Fleet Departing
CD20

Fleet Arriving at Calicut — CD21

Embarking at Rastello
CD22

Muse of History
CD23

San Gabriel, da Gama and Camoens
CD24

Archangel Gabriel, the Patron Saint
CD25

Flagship San Gabriel — CD26

Vasco da Gama — CD27

Fourth centenary of Vasco da Gama's discovery of the route to India.

1898

Azores	93-100
Macao	67-74
Madeira	37-44
Portugal	147-154
Port. Africa	1-8
Port. Congo	75-98
Port. India	189-196
St. Thomas & Prince Islands	170-193
Timor	45-52

Nos. 93-100 (8)	113.50	73.50
Nos. 67-74 (8)	250.25	170.25
Nos. 37-44 (8)	60.55	37.25
Nos. 147-154 (8)	249.05	84.90
Nos. 1-8 (8)	44.00	29.25
Nos. 75-98 (24)	78.50	64.65
Nos. 189-196 (8)	25.25	15.50
Nos. 170-193 (24)	56.30	43.00
Nos. 45-52 (8)	33.50	23.25
Set total (104) Stamps	910.90	541.55

Pombal
POSTAL TAX
POSTAL TAX DUES

Marquis de Pombal — CD28

Planning Reconstruction of Lisbon, 1755 — CD29

Pombal Monument, Lisbon — CD30

Sebastiao Jose de Carvalho e Mello, Marquis de Pombal (1699-1782), statesman, rebuilt Lisbon after earthquake of 1755. Tax was for the erection of Pombal monument. Obligatory on all mail on certain days throughout the year. Postal Tax Dues are inscribed "Multa."

1925

Angola	RA1-RA3, RAJ1-RAJ3
Azores	RA9-RA11, RAJ2-RAJ4
Cape Verde	RA1-RA3, RAJ1-RAJ3
Macao	RA1-RA3, RAJ1-RAJ3
Madeira	RA1-RA3, RAJ1-RAJ3
Mozambique	RA1-RA3, RAJ1-RAJ3
Nyassa	RA1-RA3, RAJ1-RAJ3
Portugal	RA11-RA13, RAJ2-RAJ4
Port. Guinea	RA1-RA3, RAJ1-RAJ3
Port. India	RA1-RA3, RAJ1-RAJ3
St. Thomas & Prince Islands	RA1-RA3, RAJ1-RAJ3
Timor	RA1-RA3, RAJ1-RAJ3

Nos. RA1-RA3,RAJ1-RAJ3 (6)	6.60	6.60
Nos. RA9-RA11,RAJ2-RAJ4 (6)	6.60	6.60
Nos. RA1-RA3,RAJ1-RAJ3 (6)	7.80	7.65
Nos. RA1-RA3,RAJ1-RAJ3 (6)	36.50	17.25
Nos. RA1-RA3,RAJ1-RAJ3 (6)	7.95	14.70
Nos. RA1-RA3,RAJ1-RAJ3 (6)	3.75	3.60
Nos. RA11-RA13,RAJ2-RAJ4 (6)	85.50	76.50
Nos. RA1-RA3,RAJ1-RAJ3 (6)	8.75	8.55
Nos. RA1-RA3,RAJ1-RAJ3 (6)	5.85	5.40
Nos. RA1-RA3,RAJ1-RAJ3 (6)	4.05	4.05
Nos. RA1-RA3,RAJ1-RAJ3 (6)	4.50	4.50
Nos. RA1-RA3,RAJ1-RAJ3 (6)	3.90	3.45
Set total (72) Stamps	181.75	158.85

Vasco da Gama
CD34

Mousinho de Albuquerque
CD35

Prince Henry the Navigator
CD37

Dam
CD36

Affonso de Albuquerque
CD38

Plane over Globe
CD39

1938-39

Angola	274-291, C1-C9
Cape Verde	234-251, C1-C9
Macao	289-305, C7-C15
Mozambique	270-287, C1-C9
Port. Guinea	233-250. C1-C9
Port. India	439-453, C1-C8
St. Thomas & Prince Islands	302-319, C1-C18
Timor	223-239, C1-C9

Nos. 274-291,C1-C9 (27)	129.40	22.85
Nos. 234-251,C1-C9 (27)	122.40	38.30
Nos. 289-305,C7-C15 (26)	889.60	338.55
Nos. 270-287,C1-C9 (27)	95.71	15.95
Nos. 233-250,C1-C9 (27)	130.20	49.15
Nos. 439-453,C1-C8 (23)	98.15	34.70
Nos. 302-319,323-340,C1-C18 (54)	467.70	244.80
Nos. 223-239,C1-C9 (26)	213.85	104.90
Set total (237) Stamps	2,147.	849.20

Lady of Fatima

Our Lady of the Rosary, Fatima, Portugal — CD40

1948-49

Angola	315-318
Cape Verde	266
Macao	336
Mozambique	325-328
Port. Guinea	271
Port. India	480
St. Thomas & Prince Islands	351
Timor	254

Nos. 315-318 (4)	68.00	17.25
No. 266 (1)	8.50	9.00
No. 336 (1)	90.00	30.00
Nos. 325-328 (4)	73.25	27.50
No. 271 (1)	6.50	6.00
No. 480 (1)	4.50	4.75
No. 351 (1)	8.50	7.00
No. 254 (1)	6.00	12.50
Set total (14) Stamps	265.25	114.00

A souvenir sheet of 9 stamps was issued in 1951 to mark the extension of the 1950 Holy Year. The sheet contains: Angola No. 316, Cape Verde No. 266, Macao No. 336, Mozambique No. 325, Portuguese Guinea No. 271, Portuguese India Nos. 480, 485, St. Thomas & Prince Islands No. 351, Timor No. 254. The sheet also contains a portrait of Pope Pius XII and is inscribed "Encerramento do

Ano Santo, Fatima 1951." It was sold for 11 escudos.

Holy Year

Church Bells and Dove CD41	Angel Holding Candelabra CD42

Holy Year, 1950.

1950-51

Angola	331-332
Cape Verde	268-269
Macao	339-340
Mozambique	330-331
Port. Guinea	273-274
Port. India	490-491, 496-503
St. Thomas & Prince Islands	353-354
Timor	258-259

Nos. 331-332 (2)	7.60	1.35
Nos. 268-269 (2)	7.35	4.75
Nos. 339-340 (2)	110.00	34.00
Nos. 330-331 (2)	3.00	1.60
Nos. 273-274 (2)	8.50	5.05
Nos. 490-491,496-503 (10)	14.50	7.30
Nos. 353-354 (2)	7.75	4.90
Nos. 258-259 (2)	8.75	5.00
Set total (24) Stamps	167.45	63.95

A souvenir sheet of 8 stamps was issued in 1951 to mark the extension of the Holy Year. The sheet contains: Angola No. 331, Cape Verde No. 269, Macao No. 340, Mozambique No. 331, Portuguese Guinea No. 275, Portuguese India No. 490, St. Thomas & Prince Islands No. 354, Timor No. 258, some with colors changed. The sheet contains doves and is inscribed 'Encerramento do Ano Santo, Fatima 1951.' It was sold for 17 escudos.

Holy Year Conclusion

Our Lady of Fatima — CD43

Conclusion of Holy Year. Sheets contain alternate vertical rows of stamps and labels bearing quotation from Pope Pius XII, different for each colony.

1951

Angola	357
Cape Verde	270
Macao	352
Mozambique	356
Port. Guinea	275
Port. India	506
St. Thomas & Prince Islands	355
Timor	270

No. 357 (1)	5.25	1.50
No. 270 (1)	1.75	1.25
No. 352 (1)	110.00	23.00
No. 356 (1)	3.25	1.75
No. 275 (1)	2.00	1.00
No. 506 (1)	2.50	1.60
No. 355 (1)	3.00	2.00
No. 270 (1)	3.75	2.75
Set total (8) Stamps	131.50	34.85

Medical Congress

CD44

First National Congress of Tropical Medicine, Lisbon, 1952. Each stamp has a different design.

1952

Angola	358
Cape Verde	287
Macao	364

Mozambique	359
Port. Guinea	276
Port. India	516
St. Thomas & Prince Islands	356
Timor	271

No. 358 (1)	1.50	.50
No. 287 (1)	.95	.75
No. 364 (1)	20.00	7.00
No. 359 (1)	1.90	.90
No. 276 (1)	.75	.65
No. 516 (1)	7.50	3.25
No. 356 (1)	.35	.50
No. 271 (1)	2.00	1.60
Set total (8) Stamps	34.95	14.95

Postage Due Stamps

CD45

1952

Angola	J37-J42
Cape Verde	J31-J36
Macao	J53-J58
Mozambique	J51-J56
Port. Guinea	J40-J45
Port. India	J47-J52
St. Thomas & Prince Islands	J52-J57
Timor	J31-J36

Nos. J37-J42 (6)	4.30	2.55
Nos. J31-J36 (6)	2.80	2.30
Nos. J53-J58 (6)	27.80	12.05
Nos. J51-J56 (6)	2.40	1.95
Nos. J40-J45 (6)	2.70	2.55
Nos. J47-J52 (6)	6.10	6.10
Nos. J52-J57 (6)	3.85	3.85
Nos. J31-J36 (6)	4.00	2.35
Set total (48) Stamps	53.95	33.70

Sao Paulo

Father Manuel da Nobrega and View of Sao Paulo — CD46

Founding of Sao Paulo, Brazil, 400th anniv.

1954

Angola	385
Cape Verde	297
Macao	382
Mozambique	395
Port. Guinea	291
Port. India	530
St. Thomas & Prince Islands	369
Timor	279

No. 385 (1)	.80	.50
No. 297 (1)	.95	.80
No. 382 (1)	30.00	6.00
No. 395 (1)	.75	.30
No. 291 (1)	.50	.35
No. 530 (1)	1.00	.55
No. 369 (1)	.70	.50
No. 279 (1)	2.00	1.40
Set total (8) Stamps	36.70	10.40

Tropical Medicine Congress

CD47

Sixth International Congress for Tropical Medicine and Malaria, Lisbon, Sept. 1958. Each stamp shows a different plant.

1958

Angola	409
Cape Verde	303
Macao	392
Mozambique	404
Port. Guinea	295
Port. India	569
St. Thomas & Prince Islands	371

Timor	289

No. 409 (1)	3.50	1.10
No. 303 (1)	6.75	3.25
No. 392 (1)	13.00	6.00
No. 404 (1)	3.50	1.50
No. 295 (1)	4.50	2.00
No. 569 (1)	1.75	.75
No. 371 (1)	2.75	2.00
No. 289 (1)	5.50	4.25
Set total (8) Stamps	41.25	20.85

Sports

CD48

Each stamp shows a different sport.

1962

Angola	433-438
Cape Verde	320-325
Macao	394-399
Mozambique	424-429
Port. Guinea	299-304
St. Thomas & Prince Islands	374-379
Timor	313-318

Nos. 433-438 (6)	5.50	3.20
Nos. 320-325 (6)	16.05	7.40
Nos. 394-399 (6)	129.85	28.95
Nos. 424-429 (6)	6.55	2.45
Nos. 299-304 (6)	6.00	3.00
Nos. 374-379 (6)	6.75	3.20
Nos. 313-318 (6)	11.65	5.90
Set total (42) Stamps	182.35	54.10

Anti-Malaria

Anopheles Funestus and Malaria Eradication Symbol — CD49

World Health Organization drive to eradicate malaria.

1962

Angola	439
Cape Verde	326
Macao	400
Mozambique	430
Port. Guinea	305
St. Thomas & Prince Islands	380
Timor	319

No. 439 (1)	1.75	.90
No. 326 (1)	1.90	1.60
No. 400 (1)	12.00	4.00
No. 430 (1)	2.00	.50
No. 305 (1)	1.50	.60
No. 380 (1)	2.25	1.25
No. 319 (1)	2.25	1.40
Set total (7) Stamps	23.65	10.25

Airline Anniversary

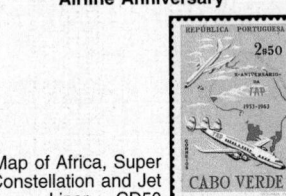

Map of Africa, Super Constellation and Jet Liner — CD50

Tenth anniversary of Transportes Aereos Portugueses (TAP).

1963

Angola	490
Cape Verde	327
Mozambique	434
Port. Guinea	318
St. Thomas & Prince Islands	381

No. 490 (1)	1.00	.35
No. 327 (1)	1.50	1.10
No. 434 (1)	.55	.25

No. 318 (1)	1.25	.60
No. 381 (1)	.80	.50
Set total (5) Stamps	5.10	2.80

National Overseas Bank

Antonio Teixeira de Sousa — CD51

Centenary of the National Overseas Bank of Portugal.

1964, May 16

Angola	509
Cape Verde	328
Port. Guinea	319
St. Thomas & Prince Islands	382
Timor	320

No. 509 (1)	.90	.30
No. 328 (1)	1.50	1.30
No. 319 (1)	.95	.60
No. 382 (1)	.70	.50
No. 320 (1)	1.50	1.30
Set total (5) Stamps	5.55	4.00

ITU

ITU Emblem and the Archangel Gabriel — CD52

International Communications Union, Cent.

1965, May 17

Angola	511
Cape Verde	329
Macao	402
Mozambique	464
Port. Guinea	320
St. Thomas & Prince Islands	383
Timor	321

No. 511 (1)	1.25	.65
No. 329 (1)	2.90	2.25
No. 402 (1)	9.00	3.00
No. 464 (1)	.65	.25
No. 320 (1)	2.50	1.00
No. 383 (1)	2.00	1.00
No. 321 (1)	2.20	1.40
Set total (7) Stamps	20.50	9.55

National Revolution

CD53

40th anniv. of the National Revolution. Different buildings on each stamp.

1966, May 28

Angola	525
Cape Verde	338
Macao	403
Mozambique	465
Port. Guinea	329
St. Thomas & Prince Islands	392
Timor	322

No. 525 (1)	.50	.25
No. 338 (1)	.85	.75
No. 403 (1)	9.00	3.75
No. 465 (1)	.65	.30
No. 329 (1)	.85	.65
No. 392 (1)	.80	.50
No. 322 (1)	2.40	1.40
Set total (7) Stamps	15.05	7.60

Navy Club

CD54

Centenary of Portugal's Navy Club. Each stamp has a different design.

1967, Jan. 31

Angola	527-528
Cape Verde	339-340
Macao	412-413
Mozambique	478-479
Port. Guinea	330-331
St. Thomas & Prince Islands	393-394
Timor	323-324

Nos. 527-528 (2)	1.75	.75
Nos. 339-340 (2)	2.70	2.30
Nos. 412-413 (2)	18.00	4.70
Nos. 478-479 (2)	1.75	.65
Nos. 330-331 (2)	1.65	.90
Nos. 393-394 (2)	3.30	1.30
Nos. 323-324 (2)	4.25	2.40
Set total (14) Stamps	33.40	13.00

Admiral Coutinho

CD55

Centenary of the birth of Admiral Carlos Viegas Gago Coutinho (1869-1959), explorer and aviation pioneer. Each stamp has a different design.

1969, Feb. 17

Angola	547
Cape Verde	355
Macao	417
Mozambique	484
Port. Guinea	335
St. Thomas & Prince Islands	397
Timor	335

No. 547 (1)	.85	.35
No. 355 (1)	.60	.25
No. 417 (1)	7.50	2.25
No. 484 (1)	.30	.25
No. 335 (1)	.50	.25
No. 397 (1)	.60	.35
No. 335 (1)	2.50	1.40
Set total (7) Stamps	12.85	5.10

Administration Reform

Luiz Augusto Rebello da Silva — CD56

Centenary of the administration reforms of the overseas territories.

1969, Sept. 25

Angola	549
Cape Verde	357
Macao	419
Mozambique	491
Port. Guinea	337
St. Thomas & Prince Islands	399
Timor	338

No. 549 (1)	.35	.25
No. 357 (1)	.65	.40
No. 419 (1)	12.50	2.00
No. 491 (1)	.30	.25
No. 337 (1)	.35	.25
No. 399 (1)	.45	.45
No. 338 (1)	1.40	.70
Set total (7) Stamps	16.00	4.30

Marshal Carmona

CD57

Birth centenary of Marshal Antonio Oscar Carmona de Fragoso (1869-1951), President of Portugal. Each stamp has a different design.

1970, Nov. 15

Angola	563
Cape Verde	359
Macao	422
Mozambique	493
Port. Guinea	340
St. Thomas & Prince Islands	403
Timor	341

No. 563 (1)	.45	.25
No. 359 (1)	.70	.50
No. 422 (1)	5.00	1.75
No. 493 (1)	.40	.25
No. 340 (1)	.45	.25
No. 403 (1)	.75	.40
No. 341 (1)	1.00	.50
Set total (7) Stamps	8.75	3.90

Olympic Games

CD59

20th Olympic Games, Munich, Aug. 26-Sept. 11. Each stamp shows a different sport.

1972, June 20

Angola	569
Cape Verde	361
Macao	426
Mozambique	504
Port. Guinea	342
St. Thomas & Prince Islands	408
Timor	343

No. 569 (1)	.65	.25
No. 361 (1)	.85	.40
No. 426 (1)	2.50	1.50
No. 504 (1)	.30	.25
No. 342 (1)	.95	.25
No. 408 (1)	.45	.25
No. 343 (1)	1.60	.80
Set total (7) Stamps	7.30	3.70

Lisbon-Rio de Janeiro Flight

CD60

50th anniversary of the Lisbon to Rio de Janeiro flight by Arturo de Sacadura and Coutinho, March 30-June 5, 1922. Each stamp shows a different stage of the flight.

1972, Sept. 20

Angola	570
Cape Verde	362
Macao	427
Mozambique	505
Port. Guinea	343
St. Thomas & Prince Islands	409
Timor	344

No. 570 (1)	.35	.25
No. 362 (1)	.85	.40
No. 427 (1)	40.00	12.00
No. 505 (1)	.30	.25
No. 343 (1)	.35	.25
No. 409 (1)	.50	.25
No. 344 (1)	1.25	.90
Set total (7) Stamps	43.60	14.30

WMO Centenary

WMO Emblem — CD61

Centenary of international meterological cooperation.

1973, Dec. 15

Angola	571
Cape Verde	363
Macao	429
Mozambique	509
Port. Guinea	344
St. Thomas & Prince Islands	410
Timor	345

No. 571 (1)	.45	.25
No. 363 (1)	.85	.40
No. 429 (1)	15.00	2.50
No. 509 (1)	.40	.25
No. 344 (1)	.55	.40
No. 410 (1)	.60	.50
No. 345 (1)	3.75	2.75
Set total (7) Stamps	21.60	7.05

FRENCH COMMUNITY
Upper Volta can be found under Burkina Faso in Vol. 1
Madagascar can be found under Malagasy in Vol. 3
Colonial Exposition

People of French Empire CD70

Women's Heads CD71

France Showing Way to Civilization CD72

"Colonial Commerce" CD73

International Colonial Exposition, Paris.

1931

Cameroun	213-216
Chad	60-63
Dahomey	97-100
Fr. Guiana	152-155
Fr. Guinea	116-119
Fr. India	100-103
Fr. Polynesia	76-79
Fr. Sudan	102-105
Gabon	120-123
Guadeloupe	138-141
Indo-China	140-142
Ivory Coast	92-95
Madagascar	169-172
Martinique	129-132
Mauritania	65-68
Middle Congo	61-64
New Caledonia	176-179
Niger	73-76
Reunion	122-125
St. Pierre & Miquelon	132-135
Senegal	138-141
Somali Coast	135-138
Togo	254-257
Ubangi-Shari	82-85
Upper Volta	66-69
Wallis & Futuna Isls.	85-88

Nos. 213-216 (4)	23.00	18.25
Nos. 60-63 (4)	22.00	22.00
Nos. 97-100 (4)	26.00	26.00
Nos. 152-155 (4)	22.00	22.00
Nos. 116-119 (4)	19.75	19.75
Nos. 100-103 (4)	18.00	18.00
Nos. 76-79 (4)	30.00	30.00
Nos. 102-105 (4)	19.00	19.00
Nos. 120-123 (4)	17.50	17.50
Nos. 138-141 (4)	19.00	19.00
Nos. 140-142 (3)	12.00	11.50
Nos. 92-95 (4)	22.50	22.50
Nos. 169-172 (4)	9.25	6.50
Nos. 129-132 (4)	21.00	21.00
Nos. 65-68 (4)	22.00	22.00
Nos. 61-64 (4)	20.00	18.50
Nos. 176-179 (4)	24.00	24.00
Nos. 73-76 (4)	20.50	20.50
Nos. 122-125 (4)	22.00	22.00
Nos. 132-135 (4)	24.00	24.00
Nos. 138-141 (4)	20.00	20.00
Nos. 135-138 (4)	22.00	22.00
Nos. 254-257 (4)	22.00	22.00

Paris International Exposition
Colonial Arts Exposition

Nos. 82-85 (4)	21.00	21.00
Nos. 66-69 (4)	19.00	19.00
Nos. 85-88 (4)	31.00	35.00
Set total (103) Stamps	548.50	543.00

"Colonial Resources"
CD74   CD77

Overseas Commerce CD75

Exposition Building and Women CD76

"France and the Empire" CD78

Cultural Treasures of the Colonies CD79

Souvenir sheets contain one imperf. stamp.

1937

Cameroun	217-222A
Dahomey	101-107
Fr. Equatorial Africa	27-32, 73
Fr. Guiana	162-168
Fr. Guinea	120-126
Fr. India	104-110
Fr. Polynesia	117-123
Fr. Sudan	106-112
Guadeloupe	148-154
Indo-China	193-199
Inini	41
Ivory Coast	152-158
Kwangchowan	132
Madagascar	191-197
Martinique	179-185
Mauritania	69-75
New Caledonia	208-214
Niger	77-83
Reunion	167-173
St. Pierre & Miquelon	165-171
Senegal	172-178
Somali Coast	139-145
Togo	258-264
Wallis & Futuna Isls.	89

Nos. 217-222A (7)	18.80	20.30
Nos. 101-107 (7)	23.60	27.60
Nos. 27-32, 73 (7)	28.10	32.10
Nos. 162-168 (7)	22.50	24.50
Nos. 120-126 (7)	24.00	28.00
Nos. 104-110 (7)	21.15	36.50
Nos. 117-123 (7)	58.50	75.00
Nos. 106-112 (7)	23.60	27.60
Nos. 148-154 (7)	19.55	21.05
Nos. 193-199 (7)	17.70	19.70
No. 41 (1)	21.00	27.50
Nos. 152-158 (7)	22.20	26.20
No. 132 (1)	9.25	11.00
Nos. 191-197 (7)	19.25	21.75
Nos. 179-185 (7)	19.95	21.70
Nos. 69-75 (7)	20.50	24.50
Nos. 208-214 (7)	39.00	50.50
Nos. 73-83 (11)	40.60	45.10
Nos. 167-173 (7)	21.70	23.20
Nos. 165-171 (7)	49.60	64.00
Nos. 172-178 (7)	21.00	23.80
Nos. 139-145 (7)	25.60	32.60
Nos. 258-264 (7)	20.40	20.40
No. 89 (1)	19.00	37.50
Set total (154) Stamps	606.55	742.10

Curie

Pierre and Marie Curie CD80

40th anniversary of the discovery of radium. The surtax was for the benefit of the Intl. Union for the Control of Cancer.

1938

Cameroun	B1
Cuba	B1-B2
Dahomey	B2
France	B76
Fr. Equatorial Africa	B1
Fr. Guiana	B3
Fr. Guinea	B2
Fr. India	B6
Fr. Polynesia	B5
Fr. Sudan	B1
Guadeloupe	B3
Indo-China	B14
Ivory Coast	B2
Madagascar	B2
Martinique	B2
Mauritania	B3
New Caledonia	B4
Niger	B1
Reunion	B4
St. Pierre & Miquelon	B3
Senegal	B3
Somali Coast	B2
Togo	B1

No. B1 (1)	10.00	10.00
Nos. B1-B2 (2)	12.00	3.35
No. B2 (1)	9.50	9.50
No. B76 (1)	21.00	12.50
No. B1 (1)	24.00	24.00
No. B3 (1)	13.50	13.50
No. B2 (1)	8.75	8.75
No. B6 (1)	10.00	10.00
No. B5 (1)	20.00	20.00
No. B1 (1)	12.50	12.50
No. B3 (1)	11.00	10.50
No. B14 (1)	12.00	12.00
No. B2 (1)	11.00	7.50
No. B2 (1)	11.00	11.00
No. B2 (1)	13.00	13.00
No. B3 (1)	7.75	7.75
No. B4 (1)	16.50	17.50
No. B1 (1)	16.50	16.50
No. B4 (1)	14.00	14.00
No. B3 (1)	21.00	22.50
No. B2 (1)	10.50	10.50
No. B2 (1)	7.75	7.75
No. B1 (1)	20.00	20.00
Set total (24) Stamps	313.25	294.60

Caillie

Rene Caillie and Map of Northwestern Africa — CD81

Death centenary of Rene Caillie (1799-1838), French explorer. All three denominations exist with colony name omitted.

1939

Dahomey	108-110
Fr. Guinea	161-163
Fr. Sudan	113-115
Ivory Coast	160-162
Mauritania	109-111
Niger	84-86
Senegal	188-190
Togo	265-267

Nos. 108-110 (3)	1.20	3.60
Nos. 161-163 (3)	1.20	3.20
Nos. 113-115 (3)	1.20	3.20
Nos. 160-162 (3)	1.05	2.55
Nos. 109-111 (3)	1.05	3.80
Nos. 84-86 (3)	2.35	2.35
Nos. 188-190 (3)	1.05	2.90
Nos. 265-267 (3)	1.05	3.30
Set total (24) Stamps	10.15	24.90

New York World's Fair

Natives and New York Skyline CD82

1939

Cameroun	223-224
Dahomey	111-112
Fr. Equatorial Africa	78-79
Fr. Guiana	169-170
Fr. Guinea	164-165
Fr. India	111-112
Fr. Polynesia	124-125
Fr. Sudan	116-117
Guadeloupe	155-156
Indo-China	203-204
Inini	42-43
Ivory Coast	163-164
Kwangchowan	133-134
Madagascar	209-210
Martinique	186-187
Mauritania	112-113
New Caledonia	215-216
Niger	87-88
Reunion	174-175
St. Pierre & Miquelon	205-206
Senegal	191-192
Somali Coast	179-180
Togo	268-269
Wallis & Futuna Isls.	90-91

Nos. 223-224 (2)	2.80	2.40
Nos. 111-112 (2)	1.60	3.20
Nos. 78-79 (2)	1.60	3.20
Nos. 169-170 (2)	2.60	2.60
Nos. 164-165 (2)	1.60	3.20
Nos. 111-112 (2)	3.00	8.00
Nos. 124-125 (2)	4.80	4.80
Nos. 116-117 (2)	1.60	3.20
Nos. 155-156 (2)	2.50	2.50
Nos. 203-204 (2)	2.05	2.05
Nos. 42-43 (2)	7.50	9.00
Nos. 163-164 (2)	1.50	3.00
Nos. 133-134 (2)	2.50	2.50
Nos. 209-210 (2)	1.50	2.50
Nos. 186-187 (2)	2.35	2.35
Nos. 112-113 (2)	1.40	2.80
Nos. 215-216 (2)	3.35	3.35
Nos. 87-88 (2)	1.60	2.80
Nos. 174-175 (2)	2.80	2.80
Nos. 205-206 (2)	4.80	6.00
Nos. 191-192 (2)	1.40	2.80
Nos. 179-180 (2)	1.40	2.80
Nos. 268-269 (2)	1.40	2.80
Nos. 90-91 (2)	5.00	6.00
Set total (48) Stamps	62.65	86.65

French Revolution

Storming of the Bastille CD83

French Revolution, 150th anniv. The surtax was for the defense of the colonies.

1939

Cameroun	B2-B6
Dahomey	B3-B7
Fr. Equatorial Africa	B4-B8, CB1
Fr. Guiana	B4-B8, CB1
Fr. Guinea	B3-B7
Fr. India	B7-B11
Fr. Polynesia	B6-B10, CB1
Fr. Sudan	B2-B6
Guadeloupe	B4-B8
Indo-China	B15-B19, CB1
Inini	B1-B5
Ivory Coast	B3-B7
Kwangchowan	B1-B5
Madagascar	B3-B7, CB1
Martinique	B3-B7
Mauritania	B4-B8
New Caledonia	B5-B9, CB1
Niger	B2-B6
Reunion	B5-B9, CB1
St. Pierre & Miquelon	B4-B8, CB1
Senegal	B3-B7
Somali Coast	B3-B7
Togo	B2-B6
Wallis & Futuna Isls.	B1-B5

Nos. B2-B6 (5)	60.00	60.00
Nos. B3-B7 (5)	47.50	47.50
Nos. B4-B8,CB1 (6)	120.00	120.00
Nos. B4-B8,CB1 (6)	79.50	79.50
Nos. B3-B7 (5)	47.50	47.50
Nos. B7-B11 (5)	28.75	32.50
Nos. B6-B10,CB1 (6)	122.50	122.50
Nos. B2-B6 (5)	50.00	50.00
Nos. B4-B8 (5)	50.00	50.00
Nos. B15-B19,CB1 (6)	85.00	85.00
Nos. B1-B5 (5)	80.00	100.00
Nos. B3-B7 (5)	43.75	43.75
Nos. B1-B5 (5)	46.25	46.25
Nos. B3-B7,CB1 (6)	65.50	65.50
Nos. B3-B7 (5)	52.50	52.50
Nos. B4-B8 (5)	42.50	42.50
Nos. B5-B9,CB1 (6)	101.50	101.50
Nos. B2-B6 (5)	60.00	60.00
Nos. B5-B9,CB1 (6)	87.50	87.50
Nos. B4-B8 (5)	67.50	72.50
Nos. B4-B8,CB1 (6)	56.50	56.50
Nos. B3-B7 (5)	45.00	45.00
Nos. B2-B6 (5)	42.50	42.50
Nos. B1-B5 (5)	80.00	110.00
Set total (128) Stamps	1,562.	1,621.

Plane over Coastal Area CD85

All five denominations exist with colony name omitted.

1940

Dahomey	C1-C5
Fr. Guinea	C1-C5
Fr. Sudan	C1-C5
Ivory Coast	C1-C5
Mauritania	C1-C5
Niger	C1-C5
Senegal	C12-C16
Togo	C1-C5

Nos. C1-C5 (5)	4.00	4.00
Nos. C1-C5 (5)	4.00	4.00
Nos. C1-C5 (5)	4.00	4.00
Nos. C1-C5 (5)	3.80	3.80
Nos. C1-C5 (5)	3.50	3.50
Nos. C1-C5 (5)	3.50	3.50
Nos. C12-C16 (5)	3.50	3.50
Nos. C1-C5 (5)	3.15	3.15
Set total (40) Stamps	29.45	29.45

Defense of the Empire

Colonial Infantryman — CD86

1941

Cameroun	B13B
Dahomey	B13
Fr. Equatorial Africa	B8B
Fr. Guiana	B10
Fr. Guinea	B13
Fr. India	B13
Fr. Polynesia	B12
Fr. Sudan	B12
Guadeloupe	B10
Indo-China	B19B
Inini	B7
Ivory Coast	B13
Kwangchowan	B7
Madagascar	B9
Martinique	B9
Mauritania	B14
New Caledonia	B11
Niger	B12
Reunion	B11
St. Pierre & Miquelon	B8B
Senegal	B14
Somali Coast	B9
Togo	B10B
Wallis & Futuna Isls.	B7

No. B13B (1)	1.60
No. B13 (1)	1.20
No. B8B (1)	3.50
No. B10 (1)	1.40
No. B13 (1)	1.40
No. B13 (1)	1.25
No. B12 (1)	3.50
No. B12 (1)	1.40
No. B10 (1)	1.00
No. B19B (1)	3.00
No. B7 (1)	1.75
No. B13 (1)	1.25
No. B7 (1)	.85

No. B9 (1)	1.50
No. B9 (1)	1.40
No. B14 (1)	.95
No. B12 (1)	1.40
No. B11 (1)	1.60
No. B8B (1)	4.50
No. B14 (1)	1.25
No. B9 (1)	1.60
No. B10B (1)	1.10
No. B7 (1)	1.75
Set total (23) Stamps	40.15

Each of the CD86 stamps listed above is part of a set of three stamps. The designs of the other two stamps in the set vary from country to country. Only the values of the Common Design stamps are listed here.

Colonial Education Fund

CD86a

1942

Cameroun	CB3
Dahomey	CB4
Fr. Equatorial Africa	CB5
Fr. Guiana	CB4
Fr. India	CB3
Fr. Polynesia	CB4
Fr. Sudan	CB4
Guadeloupe	CB3
Indo-China	CB5
Inini	CB3
Ivory Coast	CB4
Kwangchowan	CB4
Malagasy	CB5
Martinique	CB3
Mauritania	CB4
New Caledonia	CB4
Niger	CB4
Reunion	CB4
St. Pierre & Miquelon	CB3
Senegal	CB5
Somali Coast	CB3
Togo	CB4
Wallis & Futuna	CB3

No. CB3 (1)	1.10	
No. CB4 (1)	.80	5.50
No. CB5 (1)	.80	
No. CB4 (1)	1.10	
No. CB3 (1)	.40	5.50
No. CB4 (1)	.90	
No. CB4 (1)	2.00	
No. CB3 (1)	.40	5.50
No. CB5 (1)	1.10	
No. CB3 (1)	2.00	
No. CB4 (1)	1.25	
No. CB4 (1)	1.00	5.50
No. CB4 (1)	1.00	
No. CB5 (1)	.65	
No. CB3 (1)	1.00	
No. CB4 (1)	.80	
No. CB4 (1)	2.25	
No. CB4 (1)	.35	
No. CB4 (1)	.90	
No. CB5 (1)	7.00	
No. CB5 (1)	.80	6.50
No. CB3 (1)	.70	
No. CB4 (1)	.35	
No. CB3 (1)	2.00	
Set total (24) Stamps	30.65	28.50

Cross of Lorraine & Four-motor Plane CD87

1941-5

Cameroun	C1-C7
Fr. Equatorial Africa	C17-C23
Fr. Guiana	C9-C10
Fr. India	C1-C6
Fr. Polynesia	C3-C9
Fr. West Africa	C1-C3
Guadeloupe	C1-C2
Madagascar	C37-C43

Martinique...................................C1-C2
New Caledonia.........................C7-C13
Reunion C18-C24
St. Pierre & Miquelon...............C1-C7
Somali Coast C1-C7

Nos. C1-C7 (7)	6.30	6.30
Nos. C17-C23 (7)	10.40	6.35
Nos. C9-C10 (2)	3.80	3.10
Nos. C1-C6 (6)	9.30	15.00
Nos. C3-C9 (7)	13.75	10.00
Nos. C1-C3 (3)	9.50	3.90
Nos. C1-C2 (2)	3.75	2.50
Nos. C37-C43 (7)	5.60	3.80
Nos. C1-C2 (2)	3.00	1.60
Nos. C7-C13 (7)	8.85	5.00
Nos. C18-C24 (7)	7.05	5.00
Nos. C1-C7 (7)	11.60	9.40
Nos. C1-C7 (7)	13.95	11.10
Set total (71) Stamps	106.85	85.35

Somali Coast stamps are inscribed "Djibouti".

Transport
Plane
CD88

Caravan
and Plane
CD89

1942

Dahomey C6-C13
Fr. Guinea C6-C13
Fr. Sudan.................................C6-C13
Ivory Coast C6-C13
Mauritania C6-C13
Niger C6-C13
Senegal C17-C25
Togo.......................................C6-C13

Nos. C6-C13 (8)	7.15
Nos. C6-C13 (8)	5.75
Nos. C6-C13 (8)	8.00
Nos. C6-C13 (8)	11.15
Nos. C6-C13 (8)	9.75
Nos. C6-C13 (8)	6.20
Nos. C17-C25 (9)	9.45
Nos. C6-C13 (8)	6.75
Set total (65) Stamps	64.20

Red Cross

Marianne
CD90

The surtax was for the French Red Cross
and national relief.

1944

Cameroun....................................B28
Fr. Equatorial Africa B38
Fr. Guiana B12
Fr. India B14
Fr. Polynesia...............................B13
Fr. West Africa B1
Guadeloupe B12
Madagascar................................B15
Martinique...................................B11
New Caledonia B13
Reunion B15
St. Pierre & Miquelon....................B13
Somali Coast...............................B13
Wallis & Futuna Isls. B9

No. B28 (1)	2.00	1.60
No. B38 (1)	1.60	1.20
No. B12 (1)	1.75	1.25
No. B14 (1)	1.50	1.25
No. B13 (1)	2.00	1.60
No. B1 (1)	6.50	4.75
No. B12 (1)	1.40	1.00
No. B15 (1)	.90	.90
No. B11 (1)	1.20	1.20
No. B13 (1)	1.50	1.50
No. B15 (1)	1.60	1.10
No. B13 (1)	2.60	2.60
No. B13 (1)	1.75	2.00
No. B9 (1)	3.00	3.00
Set total (14) Stamps	29.30	24.95

Eboue

CD91

Felix Eboue, first French colonial administrator to proclaim resistance to Germany after
French surrender in World War II.

1945

Cameroun..............................296-297
Fr. Equatorial Africa 156-157
Fr. Guiana 171-172
Fr. India 210-211
Fr. Polynesia........................150-151
Fr. West Africa 15-16
Guadeloupe 187-188
Madagascar.........................259-260
Martinique............................196-197
New Caledonia 274-275
Reunion 238-239
St. Pierre & Miquelon.............322-323
Somali Coast........................238-239

Nos. 296-297 (2)	2.40	1.95
Nos. 156-157 (2)	2.55	2.00
Nos. 171-172 (2)	2.45	2.00
Nos. 210-211 (2)	2.20	1.95
Nos. 150-151 (2)	3.60	2.85
Nos. 15-16 (2)	2.40	2.00
Nos. 187-188 (2)	2.05	1.60
Nos. 259-260 (2)	2.00	1.45
Nos. 196-197 (2)	2.05	1.55
Nos. 274-275 (2)	3.40	3.00
Nos. 238-239 (2)	2.40	2.00
Nos. 322-323 (2)	4.40	3.45
Nos. 238-239 (2)	2.45	2.10
Set total (26) Stamps	34.35	28.30

Victory

Victory — CD92

European victory of the Allied Nations in
World War II.

1946, May 8

Cameroun..C8
Fr. Equatorial Africa C24
Fr. Guiana C11
Fr. India C7
Fr. Polynesia.................................C10
Fr. West Africa C4
Guadeloupe C3
Indo-China C19
Madagascar...................................C44
Martinique..C3
New Caledonia C14
Reunion C25
St. Pierre & Miquelon........................C8
Somali Coast....................................C8
Wallis & Futuna Isls. C1

No. C8 (1)	1.60	1.20
No. C24 (1)	1.60	1.25
No. C11 (1)	1.75	1.25
No. C7 (1)	1.00	4.00
No. C10 (1)	2.75	2.00
No. C4 (1)	1.60	1.20
No. C3 (1)	1.25	1.00
No. C19 (1)	1.00	.55
No. C44 (1)	1.00	.35
No. C3 (1)	1.30	1.00
No. C14 (1)	1.50	1.25
No. C25 (1)	1.10	.90
No. C8 (1)	2.10	2.10
No. C8 (1)	1.75	1.40
No. C1 (1)	2.25	1.90
Set total (15) Stamps	23.55	21.35

Chad to Rhine

Leclerc's Departure from
Chad — CD93

Battle at Cufra Oasis — CD94

Tanks in Action, Mareth — CD95

Normandy Invasion — CD96

Entering Paris — CD97

Liberation of Strasbourg — CD98

"Chad to the Rhine" march, 1942-44, by
Gen. Jacques Leclerc's column, later French
2nd Armored Division.

1946, June 6

Cameroun................................C9-C14
Fr. Equatorial Africa C25-C30
Fr. Guiana C12-C17
Fr. India C8-C13
Fr. Polynesia.........................C11-C16
Fr. West Africa C5-C10
Guadeloupe C4-C9
Indo-China C20-C25
Madagascar..........................C45-C50
Martinique...............................C4-C9
New Caledonia C15-C20
Reunion C26-C31
St. Pierre & Miquelon..............C9-C14
Somali Coast.........................C9-C14
Wallis & Futuna Isls. C2-C7

Nos. C9-C14 (6)	12.05	9.70
Nos. C25-C30 (6)	14.70	10.80
Nos. C12-C17 (6)	12.65	10.35
Nos. C8-C13 (6)	12.80	15.00
Nos. C11-C16 (6)	17.55	13.40
Nos. C5-C10 (6)	16.05	11.95
Nos. C4-C9 (6)	12.00	9.60
Nos. C20-C25 (6)	6.40	6.40
Nos. C45-C50 (6)	10.30	8.40
Nos. C4-C9 (6)	8.85	7.30
Nos. C15-C20 (6)	13.40	11.90
Nos. C26-C31 (6)	10.25	6.55
Nos. C9-C14 (6)	17.30	14.35

Nos. C9-C14 (6)	18.10	12.65
Nos. C2-C7 (6)	13.75	10.45
Set total (90) Stamps	196.15	158.80

UPU

French Colonials, Globe and
Plane — CD99

Universal Postal Union, 75th anniv.

1949, July 4

Cameroun......................................C29
Fr. Equatorial Africa C34
Fr. India C17
Fr. Polynesia................................C20
Fr. West Africa C15
Indo-China C26
Madagascar.................................C55
New Caledonia C24
St. Pierre & Miquelon....................C18
Somali Coast...............................C18
Togo...C18
Wallis & Futuna Isls. C10

No. C29 (1)	8.00	4.75
No. C34 (1)	16.00	12.00
No. C17 (1)	11.50	8.75
No. C20 (1)	20.00	15.00
No. C15 (1)	12.00	8.75
No. C26 (1)	4.75	4.00
No. C55 (1)	4.00	2.75
No. C24 (1)	7.50	5.00
No. C18 (1)	20.00	12.00
No. C18 (1)	14.00	10.50
No. C18 (1)	8.50	7.00
No. C10 (1)	11.00	8.25
Set total (12) Stamps	137.25	98.75

Tropical Medicine

Doctor
Treating
Infant
CD100

The surtax was for charitable work.

1950

Cameroun......................................B29
Fr. Equatorial Africa B39
Fr. India B15
Fr. Polynesia................................B14
Fr. West Africa B3
Madagascar.................................B17
New Caledonia B14
St. Pierre & Miquelon....................B14
Somali Coast...............................B14
Togo...B11

No. B29 (1)	7.25	5.50
No. B39 (1)	7.25	5.50
No. B15 (1)	6.00	4.00
No. B14 (1)	10.50	8.00
No. B3 (1)	9.50	7.25
No. B17 (1)	5.50	5.50
No. B14 (1)	6.75	5.25
No. B14 (1)	16.00	15.00
No. B14 (1)	7.75	6.25
No. B11 (1)	5.00	3.50
Set total (10) Stamps	81.50	65.75

Military Medal

Medal, Early Marine
and Colonial
Soldier — CD101

Centenary of the creation of the French Military Medal.

1952

Cameroun....................................322
Comoro Isls. 39
Fr. Equatorial Africa 186

Fr. India 233
Fr. Polynesia 179
Fr. West Africa 57
Madagascar.................................286
New Caledonia 295
St. Pierre & Miquelon 345
Somali Coast 267
Togo 327
Wallis & Futuna Isls. 149

No. 322 (1)	7.25	3.25
No. 39 (1)	45.00	37.50
No. 186 (1)	8.00	5.50
No. 233 (1)	5.50	7.00
No. 179 (1)	13.50	10.00
No. 57 (1)	8.75	6.50
No. 286 (1)	3.75	2.50
No. 295 (1)	6.50	6.00
No. 345 (1)	16.00	15.00
No. 267 (1)	9.00	8.00
No. 327 (1)	5.50	4.75
No. 149 (1)	7.25	7.25
Set total (12) Stamps	136.00	113.25

Liberation

Allied Landing, Victory Sign and Cross of Lorraine — CD102

Liberation of France, 10th anniv.

1954, June 6

Cameroun C32
Comoro Isls. C4
Fr. Equatorial Africa C38
Fr. India C18
Fr. Polynesia C22
Fr. West Africa C17
Madagascar.................................C57
New Caledonia C25
St. Pierre & Miquelon C19
Somali Coast C19
Togo C19
Wallis & Futuna Isls. C11

No. C32 (1)	7.25	4.75
No. C4 (1)	32.50	19.00
No. C38 (1)	12.00	8.00
No. C18 (1)	11.00	8.00
No. C22 (1)	10.00	8.00
No. C17 (1)	12.00	5.50
No. C57 (1)	3.25	2.00
No. C25 (1)	7.50	5.00
No. C19 (1)	19.00	12.00
No. C19 (1)	10.50	8.50
No. C19 (1)	7.00	5.50
No. C11 (1)	11.00	8.25
Set total (12) Stamps	143.00	94.50

FIDES

Plowmen CD103

Efforts of FIDES, the Economic and Social Development Fund for Overseas Possessions (Fonds d' Investissement pour le Developpement Economique et Social). Each stamp has a different design.

1956

Cameroun....................................326-329
Comoro Isls. 43
Fr. Equatorial Africa 189-192
Fr. Polynesia 181
Fr. West Africa 65-72
Madagascar................................292-295
New Caledonia 303
St. Pierre & Miquelon 350
Somali Coast 268-269
Togo 331

Nos. 326-329 (4)	6.90	3.20
No. 43 (1)	2.25	1.60
Nos. 189-192 (4)	3.20	1.65
No. 181 (1)	4.00	2.00
Nos. 65-72 (8)	16.00	6.35
Nos. 292-295 (4)	2.25	1.20
No. 303 (1)	1.90	1.10
No. 350 (1)	6.00	4.00

Nos. 268-269 (2)	5.35	3.15
No. 331 (1)	4.25	2.10
Set total (27) Stamps	52.10	26.35

Flower

 CD104

Each stamp shows a different flower.

1958-9

Cameroun....................................333
Comoro Isls. 45
Fr. Equatorial Africa 200-201
Fr. Polynesia 192
Fr. So. & Antarctic Terr. 11
Fr. West Africa 79-83
Madagascar................................301-302
New Caledonia 304-305
St. Pierre & Miquelon 357
Somali Coast 270
Togo 348-349
Wallis & Futuna Isls. 152

No. 333 (1)	1.60	.80
No. 45 (1)	5.25	4.25
Nos. 200-201 (2)	3.60	1.60
No. 192 (1)	6.50	4.00
No. 11 (1)	8.75	7.50
Nos. 79-83 (5)	10.45	5.60
Nos. 301-302 (2)	1.60	.60
Nos. 304-305 (2)	8.00	3.00
No. 357 (1)	4.50	2.25
No. 270 (1)	4.25	1.40
Nos. 348-349 (2)	1.10	.50
No. 152 (1)	3.25	3.25
Set total (20) Stamps	58.85	34.75

Human Rights

Sun, Dove and U.N. Emblem CD105

10th anniversary of the signing of the Universal Declaration of Human Rights.

1958

Comoro Isls. 44
Fr. Equatorial Africa 202
Fr. Polynesia 191
Fr. West Africa 85
Madagascar................................300
New Caledonia 306
St. Pierre & Miquelon 356
Somali Coast 274
Wallis & Futuna Isls. 153

No. 44 (1)	9.00	9.00
No. 202 (1)	2.40	1.25
No. 191 (1)	13.00	8.75
No. 85 (1)	2.40	2.00
No. 300 (1)	.80	.40
No. 306 (1)	2.00	1.50
No. 356 (1)	3.50	2.50
No. 274 (1)	3.50	2.10
No. 153 (1)	4.50	4.50
Set total (9) Stamps	41.10	32.00

C.C.T.A.

 CD106

Commission for Technical Cooperation in Africa south of the Sahara, 10th anniv.

1960

Cameroun....................................339
Cent. Africa 3
Chad...66
Congo, P.R..................................90
Dahomey 138
Gabon...150
Ivory Coast 180
Madagascar................................317

Mali...9
Mauritania...................................117
Niger...104
Upper Volta.................................89

No. 339 (1)	1.60	.75
No. 3 (1)	1.60	.75
No. 66 (1)	1.75	.50
No. 90 (1)	1.00	1.00
No. 138 (1)	.50	.25
No. 150 (1)	1.25	1.10
No. 180 (1)	1.10	.50
No. 317 (1)	.60	.30
No. 9 (1)	1.20	.50
No. 117 (1)	.75	.40
No. 104 (1)	.85	.45
No. 89 (1)	.65	.40
Set total (12) Stamps	12.85	6.90

Air Afrique, 1961

Modern and Ancient Africa, Map and Planes — CD107

Founding of Air Afrique (African Airlines).

1961-62

Cameroun....................................C37
Cent. Africa C5
Chad...C7
Congo, P.R..................................C5
Dahomey C17
Gabon...C5
Ivory Coast C18
Mauritania...................................C17
Niger...C22
Senegal C31
Upper Volta.................................C4

No. C37 (1)	1.00	.50
No. C5 (1)	1.00	.65
No. C7 (1)	1.00	.25
No. C5 (1)	1.75	.90
No. C17 (1)	.80	.40
No. C5 (1)	11.00	6.00
No. C18 (1)	2.00	1.25
No. C17 (1)	2.40	1.25
No. C22 (1)	1.75	.90
No. C31 (1)	.80	.30
No. C4 (1)	3.50	1.75
Set total (11) Stamps	27.00	14.15

Anti-Malaria

CD108

World Health Organization drive to eradicate malaria.

1962, Apr. 7

Cameroun....................................B36
Cent. Africa B1
Chad...B1
Comoro Isls. B1
Congo, P.R..................................B3
Dahomey B15
Gabon...B4
Ivory Coast B15
Madagascar................................B19
Mali...B1
Mauritania...................................B16
Niger...B14
Senegal B16
Somali Coast B15
Upper Volta.................................B1

No. B36 (1)	1.00	.45
No. B1 (1)	1.40	1.40
No. B1 (1)	1.00	.50
No. B1 (1)	3.50	3.50
No. B3 (1)	1.40	1.00
No. B15 (1)	.75	.75
No. B4 (1)	1.00	1.00
No. B15 (1)	1.25	1.25
No. B19 (1)	.75	.50
No. B1 (1)	1.25	.60
No. B16 (1)	.50	.50
No. B14 (1)	.75	.75

No. B16 (1)	1.10	.65
No. B15 (1)	7.00	7.00
No. B1 (1)	.75	.70
Set total (15) Stamps	23.40	20.55

Abidjan Games

 CD109

Abidjan Games, Ivory Coast, Dec. 24-31, 1961. Each stamp shows a different sport.

1962

Cent. Africa 19-20, C6
Chad.......................................83-84, C8
Congo, P.R.............................103-104, C7
Gabon.....................................163-164, C6
Niger.......................................109-111
Upper Volta.............................103-105

Nos. 19-20,C6 (3)	4.15	2.85
Nos. 83-84,C8 (3)	5.80	1.55
Nos. 103-104,C7 (3)	3.85	1.80
Nos. 163-164,C6 (3)	5.00	3.00
Nos. 109-111 (3)	2.60	1.25
Nos. 103-105 (3)	2.80	1.25
Set total (18) Stamps	24.20	12.20

African and Malagasy Union

Flag of Union CD110

First anniversary of the Union.

1962, Sept. 8

Cameroun....................................373
Cent. Africa 21
Chad...85
Congo, P.R..................................105
Dahomey 155
Gabon...165
Ivory Coast 198
Madagascar................................332
Mauritania...................................170
Niger...112
Senegal 211
Upper Volta.................................106

No. 373 (1)	2.00	.75
No. 21 (1)	1.25	.75
No. 85 (1)	1.25	.25
No. 105 (1)	1.50	.50
No. 155 (1)	1.25	.90
No. 165 (1)	1.60	1.25
No. 198 (1)	2.10	.75
No. 332 (1)	.80	.80
No. 170 (1)	.75	.50
No. 112 (1)	.80	.50
No. 211 (1)	.80	.50
No. 106 (1)	1.10	.75
Set total (12) Stamps	15.20	8.20

Telstar

Telstar and Globe Showing Andover and Pleumeur-Bodou — CD111

First television connection of the United States and Europe through the Telstar satellite, July 11-12, 1962.

1962-63

Andorra, French 154
Comoro Isls. C7
Fr. Polynesia C29
Fr. So. & Antarctic Terr. C5
New Caledonia C33
St. Pierre & Miquelon C26
Somali Coast C31
Wallis & Futuna Isls. C17

No. 154 (1)	2.00	1.60
No. C7 (1)	4.50	2.75
No. C29 (1)	11.50	8.00

No. C5 (1)	29.00	21.00
No. C33 (1)	25.00	18.50
No. C26 (1)	7.25	4.50
No. C31 (1)	1.00	1.00
No. C17 (1)	3.75	3.75
Set total (8) Stamps	84.00	61.10

Freedom From Hunger

World Map and Wheat Emblem CD112

U.N. Food and Agriculture Organization's "Freedom from Hunger" campaign.

1963, Mar. 21

Cameroun	B37-B38
Cent. Africa	B2
Chad	B2
Congo, P.R.	B4
Dahomey	B16
Gabon	B5
Ivory Coast	B16
Madagascar	B21
Mauritania	B17
Niger	B15
Senegal	B17
Upper Volta	B2

Nos. B37-B38 (2)	2.25	.75
No. B2 (1)	1.25	1.25
No. B2 (1)	1.10	.50
No. B4 (1)	1.40	1.00
No. B16 (1)	.80	.80
No. B5 (1)	1.00	1.00
No. B16 (1)	1.50	1.50
No. B21 (1)	.60	.45
No. B17 (1)	.60	.60
No. B15 (1)	.75	.75
No. B17 (1)	.80	.50
No. B2 (1)	.75	.70
Set total (13) Stamps	12.80	9.80

Red Cross Centenary

CD113

Centenary of the International Red Cross.

1963, Sept. 2

Comoro Isls.	55
Fr. Polynesia	205
New Caledonia	328
St. Pierre & Miquelon	367
Somali Coast	297
Wallis & Futuna Isls.	165

No. 55 (1)	7.50	6.00
No. 205 (1)	15.00	12.00
No. 328 (1)	8.00	6.75
No. 367 (1)	12.00	5.50
No. 297 (1)	6.25	6.25
No. 165 (1)	4.00	4.00
Set total (6) Stamps	52.75	40.50

African Postal Union, 1963

UAMPT Emblem, Radio Masts, Plane and Mail CD114

Establishment of the African and Malagasy Posts and Telecommunications Union.

1963, Sept. 8

Cameroun	C47
Cent. Africa	C10
Chad	C9
Congo, P.R.	C13

Dahomey	C19
Gabon	C13
Ivory Coast	C25
Madagascar	C75
Mauritania	C22
Niger	C27
Rwanda	36
Senegal	C32
Upper Volta	C9

No. C47 (1)	2.25	1.00
No. C10 (1)	1.90	.90
No. C9 (1)	1.80	.60
No. C13 (1)	1.40	.75
No. C19 (1)	.75	.25
No. C13 (1)	1.90	.80
No. C25 (1)	2.50	1.50
No. C75 (1)	1.25	.80
No. C22 (1)	1.50	.60
No. C27 (1)	1.25	.60
No. 36 (1)	1.10	.75
No. C32 (1)	1.75	.50
No. C9 (1)	1.50	.75
Set total (13) Stamps	20.85	9.80

Air Afrique, 1963

Symbols of Flight — CD115

First anniversary of Air Afrique and inauguration of DC-8 service.

1963, Nov. 19

Cameroun	C48
Chad	C10
Congo, P.R.	C14
Gabon	C18
Ivory Coast	C26
Mauritania	C26
Niger	C35
Senegal	C33

No. C48 (1)	1.25	.40
No. C10 (1)	1.80	.60
No. C14 (1)	1.60	.60
No. C18 (1)	1.25	.65
No. C26 (1)	1.00	.50
No. C26 (1)	.70	.25
No. C35 (1)	1.00	.55
No. C33 (1)	2.00	.65
Set total (8) Stamps	10.60	4.20

Europafrica

Europe and Africa Linked — CD116

Signing of an economic agreement between the European Economic Community and the African and Malagasy Union, Yaounde, Cameroun, July 20, 1963.

1963-64

Cameroun	402
Cent. Africa	C12
Chad	C11
Congo, P.R.	C16
Gabon	C19
Ivory Coast	217
Niger	C43
Upper Volta	C11

No. 402 (1)	2.25	.60
No. C12 (1)	2.50	1.75
No. C11 (1)	1.60	.50
No. C16 (1)	1.60	1.00
No. C19 (1)	1.25	.75
No. 217 (1)	1.10	.35
No. C43 (1)	.85	.50
No. C11 (1)	1.50	.80
Set total (8) Stamps	12.65	6.25

Human Rights

Scales of Justice and Globe CD117

15th anniversary of the Universal Declaration of Human Rights.

1963, Dec. 10

Comoro Isls.	56
Fr. Polynesia	206
New Caledonia	329
St. Pierre & Miquelon	368
Somali Coast	300
Wallis & Futuna Isls.	166

No. 56 (1)	7.50	6.00
No. 205 (1)	15.00	12.00
No. 329 (1)	7.00	6.00
No. 368 (1)	7.00	3.50
No. 300 (1)	8.50	8.50
No. 166 (1)	7.00	7.00
Set total (6) Stamps	52.00	43.00

PHILATEC

Stamp Album, Champs Elysees Palace and Horses of Marly CD118

Intl. Philatelic and Postal Techniques Exhibition, Paris, June 5-21, 1964.

1963-64

Comoro Isls.	60
France	1078
Fr. Polynesia	207
New Caledonia	341
St. Pierre & Miquelon	369
Somali Coast	301
Wallis & Futuna Isls.	167

No. 60 (1)	4.00	3.50
No. 1078 (1)	.25	.25
No. 206 (1)	15.00	10.00
No. 341 (1)	6.50	6.50
No. 369 (1)	11.00	8.00
No. 301 (1)	7.75	7.75
No. 167 (1)	3.00	3.00
Set total (7) Stamps	47.50	39.00

Cooperation

CD119

Cooperation between France and the French-speaking countries of Africa and Madagascar.

1964

Cameroun	409-410
Cent. Africa	39
Chad	103
Congo, P.R.	121
Dahomey	193
France	1111
Gabon	175
Ivory Coast	221
Madagascar	360
Mauritania	181
Niger	143
Senegal	236
Togo	495

Nos. 409-410 (2)	2.50	.50
No. 39 (1)	.90	.50
No. 103 (1)	1.00	.25
No. 121 (1)	.90	.35
No. 193 (1)	.80	.35
No. 1111 (1)	.25	.25
No. 175 (1)	.90	.60
No. 221 (1)	1.10	.35

No. 360 (1)	.60	.25
No. 181 (1)	.60	.35
No. 143 (1)	.80	.40
No. 236 (1)	1.60	.85
No. 495 (1)	.70	.25
Set total (14) Stamps	12.65	5.25

ITU

Telegraph, Syncom Satellite and ITU Emblem CD120

Intl. Telecommunication Union, Cent.

1965, May 17

Comoro Isls.	C14
Fr. Polynesia	C33
Fr. So. & Antarctic Terr.	C8
New Caledonia	C40
New Hebrides	124-125
St. Pierre & Miquelon	C29
Somali Coast	C36
Wallis & Futuna Isls.	C20

No. C14 (1)	18.00	9.00
No. C33 (1)	80.00	52.50
No. C8 (1)	200.00	160.00
No. C40 (1)	10.00	8.00
Nos. 124-125 (2)	32.25	27.25
No. C29 (1)	24.00	11.50
No. C36 (1)	15.00	9.00
No. C20 (1)	16.00	16.00
Set total (9) Stamps	395.25	293.25

French Satellite A-1

Diamant Rocket and Launching Installation — CD121

Launching of France's first satellite, Nov. 26, 1965.

1965-66

Comoro Isls.	C16a
France	1138a
Reunion	359a
Fr. Polynesia	C41a
Fr. So. & Antarctic Terr.	C10a
New Caledonia	C45a
St. Pierre & Miquelon	C31a
Somali Coast	C40a
Wallis & Futuna Isls.	C23a

No. C16a (1)	9.00	9.00
No. 1138a (1)	.65	.65
No. 359a (1)	3.50	3.00
No. C41a (1)	14.00	14.00
No. C10a (1)	29.00	24.00
No. C45a (1)	7.00	7.00
No. C31a (1)	14.50	14.50
No. C40a (1)	7.00	7.00
No. C23a (1)	8.50	8.50
Set total (9) Stamps	93.15	87.65

French Satellite D-1

D-1 Satellite in Orbit — CD122

Launching of the D-1 satellite at Hammaguir, Algeria, Feb. 17, 1966.

1966

Comoro Isls.	C17
France	1148

Fr. Polynesia............................C42
Fr. So. & Antarctic Terr. C11
New Caledonia.........................C46
St. Pierre & Miquelon................C32
Somali Coast..........................C49
Wallis & Futuna Isls. C24

No. C17 (1)	4.00	4.00
No. 1148 (1)	.25	.25
No. C42 (1)	7.00	4.75
No. C11 (1)	57.50	40.00
No. C46 (1)	2.25	2.00
No. C32 (1)	9.00	6.00
No. C49 (1)	4.25	2.75
No. C24 (1)	3.50	3.50
Set total (8) Stamps	87.75	63.25

Air Afrique, 1966

Planes and Air Afrique
Emblem — CD123

Introduction of DC-8F planes by Air Afrique.

1966

Cameroun..............................C79
Cent. Africa C35
Chad...................................C26
Congo, P.R.............................C42
Dahomey C42
Gabon.................................C47
Ivory Coast C32
Mauritania.............................C57
Niger..................................C63
Senegal C47
Togo C54
Upper Volta............................C31

No. C79 (1)	.80	.25
No. C35 (1)	1.00	.50
No. C26 (1)	.85	.25
No. C42 (1)	1.00	.25
No. C42 (1)	.75	.25
No. C47 (1)	.90	.35
No. C32 (1)	1.00	.60
No. C57 (1)	.60	.30
No. C63 (1)	.70	.35
No. C47 (1)	.80	.30
No. C54 (1)	.80	.25
No. C31 (1)	.75	.50
Set total (12) Stamps	9.95	4.15

African Postal Union, 1967

Telecommunications Symbols and Map
of Africa — CD124

Fifth anniversary of the establishment of the African and Malagasy Union of Posts and Telecommunications, UAMPT.

1967

Cameroun..............................C90
Cent. Africa C46
Chad...................................C37
Congo, P.R.............................C57
Dahomey C61
Gabon.................................C58
Ivory Coast C34
Madagascar............................C85
Mauritania.............................C65
Niger..................................C75
Rwanda C1-C3
Senegal C60
Togo C81
Upper Volta............................C50

No. C90 (1)	2.40	.65
No. C46 (1)	2.25	.85
No. C37 (1)	2.00	.60
No. C57 (1)	1.60	.60
No. C61 (1)	1.75	.95
No. C58 (1)	2.00	.85
No. C34 (1)	3.50	1.50
No. C85 (1)	1.25	.60
No. C65 (1)	1.25	.60
No. C75 (1)	1.40	.60

Nos. C1-C3 (3)	2.05	1.25
No. C60 (1)	1.75	.50
No. C81 (1)	1.90	.30
No. C50 (1)	1.80	.70
Set total (16) Stamps	26.90	10.55

Monetary Union

Gold Token of the Ashantis, 17-18th Centuries — CD125

West African Monetary Union, 5th anniv.

1967, Nov. 4

Dahomey 244
Ivory Coast 259
Mauritania.............................238
Niger..................................204
Senegal 294
Togo 623
Upper Volta............................181

No. 244 (1)	.65	.65
No. 259 (1)	.85	.40
No. 238 (1)	.45	.25
No. 204 (1)	.55	.25
No. 294 (1)	.60	.25
No. 623 (1)	.60	.25
No. 181 (1)	.65	.35
Set total (7) Stamps	4.35	2.40

WHO Anniversary

Sun, Flowers and WHO Emblem CD126

World Health Organization, 20th anniv.

1968, May 4

Afars & Issas 317
Comoro Isls. 73
Fr. Polynesia..........................241-242
Fr. So. & Antarctic Terr. 31
New Caledonia.........................367
St. Pierre & Miquelon................377
Wallis & Futuna Isls. 169

No. 317 (1)	3.00	3.00
No. 73 (1)	2.40	1.75
Nos. 241-242 (2)	22.00	12.75
No. 31 (1)	62.50	47.50
No. 367 (1)	4.00	2.25
No. 377 (1)	12.00	9.00
No. 169 (1)	5.75	5.75
Set total (8) Stamps	111.65	82.00

Human Rights Year

Human Rights Flame — CD127

1968, Aug. 10

Afars & Issas 322-323
Comoro Isls. 76
Fr. Polynesia..........................243-244
Fr. So. & Antarctic Terr. 32
New Caledonia.........................369
St. Pierre & Miquelon................382
Wallis & Futuna Isls. 170

Nos. 322-323 (2)	6.75	4.00
No. 76 (1)	3.25	3.25
Nos. 243-244 (2)	24.00	14.00
No. 32 (1)	55.00	47.50
No. 369 (1)	2.75	1.50
No. 382 (1)	8.00	5.50
No. 170 (1)	3.25	3.25
Set total (9) Stamps	103.00	79.00

2nd PHILEXAFRIQUE

CD128

Opening of PHILEXAFRIQUE, Abidjan, Feb. 14. Each stamp shows a local scene and stamp.

1969, Feb. 14

Cameroon...............................C118
Cent. Africa C65
Chad...................................C48
Congo, P.R.............................C77
Dahomey C94
Gabon.................................C82
Ivory Coast C38-C40
Madagascar............................C92
Mali...................................C65
Mauritania.............................C80
Niger..................................C104
Senegal C68
Togo C104
Upper Volta............................C62

No. C118 (1)	3.25	1.25
No. C65 (1)	1.75	1.75
No. C48 (1)	2.40	1.00
No. C77 (1)	2.00	1.75
No. C94 (1)	2.25	2.25
No. C82 (1)	2.00	2.00
Nos. C38-C40 (3)	14.50	14.50
No. C92 (1)	1.75	.85
No. C65 (1)	1.75	1.00
No. C80 (1)	1.90	.75
No. C104 (1)	3.00	1.90
No. C68 (1)	2.00	1.40
No. C104 (1)	2.25	.45
No. C62 (1)	4.00	3.25
Set total (16) Stamps	44.80	34.10

Concorde

Concorde in Flight CD129

First flight of the prototype Concorde supersonic plane at Toulouse, Mar. 1, 1969.

1969

Afars & Issas C56
Comoro Isls. C29
France.................................C42
Fr. Polynesia..........................C50
Fr. So. & Antarctic Terr. C18
New Caledonia.........................C63
St. Pierre & Miquelon................C40
Wallis & Futuna Isls. C30

No. C56 (1)	26.00	16.00
No. C29 (1)	18.00	12.00
No. C42 (1)	.75	.35
No. C50 (1)	55.00	35.00
No. C18 (1)	55.00	37.50
No. C63 (1)	27.50	20.00
No. C40 (1)	32.50	11.00
No. C30 (1)	15.00	10.00
Set total (8) Stamps	229.75	141.85

Development Bank

Bank Emblem — CD130

African Development Bank, fifth anniv.

1969

Cameroon...............................499
Chad...................................217
Congo, P.R.............................181-182

Ivory Coast 281
Mali...................................127-128
Mauritania.............................267
Niger..................................220
Senegal 317-318
Upper Volta............................201

No. 499 (1)	.80	.25
No. 217 (1)	.90	.25
Nos. 181-182 (2)	1.00	.50
No. 281 (1)	.70	.40
Nos. 127-128 (2)	1.00	.50
No. 267 (1)	.60	.25
No. 220 (1)	.70	.30
Nos. 317-318 (2)	1.55	.50
No. 201 (1)	.65	.30
Set total (12) Stamps	7.90	3.25

ILO

ILO Headquarters, Geneva, and
Emblem — CD131

Intl. Labor Organization, 50th anniv.

1969-70

Afars & Issas 337
Comoro Isls. 83
Fr. Polynesia..........................251-252
Fr. So. & Antarctic Terr. 35
New Caledonia.........................379
St. Pierre & Miquelon................396
Wallis & Futuna Isls. 172

No. 337 (1)	2.75	2.00
No. 83 (1)	1.25	.75
Nos. 251-252 (2)	24.00	12.50
No. 35 (1)	15.00	10.00
No. 379 (1)	2.25	1.10
No. 396 (1)	10.00	5.50
No. 172 (1)	2.75	2.75
Set total (8) Stamps	58.00	34.60

ASECNA

Map of Africa, Plane and Airport CD132

10th anniversary of the Agency for the Security of Aerial Navigation in Africa and Madagascar (ASECNA, Agence pour la Securite de la Navigation Aerienne en Afrique et a Madagascar).

1969-70

Cameroun..............................500
Cent. Africa 119
Chad...................................222
Congo, P.R.............................197
Dahomey 269
Gabon.................................260
Ivory Coast 287
Mali...................................130
Niger..................................221
Senegal 321
Upper Volta............................204

No. 500 (1)	2.00	.60
No. 119 (1)	2.00	.80
No. 222 (1)	1.00	.25
No. 197 (1)	2.00	.40
No. 269 (1)	.90	.55
No. 260 (1)	1.75	.40
No. 287 (1)	.90	.40
No. 130 (1)	.90	.40
No. 221 (1)	1.40	.70
No. 321 (1)	1.60	.50
No. 204 (1)	1.75	1.00
Set total (11) Stamps	16.20	6.35

U.P.U. Headquarters

CD133

New Universal Postal Union headquarters, Bern, Switzerland.

1970

Afars & Issas		342
Algeria		443
Cameroun		503-504
Cent. Africa		125
Chad		225
Comoro Isls.		84
Congo, P.R.		216
Fr. Polynesia		261-262
Fr. So. & Antarctic Terr.		36
Gabon		258
Ivory Coast		295
Madagascar		444
Mali		134-135
Mauritania		283
New Caledonia		382
Niger		231-232
St. Pierre & Miquelon		397-398
Senegal		328-329
Tunisia		535
Wallis & Futuna Isls.		173

No. 342 (1)	2.50	1.40
No. 443 (1)	1.10	.40
Nos. 503-504 (2)	2.60	.55
No. 125 (1)	1.75	.70
No. 225 (1)	1.20	.25
No. 84 (1)	5.50	2.00
No. 216 (1)	1.00	.25
Nos. 261-262 (2)	20.00	10.00
No. 36 (1)	40.00	27.50
No. 258 (1)	.90	.55
No. 295 (1)	1.10	.50
No. 444 (1)	.55	.25
Nos. 134-135 (2)	1.05	.50
No. 283 (1)	.60	.30
No. 382 (1)	3.00	1.50
Nos. 231-232 (2)	1.50	.60
Nos. 397-398 (2)	34.00	16.25
Nos. 328-329 (2)	1.55	.55
No. 535 (1)	.60	.25
No. 173 (1)	3.25	3.25
Set total (26) Stamps	123.75	67.55

De Gaulle

CD134

First anniversary of the death of Charles de Gaulle, (1890-1970), President of France.

1971-72

Afars & Issas		356-357
Comoro Isls.		104-105
France		1325a
Fr. Polynesia		270-271
Fr. So. & Antarctic Terr.		52-53
New Caledonia		393-394
Reunion		380a
St. Pierre & Miquelon		417-418
Wallis & Futuna Isls.		177-178

Nos. 356-357 (2)	12.50	7.50
Nos. 104-105 (2)	9.00	5.75
No. 1325a (1)	3.00	2.50
Nos. 270-271 (2)	51.50	29.50
Nos. 52-53 (2)	40.00	29.50
Nos. 393-394 (2)	23.00	11.75
No. 380a (1)	9.25	8.00
Nos. 417-418 (2)	56.50	31.00
Nos. 177-178 (2)	20.00	16.25
Set total (16) Stamps	224.75	141.75

African Postal Union, 1971

UAMPT Building, Brazzaville, Congo — CD135

10th anniversary of the establishment of the African and Malagasy Posts and Telecommunications Union, UAMPT. Each stamp has a different native design.

1971, Nov. 13

Cameroun		C177
Cent. Africa		C89
Chad		C94

Congo, P.R.		C136
Dahomey		C146
Gabon		C120
Ivory Coast		C47
Mauritania		C113
Niger		C164
Rwanda		C8
Senegal		C105
Togo		C166
Upper Volta		C97

No. C177 (1)	2.00	.50
No. C89 (1)	2.25	.85
No. C94 (1)	1.50	.50
No. C136 (1)	1.60	.75
No. C146 (1)	1.75	.80
No. C120 (1)	1.75	.70
No. C47 (1)	2.00	1.00
No. C113 (1)	1.10	.65
No. C164 (1)	1.25	.60
No. C8 (1)	2.75	2.50
No. C105 (1)	1.60	.50
No. C166 (1)	1.25	.40
No. C97 (1)	1.50	.70
Set total (13) Stamps	22.30	10.45

West African Monetary Union

African Couple, City, Village and Commemorative Coin — CD136

West African Monetary Union, 10th anniv.

1972, Nov. 2

Dahomey		300
Ivory Coast		331
Mauritania		299
Niger		258
Senegal		374
Togo		825
Upper Volta		280

No. 300 (1)	.65	.25
No. 331 (1)	1.00	.50
No. 299 (1)	.75	.25
No. 258 (1)	.65	.30
No. 374 (1)	.50	.30
No. 825 (1)	.60	.25
No. 280 (1)	.60	.25
Set total (7) Stamps	4.75	2.10

African Postal Union, 1973

Telecommunications Symbols and Map of Africa — CD137

11th anniversary of the African and Malagasy Posts and Telecommunications Union (UAMPT).

1973, Sept. 12

Cameroun		574
Cent. Africa		194
Chad		294
Congo, P.R.		289
Dahomey		311
Gabon		320
Ivory Coast		361
Madagascar		500
Mauritania		304
Niger		287
Rwanda		540
Senegal		393
Togo		849
Upper Volta		297

No. 574 (1)	1.75	.40
No. 194 (1)	1.25	.75
No. 294 (1)	1.75	.40
No. 289 (1)	1.60	.75
No. 311 (1)	1.25	.55
No. 320 (1)	1.40	.75
No. 361 (1)	2.50	1.00
No. 500 (1)	1.10	.35
No. 304 (1)	1.10	.40
No. 287 (1)	.90	.60
No. 540 (1)	3.00	2.00
No. 393 (1)	1.60	.50

No. 849 (1)	1.00	.35
No. 297 (1)	1.25	.70
Set total (14) Stamps	21.45	9.25

Philexafrique II — Essen

CD138

CD139

Designs: Indigenous fauna, local and German stamps. Types CD138-CD139 printed horizontally and vertically se-tenant in sheets of 10 (2x5). Label between horizontal pairs alternately commemoratives Philexafrique II, Libreville, Gabon, June 1978, and 2nd International Stamp Fair, Essen, Germany, Nov. 1-5.

1978-1979

Benin		C286a
Central Africa		C201a
Chad		C239a
Congo Republic		C246a
Djibouti		C122a
Gabon		C216a
Ivory Coast		C65a
Mali		C357a
Mauritania		C186a
Niger		C292a
Rwanda		C13a
Senegal		C147a
Togo		C364a

No. C286a (1)	9.00	8.50
No. C201a (1)	7.50	7.50
No. C239a (1)	7.50	4.00
No. C246a (1)	7.00	7.00
No. C122a (1)	6.50	6.50
No. C216a (1)	6.50	4.00
No. C65a (1)	9.00	9.00
No. C357a (1)	5.00	3.00
No. C186a (1)	5.50	5.00
No. C292a (1)	6.00	6.00
No. C13a (1)	4.00	4.00
No. C147a (1)	10.00	4.00
No. C364a (1)	3.00	1.50
Set total (13) Stamps	86.50	70.00

BRITISH COMMONWEALTH OF NATIONS

The listings follow established trade practices when these issues are offered as units by dealers. The Peace issue, for example, includes only one stamp from the Indian state of Hyderabad. The U.P.U. issue includes the Egypt set. Pairs are included for those varieties issued with bilingual designs se-tenant.

Silver Jubilee

Windsor Castle and King George V CD301

Reign of King George V, 25th anniv.

1935

Antigua		77-80
Ascension		33-36
Bahamas		92-95
Barbados		186-189
Basutoland		11-14

Bechuanaland Protectorate		117-120
Bermuda		100-103
British Guiana		223-226
British Honduras		108-111
Cayman Islands		81-84
Ceylon		260-263
Cyprus		136-139
Dominica		90-93
Falkland Islands		77-80
Fiji		110-113
Gambia		125-128
Gibraltar		100-103
Gilbert & Ellice Islands		33-36
Gold Coast		108-111
Grenada		124-127
Hong Kong		147-150
Jamaica		109-112
Kenya, Uganda, Tanzania		42-45
Leeward Islands		96-99
Malta		184-187
Mauritius		204-207
Montserrat		85-88
Newfoundland		226-229
Nigeria		34-37
Northern Rhodesia		18-21
Nyasaland Protectorate		47-50
St. Helena		111-114
St. Kitts-Nevis		72-75
St. Lucia		91-94
St. Vincent		134-137
Seychelles		118-121
Sierra Leone		166-169
Solomon Islands		60-63
Somaliland Protectorate		77-80
Straits Settlements		213-216
Swaziland		20-23
Trinidad & Tobago		43-46
Turks & Caicos Islands		71-74
Virgin Islands		69-72

The following have different designs but are included in the omnibus set:

Great Britain		226-229
Offices in Morocco (Sp. Curr.)		67-70
Offices in Morocco (Br. Curr.)		226-229
Offices in Morocco (Fr. Curr.)		422-425
Offices in Morocco (Tangier)		508-510
Australia		152-154
Canada		211-216
Cook Islands		98-100
India		142-148
Nauru		31-34
New Guinea		46-47
New Zealand		199-201
Niue		67-69
Papua		114-117
Samoa		163-165
South Africa		68-71
Southern Rhodesia		33-36
South-West Africa		121-124

Nos. 77-80 (4)	20.25	23.25
Nos. 33-36 (4)	58.50	127.50
Nos. 92-95 (4)	25.00	46.00
Nos. 186-189 (4)	30.00	50.30
Nos. 11-14 (4)	11.60	21.25
Nos. 117-120 (4)	15.75	36.00
Nos. 100-103 (4)	16.80	58.50
Nos. 223-226 (4)	22.35	33.55
Nos. 108-111 (4)	15.25	16.35
Nos. 81-84 (4)	21.60	24.50
Nos. 260-263 (4)	10.40	21.60
Nos. 136-139 (4)	39.75	34.40
Nos. 90-93 (4)	18.85	19.85
Nos. 77-80 (4)	55.00	14.75
Nos. 110-113 (4)	20.25	34.00
Nos. 125-128 (4)	13.05	25.25
Nos. 100-103 (4)	28.75	42.75
Nos. 33-36 (4)	36.80	67.00
Nos. 108-111 (4)	25.75	78.10
Nos. 124-127 (4)	16.70	40.60
Nos. 147-150 (4)	73.75	20.75
Nos. 109-112 (4)	24.20	50.50
Nos. 42-45 (4)	10.25	11.75
Nos. 96-99 (4)	35.75	49.60
Nos. 184-187 (4)	22.00	33.70
Nos. 204-207 (4)	44.60	58.25
Nos. 85-88 (4)	10.25	30.25
Nos. 226-229 (4)	17.50	12.05
Nos. 34-37 (4)	17.50	73.00
Nos. 18-21 (4)	17.00	15.00
Nos. 47-50 (4)	43.50	82.50
Nos. 111-114 (4)	31.15	36.50
Nos. 72-75 (4)	11.80	18.65
Nos. 91-94 (4)	16.00	20.80
Nos. 134-137 (4)	9.45	21.25
Nos. 118-121 (4)	15.75	40.00
Nos. 166-169 (4)	23.60	50.35
Nos. 60-63 (4)	29.00	38.00
Nos. 77-80 (4)	17.00	48.25
Nos. 213-216 (4)	15.00	25.10
Nos. 20-23 (4)	6.80	18.25
Nos. 43-46 (4)	18.60	37.50
Nos. 71-74 (4)	9.90	14.50
Nos. 69-72 (4)	25.00	55.25
Nos. 226-229 (4)	5.15	9.90

Nos. 67-70 (4)	13.60	30.70
Nos. 226-229 (4)	16.30	56.00
Nos. 422-425 (4)	9.35	3.95
Nos. 508-510 (3)	26.00	33.50
Nos. 152-154 (3)	49.50	45.35
Nos. 211-216 (6)	23.85	13.35
Nos. 98-100 (3)	9.65	12.00
Nos. 142-148 (7)	28.85	14.00
Nos. 31-34 (4)	12.35	13.15
Nos. 46-47 (2)	4.35	1.70
Nos. 199-201 (3)	23.00	28.50
Nos. 67-69 (3)	19.25	31.00
Nos. 114-117 (4)	9.20	17.50
Nos. 163-165 (3)	4.40	6.50
Nos. 68-71 (4)	57.50	153.00
Nos. 33-36 (4)	27.75	45.25
Nos. 121-124 (4)	13.00	36.10
Set total (245) Stamps	1,401.	2,231.

Coronation

Queen Elizabeth and King George VI CD302

1937

Aden	13-15
Antigua	81-83
Ascension	37-39
Bahamas	95-17
Barbados	190-192
Basutoland	15-17
Bechuanaland Protectorate	121-123
Bermuda	115-117
British Guiana	227-229
British Honduras	112-114
Cayman Islands	97-99
Ceylon	275-277
Cyprus	140-142
Dominica	94-96
Falkland Islands	81-83
Fiji	114-116
Gambia	129-131
Gibraltar	104-106
Gilbert & Ellice Islands	37-39
Gold Coast	112-114
Grenada	128-130
Hong Kong	151-153
Jamaica	113-115
Kenya, Uganda, Tanzania	60-62
Leeward Islands	100-102
Malta	188-190
Mauritius	208-210
Montserrat	89-91
Newfoundland	230-232
Nigeria	50-52
Northern Rhodesia	22-24
Nyasaland Protectorate	51-53
St. Helena	115-117
St. Kitts-Nevis	76-78
St. Lucia	107-109
St. Vincent	138-140
Seychelles	122-124
Sierra Leone	170-172
Solomon Islands	64-66
Somaliland Protectorate	81-83
Straits Settlements	235-237
Swaziland	24-26
Trinidad & Tobago	47-49
Turks & Caicos Islands	75-77
Virgin Islands	73-75

The following have different designs but are included in the omnibus set:

Great Britain	234
Offices in Morocco (Sp. Curr.)	82
Offices in Morocco (Fr. Curr.)	439
Offices in Morocco (Tangier)	514
Canada	237
Cook Islands	109-111
Nauru	35-38
Newfoundland	233-243
New Guinea	48-51
New Zealand	223-225
Niue	70-72
Papua	118-121
South Africa	74-78
Southern Rhodesia	38-41
South-West Africa	125-132

Nos. 13-15 (3)	2.70	5.65
Nos. 81-83 (3)	1.85	8.00
Nos. 37-39 (3)	2.75	2.75
Nos. 97-99 (3)	1.05	3.05
Nos. 190-192 (3)	1.10	1.95
Nos. 15-17 (3)	1.15	3.00
Nos. 121-123 (3)	.95	3.35
Nos. 115-117 (3)	1.25	5.00
Nos. 227-229 (3)	1.45	3.05
Nos. 112-114 (3)	1.20	2.40
Nos. 97-99 (3)	1.05	2.70
Nos. 275-277 (3)	8.25	10.35

Nos. 140-142 (3)	3.75	6.50
Nos. 94-96 (3)	.85	2.40
Nos. 81-83 (3)	2.90	2.30
Nos. 114-116 (3)	1.35	5.75
Nos. 129-131 (3)	.95	3.95
Nos. 104-106 (3)	2.25	6.45
Nos. 37-39 (3)	.85	2.15
Nos. 112-114 (3)	3.10	10.00
Nos. 128-130 (3)	1.00	.85
Nos. 151-153 (3)	17.00	17.75
Nos. 113-115 (3)	1.25	1.25
Nos. 60-62 (3)	1.25	2.35
Nos. 100-102 (3)	1.55	4.00
Nos. 188-190 (3)	1.25	1.60
Nos. 208-210 (3)	1.75	3.50
Nos. 89-91 (3)	1.00	3.35
Nos. 230-232 (3)	7.00	2.80
Nos. 50-52 (3)	3.25	8.50
Nos. 22-24 (3)	.95	2.25
Nos. 51-53 (3)	1.05	1.30
Nos. 115-117 (3)	1.45	2.05
Nos. 76-78 (3)	.95	2.15
Nos. 107-109 (3)	1.05	2.05
Nos. 138-140 (3)	.80	4.75
Nos. 122-124 (3)	1.20	1.90
Nos. 170-172 (3)	1.95	5.65
Nos. 64-66 (3)	.90	2.00
Nos. 81-83 (3)	1.10	3.50
Nos. 235-237 (3)	3.25	1.60
Nos. 24-26 (3)	.75	2.70
Nos. 47-49 (3)	1.10	3.20
Nos. 75-77 (3)	1.25	.95
Nos. 73-75 (3)	2.20	6.90
No. 234 (1)	.30	.25
No. 82 (1)	.80	.60
No. 439 (1)	.50	.25
No. 514 (1)	1.25	.50
No. 237 (1)	.35	.25
Nos. 109-111 (3)	.85	.80
Nos. 35-38 (4)	1.25	5.50
Nos. 233-243 (11)	41.90	30.40
Nos. 48-51 (4)	1.40	7.90
Nos. 223-225 (3)	1.75	2.25
Nos. 70-72 (3)	.90	2.05
Nos. 118-121 (4)	1.60	5.25
Nos. 74-78 (5)	7.60	9.35
Nos. 38-41 (4)	3.55	15.50
Nos. 125-132 (8)	5.00	8.40
Set total (189) Stamps	166.05	268.90

Peace

King George VI and Parliament Buildings, London CD303

Return to peace at the close of World War II.

1945-46

Aden	28-29
Antigua	96-97
Ascension	50-51
Bahamas	130-131
Barbados	207-208
Bermuda	131-132
British Guiana	242-243
British Honduras	127-128
Cayman Islands	112-113
Ceylon	293-294
Cyprus	156-157
Dominica	112-113
Falkland Islands	97-98
Falkland Islands Dep.	1L9-1L10
Fiji	137-138
Gambia	144-145
Gibraltar	119-120
Gilbert & Ellice Islands	52-53
Gold Coast	128-129
Grenada	143-144
Jamaica	136-137
Kenya, Uganda, Tanzania	90-91
Leeward Islands	116-117
Malta	206-207
Mauritius	223-224
Montserrat	104-105
Nigeria	71-72
Northern Rhodesia	46-47
Nyasaland Protectorate	82-83
Pitcairn Islands	9-10
St. Helena	128-129
St. Kitts-Nevis	91-92
St. Lucia	127-128
St. Vincent	152-153
Seychelles	149-150
Sierra Leone	186-187
Solomon Islands	80-81
Somaliland Protectorate	108-109
Trinidad & Tobago	62-63
Turks & Caicos Islands	90-91
Virgin Islands	88-89

The following have different designs but are included in the omnibus set:

Great Britain	264-265

Offices in Morocco (Tangier)	523-524
Aden	
Kathiri State of Seiyun	12-13
Qu'aiti State of Shihr and Mukalla	12-13
Australia	200-202
Basutoland	29-31
Bechuanaland Protectorate	137-139
Burma	66-69
Cook Islands	127-130
Hong Kong	174-175
India	195-198
Hyderabad	51-53
New Zealand	247-257
Niue	90-93
Pakistan-Bahawalpur	O16
Samoa	191-194
South Africa	100-102
Southern Rhodesia	67-70
South-West Africa	153-155
Swaziland	38-40
Zanzibar	222-223

Nos. 28-29 (2)	.95	2.50
Nos. 96-97 (2)	.50	.80
Nos. 50-51 (2)	.80	2.00
Nos. 130-131 (2)	.50	1.40
Nos. 207-208 (2)	.50	1.10
Nos. 131-132 (2)	.55	.55
Nos. 242-243 (2)	1.05	1.40
Nos. 127-128 (2)	.50	.50
Nos. 112-113 (2)	.80	.80
Nos. 293-294 (2)	.60	2.10
Nos. 156-157 (2)	.90	.70
Nos. 112-113 (2)	.50	.50
Nos. 97-98 (2)	.90	1.35
Nos. 1L9-1L10 (2)	1.30	1.00
Nos. 137-138 (2)	.75	1.75
Nos. 144-145 (2)	.60	.95
Nos. 119-120 (2)	.75	1.00
Nos. 52-53 (2)	.50	1.10
Nos. 128-129 (2)	1.85	3.75
Nos. 143-144 (2)	.50	.95
Nos. 136-137 (2)	2.00	13.50
Nos. 90-91 (2)	.65	.85
Nos. 116-117 (2)	.50	1.50
Nos. 206-207 (2)	.65	2.00
Nos. 223-224 (2)	.50	1.05
Nos. 104-105 (2)	.50	.50
Nos. 71-72 (2)	.70	2.75
Nos. 46-47 (2)	1.25	2.00
Nos. 82-83 (2)	.55	.60
Nos. 9-10 (2)	1.40	.60
Nos. 128-129 (2)	.65	.70
Nos. 91-92 (2)	.50	.50
Nos. 127-128 (2)	.50	.60
Nos. 152-153 (2)	.50	.50
Nos. 149-150 (2)	.55	.50
Nos. 186-187 (2)	.50	.50
Nos. 80-81 (2)	.50	1.50
Nos. 108-109 (2)	.70	.50
Nos. 62-63 (2)	.75	1.85
Nos. 90-91 (2)	.50	.50
Nos. 88-89 (2)	.50	.50
Nos. 264-265 (2)	.50	.50
Nos. 523-524 (2)	2.00	2.55
Nos. 12-13 (2)	.50	.90
Nos. 12-13 (2)	.50	1.25
Nos. 200-202 (3)	1.60	1.25
Nos. 29-31 (3)	2.10	2.60
Nos. 137-139 (3)	2.05	4.75
Nos. 66-69 (4)	1.50	1.25
Nos. 127-130 (4)	2.00	1.85
Nos. 174-175 (2)	6.75	2.75
Nos. 195-198 (4)	5.60	5.50
Nos. 51-53 (3)	1.50	1.70
Nos. 247-257 (11)	3.35	3.65
Nos. 90-93 (4)	1.70	2.20
No. O16 (1)	15.00	10.00
Nos. 191-194 (4)	2.05	1.00
Nos. 100-102 (3)	1.00	3.25
Nos. 67-70 (4)	1.40	1.75
Nos. 153-155 (3)	1.85	3.25
Nos. 38-40 (3)	2.40	5.50
Nos. 222-223 (2)	.65	1.00
Set total (151) Stamps	86.15	118.15

Silver Wedding

King George VI and Queen Elizabeth

CD304   CD305

1948-49

Aden	30-31
Kathiri State of Seiyun	14-15
Qu'aiti State of Shihr and Mukalla	14-15

Antigua	98-99
Ascension	52-53
Bahamas	148-149
Barbados	210-211
Basutoland	39-40
Bechuanaland Protectorate	147-148
Bermuda	133-134
British Guiana	244-245
British Honduras	129-130
Cayman Islands	116-117
Cyprus	158-159
Dominica	114-115
Falkland Islands	99-100
Falkland Islands Dep.	1L11-1L12
Fiji	139-140
Gambia	146-147
Gibraltar	121-122
Gilbert & Ellice Islands	54-55
Gold Coast	142-143
Grenada	145-146
Hong Kong	178-179
Jamaica	138-139
Kenya, Uganda, Tanzania	92-93
Leeward Islands	118-119
Malaya	
Johore	128-129
Kedah	55-56
Kelantan	44-45
Malacca	1-2
Negri Sembilan	36-37
Pahang	44-45
Penang	1-2
Perak	99-100
Perlis	1-2
Selangor	74-75
Trengganu	47-48
Malta	223-224
Mauritius	229-230
Montserrat	106-107
Nigeria	73-74
North Borneo	238-239
Northern Rhodesia	48-49
Nyasaland Protectorate	85-86
Pitcairn Islands	11-12
St. Helena	130-131
St. Kitts-Nevis	93-94
St. Lucia	129-130
St. Vincent	154-155
Sarawak	174-175
Seychelles	151-152
Sierra Leone	188-189
Singapore	21-22
Solomon Islands	82-83
Somaliland Protectorate	110-111
Swaziland	48-49
Trinidad & Tobago	64-65
Turks & Caicos Islands	92-93
Virgin Islands	90-91
Zanzibar	224-225

The following have different designs but are included in the omnibus set:

Great Britain	267-268
Offices in Morocco (Sp. Curr.)	93-94
Offices in Morocco (Tangier)	525-526
Bahrain	62-63
Kuwait	82-83
Oman	25-26
South Africa	106
South-West Africa	159

Nos. 30-31 (2)	40.40	56.50
Nos. 14-15 (2)	17.85	16.00
Nos. 14-15 (2)	18.55	12.50
Nos. 98-99 (2)	13.55	15.75
Nos. 52-53 (2)	55.55	50.45
Nos. 148-149 (2)	45.25	40.30
Nos. 210-211 (2)	18.35	13.55
Nos. 39-40 (2)	52.80	55.25
Nos. 147-148 (2)	42.85	47.75
Nos. 133-134 (2)	47.75	55.25
Nos. 244-245 (2)	24.25	28.45
Nos. 129-130 (2)	25.25	53.20
Nos. 116-117 (2)	25.25	33.50
Nos. 158-159 (2)	58.50	78.05
Nos. 114-115 (2)	25.25	32.75
Nos. 99-100 (2)	112.10	76.10
Nos. 1L11-1L12 (2)	4.25	6.00
Nos. 139-140 (2)	18.20	11.50
Nos. 146-147 (2)	21.30	21.25
Nos. 121-122 (2)	61.00	78.00
Nos. 54-55 (2)	14.25	26.25
Nos. 142-143 (2)	35.25	48.20
Nos. 145-146 (2)	21.75	21.75
Nos. 178-179 (2)	329.00	106.75
Nos. 138-139 (2)	30.35	75.25
Nos. 92-93 (2)	51.00	68.00
Nos. 118-119 (2)	7.00	8.25
Nos. 128-129 (2)	29.25	53.25
Nos. 55-56 (2)	35.25	50.25
Nos. 44-45 (2)	35.75	62.75
Nos. 1-2 (2)	35.40	49.75
Nos. 36-37 (2)	28.10	38.20
Nos. 44-45 (2)	28.00	38.05
Nos. 1-2 (2)	40.50	37.80

Nos. 99-100 (2)	27.80	37.75
Nos. 1-2 (2)	33.50	58.00
Nos. 74-75 (2)	30.25	25.30
Nos. 47-48 (2)	32.75	61.75
Nos. 223-224 (2)	40.55	45.25
Nos. 229-230 (2)	19.25	45.25
Nos. 106-107 (2)	8.75	17.25
Nos. 73-74 (2)	17.85	22.80
Nos. 238-239 (2)	35.30	45.75
Nos. 48-49 (2)	100.30	90.25
Nos. 85-86 (2)	18.25	35.25
Nos. 11-12 (2)	44.50	54.00
Nos. 130-131 (2)	32.80	42.80
Nos. 93-94 (2)	13.25	10.50
Nos. 129-130 (2)	22.25	40.25
Nos. 154-155 (2)	27.75	30.25
Nos. 174-175 (2)	52.80	67.80
Nos. 151-152 (2)	16.25	48.25
Nos. 188-189 (2)	25.25	29.75
Nos. 21-22 (2)	116.00	45.40
Nos. 82-83 (2)	13.40	13.40
Nos. 110-111 (2)	8.40	8.75
Nos. 48-49 (2)	40.30	47.75
Nos. 64-65 (2)	31.80	50.25
Nos. 92-93 (2)	16.25	22.75
Nos. 90-91 (2)	16.25	22.25
Nos. 224-225 (2)	29.60	38.00
Nos. 267-268 (2)	30.40	25.25
Nos. 93-94 (2)	17.10	25.75
Nos. 525-526 (2)	22.90	32.75
Nos. 62-63 (2)	38.50	57.75
Nos. 82-83 (2)	69.50	45.50
Nos. 25-26 (2)	41.00	42.50
No. 106 (1)	.80	1.00
No. 159 (1)	1.10	.35
Set total (136) Stamps	2,542.	2,754.

U.P.U.

Mercury and Symbols of
Communications — CD306

Plane, Ship and
Hemispheres — CD307

Mercury
Scattering
Letters over
Globe
CD308

U.P.U.
Monument,
Bern
CD309

Universal Postal Union, 75th anniversary.

1949

Aden 32-35
  Kathiri State of Seiyun..............16-19
  Qu'aiti State of Shihr and Mukalla .....
 16-19
Antigua 100-103
Ascension 57-60
Bahamas 150-153
Barbados 212-215
Basutoland 41-44
Bechuanaland Protectorate......149-152
Bermuda....................................138-141
British Guiana............................246-249
British Honduras........................137-140
Brunei..79-82
Cayman Islands.........................118-121
Cyprus 160-163
Dominica...................................116-119
Falkland Islands.........................103-106
Falkland Islands Dep...........1L14-1L17
Fiji 141-144
Gambia......................................148-151
Gibraltar....................................123-126

Gilbert & Ellice Islands...............56-59
Gold Coast................................144-147
Grenada.....................................147-150
Hong Kong 180-183
Jamaica.....................................142-145
Kenya, Uganda, Tanzania 94-97
Leeward Islands 126-129
Malaya
  Johore 151-154
  Kedah...57-60
  Kelantan.....................................46-49
  Malacca......................................18-21
  Negri Sembilan 59-62
  Pahang.......................................46-49
  Penang.......................................23-26
  Perak.......................................101-104
  Perlis..3-6
  Selangor.....................................76-79
  Trengganu...................................49-52
Malta...225-228
Mauritius....................................231-234
Montserrat.................................108-111
New Hebrides, British 62-65
New Hebrides, French 79-82
Nigeria...75-78
North Borneo.............................240-243
Northern Rhodesia.......................50-53
Nyasaland Protectorate...............87-90
Pitcairn Islands............................13-16
St. Helena.................................132-135
St. Kitts-Nevis.............................95-98
St. Lucia....................................131-134
St. Vincent.................................170-173
Sarawak....................................176-179
Seychelles.................................153-156
Sierra Leone..............................190-193
Singapore 23-26
Solomon Islands..........................84-87
Somaliland Protectorate............112-115
Southern Rhodesia 71-72
Swaziland....................................50-53
Tonga...87-90
Trinidad & Tobago 66-69
Turks & Caicos Islands 101-104
Virgin Islands...............................92-95
Zanzibar....................................226-229

The following have different designs but are
included in the omnibus set:

Great Britain..............................276-279
  Offices in Morocco (Tangier) 546-
  549
Australia...223
Bahrain...68-71
Burma..116-121
Ceylon.......................................304-306
Egypt...281-283
India..223-226
Kuwait..89-92
Oman...31-34
Pakistan-Bahawalpur 26-29, O25-O28
South Africa...............................109-111
South-West Africa.....................160-162

Nos. 32-35 (4)	5.85	8.45
Nos. 16-19 (4)	2.75	16.00
Nos. 16-19 (4)	2.60	8.00
Nos. 100-103 (4)	3.60	7.70
Nos. 57-60 (4)	11.10	9.00
Nos. 150-153 (4)	5.35	9.30
Nos. 212-215 (4)	4.40	14.85
Nos. 41-44 (4)	4.75	10.00
Nos. 149-152 (4)	3.35	7.25
Nos. 138-141 (4)	4.75	6.15
Nos. 246-249 (4)	2.75	4.20
Nos. 137-140 (4)	3.30	6.35
Nos. 79-82 (4)	9.50	8.45
Nos. 118-121 (4)	3.60	7.25
Nos. 160-163 (4)	4.60	10.70
Nos. 116-119 (4)	2.30	5.65
Nos. 103-106 (4)	14.00	17.10
Nos. 1L14-1L17 (4)	14.60	14.50
Nos. 141-144 (4)	3.35	15.75
Nos. 148-151 (4)	2.75	7.10
Nos. 123-126 (4)	5.90	8.75
Nos. 56-59 (4)	4.30	13.00
Nos. 144-147 (4)	2.55	10.35
Nos. 147-150 (4)	2.13	3.55
Nos. 180-183 (4)	66.75	19.95
Nos. 142-145 (4)	2.50	2.45
Nos. 94-97 (4)	2.90	4.00
Nos. 126-129 (4)	3.05	9.60
Nos. 151-154 (4)	4.70	8.90
Nos. 57-60 (4)	4.80	12.00
Nos. 46-49 (4)	4.25	12.65
Nos. 18-21 (4)	4.25	17.30
Nos. 59-62 (4)	3.50	10.75
Nos. 46-49 (4)	4.25	12.65
Nos. 23-26 (4)	5.10	11.75
Nos. 101-104 (4)	3.65	10.75
Nos. 3-6 (4)	3.95	14.25
Nos. 76-79 (4)	4.90	12.30
Nos. 49-52 (4)	5.55	12.25
Nos. 225-228 (4)	4.50	4.85
Nos. 231-234 (4)	3.70	7.05
Nos. 108-111 (4)	3.30	4.35
Nos. 62-65 (4)	1.60	4.25
Nos. 79-82 (4)	15.40	22.00

Nos. 75-78 (4)	2.80	9.25
Nos. 240-243 (4)	7.15	6.50
Nos. 50-53 (4)	5.00	6.50
Nos. 87-90 (4)	4.55	6.60
Nos. 13-16 (4)	15.05	14.25
Nos. 132-135 (4)	4.85	7.10
Nos. 95-98 (4)	4.35	5.55
Nos. 131-134 (4)	2.55	3.85
Nos. 170-173 (4)	2.20	5.05
Nos. 176-179 (4)	13.40	13.35
Nos. 153-156 (4)	3.00	5.15
Nos. 190-193 (4)	2.90	9.15
Nos. 23-26 (4)	19.00	13.70
Nos. 84-87 (4)	4.05	4.90
Nos. 112-115 (4)	3.95	9.95
Nos. 71-72 (4)	1.95	2.25
Nos. 50-53 (4)	2.80	4.65
Nos. 87-90 (4)	3.00	5.25
Nos. 66-69 (4)	3.55	6.80
Nos. 101-104 (4)	3.05	8.90
Nos. 92-95 (4)	2.60	5.90
Nos. 226-229 (4)	4.95	13.50
Nos. 276-279 (4)	1.35	1.00
Nos. 546-549 (4)	2.60	16.00
No. 223 (1)	.40	.40
Nos. 68-71 (4)	4.75	16.50
Nos. 116-121 (6)	7.30	5.35
Nos. 304-306 (3)	3.35	4.25
Nos. 281-283 (3)	5.75	2.70
Nos. 223-226 (4)	27.25	10.50
Nos. 89-92 (4)	6.10	10.25
Nos. 31-34 (4)	8.00	17.50
Nos. 26-29, O25-O28 (8)	2.40	44.00
Nos. 109-111 (3)	2.00	2.70
Nos. 160-162 (3)	3.00	5.50
Set total (313) Stamps	466.45	742.80

University

Arms of
University
College
CD310

Alice, Princess
of Athlone
CD311

1948 opening of University College of the
West Indies at Jamaica.

1951

Antigua 104-105
Barbados 228-229
British Guiana............................250-251
British Honduras.......................141-142
Dominica...................................120-121
Grenada.....................................164-165
Jamaica.....................................146-147
Leeward Islands 130-131
Montserrat 112-113
St. Kitts-Nevis...........................105-106
St. Lucia....................................149-150
St. Vincent.................................174-175
Trinidad & Tobago 70-71
Virgin Islands...............................96-97

Nos. 104-105 (2)	1.35	3.75
Nos. 228-229 (2)	1.75	2.65
Nos. 250-251 (2)	1.10	1.25
Nos. 141-142 (2)	1.40	2.20
Nos. 120-121 (2)	1.40	1.75
Nos. 164-165 (2)	1.20	1.60
Nos. 146-147 (2)	1.05	.70
Nos. 130-131 (2)	1.35	4.00
Nos. 112-113 (2)	.85	2.00
Nos. 105-106 (2)	1.40	2.25
Nos. 149-150 (2)	1.40	1.50
Nos. 174-175 (2)	1.00	2.15
Nos. 70-71 (2)	1.00	4.20
Nos. 96-97 (2)	1.50	3.75
Set total (28) Stamps	17.75	33.75

Coronation

Queen Elizabeth
II — CD312

1953

Aden 47
  Kathiri State of Seiyun.................28

  Qu'aiti State of Shihr and Mukalla .....
 28
Antigua 106
Ascension 61
Bahamas 157
Barbados 234
Basutoland 45
Bechuanaland Protectorate............153
Bermuda..142
British Guiana.....................................252
British Honduras................................143
Cayman Islands.................................150
Cyprus 167
Dominica..141
Falkland Islands..................................121
Falkland Islands Dependencies 1L18
Fiji 145
Gambia...152
Gibraltar...131
Gilbert & Ellice Islands........................60
Gold Coast...160
Grenada..170
Hong Kong 184
Jamaica..153
Kenya, Uganda, Tanzania 101
Leeward Islands 132
Malaya
  Johore 155
  Kedah...82
  Kelantan..71
  Malacca...27
  Negri Sembilan 63
  Pahang..71
  Penang..27
  Perak...126
  Perlis..28
  Selangor..101
  Trengganu...74
Malta..241
Mauritius..250
Montserrat 127
New Hebrides, British 77
Nigeria...79
North Borneo......................................260
Northern Rhodesia...............................60
Nyasaland Protectorate.......................96
Pitcairn Islands....................................19
St. Helena..139
St. Kitts-Nevis....................................119
St. Lucia...156
St. Vincent..185
Sarawak...196
Seychelles..172
Sierra Leone.......................................194
Singapore 27
Solomon Islands...................................88
Somaliland Protectorate.....................127
Swaziland...54
Trinidad & Tobago 84
Tristan da Cunha 13
Turks & Caicos Islands 118
Virgin Islands......................................114

The following have different designs but are
included in the omnibus set:

Great Britain.....................................313-316
  Offices in Morocco (Tangier) 579-
  582
Australia...259-261
Bahrain...92-95
Canada...330
Ceylon...317
Cook Islands...............................145-146
Kuwait..113-116
New Zealand 280-284
Niue..104-105
Oman...52-55
Samoa...214-215
South Africa......................................192
Southern Rhodesia 80
South-West Africa......................244-248
Tokelau Islands.....................................4

No. 47 (1)	1.25	1.25
No. 28 (1)	.75	1.50
No. 28 (1)	1.10	.60
No. 106 (1)	.40	.75
No. 61 (1)	1.25	2.75
No. 157 (1)	1.40	.75
No. 234 (1)	1.00	.25
No. 45 (1)	.50	.60
No. 153 (1)	.50	.35
No. 142 (1)	.85	.50
No. 252 (1)	.45	.25
No. 143 (1)	.60	.40
No. 150 (1)	.40	1.75
No. 167 (1)	1.60	.75
No. 141 (1)	.40	.40
No. 121 (1)	.90	1.50
No. 1L18 (1)	1.80	1.40
No. 145 (1)	1.00	.60
No. 152 (1)	.50	.50
No. 131 (1)	.50	.50
No. 60 (1)	.65	2.25
No. 160 (1)	1.00	.25

No. 170 (1) .30 .25
No. 184 (1) 3.00 .30
No. 153 (1) .70 .25
No. 101 (1) .40 .25
No. 132 (1) 1.00 2.25
No. 155 (1) 1.40 .30
No. 82 (1) 2.25 .60
No. 71 (1) 1.60 1.60
No. 27 (1) 1.10 1.50
No. 63 (1) 1.40 .65
No. 71 (1) 2.25 .25
No. 27 (1) 1.75 .30
No. 126 (1) 1.60 .25
No. 28 (1) 1.75 4.00
No. 101 (1) 1.75 .25
No. 74 (1) 1.50 1.00
No. 241 (1) .50 .25
No. 250 (1) 1.10 .25
No. 127 (1) .60 .45
No. 77 (1) .75 .60
No. 79 (1) .40 .25
No. 260 (1) 1.75 1.00
No. 60 (1) .70 .25
No. 96 (1) .75 .75
No. 19 (1) 2.00 3.50
No. 139 (1) 1.25 1.25
No. 119 (1) .35 .25
No. 156 (1) .70 .35
No. 185 (1) .50 .30
No. 196 (1) 1.75 1.75
No. 172 (1) .80 .80
No. 194 (1) .40 .40
No. 27 (1) 2.50 .40
No. 88 (1) 1.00 1.00
No. 127 (1) .40 .25
No. 54 (1) .30 .25
No. 84 (1) .30 .25
No. 13 (1) 1.00 1.75
No. 118 (1) .40 1.10
No. 114 (1) .40 1.00

Nos. 313-316 (4) 11.40 4.05
Nos. 579-582 (4) 10.90 5.30
Nos. 259-261 (3) 3.60 2.75
Nos. 92-95 (4) 15.25 12.75
No. 330 (1) .30 .25
No. 317 (1) 1.40 .25
Nos. 145-146 (2) 2.65 2.65
Nos. 113-116 (4) 16.00 8.50
Nos. 280-284 (5) 3.30 4.55
Nos. 104-105 (2) 2.25 1.50
Nos. 52-55 (4) 14.25 6.50
Nos. 214-215 (2) 2.50 .80
No. 192 (1) .45 .30
No. 80 (1) 7.25 7.25
Nos. 244-248 (5) 3.00 2.35
No. 4 (1) 2.75 2.75
Set total (106) Stamps 160.40 114.75

Separate designs for each country for the visit of Queen Elizabeth II and the Duke of Edinburgh.

Royal Visit 1953

1953

Aden ...62
Australia ...267-269
Bermuda ...163
Ceylon ...318
Fiji ...146
Gibraltar ...146
Jamaica ...154
Kenya, Uganda, Tanzania ...102
Malta ...242
New Zealand ...286-287

No. 62 (1) .65 4.00
Nos. 267-269 (3) 2.75 2.05
No. 163 (1) .50 .25
No. 318 (1) 1.00 .25
No. 146 (1) .65 .35
No. 146 (1) .50 .30
No. 154 (1) .50 .25
No. 102 (1) .50 .25
No. 242 (1) .35 .25
Nos. 286-287 (2) .50 .50
Set total (13) Stamps 7.90 8.45

West Indies Federation

Map of the Caribbean CD313

Federation of the West Indies, April 22, 1958.

1958

Antigua ...122-124
Barbados ...248-250
Dominica ...161-163
Grenada ...184-186
Jamaica ...175-177
Montserrat ...143-145
St. Kitts-Nevis ...136-138
St. Lucia ...170-172

St. Vincent ...198-200
Trinidad & Tobago ...86-88

Nos. 122-124 (3) 5.80 3.80
Nos. 248-250 (3) 1.60 2.90
Nos. 161-163 (3) 1.95 1.85
Nos. 184-186 (3) 1.50 1.20
Nos. 175-177 (3) 2.65 3.45
Nos. 143-145 (3) 2.35 1.35
Nos. 136-138 (3) 3.00 3.10
Nos. 170-172 (3) 2.05 2.80
Nos. 198-200 (3) 1.50 1.75
Nos. 86-88 (3) 2.35 2.35
Set total (30) Stamps 24.80 24.55

Freedom from Hunger

Protein Food CD314

U.N. Food and Agricultural Organization's "Freedom from Hunger" campaign.

1963

Aden ...65
Antigua ...133
Ascension ...89
Bahamas ...180
Basutoland ...83
Bechuanaland Protectorate ...194
Bermuda ...192
British Guiana ...271
British Honduras ...179
Brunei ...100
Cayman Islands ...168
Dominica ...181
Falkland Islands ...146
Fiji ...198
Gambia ...172
Gibraltar ...161
Gilbert & Ellice Islands ...76
Grenada ...190
Hong Kong ...218
Malta ...291
Mauritius ...270
Montserrat ...150
New Hebrides, British ...93
North Borneo ...296
Pitcairn Islands ...35
St. Helena ...173
St. Lucia ...179
St. Vincent ...201
Sarawak ...212
Seychelles ...213
Solomon Islands ...109
Swaziland ...108
Tonga ...127
Tristan da Cunha ...68
Turks & Caicos Islands ...138
Virgin Islands ...140
Zanzibar ...280

No. 65 (1) 1.50 1.75
No. 133 (1) .35 .35
No. 89 (1) 1.00 .50
No. 180 (1) .65 .65
No. 83 (1) .50 .25
No. 194 (1) .50 .50
No. 192 (1) 1.00 .50
No. 271 (1) .45 .25
No. 179 (1) .60 .25
No. 100 (1) 3.25 2.25
No. 168 (1) .55 .30
No. 181 (1) .30 .30
No. 146 (1) 10.50 2.50
No. 198 (1) 3.50 2.25
No. 172 (1) .50 .25
No. 161 (1) 4.00 2.25
No. 76 (1) 1.40 .40
No. 190 (1) .30 .25
No. 218 (1) 37.50 5.00
No. 291 (1) 2.00 2.00
No. 270 (1) .45 .25
No. 150 (1) .55 .35
No. 93 (1) .60 .25
No. 296 (1) 1.90 .75
No. 35 (1) 3.50 1.50
No. 173 (1) 2.25 1.10
No. 179 (1) .40 .40
No. 201 (1) .90 .50
No. 212 (1) 1.60 1.00
No. 213 (1) .85 .35
No. 109 (1) 3.00 .85
No. 108 (1) .50 .50
No. 127 (1) .60 .35
No. 68 (1) .75 .35
No. 138 (1) .30 .25
No. 140 (1) .50 .50
No. 280 (1) 1.50 .80
Set total (37) Stamps 90.50 32.80

Red Cross Centenary

Red Cross and Elizabeth II CD315

1963

Antigua ...134-135
Ascension ...90-91
Bahamas ...183-184
Basutoland ...84-85
Bechuanaland Protectorate ...195-196
Bermuda ...193-194
British Guiana ...272-273
British Honduras ...180-181
Cayman Islands ...169-170
Dominica ...182-183
Falkland Islands ...147-148
Fiji ...203-204
Gambia ...173-174
Gibraltar ...162-163
Gilbert & Ellice Islands ...77-78
Grenada ...191-192
Hong Kong ...219-220
Jamaica ...203-204
Malta ...292-293
Mauritius ...271-272
Montserrat ...151-152
New Hebrides, British ...94-95
Pitcairn Islands ...36-37
St. Helena ...174-175
St. Kitts-Nevis ...143-144
St. Lucia ...180-181
St. Vincent ...202-203
Seychelles ...214-215
Solomon Islands ...110-111
South Arabia ...1-2
Swaziland ...109-110
Tonga ...134-135
Tristan da Cunha ...69-70
Turks & Caicos Islands ...139-140
Virgin Islands ...141-142

Nos. 134-135 (2) 1.00 2.00
Nos. 90-91 (2) 6.75 3.35
Nos. 183-184 (2) 2.30 2.80
Nos. 84-85 (2) 1.20 .90
Nos. 195-196 (2) .95 .85
Nos. 193-194 (2) 3.00 2.80
Nos. 272-273 (2) .85 .60
Nos. 180-181 (2) 1.00 2.50
Nos. 169-170 (2) 1.10 3.00
Nos. 182-183 (2) .70 1.05
Nos. 147-148 (2) 18.00 5.50
Nos. 203-204 (2) 3.25 2.80
Nos. 173-174 (2) .80 1.00
Nos. 162-163 (2) 6.25 5.40
Nos. 77-78 (2) 2.00 3.50
Nos. 191-192 (2) .80 .50
Nos. 219-220 (2) 18.75 7.35
Nos. 203-204 (2) .75 1.65
Nos. 292-293 (2) 2.50 4.75
Nos. 271-272 (2) .85 .50
Nos. 151-152 (2) 1.00 .75
Nos. 94-95 (2) 1.00 .50
Nos. 36-37 (2) 2.50 4.00
Nos. 174-175 (2) 1.70 2.30
Nos. 143-144 (2) .90 .90
Nos. 180-181 (2) 1.25 1.25
Nos. 202-203 (2) .90 .90
Nos. 214-215 (2) 1.00 1.50
Nos. 110-111 (2) 1.25 1.15
Nos. 1-2 (2) 1.25 1.25
Nos. 109-110 (2) 1.10 1.10
Nos. 134-135 (2) 1.00 1.25
Nos. 69-70 (2) 1.15 .80
Nos. 139-140 (2) .55 1.00
Nos. 141-142 (2) .80 1.25
Set total (70) Stamps 90.15 72.70

Shakespeare

Shakespeare Memorial Theatre, Stratford-on-Avon — CD316

400th anniversary of the birth of William Shakespeare.

1964

Antigua ...151
Bahamas ...201
Bechuanaland Protectorate ...197
Cayman Islands ...171

Dominica ...184
Falkland Islands ...149
Gambia ...192
Gibraltar ...164
Montserrat ...153
St. Lucia ...196
Turks & Caicos Islands ...141
Virgin Islands ...143

No. 151 (1) .35 .25
No. 201 (1) .60 .35
No. 197 (1) .35 .35
No. 171 (1) .35 .30
No. 184 (1) .35 .35
No. 149 (1) 1.60 .50
No. 192 (1) .35 .25
No. 164 (1) .65 .55
No. 153 (1) .35 .25
No. 196 (1) .45 .25
No. 141 (1) .30 .25
No. 143 (1) .45 .45
Set total (12) Stamps 6.15 4.10

ITU

ITU Emblem CD317

Intl. Telecommunication Union, cent.

1965

Antigua ...153-154
Ascension ...92-93
Bahamas ...219-220
Barbados ...265-266
Basutoland ...101-102
Bechuanaland Protectorate ...202-203
Bermuda ...196-197
British Guiana ...293-294
British Honduras ...187-188
Brunei ...116-117
Cayman Islands ...172-173
Dominica ...185-186
Falkland Islands ...154-155
Fiji ...211-212
Gibraltar ...167-168
Gilbert & Ellice Islands ...87-88
Grenada ...205-206
Hong Kong ...221-222
Mauritius ...291-292
Montserrat ...157-158
New Hebrides, British ...108-109
Pitcairn Islands ...52-53
St. Helena ...180-181
St. Kitts-Nevis ...163-164
St. Lucia ...197-198
St. Vincent ...224-225
Seychelles ...218-219
Solomon Islands ...126-127
Swaziland ...115-116
Tristan da Cunha ...85-86
Turks & Caicos Islands ...142-143
Virgin Islands ...159-160

Nos. 153-154 (2) 1.45 1.35
Nos. 92-93 (2) 1.90 1.30
Nos. 219-220 (2) 1.35 1.50
Nos. 265-266 (2) 1.50 1.25
Nos. 101-102 (2) .85 .65
Nos. 202-203 (2) 1.10 .75
Nos. 196-197 (2) 2.15 2.25
Nos. 293-294 (2) .50 .50
Nos. 187-188 (2) .75 .75
Nos. 116-117 (2) 1.75 1.75
Nos. 172-173 (2) 1.00 .85
Nos. 185-186 (2) .55 .55
Nos. 154-155 (2) 6.75 3.15
Nos. 211-212 (2) 2.00 1.05
Nos. 167-168 (2) 9.00 5.95
Nos. 87-88 (2) .85 .60
Nos. 205-206 (2) .50 .50
Nos. 221-222 (2) 10.50 4.75
Nos. 291-292 (2) 1.10 .50
Nos. 157-158 (2) 1.05 1.15
Nos. 108-109 (2) .65 .50
Nos. 52-53 (2) 1.65 1.90
Nos. 180-181 (2) .80 .60
Nos. 163-164 (2) .60 .60
Nos. 197-198 (2) 1.25 1.25
Nos. 224-225 (2) .80 .90
Nos. 218-219 (2) .75 .60
Nos. 126-127 (2) .70 .55
Nos. 115-116 (2) .70 .70
Nos. 85-86 (2) 1.00 .65
Nos. 142-143 (2) .50 .50
Nos. 159-160 (2) .85 .85
Set total (64) Stamps 56.85 40.70

Intl. Cooperation Year

ICY Emblem CD318

1965

Antigua		155-156
Ascension		94-95
Bahamas		222-223
Basutoland		103-104
Bechuanaland Protectorate		204-205
Bermuda		199-200
British Guiana		295-296
British Honduras		189-190
Brunei		118-119
Cayman Islands		174-175
Dominica		187-188
Falkland Islands		156-157
Fiji		213-214
Gibraltar		169-170
Gilbert & Ellice Islands		104-105
Grenada		207-208
Hong Kong		223-224
Mauritius		293-294
Montserrat		176-177
New Hebrides, British		110-111
New Hebrides, French		126-127
Pitcairn Islands		54-55
St. Helena		182-183
St. Kitts-Nevis		165-166
St. Lucia		199-200
Seychelles		220-221
Solomon Islands		143-144
South Arabia		17-18
Swaziland		117-118
Tristan da Cunha		87-88
Turks & Caicos Islands		144-145
Virgin Islands		161-162

Nos. 155-156 (2)	.55	.50
Nos. 94-95 (2)	1.30	1.40
Nos. 222-223 (2)	.65	1.90
Nos. 103-104 (2)	.75	.85
Nos. 204-205 (2)	.85	1.00
Nos. 199-200 (2)	2.05	1.25
Nos. 295-296 (2)	.55	.50
Nos. 189-190 (2)	.60	.55
Nos. 118-119 (2)	.85	.85
Nos. 174-175 (2)	1.00	.75
Nos. 187-188 (2)	.55	.55
Nos. 156-157 (2)	6.00	1.65
Nos. 213-214 (2)	1.95	1.25
Nos. 169-170 (2)	1.25	2.75
Nos. 104-105 (2)	.85	.60
Nos. 207-208 (2)	.50	.50
Nos. 223-224 (2)	11.00	3.50
Nos. 293-294 (2)	.65	.50
Nos. 176-177 (2)	.80	.65
Nos. 110-111 (2)	.50	.50
Nos. 126-127 (2)	12.00	12.00
Nos. 54-55 (2)	1.60	1.85
Nos. 182-183 (2)	.95	.50
Nos. 165-166 (2)	.80	.50
Nos. 199-200 (2)	.55	.55
Nos. 220-221 (2)	.80	.60
Nos. 143-144 (2)	.70	.60
Nos. 17-18 (2)	1.20	.50
Nos. 117-118 (2)	.75	.75
Nos. 87-88 (2)	1.05	.65
Nos. 144-145 (2)	.50	.50
Nos. 161-162 (2)	.65	.50
Set total (64) Stamps	54.75	41.60

Churchill Memorial

Winston Churchill and St. Paul's, London, During Air Attack CD319

1966

Antigua		157-160
Ascension		96-99
Bahamas		224-227
Barbados		281-284
Basutoland		105-108
Bechuanaland Protectorate		206-209
Bermuda		201-204
British Antarctic Territory		16-19
British Honduras		191-194
Brunei		120-123
Cayman Islands		176-179
Dominica		189-192
Falkland Islands		158-161
Fiji		215-218

Gibraltar		171-174
Gilbert & Ellice Islands		106-109
Grenada		209-212
Hong Kong		225-228
Mauritius		295-298
Montserrat		178-181
New Hebrides, British		112-115
New Hebrides, French		128-131
Pitcairn Islands		56-59
St. Helena		184-187
St. Kitts-Nevis		167-170
St. Lucia		201-204
St. Vincent		241-244
Seychelles		222-225
Solomon Islands		145-148
South Arabia		19-22
Swaziland		119-122
Tristan da Cunha		89-92
Turks & Caicos Islands		146-149
Virgin Islands		163-166

Nos. 157-160 (4)	3.05	3.05
Nos. 96-99 (4)	10.00	6.40
Nos. 224-227 (4)	2.30	3.20
Nos. 281-284 (4)	3.00	4.95
Nos. 105-108 (4)	2.80	3.25
Nos. 206-209 (4)	2.50	2.50
Nos. 201-204 (4)	4.00	4.75
Nos. 16-19 (4)	41.20	18.00
Nos. 191-194 (4)	2.45	1.30
Nos. 120-123 (4)	7.65	6.55
Nos. 176-179 (4)	3.10	3.65
Nos. 189-192 (4)	1.15	1.15
Nos. 158-161 (4)	12.75	9.55
Nos. 215-218 (4)	4.40	3.00
Nos. 171-174 (4)	3.05	5.30
Nos. 106-109 (4)	1.50	1.30
Nos. 209-212 (4)	1.10	1.10
Nos. 225-228 (4)	52.50	11.40
Nos. 295-298 (4)	3.70	3.75
Nos. 178-181 (4)	1.60	1.55
Nos. 112-115 (4)	2.30	1.00
Nos. 128-131 (4)	8.35	8.35
Nos. 56-59 (4)	4.45	6.10
Nos. 184-187 (4)	1.85	1.95
Nos. 167-170 (4)	1.50	1.70
Nos. 201-204 (4)	1.50	1.50
Nos. 241-244 (4)	1.50	1.75
Nos. 222-225 (4)	3.20	4.35
Nos. 145-148 (4)	1.50	1.60
Nos. 19-22 (4)	2.95	2.20
Nos. 119-122 (4)	1.70	2.55
Nos. 89-92 (4)	5.95	2.70
Nos. 146-149 (4)	1.60	1.75
Nos. 163-166 (4)	1.90	1.90
Set total (136) Stamps	204.05	135.10

Royal Visit, 1966

Queen Elizabeth II and Prince Philip CD320

Caribbean visit, Feb. 4 - Mar. 6, 1966.

1966

Antigua		161-162
Bahamas		228-229
Barbados		285-286
British Guiana		299-300
Cayman Islands		180-181
Dominica		193-194
Grenada		213-214
Montserrat		182-183
St. Kitts-Nevis		171-172
St. Lucia		205-206
St. Vincent		245-246
Turks & Caicos Islands		150-151
Virgin Islands		167-168

Nos. 161-162 (2)	3.50	2.60
Nos. 228-229 (2)	3.05	3.05
Nos. 285-286 (2)	3.00	2.00
Nos. 299-300 (2)	2.35	.85
Nos. 180-181 (2)	3.45	1.80
Nos. 193-194 (2)	3.00	.60
Nos. 213-214 (2)	.80	.50
Nos. 182-183 (2)	2.00	1.00
Nos. 171-172 (2)	.90	.75
Nos. 205-206 (2)	1.50	1.35
Nos. 245-246 (2)	2.75	1.35
Nos. 150-151 (2)	1.00	.50
Nos. 167-168 (2)	1.75	1.75
Set total (26) Stamps	29.05	18.10

World Cup Soccer

Soccer Player and Jules Rimet Cup CD321

World Cup Soccer Championship, Wembley, England, July 11-30.

1966

Antigua		163-164
Ascension		100-101
Bahamas		245-246
Bermuda		205-206
Brunei		124-125
Cayman Islands		182-183
Dominica		195-196
Fiji		219-220
Gibraltar		175-176
Gilbert & Ellice Islands		125-126
Grenada		230-231
New Hebrides, British		116-117
New Hebrides, French		132-133
Pitcairn Islands		60-61
St. Helena		188-189
St. Kitts-Nevis		173-174
St. Lucia		207-208
Seychelles		226-227
Solomon Islands		167-168
South Arabia		23-24
Tristan da Cunha		93-94

Nos. 163-164 (2)	.80	.85
Nos. 100-101 (2)	2.50	2.00
Nos. 245-246 (2)	.65	.65
Nos. 205-206 (2)	1.75	1.75
Nos. 124-125 (2)	1.30	1.25
Nos. 182-183 (2)	.75	.65
Nos. 195-196 (2)	1.20	.75
Nos. 219-220 (2)	1.70	.60
Nos. 175-176 (2)	1.85	1.75
Nos. 125-126 (2)	.70	.60
Nos. 230-231 (2)	.65	.95
Nos. 116-117 (2)	1.00	1.00
Nos. 132-133 (2)	7.00	7.00
Nos. 60-61 (2)	2.00	2.00
Nos. 188-189 (2)	1.25	.60
Nos. 173-174 (2)	.85	.80
Nos. 207-208 (2)	1.15	.90
Nos. 226-227 (2)	.85	.75
Nos. 167-168 (2)	1.10	1.10
Nos. 23-24 (2)	1.90	.55
Nos. 93-94 (2)	1.25	.80
Set total (42) Stamps	32.20	27.30

WHO Headquarters

World Health Organization Headquarters, Geneva — CD322

1966

Antigua		165-166
Ascension		102-103
Bahamas		247-248
Brunei		126-127
Cayman Islands		184-185
Dominica		197-198
Fiji		224-225
Gibraltar		180-181
Gilbert & Ellice Islands		127-128
Grenada		232-233
Hong Kong		229-230
Montserrat		184-185
New Hebrides, British		118-119
New Hebrides, French		134-135
Pitcairn Islands		62-63
St. Helena		190-191
St. Kitts-Nevis		177-178
St. Lucia		209-210
St. Vincent		247-248
Seychelles		228-229
Solomon Islands		169-170
South Arabia		25-26
Tristan da Cunha		99-100

Nos. 165-166 (2)	1.15	.55
Nos. 102-103 (2)	6.60	3.35
Nos. 247-248 (2)	.80	.80
Nos. 126-127 (2)	1.35	1.35
Nos. 184-185 (2)	2.25	1.20
Nos. 197-198 (2)	.75	.75
Nos. 224-225 (2)	4.70	3.30
Nos. 180-181 (2)	6.50	4.50
Nos. 127-128 (2)	.80	.70
Nos. 232-233 (2)	.80	.50
Nos. 229-230 (2)	11.25	2.30
Nos. 184-185 (2)	1.00	1.00
Nos. 118-119 (2)	.75	.50
Nos. 134-135 (2)	8.50	8.50
Nos. 62-63 (2)	5.50	7.00
Nos. 190-191 (2)	3.50	1.50
Nos. 177-178 (2)	.60	.60
Nos. 209-210 (2)	.80	.80
Nos. 247-248 (2)	1.15	1.05
Nos. 228-229 (2)	1.25	.65
Nos. 169-170 (2)	.95	.80

Nos. 25-26 (2)	2.10	.70
Nos. 99-100 (2)	1.90	1.25
Set total (46) Stamps	64.95	43.65

UNESCO Anniversary

"Education" — CD323

"Science" (Wheat ears & flask enclosing globe). "Culture" (lyre & columns). 20th anniversary of the UNESCO.

1966-67

Antigua		183-185
Ascension		108-110
Bahamas		249-251
Barbados		287-289
Bermuda		207-209
Brunei		128-130
Cayman Islands		186-188
Dominica		199-201
Gibraltar		183-185
Gilbert & Ellice Islands		129-131
Grenada		234-236
Hong Kong		231-233
Mauritius		299-301
Montserrat		186-188
New Hebrides, British		120-122
New Hebrides, French		136-138
Pitcairn Islands		64-66
St. Helena		192-194
St. Kitts-Nevis		179-181
St. Lucia		211-213
St. Vincent		249-251
Seychelles		230-232
Solomon Islands		171-173
South Arabia		27-29
Swaziland		123-125
Tristan da Cunha		101-103
Turks & Caicos Islands		155-157
Virgin Islands		176-178

Nos. 183-185 (3)	1.90	2.50
Nos. 108-110 (3)	11.00	5.80
Nos. 249-251 (3)	2.35	2.35
Nos. 287-289 (3)	2.35	2.15
Nos. 207-209 (3)	3.80	3.90
Nos. 128-130 (3)	4.65	5.40
Nos. 186-188 (3)	2.50	1.50
Nos. 199-201 (3)	1.60	.75
Nos. 183-185 (3)	6.50	3.25
Nos. 129-131 (3)	2.50	2.45
Nos. 234-236 (3)	1.10	1.20
Nos. 231-233 (3)	49.50	24.00
Nos. 299-301 (3)	2.10	1.50
Nos. 186-188 (3)	2.40	2.40
Nos. 120-122 (3)	1.90	1.90
Nos. 136-138 (3)	7.75	7.75
Nos. 64-66 (3)	4.05	4.00
Nos. 192-194 (3)	5.25	3.65
Nos. 179-181 (3)	.90	.90
Nos. 211-213 (3)	1.15	1.15
Nos. 249-251 (3)	2.30	1.35
Nos. 230-232 (3)	2.40	2.40
Nos. 171-173 (3)	2.00	1.50
Nos. 27-29 (3)	5.50	5.50
Nos. 123-125 (3)	1.40	1.40
Nos. 101-103 (3)	2.00	1.40
Nos. 155-157 (3)	1.15	1.20
Nos. 176-178 (3)	1.40	1.30
Set total (84) Stamps	133.40	94.55

Silver Wedding, 1972

Queen Elizabeth II and Prince Philip — CD324

Designs: borders differ for each country.

1972

Anguilla		161-162
Antigua		295-296
Ascension		164-165
Bahamas		344-345
Bermuda		296-297
British Antarctic Territory		43-44
British Honduras		306-307
British Indian Ocean Territory		48-49

Brunei		186-187
Cayman Islands		304-305
Dominica		352-353
Falkland Islands		223-224
Fiji		328-329
Gibraltar		292-293
Gilbert & Ellice Islands		206-207
Grenada		466-467
Hong Kong		271-272
Montserrat		286-287
New Hebrides, British		169-170
New Hebrides, French		188-189
Pitcairn Islands		127-128
St. Helena		271-272
St. Kitts-Nevis		257-258
St. Lucia		328-329
St.Vincent		344-345
Seychelles		309-310
Solomon Islands		248-249
South Georgia		35-36
Tristan da Cunha		178-179
Turks & Caicos Islands		257-258
Virgin Islands		241-242

Nos. 161-162 (2)	1.10	1.50
Nos. 295-296 (2)	.50	.50
Nos. 164-165 (2)	.70	.70
Nos. 344-345 (2)	.60	.60
Nos. 296-297 (2)	.50	.65
Nos. 43-44 (2)	6.50	5.65
Nos. 306-307 (2)	.80	.80
Nos. 48-49 (2)	2.00	1.00
Nos. 186-187 (2)	.70	.70
Nos. 304-305 (2)	.75	.75
Nos. 352-353 (2)	.65	.65
Nos. 223-224 (2)	1.00	1.15
Nos. 328-329 (2)	.70	.70
Nos. 292-293 (2)	.50	.50
Nos. 206-207 (2)	.50	.50
Nos. 466-467 (2)	.70	.70
Nos. 271-272 (2)	1.70	1.50
Nos. 286-287 (2)	.50	.50
Nos. 169-170 (2)	.50	.50
Nos. 188-189 (2)	1.25	1.25
Nos. 127-128 (2)	.90	.85
Nos. 271-272 (2)	.60	1.20
Nos. 257-258 (2)	.65	.50
Nos. 328-329 (2)	.75	.75
Nos. 344-345 (2)	.55	.55
Nos. 309-310 (2)	.90	.90
Nos. 248-249 (2)	.50	.50
Nos. 35-36 (2)	1.40	1.40
Nos. 178-179 (2)	.70	.70
Nos. 257-258 (2)	.50	.50
Nos. 241-242 (2)	.50	.50
Set total (62) Stamps	30.10	29.15

Princess Anne's Wedding

Princess Anne and Mark Phillips — CD325

Wedding of Princess Anne and Mark Phillips, Nov. 14, 1973.

1973

Anguilla		179-180
Ascension		177-178
Belize		325-326
Bermuda		302-303
British Antarctic Territory		60-61
Cayman Islands		320-321
Falkland Islands		225-226
Gibraltar		305-306
Gilbert & Ellice Islands		216-217
Hong Kong		289-290
Montserrat		300-301
Pitcairn Islands		135-136
St. Helena		277-278
St. Kitts-Nevis		274-275
St. Lucia		349-350
St. Vincent		358-359
St. Vincent Grenadines		1-2
Seychelles		311-312
Solomon Islands		259-260
South Georgia		37-38
Tristan da Cunha		189-190
Turks & Caicos Islands		286-287
Virgin Islands		260-261

Nos. 179-180 (2)	.55	.55
Nos. 177-178 (2)	.60	.60
Nos. 325-326 (2)	1.10	1.10
Nos. 302-303 (2)	.50	.50
Nos. 60-61 (2)	1.10	1.10
Nos. 320-321 (2)	.50	.50

Nos. 225-226 (2)	.70	.60
Nos. 305-306 (2)	.55	.55
Nos. 216-217 (2)	.50	.50
Nos. 289-290 (2)	2.65	2.00
Nos. 300-301 (2)	.55	.55
Nos. 135-136 (2)	.70	.60
Nos. 277-278 (2)	.50	.50
Nos. 274-275 (2)	.50	.50
Nos. 349-350 (2)	.50	.50
Nos. 358-359 (2)	.50	.50
Nos. 1-2 (2)	.50	.50
Nos. 311-312 (2)	.65	.65
Nos. 259-260 (2)	.70	.70
Nos. 37-38 (2)	.75	.75
Nos. 189-190 (2)	.50	.50
Nos. 286-287 (2)	.50	.50
Nos. 260-261 (2)	.50	.50
Set total (46) Stamps	16.10	14.65

Elizabeth II Coronation Anniv.

CD326

CD327

CD328

Designs: Royal and local beasts in heraldic form and simulated stonework. Portrait of Elizabeth II by Peter Grugeon. 25th anniversary of coronation of Queen Elizabeth II.

1978

Ascension		229
Barbados		474
Belize		397
British Antarctic Territory		71
Cayman Islands		404
Christmas Island		87
Falkland Islands		275
Fiji		384
Gambia		380
Gilbert Islands		312
Mauritius		464
New Hebrides, British		258
New Hebrides, French		278
St. Helena		317
St. Kitts-Nevis		354
Samoa		472
Solomon Islands		368
South Georgia		51
Swaziland		302
Tristan da Cunha		238
Virgin Islands		337

No. 229 (1)	2.00	2.00
No. 474 (1)	1.35	1.35
No. 397 (1)	4.50	5.00
No. 71 (1)	6.00	6.00
No. 404 (1)	2.00	2.00
No. 87 (1)	3.50	4.00
No. 275 (1)	4.00	5.50
No. 384 (1)	1.75	1.75
No. 380 (1)	1.50	1.50
No. 312 (1)	1.25	1.25
No. 464 (1)	2.10	2.10
No. 258 (1)	1.75	1.75
No. 278 (1)	3.50	3.50
No. 317 (1)	1.75	1.75
No. 354 (1)	1.00	1.00
No. 472 (1)	2.10	2.10
No. 368 (1)	2.50	2.50
No. 51 (1)	3.00	3.00
No. 302 (1)	1.60	1.60
No. 238 (1)	1.50	1.50
No. 337 (1)	1.80	1.80
Set total (21) Stamps	50.45	52.95

Queen Mother Elizabeth's 80th Birthday

CD330

Designs: Photographs of Queen Mother Elizabeth. Falkland Islands issued in sheets of 50; others in sheets of 9.

1980

Ascension		261
Bermuda		401
Cayman Islands		443
Falkland Islands		305
Gambia		412
Gibraltar		393
Hong Kong		364
Pitcairn Islands		193
St. Helena		341
Samoa		532
Solomon Islands		426
Tristan da Cunha		277

No. 261 (1)	.40	.40
No. 401 (1)	.45	.75
No. 443 (1)	.40	.40
No. 305 (1)	.40	.40
No. 412 (1)	.40	.50
No. 393 (1)	.35	.35
No. 364 (1)	1.10	1.25
No. 193 (1)	.60	.60
No. 341 (1)	.50	.50
No. 532 (1)	.55	.55
No. 426 (1)	.50	.50
No. 277 (1)	.45	.45
Set total (12) Stamps	6.10	6.65

Royal Wedding, 1981

Prince Charles and Lady Diana — CD331

CD331a

Wedding of Charles, Prince of Wales, and Lady Diana Spencer, St. Paul's Cathedral, London, July 29, 1981.

1981

Antigua		623-627
Ascension		294-296
Barbados		547-549
Barbuda		497-501
Bermuda		412-414
Brunei		268-270
Cayman Islands		471-473
Dominica		701-705
Falkland Islands		324-326
Falkland Islands Dep.		1L59-1L61
Fiji		442-444
Gambia		426-428
Ghana		759-764
Grenada		1051-1055
Grenada Grenadines		440-443
Hong Kong		373-375
Jamaica		500-503
Lesotho		335-337
Maldive Islands		906-909
Mauritius		520-522
Norfolk Island		280-282
Pitcairn Islands		206-208
St. Helena		353-355
St. Lucia		543-549
Samoa		558-560
Sierra Leone		509-518
Solomon Islands		450-452
Swaziland		382-384
Tristan da Cunha		294-296
Turks & Caicos Islands		486-489
Caicos Island		8-11
Uganda		314-317
Vanuatu		308-310
Virgin Islands		406-408

Nos. 623-627 (5)	6.55	2.55
Nos. 294-296 (3)	1.00	1.00

Nos. 547-549 (3)	.90	.90
Nos. 497-501 (5)	10.95	10.95
Nos. 412-414 (3)	2.00	2.00
Nos. 268-270 (3)	2.15	4.50
Nos. 471-473 (3)	1.20	1.30
Nos. 701-705 (5)	8.35	2.35
Nos. 324-326 (3)	1.65	1.70
Nos. 1L59-1L61 (3)	1.45	1.45
Nos. 442-444 (3)	1.35	1.35
Nos. 426-428 (3)	.90	.90
Nos. 759-764 (9)	6.20	6.20
Nos. 1051-1055 (5)	9.85	1.85
Nos. 440-443 (3)	2.35	2.35
Nos. 373-375 (3)	3.10	2.85
Nos. 500-503 (4)	1.45	1.35
Nos. 335-337 (3)	.90	.90
Nos. 906-909 (4)	1.55	1.55
Nos. 520-522 (3)	2.15	2.15
Nos. 280-282 (3)	1.75	1.75
Nos. 206-208 (3)	1.20	1.10
Nos. 353-355 (3)	.85	.85
Nos. 543-549 (5)	7.00	7.00
Nos. 558-560 (3)	.85	.85
Nos. 509-518 (10)	15.50	15.50
Nos. 450-452 (3)	1.25	1.25
Nos. 382-384 (3)	1.30	1.25
Nos. 294-296 (3)	.90	.90
Nos. 486-489 (4)	2.20	2.20
Nos. 8-11 (4)	5.00	5.00
Nos. 314-317 (4)	3.10	3.00
Nos. 308-310 (3)	1.15	1.15
Nos. 406-408 (3)	1.10	1.10
Set total (131) Stamps	109.15	92.95

Princess Diana

CD332

CD333

Designs: Photographs and portrait of Princess Diana, wedding or honeymoon photographs, royal residences, arms of issuing country. Portrait photograph by Clive Friend. Souvenir sheet margins show family tree, various people related to the princess. 21st birthday of Princess Diana of Wales, July 1.

1982

Antigua		663-666
Ascension		313-316
Bahamas		510-513
Barbados		585-588
Barbuda		544-547
British Antarctic Territory		92-95
Cayman Islands		486-489
Dominica		773-776
Falkland Islands		348-351
Falkland Islands Dep.		1L72-1L75
Fiji		470-473
Gambia		447-450
Grenada		1101A-1105
Grenada Grenadines		485-491
Lesotho		372-375
Maldive Islands		952-955
Mauritius		548-551
Pitcairn Islands		213-216
St. Helena		372-375
St. Lucia		591-594
Sierra Leone		531-534
Solomon Islands		471-474
Swaziland		406-409
Tristan da Cunha		310-313
Turks and Caicos Islands		531-534
Virgin Islands		430-433

Nos. 663-666 (4)	8.25	7.35
Nos. 313-316 (4)	3.50	3.50
Nos. 510-513 (4)	6.00	3.85
Nos. 585-588 (4)	3.40	3.25
Nos. 544-547 (4)	9.75	7.70
Nos. 92-95 (4)	4.25	3.45
Nos. 486-489 (4)	4.75	2.95
Nos. 773-776 (4)	7.05	7.05
Nos. 348-351 (4)	2.95	2.95
Nos. 1L72-1L75 (4)	2.50	2.60
Nos. 470-473 (4)	3.25	2.95
Nos. 447-450 (4)	2.90	2.85
Nos. 1101A-1105 (7)	16.05	15.55

Nos. 485-491 (7)	17.65	17.65
Nos. 372-375 (4)	4.00	4.00
Nos. 952-955 (4)	5.50	3.90
Nos. 548-551 (4)	5.00	5.00
Nos. 213-216 (4)	1.90	1.85
Nos. 372-375 (4)	2.00	2.00
Nos. 591-594 (4)	8.70	8.70
Nos. 531-534 (4)	7.20	7.20
Nos. 471-474 (4)	2.90	2.90
Nos. 406-409 (4)	3.85	2.25
Nos. 310-313 (4)	3.65	1.45
Nos. 486-489 (4)	2.20	2.20
Nos. 430-433 (4)	3.00	3.00
Set total (110) Stamps	142.15	127.85

250th anniv. of first edition of Lloyd's List (shipping news publication) & of Lloyd's marine insurance.

CD335

Designs: First page of early edition of the list; historical ships, modern transportation or harbor scenes.

1984

Ascension	351-354
Bahamas	555-558
Barbados	627-630
Cayes of Belize	10-13
Cayman Islands	522-526
Falkland Islands	404-407
Fiji	509-512
Gambia	519-522
Mauritius	587-590
Nauru	280-283
St. Helena	412-415
Samoa	624-627
Seychelles	538-541
Solomon Islands	521-524
Vanuatu	368-371
Virgin Islands	466-469

Nos. 351-354 (4)	2.90	2.55
Nos. 555-558 (4)	4.15	2.95
Nos. 627-630 (4)	6.10	5.15
Nos. 10-13 (4)	4.85	4.85
Nos. 522-526 (5)	9.30	8.45
Nos. 404-407 (4)	3.50	3.65
Nos. 509-512 (4)	5.30	4.90
Nos. 519-522 (4)	4.20	4.30
Nos. 587-590 (4)	9.40	9.40
Nos. 280-283 (4)	2.40	2.35
Nos. 412-415 (4)	2.40	2.40
Nos. 624-627 (4)	2.55	2.35
Nos. 538-541 (4)	5.00	5.00
Nos. 521-524 (4)	4.65	3.95
Nos. 368-371 (4)	1.85	1.85
Nos. 466-469 (4)	4.25	4.25
Set total (65) Stamps	72.80	68.35

Queen Mother 85th Birthday

CD336

Designs: Photographs tracing the life of the Queen Mother, Elizabeth. The high value in each set pictures the same photograph taken of the Queen Mother holding the infant Prince Henry.

1985

Ascension	372-376
Bahamas	580-584
Barbados	660-664
Bermuda	469-473
Falkland Islands	420-424
Falkland Islands Dep	1L92-1L96
Fiji	531-535
Hong Kong	447-450
Jamaica	599-603
Mauritius	604-608
Norfolk Island	364-368
Pitcairn Islands	253-257
St. Helena	428-432
Samoa	649-653
Seychelles	567-571
Zil Elwannyen Sesel	101-105
Solomon Islands	543-547
Swaziland	476-480
Tristan da Cunha	372-376
Vanuatu	392-396

Nos. 372-376 (5)	4.65	4.65
Nos. 580-584 (5)	7.70	6.45
Nos. 660-664 (5)	8.00	6.70
Nos. 469-473 (5)	9.40	9.40
Nos. 420-424 (5)	7.35	6.65
Nos. 1L92-1L96 (5)	8.00	8.00
Nos. 531-535 (5)	6.15	6.15
Nos. 447-450 (4)	9.50	8.50
Nos. 599-603 (5)	6.15	7.00
Nos. 604-608 (5)	11.30	11.30
Nos. 364-368 (5)	5.00	5.00
Nos. 253-257 (5)	5.30	5.95
Nos. 428-432 (5)	5.25	5.25
Nos. 649-653 (5)	8.40	7.55
Nos. 567-571 (5)	8.70	8.70
Nos. 101-105 (5)	6.60	6.60
Nos. 543-547 (5)	3.95	3.95
Nos. 476-480 (5)	7.75	7.25
Nos. 372-376 (5)	5.40	5.40
Nos. 392-396 (5)	5.25	5.25
Set total (99) Stamps	139.80	135.70

Queen Elizabeth II, 60th Birthday

CD337

1986, April 21

Ascension	389-393
Bahamas	592-596
Barbados	675-679
Bermuda	499-503
Cayman Islands	555-559
Falkland Islands	441-445
Fiji	544-548
Hong Kong	465-469
Jamaica	620-624
Kiribati	470-474
Mauritius	629-633
Papua New Guinea	640-644
Pitcairn Islands	270-274
St. Helena	451-455
Samoa	670-674
Seychelles	592-596
Zil Elwannyen Sesel	114-118
Solomon Islands	562-566
South Georgia	101-105
Swaziland	490-494
Tristan da Cunha	388-392
Vanuatu	414-418
Zambia	343-347

Nos. 389-393 (5)	2.80	3.30
Nos. 592-596 (5)	2.75	3.70
Nos. 675-679 (5)	3.25	3.10
Nos. 499-503 (5)	4.65	5.15
Nos. 555-559 (5)	4.55	5.60
Nos. 441-445 (5)	3.95	4.95
Nos. 544-548 (5)	3.00	3.00
Nos. 465-469 (5)	8.75	6.75
Nos. 620-624 (5)	2.75	2.70
Nos. 470-474 (5)	2.25	2.10
Nos. 629-633 (5)	3.50	3.50
Nos. 640-644 (5)	4.10	4.10
Nos. 270-274 (5)	2.80	2.70
Nos. 451-455 (5)	2.50	3.05
Nos. 670-674 (5)	2.55	2.55
Nos. 592-596 (5)	2.70	2.70
Nos. 114-118 (5)	2.15	2.15
Nos. 562-566 (5)	2.90	2.90
Nos. 101-105 (5)	3.30	3.65
Nos. 490-494 (5)	2.15	2.15
Nos. 388-392 (5)	3.00	3.00
Nos. 414-418 (5)	3.10	3.10
Nos. 343-347 (5)	1.65	1.60
Set total (115) Stamps	75.10	77.50

Royal Wedding

Marriage of Prince Andrew and Sarah Ferguson
CD338

1986, July 23

Ascension	399-400
Bahamas	602-603
Barbados	687-688
Cayman Islands	560-561
Jamaica	629-630
Pitcairn Islands	275-276
St. Helena	460-461
St. Kitts	181-182
Seychelles	602-603
Zil Elwannyen Sesel	119-120
Solomon Islands	567-568
Tristan da Cunha	397-398
Zambia	348-349

Nos. 399-400 (2)	1.60	1.60
Nos. 602-603 (2)	2.75	2.75
Nos. 687-688 (2)	2.00	1.25
Nos. 560-561 (2)	1.70	2.35
Nos. 629-630 (2)	1.35	1.35
Nos. 275-276 (2)	2.40	2.40
Nos. 460-461 (2)	1.05	1.05
Nos. 181-182 (2)	1.50	2.25
Nos. 602-603 (2)	2.50	2.50
Nos. 119-120 (2)	2.30	2.30
Nos. 567-568 (2)	1.00	1.00
Nos. 397-398 (2)	1.40	1.40
Nos. 348-349 (2)	1.10	1.30
Set total (26) Stamps	22.65	23.50

Queen Elizabeth II, 60th Birthday

Queen Elizabeth II & Prince Philip, 1947 Wedding Portrait — CD339

Designs: Photographs tracing the life of Queen Elizabeth II.

1986

Anguilla	674-677
Antigua	925-928
Barbuda	783-786
Dominica	950-953
Gambia	611-614
Grenada	1371-1374
Grenada Grenadines	749-752
Lesotho	531-534
Maldive Islands	1172-1175
Sierra Leone	760-763
Uganda	495-498

Nos. 674-677 (4)	8.00	8.00
Nos. 925-928 (4)	5.50	6.20
Nos. 783-786 (4)	23.15	23.15
Nos. 950-953 (4)	7.25	7.25
Nos. 611-614 (4)	8.25	7.90
Nos. 1371-1374 (4)	6.80	6.80
Nos. 749-752 (4)	6.75	6.75
Nos. 531-534 (4)	5.25	5.25
Nos. 1172-1175 (4)	6.25	6.25
Nos. 760-763 (4)	5.25	5.25
Nos. 495-498 (4)	8.50	8.50
Set total (44) Stamps	90.95	91.30

Royal Wedding, 1986

CD340

Designs: Photographs of Prince Andrew and Sarah Ferguson during courtship, engagement and marriage.

1986

Antigua	939-942
Barbuda	809-812
Dominica	970-973
Gambia	635-638
Grenada	1385-1388
Grenada Grenadines	758-761
Lesotho	545-548
Maldive Islands	1181-1184
Sierra Leone	769-772
Uganda	510-513

Nos. 939-942 (4)	7.00	8.75
Nos. 809-812 (4)	14.55	14.55
Nos. 970-973 (4)	7.25	7.25
Nos. 635-638 (4)	7.80	7.80
Nos. 1385-1388 (4)	8.30	8.30
Nos. 758-761 (4)	9.00	9.00
Nos. 545-548 (4)	7.45	7.45
Nos. 1181-1184 (4)	8.45	8.45
Nos. 769-772 (4)	5.35	5.35
Nos. 510-513 (4)	9.25	10.00
Set total (40) Stamps	84.40	86.90

Lloyds of London, 300th Anniv.

CD341

Designs: 17th century aspects of Lloyds, representations of each country's individual connections with Lloyds and publicized disasters insured by the organization.

1986

Ascension	454-457
Bahamas	655-658
Barbados	731-734
Bermuda	541-544
Falkland Islands	481-484
Liberia	1101-1104
Malawi	534-537
Nevis	571-574
St. Helena	501-504
St. Lucia	923-926
Seychelles	649-652
Zil Elwannyen Sesel	146-149
Solomon Islands	627-630
South Georgia	131-134
Trinidad & Tobago	484-487
Tristan da Cunha	439-442
Vanuatu	485-488

Nos. 454-457 (4)	5.00	5.00
Nos. 655-658 (4)	8.90	4.95
Nos. 731-734 (4)	12.50	8.35
Nos. 541-544 (4)	8.00	6.60
Nos. 481-484 (4)	5.45	3.85
Nos. 1101-1104 (4)	4.25	4.25
Nos. 534-537 (4)	11.00	7.85
Nos. 571-574 (4)	8.35	8.35
Nos. 501-504 (4)	8.70	7.15
Nos. 923-926 (4)	8.80	8.80
Nos. 649-652 (4)	12.85	12.85
Nos. 146-149 (4)	11.25	11.25
Nos. 627-630 (4)	7.00	4.45
Nos. 131-134 (4)	6.30	3.70
Nos. 484-487 (4)	10.25	6.35
Nos. 439-442 (4)	7.60	7.60
Nos. 485-488 (4)	4.85	4.85
Set total (68) Stamps	141.05	116.20

Moon Landing, 20th Anniv.

CD342

Designs: Equipment, crew photographs, spacecraft, official emblems and report profiles created for the Apollo Missions. Two stamps in each set are square in format rather than like the stamp shown; see individual country listings for more information.

1989

Ascension	468-472
Bahamas	674-678
Belize	916-920
Kiribati	517-521
Liberia	1125-1129
Nevis	586-590
St. Kitts	248-252
Samoa	760-764
Seychelles	676-680
Zil Elwannyen Sesel	154-158
Solomon Islands	643-647
Vanuatu	507-511

Nos. 468-472 (5)	9.40	8.60
Nos. 674-678 (5)	23.00	19.70
Nos. 916-920 (5)	29.25	21.60
Nos. 517-521 (5)	12.50	12.50
Nos. 1125-1129 (5)	8.50	8.50
Nos. 586-590 (5)	7.50	7.50

Nos. 248-252 (5)	8.00	8.25
Nos. 760-764 (5)	9.85	9.30
Nos. 676-680 (5)	16.05	16.05
Nos. 154-158 (5)	26.85	26.85
Nos. 643-647 (5)	9.00	6.75
Nos. 507-511 (5)	8.60	8.60
Set total (60) Stamps	168.50	154.20

Queen Mother, 90th Birthday

CD343   CD344

Designs: Portraits of Queen Elizabeth, the Queen Mother. See individual country listings for more information.

1990

Ascension	491-492
Bahamas	698-699
Barbados	782-783
British Antarctic Territory	170-171
British Indian Ocean Territory	106-107
Cayman Islands	622-623
Falkland Islands	524-525
Kenya	527-528
Kiribati	555-556
Liberia	1145-1146
Pitcairn Islands	336-337
St. Helena	532-533
St. Lucia	969-970
Seychelles	710-711
Zil Elwannyen Sesel	171-172
Solomon Islands	671-672
South Georgia	143-144
Swaziland	565-566
Tristan da Cunha	480-481

Nos. 491-492 (2)	4.75	4.75
Nos. 698-699 (2)	5.25	5.25
Nos. 782-783 (2)	4.00	3.70
Nos. 170-171 (2)	6.00	6.00
Nos. 106-107 (2)	18.00	18.50
Nos. 622-623 (2)	4.00	5.50
Nos. 524-525 (2)	4.75	4.75
Nos. 527-528 (2)	6.05	6.05
Nos. 555-556 (2)	4.75	4.75
Nos. 1145-1146 (2)	3.25	3.25
Nos. 336-337 (2)	4.25	4.25
Nos. 532-533 (2)	5.25	5.25
Nos. 969-970 (2)	4.60	4.60
Nos. 710-711 (2)	6.60	6.60
Nos. 171-172 (2)	8.25	8.25
Nos. 671-672 (2)	5.00	5.30
Nos. 143-144 (2)	5.50	6.50
Nos. 565-566 (2)	4.10	4.10
Nos. 480-481 (2)	5.60	5.60
Set total (38) Stamps	109.95	112.95

Queen Elizabeth II, 65th Birthday, and Prince Philip, 70th Birthday

CD345

CD346

Designs: Portraits of Queen Elizabeth II and Prince Philip differ for each country. Printed in sheets of 10 + 5 labels (3 different) between. Stamps alternate, producing 5 different triptychs.

1991

Ascension	506a
Bahamas	731a

Belize	970a
Bermuda	618a
Kiribati	572a
Mauritius	734a
Pitcairn Islands	349a
St. Helena	555a
St. Kitts	319a
Samoa	791a
Seychelles	724a
Zil Elwannyen Sesel	178a
Solomon Islands	689a
South Georgia	150a
Swaziland	587a
Vanuatu	541a

No. 506a (1)	3.50	3.75
No. 731a (1)	4.00	4.00
No. 970a (1)	4.25	4.25
No. 618a (1)	3.50	4.00
No. 572a (1)	4.00	4.00
No. 734a (1)	4.00	4.00
No. 349a (1)	3.25	3.25
No. 555a (1)	2.75	2.75
No. 319a (1)	3.00	3.00
No. 791a (1)	3.75	3.75
No. 724a (1)	5.00	5.00
No. 178a (1)	6.25	6.25
No. 689a (1)	3.75	3.75
No. 150a (1)	4.75	7.00
No. 587a (1)	4.00	4.00
No. 541a (1)	2.50	2.50
Set total (16) Stamps	62.25	65.25

Royal Family Birthday, Anniversary

CD347

Queen Elizabeth II, 65th birthday, Charles and Diana, 10th wedding anniversary: Various photographs of Queen Elizabeth II, Prince Philip, Prince Charles, Princess Diana and their sons William and Henry.

1991

Antigua	1446-1455
Barbuda	1229-1238
Dominica	1328-1337
Gambia	1080-1089
Grenada	2006-2015
Grenada Grenadines	1331-1340
Guyana	2440-2451
Lesotho	871-875
Maldive Islands	1533-1542
Nevis	666-675
St. Vincent	1485-1494
St. Vincent Grenadines	769-778
Sierra Leone	1387-1396
Turks & Caicos Islands	913-922
Uganda	918-927

Nos. 1446-1455 (10)	21.70	20.05
Nos. 1229-1238 (10)	125.00	119.50
Nos. 1328-1337 (10)	30.20	30.20
Nos. 1080-1089 (10)	24.65	24.40
Nos. 2006-2015 (10)	25.45	22.10
Nos. 1331-1340 (10)	23.85	23.35
Nos. 2440-2451 (12)	21.40	21.15
Nos. 871-875 (5)	13.55	13.55
Nos. 1533-1542 (10)	28.10	28.10
Nos. 666-675 (10)	23.65	23.65
Nos. 1485-1494 (10)	26.75	25.90
Nos. 769-778 (10)	25.40	25.40
Nos. 1387-1396 (10)	26.35	26.35
Nos. 913-922 (10)	27.50	25.30
Nos. 918-927 (10)	17.65	17.65
Set total (147) Stamps	461.20	446.65

Queen Elizabeth II's Accession to the Throne, 40th Anniv.

CD348

Various photographs of Queen Elizabeth II with local Scenes.

1992

Antigua	1513-1518
Barbuda	1306-1311
Dominica	1414-1419
Gambia	1172-1177
Grenada	2047-2052
Grenada Grenadines	1368-1373
Lesotho	881-885

Maldive Islands	1637-1642
Nevis	702-707
St. Vincent	1582-1587
St. Vincent Grenadines	829-834
Sierra Leone	1482-1487
Turks and Caicos Islands	978-987
Uganda	990-995
Virgin Islands	742-746

Nos. 1513-1518 (6)	15.00	15.10
Nos. 1306-1311 (6)	125.25	83.65
Nos. 1414-1419 (6)	12.50	12.50
Nos. 1172-1177 (6)	15.00	14.85
Nos. 2047-2052 (6)	15.95	15.95
Nos. 1368-1373 (6)	17.00	15.35
Nos. 881-885 (5)	11.90	11.90
Nos. 1637-1642 (6)	17.55	17.55
Nos. 702-707 (6)	13.55	13.55
Nos. 1582-1587 (6)	14.40	14.40
Nos. 829-834 (6)	19.65	19.65
Nos. 1482-1487 (6)	22.50	22.50
Nos. 913-922 (10)	27.50	25.30
Nos. 990-995 (6)	19.50	19.50
Nos. 742-746 (5)	15.50	15.50
Set total (92) Stamps	362.75	317.25

CD349

1992

Ascension	531-535
Bahamas	744-748
Bermuda	623-627
British Indian Ocean Territory	119-123
Cayman Islands	648-652
Falkland Islands	549-553
Gibraltar	605-609
Hong Kong	619-623
Kenya	563-567
Kiribati	582-586
Pitcairn Islands	362-366
St. Helena	570-574
St. Kitts	332-336
Samoa	805-809
Seychelles	734-738
Zil Elwannyen Sesel	183-187
Solomon Islands	708-712
South Georgia	157-161
Tristan da Cunha	508-512
Vanuatu	555-559
Zambia	561-565

Nos. 531-535 (5)	6.10	6.10
Nos. 744-748 (5)	6.90	4.70
Nos. 623-627 (5)	7.40	7.55
Nos. 119-123 (5)	22.75	19.25
Nos. 648-652 (5)	7.60	6.60
Nos. 549-553 (5)	5.95	5.90
Nos. 605-609 (5)	5.15	5.50
Nos. 619-623 (5)	5.10	5.25
Nos. 563-567 (5)	7.80	7.75
Nos. 582-586 (5)	3.85	3.85
Nos. 362-366 (5)	5.35	5.35
Nos. 570-574 (5)	5.70	5.70
Nos. 332-336 (5)	6.60	5.50
Nos. 805-809 (5)	7.85	5.90
Nos. 734-738 (5)	10.55	10.55
Nos. 183-187 (5)	9.40	9.40
Nos. 708-712 (5)	5.00	5.30
Nos. 157-161 (5)	5.60	5.90
Nos. 508-512 (5)	8.75	8.30
Nos. 555-559 (5)	3.10	3.10
Nos. 561-565 (5)	5.20	5.15
Set total (105) Stamps	151.70	142.60

Royal Air Force, 75th Anniversary

CD350

1993

Ascension	557-561
Bahamas	771-775
Barbados	842-846
Belize	1003-1008
Bermuda	648-651
British Indian Ocean Territory	136-140
Falkland Is.	573-577
Fiji	687-691
Montserrat	830-834

St. Kitts	351-355

Nos. 557-561 (5)	15.60	14.60
Nos. 771-775 (5)	24.65	21.45
Nos. 842-846 (5)	14.15	12.85
Nos. 1003-1008 (6)	21.15	16.50
Nos. 648-651 (4)	9.65	10.45
Nos. 136-140 (5)	16.10	16.10
Nos. 573-577 (5)	10.85	10.85
Nos. 687-691 (5)	17.75	17.40
Nos. 830-834 (5)	14.10	14.10
Nos. 351-355 (5)	22.80	23.55
Set total (50) Stamps	166.80	157.85

Royal Air Force, 80th Anniv.

Design CD350 Re-inscribed

1998

Ascension	697-701
Bahamas	907-911
British Indian Ocean Terr	198-202
Cayman Islands	754-758
Fiji	814-818
Gibraltar	755-759
Samoa	957-961
Turks & Caicos Islands	1258-1265
Tuvalu	763-767
Virgin Islands	879-883

Nos. 697-701 (5)	16.10	16.10
Nos. 907-911 (5)	13.60	12.65
Nos. 136-140 (5)	16.10	16.10
Nos. 754-758 (5)	15.25	15.25
Nos. 814-818 (5)	14.00	12.75
Nos. 755-759 (5)	9.70	9.70
Nos. 957-961 (5)	15.70	14.90
Nos. 1258-1265 (2)	27.50	27.50
Nos. 763-767 (5)	7.75	7.75
Nos. 879-883 (5)	15.00	15.00
Set total (47) Stamps	150.70	147.70

End of World War II, 50th Anniv.

CD351

CD352

1995

Ascension	613-617
Bahamas	824-828
Barbados	891-895
Belize	1047-1050
British Indian Ocean Territory	163-167
Cayman Islands	704-708
Falkland Islands	634-638
Fiji	720-724
Kiribati	662-668
Liberia	1175-1179
Mauritius	803-805
St. Helena	646-654
St. Kitts	389-393
St. Lucia	1018-1022
Samoa	890-894
Solomon Islands	799-803
South Georgia	198-200
Tristan da Cunha	562-566

Nos. 613-617 (5)	21.50	21.50

Nos. 824-828 (5)	22.00	18.70
Nos. 891-895 (5)	14.20	11.90
Nos. 1047-1050 (4)	8.25	5.90
Nos. 163-167 (5)	16.25	16.25
Nos. 704-708 (5)	17.65	13.95
Nos. 634-638 (5)	18.65	17.15
Nos. 720-724 (5)	17.50	14.50
Nos. 662-668 (7)	12.55	12.55
Nos. 1175-1179 (5)	15.25	11.15
Nos. 803-805 (3)	7.50	7.50
Nos. 646-654 (9)	26.10	26.10
Nos. 389-393 (5)	16.40	16.40
Nos. 1018-1022 (5)	12.25	10.15
Nos. 890-894 (5)	15.25	14.50
Nos. 799-803 (5)	14.75	14.75
Nos. 198-200 (3)	14.50	15.50
Nos. 562-566 (5)	20.10	20.10
Set total (91) Stamps	290.65	268.55

UN, 50th Anniv.

CD353

1995

Bahamas	839-842
Barbados	901-904
Belize	1055-1058
Jamaica	847-851
Liberia	1187-1190
Mauritius	813-816
Pitcairn Islands	436-439
St. Kitts	398-401
St. Lucia	1023-1026
Samoa	900-903
Tristan da Cunha	568-571
Virgin Islands	807-810

Nos. 839-842 (4)	7.15	6.40
Nos. 901-904 (4)	7.00	5.75
Nos. 1055-1058 (4)	6.80	4.70
Nos. 847-851 (5)	5.40	5.45
Nos. 1187-1190 (4)	10.90	10.90
Nos. 813-816 (4)	4.55	4.55
Nos. 436-439 (4)	8.15	8.15
Nos. 398-401 (4)	6.15	7.15
Nos. 1023-1026 (4)	7.50	7.25
Nos. 900-903 (4)	9.35	8.30
Nos. 568-571 (4)	13.50	13.50
Nos. 807-810 (4)	7.45	7.45
Set total (49) Stamps	93.90	89.45

Queen Elizabeth, 70th Birthday

CD354

1996

Ascension	632-635
British Antarctic Territory	240-243
British Indian Ocean Territory	176-180
Falkland Islands	653-657
Pitcairn Islands	446-449
St. Helena	672-676
Samoa	912-916
Tokelau	223-227
Tristan da Cunha	576-579
Virgin Islands	824-828

Nos. 632-635 (4)	5.30	5.30
Nos. 240-243 (4)	9.45	8.35
Nos. 176-180 (5)	11.50	11.50
Nos. 653-657 (5)	13.55	11.20
Nos. 446-449 (4)	8.60	8.60
Nos. 672-676 (5)	12.45	12.70
Nos. 912-916 (5)	10.50	10.50
Nos. 223-227 (5)	10.50	10.50
Nos. 576-579 (4)	8.35	8.35
Nos. 824-828 (5)	11.30	11.30
Set total (46) Stamps	101.50	98.10

Diana, Princess of Wales (1961-97)

BAHAMAS 15c CD355

1998

Ascension	696
Bahamas	901A-902
Barbados	950
Belize	1091
Bermuda	753
Botswana	659-663
British Antarctic Territory	258
British Indian Ocean Terr.	197
Cayman Islands	752A-753
Falkland Islands	694
Fiji	819-820
Gibraltar	754
Kiribati	719A-720
Namibia	909
Niue	706
Norfolk Island	644-645
Papua New Guinea	937
Pitcairn Islands	487
St. Helena	711
St. Kitts	437A-438
Samoa	955A-956
Seycelles	802
Solomon Islands	866-867
South Georgia	220
Tokelau	252B-253
Tonga	980
Niuafo'ou	201
Tristan da Cunha	618
Tuvalu	762
Vanuatu	718A-719
Virgin Islands	878

No. 696 (1)	5.25	5.25
Nos. 901A-902 (2)	5.30	5.30
No. 950 (1)	6.25	6.25
No. 1091 (1)	10.00	10.00
No. 753 (1)	5.00	5.00
Nos. 659-663 (5)	8.25	8.80
No. 258 (1)	5.50	5.50
No. 197 (1)	5.50	5.50
Nos. 752A-753 (3)	7.40	7.40
No. 694 (1)	5.00	5.00
Nos. 819-820 (2)	5.25	5.25
No. 754 (1)	4.75	4.75
Nos. 719A-720 (2)	4.60	4.60
No. 909 (1)	1.75	1.75
No. 706 (1)	5.50	5.50
Nos. 644-645 (1)	5.60	5.60
No. 937 (1)	6.25	6.25
No. 487 (1)	4.75	4.75
No. 711 (1)	4.25	4.25
Nos. 437A-438 (2)	5.15	5.15
Nos. 955A-956 (2)	7.00	7.00
No. 802 (1)	6.25	6.25
Nos. 866-867 (2)	5.40	5.40
No. 220 (1)	4.50	5.00
Nos. 252B-253 (2)	6.00	6.00
No. 980 (1)	4.00	4.00
No. 201 (1)	6.50	6.50
No. 618 (1)	5.00	5.00
No. 762 (1)	3.50	3.50
Nos. 718A-719 (2)	8.00	8.00
No. 878 (1)	4.50	4.50
Set total (46) Stamps	171.95	173.00

Wedding of Prince Edward and Sophie Rhys-Jones

ASCENSION ISLAND 50p
The Wedding of HRH Prince Edward & Miss Sophie Rhys-Jones
Saturday 19 June 1999
CD356

1999

Ascension	729-730
Cayman Islands	775-776
Falkland Islands	729-730
Pitcairn Islands	505-506
St. Helena	733-734
Samoa	971-972
Tristan da Cunha	636-637

Virgin Islands...............908-909

Nos. 729-730 (2)	4.50	4.50
Nos. 775-776 (2)	4.95	4.95
Nos. 729-730 (2)	14.00	14.00
Nos. 505-506 (2)	7.00	7.00
Nos. 733-734 (2)	5.00	5.00
Nos. 971-972 (2)	5.00	5.00
Nos. 636-637 (2)	7.50	7.50
Nos. 908-909 (2)	7.50	7.50
Set total (16) Stamps	55.45	55.45

1st Manned Moon Landing, 30th Anniv.

ASCENSION ISLAND 15p CD357

1999

Ascension	731-735
Bahamas	942-946
Barbados	967-971
Bermuda	778
Cayman Islands	777-781
Fiji	853-857
Jamaica	889-893
Kirbati	746-750
Nauru	465-469
St. Kitts	460-464
Samoa	973-977
Solomon Islands	875-879
Tuvalu	800-804
Virgin Islands	910-914

Nos. 731-735 (5)	12.80	12.80
Nos. 942-946 (5)	14.10	14.10
Nos. 967-971 (5)	9.45	8.25
No. 778 (1)	9.00	9.00
Nos. 777-781 (5)	9.25	9.25
Nos. 853-857 (5)	9.25	8.45
Nos. 889-893 (5)	8.30	7.18
Nos. 746-750 (5)	8.60	8.60
Nos. 465-469 (5)	7.55	7.10
Nos. 460-464 (5)	11.35	11.65
Nos. 973-977 (5)	12.60	12.45
Nos. 875-879 (5)	7.50	7.50
Nos. 800-804 (5)	6.75	6.75
Nos. 910-914 (5)	11.75	11.75
Set total (66) Stamps	138.25	134.83

Queen Mother's Century

THE QUEEN MOTHER'S CENTURY
ASCENSION ISLAND 15p
CD358

1999

Ascension	736-740
Bahamas	951-955
Cayman Islands	782-786
Falkland Islands	734-738
Fiji	858-862
Norfolk Island	688-692
St. Helena	740-744
Samoa	978-982
Solomon Islands	880-884
South Georgia	231-235
Tristan da Cunha	638-642
Tuvalu	805-809

Nos. 736-740 (5)	15.50	15.50
Nos. 951-955 (5)	13.75	12.65
Nos. 782-786 (5)	8.35	8.35
Nos. 734-738 (5)	30.00	28.25
Nos. 858-862 (5)	12.80	13.25
Nos. 688-692 (5)	9.50	9.50
Nos. 740-744 (5)	16.15	16.15
Nos. 978-982 (5)	12.50	12.10
Nos. 880-884 (5)	7.50	7.00
Nos. 231-235 (5)	29.75	30.00
Nos. 638-642 (5)	18.00	18.00
Nos. 805-809 (5)	7.00	7.00
Set total (60) Stamps	180.80	177.75

Prince William, 18th Birthday

ER 15p Ascension Island CD359

2000

Ascension	755-759
Cayman Islands	797-801
Falkland Islands	762-766
Fiji	889-893
South Georgia	257-261
Tristan da Cunha	664-668
Virgin Islands	925-929

Nos. 755-759 (5)	15.50	15.50
Nos. 797-801 (5)	11.15	10.90
Nos. 762-766 (5)	24.60	22.50
Nos. 889-893 (5)	12.90	12.90
Nos. 257-261 (5)	29.00	28.75
Nos. 664-668 (5)	21.50	21.50
Nos. 925-929 (5)	14.50	14.50
Set total (35) Stamps	129.15	126.55

Reign of Queen Elizabeth II, 50th Anniv.

Ascension Island CD360

2002

Ascension	790-794
Bahamas	1033-1037
Barbados	1019-1023
Belize	1152-1156
Bermuda	822-826
British Antarctic Territory	307-311
British Indian Ocean Territory	239-243
Cayman Islands	844-848
Falkland Islands	804-808
Gibraltar	896-900
Jamaica	952-956
Nauru	491-495
Norfolk Island	758-762
Papua New Guinea	1019-1023
Pitcairn Islands	552
St. Helena	788-792
St. Lucia	1146-1150
Solomon Islands	931-935
South Georgia	274-278
Swaziland	706-710
Tokelau	302-306
Tonga	1059
Niuafo'ou	239
Tristan da Cunha	706-710
Virgin Islands	967-971

Nos. 790-794 (5)	14.10	14.10
Nos. 1033-1037 (5)	15.25	15.25
Nos. 1019-1023 (5)	12.90	12.90
Nos. 1152-1156 (5)	17.10	15.10
Nos. 822-826 (5)	18.00	18.00
Nos. 307-311 (5)	23.00	23.00
Nos. 239-243 (5)	19.40	19.40
Nos. 844-848 (5)	13.25	13.25
Nos. 804-808 (5)	23.00	22.00
Nos. 896-900 (5)	6.65	6.65
Nos. 952-956 (5)	16.65	16.65
Nos. 491-495 (5)	17.75	17.75
Nos. 758-762 (5)	15.90	15.90
Nos. 1019-1023 (5)	14.50	14.50
No. 552 (1)	8.50	8.50
Nos. 788-792 (5)	19.75	19.75
Nos. 1146-1150 (5)	12.25	12.25
Nos. 931-935 (5)	12.40	12.40
Nos. 274-278 (5)	28.00	28.50
Nos. 706-710 (5)	12.50	12.50
Nos. 302-306 (5)	14.50	14.50
No. 1059 (1)	8.00	8.00
No. 239 (1)	8.75	8.75
Nos. 706-710 (5)	18.50	18.50
Nos. 967-971 (5)	16.50	16.50
Set total (113) Stamps	387.10	384.60

Queen Mother Elizabeth (1900-2002)

CD361

2002

Ascension		799-801
Bahamas		1044-1046
Bermuda		834-836
British Antarctic Territory		312-314
British Indian Ocean Territory		245-247
Cayman Islands		857-861
Falkland Islands		812-816
Nauru		499-501
Pitcairn Islands		561-565
St. Helena		808-812
St. Lucia		1155-1159
Seychelles		830
Solomon Islands		945-947
South Georgia		281-285
Tokelau		312-314
Tristan da Cunha		715-717
Virgin Islands		979-983

Nos. 799-801 (3)	8.85	8.85
Nos. 1044-1046 (3)	9.10	9.10
Nos. 834-836 (3)	12.25	12.25
Nos. 312-314 (3)	18.75	18.75
Nos. 245-247 (3)	17.35	17.35
Nos. 857-861 (5)	15.00	15.00
Nos. 812-816 (5)	28.50	28.50
Nos. 499-501 (3)	14.00	14.00
Nos. 561-565 (5)	15.25	15.25
Nos. 808-812 (5)	12.00	12.00
Nos. 1155-1159 (5)	12.00	12.00
No. 830 (1)	6.50	6.50
Nos. 945-947 (3)	9.25	9.25
Nos. 281-285 (5)	19.50	19.50
Nos. 312-314 (3)	11.85	11.85
Nos. 715-717 (3)	16.25	16.25
Nos. 979-983 (5)	23.50	23.50
Set total (63) Stamps	249.90	249.90

Head of Queen Elizabeth II

CD362

2003

Ascension		822
Bermuda		865
British Antarctic Territory		322
British Indian Ocean Territory		261
Cayman Islands		878
Falkland Islands		828
St. Helena		820
South Georgia		294
Tristan da Cunha		731
Virgin Islands		1003

No. 822 (1)	12.50	12.50
No. 865 (1)	50.00	50.00
No. 322 (1)	9.50	9.50
No. 261 (1)	11.00	11.00
No. 878 (1)	14.00	14.00
No. 828 (1)	9.00	9.00
No. 820 (1)	9.00	9.00
No. 294 (1)	8.50	8.50
No. 731 (1)	10.00	10.00
No. 1003 (1)	10.00	10.00
Set total (10) Stamps	143.50	143.50

Coronation of Queen Elizabeth II, 50th Anniv.

CD363

2003

Ascension		823-825

Bahamas		1073-1075
Bermuda		866-868
British Antarctic Territory		323-325
British Indian Ocean Territory		262-264
Cayman Islands		879-881
Jamaica		970-972
Kiribati		825-827
Pitcairn Islands		577-581
St. Helena		821-823
St. Lucia		1171-1173
Tokelau		320-322
Tristan da Cunha		732-734
Virgin Islands		1004-1006

Nos. 823-825 (3)	12.50	12.50
Nos. 1073-1075 (3)	13.00	13.00
Nos. 866-868 (2)	14.25	14.25
Nos. 323-325 (3)	23.00	23.00
Nos. 262-264 (3)	28.00	28.00
Nos. 879-881 (3)	19.25	19.25
Nos. 970-972 (3)	10.00	10.00
Nos. 825-827 (3)	13.00	13.00
Nos. 577-581 (5)	14.40	14.40
Nos. 821-823 (3)	7.25	7.25
Nos. 1171-1173 (3)	8.75	8.75
Nos. 320-322 (3)	17.25	17.25
Nos. 732-734 (3)	16.75	16.75
Nos. 1004-1006 (3)	25.00	25.00
Set total (43) Stamps	222.40	222.40

Prince William, 21st Birthday

CD364

2003

Ascension		826
British Indian Ocean Territory		265
Cayman Islands		882-884
Falkland Islands		829
South Georgia		295
Tokelau		323
Tristan da Cunha		735
Virgin Islands		1007-1009

No. 826 (1)	7.25	7.25
No. 265 (1)	8.00	8.00
Nos. 882-884 (3)	6.95	6.95
No. 829 (1)	13.50	13.50
No. 295 (1)	8.50	8.50
No. 323 (1)	7.25	7.25
No. 735 (1)	6.00	6.00
Nos. 1007-1009 (3)	10.00	10.00
Set total (12) Stamps	67.45	67.45

Carson Products

Pop-Up Keychain Magnifier
Item # MGGN-70

$6.99 *AA**
$10.00 Retail

- This small magnifier does not compromise magnification. View up close with 7x magnification
- This magnifying glass contains the latest lens technology that minimizes distortion and provides crystal clear image quality
- Keychain magnifier built to save space. Fits inside wallet, pocket, bag, etc.
- Have this on-the-go keychain always at the ready. Durable connection will keep it safe and secure. A great pocket magnifier!
- Spring-loaded button to extend magnifier. Keep lens secure and prevent damages when not in use

MicroMini 20x LED Microscope
Item # MSMM-2800

$9.99 *AA**
$14.00 Retail

The MicroMini™ is a 20x, LED Lighted Pocket Microscope that is always at the ready! It is compact, portable and easy to use. It is so small it can fit in the palm of your hand. Clip on to any hand bag or backpack using the attached key chain. Now you can explore anything...anywhere using the LED flashlight! View fabric, flowers, foliage, printing pixels and more all up close! View the hidden objects in currency with the included UV light.Uses 3 G12 Batteries (included).

ZPix Digital Microscope
Item #MCPIX

$99.99 *AA**
$129.99 Retail

The zPix 300 is a powerful 2 megapixel zoom USB digital microscope that displays a magnified image right on your computer screen. The impressive 86x-457x effective magnification (on 21" monitor) allows you to see details of ordinary objects that you never knew existed!

4.5x Power Pre-Focused Stand Magnifier Loupe
Item #: JRHU-55

$12.60 *AA**
$14.00 Retail

The HU-55 BugLoupe™ 4.5X Power 2.65" Pre-Focused Stand Magnifier Loupe is a kids loupe magnifier for viewing Insects, Plants, Coins, Stamps, and More. You've never really seen a bug close-up until you use our 4.5x BugLoupe™ Loupe Magnifier. Professional grade acrylic optics allow you to see the finest details. Pre-focused for quick, easy viewing. Simply place the BugLoupe™ over the bug and your child will see details they've never seen before.

MicroPen Pocket Microscope
Item # MCPEN

$12.99 *AA**
$14.99 Retail

The MicroPen is a pocket size 24x-53x microscope. The light weight and portable design make this miniature microscope perfect for industrial use. The MicroPen features a built-in LED light that provides a crystal-clear image with easy to use focus and zoom adjustments.

SmartPhone Microscope
Item # MCSCOPE

$119.99 *AA**
$164.99 Retail

SAVE $45

The Smartphone Microscope now comes bundled with a smartphone adapter! With the smartphone adapter you can take pictures or video of your specimen through the microscope and share with friends and family. Connect the included adapter to your smartphone and attach to the microscope.

Bar Ruler Magnifier 1.5x
Item # MGMR-65

$9.99 *AA**
$13.00 Retail

This Bar Ruler Magnifier is a 1.5x power Bar Ruler Magnifier and features both Inches (up to 8") and Centimeters (up to 20 cm) Scales. Lie ruler flat on the page to enlarge small text. It also features a convenient handle for your reading comfort.

Prices and availability are subject to change

AmosAdvantage.com | 1-800-572-6885

British Commonwealth of Nations

Dominions, Colonies, Territories, Offices and Independent Members

Comprising stamps of the British Commonwealth and associated nations.

A strict observance of technicalities would bar some or all of the stamps listed under Burma, Ireland, Kuwait, Nepal, New Republic, Orange Free State, Samoa, South Africa, South-West Africa, Stellaland, Sudan, Swaziland, the two Transvaal Republics and others but these are included for the convenience of collectors.

1. Great Britain

Great Britain: Including England, Scotland, Wales and Northern Ireland.

2. The Dominions, Present and Past

AUSTRALIA

The Commonwealth of Australia was proclaimed on Jan. 1, 1901. It consists of six former colonies as follows:

New South Wales
Queensland
South Australia
Victoria
Tasmania
Western Australia

The following islands and territories are, or have been, administered by Australia: Australian Antarctic Territory, Christmas Island, Cocos (Keeling) Islands, Nauru, New Guinea, Norfolk Island, Papua.

CANADA

The Dominion of Canada was created by the British North America Act in 1867. The following provinces were former separate colonies and issued postage stamps:

British Columbia and
Vancouver Island
New Brunswick
Newfoundland
Nova Scotia
Prince Edward Island

FIJI

The colony of Fiji became an independent nation with dominion status on Oct. 10, 1970.

GHANA

This state came into existence March 6, 1957, with dominion status. It consists of the former colony of the Gold Coast and the Trusteeship Territory of Togoland. Ghana became a republic July 1, 1960.

INDIA

The Republic of India was inaugurated on Jan. 26, 1950. It succeeded the Dominion of India which was proclaimed Aug. 15, 1947, when the former Empire of India was divided into Pakistan and the Union of India. The Republic is composed of about 40 predominantly Hindu states of three classes: governor's provinces, chief commissioner's provinces and princely states. India also has various territories, such as the Andaman and Nicobar Islands.

The old Empire of India was a federation of British India and the native states. The more important princely states were autonomous. Of the more than 700 Indian states, these 43 are familiar names to philatelists because of their postage stamps.

CONVENTION STATES

Chamba
Faridkot
Gwalior
Jhind
Nabha
Patiala

FEUDATORY STATES

Alwar
Bahawalpur
Bamra
Barwani
Bhopal
Bhor
Bijawar
Bundi
Bussahir
Charkhari
Cochin
Dhar
Dungarpur
Duttia
Faridkot (1879-85)
Hyderabad
Idar
Indore
Jaipur
Jammu
Jammu and Kashmir
Jasdan
Jhalawar
Jhind (1875-76)
Kashmir
Kishangarh
Kotah
Las Bela
Morvi
Nandgaon
Nowanuggur
Orchha
Poonch
Rajasthan
Rajpeepla
Sirmur
Soruth
Tonk
Travancore
Wadhwan

NEW ZEALAND

Became a dominion on Sept. 26, 1907. The following islands and territories are, or have been, administered by New Zealand:

Aitutaki
Cook Islands (Rarotonga)
Niue
Penrhyn
Ross Dependency
Samoa (Western Samoa)
Tokelau Islands

PAKISTAN

The Republic of Pakistan was proclaimed March 23, 1956. It succeeded the Dominion which was proclaimed Aug. 15, 1947. It is made up of all or part of several Moslem provinces and various districts of the former Empire of India, including Bahawalpur and Las Bela. Pakistan withdrew from the Commonwealth in 1972.

SOUTH AFRICA

Under the terms of the South African Act (1909) the self-governing colonies of Cape of Good Hope, Natal, Orange River Colony and Transvaal united on May 31, 1910, to form the Union of South Africa. It became an independent republic May 3, 1961.

Under the terms of the Treaty of Versailles, South-West Africa, formerly German South-West Africa, was mandated to the Union of South Africa.

SRI LANKA (CEYLON)

The Dominion of Ceylon was proclaimed Feb. 4, 1948. The island had been a Crown Colony from 1802 until then. On May 22, 1972, Ceylon became the Republic of Sri Lanka.

3. Colonies, Past and Present; Controlled Territory and Independent Members of the Commonwealth

Abu Dhabi
Aden
Aitutaki
Alderney
Anguilla
Antigua
Ascension
Australia
Bahamas
Bahrain
Bangladesh
Barbados
Barbuda
Basutoland
Batum
Bechuanaland
Bechuanaland Prot.
Belize
Bermuda
Botswana
British Antarctic Territory
British Central Africa
British Columbia and
Vancouver Island

British East Africa
British Guiana
British Honduras
British Indian Ocean Territory
British New Guinea
British Solomon Islands
British Somaliland
Brunei
Burma
Bushire
Cameroons
Canada
Cape of Good Hope
Cayman Islands
Christmas Island
Cocos (Keeling) Islands
Cook Islands
Crete,
  British Administration
Cyprus
Dominica
East Africa & Uganda
  Protectorates
Egypt
Falkland Islands
Fiji
Gambia
German East Africa
Ghana
Gibraltar
Gilbert Islands
Gilbert & Ellice Islands
Gold Coast
Grenada
Griqualand West
Guernsey
Guyana
Heligoland
Hong Kong
Indian Native States
  (see India)
Ionian Islands
Jamaica
Jersey

Jordan
Kenya
Kenya, Uganda & Tanzania
Kiribati
Kuwait
Labuan
Lagos
Leeward Islands
Lesotho
Madagascar
Malawi
Malaya
  Federated Malay States
  Johore
  Kedah
  Kelantan
  Malacca
  Negri Sembilan
  Pahang
  Penang
  Perak
  Perlis
  Selangor
  Singapore
  Sungei Ujong
  Trengganu
Malaysia
Maldive Islands
Malta
Man, Isle of
Mauritius
Mesopotamia
Montserrat
Mozambique
Muscat
Namibia
Natal
Nauru
Nevis
New Britain
New Brunswick
Newfoundland
New Guinea
New Hebrides

New Republic
New South Wales
New Zealand
Niger Coast Protectorate
Nigeria
Niue
Norfolk Island
North Borneo
Northern Nigeria
Northern Rhodesia
North West Pacific Islands
Nova Scotia
Nyasaland Protectorate
Oman
Orange River Colony
Pakistan
Palestine
Papua New Guinea
Penrhyn Island
Pitcairn Islands
Prince Edward Island
Qatar
Queensland
Rhodesia
Rhodesia & Nyasaland
Ross Dependency
Rwanda
Sabah
St. Christopher
St. Helena
St. Kitts
St. Kitts-Nevis-Anguilla
St. Lucia
St. Vincent
Samoa
Sarawak
Seychelles
Sierra Leone
Singapore
Solomon Islands
Somaliland Protectorate
South Africa
South Arabia
South Australia

South Georgia
Southern Nigeria
Southern Rhodesia
South-West Africa
Sri Lanka
Stellaland
Straits Settlements
Sudan
Swaziland
Tanganyika
Tanzania
Tasmania
Tobago
Togo
Tokelau Islands
Tonga
Transvaal
Trinidad
Trinidad and Tobago
Tristan da Cunha
Trucial States
Turks and Caicos
Turks Islands
Tuvalu
Uganda
United Arab Emirates
Vanuatu
Victoria
Virgin Islands
Western Australia
Zambia
Zanzibar
Zimbabwe
Zululand

**POST OFFICES IN
FOREIGN COUNTRIES**
Africa
  East Africa Forces
  Middle East Forces
Bangkok
China
Morocco
Turkish Empire

Colonies, former colonies, offices, territories controlled by parent states

Belgium
Belgian Congo
Ruanda-Urundi

Denmark
Danish West Indies
Faroe Islands
Greenland
Iceland

Finland
Aland Islands

France

COLONIES PAST AND PRESENT, CONTROLLED TERRITORIES
Afars & Issas, Territory of
Alaouites
Alexandretta
Algeria
Alsace & Lorraine
Anjouan
Annam & Tonkin
Benin
Cambodia (Khmer)
Cameroun
Castellorizo
Chad
Cilicia
Cochin China
Comoro Islands
Dahomey
Diego Suarez
Djibouti (Somali Coast)
Fezzan
French Congo
French Equatorial Africa
French Guiana
French Guinea
French India
French Morocco
French Polynesia (Oceania)
French Southern & Antarctic Territories
French Sudan
French West Africa
Gabon
Germany
Ghadames
Grand Comoro
Guadeloupe
Indo-China
Inini
Ivory Coast
Laos
Latakia
Lebanon
Madagascar
Martinique
Mauritania
Mayotte
Memel
Middle Congo
Moheli
New Caledonia
New Hebrides
Niger Territory

Nossi-Be
Obock
Reunion
Rouad, Ile
Ste.-Marie de Madagascar
St. Pierre & Miquelon
Senegal
Senegambia & Niger
Somali Coast
Syria
Tahiti
Togo
Tunisia
Ubangi-Shari
Upper Senegal & Niger
Upper Volta
Viet Nam
Wallis & Futuna Islands

POST OFFICES IN FOREIGN COUNTRIES
China
Crete
Egypt
Turkish Empire
Zanzibar

Germany

EARLY STATES
Baden
Bavaria
Bergedorf
Bremen
Brunswick
Hamburg
Hanover
Lubeck
Mecklenburg-Schwerin
Mecklenburg-Strelitz
Oldenburg
Prussia
Saxony
Schleswig-Holstein
Wurttemberg

FORMER COLONIES
Cameroun (Kamerun)
Caroline Islands
German East Africa
German New Guinea
German South-West Africa
Kiauchau
Mariana Islands
Marshall Islands
Samoa
Togo

Italy

EARLY STATES
Modena
Parma
Romagna
Roman States
Sardinia
Tuscany
Two Sicilies
    Naples
    Neapolitan Provinces
    Sicily

FORMER COLONIES, CONTROLLED TERRITORIES, OCCUPATION AREAS
Aegean Islands
    Calimno (Calino)
    Caso
    Cos (Coo)
    Karki (Carchi)
    Leros (Lero)
    Lipso
    Nisiros (Nisiro)
    Patmos (Patmo)
    Piscopi
    Rodi (Rhodes)
    Scarpanto
    Simi
    Stampalia
Castellorizo
Corfu
Cyrenaica
Eritrea
Ethiopia (Abyssinia)
Fiume
Ionian Islands
    Cephalonia
    Ithaca
    Paxos
Italian East Africa
Libya
Oltre Giuba
Saseno
Somalia (Italian Somaliland)
Tripolitania

POST OFFICES IN FOREIGN COUNTRIES
"ESTERO"*
Austria
China
    Peking
    Tientsin
Crete
Tripoli
Turkish Empire
    Constantinople
    Durazzo
    Janina
Jerusalem
Salonika
Scutari
Smyrna
Valona
*Stamps overprinted "ESTERO" were used in various parts of the world.

Netherlands
Aruba
Caribbean Netherlands
Curacao
Netherlands Antilles (Curacao)
Netherlands Indies
Netherlands New Guinea
St. Martin
Surinam (Dutch Guiana)

Portugal

COLONIES PAST AND PRESENT, CONTROLLED TERRITORIES
Angola
Angra
Azores

Cape Verde
Funchal
Horta
Inhambane
Kionga
Lourenco Marques
Macao
Madeira
Mozambique
Mozambique Co.
Nyassa
Ponta Delgada
Portuguese Africa
Portuguese Congo
Portuguese Guinea
Portuguese India
Quelimane
St. Thomas & Prince Islands
Tete
Timor
Zambezia

Russia

ALLIED TERRITORIES AND REPUBLICS, OCCUPATION AREAS
Armenia
Aunus (Olonets)
Azerbaijan
Batum
Estonia
Far Eastern Republic
Georgia
Karelia
Latvia
Lithuania
North Ingermanland
Ostland
Russian Turkestan
Siberia
South Russia
Tannu Tuva
Transcaucasian Fed. Republics
Ukraine
Wenden (Livonia)
Western Ukraine

Spain

COLONIES PAST AND PRESENT, CONTROLLED TERRITORIES
Aguera, La
Cape Juby
Cuba
Elobey, Annobon & Corisco
Fernando Po
Ifni
Mariana Islands
Philippines
Puerto Rico
Rio de Oro
Rio Muni
Spanish Guinea
Spanish Morocco
Spanish Sahara
Spanish West Africa

POST OFFICES IN FOREIGN COUNTRIES
Morocco
Tangier
Tetuan

Dies of British colonial stamps

DIE A:

1. The lines in the groundwork vary in thickness and are not uniformly straight.

2. The seventh and eighth lines from the top, in the groundwork, converge where they meet the head.

3. There is a small dash in the upper part of the second jewel in the band of the crown.

4. The vertical color line in front of the throat stops at the sixth line of shading on the neck.

DIE B:

1. The lines in the groundwork are all thin and straight.

2. All the lines of the background are parallel.

3. There is no dash in the upper part of the second jewel in the band of the crown.

4. The vertical color line in front of the throat stops at the eighth line of shading on the neck.

DIE I:

1. The base of the crown is well below the level of the inner white line around the vignette.

2. The labels inscribed "POSTAGE" and "REVENUE" are cut square at the top.

3. There is a white "bud" on the outer side of the main stem of the curved ornaments in each lower corner.

4. The second (thick) line below the country name has the ends next to the crown cut diagonally.

DIE Ia.
1 as die II.
2 and 3 as die I.

DIE Ib.
1 and 3 as die II.
2 as die I.

DIE II:

1. The base of the crown is aligned with the underside of the white line around the vignette.

2. The labels curve inward at the top inner corners.

3. The "bud" has been removed from the outer curve of the ornaments in each corner.

4. The second line below the country name has the ends next to the crown cut vertically.

Wmk. 1
Crown and C C

Wmk. 2
Crown and C A

Wmk. 3
Multiple Crown
and C A

Wmk. 4
Multiple Crown
and Script C A

Wmk. 4a

Wmk. 46

Wmk. 314
St. Edward's Crown
and C A Multiple

Wmk. 373   **Wmk. 384**

Wmk. 406

British Colonial and Crown Agents watermarks

Watermarks 1 to 4, 314, 373, 384 and 406, common to many British territories, are illustrated here to avoid duplication.

The letters "CC" of Wmk. 1 identify the paper as having been made for the use of the Crown Colonies, while the letters "CA" of the others stand for "Crown Agents." Both Wmks. 1 and 2 were used on stamps printed by De La Rue & Co.

Wmk. 3 was adopted in 1904; Wmk. 4 in 1921; Wmk. 46 in 1879; Wmk. 314 in 1957; Wmk. 373 in 1974; Wmk. 384 in 1985; Wmk. 406 in 2008.

In Wmk. 4a, a non-matching crown of the general St. Edwards type (bulging on both sides at top) was substituted for one of the Wmk. 4 crowns which fell off the dandy roll. The non-matching crown occurs in 1950-52 printings in a horizontal row of crowns on certain regular stamps of Johore and Seychelles, and on various postage due stamps of Barbados, Basutoland, British Guiana, Gold Coast, Grenada, Northern Rhodesia, St. Lucia, Swaziland and Trinidad and Tobago. A variation of Wmk. 4a, with the non-matching crown in a horizontal row of crown-CA-crown, occurs on regular stamps of Bahamas, St. Kitts-Nevis and Singapore.

Wmk. 314 was intentionally used sideways, starting in 1966. When a stamp was issued with Wmk. 314 both upright and sideways, the sideways varieties usually are listed also — with minor numbers. In many of the later issues, Wmk. 314 is slightly visible.

Wmk. 373 is usually only faintly visible.

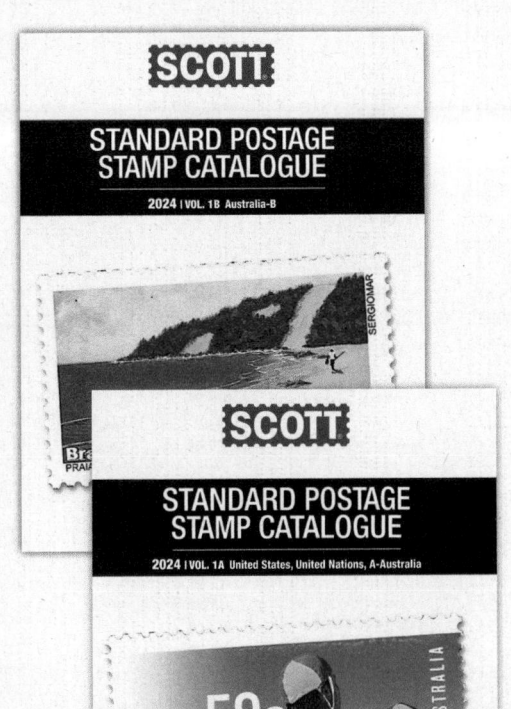

Scott Postage Stamp Checklist

Scott Postage Stamp Checklist

$9.99-$19.99 *AA**

- Provides basic information about postage stamps listed with major numbers in the Scott Standard Postage Stamp Catalogue.
- Features the country name, issue date or year, the Scott number, a description and four checkboxes; unused and used. The other two boxes can be used to label other options such as never-hinged or on cover.

Item #	Title	Retail	AA
105CK1	US Postal Stationery	19.99	14.99
112CK1	US Possessions	17.99	12.99
115CK1	US Federal and State Ducks	19.99	14.99
129CK1	US Postage semipostals through postal insurance	19.99	14.99
160CK1	US Revenues	19.99	14.99
210CK1	Australia	19.99	14.99
644CK1	Brazil	19.99	14.99
202CK1	British Islands	19.99	14.99
240CK1V2	Canada and Provinces	19.99	14.99
520CK1	China	24.99	19.99
345DMCK1	Denmark	17.99	12.99
345FICK1	Faroe Islands	12.99	9.99
345FNCK1	Finland	19.99	14.99
310CK1	France	19.99	14.99
315CK1	Germany	24.99	19.99
200CK1	Great Britain	19.99	14.99
345GRCK1	Greenland	19.99	14.99
650CK1	Guatemala	17.99	12.99
275HKCK1	Hong Kong	17.99	12.99
345ICK1	Iceland	17.99	12.99
618CK1	India	19.99	14.99
201CK1	Ireland	17.99	12.99
500CK1	Israel/Palestine	17.99	12.99
325CK1	Italy	19.99	14.99
510CK1	Japan	19.99	14.99
515CK1	Korea, South	19.99	14.99
663CK1	Liberia	17.99	12.99
341MCCK1	Macao	17.99	12.99
430CK1	Mexico	19.99	14.99
333CK1	Monaco	19.99	14.99
MMCK1	Mongolia	17.99	12.99
220CK1	New Zealand	19.99	14.99
345NRCK1	Norway	17.99	12.99
360CK1	Russia	24.99	19.99
328CK1	San Marino	19.99	14.99
345SWCK1	Sweden	17.99	12.99
365CK1	Switzerland	17.99	12.99
540CK1	Thailand	19.99	14.99
UNCK1	United Nations	19.99	14.99
375CK1	Vatican City	19.99	14.99

CANADA CHECKLIST 19

DATE	SCOTT NO.	DESCRIPTION	UNUSED	USED		
Canada						
1911-25	106	2c carmine	☐	☐	☐	☐
1911-25	107	2c yel grn ('22)	☐	☐	☐	☐
1911-25	108	3c brown ('18)	☐	☐	☐	☐
1911-25	109	3c car (I) ('23)	☐	☐	☐	☐
1911-25	110	4c ol bis ('22)	☐	☐	☐	☐
1911-25	111	5c dark blue ('12)	☐	☐	☐	☐
1911-25	112	5c violet ('22)	☐	☐	☐	☐
1911-25	113	7c yel ocher ('12)	☐	☐	☐	☐
1911-25	114	7c red brn ('24)	☐	☐	☐	☐
1911-25	115	8c blue ('25)	☐	☐	☐	☐
1911-25	116	10c plum ('12)	☐	☐	☐	☐
1911-25	117	10c blue ('22)	☐	☐	☐	☐
1911-25	118	10c bis brn ('25)	☐	☐	☐	☐
1911-25	119	20c ol grn ('25)	☐	☐	☐	☐
1911-25	120	50c blk brn ('25)	☐	☐	☐	☐
1911-25	122	$1 orange ('23)	☐	☐	☐	☐
1911-25	105c	As No. 105b, imperf, 2 panes tete beche	☐	☐	☐	☐

AmosAdvantage.com | 1-800-572-6885

NAMIBIA

nə-'mi-bē-ə

LOCATION — In southwestern Africa between Angola and South Africa, bordering on the Atlantic Ocean
GOVT. — Republic
AREA — 318,261 sq. mi.
POP. — 1,648,270 (1999 est.)
CAPITAL — Windhoek

Formerly South West Africa.

100 Cents = 1 Rand
100 Cents = 1 Dollar (1993)

Catalogue values for unused stamps in this country are for Never Hinged items.

Pres. Sam Nujoma, Map and Natl. Flag — A137

Designs: 45c, Dove, map, hands unchained, vert. 60c, Flag, map.

Perf. 14½x14, 14x14½
1990, Mar. 21   Litho.   Unwmk.
659 A137 18c shown .30 .25
660 A137 45c multicolored .60 .60
661 A137 60c multicolored 1.40 1.40
     Nos. 659-661 (3) 2.30 2.25

Independence from South Africa.

Sights of Namibia — A138

Designs: 18c, Fish River Canyon. 35c, Quiver-tree Forest. 45c, Tsaris Mountains. 60c, Dolerite Hills.

1990, Apr. 26   Perf. 14½x14
662 A138 18c multicolored .35 .30
663 A138 35c multicolored .55 .50
664 A138 45c multicolored .75 .60
665 A138 60c multicolored 1.00 .90
   a. Souvenir sheet of 1 4.25 4.25
     Nos. 662-665 (4) 2.65 2.30

No. 665a publicizes the 150th anniv. of the Penny Black. Sold for 1.50r.

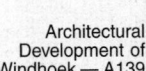

Architectural Development of Windhoek — A139

Designs: 18c, Early central business area. 35c, Modern central business area. 45c, First municipal building. 60c, Current municipal building.

1990, July 26   Perf. 14½x14
666 A139 18c multicolored .30 .30
667 A139 35c multicolored .45 .45
668 A139 45c multicolored .55 .55
669 A139 60c multicolored .85 .85
     Nos. 666-669 (4) 2.15 2.15

Farming and Ranching — A140

1990, Oct. 11   Perf. 14½x14
670 A140 20c Cornfields .25 .25
671 A140 35c Sanga cattle .40 .40
672 A140 50c Damara sheep .60 .55
673 A140 65c Irrigation .90 .95
     Nos. 670-673 (4) 2.15 2.15

Gypsum A141

Oranjemund Alluvial Diamond Mine A142

2c, Fluorite. 5c, Mimetite. 10c, Azurite. 20c, Dioptase. 30c, Tsumeb mine. 35c, Rosh Pinah mine. 40c, Diamond. 50c, Uis mine. 65c, Boltwoodite. 1r, Rossing mine. 1.50r, Wulfenite. 2r, Gold. 5r, Willemite.

1991, Jan. 2   Perf. 14½x14
674 A141 1c shown .25 .30
675 A141 2c multi .25 .30
676 A141 5c multi .30 .30
677 A141 10c multi .45 .30
679 A141 20c multi .50 .25
680 A142 25c shown .50 .30
681 A142 30c multi .65 .35
682 A142 35c multi .75 .40
683 A141 40c multi 1.00 .30
684 A142 50c multi 1.00 .35
685 A141 65c multi .95 .35
686 A142 1r multi 1.20 .50
687 A141 1.50r multi 1.60 .75
688 A141 2r multi 2.25 1.25
689 A141 5r multi 2.50 2.75
     Nos. 674-689 (15) 14.15 8.75

Nos. 676, 677 were reprinted in 1992 on phosphorescent paper.

Namibian Weather Service, Cent. — A143

20c, Weather balloon. 35c, Sunshine recorder. 50c, Measuring equipment. 65c, Gobabeb weather station.

1991, Feb. 2   Perf. 14½x14
690 A143 20c multicolored .25 .25
691 A143 35c multicolored .40 .40
692 A143 50c multicolored .55 .50
693 A143 65c multicolored .65 .60
     Nos. 690-693 (4) 1.85 1.75

Mountain Zebra — A144

20c, Four zebras. 25c, Mother suckling foal. 45c, Three zebras. 60c, Two zebras.

1991, Apr. 18   Perf. 14½x14
694 A144 20c multi 1.00 .65
695 A144 25c multi 1.10 .70
696 A144 45c multi 1.50 1.75
697 A144 60c multi 2.10 2.50
     Nos. 694-697 (4) 5.70 5.60

A souvenir sheet of 1 #696 was sold for 1.50r by the Philatelic Foundation of South Africa. Value $7.

Mountains — A145

1991, July 18   Perf. 14½x14
698 A145 20c Karas .30 .30
699 A145 25c Gamsberg .40 .40
700 A145 45c Brukkaros .55 .55
701 A145 60c Erongo .70 .70
     Nos. 698-701 (4) 1.95 1.95

Tourist Camps — A146

Designs: 20c, Bernabe De la Bat Tourist Camp, Waterberg. 25c, Von Bach Recreation Resort. 45c, Gross Barmen Hot Springs. 60c, Namutoni Rest Camp.

1991, Oct. 24   Perf. 14½x14
702 A146 20c multicolored .35 .25
703 A146 25c multicolored .45 .30
704 A146 45c multicolored .75 .60
705 A146 60c multicolored 1.15 .95
     Nos. 702-705 (4) 2.70 2.10

Windhoek Conservatoir, 21st Anniv. — A147

Designs: 20c, Artist's palette, brushes. 25c, French horn, neck of violin. 45c, Pan pipes, masks of Comedy and Tragedy, lyre. 60c, Ballet pas de deux.

1992, Jan. 30   Perf. 14x14½
706 A147 20c multicolored .25 .25
707 A147 25c multicolored .30 .25
708 A147 45c multicolored .60 .55
709 A147 60c multicolored .75 .75
     Nos. 706-709 (4) 1.90 1.80

Freshwater Fish — A148

1992, Apr. 16   Perf. 14½x14
710 A148 20c Blue kurper .35 .25
711 A148 25c Yellow fish .50 .25
712 A148 45c Carp .80 .50
713 A148 60c Catfish .95 .65
     Nos. 710-713 (4) 2.60 1.65

A souvenir sheet of 1 No. 712 was sold by the Philatelic Foundation of South Africa. Value, $5.75.

Views of Swakopmund A149

20c, Jetty. 25c, Swimming pool. 45c, State House, lighthouse. 60c, Palm beach.

1992, July 2   Perf. 14½x14
714 A149 20c multi .25 .25
715 A149 25c multi .35 .25
716 A149 45c multi .70 .55
717 A149 60c multi .95 .70
   a. Souvenir sheet of 4, #714-717 3.25 2.50
     Nos. 714-717 (4) 2.25 1.75

1992 Summer Olympics, Barcelona — A150

1992, July 24   Perf. 14½x14
718 A150 20c Runners .30 .25
719 A150 25c Flag, emblem .35 .30
720 A150 45c Swimmers .65 .55
721 A150 60c Olympic stadium .75 .65
   a. Souvenir sheet of 4, #718-721 2.75 2.75
     Nos. 718-721 (4) 2.05 1.75

No. 721a sold for 2r.

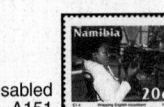

Disabled Workers — A151

Designs: 20c, Wrapping cucumbers. 25c, Finishing a woven mat. 45c, At a spinning wheel. 60c, Cleaning potted plants.

1992, Sept. 10   Perf. 14x14½
722 A151 20c multicolored .25 .25
723 A151 25c multicolored .30 .25
724 A151 45c multicolored .40 .40
725 A151 60c multicolored .55 .50
     Nos. 722-725 (4) 1.50 1.40

Endangered Animals — A152

Designs: 20c, Loxodonta africana. 25c, Tragelaphus spekei. 45c, Diceros bicornis. 60c, Lycaon pictus.

1993, Feb. 25   Perf. 14½x14
726 A152 20c multicolored .50 .25
727 A152 25c multicolored .50 .30
728 A152 45c multicolored 1.00 .50
729 A152 60c multicolored 1.25 .60
   a. Souvenir sheet of 4, #726-729 4.50 4.50
     Nos. 726-729 (4) 3.25 1.65

Namibia Nature Foundation. No. 729a sold for 2.10r.

Arrival of Simmentaler Cattle in Namibia, Cent. — A153

20c, Cows and calves. 25c, Cow and calf. 45c, Head of stud bull. 60c, Arrival on boat, 1893.

1993, Apr. 16   Perf. 14½x14
730 A153 20c multi .25 .25
731 A153 25c multi .30 .25
732 A153 45c multi .50 .40
733 A153 60c multi .80 .60
     Nos. 730-733 (4) 1.85 1.50

A souvenir sheet of one No. 732 has inscription for National Philatelic Exhibition. Sold for 3r. Value, $3.75.

Namib Desert — A154

1993, June 4   Perf. 14½x14
734 A154 30c Sossusvlei .25 .25
735 A154 40c Blutkuppe .35 .30
736 A154 65c Homeb .60 .60
737 A154 85c Moon landscape .75 .80
     Nos. 734-737 (4) 1.95 1.95

SOS Children's Village — A155

1993, Aug. 6   Litho.   Perf. 14
738 A155 30c Happiness .25 .25
739 A155 40c A loving family .30 .25
740 A155 65c Home sweet home .60 .55
741 A155 85c My village .75 .75
     Nos. 738-741 (4) 1.90 1.80

A156

Butterflies: 5c, Charaxes jasius saturnus. 10c, Acraea anemosa. 20c, Papilio nireus lyaeus. 30c, Junonia octavia sesamus. (35c), Graphium antheus. 40c, Hypolimnas misippus. 50c, Physcaeneura panda. 65c, Charaxes candiope. 85c, Junonia hierta cebrene. 90c, Colotis celimene pholoe. $1, Cacyreus dicksoni. $2, Charaxes bohemani. $2.50, Stugeta bowkeri tearei. $5, Byblia anvatara achelioa.

1993-94   Perf. 14x14½
742 A156 5c multicolored .25 .25
743 A156 10c multicolored .25 .25
744 A156 20c multicolored .25 .25
745 A156 30c multicolored .25 .25
745A A156 (35c) multicolored .55 .25
746 A156 40c multicolored .25 .25
747 A156 50c multicolored .30 .30
748 A156 65c multicolored .40 .35
749 A156 85c multicolored .50 .40
750 A156 90c multicolored .50 .40
751 A156 $1 multicolored .50 .40
752 A156 $2 multicolored 1.00 1.00
753 A156 $2.50 multicolored 1.25 1.25
754 A156 $5 multicolored 1.75 1.75
     Nos. 742-754 (14) 8.05 7.35

No. 745A is inscribed "STANDARDISED MAIL" and sold for 35c when issued.
Issued: No. 745A, 4/8/94; others, 10/1/93.

Perf. 14½x15 Syncopated Type A
1997

742a	A156	5c multicolored	.35	.35
747a	A156	50c multicolored	1.25	1.00

Issued: Nos. 742a, 747a, 3/3/97.

Coastal Angling — A157

1994, Feb. 4   Litho.   Perf. 14

755	A157	30c Blacktail	.25	.25
756	A157	40c Kob	.30	.25
757	A157	65c Steenbras	.50	.50
758	A157	85c Galjoen	.75	.70
a.		Souvenir sheet of 4, #755-758	2.75	2.75
		Nos. 755-758 (4)	1.80	1.70

Incorporation of Walvis Bay into Namibia — A158

1994, Mar. 1

759	A158	30c Quay	.45	.40
760	A158	65c Aerial view	.70	.70
761	A158	85c Map of Namibia	1.10	1.10
		Nos. 759-761 (3)	2.25	2.20

A159

Flowers: 35c, Adenolobus pechuelii. 40c, Hibiscus elliottiae. 65c, Pelargonium cortusifolium. 85c, Hoodia macrantha.

1994, Apr. 8   Litho.   Perf. 14

762	A159	35c multicolored	.25	.25
763	A159	40c multicolored	.30	.25
764	A159	65c multicolored	.50	.40
765	A159	85c multicolored	.70	.60
		Nos. 762-765 (4)	1.75	1.50

Storks of Etosha — A160

1994, June 3   Litho.   Perf. 14

766	A160	35c Yellowbilled	.50	.30
767	A160	40c Abdim's	.55	.40
768	A160	80c Openbilled	.60	.60
769	A160	$1.10 White	.80	.80
		Nos. 766-769 (4)	2.45	2.10

Trains — A161

1994, Aug. 5   Litho.   Perf. 13½x14

770	A161	35c Steam railcar	.50	.25
771	A161	70c Class Krauss	.70	.50
772	A161	80c Class 24	.75	.55
773	A161	$1.10 Class 7C	1.00	.85
		Nos. 770-773 (4)	2.95	2.25

A souvenir sheet of 1 #772 was sold for 3r by the Philatelic Foundation of South Africa. Value $2.25.

Railways in Namibia, Cent. — A162

Locomotives: 35c, Prince Edward, 1st in service. 70c, Ex-German SWA 2-8-0 tank.

80c, Class 8. $1.10, Class 33 400 diesel electric.

1995, Mar. 8   Litho.   Perf. 14

774	A162	35c multicolored	.45	.25
775	A162	70c multicolored	.70	.40
776	A162	80c multicolored	.75	.55
777	A162	$1.10 multicolored	1.10	.85
a.		Souvenir sheet of 4, #774-777	4.00	4.00
		Nos. 774-777 (4)	3.00	2.05

No. 777a sold for $3.50.
No. 777a exists inscribed "Reprint November 1996." Value $4.75.

A163

1995, Mar. 21   Litho.   Perf. 14

778	A163	(35c) multicolored	.50	.50

Independence, 5th anniv. No. 778 is inscribed "STANDARDISED MAIL" and sold for 35c on day of issue.

A164

Fossils: 40c, Geochelone stromeri. 80c, Diamantornis wardi. 90c, Prohyrax hendeyi. $1.20, Crocodylus lloydi.

1995, May 24   Litho.   Perf. 14

779	A164	40c multicolored	.55	.30
780	A164	80c multicolored	.90	.55
781	A164	90c multicolored	1.00	.60
782	A164	$1.20 multicolored	1.25	1.25
		Nos. 779-782 (4)	3.70	2.70

A souvenir sheet of 1 #780 was sold for 3r by the Philatelic Foundation of South Africa. Value $3.

Finnish Mission, 125th Anniv. — A165

Designs: 40c, Mission church, Martti Rautanen (1845-1926). 80c, Albin Savola (1867-1934), Oniipa printing press. 90c, Oxwagon, Karl Emanuel August Weikkolin (1842-91). $1.20, Dr. Selma Raino (1873-1939), Onandjokwe Hospital.

1995, July 10   Litho.   Perf. 14

783	A165	40c multicolored	.35	.25
784	A165	80c multicolored	.55	.50
785	A165	90c multicolored	.70	.65
786	A165	$1.20 multicolored	.85	.75
		Nos. 783-786 (4)	2.45	2.15

Traditional Adornments — A166

1995, Aug. 16   Litho.   Perf. 14½x14

787	A166	40c Ivory buttons	.30	.25
788	A166	80c Conus shell	.45	.40
789	A166	90c Cowrie shells	.55	.50
790	A166	$1.20 Shell button	.80	.80
		Nos. 787-790 (4)	2.10	1.95

Souvenir Sheet

Singapore '95 — A167

$1.20, Phacochoerus aethiopicus.

1995, Sept. 10   Litho.   Perf. 14

791	A167	$1.20 multi	1.60	1.60

UN, 50th Anniv. — A168

1995, Oct. 24

792	A168	40c blue & black	.45	.45

Tourism — A169

1996, Apr. 1   Litho.   Perf. 15x14

793	A169	(45c) Bogenfels Arch	.25	.25
794	A169	90c Ruacana Falls	.30	.30
795	A169	$1 Epupa Falls	.35	.30
796	A169	$1.30 Wild horses	.50	.50
		Nos. 793-796 (4)	1.40	1.35

No. 793 is inscribed "Standardised Mail" and sold for 45c on day of issue.

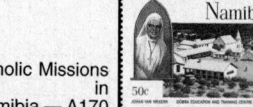

Catholic Missions in Namibia — A170

50c, Döbra Education and Training Centre. 95c, Heirachabis. $1, Windhoek St. Mary's Cathedral. $1.30, Ovamboland Old Church & School.

1996, May 27   Litho.   Perf. 15x14

797	A170	50c multicolored	.25	.25
798	A170	95c multicolored	.35	.35
799	A170	$1 multicolored	.40	.40
800	A170	$1.30 multicolored	.55	.55
		Nos. 797-800 (4)	1.55	1.55

Souvenir Sheet

CAPEX 96 A171

1996, June 8   Litho.   Perf. 14½x14

801	A171	$1.30 African lynx	1.50	1.50

UNICEF, 50th Anniv. — A172

Designs: (45c), Children have rights. $1.30, Educate the girl.

1996, June 14   Litho.   Perf. 15x14

802	A172	(45c) multicolored	.25	.25
803	A172	$1.30 multicolored	.60	.60

No. 802 is inscribed "Standard Postage" and sold for 45c on day of issue.

1996 Summer Olympic Games, Atlanta — A173

1996, June 27

804	A173	(45c) Boxing	.25	.25
805	A173	90c Cycling	.50	.40
806	A173	$1 Swimming	.30	.50
807	A173	$1.30 Running	.40	.40
		Nos. 804-807 (4)	1.45	1.55

No. 804 is inscribed "Standard Postage" and sold for 45c on day of issue.

Constellations A174

Designs: (45c), Scorpio. 90c, Sagittarius. $1, Southern Cross. $1.30, Orion.

1996, Sept. 12   Litho.   Perf. 15x14

808	A174	(45c) multicolored	.25	.25
809	A174	90c multicolored	.30	.30
810	A174	$1 multicolored	.35	.35
a.		Souvenir sheet of 1	2.00	2.00
811	A174	$1.30 multicolored	.50	.50
		Nos. 808-811 (4)	1.40	1.40

No. 808 is inscribed "Standard Postage" and sold for 45c on day of issue.
No. 810a sold for $3.50. No. 810a exists inscribed "Reprint February 17, 1997. Sold in aid of organized philately N$3.50."

Early Pastoral Pottery — A175

Designs: (45c), Urn-shaped storage vessel. 90c, Bag-shaped cooking vessel. $1, Reconstructed pot. $1.30, Large storage vessel.

1996, Oct. 17   Perf. 14x15

812	A175	(45c) multicolored	.25	.25
813	A175	90c multicolored	.35	.35
814	A175	$1 multicolored	.40	.40
815	A175	$1.30 multicolored	.45	.45
		Nos. 812-815 (4)	1.45	1.45

No. 812 is inscribed "Standard Postage" and sold for 45c on day of issue.

Ancient //Khauxa!nas Ruins, near Karasburg A176

Various views of stone wall.

1997, Feb. 6   Litho.   Perf. 15x14

816	A176	(50c) multicolored	.30	.25
817	A176	$1 multicolored	.70	.50
818	A176	$1.10 multicolored	.80	.65
819	A176	$1.50 multicolored	1.40	1.25
		Nos. 816-819 (4)	3.20	2.65

No. 816 is inscribed "Standard Postage" and sold for 45c on day of issue.

Souvenir Sheet

Hong Kong '97, Intl. Stamp Exhibition — A176a

1997, Feb. 12   Litho.   Perf. 14½x14

819A	A176a	$1.30 Sanga bull	1.25	1.25

No. 819A sold for $3.50. An inscription, "REPRINT 1 APRIL 1997," was added to a later printing of this sheet. Value $2.50.

A177

1997, Apr. 8   Litho.   Perf. 14x14½

820	A177	$2 multicolored	.90	.90

Heinrich von Stephan (1831-97), founder of UPU.

Jackass
Penguins — A178

1997, May 15   Litho.   Perf. 14x14½
821	A178	(50c) shown	.30	.30
822	A178	$1 Nesting	.40	.35
823	A178	$1.10 With young	.50	.40
824	A178	$1.50 Swimming	.60	.60
	Nos. 821-824 (4)		1.80	1.65

Souvenir Sheet
824A	A178	Sheet of 4, #b.-e.	1.75	1.75

World Wildlife Fund. No. 821 is inscribed "Standard Postage" and sold for 45c on day of issue.

Nos. 824Ab-824Ae are like Nos. 821-824 but do not have the WWF emblem. No. 824A sold for $5.

Wild
Cats — A179

1997, June 12   Litho.   Perf. 14½x14
825	A179	(45c) Felis caracal	.25	.25
826	A179	$1 Felis lybica	.40	.40
827	A179	$1.10 Felis serval	.50	.50
828	A179	$1.50 Felis nigripes	.60	.60
	Nos. 825-828 (4)		1.75	1.75

No. 825 is inscribed "Standard Postage" and sold for 45c on day of issue. A souvenir sheet containing a $5 stamp like #828 exists. Value $2.25.
See Nos. 878-881.

Helmeted
Guineafowl
A180

1997, June 5   Perf. 14½x14
829	A180	$1.20 multicolored	1.10	.90

A181

Baskets: 50c, Collecting bag. 90c, Powder basket. $1.20, Fruit basket. $2, Grain basket.

1997, July 8   Litho.   Perf. 14x14½
830	A181	50c multicolored	.25	.25
831	A181	90c multicolored	.30	.30
832	A181	$1.20 multicolored	.40	.35
833	A181	$2 multicolored	.70	.70
	Nos. 830-833 (4)		1.65	1.60

Cinderella
Waxbill — A182

60c, Blackchecked waxbill.

Perf. 14x14½ Syncopated Type A
1997, May 5   Booklet Stamps
834	A182	50c shown	.55	.45
835	A182	60c multicolored	.80	.55
a.	Booklet pane, 5 each #834-835		6.75	
	Complete booklet, #835a		7.00	

A183

Greetings
Stamps — A184

Flowers: No. 836, Catophractes alexandri. No. 837, Crinun paludosum. No. 838, Gloriosa superba. No. 839, Tribulus zeyheri. No. 840, Aptosimum pubescens.
Helmeted guineafowl: No. 841, In bed. No. 842, Holding flowers. No. 843, As music conductor. No. 844, Prepared to travel. No. 845, Wearing heart necklace.

1997, July 11   Litho.   Perf. 14x13½
Booklet Stamps
836	A183	(50c) multicolored	.40	.40
837	A183	(50c) multicolored	.40	.40
838	A183	(50c) multicolored	.40	.40
839	A183	(50c) multicolored	.40	.40
840	A183	(50c) multicolored	.40	.40
a.	Booklet pane, 2 each #836-840 + 10 labels		4.50	
	Complete booklet, #840a		4.50	
841	A184	50c multicolored	.40	.40
842	A184	50c multicolored	.40	.40
843	A184	50c multicolored	.40	.40
844	A184	$1 multicolored	.80	.80
845	A184	$1 multicolored	.80	.80
a.	Booklet pane, 2 each #841-845 + 10 labels		6.25	
	Complete booklet, #845a		6.25	

Nos. 836-840 are inscribed "Standard Postage" and sold for 45c on day of issued.

Namibian Veterinary Assoc., 50th
Anniv. — A185

1997, Sept. 12   Perf. 14
846	A185	$1.50 multicolored	.60	.60

Souvenir Sheet

Triceratops — A186

1997, Sept. 27   Litho.   Perf. 13
847	A186	$5 multicolored	2.00	2.00

World Post
Day — A187

1997, Oct. 9   Litho.   Perf. 14x15
848	A187	(45c) multicolored	.40	.30

No. 848 is inscribed "Standard Postage" and sold for 45c on day of issue.

Trees — A188

Designs: (50c), False mopane. $1, Ana tree. $1.10, Shepherd's tree. $1.50, Kiaat.

1997, Oct. 10
849	A188	(50c) multi	.25	.25
850	A188	$1 multi	.30	.30
851	A188	$1.10 multi	.30	.35
852	A188	$1.50 multi	.50	.70
	Nos. 849-852 (4)		1.35	1.60

No. 849 is inscribed "Standard Postage" and sold for 45c on day of issue.

Fauna and
Flora — A189

5c, Flame lily. 10c, Bushman poison. 20c, Camel's foot. 30c, Western rhigozum. 40c, Bluecheeked bee-eater. (50c), Rosyfaced lovebird. 50c, Laughing dove. 60c, Lappetfaced vulture. 90c, Yellowbilled hornbill. $1, Lilacbreasted roller. $1.10, Hippopotamus. ($1.20), Leopard. $1.20, Giraffe. $1.50, Elephant. $2, Lion. $4, Buffalo. $5, Black rhinoceros. $10, Cheetah.

1997, Nov. 3   Litho.   Perf. 13½
853	A189	5c multi	.25	.40
854	A189	10c multi	.25	.40
855	A189	20c multi	.25	.25
856	A189	30c multi	.25	.25
857	A189	40c multi	.25	.25
858	A189	(50c) multi	.25	.25
a.	Booklet pane of 10, perf 14x13½		2.50	
	Complete booklet, #858a		2.50	
859	A189	50c multi	.25	.25
860	A189	60c multi	.30	.25
861	A189	90c multi	.35	.30
862	A189	$1 multi	.40	.35
863	A189	$1.10 multi	.45	.40
864	A189	($1.20) multi	.50	.60
a.	Booklet pane of 10, perf 14x13½		5.50	
	Complete booklet, #864a		5.50	
865	A189	$1.20 multi	.40	.40
866	A189	$1.50 multi	.45	.45
867	A189	$2 multi	.60	.45
868	A189	$4 multi	.90	.80
869	A189	$5 multi	1.25	1.00
870	A189	$10 multi	2.25	2.00
a.	Bklt. pane, 1 ea #853-870, perf 14x13½		10.00	
	Complete booklet, #870a		10.00	
	Nos. 853-870 (18)		9.60	9.05

Self-Adhesive
Die Cut Perf. 12x12½
870B	A189	(45c) like #858	.25	.25
870C	A189	$1 like #862	.40	.30
870D	A189	($1.20) like #864	.50	.40
	Nos. 870B-870D (3)		1.15	.95

No. 858 is inscribed "Standard Postage" and sold for 50c on day issue. No. 864 is inscribed "Postcard Rate" and sold for $1.20 on day of issue. Nos. 853-854, 857, 860, 864, 866-867 and maybe others, exist imperf.
Value: $100-125 each pair.
For surcharges see #959-962, 1060-1063, 1071-1080, 1132-1040.

Christmas — A190

Various pictures of a helmeted guineafowl.

1997, Nov. 3   Perf. 13x12½
871	A190	(50c) multicolored	.25	.25
872	A190	$1 multicolored	.35	.25
873	A190	$1.10 multicolored	.40	.30
874	A190	$1.50 multicolored	.50	.50
	Nos. 871-874 (4)		1.50	1.30

Souvenir Sheet
875	A190	$5 multi, vert.	2.25	2.25

No. 871 is inscribed "Standard Postage" and sold for 50c on day of issue.

A191

1997, Nov. 27   Perf. 14x15
876	A191	(50c) multicolored	.45	.45

John Muafangejo (1943-87), artist. No. 876 is inscribed "Standard Postage" and sold for 50c on day of issue.

A192

1998, Jan. 15
877	A192	(50c) brown & gray	.35	.35

Gabriel B. Taapopi (1911-85). No. 877 is inscribed "Standard Postage" and sold for 50c on day of issue.

Wild Cats Type of 1997

Designs: $1.20, Panthera pardus. $1.90, Panthera leo, female carrying young. $2, Panthera leo, male. $2.50, Acinonyx jubatus.

1998, Jan. 26   Perf. 13x12½
878	A179	$1.20 multicolored	.60	.60
879	A179	$1.90 multicolored	.70	.60
880	A179	$2 multicolored	.75	.75
881	A179	$2.50 multicolored	.90	.90
a.	Souvenir sheet, #878-881		3.50	3.50
	Nos. 878-881 (4)		2.95	2.65

Narra Plant — A194

1998, Feb. 9   Perf. 12½x13
882	A194	$2.40 multicolored	.65	.65

Water
Awareness — A195

1998, Mar. 23   Litho.   Perf. 14x15
883	A195	(50c) multicolored	.40	.35

No. 883 is inscribed "Standard Postage" and sold for 50c on date of issue.

Nos. 885-895 were initially not available in Namibia. They were issued Nov. 23, 1997, at a Shanghai, China, stamp exhibition by a Chinese stamp dealer acting for the Namibia Post Office. There is some question whether they were sold in Namibia, but if they were, it was not until early 1998.

A197

Lunar New Year — A198

Chinese inscriptions, wood cut images of a tiger, stylized drawings of tiger in — #885: a, orange. b, light green. c, yellow. d, blue. e, dark green. f, lilac.
No. 886: Various tiger figures, Chinese inscriptions.
No. 887, Chinese inscriptions, stylized tigers.

Perf. 13½x12½
1997, Nov. 23   **Litho.**
885 A197 $2.50 Sheet of 6, #a.-f. 6.00 6.00
                  Perf. 14x13½
886 A198 $2.50 Sheet of 6, #a.-f. 6.00 6.00
            Souvenir Sheets
                Perf. 12½
887 A197 $6 multicolored   2.75 2.75
888 A198 $6 multicolored   2.75 2.75
   Nos. 887-888 each contain one 69x38mm
stamp.

Macau Returns
to China in
1999 — A199

   Designs: No. 890, Flag, building. No. 892,
Flag, Deng Xiaoping, building.
1997, Nov. 23   **Perf. 13½**
889 A199 $4.50 multicolored   2.50 2.50
            Size: 59x27mm
                Perf. 13½x13
890 A199 $4.50 multicolored   3.25 3.25
            Souvenir Sheets
                Perf. 13½x12½
891 A199 $6 multicolored   3.00 3.00
                Perf. 12½
892 A199 $6 multicolored   3.00 3.00
   Nos. 889-890 issued in sheets of 3. No. 891
contains one 62x33mm stamp, No. 892 one
69x33mm stamp.

Return of
Hong
Kong to
China
A200

   Chinese landmarks — #892A: b, Beijing,
Natl. Capital of China. c, Return of Hong Kong,
1997. d, Return of Macao, 1999. e, The Taiwan Region.
1997, Nov. 17   **Litho.**   **Perf. 14x13½**
892A A200 $3.50 Sheet of 4, #b.-
           e.   7.00 7.00
          Souvenir Sheet
                Perf. 12½
893   A200 $6 Chinese
              landmarks   2.50 2.50
   No. 893 contains one 72x41mm stamp.

Shanghai Communique, 25th
Anniv. — A201

   No. 894: a, Pres. Nixon, Mao Zedong, 1972.
b, Pres. Carter, Deng Xiaoping, 1979. c, Pres.
Reagan, Deng Xiaoping, 1984. d, Pres. Bush,
Deng Xiaoping, 1989.
$6, Nixon, Zhou Enlai, 1972.
1997, Nov. 17   **Perf. 13½x12½**
894 A201 $3.50 Sheet of 4, #a.-
           d.   5.00 5.00
          Souvenir Sheet
                Perf. 14x13½
895   A201 $6 multicolored   2.75 2.75
   No. 895 contains one 67x33mm stamp.

Owls — A204

   No. 898, Rat (prey). No. 899, Whitefaced
owl. No. 900, Barred owl. No. 901, Spotted
eagle owl. No. 902, Barn owl.
1998, Apr. 1   **Litho.**   **Perf. 13½x13**
            Booklet Stamps
898 A204   55c multi   .40   .40
              Size: 38x23mm
899 A204 $1.50 multi   .70   .70
900 A204 $1.50 multi   .70   .70
901 A204 $1.90 multi   .90   .90
              Size: 61x21mm
902 A204 $1.90 multi   .90   .90
   a. Booklet pane, #898-902   3.75
       Complete booklet, #902a   3.75
              See No. 950.

Shells — A205

   Designs: (55c), Patella granatina. $1.10,
Cymatium cutaceum africanum. $1.50, Conus
mozambicus. $6, Venus verrucosa.
1998, May 14   **Litho.**   **Perf. 12½**
903 A205 (55c) multicolored   .30   .25
904 A205 $1.10 multicolored   .45   .30
905 A205 $1.50 multicolored   .60   .60
906 A205 $6 multicolored   2.25 2.25
   a. Souvenir sheet, #903-906   4.25 4.25
       Nos. 903-906 (4)   3.60 3.40
   No. 903 inscribed "Standard Postage."

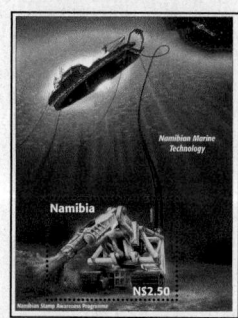

Namibian Marine Technology — A206

1998, May 18   **Litho.**   **Perf. 14½x14**
908 A206 $2.50 multicolored   2.00 2.00

Diana, Princess of Wales (1961-97)
Common Design Type
   Working for removal of land mines: a, Wearing face shield. b, Wearing Red Cross shirt. c,
In white blouse. d, With child.
1998, May 18   **Litho.**   **Perf. 14½x14**
909 CD355 $1 Sheet of 4, #a.-d. 1.75 1.75

World
Environment
Day — A207

   (55c), Namibian coast. $1.10, Okavango
sunset. $1.50, Sossusvlei. $1.90, African
moringo.
1998, June 5   **Litho.**   **Perf. 13x13½**
910 A207 (55c) multicolored   .30   .25
911 A207 $1.10 multicolored   .40   .30
912 A207 $1.50 multicolored   .45   .45
913 A207 $1.90 multicolored   .60   .55
       Nos. 910-913 (4)   1.75 1.55
   No. 910 is inscribed "Standard Postage."

Souvenir Sheet

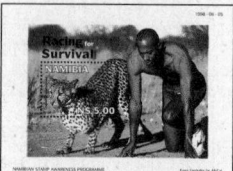

Racing
for
Survival
A208

1998, June 5   **Perf. 13**
914 A208 $5 Acinonyx jubatus   2.00 2.00

Animals and Their Young — A209

   a, Chacma baboon. b, Blue wildebeest. c,
Suricate. d, Elephant. e, Burchell's zebra.
1998, June 18   **Perf. 13½x13**
915 A209 $1.50 Sheet of 5, #a.-
           e.   2.50 2.50

Souvenir Sheet

1998 World Cup Soccer
Championships, France — A210

1998, July 1   **Litho.**   **Perf. 14**
916 A210 $5 multicolored   1.75 1.75

Flora and Fauna of the Caprivi
Strip — A211

   Designs: a, Carmine bee-eater. b, Sable
antelope. c, Lechwe. d, Woodland waterberry.
e, Nile monitor. f, African jacana. g, African
fish eagle. h, Woodland kingfisher. i, Nile crocodile. j, Black mamba.
1998, Sept. 26   **Litho.**   **Perf. 12½**
917 A211 60c Sheet of 10,
           #a.-j.   7.50 7.50
   #917b-917c, 917e are 40x40mm, #917i is
54x30mm, #917j is 32x30mm.

Souvenir Sheet

Black Rhinoceros — A212

1998, Oct. 20   **Litho.**   **Perf. 13**
918 A212 $5 multicolored   2.00 2.00
   Ilsapex '98, Intl. Philatelic Exhibition,
Johannesburg.

Souvenir Sheet

Whales
A213

1998, Oct. 9   **Litho.**   **Perf. 13½x14**
919 A213 $5 multicolored   2.25 2.25
   See Norfolk Island No. 665, South Africa
No. 1095.

Damara Dik
Dik
A214

Striped Tree
Squirrel
A215

1999, Jan. 18   **Litho.**   **Perf. 13½**
920 A214 $1.80 multi   2.50 1.50
921 A215 $2.65 multi   4.25 4.25

"Yoka" the
Snake
A216

"Yoka" the Snake
A217

   Cartoon pictures of Yoka: No. 922, Turning
head. No. 923, Wrapped around tree branch.
No. 924, Tail wrapped around branch and
female snake. No. 925, With female snake and
mouse. No. 926, In love. No. 927, Yoka tied up
in knots. No. 928, Smashed with footprint. No.
929, Female snake's tail, Yoka's head. No.
930, Female snake singing to dazed Yoka. No.
931, Lying with tail over nose.

          Serpentine Die Cut
1999, Feb. 1 **Self-Adhesive** **Litho.**
            Booklet Stamps
922 A216 $1.60 multicolored   .50   .50
923 A217 $1.60 multicolored   .50   .50
924 A216 $1.60 multicolored   .50   .50
925 A217 $1.60 multicolored   .50   .50
926 A216 $1.60 multicolored   .50   .50
927 A217 $1.60 multicolored   .50   .50
928 A216 $1.60 multicolored   .50   .50
929 A217 $1.60 multicolored   .50   .50
930 A216 $1.60 multicolored   .50   .50
931 A217 $1.60 multicolored   .50   .50
   a. Bklt. pane of 10, #922-931   5.00

   The peelable paper backing serves as a
booklet cover.

Souvenir Sheet

Passenger Liner "Windhuk" — A218

1999, Mar. 18   **Perf. 14**
932 A218 $5.50 multicolored   1.75 1.75

Gliders — A219

1999, Apr. 13   **Litho.**   **Perf. 13**
933 A219 $1.60 Zögling, 1928   .80   .80
934 A219 $1.80 Schleicher, 1998 1.00 1.00

Souvenir Sheet

IBRA '99, Nuremberg,
Germany — A220

1999, Apr. 27   Litho.   Perf. 14x14¼
935 A220 $5.50 multi   1.75 1.75

Falcons
A221

60c, Greater kestrel. $1.60, Rock kestrel.
$1.80, Red-necked falcon. $2.65, Lanner
falcon.

1999, May 18 Litho. Perf. 13¼x13½
936 A221 60c multicolored   .75   .40
937 A221 $1.20 multicolored   1.20   .90
938 A221 $1.80 multicolored   1.20 1.00
939 A221 $2.65 multicolored   1.90 2.00
      Nos. 936-939 (4)   5.05 4.30

Souvenir Sheet

Termitomyces Schimperi — A222

1999, June 19   Litho.   Perf. 13¾
940 A222 $5.50 multicolored   2.10 2.10

PhilexFrance '99 World Philatelic Exhibition.

Wetland
Birds — A223

Designs: $1.60, Wattled crane. $1.80, Burchell's sand grouse. $1.90, Rock pratincole.
$2.65, Eastern white pelican.

1999, June 28   Perf. 12¾
941 A223 $1.60 multicolored   .75   .60
942 A223 $1.80 multicolored   .90   .75
943 A223 $1.90 multicolored   1.20 1.00
944 A223 $2.65 multicolored   1.60 1.60
      Nos. 941-944 (4)   4.45 3.95

Orchids
A224

Designs: $1.60, Eulophia hereroensis.
$1.80, Ansellia africana. $2.65, Eulophia
leachii. $3.90, Eulophia speciosa.
$5.50, Eulophia walleri.

Litho. & Embossed
1999, Aug. 21   Perf. 12¾
945 A224 $1.60 multicolored   .65   .55
946 A224 $1.80 multicolored   .75   .65
947 A224 $2.65 multicolored   1.25 1.25
948 A224 $3.90 multicolored   1.60 1.60
      Nos. 945-948 (4)   4.25 4.05

Souvenir Sheet
949 A224 $5.50 multicolored   2.50 2.50

Embossing is found only on the margin of
No. 949. China 1999 World Philatelic Exhibition (No. 949).

**Owl Type of 1998
Souvenir Sheet**

1999, Sept. 30   Litho.
950 A204 $11 Like #902   5.00 5.00

Selection of stamp design as "most beautiful," 5th Stamp World Cup.

Urieta Kazahendike
(Johanna Gertze)
(1836-1935) — A225

1999, Oct. 1   Litho.   Perf. 12¾
951 A225 $20 multicolored   5.00 5.00

Souvenir Sheet

Turn of the Millennium — A226

Perf. 13¾x13¼
1999, Dec. 31   Litho.
952 A226 $9 multi   3.50 3.50

No. 952 has a holographic image. Soaking
in water may affect the hologram.

Sunset
Over
Namibia
A227

1999-2000   Perf. 13¼x13¾
953 A227 $2.20 shown   1.25 1.25
954 A227 $2.40 Sunrise   1.40 1.40

Issued: $2.20, 12/31; $2.40, 1/1/00.

Ducks — A228

Designs: $2, South African shelduck. $2.40,
Whitefaced duck. $3, Knobbilled duck. $7,
Cape shoveller.

2000, Feb. 18   Litho.   Perf. 13
955 A228 $2 multi   1.10 1.10
956 A228 $2.40 multi   1.25 1.25
957 A228 $3 multi   1.50 1.50
958 A228 $7 multi   3.25 3.25
      Nos. 955-958 (4)   7.10 7.10

Nos. 853-856
Surcharged

2000, Mar. 1   Litho.   Perf. 13½
959 A189 (65c) on 5c multi   .40   .40
960 A189 $1.80 on 30c multi   .90   .90
961 A189 $3 on 10c multi   1.50 1.50
962 A189 $6 on 20c multi   3.00 3.00
      Nos. 959-962 (4)   5.80 5.80

See No. 1000.

Independence,
10th
Anniv. — A229

2000, Mar. 21   Perf. 13¼x13¾
963 A229 65c Children   .75   .40
964 A229 $3 Flag   2.00 2.00

Passion
Play — A230

Designs: $2.10, Jesus with crown of thorns.
$2.40, Carrying cross.

2000, Apr. 1   Perf. 13¾
965 A230 $2.10 multi   .75   .75
966 A230 $2.40 multi   .85   .85

Fauna of
the
Namib
Desert
A231

Designs: a, $2, Tenebrionid beetle. b, $2
Brown hyena. c, $2, Namib golden mole. d, $2,
Shovel-snouted lizard. e, $2, Dune lark. f, $6,
Namib side-winding adder.

2000, May 22   Perf. 14½
967 A231 Sheet of 6, #a-f   9.00 9.00

The Stamp Show 2000, London.
Sizes of stamps: Nos. 967a-967c,
30x25mm; No. 967d, 30x50mm; Nos. 967e-
967f, 26x37mm. Portions of the design were
applied by a thermographic process, producing a shiny raised effect.

Welwitschia
Mirabilis — A232

Various views of Welwitschia plants.
Denominations: (65c), $2.20, $3, $4.

2000, June 21   Litho.   Perf. 13¾
968-971 A232 Set of 4   4.50 4.50

No. 968 is inscribed "Standard inland mail."

Souvenir Sheet

High Energy Stereoscopic Sytem
Telescopes — A233

2000, July 7   Perf. 13¼x13¾
972 A233 $11 multi   6.25 6.25

Fruit
Trees
A234

Designs: (65c), Jackalberry. $2, Sycamore
fig. $2.20, Bird plum. $7, Marula.

2000, Aug. 16 Litho. Perf. 13¼x14
973-976 A234 Set of 4   6.25 6.25

No. 973 is inscribed "Standard inland mail."

Souvenir Sheet

Yoka in
Etosha
A235

2000, Sept. 1   Perf. 13¼x13
977 A235 $11 multi   5.50 5.50

Coelenterates — A236

Designs: ($1), Anthothoe stimpsoni. $2.45,
Bundosoma capensis. $3.50, Anthopleura
stephensoni. $6.60, Pseudactinia flagellifera.

2001, Apr. 18   Litho.   Perf. 13¾
978-981 A236 Set of 4   5.50 5.50

No. 978 is inscribed "Standard inland mail."

Civil
Aviation — A237

Designs: ($1), Cessna 210 Turbo. $2.20,
Douglas DC-6B. $2.50, Pitts 52A. $13.20, Bell
407 helicopter.

2001, May 9   Perf. 13¼x13¾
982-985 A237 Set of 4   10.00 10.00

No. 982 is inscribed "Standard inland mail."

Renewable Energy Resources — A238

No. 986: a, Wood efficient stove. b, Biogas
digester. c, Solar cooker. d, Repair, reuse,
recycle. e, Solar water pump. f, Solar home
system. g, Solar street light. h, Solar water
heater. i, Solar telecommunication. j, Wind
water pump.

2001, Aug. 15   Perf. 13½x14
986   A238 Sheet of 10   10.00 10.00
 a.-e. ($1) Any single   .40   .40
 f.-j. $3.50 Any single   1.10 1.10

Nos. 986a-986e are inscribed "Standard
Mail."

Central Highlands Flora and
Fauna — A239

No. 987: a, ($1.00), Ruppell's parrot
(31x29mm). b, $3.50, Camel thorn
(54x29mm). c, ($1.00), Flap-necked chame-
leon (39x29mm). d, ($1.00), Klipspringer
(39x29mm). e, $3.50, Berg aloe (39x29mm). f,
$3.50, Kudu (39x39mm). g, ($1.00), Rockrunner (39x29mm). h, $3.50, Namibian rock
agama (39x39mm). i, ($1.00), Pangolin
(39x39mm). j, $3.50, Armored ground cricket
(39x29mm).

2001, Sept. 5   Perf. 12½x12¾
987 A239 Sheet of 10, #a-j   12.50 12.50

Nos. 987a, 987c, 987d, 987g, 987i are
inscribed "Standard Mail."

Tribal
Women
A240

No. 988, ($1.30): a, Mbalantu. b, Damara. c, Herero (leather headdress). d, San. e, Mafue. f, Baster.

No. 989, ($1.30): a, Mbukushu. b, Herero (flowered headdress). c, Himba. d, Kwanyama. e, Nama. f, Ngandjera/Kwaluudhi.

2002, Apr. 20   Litho.   Perf. 13¼x13
Sheets of 6, #a-f
988-989 A240   Set of 2   9.00 9.00
988g   Sheet of 6 with incorrect
          back inscriptions   10.00 10.00
989g   Sheet of 6 with incorrect
          back inscriptions   15.00 15.00

Stamps are inscribed "Standard Mail."
The back inscriptions on Nos. 988g and 989g are placed incorrectly so that the inscriptions for the stamps on the left side of the sheet have the back inscriptions of the stamps on the right side of the sheet, and vice versa.
The Mbukushu stamp on No. 989g reads "Standard Maiil."

Birds — A241

Designs: ($1.30), African hoopoe. $2.20, Paradise flycatchers. $2.60, Swallowtailed bee-eaters. $2.80, Malachite kingfisher.

2002, May 15   Perf. 13¾x13¼
990-993 A241   Set of 4   7.00 7.00

No. 990 is inscribed "Standard Mail."

Ephemeral
Rivers — A242

Designs: ($1.30), Kuiseb River floods halting movement of sand dunes, vert. (36x48mm). $2.20, Bird flying over lake of Tsauchab River flood water. $2.60, Elephants in dry bed of Hoarusib River (86x22mm). $2.80, Birds near Nossob River flood water. $3.50, Birds near Fish River, vert. (55x21mm).

2002, July 1   Perf. 13x13¼, 13¼x13
994-998 A242   Set of 5   8.00 8.00
          See No. 1023.

Namibia Post and
Telecommunications, 10th
Anniv. — A243

No. 999: a, Telephone, blue background. b, Telephone, yellow background. c, Telephone, green background. d, Telephone, lilac background. e, Picturephone, brown background. f, Mail van. g, Pillar box and letter. h, Computer. i, Dolphin with letter. j, Airplane and letters.

2002, Aug. 1   Litho.   Perf. 13¼x13
999 A243 ($1.30) Sheet of 10,
          #a-j   6.00 6.00
   k.   Sheet of 10, 2 each #a-e 6.00 6.00
   l.   Sheet of 10, 2 each #f-j 6.00 6.00

Stamps are inscribed "Standard Mail."

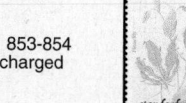

Nos. 853-854
Surcharged

2002, Oct. 21   Litho.   Perf. 13½
1000 A189 ($1.45) on 5c #853   .75 .75
1001 A189 ($1.45) on 10c #854   .75 .75

Surcharge on No. 1000 has letters that lean more to the right than those on No. 959. The two "d's" have tops that curve to the right on No. 1000, but have serifs that point left on No. 959. The cross line of the "t's" are lower on No. 1000 than on No. 959.

Prevention of
AIDS — A244

Designs: ($1.45), Cross. $2.45, Condom. $2.85, Man and hand. $11.50, Test tubes.

2002, Dec. 1   Perf. 13½x13
1002-1005 A244   Set of 4   7.00 7.00

No. 1002 is inscribed "Standard Mail."

Recent Biological
Discoveries — A245

Designs: $1.10, Sulphur bacteria. $2.45, Whiteheadia etesionamibensis. $2.85, Cunene flathead (catfish), horiz. $3.85, Zebra racer, horiz. $20, Gladiator (insect).

Perf. 13¾x13¼, 13¼x13¾
2003, Feb. 24
1006-1010 A245   Set of 5   8.25 8.25

Rural Development — A246

Designs: $1.45, Water and electricity supply. ($2.75), Conservancy formation and land use diversification. $4.40, Education and health services. ($11.50), Communication and road infrastructure.

2003, Apr. 17   Litho.   Perf. 13¼x13¾
1011-1014 A246   Set of 4   6.00 6.00

No. 1012 is inscribed "Postcard Rate" and No. 1014 is inscribed "Registered Mail."

Wetlands
A247

Designs: $1.10, Women and cattle near oshana. $2.85, Birds at Omadhiya Lakes. ($3.85), Cuvelai Drainage.

2003, June 6
1015-1017 A247   Set of 3   5.75 5.75

No. 1017 is inscribed "Non-Standard Mail."

Heroes Acre
Monuments
A248

Various monuments with inscriptions: ($1.45), Standard Mail. ($2.75), Postcard Rate. ($3.85), Non-Standard Mail.

2003, Aug. 27   Perf. 13¼
1018-1020 A248   Set of 3   4.25 4.25

Souvenir Sheet

Geological Surveying in Namibia,
Cent. — A249

2003, Sept. 10   Perf. 13¼x13¾
1021 A249 $10 multi   8.25 8.25

Souvenir Sheet

Windhoek Philatelic Society, 25th
Anniv. — A250

2003, Sept. 10
1022 A250 $10 multi   5.00 5.00

Ephemeral Rivers Type of 2002
Souvenir Sheet
2003, Dec. 8   Perf. 13¼x13
1023 A242 $3.15 Like #996   4.00 4.00

Design voted "most beautiful stamp" at 8th Stamp World Cup, Paris.

Vervet Monkeys — A251

Designs: $1.60, Adult holding fruit. $3.15, Two monkeys on tree branches. $3.40, Adult and young. ($14.25), Adult chewing on twig. $4.85, Like #1024.

2004, Jan. 30   Perf. 13
1024-1027 A251   Set of 4   8.75 8.75
Souvenir Sheet
1028 A251 $4.85 multi   3.00 3.00

No. 1027 is inscribed "Inland Registered Mail Paid." 2004 Hong Kong Stamp Expo (#1028).

Honeybees on
Flowers — A252

Honeybees on: ($1.60), Sickle bush. $2.70, Daisy. ($3.05), Aloe. $3.15, Cat's claw. ($14.25), Edging senecio. $4.85, Pretty lady.

2004, Feb. 2   Perf. 13x13¼
1029-1033 A252   Set of 5   7.75 7.75
Souvenir Sheet
1034 A252 $4.85 multi   2.75 2.75

No. 1029 is inscribed "Standard mail;" No. 1031, "Post card rate;" No. 1033, "Inland registered mail paid."

Anti-Colonial
Resistance,
Cent. — A253

2004, Mar. 23   Litho.   Perf. 13¼
1035 A253 ($1.60) multi   1.40 1.40
Souvenir Sheet
1036 A253 $5 multi   2.25 2.25

No. 1035 is inscribed "Standard Mail."

Education in
Namibia
A254

Designs: $1.60, Pre-school education enhances individual development potential. $2.75, Primary and secondary school education for all lays the foundation for equal opportunity. $4.40, Advanced learning and vocational training provide career options. ($12.65), Lifelong learning encourages personal growth and the capacity for leadership.

2004, Apr. 19   Perf. 13¼x13¾
1037-1040 A254   Set of 4   6.75 6.75

No. 1040 is inscribed "Registered Mail."

Fishing
Industry
A255

Fish and: $1.60, Ship and dockworkers. $2.75, Ship. $4.85, Workers at processing plant.

Perf. 13¼x13¾
2004, June 22   Litho.
1041-1043 A255   Set of 3   6.00 6.00

Historic Buildings
in
Bethanie — A256

Designs: ($1.60), Joseph Ferdericks House.
($3.05), Schmelen House. ($4.40), Rhenish
Mission Church. ($12.65), Stone Church.

2004, July 7   **Perf. 14x13½**
1044-1047 A256   Set of 4   8.25 8.25

No. 1044 is inscribed "Standard Mail;" No.
1045, "Postcard rate;" No. 1046, "Non-Standard Mail," No. 1047, "Registered Mail."

2004 Summer
Olympics,
Athens — A257

Designs: ($1.60), Wrestling. $2.90, Boxing,
vert. $3.40, Pistol shooting. $3.70, Mountain
biking, vert.

Perf. 14x13¼, 13¼x14
2004, Aug. 3   **Litho.**
1048-1051 A257   Set of 4   8.75 8.75
1051a Inscribed "XXVIII Olympiad"   5.00 5.00

No. 1048 is inscribed "Standard Mail."
No. 1051 has incorrect inscription "XVIII
Olympiad."
No. 1051a issued 9/14.

Miniature Sheet

Birds
A258

No. 1052: a, African fish eagles, national
bird of Namibia. b, African fish eagles, national
bird of Zimbabwe. c, Peregrine falcons,
national bird of Angola. d, Cattle egrets,
national bird of Botswana. e, Purple-crested
louries, national bird of Swaziland. f, Blue
cranes, national bird of South Africa. g, Bat-
tailed trogons. h, African fish eagles, national
bird of Zambia.

2004, Oct. 11   **Litho.**   **Perf. 14**
1052 A258 $3.40 Sheet of 8,
       #a-h   17.00 17.00

See Botswana Nos. 792-793, South Africa
No. 1342, Swaziland Nos. 727-735, Zambia
No. 1033, and Zimbabwe No. 975.

Rotary International, Cent. — A259

2005, Feb. 23   Litho.   Perf. 13x13¼
1053 A259 $3.70 multi   2.75 2.75

Pres. Hifikepunye
Pohamba — A260

2005, Mar. 21   **Perf. 13¼x14**
1054 A260 ($1.70) multi   2.25 2.25
Inscribed "Standard Mail."

Sunbirds — A261

Designs: $2.90, Marico sunbird. $3.40,
Dusky sunbird. ($4.80), White-bellied sunbird.
($15.40), Scarlet-chested sunbird.
$10, Amethyst sunbird, horiz.

2005, Apr. 14   Litho.   Perf. 13¼x14
1055-1058 A261   Set of 4   11.50 11.50
Souvenir Sheet
Perf. 14x13¼
1059 A261 $10 multi   5.00 5.00

No. 1057 is inscribed "Non-Standard Mail";
No. 1058, "Registered Inland Postage Paid."
Nos. 1055-1058 exists imperf. Value, each
pair $40.

Nos. 855, 859, 861 and 868
Surcharged

a

b

c

2005, June 7   Litho.   Perf. 13½
1060 A189(a) ($1.70) on 50c
                 #859   1.00 1.00
1061 A189(b) $2.90 on 20c
                 #855   5.00 2.00
1062 A189(c) ($4.80) on $4
                 #868   3.50 1.75
1063 A189(b) $5.20 on 90c
                 #861   2.50 1.75
    Nos. 1060-1063 (4)   12.00 6.50

Medicinal
Plants — A262

Designs: ($1.70), Nara. $2.90, Devil's claw.
($3.10), Hoodia. ($4.80), Tsamma.

2005, July 22   **Perf. 14x13¼**
1064-1067 A262   Set of 4   6.00 6.00

No. 1064 is inscribed "Standard Mail"; No.
1066, "Postcard Rate"; No. 1067, "Non-Standard Mail".

Crops — A263

Designs: $2.90, Vegetables. $3.40, Pearl
millet. ($13.70), Corn.

2005, Aug. 2   **Perf. 13¼x13¾**
1068-1070 A263   Set of 3   8.50 8.50

No. 1070 is inscribed "Registered Mail."

Nos. 855, 861, 862, 866, 868-870
Surcharged Type "b" and

d

e

f

g

2005, Aug. 10   Litho.   Perf. 13½
1070A A189(a) ($1.70) on
                 10c
                 #854 200.00 75.00
1071 A189(d) ($1.70) on
                 20c
                 #855   1.75 1.50
1071A A189(a) ($1.70) on
                 20c
                 #855
1072 A189(d) ($1.70) on
                 90c
                 #861   1.90 .75
1073 A189(d) ($1.70) on
                 $1
                 #862   1.50 1.25
1074 A189(b) $2.90 on
                 90c
                 #861   2.00 2.00
1075 A189(e) ($4.80) on
                 $1.50
                 #866   2.00 2.00
1076 A189(b) $5.20 on
                 20c
                 #855   4.00 4.00
1077 A189(f) ($15.40) on
                 $4
                 #868 4.75 4.75
1078 A189(g) ($18.50) on
                 $10
                 #870 8.00 8.00
1079 A189(b) $25 on $5
                 #869 10.00 10.00
1080 A189(b) $50 on $10
                 #870 17.50 17.50
    Nos. 1070A-1080 (11) 253.40 126.75

Gulls — A264

Designs: $3.10, Cape gulls. $4, Hartlaub's
gulls. $5.50, Sabine's gull. ($16.20), Gray-
headed gulls.

2006, Feb. 28   Litho.   Perf. 14x13¼
1081-1084 A264   Set of 4   11.50 11.50

No. 1084 is inscribed "Inland Registered
Mail Paid."

Nos. 1003, 1030,
1042 Surcharged

Methods and Perfs As Before
2006, Apr. 13
1085 A244 $3.10 on $2.45 #1003 1.60 1.25
1086 A252 $3.10 on $2.70 #1030 1.60 1.25
1087 A255 $3.10 on $2.75 #1042 1.60 1.25
    Nos. 1085-1087 (3)   4.80 3.75
Size, location and fonts of surcharges differ.

Dolphins — A265

Designs: ($1.80), Risso's dolphin. $3.10,
Southern right-whale dolphins, vert. $3.70,
Benguela dolphin. $4, Common dolphins.
$5.50, Bottlenose dolphins, vert.

Perf. 13x13¼, 13¼x13
2006, Apr. 26   **Litho.**
1088-1092 A265   Set of 5   8.25 8.25

No. 1088 is inscribed "Standard Mail."

Miniature Sheets

Traditional Roles of Men — A266

No. 1093, ($1.80): a, Father. b, Musician. c,
Carver. d, Shaman. e, Planter. f, Hunter.
No. 1094, ($1.80): a, Leader. b, Blacksmith.
c, Protector. d, Pastoralist. e, Trader. f,
Storyteller.

2006, May 24   **Perf. 13x13¼**
Sheets of 6, #a-f
1093-1094 A266   Set of 2   6.75 6.75

Nos. 862, 865
Surcharged

2006, June 20   Litho.   Perf. 13½
1095 A189 ($3.30) on $1 #862   2.25 1.60
1096 A189 ($3.30) on $1.20 #865 2.25 1.60

Nos. 1095-1096 are inscribed "Postcard
Rate." Location of surcharges differs.

Perennial
Rivers — A267

Designs: $3.10, Orange River. $5.50,
Kumene River, vert. (21x55mm). ($19.90),
Zambezi River (87x22mm).

Perf. 14x13¼, 13½ ($5.50)
2006, July 24
1097-1099 A267   Set of 3   11.50 11.50

No. 1099 is inscribed "Registered Non Standard Mail."

A268

Designs: $3.10, Construction of the rail line.
$3.70, Henschel Class NG15 locomotive No.
41. $5.50, Narrow gauge Class Jung tank
locomotive No. 9.

2006, Aug. 9   **Perf. 14¾x14**
1100-1102 A268   Set of 3   7.00 7.00
Otavi Mines and Railway Company (OMEG)
Rail Line, Cent.

Otjiwarongo,
Cent. — A269

2006, Nov. 17   **Perf. 14**
1103 A269 $1.90 multi   1.40 1.40

Printed in sheets of 10.

Flora and
Fauna — A270

Named species: 5c, Bullfrog. 10c, Mesemb. 30c, Solifuge. 40c, Jewel beetle. 60c, Compass jellyfish. ($1.90), Web-footed gecko. $2, Otjikoto tilapia. No. 1111, $6, Milkbush. No. 1112, ($6), African hawk eagle. $10, Black-faced impala. $25, Lichens. $50, Baobab tree.

2007, Feb. 15   Litho.   Perf. 14x13¼
1104	A270	5c multi	.25	.25
1105	A270	10c multi	.25	.25
1106	A270	30c multi	.25	.25
1107	A270	40c multi	.25	.25
1108	A270	60c multi	.25	.25
1109	A270	($1.90) multi	.65	.35
a.	Perf. 14		.80	.80
1110	A270	$2 multi	.75	.50
1111	A270	$6 multi	2.00	1.00
1112	A270	($6) multi	2.00	1.00
1113	A270	$10 multi	3.25	1.75
1114	A270	$25 multi	7.00	7.00
1115	A270	$50 multi	14.00	14.00
	Nos. 1104-1115 (12)		30.90	26.85

No. 1109 is inscribed "Standard Mail." No. 1112 is inscribed "Non-standard Mail."
See Nos. 1165-1168.

A271

Etosha
National
Park,
Cent.
A272

Designs: ($1.90), Otjovasandu Wilderness Area. $3.40, Okaukuejo Waterhole. ($17.20), Scientist conducting anthrax research.
No. 1119: a, Gabar goshawk (30x30mm). b, Umbrella thorn tree (50x30mm). c, Red-billed queleas (40x30mm). d, Burchell's zebras (40x30mm). e, Elephant (40x30mm). f, Blue wildebeest (40x30mm). g, Mustard tree (40x30mm). h, Black emperor dragonfly (40x40mm). i, Springbok (40x40mm). j, Ground agama (40x40mm).

Litho. With Foil Application
2007, Mar. 22   **Perf. 14x13¼**
1116-1118 A271   Set of 3   11.50 11.50
Miniature Sheet
Litho.
1119 A272 ($2.25) Sheet of
10, #a-j   12.50 12.50

No. 1116 is inscribed "Standard Mail." No. 1118, "Inland Registered Mail Paid"; Nos. 1119a-1119j, "Postcard Rate."

Dragonflies
A273

Designs: ($1.90), Blue emperor dragonfly. $3.90, Rock dropwing dragonfly. ($6), Red-veined dropwing dragonfly. ($6), Jaunty dropwing dragonfly. $6, Blue basker dragonfly.

2007, Apr. 16   Litho.   Perf. 12¾x14
1120-1123 A273   Set of 4   7.00 7.00
Souvenir Sheet
Perf. 14x13¼
1124 A273 $6 multi   3.25 3.25

No. 1120 is inscribed "Standard Mail"; No. 1123, "Non Standard Mail Paid."

Trees — A274

Designs: ($1.90), Commiphora kraeuseliana. $3.40, Commiphora wildii. $3.90, Commiphora glaucescens. ($6), Commiphora dinteri.

2007, July 20   Litho.   Perf. 13¼x13¾
1125-1128 A274   Set of 4   6.75 6.75

No. 1125 is inscribed "Standard Mail"; No. 1128, "Non-standard Mail."

Flowers — A275

Designs: ($1.90), Cheiridopsis carolischmidtii. ($6), Namibia ponderosa. ($17.20), Fenestraria rhopalophylla.

2007, Aug. 31
1129-1131 A275   Set of 3   10.00 10.00

No. 1129 is inscribed "Standard Mail"; No. 1130, "Non-standard Mail"; No. 1131, "Inland Registered Mail Paid."
Nos. 1129-1131 were each printed in sheets of 10 + 5 labels.

Nos. 861, 865, 866 and 868
Surcharged

h   i

j   k

2007, Oct. 1   Litho.   Perf. 13½
1132	A189(h)	($2) on 90c #861	1.00	.65
1133	A189(h)	($2) on $1.20 #865	1.00	.65
1134	A189(h)	($2) on $1.50 #866	1.00	.65
1135	A189(h)	($2) on $4 #868	1.00	.65
1136	A189(i)	$3.70 on $1.20 #865	1.25	1.10
1137	A189(i)	$4.20 on $1.20 #865	1.40	1.25
1138	A189(i)	$4.85 on $1.20 #865	1.60	1.50
1139	A189(j)	($6.50) on $1.20 #865	2.25	2.00
1140	A189(k)	($16.45) on $1.20 #865	7.00	8.00
	Nos. 1132-1140 (9)		17.50	16.45

Location of surcharge varies.

Miniature Sheets

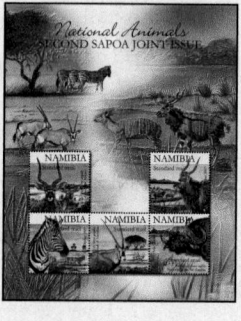

National
Animals
A276

Nos. 1141 and 1142: a, Nyala (Malawi). b, Nyala (Zimbabwe). c, Burchell's zebra (Botswana). d, Oryx (Namibia). e, Buffalo (Zambia).

2007, Oct. 9   Litho.   Perf. 13¾
Granite Paper (#1141)
Country Name in Black
1141 A276 ($2) Sheet of 5, #a-e   4.50 4.50
Litho. With Foil Application
Country Name in Silver
1142 A276 ($2) Sheet of 5, #a-e   5.00 5.00

Nos. 1141a-1141e, 1142a-1142e are inscribed "Standard Mail."
See No. 1193A, Botswana No. 838, Malawi No. 752, Zambia Nos. 1097-1101, Zimbabwe Nos. 1064-1068.

Weaver
Birds — A277

Designs: ($2), Southern masked weaver. $3.70, Red-headed weaver. ($3.90), White-browed sparrow weaver. $4.20, Sociable weaver. ($18.45), Thick-billed weaver.

2008, Feb. 28   Litho.   Perf. 13½x14
1143-1147 A277   Set of 5   11.00 11.00

No. 1143 is inscribed "Standard Mail"; No. 1145, "Postcard Rate"; No. 1147, "Inland Registered Mail Paid."

Euphorbia
Flowers — A278

Designs: ($3.90), Euphorbia virosa. $6.45, Euphorbia dregeana. ($22.95), Euphorbia damarana.
$6.45 — Type I: "E" over "I" in Latin inscription. Type II: Corrected version, no "I".

2008
1148	A278	($3.90) multi	1.10	.60
1149	A278	$6.45 multi, Type I	1.50	1.50
a.	Type II		2.25	2.25
1150	A278	($22.95) multi	5.75	5.75
	Nos. 1148-1150 (3)		8.35	7.85

Issued: Nos. 1148-1150, 3/3; No. 1149a, 5/27. No. 1148 inscribed "Postcard Rate"; No. 1150, "Registered Non-Standard Mail."

Miniature Sheet

Discovery of Diamonds in Namibia,
Cent. — A279

No. 1151: a, Uncut diamonds. b, Land mining. c, Marine mining. d, Diamond jewelry.

Litho. With Foil Application
2008, Apr. 15   **Perf. 14x13½**
1151 A279 $2 Sheet of 4, #a-d   4.75 4.75

Miniature Sheet

Traditional Houses — A280

No. 1152: a, Herero. b, Kavango. c, Owambo. d, Nama. e, Caprivi. f, San.

2008, May 27   **Litho.**
1152 A280 ($2.20) Sheet of 6, #a-f   4.00 4.00

Nos. 1152a-1152f are each inscribed "Standard Mail."

Twyfelfontein
UNESCO World
Heritage Site — A281

Rock drawings: No. 1153, ($7.20), 1156a ($2.20), Lion man. No. 1154, ($7.20), No. 1156b ($2.20), Giraffe, Dancing kudu. No. 1155, ($7.20), No. 1156c ($2.20), Elephant.

2008, June 27   **Perf. 13½x13¾**
1153-1155 A281   Set of 3   6.75 6.75
Souvenir Sheet
1156 A281 ($2.20) Sheet of 3, #a-c   2.75 2.75

Nos. 1153-1155 are each inscribed "Non-Standard Mail"; Nos. 1156a-1156c, "Standard Mail."

Ediacaran
Fossils — A282

Designs: ($2), Rangea. ($3.90), Swartpuntia. ($18.45), Pteridinium. ($22.95), Ernietta.

Litho. & Embossed
2008, Aug. 8   **Perf. 13¼x14**
1157-1160 A282   Set of 4   12.50 12.50

No. 1157 is inscribed "Standard Mail"; No. 1158, "Postcard Rate"; No. 1159, "Registered Non-standard Mail"; No. 1160, "Registered Inland Mail Paid."

2008 Summer
Olympics,
Beijing — A283

Designs: $2, Female runner, sun and Earth. $3.70, Athlete with arms raised. $3.90, Athlete at finish line. $4.20, Female runner with arms extended.

2008, Aug. 15   Litho.   Perf. 13¼x13
1161-1164 A283   Set of 4   3.75 3.75

Flora and Fauna Type of 2007

Designs: $4.10, Thimble grass. $4.60, Bronze whaler shark. $5.30, Deep sea red crab. ($18.20), False ink cap mushroom.

2008, Oct. 1   Litho.   Perf. 14x13¼
1165	A270	$4.10 multi	1.00	.80
1166	A270	$4.60 multi	1.10	.90
1167	A270	$5.30 multi	1.40	1.25
1168	A270	($18.20) multi	4.75	4.00
	Nos. 1165-1168 (4)		8.25	6.95

No. 1168 is inscribed "Registered Mail."

Eagles
A284

Designs: $4.10, Martial eagle. ($4.30), Bataleur eagle. $4.60, Verreaux's eagle. ($25.40), Tawny eagle.

2009, Feb. 2   Litho.   Perf. 13¼x13¾
1169-1172 A284   Set of 4   12.00 12.00

No. 1170 is inscribed "Postcard Rate." No. 1172, "Registered Non-Standard Mail." Nos. 1169-1172 exists imperf. Value, each $90.

New Year 2009
(Year of the
Ox) — A285

Litho. With Foil Application
2009, Apr. 10   Perf. 14x13¼
1173 A285 $2.20 multi   1.50 1.50

Miniature Sheet

Flora and Fauna of the
Brandberg — A286

No. 1174: a, Augur buzzard (30x30mm). b, Numasfels Peak (50x30mm). c, Quiver tree (40x30mm). d, CMR beetle (40x30mm). e, Leopard (40x30mm). f, Kobas (40x30mm). g, Bokmakiri (40x30mm). h, Jameson's red rock rabbit (40x40mm). i, Brandberg halfmens (40x40mm). j, Jordan's girdled lizard (40x40mm).

2009, Apr. 10   Litho.   Perf. 14x13¼
1174 A286 ($4.30)   Sheet of 10, #a-j   5.00 5.00

Nos. 1174a-1174j are each inscribed "Post-card Rate."

Souvenir Sheet

First Crossing of Africa by Automobile,
Cent. — A287

2009, May 1   Perf. 13¾x14¼
1175 A287 $7.10 multi   2.50 2.50

Wild
Horses
A288

Designs: $5.30, Two horses. $8, Three horses. ($20.40), Four horses.

2009, July 3   Perf. 13¾x14
1176-1178 A288   Set of 3   9.50 9.50

No. 1178 is inscribed "Inland Registered Mail Paid." See Nos. 1185, 1340-1342.

Souvenir Sheet

German
Higher
Private
School,
Cent.
A289

2009, Aug. 21   Litho.   Perf. 13½
1179 A289 $4.60 multi   2.00 2.00

Geckos — A290

Designs: $4.40, Festive gecko. $5, Koch's barking gecko. $6, Giant ground gecko. $7.70, Velvety thick-toed gecko. ($18.20), Bradfield's Namib day gecko.

2009, Sept. 30   Perf. 13¾
1180-1184 A290   Set of 5   11.00 11.00

No. 1184 is inscribed "Registered Mail."

Horses Type of 2009

Design: Four horses in desert.

2009, Nov. 2   Perf. 13¾x14
1185 A288 ($4.60) multi   6.00 6.00

No. 1185 is inscribed "Postcard Rate."

Miniature Sheet

Endangered Species — A291

No. 1186: a, Wattled crane. b, Gazania thermalis. c, Leatherback turtle. d, Giant quiver tree. e, Cape vulture. f, White Namib toktokkie. g, Cheetah. h, Hook-lipped rhinoceros. i, wild dog. j, Nama-padloper tortoise.

2010, Feb. 8   Perf. 13¼x13
1186 A291 ($4.60)   Sheet of 10, #a-j   25.00 25.00

Nos. 1186a-1186j are inscribed "Postcard Rate."

Independence, 20th Anniv. — A292

Perf. 13¼x13¾
2010, Mar. 21   Litho.
1187 A292 ($2.50) multi   1.00 .80

No. 1187 is inscribed "Standard mail."

Miniature Sheet

2010 World Cup Soccer
Championships, South Africa — A293

No. 1188 — Soccer players, ball, 2010 World Cup mascot and flag of: a, Namibia. b, South Africa. c, Zimbabwe. d, Malawi. e, Swaziland. f, Botswana. g, Mauritius. h, Lesotho. i, Zambia.

2010, Apr. 9   Litho.   Perf. 13½
1188 A293 ($4.60)   Sheet of 9, #a-i   14.00 14.00

Nos. 1188a-1188i are inscribed "Postcard rate." A miniature sheet containing No. 1188a and stamps from South Africa, Zimbabwe, Malawi, Swaziland, Botswana, Mauritius, Lesotho and Zambia was sold by Namibia Post for $40. The sheet apparently was not sold by any other country. See Botswana Nos. 896-905, Lesotho No. , Malawi No. 753, Mauritius No. 1086, South Africa No. 1403, Swaziland Nos. 794-803, Zambia Nos. 1115-1118, and Zimbabwe Nos. 1112-1121.

Miniature Sheet

Birds
A294

No. 1189: a, Northern black korhaan. b, Red-crested korhaan. c, Black-bellied bustard. d, Rüppell's korhaan. e, Ludwig's bustard. f, Kori bustard.

2010, Apr. 14   Perf. 13½x14
1189 A294 ($4.60)   Sheet of 6, #a-f   12.00 12.00

Nos. 1189a-1189f are inscribed "Postcard rate."

Lighthouses — A295

Designs: $4.40, Swakopmund Lighthouse. ($9.50), Diaz Point Lighthouse, Lüderitzbucht. ($18.20), Pelican Point Lighthouse, Walvis Bay.

2010, June 18   Perf. 13½x13¾
1190-1192 A295   Set of 3   10.00 10.00

No. 1191 is inscribed "Non-standard mail." No. 1192 is inscribed "Registered Mail."

Souvenir Sheet

Christuskirche, Windhoek,
Cent. — A296

2010, Aug. 6   Perf. 14
1193 A296 $5 multi   1.75 1.75

Oryx — A296a

2010, Sept. 18   Perf. 13¾
1193A A296a ($2.50) multi   4.00 4.00

No. 1193A was printed in sheets of 5 that sold for $25. The lower half of the stamp, as shown, is a generic image that could be personalized.
See No. 1141d for similarity.

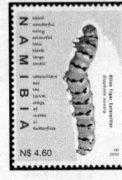

Caterpillars — A297

Designs: $4.60, Olive tiger caterpillar. $5.30, African armyworm. $6.40, Wild silk caterpillar. ($29.40), Mopane caterpillar.

2010, Oct. 1   Litho.
1194-1197 A297   Set of 4   15.00 15.00

Souvenir Sheet

World Standards Day — A298

2010, Oct. 18   Perf. 14x13½
1198 A298 $5.30 multi   1.75 1.75

Wildlife — A299

Designs: $4.60, Leopard. ($5), African elephant, vert. $5.30, Black rhinoceros. $6.40, African buffalo. ($8.50), Lion, vert.

2011, Jan. 28   Perf. 14x13¼, 13¼x14
1199-1203 A299   Set of 5   10.00 10.00

No. 1200 is inscribed "Postcard Rate." No. 1203 is inscribed "Non-standard Mail." Nos. 1199-1203 exists imperf. Value, each $65.

Miniature Sheet

Frogs
A300

No. 1204: a, Long reed frog. b, Bubbling kassina. c, Tandy's sand frog. d, Angolan reed frog.

2011, Mar. 23   Perf. 13¼x14
1204 A300 ($5)   Sheet of 4, #a-d   7.00 7.00

Nos. 1204a-1204d each were inscribed "Postcard Rate."

Souvenir Sheet

Road Safety Campaign — A301

2011, May 11   *Perf. 13x13¼*
1205 A301 $5.30 multi   8.00 8.00

Miniature Sheet

Endangered Marine Life — A302

No. 1206: a, Cape gannet (30x30mm). b, Atlantic yellow-nosed albatross (50x30mm). c, African penguin (40x30mm). d, Southern right whale (40x30mm). e, Bank cormorant (40x30mm). f, West coast steenbras (40x30mm). g, Split-fan kelp (40x40mm). h, Cape rock lobster (40x40mm).

2011, May 16   *Perf. 14x13¼*
1206 A302 $4.60 Sheet of 8,
    #a-h   12.00 12.00
    Exists imperf. Value, $220.

Personalized
Stamps — A303

Designs: No. 1207, Oryx. elephant and leopard, Etosha National Park. No. 1208, Lizard and rock paintings, Twyfelfontein UNESCO World Heritage Site. No. 1209, Bird over Fish River Canyon. No. 1210, Antelope, Sossusvlei Region. No. 1211, Rhinoceros in Community Conservation Area.

2011, June 7   *Perf. 13¼x13*
1207 A303 ($5) multi + label   2.50 2.50
1208 A303 ($5) multi + label   2.50 2.50
1209 A303 ($5) multi + label   2.50 2.50
1210 A303 ($5) multi + label   2.50 2.50
1211 A303 ($5) multi + label   2.50 2.50
   a.   Sheet of 5, #1207-1211, + 5
     labels   12.50 12.50
    Nos. 1207-1211 (5)   12.50 12.50

Nos. 1207-1211, each inscribed "Postcard rate," were printed in sheets of 5 stamps + 5 labels that could be personalized. Label shown is a generic image. Sheets of 5, including No. 1211a, each sold for $35.

Aloes — A304

Designs: ($5), Aloe gariepensis. ($8.50), Aloe variegata. ($20.90), Aloe striata ssp. karasbergensis.

2011, June 21   *Perf. 13¼x14*
1212-1214 A304   Set of 3   10.00 10.00

No. 1212 is inscribed "Postcard Rate." No. 1213 is inscribed "Non Standard Mail." No. 1214 is inscribed "Registered Mail."

Grebes — A305

Designs: No. 1215, ($2.70), Little grebe. No. 1216, ($2.70), Great crested grebe. ($23.60), Black-necked grebe, horiz.

2011, July 18   *Perf. 13¼x14, 14x13¼*
1215-1217 A305   Set of 3   8.50 8.50

Nos. 1215-1216 are each inscribed "Standard Mail." No. 1217 is inscribed "Inland Registered Mail." Nos. 1215-1217 exists imperf. Value, each $90.

Grasses
A306

Designs: ($2.70), Natal red top. $4.80, Feather-top chloris. $5.40, Urochloa brachyura. $6.50, Nine-awned grass. ($8.50), Foxtail buffalo grass.

2011, Sept. 30   *Litho.*   *Perf. 13½x14*
1218-1222 A306   Set of 5   8.00 8.00

No. 1218 is inscribed "Standard mail"; No. 1222, "Non-standard mail."

Birds — A308

Designs: 5c, Carp's tit. 10c, Hartlaub's spurfowl. 20c, Herero chat.30c, Rüppell's parrot. 50c, Rüppell's korhaan. ($2.90), White-tailed shrike. $5, Rockrunner. ($5.30), Dune lark. ($8.90), Damara hornbill. $20, Damara tern. ($21.90), Violet wood hoopoe. $100, Bare-cheeked babbler.

2012, Feb. 15   *Litho.*   *Perf. 13¼*
1224 A308   5c multi   .25 .25
1225 A308   10c multi   .25 .25
1226 A308   20c multi   .25 .25
1227 A308   30c multi   .25 .25
1228 A308   50c multi   .25 .25
1229 A308   ($2.90) multi   .80 .80
1230 A308 $5 multi   1.50 1.50
1231 A308   ($5.30) multi   1.75 1.75
1232 A308   ($8.90) multi   3.00 3.00
1233 A308 $20 multi   5.00 5.00
1234 A308   ($21.90) multi   5.75 5.75
1235 A308 $100 multi   25.00 25.00
    Nos. 1224-1235 (12)   44.05 44.05

No. 1229 is inscribed "Standard mail"; No. 1231, "Postcard rate"; No. 1232, "Non-standard mail"; No. 1234, "Registered mail." No. 1235 exists imperf. Vlaue, $105.
See Nos. 1254-1258.

Bats — A309

Designs: No. 1236, ($5.30), Straw-colored fruit bats. No. 1237, ($5.30), Egyptian slit-faced bats. No. 1238, ($5.30), Angolan epauletted fruit bats.

2012, Apr. 9   *Perf. 13¼*
Stamps + Labels
1236-1238 A309   Set of 3   6.00 6.00

Nos. 1236-1238 are inscribed "Postcard rate."

2012 Summer
Olympics and
Paralympics,
London — A310

Designs: $2.90, Shooting. $4.80, Running, vert. $5.40, Cycling. $6.50, Wheelchair racer, vert.

2012, Apr. 16   *Perf. 13x13¼, 13¼x13*
1239-1242 A310   Set of 4   6.50 6.50

Scorpions
A311

Designs: $4.80, Parabuthus villosus. ($5.30), Parabuthus namibensis. $5.40, Opistophthalmus carinatus. $6.50, Hottentotta arenaceus.

2012, June 11   *Perf. 14x13¾*
1243-1246 A311   Set of 4   8.00 8.00

Souvenir Sheets

Telecom
Namibia,
20th
Anniv.
A312

Nampost, 20th Anniv. — A313

No. 1247: a, Satellite dishes. b, Fiber-optic cable strands.
No. 1248: a, Postman in bush. b, Mail truck.

2012, July 31   *Perf. 12½*
1247 A312 $2.90 Sheet of 2, #a-
    b   2.00 2.00
1248 A313 $2.90 Sheet of 2, #a-
    b   2.00 2.00

Souvenir Sheet

Gobabeb Research and Training
Center, 50th Anniv. — A314

No. 1249: a, ($3.10), Namaqua chameleon. b, $5.10, Dune grass. c, $5.80, Flying saucer beetle.

2012, Sept. 22   *Perf. 13¼x14*
1249 A314   Sheet of 3, #a-c   5.00 5.00

No. 1249a is inscribed "Standard Mail."

Mongooses — A315

Designs: $5.10, Black mongoose. ($5.60), Yellow mongoose, vert. $5.80, Banded mongoose. $6.90, Dwarf mongoose.

Perf. 14¾x14¼, 14¼x14¾
2012, Oct. 1
1250-1253 A315   Set of 4   8.00 8.00

No. 1251 is inscribed "Postcard Rate."

Birds Type of 2012

Designs: 90c, Benguela long-billed lark. $1, Barlow's lark. $3, Rosy-faced lovebirds. $10, Gray's larks. $12, Monteiro's hornbill.

2013, Mar. 1   *Perf. 13¼*
1254 A308   90c multi   .30 .30
1255 A308 $1 multi   .30 .30
1256 A308 $3 multi   1.10 1.10
1257 A308 $10 multi   3.50 3.50
1258 A308 $12 multi   4.00 4.00
    Nos. 1254-1258 (5)   6.15 6.15

Beetles — A316

Designs: ($3.10), Glittering jewel beetle. $5.10, Red-spotted lily weevil. $5.50, Garden fruit chafer. $6.90, Lunate ladybird. ($26.50), Two-spotted ground beetle.

2013, Apr. 5   Set of 5   14.00 14.00
1259-1263 A316

No. 1259 is inscribed "Standard mail;" No. 1263, "Inland registered mail."

Miniature Sheets

Children
A317

No. 1264, ($3.10) — Inscriptions: a, Right to family, shelter & a healthy environment. b, Faith & joy. c, Right to health, nutrition & safety. d, Freedom from neglect, fear, abuse & violence. e, Love & trust. f, Freedom of identity, traditions & beliefs.

No. 1265, ($3.10) — Inscriptions: a, Right to early development support, education & information. b, Aspirations & dreams. c, Right to special care & support. d, Freedom of expression, association & participation. e, Play & creativity. f, Freedom from discrimination & exploitation.

2013, June 17   *Litho.*   *Perf. 13x13¼*
Sheets of 6, #a-f
1264-1265 A317   Set of 2   15.00 15.00

Nos. 1264a-1264f and 1265a-1265f are each inscribed "Standard mail."

Souvenir Sheet

Environmental Education — A318

2013, June 20   *Litho.*   *Perf. 13¼x13*
1266 A318 $5.10 multi   1.75 1.75

Souvenir Sheet

Man and
Woman
Riding in
Donkey
Cart
A319

2013, July 12   *Litho.*   *Perf. 13x13¼*
1267 A319 $5.80 multi   1.75 1.75

NAMIBIA

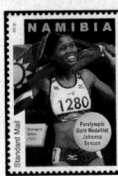

Johanna Benson, Gold
Medalist at 2012
Paralympics — A320

2013, Aug. 21   Litho.   Perf. 13¼x13
1268 A320 ($3.10) multi   1.00 1.00
1269 A320 ($6) multi + label   2.75 2.75
No. 1268 is inscribed "Standard mail" and
was printed in sheets of 10.
No. 1269 is inscribed "Postcard rate" and
was printed in sheets that sold for $40 contain-
ing 5 stamps + 5 labels that could be
personalized.

Antelopes
A321

Designs: $5.40, Elands. No. 1271, ($6),
Greater kudus. No. 1272, ($6), Gemsboks.
$6.20, Sables. $7.30, Blue wildebeests.

2013, Sept. 30   Litho.   Perf. 12½
1270-1274 A321   Set of 5   9.00 9.00
Nos. 1271 and 1272 are both inscribed
"Postcard Rate."

Wooden
Vessels — A322

Designs: ($3.30), HaMbukushu. $5.40,
BaSubiya. ($6), Naman. $6.20, AaWambo.
$7.30, OvaHerero.

2014, Feb. 10   Litho.   Perf. 14x13¼
1275-1279 A322   Set of 5   8.50 8.50
No. 1275 is inscribed "Standard Mail;" No.
1277; "Postcard Rate."

Miniature Sheet

Nocturnal Animals — A323

No. 1280: a, Southern lesser galago. b,
Cape porcupine. c, Small-spotted genet. d,
Ground pangolin. e, Aardvark. f, Aardwolf.

2014, Mar. 14   Litho.   Perf. 13¼
1280 A323 ($3.30) Sheet of 6,
       #a-f, + label   6.00 6.00
Nos. 1280a-1280f are each inscribed "Standard Mail."

Namibian Flag on
Map of
Namibia — A324

2014, May 21   Litho.   Perf. 14x13¼
1281 A324 ($3.30) multi   1.00 1.00
Souvenir Sheet
1282 A324 ($27.20) multi   7.00 7.00
No. 1281 is inscribed "Standard Mail;" No.
1282, "Inland Registered Mail."

Antelopes
A325

Designs: No. 1283, ($6), Red lechwes. No.
1284, ($6), Bushbucks. No. 1285, ($6), Red
hartebeests. No. 1286, ($6), Springboks.

2014, May 27   Litho.   Perf. 13¼x13½
1283-1286 A325   Set of 4   7.00 7.00
Nos. 1283-1286 are each inscribed "Postcard Rate."

Snakes — A326

Designs: $5.40, Black mamba. ($6), Boom-
slang. $6.20, Puff adder. $7.30, Zebra snake.

2014, June 4   Litho.   Perf. 13¾
1287-1290 A326   Set of 4   7.00 7.00
No. 1288 is inscribed "Postcard Rate."

First Visit of
Chinese Navy to
Namibia — A327

Designs: No. 1291, $3.30, Taihu. No. 1292,
$3.30, Yancheng.

2014, June 11   Litho.   Perf. 13x13¼
1291-1292 A327   Set of 2   2.00 2.00
A souvenir sheet containing two $3.30
stamps depicting Walvis Bay harbor and the
Luoyang sold for $15. Value, $2.50.

Miniature Sheet

Flora
and
Fauna of
the
Kalahari
Desert
A328

No. 1293: a, Peregrine falcon (30x30mm). b,
Cape turtle doves (50x30mm). c, Shepherd's
tree (40x30mm). d, Giraffe (40x30mm). e, African monarch butterfly (40x30mm). f, Cheetah
(40x30mm). g, Gemsbok cucumbers
(40x30mm). h, Suricates (40x40mm). i, Trum-
pet-thorn (40x40mm). j, Spotted sandveld lizard (40x40mm).

2014, July 28   Litho.   Perf. 14x13½
1293 A328 ($6) Sheet of 10,
       #a-j   17.50 17.50
Nos. 1293a-1293j are each inscribed "Postcard Rate."

In 2014 and 2015, Namibia postal
officials declared as "illegal" souvenir
sheets with a $5 denomination depict-
ing various dogs and other wildlife, and
a stamp inscribed "Postage Paid"
depicting a dog and cat.

Kingfishers
A329

Designs: ($5.70), Pied kingfishers. ($6.40),
Half-collared kingfishers. ($6.60), Woodland
kingfishers. ($7.70), Malachite kingfishers.
($28.30), Giant kingfishers.

2014, Oct. 1   Litho.   Perf. 13¼x14
1294-1298 A329   Set of 5   15.00 15.00
No. 1294 is inscribed "Zone A;" No. 1295,
"Postcard Rate;" No. 1296, "Zone B;" No.
1297, "Zone C;" No. 1298, "Inland Registered
Mail." Nos. 1294-1298 exists imperf. Vlaue,
each $60.

Souvenir Sheet

Namib Sand Sea UNESCO World
Heritage Site — A330

No. 1299: a, Sossusvlei/Deadvlei. b,
Comicus spp. c, Sandwich Harbor.

2015, Feb. 6   Litho.   Perf. 13¼
1299 A330 ($6.40) Sheet of 3,
       #a-c   2.25 2.25
Nos. 1299a-1299c are each inscribed "Postcard Rate."

Presidents of
Namibia — A331

Designs: ($3.50), Pres. Hage Geingob.
$30, Presidents Sam Nujoma, Hifikepunye
Pohamba, Hage Geingob, map and flag of
Namibia, horiz.

Litho. With Foil Application
2015, Mar. 21   Perf. 13¼x13¾
1300 A331 ($3.50) gold & multi   .80   .80
**Litho., Sheet Margin Litho. With Foil
Application**
Souvenir Sheet
Perf. 14½x14
1301 A331 $30 sil & multi   4.25 4.25
Inauguration of Pres. Geingob, Independence, 25th anniv. (No. 1301). No. 1301 contains one 75x26mm stamp.

Bee-Eaters — A332

Designs: ($3.50), White-fronted bee-eater.
$5.70, Southern carmine bee-eater, horiz.
$6.60, Swallow-tailed bee-eater, horiz. $7.70,
Little bee-eaters, horiz. ($28.30), European
bee-eater.

Perf. 14x14¼, 14¼x14
2015, May 15   Litho.
1302-1306 A332   Set of 5   7.50 7.50
No. 1302 is inscribed "Standard Mail;" No.
1306, "Inland Registered Mail." Nos. 1300-
1306 exists imperf. Value, each $65.

Antelopes
A333

Designs: No. 1307, ($6.40), Steenbok. No.
1308, ($6.40), Common duiker. No. 1309,
($6.40), Klipspringer. No. 1310, ($6.40),
Damara dik-dik.

2015, June 22   Litho.   Perf. 14¼
1307-1310 A333   Set of 4   4.25 4.25
Nos. 1307-1310 are each inscribed "Postcard Rate."

Juvenile Big Game
Animals — A334

Designs: ($3.50), Leopard. $5.70, African
elephant. $6.60, Black rhinoceros. $7.70, African buffalo. ($35.50), Lion.

2015, July 6   Litho.   Perf. 14¾x14½
1311-1315 A334   Set of 5   9.50 9.50
No. 1311 is inscribed "Standard mail;" No.
1315, "Non-standard registered mail."

Sharks
A335

Designs: $5.70, Bronze whaler shark.
($6.40), Broadnose sevengill shark. $6.60,
Great white shark. $7.70, Smooth hammer-
head shark.

2015, Aug. 19   Litho.   Perf. 14½x14
1316-1319 A335   Set of 4   5.25 5.25
No. 1317 is inscribed "Postcard Rate."

Coursers — A336

Designs: ($6.05), Burchell's courser.
($6.80), Three-banded courser. ($7), Double-
banded courser. ($8.20), Bronze-winged
courser.

2015, Oct. 1   Litho.   Perf. 13½
1320-1323 A336   Set of 4   5.00 5.00
No. 1320 is inscribed "Zone A;" No. 1321,
"Postcard Rate:" No. 1322, "Zone B;" No.
1323, "Zone C." Nos. 1320-1323 exists imperf.
Value, each $60.

Souvenir Sheet

Hong Kong 2015 Intl. Stamp
Exhibition — A337

No. 1324: a, Two rhinoceroses. b, Earth. c,
Three elephants.

2015, Nov. 22   Litho.   Perf. 13¾
1324 A337 ($6.80) Sheet of 3,
       #a-c   3.00 3.00
Nos. 1324a-1324c are each inscribed "Postcard rate."

Namibian postal officials have
declared as "illegal" eight sheets dated
"2015" having the theme of 2018 World
Cup Soccer Championships.

Allgemeine
Zeitung
Newspaper,
Cent. — A338

Newspaper masthead dated: ($3.70), July
22, 2016. ($6.80), Aug. 1, 1919.

2016   Litho.   Perf. 13
1325-1326 A338   Set of 2   1.40 1.40
1326a   Souvenir sheet of 2,
              #1325-1326   1.50 1.50
Issued: Nos. 1325-1326, 3/4; No. 1326a,
7/22/16.
No. 1325 is inscribed "Standard mail;" No.
1326, "Postcard rate."

Whydahs — A339

Designs: $6.05, Shaft-tailed whydah. $7, Long-tailed paradise whydah, vert. ($30), Pin-tailed whydah, vert.

2016, Mar. 18   Litho.   Perf. 13¼
1327-1329   A339   Set of 3   6.50 6.50
    No. 1329 is inscribed "Inland registered mail."

Miniature Sheet

Tortoises
A340

No. 1330: a, Speke's hinged tortoise. b, Namaqualand tent tortoise. c, Nama padloper. d, Angulate tortoise.

2016, May 11   Litho.   Perf. 14
1330   A340   ($3.70) Sheet of 4,
        #a-d   2.25 2.25
    Nos. 1330a-1330d are each inscribed "Standard mail."

Birds — A341

Designs: ($3.70), Cattle egret. $6.05, Green-backed heron, horiz. ($6.80), Goliath heron, horiz. $7, Squacco heron, horiz. $8.20, Black heron, horiz.

Perf. 13¼x12¾, 12¾x13¼
2016, July 7   Litho.
1331-1335   A341   Set of 5   4.75 4.75
    No. 1331 is inscribed "Standard mail;" No. 1333, "Post card rate."

Souvenir Sheet

Forestry
A342

No. 1336: a, Forestry resources used in commercial buildings and housing, arts and crafts and household utensils. b, Elephant and trees, vert. c, Fruit, soap and oils.

2016, Aug. 11   Litho.   Perf. 14x13¼
1336   A342   ($6.80) Sheet of 3,
        #a-c   3.00 3.00
    Nos. 1336a-1336c are each inscribed "Postcard rate."

Mammals
A343

Designs: ($6.60), African wild dogs. ($7.50), Spotted hyenas. ($8.80), Brown hyena.

2016, Sept. 30   Litho.   Perf. 12½x13
1337-1339   A343   Set of 3   3.50 3.50
    No. 1337 is inscribed "Zone A;" No. 1338, "Zone B;" No. 1339, "Zone C."

Wild Horses Type of 2009

Designs: No. 1340, ($7.30), Two horses (like #1176). No. 1341, ($7.30), Three horses (like #1177). No. 1342, ($7.30), Four horses (like #1178).

2016, Nov. 15   Litho.   Perf. 12½x13
1340-1342   A288   Set of 3   3.25 3.25
    Nos. 1340-1342 are each inscribed "Postcard rate."

Souvenir Sheet

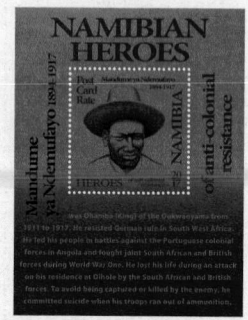

Mandume ya Ndemufayo (1894-1917), Last King of the Oukwanyama and Anti-Colonial Resistance Leader — A344

2017, Feb. 6   Litho.   Perf. 13¼
1343   A344   ($7.30) multi   1.10 1.10
    No. 1343 is inscribed "Post card rate."

Souvenir Sheet

Scouting in Namibia, Cent. A345

2017, Feb. 17   Litho.   Perf. 13¼
1344   A345   ($4) multi   .65   .65
    No. 1344 is inscribed "Standard mail."

Barbets — A346

Designs: ($6.60), Black-collared barbets. ($7.50), Crested barbets, horiz. ($8.80), Acacia pied barbets.

Perf. 13¼x13, 13x13¼
2017, Mar. 9   Litho.
1345-1347   A346   Set of 3   3.50 3.50
    No. 1345 is inscribed "Zone A;" No. 1346, "Zone B;" No. 1347, "Zone C."

Hares and Rabbits A347

No. 1348: a, Jameson's red rabbit. b, Scrub hare.

2017, Apr. 15   Litho.   Perf. 12½x13
1348   A347   ($7.30) Horiz. pair,
        #a-b   2.25 2.25
    No. 1348 is inscribed "postcard rate."

Souvenir Sheet

Protestant Reformation, 500th Anniv. — A348

2017, May 12   Litho.   Perf. 13½
1349   A348   ($7.30) multi   1.10 1.10
    No. 1349 is inscribed "Postcard Rate."

Flame Lilies — A349

Designs: ($6.60), Limestone lily. ($7.50), Flame lily. ($8.80), Namib lily, vert.

Perf. 13¼x12¾, 12¾x13¼
2017, June 15   Litho.
1350-1352   A349   Set of 3   3.50 3.50
    No. 1350 is inscribed "ZONE A." No. 1351 is inscribed "ZONE B." No. 1352 is inscribed "ZONE C."

Diamond Trains A350

Designs: No. 1353, ($7.30), (1AO) Bo Benzol-electric locomotive. No. 1354, ($7.30), Bo-Bo electric locomotive K.B.G. No. 1355, ($7.30), Bo-Bo Benzol-electric locomotive C.D.M. No. 40. No. 1356, ($7.30), Railcar No. 3 Kolmanskop.

Litho. with Foil Application
2017, July 18   Perf. 14¼x14
1353-1356   A350   Set of 4   4.50 4.50
    Nos. 1353-1356 are inscribed "Postcard Rate."

Rollers — A351

Designs: No. 1357, ($7.30), Lilac-breasted roller. No. 1358, ($7.30), Purple roller. No. 1359, ($7.30), Racket-tailed roller. No. 1360, ($7.30), Broad-billed roller. No. 1361, ($7.30), European roller.

2017, Aug. 1   Litho.   Perf. 13¼
1357-1361   A351   Set of 5   5.50 5.50
    Nos. 1357-1361 are inscribed "Postcard Rate."

Small Canines A352

Designs: ($4.00), Bat-eared fox. ($6.60), Black-backed jackal. ($7.50), Side-striped jackal. ($8.80), Aardwolf. ($32.10), Cape fox.

2017, Sept. 29   Litho.   Perf. 12½x13
1362-1366   A352   Set of 5   8.75 8.75
    No. 1362 is inscribed "Standard Mail." No. 1363 is inscribed "Zone A." No. 1364 is inscribed "Zone B." No. 1365 is inscribed "Zone C." No. 1366 is inscribed "Inland Registered Mail."

Transportation
A353

Designs: ($7.10), Ox-drawn wagon. ($8.10), Cessna 210 airplane. ($34.40), Land Rover.

2018, Mar. 12   Litho.   Perf. 14x13¼
1367-1369   A353   Set of 3   8.50 8.50
    No. 1367 is inscribed "Zone A;" No. 1368, "Zone B;" No. 1369, "Inland Registered Mail."

Birds — A354

Designs: ($4.30), Red-billed spurfowl. ($7.10), Crested francolin. ($7.90), Swainson's spurfowl. ($8.10), Coqui francolin. ($34.40), Orange River francolin.

2018, May 18   Litho.   Perf. 13¼x14
1370-1374   A354   Set of 5   10.00 10.00
    No. 1370 is inscibed "Standard Mail;" No. 1371, "Zone A;" No. 1372, "Postcard Rate;" No. 1373, "Zone B;" No. 1374, "Inland Registered Mail."

Wild Cats — A355

Designs: ($7.10), Serval. ($8.10), Caracal, vert. ($9.50), African wild cat, vert. ($34.40), Small spotted cat.

Perf. 13¼x13½, 13½x13¼
2018, July 18   Litho.
1375-1378   A355   Set of 4   9.00 9.00
    No. 1375 is inscribed "Zone A;" No. 1376, "Zone B;" No. 1377, "Zone C;" No. 1378, "Inland Registered Mail."

Whales
A356

Designs: ($4.60), Blue whale. ($7.60), Southern right whale. ($8.60), Strap-toothed whale. ($10.10), Pygmy right whale. No. 1383, ($32), Pygmy sperm whale. No. 1384, ($36.60), Pygmy killer whale.

2019, Mar. 19   Litho.   Perf. 14¼x14
1379-1384   A356   Set of 6   14.00 14.00
    No. 1379 is inscribed "Standard Mail;" No. 1380, "Zone A;" No. 1381, "Zone B;" No. 1382, "Zone C;" No. 1383, "Registered Mail;" No. 1384, "Inland Registered Mail." See No. 1385.

Whales Type of 2019

Design: No. 1385, Pygmy sperm whale, with added inscriptions of "Reprint" and Kogiidae family information.

2019, Apr. 25   Litho.   Perf. 14¼x14
1385   A356   ($32) multi   4.50 4.50
    No. 1385 is inscribed "Registered Mail."

Cuckoos
A357

Designs: ($8.40), African cuckoo. ($8.60), Diderick cuckoo, vert. ($32), Jacobin cuckoo, vert. ($36.60), Great spotted cuckoo.

2019, Apr. 25   Litho.   Perf. 14
1386-1389   A357   Set of 4   12.00 12.00
    No. 1386 is inscribed "Postcard Rate;" No. 1387, "Zone B;" No. 1388, "Registered Mail;" No. 1389, "Inland Registered Mail."

Wild Cats — A358

Designs: No. 1390, ($8.40), Lion. No. 1391, ($8.40), Cheetah. No. 1392, ($8.40), Leopard, vert.

Perf. 14¼x14, 14x14¼
2019, Aug. 1   **Litho.**
1390-1392 A358   Set of 3   3.50   3.50
   Nos. 1390-1392 are each inscribed "Postcard Rate."

Miniature Sheet

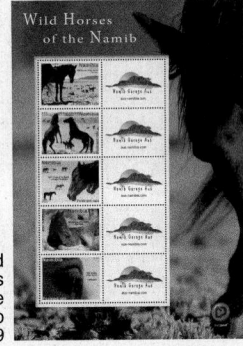

Wild Horses of the Namib A359

No. 1393 — Inscription: a, The herd. b, Living free. c, Amongst the wildlife. d, The future. e, Wild spirit.

2019, Aug. 14   **Litho.**   **Perf. 13x13¼**
1393 A359 ($8.40) Sheet of 5, #a-e, + 5 labels   7.00   7.00
   Nos. 1393a-1393e are each inscribed "Postcard rate." No. 1393 sold for $55 and had labels that could be personalized. Generic labels are shown.

Flag of Namibia — A360

2019, Oct. 2   **Litho.**   **Perf. 13¼x13**
1394 A360 ($9) multi + label   1.50   1.50
   No. 1394 is inscribed "Postcard Rate" and was printed in sheets of 5 + 5 labels that could be personalized that sold for $55. One of five different generic labels depicting Mohandas K. Gandhi is shown.

Squirrels A361

Designs: ($9.30), Damara ground squirrel. ($34.80), Striped tree squirrel. ($39.90), Tree squirrel, vert.

2020, Feb. 20   **Litho.**   **Perf. 14¼**
1395-1397 A361   Set of 3   11.00   11.00
   No. 1395 is inscribed "Postcard Rate"; No. 1396, "Registerd Mail"; No. 1397, "Inland Registered Mail."

Woodpeckers — A362

Designs: ($5.10), Bearded woodpecker. ($9.30), Bennett's woodpecker. ($9.50), Olive woodpecker, horiz. ($34.80), Golden-tailed woodpecker, horiz. ($39.90), Cardinal woodpecker, horiz.

Perf. 13¼x13, 13x13¼
2020, Apr. 2   **Litho.**
1398-1402 A362   Set of 5   10.50   10.50
   No. 1398 is inscribed "Standard Mail"; No. 1399, "Postcard Rate"; No. 1400, "Zone B"; No. 1401, "Registered Mail"; No. 1402, "Inland Registered Mail."

Batises — A363

No. 1403 — Male and female: a, ($9.30), Pririt batises. b, ($15.10), Chinspot batises.

2020, June 18   **Litho.**   **Perf. 14**
1403 A363   Vert. pair, #a-b   3.00   3.00
   No. 1403a is inscribed "Postcard Rate"; No. 1403b, "Non-standard Mail."

Black-Shouldered Kite — A365

Yellow-Billed Kite — A366

2020, Aug. 20   **Litho.**   **Perf. 14¼**
1405 A365 ($9.50) multi   1.25   1.25
1406 A366 ($49.90) multi   6.00   6.00
   No. 1406 is inscribed "Non-Standard Registered Mail."

Greater Painted Snipe — A367

African Snipe — A368

Great Snipe — A369

2021, Mar. 16   **Litho.**   **Perf. 13¼**
1407 A367 ($9.50) multi   1.30   1.30
1408 A368 ($34.80) multi   4.75   4.75
1409 A369 ($39.90) multi   5.50   5.50
   Nos. 1407-1409 (3)   11.55   11.55
   No. 1408 is inscribed "Registered Mail," and No. 1409 is inscribed "Inland Registered Mail."

Barleria Craveniae A370

Barleria Damarensis A371

Barleria Jubata — A372

Barleria Conacea Subspecies Dinteri — A373

2021, July 14   **Litho.**   **Perf. 13¼**
1410 A370 ($9.50) multi   1.30   1.30
1411 A371 ($9.50) multi   1.30   1.30
1412 A372 ($34.80) multi   5.00   5.00
1413 A373 ($39.90) multi   5.50   5.50
   Nos. 1410-1413 (4)   13.10   13.10
   No. 1412 is inscribed "Registered Mail," and No. 1413 is inscribed "Inland Registered Mail."

Mustelids — A374

Designs: No. 1414, ($9.90), Striped polecat. No. 1415, ($9.90), African striped weasel. No. 1416, ($36.10), Spotted-necked otter. No. 1417, ($36.10), African clawless otter. No. 1418, ($41.40), Honey badger.

2021, Oct. 12   **Litho.**   **Perf. 13x13¼**
1414-1418 A374   Set of 5   17.50   17.50
   Nos. 1414-1415 are each inscribed "Zone B"; Nos. 1416-1417, "Registered Mail"; No. 1418, "Inland Registered Mail".

NATAL

nə-'tal

LOCATION — Southern coast of Africa, bordering on the Indian Ocean
GOVT. — British Crown Colony
AREA — 35,284 sq. mi.
POP. — 1,206,386 (1908)
CAPITAL — Pietermaritzburg

   Natal united with Cape of Good Hope, Orange Free State and the Transvaal in 1910 to form the Union of South Africa.

    12 Pence = 1 Shilling
    20 Shillings = 1 Pound

   Values for Nos. 1-7 are for examples with complete margins and free from damage. Unused values for No. 8 on are for stamps with original gum as defined in the catalogue introduction. Very fine examples of Nos. 8-49, 61-63 and 79 will have perforations touching the design on one or more sides due to the narrow spacing of the stamps on the plates. Stamps with perfs clear of the design on all four sides are scarce and will command higher prices.

Watermark

Wmk. 5 — Small Star

Crown and V R (Victoria Regina) A1

Crown and V R (Victoria Regina) A2

Crown and Laurel — A3

A4

A5

Colorless Embossing

				Unwmk.	Imperf.
1857					
1	A1	3p	*rose*		725.
a.	Tete beche pair				55,000.
2	A2	6p	*green*		2,000.
a.	Diagonal half used as 3p on cover				16,500.
3	A3	9p	*blue*		65,000. 13,000.
4	A4	1sh	*buff*		10,500.
1858					
5	A5	1p	*blue*		1,400.
6	A5	1p	*rose*		2,200.
a.	No. 1 embossed over No. 6				
7	A5	1p	*buff*		1,450.

   Reprints: The paper is slightly glazed, the embossing sharper and the colors as follows: 1p pale blue, deep blue, carmine rose or yellow; 3p pale rose or carmine rose; 6p bright green or yellow green; 1sh pale buff or pale yellow. Bogus cancellations are found on the reprints.
   The stamps printed on surface-colored paper are revenue stamps with trimmed perforations.

   Listings of shades will be found in the *Scott Classic Specialized Catalogue.*

Queen Victoria — A6

		Engr.	**Perf. 14**
1860			
8	A6 1p rose	190.00	95.00
9	A6 3p blue	225.00	60.00
a.	Vert. pair, imperf betwn.		13,000.
1863			**Perf. 13**
10	A6 1p red	130.00	35.00
1861		**Clean-cut Perf. 14 to 16**	
11	A6 3p blue	350.00	82.50
1862		**Rough Perf. 14 to 16**	
12	A6 3p blue	175.00	45.00
a.	Imperf., pair		4,500.
b.	Horiz. or vert. pair, imperf. between	6,500.	
13	A6 6p gray	275.00	75.00
1862			**Wmk. 5**
14	A6 1p rose	180.00	82.50

   Imperforate stamps of the 1p and 3p on paper watermarked small star are proofs.

		Wmk. 1	**Perf. 12½**
1864			
15	A6 1p carmine red	140.00	50.00
16	A6 6p violet	90.00	37.50

   No. 15 imperf is a proof.

Be the change you wish to see in the world — Mahatma Gandhi / 150 YEARS OF CELEBRATING THE MAHATMA

Queen Victoria — A7

1867   **Typo.**   *Perf. 14*
17   A7   1sh green   275.00   52.50

For types A6 and A7 overprinted or surcharged see Nos. 18-50, 61-63, 76, 79.

Stamps of 1860-67 Overprinted

1869   **Overprint 12¾mm**
18	A6	1p carmine red (#15)	525.00 100.00
b.		Double overprint	
19	A6	3p blue (#12)	700.00 110.00
19A	A6	3p blue (#9)	— 725.00
19B	A6	3p blue (#11)	1,050. 325.00
20	A6	6p violet (#16)	650.00 110.00
21	A7	1sh green (#17)	30,000. 2,100.

Same Overprint 13¾mm
22	A6	1p rose (#15b)	1,200. 325.00
23	A6	3p blue (#12)	2,800. 550.00
a.		Inverted overprint	
23B	A6	3p blue (#9)	— —
23C	A6	3p blue (#11)	— 1,100.
24	A6	6p violet (#16)	2,750. 225.00
25	A7	1sh green (#17)	35,000. 3,250.

Same Overprint 14½ to 15½mm
26	A6	1p rose (#15b)	1,050. 250.00
27	A6	3p blue (#12)	— 450.00
27A	A6	3p blue (#11)	— 775.00
27B	A6	3p blue (#9)	
28	A6	6p violet (#16)	2,100. 140.00
29	A7	1sh green (#17)	32,000. 2,750.

Overprinted

30	A6	1p rose (#15b)	150.00 55.00
b.		Inverted overprint	
31	A6	3p blue (#12)	250.00 55.00
a.		Double overprint	1,800.
31B	A6	3p blue (#11)	225.00 62.50
31C	A6	3p blue (#9)	400.00 95.00
32	A6	6p violet (#16)	210.00 77.50
33	A7	1sh green (#17)	350.00 87.50

Overprinted

34	A6	1p rose (#15b)	650.00 120.00
35	A6	3p blue (#12)	825.00 120.00
35A	A6	3p blue (#11)	1,200. 375.00
35B	A6	3p blue (#9)	4,250. 925.00
36	A6	6p violet (#16)	825.00 120.00
b.		Inverted overprint	
37	A7	1sh green (#17)	37,500. 2,000.

Overprinted in Black or Red

1870-73   **Wmk. 1**   *Perf. 12½*
38	A6	1p red	120.00 16.50
39	A6	3p ultra (R) ('72)	130.00 16.50
40	A6	6p lilac ('73)	250.00 45.00
		Nos. 38-40 (3)	500.00 78.00

Overprinted in Red, Black or Green — g

1870   *Perf. 14*
41	A7	1sh green (R)	— 9,500.
42	A7	1sh green (Bk)	— 1,750.
a.		Double overprint	3,900.
43	A7	1sh green (G)	150.00 13.00

See No. 76.

Type of 1867 Overprinted

1873
44   A7   1sh brown lilac   425.00   37.50
No. 44 without overprint is a revenue.

Type of 1864 Overprinted

1874   *Perf. 12½*
45   A6   1p rose red   400.00   95.00
a.   Double overprint

Overprinted

1875
46   A6   1p rose red   185.00   70.00
b.   Double overprint   1,900.   650.00

Overprinted

1875   **Overprint 14½mm** *Perf. 12½*
47	A6	1p yellow	100.00 100.00
a.		Double overprint, one albino	275.00 —
48	A6	1p rose red	140.00 87.50
a.		Inverted overprint	2,250. 575.00
49	A6	6p violet	95.00 10.00
a.		Inverted overprint	900.00 190.00
b.		Double overprint	1,050.

Perf. 14
50	A7	1sh green	140.00 9.00
a.		Double overprint	425.00
		Nos. 47-50 (4)	475.00 206.50

The 1p yellow without overprint is a revenue.

A8   A9   A10   A11

Queen Victoria — A12

1874-78 **Typo.** **Wmk. 1** *Perf. 14*
51	A8	1p dull rose	60.00 8.50
52	A9	3p ultramarine	190.00 45.00
a.		Perf. 14x12½	2,500. 1,100.
53	A10	4p brown ('78)	210.00 20.00
54	A11	6p violet	110.00 9.00

Perf. 15½x15
55   A12   5sh claret   525.00   120.00

Perf. 14
56	A12	5sh claret ('78)	450.00 120.00
57	A12	5sh carmine	120.00 42.50

Perf. 12½
58   A10   4p brown ('78)   400.00   82.50

See Nos. 65-71. For types A8-A10 surcharged see Nos. 59-60, 72-73, 77, 80.

Surcharged in Black

n

No. 60

o

1877   *Perf. 14*
59	A8(n)	½p on 1p rose	45.00 82.50
a.		Double surcharge "1/2"	
60	A8(n)	½p on 1p rose	110.00 —

Surcharge "n" exists in 3 or more types each of the large "1/2" (No. 59) and the small "1/2" (No. 60).

"HALF" and "½" were overprinted separately; "½" may be above, below or overlapping.

Perf. 12½
61	A6(o)	½p on 1p yel	13.00 25.00
a.		Double surcharge	400.00 230.00
b.		Inverted surcharge	400.00 240.00
c.		Pair, one without surcharge	4,750. 3,000.
d.		"POTAGE"	350.00 250.00
e.		"POSAGE"	350.00 325.00
f.		"POSTAGE" omitted	2,500.
62	A6(o)	1p on 6p vio	82.50 13.00
a.		"POSTAGE" omitted	
b.		"POTAGE"	650.00 190.00
63	A6(o)	1p on 6p rose	150.00 60.00
a.		Inverted surcharge	1,750. 600.00
b.		Double surcharge	350.00
c.		Dbl. srch., one inverted	400.00 250.00
d.		Triple srch., one invtd.	
e.		Quadruple surcharge	550.00 300.00
f.		"POTAGE"	1,000. 390.00
		Nos. 61-63 (3)	245.50 98.00

No. 63 without overprint is a revenue.

A14

1880   **Typo.**   *Perf. 14*
64   A14   ½p blue green   30.00   40.00
a.   Vertical pair, imperf. between

1882-89   **Wmk. Crown and CA (2)**
65	A14	½p blue green ('84)	120.00 22.50
66	A14	½p gray green ('84)	6.00 1.40
67	A8	1p rose ('84)	8.50 .30
68	A9	3p ultra ('84)	170.00 22.00
69	A9	3p gray ('89)	12.50 5.75
70	A10	4p brown	17.50 1.90
71	A11	6p violet	14.50 2.75
		Nos. 65-71 (7)	349.00 56.60

Surcharged in Black

p   q

1885-86
72	A8(p)	½p on 1p rose	24.00 14.00
b.		Inverted surcharge	1,000.
73	A9(q)	2p on 3p gray ('86)	40.00 7.00

A17

1887
74	A17	2p ol grn, die B ('89)	6.00 1.75
a.		Die A	60.00 3.00

For explanation of dies A and B see "Dies of British Colonial Stamps" in the catalogue introduction.

Type of 1867 Overprinted Type "g" in Red

1888
76   A7   1sh orange   13.50   2.00
a.   Double overprint   3,250.

Surcharged in Black

1891
77	A10	2½p on 4p brown	17.50 17.50
a.		"PENGE"	77.50
b.		"PENN"	325.00 275.00
c.		Double surcharge	400.00 350.00
d.		As "c," in vert. pair with normal stamp	650.00 750.00
e.		Inverted surcharge	550.00 475.00
f.		Vert. pair, surcharge tete-beche	2,250. 3,000.

A20

1891, June
78   A20   2½p ultramarine   12.50   1.60

Surcharged in Red or Black

No. 79   No. 80

1895, Mar.   **Wmk. 1** *Perf. 12½*
79	A6	½p on 6p vio (R)	3.00 10.00
a.		"Ealf"	27.50 75.00
b.		"Penn'"	27.50 75.00
c.		Double surcharge, one vertical	350.00
d.		Double surcharge	350.00

Stamps with fancy "P," "T" or "A" in surcharge sell for twice as much.

Wmk. 2   *Perf. 14*
80	A8	½p on 1p rose (Bk)	3.50 2.50
a.		Double surcharge	525.00 550.00
b.		Pair, one without surcharge and the other with double surcharge	—

A23   King Edward VII — A24

1902-03 **Typo.** **Wmk. 2** *Perf. 14*
81	A23	½p blue green	7.50 .55
82	A23	1p rose	13.00 .25
83	A23	1½p blk & blue grn	4.50 6.00
84	A23	2p ol grn & scar	7.00 .45
85	A23	2½p ultramarine	2.25 6.00
86	A23	3p gray & red vio	1.60 2.75
87	A23	4p brown & scar	14.00 27.50
88	A23	5p org & black	5.00 4.00
89	A23	6p mar & bl grn	5.00 5.00
90	A23	1sh pale bl & dp rose	6.50 5.25
91	A23	2sh vio & bl grn	62.50 11.50
92	A23	2sh6p red violet	50.00 15.00
93	A23	4sh yel & dp rose	95.00 95.00

Wmk. 1
94	A24	5sh car lake & dk blue	67.50 14.00
95	A24	10sh brn & dp rose	130.00 45.00
96	A24	£1 ultra & blk	350.00 85.00
97	A24	£1 10sh vio & bl grn	600.00 140.00
		Revenue cancel	15.00
98	A24	£5 blk & vio	5,500. 1,400.
		Revenue cancel	110.00
99	A24	£10 org & grn	14,000. 6,500.
		Revenue cancel	180.00
100	A24	£20 grn & car	28,000. 19,000.
		Revenue cancel	325.00
		Nos. 81-96 (16)	821.35 323.25

1904-08   **Wmk. 3**
101	A23	½p blue green	12.00 .25
102	A23	1p rose	12.00 .25
a.		Booklet pane of 6	600.00
b.		Booklet pane of 5 + 1 label	500.00
103	A23	2p ol grn & scar	18.50 4.00
104	A23	4p brn & scar	3.50 1.60
105	A23	5p org & blk ('08)	6.50 5.00

106	A23	1sh pale bl & dp rose	90.00	9.00
107	A23	2sh vio & bl grn	75.00	55.00
108	A23	2sh6p red violet	70.00	55.00
109	A24	£1 10sh vio & org brn, chalky paper	1,900.	5,000.
		Revenue cancel		55.00
		Nos. 101-108 (8)	287.50	130.10

A25

A26

1908-09

110	A25	6p red violet	5.75	3.50
111	A25	1sh blk, grn	7.75	3.25
112	A25	2sh bl & vio, bl	19.00	3.75
113	A25	2sh6p red & blk, bl	32.00	5.50
114	A26	5sh red & grn, yell	30.00	52.50
115	A26	10sh red & grn, grn	135.00	135.00
116	A26	£1 blk & vio, red	450.00	400.00
		Nos. 110-116 (7)	679.50	603.50

OFFICIAL STAMPS

Nos. 101-103, 106 and Type A23 Overprinted

1904		Wmk. 3	Perf. 14
O1	A23	½p blue green	3.75	.45
O2	A23	1p rose	16.00	1.25
O3	A23	2p ol grn & scar	45.00	22.50
O4	A23	3p gray & red vio	27.50	5.50
O5	A23	6p mar & bl grn	87.50	82.50
O6	A23	1sh pale bl & dp rose	250.00	275.00
		Nos. O1-O6 (6)	429.75	387.20

Stamps of Natal were replaced by those of the Union of South Africa.

NAURU

nä-'ü-₀rü

LOCATION — An island on the Equator in the west central Pacific Ocean, midway between the Marshall and Solomon Islands.
GOVT. — Republic
AREA — 8½ sq. mi.
POP. — 10,605 (1999 est.)
CAPITAL — None. Parliament House is in Yaren District.

The island, a German possession, was captured by Australian forces in 1914 and, following World War I, was mandated to the British Empire. It was administered jointly by Great Britain, Australia and New Zealand.

In 1947 Nauru was placed under United Nations trusteeship, administered by Australia. On January 31, 1968, Nauru became a republic.

See North West Pacific Islands.

12 Pence = 1 Shilling
100 Cents = 1 Dollar (1966)

Catalogue values for unused stamps in this country are for Never Hinged items, beginning with Scott 39.

Watermarks

Wmk. 388 — Multiple "SPM"

Great Britain Stamps of 1912-13 Overprinted at Bottom of Stamp

NAURU

1916-23		Wmk. 33	Perf. 15x14
1	A82	½p green (#159)	2.75	12.50
2	A83	1p scarlet (#160)	2.50	14.50
3	A84	1½p red brn (#161)		
		('23)	65.00	110.00
4	A85	2p org (die I) (#162)	1.75	15.00
c.		2p deep orange (die II) (#162a) ('23)	80.00	110.00
6	A86	2½p ultra (#163)	3.00	7.50
7	A87	3p violet (#164a)	2.25	6.50
8	A88	4p slate green (#165)	2.25	9.00
9	A89	5p yel brown (#166)	2.60	16.50
10	A89	6p dull brown (#167a)	8.50	17.50
11	A90	9p blk brn (#170)	9.75	32.50
12	A90	1sh bister (#172)	8.25	27.50
		Nos. 1-12 (11)	108.60	269.00

Wmk. 34
Overprint Centered

1b	A82	½p green (#159) ('23)	5.75	62.50
2c	A83	1p scarlet (#160) ('23)	22.50	50.00
3a	A84	1½p red brn (#161) ('23)	30.00	60.00
b.		Double ovpt, one albino ('23)	200.00	
4d	A85	2p dp org (II) (#162a) ('23)	40.00	87.50
		Nos. 1b-4d (4)	98.25	260.00

On Nos. 1-12 "NAURU" is usually 12¾mm wide and at the foot of the stamp. In 1923 four values were overprinted with "NAURU" measuring 13½mm wide and across the middle of the stamp.
Forged overprints exist.

Great Britain Stamps of 1915 Overprinted

NAURU

1920		Wmk. 34	Perf. 11x12
13	A91	2sh6p lt brn	80.00	125.00
a.		2sh6p black brown	700.00	1,900.
14	A91	5sh carmine	125.00	175.00
b.		5sh rose carmine	3,000.	2,750.
15	A91	10sh lt blue (R)	300.00	450.00
c.		10sh indigo blue	14,250.	6,000.

Same Ovpt. on Great Britain No. 179a and 179b

1920				
16	A91	2sh6p gray brown	100.00	200.00
		Nos. 13-16 (4)	605.00	950.00
		Nos. 1-16 (15)	713.60	1,219.

Double and triple overprints, with one overprint albino, exist for the 1-16 overprints. Additional color shades exist for No. 13-16, and values given are for the most common varieties. For detailed listings, see Scott Classic Specialized Catalogue.

Freighter — A1

1924-48		Unwmk.	Engr.	Perf. 11
17	A1	½p orange brown	3.75	3.00
b.		Perf. 14 ('47)	2.50	14.50
18a	A1	1p green	2.75	3.50
19a	A1	1½p red	1.10	1.65
20a	A1	2p orange	7.75	9.25
21a	A1	2½p blue ('48)	6.00	4.50
c.		Horiz. pair, imperf between	18,750.	19,750.
		Vert. pair, imperf between	18,750.	19,750.
22a	A1	3p grnsh gray ('47)	8.75	24.00
23a	A1	4p olive green	8.75	16.50
24	A1	5p dk brown	4.75	8.75
25	A1	6p dark violet	5.25	22.00
26	A1	9p brown olive	10.50	21.00
27a	A1	1sh brown red	16.50	3.00
28a	A1	2sh6p slate green	35.00	45.00

29a	A1	5sh claret	42.50	60.00
30a	A1	10sh yellow	92.50	133.00
		Nos. 17-30a (14)	245.85	355.15

Two printings were made of Nos. 17-30, the first (1924-34) on unsurfaced, grayish paper (Nos. 17-30), the second (1937-48) on glazed surfaced white paper (Nos. 17a-30a). Values are for the most common type. For detailed listings, see Scott Classic Specialized Catalogue.

Stamps of Type A1 Overprinted in Black

1935, July 12		Glazed Paper	Perf. 11
31	A1	1½p red	.85	.90
32	A1	2p orange	1.50	5.75
33	A1	2½p blue	1.50	1.75
34	A1	1sh brown red	8.50	4.75
		Nos. 31-34 (4)	12.35	13.15
		Set, never hinged	385.00	

25th anniv. of the reign of George V.

George VI — A2

1937, May 10			Engr.
35	A2	1½p salmon rose	.30	1.00
36	A2	2p dull orange	.30	2.00
37	A2	2½p blue	.30	1.25
38	A2	1sh brown violet	.35	1.25
		Nos. 35-38 (4)	1.25	5.50
		Set, never hinged	1.75	

Coronation of George VI & Elizabeth.

Catalogue values for unused stamps in this section, from this point to the end of the section, are for Never Hinged items.

Casting Throw-net
A3

Anibare Bay
A4

3½p, Loading phosphate. 4p, Frigate bird. 6p, Nauruan canoe. 9p, Meeting house (domaneab). 1sh, Palms. 2sh6p, Buada lagoon. 5sh, Map.

1954, Feb. 6		Perf. 14½x14, 14x14½
39	A3	½p purple	.30	.75
40	A4	1p green	.30	.65
41	A3	3½p red	1.75	.75
42	A3	4p deep blue	3.25	2.00
43	A3	6p orange	.60	.25
44	A3	9p brown lake	.55	.25
45	A4	1sh dk rose violet	.30	.30
46	A3	2sh6p dk gray green	3.00	.75
47	A4	5sh lilac rose	8.50	2.40
		Nos. 39-47 (9)	18.55	8.10

See Nos. 58-71.

Balsam
A5

Black Lizard
A6

Capparis
A7

Coral Pinnacles
A8

White Tern — A9

2p, Micronesian pigeon, vert. 3p, Poison nut flower. 3sh3p, Nightingale reed warbler.

Perf. 13½, Perf. 14½x13½ (10p), Perf. 14½ (2sh3p)
Photo.; Engraved (10p, 2sh3p)

1963-65			Unwmk.
49	A9	2p multi ('65)	1.00	2.25
50	A6	3p red org, sl grn & yel ('64)	.40	.30
51	A5	5p gray, bl grn & yellow	.40	.70
52	A6	8p green & black	1.75	.75
53	A7	10p black ('64)	.40	.30
54	A9	1sh3p ap grn, blk & Prus bl ('65)	2.50	5.00
55	A8	2sh3p vio blue ('64)	2.25	.55
56	A6	3sh3p lt yel, bl, brn & blk ('65)	2.50	4.00
		Nos. 49-56 (8)	11.20	13.85

Issue dates: 5p, Apr. 22. 8p, July 1. 3p, 10p, 2sh3p, Apr. 16. 2p, 1sh3p, 3sh3p, May 3.

"Simpson and His Donkey" by Wallace Anderson — A9a

Perf. 13½x13

1965, Apr. 14		Photo.	Unwmk.
57	A9a	5p brt green, sepia & blk	.30	.25

See note after Australia No. 387.

Types of 1954-65
Values in Cents and Dollars

Designs: 1c, Anibare Bay. 2c, Casting throw-net. 3c, Loading phosphate. 4c, Balsam. 5c, Palms. 7c, Black lizard. 8c, Capparis. 10c, Frigate bird. 15c, White tern. 25c, Coral pinnacles. 30c, Poison nut flower. 35c, Reed warbler. 50c, Micronesian pigeon, vert. $1, Map.

Engr.; Photo. (4c, 7c, 15c, 30c-50c)			
1966		Perf. 14½x14, 14x14½
58	A4	1c dark blue	.30	.25
59	A3	2c claret	.30	.50
60	A3	3c green	.30	2.50
61	A4	4c lilac, grn & yel	.30	.25
62	A4	5c violet blue	.30	.60
63	A4	7c fawn & black	.35	.25
64	A7	8c olive green	.30	.25
65	A3	10c dark red	.40	.25
66	A9	15c ap grn, blk & Prus blue	1.00	3.00
67	A3	25c sepia	.30	1.25
68	A6	30c brick red, sl grn & yellow	.45	.35
69	A6	35c lt yel, bl, brn & black	.70	.40
70	A9	50c yel, bluish blk & brown	2.00	.75
71	A4	$1 claret	.75	1.00
		Nos. 58-71 (14)	7.75	11.60

The engraved stamps are luminescent.
Issued: 2c, 3c, 5c, 15c, 25c, 35c, 5/25; others, 2/14.

Republic

Nos. 58-71 Overprinted in Red, Black or Orange "REPUBLIC / OF / NAURU"

1968			
72	A4	1c dark blue (R)	.30	.35
73	A3	2c claret	.30	.25
74	A3	3c green	.30	.25
75	A4	4c lilac, grn & yel	.30	.25
76	A4	5c violet blue (O)	.30	.25
77	A4	7c fawn & blk (R)	.30	.25
78	A7	8c olive green (R)	.30	.25
79	A3	10c dark red	.60	.25
80	A9	15c ap grn, blk & Prus blue	2.00	3.00
81	A3	25c sepia (R)	.30	.25
82	A6	30c brick red, sl grn & yellow	.55	.25
83	A6	35c multicolored	1.40	.75
84	A9	50c yel, bluish blk & brown	1.50	1.00
85	A4	$1 claret	1.25	1.25
		Nos. 72-85 (14)	9.70	8.60

Issued: 4c, 7c, 30c, 35c, 5/15; others, 1/31.

Nauru Woman
Watching Rising
Sun — A10

Planting Seedling
and Map of
Nauru — A11

Perf. 13x13½

1968, Sept. 11   Photo.   Unwmk.
86 A10 5c multicolored   .30 .25
87 A11 10c brt blue, blk & green .30 .25

Independence of Nauru.

Flag of
Nauru — A12

1969, Jan. 31   Litho.   Perf. 13½
88 A12 15c dk vio blue, yel & org .75 .35

For overprint see No. 90.

Commission
Emblem and
Nauru — A13

1972, Feb. 7   Litho.   Perf. 14½x14
89 A13 25c blue, yellow & black   .55 .50

South Pacific Commission, 25th anniv.

No. 88 Ovptd. in
Gold

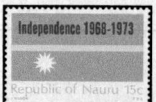

1973, Jan. 31   Perf. 13½
90 A12 15c multicolored   .35 .35

Fifth anniversary of independence.

Lotus
(Ekwena-
babae)
A14

Map of
Nauru,
Artifacts
A15

Catching
Flyingfish — A16

Designs: 2c, Kauwe iud. 3c, Rimone. 4c,
Denea. 5c, Beach morning-glory. 7c, Golden
butterflyfish. 10c, Nauruan ball game
(itsibweb). 15c, Nauruan wrestling. 20c, Snaring frigate birds. 25c, Nauruan girl with flower
garland. 30c, Men catching noddies. 50c, Frigate birds.

1973   Litho.   Perf. 13½x14
91 A14 1c pale yellow & multi   .30 .25
92 A14 2c pale ocher & multi   .35 .25
93 A14 3c pale violet & multi   .35 .25
94 A14 4c pale green & multi   .35 .35
95 A14 5c pale blue & multi   .35 .35
Perf. 14½x14, 14x14½
96 A16 7c blue & multi   .50 .90
97 A16 8c black & multi   .30 .25
98 A16 10c multicolored   .30 .25
99 A15 15c green & multi   .35 .25
100 A15 20c blue & multi   .60 .90
101 A15 25c yellow & multi   .45 .45
102 A16 30c multicolored   .55 .50
103 A16 50c multicolored   .80 .75
104 A15 $1 blue & multi   1.00 .75
    Nos. 91-104 (14)   6.55 6.45

Issue dates: Nos. 97-100, May 23; Nos. 96,
101-103, July 25; others Mar. 28, 1973.

Cooperative Store
A17

Eigigu, the
Girl in the
Moon
A18

Design: 25c, Timothy Detudamo and cooperative store emblem.

1973, Dec. 20   Litho.   Perf. 14½x14
105 A17 5c multicolored   .50 .50
106 A17 25c multicolored   .50 .50
107 A18 50c multicolored   1.00 1.25
    Nos. 105-107 (3)   2.00 2.25

50th anniversary of Nauru Cooperative
Society, founded by Timothy Detudamo.

"Eigamoiya" — A19

10c, Phosphate mining. 15c, "Nauru Chief"
plane over Nauru. 25c, Nauru chieftain with
frigate-bird headdress. 35c, Capt. J. Fearn,
sailing ship "Hunter" & map of Nauru. 50c,
"Hunter" off Nauru.

Perf. 13x13½, 13½x13
1974, May 21   Litho.
Sizes: 70x22mm (7c, 35c, 50c);
33x20mm (10c, 15c, 25c)
108 A19 7c multicolored   .70 .95
109 A19 10c multicolored   .55 .25
110 A19 15c multicolored   .70 .35
111 A19 25c multicolored   .60 .40
112 A19 35c multicolored   3.50 3.50
113 A19 50c multicolored   2.00 2.25
    Nos. 108-113 (6)   8.05 7.70

175th anniversary of Nauru's first contact
with the outside world.

Map of
Nauru
A20

Post Office
A21

UPU Emblem and: 20c, Mailman on motorcycle. $1, Flag of Nauru and UPU Building,
Bern, vert.

1974, July 23   Litho.   Perf. 14
114 A20 5c multicolored   .30 .25
Perf. 13½x13, 13x13½
115 A21 8c multicolored   .30 .25
116 A21 20c multicolored   .30 .25
117 A21 $1 multicolored   1.25 1.25
    a. Souv. sheet of 4, #114-117,
        imperf.   3.00 3.00
    Nos. 114-117 (4)   2.15 2.00

Cent. of the UPU.

Rev. P. A.
Delaporte — A22

1974, Dec. 10   Litho.   Perf. 14½
118 A22 15c brt pink & multi   .30 .30
119 A22 20c blue & multi   .50 .50

Christmas 1974. Delaporte, a German-born
American missionary, took Christianity to
Nauru and translated the New Testament into
Nauruan.

Nauru, Grain,
Albert Ellis,
Phosphate
Rock — A23

Designs: 7c, Phosphate mining and coolie
carrying load. 15c, Electric freight train, tugs
and ship. 25c, Excavator, cantilever and truck.

1975, July 23   Perf. 14½x14
120 A23 5c multicolored   .30 .30
121 A23 7c multicolored   .40 .40
122 A23 15c multicolored   1.10 1.10
123 A23 25c multicolored   1.40 1.40
    Nos. 120-123 (4)   3.20 3.20

75th anniv. of discovery of phosphate (5c);
70th anniv. of Pacific Phosphate Co. Mining
Agreement (7c); 50th anniv. of British
Phosphate Commissioners (15c); 5th anniv. of
Nauru Phosphate Corp. (25c).

Melanesian Outrigger
and Map of SPC's
Area — A24

No. 124, Micronesian outrigger. No. 125,
Polynesian double hull. No. 127, Polynesian
outrigger.

1975, Sept. 1   Litho.   Perf. 14x14½
124 A24 20c multicolored   .60 .60
125 A24 20c multicolored   .60 .60
126 A24 20c shown   .60 .60
127 A24 20c multicolored   .60 .60
    a. Block of 4, #124-127   3.25 3.25
    Nos. 124-127 (4)   2.40 2.40

South Pacific Commission Conference,
Nauru, Sept. 29-Oct. 10.
Nos. 124-127 exist imperf. Value, block of
four $50.

New Civic
Center — A25

Design: 50c, "Domaneab" (meeting house)
and flags of participating nations.

1975, Sept. 29   Litho.   Perf. 14½
128 A25 30c multicolored   .30 .25
129 A25 50c multicolored   .45 .45

South Pacific Commission Conference,
Nauru, Sept. 29-Oct. 10.
Nos. 128-129 exist imperf. Value, set $12.

Virgin Mary, Stained-
glass Window — A26

Christmas: 7c, 15c, "Suffer little children to
come unto me," stained-glass window, Orro
Protestant Church. 25c, like 5c, Yaren Catholic
Church.

1975, Nov. 7   Litho.   Perf. 14½
130 A26 5c gray blue & multi   .30 .25
131 A26 7c green & multi   .30 .25
132 A26 15c brown & multi   .30 .50
133 A26 25c lilac & multi   .30 .70
    Nos. 130-133 (4)   1.20 1.70

Frangipani
Forming Lei
Around
Nauru — A27

14c, Hand crowning Nauru with lei. 25c,
Reed warbler, birds flying from Truk to Nauru.
40c, Reunion of islanders in Boar Harbor.

1976, Jan. 31   Litho.   Perf. 14½
134 A27 10c green & multi   .30 .25
135 A27 14c violet & multi   .30 .25
136 A27 25c red & multi   .30 .25
137 A27 40c blue & multi   .30 .25
    Nos. 134-137 (4)   1.20 1.00

30th anniversary of the return of the islanders from Japanese internment on Truk.
Nos. 134-137 exist imperf. Value, set $20.

Nauru Nos. 7
and 11 — A28

15c, Nauru Nos. 10, 12. 25c, Nauru No. 13.
50c, Nauru No. 14, "Specimen."

1976, May 6   Litho.   Perf. 13½x14
138 A28 10c multicolored   .30 .25
139 A28 15c multicolored   .30 .25
140 A28 25c multicolored   .30 .25
141 A28 50c multicolored   .40 .40
    Nos. 138-141 (4)   1.30 1.15

60th anniv. of Nauru's 1st postage stamps.
Nos. 138-141 exist imperf. Value, set
$17.50.

Nauru
Shipping and
Pandanus
A29

Designs: 20c, Air Nauru Boeing 737 and
Fokker F28, and tournefortia argentea. 30c,
Earth satellite station and thespesia populnea.
40c, Area produce and cordia subcordata.

1976, July 26   Litho.   Perf. 13½x14
142 A29 10c multicolored   .30 .25
143 A29 20c multicolored   .30 .25
144 A29 30c multicolored   .30 .25
145 A29 40c multicolored   .45 .45
    Nos. 142-145 (4)   1.35 1.20

7th South Pacific Forum, Nauru, July 1976.
Nos. 142-145 exist imperf. Value, set $35.

Nauruan Children's Choir — A30

20c, Angels. Nos. 146, 148, denominations
at lower right. Nos. 147, 149, denominations at
lower left.

1976, Nov.   Litho.   Perf. 14x13½
146 15c multicolored   .30 .25
147 15c multicolored   .30 .25
    a. A30 Pair, #146-147   .55 .55
148 20c multicolored   .30 .25
149 20c multicolored   .30 .25
    a. A30 Pair, #148-149   .55 .55
    Nos. 146-149 (4)   1.20 1.00

Christmas.
Nos. 146-149 exist imperf. Value, set of two
se-tenant pairs $65.

Nauru House,
Melbourne, and Coral
Pinnacles — A32

30c, Nauru House and Melbourne skyline.

1977, Apr. 14   Photo.   Perf. 14½
150 A32 15c multicolored   .30 .25
151 A32 30c multicolored   .40 .40

Opening of Nauru House in Melbourne,
Australia.
For surcharges see Nos. 161-164.

Cable-laying Ship
Anglia, 1902 — A33

Designs: 15c, Nauru radar station. 20c, Stern of Anglia. 25c, Radar antenna.

1977, Sept. 7   Photo.   Perf. 14½
152 A33 7c multicolored   .30   .25
153 A33 15c multicolored   .30   .25
154 A33 20c multicolored   .30   .30
155 A33 25c multicolored   .40   .40
       Nos. 152-155 (4)   1.30 1.20

1st transpacific cable, 75th anniv., and 1st artificial earth satellite, 20th anniv.

Catholic Church, Yaren, and Father Kayser — A34

Designs: 25c, Congregational Church, Orro. 30c, Catholic Church, Arubo.

1977, Oct.   Photo.   Perf. 14½
156 A34 15c multicolored   .30   .25
157 A34 25c multicolored   .30   .25
158 A34 30c multicolored   .30   .25
       Nos. 156-158 (3)   .90   .75

Christmas, and 55th anniversary of first Roman Catholic Church on Nauru.

Coat of Arms of Nauru — A35

1978, Jan. 31   Litho.   Perf. 14½
159 A35 15c blue & multi   .30   .25
160 A35 60c emerald & multi .35   .35

10th anniversary of independence. Exists imperf, value $14.

Nos. 150-151 Surcharged with New Value and Two Bars

1978, Apr.   Photo.   Perf. 14½
161 A32 4c on 15c multi   1.25 1.25
162 A32 5c on 15c multi   1.25 1.25
163 A32 8c on 30c multi   1.25 1.25
164 A32 10c on 30c multi   1.25 1.25
       Nos. 161-164 (4)   5.00 5.00

Girls Catching Fish in Buada Lagoon — A36

Designs: 1c, Fisherman and family collecting shellfish. 2c, Pigs foraging near coral reef. 3c, Gnarled tree and birds. 4c, Girl catching fish with hands. 5c, Bird catching fish with hands. 10c, Ijuw Lagoon. 15c, Young girl and coral formation. 20c, Reef pinnacles, Anibare Bay. 25c, Pinnacles, Meneng shore. 30c, Frigate bird. 32c, Coconut palm and noddies. 40c, Iwiyi, wading bird. 50c, Frigate birds. $1, Pinnacles, Topside. $2, Newly uncovered pinnacles, Topside. $5, Old pinnacles, Topside.

1978-79   Photo.   Perf. 14½
165 A36 1c multicolored   .35   .25
166 A36 2c multicolored   .35   .25
167 A36 3c multicolored   .85   .75
168 A36 4c multicolored   .40   .25
169 A36 5c multicolored   .85   .75
170 A36 7c multicolored   .30 1.00
171 A36 10c multicolored   .30   .25
172 A36 15c multicolored   .30   .25
173 A36 20c multicolored   .30   .30
174 A36 25c multicolored   .30   .30
175 A36 30c multicolored   1.00   .45
176 A36 32c multicolored   1.40 1.00
177 A36 40c multicolored   1.00 1.50
178 A36 50c multicolored   1.00 1.10
179 A36 $1 multicolored   .70   .80
180 A36 $2 multicolored   .90   .90
181 A36 $5 multicolored   1.65 1.75
       Nos. 165-181 (17)   11.95 11.85

Issued: #166-169, 6/6/79; others, 5/1978. Nos. 179-181 exists on an "official black print without franking validity" numbered souvenir sheet of 3. Value, $15.

"APU" — A37

1978, Aug. 28   Litho.   Perf. 13½
182 A37 15c multicolored   .40   .90
183 A37 20c gold, blk & dk blue .60 1.10

14th General Assembly of Asian Parliamentary Union, Nauru, Aug. 28-Sept. 1. On sale during conference only.

Mother and Child — A38

Christmas: 15c, 20c, Angel over the Pacific, horiz. 30c, like 7c.

1978, Nov. 1   Litho.   Perf. 14
184 A38 7c multicolored   .30   .25
185 A38 15c multicolored   .30   .25
186 A38 20c multicolored   .30   .25
187 A38 30c multicolored   .30   .25
       Nos. 184-187 (4)   1.20 1.00

Lord Baden-Powell and Cub Scout — A39

30c, Boy Scout. 50c, Explorer.

1978, Dec. 1   Litho.   Perf. 14
188 A39 20c multicolored   .30   .25
189 A39 30c multicolored   .30   .25
190 A39 50c multicolored   .35   .35
       Nos. 188-190 (3)   .95   .85

70th anniversary of 1st Scout Troop.

Flyer A over Nauru Airfield — A40

Designs: No. 192, "Southern Cross" and Boeing 727. No. 193, "Southern Cross" and Boeing 737. 30c, Wright Flyer over Nauru.

1979, Jan.   Perf. 14½
191 A40 10c multicolored   .30   .30
192 A40 15c multicolored   .35   .35
193 A40 15c multicolored   .35   .35
a.   Pair, #192-193   .90   .90
194 A40 30c multicolored   .60   .60
       Nos. 191-194 (4)   1.60 1.60

1st powered flight, 75th anniv. and Kingsford Smith's US-Australia and Australia-New Zealand flights, 50th anniv.
Nos. 192-193 printed checkerwise.
Nos. 191-194 exist imperf. Value, set of two singles (Nos. 191, 194) and pair (193a), $70.

A41

Design: Rowland Hill, Marshall Islands No. 15 with Nauru Cancel.

1979, Feb. 27   Litho.   Perf. 14½
195 A41 5c shown   .30   .25
196 A41 15c Nauru No. 15   .30   .25
197 A41 60c Nauru No. 160   .40   .60
a.   Souvenir sheet of 3, #195-197 1.00 1.25
       Nos. 195-197 (3)   1.00 1.10

Sir Rowland Hill (1795-1879), originator of penny postage.

Dish Antenna, Earth Station, ITU Emblem A42

ITU Emblem and: 32c, Woman operating Telex machine. 40c, Radio beacon operator.

1979, Aug.   Litho.   Perf. 14½
198 A42 7c multicolored   .30   .25
199 A42 32c multicolored   .30   .30
200 A42 40c multicolored   .35   .35
       Nos. 198-200 (3)   .95   .90

Intl. Radio Consultative Committee (CCIR) of the ITU, 50th anniv.
Nos. 198-200 exist imperf. Value, set $20.

Nauruan Girl — A43

IYC Emblem, Nauruan Children: 15c, Boy. 25c, 32c, 50c, Girls, diff.

1979, Oct. 3   Litho.   Perf. 14½
201 A43 8c multicolored   .30   .25
202 A43 15c multicolored   .30   .25
203 A43 25c multicolored   .30   .25
204 A43 32c multicolored   .30   .25
205 A43 50c multicolored   .30   .25
a.   Strip of 5, #201-205   1.00 1.00

International Year of the Child.

Star, Scroll, Ekwenababa Flower — A44

Star and Flowers: 15c, Milos. 20c, Denea. 30c, Morning glories.

1979, Nov. 14   Litho.   Perf. 14½
206 A44 7c multicolored   .30   .25
207 A44 15c multicolored   .30   .25
208 A44 25c multicolored   .30   .25
209 A44 30c multicolored   .30   .25
       Nos. 206-209 (4)   1.20 1.00

Christmas.
Nos. 206-209 exist imperf. Value, set $65.

Nauruan Plane over Melbourne A45

Air Nauru, 10th Anniversary (Plane Over): 20c, Tarawa. 25c, Hong Kong. 30c, Auckland.

1980, Feb. 28   Litho.   Perf. 14½
210 A45 15c multicolored   .35   .25
211 A45 20c multicolored   .35   .25
212 A45 25c multicolored   .45   .30
213 A45 30c multicolored   .55   .40
       Nos. 210-213 (4)   1.70 1.20

Early Steam Locomotive A46

32c, Electric locomotive. 60c, Clyde diesel-hydraulic locomotive.

1980, May 6   Litho.   Perf. 15
214 A46 8c shown   .30   .25
215 A46 32c multicolored   .30   .30
216 A46 60c multicolored   .45   .45
a.   Souvenir sheet of 3, #214-216 1.50 1.75
       Nos. 214-216 (3)   1.05 1.00

Nauru Phosphate Corp., 10th anniv. No. 216a also for London 1980 Intl. Stamp Exhibition, May 6-14; Penny Black, 140th anniv.

Christmas 1980 — A47

Designs: 30c, "Glory to God in the Highest . . ." in English and Nauruan.

1980, Sept. 24   Litho.   Perf. 15
217 20c English   .30   .25
218 20c Nauruese   .30   .25
a.   A47 Pair, #217-218   .55   .55
219 30c English   .30   .25
220 30c Nauruese   .30   .25
a.   A47 Pair, #219-220   .55   .55
       Nos. 217-220 (4)   1.20 1.00

See Nos. 236-239.

Flags of Nauru, Australia, Gt. Britain and New Zealand, UN Emblem A49

30c, UN Trusteeship Council. 50c, 1968 independence ceremony.

1980, Dec. 20   Litho.   Perf. 14½
221 A49 25c shown   .30   .25
       Size: 72x22mm
       Perf. 14
222 A49 30c multicolored   .30   .30
223 A49 50c multicolored   .40   .40
       Nos. 221-223 (3)   1.00   .95

UN de-colonization declaration, 20th anniv. No. 222 printed se-tenant with label showing flags of UN and Nauru, issued Feb. 11, 1981.

Timothy Detudamo (Former Head Chief), Domaneab (Meeting House) — A50

1981, Feb.   Litho.   Perf. 14½
224 A50 20c shown   .30   .25
225 A50 30c Raymond Gadabu .30   .25
226 A50 50c Hammer DeRoburt .45   .35
       Nos. 224-226 (3)   1.05   .85

Legislative Council, 30th anniversary.

Casting Net by Hand — A51

1981   Litho.   Perf. 12
227 A51 8c multicolored   .30   .25
228 A51 20c Ancient canoe   .30   .25
229 A51 32c Powered boat   .30   .25
230 A51 40c Fishing vessel   .30   .25
a.   Souvenir sheet of 4, #230 1.75 1.75
       Nos. 227-230 (4)   1.20 1.00

Bank of Nauru, 5th Anniv. — A52

1981, July 21   Litho.   Perf. 14x14½
231 A52 $1 multicolored   1.00 1.00

ESCAP Secy. Maramis Delivering Inaugural Speech — A53

20c, Maramis, Pres. de Robert. 25c, Plaque. 30c, Raising UN flag.

1981, Oct. 24   Litho.   *Perf. 14½*
232	A53	15c shown	.30 .25
233	A53	20c multicolored	.30 .25
234	A53	25c multicolored	.30 .25
235	A53	30c multicolored	.30 .25
		Nos. 232-235 (4)	1.20 1.00

UN Day and first anniv. of Economic and Social Commission for Asia and Pacific (ESCAP) liaison office in Nauru.

Christmas Type of 1980

Christmas (Biblical Scriptures in English and Nauruan): 20c, "His Name Shall Be Called Emmanuel." 30c, "To You is Born This Day . . ."

1981, Nov. 14   Litho.   *Perf. 14½*
236	A47	20c multicolored	.30 .25
237	A48	20c multicolored	.30 .25
a.		Pair, #236-237	.50 .50
238	A47	30c multicolored	.30 .25
239	A48	30c multicolored	.30 .25
a.		Pair, #238-239	.50 .50
		Nos. 236-239 (4)	1.20 1.00

10th Anniv. of South Pacific Forum — A54

1981, Dec. 9   Litho.   *Perf. 13½x14*
240	A54	10c Globe, dish antenna	.30 .25
241	A54	20c Ship	.30 .25
242	A54	30c Jet	.35 .35
243	A54	40c Produce	.40 .40
		Nos. 240-243 (4)	1.35 1.25

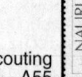

Scouting Year — A55

7c, Carrying packages. 8c, Scouts, life preserver, vert. 15c, Pottery making, vert. 20c, Inspection. 25c, Scout, cub. 40c, Troop.

1982, Feb. 23   Litho.   *Perf. 14*
244	A55	7c multicolored	.30 .25
245	A55	8c multicolored	.30 .25
246	A55	15c multicolored	.30 .25
247	A55	20c multicolored	.30 .25
248	A55	25c multicolored	.30 .30
249	A55	40c multicolored	.45 .45
a.		Souv. sheet of 6, #244-249, imperf.	1.75 1.75
		Nos. 244-249 (6)	1.95 1.75

A56

Ocean Thermal Energy Conversion — A57

Designs: No. 250, Plant under construction. No. 251, Completed plant.

1982, June 10   Litho.   *Perf. 13½*
250		Pair + 2 labels	1.00 1.00
a.-b.	A56 25c any single		.45 .45
251		Pair + 2 labels	1.50 1.50
a.-b.	A57 40c any single		.70 .70

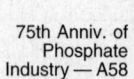

75th Anniv. of Phosphate Industry — A58

5c, Freighter Fido, 1907. 10c, Locomotive Nellie, 1907. 30c, Modern Clyde diesel train, 1982. 60c, Flagship Eigamoiya, 1969. $1, Freighters.

1982, Oct. 11   Litho.   *Perf. 14*
252	A58	5c multicolored	.30 .25
253	A58	10c multicolored	.50 .30
254	A58	30c multicolored	.90 .60
255	A58	60c multicolored	1.30 1.10
		Nos. 252-255 (4)	3.00 2.25

Souvenir Sheet
256	A58	$1 multicolored	1.75 1.75

ANPEX '82 Natl. Stamp Exhibition, Brisbane, Australia, Nos. 252-255 se-tenant with labels describing stamp. No. 256 contains one 68x27mm stamp.

Visit of Queen Elizabeth II and Prince Philip — A59

1982, Oct. 21   *Perf. 14½*
257	A59	20c Elizabeth, vert.	.30 .25
258	A59	50c Philip, vert.	.65 .40
259	A59	$1 Couple	1.10 .75
		Nos. 257-259 (3)	2.05 1.40

Christmas A60

Clergymen: 20c, Father Bernard Lahn, Catholic Mission Church. 30c, Rev. Itubwa Amram, Orro Central Church. 40c, Pastor James Aingimea, Tsiminita Memorial Church, Denigomodu. 50c, Bishop Paul Mea, Diocese of Tarawa-Nauru-Tuvalu.

1982, Nov. 17
260	A60	20c multicolored	.30 .30
261	A60	30c multicolored	.30 .40
262	A60	40c multicolored	.40 .60
263	A60	50c multicolored	.55 .80
		Nos. 260-263 (4)	1.55 2.10

15th Anniv. of Independence A61

15c, Speaker of Parliament, vert. 20c, People's Court, vert. 30c, Law Courts. 50c, Parliament.

1983, Mar. 23   Wmk. 373   *Perf. 14½*
264	A61	15c multicolored	.30 .25
265	A61	20c multicolored	.30 .25
266	A61	30c multicolored	.30 .30
267	A61	50c multicolored	.50 .50
		Nos. 264-267 (4)	1.40 1.30

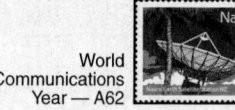

World Communications Year — A62

5c, Earth Satellite Staion NZ. 10c, Omni-directional Range Installation. 20c, Fixed-station ambulance driver. 25c, Radio Nauru broadcaster. 40c, Air mail service.

1983, May. 11   Litho.   *Perf. 14*
268	A62	5c multicolored	.30 .25
269	A62	10c multicolored	.30 .25
270	A62	20c multicolored	.30 .30
271	A62	25c multicolored	.40 .40
272	A62	40c multicolored	.60 .60
		Nos. 268-272 (5)	1.90 1.80

Angam Day (Homecoming) — A63

Perf. 14x13½

1983, Sept. 14   Litho.   Wmk. 373
273	A63	15c MV Trinza arriving	.30 .25

Size: 25x40mm
Perf. 14
274	A63	20c Elsie Agio in exile	.30 .25
275	A63	30c Baby on scale	.35 .35
276	A63	40c Children	.40 .40
		Nos. 273-276 (4)	1.35 1.25

Christmas — A64

Designs: 5c, The Holy Virgin, the Holy Child and St. John, School of Raphael. 15c, The Mystical Betrothal of St. Catherine with Jesus, School of Paolo Veronese. 50c, Madonna on the Throne Surrounded by Angels, School of Seville.

Perf. 14½x14, 14x14½

1983, Nov. 16   Litho.   Wmk. 373
277	A64	5c multi, vert.	.30 .25
278	A64	15c multi, vert.	.30 .25
279	A64	50c multi, vert.	.50 .50
		Nos. 277-279 (3)	1.10 1.00

Common Design Types pictured following the introduction.

Lloyd's List Issue
Common Design Type

20c, Ocean Queen. 25c, Enna G. 30c, Baron Minto loading phosphate. 40c, Triadic, 1940.

1984, May 23   Litho.   *Perf. 14½x14*
280	CD335	20c multicolored	.40 .35
281	CD335	25c multicolored	.50 .50
282	CD335	30c multicolored	.70 .70
283	CD335	40c multicolored	.80 .80
		Nos. 280-283 (4)	2.40 2.35

1984 UPU Congress — A65

1984, June 4   Wmk. 373   *Perf. 14*
284	A65	$1 No. 117	1.10 1.40

Coastal Scene — A66

3c, Woman, vert. 5c, Fishing vessel. 10c, Golfer. 15c, Phosphate excavation, vert. 20c, Surveyor, vert. 25c, Air Nauru jet. 30c, Elderly man, vert. 40c, Social service. 50c, Fishing, vert. $1, Tennis, vert. $2, Lagoon Anabar.

Perf. 13½x14, 14x13½

1984, Sept. 21
285	A66	1c shown	.30 .60
286	A66	3c multi	.30 .30
287	A66	5c multi	.40 .40
288	A66	10c multi	.90 .60
289	A66	15c multi	.90 .60
290	A66	20c multi	.65 .50
291	A66	25c multi	.90 .50
292	A66	30c multi	.90 .50
293	A66	40c multi	1.00 1.00
294	A66	50c multi	1.25 1.25
295	A66	$1 multi	2.50 2.50
296	A66	$2 multi	3.25 3.25
		Nos. 285-296 (12)	12.95 12.00

For surcharges see Nos. 425-427.

Local Butterflies — A67

25c, Common eggfly (female). 30c, Common eggfly (male). 50c, Wanderer (female).

1984, July 24   *Perf. 14*
297	A67	25c multicolored	.50 .50
298	A67	30c multicolored	.60 .60
299	A67	50c multicolored	.90 .90
		Nos. 297-299 (3)	2.00 2.00

Christmas A68

30c, Buada Chapel, vert. 40c, Detudamo Memorial Church, vert. 50c, Candle-light service.

1984, Nov. 14
300	A68	30c multicolored	.45 .45
301	A68	40c multicolored	.55 .55
302	A68	50c multicolored	.75 .75
		Nos. 300-302 (3)	1.75 1.75

Air Nauru, 15th Anniv. — A69

20c, Jet. 30c, Crew, vert. 40c, Fokker F28 over Nauru. 50c, Cargo handling, vert.

1985, Feb. 26   Wmk. 373   *Perf. 14*
303	A69	20c multicolored	.50 .40
304	A69	30c multicolored	.70 .60
305	A69	40c multicolored	.90 .90
306	A69	50c multicolored	1.25 1.25
		Nos. 303-306 (4)	3.35 3.15

Nauru Phosphate Corp., 15th Anniv. — A70

20c, Open-cut mining. 25c, Rail transport. 30c, Phosphate drying plant. 50c, Early steam engine.

1985, July 31
307	A70	20c multicolored	.80 .60
308	A70	25c multicolored	1.65 .90
309	A70	30c multicolored	1.40 .90
310	A70	50c multicolored	2.40 1.50
		Nos. 307-310 (4)	6.25 3.90

Christmas — A71

1985, Oct.
311		50c Canoe	1.25 1.25
312		50c Mother and child	1.25 1.25
a.	A71 Pair, #311-312		2.50 2.50

No. 312a has a continuous design.

Audubon Birth Bicentenary — A72

Illustrations of the brown noddy by John J. Audubon.

1985, Dec. 31
313	A72	10c Adult and young	.40 .40
314	A72	20c Flying	.60 .60
315	A72	30c Two adults	.75 .75
316	A72	50c Adult	1.10 1.10
		Nos. 313-316 (4)	2.85 2.85

Early Transportation A73

15c, Douglas motorcycle. 20c, Truck. 30c, German steam locomotive, 1910. 40c, Baby Austin.

1986, Mar. 5   **Wmk. 384**
317 A73 15c multicolored   1.00 .80
318 A73 20c multicolored   1.25 .90
319 A73 30c multicolored   1.50 1.50
320 A73 40c multicolored   1.90 1.90
    Nos. 317-320 (4)   5.65 5.10

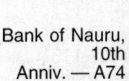

Bank of Nauru, 10th Anniv. — A74

Winning drawings of children's competition.

1986, July 21   **Litho.**   **Perf. 14**
321 A74 20c multicolored   .30 .25
322 A74 25c multicolored   .30 .30
323 A74 30c multicolored   .35 .35
324 A74 40c multicolored   .45 .45
    Nos. 321-324 (4)   1.40 1.35

Flowers — A75

20c, Plumeria rubra. 25c, Tristellateia australis. 30c, Bougainvillea cultivar. 40c, Delonix regia.

1986, Sept. 30   **Wmk. 384**
325 A75 20c multicolored   .40 .40
326 A75 25c multicolored   .60 .60
327 A75 30c multicolored   .75 .75
328 A75 40c multicolored   1.10 1.10
    Nos. 325-328 (4)   2.85 2.85

Christmas A76

1986, Dec. 8   **Wmk. 373**
329 A76 20c Men caroling   .60 .50
330 A76 $1 Carolers, invalid   2.25 2.25

Tribal Dances — A77

1987, Jan. 31
331 A77 20c Girls   .75 .75
332 A77 30c Men and women   1.00 1.00
333 A77 50c Boy, vert.   2.00 2.00
    Nos. 331-333 (3)   3.75 3.75

Artifacts — A78

25c, Hibiscus-fiber skirt. 30c, Headband, necklaces. 45c, Necklaces. 60c, Pandanus-leaf fan.

1987, July 30   **Perf. 14**
334 A78 25c multicolored   .70 .70
335 A78 30c multicolored   .80 .80
336 A78 45c multicolored   1.10 1.10
337 A78 60c multicolored   1.65 1.65
    Nos. 334-337 (4)   4.25 4.25

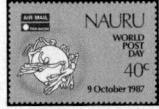

World Post Day — A79

40c, UPU emblem, airmail label.

         Perf. 14½x14
1987, Oct. 9   **Litho.**   **Wmk. 384**
338 A79 40c multicolored   1.75 1.75

Souvenir Sheet

1987, Oct. 20   *Imperf.*
339 A79 $1 Emblem, vert.   4.00 4.00

Nauru Congregational Church, Cent. — A80

Perf. 13x13½
1987, Nov. 5   **Wmk. 373**
340 A80 40c multicolored   1.50 1.50

Island Christmas Celebration A81

1987, Nov. 27   **Wmk. 384**   **Perf. 14**
341 A81 20c shown   .75 .50
342 A81 $1 Sign on building   3.00 3.00

A82   Natl. Independence, 20th Anniv. — A83

Heraldic elements independent of or as part of the natl. arms: 25c, Phosphate mining and shipping. 40c, Tomano flower, vert. 55c, Frigate bird, vert. $1, Natl. arms.

Perf. 13½x14, 14x13½
1988, May 16   **Unwmk.**
343 A82 25c multicolored   1.25 1.25
344 A82 40c multicolored   1.50 1.50
345 A82 55c multicolored   2.25 2.25

         Perf. 13
346 A83 $1 multicolored   3.75 3.75
    Nos. 343-346 (4)   8.75 8.75

Nauru Post Office, 80th Anniv. — A84

30c, Nauru highlighted on German map of the Marshall Islands, & canceled Marshall Islands #25. 50c, Letter mailed from Nauru to Dresden & post office, 1908. 70c, Post office, 1988, & Nauru #348 canceled on airmail cover.

1988, July 14   **Wmk. 384**   **Perf. 14**
347 A84 30c multicolored   .75 .75
348 A84 50c multicolored   1.10 1.10
349 A84 70c multicolored   1.75 1.75
    Nos. 347-349 (3)   3.60 3.60

String Games — A85

1988, Aug. 1   **Unwmk.**   **Perf. 13½x14**
350 A85 25c Mat   .35 .35
351 A85 40c The Pursuer   .55 .55
352 A85 55c Holding Up the Sky   .85 .85
353 A85 80c Manujie's Sword   1.25 1.25
    Nos. 350-353 (4)   3.00 3.00

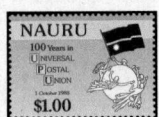

UPU, Cent. — A86

1988, Oct. 1   **Perf. 13½x14**
354 A86 $1 multicolored   1.50 1.50

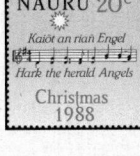

Hark! The Herald Angels Sing, by Charles Wesley (1703-91) — A87

1988, Nov. 28   **Perf. 13½**
355 A87 20c "Hark..."   .65 .65
356 A87 60c "Glory to..."   1.50 1.50
357 A87 $1 "Peace on Earth"   2.25 2.25
    Nos. 355-357 (3)   4.40 4.40

A88

15c, NIC emblem. 50c, APT, ITU emblems. $1, Mounted photograph. $2, UPU emblem, US Capitol.

1989, Nov. 19   **Perf. 14x15**
358 A88 15c multicolored   .50 .50
359 A88 50c multicolored   1.00 1.00
360 A88 $1 multicolored   2.25 2.25
361 A88 $2 multicolored   3.50 3.50
    Nos. 358-361 (4)   7.25 7.25

Annivs. and events: Nauru Insurance Corp., 15th Anniv. (15c). World Telecommunications Day and 10th anniv of the Asia-Pacific Telecommunity (50c); Photography 150th anniv. ($1); and 20th UPU Congress, Washington, DC ($2).

Christmas — A89

$1, Children opening gifts.

1989, Dec. 15   **Litho.**   **Perf. 14x15**
362 A89 20c shown   .60 .60
363 A89 $1 multicolored   2.50 2.50

A90

Legend of Eigigu, The Girl in the Moon: 25c, Eigigu works while sisters play, rocket lift-off. 30c, Eigigu climbing tree, capsule in lunar orbit. 50c, Eigigu stealing from blind woman, lunar module on moon. $1, Eigigu with husband, Maramen (the moon), astronaut stepping on moon.

1989, Dec. 22   **Litho.**   **Perf. 14x15**
364 A90 25c multicolored   3.25 3.25
365 A90 30c multicolored   3.50 3.50
366 A90 50c multicolored   6.50 6.50
367 A90 $1 multicolored   10.00 8.00
    Nos. 364-367 (4)   23.25 21.25

Limited supplies of Nos. 364-367 were available through agent.

A91

50c, Mining by hand. $1, Mechanized extraction.

1990, July 3   **Litho.**   **Perf. 14x15**
368 A91 50c multicolored   1.00 1.00
369 A91 $1 multicolored   1.50 1.50

Nauru Phosphate Corp., 20th anniv.

Christmas A92

No. 370, Children. No. 371, Telling Christmas story.

1990, Nov. 26   **Litho.**   **Perf. 14**
370   25c multicolored   1.25 1.25
371   25c multicolored   1.25 1.25
   a.   A92 Pair, #370-371   2.75 2.75

Legend of Eoiyepiang, Daughter of Thunder and Lightning — A93

1990, Dec. 24   **Litho.**   **Perf. 14x15**
372 A93 25c Woman with baby   1.25 1.00
373 A93 30c Weaving flowers   1.50 1.00
374 A93 50c Listening to storm   2.00 2.25
375 A93 $1 Couple   3.00 3.25
    Nos. 372-375 (4)   7.75 7.50

Flowers — A94

1991, July 15   **Litho.**   **Perf. 14½**
380 A94 15c Oleander   .30 .25
381 A94 20c Lily   .30 .25
382 A94 25c Passion Flower   .30 .30
383 A94 30c Lily, diff.   .40 .40
384 A94 35c Caesalpinia   .45 .45
385 A94 40c Clerodendron   .50 .50
387 A94 45c Bauhinia pinnata   .55 .55
388 A94 50c Hibiscus, vert.   .60 .60
389 A94 75c Apocynaceae   .85 .85
390 A94 $1 Bindweed, vert.   1.10 1.10
391 A94 $2 Tristellateia, vert.   2.25 2.25
392 A94 $3 Impala lily, vert.   3.00 4.00
    Nos. 380-392 (12)   10.60 11.50

Souvenir Sheet

Christmas — A95

$2, Stained glass window.

1991, Dec. 12   **Litho.**   **Perf. 14**
395 A95 $2 multicolored   4.50 4.50

Asian Development Bank, 25th Meeting — A96

1992, May 4   **Litho.**   **Perf. 14x14½**
396 A96 $1.50 multicolored   2.75 2.75

Christmas — A97

Children's drawings: 45c, Christmas trees, flags and balloons. 60c, Santa in sleigh, reindeer on flag.

1992, Nov. 23   **Litho.**   **Perf. 14½x14**
397 A97 45c multicolored   1.00 1.00
398 A97 60c multicolored   1.40 1.40

Hammer DeRoburt
(1922-1992) — A98

1993, Jan. 31   Litho.   Perf. 14x14½
399 A98 $1 multicolored   2.50 2.50
Independence, 25th anniv.

Constitution Day, 15th
Anniv. — A99

70c, Runners. 80c, Declaration of Republic.

1993, May 17   Litho.   Perf. 14x14½
400 A99 70c multi   1.20 1.20
401 A99 80c multi   1.30 1.30

24th South
Pacific Forum
A100

1993, Aug. 9   Litho.   Perf. 14½x14
402 A100 60c Seabirds   1.60 1.60
403 A100 60c Birds, dolphin   1.60 1.60
404 A100 60c Coral, fish   1.60 1.60
405 A100 60c Fish, coral, diff. 1.60 1.60
  a.   Block of 4, #402-405   8.00 8.00
  b.   Souvenir sheet of 4, #402-
       405   8.00 8.00
No. 405a is a continuous design.
No. 405b exists with SINGPEX '93 overprint, sold at the exhibition. Value, unused or
used, $10.

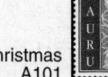

Christmas
A101

Designs: 55c, "Peace on earth..." 65c, "Hark
the Herald Angels Sing."

1993, Nov. 29   Litho.   Perf. 14½x14
406 A101 55c multicolored   1.00 1.00
407 A101 65c multicolored   1.25 1.25

Child's
Best
Friend
A102

1994, Feb. 10   Litho.   Perf. 14
408   $1 Girls, dogs   2.00 2.00
409   $1 Boys, dogs   2.00 2.00
  a.   A102 Pair, #408-409   4.00 4.00
  b.   Souvenir sheet of 2, #408-409 4.50 4.50
  c.   As "b," ovptd. in sheet margin 4.50 4.50
  d.   As "b," ovptd. in sheet margin 4.50 4.50
No. 409c ovptd. with Hong Kong '94
emblem. No. 409d ovptd. with SINGPEX '94
emblem in gold.
  Issued: #409c, 2/18/94; #409d, 8/31/94.

15th
Commonwealth
Games,
Victoria — A103

1994, Sept. 8   Litho.   Perf. 14x14½
410 A103 $1.50 Weight lifting 2.25 2.25

ICAO, 50th
Anniv. — A104

55c, Emblems. 65c, Nauru Intl. Airport. 80c,
DVOR navigational aid. $1, Airport fire
engines.

1994, Dec. 14
411 A104 55c multicolored   .65   .65
412 A104 65c multicolored   .75   .75
413 A104 80c multicolored   .95   .95
414 A104 $1 multicolored   1.25 1.25
  a.   Souvenir sheet of 4, #411-414 6.00 6.00
       Nos. 411-414 (4)   3.60 3.60

United Nations,
50th Anniv. — A105

No. 415, National flag. No. 416, National
coat of arms. No. 417, Canoe, UN emblem.
No. 418, Jet, ship, UN emblem.

1995, Jan. 1   Perf. 14x14½
415 A105 55c multicolored   1.50 1.50
416 A105 75c multicolored   1.50 1.50
417 A105 75c multicolored   1.50 1.50
418 A105 75c multicolored   1.50 1.50
  a.   Block of 4, #415-418   6.75 6.75
  b.   Souvenir sheet of 4, #415-418 7.00 7.00
Nos. 417-418 are a continuous design.

Christmas — A106

75c, Star over Bethlehem.

1994, Nov. 20   Litho.   Perf. 14½x14
419 A106 65c shown   1.25 1.10
420 A106 75c multicolored   1.40 1.30

Membership in Intl.
Olympic
Committee — A107

1994, Dec. 27   Perf. 14x14½
421 A107 50c multicolored   .60   .60

Nauru Phosphate
Corporation, 25th
Anniv. — A108

Designs: No. 422, Signing of Phosphate
Agreement, June 15, 1967. No. 423, Nauru
Pres. Bernard Dowiyogo, Australian Prime
Minister Paul Keating at signing Nauru-Austra-
lia Compact of Settlement. $2, Mining
phosphate.

1995, July 1   Litho.   Perf. 14x15
422 A108 60c multicolored   1.40 1.40
423 A108 60c multicolored   1.40 1.40
  a.   Pair, #422-423   3.50 3.50
         Souvenir Sheet
424 A108 $2 multicolored   4.00 4.00

No. 291 Surcharged & Overprinted

1995, Aug. 19   Litho.   Perf. 13½x14
425 A66 50c on 25c "at Beijing"   1.35 1.35
426 A66 $1 on 25c "at Singa-
          pore"   1.75 1.75
427 A66 $1 on 25c "at Jakarta"   1.75 1.75
  a.   Strip of 3, #425-427   6.50 6.50

UN, 50th
Anniv. — A109

Designs: 75c, Nauru coastline. $1.50, UN
headquarters, US, aerial view of Nauru.

1995, Oct. 24   Litho.   Perf. 14
428 A109 75c multicolored   1.40 1.40
429 A109 $1.50 multicolored   2.75 2.75

Christmas
A110

1995, Dec. 7   Litho.   Perf. 14
430   60c Seeking the Way   1.00 1.00
431   70c Finding the Way   1.10 1.10
  a.   A110 Pair, #430-431   2.60 2.60

Return From
Truk, 50th
Anniv. — A111

1996, Jan. 31   Perf. 12
432 A111 75c multicolored   1.20 1.20
433 A111 $1.25 multicolored   2.30 2.30
  a.   Souvenir sheet of 2, #432-433 4.00 4.00

         Souvenir Sheet

Nanjing
Stone
Carving,
Keeping
off the
Evils
A112

1996, Mar. 20   Litho.   Perf. 12
434 A112 45c multicolored   1.25 1.25
CHINA '96, 9th Asian Intl. Philatelic
Exhibition.

End of World
War II, 50th
Anniv.
A113

Designs: 75c, Children playing on old cannon. $1.50, Girls making flower leis in front of
pillbox.

1995, Sept. 13   Litho.   Perf. 14x13½
435 A113 75c multicolored   1.75 1.75
436 A113 $1.50 multicolored   3.25 3.25
  a.   Pair, Nos. 435-436 + label 7.50 7.50
  b.   As "a," ovptd. in gold on label 10.00 10.00
  c.   As "a," ovptd. in gold on label 10.00 10.00
No. 436a exists with two different labels:
one showing a war memorial, the other a dove.
Gold overprint on memorial label is Hongpex
'96 Exhibition emblem (No. 436b); on dove
label, a silhouette of a rat (No. 436c). Nos.
436a and 436b-436c may be collected as
blocks of four.
  Issued: Nos. 436b, 436c, 1996.

1996 Summer
Olympic Games,
Atlanta — A114

Discobolus and: 40c, Running pictograph,
vert. 50c, Weight lifting pictograph, vert. 60c,
Weight lifter. $1, Runner.

Perf. 13½x14, 14x13½
1996, July 21   Litho.
437 A114 40c multicolored   1.00 1.00
438 A114 50c multicolored   1.25 1.25
439 A114 60c multicolored   1.50 1.50
440 A114 $1 multicolored   1.75 1.75
       Nos. 437-440 (4)   5.50 5.50

Christmas — A115

Designs: 50c, Candles, angel with trumpet,
nativity. 70c, Angel, candles, map, fauna.

1996, Dec. 16   Litho.   Perf. 14
441 A115 50c multicolored   1.00 1.00
442 A115 70c multicolored   1.25 1.25

World Wildlife
Fund — A116

Fish: a, 20c, Dolphinfish. b, 30c, Wahoo. c,
40c, Pacific sailfish. d, 50c, Yellowfin tuna.

1997, Feb. 12   Litho.   Perf. 11½
443 A116 Strip of 4, #a.-d.   4.50 4.50

A117

Giant Buddha (various statues): a, 1c. b, 2c.
c, 5c. d, 10c. e, 12c. f, 15c. g, 25c.

1997, Feb. 12   Perf. 14
444 A117 Sheet of 7, #a.-g.   3.00 3.00
Hong Kong '97, Hong Kong's return to
China. No. 444g is 60x80mm.

A118

Designs: 80c, Engagement portrait. $1.20,
50th Wedding anniversary portrait.

1997, July 15   Litho.   Perf. 13½
445 A118 80c multicolored   1.40 1.50
446 A118 $1.20 multicolored   2.00 2.25
  a.   Souvenir sheet, #445-446   4.25 4.25
Queen Elizabeth II and Prince Philip, 50th
wedding anniv.

Christmas — A119

1997, Nov. 5   Litho.   Perf. 13½
447 A119 60c Monument   .80   .55
448 A119 80c Church   1.30 1.30
Nauru Congregational Church, 110th anniv.

         Souvenir Sheet

Commonwealth, Oceania and South
Pacific Weight Lifting
Championships — A120

Various contestants lifting weights: a, 40c. b, 60c. c, 80c. d, $1.20.

1998, Mar. 25   Litho.   Perf. 14
449 A120 Sheet of 4, #a.-d.   4.00 4.00

A121

Design: Visit of Juan Antonio Samaranch, Pres. of Intl. Olympic Committee.

1998, May 4   Perf. 13½
450 A121 $2 multicolored   2.75 2.75

Souvenir Sheet

28th Parliamentary
Conference — A122

1997, July 24   Litho.   Perf. 14
451 A122 $2 multicolored   3.25 3.25

A123

Diana, Princess of Wales (1961-97): a, In yellow. b, White blouse. c, Wearing tiara. d, White & black outfit. e, Pink hat. f, White dress.

1998, Aug. 31
452 A123 70c Sheet of 6, #a.-f.   5.25 5.25

A125

1998 Commonwealth Games, Kuala Lumpur: 40c, Gymnast on pommel horse. 60c, Throwing discus. 70c, Runner. 80c, Weight lifter.

1998, Sept. 11   Litho.   Perf. 13½x14
454 A125 40c multicolored   .60 .60
455 A125 60c multicolored   .90 .90
456 A125 70c multicolored   1.00 1.00
457 A125 80c multicolored   1.10 1.10
  a. Souvenir sheet, #454-457   3.75 3.75
    Nos. 454-457 (4)   3.60 3.60

Independence,
30th
Anniv. — A126

Squadron Leader L.H. Hicks and: $1, Band. $2, National anthem.

1998, Oct. 26   Litho.   Perf. 14
458 A126 $1 multicolored   .90 .90
459 A126 $2 multicolored   3.00 3.00
  a. Souvenir sheet, #458-459   4.25 4.25

Christmas
A127

Star, island scene and: 85c, Fish, candle, flowers. 95c, Flowers, fruits, Christmas present.

1998   Perf. 13½x12½
460 A127 85c multicolored   1.25 1.25
461 A127 95c multicolored   1.40 1.40

First Contact
with Island,
Bicent.
A128

Designs: No. 462, Sailing ship Snow Hunter. No. 463, Capt. John Fearn.

1998, Dec. 1   Perf. 12
462 A128 $1.50 multicolored   2.00 2.00
463 A128 $1.50 multicolored   2.00 2.00
  a. Pair, #462-463   4.25 4.25
  b. Souvenir sheet, #463a   4.50 4.50

Ships — A129

Designs: a, 70c, HMAS Melbourne. b, 80c, HMAS D'Amantina. c, $1.10, Traditional Nauruan canoe. d, 90c, Alcyone. e, $1, MV Rosie D.

1999, Mar. 19   Litho.   Perf. 12
464 A129 Sheet of 5, #a.-e.   6.00 6.00

Australia '99, World Stamp Expo. No. 464c is 80x30mm.

1st Manned Moon Landing, 30th Anniv.
Common Design Type

Designs: 70c, Neil Armstrong. 80c, Service module and lunar module fire towards moon. 90c, Aldrin deploying EASEP. $1, Command module enters earth atmosphere. $2, Earth as seen from moon.

Perf. 14x13¾
1999, July 20   Litho.   Wmk. 384
465 CD357 70c multicolored   .60 .60
466 CD357 80c multicolored   .85 .85
467 CD357 90c multicolored   1.00 1.00
468 CD357 $1 multicolored   2.10 1.65
    Nos. 465-468 (4)   4.55 4.10

Souvenir Sheet
Perf. 14

469 CD357 $2 multicolored   3.00 3.00

No. 469 contains one circular stamp 40mm in diameter.

China 1999 World
Philatelic
Exhibition — A130

a, Tursiops truncatus. b, Xiphias gladius.

Perf. 12¾x12½
1999, Aug. 21   Litho.   Unwmk.
470 A130 50c Sheet of 2, #a.-b.   3.75 3.75

UPU, 125th
Anniv. — A131

1999, Aug. 23   Litho.   Perf. 11¾
471 A131 $1 multicolored   1.75 1.75

Christmas — A132

Designs: 65c, Native woman. 70c, Christmas tree and candle.

Perf. 13½x13¾
1999, Nov. 10   Litho.   Wmk. 388
472 A132 65c multi   1.10 1.10
473 A132 70c multi   1.25 1.25

Millennium
A133

70c, Woman in native costume, fishermen on beach. $1.10, Satellite dish, runner, cross, airplane, crane, jeep and boat. $1.20, Man on computer, woman holding globe.

Perf. 11¾x12
2000, Jan. 1   Litho.   Wmk. 388
474 A133 70c multi   1.45 2.00
475 A133 $1.10 multi   2.30 3.25
476 A133 $1.20 multi   2.75 3.50
  a. Souvenir sheet of 3, #474-476   6.50 6.50
    Nos. 474-476 (3)   6.50 8.75

Nauru Phosphate
Corp. 30th
Anniv. — A134

Designs: $1.20, Power plant. $1.80, Phosphate train. $2, Albert Ellis.

2000, May 27   Litho.   Perf. 12½x12¾
477-479 A134 Set of 3   6.50 7.75
479a   Souv. sheet, #477-479, perf 12   6.25 7.50

No. 479a exists imperf. Value, $12.

Queen Mother,
100th
Birthday — A135

Designs: $1, Dark blue hat. $1.10, Lilac hat. $1.20, Waving, light blue hat. $1.40, Blue hat.

2000, Aug. 4   Perf. 14¼
480-483 A135 Set of 4   7.00 7.00
483a   Souvenir sheet, #480-483, perf. 13¾x13½   6.50 6.0

2000 Summer
Olympics,
Sydney — A136

Olympic rings, map of Australia, Sydney Opera House and: 90c, Running. $1, Basketball. $1.10, Weight lifting. $1.20, Olympic torch and runner.

2000   Photo.   Perf. 11¾
484-487 A136 Set of 4   8.75 8.75

Christmas — A137

Designs: 65c, Flower, girl decorating Christmas tree, star, decorated Christmas tree. 75c, Ornament, child on toy train, palm tree, gift.

2000   Litho.   Perf. 13¾x13½
488-489 A137 Set of 2   3.00 3.00
489a   Souvenir sheet #488-489   3.25 3.25
Stamps from No. 489a are perf. 14¼x14¼x13¾x14¼.

32nd
Pacific
Islands
Forum
A138

No. 490 — Island and: a, 90c, Yellow flowers, bird flying to right. b, $1, Red flowers, bird flying to left. c, $1.10, Yellow flowers, birds facing right. d, $2, Red flowers, bird facing left.

Perf. 14½x14
2001, Aug. 14   Litho.   Unwmk.
490 A138 Block of 4, #a-d   11.00 11.00
  e. Souvenir sheet, #490   12.00 12.00

Reign Of Queen Elizabeth II, 50th Anniv. Issue
Common Design Type

Designs: Nos. 491, 495a, 70c, Princess Elizabeth in uniform, 1946. Nos. 492, 495b, 80c, Wearing patterned hat. Nos. 493, 495c, 90c, Wearing hat, 1951. Nos. 494, 495d, $1, In 1997. No. 495e, $4, 1955 portrait by Annigoni (38x50mm).

Perf. 14¼x14½, 13¾ (#495e)
2002, Feb. 6   Litho.   Wmk. 373
With Gold Frames
491 CD360 70c multicolored   1.50 1.50
492 CD360 80c multicolored   1.75 1.75
493 CD360 90c multicolored   1.85 1.85
494 CD360 $1 multicolored   2.15 2.15
    Nos. 491-494 (4)   7.25 7.25

Souvenir Sheet
Without Gold Frames
495 CD360 Sheet of 5, #a-e   10.50 10.50

Miniature Sheet

In Remembrance of Sept. 11, 2001
Terrorist Attacks — A139

No. 496: a, 90c. b, $1. c, $1.10. d, $2.

Wmk. 373
2002, May 17   Litho.   Perf. 13¾
496 A139 Sheet of 4, #a-d   7.50 7.50

Butterflies — A140

No. 497: a, Parthenos sylvia. b, Delias madetes. c, Danaus philene. d, Arhopala hercules. e, Papilio canopus. f, Danaus schenkii. g, Parthenos figrina. h, Mycalesis phidon. i, Vindula sapor.
$2, Graphium agamemnon.

2002, June 28   Perf. 13¾x14¼
497 A140 50c Sheet of 9, #a-i   11.00 11.00

Souvenir Sheet
498 A140 $2 multi   4.50 4.50

Queen Mother Elizabeth (1900-2002)
Common Design Type

Designs: Nos. 499, 501a, $1.50, Wearing hat (black and white photograph). Nos. 500, 501b, $1.50, Wearing light blue hat.

Perf. 13¾x4¼
2002, Aug. 5   Litho.   Wmk. 373
With Purple Frames
499 CD361 $1.50 multicolored   3.00 3.00
500 CD361 $1.50 multicolored   3.00 3.00
Souvenir Sheet
Without Purple Frames
Perf. 14½x14¼
501 CD361   Sheet of 2, #a-b   8.00 8.00

Fire
Fighting — A141

Designs: 20c, Building fire. 50c, Blaze at
sea. 90c, Forest fire. $1, New and old fire hel-
mets. $1.10, Modern ladder truck, old pump
engine. $2, Modern and late 19th cent.
firefighters.
$5, Modern fire engine and rescue vehicle.

Perf. 14x14¼
2002, Aug. 31   Litho.   Wmk. 373
502-507 A141   Set of 6   11.00 11.00
Souvenir Sheet
508 A141 $5 multi   14.00 14.00

Roman
Catholic
Church
in Nauru,
Cent.
A142

No. 509: a, First church building, Arubo. b,
Father Friedrich Gründl, first missionary. c,
Sister Stanisla, first sister. d, Second church
building, Ibwenape. e, Brother Kalixtus Bader,
first lay brother. f, Father Alois Kayser,
missionary.

Wmk. 373
2002, Dec. 8   Litho.   Perf. 13¾
509 A142 $1.50 Sheet of 6,
#a-f   16.00 16.00

Christmas — A143

Designs: 15c, The Holy Family with Dancing
Angels, by Sir Anthony Van Dyck. $1, The
Holy Virgin with the Child, by Luca Cangiasus.
$1.20, The Holy Family with the Cat, by Rem-
brandt. $3, The Holy Family with St. John, by
Raphael.

2002, Dec. 8
510-513 A143   Set of 4   10.00 10.00

Worldwide Fund
For Nature
(WWF) — A144

Designs: 15c, Red-and-black anemone fish,
Bubble tentacle sea anemone. $1, Orange-fin
anemone fish, Leathery sea anemone. $1.20,
Pink anemone fish, Magnificent sea anemone.
$3, Clark's anemone fish, Merten's sea
anemone.

Wmk. 373
2003, Apr. 29   Litho.   Perf. 14
514-517 A144   Set of 4   10.00 10.00
517a   Miniature sheet, 4 each
#514-517   40.00 40.00

Powered
Flight,
Cent.
A145

No. 518: a, Santos-Dumont wins the
Deutsch Prize, Oct. 1901. b, USS Shenan-
doah at Lakehurst, NJ. c, R101 at Cardington
Mast, U.K., Oct. 1929. d, R34 crossing Atlan-
tic, July 1919. e, Zeppelin No. 1, 1900. f, USS
Los Angeles moored to the USS Patoka. g,
Goodyear C-71 airship. h, LZ-130 Graf
Zeppelin II at Friedrichshafen, Germany. i,
Zeppelin NT.
No. 519 — LZ-127 Graf Zeppelin: a, Over
Mt. Fuji. b, Over San Francisco. c, Exchanging
mail with Russian ice breaker, Franz Josef
Land.

2003, Oct. 26
518 A145 50c Sheet of 9, #a-i   11.00 11.00
519 A145 $2 Sheet of 3, #a-c   13.00 13.00

Bird Life
International — A146

Nauru reed warbler: No. 520, Bird on reed.
No. 521, Bird on branch with insect in beak,
vert. No. 522a, Close-up of head. No. 522b,
Bird with open beak, vert. No. 522c, Nest with
chicks.

2003, Nov. 10   Perf. 14¼x13¾
520 A146 $1.50 multi   4.75 4.75
 a.   Perf. 14¼x14½   4.75 4.75
Perf. 13¾x14¼
521 A146 $1.50 multi   4.75 4.75
 a.   Perf. 14½x14¼   4.75 4.75
Souvenir Sheet
Perf. 14¼x14½, 14½x14¼ (#522b)
522   Sheet, #520a, 521a,
522a-522c   15.00 15.00
 a.-c. A146 $1.50 Any single   3.50 3.50

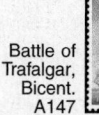

Battle of
Trafalgar,
Bicent.
A147

Designs: 25c, Aigle in action against HMS
Defiance. 50c, French "Eprouvette." 75c, San-
tissima Trinidad in action against HMS Africa.
$1, Emperor Napoleon Bonaparte, vert. $1.50,
HMS Victory. No. 528, $2.50, Vice-Admiral Sir
Horatio Nelson, vert.
No. 529, $2.50, vert.: a, Admiral Pierre Vil-
leneuve. b, Formidable.

2005, Mar. 29   Litho.   Perf. 13¼
523-528 A147   Set of 6   11.50 11.50
Souvenir Sheet
529 A147 $2.50 Sheet of 2,
#a-b   10.50 10.50

No. 527 has particles of wood from the HMS
Victory embedded in the areas covered by a
thermographic process that produces a shiny,
raised effect.

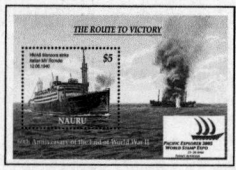

End of
World
War II,
60th
Anniv.
A148

No. 530: a, German raider Komet shells
Nauru, 1940. b, French warship Le Triomphant
assists in evacuation of civilians, 1942. c, Japanese forces occupy Nauru, 1942. d, US Air
Force B-24 Liberator aircraft bombing missions, 1943. e, USS Paddle stationed off
Nauru, 1943. f, B-25G Mitchell "Coral Princess" shot down over Nauru, 1944. g, Spitfires, Battle of Britain, 1940. h, HMAS Diaman-
tine arrives at Nauru, 1945. i, D-Day landings,
1944. j, Union Jack is hoisted again, 1945.
$5, HMAS Manoora sinks Italian MV
Romolo, 1940.

2005, Apr. 21   Perf. 13¾
530 A148 75c Sheet of 10, #a-j   13.00 13.00
Souvenir Sheet
531 A148 $5 multi   9.00 9.00
Pacific Explorer 2005 World Stamp Expo,
Sydney (No. 531).

Pope John Paul II
(1920-2005) — A149

2005, Aug. 18   Litho.   Perf. 14x14¼
532 A149 $1 multi   2.00 2.00

Rotary International,
Cent. — A150

2005, Sept. 12   Perf. 14½x14¼
533 A150 $2.50 multi   4.75 4.75

BirdLife International — A151

No. 534, 25c: a, Rota bridled white-eye. b,
Faichuk white-eye. c, Samoan white-eye. d,
Bridled white-eye. e, Long-billed white-eye. f,
Golden white-eye.
No. 535, 50c: a, Kuhl's lorikeet. b, Masked
shining parrot. c, Crimson shining parrot. d,
Blue lorikeet. e, Henderson lorikeet. f,
Ultramarine lorikeet.
No. 536, $1: a, Atoll fruit dove. b, Henderson
fruit dove. c, Cook Islands fruit dove. d, Rapa
fruit dove. e, Whistling fruit dove. f, Mariana fruit
dove.

Perf. 14¼x14½
2005, Sept. 12   Litho.
Sheets of 6, #a-f
534-536 A151   Set of 3   28.00 28.00

Christmas — A152

Stories by Hans Christian Andersen (1805-
75): 25c, The Little Fir Tree. 50c, The Wild
Swans. 75c, The Farmyard Cock and the
Weather Cock. $1, The Storks. $2.50, The
Toad. $5, The Ice Maiden.

2005, Oct. 10   Perf. 14
537-542 A152   Set of 6   16.50 16.50

Battle of Trafalgar,
Bicent. — A153

Designs: 50c, HMS Victory. $1, Ships in
battle, horiz. $5, Admiral Horatio Nelson.

2005, Oct. 18   Perf. 13½
543-545 A153   Set of 3   13.00 13.00

Anniversaries — A154

No. 546, 25c: a, Wolfgang Amadeus
Mozart. b, Piano and violin.
No. 547, 50c: a, Isambard Kingdom Brunel.
b, Chain and pulley.
No. 548, 75c: a, Edmond Halley. b, Halley's
quadrant.
No. 549, $1: a, Charles Darwin. b, Early
microscope.
No. 550, $1.25: a, Thomas Alva Edison. b,
Light bulb.
No. 551, $1.50: a, Christopher Columbus. b,
Astrolabe.

2006, May 27   Litho.   Perf. 13¼x12½
Horiz. Pairs, #a-b
546-551 A154   Set of 6   22.00 22.00
Birth of Mozart, 250th anniv., Birth of
Brunel, bicent., Birth of Halley, 350th anniv.,
Darwin's voyage on the Beagle, 175th anniv.,
Death of Edison, 75th anniv., Death of Colum-
bus, 500th anniv.

2006 World Cup
Soccer
Championships,
Germany — A155

Scenes from championship matches won
by: $1, Uruguay, 1950. $1.50, Argentina,
1978. $2, Italy, 1982. $3, Brazil, 2002.

2006, June 9   Perf. 14
552-555 A155   Set of 4   15.00 15.00

Dinosaurs
A156

Designs: 10c, Parasaurolophus. 25c,
Quetzalcoatlus. 50c, Spinosaurus. 75c, Tricer-
atops. $1, Tyrannosaurus rex. $1.50,
Euoplocephalus. $2, Velociraptor. $2.50,
Protoceratops.

2006, Aug. 14   Perf. 13¼x13½
556-563 A156   Set of 8   16.00 16.00

Miniature Sheet

Victoria
Cross,
150th
Anniv.
A157

No. 564: a, Lt. Gerald Graham carrying
wounded man. b, Pvt. Mac Gregor shooting
rifle. c, Pvt. Alexander Wright repelling a sor-
tie. d, Cpl. John Ross viewing evacuation of
the Redan. e, Sgt. McWheeney digging with
bayonet. f, Brevet Maj. G. L. Goodlake surpris-
ing enemy. Descriptions of vignettes are on
labels below each stamp.

2006, Sept. 12   Perf. 13¼x12½
564 A157 $1.50 Sheet of 6,
#a-f, + 6 la-
bels   18.00 18.00

Miniature Sheet

Inaugural Flight of the Concorde, 30th Anniv. — A158

No. 565: a, British Airways Concorde G-BOAF on ground. b, First flight of Concorde 002, 1969. c, Concorde landing. d, Queen's Golden Jubilee flypast, 2002. e, 50th anniv. of Battle of Britain, 1990. f, Concorde at 60,000 feet. g, Extreme condition testing. h, Concorde on runway. i, First commercial flight, 1976. j, Concorde above Earth. k, British Airways Concorde G-BOAF in flight. l, Two Concordes on ground.

2006, Oct. 10   **Perf. 14¼x13¾**
565 A158 $1 Sheet of 12, #a-l,
    + 3 labels   26.00 26.00

Miniature Sheet

Year of Three Kings, 70th Anniv. A159

No. 566: a, Queen Elizabeth II. b, King George V and Princess Elizabeth. c, King Edward VIII and Princess Elizabeth. d, King George VI and Princess Elizabeth.

2006, Oct. 17
566 A159 $1.50 Sheet of 4,
    #a-d   13.00 13.00

Wedding of Queen Elizabeth II and Prince Philip, 60th Anniv. — A160

Designs: $1, Couple. $1.50, Couple in coach. $2, At wedding ceremony. $3, Couple walking.
$5, Queen Elizabeth II in bridal gown.

2007, Jan. 31   **Litho.**   **Perf. 13¾**
567-570 A160   Set of 4   13.00 13.00
Souvenir Sheet
Perf. 14¼
571 A160 $5 multi   10.00 10.00
No. 571 contains one 43x57mm stamp.

Royal Air Force, 90th Anniv. A162

Aviation pioneers: No. 572, 70c, Sir Douglas Bader (1910-82), World War II fighter ace. No. 573, 70c, R. J. Mitchell (1895-1937), designer of Spitfire airplane. No. 574, 70c, Sir Frank Whittle (1907-96), inventor of jet engine. No. 575, 70c, Sir Sydney Camm (1893-1966), designer of Hawker Hurricane airplane. No. 576, 70c, Air Vice Marshal James E. "Johnnie" Johnson (1915-2001), World War II fighter ace.
$3, Avro Vulcan.

Wmk. 373
2008, May 19   **Litho.**   **Perf. 14**
572-576 A161   Set of 5   8.50 8.50
Souvenir Sheet
577 A162 $3 multi   7.00 7.00
Nos. 572-576 were each printed in sheets of 8 + central label.

2008 Summer Olympics, Beijing — A163

Designs: 15c, Bamboo, badminton. 25c, Dragon, archery. 75c, Lanterns, weight lifting. $1, Fish, diving.

Perf. 13¼
2008, Aug. 8   **Litho.**   **Unwmk.**
578-581 A163   Set of 4   5.50 5.50

A164

End of World War I, 90th Anniv. A165

World War I recruitment posters inscribed: No. 582, $1, "A Happy New Year to our Gallant Soldiers." No. 583, $1, "The Empire Needs Men." No. 584, $1, "South Australians." No. 585, $1, "Your King and Country Need You." No. 586, $1, "Britons." No. 587, $1, "An Appeal to You."
$2, Queen's Wreath of Remembrance.

Wmk. 406
2008, Sept. 16   **Litho.**   **Perf. 14**
582-587 A164   Set of 6   13.00 13.00
Souvenir Sheet
588 A165 $2 multi   4.50 4.50

Worldwide Fund for Nature (WWF) — A166

Greater frigate bird: 25c, Adult and chick. 75c, Two in flight. $1, Landing. $2, One in flight.

Perf. 13¼x13
2008, Oct. 14   **Unwmk.**
589-592 A166   Set of 4   8.25 8.25
592a   Sheet, 4 each #589-592,
    perf. 13   30.00 30.00

Naval Aviation, Cent. — A167

Designs: No. 593, $1.50, Avro 504C. No. 594, $1.50, Fairey Flycatcher. No. 595, $1.50, Short Folder. No. 596, $1.50, De Havilland Sea Vixen.
$3, Grumman Avenger in Operation Meridian, 1945.

Wmk. 406
2009, Sept. 3   **Litho.**   **Perf. 14**
593-596 A167   Set of 4   12.00 12.00
Souvenir Sheet
597 A167 $3 multi   6.00 6.00
Nos. 593-596 each were printed in sheets of 8 + central label.

Russian Space Program — A168

Flags of Russia and Nauru and: No. 598, 60c, Sputnik satellite, 1957. No. 599, 60c, Yuri Gagarin, first man in space, 1961. $1.20, Nauru Island from space. $2.25, Vostok 1. $3, International Space Station.

Perf. 14½x14
2011, Apr. 12   **Unwmk.**
598-602 A168   Set of 5   14.50 14.50

Souvenir Sheet

Wedding of Prince William and Catherine Middleton — A169

Perf. 14¾x14¼
2011, Apr. 29   **Wmk. 406**
603 A169 $5 multi   11.00 11.00

Port Development Project — A170

Wmk. 406
2018, Jan. 31   **Litho.**   **Perf. 14¼**
604 A170 50c multi   .75 .75
Republic of Nauru, 50th anniv.

Independence, 50th Anniv. — A171

Litho. & Embossed With Foil Application
2018, May 17   **Unwmk.**   **Perf. 14¼**
605 A171 $5 gold   — —
Constitution Day.

Return of Mrs. Muriel Cecil From Truk, 73rd Anniv. — A172

Perf. 14¼x14
2019, Jan. 31   **Litho.**   **Unwmk.**
606 A172 $5 multi   — —

Bishar Abdirahman Hussein, Kenyan Diplomat, Director General of Universal Postal Union International Bureau — A173

Perf. 14¼
2019, Mar. 5   **Litho.**   **Unwmk.**
607 A173 $5 multi   — —

Visit of Republic of China Pres. Tsai Ing-wen to Nauru — A174

Perf. 14¼
2019, Mar. 25   **Litho.**   **Unwmk.**
608 A174 $5 multi   — —

Pres. Baron Waqa — A175

Perf. 14¼
2019, May 17   **Litho.**   **Unwmk.**
609 A175 $5 multi   — —
Constitution Day.

Deiboe Tribe Mat Design — A177

Perf. 14¼
2020, Aug. 19   **Litho.**   **Unwmk.**
611 A177 $5 multi   — —

Return of Nauru Islanders From Truk (Chuuk) Island, 75th Anniv. — A178

Perf. 14x14¾
2021, July 10   **Litho.**   **Unwmk.**
612 A178 $5 multi   — —

Hammer DeRoburt (1922-92), First President of Nauru — A179

Perf. 14¼
2022, Oct. 20   **Litho.**   **Unwmk.**
613 A179 $5 multi   — —

SEMI-POSTAL STAMP

Miniature Sheet of 4

1996 Summer Olympics, Atlanta — SP1

Designs: a, Birds, denomination UR. b, Birds, denomination UL. c, 4 dolphins. d, 2 dolphins.

1995, Sept. 1   **Litho.**   **Perf. 12**
B1   SP1 60c +15c, #a.-d.   7.00 6.50
Surcharge for sports development in Nauru.

NEPAL

nə-'pol

LOCATION — In the Himalaya Mountains between India and Tibet
GOVT. — Republic
AREA — 56,136 sq. mi.
POP. — 24,302,653 (1999 est.)
CAPITAL — Kathmandu

Nepal stamps were valid only in Nepal and India until April 1959, when they became valid to all parts of the world.

4 Pice = 1 Anna
64 Pice = 16 Annas = 1 Rupee
100 Paisa = 1 Rupee (1958)

Catalogue values for unused stamps in this country are for Never Hinged items, beginning with Scott 103 in the regular postage section, Scott C1 in the air post section and Scott O1 in the officials section.

Nos. 1-24, 29A were issued without gum.

Sripech and Crossed
Khukris — A1

1881   Typo.   Unwmk.   Pin-perf.
European Wove Paper
1	A1	1a ultramarine	240.00	350.00
2	A1	2a purple	280.00	400.00
a.	Tete beche pair		325.00	—
3	A1	4a green	325.00	

Imperf
4	A1	1a blue	160.00	150.00
5	A1	2a purple	125.00	125.00
a.	Tete beche pair			
6	A1	4a green	240.00	400.00

No. 3 postally used is probably unique. Only 2 No. 5a are known unused. No. 5a is only known to exist used in a strip of three.

1886   Native Wove Paper   Imperf.
7	A1	1a ultramarine	90.00	120.00
a.	Tete beche pair		400.00	450.00
8	A1	2a violet	75.00	90.00
a.	Tete beche pair		400.00	525.00
9	A1	4a green	95.00	135.00
a.	Tete beche pair		600.00	700.00
	Nos. 7-9 (3)		260.00	345.00

Nos. 7-10 are clear to mostly clear designs on good quality native paper. European wove paper is of substantially higher quality, white, and lacks the wood fibers of the native paper.

Used values for Nos. 10-49 are for telegraph cancels.

Siva's Bow and Two
Khukris — A2

1899-1917   Imperf.
Native Wove Paper
10	A2	½a black, clear impression	20.00	13.50
a.	Tete beche pair		150.00	35.00
11	A2	½a red orange ('17)	1,750.	500.00
a.	Tete beche pair			2,000.

Pin-perf.
| 12 | A2 | ½a black | 30.00 | 17.50 |
| a. | Tete beche pair | | 225.00 | 55.00 |

No. 11 is known postally used on six covers.
No. 11a unused is only known in larger blocks, no unused pairs currently exist.

Type of 1881
1898-1917   Imperf.
12B	A2	½a black	35.00	35.00
13	A1	1a pale blue	60.00	60.00
a.	1a bluish green	75.00	75.00
b.	Tete beche pair	150.00	150.00
c.	As "a," tete beche pair	300.00	300.00
14	A1	2a gray violet	60.00	60.00
a.	Tete beche pair	140.00	140.00
15	A1	2a claret ('17)	100.00	32.50
a.	Tete beche pair	225.00	100.00
16	A1	2a brown ('17)	25.00	12.00
a.	Tete beche pair	55.00	42.50
17	A1	4a dull green	70.00	70.00
a.	Tete beche pair	350.00	350.00
b.	Cliche of 1a in plate of 4a ('04)	500.00	400.00
c.	As "b," pair	—	—
	Nos. 12B-17 (6)	350.00	269.50

No. 13-17 are blurry impressions on poor quality native paper.
#17b has the recut frame of the 1904 issue. #17b probably was used only on telegraph/telephone forms.

Pin-perf.
18	A1	1a pale blue	17.50	10.00
a.	Tete beche pair	325.00	—
19	A1	2a gray violet	90.00	90.00
a.	Tete beche pair	300.00	300.00
20	A1	2a claret ('17)	90.00	45.00
a.	Tete beche pair	250.00	—
21	A1	2a brown ('17)	90.00	45.00
a.	Tete beche pair	250.00	—
22	A1	4a dull green	150.00	150.00
a.	Tete beche pair	900.00	900.00

Frame Recut on All Cliches, Fewer Lines
1903-04   Native Wove Paper   Imperf.
| 23 | A1 | 1a bright blue | 20.00 | 13.00 |
| a. | Tete beche pair | 60.00 | 42.50 |

Pin-perf.
| 24 | A1 | 1a bright blue | 30.00 | |
| a. | Tete beche pair | 120.00 | |

European Wove Paper
| 23b | A1 | 1a blue | 1,500. | 1,000. |
| 23c | | Tete beche pair | 2,500. | |

Pin-perf.
| 24b | A1 | 1a blue | 1,500. | 2,000. |
| 24c | | Tete beche pair | 3,500. | |

No. 23 exists in emerald on native wove paper. All known examples are used with telegraph cancels.

Siva Mahadeva — A3

1907   Engr.   Perf. 13½
European Wove Paper
26	A3	2p brown	6.00	1.60
27	A3	4p green	6.00	1.60
28	A3	8p carmine	8.00	1.60
29	A3	16p violet	16.00	4.00
	Nos. 26-29 (4)	36.00	8.80

Type A3 has five characters in bottom panel, reading "Gurkha Sirkar." Date divided in lower corners is "1964." Outer side panels carry denomination (also on A5).

A4

1917-18   Imperf.
29A	A4	1a bright blue	12.00	5.00
b.	1a indigo	12.00	6.00
c.	Pin-perf.	17.50	15.00

No. 29A may not have been used postally.

In 1917 a telephone and telegraph system was started and remainder stocks and further printings of designs A1 and A2 were used to pay telegraphs fees. Design A4 was designed for telegraph use but was valid for postal use. After 1929 design A3 was used for telegrams. The usual telegraph cancellation is crescent-shaped.

Type of 1907 Redrawn

A5

Nine characters in bottom panel reading "Nepal Sirkar"

1930   Perf. 14, 14½
Size: 24¾x18¾mm
30	A5	2p dark brown	8.00	.55
31	A5	4p green	8.00	.80
32	A5	8p deep red	30.00	2.00
33	A5	16p dark red vio	20.00	2.00
34	A5	24p orange yellow	16.00	2.50
35	A5	32p dark ultra	20.00	2.50

Size: 26x19½mm
| 36 | A5 | 1r orange red | 24.00 | 6.00 |

Size: 28x21mm
| 37 | A5 | 5r brown & black | 27.50 | 16.00 |
| | Nos. 30-37 (8) | 153.50 | 32.35 |

On Nos. 30-37 the date divided in lower corners is "1986."

Type of 1929 Redrawn

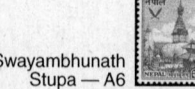

Date characters in Lower Corners read "1992"

1935   Unwmk.   Engr.   Perf. 14
38	A5	2p dark brown	4.00	.80
39	A5	4p green	4.00	1.20
40	A5	8p bright red	50.00	6.00
41	A5	16p dk red violet	16.00	2.00
42	A5	24p orange yellow	10.00	3.00
43	A5	32p dark ultra	10.00	3.00
	Nos. 38-43 (6)	94.00	16.00

Redrawn Type of 1935
Perf. 11, 11x11½, 12x11½
1941-46   Typo.
44	A5	2p black brown	.40	.40
a.	2p green (error)	8.00	8.00
45	A5	4p bright green	1.20	.80
46	A5	8p rose red	.80	.55
47	A5	16p chocolate ('42)	12.00	3.00
48	A5	24p orange ('46)	12.00	2.00
49	A5	32p deep blue ('46)	16.00	2.50

Size: 29x19½mm
50	A5	1r henna brown ('46)	32.50	20.00
	Nos. 44-50 (7)	74.90	29.25
	Set, never hinged	160.00	

Exist imperf. vert. or horiz. Full imperf. examples were not regularly issued.

Swayambhunath
Stupa — A6

Temple of
Krishna
A7

View of
Kathmandu
A8

Pashupati (Siva
Mahadeva) — A9

Designs: 4p, Temple of Pashupati. 6p, Tri-Chundra College. 8p, Mahabuddha Temple. 24p, Gueswori Temple, Patan. 32p, The 22 Fountains, Balaju.

Perf. 13½x14, 13½, 14
1949, Oct. 1   Litho.   Unwmk.
51	A6	2p brown	.50	.50
52	A6	4p green	.50	.50
53	A6	6p rose pink	1.10	.80
54	A6	8p vermilion	1.20	1.20
55	A7	16p rose lake	1.20	1.20
56	A8	20p blue	1.25	1.10
57	A8	24p carmine	2.50	2.00
58	A8	32p ultramarine	3.50	2.00
59	A9	1r red orange	16.00	20.00
	Nos. 51-59 (9)	27.75	29.30
	Set, never hinged	60.00	

King Tribhuvana Bir
Bikram — A10

1954, Apr. 15   Unwmk.   Perf. 14
Size: 18x22mm
60	A10	2p chocolate	1.10	.50
61	A10	4p green	4.00	1.75
62	A10	6p rose	.85	.50
63	A10	8p violet	.50	.55
64	A10	12p red orange	9.00	2.75

Size: 25½x29½mm
65	A10	16p red brown	.85	.50
66	A10	20p car rose	2.00	1.75
67	A10	24p rose car	1.50	1.75
68	A10	32p ultramarine	2.00	1.75
69	A10	50p rose pink	20.00	7.50
70	A10	1r vermilion	24.00	13.00
71	A10	2r orange	21.00	10.00
	Nos. 60-71 (12)	86.80	42.30
	Set, never hinged	160.00	

Map of Nepal — A11

1954, Apr. 15   Size: 29½x17½mm
72	A11	2p chocolate	1.10	1.10
73	A11	4p green	4.00	1.75
74	A11	6p rose	11.00	2.75
75	A11	8p violet	.65	.30
76	A11	12p red orange	17.00	.80

Size: 38x21½mm
77	A11	16p red brown	.85	.40
78	A11	20p car rose	1.25	.40
79	A11	24p rose lake	1.25	.40
80	A11	32p ultramarine	1.75	.70
81	A11	50p rose pink	17.50	2.50
82	A11	1r vermilion	21.00	3.00
83	A11	2r orange	15.00	3.00
	Nos. 72-83 (12)	92.35	17.10
	Set, never hinged	200.00	

Planting
Rice
A12

Throne
A13

Hanuman
Gate — A14

King
Mahendra Bir
Bikram and
Queen
Ratna — A15

Design: 8p, Ceremonial arch and elephant.

Perf. 13½x14, 11½, 13½, 14
Litho., Photo. (6p)

1956		**Granite Paper**	**Unwmk.**	
84	A12	4p green	3.50	6.75
85	A13	6p brt scar & yel		
		org	1.60	3.00
86	A12	8p dark lilac	1.25	1.50
87	A14	24p carmine rose	2.75	6.00
88	A15	1r claret	55.00	82.50
		Nos. 84-88 (5)	64.10	99.75
		Set, never hinged	135.00	

Coronation of King Mahendra Bir Bikram and Queen Ratna Rajya Lakshmi.

Mountain Village and UN Emblem A16

1956, Dec. 14		**Litho.**	**Perf. 13½**	
89	A16	12p ultra & orange	3.75	6.00
		Never hinged	7.50	

1st anniv. of Nepal's admission to the UN.

Crown of Nepal — A17

Perf. 13½x14

1957, June 22			**Unwmk.**	
		Size: 18x22mm		
90	A17	2p dull brn pur	.50	1.00
91	A17	4p light green	.70	1.00
92	A17	6p rose carmine	.50	1.00
93	A17	8p light violet	.50	1.00
94	A17	12p orange red	2.75	1.75
		Size: 25½x30mm		
95	A17	16p red brown	4.00	2.75
96	A17	20p rose carmine	6.00	3.75
97	A17	24p rose red	4.00	3.50
98	A17	32p ultramarine	5.50	3.75
99	A17	50p magenta	12.00	8.00
100	A17	1r red orange	15.00	15.00
101	A17	2r orange	10.00	11.00
		Nos. 90-101 (12)	61.45	53.50
		Set, never hinged	110.00	

Lumbini Temple — A18

1958, Dec. 10		**Typo.**	**Perf. 11**	
		Without Gum		
102	A18	6p yellow	2.00	2.00

10th anniversary of Universal Declaration of Human Rights. Exists imperf.

Catalogue values for unused stamps in this section, from this point to the end of the section, are for Never Hinged items.

Map and Flag — A19

1959, Feb. 18		**Engr.**	**Perf. 14½**	
103	A19	6p carmine & light green	.85	.50

First general elections in Nepal.

Statue of Vishnu, Changu Narayan A20

Krishna Conquering Black Serpent A21

Designs: 4p, Nepalese glacier. 6p, Golden Gate, Bhaktapur. 8p, Nepalese musk deer. 12p, Rhinoceros. 16p, 20p, 24p, 32p, 50p,

Nyatapola Temple, Bhatgaon. 1r, 2r, Himalayan impeyan pheasant. 5r, Satyr tragopan.

Perf. 13½x14, 14x13½

1959-60		**Litho.**	**Unwmk.**	
		Size: 18x22mm		
104	A20	1p chocolate	.25	.25
105	A21	2p gray violet	.25	.25
106	A20	4p light ultra	.55	.40
107	A20	6p vermilion	.55	.25
108	A21	8p sepia	.40	.25
109	A21	12p greenish gray	.55	.25
		Size: 25½x30mm		
110	A20	16p brown & lt vio	.55	.25
111	A20	20p blue & dull		
		rose	2.00	1.00
112	A20	24p green & pink	2.00	1.00
113	A20	32p brt vio & ultra	1.20	1.00
114	A20	50p rose red & grn	2.00	1.00
115	A20	1r redsh brn & bl	24.00	8.50
116	A20	2r rose lil & ultra	16.00	9.00
117	A20	5r vio & rose red		
		('60)	100.00	80.00
		Nos. 104-117 (14)	150.30	103.40

Nepal's admission to the UPU.

Spinning Wheel — A22

1959, Apr. 10		**Typo.**	**Perf. 11**	
118	A22	2p dark red brown	.75	.35

Issued to promote development of cottage industries.
Exists imperf. Value $26.

King Mahendra — A23

1959, Apr. 14				
119	A23	12p bluish black	.65	.50

Nepal's admission to UPU. Exists imperf. and ungummed. Value $200.
No. 119 exists with paper maker's watermark "LOVELY BOND / MADE IN SWEDEN". Value, unused or used, $12.

King Mahendra Opening Parliament A24

1959, July 1		**Unwmk.**	**Perf. 10½**	
120	A24	6p deep carmine	3.50	1.20

First session of Parliament. Exists imperf. Value, pair $45.

Sri Pashupati Nath — A25

1959, Nov. 19			**Perf. 11**	
		Size: 18x24½mm		
121	A25	4p dp yellow green	.80	.80
		Size: 20½x28mm		
122	A25	8p carmine	1.60	1.00
		Size: 24½x33mm		
123	A25	1r light blue	10.00	6.50
		Nos. 121-123 (3)	12.40	8.30

Renovation of Sri Pashupati Temple. Nos. 121-123 exist imperf. between.

King Mahendra — A26

1960, June 11		**Photo.**	**Perf. 14**	
		Size: 25x30mm		
124	A26	1r red lilac	1.75	1.25

King Mahendra's 40th birthday. See Nos. 147-151A. For overprint see No. O15.

Children, Temple and Mt. Everest — A27

1960		**Typo.**	**Perf. 11**	
125	A27	6p dark blue	17.50	12.00

1st Children's Day, Mar. 1, 1960. Printed in sheets of four. Exists imperf.; value $45 unused.

Mount Everest — A28

Himalaya mountain peaks: 5p, Machha Puchhre. 40p, Mansalu.

1960-61		**Photo.**	**Perf. 14**	
126	A28	5p claret & brown ('61)	.50	.25
127	A28	10p ultra & rose lilac	.70	.25
128	A28	40p vio & red brn ('61)	1.50	.85
		Nos. 126-128 (3)	2.70	1.35

King Tribhuvana — A29

1961, Feb. 18			**Perf. 13x13½**	
129	A29	10p red brown & orange	.75	.25

Tenth Democracy Day.

King Mahendra — A30

1961, June 11			**Perf. 14x14½**	
130	A30	6p emerald	.40	.40
131	A30	12p ultramarine	.55	.55
132	A30	50p carmine rose	1.20	1.20
133	A30	1r brown	2.00	2.00
		Nos. 130-133 (4)	4.15	4.15

King Mahendra's 41st birthday.

Prince Gyanendra Canceling Stamps — A31

1961		**Typo.**	**Perf. 11**	
134	A31	12p orange	40.00	40.00

Children's Day, Mar. 1, 1961. Exists imperf. Value, $75.

Malaria Eradication Emblem and Temple — A32

Design: 1r, Emblem and Nepalese flag.

1962, Apr. 7		**Litho.**	**Perf. 13x13½**	
135	A32	12p blue & lt blue	.40	.40
136	A32	1r magenta & orange	1.25	1.25

WHO drive to eradicate malaria.

King Mahendra — A33

1962, June 11		**Unwmk.**	**Perf. 13**	
137	A33	10p slate blue	.25	.25
138	A33	15p brown	.40	.40
139	A33	45p dull red brown	.75	.75
140	A33	1r olive gray	1.20	1.20
		Nos. 137-140 (4)	2.60	2.60

King Mahendra's 42nd birthday.

Bhanu Bhakta Acharya — A34

10p, Moti Ram Bhatta. 40p, Shambu Prasad.

1962		**Photo.**	**Perf. 14x14½**	
141	A34	5p orange brown	.40	.40
142	A34	10p deep aqua	.40	.40
143	A34	40p olive bister	.55	.55
		Nos. 141-143 (3)	1.35	1.35

Issued to honor Nepalese poets.

Mahendra Type of 1960 and

King Mahendra — A35

1962-66			**Perf. 14½x14**	
144	A35	1p car rose	.25	.25
145	A35	2p brt blue	.25	.25
145A	A35	3p gray ('66)	.80	.40
146	A35	5p golden brown	.25	.25
		Perf. 14x14½		
		Size: 21½x38mm		
147	A26	10p rose claret	.25	.25
148	A26	40p brown	.40	.40
149	A26	75p blue green	12.00	12.00
		Perf. 14		
		Size: 25x30mm		
150	A26	2r red orange	1.50	1.50
151	A26	5r gray green	3.25	3.25
151A	A26	10r violet ('66)	11.00	9.50
		Nos. 144-151A (10)	29.95	28.05

See No. 199. For overprints see Nos. O12-O14.

Blackboard, Book and UN Emblem — A36

1963, Jan. 6			**Perf. 14½x14**	
152	A36	10p dark gray	.50	.25
153	A36	15p brown	.65	.40
154	A36	50p violet blue	1.20	.75
		Nos. 152-154 (3)	2.35	1.40

UNESCO "Education for All" campaign.

Five-pointed Star and Hands Holding Lamps — A37

1963, Feb. 19		**Photo.**	**Unwmk.** **Perf. 13**	
155	A37	5p blue	.30	.25
156	A37	10p reddish brown	.30	.25
157	A37	50p rose lilac	.90	.55
158	A37	1r blue green	1.75	.80
		Nos. 155-158 (4)	3.25	1.85

Panchayat System and National Day.

Man, Tractor and
Wheat — A38

1963, Mar. 21   Perf. 14x14½
159 A38 10p orange   .55   .25
160 A38 15p dark ultra   .80   .40
161 A38 50p dp bl grn   1.75   .80
162 A38 1r red brown   2.50 1.40
     Nos. 159-162 (4)   5.60 2.85

FAO "Freedom from Hunger" campaign.

Map of Nepal and
Hand — A39

1963, Apr. 14   Unwmk.   Perf. 13
163 A39 10p green   .40   .25
164 A39 15p claret   .80   .40
165 A39 50p slate   1.75   .55
166 A39 1r violet blue   2.75   .90
     Nos. 163-166 (4)   5.70 2.10

Rastriya Panchayat system.

King Mahendra — A40

1963, June 11   Perf. 13
167 A40 5p violet   .30   .25
168 A40 10p brown orange   .50   .25
169 A40 15p dull green   .75   .25
     Nos. 167-169 (3)   1.55   .90

King Mahendra's 43rd birthday.

East-West
Highway on Map
of Nepal and King
Mahendra — A41

1964, Feb. 19   Photo.   Perf. 13
170 A41 10p blue & dp orange   .40   .25
171 A41 15p dk blue & dp org   .60   .25
172 A41 50p dk grn & redsh brn   1.25   .40
     Nos. 170-172 (3)   2.25   .90

Issued to publicize the East-West Highway
as "The Prosperity of the Country."

King Mahendra
Speaking Before
Microphone — A42

1964, June 11   Perf. 14
173 A42 1p brown olive   .30   .25
174 A42 2p gray   .40   .25
175 A42 2r golden brown   1.75 1.20
     Nos. 173-175 (3)   2.45 1.70

King Mahendra's 44th birthday.

Crown Prince
Birendra — A43

**   Perf. 14x14½**
1964, Dec. 28   Photo.   Unwmk.
176 A43 10p dark green   1.10   .85
177 A43 15p brown   1.10   .85

19th birthday (coming of age) of Crown
Prince Birendra Bir Bikram Shah Deva.

Nepalese Flag
and Swords,
Olympic
Emblem — A44

1964, Dec. 31   Litho.   Perf. 13x13½
178 A44 10p red & ultra   1.75   .80

18th Olympic Games, Tokyo, Oct. 10-25.

Farmer   Family
Plowing   A46
A45

Designs: 5p, Grain. 10p, Chemical plant.

1965   Photo.   Perf. 13½
179 A45 2p bl grn & char   .40   .40
180 A45 5p dull grn & brn   .40   .40
181 A45 10p gray & purple   .40   .40
182 A46 15p yellow & brown   .55   .55
     Nos. 179-182 (4)   1.75 1.75

Issued to publicize land reform.
The 2p also exists on light green paper.
Issue dates: 15p, Feb. 10; others, Dec. 16.

Mail Circling
Globe — A47

1965, Apr. 13   Perf. 14½x14
183 A47 15p rose lilac   .75   .40

Issued for Nepalese New Year.

King Mahendra — A48

**   Perf. 14x14½**
1965, June 11   Photo.   Unwmk.
184 A48 50p rose violet   1.00   .75

King Mahendra's 45th birthday.

Victims of
Revolution, 1939-
40 — A49

1965, June 11   Perf. 13
185 A49 15p bright green   .45   .40

The men executed by the Rana Government
1939-40 were: Shukra Raj Shastri, Dasharath
Chand, Dharma Bhakta and Ganga Lal
Shresta.

ITU Emblem — A50

1965, Sept. 15   Photo.   Perf. 13
186 A50 15p deep plum & black   .55   .40

Cent. of the ITU.

Devkota — A51

1965, Oct. 14   Perf. 14x14½
187 A51 15p red brown   .40   .30

Lakshmi Prasad Devkota (1908-1959), poet.

ICY
Emblem — A52

**   Engr. and Litho.**
1965, Oct. 24   Perf. 11½x12
188 A52 1r multicolored   1.20   .90

International Cooperation Year.

Nepalese Flag
and King — A53

1966, Feb. 18   Photo.   Perf. 14½x14
189 A53 15p blue & red   .80   .55

Issued for Democracy Day.

Siva, Parvati and
Pashupati
Temple — A54

1966, Feb. 18   Perf. 14
190 A54 15p violet   .50   .40

Hindu festival Maha Sivaratri.

Emblem
A55

**   Perf. 14½x14**
1966, June 10   Photo.   Unwmk.
191 A55 15p dk green & orange   .70   .40

National Philatelic Exhib., June 10-16.

King Mahendra — A56

1966, June 11   Perf. 13x13½
192 A56 15p yellow & vio brown   .45   .30

Issued for King Mahendra's 46th birthday.

Kanti Rajya
Lakshmi — A57

1966, July 5   Photo.   Perf. 14x14½
193 A57 15p golden brown   .40   .40

60th birthday of Queen Mother Kanti Rajya
Lakshmi.

Queen Ratna Rajya
Lakshmi Devi
Shah — A58

1966, Aug. 19   Photo.   Perf. 13
194 A58 15p yellow & brown   .50   .40

Issued for Children's Day.

Krishna with Consort
Radha and
Flute — A59

1966, Sept. 7
195 A59 15p dk purple & yellow   .50   .40

Krishnastami 2023, the birthday of Krishna.

King
Mahendra — A60

1966, Oct. 1   Photo.   Perf. 14½x14
196 A60 50p slate grn & dp car   4.50 1.50

Issued to commemorate the official recognition of the Nepalese Red Cross.

Opening of WHO
Headquarters
Building,
Geneva — A61

1966, Nov. 11   Photo.   Perf. 14
197 A61 1r purple   2.50 1.50

Lekhnath Paudyal — A62

1966, Dec. 29   Photo.   Perf. 14
198 A62 15p dull violet blue   .60   .50

Lekhnath Paudyal (1884-1966), poet.

**   King Type of 1962**
1967, Feb. 10   Photo.   Perf. 14½x14
199 A35 75p blue green   1.60   .80

Rama and Sita — A63

1967, Apr. 18   Litho.   Perf. 14
200 A63 15p brown & yellow   .50   .40

Rama Navami 2024, the birthday of Rama.

Buddha — A64

1967, May 23   Photo.   Perf. 13½x13
201 A64 75p orange & purple   1.00 1.00

2,511th birthday of Buddha.

King Mahendra Addressing Crowd and Himalayas A65

1967, June 11 *Perf. 13*
202 A65 15p dk brown & lt blue .50 .40
King Mahendra's 47th birthday.

Queen Ratna among Children — A66

1967, Aug. 20 Photo. *Perf. 13*
203 A66 15p pale yel & dp brown .50 .40
Issued for Children's Day on the birthday of Queen Ratna Rajya Lakshmi Devi Shah.

Durbar Square, Bhaktapur — A67

5p, Ama Dablam Mountain, ITY emblem.

1967, Oct. 24 *Perf. 13½x14*
Size: 29½x21mm
204 A67 5p violet .40 .40
Perf. 14½x14
Size: 37½x19½mm
205 A67 65p brown .80 .80
Intl. Tourist Year, 1967. See No. C2.

Official Reading Proclamation A68

1967, Dec. 16 Litho. *Perf. 13*
206 A68 15p multicolored .50 .40
"Back to the Villages" campaign.

Crown Prince Birendra, Boy Scouts and Scout Emblem — A69

1967, Dec. 29 Photo. *Perf. 14½x14*
207 A69 15p ultramarine .80 .55
60th anniv. of Boy Scouts.

Prithvi Narayan — A70

1968, Jan. 11 *Perf. 14x14½*
208 A70 15p blue & rose .80 .55
Rajah Prithvi Narayan (1779-1839), founder of modern Nepal.

Arms of Nepal — A71

1968, Feb. 19 Photo. *Perf. 14x14½*
209 A71 15p crimson & dk blue .80 .55
Issued for National Day.

WHO Emblem and Flag of Nepal — A72

1968, Apr. 7 *Perf. 13*
210 A72 1.20r dull yel, red & ultra 3.50 2.50
World Health Day (UN WHO).

Goddess Sita and Shrine — A73

1968, May 6 Photo. *Perf. 14½x14*
211 A73 15p violet & org brown .80 .40

King Mahendra, Pheasant and Himalayas — A74

1968, June 11 Photo. *Perf. 13½*
212 A74 15p multicolored 4.50 .40
King Mahendra's 48th birthday.

Flag, Children and Queen Ratna — A75

1968, Aug. 19 Litho. *Perf. 13x13½*
213 A75 5p blue grn, yel & ver .50 .30
Fourth National Children's Day.

Buddha and Human Rights Flame — A76

1968, Dec. 10 Photo. *Perf. 14½x14*
214 A76 1r dk green & red 3.00 2.00
International Human Rights Year.

Young People Dancing Around Flag — A77

1968, Dec. 28 Photo. *Perf. 14½x14*
215 A77 25p violet blue .80 .55
23rd birthday of Crown Prince Birendra, which is celebrated as Youth Festival.

UN Building, Nepalese and UN Flags — A78

1969, Jan. 1 *Perf. 13½x13*
216 A78 1r multicolored 1.25 .90
Issued to commemorate Nepal's admission to the UN Security Council for 1969-1970.

Amsu Varma — A79

Portraits: 25p, Ram Shah. 50p, Bhimsen Thapa.

1969, Apr. 13 Photo. *Perf. 14x14½*
217 A79 15p green & purple .55 .55
218 A79 25p blue green .80 .80
219 A79 50p orange brown 1.00 1.00
Nos. 217-219 (3) 2.35 2.35
Amsu Varma, 7th cent. ruler and reformer; Ram Shah, 17th cent. ruler and reformer, and Bhimsen Thapa, 18-19th cent. administrator and reformer.

ILO Emblem — A80

1969, May 1 Photo. *Perf. 14½x14*
220 A80 1r car rose, blk & lt brown 6.00 4.00
50th anniv. of the ILO.

King Mahendra — A81

1969, June 20 *Perf. 13½x13*
221 A81 25p gold & multi .50 .50
King Mahendra's 49th birthday (50th by Oriental count). Issuance delayed from June 11 to 20.

King Tribhuvana and Wives — A82

1969, July 1 *Perf. 14½x14*
222 A82 25p yellow & ol gray .50 .45
64th anniv. of the birth of King Tribhuvana.

Queen Ratna & Child Playing — A83

1969, Aug. 20 Photo. *Perf. 14x14½*
223 A83 25p gray & rose car .50 .50
5th Natl. Children's Day and to for the 41st birthday of Queen Ratna Rajya Lakshmi Devi Shah.

Rhododendron & Himalayas — A84

Flowers: No. 225, Narcissus. No. 226, Marigold. No. 227, Poinsettia.

1969, Sept. 17 Photo. *Perf. 13½*
224 A84 25p lt blue & multi .60 .45
225 A84 25p brown red & multi .60 .45
226 A84 25p black & multi .60 .45
227 A84 25p multicolored .60 .45
a. Block of 4, #224-227 3.50 3.50

Durga, Goddess of Victory — A85

1969, Oct. 17 Photo. *Perf. 14x14½*
228 A85 15p black & orange .50 .40
229 A85 50p black, bis brn & vio 1.10 1.00
Issued to celebrate the Dasain Festival.

Crown Prince Birendra and Princess Aishwarya — A86

1970, Feb. 27 Photo. *Perf. 13½*
230 A86 25p multicolored .70 .40
Wedding of Crown Prince Birendra Bir Bikram Shah Deva and Crown Princess Aishwarya Rajya Lakshmi Devi Rana, Feb. 27-28.

Agricultural Products, Cow, Fish — A87

1970, Mar. 21 Litho. *Perf. 12½*
231 A87 25p multicolored .70 .50
Issued to publicize the Agricultural Year.

Bal Bhadra Kunwar — A88

1970, Apr. 13 Photo. *Perf. 14½x14*
232 A88 1r ol bister & red lilac 1.50 1.00
Bal Bhadra Kunwar, leader in the 1814 battle of Kalanga against British forces.

King Mahendra, Mountain Peak and Crown A89

1970, June 11 Litho. *Perf. 11½*
233 A89 50p gold & multi 1.20 .60
King Mahendra's 50th birthday.

Gosainkund — A90

Lakes: 25p, Phewa Tal. 1r, Rara Daha.

1970, June 11 Photo. *Perf. 13½*
234 A90 5p dull yellow & multi .50 .40
235 A90 25p gray & multi .75 .60
236 A90 1r pink & multi 1.25 1.10
Nos. 234-236 (3) 2.50 2.10

A.P.Y. Emblem — A91

1970, July 1 *Perf. 14½x14*
237 A91 1r dark blue & blue 1.25 .90
Asian Productivity Year 1970.

Bal Mandir Building and Queen Ratna — A92

1970, Aug. 20 Photo. *Perf. 14½x14*
238 A92 25p gray & bister brn .60 .40
Issued for Children's Day. The Bal Mandir Building in Taulihawa is the headquarters of the National Children's Organization.

New UPU Headquarters, Bern — A93

1970, Oct. 9   Photo.   Perf. 14½x14
239 A93 2.50r ocher & sepia   2.50 1.75

UN Flag — A94

1970, Oct. 24   Photo.   Perf. 14½x14
240 A94 25p blue & brown   .60 .40
25th anniversary of the United Nations.

Royal Palace and Square, Patan — A95

25p, Bodhnath stupa, near Kathmandu, vert. 1r, Gauri Shankar, holy mountain.

Perf. 11x11½, 11½x11
1970, Dec. 28   Litho.
241 A95 15p multicolored   .50 .25
242 A95 25p multicolored   1.00 .50
243 A95 1r multicolored   1.75 .80
Nos. 241-243 (3)   3.25 1.55
Crown Prince Birendra's 25th birthday.

Statue of Harihar (Vishnu-Siva) — A96

1971, Jan. 26   Photo.   Perf. 14x14½
244 A96 25p bister brn & black   .60 .40

Torch and Target — A97

1971, Mar. 21   Photo.   Perf. 13½x13
245 A97 1r bluish gray & dp org   1.50 1.00
Intl. year against racial discrimination.

King Mahendra and Subjects — A98

1971, June 11   Photo.   Perf. 14½x14
246 A98 25p dull purple & blue   .70 .30
King Mahendra's 51st birthday.

Sweta Bhairab (Siva) — A99

Sculptures of Siva: 25p, Manhankal Bhairab. 50p, Kal Bhairab.

1971, July 11   Perf. 13½x13
247 A99 15p org brn & blk   .50 .40
248 A99 25p lt green & black   .60 .50
249 A99 50p blue & black   1.10 .85
Nos. 247-249 (3)   2.20 1.75

Queen Ratna Receiving Garland — A100

1971, Aug. 20   Photo.   Perf. 11½
Granite Paper
250 A100 25p gray & multi   .60 .35
Children's Day, Queen Ratna's birthday.

Map and Flag of Iran, Flag of Nepal — A101

1971, Oct. 14   Granite Paper
251 A101 1r pink & multi   1.50 .75
2500th anniversary of the founding of the Persian empire by Cyrus the Great.

UNICEF Emblem, Mother and Child — A102

1971, Dec. 11   Perf. 14½x14
252 A102 1r gray blue   1.50 1.00
25th anniversary of UNICEF.

Everest — A103

Himalayan Peaks: 1r, Kangchenjunga. 1.80r, Annapurna I.

1971, Dec. 28   Perf. 13½x13
253 A103 25p blue & brown   .40 .25
254 A103 1r dp blue & brown   .80 .50
255 A103 1.80r blue & yel brown   1.60 1.00
Nos. 253-255 (3)   2.80 1.75
"Visit Nepal."

Royal Standard — A104

1972, Feb. 19   Photo.   Perf. 13
256 A104 25p dark red & black   .75 .30
National Day.

Araniko and White Dagoba, Peking — A105

1972, Apr. 13   Litho.   Perf. 13
257 A105 15p lt blue & ol gray   .30 .25
Araniko, a 14th century Nepalese architect, who built the White Dagoba at the Miaoying Monastery, Peking, 1348.

Book Year Emblem, Ancient Book — A106

1972, Sept. 8   Photo.   Perf. 14½x14
258 A106 2p ocher & brown   .25 .25
259 A106 5p tan & black   .30 .25
260 A106 1r blue & black   1.00 .90
Nos. 258-260 (3)   1.55 1.40
International Book Year.

Heart and WHO Emblem — A107

1972, Nov. 6   Photo.   Perf. 13x13½
261 A107 25p dull grn & claret   .50 .40
"Your heart is your health," World Health Month.

King Mahendra (1920-1972) A108

1972, Dec. 15   Photo.   Perf. 13½x13
262 A108 25p brown & black   .50 .30

King Birendra — A109

1972, Dec. 28   Photo.   Perf. 13x13½
263 A109 50p ocher & purple   .60 .50
King Birendra's 27th birthday.

Northern Border Costume — A110

Nepalese Costumes: 50p, Hill dwellers. 75p, Kathmandu Valley couple. 1r, Inner Terai couple.

1973, Feb. 18   Photo.   Perf. 13
264 A110 25p dull lilac & multi   .40 .25
265 A110 50p lemon & multi   .50 .40
266 A110 75p multicolored   .75 .50
267 A110 1r multicolored   1.00 .70
a.   Block of 4, #264-267   3.25 3.25
National Day.

Babu Ram Acharya (1888-1972), Historian — A111

1973, Mar. 12   Photo.   Perf. 13
268 A111 25p olive gray & car   .50 .30

Nepalese Family and Home — A112

1973, Apr. 7   Photo.   Perf. 14½x14
269 A112 1r Prus blue & ocher   1.25 .85
25th anniv. of the WHO.

Lumbini Garden, Birthplace of Buddha A113

1973, May 17   Photo.   Perf. 13x13½
270 A113 25p shown   .40 .25
271 A113 75p Mt. Makalu   .55 .30
272 A113 1r Gorkha Village   .80 .80
Nos. 270-272 (3)   1.75 1.35

FAO Emblem, Women Farmers — A114

1973, June 29   Photo.   Perf. 14½x14
273 A114 10p dark gray & violet   .30 .25
World food program, 10th anniversary.

INTERPOL Headquarters and Emblem — A115

1973, Sept. 3
274 A115 25p bister & blue   .50 .30
50th anniversary of the International Criminal Police Organization (INTERPOL).

Shom Nath Sigdyal (1884-1972), Scholar — A116

1973, Oct. 5   Photo.   Perf. 13x13½
275 A116 1.25r violet blue   1.25 .85

Cow — A117

1973, Oct. 25   Photo.   Perf. 13½x13
276 A117 2p shown   .30 .25
277 A117 3.25r Yak   1.75 1.50
Festival of Lights (Tihar).

King Birendra A118

Perf. 13, 13½x14, 15x14½
1973-74   Photo.
278 A118 5p dark brown   .25 .25
279 A118 15p ol brn & dk brn ('74)   .30 .25
280 A118 1r reddish brn & dk brn ('74)   .80 .55
Nos. 278-280 (3)   1.35 1.05
King Birendra's 28th birthday.

National Anthem — A119

Natl. Day: 1r, Score of national anthem.

1974, Feb. 18   Photo.   Perf. 13½x13
281 A119 25p rose carmine   .50 .25
282 A119 1r deep green   .80 .65

King Janak on Throne — A120

1974, Apr. 14   Litho.   Perf. 13½
283 A120 2.50r multicolored   2.00 1.75

Children's Village and SOS Emblem A121

1974, May 20   Litho.   Perf. 13½x13
284 A121 25p ultra & red   .50 .45
25th anniv. of SOS Children's Village Intl.

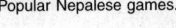
Baghchal — A122

1974, July 1   Litho.   Perf. 13
285 A122 2p Soccer   .25 .25
286 A122 2.75r shown   1.25 .90
Popular Nepalese games.

WPY Emblem — A123

1974, Aug. 19   Litho.   Perf. 13
287 A123 5p ocher & blue   .30 .25
World Population Year.

UPU Monument, Bern — A124

1974, Oct. 9   Litho.   Perf. 13
288 A124 1r olive & black   .80 .50
Centenary of Universal Postal Union.

Butterfly — A125

Designs: Nepalese butterflies.

1974, Oct. 16
289 A125 10p lt brown & multi   .25 .25
290 A125 15p lt blue & multi   .65 .30
291 A125 1.25r multicolored   1.25 .75
292 A125 1.75r buff & multi   1.50 1.10
Nos. 289-292 (4)   3.65 2.40

King Birendra — A126

1974, Dec. 28   Litho.   Perf. 13½x13
293 A126 25p gray green & black   .30 .25
King Birendra's 29th birthday.

Muktinath A127   Peacock Window A128

1974, Dec. 31   Perf. 13x13½, 13½x13
294 A127 25p multicolored   .50 .25
295 A128 1r multicolored   1.00 .55
Tourist publicity.

Guheswari Temple — A129   Rara — A130

Pashupati Temple A131   King Birendra and Queen Aishwarya A132

Designs: 1r, Throne. 1.25r, Royal Palace.

1975, Feb. 24   Litho.   Perf. 13x13½
296 A129 25p multicolored   .50 .25
Photo.   Perf. 14½x14
297 A130 50p multicolored   .50 .25
Granite Paper   Perf. 11½, 11 (A131)
298 A132 1r olive & multi   .75 .70
299 A132 1.25r multicolored   1.50 .75
300 A131 1.75r multicolored   1.00 .95
301 A132 2.75r gold & multi   1.50 1.25
a. Souvenir sheet of 3   5.50 5.50
Nos. 296-301 (6)   5.75 4.15
Coronation of King Birendra, Feb. 24, 1975.
No. 301a contains 3 imperf. stamps similar to
Nos. 298-299, 301 and label with inscription.

Tourist Year Emblem A133   Swayambhunath Stupa, Kathmandu A134

Perf. 12½x13½, 13½x12½
1975, May 25   Litho.
302 A133 2p yellow & multi   .30 .25
303 A134 25p violet & black   .40 .30
South Asia Tourism Year.

Tiger — A135

1975, July 17   Litho.   Perf. 13
304 A135 2p shown   .50 .45
305 A135 5p Deer, vert.   .50 .55
306 A135 1r Panda   1.00 1.00
Nos. 304-306 (3)   2.00 2.00
Wildlife conservation.

Queen Aishwarya and IWY Emblem A136

1975, Nov. 8   Litho.   Perf. 13
307 A136 1r lt blue & multi   .80 .40
International Women's Year.

Ganesh Peak A137   Rupse Falls A138

Kumari, Living Goddess of Nepal — A139

1975, Dec. 16   Litho.   Perf. 13½
308 A137 2p multicolored   .25 .25
309 A138 25p multicolored   .35 .30
310 A139 50p multicolored   1.00 .50
Nos. 308-310 (3)   1.60 1.05
Tourist publicity.

King Birendra — A140

1975, Dec. 28   Photo.   Perf. 13
311 A140 25p rose lil & red lil   .30 .25
King Birendra's 30th birthday.

Flag and Map of Nepal — A141

1976, Feb. 19   Litho.   Perf. 13
312 A141 2.50r dark blue & red   1.25 .80
National or Democracy Day.

Rice Cultivation A142

1976, Apr. 11   Litho.   Perf. 13
313 A142 25p multicolored   .30 .25
Agricultural development.

Flags of Nepal and Colombo Plan — A143

1976, July 1   Photo.   Perf. 13x13½
314 A143 1r multicolored   .60 .50
Colombo Plan, 25th anniversary.

Runner — A144

1976, July 31   Photo.   Perf. 13x13½
315 A144 3.25r black & ultra   1.60 1.00
21st Olympic Games, Montreal, Canada,
July 17-Aug. 1.

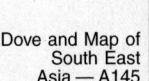
Dove and Map of South East Asia — A145

1976, Aug. 17   Litho.   Perf. 13½
316 A145 5r bister, black & ultra   2.50 1.50
5th Summit Conference of Non-aligned
Countries, Colombo, Sri Lanka, Aug. 9-19.

Folk Dances — A146

1976, Sept. 27   Litho.   Perf. 13½x13
317 A146 10p Lakha mask   .30 .25
318 A146 15p Maruni   .30 .25
319 A146 30p Jhangad   .50 .25
320 A146 1r Sebru   .75 .40
Nos. 317-320 (4)   1.85 1.15

Nepalese Lily — A147

Flowers: No. 322, Meconopsis grandis. No.
323, Cardiocrinum giganteum, horiz. No. 324,
Megacodon stylophorus, horiz.

1976-77   Litho.   Perf. 13
321 A147 30p lt ultra & multi   .55 .25
322 A147 30p brown & multi   .55 .25
323 A147 30p violet & multi   .55 .25
324 A147 30p violet & multi   .55 .25
Nos. 321-324 (4)   2.20 1.00
Issue dates: Nov. 7, 1976, Jan. 24, 1977.

King Birendra — A148

1976, Dec. 28   Photo.   Perf. 14
325 A148 5p green   .30 .25
326 A148 30p multicolored   .30 .25
King Birendra's 31st birthday.

Bell and American Bicentennial Emblem — A149

1976, Dec. 31   Litho.   Perf. 13½
327 A149 10r multicolored   3.00 2.75
American Bicentennial.

Warrior Kazi Amar Singh Thapa, Natl. Hero — A150

1977, Feb. 18   Photo.   Perf. 13x13½
328 A150 10p multicolored   .40 .25

Terracotta Figurine, Kapilavastu Excavations A151

Asoka Pillar, Lumbini — A152

1977, May 3   Photo.   Perf. 14½x14
329 A151 30p dark violet   .30 .25
330 A152 5r green & brown   1.75 1.25
Tourist publicity.

Cheer Pheasant — A153

Birds of Nepal: 5p, Great pied hornbill, vert. 1r, Green magpie. 2.30r, Nepalese laughing thrush, vert.

1977, Sept. 17   Photo.   Perf. 13
331 A153 5p multicolored   .65 .30
332 A153 15p multicolored   1.25 .30
333 A153 1r multicolored   1.75 .65
334 A153 2.30r multicolored   3.50 1.00
Nos. 331-334 (4)   7.15 2.25

Tukuche Peak, Nepalese Police Flag — A154

1977, Oct. 2
335 A154 1.25r multicolored   .85 .50
Ascent of Tukuche, Himalaya Mountains, by Nepalese police team, first anniversary.

Scout Emblem, Map of Nepal — A155

1977, Nov. 7   Litho.   Perf. 13½
336 A155 3.50r multicolored   1.25 .85
Boy Scouts of Nepal, 25th anniversary.

Dhanwantari, Health Goddess — A156

1977, Nov. 9   Photo.   Perf. 13
337 A156 30p bluish green   .30 .25
Health Day.

Flags, Map of Nepal — A157

1977, Dec. 5   Photo.   Perf. 13½
338 A157 1r multicolored   .50 .30
Colombo Plan, 26th Consultative Meeting, Kathmandu, Nov. 29-Dec. 7.

King Birendra — A158

1977, Dec. 28
339 A158 5p olive   .30 .25
340 A158 1r red brown   .55 .50
King Birendra's 32nd birthday.

Post Office Seal, New Post Office — A159

75p, Post Office date stamp & new Post Office.

1978, Apr. 14   Photo.   Perf. 14½x14
341 A159 25p org brn & blk   .25 .25
342 A159 75p bister & black   .40 .40
Centenary of Nepalese postal service.

Mt. Everest — A160

Design: 4r, Mt. Everest, different view.

1978, May 29   Photo.   Perf. 13½x13
343 A160 2.30r red brn & slate 1.25 .75
344 A160 4r grn & vio blue   1.75 1.25
1st ascent of Mt. Everest, 25th anniv.

Mountains, Trees, Environmental Emblem — A161

1978, June 5
345 A161 1r blue green & orange .50 .30
World Environment Day, June 5.

Queen Mother Ratna — A162

1978, Aug. 20   Photo.   Perf. 14
346 A162 2.30r olive gray   .80 .50
Queen Mother Ratna, 50th birthday.

Trisula River Rapids — A163

Tourist Publicity: 50p, Nepalese window. 1r, Dancer, Mahakali dance, vert.

1978, Sept. 15   Litho.   Perf. 14
347 A163 10p multicolored   .30 .25
348 A163 50p multicolored   .40 .30
349 A163 1r multicolored   .75 .50
Nos. 347-349 (3)   1.45 1.05

Human Rights Emblem — A164

1978, Oct. 10   Litho.   Perf. 13½
350 A164 25p red brown & red   .30 .25
351 A164 1r dark blue & red   .50 .30
Universal Declaration of Human Rights, 30th anniversary.

Choerospondias Axillaris — A165

Designs: 1r, Castanopsis indica, vert. 1.25r, Elaeocarpus sphaericus.

1978, Oct. 31   Photo.   Perf. 13
352 A165 5p multicolored   .30 .25
353 A165 1r multicolored   .20 .50
354 A165 1.25r multicolored   1.00 .60
Nos. 352-354 (3)   1.50 1.35

King Birendra — A166

1978, Dec. 17   Perf. 13½x14
355 A166 30p brown & indigo   .30 .25
356 A166 2r violet & black   .80 .65
King Birendra's 33rd birthday.

Kamroop and Patan Temples and Deity A167

Red Machhindra Chariot A168

Perf. 14½x14, 13½
1979   Photo., Litho.
357 A167 75p claret & olive   .60 .30
358 A168 1.25r multicolored   .60 .50
Red Machhindra Nath Festival, Lalitpur (Patan).
Issue dates: 75p, Apr. 27; 1.25r, July 25.

Bas-relief — A169

1979, May 12   Photo.   Perf. 13
359 A169 1r yellow & brown   .60 .30
Lumbini Year.

Tree Planting — A170

1979, June 29   Photo.   Perf. 13x13½
360 A170 2.30r multicolored   1.25 .75
Afforestation campaign.

Children with Flag, IYC Emblem — A172

1979, Aug. 20   Perf. 13½
362 A172 1r light brown   .60 .45
Intl. Year of the Child; Natl. Children's Day.

Mount Pabil — A173

Tourism: 50p, Swargadwari Temple. 1.25r, Altar with statues of Shiva and Parbati.

1979, Sept. 26   Photo.   Perf. 13½x13
363 A173 30p dk blue green   .30 .25
364 A173 50p multicolored   .35 .25
365 A173 1.25r multicolored   .65 .55
Nos. 363-365 (3)   1.30 1.05

Northern Shrike — A174

Design: 10r, Aethopyga ignicauda.

Perf. 14½x13½
1979, Nov. 22   Photo.
366 A174 10p shown   .30 .25
367 A174 10r multicolored   7.50 4.75
Intl. World Pheasant Assoc. Symposium, Kathmandu, Nov. 21-23. See No. C7.

Coin, Lichhavi Period, Obverse — A175

Malla Period, Obverse — A175a

Shaw Period, Obverse — A175b

Ancient Coins: No. 369, Lichhavi Period, reverse. No. 371, Malla Period, reverse. No. 373, Shah Period, reverse.

1979, Dec. 16   Photo.   Perf. 15
368 A175   5p brn & brn org   .25 .25
369 A175   5p brn & brn org   .25 .25
 a. Pair, #368-369   .55 .55
370 A175a 15p dark blue   .30 .25
371 A175a 15p dark blue   .30 .25
 a. Pair, #370-371   .65 .65
372 A175b 1r slate blue   .75 .50
373 A175b 1r slate blue   .75 .50
 a. Pair, #372-373   1.75 1.75
Nos. 368-373 (6)   2.60 2.00

King Birendra A176

Ban-Ganga Dam A177

1979, Dec. 28   Litho.   Perf. 14
374 A176 25p multicolored   .25 .25
375 A177 2.30r multicolored   .80 .65
King Birendra's 34th birthday.

Samyak Pooja Festival — A178

1980, Jan. 15   Perf. 13½
376 A178 30p vio brn & gray   .35 .25

Holy Basil — A179

30p, Himalayan valerian. 1r, Nepalese pepper. 2.30r, Himalayan rhubarb.

1980, Mar. 24   Photo.   Perf. 14x14½
377 A179 5p shown   .25 .25
378 A179 30p multicolored   .30 .25
379 A179 1r multicolored   .60 .30
380 A179 2.30r multicolored   1.25 .65
Nos. 377-380 (4)   2.40 1.45

Gyandil
Das — A180

Nepalese Writers: 30p, Shddhi Das Amatya.
1r, Pahal Man Singh Snwar. 2.30r, Jay Prithibi
Bahadur Singh.

1980, Apr. 13   Perf. 13½x13
381 A180   5p bister & rose lilac   .30   .25
382 A180   30p vio brn & lt red
                                     .30   .25
383 A180   1r blue & olive gray   .40   .30
384 A180   2.30r ol grn & dk blue   .80   .60
   Nos. 381-384 (4)   1.80 1.40

Jwalaji Dailekh
(Temple), Holy
Flame — A181

1980, Sept. 14   Litho.   Perf. 14½
385 A181   10p shown   .30   .25
386 A181   1r Godavari Pond   .50   .30
387 A181   5r Mt. Dhaulagiri   1.75 1.25
   Nos. 385-387 (3)   2.55 1.80

Temple Statue — A182

1980, Oct. 29   Perf. 14x13½
388 A182   25r multicolored   7.00 5.00
   World Tourism Conf., Manila, Sept. 27.

King Birendra's 35th
Birthday — A183

1980, Dec. 28   Litho.   Perf. 14
389 A183   1r multicolored   .60   .25

International Year of
the
Disabled — A184

1981, Jan. 1
390 A184   5r multicolored   2.00 1.40

Nepal Rastra Bank,
25th Anniv. — A185

1981, Apr. 26   Litho.   Perf. 14
391 A185   1.75r multicolored   .60   .50

Nepalese Stamp
Cent. — A186

1981, July 16
392 A186   10p No. 1   .25   .25
393 A186   40p No. 2   .30   .25
394 A186   3.40r No. 3   1.75 1.25
   a. Souvenir sheet of 3, #392-394 3.00 3.00
   Nos. 392-394 (3)   2.30 1.75

A187

1981, Oct. 30   Litho.   Perf. 14
395 A187   1.75r multicolored   .50   .40
   Intl. Hotel Assoc., 70th council meeting,
Kathmandu.

Stamp
Centenary — A188

1981, Dec. 27   Litho.   Perf. 14
396 A188   40p multicolored   .30   .25
   Nepal '81 Stamp Exhibition, Kathmandu,
Dec. 27-31.

King Birendra's 36th
Birthday — A189

1981, Dec. 28
397 A189   1r multicolored   .40   .30

Hrishikesh, Buddhist
Stone Carving,
Ridi — A190

25p, Tripurasundari Pavilion, Baitadi. 2r, Mt.
Langtang Lirung.

1981, Dec. 30
398 A190   5p shown   .25   .25
399 A190   25p multicolored   .30   .25
400 A190   2r multicolored   .75   .50
   Nos. 398-400 (3)   1.30 1.00

Royal Nepal
Academy, 25th
Anniv. — A191

1982, June 23   Litho.   Perf. 14
401 A191   40p multicolored   .35   .25

Balakrishna
Sama — A192

1982, July 21   Perf. 13½
402 A192   1r multicolored   .35   .30

Dish Antenna,
Satellite — A193

1982, Nov. 7   Litho.   Perf. 14
403 A193   5r multicolored   1.40   .80

Mt. Nuptse — A194

Intl. Union of Alpinists Assoc., 50th Anniv.
(Himalaya Peaks): b, Mt. Lhotse (31x31mm).
c, Mt. Everest (40x31mm). Continuous design.

1982, Nov. 18   Perf. 13½
404 A194   Strip of 3   3.50 3.50
   a. 25p multicolored   .25   .25
   b. 2r multicolored   .75   .50
   c. 3r multicolored   1.75   .90

9th Asian
Games — A195

1982, Nov. 19   Perf. 14
405 A195   3.40r multicolored   1.25   .80

Kulekhani Hydro-
electric
Plant — A196

1982, Dec. 2   Perf. 13½
406 A196   2r Lake, dam   1.00   .50

King Birendra's 37th
Birthday — A197

1982, Dec. 28   Perf. 12½
407 A197   5p multicolored   .40   .25

A198

1983, June 15   Litho.   Perf. 14
408 A198   50p multicolored   .50   .25
   25th anniv. of Nepal Industrial Development
Co.

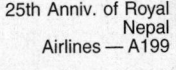

25th Anniv. of Royal
Nepal
Airlines — A199

1983, Aug. 1   Perf. 13½
409 A199   1r multicolored   .90   .30

World
Communications
Year — A200

1983, Oct. 30   Litho.   Perf. 12
410 A200   10p multicolored   .60   .25

Musical
Instruments — A201

1983, Nov. 3
411 A201   5p Sarangi   .30   .25
412 A201   10p Kwota   .50   .25
413 A201   50p Narashinga   .60   .25
414 A201   1r Murchunga   1.25   .50
   Nos. 411-414 (4)   2.65 1.25

A202

1983, Dec. 20
415 A202   4.50r multicolored   1.75 1.00
   Chakrapani Chalise (1883-1957), national
anthem composer and poet.

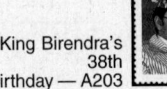

King Birendra's
38th
Birthday — A203

1983, Dec. 28   Perf. 14
416 A203   5r multicolored   1.50   .80

Temple,
Barahkshetra
A204

2.20r, Triveni pilgrimage site. 6r, Mt. Cho-
oyu.

1983, Dec. 30   Perf. 14
417 A204   1r shown   .30   .25
418 A204   2.20r multicolored   .60   .50
419 A204   6r multicolored   1.75 1.25
   Nos. 417-419 (3)   2.65 2.00

Auditor General,
25th
Anniv. — A204a

1984, June 28   Litho.   Perf. 14
419A A204a 25p Open ledger   .80   .60

A205

1984, July 1   Litho.   Perf. 14
420 A205   5r Transmission tower 1.75 1.25
   Asia-Pacific Broadcasting Union, 20th anniv.

A206

1984, July 8
421 A206   50p University emblem   .45   .25
   Tribhuvan University, 25th anniv.

A207

1984, Aug. 5
422 A207   10r Boxing   3.00 2.00
   1984 Summer Olympic Games, Los Angeles.

NEPAL

32

A208

1984, Sept. 18
423 A208 1r multicolored   .45 .25
Family Planning Assoc., 25th anniv.

Social Services
Day — A209

1984, Sept. 24
424 A209 5p multicolored   .40 .25

Wildlife — A210

10p, Gavialis gangeticus. 25p, Panthera
uncia. 50p, Antilope cervicapra.

1984, Nov. 30
425 A210 10p multicolored   .40 .30
426 A210 25p multicolored   .60 .35
427 A210 50p multicolored 1.00 .45
  Nos. 425-427 (3)   2.00 1.10

Chhinna Masta Bhagvati Temple and
Goddess Sakhandeshwari Devi,
Statue — A211

Designs: 10p, Lord Vishu the Giant, Yajna
Ceremony on Bali, bas-relief, A. D. 467, vert.
5r, Mt. Api, Himalayas, vert.

1984, Dec. 21
428 A211 10p multicolored   .25 .25
429 A211 1r multicolored   .30 .30
430 A211 5r multicolored 2.00 1.25
  Nos. 428-430 (3)   2.55 1.80

King Birendra, 39th
Birthday — A212

1984, Dec. 28
431 A212 1r multicolored   .45 .25

Sagarmatha Natl.
Park — A213

1985, May 6
432 A213 10r Mt. Everest, wildlife 6.00 2.25
King Mahendra Trust Congress for Nature
Conservation, May 6-11.

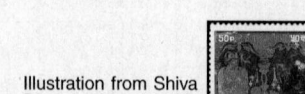

Illustration from Shiva
Dharma Purana, 13th
Cent. Book — A214

Design: Maheshware, Lord Shiva, with
brahma and vishnu. #433b, left person sitting
on wall. #433d, left person on throne.

1985, May 30
433 Strip of 5   3.50 2.50
  a.-e. A214 50p any single .40 .25
  f. Strip of 5, imperf within 4.50

#433 has a continuous design. Sizes:
#433a, 433e, 26x22mm; #433b, 433d,
24x22mm; #433c, 17x22mm.

UN, 40th Anniv. — A215

1985, Oct. 24 Litho. Perf. 13½x14
434 A215 5r multicolored 1.50 1.00

14th Eastern
Regional
Tuberculosis
Conference
A216

1985, Nov. 25
435 A216 25r multicolored 6.00 4.00

First South Asian
Regional
Cooperation
Summit — A217

1985, Dec. 8   Perf. 14
436 A217 5r Flags 1.50 1.00

Temple of
Jaleshwar,
Mohottary
Underwater
Project — A218

1r, Temple of Shaileshwari, Doti. 2r, Lake
Phoksundo, Dolpa.

1985, Dec. 15 Litho. Perf. 14x13½
437 A218 10p shown   .25 .25
438 A218 1r multicolored .55 .30
439 A218 2r multicolored 1.20 .30
  Nos. 437-439 (3)   2.00 .85

Intl. Youth Year — A219

1985, Dec. 21   Perf. 14
440 A219 1r multicolored   .45 .25

Devi Ghat Hydro-
electric Dam
Project — A220

1985, Dec. 28 Litho. Perf. 14
441 A220 2r multicolored   .85 .50

King Birendra, 40th
Birthday — A221

1985, Dec. 28
442 A221 50p Portrait   .45 .25

Panchayat System,
25th Anniv. — A222

1986, Apr. 10   Perf. 13½
443 A222 4r multicolored 1.50 1.00

Pharping
Hydroelectric
Station, 75th
Anniv. — A223

1986, Oct. 9 Litho. Perf. 14x13½
444 A223 15p multicolored   .50 .25

Architecture,
Artifacts — A224

5p, Pashupati Temple. 10p, Lumbini Fort. 1r,
Crown of Nepal.

1986, Oct. 9 Photo. Perf. 13x13½
445 A224 5p multicolored   .25 .25
446 A224 10p multicolored .30 .25
446A A224 50p like 5p ('87) .40 .25
447 A224 1r multicolored   .50 .25
  Nos. 445-447 (4)   1.45 1.00
  No. 446A issued Apr. 14.

Asian Productivity
Org., 25th
Anniv. — A225

1986, Oct. 26 Litho. Perf. 13½x14
448 A225 1r multicolored   .50 .25

Reclining
Buddha,
Kathmandu
Valley — A226

Mt. Pumori,
Khumbu
Range — A227

Perf. 14, 13½x13
1986, Oct. 26   Litho.
449 A226 60p multicolored   .30 .25
450 A227 8r multicolored 2.75 1.25

King Birendra, 41st
Birthday — A228

1986, Dec. 28 Litho. Perf. 13x13½
451 A228 1r multicolored   .45 .25

Intl. Peace Year — A229

1986, Dec. 28   Perf. 14
452 A229 10r multicolored 2.00 1.50

Social Service
Natl.
Coordination
Council, 10th
Anniv. — A230

1987, Sept. 22 Litho. Perf. 13½
453 A230 1r Natl. flag, emblem .45 .25

Birth of
Buddha — A231

Design: Asoka Pillar, enlargement of commemorative text and bas-relief of birth.

1987, Oct. 28   Perf. 14
454 A231 4r multicolored 1.25 .75

First Natl. Boy
Scout Jamboree,
Kathmandu
A232

1987, Oct. 28 Litho. Perf. 14
455 A232 1r multicolored   .85 .40

A233

1987, Nov. 2
456 A233 60p gold & lake   .30 .25
3rd SAARC (Southeast Asian Assoc. for
Regional Cooperation) Summit Conference,
Kathmandu.

A234

1987, Nov. 10
457 A234 4r multicolored 1.10 .75
Rastriya Samachar Samiti (Natl. news
agency), 25th anniv.

Intl. Year of
Shelter for the
Homeless
A235

1987, Dec. 21 Litho. Perf. 14
458 A235 5r multicolored 1.25 1.00

Kashthamandap
Temple,
Kathmandu — A236

1987, Dec. 21 Photo. Perf. 13½x13
459 A236 25p multicolored   .40 .25

Surya Bikram Gyawali
(b. 1898),
Historian — A237

1987, Dec. 21   Perf. 13x13½
460 A237 60p multicolored   .50 .25

King Birendra, 42nd
Birthday — A238

Perf. 14½x13½
1987, Dec. 28   Litho.
461 A238 25p multicolored   .50 .25

Mount Kanjiroba
A239

1987, Dec. 30 *Perf. 14*
462 A239 10r multicolored 3.00 1.75

Crown Prince Dipendra's 18th Birthday — A240

1988, Mar. 28 Litho. *Perf. 14*
463 A240 1r multicolored .50 .25

Nepal Bank, Ltd., 50th Anniv. — A241

1988, Apr. 8
464 A241 2r multicolored .50 .25

Kanti Childrens' Hospital, 25th Anniv. — A242

1988, Apr. 8
465 A242 60p multicolored .50 .25

Royal Shuklaphanta Wildlife Reserve — A243

1988, Apr. 8
466 A243 60p Swamp deer 1.00 .25

A244

1988, Aug. 20 Litho. *Perf. 14x13½*
467 A244 5r multicolored 1.25 1.00
Queen Mother Ratna Rajya Laxmi Devi Shah, 60th birthday.

Nepal Red Cross, 25th Anniv. — A245

1988, Sept. 12 Litho. *Perf. 14x13½*
468 A245 1r dull fawn & dark red .50 .25

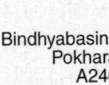

Bindhyabasini, Pokhara
A246

1988, Oct. 16 Litho. *Perf. 14½*
469 A246 15p multicolored .50 .25

King Birendra, 43rd Birthday — A247

1988, Dec. 28 Litho. *Perf. 14*
470 A247 4r multicolored 1.00 .60

A248

1989, Mar. 3 Litho. *Perf. 13½x14*
471 A248 1r Temple .50 .25
Pashupati Area Development Trust.

SAARC Year — A249

1989, Dec. 8 *Perf. 13x13½*
472 A249 60p multicolored .50 .25
Combating Drug Abuse & Trafficking.

A250

1989, Oct. 5 *Perf. 14*
473 A250 4r vio, brt grn & blk .85 .45
Asia-Pacific Telecommunity, 10th anniv.

King Birendra, 44th Birthday — A251

Perf. 13½x14½
1989, Dec. 28 Litho.
474 A251 2r multicolored .60 .25

Child Survival — A252

Design: Oral rehydration therapy, immunization, breast-feeding and growth monitoring.

1989, Dec. 31 *Perf. 13½*
475 A252 1r multicolored .50 .25

Rara Natl. Park — A253

1989, Dec. 31 *Perf. 14½x15*
476 A253 4r multicolored .60 .30

Mt. Ama Dablam — A254

1989, Dec. 31 *Perf. 14*
477 A254 5r multicolored 1.00 .60

A255

1990, Jan. 3
478 A255 1r multicolored .50 .25
Crown Prince Dipendra investiture, Jan. 3.

Temple of the Goddess Manakamana, Gorkha — A256

1990, Apr. 12 Litho. *Perf. 14½*
479 A256 60p deep blue & black .65 .25

A257

1990, Aug. 20 Litho. *Perf. 14*
480 A257 1r multicolored .50 .25
Nepal Children's Organization, 25th anniv.

Bir Hospital, Cent. — A258

1990, Sept. 13 Litho. *Perf. 14x13½*
481 A258 60p orange, blue & red .50 .25

A259

1990, Oct. 9 *Perf. 14½*
482 A259 4r multicolored .80 .50
Asian-Pacific Postal Training Center, 20th anniv.

SAARC Year of the Girl Child — A260

1990, Dec. 24 Litho. *Perf. 14½*
483 A260 4.60r multicolored 1.25 .65

Bageshwori Temple, Nepalganj — A261

Mt. Saipal — A262

1990, Dec. 24 *Perf. 13½*
484 A261 1r multicolored .50 .25
485 A262 5r multicolored 1.00 .40

B.P. Koirala (1914-82) — A263

1990, Dec. 31 *Perf. 14*
486 A263 60p red, org brn & blk .50 .25

King Birendra, 45th Birthday — A264

1990, Dec. 28
487 A264 2r multicolored .50 .25

Royal Chitwan Natl. Park — A265

1991, Feb. 10 Litho. *Perf. 14½*
488 A265 4r multicolored 1.25 .65

Restoration of Multiparty Democracy, 1st Anniv. — A266

1991, Apr. 9 Litho. *Perf. 14*
489 A266 1r multicolored .50 .25

Natl. Census — A267

1991, May 3 *Perf. 14x13½*
490 A267 60p multicolored .50 .25

A268

1991, Aug. 15 *Perf. 14½x13½*
491 A268 3r multicolored .50 .25
Federation of Nepalese Chambers of Commerce and Industry, 25th anniv.

A269

1991, Sept. 4 Litho. *Perf. 14*
492 A269 60p gray & red .50 .25
Nepal Junior Red Cross, 25th anniv.

Re-establishment of Parliament, 1st Session — A270

1991, Sept. 10   *Perf. 14½*
493 A270 1r multicolored   .50 .25

Constitution Day — A271

1991, Nov. 9   **Litho.**   *Perf. 15x14*
494 A271 50p multicolored   .65 .25

Mt. Kumbhakarna A272

1991, Oct.   **Litho.**   *Perf. 13½x14*
495 A272 4.60r multicolored   .75 .30

Vivaha Mandap — A274

1991, Dec. 11   *Perf. 11½*
497 A274 1r multicolored   .50 .25

SAARC Year of Shelter — A275

1991, Dec. 28   *Perf. 13½x14*
498 A275 9r multicolored   1.25 .75

King Birendra, 46th Birthday — A276

1991, Dec. 28   *Perf. 14x13½*
499 A276 8r multicolored   1.25 .60

Nepal Philatelic Society, 25th Anniv. — A277

1992, July 11   **Litho.**   *Perf. 13*
500 A277 4r multicolored   .60 .30

Protect the Environment A278

1992, Oct. 24   **Litho.**   *Perf. 12½x13*
501 A278 60p multicolored   .65 .25

Rights of the Child — A279

1992, Oct. 24   *Perf. 13½x13*
502 A279 1r multicolored   .50 .25

Temples — A280

75p, Thakurdwara. 1r, Namo Buddha. 2r, Narijhowa. 11r, Dantakali.

1992, Nov. 10   *Perf. 14*
503 A280 75p multicolored   .30 .25
504 A280 1r multicolored   .35 .25
505 A280 2r multicolored   .45 .25
506 A280 11r multicolored   2.25 1.00
   Nos. 503-506 (4)   3.35 1.75
   No. 506 is airmail.

A281

1992, Dec. 20 Photo.   *Perf. 13x13½*
507 A281 40p brown & green   .50 .25
Agricultural Development Bank, 25th anniv.

Birds — A282

1r, Pin-tailed green pigeon. 3r, Bohemian waxwing. 25r, Rufous-tailed finch lark.

1992, Dec. 20   **Litho.**   *Perf. 11½*
508 A282 1r multicolored   .30 .25
509 A282 3r multicolored   .60 .30
510 A282 25r multicolored   4.75 2.50
   Nos. 508-510 (3)   5.65 3.05

King Birendra, 47th Birthday — A283

1992, Dec. 28   *Perf. 12½x13*
511 A283 7r multicolored   1.10 .45

Poets — A284

Designs: No. 512, Pandit Kulchandra Gautam. No. 513, Chittadhar Hridaya. No. 514, Vidyapati. No. 515, Teongsi Sirijunga.

1992, Dec. 31   *Perf. 11½*
512 A284 1r blue & multi   .80 .25
513 A284 1r brown & multi   .80 .25
514 A284 1r tan & multi   .80 .25
515 A284 1r gray & multi   .80 .25
   Nos. 512-515 (4)   3.20 1.00

1992 Summer Olympics, Barcelona — A285

1992, Dec. 31
516 A285 25r multicolored   3.00 2.00

Fish — A286

Designs: 25p, Tor putitora. 1r, Schizothorax plagiostomus. 5r, Anguilla bengalensis, temple of Chhabdi Barahi. 10r, Psilorhynchus pseudecheneis.

1993, Aug. 6   **Litho.**   *Perf. 11½*
Granite Paper
517 A286 25p multicolored   .50 .25
518 A286 1r multicolored   .55 .40
519 A286 5r multicolored   1.25 .90
520 A286 10r multicolored   2.25 1.00
   a.   Souvenir sheet of 4, #517-520   7.00 7.00
   Nos. 517-520 (4)   4.55 2.55

World AIDS Day — A287

1993, Dec. 1   **Litho.**   *Perf. 13½x14½*
521 A287 1r multicolored   .50 .25

Tanka Prasad Acharya — A288

1r, Sundare Sherpa. 7r, Siddhi Charan Shrestha. 15r, Falgunand.

1993, Dec. 2   *Perf. 13½*
522 A288 25p shown   .25 .25
523 A288 1r multicolored   .30 .25
524 A288 7r multicolored   .75 .40
525 A288 15r multicolored   1.50 1.00
   Nos. 522-525 (4)   2.80 1.90

Holy Places — A289

1.50r, Halesi Mahadev, Khotang. 5r, Devghat, Tanahun. 8r, Bagh Bhairab, Kirtipur.

Perf. 13½x14½
1993, Dec. 28   **Litho.**
526 A289 1.50r multicolored   .25 .25
527 A289 5r multicolored   .60 .50
528 A289 8r multicolored   1.00 .80
   Nos. 526-528 (3)   1.85 1.55

Tourism — A290

Designs: 5r, Tushahiti Sundari Chowk, Patan. 8r, White water rafting.

1993, Dec. 28
529 A290 5r multicolored   .60 .30
530 A290 8r multicolored   .90 .50

King Birendra, 48th Birthday — A291

1993, Dec. 28   *Perf. 14*
531 A291 10r multicolored   1.00 .60

Large Building, Courtyard A293

Pagoda, Courtyard A293a

Monument A294

Arms A295

Fort A296

Mt. Everest A299

Pagoda (Nyata Pola) A300

Map of Nepal A301

Design: 50p, Pagoda, vert.

Perf. 14½, 12, (#533A, 538, 540), 14¼x14

Photo., Litho. (#533A, 535A, 538, 540)

1994-96
533 A293 10p green   .45 .25
533A A293a 10p claret & black   .45 .25
534 A294 20p violet brown   .45 .25
535 A295 25p carmine, 21x23mm   .45 .25
535A A295 25p carmine, 21x26mm   .75 .25
536 A296 30p slate   .45 .25
537 A293 50p dark blue   .45 .25
538 A293a 50p black & claret   .45 .25
539 A299 1r multicolored   1.00 .25
539A A300 1r blue & claret   .75 .25
   Perf. 14½x13½
540 A301 5r multicolored   .75 .35
   Nos. 533-540 (11)   6.40 2.85

Issued: 20p, No. 535, 30p, 5/17/94; No. 539, 7/6/94; 5r, 9/22/94; Nos. 533, 537, 1995; No. 535A, 8/2/96. Nos. 533A, 538, 539A, 10/9/96.

Pasang Lhamu Sherpa (1960-1993) — A304

1994, Sept 2   **Litho.**   *Perf. 14*
544 A304 10r multicolored   1.00 .60

Stop Smoking Campaign — A305

1994, Sept. 26   *Perf. 13½x14*
545 A305 1r multicolored   .75 .25

Mail Transport — A306

1994, Oct. 9   *Perf. 13x13½*
546 A306 1.50r multicolored   .80 .25

Traditional Weapons — A307

No. 547: a, Daggers, scabbards. b, Yataghans. c, Sabers, shield. d, Carved stone daggers.

1994, Oct. 9 — *Perf. 14*
547 A307 5r Block of 4, #a.-d.   3.25 3.25

ILO, 75th Anniv. — A308

1994, Oct. 9 — *Perf. 13*
548 A308 15r blue & gold   2.00 1.25

World Food Day A309

1994, Oct. 23 — *Perf. 14*
549 A309 25r multicolored   3.00 2.00

Orchids — A310

a, Dendrobium densiflorum. b, Coelogyne flaccida. c, Cymbidium devonianum. d, Coelogyne corymbosa.

1994, Nov. 7 — *Perf. 14x13½*
550 A310 10r Block of 4, #a.-d.   4.00 3.00

Intl. Year of the Family — A311

1994, Dec. 5 — *Perf. 12½x13*
551 A311 9r green & red   1.00 .60

ICAO, 50th Anniv. — A312

1994, Dec. 7
552 A312 11r blue & gold   1.25 .80

Mushrooms — A313

1994, Dec. 20 — *Perf. 14*
553 A313 7r Cordyceps sinensis   1.10 .50
554 A313 7r Morchella conica   1.10 .50
555 A313 7r Amanita caesarea   1.10 .50
556 A313 7r Russula nepalensis   1.10 .50
 Nos. 553-556 (4)   4.40 2.00

Famous Men — A314

Designs: 1r, Dharanidhar Koirala, poet. 2r, Narayan Gopal Guruwacharya, singer. 6r, Bahadur Shah, military leader. 7r, Balaguru Shadananda, religious leader.

1994, Dec. 23 *Perf. 13½x14, 14x13½*
557 A314 1r multicolored   .35 .25
558 A314 2r multicolored   .35 .25
559 A314 6r multicolored   .90 .50
560 A314 7r multicolored   1.00 .55
 Nos. 557-560 (4)   2.60 1.55

King Birendra, 49th Birthday — A315

1994, Dec. 28 — *Perf. 14*
561 A315 9r multicolored   1.00 .70

Tilicho Lake, Manang — A316

11r, Taleju Temple, Katmandou, vert.

1994, Dec. 28 *Perf. 13½x14, 14x13½*
562 A316 9r multicolored   1.10 .70
563 A316 11r multicolored   1.40 .80

Care of Children — A317

No. 564: a, Vaccination. b, Education. c, Playground activities. d, Stamp collecting.

1994, Dec. 30 — *Perf. 14*
564 A317 1r Block of 4, #a.-d.   1.00 .80

Fight Against Cancer — A318

1995, June 23 *Litho.* *Perf. 14x13½*
565 A318 2r red & black   .50 .25

A319

Famous People: a, Bhim Nidhi Tiwari, writer. b, Yuddha Prasad Mishra, writer. c, Chandra Man Singh Maskey, artist. d, Parijat, writer.

1995, July 11 — *Perf. 14*
566 A319 3r Block of 4, #a.-d.   2.00 2.00

A320

Famous Men: 15p, Bhakti Thapa, warrior. 1r, Madan Bhandari, politician. 4r, Prakash Raj Kaphley, human rights activist.

1995, Sept. 1 *Litho.* *Perf. 14x13½*
567 A320 15p multicolored   .30 .25
568 A320 1r multicolored   .30 .25
569 A320 4r multicolored   .50 .30
 Nos. 567-569 (3)   1.10 .80

Animals — A321

Designs: a, Bos gaurus. b, Felis lynx. c, Macaca assamensis. d, Hyaena hyaena.

1995, Sept. 1 *Litho.* *Perf. 12*
570 A321 10p Block of 4, #a.-d.   6.00 6.00

Tourism — A322

1r, Bhimeshwor Temple, Dolakha, vert. 5r, Ugra Tara Temple, Dadeldhura. 7r, Mt. Nampa. 18r, Thanka art, Nrity Aswora, vert.

 Perf. 14x13½, 13½x14
1995, Nov. 8 *Litho.*
574 A322 1r multicolored   .25 .25
575 A322 5r multicolored   .60 .35
576 A322 7r multicolored   1.00 .50
 Size: 26x39mm
577 A322 18r multicolored   2.50 1.25
 Nos. 574-577 (4)   4.35 2.35

FAO, 50th Anniv. — A323

1995, Oct. 16 *Litho.* *Perf. 13½x14*
578 A323 7r multicolored   .90 .45

UN, 50th Anniv. — A324

1995, Oct. 22 *Litho.* *Perf. 11½*
Granite Paper
579 A324 50r multicolored   6.00 3.50

Lumbini, Birth Place of Gautama Buddha — A325

1995, Dec. 23 *Litho.* *Perf. 14*
580 A325 20r multicolored   3.00 1.50

King Birendra, 50th Birthday
A326   A327

1995, Dec. 28 — *Perf. 12*
Granite Paper (No. 581)
581 A326 1r multicolored   .50 .25
 Perf. 13x13½
582 A327 12r multicolored   1.50 .95

SAARC, 10th Anniv. — A328

1995, Dec. 28 — *Perf. 13½*
583 A328 10r multicolored   1.50 .70

Karnali Bridge A329

1996, May 13 *Litho.* *Perf. 14*
584 A329 7r multicolored   1.00 .50

1996 Summer Olympic Games, Atlanta — A330

1996, Oct. 9 *Photo.* *Perf. 12*
Granite Paper
585 A330 7r multicolored   1.00 .45

Kaji Kalu Pande A331   Hem Raj Sharma, Grammarian A332

#587, Pushpa Lal Shrestha. #589, Padma Prasad Bhattarai, scholar, philosopher. #590, Suvarna Shamsher Rana. #591, Bhawani Bhikshu, novelist, writer.

 Perf. 13½x14, 14x13½
1996, Aug. 6 *Litho.*
586 A331 75p multicolored   .35 .25
587 A331 1r multicolored   .35 .25
588 A332 1r multicolored   .35 .25
589 A332 3r multicolored   .35 .25
590 A331 5r multicolored   .60 .30
591 A332 5r multicolored   .60 .30
 Nos. 586-591 (6)   2.60 1.60
 See Nos. 614-615.

Asoka Pillar, Lumbini — A333

1996, Dec. 1 *Litho.* *Perf. 11½*
592 A333 12r multicolored   2.00 1.00

Tourism — A334

Designs: 1r, Arjun Dhara, Jhapa. 2r, Palace of Nuwakot. 8r, Traditional Gaijatra, Bhaktapur. 10r, Begnash Lake, Kaski.

1996, Nov. 20   Litho.   Perf. 14
593 A334   1r multicolored   .35   .25
594 A334   2r multicolored   .35   .25
595 A334   8r multicolored   1.25   .60
596 A334 10r multicolored   1.50   .90
      Nos. 593-596 (4)   3.45   2.00

Butterflies and Birds — A335

Designs: a, Krishna pea-cock butterfly. b, Great Himalayan barbet. c, Sarus crane. d, Northern junglequeen butterfly.

1996, Nov. 20   Litho.   Perf. 14
597 A335 5r Block of 4, #a.-d.   4.25   4.25

Annapurna Mountain Range — A336

Designs: a, Annapurna South, Annapurna I. b, Machhapuchhre, Annapurna III. c, Annapurna IV, Annapurna II.

1996, Dec. 28   Litho.   Perf. 14
601 A336 18r Strip of 3, #a.-c. 7.00   7.00

King Birendra, 51st Birthday — A337

1996, Dec. 28   Photo.   Perf. 12
Granite Paper
602 A337 10r multicolored   1.00   .65

Accession of King Birendra to Throne, 25th Anniv. — A338

1997, Feb. 1   Litho.   Perf. 14
603 A338 2r multicolored   1.00   .25

Nepal Postal Service — A339

1997, Apr. 12   Litho.   Perf. 14
604 A339 2r brown & red   .60   .25

Nepalese-Japanese Diplomatic Relations, 40th Anniv. — A340

1997, Apr. 6   Photo.   Perf. 12
605 A340 18r multicolored   2.50   1.25

Visit Nepal '98 — A341

2r, Emblem. 10r, Upper Mustang. 18r, Rafting Sunkoshi. 20r, Changunarayan (Bhaktapur), vert.

1997, July 6   Litho.   Perf. 14
606 A341   2r multicolored   .25   .25
607 A341 10r multicolored   1.00   .60
608 A341 18r multicolored   1.75   1.25
609 A341 20r multicolored   2.00   1.40
      Nos. 606-609 (4)   5.00   3.50

A342

Traditional costumes.

1997, Sept. 30   Litho.   Perf. 14
610 A342 5r Rana Tharu   .50   .30
611 A342 5r Gurung   .50   .30
612 A342 5r Chepang   .50   .30
      Nos. 610-612 (3)   1.50   .90

A343

1997, Sept. 30   Perf. 11½
613 A343 20r multicolored   2.25   1.50

Diplomatic relations between Nepal and US, 50th anniv.

Personality Type of 1996

Designs: No. 614, Riddhi Bahadur Malla, writer. No. 615, Dr. K.I. Singh, political leader.

1997, Nov. 6   Litho.   Perf. 11½
614 A332 2r multicolored   .45   .25
615 A332 2r multicolored   .45   .25

A344

Traditional Technology — A345

#616, Janto (grinder), horiz. #617, Dhiki, horiz. #618, Okhal. #619, Kol (oil mill).

1997, Dec. 29   Litho.   Perf. 14
616 A344 5r multicolored   .60   .35
617 A344 5r multicolored   .60   .35
618 A344 5r multicolored   .60   .35
619 A345 5r multicolored   .60   .35
      Nos. 616-619 (4)   2.40   1.40

Flowers — A346

40p, Jasminum gracile. 1r, Callistephus chinensis. 2r, Manglietia insignis. 15r, Luculia gratissima.

1997, Dec. 11
620 A346 40p multicolored   .25   .25
621 A346   1r multicolored   .25   .25
622 A346   2r multicolored   .35   .25
623 A346 15r multicolored   2.00   .90
      Nos. 620-623 (4)   2.85   1.65

King Birendra, 52nd Birthday — A347

1997, Dec. 29   Photo.   Perf. 11½
624 A347 10r multicolored   1.00   .75

Visit Nepal '98 — A348

Designs: 2r, Sunrise, Shree Antudanda, Ilam. 10r, Maitidevi Temple, Kathmandu. 18r, Great Reunification Gate, Kapilavastu. 20r, Mt. Cholatse, Solukhumbu, vert.

1998, May 8   Photo.   Perf. 11½
625 A348   2r multicolored   .25   .25
626 A348 10r multicolored   1.10   .65
627 A348 18r multicolored   2.00   1.25
628 A348 20r multicolored   2.25   1.40
      Nos. 625-628 (4)   5.60   3.55

Famous People — A349

Designs: 75p, Ram Prasad Rai, freedom fighter. 1r, Imansingh Chemjong, philologist. No. 631, Tulsi Meher Shrestha, social worker. No. 632, Dadhi Ram Marasini, Sanskrit expert. 5.40r, Mahananda Sapkota, linguist.

1998, June 26   Litho.   Perf. 14x13½
629 A349 75p brown & black   .25   .25
630 A349   1r rose lilac & black   .25   .25
631 A349   2r blue & black   .30   .25
632 A349   2r olive & black   .30   .25
633 A349 5.40r red & black   .65   .30
      Nos. 629-633 (5)   1.75   1.30

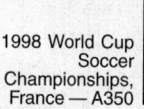

1998 World Cup Soccer Championships, France — A350

1998, June 26   Perf. 14
634 A350 12r multicolored   1.50   .85

Ganesh Man Singh (1915-97), Senior Democratic Leader — A351

1998, Sept. 18   Photo.   Perf. 11½
635 A351 5r multicolored   .60   .35

A352

1998, Oct. 9   Litho.   Perf. 13½x13
636 A352 10r multicolored   1.25   .70

Peace Keeping Mission of the Royal Nepalese Army, 40th Anniv.

Save Sight, Prevent Blindness — A353

Snakes — A354

1998, Nov. 29   Photo.   Perf. 12
Granite Paper
637 A353 1r multicolored   .40   .25

1.70r, King cobra. 2r, Golden tree snake. 5r, Asiatic rock python. 10r, Karan's pit viper.

1998, Nov. 29   Litho.   Perf. 14
638 A354 1.70r multicolored   .30   .25
639 A354   2r multicolored   .35   .25
640 A354   5r multicolored   .90   .30
641 A354 10r multicolored   1.75   .75
      Nos. 638-641 (4)   3.30   1.55

Universal Declaration of Human Rights, 50th Anniv. — A355

1998, Dec. 10   Litho.   Perf. 14
642 A355 10r multicolored   1.10   .65

A356

1998, Dec. 27   Perf. 14x13½
643 A356 10r multicolored   1.10   .60

Asian and Pacific Decade of Disabled Persons, 1993-2002.

A357

1998, Dec. 29   Perf. 13x13½
644 A357 2r multicolored   .40   .25

King Birendra, 53rd birthday.

Marsyangdi Dam and Hydro-Electric Power Station — A358

1998, Dec. 29   Perf. 11½
Granite Paper
645 A358 12r multicolored   1.35   .85

Nepal Eye Hospital, 25th Anniv. — A359

1999, Apr. 8   Litho.   Perf. 14
646 A359 2r multicolored   .50   .40

Tourism — A360

Designs: No. 647, Kalika Bhagawati Temple, Baglung. No. 648, Chandan Nath Temple, vert. 12r, Bajra Yogini Temple, Sankhu, vert. No. 650, Mt. Everest. No. 651, Lumbini Pillar Script translated into English.

1999, June 7 *Perf. 13½x13, 13x13½*
647	A360	2r multicolored	.35	.25
648	A360	2r multicolored	.35	.25
649	A360	12r multicolored	1.75	1.10
650	A360	15r multicolored	2.00	1.25
651	A360	15r multicolored	2.00	1.25
		Nos. 647-651 (5)	6.45	4.10

Tetracerus Quadricornis — A361

No. 653, Ovis ammon hodgsonii.

Granite Paper

1999, June 7   Photo.   *Perf. 11¾*
652	A361	10r shown	1.40	.85
653	A361	10r multicolored	1.40	.85

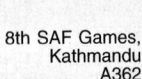

8th SAF Games, Kathmandu — A362

Perf. 13½x14¼

1999, Sept. 30   Litho.
654	A362	10r multicolored	1.40	.85

UPU, 125th Anniv. — A363

1999, Oct. 9   *Perf. 13½*
655	A363	15r multicolored	1.60	1.60

Famous People — A364

Designs: No. 656, Ram Narayan Mishra (1922-67), freedom fighter. No. 657, Bhupi Sherchan (1935-89), poet. No. 658, Master Mitrasen (1895-1946), writer. No. 659, Rudra Raj Pandey (1901-87), writer. No. 660, Gopal Prasad Rimal (1917-73), writer. No. 661, Mangaladevi Singh (1924-96), politician.

1999, Nov. 20   Litho.   *Perf. 13¾*
656	A364	1r multicolored	.30	.25
657	A364	1r multicolored	.30	.25
658	A364	1r multicolored	.30	.25
659	A364	2r multicolored	.35	.25
660	A364	2r multicolored	.35	.25
661	A364	2r multicolored	.35	.25
		Nos. 656-661 (6)	1.95	1.50

Dances — A365

1999, Dec. 26   Litho.   *Perf. 11¾x12*
662	A365	5r Sorathi	.75	.45
663	A365	5r Bhairav	.75	.45
664	A365	5r Jhijhiya	.75	.45
		Nos. 662-664 (3)	2.25	1.35

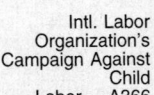

Intl. Labor Organization's Campaign Against Child Labor — A366

1999, Dec. 29   *Perf. 13½x14¼*
665	A366	12r multi	1.60	1.00

A367

1999, Dec. 29   *Perf. 14¼x13½*
666	A367	5r multi	.70	.50

King Birendra's 54th birthday.

A368

2000, Apr. 2   Photo.   *Perf. 12x11¾*
Granite Paper
667	A368	15r multi	2.00	1.75

Queen Aishwarya Rajya Laxmi Devi Shah, 50th birthday (in 1999).

Radio Nepal, 50th Anniv. — A369

2000, Apr. 2   Litho.   *Perf. 13½x14¼*
668	A369	2r multi	.45	.25

Gorkhapatra Newspaper, Cent. — A370

2000, May 5   *Perf. 14*
669	A370	10r multi	1.25	1.25

Tourism — A371

Designs: 12r, Tchorolpa Glacial Lake, Dolakha. 15r, Dakshinkali Temple, Kathmandu. 18r, Annapurna.

2000, June 30   Litho.   *Perf. 13¾x14*
670-672	A371	Set of 3	5.75	5.75

First ascent of Annapurna, 50th anniv. (No. 672).

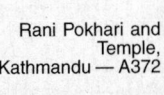

Rani Pokhari and Temple, Kathmandu — A372

Frame color: 50p, Orange. 1r, Blue. 2r, Brown.

2000, July 7   Photo.   *Perf. 11½*
673-675	A372	Set of 3	.70	.70

Geneva Conventions, 50th Anniv. — A373

2000, Sept. 7   Litho.   *Perf. 13½x14¼*
676	A373	5r multi	.75	.70

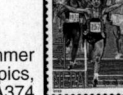

2000 Summer Olympics, Sydney — A374

2000, Sept. 7   Photo.   *Perf. 11¾x12*
Granite Paper
677	A374	25r multi	3.75	3.25

Famous People — A375

Designs: No. 678, 2r, Hridayachandra Singh Pradhan, writer (olive green frame). No. 679, 2r, Thir Bam Malla, revolutionary (brown frame). No. 680, 5r, Krishna Prasad Koirala, social reformer (indigo frame). No. 681, 5r, Manamohan Adhikari, politician (red frame).

2000, Sept. 7   Litho.   *Perf. 14*
678-681	A375	Set of 4	1.70	1.70

Worldwide Fund for Nature (WWF) — A376

#682, Bengal florican. #683, Lesser adjutant stork. #684, Female greater one-horned rhinoceros and calf. #685, Male greater one-horned rhinoceros.

2000, Nov. 14   Photo.   *Perf. 11¾*
Granite Paper
682-685	A376	10r Set of 4	5.75	5.25

King Birendra's 55th Birthday — A377

2000, Dec. 28   Photo.   *Perf. 12x11¾*
Granite Paper
686	A377	5r multi	.80	.65

Flowers — A378

Designs: No. 687, Talauma hodgsonii. No. 688, Mahonia napaulensis. No. 689, Dactylorhiza hatagirea, vert.

2000, Dec. 28   *Perf. 11¾x12, 12x11¾*
Granite Paper
687-689	A378	5r Set of 3	2.60	2.10

Establishment of Democracy, 50th Anniv. — A379

Perf. 11¾x11½

2001, Feb. 16   Photo.
Granite Paper
690	A379	5r King Tribhuvan	.80	.65

2001 Census — A380

2001, Apr. 17   Photo.   *Perf. 11¾*
Granite Paper
691	A380	2r multi	.50	.25

Famous Nepalese — A381

Designs: No. 692, 2r, Khaptad Baba (bright pink background, white Nepalese numeral at UR), ascetic. No. 693, 2r, Bhikkhu Pragyananada Mahathera (red violet background), religious teacher. No. 694, 2r, Guru Prasad Mainali (pink background, red Nepalese numeral at UR), writer. No. 695, 2r, Tulsi Lal Amatya (brown violet background), politician. No. 696, 2r, Madan Lal Agrawal (light blue background), industrialist.

Perf. 14¼x13½

2001, June 29   Litho.
692-696	A381	Set of 5	1.25	1.25

Ficus Religiosa — A382

2001, Nov. 2   Litho.   *Perf. 14¼x13½*
697	A382	10r multi	1.40	1.40

UN High Commissioner for Refugees, 50th Anniv. — A383

2001, Nov. 2   *Perf. 14*
698	A383	20r multi	2.75	2.50

Herbs — A384

Designs: 5r, Water pennywort. 15r, Rockfoil. 30r, Himalayan yew.

2001, Nov. 2   *Perf. 13¾*
699-701	A384	Set of 3	7.50	7.50

Nepalese Flag — A385

2001, Nov. 28   *Perf. 14*
702	A385	10r multi	.50	.40

King Birendra (1945-2001) — A386

2001, Dec. 28   *Perf. 14¼x13½*
703	A386	15r multi	2.25	1.75

Year of Dialogue Among Civilizations A387

2001, Dec. 28   *Perf. 14*
704	A387	30r multi	4.00	3.75

Tourism — A388

Designs: 2r, Amargadi Fort. 5r, Hiranyavarna Mahavihar, vert. 15r, Jugal Mountain Range.

Perf. 13½x14¼, 14¼x13½
2001, Dec. 28
705-707 A388 Set of 3   3.50 3.50

Nepal Scouts, 50th Anniv. — A389

2002, Apr. 9   Litho.   Perf. 14¼x13½
708 A389 2r red brn & olive   .50 .35

2002 World Cup Soccer Championships, Japan and Korea — A390

2002, May 31   Litho.   Perf. 13½x12¾
709 A390 15r multi   2.10 2.10

King Gyanendra's Accession to Throne, 1st Anniv. — A391

2002, June 5   Perf. 13¾
710 A391 5r multi   .70 .70

King Birendra (1945-2001) and Queen Aishwarya (1949-2001) — A392

2002, June 5   Perf. 14
711 A392 10r multi   .80 .80

Paintings A393

Designs: No. 712, 5r, Pearl, by King Birendra. No. 713, 5r, Aryabalokiteshwor, by Siddhimuni Shakya, vert.

Perf. 13½x13¾, 13¾x13½
2002, July 29
712-713 A393 Set of 2   1.40 1.40

Insects — A394

Designs: 3r, Leaf beetle. 5r, Locust.

2002, Sept. 6   Perf. 14
714-715 A394 Set of 2   1.25 1.25

Societal Messages — A395

Designs: 1r, Untouchable family behind barbed wire (untouchables should not be discriminated against). 2r, Children and parents waving (female children should not be discriminated against).

2002, Sept. 6   Perf. 14¼x14
716-717 A395 Set of 2   .70 .70

Intl. Year of Mountains — A396

2002, Oct. 9   Litho.   Perf. 14
718 A396 5r multi   .80 .65

Tourism — A397

Designs: No. 719, 5r, Mt. Nilgiri, Mustang. No. 720, 5r, Pathibhara Devisthan, Taplejung. No. 721, 5r, Ramgram Stupa, Hawalparasi. No. 722, 5r, Galeshwor Mahadevsthan, Myagdi.

2002, Oct. 9
719-722 A397 Set of 4   3.25 2.75

South Asian Association for Regional Cooperation Charter Day — A398

2002, Dec. 8   Perf. 13½x12¾
723 A398 15r multi   2.00 1.60

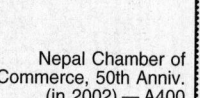

Famous Men — A399

Designs: 2r, Dava Bir Singh Kansakar, social worker. 25r, Rev, Ekai Kawaguchi (1866-1945), Buddhist scholar.

2002, Dec. 8   Perf. 13x13½
724-725 A399 Set of 2   3.50 3.50

Nepal Chamber of Commerce, 50th Anniv. (in 2002) — A400

2003, Apr. 10   Litho.   Perf. 14
726 A400 5r multi   .60 .60

Industry and Commerce Day — A401

2003, Apr. 11   Perf. 13½x12¾
727 A401 5r multi   .60 .60

First Ascent of Mt. Everest, 50th Anniv. — A402

2003, May 29   Litho.   Perf. 13½x14¼
728 A402 25r multi   3.25 3.25

Babu Chiri Sherpa (1965-2001), Mountaineer A403

2003, June 27   Perf. 14
729 A403 5r multi   .75 .60

King Gyanendra, 56th Birthday — A404

2003, July 7   Perf. 13½x14¼
730 A404 5r multi   .75 .65

Tea Garden, Eastern Nepal — A405

2003, July 7   Perf. 14
731 A405 25r multi   3.00 3.00

Dr. Dilli Raman Regmi (1913-2001), Politician and Historian — A406

2003, Aug. 31
732 A406 5r brown & blk   .60 .60

Gopal Das Shrestha (1930-98), Journalist — A407

2003, Sept. 23   Litho.   Perf. 14
733 A407 5r multi   .60 .60

Export Year 2003 — A408

2003, Oct. 9   Perf. 13½x14
734 A408 25r multi   3.00 3.00

Sankhadhar Sakhwaa, Initiator of Nepalese Calendar — A409

2003, Oct. 26   Perf. 13½x12¾
735 A409 5r multi   .60 .60

Flowers A410

No. 736: a, Lotus. b, Picrorhiza. c, Himalayan rhubarb. d, Night jasmine.

Perf. 14¼x13½
2003, Dec. 23   Litho.
736 A410 10r Block of 4, #a-d   4.50 4.50

Tourism — A411

Designs: No. 737, 5r, Kali Gandaki "A" hydroelectric dam site. No. 738, 5r, Ganesh idol, Kageshwar, vert. 30r, Buddha icon, Swayambhunath.

2003, Dec. 23   Perf. 14
737-739 A411 Set of 3   4.50 4.50

Social Services of United Mission to Nepal, 50th Anniv. — A412

2004, Mar. 5   Litho.   Perf. 14
740 A412 5r multi   .60 .60

National Society of Comprehensive Eye Care, 25th Anniv. — A413

2004, Mar. 25
741 A413 5r multi   .65 .65

Marwadi Sewa Samiti, 50th Anniv. — A414

2004, Apr. 9
742 A414 5r multi   .65 .65

King Gyanendra, 57th Birthday — A415

2004, July 7   Litho.   Perf. 14
743 A415 5r multi   .65 .65

Management Education, 50th Anniv. — A416

2004, Sept. 24   Litho.   Perf. 14
744 A416 5r multi   .60 .60

Asia-Pacific Telecommunity, 25th Anniv. — A417

2004, Sept. 24
745 A417 5r multi   .65 .65

FIFA (Fédération Internationale de Football Association), Cent. — A418

2004, Sept. 24
746 A418 20r multi   2.00 2.00

Mountains — A419

No. 747: a, Mt. Everest. b, Mt. Kanchenjunga Main. c, Mt. Lhotse. d, Mt. Makalu I. e, Mt. Cho Oyu. f, Mt. Dhaulagiri. g, Mt. Manasalu. h, Mt. Annapurna I.

2004, Oct. 19   Litho.   Perf. 14
747   A419   Block of 8   8.00 8.00
a.-h.   10r Any single   1.00 1.00

Famous Men — A420

Designs: No. 748, 5r, Nayaraj Panta (1913-2002), historian. No. 749, 5r, Narahari Nath (1914-2003), yogi.

2004, Nov. 3
748-749   A420   Set of 2   1.20 1.20

Flora and Fauna A421

No. 750: a, Rufous piculet woodpecker. b, Giant atlas moth. c, Serma guru. d, High altitude rice.

2004, Nov. 3
750   A421   10r Block of 4, #a-d   4.00 4.00

Mayadevi Temple, Lumbini — A422

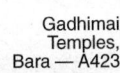

Gadhimai Temples, Bara — A423

2004, Nov. 30   Perf. 13½x13
751   A422   10r multi   1.40 1.00
752   A423   10r multi   1.40 1.00

Madan Puraskar Trust, 50th Anniv. — A424

2004, Dec. 13   Perf. 14
753   A424   5r multi   .55 .55

Sculptures — A425

No. 754: a, Jayavarma. b, Umamaheshwar. c, Vishwarupa. d, Banshagopal.

2004, Dec. 27   Perf. 13½
754   A425   10r Block of 4, #a-d   4.00 4.00

Nepal Rastra Bank, 50th Anniv. (in 2006) — A426

2005, Apr. 27   Litho.   Perf. 14
755   A426   2r multi   .60 .60

First Ascent of Mt. Makalu, 50th Anniv. — A427

2005, May 15
756   A427   10r multi   1.00 1.00

First Ascent of Mt. Kanchanjunga, 50th Anniv. — A428

2005, May 25
757   A428   12r multi   1.25 1.25

King Gyanendra, 58th Birthday — A429

2005, July 7   Litho.   Perf. 14
758   A429   5r multi   .55 .55

Life of Buddha — A430

No. 759: a, Birth at Lumbini. b, Enlightenment at Bodhagaya. c, First Sermon at Sarnath. d, Mahaparinirvana at Kushinagar.

2005, July 21
759   Horiz. strip of 4, any
    background color   4.00 4.00
a.-d.   10r Any single, any background color   1.00 1.00
    Sheet of 4 horiz. strips   16.00 —

The sheet has four horizontal strips with background colors of yellow, green, red and purple.

Queen Mother Ratna Rajya Laxmi Devi Shah — A431

2005, Aug. 20
760   A431   20r multi   2.00 2.00

Fruits and Nuts — A432

No. 761: a, Indian gooseberry. b, Walnut. c, Wood apple. d, Golden evergreen raspberry.

2005, Aug. 20
761   A432   10r Block of 4, #a-d   4.00 4.00

Mammals A433

No. 762: a, Gangetic dolphin. b, Indian pangolin. c, Asiatic wild elephant. d, Clouded leopard.

2005, Aug. 31   Litho.   Perf. 14
762   Horiz. strip of 4, any
    background color   4.00 4.00
a.-d.   A433 10r Any single, any background color   1.00 1.00
    Sheet of 4 horiz. strips   16.00 —

The sheet has four horizontal strips with background colors of yellow, green, red and purple.

Late Bhupalmansingh Karki, Social Worker — A434

2005, Sept. 24
763   A434   2r multi   .60 .60

Tourism A435

No. 764: a, Ghodaghodi Lake, Kailali. b, Budhasubba, Sunasari. c, Kalinchok Bhagawati, Dolakha. d, Panauti City, Kabhrepalanchok.

2005, Oct. 9
764   A435   5r Block of 4, #a-d   2.00 2.00

Diplomatic Relations Between Nepal and People's Republic of China, 50th Anniv. — A436

2005, Dec. 26
765   A436   30r multi   3.25 3.25

Admission to United Nations, 50th Anniv. — A437

2005, Dec. 26
766   A437   50r multi   5.50 5.50

Tribal Ornaments — A438

No. 767 — Ornaments of: a, Limbu tribes. b, Tharu tribes. c, Newar tribes. d, Sherpa tribes.

2005, Dec. 26
767   A438   25r Block of 4, #a-d   11.00 11.00

King Tribhuvan (1906-55) — A439

2006, Feb. 17   Litho.   Perf. 13¼x13
768   A439   5r multi   .55 .55

Democracy Day.

Queen Komal Rajya Laxmi Devi Shah — A440

2006, Mar. 8
769   A440   5r multi   .55 .55

Intl. Women's Day.

World Hindu Federation, 25th Anniv. — A441

2006, Apr. 6   Perf. 12¾
770   A441   2r multi   .35 .35

First Ascent of Mt. Lhotse, 50th Anniv. — A442

First Ascent of Mt. Manaslu, 50th Anniv. — A443

2006, May 9   Perf. 13x13¼
771   A442   25r multi   2.50 2.50
772   A443   25r multi   2.50 2.50

Supreme Court, 50th Anniv. — A444

2006, May 21
773   A444   5r multi   .65 .65

Fauna, Flora and Mushrooms — A445

Designs: No. 774, Imperial butterfly. No. 774A, Nepalese primrose. No., 774B, Chaffer beetle. No. 774C, Beautiful stream frog. No. 774D, White pine mushroom.

2006, June 12   Perf. 12¾
774-774D   Set of 5   5.50 5.50
e.   Horiz. strip of 5, #774-774D   7.00 7.00

Nos. 774-774D were printed in sheets of 50 stamps, containing ten of each stamp, but containing only two horizontal strips of the stamps.

40   **NEPAL**

Diplomatic Relations Between Nepal and Russia, 50th Anniv. — A446

2006, Aug. 22   *Perf. 13¼x13*
775   A446   30r multi
                      1.75   1.75

Diplomatic Relations Between Nepal and Japan, 50th Anniv. — A447

2006, Sept. 1   *Perf. 13x13¼*
776   A447   30r multi
                      1.75   1.75

Mt. Everest   Stag Beetle
A448   A449

2006, Sept. 19   *Perf. 14¼x14*
777   A448   1r blk & bl grn   .25   .25
778   A449   2r black   .35   .35

          Perf. 14x13¾
          Size: 29x25mm

779   A448   5r blk, pink & blue   .55   .35
     Nos. 777-779 (3)   1.15   .95

Membership in UPU, 50th Anniv. — A450

2006, Oct. 9   *Perf. 13x13¼*
780   A450   15r multi
                      1.00   1.00

Nepalese Postage Stamps, 125th Anniv. — A451

Designs: 5r, #1. 20r, #2. 100r, #3. 125r, #1-3.

2006, Oct. 9   *Perf. 13¼*
781-783   A451   Set of 3   7.50   7.50
          Size: 91x75mm
               Imperf
784   A451   125r multi   7.50   7.50

No. 784 contains a perforated label that is not valid for postage showing Nepal #1-3.

Birth of Buddha, 2550th Anniv. — A452

2006, Dec. 20   *Perf. 13¼x13*
785   A452   30r multi
                      1.75   1.75

Chhatrapati Free Clinic, 50th Anniv. — A453

2007, Feb. 6   *Litho.*   *Perf. 13x13¼*
786   A453   2r multi
                      .55   .55

Mt. Everest — A454

2007, Mar. 14
787   A454   5r multi   .80   .80

       Miniature Sheet

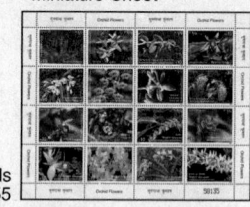

Orchids
A455

No. 788: a, Satyrium nepalense. b, Dendrobium heterocarpum. c, Pelantheria insectifera. d, Coelogyne ovalis. e, Coelogyne cristata. f, Dendrobium chrysanthum. g, Phalaenopsis mannii. h, Dendrobium densiflorum. i, Esmeralda clarkei. j, Acampe rigida. k, Bulbophyllum leopardinum. l, Dendrobium fimbriatum. m, Arundina graminifolia. n, Dendrobium moschatum. o, Rhynchostylis retusa. p, Cymbidium devonianum.

2007, Apr. 12
788   A455   10r Sheet of 16, #a-
         p   10.00   10.00

Sports — A456

Designs: No. 789, 5r, Taekwondo. No. 790, 5r, Cricket.

2007   *Perf. 13x13¼*
789-790   A456   Set of 2   .90   .90
Issued: No. 789, 4/25; No. 790, 4/28.

       Miniature Sheet

Martyrs of the Democratic Movement — A457

No. 791: a, Setu B. K. b, Tulasi Chhetri. c, Anil Lama. d, Umesh Chandra Thapa. e, Chakraraj Joshi. f, Chandra Bayalkoti. g, Devilal Poudel. h, Govindanath Sharma. i, Prof. Hari Raj Adhikari. j, Horilal Rana Tharu. k, Lal Bahadur Bista. l, Mohamad Jahangir. m, Pradhumna Khadka. n, Rajan Giri. o, Suraj Bishwas. p, Sagun Tamrakar. q, Bhimsen Dahal. r, Shivahari Kunwar. s, Basudev Ghimire. t, Bishnu Prasad Panday. u, Yamlal Lamichhane. v, Deepak Kami. w, Darshanial Yadab. x, Tahir Hussain Ansari. y, Hiralal Gautam.

2007, June 4   *Perf. 12½*
791   A457   2r Sheet of 25, #a-y   15.00   15.00

Diplomatic Relations Between Nepal and Sri Lanka, 50th Anniv. — A458

2007, July 1   *Perf. 13x13¼*
792   A458   5r multi   .50   .50

Diplomatic Relations Between Nepal and Egypt, 50th Anniv. — A459

2007, July 24
793   A459   5r multi   .50   .50

Scouting, Cent. — A460

2007, Sept. 4
794   A460   2r multi   .55   .55

Nepal Cancer Relief Society, 25th Anniv. — A461

2007, Sept. 17
795   A461   1r multi   .45   .45

Nepalese Parliament Building and Documents — A462

No. 796, 1r: a, Reinstatement of the House of Representatives. b, Proclamation of the House of Representatives.
No. 797, 1r: a, Constitution of Legislature-Parliament. b, Interim Constitution of Nepal.

2007, Dec. 28   *Litho.*   *Perf. 13x13¼*
        Horiz. Pairs, #a-b
796-797   A462   Set of 2   .90   .90

Chhaya Devi Parajuli (1918-2006), Politician — A463

2007, Dec. 30
798   A463   2r multi   .50   .50

Famous People A464

No. 799, 5r: a, Shivapuri Baba (1862-1963), religious leader. b, Mahesh Chandra Regmi (1929-2003), writer.
No. 800, 5r: a, Princess Bhrikuti (617-49). b, Pundit Udayananda Arjyal, writer.
No. 801, 5r: a, Ganesh Lal Shrestha, musician. b, Tara Devi (1945-2006), singer.

2007, Dec. 30   *Litho.*
        Horiz. Pairs, #a-b
799-801   A464   Set of 3   3.00   3.00

Tourism — A465

No. 802: a, Mt. Abi. b, Shree Bhageshwor Temple, Dadeldhura. c, Shree Shaillya Malikarjun Temple, Darchula. d, Shiddakali Temple, Bhojpur. e, Buddha's Victory over the Mara.

2007, Dec. 30
802   Vert. strip of 5   2.00   2.00
   a.-e.   A465   5r Any single   .35   .35

Diplomatic Relations Between Nepal and Germany, 50th Anniv. — A466

2008, Apr. 2   *Litho.*   *Perf. 13x13¼*
803   A466   25r multi
                      1.50   1.50

Nativity of Buddha — A467

2008, July 18   *Perf. 13¼x13*
804   A467   2r multi
                      1.00   1.00

Nepal Coat of Arms — A468

2008, Aug. 21
805   A468   1r multi   .50   .50

2008 Summer Olympics, Beijing — A469

2008, Aug. 21   *Perf. 12¾*
806   A469   15r multi
                      1.00   1.00

National Anthem and Flag of Nepal — A470

2008, Nov. 13   *Litho.*   *Perf. 13¼x13*
807   A470   1r multi   .60   .60

Kaiser Library, Cent. — A471

2008, Nov. 13   *Perf. 13x13¼*
808   A471   5r multi   .50   .50

Dr. Harka Gurung (1935-2006), Minister of Tourism, and Dr. Harka Gurung Peak — A472

2008, Dec. 24   *Litho.*
        Granite Paper
809   A472   5r multi   .60   .60

Flora, Fauna and Mushrooms — A473

No. 810: a, Serpentine. b, Long-horned beetle. c, Russula chloroides. d, Golden monitor lizard.

2008, Dec. 24   *Perf. 13x13¼*
Granite Paper
810 A473   Block or horiz. strip of 4, #a-d   2.25   2.25
a.-d.   5r Any single   .50   .50

Tourism — A474

No. 811: a, Mustang village, Mustang District. b, Syarpu Lake, Rukum District. c, Jaljala Hill, Rolpa District. d, Pindeswor Babadham, Dharan. e, Shree Kumair Chariot Festival, Kathmandu.

2008, Dec. 24   Litho.
Granite Paper
811   Vert. strip of 5   3.25   3.25
a.-e. A474 5r Any single   .45   .45

Family Planning Association of Nepal, 50th Anniv. — A475

2009, Sept. 14   Litho.   *Perf. 13x13¼*
Granite Paper
812 A475 1r multi   .35   .35

Office of Auditor General, 50th Anniv. — A476

2009, Sept. 14   *Perf. 13x13¼*
Granite Paper
813 A476 5r multi   .60   .60

Tribhuvan University, 50th Anniv. — A477

2009, Sept. 14   Litho.
Granite Paper
814 A477 5r multi   .60   .60

Birthplace of Buddha UNESCO World Heritage Site, Lumbini — A478

No. 815: a, Nativity sculpture and marker stone. b, Holy Pond. c, Asoka pillar. d, Excavated stupas. e, Mayadevi Temple.

2009, Sept. 14   *Perf. 13x13¼*
Granite Paper
815   Horiz. strip of 5   4.50   4.50
a.-e. A478 10r Any single   .50   .50

Establishment of Federal Democratic Republic — A479

2009, Oct. 8   Granite Paper   Litho.
816 A479 2r multi   1.00   1.00

Miniature Sheet

Butterflies — A480

No. 817: a, Common Apollo. b, Striped blue crow. c, Common yellow swallowtail. d, Swinhoe's nawab. e, Great satyr. f, Large cabbage white. g, Common tiger. h, Common brimstone. i, Yellow orange tip. j, Glassy blue bottle. k, Banded Apollo. l, Blue admiral. m, Lime swallowtail. n, Red Helen. o, Spot swordtail. p, Green sapphire.

2009, Oct. 8   *Perf. 13x13¼*
Granite Paper
817 A480 10p Sheet of 16, #a-p   11.00   11.00

Govinda Biyogi (1929-2006), Journalist — A481

2009, Nov. 2   *Perf. 13¾x13½*
Granite Paper
818 A481 5r multi   .60   .60

Guruji Mangal Das (1896-1985), Religious Leader — A482

2009, Nov. 9   Granite Paper   Litho.
819 A482 5r multi   .50   .50

Art A483

No. 820: a, Tej Bahadur Chitrakar (1898-1971), painter. b, Tribute to the Forefathers, painting by Chitrakar.

2009, Dec. 5   *Perf. 13½x13¼*
Granite Paper
820 A483 5r Horiz. pair, #a-b   .90   .90

Ramesh Vikal (1928-2008), Writer — A484

2009, Dec. 27   *Perf. 13¼x13½*
Granite Paper
821 A484 2r multi   .60   .60

Krishna Sen Ichhuk (1956-2002), Journalist — A485

2009, Dec. 27   *Perf. 13½x13¼*
Granite Paper
822 A485 5r multi   .50   .50

Laxmi Prasad Devkota (1909-59), Poet — A486

2009, Dec. 31   *Perf. 13¼x13½*
Granite Paper
823 A486 1r multi   .60   .60

Chhath Festival — A487

2009, Dec. 31   Litho.
Granite Paper
824 A487 5r multi   .60   .60

Lahurya Folk Dance — A488

2009, Dec. 31   *Perf. 13¼x13½*
Granite Paper
825 A488 5r multi   .65   .65

Kayaking — A489

2009, Dec. 31
826 A489 10r multi   .80   .80

Mountain Biking — A490

2009, Dec. 31
827 A490 10r multi   .80   .80

Nepal Television, 25th Anniv. — A491

2010, Jan. 31   *Perf. 13½x13¼*
828 A491 2r multi   .50   .50

Worldwide Fund for Nature (WWF) — A492

Perf. 13¼x13½
2010, Sept. 14   Litho.
829 A492 5r multi   .75   .75
New Year 2010 (Year of the Tiger).

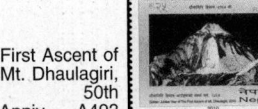

First Ascent of Mt. Dhaulagiri, 50th Anniv. — A493

2010, Sept. 26
830 A493 25r multi   1.75   1.75

Pemba Doma Sherpa (1970-2007), Mountaineer A494

2010, Sept. 26
831 A494 25r multi   1.75   1.75

Kankalini Mai Temple — A495

2010, Dec. 1
832 A495 2r multi   .55   .55   Litho.

Maru Ganesh Temple — A496

2010, Dec. 1
833 A496 2r multi   .50   .50

Bhairab Aryal (1936-76), Writer — A497

2010, Dec. 1
834 A497 5r multi   .50   .50

Natikaji Shrestha (1925-2003), Musician — A498

2010, Dec. 1   *Perf. 13½x13¼*
835 A498 5r multi   .50   .50

Jibraj Ashrit (1944-93), Politician — A499

2010, Dec. 1   *Perf. 13¼x13½*
836 A499 5r multi   .50   .50

Bhagat Sarbajit Bishwokarma (1893-1955), Social Reformer — A500

2010, Dec. 5   *Perf. 13½x13¼*
837 A500 5r multi   .50   .50

Mahasthabir Bhikshu Amritandanda (1918-90), Religious Leader — A501

2010, Dec. 7   *Perf. 13¼x13½*
838 A501 5r multi   .50   .50

Sadhana Adhikari (1925-2005), Politician A502

2010, Dec. 9   **Litho.**
839   A502   5r multi   .50   .50

Mai Pokhari Lake — A503

2010, Dec. 12
840   A503   2r multi   .60   .60

Global Handwashing Day — A504

2010, Dec. 30
841   A504   2r multi   .50   .50

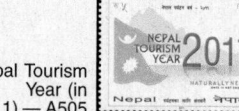

Nepal Tourism Year (in 2011) — A505

2010, Dec. 30
842   A505   5r multi   .55   .55

Stamps and Postmarks A506

Designs: No. 843, 1r, Nepal #1, 1881 Kathmandu postmark. No. 844, 1r, Nepal #27, 1910 Birganj postmark. No. 845, 2r, Nepal #26, 1915 Bethari postmark. No. 846, 2r, Nepal postal stationery indicia, 1934 Kanchanpur postmark. 3r, Nepal #53, 1952 Tamghas / Gulmi postmark.

2011, June 13   **Perf. 13¼x13½**
843-847   A506   Set of 5   1.00 1.00

Turtles — A507

No. 848: a, Ganges softshell turtle. b, Tricarinate Hill turtle. c, Elongated tortoise. d, Common roofed turtle.

2011, Aug. 28   **Perf. 13¾x13½**
          Granite Paper
848   Horiz. strip or block of 4   2.25 2.25
a.-d.   A507   10r Any single   .50   .50

Mohan Gopal Khetan (1947-2007), Industrialist A508

2011, Nov. 22   **Litho.**
          Granite Paper
849   A508   5r multi   .50   .50

Yagyaraj Sharma Aryjal (1903-89), Musician A509

2011, Nov. 23   **Perf. 13¾x13½**
          Granite Paper
850   A509   10r multi   .60   .60

Shankar Lamichhane (1928-76), Writer — A510

2011, Nov. 23   **Perf. 13½x13¾**
          Granite Paper
851   A510   10r multi   .60   .60

Ekdev Aale (1923-68), Politician — A511

2011, Nov. 23   **Litho.**
          Granite Paper
852   A511   10r multi   .60   .60

Motidevi Shrestha (1913-97), Politician — A512

2011, Nov. 23   **Perf. 13½x13¾**
          Granite Paper
853   A512   10r multi   .60   .60

Rishikesh Shaha (1925-2002), Human Rights Activist — A513

2011, Dec. 9   **Granite Paper**
854   A513   5r multi   .60   .60

Religious Sites — A514

Designs: 1r, Badimalika, Bajura. No. 856, 2r, Tansen Bhagawati, Palpa. No. 857, 2r, Siddha Ratannath Temple, Dang. No. 858, 2r, Deuti Bajai, Surkhet. No. 859, 2r, Bhat Bhateni Mai, Kathmandu. No. 860, 5r, Shree Baidhyanath Temple, Achham. No. 861, 5r, Gajurmukhi Dham, Ilam. 25r, Yetser Jangchubling Monastery, Upper Dolpa.
No. 863, 2r, vert.: a, Shree Aryavalokiteswora Seto Machhindranath, Kathmandu. b, Shree Aryavalokiteswora Seto Machhindranath Rath, Kathmandu.

2011, Dec. 30   **Perf. 13¾x13½**
          Granite Paper
855-862   A514   Set of 8   4.00 4.00
          Perf. 13½x13¾
863   A514   2r Horiz. pair, #a-b   .70   .70

Nepalese Landscapes A515

Designs: No. 864, 10r, Panch Pokhari, Sindhupalchok. No. 865, 10r, Mt. Mera Peak. No. 866, 10r, Badaiya Taal, Bardiya.

2011, Dec. 30   **Perf. 13¾x13½**
          Granite Paper
864-866   A515   Set of 3   1.75 1.75

A516

A517

A518

Cave Murals, Upper Mustang A519

2011, Dec. 30   **Litho.**
          Granite Paper
867   Horiz. strip of 4   2.25 2.25
a.   A516   10r multi   .50   .50
b.   A517   10r multi   .50   .50
c.   A518   10r multi   .50   .50
d.   A519   10r multi   .50   .50

Ramesh Kumar Mahato, Martyr — A520

2012, Jan. 19   **Perf. 13½x13¾**
          Granite Paper
868   A520   10r multi   .50   .50
          Dated 2011.

Gajendra Narayan Singh (1929-2002), Politician — A521

2012, Jan. 19   **Litho.**
          Granite Paper
869   A521   10r multi   .50   .50
          Dated 2011.

Girija Prasad Koirala (1924-2010), Prime Minister — A522

2012, Feb. 11   **Perf. 13¾x13½**
          Granite Paper
870   A522   10r multi   .50   .50
          Dated 2011.

Nepalese National News Agency, 50th Anniv. — A523

2012, Feb. 19   **Perf. 13½x13¾**
          Granite Paper
871   A523   10r multi   .60   .60

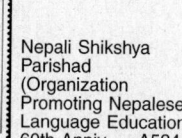

Nepali Shikshya Parishad (Organization Promoting Nepalese Language Education), 60th Anniv. — A524

2012, July 29   **Granite Paper**
872   A524   5r multi   .60   .60

Biodiversity — A525

No. 873: a, Delphinium himalayai. b, Dendrobium eriiflorum. c, Podophyllum hexandrum. d, Ganodermna lucidum. e, Prinia burnesii nepalicola. f, Gyps bengalensis. g, Caprolagus hispidus. h, Cyrtopodion markuscombaii.

2012, July 29   **Granite Paper**
873   A525   10r Block of 8, #a-h   4.50 4.50

Dead Sea, Mt. Everest, Flags of Israel and Nepal — A526

2012, Sept. 4   **Perf. 13½x13¾**
          Granite Paper
874   A526   35r multi   2.25 2.25
          Souvenir Sheet
875   A526   50r multi   5.50 5.50
          See Israel No. 1944.

B.P. Koirala Museum, Kathmandu, 8th Anniv. — A527

2012, Sept. 10   **Perf. 13¾x13½**
          Granite Paper
876   A527   10r multi   .70   .70

Lions International Blindness Prevention Campaign A528

2012, Sept. 25   **Litho.**
          Granite Paper
877   A528   5r multi   .50   .50

World AIDS Day — A529

2012, Dec. 13 *Perf. 13½x13¾*
Granite Paper
878 A529 5r multi .45 .45

Mt. Everest — A530

2012, Dec. 13 *Perf. 13¾x13½*
Granite Paper
879 A530 10r multi .75 .75

Asian-Pacific Postal Union, 50th Anniv. — A531

2012, Dec. 13 **Granite Paper**
880 A531 35r multi 2.00 2.00

Intl. Year of Cooperatives A532

2012, Dec. 24 **Litho.**
Granite Paper
881 A532 20r multi 1.25 1.25

Sports — A533

Designs: No. 882, 25r, Elephant soccer. No. 883, 25r, Bungee jumping, vert.

Perf. 13¾x13½, 13½x13¾
2012, Dec. 28 **Granite Paper**
882-883 A533 Set of 2 2.75 2.75

Krishna Prasad Bhattarai (1924-2011), Prime Minister — A534

2012, Dec. 23 *Perf. 13¾x13½*
884 A534 10r multi .60 .60

Bhikshu Sudarshan (1938-2002), Monk — A535

Perf. 13¾x13½
2012, Dec. 31 **Litho.**
885 A535 5r multi .50 .50

Basudev Luintel, Writer — A536

Perf. 13¾x13½
2012, Dec. 31 **Litho.**
886 A536 5r black .50 .50

Ali Miyan, Poet — A537

Perf. 13¾x13½
2012, Dec. 31 **Litho.**
Granite Paper
887 A537 10r multi .50 .50

Ramniwas Pandeya, Educator A538

Perf. 13¾x13½
2012, Dec. 31 **Litho.**
Granite Paper
888 A538 10r multi .50 .50

Bhuvaneswor Patheya, Writer — A539

Perf. 13¾x13½
2012, Dec. 31 **Litho.**
Granite Paper
889 A539 10r multi .50 .50

Khagendra Bahadur Basnet, Activist for Rights of the Disabled — A540

Perf. 13¾x13½
2012, Dec. 31 **Litho.**
Granite Paper
890 A540 10r multi .50 .50

Kishore and Kumar Narsingh Rama, Architects A541

Perf. 13¾x13½
2012, Dec. 31 **Litho.**
Granite Paper
891 A541 10r multi .50 .50

Karuna (1920-2008) and Lupau Ratna Tuladhar (1918-93), Operators of First Public Bus Service in Nepal — A542

Perf. 13¾x13½
2012, Dec. 31 **Litho.**
Granite Paper
892 A542 10r multi .50 .50

Visit Lumbini Year — A543

Perf. 13¾x13½
2012, Dec. 31 **Litho.**
Granite Paper
893 A543 20r multi 1.20 1.20

Rajmansingh Chitrakar (1797-1865), Painter — A544

No. 894 — Chitrakar and his paintings of: a, Tibetan antelopes. b, Birds.

Perf. 13¾x13½
2012, Dec. 31 **Litho.**
Granite Paper
894 A544 10r Horiz. pair, #a-b 1.20 1.20

Pandit Ramakanta Jha, Politician — A545

2013, Jan. 18 Litho. *Perf. 13¾x13½*
895 A545 10r multi .55 .55

Nepalese Partnership With World Bank Group, 50th Anniv. — A546

Perf. 13¾x13½
2013, Mar. 18 **Litho.**
Granite Paper
896 A546 10r multi .60 .60

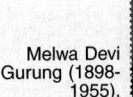

Melwa Devi Gurung (1898-1955), Singer — A547

Perf. 13¾x13½
2013, June 10 **Litho.**
Granite Paper
897 A547 5r multi .50 .50

Lake Salpa — A548

Lomanthang Durbar — A549

Salhes Garden, Lok Nayak Raja Salhes A550

Sahashra Dhara Jatra Festival A551

Perf. 13¾x13½
2013, June 10 **Litho.**
Granite Paper
898 A548 10r multi .60 .60
899 A549 10r multi .60 .60
900 A550 10r multi .60 .60
Perf. 13½x13¾
901 A551 10r multi .60 .60
Nos. 898-901 (4) 2.40 2.40

Ramraja Prasad Singh (1935-2012), Politician — A552

Moti Kaji Shakya (1913-97), Sculptor — A553

Bhimbahadur Tamang (1933-2012), Politician — A554

Basudev Prasad Dhungana (1933-2012), Advocate for Senior Citizens A555

Harihar Gautam (1901-65), Social Worker A556

Gopal Pande (1913-78), Writer — A557

2013, Oct. 9 Litho. *Perf. 13¾x13½*
Granite Paper
902 A552 10r multi .55 .55
903 A553 10r multi .55 .55
904 A554 10r multi .55 .55
905 A555 10r multi .55 .55
Perf. 13½x13¾
906 A556 10r multi .55 .55
907 A557 10r multi .55 .55
Nos. 902-907 (6) 3.30 3.30

Nepal Red Cross Society, 50th Anniv. — A558

2013, Oct. 9 Litho. *Perf. 13¾x13½*
Granite Paper
908 A558 50r multi 2.75 2.75

Batsaladevi Bhagawali, Dhadhing A559

2013, Oct. 30 Litho. *Perf. 13¾x13½*
909 A559 1r multi .65 .65

Rupchandra Bista (1933-99), Politician — A560

Kewalpure Kisan (1926-2011), Poet — A561

Rupak Raj Sharma (1954-92), Soccer Player — A562

Ram Sharan Darnal (1937-2011), Music Researcher A563

Diamond Shumsher Rana (1919-2011), Writer — A564

2013, Oct. 30   Litho.   Perf. 13¾x13½
910 A560 5r multi   .40   .40
Granite Paper
911 A561 5r multi   .40   .40
912 A562 10r multi   .65   .65
913 A563 10r multi   .65   .65
914 A564 20r multi   1.25 1.25
        Nos. 910-914 (5)   3.35 3.35

Bagalamukhi Devi, Lalitpur — A565

Rajdevi Temple, Saptari — A566

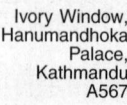

Ivory Window, Hanumandhoka Palace, Kathmandu A567

Kakre Bihar, Surkhet — A568

Argha Bhagawati, Arghakhanchi A569

2013, Dec. 31   Litho.   Perf. 13¼
Granite Paper
915 A565 1r multi   .50   .50
916 A566 1r multi   .50   .50
917 A567 5r multi   .50   .50
918 A568 5r multi   .50   .50
919 A569 5r multi   .50   .50
        Nos. 915-919 (5)   2.50 2.50

Shankar Koirala (1930-97), Writer A570

Ramhari Sharma (1916-2012), Politician A571

Bhanubhakta Acharya (1814-68), Poet — A572

Dr. Dilliraman Regmi (1913-2001), Historian — A573

2013, Dec. 31   Litho.   Perf. 13¼
Granite Paper
920 A570 3r multi   .50   .50
921 A571 3r multi   .50   .50
922 A572 10r multi   .60   .60
923 A573 10r multi   .60   .60
        Nos. 920-923 (4)   2.20 2.20

Museums A574

Designs: No. 924, 20r, National Art Museum, Bhaktapur. No. 925, 20r, International Mountain Museum, Kaski. No. 926, 20r, Patan Museum, Patan. 35r, National Museum, Chhauni.

2013, Dec. 31   Litho.   Perf. 13¼
Granite Paper
924-927 A574 Set of 4   5.50 5.50

Kathmandu Valley World Heritage Property — A575

Designs: No. 928, 25r, Bhaktapur Durbar Square Monument Zone. No. 929, 25r, Bauddhanath Monument Zone. No. 930, 25r, Changu Narayan Monument Zone. No. 931, 30r, Swayambhu Monument Zone. No. 932, 30r, Hanumandhoka Durbar Square Monument Zone. No. 933, 30r, Pashupati Monument Zone. No. 934, 30r, Patan Durbar Square Monument Zone.

2013, Dec. 31   Litho.   Perf. 13¼
Granite Paper
928-934 A575 Set of 7   11.00 11.00

Rara Lake, Mugu — A576

2013, Dec. 31   Litho.   Perf. 13¼
Granite Paper
935 A576 40r multi   2.25 2.25

Flora — A577

Designs: No. 936, 40r, Wild asparagus. No. 937, 40r, Chireta. No. 938, 40r, Long pepper. No. 939, 40r, Fragrant wintergreen.

2013, Dec. 31   Litho.   Perf. 13¼
Granite Paper
936-939 A577 Set of 4   9.00 9.00

Extinct Animals and Their Fossils — A578

Designs: No. 940, 50r, Giraffa punjabensis and fossil molar teeth. No. 941, 50r, Ramapithecus sivalensis and fossil molar

teeth. No. 942, 50r, Hexaprotodon sivalensis and fossil skull. No. 943, 50r, Archidiskidon planifrons and fossil skull.

2013, Dec. 31   Litho.   Perf. 13¼
Granite Paper
940-943 A578 Set of 4   12.00 12.00

Ascent of Mt. Everest, 60th Anniv., — A579

2013, Dec. 31   Litho.   Perf. 13¼
Granite Paper
944 A579 100r multi   5.50 5.50

Rishikesh Temple, Ridi — A580

2014, Oct. 9   Litho.   Perf. 13¼
Granite Paper
945 A580 5r multi   .50   .50

Narayanhiti Palace Museum, Kathmandu A581

2014, Oct. 9   Litho.   Perf. 13¼
Granite Paper
946 A581 20r multi   1.25 1.25

Scouting in Nepal, 60th Anniv. — A582

2014, Oct. 9   Litho.   Perf. 13¼
Granite Paper
947 A582 30r multi   2.25 1.50

Ascent of Mt. Cho-Oyu, 60th Anniv. — A583

2014, Oct. 9   Litho.   Perf. 13¼
Granite Paper
948 A583 100r multi   5.50 5.50

Manakamana Cable Car — A584

2014, Oct. 30   Litho.   Perf. 13¼
Granite Paper
949 A584 50r multi   3.00 3.00

Junior Chamber International of Nepal, 50th Anniv. — A585

2014, Nov. 11   Litho.   Perf. 13¼
Granite Paper
950 A585 10r multi   .50   .50

Kathmandu Buildings — A586

Designs: 1r, Shivaparbati Temple. 2r, Kumari Ghar.

2014, Dec. 9   Litho.   Perf. 13¼
Granite Paper
951-952 A586 Set of 2   .80   .80

Natural History Museum, Kathmandu — A587

2014, Dec. 9   Litho.   Perf. 13¼
Granite Paper
953 A587 1r multi   .35   .35

Aadeshwor Mahadev, Kathmandu — A588

2014, Dec. 9   Litho.   Perf. 13¼
Granite Paper
954 A588 1r multi   .35   .35

2014 International Cricket Council World Twenty 20 Competition, Bangladesh — A589

2014, Dec. 9   Litho.   Perf. 13¼
Granite Paper
955 A589 2r multi   .35   .35

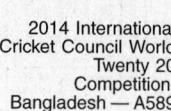

Female Community Health Volunteers Program, 25th Anniv. (in 2013) — A590

2014, Dec. 9   Litho.   Perf. 13¼
Granite Paper
956 A590 3r multi   .35   .35

Koteshwor Mahadev, Kathmandu — A591

2014, Dec. 9   Litho.   Perf. 13¼
Granite Paper
957 A591 4r multi   .45   .45

Prem Bahadur Kansakar (1917-91), Social Worker — A592

2014, Dec. 9   Litho.   Perf. 13¼
Granite Paper
958 A592 5r multi   .50   .50

Paragliding, Kaski — A593

2014, Dec. 9   Litho.   Perf. 13¼
Granite Paper
959 A593 10r multi   .55 .55

Miniature Sheets

Moths — A594

No. 960, 10r: a, Acherontia lachesis. b, Asota producta. c, Argina argus. d, Biston contectaria.
No. 961, 10r: a, Brahmaea wallichii. b, Campylotes histrionicus. c, Dermaleipa (Lagoptera) juno. d, Episteme adulatrix.
No. 962, 10r: a, Erasmia pulchella. b, Eterusia aedea edocla. c, Eudocima salaminia. d, Gynautocera papilionaria.

2014, Dec. 9   Litho.   Perf. 13¼
Granite Paper
Sheets of 4, #a-d
960-962 A594   Set of 3   6.75 6.75

Miniature Sheet

Birthplace of Buddha — A595

No. 963: a, Birthplace of Lord Buddha, Lumbini. b, Ashoka Pillar, Lumbini. c, Ramagrama, Nawalparasi. d, Tilaurakot, Kapilavastu.

2014, Dec. 9   Litho.   Perf. 13¼
Granite Paper
963 A595 20r Sheet of 4, #a-d   4.50 4.50

2014 Winter Olympics, Sochi, Russia — A596

2014, Dec. 10   Litho.   Perf. 13¼
Granite Paper
964 A596 2r multi   .50 .50

Tenzing-Hillary Everest Marathon — A597

2014, Dec. 19   Litho.   Perf. 13¼
Granite Paper
965 A597 3r multi   .40 .40

B. P. Koirala (1914-82), Prime Minister — A598

2014, Dec. 31   Litho.   Perf. 13¼
Granite Paper
966 A598 10r multi   .40 .40

Dwarika Bhakta Mathema (1902-68), Musician — A599

2015, July 1   Litho.   Perf. 13¼
Granite Paper
967 A599 1r multi   .25 .25

Chandeshwori Temple, Banepa — A600

Makwanpur Gadhi, Makwanpur A601

Lamjung Durbar, Lamjung — A602

Siddha Pokhari, Bhaktapur A603

Doleshwor Mahadev, Bhaktapur A604

Sindhuli Gadhi, Sindhuli — A605

Kaliyadaman, Sundari Chowk, Hanumandhoka A606

Mohankali Dhungedhara, Hanumandhoka A607

Taleju Temple, Nuwakot — A608

Bulbule Lake, Surkhet — A609

2015, July 1   Litho.   Perf. 13¼
Granite Paper
968 A600 1r multi   .35 .30
969 A601 1r multi   .35 .30
970 A602 2r multi   .35 .30
971 A603 2r multi   .35 .30
972 A604 5r multi   .35 .30
973 A605 5r multi   .35 .30
974 A606 5r multi   .35 .30
975 A607 8r multi   .35 .30
976 A608 10r multi   .35 .30
977 A609 10r multi   .35 .30
    Nos. 968-977 (10)   3.50 3.00

Fewa Lake and Machhapuchchhre, Kaski — A610

Serpentine Die Cut 12¼
2015, July 1   Litho.
Self-Adhesive
978 A610 60r multi   1.40 1.00

A611

A612

A613

B.P. Koirala Highway, Flags of Nepal and Japan — A614

2015, July 1   Litho.   Perf. 13¼
Granite Paper
979   Strip of 4   2.25 2.25
  a. A611 10r multi   .50   .30
  b. A612 10r multi   .50   .30
  c. A613 10r multi   .50   .30
  d. A614 10r multi   .50   .30
    Nepal-Japan cooperation.

Prehistoric Elephants A615

Emblem of Tribhuvan University Natural History Museum and: No. 980, 10r, Deinotherium indicum. No. 981, 10r, Elephas hysudricus. No. 982, 10r, Elephas namadicus. No. 983, 10r, Gomphotherium sp. No. 984, 10r, Stegodon bombifrons. No. 985, 10r, Stegodon ganesa.

2015, July 7   Litho.   Perf. 13¼
Granite Paper
980-985 A615   Set of 6   4.50 4.50

A616

2015, Aug. 1   Litho.   Perf. 13¼
Granite Paper
986 A616 20r multi   .90 .90

Diplomatic Relations Between Nepal and People's Republic of China, 60th Anniv.

Narasimha, Hanumandhoka A617

Nautale Durbar, Hanumandhoka A618

Rani Mahal, Palpa — A619

Gaddi Baithak, Hanumandhoka A620

2015, Aug. 11   Litho.   Perf. 14x13½
Granite Paper
987 A617 10r multi   .40   .40
           Perf. 13½x14
988 A618 10r multi   .40   .40
989 A619 25r multi   .75   .75
990 A620 35r multi   1.10 1.10
    Nos. 987-990 (4)   2.65 2.65

Miniature Sheet

Ascent of Mounts Kanchenjunga and Makalu, 60th Anniv. — A621

No. 991: a, Mt. Kanchenjunga. b, Mt. Makalu. c, Airplane over mountains. d, Unnamed mountains. e, Hillary Peak. f, Tenzing Peak.

**   Perf. 13½x13¼**
2015, Aug. 11   Litho.
Granite Paper
991 A621 10r Sheet of 6, #a-f 3.25 3.25

Non-Violence, Harmony, Morality and Freedom From Addiction — A622

2015, Aug. 16   Litho.   Perf. 13¼
Granite Paper
992 A622 25r multi   .70 .70

Wildlife Reserves and National Parks — A623

Designs: 1r, Koshi Tappu Wildlife Reserve. No. 994, 2r, Sagarmatha National Park. No. 995, 2r, Chitwan National Park. No. 996, 5r, Shuklaphanta Wildlife Reserve. No. 997, 5r, Lamtang National Park.

2015, Oct. 2 Litho. Perf. 13¼
Granite Paper
993-997 A623 Set of 5   1.25 1.25

Flora — A624

Designs: No. 998, 10r, Abies spectabilis. No. 999, 10r, Gentiana robusta. No. 1000, 10r, Lilium nepalense. No. 1001, 10r, Maharanga emodi. No. 1002, 10r, Paris polyphylla. No. 1003, 10r, Saussurea gossipiphora.

2015, Oct. 2 Litho. Perf. 13¼
Granite Paper
998-1003 A624 Set of 6   3.25 3.25

Sarbeshwor Mahadev, Lalitpur — A625

2015, Oct. 9 Litho. Perf. 13¼
Granite Paper
1004 A625 3r multi   .40 .30

Earthquake Survival Techniques A626

2015, Oct. 9 Litho. Perf. 13¼
Granite Paper
1005 A626 5r multi   .40 .40

18th South Asian Association for Regional Cooperation Summit, Kathmandu, 1st Anniv. — A627

2015, Oct. 9 Litho. Perf. 13¼
Granite Paper
1006 A627 10r multi   .50 .50

Famous Men — A628

Designs: No. 1007, 8r, Deviprasad Uprety (1912-92), social worker. No. 1008, 8r, Nagendra Prasad Rijal (1927-94), politician. No. 1009, 8r, Yadav Prasad Pant (1915-2007), economist. No. 1010, 8r, Shreeprasad Parajuli (1911-62), martyr. No. 1011, 8r, Ganeshman Singh (1915-97), politician. No. 1012, 8r, Siddhi Charan Shrestha (1912-92), poet, vert.

2015, Dec. 31 Litho. Perf. 13¼
Granite Paper
1007-1012 A628 Set of 6   3.25 3.25

Diplomatic Relations Between Nepal and Japan, 60th Anniv. — A630

2016, Nov. 3 Litho. Perf. 12½
Granite Paper
1014 A630 10r multi   1.00 1.00

Nepal Philatelic Society, 50th Anniv. — A631

Serpentine Die Cut 11
2016, Nov. 3 Litho.
Self-Adhesive
Granite Paper
1015 A631 10r multi   .50 .50

Federation of Nepal Chambers of Commerce and Industry, 50th Anniv. — A632

Serpentine Die Cut 11
2016, Nov. 3 Litho.
Self-Adhesive
Granite Paper
1016 A632 10r multi   .50 .50

Bal Bahadur Rai (1921-2010), Politician A633

Lakhan Thapa Magar (1834-77), Revolutionist and First Martyr of Nepal — A634

Mahendra Narayan Nidhi (1922-99), Politician A635

Yogmaya Neupane (1867-1941), Social Reformer A636

Dev S. J. B. Rana (1862-1914), Social Reformer A637

Ratna Kumar Bantawa (1952-79), Politician and Martyr — A638

2016 Litho. Perf. 12½
Granite Paper
1017 A633 10r multi   .50 .50
1018 A634 10r multi   .50 .50
1019 A635 10r multi   .50 .50
1020 A636 10r multi   .50 .50
1021 A637 10r multi   .50 .50
1022 A638 10r multi   .50 .50
   Nos. 1017-1022 (6)   3.00 3.00

Aadilinga Kusheshwor Mahadev, Sindhuli — A639

Chandanbharateshwor Mahadev, Kathmandu — A640

Shree Parroha Parmeshwor Shiva Jyotirlinga, Rupandehi A641

Siddhakali Temple, Bhojpur A642

Matsyanarayan Temple, Kathmandu A643

Hatuwaghadi, Capital of Majh Kirat, Bhojpur — A644

2016 Litho. Perf. 12½
Granite Paper
1023 A639 1r multi   .30 .30
1024 A640 5r multi   .30 .30
1025 A641 5r multi   .30 .30
1026 A642 10r multi   .50 .50
1027 A643 10r multi   .50 .50
1028 A644 10r multi   .50 .50
   Nos. 1023-1028 (6)   2.40 2.40

Bhringareshwor Mahadev, Lalitpur A645

2016 Litho. Serpentine Die Cut 11
Self-Adhesive
Granite Paper
1029 A645 2r multi   .30 .30

First Issue of Gorkhapatra Daily, 1901 — A646

2016 Litho. Serpentine Die Cut 11
Self-Adhesive
Granite Paper
1030 A646 10r multi   .50 .50

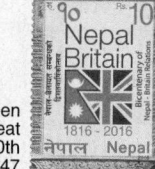

Relations Between Nepal and Great Britain, 200th Anniv. — A647

2016 Litho. Serpentine Die Cut 11
Self-Adhesive
Granite Paper
1031 A647 10r multi   1.00 1.00

Constitution of Nepal — A648

2016 Litho. Serpentine Die Cut 11
Self-Adhesive
Granite Paper
1032 A648 10r multi   .50 .50

Francolinus Francolinus A649

2016 Litho. Serpentine Die Cut 11
Self-Adhesive
Granite Paper
1033 A649 25r multi   2.25 2.25

Beetles A650

Designs: No. 1034, 20r, Therates nepalensis. No. 1035, 20r, Mylabris phalerata. No. 1036, 20r, Dorcus nepalensis. No. 1037, 20r, Odontolabis (Calcodes) cuvera.

2016 Litho. Serpentine Die Cut 11
Self-Adhesive
Granite Paper
1034-1037 A650 Set of 4   6.50 6.50

Rhododendrons A651

Designs: No. 1038, 20r, Rhododendron ciliatum. No. 1039, 20r, Rhododendron dalhousiae. No. 1040, 20r, Rhododendron fulgens. No. 1041, 20r, Rhododendron glaucophyllum.

2016 Litho. Serpentine Die Cut 11
Self-Adhesive
Granite Paper
1038-1041 A651 Set of 4   6.50 6.50

Mountains A652

Designs: 35r, Mt. Manaslu. 100r, Mt. Lhotse.

2016 Litho. *Serpentine Die Cut 11*
Self-Adhesive
Granite Paper
1042-1043 A652 Set of 2 11.00 11.00

Prehistoric
Mammals
A653

Designs: No. 1044, 10r, Dorcatherium. No. 1045, 10r, Hipparion. No. 1046, 10r, Pachyportax. No. 1047, 10r, Hemibos acuticornis. 100r, Brachypotherium perimense. 200r, Giraffokeryx punjabiensis.

Serpentine Die Cut 11
2017, Sept. 22 **Litho.**
Self-Adhesive
Granite Paper
1044-1049 A653 Set of 6 16.00 16.00

Mammals
A654

Designs: No. 1050, 10r, Marbled cat. No. 1051, 10r, Large Indian civet. No. 1052, 10r, Pygmy hog. No. 1053, 10r, Black giant squirrel. No. 1054, 20r, Crested porcupine. No. 1055, 20r, Roylei's pika.

Serpentine Die Cut 11
2017, Sept. 22 **Litho.**
Self-Adhesive
Granite Paper
1050-1055 A654 Set of 6 4.50 4.50

Flora — A655

Designs: No. 1056, 1r, Dryopteris cochleata. No. 1057, 1r, Lycopodium japonicum. No. 1058, 2r, Cyathea spinulosa. No. 1059, 2r, Drynaria propinqua. No. 1060, 3r, Nephrolepis cordifolia. No. 1061, 3r, Tectaria coadunate.

2017 Litho. Perf. 12½
Granite Paper
1056-1061 A655 Set of 6 1.75 1.75

Containers — A656

Designs: 3r, Theki Madani. 8r, Karuwa.

2017 Litho. Perf. 12½
Granite Paper
1062-1063 A656 Set of 2 .90 .90

Famous
Men — A657

Designs: No. 1064, 10r, Janakabi Keshari Dharmaraj Thapa (1924-2014), folk singer. No. 1065, 10r, Saroj Prasad Koirala (1929-73), politician.

2017 Litho. Perf. 12½
Granite Paper
1064-1065 A657 Set of 2 1.20 1.20

Pokali
Waterfall — A658

2017 Litho. Perf. 12½
Granite Paper
1066 A658 1r multi .40 .30

Ugratara
Temple,
Dadeldhura
A659

2017 Litho. Perf. 12½
Granite Paper
1067 A659 1r multi .40 .30

Shreeantu
A660

2017 Litho. Perf. 12½
Granite Paper
1068 A660 2r multi .40 .30

Rauta
Pokhari — A661

2017 Litho. Perf. 12½
Granite Paper
1069 A661 2r multi .40 .30

Tansen Bhairav,
Palpa — A662

2017 Litho. Perf. 12½
Granite Paper
1070 A662 2r multi .40 .30

Junge Mahadev
Statue,
Banke — A663

2017 Litho. Perf. 12½
Granite Paper
1071 A663 2r multi .40 .30

Flag of
Nepal — A664

2017 Litho. Perf. 12½
Granite Paper
1072 A664 5r multi .40 .30

Pandit Amrit
Nath Mishra
(1920-2015),
Srimadbhagwat
Savant — A665

2017 Litho. Perf. 12½
Granite Paper
1073 A665 10r multi .90 .90

Nepal Election
Commission, 50th
Anniv. — A666

2017 Litho. Perf. 12½
Granite Paper
1074 A666 10r multi .90 .90

Foods
A667

No. 1075: a, Yomari. b, Sel. c, Anarasa. d, Lakhamari.

2017 Litho. Perf. 12½
Granite Paper
1075 A667 1r Block of 4, #a-d 1.20 1.20

Jewelry
A668

No. 1076: a, Bulaki. b, Hasuli. c, Tilhari. d, Kalli.

2017 Litho. Perf. 12½
Granite Paper
1076 A668 500r Block of 4, #a-d 85.00 85.00

Four
Martyrs — A669

2017 Litho. Perf. 12½
Granite Paper
1077 A669 10r multi .90 .90

Bel Biwaha — A670

2017 Litho. Perf. 12½
Granite Paper
1078 A670 20r multi 1.75 1.75

Bratabandha
A671

2017 Litho. Perf. 12½
Granite Paper
1079 A671 35r multi 2.40 2.40

Wedding
Costumes — A672

Costumes of newly-wedded: 10r, Tharu couple. 20r, Limbu couple.

2017 Litho. Perf. 12½
Granite Paper
1080-1081 A672 Set of 2 2.50 2.50

Landscapes
A673

Designs: 5r, Gajedi Lake, Rupandehi. 35r, Khangchung (UIAA Peak), Solukhumbu.

2017 Litho. Perf. 12½
Granite Paper
1082-1083 A673 Set of 2 3.00 3.00

Temples — A674

Designs: 2r, Sarshwor Mahadev, Siraha. 5r, Mahalaxmi Temple, Lalitpur. 10r, Kshemadevi Temple, Sindhupalchowk.

2017 Litho. Perf. 12½
Granite Paper
1084-1086 A674 Set of 3 1.75 1.75

First Paper
Banknotes of
Nepal — A675

Front and back of: 5r, Five-rupee note. 10r, Ten-rupee note. 100r, One hundred-rupee note.

2017 Litho. Perf. 12½
Granite Paper
1087-1089 A675 Set of 3 6.00 6.00

Famous
Men — A676

Designs: No. 1090, 5r, Master Ratadnas Prakash (1913-92), musician. No. 1091, 5r, Dronacharya Chhetri (1945-93), politician. No. 1092, 10r, Durga Nanda Jha (1942-64), martyr. No. 1093, 10r, Yagya Bahadur Thapa (1913-78), martyr. No. 1094, 10r, Gaurishankar Khadka (1959-2009), politician. No. 1095, 10r, Gambhir Bahadur Thapa (1924-2009), social worker.

2017   Litho.   Perf. 12½
            Granite Paper
1090-1095 A676   Set of 6   4.50 4.50

Ram Prasad Rai
(1909-52), Leader of
1951
Revolution — A677

2018   Litho.   Perf. 12½
            Granite Paper
1096 A677 10r multi   .90 .90

Alam Devi
Temple,
Syangja
A678

2019   Litho.   Perf. 12½
            Granite Paper
1097 A678 5r multi   .90 .90

Flora — A679

Designs: No. 1098, 5r, Daphne bholua. No. 1099, 5r, Girardinia diversifolia. No. 1100, 5r, Agave americana.

2019   Litho.   Perf. 12½
            Granite Paper
1098-1100 A679   Set of 3   1.60 1.60

Snails
A680

No. 1101: a, Rishetia kathmandica. b, Rishetia nagarjunesis. c, Rishetia rishikeshi. d, Rishetia tribhuvana.

2019   Litho.   Perf. 12½
            Granite Paper
1101 A680 5r Block of 4, #a-d   2.25 2.25

Tongue
Piercing
Ceremony
A681

2019   Litho.   Perf. 12½
            Granite Paper
1102 A681 10r multi   .90 .90

Yadunath Khanal
(1913-2004),
Diplomat — A682

2019   Litho.   Perf. 12½
            Granite Paper
1103 A682 10r multi   .90 .90

Amber Gurung
(1938-2016),
Composer and
Musician
A683

2019   Litho.   Perf. 12½
            Granite Paper
1104 A683 10r multi   .90 .90

Nararaj Dhakal
(1920-2004),
Musician
A684

2019   Litho.   Perf. 12½
            Granite Paper
1105 A684 10r multi   .90 .90

Toni Hagen
(1917-2003),
Geologist
A685

2019   Litho.   Perf. 12½
            Granite Paper
1106 A685 20r multi   1.60 1.60

Buddha — A686

2019   Litho.   Perf. 12½
            Granite Paper
1107 A686 20r multi   1.60 1.60

Diplomatic
Relations
Between Nepal
and Sri Lanka,
60th
Anniv. — A687

2019   Litho.   Perf. 12½
            Granite Paper
1108 A687 25r multi   2.75 2.75

Souvenir Sheet

Temal Jatra, Boudhanath
Stupa — A688

2019   Litho.   Perf. 12½
            Granite Paper
1109 A688 50r multi   5.50 5.50

Securities
Board of
Nepal, 25th
Anniv. — A689

            Serpentine Die Cut 11
2020, Jan. 1   Litho.
            Self-Adhesive
1110 A689 5r multi   — —

2021
Census — A690

2020, Jan. 1   Litho.   Perf. 12½
            Granite Paper
1111 A690 10r bl grn & blk   — —

100th Birthday of
Dr. Satya Mohan
Joshi,
Writer — A691

2020, Jan. 1   Litho.   Perf. 12½
            Granite Paper
1112 A691 10r multi   — —

Ramdhuni
Temple,
Sunsari
A692

            Serpentine Die Cut 11
2020, Jan. 1   Litho.
            Self-Adhesive
1113 A692 10r multi   — —

Lumbini Peace
Marathon
A693

            Serpentine Die Cut 11
2020, Jan. 1   Litho.
            Self-Adhesive
1114 A693 20r multi   — —

Mount Everest
Skydivers
A694

2020, Jan. 1   Litho.   Perf. 12½
            Granite Paper
1115 A694 30r multi   — —

Flora — A695

Designs: No. 1116, Berberis pendryi. No. 1117, Begonia tribenensis. No. 1118, Begonia leptoptera. No. 1119, Berberis mucrifolia.

2020, Jan. 1   Litho.   Perf. 12½
            Granite Paper
1116-1119 A695 10r Set of 4   — —

Tourism
A696

Designs: 5r, Galeshwor Mahadev Temple, Myagdi. No. 1121, 10r, Resunga Yagyashala, Gulmi. No. 1122, 10r, Sirubari, Syangja. No. 1123, 10r, Ghale Gaun, Lamjung.

            Serpentine Die Cut 11
2020, Jan. 1   Litho.
            Self-Adhesive
1120-1123 A696   Set of 4

Nepal Rastra
Bank's First 1-
Rupee
Banknote
A697

No. 1124: a, Front of banknote (with black serial number). b, Back of banknote.

2020, Jan. 1   Litho.   Perf. 12½
            Granite Paper
1124 A697 10r Vert. pair, #a-b   — —

Musical Instruments — A698

No. 1125: a, Damaahaa. b, Sahane. c, Karnaal. d, Dholaki. e, Jhurmaa. f, Tyaamko. g, Narasingaa. h, Panchai baajaa.

            Serpentine Die Cut 11
2020, Jan. 1   Litho.
            Self-Adhesive
1125 A698 20r Block of 8, #a-h

Nepal Chamber of Commerce, 70th Anniv. — A699

Serpentine Die Cut 11
2021, Dec. 29   Litho.
Self-Adhesive
1126 A699 5r multi   — —

Spiny Babbler — A700

Serpentine Die Cut 11
2021, Dec. 29   Litho.
Self-Adhesive
1127 A700 10r multi   — —

Hiking Routes and Bases — A701

Designs: 10r, Ghandruk, Kaski. No. 1129, 20r, Everest Base Camp Route. No. 1130, 20r, Manaslu Circuit Route. No. 1131, 20r, Mardi Himal Trekking Route. No. 1132, 20r, Annapurna Base Camp Route.

Serpentine Die Cut 11
2021, Dec. 29   Litho.
Self-Adhesive
1128-1132 A701 Set of 5   — —
Nos. 1129-1132 have white denominations.

Mountains A702

Designs: No. 1133, 10r, Mt. Everest. No. 1134, 10r, Mt. Cho-Oyu. No. 1135, 10r, Mt. Dhaulagiri. No. 1136, 10r, Mt. Annapurna. No. 1137, 10r, Mt. Kanchenjunga (main peak). No. 1138, 10r, Mt. Lhotse. No. 1139, 10r, Mt. Makalu. No. 1140, 10r, Mt. Manaslu.

Serpentine Die Cut 11
2021, Dec. 29   Litho.
Self-Adhesive
1133-1140 A702 Set of 8   — —

Sustainable Development Goals — A703

Various works of Mithla art and sustainable development goal: No. 1141, Goal 1, No poverty.
No. 1142: a, Goal 2, Zero hunger. b, Goal 3, Good health and well-being. c, Goal 4, Quality education. d, Goal 5, Gender equality.
No. 1143: a, Goal 6, Clean water and sanitation. b, Goal 7, Affordable and clean energy. c, Goal 8, Decent work and economic growth. d, Goal 9, Industry, innovation and infrastructure.
No. 1144: a, Goal 10, Reduced inequalities. b, Goal 11, Sustainable cities and communities. c, Goal 12, Responsible consumption and production. d, Goal 13, Climate action.

No. 1145: a, Goal 14, Life below water. b, Goal 15, Life on land. c, Goal 16, Peace, justice and strong institutions. d, Goal 17, Partnerships for the goals.

Serpentine Die Cut 11
2021, Dec. 29   Litho.
Self-Adhesive
1141 A703 10r multi   — —
1142   Horiz. strip of 4   — —
a.-d. A703 10r Any single   — —
1143   Horiz. strip of 4   — —
a.-d. A703 10r Any single   — —
1144   Horiz. strip of 4   — —
a.-d. A703 10r Any single   — —
1145   Horiz. strip of 4   — —
a.-d. A703 10r Any single   — —

Panchadewal Temple, Baitadi — A704

Mandavya Rishi Temple, Palpa — A705

2022   Litho.   Perf. 12½
Granite Paper
1146   Vert. pair   — —
a. A704 5r multi   — —
b. A705 5r multi   — —

Sinja Valley, Jumla — A706

2022   Litho.   Perf. 12½
Granite Paper
1147 A706 10r multi   — —

Kaji Kalu Pandey Graveyard, Kathmandu — A707

2022   Litho.   Perf. 12½
Granite Paper
1148 A707 10r multi   — —

Palpa Durbar Museum, Palpa — A708

2022   Litho.   Perf. 12½
Granite Paper
1149 A708 10r multi   — —

Kalinchowk Bhagawati, Dolakha A709

Tanadevi Temple, Kathmandu A710

Saileshwori Bhagawati Temple, Doti — A711

Rambhadevi Temple, Palpa — A712

2022   Litho.   Perf. 12½
Granite Paper
1150   Vert. strip of 4   — —
a. A709 5r multi   — —
b. A710 5r multi   — —
c. A711 5r multi   — —
d. A712 5r multi   — —

Man and Woman Wearing Jirel Costumes and Ornaments A713

Shadar Pidar (Koech) Festival of Sunuwar A714

Man and Woman Wearing Surel Costumes A715

Man and Woman Wearing Tamang Costumes, Damphu Drum A716

Thami Ethnic Culture — A717

2022   Litho.   *Serpentine Die Cut 11*
Granite Paper
Self-Adhesive
1151   Vert. strip of 5   — —
a. A713 10r multi   — —
b. A714 10r multi   — —
c. A715 10r multi   — —
d. A716 10r multi   — —
e. A717 10r multi   — —

Rhododendrons A718

No. 1152: a, Rhododendron thomsonii. b, Rhododendron campanulatum.
No. 1153: a, Pink Rhododendron arboreum. b, Red Rhododendron arboreum. c, Rhododendron lepidotum. d, White Rhododendron arboreum.

2022   Litho.   Perf. 12½
Granite Paper
1152   Horiz. pair   — —
a.-b. A718 20r Either single   — —
1153   Horiz. strip of 4   — —
a.-d. A718 20r Any single   — —

A719   A720

A721

Workers of the COVID-19 Pandemic — A722

2022, Dec. 18   Litho.   Perf. 12½
Granite Paper
1154   Horiz. strip of 4   — —
a. A719 10r multi   — —
b. A720 10r multi   — —
c. A721 10r multi   — —
d. A722 10r multi   — —

Khaptad National Park, Doti — A723

Panini Tapobhumi, Arghakhanchi A724

Statue of Shrawan Kumar and Aandhikhola, Syangja A725

Tribeni Temple, Khaptad National Park, Doti — A726

Taudaha Lake, Kathmandu A727

2022, Oct. 9   Litho.   Perf. 12½
Granite Paper
1155   Horiz. strip of 5   — —
a. A723 5r multi   — —
b. A724 5r multi   — —
c. A725 5r multi   — —
d. A726 5r multi   — —
e. A727 5r multi   — —

Medicinal Plants — A728

No. 1156: a, Didymocarpus nepalensis. b, Tinospora sinensis. c, Justicia adhatoda. d, Acorus calamus.

2022, Oct. 9   Litho.   Perf. 12½
Granite Paper
1156	Horiz. strip of 4	—	—
a.-d.	A728 10r Any single	—	—

Mountain Peaks — A729

No. 1157: a, Island Peak. b, Abi Peak. c, Lobuche Peak. d, Chulu East Peak. e, Pisang Peak.

Serpentine Die Cut 11
2022, Oct. 9   Litho.
Self-Adhesive
Granite Paper
1157	Horiz. strip of 5	—	—
a.-e.	A729 10r Any single	—	—

AIR POST STAMPS

Catalogue values for unused stamps in this section are for Never Hinged items.

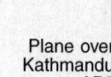

Bird over Kathmandu — AP1

Rough Perf 11½
1958, Oct. 16   Typo.   Unwmk.
Without Gum
C1	AP1	10p dark blue	4.00 2.00

Plane over Kathmandu AP2

1967, Oct. 24   Photo.   Perf. 13½x13
C2	AP2	1.80r multicolored	2.00 1.50

International Tourist Year.

God Akash Bhairab and Nepal Airlines Emblem — AP3

Map of Nepal with Airlines Network — AP4

Design: 2.50r, Plane over Himalayas.

Perf. 14½x14, 13 (65p)
1968, July 1   Photo.
C3	AP3	15p blue & bis brn	.50 .50
C4	AP4	65p violet blue	1.25 1.00
C5	AP3	2.50r dp blue & scar	3.75 2.75
		Nos. C3-C5 (3)	5.50 4.25

10th anniv. of the Royal Nepal Airlines Corp.

Flyer and Jet — AP5

1978, Dec. 12   Photo.   Perf. 13
C6	AP5	2.30r blue & ocher	1.25 .80

75th anniversary of 1st powered flight.

Pheasant Type of 1979

3.50r, Impeyan pheasant, horiz.

1979, Nov. 22 Photo.   Perf. 14½x14
C7	A174	3.50r multicolored	2.25 1.75

OFFICIAL STAMPS

Catalogue values for unused stamps in this section are for Never Hinged items.

Soldiers and Arms of Nepal — O1

Perf. 13½
1959, Nov. 1   Litho.   Unwmk.
Size: 29x17½mm
O1	O1	2p reddish brown	.25 .25
O2	O1	4p yel green	.25 .25
O3	O1	6p salmon pink	.25 .25
O4	O1	8p brt violet	.30 .25
O5	O1	12p red orange	.35 .25

Size: 37½x21½mm
O6	O1	16p red brown	.50 .35
O7	O1	24p carmine	.60 .50
O8	O1	32p rose car	1.00 .70
O9	O1	50p ultramarine	1.75 1.25
O10	O1	1r rose red	3.25 2.25
O11	O1	2r orange	6.50 5.00
		Nos. O1-O11 (11)	15.00 11.30

Nos. 144-146 and 124 Overprinted in Black

1960-62   Photo.   Perf. 14½x14
Overprint 12½mm Long
O12	A35	1p carmine rose ('62)	.25 .25
O13	A35	2p bright blue ('62)	.25 .25
O14	A35	5p golden brown ('62)	.35 .35
		Nos. O12-O14 (3)	.85 .85

Perf. 14
Overprint 14½mm Long
O15	A26	1r red lilac	1.25 1.25

The overprint, "Kaj Sarkari" in Devanagari characters means "Service." Five other denominations, 10p, 40p, 75p, 2r and 5r, were similarly overprinted but not issued. Value, 5 values $3. A few exist on 1960 first day covers.

In 1983 substantial quantities of the set of nine values were sold as remainders by the Post Office at face value (under $1 for the set).

The existence of covers from 1985-86 indicate that some of these may have been used as regular postage stamps.

NETHERLANDS
'ne-thər-lən͟dz

(Holland)

LOCATION — Northwestern Europe, bordering on the North Sea
GOVT. — Kingdom
AREA — 16,029 sq. mi.
POP. — 15,807,641 (1999 est.)

CAPITAL — Amsterdam
100 Cents = 1 Gulden (Guilder or Florin)
100 Cents = 1 Euro (2002)

Catalogue values for unused stamps in this country are for Never Hinged items, beginning with Scott 216 in the regular postage section, Scott B123 in the semi-postal section, Scott C13 in the airpost section, Scott J80 in the postage due section and Scott O44 in the official section.

Values for unused stamps are for examples with original gum as defined in the catalogue introduction. Very fine examples of Nos. 4-12 will have perforations touching the frameline on one or more sides due to the narrow spacing of the stamps on the plates. Stamps with perfs clear on all four sides are very scarce and command higher prices.

Watermarks

Wmk. 158   Wmk. 202 — Circles

King William III — A1

Wmk. 158
1852, Jan. 1   Engr.   Imperf.
1	A1	5c blue	400.00	35.00
a.		5c light blue	450.00	40.00
b.		5c steel blue	750.00	100.00
c.		5c dark blue	450.00	35.00
2	A1	10c carmine	450.00	27.50
3	A1	15c orange	775.00	130.00

In 1895 the 10c was privately reprinted in several colors on unwatermarked paper by Joh. A. Moesman, whose name appears on the back.

King William III — A2

1864   Unwmk.   Perf. 12½x12
4	A2	5c blue	300.00	16.00
5	A2	10c lake	425.00	8.00
6	A2	15c orange	1,050.	100.00
a.		15c yellow	1,350.	115.00

The paper varies considerably in thickness. It is sometimes slightly bluish, also vertically ribbed.

William III — A3

1867   Perf. 12¾x11¾
7	A3	5c ultra	115.00	2.75
8	A3	10c lake	225.00	4.75
9	A3	15c orange brn	640.00	35.00
10	A3	20c dk green	625.00	24.00
11	A3	25c dk violet	2,100.	110.00
12	A3	50c gold	2,500.	160.00

The paper of Nos. 7-22 sometimes has an accidental bluish tinge of varying strength. During its manufacture a chemical whitener (bluing agent) was added in varying quantities. No particular printing was made on bluish paper.

Two varieties of numerals in each value, differing chiefly in the thickness.

Oxidized copies of the 50c are worth much less.

Imperforate varieties of Nos. 7-12 are proofs.

See the *Scott Specialized Catalogue* for listings by perforations.

1869   Perf. 10½x10
7c	A3	5c ultra	225.00	11.50
8c	A3	10c lake	230.00	7.75
9c	A3	15c orange brown	2,700.	1,150.
10c	A3	20c dark green	1,550.	155.00

Coat of Arms — A4

1869-71   Typo.   Perf. 13¼, 14
17	A4	½c red brown ('71)	24.00	3.75
c.		Perf. 14	2,300.	875.00
18	A4	1c black	210.00	70.00
19	A4	1c green	15.50	2.25
c.		Perf. 14	27.50	5.50
20	A4	1½c rose	150.00	77.50
b.		Perf. 14	175.00	97.50
21	A4	2c buff	60.00	15.00
c.		Perf. 14	55.00	14.00
22	A4	2½c violet ('70)	475.00	70.00
c.		Perf. 14	775.00	425.00

Imperforate varieties are proofs.

A5   A6

Perf. 12½, 13, 13½, 13x14, 14, 12½x12 and 11½x12
1872-88
23	A5	5c blue	11.50	.30
a.		5c ultra	14.00	1.25
24	A5	7½c red brn ('88)	35.00	18.00
25	A5	10c rose	57.50	1.60
26	A5	12½c gray ('75)	62.50	2.40
27	A5	15c brn org	350.00	5.25
28	A5	20c green	425.00	5.00
29	A5	22½c dk grn ('88)	77.50	42.50
30	A5	25c dull vio	525.00	4.00
31	A5	50c bister	650.00	11.00
32	A5	1g gray vio ('88)	480.00	40.00
33	A6	2g50c rose & ultra	900.00	105.00

Imperforate varieties are proofs.

Numeral of Value — A7

HALF CENT:
Type I — Fraction bar 8 to 8½mm long.
Type II — Fraction bar 9mm long and thinner.

Perf. 12½, 13½, 14, 12½x12, 11½x12
1876-94
34	A7	½c rose (II)	11.50	.30
a.		½c rose (I)	15.00	.50
c.		Laid paper		60.00
d.		Perf. 14 (I)	1,950.	575.00
35	A7	1c emer grn ('94)	2.75	.25
b.		As "c," laid paper	70.00	7.25
c.		1c green	8.00	.25
36	A7	2c olive yel ('94)	32.50	2.75
a.		2c yellow	65.00	3.50
37	A7	2½c violet ('94)	14.00	.30
b.		2½c dark violet ('94)	17.50	.45
c.		2½c lilac	100.00	.80
d.		Laid paper		
		Nos. 34-37 (4)	60.75	3.60

Imperforate varieties are proofs.

Princess Wilhelmina — A8

1891-94   Perf. 12½
40	A8	3c orange ('94)	8.00	2.30
a.		3c orange yellow ('92)	11.50	2.75
41	A8	5c lt ultra ('94)	4.00	.25
a.		5c dull blue	5.00	.25
42	A8	7½c brown ('94)	15.00	6.25
a.		7½c red brown	27.50	6.25
43	A8	10c brt rose ('94)	23.50	1.60
a.		10c brick red	45.00	2.40
44	A8	12½c bluish gray ('94)	23.50	1.60
a.		12½c gray	40.00	1.75
45	A8	15c yel brn ('94)	60.00	5.00
a.		15c orange brown	80.00	5.50
46	A8	20c green ('94)	70.00	3.00
a.		20c yellow green	80.00	4.00

47	A8	22½c dk grn ('94)	32.50	13.50
a.		22½c deep blue green	55.00	13.50
48	A8	25c dl vio ('94)	110.00	6.00
a.		25c dark violet	110.00	6.00
49	A8	50c yel brn ('94)	550.00	20.00
a.		50c bister	575.00	27.50
50	A8	1g gray vio	625.00	77.50

The paper used in 1891-93 was white, rough and somewhat opaque. In 1894, a thinner, smooth and sometimes transparent paper was introduced.

The 5c orange was privately produced.

Princess Wilhelmina — A9

1893-96   *Perf. 11½x11*

51	A9	50c emer & yel brn ('96)	80.00	15.00
a.		Perf. 11	2,500.	200.00
52	A9	1g brn & ol grn ('96)	200.00	22.50
a.		Perf. 11	225.00	60.00
53	A9	2g 50c brt rose & ultra	400.00	130.00
a.		2g 50c lil rose & ultra, perf. 11	475.00	130.00
b.		Perf. 11 ½	500.00	140.00

Perf. 11

54	A9	5g brnz grn & red brn ('96)	700.00	425.00

A10

Queen Wilhelmina — A11

Perf. 12½ (#70, 73, 75-77, 81-82), 11½, 11½x11, 11x11½

1898-1924

55	A10	½c violet	.45	.25
56	A10	1c red	.90	.25
b.		Imperf., pair	2,000.	
57	A10	1½c ultra ('08)	6.00	.85
58	A10	1½c dp blue ('13)	3.00	.35
59	A10	2c yellow brn	3.75	.25
60	A10	2½c deep green	3.25	.25
b.		Imperf., pair	6,250.	
61	A11	3c orange	16.50	3.25
62	A11	3c pale ol grn ('01)	1.10	.25
63	A11	4c claret ('21)	1.60	1.10
64	A11	4½c violet ('19)	3.75	3.75
65	A11	5c car rose	1.60	.25
66	A11	7½c brown	.75	.25
a.		Tête bêche pair ('24)	80.00	72.50
67	A11	10c gray lilac	6.25	.25
68	A11	12½c blue	3.25	.30
69	A11	15c yellow brn	100.00	3.25
70	A11	15c bl & car ('08)	6.25	.25
71	A11	17½c vio ('06)	50.00	12.00
73	A11	17½c ultra & brn ('10)	15.00	.90
74	A11	20c yellow green	150.00	.75
75	A11	20c ol grn & gray ('08)	10.00	.50
76	A11	22½c brn & ol grn	9.25	.60
77	A11	25c rose pink & bl	9.25	.45
78	A11	30c lil & vio brn ('17)	24.00	.50
79	A11	40c grn & org ('20)	34.00	1.10
80	A11	50c brnz grn & red brn	110.00	1.10
81	A11	50c gray & vio ('14)	70.00	1.10
a.		Perf 11½x11	70.00	16.50
82	A11	60c ol grn & grn ('20)	34.00	1.10
a.		Perf 11½	200.00	20.00
		Nos. 55-82 (27)	673.90	35.20
		Set, never hinged	3,000.	

See Nos. 107-112. For overprints and surcharges see Nos. 102-103, 106, 117-123, 135-136, O1-O8.

A12

     I   II

Type I — The figure "1" is 3¾mm high and 2¾mm wide.
Type II — The figure "1" is 3½mm high and 2½mm wide, it is also thinner than in type I.

Perf. 11, 11x11½, 11½, 11½x11

1898-1905   Engr.

83	A12	1g dk grn, II ('99)	52.50	.75
a.		1g dark green, I ('98)	190.00	110.00
84	A12	2½g brn lil ('99)	100.00	3.25
85	A12	5g claret ('99)	225.00	6.00
86	A12	10g orange ('05)	775.00	675.00
		Set, never hinged	2,975.	

For surcharge see No. 104.

Admiral M. A. de Ruyter and Fleet — A13

1907, Mar. 23   Typo.   Perf. 12x12½

87	A13	½c blue	2.00	1.25
88	A13	1c claret	3.50	2.25
89	A13	2½c vermilion	6.00	2.25
		Nos. 87-89 (3)	11.50	5.75
		Set, never hinged	37.00	

De Ruyter (1607-1676), naval hero. For surcharges see Nos. J29-J41.

King William I — A14

Designs: 2½c, 12½c, 1g, King William I. 3c, 20c, 2½g, King William II. 5c, 25c, 5g, King William III. 10c, 50c, 10g, Queen Wilhelmina.

Perf. 11½x11, 11½ (#97, 100-101)

1913, Nov. 29   Engr.

90	A14	2½c green, *grn*	.80	.80
91	A14	3c buff, *straw*	1.80	1.50
92	A14	5c rose red, *sal*	1.25	.90
93	A14	10c black brown	4.25	2.40
94	A14	12½c vio blue, *bl*	3.00	1.90
95	A14	20c orange brn	13.00	11.00
96	A14	25c blue	15.00	8.75
97	A14	50c yel grn	32.50	27.50
98	A14	1g claret	47.50	20.00
a.		Perf. 11½	60.00	20.00
99	A14	2½g purple	120.00	50.00
100	A14	5g yel, *straw*	225.00	40.00
101	A14	10g red, *straw*	800.00	725.00
		Nos. 90-101 (12)	1,264.	889.75
		Set, never hinged	2,285.	

Centenary of Dutch independence. For surcharge see No. 105.

No. 78 Surcharged in Red or Black

a   b

1919, Dec. 1   Perf. 12½

102	A11 (a)	40c on 30c (R)	25.00	4.50
103	A11 (b)	60c on 30c (Bk)	25.00	4.50
		Set, never hinged	210.00	

Nos. 86 and 101 Surcharged in Black

1920, Aug. 17   Perf. 11, 11½

104	A12	2.50g on 10g	145.00	80.00
		Never hinged	350.00	
105	A14	2.50g on 10g	160.00	100.00
		Never hinged	400.00	
		Set, never hinged	750.00	

No. 64 Surcharged in Red

1921, Mar. 1   Typo.   Perf. 12½

106	A11	4c on 4½c vio	3.75	1.40
		Never hinged	7.00	

A17

1921-22   Typo.   Perf. 12½

107	A17	5c green ('22)	13.00	.25
108	A17	12½c vermilion ('22)	19.00	1.75
109	A17	20c blue	31.00	.25
		Nos. 107-109 (3)	63.00	2.25
		Set, never hinged	215.00	

Queen Type of 1898-99, 10c Redrawn

1922   Perf. 12½

110	A11	10c gray	27.50	.25
		Never hinged	85.00	

Imperf

111	A11	5c car rose	7.00	7.00
		Never hinged	13.00	
112	A11	10c gray	7.00	7.00
		Never hinged	13.00	
		Nos. 110-112 (3)	41.50	14.25

In redrawn 10c the horizontal lines behind the Queen's head are wider apart.

Orange Tree and Lion of Brabant A18

Post Horn and Lion A19

Numeral of Value — A20

1923, Mar. 9   Perf. 12½

113	A18	1c dark violet	.55	.50
		Never hinged	2.00	
114	A18	2c orange	5.00	.25
		Never hinged	10.00	
115	A19	2½c bluish green	1.50	.65
		Never hinged	4.00	
116	A20	4c deep blue	1.25	.60
		Never hinged	3.25	
		Nos. 113-116 (4)	8.30	2.00
		Set, never hinged	19.50	

See No. 244 and compare to No. 115.

Nos. 56, 58, 62, 65, 68, 73, 76 Surcharged in Various Colors

c   d

1923, July   Perf. 12½

117	A10(c)	2c on 1c (Bl)	.45	.25
		Never hinged	1.00	
118	A10(c)	2c on 1½c (Bk)	.45	.25
		Never hinged	1.00	
119	A11(d)	10c on 3c (Br)	4.00	.25
		Never hinged	13.00	
120	A11(d)	10c on 5c (Bk)	8.00	.50
		Never hinged	22.50	
121	A11(d)	10c on 12½c (R)	6.50	.75
		Never hinged	24.00	

Perf. 11½x11

122	A11(d)	10c on 17½c (R)	2.75	2.60
		Never hinged	8.25	
a.		Perf. 11½	1,600.	800.00
b.		Perf. 12½	4.00	4.00
		Never hinged	8.00	
123	A11(d)	10c on 22½c (R)	2.75	2.60
		Never hinged	8.25	
a.		Perf. 11½	3.00	3.50
		Never hinged	6.50	
b.		Perf. 12½	4.00	4.00
		Never hinged	8.00	
		Nos. 117-123 (7)	24.90	7.20
		Set, never hinged	78.00	

Queen Wilhelmina
A21   A22

Perf. 11½x12½, 11½x12 (5c)

1923, Oct.   Engr.

124	A22	2c myrtle green	.25	.25
		Never hinged	1.10	
a.		Vert. pair, imperf. between	2,400.	
125	A21	5c green	.40	.25
		Never hinged	1.10	
a.		Vert. pair, imperf. between	1,800.	
126	A22	7½c carmine	.50	.25
		Never hinged	2.25	
127	A22	10c vermilion	.40	.25
		Never hinged	1.60	
a.		Vert. pair, imperf. between	550.00	575.00
128	A22	20c ultra	3.75	1.00
		Never hinged	9.00	
129	A22	25c yellow	5.00	1.10
		Never hinged	15.00	

Perf. 11½

130	A22	35c orange	5.00	3.00
		Never hinged	15.00	
131	A22	50c black	15.00	1.00
		Never hinged	45.00	
132	A21	1g red	30.00	7.25
		Never hinged	65.00	
133	A21	2½g black	190.00	200.00
		Never hinged	450.00	
134	A21	5g dark blue	175.00	175.00
		Never hinged	360.00	
		Nos. 124-134 (11)	425.30	389.35
		Set, never hinged	975.00	

25th anniv. of the assumption as monarch of the Netherlands by Queen Wilhelmina at the age of 18.

No. 119 Overprinted in Red

No. 73 With Additional Surcharge in Blue

1923   Typo.   Perf. 12½

135	A11	10c on 3c	1.10	1.00
		Never hinged	3.00	
136	A11	1g on 17½c	62.50	15.00
		Never hinged	190.00	
a.		Perf. 11½	95.00	40.00
b.		Perf. 11½x11	80.00	30.00

Stamps with red surcharge were prepared for use as Officials but were not issued.

Queen Wilhelmina — A23

1924, Sept. 6   Photo.   Perf. 12½
137	A23	10c slate green	32.50	32.50
		Never hinged	65.00	
138	A23	15c gray black	40.00	40.00
		Never hinged	70.00	
139	A23	35c brown orange	32.50	32.50
		Never hinged	65.00	
		Nos. 137-139 (3)	105.00	105.00
		Set, never hinged	200.00	

These stamps were available solely to visitors to the International Philatelic Exhibition at The Hague and were not obtainable at regular post offices. Set of three on international philatelic exhibition cover dataed Sept. 6-12, 15-17, 1924, value, $110. Set of three on Netherland Philatelic Exhibition cover dated Sept. 13-14, value, $150.

See Nos. 147-160, 172-193. For overprints and surcharge see Nos. 194, Q11, O13-O15.

Ship in Distress — A23a

Lifeboat — A23b

1924, Sept. 15   Litho.   Perf. 11½
140	A23a	2c black brn	3.25	2.25
		Never hinged	7.25	
141	A23b	10c orange brn	5.50	1.75
		Never hinged	13.00	

Centenary of Royal Dutch Lifeboat Society.

Type A23 and

Gull — A24

1924-26   Unwmk.   Perf. 12½
142	A24	1c deep red	.75	.90
		Never hinged	1.50	
143	A24	2c red orange	2.60	.35
		Never hinged	9.00	
144	A24	2½c deep green	3.00	1.10
		Never hinged	6.00	
145	A24	3c yel grn ('25)	16.50	1.50
		Never hinged	50.00	
146	A24	4c dp ultra	3.25	.95
		Never hinged	15.00	

Photo.
147	A23	5c dull green	3.50	.75
		Never hinged	8.00	
148	A23	6c org brn ('25)	.75	.50
		Never hinged	1.40	
149	A23	7½c orange ('25)	.35	.25
		Never hinged	1.10	
150	A23	9c org red & blk ('26)	1.50	1.25
		Never hinged	3.00	
151	A23	10c red, shades	1.50	.25
		Never hinged	5.50	
152	A23	12½c deep rose	1.60	.35
		Never hinged	4.50	
153	A23	15c ultra	6.00	.45
		Never hinged	15.00	
154	A23	20c dp blue ('25)	10.00	.60
		Never hinged	22.00	
155	A23	25c olive bis ('25)	22.50	.85
		Never hinged	40.00	
156	A23	30c violet	13.00	.65
		Never hinged	40.00	
157	A23	35c olive brn ('25)	30.00	6.00
		Never hinged	80.00	
158	A23	40c dp brown	35.00	.75
		Never hinged	200.00	
159	A23	50c blue grn ('25)	60.00	.60
		Never hinged	275.00	
160	A23	60c dk violet ('25)	27.50	.80
		Never hinged	100.00	
		Nos. 142-160 (19)	239.30	18.85
		Set, never hinged	725.00	

See Nos. 164-171, 243A-243Q. For overprints and surcharges see Nos. 226-243, O9-O10.

Syncopated Perforations

Type A   Type B

Type C

These special "syncopated" or "interrupted" perforations, devised for coil stamps, are found on Nos. 142-156, 158-160, 164-166, 168-185, 187-193 and certain semipostals of 1925-33, between Nos. B9 and B69. There are four types:

A (1st stamp is #142a.) On two shorter sides, groups of four holes separated by blank spaces equal in width to two or three holes.

B (1st stamp is #164a.) As "A," but on all four sides.

C (1st stamp is #164b.) On two shorter sides, end holes are omitted.

D (1st stamp is #174c.) Four-hole sequence on horiz. sides, three-hole on vert. sides.

Syncopated, Type A (2 Sides)
1925-26
142a	A24	1c deep red	.75	.80
		Never hinged	1.60	
143a	A24	2c red orange	2.60	2.60
		Never hinged	4.50	
144a	A24	2½c deep green	2.60	1.60
		Never hinged	4.50	
145a	A24	3c yellow green	17.50	17.50
		Never hinged	42.50	
146a	A24	4c deep ultra	2.25	2.25
		Never hinged	7.50	
147a	A23	5c dull green	5.50	3.00
		Never hinged	9.75	
148a	A23	6c orange brown	110.00	100.00
		Never hinged	170.00	
149a	A23	7½c orange	1.10	1.10
		Never hinged	1.60	
150a	A23	9c org red & blk	1.90	1.60
		Never hinged	2.50	
151a	A23	10c red	9.00	3.00
		Never hinged	16.50	
152a	A23	12½c deep rose	1.75	1.75
		Never hinged	3.25	
153a	A23	15c ultra	90.00	6.25
		Never hinged	225.00	
154a	A23	20c deep blue	11.00	4.75
		Never hinged	20.00	
155a	A23	25c olive bister	40.00	40.00
		Never hinged	105.00	
156a	A23	30c violet	15.00	11.50
		Never hinged	30.00	
158a	A23	40c deep brown	55.00	47.50
		Never hinged	210.00	
159a	A23	50c blue green	60.00	23.00
		Never hinged	240.00	
160a	A23	60c dark violet	30.00	11.50
		Never hinged	75.00	
		Nos. 142a-160a (18)	456.20	279.70
		Set, never hinged	1,070.	

A25

1925-30   Engr.   Perf. 11½
161	A25	1g ultra	8.00	.65
		Never hinged	25.00	
162	A25	2½g car ('27)	90.00	3.00
		Never hinged	175.00	
163	A25	5g gray blk	160.00	2.50
		Never hinged	300.00	
		Nos. 161-163 (3)	258.00	6.15

Types of 1924-26 Issue
Perf. 12½, 13½x12½, 12½x13½
1926-39   Wmk. 202   Litho.
164	A24	½c gray ('28)	.90	1.00
165	A24	1c dp red ('27)	.25	.25
166	A24	1½c red vio ('28)	1.10	.25
c.		"CEN" for "CENT"	165.00	275.00
d.		"GENT" for "CENT"	120.00	115.00
167	A24	1½c gray ('35)	.25	.25
a.		1½c dark gray	.25	
168	A24	2c dp org	.25	.25
a.		2c red orange	.25	
169	A24	2½c green ('27)	2.75	.25
170	A24	3c yel grn ('27)	.25	.25
171	A24	4c dp ultra ('27)	.25	.25

Photo.
172	A23	5c dp green	.25	.25
173	A23	6c org brn ('27)	.25	.25
174	A23	7½c dk vio ('27)	3.25	.25
175	A23	7½c red ('28)	.35	.25
176	A23	9c org red & blk ('28)	11.00	12.00
b.		Value omitted	14.00.	
177	A23	10c red	1.30	.25
178	A23	10c dl vio ('29)	2.50	.25
179	A23	12½c dp rose ('27)	42.50	4.50
180	A23	12½c ultra ('28)	.25	.25
181	A23	15c ultra	7.25	.25
182	A23	15c orange ('29)	1.30	.25
183	A23	20c dp blue ('27)	.25	.25
184	A23	21c ol brn ('31)	25.00	.90
185	A23	22½c ol brn ('27)	7.25	3.00
186	A23	22½c dp org ('39)	15.50	16.00
187	A23	25c ol bis ('27)	4.50	.25
188	A23	27½c gray ('28)	4.50	.90
189	A23	30c violet	5.00	.25

190	A23	35c olive brn	62.50	12.50
191	A23	40c dp brown	9.00	.25
192	A23	50c blue grn	5.00	.25
193	A23	60c black ('29)	57.50	.90
		Nos. 164-193 (30)	279.20	56.95
		Set, never hinged	640.00	

Syncopated, Type A (2 Sides), 12½
1926-27
168b	A24	2c deep orange	.40	.40
170a	A24	3c yellow green	.60	.60
171a	A24	4c deep ultra	.60	.60
172a	A23	5c deep green	.70	.60
173a	A23	6c orange brown	.40	.45
174a	A23	7½c dark violet	4.50	2.00
177a	A23	10c red	1.00	.85
181a	A23	15c ultra	7.00	3.00
185a	A23	22½c olive brown	7.00	2.50
187a	A23	25c olive bister	20.00	18.00
189a	A23	30c violet	19.00	12.00
190a	A23	35c olive brown	77.50	22.50
191a	A23	40c deep brown	50.00	40.00
		Nos. 168b-191a (13)	188.70	103.50
		Set, never hinged	360.00	

1928   Syncopated, Type B (4 Sides)
164a	A24	½c gray	.50	.50
165a	A24	1c deep red	.50	.30
166a	A24	1½c red violet	.50	.30
168c	A24	2c deep orange	.80	.80
169a	A24	2½c green	2.00	.35
170b	A24	3c yellow green	.75	.75
171b	A24	4c deep ultra	.75	.75
172b	A23	5c deep green	1.00	.75
173b	A23	6c orange brown	.70	.75
174b	A23	7½c dark violet	3.50	2.00
175a	A23	7½c red	.35	.35
176a	A23	9c org red & blk	9.00	10.00
178a	A23	10c dull violet	4.50	3.50
179a	A23	12½c deep rose	80.00	85.00
180a	A23	12½c ultra	1.50	.75
181b	A23	15c ultra	7.00	2.00
182a	A23	15c orange	1.00	.75
183a	A23	20c deep blue	6.50	3.50
187b	A23	25c olive bister	17.00	10.00
188a	A23	27½c gray	5.00	2.00
189b	A23	30c violet	15.00	8.00
190b	A23	35c olive brown	34.00	25.00
192a	A23	50c blue green	50.00	45.00
193a	A23	60c black	36.00	25.00
		Nos. 164a-193a (24)	277.85	228.10
		Set, never hinged	525.00	

Syncopated, Type C (2 Sides, Corners Only)
1930
164b	A24	½c gray	1.00	.70
165b	A24	1c deep red	1.00	.40
166b	A24	1½c red violet	.90	.25
168d	A24	2c deep orange	.80	.70
169b	A24	2½c green	2.75	.25
170c	A24	3c yellow green	1.10	.50
171c	A24	4c deep ultra	.50	.25
172c	A23	5c deep green	.70	.70
173c	A23	6c orange brown	.70	.70
178b	A23	10c dull violet	8.00	7.00
183b	A23	20c deep blue	7.75	3.75
184a	A23	21c olive brown	25.00	9.00
189c	A23	30c violet	12.00	7.00
192b	A23	50c blue green	45.00	45.00
		Nos. 164b-192b (14)	107.20	76.20
		Set, never hinged	225.00	

Syncopated, Type D (3 Holes Vert., 4 Holes Horiz.)
1927
174c	A23	7½c dark violet	2,750.	2,100.
		Never hinged	3,750.	

No. 185 Surcharged in Red

1929, Nov. 11   Perf. 12½
194	A23	21c on 22½c ol brn	19.00	1.40
		Never hinged	47.50	

Queen Wilhelmina — A26

1931, Oct.   Photo.   Perf. 12½
195	A26	70c dk bl & red	29.00	.75
		Never hinged	110.00	
a.		Perf. 14½x13½ ('39)	50.00	11.00
		Never hinged	190.00	

See No. 201.

Arms of the House of Orange A27

William I A28

Designs: 5c, William I, Portrait by Goltzius. 6c, Portrait of William I by Van Key. 12½c, Portrait attributed to Moro.

1933, Apr. 1   Unwmk.   Engr.
196	A27	1½c black	.55	.40
197	A28	5c dark green	1.75	.40
198	A28	6c dull violet	2.75	.30
199	A28	12½c deep blue	17.00	3.50
		Nos. 196-199 (4)	22.05	4.60
		Set, never hinged	55.00	

400th anniv. of the birth of William I, Count of Nassau and Prince of Orange, frequently referred to as William the Silent.

Star, Dove and Sword — A31

1933, May 18   Photo.   Wmk. 202
200	A31	12½c dp ultra	8.00	.75
		Never hinged	26.50	

For overprint see No. O12.

Queen Wilhelmina Design of 1931
Queen Wilhelmina and ships.

Perf. 14½x13½
1933, July 26   Wmk. 202
201	A26	80c Prus bl & red	100.00	2.90
		Never hinged	320.00	

Willemstad Harbor — A33

Van Walbeeck's Ship — A34

Perf. 14x12½
1934, July 2   Engr.   Unwmk.
202	A33	6c violet blk	3.50	.25
203	A34	6c dull blue	20.00	3.00
		Set, never hinged	70.00	

Tercentenary of Curacao.

Minerva A35

Design: 12½c, Gisbertus Voetius.

Wmk. 202
1936, May 15   Photo.   Perf. 12½
204	A35	6c brown lake	2.50	.25
205	A35	12½c indigo	4.50	4.50
		Set, never hinged	16.00	

300th anniversary of the founding of the University at Utrecht.

Boy Scout Emblem A37

"Assembly" A38

Mercury — A39

1937, Apr. 1   Perf. 14½x13½
206	A37	1½c multicolored	.40	.25
207	A38	6c multicolored	1.25	.25
208	A39	12½c multicolored	4.00	1.40
		Nos. 206-208 (3)	5.65	1.90
		Set, never hinged	12.00	

Fifth Boy Scout World Jamboree, Vogelenzang, Netherlands, 7/31-8/13/37.

Wilhelmina — A40

1938, Aug. 27   Perf. 12½x12
209	A40	1½c black	.25	.25
210	A40	5c red orange	.30	.25
211	A40	12½c royal blue	4.00	1.60
		Nos. 209-211 (3)	4.55	2.10
		Set, never hinged	13.50	

Reign of Queen Wilhelmina, 40th anniv.

St. Williibrord — A41

Design: 12½c, St. Willibrord as older man.

Perf. 12½x14
1939, June 15   Engr.   Unwmk.
212	A41	5c dk slate grn	.75	.25
213	A41	12½c slate blue	5.00	2.75
		Set, never hinged	14.00	

12th centenary of the death of St. Willibrord.

Woodburning Engine — A43

Design: 12½c, Streamlined electric car.

Perf. 14½x13½
1939, Sept. 1   Photo.   Wmk. 202
214	A43	5c dk slate grn	.80	.25
215	A43	12½c dark blue	8.00	4.00
		Set, never hinged	22.50	

Centenary of Dutch Railroads.

> **Catalogue values for unused stamps in this section, from this point to the end of the section, are for Never Hinged items.**

Queen Wilhelmina — A45

1940-47   Perf. 13½x12½
216	A45	5c dk green	.25	.25
216B	A45	6c hn brn ('47)	.50	.25
217	A45	7½c brt red	.25	.25
218	A45	10c brt red vio	.25	.25
219	A45	12½c sapphire	.25	.25
220	A45	15c light blue	.25	.25
220B	A45	17½c slate bl ('46)	1.10	.65
221	A45	20c purple	.55	.25
222	A45	22½c olive grn	1.75	1.60
223	A45	25c rose brn	.45	.25
224	A45	30c bister	.95	.35
225	A45	40c brt green	1.60	.65
225A	A45	50c orange ('46)	6.75	.65
225B	A45	60c pur brn ('46)	6.75	1.90
		Nos. 216-225B (14)	21.65	7.80

Imperf. examples of Nos. 216, 218-220 were released through philatelic channels during the German occupation, but were never issued at any post office. Value, set, $1.
For overprints see Nos. O16-O24.

Type of 1924-26 Surcharged in Black or Blue

Perf. 12½x13½
1940, Oct.   Photo.   Wmk. 202
226	A24	2½c on 3c ver	4.00	.25
227	A24	5c on 3c lt grn	.25	.25
228	A24	7½c on 3c ver	.25	.25
a.		Pair, #226, 228	5.00	1.50
229	A24	10c on 3c lt grn	.25	.25
230	A24	12½c on 3c lt bl		
		(Bl)	.35	.35
231	A24	17½c on 3c lt grn	1.00	.55
232	A24	20c on 3c lt grn	.70	.25
233	A24	22½c on 3c lt grn	2.75	3.75
234	A24	25c on 3c lt grn	1.25	.35
235	A24	30c on 3c lt grn	1.10	.40
236	A24	40c on 3c lt grn	2.00	1.75
237	A24	50c on 3c lt grn	1.25	.55
238	A24	60c on 3c lt grn	1.35	1.00
239	A24	70c on 3c lt grn	7.25	7.25
240	A24	80c on 3c lt grn	9.25	8.50
241	A24	1g on 3c lt grn	29.00	25.00
242	A24	2.50g on 3c lt grn	32.00	29.00
243	A24	5g on 3c lt grn	32.00	29.00
		Nos. 226-243 (18)	126.00	111.70
		Set, hinged	80.00	

No. 228a is from coils.

Gull Type of 1924-26
1941
243A	A24	2½c dk green	1.00	.25
b.		Booklet pane of 6	15.00	
243C	A24	5c brt green	.25	.25
s.		Booklet pane of 6	15.00	
243E	A24	7½c henna	.25	.25
r.		Pair, #243A, 243E	2.50	2.50
t.		Booklet pane of 6	15.00	
243G	A24	10c brt violet	.60	.25
243H	A24	12½c ultra	.35	.25
u.		Booklet pane of 6	15.00	
243J	A24	15c lt blue	.60	.30
243K	A24	17½c red org	.25	.25
243L	A24	20c lt violet	.85	.25
243M	A24	22½c dk ol grn	.25	.30
243N	A24	25c lake	.35	.25
243O	A24	30c olive	2.25	.25
243P	A24	40c emerald	.25	.25
243Q	A24	50c orange brn	.25	.25
		Nos. 243A-243Q (13)	7.50	3.35

No. 243Er is from coils.

Stamps from coils have designs that are 21½mm wide instead of 22¼mm width of the sheet stamps. Stamps are Nos. 496-498, 663-664, 681-682, 705-706, 708-772, 719, 721, 736, 749, 794, 797, 800, 809, 982.

Post Horn and Lion — A46

Gold Surcharge
1943, Jan. 15   Photo.   Perf. 12½x12
244	A46	10c on 2½c yel	.25	.25
a.		Surcharge omitted	6,000.	6,500.

Founding of the European Union of Posts and Telegraphs at Vienna, Oct. 19, 1942.
See No. 115.

Sea Horse — A47

Triple-crown Tree — A48

Admiral M. A. de Ruyter — A54

Designs: 2c, Swans. 2½c, Tree of Life. 3c, Tree with snake roots. 4c, Man on horseback. 5c, Rearing white horses. 10c, Johan Evertsen. 12½c, Martin Tromp. 15c, Piet Hein. 17½c, Willem van Ghent. 20c, Witte de With. 22½c, Cornelis Evertsen. 25c, Tjerk de Vries. 30c, Cornelis Tromp. 40c, Cornelis Evertsen De Jongste.

Perf. 12x12½, 12½x12
1943-44   Photo.   Wmk. 202
245	A47	1c black	.25	.25
246	A48	1½c rose lake	.25	.25
247	A47	2c dk blue	.25	.25
248	A48	2½c dk blue grn	.25	.25
249	A47	3c copper red	.25	.25
250	A48	4c black brown	.25	.25
251	A47	5c dull yel grn	.25	.25

Unwmk.
252	A54	7½c henna brn	.25	.25
a.		Thinner numerals and letters ('44)	.25	.25
253	A54	10c dk green	.25	.25
254	A54	12½c blue	.25	.25
255	A54	15c dull lilac	.25	.25
256	A54	17½c slate ('44)	.25	.25
257	A54	20c dull brown	.25	.25
258	A54	22½c org red	.25	.25
259	A54	25c vio rose ('44)	.35	.55
260	A54	30c cobalt bl ('44)	.25	.25

Engr.
261	A54	40c bluish blk	4.35	4.55

In 1944, 200,000 examples of No. 247 were privately punched with a cross and printed on the back with a number and the words "Prijs 15 Cent toeslag ten bate Ned. Roode Kruis." These were sold at an exhibition, the surtax going to the Red Cross. The Dutch post office tolerated these stamps.

Soldier A64

S. S. "Nieuw Amsterdam" A65

Pilot A66

Cruiser "De Ruyter" A67

Queen Wilhelmina — A68

Perf. 12, 12½
1944-46   Unwmk.   Engr.
262	A64	1½c black	.25	.25
263	A65	2½c yellow grn	.25	.25
264	A66	3c dull red brn	.25	.25
265	A67	5c dk blue	.25	.25
266	A68	7½c vermilion	.25	.25
267	A68	10c yellow org	.25	.25
268	A68	12½c ultra	.25	.25
269	A68	15c dl red brn ('46)	1.30	1.25
270	A68	17½c gray grn ('46)	.75	.85
271	A68	20c violet	.35	.25
272	A68	22½c rose red ('46)	.90	1.00
273	A68	25c brn org ('46)	1.00	1.10
274	A68	30c blue grn	.25	.25
275	A68	40c dk vio brn ('46)	2.00	2.10
276	A68	50c red vio ('46)	1.10	.85
		Nos. 262-276 (15)	9.40	9.40

These stamps were used on board Dutch war and merchant ships until Netherlands' liberation.

Lion and Dragon — A69

1945, July 14   Perf. 12½x14
277	A69	7½c red orange	.25	.25

Netherlands' liberation or "rising again."

Queen Wilhelmina — A70

A71

1946   Engr.   Perf. 13½x14
278	A70	1g dark blue	2.50	.60
279	A70	2½g brick red	125.00	8.00
280	A70	5g dk olive grn	125.00	22.00
281	A70	10g dk purple	125.00	22.00
		Set, hinged	377.50	52.60
			200.00	

Perf. 12½x13½
1946-47   Wmk. 202   Photo.
282	A71	1c dark red	.25	.25
283	A71	2c ultra	.25	.25
284	A71	2½c dp orange ('47)	3.50	1.00
285	A71	4c olive green	.30	.25
		Nos. 282-285 (4)	4.30	1.75

The 1c was reissued in 1969 on phosphorescent paper in booklet pane No. 345b. The 4c was reissued on fluorescent paper in 1962. The 2c was issued in coils in 1972. Every fifth stamp has black control number on back. See Nos. 340-343A, 404-406.

Queen Wilhelmina A72   A73

1947-48   Perf. 13½x12½
286	A72	5c olive grn ('48)	1.00	.25
287	A72	6c brown black	.30	.25
288	A72	7½c dp red brn ('48)	.40	.25
289	A72	10c brt red vio	.75	.25
290	A72	12½c scarlet ('48)	.75	.25
291	A72	15c purple	7.00	.25
292	A72	20c deep blue	7.00	.25
293	A72	22½c ol brn ('48)	.75	.65
294	A72	25c ultra	14.00	.25
295	A72	30c dp orange	14.00	.25
296	A72	35c dk blue grn	14.00	.45
297	A72	40c henna brown	15.50	.45

Engr.
298	A73	45c dp bl ('48)	16.50	8.50
299	A73	50c brown ('48)	11.50	.35
300	A73	60c red ('48)	14.50	1.90
		Nos. 286-300 (15)	117.95	14.65
		Set, hinged	60.00	

For surcharge see No. 330.

Type of 1947
1948   **Photo.**
301	A72	6c gray blue	.50	.25

Queen Wilhelmina — A74

Perf. 12½x14
1948, Aug. 30   Engr.   Unwmk.
302	A74	10c vermilion	.25	.25
303	A74	20c deep blue	1.25	1.00

Reign of Queen Wilhelmina, 50th anniv.

Queen Juliana — A75

Perf. 14x13
1948, Sept. 7   Photo.   Wmk. 202
304	A75	10c dark brown	1.10	.25
305	A75	20c ultra	1.40	.45

Investiture of Queen Juliana, Sept. 6, 1948.

Queen Juliana — A76

1949   **Perf. 13½x12½**
306	A76	5c olive green	.65	.25
307	A76	6c gray blue	.35	.25
308	A76	10c deep orange	.35	.25
309	A76	12c orange red	1.90	1.75
310	A76	15c olive brown	3.75	.25
311	A76	20c brt blue	3.25	.25
312	A76	25c orange brn	8.75	.25
313	A76	30c violet	6.25	.25
314	A76	35c gray	21.00	.25
315	A76	40c red violet	35.00	.25
316	A76	45c red orange	1.30	.70
317	A76	50c blue green	8.75	.25
318	A76	60c red brown	12.50	.25
		Nos. 306-318 (13)	103.80	5.20

See No. 325-327. For surcharge see No. B248.

Queen Juliana — A77

1949 Unwmk. Engr. Perf. 12½x12
319	A77	1g rose red	3.25	.25
320	A77	2½g black brn	190.00	1.25
321	A77	5g orange brn	340.00	3.50
322	A77	10g dk vio brn	240.00	11.50
		Nos. 319-322 (4)	773.25	17.50
		Set, hinged	350.00	

Two types exist of No. 321.

Post Horns Entwined — A78

Perf. 11½x12½
1949, Oct. 1   Photo.   Wmk. 202
323	A78	10c brown red	.60	.25
324	A78	20c dull blue	4.50	1.75

75th anniversary of the UPU.

Juliana Type of 1949
1950-51   **Perf. 13½x12½**
325	A76	12c scarlet ('51)	5.00	1.00
326	A76	45c violet brn	40.00	.45
327	A76	75c car rose ('51)	60.00	1.50
		Nos. 325-327 (3)	105.00	2.95

Janus Dousa — A79

Design: 20c, Jan van Hout.

1950, Oct. 3   **Perf. 11½x13**
328	A79	10c olive brown	2.60	.25
329	A79	20c deep blue	2.60	1.10

375th anniversary of the founding of the University of Leyden.

No. 288 Surcharged in Black

1950, May   **Perf. 13½x12½**
330	A72	6c on 7½c dp red brn	1.10	.25

Miner — A80

Perf. 12x12½
1952, Apr. 16   Engr.   Unwmk.
331	A80	10c dark blue	1.30	.25

50th anniversary of the founding of Netherlands' mining and chemical industry.

Telegraph Poles and Train of 1852 — A81

Designs: 6c, Radio towers. 10c, Mail Delivery 1852. 20c, Modern postman.

1952, June 28   **Perf. 13x14**
332	A81	2c gray violet	.40	.25
333	A81	6c vermilion	.50	.25
334	A81	10c green	.50	.25
335	A81	20c gray blue	4.00	1.60
		Nos. 332-335 (4)	5.40	2.35

Centenary of Dutch postage stamps and of the telegraph service.

1952, June 28
336	A81	2c chocolate	14.00	10.00
337	A81	6c dk bluish grn	14.00	10.00
338	A81	10c brown carmine	14.00	10.00
339	A81	20c violet blue	14.00	10.00
		Nos. 336-339 (4)	56.00	40.00

Nos. 336 to 339 sold for 1.38g, which included the price of admission to the International Postage Stamp Centenary Exhibition, Utrecht.

Numeral Type of 1946-47
Perf. 12½x13½
1953-57   Wmk. 202   Photo.
340	A71	3c dp org brn	.30	.25
341	A71	5c orange	.25	.25
342	A71	6c gray ('54)	.30	.25
343	A71	7c red org	.25	.25
343A	A71	8c brt lilac ('57)	.25	.25
		Nos. 340-343A (5)	1.35	1.25

The 5c and 7c perf. on 3 sides, and with watermark vertical, are from booklet panes Nos. 346a-346b. The 5c perf. on 3 sides, with wmk. horiz., is from No. 349a.
In 1972 the 5c was printed on phosphorescent paper.

A82

1953-71   Wmk. 202   Perf. 13½x12½
344	A82	10c dk red brn	.25	.25
a.		Bklt. pane of 6 (1 #344 + 5 #346C)('65)	5.00	
345	A82	12c dk Prus grn ('54)	.25	.25
a.		Bklt. pane of 7 + label (5 #345 + 2 #347)('67)	5.50	
b.		Bklt. pane, 4 #282 + 8 #345 ('69)	12.50	
346	A82	15c dp carmine	.25	.25
a.		Bklt. pane of 8 (2 #341 in vert. pair + 6 #346)('64)	17.00	
b.		Bklt. pane of 12 (10 #343 + 2 #346)('64)	12.50	
e.		Bklt. pane of 8 (2 #341 in horiz. pair + 6 #346)('70)	9.00	
346C	A82	18c dull bl ('65)	.25	.25
a.		Bklt. pane of 10 (8 #343A + 2 #346C)('65)	4.50	
347	A82	20c dk gray	.25	.25
b.		Bklt. pane of 5 + label ('66)	4.00	
347A	A82	24c olive ('63)	.30	.25
348	A82	25c deep blue	.95	.25
349	A82	30c deep orange	.25	.25
a.		Bklt. pane of 5 + label (2 #341 + 3 #349)('71)	22.50	
350	A82	35c dk ol brn ('54)	.70	.25
351	A82	37c aqua ('58)	.35	.25
352	A82	40c dk slate	.35	.25
353	A82	45c scarlet	.30	.25
354	A82	50c dk bl grn	.55	.25
355	A82	60c brown bister	.70	.25
356	A82	62c dl red lil ('58)	.80	.80
357	A82	70c blue ('57)	.70	.25
358	A82	75c deep plum	.70	.25
359	A82	80c brt vio ('58)	.70	.25
360	A82	85c brt bl grn ('56)	.85	.25
360A	A82	95c org brn ('67)	.85	.35
		Nos. 344-360A (20)	10.40	5.65

Coils of the 12, 15, 20, 25, 30, 40, 45, 50, 60, 70, 75 and 80c were issued in 1972. Black control number on back of every fifth stamp. Watermark is vertical on some stamps from booklet panes.
Some booklet panes, Nos. 344a, 347b, 349a, etc., have a large selvage the size of four or six stamps, with printed inscription and sometimes illustration.
Phosphorescent paper was introduced in 1967 for the 12, 15, 20 and 45c; in 1969 for the 25c, and in 1971 for the 30, 40, 50, 60, 70, 75 and 80c.
Of the booklet panes, Nos. 345a, 345b, 346d, 346e and 347b were issued on both ordinary and phosphorescent paper, and No. 349a only on phosphorescent paper.
See No. 407. For surcharge see No. 374.

Queen Juliana — A83

Perf. 12½x12
1954-57   Unwmk.   Engr.
361	A83	1g vermilion	1.00	.25
362	A83	2½g dk green ('55)	4.25	.25
363	A83	5g black ('55)	2.60	.35
364	A83	10g vio bl ('57)	8.25	1.60
		Nos. 361-364 (4)	16.10	2.45

St. Boniface — A84

1954, June 16
365	A84	10c blue	1.25	.25

1200th anniv. of the death of St. Boniface.

Queen Juliana — A84a

Wmk. 202
1954, Dec. 15   Photo.   Perf. 13½
366	A84a	10c scarlet	.75	.25

Issued to publicize the Charter of the Kingdom, adopted December 15, 1954.
See Netherlands Antilles No. 232, Surinam No. 264.

Flaming Sword — A85

1955, May 4   Perf. 12½x12
367	A85	10c crimson	.80	.25

10th anniv. of Netherlands' liberation.

"Rebuilding Europe" — A86

1956, Sept. 15 Unwmk. Perf. 13x14
368	A86	10c rose brn & blk	1.75	.25
369	A86	25c brt bl & blk	24.00	1.25

Europa. Issued to symbolize the cooperation among the six countries comprising the Coal and Steel Community.

Admiral M. A. de Ruyter — A87

30c, Flagship "De Zeven Provincien."

1957, July 2   Engr.   Perf. 12½x12
370	A87	10c orange	.35	.25
371	A87	30c dk blue	2.60	1.10

Adm. M. A. de Ruyter (1607-1676).

"United Europe" — A88

1957, Sept. 16   Photo.   Perf. 13x14
372	A88	10c blk, gray & ultra	.70	.25
373	A88	30c dull grn & ultra	3.25	1.25

United Europe for peace and prosperity.

No. 344 Surcharged in Silver with New Value and Bars
Perf. 13½x12½
1958, May 16   Photo.   Wmk. 202
374	A82	12c on 10c	.80	.25
a.		Double surcharge	400.00	400.00
b.		Inverted surcharge	400.00	400.00

Common Design Types pictured following the introduction.

Europa Issue, 1958
Common Design Type
Perf. 13x14
1958, Sept. 13   Litho.   Unwmk.
Size: 22x33mm
375	CD1	12c org ver & blue	.25	.25
376	CD1	30c blue & red	1.00	.50

NATO Emblem — A89

1959, Apr. 3   Perf. 12½x12
377	A89	12c yel org & blue	.25	.25
378	A89	30c red & blue	.50	.40

10th anniversary of NATO.

Europa Issue, 1959.
Common Design Type
1959, Sept. 19   Perf. 13x14
Size: 22x33mm
379	CD2	12c crimson	.50	.25
380	CD2	30c yellow grn	1.60	1.60

Easy Online Bidding

STANLEY GIBBONS AUCTIONS

Postiljonen

POSTZEGELVEILING RIJNMOND

PhilaSearch

Oslo Frimerke- og Myntauksjoner AS

Raritan Stamps, Inc.

CHERRYSTONE PHILATELIC AUCTIONEERS

Philasearch.com

DE NEDERLANDSCHE POSTZEGEL- EN MUNTENVEILING B.V.

Schuyler Rumsey Philatelic Auctions

DRESDNER brief marken AUKTION
Organisationsgesellschaft mbH

VAN DIETEN POSTZEGELVEILINGEN

Kelleher & Rogers

SKANFIL Auksjoner as

Soler y Llach SL

LUGDUNUM Thierry LALLEVÉE

LA POSTALE PHILATÉLIE

GM

Rietdijk Aº 1919

UNIVERSAL PHILATELIC AUCTIONS SINCE 1958

Briefmarkenauktionen Schulz NÜRNBERG

Colonial Stamp Co.

CORBITTS

François FELDMAN

DR. PHIL. W. DERICHS KÖLN D Briefmarkenauktion

CORINPHILA VEILINGEN

Argyll Etkin Limited

Plumridge & Co.

BOULE

AG AUCTIONGALLERY

SUOMEN FILATELIAPALVELU OY

Postzegelveilingen VAN LOOY VAN LOOY

Eastern Auctions

iberphil AUCTIONS

RAUHUT & KRUSCHEL BRIEFMARKEN - AUKTIONSHAUS

Bielefelder AUKTION

Victoria Stamp Company

C.G. Auctions

JalilStamps.com
Philatino.com

CERES Philatélie

STATUS INTERNATIONAL PUBLIC AUCTIONEERS

CAVENDISH PHILATELIC AUCTIONS LTD.

SPINK LONDON 1666

Robert A. Siegel AUCTION GALLERIES, INC.

AUKTIONSHAUS FELZMANN Ihr Partner für hochwertige Philatelie und Numismatik

Auktionshaus Dr. Reinhard Fischer

classicphil

and many more

Douglas DC-8 and World Map — A90

Design: 30c, Douglas DC-8 in flight.

1959, Oct. 5   Engr.   Perf. 14x13
381 A90 12c carmine & ultra .25 .25
382 A90 30c dp blue & dp grn .90 .90
40th anniversary of the founding of KLM, Royal Dutch Airlines.

J. C. Schroeder van der Kolk — A91

Design: 30c, Johannes Wier.

Perf. 12½x12
1960, July 18   Unwmk.
383 A91 12c red .55 .40
384 A91 30c dark blue 2.75 2.00
Issued to publicize Mental Health Year and to honor Schroeder van der Kolk and Johannes Wier, pioneers of mental health.

Europa Issue, 1960
Common Design Type
1960, Sept. 19   Photo.   Perf. 12x12½
Size: 27x21mm
385 CD3 12c car rose & org .40 .40
386 CD3 30c dk blue & yel 1.60 1.60
1st anniv. of CEPT. Spokes symbolize 19 founding members of Conference.

Europa Issue, 1961
Common Design Type
1961, Sept. 18   Perf. 14x13
Size: 32½x21½mm
387 CD4 12c golden brown .25 .25
388 CD4 30c Prus blue .25 .25

Queen Juliana and Prince Bernhard — A92

Perf. 14x13
1962, Jan. 5   Unwmk.   Photo.
389 A92 12c dk red .25 .25
390 A92 30c dk green 1.00 .65
Silver wedding anniversary of Queen Juliana and Prince Bernhard.

Telephone Dial — A93

Designs: 12c, Map showing telephone network. 30c, Arch and dial, horiz.

1962, May 22   Perf. 13x14, 14x13
391 A93 4c brown red & blk .25 .30
392 A93 12c brown ol & blk .50 .30
393 A93 30c black, bis & Prus bl 1.40 1.40
Nos. 391-393 (3) 2.15 2.00
Completion of the automation of the Netherlands telephone network.

Europa Issue, 1962
Common Design Type
1962, Sept. 17   Perf. 14x13
Size: 33x22mm
394 CD5 12c lemon, yel & blk .25 .25
395 CD5 30c blue, yel & blk 1.10 .65

Polder with Canals and Windmills — A94

Design: 4c, Cooling towers, Limburg State Coal Mines. 10c, Dredging in Delta.

Perf. 12½x13½
1962-72   Wmk. 202   Photo.
399 A94 4c dk blue ('63) .25 .25
401 A94 6c grn & dk grn .40 .25
402 A94 10c dp claret ('63) .25 .25
a. Booklet pane of 10 ('66) 3.50

403 A94 10c dp claret ('72) .25 .25
Nos. 399-403 (4) 1.15 1.00
No. 403 was issued in coils in 1972. Every fifth stamp has black control number on back. See No. 461Ab.

Types of 1946 and 1953
1962-73   Unwmk.
Phosphorescent Paper
404 A71 4c olive green 1.30 1.30
405 A71 5c orange ('73) 1.30 1.30
406 A71 8c bright lilac 6.00 8.50
407 A82 12c dk Prus green 1.30 1.30
Nos. 404-407 (4) 9.90 12.40
The 5c is from booklets and has the phosphor on the front only.
Issue dates: 5c, Jan. 12; others Aug. 27. See Nos. 460d, 461c, 461d and 463a.

Wheat Emblem and Globe — A95

1963, Mar. 21   Photo.   Perf. 14x13
413 A95 12c dl bl, dk bl & yel .25 .25
414 A95 30c dl car, rose & yel .80 .80
FAO "Freedom from Hunger" campaign.

Inscription in Circle — A96

Perf. 13x14
1963, May 7   Unwmk.   Litho.
415 A96 30c brt blue, blk & grn 1.00 1.00
1st Intl. Postal Conf., Paris, cent.

Europa Issue, 1963
Common Design Type
1963, Sept. 16   Photo.   Perf. 14x13
Size: 33x22mm
416 CD6 12c red brown & yel .30 .25
417 CD6 30c Prus green & yel 1.00 .75

Prince William of Orange Landing at Scheveningen — A97

Designs: 12c, G. K. van Hogendorp, A. F. J. A. Graaf van der Duyn van Maasdam and L. Graaf van Limburg Stirum, Dutch leaders, 1813. 30c, Prince William taking oath of allegiance.

Size: 27½x27½mm
1963, Nov. 18   Photo.   Perf. 12x12½
418 A97 4c dull bl, blk & brn .25 .25
419 A97 5c dk grn, blk & red .25 .25
420 A97 12c olive & blk .25 .25
421 A97 30c maroon & blk .50 .50
Nos. 418-421 (4) 1.25 1.25
150th anniversary of the founding of the Kingdom of the Netherlands.

Knights' Hall, The Hague — A98

1964, Jan. 9   Perf. 14x13
422 A98 12c olive & blk .25 .25
500th anniversary of the meeting of the States-General (Parliament).

Arms of Groningen University — A99

Design: 30c, Initials "AG" and crown.

1964, June 16   Engr.   Perf. 12½x12
423 A99 12c slate .25 .25
424 A99 30c yellow brown .25 .25
350th anniv. of the University of Groningen.

Railroad Light Signal — A100

Design: 40c, Electric locomotive.

1964, July 28   Photo.   Perf. 14x13
425 A100 15c black & brt grn .25 .25
426 A100 40c black & yellow .65 .55
125th anniv. of the Netherlands railroads.

Bible, Chrismon and Dove — A101

1964, Aug. 25   Unwmk.
427 A101 15c brown red .25 .25
150th anniversary of the founding of the Netherlands Bible Society.

Europa Issue, 1964
Common Design Type
1964, Sept. 14   Photo.   Perf. 13x14
Size: 22x33mm
428 CD7 15c dp olive grn .25 .25
429 CD7 20c yellow brown .50 .35

Benelux Issue

King Baudouin, Queen Juliana and Grand Duchess Charlotte — A101a

Size: 33x22mm
1964, Oct. 12   Perf. 14x13
430 A101a 15c purple & buff .25 .25
20th anniversary of the signing of the customs union of Belgium, Netherlands and Luxembourg.

Queen Juliana — A102

1964, Dec. 15   Photo.   Perf. 13x14
431 A102 15c green .25 .25
10th anniversary of the Charter of the Kingdom of the Netherlands.

"Killed in Action" and "Destroyed Town" — A103

Statues: 15c, "Docker" Amsterdam, and "Killed in Action" Waalwijk. 40c, "Destroyed Town" Rotterdam, and "Docker" Amsterdam.

1965, Apr. 6   Photo.   Perf. 12x12½
432 A103 7c black & dk red .25 .25
433 A103 15c black & dk olive .25 .25
434 A103 40c black & dk red .70 .60
Nos. 432-434 (3) 1.20 1.10
Resistance movement of World War II.

Knight Class IV, Order of William — A104

1965, Apr. 29   Perf. 13x14
435 A104 1g gray .75 .50
150th anniversary of the establishment of the Military Order of William.

ITU Emblem — A105

1965, May 17   Litho.   Perf. 14x13
436 A105 20c dull bl & tan .25 .25
437 A105 40c tan & dull bl .30 .30
Centenary of the International Telecommunication Union.

Europa Issue, 1965
Common Design Type
1965, Sept. 27   Photo.
Size: 33x22mm
438 CD8 18c org brn, dk red & blk .25 .25
439 CD8 20c sapphire, brn & blk .30 .25

Marines of 1665 and 1965 — A106

1965, Dec. 10   Engr.   Perf. 13x14
440 A106 18c dk vio bl & car .25 .25
Netherlands Marine Corps, 300th anniv.

Europa Issue, 1966
Common Design Type
1966, Sept. 26   Photo.   Perf. 13x14
Size: 22x33mm
441 CD9 20c citron .25 .25
442 CD9 40c dull blue .60 .25

Assembly Hall, Delft University — A107

1967, Jan. 5   Litho.   Perf. 14x13
443 A107 20c dl sage grn & sepia .25 .25
125th anniversary of the founding of the Delft University of Technology.

Europa Issue, 1967
Common Design Type
Perf. 13x14
1967, May 2   Unwmk.   Photo.
Ordinary Paper
Size: 22x32½mm
444 CD10 20c dull blue .35 .25
445 CD10 45c dull vio brn .75 .60
Wmk. 202
446 CD10 20c dull blue .65 .30
447 CD10 45c dull vio brn .95 .90
Nos. 444-447 (4) 2.70 2.05
Nos. 446-447 are on phosphorescent paper.

Stamp of 1852, #1 — A108

1967, May 8   Engr.   Unwmk.
448 A108 20c shown   1.75 1.75
449 A108 25c No. 5   1.75 1.75
450 A108 75c No. 10   1.75 1.75
     Nos. 448-450 (3)   5.25 5.25

AMPHILEX 67, Amsterdam, May 11-21. Sold only in complete sets together with a 2.50g admission ticket to Amsterdam Philatelic Exhibition. Issued in sheets of 10 (5x2).

Coins and Punched Card — A109

1968, Jan. 16   Photo.   Perf. 14x13
451 A109 20c ver, blk & dl yel   .25 .25

50th anniversary of the postal checking service.

Luminescence

All commemorative issues from No. 451 to No. 511 are printed on phosphorescent paper except No. 478 which is printed with phosphorescent ink, and Nos. 490-492. Some later issues are tagged.

Europa Issue, 1968
Common Design Type
1968, Apr. 29   Photo.   Perf. 14x13
Size: 32½x22mm
452 CD11 20c deep blue   .30 .25
453 CD11 45c crimson   .75 .45

National Anthem — A110

1968, Aug. 27   Litho.   Perf. 13x14
454 A110 20c gray, org, car & dk bl .25 .25

400th anniversary of the national anthem "Wilhelmus van Nassouwe."

Fokker F.2, 1919, and Friendship F.29 — A111

Planes: 12c, Wright A, 1909, and Cessna sports plane. 45c, De Havilland DH-9, 1919, and Douglas DC-9.

1968, Oct. 1   Photo.   Perf. 14x13
455 A111 12c crim, pink & blk   .25 .25
456 A111 20c brt grn, bl grn & blk .25 .25
457 A111 45c brt grn, lt grn & blk 1.00 1.00
     Nos. 455-457 (3)   1.50 1.50

50th anniv. of the founding in 1919 of Royal Dutch Airlines and the Royal Netherlands Aircraft Factories Fokker, and the 60th anniv. in 1967 of the Royal Netherlands Aeronautical Assoc.

"iao" — A112

Design is made up of 28 minute lines, each reading "1919 internationale arbeids-organisatie 1969".

1969, Feb. 25   Engr.   Perf. 14x13
458 A112 25c brick red & blk   .35 .25
459 A112 45c ultra & blue   .75 .65

International Labor Organization, 50th anniv.

A113

Queen Juliana — A114

Perf. 13½ horiz. x 12½ on one vert. side
1969-75   Photo.
460   A113 25c orange ver   .80 .25
 a.   Bklt. pane of 4 + 2 labels 10.00
460B A113 25c dull red ('73)   1.00 .25
 c.   Booklet pane of 6 (#460B + 5 #461A) 15.00
 d.   Booklet pane of 12 (5 #405 + 7 #460B) 14.00

Perf. 13x12½
461   A113 30c choc ('72)   .25 .25
 d.   Bklt. pane of 10 (4 #405 + 6 #461 + 2 labels)('74) 2.75
       Complete booklet, #461d   2.75
461A A113 35c grnsh bl ('72)   .25 .25
 b.   Bklt. pane of 5 (3 #403, 2 #461A + label) ('72) 11.00
 c.   Bklt. pane of 10 (5 #405 + 5 #461A + 2 labels)('75) 3.00
       Complete booklet, #461c   3.00
462   A113 40c car rose ('72)   .35 .25
 a.   Bklt. pane of 5 + label ('73) 5.50
463   A113 45c ultra ('72)   .35 .25
 a.   Bklt. pane of 8 (4 #405 + 4 #463) ('74) 2.00
       Complete booklet, #463a   2.00
464   A113 50c lilac ('72)   .40 .25
 a.   Bklt. pane of 4 + 2 labels ('75) 2.00
       Complete booklet, #464a   2.00
465   A113 60c slate bl ('72)   .50 .25
 a.   Bklt. pane of 5 + label ('80) 3.00
466   A113 70c bister ('72)   .60 .25
467   A113 75c green ('72)   .60 .25
468   A113 80c red org ('72)   .65 .25
468A A113 90c gray ('75)   .65 .25

Perf. 13x14
469   A114   1g yel green   .65 .25
470   A114   1.25g maroon   .80 .25
471   A114   1.50g yel bis ('71)   1.00 .25
471A A114   2g dp rose lil ('72) 1.10 .25
472   A114   2.50g grnsh bl   1.40 .25
473   A114   5g gray ('70)   2.75 .25
474   A114   10g vio bl ('70)   5.50 .85
      Nos. 460-474 (19)   19.60 5.35

Both 25c stamps issued only in booklets.
Printings were both ordinary and phosphorescent paper for Nos. 460, 460a, 469, 471-474.
Coil printings were issued later for Nos. 461, 462-472. Black control number on back of every fifth stamp.
Booklet panes have a large selvage the size of 4 or 6 stamps, with printed inscription. See No. 542.

Europa Issue, 1969
Common Design Type
1969, Apr. 28   Photo.   Perf. 14x13
Size: 33½x22mm
475 CD12 25c dark blue   .25 .25
476 CD12 45c red   1.10 .75

A114a

Möbius strip in Benelux colors.

1969, Sept. 8   Photo.   Perf. 13x14
477 A114a 25c multicolored   .25 .25

25th anniversary of the signing of the customs union of Belgium, Netherlands and Luxembourg.

A115

Photo. & Engr.
1969, Sept. 30   Perf. 13x14
478 A115 25c yellow grn & maroon .25 .25

Desiderius Erasmus (1469-1536), scholar.

Queen Juliana and Rising Sun — A116

1969, Dec. 15   Photo.   Perf. 14x13
479 A116 25c blue & multi   .25 .25

15th anniversary of the Charter of the Kingdom of the Netherlands.

Prof. E. M. Meijers — A117

1970, Jan. 13   Photo.   Perf. 14x13
480 A117 25c blue, vio bl & grn   .25 .25

Issued to publicize the new Civil Code and to honor Prof. Meijers, who prepared it.

Dutch Pavilion, EXPO '70 — A118

1970, Mar. 10   Photo.   Perf. 14x13
481 A118 25c multicolored   .25 .25

EXPO '70 International Exposition, Osaka, Japan, Mar. 15-Sept. 13.

"V" for Victory — A119

1970, Apr. 21   Photo.   Perf. 13x14
482 A119 12c red, ultra, brn ol & lt bl .25 .25

25th anniv. of liberation from the Germans.

Europa Issue, 1970
Common Design Type
1970, May 4   Photo.   Perf. 14x13
Size: 32½x21½mm
483 CD13 25c carmine   .30 .25
484 CD13 45c dk blue   1.00 .90

Panels A120

Globe A121

1970, June 23   Photo.   Perf. 13x14
485 A120 25c gray, blk & brt grn   .30 .25
486 A121 45c ultra, blk & pur   .60 .50

#485 publicizes the meeting of the interparliamentary Union; #486 the UN 25th anniv.

Punch Cards — A122

1971, Feb. 16   Photo.   Perf. 14x13
487 A122 15c dp rose lilac   .25 .25

14th national census, 1971.

Europa Issue, 1971
Common Design Type
1971, May 3   Photo.   Perf. 14x13
Size: 33x22mm
488 CD14 25c lil rose, yel & blk   .40 .25
489 CD14 45c ultra, yel & blk   .80 .70

No. 488 was issued in coils and sheets. In the coils every fifth stamp has a black control number on the back.

Prince Bernhard, Fokker F27, Boeing 747 B — A123

Designs: 15c, Stylized carnation (Prince Bernhard Fund). 20c, Giant Panda (World Wildlife Fund). 15c, 20c horiz.

Photo., Litho. (20c)
1971, June 29   Perf. 13x14
490 A123 15c black & yellow   .30 .25
491 A123 20c multicolored   .75 .30
492 A123 25c multicolored   .30 .25
     Nos. 490-492,B475 (4)   2.95 2.40

60th birthday of Prince Bernhard. See No. B475.

Map of
Delta — A124

1972, Feb. 15   Photo.   *Perf. 14x13*
493 A124 20c bl, grn, blk & red   .25 .25
 Publicity for the Delta plan, a project to
shorten the coastline and to build roads.

Europa Issue 1972
Common Design Type
1972, May 5   Photo.   *Perf. 13x14*
Size: 22x33mm
494 CD15 30c blue & bis   .40 .25
495 CD15 45c orange & bis   .80 .65
 No. 494 was issued in coils and sheets. In
the coils every fifth stamp has a black control
number on the back.

Thorbecke
Quotation — A126

1972, June 2   Photo.   *Perf. 14x13*
496 A126 30c lt ultra & blk   .40 .25
 Jan Rudolf Thorbecke (1798-1872), statesman, who said: "There is more to be done in
the world than ever before."

Dutch Flag — A127

1972   *Perf. 13x14*
497 A127 20c blue & multi   .30 .25
498 A127 25c blue & multi   .60 .25
 400th anniversary of the Dutch flag.
Issue dates: 20c, July 4; 25c, Nov. 1.

Woman
Hurdler — A128

 30c, Woman swimmer. 45c, Bicycling.

1972, July 11   *Perf. 14x13*
499 A128 20c multicolored   .25 .25
500 A128 30c crimson & multi   .30 .25
501 A128 45c violet & multi   .60 .60
  Nos. 499-501 (3)   1.15 1.10
 20th Olympic Games, Munich, 8/26-9/11.

Red Cross — A129

1972, Aug. 15   Photo.   *Perf. 13x14*
502 A129 5c red   .25 .25
  Nos. 502,B485-B488 (5)   2.90 2.75
 Netherlands Red Cross.

Tulips — A130

1973, Mar. 20   Photo.   *Perf. 14x13*
503 A130 25c rose, brt grn & blk   .40 .25
 Dutch flower and bulb exports.

Europa Issue 1973
Common Design Type
1973, May 1   Photo.   *Perf. 14x13*
Size: 32½x22mm
504 CD16 35c bright blue   .40 .25
505 CD16 50c purple   .80 .70

Hockey
A132

Woman
Gymnast
A133

Antenna, Burum
A134

Rainbow,
Measures
A135

Photo. (25c, 35c); Litho. (30c, 50c)
1973, July 31   *Perf. 13x14, 14x13*
506 A132 25c black & green   .35 .25
507 A133 30c gray & multi   .80 .50
508 A134 35c blue & multi   .50 .30
509 A135 50c blue & multi   .80 .70
  Nos. 506-509 (4)   2.45 1.75
 Netherlands Hockey Assoc., 75th anniv.
(25c); Rhythmical Gymnastics World Championship, Rotterdam (30c); inauguration of satellite ground station at Burum (35c); cent. of intl.
meteorological cooperation (50c).

Queen Juliana,
Dutch and House
of Orange
Colors — A136

Engr. & Photo.
1973, Sept. 4   *Perf. 13x12*
510 A136 40c silver & multi   .40 .25
 25th anniversary of reign of Queen Juliana.

Chain with Open
Link — A137

1973, Oct. 16   Photo.   *Perf. 13x14*
511 A137 40c grn, blk, gold & sil   .40 .25
 Development Corporation.

Nature and Environment — A138

1974, Feb. 19   Photo.   *Perf. 13x14*
512 A138   Strip of 3   1.75 1.75
  a.   25c Bird of prey   .55 .35
  b.   25c Tree   .55 .35
  c.   25c Fisherman in boat and frog .55 .35
 75th anniv. of the Netherlands Assoc. for
the Protection of Birds and of the State Forestry Service.

Soccer
Ball — A139

Tennis
Ball — A140

Perf. 14x13, 13x14
1974, June 5   Photo.
513 A139 25c multicolored   .40 .25
514 A140 40c multicolored   .40 .25
 World Cup Soccer Championship, Munich,
June 13-July 7 (25c) and 75th anniversary of
the Royal Dutch Lawn Tennis Association
(40c).

Cattle
A141

Pierced
Crab under
Lens
A142

Shipwreck Seen Through
Binoculars — A143

1974, July 30   *Perf. 13x14*
515 A141 25c multicolored   1.20 1.20
516 A142 25c sal pink & multi   .90 .30
517 A143 40c dk violet & multi   .90 .30
  Nos. 515-517 (3)   3.00 1.80
 Cent. of the Netherlands Cattle Herdbook
Soc. (#515); 25th anniv. of Queen Wilhelmina
Fund (for cancer research) (#516); sesquicentennial of Royal Dutch Lifeboat Soc. (#517).

BENELUX Issue

"BENELUX"
A143a

1974, Sept. 10   Photo.   *Perf. 14x13*
518 A143a 30c bl grn, dk grn & lt bl .35 .25
 30th anniv. of the signing of the customs
union of Belgium, Netherlands and
Luxembourg.

Council of
Europe
Emblem
A144

NATO
Emblem
and Sea
Gull
A145

1974, Sept. 10   *Perf. 13x14*
519 A144 45c black, bl & yel   .40 .25
520 A145 45c dk blue & silver   .40 .25
 25th anniv. of Council of Europe (No. 519)
and of North Atlantic Treaty Organization (No.
520).

Letters and Hands,
Papier-maché
Sculpture — A146

1974, Oct. 9
521 A146 60c purple & multi   .35 .25
 Centenary of Universal Postal Union.

People and
Map of Dam
Square
A147

Brain with
Window
Symbolizing
Free
Thought
A148

 Design: No. 523, Portuguese Synagogue
and map of Mr. Visser Square. 35c, No. 526,
like No. 522.

1975   Photo.   *Perf. 13x14*
522 A147 30c multicolored   .35 .25
523 A147 30c multicolored   .35 .25
524 A147 35c multicolored   .40 .25
525 A148 45c dp blue & multi   .30 .25
  Nos. 522-525 (4)   1.40 1.00

Coil Stamps
Perf. 13 Horiz.
526 A147 30c multicolored   .35 .25
527 A147 35c multicolored   .40 .25

 700th anniv. of Amsterdam (No. 522); 300th
anniv. of the Portuguese Synagogue in
Amsterdam (No. 523) and 400th anniv. of the
founding of the University of Leyden and the
beginning of higher education in the Netherlands (No. 525).
 Issue dates: Nos. 522-523, 525-526, Feb.
26; Nos. 524, 527, Apr. 1.

Eye Looking over Barbed
Wire — A149

1975, Apr. 29   Photo.   *Perf. 13x14*
528 A149 35c black & carmine   .40 .25
 Liberation of the Netherlands from Nazi
occupation, 30th anniversary.

Company Emblem
and "Stad
Middelburg" — A150

1975, May 21   Photo.   *Perf. 14x13*
529 A150 35c multicolored   .50 .25
 Zeeland Steamship Company, centenary.

Albert Schweitzer in
Boat — A151

1975, May 21
530 A151 50c multicolored   .50 .25
 Albert Schweitzer (1875-1965), medical
missionary.

Symbolic Metric
Scale — A152

1975, July 29   Litho.   *Perf. 14x13*
531 A152 50c multicolored   .50 .25
 Cent. of Intl. Meter Convention, Paris, 1875.

Playing Card with
Woman, Man, Pigeons,
Pens — A153

1975, July 29   *Perf. 13x14*
532 A153 35c multicolored   .50 .25
 International Women's Year 1975.

Fingers Reading Braille — A154

1975, Oct. 7   Photo.   Perf. 13x14
533 A154 35c multicolored   .50 .25
Sesquicentennial of the invention of Braille system of writing for the blind by Louis Braille (1809-1852).

Rubbings of 25¢ Coins — A155

1975, Oct. 7   Perf. 14x13
534 A155 50c green, blk & bl   .50 .25
To publicize the importance of saving.

Lottery Ticket, 18th Century — A156

1976, Feb. 3   Photo.   Perf. 14x13
535 A156 35c multicolored   .40 .25
250th anniversary of National Lottery.

Queen Type of 1969 and

A157

1976-86   Photo.   Perf. 12½x13½
536 A157 5c gray   .25 .25
   Booklet Panes
  a. (3 #536, 2 #537, 3 #542)   3.00
    Complete booklet, #536a   3.00
  b. (4 #536, 2 #537, 4 #539 + 2 labels)   2.00
    Complete booklet, #536b   2.00
  c. (#536, 2 #537, 5 #542)   3.00
    Complete booklet, #536c   3.00
  d. (4 #536, 7 #539 + label)   3.00
    Complete booklet, #536d   3.00
  e. (2 #536, 2 #540, 4 #541)   3.00
    Complete booklet, #536e   3.00
  f. (5 #536, 2 #537, 2 #540, 3 #542) + 2 labels   4.00
    Complete booklet, #536f   4.00
  g. (1 #536, 2 #537, 5 #543) ('86)   3.00
    Complete booklet, #536g   3.00
537 A157 10c ultra   .25 .25
538 A157 25c violet   .25 .25
539 A157 40c sepia   .40 .25
540 A157 45c brt blue   .40 .25
541 A157 50c lil rose ('80)   .40 .25
  a. Bklt. pane, 5 each #537, 541 + 2 labels   2.75
    Complete booklet, #541a   2.75
542 A113 55c carmine   .60 .25
543 A157 brt grn ('81)   .55 .25
544 A157 60c apple grn ('81)   .65 .25
545 A157 65c dk red brn ('86)   .95 .25
    Nos. 536-545 (10)   4.70 2.50

Compare No. 544 with No. 791. No. 542 also issued in coils with control number on the back of every 5th stamp.
See Nos. 903-905.

Coil Stamps

1976-86   Perf. 13½ Vert.
546 A157 5c slate gray   .25 .25
547 A157 10c ultra   .25 .25
548 A157 25c violet   .30 .25
549 A157 40c sepia ('77)   .50 .25
550 A157 45c brt blue   .50 .25
551 A157 50c brt rose ('79)   .75 .25
552 A157 55c brt grn ('81)   .75 .25
553 A157 60c apple grn ('81)   .85 .25
554 A157 65c dk red brn ('86)   .95 .25
    Nos. 546-554 (9)   5.10 2.25

See Nos. 772, 774, 786, 788, 791.

De Ruyter Statue, Flushing — A158

1976, Apr. 22   Photo.   Perf. 14x13
555 A158 55c multicolored   .50 .25
Adm. Michiel Adriaenszon de Ruyter (1607-1676), Dutch naval hero, 300th death anniversary.

Van Prinsterer and Page — A159

1976, May 19   Photo.   Perf. 14x13
556 A159 55c multicolored   .40 .25
Guillaume Groen van Prinsterer (1801-1876), statesman and historian.

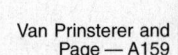

Women Waving American Flags — A160

Design is from a 220-year old permanent wooden calendar from Ameland Island.

1976, May 25   Litho.
557 A160 75c multicolored   .60 .25
American Bicentennial.

Marchers — A161

1976, June 15   Photo.   Perf. 14x13
558 A161 40c multicolored   .50 .25
Nijmegen 4-day march, 60th anniversary.

A number of stamps issued from 1970 on appear to have parts of the designs misregistered, blurry, or look off-center. These stamps are deliberately designed that way. Most prominent examples are Nos. 559, 582, 602, 656, 711-712, 721, B638-B640, B662-B667.

Runners — A162

1976, June 15   Litho.   Tagged
559 A162 55c multicolored   .55 .25
Royal Dutch Athletic Soc., 75th anniv.

Printing: One Communicating with Many — A163

1976, Sept. 2   Photo.   Perf. 13x14
560 A163 45c blue & red   .50 .25
Netherlands Printers Organization, 75th anniv.

Sailing Ship and City — A164

Design: 75c, Sea gull over coast.

1976, Sept. 2   Litho.   Perf. 14x13
Tagged
561 A164 40c bister, red & bl   .50 .25
562 A164 75c ultra, yel & red   .70 .45
Zuider Zee Project, the conversion of water areas into land.

Radiation of Heat and Light A165

Ballot and Pencil A166

Perf. 13x14, 14x13
1977, Jan. 25   Photo.
563 A165 40c multicolored   .45 .25
564 A166 45c black, red & ocher   .45 .25

Coil Stamps
Perf. 13 Horiz.
565 A165 40c multicolored   .35 .25
Perf. 13 Vert.
566 A166 45c multicolored   .35 .25
Publicity for wise use of energy (40c) and forthcoming elections (45c). Nos. 565-566 have black control number on back of every 5th stamp.
For overprint see No. 569.

Spinoza — A167

1977, Feb. 21   Photo.   Perf. 13x14
567 A167 75c multicolored   .80 .25
Baruch Spinoza (1632-1677), philosopher, 300th death anniversary.

Delft Bible Text, Old Type, Electronic "a" — A168

1977, Mar. 8   Perf. 14x13
568 A168 55c ocher & black   .50 .25
Delft Bible (Old Testament), oldest book printed in Dutch, 500th anniversary. Printed in sheets of 50 se-tenant with label inscribed with description of stamp design and purpose.

No. 564 Overprinted in Blue

1977, Apr. 15   Photo.   Perf. 14x13
569 A166 45c multicolored   .40 .25
Elections of May 25.

Kaleidoscope of Activities — A169

1977, June 9   Litho.   Perf. 13x14
570 A169 55c multicolored   .45 .25
Netherlands Society for Industry and Commerce, bicentenary.

Man in Wheelchair Looking at Obstacles A170

Engineer's Diagram of Water Currents A171

Teeth, Dentist's Mirror — A172

1977, Sept. 6   Photo.   Perf. 14x13
571 A170 40c multicolored   .45 .25
Litho.
572 A171 45c multicolored   .45 .25
Perf. 13x14
573 A172 55c multicolored   .45 .25
    Nos. 571-573 (3)   1.35 .75
50th anniversaries of AVO (Actio vincit omnia), an organization to help the handicapped (40c), and of Delft Hydraulic Laboratory (45c); centenary of Dentists' Training in the Netherlands (55c).

"Postcode" — A173

1978, Mar. 14   Photo.   Perf. 14x13
574 A173 40c dk blue & red   .45 .25
575 A173 45c red, dk & lt bl   .50 .25
Introduction of new postal code.

European Human Rights Treaty — A174

1978, May 2   Photo.   Perf. 13x14
576 A174 45c gray, blue & blk   .50 .25
European Treaty of Human Rights, 25th anniv.

Europa Issue

Haarlem City Hall — A175

1978, May 2
577 A175 55c multicolored   .80 .25

Chess Board and Move Diagram A176

Korfball A177

1978, June 1   Photo.   Perf. 13x14
578 A176 40c multicolored   .40 .25
Litho.
579 A177 45c red & vio bl   .50 .25
18th IBM Chess Tournament, Amsterdam, July 12, and 75th anniversary of korfball in the Netherlands.

Man Pointing to his Kidney A178

Heart, Torch, Gauge and Clouds A179

1978, Aug. 22 Photo.   Perf. 13x13½
580 A178 40c multicolored   .45   .25
            Perf. 13x14
581 A179 45c multicolored   .45   .25
Importance of kidney transplants and drive against hypertension.

Epaulettes, Military Academy — A180

1978, Sept. 12 Photo.   Perf. 13x14
582 A180 55c multicolored   .50   .25
Royal Military Academy, sesquicentennial. Printed in continuous design in sheets of 100 (10x10).

Verkade as Hamlet — A181

1978, Oct. 17 Photo.   Perf. 14x13
583 A181 45c multicolored   .50   .25
Eduard Rutger Verkade (1878-1961), actor and producer.

Clasped Hands and Arrows — A182

1979, Jan. 23 Engr.   Perf. 13x14
584 A182 55c blue   .60   .25
Union of Utrecht, 400th anniversary.

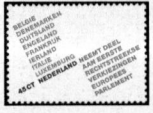

European Parliament — A183

1979, Feb. 20 Litho.   Perf. 13½x13
585 A183 45c blue, blk & red   .50   .25
European Parliament, first direct elections, June 7-10.

Queen Juliana — A184

1979, Mar. 13 Photo.   Perf. 13½x14
586 A184 55c multicolored   .60   .25
70th birthday of Queen Juliana.

A185

Europa: 55c, Dutch Stamps and magnifying glass. 75c, Hand on Morse key, and ship at sea.

1979, May 2 Litho.   Perf. 13x13½
587 A185 55c multicolored   .50   .25
588 A185 75c multicolored   1.00   .30

A186

Map of Netherlands with chamber locations.

1979, June 5 Litho.   Perf. 13x14
589 A186 65c multicolored   .50   .25
Netherlands Chambers of Commerce and 175th anniversary of Maastricht Chamber.

Soccer — A187

1979, Aug. 28 Litho.   Perf. 14x13
590 A187 45c multicolored   .50   .25
Centenary of soccer in the Netherlands.

Suffragettes — A188

1979, Aug. 28 Photo.   Perf. 13x14
591 A188 55c multicolored   .60   .25
Voting right for women, 60th anniversary.

Inscribed Tympanum and Architrave — A189

1979, Oct. 2 Photo.   Perf. 14x13
592 A189 40c multicolored   .45   .25
Joost van den Vondel (1587-1679), Dutch poet and dramatist.

"Gay Company," Tile Floor — A190

1979, Oct. 2
593 A190 45c multicolored   .50   .25
Jan Steen (1626-1679), Dutch painter.

Alexander de Savornin Lohman (1837-1924) — A191

Politicians: 50c, Pieter Jelles Troelstra (1860-1930), Social Democratic Workmen's Party leader. 60c, Pieter Jacobus Oud (1886-1968), mayor of Rotterdam.

1980, Mar. 4 Photo.   Perf. 13x13½
594 A191 45c multicolored   .40   .25
595 A191 50c multicolored   .45   .25
596 A191 60c multicolored   .55   .25
        Nos. 594-596 (3)   1.40   .75

British Bomber Dropping Food, Dutch Flag A192

Anne Frank A193

Perf. 13x14, 14x13
1980, Apr. 25   Photo.
597 A192 45c multicolored   .55   .25
598 A193 60c multicolored   .60   .25
35th anniv. of liberation from the Germans.

Queen Beatrix, Palace — A194

1980, Apr. 30 Perf. 13x14, 13x13½
599 A194 60c multicolored   .60   .25
   a.   Perf. 12¾x13¼   2.00 1.00
Installation of Queen Beatrix.
See No. 608.

Boy and Girl Inspecting Stamp — A195

1980, May 1   Perf. 14x13
600 A195 50c multicolored   .50   .25
Youth philately: NVPH Stamp Show, s'Gravenhagen, May 1-3 and JUPOSTEX Stamp Exhibition, Eindhoven, May 23-27. No. 600 printed se-tenant with label.

Bridge Players, "Netherlands" Hand — A196

1980, June 3 Litho.   Perf. 13x14
601 A196 50c multicolored   .55   .25
6th Bridge Olympiad, Valkenburg, 9/27-10/11.

Truck Transport — A197

60c, Two-axle railway hopper truck. 80c, Inland navigation barge.

1980, Aug. 26 Photo.   Perf. 13½x13
602 A197 50c shown   .45   .25
603 A197 55c multicolored   .55   .25
604 A197 80c multicolored   .75   .25
        Nos. 602-604 (3)   1.75   .75

Queen Wilhelmina, Excerpt from Speech, Netherlands Flag — A198

80c, Winston Churchill, British flag.

1980, Sept. 23 Litho.   Perf. 13½x13
605 A198 60c shown   .50   .25
606 A198 80c multicolored   1.00   .30
        Europa.

Abraham Kuyper, University Emblem, "100" — A199

1980, Oct. 14 Litho.   Perf. 13½x13
607 A199 50c multicolored   .55   .25
Free University centennial (founded by Kuyper).

Queen Beatrix Type of 1980
1981, Jan. 6 Photo.   Perf. 12¾x13¼
608 A194 65c multicolored   .70   .25
   a.   Perf. 12¾x14   2.50 1.00

Parcel — A200

Designs: 55c, Dish antenna and telephone. 65c, Bank books.

1981, May 19 Litho.   Perf. 13½x13
609 A200 45c multicolored   .50   .25
610 A200 55c multicolored   .50   .25
611 A200 65c multicolored   .50   .25
   a.   Souvenir sheet of 3, #609-611 1.35 1.00
Centenaries: Parcel Post Service (45c); Public telephone service (55c); National Savings Bank (65c).

Huis ten Bosch (Royal Palace), The Hague — A201

1981, June 16 Litho.   Perf. 13½x13
612 A201 55c multicolored   .60   .25

Europa Issue

Carillon — A202

1981, Sept. 1 Litho.   Perf. 13½x13
613 A202 45c shown   .50   .25
614 A202 65c Barrel organ   .65   .25

450th Anniv. of Council of State — A203

1981, Oct. 1 Photo.   Perf. 13½x13
615 A203 65c multi   .70   .25

Excavator and Ship's Screw (Exports) — A204

55c, Cast iron component, scale. 60c, Tomato, lettuce. 65c, Egg, cheese.

1981, Oct. 20 Photo.   Perf. 13½x13
616 A204 45c shown   .45   .25
617 A204 55c multi   .50   .25
618 A204 60c multi   .60   .25
619 A204 65c multi   .65   .25
        Nos. 616-619 (4)   2.20 1.00

Queen Beatrix — A205

Black Vignette
1981-86   Photo.   Perf. 13½x12½
620 A205 65c tan   .55   .25
621 A205 70c lt vio ('82)   .70   .25
   a.   Bklt. pane, 4 #536, 4 #621   3.00
         Complete booklet, #621a   3.00
622 A205 75c pale pink ('82)   .70   .25
   a.   Bklt. pane of 4 ('86)   3.00
623 A205 90c lt grn('82)   .70   .25
624 A205 1g lt vio('82)   .70   .25
625 A205 1.40g pale grn('82)   1.15   .25
626 A205 2g lem ('82)   1.40   .25
627 A205 3g pale vio ('82)   2.10   .25
628 A205 4g brt yel grn ('82)   2.60   .25
629 A205 5g lt grnsh bl ('82)   2.60   .25
630 A205 6.50g lt lil rose ('82)   3.75   .30
631 A205 7g pale bl ('86)   4.50   .40
        Nos. 620-631 (12)   21.85 3.20

Coil Stamps
Perf. 13½ Horiz.
632 A205 70c lt vio ('82)   .80   .25
633 A205 75c pale pink ('86)   .80   .25
634 A205 1g lt vio ('82)   .80   .25
635 A205 2g lem ('82)   1.60   .25
636 A205 6.50g lt lil rose ('82)   5.50   .55
637 A205 7g pale bl ('86)   6.50   .75
        Nos. 632-637 (6)   16.00 2.30
See Nos. 685-699.

University of Amsterdam, 350th Anniv. — A206

1982, Jan. 14   Litho.   Perf. 13½x13
638 A206 65c multi   .60 .25

Royal Dutch Skating Assoc. Centenary — A207

1982, Feb. 26   Litho.   Perf. 13x13½
639 A207 45c multi   .50 .25

Bicentenary of US-Netherlands Diplomatic Relations — A208

1982, Apr. 20   Photo.   Perf. 13½x13
640 A208 50c multi   .50 .25
641 A208 65c multi   .70 .25

See US No. 2003.

Sandwich Tern and Eider Duck, Waddenzee A209

1982, June 8   Litho.   Perf. 13½x13
642 A209 50c shown   .55 .25
643 A209 70c Barnacle geese   .75 .25

Dutch Road Safety Assoc, 50th Anniv. — A210

1982, Aug. 24   Photo.   Perf. 13x14
644 A210 60c multi   .50 .25

Europa 1982 — A211

Fortification Layouts.

1982, Sept. 16   Litho.   Perf. 13x13½
645 A211 50c Enkhuizen, 1590   .60 .25
646 A211 70c Coevorden, 1680   .75 .25

Royal Palace, Dam Square, Amsterdam — A212

50c, Facade, cross-section. 60c, Aerial view.

1982, Oct. 5   Litho.   Perf. 13x13½
647 A212 50c multi   .50 .25
648 A212 60c multi   .55 .25

Royal Dutch Touring Club Centenary — A213

1983, Mar. 1   Litho.   Perf. 13½x13
649 A213 70c multi   .70 .25

  A214

Europa: 50c, Netherlands Newspaper Publishers Assoc., 75th anniv. 70c, Launching of European Telecommunication Satellite Org. ECS F-1 rocket, June 3.

1983, May 17   Litho.   Perf. 13x13½
650 A214 50c multi   .50 .25
651 A214 70c multi   .70 .25

A215

De Stijl ("The Style") Modern Art Movement, 1917-31: 50c, Composition 1922, by P. Mondriaan. 65c, Maison Particuliere contra Construction, by C. van Eesteren and T. van Doesburg.

1983, June 21   Litho.   Perf. 13x13½
652 A215 50c multi   .50 .25
653 A215 65c multi   .65 .25

Symbolic Separation of Church — A216

1983, Oct. 11   Litho.   Perf. 13x13½
654 A216 70c multi   .70 .25

Martin Luther (1483-1546).

2nd European Parliament Election, June 14 — A217

1984, Mar. 13   Litho.   Perf. 13½x13
655 A217 70c multicolored   .70 .25

St. Servatius (d. 384) — A218

1984, May 8   Photo.   Perf. 13x14
656 A218 60c Statue, 1732   .60 .25

Europa (1959-84) — A219

1984, May 22   Perf. 13½x13
657 A219 50c blue   .50 .25
  a.   Perf. 14x13   3.00 2.50
658 A219 70c yellow green   .70 .30
  a.   Perf. 14x13   3.00 2.50

Perf. 14x13 stamps are coils. Every fifth stamp has a control number on the back.

William of Orange (1533-84) — A220

1984, July 10   Photo.   Perf. 14x13
659 A220 70c multicolored   .70 .25

World Wildlife Fund — A221

1984, Sept. 18   Litho.   Perf. 14x13
660 A221 70c Pandas, globe   1.00 .25

11th Intl. Small Business Congress, Amsterdam, Oct. 24-26 — A222

1984, Oct. 23   Litho.   Perf. 13x13½
661 A222 60c Graph, leaf   .60 .25

Guide Dog Fund — A223

60c, Sunny, first guide dog.

Photogravure and Engraved
1985, Jan. 22   Perf. 14x13
662 A223 60c multi   .60 .25

 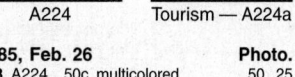

A224   Tourism — A224a

1985, Feb. 26   Photo.
663 A224 50c multicolored   .50 .25
664 A224a 70c multicolored   .70 .25

Cent. of the Tourist office "Geuldal," and 50th anniv. of the Natl. Park "De Hoge Veluwe."

Liberation from German Forces, 40th Anniv. — A225

Designs: 50c, Jewish star, mastheads of underground newspapers, resistance fighter. 60c, Allied supply air drop, masthead of The Flying Dutchman, Polish soldier at Arnhem. 65c, Liberation Day in Amsterdam, masthead, first edition of Het Parool (underground newspaper), American cemetery at Margraten. 70c, Dutch women in Japanese prison camp, Japanese occupation currency, building of the Burma Railway.

1985, May 5   Photo.   Perf. 14x13
665 A225 50c blk, buff & red   .55 .25
666 A225 60c blk, buff & brt bl   .65 .25
667 A225 65c blk, buff & org   .70 .50
668 A225 70c blk, buff & brt grn   .75 .25
    Nos. 665-668 (4)   2.65 1.25

WWII resistance effort (1940-1945) and liberation of Europe, 1945.

Europa '85 — A226

50c, Piano keyboard. 70c, Stylized organ pipes.

1985, June 4   Litho.   Perf. 13x13½
669 A226 50c multi   .85 .25
670 A226 70c multi   1.15 .30

Natl. Museum of Fine Arts, Amsterdam, Cent. — A227

Anniversaries and events: 50c, Museum in 1885, 1985. 60c, Nautical College, Amsterdam, bicent.: Students training. 70c, SAIL-85, Amsterdam: Sailboat rigging.

1985, July 2   Photo.   Perf. 13½x13
671 A227 50c multicolored   .50 .25
672 A227 60c multicolored   .60 .25

Perf. 14x13
673 A227 70c multicolored   .70 .25
    Nos. 671-673 (3)   1.80 .75

Wildlife Conservation A228

Designs: 50c, Porpoise, statistical graph. 70c, Seal, molecular structure models.

1985, Sept. 10   Litho.   Perf. 13½x13
674 A228 50c multicolored   .55 .30
675 A228 70c multicolored   .75 .30

Penal Code, Cent. — A229   Amsterdam Datum Ordinance, 300th Anniv. — A230

Lithographed, Photogravure (60c)
1986, Jan. 21   Perf. 14x13
676 A229 50c Text   .55 .30
677 A230 60c Elevation gauge   .65 .25

Sexbierum Windmill Test Station Inauguration A231

1986, Mar. 4   Litho.   Perf. 14x13
678 A231 70c multicolored   .75 .25

Het Loo Palace Gardens, Apeldorn — A232

1986, May 13   Litho.   Perf. 13x14
679 A232 50c shown   .60 .30

Photo.
680 A232 70c Air and soil pollution   .80 .25

Europa 1986.

Utrecht Cathedral — A233

60c, German House, c.1350. 70c, Utrecht University charter, horiz.

1986, June 10   Photo.   Perf. 13x14
681 A233 50c shown   .55 .30
682 A233 60c multicolored   .65 .30

Perf. 14x13
683 A233 70c multicolored   .75 .30
    Nos. 681-683 (3)   1.95 .90

Cathedral restoration, 1986. Heemschut Conservation. Soc., 75th anniv. Utrecht University, 350th anniv.

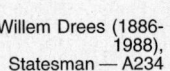

Willem Drees (1886-
1988),
Statesman — A234

1986, July 1 Litho. Perf. 13x13½
684 A234 55c multicolored .60 .25

Queen Type of 1981
1986-90 Photo. Perf. 13½x12½
685 A205 1.20g citron & blk .90 .25
686 A205 1.50g lt rose vio & blk .85 .25
688 A205 2.50g tan & blk 1.35 .25
694 A205 7.50g lt grn & blk 5.00 1.00
 Nos. 685-694 (4) 8.10 1.75

Coil Stamps
Perf. 13½ Horiz.
697 A205 1.50g lt rose vio & blk 1.25 .25
699 A205 2.50g tan & blk 2.00 .25

Issue dates: Nos. 685, 688, 699, 9/23. Nos. 686, 697, 8/19. 7.50g, 5/29/90.

Billiards — A235

Perf. 14x13, 13x14
1986, Sept. 9 Photo.
705 A235 75c shown .80 .30
706 A235 75c Checkers, vert. .80 .25

Royal Dutch Billiards Assoc., Checkers Association, 75th annivs.

Delta Project
Completion — A236

65c, Storm-surge barrier. 75c, Barrier withstanding flood.

1986, Oct. 7 Photo. Perf. 14x13
708 A236 65c multicolored .70 .30
709 A236 75c multicolored .80 .25

Princess Juliana and
Prince Bernhard, 50th
Wedding Anniv. — A237

1987, Jan. 6 Photo. Perf. 13x14
710 A237 75c multicolored .85 .25

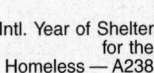

Intl. Year of Shelter
for the
Homeless — A238

Designs: 75c, Salvation Army, cent.

1987, Feb. 10 Photo. Perf. 14x13
711 A238 65c multicolored .95 .30
712 A238 75c multicolored 1.05 .25

Dutch
Literature — A239

Authors: 55c, Eduard Douwes Dekker (1820-1887) and De Harmonie Club, Batavia. 75c, Constantijn Huygens (1596-1687) and Scheveningseweg, The Hague.

1987, Mar. 10 Litho. Perf. 13½x13
713 A239 55c multicolored .60 .25
714 A239 75c multicolored .80 .25

Europa
1987 — A240

Modern architecture: 55c, Scheveningen Dance Theater, designed by Rem Koolhaas. 75c, Montessori School, Amsterdam, designed by Herman Hertzberger.

1987, May 12 Litho. Perf. 14x13
715 A240 55c multicolored .95 .25
716 A240 75c multicolored 1.05 .25

Produce Auction at
Broeck op
Langedijk,
1887 — A241

Designs: 65c, Field in Groningen Province, signatures of society founders. 75c, Auction, bidding, price indicator, 1987.

1987, June 16 Photo. Perf. 14x13
717 A241 55c shown .55 .25
718 A241 65c multicolored .65 .25
719 A241 75c multicolored .75 .75
 Nos. 717-719 (3) 1.95 .75

Sale of produce by auction in the Netherlands, cent., and Groningen Agricultural Society, 150th anniv. (No. 718).

Union of the Netherlands
Municipalities, 75th
Anniv. — A242

1987, Oct. 6 Litho. Perf. 13x14
720 A242 75c multicolored .80 .25

Noordeinde Palace,
The Hague — A243

1987, Oct. 27 Photo. Perf. 14x13
721 A243 65c multicolored .70 .25

A244

Booklet Stamps
Perf. 13½x13 on 3 Sides
1987, Dec. 1 Photo.
722 A244 50c dk ultra, emer & dk red .50 .25
723 A244 50c dk red, dk ultra & yel .50 .25
724 A244 50c dk ultra, yel & dk red .50 .25
725 A244 50c dk red, emer & yel .50 .25
726 A244 50c emer, dk red & dk ultra .50 .25
 a. Bklt. pane, 4 each #722-726 10.00 13.00
  Complete booklet #726a 10.00
 Nos. 722-726 (5) 2.50 1.25

Netherlands Cancer
Institute, 75th
Anniv. — A246

1988, Apr. 19 Litho. Perf. 13½x12½
728 A246 75c multicolored .80 .25

Europa
1988 — A247

Modern transportation meeting ecological requirements: 55c, Cyclist, rural scenery, chemical formulas, vert. 75c, Cyclists seen through car-door mirror.

1988, May 17 Litho. Perf. 13x13½
729 A247 55c multicolored .95 .25
Perf. 13½x13
730 A247 75c multicolored 1.05 .25

A248

Designs: 65c, Prism splitting light as discovered by Sir Isaac Newton, planet Saturn as observed by Christian Huygens, and pendulum clock, c. 1688. 75c, William of Orange (1650-1702) and Mary II (1662-1694).

1988, June 14 Perf. 14x13
731 A248 65c multicolored .70 .25
732 A248 75c multicolored .80 .25

No. 731, Coronation of William III and Mary Stuart, King and Queen of England, 300th anniv. (in 1989). No. 732, Arrival of Dutch William in England, 300th anniv.

Modern Art — A249

Paintings by artists belonging to Cobra: 55c, *Cobra Cat*, 1950, by Appel. 65c, *Stag Beetle*, 1948, by Corneille. 75c, *Fallen Horse*, 1950, by Constant.

1988, July 5 Litho. Perf. 13½x13
733 A249 55c multicolored .70 .50
734 A249 65c multicolored .80 .50
735 A249 75c multicolored .90 .30
 Nos. 733-735 (3) 2.40 1.30

Each stamp printed se-tenant with label picturing the featured artist's signature.
Cobra, an intl. organization established in 1948 by expressionist artists from Copenhagen, Brussels and Amsterdam.

Australia
Bicentennial — A250

1988, Aug. 30 Photo. Perf. 13x14
736 A250 55c multicolored .80 .25

A251 A252

1988, Sept. 27 Litho. Perf. 13x13½
737 A251 75c dk green & green .80 .25
738 A252 75c bright violet .80 .25

Erasmus University, Rotterdam, 75th anniv. (#737), Amsterdam Concertgebouw & Orchestra, cent. (#738).

Holiday Greetings — A253

1988, Dec. 1 Photo. Perf. 13½x12½
739 A253 50c multicolored .55 .25

"Holland," etc.
Stamps inscribed "Holland," "Stadspost," etc., are private issues. In some cases overprints or surcharges on Netherlands stamps may be created.

Privatization of the Netherlands Postal
Service
A254

Mailbox, sorting machine, mailbag, mailman, telephone key pad, fiber optics cable, microwave transmitter & telephone handset.

Litho. & Engr.
1989, Jan. 3 Perf. 13x13½
740 A254 75c multicolored .85 .25

Dutch Trade
Unions — A255

1989, Feb. 7 Litho. Perf. 13x13½
741 A255 55c shown .60 .25
Photo.
Perf. 13x14
742 A255 75c Hands, mouths .80 .25

NATO, 40th
Anniv. — A256

1989, Mar. 14 Litho. Perf. 14x13
743 A256 75c multicolored .80 .25

Europa
1989 — A257

Children's games (string telephone): 55c, Boy. 75c Girl.

1989, May 9 Litho. Perf. 13½x13
744 A257 55c multicolored .95 .25
745 A257 75c multicolored 1.05 .25

Dutch Railways,
150th
Anniv. — A258

1989, June 20 Litho. Perf. 13½x13
746 A258 55c Rails .55 .25
747 A258 65c Trains .65 .25
Perf. 14x13
748 A258 75c Passengers .75 .25
 Nos. 746-748 (3) 1.95 .75

Royal Dutch Soccer
Assoc., Cent. — A259

1989, Sept. 5 Photo. Perf. 13x14
749 A259 75c multicolored .75 .25

Treaty of London, 150th
Anniv. — A260

Map of Limburg Provinces

1989, Oct. 2 Litho. Perf. 13x14
750 A260 75c multicolored .75 .25
See Belgium No. 1327.

A261

Perf. 13x13x13½

1989, Nov. 30 Photo.
751 A261 50c multicolored .55 .25

Sold only in sheets of 20.

Anniversaries — A262

Designs: 65c, Leiden coat of arms (tulip), and layout of the Hortus Botanicus in 1601. 75c, Assessing work conditions (clock, sky, wooden floor), horiz.

1990, Feb. 6 Litho. **Perf. 13x13½**
752 A262 65c multicolored .70 .25

Perf. 13½x13
753 A262 75c multicolored .80 .25

Hortus Botanicus, Leiden, 400th anniv. (65c); Labor Inspectorate, cent. (75c).

Vincent van Gogh (1853-1890) — A263

Details of works by van Gogh: 55c, *Self-portrait*, pencil sketch, 1886-87. 75c, *The Green Vineyard*, painting, 1888.

1990, Mar. 6 **Perf. 13x13½**
754 A263 55c multicolored .65 .25
755 A263 75c multicolored .85 .25

Rotterdam Reconstruction A264

1990, May 8 Litho. **Perf. 13½x13**
756 A264 55c shown .55 .25
757 A264 65c Diagram .65 .25
758 A264 75c Modern bldgs. .75 .25
Nos. 756-758 (3) 1.95 .75

Europa — A264a

Post offices.

1990, June 12
759 A264a 55c Veere .95 .25
760 A264a 75c Groningen 1.05 .25

Dutch East India Co. Ships A265

Sail '90 A266

1990, July 3 **Perf. 13x13½**
761 A265 65c multicolored .65 .25
762 A266 75c multicolored .75 .25

Queens of the House of Orange — A267

1990, Sept. 5 Litho. **Perf. 13½**
763 A267 150c multicolored 1.50 .90

Century of rule by Queens Emma, Wilhelmina, Juliana and Beatrix.

A268

1990, Oct. 9 Photo. **Perf. 13x14**
764 A268 65c multicolored .70 .30

Natl. emergency phone number.

A269

1990, Nov. 29 Photo. **Perf. 14**
765 A269 50c multicolored .55 .25
a. Tete-beche pair 1.10 .30

All pairs in sheet are tete-beche.

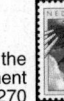

Threats to the Environment A270

1991, Jan. 30 Litho. **Perf. 13½x13**
766 A270 55c Air pollution .55 .25
767 A270 65c Water pollution .65 .25
768 A270 75c Soil pollution .75 .25
Nos. 766-768 (3) 1.95 .75

General Strike, 50th Anniv. — A271

1991, Feb. 25 Photo. **Perf. 14x13**
769 A271 75c multicolored .80 .25

Queen Beatrix and Prince Claus, 25th Wedding Anniv. — A272

1991, Mar. 11 Litho. **Perf. 13½x13**
770 75c shown .80 .30
771 75c Riding horses .80 .30
a. A272 Pair, #770-771 1.60 1.20

Numeral Type of 1976 and

Queen Beatrix — A273

Perf. 12½x13½, 13½x12½
1991-94 Photo.
772 A157 70c gray violet .75 .25
a. Booklet pane, 5 each #537, 772 5.00
773 A273 75c green 1.00 .25
a. Bklt. pane of 4 + 2 labels 4.00 2.00
Complete booklet, #773a 4.00
774 A157 80c red lilac 1.00 .25
774A A273 80c red brown 1.00 .25
b. Booklet pane of 5 + label 4.00
Complete booklet, #774Ab 4.00
775 A273 90c blue 1.00 .25
776 A273 1g purple 1.00 .40
777 A273 1.30g gray blue 1.10 .25
778 A273 1.40g gray olive 1.10 .25
779 A273 1.60g magenta 1.40 .25
780 A273 2g yel brown 1.75 .80
781 A273 2.50g red lilac 2.25 1.20

782 A273 3g blue 2.50 1.20
783 A273 5g brown red 4.25 1.15

Perf. 14x13, Syncopated
784 A273 7.50g purple 8.00 2.75
785 A273 10g green 5.00 1.00
Nos. 772-785 (15) 33.10 11.50

Coil Stamps
Perf. 13½ Vert. (A157), Horiz. (A273)
786 A157 70c gray violet .75 .25
787 A273 75c green .95 .50
788 A157 80c red lilac .90 .25
789 A273 80c red brown .90 .25
790 A273 1.60g magenta 1.75 .50
Nos. 786-790 (5) 5.25 1.75

Booklet Stamp
Perf. 12½x13½
791 A157 60c lemon .65 .25
a. Bklt. pane, 2 #791, 4 #772 4.50

Issued: 75c, 3/14/91; 60c, 70c, #774, 1.60g, 6/25/91; #774A, 789, 1.30g, 1.40g, 9/3/91; 1g, 2g, 3g, 5g, 11/11/92; 90c, 2/2/93; 2.50g, 9/7/93; 10g, 11/29/93; 7.50g, 11/28/94.
See #902, 906-913, 1091-1104, 1216, 1218-1221, 1223.

A274

A275

Designs: 55c, Gerard Philips, carbon filament experiments, 1890. 65c, Electrical wiring. 75c, Laser video disk experiment.

Perf. 13x14, 14x13
1991, May 15 Photo.
792 A274 55c multicolored .55 .25
793 A275 65c multicolored .65 .25
794 A274 75c multicolored .75 .25
Nos. 792-794 (3) 1.95 .75

Philips Electronics, cent. (Nos. 792, 794). Netherlands Normalization Institute, 75th anniv. (No. 793).

A276

Europa: 75c, Ladders to another world.

1991, June 11 Litho. **Perf. 13x13½**
795 A276 55c multicolored .95 .30
796 A276 75c multicolored 1.05 .25

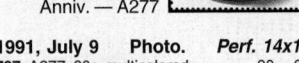

Nijmegen Four Days Marches, 75th Anniv. — A277

1991, July 9 Photo. **Perf. 14x13**
797 A277 80c multicolored .90 .25

Dutch Nobel Prize Winners — A278

Designs: 60c, Jacobus H. Van't Hoff, chemistry, 1901. 70c, Pieter Zeeman, physics, 1902. 80c, Tobias M. C. Asser, peace, 1911.

1991, Sept. 3 **Perf. 14x13**
798 A278 60c multicolored .65 .25
799 A278 70c multicolored .70 .25
800 A278 80c multicolored .80 .25
Nos. 798-800 (3) 2.15 .75

Public Libraries, Cent. — A279

A280

1991, Oct. 1 Litho. **Perf. 13½x13**
801 A279 70c Children reading .75 .25
802 A279 80c Books .85 .25

1991, Nov. 28 Photo. **Perf. 14**
803 A280 55c multicolored .50 .25

Delft University of Technology, Sesquicent. A281

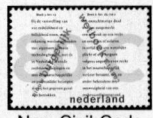

New Civil Code A282

1992, Jan. 7 Litho. **Perf. 13½x13**
804 A281 60c multicolored .65 .25
805 A282 80c multicolored .85 .25

Souvenir Sheet

A283

1992 Olympics, Albertville and Barcelona: No. 806a, Volleyball, rowing. b, Shotput, rowing. c, Speedskating, rowing. d, Field hockey.

1992, Feb. 4 Litho. **Perf. 13x14**
806 A283 80c Sheet of 4, #a.-d. 3.00 3.00

Tulips — A284

Map — A284a

1992, Feb. 25 Litho. **Perf. 13x12½**
807 A284 70c multicolored .75 .25

Photo.
Perf. 13x14
808 A284a 80c multicolored .85 .25

Expo '92, Seville.

Discovery of New Zealand and Tasmania by Abel Tasman, 350th Anniv. — A285

1992, Mar. 12 Photo. **Perf. 14x13**
809 A285 70c multicolored .75 .25

A286

A287

1992, Apr. 28 Litho. **Perf. 13x13½**
810 A286 60c multicolored .65 .25
811 A287 80c multicolored .85 .25

Royal Assoc. of Netherlands Architects, 150th Anniv. (#810). Opening of Building for Lower House of States General (#811).

Discovery of America, 500th Anniv. — A288

Perf. 13½x13, 13x13½
1992, May 12 Litho.
812 A288 60c Globe, Columbus .60 .30
813 A288 80c Sailing ship, vert. .75 .25

Europa. On normally centered stamps the white border appears at the left side of No. 813.

Royal Netherlands Numismatics Society, Cent. — A289

1992, May 19 Photo. **Perf. 13x14**
814 A289 70c multicolored .75 .25

Netherlands Pediatrics Society, Cent. — A290

1992, June 16 Litho. **Perf. 13½x13**
815 A290 80c multicolored .90 .25

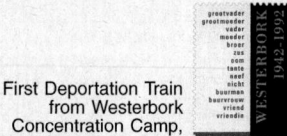

First Deportation Train from Westerbork Concentration Camp, 50th Anniv. — A291

1992, Aug. 25 **Perf. 13x13½**
816 A291 70c multicolored .75 .25

Single European Market — A292

1992, Oct. 6 **Perf. 13½x13**
817 A292 80c multicolored .80 .25

Queen Beatrix, 12½ Years Since Investiture — A293

1992, Oct. 30 **Perf. 13x13½**
818 A293 80c multicolored .80 .25

Christmas Rose A294

1992, Nov. 30 Photo. **Perf. 14**
819 55c Red flower .60 .25
820 55c Silver flower .60 .25
a. A294 Pair, #819-820 1.25 .25

Netherlands Cycle and Motor Industry Assoc. (RAI), Cent. — A295

Designs: 70c, Couple riding bicycle. 80c, Early automobile.

1993, Jan. 5 Litho. **Perf. 13½x13**
821 A295 70c multicolored .80 .25
822 A295 80c black & yellow .90 .25

A296 | Greeting Stamps — A296a

Geometric shapes.

1993, Feb. 2 Photo. **Perf. 14x13½**
823 A296 70c multi .70 .25
824 A296a 70c multi, diff. .70 .25
a. Tete-beche pair, #823-824 1.40 .40

Mouth-to-mouth Resuscitation A297 | Royal Horse Artillery Lead Driver, Horses A298

Leaf, Insect Pests — A299

1993, Feb. 16 Litho. **Perf. 13x13½**
825 A297 70c multicolored .85 .25
826 A298 80c multicolored .85 .25
827 A299 80c multicolored .85 .25
Nos. 825-827 (3) 2.55 .75

Royal Netherlands First Aid Assoc., cent. (#825). Royal Horse Artillery, bicent. (#826). University of Agriculture, 75th anniv. (#827).
On No. 826, normally centered stamps show design extending to top and right sides only.

Royal Dutch Notaries' Assoc., 150th Anniv. A300

Litho. & Engr.
1993, Mar. 2 **Perf. 14x13**
828 80c Top half of emblem .90 .25
829 80c Bottom half of emblem .90 .25
a. A300 Pair, #828-829 1.80 .40

No. 829a has continuous design.

Butterflies — A301

Designs: 70c, Pearl-bordered fritillary (Zilvervlek). 80c, Large tortoiseshell (Grote vos). 90c, Large white (Koolwitje). 160c, Polyommatus icarus.

1993, Mar. 23 Photo.
830 A301 70c black & multi .80 .50
831 A301 80c yellow & multi .80 .30
832 A301 90c green & multi .80 .80
Nos. 830-832 (3) 2.40 1.60
Souvenir Sheet
833 A301 160c red & multi 2.40 2.40

On normally centered stamps the white border appears at the right side.

Radio Orange A302

Designs: No. 834, Woman broadcasting. No. 835, Man listening.

1993, May 5 Photo. **Perf. 14x13**
834 80c orange red & purple .85 .25
835 80c purple & orange red .85 .25
a. A302 Pair, #834-835 1.90 .40

European Youth Olympic Days — A303

Symbols of Olympic sports.

1993, June 1 **Perf. 13x14**
836 A303 70c blue & multi .70 .25
837 A303 80c yellow & multi .80 .25

Europa — A304

Contemporary sculpture by: 70c, Wessel Couzijn. 80c, Per Kirkeby. 160c, Naum Gabo, vert.

Perf. 13½x13, 13x13½
1993, July 6 Litho.
838 A304 70c blk, blue & grn .85 .40
839 A304 80c black, red & yel .85 .30
840 A304 160c black, blue & pur 1.60 1.40
Nos. 838-840 (3) 3.30 2.10

Dutch Nobel Prize Winners — A305

Designs: 70c, J.D. van der Waals, physics, 1910. 80c, Willem Einthoven, medicine, 1924. 90c, Christiaan Eijkman, medicine, 1929.

1993, Sept. 7 Litho. **Perf. 13x13½**
841 A305 70c multicolored .60 .35
842 A305 80c multicolored .70 .25
843 A305 90c multicolored .80 .80
Nos. 841-843 (3) 2.10 1.40

Letter Writing Day A306

1993, Sept. 14 Photo. **Perf. 14x13**
844 80c Pencils, pen .75 .25
b. Perf. 14x13½ ('94) 2.50 .25
845 80c Envelope, contents .75 .25
a. A306 Pair, #844-845 1.60 .45
b. Perf. 14x13½ ('94) 2.50 .25
c. Pair, #844b-845b ('94) 5.00 1.00

Stamp Day — A307

80c, Dove with envelope.

1993, Oct. 8 Litho. **Perf. 13½x13**
846 A307 70c shown .70 .30
847 A307 80c multicolored .80 .25

December Stamps A308

Clock hand pointing to "12:" and: No. 848, Star, candle, Christmas tree. No. 849, Fireworks.

1993, Nov. 29 Photo. **Perf. 12**
848 A308 55c blue & multi .60 .25
849 A308 55c red & multi .60 .25
a. Pair, #848-849 1.25 .25

Issued in sheets of 20, 10 each #848-849 + label. Each stamp contains perforations placed within the design to resemble snowflakes.

Piet Mondrian (1872-1944), Painter — A309

Details from paintings: 70c, The Red Mill. 80c, Rhomboid with Yellow Lines. 90c, Broadway Boogie Woogie.

1994, Feb. 1 Litho. **Perf. 13½x13**
850 A309 70c multicolored .70 .45
851 A309 80c multicolored .75 .40
852 A309 90c multicolored .85 .85
Nos. 850-852 (3) 2.30 1.70

Wild Flowers — A310

70c, Downy rose. 80c, Daisy. 90c, Woods forget-me-not. 160c, Fire lily croceum.

1994, Mar. 15 Photo. **Perf. 14]x13**
853 A310 70c multi .70 .40
854 A310 80c multi .80 .30
855 A310 90c multi .90 .90
Nos. 853-855 (3) 2.40 1.60
Souvenir Sheet
856 A310 160c multi 2.50 2.50

Dutch Aviation, 75th Anniv. — A311

1994, Apr. 6 Litho. **Perf. 13½x13**
857 A311 80c KLM .85 .25
858 A311 80c Fokker .85 .25
859 A311 80c NLR .85 .25
Nos. 857-859 (3) 2.55 .75

Planetarium, Designed by Eise Eisinga — A312

Design: 90c, Television image of moon landing, footprint on moon.

1994, May 5 Photo. **Perf. 13x14**
860 A312 80c multicolored .80 .25
861 A312 90c multicolored 1.00 .80

First manned moon landing, 25th anniv. (#861).

1994 World Cup Soccer Championships, U.S. — A313

1994, June 1
862 A313 80c multicolored .90 .60

No. 862 printed with se-tenant label.

Stock Exchange Floor, Initials KPN — A314

1994, June 13 Litho. **Perf. 13½**
863 A314 80c multicolored .90 .25

Offering of shares in Royal PTT Netherlands NV (KPN).

Bicycle, Car, Road Sign — A315

80c, Silhouettes of horses, riders, carriage.

1994, June 14 Photo. *Perf. 14x13*
864 A315 70c multicolored .75 .25

Litho.
Perf. 13½x13
865 A315 80c multicolored .85 .25

First road signs placed by Dutch motoring assoc. (ANWB), cent. (#864). World Equestrian Games, The Hague (#865).

War in Dutch East Indies (1941-45) A316

Operation Market Garden (1944) A316a

Perf. 14x13, 13x14
1994, Aug. 15 Photo.
866 A316 80c multicolored .75 .25
867 A316a 90c multicolored .95 .75

Lighthouses A317

Designs: 70c, Brandaris, Terschelling Island. 80c, Ameland Island, vert. 90c, Vlieland Island, vert.

Perf. 13½x13, 13x13½
1994, Sept. 13 Litho.
868 A317 70c multicolored 1.00 .50
869 A317 80c multicolored 1.00 .25
870 A317 90c multicolored 1.00 .90
Nos. 868-870 (3) 3.00 1.65

December Stamps — A318

1994, Nov. 28 Photo. *Perf. 13½*
871 A318 55c Snowflake, tree .55 .25
872 A318 55c Candle, star .55 .25
a. Pair, #871-872 1.10 .50
b. Min. sheet, 10 #872a + label 11.00 8.00

One stamp in #872a is rotated 90 degrees to the other stamp.

Cow, Dutch Products — A319

1995, Jan 2 Photo. *Perf. 14x13½*
873 A319 100c multicolored 1.25 .30

Hendrik Nicolaas Werkman (1882-1945), Printer A320

Mesdag Museum Restoration A321

Mauritius No. 2 — A322

1995, Jan. 17 Litho. *Perf. 14x13½*
874 A320 80c multicolored 1.00 .35
875 A321 80c multicolored 1.00 .35

Litho. & Engr.
Perf. 13½x14
876 A322 80c multicolored 1.00 .35
Nos. 874-876 (3) 3.00 1.05

Acquisition of Mauritius No. 2 by Netherlands PTT Museum (#876).

Motion Pictures, Cent. — A323

70c, Joris Iven, documentary film maker. 80c, Scene from film, "Turkish Delight," 1972.

1995, Feb. 28 Photo. *Perf. 14x13*
877 A323 70c multicolored .70 .25
878 A323 80c multicolored .80 .25

Mahler Festival — A324

Design: 80c, Gustav Mahler, (1860-1911), composer, 7th Symphony score.

1995, Mar. 21 Litho. *Perf. 13½x13*
879 A324 80c blue & black .90 .25

Institute of Registered Accountants, Cent. — A325

Assoc. of Building Contractors, Cent. — A326

1995, Mar. 28
880 A325 80c multicolored .80 .30
881 A326 80c multicolored .80 .30

50th Anniversaries — A327

Designs: No. 882, End of World War II, "45, 95" No. 883, Liberation of the Netherlands, "40, 45." No. 884, Founding of the UN, "50."

1995, May 3 Litho. *Perf. 13x13½*
882 A327 80c multicolored .80 .30
883 A327 80c multicolored .80 .30
884 A327 80c multicolored .80 .30
Nos. 882-884 (3) 2.40 .90

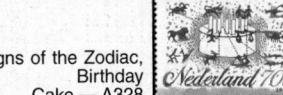

Signs of the Zodiac, Birthday Cake — A328

1995, May 22 Photo. *Perf. 14x13½*
885 A328 70c multicolored 1.10 .30

18th World Boy Scout Jamboree A329

Sail Amsterdam '95 A330

Perf. 13x13½, 13½x13
1995, June 6 Litho.
886 A329 70c multicolored .70 .35
887 A330 80c multicolored .80 .25

Birds of Prey — A330a

Perf. 13x14, 14x13
1995, Sept. 5 Photo.
888 A330a 70c Kestrel, vert. .80 .25
889 A330a 80c Hen harrier .80 .25
890 A330a 100c Red kite 1.00 1.00
Nos. 888-890 (3) 2.60 1.50

Souvenir Sheet
891 A330a 160c Honey buzzard 2.75 2.75

Nobel Prize Winners — A331

No. 892, F. Zernike, physics, 1953. No. 893, P.J.W. Debye, chemistry, 1936. No. 894, J. Tinbergen, economics, 1969.

1995, Sept. 26 Litho. *Perf. 13½x13*
892 A331 80c green & multi .80 .25
893 A331 80c blue & multi .80 .25
894 A331 80c red & multi .80 .25
Nos. 892-894 (3) 2.40 .75

Dutch Cabaret, Cent. — A332

Designs: 70c, Eduard Jacobs (1868-1914), Jean-Louis Pisuisse (1880-1927). 80c, Wim Kan (1911-83), Freek de Jonge (b. 1944).

1995, Oct. 17 Litho. *Perf. 13½x14*
895 A332 70c multicolored .70 .25
896 A332 80c multicolored .80 .25

Numeral Type of 1976 and Queen Type of 1991
1995-2001 Photo. *Perf. 13½x12½*
902 A273 1.50g green 1.50 .40

Self-Adhesive (Nos. 903-911)
Booklet Stamps
Die Cut Perf. 14¼
903 A157 5c gray .25 .25
a. Double-sided pane of 10 .45
904 A157 10c ultramarine .25 .25
a. Double-sided pane of 10 .85
905 A157 25c violet .30 .25
a. Double sided pane of 10 3.00
906 A273 85c blue green .95 .25
a. Booklet pane of 5 5.00
907 A273 1g purple 1.10 .25
a. Booklet pane of 5 5.50
908 A273 1.10g blue 1.25 .25
a. Booklet pane of 5 6.25
909 A273 1.45g green 1.60 .30
a. Booklet pane of 5 8.00
910 A273 2.50g red lilac 2.75 .55
a. Booklet pane of 5 14.00
911 A273 5g brown red 5.50 1.10
a. Booklet pane of 5 27.50
Nos. 903-911 (9) 13.95 3.45

Coil Stamps
Perf. 13½ Horiz.
912 A273 1g gray violet 1.10 .25
913 A273 1.10g blue 1.25 .25

Issued: No. 912, 10/5; 1.50g, 3/17/98, No. 913, 8/1/00; 5c, 10c, 25c, 6/18/01; 85c, 1.45g, 7/2/01; Nos. 907, 908, 2.50g, 5g, 9/3/01. 85c has added euro denomination.

December Stamps — A333

Serpentine Die Cut 12½x13
1995, Nov. 27 Self-Adhesive
916 A333 55c Children, star .70 .25
917 A333 55c Children, stars .70 .25
a. Pair, #916-917 1.40 .50

Issued in sheets of 20, checkerboard style. Nos. 916-917 exist imperf. Value, $62.50 for pair.

Paintings by Johannes Vermeer (1632-75) — A334

Entire paintings or details: 70c, A Lady Writing a Letter, with Her Maid. 80c, The Love Letter. 100c, A Woman in Blue Reading a Letter.

1996, Feb. 27 Litho. *Perf. 13x13½*
918 A334 70c multicolored .85 .45
919 A334 80c multicolored .90 .30
920 A334 100c multicolored 1.10 1.00
a. Souvenir sheet, Nos. 918-920 3.25 3.25
Nos. 918-920 (3) 2.85 1.75

Spring Flowers — A335

Designs: 70c, Daffodil bulb, garden tools. 80c, Closeup of woman, tulip. 100c, Snake's head (fritillaria). 160c, Crocuses.

1996, Mar. 21 Litho. *Perf. 13½x13*
921 A335 70c multicolored .85 .40
922 A335 80c multicolored .90 .30
923 A335 100c multicolored 1.10 1.00
Nos. 921-923 (3) 2.85 1.70

Souvenir Sheet
924 A335 160c multicolored 2.10 1.90

A336

1996, Apr. 1 *Perf. 13x13½*
925 A336 70c Moving stamp .85 .40

No. 925 was sold in sheets of 20. See #951.

Comic Strips, Cent. — A337

Mr. Olivier B. Bommel, by Marten Toonder: a, O.B. Bommel goes on holiday. b, O.B. Bommel receives letter.

1996, May 14 Litho. *Perf. 13½x13*
926 Sheet of 2 + 2 labels 2.60 2.60
a. A337 70c multicolored 1.25 1.00
b. A337 80c multicolored 1.25 1.00

Vacations — A338

Scene, flower: No. 927, Beach, sunflower. No. 928, Cyclists, gerbera. 80c, Gables in Amsterdam, cornflower. 100c, Windmills at "Zaanse Schans'" open air museum, anemone.

1996, May 31
927 A338 70c multicolored .85 .25
928 A338 70c multicolored .85 .45
929 A338 80c multicolored .85 .25
930 A338 100c multicolored .85 .45
Nos. 927-930 (4) 3.40 1.40

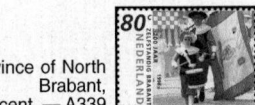

Province of North Brabant, Bicent. — A339

1996, June 13 Litho. *Perf. 13½x13*
931 A339 80c multicolored .90 .25

Sporting
Events — A340

Designs: 70c, Lighting the Olympic Torch, 1996 Summer Olympic Games, Atlanta. 80c, Tour de France cycling race. 100c, Euro '96 Soccer Championships, Wembley Stadium, England. 160c, Olympic rings, track sports, Atlanta stadium.

1996, June 25
932 A340 70c multicolored .80 .25
933 A340 80c multicolored .80 .25
934 A340 100c multicolored 1.00 .75
935 A340 160c multicolored 1.50 .80
  Nos. 932-935 (4) 4.10 2.05

Erasmus Bridge,
Rotterdam — A341

Designs: No. 936, Martinus Nijhoff Bridge over Waal River, horiz. No. 938, Wijker Tunnel under North Sea Canal, horiz.

1996, Aug. 6   Perf. 13½x13, 13x13½
936 A341 80c multicolored .85 .25
937 A341 80c shown .85 .25
938 A341 80c multicolored .85 .25
  Nos. 936-938 (3) 2.55 .75

UNICEF, 50th
Anniv. — A342

Designs: 70c, School children from Ghana. 80c, Girl from Ghana with tray on head.

1996, Sept. 3   Perf. 13x13½
939 A342 70c multicolored .80 .25
940 A342 80c multicolored .80 .25

Sesame Street in
Netherlands, 20th
Anniv. — A343

70c, Bert & Ernie. 80c, Pino, Ieiemienie & Tommie.

1996, Sept. 3   Perf. 13½x13
941 A343 70c multicolored .80 .25
942 A343 80c multicolored .75 .25

Nos. 941-942 were issued in sheets of 100 and sheets of 10. On Jan. 1, 1997, No. 942 was reprinted reading "Tien voor je post" instead of "Tien voor je brief" in the top selvage.

Voyages of
Discovery — A344

Voyages of: 70c, Petrus Plancius (1552-1622), cartographer. #944, Willem Barents (d. 1597). #945, Cornelis de Houtman (1540-99). 100c, Mahu en De Cordes (1598-1600).

1996, Oct. 1
943 A344 70c multicolored .75 .40
944 A344 80c multicolored .75 .30
945 A344 80c multicolored .75 .30
946 A344 100c multicolored 1.15 1.15
  Nos. 943-946 (4) 3.40 2.15

December
Stamps — A345

Collage of faces, hands: No. 947, Wing, ear, hands. No. 948, Mouth, two faces. No. 949, Woman with eyes closed, hand. No. 950, Eyes, face with mouth open.

Serpentine Die Cut 9 Horiz.
1996, Nov. 26   Self-Adhesive
947 A345 55c multicolored .50 .25
948 A345 55c multicolored .50 .25
949 A345 55c red violet & multi .50 .25
950 A345 55c blue & multi .50 .25
  a.   Block or strip of 4, #947-950 2.00
  Issued in sheets of 20.

Moving Stamp Type of 1996
Die Cut Perf. 13
1997, Jan. 2   Photo.
Self-Adhesive
951 A336 80c like No. 925 .90 .25
  No. 951 sold in panes of 20.

Business
Stamps — A346

Geometric designs.

Coil Stamps
*Sawtooth Die Cut 13½ Horiz.,
Syncopated (on 1 Side)*
1997, Jan. 2   Self-Adhesive
952 A346 80c pink & multi .75 .25
953 A346 160c green & multi 1.40 .25

Cross-Country
Skating
Championships
A347

1997, Jan. 4   Photo.   Perf. 14x13
954 A347 80c multicolored .90 .25

Surprise
Stamps — A348

Inscriptions beneath scratch-off heart-shaped panels: b, Schrijf me. c, Groetjes. d, Ik hou van je. e, Tot gauw. f, Ik denk aan je. g, XXX-jes. h, Ik mis je. i, Geintje. j, Zomaar. k, Wanneer?

1997, Jan. 21   Perf. 14x13½
955   Sheet of 10 7.50 6.50
  a.   A348 80c Any single, unscratch-
       ed heart .75 .65
  b.-k. A348 80c Any single, scratched
       heart .25
Unused value for #955a is with attached selvage. Inscriptions are shown in selvage beside each stamp.

Nature and
Environment
A349

1997, Feb. 25   Litho.   Perf. 13½x13
956 A349 80c Pony .90 .30
957 A349 100c Sheep 1.10 1.00

Souvenir Sheet
958 A349 160c Sheep, diff. 2.10 2.10

Suske & Wiske
Comic Strip
Characters — A350

#959, Suske, Wiske, Tante Sidonia, & Lambik. #960a, Jerome making exclamation.

Perf. 13½x12½
1997, Mar. 18   Litho.
959 A350 80c multicolored .85 .25

Souvenir Sheet
960   Sheet of 2, #959, 960a 2.60 2.10
  a.   A350 80c violet & red 1.25 .90

A351

Greetings
Stamps — A352

#961, Birthday cake. #962, Amaryllis surrounded by cup of coffee, two glasses of wine, hand writing card, candlelight.

1997, May 6   Photo.   Perf. 14x13½
961 A351 80c multicolored .80 .25
962 A352 80c multicolored .80 .25
  See No. 1035.

Marshall Plan, 50th Anniv.
A353

Designs: No. 963, Map of Europe. No. 964, Flag, quotation from George C. Marshall.

1997, May 27   Litho.   Perf. 13½x13
963   80c multicolored .85 .30
964   80c multicolored .85 .30
  a.   A353 Pair, #963-964 1.75 1.75

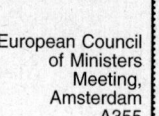

Court of Audit,
550th
Anniv. — A354

1997, May 27   Perf. 13½x13
965 A354 80c multicolored .85 .30

European Council
of Ministers
Meeting,
Amsterdam
A355

1997, June 17   Litho.   Perf. 13½
966 A355 100c multicolored 1.40 1.10

Water
Recreation — A356

80c, Swimming, row boat. 1g, Sailboats.

1997, July 1   Perf. 13½x13
967 A356 80c multicolored .85 .25
968 A356 1g multicolored 1.00 .55

Royal Institute of
Engineers, 150th
Anniv. — A357

1997, Aug. 5
969 A357 80c multicolored .90 .25

Netherlands
Asthma Center,
Cent. — A358

1997, Aug. 5
970 A358 80c multicolored .90 .25

Horticultural
Education at
Florens College,
Aalsmeer,
Cent. — A359

1997, Aug. 5
971 A359 80c multicolored .90 .25

Franz Schubert
(1797-1828),
Composer — A360

1997, Aug. 5
972 A360 80c multicolored .90 .25

A361   Youth
Stamps — A362

1997, Sept. 2
973 A361 80c multicolored .75 .25
  a.   Bkit. pane of 5 + 2 labels 5.00
       Complete booklet, #973a 5.00
974 A362 80c multicolored .75 .25
  a.   Perf. 14x13 50.00 50.00
Issued: No. 973a, 7/6/99.
Booklet stamps differ from sheet stamps: the year date is closer to the edge.

Birth
Announcement
Stamp — A363

Die Cut Perf. 13½x13
1997, Oct. 7   Photo.
Self-Adhesive
975 A363 80c multicolored .80 .25
  a.   Litho. ('99) 1.25 1.25
  See Nos. 1033, 1071, 1109, 1260.

A364

December Stamps: Stylized people head to head showing either a star or heart in the center.

Serpentine Die Cut
1997, Nov. 25   Photo.
Self-Adhesive
Background Colors
976 A364 55c yellow .55 .25
977 A364 55c blue .55 .25
978 A364 55c orange .55 .25
979 A364 55c red .55 .25
980 A364 55c yellow green .55 .25
981 A364 55c dark green .55 .25
  a.   Sheet, 3 ea #976, 978-979,
       981, 4 ea #977, 980 11.00 11.00

Death Announcement
Stamp — A365

1998, Jan. 2   Litho.   Perf. 13½
982 A365 80c gray blue .80 .25
  See Nos. 1059, 1072, 1110, 1261. Compare with Types A580 and A824.

Delftware — A366

100c, Cow, tiles with pictures of sailing ships. 160c, Tiles, one picturing boy standing on head.

1998, Jan. 2   Photo.   Die Cut
Self-Adhesive
983 A366 100c multicolored .95 .50
984 A366 160c multicolored 1.50 1.00

Issued in both coil strips and sheets with priority labels.

A368

Growing Fruit in the Four Seasons: No. 986, Orchard in bloom, spring. No. 987, Strawberries, summer. No. 988, Harvesting, autumn. No. 989, Pruning, winter.

1998, Feb. 17 Litho. Perf. 13x13½
Booklet Stamps
986 A368 80c multicolored .95 .80
987 A368 80c multicolored .95 .80
988 A368 80c multicolored .95 .80
989 A368 80c multicolored .95 .80
 a. Booklet pane, #986-989 4.00
 Complete booklet, #989a 4.00

A369

Die Cut Perf. 13½
1998, Mar. 17 Photo.
Self-Adhesive
990 A369 80c multicolored .80 .25
 a. Litho. ('99) 4.00 4.00

Marriage and wedding anniversaries. No. 990 was issued in sheets of 10.
See No. 1034.

Anniversaries A370

#991, Men shaking hands, Treaty of Munster, 350th anniv. #992, Statue of John Rudolf Thorbecke, Dutch constitution, 150th anniv. #993, Child on swing, Universal Declaration of Human Rights, 50th anniv.

1998, Mar. 17 Litho. Perf. 13½x13
991 A370 80c multicolored .85 .25
992 A370 80c multicolored .85 .25
993 A370 80c multicolored .85 .25
 a. Strip of 3, #991-993 2.60 2.60

Letter Writing Day — A371

1998, May 8 Litho. Perf. 13½
994 A371 80c multicolored .85 .25

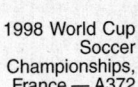

1998 World Cup Soccer Championships, France — A372

1998, May 19 Litho. Perf. 13½
995 A372 80c multicolored .90 .25

Rabo Bank, Cent. — A373

1998, May 19 Perf. 13½x13
996 A373 80c multicolored .85 .25

Royal Netherlands Field Hockey Federation, Cent. — A374

1998, May 19
997 A374 80c multicolored .85 .25

Central Administration in Friesland, 500th Anniv. — A375

1998, June 9 Litho. Perf. 13½x13
998 A375 80c multicolored .85 .25

Water Management A375a

1998, June 9
999 A375a 80c shown .80 .25
1000 A375a 1g Aerial view 1.00 .75

Split of Royal Netherlands PTT — A376

#1001, TNT Post Groep. #1002, KPN NV.

1998, June 29
1001 80c red, black & blue .85 .25
1002 80c blue, blk & grn .85 .25
 a. A376 Vert. pair, #1001-1002 1.75 1.75

No. 1002a is a continuous design.

Natl. Library of the Netherlands, Bicent. — A377

1998, July 7
1003 A377 80c multicolored .85 .25

A378

No. 1004, Maurits Cornelis Escher (1898-1972), Graphic Artist. No. 1005, Simon Vestdijk (1898-1971), writer.

1998, July 7 Perf. 13x13½
1004 A378 80c multicolored .85 .40
1005 A378 80c multicolored .85 .40
 a. Pair, #1004-1005 1.75 1.75

Souvenir Sheet

A379

Inauguration of Queen Wilhelmina, Cent.: a, Queen Wilhelmina. b, Gilded Coach.

1998, Sept. 1 Litho. Perf. 13x13½
1006 A379 80c Sheet of 2, #a.-b. 2.60 2.60

Greetings Stamps — A380

Colors of stamp edges, clockwise from side adjacent to "Neder:" No. 1007: a, yellow, orange, red, red. b, red, orange, pink, yellow orange. c, red, orange, rose, orange. d, orange, red, light orange, yellow orange. e, yellow, orange, pink, red.

Serpentine Die Cut Perf. 13½x13
1998, Sept. 1 Litho.
Self-Adhesive
1007 80c Sheet of 10, 2 each #a.-e. 8.00
 a.-e. A380 any single 1.00 .50

Each side of No. 1007 contains a pane of 1 each #1007a-1007e and 10 different self-adhesive labels.

Nos. 1008-1011 are unassigned.

Pets — A381

1998, Sept. 22 Perf. 13½x13
1012 A381 80c Dog .80 .30
 a. Bklt. pane of 5 + 2 labels 4.75
 Complete booklet, #1012a 4.75
1013 A381 80c Kittens .80 .40
1014 A381 80c Rabbits 1.00 .80
 Nos. 1012-1014 (3) 2.60 1.50
Issued: No. 1012a, 7/6/99.

Jan, Jans en de Kinderen Comic Strip, by Jan Kruis — A382

Characters: No. 1015, Writing letters. No. 1016, In automobile, mailing letter.

1998, Oct. 6 Litho. Perf. 13½x13
1015 A382 80c multicolored .85 .25
 a. Booklet pane, 10 #1015 + 20 labels 8.50
 Complete booklet, #1015a 8.50
1016 A382 80c multicolored 1.50 .25
 a. Sheet of 2, #1015-1016 + 3 labels 2.60 2.50

December Stamps — A383

25c, Stylized tree, house on top of earth.
No. 1018:
Silhouetted against moon: a, Rabbit. b, House. c, Bird. d, Tree. e, Deer.
Silhouetted against horizon: f, Rabbit. g, House. h, Bird. i, Tree. j, Deer.
House with: k, Rabbit. l, Heart. m. Bird. n, Tree. o, Deer.
Tree with: p, Rabbit. q, House. r, Bird. s, Heart. t, Deer.

1998-99 Litho. Perf. 13
1017 A383 25c multicolored .30 .25
Self-Adhesive
Die Cut Perf. 9
1018 A383 55c Sheet of 20, #a.-t. 10.00 3.25
Issued: #1018, 11/24; #1017, 1/5/99.

Introduction of the Euro — A384

1999, Jan. 5 Litho. Perf. 13x12½
1019 A384 80c multicolored .85 .25

Netherlands Postal Services, Bicent. A385

1999, Jan. 15 Litho. Perf. 13½x14
1020 A385 80c multi + label .90 .80
See No. 1039

A386

1999, Feb. 2 Litho. Perf. 12¾x13¼
1021 A386 80c Spoonbill .85 .25
1022 A386 80c Globe, tern .85 .25

Protection of birds and migrating waterfowl. Netherlands Society for Protection of Birds, cent (#1021). African-Eurasian Waterbird Agreement (#1022).

A387

1999, Feb. 2 Perf. 12¾x13¼
Booklet Stamp
1023 A387 80c multicolored .85 .25
 a. Booklet pane of 4 3.50
 Complete booklet, #1023a 3.50

Royal Dutch Lawn Tennis Assoc., cent.

Views During the Four Seasons — A388

Designs: a, Haarlemmerhout in fall. b, Sonsbeek in winter. c, Weerribben in spring. d, Keukenhof in summer.

1999, Mar. 2 Litho. Perf. 13¼x12¾
1024 A388 Booklet pane of 4, #a.-d. 4.00 4.00
 a.-d. 80c Any single .90 .80
 Complete booklet, #1024 4.25

I Love Stamps — A389

1999, May 6 Litho. Perf. 13¼x12¾
1025 A389 80c I Love Stamps .80 .40
1026 A389 80c Stamps Love Me 1.00 .75
 a. Booklet pane, 3 #1025, 2 #1026 + 2 labels 4.50
 Complete booklet, #1026a 4.50

Nos. 1025-1026 each contain a hologram. Soaking may affect the hologram.

Maritime Anniversaries — A390

1999, May 6 Litho. Perf. 12¾x13¼
1027 A390 80c Freighters .80 .25
1028 A390 80c Lifeboats .80 .25

Schuttevaer Ship Masters Assoc., 150th anniv. (#1027). Netherlands Lifeboat Assoc., 175th anniv. (#1028).

Paintings — A391

No. 1029: a, The Goldfinch, by Carel Fabritius. b, Self-portrait, by Rembrandt. c, Self-portrait, by Judith Leyster. d, St. Sebastian, by Hendrick Ter Brugghen. e, Beware of Luxury, by Jan Steen. f, The Sick Child, by Gabriel Metsu. g, Gooseberries, by Adriaen Coorte. h,

View of Haarlem, by Jacob van Ruisdael. i, Mariaplaats Utrecht, by Pieter Saenredam. j, Danae, by Rembrandt. 1g, The Jewish Bride, by Rembrandt.

1999, June 8 Litho. Perf. 13¼x13¾
1029   Sheet of 10, #a.-j.   9.00 9.00
a.-j. A391 80c any single   .85 .85
Self-Adhesive
Die Cut Syncopated
1030   A391 1g multicolored   1.25 .95

No. 1030 issued in sheets of 5 stamps and blue priority mail etiquettes.

A392

1999, July 6 Litho. Perf. 13¼x12¾
1031   A392 80c multicolored   .90 .25
Self-Adhesive
Die Cut 13½ Syncopated Horiz.
1032   A392 80c multicolored   .90 .25

Birth Announcement Type of 1997 and Marriage Type of 1998
1999, July 6 Litho. Perf. 13¼x12¾
Booklet Stamps
1033   A363 80c multicolored   .90 .25
a. Booklet pane of 5 + 2 labels   4.50
Complete booklet, #1033a   4.50
Perf. 13¼
1034   A369 80c multicolored   .90 .25
a. Booklet pane of 5 + 2 labels   4.50
Complete booklet, #1034a   4.50

Greetings Type of 1997
Die Cut 13½ Syncopated Horiz.
1999, July 6 Litho.
Self-Adhesive
1035   A352 80c multicolored   1.25 .50

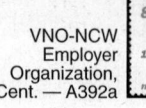
VNO-NCW Employer Organization, Cent. — A392a

1999, Sept. 7 Litho. Perf. 13¼x12¾
1036   A392a 80c multicolored   .85 .25

Tintin — A393

No. 1037, Tintin, Snowy in space suits. No. 1038a, Tintin, Snowy, Capt. Haddock in spacecraft.

1999, Oct. 8 Perf. 13¼x12¾
1037   A393 80c multicolored   .25 .25
a. Booklet pane of 5 + 2 labels   7.75
Complete booklet, #1037a   8.00
Souvenir Sheet
1038   Sheet of 2, #1037, 1038a   3.25 2.75
a. A393 80c multicolored   1.50 1.25

Postal Service Bicentennial Type
Souvenir Sheet
1999, Oct. 15 Litho. Perf. 13¼x13¾
1039   A385 5g multicolored   5.00 5.00

The numeral in the denomination is made up of perforations.

Millennium — A394

Highlights of the 20th Century: a, Construction of barrier dam, 1932. b, Satellite. c, Amsterdam Bourse, 1903, designed by H. P. Berlage. d, Empty highway, 1973-74 oil crisis. e, Prime Minister Willem Drees's social welfare programs, 1947. f, Flood control projects 1953-97. g, European soccer champions, 1988. h, Liberation, 1945. i, Woman suffrage. j, Eleven-city skating race.

1999, Oct. 25 Litho. Perf. 13¼x12¾
1040   Sheet of 10   8.00 8.00
a.-j. A394 80c any single   .80 .80

December Stamps — A395

Designs: a, Santa's head. b, Angel, musical notes, vert. c, Ornaments in box. d, Crescent-shaped Santa's head, vert. e, Santa, four trees. f, Clock, vert. g, Skater. h, Tree of people holding candles, vert. i, Man and woman. j, Woman, tree, star, vert. k, Angel, musical score. l, Hand, vert. m, Tree. n, Cat with crown, vert. o, Bird, house. p, Baby as angel, vert. q, Dog with cap. r, Angel with halo, vert. s, Family in house. t, Tree with presents, vert.

Serpentine Die Cut 7
1999, Nov. 30 Photo.
Self-Adhesive
1041   A395 Sheet of 20, #a-t   10.00
a.-t. 55c any single   .50 .25

A396

2000, Jan. 4 Litho. Perf. 13x12¾
1042   A396 25c multi   .30 .25

Souvenir Sheet

Holy Roman Emperor Charles V (1500-58) — A397

Designs: a, Gulden coin, Charles' aunt and guardian, Margaret of Austria, Charles V on Horseback in Bologna, by Juan de la Corte. b, Map of the Netherlands, Charles V on Horseback at the Battle of Mühlberg, by Titian, Charles' daughter, Margaret of Parma.

2000, Jan. 4 Perf. 13¼
1043   A397 Sheet of 2 + label   2.25 2.00
a.-b. 80c Any single   1.00 1.00

Greetings — A398

Color of denomination or country name and hands (back or palm) with written messages: a, Pink, back. b, Pink, palm. c, Orange, back. d, Orange, palm. e, Green, back. f, Green, palm. g, Blue, back. h, Blue, palm. i, Red, back. j, Red, palm.

Perf. 13¼x13¾
2000, Feb. 29 Litho.
1044   A398 Sheet of 10, #a-j   8.00 8.00
a.-j. 80c any single   .75 .75

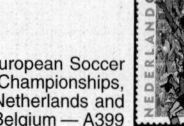
European Soccer Championships, Netherlands and Belgium — A399

2000, Mar. 25 Perf. 12¾x13¼
Booklet Stamps
1045   A399 80c Crowd, players   .75 .25
1046   A399 80c Crowd, ball   1.10 .75
a. Booklet pane, 3 #1045, 2 #1046 + 2 labels   4.50
Booklet, #1046a   4.50

See Belgium No. 1796.

Items in Rijksmuseum — A400

a, Feigned Sorrow (woman wiping eye), by Cornelis Troost. b, Harlequin and Colombine, Meissen porcelain piece, by J. J. Kändler. c, Kabuki Actor Ebizo Ichikawa IV, by Sharaku. d, Apsara from India. e, Carved head of St. Vitus. f, Woman in Turkish Costume, by Jean Etienne Liotard. g, J. van Speyk (man with epaulet), by J. Schoemaker Doyer. h, Engraving of King Saul, by Lucas van Leyden. i, Statue, L'Amour Menacant, by E. M. Falconet. j, Photograph of two men, by C. Ariens. 100c, The Night Watch, by Rembrandt.

2000, Apr. 14 Perf. 13¼x13¾
1047   A400 Sheet of 10, #a-j   11.00 11.00
a.-j. 80c any single   1.00 1.00

Die Cut Syncopated
Self-Adhesive
1048   A400 100c multi   1.10 .90

#1048 issued in sheets of 5 + 5 priority mail etiquettes.
See Nos. 1051, 1053.

Doe Maar, Popular Musical Group — A401

2000, May 2 Litho. Perf. 13¼x12¾
1049   A401 80c Song titles   1.00 .75
1050   A401 80c Album cover   .75 .35
a. Booklet pane, 2 #1049, 3 #1050, + 2 labels   4.25
Booklet, #1050a   4.25

Rijksmuseum Type of 2000 with Priority Mail Emblem Added and

Dutch Landscape, by Jeroen Krabbé — A402

Designs: Nos. 1051, 1053, The Night Watch, by Rembrandt.
Die cut perf. 4 on right side and right parts of top and bottom sides.

Die Cut Similar to Sync.
2000, Aug. 1 Litho.
Self-Adhesive
1051   A400 110c pur & multi   1.25 .60
Die Cut Sync.
1052   A402 110c multi   1.25 .60
Coil Stamp
Die Cut Similar to Sync.
1053   A400 110c blue & multi   3.25 1.60
Nos. 1051-1053 (3)   5.75 2.80

Nos. 1051-1052 issued in sheets of 5. No. 1051 lacks die cut "holes" on left side and at upper left. No. 1053 lacks die cut "holes" on left side, but has only two at upper left.

Sail 2000, Amsterdam Harbor — A403

No. 1054: a, Block and Libertad, Argentina. b, Figurehead and Amerigo Vespucci, Italy. c, Unfurled white sail, Dar Mlodziezy, Poland. d, Ship's wheel, Europa, Netherlands. e, Bell, Kruzenshtern, Russia. f, Deckhand adjusting sail, Sagres II, Portugal. g, Green sail, Alexander von Humboldt, Germany. h, Crewmen on bowsprit, Sedov, Russia. i, Spreaders, furled sails and ropes, Mir, Russia. j, Rope, Oosterschelde, Netherlands.

Perf. 13¼x12¾
2000, Aug. 21 Litho.
1054   A403 Sheet of 10   9.25 9.25
a.-j. 80c Any single   .90 .45

Sjors and Sjimmie — A404

Comic strip characters: No. 1055, Rollerblading. No. 1056, In go-kart. No. 1057, Wearing headphones. No. 1058, Hanging on rope.

2000, Sept. 23
1055   A404 80c multi   1.25 .60
1056   A404 80c multi   1.25 .60
a. Pair, #1055-1056   2.50 1.25
1057   A404 80c multi   .90 .45
a. Souvenir sheet, #1056-1057   3.00 3.00
Booklet Stamp
1058   A404 80c multi   1.25 .60
a. Booklet pane, 3 #1057, 2 #1058 + 2 labels   5.25
Booklet, #1058a   5.25
Nos. 1055-1058 (4)   4.65 2.25

Death Announcement Type of 1998
Die Cut Perf. 13¼
2000, Oct. 10 Photo.
Self-Adhesive
1059   A365 80c gray blue   .90 .50

Endangered Species — A405

Designs: No. 1060, Aeshna viridis (Groene glazenmaker). No. 1061, Misgurnus fossilis (Grote modderkruiper).

2000, Oct. 10 Litho. Perf. 13¼x12¾
Booklet Stamps
1060   A405 80c multi   .90 .50
1061   A405 80c multi   1.10 .50
a. Booklet pane 3 #1060, 2 #1061 + 2 labels   5.00
Booklet, #1061a   5.00

Souvenir Sheet

Amphilex 2002 Intl. Stamp Show, Amsterdam — A406

No. 1062: a, Boat. b, Carriage.

2000, Oct. 10
1062   A406 Sheet of 2   2.10 2.10
a.-b. 80c Any single   .90 .50

Christmas — A407

No. 1063: a, Woman, man with tree on shoulder. b, Woman, child decorating tree. c, Couple dancing. d, Tuba player. e, Man carrying hat and tree. f, Man with child on shoulder. g, Woman reading. h, Couple kissing. i, Piano player. j, Woman at window. k, Woman in chair. l, Santa by fire. m, Snowman. n, Couple in front of house. o, Violin player. p, Children on sled. q, Man writing letter. r, Woman with food tray. s, Four people. t, Woman asleep.

Serpentine Die Cut 14½x15

2000, Nov. 28   **Photo.**
Self-Adhesive

1063	A407	Sheet of 20	11.00	
a.-t.	60c Any single		.55	.25

A408

2001, Jan. 2   **Litho.**   *Perf. 12¾x13¼*
1064	A408	20c multi	.25	.25

Royal Dutch Nature Society, Cent. — A409

No. 1065: a, Whinchat thrush. b, People in rowboat. c, Fox. d, People with binoculars. e, Scotch rose and June beetles.

2001, Jan. 26   **Litho.**   *Perf. 13½x12¾*
1065		Booklet pane of 5, #a-e, +2 labels	5.25	5.25
a.-e.	A409 80c Any single		1.00	.75
	Booklet, #1065		6.00	

Rotterdam, 2001 European Cultural Capital — A410

Die Cut Similar to Sync.

2001, Mar. 14   **Litho.**
Self- Adhesive
1066	A410 110c multi		1.50	.90

Printed in sheets of 5. Die cutting has no "holes" at left, but has "holes" at top and bottom at the thin vertical line.

Book Week A411

No. 1067: a, Quote by Edgar du Perron. b, Photograph by Ulay. c, Quote by Hafid Bouazza. d, Photograph by Ed van der Elsken. e, Quote by Adriaan van Dis. f, Photograph by Anton Corbijn. g, Quote by Kader Abdolah. h,

---

Photographs by Celine van Balen. i, Quote by Ellen Ombre. j, Photograph by Cas Oorthuys.

2001, Mar. 14   *Perf. 13¼x13¾*
1067	A411	Sheet of 10	7.25	7.25
a.-j.	80c Any single		.90	.25

Souvenir Sheet

Max Euwe (1901-81), Chess Champion — A412

No. 1068: a, Chessboard. b, Euwe, chess pieces.

2001, Apr. 3   *Perf. 13¼x12¾*
1068	A412	Sheet of 2	2.25	2.25
a.-b.	80c Any single		1.00	.90

Souvenir Sheet

Intl. Volunteers Year — A413

No. 1069: a, Rescue workers. b, People with animal cages.

2001, Apr. 3
1069	A413	Sheet of 2	2.25	2.25
a.-b.	80c Any single		1.00	.75

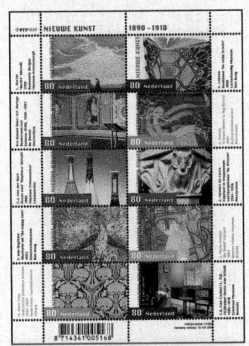

Art of 1892-1910 — A414

Art: a, "Autumn," L. Gestel. b, Book cover for "De Stille Kracht," C. Lebeau. c, Burcht Federal Council Hall, R. N. Roland Holst and H. P. Berlage. d, "O grave, where is thy victory?," J. Toorop. e, Vases from "Amphoras," C. J. van der Hoef. f, De Utrecht office building capital, J. Mendes da Costa. g, Illustration from "The Happy Owls," T. van Hoytema. h, "The Bride," J. Thorn Prikker. i, Printed fabric, M. Duco Crop. j, Dentz van Schaik period room, Central Museum, Utrecht, C. A. Lion Cachet and L. Zijl.

2001, May 15   *Perf. 14¾*
1070	A414	Sheet of 10	7.25	7.25
a.-j.	80c Any single		.70	.50

Birth Announcement Type of 1997 with Added Euro Denomination
Die Cut Perf. 13¼x12¾

2001, July 2   **Litho.**
Booklet Stamp
Self-Adhesive
1071	A363 85c multi		1.10	.80
a.	Booklet pane of 5		6.00	

Death Announcement Type of 1998 with Added Euro Denomination
Die Cut Perf. 13¼

2001, July 2   **Litho.**
Self-Adhesive
1072	A365 85c gray blue		1.25	1.00

Wedding Stamp — A415

Die Cut Perf. 13¼x12¾

2001, July 2   **Photo.**
Booklet Stamp
Self-Adhesive
1073	A415 85c multi		1.10	.25
a.	Booklet pane of 5		5.50	

See No. 1111.

A416

2001, July 2   **Booklet Stamp**
Self-Adhesive
1074	A416 85c multi		1.10	.50
a.	Booklet pane of 10		11.00	

See No. 1112.

Arrows — A417

Serpentine Die Cut 14x13½

2001, July 2   **Coil Stamp**   **Photo.**
Self-Adhesive
1075	A417 85c pur & silver		1.00	.50

See Nos. 1105-1106.

Change of Address Stamp — A418

Die Cut Perf. 14½x14

2001, July 2   **Photo.**
Self-Adhesive
1076	A418 85c orange & blk		1.25	.80

See No. 1113.

Polder — A419

Coast at Zandvoort A420

Design: 1.65g, Cyclists on Java Island, Amsterdam.

2001, July 2   *Die Cut Perf. 13¼x12¾*
Booklet Stamps
Self-Adhesive
1077	A419 85c multi		1.25	.50
a.	Booklet pane of 5		6.25	

Serpentine Die Cut 12¾ Syncopated
1078	A420 1.20g multi		1.50	1.10
a.	Booklet pane of 5		7.50	
1079	A420 1.65g multi		2.00	1.75
a.	Booklet pane of 5		10.00	

Nos. 1078 and 1079 have rouletting between stamp and etiquette.
See Nos. 1114-1116.

Cartoon Network Cartoons — A421

No. 1080: a, Tom and Jerry. b, The Flintstones. c, Johnny Bravo. d, Dexter's Laboratory. e, The Powerpuff Girls.

Perf. 13½x12¾

2001, Aug. 28   **Litho.**
1080	A421	Booklet pane of 5, #a-e, + 2 labels	5.00	3.75
a.-e.	85c Any single		.95	.60
	Booklet, #1080		6.00	

Greetings — A422

No. 1081: a, Veel Geluk (9 times). b, Gefeliciteerd! (11 times). c, Veel Geluk (4 times), horiz. d, Gefeliciteerd! (5 times), horiz. e, Proficiat (7 times). f, Succes! (7 times). g, Van Harte. . . (9 times). h, Proficiat (3 times), horiz. i, Succes! (3 times), horiz. j, Van Harte. . . (4 times), horiz.

Die Cut Perf. 13x13¼, 13¼x13

2001, Sept. 3   **Photo.**
Self-Adhesive
1081		Booklet of 10	10.50	
a.-j.	A422 85c Any single		.95	.75

See No. 1117.

Change From Guilder to Euro Currency — A423

Etched on Silver Foil

2001, Sept. 25   *Die Cut Perf. 12¾*
Self-Adhesive
1082	A423 12.75g Guilder coins		9.50	6.50

Cancels can be easily removed from these stamps.

Souvenir Sheet

Royal Dutch Association of Printers, Cent. — A424

No. 1083 — Magnifying glass and: a, Color dots. b, Spectrum.

Photo. & Embossed

2001, Oct. 12   *Perf. 14x13½*
1083	A424	Sheet of 2	2.00	1.75
a.-b.	85c Any single		.95	.75

Souvenir Sheet

Dutch Stamps, 150th Anniv. (in 2002) A425

No. 1084: a, Waigaat Canal and ramparts, Williamstad, Curacao. b, Pangka sugar refinery, Java Island, Netherlands Indies.

2001, Oct. 12   **Photo.**   *Perf. 14x13½*
1084	A425	Sheet of 2	2.00	2.00
a.-b.	85c Any single		.95	.25

Amphilex 2002 Intl. Stamp Show, Amsterdam.

December Stamps — A426

No. 1085: a, Clock, grapes. b, Grapes, stars, doughnut balls. c, Doughnut balls, spire of church tower. d, Cherub. e, Champagne bottle. f, Wreath, roof. g, Windows of church tower. h, Ornament on Christmas tree. i, Christmas tree on sign. j, Cake in window. k, Christmas tree with ornaments, church tower. l, Santa Claus. m, Mug of hot chocolate on sign, snowman's head. n, Candles in window. o, Church tower, decorated market stalls. p, Reindeer. q, Snowman. r, Wrapped gift. s, Bonfire. t, Children on sled.

Serpentine Die Cut 13¼x13

2001, Nov. 27   **Photo.**
Self-Adhesive
1085	A426	Sheet of 20	10.50	
a.-t.	A426 60c Any single		.50	.25

100 Cents = 1 Euro (€)

Queen Type of 1991, Arrows Type of 2001 With Euro Denominations Only and

A427

Die Cut Perf. 14¼, Serpentine Die Cut 14 (#1086, 12c), Serpentine Die Cut 14¼ (55c, 57c 70c, 72c), Perf 14¼x13½ (#1087, 5c, 10c)

Photo, Litho (5c, 12c)

2002-05		**Self-Adhesive**	
1086	A427	2c red	.25 .25
a.		Booklet pane of 5	.25

Water-Activated Gum

1087	A427	2c red	.25 .25
1088	A427	5c red violet	.25 .25
1089	A427	10c blue	.25 .25

Self-Adhesive Booklet Stamps

1090	A427	12c green	.30 .25
a.		Booklet pane of 5	1.50
1091	A273	25c brn & dk grn	.60 .25
a.		Booklet pane of 5	3.00
1092	A273	39c bl grn & red	.95 .25
a.		Booklet pane of 5	4.75
b.		Booklet pane of 10	9.50
1093	A273	40c bl & brn	.95 .25
a.		Booklet pane of 5	4.75
1094	A273	50c fawn & emer	1.25 .25
a.		Booklet pane of 5	6.25
1095	A273	55c lilac & brown	1.40 .25
a.		Booklet pane of 5	7.00
1096	A273	57c brn & blue grn	1.50 .30
a.		Booklet pane of 5	7.50
1097	A273	61c pur & red brn	1.60 .30
a.		Booklet pane of 5	8.00
1098	A273	65c grn & pur	1.60 .30
a.		Booklet pane of 5	8.00
1099	A273	70c ol grn & bl grn	1.75 .30
a.		Booklet pane of 5	8.75
1100	A273	72c blue & brt vio	1.90 .30
a.		Booklet pane of 5	9.50
1101	A273	76c olive & grn	2.00 .30
a.		Booklet pane of 5	10.00
1102	A273	78c bl & ol brn	1.90 .30
a.		Booklet pane of 5	9.50
1103	A273	€1 grn & blue	2.40 .40
a.		Booklet pane of 5	12.00
1104	A273	€3 red vio & grn	7.25 1.25
a.		Booklet pane of 5	37.50
		Nos. 1086-1104 (19)	28.35 6.25

Coil Stamps
Self-Adhesive
Serpentine Die Cut Perf. 14x13½

1105	A417	39c pur & silver	.95 .25
1106	A417	78c blue & gold	1.90 .30

Issued: 12c, 25c, 39c, 40c, 50c, 65c, 78c, €1, €3, 1/2/02; 2c (#1086), 1/28/02; 2c (#1087), 9/2/02; 10c, 11/26/02; 5c, 55c, 70c, 1/2/03; 57c, 72c, 1/2/04; 61c, 76c, 1/3/05. See No. 1259.

Souvenir Sheet

Wedding of Prince Willem-Alexander and Máxima Zorreguieta — A428

No. 1108: a, Portraits. b, Names.

2002, Jan. 10	**Photo.**		**Perf. 14**
1108	A428	Sheet of 2	2.00 2.00
a.-b.		39c Either single	.95 .50

Types of 1998-2001 With Euro Denominations Only
Die Cut Perf. 13¼x12¾
Photo., Litho. (#1110)

2002, Jan. 28		**Self-Adhesive**	
1109	A363	39c multi	.95 .50
a.		Booklet pane of 5	4.75

Die Cut Perf. 13¼

1110	A365	39c gray blue	.95 .50

Die Cut Perf. 13¼x12¾

1111	A415	39c multi	.95 .50
a.		Booklet pane of 5	4.75
1112	A416	39c multi	.95 .50
a.		Booklet pane of 10	9.50

Die Cut Perf. 14½x14

1113	A418	39c orange & blk	1.00 .50

Die Cut Perf. 13¼x12¾

1114	A419	39c multi	.95 .50
a.		Booklet pane of 5	4.75

Serpentine Die Cut 12¾ Syncopated

1115	A420	54c Like #1078	1.25 .50
a.		Booklet pane of 5	6.25

1116	A420	75c Like #1079	1.75 .50
a.		Booklet pane of 5	8.75
		Nos. 1109-1116 (8)	8.75 4.00

Nos. 1115-1116 have rouletting between stamp and etiquette.

Greetings Type of 2001 with Euro Denominations Only

No. 1117: a, Veel Geluk (9 times). b, Gefeliciteerd! (11 times). c, Veel Geluk (4 times), horiz. d, Gefeliciteerd! (5 times), horiz. e, Proficiat (7 times). f, Succes! (7 times). g, Van Harte. . . (9 times). h, Proficiat (3 times), horiz. i, Succes! (3 times), horiz. j, Van Harte. . . (4 times), horiz.

Die Cut Perf. 13x13¼, 13¼x13

2002, Jan. 28			**Photo.**
		Self-Adhesive	
1117		Booklet of 10	10.00
a.-j.	A422	39c Any single	.95 .70

Provinces — A429

2002		**Litho.**	**Perf. 14½x14¾**
1118	A429	39c Friesland	.95 .95
1119	A429	39c Drenthe	.95 .95
1120	A429	39c Noord-Holland	.95 .95
1121	A429	39c Gelderland	.95 .95
1122	A429	39c Noord-Brabant	.95 .95
1123	A429	39c Groningen	.95 .95
1124	A429	39c Zuid-Holland	.95 .95
1125	A429	39c Utrecht	.95 .95
1126	A429	39c Limburg	.95 .95
1127	A429	39c Overijssel	.95 .95
1128	A429	39c Zeeland	.95 .95
1129	A429	39c Flevoland	.95 .95
a.		Souvenir sheet of 12, #1118-1129	11.40
		Nos. 1118-1129 (12)	11.40 11.40

Nos. 1118-1129 each were issued in sheets of 12 + 6 labels.
Issued: No. 1118, 3/12; No. 1119, 3/26; No. 1120, 4/9; No. 1121, 4/23. No. 1122, 5/7; No. 1123, 5/21. No. 1124, 6/4; No. 1125, 6/18; No. 1126, 7/2. No. 1127, 7/16; No. 1128, 7/30; No. 1129, 8/13.

Efteling Theme Park, 50th Anniv. — A430

Characters: a, Bald man. b, Jester. c, Fairy. d, Man with thumb extended. e, Man with mouth open.

Serpentine Die Cut 13¼x12¾

2002, May 14			**Photo.**
		Self-Adhesive	
1130		Booklet pane of 5	4.75
a.-e.	A430	39c Any single	.95 .50

Europa — A431

Designs: No. 1131, Lions and circus tent. No. 1132, Acrobats, juggler, animal acts.

Perf. 14½x14¾

2002, June 11			**Litho.**
1131	A431	54c multi	1.50 .75
1132	A431	54c multi	1.50 .75
a.		Tete-beche pair, #1131-1132	3.50 3.25

Landscape Paintings — A432

No. 1133: a, West Indian Landscape, by Jan Mostaert. b, Landscape with Cows, by Aelbert Cuyp. c, Grain Field, by Jacob van Ruisdael. d, Path in Middelharnis, by Meindert Hobbema. e, Italian Landscape, by Hendrik Vogel. f, Normandy Landscape, by Andreas Schelfhout. g, Landscape with Canal, by Jan Toorop. h, Landscape, by Jan Sluijters. i, Kismet, by Michael Raedecker. j, Untitled painting, by Robert Zandvliet. Names of artwork and artist are on sheet margins adjacent to stamps.

2002, June 11	**Photo.**		**Perf. 14½**
1133	A432	Sheet of 10	9.25 6.25
a.-j.		39c Any single	.90 .50

A433

Die Cut Perf. 14¼

2002, July	**Coil Stamps**		**Photo.**
1134	A433	39c blue & red	.95 .50
1135	A433	78c green & red	1.90 .75

See Nos. 1157, 1173.

Souvenir Sheet

Amphilex 2002 Intl. Stamp Exhibition, Amsterdam — A434

No. 1136: a, One ship. b, Two ships.

2002, Aug. 30	**Litho.**		**Perf. 14x13½**
1136	A434	Sheet of 2	1.90 1.90
a.-b.		39c Either single	.95 .95

Dutch stamps, 150th anniv.; Dutch East India Company, 400th anniv.

Industrial Heritage A435

No. 1137: a, Spakenberg shipyard, 1696. b, Dedemsvaart lime kilns, 1820. c, Cruquius steam pumping station, 1849. d, Heerlen coal mine shaft, 1898. e, Hengelo salt pumping tower, 1918. f, Weidum windmotor, 1920. g, Zevenaar brick oven, 1925. h, Breda brewery, 1926. i, Water works, Tilburg, 1927. j, Schoonebeck oil well pump, 1947.

2002, Sept. 24			**Perf. 14½x14¾**
1137	A435	Sheet of 10	9.50 9.50
a.-j.		39c Any single	.95 .25

December Stamps — A436

No. 1138: a, Person, child, fence and trees. b, Man seated, trees. c, Head facing left. d, Red tree, person in black. e, Woman with white hair, tree. f, Person standing in grass. g, Man standing with legs crossed. h, Woman, windmill. i, Man on stool. j, Face with black lips. k, Man standing near tree, with bent knee. l, Man standing near trees, both hands in pockets. m, Two people seated. n, Person with black hair. o, Man with child on shoulders. p, Face, with black hair and eye looking right. q, Person with gold lips looking left. r, Head of person near shore. s, Person with sunglasses standing near shore. t, Woman with arms extended.

Serpentine Die Cut 13

2002, Nov. 26			**Photo.**
		Self-Adhesive	
1138	A436	Sheet of 20	12.00
a.-t.		29c Any single	.60 .25

Paintings by Vincent Van Gogh — A437

Designs: 39c, Self-portrait, 1886. 59c, Sunflowers, 1887. 75c, The Sower, 1888.

Die Cut Perf. 14¼

2003, Jan. 2			**Photo.**
		Booklet Stamps	
		Self-Adhesive	
1139	A437	39c multi	.95 .50
a.		Booklet pane of 10	9.50

Serpentine Die Cut 13¼ Syncopated

1140	A437	59c multi + etiquette	1.40 1.10
a.		Booklet pane of 5+5 etiquettes	7.00
1141	A437	75c multi + etiquette	1.75 1.50
a.		Booklet pane of 5+5 etiquettes	8.75

A row of rouletting separates stamps from the etiquettes.

Paintings by Vincent Van Gogh A438

No. 1142: a, Autumn Landscape with Four Trees, 1885. b, The Potato Eaters, 1885. c, Four Cut Sunflowers, 1887. d, Self-portrait with Gray Felt Hat, 1887-88. e, The Zouave, 1888. f, The Cafe Terrace on the Place du Forum, at Night, 1888. g, Pine Trees and Dandelions in the Garden of Saint-Paul Hospital, 1890. h, Blossoming Almond Tree, 1890. i, View of Auvers, 1890. j, Wheat Field with Crows, 1890.

2003, Jan. 2	**Litho.**		**Perf. 14½**
1142	A438	Sheet of 10	10.00 10.00
a.-j.		39c Any single	.95 .60

Water Control A439

No. 1143: a, North Pier, Ijmuiden, 1869. b, Hansweert Lock, 1865. c, Damming of the Wieringermeer, 1929. d, Ijsselmeer Dam (no date). e, Water breaching dike at Willemstad, 1953. f, Repairing dike at Stavenisse, 1953. g, Damming of the Zandkreek, 1960. h, Damming of the Grevelingen, 1964. i, Oosterschelde flood barrier, 1995. j, High water in Roermond, 1993.

2003, Feb. 1			**Photo.**
1143	A439	Sheet of 10	8.75 8.75
a.-j.		39c Any single	.85 .60

Johann Enschedé and Sons, Printers, 300th Anniv. — A440

No. 1144: a, Binary code, mathematics symbols. b, Fleischman's musical notation symbols.

Litho. & Embossed

2003, Mar. 4   Perf. 14x12¾
1144	A440	Horiz. pair	1.60 1.00
a.-b.		39c Either single	.80 .50

No. 1144a has photogravure back printing that can be seen through blank triangle on face of stamp.

Souvenir Sheets

Island Fauna A441

No. 1145: a, Eurasian oyster catcher and pilings. b, Spoonbill, horiz. c, Eider. d, Harbor seal, horiz.
No. 1146: a, Sea gull. b, Stone curlew, horiz. c, Gull and seals. d, Crab, horiz.

2003, May 6   Litho.   Perf. 14½
1145	A441	Sheet of 4	4.25 4.25
a.-d.		39c Any single	.90 .60
1146	A441	Sheet of 4	5.25 5.25
a.-d.		59c Any single	1.25 .80

A442

Personalized Stamps — A443

No. 1147: a, Flowers. b, Flag. c, Gift. d, Martini glass. e, Medal. f, Guitar. g, Balloons. h, Paper cut-outs. i, Cake. j, Party hat.
No. 1148 — Numeral color: a, Bright blue. b, Dull green. c, Lilac. d, Red violet. e, Dull orange. f, Yellow green. g, Olive. h, Dull blue. i, Red. j, Orange brown.

Perf. 13½x12¾

2003, May 20   Photo.
1147	A442	Sheet of 10 + 10 labels	9.00 9.00
a.-j.		39c Any single	.90 .25
1148	A443	Sheet of 10 + 10 labels	9.00 9.00
a.-j.		39c Any single	.90 .25

Labels could be personalized for an additional fee.

Douwe Egberts Co., 250th Anniv. — A444

2003, June 3   Litho.   Perf. 14½x14¾
1149		39c Spotted cup	.95 .45
1150		39c White cup	.95 .45
a.		A444 Horiz. pair, #1149-1150	1.90 1.90

Land, Air and Water A445

2003, June 24
1151		39c Airplane at UL	.95 .45
1152		39c Fish at LR	.95 .45
a.		A445 Horiz. pair, #1151-1152	1.90 .90

Nelson Mandela, 85th Birthday, and Nelson Mandela Children's Fund — A446

2003, July 18
1153		39c Mandela	.95 .45
1154		39c Children's Fund	.95 .45
a.		A446 Horiz. pair, #1153-1154	1.90 .90

"From Me to You" — A447

Die Cut Perf. 14¼x14½

2003, Sept. 1   Photo.

Booklet Stamp
Self-Adhesive
1155	A447	39c multi	.90 .50
a.		Booklet pane of 5	4.50

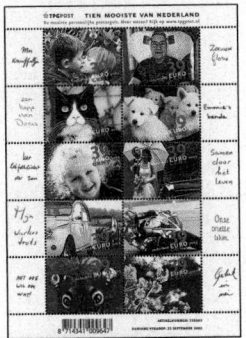

Photographs — A448

No. 1156: a, Children kissing. b, Woman. c, Cat. d, Puppies. e, Girl. f, Bride and groom. g, Automobiles. h, Motorcycle race. i, Butterfly. j, Flowers and sky.

Perf. 14½x14¾

2003, Sept. 23   Litho.
1156	A448	Sheet of 10	9.50 9.50
a.-j.		39c Any single	.90 .65

Numeral Type of 2002
Die Cut Perf. 13½

2003, Oct. 2   Photo.

Self-Adhesive
Stamp + Label
1157	A433	39c Prus bl & red	1.15 .75

No. 1157 has "2003" year date and was printed in sheets of 50 stamps + 50 labels. Labels could be personalized for an additional fee.

Stamp Collecting — A449

2003, Oct. 20   Litho.   Perf. 14½x14¾
1158	A449	39c multi	.95 .50

A booklet containing 2 booklet panes of 4 #1158 and three different imperf incomplete progressive proofs of these panes sold for €9.95.

A450

December Stamps — A451

Designs: No. 1159, Five-pointed star.
No. 1160: a, Family. b, Open gift box. c, Cat and dog. d, Christmas tree. e, Toast. f, Bell. g, Hand with pencil. h, Head of reindeer. i, Hand with flower. j, Holly leaf and berries. k, Candle. l, Eight-pointed star. m, Man and woman. n, Snowman. o, Fireplace. p, Angel. q, Man and woman dancing. r, Round Christmas ornament. s, Mother and child. t, Treetop ornament.

Perf. 13½x12¾

2003, Nov. 25   Litho.
1159	A450	29c multi + label	.75 .75

Photo.
Self-Adhesive
Serpentine Die Cut 13
1160	A451	Sheet of 20	15.00
a.-t.		29c Any single	.60 .25

No. 1159 was printed in sheets of 10 stamps + 10 labels. Labels could be personalized. No. 1160 is printed with panel of thermochromic ink which reveals a message when warmed.

Queen Beatrix and Family A452

No. 1161: a, Princess Beatrix as infant with Queen Juliana and Prince Bernhard, 1938. b, Princess Beatrix playing on swings with Princess Irene, 1943. c, Princess Beatrix with horse, 1951. d, Princess Beatrix reading book, 1964. e, Princess Beatrix talking with Prince Claus, 1965. f, Princess Beatrix, Prince Claus and infant Prince Willem-Alexander, 1967. g, Princess Beatrix, Prince Claus and three young sons, 1975. h, Queen Beatrix and Prince Claus dancing, 1998. i, Royal Family, 1999. j, Queen at art exhibition, 2000.

2003, Dec. 9   Photo.   Perf. 14¼
1161	A452	Sheet of 10	9.50 9.50
a.-j.		39c Any single	.95 .60

A booklet containing five panes each with two horizontally adjacent stamps from Nos. 1161a-1161j, in perf 13½x13¾, sold for €9.95.

Souvenir Sheet

Birth of Princess Catharina-Amalia — A453

2003, Dec. 16   Litho.   Perf. 13¾
1162	A453	39c multi	1.00 .75

See footnote below No. 1174.

Paintings — A454

Designs: 61c, Woman Reading a Letter, by Gabriel Metsu. 77c, The Letter, by Jan Vermeer.

Serpentine Die Cut 13 Horiz. Syncopated

2004, Jan. 2   Photo.

Booklet Stamps
Stamp + Detachable Etiquette
1163	A454	61c multi	1.20 .50
a.		Booklet pane of 5	6.00
1164	A454	77c multi	1.45 .65
a.		Booklet pane of 5	7.25

Royal Netherlands Meteorological Institute, 150th Anniv. — A455

Designs: No. 1165, Rain (rainbow at left). No. 1166, Sun (rainbow at right).

2004, Jan. 31   Litho.   Perf. 14½x14¾
1165		39c multi	.80 .60
1166		39c multi	.80 .60
a.		A455 Horiz. pair, #1165-1166	2.00 .50

Retangles — A456

Die Cut Perf. 14¼

2004, Mar. 2   Photo.

Self-Adhesive
1167	A456	39c red & multi	.90 .60
1168	A456	78c green & multi	1.75 1.00

See Nos. 1263-1264.

Spyker Automobiles — A457

Designs: No. 1169, 1922 Spyker. No. 1170, 2003 Spyker C8 Double 12 R.

2004, May 10   Litho.   Perf. 14½
1169		39c multi	.90 .65
1170		39c multi	.90 .65
a.		A457 Horiz. pair, #1169-1170	1.80 1.80

A booklet containing four panes of perf 13¼x13 stamps (one pane of two No. 1169, one pane of two No. 1170, two panes containing two each of Nos. 1169-1170) sold for €9.95.

Expansion of European Union — A458

No. 1171 — Map, flag and stamps of new European Union members: a, Czech Republic. b, Lithuania. c, Estonia. d, Poland. e, Malta. f, Hungary. g, Latvia. h, Slovakia. i, Cyprus. j, Slovenia.

2004, May 10   Perf. 14½
1171	A458	Sheet of 10	10.00 10.00
a.-j.		39c Any single	.90 .75

Numeral
A459

Perf. 13½x12¾

2004, June 1 **Photo.**
1172 A459 39c multi + label .95 .70
Labels could be personalized.

Numeral Type of 2002
2004, June 23 *Die Cut Perf. 13½*
Self-Adhesive
Stamp + Label

1173 A433 39c org red & blue 1.10 1.10
No. 1173 has "2004" year date and has Olympic Torch Relay label.

Miniature Sheet

Prince Willem-Alexander, Princess Máxima and Princess Catharina-Amalia — A460

No. 1174: a, Prince Willem-Alexander and Princess Máxima announcing engagement. b, Princess Máxima showing engagement ring. c, Prince Willem-Alexander (without hat) and Princess Máxima looking at each other at wedding ceremony. d, Prince Willem-Alexander and Princess Máxima looking ahead at wedding ceremony. e, Prince Willem-Alexander and Princess Máxima kissing. f, Prince Willem-Alexander (with hat) looking at Princess Máxima. g, Prince Willem-Alexander and Princess Máxima looking at Princess Catharina-Amalia. h, Prince Willem-Alexander and Princess Máxima looking at book, Princess Máxima holding Princess Catharina-Amalia. i, Baptism of Princess Catharina-Amalia. j, Clergyman holding ceremony notes and touching head of Princess Catharina-Amalia at baptism.

2004, June 23 **Litho.** **Perf. 13¾**
1174 A460 Sheet of 10 9.50 9.50
a.-j. 39c Any single .90 .65

A booklet containing five panes, each with two horizontally adjacent stamps of Nos. 1174a-1174j, and a booklet pane of No. 1162, sold for €9.95.

Veluwe Nature Park A461

No. 1175: a, Rabbit. b, Bird. c, Doe. d, Boar. No. 1176: a, Fox. b, Woodpecker. c, Buck. d, Ram.

2004, July 6 **Photo.** **Perf. 13¼x12¾**
1175 A461 Sheet of 4 4.50 4.50
a.-d. 39c Any single 1.00 .40
1176 A461 Sheet of 4 + 4 etiquettes 5.50 5.50
a.-d. 61c Any single 1.25 .50

Souvenir Sheet

Greeting Card Week A462

No. 1177: a, Pen nib. b, Hand. c, Head.

Perf. 13¼x13¾
2004, Sept. 1 **Photo.**
1177 A462 Sheet of 3 + 2 labels 2.50 2.50
a.-c. 39c Any single .80 .60

Paintings by Carel Fabritius (1622-54) — A463

No. 1178: a, Mercurius en Argus, c. 1645-47. b, Self-portrait, c. 1645. c, Mercurius en Aglauros, c. 1645-47. d, Abraham de Potter, 1649. e, Hagar en de Engel, c. 1643-45. f, De Schildwacht, c. 1654. g, Hera, c. 1643. h, Self-portrait, 1654. i, Self-portrait, c. 1647-48. j, Het Puttertje, 1654.

2004, Sept. 24 **Litho.** **Perf. 14½**
1178 A463 Sheet of 10 12.00 12.00
a.-f. 39c Any single .90 .70
g.-j. 78c Any single 1.60 1.25

Snowman A464

December Stamps A465

No. 1180: a, Shadows. b, People with gifts. c, Girl and dog. d, Children. e, Sheep. f, Polar bears. g, Children making snowman. h, People dragging Christmas tree. i, Man and woman in water. j, People around Christmas tree.

Perf. 13½x12¾
2004, Nov. 25 **Litho.**
1179 A464 29c multi + label .85 .85
Photo.
Self-Adhesive
Serpentine Die Cut 12¾x13¼
1180 Block of 10 8.00
a.-j. A465 29c Any single .80 .25

Hearts — A466

Serpentine Die Cut 14¼
2005, Jan. 3 **Photo.**
Self-Adhesive
1181 A466 39c multi 1.00 .25
a. Booklet pane of 10 10.00
See No. 1262.

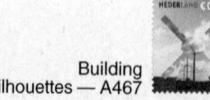

Building Silhouettes — A467

Designs: 39c, Windmill and field. 65c, House and brick wall. 81c, Greenhouse and field.

Serpentine Die Cut 14¼
2005, Jan. 3 **Self-Adhesive**
1182 A467 39c multi 1.00 .25
a. Booklet pane of 10 10.00
Serpentine Die Cut 13¼ Horiz. Syncopated
1183 A467 65c multi + etiquette 1.75 .45
a. Booklet pane of 5 8.75

1184 A467 81c multi + etiquette 2.10 .50
a. Booklet pane of 5 10.50
Nos. 1182-1184 (3) 4.85 1.20
On Nos. 1183 and 1184 a row of rouletting separates stamp from etiquette.

Netherlands Views — A468

2005 **Litho.** **Perf. 14¼**
1185 A468 39c shown 1.00 .25
1186 A468 39c Nijmegen 1.00 .25
1187 A468 39c Rotterdam 1.00 .25
1188 A468 39c Weesp 1.00 .25
1189 A468 39c Monnickendam .95 .25
1190 A468 39c Goes .95 .25
1191 A468 39c Boalsert 1.00 .25
1192 A468 39c Amsterdam 1.00 .25
1193 A468 39c Roermond .95 .25
a. Souvenir sheet, #1186, 1187, 1190, 1192, 1193 5.00 5.00
1194 A468 39c Papendrecht .95 .25
a. Souvenir sheet, #1185, 1188, 1189, 1191, 1194 5.00 5.00
Nos. 1185-1194 (10) 9.80 2.50

Issued: Nos. 1185-1186, 2/8; Nos. 1187-1188, 4/12; Nos. 1189-1190, 6/14. Nos. 1191-1192, 8/9; Nos. 1193-1194, 1193a, 1194a, 10/14.

A booklet containing five panes, each with the two stamps issued on the same day with perf. 13½x12¾, sold for €9.95.

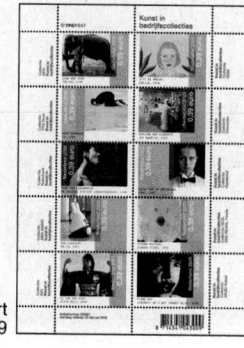

Art A469

No. 1195: a, Trying, by Liza May Post. b, Emilie, by Sidi El Karchi. c, ZT, by Koen Vermeule. d, Het Bedrijf, by Lieshout Studio. e, Me Kissing Vinoodh (Passionately), by Inez van Lamsweerde. f, Lena, by Carla van de Puttelaar. g, Nr. 13, by Tom Claasen. h, Untitled, by Pieter Kusters. i, Witte Roos, by Ed van der Kooy. j, Portrait of a Boy (Grand Prix), bu Tiong Ang.

2005, Feb. 25 **Litho.** **Perf. 14½**
1195 A469 Sheet of 10 10.00 10.00
a.-j. 39c Any single 1.00 .50

Business Symbols — A470

Die Cut Perf. 14¼
2005, Mar. 22 **Litho.**
Self-Adhesive
1196 A470 39c multi 1.00 .25

Souvenir Sheets

Natuurmonumenten, Cent. — A471

No. 1197: a, Cormorant. b, Dragonfly. c, Water lily. d, Fish.
No. 1198: a, Bird. b, Butterfly. c, Lizard. d, Sheep.

2005, Mar. 22 **Photo.** **Perf. 13¼x13**
1197 A471 Sheet of 4 4.00 4.00
a.-d. 39c Any single 1.00 .25
1198 A471 Sheet of 4 + 4 etiquettes 6.75 6.75
a.-d. 65c Any single 1.60 .40

A booklet containing four panes, each with two litho., perf 14x13¾ stamps like Nos.

1197a-1197d and 1198a-1198d, sold for €9.95.

Souvenir Sheet

Queen Beatrix, 25th Anniv. of Reign A472

Photos: a, Coronation, 1980. b, Giving speech, 1991. c, With Nelson Mandela, 1999. d, Visiting colonies, 1999. e, At European Parliament, 2004.

2005, Apr. 30 **Litho.** **Perf. 13¼x13¾**
1199 A472 Sheet of 5 16.00 16.00
a. 39c multi 1.00 .25
b. 78c multi 2.00 .50
c. 117c multi 3.00 .75
d. 156c multi 4.00 1.00
e. 225c multi 6.00 1.50
f. Booklet pane of 1, #1199a 1.75
g. Booklet pane of 1, #1199b 3.25 —
h. Booklet pane of 1, #1199c 5.00 —
i. Booklet pane of 1, #1199d 6.50 —
j. Booklet pane of 1, #1199e 9.50 —
Complete booklet, #1199f-1199j 26.00

Complete booklet sold for €9.95.

Numerals — A473

Die Cut Perf. 14¼
2005, May 24 **Photo.**
Coil Stamps
Self-Adhesive
1200 A473 39c bronze .95 .25
1201 A473 78c silver 1.90 .50

Souvenir Sheet

Greeting Card Week A474

No. 1202: a, Red background, denomination in white. b, Yellow background, denomination in red. c, Blue background, denomination in red.

2005, Sept. 1 **Litho.** **Perf. 13½x13¾**
1202 A474 Sheet of 3 + 2 labels 3.00 3.00
a.-c. 39c Any single 1.00 .25

Farm Technology — A475

Sheep and: No. 1203, Dutch windmills. No. 1204, Chinese water wheel.

2005, Sept. 22 **Litho.** **Perf. 14½**
1203 81c multi 2.00 .50
1204 81c multi 2.00 .50
a. A475 Horiz. pair, #1203-1204 4.00 1.00
See People's Republic of China Nos. 3452-3453.

World Press Photo, 50th Anniv. A476

No. 1205 — Silver Camera award-winning news photographs by: a, Douglas Martin, 1957. b, Héctor Rondón Lovera, 1962. c, Co Rentmeester, 1967. d, Hanns-Jörg Anders, 1969. e, Ovie Carter, 1974. f, David Burnett, 1979. g, Anthony Suau, 1987. h, Georges Merillon, 1990. i, Claus Bjorn Larsen, 1999. j, Arko Datta, 2004.

2005, Oct. 8 **Litho.**
1205 A476 Sheet of 10 9.50 9.50
a.-j. 39c Any single .95 .25

Trains — A477

Designs: No. 1206, Blue Angel. No. 1207, Locomotive 3737. No. 1208, ICE. No. 1209, Koploper.

2005, Oct. 14   **Litho.**

1206	A477	39c blue & multi	.95	.25
1207	A477	39c green & multi	.95	.25
1208	A477	39c red & multi	.95	.25
1209	A477	39c yel & multi	.95	.25
a.		Block of 4, #1206-1209	3.80	1.00

A478

December Stamps — A479

No. 1211: a, Flames and hearts. b, Gifts. c, Comets. d, Bells. e, Doves. f, Snowmen. g, Ornaments. h, Ice skates. i, Christmas trees. j, Champagne flutes.

Perf. 13½x12¾

2005, Nov. 24   **Litho.**

1210	A478	29c multi + label	.70	.25

Photo.

1211	A479	Sheet of 10	7.00	7.00
a.-j.		29c Any single	.70	.25

Labels on No. 1210 could be personalized for a fee.

Modern Art — A480

No. 1212: a, Koe in de Optrekkende Avondmist, by Ed van der Elsken. b, Double Dutch, by Berend Strik. c, Hollandse Velden, by Hans van der Meer. d, Tomorrow, by Marijke van Warmerdam. e, A Day in Holland/Holland in a Day, by Barbara Visser. f, Composite mit Rode Ruit, by Daan van Golden. g, Untitled work, by J. C. J. Vanderhayden. h, De Groene Kathedraal, by Mariana Boozem. i, Hollandpan, by John Körmerling. j, Drijfbeeld, by Atelier Van Lieshout.

No. 1213: a, Study for Horizon, by Sigurdur Gudmundsson. b, Lost Luggage Depot, by Jeff Wall. c, 11,000 Tulipes, by Daniel Buren. d, Flets & Stal, by FAT. e, Double Sunset, by Olafur Eliasson.

No. 1214: a, Untitled, by Dustin Larson. b, Working Progress, by Tadashi Kawamata. c, Boerderijgezichten, by Sean Snyder. d, Toc Toc, by Amalia Pica. e, Freude, by Rosemarie Trockel.

Serpentine Die Cut 14¼

2006, Jan. 2   **Litho.**

Self-Adhesive

1212		Booklet pane of 10	9.50	
a.-j.	A480	39c Any single	.95	.25

Serpentine Die Cut 13 Vert. Syncopated

1213		Booklet pane of 5 + 5 etiquettes	8.50	
a.-e.	A480	69c Any single + etiquette	1.60	.40
1214		Booklet pane of 5 + 5 etiquettes	10.50	
a.-e.	A480	85c Any single + etiquette	2.00	.50

On Nos. 1213 and 1214, a row of microrouletting separates stamps from etiquettes.

Queen Type of 1991
Die Cut Perf. 14¼ Syncopated

2006-09   **Photo.**

Self-Adhesive
Booklet Stamps

1216	A273	44c rose & ol grn	1.25	.25
a.		Booklet pane of 10	12.50	

Die Cut Perf. 14¼

1218	A273	44c rose & ol grn	1.25	.25
a.		Booklet pane of 10	12.50	
1219	A273	67c bl grn & blue	1.75	.30
a.		Booklet pane of 5	8.75	
1220	A273	74c gray grn & pur	2.10	.50
a.		Booklet pane of 5	10.50	
1221	A273	80c blue & red vio	2.00	.50
a.		Booklet pane of 5	10.00	
1223	A273	88c lilac & gray grn	2.40	.40
a.		Booklet pane of 5	12.00	
		Nos. 1216-1223 (6)	10.75	2.20

Issued: 80c, 1/2; 44c, 67c, 88c, 12/11; 74c, 1/2/09.

Netherlands Tourism Areas — A481

2006   **Litho.**   **Perf. 14½x14¼**

1240	A481	39c Leiden	.95	.25
1241	A481	39c Sittard	.95	.25
1242	A481	39c Vlieland	1.00	.25
1243	A481	39c Woudrichem	1.00	.25
1244	A481	39c Enkhuizen	1.00	.25
a.		Souvenir sheet, #1240-1244	5.00	5.00
1245	A481	39c Schoonhoven	1.00	.25
1246	A481	39c Zutphen	1.00	.25
1247	A481	39c Deventer	1.00	.25
1248	A481	39c Zwolle	1.00	.25
1249	A481	39c Kampen	1.00	.25
a.		Souvenir sheet, #1245-1249	5.00	5.00
		Nos. 1240-1249 (10)	9.90	2.50

Issued: No. 1240, 2/1; No. 1241, 2/3; No. 1242, 4/28; No. 1243, 5/24; Nos. 1244-1245, 6/2; Nos. 1246-1247, 8/4; Nos. 1248-1249, 9/1. Nos. 1244a, 1249a, 10/10.

A booklet containing five panes of one each of Nos. 1240-1241, 1242-1243, 1244-1245, 1246-1247, and 1248-1249 sold for €9.95.

Souvenir Sheet

Dutch Speed Skating Gold Medalists in the Winter Olympics — A482

No. 1250: a, Ard Schenk. b, Yvonne van Gennip.

Litho. With Three-Dimensional Plastic

2006, Feb. 10   *Serpentine Die Cut 9*

Self-Adhesive

1250	A482	Sheet of 2	1.90	
a.-b.		39c Either single	.95	.50

The two stamps and a top and bottom sheet margin are affixed to a sheet of backing paper. A booklet containing five examples of No. 1250 sold for €9.95.

Personalized Stamp — A483

2006, May 1   **Litho.**   **Perf. 13½x14**

1251	A483	39c multi	1.00	.25

No. 1251, showing Dutch soccer player Dirk Kuyt, sold for face value to the public and is the generic image for this stamp. Stamps depicting twenty other Dutch soccer players (Edwin van der Sar, Arjen Robben, Mark van Bommel, Ron Vlaar, Giovanni van Bronckhorst, Khalid Boulahrouz, Romeo Castelen, Jan Vennegoor of Hesselink, Urby Emanuelson, Ruud van Nistelrooy, Henk Timmer, Rafael van der Vaart, Hedwiges Maduro, Wesley Sneijder, Robin van Persie, Nigel de Jong, Barry Opdam, Joris Mathijsen, Denny Landzaat, and Phillip Cocu) were produced by postal authorities to sell as a special set for

---

€12.95 per sheet of 10 different players. Examples of No. 1251 with other images are personalized stamps that sold for €12.95 per sheet of 10 stamps.

Miniature Sheet

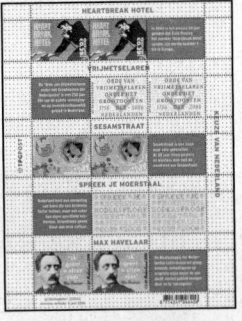

Stamps Chosen By the Public A484

No. 1252: a, Elvis Presley. b, Masonic emblem. c, Muppets Purk and Pino. d, Needlepoint design of sayings in languages used in Twente, Limburg and Friesland. e, Max Havelaar, fictional character.

2006, June 10   **Perf. 14½**

1252	A484	Sheet of 10, 2 each #a-e, + 17 labels	10.00	10.00
a.-e.		39c Any single	1.00	.25

Heartbreak Hotel, by Presley, 50th anniv., Dutch Grand Masonic Lodge, 250th anniv.; Dutch version of Sesame Street. 30th anniv.

Rembrandt (1606-69), Painter — A485

No. 1253: a, Bearded Man in Oriental Cape and Robe. b, Old Woman Seated at a Table. c, Saskia van Uylenburgh. d, Rembrandt's Son, Titus. e, Portrait of a Woman at the Window. €6.45, Self-portrait with Saskia.

2006, June 15   **Litho.**   **Perf. 13¾**

1253	A485	Block of 5 + label	5.00	5.00
a.-e.		39c Any single	1.00	.25

Souvenir Sheet
Litho. & Engr.
On Thin Card

1254	A485	€6.45 tan & black	17.00	17.00

See Germany No. 2387. A booklet containing two panes, each containing Nos. 1253a, 1253b, and 1253d, one pane of No. 1253c and Germany No. 2387, and one pane containing two No. 1253e, sold for €9.95. The booklet was withdrawn from sale after it was discovered that the German stamp in the booklet was printed with perforations and tagging without the authorization of German postal authorities, but most of the booklets produced had already been distributed. Value, $80.

Drawing by Karel Appel (1921-2006) — A486

2006, Sept. 1   **Litho.**   **Perf. 13¼x14**

1255	A486	39c multi	1.00	.25

A booklet containing five panes of 2 No. 1255 sold for €9.95.

Miniature Sheet

Endangered Animals — A487

No. 1256: a, Giraffe. b, Butterfly. c, Manchurian crane. d, Francois' leaf monkey. e, Blue poison dart frog. f, Red panda. g, Lowland gorilla. h, Sumatran tiger. i, Asian lion. j, Indian rhinoceros. k, Asian elephant. l, Pygmy hippopotamus.

2006, Oct. 4   **Perf. 13¾**

1256	A487	Sheet of 12	12.00	12.00
a.-l.		39c Any single	1.00	.25

A booklet containing one pane each of Nos. 1256a-1256c, 1256d-1256f, 1256g-1256i, and 1256j-1256l sold for €9.95.

Renaming of Postal Corporation as TNT Post — A488

2006, Oct. 16   **Litho.**   **Perf. 14½**

1257	A488	39c multi	1.00	.25

Snowflakes — A489

No. 1258: a, Small blue green, large dark blue flakes. b, Large pink, small red flakes. c, Small pink, large brown flakes. d, Large blue, small red flakes. e, Small blue green, large brown flakes. f, Small blue, large red flakes. g, Large green, small brown flakes. h, Small blue, large pink flakes. i, Large red, small brown flakes. j, Small pink, large blue green flakes.

Serpentine Die Cut 12¾x13¼

2006, Nov. 23   **Photo.**

Self-Adhesive

1258		Block of 10	7.75	
a.-j.	A489	29c Any single	.75	.25

Numeral and "NL" Type of 2002
Perf. 14¼x13½

2006, Dec. 11   **Photo.**

1259	A427	3c brown	.25	.25

Birth Announcement Type of 1997
Serpentine Die Cut 13¼x12¾

2006, Dec. 11   **Photo.**

Self-Adhesive

1260	A363	44c multi	1.25	.30

Death Announcement Type of 1997
Serpentine Die Cut 13¼

2006, Dec. 11   **Photo.**

Self-Adhesive

1261	A365	44c multi	1.25	.30

Hearts Type of 2005
Serpentine Die Cut 14½x14¼

2006, Dec. 11   **Litho.**

Self-Adhesive

1262	A466	44c multi	1.25	.30
a.		Booklet pane of 10	12.50	

Rectangles Type of 2004
Die Cut Perf. 14¼x14½

2006, Dec. 11   **Photo.**

Self-Adhesive

1263	A456	44c multi	1.25	.30
1264	A456	88c multi	2.40	.40

Dutch Products — A490

No. 1265: a, Glide glass goblet. b, Revolt chair. c, Heineken beer bottle. d, Bugaboo stroller. e, Lapin kettle. f, Milk bottle lamp. g, Carrier bicycle. h, Fluorescent screw-bottom lightbulb. i, Unox smoked sausage. j, Tulip. 72c, Clap skates. 89c, Cheese slicer.

Die Cut Perf. 14¼

2006, Dec. 11		**Photo.**	
Self-Adhesive			
1265	Booklet pane of 10	12.50	
a.-j.	A490 44c Any single	1.25	.25

Serpentine Die Cut 11

1266	A490 72c multi + etiquette	1.90	.30
a.	Booklet pane of 5 + 5 etiquettes	9.50	
1267	A490 89c multi + etiquette	2.40	.40
a.	Booklet pane of 5 + 5 etiquettes	12.00	

On Nos. 1266-1267, a row of microrouletting separates stamps from etiquettes.

Numerals — A491

2007, Jan. 2	*Die Cut Perf. 14¼x14½*		
Self-Adhesive			
1268	A491 44c multi	1.25	.30
a.	Serpentine die cut 13½ + label	1.25	.30
1269	A491 88c multi, vert.	2.40	.40

The generic label on No. 1268a depicts a mailbox. These labels could be personalized for an additional fee.

A492

Personalized Stamps — A493

2007	**Litho.**	**Perf. 14x13½**	
1270	A492 44c multi	1.25	.30

Self-Adhesive

Serpentine Die Cut 13¼x13

1271	A493 44c multi	1.25	.30

Issued: No. 1270, 1/2; No. 1271, 9/21. The generic vignettes of Nos. 1270 (Royal Dutch Mint), and 1271 (Mathematician L. E. J. Brouwer), which sold for face value, are shown. These stamps, printed in sheets of 10, could be personalized with horizontal or vertical images for an additional fee.

Netherlands Tourism Areas — A494

2007	**Litho.**	**Perf. 14½x14¼**	
1272	A494 44c Gouda	1.25	.30
1273	A494 44c Groningen	1.25	.30
1274	A494 44c Vlissingen	1.25	.30
1275	A494 44c Hoorn	1.25	.30
1276	A494 44c Leerdam	1.25	.30
1277	A494 44c Den Helder	1.25	.30
1278	A494 44c Lelystad	1.25	.30
1279	A494 44c Den Haag (The Hague)	1.25	.30
a.	Souvenir sheet, #1274-1275, 1277-1279	6.25	6.25
1280	A494 44c Utrecht	1.25	.30
1281	A494 44c Edam	1.25	.30
a.	Souvenir sheet, #1272-1273, 1276, 1280-1281	6.25	6.25
	Nos. 1272-1281 (10)	12.50	3.00

Issued: Nos. 1272-1273, 2/7; No. 1274, 3/23; No. 1275, 3/26; No. 1276, 4/13; No. 1277, 7/24; No. 1278, 8/8; No. 1279, 8/15. Nos. 1279a, 1281a, 10/17; No. 1280, 10/3; No. 1281, 10/10. A booklet containing five panes of one each of Nos. 1272-1273, 1274-

1275, 1276-1277, 1278-1279, and 1280-1281 in perf. 13½x12½ sold for €9.95.

Trees in Spring A495

Trees in Summer A496

Trees in Autumn A497

Trees in Winter A498

Designs: No. 1282, Lime tree. No. 1283, Horse chestnut bud. No. 1284, Bark of plane tree. No. 1285, Oak tree. No. 1286, Maple samaras. No. 1287, Trunk and branches of beech tree. No. 1288, Black alder tree. No. 1289, White willow tree in water.

2007	**Litho.**	**Perf. 14½**	
1282	44c multi	1.25	.30
1283	44c multi	1.25	.30
a.	A495 Horiz. pair, #1282-1283	2.50	.60
1284	44c multi	1.25	.30
1285	44c multi	1.25	.30
a.	A496 Horiz. pair, #1284-1285	2.50	.60
1286	44c multi	1.25	.30
1287	44c multi	1.25	.30
a.	A497 Horiz. pair, #1286-1287	2.50	.60
1288	44c multi	1.25	.30
1289	44c multi	1.25	.30
a.	A498 Horiz. pair, #1288-1289	2.50	.60
	Nos. 1282-1289 (8)	10.00	2.40

Issued: Nos. 1282-1283, 3/23; Nos. 1284-1285, 6/21; Nos. 1286-1287, 9/21; Nos. 1288-1289, 11/12.

Miniature Sheet

Flowers A499

No. 1290: a, Yellow and white toadflax at L, blue lobelia at R, red pinks at LR. b, Blue lobelias and white petunia. c, Yellow and white toadflax at UL, red pinks at UR and LL, sky at LR. d, Red snapdragon at UL, blue lobelia at top, white petunias at UR, red and white petunias at bottom, sky at LL. e, Red pinks at top, white toadflax at UL and LL, sky at R. f, Red and white petunias at R, sky at left. g, White toadflax at L, pink snapdragons at LR, sky at UR. h, Red and white petunia at top, pink snapdragons at LL, red violet toadflax at LR, sky at UL. i, White toadflax at UL, red and white snapdragons at UR, white and red pinks at LL. j, Red violet toadflax.

Litho & Embossed

2007, May 1		**Perf. 13½**	
1290	A499 Sheet of 10	15.00	15.00
a.-h.	44c Any single	1.25	.30
i.-j.	88c Any single	2.50	.30

Flower seeds are sealed under a round piece of adhesive tape in the embossed circle in the center of the stamps. The left and right sheet selvage contains instructions on planting the stamps and seeds. A booklet containing five panes, each containing one of the five horizontal pairs of stamps from the sheet and the adjacent selvage, sold for €9.95.

Europa A500

2007, July 26	**Litho.**	**Perf. 13½**	
1291	72c Moon	2.00	.50
1292	72c Sun	2.00	.50
a.	A500 Pair, #1291-1292	4.00	1.00

Scouting, cent. Printed in sheets of 10. Sheet margins inscribed "Priority" serve as etiquettes. A booklet containing three different panes, each containing a horizontal pair and two etiquettes, sold for €9.95.

Greeting Card Weeks — A501

2007, Sept. 3		**Perf. 13¾**	
1293	A501 44c multi	1.25	.30

Printed in sheets of 3.

Kingdom of the Netherlands, Bicent. — A502

Litho. & Embossed

2007, Sept. 11		**Perf. 13¼**	
Booklet Stamp			
1294	A502 €6.45 multi	29.00	15.00
	Complete booklet	29.00	

No. 1294 was sold only in a booklet pane of one stamp in a booklet containing one pane, which sold for €9.95.

A503   A504

A505   A506

A507   A508

A509   A510

Snowflakes and Trees A511   A512

A513   A514

A515   A516

A517   A518

A519   A520

A521   A522

Fireworks A521   A522

Serpentine Die Cut 12¾x13¼

2007, Nov. 22		**Photo.**	
Self-Adhesive			
1295	Block of 10	8.50	
a.	A503 29c multi	.85	.25
b.	A504 29c multi	.85	.25
c.	A505 29c multi	.85	.25
d.	A506 29c multi	.85	.25
e.	A507 29c multi	.85	.25
f.	A508 29c multi	.85	.25
g.	A509 29c multi	.85	.25
h.	A510 29c multi	.85	.25
i.	A511 29c multi	.85	.25
j.	A512 29c multi	.85	.25

Litho.

Serpentine Die Cut 12¾

1296	Block of 10	13.00	
a.	A513 29c multi, unscratched panel	1.25	.30
b.	A514 29c multi, unscratched panel	1.25	.30
c.	A515 29c multi, unscratched panel	1.25	.30
d.	A516 29c multi, unscratched panel	1.25	.30
e.	A517 29c multi, unscratched panel	1.25	.30
f.	A518 29c multi, unscratched panel	1.25	.30
g.	A519 29c multi, unscratched panel	1.25	.30
h.	A520 29c multi, unscratched panel	1.25	.30
i.	A521 29c multi, unscratched panel	1.25	.30
j.	A522 29c multi, unscratched panel	1.25	.30
k.-t.	#1296a-1296j, any single, scratched panel		.30

No. 1296 sold for €4.40, with €1.50 of the total going towards lottery prizes awarded to the sender of and mail recipient of stamps with prizes found under the scratch-off panel at the bottom of the stamps. Scratch-off panels are separated from the stamps by a row of rouletting.

Ecology — A523

No. 1297: a, Hybrid vehicle with electric plug. b, House and sun (solar energy). c, Cow with electric plug (biofuels). d, Wind generators. e, Trees. f, Flowers, carpoolers in automobile. g, "Groen" with electric plug. h, Truck (soot filters). i, Birds and envelope (green mail). j, Insulated house.

75c, Bicycle with globe hemispheres as wheels. 92c, Heart-shaped globe.

Die Cut Perf. 14¼

2008, Jan. 2   **Litho.**

Self-Adhesive

| 1297 | Booklet pane of 10 | 13.00 | |
| a.-j. | A523 44c Any single | 1.25 | .30 |

Photo.

Serpentine Die Cut 11

| 1298 | A523 75c multi + etiquette | 2.25 | .55 |
| 1299 | A523 92c multi + etiquette | 2.75 | .70 |

On Nos. 1298-1299 a row of microrouletting separates stamps from etiquettes.
See Nos. 1324-1325.

A524   A525

A526   A527

A528   A529

Personalized Stamps — A530

2008   **Litho.**   **Perf. 14x13½**

| 1300 | A524 44c multi | 1.25 | .30 |

Perf. 13½x14

| 1301 | A525 44c multi | 1.25 | .30 |

Perf. 13½x13, 13x13½

1302	Horiz. strip of 5	6.50	3.25
a.	A526 44c multi	1.25	.30
b.	A527 44c multi	1.25	.30
c.	A528 44c multi	1.25	.30
d.	A529 44c multi	1.25	.30
e.	A530 44c multi	1.25	.30

Issued: Nos. 1300-1301, 1/2; No. 1302, 3/18. The generic vignettes of Nos. 1300 (Netherlands Federation of Philatelic Associations, cent.), 1301 (Netherlands Association of Stamp Dealers, 80th anniv.), and 1302 (winning art for personalized stamp design contest), which sold for face value, are shown. These stamps, printed in sheets of 10, could be personalized for an additional fee. A booklet containing 5 panes of Nos. 1300-1301, each with different pane margins, sold for €9.95. Other booklets containing panes of Nos. 1300 or 1301 with different vignettes exist. These booklets usually sold for €9.95, and may contain fewer than ten stamps.

Netherlands Tourism Areas — A531

2008   **Litho.**   **Perf. 14½x14¼**

1303	A531 44c Sneek	1.40	.35
1304	A531 44c Coevorden	1.40	.35
1305	A531 44c Heusden	1.40	.35
1306	A531 44c Amersfoort	1.40	.35
1307	A531 44c Zoetermeer	1.40	.35
a.	Souvenir sheet of 5, #1303-1307	7.00	3.50
	Nos. 1303-1307 (5)	7.00	1.75

Issued: Nos. 1303-1304, 3/25; Nos. 1305-1306, 4/22; No. 1307, 6/3; No. 1307a, 6/12. A booklet containing five panes, with each pane containing two perf. 13½x12¾ examples of each stamp, sold for €9.95.

Europa — A532

2008, May 20   Litho.   Perf. 13½x12¾

| 1308 | A532 75c multi | 2.40 | .60 |
| a. | Tete-beche pair | 4.80 | 1.25 |

Sheet margins, inscribed "Priority," served as etiquettes.

Royal Netherlands Academy of Arts and Sciences, 200th Anniv. — A533

European Central Bank, 10th Anniv. — A534

AEX Stock Index, 25th Anniv. — A535

Bruna Bookshop Chain, 140th Anniv. — A536

Royal Dutch Tourist Board, 125th Anniv. — A537

2008, May 20   **Perf. 13¼x12¾**

1309	Vert. strip of 5	7.00	3.50
a.	A533 44c multi	1.40	.35
b.	A534 44c multi	1.40	.35
c.	A535 44c multi	1.40	.35
d.	A536 44c multi	1.40	.35
e.	A537 44c multi	1.40	.35

Souvenir Sheet

Rembrandt Association, 125th Anniv. — A538

2008, June 12   **Perf. 13¾**

| 1310 | A538 €6.65 multi | 21.00 | 10.50 |

Dutch Food Products — A539

Designs: No. 1311, Container of adobo seasoning mix, Madame Jeannette peppers, Edam cheese. No. 1312, Peas, can of condensed milk, papaya, vert. No. 1313, Ham, plantain, bottle of Ponche Pistachio liqueur, vert.

2008, July 8   **Perf. 13¾**

1311	A539 92c multi	3.00	.75
1312	A539 92c multi	3.00	.75
1313	A539 92c multi	3.00	.75
a.	Souvenir sheet of 5, #1311-1313, Aruba #330, Netherlands Antilles #1187, + 3 etiquettes, 144x75mm	9.00	4.50
b.	Booklet pane, as "a," 150x102mm	15.50	
	Complete booklet, 2 #1313b	31.00	
	Nos. 1311-1313 (3)	9.00	2.25

No. 1313a sold for €2.76. Complete booklet sold for €9.95. Nos. 1312-1313 were available only in Nos. 1313a and 1313b. No. 1311 was available in Nos. 1313a, 1313b, Aruba No. 332a, and Netherlands Antilles No. 1189a.

Miniature Sheet

Zodiac Constellations — A540

No. 1314: a, Ram (Aries). b, Stier (Taurus). c, Tweeling (Gemini). d, Kreeft (Cancer). e, Leeuw (Leo). f, Maagd (Virgo). g, Weegschaal (Libra). h, Schorpioen (Scorpio). i, Boogschutter (Sagittarius). j, Steenbok (Capricorn). k, Waterman (Aquarius). l, Vissen (Pisces).

2008, Sept. 1   Litho.   Perf. 13¾

| 1314 | A540 | Sheet of 12 | 15.00 | 15.00 |
| a.-l. | 44c Any single | | 1.25 | .30 |

Greeting Card Weeks — A541

2008, Sept. 1   **Perf. 14½**

| 1315 | A541 44c multi | 1.25 | .30 |

Printed in sheets of 3.

Gnomes — A542

Designs: No. 1316, Pinkeltje. No. 1317, Wipneus en Pim. No. 1318, Piggelmee. No. 1319, Paulus de boskabouter. No. 1320, De Kabouter.

2008, Oct. 1   **Perf. 13½x12¾**

1316	A542 75c multi	2.10	.50
1317	A542 75c multi	2.10	.50
1318	A542 75c multi	2.10	.50
1319	A542 75c multi	2.10	.50
1320	A542 75c multi	2.10	.50
a.	Vert. strip of 5, #1316-1320	10.50	2.50

Nos. 1316-1320 were printed in sheets of 10, containing two of each stamp. The other strip in the sheet is in a different stamp order and the two strips in the sheet are tete-beche.

Miniature Sheet

Mushrooms — A543

No. 1321 — Early and late stages of mushroom's life: a, Inktviszwam (early). b, Aardater (early). c, Vliegenzwam (early). d, Nestzwam (early). e, Inktzwam (early). f, Inktviszwam (late). g, Aardater (late). h, Vliegenzwam (late). i, Nestzwam (late). j, Inktzwam (late).

2008, Oct. 1   **Perf. 14½**

| 1321 | A543 | Sheet of 10 | 12.50 | 12.50 |
| a.-j. | 44c Any single | | 1.25 | .30 |

A booklet containing 5 panes, each showing a vertical pair from the sheet (same mushroom in different stages), sold for €9.95.

A544

December Stamps — A545

No. 1323: a, Building with large clock face and gift. b, Three dark envelopes, left half of Christmas tree. c, Right half of Christmas tree, top of ladder. d, Bell, Christmas tree. e, Building, gifts. f, Christmas tree, building with people on roof. g, Building, knife, fork and candle. h, House, bottom of ladder. i, Postcard, left side of fireplace. j, Right side of fireplace, fork and spoon.

Serpentine Die Cut 12

2008, Nov. 18   **Self-Adhesive**

1322	A544 34c multi	.90	.25
1323	A545 Block of 10	9.00	
a.-j.	34c Any single	.90	.25

The vignette of No. 1322 could be personalized for a fee.

Ecology Types of 2008

Designs: 77c, Bicycle with globe hemispheres as wheels. 95c, Heart-shaped globe.

Serpentine Die Cut 11

2009, Jan. 2   **Photo.**

Booklet Stamps

Self-Adhesive

1324	A523 77c multi + etiquette	2.25	.55
a.	Booklet pane of 5	11.50	
1325	A523 95c multi + etiquette	2.75	.70
a.	Booklet pane of 5	14.00	

On Nos. 1324-1325 a row of microrouletting separates stamps from etiquettes.

Miniature Sheet

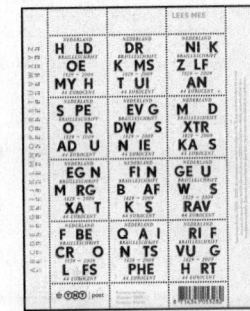

Braille Alphabet, 180th Anniv. — A546

No. 1326 — Letters (on front and back), and in Braille: a, Hulde roem mythe. b, Adres komst thuis. c, Uniek zelfs dank. d, Super zodra adieu. e, Hevig dwars naief. f, Moed extra kans. g, Begin marge exact. h, Afijn bekaf kus. i, Geluk wens bravo. j, Fabel credo liefs. k, Quasi niets ophef. l, Brief vurig hart.

Litho., Photo & Embossed

2009, Jan. 10   **Perf. 13¾**

1326	A546	Sheet of 12	14.00	14.00
a.-l.	44c Any single		1.10	.30
m.	Booklet pane of 3, #1326a-1326c	6.50	—
n.	Booklet pane of 3, #1326d-1326f	6.50	—
o.	Booklet pane of 3, #1326g-1326i	6.50	—
p.	Booklet pane of 3, #1326j-1326l	6.50	—
	Complete booklet, #1326m-1326p	26.00	

Louis Braille (1809-52), educator of the blind. Complete booklet sold for €9.95.

A547

Personalized Stamps — A548

Serpentine Die Cut 12

2009, Mar. 10			Litho.	
Self-Adhesive				
1327	A547	44c multi	1.25	.30
1328	A548	44c multi	1.25	.30

The generic vignettes of Nos. 1327 (Dutch Golf Federation) and 1328 (Dutch Stamp Collectors' Association), which sold at face value, are shown. These stamps, printed in sheets of 10, could be personalized for an additional fee. See Nos. 1300-1301 for perforated stamps having these frames.

Netherlands Tourism Areas — A549

2009			Litho.	Perf. 14½x14¼
1329	A549	44c Assen	1.25	.30
1330	A549	44c Tilburg	1.25	.30
1331	A549	44c Oosterhout	1.25	.30
1332	A549	44c Roosendaal	1.25	.30
1333	A549	44c Delfzijl	1.25	.30
a.	Souvenir sheet of 5, #1329-1333		6.25	3.25
	Nos. 1329-1333 (5)		6.25	1.50

Issued: Nos. 1329-1330, 3/10; Nos. 1331-1332, 4/28; No. 1333, 6/16; No. 1333a, 6/12. A booklet containing five panes, with each pane containing two perf. 13½x12¾ examples of each stamp, sold for €9.95.

Europa A550

Designs: No. 1334, Map of low frequency array radio telescopes superimposed on map of Europe. No. 1335, Sketch of Saturn and Titan, telescope lens of Christiaan Huygens.

2009, Apr. 7		Litho.	Perf. 13¼x12¾
1334		77c multi	2.10	.50
1335		77c multi	2.10	.50
a.	A550 Horiz. pair, #1334-1335	4.20	1.00

Intl. Year of Astronomy. Sheet margins serve as etiquettes. No. 1335 is upside-down in relation to No. 1334.

Souvenir Sheet

Queens Wilhelmina, Juliana and Beatrix — A551

2009, Apr. 28		Litho. & Engr.	Perf. 13¾
1336	A551	€7 multi	19.00	9.50
a.	Booklet pane of 1		27.00	—
	Complete booklet, #1336a		27.00	

Size of No. 1336a: 145x102mm. Complete booklet sold for €9.95.

Flasks, Artist's Mannequin, Party Streamer A552

Atlas Sheltering Figurines — A554

Window, Egg, Binoculars A553

Coffee Service — A555

Blocks, Pictures of Children — A556

2009, May 12		Photo.	Perf. 14½
1337		Vert. strip of 5	6.25	3.25
a.	A552	44c multi	1.25	.30
b.	A553	44c multi	1.25	.30
c.	A554	44c multi	1.25	.30
d.	A555	44c multi	1.25	.30
e.	A556	44c multi	1.25	.30

Dutch Cancer Society, 60th anniv. (No. 1337a); Netherlands Bird Protection Society, 110th anniv. (No. 1337b); Cordaid Mensen in Nood (Men in Need), 95th anniv. (No. 1337c); National Sunflower Society, 60th anniv. (No. 1337d); SOS Children's Village, 60th anniv. (No. 1337e).

Music A557

No. 1338: a, Tuba, trumpet and saxophone players. b, "When you sing you begin with Do Re Mi." c, Baton twirlers. d, "Jauchzet, frohlocket." e, Sousaphone players. f, "Para bailar la bamba."

2009, July 14		Litho.	Perf. 13½
1338	A557	Block of 6	13.50	6.75
a.-f.	77c Any single		2.25	.60

World Music Contest, Kerkrade and Europa Cantat, Utrecht. Printed in sheets of 10 containing Nos. 1338e, 1338f, and 2 each Nos. 1338a-1338d. Sheet margins served as etiquettes. Stamps showing text are upside-down in relation to stamps showing people.

Miniature Sheet

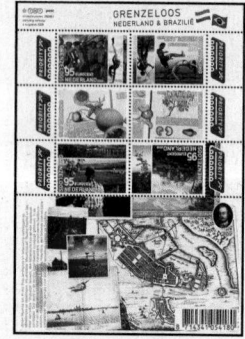

Dutch Connections With Brazil — A558

No. 1339: a, Tarairu Tribe War Dance, painting by Albert Eckhout, man standing on one hand. b, Capoeira performers, Tarairu tribesman. c, Passion fruit, and scientific book picturing passion fruit blossom. d, Cashews and scientific book picturing cashew tree. e, Sugar Plantation, painting by Frans Post; farmer looking at livestock. f, Church, Olinda, painting by Post; rose bush.

2009, Aug. 4			Perf. 13½x12¾
1339	A558	Sheet of 6	16.50	8.25
a.-f.	95c Any single		2.75	.70

No. 1339 was printed with three different illustrations in the bottom sheet margin, with each sheet having a different arrangement of stamps. Sheet margins at left and right served as etiquettes.

Athletes and Their Mentors — A559

No. 1340: a, Anthony van Assche, gymnast, and mentor Jochem Uytdehaage. b, Leon Commandeur, cyclist, and mentor Johan Kenkhuis. c, Mike Marissen, swimmer, and mentor Bas van de Goor. d, Maureen Groefsema, judoist, and mentor Lobke Berkhout. e, Aniek van Koot, wheelchair tennis player, and mentor Marko Koers.

2009, Aug. 25		Photo.	Perf. 14½
1340		Vert. strip of 5	6.25	3.25
a.-e.	A559 44c Any single		1.25	.30

Stichting Sporttop, Olympic athlete development organization.

Greeting Card Week — A560

2009, Sept. 7		Litho.	Perf. 14½
1341	A560	44c multi	1.40	.35

Miniature Sheets

Birthday Greetings — A561

"88" and: Nos. 1342a, 1343e, "Gefeliciteerd!" Nos. 1342b, 1343b, "Hoera!" Nos. 1342c, 1343c, "Proficiat!" Nos. 1342d, 1343d, "Nog Vele Jaren!" Nos. 1342e, 1343a, "Van Harte!"

2009, Sept. 22		Litho.	Perf. 13½
1342	A561	Sheet of 5	7.00	3.50
a.-e.	44c Any single		1.40	.35

Self-Adhesive
Serpentine Die Cut 13¼x13
Stamp Size: 20x25mm

1343	A561	Sheet of 5	7.00	
a.-e.	44c Any single		1.40	.35

Lines in the "88" on each stamp could be colored in to create all ten digits. Unused values are for stamps without any such alterations. Used values are for stamps with or without alterations.

A562

Personalized Stamps — A563

2009-10			Perf. 13¼
1344	A562	44c multi	1.40	.35

Self-Adhesive
Serpentine Die Cut 12½

1345	A563	44c multi	1.25	.30

Issued: No. 1344, 10/1; No. 1345, 1/12/10. The generic vignettes for Nos. 1344 (Stamp Day) and 1345 (Wadden Sea Society), which sold at face value, are shown. These stamps, printed in sheets of 10, could be personalized for an additional fee. A booklet containing five panes, each with two examples of No. 1344 with the Stamp Day vignette sold for €9.95.

Miniature Sheet

Powered Flight in the Netherlands, Cent. — A564

No. 1346: a, Medical helicopter. b, Boeing 747. c, Apache helicopter. d, Terminal B, Schiphol Airport. e, Fokker F-27. f, Lockheed Super Constellation. g, Fokker F-18 "Pelikaan." h, Douglas DC-2 "Uiver" in Melbourne race. i, Wright Flyer. j, Fokker Spin, piloted by Anthony Fokker.

2009, Oct. 1			Perf. 13½
1346	A564	Sheet of 10	14.00	7.00
a.-j.	44c Any single		1.40	.35

A booklet containing five panes, each with a different horizontal pair from No. 1346, sold for €9.95.

December Stamps — A565

No. 1347: a, Green gift, pink ribbon, red background. b, Candelabra on yellow gift, blue background. c, Christmas tree on light blue gift, bright yellow green background. d, Light pink gift, red ribbon, gray background. e, Woman holding glass on yellow gift, pink background. f, Man holding glass on yellow gift, gray background. g, Christmas tree on blue gift, pink background. h, Red violet gift, red ribbon, carmine background. i, Christmas tree on yellow gift, blue background. j, Christmas tree on blue gift, red background.

Serpentine Die Cut 12¾x13¼

2009, Nov. 19			Self-Adhesive
1347		Block of 10	10.00	
a.-j.	A565 34c Any single		1.00	.25

Netherlands Tourism Areas — A566

2010			Litho.	Perf. 14½x14¼
1348	A566	44c Haarlem	1.25	.35
1349	A566	44c Middelburg	1.25	.35
1350	A566	44c Maastricht	1.25	.35
1351	A566	44c Arnhem	1.25	.35
1352	A566	44c Leeuwarden	1.10	.30
a.	Souvenir sheet of 5, #1348-1352		6.25	3.25

Issued: Nos. 1348-1349, 1/12. Nos. 1350-1351, 3/29; Nos. 1352, 1352a, 6/22. A booklet containing five panes, with each pane containing two perf. 13½x12¾ examples of each stamp, sold for €9.95.

Miniature Sheet

Dutch Patent Act, Cent. A567

No. 1353: a, Submarine invented by Cornelis Drebbel, 1620. b, Light-emitting diode lighting invented by Philips, 2007. c, Artificial kidney invented by Willem Kolff, 1943. d, VacuVin vacuum sealer for wine bottles invented by Bernd Schneider. e, Milking robot invented by Van der Lely, 1987. f, Bicycle chain case invented by Wilhelmine J. van der Woerd. g, Automated handwriting recognition invented by TNT Post, 1980. h, Solar-powered vehicle invented by Solar Team Twente. i, Dyneema fiber invented by DSM, 1979. j, Telescope invented by Hans Lippershey, 1608.

2010, Feb. 9		Litho.	Perf. 13¼x12¾
1353	A567	Sheet of 10	12.50	6.25
a.-j.	44c Any single		1.25	.35

A booklet containing five panes, with each pane containing a horizontal pair from the sheet, sold for €9.95.

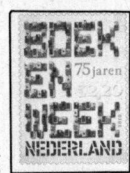

75th Book
Week — A568

2010, Mar. 9   Litho.   Imperf.
1354 A568 €2.20 multi   6.00 3.00

No. 1354 is printed as a miniature book made up of two pieces of paper of different sizes. Both pieces of paper are printed on both sides, and are glued together. The cover of the book is the longer of the two pieces of paper, and is folded into three parts. The stamp, the front cover of the book, is the middle part of this piece of paper. The gum, applied to the left of the stamp, becomes the book's back cover when the longer piece of paper is folded. A photograph of a man holding a book, is to the right of the stamp, and is the book's first page. Text appears on the reverse of this picture and the stamp, and another picture depicting a man reading a book is printed on the back of the gum. The second piece of paper, folded in half to constitute four pages of the book, has text only, and is glued to the back of longer sheet where the fold between the stamp and the photo is found. Values are for the complete item.

VVV, Dutch Tourist Information Office, 125th Anniv. — A569

Royal Tropical Institute, Cent. — A570

Duinrell Amusement Park, Wassenaar, 75th Anniv. — A571

Euromast Tower, Rotterdam, 50th Anniv. — A572

Djoser Travel, 25th Anniv. — A573

2010, Mar. 23   Photo.   Perf. 14½
1355   Vert. strip of 5   6.25 3.25
  a. A569 44c multi   1.25   .35
  b. A570 44c multi   1.25   .35
  c. A571 44c multi   1.25   .35
  d. A572 44c multi   1.25   .35
  e. A573 44c multi   1.25   .35

Greeting Card Weeks — A574

2010, Mar. 29   Litho.
1356 A574 44c multi   1.25   .35
  Printed in sheets of 3.

Souvenir Sheet

Breskens Lighthouse — A575

2010, Apr. 27   Perf. 13¾
1357 A575 €7 multi   19.00 9.50

Personalized Stamp — A576

2010, July 1   Litho.   Perf. 13½x14
1358 A576 1 gray & black   1.10   .30

The generic vignette of No. 1358, which sold for the franking value of 44c, and was printed in sheets of 10, is shown. The vignette part of the stamp could be personalized for an additional fee. Booklets containing stamps showing different vignettes that could not be personalized sold for €9.95.

Rectangles — A577

2010, July 1   Die Cut Perf. 14¼
Self-Adhesive
1359 A577 1 multi   1.10   .30
  Sold for 44c on day of issue. Compare with type A456.

Birth Announcement Stamp — A578

2010, July 1   Die Cut Perf. 14¼
Self-Adhesive
1360 A578 1 multi   1.10   .30
  Sold for 44c on day of issue.

Hearts — A579

2010, July 1   Die Cut Perf. 14¼
Self-Adhesive
1361 A579 1 multi   1.10   .30
  a.   Booklet pane of 10   11.00
  Sold for 44c on day of issue. Compare with type A466.

Death Announcement Stamp — A580

Serpentine Die Cut 11¾
2010, July 1   Photo.
Self-Adhesive
1362 A580 1 multi   1.10   .30
  Sold for 44c on day of issue. Compare with types A365 and A824.

Numerals
A581   A582

Serpentine Die Cut 13½
2010, July 1   Litho.
Self-Adhesive
1363 A581 1 multi + label   1.10   .30
Coil Stamps
Photo.
Die Cut Perf. 14¼
1364 A581 1 multi   1.10   .30
1365 A582 2 multi   2.25   .60
  On day of issue Nos. 1363-1364 each sold for 44c, and No. 1365 sold for 88c. Label on No. 1363 could be personalized. Compare with type A491.

Queen Beatrix With Large Numeral — A583

Die Cut Perf. 14¼ Syncopated
2010, July 1   Photo.
Booklet Stamps
Self-Adhesive
1366 A583 1 metallic blue & lil 1.10   .30
  a.   Booklet pane of 10   11.00
Die Cut Perf. 14¼
1367 A583 2 gold & metallic grn 2.25   .60
  a.   Booklet pane of 5   11.50
  On day of issue, No. 1366 sold for 44c and No. 1367 sold for 88c. Compare with Type A273.

A584

A585

Ecology — A586

No. 1368: a, Hybrid vehicle with electric plug. b, House and sun (solar energy). c, Cow with electric plug (biofuels). d, Wind generators. e, Trees. f, Flowers, carpoolers in automobile. g, "Groen" with electric plug. h, Truck (soot filters). i, Birds and envelope (green mail). j, Insulated house.

Die Cut Perf. 14¼
2010, July 1   Litho.
Booklet Stamps
Self-Adhesive
1368   Booklet pane of 10   11.00
  a.-j. A584 1 Any single   1.10   .30
Photo.
Serpentine Die Cut 11
1369 A585 1 Europa multi + etiquette 2.00   .50
  a.   Booklet pane of 5 + 5 etiquettes 10.00
1370 A586 1 Wereld multi + etiquette 2.40   .60
  a.   Booklet pane of 5 + 5 etiquettes 12.00
  On Nos. 1369-1370 a row of microrouletting separates stamps from etiquettes. On day of issue, Nos. 1368a-1368j each sold for 44c; No. 1369, for 77c; No. 1370, for 95c. Compare with type A523.

Miniature Sheet

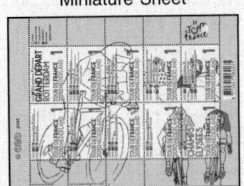

Start of 2010 Tour de France in Rotterdam — A587

No. 1371 — Dates and stages of the Tour de France: a, July 3 (preliminary stage). b, July 4-6 (stages 1-3). c, July 7-9 (stages 4-6). d, July 10-12 (stages 7-8). e, July 13-15 (stages 9-11). f, July 16-17 (stages 12-13). g, July 18-19 (stages 14-15). h, July 20-22 (stages 16-17). i, July 23-24 (stages 18-19). j, July 25 (stage 20).

2010, July 1   Photo.   Perf. 14½
1371   Sheet of 10   11.00 5.50
  a.-j.   1 Any single   1.10   .30
  On day of issue, Nos. 1371a-1371j each sold for 44c.

Miniature Sheet

Royal Dutch Forestry Association, Cent. — A588

No. 1372: a, Maple leaves, forest canopy, tip of jay's wing, "1" in white at LR. b, Maple leaves, forest canopy, "1" in brown at UL. c, Jay, forest canopy, "1" in brown at LR. d, Forest canopy, rose leaves, "1" in white at UL. e, Rose hips and leaves, "1" in white at LR. f, Rose leaves, tree trunks, "1" in brown at UL. g, Rose hips, logs, bracken leaves, "1" in brown at LR. h, Bracken leaves, logs, "1" in white at UL. i, Tree roots, moss, "1" in white at LR. j, Tree roots, mushrooms, "1" in brown at UL.

Perf. 13¼x12¾
2010, Aug. 17   A588   Litho.
1372 A588 Sheet of 10   12.50 6.25
  a.-j.   1 Any single   1.25   .35
  On day of issue, Nos. 1372a-1372j each sold for 44c. A booklet containing five panes, each showing a horizontal pair from the sheet, sold for €9.95.

Miniature Sheet

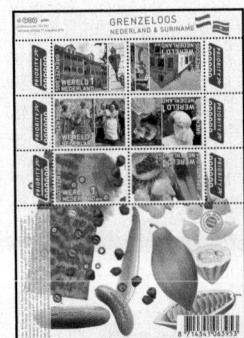

Dutch Connections With Surinam — A589

No. 1373: a, Building with balconies and dormers, lamp. b, Building with stairway, hand rail. c, Women in native dress. d, Two women, one upside-down. e, Wood, feathers, achiote seeds. f, Onions, achiote fruit, tobacco.

2010, Aug. 17   Litho.   Perf. 13½x13
1373 A589 Sheet of 6   15.00 7.50
  a.-f.   1 Wereld Any single 2.50   .65
  No. 1373 was printed with three different illustrations in the bottom sheet margin, with each sheet having a different arrangement of stamps. Sheet margins at left and right served as etiquettes. On day of issue Nos. 1373a-1373f each sold for 95c.

Personalized Stamp — A590

2010, Sept. 14 Litho. Perf. 13½x14
1374 A590 1 multi   1.25   .35
  The generic vignette shown on this stamp, commemorating Stamp Day, sold for 44c on day of issue. This stamp, printed in sheets of 10, could be personalized for an additional fee. A booklet containing five panes, each with two examples of No. 1374 with the generic vignette, sold for €9.95.

Woman and Windmill A591

Litho. With 3-Dimensional Plastic Affixed
Serpentine Die Cut 9x8¾
2010, Sept. 29   **Self-Adhesive**
1375   A591   5 multi   6.25   1.60
Sold for €2.20 on day of issue.

Stop AIDS Campaign — A592

No. 1376: a, African woman with "Stop AIDS Now!" poster on head. b, African woman, ribbon. c, Hand holding pill, ribbon. d, African woman pointing to ribbon. e, Ribbon, heads of African man and woman. f, African woman wearing headdress.

2010, Oct. 12   **Litho.**   *Perf. 14½*
1376   A592   Block of 6   7.50   3.75
   a.-f.   1 Any single   1.25   .35
Nos. 1376a-1376f each sold for 44c on day of issue.

Personalized Stamp — A593

2010, Nov. 23   **Litho.**   *Perf. 13½x14*
1377   A593   (34c) multi   .95   .25
The generic vignette shown on this stamp depicts Snoopy. This stamp, printed in sheets of 10, could be personalized for an additional fee.

December Stamps — A594

No. 1378: a, Santa Claus carrying tree. b, Bell and ribbon. c, Rocking horse and flowers. d, Embroidered heart. e, Deer, flower and candle on Christmas card. f, Deer and ribbon. g, Santa Claus. h, Handshake and flowers on Christmas card. i, Angel with flowers. j, Gingerbread house.

Serpentine Die Cut 12¾
2010, Nov. 23   **Self-Adhesive**
1378   Block of 10   9.50
   a.-j.   A594 (34c) Any single   .95   .25
   k.   Booklet pane of 10, #1378a-
       1378j   13.50
     Complete booklet, 2 #1378k   27.00
Complete booklet sold for €9.95.

Personalized Stamp — A595

Die Cut Perf. 13x13¼
2011, Jan. 10   **Litho.**
       Self-Adhesive
1379   A595   1 black   1.25   .35
The generic vignette of No. 1379 depicting St. John's Cathedral, 's Hertogenbosch, which sold for the franking value of 46c and printed in sheets of 10, is shown. The vignette part of the

---

stamp could be personalized for an additional fee.

Netherlands Tourism Areas — A596

2011   *Perf. 14½x14¼*
1380   A596   1 Almere   1.25   .35
1381   A596   1 Eindhoven   1.25   .35
1382   A596   1 Apeldoorn   1.40   .45
1383   A596   1 Breda   1.40   .45
1384   A596   1 Enschede   1.40   .45
   a.   Souvenir sheet of 5, #1380-
      1384   6.75   3.50
    Nos. 1380-1384 (5)   6.70   2.05
Issued: Nos. 1380-1381, 1/10; Nos. 1382-1383, 4/11; Nos. 1384, 1384a, 5/23. On day of issue, Nos. 1380-1384 each sold for 46c. A booklet containing five panes, with each pane containing two perf. 13½x12¾ examples of each stamp, sold for €9.95.

Personalized Stamp — A597

2011, Jan. 31   *Perf. 13¾*
1385   A597   1 multi   1.25   .35
The generic vignette of No. 1385 depicting a great tit, which sold for the franking value of 46c and printed in sheets of 10, is shown. The vignette part of the stamp could be personalized for an additional fee. Numerous stamps depicting different birds in the vignette were created after Jan. 31 by postal authorities. An electronic audio pen which sold for €39.95 would play the song of the bird when placed near the stamp. Numerous stamps depicting recording artists in the vignette began appearing in 2012.

Miniature Sheet

Utrecht University, 375th Anniv. — A598

No. 1386 — Various anniversaries at Utrecht University: a, 90th anniv. of psychology studies (brain). b, 100th anniv. of Unitas Student Society (owl). c, 65th birthday of Gerard t'Hooft. 1999 Nobel Physics laureate (t'Hooft). d, 125th anniv. of Utrecht University Foundation (globe). e, 50th anniv. of Utrecht Science Park de Uithof (aerial view of park). f, 190th anniv. of veterinary medicine program (horse). g, 45th anniv. of Institute of Theater Studies (theater spotlight). h, 250th anniv. of death of Petrus van Musschenbroek, professor of mathematics and philosophy (van Musschenbroek). i, 25th anniv. of Mebiose Student Association for the Biological Sciences (stylized DNA molecule). j, 325th anniv. of Senaatzaal Portrait Gallery (Senaatzaal).

2011, Mar. 28   *Perf. 13¼x12¾*
1386   A598   Sheet of 10   14.00   7.00
   a.-j.   1 Any single   1.40   .45
Nos. 1386a-1386j each sold for 46c on day of issue. A booklet containing 5 panes, each containing a horizontal pair of stamps on the sheet, sold for €9.95.

Miniature Sheet

City of the Netherlands — A599

No. 1387 — Inscriptions in bold type: a, Kenniscluster, Arnhem (black-framed code box). b, Kenniscluster, Arnhem (building). c, Parkeertoren Nederland (black-framed code box). d, Parkeertoren Nederland (building). e, De Boekenberg, Spijkenisse (black-framed code box). f, Skytower, Amsterdam (building). g, Skytower, Amsterdam (black-framed code box). h, De Boekenberg, Spijkenisse (building). i, Windpost, Maasvlakte (black-framed code box). j, Windpost, Maasvlakte (building). k, Map of the Netherlands.

2011, Mar. 28   *Perf. 13¼*
1387   A599   Sheet of 12,
       #1387a-1387j, 2
       #1387k   17.00   8.50
On day of issue, Nos. 1387a-1387k each sold for 46c. The code boxes activate an augmented reality application when scanned by a webcam when visting the www.toekomstinbeweging.nl website.

Greeting Card Week — A600

2011, Apr. 18   *Perf. 14½*
1388   A600   1 multi   1.40   .45
No. 1388 sold for 46c on day of issue. Printed in sheets of 3.

Organization for Economic Cooperation and Development, 50th Anniv. — A601

Royal Dutch Billiards Federation, Cent. — A602

Royal Dutch Checkers Federation, Cent. — A603

Loevenstein Castle, 650th Anniv. — A604

Association of Dutch Composers, Cent. — A605

2011, May 2   *Perf. 13¼x12¾*
1389   Vert. strip of 5   7.00   3.50
   a.   A601 1 multi   1.40   .45
   b.   A602 1 multi   1.40   .45
   c.   A603 1 multi   1.40   .45
   d.   A604 1 multi   1.40   .45
   e.   A605 1 multi   1.40   .45
Nos. 1389a-1389e each sold for 46c on day of issue.

Miniature Sheet

Netherlands Society for Microbiology, Cent. — A606

No. 1390 — Various microorganisms and inscription: a, Wijn / Gist (wine / yeast). b, Penicilline / Schimmel (penicillin / mold). c, Kaas / Melkzuurbacterie (cheese / lactic bacteria). d, Biogas / Archebacterie (biogas / archaea). e, Groenbemesting / Bacterie (green manure / bacteria). f, Biodiesel / Alg. (biodiesel / algae). g, Afvalwaterzuivering / Bacterie (waste water purification / bacteria). h, Compost / Schimmel (compost / mold). i, Desinfectie / Bacterievirus (disinfectant / bacteriophage). j, Zelfhelend beton / bacterie (self-curing concrete / bacteria).

2011, May 27
1390   A606   Sheet of 10   14.00   7.00
   a.-j.   1 Any single   1.40   .45
Nos. 1390a-1390j each sold for 46c on day of issue. A booklet containing 5 panes, each containing a horizontal pair of stamps on the sheet, sold for €9.95.

Initial Public Offering of Royal Post NL Stock — A607

2011, May 31   **Litho.**
1391   A607   1 multi   1.40   .45
No. 1391 sold for 46c on day of issue.

Miniature Sheet

Dutch Connections With South Africa — A608

No. 1392: a, Dutch-style South African houses in elephant (olifant). b, Poem by Ingrid Jonker in leopard (luipaard). c, Grapes in buffalo (buffel). d, South African house in rhinoceros (neushoorn). e, Painting of Jan van Riebeeck arriving at Cape of Good Hope in lion (leeuw). f, Dutch East India Company pottery in penguin (pinguin).

2011, July 25   *Perf. 13¼x12¾*
1392   A608   Sheet of 6   16.50   8.25
   a.-f.   1 Wereld Any single   2.75   .85
No. 1392 was printed with three different illustrations in the bottom sheet margin, with each sheet having a different arrangement of stamps. Sheet margins at left and right served as etiquettes. On day of issue Nos. 1392a-1392f each sold for 95c.

De Bond Heemschut Historical Preservation Society, Cent. — A609

No. 1393: a, American Embassy, The Hague. b, Amerongen Castle. c, Tricot factory, Winterswijk. d, Noord-Zuid-Hollands Coffee House, Amsterdam. e, St. Servatius Bridge, Maastricht. f, Synagogue, Groningen.

2011, Aug. 22 **Perf. 13¼x12¾**
| 1393 | A609 | Block of 6 | 7.50 | 3.75 |
| a.-f. | | 1 Any single | 1.25 | .35 |

Nos. 1393a-1393f each sold for 46c on day of issue.

A610

A611

Ecology — A612

No. 1394: a, Shirt on clothesline. b, Stylized plant. c, Bird. d, Hen. e, Kites. f, House. g, Laptop computer. h, Suitcase and leaf, horiz. i, Butterfly, horiz. j, Electric vehicle and plug, horiz.

Die Cut Perf. 14¼
2011, Sept. 1 **Litho.**
Booklet Stamps
Self-Adhesive
| 1394 | | Booklet pane of 10 | 12.50 | |
| a.-j. | | A610 1 Any single | 1.25 | .35 |

Photo.
Serpentine Die Cut 11
1395	A611 1 Europa multi + eti-quette		2.25	.60
a.	Booklet pane of 5		11.50	
1396	A612 1 Wereld multi + eti-quette		2.60	.80
a.	Booklet pane of 5		13.00	

On Nos. 1395-1396 a row of microrouletting separates stamps from etiquettes. On day of issue, Nos. 1394a-1394j each sold for 46c,; No. 139, for 79c; No. 1396, for 95c.

Miniature Sheet

Herman Renz Circus, Cent. A613

No. 1397: a, Fire eater. b, Snake handler. c, Clown. d, Trained horse. e, Man balancing hat on nose. f, Tumbling act. g, Lion. h, Acrobat lifting another acrobat. i, Elephant. j, Unicyclist on tightrope.

Perf. 12¾x13¼
2011, Sept. 19 **Litho.**
| 1397 | A613 | Sheet of 10 | 12.50 | 6.25 |
| a.-j. | | A613 1 Any single | 1.25 | .30 |

On day of issue, Nos. 1397a-1397j each sold for 46c.

Queen Wilhelmina (1880-1962) — A614

2011, Oct. 14 **Perf. 13¼x13½**
| 1398 | A614 1 multi | | 1.25 | .30 |

Stamp Day. No. 1398 sold for 46c on day of issue. A booklet containing five panes, each containing two No. 1398, sold for €9.95.

Postcrossing.com — A615

No. 1399 — Postcards depicting: a, Sunset, man and woman kissing under umbrella, donkey and house, puppies, nesting dolls, Eiffel Tower, Asian woman, beach in Rio. b, Baby surrounded by sunflower petals, sheep, beach, bull fight, Sphinx and Pyramid, Cuban car, building in Finland. c, Bridge, fish and coral, building in Antwerp, Belgium, Taj Mahal, Asian woman, soccer players, tower and Arabic text. d, Flamingo in Miami, beach in Rio, Petronas Towers, Kuala Lumpur, Acropolis, buildings in Warsaw, Big Ben and statue, London, woman, and China Central Television Building, Beijing. e, Boat and building in Finland, Prague and Hradcany Castle, tulips, chimpanzee wearing cowboy hat, Hong Kong skyline, Asian woman, bird, comic strip. f, Cat, windmill and tulips, Netherlands, Cliffs of Moher, Ireland, Calgary skyline, churches, St. Petersburg, Russia, Great Wall of China, woman praying, two boys.

2011, Oct. 14 **Perf. 13¼x12¾**
1399	A615	Block of 6 + 6 eti-quettes	15.00	7.50
a.-c.		1 Europa Any single	2.25	.60
d.-f.		1 Wereld Any single	2.60	.80

On day of issue Nos. 1399a-1399c each sold for 79c, and Nos. 1399d-1399f each sold for 95c.

December Stamps — A616

No. 1400: a, Candle. b, Reindeer, bird and fir trees. c, Bird on heart. d, Three Christmas ornaments. e, Church and houses. f, Reindeer with Christmas ornament, birds and candles on antlers. g, Angel with candles. h, Bird, holding Christmas ornament on fir branch. i, Snowman. j, Squirrel and Christmas ornament.

Serpentine Die Cut 12½
2011, Nov. 22 **Litho.**
Self-Adhesive
| 1400 | | Block of 10 | 10.00 | |
| a.-j. | | A616 (36c) Any single | 1.00 | .30 |

Personalized Stamp — A617

2011, Nov. 22 *Die Cut Perf. 13x13¼*
Self-Adhesive
| 1401 | A617 (36c) multi | | 1.00 | .30 |

The generic vignette shown on this stamp depicts two birds under mistletoe. This stamp could be personalized for an additional fee.

A618

Personalized Stamps — A619

2012, Jan. 2 **Litho.** **Perf. 13½x14**
| 1402 | A618 1 Europa black | 2.25 | .55 |
| 1403 | A619 1 Wereld black | 2.50 | .65 |

The generic vignettes of Nos. 1402 and 1403, which are shown, sold for the franking value of 85c and 95c, respectively. Nos. 1402 and 1403 each were printed in sheets of 10. The vignette parts of the stamp could be personalized for an additional fee.

Country Houses — A620

Country houses in: No. 1404, Mattemburgh. No. 1405, Amstenrade. No. 1406, Trompenburg. No. 1407, Vollenhoven. No. 1408, Middachten.

2012 **Perf. 14½x14¼**
1404	A620 1 multi		1.40	.35
a.	Perf. 13½x12¾		2.50	2.50
b.	Booklet pane of 2 #1404a		5.00	5.00
1405	A620 1 multi		1.40	.35
a.	Perf. 13½x12¾		2.50	2.50
b.	Booklet pane of 2 #1405a		5.00	5.00
1406	A620 1 multi		1.40	.35
a.	Perf. 13½x12¾		2.50	2.50
b.	Booklet pane of 2 #1406a		5.00	5.00
1407	A620 1 multi		1.40	.35
a.	Perf. 13½x12¾		2.50	2.50
b.	Booklet pane of 2 #1407a		5.00	5.00
1408	A620 1 multi		1.25	.35
a.	Perf. 13½x12¾		2.50	2.50
b.	Booklet pane of 2 #1408a		5.00	5.00
	Complete booklet, #1404b, 1405b, 1406b, 1407b, 1408b		25.00	
c.	Souvenir sheet of 5, #1404-1408		7.00	3.50
	Nos. 1404-1408 (5)		6.85	1.75

Issued: Nos. 1404-1405, 1/30; Nos. 1406-1407, 2/27; Nos. 1404a, 1404b, 1405a, 1405b, 1406a, 1406b, 1407a, 1407b, 1408, 1408a, 1408b, 1408c, 5/21. Nos. 1404-1408 each sold for 50c on day of issue. Complete booklet sold for €9.95 on day of issue.

Dutch Salvation Army, 125th Anniv. — A621

2012, Feb. 27 **Perf. 13¼x13½**
| 1409 | A621 1 multi | | 1.40 | .35 |

No. 1409 sold for 50c on day of issue.

Albert Heijn Grocery Stores, 125th Anniv. — A622

Designs: No. 1410, Original store, employee with first delivery bicycle. No. 1411, Coffee beans, coffee plant workers. No. 1412, Hamster, shoppers in grocery store. No. 1413, Shopper with child in shopping cart, store employees.

Serpentine Die Cut 13¼x13
2012, Feb. 27 **Self-Adhesive**
1410	A622 1 multi		1.40	.35
1411	A622 1 multi		1.40	.35
1412	A622 1 multi		1.40	.35
1413	A622 1 multi		1.40	.35
	Nos. 1410-1413 (4)		5.60	1.40

Nos. 1410-1413 each sold for 50c on day of issue.

Greeting Card Week — A623

2012, Mar. 26 **Perf. 13¼x13½**
| 1414 | A623 1 multi | | 1.40 | .35 |

No. 1414 sold for 50c on day of issue. Printed in sheets of 3.

A624

Tourism A625

No. 1415: a, National Maritime Museum, Dutch East Indiaman "The Amsterdam," country name in white. b, Muziekgebouw Concert Hall, cruise ship "MSC Lirica," country name in gold.
No. 1416: a, The Bend in the Herengracht Canal, painting by Gerrit Berckheyde, country name in white. b, Skinny Bridge over Amstel River, country name in gold.

2012, Mar. 26 **Litho.**
1415	A624	Horiz. pair	2.80	1.40
a.-b.		1 Either single	1.40	.35
1416	A625	Pair	4.50	2.25
a.-b.		1 Europa Either single	2.25	.60

Europa (#1416b). On day of issue, Nos. 1415a-1415b each sold for 50c and Nos. 1416a-1416b each sold for 85c.

Netherlands Open Air Museum, Cent. — A626

Historical photographs: Nos. 1417a, 1417k, Women cleaning (green, at left), Marketplace (black, at right). Nos. 1417b, 1417l, Marketplace (black, at left). Woman sewing (purple, at right). Nos. 1417c, 1417m, Children with smartphone (rose, at left), Children crossing street (blue, at right). Nos. 1417d, 1417n, Children crossing street (blue, at left), Children playing (black, at right). Nos. 1417e, 1417o, Cots and worker at migrant worker's lodging (blue, at left), Sod hut (purple at right). Nos. 1417f, 1417p, Sod hut (purple, at left), Children watching television (rose, at right). Nos. 1417g, 1417q, Campers and van (purple, at left), Children with tablet and camp light (green, at right). Nos. 1417h, 1417r, Children with tablet and camp light (green, at left), Hockey players at Netherlands Open Air Museum (blue, at right). Nos. 1417i, 1417s, People boarding airplane at Schiphol Airport (black, at left), Car at gas station (rose, at right). Nos. 1417j, 1417t, Car at gas station (rose, at left), Hay cart (green, at right).

2012, Apr. 23 **Perf. 13¼x12¾**
1417	A626	Sheet of 10	14.00	7.00
a.-j.		1 Any single	1.40	.35
k.-t.		Any single, perf. 14½	2.60	2.60
u.		Booklet pane of 2, #1417k-1417l	5.25	
v.		Booklet pane of 2, #1417m-1417n	5.25	
w.		Booklet pane of 2, #1417o-1417p	5.25	
x.		Booklet pane of 2, #1417q-1417r	5.25	
y.		Booklet pane of 2, #1417s-1417t	5.25	
		Complete booklet, #1417u, 1417v, 1417w, 1417x, 1417y	26.50	

Nos. 1417a-1417t each sold for 50c on day of issue.

Miniature Sheet

Madurodam Miniature Park, 60th Anniv. — A627

No. 1418 — Miniatures of: a, Dutch East India ship. b, Windmills and building. c, Cheese market (crowd in plaza in front of building). d, Port of Rotterdam and tanker ships. e, Field of flowers. f, Rijksmuseum. g, Schiphol Airport. h, Delta Works (people near white conneted pipes). i, Maasvlakte 2 port project (dredger). j, Binnenhof, horses and carriages.

2012, May 21   **Perf. 13¼x13½**
1418	A627	Sheet of 10	12.50	6.25
a.-j.		1 Any single	1.25	.35

Nos. 1418a-1418j each sold for 50c on day of issue.

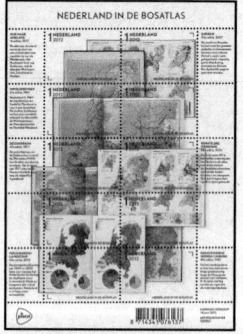

Maps of the Netherlands from the Bosatlas — A628

Designs: Nos. 1419a, 1419k, Upper left section of map from 1877 atlas, upper part of page 62 from 2007 atlas. Nos. 1419b, 1419l, Upper right section of map from 1877 atlas, upper sections of pages 62 and 63 from 2007 atlas. Nos. 1419c, 1419m, Section of map from 1877 atlas, upper left section of page 60 from 1961 atlas. Nos. 1419d, 1419n, Section of map from 1877 atlas, lower section of page 63 from 2007 atlas, upper right section of page 61 from 1961 atlas. Nos. 1419e, 1419o, Section of map from page 60 of 1961 atlas, sections of pages depicting South Netherlands (Zuid-Nederland) from 1971 atlas, upper left section of page 60 from 2001 atlas. Nos. 1419f, 1419p, Section of page 61 from 1961 atlas, upper right section of pages 60 and upper left section of 61 from 2001 atlas. Nos. 1419g, 1419q, Lower section of South Netherlands map from 1971 atlas, lower section of page 60 from 2001 atlas, upper sections of pages 59 from 2012 atlas. Nos. 1419h, 1419r, Lower sections of pages 60 and 61 from 2001 atlas, upper right section of page 39 from 2012 atlas, section of page from 1981 atlas. Nos. 1419i, 1419s, Lower sections of pages 38 and 39 from 2012 atlas. Nos. 1419j, 1419t, Lower right section of page 39 from 2012 atlas, lower right section of page from 1981 atlas.

2012, June 18   **Perf. 13¼x12¾**
1419	A628	Sheet of 10	12.50	6.25
a.-j.		1 Any single	1.25	.35
k.-t.		Any single, perf. 14½	2.50	2.50
u.		Booklet pane of 2, #1419k-1419l	5.00	
v.		Booklet pane of 2, #1419m-1419n	5.00	
w.		Booklet pane of 2, #1419o-1419p	5.00	
x.		Booklet pane of 2, #1419q-1419r	5.00	
y.		Booklet pane of 2, #1419s-1419t	5.00	
		Complete booklet, #1419u, 1419v, 1419w, 1419x, 1419y	25.00	

Nos. 1419a-1419j each sold for 50c on day of issue. Complete booklet sold for €9.95.

Miniature Sheet

Netherlands Olympic Committee and Netherlands Sports Federation, Cent. — A629

No. 1420 — Athletes: a, Sjoukje Dijkstra, figure skater. b, Anton Geesink, judoka. c, Nico Rienks, rower. d, Ellen van Langen, runner. e, Field hockey player. f, Leontien Zijlaard-van Moorsel, cyclist. g, Esther Vergeer, Paralympian tennis player. h, Maarten van der Weijden, swimmer. i, Anky van Grunsven, dressage. j, Nicolien Sauerbreij, snowboarder.

2012, July 4   **Perf. 13¼x13½**
1420	A629	Sheet of 10	12.50	6.25
a.-j.		1 Any single	1.25	.35

Nos. 1420a-1420j each sold for 50c on day of issue.

Miniature Sheet

Seasons Magazine, 20th Anniv. — A630

No. 1422 — Photography from magazine with inscription at LR: a, Esdoorn (maple leaves). b, IJsbloem (frost flower). c, Peul (snow peas). d, Dahlia. e, Kievitsbloem (fritillaries). f, Lijsterbes (rowanberries). g, Rode zonnehoed (Purple coneflower). h, Rimpelroos, Rozenbottel, Rozengeranium (Rugosa rose, rose hips, rose geranium). i, Tulp (tulips). j, Blauwe bes (blueberries).

2012, July 16   **Perf. 13½x13¼**
1421	A630	Sheet of 10	12.50	6.25
a.-j.		1 Any single	1.25	.35

Nos. 1421a-1421j each sold for 50c on day of issue.

Cattle Breeds A631

Designs: Nos. 1422a, 1422g, Maas-Rijn-Ijsselvee (Meuse-Rhine-Issel). Nos. 1422b, 1422h, Blaarkop. Nos. 1422c, 1422i, Fries-Hollands (Dutch Friesian). Nos. 1422d, 1422j, Lakenvelder (Dutch Belted). Nos. 1422e, 1422k, Brandrode Rund. Nos. 1422f, 1422l, Witrik.

2012, Aug. 13   **Perf. 13¼x12¾**
1422	A631	Block of 6	8.50	4.25
a.-f.		1 Any single	1.40	.35
g.-l.		1 Any single, perf. 14½	2.60	2.60
m.		Booklet pane of 2 #1422g	5.25	—
n.		Booklet pane of 2 #1422h	5.25	—
o.		Booklet pane of 2 #1422i	5.25	—
p.		Booklet pane of 2 #1422j	5.25	—
q.		Booklet pane of 2, #1422k, 1422l	5.25	—
		Complete booklet, #1422m, 1422n, 1422o, 1422p, 1422q	26.50	

Nos. 1422a-1422f each sold for 50c on day of issue. Complete booklet sold for €9.95 on day of issue.

Miniature Sheet

Dutch Connections With Indonesia — A632

No. 1423: a, Hella Haasse (1918-2011), writer, cattle and tea planters. b, Tjalie Robinson (1911-74), writer, dog on chain. c, Hendrik Petrus Berlage (1856-1934), architect, Gemeentemuseum, The Hague. d, Charles Prosper Wolff Schoemaker (1882-1949), architect, (wearing hat), Villa Isola, Bandung, Indonesia. e, Andy Tielman (1936-2011), musician, Anneke Grönloh, singer. f, Chevrotain, Indonesian shadow puppet.

2012, Aug. 13   **Perf. 13½x13¼**
1423	A632	Sheet of 6	15.00	7.50
a.-f.		1 Wereld Any single	2.50	.65

No. 1423 was printed with three different illustrations in the bottom sheet margin, with each sheet having a different arrangement of stamps. Sheet margins at left and right served as etiquettes. On day of issue, Nos. 1423a-1423f each sold for 95c.

Royal Carré Theater, Amsterdam, 125th Anniv. — A633

No. 1424: a, Theater. b, Toon Hermans, microphone, balloons. c, Oscar Carré's circus horses. d, Two male ballet dancers. e, Guitarist and lights. f, Two dancers from *Cats*. g, Tightrope artist with unicycle. h, Ballerina. i, Circus elephants. j, Chandeliers and "125.".

2012, Sept. 10   **Perf. 12¾x13¼**
1424	A633	Sheet of 10	14.00	7.00
a.-j.		1 Any single	1.40	.35
k.		Booklet pane of 2, #1424a, 1424c	5.25	—
l.		Booklet pane of 2, #1424b, 1424j	5.25	—
m.		Booklet pane of 2, #1424e, 1424f	5.25	—
n.		Booklet pane of 2, #1424d, 1424h	5.25	—
o.		Booklet pane of 2, #1424g, 1424i	5.25	—
		Complete booklet, #1424k, 1424l, 1424m, 1424n, 1424o	26.50	

On day of issue, Nos. 1424a-1424j each sold for 50c and complete booklet sold for €9.95.

Miniature Sheet

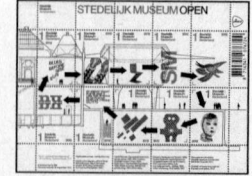

Reopening of Stedelijk Museum, Amsterdam — A634

No. 1425 — Arrows and: a, Blues Before Sunrise poster, by Mevis & Van Deursen. b, As I Opened Fire, by Roy Lichtenstein (cannons). c, Zig-zag chair prototype, by Gerrit Rietveld. d, Musuem logo (SM), by Wim Crouwel. e, Mural, by Karel Appel. f, Now 2, by Willem Sandberg (nu). g, An Object Made. ., by Lawrence Weiner (text, man on staircase). h, Suprematist Composition (Eight Red Rectangles), by Kazimir Malevich. i, Empathy Displacement 7, by Mike Kelley (polka-dotted

object). j, Barbie (With Pearl Necklace), by Marlene Dumas (doll's head).

2012, Sept. 24   **Perf. 13½x13¼**
1425	A634	Sheet of 10	14.00	7.00
a.-j.		1 Any single	1.40	.35

Nos. 1425a-1425j each sold for 50c on day of issue.

Souvenir Sheet

Children's Book Week — A635

No. 1426: a, Bird. b, Butterfly.

2012, Oct. 8   **Rouletted**
On Cardboard
1426	A635	Sheet of 2	13.00	6.50
a.-b.		5 Either single	6.50	3.25

Nos. 1426a-1426b each sold for €2.50. Parts of the stamps pop up when the cardboard slide on each stamp is pulled out.

Queen Juliana — A636

2012, Oct. 19   **Perf. 13¼x14**
1427	A636	1 multi	1.25	.35
a.		Booklet pane of 2	5.00	
		Complete booket, 5 #1427a	25.00	

Stamp Day. No. 1427 sold for 50c on day of issue. Complete booklet sold for €9.95 and contains five examples of No. 1427a, each with a different pane margin.

December Stamps A637

No. 1428 — Christmas knitting patterns featuring: a, Christmas trees and red violet hearts. b, Candles. c, Christmas trees and green hearts. d, Reindeer. e, Snowmen. f, Angels with horns. g, Red reindeer and heart. h, Poinsettias. i, Christmas ornaments and poinsettias. j, Angels and musical notes.

Serpentine Die Cut 12¾x12½
2012, Nov. 20   **Self-Adhesive**
1428	A637	Block of 10	11.00	
a.-j.		(40c) Any single	1.10	.30

A638

Personalized Stamps — A639

2013, Jan. 2   Litho.   Perf. 13¼x14
1429 A638 1 multi   1.50 1.50

Self-Adhesive

1430 A639 1 multi   1.50 1.50

Nos. 1429-1430 each sold for 54c on day of issue. Vignettes shown are the generic images available on the day of issue. Vignettes could be personalized for a fee.

Traditional Women's Head Coverings — A640

Head covering from: No. 1431, Bunschoten-Spakenburg. No. 1432, Staphorst. No. 1433, Marken. No. 1434, Walcheren. No. 1435, Noordwest-Veluwe.

2013   Litho.   Perf. 14½x14¼

1431	A640 1 multi	1.50	1.50
a.	Perf. 13½x12½	2.75	2.75
b.	Booklet pane of 2 #1431a	5.50	
1432	A640 1 multi	1.50	1.50
a.	Perf. 13½x12½	2.75	2.75
b.	Booklet pane of 2 #1432a	5.50	
1433	A640 1 multi	1.40	1.40
a.	Perf. 13½x12½	2.75	2.75
b.	Booklet pane of 2 #1433a	5.50	
1434	A640 1 multi	1.40	1.40
a.	Perf. 13½x12½	2.75	2.75
b.	Booklet pane of 2 #1434a	5.50	
1435	A640 1 multi	1.50	1.50
a.	Perf. 13½x12½	2.75	2.75
b.	Booklet pane of 2 #1435a	5.50	
	Complete booklet, #1431b, 1432b, 1433b, 1434b, 1435b	27.50	
c.	Souvenir sheet of 5, #1431-1435	7.50	7.50
	Nos. 1431-1435 (5)	7.30	7.30

Issued: Nos. 1431-1432, 1/2; Nos. 1433-1434, 2/25; Nos. 1431a-1431b, 1432a-1432b, 1433a-1433b, 1434a-1434b, 1435-1435c, 5/21. Nos. 1431-1435 each sold for 54c on day of issue. Complete booklet sold for €9.95.

Miniature Sheet

Netherlands Land Development Society, 125th Anniv. — A641

No. 1436 — Construction projects developed by Arcadis and KNHM: a, Millau Viaduct, France. b, Train under Zanderij Crailoo Wildlife Crossing Bridge. c, Lighthouse, flags and grass-covered dunes. d, Floriade (terraced garden), Venlo. e, Olympic Stadium, London. f, Storm barrier, New Orleans, Louisiana. g, Garden on Meuse River, Rotterdam. h, Water, trees and tower in distance (Kern met Pit Contest). i, Amsterdam Bijlmer ArenA railway station. j, Model constructed for Artcadia children's art and technology contest.

2013, Jan. 28   Litho.   Perf. 13¼x13½
1436 A641   Sheet of 10   15.00 15.00
a.-j.   1 Any single   1.50   1.50

Nos. 1436a-1436j each sold for 54c on day of issue.

Miniature Sheet

Animals in Burgers' Zoo, Arnhem A642

No. 1437: a, Panthera pardus kotiya (Sri Lankan leopards). b, Pterapogon kauderni (Banggai cardinalfish) witheggs in mouth. c, Giraffa camelopardalis rothschildi (giraffes). d, Anodorhynchus hyacinthinus (hyacinth macaws). e, Ceratotherium simum (white rhinoceroses). f, Equus quagga boehmi (Grant's zebras). g, Nomascus gabriellae (yellow-cheeked gibbons). h, Iguana iguana (green iguanas). i, Spheniscus demersus (jackass penguins). j, Pan troglodytes (chimpanzees).

Perf. 13¼x12¾

2013, Feb. 25   Litho.

1437	A642 Sheet of 10	14.00	14.00
a.-j.	1 Any single	1.40	1.40
k.	Booklet pane of 2, #1437a-1437b	5.25	—
l.	Booklet pane of 2, #1437c-1437d	5.25	—
m.	Booklet pane of 2, #1437e-1437f	5.25	—
n.	Booklet pane of 2, #1437g-1437h	5.25	—
o.	Booklet pane of 2, #1437i-1437j	5.25	—
	Complete booklet, #1437k, 1437l, 1437m, 1437n, 1437o	26.50	

Nos. 1437a-1437j each sold for 54c on day of issue. Complete booklet sold for €9.95.

Famous Women A643

No. 1438: a, Alexandrine Tinne (1835-69), explorer of Sahara region. b, Belle van Zuylen (1740-1805), writer. c, Trijn van Leemput (c. 1530-1607), heroine in Eighty Years' War. d, Maria van Oosterwijck (1630-93), painter. e, Mary, Duchess of Burgundy (1457-82). f, Anna Zernike (1887-1972), theologian, first female minister in Netherlands.

Perf. 13¼x12¾

2013, Mar. 25   Litho.
1438 A643   Block of 6   8.50 8.50
a.-f.   1 Any single   1.40   1.40

Nos. 1438a-1438f each sold for 54c on day of issue.

Miniature Sheet

Reopening of Main Building of Rijksmuseum — A644

No. 1439: a, Right part of *The Gallant Conversation*, by Gerard ter Borch, left part of *Interior of the Church of St. Odulphus in Assendelft*, by Pieter Jansz. b, Right part of *Interior of the Church of St. Odolphus in Assendelft, Mary Magdalene*, by Jan van Scorel. c, *Still Life of Fruits and Flowers*, by Balthasar van der Ast, left part of *Still Life with Flowers*, by Hans Bollongier. d, Right part of *Still Life with Flowers*, left part of *Vivi in a Red Dress in a Forest*, by Jacob Olie, Jr. e, Right edge of *Sheet with Five Butterflies a Wasp and*

Two Flies, by Pieter Withoos, Bunya no Yasu-hide from *Modern Parody on the Six Poets and Six Flowers*, by Kunisada Utagawa, left edge of *Italian Landscape with Stone Pines*, by Hendrik Voogd. f, Right part of *Italian Land-cape with Stone Pines*, left part of *The Threatened Swan*, by Jan Asselijn. g, Right part of *Still Life with Gilded Cup*, by Willem Claesz, *The Milkmaid*, by Johannes Vermeer. h, *Still Life with Cheeses*, by Floris Claesz van Dijck, left part of tile from Sommelsdijk Orphanage. i, Right part of *Gerard Andriesz Bicker*, by Bartholomeus van der Helst, left part of *Portrait of Giuliano da Sangallo*, by Piero di Cosomo. j, Right part of *Portrait of Giuliano da Sangallo*, left part of *The Night Watch*, by Rembrandt.

Perf. 13¼x12¾

2013, Mar. 25   Litho.
1439 A644   Sheet of 10   14.00 14.00
a.-j.   1 Any single   1.40   1.40

Nos. 1439a-1439j each sold for 54c on day of issue.

Abdication of Queen Beatrix — A645

2013, Mar. 25 Litho. Perf. 14x13½
1440 A645 1 blue & blk   1.40 1.40

No. 1440 sold for 54c on day of issue.

Europa A646

No. 1441: a and c, Modern mail vans (2013 Renault Kangoo, 1976 Simca 1100 VF, 2010 Fiat Fiorino, 1974 Daf 33). b and d, Old mail vans (1960 Bedford CA, 1936, Opel P4, 1956 Opel Blitz, 1918 GMC).

2013, Apr. 22 Litho. Perf. 13¼x12¾

1441	A646 Pair	4.80	4.80
a.-b.	1 Europa Either single	2.40	2.40
c.-d.	1 Europa Either single, perf. 14½	4.25	4.25
e.	Booklet pane of 2, #1441c-1441d	8.75	—
	Complete booklet, 3 #1441e	26.50	

Nos. 1441a-1441b each sold for 90c on day of issue. Complete booklet sold for €9.95, and contains three panes of No. 1441e with different orientations of the stamps.

Ascension to Throne of King Willem-Alexander — A647

Perf. 14¼x14 Syncopated
2013, Apr. 30   Litho.
Booklet Stamps
Self-Adhesive

1442	A647 1 blk, red & bl	1.40	1.40
a.	Booklet pane of 10	14.00	
1443	A647 2 blk, bl & grn	3.00	3.00
a.	Booklet pane of 5	15.00	

On day of issue, No. 1442 sold for 54c and No. 1443 sold for €1.08.

King Willem-Alexander A648

2013, May 21 Litho. Perf. 14x13½
1444 A648 1 red & blk   1.50 1.50

No. 1444 sold for 54c on day of issue.

Writers — A649

No. 1445: a, Simon Carmiggelt (1913-87). b, Gerrit Kouwenaar. c, Louis Couperus

(1863-1923). d, Adriaan Roland Holst (1888-1976). e, Godfried Bomans (1913-71).

2013, May 21   Litho.   Perf. 14½
1445   Horiz. strip of 5   7.50 7.50
a.-e.   A649 1 Any single   1.50   1.50

Nos. 1445a-1445e each sold for 54c on day of issue. Printed in sheets containing 2 each of Nos. 1445a-1445e + 5 central labels.

World Blood Donor Day — A650

No. 1446: a, Queen, "1" in red. b, King, "1" in white.

2013, June 17   Litho.   Perf. 14½
1446 A650   Pair   3.00 3.00
a.-b.   1 Either single   1.50   1.50

On day of issue Nos. 1446a-1446b each sold for 54c.

Miniature Sheet

Windmills — A651

No. 1447 — Various windmill types located in: a and k, Schermer. b and l, Burgwerd. c and m, Heeswijk-Dinther. d and n, Hoornaar. e and o, Zaandam. f and p, Wijk bij Duurstede. g and q, Klein Genhout. h and r, Zeddam. i and s, Nieuw- en Sint Joosland. j and t, Roderwolde.

2013, June 17   Litho.   Perf. 14½

1447	A651 Sheet of 10	15.00	15.00
a.-j.	1 Any single	1.50	1.50
k.-t.	1 Any single, perf. 12¾x13¼	2.75	2.75
u.	Booklet pane of 2, #1447k, 1447p	5.50	—
v.	Booklet pane of 2, #1447l, 1447q	5.50	—
w.	Booklet pane of 2, #1447m, 1447r	5.50	—
x.	Booklet pane of 2, #1447n, 1447s	5.50	—
y.	Booklet pane of 2, #1447o, 1447t	5.50	—
	Complete booklet, #1447u, 1447v, 1447w, 1447x, 1447y	27.50	

Nos. 1447a-1447j each sold for 54c on day of issue. Complete booklet sold for €9.95.

Miniature Sheet

Royal Dutch Swimming Association, 125th Anniv. — A652

No. 1448: a, People standing at edge of pool. b, Two synchronized divers. c, Water polo player. d, Diver about to enter water. e, People standing at edge of pool, people lined up on diving platform. f, Two synchronized swimmers. g, Swimmer and lane barriers. h, Teacher and children learning how to swim. i, Swimmer's head near edge of pool. j, Swimmer bent over ready to start race.

2013, Aug. 12   Litho.   Perf. 14½
1448 A652   Sheet of 10   16.00 16.00
a.-j.   1 Any single   1.60   1.60

Nos. 1448a-1448j each sold for 60c on day of issue.

Miniature Sheet

Dutch Connections With Belgium — A653

No. 1449: a, Museum aan de Stroom, Antwerp, Belgium, designed by Neutelings Riedijk Architectural Agency. b, Design for Hoenderloo Museum, by Henry van de Velde. c, Twelve books, country name at left. d, Thirteen books, country name at right. e, Après-midi à Amsterdam, by Rik Wouters. f, De Vlakte, by Jakob Smits.

Perf. 13¼x12¾

2013, Aug. 12		Litho.
1449	A653	Sheet of 6	16.50 16.50
a.-f.	1 Wereld Any single	2.75 2.75

Nos. 1449a-1449f each sold for €1 on day of issue. No. 1449 was printed with three different illustrations in the bottom sheet margin, with each stamp having a different arrangement of stamps. Sheet margins at left and right served as etiquettes.

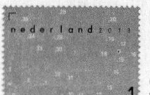

Greeting Card Week — A654

2013, Sept. 9		Litho.	**Perf. 14½**
1450	A654	1 multi	1.60 1.60

No. 1450 sold for 60c on day of issue and was printed in sheets of 3.

Miniature Sheet

Peace Palace, The Hague, Cent. A655

No. 1451 — Details of architectural or artistic items of the Peace Palace in circle at left, word at top in inner ring of words in circle at right: a and k, Detail of wall tile, Artes. b and l, Bronze medallion on entrance gates, Amicitia. c and m, Stained-glass window in Central Hall, Iustitia. d and n, Portrait of Hugo de Groot, by Michiel Jansz.van Mierevelt, Mercatura. e and o, Marble floor in Entrance Hall, Scientia. f and p, Relief sculpture by Toon Dupuis, Veritas. g and q, Prestudy for unmade tapestry, Concordia. h and r, Tile panel, Securitas. i and s, Peace Goddess with Child, by Herman Rosse, Prosperitas. j and t, Stained-glass window depicting locomotive, Industria.

2013, Sept. 9		Litho.	**Perf. 13¼x12¾**
1451	A655	Sheet of 10	16.00 16.00
a.-j.	1 Any single	1.60 1.60
k.-t.	1 Any single, perf. 14½	2.75 2.75
u.	Booklet pane of 2, #1451k-1451l	5.50 —
v.	Booklet pane of 2, #1451m-1451n	5.50 —
w.	Booklet pane of 2, #1451o-1451p	5.50 —
x.	Booklet pane of 2, #1451q-1451r	5.50 —
y.	Booklet pane of 2, #1451s-1451t	5.50 —

Complete booklet, #1451u, 1451v, 1451w, 1451x, 1451y   27.50

Nos. 1451a-1451j each sold for 60c on day of issue. Complete booklet sold for €9.95.

Airplanes and Queen Wilhelmina From Type AP5 — A656

2013, Oct. 18		Litho.	**Perf. 14x13½**
1452	A656	1 multi	1.60 1.60
a.	Booklet pane of 2	5.50 —
	Complete booklet, 5 #1452a	27.50

Stamp Day. No. 1452 sold for 60c on day of issue. Complete booklet sold for €9.95.

Legend of St. Nicholas (Santa Claus) — A657

No. 1453: a, St. Nicholas on horse, Black Peter, and Moon. b, Black Peter with gift. c, Moon, tree and house. d, St. Nicholas with crozier. e, Shoe filled with gifts.

2013, Nov. 4		Litho.	**Perf. 13¾x13¼**
1453		Horiz. strip of 5	8.00 8.00
a.-e.	A657 1 Any single	1.60 1.60

Nos. 1453a-1453e sold for 60c on day of issue and emit a spice scent when scratched.

Miniature Sheet

December Stamps — A658

No. 1454: a, Buildings at night, comet in sky over Christmas tree. b, Buildings at night, Christmas tree. c, Buildings at night, people viewing fireworks. d, Buildings at night, Christmas tree, large star at left, Moon over top of tower. e, Buildings at night, large star at left, Christmas trees. f, Buildings at night, people viewing large star at right. g, Buildings at night, Christmas tree, man running. h, Buildings at night, clock on tower at right. i, Girl on ice skates looking at bird in tree. j, Boy in sled on ice, man ice skating. k, Two ice skaters, windmill. l, Boy in sled on ice, tower at right. m, Snowman, star and top of Christmas tree. n, Man pulling Christmas tree on cart. o, Dog looking at postman on bicycle. p, Woman holding dog's leash, tower at right. q, Man and woman under mistletoe. r, Birds under bridge, Christmas tree. s, Buildings in day, Christmas tree. t, Buidlings in day, tower at right.

Serpentine Die Cut 12½x12¼

2013, Nov. 19		Litho.
1454	A658	Sheet of 20	30.00
a.-t.	(55c) Any single	1.50 1.50

Kingdom of the Netherlands, 200th Anniv. — A659

No. 1455: a, Landing of Willem I, 1813, King Willem I, flag of the Netherlands. b, List of monarchs.

2013, Nov. 30		Litho.	**Perf. 14½**
1455	A659	Pair, #a-b	7.00 7.00
a.-b.	2 Either single	3.50 3.50

On day of issue Nos. 1455a-1455b both sold for €1.28.

King Willem-Alexander
A660   A661

Die Cut Perf. 14¼ Syncopated

2013, Nov. 30			Photo.

Booklet Stamps
Self-Adhesive

1456	A660	1 blue & blk	1.75 1.75
a.	Booklet pane of 10	17.50
b.	Dated "2014"	—
d.	Dated "2015"	1.60 1.60
e.	Booklet pane of 10 #1456d	16.00
n.	Dated "2020"	2.10 2.10
o.	Booklet pane of 10 #1456n	21.00

Issued: No. 1456n, 6/9/20; No. 1458n, 7/15/20.

Serpentine Die Cut 11¼

1457	A661	1 Internationaal gray & blk	3.00 3.00
a.	Booklet pane of 5	15.00
b.	Dated "2014"	—
d.	Dated "2015"	2.60 2.60
e.	Booklet pane of 5 #1457d	13.00
h.	Dated "2017"	—
i.	Booklet pane of 5 #1457h	—
j.	Dated "2018"	—
k.	Booklet pane of 5 #1457j	—
n.	Dated "2020"	—
o.	Booklet pane of 5 #1457n	—

Die Cut Perf. 14¼

1458	A660	2 ver & blk	3.50 3.50
a.	Booklet pane of 5	17.50
b.	Dated "2014"	—
d.	Dated "2015"	3.25 3.25
e.	Booklet pane of 5 #1458d	16.50
n.	Dated "2020"	4.25 4.25
o.	Booklet pane of 5 #1458n	21.50
	Nos. 1456-1458 (3)	8.25 8.25

On day of issue, No. 1456 sold for 64c; No. 1457, for €1.05; No. 1458, for €1.28.
Issued: Nos. 1456b, 1457b, 1458b, 10/23/14; Nos. 1456d, 1456e, 1457d, 1457e, 1458d, 1458e, 1/5/15; No. 1457h, 6/16/17; No. 1457j, 6/1/18; No. 1457n, 7/15/20; No. 1456nm 6/9/20; No. 1458n, 7/15/20.
On day of issues, No. 1456b sold for 64c; No. 1456d, 69c; No. 1457b, €1.05; No. 1457d, €1.15; No. 1458b, €1.28;No. 1458d, €1.38.

Numerals
A662   A663

Die Cut Perf. 13½ Syncopated

2014, Jan. 2	Coil Stamps	Litho.

Self-Adhesive

1459	A662	1 multi	1.75 1.75
1460	A663	2 multi	3.50 3.50

On day of issue, No. 1459 sold for 64c; No. 1460, for €1.28.

A664

Dutch Items A665

Designs: No. 1461a, Frisian flat-bottomed boat. Nos. 1461b, 1462a, Windmill. No. 1461c, Wedge of Gouda cheese. Nos. 1461d, 1462d, House with step-gable roof. No. 1461e, Boy and girl in Dutch costumes kissing. Nos. 1461f, 1462b, Bicycle. Nos. 1461g, 1462c, Holstein-Frisian cow. Nos. 1461h, 1462e, Tulip. No. 1461i, Ice skate. No. 1461j, Wooden shoe.

Die Cut Perf. 14¼

2014, Jan. 2		Litho.

Self-Adhesive

1461	A664	Booklet pane of 10	17.50
a.-j.	1 Any single	1.75 1.75

Serpentine Die Cut 11¼

1462	A665	Booklet pane of 5	15.00
a.-e.	1 Internationaal Any single	3.00 3.00

On day of issue, Nos. 1461a-1461j each sold for 64c; Nos. 1462a-1462 each sold for €1.05.

Miniature Sheet

Automobiles in Louwman Museum Collection — A666

No. 1463: a, 1887 De Dion-Bouton & Trépardoux. b, 1910 Brooke Swan Car. c, 1912 Eysink. d, 1912 Spyker. e, 1932 Bugatti. f, 1935 Duesenberg. g, 1936 Toyota. h, 1960 Porsce race car. i, 1964 Aston Martin. j, 1965 Ferrari.

2014, Jan. 27	Litho.	**Perf. 13¼x13½**
1463	A666	Sheet of 10	17.50 17.50
a.-j.	1 Any single	1.75 1.75
k.	Booklet pane of 2, #1463a-1463b	6.75 —
l.	Booklet pane of 2, #1463c-1463d	6.75 —
m.	Booklet pane of 2, #1463e-1463f	6.75 —
n.	Booklet pane of 2, #1463g-1463h	6.75 —
o.	Booklet pane of 2, #1463i-1463j	6.75 —
	Complete booklet, #1463k-1463o	34.00

On day of issue, Nos. 1463a-1463j each sold for 64c. Complete booklet sold for €12.45.

Ceramics — A667

Ceramics from: No. 1464, Loosdrecht. No. 1465, Tegelen. No. 1466, Harlingen. No. 1467, Makkum. No. 1468, Delft.

2014 Litho. *Perf. 14½x14¼*
1464	A667	1 multi	1.75	1.75
a.		Perf. 13½x12½	3.25	3.25
b.		Booklet pane of 2 #1464a	6.75	
1465	A667	1 multi	1.75	1.75
a.		Perf. 13½x12½	3.25	3.25
b.		Booklet pane of 2 #1465a	6.75	
1466	A667	1 multi	1.75	1.75
a.		Perf. 13½x12½	3.25	3.25
b.		Booklet pane of 2 #1466a	6.75	
1467	A667	1 multi	1.75	1.75
a.		Perf. 13½x12½	3.25	3.25
b.		Booklet pane of 2 #1467a	6.75	
1468	A667	1 multi	1.75	1.75
a.		Perf. 13½x12½	3.25	3.25
b.		Booklet pane of 2 #1468a	6.75	
		Complete booklet, #1464b, 1465b, 1466b, 1467b, 1468b	34.00	
c.		Souvenir sheet of 5, #1464-1468	8.75	8.75

Issued: Nos. 1464, 1465, 1/27; Nos. 1466, 1467, 2/24; Nos. 1464a, 1464b, 1465a, 1465b, 1466a, 1466b, 1467a, 1467b, 1468, 1468a, 1468b, 1468c, 5/19. On day of issue, Nos. 1464-1468 each sold for 64c. Complete booklet sold for €12.45.

Youth Philately Day A668

No. 1469: a, Carrier pigeon (duif). b, Hedgehog (egel).

2014, Mar. 24 Litho. *Die Cut* **Self-Adhesive**
1469	A668	Pair, #a-b	3.50
a.-b.		1 Either single	1.75 1.75

Printed in sheets of 10 containing five each Nos. 1469a-1469b, with adjacent stamps at different distances from each other. On day of issue, Nos. 1469a-1469b each sold for 64c.

Constitution of the Kingdom of the Netherlands, 200th Anniv. A669

No. 1470: a, King Willem-Alexander, text from coronation oath, blue panel. b, Statue of King Willem I, text from oath to the Constitution, red panel.

Perf. 13½x13¼
2014, Mar. 29 Litho.
1470	A669	Pair, #a-b	7.00 7.00
a.-b.		2 Either single	3.50 3.50

On day of issue, Nos. 1470a-1470b each sold for €1.28.

Europa A670

No. 1471 — Drie Pruiken Barrel Organ: a, Internal machinery. b, Front of organ with figurines and builder's name.

2014, Apr. 22 Litho. *Perf. 13¼x13½*
1471	A670	Horiz. pair	6.00 6.00
a.-b.		1 Internationaal Either single	3.00 3.00

On day of issue, Nos. 1471a-1471b each sold for €1.05.

Miniature Sheet

Orchids — A671

No. 1472: a, Gymnadenia conopsea. b, Orchis militaris. c, Orchis anthropophora. d, Anacamptis pyramidalis. e, Dactylorhiza maculata. f, Orchis purpurea. g, Platanthera bifolia. h, Orchis mascula. i, Coeloglossum viride. j, Orchis simia.

2014, Apr. 22 Litho. *Perf. 13½x13¼*
1472	A671	Sheet of 10	17.50	17.50
a.-j.		1 Any single	1.75	1.75
k.		Booklet pane of 2, #1472a, 1472f	7.00	—
l.		Booklet pane of 2, #1472b, 1472g	7.00	—
m.		Booklet pane of 2, #1472c, 1472h	7.00	—
n.		Booklet pane of 2, #1472d, 1472i	7.00	—
o.		Booklet pane of 2, #1472e, 1472j	7.00	—
		Complete booklet, #1472k-1472o	35.00	

On day of issue, Nos. 1472a-1472j each sold for 64c. Complete booklet sold for €12.45.

Miniature Sheet

2014 World Cup Soccer Championships, Brazil — A672

No. 1473 — Dutch lion, soccer ball with host county flag and year: a, Italy, 1934. b, France, 1938. c, West Germany, 1974. d, Argentina, 1978. e, Italy, 1990. f, United States, 1994. g, France, 1998. h, Germany, 2006. i, South Africa, 2010, j, Brazil, 2014.

2014, May 19 Litho. *Perf. 13¼x13½*
1473	A672	Sheet of 10	17.50	17.50
a.-j.		1 Any single	1.75	1.75

On day of issue, Nos. 1473a-1473j sold for 64c.

Personalized Stamp — A673

2014, July 1 Litho. *Perf. 13½x14*
1474	A673	1 Internationaal multi	3.00 3.00

No. 1474 sold for €1.05 on day of issue. The vignette shown is the generic image available on the day of issue. Vignettes could be personalized for a fee.

Miniature Sheet

Dutch Connections With Japan — A674

No. 1475: a, Gentaku Otsuki (1757-1827), Japanese expert on the Dutch ("1" at UL). b, Philipp Franz von Siebold (1796-1866), physician in Japan ("1" at UR). c, The Courtesan, by Vincent van Gogh ("1" at UL). d, The Red Kimono, by George Hendrik Breitner ("1" at UR). e, Dutch ship Liefde ("1" at UL). f, Dejima

Island, detail of painting by Keiga Kawahara ("1" at UR).

2014, July 14 Litho. *Perf. 13¼x13½*
1475	A674	Sheet of 6	18.00	18.00
a.-f.		1 Internationaal Any single	3.00	3.00

Nos. 1475a-1475f each sold for €1.05 on day of issue. No. 1475 was printed with three different illustrations in the bottom sheet margin, with each sheet having a different arrangement of stamps. Sheet margins at left and right served as etiquettes.

Royal Family Riding Bicycles — A675

King Willem-Alexander and Queen Máxima at 2014 Winter Olympics — A676

King Willem-Alexander and Queen Máxima — A677

2001 Announcement of Engagement A678

Royal Family in New York City A679

2014, Aug. 2 Litho. *Perf. 13¼x13½*
1476		Vert. strip of 5	8.75	8.75
a.	A675	1 multi	1.75	1.75
b.	A676	1 multi	1.75	1.75
c.	A677	1 multi	1.75	1.75
d.	A678	1 multi	1.75	1.75
e.	A679	1 multi	1.75	1.75

12½ year anniv. of marriage of King Willem-Alexander and Queen Máxima. Printed in sheets containing two vertical strips. Nos. 1476a-1476e each sold for 64c on day of sale.

Miniature Sheet

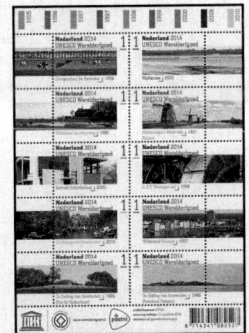

UNESCO World Heritage Sites in the Netherlands — A680

No. 1477: a, Beemster Polder, 1999. b, Wadden Sea, 2009. c, Schokland and Surroundings, 1995. d, Windmill Network at Kinderdijk-Elshout, 1997. e, Rietveld Schröder House, 2000. f, D.F. Wouda Steam Pumping Station, 1998. g, Canal Ring of Amsterdam, 2010. h, Willemstad, Curaçao, 1997. i, Fort near Spijkerboor, Defense Ring of Amsterdam, 1996. j, Pampus Island Fort, Defense Ring of Amsterdam, 1996.

Perf. 13¼x13½
2014, Aug. 11 Litho.
1477	A680	Sheet of 10	17.50	17.50
a.-j.		1 Any single	1.75	1.75
k.		Booklet pane of 2, #1477a-1477b	6.75	
l.		Booklet pane of 2, #1477c-1477d	6.75	
m.		Booklet pane of 2, #1477e-1477f	6.75	
n.		Booklet pane of 2, #1477g-1477h	6.75	
o.		Booklet pane of 2, #1477i-1477j	6.75	
		Complete booklet, #1477k-1477o	34.00	

On day of issue, Nos. 1477a-1477j each sold for 64c. Complete booklet sold for €12.45.

Miniature Sheet

Railways in the Netherlands, 175th Anniv. — A681

No. 1478: a, Locomotives and electric cable towers. b, Locomotive, clock with second hand, Arnhem train station stairway and escalator. c, Tile work and Haarlem station. d, Electric locomotive and map of railway line stations. e, Vertical lift railway bridge, green track signal. f, Emblem for Tienertoer reduced rate program, winged wheel emblem. g, Locomotive and red track signal. h, Clock without second hand, Rotterdam train station. i, New and old symbols for Netherlands Railways, track network. j, Locomotive, Netherlands #215.

2014, Sept. 8 Litho. *Perf. 13¼x13½*
1478	A681	Sheet of 10	16.00	16.00
a.-j.		1 Any single	1.60	1.60
k.		Booklet pane of 2, #1478a-1478b	6.50	—
l.		Booklet pane of 2, #1478c-1478d	6.50	—
m.		Booklet pane of 2, #1478e-1478f	6.50	—
n.		Booklet pane of 2, #1478g-1478h	6.50	—
o.		Booklet pane of 2, #1478i-1478j	6.50	—
		Complete booklet, #1478k-1478o	32.50	

On day of issue, Nos. 1478a-1478j each sold for 64c. Complete booklet sold for €12.45.

Hardwell, Disk Jockey A682

Tiesto, Disk Jockey A683

Afrojack, Disk Jockey A684

Dash Berlin, Disk Jockey A685

Armin Van Buuren, Disk Jockey — A686

2014, Oct. 6 Litho. *Perf. 13½x13¼*
1479		Horiz. strip of 5	8.00	8.00
a.	A682	1 multi	1.60	1.60
b.	A683	1 multi	1.60	1.60
c.	A684	1 multi	1.60	1.60
d.	A685	1 multi	1.60	1.60
e.	A686	1 multi	1.60	1.60

Printed in sheets containing two strips. On day of issue, Nos. 1479a-1479e each sold for 64c.

Stamp Day — A687

2014, Oct. 17 Litho. *Perf. 13x13¼*
1480 A687 1 multi   1.60 1.60
  a.   Booklet pane of 2   6.25
    Complete booklet, 5 #1480a   31.50

On day of issue No. 1480 sold for 64c. Complete booklet sold for €12.45. The five examples of No. 1480a in the complete booklet have different margins.

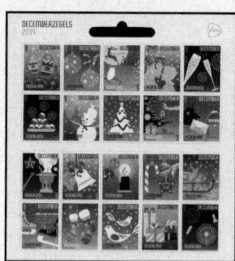

December Stamps — A688

No. 1481: a, Mittens. b, Two round Christmas ornaments. c, Owl, Santa's sleigh in flight. d, People kissing under mistletoe. e, Champagne flutes. f, Plate of Christmas pastries. g, Snowman. h, Christmas tree. i, Hand placing ornament on Christmas tree. j, House, envelope, mailbox. k, Fondue pot and Christmas ornament. l, Bells. m, Candle. n, Candy cane and Christmas ornament. o, Reindeer and sleigh. p, Ice skates. q, Stockings. r, Birds. s, Wrapped gifts. t, Rockets and fireworks.

Serpentine Die Cut 12½
2014, Nov. 17   Photo.
Self-Adhesive
1481 A688   Booklet pane of 20   30.00
  a.-t.   (59c) Any single   1.50 1.50

Miniature Sheet

Dutch Top 40 Music Rankings, 50th Anniv. — A689

No. 1482: a, "Radar Love," by Golden Earring. b, "One Way Wind," by The Cats. c, "Willempie," by André van Duin. d, "Mon Amour," by BZN. e, "No Limit," by 2 Unlimited. f, "Vlieg Met Me Mee," by Paul de Leeuw. g, "Dromen Zijn Bedrog," by Marco Borsato. h, "We're Going to Ibiza!" by Vengaboys. i, "Cupido," by Jan Smit. j, "Birds," by Anouk.

2015, Jan. 5   Litho.   *Perf. 13½x13¼*
1482 A689   Sheet of 10   16.00 16.00
  a.-j.   1 Any single   1.60 1.60

On day of issue, Nos. 1482a-1482j each sold for 69c.

Fortified Towns — A690

Fortifications of: No. 1483, Bourtange. No. 1484, Elburg. No. 1485, Naarden. No. 1486, Willemstad. No. 1487, Hulst.

2015   Litho.   *Perf. 14½x14¼*
1483 A690 1 multi   1.60 1.60
  a. Perf. 13½x12¾   2.75 2.75
  b. Booklet pane of 2 #1483a   5.50
1484 A690 1 multi   1.60 1.60
  a. Perf. 13½x12¾   2.75 2.75
  b. Booklet pane of 2 #1484a   5.50
1485 A690 1 multi   1.60 1.60
  a. Perf. 13½x12¾   2.75 2.75
  b. Booklet pane of 2 #1485a   5.50
1486 A690 1 multi   1.60 1.60
  a. Perf. 13½x12¾   2.75 2.75
  b. Booklet pane of 2 #1486a   5.50
1487 A690 1 multi   1.60 1.60
  a. Perf. 13½x12¾   2.75 2.75
  b. Booklet pane of 2 #1487a   5.50
    Complete booklet, #1483b, 1484b, 1485b, 1486b, 1487b   27.50
  c. Souvenir sheet of 5, #1483-1487   8.00 8.00
    Nos. 1483-1487 (5)   8.00 8.00

Issued: Nos. 1483, 1484, 1485, 2/2/15. Nos. 1483a, 1484a, 1485a, 1486, 1486a, 1487, 1487b, 5/26/15. Nos. 1483-1487 each sold for 69c on day of issue. Complete booklet sold for €12.45.

Baby Carriage, Baby Bottle, Rocking Horse and Baby Toys — A691

Die Cut Perf. 14¼x14½
2015, Mar. 2   Photo.
Self-Adhesive
1488 A691 1 multi   1.60 1.60

No. 1488 sold for 69c on day of issue.

Map of Netherlands and Royal Items A692

No. 1489 — Map and: a, Royal arms, inscription "Koning Willem-Alexander / 2013." b, Signature of King William I. inscription "Koning Willem I / 1815."

2015, Mar. 2   Litho.   *Perf. 13½x13¼*
1489 A692   Pair, #a-b   6.50 6.50
  a.-b.   2 Either single   3.25 3.25

On day of issue, Nos. 1489a and 1489b each sold for €1.38.

Bridges A693

No. 1490: a and k, High speed railroad Bridge, Moerdijk, 2006. b and l, Ehzer Bridge, Almen, 1946. c and m, Kolenhaven Bridge, Delft, 2004. d and n, Cable-stayed bridge, Heusden, 1989. e and o, Zouthaven Bridge, Amsterdam, 2005. f and p, Jan Waaijer Bridge, Zoetermeer, 2013. g and q, De Oversteek Bridge, Nijmegen, 2013. h and r, Zeeland Bridge, Oosterschelde, 1965. i and s, Hanzeboog Bridge, Zwolle, 2011. j and t, Nescio Bridge, Amsterdam, 2006.

Perf. 13½x12¾
2015, Mar. 30   Litho.
1490 A693   Sheet of 10   16.00 16.00
  a.-j.   1 Any single   1.60 1.60
  k.-t.   1 Any single, perf. 14½x14¼   2.75 2.75
  u.   Booklet pane of 2, #1490k-1490l   5.50
  v.   Booklet pane of 2, #1490m-1490n   5.50
  w.   Booklet pane of 2, #1490o-1490p   5.50
  x.   Booklet pane of 2, #1490q-1490r   5.50
  y.   Booklet pane of 2, #1490s-1490t   5.50
    Complete booklet, #1490u, 1490v, 1490w, 1490x, 1490y   27.50

On day of issue, Nos. 1490a-1490j each sold for 69c. Complete booklet sold for €12.45. Descriptions of the bridges shown are found on the adjacent sheet selvage.

Hearts and Dots — A694

Die Cut Perf. 14¼x14½
2015, Apr. 28   Photo.
Booklet Stamp
Self-Adhesive
1491 A694 1 multi   1.60 1.60
  a.   Booklet pane of 10   16.00

No. 1491 sold for 69c on day of issue.

Toys and Games A695

No. 1492: a, Video game equipment. b, Rubik's cube.
No. 1493: a, Robot and wind-up key. b, Board game.

2015, Apr. 28   Litho.   *Perf. 13¼x13½*
1492 A695   Horiz. pair   3.25 3.25
  a.-b.   1 Either single   1.60 1.60
1493 A695   Horiz. pair   5.25 5.25
  a.-b.   1 International Either single   2.60 2.60

Europa (No. 1493). On day of issue, Nos. 1492a-1492b each sold for 69c; Nos. 1493a-1493b, €1.15.

Flora and Fauna of the Naardermeer Nature Reserve — A696

No. 1494: a and k, Alnus glutinosa. b and l, Phalacrocorax carbo. c and m, Phragmites australis. d and n, Acrocephalus scirpaceus. e and o, Dactylorhiza majalis subspecies praetermissa. f and p, Natrix natrix. g and q, Nymphaea alba. h and r, Podiceps cristatus. i and s, Nymphoides peltata. j and t, Esox lucius.

2015, Apr. 28   Litho.   *Perf. 13¼x12¾*
1494 A696   Sheet of 10   16.00 16.00
  a.-j.   1 Any single   1.60 1.60
  k.-t.   1 Any single, perf. 14¼x14¼   2.75 2.75
  u.   Booklet pane of 2, #1494s-1494t   5.50
  v.   Booklet pane of 2, #1494q-1494r   5.50
  w.   Booklet pane of 2, #1494o-1494p   5.50
  x.   Booklet pane of 2, #1494m-1494n   5.50
  y.   Booklet pane of 2, #1494k-1494l   5.50
    Complete booklet, #1494u, 1494v, 1494w, 1494x, 1494y   27.50

On day of issue, Nos. 1494a-1494j each sold for 69c. Complete booklet sold for €12.45.

Volvo Ocean Race A697

No. 1495: a, Three crewmembers on boat. b, Wave crashing against sailboat with Volvo Ocean Race emblem on bow. c, Sailboats in harbor. d, Four crewmembers in protective gear. e, View from mast of crew on deck. f, Boat with sail inscribed "Vestas."

2015, May 26   Litho.   *Perf. 13¼x13¾*
1495 A697   Block of 6   9.75 9.75
  a.-f.   1 Any single   1.60 1.60

On day of issue, Nos. 1495a-1495f each sold for 69c.

King William II (1792-1849) — A698

Perf. 13½x13¼
2015, June 22   Litho.
1496 A698 1 Internationaal multi   2.60 2.60

Battle of Waterloo, 200th anniv. No. 1496 sold for €1.15 on day of issue.

Simple Science Experiments — A699

No. 1497: a, Match under egg passing through neck of bottle. b, Water in heated balloon. c, Battery made of lemons. d, Optical illusion of pencil behind glass of water. e, Lightbulb and positively and negatively charged balloons.

2015, July 20   Litho.   *Perf. 13½x13¼*
1497   Horiz. strip of 5   7.50 7.50
  a.-e.   A699 1 Any single   1.50 1.50

On day of issue, Nos. 1497a-1497e each sold for 69c.

Famous Men and Excerpts From Their Letters A700

No. 1498: a and k, Vincent van Gogh (1853-90), painter. b and l, Signature and excerpt from letter by van Gogh. c and m, Signature and excerpt from letter by Leo Vroman (1915-2014), poet. d and n, Vroman. e and o, Rembrandt van Rijn (1606-69), painter. f and p, Signature and excerpt from letter by Rembrandt. g and q, Signature and excerpt from letter by Desiderius Erasmus (1466-1536), theologian. h and r, Erasmus. i and s, Christiaan Huygens (1629-95), scientist. j and t, Signature and excerpt of letter by Huygens.

Perf. 13½x12¾
2015, Aug. 17   Litho.
1498 A700   Sheet of 10 + 5 labels   16.00 16.00
  a.-j.   1 Any single   1.60 1.60
  k.-t.   1 Any single, perf. 14½   2.75 2.75
  u.   Booklet pane of 2, #1498k-1498l   5.50
  v.   Booklet pane of 2, #1498m-1498n   5.50
  w.   Booklet pane of 2, #1498o-1498p   5.50
  x.   Booklet pane of 2, #1498q-1498r   5.50
  y.   Booklet pane of 2, #1498s-1498t   5.50
    Complete booklet, #1498u, 1498v, 1498w, 1498x, 1498y   27.50

On day of issue, Nos. 1498a-1498j each sold for 69c. Complete booklet sold for €12.45.

Miniature Sheet

Photographs of Animals by Charlotte Dumas — A701

No. 1499 — Title of photograph: a, Retrieved (retriever named Guinness and trailer in background), 2011. b, Day is Done, 2004 (horse named Isolde, white wall behind horse), 2004. c, Reverie (wolf named Taza sleeping), 2005. d, Tiger Tiger (tiger named

Zeus), 2007. e, Heart Shaped Hole (dog named Tom Tom standing next to wall), 2008. f, Retrieved (dog named Moxie sitting on dock), 2011. g, Randagi (street dog laying on step), 2006. h, Anima (horse named Ringo in darkened stall), 2012. i, The Widest Prairies (horse named Rocky Road standing in field), 2013. j, Casa Voyageurs (cat named Kat), 2012.

Perf. 13¼x13½

2015, Sept. 14			Litho.
1499	A701	Sheet of 10	16.00 16.00
a.-j.	1 Any single		1.60 1.60

On day of issue Nos. 1499a-1499j each sold for 69c. Titles of photographs are in sheet selvage adjacent to each stamp.

Miniature Sheet

Dutch Connections With the United States of America — A702

No. 1500: a, "Jan Kees" on pinstriped uniform in script of New York Yankees emblem. b, New York City subway signs using Dutch spellings of Harlem and Brooklyn. c, City Hall, The Hague, designed by Richard Meier. d, High Line Linear Park, New York City. e, Hotdog USA, by Jan Cremer. f, Photograph of breakedancer Kid Freeze holding boom box, by Jamel Shabazz.

Perf. 13¼x13½

2015, Sept. 14			Litho.
1500	A702	Sheet of 6	16.00 16.00
a.-f.	1 International single		2.60 2.60

Nos. 1500a-1500f each sold for €1.15 on day of issue. No. 1500 was printed with three different illustrations in the bottom sheet margin, with each sheet having a different arrangement of stamps. Sheet margins at left and right served as etiquettes.

Miniature Sheet

Netherlands at Night as Seen From Space — A703

No. 1501: a, West Frisian Islands. b, Northern Netherlands (area around Groningen and Leeuwarden). c, North Holland Province (area around Alkmaar). d, Drenthe and Overijssel Provinces (area around Hoogeveen and Meppel). e, Area around Amsterdam and Utrecht. f, Flevoland Province (area around Deventer and Apeldoorn). g, Area around Rotterdam. h, Area around Nijmegen and 's Hertogenbosch. i, Zeeland Province and North Brabant Province area north of Belgian border. j, Southeastern Netherlands (area around Eindhoven and Echt).

Perf. 13¼x13½

2015, Oct. 12			Litho.
1501	A703	Sheet of 10	16.00 16.00
a.-j.	1 Any single		1.60 1.60

On day of issue Nos. 1501a-1501j each sold for 69c.

Ship Models at Rotterdam Maritime Museum — A704

No. 1502: a and k, Aegir. b and l, Bomschuit. c and m, Trio. d and n, Sindoro. e and o, Sultan van Koetei. f and p, Fairmount Expedition. g and q, Mataró. h and r, Assahan. i and s, Nedlloyd Houtman. j and t, Padmos/Blijdorp.

2015, Oct. 12		Litho.	Perf. 13½x12¾
1502	A704	Sheet of 10	16.00 16.00
a.-j.	1 Any single		1.60 1.60
k.-t.	1 Any single, perf. 14½		2.75 2.75
u.	Booklet pane of 2, #1502q, 1502t		5.50 —
v.	Booklet pane of 2, #1502l, 1502m		5.50 —
w.	Booklet pane of 2, #1502r, 1502o		5.50 —
x.	Booklet pane of 2, #1502r, 1502s		5.50 —
y.	Booklet pane of 2, #1502k, 1502p		5.50 —
	Complete booklet, #1502u, 1502v, 1502w, 1502x, 1502y		27.50

On day of issue Nos. 1502a-1502j each sold for 69c. Complete booklet sold for €12.45.

Netherlands No. 266 — A705

2015, Oct. 16		Litho.	Perf. 13½x14
1503	A705	1 multi	1.60 1.60
a.	Booklet pane of 2		5.50 —
	Complete booklet, 5 #1503a		27.50

No. 1503 sold for 69c on day of issue. Complete booklet sold for €12.45. The five examples of No. 1503a in the complete booklet have different margins.

December Stamps — A706

No. 1504 — Snowflakes and: a, Fox in den, deer and bird. b, Woman and deer. c, Bird on woman's hand. d, Swans. e, Polar bear and bird. f, Rabbits. g, Squirrels. h, Birds in flight. i, Woman and dog. j, Rabbit, bird, fawn, and deer.

Serpentine Die Cut 12½x12¾

2015, Nov. 24			Photo.
Self-Adhesive			
1504	A706	Block of 10	14.00
a.-j.	(64c) Any single		1.40 1.40

The Hay Wagon, by Hieronymus Bosch (c. 1450-1516) — A707

No. 1505 — Painting details: a and k, Man holding stick, woman holding infant. b and l, Wagon wheel, woman holding stick. c and m, Man in blue with lifted arms at side of wagon. d and n, Man in red looking at wagon wheel from behind. e and o, People with heads of animals.

f and p, Man holding stick and carrying infant on back, child. g and q, Bird roasting on a spit. h and r, Man looking in woman's mouth. i and s, Bagpipe player and nun holding hay. j and t, Woman reaching in bag of hay, monk holding glass.

2016, Jan. 4		Litho.	Perf. 13½x13¼
1505	A707	Sheet of 10	16.00 16.00
a.-j.	1 Any single		1.60 1.60
k.	Booklet pane of 2, #1505a, 1505f		5.50 —
l.	Booklet pane of 2, #1505b, 1505g		5.50 —
m.	Booklet pane of 2, #1505c, 1505h		5.50 —
n.	Booklet pane of 2, #1505d, 1505i		5.50 —
o.	Booklet pane of 2, #1505e, 1505j		5.50 —
	Complete booklet, #1505k, 1505l, 1505m, 1505n, 1505o		27.50

On day of issue, Nos. 1505a-1505j each sold for 73c. Complete booklet sold for €12.45.

Fishing Communities — A708

Designs: No. 1506, Urk. No. 1507, Zoutkamp. No. 1508, Volendam. No. 1509, Arnemuiden. No. 1510, Scheveningen.

2016		Litho.	Perf. 14½x14¼
1506	A708	1 multi	1.60 1.60
a.	Perf. 13½x12¾		2.75 2.75
b.	Booklet pane of 2 #1506a		5.50 —
1507	A708	1 multi	1.60 1.60
a.	Perf. 13½x12¾		2.75 2.75
b.	Booklet pane of 2 #1507a		5.50 —
1508	A708	1 multi	1.60 1.60
a.	Perf. 13½x12¾		2.75 2.75
b.	Booklet pane of 2 #1508a		5.50 —
1509	A708	1 multi	1.60 1.60
a.	Perf. 13½x12¾		2.75 2.75
b.	Booklet pane of 2 #1509a		5.50 —
1510	A708	1 multi	1.60 1.60
a.	Perf. 13½x12¾		2.75 2.75
b.	Booklet pane of 2 #1510a		5.50 —
	Complete booklet, #1506b, 1507b, 1508b, 1509b, 1510b		27.50
c.	Souvenir sheet of 5, #1506-1510		8.00 8.00
	Nos. 1506-1510 (5)		8.00 8.00

Issued: Nos. 1506, 1507, 1508, 2/1. Nos. 1506a, 1507a, 1508a, 1509, 1509a, 1510, 1510a, 1510b, 1510c, 5/23. Nos. 1506-1510 each sold for 73c on day of issue. Complete booklet sold for €12.45.

Miniature Sheet

Postcrossing — A709

No. 1511 — Inscriptions: a, Deltawerken (Delta works). b, De Waddeneiland (Wadden Island). c, De Hoge Veluwe (Hoge Veluwe National Park). d, Het Binnenhof (Binnenhof, The Hague) e, Alkmaar Kaasmarkt (Alkmaar Cheese Market). f, Bollenvelden (Flower fields). g, Giethoorn. h, Marken. i, Zaanse Schans. j, Nacht Wacht (Night Watch).

Perf. 13¼x13½

2016, Mar. 29			Litho.
1511	A709	Sheet of 10	30.00 30.00
a.-j.	1 International Any single		

On day of issue Nos. 1511a-1511j each sold for €1.25. Sheet margins at left and right served as etiquettes.

Europa A710

No. 1512: a, Painter with roller, buildings, wind generators, bicyclist. b, Bicycle.

2016, Apr. 25		Litho.	Perf. 13¼x13½
1512	A710	Pair	6.00 6.00
a.-b.	1 International Either single		3.00 3.00

Think Green Issue.
On day of issue, Nos. 1512a-1512b each sold for €1.25.

Miniature Sheet

Birds From Griend in the Wadden Islands A711

No. 1513: a, Thalasseus sandvicensis in flight. b, Two Haematopus ostralegus in flight. c, Tadorna tadorna with bill in water. d, Limosa lapponica with beak in water. e, Two Calidris alpina on land. f, Pluvialis squatarola walking. g, Charadrius hiaticula on nest. h, Sterna hirundo on nest. i, Head of Calidris canutus. j, Head of Somateria mollissima.

2016, Apr. 25		Litho.	Perf. 13¼x13½
1513	A711	Sheet of 10	17.50 17.50
a.-j.	1 Any single		1.75 1.75
k.	Booklet pane of 2, #1513a-1513b		6.00 —
l.	Booklet pane of 2, #1513c-1513d		6.00 —
m.	Booklet pane of 2, #1513e-1513f		6.00 —
n.	Booklet pane of 2, #1513g-1513h		6.00 —
o.	Booklet pane of 2, #1513i-1513j		6.00 —
	Complete booklet, #1513k, 1513l, 1513m, 1513n, 1513o		30.00

Latin names of birds are on the selvage to left or right of the stamps. On day of issue Nos. 1513a-1513j each sold for 73c. Complete booklet sold for €12.45.

Wolfgang Amadeus Mozart in the Netherlands — A712

No. 1514: a, Musical score at left, Mozart at right. b, Mozart at left, Müller Organ, Church of St. Bavo, Haarlem.

2016, May 23		Litho.	Perf. 13¼x13½
1514	A712	Horiz. pair	3.25 3.25
a.-b.	1 Either single		1.60 1.60

On day of issue, Nos. 1514a-1514b each sold for 73c.

Photographs by Ed van der Elsken (1925-90) — A713

No. 1501: a, Women crossing street, women standing on street corner. b, People lying on grass, woman and girls. c, Man lighting cigarette near car, woman and child wearing helmets on bicycle. d, People kissing. e, Women standing near track lanes, men on motorcycles. f, Man with tattoos on cobblestone street, man, woman holding child and cigarette. g, Man and woman holding gardening tools, man, woman pushing baby carriage. h, Man and woman walking past older woman at street corner, woman adjusting shoe near fence. i, Young woman standing in field, man, woman and child standing on vehicle rails. j, Man and woman on crowded street, seated woman.

2016, May 23 Litho. Perf. 13¼x13½
1515	A713	Sheet of 10	16.00	16.00
a.-j.		1 Any single	1.60	1.60

On day of issue Nos. 1515a-1515j each sold for 73c.

Comic Book Characters by Marten Toonder A714

No. 1516: a, Tom Poes. b, Olivier B. Bommel.

2016, June 3 Litho. Perf. 13½x13¼
1516	A714	Pair	3.25	3.25
a.-b.		1 Either single	1.60	1.60

Tom Poes, 75th anniv. On day of issue, Nos. 1516a-1516b each sold for 73c.

Europride Amsterdam 2016 Gay Pride Festival A715

No. 1517: a, Woman, stars at top of circle. b, Man, stars at bottom of circle.

2016, July 18 Litho. Perf. 13½x13¼
1517	A715	Pair	3.25	3.25
a.-b.		1 Either single	1.60	1.60

On day of issue, Nos. 1517a-1517b each sold for 73c.

Souvenir Sheet

2016 Summer Olympics, Rio de Janeiro — A716

No. 1518 — Netherlands team emblem on winner's platform in: a, Gold (36x50mm). b, Silver (36x25mm). c, Bronze (36x25mm).

2016, July 18 Litho. Perf. 14½
1518	A716	Sheet of 3	5.00	5.00
a.-c.		1 Any single	1.60	1.60

On day of issue, Nos. 1518a-1518c each sold for 73c.

Miniature Sheet

Apple and Pear Varieties A717

No. 1513: a, Cox's orange pippeling apples. b, Brielsche Calville apples. c, Bezy van Schonauwen pears. d, Winterriet pears. e, Rode Herftscalville apples. f, Ananas Reinette apples. g, Williams pears. h, Ponds pears. i, Schone van Boskoop apples. j, Zoete Ermgaard apples.

Perf. 13¼x13½
2016, Aug. 15 Litho.
1519	A717	Sheet of 10	17.50	17.50
a.-j.		1 Any single	1.75	1.75
k.		Booklet pane of 2, #1519a-1519b	6.00	—

---

l.		Booklet pane of 2, #1519c-1519d	6.00	—
m.		Booklet pane of 2, #1519e-1519f	6.00	—
n.		Booklet pane of 2, #1519g-1519h	6.00	—
o.		Booklet pane of 2, #1519i-1519j	6.00	—
		Complete booklet, #1519k, 1519l, 1519m, 1519n, 1519o	30.00	

On day of issue Nos. 1519a-1519j each sold for 73c. Complete booklet sold for €12.45.

Miniature Sheet

Dutch Connections With Australia — A718

No. 1520: a, Sydney Harbour Bridge. b, Moving crate of 100,000th Dutch emigrant to Australia on dock. c, Radio telescope in Australian desert. d, Water purification plant. e, Nautical chart showing Dirk Hartog's Island. f, Dutch East India Company ship Duyfken.

Perf. 13¼x13½
2016, Aug. 15 Litho.
1520	A718	Sheet of 6	18.00	18.00
a.-f.		1 Internationaal Any single	3.00	3.00

Nos. 1520a-1520f each sold for €1.25 on day of issue. No. 1520 was printed with three different illustrations in the bottom sheet margin, with each sheet having a different arrangement of stamps. Sheet margins at left and right served as etiquettes.

Schiphol Airport, Cent. — A719

No. 1521: a, Airplanes, terminal and control tower. b, Airport check-in area. c, Sign to Gates B21-B33. d, Airplane and portable boarding stairway. e, Old KLM ticket counter and waiting room.

Perf. 13¼x13½
2016, Sept. 12 Litho.
1521		Vert. strip of 5	8.00	8.00
a.-e.	A719	1 Any single	1.60	1.60

On day of issue, Nos. 1521a-1521c each sold for 73c.

Photographs of Model Doutzen Kroes by Anton Corbijn — A720

No. 1522 — Kroes: a, With arms raised, no blue violet circle. b, Wearing white panties, blue violet circle over lower back. c, With two blue violet circles over eyes. d, Wearing black swimsuit, blue violet circle at UR. e, Facing left, wearing swimsuit with white straps, large blue violet circle at UR. f, With large blue violet circle over back of ear, jaw and neck. g, Wearing white swimsuit, blue violet circle over legs. h, Topless, with arms crossed, blue violet circle at UR. i, Wearing white swimsuit, looking at hands, small blue violet circle above fingers. j, Wearing black swimsuit, blue violet circle over fingertips.

Perf. 13½x13¼
2016, Sept. 12 Litho.
1522	A720	Sheet of 10	16.00	16.00
a.-j.		1 Any single	1.60	1.60

On day of issue Nos. 1522a-1522j each sold for 73c.

Miniature Sheet

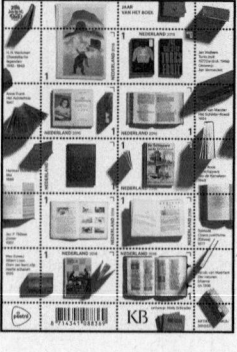

Book Year A721

No. 1523: a, Illustration from *Chassidische Legenden*, by H. N. Werkman. b, Cover of *Turks Fruit*, by Jan Wolkers. c, Photograph and title page of the *Het Achterhuis (Diary of Anne Frank)*. d, Pages from *Het Schilder-Boeke*, by Karel van Mander. e, *Mei*, by Herman Gorter. f, Cover of *De Schippers van de Kameleon*, by H. de Roos. g, Pages and illustrations of insects from *Zomer*, by Jac. P. Thijsse. h, Title page from *Opera Postuma / Ethica*, by Spinoza. i, Cover of *Oom Jan Leert Zijn Neefje Schaken*, by Max Euwe and Alber Loon. j, Pages with illustrations from *Der Naturen Bloeme*, by Jacob van Maerlant.

Perf. 13¼x13½
2016, Sept. 12 Litho.
1523	A721	Sheet of 10	16.00	16.00
a.-j.		1 Any single	1.60	1.60
k.		Booklet pane of 2, #1523a-1523b	5.50	
l.		Booklet pane of 2, #1523c-1523d	5.50	
m.		Booklet pane of 2, #1523e-1523f	5.50	
n.		Booklet pane of 2, #1523g-1523h	5.50	
o.		Booklet pane of 2, #1523i-1523j	5.50	
		Complete booklet, #1523k, 1523l, 1523m, 1523n, 1523o	27.50	

Titles and authors are on the selvage to left or right of the stamps. On day of issue Nos. 1523a-1523j each sold for 73c. Complete booklet sold for €12.45.

Kings William I, William II, William III, Queen Wilhelmina — A722

2016, Oct. 14 Litho. Perf. 13¼x13
1524	A722	1 multi	1.60	1.60
a.		Booklet pane of 2	5.50	
		Complete booklet, 5 #1524a	27.50	

No. 1524 sold for 73c on day of issue. Complete booklet sold for €12.45. The five examples of No. 1524a in the complete booklet have different margins.

December Stamps — A723

Designs: No. 1525, Fingers of people making five-pointed star. No. 1526, Gifts on sled. No. 1527, Ice skate. No. 1528, Snow sphere with snowman. No. 1529, Squirrels. No. 1530, Snowflake, Christmas tree and Star of Bethlehem ornaments. No. 1531, Bicycle carrying Christmas tree. No. 1532, Two Christmas ornaments and drink mug. No. 1533, Two champagne glasses. No. 1534, Silhouette of person wearing stocking cap and scarf, Dutch building. No. 1535, Bells, record on turntable.

Serpentine Die Cut 12½
2016, Nov. 14 Litho.
Self-Adhesive
1525	A723	(65c) multi	1.40	1.40
1526	A723	(65c) multi	1.40	1.40
1527	A723	(65c) multi	1.40	1.40
1528	A723	(65c) multi	1.40	1.40

1529	A723	(65c) multi	1.40	1.40
1530	A723	(65c) multi	1.40	1.40
1531	A723	(65c) multi	1.40	1.40
1532	A723	(65c) multi	1.40	1.40
1533	A723	(65c) multi	1.40	1.40
1534	A723	(65c) multi	1.40	1.40
1535	A723	(65c) multi	1.40	1.40
a.		Block of 11, #1525-1535	15.50	
		Nos. 1525-1535 (11)	15.40	15.40

Nos. 1525-1535 are each inscribed "December" at UR, and were printed in sheets of 21, containing No. 1525 and two each Nos. 1526-1535.

Miniature Sheet

Dutch Chicken Breeds A724

No. 1536: a, Twents hoen. b, Lakenvelder. c, Hollands kuifhoen. d, Kraaikop. e, Nederlandse Uilebaard. f, Noord-Hollands hoen. g, Hollandse kriel. h, Fries hoen. i, Barnevelder. j, Welsumer.

2017, Jan. 2 Litho. Perf. 13¼x12¾
1536	A724	Sheet of 10	16.00	16.00
a.-j.		1 Any single	1.60	1.60
k.-t.		1 As #1536a-1536j, any single, perf. 14¼x14½	1.60	1.60
u.		Booklet pane of 2, #1536k-1536l	5.25	—
v.		Booklet pane of 2, #1536m-1536n	5.25	—
w.		Booklet pane of 2, #1536o-1536p	5.25	—
x.		Booklet pane of 2, #1536q-1536r	5.25	—
y.		Booklet pane of 2, #1536s-1536t	5.25	—
		Complete booklet, #1536u, 1536v, 1536w, 1536x, 1536y	26.50	

Breed are on the selvage to left or right of the stamps. On day of issue Nos. 1536a-1536j each sold for 78c. Complete booklet sold for €12.45.

Silver-Studded Blue Butterflies — A725

Tulips A726

Die Cut Perf. 14½
2017, Jan. 30 Litho.
Self-Adhesive Coil Stamps
1537	A725	1 multi	1.75	1.75
1538	A726	1 Internationaal multi	3.00	3.00

On day of issue, No. 1537 sold for 78c; No. 1538, €1.33. Country name, "1," "Internationaal" and codes were printed on the labels by the vending machine at the time of sale. Stamps with other denominations could not be printed.

River Valley Communities — A727

Designs: No. 1539, Church, Oud-Avereest, map of Reest River. No. 1540, Saxon Farm, map of Drentsche Aa River. No. 1541, Fort Asperen, map of Linge River. No. 1542, Vaantje Ferryhouse, map of Dommel River. No. 1543, Wooden house, map of Geul River.

2017 Litho. Perf. 14¼
1539	A727	1 multi	1.75	1.75
a.		Perf. 13½x12¾	2.75	2.75
b.		Booklet pane of 2 #1539a	5.50	

NETHERLANDS   87

1540	A727	1 multi	1.75	1.75
a.		Perf. 13½x12¾	2.75	2.75
b.		Booklet pane of 2 #1540a	5.50	—
1541	A727	1 multi	1.75	1.75
a.		Perf. 13½x12¾	2.75	2.75
b.		Booklet pane of 2 #1541a	5.50	—
1542	A727	1 multi	1.75	1.75
a.		Perf. 13½x12¾	2.75	2.75
b.		Booklet pane of 2 #1542a	5.50	—
1543	A727	1 multi	1.75	1.75
a.		Perf. 13½x12¾	2.75	2.75
b.		Booklet pane of 2 #1543a	5.50	—
		Complete booklet, #1539b, 1540b, 1541b, 1542b, 1543b	27.50	
c.		Souvenir sheet of 5, #1539-1543	8.75	8.75
		Nos. 1539-1543 (5)	8.75	8.75

Issued: Nos. 1539, 1540, 1541, 1/30. Nos. 1539a, 1540a, 1541a, 1542, 1542a, 1543, 1543a, 1543c, 5/22. Nos. 1539-1543 each sold for 78c on day of issue. Complete booklet sold for €12.45.

Europa
A728

No. 1544: a, Doornenburg Castle, three coats of arms at left. b, Ammersoyen Castle, coat of arms at right.

Perf. 13½x12¾

2017, Feb. 20			Litho.
1544	A728	Horiz. pair	5.75	5.75
a.-b.		1 Internationaal Either single	2.75	2.75

On day of issue, Nos. 1544a-1544b each sold for €1.33.

Miniature Sheet

Special
Moments
A729

No. 1545 — Inscription: a, Gefeliciteerd (31x27mm heart-shaped stamp). b, Liefs (31x27mm heart-shaped stamp). c, Veel geluk (31x27mm heart-shaped stamp). d, Sterkte (28x29mm). e, Succes (28x29mm). f, Hoera (28x29mm). g, Fijne dag (28x29mm). h, Proficiat (31x27mm heart-shaped stamp). i, Voor jou (31x27mm heart-shaped stamp). j, Beterschap (31x27mm heart-shaped stamp).

*Die Cut (heart-shaped stamps),
Serpentine Die Cut 14¼*

2017, Mar. 27			Litho.
		Self-Adhesive	
1545	A729	Sheet of 10 + 7 stickers	17.50	
a.-j.		1 Any single	1.75	1.75

On day of issue, Nos. 1545a-1545j each sold for 78c.

Miniature Sheet

De Stijl Art Movement, Cent. — A730

No. 1546: a, Drawing by Theo van Doesburg (1883-1931), red and blue panels, "1" under red panel. b, Drawing by van Doesburg, yellow and blue panels. c, Drawing by van Doesburg, red and yellow panels. d, Painting of diamond with horizontal and vertical lines by Piet Mondriaan (1872-1944), blue and yellow panels. e, Model of restaurant, by J.J. P. Oud (1890-1963), red and yellow panels, vert. f, De Stijl magazine cover by van Doesburg, yellow and red panels. g, Drawing by van Doesburg, red and blue panels, "1" not under colored panel. h, Chair by Gerrit Rietveld (1888-1964), red and blue panels, vert. i, Architectural drawing by Cornelis van Eesteren (1897-1988), blue and yellow panels. j, Painting of rectangles and squares by Mondrian, yellow and blue panels.

Perf. 13¼x12¾

2017, Mar. 27			Litho.
1546	A730	Sheet of 10	17.50	17.50
a.-j.		1 Any single	1.75	1.75

On day of issue, Nos. 1546a-1546j each sold for 78c.

Miniature Sheet

King Willem-Alexander, 50th
Birthday — A731

No. 1547 — Photograph of King Willem-Alexander: a, Reading book as teenager. b, Standing on stairway. c, Standing in boat near bridge. d, Standing in front of building, wearing winter jacket. e, Wearing blue suit and tie. f, With Queen Máxima.

2017, Apr. 24			Litho.	*Perf. 14½*
1547	A731	Sheet of 6	10.50	10.50
a.-f.		1 Any single	1.75	1.75

On day of issue, Nos. 1547a-1547f each sold for 78c.

Plants in
Dutch
Botanical
Gardens
A732

No. 1548: a, Echinacea purpurea. b, Metasequoia glyptostroboides. c, Pyrostegia venusta. d, Sarracenia flava. e, Veratrum nigrum. f, Ginkgo biloba. g, Arum italicum. h, Vanilla planifolia. i, Clerodendrum trichotomum. j, Atropa belladonna.

2017, Apr. 24		Litho.	*Perf. 12¾x13¼*
1548	A732	Sheet of 10	17.50	17.50
a.-j.		1 Any single	1.75	1.75
k.		Booklet pane of 2, #1548a, 1548f	5.50	—
l.		Booklet pane of 2, #1548b, 1548g	5.50	—
m.		Booklet pane of 2, #1548c, 1548h	5.50	—
n.		Booklet pane of 2, #1548d, 1548i	5.50	—
o.		Booklet pane of 2, #1548e, 1548j	5.50	—
		Complete booklet, #1548k, 1548l, 1548m, 1548n, 1548o	27.50	

On day of issue, Nos. 1548a-1548j each sold for 78c. Complete booklet sold for €12.45.

Netherlands Red Cross,
150th Anniv. — A733

No. 1549: a, Red Cross worker comforting elderly woman. b, Child and Red Cross banner. c, Red Cross worker examining woman's arm.

2017, May 22		Litho.	*Perf. 14½*
1549		Vert. strip of 3	5.25	5.25
a.-c.	A733	1 Any single	1.75	1.75

On day of issue, Nos. 1549a-1549c each sold for 78c.

Foods
A734

Designs: Nos. 1550a, 1550k, Bossche bol. Nos. 1550b, 1550l, Limburgse vlaai. Nos. 1550c, 1550m, Drents kniepertie. Nos. 1550d, 1550n, Fries suikerbrood. Nos. 1550e, 1550o, Zwolse balletjes. Nos. 1550f, 1550p, Goudse stroopwafel. Nos. 1550g, 1550q, Zeeuwse bolus. Nos. 1550h, 1550r, Groningse eierbal.

Nos. 1550i, 1550s, Amsterdamse ui. Nos. 1550j, 1550t, Tielse kermiskoek.

2017, June 19		Litho.	*Perf. 14½*
1550	A734	Sheet of 10	17.50	17.50
a.-j.		1 Any single	1.75	1.75
k.-t.		1 Any single, perf. 12¾x13¼	3.00	3.00
u.		Booklet pane of 2, #1550k, 1550p	6.00	
v.		Booklet pane of 2, #1550l, 1550q	6.00	
w.		Booklet pane of 2, #1550m, 1550r	6.00	
x.		Booklet pane of 2, #1550n, 1550s	6.00	
y.		Booklet pane of 2, #1550o, 1550t	6.00	
		Complete booklet, #1550u, 1550v, 1550w, 1550x, 1550y	30.00	

On day of issue, Nos. 1550a-1550j each sold for 78c. Complete booklet sold for €12.45.

Northern
Gannet — A735

Tub
Gurnard — A736

Brown
Crab — A737

Bladder Wrack
and
Seaweed — A738

Spotted Ray Egg
Case and
Shells — A739

2017, July 17	Litho.	*Perf. 13¼x12¾*
1551		Vert. strip of 5	9.50	9.50
a.	A735	1 multi	1.90	1.90
b.	A736	1 multi	1.90	1.90
c.	A737	1 multi	1.90	1.90
d.	A738	1 multi	1.90	1.90
e.	A739	1 multi	1.90	1.90
f.	A735	1 multi, perf. 14½	3.00	3.00
g.	A736	1 multi, perf. 14½	3.00	3.00
h.	A737	1 multi, perf. 14½	3.00	3.00
i.	A738	1 multi, perf. 14½	3.00	3.00
j.	A739	1 multi, perf. 14½	3.00	3.00
k.		Booklet pane of 2 #1551f	6.00	—
l.		Booklet pane of 2 #1551g	6.00	—
m.		Booklet pane of 2 #1551h	6.00	—
n.		Booklet pane of 2 #1551i	6.00	—
o.		Booklet pane of 2 #1551j	6.00	—
		Complete booklet, #1551k, 1551l, 1551m, 1551n, 1551o	30.00	

On day of issue, Nos. 1551a-1551j each sold for 78c. Complete booklet sold for €12.45.

Miniature Sheet

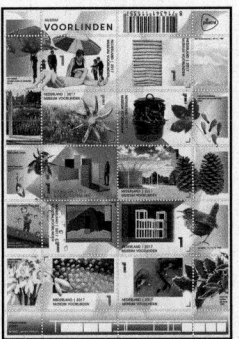

Art in Voorlinden Museum — A740

No. 1552: a, Couple Under an Umbrella, by Ron Mueck, and museum visitors. b, R81-4, by Jan Schoonhoven. c, Flowers and Voorlinden Museum landscaping, by Piet Oudolf. d, Casserole des Moules Noire, by Marcel Broodthaers, and leaf. e, The Performance, by Esther Tielemans. f, Voorlinden Museum and pine cone. g, California #10, by Etel Adnan. h, 2x7x7 by Sol Lewitt, and bird. i, Untitled, by Robert Zandvliet, and flower. j, Larmes de Verre, by Man Ray, and leaf.

2017, July 17		Litho.	*Perf. 14½*
1552	A740	Sheet of 10	19.00	19.00
a.-j.		1 Any single	1.90	1.90

On day of issue, Nos. 1552a-1552j each sold for 78c.

Souvenir Sheet

Multilateral Philatelic Exhibition,
s'Hertogenbosch — A741

No. 1553: a, Zoete Lieve Gerritje Statue, St. John's Cathedral, s'Hertogenbosch. b, Duke's Palace, Remembrance Monument, Luxembourg Philharmonid, Luxembourg, Church of the Assumption, Ljubljana, Slovenia.

2017, Aug. 25		Litho.	*Perf. 14½*
1553	A741	Sheet of 2	5.25	5.25
a.		1 multi	1.90	1.90
b.		1 Internationaal multi	3.25	3.25

On day of issue, No. 1553a sold for 78c, and No. 1553b sold for €1.33. A souvenir sheet containing No. 1553a and Luxembourg No. 1470a was given to standing order customers of Luxembourg Post, and this sheet was sold together with Netherlands No. 1553 and Luxembourg No. 1470 for €15.

Miniature Sheet

Buildings Reconstructed After World
War II — A742

No. 1554: a, Velser Tunnel Ventilation Building, Velsen, 1957 (turquoise green panel at center right). b, Purfina gas station, Arnhem, 1957 (turquoise green panel at center left). c, Industriegebouw, Rotterdam, 1953, (yellow green panel at center left). d, Van Leer Drum Factory, Amstelveen, 1958 (yellow green panel at center right). e, Soesterkwartier residential district, Amersfoort, 1957 (pink panel at center right). f, Gemeenteflat (tree in front of building), Maastricht, 1950 (pink panel at center right). g, De Ploeg Weaving Mill, Bergeijk, 1958 (pale dull green panel at center right). h, Blast furnace at steel factory, IJmuiden, 1951 (pale dull green panel at center left). i, Faculty of Geodesy building, Wageningen, 1953 (orange brown panel at center left). j, Second Liberal Christian Lyceum, The Hague, 1954 (orange brown panel at center right).

Perf. 13¼x12¾

2017, Sept. 11			Litho.
1554	A742	Sheet of 10	19.00	19.00
a.-j.		1 Any single	1.90	1.90

On day of issue, Nos. 1554a-1554j each sold for 78c.

Miniature Sheet

Viktor & Rolf, Fashion Designers, 25th
Anniv. — A743

No. 1555 — Ink spots and drawings of: a, Flower. b, Red high-heeled shoe and eye. c, Woman's face covered by long hair. d, Dress and bow. e, Woman's face and ampersand. f, Woman's head and black curved line. g, Faceless woman wearing dress with puffed shoulders. h, Tan high-heeled shoe. i, Arrows and "V&R". j, Woman with yellow green and pink dress.

2017, Sept. 11   Litho.   *Perf. 14½*
1555	A743	Sheet of 10	19.00	19.00
a.-j.		1 Any single	1.90	1.90

On day of issue, Nos. 1555a-1555j each sold for 78c.

Wood Engraving and Portrait of Princess Wilhelmina Used on 1891-96 Stamps — A744

2017, Oct. 20   Litho.   *Perf. 13¼x14*
1556	A744	1 multi	1.90	1.90
a.		Booklet pane of 2	6.00	6.00
		Complete booklet, 5 #1556a	30.00	

Stamp Day. On day of issue, No. 1556 sold for 78c. Stamps are printed tete-beche on No. 1556a. Complete booklet sold for €12.45 and contains five examples of No. 1556a, each with a different pane margin.

George Michael (1963-2016), Rock Musician A745

String of Christmas Lights A746

Candle Flame A747

Woman and Stars A748

Fork, G Clef and Musical Notes A749

Christmas Bell and Birds A750

Turkey A751

Stylized Christmas Tree, Hands and Accordion A752

Winter Painting and People Holding Champagne Flutes A753

Christmas Cake A754

Serpentine Die Cut 11

2017, Nov. 20   Photo.

Self-Adhesive
1557		Block of 10	17.50	
a.	A745 (73c) multi		1.75	1.75
b.	A746 (73c) multi		1.75	1.75
c.	A747 (73c) multi		1.75	1.75
d.	A748 (73c) multi		1.75	1.75
e.	A749 (73c) multi		1.75	1.75
f.	A750 (73c) multi		1.75	1.75
g.	A751 (73c) multi		1.75	1.75

---

h.	A752 (73c) multi		1.75	1.75
i.	A753 (73c) multi		1.75	1.75
j.	A754 (73c) multi		1.75	1.75

Printed in sheets of 20 containing two each of Nos. 1557a-1557j.

Miniature Sheet

Reptiles and Amphibians — A755

No. 1558 — Inscriptions: a, Levendbarende hagedis. b, Rugstreeppad. c, Kamsalamander. d, Adder. e, Boomkikker. f, Geelbuikvuurpad. g, Gladde slang. h, Ringslang. i, Heikikker. j, Knoflookpad.

2018, Jan. 2   Litho.   *Perf. 13½x14*

Self-Adhesive
1558	A755	Sheet of 10	20.00	20.00
a.-j.		1 Any single	2.00	2.00

Nos. 1558a-1558j each sold for 83c on day of issue. Latin names of animals are found in the sheet margin above or below the stamp.

City Gates — A756

City gates in: No. 1559, Hattem. No. 1560, Vianen. No. 1561, Bergen op Zoom. No. 1562, Culemborg. No. 1563, Zierikzee.

2018   Litho.   *Perf. 14½x14¼*
1559	A756	1 black	2.10	2.10
a.		Perf. 13½x12¾	3.00	3.00
b.		Booklet pane of 2 #1559a	6.00	—
1560	A756	1 black	2.10	2.10
a.		Perf. 13½x12¾	3.00	3.00
b.		Booklet pane of 2 #1560a	6.00	—
1561	A756	1 black	2.10	2.10
a.		Perf. 13½x12¾	3.00	3.00
b.		Booklet pane of 2 #1561a	6.00	—
1562	A756	1 black	1.90	1.90
a.		Perf. 13½x12¾	3.00	3.00
b.		Booklet pane of 2 #1562a	6.00	—
1563	A756	1 black	1.90	1.90
a.		Perf. 13½x12¾	3.00	3.00
b.		Booklet pane of 2 #1563a	6.00	—
		Complete booklet, #1559b, 1560b, 1561b, 1562b, 1563b	30.00	
c.		Souvenir sheet of 5, #1559-1563	10.50	10.50
		Nos. 1559-1563 (5)	10.10	10.10

Issued: Nos. 1559-1561, 1/29; Nos. 1562-1563, 1559a-1563a, 1563c, 6/4. Nos. 1559-1563 each sold for 83c on day of issue. Complete booklet sold for €12.45.

Miniature Sheet

Children's Birthday Party — A757

No. 1564: a, Child sitting in chair reading book, child opening gift, child holding gift, woman greeting attendees. b, Woman and line of children holding gifts. c, Man giving child gift, girl holding gift, two other children. d, Old woman sitting in chair with hands raised, three children. e, Boy, girl and cat. f, Boy annoying man sitting in chair, boy eating birthday cake.

Perf. 13¼x12¾

2018, Feb. 19   Litho.
1564	A757	Sheet of 6	13.00	13.00
a.-f.		1 Any single	2.10	2.10

Nos. 1564a-1564f each sold for 83c on day of issue.

Rijksmuseum van Oudheden (National Museum of Antiquities), Leiden, 200th Anniv. — A758

No. 1565: a and k, Bronze statue of cat, Egypt, 700-300 B.C. b and l, Golden lion's head, Iran, 400 B.C. c and m, Terracotta statue of Eros, Asia Minor, 200-100 B.C. d and n, Gold fibula with precious stones, Wijk bij Duurstede, 800 A.D. e and o, Glass bead depicting face, Egypt, 500-200 B.C. f and p, Wooden case for mummy of Peftjauneith, Egypt, 664-525 B.C. g and q, Wooden figurine of man, Willemstad, Netherlands, 5500-5200 B.C. h and r, Bronze sword, Ommerschans, 1500-1350 B.C. i and s, Marble statue of Bacchus, Italy, 100-200 A.D. j and t, Semi-precious stone sculpture of Empress Livia, Naples area, 10 A.D.

2018, Feb. 19   Litho.   *Perf. 14½*
1565	A758	Sheet of 10	21.00	21.00
a.-j.		1 Any single	2.10	2.10
k.-t.		1 Any single, perf. 12¾x13½	3.00	3.00
u.		Booklet pane of 2, #1565k, 1565p	6.00	—
v.		Booklet pane of 2, #1565l, 1565q	6.00	—
w.		Booklet pane of 2, #1565m, 1565r	6.00	—
x.		Booklet pane of 2, #1565n, 1565s	6.00	—
y.		Booklet pane of 2, #1565o, 1565t	6.00	—
		Complete booklet, #1565u, 1565v, 1565w, 1565x, 1565y	30.00	

Nos. 1565a-1565l each sold for 83c on day of issue. Complete booklet sold for €12.45.

Europa A759

No. 1566: a and c, Dedemsvaart Canal swing bridge, Musselkanaal. b and d, Kwakelbrug bascule bridge (with hanging chain), Edam.

2018, Mar. 26   Litho.   *Perf. 13½x13*
1566	A759	Horiz. pair	7.00	7.00
a.-b.		1 International Either single	3.50	3.50
c.-d.		1 International Perf. 14½x14¼, either single	5.00	5.00
e.		Booklet pane of 2, #1566c-1566d	10.00	
f.		Booklet pane of 2 #1566c	10.00	
g.		Booklet pane of 2 #1566d	10.00	
		Complete booklet, #1566e, 1566f, 1566g	30.00	

Nos. 1566a-1566b each sold for €1.40 on day of issue. Complete booklet sold for €12.45.

Miniature Sheet

Wild Flowers A760

No. 1567 — Inscriptions: a, Fluitenkruid. b, Hazenpootje. c, Wondklaver. d, Madeliefje. e, Gewone ossentong. f, Pinksterbloem. g, Trilgras. h, Paarse morgenster. i, Paardenbloem. j, Smalle weegbree.

2018, Apr. 9   Litho.   *Perf. 13½x14*

Self-Adhesive
1567	A760	Sheet of 10	20.00	20.00
a.-j.		1 Any single	2.00	2.00

Nos. 1567a-1567j each sold for 83c on day of issue. Latin names of flowers are found in the sheet margin above or below the stamp.

Nederland A761

Personalized Stamps — A762

2018, Apr. 23   Litho.   *Perf. 13½x14*
1568	A761	1 multi	2.00	2.00
1569	A762	1 Internationaal multi	3.50	3.50

Self-Adhesive
1570	A761	1 multi	2.00	

On day of issue, Nos. 1568 and 1570 each sold for 83c, and No. 1569 sold for €1.40. The vignettes shown are the generic images available on the day of issue. Vignettes could be personalized for a fee. Used examples of Nos. 1568 and 1570 may be indistinguishable.

In 2019, self-adhesive stamps of type A761, etched on gold foil were produced in limited quantities, packed in an airtight box and sold for €50. In 2022, self-adhesive stamps of type A761, etched on silver foil were produced in limited quantities, packed in a folder and sold for €25.

Groninger Museum's Exhibition of Avant-Garde Art by Members of the De Ploeg Artists Collective — A763

No. 1571: a and k, *Blauwborgje, Shadow*, by Alida Pott, and *After the Visit*, by Jan Altink. b and l, *Dike Along the Rietdiep*, by Altink, *Portrait of a Grammar School Student*, by Jan Jordens, and left half of *Groningen Landscape with Canal*, by Jan Wiegers. c and m, Right half of Wiegers painting and *Composition with Diagonal*, by Wobbe Alkema. d and n, *Groningen May Fair*, by Johan Dijkstra, and left half of *Fish Market*, by George Martens. e and o, Right half of Martens painting and *Seated Nude*, by Wiegers. f and p, Lower portion of Pott painting, *Blauwborgje*, by Job Hansen, upper left portion of *Portrait of George Martens*, by Ekke Kleima, and left half of *Landscape Composition*, by Jan van der Zee. g and q, Right half of van der Zee painting, and *Student Path*, by Dijkstra. h and r, *Portrait of Jan Altink*, by Wiegers, and *Courtyard in Winter*, by Dijkstra. i and s, *Kattendiep in the Rain*, by Martens, *Portrait of H. N. Werkman*, by Altink, and upper left portion of *Façade*, by H. N. Werkman. j and t, Upper right portion of Werkman painting, *Portrait of Alida Pott*, by Martens, and *Composition with the Letter O*, by Werkman.

2018, May 22   Litho.   *Perf. 13x13½*
1571	A763	Sheet of 10	20.00	20.00
a.-j.		1 Any single	2.00	2.00
k.-t.		1 Perf. 12¾x13¼, any single	3.00	3.00
u.		Booklet pane of 2, #1571k, 1571p	6.00	
v.		Booklet pane of 2, #1571l, 1571q	6.00	
w.		Booklet pane of 2, #1571m, 1571r	6.00	
x.		Booklet pane of 2, #1571n, 1571s	6.00	
y.		Booklet pane of 2, #1571o, 1571t	6.00	
		Complete booklet, #1571u, 1571v, 1571w, 1571x, 1571y	30.00	

De Ploeg Artists Collective, cent. On day of issue, Nos. 1571a-1571j each sold for 83c. Complete booklet sold for €12.45. Names of the artists of the painting are found in the upper and lower sheet margins on No. 1571.

Miniature Sheet

Insects
and
Spiders
A764

No. 1572 — Inscriptions: a, Grote beer. b,
Pyjamawants. c, Meikever. d, Zwartbruine
wegmier. e, Olifantsrups. f, Citroenlieveheer-
sbeestje. g, Gewone pantserjuffer. h, Kruispin.
i, Kleine vuurvlinder. j, Moerassprinkhaan.

2018, June 4 Litho. *Perf. 13½x14*
Self-Adhesive
| 1572 | A764 | Sheet of 10 | 20.00 | 20.00 |
| a.-j. | | 1 Any single | 2.00 | 2.00 |

Nos. 1572a-1572j each sold for 83c on day
of issue. Latin names of insects and spider are
found in the sheet margin above or below the
stamp.

Dutch
Guilder
Currency
A765

No. 1573: a and k, Gold lily guilder, c. 1355.
b and l, 1574 paper emergency coin from Leiden. c and m, 1680 proof silver state guilder. d
and n, 1818 proof coins from reign of King
William I. e and o, 1949 2½-guilder note,
Queen Juliana. f and p, Model of 1982 2½-
guilder coin for coronation of Queen Beatrix. g
and q, 1860 1000-guilder note. h and r, 1945
10-guilder note. i and s, 1986 250-guilder
note, j and t, 1997 10-guilder note.

2018, July 23 Litho. *Perf. 13¼x12¾*
1573	A765	Sheet of 10	20.00	20.00
a.-j.		1 Any single	2.00	2.00
k.-t.		1 Perf. 14¼x14½, any single	3.00	3.00
u.		Booklet pane of 2, #1573k,		
		1573l	6.00	—
v.		Booklet pane of 2, #1573m,		
		1573n	6.00	—
w.		Booklet pane of 2, #1573o,		
		1573p	6.00	—
x.		Booklet pane of 2, #1573q,		
		1573r	6.00	—
y.		Booklet pane of 2, #1573s,		
		1573t	6.00	—
		Complete booklet, #1573u,		
		1573v, 1573w, 1573x,		
		1573y	30.00	

On day of issue, Nos. 1573a-1573j each
sold for 83c. Complete booklet sold for
€12.45.

Van Nelle
Factory,
Rotterdam,
1931 — A766

Zonnestraal
Sanatorium,
Hilversum,
1928 — A767

Coöperatie de
Volharding
Building, The
Hague,
1928 — A768

Glaspaleis
Department
Store, Heerlen,
1935 — A769

House, Utrecht,
1931 — A770

Perf. 13¼x12¾
2018, Sept. 17 Litho.
1574		Vert. strip of 5	10.00	10.00
a.	A766	1 multi	2.00	2.00
b.	A767	1 multi	2.00	2.00
c.	A768	1 multi	2.00	2.00
d.	A769	1 multi	2.00	2.00
e.	A770	1 multi	2.00	2.00

On day of issue, Nos. 1574a-1574e each
sold for 83c.

Miniature Sheet

Mushrooms — A771

No. 1575 — Inscriptions: a, Sparrenveertje.
b, Vliegenzwam. c, Takruitertjes. d, Broze russula. e, Knopschimmel op mycena. f,
Heideknotszwam. g, Plooivlieswaaiertje. h,
Echte kopergroenzwam. i, Grote bloedsteel-
mycena. j, Grote sponszwam.

2018, Sept. 17 Litho. *Perf. 13½x14*
Self-Adhesive
| 1575 | A771 | Sheet of 10 | 20.00 | 20.00 |
| a.-j. | | 1 Any single | 2.00 | 2.00 |

Nos. 1575a-1575j each sold for 83c on day
of issue. Latin names of mushrooms are found
in the sheet margin above or below the stamp.

Miniature Sheet

Garden Vegetables — A772

No. 1576: a, Sla (lettuce). b, Aubergine
(eggplant). c, Venkel (fennel). d, Radijs (rad-
ishes). e, Zoete aardappel (sweet potato). f,
Raapstelen (turnip greens).

2018, Oct. 19 Litho. *Perf. 14½*
| 1576 | A772 | Sheet of 6 | 11.50 | 11.50 |
| a.-f. | | 1 Any single | 1.90 | 1.90 |

Nos. 1576a-1576f each sold for 83c on day
of issue.

Stamp Day — A773

2018, Oct. 19 Litho. *Perf. 13½x14*
1577	A773	1 multi	1.90	1.90
a.		Booklet pane of 2	5.75	
		Complete booklet, 5 #1577a	29.00	

No. 1577 sold for 83c on day of issue. Complete booklet sold for €12.45.

December
Stamps — A774

No. 1578: a, Dutch buildings. b, Sweater. c,
Adult and child ice skating. d, Cat and Christmas tree ornament on tree. e, Holiday foods
and table setting. f, Dove carrying letter. g,
Snow globe. h, Christmas tree, envelopes and
gift. i, Gift boxes. j, Man and woman watching
fireworks display.

Serpentine Die Cut 11
2018, Nov. 5 Litho.
Self-Adhesive
| 1578 | | Block of 10 | 17.50 | |
| a.-j. | A774 (78c) Any single | 1.75 | 1.75 |

Printed in sheets of 20 containing two each
Nos. 1578a-1578j.

Personalized
Stamp — A775

2018, Dec. 5 Litho. *Perf. 13½x14*
Self-Adhesive
| 1579 | A775 (78c) multi | 1.75 | 1.75 |

The vignettes shown is the generic image
available on the day of issue. Vignettes could
be personalized for a fee.

Miniature Sheet

Mammals — A776

No. 1580 — Inscriptions: a, Wilde kat. b,
Ingekorven vleermuis. c, Wolf. d, Grijze
zeehond. e, Hermelijn. f, Bunzing. g,
Europese otter. h, Vos. i, Das. j, Konijn.

2019, Jan. 2 Litho. *Perf. 13½x14*
Self-Adhesive
| 1580 | A776 | Sheet of 10 | 20.00 | 20.00 |
| a.-j. | | 1 Any single | 2.00 | 2.00 |

Nos. 1580a-1580j each sold for 87c on day
of issue. Latin names of mammals are found in
the sheet margin above or below the stamp.

Islands — A777

Tourist attractions, landmarks and items
from islands and map of: No. 1581, Texel. No.
1582, Vlieland. No. 1583, Terschelling. No.
1584, Ameland. No. 1585, Schiermonnikoog.

2019 Litho. *Perf. 14¼*
1581	A777	1 multi	2.00	2.00
a.		Booklet pane of 5	14.00	
		Complete booklet, 2 #1581a	28.00	
1582	A777	1 multi	2.00	2.00
a.		Booklet pane of 5	14.00	
		Complete booklet, 2 #1582a	28.00	
1583	A777	1 multi	2.00	2.00
a.		Booklet pane of 5	14.00	
		Complete booklet, 2 #1583a	28.00	
1584	A777	1 multi	2.00	2.00
a.		Booklet pane of 5	14.00	
		Complete booklet, 2 #1584a	28.00	
1585	A777	1 multi	2.00	2.00
a.		Booklet pane of 5	14.00	
		Complete booklet, 2 #1585a	28.00	
b.		Souvenir sheet of 5, #1581-		
		1585	10.00	10.00
		Nos. 1581-1585 (5)	10.00	10.00

Issued: No. 1581, 1/2; No. 1582, 2/25; No.
1583, 3/25; No. 1584, 4/23; No. 1585, 5/20.
Nos. 1581-1585 each sold for 87c on day of
issue. Each complete booklet sold for €12.45.

Souvenir Sheet

Dutch
Postal
Services,
220th
Anniv.
A778

No. 1586: a, Six envelopes, three packages.
b, Three envelopes, six packages.

2019, Jan. 24 Litho. *Perf. 14¼*
| 1586 | A778 | Sheet of 2 | 4.00 | 4.00 |
| a.-b. | | 1 Either single | 2.00 | 2.00 |

Nos. 1586a-1586b each sold for 87c on day
of issue.

Self-portraits of Rembrandt van Rijn
(1606-69) — A779

No. 1587: a, Self-portrait in a Soft Cap (c.
1634). b, Self-portrait in a Fur Cap (1630).

2019, Feb. 15 Litho. *Perf. 13¼x14*
| 1587 | A779 | Horiz. pair | 4.00 | 4.00 |
| a.-b. | | 1 Either single | 2.00 | 2.00 |

Nos. 1587a-1587b each sold for 87c on day
of issue. Printed in sheets containing 3
#1578a and 2 #1578b.

Miniature Sheet

Plants
A780

No. 1588 — Inscriptions: a, Armbloemig
look. b, Gewoon speenkruid. c, Herfsttuloos.
d, Bosgeelster. e, Gewoon sneeuwklokje. f,
Wilde kievitsbloem. g, Kraailook. h, Gewone
vogelmelk. i, Wilde hyacint. j, Winterakoniet.

2019, Feb. 25 Litho. *Perf. 13½x14*
Self-Adhesive
| 1588 | A780 | Sheet of 10 | 20.00 | 20.00 |
| a.-j. | | 1 Any single | 2.00 | 2.00 |

Nos. 1588a-1588j each sold for 87c on day
of issue. Latin names of plants are found in
the sheet margins above or below the stamps.

Souvenir Sheet

Dutch Aviation Centenaries — A781

No. 1589: a, Fokker F. XXII (tail inscription
PH-AJP), fuselage of Douglas DC-2 (tail
inscription PH-AJU), tail of Fokker F27 Friendship (tail inscription PH-SAD). b, Fuselage of
Fokker F27 Friendship, Fokker 50 (small KLM
airplane). c, Cessna 550 Citation II (tail
inscription PH-LAB), tail of Fokker 70 (fuselage inscription PH-KZU), wing tip of KLM jet.

2019, Mar. 11 Litho. *Perf. 14x13½*
| 1589 | A781 | Sheet of 3 | 6.00 | 6.00 |
| a.-c. | | 1 Any single | 2.00 | 2.00 |

Centenaries of KLM (Royal Dutch Arilines),
Fokker (aircraft manufacturer), and the Netherlands Aerospace Center. Nos. 1589a-1589c
each sold for 87c on day of issue.

Europa
A782

No. 1590 — Inscriptions: a, Putter (goldfinch). b, Pestvogel (Bohemian waxwing).

2019, Apr. 23 Litho. *Perf. 13¼x12¾*
| 1590 | A782 | Horiz. pair | 6.50 | 6.50 |
| a.-b. | | 1 Internationaal Either single | 3.25 | 3.25 |

Nos. 1590a-1590b each sold for €1.45 on
day of issue.

Miniature Sheet

Birds
A783

No. 1591 — Inscriptions: a, Pimpelmees (blue tit). b, Winterkoning (wren). c, Roodborst (robin). d, Huismus (house sparrow). e, Goudhaan (goldcrest). f, Koolmees (great tit).

2019, May 20 Litho. *Perf. 13¼x12¾*
1591 A783 Sheet of 6 12.00 12.00
a.-f. 1 Any single 2.00 2.00

Nos. 1591a-1591f each sold for 87c on day of issue. Latin names of plants are found in the sheet margins to left or right of the stamps.

Miniature Sheet

Butterflies and Moths — A784

No. 1592 — Inscriptions: a, Gentiaan blauwtje. b, Aardbeivlinder. c, Groentje. d, Kleine vos. e, Lieveling. f, Bruine vuurvlinder. g, Icarus blauwtje. h, Sint-Jansvlinder. i, Nachtpauwoog. j, Phegeavlinder.

2019, June 11 Litho. *Perf. 13½x14*
Self-Adhesive
1592 A784 Sheet of 10 20.00 20.00
a.-j. 1 Any single 2.00 2.00

Nos. 1592a-1592j each sold for 87c on day of issue. Latin names of plants are found in the sheet margins above or below the stamps.

Pearls
A785

Julius Caesar, Died 44 B.C.
A786

Nadia
A787

Portrait #5
A788

Portrait of Alex — A789

2019, July 1 Litho. *Perf. 13x13¼*
1593 Horiz. strip of 5 10.00 10.00
a. A785 1 multi 2.00 2.00
b. A786 1 multi 2.00 2.00
c. A787 1 multi 2.00 2.00
d. A788 1 multi 2.00 2.00
e. A789 1 multi 2.00 2.00

Photographs by Erwin Olaf. Nos. 1593a-1593e each sold for 87c on day of issue.

Miniature Sheets

A790

Public Transportation — A791

No. 1594 — a, Emmeloord-Lelystad regional bus route 146. b, Zwolle-Stadskanaal local train. c, Geuzenveld District-Amsterdam Central Station tram route 13. d, Brakel-Herwijne ferry service. e, Goes-Zierikzee regional bus route 132. f, Den Helder-Maastricht intercity train.

No. 1595: a, Leeuwarden-Rotterdam intercity train. b, Paddepoel District-De Wijert District city bus route 5. c, Amsterdam Noord-Amsterdam Zuid subway train line 52. d, Amsterdam-Berlin train. e, Den Haag HS Station-Duindorp District tram route 12. f, Arnhem-Winterswijk local train.

Perf. 13¼x12¾
2019, Aug. 19 Litho.
1594 A790 Sheet of 6 11.50 11.50
a.-f. 1 Any single 1.90 1.90
1595 A791 Sheet of 6 19.50 19.50
a.-f. 1 Internationaal Any single 3.25 3.25

On day of issue, Nos. 1594a-1594f each sold for 87c; Nos. 1595a-1595f, €1.45. Sheet margins at left and right served as etiquettes.

Miniature Sheet

Trees
A792

No. 1596 — Inscriptions: a, Beuk ("1" at LR). b, Zomerlinde. c, No inscription (leaves, "1" at LL). d, Ratelpopulier. e, Gewone es. f, Mispel. g, No inscription (leaves, "1" at right). h, Linde. i, Beuk ("1" at left). j, Ruwe berk.

2019, Sept. 16 Litho. *Perf. 13½x14*
Self-Adhesive
1596 A792 Sheet of 10 19.00 19.00
a.-j. 1 Any single 1.90 1.90

Nos. 1596a-1596j each sold for 87c on day of issue. Latin names of plants are found in the sheet margins above or below the stamps.

Miniature Sheet

Marbles and Beads
A793

No. 1597: a, Large light green and red marble, one bead. b, Large green and red marble, small green marble. c, Small green marble with yellow spiral, large blue and red marble. d, Small blue and yellow marble, large light green marble. e, One small blue and pink marble, One small green and red marble, three beads. f, Large green and yellow marble, two beads.

2019, Oct. 18 Litho. *Perf. 13¼x12¾*
1597 A793 Sheet of 6 19.50 19.50
a.-f. 1 Internationaal Any single 3.25 3.25

On day of issue, Nos. 1597a-1597f each sold for €1.45. Sheet margins at left and right served as etiquettes.

Stamp Day A794

No. 1598 — Seagull in: a, Orange. b, Green.

2019, Nov. 1 Litho. *Perf. 14x13¼*
1598 A794 Horiz. pair 4.00 4.00
a.-b. 1 Either single 2.00 2.00
c. Booklet pane of 2, #1598a-1598b 5.50
Complete booklet, 5 #1598c 28.00

Nos. 1598a-1598b each sold for 87c on day of issue. No. 1598 was printed in sheets containing 5 pairs. Complete booklet sold for €12.45, and contains five panes with different pane margins.

Woman With Horn
A795

Boy on Reindeer
A796

Man Holding String of Lights
A797

Raccoon With Gift and Torch
A798

Woman With Cake
A799

Pig on Sled
A800

Woman With Lantern
A801

Chickens
A802

Man Carrying Christmas Tree
A803

Polar Bear Mailing Letters
A804

Serpentine Die Cut 11¼
2019, Nov. 4 Litho.
Self-Adhesive
1599 Block of 10 19.00
a. A795 (82c) multi 1.90 1.90
b. A796 (82c) multi 1.90 1.90
c. A797 (82c) multi 1.90 1.90
d. A798 (82c) multi 1.90 1.90
e. A799 (82c) multi 1.90 1.90
f. A800 (82c) multi 1.90 1.90
g. A801 (82c) multi 1.90 1.90
h. A802 (82c) multi 1.90 1.90
i. A803 (82c) multi 1.90 1.90
j. A804 (82c) multi 1.90 1.90

Printed in sheets of 20 containing two each of Nos. 1599a-1599j.

Souvenir Sheet

Arrows
A805

Zigzag Die Cut 6¾
2020, Jan. 2 Litho.
Self-Adhesive
1600 A805 (€4.40) multi 10.00 10.00

Miniature Sheet

Owls and Birds of Prey
A806

No. 1601 — Inscriptions: a, Visarend. b, Wespendief. c, Rode wouw. d, Velduil. e, Grauwe kiekendief. f, Torenvalk. g, Blauwe kiekendief. h, Boomvalk. i, Ransuil. j, Zeearend.

2020, Jan. 2 Litho. *Perf. 13¼x14*
Self-Adhesive
1601 A806 Sheet of 10 21.00 21.00
a.-j. 1 Any single 2.10 2.10

Nos. 1601a-1601j each sold for 91c on day of issue. Latin names of birds are found in the sheet margin above or below the stamp.

Dutch Foods — A807

Designs: No. 1602, Rookworst. No. 1603, Carrots. No. 1604, Hagelslag (chocolate sprinkles) on bread. No. 1605, Tompouce (custard-filled pastry). No. 1606, Bitterballen (meatballs).

2020 Litho. *Perf. 14x13¼*
1602 A807 1 multi 2.10 2.10
a. Booklet pane of 2 5.50
1603 A807 1 multi 2.10 2.10
a. Booklet pane of 2 5.50
1604 A807 1 multi 2.00 2.00
a. Booklet pane of 2 5.50
1605 A807 1 multi 2.00 2.00
a. Booklet pane of 2 5.50

1606	A807 1 multi	2.10	2.10
a.	Booklet pane of 2	5.50	
	Complete booklet, #1602a, 1603a, 1604a, 1605a, 1606a	27.50	
	Nos. 1602-1606 (5)	10.30	10.30

Issued: No. 1602, 1/2; No. 1603, 2/24; No. 1604, 3/23; No. 1605, 4/6; Nos. 1602a, 1603a, 1604a, 1605a, 1606, 1606a, 6/15. Complete booklet sold for €12.45. On day of issue, Nos. 1602-1606 each sold for 91c.

Miniature Sheet

Farmland Birds A808

No. 1607 — Inscriptions: a, Gele kwikstaart. b, Slobeend. c, Grutto. d, Wulp. e, Zomertortel. f, Patrijs. g, Kievit. h, Steenuil. i, Tureluur. j, Veldleeuwerik.

2020, Feb. 24   Litho.   Perf. 13¼x14
Self-Adhesive

1607	A808	Sheet of 10	21.00	21.00
a.-j.	1 Any single		2.10	2.10

Nos. 1607a-1607j each sold for 91c on day of issue. Latin names of birds are found in the sheet margin above or below the stamp.

Cartographers and Their Maps of the Low Countries — A809

No. 1608: a, Abraham Ortelius (1527-98), 1571 map in oval. b, Gerard de Jode (1509-91), 1578 map with compass rose at left. c, Gerard Mercator (1512-94), wearing hat, holding compass and globe at left, 1585 map with rectangular legend at upper left. d, Jodocus Hondius (1563-1612), holding compass and globe at right, 1606 map with red and green regions. e, Willem Janszoon Blaeu (1571-1638), 1630 map with large ships at upper right. f, Johannes Janssonius (1588-1664), 1638 map with three small ships at top.

Perf. 13¼x12¾
2020, Mar. 23   Litho.

1608	A809	Sheet of 6	19.50	19.50
a.-f.	1 Internationaal Any single		3.25	3.25
g.	Booklet pane of 2, #1608a-1608b	9.00	
h.	Booklet pane of 2, #1608c-1608d	9.00	
i.	Booklet pane of 2, #1608e-1608f	9.00	
	Complete booklet, #1608g-1608i	27.00	

On day of issue, Nos. 1608a-1608f each sold for €1.50. Cartographer's names are found in the sheet selvage to the left or right of each stamp. The selvage to the left or right of the stamps served as etiquettes. The complete booklet sold for €12.45.

People Born in Freedom A810

No. 1609: a, Yvette Hartman-Mercier, expectant mother due to give birth May 5, 2020. b, Jan van der Linden, born May 5, 1945.

2020, Apr. 16   Litho.   Perf. 14¼x14½

1609	A810	Pair	4.00	4.00
a.-b.	1 Either single		2.00	2.00
c.	As #1609a, perf. 12¾x13¼	2.25	2.25

d.	As #1609b, perf. 12¾x13¼	2.25	2.25
e.	Booklet pane of 3, #1609d, 2 #1609c	6.75	
f.	Booklet pane of 3, #1609c, 2 #1609d	6.75	
	Complete booklet, 2 each #1609e-1609f	27.00	

Restoration of freedom after World War II, 75th anniv. On day of issue, Nos. 1609a-1609b each sold for 91c. The panes in the complete booklet have different pane margins. Complete booklet sold for €12.45.

Miniature Sheet

Stylized Faces A811

No. 1610: a, Lilac face with stars for eyes. b, Light blue face with eyes looking upward. c, Brown face with winking eye. d, Light green face with frown. e, Pale orange face with hearts for eyes. f, Yellow face laughing and crying.

2020, May 11   Litho.   Perf. 14½

1610	A811	Sheet of 6	12.00	12.00
a.-f.	1 Any single		2.00	2.00

On day of issue, Nos. 1610a-1610f each sold for 91c.

Europa A812

No. 1611: a, Postrider on horseback. b, Horse-drawn postal coach.

2020, May 11   Litho.   Perf. 13¼x12¾

1611	A812	Horiz. pair	7.00	7.00
a.-b.	1 Internationaal Either single		3.50	3.50
c.	Booklet pane of 2, #1611a-1611b + 2 etiquettes.	7.00	
	Complete booklet, 4 #1611c	28.00	

Ancient Postal Routes.
On day of issue, Nos. 1611a-1611b each sold for €1.50. Sheet selvage to left or right of the stamps served as etiquettes. Each booklet pane has a different pane margin. Complete booklet sold for €12.45.

Miniature Sheet

Coastal Birds A813

No. 1612 — Inscriptions: a, Dwergstern. b, Kleine jager. c, Steenloper. d, Sneeuwgors. e, Drieteenmeeuw. f, Grote mantelmeeuw. g, Strandleeuwerik. h, Kluut. i, Paarse strandloper. j, Strandplevier.

2020, June 15   Litho.   Perf. 13¼x14
Self-Adhesive

1612	A813	Sheet of 10	21.00	21.00
a.-j.	1 Any single		2.10	2.10

Nos. 1612a-1612j each sold for 91c on day of issue. Latin names of birds are found in the sheet margin above or below the stamp.

Bicycle Parts A814

No. 1613 — Detail of: a, Reflector. b, Fietsframe (bicycle frame). c, Handvat (handlebar grip). d, Fietsbel (bicycle bell). e, Buitenband (tire tread). f, Binnenband (inner tube).

Perf. 13¼x12¾
2020, Aug. 17   Litho.

1613	A814	Sheet of 6	13.50	13.50
a.-f.	1 Any single		2.25	2.25
g.	As #1613a, perf. 14¼	3.00	3.00
h.	As #1613b, perf. 14¼	3.00	3.00
i.	As #1613c, perf. 14¼	3.00	3.00
j.	As #1613d, perf. 14¼	3.00	3.00
k.	As #1613e, perf. 14¼	3.00	3.00
l.	As #1613f, perf. 14¼	3.00	3.00
m.	Booklet pane of 2, #1613g-1613h	6.00	—
n.	Booklet pane of 2, #1613i-1613j	6.00	—
o.	Booklet pane of 2, #1613k-1613l	6.00	—
	Complete booklet, #1313o, 2 each #1613m-1613n	30.00	

On day of issue, Nos. 1613a-1613f each sold for 91c. Each booklet pane has a different pane margin. Complete booklet sold for €12.45.

Miniature Sheet

Forest and Heathland Birds — A815

No. 1614 — Inscriptions: a, Raaf. b, Zwarte mees. c, Keep. d, Grote bonte specht. e, Gekraagde roodstaart. f, Grauwe vliegenvanger. g, Klapekster. h, Korhoen. i, Draaihals. j, Matkop.

2020, Sept. 14   Litho.   Perf. 13¼x14
Self-Adhesive

1614	A815	Sheet of 10	22.50	22.50
a.-j.	1 Any single		2.25	2.25

Nos. 1614a-1614j each sold for 91c on day of issue. Latin names of birds are found in the sheet margin above or below the stamp.

A816

A817

A818

A819

A820

Kaleidoscopic Curves — A821

2020, Sept. 14   Litho.   Perf. 13¼x13

1615		Miniature sheet of 6	21.00	21.00
a.	A816 1 Internationaal multi		3.50	3.50
b.	A817 1 Internationaal multi		3.50	3.50
c.	A818 1 Internationaal multi		3.50	3.50
d.	A819 1 Internationaal multi		3.50	3.50
e.	A820 1 Internationaal multi		3.50	3.50
f.	A821 1 Internationaal multi		3.50	3.50

On day of issue, Nos. 1615a-1615f each sold for €1.50. The sheet selvage to the left and right of each stamp served as etiquettes.

Stamp Day A822

No. 1616 — Color of large "1": a, White. b, Red.

2020, Oct. 16   Litho.   Perf. 13½x14

1616	A822	1 Pair	4.25	4.25
a.-b.	1 Either single		2.10	2.10
c.	Booklet pane of 2, #1616a-1616b	5.75	5.75
	Complete booklet, 5 #1616c			

On day of issue, Nos. 1616a-1616b each sold for 91c. In the complete booklet, each example of No. 1616c has a different booklet

pane margin. The complete booklet sold for €12.45.

Martin Garrix, Music Producer and DJ — A823

2020, Oct. 21   Litho.   Perf. 13¼x13¾

1617	A823 1 multi	2.10	2.10

No. 1617 sold for 91c on day of issue.

Death Announcement Stamp — A824

Serpentine Die Cut 11¾
2020, Nov. 2   Litho.
Self-Adhesive

1618	A824 2 blk & ol sepia	4.25	4.25

No. 1618 sold for €1.82 on day of issue.

Clock, High-heeled Shoe, and Camera Christmas Ornaments A825

Flamingo Christmas Ornament A826

Robot in Box Christmas Ornament A827

Donut, Gingerbread House, and Diamond Christmas Ornaments A828

Dog Wearing Stocking Cap Christmas Ornament A829

Heart and Banner Christmas Ornament A830

Car, House, and Round Starred Christmas Ornaments A831

Nutcracker and Candy Cane Christmas Ornaments A832

Tiger's Head in Box Christmas Ornament A833

Postcard and Hummingbird Christmas Ornaments A834

Serpentine Die Cut 11

2020, Nov. 16   **Litho.**
Self-Adhesive
1619		Block of 10	21.00
a.	A825 (86c) multi		2.10 2.10
b.	A826 (86c) multi		2.10 2.10
c.	A827 (86c) multi		2.10 2.10
d.	A828 (86c) multi		2.10 2.10
e.	A829 (86c) multi		2.10 2.10
f.	A830 (86c) multi		2.10 2.10
g.	A831 (86c) multi		2.10 2.10
h.	A832 (86c) multi		2.10 2.10
i.	A833 (86c) multi		2.10 2.10
j.	A834 (86c) multi		2.10 2.10

Printed in sheets of 20 containing two each of Nos. 1619a-1619j.

Miniature Sheet

Heathland Flora and Fauna of Dwingelderveld National Park — A835

No. 1620 — Inscriptions: a, Drents heideschaap. b, Geelgors. c, Zandhagedis. d, Hazelworm. e, Bijenwolf. f, Kraanvogel. g, Groveden. h, Veenmos. i, Ringslang. j, Ree.

2021, Jan. 4   Litho.   Perf. 14x13¼
Self-Adhesive
1620	A835	Sheet of 10	24.00 24.00
a.-j.		1 Any single	2.40 2.40

Nos. 1620a-1620j each sold for 96c on day of issue. Latin names of flora and fauna are found in the sheet margin to left or right of the stamp.

Stolp Farmhouse A836

Wooden Houses — A837

Canal Houses — A838

Houseboats A839

Terraced Houses — A840

2021   Litho.   Perf. 13x13¼
1621	A836	1 multi	2.40 2.40
a.		Booklet pane of 2	6.00 —
1622	A837	1 multi	2.40 2.40
a.		Booklet pane of 2	6.00 —
1623	A838	1 multi	2.25 2.25
a.		Booklet pane of 2	6.00 —
1624	A839	1 multi	2.40 2.40
a.		Booklet pane of 2	6.00 —

1625	A840	1 multi	2.25	2.25
a.		Booklet pane of 2	6.00	
		Complete booklet, #1621a, 1622a, 1623a, 1624a, 1625a	30.00	
		Nos. 1621-1625 (5)	11.70	11.70

Issued: No. 1621, 1/4; No. 1622, 2/22; No. 1623, 3/22; No. 1624, 4/6; Nos. 1621a, 1622a, 1623a, 1624a, 1625, 1625a, 6/14. Nos. 1621-1625 each sold for 96c on day of issue. The complete booklet sold for €12.45.

Miniature Sheet

Marshland Flora and Fauna of De Onlanden Nature Reserve — A841

No. 1626 — Inscriptions: a, Kemphaan. b, Grote zilverreiger. c, Smient. d, Groene glazenmaker. e, Grote klaproos. f, Klein hoefblad. g, Gewone margriet. h, Brasem. i, Otter. j, Bruine vuurvlinder.

2021, Feb. 22   Litho.   Perf. 14x13¼
Self-Adhesive
1626	A841	Sheet of 10	24.00 24.00
a.-j.		1 Any single	2.40 2.40

Nos. 1626a-1626j each sold for 96c on day of issue. Latin names of flora and fauna are found in the sheet margin to left or right of the stamp.

Sustainability — A842

No. 1627 — Arms and: a, Western Europe and Western Africa. b, Eastern Europe, Eastern and Southern Africa and Western Asia.

2021, Mar. 22   Litho.   Perf. 13¼x13
1627	A842	Horiz. pair	4.50	4.50
a.-b.		1 Either single	2.25	2.25
c.		Vert. tete-beche pair, #1627a-1627b	4.50	4.50
d.		As #1627a, perf. 14½	3.00	3.00
e.		As #1627b, perf. 14½	3.00	3.00
f.		Booklet pane of 2, #1627d-1627e	6.00	—
		Complete booklet, 5 #1627f	30.00	

Nos. 1627a-1627b each sold for 96c on day of issue, and was printed in sheets containing 3 pairs. Complete booklet sold for €12.45.

Endangered Animals — A843

No. 1628 — Bees and hexagons: a, To right of inscriptions. b, To left of inscriptions.

2021, May 10   Litho.   Perf. 13¼x13
1628	A843	Vert. pair	7.50	7.50
a.-b.		1 International Either single	3.75	3.75
c.		As #1628a, perf. 14x13¾	5.00	5.00
d.		As #1628b, perf. 14x13¾	5.00	5.00
e.		Booklet pane of 2, #1628c-1628d	10.00	—
		Complete booklet, 3 #1628e	30.00	

Europa. Nos. 1628a-1628b each sold for €1.55 on day of issue, and was printed in sheets containing 3 pairs. The sheet margins to the left and right of the stamps served as etiquettes. The three examples of No. 1628e in the complete booklet have different marginal text. Complete booklet sold for €12.45.

Miniature Sheet

Queen Máxima, 50th Birthday A844

No. 1629 — Queen Máxima: a, Black-and-white photograph, 1999 (36x50mm). b, Wearing crown, 2013 (36x25mm). c, Holding headphones, 2018 (36x25mm). d, With husband, King Willem-Alexander and mother-in-law, Princess Beatrix, 2015 (36x25mm). e, With Indonesians in Jakarta, 2018 (36x25mm).

2021, May 17   Litho.   Perf. 14½
1629	A844	Sheet of 5	12.00 12.00
a.-e.		1 Any single	2.40 2.40

Nos. 1629a-1629e each sold for 96c on day of issue.

Miniature Sheet

Flora and Fauna of Duin en Kruidberg Dunes — A845

No. 1630 — Inscriptions: a, Duin parelmoervlinder. b, Konin. c, Vos. d, Duindoorn. e, Parnassia. f, Damhert. g, Nachtegaal. h, Duinviooltje. i, Grote tijm. j, Konikpaard.

2021, June 14   Litho.   Perf. 14x13¼
Self-Adhesive
1630	A845	Sheet of 10	22.50 22.50
a.-j.		1 Any single	2.25 2.25

Nos. 1630a-1630j each sold for 96c on day of issue. Latin names of flora and fauna are found in the sheet margin to left or right of the stamp.

Miniature Sheet

Flora and Fauna of Haarzuilens Country Estate — A846

No. 1631 — Inscriptions: a, Haas. b, Schaatsenrijder. c, Beuk. d, Boomklever. e, Buizerd. f, Gewone esdoorn. g, Bastaardkikker. h, Knotwilg. i, Viervlek. j, Tamme kastanje.

2021, Aug. 16   Litho.   Perf. 14x13¼
Self-Adhesive
1631	A846	Sheet of 10	22.50 22.50
a.-j.		1 Any single	2.25 2.25

Nos. 1631a-1631j each sold for 96c on day of issue. Latin names of flora and fauna are found in the sheet margin to left or right of the stamp.

Miniature Sheet

Innovation in the Netherlands — A847

No. 1632 — Inscriptions: a, Biobrandstof (biofuel created from elephant dung). b, 4Fold (foldable shipping containers). c, Variable stiffness (printable 3-D structures with flexible stiffness). d, Kitepower (wind energy system). e, Zandmotor (artifical sandbanks). f, Tiler (tile for charging electric bicycles and light vehicles). g, Bluebloqs (system for rainwater treatment, storage and reuse). h, Innozowa (floating solar panels). i, Gaming @ the Dentist (video game for pain distraction). j, Exo-l (3-D printed external ankle ligament).

2021, Aug. 16   Litho.   Perf. 14x13¼
1632	A847	Sheet of 10	22.50 22.50
a.-j.		1 Any single	2.25 2.25
k.		Booklet pane of 2, #1632a-1632b	6.00
l.		Booklet pane of 2, #1632c-1632d	6.00
m.		Booklet pane of 2, #1632e-1632f	6.00
n.		Booklet pane of 2, #1632g-1632h	6.00
o.		Booklet pane of 2, #1632i-1632j	6.00
		Complete booklet, #1632k, 1632l, 1632m, 1632n, 1632o	30.00

Nos. 1632a-1632j each sold for 96c on day of issue. Complete booklet sold for €12.45.

Miniature Sheet

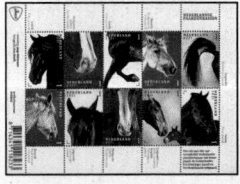

Dutch Horse Breeds A848

No. 1633: a, Head of black Friesian horse facing left. b, Nose of Gelderland horse. c, Chest and front legs of black Friesian horse. d, Head of Dutch draft horse, eye visible. e, Tail of Groningen horse. f, Head of Dutch draft horse, eye hidden. g, Top of head of Groningen horse. h, Eyes and nose of Gelderland horse. i, Heads of Groningen horse and foal. j, Head of black Friesian horse facing right.

Perf. 12¾x13¼
2021, Sept. 13			**Litho.**
1633	A848	Sheet of 10	22.50 22.50
a.-j.		1 Any single	2.25 2.25
k.		Booklet pane of 2, #1633a,1633f	5.75 —
l.		Booklet pane of 2, #1633b,1633g	5.75 —
m.		Booklet pane of 2, #1633c,1633h	5.75 —
n.		Booklet pane of 2, #1633d,1633i	5.75 —
o.		Booklet pane of 2, #1633e,1633j	5.75 —
		Complete booklet, #1633k, 1633l, 1633m, 1633n, 1633o	29.00

Nos. 1633a-1633j each sold for 96c on day of issue. Complete booklet sold for €12.45.

Miniature Sheet

Hands
A849

No. 1634: a, Gray hand. b, Orange hand. c, Light blue hand pointing to left. d, Purple hand with fingers outstretched. e, Purple hand with index finger pointing upward. f, Light blue hand with palm up.

Perf. 13¼x12¾

2021, Sept. 13		**Litho.**		
1634	A849	Sheet of 6	22.50	22.50
a.-f.		1 Internationaal Any single	3.75	3.75

Nos. 1634a-1634f each sold for €1.55 on day of issue and sheet margins to left or right of the stamp served as etiquettes,

Stamp Day
A850

No. 1653: a, Half of stylized coat of arms with two lions. b, Half of stylized coat of arms with one lion.

2021, Oct. 15		**Litho.**	**Perf. 14x13½**	
1635	A850	Pair	4.50	4.50
a.-b.		1 Either single	2.25	2.25
c.		Booklet pane of 2, #1635a-1635b	5.75	—
		Complete booklet, 5 #1635c	29.00	

Nos. 1635a-1635b each sold for 96c on day of issue. The complete booklet sold for €12.45 and contains five examples of No. 1635c, each with different pane margins.

Mole With Candy Cane and Backpack
A851

Blue Tits Under Mistletoe
A852

Fox Carrying Letter
A853

Mouse in Postal Car
A854

Badger Decorating Christmas Tree
A855

Mice Decorating Peacock
A856

Squirrel Pushing Sled
A857

Hare, Squirrel and Dog Skating
A858

Hare With Poinsettias
A859

Deer With Christmas Ornaments
A860

Serpentine Die Cut 11¼

2021, Nov. 15			**Litho.**	
Self-Adhesive				
1636		Block of 10	21.00	
a.	A851	(91c) multi	2.10	2.10
b.	A852	(91c) multi	2.10	2.10
c.	A853	(91c) multi	2.10	2.10
d.	A854	(91c) multi	2.10	2.10
e.	A855	(91c) multi	2.10	2.10
f.	A856	(91c) multi	2.10	2.10
g.	A857	(91c) multi	2.10	2.10
h.	A858	(91c) multi	2.10	2.10
i.	A859	(91c) multi	2.10	2.10
j.	A860	(91c) multi	2.10	2.10

Printed in sheets of 20 containing two each of Nos. 1636a-1636j.

Dutch Sports — A861

Designs: No. 1637, Skating. No. 1638, Field hockey. No. 1639, Cycling. No. 1640, Sailing. No. 1641, Soccer.

2022		**Litho.**	**Perf. 13½x13**	
1637	A861	1 multi	2.25	2.25
a.		Booklet pane of 2	5.00	
1638	A861	1 multi	2.25	2.25
a.		Booklet pane of 2	5.00	
1639	A861	1 multi	2.10	2.10
a.		Booklet pane of 2	5.00	
1640	A861	1 multi	2.10	2.10
a.		Booklet pane of 2	5.00	
1641	A861	1 multi	2.00	2.00
a.		Booklet pane of 2	5.00	
		Complete booklet, #1637a, 1638a, 1639a, 1640a, 1641a	25.00	
		Nos. 1637-1641 (5)	10.70	10.70

Issued: No. 1637, 1/3; No. 1638, 3/21; No. 1639, 4/4; No. 1640, 5/9; Nos. 1637a, 1638a, 1639a, 1640a, 1641, 1641a, 8/15. Complete booklet sold for €12.45. On day of issue, Nos. 1637-1641 each sold for 96c.

Miniature Sheets

Flora and Fauna of Fort Ellewoutsdijk — A862

Flora and Fauna of Nieuwkoopse Plassen — A863

No. 1642 — Inscriptions: a, Noordzeekrab. b, Zwartkopmeeuw. c, Rosse grutto. d, Kokkel. e, Kortarige zeekraal. f, Verandelijke steurgarnaal. g, Gewone mossel. h, Kleine zee-eik. i, Zeehond. j, Gewone zeester.

No. 1643 — Inscriptions: a, Zwarte stern. b, Glassnijder. c, Rietorchis. d, Echte koekoeksbloem. e, Kleine modderkruiper. f, Wateraardbei. g, Kleine lisdodde. h, Krabbenscheer. i, Witte waterlelie. j, Roerdomp.

2022		**Litho.**	**Perf. 13x13¼**	
Self-Adhesive				
1642	A862	Sheet of 10	22.50	22.50
a.-j.		1 Any single	2.25	2.25
1643	A863	Sheet of 10	22.50	22.50
a.-j.		1 Any single	2.25	2.25

Issued: No. 1642, 1/3; No. 1643, 2/21. Nos. 1642a-1642j, 1643a-1643j each sold for 96c on day of issue. Latin names of flora and fauna are found in the sheet margin to left or right of the stamp.

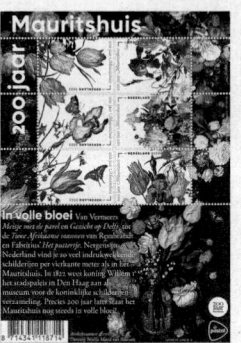

Mauritshuis Museum, The Hague, 200th Anniv. — A864

No. 1644 — Various flowers from Mauritshuis still-life paintings: a, White and redstriped tulips. b, Iris, lilies and bee. c, Iris and butterfly. d, Yellow iris and tulips. e, Tulip and butterfly. f, Blue irises and tulips.

2022, Feb. 21		**Litho.**	**Perf. 14½**	
1644	A864	Sheet of 6	13.50	13.50
a.-f.		1 Any single	2.25	2.25
g.		Booklet pane of 2, #1644a-1644b	5.75	—
h.		Booklet pane of 2, #1644c-1644d	5.75	—
i.		Booklet pane of 2, #1644e-1644f	5.75	—
		Complete booklet, #1644i, 2 each #1644g-1644h	29.00	

Nos. 1644a-1644f each sold for 96c on day of issue. Complete booklet sold for €12.45. The two examples of Nos. 1644g-1644h in the booklet have different pane margins.

Delftware Tulip Vases
A865

No. 1645 — Various vases from late 17th-early 18th centuries: a, Vase, pale orange background. b, Four vases. c, Three vases, tall vase at right. d, Vase, gray background. e, Vase, light blue background. f, Three vases, tall vase at left.

2022, Mar. 21		**Litho.**	**Perf. 14½**	
1645	A865	Sheet of 6	13.50	13.50
a.-f.		1 Any single	2.25	2.25
g.		Booklet pane of 2, #1645a-1645b	5.50	—
h.		Booklet pane of 2, #1645c-1645d	5.50	—

i.		Booklet pane of 2, #1645e-1645f	5.50	—
		Complete booklet, #1645i, 2 each #1645g-1645h	27.50	

Nos. 1645a-1645f each sold for 96c on day of issue. Complete booklet sold for €12.45. The two examples of Nos. 1645g-1645h in the booklet have different pane margins.

Europa
A866

No. 1646 — Folktale of the Lady of Stavoren: a, Ring on hand of the Lady of Stavoren. b, Head of Lady of Stavoren.

2022, May 9		**Litho.**	**Perf. 13½x13**	
1646	A866	Horiz. pair	4.25	4.25
a.-b.		1 Either single	2.10	2.10

Nos. 1646a-1646b each sold for 96c on day of issue. Booklets containing three panes, with each pane comprised of a pair of perf. 14x13½ examples of Nos. 1646a-1646b, sold for €12.45.

Miniature Sheet

Flora and Fauna of Mount Saint Peter
A867

No. 1647 — Inscriptions: a, Kleine pimpernel. b, Baardvleermuis. c, Gehakkelde aurelia. d, Wilde marjolein. e, Das. f, Bijenorchis. g, Kalketrip. h, Oehoe. i, Gevlekte aronskelk. j, Boswitje.

2022, June 13		**Litho.**	**Perf. 13x13¼**	
Self-Adhesive				
1647	A867	Sheet of 10	20.00	20.00
a.-j.		1 Any single	2.00	2.00

Nos. 1647a-1647j each sold for 96c on day of issue. Latin names of flora and fauna are found in the sheet margin to left or right of the stamp.

King William I (1772-1843)
A868

King William I and Queen Wilhelmina of Prussia (1774-1837)
A869

Fulda Palace Castle, Germany — A870

2022, June 20		**Litho.**	**Perf. 13½x13**	
1648	A868	1 Internationaal multi	3.25	3.25
a.		Perf. 14x13½	4.25	4.25
1649	A869	1 Internationaal multi	3.25	3.25
a.		Horiz. pair, #1648-1649	6.50	6.50
b.		Perf. 14x13½	4.25	4.25
c.		Booklet pane of 2, #1648a-1649b	8.75	
1650	A870	1 Internationaal multi	3.25	3.25
a.		Perf. 14x13½	4.25	4.25
b.		Booklet pane of 2, #1650a #1649c	8.75	
		Complete booklet, #1650b, 2 #1649c	26.50	
		Nos. 1648-1650 (3)	9.75	9.75

Printed in sheets of 6 containing 2 each Nos. 1648-1650. Sheet margins at left or right of stamps served as etiquettes. Nos. 1648-1650 each sold for €1.55 on day of issue. The complete booklet sold for €12.45. The two examples of No. 1649c in the booklet have different pane margins.

Miniature Sheet

Flora and Fauna of Leuvenum Woods — A871

No. 1651 — Inscriptions: a, Fluiter. b, Edelhert. c, Porseleinzwam. d, Boommarter. e, Wolf. f, Open rendiermos. g, Gewone eikvaren. h, Wild zwijn. i, Vuurgoudhaan. j, Gewone mestkever.

2022, Aug. 15   Litho.   Perf. 13x13¼
Self-Adhesive
1651 A871 Sheet of 10   20.00 20.00
a.-j.   1 Any single   2.00   2.00

Nos. 1651a-1651j each sold for 96c on day of issue. Latin names of flora and fauna are found in the sheet margin to left or right of the stamp.

Miniature Sheet

Futuristic Mythological Beast — A872

No. 1652 — Color of beast's appendage: a, Lilac. b, Green. c, Blue. d, Purple. e, Green, diff. f, Olive green.

2022, Sept. 26   Litho.   Perf. 13¼x12¾
1652 A872 Sheet of 6   18.00 18.00
a.-f.   1 Internationaal Any single   3.00   3.00

Nos. 1652a-1652f each sold for €1.55 on day of issue. Sheet margins at left or right of stamps served as etiquettes.

Stamp Day A873

No. 1653: a, Admiral Michiel A. de Ruyter (1607-76). b, Naval battle between Dutch and English ships.

2022, Oct. 17   Litho.   Perf. 13½x14
1653 A873 Horiz. pair   3.80   3.80
a.-b.   1 Either single   1.90   1.90
c.   Booklet pane of 2, #1653a-
       1653b   5.00   —
     Complete booklet, 5 #1653c 25.00

Nos. 1653a-1653b each sold for 96c on day of issue. Complete booklet sold for €12.45. The five examples of No. 1653c in the booklet each have different pane margins.

SEMI-POSTAL STAMPS

Design Symbolical of the Four Chief Means for Combating Tuberculosis: Light, Water, Air and Food — SP1

Perf. 12½

1906, Dec. 21		**Typo.**	**Unwmk.**
B1	SP1 1c (+1c) rose red	20.00	11.00
B2	SP1 3c (+3c) pale ol grn	30.00	26.00
B3	SP1 5c (+5c) gray	30.00	15.00
	Nos. B1-B3 (3)	80.00	52.00
	Set, never hinged	475.00	

Surtax aided the Society for the Prevention of Tuberculosis.
Nos. B1-B3 canceled-to-order "AMSTERDAM 31.07 10-12 N," sell at $3 a set.

Symbolical of Charity — SP2   SP3

1923, Dec. 15		**Perf. 11½**	
B4	SP2 2c (+5c) vio bl	17.00	17.00
B5	SP3 10c (+5c) org red	17.00	17.00
	Set, never hinged	85.00	

The surtax was for the benefit of charity.

Allegory, Charity Protecting Child — SP6

1924, Dec. 15	**Photo.**	**Perf. 12½**	
B6	SP6 2c (+2c) emer	1.80	1.80
B7	SP6 7½c (+3½c) dk brn	6.75	8.00
B8	SP6 10c (+2½c) vermilion	4.00	1.80
	Nos. B6-B8 (3)	12.55	11.60
	Set, never hinged	26.00	

These stamps were sold at a premium over face value for the benefit of Child Welfare Societies.

Arms of North Brabant SP7   Arms of Gelderland SP8

Arms of South Holland — SP9

1925, Dec. 17		**Perf. 12½**	
B9	SP7 2c (+2c) grn & org	.85	.75
B10	SP8 7½c (+3½c) pur & bl gray	4.25	4.50
B11	SP9 10c (+2½c) red & yel org	3.50	.45
	Nos. B9-B11 (3)	8.60	5.70
	Set, never hinged	19.00	

Surtax went to Child Welfare Societies.

Syncopated Perfs., Type A

B9a	SP7	2c (+2c)	19.00	22.00
B10a	SP8	7½c (+3½c)	37.50	37.50
B11a	SP9	10c (+2½c)	65.00	52.50
	Nos. B9a-B11a (3)		121.50	112.00
	Set, never hinged		300.00	

Arms of Utrecht SP10   Arms of Zeeland SP11

Arms of North Holland SP12   Arms of Friesland SP13

1926, Dec. 1	**Wmk. 202**	**Perf. 12½**	
B12	SP10 2c (+2c) sil & red	.50	.40
B13	SP11 5c (+3c) grn & gray bl	1.40	.75
B14	SP12 10c (+3c) red & gold	2.10	.35
B15	SP13 15c (+3c) ultra & yel	5.50	6.00
	Set, never hinged	9.50	7.50
		30.00	

The surtax on these stamps was devoted to Child Welfare Societies.

Syncopated Perfs., Type A

B12a	SP10	2c (+2c)	5.25	5.25
B13a	SP11	5c (+3c)	8.25	8.25
B14a	SP12	10c (+3c)	15.00	8.75
B15a	SP13	15c (+3c)	16.50	16.50
	Nos. B12a-B15a (4)		45.00	38.75
	Set, never hinged		125.00	

King William III SP14   Red Cross and Doves SP18

Designs: 3c, Queen Emma. 5c, Prince Consort Henry. 7½c, Queen Wilhelmina.

1927, June	**Photo.**	**Unwmk.**	
B16	SP14 2c (+2c) scar	3.25	2.75
	Engr.		
B17	SP14 3c (+2c) dp grn	6.75	7.50
B18	SP14 5c (+3c) slate bl	1.35	1.25
	Photo.		
B19	SP14 7½c (+3½c) ultra	4.25	1.60
B20	SP18 15c (+5c) ultra & red	9.25	8.50
	Nos. B16-B20 (5)	24.85	21.60
	Set, never hinged	65.00	

60th anniversary of the Netherlands Red Cross Society. The surtaxes in parentheses were for the benefit of the Society.

Arms of Drenthe SP19   Arms of Groningen SP20

Arms of Limburg SP21   Arms of Overijssel SP22

1927, Dec. 15	**Wmk. 202**	**Perf. 12½**	
B21	SP19 2c (+2c) dp rose & vio	.35	.30
B22	SP20 5c (+3c) ol grn & yel	1.50	1.25
B23	SP21 7½c (+3½c) red & blk	3.25	.35
B24	SP22 15c (+3c) ultra & org brn	4.75	4.25
	Nos. B21-B24 (4)	9.85	6.15
	Set, never hinged	31.00	

The surtax on these stamps was for the benefit of Child Welfare Societies.

Syncopated Perfs., Type A

B21a	SP19	2c (+2c)	2.25	2.25
B22a	SP20	5c (+3c)	4.00	4.00
B23a	SP21	7½c (+3½c)	6.00	6.00
B24a	SP22	15c (+3c)	11.00	7.75
	Nos. B21a-B24a (4)		23.25	20.00
	Set, never hinged		75.00	

Rowing SP23   Fencing SP24

Soccer SP25   Yachting SP26

Putting the Shot SP27   Running SP28

Riding SP29   Boxing SP30

Perf. 11½, 12, 11½x12, 12x11½

1928, Mar. 27		**Litho.**	
B25	SP23 1½c (+1c) dk grn	3.00	3.00
B26	SP24 2c (+1c) red vio	3.00	3.75
B27	SP25 3c (+1c) green	4.50	4.50
B28	SP26 5c (+1c) lt bl	3.75	4.50
B29	SP27 7½c (+2½c) org	3.75	2.25
B30	SP28 10c (+2c) scarlet	6.75	5.25
B31	SP29 15c (+2c) dk bl	9.00	5.25
B32	SP30 30c (+3c) dk brn	19.00	19.00
	Nos. B25-B32 (8)	52.75	45.25
	Set, never hinged	170.00	

The surtax on these stamps was used to help defray the expenses of the Olympic Games of 1928.

Jean Pierre Minckelers — SP31

5c, Hermann Boerhaave. 7½c, Hendrik Antoon Lorentz. 12½c, Christiaan Huygens.

1928, Dec. 10	**Photo.**	**Perf. 12x12½**	
B33	SP31 1½c (+1½c) vio	.55	.40
B34	SP31 5c (+3c) grn	1.75	.60
	Perf. 12		
B35	SP31 7½c (+2½c) ver	3.50	.25
a.	Perf. 12x12½	4.75	.50
B36	SP31 12½c (+3½c) ultra	9.75	7.50
a.	Perf. 12x12½	77.50	15.00
	Nos. B33-B36 (4)	15.55	8.75
	Set, never hinged	45.00	

The surtax on these stamps was for the benefit of Child Welfare Societies.

Child on Dolphin — SP35

1929, Dec. 10	**Litho.**	**Perf. 12½**	
B37	SP35 1½c (+1½c) gray	1.75	.40
B38	SP35 5c (+3c) blue	2.50	.75
B39	SP35 6c (+4c) scarlet	2.00	.35
B40	SP35 12½c (+3½c) dk bl	14.00	9.75
	Nos. B37-B40 (4)	20.25	11.25
	Set, never hinged	72.50	

Surtax for child welfare.

Syncopated Perfs., Type B

B37a	SP35	1½c (+1½c)	3.75	3.00
B38a	SP35	5c (+3c)	4.50	4.00
B39a	SP35	6c (+4c)	3.75	3.00
B40a	SP35	12½c (+3½c)	18.00	14.00
	Nos. B37a-B40a (4)		30.00	24.00
	Set, never hinged		125.00	

Rembrandt and His "Cloth Merchants of Amsterdam" — SP36

Perf. 11½
1930, Feb. 15   Engr.   Unwmk.

B41	SP36	5c (+5c) bl grn	6.75	6.00
B42	SP36	6c (+5c) gray blk	5.25	3.50
B43	SP36	12½c (+5c) dp bl	9.00	8.00
		Nos. B41-B43 (3)	21.00	17.50
		Set, never hinged	62.50	

Surtax for the benefit of the Rembrandt Soc.

"Spring" — SP37

5c, Summer. 6c, Autumn. 12½c, Winter.

1930, Dec. 10   Perf. 12½

B44	SP37	1½c (+1½c) lt red	1.75	.45
B45	SP37	5c (+3c) gray grn	2.25	.60
B46	SP37	6c (+4c) claret	1.75	.45
B47	SP37	12½c (+3½c) lt ultra	16.00	8.50
		Nos. B44-B47 (4)	21.75	10.00
		Set, never hinged	62.50	

Surtax was for Child Welfare work.

Syncopated Perfs., Type C

B44a	SP37	1½c (+1½c)	4.00	3.75
B45a	SP37	5c (+3c)	4.75	4.50
B46a	SP37	6c (+4c)	4.00	3.75
B47a	SP37	12½c (+3½c)	19.00	14.00
		Nos. B44a-B47a (4)	31.75	26.00
		Set, never hinged	85.00	

Stained Glass Window and Detail of Repair Method — SP41

6c, Gouda Church and repair of window frame.

Wmk. 202
1931, Oct. 1   Photo.   Perf. 12½

B48	SP41	1½c (+1½c) bl grn	17.00	15.00
B49	SP41	6c (+4c) car rose	20.00	17.00
		Set, never hinged	80.00	

Deaf Mute Learning Lip Reading — SP43

Designs: 5c, Mentally retarded child. 6c, Blind girl learning to read Braille. 12½c, Child victim of malnutrition.

1931, Dec. 10   Perf. 12½

B50	SP43	1½c (+1½c) ver & ultra	1.90	1.25
B51	SP43	5c (+3c) Prus bl & vio	5.25	1.25
B52	SP43	6c (+4c) vio & grn	5.25	1.25
B53	SP43	12½c (+3½c) ultra & dp org	29.00	21.00
		Nos. B50-B53 (4)	41.40	24.75
		Set, never hinged	125.00	

The surtax was for Child Welfare work.

Syncopated Perfs., Type C

B50a	SP43	1½c (+1½c)	3.75	4.00
B51a	SP43	5c (+3c)	7.50	7.75
B52a	SP43	6c (+4c)	7.50	7.75
B53a	SP43	12½c (+3½c)	27.00	19.50
		Nos. B50a-B53a (4)	45.75	39.00
		Set, never hinged	150.00	

Drawbridge — SP47

Designs: 2½c, Windmill and Dikes. 6c, Council House, Zierikzee. 12½c, Flower fields.

1932, May 23   Perf. 12½

B54	SP47	2½c (+1½c) turq	7.00	5.00
B55	SP47	6c (+4c) gray blk & blk	10.50	5.00
B56	SP47	7½c (+3½c) brt red & blk	30.00	12.50
B57	SP47	12½c (+2½c) ultra & blk	32.50	19.00
		Nos. B54-B57 (4)	80.00	41.50
		Set, never hinged	225.00	

The surtax was for the benefit of the National Tourist Association.

Furze and Boy — SP51

Designs (Heads of children and flowers typifying the seasons): 5c, Cornflower. 6c, Sunflower. 12½c, Christmas rose.

1932, Dec. 10   Perf. 12½

B58	SP51	1½c (+1½c) brn & yel	2.10	.45
B59	SP51	5c (+3c) red org & ultra	2.75	.75
B60	SP51	6c (+4c) dk grn & ocher	2.10	.35
B61	SP51	12½c (+3½c) ocher & ultra	27.50	18.00
		Nos. B58-B61 (4)	34.45	19.55
		Set, never hinged	110.00	

The surtax aided Child Welfare Societies.

Syncopated Perfs., Type C

B58a	SP51	1½c (+1½c)	3.50	3.50
B59a	SP51	5c (+3c)	4.25	4.25
B60a	SP51	6c (+4c)	4.25	4.25
B61a	SP51	12½c (+3½c)	32.50	20.00
		Nos. B58a-B61a (4)	44.50	32.00
		Set, never hinged	135.00	

Monument at Den Helder SP55

The "Hope," A Church and Hospital Ship SP56

Lifeboat in a Storm SP57

Dutch Sailor and Sailors' Home SP58

1933, June 10   Perf. 14½x13½

B62	SP55	1½c (+1½c) dp red	3.50	2.60
B63	SP56	5c (+3c) bl grn & red org	10.50	4.25
B64	SP57	6c (+4c) dp grn	16.00	3.25
B65	SP58	12½c (+3½c) ultra	24.00	16.00
		Nos. B62-B65 (4)	54.00	26.10
		Set, never hinged	135.00	

The surtax was for the aid of Sailors' Homes.

Child Carrying the Star of Hope, Symbolical of Christmas Cheer — SP59

1933, Dec. 11   Perf. 12½

B66	SP59	1½c (+1½c) sl & org brn	1.50	.55
B67	SP59	5c (+3c) dk brn & ocher	2.00	.65
B68	SP59	6c (+4c) bl grn & gold	2.50	.55
B69	SP59	12½c (+3½c) dk bl & sil	25.00	18.00
		Nos. B66-B69 (4)	31.00	19.75
		Set, never hinged	100.00	

The surtax aided Child Welfare Societies.

Syncopated Perfs., Type C

B66a	SP59	1½c (+1½c)	1.90	.80
B67a	SP59	5c (+3c)	2.60	.90
B68a	SP59	6c (+4c)	3.25	.80
B69a	SP59	12½c (+3½c)	27.50	24.50
		Nos. B66a-B69a (4)	35.25	27.00
		Set, never hinged	130.00	

Queen Wilhelmina SP60

Princess Juliana SP61

Perf. 12½
1934, Apr. 28   Engr.   Unwmk.

B70	SP60	5c (+4c) dk vio	11.50	3.00
B71	SP61	6c (+5c) blue	10.50	3.75
		Set, never hinged	55.00	

The surtax was for the benefit of the Anti-Depression Committee.

Dowager Queen Emma — SP62

1934, Oct. 1   Perf. 13x14

B72	SP62	6c (+2c) blue	11.50	1.40
		Never hinged	28.00	

Surtax for the Fight Tuberculosis Society.

Poor Child — SP63

1934, Dec. 10   Photo.   Wmk. 202

B73	SP63	1½c (+1½c) olive	1.40	.45
B74	SP63	5c (+3c) rose red	2.40	1.00
B75	SP63	6c (+4c) bl grn	2.40	.25
B76	SP63	12½c (+3½c) ultra	22.50	16.00
		Nos. B73-B76 (4)	28.70	17.70
		Set, never hinged	100.00	

The surtax aided child welfare.

Henri D. Guyot SP64

F. C. Donders SP66

A. J. M. Diepenbrock SP65

J. P. Sweelinck SP67

Perf. 12½ x 12, 12
1935, June 17   Engr.   Unwmk.

B77	SP64	1½c (+1½c) dk car	1.50	1.50
B78	SP65	5c (+3c) blk brn	4.00	4.00

B79	SP66	6c (+4c) myr grn	4.50	.50
B80	SP67	12½c (+3½c) dp bl	24.00	6.00
		Nos. B77-B80 (4)	34.00	12.00
		Set, never hinged	100.00	

Surtax for social and cultural projects.

Netherlands Map, DC-3 Planes' Shadows — SP68

Perf. 14x13
1935, Oct. 16   Photo.   Wmk. 202

B81	SP68	6c (+4c) brn	24.00	7.50

Surtax for Natl. Aviation.

Girl Picking Apple — SP69

1935, Dec. 4   Perf. 14½x13½

B82	SP69	1½c (+1½c) crim	.50	.55
B83	SP69	5c (+3c) dk yel grn	1.40	1.05
B84	SP69	6c (+4c) blk brn	1.25	.55
B85	SP69	12½c (+3½c) ultra	20.00	7.50
		Nos. B82-B85 (4)	23.15	9.65
		Set, never hinged	110.00	

The surtax aided child welfare.

H. Kamerlingh Onnes SP70

Msgr. H. J. A. M. Schaepman SP72

Dr. A. S. Talma SP71

Desiderius Erasmus SP73

Perf. 12½x12
1936, May 1   Engr.   Unwmk.

B86	SP70	1½c (+1½c) brn blk	.65	.75
B87	SP71	5c (+3c) dl grn	4.00	3.25
B88	SP72	6c (+4c) dk red	3.25	.50
B89	SP73	12½c (+3½c) dl bl	11.50	2.50
		Nos. B86-B89 (4)	19.40	7.00
		Set, never hinged	67.50	

Surtax for social and cultural projects.

Cherub — SP74

Perf. 14½x13½
1936, Dec. 1   Photo.   Wmk. 202

B90	SP74	1½c (+1½c) lil gray	.50	.30
B91	SP74	5c (+3c) turq grn	2.00	.75
B92	SP74	6c (+4c) dp red brn	1.90	.25
B93	SP74	12½c (+3½c) ind	14.00	4.75
		Nos. B90-B93 (4)	18.40	6.05
		Set, never hinged	52.50	

The surtax aided child welfare.

Jacob Maris
SP75

Franciscus
de la Boe
Sylvius
SP76

Joost van
den Vondel
SP77

Antoni van
Leeuwenhoek
SP78

Perf. 12½x12

1937, June 1   Engr.   Unwmk.

B94	SP75	1½c (+1½c) blk brn	.50 .40
B95	SP76	5c (+3c) dl grn	4.00 2.75
B96	SP77	6c (+4c) brn vio	1.00 .25
B97	SP78	12½c (+3½c) dl bl	7.00 1.25
	Nos. B94-B97 (4)		12.50 4.65
	Set, never hinged		40.00

Surtax for social and cultural projects.

"The Laughing Child" after
Frans Hals — SP79

Perf. 14½x13½

1937, Dec. 1   Photo.   Wmk. 202

B98	SP79	1½c (+1½c) blk	.25 .25
B99	SP79	3c (+2c) grn	1.50 1.00
B100	SP79	4c (+2c) hn brn	.60 .45
B101	SP79	5c (+3c) bl grn	.50 .25
B102	SP79	12½c (+3½c) dk bl	7.25 1.40
	Nos. B98-B102 (5)		10.10 3.35
	Set, never hinged		35.00

The surtax aided child welfare.

Marnix van
Sint
Aldegonde
SP80

Otto
Gerhard
Heldring
SP81

Maria
Tesselschade
SP82

Hermann
Boerhaave
SP84

Harmenszoon Rembrandt
van Rijn — SP83

Perf. 12½x12

1938, May 16   Engr.   Unwmk.

B103	SP80	1½c (+1½c) sep	.30 .35
B104	SP81	3c (+2c) dk grn	.55 .35
B105	SP82	4c (+2c) rose lake	1.75 1.75
B106	SP83	5c (+3c) dk sl grn	2.25 .35
B107	SP84	12½c (+3½c) dl bl	7.75 1.00
	Nos. B103-B107 (5)		12.60 3.80
	Set, never hinged		34.00

The surtax was for the benefit of cultural and
social relief.

Child with Flowers, Bird
and Fish — SP85

Perf. 14½x13½

1938, Dec. 1   Photo.   Wmk. 202

B108	SP85	1½c (+1½c) blk	.25 .25
B109	SP85	3c (+2c) mar	.30 .25
B110	SP85	4c (+2c) dk bl grn	.60 .80
B111	SP85	5c (+3c) hn brn	.25 .25
B112	SP85	12½c (+3½c) dp bl	9.00 1.75
	Nos. B108-B112 (5)		10.40 3.30
	Set, never hinged		35.00

The surtax aided child welfare.

Matthijs
Maris
SP86

Anton
Mauve
SP87

Gerard van
Swieten
SP88

Nikolaas
Beets
SP89

Peter Stuyvesant — SP90

Perf. 12½x12

1939, May 1   Engr.   Unwmk.

B113	SP86	1½c (+1½c) sepia	.60 .60
B114	SP87	2½c (+2½c) gray grn	3.00 2.75
B115	SP88	3c (+3c) ver	.80 1.00
B116	SP89	5c (+3c) dk sl grn	2.00 .30
B117	SP90	12½c (+3½c) indigo	5.00 .85
	Nos. B113-B117 (5)		11.40 5.50
	Set, never hinged		40.00

The surtax was for the benefit of cultural and
social relief.

Child Carrying
Cornucopia — SP91

Perf. 14½x13½

1939, Dec. 1   Photo.   Wmk. 202

B118	SP91	1½c (+1½c) blk	.25 .25
B119	SP91	2½c (+2½c) dk ol grn	3.75 2.00
B120	SP91	3c (+3c) hn brn	.40 .25
B121	SP91	5c (+3c) dk grn	.85 .25
B122	SP91	12½c (+3½c) dk bl	4.00 1.00
	Nos. B118-B122 (5)		9.25 3.75
	Set, never hinged		40.00

The surtax was used for destitute children.

> **Catalogue values for unused
> stamps in this section, from this
> point to the end of the section, are
> for Never Hinged items.**

Vincent van
Gogh
SP92

E. J.
Potgieter
SP93

Petrus
Camper
SP94

Jan Steen
SP95

Joseph Scaliger — SP96

Perf. 12½x12

1940, May 11   Engr.   Wmk. 202

B123	SP92	1½c +1½c brn blk	4.00 .35
B124	SP93	2½c +2½c dk grn	7.00 .65
B125	SP94	3c +3c car	4.00 .65
B126	SP95	5c +3c dp grn	10.00 .30
B127	SP96	12½c +3½c dp bl	8.00 1.10
a.	Booklet pane of 4		140.00

Surtax for social and cultural projects.

Type of 1940 Surcharged
in Black

1940, Sept. 7

B128	SP95	7½c +2½c on 5c +3c dk red	.80 .30
	Nos. B123-B128 (6)		33.80 3.35

Child with Flowers and
Doll — SP97

Perf. 14½x13½

1940, Dec. 2   Photo.   Wmk. 202

B129	SP97	1½c +1½c dl bl gray	1.00 .25
B130	SP97	2½c +2½c dp ol	2.75 .55
B131	SP97	4c +3c royal bl	3.00 .60
B132	SP97	5c +3c dk bl grn	3.00 .25
B133	SP97	7½c +3½c hn	1.40 .25
	Nos. B129-B133 (5)		11.15 1.90

The surtax was used for destitute children.

Dr.
Antonius
Mathijsen
SP98

Dr. Jan
Ingenhousz
SP99

Aagje
Deken
SP100

Johannes
Bosboom
SP101

A. C. W.
Staring — SP102

Perf. 12½x12

1941, May 29   Engr.   Wmk. 202

B134	SP98	1½c +1½c blk brn	.65 .25
B135	SP99	2½c +2½c dk sl grn	.65 .25
B136	SP100	4c +3c red	.65 .25
B137	SP101	5c +3c slate grn	.65 .25
B138	SP102	7½c +3½c rose vio	.65 .25
	Nos. B134-B138 (5)		3.25 1.25

The surtax was for cultural and social relief.

Rembrandt's Painting of
Titus, His Son — SP103

Perf. 14½x13½

1941, Dec. 1   Photo.   Wmk. 202

B139	SP103	1½c +1½c vio blk	.35 .25
B140	SP103	2½c +2½c dk ol	.35 .25
B141	SP103	4c +3c royal blue	.35 .25
B142	SP103	5c +3c dp grn	.35 .25
B143	SP103	7½c +3½c dp henna brn	.35 .25
	Nos. B139-B143 (5)		1.75 1.25

The surtax aided child welfare.

Legionary
SP104   SP105

1942, Nov. 1   Perf. 12½x12, 12x12½

B144	SP104	7½c +2½c dk red	.75 .50
a.	Sheet of 10		100.00 100.00
B145	SP105	12½c +87½c ultra	5.50 6.25
a.	Sheet of 4		75.00 80.00

The surtax aided the Netherlands Legion.
#B144a, B145a measure 155x111mm and
94x94mm respectively.

19th Century Mail
Cart — SP108

1943, Oct. 9   Unwmk.   Perf. 12x12½

B148	SP108	7½c +7½c henna brn	.25 .25

Issued to commemorate Stamp Day.

Child and
House — SP109

#B150, Mother & Child. #B151, Mother $
Children. #B152, Child Carrying Sheaf of
Wheat. #B153, Mother & Children, diff.

Perf. 12½x12

1944, Mar. 6   Wmk. 202

B149	SP109	1½c +3½c dl blk	.25 .25
B150	SP109	4c +3½c rose lake	.25 .25
B151	SP109	5c +5c dk bl grn	.25 .25
B152	SP109	7½c +7½c dp hn brn	.25 .25
B153	SP109	10c +40c royal blue	.25 .25
	Nos. B149-B153 (5)		1.25 1.25

The surtax aided National Social Service
and winter relief.

Child — SP114

1945, Dec. 1   Photo.   Perf. 14½x13½

B154	SP114	1½c +2½c gray	.25 .25
B155	SP114	2½c +3½c dk bl grn	.25 .25
B156	SP114	5c +5c brn red	.25 .25
B157	SP114	7½c +4½c red	.25 .25
B158	SP114	12½c +½c brt bl	.25 .25
	Nos. B154-B158 (5)		1.25 1.25

The surtax was for Child Welfare.

Fortuna — SP115

Perf. 12½x12
1946, May 1   Engr.   Unwmk.

B159	SP115	1½c +3½c brn blk	.40	.30
B160	SP115	2½c +5c dl grn	.45	.45
B161	SP115	5c +10c dk vio	.45	.45
B162	SP115	7½c +15c car lake	.40	.30
B163	SP115	12½c +37½c dk bl	.75	.55
	Nos. B159-B163 (5)		2.45	2.05

The surtax was for victims of World War II.

Princess Irene — SP116

Designs: Nos. B165, B167, Princess Margriet. Nos. B168-B169, Princess Beatrix.

1946, Sept. 16

B164	SP116	1½c +1½c blk brn	.40	.40
B165	SP116	2½c +1½c bl grn	.40	.40
B166	SP116	4c +2c magenta	.50	.40
B167	SP116	5c +2c brown	.50	.40
B168	SP116	7½c +2½c red	.40	.25
B169	SP116	12½c +7½c dk bl	.40	.50
	Nos. B164-B169 (6)		2.60	2.35

The surtax was for child welfare and anti-tuberculosis work.

Child on Merry-go-round — SP119

1946, Dec. 2   Photo.   Wmk. 202

B170	SP119	2c +2c lil gray	.35	.30
B171	SP119	4c +2c dk grn	.35	.30
B172	SP119	7½c +2½c brt red	.35	.30
B173	SP119	10c +5c dp plum	.45	.25
B174	SP119	20c +5c dp bl	.50	.45
	Nos. B170-B174 (5)		2.00	1.60

The surtax was for child welfare.

Dr. Hendrik van Deventer SP120

Peter Cornelisz Hooft SP121

Johan de Witt SP122

Jean F. van Royen SP123

Hugo de Groot — SP124

1947, Aug. 1   Engr.   Unwmk.

B175	SP120	2c +2c dark red	.55	.30
B176	SP121	4c +2c dk green	.90	.40
B177	SP122	7½c +2½c dk pur brn	1.40	.40
B178	SP123	10c +5c brown	1.40	.25
B179	SP124	20c +5c dk blue	.85	.40
	Nos. B175-B179 (5)		5.10	1.75

The surtax was for social and cultural purposes.

Children SP125

Infant SP126

1947, Dec. 1   Photo.   Perf. 13x14

B180	SP125	2c +2c red brn	.25	.25
B181	SP126	4c +2c bl grn	.60	.40
B182	SP126	7½c +2½c sepia	.60	.55
B183	SP126	10c +5c dk red	.80	.25
B184	SP126	20c +5c blue	.90	.70
	Nos. B180-B184 (5)		3.15	2.15

The surtax was for child welfare.

Hall of Knights, The Hague — SP127

Designs: 6c+4c, Royal Palace, Amsterdam. 10c+5c, Kneuterdyk Palace, The Hague. 20c+5c, New Church, Amsterdam.

1948, June 17   Engr.   Perf. 13½x14

B185	SP127	2c +2c dk brn	1.15	.50
B186	SP127	6c +4c grn	1.25	.50
B187	SP127	7½c +5c brt red	.85	.30
B188	SP127	20c +5c deep blue	1.25	.70
	Nos. B185-B188 (4)		4.50	2.00

The surtax was for cultural and social purposes.

Boy in Kayak — SP128

5c+3c, Swimming. 6c+4c, Sledding. 10c+5c, Swinging. 20c+8c, Figure skating.

1948, Nov. 15   Photo.   Perf. 13x14

B189	SP128	2c +2c yel grn	.25	.25
B190	SP128	5c +3c dk bl grn	1.50	.50
B191	SP128	6c +4c gray	.80	.25
B192	SP128	10c +5c red	.35	.25
B193	SP128	20c +8c blue	1.50	.75
	Nos. B189-B193 (5)		4.40	2.00

The surtax was for child welfare.

Beach Terrace — SP129

Boy and Girl Hikers — SP130

Campers SP131

Reaping SP132

Sailboats — SP133

1949, May 2   Wmk. 202   Perf. 14x13

B194	SP129	2c +2c bl & org yel	1.10	.25
B195	SP130	5c +3c bl & yel	1.75	1.00
B196	SP131	6c +4c dk bl grn	1.60	.35
B197	SP132	10c +5c bl & org yel	1.90	.25
B198	SP133	20c +5c blue	2.40	1.25
	Nos. B194-B198 (5)		8.75	3.10

The surtax was for cultural and social purposes.

Hands Reaching for Sunflower — SP134

Perf. 14½x13½
1949, Aug. 1   Photo.   Unwmk.
Flower in Yellow

B199	SP134	2c +3c gray	.95	.25
B200	SP134	6c +4c red brown	1.50	.30
B201	SP134	10c +5c brt blue	2.40	.25
B202	SP134	30c +10c dk brown	5.25	2.40
	Nos. B199-B202 (4)		10.10	3.20

The surtax was for the Red Cross and for Indonesia Relief work.

"Autumn" — SP135

5c+3c, "Summer." 6c+4c, "Spring." 10c+5c, "Winter." 20c+7c, "New Year."

1949, Nov. 14   Engr.   Perf. 13x14

B203	SP135	2c +3c brown	.25	.25
B204	SP135	5c +3c red	3.50	1.50
B205	SP135	6c +4c dull green	2.50	.30
B206	SP135	10c +5c gray	.25	.25
B207	SP135	20c +7c blue	3.50	1.50
	Nos. B203-B207 (5)		10.00	3.80

The surtax was for child welfare.

Figure from PTT Monument, The Hague SP136

Grain Binder SP137

Designs: 4c+2c, Dike repairs. 5c+3c, Apartment House, Rotterdam. 10c+5c, Bridge section being towed. 20c+5c, Canal freighter.

1950, May 2   Perf. 12½x12, 12x12½

B208	SP136	2c +2c brn	2.10	1.10
B209	SP136	4c +2c dk green	6.50	5.75
B210	SP136	5c +3c gray	5.50	4.50
B211	SP137	6c +4c purple	2.75	.75
B212	SP137	10c +5c indigo	3.75	.40
B213	SP137	20c +5c dp bl	7.50	9.50
	Nos. B208-B213 (6)		28.10	22.00

The surtax was for social and cultural works.

Church Ruins and Good Samaritan — SP138

1950, July 17   Photo.   Perf. 12½x12

B214	SP138	2c +2c ol brn	4.75	2.40
B215	SP138	5c +3c brn red	6.25	7.25
B216	SP138	6c +4c dp grn	3.75	3.25
B217	SP138	10c +5c brt lil rose	13.50	.80
B218	SP138	20c +5c ultra	19.00	24.00
	Nos. B214-B218 (5)		47.25	37.70

The surtax was for the restoration of ruined churches.

Baby and Bees — SP139

Designs: 5c+3c, Boy and rooster. 6c+4c, Girl feeding birds. 10c+5c, Boy and fish. 20c+7c, Girl, butterfly and toad.

1950, Nov. 13   Perf. 13x12

B219	SP139	2c +3c car	.30	.25
B220	SP139	5c +3c ol grn	8.25	4.25
B221	SP139	6c +4c dk bl grn	2.40	.65
B222	SP139	10c +5c lilac	.30	.25
B223	SP139	20c +7c blue	8.75	7.50
	Nos. B219-B223 (5)		20.00	12.90

The surtax was to aid needy children.

Hillenraad Castle SP140

Bergh Castle SP141

Castles: 6c+4c, Hernen. 10c+5c, Rechteren. 20c+5c, Moermond.

Perf. 12x12½, 12½x12
1951, May 15   Engr.   Unwmk.

B224	SP140	2c +2c purple	1.75	1.00
B225	SP141	5c +3c dk red	5.50	6.00
B226	SP140	6c +4c dk brown	3.50	1.00
B227	SP141	10c +5c dk green	4.00	.25
B228	SP141	20c +5c dp blue	5.50	6.00
	Nos. B224-B228 (5)		20.25	14.25

The surtax was for cultural, medical and social purposes.

Girl and Windmill — SP142

Designs: 5c+3c, Boy and building construction. 6c+4c, Fisherboy and net. 10c+5c, Boy, chimneys and steelwork. 20c+7c, Girl and apartment house.

1951, Nov. 12   Photo.   Perf. 13x14

B229	SP142	2c +3c dp green	.60	.25
B230	SP142	5c +3c sl vio	5.25	3.50
B231	SP142	6c +4c dk brown	3.50	.70
B232	SP142	10c +5c red brn	.30	.25
B233	SP142	20c +7c dp bl	5.25	6.50
	Nos. B229-B233 (5)		14.90	11.20

The surtax was for child welfare.

Jan van Riebeeck — SP143

1952, Mar.   Perf. 12½x12

B234	SP143	2c +3c dk gray	3.25	2.25
B235	SP143	6c +4c dk bl grn	4.00	3.00
B236	SP143	10c +5c brt red	4.50	2.25
B237	SP143	20c +5c brt blue	3.25	3.00
	Nos. B234-B237 (4)		15.00	10.50

Tercentenary of Van Riebeeck's landing in South Africa. Surtax was for Van Riebeeck monument fund.

Scotch Rose — SP144

Designs: 5c+3c, Marsh marigold. 6c+4c, Tulip. 10c+5c, Ox-eye daisy. 20c+5c, Cornflower.

1952, May 1

B238	SP144	2c +2c cer & dl grn	.60	.50
B239	SP144	5c +3c dp grn & yel	2.40	3.00
B240	SP144	6c +4c red & dl grn	1.60	1.10
B241	SP144	10c +5c org yel & dl grn	1.20	.35
B242	SP144	20c +5c bl & dl grn	6.25	5.25
	Nos. B238-B242 (5)		12.05	10.20

The surtax was for social, cultural and medical purposes.

Girl and Dog — SP145

2c+3c, Boy & goat. 5c+3c, Girl on donkey. 10c+5c, Boy & kitten. 20c+7c, Boy & rabbit.

Design in Black
Perf. 12x12½
1952, Nov. 17   **Unwmk.**

B243	SP145	2c +3c olive	.25 .25
B244	SP145	5c +3c dp rose	1.90 1.45
B245	SP145	6c +4c aqua	1.35 .40
B246	SP145	10c +5c org yel	.25 .25
B247	SP145	20c +7c blue	4.50 4.25
		Nos. B243-B247 (5)	8.25 6.60

The surtax was for child welfare.

No. 308 Surcharged in Black

Perf. 13½x13
1953, Feb. 10   **Wmk. 202**

B248	A76	10c +10c org yel	.50 .25

The surtax was for flood relief.

Hyacinth — SP146

Designs: 5c+3c, African Marigold. 6c+4c, Daffodil. 10c+5c, Anemone. 20c+5c, Iris.

1953, May 1   **Unwmk.**   *Perf. 12½x12*

B249	SP146	2c +2c vio & grn	.65 .50
B250	SP146	5c +3c dp org & grn	2.25 3.25
B251	SP146	6c +4c grn & yel	1.30 1.00
B252	SP146	10c +5c dk red & grn	2.90 .50
B253	SP146	20c +5c dp ultra & grn	9.00 9.00
		Nos. B249-B253 (5)	16.10 14.25

The surtax was for social, cultural and medical purposes.

Red Cross on Shield — SP147

Designs: 6c+4c, Man holding lantern. 7c+5c, Worker and ambulance at flood. 10c+5c, Nurse giving blood transfusion. 25c+8c, Red Cross flags.

Cross in Red
1953, Aug. 24   **Engr.**

B254	SP147	2c +3c dk ol	.60 .45
B255	SP147	6c +4c dk vio brn	3.50 3.25
B256	SP147	7c +5c dk gray	.75 .45
B257	SP147	10c +5c red	.60 .25
B258	SP147	25c +8c dp bl	4.50 4.25
		Nos. B254-B258 (5)	9.95 8.65

The surtax was for the Red Cross.

Spade, Flag, Bucket and Girl's Head — SP148

Head of child and: 5c+3c, Apple. 7c+5c, Pigeon. 10c+5c, Sailboat. 25c+8c, Tulip.

1953, Nov. 16   **Litho.**   *Perf. 12x12½*

B259	SP148	2c +3c yel & bl gray	.25 .25
B260	SP148	5c +3c ap grn & brn car	2.25 3.50
B261	SP148	7c +5c lt bl & sep	2.25 1.30
B262	SP148	10c +5c ol bis & lil	.25 .25
B263	SP148	25c +8c pink & bl grn	6.00 8.00
		Nos. B259-B263 (5)	11.00 13.30

The surtax was for child welfare.

Martinus Nijhoff, Poet — SP149

5c+3c, Willem Pijper, composer. 7c+5c, H. P. Berlage, architect. 10c+5c, Johan Huizinga, historian. 25c+8c, Vincent van Gogh, painter.

1954, May 1   **Photo.**   *Perf. 12½x12*

B264	SP149	2c +3c dp bl	1.75 1.50
B265	SP149	5c +3c ol brn	2.00 2.00
B266	SP149	7c +5c dk red	2.60 1.20
B267	SP149	10c +5c dl grn	5.25 .60
B268	SP149	25c +8c plum	6.75 7.75
		Nos. B264-B268 (5)	18.35 13.05

The surtax was for social and cultural purposes.

Boy Flying Model Plane — SP150

Portrait: 10c+4c, Albert E. Plesman.

1954, Aug. 23   *Perf. 12½x12*

B269	SP150	2c +2c ol grn	.75 .65
B270	SP150	10c +4c dk gray bl	2.10 .65

The surtax was for the Netherlands Aviation Foundation.

Children Making Paper Chains SP151

Girl Brushing Teeth SP152

7c+5c, Boy sailing toy boat. 10c+5c, Nurse drying child. 25c+8c, Young convalescent, drawing.

Perf. 12x12½, 12½x12
1954, Nov. 15

B271	SP151	2c +3c brn	.25 .25
B272	SP152	5c +3c ol grn	2.75 2.75
B273	SP152	7c +5c gray bl	1.00 .50
B274	SP152	10c +5c brn red	.25 .25
B275	SP152	25c +8c dp bl	5.75 4.75
		Nos. B271-B275 (5)	10.00 8.50

The surtax was for child welfare.

Factory, Rotterdam SP153

Amsterdam Stock Exchange SP154

5c+3c, Post office, The Hague. 10c+5c, Town hall, Hilversum. 25c+8c, Office building, The Hague.

1955, Apr. 25   **Engr.**

B276	SP153	2c +3c brnsh bis	1.25 1.00
B277	SP153	5c +3c bl grn	2.25 2.75
B278	SP154	7c +5c rose brn	1.25 1.00
B279	SP153	10c +5c steel bl	1.75 .25
B280	SP153	25c +8c choc	6.75 7.00
		Nos. B276-B280 (5)	13.25 12.00

The surtax was for social and cultural purposes.

Microscope and Crab — SP155

1955, Aug. 15   **Photo.**   *Perf. 12½x12*
Crab in Red

B281	SP155	2c +3c dk gray	.65 .55
B282	SP155	5c +3c dk grn	1.40 1.45
B283	SP155	7c +5c dk vio	1.15 .60
B284	SP155	10c +5c dk bl	.95 .25
B285	SP155	25c +8c olive	4.50 3.75
		Nos. B281-B285 (5)	8.65 6.60

The surtax was for cancer research.

Willem van Loon by Dirck Santvoort — SP156

Portraits: 5+3c, Boy by Jacob Adriaanszoon Backer. 7+5c, Girl by unknown artist. 10+5c, Philips Huygens by Adriaan Hanneman. 25+8c, Constantijn Huygens by Adriaan Hanneman.

1955, Nov. 14   **Unwmk.**

B286	SP156	2c +3c dk grn	.35 .25
B287	SP156	5c +3c dp car	2.10 1.75
B288	SP156	7c +5c dl red brn	2.10 .60
B289	SP156	10c +5c dp bl	.35 .25
B290	SP156	25c +8c purple	5.50 5.00
		Nos. B286-B290 (5)	10.40 7.90

The surtax was for child welfare.

Farmer Wearing High Cap — SP157

Rembrandt Etchings: 5c+3c, Young Tobias with Angel. 7c+5c, Persian Wearing Fur Cap. 10c+5c, Old Blind Tobias. 25c+8c, Self-portrait of 1639.

1956, Apr. 23   **Engr.**   *Perf. 13½x14*

B291	SP157	2c +3c dk gray bl	1.25 1.60
B292	SP157	5c +3c ol grn	2.25 2.25
B293	SP157	7c +5c brown	2.50 2.50
B294	SP157	10c +5c dk grn	6.00 .35
B295	SP157	25c +8c redsh	9.25 9.25
		Nos. B291-B295 (5)	21.25 15.95

350th anniv. of the birth of Rembrandt van Rijn.
Surtax for social and cultural purposes.

Sailboat — SP158

Designs: 5c+3c, Woman runner. 7c+5c, Amphora depicting runners. 10c+5c, Field hockey. 25c+8c, Waterpolo player.

1956, Aug. 27   **Litho.**   *Perf. 12½x12*

B296	SP158	2c +3c brt bl & blk	.70 .80
B297	SP158	5c +3c dl yel & blk	1.00 1.15
B298	SP158	7c +5c red brn & blk	1.00 1.15
B299	SP158	10c +5c gray & blk	1.25 .40
B300	SP158	25c +8c brt grn & blk	2.60 3.50
		Nos. B296-B300 (5)	6.55 7.00

16th Olympic Games at Melbourne, Nov. 22-Dec. 8, 1956.
The surtax was for the benefit of the Netherlands Olympic Committee.

Boy by Jan van Scorel — SP159

Children's Portraits: 5c+3c, Boy, 1563. 7c+5c, Girl, 1563. 10c+5c, Girl, 1590. 25c+8c, Eechie Pieters, 1592.

1956, Nov. 12   **Photo.**   **Unwmk.**

B301	SP159	2c +3c blk vio	.35 .25
B302	SP159	5c +3c ol grn	1.60 .65
B303	SP159	7c +5c brn vio	1.75 1.25
B304	SP159	10c +5c dp red	.30 .25
B305	SP159	25c +8c dk bl	3.25 2.90
		Nos. B301-B305 (5)	7.25 5.30

The surtax was for child welfare.

Motor Freighter — SP160

Ships: 6c+4c, Coaster. 7c+5c, "Willem Barendsz." 10c+8c, Trawler. 30c+8c, S. S. "Nieuw Amsterdam."

1957, May 13   **Photo.**   *Perf. 14x13*

B306	SP160	4c +3c brt bl	1.00 1.00
B307	SP160	6c +4c brt vio	2.00 2.00
B308	SP160	7c +5c dk car rose	1.25 1.10
B309	SP160	10c +8c grn	2.10 .40
B310	SP160	30c +8c choc	3.25 3.00
		Nos. B306-B310 (5)	9.60 7.50

The surtax was for social and cultural purposes.

White Pelican Feeding Young — SP161

Designs: 6c+4c, Vacation ship, "Castle of Staverden." 7c+5c, Cross and dates: 1867-1957. 10c+8c, Cross and laurel wreath. 30c+8c, Globe and Cross.

1957, Aug. 19   **Litho.**   *Perf. 12x12½*
Cross in Red

B311	SP161	4c +3c bl & red	.65 .60
B312	SP161	6c +4c dk grn	.85 .85
B313	SP161	7c +5c dk grn & pink	.85 .85
B314	SP161	10c +8c yel org	.75 .25
B315	SP161	30c +8c vio bl	1.90 1.90
		Nos. B311-B315 (5)	5.00 4.45

90th anniversary of the founding of the Netherlands Red Cross.

Girl by B. J. Blommers — SP162

Girls' Portraits by: 6c+4c, William B. Tholen. 8c+4c, Jan Sluyters. 12c+9c, Matthijs Maris. 30c+9c, Cornelis Kruseman.

1957, Nov. 18   **Photo.**   *Perf. 12½x12*

B316	SP162	4c +4c dp car	.30 .25
B317	SP162	6c +4c ol grn	1.50 2.00
B318	SP162	8c +4c gray	1.60 1.90
B319	SP162	12c +9c dp claret	.25 .25
B320	SP162	30c +9c dk bl	4.50 4.75
		Nos. B316-B320 (5)	8.15 9.15

The surtax was for child welfare.

Woman from Walcheren, Zeeland — SP163

Regional Costumes: 6c+4c, Marken. 8c+4c, Scheveningen. 12c+9c, Friesland. 30c+9c, Volendam.

1958, Apr. 28   **Photo.**   **Unwmk.**

B321	SP163	4c +4c blue	.95 .60
B322	SP163	6c +4c bister	1.60 1.60
B323	SP163	8c +4c dk car rose	2.90 1.60
B324	SP163	12c +9c org brn	1.60 .25
B325	SP163	30c +9c vio	5.00 5.25
		Nos. B321-B325 (5)	12.05 9.30

Surtax for social and cultural purposes.

Girl on Stilts and Boy on Tricycle — SP164

Children's Games: 6c+4c, Boy and girl on scooters. 8c+4c, Leapfrog. 12c+9c, Roller skating. 30c+9c, Boy in toy car and girl jumping rope.

1958, Nov. 17 Litho.
B326	SP164	4c +4c lt bl	.25	.25
B327	SP164	6c +4c dp red	1.60	1.60
B328	SP164	8c +4c brt bl grn	1.30	.75
B329	SP164	12c +9c red org	.25	.25
B330	SP164	30c +9c dk bl	3.25	3.00
	Nos. B326-B330 (5)		6.65	5.85

The surtax was for child welfare.

Tugs and Caisson — SP165

Designs: 6c+4c, Dredger. 8c+4c, Laborers making fascine mattresses. 12c+9c, Grab cranes. 30c+9c, Sand spouter.

1959, May 11 Perf. 14x13
B331	SP165	4c +4c dk bl, bl grn	1.00	1.00
B332	SP165	6c +4c red org, gray	1.00	1.30
B333	SP165	8c +4c bl vio, lt bl	1.00	1.00
B334	SP165	12c +9c bl grn, brt yel	1.75	.25
B335	SP165	30c +9c dk brn, brick red	3.25	4.50
	Nos. B331-B335 (5)		8.00	8.05

Issued to publicize the endless struggle to keep the sea out and the land dry.
The surtax was for social and cultural purposes.

Child in Playpen — SP166

Designs: 6c+4c, Playing Indian. 8c+4c, Child feeding geese. 12c+9c, Children crossing street. 30c+9c, Doing homework.

1959, Nov. 16 Perf. 12½x12
B336	SP166	4c +4c dp rose & dk bl	.25	.25
B337	SP166	6c +4c red brn & emer	1.00	1.00
B338	SP166	8c +4c red & bl	1.75	1.10
B339	SP166	12c +9c grnsh bl, org & gray	.25	.25
B340	SP166	30c +9c yel & bl	2.90	2.75
	Nos. B336-B340 (5)		6.15	5.35

The surtax was for child welfare.

Refugee Woman — SP167

1960, Apr. 7 Photo. Perf. 13x14
B341	SP167	12c +8c dp claret	.50	.30
B342	SP167	30c +10c dk ol grn	2.25	2.00

Issued to publicize World Refugee Year, July 1, 1959-June 30, 1960. The surtax was for aid to refugees.

Tulip — SP168

Flowers: 6c+4c, Gorse. 8c+4c, White waterlily, horiz. 12c+8c, Red poppy. 30c+10c, Blue sea holly.

Perf. 12½x12, 12x12½
1960, May 23 Unwmk.
B343	SP168	4c +4c gray, grn & red	.95	.75
B344	SP168	6c +4c sal, grn & yel	1.25	1.60
B345	SP168	8c +4c multi	1.75	1.60
B346	SP168	12c +8c dl org, red & grn	1.60	.30
B347	SP168	30c +10c yel, grn & ultra	3.00	4.50
	Nos. B343-B347 (5)		8.55	8.75

The surtax was for child welfare.

Girl from Marken — SP169

Regional Costumes: 6c+4c, Volendam. 8c+4c, Bunschoten. 12c+9c, Hindeloopen. 30c+9c, Huizen.

1960, Nov. 14 Perf. 12½x12
B348	SP169	4c +4c multi	.35	.25
B349	SP169	6c +4c multi	1.60	2.00
B350	SP169	8c +4c multi	3.00	2.00
B351	SP169	12c +9c multi	.35	.25
B352	SP169	30c +9c multi	3.75	4.50
	Nos. B348-B352 (5)		9.05	9.00

The surtax was for child welfare.

Herring Gull — SP170

Birds: 6c+4c, Oystercatcher, horiz. 8c+4c, Curlew. 12c+8c, Avocet, horiz. 30c+10c, Lapwing.

Perf. 12½x12, 12x12½
1961, Apr. 24 Litho. Unwmk.
B353	SP170	4c +4c yel & grnsh gray	.70	.95
B354	SP170	6c +4c fawn & blk	1.40	1.75
B355	SP170	8c +4c ol & red brn	.70	1.10
B356	SP170	12c +8c lt bl & gray	1.90	.40
B357	SP170	30c +10c grn & blk	1.90	2.40
	Nos. B353-B357 (5)		6.60	6.60

The surtax was for social and cultural purposes.

St. Nicholas on his Horse — SP171

Holiday folklore: 6c+4c, Epiphany. 8c+4c, Palm Sunday. 12c+9c, Whitsun bride, Pentecost. 30c+9c, Martinmas.

1961, Nov. 13 Perf. 12½x12
B358	SP171	4c +4c brt red	.25	.25
B359	SP171	6c +4c brt bl	.90	.75
B360	SP171	8c +4c olive	.80	.75
B361	SP171	12c +9c dp grn	.25	.25
B362	SP171	30c +9c dp org	2.40	2.40
	Nos. B358-B362 (5)		4.60	4.40

The surtax was for child welfare.

SP172

Designs: 4c+4c, Cat, Roman sculpture, horiz. 6c+4c, Fossil Ammonite. 8c+4c, Christian Huygens' Pendulum Clock by van Ceulen. 12c+8c, Figurehead from admiralty ship model. 30c+10c, Guardsmen Hendrick van Berckenrode and Jacob van Lourensz, by Frans Hals, horiz.

Perf. 14x13, 13x14
1962, Apr. 27 Photo.
B363	SP172	4c +4c ol grn	.85	.85
B364	SP172	6c +4c gray	.70	.85
B365	SP172	8c +4c maroon	1.00	1.25
B366	SP172	12c +8c olive bis	1.00	.35
B367	SP172	30c +10c indigo	1.05	1.25
	Nos. B363-B367 (5)		4.60	4.55

The surtax was for social and cultural purposes. Issued to publicize the International Congress of Museum Experts, July 4-11.

Children Cooking — SP173

Children's Activities: 6c+4c, Bicycling. 8c+4c, Watering flowers. 12c+9c, Feeding chickens. 30c+9c, Music making.

1962, Nov. 12 Perf. 12½x12
B368	SP173	4c +4c red	.25	.25
B369	SP173	6c +4c yel bis	.75	.60
B370	SP173	8c +4c ultra	1.05	1.15
B371	SP173	12c +9c dp grn	.25	.25
B372	SP173	30c +9c dk car rose	1.75	1.90
	Nos. B368-B372 (5)		4.05	4.15

The surtax was for child welfare.

Gallery Windmill — SP174

Windmills: 6c+4c, North Holland polder mill. 8c+4c, South Holland polder mill, horiz. 12c+8c, Post mill. 30c+10c, Wip mill.

Perf. 13x14, 14x13
1963, Apr. 24 Litho. Unwmk.
B373	SP174	4c +4c dk bl	.85	1.00
B374	SP174	6c +4c dk pur	.85	1.00
B375	SP174	8c +4c dk grn	1.05	1.20
B376	SP174	12c +8c blk	1.05	.30
B377	SP174	30c +10c dk car	1.60	1.75
	Nos. B373-B377 (5)		5.40	5.25

The surtax was for social and cultural purposes.

Roadside First Aid Station — SP175

Designs: 6c+4c, Book collection box. 8c+4c, Crosses. 12c+9c, International aid to Africans. 30c+9c, First aid team.

1963, Aug. 20 Perf. 14x13
B378	SP175	4c +4c dk bl & red	.40	.40
B379	SP175	6c +4c dl pur & red	.40	.40
B380	SP175	8c +4c blk & red	.75	.55
B381	SP175	12c +9c red brn & red	.25	.25
B382	SP175	30c +9c yel grn & red	1.20	1.20
	Nos. B378-B382 (5)		3.00	2.80

Centenary of the Intl. Red Cross. The surtax went to the Netherlands Red Cross.

Seeing-Eye Dog — SP177

8c+5c, Three red deer. 12c+9c, Three kittens. 30c+9c, European bison and young.

1964, Apr. 21 Perf. 12x12½
B388	SP177	5c +5c gray ol, red & blk	.35	.35
B389	SP177	8c +5c dk red, pale brn & blk	.25	.25
B390	SP177	12c +9c dl yel, blk & gray	.35	.25
B391	SP177	30c +9c bl, gray & blk	.60	.55
	Nos. B388-B391 (4)		1.55	1.40

The surtax was for social and cultural purposes.

Child Painting — SP178

"Artistic and Creative Activities of Children": 10c+5c, Ballet dancing. 15c+10c, Girl playing the flute. 20c+10c, Little Red Riding Hood (masquerading children). 40c+15c, Boy with hammer at work bench.

Perf. 13x14
1964, Nov. 17 Photo. Unwmk.
B392	SP178	7c +3c lt ol grn & bl	.45	.35
B393	SP178	10c +5c red, brt pink & grn	.40	.35
B394	SP178	15c +10c yel bis, blk & yel	.25	.25
B395	SP178	20c +10c brt pink, brn & red	.75	.50
B396	SP178	40c +15c bl & yel grn	.95	.70
	Nos. B392-B396 (5)		2.80	2.15

The surtax was for child welfare.

View of Veere — SP179

Views: 10c+6c, Thorn. 18c+12c, Dordrecht. 20c+10c, Staveren. 40c+10c, Medemblik.

1965, June 1 Litho. Perf. 14x13
B397	SP179	8c +6c yel & blk	.25	.30
B398	SP179	10c +6c grnsh bl & blk	.40	.35
B399	SP179	18c +12c sal & blk	.30	.30
B400	SP179	20c +10c bl & blk	.40	.35
B401	SP179	40c +10c ap grn & blk	.45	.45
	Nos. B397-B401 (5)		1.80	1.75

The surtax was for social and cultural purposes.

Child — SP180

Designs by Children: 10c+6c, Ship. 18c+12c, Woman, vert. 20c+10c, Child, lake and swan. 40c+10c, Tractor.

Perf. 14x13, 13x14
1965, Nov. 16 Photo.
B402	SP180	8c +6c multi	.25	.25
B403	SP180	10c +6c multi	.50	.50
B404	SP180	18c +12c multi	.25	.25
a.	Min. sheet of 11, 5 #B402, 6 #B404 + label		16.00	23.50
B405	SP180	20c +10c multi	.75	.60
B406	SP180	40c +10c multi	1.00	.85
	Nos. B402-B406 (5)		2.75	2.45

The surtax was for child welfare.

"Help them to a safe haven" — SP181

"Aunt Lucy Sat on a Goosey" — SP176

Nursery Rhymes: 6c+4c, "In the Hague there lives a count." 8c+4c, "One day I passed a puppet's fair." 12c+9c, "Storky, storky, Billy Spoon." 30c+9c, "Ride on in a little buggy."

1963, Nov. 12 Litho. Perf. 13x14
B383	SP176	4c +4c grnsh bl & dk bl	.25	.25
B384	SP176	6c +4c org red & sl grn	1.10	.60
B385	SP176	8c +4c dl grn & dk brn	1.60	.50
B386	SP176	12c +9c yel & dk pur	.25	.25
B387	SP176	30c +9c rose & blksh lil	1.60	1.40
	Nos. B383-B387 (5)		4.80	3.00

The surtax was for mentally and physically handicapped children.

1966, Jan. 31   Photo.   Perf. 14x13
B407 SP181 18c +7c blk & org
    yel   .30 .25
B408 SP181 40c +20c blk & red .25 .25
   a.   Min. sheet of 3, #B407, 2
       #B408   1.60 1.20

The surtax was for the Intergovernmental Committee for European Migration (ICEM). The message on the stamps was given and signed by Queen Juliana.

Inkwell, Goose Quill and Book — SP182

Designs: 12c+8c, Fragment of Gysbert Japicx manuscript. 20c+10c, Knight on horseback, miniature from "Roman van Walewein" manuscript, 1350. 25c+10c, Initial "D" from "Ferguut" manuscript, 1350. 40c+20c, Print shop, 16th century woodcut.

1966, May 3   Perf. 13x14
B409 SP182 10c +5c multi   .30 .35
B410 SP182 15c +8c multi   .30 .35
B411 SP182 20c +10c multi   .45 .35
B412 SP182 25c +10c multi   .60 .50
B413 SP182 40c +20c multi   .45 .50
  Nos. B409-B413 (5)   2.10 2.05

Gysbert Japicx (1603-1666), Friesian poet, and the 200th anniversary of the founding of the Netherlands Literary Society.

The surtax was for social and cultural purposes.

Infant — SP183

Designs: 12c+8c, Daughter of the painter S. C. Lixenberg. 20c+10c, Boy swimming. 25c+10c, Dominga Blazer, daughter of Carel Blazer, photographer of this set. 40c+20c, Boy and horse.

1966, Nov. 15   Photo.   Perf. 14x13
B414 SP183 10c +5c dp org & bl .25 .25
B415 SP183 12c +8c ap grn &
    red   .25 .25
B416 SP183 20c +10c brt bl &
    red   .25 .25
   a.   Min. sheet of 12, 4 #B414, 5
      #B415, 3 #B416   2.00 2.00
B417 SP183 25c +10c brt rose lil
    & dk bl   .65 .65
B418 SP183 40c +20c dp car &
    dk grn   .65 .65
  Nos. B414-B418 (5)   2.05 2.05

The surtax was for child welfare.

Whelk Eggs — SP184

15c+10c, Whelk. 20c+10c, Mussel with acorn shells. 25c+10c, Jellyfish. 45c+20c, Crab.

1967, Apr. 11   Unwmk.   Litho.
B419 SP184 12c +8c ol grn &
    tan   .25 .25
B420 SP184 15c +10c lt bl, ultra
    & blk   .25 .25
B421 SP184 20c +10c gray, blk
    & red   .25 .25
B422 SP184 25c +10c brn car,
    plum & ol brn   .50 .50
B423 SP184 45c +20c multi   .70 .65
  Nos. B419-B423 (5)   1.95 1.90

Red Cross and Dates Forming Cross — SP185

15c+10c, Crosses. 20c+10c, Initials "NRK" forming cross. 25c+10c, Maltese cross and crosses. 45c+20c, "100" forming cross.

1967, Aug. 8   Perf. 14x13
B424 SP185 12c +8c dl bl & red .30 .30
B425 SP185 15c +10c red   .35 .35
B426 SP185 20c +10c ol & red .30 .30

B427 SP185 25c +10c ol grn &
    red   .45 .45
B428 SP185 45c +20c gray & red .70 .70
  Nos. B424-B428 (5)   2.10 2.10

Centenary of the Dutch Red Cross.

"Lullaby for the Little Porcupine" — SP186

Nursery Rhymes: 15c+10c, "Little Whistling Kettle." 20c+10c, "Dikkertje Dap and the Giraffe." 25c+10c, "The Nicest Flowers." 45c+20c, "Pippeljoentje, the Little Bear."

1967, Nov. 7   Litho.   Perf. 13x14
B429 SP186 12c +8c multi   .25 .25
B430 SP186 15c +10c multi   .25 .25
B431 SP186 20c +10c multi   .25 .25
   a.   Min. sheet of 10, 3 #B429, 4
      #B430, 3 #B431   4.00 4.00
B432 SP186 25c +10c multi   1.10 .75
B433 SP186 45c +20c multi   1.15 .75
  Nos. B429-B433 (5)   3.00 2.25

The surtax was for child welfare.

St. Servatius Bridge, Maastricht SP187

Bridges: 15c+10c, Narrow Bridge, Amsterdam. 20c+10c, Railroad Bridge, Culenborg. 25c+10c, Van Brienenoord Bridge, Rotterdam. 45c+20c, Zeeland Bridge, Schelde Estuary.

1968, Apr. 9   Photo.   Perf. 14x13
B434 SP187 12c +8c green   .35 .35
B435 SP187 15c +10c ol brn   .50 .50
B436 SP187 20c +10c rose red .30 .25
B437 SP187 25c +10c gray   .35 .35
B438 SP187 45c +20c ultra   .60 .60
  Nos. B434-B438 (5)   2.10 2.05

Goblin — SP188

Fairy Tale Characters: 15c+10c, Giant. 20c+10c, Witch. 25c+10c, Dragon. 45c+20c, Magician.

1968, Nov. 12   Photo.   Perf. 14x13
B439 SP188 12c +8c grn, pink
    & blk   .25 .25
B440 SP188 15c +10c bl, pink
    & blk   .25 .25
B441 SP188 20c +10c bl, emer
    & blk   .25 .25
   a.   Min. sheet of 10, 3 #B439,
      4 #B440, 3 #B441 4.00 4.00
B442 SP188 25c +10c org red,
    org & blk   1.25 1.25
B443 SP188 45c +20c yel, org
    & blk   1.25 1.25
  Nos. B439-B443 (5)   3.25 3.25

The surtax was for child welfare.

Villa Huis ter Heide, 1915 — SP189

Contemporary Architecture: 15c+10c, House, Utrecht, 1924. 20c+10c, First open-air school, Amsterdam, 1960. 25c+10c, Burgweeshuis (orphanage), Amsterdam, 1960. 45c+20c, Netherlands Congress Building, The Hague, 1969.

1969, Apr. 15   Photo.   Perf. 14x13
B444 SP189 12c +8c lt brn & sl .65 .65
B445 SP189 15c +10c bl, gray &
    red   .65 .65
B446 SP189 20c +10c vio & blk .65 .65
B447 SP189 25c +10c grn & gray .65 .65
B448 SP189 45c +20c gray, bl &
    yel   .65 .65
  Nos. B444-B448 (5)   3.25 3.25

Surtax for social and cultural purposes.

Stylized Crab — SP190

1969, Aug. 12   Photo.   Perf. 13x14
B449 SP190 12c +8c vio   .55 .55
B450 SP190 25c +10c org   .80 .35
B451 SP190 45c +20c bl grn 1.25 1.25
  Nos. B449-B451 (3)   2.60 2.15

20th anniv. of the Queen Wilhelmina Fund. The surtax was for cancer research.

Child with Violin — SP191

12c+8c, Child with flute. 20c+10c, Child with drum. 25c+10c, Three children singing, horiz. 45c+20c, Two girls dancing, horiz.

1969, Nov. 11   Perf. 13x14, 14x13
B452 SP191 12c +8c ultra, blk
    & yel   .25 .25
B453 SP191 15c +10c blk &
    red   .25 .25
B454 SP191 20c +10c red, blk
    & yel   2.00 1.60
B455 SP191 25c +10c yel, blk
    & red   .25 .25
   a.   Min. sheet of 10, 4 #B452,
      4 #B453, 2 #B455 5.00 5.00
B456 SP191 45c +20c grn, blk
    & red   2.10 1.60
  Nos. B452-B456 (5)   4.85 3.95

The surtax was for child welfare.

Isometric Projection from Circle to Square — SP192

Designs made by Computer: 15c+10c, Parallel planes in a cube. 20c+10c, Two overlapping scales. 25c+10c, Transition phases of concentric circles with increasing diameters. 45c+20c, Four spirals.

Lithographed and Engraved
1970, Apr. 7   Perf. 13x14
B457 SP192 12c +8c yel & blk   .80 .80
B458 SP192 15c +10c sil & blk   .80 .80
B459 SP192 20c +10c blk   .80 .80
B460 SP192 25c +10c brt bl &
    blk   .80 .80
B461 SP192 45c +20c sil &
    white   .80 .80
  Nos. B457-B461 (5)   4.00 4.00

Surtax for social and cultural purposes.

Bleeding Heart — SP193

1970, July 28   Photo.   Perf. 13x14
B462 SP193 12c +8c org yel, red
    & blk   .60 .60
B463 SP193 25c +10c pink, red
    & blk   .60 .40
B464 SP193 45c +20c brt grn,
    red & blk   .60 .60
  Nos. B462-B464 (3)   1.80 1.60

The surtax was for the Netherlands Heart Foundation.

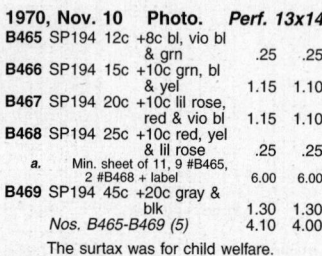

Toy Block — SP194

1970, Nov. 10   Photo.   Perf. 13x14
B465 SP194 12c +8c bl, vio bl
    & grn   .25 .25
B466 SP194 15c +10c grn, bl
    & yel   1.15 1.10
B467 SP194 20c +10c lil rose,
    red & vio bl   1.15 1.10
B468 SP194 25c +10c red, yel
    & lil rose   .25 .25
   a.   Min. sheet of 11, 9 #B465,
      2 #B468 + label   6.00 6.00
B469 SP194 45c +20c gray &
    blk   1.30 1.30
  Nos. B465-B469 (5)   4.10 4.00

The surtax was for child welfare.

St. Paul — SP195

Designs: 15c+10c, "50" and people. 25c+10c, Joachim and Ann. 30c+15c, John the Baptist and the Scribes. 45c+20c, St. Anne. The sculptures are wood, 15th century, and in Dutch museums.

1971, Apr. 20   Litho.   Perf. 13x14
B470 SP195 15c +10c multi   .80 .80

Lithographed and Photogravure
B471 SP195 20c +10c gray,
    grn & blk   .80 .80
B472 SP195 25c +10c buff,
    org & blk   .80 .50
B473 SP195 30c +15c gray, bl
    & blk   .80 .80
B474 SP195 45c +20c pink,
    ver & blk   .80 .80
  Nos. B470-B474 (5)   4.00 3.70

50th anniversary of the Federation of Netherlands Universities for Adult Education.

Detail from Borobudur — SP196

1971, June 29   Litho.   Perf. 13x14
B475 SP196 45c +20c pur, yel &
    blk   1.60 1.60

60th birthday of Prince Bernhard. Surtax for Save Borobudur Temple Fund.

"Earth" — SP197

Designs: 20c+10c, "Air" (butterfly). 25c+10c, "Sun," horiz. 30c+15c, "Moon," horiz. 45c+20c, "Water" (child looking at reflection).

           Perf. 13x14, 14x13
1971, Nov. 9   Photo.
B476 SP197 15c +10c blk, lil &
    org   .25 .30
B477 SP197 20c +10c yel, blk
    & rose lil   .25 .30
B478 SP197 25c +10c multi   .25 .30
   a.   Min. sheet of 9, 6 #B476,
      #B477, 3 #B478   4.50 8.75
B479 SP197 30c +15c bl, blk &
    pur   .95 .75
B480 SP197 45c +20c grn, blk
    & bl   1.35 1.40
  Nos. B476-B480 (5)   3.05 3.05

The surtax was for child welfare.

Luminescence
Some semipostal issues from Nos. B481-B484 onward are on phosphorescent paper.

Stylized Fruits — SP198

1972, Apr. 11   Litho.   *Perf. 13x14*
B481 SP198 20c +10c shown   .75   .75
B482 SP198 25c +10c Flower   .75   .75
B483 SP198 30c +15c "Sunlit
        Landscape"   .75   .40
B484 SP198 45c +25c "Music"   .75   .75
      Nos. B481-B484 (4)   3.00   2.65

Summer festivals: Nos. B481-B482 publicize the Floriade, flower festival; Nos. B483-B484 the Holland Festival of Arts.

Red Cross, First
Aid — SP199

Red Cross and: 25c+10c, Blood bank. 30c+15c, Disaster relief. 45c+25c, Child care.

1972, Aug. 15   *Perf. 13x14*
B485 SP199 20c +10c brt pink &
        red   .40   .40
B486 SP199 25c +10c org & red .85   .85
B487 SP199 30c +15c blk & red .55   .44
B488 SP199 45c +25c ultra & red .85   .85
      Nos. B485-B488 (4)   2.65   2.50

Surtax for the Netherlands Red Cross.

Prince Willem-Alexander
SP200

Photographs of Dutch Princes: 30c+10c, Johan Friso. 35c+15c, Constantijn. 50c+20c, Johan Friso, Constantijn and Willem-Alexander. All are horizontal.

**   *Perf. 13x14, 14x13***
1972, Nov. 7   Photo.
B489 SP200 25c +15c multi   .25   .25
B490 SP200 30c +10c multi   .65   .50
B491 SP200 35c +15c multi   .60   .25
  a.   Min. sheet of 7, 4 #B489,
        #B490, 2 #B491 + label 4.00   4.00
B492 SP200 50c +20c multi   2.10   2.00
      Nos. B489-B492 (4)   3.60   3.00

Surtax was for child welfare.

"W. A. Scholten,"
1874 — SP201

Ships: 25c+15c, Flagship "De Seven Provincien," 1673, vert. 35c+15c, "Veendam," 1923. 50c+20c, Zuider Zee fish well boat, 17th century, vert.

1973, Apr. 10   Litho.
B493 SP201 25c +15c multi   .80   .80
B494 SP201 30c +10c multi   .80   .80
B495 SP201 35c +15c multi   .80   .50
B496 SP201 50c +20c multi   .80   .80
      Nos. B493-B496 (4)   3.20   2.90

Tercentenary of the Battle of Kijkduin and centenary of the Holland-America Line. Surtax for social and cultural purposes.

Chessboard — SP202

Games: 30c+10c, Tick-tack-toe. 40c+20c, Maze. 50c+20c, Dominoes.

1973, Nov. 13   Photo.   *Perf. 13x14*
B497 SP202 25c +15c multi   .25   .25
B498 SP202 30c +10c multi   .55   .45
B499 SP202 40c +20c multi   .25   .25
  a.   Min. sheet of 6, 2 #B497,
        #B498, 3 #B499   4.50   4.50
B500 SP202 50c +20c multi   1.60   1.60
      Nos. B497-B500 (4)   2.65   2.55

Surtax was for child welfare.

Music   Herman
Bands   Heijermans
SP203   SP204

Designs: 30c+10c, Ballet dancers and traffic lights. 50c+20c, Kniertje, the fisher woman, from play by Heijermans.

1974, Apr. 23   Litho.   *Perf. 13x14*
B501 SP203 25c +15c multi   .75   .75
B502 SP203 30c +10c multi   .75   .75
                Photo.
B503 SP204 40c +20c multi   .75   .40
B504 SP204 50c +20c multi   .75   .75
      Nos. B501-B504 (4)   3.00   2.65

Surtax was for various social and cultural institutions.

Boy with Hoop — SP205

Designs: 35c+20c, Girl and infant. 45c+20c, Two girls. 60c+20c, Girl sitting on balustrade. Designs are from turn-of-the-century photographs.

1974, Nov. 12   Photo.   *Perf. 13x14*
B505 SP205 30c +15c brown   .25   .25
B506 SP205 35c +20c maroon   .55   .45
B507 SP205 45c +20c black brn .55   .25
  a.   Min. sheet of 6, 4 #B505,
        #B506, #B507   3.00   3.00
B508 SP205 60c +20c indigo   1.45   1.35
      Nos. B505-B508 (4)   2.80   2.20

Surtax was for child welfare.

Beguinage,   Cooper's
Amsterdam   Gate,
SP206   Middelburg
                   SP207

Designs: 35c+20c, St. Hubertus Hunting Lodge, horiz. 60c+20c, Orvelte Village, horiz.

**   *Perf. 14x13, 13x14***
1975, Apr. 4   Litho.
B509 SP206 35c +20c multi   .55   .50
B510 SP206 40c +15c multi   .55   .50
B511 SP207 50c +20c multi   .70   .50
B512 SP207 60c +20c multi   .90   .90
      Nos. B509-B512 (4)   2.70   2.40

European Architectural Heritage Year 1975. Surtax was for various social and cultural institutions.

Orphans, Sculpture,
1785 — SP208

40c+15c, Milkmaid, 17th cent. 50c+25c, Aymon's 4 sons on steed Bayard, 17th cent. 60c+25c, Life at orphanage, 1557. All designs are after ornamental stones from various buildings.

1975, Nov. 11   Photo.   *Perf. 14x13*
B513 SP208 35c +15c multi   .25   .25
B514 SP208 40c +15c multi   .70   .40
B515 SP208 50c +25c multi   .35   .25
  a.   Min. sheet of 5, 3 #B513, 2
        #B515 + label   2.00   2.00
B516 SP208 60c +25c multi   1.00   .70
      Nos. B513-B516 (4)   2.30   1.60

Surtax was for child welfare.

Hedgehog   Book with
SP209   "ABC" and
               Grain; Open
                  Field
                 SP210

Green Frog   People and
and Spawn   Initials of Social
SP212   Security Acts
                  SP211

**   *Perf. 14x13, 13x14***
1976, Apr. 6   Litho.
B517 SP209 40c +20c multi   .65   .50
B518 SP210 45c +20c multi   .60   .50
                Photo.
B519 SP211 55c +20c multi   .60   .25
B520 SP212 75c +25c multi   .80   .70
      Nos. B517-B520 (4)   2.65   1.95

Surtax for various social and cultural institutions. #B517, B520 for wildlife protection; #B518 cent. of agricultural education and 175th anniv. of elementary education legislation; #B519 75th anniv. of social legislation and the Social Insurance Bank.

Patient Surrounded by
Caring Hands — SP213

1976, Sept. 2   Litho.   *Perf. 13x14*
B521 SP213 55c +25c multi   .55   .45

Dutch Anti-Rheumatism Assoc., 50th anniv.

Netherlands No.
41 — SP214

Designs: No. B523, #64. No. B524, #155. No. B525, #294. No. B526, #220.

1976, Oct. 8   Litho.   *Perf. 13x14*
B522 SP214 55c +55c multi   .75   .70
B523 SP214 55c +55c multi   .75   .70
B524 SP214 55c +55c multi   .75   .70
  a.   Strip of 3, #B522-B524 2.25   2.25
                Photo.
B525 SP214 75c +75c multi   .75   .70
B526 SP214 75c +75c multi   .75   .70
  a.   Pair, #B525-B526   1.50   1.50
      Nos. B522-B526 (5)   3.75   3.50

Amphilex 77 Philatelic Exhibition, Amsterdam, May 26-June 5, 1977. No. B526a printed checkerwise.

See Nos. B535-B538.

Soccer — SP215

Children's Drawings: 45c+20c, Sailboat. 55c+20c, Elephant. 75c+25c, Mobile home.

1976, Nov. 16   Photo.   *Perf. 14x13*
B527 SP215 40c +20c multi   .25   .25
B528 SP215 45c +20c multi   .30   .25
B529 SP215 55c +20c multi   .35   .25
  a.   Min. sheet of 6, 2 each
        #B527-B529   2.40   2.40
B530 SP215 75c +25c multi   1.10   .80
      Nos. B527-B530 (4)   2.00   1.55

Surtax was for child welfare.

Hot Room, Thermal
Bath,
Heerlen — SP216

45c+20c, Altar of Goddess Nehalennia, 200 A.D., Eastern Scheldt. 55c+20c, Part of oaken ship, Zwammerdam. 75c+25c, Helmet with face, Waal River at Nijmegen.

1977, Apr. 19   Photo.   *Perf. 14x13*
B531 SP216 40c +20c multi   .45   .30
B532 SP216 45c +20c multi   .50   .30
B533 SP216 55c +20c multi   .50   .30
B534 SP216 75c +25c multi   .65   .50
      Nos. B531-B534 (4)   2.10   1.40

Archaeological finds of Roman period. Surtax for various social and cultural institutions.

Type of 1976

Designs: No. B535, Netherlands #83. No. B536, Netherlands #128. No. B537, Netherlands #211. No. B538, Netherlands #302.

1977, May 26   Litho.   *Perf. 13x14*
B535 SP214 55c +45c multi   .55   .30
B536 SP214 55c +45c multi   .55   .30
  a.   Pair, #B535-B536   1.10   1.10
B537 SP214 55c +45c multi   .55   .30
B538 SP214 55c +45c multi   .55   .30
  a.   Souv. sheet of 2, #B535,
        B538   1.25   1.25
  b.   Pair, #B537-B538   1.10   1.10
      Nos. B535-B538 (4)   2.20   1.20

Amphilex 77 International Philatelic Exhibition, Amsterdam May 26-June 5. No. B538a sold at Exhibition only.

Risk of
Drowning — SP217

Childhood Dangers: 45c+20c, Poisoning. 55c+20c, Following ball into street. 75c+25c, Playing with matches.

1977, Nov. 15   Photo.   *Perf. 13x14*
B539 SP217 40c +20c multi   .40   .25
B540 SP217 45c +20c multi   .40   .25
B541 SP217 55c +20c multi   .40   .25
  a.   Min. sheet of 6, 2 each
        #B539-B541   2.50   2.40
B542 SP217 75c +25c multi   .80   .80
      Nos. B539-B542 (4)   2.00   1.55

Surtax was for child welfare.

Anna Maria   Delft Plate
van   SP219
Schuurman
SP218

Designs: 45c+20c, Part of letter written by author Belle van Zuylen (1740-1805). 75c+25c, Makkum dish with dog.

1978, Apr. 11   Litho.   *Perf. 13x14*
B543 SP218 40c +20c multi   .40   .30
B544 SP218 45c +20c multi   .50   .30
                Photo.
B545 SP219 55c +20c multi   .55   .30
B546 SP219 75c +20c multi   .60   .45
      Nos. B543-B546 (4)   2.05   1.35

Dutch authors and pottery products.

Red Cross and World Map — SP220

1978, Aug. 22   Photo.   Perf. 14x13
B547 SP220 55c +25c multi .50 .40
a.   Souvenir sheet of 3 1.50 1.50
Surtax was for Dutch Red Cross.

Boy Ringing Doorbell — SP221

Designs: 45c+20c, Child reading book. 55c+20c, Boy writing "30x Children for Children," vert. 75c+25c, Girl at blackboard, arithmetic lesson.

Perf. 14x13, 13x14
1978, Nov. 14   Photo.
B548 SP221 40c +20c multi .40 .25
B549 SP221 45c +20c multi .40 .25
B550 SP221 65c +20c multi .40 .25
a.   Min. sheet of 6, 2 each #B548-B550 2.40 2.25
B551 SP221 75c +25c multi .80 .65
    Nos. B548-B551 (4) 2.00 1.40
Surtax was for child welfare.

Psalm Trilogy, by Jurriaan Andriessen SP222

Birth of Christ (detail) Stained-glass Window SP223

Designs: 45c+20c, Amsterdam Toonkunst Choir. 75c+25c, William of Orange, stained-glass window, 1603. Windows from St. John's Church, Gouda.

1979, Apr. 3   Photo.   Perf. 13x14
B552 SP222 40c +20c multi .40 .30
B553 SP222 55c +20c multi .50 .30
B554 SP223 55c +20c multi .55 .25
B555 SP223 75c +25c multi .60 .45
    Nos. B552-B555 (4) 2.05 1.30
Surtax for social and cultural purposes.

Child Sleeping Under Blanket — SP224

Designs: 45c+20c, Infant. 55c+20c, African boy, vert. 75c+25c, Children, vert.

1979, Nov. 13   Perf. 14x13, 13x14
B556 SP224 40c +20c blk, red & yel .40 .30
B557 SP224 45c +20c blk & red .40 .30
B558 SP224 45c +20c blk & yel .40 .30
a.   Min. sheet, 2 each #B556-B558 2.75 2.75
B559 SP224 75c +25c blk, ultra & red .75 .55
    Nos. B556-B559 (4) 1.95 1.45
Surtax was for child welfare (in conjuction with International Year of the Child).

Roads Through Sand Dunes — SP225

50c+20c, Park mansion vert. 60c+25c, Sailing. 80c+35c, Bicycling, moorlands.

Perf. 14x13, 13x14
1980, Apr. 15   Litho.
B560 SP225 45c +20c multi .60 .30
B561 SP225 50c +20c multi .60 .30
B562 SP225 60c +25c multi .60 .30
B563 SP225 80c +35c multi .80 .45
    Nos. B560-B563 (4) 2.60 1.35
Society for the Promotion of Nature Preserves, 75th anniv. Surtax for social and cultural purposes.

Wheelchair Basketball — SP226

1980, June 3   Litho.   Perf. 13x14
B564 SP226 60c +25c multi .80 .40
Olympics for the Disabled, Arnhem and Veenendaal, June 21-July 5. Surtax was for National Sports for the Handicapped Fund.

Harlequin and Girl Standing in Open Book — SP227

Designs: 50c+20c, Boy on flying book, vert. 60c+30c, Boy reading King of Frogs, vert. 80c+30c, Boy "engrossed" in book.

Perf. 14x13, 13x14
1980, Nov. 11   Photo.
B565 SP227 45c +20c multi .45 .25
B566 SP227 50c +20c multi .55 .30
B567 SP227 60c +30c multi .55 .25
a.   Min. sheet of 5, 2 #B565, 3 #B567 + label 2.50 2.50
B568 SP227 80c +30c multi .90 .60
    Nos. B565-B568 (4) 2.45 1.40
Surtax was for child welfare.

Salt Marsh with Outlet Ditch at Low Tide — SP228

Designs: 55c+25c, Dike. 60c+25c, Land drainage. 65c+30c, Cultivated land.

1981, Apr. 7   Photo.   Perf. 13x14
B569 SP228 45c +20c multi .50 .30
B570 SP228 55c +25c multi .55 .30
B571 SP228 60c +25c multi .65 .30
B572 SP228 65c +25c multi .75 .30
    Nos. B569-B572 (4) 2.45 1.20

Intl. Year of the Disabled — SP229

Various people.

Perf. 14x13, 13x14
1981, Nov. 10   Photo.
B573 SP229 45c +25c multi .45 .25
B574 SP229 55c +20c multi, vert .50 .35
B575 SP229 60c +25c multi, vert. .60 .35
B576 SP229 65c +30c multi .65 .25
a.   Min. sheet of 5, 3 #B573, 2 #B576 + label 2.25 2.40
    Nos. B573-B576 (4) 2.20 1.20
Surtax was for child welfare.

Floriade '82, Amsterdam, Apr. — SP230

No. B578, Anemones. No. B579, Roses. No. B580, African violets.

1982, Apr. 7   Litho.   Perf. 13½x13
B577 SP230 50c +20c shown .65 .35
B578 SP230 60c +25c multi .65 .35
B579 SP230 60c +25c multi .65 .35
B580 SP230 70c +30c multi .65 .40
    Nos. B577-B580 (4) 2.60 1.45
Surtax was for culture and social welfare institutions.

Birds on Child's Head — SP231

Children and Animals: 60c+20c, Boy and cat. 65c+20c, Boy and rabbit. 70c+30c, Boy and bird.

1982, Nov. 16   Photo.   Perf. 13x14
B581 SP231 50c +30c multi .35 .25
B582 SP231 60c +20c multi .50 .25
a.   Min. sheet of 5, 4 #B581, #B582 3.00 2.75
B583 SP231 65c +20c multi .75 .60
B584 SP231 70c +30c multi .85 .60
    Nos. B581-B584 (4) 2.45 1.70
Surtax was for child welfare.

Johan van Oldenbarneveldt (1547-1619), Statesman, by J. Houbraken SP232

Portrait of Saskia van Uylenburch, by Rembrandt (1606-1669) — SP232a

Paintings: 60c+25c, Willem Jansz Blaeu (1571-1638), cartographer, by Thomas de Keijser. 65c+25c, Hugo de Groot (1583-1645), statesman, by J. van Ravesteyn.

1983, Apr. 19   Photo.   Perf. 14x13
B585 SP232 50c +20c multi .75 .35
B586 SP232 60c +25c multi .75 .35
B587 SP232 65c +25c multi .75 .50
B588 SP232a 70c +30c multi .75 .50
    Nos. B585-B588 (4) 3.00 1.70
Surtax was for cultural and social welfare institutions.

Red Cross Workers — SP233

Designs: 60c+20c, Principles. 65c+25c, Sociomedical work. 70c+30c, Peace.

1983, Aug. 30   Photo.   Perf. 13x14
B589 SP233 50c +25c multi .75 .45
B590 SP233 60c +20c multi .75 .50
B591 SP233 65c +25c multi .75 .50
B592 SP233 70c +30c multi .75 .70
a.   Bklt. pane, 4 #B589, 2 #B592 4.75 4.75
    Complete booklet, #B592a 4.75
    Nos. B589-B592 (4) 3.00 2.15
Surtax was for Red Cross.

Children's Christmas — SP235

No. B596, Ox & donkey. No. B597, Snowman. No. B598, Stars. No. B599, Epiphany.

1983, Nov. 16   Photo.   Perf. 14x13
B596 SP235 50c +10c multi .65 .45
B597 SP235 50c +25c multi .40 .25
B598 SP235 60c +30c multi .75 .60
B599 SP235 70c +30c multi .60 .25
a.   Min. sheet, 4 #B597, 2 #B599 3.75 3.25
    Nos. B596-B599 (4) 2.40 1.55
Surtax was for Child Welfare.

Eurasian Lapwings — SP236

Birds: 60c+25c, Ruffs. 65c+25c, Redshanks, vert. 70c+30c, Black-tailed godwits, vert.

1984, Apr. 3   Perf. 14x13, 13x14
B600 SP236 50c +20c multi .65 .35
B601 SP236 60c +25c multi .65 .35
B602 SP236 65c +25c multi .65 .55
B603 SP236 70c +30c multi .65 .55
a.   Bklt. pane, 2 #B600, 2 #B603 3.50 3.50
    Complete booklet, #B603a 3.75
    Nos. B600-B603 (4) 2.60 1.80
Surtax was for cultural and social welfare institutions.

FILACENTO '84 — SP237

Centenary of Organized Philately: 50c+20c, Eye, magnifying glass (36x25mm). 60c+25c, Cover, 1909 (34½x25mm). 70c+30c, Stamp club meeting, 1949 (34½x24mm).

1984, June 13   Litho.   Perf. 14x13
B604 SP237 50c +20c multi .60 .55
B605 SP237 60c +25c multi .70 .55
B606 SP237 70c +30c multi .80 .55
a.   Souv. sheet of 3, #B604-B606 2.50 2.40
    Nos. B604-B606 (3) 2.10 1.65
No. B606a issued Sept. 5, 1984.

Comic Strips — SP238

No. B607, Music lesson. No. B608, Dentist. No. B609, Plumber. No. B610, King.

1984, Nov. 14   Litho.   Perf. 13x13½
B607 SP238 50c +25c multi .40 .30
B608 SP238 60c +20c multi 1.05 .60
B609 SP238 65c +20c multi 1.15 .80
B610 SP238 70c +30c multi .65 .30
a.   Min. sheet, 2 #B607, 2 #B610 4.00 3.75
    Nos. B607-B610 (4) 3.25 2.00
Surtax was for child welfare.

Winterswijk Synagogue, Holy Arc — SP239

Religious architecture: 50+20c, St. Martin's Church, Zaltbommel, vert. 65+25c, Village Congregational Church, Bolsward, vert. 70+30c, St. John's Cathedral, 'S-Hertogenbosch, detail of buttress.

Perf. 13x14, 14x13
1985, Mar. 26   Photo.
B611 SP239 50c +20c gray & brt bl .80 .50
B612 SP239 60c +20c dk red brn, Prus bl & pck bl .80 .55
B613 SP239 65c +25c sl bl, red brn & gray ol .80 .55
B614 SP239 70c +30c gray, brt bl & bis .80 .40
a.   Bklt. pane, 2 #B611, 2 #B614 4.00 4.00
    Complete booklet, #B614a 4.00
    Nos. B611-B614 (4) 3.20 2.00
Surtax for social and cultural purposes.

Traffic Safety — SP240

No B615, Photograph, lock, key. No. B616, Boy, target. No. B617, Girl, hazard triangle. No. B618, Boy, traffic sign.

1985, Nov. 13   Photo.   Perf. 13x14

B615	SP240 50c +25c multi	.45	.35
B616	SP240 60c +20c multi	.75	.65
B617	SP240 65c +20c multi	.75	.65
B618	SP240 70c +30c multi	.85	.35
a.	Souv. sheet, 4 #B615, 2 #B618	3.75	3.25
	Nos. B615-B618 (4)	2.80	2.00

Surtax was for child welfare organizations.

Antique Measuring Instruments SP241

No. B619, Balance. No. B620, Clock mechanism. No. B621, Barometer. No. B622, Jacob's staff.

Perf. 13½x13, 13x13½

1986, Apr. 8   Litho.

B619	SP241 50c +20c multi	.50	.45
B620	SP241 60c +25c multi	.50	.45
B621	SP241 65c +25c multi	.50	.45
B622	SP241 70c +30c multi	.50	.45
a.	Bklt. pane, 2 each #B619, B622	4.00	4.00
	Complete booklet, #B622a	4.00	
	Nos. B619-B622 (4)	2.00	1.80

Nos. B620-B621 vert.

Youth and Culture — SP242

No. B623, Music. No. B624, Visual arts. No. B625, Theater.

1986, Nov. 12   Litho.   Perf. 14x13

B623	SP242 55c +25c multi	.75	.45

Perf. 13½x13

B624	SP242 65c +35c multi	.90	.45
B625	SP242 75c +35c multi	1.00	.45
a.	Min. sheet of 5, #B623, 2 each #B624-B625, perf. 14x13	4.00	3.75
	Nos. B623-B625 (3)	2.65	1.35

Surtax for child welfare organizations.

Traditional Industries — SP243

Designs: 55c+30c, Steam pumping station, Nijkerk. 65c+35c, Water tower, Deventer. 75c+35c, Brass foundry, Joure.

1987, Apr. 7   Photo.   Perf. 14x13

B626	SP243 55c +30c multi	.90	.65
B627	SP243 65c +35c multi	1.05	.65
B628	SP243 75c +35c multi	1.20	.85
a.	Bklt. pane, 2 #B626, 2 #B628	4.25	4.25
	Complete booklet, #B628a	4.25	
	Nos. B626-B628 (3)	3.15	2.15

Surtax for social and cultural welfare organizations.

Red Cross — SP244

1987, Sept. 1   Photo.   Perf. 14x13

B629	SP244 55c +30c multi	.90	.75
B630	SP244 65c +35c multi, diff.	1.05	.75
B631	SP244 75c +35c multi, diff.	1.20	.75
a.	Bklt. pane, 2 #B629, 2 #B631	4.25	4.25
	Complete booklet, #B631a	4.25	
	Nos. B629-B631 (3)	3.15	2.25

Surtax for nat'l. Red Cross.

Youth and Professions SP245

No. B632, Woodcutter, vert. No. B633, Sailor. No. B634, Pilot.

Perf. 13x14, 14x13

1987, Nov. 11   Photo.

B632	SP245 55c +25c multi	.90	.60
B633	SP245 65c +35c multi	1.05	.90
B634	SP245 75c +35c multi	1.20	.25
a.	Miniature sheet of 5, #B632, 2 #B633, 2 #B634	4.00	4.00
	Nos. B632-B634 (3)	3.15	1.35

Surtax for child welfare organizations.

FILACEPT '88, October 18, The Hague — SP246

Designs: 55c +55c, Narcissus cyclamineus and poem "I call you flowers," by Jan Hanlo. No. B636, Rosa gallica versicolor. No. B637, Eryngium maritimum and map of The Hague from 1270.

1988, Feb. 23   Litho.   Perf. 13½x13

B635	SP246 55c +55c multi	1.00	.90
B636	SP246 75c +70c multi	1.00	.90
B637	SP246 75c +70c multi	1.00	.90
a.	Min. sheet of 3 + 3 labels, #B635-B637	3.25	3.25
	Nos. B635-B637 (3)	3.00	2.70

Surtax helped finance exhibition. No. B637a issued Oct. 18, 1988.

Man and the Zoo — SP247

No B638, Equus quagga quagga. No. B639, Carribean sea cow. No. B640, Sam the orang-utan, vert.

Perf. 14x13, 13x14

1988, Mar. 22   Photo.

B638	SP247 55c +30c multi	1.00	.90
B639	SP247 65c +35c multi	1.00	1.00
B640	SP247 75c +35c multi	1.00	.80
a.	Bklt. pane, 2 #B638, 2 #B640	4.00	4.00
	Complete booklet, #B640a	4.00	
	Nos. B638-B640 (3)	3.00	2.70

Natural Artis Magistra zoological soc., 150th anniv. Surtax for social and cultural welfare organizations.

Royal Dutch Swimming Federation, Cent. — SP248

Children's drawings on the theme "Children and Water." No. B641, Rain. No. B642, Getting Ready for the Race. No. B643, Swimming Test.

1988, Nov. 16   Photo.   Perf. 14x13

B641	SP248 55c +25c multi	.75	.55
B642	SP248 65c +35c multi	.90	.55
B643	SP248 75c +35c multi	1.00	.30
a.	Min. sheet of 5, #B641, 2 each #B642-B643	4.75	4.75
	Nos. B641-B643 (3)	2.65	1.40

Surtax to benefit child welfare organizations.

Ships — SP249

Designs: No. B644, Pleasure yacht (boyer), vert. No. B645, Zuiderzee fishing boat (smack). No. B646, Clipper.

Perf. 13x14, 14x13

1989, Apr. 11   Photo.

B644	SP249 55c +30c multi	1.00	.80
B645	SP249 65c +35c multi	1.00	.80
B646	SP249 75c +35c multi	1.00	.80
a.	Bklt. pane, 2 #B644-B645, 2 #B646	4.00	4.00
	Complete booklet, #B646a	4.00	
	Nos. B644-B646 (3)	3.00	2.40

Surtax for social and cultural organizations.

Children's Rights — SP250

1989, Nov. 8   Litho.   Perf. 13½x13

B647	SP250 55c +25c Housing	.75	.55
B648	SP250 65c +35c Food	.90	.45
B649	SP250 75c +35c Education	1.00	.35
a.	Min. sheet of 5, #B647, 2 each #B648-B649	4.00	4.00
	Nos. B647-B649 (3)	2.65	1.35

UN Declaration of Children's Rights, 30th anniv. Surtax for child welfare.

Summer Weather — SP251

No. B650, Girl, flowers. No. B651, Clouds, isobars, vert. No. B652, Weather map, vert.

Perf. 14x13, 13x14

1990, Apr. 3   Photo.

B650	SP251 55c +30c multi	1.00	.75
B651	SP251 65c +35c multi	1.00	.85
B652	SP251 75c +35c multi	1.00	.75
a.	Bklt. pane #B650-B651, 2 #B652	4.00	4.00
	Complete booklet, #B652a	4.00	
	Nos. B650-B652 (3)	3.00	2.35

Surtax for social & cultural welfare organizations.

Children's Hobbies — SP252

No. B653, Riding. No. B654, Computers. No. B655, Philately.

1990, Nov. 7   Litho.   Perf. 13½x13

B653	SP252 55c +25c multi	.75	.75
B654	SP252 65c +35c multi	.85	.45
B655	SP252 75c +35c multi	1.00	.25
a.	Souv. sheet of 5, #B653, 2 each #B654-B655	4.00	4.00
	Nos. B653-B655 (3)	2.60	1.45

Surtax for child welfare.

Dutch Farms — SP253

55c+30c, Frisian farm, Wartena. 65c+35c, Guelders T-style farm, Kesteren. 75c+35c, Closed construction farm, Nuth (Limburg).

1991, Apr. 16   Litho.   Perf. 13½x13

B656	SP253 55c +30c multi	1.00	.90
a.	Photo.	.75	.30
B657	SP253 65c +35c multi	1.00	.90
B658	SP253 75c +35c multi	1.00	.90
a.	Photo.	.75	.30
b.	Bklt. pane, 2 #B656a, 3 #B658a	4.00	4.00
	Complete booklet, #B658b	4.00	
	Nos. B656-B658 (3)	3.00	2.70

Surtax for social and cultural welfare organizations.

Children Playing — SP254

No. B659, Doll, robot. No. B660, Cycle race. No. B661, Hide and seek.

1991, Nov. 6   Litho.   Perf. 13½x13

B659	SP254 60c +30c multi	.60	.90
a.	Photo., perf. 14x13½	.60	.30
B660	SP254 70c +35c multi	.70	.70
B661	SP254 80c +40c multi	.80	.40
a.	Photo., perf. 14x13½	.80	.40
b.	Min. sheet, 4 #B659a, 2 #B661a	4.00	4.00
	Nos. B659-B661 (3)	2.10	1.40

Floriade 1992, World Horticultural Exhibition — SP255

Various plants and flowers.

1992, Apr. 7   Litho.   Perf. 13½x13

B662	SP255 60c +30c multi	1.00	1.00
a.	Photo., perf. 14x13½	.70	.40

B663	SP255 70c +35c multi	1.00	1.00
a.	Photo., perf. 14x13½	.80	.70
B664	SP255 80c +40c multi	1.00	1.00
a.	Photo., perf. 14x13½	3.50	3.00
b.	Booklet pane of 6, 3 #B662a, 2 #B663a, #B664a	7.25	
	Complete booklet, #B664b	7.25	
	Nos. B662-B664 (3)	3.00	3.00

Surtax for social and cultural welfare organizations.

Stamps in No. 664b are tete-beche (1 pair of B662a, 1 pair of B663a, 1 pair of B662a and B664a).

Netherlands Red Cross, 125th Anniv. — SP256

No. B665, Shadow of cross. No B666, Aiding victim. No. B667, Red cross on bandage.

1992, Sept. 8   Litho.   Perf. 13½x13

B665	SP256 60c +30c multi	1.00	1.00
a.	Photo., perf. 14 on 3 sides	.70	.40
B666	SP256 70c +35c multi	1.00	1.00
a.	Photo., perf. 14 on 3 sides	.80	.70
B667	SP256 80c +40c multi	1.00	1.00
a.	Photo., perf. 14 on 3 sides	3.50	3.00
b.	Bklt. pane, 3 #B665a, 2 #B666a, 1 #B667a	7.25	
	Complete booklet, #B667b	7.25	
	Nos. B665-B667 (3)	3.00	3.00

On normally centered stamps, the white border appears on the top, bottom and right sides only.

Children Making Music — SP257

No. B668, Saxophone player. No. B669, Piano player. No. B670, Bass player.

1992, Nov. 11   Litho.   Perf. 13x13½

B668	SP257 60c +30c multi	.70	.40
a.	Photo., perf. 13½x14	.70	.40
B669	SP257 70c +35c multi	.75	.60
a.	Photo., perf. 13½x14	.75	.60
B670	SP257 80c +40c multi	.85	.85
a.	Photo., perf. 13½x14	.85	.85
b.	Min. sheet, 3 #B668a, 2 #B669a, #B670a	4.50	4.50
	Nos. B668-B670 (3)	2.30	1.85

Senior Citizens — SP258

1993, Apr. 20   Litho.   Perf. 13x13½

B671	SP258 70c +35c shown	1.10	1.10
a.	Photo., perf. 13½x14	2.75	2.75
B672	SP258 70c +35c couple	1.10	1.10
a.	Photo., perf. 13½x14	.80	.70
B673	SP258 80c +40c woman	1.10	1.10
a.	Photo., perf. 13½x14	.70	.60
b.	Booklet pane, 1 #B671a, 2 #B672a, 3 #B673a	6.45	6.45
	Complete booklet, #B673b	6.45	
	Nos. B671-B673 (3)	3.30	3.30

Children and the Media — SP259

Designs: No. B674, Child wearing newspaper hat. No. B675, Elephant wearing earphones. 80c + 40c, Television, child's legs.

1993, Nov. 17   Litho.   Perf. 13½x13

B674	SP259 70c +35c multi	.90	.90
a.	Photo., perf. 14x13½	.90	.90
B675	SP259 70c +35c multi	.90	.90
a.	Photo., perf. 14x13½	.90	.90
B676	SP259 80c +40c multi	.90	.90
a.	Photo., perf. 14x13½	.90	.90
b.	Min. sheet, 2 each #B674a-B676a	5.50	5.50
	Nos. B674-B676 (3)	2.70	2.70

FEPAPOST '94 — SP260

Birds: 70c+60c, Branta leucopsis. 80c+70c, Luscinia svecica. 90c+80c, Anas querquedula.

1994, Feb. 22   Litho.   Perf. 14x13

B677	SP260	70c +60c multi	1.20	1.20
B678	SP260	80c +70c multi	1.20	1.20
B679	SP260	90c +80c multi	1.20	1.20
a.	Min. sheet, #B677-B679 + 3			
	labels, perf. 13½x13		3.75	3.75
	Nos. B677-B679 (3)		3.60	3.60

Issued: No. B679a, 10/17/94.

Senior Citizens — SP261

Designs: 80c+40c, Man talking on telephone seen from behind. 90c+35c, Man in suit talking on telephone.

1994, Apr. 26   Litho.   Perf. 13x13½

B680	SP261	70c +35c shown	1.00	.90
a.	Photo., perf. 13½x14		.80	.70
B681	SP261	80c +40c multi	1.00	.75
a.	Photo., perf. 13½x14		.90	.80
B682	SP261	90c +35c multi	1.00	1.00
a.	Photo., perf. 13½x14		3.50	3.00
b.	Booklet pane, 2 #B680a, 3			
	#B681a, #B682a		8.00	
	Nos. B680-B682 (3)		3.00	2.65

Child Welfare Stamps — SP262

Designs: 70c+35c, Holding ladder for woman painting. 80c+40c, Helping to balance woman picking cherries, vert. 90c+35c, Supporting boy on top of play house, vert.

Perf. 13½x13, 13x13½

1994, Nov. 9   Litho.

B683	SP262	70c +35c multi	.90	.50
a.	Perf. 14x13		.90	.80
B684	SP262	80c +40c multi	.90	.50
a.	Perf. 13x14		.90	.60
B685	SP262	90c +35c multi	1.35	1.35
a.	SP262 Miniature sheet, 2			
	#B683a, 3 #B684a, 1			
	#B685b		5.25	5.25
b.	Perf. 13x14		1.35	1.35
	Nos. B683-B685 (3)		3.15	2.35

Senior Citizens — SP263

Designs: 70c+35c, Indonesia #1422 on postcard. 80c+40c, Couple seen in bus mirror. 100c+45c, Grandparents, child at zoo.

1995, Apr. 11   Litho.   Perf. 13½x13

B686	SP263	70c +35c multi	.90	.90
B687	SP263	80c +40c multi	.90	.50
B688	SP263	100c +45c multi	.90	.90
a.	Miniature sheet, 2 #B686, 3			
	#B687, 1 #B688		6.00	6.00
	Nos. B686-B688 (3)		2.70	2.30

Child Welfare Stamps — SP264

Computer drawings by children: 70c+35c, Dino, by S. Stegeman. 80c+40c, The School Teacher, by L. Ensing, vert. 100c+50c, Children and Colors, by M. Jansen.

Perf. 13½x13, 13x13½

1995, Nov. 15   Litho.

B689	SP264	70c +35c multi	1.10	.75
B690	SP264	80c +40c multi	1.10	.75
B691	SP264	100c +50c multi	1.10	1.10
a.	Min. sheet of 6, 2 #B689, 3			
	#B690, 1 #B691		6.75	6.75
	Nos. B689-B691 (3)		3.30	2.60

Senior Citizens — SP265

No. B692, Swimming. No. B693, Babysitting. No. B694, Playing piano.

1996, Apr. 23   Litho.   Perf. 13¼x12¾

B692	SP265	70c +35c multi	.95	.50
B693	SP265	80c +40c multi	.95	.50
B694	SP265	100c +50c multi	1.75	1.10
a.	Sheet of 6, 2 #B692, 3			
	#B693, 1 #B694, perf.			
	13x12½		6.50	6.50
	Nos. B692-B694 (3)		3.65	2.10

Child Welfare Stamps — SP266

Designs: 70c+35c, Baby, books. No. B696, Boy, toys. No. B697, Girl, tools.

Perf. 12¾x13¼

1996, Nov. 6   Litho.

B695	SP266	70c +35 multi	1.00	.50
B696	SP266	80c +40c multi	1.00	.50
B697	SP266	100c +50c multi	1.00	.50
a.	Sheet of 2 each, #B695-B697		6.00	6.00
	Nos. B695-B697 (3)		3.00	1.50

Senior Citizens — SP267

Designs: No. B698, Rose in full bloom. No. B699, Stem of rose. No. B700, Rose bud.

1997, Apr. 15   Litho.   Perf. 13¼x12¾

B698	SP267	80c +40c multi	1.10	.80
B699	SP267	80c +40c multi	1.10	.80
B700	SP267	80c +40c multi	1.10	.80
a.	Min. sheet, 2 each #B698-B700		6.75	6.75
	Nos. B698-B700 (3)		3.30	2.40

Netherlands Red Cross — SP268

1997, May 27   Litho.   Perf. 12¾x13¼

B701	SP268	80c +40c multi	1.30	1.20

Child Welfare Stamps — SP269

Children's Fairy Tales: No. B702, Hunter with wolf, from "Little Red Riding Hood." No. B703, Dropping loaves of bread, from "Tom Thumb." No. B704, Man opening bottle, from "Genie in the Bottle."

Perf. 13¼x12¾

1997, Nov. 12   Litho.

B702	SP269	80c +40c multi	1.10	.50
B703	SP269	80c +40c multi	1.10	.50
B704	SP269	80c +40c multi	1.10	.50
a.	Min. sheet of 2 each, #B702-B704		6.75	6.75
	Nos. B702-B704 (3)		3.30	1.50

Senior Citizens — SP270

#B705, Sports shoe. #B706, Note on paper. #B707, Wrapped piece of candy.

1998, Apr. 21   Litho.   Perf. 13¼x12¾

B705	SP270	80c +40c multi	1.25	1.25
B706	SP270	80c +40c multi	1.25	1.25
B707	SP270	80c +40c multi	1.25	1.25
a.	Sheet, 2 each #B705-B707		7.50	7.50
	Nos. B705-B707 (3)		3.75	3.75

Child Welfare Stamps — SP271

#B708, Elephant riding horse. #B709, Pig, rabbit decorating cake. #B710, Pig, goose, rabbit carrying flower, frog carrying flag.

Perf. 13¼x12¾

1998, Nov. 11   Litho.

B708	SP271	80c +40c multi	1.25	.50
B709	SP271	80c +40c multi	1.25	.50
B710	SP271	80c +40c multi	1.25	.50
a.	Sheet, 2 each #B708-B710		7.50	7.50
	Nos. B708-B710 (3)		3.75	1.50

Intl. Year of Older Persons — SP272

No. B711, Woman. No. B712, Black man. No. B713, Caucasian man.

1999, Apr. 13   Litho.   Perf. 13¼x12¾

B711	SP272	80c +40c multi	1.25	1.00
B712	SP272	80c +40c multi	1.25	1.00
B713	SP272	80c +40c multi	1.25	1.00
a.	Min. sheet, 2 ea #B711-B713		7.50	7.50
	Nos. B711-B713 (3)		3.75	3.00

Child Welfare Stamps — SP273

Designs: No. B714, Boy on tow truck. No. B715, Girl and chef. No. B716, Children stamping envelope.

Perf. 13¼x12¾

1999, Nov. 10   Litho.

B714	SP273	80c +40c multi	1.25	.60
B715	SP273	80c +40c multi	1.25	.60
B716	SP273	80c +40c multi	1.25	.60
a.	Sheet, 2 each #B714-B716		7.50	7.50
	Nos. B714-B716 (3)		3.75	1.80

Senior Citizens — SP274

No. B717, Swimmers. No. B718, Bowlers. No. B719, Fruit picker.

2000, Apr. 4   Litho.   Perf. 13¼x12¾

B717	SP274	80c +40c multi	1.40	1.40
B718	SP274	80c +40c multi	1.40	1.40
B719	SP274	80c +40c multi	1.40	1.40
a.	Souvenir sheet, 2 each			
	#B717-B719		8.50	8.50
	Nos. B717-B719 (3)		4.20	4.20

Souvenir Sheet

Child Welfare — SP275

Designs: Nos. B720a, B721, Children with masks. No. B720b, Child with ghost costume. No. B720c, Child on alligator. Nos. B720d, B722, Child in boat. Nos. B720e, B723, Children cooking. No. B720f, Children in dragon costume.

2000, Nov. 8   Litho.   Perf. 13¼x12¾

B720	SP275	Sheet of 6	5.00	5.00
a.-f.	80c +40c Any single		.75	.75

Self-Adhesive

Serpentine Die Cut 15

B721	SP275	80c +40c multi	2.25	1.25
B722	SP275	80c +40c multi	2.25	1.25
B723	SP275	80c +40c multi	2.25	1.25
	Nos. B721-B723 (3)		6.75	3.75

Flowers — SP276

Designs: No. B724a, Caryopteris. Nos. B724b, B725, Helenium. Nos. B724c, B726, Alcea rugosa. No. B724d, Euphorbia schillingii. No. B724e, B727, Centaurea dealbata. No. B724f, Inula hookeri.

2001, Apr. 24   Litho.   Perf. 13¼x12¾

B724		Sheet of 6	6.00	6.00
a.-f.	SP276 80c+40c Any single		1.00	1.00

Serpentine Die Cut 14⅜x15

Self-Adhesive

B725	SP276	80c +40c multi	1.40	1.40
B726	SP276	80c +40c multi	1.40	1.40
B727	SP276	80c +40c multi	1.40	1.40
a.	Booklet, 10 each #B725-727		42.50	
	Nos. B725-B727 (3)		4.20	4.20

Children and Computers SP277

Black figure: No. B728a, Retrieving letter from printer. No. B728b, Crossing road with letter. No. B728c, Sliding down green vine. No. B728d, Posting letter. Nos. B728e, B729, Crossing river on log. No. B728f, Swinging on rope.

2001, Nov. 6   Photo.   Perf. 14x13½

B728		Sheet of 6	6.75	6.75
a.-f.	SP277 85c +40c Any single		1.00	.90

Self-Adhesive

Die Cut Perf. 13¼x13

B729	SP277	85c +40c multi	2.50	1.50

Surtax for Dutch Children's Stamp Foundation.

SP278

SP279

SP280

SP281

SP282

Floriade 2002 — SP283

2002, Apr. 2   Litho.   Perf. 14⅜x14½

B730	SP278	39c +19c multi	1.20	.65
B731	SP279	39c +19c multi	1.20	.65
B732	SP280	39c +19c multi	1.20	.65
B733	SP281	39c +19c multi	1.20	.65
B734	SP282	39c +19c multi	1.20	.65
B735	SP283	39c +19c multi	1.20	.65
a.	Block of 6, #B730-B735		7.00	7.00

Nos. B730-B735 are impregnated with a floral scent.

Surtax for National Help the Aged Fund.

Blossom Walk, 10th Anniv. — SP284

2002, Apr. 27   Litho.   Perf. 14⅜x14½

B736	SP284	39c +19c multi	1.25	.90

Surtax for Red Cross.

Children
SP285

No. B737: a, Child with red head, red cat. b, Child with green head, blue father. c, Child with red head, blue ball. d, Child with yellow head, green pet dish. e, Child with brown head, legs of child. f, Child with yellow head, blue dog.

2002, Nov. 5	Photo.	Perf. 14x13½	
B737	SP285	Sheet of 6	6.75 6.75
a.-f.		39c +19c Any single	1.10 .85

Surtax for Dutch Children's Stamp Foundation.

Flowers — SP286

No. B738: a, Orange yellow lilies of the Incas. b, Lilac sweet peas. c, Pansies. d, Red orange and yellow trumpet creepers. e, Red campions. f, Purple, white and yellow irises.

2003, Apr. 8	Photo.	Perf. 14½x14¾	
B738	SP286	Block of 6	7.50 7.50
a.-f.		39c +19c Any single	1.25 1.25

Souvenir Sheet

Items in
a Child's
Life
SP287

No. B739: a, Note pad, radio, ballet shoes. b, Theater masks, book. c, Microphone, musical staff, paintbrush. d, Violin, soccer ball, television. e, Television, drum, light bulbs. f, Light bulbs, trombone, hat, headphones.

2003, Nov. 4		Perf. 14x13½	
B739	SP287	Sheet of 6	7.25 7.25
a.-f.		39c +19c Any single	1.15 .85

Flowers
SP288

No. B740 — Various flowers with background color of: a, Lilac. b, Pink. c, Brownish gray. d, Ocher. e, Blue gray. f, Olive.

2004, Apr. 6	Photo.	Perf. 14¾x14½	
B740	SP288	Block of 6	7.50 7.50
a.-f.		39c + 19c any single	1.25 .75

Souvenir Sheet

Fruit and
Sports
SP289

No. B741: a, Watermelon, soccer. b, Lemon, rope jumping. c, Orange, cycling. d, Pear, skateboarding. e, Banana, sit-ups. f, Strawberry, weight lifting.

2004, Nov. 9	Photo.	Perf. 14½	
B741	SP289	Sheet of 6	7.50 7.50
a.-f.		39c +19c Any single	1.25 .85

December
Stamps — SP290

No. B742 — Inscriptions: a, Novib. b, Stop AIDS Now. c, Natuurmonumenten. d, KWF Kankerbestrijding. e, UNICEF. f, Plan Nederland. g, Tros Helpt. h, Greenpeace. i, Artsen Zonder Grenzen (Doctors Without Borders). j, World Food Program.

Serpentine Die Cut 8¾x9

2004, Nov. 25		Self-Adhesive	
B742		Block of 10	9.00 9.00
a.-j.	SP290	29c +10c Any single	.90 .80

The surtax went to the various organizations named on the stamps.

Souvenir Sheets

SP291

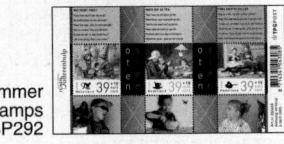

Summer
Stamps
SP292

No. B743 — Illustrations for children's stories and silhouette of: a, Children and barrel. b, Two children. c, Frying pan.

No. B744 — Illustrations for children's stories and silhouette of: a, Monkey. b, Cup, saucer and spoon. c, Cat playing with ball.

2005, Apr. 5	Litho.	Perf. 13¼x13¾	
B743	SP291	Sheet of 3 + 2 labels	4.00 4.00
a.-c.		39c +19c Any single	1.25 1.25
B744	SP292	Sheet of 3 + 2 labels	4.00 4.00
a.-c.		39c +19c Any single	1.25 1.25

Miniature Sheet

Miffy the
Bunny,
by Dick
Bruna
SP293

No. B745: a, Bunny and dog. b, Four bunnies. c, Bunny holding teddy bear. d, Bunny writing letter. e, White and brown bunnies. f, Six bunnies.

2005, Nov. 8	Photo.	Perf. 14½	
B745	SP293	Sheet of 6	8.50 8.50
a.-f.		39c+19c Any single	1.40 1.40

The surtax went to the Foundation for Children's Welfare Stamps. A booklet containing four panes of two stamps sold for €9.95.

SP294 SP295

SP296 SP297

SP298 SP299

SP300 SP301

Religious Art from
Museum
Catharijnconvent, Utrecht
SP302 SP303

Serpentine Die Cut 8¾x9

2005, Nov. 24		Litho.	
B746		Booklet pane of 10	9.50
a.	SP294	29c+10c multi	.95 .95
b.	SP295	29c+10c multi	.95 .95
c.	SP296	29c+10c multi	.95 .95
d.	SP297	29c+10c multi	.95 .95
e.	SP298	29c+10c multi	.95 .95
f.	SP299	29c+10c multi	.95 .95
g.	SP300	29c+10c multi	.95 .95
h.	SP301	29c+10c multi	.95 .95
i.	SP302	29c+10c multi	.95 .95
j.	SP303	29c+10c multi	.95 .95

The surtax went to the various organizations named on the margin and backing paper of the booklet pane.

Souvenir Sheets

SP304

Illustrations From Reading
Boards — SP305

No. B747: a, Monkey and birds. b, Walnut. c, Cat.

No. B748: a, Boy playing with game. b, Girl holding rattle. c, Girl playing with doll.

2006, Apr. 4	Litho.	Perf. 13½x13¾	
B747	SP304	Sheet of 3 + 2 labels	4.25 4.25
a.-c.		39c +19c Any single	1.40 1.40
B748	SP305	Sheet of 3 + 2 labels	4.25 4.25
a.-c.		39c +19c Any single	1.40 1.40

Surtax for National Fund for Care of the Elderly.

Souvenir Sheet

Children
SP306

No. B749: a, Six children, boy in orange shirt with hands up and with foot on ball. b, Eight children, girl in red shirt with hands in air. c, Six children, girl at right standing. d, Six children, boy in orange shirt with hands down and kicking ball. e, Eight children, girl in red shirt with hands at waist. f, Six children, girl at right seated.

2006, Nov. 7	Photo.	Perf. 14½	
B749	SP306	Sheet of 6	9.25 9.25
a.-f.		39c +19c Any single	1.50 1.50

Surtax for Dutch Children's Stamp Foundation.

SP307 SP308

SP309

SP311

SP310

SP312

SP313 SP314

SP315

Children Wearing Angel
Costumes — SP316

Serpentine Die Cut 8¾x9

2006, Nov. 23		Litho.	
		Self-Adhesive	
B750		Block of 10	10.50 10.50
a.	SP307	29c +10c multi	1.00 1.00
b.	SP308	29c +10c multi	1.00 1.00
c.	SP309	29c +10c multi	1.00 1.00
d.	SP310	29c +10c multi	1.00 1.00
e.	SP311	29c +10c multi	1.00 1.00
f.	SP312	29c +10c multi	1.00 1.00
g.	SP313	29c +10c multi	1.00 1.00
h.	SP314	29c +10c multi	1.00 1.00
i.	SP315	29c +10c multi	1.00 1.00
j.	SP316	29c +10c multi	1.00 1.00

The surtax went to the various organizations named in the sheet selvage.

Souvenir Sheets

Beach
Activities
SP317

No. B751: a, Woman pulling dress up in surf, boy in water. b, Woman standing in surf, children on ponies on beach. c, Children on ponies on beach, children playing on beach.

No. B752: a, Children playing on beach, family posing for photograph on beach. b, Boy waving, people in large beach chair. c, Boy on sail-powered beach cart, family digging sand at shore.

2007, Apr. 4	Litho.	Perf. 13¼x12¾	
B751	SP317	Sheet of 3	5.50 5.50
a.-c.		44c +22c Any single	1.75 1.75
B752	SP317	Sheet of 3	5.50 5.50
a.-c.		44c +22c Any single	1.75 1.75

Surtax for National Fund for Senior Citizen's Help.

Netherlands Red
Cross, 140th
Anniv. — SP318

2007, July 19		Perf. 13¼	
B753	SP318	44c +22c multi	1.90 1.90

Surtax for Netherlands Red Cross. Printed in sheets of 3.

Miniature Sheet

Children
and
Safety
SP319

No. B754 — Child: a, Watching television. b, And building at night. c, In bed. d, And computer. e, And kitten. f, Reading book.

2007, Nov. 6　Litho.　Perf. 14½
B754　SP319　Sheet of 6　12.00　12.00
　a.-f.　44c +22c any single　2.00　2.00

Surtax for Foundation for Children's Welfare Stamps.

SP320

Forget-me-nots — SP321

No. B755: a, Forget-me-not, head-on view. b, Purple crane's bill geranium. c, Pink Japanese anemone.

No. B756: a, Purple larkspur. b, Globe thistle. c, Forget-me-not, side view.

2008, Apr. 1　Litho.　Perf. 14½
B755　SP320　Sheet of 3　6.25　6.25
　a.-c.　44c+22c Any single　2.00　2.00
B756　SP321　Sheet of 3　6.25　6.25
　a.-c.　44c+22c Any single　2.00　2.00

Surtax for National Fund for Elderly Assistance.

Miniature Sheet

Children's Education — SP322

No. B757 — Letters of word "Onderwijs" (education): a, "O." b, "ND." c, "ER." d, "W." e, "IJ." f, "S."

2008, Nov. 4　Photo.　Perf. 14½
B757　SP322　Sheet of 6　10.00　10.00
　a.-f.　44c+22c Any single　1.60　1.60

Surtax for Foundation for Children's Welfare Stamps.

Miniature Sheet

Elder
Care
SP323

No. B758: a, Couple dancing. b, Woman with bag cart. c, Ballet dancer. d, Woman with guide dog. e, Man playing trumpet. f, Woman holding diploma.

2009, Apr. 7　Litho.　Perf. 14½
B758　SP323　Sheet of 6　10.50　10.50
　a.-f.　44c +22c Any single　1.75　1.75

Surtax for National Fund for Elderly Assistance.

Miniature Sheet

Children's Activities — SP324

No. B759 — Stylized children: a, With pencil. b, With magnifying glasses. c, Watching falling star. d, Playing. e, Reading newspaper. f, With stylized Pegasus.

2009, Nov. 3　Photo.　Perf. 14½
B759　SP324　Sheet of 6　12.00　12.00
　a.-f.　44c+22c Any single　2.00　2.00

Surtax for Foundation for Children's Welfare Stamps.

Miniature Sheet

Famous
People
SP325

No. B760 — Silhouettes of: a, Ramses Shaffy (1933-2009), singer and actor. b, Fanny Blankers-Koen (1918-2004), Olympic gold medalist. c, Mies Bouwman, television personality. d, Willy Alberti (1926-85), singer. e, Dick Bruna, writer and illustrator. f, Annie M. G. Schmidt (1911-95), writer.

2010, Apr. 27　Litho.　Perf. 14½
B760　SP325　Sheet of 6　10.50　10.50
　a.-f.　44c + 22c Any single　1.75　1.75

Surtax for National Fund for Elderly Assistance.

Miniature Sheet

Children and Mathematical Symbols — SP326

No. B761: a, Boy with red shirt. b, Boy with dark gray shirt, hand near head. c, Boy with gray shirt, hand in front of chest. d, Girl with red and orange dress. e, Girl with arms clasped behind head. f, Girl with arm raised.

2010, Nov. 9　　　Perf. 14x13¾
B761　SP326　Sheet of 6　11.00　11.00
　a.-f.　1 + 22c Any single　1.75　1.75

Nos. B761a-B761f each had a franking value of 44c, with the 22c surtax going to the Foundation for Children's Welfare Stamps.

Miniature Sheet

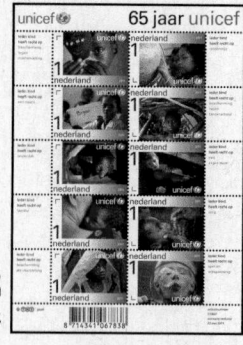

UNICEF,
65th
Anniv.
SP327

No. B762: a, Child holding doll. b, Children touching globe. c, Boy holding card showing his name. d, Boy carrying branches. e, Boy looking out of broken window. f, Boy playing violin. g, Mother holding child. h, Child receiving medicine. i, Child using dog food bag as hood. j, Child blowing bubbles.

2011, May 23　　　Perf. 13¼x12¾
B762　SP327　Sheet of 10　19.00　19.00
　a.-j.　1 + (20c) Any single　1.90　1.90
　k.　Booklet pane of 2,
　　　#B762a-B762b　5.75　—
　l.　Booklet pane of 2,
　　　#B762c-B762d　5.75　—
　m.　Booklet pane of 2,
　　　#B762e-B762f　5.75　—
　n.　Booklet pane of 2,
　　　#B762g-B762h　5.75　—
　o.　Booklet pane of 2,
　　　#B762i-B762j　5.75　—
　　　Complete booklet,
　　　#B762k-B762o　29.00

Nos. B762a-B762j each had a franking value of 46c, with the 20c surtax going to UNICEF. Complete booklet sold for €9.95.

Miniature Sheet

Children
at Play
SP328

No. B763 — Child wearing: a, Orange shirt. b, Light green shirt. c, Pink shirt. d, Purple shirt. e, Blue green shirt. f, White shirt.

2011, Oct. 29　Photo.　Perf. 14½
B763　SP328　Sheet of 6　11.50　11.50
　a.-f.　1 + 23c Any single　1.90　1.90

Nos. B763a-B763f each had a franking value of 46c, with the 23c surtax going to the Foundation for Children's Welfare Stamps.

Red Cross — SP329

No. B764: a, Cross in red, text "Eerste Hulp bij ongelukken." b, Woman in cross, text "Eerste Hulp dóór iedereen." c, Hand and child's head in cross, text "Eerste Hulp vóór iedereen."

2012, Jan. 30　Litho.　Perf. 13¼x13½
B764　SP329　Horiz. strip of 3　6.00　6.00
　a.-c.　1 +25c any single　2.00　2.00

Nos. B764a-B764c each had a franking value of 50c, with the 25c surtax going to the Dutch Red Cross. No. B764 was printed in sheets containing two strips.

Miniature Sheet

Princesses — SP330

No. B765: a, Princess Catharina-Amalia. b, Princesses Alexia, Ariane and Catharina-Amalia (five buttons on blouse of Princess Ariane visible). c, Princess Ariane. d, Princesses Catharina-Amalia, Alexia and Ariane (Catharina-Amalia at left). e, Princess Alexia. f, Princesses Alexia, Ariane and Catharina-Amalia (three buttons on blouse of Princess Ariane visible).

2012, Nov. 6　Photo.　Perf. 14½
B765　SP330　Sheet of 6　11.50　11.50
　a.-f.　1 + 25c Any single　1.90　1.90

Nos. B765a-B765f each had a franking value of 50c, with the 23c surtax going to the Foundation for Children's Welfare Stamps.

Miniature Sheet

Ethiopian
Children
SP331

No. B766: a, Boy, multiplication table. b, Boy holding bundle of sticks. c, Girl carrying young boy on her back. d, Girl, letters of Amharic alphabet. e, Boy, poster with pictures and English words. f, Boy carrying goat.

2013, Nov. 4　Litho.　Perf. 14½
B766　SP331　Sheet of 6　14.50　14.50
　a.-f.　1+30c Any single　2.40　2.40

Nos. B766a-B766f each had a franking value of 60c on the day of issue, with the 30c surtax going to th Foundation for Children's Welfare Stamps.

Miniature Sheet

Children in Works from the Rijksmuseum — SP332

No. B767: a, Children at the beach (36x25mm). b, Children riding donkey (36x25mm). c, Girl wearing kimono (36x25mm). d, Girl and boys near piano (36x25mm). e, Boy on skateboard (36x50mm).

2014, Nov. 3　Litho.　Perf. 14½
B767　SP332　Sheet of 5　12.00　12.00
　a.-e.　1+32c Any single　2.40　2.40

Nos. B767a-B767b had a franking value of 64c on the day of issue, with the 32c surtax going to the Foundation for Children's Welfare Stamps.

Miniature Sheet

Illustrations From Little Golden Books Series of Children's Books — SP333

No. B768: a, Sofa, toys strung together with cart containing dog and cat. b, Bird chasing cat in tree away from nest. c, Child pulling toys strung together. d, Duck, goose and house. e, Cat on mitten. f, Duck, goose, cat and pig.

2015, Nov. 2　Litho.　Perf. 13¼
B768　SP333　Sheet of 6　13.50　13.50
　a.-f.　1+34c Any single　2.25　2.25

Nos. B768a-B768f each had a franking value of 69c on the day of issue, with the 34c surcharge going to the Foundation for Children's Welfare Stamps.

Miniature Sheet

Illustrations of Bus and Passengers by Fiep Westendorp (1916-2004) — SP334

No. B769: a, Children with hats and bird cage, child cutting cake. b, Snake, turtles, birds, cat, dog, child. c, Children and chef. d, Bird and musicians. e, Eight children. f, Cats and bus driver.

2016, Nov. 7   Litho.   Perf. 13¼x13½
B769   SP334   Sheet of 6   14.00 14.00
a.-f.   1+36c Any single   2.25   2.25

Nos. B769a-B769f each had a franking value of 73c on the day of issue, with the 36c surcharge going to the Foundation for Children's Welfare Stamps.

Miniature Sheet

Characters From *Jan, Jans, and the Children* Comic Strip, by Jan Kruis — SP335

No. B770: a, Jan and son, Gertje. b, Jans and daughter, Karlijn. c, Grandfather and cat. d, Catootje and dog. e, Jeroen holding letter. f, Cat in basket.

2017, Oct. 9   Litho.   Perf. 14½
B770   SP335   Sheet of 6   16.50 16.50
a.-f.   1+38c Any single   2.75   2.75

Nos. B770a-B770f each had a franking value of 78c on the day of issue, with the 38c surcharge going to the Foundation for Children's Welfare Stamps.

Miniature Sheet

Characters From the Children's Television Series *The Daily Fable* — SP336

No. B771: a, Myra and Martha Hamster and water wheel (36x25mm). b, Mr. Owl (36x50mm). c, Boris the Wolf hammering sign and Miss Stork with picnic basket (36x25mm). d, Crox the Raven and Cunningham the Foxx (36x25mm). e, Fred and Bart Beaver in chairs under umbrella (36x25mm).

2018, Oct. 8   Litho.   Perf. 14¼x14½
B771   SP336   Sheet of 5   15.00 15.00
a.-e.   1+41c Any single   3.00   3.00

The Daily Fable, 50th anniv. Nos. B771a-B771e each had a franking value of 83c on day of issue, with the surtax of 41c going to the Foundation for Children's Welfare Stamps.

Nieuwe Avonturen van Pietje Bell, by Chris van Abkoude SP337

De Drieling te Paard, by Trix van Brussel SP338

Uit het Leven van Dik Trom, by Johan Kieviet SP339

Kruimeltje, by Chris van Abkoude SP340

De Schippers van de Kameleon, by Hotze de Roos — SP341

2019, Oct. 3   Litho.   Perf. 13¼x13
B772   Horiz. strip of 5   15.00 15.00
a.   SP337   1+43c multi   3.00   3.00
b.   SP338   1+43c multi   3.00   3.00
c.   SP339   1+43c multi   3.00   3.00
d.   SP340   1+43c multi   3.00   3.00
e.   SP341   1+43c multi   3.00   3.00

Children's books. Nos. B772a-B772e each had a franking value of 87c on day of issue, with the surtax of 43c going to the Foundation for Children's Welfare Stamps. Printed in sheets containing two each Nos. B772a-B772e.

Miniature Sheet

Miffy, the Bunny, by Dick Bruna, 65th Anniv. SP342

No. B773: a, Miffy and parents in car (36x25mm). b, Auntie Alice holding tray of drinks (36x25mm). c, Boris and Barbara with balloon (36x25mm). d, Poppy and Grunty Pig dancing (36x25mm). e, Miffy and birthday cake (36x50mm).

2020, Oct. 5   Litho.   Perf. 14¼
B773   SP342   Sheet of 5   16.50 16.50
a.-e.   1 + 45c Any single   3.25   3.25

On day of issue, Nos. B773a-B773e each had a franking value of 91c, with the 45c surtax going to the Foundation for Children's Welfare Stamps.

Miniature Sheet

Tom Puss, Comic Strip by Martin Toonder (1912-2005), 80th Anniv. — SP343

No. B774: a, Marquis de Canteclaer holding eyeglasses (36x25mm). b, Tom Puss and Mr. Bumble (36x50mm). c, Joost, the butler, and castle (36x25mm). d, Doddeltje and mushrooms (36x25mm). e, Wammes Waggel with accordion (36x25mm).

2021, Oct. 11   Litho.   Perf. 14½
B774   SP343   Sheet of 5   17.50 17.50
a.-e.   1 + 48c Any single   3.50   3.50

On day of issue, Nos. B774a-B774e each had a franking value of 96c, with the 48c surtax going to the Foundation for Children's Welfare Stamps.

Miniature Sheet

Donald Duck Magazine, 70th Anniv. — SP344

No. B775: a, May and Dewey (36x25mm). b, Donald and Huey (36x50mm). c, Louie at computer (36x25mm). d, Scrooge McDuck (36x25mm). e, April on bicycle, and June with skateboard. (36x25mm).

2022, Oct. 10   Litho.   Perf. 14½
B775   SP344   Sheet of 5   15.00 15.00
a.-e.   1 + 48c Any single   3.00   3.00

On day of issue, Nos. B775a-B775e each had a franking value of 96c, with the 48c surtax going to the Foundation for Children's Welfare Stamps.

AIR POST STAMPS

Stylized Seagull — AP1

Perf. 12½
1921, May 1   Unwmk.   Typo.
C1   AP1   10c red   1.90   1.25
C2   AP1   15c yellow grn   5.25   2.10
C3   AP1   60c dp blue   23.00   .50
     Nos. C1-C3 (3)   30.15   3.85
     Set, never hinged   260.00

Nos. C1-C3 were used to pay airmail fee charged by the carrier, KLM.

Lt. G. A. Koppen AP2

Capt. Jan van der Hoop AP3

Wmk. Circles (202)
1928, Aug. 20   Litho.   Perf. 12
C4   AP2   40c orange red   .50   .25
C5   AP3   75c blue green   .50   .25
     Set, never hinged   2.00

Mercury — AP4

Perf. 11½
1929, July 16   Unwmk.   Engr.
C6   AP4   1½g gray   2.25   1.40
C7   AP4   4½g carmine   2.25   4.00
C8   AP4   7½g blue green   26.00   4.00
     Nos. C6-C8 (3)   30.50   9.40
     Set, never hinged   75.00

Queen Wilhelmina — AP5

Perf. 12½, 14x13
1931, Sept. 24   Photo.   Wmk. 202
C9   AP5   36c org red & dk bl   13.00   .75
     Never hinged   70.00

Fokker Pander — AP6

1933, Oct. 9   Perf. 12½
C10 AP6   30c dark green   .75   .75
     Never hinged   1.50

Nos. C10-C12 were issued for use on special flights.

Crow in Flight — AP7

1938-53   Perf. 13x14
C11 AP7   12½c dk blue & gray   .35   .25
C12 AP7   25c dk bl & gray   2.25   1.60
     ('53)
     Set, never hinged   4.25

Catalogue values for unused stamps in this section, from this point to the end of the section, are for Never Hinged items.

Seagull — AP8

Perf. 13x14
1951, Nov. 12   Engr.   Unwmk.
C13 AP8   15g gray   225.00 80.00
C14 AP8   25c blue gray   225.00 80.00
     Set, hinged   250.00

Airplane — AP9

1966, Sept. 2   Litho.   Perf. 14x13
C15 AP9   25c gray, blk & bl   .25   .35
     Issued for use on special flights.

AP10

1980, May 13   Photo.   Perf. 13x14
C16 AP10 1g multicolored   1.00   1.00

REGISTRATION STAMPS

Personalized Stamp — R1

Die Cut Perf. 12¾x12½
Etched on Silver Foil
2011, Oct. 10   Self-Adhesive
F1   R1   (€7) silver   19.00 19.00

The vignette portion of No. F1 could be personalized for €34.95. The image shown, depicting Piet Hein and a warship, is a generic image. Starting in 2013, stamps with different images were produced in limited quantities and sold at prices above face value were sold by Netherlands Post.

Souvenir Sheet

Bull's Head, Tulips and QR Code — R2

Litho. With Foil Application
2022, Sept. 22   Die Cut Perf. 10x9¾
Self-Adhesive

F2	R2	R multi	18.00 18.00

Crypto stamp. No. F2 sold for €9.05 on day of issue. See Austria No.

MARINE INSURANCE STAMPS

Floating Safe Attracting Gulls MI1

Floating Safe with Night Flare MI2

Fantasy of Floating Safe — MI3

Perf. 11½
1921, Feb. 2   Unwmk.   Engr.

GY1	MI1	15c slate grn	11.00	75.00
GY2	MI1	60c car rose	15.00	75.00
GY3	MI1	75c gray brn	18.50	75.00
GY4	MI2	1.50g dk blue	65.00	425.00
GY5	MI2	2.25g org brn	110.00	550.00
GY6	MI3	4½g black	165.00	675.00
GY7	MI3	7½g red	250.00	925.00
		Nos. GY1-GY7 (7)	634.50	2,800.
		Set, never hinged	1,500.	

POSTAGE DUE STAMPS

Postage due types of Netherlands were also used for Netherlands Antilles, Netherlands Indies and Surinam in different colors.

D1

Unwmk.
1870, May 15   Typo.   Perf. 13

J1	D1	5c brown, *org*	72.50	15.00
J2	D1	10c violet, *bl*	150.00	20.00
a.		Perf 12½x12	300.00	32.50

D2

Type I — 34 loops. "T" of "BETALEN" over center of loop; top branch of "E" of "TE" shorter than lower branch.
Type II — 33 loops. "T" of "BETALEN" between two loops.
Type III — 32 loops. "T" of "BETALEN" slightly to the left of loop; top branch of first "E" of "BETALEN" shorter than lower branch.
Type IV — 37 loops. Letters of "PORT" larger than in the other three types.
Imperforate varieties are proofs.

Perf. 11½x12, 12½x12, 12½, 13½
1881-87   Value in Black

J3	D2	1c lt blue (III)	11.00	11.00
a.		Type I	15.00	18.00
b.		Type II	20.00	20.00
c.		Type IV	47.50	52.50
J4	D2	1½c lt blue (III)	15.00	15.00
a.		Type I	18.00	18.00
b.		Type II	24.00	24.00
c.		Type IV	75.00	75.00
J5	D2	2½c lt blue (III)	37.50	5.00
a.		Type I	45.00	5.50
b.		Type II	50.00	6.00
c.		Type IV	210.00	125.00
J6	D2	5c lt blue (III) ('87)	140.00	3.50
a.		Type I	50.00	5.00
b.		Type II	130.00	5.25
c.		Type IV	1,250.	350.00

J7	D2	10c lt blue (III) ('87)	92.50	4.00
a.		Type I	115.00	4.50
b.		Type II	125.00	5.00
c.		Type IV	2,500.	375.00
J8	D2	12½c lt blue (III)	95.00	25.00
a.		Type I	165.00	40.00
b.		Type II	130.00	45.00
c.		Type IV	350.00	100.00
J9	D2	15c lt blue (III)	90.00	4.00
a.		Type I	105.00	4.50
b.		Type II	120.00	5.00
c.		Type IV	130.00	25.00
J10	D2	20c lt blue (III)	35.00	4.00
a.		Type I	47.50	4.25
b.		Type II	50.00	5.50
c.		Type IV	137.50	27.50
J11	D2	25c lt blue (III)	210.00	3.50
a.		Type I	230.00	3.00
b.		Type II	275.00	4.50
c.		Type IV	425.00	170.00

Value in Red

J12	D2	1g lt blue (III)	85.00	30.00
a.		Type I	85.00	37.50
b.		Type II	100.00	40.00
c.		Type IV	175.00	75.00
		Nos. J3-J12 (10)	811.00	105.00

See Nos. J13-J26, J44-J60. For surcharges see Nos. J27-J28, J42-J43, J72-J75.

1896-1910   Perf. 12½
Value in Black

J13	D2	½c dk bl (I) ('01)	.40	.35
J14	D2	1c dk bl (I)	1.65	.35
a.		Type III	2.50	3.25
J15	D2	1½c dk blue (I)	.75	.35
a.		Type III	2.50	2.50
J16	D2	2½c dk blue (I)	1.50	.75
a.		Type III	3.25	.55
J17	D2	3c dk bl (I) ('10)	1.65	1.10
J18	D2	4c dk bl (I) ('09)	1.65	2.25
J19	D2	5c dk blue (I)	13.00	.35
a.		Type III	16.00	.55
J20	D2	6½c dk bl (I) ('07)	45.00	45.00
J21	D2	7½c dk bl (I) ('04)	1.75	.55
J22	D2	10c dk bl (I)	35.00	.55
a.		Type III	52.50	1.50
J23	D2	12½c dk blue (I)	30.00	1.10
a.			45.00	3.50
J24	D2	15c dk blue (I)	35.00	.90
a.			55.00	1.00
J25	D2	20c dk blue (I)	20.00	8.00
a.		Type III	20.00	8.75
J26	D2	25c dk blue (I)	45.00	.75
a.			50.00	1.00
		Nos. J13-J26 (14)	232.35	62.35

Surcharged in Black

1906, Jan. 10   Perf. 12½

J27	D2	50c on 1g lt bl (III)	125.00	110.00
a.		50c on 1g light blue (III)	165.00	140.00
b.		50c on 1g light blue (II)	175.00	150.00

Surcharged in Red

1906, Oct. 6

J28	D2	6½c on 20c dk bl (I)	5.50	5.00

Nos. 87-89 Surcharged

1907, Nov. 1

J29	A13	½c on 1c claret	1.25	1.25
J30	A13	1c on 1c claret	.50	.50
J31	A13	1½c on 1c claret	.50	.50
J32	A13	2½c on 1c claret	1.25	1.25
J33	A13	5c on 2½c ver	1.40	.40
J34	A13	6½c on 2½c ver	3.50	3.50
J35	A13	7½c on ½c blue	2.00	1.25
J36	A13	10c on ½c blue	1.75	.75
J37	A13	12½c on ½c blue	5.00	4.75
J38	A13	15c on 2½c ver	6.00	4.00
J39	A13	25c on ½c blue	9.00	8.50
J40	A13	50c on ½c blue	42.50	40.00
J41	A13	1g on ½c blue	60.00	55.00
		Nos. J29-J41 (13)	134.65	121.65

Two printings of the above surcharges were made. Some values show differences in the setting of the fractions; others are practically impossible to distinguish.

No. J20 Surcharged in Red

1909, June

J42	D2	4c on 6½c dark blue	5.50	5.00
		Never hinged	20.00	

No. J12 Surcharged in Black

1910, July 11

J43	D2	3c on 1g lt bl, type III	30.00	27.50
		Never hinged	100.00	
a.		Type I	37.50	40.00
		Never hinged	110.00	
b.		Type II	40.00	40.00
		Never hinged	125.00	

Type I
1912-21   Perf. 12½, 13½x13
Value in Color of Stamp

J44	D2	½c pale ultra	.25	.25
J45	D2	1c pale ultra ('13)	.25	.25
J46	D2	1½c pale ultra ('15)	1.90	1.50
J47	D2	2½c pale ultra	.25	.25
J48	D2	3c pale ultra	.40	.40
J49	D2	4c pale ultra ('13)	.25	.25
J50	D2	4½c pale ultra ('16)	5.25	5.00
J51	D2	5c pale ultra	.25	.25
J52	D2	5½c pale ultra ('16)	5.00	5.00
J53	D2	7c pale ultra ('21)	2.25	2.25
J54	D2	7½c pale ultra ('13)	2.50	1.00
J55	D2	10c pale ultra ('13)	.40	.40
J56	D2	12½c pale ultra ('13)	.40	.40
J57	D2	15c pale ultra ('13)	.40	.40
J58	D2	20c pale ultra ('20)	.40	.25
J59	D2	25c pale ultra ('17)	80.00	.60
J60	D2	50c pale ultra ('20)	.40	.25
		Nos. J44-J60 (17)	100.55	18.70
		Set, never hinged	450.00	

D3

1921-38   Typo.   Perf. 12½, 13½x12½

J61	D3	3c pale ultra ('28)	.25	.25
J62	D3	6c pale ultra ('27)	.25	.25
J63	D3	7c pale ultra ('28)	.45	.45
J64	D3	7½c pale ultra ('26)	.45	.45
J65	D3	8c pale ultra ('38)	.45	.45
J66	D3	9c pale ultra ('30)	.45	.45
J67	D3	11c ultra ('21)	12.50	4.00
J68	D3	12c pale ultra ('28)	.45	.30
J69	D3	25c pale ultra ('25)	.45	.30
J70	D3	30c pale ultra ('35)	.45	.30
J71	D3	1g ver ('21)	.60	.30
		Nos. J61-J71 (11)	16.75	7.50
		Set, never hinged	50.00	

Stamps of 1912-21 Surcharged

1923, Dec.   Perf. 12½

J72	D2	1c on 3c ultra	.75	.65
J73	D2	2½c on 7c ultra	1.20	.65
J74	D2	25c on 1½c ultra	8.00	.65
J75	D2	25c on 7½c ultra	10.00	.65
		Nos. J72-J75 (4)	19.95	2.60
		Set, never hinged	57.50	

Nos. 56, 58, 62, 65 Surcharged

1924, Aug.

J76	A11	4c on 3c ol grn	1.10	1.10
J77	A10	5c on 1c red	.75	.40
a.		Surcharge reading down	500.00	450.00
J78	A10	10c on 1½c blue	1.10	.60
a.		Tête bêche pair	8.50	10.00
J79	A11	12½c on 5c car	1.50	.60
a.		Tête bêche pair	8.50	10.00
		Nos. J76-J79 (4)	4.45	2.70
		Set, never hinged	14.50	

The 11c on 22½c and 15c on 17½c exist. These were used by the postal service for accounting of parcel post fees.

> **Catalogue values for unused stamps in this section, from this point to the end of the section, are for Never Hinged items.**

D5

Perf. 13½x12½
1947-58   Wmk. 202   Photo.

J80	D5	1c light blue ('48)	.25	.25
J81	D5	3c light blue ('48)	.40	.30
J82	D5	4c light blue	8.50	.85
J83	D5	5c light blue ('48)	.25	.25
J84	D5	6c light blue ('50)	.35	.35
J85	D5	7c light blue	.25	.30
J86	D5	8c light blue ('48)	.25	.25
J87	D5	10c light blue	.25	.25
J88	D5	11c light blue	.35	.45
J89	D5	12c light blue ('48)	.80	.85
J90	D5	14c light blue ('53)	.80	.65
J91	D5	15c light blue	.35	.25
J92	D5	16c light blue	.70	.80
J93	D5	20c light blue	.35	.30
J94	D5	24c light blue ('57)	.95	1.10
J95	D5	25c light blue ('48)	.35	.30
J96	D5	26c light blue ('58)	1.90	2.10
J97	D5	30c light blue ('48)	.50	.25
J98	D5	35c light blue	.65	.25
J99	D5	40c light blue	.65	.25
J100	D5	50c light blue ('48)	.80	.30
J101	D5	60c light blue ('58)	.85	.45
J102	D5	85c light blue ('50)	13.00	.55
J103	D5	90c light blue ('56)	2.40	.60
J104	D5	95c light blue ('57)	2.40	.60
J105	D5	1g carmine ('48)	1.90	.25
J106	D5	1.75g carmine ('57)	4.50	.35
		Nos. J80-J106 (27)	44.70	13.50

OFFICIAL STAMPS

Regular Issues of 1898-1908 Overprinted

1913   Typo.   Unwmk.   Perf. 12½

O1	A10	1c red	4.00	2.75
O2	A10	1½c ultra	1.00	2.25
O3	A10	2c yellow brn	7.00	7.00
O4	A10	2½c dp green	16.00	12.00
O5	A11	3c olive grn	4.00	1.00
O6	A11	5c carmine rose	4.00	4.50
O7	A11	10c gray lilac	35.00	37.50
		Nos. O1-O7 (7)	71.00	67.00

Same Overprint in Red on No. 58
1919

O8	A10	1½c deep blue (R)	100.00	110.00

Nos. O1 to O8 were used to defray the postage on matter relating to the Poor Laws. Counterfeit overprints exist.

For the International Court of Justice

Regular Issue of 1926-33 Overprinted in Gold

1934   Wmk. 202   Perf. 12½

O9	A24	1½c red violet	1.50
O10	A24	2½c deep green	1.50
O11	A23	7½c red	2.25
O12	A31	12½c deep ultra	22.50
O13	A23	15c orange	2.00
O14	A23	30c violet	2.25
a.		Perf. 13½x12½	2.25
		Nos. O9-O14 (6)	32.00

Same Overprint on No. 180 in Gold
1937   Perf. 13½x12½

O15	A23	12½c ultra	16.00

"Mint" Officials
Nos. O9-O15, O20-O43 were sold to the public only canceled. Uncanceled, they were obtainable only by favor of an official or from UPU specimen stamps.

Same on Regular Issue of
1940 Overprinted in Gold

1940   **Perf. 13½x12½**

O16	A45	7½c bright red	27.50	7.00
O17	A45	12½c sapphire	27.50	7.00
O18	A45	15c lt blue	27.50	7.00
O19	A45	30c bister	27.50	7.00
		Nos. O16-O19 (4)	110.00	28.00

A second printing with more open letters exists. Value, $750.

Nos. 217 to 219, 221 and
223 Overprinted in Gold

1947

O20	A45	7½c bright red	1.10
O21	A45	10c brt red violet	1.10
O22	A45	12½c sapphire	1.10
O23	A45	20c purple	1.10
O24	A45	25c rose brown	1.10
		Nos. O20-O24 (5)	5.50

O1

     Perf. 14½x13½

1950   **Unwmk.**   **Photo.**

O25	O1	2c ultra	8.75
O26	O1	4c olive green	8.75

Palace of   Queen
Peace, The   Juliana
Hague   O3
O2

1951-58   **Perf. 12½x12**

O27	O2	2c red brown	.40
O28	O2	3c ultra ('53)	.40
O29	O2	4c deep green	.40
O30	O2	5c olive brn ('53)	.40
O31	O2	6c olive grn ('53)	.80
O32	O2	7c red ('53)	.60

Engr.

O33	O3	6c brown vio	5.50
O34	O3	10c dull green	.25
O35	O3	12c rose red	.75
O36	O3	15c rose brn ('53)	.25
O37	O3	20c dull blue	.25
O38	O3	25c violet brn	.25
O39	O3	30c rose lil ('58)	.35
O40	O3	1g slate gray	.80
		Nos. O27-O40 (14)	11.40

1977, May   **Photo.**   **Perf. 12½x12**

O41	O2	40c brt grnsh blue	.50
O42	O2	45c brick red	.50
O43	O2	50c brt rose lilac	.50
		Nos. O41-O43 (3)	1.50

Catalogue values for unused stamps in this section, from this point to the end of the section, are for Never Hinged items.

Peace Palace, The
Hague — O4

Palm, Sun and Column
— O4a

1989-94   **Litho.**

O44	O4	5c blk & org yel	.25	.25
O45	O4	10c black & blue	.25	.25
O46	O4	25c black & red	.30	.30
O47	O4	50c black & yel grn	.60	.60
O48	O4	55c black & pink	.55	.55
O49	O4	60c black & bister	.75	.75
O50	O4	65c black & bl grn	.75	.75
O51	O4	70c blk & gray bl	.90	.90
O52	O4	75c black & yellow	.70	.70
O53	O4	80c black & gray grn	1.00	1.00
O54	O4	1g black & orange	1.10	1.10
O55	O4	1.50g blk & blue	1.60	1.60
O56	O4	1.60g blk & rose brn	2.00	2.00

Litho. & Engr.

O57	O4a	5g multicolored	5.50	5.50
O58	O4a	7g multicolored	6.50	6.50
		Nos. O44-O58 (15)	22.75	22.75

Issued: 55c, 75c, 7g, 10/24/89; 65c, 1g, 1.50g, 5g, 10/23/90; 5c, 10c, 25c, 50c, 60c, 70c, 80c, 10/22/91; 1.60g, 11/28/94.

Intl. Court of   Emblem of
Justice — O5   Intl. Court of
              Justice — O6

2004, Jan. 2   **Litho.**   **Perf. 14¾x14½**

O59	O5	39c multi	1.00	1.00
O60	O6	61c multi	1.60	1.60

Intl. Court of   Emblem of
Justice   Intl. Court of
O7   Justice
                O8

Doves — O9

2011, Apr. 11   **Perf. 13½x13¼**

O61	O7	1 multi	1.40	1.40
O62	O8	1 Europa multi	2.40	2.40
O63	O9	1 Wereld multi	2.75	2.75
		Nos. O61-O63 (3)	6.55	6.55

On day of issue, Nos. O61-O63 each sold for 46c, 79c, and 95c, respectively.

Intl. Court of Justice,
70th Anniv. — O10

2016, Apr. 25   **Litho.**   **Perf. 13½x13¼**

O64	O10	1 Internationaal multi	3.00	3.00

NETHERLANDS ANTILLES

'ne-<u>th</u>ər-lənd̯z an-'ti-lēz

(Curaçao)

LOCATION — Two groups of islands about 500 miles apart in the West Indies, north of Venezuela
AREA — 383 sq. mi.
POP. — 207,333 (1995)
CAPITAL — Willemstad

Formerly a colony, Curaçao, Netherlands Antilles became an integral part of the Kingdom of the Netherlands under the Constitution of 1954. On Jan. 1, 1986, the island of Aruba achieved a separate status within the Kingdom and began issuing its own stamps.

100 Cents = 1 Gulden

Catalogue values for unused stamps in this country are for Never Hinged items, beginning with Scott 164 in the regular postage section, Scott B1 in the semipostal section, Scott C18 in the airpost section, Scott CB9 in the airpost semi-postal section, and Scott J41 in the postage due section.

Values for unused examples of Nos. 1-44 are for stamps without gum.

Watermark

Wmk. 202 — Circles

King William III — A1

Regular Perf. 11½, 12½, 11½x12, 12½x12, 13½x13, 14

1873-79		Typo.	Unwmk.	
1	A1	2½c green	6.00	9.50
2	A1	3c bister	57.50	115.00
3	A1	5c rose	14.00	13.50
4	A1	10c ultra	80.00	19.00
5	A1	25c brown orange	57.50	9.50
6	A1	50c violet	2.00	1.90
7	A1	2.50g bis & pur ('79)	50.00	45.00
		Nos. 1-7 (7)	267.00	213.40

See bluish paper note with Netherlands #7-22.
The gulden denominations, Nos. 7 and 12, are of larger size.
See 8-12. For surcharges see #18, 25-26.

Perf. 14, Small Holes

1b	A1	2½c	18.00	21.00
2b	A1	3c	70.00	135.00
3b	A1	5c	20.00	28.00
4b	A1	10c	115.00	97.50
5b	A1	25c	80.00	7.50
6b	A1	50c	40.00	37.50
		Nos. 1b-6b (6)	343.00	326.50

"Small hole" varieties have the spaces between the holes wider than the diameter of the holes.

1886-89		**Perf. 11½, 12½, 12½x12**		
8	A1	12½c yellow	130.00	52.50
9	A1	15c olive ('89)	40.00	22.50
10	A1	30c pearl gray ('89)	45.00	52.50
11	A1	60c olive bis ('89)	55.00	19.00
12	A1	1.50g lt & dk bl ('89)	120.00	102.50
		Nos. 8-12 (5)	390.00	249.00

Nos. 1-12 were issued without gum until 1890. Imperfs. are proofs.

Numeral — A2

1889		**Perf. 12½**		
13	A2	1c gray	1.60	1.60
14	A2	2c violet	1.60	2.25
15	A2	2½c green	5.75	5.25
16	A2	3c bister	6.50	6.00
17	A2	5c rose	25.00	1.90
		Nos. 13-17 (5)	40.45	17.00

No. 13 the numeral in the center is in italics, but Nos. 14-17 do not.

Black Handstamped Surcharge

1891		**Perf. 12½x12**		
		Without Gum		
18	A1	25c on 30c pearl gray	18.00	15.00

No. 18 exists with double surcharge, value $225, and with inverted surcharge, value $275.

Queen Wilhelmina — A4

1892-96		**Perf. 12½**		
19	A4	10c ultra ('95)	1.60	1.60
20	A4	12½c green	18.50	10.50
21	A4	15c rose ('93)	4.00	3.00
22	A4	25c brown orange	145.00	3.75
23	A4	30c gray ('96)	4.00	7.50
		Nos. 19-23 (5)	173.10	26.35

No. 4 Handstamped Surcharge in Magenta

No. 10 Handstamped Surcharge in Black

1895		**Perf. 12½, 13½x13**		
25	A1	2½c on 10c ultra	16.00	11.50
		Perf. 12½x12		
26	A1	2½c on 30c gray	160.00	7.50

Nos. 25-26 exist with surcharge double or inverted.
No. 26 and No. 25, perf. 13½x13, were issued without gum.

Netherlands No. 77 Surcharged in Black

1902, Jan. 1		**Perf. 12½**		
27	A11	25c on 25c rose pink & bl	2.00	1.90

Netherlands No. 84 Surcharged in Black

1901, May 1		**Engr.**	**Perf. 11½x11**	
28	A12	1.50g on 2.50g brn lil	22.00	26.00

Netherlands No. 68 Surcharged in Black

1902, Mar. 1		**Typo.**	**Perf. 12½**	
29	A11	12½c on 12½c blue	28.00	9.50

A9

A10

1904-08				
30	A9	1c olive green	2.00	1.90
31	A9	2c yellow brown	18.00	3.75
32	A9	2½c blue green	8.00	.75
33	A9	3c orange	10.00	5.75
34	A9	5c rose red	10.00	1.15
35	A9	7½c gray ('08)	32.00	9.50
36	A10	10c slate	24.00	1.90
37	A10	12½c deep blue	2.00	.75
38	A10	15c brown	20.00	13.50
39	A10	22½c brn & ol ('08)	20.00	13.50
40	A10	25c violet	24.00	3.75
41	A10	30c brown orange	50.00	17.00
42	A10	50c red brown	40.00	10.50
		Nos. 30-42 (13)	260.00	83.70

Queen Wilhelmina — A11

1906, Nov. 1		**Engr.**	**Perf. 11½**	
		Without Gum		
43	A11	1½g red brown	40.00	30.00
44	A11	2½g slate blue	40.00	34.00

A12

Queen Wilhelmina
A13   A14

Perf. 12½, 11, 11½, 11x11½

1915-33			**Typo.**	
45	A12	½c lilac ('20)	1.60	1.60
46	A12	1c olive green	.40	.25
47	A12	1½c blue ('20)	.40	.25
48	A12	2c yellow brn	1.60	1.35
49	A12	2½c green	1.00	.40
50	A12	3c yellow	3.00	1.90
51	A12	3c green ('26)	3.00	2.60
52	A12	5c rose	2.40	.40
53	A12	5c green ('22)	5.00	2.60
54	A12	5c lilac ('26)	2.40	.25
55	A12	7½c drab	1.45	.25
56	A12	7½c bister ('20)	1.45	.25
57	A12	10c lilac ('22)	5.75	5.75
58	A12	10c rose ('26)	5.00	1.90
59	A13	10c car rose	27.00	3.75
60	A13	12½c blue	3.00	.75
61	A13	12½c red ('22)	2.60	1.90
62	A13	15c olive grn	1.00	1.60
63	A13	15c lt blue ('26)	5.00	3.00
64	A13	20c blue ('22)	8.00	3.00
65	A13	20c olive grn ('26)	3.25	2.25
66	A13	22½c orange	3.25	3.00
67	A13	25c red violet	4.00	1.60
68	A13	30c slate	4.00	1.60
69	A13	35c sl & red ('22)	3.25	6.00

Perf. 11½x11, 11½, 12½, 11

		Engr.		
70	A14	50c green	4.00	.40
71	A14	1½g violet	18.00	13.50
72	A14	2½g carmine	26.00	24.00
a.		Perf. 12½ ('33)	160.00	340.00
		Nos. 45-72 (28)	146.80	86.10

Some stamps of 1915 were also issued without gum.
For surcharges see #74, 107-108, C1-C3.

A15

Laid Paper
Without Gum

1918, July 16		**Typo.**	**Perf. 12**	
73	A15	1c black, buff	6.00	3.75

"HAW" are the initials of Postmaster H. A. Willemsen.

No. 60 Surcharged in Black

1918, Sept. 1			**Perf. 12½**	
74	A13	5c on 12½c blue	4.00	2.60
a.		"5" 2½mm wide	72.50	45.00
b.		Double surcharge		1,350.
c.		As "a," double surcharge		1,800.

The "5" of No. 74 is 2.75mm wide. Illustration shows No. 74a surcharge.

Queen Wilhelmina — A16

1923		**Engr.**	**Perf. 11½, 11x11½**	
75	A16	5c green	2.00	3.00
76	A16	7½c olive grn	2.00	3.00
77	A16	10c car rose	4.00	4.50
78	A16	20c indigo	4.00	4.50
a.		Perf. 11x11½	4.00	5.75
79	A16	1g brown vio	40.00	37.50
80	A16	2½g gray black	85.00	180.00
81	A16	5g brown	105.00	225.00
a.		Perf. 11x11½	600.00	475.00
		Nos. 75-81 (7)	242.00	457.50

25th anniv. of the assumption of the government of the Netherlands by Queen Wilhelmina, at the age of 18.
Nos. 80-81 with clear cancel between Aug. 1, 1923 and Apr. 30, 1924, sell for considerably more.

Types of Netherlands Marine Insurance Stamps, Inscribed "CURAÇAO" Surcharged in Black

1927, Oct. 3				
87	MI1	3c on 15c dk green	.80	.75
88	MI1	10c on 60c car rose	.80	.75
89	MI1	12½c on 75c gray brn	.80	.75
90	MI2	15c on 1.50g dk bl	4.00	3.75
a.		Double surcharge	1,600.	
91	MI2	25c on 2.25g org brn	9.75	9.00
92	MI3	30c on 4½g black	10.50	9.75
93	MI3	50c on 7½g red	9.75	9.00
		Nos. 87-93 (7)	36.40	33.75

Nos. 90, 91 and 92 have "FRANKEER-ZEGEL" in one line of small capitals. Nos. 90 and 91 have a heavy bar across the top of the stamp.

Queen Wilhelmina — A17

1928-30		**Engr.**	**Perf. 11½, 12½**	
95	A17	6c orange red ('30)	2.40	.40
a.		Booklet pane of 6		
96	A17	7½c orange red	.80	.60
97	A17	10c carmine	1.60	.60
98	A17	12½c red brown	1.60	1.35
a.		Booklet pane of 6		
99	A17	15c dark blue	1.60	.60
a.		Booklet pane of 6		
100	A17	20c blue black	6.00	.95
101	A17	21c yellow grn ('30)	10.00	11.50
102	A17	25c brown vio	4.00	2.10
103	A17	27½c black ('30)	14.50	15.00
104	A17	30c deep green	6.00	1.15
105	A17	35c brnsh black	2.00	3.75
		Nos. 95-105 (11)	50.50	38.00

No. 96 Surcharged in Black with Bars over Original Value

1929, Nov. 1

106	A17	6c on 7½c org red	1.60	1.15
a.		Inverted surcharge	280.00	260.00

No. 51 Surcharged in Red

1931, Mar. 1   Typo.   Perf. 12½

107	A12	2½c on 3c green	1.20	1.15

No. 49 Surcharged in Red

1932, Oct. 29

108	A12	1½c on 2½c grn	4.00	3.75

Prince William I, Portrait by Van Key — A18

1933   Photo.   Perf. 12½

109	A18	6c deep orange	2.00	1.15

400th birth anniv. of Prince William I, Count of Nassau and Prince of Orange, frequently referred to as William the Silent.

Willem Usselinx A19

Van Walbeeck's Ship A22

Designs: 2½c, 5c, 6c, Frederik Hendrik. 10c, 12½c, 15c, Jacob Binckes. 27½c, 30c, 50c, Cornelis Evertsen the Younger. 1.50g, 2.50g, Louis Brion.

1934, Jan. 1   Engr.   Perf. 12½

110	A19	1c black	1.40	1.60
111	A19	1½c dull violet	1.00	.40
112	A19	2c orange	1.60	1.90
113	A19	2½c dull green	1.20	1.60
114	A19	5c black brn	1.20	1.60
115	A19	6c violet bl	1.60	.40
116	A19	10c lake	4.00	1.60
117	A19	12½c bister brn	9.00	7.50
118	A19	15c blue	3.00	1.90
119	A22	20c black	4.50	3.75
120	A22	21c brown	20.00	13.50
121	A22	25c dull green	20.00	13.50
122	A19	27½c brown vio	20.00	19.00
123	A19	30c scarlet	14.00	7.50
124	A19	50c orange	14.00	11.50
125	A19	1.50g indigo	60.00	57.50
126	A19	2.50g yellow grn	65.00	65.00
		Nos. 110-126 (17)	241.50	209.75

3rd centenary of the founding of the colony.

Numeral A25

Queen Wilhelmina A26

1936, Aug. 1   Litho.   Perf. 13½x13
Size: 18x22mm

127	A25	1c brown black	.25	.25
128	A25	1½c deep ultra	.25	.25
129	A25	2c orange	.25	.25
130	A25	2½c green	.25	.25
131	A25	5c scarlet	.25	.25

Engr.
Perf. 12½
Size: 20¼x30½mm

132	A26	6c brown vio	.80	.25
133	A26	10c orange red	1.20	.25
134	A26	12½c dk bl grn	1.60	.75
135	A26	15c dark blue	1.60	.75
136	A26	20c orange yel	1.60	.75

137	A26	21c dk gray	3.75	3.75
138	A26	25c brown lake	1.60	1.15
139	A26	27½c violet brn	3.25	3.00
140	A26	30c olive brn	.80	.70

Perf. 13x14
Size: 22x33mm

141	A26	50c dull yel grn	4.00	.40
a.		Perf. 14	60.00	.40
142	A26	1.50g black brn	18.00	11.50
a.		Perf. 14	80.00	37.50
143	A26	2.50g rose lake	18.00	13.50
a.		Perf. 14	20.00	19.00
		Nos. 127-143 (17)	57.45	38.00

See Nos. 147-151. For surcharges see Nos. B1-B3.

Queen Wilhelmina — A27

Perf. 12½x12
1938, Aug. 27   Photo.   Wmk. 202

144	A27	1½c dull purple	.40	.40
145	A27	6c red orange	.80	.75
146	A27	15c royal blue	1.60	1.15
		Nos. 144-146 (3)	2.80	2.30

Reign of Queen Wilhelmina, 40th anniv.

Numeral Type of 1936 and

Queen Wilhelmina — A28

1941-42   Unwmk.   Litho.   Perf. 12½
Thick Paper
Size: 17¾x22mm

147	A25	1c gray brn ('42)	3.00	2.60
148	A25	1½c dull blue ('42)	9.75	.40
149	A25	2c lt orange ('42)	9.75	8.25
150	A25	2½c green ('42)	2.40	1.60
151	A25	5c crimson ('42)	2.00	1.15

Photo.
Perf. 12½, 13
Size: 18½x23mm

152	A28	6c rose violet	3.00	2.25
153	A28	10c red orange	3.00	1.15
154	A28	12½c lt green	3.25	1.15
155	A28	15c brt ultra	8.00	2.60
156	A28	20c orange	3.00	1.90
157	A28	21c gray	12.00	7.50
158	A28	25c brown lake	5.00	2.60
159	A28	27½c deep brown	20.00	16.50
160	A28	30c olive bis	18.00	4.50

Size: 21x26½mm

161	A28	50c olive grn ('42)	24.00	.75
162	A28	1½g gray ol ('42)	30.00	2.25
163	A28	2½g rose lake ('42)	32.00	1.90
		Nos. 147-163 (17)	188.15	59.05

Imperfs. are proofs.
See Nos. 174-187.

> **Catalogue values for unused stamps in this section, from this point to the end of the section, are for Never Hinged items.**

Bonaire A29

St. Eustatius A30

Designs: 2c, View of Saba. 2½c, St. Maarten. 5c, Aruba. 6c, Curaçao.

Perf. 13x13½, 13½x13 (No. 165)
1943, Feb. 1   Engr.   Unwmk.

164	A29	1c rose vio & org brn	.30	.25
165	A30	1½c dp bl & yel grn	.30	.25
166	A29	2c sl blk & org brn	.60	.35
167	A29	2½c grn & org	.35	.25
168	A29	5c red & slate blk	1.15	.25
169	A29	6c rose lil & lt bl	.85	.80
		Nos. 164-169 (6)	3.55	2.15

Royal Family — A35

1943, Nov. 8   Perf. 13½x13

170	A35	1½c deep orange	.45	.40
171	A35	2½c red	.45	.40
172	A35	6c black	1.30	1.20
173	A35	10c deep blue	1.30	1.20
		Nos. 170-173 (4)	3.50	3.20

Princess Margriet Francisca of the Netherlands.

Wilhelmina Type of 1941
1947   Photo.   Perf. 13½x13
Size: 18x22mm

174	A28	6c brown vio	1.60	1.90
175	A28	10c orange red	1.60	1.90
176	A28	12½c dk blue grn	1.60	1.90
177	A28	15c dark blue	1.60	2.25
178	A28	20c orange yel	1.60	3.25
179	A28	21c dark gray	2.75	3.25
180	A28	25c brown lake	.35	.25
181	A28	27½c chocolate	2.25	2.40
182	A28	30c olive bister	1.90	1.30
183	A28	50c dull yel grn	2.00	.25

Perf. 13½x14
Engr.
Size: 25x31¼mm

184	A28	1½g dark brown	6.00	1.90
185	A28	2½g rose lake	60.00	27.00
186	A28	5g olive green	120.00	170.00
187	A28	10g red orange	145.00	275.00
		Nos. 174-187 (14)	348.25	492.55

Used values for Nos. 186-187 are for genuinely canceled copies clearly dated before the end of 1949.

A36

Queen Wilhelmina — A37

1948   Unwmk.   Photo.   Perf. 13½x13

188	A36	6c dk vio brn	1.05	.95
189	A36	10c scarlet	1.05	1.20
190	A36	12½c dk blue grn	1.05	.80
191	A36	15c deep blue	1.05	.95
192	A36	20c red orange	1.05	1.90
193	A36	21c black	1.05	1.90
194	A36	25c brt red vio	.35	.25
195	A36	27½c henna brn	17.50	16.00
196	A36	30c olive brown	16.50	1.15
197	A36	50c olive green	14.50	.25

Perf. 12½x12
Engr.

198	A37	1.50g chocolate	28.00	6.50
		Nos. 188-198 (11)	83.15	31.85

Queen Wilhelmina — A38

1948, Aug. 30   Perf. 13x14

199	A38	6c vermilion	.70	.55
200	A38	12½c deep blue	.70	.55

Reign of Queen Wilhelmina, 50th anniv.

Queen Juliana — A39

Perf. 14x13½
1948, Oct. 18   Photo.   Wmk. 202

201	A39	6c red brown	.75	.45
202	A39	12½c dark green	.75	.45

Investiture of Queen Juliana, Sept. 6, 1948. Nos. 201-202 were issued in Netherlands Sept. 6.

Ship of Ojeda A40

Alonso de Ojeda A41

Perf. 14x13, 13x14
1949, July 26   Photo.   Unwmk.

203	A40	6c olive green	4.00	2.25
204	A41	12½c brown red	4.25	3.00
205	A40	15c ultra	4.75	3.25
		Nos. 203-205 (3)	13.00	8.50

450th anniversary of the discovery of Curaçao by Alonso de Ojeda, 1499.

Post Horns Entwined — A42

1949, Oct. 3   Perf. 12x12½

206	A42	6c brown red	4.75	2.50
207	A42	25c dull blue	4.75	1.30

UPU, 75th anniversary.

A43

A44

Queen Juliana — A45

1950-79   Photo.   Perf. 13x13½

208	A43	1c red brown	.25	.25
209	A43	1½c blue	.25	.25
210	A43	2c orange	.25	.25
211	A43	2½c green	1.20	.25
212	A43	3c purple	.35	.25
212A	A43	4c yel grn ('59)	.95	.40
213	A43	5c dark red	.25	.25

Perf. 13½x13

214	A44	6c deep plum	1.60	.25
215	A44	7½c red brn ('54)	5.50	.25
216	A44	10c red	2.25	.25
a.		Redrawn ('79)	1.75	1.60
217	A44	12½c dk green	2.75	.25
218	A44	15c deep blue	2.75	.25
a.		Redrawn ('79)	.25	.25
219	A44	20c orange	3.25	.25
a.		Redrawn ('79)	.25	.25
220	A44	21c black	4.00	2.25
221	A44	22½c blue grn ('54)	6.25	.25
222	A44	25c violet	5.25	.25
a.		Redrawn ('79)	.25	.25
223	A44	27½c henna brn	8.25	1.90
224	A44	30c olive brown	12.50	.25
225	A44	50c olive green	12.50	.25

Perf. 12½x12
Engr.

226	A45	1½g slate grn	40.00	.40
227	A45	2½g black brn	40.00	1.90
228	A45	5g rose red	60.00	17.00
229	A45	10g dk vio brn	190.00	65.00
		Nos. 208-229 (23)	400.35	92.85

Nos. 216a, 218a, 219a and 222a are from booklets Nos. 427a and 428a. Background design is sharper and stamps have one or two straight edges.
See Nos. 427-429. For surcharge see No. B20.

Fort Beekenburg — A46

Perf. 13½x12½

1953, June 16   Photo.
230 A46 22½c olive brown   6.00 .90
Founding of Fort Beekenburg, 250th anniv.

Beach at
Aruba — A47

1954, May 1   Perf. 11x11½
231 A47 15c dk bl, sal & dp bl   6.00 3.00
3rd congress of the Caribbean Tourist
Assoc., Aruba, May 3-6.

Queen Juliana — A48

1954, Dec. 15   Perf. 13½
232 A48 7½c olive green   1.40 1.00
Charter of the Kingdom, adopted Dec. 15,
1954. See Netherlands No. 366, Surinam No.
264.

Beach — A49

Petroleum
Refinery,
Aruba
A50

1955, Dec. 5   Litho.   Perf. 12
233 A49 15c chnt, bl & emer   3.25 2.60
234 A50 25c chnt, bl & emer   4.00 3.25
Caribbean Commission, 21st meeting, Aruba.

St. Annabaai
Harbor and
Flags — A51

1956, Dec. 6   Unwmk.   Perf. 14x13
235 A51 15c lt bl, blk & red   .40 .40
Caribbean Commission, 10th anniversary.

Man Watching
Rising Sun — A52

1957, Mar. 14   Photo.   Perf. 11x11½
236 A52 15c black & yellow   .40 .40
1st Caribbean Mental Health Conference,
Aruba, Mar. 14-19.

Tourism — A53

1957, July 1   Litho.   Perf. 14x13
237 A53 7½c Saba   .80 .50
238 A53 15c St. Maarten   .80 .50
239 A53 25c St. Eustatius   .80 .50
    Nos. 237-239 (3)   2.40 1.50

Curaçao
Intercontinental
Hotel — A54

1957, Oct. 12   Perf. 14x13
240 A54 15c lt ultra   .40 .40
Intercontinental Hotel, Willemstad, opening.

Map of
Curaçao — A55

1957, Dec. 10   Perf. 14x13½
241 A55 15c indigo & lt bl   .80 .70
International Geophysical Year.

Flamingoes,
Bonaire — A56

Designs: 7½c, 8c, 25c, 1½g, Old buildings,
Curaçao. 10c, 5g, Extinct volcano and palms,
Saba. 15c, 30c, 1g, Fort Willem III, Aruba.
20c, 35c, De Ruyter obelisk, St. Eustatius.
12c, 40c, 2½g, Town Hall, St. Maarten.

1958-59   Litho.   Perf. 14x13
      Size: 33x22mm

242 A56   6c lt ol grn & pink   2.25 .25
243 A56   7½c red brn & org   .25 .25
244 A56   8c dk bl & org ('59)   .25 .25
245 A56   10c gray & org yel   .25 .25
246 A56   12c bluish grn & gray
      ('59)   .25 .25
247 A56   15c grn & lt ultra   .25 .25
   a.   15c green & lilac   .25 .25
248 A56   20c crim & gray   .25 .25
249 A56   25c Prus bl & yel grn   .30 .25
250 A56   30c brn & bl grn   .30 .25
251 A56   35c gray & rose ('59)   .40 .25
252 A56   40c mag & grn   .45 .25
253 A56   50c grysh brn & pink   .45 .25
254 A56   1g brt red & gray   1.00 .25
255 A56   1½g rose vio & pale
      brn   1.35 .25
256 A56   2½g blue & citron   2.60 .30
257 A56   5g lt red brn & rose
      lil   5.00 .60
    Nos. 242-257 (16)   15.60 4.40

See Nos. 340-348, 400-403. For surcharge
see No. B58.
Nos. 242, 244-246, and 248-257 were
printed on glossy and matte paper. Nos. 243
and 247 were printed on matte paper only. No.
247a was printed on glossy paper only.

Globe — A57

1958, Oct. 16   Perf. 11x11½
258 A57 7½c blue & lake   .25 .25
259 A57 15c red & ultra   .40 .40
50th anniv. of the Netherlands Antilles
Radio and Telegraph Administration.

Hotel Aruba
Caribbean — A58

1959, July 18   Perf. 14x13
260 A58 15c multi   .40 .40
Opening of the Hotel Aruba Caribbean,
Aruba.

Sea Water
Distillation
Plant — A59

1959, Oct. 16   Photo.   Perf. 14x13
261 A59 20c bright blue   .50 .50
Opening of sea water distillation plant at
Balashi, Aruba.

Netherlands Antilles
Flag — A60

1959, Dec. 14   Litho.   Perf. 13½
262 A60 10c ultra & red   .50 .40
263 A60 20c ultra, yel & red   .50 .40
264 A60 25c ultra, grn & red   .50 .40
    Nos. 262-264 (3)   1.50 1.20
5th anniv. of the new constitution (Charter of
the Kingdom).

Fokker "Snip" and
Map of
Caribbean — A61

Designs: 20c, Globe showing route flown,
and plane. 25c, Map of Atlantic ocean and
view of Willemstad. 35c, Map of Atlantic ocean
and plane on Aruba airfield.

1959, Dec. 22   Unwmk.   Perf. 14x13
265 A61 10c yel, lt & dk bl   .80 .40
266 A61 20c yel, lt & dk bl   .80 .40
267 A61 25c yel, lt & dk bl   .80 .25
268 A61 35c yel, lt & dk bl   .80 .55
    Nos. 265-268 (4)   3.20 1.60
25th anniv. of Netherlands-Curaçao air
service.

Msgr. Martinus J.
Niewindt — A62

1960, Jan. 12   Photo.   Perf. 13½
269 A62 10c deep claret   .95 .50
270 A62 20c deep violet   .95 .55
271 A62 25c olive green   .95 .55
    Nos. 269-271 (3)   2.85 1.60
Death centenary of Monsignor Niewindt,
first apostolic vicar for Curaçao.

Worker, Flag and
Factories — A63

1960, Apr. 29   Perf. 12½x13½
272 A63 20c multi   .50 .50
Issued for Labor Day, May 1, 1960.

US Brig
"Andrea Doria"
and Gun at Fort
Orange, St.
Eustatius
A64

1961, Nov. 16   Litho.   Perf. 14x13½
273 A64 20c bl, red, grn & blk   .80 .65
185th anniv. of 1st salute by a foreign power
to the US flag flown by an American ship.

Queen Juliana and
Prince
Bernhard — A64a

1962, Jan. 31   Photo.   Perf. 14x13
274 A64a 10c deep orange   .50 .35
275 A64a 25c deep blue   .50 .35
Silver wedding anniversary of Queen Juliana and Prince Bernhard.

Benta Player — A65

6c, Corn masher. 20c, Petji kerchief. 25c,
"Jaja" (nurse) with child, sculpture.

Perf. 12½x13½

1962, Mar. 14   Photo.
276 A65   6c red brn & yel   .40 .25
277 A65   10c shown   .40 .25
278 A65   20c crim, ind & brt grn   .40 .30
279 A65   25c brt grn, brn & gray   .40 .30
   a.   Souvenir sheet of 4, #276-279   2.00 1.25
    Nos. 276-279 (4)   1.60 1.10

Emblem of Family
Relationship — A66

25c, Emblem of mental health (cross).

1963, Apr. 17   Litho.   Perf. 14x13½
280 A66 20c dk blue & ocher   .40 .40
281 A66 25c blue & red   .40 .40
Fourth Caribbean Conference for Mental
Health, Curaçao, Apr. 17-23.

Dove with Olive
Branch — A67

1963, July 1   Unwmk.   Perf. 14x13
282 A67 25c org yel & dk brn   .40 .35
Centenary of emancipation of the slaves.

Hotel
Bonaire — A68

1963, Aug. 31   Perf. 14x13
283 A68 20c dk red brown   .40 .30
Opening of Hotel Bonaire on Bonaire.

Prince William of
Orange Taking Oath of
Allegiance — A69

1963, Nov. 21   Photo.   Perf. 13½x14
284 A69 25c green, blk & rose   .40 .35
150th anniversary of the founding of the
Kingdom of the Netherlands.

Chemical
Equipment — A70

1963, Dec. 10   Litho.   Perf. 14x13½
285 A70 20c bl grn, brt yel grn &
      red   .50 .50
Opening of chemical factories on Aruba.

Airmail Letter and Wings — A71

Design: 25c, Map of Caribbean, Miami-Curaçao route and planes of 1929 and 1964.

1964, June 22   Photo.   Perf. 11x11½
286 A71 20c lt bl, red & ultra   .40 .40
287 A71 25c lt grn, bl, red & blk   .40 .40

35th anniversary of the first regular Curaçao airmail service.

Map of the Caribbean — A72

1964, Nov. 30   Litho.   Unwmk.
288 A72 20c ultra, org & dk red   .40 .35

5th meeting of the Caribbean Council, Curaçao, Nov. 30-Dec. 4.

Netherlands Antilles Flags, Map of Curaçao and Crest — A73

1964, Dec. 14   Litho.   Perf. 11½x11
289 A73 25c lt bl & multi   .40 .35

10th anniversary of the Charter of the Kingdom of the Netherlands. The flags, shaped like seagulls, represent the six islands comprising the Netherlands Antilles.

Princess Beatrix — A74

1965, Feb. 22   Photo.   Perf. 13½x14
290 A74 25c brick red   .40 .40

Visit of Princess Beatrix of Netherlands.

ITU Emblem, Old and New Communication Equipment A75

1965, May 17   Litho.   Perf. 13½
291 A75 10c brt bl & dk bl   .25 .25

ITU, centenary.

Shell Refinery, Curaçao — A76

10c, Catalytic cracking installation, vert. 25c, Workers operating manifold, primary distillation plant, vert.

Perf. 13½x14, 14x13½
1965, June 22   Photo.
292 A76 10c blk, red & yel   .40 .35
293 A76 20c multi   .40 .35
294 A76 25c multi   .40 .35
        Nos. 292-294 (3)   1.20 1.05

50th anniv. of the oil industry in Curaçao.

Floating Market, Curaçao — A77

Designs (flag and): 2c, Divi-divi tree and Haystack Mountain, Aruba. 3c, Lace, Saba. 4c, Flamingoes, Bonaire. 5c, Church ruins, St. Eustatius. 6c, Lobster, St. Maarten.

1965, Aug. 25   Litho.   Perf. 14x13
295 A77 1c lt grn, ultra & red   .25 .25
296 A77 2c yel, ultra & red   .25 .25
297 A77 3c chlky bl, ultra & red   .25 .25
298 A77 4c org, ultra & red   .25 .25
299 A77 5c lt bl, ultra & red   .25 .25
300 A77 6c pink, ultra & red   .25 .25
        Nos. 295-300 (6)   1.50 1.50

Marine Guarding Beach — A78

1965, Dec. 10   Photo.   Perf. 13x10½
301 A78 25c multi   .25 .25

Netherlands Marine Corps, 300th anniv.

Budgerigars, Wedding Rings and Initials — A79

1966, Mar. 10   Photo.   Perf. 13½x14
302 A79 25c gray & multi   .35 .25

Issued to commemorate the marriage of Princess Beatrix and Claus van Amsberg.

M. A. de Ruyter and Map of St. Eustatius A80

1966, June 19   Photo.   Perf. 13½
303 A80 25c vio, ocher & lt bl   .25 .25

Visit of Adm. Michiel Adriaanszoon de Ruyter (1607-1676) to St. Eustatius, 1666.

Liberal Arts and Grammar — A81

10c, Rhetoric and dialectic. 20c, Arithmetic and geometry. 25c, Astronomy and music.

Perf. 13½x12½
1966, Sept. 19   Litho.   Unwmk.
304 A81 6c yel, bl & blk   .25 .25
305 A81 10c yel grn, red & blk   .25 .25
306 A81 20c bl, yel & blk   .35 .25
307 A81 25c red, yel grn & blk   .35 .25
        Nos. 304-307 (4)   1.20 1.00

25th anniversary of secondary education.

Cruiser — A82

Ships: 10c, Sailing ship. 20c, Tanker. 25c, Passenger ship.

Perf. 13½x14
1967, Mar. 29   Litho.   Unwmk.
308 A82 6c lt & dk grn   .35 .25
309 A82 10c org & brn   .35 .25
310 A82 20c sep & brn   .35 .25
311 A82 25c chlky bl & dk grn   .35 .25
        Nos. 308-311 (4)   1.40 1.00

60th anniv. of *Onze Vloot* (Our Fleet), an organization which publicizes the Dutch navy and merchant marine and helps seamen.

Manuel Carlos Piar (1777-1817), Independence Hero — A83

1967, Apr. 26   Photo.   Perf. 14x13
312 A83 20c red & blk   .35 .25

Discobolus after Myron — A84

10c, Hand holding torch, & Olympic rings. 25c, Stadium, doves & Olympic rings.

1968, Feb. 19   Litho.   Perf. 13x14
313 A84 10c multi   .45 .30
314 A84 20c dk brn, ol & yel   .45 .30
315 A84 25c bl, dk bl & brt yel
               grn   .45 .30
        Nos. 313-315 (3)   1.35 .90

19th Olympic Games, Mexico City, 10/12-27.

Friendship 500 — A84a

Designs: 20c, Beechcraft Queen Air. 25c, Friendship and DC-9.

1968, Dec. 3   Litho.   Perf. 14x13
315A A84a 10c dl yel, blk & brt
                   bl   .45 .30
315B A84a 20c tan, blk & brt bl   .45 .30
315C A84a 25c sal pink, blk &
                   brt bl   .45 .30
        Nos. 315A-315C (3)   1.35 .90

Dutch Antillean Airlines (ALM).

Map of Bonaire, Radio Mast and Waves — A85

1969, Mar. 6   Perf. 14x13½
316 A85 25c bl, emer & blk   .35 .30

Opening of the relay station of the Dutch World Broadcasting System on Bonaire.

Code of Law — A86

Designs: 25c, Scales of Justice.

Perf. 12½x13½
1969, May 19   Photo.
317 A86 20c dk grn, yel grn &
               gold   .35 .30
318 A86 25c vio bl, bl & gold   .35 .30

Court of Justice, centenary.

ILO Emblem, Cactus and House — A87

1969, Aug. 25   Litho.   Perf. 14x13
319 A87 10c bl & blk   .35 .25
320 A87 25c dk red & blk   .35 .25

ILO, 50th anniversary.

Queen Juliana and Rising Sun — A87a

1969, Dec. 12   Photo.   Perf. 14x13
321 A87a 25c bl & multi   .45 .30

15th anniv. of the Charter of the Kingdom of the Netherlands. Phosphorescent paper.

Radio Bonaire Studio and Transmitter A88

Design: 15c, Radio waves and cross set against land, sea and air.

1970, Feb. 5   Photo.   Perf. 12½x13½
322 A88 10c multi   .25 .25
323 A88 15c multi   .25 .25

5th anniv. of the opening of the Trans World Missionary Radio Station, Bonaire.

Altar, St. Anna's Church, Otraband 1752 — A89

20c, Interior, Synagogue at Punda, 1732, horiz. 25c, Pulpit, Fort Church, Fort Amsterdam, 1769.

Perf. 13½x14, 14x13½
1970, May 12   Photo.
324 A89 10c gold & multi   .45 .30
325 A89 20c gold & multi   .45 .30
326 A89 25c gold & multi   .45 .30
        Nos. 324-326 (3)   1.35 .90

St. Theresia Church, St. Nicolaas — A90

1971, Feb. 9   Litho.   Perf. 14x13½
327 A90 20c dl bl, gray & rose   .35 .30

40th anniversary of the Parish of St. Theresia at St. Nicolaas, Aruba.

A91

1971, Feb. 24   Perf. 13½x14
328 A91 25c Lions emblem   .45 .40

Lions Club in the Netherlands Antilles, 25th anniversary.

A91a

Prince Bernhard, Fokker F27, Boeing 747B.

1971, June 29   Photo.   Perf. 13x14
329 A91a 45c multi   .85 .60

60th birthday of Prince Bernhard.

Pedro Luis Brion (1782-1821), Naval Commander in Fight for South American Independence — A92

1971, Sept. 27   Photo.   *Perf. 13x12½*
330 A92 40c multi   .45   .40

Flamingoes, Bonaire — A93

Designs: 1c, Queen Emma Bridge, Curaçao. 2c, The Bottom, Saba. 4c, Water tower, Aruba. 5c, Fort Amsterdam, St. Maarten. 6c, Fort Orange, St. Eustatius.

1972, Jan. 17   Litho.   *Perf. 13½x14*
331 A93 1c yel & multi   .30   .25
332 A93 2c yel grn & multi   .30   .25
333 A93 3c dp org & multi   .30   .25
334 A93 4c brt bl & multi   .30   .25
335 A93 5c red org & multi   .30   .25
336 A93 6c lil rose & multi   .30   .25
        Nos. 331-336 (6)   1.80 1.50

Ship in Dry Dock — A94

1972, Apr. 7   *Perf. 14x13½*
337 A94 30c bl gray & multi   .45   .40
Inauguration of large dry dock facilities in Willemstad.

Juan Enrique Irausquin — A95

1972, June 20   Photo.   *Perf. 13x14*
338 A95 30c deep orange   .45   .40
Irausquin (1904-1962), financier and patriot.

Costa Gomez — A96

1972, Oct. 27   Litho.
339 A96 30c yel grn & blk   .45   .40
Moises Frumencio da Costa Gomez (1907-1966), lawyer, legislator, patriot.

Island Series Type of 1958-59

Designs: 45c, 85c, Extinct volcano and palms, Saba. 55c, 90c, De Ruyter obelisk, St. Eustatius. 65c, 75c, 10g, Flamingoes, Bonaire. 70c, Fort Willem III, Aruba. 95c, Town Hall, St. Maarten.

1973, Feb. 12   Litho.   *Perf. 14x13*
                Size: 33x22mm
340 A56 45c vio bl & lt bl   .50   .25
341 A56 55c dk car rose &
                emer   .55   .25
342 A56 65c green & pink   .80   .30
343 A56 70c gray vio & org   1.30   .50
344 A56 75c brt lilac & salmon   .70   .50
345 A56 85c brn ol & apple
                grn   .80   .60
346 A56 90c blue & ocher   .95   .75
347 A56 95c orange & yellow   1.10   .80
348 A56 10g brt ultra & sal   8.75 4.25
        Nos. 340-348 (9)   15.45 8.20

Mailman — A97

Designs: 15c, King William III from 1873 issue. 30c, Emblem of Netherlands Antilles postal service.

1973, May 23   Photo.   *Perf. 13x14*
349 A97 15c lil, gold & vio   .40   .35
350 A97 20c dk grn & multi   .50   .50
351 A97 30c org & multi   .50   .40
        Nos. 349-351 (3)   1.40 1.15
Centenary of first stamps of Netherlands Antilles.

Cable Linking Aruba, Curaçao and Bonaire — A98

30c, 6 stars symbolizing the islands, cable. 45c, Saba, St. Maarten and St. Eustatius linked by cable.

1973, June 20   Litho.   *Perf. 14x13*
352 A98 15c multi   .50   .45
353 A98 30c multi   .50   .45
354 A98 45c multi   .50   .45
   a. Souvenir sheet of 3, #352-354 1.60 1.60
        Nos. 352-354 (3)   1.50 1.35
Inauguration of the inter-island submarine cable.

Queen Juliana, Netherlands Antilles and House of Orange Colors — A99a

Engr. & Photo.
1973, Sept. 4   *Perf. 12½x12*
355 A99a 15c silver & multi   .55   .55
25th anniversary of reign of Queen Juliana.

Jan Hendrik Albert Eman — A99

1973, Oct. 17   Litho.   *Perf. 13x14*
356 A99 30c lt yel grn & blk   .40   .40
Eman (1888-1957), founder of the People's Party in Aruba, member of Antillean Parliament.

Lionel Bernard Scott — A100

1974, Jan. 28
357 A100 30c lt bl & multi   .40   .40
Scott (1897-1966), architect and statesman.

Family at Supper — A101

Designs: 12c, Parents watching children at play. 15c, Mother and daughter sewing, father and son gardening.

1974, Feb. 18   Litho.   *Perf. 13x14*
358 A101 6c bl & multi   .30   .30
359 A101 12c bis & multi   .35   .30
360 A101 15c grn & multi   .35   .30
        Nos. 358-360 (3)   1.00   .90
Planned parenthood and World Population Year.

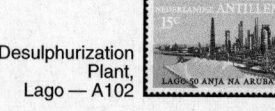

Desulphurization Plant, Lago — A102

Designs: 30c, Distillation plant. 45c, Lago refinery at night.

1974, Aug. 12   Litho.   *Perf. 14x13*
361 A102 15c lt bl, blk & yel   .35   .30
362 A102 30c lt bl, blk & yel   .40   .40
363 A102 45c dk brn & multi   .55   .55
        Nos. 361-363 (3)   1.30 1.25
Oil industry in Aruba, 50th anniversary.

UPU Emblem — A103

1974, Oct. 9   Litho.   *Perf. 13x14*
364 A103 15c yel grn, blk & gold   .50   .45
365 A103 30c bl, blk & gold   .50   .45
Centenary of Universal Postal Union.

Queen Emma Bridge — A104

Willemstad Bridges: 30c, Queen Juliana Bridge. 40c, Queen Wilhelmina Bridge.

1975, Feb. 5   Litho.   *Perf. 14x13*
366 A104 20c ultra & multi   .50   .45
367 A104 30c ultra & multi   .50   .45
368 A104 40c ultra & multi   .60   .50
        Nos. 366-368 (3)   1.60 1.45
Dedication of new Queen Juliana Bridge spanning Curaçao Harbor.

Salt Crystals — A105

Designs: 20c, Solar salt pond. 40c, Map of Bonaire and location of solar salt pond, vert.

**   *Perf. 14x13, 13x14***
1975, Apr. 24   Litho.
369 A105 15c multi   .55   .40
370 A105 20c multi   .55   .45
371 A105 40c multi   .65   .45
        Nos. 369-371 (3)   1.75 1.30

Bonaire's salt industry.

Aruba Airport, 1935 and Fokker F-18 — A106

30c, Aruba Airport, 1950, & Douglas DC-9. 40c, New Princess Beatrix Airport & Boeing 727.

1975, June 19   Litho.   *Perf. 14x13*
372 A106 15c vio & multi   .45   .35
373 A106 30c blk & multi   .45   .35
374 A106 40c yel & multi   .45   .45
        Nos. 372-374 (3)   1.35 1.15
40th anniversary of Aruba Airport.

International Women's Year Emblem — A107

12c, "Women's role in social development." 20c, Embryos within female & male symbols.

1975, Aug. 1   Photo.   *Perf. 14x13*
375 A107 6c multi   .35   .25
376 A107 12c multi   .40   .30
377 A107 20c multi   .50   .40
        Nos. 375-377 (3)   1.25   .95
International Women's Year 1975.

Beach, Aruba — A108

Tourist Publicity: No. 379, Beach pavilion and boat, Bonaire. No. 380, Table Mountain and Spanish Water, Curaçao.

1976, June 21   Litho.   *Perf. 14x13*
378 A108 40c blue & multi   .55   .50
379 A108 40c blue & multi   .55   .50
380 A108 40c blue & multi   .55   .50
        Nos. 378-380 (3)   1.65 1.50

Julio Antonio Abraham — A109

1976, Aug. 10   Photo.   *Perf. 13x14*
381 A109 30c tan & claret   .65   .45
Julio Antonio Abraham (1909-1960), founder of Democratic Party of Bonaire.

Dike and Produce — A110

1976, Sept. 21   Litho.
382 A110 15c shown   .50   .40
383 A110 35c Cattle   .55   .45
384 A110 45c Fish   .55   .55
        Nos. 382-384 (3)   1.60 1.40
Agriculture, husbandry and fishing in Netherlands Antilles.

Plaque, Fort Oranje Memorial — A111

Designs: 40c, Andrea Doria in St. Eustatius harbor receiving salute. 55c, Johannes de Graaff, Governor of St. Eustatius, holding Declaration of Independence.

1976, Nov. 16   Litho.   *Perf. 14x13*
385 A111 25c multi   .60   .40
386 A111 40c multi   .60   .40
387 A111 55c multi   .60   .55
        Nos. 385-387 (3)   1.80 1.35
First gun salute to US flag, St. Eustatius, Nov. 16, 1776.
See No. 619.

Dancer with Cactus Headdress — A112

Carnival: 35c, Woman in feather costume. 40c, Woman in pompadour costume.

1977, Jan. 20   Litho.   *Perf. 13x14*
388 A112 25c multi   .60   .45
389 A112 35c multi   .60   .45
390 A112 40c multi   .60   .45
        Nos. 388-390 (3)   1.80 1.35

Bird Petroglyph, Aruba — A113

Indian Petroglyphs: 35c, Loops and spiral, Savonet Plantation, Curaçao. 40c, Tortoise, Onima, Bonaire.

1977, Mar. 29
391 A113 25c red & multi .60 .45
392 A113 35c brn & multi .60 .45
393 A113 40c yel & multi .60 .45
Nos. 391-393 (3) 1.80 1.35

A114

Tropical Trees: 25c, Cordia Sebestena. 40c, East Indian walnut, vert. 55c, Tamarind.

1977, July 20   Perf. 14x13, 13x14
394 A114 25c blk & multi .50 .45
395 A114 40c blk & multi .60 .45
396 A114 55c blk & multi .65 .60
Nos. 394-396 (3) 1.75 1.50

A115

Designs: 20c, Chimes, Spritzer & Fuhrmann Building. 40c, Globe with Western Hemisphere and sun over Curaçao. 55c, Diamond ring and flag of Netherlands Antilles.

1977, Sept. 27   Perf. 13x14
397 A115 20c brt grn & multi .50 .45
398 A115 40c yel & multi .60 .45
399 A115 55c bl & multi .65 .60
Nos. 397-399 (3) 1.75 1.50

Spritzer & Fuhrmann, jewelers of Netherlands Antilles, 50th anniversary.

Island Series Type of 1958-59

Designs: 20c, 35c, 55c, De Ruyter obelisk, St. Eustatius. 40c, Town Hall, St. Maarten.

Perf. 13½ Horiz.

1977, Nov. 30   Photo.
Size: 39x22mm
400 A56 20c crim & gray 1.40 1.40
a. Bklt. pane of 6 (2 #400, 4 #402) 5.00
401 A56 35c gray & rose 3.75 3.00
a. Bklt. pane of 4 (1 #401, 3 #403) 6.00
402 A56 40c magenta & grn .50 .50
403 A56 55c dk car rose & emer .70 .70
Nos. 400-403 (4) 6.35 5.60

Nos. 400-403 issued in booklets only. No. 400a has label with red inscription in size of 3 stamps; No. 401a has label with dark carmine rose inscription in size of 2 stamps.

Winding Road, Map of Saba — A116

Tourism: 35c, Ruins of Synagogue, map of St. Eustatius. 40c, Greatbay, Map of St. Maarten.

1977, Nov. 30   Litho.   Perf. 14x13
404 A116 25c multi .30 .25
405 A116 35c multi .35 .30
406 A116 40c multi .35 .35
Nos. 404-406 (3) 1.00 .90

Tete-beche gutter pairs exist.

Treasure Chest — A117

Designs: 20c, Logo of Netherlands Antilles Bank. 40c, Safe deposit door.

1978, Feb. 7   Litho.   Perf. 14x13
407 A117 15c brt & dk bl .25 .25
408 A117 20c org & gold .25 .25
409 A117 40c brt & dk grn .25 .25
Nos. 407-409 (3) .75 .75

Bank of Netherlands Antilles, 150th anniv. Tete-beche gutter pairs exist.

Flamboyant — A118

Flowers: 25c, Erythrina velutina. 40c, Guaiacum officinale, horiz. 55c, Gliricidia sepium, horiz.

Perf. 13x14, 14x13

1978, May 31   Litho.
410 A118 15c multi .25 .25
411 A118 25c multi .25 .25
412 A118 40c multi .40 .30
413 A118 55c multi .50 .45
Nos. 410-413 (4) 1.40 1.25

Polythysana Rubrescens — A119

Butterflies: 25c, Caligo eurilochus. 35c, Prepona omphale amesis. 40c, Morpho aega.

1978, June 20   Perf. 13x14
414 A119 15c multi .50 .30
415 A119 25c multi .50 .30
416 A119 35c multi .50 .35
417 A119 40c multi .60 .45
Nos. 414-417 (4) 2.10 1.40

"Conserve Energy" — A120

1978, Aug. 31   Litho.   Perf. 13x14
418 A120 15c org & blk .30 .30
419 A120 20c dp grn & blk .40 .30
420 A120 40c dk red & blk .45 .40
Nos. 418-420 (3) 1.15 1.00

Morse Ship-to-Shore Service — A121

Designs: 40c, Ship-to-shore telex service. 55c, Future radar-satellite service, vert.

Perf. 14x13, 13x14

1978, Oct. 16   Litho.
421 A121 20c multi .35 .35
422 A121 40c multi .45 .45
423 A121 55c multi .50 .50
Nos. 421-423 (3) 1.30 1.30

Ship-to-shore communications, 70th anniv.

Villa Maria Waterworks A122

35c, Leonard B. Smith, vert. 40c, Opening of Queen Emma Bridge, Willemstad, 1888.

1978, Dec. 13
424 A122 25c multi .30 .25
425 A122 35c multi .40 .30
426 A122 40c multi .45 .40
Nos. 424-426 (3) 1.15 .95

L. B. Smith, engineer, 80th death anniv.

Queen Juliana Type of 1950

1979, Jan. 11   Photo.   Perf. 13½x13
427 A44 5c dp yel .25 .25
a. Bklt. pane of 10 (4 #427, 1 #216a, 2 #222a, 3 #429) 4.00
428 A44 30c brown 1.05 1.05
a. Bklt. pane of 10 (1 #428, 4 #218a, 3 #219a, 2 #222a) 4.00
429 A44 40c brt bl .35 .35
Nos. 427-429 (3) 1.65 1.65

Nos. 427-429 issued in booklets only. Nos. 427a-428a have 2 labels and selvages the size of 6 stamps. Background design of booklet stamps sharper than 1950 issue. All stamps have 1 or 2 straight edges.

Goat and Conference Emblem — A123

75c, Horse & map of Curaçao. 150c, Cattle, Netherlands Antilles flag, UN & Conf. emblems.

1979, Apr. 18   Litho.   Perf. 14x13
437 A123 50c multi .40 .35
438 A123 75c multi .55 .50
439 A123 150c multi .85 .95
a. Souv. sheet of 3, perf. 13½x13 2.00 2.00
Nos. 437-439 (3) 1.80 1.80

12th Inter-American Meeting at Ministerial Level on Foot and Mouth Disease and Zoonosis Control, Curaçao, Apr. 17-20. No. 439a contains Nos. 437-439 in changed colors.

Dutch Colonial Soldier, Emblem — A124

1979, July 4   Litho.   Perf. 13x14
440 A124 1g multi .65 .60
Nos. 440,B166-B167 (3) 1.45 1.30

Netherlands Antilles Volunteer Corps, 50th anniv.

A125

Flowering Trees: 25c, Casearia Tremula. 40c, Cordia cylindro-stachya. 1.50g, Melochia tomentosa.

1979, Sept. 3   Litho.   Perf. 13x14
441 A125 25c multi .40 .30
442 A125 40c multi .50 .45
443 A125 1.50g multi 1.00 1.00
Nos. 441-443 (3) 1.90 1.75

A126

Designs: 65c, Dove and Netherlands flag. 1.50g, Dove and Netherlands Antilles flag.

1979, Dec. 6   Litho.   Perf. 13x14
444 A126 65c multi .55 .50
445 A126 1.50g multi 1.00 1.05

Constitution, 25th anniversary.

Map of Aruba, Foundation Emblem — A127

1g, Foundation headquarters, Aruba.

1979, Dec. 18   Perf. 14x13
446 A127 95c multi .70 .70
447 A127 1g multi .85 .85

Cultural Foundation Center, Aruba, 30th anniv.

Cupola, 1910, Fort Church — A128

1980, Jan. 9   Perf. 13x14
448 A128 100c multi .85 .70
Nos. 448,B172-B173 (3) 1.65 1.50

Fort Church, Curaçao, 210th anniv. (1979).

Rotary Emblem — A129

Designs: 50c, Globe and cogwheels. 85c, Cogwheel and Rotary emblem.

1980, Feb. 22   Litho.   Perf. 14x13
449 A129 45c multi .45 .35
450 A129 50c multi .45 .35
451 A129 85c multi .60 .60
a. Souvenir sheet of 3, #449-451, perf. 13½x13 1.75 1.60
b. Strip of 3, #449-451 1.60 1.60

Rotary Intl., 75th anniv. No. 451a has continuous design.

Coin Box, 1905 — A130

Post Office Savings Bank of Netherlands Antilles, 75th Anniv.: 150c, Coin box, 1980.

1980, Apr. 2   Litho.   Perf. 14x13
452 A130 25c multi .35 .35
453 A130 150c multi 1.10 1.10

Netherlands Antilles No. 200, Arms — A131

60c, No. 290, royal crown.

1980, Apr. 29   Photo.
454 A131 25c shown .30 .30
455 A131 60c multicolored .45 .45
a. Bklt. pane of 5 + 3 labels (#428, 2 #454, 2 #455) 3.50

Abdication of Queen Juliana of the Netherlands.
Tete-beche gutter pairs exist.

Sir Rowland Hill (1795-1879), Originator of Penny Postage — A132

60c, London 1980 emblem. 1g, Airmail label.

1980, May 6   Litho.
456 A132 45c shown .40 .40
457 A132 60c multicolored .50 .50
458 A132 1g multicolored .80 .80
a. Souv. sheet of 3, perf. 13½x14 1.75 1.40
Nos. 456-458 (3) 1.70 1.70

London 1980 Intl. Stamp Exhibition, May 6-14. No. 458a contains Nos. 456-458 in changed colors.

Leptotila Verreauxi — A133

1980, Sept. 3   Litho.   Perf. 14x13
459 A133 25c shown .70 .30
460 A133 60c Mockingbird .85 .50
461 A133 85c Coereba flaveola 1.05 .65
Nos. 459-461 (3) 2.60 1.45

Rudolf Theodorus
Palm — A134

1g, Score, hand playing piano.

1981, Jan. 27   Litho.   Perf. 13x14
462 A134 60c shown .60 .60
463 A134 1g multicolored 1.00 .85

Palm, composer, birth centenary.

Alliance Mission
Emblem, Map of
Aruba — A135

1981, Mar. 24   Perf. 14x13
464 A135 30c shown .35 .35
465 A135 50c Curaçao .60 .45
466 A135 1g Bonaire map .95 .85
Nos. 464-466 (3) 1.90 1.65

Evangelical Alliance Mission anniversaries:
35th in Aruba, 50th in Curaçao, 30th in
Bonaire.

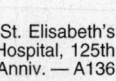

St. Elisabeth's
Hospital, 125th
Anniv. — A136

1981, June 24   Litho.   Perf. 14x13
467 A136 60c Gateway .55 .55
468 A136 1.50g shown 1.30 1.30

Oregano
Blossom — A137

1981, Nov. 24   Litho.   Perf. 13x14
469 A137 45c shown .50 .40
470 A137 70c Flaira .80 .65
471 A137 100c Welisali 1.00 .80
Nos. 469-471 (3) 2.30 1.85

Ship Pilot Service
Cent. — A138

Designs: Various ships.

1982, Jan. 13   Litho.   Perf. 13x14
472 A138 70c multi 1.05 .80
473 A138 85c multi 1.15 .85
474 A138 1g multi 1.20 .90
Nos. 472-474 (3) 3.40 2.55

A139

1982, Mar. 15   Litho.   Perf. 13x14
475 A139 75c Altar 1.05 .65
476 A139 85c Building 1.15 .65
477 A139 150c Pulpit 1.60 1.10
Nos. 475-477 (3) 3.80 2.40

Community Mikve Israel-Emanuel Synagogue, 250th anniv.

Flags, Peter
Stuyvesant — A140

1982, Apr. 21   Litho.   Perf. 13x14
478 A140 75c multicolored 1.15 .90
a.   Souvenir sheet 1.25 1.25

US-Netherlands diplomatic relations
bicentenary.
See No. 619b.

A141

1982, May 5
479 A141 35c Radar screen .65 .35
480 A141 75c Control tower 1.05 .65
481 A141 150c Antenna 1.60 1.10
Nos. 479-481 (3) 3.30 2.10

Intl. Air Traffic Controllers' Year.

A142

45c, Emblem. 85c, Mail bag. 150c, Flags of
France, Netherland Antilles.

1982, June 9   Litho.   Perf. 13x14
482 A142 45c multi .65 .45
483 A142 85c multi .90 .70
484 A142 150c multi 1.45 1.10
a.   Souvenir sheet of 3, #482-484 3.00 2.50
Nos. 482-484 (3) 3.00 2.25

PHILEXFRANCE '82 Stamp Exhibition,
Paris, June 11-21.

Brown
Chromis — A143

1982, Sept. 15   Litho.   Perf. 14x13
485 A143 35c shown .85 .45
486 A143 75c Spotted trunkfish 1.15 .80
487 A143 85c Blue tang 1.30 .90
488 A143 100c French angelfish 1.40 .95
Nos. 485-488 (4) 4.70 3.10

Natural Bridge,
Aruba — A144

45c, Lac-Bay, Bonaire. 100c, Willemstad,
Curaçao.

1983, Apr. 12   Litho.   Perf. 14x13
489 A144 35c shown .60 .45
490 A144 45c multi .70 .55
491 A144 100c multi 1.40 1.05
Nos. 489-491 (3) 2.70 2.05

World Communications
Year — A145

1983, May 17   Litho.   Perf. 13x14
492 A145 1g multi 1.40 1.25
a.   Souvenir sheet 1.60 1.25

BRASILIANA
'83 — A146

45c, Ship, postal building, Waaigat. 55c,
Flags, emblem. 100c, Governor's Palace,
Sugar Loaf Mt.

1983, June 29   Litho.   Perf. 13x14
493 A146 45c multi .80 .65
494 A146 55c multi .85 .75
495 A146 100c multi 1.25 1.15
a.   Souvenir sheet of 3, #493-495 3.00 2.50
Nos. 493-495 (3) 2.90 2.55

Fruit Tree — A147

45c, Mangifera indica. 55c, Malpighia
punicifolia. 100c, Citrus aurantifolia.

1983, Sept. 13   Litho.   Perf. 13x14
496 A147 45c multicolored 1.00 .65
497 A147 55c multicolored 1.05 .70
498 A147 100c multicolored 1.60 1.15
Nos. 496-498 (3) 3.65 2.50

Local Government
Buildings — A148

1983, Dec. 20   Litho.   Perf. 14x13
499 A148 20c Saba .35 .25
500 A148 25c St. Eustatius .35 .25
501 A148 30c St. Maarten .40 .35
502 A148 35c Aruba 2.40 .40
503 A148 45c Bonaire .60 .45
a.   Perf. 13½ horiz. ('86) 2.40 1.30
504 A148 55c Curaçao .80 .55
a.   Perf. 13½ horiz. ('86) 2.40 1.30
b.   Bkt. pane of 4 + label (2 #503a, 504a) ('86) 10.00
Nos. 499-504 (6) 4.90 2.25

See Nos. 515-520, 543A-555.

Amigoe di Curaçao
Newspaper
Centenary — A149

45c, Copy programming. 55c, Printing
press. 85c, Man reading newspaper.

1984, Jan. 5   Litho.
505 A149 45c multicolored .75 .60
506 A149 55c multicolored .85 .65
507 A149 85c multicolored 1.30 1.05
Nos. 505-507 (3) 2.90 2.30

40th Anniv. of Intl.
Civil Aviation
Org. — A150

Various emblems.

1984, Feb. 28   Litho.   Perf. 14x13
508 A150 25c Winair .65 .35
509 A150 45c ICAO .95 .60
510 A150 55c ALM 1.05 .65
511 A150 100c Plane 1.60 1.05
Nos. 508-511 (4) 4.25 2.65

Chamber of Commerce and Industry
Centenary — A151

45c, Bonnet maker. 55c, Emblem. 100c,
River, bridge, boat.

1984, May 29   Litho.   Perf. 13½
512 A151 45c multicolored 1.20 .80
513 A151 55c multicolored 1.25 .80
514 A151 100c multicolored 1.75 1.10
Nos. 512-514 (3) 4.20 2.70

Govt. Building Type of 1983

1984, June 26   Litho.   Perf. 14x13
515 A148 60c like 20c .65 .55
516 A148 65c like 25c .75 .60
517 A148 75c like 30c 1.00 .80
518 A148 85c like 35c 3.00 .90
519 A148 90c like 45c 1.15 .90
520 A148 95c like 55c 1.20 .95
Nos. 515-520 (6) 7.75 4.70

For surcharges see Nos. B306-B307.

Local Birds — A152

45c, Tiaris bicolor. 55c, Zonotrichia capensis. 150c, Chlorostilbon mellisugus.

1984, Sept. 18   Litho.   Perf. 14x13
521 A152 45c multi 1.15 .65
522 A152 55c multi 1.30 .85
523 A152 150c multi 2.25 1.60
Nos. 521-523 (3) 4.70 3.10

Eleanor Roosevelt
(1884-1962) — A153

45c, At Hyde Park. 85c, Portrait. 100c,
Reading to children.

1984, Oct. 11   Litho.   Perf. 13x14
524 A153 45c multi .80 .55
525 A153 85c multi 1.30 .90
526 A153 100c multi 1.40 .95
Nos. 524-526 (3) 3.50 2.40

Tete-beche gutter pairs exist.

Flamingos — A154

1985, Jan. 9   Litho.   Perf. 14x13
527 A154 25c Adult pullets .85 .55
528 A154 45c Juveniles 1.25 .65
529 A154 55c Adults wading 1.25 .80
530 A154 100c Adults flying 1.90 1.15
Nos. 527-530 (4) 5.25 3.15

Curaçao Masonic Lodge
Bicent. — A155

45c, Compass, sun, moon and stars. 55c,
Doorway, columns and 5 steps. 100c, Star, 7
steps.

1985, Feb. 21   Litho.   Perf. 13x14
531 A155 45c multi 1.75 .65
532 A155 55c multi 1.75 .85
533 A155 100c multi 2.10 1.35
Nos. 531-533 (3) 5.60 2.85

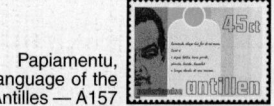

UN, 40th
Anniv. — A156

1985, June 5   Litho.   Perf. 14x13
534 A156 55c multi 1.05 .70
535 A156 1g multi 1.60 1.15

Papiamentu,
Language of the
Antilles — A157

45c, Pierre Lauffer (1920-1981), author and poem Patria. 55c, Waves of Papiamentu.

1985, Sept. 4   Litho.   Perf. 14x13
536 A157 45c multi   .70 .55
537 A157 55c multi   .85 .65

Tete-beche gutter pairs exist.

Flora — A158

5c, Calotropis procera. 10c, Capparis flexuosa. 20c, Mimosa distachya. 45c, Ipomoea nil. 55c, Heliotropium ternatum. 1.50g, Ipomoea incarnata.

1985, Nov. 6   Perf. 13x14
538 A158   5c multi   .50 .25
539 A158   10c multi   .50 .25
540 A158   20c multi   .70 .35
541 A158   45c multi   1.05 .55
542 A158   55c multi   1.20 .60
543 A158 1.50g multi   1.90 1.30
      Nos. 538-543 (6)   5.85 3.30

Govt. Building Type of 1983
1985-89   Perf. 14x13
543A A148   70c like 20c
                    ('88)   1.00 .40
543B A148   85c like 45c
                    ('88)   1.15 .45
544 A148   1g like 20c   1.40 .90
545 A148 1.50g like 25c   1.75 1.15
546 A148 2.50g like 30c
                    ('86)   2.00 1.60
551 A148   5g like 45c
                    ('86)   4.00 3.00
554 A148   10g like 55c
                    ('87)   8.00 4.75
555 A148   15g like 20c
                    ('89)   12.00 7.75
      Nos. 543A-555 (8)   31.30 20.00

Issued: 70c, 85c, 3/16; 1g, 1.50g, 12/4; 2.50g, 1/8; 5g, 12/3; 10g, 5/20; 15g, 2/8.
For surcharge see No. B308.

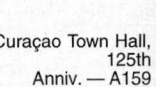

Curaçao Town Hall, 125th Anniv. — A159

1986, Jan. 8   Perf. 14x13, 13x14
561 A159 5c Town Hall   .35 .25
562 A159 15c State room, vert.   .40 .25
563 A159 25c Court room   .60 .35
564 A159 55c Entrance, vert.   1.00 .60
      Nos. 561-564 (4)   2.35 1.45

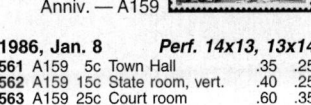

Amnesty Intl., 25th Anniv. — A160

45c, Prisoner chained. 55c, Peace bird imprisoned. 100c, Prisoner behind bars.

1986, May 28   Litho.   Perf. 14x13
565 A160 45c multi   .80 .50
566 A160 55c multi   .90 .55
567 A160 100c multi   1.25 .85
      Nos. 565-567 (3)   2.95 1.90

Mailboxes — A161

10c, PO mailbox. 25c, Steel mailbox, vert. 45c, Mailbox on brick wall, vert. 55c, Pillar box, vert.

**   Perf. 14x13, 13x14**
1986, Sept. 3   Litho.
568 A161 10c multi   .30 .25
569 A161 25c multi   .45 .25
570 A161 45c multi   .70 .50
571 A161 55c multi   .85 .60
      Nos. 568-571 (4)   2.30 1.60

Friars of Tilburg in the Antilles, Cent. — A162

10c, Brother Mauritius Vliegendehond, residence, 1886. 45c, Monsignor Ferdinand Kieckens, St. Thomas College, Roodeweg. 55c, Father F.S. de Beer, 1st general-superior, & college courtyard.

1986, Nov. 13   Litho.   Perf. 13x14
572 A162 10c multi   .35 .25
573 A162 45c multi   .80 .55
574 A162 55c multi   .95 .65
      Nos. 572-574 (3)   2.10 1.40

Princess Juliana & Prince Bernhard, 50th Wedding Anniv. — A163

1987, Jan. 7   Litho.   Perf. 13x14
575 A163 1.35g multi   2.50 1.25
   a.   Souvenir sheet   3.00 2.50

Maduro Holding, Inc., Sesquicent. — A164

70c, Expansion map. 85c, Corporate divisions. 1.55g, S.E.L. Maduro, founder.

1987, Jan. 26
576 A164 70c multi   .85 .55
577 A164 85c multi   1.05 .65
578 A164 1.55g multi   1.75 1.30
      Nos. 576-578 (3)   3.65 2.50

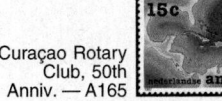

Curaçao Rotary Club, 50th Anniv. — A165

15c, Map of the Antilles. 50c, Rotary headquarters. 65c, Map of Curaçao.

1987, Apr. 2   Litho.   Perf. 14x13
579 A165 15c multicolored   .40 .25
580 A165 50c multicolored   .75 .55
581 A165 65c multicolored   1.00 .60
      Nos. 579-581 (3)   2.15 1.40

Bolivar-Curaçao Friendship, 175th Anniv. — A166

60c, Octagon, residence of Simon Bolivar in Curaçao. 70c, Bolivarian Soc. Headquarters, 1949, Willemstad. 80c, Octagon interior (bedroom). 90c, Manual Carlos Piar, Simon Bolivar (1783-1830) & Pedro Luis Brion.

1987, July 24   Litho.   Perf. 14x13
582 A166 60c multi   .75 .55
583 A166 70c multi   .80 .60
584 A166 80c multi   1.05 .80
585 A166 90c multi   1.15 .85
      Nos. 582-585 (4)   3.75 2.80

Bolivarian Society, 50th anniv. (70c, 90c).

Antilles Natl. Parks Foundation, 25th Anniv. — A167

70c, Phaethon lepturus. 85c, Odocoileus virginianus curassavicus. 1.55g, Iguana iguana.

1987, Dec. 1   Litho.   Perf. 14x13
586 A167 70c multi   .90 .55
587 A167 85c multi   1.05 .65
588 A167 1.55g multi   1.75 1.30
      Nos. 586-588 (3)   3.70 2.50

The Curaçao Courant, 175th Anniv. — A168

Designs: 55c, 19th Cent. printing press, lead type. 70c, Keyboard, modern press.

1987, Dec. 11
589 A168 55c multi   .80 .55
590 A168 70c multi   .85 .60

Mijnmaatschappij Phosphate Mining Co., Curaçao, 75th Anniv. — A169

40c, William Godden, founder. 105c, Processing plant. 155c, Tafelberg.

1988, Jan. 21
591 A169 40c multicolored   .70 .40
592 A169 105c multicolored   1.30 .85
593 A169 155c multicolored   1.75 1.15
      Nos. 591-593 (3)   3.75 2.40

States of the Netherlands Antilles, 50th Anniv. — A170

Designs: 65c, John Horris Sprockel, 1st president, and natl. colors, crest. 70c, Development of state elections, women's suffrage. 155c, Natl. colors, crest, constellation representing the 5 islands and separation of Aruba.

1988, Apr. 5   Litho.
594 A170 65c multi   .85 .60
595 A170 70c multi   1.05 .60
596 A170 155c multi   1.75 1.15
      Nos. 594-596 (3)   3.65 2.35

Abolition of Slavery, 125th Anniv. — A171

190c, Slave Wall, Curaçao.

1988, July 1   Litho.   Perf. 14x13
597 A171 155c shown   1.60 1.05
598 A171 190c multicolored   1.90 1.20

3rd Conference for Great Cities of the Americas, Curaçao, Aug. 24-27 — A172

1988, Aug. 24   Litho.
599 A172 80c shown   1.05 .60
600 A172 155c Bridge, globe   1.60 1.05

Interamerican Foundation of Cities conference on building bridges between peoples.

Charles Ernst Barend Hellmund (1896-1952) — A173

Men and women who initiated community development: 65c, Atthelo Maud Edwards Jackson (1901-1970). 90c, Nicolaas Debrot (1902-1981). 120c, William Charles De La Try Ellis (1881-1977).

1988, Sept. 20   Perf. 13x14
601 A173 55c multi   .70 .40
602 A173 65c multi   .75 .50
603 A173 90c multi   1.20 .75
604 A173 120c multi   1.25 .85
      Nos. 601-604 (4)   3.90 2.50

Tete-beche gutter pairs exist.

Cacti — A174

55c, Cereus hexagonus. 115c, Melocactus. 125c, Opuntia wentiana.

1988, Dec. 13   Litho.   Perf. 13x14
605 A174 55c multicolored   .85 .55
606 A174 115c multicolored   1.35 .85
607 A174 125c multicolored   1.60 1.05
      Nos. 605-607 (3)   3.80 2.45

A175

1989, Mar. 9   Litho.   Perf. 14x13
608 A175 65c Crested quail   1.30 .75
609 A175 115c Dogs, cats   1.45 1.10

Wildlife Protection and Curaçao Foundation for the prevention of cruelty to animals.

Cruise Ships at St. Maarten and Curaçao — A176

1989, May 8   Litho.
610 A176 70c Great Bay Harbor   1.05 .75
611 A176 155c St. Annabay   1.75 1.45

Tourism.

A177

Social and Political Figures: 40c, Paula Clementina Dorner (1901-1969), teacher. 55c, John Aniceto de Jongh (1885-1951), pharmacist, Parliament member. 90c, Jacobo Palm (1887-1982), composer. 120c, Abraham Mendes Chumaceiro (1841-1902), political reformer.

1989, Sept. 20   Litho.   Perf. 13x14
612 A177 40c multi   .70 .45
613 A177 55c multi   .80 .55
614 A177 90c multi   1.15 .75
615 A177 120c multi   1.40 1.05
      Nos. 612-615 (4)   4.05 2.80

A178

30c, 7 Symptoms of cancer. 60c, Radiation treatment. 80c, Fund emblem, healthy person.

1989, Nov. 7   Litho.
616 A178 30c multi   .60 .45
617 A178 60c multi   .95 .70
618 A178 80c multi   1.15 .70
      Nos. 616-618 (3)   2.70 1.85

Queen Wilhelmina Fund, 40th anniv. Nos. 616-618 printed se-tenant with inscribed labels.

Souvenir Sheet

World Stamp Expo '89 and 20th UPU Congress, Washington, DC — A179

Designs: 70c, Monument, St. Eustatius, where the sovereignty of the US was 1st recognized by a foreign officer, Nov. 16, 1776. 155c, Peter Stuyvesant, flags representing bicent. of US-Antilles diplomatic relations, vert. 250c, 9-Gun salute of the Andrea Doria.

1989, Nov. 17   Litho.   *Perf. 13*
619   Sheet of 3   5.75 4.50
a. A179 70c multicolored   1.15   .75
b. A179 155c multicolored   1.75 1.30
c. A179 250c multicolored   2.60 2.25

Fireworks — A180

100c, Ornaments on tree.

1989, Dec. 1   *Perf. 13½x14*
620   A180 30c multicolored   .60   .40
621   A180 100c multicolored   1.30   .90

Christmas 1989 and New Year 1990. Nos. 620-621 printed se-tenant with labels inscribed "Merry X-mas and Happy New Year" in four languages.

Flowering plants — A181

30c, Tephrosia cinerea. 55c, Erithalis fruticosa. 65c, Evolvulus antillanus. 70c, Jacquinia arborea. 125c, Tournefortia gnaphalodes. 155c, Sesuvium portulacastrum.

1990, Jan. 31   Litho.   *Perf. 13x14*
622   A181 30c multi   .40   .35
623   A181 55c multi   .75   .55
624   A181 65c multi   .80   .60
625   A181 70c multi   .90   .70
626   A181 125c multi   1.60 1.30
627   A181 155c multi   2.00 1.60
       Nos. 622-627 (6)   6.45 5.10

Dominican Nuns in the Netherlands Antilles, Cent. — A182

10c, Nurse, flag, map. 55c, St. Rose Hospital and St. Martin's Home. 60c, St. Joseph School.

1990, May 7   Litho.   *Perf. 14x13*
628   A182 10c multicolored   .25   .25
629   A182 55c multicolored   .75   .50
630   A182 60c multicolored   .85   .60
       Nos. 628-630 (3)   1.85 1.35

A183

Poets: 40c, Carlos Alberto Nicolaas-Perez (1915-1989). 60c, Evert Stephanus Jordanus Kruythoff (1893-1967). 80c, John De Pool (1873-1947). 150c, Joseph Sickman Corsen (1853-1911).

1990, Aug. 8   Litho.   *Perf. 13x14*
631   A183 40c multicolored   .55   .35
632   A183 60c multicolored   .80   .60
633   A183 80c multicolored   1.00   .75
634   A183 150c multicolored   1.75 1.60
       Nos. 631-634 (4)   4.10 3.30

Netherlands Queens — A184

No. 635, Emma. No. 636, Wilhelmina. No. 637, Juliana. No. 638, Beatrix. 250c, Four Queens, horiz.

1990, Sept. 5   *Perf. 13x14*
635   A184 100c multi   1.45 1.05
636   A184 100c multi   1.45 1.05
637   A184 100c multi   1.45 1.05
638   A184 100c multi   1.45 1.05
       Nos. 635-638 (4)   5.80 4.20
Souvenir Sheet
Perf. 14x13
639   A184 250c multi   6.25 5.00

Oil Refining in Curaçao, 75th Anniv. — A185

1990, Oct. 1   Litho.   *Perf. 14x13*
640   A185 100c multicolored   1.60 1.25

Christmas — A186

1990, Dec. 5   Litho.   *Perf. 13½x14*
641   A186 30c Gifts   .60   .30
642   A186 100c shown   1.60   .95

25th anniv. of Bon Bisina Project (No. 641). Nos. 641-642 each printed with se-tenant label showing holiday greetings.

Express Mail Service, 5th Anniv. — A187

1991, Jan. 16   Litho.   *Perf. 14x13*
643   A187 20g multicolored   15.00 12.50

Fish — A188

Designs: 10c, Scuba diver, French grunt. 40c, Spotted trunkfish. 55c, Coppersweeper. 75c, Skindiver, yellow goatfish. 100c, Blackbar soldierfish.

1991, Mar. 13   *Perf. 13x14*
644   A188 10c multicolored   .60   .25
645   A188 40c multicolored   .70   .50
646   A188 55c multicolored   .85   .75
647   A188 75c multicolored   1.05 1.00
648   A188 100c multicolored   1.60 1.20
       Nos. 644-648 (5)   4.80 3.70

Greetings — A189

1991, May 8   *Perf. 14x13*
649   A189 30c Good luck   .45   .40
650   A189 30c Thank you   .45   .40
651   A189 30c Love you   .45   .40
652   A189 30c Happy day   .45   .40
653   A189 30c Get well soon   .45   .40
654   A189 30c Happy birthday   .45   .40
       Nos. 649-654 (6)   2.70 2.40

Lighthouses — A190

30c, Westpoint, Curaçao. 70c, Willem's Tower, Bonaire. 115c, Little Curaçao, Curaçao.

1991, June 19   Litho.   *Perf. 13x14*
655   A190 30c multicolored   2.50 1.30
656   A190 70c multicolored   2.50 1.30
657   A190 115c multicolored   2.50 1.30
       Nos. 655-657 (3)   7.50 3.90

Peter Stuyvesant College, 50th Anniv. — A191   Espamer '91 — A192

1991, July 5   *Perf. 14x13, 13x14*
658   A191 65c multicolored   .90   .85
659   A192 125c multicolored   1.75 1.75

Christmas — A193

1991, Dec. 2   Litho.   *Perf. 13½x14*
660   A193 30c shown   .45   .40
661   A193 100c Angel, shepherds   1.40 1.25

Nos. 660-661 printed with se-tenant labels.

  A194

Litho. & Typo.
1991, Dec. 16   *Perf. 13x14*
662   A194 30c J. A. Correa   .80   .45
663   A194 70c "75", coat of arms   1.30   .90
664   A194 155c I. H. Capriles   1.90 1.60
a.   Strip of 3, #662-664   4.00 3.00

Maduro and Curiel's Bank NV, 75th anniv.

Odocoileus Virginianus — A195

1992, Jan. 29   Litho.   *Perf. 14x13*
666   A195 5c Fawn   .95   .70
667   A195 10c Two does   .95   .70
668   A195 30c Buck   .95   .70
669   A195 40c Buck & doe in water   .95   .70
670   A195 200c Buck drinking   3.00 2.25
671   A195 355c Buck, diff.   5.00 4.00
       Nos. 666-671 (6)   11.80 9.05

World Wildlife Fund. Nos. 670-671 are airmail and do not have the WWF emblem. Nos. 670-671 are airmail.

Souvenir Sheet

Discovery of America, 500th Anniv. — A196

Designs: a, 250c, Alhambra, Granada, Spain. b, 500c, Carthusian Monastery, Seville, Spain.

1992, Apr. 1   Litho.   *Perf. 14x13*
672   A196 Sheet of 2, #a.-b.   11.50 9.00
#672a, Granada '92. #672b, Expo '92, Seville.

Discovery of America, 500th Anniv. — A197

250c, Sailing ship. 500c, Map, Columbus.

1992, May 13   Litho.   *Perf. 14x13*
673   A197 250c multicolored   3.25 2.60
674   A197 500c multicolored   6.50 5.25

World Columbian Stamp Expo '92, Chicago.

Container Terminal, Curaçao — A198

1992, June 26
675   A198 80c multi   1.15   .90
676   A198 125c multi, diff.   1.60 1.35

Famous People — A199

Designs: 30c, Angela Altagracia de Lannoy-Willems (1913-1983), politician and social activist. 40c, Lodewijk Daniel Gerharts (1901-1983), politician and promoter of tourism for Bonaire. 55c, Cyrus Wilberforce Wathey (1901-1969), businessman and philanthropist. 70c, Christiaan Winkel (1899-1962), deputy governor of Netherlands Antilles. 100c, Franciscan Nuns of Roosendaal, educational and charitable group, 150th anniversary of arrival in Curaçao.

1992, Sept. 1   Litho.   *Perf. 13x14*
677   A199 30c grn & blk, *tan*   .45   .40
678   A199 40c blue & blk, *tan*   .60   .45
679   A199 55c yel org & blk, *tan*   .75   .60
680   A199 70c lake & blk, *tan*   .85   .70
681   A199 100c blue & blk, *tan*   1.15 1.15
       Nos. 677-681 (5)   3.80 3.30

Queen Beatrix's 1992 Visit — A200

Designs: 70c, Queen in white hat, Prince Claus. 100c, Queen signing jubilee register. 175c, Queen in black hat, Prince Claus, native girl.

1992, Nov. 9   Litho.   *Perf. 14x13*
682   A200 70c multicolored   .95   .80
683   A200 100c multicolored   1.30 1.15
684   A200 175c multicolored   2.10 1.90
       Nos. 682-684 (3)   4.35 3.85

Queen Beatrix's accession to the throne, 12½ year anniv. (#683).

Christmas — A201

30c, Nativity scene. 100c, Mary, Joseph, vert.

Perf. 14x13½, 13½x14
1992, Dec. 1   Litho.
685   A201 30c multi   .55   .40
686   A201 100c multi   1.45 1.05

No. 686 printed with se-tenant label.

Flowers — A202

75c, Hibiscus. 90c, Helianthus annuus. 175c, Ixora. 195c, Rosea.

1993, Feb. 3   Litho.   *Perf. 13x14*
687   A202 75c multi   1.05   .75
688   A202 90c multi   1.25 1.00
689   A202 175c multi   2.10 1.75
690   A202 195c multi   2.40 2.10
       Nos. 687-690 (4)   6.80 5.60

Anniversaries
A203

Map of islands and: 65c, Airplane, air routes. 75c, Natl. Laboratory, scientist using microscope. 90c, Airplane at Princess Juliana Intl. Airport. 175c, Yellow and white crosses.

1993, Mar. 9   **Perf. 14x13**
691 A203 65c multicolored .85 .65
692 A203 75c multicolored .95 .70
693 A203 90c multicolored 1.15 .95
694 A203 175c multicolored 2.00 1.75
Nos. 691-694 (4) 4.95 4.05

Princess Juliana Intl. Airport, 50th anniv. (#691, 693). Natl. Laboratory, 75th anniv. (#692). Princess Margaret White/Yellow Cross Foundation for District Nursing, 50th anniv. (#694).

Dogs — A204

1993, May 26   **Litho.**   **Perf. 13x14**
695 A204 65c Pekingese .85 .70
696 A204 90c Poodle 1.15 1.00
697 A204 100c Pomeranian 1.40 1.10
698 A204 175c Papillon 2.10 1.75
Nos. 695-698 (4) 5.50 4.55

Entry of
Netherlands Antilles
into UPAEP — A205

Designs: 150c, Indian cave painting, Bonaire. 200c, Emblem of Brasiliana '93, flag of Netherlands Antilles. 250c, Map of Central and South America, Netherlands Antilles, Spain, and Portugal, document being signed.

1993, July 15   **Litho.**   **Perf. 14x13**
699 A205 150c multicolored 2.60 1.60
700 A205 200c multicolored 3.00 2.10
701 A205 250c multicolored 3.50 2.60
Nos. 699-701 (3) 9.10 6.30

Brasiliana '93 (#700).

Contemporary
Art — A206

1993, July 23   **Litho.**   **Perf. 13x14**
702 A206 90c silver & multi 1.15 .95
703 A206 150c gold & multi 1.75 1.50

US Consulate
General in
Netherlands
Antilles,
Bicent. — A207

65c, American Consulate. 90c, Coats of Arms. 175c, Eagle in flight.

1993, Nov. 16   **Litho.**   **Perf. 14x13**
704 A207 65c multicolored .80 .70
705 A207 90c multicolored 1.20 1.00
706 A207 175c multicolored 2.00 1.75
Nos. 704-706 (3) 4.00 3.45

Christmas — A208

Designs: 30c, Mosaic of mother and child. 115c, Painting of Mary holding Christ.

1993, Dec. 1   **Perf. 13x14**
707 A208 30c multicolored .55 .35
708 A208 115c multicolored 1.45 1.30

Dogs — A209

1994, Feb. 2   **Litho.**   **Perf. 14x13**
709 A209 65c Basset 1.00 .85
710 A209 75c Pit bull terrier 1.15 .95
711 A209 90c Cocker spaniel 1.35 1.15
712 A209 175c Chow 2.40 2.00
Nos. 709-712 (4) 5.90 4.95

Birds — A210

50c, Polyborus plancus. 95c, Pavo muticus. 100c, Ara macao. 125c, Icterus icterus.

1994, Mar. 2   **Litho.**   **Perf. 13x14**
713 A210 50c multicolored 1.75 .75
714 A210 95c multicolored 1.75 1.35
715 A210 100c multicolored 1.75 1.35
716 A210 125c multicolored 2.25 1.60
Nos. 713-716 (4) 7.50 5.05

A211

Famous People: 65c, Joseph Husurell Lake (1925-76), politician, journalist. 75c, Efrain Jonckheer (1917-87), diplomat. 100c, Michiel Martinus Romer (1865-1937), educator. 175c, Carel Nicolaas Winkel (1882-1973), public official, social worker.

1994, Apr. 8
717 A211 65c olive & blk, grn .80 .80
718 A211 75c brn & blk, lt brn .95 .95
719 A211 100c grn & blk, bl 1.25 1.25
720 A211 175c brn & blk, tan 2.25 2.25
Nos. 717-720 (4) 5.25 5.25

A212

1994 World Cup Soccer Championships, US: 90c, Socks, soccer shoes, horiz. 150c, Shoe, ball. 175c, Whistle, horiz.

Perf. 14x13, 13x14
1994, May 4   **Litho.**
721 A212 90c multicolored 1.20 1.05
722 A212 150c multicolored 1.90 1.75
723 A212 175c multicolored 2.10 2.00
Nos. 721-723 (3) 5.20 4.80

A213

ILO, 75th Anniv.: 90c, Declaration, chair, gavel. 110c, "75" over heart. 200c, Wind-blown tree.

1994, June 1   **Litho.**   **Perf. 13x14**
724 A213 90c multicolored 1.20 1.10
725 A213 110c multicolored 1.35 1.25
726 A213 200c multicolored 2.60 2.50
Nos. 724-726 (3) 5.15 4.85

Wildlife — A214

Designs: 10c, Ware-wara, blenchi, parakeet, dolphin. 35c, Dolphin, pelican, troupial. 50c, Iguana, fish, lobster, sea hedgehog. 125c, Sea hedgehog, sea apple, fish, turtle, flamingos, ducks.

1994, Aug. 4   **Litho.**   **Perf. 14x13**
727 A214 10c multicolored .75 .40
728 A214 35c multicolored .75 .55
729 A214 50c multicolored .80 .75
730 A214 125c multicolored 1.75 1.75
a. Souvenir sheet #727-730 5.00 4.50
Nos. 727-730 (4) 4.05 3.45

PHILAKOREA '94 (#730a).

FEPAPOST
'94 — A215

2.50g, Netherlands #277. 5g, #109.

1994, Oct. 5   **Litho.**   **Perf. 14x13**
731 A215 2.50g multicolored 3.00 3.25
732 A215 5g multicolored 6.00 6.25
a. Souv. sheet of 2, #731-732, perf. 13½x13 10.00 8.25

Christmas — A216

115c, Hands holding earth.

1994, Dec. 1   **Litho.**   **Perf. 14x13**
733 A216 30c shown .85 .45
734 A216 115c multicolored 1.75 1.45

Curaçao
Carnivals — A217

Carnival scene and: 125c, Buildings, Willemstad. 175c, Floating market. 250c, House with thatched roof.

1995, Jan. 19   **Litho.**   **Perf. 14x13**
735 A217 125c multicolored 1.60 1.45
736 A217 175c multicolored 2.25 1.90
737 A217 250c multicolored 3.00 2.60
Nos. 735-737 (3) 6.85 5.95

Mgr. Verriet Institute for
Physically Handicapped,
50th Anniv. — A218

Design: 90c, Cedric Virginie, handicapped worker at Public Library.

1995, Feb. 2   **Litho.**   **Perf. 13x14**
738 A218 65c multicolored .80 .75
739 A218 90c multicolored 1.15 1.05

Dogs — A219

1995, Mar. 29   **Litho.**   **Perf. 14x13**
740 A219 75c Doberman 1.20 1.00
741 A219 85c Shepherd 1.45 1.20
742 A219 100c Bouvier 1.60 1.30
743 A219 175c St. Bernard 2.60 2.10
Nos. 740-743 (4) 6.85 5.60

Flags, Coats of
Arms of Island
Territories — A220

10c, Bonaire. 35c, Curaçao. 50c, St. Maarten. 65c, Saba. 75c, St. Eustatius, natl. flag, coat of arms. 90c, Flags of territories, natl. coat of arms.

1995, June 30   **Litho.**   **Perf. 14x13**
744 A220 10c multicolored .25 .30
745 A220 35c multicolored .60 .45
746 A220 50c multicolored .75 .60
a. St. Maarten flag colors reversed 60.00 —
747 A220 65c multicolored .90 .80
748 A220 75c multicolored 1.05 .85
749 A220 90c multicolored 1.20 1.15
a. St. Maarten flag colors reversed 60.00 —
Nos. 744-749 (6) 4.75 4.15

Nos. 746a and 749a show the colors of the St. Maarten flag reversed: blue on top, red on bottom. Both were quickly withdrawn from sale after the error was discovered. Used examples exist.

Domestic Cats — A221

Designs: 25c, Siamese sealpoint. 60c, Maine coon. 65c, Egyptian silver mau. 90c, Angora. 150c, Persian blue smoke.

1995, Sept. 29   **Litho.**   **Perf. 13x14**
750 A221 25c multicolored .70 .35
751 A221 60c multicolored 1.05 .70
752 A221 65c multicolored 1.15 .80
753 A221 90c multicolored 1.40 1.15
754 A221 150c multicolored 2.10 1.75
Nos. 750-754 (5) 6.40 4.75

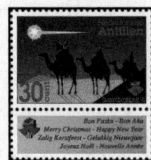

Christmas and New
Year — A222

Designs: 30c, Three Magi following star. 115c, Fireworks above houses, Handelskade.

1995, Dec. 1   **Litho.**   **Perf. 13½x13**
755 A222 30c multicolored .60 .40
756 A222 115c multicolored 1.60 1.30

Nos. 755-756 each printed with se-tenant label.

A223

Curaçao Lions Club, 50th Anniv.: 75c, List of services to community. 105c, Seal. 250c, Hands clasp.

1996, Feb. 26   **Litho.**   **Perf. 13x14**
757 A223 75c multicolored 1.20 .80
758 A223 105c multicolored 1.45 1.20
759 A223 250c multicolored 3.25 3.00
Nos. 757-759 (3) 5.90 5.00

A224

1996, Apr. 12   **Litho.**   **Perf. 13x14**
760 A224 85c shown .80 .65
761 A224 175c Telegraph key 1.20 .80
Radio, cent.

A225

1996, Apr. 12
762 A225 60c shown   1.15 1.05
763 A225 75c Tornado, sun   2.10 1.90

Dr. David Ricardo Capriles Clinic, 60th anniv.

A226

1996, May 8   Litho.   Perf. 13x14
764 A226 85c shown   1.15 1.15
765 A226 225c Bible   3.00 2.60

Translation of the Bible into Papiamentu.
Nos. 764-765 exist imperf. Value, set $90.

CAPEX '96 — A227

Butterflies: 5c, Agraulis vanillae. 110c, Callithea philotima. 300c, Parthenos sylvia. 750c, Euphaedra francina.

1996, June 5   Litho.   Perf. 14x13
766 A227   5c multicolored   .90   .25
767 A227 110c multicolored   1.75 1.30
768 A227 300c multicolored   4.50 3.50
  a.   Souvenir sheet of 2, #767-
       768   7.50 5.75
769 A227 750c multicolored   10.50 8.50
       Nos. 766-769 (4)   17.65 13.55

Nos. 766-769 exist imperf. Value, set $120.
No. 768a exists imperf. Value, $110.

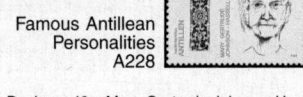

Famous Antillean
Personalities
A228

Designs: 40c, Mary Gertrude Johnson Hassel (1853-1939), introduced drawn thread (Spanish work) to Saba. 50c, Cornelis Marten (Papa Cornes) (1749-1852), spiritual care giver on Bonaire. 75c, Phelippi Benito Chakutoe (1891-1967), union leader. 85c, Christiaan Josef Hendrikus Engels (1907-80), physician, painter, pianist, poet.

1996, Aug. 21   Litho.   Perf. 14x13
770 A228 40c orange & black   .65   .50
771 A228 50c green & black   .70   .55
772 A228 75c brown & black   1.05   .80
773 A228 85c blue & black   1.10 1.05
       Nos. 770-773 (4)   3.50 2.90

Horses — A229

1996, Sept. 26   Litho.   Perf. 14x13
774 A229 110c Shire   1.60 1.25
775 A229 225c Shetland pony   3.25 2.50
776 A229 275c Thoroughbred   3.50 3.25
777 A229 350c Przewalski   4.75 4.00
       Nos. 774-777 (4)   13.10 11.00

Christmas — A230

35c, Money bag, straw hat, candy cane, gifts, poinsettias, star. 150c, Santa Claus.

Serpentine Die Cut 13x13½
1996, Dec. 2   Litho.
Self-Adhesive
778 A230 35c multicolored   .80   .40
779 A230 150c multicolored   2.00 1.60

Mushrooms
A231

40c, Galerina autumnalis. 50c, Amanita virosa. 75c, Boletus edulis. 175c, Amanita muscaria.

1997, Feb. 19   Litho.   Perf. 14x13
780 A231 40c multicolored   1.00   .55
781 A231 50c multicolored   1.20   .65
782 A231 75c multicolored   1.75   .90
783 A231 175c multicolored   3.00 2.25
       Nos. 780-783 (4)   6.95 4.35

Birds — A232

5c, Melopsittacus undulatus. 25c, Cacatua leadbeateri leadbeateri. 50c, Amazona barbadensis. 75c, Ardea purperea. 85c, Chrysolampis mosquitus. 100c, Balearica pavonina. 110c, Pyrocephalus rubinus. 125c, Phoenicopterus ruber. 200c, Pandion haliaetus. 225c, Ramphastos sulfuratus.

1997, Mar. 26   Litho.   Perf. 13x14
784 A232   5c multicolored   1.10   .35
785 A232 25c multicolored   1.35   .35
786 A232 50c multicolored   1.60   .60
787 A232 75c multicolored   2.00   .80
788 A232 85c multicolored   2.10 1.00
789 A232 100c multicolored   2.40 1.20
790 A232 110c multicolored   2.40 1.20
791 A232 125c multicolored   2.50 1.45
792 A232 200c multicolored   3.50 2.25
793 A232 225c multicolored   4.00 2.60
       Nos. 784-793 (10)   22.95 11.80

Greetings
Stamps — A233

No. 799A, like #794. No. 799B, Correspondence in 3 languages. No. 799C, Positivism, flower, sun. 799D, like #795. No. 799E, Success, rising sun. 85c, like #796. 100c, like #797. #799H, like #798. No. 799I, Love, silhouette of couple. 225c, like #799.

1997, Apr. 16
794 A233 40c Love   .55   .50
795 A233 75c Positivism   .90   .80
796 A233 85c Mother's Day   1.05 1.05
797 A233 100c Correspondence   1.15 1.15
798 A233 110c Success   1.30 1.30
799 A233 225c Congratulations   2.60 2.60
       Nos. 794-799 (6)   7.55 7.40
Booklet Stamps
Size: 21x25mm
Perf. 13x14 on 3 Sides
799A A233 40c multicolored   .75   .75
799B A233 40c multicolored   .75   .75
799C A233 75c multicolored   1.15 1.15
799D A233 75c multicolored   1.15 1.15
799E A233 75c multicolored   1.15 1.15
799F A233 85c multicolored   1.15 1.15
799G A233 100c multicolored   1.60 1.60
799H A233 110c multicolored   1.60 1.60
799I A233 110c multicolored   1.60 1.60
799J A233 225c multicolored   3.00 3.00
  k.   Booklet pane of 10, #799A-
       799J + label   13.50
       Complete booklet, #799k   11.75

Stamps arranged in booklet out of Scott order.

Signs of the
Chinese
Calendar — A234

Stylized designs.

1997, May 19   Litho.   Perf. 14x13
800 A234   5c Rat   .25   .25
801 A234   5c Ox   .25   .25
802 A234   5c Tiger   .25   .25
803 A234 40c Rabbit   .65   .45
804 A234 40c Dragon   .65   .45
805 A234 40c Snake   .65   .45
806 A234 75c Horse   1.05   .75
807 A234 75c Goat   1.05   .75
808 A234 75c Monkey   1.05   .75
809 A234 100c Rooster   1.25 1.05
810 A234 100c Dog   1.25 1.05
811 A234 100c Pig   1.25 1.05
  a.   Souvenir sheet of 12, #800-811 10.25 9.75
       Nos. 800-811 (12)   9.60 7.50

No. 811a for PACIFIC 97. Issued: 5/19/97.

Coins — A235

85c, Plaka, 2½ cent. 175c, Stuiver, 5 cent. 225c, Fuèrtè, 2½ gulden.

1997, Aug. 6   Perf. 13x14
812 A235 85c multi   1.15 1.00
813 A235 175c multi   2.25 1.90
814 A235 225c multi   3.00 2.50
       Nos. 812-814 (3)   6.40 5.40

A236

Shanghai '97, Intl.
Stamp
Exhibition — A237

15c, Nampu Grand Bridge, Shanghai. 40c, Giant panda, horiz. 75c, Tiger, New Year 1998.
90c, Buildings in downtown Shanghai.

Perf. 14x13, 13x14
1997, Nov. 19   Litho.
815 A236 15c multicolored   .85   .45
816 A237 40c multicolored   1.30   .90
817 A237 75c multicolored   1.75 1.35
       Nos. 815-817 (3)   3.90 2.70
Souvenir Sheet
818 A236 90c multicolored   3.00 2.75

No. 818 exists imperf. Value, $100.

A238

Christmas and New Year: 35c, Left panel of triptych from Roman Catholic Church, Willemstad. 150c, Champagne bottle being opened, calendar.

1997, Dec. 1   Perf. 13x14
819 A238 35c multicolored   .80   .40
820 A238 150c multicolored   2.00 1.60

A239

Total Solar Eclipse, Curacao: 85c, Sun partially covered by moon's shadow. 110c, Outer edge of sun showing beyond moon's shadow. 225c, Total solar eclipse.
750c, Hologram of the eclipse.

1998, Feb. 26   Litho.   Perf. 13x14
821 A239 85c multicolored   1.45 1.20
822 A239 110c multicolored   2.00 1.40
823 A239 225c multicolored   3.50 3.00
       Nos. 821-823 (3)   6.95 5.60
Souvenir Sheet
824 A239 750c multicolored   12.50 11.50

No. 824 contains a hologram which may be damaged by soaking.

ISRAEL '98 World
Stamp
Exhibition — A240

Designs: 40c, Dead Sea. 75c, Zion Gate, Jerusalem. 110c, Masada.
225c, Mikvé Israel-Emanuel Synagogue, Curacao.

1998, Apr. 29   Litho.   Perf. 13x14
825 A240 40c multicolored   .90   .70
826 A240 75c multicolored   1.10   .95
827 A240 110c multicolored   1.60 1.45
       Nos. 825-827 (3)   3.60 3.10
Souvenir Sheet
828 A240 225c multicolored   3.75 3.50

Elias Moreno
Brandao & Sons,
Car Dealership,
75th Anniv. — A241

Chevrolet automobiles: 40c, 1923 Superior, Elias Moreno Brandao. 55c, 1934 Roadster. 75c, 1949 Styleline Deluxe. 110c, 1957 Bel Air Convertible. 225c, 1963 Corvette "Stingray." 500c, 1970 Chevelle SS-454.

1998, May 4   Perf. 14x13
829 A241 40c multicolored   1.20   .55
830 A241 55c multicolored   1.30   .90
831 A241 75c multicolored   1.60   .90
832 A241 110c multicolored   2.10 1.35
833 A241 225c multicolored   3.50 3.00
834 A241 500c multicolored   8.00 6.50
       Nos. 829-834 (6)   17.70 13.20

A242

Advisory Council, 50th Anniv.: 75c, Natl. flag, natl. arms. 85c, Gavel, stars, natl. arms.

1998, June 1   Litho.   Perf. 13x14
835 A242 75c multicolored   1.05   .85
836 A242 85c multicolored   1.20 1.05

A243

Famous People: 40c, Christina Elizabeth Flanders (1908-96). 75c, Abraham Jesurun Dz. (1839-1918). 85c, Gerrit Simeon Newton (1884-1949). 110c, Eduardo Adriana (1925-97).

1998, June 24   Perf. 13
837 A243 40c multicolored   .60   .55
838 A243 75c multicolored   1.05   .90
839 A243 85c multicolored   1.15 1.05
840 A243 110c multicolored   1.60 1.35
       Nos. 837-840 (4)   4.40 3.85

Mailboxes — A244

1998, July 29   Litho.   Perf. 13x14
841 A244 15c Ireland   .35   .30
842 A244 40c Nepal   .70   .55
843 A244 75c Uruguay   1.15   .90
844 A244 85c Curacao   1.20 1.20
       Nos. 841-844 (4)   3.40 2.95

See Nos. 932-935.

A245

Privatization of Natl. Postal Service: 75c, Globe, map of North and South America, horiz. 110c, Numbers and tree on screen. 225c, #207 and #846, horiz.

1998, Aug. 5   *Perf. 13*
845 A245 75c multicolored   1.05   .90
846 A245 110c multicolored   1.60 1.35
847 A245 225c multicolored   3.00 3.00
     Nos. 845-847 (3)   5.65 5.25

A246

Endangered Species: 5c, Black rhinoceros, horiz. 75c, White-tailed hawk. 125c, White-tailed deer, horiz. 250c, Tiger.

1998, Aug. 26   *Perf. 13½*
848 A246   5c multicolored   1.20   .85
849 A246   75c multicolored   1.60 1.30
850 A246 125c multicolored   2.40 1.75
851 A246 250c multicolored   3.75 3.00
     Nos. 848-851 (4)   8.95 6.90

Intl. Year of the Ocean — A247

1998, Sept. 30   *Litho.*   *Perf. 13*
852 A247 275c Mako shark   5.25 3.50
853 A247 350c Manta ray   6.25 4.25

1998 Philatelic Exhibition, The Hague, Netherlands A248

1998, Oct. 8   *Perf. 14x13*
854 A248 225c No. 213   3.00 3.00
855 A248 500c No. 218   5.75 5.75
    Souvenir Sheet
856 A248 500c Nos. 61, 218   6.75 6.50

Price Waterhouse Coopers in Netherlands Antilles, 60th Anniv. — A249

Emblems, company buildings in Julianaplein, minerals: 75c, Lapis lazuli. 225c, Pyrite.

1998, Nov. 13   *Perf. 13½*
857   75c multicolored   1.60 1.60
858   225c multicolored   3.00 2.25
  a. A249 Pair, #857-858   4.50 3.75

Christmas — A250

Children's drawings: 35c, Christmas tree, vert. 150c, Mail box at Christmas.

Perf. 13x14, 14x13
1998, Dec. 1   *Litho.*
859 A250 35c multicolored   .65 .65
860 A250 150c multicolored   2.10 1.90

Avila Beach Hotel, 50th Anniv. — A251

Designs: 75c, Exterior view of hotel, Dr. Pieter Hendrik Maal. 110c, Beach, delonix regia. 225c, Mesquite tree, porposis juliflora.

1999, Feb. 3   *Litho.*   *Perf. 14x13*
861 A251 75c multicolored   1.10   .90
862 A251 110c multicolored   1.60 1.35
863 A251 225c multicolored   3.00 2.75
     Nos. 861-863 (3)   5.70 5.00

A252

Designs: 75c, Rabbit, Great Wall of China. No. 865, Rabbit, Jade Pagoda, Beijing, vert. No. 866, Rabbit, landscape, vert.

Perf. 14x13, 13x14
1999, Mar. 30   *Litho.*
864 A252 75c multicolored   1.60   .90
865 A252 225c multicolored   3.75 2.60
    Souvenir Sheet
     Perf. 13x13½
866 A252 225c multicolored   4.50 3.50

New Year 1999 (Year of the Rabbit) and China '99, World Stamp Exhibition, Beijing.

Government Correctional Institute (GOG) for Youth, 50th Anniv. — A253

Design, traditional musical instrument: 40c, Couple dancing, wiri. 75c, Building, bamba. 85c, Man using file and vise, triangle.

Perf. 13x14, 14x13
1999, Apr. 28   *Litho.*
867 A253 40c multi, vert.   .75 .55
868 A253 75c multi, vert.   1.20 .90
869 A253 85c multi   1.35 1.10
     Nos. 867-869 (3)   3.30 2.55

Recorded History of Curacao, 500th Anniv — A254

Curacao 500 emblem and: 75c, Ship launching. 110c, Houses on Rifwater, Otrobanda, Pasa Kontrami Bridge. 175c, #870-871. 225c, Fort Beeckenburg. 500c, #204, sailing ship.

1999, May 19   *Perf. 14x13*
870 A254 75c multicolored   1.35 .85
871 A254 110c multicolored   1.75 1.30
872 A254 175c multicolored   2.60 2.10
873 A254 225c multicolored   3.25 2.60
874 A254 500c multicolored   6.50 6.00
     Nos. 870-874 (5)   15.45 12.85

Nos. 870-874 exist imperf. Value, $120.

Wilson "Papa" Godett (1932-95), Politician — A255

1999, May 28   *Perf. 13x14*
875 A255 75c multicolored   1.25 1.00

No. 875 exists imperf. Value, $57.50.

Millennium A256

Designs: 5c, Indians, map. 10c, Indian, ship, armored horseman. 40c, Flags of islands, Autonomy monument, Curacao, autonomy document. 75c, Telephone, #5. 85c, Airplane. 100c, Oil refinery. 110c, Satellite dish, underwater cable. 125c, Tourist ship, bridge. 225c, Island residents, music box. 350c, Birds, cacti.

1999, Aug. 4   *Litho.*   *Perf. 13½*
876 A256 5c multicolored   .45 .45
877 A256 10c multicolored   .45 .45
878 A256 40c multicolored   .90 .75
879 A256 75c multicolored   1.35 1.15
880 A256 85c multicolored   1.35 1.35
881 A256 100c multicolored   1.35 1.35
882 A256 110c multicolored   1.75 1.60
883 A256 125c multicolored   2.25 2.00
884 A256 225c multicolored   3.25 3.25
885 A256 350c multicolored   5.00 5.00
    Size: 31x31mm
    Self-Adhesive
    Serpentine Die Cut 8
886 A256 5c multicolored   .45 .45
887 A256 10c multicolored   .45 .45
888 A256 40c multicolored   .90 .75
889 A256 75c multicolored   1.35 1.15
890 A256 85c multicolored   1.35 1.35
891 A256 100c multicolored   1.35 1.35
892 A256 110c multicolored   1.75 1.60
893 A256 125c multicolored   2.25 2.00
894 A256 225c multicolored   3.25 3.25
895 A256 350c multicolored   5.00 5.00
     Nos. 876-895 (20)   36.20 34.70

A257

Designs: 150c, Church of the Conversion of St. Paul, Saba. 250c, Flamingo, Bonaire. 500c, Courthouse of Philipsburg, St. Martin.

1999, Oct. 1   *Litho.*   *Perf. 14x13*
896 A257 150c multicolored   3.00 1.60
897 A257 250c multicolored   3.75 2.75
898 A257 500c multicolored   6.50 5.50
     Nos. 896-898 (3)   13.25 9.85

Flowers A258

Designs: No. 899, Allamanda. No. 900, Bougainvillea. No. 901, Gardenia jasminoides. No. 902, Saintpaulia ionantha. No. 903, Cymbidium. No. 904, Strelitzia. No. 905, Cassia fistula. No. 906, Phalaenopsis. No. 907, Doritaenopsis. No. 908, Guzmania. No. 909, Caralluma hexagona. No. 910, Catharanthus roseus.

1999, Nov. 15   *Perf. 13½*
899 A258 40c multicolored   1.10 1.00
900 A258 40c multicolored   1.10 1.00
  a. Pair, #899-900   2.25 2.25
901 A258 40c multicolored   1.10 1.00
902 A258 40c multicolored   1.10 1.00
  a. Pair, #901-902   2.25 2.25
903 A258 75c multicolored   1.25 1.10
904 A258 75c multicolored   1.25 1.10
  a. Pair, #903-904   2.50 2.50
905 A258 75c multicolored   1.25 1.10
906 A258 75c multicolored   1.25 1.10
  a. Pair, #905-906   2.75 2.75
907 A258 110c multicolored   2.00 1.75
908 A258 110c multicolored   2.00 1.75
  a. Pair, #907-908   4.00 4.00
909 A258 225c multicolored   3.25 3.00
910 A258 225c multicolored   3.25 3.00
  a. Pair, #909-910   6.50 6.50
     Nos. 899-910 (12)   19.90 17.90

Christmas A259   Year 2000 A260

1999, Dec. 1   *Litho.*   *Perf. 13x14*
911 A259 35c multi   .90 .40
912 A260 150c multi   2.25 1.60

Greetings Stamps — A261

#913, 40c, #918, 150c, Hearts, roses. #914, 40c, #919, 150c, Mothers, globe. #915, 40c, Father, baby, blocks. #916, 75c, Dog in gift box. #917, 110c, Butterfly, flowers in vase. #920, 225c, Hands, rings.

2000, Jan. 27   *Litho.*   *Perf. 13x14*
913-920 A261   Set of 8   12.50 11.50

New Year 2000 (Year of the Dragon) — A262

2000, Feb. 28   *Perf. 14x13*
921 A262 110c shown   2.00 1.90
    Souvenir Sheet
922 A262 225c Two dragons   4.50 3.25

Fauna — A263

Designs: 40c, Red eye tree toad. 75c, King penguin, vert. 85c, Killer whale, vert. 100c, African elephant, vert. 110c, Chimpanzee, vert. 225c, Indian tiger.

2000, Mar. 29   *Perf. 14x13, 13x14*
923-928 A263   Set of 6   14.00 11.50

Space — A264

Designs: 75c, Space Shuttle. No. 930, 225c, Astronaut, flag, space station.

2000, June 21   *Litho.*   *Perf. 13x14*
929-930 A264   Set of 2   5.00 4.50
    Souvenir Sheet
     Perf. 13x13¼
931 A264 225c Colonized planet   4.50 4.50

World Stamp Expo 2000, Anaheim.

Mailbox Type of 1998

Mailboxes from: 110c, Mexico. 175c, Dubai. 350c, England. 500c, United States.

2000, Aug. 8   *Perf. 13x14*
932-935 A244   Set of 4   16.50 14.00

Nos. 932-935 exist imperf. Value, set $120.

2000 Summer Olympics, Sydney — A265

75c, Cycling. No. 937, 225c, Running.

2000, Aug. 8   *Litho.*   *Perf. 13x14*
936-937 A265   Set of 2   5.25 5.00
    Souvenir Sheet
938 A265 225c Swimming   4.50 4.50
Nos. 936-938 exist imperf. Value, set $200.

Social Insurance Bank, 40th Anniv. — A266

Designs: 75c, People, islands, vert. 110c, Hands. 225c, Emblem, vert.

2000, Sept. 1   *Perf. 13x14, 14x13*
939-941 A266   Set of 3   6.25 5.75

Christmas — A267

Songs: 40c, Jingle Bells, vert. 150c, We Wish You a Merry Christmas.

2000, Nov. 15   *Perf. 13x14, 14x13*
942-943 A267   Set of 2   3.25 3.25

New Year 2001 (Year of the Snake) — A268

Designs: 110c, Red milk snake. 225c, Indian cobra, vert.

2001, Jan. 17   Litho.   Perf. 14x13
944 A268 110c multi   2.40 1.90

Souvenir Sheet
Perf. 13x14
945 A268 225c multi   4.50 4.50

Hong Kong 2001 Stamp Exhibition — A269

Designs: 25c, Birds in forest. 40c, Palm trees and waterfall. 110c, Spinner dolphins.

2001, Feb. 1   Perf. 13x14
946-948 A269   Set of 3   4.25 3.75

Cats and Dogs — A270

Designs: 55c, Persian shaded golden. 75c, Burmese bluepoint. 110c, Beagle and American wirehair. 175c, Golden retriever. 225c, German shepherd. 750c, British shorthair black-silver marble.

2001, Mar. 7   Litho.   Perf. 13x14
949-954 A270   Set of 6   24.00 20.00

Ships — A271

Designs: 110c, Z. M. Mars. 275c, Z. M. Alphen. 350c, Z. M. Curaçao, horiz. 500c, Schooner Pioneer, horiz.

2001, Apr. 26   Perf. 13x14, 14x13
955-958 A271   Set of 4   19.00 17.50

Fedjai the Postal Worker — A272

Fedjai: 5c, On bicycle. 40c, With children. 75c, Looking at nest in mailbox. 85c, Talking with woman. 100c, Chased atop mailbox by dog. 110c, Looking at boy's stamp album.

2001, June 5   Perf. 13x14
959-964 A272   Set of 6   8.75 7.50

See No. 1012.

Cave Bats — A273

Designs: 85c, Map of bat species in Kueba Bosá. 110c, Leptonycteris nivalis curasaoe. 225c, Glosophaga elongata.

2001, Aug. 20   Litho.   Perf. 14x13
965-967 A273   Set of 3   7.50 6.25

Birds A274

No. 968: a, 10c, Trochilus polytmus. b, 85c, Pelecanus onocrotalus. c, 110c, Erythrura gouldiae. d, 175c, Passerina ciris. e, 250c, Fratercula arctica. f, 375c, Anhinga anhinga.

2001, Sept. 28   Perf. 12¾x13½
968 A274   Block of 6, #a-f   17.50 16.50

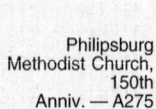

Philipsburg Methodist Church, 150th Anniv. — A275

Map of St. Maarten and: 75c, Church building. 110c, Bibles.

2001, Oct. 19   Perf. 14x13
969-970 A275   Set of 2   3.50 3.25

Christmas and New Year's Day — A276

Designs: 40c, Clock, people from 8 countries. 150c, Dove, poinsettias, baby Jesus, and people from 4 countries, vert.

2001, Nov. 15   Litho.
Perf. 13½x12¾, 12¾x13½
971-972 A276   Set of 2   3.50 3.00

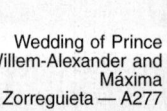

Wedding of Prince Willem-Alexander and Máxima Zorreguieta — A277

Designs: 75c, Prince. 110c, Máxima. No. 975: a, 2.25f, Prince. b, 2.75f, Máxima.

2002, Feb. 2   Litho.   Perf. 12¾x14
973-974 A277   Set of 2   3.25 3.00

Souvenir Sheet
Perf. 12¾x13½
975 A277   Sheet of 2, #a-b   8.75 7.50

New Year 2002 (Year of the Horse) — A278

Designs: 25c, Horse rearing. 95c, Horse's head.

2002, Mar. 1   Perf. 12¾x14
976 A278 25c multi   1.25 1.25

Souvenir Sheet
Perf. 12¾x13½
977 A278 95c multi   3.00 2.50

Flora & Fauna — A279

Designs: 50c, Chlorostilbon mellisugus and Passiflora foetida, vert. 95c, Anolis lineatus and Cordia sebestena. 120c, Odonata. 145c, Coenobita clypeatus. 285c, Polistes versicolor, vert.

Perf. 12¾x13½, 13½x12¾
2002, Mar. 27   Litho.
978-982 A279   Set of 5   11.00 10.00

Butterflies — A280

Designs: 25c, Dryas iulia, vert. 145c, Danaus plexippus. 400c, Mechanitis polymnia. 500c, Pyrhapygopsis socrates.

Perf. 12¾x13½, 13½x12¾
2002, May 22   Litho.
983-986 A280   Set of 4   17.50 16.50

Fedjai the Postal Worker Type of 2001

Fedjai: 10c, Jumping rope with children, horiz. 55c, Scolding dog. 95c, Delivering letter to child. 240c, Helping elderly lady across street.

Perf. 13¾x12¾, 12¾x13¾
2002, July 31
987-990 A272   Set of 4   8.25 8.25

Amphilex 2002 Intl. Stamp Exhibition, Amsterdam — A281

Details from the 1885 version of "The Potato Eaters," by Vincent Van Gogh: 70c, 95c, 145c, 240c. 550c, Entire painting, horiz.

Perf. 12¾x13½
2002, Aug. 26   Litho.
991-994 A281   Set of 4   8.75 8.75

Souvenir Sheet
Perf. 14x12¾
995 A281 550c multi   8.75 8.75

Orchids — A282

Designs: 95c, Wingfieldara casseta. 285c, Cymbidium Magna Charta. 380c, Brassolaeliocattleya. 750c, Miltonia spectabilis.

2002, Sept. 27   Perf. 12¾x14
996-999 A282   Set of 4   22.50 21.00

Christmas and New Year — A283

Designs: 95c, Christmas tree decorations. 240c, Lanterns.

2002, Nov. 15   Perf. 14x12¾
1000-1001 A283   Set of 2   5.00 4.75

Birds A284

No. 1002: a, 5c, Buteogallus meridionalis. b, 20c, Capito niger. c, 30c, Ara macao. d, 35c, Jacamerops aurea. e, 70c, Florisuga mellivora. f, 85c, Haematoderus militaris. g, 90c, Aratinga aurea. h, 95c, Psarocolius viridis. i, 100c, Sturnella magna, horiz. j, 145c, Aratinga

solstitialis, horiz. k, 240c, Trogon viridis. l, 285c, Rhamphastos tucanus.

2002, Dec. 11   Litho.   Perf. 13x14
1002 A284   Block of 12, #a-l   20.00 20.00

New Year 2003 (Year of the Ram) — A285

Chinese character and: 25c, Ram's head. 95c, Ram.

2003, Feb. 3
1003 A285 25c multi   1.25 1.25

Souvenir Sheet
1004 A285 95c multi   2.40 1.90

Butterflies — A286

No. 1005: a, 5c, Rhetus arcius, vert. b, 10c, Evenus teresina. c, 25c, Bhutanitis thaidina. d, 30c, Semomesia capanea. e, 45c, Papilio machaon. f, 55c, Papilio multicaudata, vert. g, 65c, Graphium weiskei, vert. h, 95c, Ancyluris formosissima venabalis, vert. i, 100c, Euphaedra neophron. j, 145c, Ornithoptera goliath samson. k, 275c, Ancyluris colubra, vert. l, 350c, Papilio lorquinianus, vert.

Perf. 12¾x14 (vert. stamps), 14x12¾
2003, Apr. 23   Litho.
1005 A286   Block of 12, #a-l   21.00 20.00

Printed in sheets of 2 blocks separated by a central gutter.

Miniature Sheet

Musical Instruments — A287

No. 1006: a, 20c, Trumpet. b, 75c, Percussion instruments. c, 145c, Tenor saxophone. d, 285c, Double bass.

2003, May 28   Perf. 12¾x14
1006 A287   Sheet of 4, #a-d   7.50 7.50

Johann Enschedé and Sons, Printers, 300th Anniv. — A288

No. 1007: a, 70c, 25-florin bank note, 1827. b, 95c, #4. c, 145c, Revenue stamp. d, 240c, Portion of 1967 bank note. 550c, Enschedé headquarters, Netherlands.

2003, June 3
1007 A288   Sheet of 4, #a-d   8.75 8.75

Souvenir Sheet
1008 A288 550c multi   7.50 7.50

Bank of the Netherlands Antilles, 175th Anniv. — A289

Designs: 95c, Portion of 10-guilder banknote with serial number magnified. 145c, Road map, Bank headquarters. 285c, Early bank document, vert.

Perf. 14x12¾, 12¾x14
2003, June 26
1009-1011 A289 Set of 3 7.00 7.00

Fedjai, the Postal Worker Type of 2001
Miniature Sheet

No. 1012: a, 30c, Fedjai giving gift to Angelina. b, 95c, Fedjai and Angelina at wedding. c, 145c, Fedjai taking pregnant wife on bicycle, horiz. d, 240c, Fedjai shows son to co-workers.

Perf. 12¾x14, 14x12¾ (#1012c)
2003, June 31
1012 A272 Sheet of 4, #a-d 7.50 6.25

Ships A290

No. 1013: a, 5c, Egyptian boat, 15th cent. B.C. b, 5c, Ship of King Tutankhamen. c, 35c, Picture from Greek vase depicting Ulysses and the Sirens. d, 35c, Egyptian river boat. e, 40c, Greek dromond. f, 40c, Illustration from 15th cent. edition of Virgil's Aeneid. g, 60c, Javanese fusta. h, 60c, Greek trade ship. i, 75c, Venetian cog, 16th cent. j, 75c, Mora from Bayeux Tapestry. k, 85c, HMS Pembroke, ship of Capt. James Cook, vert. l, 85c, Savannah, first transatlantic steamship, 1819, vert.
Illustration reduced.

Perf. 14x12¾, 12¾x14 (vert. stamps)
2003, Aug. 7
1013 A290 Block of 12, #a-l 10.00 9.00

Miniature Sheets

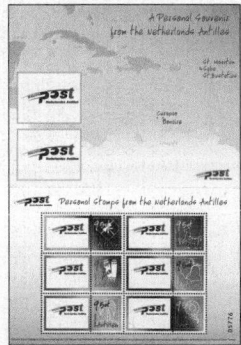

Personalized Stamps — A291

Designs: Nos. 1014a, 1015a, Gift. Nos. 1014b, 1015b, Rocking horse. Nos. 1014c, 1015c, Conga drums. Nos. 1014d, 1015d, Bells. Nos. 1014e, 1015e, Palm tree. Nos. 1014f, 1015f, Flower.

2003, Sept. 17 Litho. Perf. 13¼x14
1014 A291 95c Sheet of 6, #a-f, + 6 labels 10.00 9.00
1015 A291 145c Sheet of 6, #a-f, + 6 labels 15.00 14.00

Labels could be personalized. Nos. 1014-1015 each sold for $6 and $8.50 respectively in US funds.

Cats A292

No. 1016: a, 5c, Bombay. b, 20c, Persian sealpoint. c, 25c, British shorthair blotchy. d, 50c, British blue. e, 65c, Persian chinchilla. f, 75c, Tonkinese red point. g, 85c, Balinese lilac tabbypoint. h, 95c, Persian shaded cameo. i, 100c, Burmilla. j, 145c, Chocolate tortie shaded silver eastern shorthair. k, 150c, Devon Rex silver tabby. l, 285c, Persian black tabby.

2003, Sept. 29 Perf. 12¾x14
1016 A292 Block of 12, #a-l 18.00 17.00

Souvenir Sheet

Christmas and New Year's Day — A293

No. 1017 — Cacti with faces and Christmas lights and: a, 75c, Star. b, 240c, Clock.

2003, Nov. 17 Litho. Perf. 13x14
1017 A293 Sheet of 2, #a-b 3.75 3.75

Airport Code and Local Attraction A294 | Curves and Lines A295

Designs: 50c, BON (Bonaire), slave hut. 75c, CUR (Curaçao), Handelskade, Willemstad. 95c, SAB (Saba), Holy Rosary Roman Catholic Church, Hell's Gate, Anglican Church, Valley. 120c, EUX (St. Eustatius), Simon Docker House, Fort Orange. 145c, SXM (St. Maarten), bird at sunset. 240c, CUR, Queen Emma Bridge. 285c, SXM, Simpson Bay.

2003, Nov. 27 Perf. 13½x12¾
1018 A294 50c multi .65 .65
1019 A294 75c multi 1.00 1.00
1020 A294 95c multi 1.20 1.20
1021 A294 120c multi 1.45 1.45
1022 A294 145c multi 1.60 1.60
1023 A294 240c multi 2.75 2.75
1024 A294 285c multi 3.25 3.25
1025 A295 380c multi 4.25 4.25
Nos. 1018-1025 (8) 16.15 16.15

Birth of Princess Catharina-Amalia, Dec. 7, 2003 — A296

No. 1026: a, 145c, Princess Catharina-Amalia. b, 380c, Prince Willem-Alexander and Princess Catharina-Amalia.

2004, Jan. 16 Perf. 13½x13¾
1026 A296 Horiz. pair, #a-b 5.75 5.75
c. Miniature sheet, #1026a, 1026b + central label 5.75 5.75

New Year 2004 (Year of the Monkey) — A297

Designs: 95c, Golden snub-nosed monkey. 145c, Monkey holding peach, on fan.

2004, Jan. 21 Perf. 13x13½
1027 A297 95c multi 2.00 2.00
Souvenir Sheet
1028 A297 145c multi + 2 labels 2.50 2.50

Houses and Mansions — A298

No. 1029: a, 10c, Belvedère, L. B Smithplein 3. b, 25c, Hoogstraat 27. c, 35c, Landhuis Brievengat. d, 65c, Scharlooweg 102. e, 95c, Hoogstraat 21-25. f, 145c, Villa Maria, Van den Brandhofstraat 6 t/m 6. g, 275c, Werfstraat 6. h, 350c, Landhuis Ronde Klip.

2004, Feb. 20 Perf. 13½x13
1029 A298 Block of 8, #a-h 11.50 11.50
See No. 1066.

Wild Animals A299

No. 1030: a, 5c, Loxodonta africana. b, 10c, Loxodonta africana, diff. c, 25c, Loxodonta africana, diff. d, 35c, Pan troglodytes. e, 45c, Pan troglodytes, diff. f, 55c, Pan troglodytes, diff. g, 65c, Ursus maritimus. h, 95c, Ursus maritimus, diff. i, 100c, Ursus maritimus, diff. j, 145c, Panthera leo. k, 275c, Panthera leo, diff. l, 350c, Panthera leo, diff.

2004, Mar. 31
1030 A299 Block of 12, #a-l 16.00 16.00

Transportation — A300

No. 1031: a, 10c, Diesel locomotive, 1977. b, 55c, Water dealer and cart, 1900. c, 75c, 1903 Ford Model A. d, 85c, Oil tanker, 2004. e, 95c, 1903 Wright Flyer. f, 145c Penny Farthing bicycles, 1871.

2004, Apr. 27
1031 A300 Block of 6, #a-f 7.50 7.50

String Instruments A301

No. 1032: a, 70c, Harp. b, 95c, Lute. c, 145c, Violin, horiz. d, 240c, Zither, horiz.

2004, May 26 Perf. 13x13½, 13½x13
1032 A301 Block of 4, #a-d 7.50 7.50

Dogs A302

No. 1033: a, 5c, Miniature pinscher. b, 5c, Pomeranian. c, 35c, Longhaired teckel. d, 35c, Shih tzu. e, 40c, Boxer. f, 40c, Jack Russell terrier. g, 60c, Basset hound. h, 60c, Braque de l'Ariege. i, 75c, Afghan hound. j, 75c, Old English sheepdog (bobtail). k, 85c, Entelbucher Sennen. l, 85c, Mastiff.

2004, June 22 Perf. 13x13½
1033 A302 Block of 12, #a-l 12.50 12.50

World Stamp Championship 2004, Singapore — A303

No. 1034: a, 95c, Ship in St. Annabay Harbor, Curaçao, dragon. b, 95c, Flags of Singapore and Netherlands Antilles, lion. c, 145c, Brionplein houses, Curaçao, dragon. d, 145c, Ships at Dr. A. C. Wathey Cruise and Cargo Facility, St. Maarten, lion.
500c, Like No. 1034b.

2004, Aug. 23 Perf. 13½x13
1034 A303 Block of 4, #a-d 5.75 5.75
Souvenir Sheet
1035 A303 500c multi 5.75 5.75

Fish and Ducks — A304

No. 1036: a, Pomacanthus paru. b, Epinephelus guttatus. c, Mycteroperca interstitialis. d, Holacanthus isabelita. e, Epinephelus itajara. f, Holacanthus ciliaris. g, Anas americana, Sphyreana barracuda. h, Anas discors. i, Anas bahamensis. j, Aythya affinis.

2004, Sept. 28
1036 Block of 10 15.00 15.00
a. A304 30c multi .65 .65
b. A304 65c multi .80 .80
c. A304 70c multi .90 .90
d. A304 75c multi .90 .90
e. A304 85c multi 1.00 1.00
f. A304 95c multi 1.05 1.05
g. A304 100c multi 1.05 1.05
h. A304 145c multi 1.60 1.60
i. A304 250c multi 2.60 2.60
j. A304 285c multi 3.00 3.00

Birds — A305

Designs: 10c, Icterus icterus. 95c, Coereba flaveola. 100c, Zonotrichia capensis. 145c, Sterna hirundo. 250c, Phoenicopterus ruber. 500c, Buteo albicaudatus.

2004, Oct. 8
1037-1042 A305 Set of 6 15.00 15.00

Miniature Sheets

Coats of Arms and Flags A306

Nos. 1043 and 1044 — Arms of: a, Bonaire. b, Curacao. c, Saba. d, St. Eustatius. e, St. Maarten. f, Flags of Islands of Netherlands Antilles.

2004, Oct. Litho. Perf. 13½x13¾
1043 A306 95c Sheet of 6, #a-f, + 6 labels 12.50 12.50

1044 A306 145c Sheet of 6,
  #a-f, + 6 la-
  bels   20.00 20.00

Labels on Nos. 1043-1044 could be personalized. The two sheets together sold for
€12.42.

Turtles — A307

Designs: 100c, Loggerhead turtle. 145c,
Kemp's Ridley turtle. 240c, Green turtle. 285c,
Olive Ridley turtle. 380c, Hawksbill turtle.
500c, Leatherback turtle.

2004, Dec. 10   Litho.   Perf. 13½x13
1045-1050 A307   Set of 6   22.00 22.00

Buildings
A308

Beach
Scene
A309

Self-Adhesive

2004   Litho.   Die Cut
1051 A308 145c multi   3.50 3.50
1052 A309 145c multi   3.50 3.50
   a.   Horiz. pair, #1051-1052   7.00

Nos. 1051-1052 were printed in sheets of 10
containing five of each stamp at the right of the
sheet. At the left of the sheet are three stamp-
like vignettes lacking die cutting that were not
valid for postage. The spaces at the right of
the stamps where the birds are shown in the
illustration was intended for personalization by
customers on cruise ships that came to St.
Maarten or Curacao. The three stamp-like
vignettes at the left of the sheet also show the
same personalized picture. Four different
sheets, each depicting different birds in the
space for personalization on each stamp and
the three vignettes at the left of the sheet,
were created as exemplars. The sheets,
depicting birds or a personalized image, sold
for $20 in US currency. The stamps were for
postage for postcards mailed anywhere in the
world.

Flowers — A310

Designs: 65c, Hibiscus rosa sinensis. 76c,
Plumbago auriculata. 97c, Tecoma stans.
100c, Ixora coccinea. 122c, Catharanthus
roseus. 148c, Lantana camara. 240c, Trades-
cantia pallida. 270c, Nerium oleander. 285c,
Plumeria obtusa. 350c, Bougainvillea
spectabilis.

2005, Jan. 3   Litho.   Perf. 13½x13
1053 A310 65c multi   .80   .80
1054 A310 76c multi   .90   .90
1055 A310 97c multi   1.05 1.05
1056 A310 100c multi   1.15 1.15
1057 A310 122c multi   1.30 1.30
1058 A310 148c multi   1.60 1.60
1059 A310 240c multi   2.50 2.50
1060 A310 270c multi   3.00 3.00
1061 A310 285c multi   3.00 3.00
1062 A310 350c multi   3.75 3.75
   Nos. 1053-1062 (10)   19.05 19.05

New Year 2005 (Year of
the Rooster) — A311

Designs: 145c, Rooster and Chinese character. 500c, Two roosters.

2005, Feb. 9   Perf. 13x13½
1063 A311 145c multi   1.90 1.90
Souvenir Sheet
1064 A311 500c multi   5.75 5.75

Souvenir Sheet

Queen
Beatrix,
25th
Anniv. of
Reign
A312

Photos: a, Coronation, 1980. b, Giving
speech, 1991. c, With Nelson Mandela, 1999.
d, Visiting colonies, 1999. e, At European Parliament, 2004.

2005, Apr. 30   Perf. 13¼x13¾
1065 A312   Sheet of 5   13.50 13.50
   a.   50c multi   .75   .75
   b.   97c multi   1.05 1.05
   c.   145c multi   1.50 1.50
   d.   285c multi   3.00 3.00
   e.   550c multi   5.75 5.75

Houses & Mansions Type of 2004

No. 1066: a, 10c, Scharlooweg 76. b, 21c,
Landhuis Zeelandia. c, 25c, Berg Altena. d,
35c, Landhuis Dokterstuin. e, 97c, Landhuis
Santa Martha. f, 148c, Landhuis Seri Papaya.
g, 270c, Landhuis Rooi Katooje. h, 300c,
Plaza Horacio Hoyer 19.

2005, May 31   Perf. 13½x13
1066 A298   Block of 8, #a-h   10.50 10.50

Paintings by
Vincent van
Gogh
A313

No. 1067: a, 10c, Vase with Fourteen Sunflowers, detail. b, 65c, Sunflowers, detail. c,
80c, Self-portrait. d, 120c, Sunflowers, detail,
diff. e, 150c, Vase with Fourteen Sunflowers. f,
175c, Joseph Roulin.
500c, Sunflowers, detail, diff.

2005, June 16   Perf. 13x13½
1067 A313   Block of 6, #a-f   10.00 10.00
Souvenir Sheet
1068 A313 500c multi   8.00 8.00

Otrobanda Section of Willemstad,
300th Anniv. (in 2007) — A314

No. 1069: a, 100c, Breedestraat. b, 150c,
Wharf area. c, 285c, Rifwater. d, 500c, Brionplein bus stop.

2005, July 28   Perf. 13½x13
1069 A314   Block of 4, #a-d   12.00 12.00
   See Nos. 1108-1111, 1157-1160.

Fruit — A315

2005, Aug. 31
1070   Block of 10   15.00 15.00
   a.   A315 25c Papaya   .50   .50
   b.   A315 45c Pomegranates   .65   .65
   c.   A315 70c Mango   .80   .80
   d.   A315 75c Bananas   .90   .90
   e.   A315 85c Cashews   1.00 1.00
   f.   A315 97c Soursops   1.05 1.05
   g.   A315 145c Tamarinds   1.60 1.60
   h.   A315 193c Watermelons   2.00 2.00
   i.   A315 270c Gennips   3.00 3.00
   j.   A315 300c Sea grapes   3.25 3.25
   See Nos. 1247-1256.

Worldwide Fund for Nature
(WWF) — A316

No. 1071: a, 51c, Blushing star coral. b,
148c, Rose coral. c, 270c, Smooth flower
coral. d, 750c, Symmetrical brain coral.

2005, Sept. 29
1071 A316   Block of 4, #a-d   14.00 14.00

Musical Instruments
A317

Designs: 55c, Bandoneon. 97c, Bagpipe,
vert. 145c, Vina. 195c, Samisen, vert. 240c,
Shofar. 285c, Kaha di orgel, vert.

2005, Nov. 8   Perf. 13½x13, 13x13½
1072-1077 A317   13.00 13.00

A318

Santa Claus and: 10c, Children's hands.
97c, Children, horiz. 148c, Ornament, horiz.
580c, Chair.

Perf. 13x13½, 13½x13
2005, Nov. 17
1078-1081 A318   Set of 4   9.50 9.50
   Christmas.

A319

Designs: 97c, Aerial view of St. Elizabeth
Hospital, Willemstad. 145c, Stained glass window in hospital chapel. 300c, Entrance to first
community hospital.

2005, Dec. 2   Perf. 13x13½
1082-1084 A319   Set of 3   6.25 6.25
   St. Elizabeth Hospital, 150th anniv.

New Year 2006
(Year of the
Dog) — A320

Chinese character and: 100c, Porcelain
dogs. 149c, Various dog breeds.
500c, Dog and zodiac animals.

2006, Jan. 30   Perf. 13½x13
1085-1086 A320   Set of 2   3.25 3.25
Souvenir Sheet
1087 A320 500c multi   5.75 5.75

Equines — A321

No. 1088: a, Turkmenian Kulan. b, Rhine-
land heavy draft horse. c, Donkey. d, Mule. e,
Hanoverian and Arabian horses.

Perf. 13¼x12¾
2006, Feb. 24   Litho.
1088   Horiz. strip of 5   14.00 14.00
   a.   A321 50c multi   .65   .65
   b.   A321 100c multi   1.05 1.05
   c.   A321 149c multi   1.60 1.60
   d.   A321 285c multi   3.00 3.00
   e.   A321 550c multi   6.00 6.00

Frogs — A322

Designs: 55c, Hyla cinerea. 100c, Dendrobates tinctorius. 149c, Dendrobates azureus.
405c, Epipedobates tricolor.

2006, Mar. 10   Perf. 13¼x12¾
1089-1092 A322   Set of 4   9.50 9.50

Butterflies — A323

Designs: 24c, Danaus chrysippus. 53c, Prepona praeneste. 100c, Caligo uranus. 149c,
Ituna lamirus. 285c, Euphaedra gausape.
335c, Morpho hecuba.

2006, Apr. 7
1093-1098 A323   Set of 6   11.50 11.50

Orchids — A324

No. 1099: a, Brassolaeliocattleya Susan
Harry M. G. R. b, Miltoniopsis Jean Sabourin.
c, Promenaea xanthina Sylvan Sprite. d,
Paphiopedilum Streathamense Wedgewood,
vert. e, Cattleya chocoensis Linden, vert. f,
Disa kewensis Rita Helen, vert.

**Perf. 13¼x12¾, 12¾x13¼ (vert.
stamps)**
2006, Apr. 26
1099   Block of 6   22.50 22.50
   a.   A324 153c multi   1.90 1.90
   b.   A324 240c multi   2.60 2.60
   c.   A324 285c multi   3.25 3.25
   d.   A324 295c multi   3.25 3.25
   e.   A324 380c multi   4.00 4.00
   f.   A324 500c multi   5.25 5.25

Automobiles
A325

Designs: 51c, 1976 MGB. 100c, 1963 Studebaker Avanti. 149c, 1953 Pegaso Cabriolet.
153c, 1939 Delage Aerosport. 195c, 1924 His-
pano-Suiza Boulogne. 750c, 1903 Pierce
Arrow Motorette.

2006, May 10   Perf. 13¼x12¾
1100-1105 A325   Set of 6   16.00 16.00

Washington 2006 World Philatelic
Exhibition — A326

No. 1106: a, 100c, Mailboxes of United
States and Netherlands Antilles. b, 100c,
Queen Emma Bridge, Curaçao, George
Washington Bridge, New York and New
Jersey. c, 149c, UPU emblem. d, 149c, Fokker
F18-Snip, Fokker F4 airplanes.

405c, U.S. Capitol, Palace of the Governor of the Netherlands Antilles.

2006, May 26
1106 A326   Block of 4, #a-d   5.75 5.75
Souvenir Sheet
1107 A326 405c multi   4.75 4.75

Otrobanda Type of 2005

Designs: 100c, Hoogstraat. 149c, Emmabrug. 335c, Pasa Kontrami. 500c, Seaman's Home.

2006, June 16
1108-1111 A314   Set of 4   11.50 11.50

Greetings — A327

Designs: 52c, Bless you. 55c, Love. 77c, All the best. 95c, Regards. 1.00g, Go for it. 1.49g, Tolerance. 1.53g, Positivism. 2.85g, Keep on going. 3.35g, Success. 4.05g, Be good.

2006, July 31
1112-1121 A327   Set of 10   18.50 18.50
See No. 1239-1245.

Birds — A328

No. 1122: a, Taeniopygia guttata. b, Parus caeruleus, vert. c, Pitta genus. d, Pyrrhula pyrrhula, vert. e, Calospiza fastuosa. f, Cosmopsarus regius, vert. g, Coracias caudatus, vert. h, Merops apiaster, vert. i, Icterus nigrogularis. j, Dendrocopus major, vert. k, Amazona barbadensis. l, Alcedo atthis, vert.

Perf. 13¼x12¾, 12¾x13¼ (vert. stamps)

2006, Aug. 18
1122   Block of 12   9.50 9.50
a.-b. A328 5c Either single   .60   .60
c.-d. A328 35c Either single   .60   .60
e.-f. A328 60c Either single   .60   .60
g.-h. A328 75c Either single   .65   .65
i.-j. A328 85c Either single   .75   .75
k.-l. A328 100c Either single .90   .90

Miniature Sheets

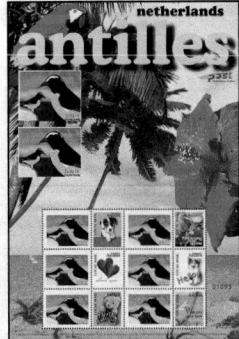

Personalized Stamps — A329

Nos. 1123 and 1124: a, Dog, "Thank you." b, Flower, "Missing you." c, Hearts, "Love you." d, Cat, "Hello." e, Teddy bear, "Hugs & kisses." f, Dolphin, "Wish you were here."

Perf. 13¼x13¾

2006, Aug. 26   Litho.
Stamps Inscribed "Local Mail"
1123 A329   (1g) Sheet of 6,
             #a-f, + 6
             labels   11.50 11.50
Stamps Inscribed "International Mail"
1124 A329 (1.49g) Sheet of 6,
             #a-f, + 6
             labels   17.00 17.00

On day of issue, No. 1123 sold for 10g, and No. 1124 sold for 15g. Labels could be personalized. Labels shown are generic.

Rembrandt (1606-69), Painter A330

No. 1125: a, 70c, The Nightwatch (detail of girl). b, 100c, De Staalmeesters. c, 153c, The Jewish Bride (detail). d, 285c, Self-portrait. 550c, The Nightwatch (detail of men).

Perf. 12¾x13¼

2006, Sept. 28   Litho.
1125 A330   Block of 4, #a-d   7.50 7.50
Souvenir Sheet
1126 A330 550c multi   7.00 7.00

Souvenir Sheet

Royal Visit of Queen Beatrix A331

No. 1127 — Various photos of Queen Beatrix with background colors of: a, 149c, Red. b, 285c, Blue. c, 335c, Yellow. d, 750c, Orange.

2006, Nov. 13   **Perf. 13¼x12¾**
1127 A331   Sheet of 4, #a-d   17.00 17.00

Christmas — A332

Designs: 45c, Candles. 100c, Bells. 149c, Candles. 215c, Bells. 285c, Steeple. 380c, Flower.

2006, Nov. 15
1128-1133 A332   Set of 6   13.00 13.00

Fauna — A333

No. 1134: a, Cacatua leadbeateri leadbeateri. b, Aptenocytes patagonica. c, Pan troglodytes. d, Stenella longirostris. e, Anolis lineatus and Cordia sebestina, horiz. f, Passerina ciris. g, Dryas iulia. h, Bombay cat. i, Epinephelus guttatus, horiz. j, Panthera leo, horiz. k, Pomeranian dog. l, Hawksbill turtle, horiz.

Perf. 12¾x13¼, 13¼x12¾

2007, Jan. 26   Litho.
1134   Block of 12   15.50 15.50
a. A333 3c multi   .40   .40
b. A333 25c multi   .45   .45
c. A333 53c multi   .65   .65
d. A333 60c multi   .75   .75
e. A333 80c multi   .90   .90
f. A333 81c multi   .90   .90
g. A333 95c multi   1.10   1.10
h. A333 106c multi   1.20   1.20
i. A333 145c multi   1.60   1.60
j. A333 157c multi   1.60   1.60
k. A333 161c multi   1.60   1.60
l. A333 240c multi   2.50   2.50

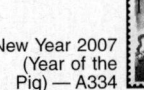

New Year 2007 (Year of the Pig) — A334

Designs: 104c, Berkshire pig. 155c, Wart hog. 500c, Pig, vert.

2007, Feb. 20   **Perf. 13¼x12¾**
1135-1136 A334   Set of 2   3.00 3.00
Souvenir Sheet
Perf. 12¾x13¼
1137 A334 500c multi   5.75 5.75

Islands — A335

Designs: 1c, Flag of Bonaire, divers and marine life. 2c, Flag of Curaçao, royal poinciana flowers. 3c, Flag of Saba, The Bottom. 4c, Flag of Statia (St. Eustatius), cannons at Fort Orange. 5c, Flag of St. Maarten, cruise ship and pier. 104c, Map of Bonaire, flamingos, horiz. 285c, Map of Curaçao, Chobolobo Landhouse, laraha tree, horiz. 335c, Map of Saba, houses, horiz. 405c, Map of Statia, oil storage tanks, horiz. 500c, Map of St. Maarten, Guavaberry Emporium, horiz.

Perf. 12¾x13¼, 13¼x12¾

2007, Mar. 1
1138 A335   1c multi   .25   .25
1139 A335   2c multi   .25   .25
1140 A335   3c multi   .25   .25
1141 A335   4c multi   .25   .25
1142 A335   5c multi   .25   .25
1143 A335 104c multi   1.25   1.25
1144 A335 285c multi   3.50   3.50
1145 A335 335c multi   4.00   4.00
1146 A335 405c multi   4.75   4.75
1147 A335 500c multi   6.00   6.00
    Nos. 1138-1147 (10)   20.75 20.75
See Nos. 1221-1226.

Ananzi the Spider — A336

No. 1148 — Ananzi with: a, Turtle. b, Shark. c, Parrot. d, Cow. e, Dog. f, Goat. g, Chicken. h, Donkey.

2007, Mar. 21   **Perf. 13¼x12¾**
1148   Block of 8   10.00 10.00
a.-h. A336 104c Any single 1.25   1.25

Saba Lace Designs — A337

Various lace designs with background colors of: 59c, Red. 80c, Green. 95c, Blue. 104c, Red. 155c, Green. 159c, Blue.

2007, Apr. 20   **Perf. 12¾x13¼**
1149-1154 A337   Set of 6   7.50 7.50

Marine Life — A338

No. 1155: a, School of fish and sea floor. b, Portuguese man-of-war. c, Coral reef. d, Sea turtle. e, Sea anemones. f, Fish.

2007, May 22
1155   Block of 6   18.00 18.00
a. A338 104c multi   1.00   1.00
b. A338 155c multi   1.45   1.45
c. A338 195c multi   1.75   1.75
d. A338 335c multi   3.25   3.25
e. A338 405c multi   3.75   3.75
f. A338 525c multi   4.75   4.75

Fruits and Vegetables — A339

No. 1156: a, Grapes, Brussels sprouts, tomatoes, peppers and bananas. b, Pumpkins. c, Cucumber, tomatoes, corn, leeks. d, Strawberries, orange, peaches, pineapple. e, Avocados, horiz. f, Lemons, horiz. g, Peppers, corn, potato, mushrooms, horiz. h, Mangos, horiz.

Perf. 12¾x13¼, 13¼x12¾

2007, June 19
1156   Block of 8   11.50 11.50
a. A339 10c multi   .30   .30
b. A339 25c multi   .30   .30
c. A339 35c multi   .40   .40
d. A339 65c multi   .70   .70
e. A339 95c multi   1.00   1.00
f. A339 145c multi   1.60   1.60
g. A339 275c multi   2.75   2.75
h. A339 350c multi   3.50   3.50

Otrabanda Type of 2005

Designs: 104c, Brionplein Square. 155c, Jopi Building and Hotel Otrabanda. 285c, Kura Hulanda. 380c, Luna Blou.

2007, July 26   **Perf. 13¼x12¾**
1157-1160 A314   Set of 4   9.50 9.50

Nature A340

No. 1161: a, 30c, Nautilus shell. b, 65c, Turtles on beach. c, 70c, Grasshopper. d, 75c, Cactus. e, 85c, Swamp. f, 95c, Bird on cactus. g, 104c, Surf spray at rocks. h, 145c, Plants near water. i, 250c, Rainbow in rainforest. j, 285c, Sun on horizon.

Perf. 12¾x 13¼
2007, Aug. 22   Litho.
1161 A340   Block of 10, #a-j   13.00 13.00

Paintings by Dutch Artists A341

No. 1162: a, 104c, Portrait of a Man (probably Nicolaes Hasselaer), by Frans Hals. b, 104c, Wedding of Isaak Abrahamsz Massa and Beatrix van der Lean, by Hals. c, 155c, The Merry Drinker, by Hals. d, 155c, Serenade, by Judith Leyster. 550c, The Meagre Company, by Hals, horiz.

2007, Sept. 20   **Perf. 12¾x13¼**
1162 A341   Block of 4, #a-d   7.00 7.00

Souvenir Sheet
Perf. 13¼x12¾

1163 A341 550c multi   6.25 6.25

Dutch
Royalty
A342

No. 1164: a, 50c, Queen Emma (1858-
1934). b, 104c, Queen Wilhelmina (1880-
1962). c, 155c, Queen Juliana (1909-2004). d,
285c, Queen Beatrix. e, 380c, Princess Máxima. f, 550c, Princess Catharina-Amalia.

2007, Oct. 10   Perf. 12¾x13¼
1164 A342   Block of 6, #a-f   15.50 15.50

Christmas and New
Year — A343

Designs: 48c, Candle. 104c, Gifts under
Christmas tree. 155c, Musical notes and song
lyrics, horiz. 215c, "2008" above "2007," horiz.

Perf. 12¾x13¼, 13¼x12¾
2007, Nov. 15   Litho.
1165-1168 A343   Set of 4   5.25 5.25

Mailboxes
A344

No. 1169 — Various mailboxes with panel
color of: a, 20c, Yellow. b, 104c, Green. c,
240c, Light blue. d, 285c, Lilac. e, 380c,
Orange. f, 500c, Brown.

2007, Dec. 3   Perf. 12¾x13¼
1169 A344   Block of 6, #a-f   15.50 15.50

Lighthouses
A345

No. 1170: a, Fort Oranje, Bonaire. b,
Malmok, Bonaire. c, Noordpunt, Curaçao. d,
Klein Curaçao. e, Willemstoren, Bonaire. f,
Bullenbaai, Curaçao.

2008, Jan. 21
1170 A345 158c Block of 6,
                    #a-f   12.00 12.00

New Year 2008 (Year of
the Rat) — A346

Designs: 106c, Stylized rat. 158c, Rat.
500c, Rat on branch, horiz.

2008, Feb. 7   Perf. 12¾x13¼
1171-1172 A346   Set of 2   3.00 3.00

Souvenir Sheet
Perf. 13¼x12¾
1173 A346 500c multi   5.50 5.50

Dutch
Royalty
A347

No. 1174: a, 75c, Princess Catharina-
Amalia. b, 100c, Princess, diff. c, 125c, Crown
Prince Willem-Alexander. d, 250c, Crown
Prince, diff. e, 375c, Queen Beatrix. f, 500c,
Queen, diff.

2008, Feb. 28   Perf. 12¾x13¼
1174 A347   Block of 6, #a-f   15.50 15.50

Global
Warming
A348

No. 1175: a, 50c, Smokestacks. b, 75c,
Polar bear. c, 125c, Windmills. d, 250c, Beach
and lighthouse.

2008, Mar. 20   Perf. 13¼x12¾
1175 A348   Block of 4, #a-d   6.25 6.25

2008
Summer
Olympics,
Beijing
A349

No. 1176: a, 25c, Runner. b, 35c, Gymnast
on rings. c, 75c, Swimmer. d, 215c, Cyclist.

2008, Apr. 1   Perf. 12¾x13¼
1176 A349   Block of 4, #a-d   4.00 4.00

Stamp
Passion
Philatelic
Exhibition,
the
Netherlands
A350

No. 1177: a, 75c, Netherlands Antilles
#C14. b, 100c, Netherlands Antilles #29. c,
125c, Netherlands Antilles #CB19. d, 250c,
Netherlands #O32. e, 375c, Netherlands
#134. f, 500c, Netherlands Antilles #187.

2008, Apr. 11
1177 A350   Block of 6, #a-f   14.00 14.00
    Images of stamps shown on Nos. 1177a,
1177c and 1177e are distorted.

Catholic Diocese of
Netherlands Antilles and
Aruba, 50th
Anniv. — A351

Designs: 59c, Chapel of Alto Vista, Aruba.
106c, Cross at Seru Largu, Bonaire. 158c, St.
Ann Church, Curaçao. 240c, Sacred Heart
Church, Saba. 285c, Roman Catholic Church
of Oranjestad, St. Eustatius. 335c, Mary Star
of the Sea Church, St. Maarten.

2008, Apr. 28
1178-1183 A351   Set of 6   11.50 11.50

Dolls
Depicting
Women
Doing Work
A352

No. 1184: a, 145c, Pounding corn (Batidó di
maíshi den pilon). b, 145c, Selling fish
(Bendedó di piská). c, 145c, Baking fish
(Hasadó di masbangu riba bleki). d, 145c,
Roasting coffee beans (Totadó di kòfi). e,
155c, Scrubbing clothes on scrub board
(Labadera). f, 155c, Carrying basket of clothes
(Labadó di paña na laman). g, 155c, Grinding
corn on coral (Muladó di maíshi chikí riba
pieda). h, 155c, Weaving hat (Trahadó di
sombré).

2008, May 15
1184 A352   Block of 8, #a-h   11.50 11.50

Paintings by Johannes Vermeer (1632-
75) — A353

No. 1185: a, 145c, Little Street. b, 145c, Girl
with Pearl Earring. c, 155c, Woman in Blue
Reading Letter. d, 155c, The Love Letter.
500c, The Milkmaid.

2008, June 23
1185 A353   Sheet of 4, #a-d, +
                    2 labels   7.50 7.50
Souvenir Sheet
1186 A353 500c multi   5.75 5.75

Windows — A354

Various windows.

2008, July 8 *Perf. 13¾*

1187 A354 5c multi .50 .50
1188 A354 106c multi, vert. 1.60 1.60
1189 A354 285c multi, vert., diff. 3.25 3.25
a. Souvenir sheet of 5, # 1187-1189, Aruba #330, Netherlands #1311, + etiquette 15.00 15.00

Nos. 1188-1189 were only available in No. 1189a. No. 1187 also was available in Aruba No. 332a and in Netherlands Nos. 1313a and 1313b.

Shells — A355

No Country Name — A355a

Designs: 20c, Cypraea zebra. 40c, Charonia variegata. 65c, Calliostoma armillata. 106c, Strombus gigas. 158c, Pina carnea. 285c, Olivia sayana. 335c, Natica canrena. 405c, Voluta musica.

Perf. 13¼x12¾

2008, Sept. 19 **Litho.**

1190 A355 20c multi 1.00 1.00
1191 A355 40c multi 1.00 1.00
1192 A355 65c multi 1.00 1.00
1193 A355a 106c multi, without country name 1.10 1.10
a. With country name 3.00 3.00
1194 A355 158c multi 1.60 1.60
1195 A355 285c multi 3.00 3.00
1196 A355 335c multi 3.25 3.25
1197 A355 405c multi 4.00 4.00
Nos. 1190-1197 (8) 15.95 15.95

African Animals A356

No. 1198: a, 75c, Giraffes, vert. b, 150c, Elephants. c, 175c, Cheetahs. d, 250c, Zebras.
No. 1199, Impalas, vert.

Perf. 13¼x12¾, 12¾x13¼ (vert. stamps)

2008, Oct. 2

1198 A356 Block of 4, #a-d 7.50 7.50

Souvenir Sheet

1199 A356 250c multi 3.00 3.00

Christmas and New Year's Day — A357

Designs: 50c, Plate of basil. 106c, Flowers. 158c, Fishermen in boat. 215c, Dock.

Perf. 13¼x12¾

2008, Nov. 14 **Litho.**

1200-1203 A357 Set of 4 5.50 5.50

Traditional Costumes — A358

No. 1204: a, 100c, Antillean girl. b, 104c, Dutch boy. c, 155c, Japanese girl.

2008, Nov. 27 *Perf. 12¾x13¼*

1204 A358 Horiz. strip of 3, #a-c 4.00 4.00

Birds — A359

No. 1205: a, Kasuaris (cassowary). b, Struisvogel (ostrich). c, Pinguin (penguin). d, Kalkoen (wild turkey). e, Aalscholver (cormorant), horiz. f, Mandarijneend (Mandarin duck), horiz. g, Putter-distelvink (goldfinch), horiz. h, Groene reiger (green heron), horiz.

Perf. 12¾x13¼, 13¼x12¾ (horiz. stamps)

2008, Dec. 12

1205 A359 158c Block of 8, #a-h 14.00 14.00

Flowers — A360

No. 1206: a, Nelumbo nucifera. b, Chrysanthemum leucanthemum. c, Hepatica nobilis. d, Cistus incanus. e, Alamanda. f, Wise portia.

2009, Jan. 26 **Litho.** *Perf. 13¼x12¾*

1206 Block of 6 16.00 16.00
a. A360 75c multi .70 .70
b. A360 150c multi 1.10 1.10
c. A360 200c multi 1.60 1.60
d. A360 225c multi 2.10 2.10
e. A360 350c multi 3.50 3.50
f. A360 500c multi 5.00 5.00

New Year 2009 (Year of the Ox) — A361

Chinese character and: 110c, Outline of ox. 168c, Ox, horiz.

Perf. 12¾x13¼, 13¼x12¾

2009, Feb. 19

1207-1208 A361 Set of 2 3.00 3.00

Butterflies — A362

No. 1209: a, 25c, Lycaena phlaeas. b, 35c, danaus plexippus. c, 50c, Nymphalis antiopa. d, 105c, Carterocephalus palaemon. e, 115c, Inachis io. f, 155c, Phyciodes tharos. g, 185c, Papilio glaucus. h, 240c, Dryas iulia. i, 315c, Libytheana carinenta. j, 375c, Melanis pixe. k, 400c, Asterocampa celtis. l, 1000c, Historis acheronta.

2009, Mar. 2 *Perf. 13¼x12¾*

1209 A362 Block of 12, #a-l 32.00 32.00

Birds A363

No. 1210: a, 10c, Daptrius americanus. b, 45c, Amazona amazonica. c, 80c, Querula purpurata. d, 145c, Aratinga leucophthalmus. e, 190c, Xipholena punicea. f, 235c, Celeus torquatus. g, 285c, Lamprospiza melanoleuca. h, 300c, Selenidera culik. i, 335c, Amazila viridigaster. j, 425c, Tangara gyrola. k, 450c, Nyctibius grandis. l, 500c, Galbula leucogastra.

2009, Apr. 20 *Perf. 12¾x13¼*

1210 A363 Block of 12, #a-l 32.00 32.00

Telecommunications and Posts Department, Cent. — A364

Designs: 59c, Ship, telegraph operator. 110c, Person on telephone, room with radio and television. 164c, Person at computer, satellite dish, street scene.

2009, May 18 *Perf. 13¼x12¾*

1211-1213 A364 Set of 3 3.50 3.50

Pianos — A365

Pianos manufactured by: 175c, J. B. & Sons, 1796. 225c, J. Schantz, 1818, vert. 250c, Steinway-Welt, 1927, vert. 350c, Yamaha, 2007.

Perf. 13¼x12¾, 12¾x13¼

2009, June 1

1214-1217 A365 Set of 4 11.50 11.50

Nos. 1214-1217 were printed in a sheet of 8 containing two of each stamp, with a central label.

Miniature Sheets

A366

A367

Coca-Cola Bottling on Curaçao, 70th Anniv. — A368

No. 1218 — Fria soft drinks: a, No bottle shown. b, Bottle with pink drink, parts of blue balls at UL and bottom. c, Bottle with purple drink, parts of red ball at UL and purple ball at right. d, Bottle with yellow drink, parts of green ball at UL and purple ball at LR. e, Bottle with orange drink, parts of purple ball at UL and red ball at LL. f, Bottle with red drink, parts of purple ball at UL, blue ball at LR. g, Bottle with pale pink drink, part of red ball at LR. h, Bottle with yellow-green drink, part of orange ball at LR.

No. 1219: a, Coca-Cola advertisement showing couple on beach and bottle. b, Women around counter with two Coca-Cola advertisements. c, Coca-Cola building with awning at left. d, Man at vending machine. e, Man and automobile in front of building with Coca-Cola advertisement, vert. f, Two men holding bottles of Coca-Cola. g, Men and women around a counter. h, Delivery truck.

No. 1220: a, 106c, 1899 Coca-Cola bottle. b, 106c, 1900 Coca-Cola bottle. c, 158c, 1905 Coca-Cola bottle. d, 158c, 1913 Coca-Cola bottle. e, 158c, 1915 Coca-Cola bottle. f, 285c, Woman holding glass of Coca-Cola and blue-striped umbrella. g, 285c, Woman holding glass of Coca-Cola and yellow umbrella. h, 285c, 1923 Coca-Cola bottle.

Perf. 12¾x13¼, 13¼x12¾

2008, Dec. 23 **Litho.**

1218 A366 106c Sheet of 8, #a-h 8.50 8.50
1219 A367 158c Sheet of 8, #a-h 13.00 13.00
1220 A368 Sheet of 8, #a-h 15.00 15.00
Nos. 1218-1220 (3) 36.50 36.50

Islands Type of 2007

Designs: 30c, Flag of Bonaire, divers and marine life. 59c, Map of Statia, oil storage tanks, horiz. 110c, Flag of Curaçao, royal poinciana flowers. 164c, Flag of St. Maarten, cruise ship and pier. 168c, Map of bonaire, flamingos, horiz. 285c, Map of Saba, houses, horiz.

Perf. 12¾x13¼, 13¼x12¾

2009, Jan.

1221 A335 30c multi 1.00 1.00
1222 A335 59c multi 1.00 1.00
1223 A335 110c multi 1.40 1.40
1224 A335 164c multi 1.60 1.60
1225 A335 168c multi 1.75 1.75
1226 A335 285c multi 3.00 3.00
Nos. 1221-1226 (6) 9.75 9.75

Souvenir Sheet

Birds A369

No. 1227: a, 5g, Celeus undatus. b, 10g, Todopleura fusca.

2009, July 20 *Perf. 13¼x12¾*

1227 A369 Sheet of 2, #a-b 15.00 15.00

Sailing Ships A370

No. 1228: a, 1c, Merchantman, 200. b, 2c, Caravel, 1490. c, 3c, Naos, 1492. d, 4c, Constant, 1605. e, 5c, Merchant ship, 1620. f, 80c, Vasa, 1628. g, 220c, Hoys, 1730. h, 275c, Bark, 1750. i, 385c, Schooner, 1838. j, 475c, Sailing rig, 1884. k, 500c, Fifie, 1903. l, 750c, Junk, 1938.

2009, Aug. 31

1228 A370 Block of 12, #a-l 28.00 28.00

Snakes
A371

No. 1229: a, 275c, Bothriopsis bilineata. b, 325c, Bothriechis schlegelii. c, 340c, Agkistrodeon piscivorous. d, 390c, Erythrolamprus aesculapii. e, 420c, Atropoides mexicanus. f, 450c, Bothriechis nigroviridis.

2009, Oct. 5
1229 A371   Block of 6, #a-f   26.00 26.00

Aviation
Pioneers — A372

Designs: 59c, Freddy Johnson (1932-2001). 110c, Norman Chester Wathey (1925-2001). 164c, José Dormoy (1925-2007).

Perf. 13¼x12¾
2009, Nov. 10   **Litho.**
1230-1232 A372   Set of 3   3.50 3.50

Airplanes — A373

No. 1233: a, Wright Flyer, 1903. b, DST Skysleeper, 1935. c, Cessna 170, 1948. d, Lockheed Constellation, 1943. e, De Havilland Comet, 1949. f, BAC Super VC10, 1962.

2009, Nov. 16
1233   Block of 6   21.00 21.00
  a. A373 55c multi   1.00 1.00
  b. A373 100c multi   1.20 1.20
  c. A373 205c multi   2.00 2.00
  d. A373 395c multi   4.00 4.00
  e. A373 645c multi   6.00 6.00
  f. A373 800c multi   7.00 7.00

Hanukkah
A374

Christmas
A375

Kwanzaa
A376

New Year's
Day
A377

2009, Nov. 30   **Perf. 12¾x13¼**
1234 A374 50c multi   .50 .50
1235 A375 110c multi   1.10 1.10
1236 A376 168c multi   1.75 1.75
1237 A377 215c multi   2.25 2.25
  Nos. 1234-1237 (4)   5.60 5.60

Fruit — A378

2009, Dec. 28   **Litho.**
1238   Block of 8 + label   20.00 20.00
  a. A378 20c Sapodilla   1.00 1.00
  b. A378 45c Pineapple   1.00 1.00
  c. A378 125c Mamey sapote   1.30 1.30
  d. A378 145c Avocado   1.60 1.60
  e. A378 160c Mangosteen   1.60 1.60
  f. A378 210c Rambutan   2.00 2.00
  g. A378 295c Pomelo   3.00 3.00
  h. A378 1000c Watermelon   9.00 9.00

Greetings Type of 2006

Designs: 32c, Bless you. 60c, Love. 81c, All the best. 87c, Regards. 1.06g, Go for it. 1.57g, Tolerance. 1.61g, Positivism.

2009   **Perf. 13¼x12¾**
1239-1245 A327   Set of 7   10.00 10.00

Flowers
A379

No. 1246: a, 50c, Opuntia basilaris. b, 75c, Aristolochiaceae. c, 125c, Protea cynaroides. d, 175c, Louisiana iris. e, 200c, Spontaneous frangipani. f, 250c, Red azaleas. g, 300c, English Heritage rose. h, 350c, Aquilegia. i, 475c, Octavia Hill rose. j, 500c, Tea rose.

2010, Jan. 25 Litho. Perf. 13¼x12¾
1246 A379   Block of 10, #a-j   26.00 26.00

Fruit Type of 2005

2010, Feb. 1   Litho. Perf. 13¼x12¾
1247 A315   1c Papaya   .30 .30
1248 A315   5c Pomegranates   .30 .30
1249 A315   30c Mangos   .30 .30
1250 A315   59c Bananas   .60 .60
1251 A315   79c Cashews   .80 .80
1252 A315   111c Soursops   1.10 1.10
1253 A315   164c Tamarinds   1.75 1.75
1254 A315   170c Watermelons   1.75 1.75
1255 A315   199c Gennips   2.00 2.00
1256 A315   285c Sea grapes   3.00 3.00
  Nos. 1247-1256 (10)   11.90 11.90

New Year 2010 (Year of
the Tiger) — A380

Designs: 111c, Tiger cub. 164c, Tiger and cub. 170c, White tiger.

2010, Feb. 1   **Perf. 12¾x13¼**
1257-1259 A380   Set of 3   5.00 5.00

Butterflies — A381

No. 1260: a, 20c, Thersamonia thersamon. b, 50c, Acraea natalica. c, 80c, Vanessa carye. d, 100c, Apodemia mormo. e, 125c, Siproeta stelenes meridionalis. f, 175c, Anartia amathea. g, 200c, Doxocopa laure. h, 250c, Euphaedra uganda. i, 350c, Precis westermannii. j, 450c, Precis octavia. k, 500c, Euphaedra neophron. l, 700c, Vanessa cardui.

2010, Mar. 1   **Perf. 13¼x12¾**
1260 A381   Block of 12, #a-l   34.00 34.00

Paintings by Vincent Van
Gogh — A382

Designs: 200c, Self-portrait, 1888. 400c, Agostina Segatori, 1887. 500c, Arlesian Woman, 1888. 700c, Emperor Moth, 1889.

2010, Apr. 7   **Perf. 12¾x13¼**
1261 A382 200c multi   4.00 4.00
1262 A382 400c multi   4.50 4.50
1263 A382 500c multi   5.50 5.50
1264 A382 700c multi   6.75 6.75
  Nos. 1261-1264 (4)   20.75 20.75

Nos. 1261-1264 were printed in sheets of 8 containing two of each stamp with a central label.

Birds
A383

No. 1265: a, 75c, Pipra aureola. b, 150c, Neopelma chrysocephalum. c, 200c, Oxyruncus cristatus. d, 225c, Automolus rufipileatus. e, 350c, Empidonomus varius. f, 500c, Veniliornis sanguineus.

2010, May 10
1265 A383   Block of 6, #a-f   18.50 18.50

Ships
A384

No. 1266 — Inscriptions: a, 100c, Osberg, 800. b, 125c, Dromon, 910. c, 175c, Cocca, 1500. d, 200c, Mary, 1661. e, 250c, Houtport, 1700. f, 300c, Santissima Trinidad, 1769. g, 350c, Vrachtschip, 1800. h, 400c, Amistad, 1839. i, 450c, Oorlogsschip, 1840. j, 650c, Nederlands schip, 1850.

2010, June 14   **Perf. 13¼x12¾**
1266 A384   Block of 10, #a-j   33.00 33.00   **Litho.**

Netherlands Antilles Stamps — A385

No. 1267: a, 25c, #109. b, 50c, #140. c, 100c, #77. d, 250c, #144. e, 275c, #290. f, 300c, #75. g, 400c, #C34. h, 600c, #200. No. 1268: a, 700c, #204. b, 800c, #141.

2010, July 19   **Perf. 12¾x13¼**
1267 A385   Block of 8, #a-h   22.50 22.50
Souvenir Sheet
1268 A385   Sheet of 2, #a-b   17.00 17.00
Image of stamp on No. 1267d is distorted.

TeleCuraçao, 50th
Anniv. — A386

Television showing: 59c, Cameraman. 111c, Transmission tower. 164c, 50th anniversary emblem.

2010, Aug. 2 Litho. Perf. 13¼x12¾
1269-1271 A386   Set of 3   3.75 3.75

Pocket Watches — A387

No. 1272 — Watches made by: a, Ulysse, 1890. b, Hampden, 1910. c, Elgin, 1924. d, Illinois, 1928. e, Vacheron, 1955.

2010, Sept. 6   **Perf. 12¾x13¼**
1272   Horiz. strip of 5   14.00 14.00
  a. A387 125c multi   2.00 2.00
  b. A387 175c multi   2.00 2.00
  c. A387 250c multi   2.50 2.50
  d. A387 300c multi   3.00 3.00
  e. A387 350c multi   3.00 3.00

On Oct. 10, 2010, the Netherlands Antilles was dissolved, being replaced by three entities: Caribbean Netherlands, Curaçao and St. Martin.

SEMI-POSTAL STAMPS

Catalogue values for unused stamps in this section are for Never Hinged items.

Nos. 132, 133 and 135
Surcharged in Black

1947, Dec. 1   Unwmk.   Perf. 12½
B1 A26 1½c + 2½c on 6c   1.05 1.00
B2 A26 2½c + 5c on 10c   1.05 1.00
B3 A26 5c + 7½c on 15c   1.05 1.00
  Nos. B1-B3 (3)   3.15 3.00

The surtax was for the National Inspanning Welzijnszorg in Nederlandsch Indie, relief organization for Netherlands Indies.

Curaçao Children
SP1   SP2

Design: Nos. B6, B9, Girl.

1948, Nov. 3   Photo.   Perf. 12½x12
B4 SP1   6c + 10c ol brn   2.50 1.60
B5 SP2   10c + 15c brt red   2.50 1.60
B6 SP2   12½c + 20c Prus grn   2.50 1.75
B7 SP1   15c + 25c brt bl   2.50 1.75
B8 SP2   20c + 30c red brn   2.50 1.90
B9 SP2   25c + 35c purple   2.50 1.90
  Nos. B4-B9 (6)   15.00 10.50

The surtax was for child welfare and the White/Yellow Cross Foundation.

Leapfrog — SP4

Designs: 5c+2½c, Flying kite. 6c+2½c, Girls swinging. 12½c+5c, "London Bridge." 25c+10c, Rolling hoops.

Perf. 14½x13½

1951, Aug. 16   **Unwmk.**

B10	SP4	1½c + 1c pur	11.50	4.25
B11	SP4	5c + 2½c brn	11.50	4.25
B12	SP4	6c + 2½c blue	11.50	4.25
B13	SP4	12½c + 5c red	11.50	4.25
B14	SP4	25c + 10c dl grn	11.50	4.25
	Nos. B10-B14 (5)	57.50	21.25

The surtax was for child welfare.

Ship and Gull — SP5

Designs: 6c+4c, Sailor and lighthouse. 12½c+7c, Prow of sailboat. 15c+10c, Ships. 25c+15c, Ship, compass and anchor.

1952, July 16   **Perf. 13x14**

B15	SP5	1½c + 1c dk grn	9.50	1.90
B16	SP5	6c + 4c choc	16.50	4.25
B17	SP5	12½c + 7c red vio	12.00	4.25
B18	SP5	15c + 10c dp bl	14.00	5.00
B19	SP5	25c + 15c red	13.00	3.75
	Nos. B15-B19 (5)	65.00	19.15

The surtax was for the seamen's welfare fund.

No. 226 Surcharged in Black

1953, Feb. 21

B20	A45	22½c + 7½c on 1½g	2.40	1.25

The surtax was for flood relief in the Netherlands.

Tribulus Cistoides — SP6

Flowers: 7½c+5c, Yellow hibiscus. 15c+5c, Oleander. 22½c+7½c, Cactus. 25c+10c, Red hibiscus.

1955, May 17   Photo.   Perf. 14x13
Flowers in Natural Colors

B21	SP6	1½c + 1c bl grn & dk bl	3.00	.95
B22	SP6	7½c + 5c dp ultra	4.00	1.90
B23	SP6	15c + 5c ol grn	4.00	2.25
B24	SP6	22½c + 7½c dk bl	4.00	1.90
B25	SP6	25c + 10c ind & gray	4.00	1.90
	Nos. B21-B25 (5)	19.00	8.90

The surtax was for child welfare.

Prince Bernhard and Queen Juliana — SP7

1955, Oct. 19   **Perf. 11x12**

B26	SP7	7½c + 2½c rose brn	.40	.25
B27	SP7	22½c + 7½c dp bl	1.20	.95

Royal visit to the Netherlands Antilles, Oct. 1955.
Surtax paid for a gift.

Lord Baden-Powell SP8

1957, Feb. 22   **Perf. 14x13½**

B28	SP8	6c + 1½c org yel	.95	.45
B29	SP8	7½c + 2½c dp grn	.95	.45
B30	SP8	15c + 5c red	.95	.45
	Nos. B28-B30 (3)	2.85	1.35

50th anniv. of the Boy Scout movement.

Soccer Player — SP9   Map of Central America and the Caribbean — SP10

Designs: 15c+5c, Goalkeeper catching ball. 22½c+7½c, Men playing soccer.

1957, Aug. 6   Perf. 12x11, 11x12

B31	SP9	6c + 2½c org	1.90	.70
B32	SP10	7½c + 5c dk red	1.90	1.00
B33	SP9	15c + 5c brt bl grn	1.90	1.00
B34	SP9	22½c + 7½c brt bl	1.90	1.00
	Nos. B31-B34 (4)	7.60	3.70

8th Central American and Caribbean Soccer Championships, Aug. 11-25.
Surtax was for organizing costs.

American Kestrel — SP11

Birds: 7½+1½c, Yellow oriole. 15+2½c, Common ground doves. 22½+2½c, Brown-throated parakeet.

1958, Apr. 15   Photo.   Perf. 13½x14

B35	SP11	2½c + 1c multi	1.75	.95
B36	SP11	7½c + 1½c multi	1.75	.95
B37	SP11	15c + 2½c multi	1.75	.95
B38	SP11	22½c + 2½c multi	1.75	.95
	Nos. B35-B38 (4)	7.00	3.80

The surtax was for child welfare.

Flag and Map — SP12

1958, Dec. 1   Litho.   Perf. 13½
Cross in Red

B39	SP12	6c + 2c red brn	.95	.45
B40	SP12	7½c + 2½c bl grn	.95	.45
B41	SP12	15c + 5c org yel	.95	.45
B42	SP12	22½c + 7½c blue	.95	.45
	Nos. B39-B42 (4)	3.80	1.80

The surtax was for the Red Cross.

Community House, Zeeland — SP13

Historic buildings: 7½c+2½c, Molenplein. 15c+5c, Saba, vert. 22½c+7½c, Scharlooburg. 25c+7½c, Community House, Brievengat.

Perf. 14x13½, 13½x14
1959, Sept. 16   Litho.

B43	SP13	6c + 1½c multi	1.40	.90
B44	SP13	7½c + 2½c multi	1.40	.90
B45	SP13	15c + 5c multi	1.40	.90
B46	SP13	22½c + 7½c dk bl multi	1.40	.90
B47	SP13	25c + 7½c multi	1.40	.90
	Nos. B43-B47 (5)	4.90	4.50

The surtax went to the Foundation for the Preservation of Historical Monuments.

Fish — SP14

Designs. 10c+2c, SCUBA diver with spear gun, vert. 25c+5c, Two fish.

1960, Aug. 24   Photo.   Perf. 13½

B48	SP14	10c + 2c sapphire	1.50	.85
B49	SP14	20c + 3c multi	1.75	1.15
B50	SP14	25c + 5c blk, brt pink & dk bl	1.75	1.15
	Nos. B48-B50 (3)	5.00	3.15

The surtax was for the fight against cancer.

Infant — SP15

Designs: 10c+3c, Girl and doll. 20c+6c, Boy on beach. 25c+8c, Children in school.

1961, July 24   Litho.   Perf. 13½x14
Designs in Black

B51	SP15	6c + 2c lt yel grn	.55	.30
B52	SP15	7½c + 3c rose red	.55	.30
B53	SP15	20c + 6c yellow	.55	.30
B54	SP15	25c + 8c orange	.55	.30
	Nos. B51-B54 (4)	2.20	1.20

The surtax was for child welfare.

Globe and Knight — SP16

1962, May 2   Perf. 13½x14½

B55	SP16	10c + 5c green	1.10	.65
B56	SP16	20c + 10c carmine	1.10	.65
B57	SP16	25c + 10c dk bl	1.10	.65
	Nos. B55-B57 (3)	3.30	1.95

Intl. Candidates Chess Tournament, Willemstad, May-June.

No. 248 Surcharged

1963, Mar. 21

B58	A56	20c + 10c crimson & gray	.50	.50

FAO "Freedom from Hunger" campaign.

Child and Flowers — SP17

Designs: 6c+3c, Three girls and flowers, horiz. 10c+5c, Girl with ball and trees, horiz. 20c+10c, Three boys with flags, horiz. 25c+12c, Singing boy.

Perf. 14½x13½, 13½x14½
1963, Oct. 23   Photo.   Unwmk.

B59	SP17	5c + 2c multi	.40	.25
B60	SP17	6c + 3c multi	.40	.25
B61	SP17	10c + 5c multi	.40	.25
B62	SP17	20c + 10c multi	.40	.25
B63	SP17	25c + 12c multi	.40	.25
	Nos. B59-B63 (5)	2.00	1.25

Surtax for child welfare.

Bougainvillea SP18

Designs: 10c+5c, Wild rose. 20c+10c, Chalice flower. 25c+11c, Bellisima.

1964, Oct. 21   Perf. 14x13
Flowers in Natural Colors

B64	SP18	6c + 3c bl vio & blk	.40	.25
B65	SP18	10c + 5c yel brn, yel & blk	.40	.25
B66	SP18	20c + 10c dull red & blk	.40	.25
B67	SP18	25c + 11c citron & brn	.40	.25
	Nos. B64-B67 (4)	1.60	1.00

The surtax was for child welfare.

Sea Anemones and Star Coral — SP19

Corals: 6c+3c, Blue cup sponges. 10c+5c, Green cup sponges. 25c+11c, Basket sponge, knobbed brain coral and reef fish.

1965, Nov. 10   Photo.   Perf. 14x13½

B68	SP19	6c + 3c multi	.25	.25
B69	SP19	10c + 5c multi	.25	.25
B70	SP19	20c + 10c multi	.35	.25
B71	SP19	25c + 11c multi	.35	.25
	Nos. B68-B71 (4)	1.20	1.00

The surtax was for child welfare.

ICEM Type of Netherlands
1966, Jan. 31   Photo.   Perf. 14x13

B72	SP181	35c + 15c brn & dl yel	.25	.25

The surtax was for the Intergovernmental Committee for European Migration (ICEM). The message on the stamps was given and signed by Queen Juliana.

Girl Cooking — SP20

Youth at Work: 10c+5c, Nurse's aide with infant. 20c+10c, Young metalworker. 25c+11c, Girl ironing.

1966, Nov. 15   Perf. 13½

B73	SP20	6c + 3c multi	.25	.25
B74	SP20	10c + 5c multi	.25	.25
B75	SP20	20c + 10c multi	.25	.25
B76	SP20	25c + 11c multi	.25	.25
	Nos. B73-B76 (4)	1.00	1.00

The surtax was for child welfare.

Helping Hands Supporting Women — SP21

1967, July 4   Litho.   Perf. 13x14

B77	SP21	6c + 3c bl & blk	.25	.25
B78	SP21	10c + 5c brt pink & blk	.25	.25
B79	SP21	20c + 10c lilac	.25	.25
B80	SP21	25c + 11c dk bl	.25	.25
	Nos. B77-B80 (4)	1.00	1.00

The surtax was for various social and cultural institutions.

Nanzi the Spider and the Tiger — SP22

Nanzi Stories (Folklore): 6c+3c, Princess Longnose, vert. 10c+5c, The Turtle and the Monkey. 25c+11c, Adventure of Shon Arey, vert.

Perf. 14x13, 13x14
1967, Nov. 15   Photo.

B81	SP22	6c + 3c dk red, pink & org	.25	.25
B82	SP22	10c + 5c vio bl & org	.25	.25
B83	SP22	20c + 10c grn & org	.25	.25
B84	SP22	25c + 11c brt bl & org	.25	.25
	Nos. B81-B84 (4)	1.00	1.00

The surtax was for child welfare.

Lintendans (Dance) and Koeoekoe House — SP23

1968, May 29 Litho. *Perf. 14x13*

B85	SP23	10c + 5c multi	.25	.25
B86	SP23	15c + 5c multi	.25	.25
B87	SP23	20c + 10c multi	.25	.25
B88	SP23	25c + 10c multi	.25	.25
		Nos. B85-B88 (4)	1.00	1.00

The surtax was for various social and cultural institutions.

Boy and Pet Cat — SP24

Designs: 6c+3c, Boy and goat. 10c+5c, Girl and poodle. 25c+11c, Girl and duckling.

1968, Nov. 13 Photo. *Perf. 13½*

B89	SP24	6c + 3c multi	.40	.25
B90	SP24	10c + 5c multi	.40	.25
B91	SP24	20c + 10c multi	.40	.25
B92	SP24	25c + 11c multi	.40	.25
		Nos. B89-B92 (4)	1.60	1.00

The surtax was for child welfare.

Carnival Headpiece — SP25

Folklore: 15c+5c, Harvest-home festival. 20c+10c, Feast of St. John (dancers & cock). 25c+10c, "Dande" New Year's celebration.

1969, July 23 Litho. *Perf. 13½*

B93	SP25	10c + 5c multi	.30	.25
B94	SP25	15c + 5c multi	.30	.25
B95	SP25	20c + 10c multi	.35	.30
B96	SP25	25c + 10c multi	.35	.30
		Nos. B93-B96 (4)	1.30	1.10

The surtax was for various social and cultural institutions.

Boy Playing Guitar — SP26

Designs: 10c+5c, Girl with English flute. 20c+10c, Boy playing the marimula. 25c+11c, Girl playing the piano.

1969, Nov. 3 Litho. *Perf. 14x13*

B97	SP26	6c + 3c org & vio	.40	.30
B98	SP26	10c + 5c yel & brt grn	.40	.35
B99	SP26	20c + 10c bl & car	.40	.35
B100	SP26	25c + 11c pink & brn	.40	.35
		Nos. B97-B100 (4)	1.60	1.35

The surtax was for child welfare.

Printing Press and Quill — SP27

Mass Media: 15c+5c, Filmstrip and reels. 20c+10c, Horn and radio mast. 25c+10c, Television antenna and eye focused on globe.

1970, July 14 Litho. *Perf. 13½*

B101	SP27	10c + 5c multi	.40	.35
B102	SP27	15c + 5c multi	.40	.35
B103	SP27	20c + 10c multi	.40	.35
B104	SP27	25c + 10c multi	.40	.35
		Nos. B101-B104 (4)	1.60	1.40

The surtax was for various social and cultural institutions.

Mother and Child — SP28

Designs: 10c+5c, Girl holding piggy bank. 20c+10c, Boys wrestling (Judokas). 25c+11c, Youth carrying small boy on his shoulders.

1970, Nov. 16 *Perf. 13½x14*

B105	SP28	6c + 3c multi	.40	.30
B106	SP28	10c + 5c multi	.40	.30
B107	SP28	20c + 10c multi	.40	.30
B108	SP28	25c + 11c multi	.40	.30
		Nos. B105-B108 (4)	1.60	1.20

The surtax was for child welfare.

Charcoal Burner — SP29

Kitchen Utensils: 15c+5c, Earthenware vessel for water. 20c+10c, Baking oven. 25c+10c, Soup plate, stirrer and kneading stick.

1971, May 12 *Perf. 14x13½*

B109	SP29	10c + 5c multi	.50	.40
B110	SP29	15c + 5c multi	.50	.40
B111	SP29	20c + 10c multi	.50	.40
B112	SP29	25c + 10c multi	.50	.40
		Nos. B109-B112 (4)	2.00	1.60

Surtax was for various social and cultural institutions.

Homemade Dolls and Comb — SP30

Homemade Toys: 20c+10c, Carts. 30c+15c, Musical top made from calabash.

1971, Nov. 16 *Perf. 13½x14*

B113	SP30	15c + 5c multi	.55	.50
B114	SP30	20c + 10c multi	.55	.50
B115	SP30	30c + 15c multi	.55	.50
		Nos. B113-B115 (3)	1.65	1.50

Surtax was for child welfare.

Steel Band — SP31

Designs: 20c+10c, Harvest festival (Seu). 30c+15c, Tambu dancers.

1972, May 16

B116	SP31	15c + 5c multi	.80	.65
B117	SP31	20c + 10c multi	.80	.65
B118	SP31	30c + 15c multi	.80	.65
		Nos. B116-B118 (3)	2.40	1.95

Surtax was for various social and cultural institutions.

Child at Play on Ground — SP32

Designs: 20c+10c, Child playing in water. 30c+15c, Child throwing ball into air.

1972, Nov. 14 Litho. *Perf. 14x13*

B119	SP32	15c + 5c multi	.65	.65
B120	SP32	20c + 10c multi	.65	.65
B121	SP32	30c + 15c multi	.65	.65
		Nos. B119-B121 (3)	1.95	1.95

Surtax was for child welfare.

Pedestrian Crossing, Traffic Sign — SP33

Designs: 15c+7c, School crossing. 40c+20c, Traffic light, road and car.

1973, Apr. 9 Litho. *Perf. 13x14*

B122	SP33	12c + 6c multi	.80	.65
B123	SP33	15c + 7c multi	.80	.65
B124	SP33	40c + 20c multi	.80	.65
		Nos. B122-B124 (3)	2.40	1.95

Surtax was for various social and cultural institutions.

"1948-73" — SP34

20c+10c, Children. 30c+15c, Mother & child.

1973, Nov. 19 Litho. *Perf. 14x13*

B125	SP34	15c + 5c multi	.60	.60
B126	SP34	20c + 10c multi	.60	.60
a.		Min. sheet, 2 ea #B125-B126	3.25	3.00
B127	SP34	30c + 15c multi	.70	.70
		Nos. B125-B127 (3)	1.90	1.90

Child Welfare semi-postal stamps, 25th anniv.

Girl Combing her Hair — SP35

15c+7c, Young people listening to rock music. 40c+20c, Drummer, symbolizing rock music.

1974, Apr. 9 Litho. *Perf. 14x13*

B128	SP35	12c + 6c multi	.90	.70
B129	SP35	15c + 7c multi	.90	.70
B130	SP35	40c + 20c multi	.90	.70
		Nos. B128-B130 (3)	2.70	2.10

Surtax was for various social and cultural institutions.

Child, Saw and Score — SP36

Designs: 20c+10c, Footprints in circle. 30c+15c, Moon and sun. Each design includes score of a children's song.

1974, Nov. 12 Litho. *Perf. 13x14*

B131	SP36	15c + 5c multi	.90	.60
B132	SP36	20c + 10c multi	.90	.60
B133	SP36	30c + 15c multi	.90	.60
		Nos. B131-B133 (3)	2.70	1.80

Surtax was for child welfare.

Carved Stone Grid, Flower Pot SP37

Jewish Tombstone, Mordecai's Procession SP38

Design: 40c+20c, Ornamental stone from facade of Jewish House, 1728.

1975, Mar. 21 Litho. *Perf. 13x14*

B134	SP37	12c + 6c multi	.60	.60
B135	SP38	15c + 7c multi	.60	.60
B136	SP37	40c + 20c multi	.60	.60
		Nos. B134-B136 (3)	1.80	1.80

Surtax was for various social and cultural institutions.

Children Building Curaçao Windmill — SP39

Designs: 20c+10c, Girl molding clay animal. 30c+15c, Children drawing picture.

1975, Nov. 12 Litho. *Perf. 14x13*

B137	SP39	15c + 5c multi	.60	.60
B138	SP39	20c + 10c multi	.60	.60
B139	SP39	30c + 15c multi	.60	.60
		Nos. B137-B139 (3)	1.80	1.80

Surtax was for child welfare.

Carrying a Child — SP40

Designs: Different ways of carrying a child. 40c+18c is vertical.

Perf. 14x13, 13x14

1976, Oct. 4 Litho.

B140	SP40	20c + 10c multi	.60	.60
B141	SP40	25c + 12c multi	.60	.60
B142	SP40	40c + 18c multi	.60	.60
		Nos. B140-B142 (3)	1.80	1.80

Surtax was for child welfare.

Composite: Aces of Hearts, Clubs, Diamonds and Spades — SP41

Designs: 25c+12c, "King" and inscription. 40c+18c, Hand holding cards; map of Aruba as ace of hearts, horiz.

Perf. 13x14, 14x13

1977, May 6 Litho.

B143	SP41	20c + 10c red & blk	.50	.35
B144	SP41	25c + 12c multi	.50	.35
a.		Min. sheet, 2 ea #B143-B144	1.40	1.10
B145	SP41	40c + 18c multi	.65	.45
		Nos. B143-B145 (3)	1.65	1.15

Central American and Caribbean Bridge Championships, Aruba.

Souvenir Sheet

1977, May 26 *Perf. 13½x14*

B146	SP41	Sheet of 3	3.50	2.50

Amphilex 77 International Philatelic Exhibition, Amsterdam, May 26-June 5. No. B146 contains 3 stamps similar to Nos. B143-B145 with bright green background.

Children and Toys — SP42

Children playing with fantasy animals.

1977, Oct. 25 Litho. *Perf. 14x13*

B147	SP42	15c + 5c multi	.35	.25
B148	SP42	20c + 10c multi	.45	.35
B149	SP42	25c + 12c multi	.55	.45
B150	SP42	40c + 18c multi	.65	.45
a.		Min. sheet, 2 ea #B148, B150	2.40	1.60
		Nos. B147-B150 (4)	2.00	1.50

Surtax was for child welfare.

Water Skiing — SP43

Designs: 20c+10c, Sailing. 25c+12c, Soccer. 40c+18c, Baseball.

1978, Mar. 31   **Litho.**   **Perf. 13x14**
B151 SP43 15c + 5c multi   .25   .25
B152 SP43 20c + 10c multi   .25   .25
B153 SP43 25c + 12c multi   .25   .25
B154 SP43 40c + 18c multi   .25   .25
   Nos. B151-B154 (4)   1.00 1.00

Surtax was for sports. Tete-beche gutter pairs exist.

Red Cross — SP44

1978, Sept. 19   **Litho.**   **Perf. 14x13**
B155 SP44 55c + 25c red & blk   .40   .40
   a.   Souv. sheet of 3, perf. 13½x13   2.00 1.60

Henri Dunant (1828-1910), founder of Red Cross. Surtax for the Red Cross. Tete-beche gutter pairs exist.

Roller Skating — SP45

Children's Activities: 20c+10c, Kite flying. 25c+12c, Playing marbles. 40c+ 18c, Bicycling.

1978, Nov. 7   **Litho.**   **Perf. 13x14**
B156 SP45 15c + 5c multi   .45   .35
B157 SP45 20c + 10c multi   .50   .40
   a.   Min. sheet, 2 ea #B156-B157   1.75 1.50
B158 SP45 25c + 12c multi   .55   .45
B159 SP45 40c + 18c multi   .60   .50
   Nos. B156-B159 (4)   2.10 1.70

Surtax was for child welfare.

Carnival King — SP46

25th Aruba Carnival: 75c+20c, Carnival Queen and coat of arms.

1979, Feb. 20   **Litho.**   **Perf. 13x14**
B160 SP46 40c + 10c multi   .50   .45
B161 SP46 75c + 20c multi   .75   .70

Regatta Emblem — SP47

Designs: 35c+10c, Race. 40c+15c, Globe and yacht, horiz. 55c+25c, Yacht, birds and sun.

     Perf. 13x14, 14x13
1979, May 16   **Litho.**
B162 SP47 15c + 5c multi   .25   .25
B163 SP47 35c + 10c multi   .35   .30
B164 SP47 40c + 15c multi   .45   .35
B165 SP47 55c + 25c multi   .55   .40
   a.   Souv. sheet of 4, #B162-B165   1.75 1.60
   Nos. B162-B165 (4)   1.60 1.30

12th International Sailing Regatta, Bonaire. #B164 in souvenir sheet is perf 13x14.

Volunteer Corps Type, 1979

15c+10c, Soldiers, 1929 and 1979. 40c+20c, Soldier guarding oil refinery, Guard emblem.

1979, July 4   **Litho.**   **Perf. 13x14**
B166 A124 15c + 10c multi   .35   .30
B167 A124 40c + 20c multi   .45   .40

Girls Reading Book, IYC Emblem — SP48

IYC Emblem and Children's Drawings: 25c+12c, Infant and cat. 35c+15c, Girls walking under palm trees. 50c+20c, Children wearing adult clothing.

1979, Oct. 24   **Litho.**   **Perf. 13x14**
B168 SP48 20c + 10c multi   .35   .35
B169 SP48 25c + 12c multi   .40   .35
B170 SP48 35c + 15c multi   .45   .40
   a.   Souv. sheet, 2 ea #B168,   B170   1.50 1.60
B171 SP48 50c + 20c multi   .55   .50
   Nos. B168-B171 (4)   1.75 1.60

International Year of the Child. Surtax for child welfare.

Fort Church Type of 1980

Designs: 20c+10c, Brass chandelier, 1909, horiz. 50c+25c, Pipe organ.

     Perf. 14x13, 13x14
1980, Jan. 9   **Litho.**
B172 A128 20c + 10c multi   .35   .35
B173 A128 50c + 25c multi   .45   .45

Volleyball, Olympic Rings — SP49

Designs: 25c+10c, Woman gymnast. 30c+15c, Male gymnast. 60c+25c, Basketball.

1980, June 25   **Litho.**   **Perf. 13x14**
B174 SP49 25c + 10c multi   .35   .30
B175 SP49 30c + 15c multi   .40   .35
B176 SP49 45c + 20c multi   .55   .50
B177 SP49 60c + 25c multi   .65   .55
   a.   Souvenir sheet of 6, 3 each   #B174, B177, perf. 14x13½   2.25 1.90
   Nos. B174-B177 (4)   1.95 1.70

22nd Summer Olympic Games, Moscow, July 19-Aug. 3.

St. Maarten Landscape — SP50

Children's Drawings: 30c+15c, House in Bonaire. 40c+20c, Child at blackboard. 60c+25c, Dancers, vert.

     Perf. 14x13, 13x14
1980, Oct. 22   **Litho.**
B178 SP50 25c + 10c multi   .40   .25
B179 SP50 30c + 15c multi   .50   .40
B180 SP50 40c + 20c multi   .55   .45
B181 SP50 60c + 25c multi   .65   .45
   a.   Souvenir sheet of 6+ 4 labels,   3 each #B178, B181   3.00 2.25
   Nos. B178-B181 (4)   2.10 1.55

Surtax was for child welfare.
#B178 in souvenir sheet is perf 13x14.

Girl Using Sign Language — SP51

Designs: 25c+10c, Blind woman. 30c+15c, Man in wheelchair. 45c+20c, Infant in walker.

1981, Apr. 7   **Litho.**   **Perf. 13x14**
B182 SP51 25c + 10c multi   .45   .40
B183 SP51 30c + 15c multi   .50   .50
B184 SP51 45c + 20c multi   .65   .65
B185 SP51 60c + 25c multi   .75   .70
   Nos. B182-B185 (4)   2.35 2.25

International Year of the Disabled. Surtax was for handicapped children.

Tennis Player — SP52

1981, May 27   **Litho.**   **Perf. 13x14**
B186 SP52 30c + 15c shown   .60   .50
B187 SP52 50c + 20c Diving   .80   .60
B188 SP52 70c + 25c Boxing   1.00   .80
   a.   Min. sheet of 3, #B186-B188   2.50 2.50
   Nos. B186-B188 (3)   2.40 1.90

Surtax was for sporting events.

Den Mother and Cub Scout — SP53

Scouting in Netherlands Antilles, 50th Anniv.: 70c+25c, van der Maarel, national founder. 1g+50c, Ronde Klip (headquarters).

1981, Sept. 16   **Litho.**   **Perf. 14x13**
B189 SP53 45c + 20c multi   .95   .75
B190 SP53 70c + 25c multi   1.20   .95
B191 SP53 1g + 50c multi   1.60 1.35
   a.   Min. sheet of 3, #B189-B191,   perf. 13½x13   4.00 3.25
   Nos. B189-B191 (3)   3.75 3.05

Surtax was for various social and cultural institutions.

Girl and Teddy Bear — SP54

Designs: 35c+15c, Mother and child. 45c+20c, Two children. 55c+25c, Boy and cat.

1981, Oct. 21   **Litho.**   **Perf. 13x14**
B192 SP54 35c + 15c multi   .50   .45
B193 SP54 45c + 20c multi   .60   .50
B194 SP54 55c + 25c multi   .75   .65
   a.   Min. sheet of 2 + label   2.50 2.00
B195 SP54 85c + 40c multi   1.10   .95
   Nos. B192-B195 (4)   2.95 2.55

Surtax for child welfare.

Fencing — SP55

1982, Feb. 17   **Litho.**   **Perf. 14x13**
B196 SP55 35c + 15c shown   .75   .50
B197 SP55 45c + 20c Judo   1.00   .60
B198 SP55 70c + 35c Soccer   1.25   .95
   a.   Miniature sheet of 2 + label   3.50 2.00
B199 SP55 85c + 40c Bicycling   1.50 1.10
   Nos. B196-B199 (4)   4.50 3.15

Surtax was for sporting events.

Girl Playing Accordion — SP56

1982, Oct. 20   **Litho.**
B200 SP56 35c + 15c shown   .85   .50
B201 SP56 75c + 35c Guitar   1.40 1.00
B202 SP56 85c + 40c Violin   1.60 1.10
   a.   Min. sheet of 3, #B200-B202   4.00 3.25
   Nos. B200-B202 (3)   3.85 2.60

Surtax for child welfare.

Traditional House, Saba — SP57

1982, Nov. 17   **Litho.**
B203 SP57 35c + 15c shown   .95   .65
B204 SP57 75c + 35c Aruba   1.40   .95
B205 SP57 85c + 40c Curaçao   1.40   .95
   a.   Souv. sheet of 3, #B203-B205   4.00   3.25
   Nos. B203-B205 (3)   3.75 2.55

Surtax was for various social and cultural institutions.

High Jump — SP58

No. B207, Weight lifting. No. B208, Wind surfing.

1983, Feb. 22   **Litho.**
B206 SP58 35c + 15c shown   .75   .60
B207 SP58 45c + 20c multi   1.10   .75
B208 SP58 85c + 40c multi   1.75 1.20
   Nos. B206-B208 (3)   3.60 2.55

Surtax was for sporting events.

Child with Lizard — SP59

No. B210, Child with insects. No. B211, Child with animal.

1983, Oct. 18   **Litho.**   **Perf. 13x14**
B209 SP59 45c + 20c shown   1.00   .75
B210 SP59 55c + 25c multi   1.25   .90
B211 SP59 100c + 50c multi   2.00 1.50
   a.   Souv. sheet of 3, #B209-B211   4.50 3.25
   Nos. B209-B211 (3)   4.25 3.15

Surtax was for Childrens' Charity.

Pre-Columbian Artifacts — SP60

1983, Nov. 22   **Litho.**   **Perf. 13x14**
B212 SP60 45c + 20c multi   1.00   .85
B213 SP60 55c + 25c multi   1.25 1.00
B214 SP60 85c + 40c multi   1.50 1.10
B215 SP60 100c + 50c multi   1.90 1.50
   Nos. B212-B215 (4)   5.65 4.45

Curaçao Baseball Federation, 50th Anniv. — SP61

1984, Mar. 27   **Litho.**   **Perf. 14x13**
B216 SP61 25c + 10c Catching   1.20   .50
B217 SP61 45c + 20c Batting   1.70   .85
B218 SP61 55c + 25c Pitching   2.10 1.05
B219 SP61 85c + 40c Running   2.40 1.30
   a.   Min. sheet of 3, #B217-B219   6.00 3.75
   Nos. B216-B219 (4)   7.40 3.70

Surtax was for baseball fed., 1984 Olympics.

Microphones, Radio — SP62

Designs: 55c+25c, Radio, record player. 100c+50c, Record players.

1984, Apr. 24   **Litho.**   **Perf. 14x13**
B220 SP62 45c + 20c multi   1.45   .90
B221 SP62 55c + 25c multi   1.75 1.15
B222 SP62 100c + 50c multi   2.10 1.60
   Nos. B220-B222 (3)   5.30 3.65

Surtax was for social and cultural institutions.

Boy Reading — SP63

Designs: 55c+25c, Parents reading to children. 100c+50c, Family worship.

1984, Nov. 7   Litho.   Perf. 13x14
B223 SP63 45c + 20c multi   1.05 .90
B224 SP63 55c + 25c multi   1.35 1.15
B225 SP63 100c + 50c multi   1.75 1.45
  a. Souv. sheet of 3, #B223-B225   4.50 3.75
  Nos. B223-B225 (3)   4.15 3.50

Surtax was for children's charity.

Soccer Players — SP64

1985, Mar. 27   Litho.   Perf. 14x13
B226 SP64 10c + 5c multi   .60 .35
B227 SP64 15c + 5c multi   .65 .40
B228 SP64 45c + 20c multi   1.15 .85
B229 SP64 55c + 25c multi   1.40 1.05
B230 SP64 85c + 40c multi   1.90 1.45
  Nos. B226-B230 (5)   5.70 4.10

The surtax was for sporting events.

Intl. Youth Year — SP65

No. B231, Youth, computer keyboard. No. B232, Girl listening to music. No. B233, Youth breakdancing.

1985, Apr. 29   Litho.
B231 SP65 45c + 20c multi   1.20 .90
B232 SP65 55c + 25c multi   1.60 1.15
B233 SP65 100c + 50c multi   2.25 1.60
  Nos. B231-B233 (3)   5.05 3.65

Surtax for youth, social and cultural organizations.

Children — SP66

No. B234, Eskimo. No. B235, African. No. B236, Asian. No. B237, Dutch. No. B238, American Indian.

1985, Oct. 16   Litho.   Perf. 13x14
B234 SP66 5c + 5c multi   .45 .25
B235 SP66 10c + 5c multi   .55 .30
B236 SP66 25c + 10c multi   .80 .45
B237 SP66 45c + 20c multi   1.40 .80
B238 SP66 55c + 25c multi   1.40 .95
  a. Souv. sheet of 3, #B236-B238   4.00 2.25
  Nos. B234-B238 (5)   4.60 2.75

Surtax for child welfare.

Sports — SP67

No. B239, Running. No. B240, Horse racing. No. B241, Car racing. No. B242, Soccer.

1986, Feb. 19   Litho.   Perf. 13x14
B239 SP67 15c + 5c multi   1.05 .45
B240 SP67 25c + 10c multi   1.25 .65
B241 SP67 45c + 20c multi   1.60 .85
B242 SP67 55c + 25c multi   1.75 1.05
  Nos. B239-B242 (4)   5.65 3.00

Surtax for the natl. Sports Federation.

Handicrafts — SP68

1986, Apr. 29
B243 SP68 30c + 15c Painting   1.05 .60
B244 SP68 45c + 20c Sculpting 1.25 .65
B245 SP68 55c + 25c Ceramics   1.50 .90
  Nos. B243-B245 (3)   3.80 2.15

Surtax for Curaçao Social & Cultural Care.

Sports — SP69

1986, Oct. 15   Litho.   Perf. 13x14
B246 SP69 20c + 10c Soccer   .70 .40
B247 SP69 25c + 15c Tennis   .90 .45
B248 SP69 45c + 20c Judo   1.05 .65
B249 SP69 55c + 20c Baseball   1.25 .85
  a. Min. sheet of 2, #B248-B249   2.60 1.60
  Nos. B246-B249 (4)   3.90 2.35

Surtax for the natl. Sports Foundation.

Social and Cultural Programs — SP70

No. B250, Musicians. No. B251, Handicapped. No. B252, Pavilion.

1987, Mar. 11   Litho.
B250 SP70 35c + 15c multi   .80 .55
B251 SP70 45c + 25c multi   1.25 .65
B252 SP70 85c + 40c multi   1.60 1.05
  Nos. B250-B252 (3)   3.65 2.25

Surtax for the Jong Wacht (Youth Guard) and the natl. Red Cross.

Boy in Various Stages of Growth — SP71

1987, Oct. 21   Litho.   Perf. 14x13
B253 SP71 40c + 15c Infant   1.00 .65
B254 SP71 55c + 25c Toddler   1.25 .85
B255 SP71 115c + 50c Boy   1.60 1.15
  a. Souv. sheet of 3, #B253-B255   4.25 2.75
  Nos. B253-B255 (3)   3.85 2.65

Surtax benefited Child Care programs.

Queen Emma Bridge, Cent. — SP72

55c+25c, Bridge, vert. 115c+55c, View of Willemstad Harbor and quay. 190c+60c, Flags of the Netherlands, Antilles and US, Leonard B. Smith, engineer.

1988, May 9   Perf. 13x14, 14x13
B256 SP72 55c + 25c multi   1.15 .60
B257 SP72 115c + 55c multi   1.75 1.10
B258 SP72 190c + 60c multi   3.00 2.00
  Nos. B256-B258 (3)   5.90 3.70

Surtax for social and cultural purposes.

Youth Care Campaign — SP73

No. B259, Girl, television. No. B260, Boy, portable stereo. No. B261, Girl, computer.

1988, Oct. 26   Litho.   Perf. 14x13
B259 SP73 55c + 25c multi   1.05 .65
B260 SP73 65c + 30c multi   1.15 .80
B261 SP73 115c + 55c multi   1.60 1.15
  a. Souv. sheet of 3, #B259-B261   5.25 2.75
  Nos. B259-B261 (3)   3.80 2.60

Surtax for child welfare.

Curaçao Stamp Assoc., 50th Anniv. SP75

Designs: 30c+10c, Type A25 and No. 461 under magnifying glass. 55c+20c, Simulated stamp (learning to use tongs). 80c+30c, Barn owl, album, magnifying glass, tongs.

1989, Jan. 18   Litho.   Perf. 13x14
B264 30c + 10c multi   1.25 .55
B265 55c + 20c multi   1.25 .85
B266 80c + 30c multi   1.25 .95
  a. Strip of 3, #B264-B266   3.75 3.00

No. B266a has a continuous design. Surtaxed for welfare organizations.

Child and Nature — SP76

No. B267, Girl, boy, tree. No. B268, Playing on beach. No. B269, Father and child. No. B270, At the beach, diff.

1989, Oct. 25   Litho.   Perf. 14x13
B267 SP76 40c + 15c multi   1.00 .60
B268 SP76 65c + 30c multi   1.15 .80
B269 SP76 115c + 55c multi   1.75 1.30
  Nos. B267-B269 (3)   3.90 2.70

Souvenir Sheet
B270 SP76 155c + 75c multi   3.75 2.10

Surtax for child welfare.

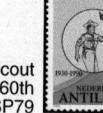

Natl. Girl Scout Movement, 60th Anniv. SP77

Totolika, 60th Anniv. SP78

Natl. Boy Scout Movement, 60th Anniv. — SP79

1990, Mar. 7   Litho.   Perf. 13x14
B271 SP77 30c + 10c multi   .80 .55
B272 SP78 40c + 15c multi   1.05 .75
B273 SP79 155c + 65c multi   3.00 2.50
  Nos. B271-B273 (3)   4.85 3.80

Parents' and Friends Association of Persons with a Mental Handicap (Totolika). Surtax for social and cultural purposes.

SP80

1990, June 13   Litho.   Perf. 13x14
B274 SP80 65c + 30c multi   1.15 .75

Sport Unie Brion Trappers Soccer Club. Exists in tete-beche gutter pairs.

Anti-drug Campaign — SP81

1990, June 13
B275 SP81 115c + 55c multi   1.75 1.35

Exists in tete-beche gutter pairs.

Youth Care Campaign — SP82

No. B276, Bees, flowers. No. B277, Dolphins. No. B278, Donkey, bicycle. No. B279, Goat, house. No. B280, Rabbit. No. B281, Lizard, moon.

1990, Oct. 31   Litho.   Perf. 14x13
B276 SP82 30c + 5c multi   .70 .40
B277 SP82 55c + 10c multi   1.05 .60
B278 SP82 65c + 15c multi   1.15 .80
B279 SP82 100c + 20c multi   1.75 1.20
B280 SP82 115c + 25c multi   1.90 1.30
B281 SP82 155c + 25c multi   3.25 2.10
  Nos. B276-B281 (6)   9.80 6.40

Surtax for child welfare. See Nos. B285-B288.

Social and Cultural Care — SP83

Designs: 30c+10c, Youth philately. 65c+25c, St. Vincentius Brass Band, 50th anniv. 155c+55c, Curaçao Community Center Federation.

1991, Apr. 3   Litho.   Perf. 14x13
B282 SP83 30c + 10c multi   .85 .60
B283 SP83 65c + 25c multi   1.35 1.00
B284 SP83 155c + 55c multi   3.00 2.25
  Nos. B282-B284 (3)   5.20 3.85

Youth Care Campaign Type of 1990

Fight illiteracy: 40c+15c, Octopus holding numbers and letters. 65c+30c, Birds, blackboard. 155c+65c, Turtle telling time. No. B288a, Owl, flag. b, Books, bookworms. c, Seahorse.

1991, Oct. 31   Litho.   Perf. 14x13
B285 SP82 40c + 15c multi   1.15 .80
B286 SP82 65c + 30c multi   1.45 1.35
B287 SP82 155c + 65c multi   3.00 3.00
  Nos. B285-B287 (3)   5.60 5.15

Souvenir Sheet
Imperf
B288   Sheet of 3   6.25 5.00
  a. SP82 55c + 25c multi   2.00 1.60
  b. SP82 100c + 35c multi   2.00 1.60
  c. SP82 115c + 50c multi   2.00 1.60

Surtax for child welfare.

SP84

1992 Summer Olympics, Barcelona: a, 30c + 10c, Triangle and oval. b, 55c + 25c, Globe showing location of Netherland Antilles, flag. c, 115c + 55c, Emblem of Netherlands Antilles Olympic Committee.

1992, Mar. 4   Litho.   Perf. 13x14
B289 SP84 Strip of 3, #a.-c.   4.50 3.75

Netherlands Antilles Olympic Committee, 60th Anniv.

SP85

No. B290, Spaceship. No. B291, Robot. No. B292, Extraterrestrial.
No. B293, Extraterrestrial, diff.

1992, Oct. 28   Litho.   Perf. 13x14
B290 SP85 30c +10c multi   .65   .50
B291 SP85 70c +30c multi   1.15   1.15
B292 SP85 100c +40c multi   1.75   1.60
    Nos. B290-B292 (3)   3.55   3.25

Souvenir Sheet
B293 SP85 155c +70c multi   3.50   3.25

Surtax for child welfare.

SP86

Designs: 65c+25c, Fire safety, child playing with blocks. 90c+35c, Child fastening auto safety belt, vert. 175c+75c, Child wearing flotation equipment while swimming. 35c+15c, Alert child studying.

Perf. 14x13, 13x14
1993, Oct. 27   Litho.
B294 SP86 65c +25c multi   1.25   1.05
B295 SP86 90c +35c multi   1.50   1.35
B296 SP86 175c +75c multi   3.00   2.75
    Nos. B294-B296 (3)   5.75   5.15

Souvenir Sheet
Perf. 13½x13
B297 SP86 35c +15c Sheet of 5
    + label   5.00   5.00

Surtax for child welfare.

Intl. Year of the
Family — SP87

No. B298, Woman, baby. No. B299, Daughter, father. No. B300, Grandparents. No. B301, Intl. emblem.

1994, Oct. 26   Litho.   Perf. 13x14
B298 SP87 35c +15c multi   .60   .55
B299 SP87 65c +25c multi   1.10   1.05
B300 SP87 90c +35c multi   2.00   1.75
    Nos. B298-B300 (3)   3.70   3.35

Souvenir Sheet
B301 SP87 175c +75c multi   3.75   3.75

Surtax for the benefit of the Antillean Youth Care Federation.

Slave Rebellion in
Curaçao,
Bicent. — SP88

Designs: 30c+10c, Monument, bird with outstretched wings. 45c+15c, Bird, bell tower.

1995, Aug. 17   Litho.   Perf. 14x13
B302 SP88 30c +10c multi   .75   .65
B303 SP88 45c +15c multi   1.15   1.00

Youth
Philately — SP89

Stamp drawings by children from: 65c+25c, Curaçao, Bonaire. 75c+35c, St. Maarten, St. Eustatius, Saba.

1995, Aug. 17
B304 SP89 65c +25c multi   1.40   1.05
B305 SP89 75c +35c multi   1.50   1.20

Nos. 516-517, 544
Surcharged in Red
Brown

1995, Sept. 22   Litho.   Perf. 14x13
B306 A148 65c +65c on #516   1.75   1.60
B307 A148 75c +75c on #517   2.00   1.75
B308 A148 1g +1g on #544   2.40   2.25
    Nos. B306-B308 (3)   6.15   5.60
Surcharge for hurricane relief.

Child Welfare
Stamps — SP91

Promotion of Children's Good Deeds: 35c+15c, Helping elderly across street. 65c+25c, Reading newspaper to blind person. 90c+35c, Caring for younger sibling. 175c+75c, Giving flowers to sick person.

1995, Oct. 25   Litho.   Perf. 14x13
B309 SP91 35c +15c multi   .65   .60
B310 SP91 65c +25c multi   1.15   1.05
B311 SP91 90c +35c multi   1.45   1.35
B312 SP91 175c +75c multi   3.00   2.75
    Nos. B309-B312 (4)   6.25   5.75

Surtax for various youth organizations.

Child Welfare
Stamps — SP92

UNICEF, 50th anniv.: 40c+15c, Child wandering streets. 75c+25c, Child labor in Asia. 110c+45c, Child in wartime (former Yugoslavia), vert. 225c+100c, Caribbean poverty, vert.

Perf. 14x13, 13x14
1996, Oct. 23   Litho.
B313 SP92 40c +15c multi   .75   .65
B314 SP92 75c +25c multi   1.30   1.20
B315 SP92 110c +45c multi   1.90   1.75
B316 SP92 225c +100c multi   4.00   3.75
    Nos. B313-B316 (4)   7.95   7.35

Social and Cultural Care
Stamps — SP93

Designs: 40c+15c, Curaçao Foundation for the cure and resettlement of ex-prisoners, 50th anniv. 75c+30c, ABVO (General Union of Public Servants), 60th anniv. 85c+40c, 110c+50c, Red Cross Corps section, Curaçao, 65th anniv.

1997, Jan. 16   Litho.   Perf. 13x14
B317 SP93 40c +15c multi   .90   .65
B318 SP93 75c +30c multi   1.30   1.20
B319 SP93 85c +40c multi   1.60   1.60
B320 SP93 110 +50c multi   1.90   1.75
    Nos. B317-B320 (4)   5.70   5.20

Child Welfare
Stamps — SP94

Musical notes, musical instruments: 40c+15c, Drums. 75c+25c, Piano. 110c+45c, Flute. 225c+100c, Guitar.

1997, Oct. 22   Litho.   Perf. 14x13
B321 SP94 40c +15c multi   .80   .65
B322 SP94 75c +25c multi   1.20   1.15
B323 SP94 110c +45c multi   2.00   1.75
B324 SP94 225c +100c multi   3.00   2.50
    Nos. B321-B324 (4)   7.00   6.05

Social and Cultural
Care — SP95

No. B325, Curaçao Museum, 50th anniv. No. B326, Seawater Desalination, 70th anniv. 75c+25c, Water area, Lac Cai Bonaire, vert. 85c+40c, Water area, Klein-Bonaire, vert.

Perf. 14x13, 13x14
1998, Mar. 9   Litho.
B325 SP95 40c +15c multi   .85   .70
B326 SP95 40c +15c multi   .85   .70
B327 SP95 75c +25c multi   1.45   1.30
B328 SP95 85c +40c multi   1.90   1.75
    Nos. B325-B328 (4)   5.05   4.45

Child Welfare
Stamps — SP96

Universal Rights of the Child: 40c+15c, Child holding cutouts representing family. 75c+25c, Children eating watermelon. 110c+45c, Handicapped children drawing pictures. 225c+100c, Children holding cans with string to play telephone.

1998, Oct. 28   Litho.   Perf. 13x14
B329 SP96 40c +15c multi   .85   .70
B330 SP96 75c +25c multi   1.30   1.20
B331 SP96 110c +45c multi   2.00   1.90
B332 SP96 225c +100c multi   4.25   4.00
    Nos. B329-B332 (4)   8.40   7.80

Buildings — SP97

Willemstad buildings on World Heritage List: 40c+15c, Houses, Ijzerstraat neighborhood, horiz. 75c+30c, Postal Museum. 110c+50c, "Bridal Cake" building, Scharloo area, horiz.

Perf. 14x13, 13x14
1999, Sept. 28   Litho.
B333 SP97 40c +15c multi   .80   .70
B334 SP97 75c +30c multi   1.45   1.30
B335 SP97 110c +50c multi   2.10   1.90
    Nos. B333-B335 (3)   4.35   3.90

Sports — SP98

1999, Oct. 27   Perf. 13x14
B336 SP98 40c +15c Basketball   1.30   .80
B337 SP98 75c +25c Golf   1.75   1.30
B338 SP98 110c +45c Fencing   2.60   1.90
B339 SP98 225c +100c Tennis   4.75   4.00
    Nos. B336-B339 (4)   10.40   8.00

Social and Cultural
Care — SP99

Designs: 75c+30c, Children playing. 110c+50c, Chemistry lesson. 225c+100c, Arithmetic lesson, vert.

Perf. 14x13, 13x14
2000, Apr. 28   Litho.
B340-B342 SP99 Set of 3   8.25   7.00

Youth
Care — SP100

Designs: 40c+15c, Child reaching up, vert. 75c+25c, Children learning with computers. 110c+45c, Children playing with toy boat. 225c+100c, Children and map, vert.

Perf. 13x14, 14x13
2000, Oct. 25   Litho.
B343-B346 SP100 Set of 4   9.50   8.75

Caribbean Postal
Union, 5th
Anniv. — SP101

Designs: 75c+25c, Pen, emblem. 110c+45c, Emblem. 225c+100c, Globe, emblem.

2001, May 21   Litho.   Perf. 13¼x13¾
B347-B349 SP101 Set of 3   10.00   8.25

Youth
Care — SP102

Designs: 40c+15c, Boy feeding baby. 75c+25c, Girls dancing, vert. 110c+45c, Boy pushing woman in wheelchair, vert.

Perf. 13½x12¾, 12¾x13½
2001, Oct. 24   Litho.
B350-B352 SP102 Set of 3   6.25   5.75

2002 World Cup Soccer
Championships, Japan
and Korea — SP103

Soccer player with: 95c+35c, Ball of flags. 145c+55c, Ball with map. 240c+110c, Ball.

2002, June 25   Litho.   Perf. 12¾x14
B353-B355 SP103 Set of 3   11.00 10.00

Youth
Care — SP104

"Dialogue among civilizations:" 50c+15c, Lion and fish. 95c+35c, Kangaroo and iguana. 145c+55c, Goat and penguin. 240c+110c, Lizard and toucan.

2002, Oct. 24   Perf. 14x12¾
B356-B359 SP104 Set of 4   11.25 11.25

Miniature Sheet

Maps of the Netherlands
Antilles — SP105

No. B360: a, 25c+10c, Portion of 1688 map by Hendrick Doncker showing Curaçao and Bonaire. b, 30c+15c, Portion of Doncker map showing St. Maarten, Saba and St. Eustatius, vert. c, 55c+25c, Modern map of Curaçao and Bonaire. d, 85c+35c, Modern map of St. Maarten, Saba and St. Eustatius, vert. e, 95c+40c, Modern map of Caribbean Islands.

Perf. 14x12¾, 12¾x14 (vert. stamps)
2003, Mar. 19   Litho.
B360 SP105   Sheet of 5, #a-e   7.50 7.00

Miniature Sheet

Youth Care SP106

No. B361: a, 50c+15c, Boy taking shower. b, 95c+35c, Girl with umbrella. c, 145c+55c, Boy with watering can. d, 240c+110c, Hands in water from open faucet.

2003, Oct. 22   Litho.   *Perf. 13x14*
B361 SP106   Sheet of 4, #a-d   9.50 8.50

Intl. Year of Fresh Water.

Youth Care — SP107

No. B362: a, Boy, girl, slave huts. b, Girl, Autonomy Monument. c, Boy, girl, broken stone walls built by slaves. d, Boy, girl, wall of plantation house. e, Boy, preamble of Netherlands Constitution.

2004, Oct. 20   *Perf. 13½x13*
B362   Horiz. strip of 5   8.25 8.25
   a.   SP107 50c +15c multi   .75 .75
   b.-c.   SP107 95c +35c either single   1.50 1.50
   d.-e.   SP107 145c +55c either single   2.25 2.25

Autonomy of the Netherlands Antilles, 50th anniv. (Nos. B362b, B362e), Intl. Year Commemorating the Struggle Against Slavery and its Abolition (Nos. B362a, B362c, B362d).

Intl. Year of Sports and Physical Education — SP108

Designs: 55c+20c, Soccer. 97c+36c, Table tennis. 148c+56c, Tennis. 240c+110c, Baseball.

2005, Dec. 24   Litho.   *Perf. 13x13½*
B363-B366 SP108   Set of 4   9.50 9.50

Youth Care — SP109

Hatted globes showing: 55c+20c, North and South America. 100c+45c, Africa. 149c+61c, Europe, Africa and Asia. 285c+125c, Africa and Asia.

2006, Oct. 23   Litho.   *Perf. 12¾x13¼*
B367-B370 SP109   Set of 4   8.25 8.25

Youth Care — SP110

Family: 59c+26c, Praying at dinner table. 104c+46c, Respecting flag. 155c+65c, As baseball team. 285c+125c, Studying together.

2007, Oct. 24   Litho.   *Perf. 13¼x12¾*
B371-B374 SP110   Set of 4   8.25 8.25

Youth Care — SP111

Potato: 59c+26c, As potato farmer. 1.06g+46c, Peeling potatoes. 1.58g+65c, Eating French fries. 2.85g+1.25g, Family.

2008, Oct. 23 Litho.   *Perf. 12¾x13¼*
B375-B378 SP111   Set of 4   9.00 9.00

Intl. Year of the Potato.

Youth Care — SP112

Designs: 59c+26c, Galileo Galilei and silhouette of boy. 110c+45c, Silhouettes of stargazers and telescope. 168c+75c, Silhouettes of children watching space shuttle. 285c+125c, Men walking on Moon.

2009, Oct. 26 Litho.   *Perf. 12¾x13¼*
B379-B382 SP112   Set of 4   8.50 8.50

Intl. Year of Astronomy.

AIR POST STAMPS

Regular Issues of 1915-22 Surcharged in Black

Perf. 12½
1929, July 6   Typo.   Unwmk.
C1 A13   50c on 12½c red   18.00 21.00
C2 A13   1g on 20c blue   18.00 21.00
C3 A13   2g on 15c ol grn   45.00 52.50
   Nos. C1-C3 (3)   81.00 94.50

Excellent forgeries exist.

Allegory, "Flight" — AP1

1931-39   Engr.
C4 AP1   10c Prus grn ('34)   .25 .25
C5 AP1   15c dull blue ('38)   .40 .25
C6 AP1   20c red   1.00 .25
C7 AP1   25c gray ('38)   .80 .90
C8 AP1   30c yellow ('39)   .40 .40
C9 AP1   35c dull blue   1.20 1.15
C10 AP1   40c green   .80 .55
C11 AP1   45c orange   2.00 2.00
C12 AP1   50c lake ('38)   1.20 .60
C13 AP1   60c brown vio   .80 .40
C14 AP1   70c black   6.50 .50
C15 AP1   1.40g brown   4.00 5.00
C16 AP1   2.80g bister   5.00 5.25
   Nos. C4-C16 (13)   24.35 19.00

No. C6 Surcharged in Black

1934, Aug. 25
C17 AP1 10c on 20c red   20.00 15.00

Catalogue values for unused stamps in this section, from this point to the end of the section, are for Never Hinged items.

Map of the Atlantic — AP2   Plane over Islands — AP3

Map of Curaçao, Aruba and Bonaire — AP4   Planes — AP5

Plane — AP6

1942, Oct. 20   *Perf. 13x13½*
C18 AP2   10c grn & bl   .80 .25
C19 AP3   15c rose car & yel grn   .80 .25
C20 AP4   20c red brn & grn   .80 .25
C21 AP5   25c dp ultra & org brn   .80 .25
C22 AP6   30c red & lt vio   .80 .75
C23 AP2   35c dk vio & ol grn   1.20 .55
C24 AP3   40c gray ol & chnt   1.60 .55
C25 AP4   45c dk red & blk   .80 .25
C26 AP5   50c vio & blk   2.00 .25
C27 AP6   60c lt yel brn & dl bl   3.25 1.15
C28 AP2   70c red brn & Prus bl   3.25 1.15
C29 AP3   1.40g bl vio & sl grn   20.00 2.10
C30 AP4   2.80g int bl & lt bl   28.00 5.75
C31 AP5   5g rose lake & sl grn   45.00 19.00
C32 AP6   10g grn & red brn   52.50 28.00
   Nos. C18-C32 (15)   161.60 60.50

For surcharges see Nos. CB9-CB12.

Plane and Post Horn AP7   DC-4 above Waves AP8

1947   Photo.   *Perf. 12½x12*
C32A AP7   6c gray blk   .65 .25
C33 AP7   10c deep red   .65 .25
C33A AP7   12½c plum   .90 .25
C34 AP7   15c deep blue   .90 .30
C35 AP7   20c dl yel grn   1.10 .35
C36 AP7   25c org yel   1.10 .25
C37 AP7   30c lilac gray   1.35 .55
C38 AP7   35c org red   1.35 .70
C39 AP7   40c blue grn   1.35 .70
C40 AP7   45c brt violet   1.60 1.05
C41 AP7   50c carmine   1.60 .25
C42 AP7   60c brt blue   2.10 .65
C43 AP7   70c brown   3.75 1.50

Engr.
Perf. 12x12½
C44 AP8   1.50g black   2.75 .90
C45 AP8   2.50g dk car   15.50 4.00
C46 AP8   5g green   32.00 8.25
C47 AP8   7.50g dk blue   130.00 95.00
C48 AP8   10g dk red vio   82.50 34.00
C49 AP8   15g red org   110.00 95.00
C50 AP8   25g chocolate   110.00 95.00
   Nos. C32A-C50 (20)   501.15 339.20

AIR POST SEMI-POSTAL STAMPS

Flags of the Netherlands and the House of Orange with Inscription "Netherlands Shall Rise Again" — SPAP1

Engr. & Photo.
1941, Dec. 11   Unwmk.   *Perf. 12*
CB1 SPAP1   10c + 10c multi   32.00 26.00
CB2 SPAP1   15c + 25c multi   32.00 26.00
CB3 SPAP1   20c + 25c multi   32.00 26.00
CB4 SPAP1   25c + 25c multi   32.00 26.00
CB5 SPAP1   30c + 50c multi   32.00 26.00
CB6 SPAP1   35c + 50c multi   32.00 26.00
CB7 SPAP1   40c + 50c multi   32.00 26.00
CB8 SPAP1   50c + 100c multi   32.00 26.00
   Nos. CB1-CB8 (8)   256.00 208.00

The surtax was used by the Prince Bernhard Committee to purchase war material for

---

the Netherlands' fighting forces in Great Britain.

Catalogue values for unused stamps in this section, from this point to the end of the section, are for Never Hinged items.

Nos. C29-C32 Surcharged in Black

1943, Dec. 1   *Perf. 13x13½*
CB9 AP3   40c + 50c on 1.40g   9.00 8.25
CB10 AP4   45c + 50c on 2.80g   9.00 8.25
CB11 AP5   50c + 75c on 5g   9.00 8.25
CB12 AP6   60c + 100c on 10g   9.00 8.25
   Nos. CB9-CB12 (4)   36.00 33.00

The surtax was for the benefit of prisoners of war. These stamps were not sold to the public in the normal manner. All were sold in sets by advance subscription, the majority to philatelic speculators.

On No. CB9 overprint reads: "Voor / Krijgsgevangenen."

Princess Juliana — SPAP2

Engr. & Photo.
1944, Aug. 16   *Perf. 12*
Frame in carmine & deep blue, cross in carmine
CB13 SPAP2   10c + 10c lt brn   2.75 2.50
CB14 SPAP2   15c + 25c turq grn   2.75 2.50
CB15 SPAP2   20c + 25c dk ol gray   2.75 2.50
CB16 SPAP2   25c + 25c slate   2.75 2.50
CB17 SPAP2   30c + 50c sepia   2.75 2.50
CB18 SPAP2   35c + 50c chnt   2.75 2.50
CB19 SPAP2   40c + 50c grn   2.75 2.50
CB20 SPAP2   50c + 100c dk vio   2.75 2.50
   Nos. CB13-CB20 (8)   22.00 20.00

The surtax was for the Red Cross.

Map of Netherlands Indies — SPAP3

Map of Netherlands SPAP4

Photo. & Typo.
1946, July 1   *Perf. 11x11½*
CB21 SPAP3   10c + 10c   1.75 1.60
CB22 SPAP3   15c + 25c   1.75 1.60
CB23 SPAP3   20c + 25c   1.75 1.60
CB24 SPAP3   25c + 25c   1.75 1.60
CB25 SPAP3   30c + 50c   1.75 1.60
   a.   Double impression of denomination   400.00 475.00
CB26 SPAP3   35c + 50c   1.75 1.60
CB27 SPAP3   40c + 75c   1.75 1.60
CB28 SPAP3   50c + 100c   1.75 1.60
CB29 SPAP4   10c + 10c   1.75 1.60
CB30 SPAP4   15c + 25c   1.75 1.60
CB31 SPAP4   20c + 25c   1.75 1.60
CB32 SPAP4   25c + 25c   1.75 1.60
CB33 SPAP4   30c + 50c   1.75 1.60
CB34 SPAP4   35c + 50c   1.75 1.60
CB35 SPAP4   40c + 75c   1.75 1.60
CB36 SPAP4   50c + 100c   1.75 1.60
   Nos. CB21-CB36 (16)   28.00 25.60

The surtax on Nos. CB21 to CB36 was for the National Relief Fund.

POSTAGE DUE STAMPS

D1

Type I — 34 loops. "T" of "BETALEN" over center of loop, top branch of "E" of "TE" shorter than lower branch.
Type II — 33 loops. "T" of "BETALEN" over center of two loops.
Type III — 32 loops. "T" of "BETALEN" slightly to the left of loop, top of first "E" of "BETALEN" shorter than lower branch.

Value in Black

1889   Unwmk.   Typo.   Perf. 12½
Type III

J1	D1	2½c green	3.00	4.50
J2	D1	5c green	3.00	2.60
J3	D1	10c green	35.00	34.00
J4	D1	12½c green	400.00	210.00
J5	D1	15c green	28.00	22.50
J6	D1	20c green	16.00	11.50
J7	D1	25c green	200.00	150.00
J8	D1	30c green	14.00	11.50
J9	D1	40c green	18.00	11.50
J10	D1	50c green	40.00	30.00

Nos. J1-J10 were issued without gum.

Type I

J1a	D1	2½c	5.00	4.50
J2a	D1	5c	40.00	30.00
J3a	D1	10c	45.00	35.00
J4a	D1	12½c	450.00	225.00
J5a	D1	15c	32.00	22.50
J6a	D1	20c	80.00	57.50
J7a	D1	25c	600.00	350.00
J8a	D1	30c	80.00	67.50
J9a	D1	40c	80.00	67.50
J10a	D1	50c	50.00	37.50

Type II

J1b	D1	2½c	8.00	5.75
J2b	D1	5c	200.00	170.00
J3b	D1	10c	45.00	42.50
J4b	D1	12½c	475.00	260.00
J5b	D1	15c	32.00	26.00
J6b	D1	20c	450.00	425.00
J7b	D1	25c	1,600.	1,600.
J8b	D1	30c	450.00	375.00
J9b	D1	40c	450.00	375.00
J10b	D1	50c	60.00	75.00

D2

Value in Black

1892-98   Value in Black   Perf. 12½

J11	D2	2½c green (III)	.80	1.15
J12	D2	5c green (III)	1.20	1.60
J13	D2	10c green (III)	2.00	1.90
J14	D2	12½c green (III)	2.00	1.90
J15	D2	15c green (III) ('95)	3.00	1.90
J17	D2	25c green (III)	12.00	1.15
		Nos. J11-J17 (6)	21.00	9.60

Type I

J11a	D2	2½c	.80	1.15
J12a	D2	5c	3.00	2.60
J13a	D2	10c	3.00	2.25
J14a	D2	12½c	2.40	1.90
J16	D2	20c green ('95)	4.00	1.90
J17a	D2	25c	12.00	1.90
J18	D2	30c green ('95)	40.00	34.00
J19	D2	40c green ('95)	50.00	34.00
J20	D2	50c green ('95)	50.00	34.00

Type II

J11b	D2	2½c	20.00	20.00
J12b	D2	5c	1.20	1.60
J13b	D2	10c	2.00	1.90
J14b	D2	12½c	8.00	7.50
J17b	D2	25c	10.00	9.50
		Nos. J11b-J17b (5)	41.20	40.50

The editors would like to see documented evidence of existence the following: 15c type I; 15c, 20c, 30c, 40c, 50c type II; 20c type III.
Nos. J18-J20 are printed on porous paper.

Type I
On Yellowish or White Paper
Value in Color of Stamp

1915   Perf. 12½, 13½x12½

J21	D2	2½c green	.65	.75
J22	D2	5c green	.65	.75
J23	D2	10c green	.65	.75
J24	D2	12½c green	.80	1.15
J25	D2	15c green	1.45	1.60
J26	D2	20c green	.80	1.60
J27	D2	25c green	.25	.40
J28	D2	30c green	3.00	3.75
J29	D2	40c green	3.00	3.75
J30	D2	50c green	2.00	3.00
		Nos. J21-J30 (10)	13.25	17.50

1944   Perf. 11½

J23a	D2	10c yellow green	40.00	37.50
J24a	D2	12½c yellow green	40.00	30.00
J27a	D2	25c yellow green	100.00	3.75
		Nos. J23a-J27a (3)	180.00	71.25

Nos. J23a-J27a designs are 18x22½mm; Nos. J21-J30 designs are 18x21½mm.

Type of 1915
Type I
Value in Color of Stamp
Perf. 13½x13

1948-49   Unwmk.   Photo.

J31	D2	2½c bl grn ('48)	2.40	3.00
J32	D2	5c bl grn ('48)	2.40	3.00
J33	D2	10c blue green	10.00	10.50
J34	D2	12½c blue green	10.00	5.25
J35	D2	15c blue green	17.00	34.00
J36	D2	20c blue green	17.00	34.00
J37	D2	25c blue green	2.60	.75
J38	D2	30c blue green	17.00	34.00
J39	D2	40c blue green	17.00	34.00
J40	D2	50c blue green	17.00	34.00
		Nos. J31-J40 (10)	112.40	192.50

> **Catalogue values for unused stamps in this section, from this point to the end of the section, are for Never Hinged items.**

D3

1953-59   Photo.

J41	D3	1c dk blue grn ('59)	.25	.40
J42	D3	2½c dk blue grn	.60	.75
J43	D3	5c dk blue grn	.25	.40
J44	D3	6c dk blue grn ('59)	.75	.90
J45	D3	7c dk blue grn ('59)	.75	.90
J46	D3	8c dk blue grn ('59)	.75	.90
J47	D3	9c dk blue grn ('59)	.75	.90
J48	D3	10c dk blue grn	.30	.40
J49	D3	12½c dk blue grn	.30	.40
J50	D3	15c dk blue grn	.75	.90
J51	D3	20c dk blue grn	.75	.90
J52	D3	25c dk blue grn	.60	.25
J53	D3	30c dk blue grn	1.60	1.90
J54	D3	35c dk blue grn ('59)	1.60	1.90
J55	D3	40c dk blue grn	1.60	1.90
J56	D3	45c dk blue grn ('59)	1.60	1.90
J57	D3	50c dk blue grn	1.60	1.90
		Nos. J41-J57 (17)	14.80	17.50

NETHERLANDS INDIES

ˈne-thər-lənd͜z ˈin-dēs

(Dutch Indies, Indonesia)

LOCATION — East Indies
GOVT. — Dutch colony
AREA — 735,268 sq. mi.
POP. — 76,000,000 (estimated 1949)
CAPITAL — Jakarta (formerly Batavia)

Netherlands Indies consisted of the islands of Sumatra, Java, the Lesser Sundas, Madura, two thirds of Borneo, Celebes, the Moluccas, western New Guinea and many small islands.

Netherlands Indies changed its name to Indonesia in 1948. The Netherlands transferred sovereignty on Dec. 28, 1949, to the Republic of the United States of Indonesia (see "Indonesia"), except for the western part of New Guinea (see "Netherlands New Guinea"). The Republic of Indonesia was proclaimed Aug. 15, 1950.

100 Cents = 1 Gulden
100 Sen = 1 Rupiah (1949)

> **Catalogue values for unused stamps in this country are for Never Hinged items, beginning with Scott 250 in the regular postage section, Scott B57 in the semipostal section, and Scott J43 in the postage due section.**

Values for unused stamps are for examples with original gum as defined in the catalogue introduction. Very fine examples of No. 2 will have perforations touching the frameline on one or more sides due to the narrow spacing of the stamps on the plates. Stamps with perfs clear of the framelines on all four sides are scarce and will command higher prices.

Watermarks

Wmk. 202 — Circles

Wmk. 228 — Small Crown and C of A Multiple

King William III — A1

Unwmk.

1864, Apr. 1   Engr.   Imperf.

1	A1	10c lake	325.00	100.00

1868   Perf. 12½x12

2	A1	10c lake	1,250.	180.00

Privately perforated examples of No. 1 sometimes are mistaken for No. 2.

King William III — A2

ONE CENT:
Type I — "CENT" 6mm long.
Type II — "CENT" 7½mm long.

Perf. 11½x12, 12½, 12½x12, 13x14, 13½, 14, 13½x14

1870-88   Typo.

3	A2	1c sl grn, type I	20.00	8.00
a.		Perf. 13x14, small holes	16.00	6.50
4	A2	1c sl grn, type II	9.75	2.40
5	A2	2c red brown	13.00	5.00
a.		2c fawn	13.00	5.00
6	A2	2c violet brn	100.00	120.00
7	A2	2½c orange	65.00	30.00
8	A2	5c pale green	97.50	6.50
a.		Perf. 14, small holes	90.00	11.00
b.		Perf. 13x14, small holes	115.00	8.00
9	A2	10c orange brn	40.00	.40
a.		Perf. 14, small holes	35.00	.80
b.		Perf. 13x14, small holes	57.50	3.25
10	A2	12½c gray	9.75	3.25
a.		Perf. 12½x12	1,900.	

11	A2	15c bister	40.00	3.00
a.		Perf. 13x14, small holes	57.50	4.00
12	A2	20c ultra	145.00	3.75
a.		Perf. 13x14, small holes	120.00	4.50
b.		Perf. 14, small holes	160.00	5.75
13	A2	25c dk violet	50.00	1.60
a.		Perf. 13x14, small holes	57.50	4.75
c.		Perf. 14, large holes	800.00	220.00
14	A2	30c green	65.00	5.00
15	A2	50c carmine	40.00	1.50
a.		Perf. 14, small holes	34.00	4.00
b.		Perf. 13x14, small holes	50.00	3.25
c.		Perf. 14, large holes	42.50	4.00
16	A2	2.50g green & vio	110.00	26.00
b.		Perf. 14, small holes	100.00	28.00
c.		Perf. 14, large holes	100.00	28.00
		Nos. 3-16 (14)	805.00	216.40

Imperforate examples of Nos. 3-16 are proofs. The 1c red brown and 2c yellow are believed to be bogus.
"Small hole" varieties have the spaces between the holes wider than the diameter of the holes.

Numeral of Value — A3

1883-90   Perf. 12½ Large Holes

17	A3	1c slate grn ('88)	1.20	.25
a.		Perf. 12½x12	3.00	1.60
18	A3	2c brown ('84)	1.20	.25
a.		Perf. 12½x12	3.00	.80
b.		Perf. 11½x12	80.00	50.00
19	A3	2½c yellow	1.20	.80
a.		Perf. 12½x12	3.00	1.60
b.		Perf. 11½x12	24.00	24.00
20	A3	3c lilac ('90)	2.00	.25
21	A3	5c green ('87)	14.50	.40
a.		Perf. 12½x12, large holes	60.00	26.00
22	A3	5c ultra ('90)	14.50	.25
		Nos. 17-22 (6)	34.60	2.20

For surcharges and overprint see Nos. 46-47, O4.

Queen Wilhelmina — A4

1892-97   Perf. 12½

23	A4	10c orange brn ('95)	8.00	.40
24	A4	12½c gray ('97)	12.00	32.50
25	A4	15c bister ('95)	20.00	2.40
26	A4	20c ultra ('93)	60.00	1.60
27	A4	25c violet	35.00	2.00
28	A4	30c green ('94)	50.00	3.75
29	A4	50c carmine ('93)	40.00	2.00
30	A4	2.50g org brn & ultra	140.00	45.00
		Nos. 23-30 (8)	365.00	89.65

For overprints see Nos. O21-O27.

Netherlands Nos. 67-69, 74, 77, 80 Surcharged in Black

1900, July 1

31	A11	10c on 10c gray lil	5.00	.25
32	A11	12½c on 12½c blue	5.00	.60
33	A11	15c on 15c yel brn	5.00	.60
34	A11	20c on 20c yel grn	22.00	.60
35	A11	25c on 25c car & bl	16.00	.60
36	A11	50c on 50c brnz grn & red brn	35.00	1.20

Netherlands No. 84 Surcharged in Black

1902   Perf. 11½x11

37	A12	2.50g on 2½g brn lil	70.00	20.00
a.		Perf. 11	72.50	24.00
		Nos. 31-37 (7)	158.00	23.85

A6

1902-09   Perf. 12½

38	A6	½c violet	.80	.25
39	A6	1c olive grn	.80	.25
a.		Booklet pane of 6		
b.		Complete booklet, 4 #39a	24.00	
40	A6	2c yellow brn	4.00	.25
41	A6	2½c green	2.40	.25
a.		Booklet pane of 6		
42	A6	3c orange	4.00	1.20
43	A6	4c ultra ('09)	14.00	8.50
44	A6	5c rose red	6.00	.25
a.		Booklet pane of 6		
45	A6	7½c gray ('08)	4.00	.40
		Nos. 38-45 (8)	36.00	11.35

For overprints see Nos. 63-69, 81-87, O1-O9.

Nos. 18, 20 Surcharged

1902

46	A3	½c on 2c yel brn	.25	.25
a.		Double surcharge	160.00	160.00
47	A3	2½c on 3c violet	.25	.25
a.		Double surcharge	1,800.	

Queen Wilhelmina — A9

1903-08

48	A9	10c slate	5.00	.25
a.		Booklet pane of 6		
b.		Complete booklet, 4 #48a	2,000.	
49	A9	12½c deep blue ('06)	2.40	.25
a.		Booklet pane of 6		
b.		Complete booklet, #39a, #41a, #44a, #49a; 2 #48a	2,000.	
50	A9	15c chocolate ('06)	10.00	2.00
a.		Ovptd. with 2 horiz. bars	2.00	.80

51	A9	17½c bister ('08)	4.00	.25
52	A9	20c grnsh slate	2.40	1.60
53	A9	20c olive grn ('05)	32.00	.80
54	A9	22½c brn & ol grn ('08)	4.00	.30
55	A9	25c violet ('04)	16.00	.30
56	A9	30c orange brn	34.00	.40
57	A9	50c red brown ('04)	32.00	.40
		Nos. 48-57 (10)	141.80	6.55

For overprints and surcharges see Nos. 58, 70-78, 88-96, 139, O10-O18.

No. 52 Surcharged in Black

Type I

Type II

Two Types of "10":
Type I — Skinny 1 with almost straight flag.
Type II — Fat 1 with rising flag.

1905, July 6

58	A9	10c on 20c grnsh slate	3.00	1.20
a.		Type II	4.75	4.75

Queen Wilhelmina — A10

1905-12   Engr.   Perf. 11x11½

59	A10	1g dp claret ('06)	65.00	.40
a.		Perf. 11½x11	65.00	6.00
b.		Perf. 11	80.00	6.00
60	A10	1g dl lil, bl ('12)	60.00	8.00
a.		Perf. 11	72.50	57.50
61	A10	2½g slate bl ('05)	77.50	2.00
a.		Perf. 11½	77.50	2.00
b.		Perf. 11½x11	80.00	2.00
c.		Perf. 11	900.00	
62	A10	2½g sl bl, bl ('12)	120.00	40.00
a.		Perf. 11	130.00	92.50
		Nos. 59-62 (4)	322.50	50.40

Sheets of Nos. 60 & 62 were soaked in an indigo solution.
For overprints and surcharge see Nos. 79-80, 97-98, 140, O19-O20.

Previous Issues Overprinted

1908, July 1

63	A6	½c violet	.60	.30
64	A6	1c olive grn	.60	.30
65	A6	2c yellow brn	2.00	3.00
66	A6	2½c green	1.20	.30
67	A6	3c orange	1.20	1.20
68	A6	5c rose red	3.25	.40
69	A6	7½c gray	3.00	3.00
70	A9	10c slate	1.20	.25
71	A9	12½c dp blue	10.00	2.40
72	A9	15c choc (#50a)	5.00	4.00
73	A9	17½c bister	2.25	2.00
74	A9	20c olive grn	10.00	2.40
75	A9	22½c brn & ol grn	8.00	7.00
76	A9	25c violet	8.00	.40
77	A9	30c orange brn	16.00	2.25
78	A9	50c red brown	8.00	.80
79	A10	1g dull lilac (#59)	60.00	6.00
b.		Perf. 11½x11	60.00	6.00
c.		Perf. 11	80.00	8.00
80	A10	2½g slate blue (#61b)	100.00	65.00
		Nos. 63-80 (18)	240.30	101.00

The above stamps were overprinted for use in the territory outside of Java and Madura, stamps overprinted "Java" being used in these latter places.
The 15c is overprinted, in addition, with two horizontal lines, 2½mm apart.
The overprint also exists on Nos. 59a-59b. Same values.

Overprint Reading Down

63a	A6	½c	.80	6.00
64a	A6	1c	.80	4.00
65a	A6	2c	4.00	8.00
66a	A6	2½c	1.60	4.00
67a	A6	3c	35.00	90.00
68a	A6	5c	4.00	3.25
70a	A9	10c	1.20	4.00
71a	A9	12½c	6.00	12.00
72a	A9	15c	32.50	75.00
74a	A9	20c	12.50	20.00
75a	A9	22½c	2,200.	2,800.

76a	A9	25c	8.00	12.00
77a	A9	30c	14.00	32.50
78a	A9	50c	10.00	24.00
79a	A10	1g	200.00	240.00
d.		Double overprint	180.00	200.00
80a	A10	2½g	2,800.	4,000.

Overprinted

1908, July 1

81	A6	½c violet	.25	.25
b.		Double overprint	600.00	
82	A6	1c olive grn	.60	.40
83	A6	2c yellow brn	2.40	2.60
84	A6	2½c green	1.60	.25
85	A6	3c orange	1.20	1.00
86	A6	5c rose red	2.40	.25
87	A6	7½c gray	2.00	1.75
88	A9	10c slate	1.40	.25
89	A9	12½c deep blue	2.00	.80
b.		Dbl. ovpt., one inverted	150.00	150.00
90	A9	15c choc (on No. 50a)	3.75	3.75
91	A9	17½c bister	2.00	.80
92	A9	20c olive grn	10.00	.80
93	A9	22½c brn & ol grn	5.25	3.00
94	A9	25c violet	5.25	.40
95	A9	30c orange brn	28.00	3.00
96	A9	50c red brown	20.00	.80
97	A10	1g dull lilac (#59a)	50.00	3.25
b.		Perf. 11	52.50	4.00
98	A10	2½g slate blue (#61b)	72.50	60.00
		Nos. 81-98 (18)	210.60	83.35

Inverted Overprint

81a	A6	½c	1.25	4.00
82a	A6	1c	.75	4.00
83a	A6	2c	3.00	12.00
84a	A6	2½c	3.25	8.00
85a	A6	3c	28.00	40.00
86a	A6	5c	3.00	6.00
88a	A9	10c	1.60	4.00
89a	A9	12½c	4.00	8.00
90a	A9	15c	4.00	16.00
92a	A9	20c	16.00	16.00
94a	A9	25c	6.00	16.00
95a	A9	30c	28.00	40.00
96a	A9	50c	20.00	28.00
97a	A10	1g Perf. 11	160.00	220.00
98a	A10	2½g	2,800.	4,000.

A11

Queen Wilhelmina A12   A13

Typo., Litho. (#114A)

1912-40   Perf. 12½

101	A11	½c lt vio	.25	.25
102	A11	1c olive grn	.25	.25
103	A11	2c yellow brn	.60	.25
104	A11	2c gray blk ('30)	.60	.25
105	A11	2½c green	1.40	.25
106	A11	2½c lt red ('22)	.80	.25
107	A11	3c yellow	.60	.25
108	A11	3c green ('29)	1.20	.25
109	A11	4c gray blue	1.20	.25
110	A11	4c dp grn ('28)	1.20	.25
111	A11	4c yellow ('30)	8.00	5.00
112	A11	5c rose	1.25	.25
113	A11	5c green ('22)	1.20	.25
114	A11	5c chlky bl ('28)	.80	.25
114A	A11	5c ultra ('40)	.80	.30
115	A11	7½c bister	.80	.25
116	A11	10c lilac ('22)	8.00	.25
117	A12	10c car rose ('14)	1.20	.25
118	A12	12½c dull bl ('14)	1.10	.25
119	A12	12½c red ('22)	1.10	.30
120	A12	15c blue ('29)	8.00	.25
121	A12	17½c red brn ('15)	1.10	.25
122	A12	20c green ('15)	2.00	.25
123	A12	20c blue ('22)	2.00	.25
124	A12	20c orange ('32)	14.00	.30
125	A12	22½c orange ('15)	2.00	.25
126	A12	25c red vio ('15)	2.00	.80
127	A12	30c slate ('15)	2.00	.25
128	A12	32½c vio & red ('22)	2.00	.25
129	A12	35c org brn ('29)	7.25	.60
130	A12	40c green ('22)	4.00	.25

Perf. 11½   Engr.

131	A13	50c green ('13)	6.00	.25
a.		Perf. 11x11½	6.00	.25
b.		Perf. 12½	6.00	.40
c.		Vert. pair, imperf. betwn.		1,600.
132	A13	60c dp blue ('22)	6.00	.25
133	A13	80c orange ('22)	6.00	.30
134	A13	1g brown ('13)	6.00	.25
a.		Perf. 11x11½		.30
135	A13	1.75g dk vio, perf. 12½ ('31)	20.00	2.00
136	A13	2½g car ('13)	16.00	.50
a.		Perf. 11x11½	16.00	4.00
b.		Perf. 12½	16.00	.70
		Nos. 101-136 (37)	132.70	17.10

For surcharges and overprints see Nos. 137-138, 144-150, 102a-123a, 158, 194-195, B1-B3, C1-C5.

Water Soluble Ink
Some values of types A11 and A12 and late printings of types A6 and A9 are in soluble ink. The design disappears when immersed in water.

Nos. 105, 109, 54, 59 Surcharged

No. 137   No. 138

No. 139   No. 140

1917-18   Typo.   Perf. 12½

137	A11	½c on 2½c	.30	.30
138	A11	1c on 4c ('18)	.55	.55
139	A9	17½c on 22½c ('18)	2.00	.75
a.		Inverted surcharge	350.00	725.00

Perf. 11x11½

140	A10	30c on 1g ('18)	6.50	1.75
a.		Perf. 11½x11	130.00	120.00
		Nos. 137-140 (4)	9.35	3.35

Nos. 121, 125, 131, 134 Surcharged in Red or Blue

On A12   On A13

Two types of 32½c on 50c:
I — Surcharge bars spaced as in illustration.
II — Bars more closely spaced.

1922, Jan.   Perf. 12½

144	A12	12½c on 17½c ('R)	.75	.25
145	A12	12½c on 22½c ('R)	.75	.25
146	A12	20c on 22½c (Bl)	.75	.25
a.		Double overprint	1,800.	

Perf. 11½, 11x11½

147	A13	32½c on 50c (Bl) (I, perf. 11½)	1.50	.25
a.		Type II, perf. 11½	10.00	.25
b.		Type I, perf. 11x11½	1,000.	6.00
c.		Type II, perf. 11x11½	20.00	1.60
148	A13	40c on 50c (R)	4.00	.45
149	A13	60c on 1g (Bl)	6.50	.40
150	A13	80c on 1g (R)	8.00	1.20
		Nos. 144-150 (7)	22.25	3.05

Stamps of 1912-22 Overprinted in Red, Blue, Green or Black

a   b

No. 145a

1922, Sept. 18   **Typo.**   **Perf. 12½**

102a	A11(a)	1c ol grn (R)	8.00	8.00
103a	A11(a)	2c yel brn (Bl)	8.00	8.00
106a	A11(a)	2½c lt red (G)	57.50	65.00
107a	A11(a)	3c yellow (R)	8.00	8.00
109a	A11(a)	4c ultra (R)	32.50	40.00
113a	A11(a)	5c green (R)	12.00	8.00
115a	A11(a)	7½c drab (Bl)	8.00	8.00
116a	A11(a)	10c lilac (Bl)	65.00	92.50
145a	A12(b)	12½c on 22½c org (Bl)	8.00	8.00
121a	A12(b)	17½c red brn (Bk)	8.00	8.00
123a	A12(b)	20c blue (Bk)	8.00	8.00
		Nos. 102a-123a (11)	223.00	261.50

Issued to publicize the 3rd Netherlands Indies Industrial Fair at Bandoeng, Java.
Nos. 102a-123a were sold at a premium for 3, 4, 5, 6, 8, 9, 10, 12½, 15, 20 and 22½ cents respectively.

Queen Wilhelmina — A15

1923, Aug. 31   **Engr.**   **Perf. 11½**

151	A15	5c myrtle green	.25	.25
a.		Perf. 11½x11	1,000.	125.00
b.		Perf. 11x11½	4.00	.75
152	A15	12½c rose	.25	.25
a.		Perf. 11x11½	1.25	.25
b.		Perf. 11½x11	1.75	.75
c.		Vert. pair, imperf. btwn.	1,000.	
153	A15	20c dark blue	.75	.25
a.		Perf. 11½x11	4.00	.75
154	A15	50c red orange	2.00	.75
a.		Perf. 11x11½	6.00	1.25
b.		Perf. 11½x11	3.00	.90
c.		Perf. 11	6.00	1.25
155	A15	1g brown vio	4.50	.75
a.		Perf. 11½x11	8.00	.80
156	A15	2½g gray black	40.00	40.00
157	A15	5g orange brown	125.00	100.00
		Nos. 151-157 (7)	172.75	182.25

25th anniversary of the assumption of the government of the Netherlands by Queen Wilhelmina, at the age of 18.

No. 123 Surcharged

1930, Dec. 13   **Typo.**   **Perf. 12½**

158	A12	12½c on 20c bl (R)	.80	.25
a.		Inverted surcharge	375.00	725.00

Prince William I, Portrait by Van Key — A16

1933, Apr. 18   **Photo.**

163	A16	12½c deep orange	1.60	.40

400th anniv. of the birth of Prince William I, Count of Nassau and Prince of Orange, frequently referred to as William the Silent.

Rice Field Scene A17   Queen Wilhelmina A18

Queen Wilhelmina — A19

1933-37   **Unwmk.**   **Perf. 11½x12½**

164	A17	1c lilac gray ('34)	.25	.25
165	A17	2c plum ('34)	.25	.25
166	A17	2½c bister ('34)	.25	.25
167	A17	3c yellow grn ('34)	.25	.25
168	A17	3½c dark gray ('37)	.25	.25

169	A17	4c dk olive ('34)	1.00	.25
170	A17	5c ultra ('34)	.25	.25
171	A17	7½c violet ('34)	1.00	.25
172	A17	10c ver ('34)	1.90	.25
173	A18	10c ver ('37)	.60	.25
174	A18	12½c dp org ('34)	.60	.25
a.		12½c light orange, perf. 12½ ('33)	8.00	.40
175	A18	15c ultra ('34)	.60	.25
176	A18	20c plum ('34)	.80	.25
177	A18	25c blue grn ('34)	2.25	.25
178	A18	30c lilac gray ('34)	3.75	.25
179	A18	32½c bister ('34)	8.00	8.00
180	A18	35c violet ('34)	6.00	2.10
181	A18	40c yel grn ('34)	3.00	.25
182	A18	42½c yellow ('34)	3.00	1.25

1934, Jan 16   **Perf. 12½**

183	A19	50c lilac gray	6.00	.25
184	A19	60c ultra	6.00	.80
185	A19	80c vermilion	8.00	1.20
186	A19	1g violet	8.00	.40
187	A19	1.75g yellow grn	20.00	13.50
188	A19	2.50g plum	20.00	2.00
		Nos. 164-188 (25)	102.00	33.50

See Nos. 200-225. For overprints and surcharges see Nos. 271-275, B48, B57.

Water Soluble Ink
Nos. 164-188 and the first printing of No. 163 have soluble ink and the design disappears when immersed in water.

Nos. C6-C7, C14, C9-C10 Surcharged in Black

a

b

1934   **Typo.**   **Perf. 12½x11½, 12½**

189	AP1(a)	2c on 10c	.75	.45
190	AP1(a)	2c on 20c	.75	.25
191	AP3(b)	2c on 30c	.75	1.20
192	AP1(a)	42½c on 75c	7.00	.25
193	AP1(a)	42½c on 1.50g	7.00	.40
		Nos. 189-193 (5)	16.25	2.55

Nos. 127-128 Surcharged with New Value in Red or Black

1937, Sept.   **Perf. 12½**

194	A12	10c on 30c (R)	3.00	.25
a.		Double surcharge	675.00	2,400.
195	A12	10c on 32½c (Bk)	3.00	.35

Wilhelmina — A20

Perf. 12½x12

1938, Aug. 30   **Photo.**   **Wmk. 202**

196	A20	2c dull purple	.25	.25
197	A20	10c car lake	.25	.25
198	A20	15c royal blue	1.25	1.25
199	A20	20c red orange	.75	.40
		Nos. 196-199 (4)	2.50	2.15

40th anniv. of the reign of Queen Wilhelmina.

Types of 1933-37

1938-40   **Photo.**   **Perf. 12½x12**

200	A17	1c lilac gray ('39)	.40	.80
201	A17	2c plum ('39)	.25	.25
202	A17	2½c bister ('39)	.75	.75
203	A17	3c yellow grn ('39)	1.50	1.50
205	A17	4c gray ol ('39)	1.50	1.50
206	A17	5c ultra ('39)	.25	.25
a.		Perf. 12x12½	1.50	.75
207	A17	7½c violet ('39)	3.00	1.50
208	A18	10c ver ('39)	.25	.25
210	A18	15c ultra ('39)	.25	.25
211	A18	20c plum ('39)	.25	.25
a.		Perf. 12x12½	1.50	.75
212	A18	25c blue grn ('39)	24.00	24.00
213	A18	30c lilac gray ('39)	10.00	5.00
215	A18	35c violet ('39)	5.75	1.60
216	A18	40c dp yel grn ('40)	5.75	.25

Perf. 12½

218	A19	50c lilac gray ('40)	275.00	
219	A19	60c ultra ('39)	14.00	8.00
220	A19	80c ver ('39)	75.00	65.00
221	A19	1g violet ('39)	30.00	4.00
223	A19	2g Prus green	26.00	14.00
225	A19	5g yellow brn	24.00	14.00
		Nos. 200-216,219-225 (19)	222.90	143.15

The note following No. 188 applies also to this issue.
The 50c was sold only at the philatelic window in Amsterdam.

War Dance of Nias Island A23   Legong Dancer of Bali A24

Wayang Wong Dancer of Java A25   Padjogé Dancer, Southern Celebes A26

Dyak Dancer of Borneo — A27

1941   **Unwmk.**   **Perf. 12½**

228	A23	2½c rose violet	.60	.80
229	A24	3c green	.60	.80
230	A25	4c olive green	.50	.80
231	A26	5c blue	.25	.25
232	A27	7½c dark violet	.60	.35
		Nos. 228-232 (5)	2.55	3.00

See Nos. 279-280, 293, N38.
Imperfs. are printers waste.

A28   Queen Wilhelmina A28a

1941   **Perf. 12½**

Size: 18x22¾mm

234	A28	10c red orange	.80	.40
a.		Perf. 13½	.40	.40
235	A28	15c ultra	4.00	4.00
236	A28	17½c orange	2.00	2.00
237	A28	20c plum	40.00	120.00
238	A28	25c Prus green	50.00	1.75
239	A28	30c olive bis	7.00	3.25
240	A28	35c purple	160.00	400.00
241	A28	40c yellow grn	18.50	8.00

Perf. 13½

Size: 20½x26mm

242	A28	50c car lake	7.25	1.60
243	A28	60c ultra	6.50	1.60
244	A28	80c red orange	6.50	1.60
245	A28	1g purple	6.50	.80
246	A28	2g Prus green	20.00	2.40
247	A28	5g bis, perf. 12½	350.00	3,000.
248	A28	10g green	42.50	24.00

Size: 26x32mm

249	A28a	25g orange	260.00	160.00
		Nos. 234-249 (16)	981.55	3,731.

Nos. 242-246 come with pin-perf 13½.
Small hole, large hole, comb and line perforation varieties exist.
Nos. 242-246 exist on thick paper in darker colors. These are proofs.
The 10c comes in two types: 1¼mm between "10" and "CENT," and 1¾mm.

For overprints and surcharge see Nos. 276-278, J43-J46.

Catalogue values for unused stamps in this section, from this point to the end of the section, are for Never Hinged items.

Rice Fields — A29   Barge on Java Lake — A30

University of Medicine, Batavia — A31   Palms on Shore — A32

Plane over Bromo Volcano — A33

Queen Wilhelmina
A34   A35

1945-46, Oct. 1   **Engr.**   **Perf. 12**

250	A29	1c green	.60	.25
251	A30	2c rose lilac	.60	.35
252	A31	2½c dull lilac	.60	.25
253	A32	5c blue	.40	.25
254	A33	7½c olive gray	.80	.25
255	A34	10c red brown	.40	.25
256	A34	15c dark blue	.40	.25
257	A34	17½c rose lake	.40	.25
258	A34	20c sepia	.40	.25
259	A34	30c slate gray	.40	.25
260	A35	60c gray black	.80	.25
261	A35	1g blue green	1.20	.25
262	A35	2½g red orange	3.75	.75
		Nos. 250-262 (13)	10.75	3.85

For surcharge see No. 304.
Issued: 15c, 1946, others 10/1/45.

Railway Viaduct Near Soekaboemi A36   Dam and Power Station A37

Palm Tree and Menangkabau House — A38

Huts on Piles A39   Buddhist Stupas A40

Perf. 14½x14

1946   **Typo.**   **Wmk. 228**

263	A36	1c dark green	.35	.25
264	A37	2c black brown	.35	.25
265	A38	2½c scarlet	.35	.25
266	A39	5c indigo	.35	.25
267	A40	7½c ultra	.35	.25
		Nos. 263-267 (5)	1.75	1.25

Nos. 265, 267, 263 Surcharged

1947, Sept. 25

268	A38	3c on 2½c scar	.35	.25
269	A40	3c on 7½c ultra	.35	.25
a.		Double surcharge	200.00	200.00
270	A36	4c on 1c dk green	.35	.25
		Nos. 268-270 (3)	1.05	.75

No. 219 Surcharged with New Value and Bars in Red

1947, Sept. 25   **Wmk. 202**   **Perf. 12½**

271	A19	45c on 60c ultra	1.45	1.00

Nos. 212, 218 and 220 Overprinted "1947" in Red or Black

1947, Sept. 25   **Perf. 12½x12, 12½**

272	A18	25c blue green (R)	.40	.25
a.		Unwmkd.		260.00
273	A19	50c lilac gray (R)	.80	.35
274	A19	80c vermilion	1.20	1.20
a.		Unwmkd.	500.00	240.00
		Nos. 272-274 (3)	2.40	1.80

Bar above "1947" on No. 274.

Nos. 174, 241, 247 and Type of 1941 Overprinted "1947" in Black

Perf. 12½, 12½x12 (2g)

1947, Sept. 25   **Unwmk.**

275	A18	12½c deep orange	.40	.25
276	A28	40c yellow green	.80	.25
277	A28	2g Prus green	4.00	1.40
278	A28	5g bister	11.00	9.75
		Nos. 275-278 (4)	16.20	11.65

The overprint is vertical on Nos. 276-278.

Dancer Types of 1941, 1945

1948, May 13   **Litho.**   **Perf. 12½**

279	OS21	3c rose red	.25	.25
280	A24	4c dull olive grn	.25	.25

Queen Wilhelmina — A41

1948   **Photo.**   **Perf. 12½**

Size: 18x22mm

281	A41	15c red orange	.80	2.00
282	A41	20c brt blue	.30	.30
283	A41	25c dk green	.30	.30
284	A41	40c dp yellow grn	.30	.30
285	A41	45c plum	.60	.80
286	A41	50c red brown	.50	.30
287	A41	80c brt red	.60	.60

Perf. 13

Size: 20½x26mm

288	A41	1g deep violet	.30	.30
a.		Perf. 12½ x 12	1.20	.60
289	A41	10g green	32.50	15.00
290	A41	25g orange	60.00	60.00
		Nos. 281-290 (10)	96.20	79.90

See Nos. 291-292. For overprints see Nos. 294-303.

Wilhelmina Type of 1948 Inscribed "1898-1948"

1948, Aug. 31   **Perf. 12½x12**

Size: 21x26½mm

291	A41	15c orange	.40	.40
292	A41	20c ultra	.40	.30

Reign of Queen Wilhelmina, 50th anniv.

Dancer Type of 1941

1948, Sept.   **Photo.**   **Perf. 12½**

293	A27	7½c olive bister	.80	.75

Juliana Type of Netherlands 1948

Perf. 14½x13½

1948, Sept. 25   **Wmk. 202**

293A	A75	15c red orange	.50	.35
293B	A75	20c deep ultra	.50	.35

Investiture of Queen Juliana, Sept. 6, 1948.

Indonesia

Nos. 281 to 287 Overprinted in Black

Two types of overprint:
I — Shiny ink, bar 1.8mm wide. By G. C. T. van Dorp & Co.
II — Dull ink, bar 2.2mm. By G. Kolff & Co.

1948   **Perf. 12½**

294	A41	15c red orange (I)	1.75	.25
a.		Type II	.95	.25
295	A41	20c bright blue (I)	.25	.25
a.		Type II	.50	.25
296	A41	25c dark green (I)	.25	.25
a.		Type II	.25	.25
297	A41	40c dp yel grn (I)	.25	.25
298	A41	45c plum ('49) (II)	1.10	.90
299	A41	50c red brn ('49) (II)	.25	.25
300	A41	80c bright red (I)	1.00	.25
a.		Type II	1.10	

Nos. 288-290 Overprinted in Black

Two Bars

Perf. 12½x12

301	A41	1g deep violet	1.25	.25
a.		As #301, with three bars	8.00	.35
b.		Perf. 13	2.75	.30

Perf. 13

302	A41	10g green	92.50	30.00
303	A41	25g orange	125.00	57.50
		Nos. 294-303 (10)	223.60	90.15

Same Overprint in Black on No. 262

1949   **Engr.**   **Perf. 12**

Bars 28½mm long

304	A35	2½g red orange	52.50	9.75

A42

Tjandi Puntadewa Temple Entrance, East Java
A43

Detail, Temple of the Dead, Bedjuning, Bali
A44

Menangkabau House, Sumatra — A45   Toradja House, Celebes — A46

Designs: 5r, 10r, 25r, Temple entrance.

Perf. 12½, 11½

1949   **Unwmk.**   **Photo.**

307	A42	1s gray	.30	.25
a.		Perf. 11½	.60	.80
308	A42	2s claret	.60	.25
a.		Perf. 11½	30.00	30.00
309	A42	2½s olive brown	.30	.25
a.		Perf. 11½	.30	.25
310	A42	3s rose pink	.60	.25
a.		Perf. 11½	1.50	1.40
311	A42	4s green	.60	.60
312	A42	5s blue	.30	.25
a.		Perf. 11½	1.10	.25
313	A42	7½s dark green	.60	.25
a.		Perf. 11½	1.10	.60
314	A42	10s violet	.30	.25
a.		Perf. 11½		475.00
315	A42	12½s brt red	1.90	.25
a.		Perf. 11½	2.25	1.75
316	A43	15s rose red	.30	.25
a.		Perf. 12½	1.75	.60
317	A43	20s gray black	.30	.25
a.		Perf. 12½	.95	.25
318	A43	25s ultra	.30	.25
a.		Perf. 12½	.95	.25
319	A44	30s brt red	1.10	.25
a.		Perf. 12½	1.10	.25
320	A44	40s gray green	.60	.25
a.		Perf. 12½	.30	.25
321	A44	45s claret	.60	3.75
a.		Perf. 12½	2.75	.50
322	A45	50s orange brn	.60	.25
a.		Perf. 12½	1.50	.25
323	A45	60s brown	.80	1.90
a.		Perf. 12½	1.50	.25
324	A45	80s scarlet	1.15	.25
a.		Perf. 12½	4.00	

The 4s is perf. 12½. The 25s, 30s, 40s, 50s, 60s come both 12½ and 11½, same values.

Perf. 12½, 12¼

325	A46	1r purple	.80	.25
a.		Perf. 12¼	.80	.25
326	A46	2r gray green	4.75	.25
a.		Perf. 12¼	4.75	.25
327	A46	3r red violet	95.00	.25
328	A46	5r dk brown	67.50	.40
329	A46	10r gray	82.50	1.90
330	A46	25r orange brn	.80	1.90
		Nos. 307-330 (24)	262.60	14.95

Nos. 307-330 remained on sale in Indonesia Republic post offices until May 23, 1958, and were valid for postage until June 30, 1958.
For surcharge, see Indonesia Nos. 335-358.
Nos. 325-330 exist with both large and small holes.

Globe and Arms of Bern — A48

1949, Oct. 1   **Perf. 12½**

331	A48	15s bright red	1.15	.40
332	A48	25s ultra	1.15	.40

Nos. 307-330 remained on sale in Indonesia Republic post offices until May 23, 1958, and were valid for postage until June 30, 1958. 75th anniv. of UPU.
See Indonesia (republic) for subsequent listings.

SEMI-POSTAL STAMPS

Regular Issue of 1912-14 Surcharged in Carmine

1915, June 10   **Unwmk.**   **Perf. 12½**

B1	A11	1c + 5c ol grn	4.50	4.50
B2	A11	5c + 5c rose	4.50	4.50
B3	A12	10c + 5c rose	7.25	7.25
		Nos. B1-B3 (3)	16.25	16.25

Surtax for the Red Cross.

Bali Temple SP1   Watchtower SP2

Menangkabau Compound — SP3

Borobudur Temple, Java — SP4

Perf. 11½x11, 11x11½

1930, Dec. 1   **Photo.**

B4	SP1	2c (+ 1c) vio & brn	1.00	.80
B5	SP2	5c (+ 2½c) dk grn & brn	4.75	2.50
B6	SP3	12½c (+ 2½c) dp red & brn	3.25	.50
B7	SP4	15c (+ 5c) ultra & brn	5.75	5.75
		Nos. B4-B7 (4)	14.75	9.55

Surtax for youth care.

Farmer and Carabao — SP5

5c, Fishermen. 12½c, Dancers. 15c, Musicians.

1931, Dec. 1   **Engr.**   **Perf. 12½**

B8	SP5	2c (+ 1c) olive bis	3.00	2.00
B9	SP5	5c (+ 2½c) bl grn	4.25	3.75
B10	SP5	12½c (+ 2½c) dp red	3.25	.55
B11	SP5	15c (+ 5c) dl bl	8.25	7.00
		Nos. B8-B11 (4)	18.75	13.30

The surtax was for the aid of the Leper Colony at Salatiga.

Weaving — SP9

5c, Plaiting rattan. 12½c, Woman batik dyer. 15c, Coppersmith.

1932, Dec. 1   **Photo.**   **Perf. 12½**

B12	SP9	2c (+ 1c) dp vio & bis	.40	.40
B13	SP9	5c (+ 2½c) dp grn & bis	2.50	2.00
B14	SP9	12½c (+ 2½c) brt rose & bis	.85	.30
B15	SP9	15c (+ 5c) bl & bis	3.25	3.00
		Nos. B12-B15 (4)	7.00	5.70

The surtax was donated to the Salvation Army.

Woman and Lotus — SP13

Designs: 5c, "The Light that Shows the Way." 12½c, YMCA emblem. 15c, Jobless man.

1933, Dec. 1   **Perf. 12½**

B16	SP13	2c (+ 1c) red vio & ol bis	.65	.30
B17	SP13	5c (+ 2½c) grn & ol bis	2.25	1.90
B18	SP13	12½c (+ 2½c) ver & ol bis	2.50	.30
B19	SP13	15c (+ 5c) bl & ol bis	2.75	2.00
		Nos. B16-B19 (4)	8.15	4.50

The surtax was for the Amsterdam Young Men's Society for Relief of the Poor in Netherlands Indies.

Dowager Queen Emma — SP17

1934, Sept. 15   **Perf. 13x14**

B20	SP17	12½c (+ 2½c) blk brn	1.25	.45

Issued in memory of the late Dowager Queen Emma of Netherlands. The surtax was for the Anti-Tuberculosis Society.

A Pioneer at Work — SP18

Designs: 5c, Cavalryman rescuing wounded native. 12½c, Artilleryman under fire. 15c, Bugler.

1935   **Perf. 12½**

B21	SP18	2c (+ 1c) dp mag & bis	1.25	1.00
B22	SP18	5c (+ 2½c) grn & bis	3.25	2.25
B23	SP18	12½c (+ 2½c) red org & bis	3.25	.25
B24	SP18	15c (+ 5c) brt bl & bis	4.50	4.50
		Nos. B21-B24 (4)	12.25	8.00

The surtax was for the Indies Committee of the Christian Military Association for the East and West Indies.

Child Welfare Work — SP22

1936, Dec. 1   Size: 23x20mm
B25	SP22	2c (+ 1c) plum	1.00	.60

Size: 30x26½mm
B26	SP22	5c (+ 2½c) gray vio	1.25	1.10
B27	SP22	7½c (+ 2½c) dk vio	1.25	1.25
B28	SP22	12½c (+ 2½c) red org	1.25	.30
B29	SP22	15c (+5c) brt bl	2.00	1.75
		Nos. B25-B29 (5)	6.75	5.00

Surtax for Salvation Army.

Boy Scouts — SP23

1937, May 1
B30	SP23	7½c + 2½c dk ol brn	1.25	1.00
B31	SP23	12½c + 2½c rose car	1.25	.50

Fifth Boy Scout World Jamboree, Vogelenzang, Netherlands, July 31-Aug. 13, 1937. Surtax for Netherlands Indies Scout Association.

Sifting Rice — SP24

Designs: 3½c, Mother and children. 7½c, Plowing with carabao team. 10c, Carabao team and cart. 20c, Native couple.

1937, Dec. 1
B32	SP24	2c (+ 1c) dk brn & org	1.10	.80
B33	SP24	3½c (+ 1½c) gray	1.10	.80
B34	SP24	7½c (+ 2½c) Prus grn & org	1.25	.95
B35	SP24	10c (+ 2½c) car & org	1.25	.25
B36	SP24	20c (+5c) brt bl	1.25	1.10
		Nos. B32-B36 (5)	5.95	3.90

Surtax for the Public Relief Fund for indigenous poor.

Modern Plane — SP28

Design: 20c, Plane nose facing left.

Wmk. 202
1938, Oct. 15   Photo.   Perf. 12½
B36A	SP28	17½c (+5c) olive brn	.85	.85
B36B	SP28	20c (+5c) slate	.85	.55

10th anniversary of the Dutch East Indies Royal Air Lines (K. N. I. L. M.). Surtax for the Aviation Fund in the Netherlands Indies.

Nun and Child
SP29   SP30

Designs: 7½c, Nurse examining child's arm. 10c, Nurse bathing baby. 20c, Nun bandaging child's head.

1938, Dec. 1   Wmk. 202   Perf. 12½
B37	SP29	2c (+ 1c) vio	.60	.45

Perf. 11½x12
B38	SP30	3½c (+ 1½c) brt grn	1.00	.90

Perf. 12x11½
B39	SP30	7½c (+ 2½c) cop red	.80	.85
B40	SP30	10c (+ 2½c) ver	.90	.25
B41	SP30	20c (+5c) brt ultra	1.00	.95
		Nos. B37-B41 (5)	4.30	3.40

The surtax was for the Central Mission Bureau in Batavia.

Social Workers SP34

Indonesian Nurse Tending Patient SP35

European Nurse Tending Patient — SP36

Perf. 13x11½, 11½x13
1939, Dec. 1   Photo.
B42	SP34	2c (+ 1c) purple	.25	.25
B43	SP35	3½c (+ 1½c) bl grn & pale bl grn	.30	.25
B44	SP34	7½c (+ 2½c) cop brn	.25	.25
B45	SP35	10c (+ 2½c) scar & pink	1.40	.80
B46	SP36	10c (+ 2½c) scar	1.40	.80
B47	SP36	20c (+ 5c) dk bl	.40	.35
		Nos. B42-B47 (6)	4.00	2.70

No. B44 shows native social workers. Nos. B45 and B46 were issued se-tenant vertically and horizontally. The surtax was used for the Bureau of Social Service.

No. 174 Surcharged in Brown

1940, Dec. 2   Unwmk.   Perf. 12x12½
B48	A18	10c + 5c on 12½c dp org	1.10	.40

SP37

Netherlands coat of arms and inscription "Netherlands Shall Rise Again"

1941, May 10   Litho.   Perf. 12½
B49	SP37	5c + 5c multi	.25	.25
B50	SP37	10c + 10c multi	.25	.25
B51	SP37	1g + 1g multi	9.00	6.75
		Nos. B49-B51 (3)	9.50	7.25

The surtax was to purchase fighter planes for Dutch pilots fighting with the Royal Air Force in Great Britain.

SP38

Designs: 2c, Doctor and child, 3½c, Rice eater. 7½c, Nurse and patient. 10c, Nurse and children. 15c, Basket weaver.

1941, Sept. 22   Photo.
B52	SP38	2c (+ 1c) yel grn	.60	.55
B53	SP38	3½c (+ 1½c) vio brn	4.00	3.50
B54	SP38	7½c (+ 2½c) vio	3.25	2.75
B55	SP38	10c (+ 2½c) dk red	.90	.25
B56	SP38	15c (+ 5c) saph	9.50	6.00
		Nos. B52-B56 (5)	18.25	13.05

The surtax was used for various charities.

> **Catalogue values for unused stamps in this section, from this point to the end of the section, are for Never Hinged items.**

Indonesia

No. 208 Surcharged in Black

Perf. 12½x12
1948, Feb. 2   Wmk. 202
B57	A18	15c + 10c on 10c	.25	.25
a.		Inverted surcharge	210.00	210.00

The surtax was for war victims and other charitable purposes.

AIR POST STAMPS

Regular Issues of 1913-1923 Surcharged in Black or Blue

Nos. 119 & 126 Surcharged

No. 133 Surcharged

No. 134 Surcharged

No. 136 Surcharged

Perf. 12½, 11½
1928, Sept. 20   Unwmk.
C1	A12	10c on 12½c red	1.25	1.25
C2	A12	20c on 25c red vio	3.00	3.00
C3	A13	40c on 80c org	3.00	3.00
C4	A13	75c on 1g brn (Bl)	1.25	1.25
C5	A13	1½g on 2½g car	8.00	8.00
		Nos. C1-C5 (5)	16.50	16.50

On Nos. C4 and C5 there are stars over the original values and the airplane is of different shape. On No. C3 there are no bars under "OST."

Planes over Temple — AP1

1928, Dec. 1   Litho.   Perf. 12½x11½
C6	AP1	10c red violet	.40	.25
C7	AP1	20c brown	1.00	.75
C8	AP1	40c rose	1.20	.75
C9	AP1	75c green	3.25	.25
C10	AP1	1.50g orange	6.25	.75
		Nos. C6-C10 (5)	12.10	2.75

For surcharges see Nos. 189-190, 192-193, C11-C12, C17.

No. C8 Surcharged in Black or Green

1930-32
C11	AP1	30c on 40c rose	2.00	.25
C12	AP1	30c on 40c rose (G) ('32)	2.40	.25

Pilot at Controls of Plane — AP2

1931, Apr. 1   Photo.   Perf. 12½
C13	AP2	1g blue & brown	16.00	18.00

Issued for the first air mail flight from Java to Australia.

Landscape and Garudas — AP3

1931, May
C14	AP3	30c red violet	3.25	.25
C15	AP3	4½g bright blue	9.00	3.25
C16	AP3	7½g yellow green	12.00	4.50
		Nos. C14-C16 (3)	24.25	8.00

For surcharge see No. 191.

No. C10 Surcharged in Blue

1932, July 21   Perf. 12½x11½
C17	AP1	50c on 1.50g org	3.25	.60
a.		Inverted surcharge	2,200.	2,800.

Airplane — AP4

1933, Oct. 18   Photo.   Perf. 12½
C18	AP4	30c deep blue	1.50	1.50

MARINE INSURANCE STAMPS

Floating Safe Attracting Gulls MI1

Floating Safe with Night Flare MI2

Artistic Fantasy of Floating Safe — MI3

Perf. 11½
1921, Nov. 1   Unwmk.   Engr.
GY1	MI1	15c slate green	12.50	60.00
GY2	MI1	60c rose	12.50	90.00
GY3	MI1	75c gray brn	12.50	120.00
GY4	MI2	1.50g dark blue	37.50	325.00
GY5	MI2	2.25g org brn	45.00	475.00
GY6	MI3	4½g black	80.00	800.00
GY7	MI3	7½g red	100.00	925.00
		Nos. GY1-GY7 (7)	300.00	2,795.

POSTAGE DUE STAMPS

D1

D2

1845-46   Unwmk.   Typeset   Imperf.
Bluish Paper
J1	D1	black ('46)		1,650.
J2	D2	black		2,000.
a.		"Maill" instead of "Mail"		3,200.

D3

1874   Typo.   Perf. 12½x12, 13x14
J3	D3	5c ocher	300.00	275.00
J4	D3	10c green, yel	240.00	155.00
J5	D3	15c ocher, org	40.00	24.00
a.		Perf. 11½x12	65.00	65.00

J6	D3	20c green, *blue*	60.00	24.00
a.		Perf. 11½x12	110.00	45.00
		Nos. J3-J6 (4)	640.00	478.00

D4

Type I — 34 loops. "T" of "Betalen" over center of loop, top branch of "E" of "Te" shorter than lower branch.

Type II — 33 loops. "T" of "Betalen" over center of two loops.

Type III — 32 loops. "T" of "Betalen" slightly to the left of loop, top branch of first "E" of "Betalen" shorter than lower branch.

Type IV — 37 loops and letters of "PORT" larger than in the other three types.

Value in Black

Perf. 11½x12, 12½, 12½x12, 13½

1882-88				Type III
J7	D4	2½c carmine	.75	1.25
J8	D4	5c carmine	.75	.75
J9	D4	10c carmine	4.00	4.00
J10	D4	15c carmine	4.00	3.25
J11	D4	20c carmine	100.00	1.25
J12	D4	30c carmine	3.75	4.50
J13	D4	40c carmine	2.40	3.25
J14	D4	50c deep salmon	1.25	1.60
J15	D4	75c carmine	1.25	1.60
		Nos. J7-J15 (9)	118.15	20.95

Type I

J7a	D4	2½c carmine	.75	1.60
J8a	D4	5c carmine	.75	1.25
J9a	D4	10c carmine	5.00	6.00
J10a	D4	15c carmine	5.00	5.75
J11a	D4	20c carmine	120.00	1.25
J12a	D4	30c carmine	6.00	8.00
J13a	D4	40c carmine	2.40	3.25
J14a	D4	50c deep salmon	2.00	2.40
J15a	D4	75c carmine	2.00	2.40
		Nos. J7a-J15a (9)	143.15	31.50

Type II

J7b	D4	2½c carmine	.75	2.00
J8b	D4	5c carmine	.75	1.25
J9b	D4	10c carmine	6.00	6.00
J10b	D4	15c carmine	6.00	6.00
J11b	D4	20c carmine	120.00	3.25
J12b	D4	30c carmine	10.00	10.00
J13b	D4	40c carmine	3.25	4.00
J14b	D4	50c deep salmon	2.00	2.50
J15b	D4	75c carmine	1.60	2.50
		Nos. J7b-J15b (9)	150.35	37.50

Type IV

J7c	D4	2½c carmine	4.00	6.00
J8c	D4	5c carmine	2.00	6.00
J9c	D4	10c carmine	27.50	40.00
J10c	D4	15c carmine	24.00	27.50
J11c	D4	20c carmine	250.00	12.50
J13c	D4	40c carmine	4.00	6.00
J14c	D4	50c deep salmon	16.00	24.00
J15c	D4	75c carmine	2.00	3.00
		Nos. J7c-J15c (8)	330.00	128.00

D5

1892-95		Type I	**Perf. 12½**	
J16	D5	10c carmine	2.50	.40
J17	D5	15c carmine ('95)	22.00	3.00
J18	D5	20c carmine	5.50	.25
		Nos. J16-J18 (3)	30.00	3.65

Type III

J16a	D5	10c dull red	5.00	3.00
J18a	D5	20c dull red	6.00	2.00

Type II

J16b	D5	10c dull red	16.00	16.00
J18b	D5	20c dull red	10.00	10.00

1906-09				Type I
J19	D5	2½c carmine ('08)	1.60	.30
J20	D5	5c carmine ('09)	5.00	.25
J21	D5	30c carmine	30.00	10.00
J22	D5	40c carmine ('09)	26.00	3.25
J23	D5	50c carmine ('09)	18.00	1.60
J24	D5	75c carmine ('09)	34.00	5.25
		Nos. J19-J24 (6)	114.60	20.65

Value in Color of Stamp

1913-39			**Perf. 12½**	
J25	D5	1c salmon ('39)	.25	25.00
J26	D5	2½c salmon	.25	.25
J27	D5	3½c salmon ('39)	.25	25.00
J28	D5	5c salmon	.25	.25
J29	D5	7½c salmon ('22)	.25	.25
J30	D5	10c salmon	.25	.25
J31	D5	12½c salmon ('22)	3.25	.40
J32	D5	15c salmon	3.25	.40
J33	D5	20c salmon	.25	.25
J34	D5	25c salmon ('22)	.25	.25
J35	D5	30c salmon	.25	.25
J36	D5	37½c salmon ('30)	18.00	20.00
J37	D5	40c salmon	.25	.25

J38	D5	50c salmon	2.40	.25
J39	D5	75c salmon	3.25	2.40
		Nos. J25-J39 (15)	32.65	75.45

Thick White Paper
Invisible Gum
Numerals Slightly Larger

1941		Litho.	**Perf. 12½**	
J25a	D5	1c light red	.75	12.00
J28a	D5	5c light red	.75	12.00
J30a	D5	10c light red	8.00	24.00
J32a	D5	15c light red	1.00	12.00
J33a	D5	20c light red	.80	12.00
J35a	D5	30c light red	1.25	12.00
J37a	D5	40c light red	1.00	12.00
		Nos. J25a-J37a (7)	13.55	96.00

No. J36 Surcharged with New Value

1937, Oct. 1		Unwmk.	**Perf. 12½**	
J40	D5	20c on 37½c salmon	.80	.40

D6

1939-40				
J41	D6	1g salmon	6.00	8.00
J42	D6	1g blue ('40)	.40	*4.00*
a.		1g lt bl, thick paper, invisible gum	.80	12.00

> **Catalogue values for unused stamps in this section, from this point to the end of the section, are for Never Hinged items.**

Nos. 234, 237 and 241 Surcharged or Overprinted in Black

1946, Mar. 11			Photo.	
J43	A28	2½c on 10c red org	1.25	1.25
J44	A28	10c red orange	2.00	2.00
J45	A28	20c plum	6.00	6.00
J46	A28	40c yellow green	45.00	45.00
		Nos. J43-J46 (4)	54.25	54.25

D7

Perf. 14½x14

1946, Aug. 14		Wmk. 228	Typo.	
J47	D7	1c purple	.75	1.25
J48	D7	2½c brn org	2.00	2.00
J49	D7	3½c ultra	.75	1.25
J50	D7	5c red orange	.75	1.25
J51	D7	7½c Prus green	.75	1.25
J52	D7	10c deep magenta	.75	1.25
J53	D7	20c light ultra	.75	1.25
J54	D7	25c olive	.75	1.25
J55	D7	30c red brown	1.25	1.50
J56	D7	40c yellow grn	1.25	1.50
J57	D7	50c yellow	1.60	1.50
J58	D7	75c aqua	1.60	1.50
J59	D7	100c apple green	1.60	1.50
		Nos. J47-J59 (13)	14.55	18.25

1948		Litho. Unwmk.	**Perf. 12½**	
J59A	D7	2½c brown orange	1.25	*2.00*

OFFICIAL STAMPS

Regular Issues of 1883-1909 Overprinted

1911, Oct. 1		Typo.	Unwmk.	
O1	A6	½c violet	1.00	8.00
O2	A6	1c olive grn	.25	.80
O3	A6	2c yellow brn	.25	.25
O4	A3	2½c yellow	.75	.75
O5	A6	2½c blue grn	2.00	2.00
O6	A6	3c orange	.65	.65
O7	A6	4c ultra	.25	.25
O8	A6	5c rose red	1.20	1.00
b.		Double overprint	1,600.	400.00
O9	A6	7½c gray	3.00	3.00
O10	A9	10c slate	.25	.25
O11	A9	12½c deep blue	3.00	3.00

O12	A9	15c chocolate	1.00	1.00
a.		Overprinted with two bars	40.00	120.00
b.		As "a," "Dienst" inverted	50.00	
O13	A9	17½c bister	4.00	3.00
O14	A9	20c olive grn	1.00	.65
O15	A9	22½c brn & ol grn	4.00	4.00
O16	A9	25c violet	2.40	2.00
O17	A9	30c orange brn	1.25	.75
O18	A9	50c red brown	16.00	10.00
O19	A10	1g dull lilac	4.00	2.00
O20	A10	2½g slate blue	34.00	35.00
		Nos. O1-O20 (20)	80.25	78.35

The overprint reads diagonally downward on Nos. O1-O3 and O5-O9.

Overprint Inverted

O1a	A6	½c	60.00	120.00
O2a	A6	1c	4.00	20.00
O3a	A6	2c	4.00	20.00
O5a	A6	2½c	12.00	28.00
O6a	A6	3c	120.00	40.00
O8a	A6	5c	4.00	20.00
O10a	A9	10c	4.00	8.00
O11a	A9	12½c	40.00	60.00
O14a	A9	20c	200.00	60.00
O16a	A9	25c	1,400.	1,400.
O17a	A9	30c	200.00	120.00
O18a	A9	50c	40.00	32.50
O19a	A10	1g	575.00	1,000.
O20a	A10	2½g	240.00	650.00

D

Regular Issue of 1892-1894 Overprinted

1911, Oct. 1				
O21	A4	10c orange brn	2.40	1.60
O22	A4	12½c gray	4.00	12.00
O23	A4	15c bister	4.00	4.00
O24	A4	20c blue	4.00	2.40
O25	A4	25c lilac	16.00	10.00
O26	A4	50c carmine	50.00	25.00
O27	A4	2.50g org brn & bl	67.50	65.00
		Nos. O21-O27 (7)	101.90	97.00

Inverted Overprints

O21a	A4	10c	15.00	50.00
O22a	A4	12½c	425.00	400.00
O23a	A4	15c	425.00	325.00
O24a	A4	20c	165.00	175.00
O25a	A4	25c	800.00	900.00
O26a	A4	50c	15.00	75.00
O27a	A4	2.50g	1,150.	1,450.

Handstamped overprints exist on Nos. O21, O26, O27. Handstamps differ from machine overprints in that the ink is flatter, the quality is poorer, and the "D" is usually slightly angled. The machined printed overprints are always parallel.

A handstamped "D" exists on regular-issue No. 28; however, this was created in limited quantities and was never issued. Value, $2,200.

OCCUPATION STAMPS

Issued under Japanese Occupation

During the Japanese occupation of the Netherlands Indies, 1942-45, the occupation forces applied a great variety of overprints to supplies of Netherlands Indies stamps of 1933-42. A few typical examples are shown above.

Most of these overprinted stamps were for use in limited areas, such as Java, Sumatra, Bangka and Billiton, etc. The anchor overprints were applied by the Japanese naval authorities for areas under their control.

For a time, stamps of Straits Settlements and some of the Malayan states, with Japanese overprints, were used in Sumatra and the Riouw archipelago. Stamps of Japan without overprint were also used in the Netherlands Indies during the occupation.

For Use in Java and Sumatra
100 Sen (Cents) = 1 Rupee (Gulden)

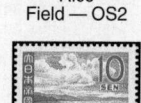

Globe Showing Japanese Empire — OS1

Farmer Plowing Rice Field — OS2

Mt. Semeru, Java's Highest Active Volcano — OS3

Bantam Bay, Northwest Java — OS4

Values in Sen

Perf. 12½

1943, Mar. 9		Unwmk.	Litho.	
N1	OS1	2s red brown	2.50	4.25
N2	OS2	3½s carmine	1.75	1.25
N3	OS3	5s green	5.00	1.25
N4	OS4	10s light blue	15.00	2.50
		Nos. N1-N4 (4)	24.25	9.25

Issued to mark the anniversary of Japan's "Victory" in Java.

For Use in Java (also Sumatra, Borneo and Malaya)

Javanese Dancer OS5

Javanese Puppet OS6

Buddha Statue, Borobudur OS7

Map of Java OS8

Sacred Dancer of Djokja Palace, and Borobudur OS9

Bird of Vishnu, Map of Java and Mt. Semeru OS10

Plowing with Carabao OS11

Terraced Rice Fields OS12

Values in Cents, Sen or Rupees

1943-44		Unwmk.	**Perf. 12½**	
N5	OS5	3½c rose red	2.00	1.00
N6	OS6	5c yellow grn	3.50	.80
N7	OS7	10c dk blue	4.00	.60
N8	OS8	20c olive brn	1.40	.80
N9	OS9	40c rose lilac	3.50	1.20
N10	OS10	60c red orange	2.50	1.20
N11	OS11	80s fawn ('44)	4.50	3.75
N12	OS12	1r violet ('44)	22.50	3.00
		Nos. N5-N12 (8)	43.90	12.35

Indies Soldier — OS13

1943, Apr.
N13	OS13	3½c rose	11.00	10.00
N14	OS13	10c blue	35.00	4.25

Issued to commemorate reaching the postal savings goal of 5,000,000 gulden.

For Use in Sumatra

Batak Tribal House OS14

Menangkabau House OS15

Plowing with Carabao OS16

Nias Island Scene OS17

Carabao Canyon — OS18

1943   Unwmk.   Perf. 12½
N15	OS14	1c olive green	.55	1.00
N16	OS14	2c brt yel grn	.55	1.00
N17	OS14	3c bluish green	.55	1.00
N18	OS15	3½c rose red	2.10	1.00
N19	OS15	4c ultra	1.25	1.00
N20	OS15	5c red orange	1.50	1.00
N21	OS16	10c blue gray	4.75	.50
N22	OS16	20c orange brn	1.00	.50
N23	OS17	30c red violet	2.25	1.00
N24	OS17	40c dull brown	2.50	1.00
N25	OS18	50c bister brn	2.50	2.50
N26	OS18	1r lt blue vio	35.00	10.00
		Nos. N15-N26 (12)	54.50	16.50

For Use in the Lesser Sunda Islands, Molucca Archipelago and Districts of Celebes and South Borneo Controlled by the Japanese Navy

Japanese Flag, Island Scene OS19

Mt. Fuji, Kite, Flag, Map of East Indies OS20

Values in Cents and Gulden

1943   Wmk. 257   Typo.   Perf. 13
N27	OS19	2c brown	1.25	11.50
N28	OS19	3c yellow grn	1.25	10.50
N29	OS19	3½c brown org	4.00	10.50
N30	OS19	5c blue	.80	3.75
N31	OS19	10c carmine	1.00	3.75
N32	OS19	15c ultra	1.20	10.00
N33	OS19	20c dull violet	1.75	3.75

Engr.
N34	OS20	25c orange	6.00	11.50
N35	OS20	30c blue	6.00	6.25
N36	OS20	50c slate green	8.50	9.00
N37	OS20	1g brown lilac	37.50	20.00
		Nos. N27-N37 (11)	69.25	100.50

Issued under Nationalist Occupation

Menari Dancer of Amboina — OS21

Perf. 12½
1945, Aug.   Photo.   Unwmk.
N38	OS21	2c carmine	.25	.35

This stamp was prepared in 1941 or 1942 by Netherlands Indies authorities as an addition to the 1941 "dancers" set, but was issued in 1945 by the Nationalists (Indonesian Republic). It was not recognized by the Dutch. Exists imperforate.

NETHERLANDS NEW GUINEA

'ne-ther-lən͟d͟z 'nü 'gi-nē

(Dutch New Guinea)

LOCATION — Western half of New Guinea, southwest Pacific Ocean
GOVT. — Former Overseas Territory of the Netherlands
AREA — 151,789 sq. mi.
POP. — 730,000 (est. 1958)
CAPITAL — Hollandia

Netherlands New Guinea came under temporary United Nations administration Oct. 1, 1962, when stamps of this territory overprinted "UNTEA" were introduced to replace issues of Netherlands New Guinea. See West New Guinea (West Irian) in Vol. 6.

100 Cents = 1 Gulden

> **Catalogue values for all unused stamps in this country are for Never Hinged items.**

A1

A2

Queen Juliana — A3

Perf. 12½x13½
1950-52   Unwmk.   Photo.
1	A1	1c slate blue	.35	.25
2	A1	2c deep org	.35	.25
3	A1	2½c olive brn	.50	.25
4	A1	3c deep plum	1.75	1.25
5	A1	4c blue grn	1.75	1.25
6	A1	5c ultra	3.50	.25
7	A1	7½c org brown	.55	.25
8	A1	10c purple	1.75	.25
9	A1	12½c crimson	1.75	1.60

Perf. 13½x12½
10	A2	15c brown org	2.50	.75
11	A2	20c blue	1.15	.25
12	A2	25c orange red	1.15	.25
13	A2	30c dp blue ('52)	10.00	.40
14	A2	40c blue grn	1.75	.25
15	A2	45c brown ('52)	5.50	.80
16	A2	50c deep orange	1.50	.25
17	A2	55c brown blk ('52)	10.00	.60
18	A2	80c purple	12.00	3.00

Engr.   Perf. 12½x12
19	A3	1g red	15.00	1.40
20	A3	2g yellow brn ('52)	12.00	1.40
21	A3	5g dk olive grn	17.50	1.40
		Nos. 1-21 (21)	102.30	15.70

For surcharges see Nos. B1-B3.

Bird of Paradise A4

Queen Victoria Crowned Pigeon A5

Queen Juliana — A6

10c, 15c, 20c, Bird of Paradise with raised wings.

Photo.; Litho. (Nos. 24, 26, 28)
1954-60   Perf. 12½x12
22	A4	1c ver & yel ('58)	.40	.25
23	A4	5c choc & yel	.40	.25
24	A5	7c org red, bl & brn vio ('59)	.55	.35
25	A4	10c aqua & red brn	.40	.25
26	A5	12c grn, bl & brn vio ('59)	.55	.35
27	A4	15c dp yel & red brn	.40	.25
28	A5	17c brn vio & bl ('59)	.55	.25
29	A4	20c lt bl grn & red brn ('56)	1.20	.60
30	A6	25c red	.40	.25
31	A6	30c deep blue	.95	.25
32	A6	40c dp orange ('60)	2.50	2.00
33	A6	45c dk olive ('58)	1.20	1.25
34	A6	55c dk blue grn	.75	.25
35	A6	80c dl gray vio	1.60	.40
36	A6	85c dk vio brn ('56)	2.00	.55
37	A6	1g plum ('59)	5.25	2.25
		Nos. 22-37 (16)	18.70	9.75

Stamps overprinted "UNTEA" are listed under West Irian in Vol. 6.
For surcharges see Nos. B4-B6.

Papuan Watching Helicopter — A7

1959, Apr. 10   Photo.   Perf. 11½x11
38	A7	55c red brown & blue	1.75	1.00

1959 expedition to the Star Mountains of New Guinea.

Mourning Woman — A8

1960, Apr. 7   Unwmk.   Perf. 13x14
39	A8	25c blue	.75	.60
40	A8	30c yellow bister	.75	.60

World Refugee Year, 7/1/59-6/30/60.

Council Building — A9

1961, Apr. 5   Litho.   Perf. 11x11½
41	A9	25c bluish green	.30	.40
42	A9	30c rose	.30	.40

Inauguration of the New Council.

School Children Crossing Street — A10

Design: 30c, Men looking at traffic sign.

1962, Mar. 16   Photo.   Perf. 14x13
43	A10	25c dp blue & red	.40	.40
44	A10	30c brt green & red	.40	.40

Need for road safety.

Queen Juliana and Prince Bernhard — A11

1962, Apr. 28   Unwmk.   Perf. 14x13
45	A11	55c olive brown	.40	.50

Silver wedding anniv.

Tropical Beach — A12

Design: 30c, Palm trees on beach.

1962, July 18   Perf. 14x13
46	A12	25c multicolored	.30	.40
47	A12	30c multicolored	.30	.40

5th So. Pacific Conf., Pago Pago, July 1962.

SEMI-POSTAL STAMPS

Regular Issue of 1950-52 Surcharged in Black

Perf. 12½x13½
1953, Feb. 9   Unwmk.   Photo.
B1	A1	5c + 5c ultra	12.00	9.50

Perf. 13½x12½
B2	A2	15c + 10c brn org	12.00	9.50
B3	A2	25c + 10c org red	12.00	9.50
		Nos. B1-B3 (3)	36.00	28.50

The tax was for flood relief work in the Netherlands.

Nos. 23, 25, 27 Surcharged in Red

1955, Nov. 1   Perf. 12½x12
B4	A4	5c + 5c	1.75	1.50
B5	A4	10c + 10c	1.75	1.50
B6	A4	15c + 10c	1.75	1.50
		Nos. B4-B6 (3)	5.25	4.50

The surtax was for the Red Cross.

Leprosarium — SP1

10c+5c, 30c+10c, Young Papuan and huts.

Perf. 12x12½
1956, Dec. 15   Unwmk.   Photo.
B7	SP1	5c + 5c dk slate grn	1.25	.95
B8	SP1	10c + 5c brn violet	1.25	.95
B9	SP1	25c + 10c brt blue	1.25	.95
B10	SP1	30c + 10c ocher	1.25	.95
		Nos. B7-B10 (4)	5.00	3.80

The surtax was for the fight against leprosy.

Papuan Girl and Beach Scene — SP2

10c+5c, 30c+10c, Papuan boy and pile dwelling.

1957, Oct. 1　　　Perf. 12½x12

B11	SP2	5c + 5c maroon	1.25	.95
B12	SP2	10c + 5c slate grn	1.25	.95
B13	SP2	25c + 10c brown	1.25	.95
B14	SP2	30c + 10c dark blue	1.25	.95
		Nos. B11-B14 (4)	5.00	3.80

The surtax was to fight infant mortality.

Ancestral Image, North Coast New Guinea — SP3

Design: 10c+5c, 30c+10c, Bowl in form of human figure, Asmat-Papua.

1958, Oct. 1　Litho.　Perf. 12½x12

B15	SP3	5c + 5c bl, blk & red	1.25	.95
B16	SP3	10c + 5c rose lake, blk, red & yel	1.25	.95
B17	SP3	25c + 10c bl grn, blk & red	1.25	.95
B18	SP3	30c + 10c ol gray, blk & yel	1.25	.95
		Nos. B15-B18 (4)	5.00	3.80

The surtax was for the Red Cross.

Bignonia — SP4

Flowers: 10c+5c, Orchid. 25c+10c, Rhododendron. 30c+10c, Gesneriacea.

1959, Nov. 16　Photo.　Perf. 12½x13

B19	SP4	5c + 5c car rose & grn	.80	.70
B20	SP4	10c + 5c ol, yel & lil	.80	.70
B21	SP4	25c + 10c red, org & grn	.80	.70
B22	SP4	30c + 10c vio & grn	.80	.70
		Nos. B19-B22 (4)	3.20	2.80

Birdwing — SP5

Various Butterflies.

Perf. 13x12½
1960, Sept. 1　Unwmk.　Litho.

B23	SP5	5c + 5c lt bl, blk, emer & yel	1.40	1.25
B24	SP5	10c + 5c sal, blk & bl	1.40	1.25
B25	SP5	25c + 10c yel, blk & org red	1.40	1.25
B26	SP5	30c + 10c lt grn, brn & yel	1.40	1.25
		Nos. B23-B26 (4)	5.60	5.00

Surtax for social care.

Rhinoceros Beetle and Coconut Palm Leaf — SP6

Beetles & leaves of host plants: 10c+5c, Ectocemus 10-maculatus Montri, a primitive weevil. 25c+10c, Stag beetle. 30c+10c, Tortoise beetle.

1961, Sept. 15　　　Perf. 13x12½
Beetles in Natural Colors

B27	SP6	5c + 5c deep org	.70	.50
B28	SP6	10c + 5c lt ultra	.70	.50
B29	SP6	25c + 10c citron	.70	.50
B30	SP6	30c + 10c green	.70	.50
		Nos. B27-B30 (4)	2.80	2.00

Surtax for social care.

Crab — SP7

Designs: 10c+5c, Lobster, vert. 25c+10c, Spiny lobster, vert. 30c+10c, Shrimp.

Perf. 14x13, 13x14
1962, Sept. 17　　　Unwmk.

B31	SP7	5c + 5c red, grn, brn & yel	.30	.25
B32	SP7	10c + 5c Prus bl & yel	.30	.25
B33	SP7	25c + 10c multicolored	.30	.25
B34	SP7	30c + 10c bl, org red & yel	.35	.30
		Nos. B31-B34 (4)	1.25	1.05

The surtax on Nos. B19-B34 went to various social works organizations.

POSTAGE DUE STAMPS

D1

Perf. 13½x12½
1957　　Photo.　　Unwmk.

J1	D1	1c vermilion	.50	.45
J2	D1	5c vermilion	1.25	1.10
J3	D1	10c vermilion	2.75	2.50
J4	D1	25c vermilion	3.25	2.90
J5	D1	40c vermilion	3.25	2.90
J6	D1	1g blue	5.25	5.25
		Nos. J1-J6 (6)	16.25	15.10

NEVIS

'nē-vəs

LOCATION — West Indies, southeast of Puerto Rico
GOVT. — A former presidency of the Leeward Islands Colony (British)
AREA — 36 sq. mi.
POP. — 8,794 (1991)

Nevis stamps were discontinued in 1890 and replaced by those of the Leeward Islands. From 1903 to 1956 stamps of St. Kitts-Nevis and Leeward Islands were used concurrently. From 1956 to 1980 stamps of St. Kitts-Nevis were used. While still a part of St. Kitts-Nevis, Nevis started issuing stamps in 1980.

See Leeward Islands and St. Kitts-Nevis.

12 Pence = 1 Shilling
100 Cents = 1 Dollar

> Catalogue values for unused stamps in this country are for Never Hinged items, beginning with Scott 100 in the regular postage section and Scott O1 in the officials section.

Unused examples of Nos. 1-8 almost always have no original gum, and they are valued without gum. These stamps with original gum are worth more. Other issues are valued with original gum as defined in the catalogue introduction. Very fine examples of Nos. 1-8, will have perforations touching the design on at least one side due to the narrow spacing of the stamps on the plates. Stamps with perfs clear of the design on all four sides are scarce and will command higher prices.

Medicinal Spring
A1　　　A2

A3

A4

1861　　Unwmk.　Engr.　Perf. 13
Bluish Wove Paper

1	A1	1p lake rose	325.00	140.00
2	A2	4p dull rose	950.00	200.00
3	A3	6p gray	775.00	260.00
4	A4	1sh green	1,100.	250.00

Grayish Wove Paper

5	A1	1p lake rose	115.00	60.00
6	A2	4p dull rose	170.00	80.00
7	A3	6p lilac gray	175.00	65.00
8	A4	1sh green	400.00	95.00

1867　White Wove Paper　Perf. 15

9	A1	1p red	67.50	55.00
10	A2	4p orange	155.00	25.00
11	A4	1sh yellow green	925.00	125.00
12	A4	1sh blue green	325.00	45.00

Laid Paper

13	A4	1sh yel green	25,000.	6,750.
		Manuscript cancel		3,000.

No. 13 values are for stamps with design cut into on one or two sides.

1876　　Wove Paper　　Litho.

14	A1	1p rose	35.00	25.00
14A	A1	1p red	45.00	30.00
b.		1p vermilion	45.00	45.00
c.		Imperf., pair	1,900.	
d.		Half used as ½p on cover		4,500.
15	A2	4p orange	190.00	45.00
a.		Imperf.		
b.		Vert. pair, imperf. between	12,750.	
16	A3	6p olive gray	250.00	250.00
17	A4	1sh gray green	100.00	125.00
a.		1sh dark green	135.00	175.00
b.		Horiz. strip of 3, perf. all around & imperf. btwn.	20,000.	

Perf. 11½

18	A1	1p vermilion	65.00	60.00
a.		Horiz. pair, imperf. btwn.		
b.		Half used as ½p on cover		4,500.
c.		Imperf., pair	1,200.	
		Nos. 14-18 (6)	685.00	535.00

Queen Victoria — A5

1879-80　Typo.　Wmk. 1　Perf. 14

19	A5	1p violet ('80)	90.00	55.00
a.		Diagonal half used as ½p on cover		1,500.
20	A5	2½p red brown	175.00	100.00

1882-90　　Wmk. Crown and CA (2)

21	A5	½p green ('83)	14.00	27.50
22	A5	1p violet	125.00	50.00
a.		Half used as ½p on cover		900.00
23a	A5	1p carmine ('84)	20.00	20.00
24	A5	2½p red brown	140.00	55.00
25	A5	2½p ultra ('84)	24.00	27.50
26	A5	4p blue	400.00	55.00
27	A5	4p gray ('84)	25.00	10.00
28	A5	6p green ('83)	500.00	400.00
29	A5	6p brown org ('86)	27.50	77.50
30	A5	1sh violet ('90)	125.00	225.00
		Nos. 21-30 (10)	1,401.	947.50

Half of No. 22 Surcharged in Black or Violet

1883

31	A5	½p on half of 1p	1,100.	60.00
a.		Double surcharge		450.00
b.		Unsevered pair	7,500.	
c.		Surcharged on half of 1p revenue stamp		600.00
32	A5	½p on half of 1p (V)	1,250.	55.00
a.		Double surcharge		450.00
b.		Unsevered pair	7,500.	
c.		Surcharged on half of 1p revenue stamp		600.00

Surcharge reads up or down.

> Catalogue values for unused stamps in this section, from this point to the end of the section, are for Never Hinged items.

St. Kitts-Nevis Nos. 357-369 Ovptd.

Perf. 14½x14
1980, June 23　Litho.　Wmk. 373

100	A61	5c multicolored	.25	.25
101	A61	10c multicolored	.25	.25
102	A61	12c multicolored	.25	.30
103	A61	15c multicolored	.25	.25
104	A61	25c multicolored	.25	.25
a.		Unwatermarked	1.00	1.75
105	A61	30c multicolored	.25	.25
106	A61	40c multicolored	.30	.30
107	A61	45c multicolored	.65	.50
108	A61	50c multicolored	.30	.30
109	A61	55c multicolored	.40	.25
110	A61	$1 multicolored	.30	.30
a.		Unwatermarked	2.50	5.00
111	A61	$5 multicolored	1.00	1.00
112	A61	$10 multicolored	2.00	1.50
		Nos. 100-112 (13)	6.45	5.70

The bars cover "St. Christopher" and "Anguilla."

80th Birthday of Queen Mother Elizabeth — A6

1980, Sept. 4　　　Perf. 14

113	A6	$2 multicolored	.40	.50

Ships and Boats — A6a

5c, Nevis lighter. 30c, Local fishing boat. 55c, Caona. $3, Windjammer's S.V. Polynesia.

1980, Oct. 8

114	A6a	5c multicolored	.25	.25
115	A6a	30c multicolored	.25	.25
116	A6a	55c multicolored	.25	.25

Size: 38x52mm

117	A6a	$3 multicolored	.55	.55
a.		Perf. 12½x12	.55	.55
b.		Booklet pane of 3 #117a	1.75	1.75
		Nos. 114-117 (4)	1.30	1.30

No. 117b separated into three parts by roulettes running vert. through the margin surrounding the stamps. For overprint see No. 538.

Christmas — A7

1980, Nov. 20　　　Perf. 14

118	A7	5c Mother and child	.30	.30
119	A7	30c Heralding angel	.30	.30
120	A7	$2.50 Three kings	.60	.60
		Nos. 118-120 (3)	1.20	1.20

A8

Landmarks — A9

5c, Charlestown Pier. 10c, Court House & Library. 15c, New River Mill. 20c, Nelson Museum. 25c, St. James' Parish Church. 30c, Nevis Lane. 40c, Zetland Plantation. 45c, Nisbet Plantation. 50c, Pinney's Beach. 55c, Eva Wilkin's Studio. $1, Nevis at dawn. $2.50, Ft. Charles ruins. $5, Old Bath House. $10, Nisbet's Beach.

1981, Feb. 5
No Date Imprint Below Design

121	A8	5c multicolored	.25	.25
122	A8	10c multicolored	.25	.25
123	A9	15c multicolored	.25	.25
124	A9	20c multicolored	.25	.25
125	A9	25c multicolored	.25	.25
126	A9	30c multicolored	.25	.25
127	A9	40c multicolored	.25	.25
128	A9	45c multicolored	.25	.25
129	A9	50c multicolored	.25	.25
130	A9	55c multicolored	.30	.30
131	A9	$1 multicolored	.55	.55
132	A9	$2.50 multicolored	.75	.75
133	A9	$5 multicolored	1.25	1.25
134	A9	$10 multicolored	2.50	2.50
		Nos. 121-134 (14)	7.60	7.60

For surcharges see Nos. 169-181.

1982, June 9
Inscribed "1982" Below Design

121a	A8	5c multicolored	.30	.30
122a	A8	10c multicolored	.30	.30
123a	A9	15c multicolored	.25	.25
124a	A9	20c multicolored	.25	.25
125a	A9	25c multicolored	.25	.25
126a	A9	30c multicolored	.25	.25
127a	A9	40c multicolored	.25	.25
128a	A9	45c multicolored	.25	.25
129a	A9	50c multicolored	.25	.25
130a	A9	55c multicolored	.30	.30
131a	A9	$1 multicolored	.55	.55
132a	A9	$2.50 multicolored	.75	.75
133a	A9	$5 multicolored	1.25	1.25
134a	A9	$10 multicolored	2.50	2.50
		Nos. 121a-134a (14)	7.70	7.70

1983
Inscribed "1983" Below Design

124b	A9	20c multicolored	.50	.25
125b	A9	25c multicolored	.50	.25
126b	A9	30c multicolored	.50	.25
127b	A9	40c multicolored	.50	.25
128b	A9	45c multicolored	.50	.25
129b	A9	50c multicolored	.50	.25
130b	A9	55c multicolored	.50	.25
132b	A9	$2.50 multicolored	1.25	1.00
		Nos. 124b-132b (8)	4.75	2.75

Prince Charles, Lady Diana, Royal Yacht Charlotte — A9a

Prince Charles and Lady Diana A9b

No. 135, Couple, *Royal Caroline.* No. 136, Couple. No. 137, Couple, *Royal Sovereign.* No. 139, Couple, HMY *Britannia.*

1981, June 23   Wmk. 373   Perf. 14

135	A9a	55c multicolored	.25	.25
a.		Bklt. pane of 4, perf. 12, unwmkd.	.90	.90
136	A9b	55c multicolored	.25	.25
137	A9b	$2 multicolored	.50	.50
138	A9b	$2 like No. 136	.50	.50
a.		Bklt. pane of 2, perf. 12, unwmkd.	1.40	1.40
139	A9a	$5 multicolored	1.10	1.10
140	A9b	$5 like No. 136	1.10	1.10
		Nos. 135-140 (6)	3.70	3.70

Souvenir Sheet

1981, Dec. 14   Perf. 12
141 A9b $4.50 like No. 136   1.75 1.75

Stamps of the same denomination issued in sheets of 7 (6 type A9a and 1 type A9b). For surcharges see Nos. 453-454.

Butterflies — A10

5c, Zebra. 30c, Malachite. 55c, Southern dagger tail. $2, Large orange sulphur.

1982, Feb. 16   Perf. 14

142	A10	5c multicolored	.30	.30
143	A10	30c multicolored	.30	.30
144	A10	55c multicolored	.30	.30
145	A10	$2 multicolored	1.40	1.40
		Nos. 142-145 (4)	2.30	2.30

For overprint see No. 452.

1983, June 8

30c, Tropical chequered skipper. 55c, Caribbean buckeye, vert. $1.10, Common long-tailed skipper, vert. $2, Mimic.

146	A10	30c multicolored	.50	.50
147	A10	55c multicolored	.50	.50
148	A10	$1.10 multicolored	.75	.75
149	A10	$2 multicolored	1.00	1.00
		Nos. 146-149 (4)	2.75	2.75

21st Birthday of Princess Diana, July 1 — A11

30c, Caroline of Brunswick. 55c, Brunswick arms. $5, Diana.

1982, June 22   Perf. 13½x14

150	A11	30c multi	.25	.25
151	A11	55c multi	.30	.30
152	A11	$5 multi	1.20	1.20
		Nos. 150-152 (3)	1.75	1.75

For surcharge see No. 449.

Nos. 150-152 Overprinted "ROYAL BABY"

1982, July 12

153	A11	30c multicolored	.25	.25
154	A11	55c multicolored	.35	.35
155	A11	$5 multicolored	1.25	1.25
		Nos. 153-155 (3)	1.85	1.85

Birth of Prince William of Wales, June 21.

Scouting, 75th Anniv. — A12

1982, Aug. 18

156	A12	5c Cycling	.35	.35
157	A12	30c Running	.45	.45
158	A12	$2.50 Building campfire	.90	.90
		Nos. 156-158 (3)	1.70	1.70

For overprints see Nos. 447, 455.

Christmas A13

Illustrations by youths — 15c, Eugene Seabrookes. 30c, Kharenzabeth Glasgow. $1.50, David Grant. $2.50, Leonard Huggins. Nos. 159-160 vert.

1982, Oct. 20   Perf. 13½x14, 14x13½

159	A13	15c multicolored	.35	.35
160	A13	30c multicolored	.35	.35
161	A13	$1.50 multicolored	.45	.45
162	A13	$2.50 multicolored	.85	.85
		Nos. 159-162 (4)	2.00	2.00

Coral — A14

15c, Tube sponge. 30c, Stinging coral. 55c, Flower coral. $3, Sea rod, red fire sponge.

1983, Jan. 12   Perf. 14

163	A14	15c multicolored	.25	.25
164	A14	30c multicolored	.40	.40
165	A14	55c multicolored	.40	.40
166	A14	$3 multicolored	1.20	1.20
a.		Souvenir sheet of 4, #163-166	2.50	2.50
		Nos. 163-166 (4)	2.25	2.25

For overprints see Nos. 446, 448.

Commonwealth Day — A15

55c, HMS *Boreas* off Nevis. $2, Lord Nelson, *Boreas.*

1983, Mar. 14
167 A15 55c multicolored   .40 .40
168 A15 $2 multicolored   1.00 1.00

Nos. 121a and 123a-134a Ovptd.

No. 169   No. 170-181

1983, Sept. 19

169	A8	5c multicolored	.25	.25
c.		Overprint larger with serifed letters	1.25	2.25
170	A9	15c multicolored	.25	.25
171	A9	20c multicolored	.25	.25
172	A9	25c multicolored	.25	.25
173	A9	30c multicolored	.25	.25
174	A9	40c multicolored	.25	.30
175	A9	45c multicolored	.30	.30
176	A9	50c multicolored	.30	.40
177	A9	55c multicolored	.35	.45
178	A9	$1 multicolored	.45	.45
179	A9	$2.50 multicolored	.45	.70
180	A9	$5 multicolored	.55	.85
181	A9	$10 multicolored	.75	1.10
		Nos. 169-181 (13)	4.65	5.90

The overprints on Nos. 169a and 169c were applied locally.

Nos. 121, 123-127, 130-134 Ovptd.

1983

169a	A8	5c multicolored, larger ovpt.	15.00	12.00
170a	A9	15c multicolored	42.50	42.50
171a	A9	20c multicolored	6.00	6.00
172a	A9	25c multicolored	6.00	6.00
173a	A9	30c multicolored	1.10	1.10
174a	A9	40c multicolored	1.00	1.00
177a	A9	55c multicolored	1.00	1.00
178a	A9	$1 multicolored	1.00	1.00
179a	A9	$2.50 multicolored	1.40	1.40
180a	A9	$5 multicolored	2.50	2.50
181a	A9	$10 multicolored	4.50	4.50
		Nos. 169a-181a (11)	82.00	79.00

Nos. 124b-132b and Additional values inscribed "1983" Ovptd.

1983

170b	A9	15c multicolored	1.75	1.00
171b	A9	20c multicolored	1.75	1.00
172b	A9	25c multicolored	1.75	1.00
173b	A9	30c multicolored	1.75	1.00
174b	A9	40c multicolored	1.75	1.00
175b	A9	45c multicolored	1.75	1.00
176b	A9	50c multicolored	1.75	1.00
177b	A9	55c multicolored	1.75	1.00
178b	A9	$1 multicolored	2.25	1.25
179b	A9	$2.50 multicolored	1.75	1.00
180b	A9	$5 multicolored	3.00	3.00
181b	A9	$10 multicolored	6.00	6.00
		Nos. 170b-181b (12)	27.00	19.25

1st Manned Flight, Bicent. — A16

10c, Montgolfier Balloon, 1783, vert. 45c, Lindbergh's Sikorsky S-38 carrying mail, 1929. 50c, Beechcraft Twin Bonanza. $2.50, Sea Harrier, 1st operational V/STOL fighter.

1983, Sept. 28   Wmk. 380

182	A16	10c multicolored	.25	.25
183	A16	45c multicolored	.25	.25
184	A16	50c multicolored	.25	.25
185	A16	$2.50 multicolored	.75	.75
a.		Souvenir sheet of 4, #182-185	1.75	1.75
		Nos. 182-185 (4)	1.50	1.50

Christmas A17

1983, Nov. 7

186	A17	5c Nativity	.25	.25
187	A17	30c Shepherds, flock	.25	.25
188	A17	55c Angels	.25	.25
189	A17	$3 Youths	.90	.90
a.		Souvenir sheet of 4, #186-189	1.60	1.60
		Nos. 186-189 (4)	1.65	1.65

Leaders of the World
Large quantities of some Leaders of the World issues were sold at a fraction of face value when the printer was liquidated.

A18

Leaders of the World: Locomotives — No. 190, 1882 Class Wee Bogie, UK. No. 191, 1968 JNR Class EF81, Japan. No. 192, 1878 Snowdon Ranger, UK. No. 193, 1927 P.O. Class 5500, France. No. 194, 1859 Connor Single Class. No. 195, 1904 Large Belpaire Passenger, UK. No. 196, 1829 Stourbridge Lion, US. No. 197, 1934 Cock O' The North. No. 198, 1945 County of Oxford, GB. No. 199, 1940 SNCF Class 240P, France. No. 200, 1851 Comet, UK. No. 201, 1904 County Class, UK. No. 202, 1926 JNR Class 7000, Japan. No. 203, 1877 Nord L'Outrance, France. No. 204, 1919 CM St.P&P Bipolar, US. No. 205, 1897 Palatinate Railway Class P3, Germany. No. 206, 1908 Class 8H, UK. No. 207, 1927 King George V. No. 208, 1951 Britannia. No. 209, 1924 Pendennis Castle. No. 210, 1960 Evening Star. No. 211, 1934 Stanier Class 5, GB. No. 212, 1946 Winston Churchill Battle of Britain. No. 213, 1935 Mallard A4. No. 214, 1899 Q.R. Class PB-15, Australia. No. 215, 1836 C&St.L Dorchester, Canada. No. 216, 1953 U.P. Gas Turbine, US. No. 217, 1969 U.P. Centennial Class, US. No. 218, 1866 No. 23 Class A, UK. No. 219, 1955 NY, NH & HR FL9, US. No. 220, 1837 B&O Lafayette, US. No. 221, 1964 JNR Shin-Kansen, Japan. No. 222, 1928 DRG Class 64, Germany. No. 223, 1882 D&RGR Class C-16, US.

1983-86 Litho. Unwmk. Perf. 12½
Se-tenant Pairs, #a.-b.
a. — Side and front views.
b. — Action scene.

190	A18	1c multicolored	.25	.25
191	A18	5c multicolored	.25	.25
192	A18	5c multicolored	.25	.25
193	A18	10c multicolored	.25	.25
194	A18	15c multicolored	.25	.25
195	A18	30c multicolored	.25	.25
196	A18	30c multicolored	.25	.25
197	A18	45c multicolored	.25	.25
198	A18	55c multicolored	.25	.25
199	A18	60c multicolored	.25	.25
200	A18	60c multicolored	.25	.25
201	A18	60c multicolored	.25	.25
202	A18	60c multicolored	.25	.25
203	A18	75c multicolored	.25	.25
204	A18	75c multicolored	.25	.25
205	A18	75c multicolored	.25	.25
206	A18	90c multicolored	.25	.25
207	A18	$1 multicolored	.30	.30
208	A18	$1 multicolored	.30	.30
209	A18	$1 multicolored	.30	.30
210	A18	$1 multicolored	.30	.30
211	A18	$1 multicolored	.30	.30
212	A18	$1 multicolored	.30	.30
213	A18	$1 multicolored	.30	.30
214	A18	$1 multicolored	.30	.30
215	A18	$1 multicolored	.30	.30
216	A18	$1.50 multicolored	.45	.45
217	A18	$1.50 multicolored	.45	.45
218	A18	$2 multicolored	.60	.60
219	A18	$2 multicolored	.60	.60
220	A18	$2 multicolored	.60	.60
221	A18	$2.50 multicolored	.85	.85
222	A18	$2.50 multicolored	.85	.85
223	A18	$3 multicolored	.85	.85
		Nos. 190-223 (34)	12.20	12.20

Issued: #190, 200, 218, 4/26/85; #191, 193, 199, 221, 10/29/84; #192, 195, 201, 203, 214, 222, 7/26/85; #194, 197, 202, 204, 215, 217, 220, 223, 10/1/86; #196, 205, 216, 219, 1/30/86; #198, 206-213, 11/10/83.

British Monarchs, Scenes from History — A20

#258a, Boer War. #258b, Queen Victoria. #259a, Signing of the Magna Carta. #259b, King John. #260a, Victoria, diff. #260b, Osborne House. #261a, John, diff. #261b, Newark Castle, Nottinghamshire. #262a, Battle of Dettingen. #262b, King George II. #263a, George II, diff. #263b, Bank of England, 1732. #264a, George II's coat of arms. #264b, George II, diff. #265a, John's coat of arms. #265b, John, diff. #266a, Victoria's coat of arms. #266b, Victoria, diff.

1984

258	A20	5c Pair, #a.-b.	.25	.25
259	A20	5c Pair, #a.-b.	.25	.25
260	A20	50c Pair, #a.-b.	.25	.25
261	A20	55c Pair, #a.-b.	.25	.25
262	A20	60c Pair, #a.-b.	.25	.25
263	A20	75c Pair, #a.-b.	.25	.25
264	A20	$1 Pair, #a.-b.	.25	.25
265	A20	$2 Pair, #a.-b.	.60	.60
266	A20	$3 Pair, #a.-b.	.50	.50
		Nos. 258-266 (9)	2.85	2.85

Issued: #258, 260, 262-264, 266, 4/11; others, 11/20.

Tourism — A22

No. 276, Golden Rock Inn. No. 277, Rest Haven Inn. No. 278, Cliffdwellers Hotel. No. 279, Pinney's Beach Hotel.

1984, May 16   Wmk. 380   Perf. 14

276	A22	55c multicolored	.40	.40
277	A22	55c multicolored	.40	.40
278	A22	55c multicolored	.40	.40
279	A22	55c multicolored	.40	.40
		Nos. 276-279 (4)	1.60	1.60

Seal of the Colony — A22a

1984, June 8   Wmk. 380   Perf. 14

279A	A22a	$15 dull red	2.00	5.25

Tourism Type of 1984

No. 280, Croney's Old Manor Hotel. No. 281, Montpelier Plantation Inn. No. 282, Nisbet's Plantation Inn. No. 283, Zetland Plantation Inn.

1985, Feb. 12

280	A22	$1.20 multicolored	.65	.65
281	A22	$1.20 multicolored	.65	.65
282	A22	$1.20 multicolored	.65	.65
283	A22	$1.20 multicolored	.65	.65
		Nos. 280-283 (4)	2.60	2.60

A23

Leaders of the World: Classic cars — No. 285, 1932 Cadillac V16 Fleetwood Convertible, US. No. 286, 1935 Delahaye Type 35 Cabriolet, France. No. 287, 1916 Packard Twin Six Touring Car, US. No. 288, 1929 Lagonda Speed Model Touring Car, GB. No. 289, 1958 Ferrari Testarossa, Italy. No. 290, 1934 Voisin Aerodyne, France. No. 291, 1912 Sunbeam Coupe De L'Auto, GB. No. 292, 1936 Adler Trumpf, Germany. No. 293, 1886 Daimler 2-Cylinder, Germany. No. 294, 1930 Riley Brooklands Nine, UK. No. 295, 1967 Jaguar E-Type 4.2 Liter, GB. No. 296, 1970 Porsche

911 S Targa, Germany. No. 297, 1948 Cisitalia Pinnifarina Coupe, Italy. No. 298, 1885 Benz Three-wheeler, Germany. No. 299, 1966 Alfa Romeo GTA, Italy. No. 300, 1947 Volkswagen Beetle, Germany. No. 301, 1963 Buick Riviera, US. No. 302, 1947 MG TC, GB. No. 303, 1960 Cooper Climax, UK. No. 304, 1957 Maserati Tipo 250F, Italy. No. 305, 1913 Pierce Arrow Type 66, US. No. 306, 1904 Ford 999, US. No. 307, 1980 Porsche 928S, Germany. No. 308, 1910 Oldsmobile Limited, US. No. 309, 1951 Jaguar C-Type, UK. No. 310, 1928 Willys-Knight 66A, US. No. 311, 1933 MG K3 Magnette, GB. No. 312, 1937 Lincoln Zephyr, US. No. 313, 1937 ERA 1.5 l B Type, UK. No. 314, 1953 Studebaker Starliner, US. No. 315, 1926 Pontiac 2-door, US. No. 316, 1966 Cobra Roadster 289, US. No. 317, 1930 MG M-Type Midget, UK. No. 318, 1966 Aston Martin DB6 Hardtop, GB. No. 319, 1932 Pierce Arrow V12, US. No. 320, 1971 Rolls Royce Corniche, UK. No. 321, 1953 Chevrolet Corvette, UK. No. 322, 1919 Cunningham V-8, US.

1984-86   Unwmk.   Perf. 12½
Se-tenant Pairs, #a.-b.
a. — Side and front views.
b. — Action scene.

285	A23	1c multicolored	.25	.25
286	A23	1c multicolored	.25	.25
287	A23	5c multicolored	.25	.25
288	A23	5c multicolored	.25	.25
289	A23	5c multicolored	.25	.25
290	A23	10c multicolored	.25	.25
291	A23	10c multicolored	.25	.25
292	A23	10c multicolored	.25	.25
293	A23	15c multicolored	.25	.25
294	A23	15c multicolored	.25	.25
295	A23	30c multicolored	.25	.25
296	A23	35c multicolored	.25	.25
297	A23	35c multicolored	.25	.25
298	A23	45c multicolored	.25	.25
299	A23	45c multicolored	.25	.25
300	A23	50c multicolored	.25	.25
301	A23	50c multicolored	.25	.25
302	A23	55c multicolored	.25	.25
303	A23	60c multicolored	.25	.25
304	A23	60c multicolored	.25	.25
305	A23	60c multicolored	.25	.25
306	A23	75c multicolored	.25	.25
307	A23	75c multicolored	.25	.25
308	A23	75c multicolored	.25	.25
309	A23	$1 multicolored	.30	.30
310	A23	$1 multicolored	.30	.30
311	A23	$1.15 multicolored	.35	.35
312	A23	$1.50 multicolored	.40	.40
313	A23	$1.50 multicolored	.40	.40
314	A23	$1.75 multicolored	.45	.45
315	A23	$2 multicolored	.55	.55
316	A23	$2.50 multicolored	.70	.70
317	A23	$2.50 multicolored	.70	.70
318	A23	$3 multicolored	.75	.75
319	A23	$3 multicolored	.75	.75
320	A23	$3 multicolored	.75	.75
321	A23	$3 multicolored	.75	.75
322	A23	$3 multicolored	.75	.75
		Nos. 285-322 (38)	13.90	13.90

Issued: #285, 287, 293, 296, 298, 302, 316, 318, 7/25/84; #286, 289-290, 301, 303, 306, 317, 320, 2/20/85; #288, 295, 300, 319, 10/23/84; #291, 297, 307, 311-312, 315, 10/4/85; #292, 303, 308-309, 313, 321, 1/30/86; #294, 299, 305, 310, 314, 322, 8/15/86.

Culturama Carnival, 10th Anniv. — A24a

30c, Carpentry. 55c, Weaving mats and baskets. $1, Ceramics. $3, Carnival queen, folk dancers.

Wmk. 380
1984, Aug. 1   Litho.   Perf. 14

361	A24a	30c multicolored	.25	.25
362	A24a	55c multicolored	.25	.25
363	A24a	$1 multicolored	.25	.25
364	A24a	$3 multicolored	.65	.65
		Nos. 361-364 (4)	1.40	1.40

Flowers — A24b

5c, Yellow bell. 10c, Plumbago. 15c, Flamboyant. 20c, Eyelash orchid. 30c, Bougainvillea. 40c, Hibiscus. 50c, Night-blooming cereus. 55c, Yellow mahoe. 60c, Spider lily. 75c, Scarlet cordia. $1, Shell ginger. $3, Blue petrea. $5, Coral hibiscus. $10, Passion flower.

1984, Aug. 8
No Date Imprint Below Design

365	A24b	5c multi	.25	.25
366	A24b	10c multi	.25	.25
367	A24b	15c multi	.25	.25
368	A24b	20c multi	.25	.25
a.		Inscribed "1986"	.80	.35
369	A24b	30c multi	.25	.25
370	A24b	40c multi	.25	.25
a.		Inscribed "1986"	.50	.35
371	A24b	50c multi	.25	.25
372	A24b	55c multi	.25	.25
373	A24b	60c multi	.30	.30
374	A24b	75c multi	.35	.35
375	A24b	$1 multi	.30	.40
376	A24b	$3 multi	.60	1.10
377	A24b	$5 multi	1.10	2.00
378	A24b	$10 multi	2.25	3.50
		Nos. 365-378 (14)	6.90	9.65

Nos. 368a and 370a issued 7/23/86.

Independence of St. Kitts and Nevis, 1st Anniv. — A26

15c, Picking cotton. 55c, Hamilton House. $1.10, Self-sufficiency in food production. $3, Pinney's Beach.

1984, Sept. 18

379	A26	15c multi	.25	.25
380	A26	55c multi	.25	.25
381	A26	$1.10 multi	.40	.40
382	A26	$3 multi	.70	1.00
		Nos. 379-382 (4)	1.60	1.90

Leaders of the World A27

Cricket players and team emblems and match scenes: No. 383, C.P. Mead, England. No. 384, J.D. Love, Yorkshire. No. 385, S.J. Dennis, Yorkshire. No. 386, J.B. Statham, England. No. 387, Sir Learie Constantine, West Indies. No. 388, B.W. Luckhurst, Kent. No. 389, Sir Leonard Hutton, England. No. 390, B.L. D'Oliveira, England.

Pairs, #a.-b.

1984   Unwmk.   Perf. 12½

383	A27	5c multicolored	.25	.25
384	A27	5c multicolored	.25	.25
385	A27	15c multicolored	.25	.25
386	A27	25c multicolored	.25	.25
387	A27	55c multicolored	.25	.25
388	A27	55c multicolored	.25	.25
389	A27	$2.50 multicolored	.50	1.25
390	A27	$2.50 multicolored	.50	1.25
		Nos. 383-390 (8)	2.50	4.00

Issued: #383, 386, 389, 10/23; others, 11/20.

Christmas A29

Musicians from local bands: 15c, Flutist and drummer of the Honeybees Band. 40c, Guitar and barhow players of the Canary Birds Band. 60c, Shell All Stars steel band. $3, Choir, organist, St. John's Church, Fig Tree.

1984, Nov. 2   Wmk. 380   Perf. 14

399-402	A29	Set of 4	2.25	2.25

Birds — A30

1985, Mar. 19

403	A30	20c Broad-winged hawk	1.10	.25
404	A30	40c Red-tailed hawk	1.25	.35
405	A30	60c Little blue heron	1.25	.45
406	A30	$3 Great white heron	2.75	2.25
		Nos. 403-406 (4)	6.35	3.30

Leaders of the World A31

Birds: #407a, Painted bunting. #407b, Golden-crowned kinglet. #408a, Eastern bluebird. #408b, Northern cardinal. #409a, Common flicker. #409b, Western tanager. #410a, Belted kingfisher. #410b, Mangrove cuckoo. #411a, Yellow warbler. #411b, Cerulean warbler. #412a, Sage thrasher. #412b, Evening grosbeak. #413a, Burrowing owl. #413b, Long-eared owl. #414a, Blackburnian warbler. #414b, Northern oriole.

1985   Unwmk.   Perf. 12½

407	A31	1c Pair, #a.-b.	.25	.25
408	A31	5c Pair, #a.-b.	.25	.25
409	A31	40c Pair, #a.-b.	.40	.40
410	A31	55c Pair, #a.-b.	.45	.45
411	A31	60c Pair, #a.-b.	.50	.50
412	A31	60c Pair, #a.-b.	.50	.50
413	A31	$2 Pair, #a.-b.	1.50	1.50
414	A31	$2.50 Pair, #a.-b.	1.75	1.75
		Nos. 407-414 (8)	5.60	5.60

John J. Audubon, ornithologist, birth bicent. Issued: 1c, 40c, #412, $2.50, 6/3; others, 3/25.

Girl Guides, 75th Anniv. — A32

15c, Troop, horiz. 60c, Uniforms, 1910, 1985. $1, Lord and Lady Baden-Powell. $3, Princess Margaret.

1985, June 17   Wmk. 380   Perf. 14

423	A32	15c multicolored	.25	.25
424	A32	60c multicolored	.25	.25
425	A32	$1 multicolored	.35	.35
426	A32	$3 multicolored	.90	1.25
		Nos. 423-426 (4)	1.75	2.10

Queen Mother Elizabeth A33

#427a, 432a, Black hat, white plume. #427b, 432b, Blue hat, pink feathers. #428a, Blue hat. #428b, Tiara. #429a, Violet & blue hat. #429b, Blue hat. #430a, 433a, Light blue hat. #430b, 433b, Black hat. #431a, As a child, c. 1910. #431b, Queen consort, c. 1945.

1985, July 31   Unwmk.   Perf. 12½

427	A33	45c Pair, #a.-b.	.25	.25
428	A33	75c Pair, #a.-b.	.30	.30
429	A33	$1.20 Pair, #a.-b.	.55	.55
430	A33	$1.50 Pair, #a.-b.	.70	.70
		Nos. 427-430 (4)	1.80	1.80

Souvenir Sheets

431	A33	$2 Sheet of 2, #a.-b.	2.00	2.00
432	A33	$3.50 Sheet of 2, #a.-b.	2.00	2.00
433	A33	$6 Sheet of 2, #a.-b.	4.00	4.00

Issued: #432-433, 12/27; others, 7/31. For overprints see No. 450.

Great Western Railway, 150th Anniv. A34

Railway engineers and their achievements: #438a, Isambard Brunel. #438b, Royal Albert Bridge, 1859. #439a, William Dean. #439b, Lord of the Isles, 1895. #440a, Lode Star, 1907. #440b, G.J. Churchward. #441a, Pendennis Castle Class, 1924. #441b, C.B. Collett.

1985, Aug. 31
438	A34	25c Pair, #a.-b.	.25	.25
439	A34	50c Pair, #a.-b.	.30	.30
440	A34	$1 Pair, #a.-b.	.50	.50
441	A34	$2.50 Pair, #a.-b.	1.30	1.30
		Nos. 438-441 (4)	2.35	2.35

Nos. 163, 157, 164, 151, 427, 144, 139-140 and 158 Ovptd. or Srchd. "CARIBBEAN ROYAL VISIT 1985" in 2 or 3 Lines

Perf. 14, 12½ (45c)

1985, Oct. 23   Wmk. as Before
446	A14	15c No. 163	1.00	1.00
447	A12	30c No. 157	2.00	2.00
448	A14	30c No. 164	1.00	1.00
449	A11	40c on 55c No. 151	2.25	2.25
450	A33	45c Pair, #a.-b.	3.00	3.00
452	A10	55c No. 144	2.25	2.25
453	A9a	$1.50 on $5 No. 139	3.75	3.75
454	A9b	$1.50 on $5 No. 140	13.00	16.00
455	A12	$2.50 No. 158	4.00	4.00
		Nos. 446-455 (9)	32.25	35.25

Christmas — A36

Anglican, Roman Catholic and Methodist churches — 10c, St. Paul's, Charlestown. 40c, St. Theresa, Charlestown. 60c, Methodist Church, Gingerland. $3, St. Thomas, Lowland.

1985, Nov. 5   Wmk. 380   Perf. 15
456	A36	10c multicolored	.25	.25
457	A36	40c multicolored	.30	.30
458	A36	60c multicolored	.40	.40
459	A36	$3 multicolored	1.25	1.25
		Nos. 456-459 (4)	2.20	2.20

Spitfire Fighter Plane, 50th Anniv. A37

$1, Prototype K.5054, 1936. $2.50, Mk.1A, 1940. $3, Mk.XII, 1944. $4, Mk.XXIV, 1948. $6, Seafire Mk.III.

1986, Mar. 24   Unwmk.   Perf. 12½
460	A37	$1 multi	.30	.30
461	A37	$2.50 multi	.70	.70
462	A37	$3 multi	.80	.80
463	A37	$4 multi	1.20	1.20
		Nos. 460-463 (4)	3.00	3.00

Souvenir Sheet
464	A37	$6 multi	3.00	3.00

No. 464 exists imperf. Value, $12.50 unused.

Discovery of America, 500th Anniv. (in 1992) — A38

#465a, American Indian. #465b, Columbus trading with Indians. #466a, Columbus's coat of arms. #466b, Breadfruit. #467a, Galleons. #467b, Columbus.

1986, Apr. 11
465	A38	75c Pair, #a.-b.	.90	.90
466	A38	$1.75 Pair, #a.-b.	2.25	2.25
467	A38	$2.50 Pair, #a.-b.	3.25	3.25
		Nos. 465-467 (3)	6.40	6.40

Souvenir Sheet
468	A38	$6 Columbus, diff.	6.50	6.50

Printed in continuous designs picturing various maps of Columbus's voyages.

Queen Elizabeth II, 60th Birthday A39

Various portraits.

1986, Apr. 21
472	A39	5c multicolored	.25	.25
473	A39	75c multicolored	.25	.25
474	A39	$2 multicolored	.50	.50
475	A39	$8 multi, vert.	2.00	2.00
		Nos. 472-475 (4)	3.00	3.00

Souvenir Sheet
476	A39	$10 multicolored	6.00	6.00

1986 World Cup Soccer Championships, Mexico — A40

1c, Character trademark. 2c, Brazilian player. 5c, Danish player. 10c, Brazilian, diff. 20c, Denmark vs. Spain. 30c, Paraguay vs. Chile. 60c, Italy vs. W. Germany. 75c, Danish team. $1, Paraguayan team. $1.75, Brazilian team. $3, Italy vs. England. $6, Italian team.

Size of 75c, $1, $1.75, $6: 56x35½mm

Perf. 15, 12½ (75c, $1, $1.75, $6)

1986, May 16
477	A40	1c multicolored	.25	.25
478	A40	2c multicolored	.25	.25
479	A40	5c multicolored	.25	.25
480	A40	10c multicolored	.25	.25
481	A40	20c multicolored	.25	.25
482	A40	30c multicolored	.25	.25
483	A40	60c multicolored	.35	.35
484	A40	75c multicolored	.50	.50
485	A40	$1 multicolored	.70	.70
486	A40	$1.75 multicolored	.80	.80
487	A40	$3 multicolored	1.30	1.30
488	A40	$6 multicolored	2.50	2.50
		Nos. 477-488 (12)	7.65	7.65

Souvenir Sheets
Perf. 12½
489	A40	$1.50 like $1.75	1.90	1.90
490	A40	$2 like $6	2.10	2.10

Perf. 15
491	A40	$2 like 20c	2.10	2.10
492	A40	$2.50 like 60c	2.50	2.50
493	A40	$4 like 30c	3.50	3.50

Nos. 478-483 and 487 vert.

Local Industry — A41

1986, July 18   Wmk. 380   Perf. 14
494	A41	15c Textile	.35	.35
495	A41	40c Carpentry	.50	.50
496	A41	$1.20 Agriculture	1.40	1.40
497	A41	$3 Fishing	3.25	3.25
		Nos. 494-497 (4)	5.50	5.50

A42

Wedding of Prince Andrew and Sarah Ferguson A43

#498a, Andrew. #498b, Sarah. #499a, Andrew at the races, horiz. #499b, Andrew in Africa, horiz.

1986, July 23   Unwmk.   Perf. 12½
498	A42	60c Pair, #a.-b.	.40	.40
499	A42	$2 Pair, #a.-b.	1.25	1.25

Souvenir Sheet
500	A43	$10 Couple on Balcony	4.00	4.00

Printed in vert. and horiz. pairs. For overprints see Nos. 521-522.

Coral — A44

1986, Sept. 8   Wmk. 380   Perf. 15
503	A44	15c Gorgonia	.25	.25
504	A44	60c Fire coral	.30	.30
505	A44	$2 Elkhorn coral	.90	.90
506	A44	$3 Feather star	1.20	1.20
		Nos. 503-506 (4)	2.65	2.65

A45

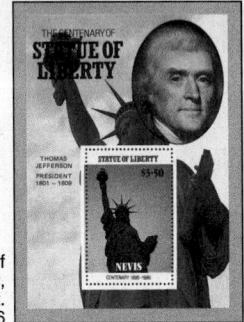

Statue of Liberty, Cent. A46

15c, Statue, World Trade Center. 25c, Statue, tall ship. 40c, Under renovation (front). 60c, Renovation (side). 75c, Statue, Operation Sail. $1, Tall ship. $1.50, Renovation (arm, head). $2, Ship flying Liberty flag. $2.50, Statue, Manhattan. $3, Workers on scaffold. $3.50, Statue at dusk. $4, Head. $4.50, Torch struck by lightning. $5, Torch, blazing sun.

All stamps are vertical except the $1 & $2.

1986, Oct. 28   Unwmk.   Perf. 14
507	A45	15c multicolored	.25	.25
508	A45	25c multicolored	.25	.25
509	A45	40c multicolored	.25	.25
510	A45	60c multicolored	.40	.40
511	A45	75c multicolored	.50	.50
512	A45	$1 multicolored	.65	.65
513	A45	$1.50 multicolored	.85	.85
514	A45	$2 multicolored	1.10	1.10
515	A45	$2.50 multicolored	1.25	1.25
516	A45	$3 multicolored	1.60	1.60
		Nos. 507-516 (10)	7.10	7.10

Souvenir Sheets
517	A46	$3.50 multicolored	2.10	2.10
518	A46	$4 multicolored	2.25	2.25
519	A46	$4.50 multicolored	2.50	2.50
520	A46	$5 multicolored	2.75	2.75

Nos. 498-499 Ovptd. "Congratulations to T.R.H. The Duke & Duchess of York"

1986, Nov. 17   Perf. 12½
521	A42	60c Pair, #a.-b.	.45	.45
522	A42	$2 Pair, #a.-b.	1.50	1.50

Sports — A47

1986, Nov. 21   Perf. 14
525	A47	10c Sailing	.30	.30
526	A47	25c Netball	.30	.30
527	A47	$2 Cricket	2.00	2.00
528	A47	$3 Basketball	3.00	3.00
		Nos. 525-528 (4)	5.60	5.60

Christmas A48

Churches: 10c, St. George's Anglican Church, Gingerland. 40c, Methodist Church,

Fountain. $1, Charlestown Methodist Church. $5, Wesleyan Holiness Church, Brown Hill.

1986, Dec. 8
529	A48	10c multicolored	.25	.25
530	A48	40c multicolored	.30	.30
531	A48	$1 multicolored	.75	.75
532	A48	$5 multicolored	2.75	2.75
		Nos. 529-532 (4)	4.05	4.05

US Constitution — A49

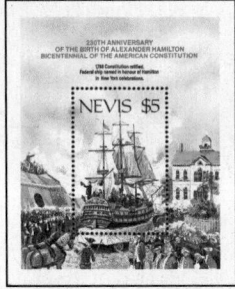

Christening of the Hamilton, 1788 — A50

US Constitution, bicent. and 230th anniv. of the birth of Alexander Hamilton: 40c, Alexander Hamilton, Hamilton House. 60c, Hamilton. $2, George Washington and members of the 1st presidential cabinet.

1987, Jan. 11
533	A49	15c shown	.25	.25
534	A49	40c multicolored	.30	.30
535	A49	60c multicolored	.45	.45
536	A49	$2 multicolored	1.10	1.10
		Nos. 533-536 (4)	2.10	2.10

Souvenir Sheet
537	A50	$5 shown	7.50	7.50

No. 117 Overprinted

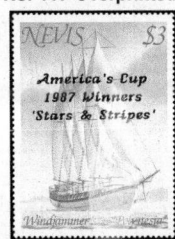

1987, Feb. 20   Wmk. 373
538	A6a	$3 multicolored	1.50	1.50

A51

1987, Mar. 11   Wmk. 380
539	A51	15c Fig Tree Church	.35	.35
540	A51	60c Frances Nisbet	.75	.75
541	A51	$1 HMS Boreas	1.25	1.25
542	A51	$3 Capt. Nelson	3.00	3.00
		Nos. 539-542 (4)	5.35	5.35

Souvenir Sheet
543		Sheet of 2, #542, 543a	5.25	5.25
a.		A51 $3 like No. 540	3.50	3.50

Wedding of Capt. Horatio Nelson and Frances Nisbet, Bicent.

A52

#544a, Queen angelfish. #544b, Blue angelfish. #545a, Blue thum. #545b, Red thum. #546a, Red hind. #546b, Rock hind. #547a, Coney Butterfish. #547b, Coney butterfish, diff.

1987, July 22	**Unwmk.**	**Perf. 15**	
544 A52	60c Pair, #a.-b.	.70	.70
545 A52	$1 Pair, #a.-b.	1.25	1.25
546 A52	$1.50 Pair, #a.-b.	1.75	1.75
547 A52	$2.50 Pair, #a.-b.	3.00	3.00
Nos. 544-547 (4)		6.70	6.70

Mushrooms — A53

15c, Panaeolus antillarum. 50c, Pycnoporus sanguineus. $2, Gymnopilus chrysopellus. $3, Cantharellus cinnabarinus.

1987, Oct. 16	**Wmk. 384**	**Perf. 14**	
552 A53	15c multicolored	.40	.40
553 A53	50c multicolored	1.00	1.00
554 A53	$2 multicolored	2.50	2.50
555 A53	$3 multicolored	3.00	3.00
Nos. 552-555 (4)		6.90	6.90

Christmas
A54

1987, Dec. 4		**Perf. 14½**	
556 A54	10c Rag doll	.25	.25
557 A54	40c Coconut boat	.25	.25
558 A54	$1.20 Sandbox cart	.50	.50
559 A54	$5 Two-wheeled cart	2.00	2.00
Nos. 556-559 (4)		3.00	3.00

Sea Shells — A55

1988, Feb. 15		**Perf. 14x14½**	
560 A55	15c Hawk-wing conch	.30	.30
561 A55	40c Roostertail conch	.40	.40
562 A55	60c Emperor helmet	.50	.50
563 A55	$2 Queen conch	1.30	1.30
564 A55	$3 King helmet	1.75	1.75
Nos. 560-564 (5)		4.25	4.25

Intl. Red Cross and Red Crescent Organizations, 125th Anniv. — A56

Activities: 15c, Visiting the sick and the elderly. 40c, First aid training. 60c, Wheelchairs for the disabled. $5, Disaster relief.

1988, June 20		**Perf. 14½x14**	
565 A56	15c multicolored	.25	.25
566 A56	40c multicolored	.25	.25
567 A56	60c multicolored	.35	.35
568 A56	$5 multicolored	2.50	2.50
Nos. 565-568 (4)		3.35	3.35

1988 Summer Olympics, Seoul — A57

1988, Aug. 26		**Perf. 14**	
569	Strip of 4	3.00	3.00
a.	A57 10c Runner at starting block	.25	.25
b.	A57 $1.20 Leaving block	.55	.55
c.	A57 $2 Full stride	.95	.95
d.	A57 $3 Crossing finish line	1.40	1.40
e.	Souvenir sheet of 4, #569a-569d	3.00	3.00

Printed se-tenant in a continuous design. Stamps in No. 569e are 23½x36½.

Independence, 5th Anniv. — A58

1988, Sept. 19	**Wmk. 373**	**Perf. 14½**	
570 A58	$5 multicolored	2.50	2.50

Common Design Types pictured following the introduction.

Lloyds of London
Common Design Type

Designs: 15c, Act of Parliament incorporating Lloyds, 1871. 60c, *Cunard Countess* in Nevis Harbor, horiz. $2.50, Space shuttle, deployment of satellite in space, horiz. $3, *Viking Princess* on fire in the Caribbean, 1966.

1988, Oct. 31	**Wmk. 384**	**Perf. 14**	
571 CD341	15c multicolored	.45	.45
572 CD341	60c multicolored	.90	.90
573 CD341	$2.50 multicolored	2.50	2.50
574 CD341	$3 multicolored	4.50	4.50
Nos. 571-574 (4)		8.35	8.35

Christmas Flowers — A59

1988, Nov. 7		**Perf. 14½**	
575 A59	15c Poinsettia	.25	.25
576 A59	40c Tiger claws	.25	.25
577 A59	60c Sorrel flower	.35	.35
578 A59	$1 Christmas candle	.60	.60
579 A59	$5 Snow bush	2.40	2.40
Nos. 575-579 (5)		3.85	3.85

Battle of Frigate Bay, 1782 — A60

Exhibition emblem & maps. #580a-580c in a continuous design.

1989, Apr. 17		**Perf. 14**	
580 A60	Strip of 3	3.75	3.75
a.	50c multicolored	.30	.30
b.	$1.20 multicolored	.80	.80
c.	$2 multicolored	1.40	1.40

Size: 34x47mm		
	Perf. 14x13½	
581 A60	$3 Map of Nevis, 1764	3.00 3.00

French revolution bicent., PHILEXFRANCE '89.

Nocturnal Insects and Frogs — A61

1989, May 15			
582 A61	10c Cicada	.30	.30
583 A61	40c Grasshopper	.50	.50
584 A61	60c Cricket	.85	.85
585 A61	$5 Tree frog	4.50	4.50
a.	Souvenir sheet of 4, #582-585	7.00	7.00
Nos. 582-585 (4)		6.15	6.15

Moon Landing, 20th Anniv.
Common Design Type

Apollo 12: 15c, Vehicle Assembly Building, Kennedy Space Center. 40c, Crew members Charles Conrad Jr., Richard Gordon and Alan Bean. $2, Mission emblem. $3, Moon operation in the Sun's glare. $6, Buzz Aldrin deploying passive seismic experiment package on the lunar surface, Apollo 11 mission.

1989, July 20		**Perf. 14x13½**	
Size of Nos. 587-588: 29x29mm			
586 CD342	15c multicolored	.25	.25
587 CD342	40c multicolored	.25	.25
588 CD342	$2 multicolored	1.25	1.25
589 CD342	$3 multicolored	1.75	1.75
Nos. 586-589 (4)		3.50	3.50

Souvenir Sheet

590 CD342	$6 multicolored	4.00	4.00

Queen Conchs (*Strombus gigas*) — A62

1990, Jan. 31			
591 A62	10c shown	.35	.35
592 A62	40c Conch, diff	.65	.65
593 A62	60c Conch, diff	1.50	1.50
594 A62	$1 Conch, diff	2.25	2.25
Nos. 591-594 (4)		4.75	4.75

Souvenir Sheet

595 A62	$5 Fish and coral	5.75	5.75

World Wildlife Fund.

Wyon Portrait of Victoria — A63

40c, Engine-turned background. 60c, Heath's engraving. $4, Inscriptions added. $5, Completed design.

	Perf. 14x15		
1990, May 3	**Litho.**	**Unwmk.**	
596 A63	15c brn, blk, tan	.25	.25
597 A63	40c grn, blk, lt grn	.30	.30
598 A63	60c blk, gray	.50	.50
599 A63	$4 blue, blk, lt blue	2.75	2.75
Nos. 596-599 (4)		3.80	3.80

Souvenir Sheet

600 A63	$5 multicolored	4.50	4.50

Penny Black, 150th anniv. No. 600 for Stamp World London '90.

A64

1990, May 3		**Perf. 13½**	
601 A64	15c brown	.25	.25
602 A64	40c deep green	.30	.30
603 A64	60c violet	.50	.50
604 A64	$4 bright ultra	3.25	3.25
Nos. 601-604 (4)		4.30	4.30

Souvenir Sheet

605 A64	$5 gray, lake & buff	5.50	5.50

Penny Black 150th anniversary and commemoration of the Thurn & Taxis postal service.

Crabs — A65

Designs include UPAE and discovery of America anniversary emblems.

1990, June 25	**Litho.**	**Perf. 14**	
606 A65	5c Sand fiddler	.25	.25
607 A65	15c Great land crab	.25	.25
608 A65	20c Blue crab	.30	.30
609 A65	40c Stone crab	.40	.40
610 A65	60c Mountain crab	.60	.60
611 A65	$2 Sargassum crab	1.40	1.40
612 A65	$3 Yellow box crab	2.00	2.00
613 A65	$4 Spiny spider crab	2.75	2.75
Nos. 606-613 (8)		7.95	7.95

Souvenir Sheets

614 A65	$5 Wharf crab	4.00	4.00
615 A65	$5 Sally lightfoot	4.00	4.00

Queen Mother 90th Birthday
A66   A67

1990, July 5			
616 A66	$2 shown	1.25	1.25
617 A66	$2 shown	1.25	1.25
618 A66	$2 Queen Consort, diff.	1.25	1.25
a.	Strip of 3, #616-618	3.75	3.75

Souvenir Sheet

619 A67	$6 Coronation Portrait, diff.	4.00	4.00

Nos. 616-618 printed in sheet of 9.

A68

Players from participating countries.

1990, Oct. 1	**Litho.**	**Perf. 14**	
620 A68	10c Cameroun	.25	.25
621 A68	25c Czechoslovakia	.25	.25
622 A68	$2.50 England	2.00	2.00
623 A68	$5 West Germany	4.00	4.00
Nos. 620-623 (4)		6.50	6.50

Souvenir Sheets

624 A68	$5 Spain	3.50	3.50
625 A68	$5 Argentina	3.50	3.50

World Cup Soccer Championships, Italy.

A69

Christmas (Orchids): 10c, Cattleya deckeri. 15c, Epidendrum ciliare. 20c, Epidendrum fragrans. 40c, Epidendrum ibaguense. 60c, Epidendrum latifolium. $1.20, Maxillaria conferta. $2, Epidendrum strobiliferum. $3, Brassavola cucullata. $5, Rodriguezia lanceolata.

	Unwmk.		
1990, Nov. 19	**Litho.**	**Perf. 14**	
626 A69	10c multicolored	.30	.30
627 A69	15c multicolored	.30	.30
628 A69	20c multicolored	.30	.30
629 A69	40c multicolored	.45	.45
630 A69	60c multicolored	.70	.70
631 A69	$1.20 multicolored	1.30	1.30
632 A69	$2 multicolored	2.25	2.25
633 A69	$3 multicolored	3.00	3.00
Nos. 626-633 (8)		8.60	8.60

Souvenir Sheet

634 A69	$5 multicolored	7.00	7.00

Peter Paul Rubens
(1577-1640),
Painter — A70

Details from The Feast of Achelous: 10c,
Pitchers. 40c, Woman at table. 60c, Two
women. $4, Achelous feasting. $5, Complete
painting, horiz.

1991, Jan. 14   Litho.   Perf. 13½
635	A70	10c multicolored	.30	.30
636	A70	40c multicolored	.50	.50
637	A70	60c multicolored	.80	.80
638	A70	$4 multicolored	3.75	3.75
		Nos. 635-638 (4)	5.35	5.35

Souvenir Sheet
639	A70	$5 multicolored	5.25	5.25

Butterflies
A71

5c, Gulf fritillary. 10c, Orion. 15c, Dagger
wing. 20c, Red anartia. 25c, Caribbean buckeye. 40c, Zebra. 50c, Southern dagger tail.
60c, Silver spot. 75c, Doris. $1, Mimic. $3,
Monarch. $5, Small blue grecian. $10, Tiger.
$20, Flambeau.

1991, Mar.   Perf. 14
No Date Imprint Below Design
640	A71	5c multicolored	.25	.25
641	A71	10c multicolored	.25	.25
642	A71	15c multicolored	.25	.25
643	A71	20c multicolored	.25	.25
644	A71	25c multicolored	.25	.25
645	A71	40c multicolored	.35	.35
646	A71	50c multicolored	.50	.50
647	A71	60c multicolored	.55	.55
648	A71	75c multicolored	.65	.65
649	A71	$1 multicolored	.90	.90
650	A71	$3 multicolored	2.75	2.75
651	A71	$5 multicolored	4.50	4.50
652	A71	$10 multicolored	9.00	9.00
653	A71	$20 multicolored	18.00	18.00
		Nos. 640-653 (14)	38.45	38.45

For overprints see Nos. O41-O54.

1992, Mar. 1   "1992" Below Design
640a	A71	5c multicolored	.25	.25
641a	A71	10c multicolored	.25	.25
642a	A71	15c multicolored	.25	.25
643a	A71	20c multicolored	.25	.25
644a	A71	25c multicolored	.30	.25
645a	A71	40c multicolored	.40	.25
646a	A71	50c multicolored	.50	.50
648b	A71	75c multicolored	.65	.65
648A	A71	80c multicolored	1.50	1.50
649a	A71	$1 multicolored	.90	.90
650a	A71	$3 multicolored	2.75	2.75
651a	A71	$5 multicolored	4.50	4.50
652a	A71	$10 multicolored	9.00	9.00
653a	A71	$20 multicolored	18.00	18.00
		Nos. 640a-653a (14)	39.50	39.30

1994   "1994" Below Design
640b	A71	5c multicolored	.40	.40
641b	A71	10c multicolored	.40	.40
644b	A71	25c multicolored	.40	.40
646b	A71	50c multicolored	.40	.40
648Ab	A71	80c multicolored	1.75	1.75
		Nos. 640b-648Ab (5)	3.35	3.35

Space Exploration-Discovery
Voyages — A72

15c, Viking Mars lander. 40c, Apollo 11 lift-
off. 60c, Skylab. 75c, Salyut 6. $1, Voyager 1.
$2, Venera 7. $4, Gemini 4. $5, Luna 3.
No. 662, Sailing ship, vert. No. 663, Columbus' landfall.

1991, Apr. 22   Litho.   Perf. 14
654	A72	15c multi	.25	.25
655	A72	40c multi	.30	.30
656	A72	60c multi	.45	.45
657	A72	75c multi	.55	.55
658	A72	$1 multi	.75	.75
659	A72	$2 multi	1.25	1.25
660	A72	$4 multi	2.50	2.50
661	A72	$5 multi	3.25	3.25
		Nos. 654-661 (8)	9.30	9.30

Souvenir Sheet
662	A72	$6 multi	5.00	5.00
663	A72	$6 multi	5.00	5.00

Discovery of America, 500th anniv. (in
1992) (No. 663).

Miniature Sheet

Birds — A73

Designs: a, Magnificent frigatebird. b, Roseate tern. c, Red-tailed hawk. d, Zenaida dove.
e, Bananaquit. f, American kestrel. g, Grey
kingbird. h, Prothonotary warbler. i, Blue-
hooded euphonia. j, Antillean crested hummingbird. k, White-tailed tropicbird. l, Yellow-
bellied sapsucker. m, Green-throated carib. n,
Purple-throated carib. o, Black-bellied tree
duck. p, Ringed kingfisher. q, Burrowing owl. r,
Ruddy turnstone. s, Great white heron. t, Yellow-crowned night heron.

1991, May 28
664	A73	40c Sheet of 20, #a.-t.	16.00	16.00

Souvenir Sheet
665	A73	$6 Great egret	11.00	11.00

Royal Family Birthday, Anniversary
Common Design Type

No. 674, Elizabeth, Philip. No. 675, Charles,
Diana & family.

1991, July 5   Litho.   Perf. 14
666	CD347	10c multicolored	.30	.30
667	CD347	15c multicolored	.30	.30
668	CD347	40c multicolored	.45	.45
669	CD347	50c multicolored	.60	.60
670	CD347	$1 multicolored	1.00	1.00
671	CD347	$2 multicolored	1.75	1.75
672	CD347	$4 multicolored	3.75	3.75
673	CD347	$5 multicolored	4.50	4.50
		Nos. 666-673 (8)	12.65	12.65

Souvenir Sheets
674	CD347	$5 multicolored	5.50	5.50
675	CD347	$5 multicolored	5.50	5.50

10c, 50c, $1, Nos. 673, 675, Charles and
Diana, 10th Wedding Anniv. Others, Queen
Elizabeth II 65th birthday.

Japanese
Trains — A74

Locomotives: 10c, C62 Steam, vert. 15c,
C56 Steam. 40c, Streamlined C55, steam.
60c, Class 1400 Steam. $1, Class 485 bonnet
type rail diesel car, vert. $2, C61 Steam, vert.
$3, Class 485 express train. $4, Class 7000
electric train. No. 684, D51 Steam. No. 685,
Hikari bullet train.

1991, Aug. 12
676-683	A74	Set of 8	13.50	13.50

Souvenir Sheets
684-685	A74	$5 Set of 2	11.00	11.00

Phila Nippon '91.

Christmas — A75

Paintings by Albrecht Durer: 10c, Mary
Being Crowned by an Angel. 40c, Mary with
the Pear. 60c, Mary in a Halo. $3, Mary with
the Crown of Stars and Scepter. No. 690, The
Holy Family. No. 691, Mary at the Yard Gate.

1991, Dec. 20   Litho.   Perf. 13½
686	A75	10c yel green & blk	.25	.25
687	A75	40c org brown & blk	.30	.30
688	A75	60c blue & black	.45	.45
689	A75	$3 brt magenta & blk	1.90	1.90
		Nos. 686-689 (4)	2.90	2.90

Souvenir Sheets
690	A75	$6 black	5.00	5.00
691	A75	$6 black	5.00	5.00

A76

Mushrooms: 15c, Marasmius
haematocephalus. 40c, Psilocybe cubensis.
60c, Hygrocybe acutoconica. 75c, Hygrocybe
occidentalis. $1, Boletellus cubensis. $2,
Gymnopilus chrysopellus. $4, Cantharellus
cinnabarinus. $5, Chlorophyllum molybdites.
No. 700, Our Lady of the Snows (8 mushrooms). No. 701, Our Lady of the Snows (4
mushrooms), diff.

1991, Dec. 20   Litho.   Perf. 14
692-699	A76	Set of 8	10.00	10.00

Souvenir Sheet
700-701	A76	$6 Set of 2	10.00	10.00

**Queen Elizabeth II's Accession to
the Throne, 40th Anniv.**
Common Design Type

1992, Feb. 26   Litho.   Perf. 14
702	CD348	10c multicolored	.25	.25
703	CD348	40c multicolored	.30	.30
704	CD348	$1 multicolored	.75	.75
705	CD348	$5 multicolored	3.25	3.25
		Nos. 702-705 (4)	4.55	4.55

Souvenir Sheets
706	CD348	$6 Queen, people on beach	4.50	4.50
707	CD348	$6 Queen, seashell	4.50	4.50

A77

Gold medalists: 20c, Monique Knol, France,
cycling. 25c, Roger Kingdom, US, 110-meter
hurdles. 50c, Yugoslavia, water polo. 80c, Anja
Fichtel, West Germany, foil. $1, Said Aouita,
Morocco, 5000-meters. $1.50, Yuri Sedykh,
USSR, hammer throw. $3, Yelena Shushu-
nova, USSR, gymnastics. $5, Vladimir
Artemov, USSR, gymnastics. No. 716, Florence Griffith-Joyner, US, 100-meter dash.
No. 717, Naim Suleymanoglu, Turkey, weight
lifting.

1992, May 7   Litho.   Perf. 14
708-715	A77	Set of 8	10.50	10.50

Souvenir Sheets
716-717	A77	$6 Set of 2	7.25	7.25

1992 Summer Olympics, Barcelona. All athletes except those on $1 and $1.50 won gold
medals in 1988. No. 715 incorrectly spelled
"Valimir."

Spanish
Art — A78

Designs: 20c, Landscape, by Mariano For-
tuny, vert. 25c, Dona Juana la Loca, by Fran-
cisco Pradilla Ortiz. 50c, Idyll, by Fortuny, vert.
80c, Old Man in the Sun, by Fortuny, vert. $1,
$2, The Painter's Children in the Japanese
Salon (different details), vert., by Fortuny. $3,
Still Life (Sea Bream and Oranges), by Luis
Eugenio Melendez. $5, Still Life (Box of
Sweets, Pastry, and Other Objects), by
Melendez, vert. No. 726, Moroccans by For-
tuny. No. 727, Bullfight, by Fortuny.

1992, June 1   Litho.   Perf. 13x13½, 13½x13
718-725	A78	Set of 8	10.00	10.00

Size: 120x95mm
Imperf
726-727	A78	$6 Set of 2	6.50	6.50

Granada '92.

A79

1992, July 6   Perf. 14
728	A79	20c Early compass	.50	.50
729	A79	50c Manatee	.50	.50
730	A79	80c Green turtle	.80	.80
731	A79	$1.50 Santa Maria	1.40	1.40
732	A79	$3 Queen Isabella	2.75	2.75
733	A79	$5 Pineapple	4.75	4.75
		Nos. 728-733 (6)	10.70	10.70

Souvenir Sheets
734	A79	$6 Storm petrel, horiz.	5.50	5.50
735	A79	$6 Pepper, horiz.	5.50	5.50

Discovery of America, 500th anniv. World
Columbian Stamp Expo '92, Chicago.

A80

1992, Aug. 24   Perf. 14½
736	A80	$1 Coming ashore	.80	.80
737	A80	$2 Natives, ships	1.50	1.50

Discovery of America, 500th anniv. Organization of East Caribbean States.

Wolfgang Amadeus
Mozart, Bicent. of
Death (in 1991) — A81

1992, Oct.   Litho.   Perf. 14
738	A81	$3 multicolored	3.00	3.00

Souvenir Sheet
739	A81	$6 Don Giovanni	5.25	5.25

Mickey's Portrait
Gallery — A82

10c, Minnie Mouse, 1930. 15c, Mickey
Mouse. 40c, Donald Duck. 80c, Mickey
Mouse, 1930. $1, Daisy Duck. $2, Pluto. $4,
Goofy. $5, Goofy, 1932.
No. 748, Plane Crazy. No. 749, Mickey,
Home Sweet Home, horiz.

1992, Nov. 9   Litho.   Perf. 13½x14
740	A82	10c multicolored	.25	.25
741	A82	15c multicolored	.35	.35
742	A82	40c multicolored	.45	.45
743	A82	80c multicolored	.75	.75
744	A82	$1 multicolored	1.00	1.00
745	A82	$2 multicolored	1.75	1.75
746	A82	$4 multicolored	3.50	3.50
747	A82	$5 multicolored	4.00	4.00
		Nos. 740-747 (8)	12.05	12.05

Souvenir Sheet
Perf. 14x13½
748	A82	$6 multicolored	6.00	6.00
749	A82	$6 multicolored	6.00	6.00

Christmas — A83

Details or entire paintings: 20c, The Virgin and Child Between Two Saints, by Giovanni Bellini. 40c, The Virgin and Child Surrounded by Four Angels, by Master of the Castello Nativity. 50c, Virgin and Child Surrounded by Angels with St. Frediano and St. Augustine, by Fra Filippo Lippi. 80c, The Virgin and Child Between St. Peter and St. Sebastian, by Giovanni Bellini. $1, The Virgin and Child with St. Julian and St. Nicholas of Myra, by Lorenzo Di Credi. $2, Saint Bernardino and a Female Saint Presenting a Donor to Virgin and Child, by Francesco Bissolo. $4, Madonna and Child with Four Cherubs, Ascribed to Barthel Bruyn. $5, The Virgin and Child, by Quentin Metsys. No. 758, The Virgin and Child Surrounded by Two Angels, by Perugino. No. 759, Madonna and Child with the Infant St. John and Archangel Gabriel, by Sandro Botticelli.

1992, Nov. 16   Litho.   Perf. 13½x14
750-757 A83   Set of 8   10.00 10.00

Souvenir Sheet
758-759 A83 $6 Set of 2   9.50   9.50

Empire State Building, New York City — A84

1992, Oct. 28   Litho.   Perf. 14
760 A84 $6 multicolored   5.00 5.00
Postage Stamp Mega Event '92, New York City.

A85

A89

A86

A87

A88

A90

A92

A91

Anniversaries and Events — A93

Designs: 15c, Japanese launch vehicle H-2. 50c, Hindenburg on fire, 1937. 75c, Charles de Gaulle, Konrad Adenauer. No. 764, Horatio Nelson Museum, Nevis. No. 765, Red Cross emblem, Nevis. No. 766, America's Cup yacht *Resolute*, 1920, vert. No. 767, St. Thomas Anglican Church. No. 768, Care Bear, butterfly and flower. No. 770, Blue whale. No. 771, WHO, ICN, FAO emblems, graph showing population growth. vert. No. 772, Lion, Lion's Intl. emblem. No. 773, John F. Kennedy, Adenauer. No. 774, Lebaudy, first flying machine with mechanical engine. No. 775, Soviet Energia launch vehicle SL-17.
Elvis Presley: No. 776a, Portrait. b, With guitar. c, With microphone.
Details or entire paintings, by Georges de La Tour: No. 777a, The Cheater (left). b, The Cheater (center). c, The Cheater (right). d, St. Joseph, the Carpenter. e, Saint Thomas. f, Adoration of the Shepherds (left). g, Adoration of the Shepherds (right). h, La Madeleine a La Veilleuse.
No. 778, Care Bear, palm tree, vert. No. 779, Manned maneuvering unit in space. No. 780, Count Zeppelin taking off from Goppingen for Friedrichshafen. No. 781, Adenauer. No. 782, America's Cup yacht. No. 783, The Angel Departing from the Family of Tobias, by Rembrandt.

1993   Litho.   Perf. 14
761 A85   15c multicolored   .25   .25
762 A86   50c multicolored   .40   .40
763 A87   75c multicolored   .80   .80
764 A88   80c multicolored   .90   .90
765 A88   80c multicolored   .90   .90
766 A89   80c multicolored   .60   .60
767 A88   80c multicolored   .60   .60
768 A90   80c multicolored   .60   .60
770 A88 $1 multicolored   .75   .75
771 A91 $3 multicolored   3.50   3.50
772 A85 $3 multicolored   3.00   3.00
773 A87 $5 multicolored   3.00   3.00
774 A86 $5 multicolored   3.50   3.50
775 A85 $5 multicolored   3.50   3.50

Perf. 14
776 A92 $1 Strip of 3, #a.-c.   2.25   2.25
       Nos. 761-776 (15)   24.55 24.55

Miniature Sheet
Perf. 12
777 A93 $1 Sheet of 8, #a.-h.
              + label   8.50   8.50

Souvenir Sheets
Perf. 14
778 A90 $2 multicolored   2.00   2.00
779 A85 $6 multicolored   5.25   5.25
780 A85 $6 multicolored   5.25   5.25
781 A87 $6 multicolored   5.50   5.50
782 A89 $6 multicolored   4.00   4.00

Perf. 14½
783 A92 $6 multicolored   6.00   6.00
Intl. Space Year (#761, 775, 779). Count Zeppelin, 75th anniv. of death (#762, 774, 780). Konrad Adenauer, 25th anniv. of death (#763, 773, 781). Anglican Church in Nevis, 150th anniv. Opening of Horatio Nelson Museum (#764). Nevis and St. Kitts Red Cross, 50th anniv. (#765). America's Cup yacht race (#766, 782). (#767). Lions Intl., 75th anniv. (#772). Earth Summit, Rio de Janeiro (#768, 770, 778). Intl. Conference on Nutrition, Rome (#771). Elvis Presley, 15th death anniv. (in 1992) (#776). Louvre Art Museum, bicent. (#777, 783).
Nos. 779-781 have continuous designs.
No. 783 contains one 55x89mm stamp.
Issued: No. 767, Mar.; others, Jan. 14.

Tropical Flowers — A94

1993, Mar. 26   Litho.   Perf. 14
784 A94   10c Frangipani   .25   .25
785 A94   25c Bougainvillea   .25   .25
786 A94   50c Allamanda   .50   .50
787 A94   80c Anthurium   .80   .80
788 A94 $1 Ixora   1.00   1.00
789 A94 $2 Hibiscus   2.00   2.00
790 A94 $4 Shrimp plant   4.00   4.00
791 A94 $5 Coral vine   5.00   5.00
       Nos. 784-791 (8)   13.80 13.80

Souvenir Sheets
792 A94 $6 Lantana   4.50   4.50
793 A94 $6 Petrea   4.50   4.50

Butterflies — A95

10c, Antillean blue. 25c, Cuban crescentspot. 50c, Ruddy daggerwing. 80c, Little yellow. $1, Atala. $1.50, Orange-barred giant sulphur. $4, Tropic queen. $5, Malachite.
No. 802, Polydamas swallowtail. No. 803, West Indian Buckeye.

1993, May 17   Litho.   Perf. 14
794 A95   10c multicolored   .30   .30
795 A95   25c multicolored   .30   .30
796 A95   50c multicolored   .60   .60
797 A95   80c multicolored   .90   .90
798 A95 $1 multicolored   1.00   1.00
799 A95 $1.50 multicolored   1.40   1.40
800 A95 $4 multicolored   4.00   4.00
801 A95 $5 multicolored   5.00   5.00
       Nos. 794-801 (8)   13.50 13.50

Souvenir Sheets
802 A95 $6 multicolored   5.75   5.75
  a. Ovptd. in sheet margin   5.00   5.00
803 A95 $6 multicolored   5.75   5.75
  a. Ovptd. in sheet margin   5.00   5.00
Location of Hong Kong '94 emblem on Nos. 802a-803a varies.
Nos. 802a, 803a issued Feb. 18, 1994.

Miniature Sheet

Coronation of Queen Elizabeth II, 40th Anniv. — A96

Designs: a, 10c, Official coronation photograph. b, 80c, Queen, wearing Imperial Crown of State. c, $2, Queen, sitting on throne during ceremony. d, $4, Prince Charles kissing mother's hand.
$6, Portrait, "Riding on Worcran in the Great Park at Windsor," by Susan Crawford, 1977.

1993, June 2   Litho.   Perf. 13½x14
804 A96   Sheet, 2 ea #a.-d.   10.00 10.00

Souvenir Sheet
Perf. 14
805 A96 $6 multicolored   4.00   4.00
No. 805 contains one 28x42mm stamp.

Independence of St. Kitts and Nevis, 10th Anniv. — A97

Designs: 25c, Natl. flag, anthem. 80c, Brown pelican, map of St. Kitts and Nevis.

1993, Sept. 19   Litho.   Perf. 13½
807 A97   25c multicolored   .50   .50
808 A97   80c multicolored   1.50   1.50

1994 World Cup Soccer Championships, US — A98

Soccer players: 10c, Garaba, Hungary; Platini, France. 25c, Maradona, Argentina;

Bergomi, Italy. 50c, Fernandez, France; Rats, Russia. 80c, Munoz, Spain. $1, Elkjaer, Denmark; Goicoechea, Spain. $2, Coelho, Brazil; Tigana, France. $3, Troglio, Argentina; Alejnikov, Russia. No. 816, $5, Karas, Poland; Costa, Brazil.
Each $5: No. 817, Belloumi, Algeria. No. 818, Steven, England, vert.

1993, Nov. 9   Litho.   Perf. 14
809-816 A98   Set of 8   10.00 10.00

Souvenir Sheets
817-818 A98   Set of 2   16.00 16.00

Christmas — A99

Works by Albrecht Durer: 20c, Annunciation of Mary. 40c, The Nativity. 50c, Holy Family on a Grassy Bank. 80c, The Presentation of Christ in the Temple. $1, Virgin in Glory on the Crescent. $1.60, The Nativity, diff. $3, Madonna and Child. $5, The Presentation of Christ in the Temple (detail).
Each $6: No. 827, Mary with Child and the Long-Tailed Monkey, by Durer. No. 828, The Rest on the Flight into Egypt, by Fragonard, horiz.

1993, Nov. 30   Perf. 13
819-826 A99   Set of 8   10.00 10.00

Souvenir Sheets
827-828 A99   Set of 2   16.00 16.00

Tuff Mickey A100

Disney's Mickey Mouse playing: 10c, Basketball. 50c, Volleyball. $1, Soccer. $5, Boxing. No. 837, $6, Tug-of-war. No. 838, Ringing carnival bell with hammer, vert.
Disney's Minnie Mouse: 25c, Welcome to my island, vert. 80c, Sunny and snappy, vert. $1.50, Happy hoopin', vert. $4, Jumping for joy, vert.

Perf. 14x13½, 13½x14
1994, Mar. 15   Litho.
829 A100   10c multicolored   .25   .25
830 A100   25c multicolored   .25   .25
831 A100   50c multicolored   .55   .55
832 A100   80c multicolored   .80   .80
833 A100 $1 multicolored   .90   .90
834 A100 $1.50 multicolored   1.10   1.10
835 A100 $4 multicolored   3.00   3.00
836 A100 $5 multicolored   3.75   3.75
       Nos. 829-836 (8)   10.60 10.50

Souvenir Sheets
837 A100 $6 multicolored   6.00   6.00
838 A100 $6 multicolored   6.00   6.00

Hummel Figurines — A101

Designs: 5c, Umbrella Girl. 25c, For Father. 50c, Apple Tree Girl. 80c, March Winds. $1, Have the Sun in Your Heart. $1.60, Blue Belle. $2, Winter Fun. $5, Apple Tree Boy.

1994, Apr. 6   Litho.   Perf. 14
839-846 A101   Set of 8   10.00 10.00
845a   Souv. sheet, #839, 843-845 3.50   3.50
846a   Souv. sheet, #840-842, 846 5.75   5.75

Beekeeping A102

Designs: 50c, Beekeeper cutting wild nest of bees. 80c, Group of beekeepers, 1987. $1.60, Decapping frames of honey. $3, Queen bee rearing.

$6, Queen bee, worker bees, woman extracting honey.

1994, June 13   Litho.   Perf. 14
847-850 A102 Set of 4   7.75 7.75
Souvenir Sheet
851 A102 $6 multicolored   8.00 8.00
a.   Ovptd. in sheet margin   5.75 5.75

No. 851a Overprinted "2nd Caribbean Beekeeping Congress / August 14-18, 2000" in sheet margin. Issued 8/14/00.
Issued: No. 851a, 8/17/00.

Miniature Sheet

Cats
A103

Designs: a, Blue point Himalayan. b, Black & white Persian. c, Cream Persian. d, Red Persian. e, Persian. f, Persian black smoke. g, Chocolate smoke Persian. h, Black Persian.
Each $6: No. 853, Brown tabby Persian. No. 854, Silver tabby Persian.

1994, July 20
852 A103 80c Sheet of 8, #a.-h.   8.25 8.25
Souvenir Sheets
853-854 A103 Set of 2   19.00 19.00

A104

Marine Life — A104a

Designs: 10c, Striped burrfish. 25c, Black coral, white & yellow, vert. 40c, Black coral, white & red, vert. 50c, Black coral, yellow & green, vert. 80c, Black coral, spiral-shaped, vert. $1, Blue-striped grunt. $1.60, Blue angelfish. $3, Cocoa damselfish.
No. 864a, Flameback angelfish. b, Reef bass. c, Honey gregory. d, Saddle squirrelfish. e, Cobalt chromis. f, Cleaner goby. g, Slendertail cardinalfish. h, Royal gramma.
Each $6: No. 865, Sailfish, vert. No. 866, Blue marlin.

1994, July 25   Litho.   Perf. 14
856-863 A104 Set of 8   7.25 7.25
860a   Strip of 4, #857-860   3.75 3.75
860b   Min. sheet, 3 each #857-860   11.50 11.50
Miniature Sheet of 8
864 A104a 50c #a.-h.   8.50 8.50
i.   Ovptd. in sheet margin   3.75 3.75
Souvenir Sheets
865-866 A104a Set of 2   19.00 19.00

Nos. 857-860, World Wildlife Fund. No. 864i overprinted in sheet margin with PHILAKOREA '94 emblem.
Issued: #864i, 8/16; #860b, 7/25.

Local Architecture
A105

Designs: 25c, Residence, Barnes Ghaut Village. 50c, House above grocery store, Newcastle. $1, Treasury Building, Charlestown. $5, House above supermarket, Charlestown. $6, Apartment houses.

1994, Aug. 22
867-870 A105 Set of 4   7.25 7.25
Souvenir Sheet
871 A105 $6 multicolored   4.75 4.75

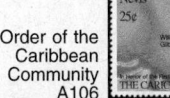
Order of the Caribbean Community
A106

First award recipients: 25c, William Demas, economist, Trinidad and Tobago. 50c, Sir Shridath Ramphal, statesman, Guyana. $1, Derek Walcott, writer, Nobel Laureate, St. Lucia.

1994, Sept. 1
872-874 A106 Set of 3   3.00 3.00

Miniature Sheet of 8

PHILAKOREA '94 — A107

Folding screen, longevity symbols embroidered on silk, Late Choson Dynasty: a, #1. b, #2. c, #3. d, #4. e, #5. f, #6. g, #7. h, #8.

1994   Litho.   Perf. 14
875 A107 50c #a.-h.   6.00 6.00

Christmas — A108

Different details from paintings: 20c, 40c, 50c, $5, The Virgin Mary as Queen of Heaven, by Jan Provost. 80c, $1, $1.60, $3, Adoration of the Magi, by Workshop of Hugo van der Goes.
No. 884, The Virgin Mary as Queen of Heaven (complete). $6, Adoration of the Magi (complete).

1994, Dec. 1   Litho.   Perf. 14
876-883 A108 Set of 8   8.00 8.00
Souvenir Sheets
884 A108 $5 multicolored   4.25 4.25
885 A108 $6 multicolored   5.00 5.00

Disney Valentines
A109

Designs: 10c, Mickey, Minnie. 25c, Donald, Daisy. 50c, Pluto, Fifi. 80c, Clarabelle, Horace Horsecollar. $1, Pluto, Figaro. $1.50, Polly, Peter Penguin. $4, Prunella Pullet, Hick Rooster. $5, Jenny Wren, Cock Robin.
Each $6: No. 894, Minnie, vert. No. 895, Daisy, vert.

1995, Feb. 14   Litho.   Perf. 14x13½
886-893 A109 Set of 8   10.00 10.00
Souvenir Sheets
Perf. 13½x14
894-895 A109 Set of 2   10.00 10.00

Birds — A110

Designs: 50c, Hooded merganser. 80c, Green-backed heron. $2, Double crested cormorant. $3, Ruddy duck.
Hummingbirds: No. 900a, Rufous-breasted hermit. b, Purple-throated carib. c, Green mango. d, Bahama woodstar. e, Hispaniolan emerald. f, Antillean crested. g, Green-throated carib. h, Antillean mango. i, Vervian. j, Jamaican mango. k, Cuban emerald. l, Blue-headed.
Each $6: No. 901, Black skimmer. No. 902, Snowy plover.

1995, Mar. 30   Litho.   Perf. 14
896-899 A110 Set of 4   3.75 3.75

Miniature Sheet of 12
900 A110 50c #a.-l.   10.50 10.50
Souvenir Sheets
901-902 A110 Set of 2   10.00 10.00

Dogs — A111

Designs: 25c, Pointer. 50c, Old Danish pointer. $1, German short-haired pointer. $2, English setter.
No. 907a, Irish setter. b, Weimaraner. c, Gordon setter. d, Britanny spaniel. e, American cocker spaniel. f, English cocker spaniel. g, Labrador retriever. h, Golden retriever. i, Flat-coated retriever.
Each $6: #908, Bloodhound. #909, German shepherd.

1995, May 23   Litho.   Perf. 14
903-906 A111 Set of 4   3.75 3.75
Miniature Sheet of 9
907 A111 80c #a.-i.   11.00 11.00
Souvenir Sheets
908-909 A111 Set of 2   11.00 11.00

Cacti — A112

Designs: 40c, Schulumbergera truncata. 50c, Echinocereus pectinatus. 80c, Mammillaria zelmanniana alba. $1.60, Lobivia hertriehiana. $2, Hamatocactus setispinus. $3, Astrophytum myriostigma.
Each $6: No. 916, Opuntia robusta. No. 917, Rhipsalidopsis gaertneri.

1995, June 20   Litho.   Perf. 14
910-915 A112 Set of 6   6.50 6.50
Souvenir Sheets
916-917 A112 Set of 2   10.00 10.00

Miniature Sheets of 6 or 8

End of World War II, 50th Anniv. A113

Famous World War II Personalities: No. 918: a, Clark Gable. b, Audie Murphy. c, Glenn Miller. d, Joe Louis. e, Jimmy Doolittle. f, John Hersey. g, John F. Kennedy. h, Jimmy Stewart.
Planes: No. 919: a, F4F Wildcat. b, F4U-1A Corsair. c, Vought SB2U Vindicator. d, F6-F Hellcat. e, SDB Dauntless. f, TBF-1 Avenger.
Each $6: No. 920, Jimmy Doolittle, vert. No. 921, Fighter plane landing on aircraft carrier.

1995, July 20
918 A113 $1.25 #a.-h. + label   10.00 10.00
919 A113 $2 #a.-f. + label   11.00 11.00
Souvenir Sheets
920-921 A113 Set of 2   15.00 15.00

UN, 50th Anniv. A114

People of various races: No. 922a, $1.25, Two men, child. b, $1.60, Man wearing turban, man with beard, woman. c, $3, Two men in business suits, woman.
$6, Nelson Mandela.

1995, July 20   Litho.   Perf. 14
922 A114 Strip of 3, #a.-c.   4.00 4.00
Souvenir Sheet
923 A114 $6 multicolored   4.25 4.25

No. 922 is a continuous design.

1995 Boy Scout Jamboree, Holland — A115

Scouts in various activities: No. 924a, $1, Two wearing backpacks. b, $2, One holding rope, one wearing backpack. c, $4, One crossing rope bridge, one looking at map, natl. flag. $6, Scout in kayak.

1995, July 20
924 A115 Strip of 3, #a.-c.   5.00 5.00
Souvenir Sheet
925 A115 $6 multicolored   5.50 5.50

No. 924 is a continuous design.

Rotary Intl., 90th Anniv. — A116

Designs: $5, Rotary emblem, natl. flag. $6, Rotary emblem, beach.

1995, July 20
926 A116 $5 multicolored   3.75 3.75
Souvenir Sheet
927 A116 $6 multicolored   4.50 4.50

Queen Mother, 95th Birthday
A117

No. 928: a, Drawing. b, Pink hat. c, Formal portrait. d, Green blue hat.
$6, Wearing crown jewels.

1995, July 20   Perf. 13½x14
928 A117 $1.50 Block or strip of 4, #a.-d.   4.50 4.50
Souvenir Sheet
928E A117 $6 multicolored   4.75 4.75

No. 928 was issued in sheets of 2.
Sheets of Nos. 928 and 928E exist with margins overprinted with black border and text "In Memoriam 1900-2002."

FAO, 50th anniv. A118

No. 929a, 40c, Woman with tan sari over head. b, $2, FAO emblem, two infants. c, $3, Woman with blue sari over head.
$6, Man with hands around hoe handle.

1995, July 20   Perf. 14
929 A118 Strip of 3, #a.-c.   4.25 4.25
Souvenir Sheet
930 A118 $6 multicolored   4.75 4.75

No. 929 is a continuous design.

Miniature Sheet of 9

100th ANNIVERSARY OF THE NOBEL PRIZES

Nobel Prize Recipients — A119

No. 931: a, Emil A. von Behring, medicine, 1901. b, Wilhelm Roentgen, physics, 1901. c, Paul J.L. Heyse, literature, 1910. d, Le Duc Tho, peace, 1973. e, Yasunari Kawabata, 1968. f, Tsung-Dao Lee, physics, 1957. g, Werner Heisenberg, physics, 1932. h, Johannes Stark, physics, 1919. i, Wilhelm Wien, physics, 1911.
$6, Kenzaburo Oe, literature, 1994.

1995, July 20
931 A119 $1.25 #a.-i.   9.50 9.50
Souvenir Sheet
932 A119 $6 multicolored   4.75 4.75

Souvenir Sheet

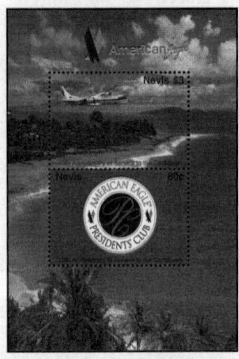

American Eagle Service, 10th Anniv. — A120

a, 80c, President's Club Emblem. b, $3, Airplane over beach.

1995, Aug. 28   Litho.   Perf. 14
933 A120   Sheet of 2, #a.-b.   3.50 3.50

Miniature Sheet of 16

UNDERWATER TREASURES

Marine Life A121

No. 934: a, Great egrets. b, 17th cent. ship. c, Marlin. d, Herring gulls. e, Nassau groupers. f, Manta ray. g, Leopard shark, hammerhead shark. h, Hourglass dolphins. i, Spanish hogfish. j, Jellyfish, sea horses. k, Angel fish. l, Hawsbill turtle. m, Octopus vulgaris (i, j, m). n, Moray eel (o). o, Queen angelfish, butterlyfish. p, Ghost crab, sea star.
Each $6: No. 935, Nassau grouper. No. 936, Queen angelfish, vert.

1995, Sept. 1
934 A121 50c #a.-p.   9.00 9.00
Souvenir Sheets
935-936 A121 Set of 2   11.00 11.00
Singapore '95 (#935-936).

Natl. Telephone Co., SKANTEL Ltd., 10th Anniv. — A122

Designs: $1, Repairman working on telephone. $1.50, Company sign on building. $5, Front of SKANTEL's Nevis office, horiz.

1995, Oct. 23   Litho.   Perf. 14
937 A122 $1 multicolored   .90 .90
938 A122 $1.50 multicolored   1.25 1.25
Souvenir Sheet
939 A122 $5 multicolored   4.25 4.25

Christmas Paintings, by Duccio di Buoninsegna (1250-1318) A123

Details or entire paintings: 20c, Rucellai Madonna and Child. 50c, Border angel from Rucellai Madonna facing left. 80c, Madonna and Child. $1, The Annuniciation. $1.60, Madonna and Child. $3, Border angel from Rucellai Madonna facing right.
No. 946, Nativity with Prophets Isiah and Ezekiel. No. 947, Crevole Madonna.

1995, Dec. 1   Litho.   Perf. 13½x14
940-945 A123   Set of 6   7.00 7.00
Souvenir Sheets
946 A123 $5 multicolored   4.50 4.50
947 A123 $6 multicolored   5.25 5.25

Four Seasons Resort, 5th Anniv. — A124

Designs: 25c, Beach, resort buildings. 50c, Sailboats on beach. 80c, Golf course. $2, Premier Simeon Daniel laying cornerstone. $6, Lounge chair on beach, sunset.

1996, Feb. 14   Litho.   Perf. 14
948-951 A124   Set of 4   2.50 2.50
Souvenir Sheet
952 A124 $6 multicolored   4.25 4.25

New Year 1996 (Year of the Rat) — A125

Rat, various plant life, with olive margin: Nos. 953: a, Looking up at butterfly. b, Crawling left. c, Looking up at horsefly. d, Looking up at dragonfly.
Nos. 954a-954d: like Nos. 953a-953d, with yellow brown margin.
$3, Berries over rat.

1996, Feb, 28
953 A125 $1 Block of 4, #a.-d.   3.00 3.00
Miniature Sheet
954 A125 $1 Sheet of 4, #a.-d.   3.00 3.00
Souvenir Sheet
955 A125 $3 multicolored   3.00 3.00
No. 953 was issued in sheets of 16 stamps.

Pagodas of China — A126

#956: a, Qian Qing Gong, 1420, Beijing. b, Qi Nian Dian, Temple of Heaven, Beijing. c, Zhongnanhai, Beijing. d, Da Zing Hall, Shenyang Palace. e, Temple of the Sleeping Buddha, Beijing. f, Huang Qiong Yu, Alter of Heaven, Beijing. g, Grand Bell Temple, Beijing. h, Imperial Palace, Beijing. i, Pu Tuo Temple.
$6, Summer Palace of emperor Wan Yanliang, 1153, Beijing, vert.

1996, May 15   Litho.   Perf. 14
956 A126 $1 Sheet of 9, #a.-i.   6.25 6.25
Souvenir Sheet
957 A126 $6 multicolored   4.00 4.00
CHINA '96, 9th Asian Intl. Philatelic Exhibition (#956).

Queen Elizabeth II, 70th Birthday — A127

Queen wearing: a, Blue dress, pearls. b, Formal white dress. c, Purple dress, hat.
$6, In uniform at trooping of the color.

1996, May 15   Litho.   Perf. 13½x14
958 A127 $2 Strip of 3, #a.-c.   3.75 3.75
Souvenir Sheet
959 A127 $6 multicolored   3.75 3.75
No. 958 was issued in sheets of 9 stamps with each strip in a different order.

1996 Summer Olympic Games, Atlanta — A128

Designs: 25c, Ancient Greek athletes boxing. 50c, Mark Spitz, gold medalist, swimming, 1972. 80c, Siegbert Horn, kayak singles gold medalist, 1972. $3, Siegestor Triumphal Arch, Munich, vert.
Pictures inside gold medals: No. 964, vert.: a, Jim Thorpe. b, Glenn Morris. c, Bob Mathias. d, Rafer Johnson. e, Bill Toomey. f, Nikolay Avilov. g, Bruce Jenner. h, Daley Thompson. i, Christian Schenk.
Each $5: No. 965, Willi Holdorf, vert. No. 966, Hans-Joachim Walde, silver medal, vert.

1996, May 28   Perf. 14
960-963 A128   Set of 4   3.50 3.50
964 A128 $1 Sheet of 9, #a.-i.   6.75 6.75
Souvenir Sheets
965-966 A128   Set of 2   12.00 12.00
Olymphilex '96 (#965).

UNESCO, 50th Anniv. — A129

25c, Cave paintings, Tassili N'Ajjer, Algeria. $2, Tikal Natl. Park, Guatemala, vert. $3, Temple of Hera at Samos, Greece. $6, Pueblo, Taos, US.

1996, July 1   Litho.   Perf. 14
967-969 A129   Set of 3   4.50 4.50
Souvenir Sheet
970 A129 $6 multicolored   4.25 4.25

UNICEF, 50th Anniv. — A130

25c, Children reading book. 50c, Girl receiving innoculation. $4, Faces of young people.

$6, Girl, vert.
1996, July 1
971-973 A130   Set of 3   4.25 4.25
Souvenir Sheet
974 A130 $6 multicolored   4.25 4.25

Disney's Sweethearts A131

Designs: a, Pocahontas, John Smith, Flit. b, Mowgli, The Girl, Kaa. c, Belle, Beast, Mrs. Potts, Chip. d, Cinderella, Prince Charming, Jaq. e, Pinocchio, Dutch Girl Marionette, Jiminy Cricket. f, Grace Martin, Henry Coy. g, Snow White, Prince. h, Aladdin, Jasmine, Abu. i, Pecos Bill, Slue Foot Sue.
Each $6: No. 977, Sleeping Beauty, Prince Phillip, vert. No. 978, Ariel, Eric.

Perf. 14x13½, 13½x14
1996, June 17   Litho.
975 A131 $2 Sheet of 9, #a.-i.   17.50 17.50
Souvenir Sheets
977-978 A131   Set of 2   11.00 11.00
A number has been reserved for an additional sheet with this set.

American Academy of Ophthalmology, Cent. — A132

1996, July 1   Litho.   Perf. 14
979 A132 $5 multicolored   4.00 4.00

Flowers — A133

Designs: 25c, Rothmannia longiflora. 50c, Gloriosa simplex. $2, Catharanthus roseus. $3, Plumbago auriculata.
No. 984: a, Monodora myristica. b, Giraffa camelopardalis. c, Adansonia digitata. d, Ansellia gigantea. e, Geissorhiza rochensis. f, Arctotis venusta. g, Gladiohis cardinalis. h, Eucomis bicolor. i, Protea obtusifolia.
$5, Stelitzia reginae.

1996, Sept. 24   Litho.   Perf. 14
980-983 A133   Set of 4   4.25 4.25
984 A133 $1 Sheet of 9, #a.-i.   6.75 6.75
Souvenir Sheet
985 A133 $5 multicolored   3.75 3.75

Christmas A134

Designs: 25c, Western meadowlark, vert. 50c, American goldfinch. 80c, Santa in sleigh, reindeer. $1, Western meadowlark, diff., vert. $1.60, Mockingbird, vert. $5, Yellow-rumped caleque.
Each $6: No. 992, Macaw. No. 993, Vermilion flycatcher.

1996, Dec. 2   Litho.   Perf. 14
986-991 A134   Set of 6   6.75 6.75
Souvenir Sheets
992-993 A134   Set of 2   8.50 8.50

New Year 1997 (Year of the Ox) A135

Painting, "Five Oxen," by Han Huang: a, 50c. b, 80c. c, $1.60. d, $2.

1997, Jan. 16   Litho.   Perf. 14x15
994 A135 Sheet of 4, #a.-d. + label   4.00 4.00

A136

Pandas: a, Eating leaves on branch. b, Face, eating. c, Paws holding object. d, Hanging upside down. e, Lying between tree branch. f, Climbing tree.
$5, Mother, cub.

1997, Feb. 12   Litho.   Perf. 14
995 A136 $1.60 Sheet of 6, #a.-f.   9.50 9.50
Souvenir Sheet
996 A136 $5 multicolored   3.75 3.75

Hong Kong '97.

A137

Cricket Players: 25c, Elquemedo Willet. 80c, Stuart Williams. $2, Keith Arthurton.
Each $5: No. 1000, Willet, Arthurton, Williams, 1990 Nevis team. No. 1001, Williams, Arthurton, 1994 West Indies team, vert.

1997, May 1   Litho.   Perf. 14
997-999 A137 Set of 3   2.25 2.25
Souvenir Sheets
1000-1001 A137 Set of 2   7.00 7.00

Queen Elizabeth II, Prince Philip, 50th Wedding Anniv. — A138

No. 1002: a, Queen Elizabeth II. b, Royal arms. c, Prince, Queen in red hat. d, Queen in blue coat, Prince. e, Caernarfon Castle. f, Prince Philip.
$5, Queen wearing crown.

1997, May 29   Litho.   Perf. 14
1002 A138 $1 Sheet of 6, #a.-f.   5.00 5.00
Souvenir Sheet
1003 A138 $5 multicolored   3.75 3.75

Paintings by Hiroshige (1797-1858) A139

No. 1004: a, Scattered Pines, Tone River. b, Nakagawa River Mouth. c, Niijuku Ferry. d, Horie and Nekozane. e, View of Konodai and the Tone River. f, Maple Trees at Mama, Tekona Shrine & Bridge.
Each $6: No. 1005, Mitsumata Wakarenofuchi. No. 1006, Moto-Hachinan Shrine, Sunamura.

1997, May 29   Perf. 13½x14
1004 A139 $1.60 Sheet of 6, #a.-f. 7.00 7.00
Souvenir Sheets
1005-1006 A139 Set of 2   8.00 8.00

Paul Harris (1868-1947), Founder of Rotary Intl. — A140

$2, Literacy promotion, portrait of Harris.
$5, Rotary Village Corps coaching soccer for youths in Chile.

1997, May 29   Perf. 14
1007 A140 $2 multicolored   1.75 1.75
Souvenir Sheet
1008 A140 $5 multicolored   3.75 3.75

Heinrich von Stephan (1831-97) A141

No. 1009: a, Russian Reindeer Post, 1859. b, Von Stephan, UPU emblem. c, Steamboat, City of Cairo, 1800's.
$5, Portrait of Von Stephan, Bavarian postal messenger, 1640.

1997, May 29
1009 A141 $1.60 Sheet of 3, #a.-c. 3.25 3.25
Souvenir Sheet
1010 A141 $5 multicolored   3.50 3.50

PACIFIC 97.

Butterflies and Moths — A142

10c, Crimson speckled. 25c, Purple emperor. 50c, Regent skipper. 80c, Provence burnet moth. $1, Common wall butterfly. $4, Cruiser butterfly.
No. 1017: a, Red-lined geometrid. b, Boisduval's autumnal moth. c, Blue pansy. d, Common clubtail. e, Tufted jungle queen. f, Lesser marbled fritillary. g, Peacock royal. h, Emperor gum moth. i, Orange swallow-tailed moth.
Each $5: No. 1018, Jersey tiger. No. 1019, Japanese emperor.

1997, May 12   Litho.   Perf. 14
1011-1016 A142 Set of 6   5.50 5.50
1017 A142 $1 Sheet of 9, #a.-i.   7.25 7.25
Souvenir Sheets
1018-1019 A142 Set of 2   7.50 7.50

Souvenir Sheet

Mother Goose A143

1997, May 29
1020 A143 $5 Boy, two pigeons   3.75 3.75

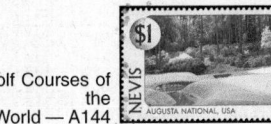

Golf Courses of the World — A144

Designs: a, Augusta National, U.S. b, Cabo Del Sol, Mexico. c, Cypress Point, U.S. d, Lost City, South Africa. e, Moscow Country Club, Russia. f, New South Wales, Australia. g, Royal Montreal, Canada. h, St. Andrews, Scotland. i, Four Seasons Resort, Nevis.

1997, July 15
1021 A144 $1 Sheet of 9, #a.-i.   7.25 7.25

Mushrooms — A145

Designs: 25c, Cantharellus cibarius. 50c, Stropharia aeruginosa. $3, Lactarius turpis. $4, Entoloma Jypeatum.
No. 1026: a, Suillus luteus. b, Amanita musearia. c, Lactarius rufus. d, Amanita rubescens. e, Armillaria mellea. f, Russula sardonia.
No. 1027: a, Boletus edulis. b, Pholiota lenta. c, Cortinarius bolaris. d, Coprinus picaceus. e, Amanita phalloides. f, Cystolepiota aspera.
Each $5: No. 1028, Gymnopilus junonius. No. 1029, Galerina mutabilis, philiota auriuella.

1997, Aug. 12   Litho.   Perf. 13
1022-1025 A145 Set of 4   6.00 6.00
Sheets of 6
1026 A145 80c #a.-f.   3.75 3.75
1027 A145 $1 #a.-f.   4.50 4.50
Souvenir Sheets
1028-1029 A145 Set of 2   8.00 8.00

Diana, Princess of Wales (1961-97) — A146

Various portraits.

1997, Sept. 19   Litho.   Perf. 14
1030 A146 $1 Sheet of 9, #a.-i.   7.00 7.00

Trains — A147

Designs: 10c, New Pacific type, Victorian Government Railways, Australia. 50c, Express locomotive, Imperial Government Railways, Japan. 80c, Turbine driven locomotive, London, Midland & Scottish Railway. $1, Electric passenger & freight locomotive, Swiss Federal Railways. $2, 3 cylinder compound express locomotive, London, Midland, Scottish Railway. $3, Express locomotive Kestrel, Great Northern Railway, Ireland.
No. 1037: a, 2-8-2 Mikado, Sudan Government Railways. b, Mohammed Ali El Kebir locomotive, Egyptian State Railways. c, "Schools" class locomotive, Southern Railway. d, Drum Battery Train, Great Southern Railways, Ireland. e, "Pacific" express locomotive, German State Railways. f, Mixed traffic locomotive, Canton-Hankow Railway, China.
Each $5: No. 1038, "King" class express, Great Western Railway. No. 1039, High pressure locomotive, London, Midland and Scottish Railway.

1997, Sept. 29   Litho.   Perf. 14
1031-1036 A147 Set of 6   6.00 6.00
1037 A147 $1.50 Sheet of 6, #a.-f.   7.00 7.00
Souvenir Sheets
1038-1039 A147 Set of 2   7.75 7.75

Christmas — A148

Entire paintings or details: 20c, 25c, Diff. details from Selection of Angels, by Durer. 50c, Andromeda and Perseus, by Rubens. 80c, $1.60, Diff. details from Astronomy, by Raphael. $5, Holy Trinity, by Raphael.

Each $5: No. 1046, Ezekiel's Vision, by Raphael, horiz. No. 1047, Justice, by Rapahel, horiz.

1997, Nov. 26   Litho.   Perf. 14
1040-1045 A148 Set of 6   6.50 6.50
Souvenir Sheets
1046-1047 A148 Set of 2   7.00 7.00

New Year 1998 (Year of the Tiger) A149

Tigers: No. 1048: a, Jumping right. b, Looking back over shoulder. c, Jumping left. d, Looking forward.
No. 1049, Tiger, vert.

1998, Jan. 19   Litho.   Perf. 14
1048 A149 80c Sheet of 4, #a.-d.   4.00 4.00
Souvenir Sheet
1049 A149 $2 multicolored   2.25 2.25

Social Security of St. Kitts and Nevis, 20th Anniv. — A150

Designs: 30c, Logo, vert. $1.20, Front of Social Security building.
$6, Social Security staff, Charlestown, Nevis.

1998, Feb. 2   Litho.   Perf. 13
1050 A150 30c multicolored   .30   .30
1051 A150 $1.20 multicolored   .90   .90
Souvenir Sheet
Perf. 13½x13
1052 A150 $6 multicolored   4.50 4.50

No. 1052 contains one 56x36mm stamp.

Fruit — A151

1998, Mar. 9   Perf. 14
No Year Imprint Below Design
1053 A151 5c Soursop   .25   .25
1054 A151 10c Carambola   .25   .25
1055 A151 25c Guava   .25   .25
1056 A151 30c Papaya   .25   .25
1057 A151 50c Mango   .40   .40
1058 A151 60c Golden apple   .45   .45
1059 A151 80c Pineapple   .60   .60
1060 A151 90c Watermelon   .70   .70
1061 A151 $1 Bananas   .75   .75
1062 A151 $1.80 Orange   1.40 1.40
1063 A151 $3 Honeydew   2.25 2.25
1064 A151 $5 Cantaloupe   3.75 3.75
1065 A151 $10 Pomegranate   7.50 7.50
1066 A151 $20 Cashew   15.00 15.00
    Nos. 1053-1066 (14)   33.80 33.80

For overprints see #O55-O66.

2000, Mar. 22
Inscribed "2000" Below Design
1054a A151 10c multicolored   .25   .25
1056a A151 30c multicolored   .40   .25
1059a A151 80c multicolored   .90   .60
1062a A151 $1.80 multicolored   1.75 1.40
1064a A151 $5 multicolored   4.00 4.00
1065a A151 $10 multicolored   7.50 7.50
    Nos. 1054a-1065a (6)   14.80 14.00

Endangered Species — A152

Designs: 30c, Fish eagle. 80c, Summer tangers. 90c, Orangutan. $1.20, Tiger. $2, Cape pangolin. $3, Moatzin.
No. 1073: a, Chimpanzee. b, Keel-billed toucan. c, Chaco peccary. d, Spadefoot toad. e, Howler monkey. f, Alaskan brown bear. g, Koala. h, Spiny pelican. i, Iguana.

Each $5: No. 1074, Mandrill. No. 1075, Polar bear.

1998, Mar. 31   Litho.   Perf. 14
1067-1072 A152 Set of 6   6.50 6.50
1073 A152 $1 Sheet of 9, #a.-i. 7.00 7.00
Souvenir Sheets
1074-1075 A152 Set of 2   8.50 8.50

Aircraft — A153

Designs: 10c, Boeing 747 200B. 90c, Cessna 185 Skywagon. $1.80, McDonnell Douglas DC-9 SO. $5, Airbus A300 B4.
No. 1080: a, Northrop B-2A. b, Lockheed SR-71A. c, Beechcraft T-44A. d, Sukhoi Su-27UB. e, Hawker Siddeley (BAe) Harrier GR.MK1. f, Boeing E-3A Sentry. g, Convair B-36H. h, IAI Kfir C2.
Each $5: No. 1081, Lockheed F-117A. No. 1082, Concorde G-BOAA.

1998, May 19   Litho.   Perf. 14
1076-1079 A153 Set of 4   5.75 5.75
1080 A153 $1 Sheet of 8, #a.-h. 6.00 6.00
Souvenir Sheets
1081-1082 A153 Set of 2   7.75 7.75

Nos. 1081-1082 each contain 1 57x42mm stamp.

Chaim Topol Portraying Tevye from "Fiddler on the Roof" — A154

1998, May 17   Litho.   Perf. 13½
1083 A154 $1.60 multicolored   1.75 1.75

Israel '98. Issued in sheets of 6.

A155   A155a

Voice of Nevis (VON) Radio, 10th Anniv. — A155b

20c, Logo of Nevis Broadcasting Co., vert. 30c, Evered "Webbo" Herbert, station manager at controls. $1.20, Exterior of offices and studios.
$5, Merritt Herbert, managing director, opening ceremony, 1988.

1998, June 18   Perf. 14
1084 A155   20c blk & vio   .25   .25
1085 A155a 30c multicolored   .50   .50
1086 A155a $1.20 multicolored   .85   .85
Souvenir Sheet
1087 A155b $5 multicolored   3.50 3.50

Intl. Year of the Ocean — A156

30c, Butterflyfish. 80c, Bicolor cherub. $1.20, Silver badgerfish. $2, Asfur angelfish.
No. 1092, vert: a, Copperbanded butterlyfish. b, Forcepsfish. c, Double-saddled butterflyfish. d, Blue surgeonfish. e, Orbiculate batfish. f, Undulated triggerfish. g, Rock beauty. h, Flamefish. i, Queen angelfish.

No. 1093: a, Pygama cardinal fish. b, Wimplefish. c, Long-nosed filefish. d, Oriental sweetlips. e, Blue spotted boxfish. f, Blue stripe angelfish. g, Goldrim tang. h, Royal gramma. i, Common clownfish.
Each $5: No. 1094, Longhorned cowfish, vert. No. 1095, Red-faced batfish, vert.

1998, Aug. 18   Litho.   Perf. 14
1088-1091 A156 Set of 4   5.75 5.75
1092 A156 90c Sheet of 9, #a.-i. 6.25 6.25
1093 A156 $1 Sheet of 9, #a.-i.   7.00 7.00
Souvenir Sheets
1094-1095 A156 Set of 2   8.75 8.75

Princess Diana (1961-97) — A157

1998, Oct. 15   Litho.   Perf. 14
1096 A157 $1 multicolored   .75   .75

No. 1096 was issued in sheets of 6.

Mahatma Gandhi (1869-1948) — A158

Portraits: No. 1097, In South Africa, 1914. No. 1098, At Downing Street, London.

1998, Oct. 15
1097 A158 $1 multicolored   1.00 1.00
1098 A158 $1 multicolored   1.00 1.00

Nos. 1097-1098 were each issued in sheets of 6.

Royal Air Force, 80th Anniv. — A159

Aircraft — #1100: a, Panavia Tornado F3 ADV. b, Panavia Tornado F3 IDV. c, Tristar K Mk1 Tanker refueling Panavia Tornado. d, Panavia Tornado GRI.
Each $5: No. 1101, Wessex helicopter, fighter plane. No. 1102, Early aircraft, birds.

1998, Oct. 15   Litho.   Perf. 14
1100 A159 $2 Sheet of 4, #a.-d. 7.00 7.00
Souvenir Sheets
1101-1102 A159 Set of 2   9.25 9.25

1998 World Scouting Jamboree, Chile — A160

Designs: a, Four Boy Scouts from around the world. b, Boy Scout accompanying Gettysburg veterans, 1913. c, First black troop, Virginia, 1928.

1998, Oct. 15
1103 A160 $3 Sheet of 3, #a.-c. 7.00 7.00

Independence, 15th Anniv. — A161

Design: Prime Minister Kennedy Simmonds receiving constitutional instruments from Princess Margaret, Countess of Snowden.

1998, Oct. 15   Litho.   Perf. 14
1104 A161 $1 multicolored   1.10 1.10

Organization of American States, 50th Anniv. — A162

1998, Oct. 15   Perf. 14
1105 A162 $1 multicolored   .90   .90

Enzo Ferrari (1898-1988), Automobile Manufacturer — A163

No. 1106: a, 365 California. b, Pininfarina's P6. c, 250 LM.
$5, 212 Export Spyder.

1998, Oct. 15
1106 A163 $2 Sheet of 3, #a.-c. 5.50 5.50
Souvenir Sheet
1107 A163 $5 multicolored   4.75 4.75

No. 1107 contains one 91x35mm stamp.

Christmas A164

Designs: 25c, Kitten, Santa. 60c, Kitten, ornament. 80c, Kitten in sock, vert. 90c, Puppy, presents. $1, Cherub sleeping, birds. $3, Child making snowball, vert.
Each $5: No. 1114, Family, vert. No. 1115, Two dogs.

1998, Nov. 24   Litho.   Perf. 14
1108-1113 A164 Set of 6   5.25 5.25
Souvenir Sheets
1114-1115 A164 Set of 2   7.75 7.75

New Year 1999 (Year of the Rabbit) A165

Color of pairs of rabbits — #1116: a, brown & gray. b, brown & white. c, brown. d, white & black spotted.
$5, Adult white rabbit, 3 bunnies.

1999, Jan. 4   Litho.   Perf. 14
1116 A165 $1.60 Sheet of 4, #a.-d. 5.25 5.25
Souvenir Sheet
1117 A165 $5 multicolored   4.50 4.50

No. 1117 contains one 58x47mm stamp.

Disney Characters Playing Basketball — A166

Basketball in background — #1118, each $1: a, Mickey in green. b, Donald. c, Minnie. d, Goofy. e, One of Donald's nephews. f, Goofy, Mickey. g, Mickey in purple. h, Huey, Dewey, Louie.
Green & white background — #1119, each $1: a, Mickey in purple. b, Goofy. c, Minnie in puple. d, Mickey in yellow & gray. e, Minnie in yellow. f, Donald. g, Donald & Mickey. h, One of Donald's nephews.
No. 1120, $5, Minnie, green bow, horiz. No. 1121, $5, Minnie, purple bow, horiz. No. 1122,

$6, Mickey in purple, horiz. No. 1123, $6, Mickey in yellow, horiz.

Perf. 13½x14, 14x13½
1998, Dec. 24   Litho.
Sheets of 8, #a-h
1118-1119 A166   15.00 15.00
Souvenir Sheets
1120-1121 A166 Set of 2   8.00 8.00
1122-1123 A166 Set of 2   10.00 10.00

Mickey Mouse, 70th anniv.

1998 World Cup Soccer Players — A167

No. 1124: a, Laurent Blanc, France. b, Dennis Bergkamp, Holland. c, David Sukor, Croatia. d, Ronaldo, Brazil. e, Didier Deschamps, France. f, Patrick Kluivert, Holland. g, Rivaldo, Brazil. h, Zinedine Zidane, France.
$5, Zinedine Zidane, close-up.

1999, Jan. 18   Perf. 13½
1124 A167 $1 Sheet of 8, #a.-h. 5.50 5.50
Souvenir Sheet
1125 A167 $5 multicolored   4.00 4.00

Australia '99, World Stamp Expo — A168

Dinosaurs: 30c, Kritosaurus. 60c, Oviraptor. 80c, Eustreptospondylus. $1.20, Tenontosaurus. $2, Ouranosaurus. $3, Muttaburrasaurus.
No. 1132, $1.20: a, Edmontosaurus. b, Avimimus. c, Minmi. d, Segnosaurus. e, Kentrosaurus. f, Deinonychus.
No. 1133, #1.20: a, Saltasaurus. b, Compsoganthus. c, Hadrosaurus. d, Tuojiangosaurus. e, Euoplocephalus. f, Anchisaurus.
Each $5: #1134, Triceratops. #1135, Stegosaurus.

1999, Feb. 22   Litho.   Perf. 14
1126-1131 A168 Set of 6   6.00 6.00
Sheets of 6, #a-f
1132-1133 A168 Set of 2   11.00 11.00
Souvenir Sheets
1134-1135 A168 Set of 2   7.50 7.50

World Leaders of the 20th Century — A169

No. 1136: a, Emperor Haile Selassie (1892-1975), Ethiopia. b, Selassie, Ethiopian warriors, flag. c, David Ben-Gurion (1886-1973), Prime Minister of Israel. d, Ben-Gurion, Israeli flag. e, Pres. Franklin Roosevelt (1882-1945), Eleanor Roosevelt (1884-1962), UN emblem. f, Roosevelts campaigning, US GI in combat. g, Mao Tse-tung (1893-1976), Chinese leader, 1934 Long March. h, Poster of Mao, soldier.
Each $5: No. 1137, Gandhi. No. 1138, Nelson Mandela.

1999, Mar. 8
1136 A169 90c Sheet of 8, #a.-h. 6.75 6.75
Souvenir Sheets
1137-1138 A169 Set of 2   8.00 8.00

Nos. 1136b-1136c, 1136f-1136g are each 53x38mm.

Birds — A170

No. 1139, each $1.60: a, Yellow warbler. b, Common yellowthroat. c, Painted bunting. d, Belted kingfisher. e, American kestrel. f, Northern oriole.
No. 1140, each $1.60: a, Malachite kingfisher. b, Lilac-breasted roller. c, Swallow-tailed bee-eater. d, Eurasian jay. e, Black-collared apalis. f, Gray-backed camaroptera.
Each $5: No. 1141, Banaquit. No. 1142, Ground scraper thrush, vert.

1999, May 10   Litho.   Perf. 14
Sheets of 6, #a-f
1139-1140 A170 Set of 2   15.00 15.00
Souvenir Sheets
1141-1142 A170 Set of 2   8.00 8.00

Orchids — A171

Designs: 20c, Phaius hybrid, vert. 25c, Cuitlauzina pendula, vert. 50c, Bletilla striata, vert. 80c, Cymbidium "Showgirl," vert. $1.60, Zygopetalum crinitium. $3, Dendrobium nobile.
No. 1149, vert., each $1: a, Cattleya pumpernickel. b, Odontocidium Arthur Elle. c, Neostylis Lou Sneary. d, Phalaenopsis Aprodite. e, Arkundina graminieolia. f, Cymbidium Hunter's Point. g, Rynchoatylis coelestis. h, Cymbidium Elf's castle.
No. 1150, vert., each $1: a, Cattleya intermedia. b, Cattleya Sophia Martin. c, Phalaenopsis Little Hal. d, Laeliocattleya alisal "Rodeo." e, Laelia lucasiana fournieri. f, Cymbidium Red beauty. g, Sobralia sp. h, Promenaea xanthina.
Each $5: No. 1151, Philippine wind orchid. No. 1152, Dragon's mouth.

1999, June 15   Litho.   Perf. 14
1143-1148 A171 Set of 6   5.50 5.50
Sheets of 8, #a-h
1149-1150 A171   14.50 14.50
Souvenir Sheets
1151-1152 A171 Set of 2   8.00 8.00

Wedding of Prince Edward and Sophie Rhys-Jones — A172

No. 1153, each $2: a, Sophie in checked suit. b, Couple walking across grass. c, Sophie in black hat, suit, d, Prince Edward in white shirt.
No. 1154, each $2: a, Couple standing in front of building. b, Sophie wearing large hat. c, Sophie in black dress. d, Edward in striped shirt.
Each $5: No. 1155, Couple posing for engagement photo, horiz. No. 1156, Edward kissing Sophie, horiz.

1999, June 19   Litho.   Perf. 14¼
Sheets of 4, #a-d
1153-1154 A172 Set of 2   11.00 11.00
Souvenir Sheets
1155-1156 A172 Set of 2   7.00 7.00

IBRA '99, World Stamp Exhibition, Nuremberg — A173

Beuth 2-2-2 locomotive and: 30c, Baden #1. 80c, Brunswick #1.
Sailing ship Kruzenshstern and: 90c, Bergedorf #2 & #1a. $1, Bremen #1.
$5, Regensburg air post label on cover.

1999, July 1   Perf. 14x14½
1157-1160 A173 Set of 4   2.50 2.50
Souvenir Sheet
1161 A173 $5 multicolored   3.50 3.50

Souvenir Sheets

PhilexFrance '99, World Philatelic Exhibition — A174

Trains: No. 1162, $5: First Class Carriage, 1837. No. 1163, $5: 141.R Mixed Traffic 2-8-2, 1949.

1999, July 1   Perf. 14x13½
1162-1163 A174 Set of 2   8.25 8.25

Paintings by Hokusai (1760-1849) A175

Details or entire paintings — #1164: a, (Five) Women Returning Home at Sunset. b, The Blind. c, (Four) Women Returning Home at Sunset. d, A Young Man on a White Horse. e, The Blind (man with beard). f, A Peasant Crossing a Bridge.
No. 1165: a, Poppies (one in bloom). b, The Blind (man with goatee). c, Poppies. d, Abe No Nakamaro Gazing at the Moon from a Terrace. e, The Blind. f, Cranes on a Snowy Pine.
Each $5: No. 1166, Carp in a Waterfall. No. 1167, A Rider in the Snow.

1999, July 1   Perf. 13½x14
Sheets of 6
1164 A175 $1 #a.-f.   4.25 4.25
1165 A175 $1.60 #a.-f.   6.75 6.75
Souvenir Sheets
1166-1167 A175 Set of 2   7.75 7.75

Culturama Festival, 25th Anniv. — A176

Designs: 30c, Steel drummers. 80c, Clowns. $1.80, Masqueraders with "Big Drum." No. 1171, $5, String band.
No. 1172, Masquerade dancers.

1999, July 1   Litho.   Perf. 14
1168-1171 A176 Set of 4   5.50 5.50
Souvenir Sheet
1172 A176 $5 multicolored   3.75 3.75
No. 1172 contains one 51x38mm stamp.

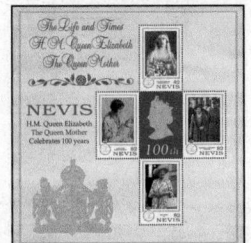

Queen Mother — A177

Queen Mother (b. 1900): No. 1173: a, In bridal gown, 1923. b, With Princess Elizabeth, 1926. c, With King George VI in World War II. d, Wearing hat, 1983.
$6, Wearing tiara, 1957.

Gold Frames
1999, Aug. 4   Sheet of 4   Perf. 14
1173 A177 $2 #a.-d., + label   5.50 5.50

Souvenir Sheet
Perf. 13¾
1174 A177 $6 multicolored   4.25 4.25
No. 1174 contains one 38x51mm stamp. See Nos. 1287-1288.

Christmas — A178

30c, Adoration of the Magi, by Albrecht Durer. 90c, Canigiani Holy Family, by Raphael. $1.20, The Nativity, by Durer. $1.80, Madonna Surrounded by Angels, by Peter Paul Rubens. $3, Madonna Surrounded by Saints, by Rubens.
$5, Madonna and Child by a Window, by Durer, horiz.

1999, Nov. 12   Litho.   Perf. 14
1175-1179 A178 Set of 5   5.50 5.50
Souvenir Sheet
1180 A178 $5 multicolored   3.75 3.75

Millennium — A179

Scenes of Four Seasons Resort: a, Aerial view. b, Palm tree, beach. c, Golf course. d, Couple on beach.

1999   Litho.   Perf. 14¼x13¾
1181 A179 30c Sheet of 4, #a.-d.   .90 .90

Flowers — A180

Various flowers making up a photomosaic of Princess Diana.

1999, Dec. 31   Litho.   Perf. 13¾
1182 A180 $1 Sheet of 8, #a.-h.   6.00 6.00

New Year 2000 (Year of the Dragon) A181

No. 1183: a, Dragon showing 9 claws. b, Dragon showing 10 claws. c, Dragon showing 5 claws. d, Dragon showing 8 claws.
$5, Dragon, vert.

2000, Feb. 5   Perf. 14
1183 A181 $1.60 Sheet of 4, #a.-d.   4.25 4.25
Souvenir Sheet
Perf. 13¾
1184 A181 $5 multi   4.00 4.00
No. 1184 contains one 38x50mm stamp.

Millennium — A182

No. 1185 — Highlights of 1700-1750: a, Jonathan Swift writes "Gulliver's Travels." b, Manchu Dynasty flourishes in China. c,

Bartolomeo Cristofori invents piano. d, Capt. William Kidd hanged for piracy. e, Astronomer William Herschel born. f, George I succeeds Queen Anne as British ruler. g, Russian treaty with China. h, Bubonic plague hits Austria and Germany. i, Kaigetsudo paints "Standing Woman." j, Queen Anne ascends to English throne. k, Anders Celsius invents centigrade scale for thermometer. l, Vitus Bering discovers Alaska and Aleutian Islands. m, Edmond Halley predicts return of comet. n, John and Charles Wesley found Methodism movement. o, Isaac Newton publishes "Opticks." p, England and Scotland form Great Britain (60x40mm). q, Johann Sebastian Bach composes "The Well-Tempered Clavier."
No. 1186 — Highlights of the 1990s: a, Boris Yeltsin becomes prime minister of Russian Federation. b, Gulf War begins. c, Civil War in Bosnia. d, Signing of the Oslo Accords. e, John Major, Albert Reynolds search for peace in Northern Ireland. f, F.W. De Klerk, Nelson Mandela end apartheid in South Africa. g, Cal Ripken, Jr. breaks record for most consecutive baseball games played. h, Kobe, Japan earthquake. i, Inca girl, believed to be 500 years old, found in ice. j, Sojourner beams back images from Mars. k, Dr. Ian Wilmot clones sheep "Dolly." l, Princess Diana dies in car crash. m, Hong Kong returned to China. n, Septuplets born and survive. o, Guggenheim Museum in Bilbao, Spain completed. p, Countdown to year 2000 (60x40mm). q, Pres. William J. Clinton impeached.

2000, Jan. 4   Litho.   Perf. 12¾x12½
Sheets of 17
1185 A182 30c #a.-q., + label   6.75 6.75
1186 A182 50c #a.-q., + label 10.00 10.00
Misspellings and historical inaccuracies abound on Nos. 1185-1186.

Tropical Fish — A183

Designs: 30c, Spotted scat. 80c, Platy variatus. 90c, Emerald betta. $4, Cowfish.
No. 1191, each $1: a, Oriental sweetlips. b, Royal gramma. c, Threadfin butterflyfish. d, Yellow tang. e, Bicolor angelfish. f, Catalina goby. g, False cleanerfish. h, Powder blue surgeon.
No. 1192, each $1: a, Sailfin tang. b, Black-capped gramma. c, Majestic snapper. d, Purple firefish. e, Clown trigger. f, Yellow longnose. g, Clown wrasse. h, Yellow-headed jawfish.
Each $5: No. 1193, Clown coris. No. 1194, Clown killifish.

2000, Mar. 27   Perf. 14
1187-1190 A183 Set of 4   5.50 5.50
Sheets of 8, #a.-h.
1191-1192 A183 Set of 2   13.50 13.50
Souvenir Sheets
1193-1194 A183 Set of 2   8.50 8.50

Dogs — A184

Designs: 10c, Miniature pinscher. 20c, Pyrenean mountain dog. 30c, Welsh Springer spaniel. 80c, Alaskan malamute. $2, Bearded collie. $3, Amercian cocker spaniel.
No. 1201, horiz.: a, Beagle. b, Basset hound. c, St. Bernard. d, Rough collie. e, Shih tzu. f, American bulldog.
No. 1202, horiz.: a, Irish red and white setter. b, Dalmatian. c, Pomeranian. d, Chihuahua. e, English sheepdog. f, Samoyed.
Each $5: No. 1203, Leonberger. No. 1204, Longhaired miniature dachshund, horiz.

2000, May 1   Litho.   Perf. 14
1195-1200 A184 Set of 6   5.25 5.25
1201 A184 90c Sheet of 6, #a-f   4.50 4.50
1202 A184 $1 Sheet of 6, #a-f   5.00 5.00
Souvenir Sheets
1203-1204 A184 Set of 2   8.50 8.50

100th Test Match at
Lord's Ground — A185

Designs: $2, Elquemede Willett. $3, Keith
Arthurton.
$5, Lord's Ground, horiz.

2000, June 10
1205-1206 A185 Set of 2   4.00 4.00
Souvenir Sheet
1207 A185 $5 multi   4.00 4.00

First
Zeppelin
Flight,
Cent.
A186

No. 1208: a, LZ-129. b, LZ-1. c, LZ-11.
$5, LZ-127.

2000, June 10   **Perf. 14**
1208 A186 $3 Sheet of 3, #a-c   7.00 7.00
Souvenir Sheet
Perf. 14¼
1209 A186 $5 multi   4.25 4.25

No. 1208 contains three 38x25mm stamps.

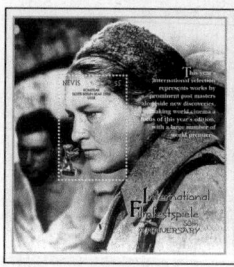

Berlin
Film
Festival,
50th
Anniv.
A187

No. 1210: a, Rani Radovi. b, Salvatore Giu-
liano. c, Schoenzeit für Füchse. d, Shirley
MacLaine. e, Simone Signoret. f, Sohrab
Shahid Saless.
$5, Komissar.

2000, June 10   **Perf. 14**
1210 A187 $1.60 Sheet of 6, #a-f 7.00 7.00
Souvenir Sheet
1211 A187 $5 multi   4.00 4.00

Spacecraft — A188

No. 1212, each $1.60: a, Mars IV probe. b,
Mars Water. c, Mars 1. d, Viking. e, Mariner 7.
f, Mars Surveyor.
No. 1213, each $1.60: a, Mariner 9. b, Mars
3. c, Mariner 4. d, Planet B. e, Mars Express
Lander. f, Mars Express.
Each $5: No. 1214, Mars Observer. No.
1215, Mars Climate Observer, vert.

2000, June 10   **Sheets of 6, #a-f**
1212-1213 A188 Set of 2   15.00 15.00
Souvenir Sheets
1214-1215 A188 Set of 2   8.00 8.00

Souvenir Sheets

2000 Summer Olympics,
Sydney — A189

No. 1216: a, Gisela Mauermeyer. b, Uneven
bars. c, Wembley Stadium, London, and British flag. d, Ancient Greek horse racing.

2000, June 10
1216 A189 $2 Sheet of 4, #a-d   5.00 5.00

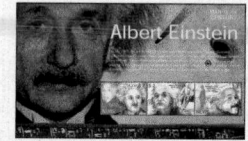

Albert Einstein (1879-1955) — A190

No. 1217: a, Sticking out tongue. b, Riding
bicycle. c, Wearing hat.

2000, June 10
1217 A190 $2 Sheet of 3, #a-c   5.50 5.00

Public Railways, 175th Anniv. — A191

No. 1218: a, Locomotion No. 1, George Stephenson. b, Trevithick's 1804 drawing of
locomotive.

2000, June 10
1218 A191 $3 Sheet of 2, #a-b   4.75 4.75

Johann Sebastian Bach (1685-
1750) — A192

2000, June 10
1219 A192 $5 multi   4.25 4.25

Prince
William,
18th
Birthday
A193

No. 1220: a, Reaching to shake hand. b, In
ski gear. c, With jacket open. d, In sweater.
$5, In suit and tie.

2000, June 21   **Perf. 14**
1220 A193 $1.60 Sheet of 4,
      #a-d   4.25 4.25
Souvenir Sheet
Perf. 13¾
1221 A193 $5 multi   4.00 4.00

No. 1220 contains four 28x42mm stamps.

Souvenir Sheets

Bob Hope, Entertainer — A194

No. 1222: a, Wearing Air Force Ranger uniform. b, With Sammy Davis, Jr. c, With wife,
Dolores. d, On golf course. e, In suit behind
microphone. f, Walking.

2000, July 10   **Perf. 14**
1222 A194 $1 Sheet of 6, #a-f   5.75 5.75

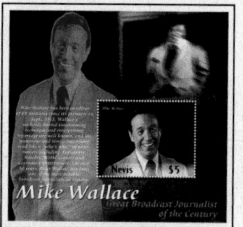

Mike Wallace, Broadcast
Journalist — A195

2000, July 10   **Perf. 13¾**
1223 A195 $5 multi   4.00 4.00

Carifesta VII — A196

Designs: 30c, Emblem. 90c, Festival participants. $1.20, Dancer.

2000, Aug. 17   **Perf. 14**
1224-1226 A196 Set of 3   2.25 2.25

Monarchs — A197

No. 1227: a, King Edward III of England,
1327-77. b, Holy Roman Emperor Charles V
(Charles I of Spain), 1520-56. c, Holy Roman
Emperor Joseph II of Austria-Hungary, 1780-
90. d, King Henry II of Germany, 1002-24. e,
King Louis IV of France, 936-54. f, King Louis
II of Bavaria, 1864-86.
$5, King Louis IX of France, 1226-70.

2000, Aug. 1   Litho.   Perf. 13¾
1227 A197 $1.60 Sheet of 6, #a-f 8.00 8.00
Souvenir Sheet
1228 A197 $5 multi   4.25 4.25

David Copperfield,
Magician — A198

2000, Aug. 10   **Perf. 14**
1229 A198 $1.60 multi   2.00 2.00
Printed in sheets of 4.

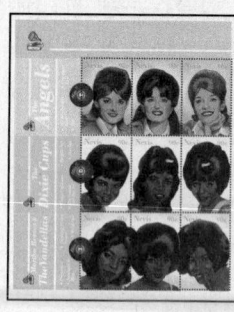

Female
Singing
Groups
A199

Singers from the Angels (a-c, blue background), Dixie Cups (d-f, yellow background)
and Martha Reeves and the Vandellas (g-i,
pink background): a, Record half. b, Woman
with long hair. c, Woman with mole on chin. d,
Record half. e, Woman with mole on cheek. f,
Woman, no mole. g, Record half. h, Woman,
not showing teeth. i, Woman showing teeth.

2000, Aug. 10
1230 A199 90c Sheet of 9, #a-i   6.25 6.25

Butterflies
A200

Designs: 30c, Zebra. 80c, Julia. $1.60,
Small flambeau. $5, Purple mort bleu.
No. 1235, $1: a, Ruddy dagger. b, Common
morpho. c, Banded king shoemaker. d, Figure
of eight. e, Grecian shoemaker. f, Mosaic.
No. 1236, $1: a, White peacock. b, Hewit-
son's blue hairstreak. c, Tiger pierid. d, Gold
drop helicopsis. e, Cramer's mesene. f, Red-
banded pereute.
No. 1237, $5, Common mechanitis. No.
1238, $5, Hewitson's pierella.

2001, Mar. 22
1231-1234 A200 Set of 4   6.00 6.00
Sheets of 6, #a-f
1235-1236 A200 Set of 2   9.50 9.50
Souvenir Sheets
1237-1238 A200 Set of 2   7.75 7.75

Flowers — A201

Designs: 30c, Golden elegance oriental lily.
80c, Frangipani. $1.60, Garden zinnia. $5,
Rose elegance lily.
No. 1243, 90c: a, Star of the march. b, Tiger
lily. c, Mont Blanc lily. d, Torch ginger. e, Cat-
tleya orchid. f, Saint John's wort.
No. 1244, $1: a, Culebra. b, Rubellum lily. c,
Silver elegance oriental lily. d, Chinese hibis-
cus. e, Tiger lily. f, Royal poinciana.
No. 1245, $1.60: a, Epiphyte. b, Enchant-
ment lily. c, Glory lily. d, Purple granadilla. e,
Jacaranda. f, Shrimp plant.
No. 1246, $5, Dahlia. No. 1247, $5, Bird of
Paradise.

2000, Oct. 30
1239-1242 A201 Set of 4   6.00 6.00
Sheets of 6, #a-f
1243-1245 A201 Set of 3   17.00 17.00
Souvenir Sheets
1246-1247 A201 Set of 2   7.75 7.75

The Stamp Show 2000, London (Nos. 1243-
1247).

Christmas — A203

Designs: 30c, The Coronation of the Virgin, by Diego Velazquez, vert. 80c, The Immaculate Conception, by Velazquez, vert. 90c, Madonna and Child, by Titian. $1.20, Madonna and Child With St. John the Baptist and St. Catherine, by Titian.
$6, Madonna and Child With St. Catherine, by Titian.

2000, Dec. 4	**Litho.**		**Perf. 13½**	
1249-1252	A203	Set of 4	2.40	2.40
Souvenir Sheet				
1253	A203	$6 multi	4.50	4.50

New Year 2001 (Year of the Snake) A204

No. 1254: a, Snake coiled on branch, facing right. b, Snake coiled on branch, facing left. c, Snake on ground, facing right. d, Snake on ground, facing left.
$5, Snake raising head.

2001, Jan. 4			**Perf. 14**	
1254	A204	$1.60 Sheet of 4, #a-d	5.00	5.00
Souvenir Sheet				
1255	A204	$5 multi	4.00	4.00

195th Annual Leeward Islands Methodist Church District Conference — A205

Churches: a, Charlestown. b, Jessups. c, Clifton. d, Trinity. e, Combermere. f, Gingerland. g, New River.

2001, Jan. 23				
1256	A205	50c Sheet of 7, #a-g	2.50	2.50

Garden of Eden A206

No. 1257, $1.60: a, Red-crested woodpecker, unicorn. b, African elephant. c, Siberian tiger. d, Greater flamingo, Adam and Eve. e, Hippopotamus. f, Harlequin frog.
No. 1258, $1.60: a, Giraffe. b, Rainbow boa constrictor. c, Mountain cottontail rabbit. d, Bluebuck antelope. e, Red fox. f, Box turtle.
No. 1259, $5, Bald eagle. No. 1260, $5, Blue and gold macaw, vert. No. 1261, $5, Toucan, vert. No. 1262, $5, Koala, vert.

2001, Jan. 31			**Perf. 14**	
Sheets of 6, #a-f				
1257-1258	A206	Set of 2	14.50	14.50
Souvenir Sheets				
1259-1262	A206	Set of 4	15.00	15.00

Mushrooms — A207

Designs: 20c, Clavulinopsis corniculata. 25c, Cantharellus cibarius. 50c, Chlorociboria aeruginascens. 80c, Auricularia auricula judae. $2, Peziza vesiculosa. $3, Mycena acicula.
No. 1269, $1: a, Entoloma incanum. b, Entoloma nitidum. c, Stropharia cyanea. d, Otidea onotica. e, Aleuria aurantia. f, Mitrula paludosa. g, Gyromitra esculenta. h, Helvella crispa. i, Morchella semilibera.
No. 1270, $5, Omphalotus olearius. No. 1271, $5, Russula sardonia.

2001, May 15		**Litho.**	**Perf. 14**	
1263-1268	A207	Set of 6	5.50	5.50
1269	A207	$1 Sheet of 9, #a-i	7.50	7.50
Souvenir Sheets				
1270-1271	A207	Set of 2	8.25	8.25

Tale of Prince Shotoku A208

No. 1272, $2: a, Conception of Prince Shotoku. b, At six. c, At ten. d, At eleven.
No. 1273, $2: a, At sixteen (soldiers at gate). b, At sixteen (soldiers on horseback). c, At thirty-seven. d, At forty-four.

2001, May 31			**Perf. 13¾**	
Sheets of 4, #a-d				
1272-1273	A208	Set of 2	12.00	12.00
Phila Nippon '01, Japan.				

Queen Victoria (1819-1901) — A209

No. 1274: a, Prince Albert. b, Queen Victoria (flower in hair). c, Alexandrina Victoria. d, Duchess of Kent. e, Queen Victoria (as old woman). f, Prince of Wales.
$5, Queen Victoria (with tiara).

2001, July 9		**Litho.**	**Perf. 14**	
1274	A209	$1.20 Sheet of 6, #a-f	5.50	5.50
Souvenir Sheet				
1275	A209	$5 multi	3.75	3.75

Queen Elizabeth II, 75th Birthday A210

No. 1276: a, Blue hat. b, Tiara. c, Yellow hat. d, Tan hat. e, Red hat. f, No hat.
$5, Blue hat, diff.

2001, July 9				
1276	A210	90c Sheet of 6, #a-f	4.00	4.00
Souvenir Sheet				
1277	A210	$5 multi	3.75	3.75

Flags of the Caribbean Community — A211

No. 1278: a, Antigua & Barbuda. b, Bahamas. c, Barbados. d, Belize. e, Dominica. f, Grenada. g, Guyana. h, Jamaica. i, Montserrat. j, St. Kitts & Nevis. k, St. Lucia. l, Surinam. m, St. Vincent & the Grenadines. n, Trinidad & Tobago.

2001, Dec. 3		**Litho.**	**Perf. 14**	
1278	A211	90c Sheet of 14, #a-n	11.00	11.00

Christmas A212

Flowers: 30c, Christmas candle, vert. 90c, Poinsettia. $1.20, Snowbush. $3, Tiger claw, vert.

2001, Dec. 3				
1279-1282	A212	Set of 4	4.25	4.25

2002 World Cup Soccer Championships, Japan and Korea — A213

No. 1283, $1.60: a, Moracana Stadium, Brazil, 1950. b, Ferenc Puskas, 1954. c, Luis Bellini, 1958. d, Mauro, 1962. e, Cap, 1966. f, Banner, 1970.
No. 1284, $1.60: a, Passarella, 1978. b, Dino Zoff, 1982. c, Azteca Stadium, Mexico, 1986. d, San Siro Stadium, Italy, 1990. e, Dennis Bergkamp, Netherlands, 1994. f, Stade de France, 1998.
No. 1285, $5, Head from Jules Rimet Cup, 1930. No. 1286, $5, Head and globe from World Cup trophy, 2002.

2001, Dec. 10			**Perf. 13¾x14¼**	
Sheets of 6, #a-f				
1283-1284	A213	Set of 2	13.00	13.00

Souvenir Sheets
Perf. 14½x14¼

1285-1286	A213	Set of 2	7.25	7.25

Queen Mother Type of 1999 Redrawn

No. 1287: a, In bridal gown, 1923. b, With Princess Elizabeth, 1926. c, With King George VI in World War II. d, Wearing hat, 1983.
$6, Wearing tiara, 1957.

2001, Dec. 13			**Perf. 14**	
Yellow Orange Frames				
1287	A177	$2 Sheet of 4, #a-d, + label	6.00	6.00
Souvenir Sheet				
Perf. 13¾				
1288	A177	$6 multi	4.50	4.50

Queen Mother's 101st birthday. No. 1288 contains one 38x51mm stamp with a bluer background than that found on No. 1174. Sheet margins of Nos. 1287-1288 lack embossing and gold arms and frames found on Nos. 1173-1174.

Reign of Queen Elizabeth II, 50th Anniv. A214

No. 1289: a, Queen with Prince Philip. b, Prince Philip. c, Queen with yellow dress. d, Queen touching horse.
$5, Queen with Prince Philip, diff.

2002, Feb. 6			**Perf. 14¼**	
1289	A214	$2 Sheet of 4, #a-d	5.75	5.75
Souvenir Sheet				
1290	A214	$5 multi	3.75	3.75

New Year 2002 (Year of the Horse) A215

Horse paintings by Ren Renfa: a, Brown and white horse. b, Horse with ribs showing. c, Horse with tassel under neck. d, Gray horse.

2002, Mar. 4			**Perf. 13¼**	
1291	A215	$1.60 Sheet of 4, #a-d	4.50	4.50

Insects, Birds and Whales A216

No. 1292, $1.20: a, Beechey's bee. b, Banded king shoemaker butterfly. c, Streaked sphinx caterpillar. d, Hercules beetle. e, South American palm beetle. f, Giant katydid.
No. 1293, $1.60: a, Roseate spoonbill. b, White-tailed tropicbird. c, Ruby-throated tropicbird. d, Black skimmer. e, Black-necked stilt. f, Mourning dove.
No. 1294, $1.60: a, Sperm whale. b, Sperm and killer whales. c, Minke whales. d, Fin whale. e, Blainville's beaked whale. f, Pygmy sperm whale.
No. 1295, $5, Click beetle. No. 1296, $5, Royal tern. No. 1297, $5, Humpback whale, vert.

2002, Aug. 15 Litho. Perf. 14
Sheets of 6, #a-f
1292-1294 A216 Set of 3 21.00 21.00
Souvenir Sheets
1295-1297 A216 Set of 3 12.00 12.00
APS Stampshow (#1293).

United We
Stand — A217

2002, Aug. 26
1298 A217 $2 multi 1.50 1.50
Printed in sheets of 4.

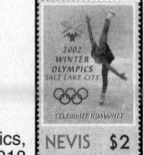

2002 Winter Olympics,
Salt Lake City — A218

Designs: No. 1299, $2, Figure skating. No.
1300, $2, Freestyle skiing.

2002, Aug. 26
1299-1300 A218 Set of 2 3.00 3.00
 a. Souvenir sheet, #1299-1300 3.25 3.25

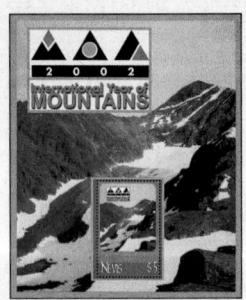

Intl. Year of Mountains — A219

No. 1301: a, Mt. Assiniboine, Canada. b, Mt.
Atitlán, Guatemala. c, Mt. Adams, US. d, Matterhorn, Switzerland and Italy. e, Mt. Dhaulagiri, Nepal. f, Mt. Chamlang, Nepal.
$5, Mt. Kvaenangen, Norway.

2002, Aug. 26
1301 A219 $2 Sheet of 6, #a-f 8.50 8.50
Souvenir Sheet
1302 A219 $5 multi 3.50 3.50

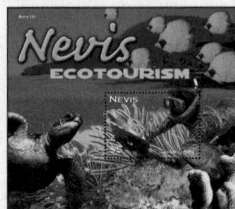

Ecotourism — A220

No. 1303: a, Horseback riding on beach. b,
Windsurfing. c, Pinney's Beach. d, Cross-
country hike. e, Robert T. Jones Golf Course.
f, Scuba safaris.
$5, Coral reef snorkeling.

2002, Aug. 26
1303 A220 $1.60 Sheet of 6, #a-f 8.00 8.00
Souvenir Sheet
1304 A220 $5 multi 3.75 3.75

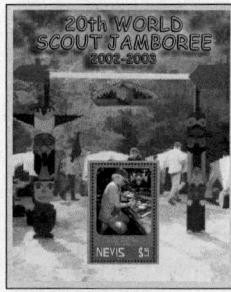

20th World Scout Jamboree,
Thailand — A221

No. 1305: a, Scouts in two canoes. b,
Scouts in one canoe. c, Scout on rope bridge.
d, Scouts in inflatable rafts.
$5, Scout working on leatherwork project.

2002, Aug. 26
1305 A221 $2 Sheet of 4, #a-d 6.00 6.00
Souvenir Sheet
1306 A221 $5 multi 3.75 3.75

Souvenir Sheet

Artwork of Eva Wilkin (1898-
1989) — A222

No. 1307: a, Unnamed painting of windmill.
b, Nevis Peak (sepia toned). c, Fig Tree
Church. d, Nevis Peak (full color).

2002, Sept. 23
1307 A222 $1.20 Sheet of 4,
 #a-d 3.75 3.75

Japanese Art — A223

No. 1308: a, Golden Pheasants and Loquat,
by Shoei Kano. b, Flowers and Birds of the
Four Seasons (snow-covered branches), by
Koson Ikeda. c, Pheasants and Azaleas, by
Kano. d, Flowers and Birds of the Four Sea-
sons (tree and hill), by Ikeda.
No. 1309, $3: a, Flying bird from Birds and
Flowers of Summer and Autumn, by Terutada
Shikibu. b, Red flower, from Birds and Flowers
of Summer and Autumn, by Shikibu.
No. 1310, $3: a, White flower from Birds and
Flowers of Summer and Autumn, by Shikibu.
b, Perched bird from Birds and Flowers of
Summer and Autumn, by Shikibu.
No. 1311, $3, horiz.: a, Bird facing right,
from Two Birds on Willow and Peach Trees, by
Buson Yosa. b, Bird facing left, from Two Birds
on Willow and Peach Trees, by Yosa.
No. 1312, $5, Golden Pheasants Among
Rhododendrons, by Baiitsu Yamamoto. No.
1313, $5, Muskrat and Camellias, by Neko
Jako, horiz.

2002 Perf. 14x13¾
1308 A223 $2 Sheet of 4, #a-d 6.00 6.00
Sheets of 2, #a-b
Perf. 13¾
1309-1311 A223 Set of 3 13.50 13.50
Souvenir Sheets
1312-1313 A223 Set of 2 7.50 7.50
No. 1308 contains four 29x80mm stamps.

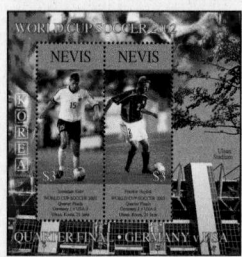

2002 World Cup Soccer Championship
Quarterfinal Matches — A224

No. 1314, $1.20: a, Claudio Reyna and Tor-
sten Frings. b, Michael Ballack and Eddie
Pope. c, Sebastian Kehl and Brian McBride. d,
Puyol and Eul Yong Lee. e, Jin Cheul Choi and
Gaizka Mendieta. f, Juan Valeron and Jin
Cheul Choi.
No. 1315, $1.60: a, Emile Heskey and
Edmilson. b, Rivaldo and Sol Campbell. c,
Ronaldinho and Nicky Butt. d, Ilhan Mansiz
and Omar Daf. e, Hasan Sas and Papa Bouba
Diop. f, Lamine Diatta and Hakan Sukur.
No. 1316, $3: a, Sebastian Kehl. b, Frankie
Hejduk.
No. 1317, $3: a, Hong Myung Bo. b, Gaizka
Mendieta.
No. 1318, $3: a, David Beckham and Roque
Junior. b, Paul Scholes and Rivaldo.
No. 1319, $3: a, Alpay Ozalan. b, Khalilou
Fadiga.

2002, Nov. 4 Litho. Perf. 13¼
Sheets of 6, #a-f
1314-1315 A224 Set of 2 12.50 12.50
Souvenir Sheets of 2, #a-b
1316-1319 A224 Set of 4 18.00 18.00

Christmas — A225

Religious art: 30c, Madonna and Child
Enthroned with Saints, by Perugino. 80c, Adoration of the Magi, by Domenico Ghirlandaio.
90c, San Zaccaria Altarpiece, by Giovanni Bellini. $1.20, Presentation at the Temple, by Bel-
lini. $5, Madonna and Child, by Simone
Martini.
$6, Maestà, by Martini.

2002, Nov. 4 Perf. 14¼
1320-1324 A225 Set of 5 6.25 6.25
Souvenir Sheet
Perf. 14x14¼
1325 A225 $6 multi 4.50 4.50

New Year 2003 (Year
of the Ram) — A226

2003, Feb. 10 Perf. 14x13¾
1326 A226 $2 multi 2.50 2.50
Printed in sheets of 4.

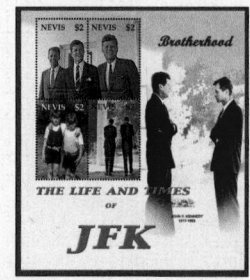

Pres. John F. Kennedy (1917-
63) — A227

No. 1327, $2: a, Robert and Edward Ken-
nedy. b, John F. Kennedy. c, Joseph P., Jr.,

and John F. Kennedy as children. d, Robert
and John F. Kennedy.
No. 1328, $2: a, Taking oath of office, 1961.
b, At cabinet oath ceremony, 1961. c, With
Russian foreign minister Andrei Gromyko,
1963. d, Cuban Missile Crisis, 1962.

2003, Mar. 10 Litho. Perf. 14
Sheets of 4, #a-d
1327-1328 A227 Set of 2 12.00 12.00

Elvis Presley (1935-
77) — A228

2003, Mar. 10 Litho. Perf. 14
1329 A228 $1.60 multi 1.60 1.60
Printed in sheets of 6.

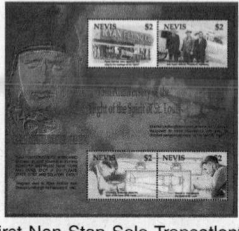

First Non-Stop Solo Transatlantic
Flight, 75th Anniv. — A229

No. 1330, $2: a, Ryan Airlines crew
attaches wing to fuselage of the Spirit of St.
Louis. b, Charles Lindbergh, Donald Hall and
President of Ryan Flying Co. c, Lindbergh
planning flight. d, Hall designing Spirit of St.
Louis.
No. 1331, $2: a, Hall. b, Lindbergh. c, Auto-
mobile towing Spirit of St. Louis from Ryan
factory. d, Spirit of St. Louis being towed at
Curtiss Field.

2003, Mar. 10 Sheets of 4, #a-d
1330-1331 A229 Set of 2 12.00 12.00

Princess Diana (1961-97) — A230

No. 1332: a, Wearing light blue and white
dress. b, Wearing light green dress, pearl
necklace. c, Wearing black gown. d, Wearing
black and white hat and pearls.
$5, Wearing black dress and necklace.

2003, Mar. 10 Perf. 12¼
1332 A230 $2 Sheet of 4, #a-d 6.00 6.00
Souvenir Sheet
1333 A230 $5 multi 3.75 3.75

Marlene Dietrich (1901-92) — A231

No. 1334: a, With cigarette, country name at
right. b, With cigarette, country name at left. c,
Close-up. d, Wearing hat and white jacket.
$5, Wearing dress.

2003, Mar. 10 Perf. 14
1334 A231 $1.60 Sheet, #a-b, 2
 each #c-d 6.75 6.75
Souvenir Sheet
1335 A231 $5 multi 3.75 3.75

Coronation of Queen Elizabeth II, 50th
Anniv. — A232

No. 1336: a, Queen as young woman. b,
Queen as older woman. c, Queen wearing
glasses.
$5, Queen wearing tiara.

2003, May 13
1336 A232 $3 Sheet of 3, #a-c   7.00 7.00
Souvenir Sheet
1337 A232 $5 multi   4.25 4.25

Prince
William,
21st
Birthday
A233

No. 1338: a, Wearing suit, showing teeth. b,
Wearing suit. c, Wearing sweater.
$5, Wearing suit, diff.

2003, May 13
1338 A233 $3 Sheet of 3, #a-c   7.00 7.00
Souvenir Sheet
1339 A233 $5 multi   4.00 4.00

Powered
Flight,
Cent.
A234

No. 1340: a, A. V. Roe triplane. b, A. V. Roe
Type D biplane. c, Avro Type F. d, Avro 504.
$5, Avro 561.

2003, May 13
1340 A234 $1.80 Sheet of 4, #a-
d   5.75 5.75
Souvenir Sheet
1341 A234 $5 multi   4.00 4.00

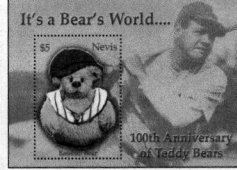

Teddy
Bears,
Cent. (in
2002)
A235

No. 1342: a, Abraham Lincoln bear. b,
Napoleon bear. c, King Henry VIII bear. d,
Charlie Chaplin bear.
$5, Baseball bear.

2003, May 13   *Perf. 13¼*
1342 A235 $2 Sheet of 4, #a-d   5.50 5.50
Souvenir Sheet
1343 A235 $5 multi   3.75 3.75

Tour de
France
Bicycle
Race,
Cent.
A236

No. 1344: a, Gustave Garrigou, 1911. b,
Odile Defraye, 1912. c, Philippe Thys, 1913. d,
Thys, 1914.
$5, François Faber.

2003, May 13
1344 A236 $2 Sheet of 4, #a-d   7.00 7.00
Souvenir Sheet
1345 A236 $5 multi   5.50 5.50

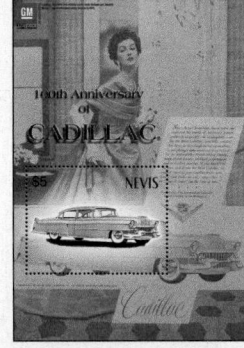

General Motors Automobiles — A237

No. 1346, $2 — Cadillacs: a, 1933 355-C
V8 sedan. b, 1953 Eldorado. c, 1977 Coupe
de Ville. d, 1980 Seville Elegante.
No. 1347, $2 — Corvettes: a, 1970. b, 1974.
c, 1971. d, 1973.
No. 1348, $5, 1954 Cadillac. No. 1349, $5,
1997 C5 Corvette.

2003, May 13
Sheets of 4, #a-d
1346-1347 A237 Set of 2   12.00 12.00
Souvenir Sheets
1348-1349 A237 Set of 2   7.50 7.50

Orchids — A238

Designs: 20c, Phalaenopsis joline, vert.
$1.20, Vanda thonglor, vert. No. 1352, $2,
Potinara. $3, Lycaste aquila.
No. 1354, $2: a, Brassolaelia cattleya. b,
Cymbidium claricon. c, Calanthe vestita. d,
Odontoglossum crispum.
$5, Odontioda brocade.

2003, Oct. 24   *Perf. 14*
1350-1353 A238 Set of 4   5.00 5.00
1354 A238 $2 Sheet of 4, #a-d   6.25 6.25
Souvenir Sheet
1355 A238 $5 multi   4.00 4.00

Butterflies
A239

Designs: 30c, Perisama bonplandii. 90c,
Danaus formosa. $1, Amauris vashti. $3,
Lycorea ceres.
No. 1360: a, Kallima rumia. b, Nessaea
ancaeus. c, Callicore cajetani. d, Hamadryas
guatemalena.
$5, Euphaedra medon.

2003, Oct. 24
1356-1359 A239 Set of 4   4.25 4.25
1360 A239 $2 Sheet of 4, #a-d   6.25 6.25
Souvenir Sheet
1361 A239 $5 multi   4.00 4.00

Marine Life — A240

Designs: 30c, Epinephelus striatus, vert.
80c, Acropora, vert. 90c, Myripristis hexagona.
No. 1365, $5, Trichechus manatus.
No. 1366: a, Lioices latus. b, Chelmon rostratus. c, Epinephelus merra. d, Acanthurus
coeruleus.
No. 1367, $5, Haemulon sciurus.

2003, Oct. 24
1362-1365 A240 Set of 4   5.50 5.50
1366 A240 $2 Sheet of 4, #a-d   6.25 6.25
Souvenir Sheet
1367 A240 $5 multi   4.00 4.00

A241

Christmas — A241a

Designs: 30c, Madonna of the Magnificat,
by Botticelli. 90c, Madonna with the Long
Neck, by Il Parmigianino. $1.20, Virgin and
Child With St. Anne, by Leonardo da Vinci. $5,
Madonna and Child and Scenes from the Life
of St. Anne, by Filippo Lippi.
$6, Conestabile Madonna, by Raphael.

2003, Nov. 5   *Perf. 14¼*
1368-1371 A241 Set of 4   5.00 5.00
Souvenir Sheet
1372 A241a $6 multi   4.25 4.25

World AIDS
Day — A242

National flag, AIDS ribbon and: 90c, Stylized
men. $1.20, Map.

2003, Dec. 1   *Perf. 14*
1373-1374 A242 Set of 2   1.75 1.75

New Year 2004
(Year of the
Monkey) — A243

Designs: $1.60, Monkey King and Chinese
text. $3, Monkey King.

2004, Feb. 16   Litho.   *Perf. 13¼*
1375 A243 $1.60 red & black   1.25 1.25
Souvenir Sheet
Perf. 13¼x13
1376 A243 $3 multi   2.75 2.75
No. 1375 printed in sheets of 4. No. 1376
contains one 30x40mm stamp.

Girl Guides in Nevis,
50th Anniv. — A244

Designs: 30c, Badges. 90c, Guide and
guide leader, horiz. $1.20, Lady Olave Baden-
Powell. $5, Guides wearing t-shirts.

2004, Feb. 22   *Perf. 14*
1377-1380 A244 Set of 4   5.50 5.50

Paintings in
the
Hermitage,
St.
Petersburg,
Russia
A245

Designs: 30c, Still Life with a Drapery, by
Paul Cézanne. 90c, The Smoker, by Cézanne,
vert. $2, Girl with a Fan, by Pierre Auguste
Renoir, vert. No. 1384, $5, Grove, by André
Derain, vert.
No. 1385, Lady in the Garden (Sainte
Adresse), by Claude Monet.

2004, Mar. 4   *Perf. 13¼*
1381-1384 A245 Set of 4   6.25 6.25
Imperf
Size: 94x74mm
1385 A245 $5 multi   3.75 3.75

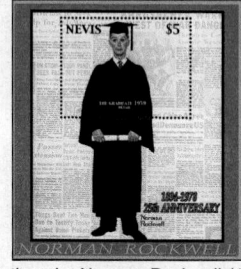

Paintings by Norman Rockwell (1894-
1978) — A246

No. 1386, vert.: a, The Morning After. b,
Solitaire. c, Easter Morning. d, Walking to
Church.
$5, The Graduate.

2004, Mar. 4   *Perf. 13¼*
1386 A246 $2 Sheet of 4, #a-d   6.00 6.00
Souvenir Sheet
1387 A246 $5 multi   4.00 4.00

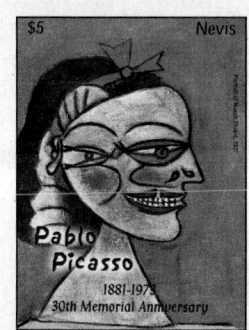

Paintings by Pablo Picasso (1881-
1973) — A247

No. 1388, $2: a, Woman with a Hat. b,
Seated Woman. c, Portrait of Nusch Eluard. d,
Woman in a Straw Hat.
No. 1389, $2: a, L'Arlésienne. b, The Mirror.
c, Repose. d, Portrait of Paul Eluard.
No. 1390, Portrait of Nusch Eluard, diff. No.
1391, Reclining Woman with a Book, horiz.

2004, Mar. 4   *Perf. 13¼*
Sheets of 4, #a-d
1388-1389 A247 Set of 2   12.00 12.00
Imperf
1390 A247 $5 shown   4.00 4.00
Size: 100x75mm
1391 A247 $5 multi   4.00 4.00
ASDA Mega-Event, New York (#1389).

A248

Marilyn Monroe A249

No. 1393 — Placement of stamp on sheet: a, UL. b, UR. c, LL. d, LR.

2004, June 17   **Perf. 13½x13¼**
1392 A248 60c multi   .70 .70

Perf. 13¼
1393 A249 $2 Sheet of 4, #a-d   6.00 6.00

John Denver (1943-97), Musician — A250

Placement of stamp on sheet: a, Top left. b, Top right. c, Bottom left. d, Bottom right.

2004, June 17
1394 A250 $1.20 Sheet of 4, #a-d   3.75 3.75

2004 Summer Olympics, Athens — A251

Designs: 30c, Commemorative medal, 1968 Mexico City Olympics. 90c, Pentathlon. $1.80, Avery Brundage, Intl. Olympic Committee President. $3, Women's tennis, 1920 Antwerp Olympics, horiz.

2004, Sept. 7   **Litho.**   **Perf. 14¼**
1395-1398 A251   Set of 4   4.50 4.50

Intl. Year of Peace A252

No. 1399: a, Country name at right, dove's feet not visible. b, Country name at left. c, Country name at right, dove's feet visible.

2004, Sept. 7
1399 A252 $3 Sheet of 3, #a-c   7.00 7.00

Souvenir Sheet

Deng Xiaoping (1904-97), Chinese Leader — A253

2004, Sept. 7   **Perf. 14**
1400 A253 $5 multi   4.00 4.00

D-Day, 60th Anniv. A254

No. 1401: a, HMCS Penetang. b, Landing Craft Infantry (Large). c, LCT (6). d, Landing Craft Tank (Rocket). e, Landing Barge Kitchen. f, Battleship Texas.
$6, HMS Scorpion.

2004, Sept. 7
1401 A254 $1.20 Sheet of 6, #a-f 5.50 5.50

Souvenir Sheet
1402 A254 $6 multi   4.50 4.50

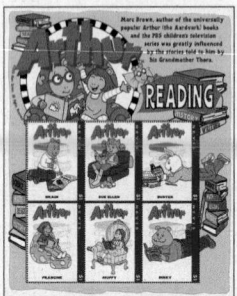

Arthur and Friends A255

No. 1403 — Characters reading: a, Brain. b, Sue Ellen. c, Buster. d, Francine. e, Muffy. f, Binky.
No. 1404, $2 — Characters, with purple background: a, Arthur. b, D. W. c, Francine, looking right. d, Buster, diff.
No. 1405, $2 — Characters, with lilac background: a, Binky, diff. b, Sue Ellen, diff. c, Brain, diff. d, Francine, looking left.

2004, June 17   **Litho.**   **Perf. 14¼**
1403 A255 $1 Sheet of 6, #a-f   4.50 4.50

Sheets of 4, #a-d
1404-1405 A255   Set of 2   12.00 12.00

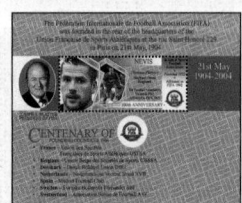

FIFA (Fédération Internationale de Football Association), Cent. — A256

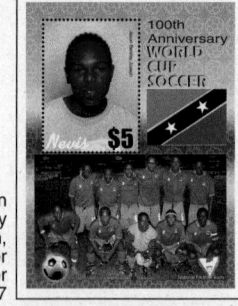

Jason Berkley Joseph, Soccer Player A257

No. 1406: a, Nery Pumpido. b, Gary Lineker. c, Thomas Hassler. d, Sol Campbell. No. 1407, Michael Owen.

2004, Nov. 29   **Perf. 12¾x12½**
1406 A256 $2 Sheet of 4, #a-d   6.00 6.00

Souvenir Sheets
1407 A256 $5 multi   4.00 4.00
1408 A257 $5 multi   4.00 4.00

Marginal inscription on No. 1408, "100th Anniversary World Cup Soccer" is incorrect as the first World Cup was held in 1930.

Elvis Presley (1935-77) — A258

No. 1409 — Wearing checked shirt: a, Blue background. b, Bright red violet background.
No. 1410 — Color of sweater: a, Red. b, Orange yellow. c, Blue. d, Blue green. e, Red violet. f, Bright green.

2004, Nov. 29   **Perf. 13½x13¼**
1409 A258 $1.20 Pair, #a-b   3.50 3.50
1410 A258 $1.20 Sheet of 6, #a-f 5.50 5.50

No. 1409 printed in sheets of 3 pairs.

Christmas — A259

Paintings by Norman Rockwell: 25c, Santa's Good Boys. 30c, Ride 'em Cowboy. 90c, Christmas Sing Merrilie. No. 1414, $5, The Christmas Newsstand.
No. 1415, $5, Is He Coming.

2004, Dec. 1   **Perf. 12**
1411-1414 A259   Set of 4   5.00 5.00

Imperf
Size: 63x73mm
1415 A259 $5 multi   3.75 3.75

Locomotives, 200th Anniv. — A260

No. 1416: a, Steam Idyll, Indonesia. b, 2-8-2, Syria. c, Narrow gauge Mallet 0-4-4-0T, Portugal. d, Western Pacific Bo-Bo Road Switcher, US.
$5, LMS 5305, Great Britain.

2004, Dec. 13   **Perf. 13¼x13½**
1416 A260 $3 Sheet of 4, #a-d   9.00 9.00

Souvenir Sheet
1417 A260 $5 multi   4.50 4.50

Reptiles and Amphibians — A261

No. 1418: a, Gekko gecko. b, Eyelash viper. c, Green iguana. d, Whistling frog.
$5, Hawksbill turtle.

2005, Jan. 10   **Perf. 14**
1418 A261 $1.20 Sheet of 4, #a-d   4.50 4.50

Souvenir Sheet
1419 A261 $5 multi   4.50 4.50

Mushrooms — A262

No. 1420: a, Xeromphalina campanella. b, Calvatia sculpta. c, Mitrula elegans. d, Aleuria aurantia.
$5, Scarlet cup.

2005, Jan. 10
1420 A262 $2 Sheet of 4, #a-d   7.00 7.00

Souvenir Sheet
1421 A262 $5 multi   4.50 4.50

Hummingbirds — A263

No. 1422: a, Rufous hummingbird. b, Green-crowned brilliant. c, Ruby-throated hummingbird. d, Purple-throated Carib.
$5, Magnificent hummingbird.

2005, Jan. 10   **Litho.**   **Perf. 14**
1422 A263 $2 Sheet of 4, #a-d   7.00 7.00

Souvenir Sheet
1423 A263 $5 multi   4.50 4.50

Sharks A264

No. 1424: a, Zebra shark. b, Caribbean reef shark. c, Blue shark. d, Bronze whaler.
$5, Blacktip reef shark.

2005, Jan. 10
1424 A264 $2 Sheet of 4, #a-d   7.00 7.00

Souvenir Sheet
1425 A264 $5 multi   4.50 4.50

Artist's Depictions of Hawksbill Turtles — A265

Artist: 30c, Leon Silcott. 90c, Kris Liburd. $1.20, Alice Webber. $5, Jeuaunito Huggins.

2005, Jan. 10
1426-1429 A265   Set of 4   6.00 6.00

Souvenir Sheet

New Year 2005 (Year of the Rooster) A266

No. 1430: a, Rooster, blue green background. b, Rooster silhouette, light green background. c, Rooster silhouette, blue background. d, Rooster, red violet background.

2005, Jan. 17   *Perf. 12*
1430 A266 75c Sheet of 4, #a-d   2.50 2.50

Friedrich von Schiller (1759-1805), Writer — A267

No. 1431: a, Schiller, country name in pink. b, Schiller, country name in blue. c, Schiller's birthplace, Marbach, Germany. $5, Statue of Schiller, Chicago.

2005, May 16   *Perf. 12¾*
1431 A267 $3 Sheet of 3, #a-c   6.00 6.00
        Souvenir Sheet
1432 A267 $5 multi   3.50 3.50

Rotary International, Cent. — A268

No. 1433, vert.: a, Barefoot child. b, Vaccination of child. c, Child with crutches and braces. $5, Woman and children.

2005, May 16
1433 A268 $3 Sheet of 3, #a-c   6.00 6.00
        Souvenir Sheet
1434 A268 $5 multi   3.50 3.50

Hans Christian Andersen (1805-75), Author — A269

No. 1435: a, The Little Mermaid. b, Thumbelina. c, The Snow Queen. d, The Emperor's New Clothes. $6, Andersen.

2005, May 16
1435 A269 $2 Sheet of 4, #a-d   6.00 6.00
        Souvenir Sheet
1436 A269 $6 multi   4.50 4.50

World Cup Soccer Championships, 75th Anniv. — A270

No. 1437: a, Brazil, 1958 champions. b, Scene from 1958 Brazil-Sweden final. c, Rasunda Stadium, Stockholm. d, Pele. $5, 1958 Brazil team celebrating victory.

2005, May 16   *Litho.*
1437 A270 $2 Sheet of 4, #a-d   6.00 6.00
        Souvenir Sheet
1438 A270 $5 multi   3.75 3.75

End of World War II, 60th Anniv. A271

No. 1439, $2: a, Gen. Charles de Gaulle. b, Gen. George S. Patton. c, Field Marshal Bernard Montgomery. d, Liberation of concentration camps. e, Political cartoon about end of war.
No. 1440, $2, horiz. — VJ Day: a, Flight crew of the Enola Gay. b, Atomic bomb mushroom cloud. c, Souvenir of Japanese surrender ceremony. d, Japanese delegation on USS Missouri. e, Gen. Douglas MacArthur speaking at surrender ceremony.

2005, May 16   *Perf. 12¾*
        Sheets of 5, #a-e
1439-1440 A271   Set of 2   16.50 16.50

Battle of Trafalgar, Bicent. — A272

Various ships and: 30c, Admiral William Cornwallis. 90c, Capt. Maurice Suckling. $1.20, Fleet Admiral Earl Howe. $3, Sir John Jervis.
$5, Earl Howe on the quarterdeck of the Queen Charlotte.

2005, May 16   *Perf. 12¾*
1441-1444 A272   Set of 4   5.00 5.00
        Souvenir Sheet
        Perf. 12
1445 A272 $5 multi   4.25 4.25

A273

Prehistoric Animals — A274

Designs: 30c, Tyrannosaurus rex. No. 1447, $5, Hadrosaur.
No. 1448, $1.20: a, Apatosaurus. b, Camarasaurus. c, Iguanodon. d, Edmontosaurus. e, Centrosaurus. f, Euoplocephalus.
No. 1449, $1.20: a, Ouranosaurus. b, Parasaurolophus. c, Psittacosaurus. d, Stegosaurus. e, Scelidosaurus. f, Hypsilophodon.
No. 1450, $1.20, vert.: a, Deinotherium. b, Platybelodon. c, Palaeoloxodon. d, Arsinotherium. e, Procoptodon. f, Macrauchenia.
No. 1451, $5, Brontotherium. No. 1452, $5, Daspletosaurus. No. 1453, $5, Pliosaur.

2005, June 7   *Perf. 12¾*
1446-1447 A273   Set of 2   4.25 4.25
        Sheets of 6, #a-f
1448-1450 A274   Set of 3   16.50 16.50
        Souvenir Sheets
1451-1453 A274   Set of 3   11.50 11.50

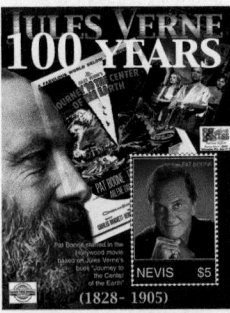

Jules Verne (1828-1905), Writer — A275

No. 1454 — Story characters: a, Captain Nemo, *20,000 Leagues Under the Sea.* b, Michael Strogoff, *Michael Strogoff.* c, Phileas Fogg, *Around the World in 80 Days.* d, Captain Cyrus Smith, *Mysterious Island.*
$5, Pat Boone, actor in movie, *Journey to the Center of the Earth.*

2005, June 17
1454 A275 $2 Sheet of 4, #a-d   6.50 6.50
        Souvenir Sheet
1455 A275 $5 multi   4.25 4.25
        2005 National Topical Stamp Show, Milwaukee (#1455).

Vatican City No. 66   Pope John
A276   Paul II (1920-
                       2005)
                       A277

2005, July 12   *Perf. 13x13¼*
1456 A276 90c multi   1.00 1.00
        Perf. 13½x13¼
1457 A277 $4 multi   4.50 4.50

National Basketball Association Players — A278

Designs: No. 1458, $1, Shareef-Abdur Rahim (shown), Portland Trail Blazers. No. 1459, $1, Shaun Livingston, Los Angeles Clippers. No. 1460, $1, Vince Carter, New Jersey Nets. No. 1461, $1, Rasheed Wallace, Detroit Pistons.
No. 1462: a, Theo Ratliff, Portland Trail Blazers. b, Portland Trail Blazers emblem.

2005, July 26   *Perf. 14*
1458-1461 A278   Set of 4   3.00 3.00
1462 A278 $1 Sheet, 10 #1462a, 9.00 9.00
        2 #1462b

Sun Yat-sen (1866-1925), Chinese Leader — A279

No. 1463: a, Wearing blue suit, harbor in background. b, Wearing suit and tie. c, Wearing blue suit, statue in background. d, Wearing brown red suit.

2005, Aug. 19   *Litho.*   *Perf. 14*
1463 A279 $2 Sheet of 4, #a-d   5.00 5.00
        Taipei 2005 Intl. Stamp Exhibition.

Christmas — A280

Designs: 25c, Madonna and the Angels, by Fra Angelico. 30c, Madonna and the Child, by Fra Filippo Lippi. 90c, Madonna and Child, by Giotto. $4, Madonna of the Chair, by Raphael. $5, Adoration of the Magi, by Giovanni Batista Tiepolo, horiz.

2005, Dec. 1   *Perf. 13½*
1464-1467 A280   Set of 4   4.75 4.75
        Souvenir Sheet
1468 A280 $5 multi   4.25 4.25

U.S. Forest Service, Cent. (in 2005) — A281

No. 1469, vert.: a, Eldorado National Forest, California. b, Pisgah National Forest, North Carolina. c, Chattahoochee-Oconee National Forests, Georgia. d, Nantahala National Forest, North Carolina. e, Bridger-Teton National Forest, Wyoming. f, Mount Hood National Forest, Oregon.
No. 1470, $6, Klamath National Forest, California. No. 1471, $6, The Source Rain Forest Walk, Nevis, vert.

2006, Jan. 3
1469 A281 $1.60 Sheet of 6, #a-f 7.25 7.25
        Souvenir Sheets
1470-1471 A281   Set of 2   9.00 9.00

A Dog, by Ren Xun — A282

2006, Jan. 3
1472 A282 75c multi   .80 .80
        New Year 2006 (Year of the Dog). Printed in sheets of 4.

Queen Elizabeth II, 80th Anniv. A283

No. 1473 — Queen wearing: a, Black hat with feather. b, No hat. c, Tiara. d, White hat. $5, As young woman.

2006, Mar. 20   Litho.   Perf. 13¼
1473 A283 $2 Sheet of 4, #a-d   6.50 6.50
Souvenir Sheet
1474 A283 $5 multi   4.00 4.00

2006 Winter Olympics, Turin A284

Designs: 25c, U.S. #1796. 30c, Italy #705. 90c, Italy #707. $1.20, Emblem of 1980 Lake Placid Winter Olympics, vert. $4, Italy #708. $5, Emblem of 1956 Cortina d'Ampezzo Winter Olympics.

Perf. 14¼ (25c, $1.20), 13¼
2006, Apr. 24
1475-1480 A284   Set of 6   8.75 8.75

Mohandas K. Gandhi (1869-1948), Humanitarian A285

2006, May 27   Perf. 12x11½
1481 A285 $3 multi   3.00 3.00

Rembrandt (1606-69), Painter — A286

No. 1482 — Various men from The Anatomy Lesson of Dr. Tulp. $6, Bald-headed Old Man.

2006, June 23   Perf. 13¼
1482 A286 $2 Sheet of 4, a-d   6.00 6.00
Imperf
Size: 70x100mm
1483 A286 $6 multi   4.50 4.50

Miniature Sheets

Space Achievements — A287

No. 1484 — Apollo-Soyuz: a, Liftoff of Saturn IB rocket . b, Astronaut Donald K. Slayton, Cosmonaut Aleksei A. Leonov. c, Liftoff of Soyuz 19. d, Soyuz in space. e, American and Soviet crews, model of docked spacecraft. f, Apollo in space.
No. 1485 — Viking I: a, Liftoff of Titan Centaur rocket. b, Viking I in flight. c, Model of Viking I on Mars. d, Mars.

2006, Sept. 11   Perf. 13¼
1484 A287 $2 Sheet of 6, #a-f   9.50 9.50
1485 A287 $3 Sheet of 6, #a-f   9.50 9.50

Christmas A288

Designs: 25c, Charlestown Christmas tree. 30c, Snowman decoration. 90c, Reindeer decorations. $4, Christmas tree and gifts, vert. $6, Santa Claus and children.

2006, Dec. 8
1486-1489 A288   Set of 4   4.25 4.25
Souvenir Sheet
1490 A288 $6 multi   4.50 4.50

Scouting, Cent. — A289

Designs: $3, Flags, Map of Great Britain and Ireland. $5, Flags, bird, map, horiz.

2007, Jan. 29   Litho.   Perf. 13¼
1491 A289 $3 multi   2.25 2.25
Souvenir Sheet
1492 A289 $5 multi   3.75 3.75
No. 1491 printed in sheets of 4.

Miniature Sheet

Marilyn Monroe (1926-62), Actress — A290

No. 1493 — Monroe: a, With head tilted. b, Wearing necklace. c, With lips closed. d, Wearing sash.

2007, Jan. 29
1493 A290 $2 Sheet of 4, #a-d   6.50 6.50

Cricket World Cup — A291

Designs: 90c, Cricket World Cup emblem, flag of St. Kitts and Nevis, map of Nevis. $2, Emblem and Runako Morton. $6, Emblem.

2007, May 1   Perf. 14
1494-1495 A291   Set of 2   2.25 2.25
Souvenir Sheet
1496 A291 $6 multi   4.50 4.50

Shells — A292

Designs: 10c, Flame helmet. 25c, Rooster tail conch. 30c, Beaded periwinkle. 60c, Emperor helmet. 80c, Scotch bonnet. 90c Milk conch. $1, Beaded periwinkle, diff. $1.20, Alphabet cone. $1.80, Measled cowrie. $3, King helmet. $5, Atlantic hairy triton. $10, White-lined mitre. $20, Reticulated cowrie.

2007, July 5   Perf. 12½x13¼
1497 A292 10c multi   .25 .25
1498 A292 25c multi   .25 .25
1499 A292 30c multi   .30 .30
1500 A292 60c multi   .50 .50
1501 A292 80c multi   .65 .65
1502 A292 90c multi   .75 .75
1503 A292 $1 multi   .80 .80
1504 A292 $1.20 multi   1.00 1.00
1505 A292 $1.80 multi   1.50 1.50

1506 A292 $3 multi   2.40 2.40
1507 A292 $5 multi   4.00 4.00
1508 A292 $10 multi   7.25 7.25
1509 A292 $20 multi   14.50 14.50
   Nos. 1497-1509 (13)   34.15 34.15

Worldwide Fund for Nature (WWF) — A293

No. 1510 — Rainbow parrotfish: a, Facing left, white coral above fish. b, Two parrotfish. c, Facing left, ocean floor below fish. d, Facing right.

2007, July 23   Perf. 13½
1510   Strip of 4   4.00 4.00
a.-d.   A293 $1.20 Any single   .95 .95
e.   Miniature sheet, 2 each #1510a-1510d   7.75 7.75

Flowers A294

No. 1511: a, Wild cilliment. b, Jumbie beads. c, Wild sage. d, Blood flower. $6, Pink trumpet.

2007, July 23   Perf. 13¼
1511 A294 $2 Sheet of 4, #a-d   6.00 6.00
Souvenir Sheet
1512 A294 $6 multi   4.25 4.25

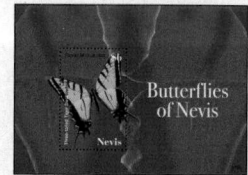

Butterflies — A295

No. 1513: a, Zetides swallowtail. b, Hahnel's Amazon swallowtail. c, Haitian mimic. d, Marbled white. $6, Three-tailed tiger swallowtail.

2007, July 23
1513 A295 $2 Sheet of 4, #a-d   6.25 6.25
Souvenir Sheet
1514 A295 $6 multi   4.75 4.75

Miniature Sheet

Elvis Presley (1935-77) — A296

No. 1515 — Various photographs of Presley with: a, Denomination in white, country name in violet, laces showing on shirt. b, Denomination in blue. c, Denomination in bister. d, Denomination and country name in pink. e, Denomination in white, country name in pink.

f, Denomination in white, country name in violet, laces not showing on shirt.

2007, Aug. 13
1515 A296 $1.20 Sheet of 6, #a-f 5.00 5.00

Princess Diana (1961-97) — A297

No. 1516: a, With head on hands. b, Wearing black dress. c, Wearing pink jacket. d, Wearing white dress. $6, Wearing hat.

2007, Aug. 13
1516 A297 $2 Sheet of 4, #a-d   5.50 5.50
Souvenir Sheet
1517 A297 $6 multi   4.25 4.25

Miniature Sheets

Concorde — A298

No. 1518, $1.20 — Concorde with portions of globe in background: a, Western United States. b, Central United States. c, Atlantic Ocean and Eastern Canada. d, Central Pacific Ocean. e, Central America. f, Northeastern South America.
No. 1519, $1.20 — Concorde with: a, Green frame, white denomination. b, Red frame, blue denomination. c, Green frame, yellow denomination. d, Red frame, yellow denomination. e, Green frame, blue denomination. f, Red frame, white denomination.

2007, Aug. 13   Litho.   Perf. 13¼
Sheets of 6, #a-f
1518-1519 A298   Set of 2   11.00 11.00

Pope Benedict XVI — A299

2007, Oct. 24
1520 A299 $1 multi   .90 .90
Printed in sheets of 8.

Miniature Sheet

Wedding of Queen Elizabeth II and Prince Philip, 60th Anniv. A300

No. 1521 — Couple: a, Queen wearing tiara. b, Waving. c, Wearing feathered hats. d, In gilded coach, Queen in blue, waving. e, In coach, Queen with red hat, waving. f, On balcony, Queen waving.

2007, Oct. 24
1521 A300 $1.20 Sheet of 6, #a-f 6.00 6.00

Miniature Sheet

Inauguration of Pres. John F. Kennedy, 46th Anniv. — A301

No. 1522: a, Jacqueline Kennedy. b, John F. Kennedy, hands at side. c, John F. Kennedy, clapping. d, Vice president Lyndon B. Johnson.

2007, Nov. 28
1522 A301 $3 Sheet of 4, #a-d   8.00 8.00

First Helicopter Flight, Cent. — A302

No. 1523, horiz.: a, Westland Sea King. b, Schweizer N330TT. c, Sikorsky R-4/R-5. d, PZL Swidnik.
$6, MIL V-12.

2007, Nov. 28
1523 A302 $3 Sheet of 4, #a-d   9.00 9.00
Souvenir Sheet
1524 A302 $6 multi   4.50 4.50

Paintings by Qi Baishi (1864-1957) — A303

No. 1525: a, Begonias and Rock. b, Mother and Child. c, Fish and Bait. d, Solitary Hero.
$6, Chrysanthemums and Insects.

2007, Nov. 28   **Perf. 12½**
1525 A303 $3 Sheet of 4, #a-d   8.00 8.00
Souvenir Sheet
Perf. 13¼
1526 A303 $6 multi   4.00 4.00
No. 1525 contains four 32x80mm stamps.

Christmas — A304

Paintings: 25c, The Rest on the Flight Into Egypt, by Federico Barocci. 30c, The Annunciation, by Barocci. 90c, The Annunciation, by Cavalier d'Arpino. $4, The Rest on the Flight Into Egypt, by Francesco Mancini.
$5, The Virgin and Child Between Saints Peter and Paul and the Twelve Magistrates of the Rota, by Antoniazzo Romano.

2007, Dec. 3   Perf. 11¼x11½
1527-1530 A304   Set of 4   4.25 4.25
Souvenir Sheet
Perf. 13½
1531 A304 $5 multi   3.75 3.75

Miniature Sheet

Ferrari Automobiles, 60th Anniv. — A305

No. 1532: a, 1997 F 355 F1 GTS. b, 1985 412. c, 1964 158 F1. d, 1953 375 MM. e, 1967 330 P4. f, 1978 512 BB LM. g, 1974 312 B3-74. h, 1982 308 GTB Quattrovalvole.

2007, Dec. 10   Perf. 13¼
1532 A305 $1 Sheet of 8, #a-h   6.00 6.00

Miniature Sheet

2008 Summer Olympics, Beijing — A306

No. 1533: a, Cycling. b, Kayaking. c, Sailing. d, Equestrian.

2008, Mar. 8   Litho.   Perf. 12¾
1533 A306 $2 Sheet of 4, #a-d   6.00 6.00

Israel 2008 Intl. Philatelic Exhibition — A307

No. 1534 — Sites in Israel: a, Mt. Masada. b, Red Sea and mountains. c, Dead Sea. d, Sea of Galilee.
$5, Mt. Hermon.

2008, May 21   Litho.   Perf. 11½x11¼
1534 A307 $1.50 Sheet of 4, #a-d   4.50 4.50
Souvenir Sheet
1535 A307 $5 multi   3.75 3.75

32nd America's Cup Yacht Races A308

No. 1536 — Various yachts: a, $1.20. b, $1.80. c, $3. d, $5.

2007, Dec. 31   Litho.   Perf. 13½
1536 A308   Block of 4, #a-d   8.25 8.25
No. 1536 was not made available until late 2008.

Miniature Sheets

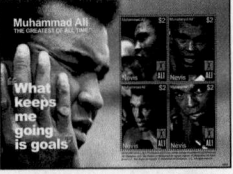

Muhammad Ali, Boxer — A310

No. 1537 — Ali: a, In ring with fists at side. b, In ring, opponent at right. c, In ring, opponent punching. d, With arm on ropes. e, With arms raised. f, Receiving trophy.
No. 1538 — Ali: a, Facing left, face in background. b, With microphones, at bottom. c, Facing left, with microphone at left. d, With large microphone at LL.

2008, Sept. 3   Litho.   Perf. 11½x12
1537 A309 $1.80 Sheet of 6, #a-f 7.75 7.75
Perf. 13¼
1538 A310 $2 Sheet of 4, #a-d   6.00 6.00

Miniature Sheet

Elvis Presley (1935-77) — A311

No. 1539 — Presley with guitar: a, Microphone at right, both hands on guitar. b, Microphone at left, hand on neck of guitar. c, With audience at LL. d, Microphone at left, no hands shown. e, Wearing blue shirt. f, Microphone at right, with hands off guitar.

2008, Sept. 3   Perf. 13¼
1539 A311 $1.80 Sheet of 6, #a-f 8.00 8.00

Miniature Sheet

Visit to New York of Pope Benedict XVI A312

No. 1540 — Pope Benedict XVI and background with: a, Gray spot to left of "N" in "Nevis." b, Left half of United Nations emblem. c, Right half of United Nations Emblem. d, Gray spot between "E" and "V" in "Nevis."

2008, Sept. 17
1540 A312 $2 Sheet of 4, #a-d   6.25 6.25

Geothermal Well — A313

2008, Sept. 19   Perf. 11½
1541 A313 $5 multi   4.50 4.50
Independence, 25th anniv.

A314

Space Exploration, 50th Anniv. — A315

No. 1542: a, Galileo spacecraft with arms extended, stars in background. b, Galileo on booster rocket. c, Galileo probe. d, Technical drawing of Galileo probe. e, Galileo, planet and moon. f, Technical drawing of Galileo.
No. 1543: a, Voyager 1 and ring diagram. b, Io, Ganymede, Voyager 1 and Callisto. c, Ganymede, Europa, Callisto and Voyager 1. d, Voyager 1 and radiating line diagram. e, Voyager 1, Titan and Dione. f, Titan, Voyager 1 and Enceladus.
No. 1544: a, Technical drawing of Apollo 11 command module. b, Saturn V rocket on launch pad. c, Edwin E. Aldrin on Moon. d, Technical drawing of Apollo 11 lunar module.
No. 1545: a, Van Allen radiation belt. b, Technical drawing of Explorer 1. c, James Van Allen. d, Explorer 1 above Earth.

2008, Dec. 3   Perf. 13¼
1542 A314 $1.50 Sheet of 6, #a-f 7.00 7.00
1543 A315 $1.50 Sheet of 6, #a-f 7.00 7.00
1544 A314 $2 Sheet of 4, #a-d   6.25 6.25
1545 A315 $2 Sheet of 4, #a-d   6.25 6.25

Christmas A316

Traditional holiday foods: 25c, Roast pig. 30c, Fruit cake. 80c, Pumpkin pie. 90c, Sorrel drink. $2, Fruit cake, diff.
$6, Baked ham and turkey, vert.

2008, Dec. 5   Perf. 11½
1546-1550 A316   Set of 5   3.25 3.25
Souvenir Sheet
1551 A316 $6 multi   4.75 4.75

Miniature Sheet

Inauguration of U.S. President Barack Obama — A317

No. 1552 — Pres. Obama and, in background: a, Window. b, Flag and chair. c, White House and flowers. d, Chair.

2009, Jan. 20   Litho.   Perf. 11½x12
1552 A317 $3 Sheet of 4, #a-d   8.25 8.25

Agricultural Open Day, 15th Anniv. — A318

Designs: 25c, Fruits and packaged foods. 30c, Fruits. 90c, Goats. $5, Workers propagating plants.
$6, Entertainment at fair.

2009, Mar. 26   Perf. 11½
1553-1556 A318   Set of 4   5.00 5.00
Souvenir Sheet
Perf. 13½
1557 A318 $6 multi   4.75 4.75
No. 1557 contains one 51x37mm stamp.

Miniature Sheets

A319

China 2009 World Stamp Exhibition, Luoyang — A320

No. 1558 — Olympic Sports: a, Shooting. b, Field hockey. c, Taekwondo. d, Softball.
No. 1559 — Emperor Hsuan-yeh (Kangxi) (1654-1722): a, Wearing blue robe. b, Wearing Robe with blue sleeves. c, Wearing robe with yellow sleeves. d, At desk.

2009, Apr. 10   **Perf. 14x14¾**
1558 A319 $1.40 Sheet of 4, #a-d   4.25 4.25
         Perf. 12¾x12½
1559 A320 $1.40 Sheet of 4, #a-d   4.25 4.25

Charles Darwin (1809-82), Naturalist — A321

No. 1560, horiz.: a, Marine iguana. b, Statue of Darwin, Shrewsbury, England. c, Platypus. d, Vampire bat. e, Painting of Darwin by George Richmond. f, Large ground finch.
$6, 1881 colorized photograph of Darwin

2009, June 15   **Perf. 11½**
1560 A321 $2 Sheet of 6, #a-f   9.00 9.00
     Souvenir Sheet
        Perf. 13¼
1561 A321 $6 multi   4.50 4.50
No. 1560 contains six 40x30mm stamps.

Dolphins and Whales A322

No. 1562: a, Amazon River dolphin. b, Indus river dolphin. c, Atlantic white-sided dolphin. d, La Plata dolphin. e, Peale's dolphin. f, White-beaked dolphin.
No. 1563: a, Long-finned pilot whale. b, Short-finned pilot whale.
No. 1564: a, Killer whale. b, Pygmy killer whale.

2009, June 15   **Perf. 13¼**
1562 A322 $2 Sheet of 6, #a-f   9.00 9.00
     Souvenir Sheets
1563 A322 $3 Sheet of 2, #a-b   4.75 4.75
1564 A322 $3 Sheet of 2, #a-b   4.75 4.75

Souvenir Sheets

A323

A324

A325

Elvis Presley (1935-77) — A326

2009, June 15   **Perf. 13¼**
1565 A323 $6 multi   4.50   4.50
1566 A324 $6 multi   4.50   4.50
1567 A325 $6 multi   4.50   4.50
1568 A326 $6 multi   4.50   4.50
    Nos. 1565-1568 (4)   18.00 18.00

Miniature Sheet

Pres. Abraham Lincoln (1809-65) — A327

No. 1569: a, Lincoln Memorial and Reflecting Pool. b, Front view of Lincoln sculpture in Lincoln Memorial. c, Head and hand of Lincoln sculpture. d, Aerial view of Lincoln Memorial.

2009, Aug. 20
1569 A327 $2.50 Sheet of 4, #a-d   7.25 7.25

Miniature Sheet

The Three Stooges A328

No. 1570: a, Moe Howard, Curly Howard and Larry Fine. b, Curly Howard. c, Moe Howard. d, Larry Fine.

2009, Aug. 20   **Perf. 11½**
1570 A328 $2.50 Sheet of 4, #a-d   7.25 7.25

Miniature Sheet

Pope Benedict XVI A329

No. 1571 — Pope Benedict XVI: a, Wearing miter, brown frame. b, Wearing miter, bister frame. c, Wearing zucchetto and eyeglasses, brown frame. d, Wearing zucchetto and eyeglasses, bister frame.

2009, Aug. 20
1571 A329 $3 Sheet of 4, #a-d   9.00 9.00

Miniature Sheets

A330

Michael Jackson (1958-2009) — A331

No. 1572 — Jackson with country name in: a, Blue. b, Yellow. c, Lilac. d, Red.
No. 1573 — Jackson: a, With microphone near mouth, hands raised. b, With arms extended to side. c, Holding microphone. d, With people in background.

     Perf. 11¼x11½
2009, Sept. 25   **Litho.**
1572 A330 $2 Sheet of 4, #a-d   6.00 6.00
     Perf. 11½x12
1573 A331 $3 Sheet of 4, #a-d   8.50 8.50

Worldwide Fund for Nature (WWF) — A332

No. 1574 — Caribbean reef squid with denomination in: a, Pink and blue. b, Pink. c, Orange and red. d, Green and blue.

2009, Dec. 1   **Perf. 13¼**
1574   Strip or block of 4   6.25   6.25
a.-d. A332 $2 Any single   1.50   1.50
e.   Sheet of 8, 2 each #1574a-1574d   12.00 12.00

Flowers — A333

Designs: 25c, Genipa americana. 50c, Clusia rosea. 80c, Browallia americana. 90c, Bidens alba. $1, Begonia odorata. $5, Jatropha gossypiifolia.
No. 1581: a, Crantzia cristata. b, Selaginella flabellata. c, Hibiscus tiliaceus. d, Heliconia psittacorum.

2009, Dec. 1   **Litho.**   **Perf. 13x13¼**
1575-1580 A333   Set of 6   6.75 6.75
1581 A333 $2.50 Sheet of 4, #a-d   8.00 8.00

Christmas A334

Designs: 25c, Magi on camels. 30c, Holy Family. 90c, Magus and camel in stars. $5, Holy Family and angels.

2009, Dec. 7   **Litho.**   **Perf. 14¾x14¼**
1582-1585 A334   Set of 4   5.00 5.00

First Man on the Moon, 40th Anniv. A335

No. 1586: a, Astronaut Neil Armstrong, Saturn V rocket. b, Astronauts Edwin "Buzz" Aldrin and Michael Collins. c, Apollo 11 command module, Moon. d, Apollo 11 lunar module leaving Moon.
$6, Armstrong and lunar module.

2009, Dec. 30   **Litho.**   **Perf. 11½x12**
1586 A335 $2.50 Sheet of 4, #a-d   8.00 8.00
     Souvenir Sheet
      Perf. 11½x11¼
1587 A335 $6 multi   5.00 5.00
    Intl. Year of Astronomy.

Miniature Sheet

Elvis Presley (1935-77) — A336

No. 1588 — Presley wearing: a, Black jacket. b, Brown suit and blue shirt. c, White shirt with red neckerchief. d, Blue shirt.

2010, Mar. 2   **Litho.**   **Perf. 12x11½**
1588 A336 $2.50 Sheet of 4, #a-d   7.25 7.25

Ferrari Race Cars and Parts — A337

No. 1589, $1.25: a, Engine diagram of 1947 125 S. b, 1947 125 S.
No. 1590, $1.25: a, Engine of 1951 500 F2. b, 1951 500 F2.
No. 1591, $1.25: a, Exhaust pipe of 1953 553 F2. b, 1953 553 F2.
No. 1592, $1.25: a, Engine of 1957 Dino 156 F2. b, 1957 Dino 156 F2.

2010, Mar. 2 ***Perf. 12***

Vert. Pairs, #a-b

1589-1592 A337 Set of 4 8.00 8.00

Mushrooms — A338

Designs: 25c, Psilocybe guilartensis. 80c, Alboleptonia flavifolia. $1, Agaricus sp. $5, Psilocybe caerulescens.
No. 1597: a, Psilocybe portoricensis. b, Boletus ruborculus. c, Psilocybe plutonia (one). d, Alboleptonia largentii. e, Psilocybe plutonia (three). f, Collybia aurea.

2010, Mar. 24 Litho. ***Perf. 11½***

1593-1596 A338 Set of 4 5.25 5.25
1597 A338 $1.50 Sheet of 6, #a-f 6.75 6.75

A339

A340

Birds A341

Designs: 30c, Great blue heron. 90c, Magnificent frigatebird. $1, Masked booby. $5, Great egret.
No. 1602: a, White-tailed tropicbird. b, Audubon's shearwater. c, Red-billed tropicbird. d, Leach's storm petrel.
No. 1603: a, Brown pelican. b, Brown booby.

2010, May 21 ***Perf. 11½***

1598-1601 A339 Set of 4 6.00 6.00
1602 A340 $2 Sheet of 4, #a-d 6.50 6.50

Souvenir Sheet

Perf. 11½x12

1603 A341 $3 Sheet of 2, #a-b 5.00 5.00

Miniature Sheets

A342

Election of Pres. John F. Kennedy, 50th Anniv. A343

No. 1604 — Denomination in red: a, Kennedy. b, USSR Premier Nikita Khrushchev. c, Khrushchev on sofa. d, Kennedy on sofa.
No. 1605 — Denomination in white: a, Pres. Richard M. Nixon, color photograph. b, Kennedy, color photograph. c, Kennedy, black-and-white photograph. d, Nixon, black-and-white photograph.

2010, May 21 Litho. ***Perf. 13¼***

1604 A342 $3 Sheet of 4, #a-d 8.50 8.50
1605 A343 $3 Sheet of 4, #a-d 8.50 8.50

Girl Guides, Cent. A344

No. 1606: a, Four Girl Guides and adult leader. b, Four Girl Guides. c, Girl Guide climbing rock. d, Three Girl Guides.
$6, Four Girl Guides, vert.

2010, May 21 ***Perf. 11½x12***

1606 A344 $3 Sheet of 4, #a-d 9.00 9.00

Souvenir Sheet

Perf. 11¼x11½

1607 A344 $6 multi 4.50 4.50

A345

Whales A346

Designs: $1.20, Minke whale. $1.80, Northern right whale. $3, Fin whale. $5, Sei whale.
$6, Blue whale.

2010, July 14 ***Perf. 13x13¼***

1608-1611 A345 Set of 4 9.00 9.00

Souvenir Sheet

1612 A346 $6 multi 5.00 5.00

Souvenir Sheet

Sea Mammals — A347

No. 1613: a, Caribbean monk seal. b, West Indian manatee.

2010, July 14

1613 A347 $3 Sheet of 2, #a-b 5.00 5.00

Miniature Sheet

John F. Kennedy's 1960 US Presidential Campaign Buttons — A348

No. 1614: a, "Vote Kennedy for President." b, "For President John F. Kennedy." c, "Kennedy Johnson." d, "America Needs Kennedy Johnson."

2010, Sept. 8 ***Perf.***

1614 A348 $2 Sheet of 4, #a-d 6.50 6.50

Orchids A349

No. 1615, horiz.: a, Heart-lipped brassavola. b, Waunakee Sunset. c, Moss-loving cranichis. d, Longclaw orchid. e, Golden yellow cattleya. f, Fat Cat.
$6, Von Martin's brassavola.

2010, Sept. 8 ***Perf. 11½x12***

1615 A349 $2 Sheet of 6, #a-f 9.50 9.50

Souvenir Sheet

Perf. 11½

1616 A349 $6 multi 5.00 5.00

Henri Dunant (1828-1910), Founder of Red Cross — A350

No. 1617 — Dunant and: a, Bertha von Suttner. b, Victor Hugo. c, Charles Dickens. d, Harriet Beecher Stowe.
$6, Dunant and scene of abolition of slavery in Washington, DC.

2010, Sept. 8 ***Perf. 13x13¼***

1617 A350 $2.50 Sheet of 4, #a-d 7.50 7.50

Souvenir Sheet

1618 A350 $6 multi 4.50 4.50

A351

Princess Diana (1961-97) — A352

No. 1619 — Princess Diana wearing: a, Black hat, black jacket. b, Black and white hat, white dress. c, Tiara.
$3, White dress, no hat.

2010, Dec. 6 ***Perf. 12***

1619 A351 $2 Vert. strip of 3, #a-c 4.50 4.50
1620 A352 $3 multi 2.25 2.25

No. 1619 was printed in sheets containing 2 of each stamp. No. 1620 was printed in sheets of 4.

Christmas — A353

Paintings: 30c, Annunciation, by Paolo Uccello. 90c, The Altarpiece of the Rose Garlands, by Albrecht Dürer. $1.80, Like 30c. $2, Sistine Madonna, by Raphael. $2.30, Like $2. $3, The Adoration of the Magi, by Giotto di Bondone.

2010, Dec. 6 ***Perf. 12***

1621-1626 A353 Set of 6 8.00 8.00

A354

Pres. Abraham Lincoln (1809-65) — A355

No. 1628 — Lincoln: a, With buff background. b, With gray background. c, Oval photograph. d, With black background.

2010, Dec. 10 ***Perf. 11½***

1627 A354 $2 black 1.50 1.50
1628 A355 $2 Sheet of 4, #a-d 6.00 6.00

Bank of Nevis — A356

Designs: 30c, Old building. $5, New building.

2010, Dec. 9 Litho. ***Perf. 11¼x11½***

1629-1630 A356 Set of 2 4.00 4.00

Pope John Paul II (1920-2005) — A357

Pope John Paul II wearing: $3, Miter. $4, Red hat.

2010, Dec. 10 ***Perf. 14x14¾***

1631-1632 A357 Set of 2 5.00 5.00

No. 1631 was printed in sheets of 4; No. 1632, in sheets of 3.

Elvis Presley (1935-77) — A358

Presley wearing: No. 1633, $3, Black jacket, white shirt. No. 1634, $3, Red shirt.

2010, Dec. 10
1633-1634 A358   Set of 2   4.00 4.00
Nos. 1633-1634 each were printed in sheets of 4.

2010 World Cup Soccer Championships, South Africa — A359

No. 1635, $1.50: a, Marek Hamsik. b, Giovanni Van Bronckhorst. c, Robert Vittek. d, Eljero Elia. e, Miroslav Stoch. f, Dirk Kuyt.
No. 1636, $1.50: a, Lucio. b, Alexis Sanchez. c, Dani Alves. d, Arturo Vidal. e, Gilberto Silva. f, Rodrigo Tello.
No. 1637, $1.50: a, Liedson. b, Xavi Hernandez. c, Simao. d, Jasper Juinen. e, Cristiano Ronaldo. f, David Villa.
No. 1638, $1.50: a, Paulo Da Silva. b, Yoshito Okubo. c, Edgar Barreto. d, Yuichi Komano. e, Cristian Riveros. f, Yasuhito Endo.
No. 1639, $1.50: a, Netherlands coach Bert van Marwijk. b, Joris Mathijsen.
No. 1640, $1.50: a, Brazil coach Dunga. b, Kaka.
No. 1641, $1.50: a, Spain coach Vicente del Bosque. b, Sergio Ramos.
No. 1642, $1.50: a, Paraguay coach Gerardo Martino. b, Roque Santa Cruz.

2010, Dec. 10   *Perf. 12*
Sheets of 6, #a-f
1635-1638 A359   Set of 4   27.00 27.00
Souvenir Sheets of 2, #a-b
1639-1642 A359   Set of 4   10.00 10.00

Trip to India of U.S. President Barack Obama — A360

No. 1643: a, Barack and Michelle Obama leaving Air Force One. b, Pres. Obama addressing Indian students in Mumbai. c, Pres. Obama signing Mumbai terrorist attacks condolence book. d, Pres. Obama and Indian Prime Minister Manmohan Singh. $6, Pres. Obama addressing Indian students in Mumbai, horiz.

2010, Dec. 10   *Perf. 14¼x14¾*
1643 A360 $3 Sheet of 4, #a-d   9.00 9.00
Souvenir Sheet
Perf. 14¾x14¼
1644 A360 $6 multi   4.50 4.50
Indipex 2011, New Delhi.

Engagement of Prince William and Catherine Middleton — A361

No. 1645: a, Arms of Prince William (38mm diameter). b, Buckingham Palace (86x40mm arc-shaped). c, Catherine Middleton, black-and-white photo (86x40mm arc-shaped). d, Prince William, black-and-white photo (86x40mm arc-shaped).
No. 1646: a, Couple (86x40mm arc-shaped). b, Catherine Middleton, color photo (86x40mm arc-shaped). c, Prince William, color photo (86x40mm arc-shaped). $6, Couple, diff.

2010, Dec. 30   *Perf. 13*
1645 A361 $3 Sheet of 4, #a-d   9.00 9.00
1646 A361 $3 Sheet of 4,
    #1645a, 1646a-
    1646c   9.00 9.00
Souvenir Sheet
Perf. 11½x11¼
1647 A361 $6 multi   4.50 4.50
No. 1647 contains one 40x30mm stamp.

Miniature Sheets

A362

Pope Benedict XVI A363

No. 1648 — Pope Benedict XVI with: a, Part of white stole outside frame line at LR. b, Black areas outside of frame line.
No. 1649 — Pope Benedict with: a, Windows under "N," "V" and "S" in country name. b, Protruding corner of ceiling to left of "N" in country name. c, White area under "N" in country name. d, Cross and head of statue under "V" of country name.

2011, Mar. 30   *Perf. 13 Syncopated*
1648 A362 $3 Sheet of 4,
    #1648a, 3
    #1648b   9.00 9.00
1649 A363 $3 Sheet of 4, #a-d   9.00 9.00

Mohandas K. Gandhi (1869-1948), Indian Nationalist — A364

Gandhi and: No. 1650, $3, Orange panel at bottom. No. 1651, $3, Red brown panel at left.

2011, Mar. 30   *Perf. 12*
1650-1651 A364   Set of 2   5.00 5.00
Nos. 1650-1651 each were printed in sheets of 4.

A365

A366

A367

A368

A369

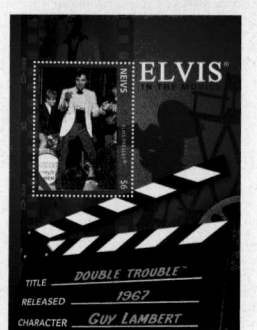

Elvis Presley (1935-77) — A370

No. 1652 — Presley and: a, Country name in white at UL. b, Country name in black at LR, Presley holding microphone. c, No country name. d, Country name in black at LL, no microphone shown.
No. 1653 — Presley: a, Head and neck only. b, Wearing hat. c, Wearing jacket. d, Touching his chin.

2011, Mar. 30   *Perf. 13 Syncopated*
1652 A365 $3 Sheet of 4, #a-d   9.00 9.00
1653 A366 $3 Sheet of 4, #a-d   9.00 9.00
Souvenir Sheets
Perf. 12½
1654 A367 $6 multi   4.50 4.50
1655 A368 $6 multi   4.50 4.50
1656 A369 $6 multi   4.50 4.50
1657 A370 $6 multi   4.50 4.50
    Nos. 1654-1657 (4)   18.00 18.00

Miniature Sheets

Cats of the World *(longhair cats)*   Cats A371

No. 1658, $2.50: a, Maine Coon cat. b, Norwegian Forest cat. c, Ragdoll cat. d, Turkish Angora cat.
No. 1659, $2.50: a, Russian Blue cat. b, Siamese cat. c, Abyssinian cat. d, Bombay cat.

2011, Apr. 4   *Perf. 12*
Sheets of 4, #a-d
1658-1659 A371   Set of 2   15.00 15.00

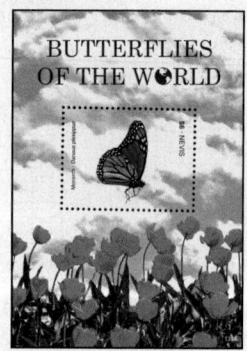

Butterflies — A372

No. 1660: a, Meadow argus. b, Gulf fritillary. c, Eastern tiger swallowtail. d, Gabb's checkerspot. e, Indian leafwing. f, Blue diadem. $6, Monarch butterfly.

2011, Apr. 4   *Perf. 13 Syncopated*
1660 A372 $2 Sheet of 6, #a-f   10.00 10.00
Souvenir Sheet
Perf. 12
1661 A372 $6 multi   5.00 5.00

British Royalty — A373

Designs: No. 1662, Prince Philip.
No. 1663 — Queen Elizabeth II wearing: a, White dress. b, Lilac dress.
No. 1664, King George V. No. 1665, King George VI.

2011, Apr. 4   *Perf. 13 Syncopated*
1662 A373 $2 multi   1.50 1.50
1663 A373 $2 Pair, #a-b   3.00 3.00
1664 A373 $3 multi   2.25 2.25
1665 A373 $3 multi   2.25 2.25
    Nos. 1662-1665 (4)   9.00 9.00

Nos. 1662, 1664-1665 each were printed in sheets of 4. No. 1663 was printed in sheet containing two pairs.

Miniature Sheets

2011 Cricket World Cup, India, Bangladesh and Sri Lanka — A374

No. 1666 — Inscribed "South Africa," with dull orange background: a, A. B. De Villiers batting. b, Close-up of De Villiers. c, Posed photograph of South Africa team. d, Cricket World Cup.

No. 1667 — Inscribed "South Africa," with orange background: a, Like #1666a. b, Like #1666b. c, South Africa team celebrating. d, Like #1666d.

No. 1668 — Inscribed "Pakistan," with olive green background: a, Shoaib Akhtar running. b, Close-up of Akhtar. c, Pakistan team. d Like #1666d.

No. 1669 — Inscribed "Sri Lanka," with red brown background: a, Kumar Sangakkara on cricket pitch. b, Close-up of Sangakkara. c, Sri Lanka team. d, Like #1666d.

No. 1670 — Inscribed "West Indies," with dark red background: a, Chris Gayle holding on cricket bat. b, Close-up of Gayle. c, West Indies team. d, Like #1666d.

2011, Apr. 4   *Perf. 12*
1666 A374 $3 Sheet of 4, #a-d   9.00   9.00
1667 A374 $3 Sheet of 4, #a-d   9.00   9.00
1668 A374 $3 Sheet of 4, #a-d   9.00   9.00
1669 A374 $3 Sheet of 4, #a-d   9.00   9.00
1670 A374 $3 Sheet of 4, #a-d   9.00   9.00
   Nos. 1666-1670 (5)   45.00 45.00

Wedding of Prince William and Catherine Middleton — A375

No. 1671: a, Groom facing right. b, Bride waving.

No. 1672: a, Bride. b, Groom facing forward. c, Couple in coach, facing left, groom waving.

No. 1673: a, Couple standing. b, Couple in coach, facing right, groom waving.

2011, Apr. 29   *Litho.*   *Perf. 12*
1671 A375 $3 Pair, #a-b   4.50 4.50
1672 A375 $3 Sheet of 4,
      #1672a-1672b, 2
      #1672c   9.00 9.00
      Souvenir Sheet
1673 A375 $6 Sheet of 2, #a-b   9.00 9.00

No. 1671 was printed in sheets containing two pairs.

Miniature Sheets

Pres. Abraham Lincoln (1809-65) — A376

No. 1674, $2: a, Union soldier. b, Civil War era illustration with shield, books, wounded snake. c, Union soldiers in trenches. d, Lincoln.

No. 1675, $2 — Lincoln and quotes: a, "Government of the people, by the people, for the people shall not perish from the Earth." b, "The best way to destroy an enemy is to make him a friend." c, "A house divided against itself cannot stand." d, "Avoid popularity if you would have peace."

2011, June 20   *Perf. 13 Syncopated*
      Sheets of 4, #a-d
1674-1675 A376 Set of 2   12.00 12.00
   U.S. Civil War, 150th anniv.

Miniature Sheets

Princess Diana (1961-97) — A377

No. 1676, $2 — Red panel, Princess Diana: a, Facing forward, wearing dress with dark collar. b, Wearing sailor's cap. c, Facing left, wearing striped blouse. d, Wearing maroon hat.

No. 1677, $2 — Yellow panel, Princess Diana wearing: a, Purple jacket. b, Black and white hat. c, Black jacket. d, Red dress.

2011, June 20   *Perf. 12*
      Sheets of 4, #a-d
1676-1677 A377 Set of 2   12.00 12.00

A378

A379

Marine Life A380

Designs: 10c, Blue stripe grunt. 30c, Red hind. 40c, Red snapper. $5, Old wife.

No. 1682: a, Spotfin butterflyfish. b, Caribbean reef squid. c, Chubs. d, Surgeonfish. e, Blue-headed wrasse. f, Long-spine porcupinefish.

$6, Anemonefish.

2011, July 6   *Perf. 12*
1678-1681 A378 Set of 4   4.50 4.50
1682 A379 $2 Sheet of 6, #a-f   9.00 9.00
      Souvenir Sheet
1683 A380 $6 multi   4.50 4.50

Shells — A381

Designs: 20c, Scaphella junonia. 30c, Strombus gigas. $1.80, Busycon contrarium. $5, Arca zebra.

No. 1688: a, Charonia variegata. b, Cypraea aurantium. c, Cyphoma gibbosa. d, Chicoreus articulatus.

No. 1689, $6, Thais deltoidea. No. 1690, $6, Cittarium pica.

2011, July 25   *Perf. 12*
1684-1687 A381 Set of 4   6.00 6.00
      Perf. 13 Syncopated
1688 A381 $2.50 Sheet of 4,
      #a-d   8.00 8.00
      Souvenir Sheets
1689-1690 A381 Set of 2   10.00 10.00

Pres. John F. Kennedy (1917-63) — A382

No. 1691 — Kennedy: a, In front of window next to other man. b, With lectern visible. c, With other man in front of microphones. d, Greeting youths.

$6, Kennedy on path shoveled in snow.

2011, Aug. 29   *Perf. 12*
1691 A382 $3 Sheet of 4, #a-d   9.00 9.00
      Souvenir Sheet
1692 A382 $6 multi   4.75 4.75

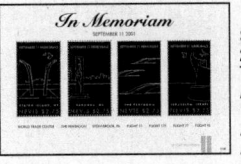
Sept. 11, 2001 Terrorist Attacks, 10th Anniv. A383

No. 1693 — Memorials at: a, Staten Island, New York. b, Bayonne, New Jersey. c, Pentagon. d, Jerusalem, Israel.

$6, Ground Zero Reflecting Pools.

2011, Sept. 9   *Litho.*
1693 A383 $2.75 Sheet of 4,
      #a-d   8.25 8.25
      Souvenir Sheet
1694 A383 $2.75 multi   4.75 4.75

Miniature Sheet

Inter Milan Soccer Team A384

No. 1695: a, Team photo, 1910. b, Giorgio Muggiani, team founder. c, Angelo Moratti, past president of team. d, Heleno Herrera, coach. e, Team celebrating 2011 TIM Cup championship. f, Giacinto Facchetti, player and team president. g, Sandro Mazzola, player. h, Mario Corso, player. i, Luis Suarez, player.

2011, Sept. 13   *Perf. 12¾*
1695 A384 $1.50 Sheet of 9,
      #a-i   10.00 10.00

Dogs of the World A385

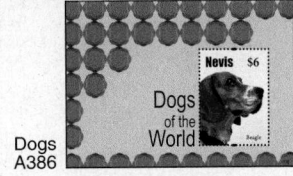
Dogs A386

No. 1696: a, Alaskan malamute. b, Yorkshire terrier. c, Black Labrador retriever. d, Dachshund.

$6, Beagle.

2011, Oct. 14   *Perf. 13 Syncopated*
1696 A385 $2.75 Sheet of 4,
      #a-d   8.50 8.50
      Souvenir Sheet
1697 A386 $6 multi   4.75 4.75

Christmas — A387

Paintings by Melchior Broederlam: 25c, Annunciation. 30c, Visitation. 90c, Presentation in the Temple. $5, Flight into Egypt.

2011, Nov. 7   *Perf. 12*
1698-1701 A387 Set of 4   4.75 4.75

Reptiles A388

No. 1702: a, Anegada ground iguana. b, Antilles racer. c, Brown anole. d, Lesser Antillean iguana.

$6, Anegada ground iguana, horiz.

2011, Nov. 14   *Litho.*   *Perf. 12*
1702 A388 $3 Sheet of 4, #a-d   9.00 9.00
      Souvenir Sheet
      Perf. 12½
1703 A388 $6 multi   4.75 4.75

No. 1703 contains one 51x38mm stamp.

Miniature Sheets

First Man in Space, 50th Anniv. A389

No. 1704 — Planets: a, Neptune. b, Uranus. c, Earth and Mars. d, Venus and Mercury. e, Jupiter. f, Saturn.

No. 1705 — Phases of the Moon: a, Full (country name in black). b, Waxing gibbous ("N" of country name in white). c, First quarter ("NE" and part of "V" of country name in white). d, Waxing crescent (country name in white).

2011, Dec. 16   *Perf. 12½x12*
1704 A389 $2 Sheet of 6, #a-f   9.50 9.50
      Perf. 13
1705 A389 $3 Sheet of 4, #a-d   9.50 9.50

No. 1705 contains four 35mm diameter stamps.

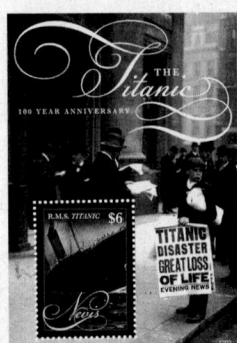
Sinking of the Titanic, Cent. A390

No. 1706: a, Stowaway on rope. b, Grand Staircase of the Olympic. c, Titanic at Southampton dock. d, Reading and writing room.

$6, Titanic sinking.

2012, Feb. 8   *Perf. 13 Syncopated*
1706 A390 $3 Sheet of 4, #a-d   9.00 9.00

Souvenir Sheet
Perf. 12
1707 A390 $6 multi   4.50 4.50

Elvis Presley (1935-77) — A391

No. 1708 — Presley: a, With guitar and gray
suit, no microphone. b, With guitar, gray suit,
microphone on stand. c, With beige suit. d,
With guitar, white suit, holding microphone.
$9, Presley in gray suit playing guitar.

2012, Mar. 26   *Perf. 12*
1708 A391 $2.50 Sheet of 4, #a-
        d   7.50 7.50
Souvenir Sheet
Perf. 13¼
1709 A391 $9 multi   6.75 6.75

Medicinal   Nevis Coat of
Spring   Arms
A392   A393

2012, June 14   *Perf. 11¼*
1710 A392 $100 multi   75.00 75.00
1711 A393 $150 multi   110.00 110.00

Reign of
Queen
Elizabeth
II, 60th
Anniv.
A394

No. 1712 — Various photographs of Queen
Elizabeth II with denomination at: a, LR. b, LL.
c, UR. d, UL.
$10, Queen Elizabeth II wearing tiara.

2012, July 25   *Perf. 13¾*
1712 A394 $3 Sheet of 4, #a-d   9.50 9.50
Souvenir Sheet
1713 A394 $10 multi   8.00 8.00

Charles Dickens
(1812-70),
Writer — A395

Designs: $3.50, Dickens.
No. 1715: a, Books by Dickens. b, Dickens,
diff.

2012, Aug. 7   Litho.
1714 A395 $3.50 multi   2.60 2.60
Souvenir Sheet
1715 A395 $4.50 Sheet of 2, #a-
        b   6.75 6.75
No. 1714 was printed in sheets of 4.

Miniature Sheet

Stingrays
A396

No. 1716: a, Caribbean whiptail. b, Lesser
electric ray. c, Giant manta ray. d, Southern
stingray. e, Spotted eagle ray.

2012, Aug. 7   *Perf. 12*
1716 A396 $3 Sheet of 5, #a-e 12.00 12.00

Illustrations From *Peter Pan*, by James
M. Barrie (1860-1937) — A397

No. 1717 — Various illustrations with upper
panel in: a, Green. b, Yellow green. c, Dull
brown. d, Blue.
$6, Yellow green panel at right.

2012, Aug. 9   *Perf. 13 Syncopated*
1717 A397 $3 Sheet of 4, #a-d   9.00 9.00
Souvenir Sheet
1718 A397 $6 multi   4.50 4.50

Miniature Sheet

Butterflies — A398

No. 1719: a, Hamadryas amphinome. b,
Lycorea halia atergatis. c, Marpesia eleuchea
bahamensis. d, Pyrisitia proterpia, with antennae. e, Pyrisitia proterpia, without antennae. f,
Pyrrhocalles antiqua.

2012, Nov. 28   *Perf. 12*
1719 A398 $2.50 Sheet of 6,
        #a-f   12.00 12.00

Beetles
A399

No. 1720: a, Lema biornata. b, Lema
splendida. c, Lema minuta. d, Lema dorsalis.
No. 1721: a, Stilodes heydeni. b, Stilodes
leoparda.

2012, Nov. 28   *Perf. 13¾*
1720 A399 $2.50 Sheet of 4, #a-
        d   7.50 7.50
Souvenir Sheet
1721 A399 $4 Sheet of 2, #a-
        b   6.00 6.00

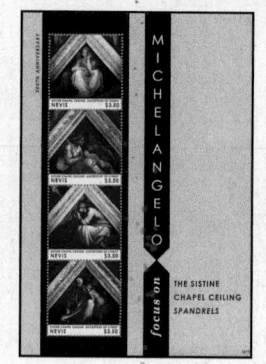

Painting of the Sistine Chapel Ceiling
by Michelangelo, 500th Anniv. — A400

No. 1722 — Details from Ancestors of
Christ: a, Man with hand at face. b, Woman,
man and infant. c, Woman kissing child. d,
Woman and naked child at right.
$9, The Creation of Adam, horiz.

2012, Nov. 28   *Perf. 13¾*
1722 A400 $3.50 Sheet of 4,
        #a-d   10.50 10.50
Souvenir Sheet
Perf. 12
1723 A400 $9 multi   6.75 6.75
No. 1723 contains one 80x30mm stamp.

Souvenir Sheets

Elvis Presley (1935-77) — A401

Presley: No. 1724, $9, Playing guitar, purple
frame, country name in red. No. 1725, $9,
With two women, black frame and country
name. No. 1726, $9, With band, playing guitar,
red frame and country name. No. 1727, $9,
Holding microphone, red frame and country
name. No. 1728, $9, Holding microphone,
gray frame and country name.

2012, Nov. 28   *Perf. 12¾*
1724-1728 A401   Set of 5   34.00 34.00

Christmas — A402

Paintings by Caravaggio: 25c, Adoration of
the Shepherds. 30c, Annunciation. 90c, Holy
Family with St. John the Baptist. $1, Nativity
with St. Francis and St. Lawrence. $3, Rest on
the Flight into Egypt. $5, Madonna of the
Rosary.

2012, Nov. 28   Litho.
1729-1734 A402   Set of 6   7.75 7.75

Coronation of Queen Elizabeth II, 60th
Anniv. — A403

No. 1735 — Queen Elizabeth II: a, Holding
orb. b, Wearing blue hat. c, Wearing pink hat.
d, Wearing sash.
$9, Queen Elizabeth II wearing crown,
waving.

2013, Apr. 13   *Perf. 13 Syncopated*
1735 A403 $3.25 Sheet of 4, #a-
        d   9.75 9.75
Souvenir Sheet
1736 A403 $9 multi   6.75 6,75

Miniature Sheets

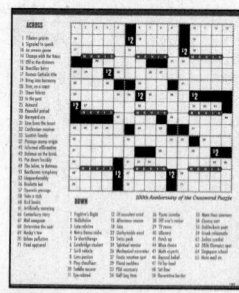

Crossword Puzzles, Cent. — A404

No. 1737, $2 — Stamps with green panels
and numbered squares: a, 1-5, 14, 17, 20, 23-
25. b, 6-9, 15, 18, 21, 26-27. c, 10-13, 16, 19,
22. d, 28-29, 32-33, 37, 42, 45-48. e, 30, 34-
36, 38, 43, 49-50. f, 31, 39-41, 44, 51. g, 52,
57, 60, 66, 69. h, 53-54, 58, 61-63, 67, 70. i,
55-56, 59, 64-65, 68, 71.
No. 1738, $2 — Stamps with red panels and
numbered squares: a, 1-5, 14, 17, 20, 22, 23.
b, 6-9, 15, 18, 21, 24. c, 10-13, 16, 19, d, 25,
29, 32-33, 37, 40-43. e, 26-27, 30, 34, 44. f,
28, 31, 35-36, 38-39, 45. g, 46-47, 49, 52, 56,
59. h, 48, 50-51, 53, 57, 60. i, 54-55, 58, 61.

2013, Apr. 3   *Perf. 13¾*
Sheets of 9, #a-i
1737-1738 A404   Set of 2   25.00 25.00

On Nos. 1737-1738, crossword puzzle clues
are in sheet margins and puzzle answers are
printed on the backs of the stamps.

Personalizable Stamp — A405

2013, Apr. 22   *Perf. 14x14¾*
1739 A405 $3 multi   2.25 2.25

No. 1739 was printed in sheets of 9 and presumably could be personalized for an extra fee.

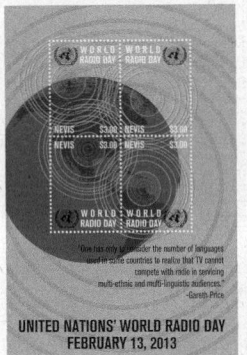

World Radio Day A406

No. 1740 — Radio antennae and concentric circles with United Nations emblem at: a, UL. b, UR. c, LL. d, LR.
$8, Radio antenna, concentric circles, United Nations emblem at LL.

2013, Apr. 25   *Perf. 12*
1740 A406 $3 Sheet of 4, #a-d   9.00 9.00
Souvenir Sheet
1741 A406 $8 multi   6.00 6.00

Hummingbirds — A407

No. 1742: a, Antillean mango. b, Ruby-throated hummingbird. c, Purple-throated carib. d, Long-billed starthroat.
No. 1743: a, Green-throated carib. b, Tufted coquette.

2013, Apr. 25   *Perf. 13¾*
1742 A407 $3.25 Sheet of 4, #a-d   10.50 10.50
Souvenir Sheet
1743 A407 $4.50 Sheet of 2, #a-b   7.50 7.50

Nos. 1742 and 1743 exist imperf. Value, set $25.

Bees A408

No. 1744: a, Bicyrtes quadrifasciatus. b, Bembix americana. c, Ammophila apicalis. d, Ectemnius continuus.
$8, Bicyrtes quadrifasciatus, diff.

2013, Apr. 25   *Perf. 12*
1744 A408 $4 Sheet of 4, #a-d 12.00 12.00
Souvenir Sheet
1745 A408 $8 multi   6.00 6.00

Fruit A409

No. 1746: a, Lemon. b, Persimmons. c, Yellow plum. d, Oranges.
$9, Peach, vert.

2013, June 3   *Perf. 13¾*
1746 A409 $3.25 Sheet of 4, #a-d   9.75 9.75
Souvenir Sheet
Perf. 12½
1747 A409 $9 multi   6.75 6.75

No. 1747 contains one 38x51mm stamp.

Turtles A410

No. 1748: a, Desert tortoise. b, African helmeted turtle. c, Redbelly turtle. d, Red-eared slider.
$9, Gulf Coast box turtle.

2013, June 3   *Perf. 13 Syncopated*
1748 A410 $3.25 Sheet of 4, #a-d   9.75 9.75
Souvenir Sheet
1749 A410 $9 multi   6.75 6.75

Parrots A411

No. 1750: a, Imperial amazon. b, Cuban amazon. c, Hispanolian parrot. d, St. Vincent amazon.
$9, St. Lucia amazon, vert.

2013, June 3   *Perf. 13¾*
1750 A411 $3.25 Sheet of 4, #a-d   9.75 9.75
Souvenir Sheet
Perf. 12½
1751 A411 $9 multi   6.75 6.75

No. 1751 contains one 38x51mm stamp.

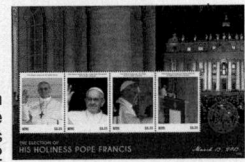

Election of Pope Francis A412

No. 1752 — Pope Francis: a, Waving, orange background. b, Waving, black background. c, Facing right. d, On balcony with assistant.
$9, Pope Francis, assistant with microphone.

2013, June 3   *Perf. 14*
1752 A412 $3.25 Sheet of 4, #a-d   9.75 9.75
Souvenir Sheet
Perf. 12½
1753 A412 $9 multi   6.75 6.75

No. 1753 contains one 38x51mm stamp.

Souvenir Sheet

Elvis Presley (1935-77) — A413

Litho., Margin Embossed
2013, July 8   *Imperf.*
Without Gum
1754 A413 $20 black   16.00 16.00

Birth of Prince George of Cambridge — A414

No. 1755: a, Duke and Duchess of Cambridge, Prince George. b, Prince George. c, Duchess of Cambridge, Prince George. d, Duke of Cambridge, Prince George.
No. 1756: a, Duke and Duchess of Cambridge, Prince George, diff. b, Prince George, diff.

2013, Sept. 10   Litho.   *Perf. 12x12½*
1755 A414 $3.25 Sheet of 4, #a-d   9.75 9.75
Souvenir Sheet
1756 A414 $4.75 Sheet of 2, #a-b   7.00 7.00

Flora of Thailand A415

No. 1757: a, Pineapple. b, Papayas. c, Red pineapple. d, Plumeria. e, Magnolia. f, Camellia.
$9, Bromeliad, vert.

2013, Aug. 26   Litho.   *Perf. 13¾*
1757 A415 $2.50 Sheet of 6, #a-f   10.50 10.50
Souvenir Sheet
Perf. 12½
1758 A415 $9 multi   6.25 6.25

Thailand 2013 World Stamp Exhibition, Bangkok. No. 1758 contains one 38x51mm stamp.

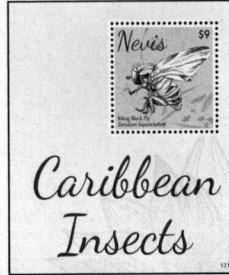

Insects A416

No. 1759: a, Citrus root weevil. b, West Indian firetail. c, Catarina. d, Field cricket.
$9, Biting black fly.

2013, Sept. 17   Litho.   *Perf. 12½*
1759 A416 $3.50 Sheet of 4, #a-d   10.50 10.50
Souvenir Sheet
1760 A416 $9 multi   6.25 6.25

Independence, 30th Anniv. — A417

Designs: 30c, Soldiers handling flag. $5, National anthem, vert. (30x50mm). $10, Soldiers on parade.
$9, Map of St. Kitts and Nevis, vert.

Perf. 12½x13¼, 12 ($5)
2013, Sept. 19   Litho.
1761-1763 A417 Set of 3   10.50 10.50
Souvenir Sheet
Perf. 13¼x12½
1764 A417 $9 multi   6.25 6.25

Christmas — A418

Paintings by Carlo Crivelli: 30c, Adoration of the Shepherds. 90c, Christ Blessing. $2, Immaculate Conception. $5, Madonna d'Ancona.

2013, Dec. 2   Litho.   *Perf. 12½*
1765-1768 A418 Set of 4   6.25 6.25

Fish — A419

Designs: 10c, Barred hogfish. 15c, Bluefaced angelfish (Pomacanthus xanthometopon). 20c, Comb grouper. 30c, Spotfin hogfish. 90c, Yellow jack. $1, Broadbarred firefish. $1.20, Queen angelfish. $2, Stoplight parrotfish. $3, Tiger grouper. $5, Titan triggerfish. $10, Blue-striped grunt. $20, Flameback angelfish.

2013, Dec. 4   Litho.   *Perf. 13¾*
1769	A419	10c multi	.25	.25
1770	A419	15c multi	.25	.25
1771	A419	20c multi	.25	.25
1772	A419	30c multi	.25	.25
1773	A419	90c multi	.65	.65
1774	A419	$1 multi	.75	.75
1775	A419	$1.20 multi	.90	.90
1776	A419	$2 multi	1.50	1.50
1777	A419	$3 multi	2.25	2.25
1778	A419	$5 multi	3.75	3.75
1779	A419	$10 multi	7.50	7.50
1780	A419	$20 multi	15.00	15.00
Nos. 1769-1780 (12)			33.30	33.30

A420

A421

A422

Nelson Mandela (1918-2013),
President of South Africa — A423

No. 1782 — Mandela: a, Wearing blue and white shirt with AIDS ribbon below top button. b, Wearing black and white shirt, person in background. c, Waving. d, Wearing black and white shirt.

2013, Dec. 15   Litho.   Perf. 13¾
1781 A420 $4 multi   3.00   3.00
1782 A421 $4 Sheet of 4, #a-
          d   11.50   11.50
Souvenir Sheets
1783 A422 $14 multi   10.00   10.00
1784 A423 $14 multi   10.00   10.00
No. 1781 was printed in sheets of 4.

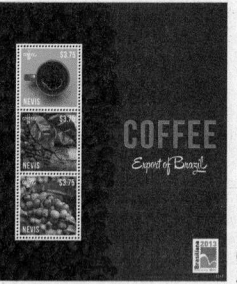

Coffee
A424

No. 1785: a, Cup of coffee. b, Leaves and roasted beans. c, Coffee berries.
$9, Roasted bean.

2013, Nov. 18   Litho.   Perf. 12½
1785 A424 $3.75 Sheet of 3, #a-
          c   8.25   8.25
Souvenir Sheet
1786 A424 $9 multi   6.50   6.50
2013 Brasiliana Intl. Philatelic Exhibition, Rio de Janeiro.

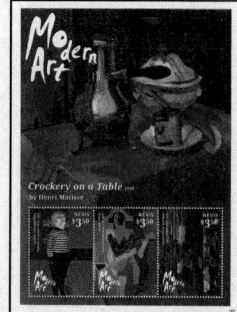

Modern
Art
A425

No. 1787, $3.50: a, Charles au Jersey Rayé, by Henri Evenepoel. b, Harlequin with Guitar, by Juan Gris. c, Katedrala, by Frantisek Kupka.
No. 1788, $3.50: a, Madras Rouge, by Henri Matisse. b, Nude with a Parrot, by George Bellows. c, The Old Guitarist, by Pablo Picasso.
No. 1789, $9, Senecio, by Paul Klee. No. 1790, $9, Udnie, by Francis Picabia.

2014, Jan. 3   Litho.   Perf. 12¾
Sheets of 3, #a-c
1787-1788 A425 Set of 2 15.50   15.50
Souvenir Sheets
1789-1790 A425 Set of 2 13.50   13.50

Alexander Hamilton (1755-1804), First U.S. Treasury Secretary — A426

Designs: 30c, Portrait of Hamilton. 90c, Statue of Hamilton, U.S. Treasury Building. $10, Parchment scrolls.
$9, Nevis Heritage Center, horiz.

2014, Jan. 11   Litho.   Perf. 14
1791-1793 A426 Set of 3   8.25   8.25
Souvenir Sheet
Perf. 12
1794 A426 $9 multi   6.50   6.50
No. 1794 contains one 50x30mm stamp.

Miniature Sheets

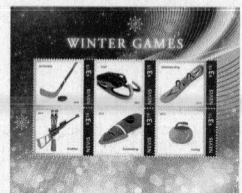

2014 Winter Olympics, Sochi,
Russia — A427

No. 1795: a, Ice hockey stick and puck. b, Luge. c, Snowboard. d, Biathlon skis and rifle. e, Bobsled. f, Curling stone.
No. 1796, vert.: a, Ski jumping. b, Speed skating. c, Alpine skiing. d, Figure skating.

2014, Mar. 5   Litho.   Perf. 12
1795 A427 $3.15 Sheet of 6,
          #a-f   14.00   14.00
1796 A427 $4.75 Sheet of 4,
          #a-d   14.00   14.00
No. 1796 contains four 30x50mm stamps.

World
War I,
Cent.
A428

No. 1797, $3.15: a, Recruitment station, Trafalgar Square, London, 1914. b, Man wearing body armor, 1915. c, French machine gunners take position, 1917. d, Fort Brady, 1915. e, World War I photographer, 1917. f, Medical officer in a gas mask, 1915.
No. 1798, $3.15 — War posters from: a, France, 1915. b, Great Britain, 1914. c, United States, 1914. d, Germany, 1914. e, Australia, 1914. f, Italy, 1914.
No. 1799, $5: a, French soldiers in a trench at Berry-au-Bac, 1914. b, French soldier standing in the entrance to a trench, 1914.
No. 1800, $5 — War recruitment posters from: a, Great Britain, 1914. b, United States, 1917.

2014, Mar. 5   Litho.   Perf. 12¾
Sheets of 6, #a-f
1797-1798 A428 Set of 2 27.00   27.00
Souvenir Sheets of 2, #a-b
1799-1800 A428 Set of 2 14.00   14.00

Characters from *Downton Abbey* Television Series — A429

No. 1801: a, Anna. b, Ivy. c, Daisy. d, Alfred Nugent.
$9, Tom Branson and Lady Sybil Crawley, horiz.

2014, Mar. 5   Litho.   Perf. 14
1801 A429 $3.25 Sheet of 4, #a-
          d   9.75   9.75
Souvenir Sheet
1802 A429 $9 multi   6.75   6.75

Worldwide Fund for Nature
(WWF) — A430

Nos. 1803 and 1804 — Caribbean reef shark: a, One shark, nose pointing to UR. b, Two sharks and fish. c, One shark with nose pointing to UL and fish. d, One shark with nose pointing left and fish.

2014, Apr. 2   Litho.   Perf. 14
1803 A430 $2.50 Block or vert.
          strip of 4, #a-d 7.50   7.50
1804 A430 $2.75 Block or vert.
          strip of 4, #a-d 8.25   8.25

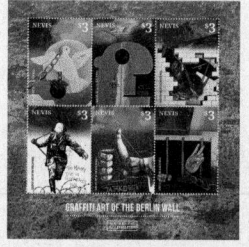

Berlin
Wall
Graffiti
Art
A431

No. 1805: a, Dove, ball and chain. b, Pink stylized face. c, Reproduction of inner left cover of Pink Floyd's *The Wall* album (Marching hammers and broken wall). d, Soldier and barbed wire. e, Hand with upraised, chained thumb. f, Hands at prison window, chain.
No. 1806: a, Two stylized heads. b, Reproduction of inner right cover of Pink Floyd's *The Wall* album (mother, teacher and creature).

2014, June 23   Litho.   Perf. 12¾
1805 A431 $3 Sheet of 6, #a-f 13.50 13.50
Souvenir Sheet
1806 A431 $5 Sheet of 2, #a-b   7.50   7.50
Fall of Berlin Wall, 25th anniv.

Orchids
A432

No. 1807: a, Phalaenopsis. b, Phalaenopsis Sogo Yukidian. c, Aerides houlettiana. d, Zygopetalum crinitum.
No. 1808: a, Laelia gouldiana. b, Miltonia regnellii. c, Epidendrum fulgens. d, Cattleya alaorii.
No. 1809, vert.: a, Pink phalaenopsis, diff. b, Miltonia. No. 1810, vert.: a, Yellow phalaenopsis. b, Miltoniopsis.

2014, July 7   Litho.   Perf. 14
1807 A432 $4 Sheet of 4, #a-d 12.00 12.00
1808 A432 $4 Sheet of 4, #a-d 12.00 12.00
Souvenir Sheet
1809 A432 $9 Sheet of 2, #a-b 13.50 13.50
1810 A432 $9 Sheet of 2, #a-b 13.50 13.50

Nevis Financial Services Department, 30th Anniv. — A433

Background color: 30c, Purple. $2, Greenish blue. $5, Blue.

2014, June 20   Litho.   Perf. 13¼
1811-1813 A433 Set of 3   5.50   5.50

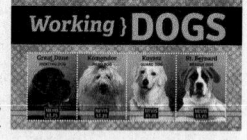

Dogs
A434

No. 1814, $3.25: a, Great Dane. b, Komondor. c, Kuvasz. d, St. Bernard.
No. 1815, $3.25: a, Italian greyhound. b, Pomeranian. c, Chihuahua. d, Japanese chin.
No. 1816, $5: a, Newfoundland. b, Alaskan malamute.
No. 1817, $5: a, Mini pinshcer. b, Chinese crested.

2014, Aug. 14   Litho.   Perf. 14
Sheets of 4, #a-d
1814-1815 A434 Set of 2 19.50   19.50
Souvenir Sheets of 2, #a-b
1816-1817 A434 Set of 2 15.00   15.00

A435

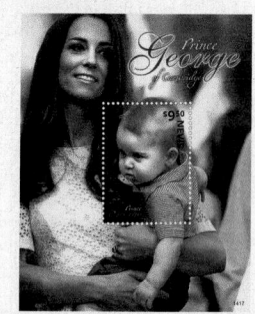

Prince George of Cambridge — A436

No. 1818 — Prince George wearing: a, Blue and white striped shirt. b, White shirt.
No. 1819, $9.50, Prince George (shown). No. 1820, $9.50, Prince George (close-up).

2014, Aug. 14   Litho.   Perf. 14
1818 A435 $3.25 Vert. pair,
          #a-b   5.00   5.00
Souvenir Sheets
Perf. 12
1819-1820 A436 Set of 2 14.00   14.00
No. 1818 was printed in sheets containing three pairs. One example of No. 1818b has a different background, showing the shirt and tie of Prince William.

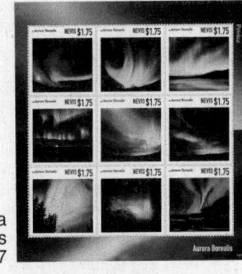

Aurora Borealis
A437

No. 1821, Various depictions of the Aurora Borealis, as shown.
$10, Aurora Borealis, diff.

2014, Sept. 3   Litho.   *Perf. 13¾*
1821 A437 $1.75 Sheet of 9,
          #a-i   12.00 12.00
Souvenir Sheet
1822 A437 $10 multi   7.50 7.50

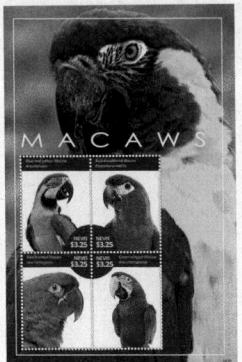

Macaws
A438

No. 1823, $3.25: a, Blue and yellow macaw. b, Red-shouldered macaw. c, Red-fronted macaw. d, Green-winged macaw.
No. 1824, $3.25: a, Indigo macaw. b, Hyacinth macaw. c, Blue-headed macaw. d, Great green macaw.
No. 1825, $5: a, Scarlet macaaw. b, Golden-collared macaw.
No. 1826, $5: a, Blue and yellow macaw, diff. b, Blue-throated macaw.

2014, Sept. 3   Litho.   *Perf. 14*
Sheets of 4, #a-d
1823-1824 A438 Set of 2   19.50 19.50
Souvenir Sheets of 2, #a-b
1825-1826 A438 Set of 2   15.00 15.00

Ducks — A439

No. 1827, $3.25: a, Marbled duck. b, Tufted duck. c, Barrow's goldeneye. d, King eider.
No. 1828, $3.25: a, Wood duck. b, Rosy-billed pochard. c, Puna teal. d, Maned duck.
No. 1829, $10, Indian whistling ducks, vert. No. 1830, $10, Yellow-billed ducks, vert.

2014, Sept. 4   Litho.   *Perf. 13¾*
Sheets of 4, #a-d
1827-1828 A439 Set of 2   19.50 19.50
Souvenir Sheets
Perf. 12
1829-1830 A439 Set of 2   15.00 15.00
Nos. 1829-1830 each contain one 30x40mm stamp.

A440

Coral Reefs
A441

Various corals and fish, as shown.

2014, Sept. 4   Litho.   *Perf. 12*
1831 A440 $3.25 Sheet of 8.
          #a-h   19.50 19.50
Souvenir Sheet
1832 A441 $5 Sheet of 2,
          #a-b   7.50 7.50

Visit of Pope Francis to Israel — A442

Designs: $1.25, Pope Francis seated with Israeli President Shimon Peres.
No. 1834 — Pope Francis: a, Standing at Church of the Holy Sepulchre. b, Kneeling at Church of the Holy Sepulchre. c, At Yad Vashem Holocaust Museum. d, At Dome of the Rock.
No. 1835, $9.50, Pope Francis facing left. and praying at Yad Vashem Holocaust Museum. No. 1836, $9.50, Pope Francis facing right and praying at the Wailing Wall.

2014, Oct. 14   Litho.   *Perf. 14*
1833 A442 $1.25 multi   .95   .95
Perf. 12
1834 A442 $3.25 Sheet of 4,
          #a-d   9.75 9.75
Souvenir Sheets
1835-1836 A442 Set of 2   14.00 14.00

Cicely Tyson, Actress — A443

2014, Jan. 1   Litho.   *Perf. 14*
1837 A443 $3.25 multi   2.40 2.40
No. 1837 was printed in sheets of 4.

40th Culturama Festival — A444

Designs: $5, Crowd watching performers. No. 1839, $10, Dancers and crowd.
No. 1840, $10, King Meeko and King Dis and Dat, musicians.

2014, Aug. 1 Litho. *Perf. 13¼x12½*
1838-1839 A444 Set of 2   11.00 11.00
Souvenir Sheet
Perf. 12x12½
1840 A444 $10 multi   7.50 7.50

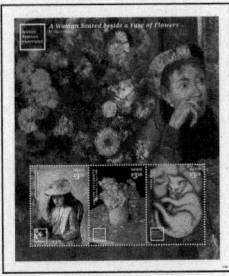

Paintings
A445

No. 1841, $3.50: a, The Artist's Daughter, by Camille Pissarro. b, Yellow Roses in a Vase, by Gustave Caillebotte. c, Kitten, by Franz Marc.
No. 1842, $3.50: a, Clump of Chrysanthemums, by Caillebotte. b, Woman Combing Her Hair, by Edgar Degas. c, Still Life with a Curtain, by Paul Gauguin.
No. 1843, $10, Road in Maine, by Edward Hopper. No. 1844, $10, Baby Reaching for an Apple, by Mary Cassatt.

2014, Oct. 14 Litho. *Perf. 12¾x12½*
Sheets of 3, #a-c
1841-1842 A445 Set of 2   15.50 15.50
Size:100x100mm
Imperf
1843-1844 A445 Set of 2   15.00 15.00

Christmas — A446

Paintings by Raphael: 30c, Madonna of Foligno. 90c, The Transfiguration. $2, Madonna of Loreto. $5, Madonna del Baldacchino.

2014, Oct. 24   Litho.   *Perf. 12½*
1845-1848 A446 Set of 4   6.00 6.00

Steam Locomotives of 1857 — A447

No. 1849, $3.25: a, Queen Class of Engines. b, Fourth and Fifth Lots Coupled. c, Eight Feet Passenger Engine. d, Third Lot Coupled.
No. 1850, $3.25: a, Five Feet Tank Engine. b, Sixth and Seventh Lots Coupled. c, Bogie Engine. d, Six Feet Tank Engine.
No. 1851, $10, Seven Feet Coupled Engine. No. 1852, $10, 6 Feet 6 Inches Coupled.

2014, Nov. 3   Litho.   *Perf. 12*
Sheets of 4, #a-d
1849-1850 A447 Set of 2   19.50 19.50
Souvenir Sheets
1851-1852 A447 Set of 2   15.00 15.00

A448

Whales and Dolphins
A449

No. 1853, Various photographs of killer whale, as shown.
No. 1854, Various photographs of humpback whale, as shown.
No. 1855, $10, Pygmy killer whale. No. 1856, $10, Sperm whale.

Perf. 13 Syncopated
2014, Dec. 16
1853 A448 $3.15 Sheet of 6,
          #a-f   14.00 14.00
1854 A449 $3.25 Sheet of 4,
          #a-d   9.75 9.75
Souvenir Sheets
1855-1856 A449 Set of 2   15.00 15.00

Rosetta Mission
A450

No. 1857: a, Philae landing on Comet 67P. b, Philae passing Earth. c, Philae passing Mars. d, Philae break away.
$10, Philae's descent to Comet 67P.

2015, Jan. 1   Litho.   *Perf. 13¾*
1857 A450 $3.25 Sheet of 4, #a-
          d   9.75 9.75
Souvenir Sheet
1858 A450 $10 multi   7.50 7.50

Prehistoric Mammals — A451

No. 1859, $3.25: a, Daeodon. b, Pseudaelurus. c, Stenomylus. d, Amebelodon.
No. 1860, $3.25: a, Megacerops. b, Synthetoceras. c, Merychyrus. d, Prosthennops.
No. 1861, $10, Saber-toothed cat. No. 1862, $10, Woolly mammoth.

2015, Jan. 21   Litho.   *Perf. 14*
Sheets of 4, #a-d
1859-1860 A451 Set of 2   19.50 19.50
Souvenir Sheets
Perf. 12
1861-1862 A451 Set of 2   15.00 15.00

Volcanoes — A452

No. 1863: a, Klyuchevskoy Volcano, Russia (80x30mm). b, Popocatépetl Volcano, Mexico (40x30mm). c, Kamchatka Volcano, Russia (40x60mm). d, Kilauea Volcano, U.S. (40x30mm). e, Nevis Peak, Nevis (40x30mm). f, Yasur Volcano, Vanuatu (40x30mm). $10, Mt. Fuji, Japan.

2015, Mar. 2　　　Litho.　　　Perf. 14
1863 A452 $3.15 Sheet of 6,
　　#a-f　　　　　　14.00 14.00
Souvenir Sheet
Perf. 12
1864 A452 $10 multi　　　　7.50 7.50
No. 1864 contains one 65x32mm triangular stamp.

Birds
A453

No. 1865: a, Scarlet ibis on tree branch. b, Greater flamingo. c, Scarlet ibis on rock with wings extended. d, Roseate spoonbill. e, Scarlet ibis on rock looking left. f, Caribbean flamingo. $10, Caribbean flamingo, diff.

2015, Mar. 2　　　Litho.　　　Perf. 14
1865 A453 $4 Sheet of 6, #a-
　　f　　　　　　　18.00 18.00
Souvenir Sheet
1866 A453 $10 multi　　　　7.50 7.50
No. 1866 contains one 30x80mm stamp.

Loggerhead Sea Turtles — A454

No. 1867, Various photographs.
$10, Loggerhead sea turtle, diff.

2015, Mar. 24　　　Litho.　　　Perf. 14
1867 A454 $3.15 Sheet of 6,
　　#a-f　　　　　　14.00 14.00
Souvenir Sheet
Perf. 12
1868 A454 $10 multi　　　　7.50 7.50

Pope
Benedict
XVI
A455

No. 1869: a, Pope Benedict XVI on balcony with arms extended. b, Pope Benedict XVI wearing red zuchetto. c, Smoke announcing election of Pope Benedict XVI. d, Crowd at inauguration of Pope Benedict XVI. e, Pope Benedict XVI wearing miter. f, Pope Benedict XVI wearing white zuchetto. $10, Pope Benedict XVI seated.

2015, Mar. 24　　　Litho.　　　Perf. 14
1869 A455 $3.15 Sheet of 6,
　　#a-f　　　　　　14.00 14.00
Souvenir Sheet
Perf. 12
1870 A455 $10 multi　　　　7.50 7.50

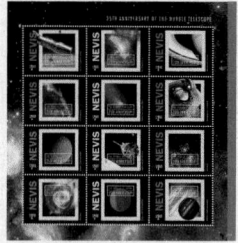

Hubble Space Telescope, 25th
Anniv. — A456

No. 1871: a, Hubble Space Telescope above Earth. b, Crab Nebula. c, Rings of Saturn. d, Orion Nebula. e, Comet. f, Astronaut repairing telescope. g, Mars. h, Hubble Space Telescope, Earth at LL corner. i, NGC 3603. j, NGC 6543. k, Neptune. l, A moon in front of Jupiter. $10, Hubble Space Telescope, diff.

2015, Mar. 24　　　Litho.　　　Perf. 14
1871 A456 $1.60 Sheet of 12,
　　#a-l　　　　　　14.50 14.50
Souvenir Sheet
Perf. 12½
1872 A456 $10 multi　　　　7.50 7.50
No. 1872 contains one 51x38mm stamp.

International Year of Light — A457

No. 1873 — UNESCO emblem, light and inscription: a, Incandescent. b, Halogen. c, Fluorescent. d, LED. e, Laser. $10, UNESCO emblem and "2015 / International / Year of / Light."

2015, Apr. 15　　　Litho.　　　Perf. 12
1873 A457 $3.25 Sheet of 5,
　　#a-e　　　　　　12.00 12.00
Souvenir Sheet
Perf. 12¾
1874 A457 $10 multi　　　　7.50 7.50
No. 1874 contains one 38x51mm stamp.

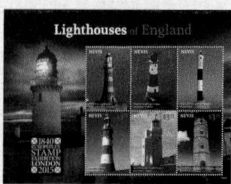

English Lighthouses — A458

No. 1875: a, Roker Pier Lighthouse. b, Beachy Head Lighthouse. c, New Lighthouse at Dungeness. d, Smeaton's Tower. e, St. Catherine's Lighthouse. f, Flamborough Head Lighthouse. $10, Needles Lighthouse.

2015, Apr. 15　　　Litho.　　　Perf. 14
1875 A458 $3.15 Sheet of 6,
　　#a-f　　　　　　14.00 14.00
Souvenir Sheet
1876 A458 $10 multi　　　　7.50 7.50
Europhilex Stamp Exhibition, London.

2015 Cricket
World Cup,
Australia and New
Zealand — A459

Designs: $4, Hagley Oval, Christchurch, New Zealand.
$10, Cricket World Cup, vert.

2015, May 4　　　Litho.　　　Perf. 14
1877 A459 $4 multi　　　　3.00 3.00
Souvenir Sheet
Perf. 12
1878 A459 $10 multi　　　　7.50 7.50

First
Battle of
Ypres,
Cent. (in
2014)
A460

No. 1879: a, Second Scots Guards testing trench, Ghent. b, Second Battalion Scots Guards. c, Sikh Regiment, Ypres. d, Naval armored car, Menin Road. $10, British medics aid wounded comrade.

2015, Nov. 1　　　Litho.　　　Perf. 12
1879 A460 $3.25 Sheet of 4, #a-
　　d　　　　　　　9.75 9.75
Souvenir Sheet
Perf. 12½
1880 A460 $10 multi　　　　7.50 7.50
No. 1880 contains one 51x38mm stamp.

Christmas — A461

Paintings by Bartolomé Esteban Murillo: 30c, The Annunciation. 90c, Nativity. $2, Madonna and Child. $5, Adoration of the Shepherds.

2015, Nov. 2　　　Litho.　　　Perf. 14
1881-1884 A461　Set of 4　　6.00 6.00

Queen Elizabeth II, Longest-Reigning
British Monarch — A462

No. 1885 — Various photographs of Queen Elizabeth II with denomination in: a, Magenta. b, Turquoise green. c, Violet gray. d, Ochre. e, Black. f, Gray. $10, Queen Elizabeth II wearing pink and white dress.

2015, Nov. 25　　　Litho.　　　Perf. 14
1885 A462 $3.15 Sheet of 6,
　　#a-f　　　　　　14.00 14.00
Souvenir Sheet
Perf. 12¾
1886 A462 $10 multi　　　　7.50 7.50
No. 1886 contains one 38x51mm stamp.

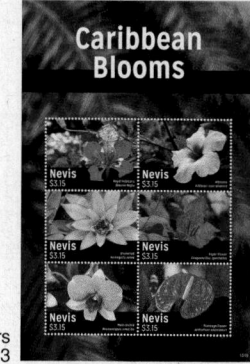

Flowers
A463

No. 1887: a, Royal poinciana. b, Hibiscus. c, Bromeliad. d, Paper flower. e, Moth orchid. f, Flamingo flower. $10, Red palulu, vert.

2015, Dec. 7　　　Litho.　　　Perf. 14
1887 A463 $3.15 Sheet of 6,
　　#a-f　　　　　　14.00 14.00
Souvenir Sheet
Perf. 12
1888 A463 $10 multi　　　　7.50 7.50
No. 1888 contains one 30x50mm stamp.

Bank of Nevis
Limited, 30th
Anniv. — A464

Designs: 30c, Bank building. 90c, Bank building, diff. $5, Sir Simeon Daniel (1934-2012), premier of Nevis, bank founder, vert.

2015, Dec. 9　　　Litho.　　　Perf. 14
1889-1891 A464　Set of 3　　4.75 4.75

Kingfishers — A465

No. 1892: a, Belted kingfisher. b, Ringed kingfisher. c, Green and rufous kingfisher. d, Green kingfisher, showing breast. e, Amazon kingfisher. f, Green kingfisher, showing back. $10, Belted kingfisher in flight.

2015, Dec. 17　　　Litho.　　　Perf. 13¾
1892 A465 $3.15 Sheet of 6,
　　#a-f　　　　　　14.00 14.00
Souvenir Sheet
1893 A465 $10 multi　　　　7.50 7.50

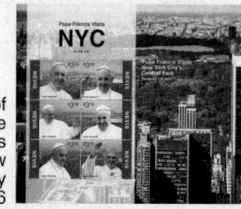

Visit of
Pope
Francis
to New
York City
A466

No. 1894, Various photographs of Pope Francis, as shown.
$10, Pope Francis looking forward with left arm raised.

2015, Dec. 17　　　Litho.　　　Perf. 14
1894 A466 $3.15 Sheet of 6,
　　#a-f　　　　　　14.00 14.00
Souvenir Sheet
Perf. 12
1895 A466 $10 multi　　　　7.50 7.50

1896 Olympic Champions — A467

No. 1896: a, Herman Weingärtner, horizontal bar. b, Carl Schuhmann, horse vault. c, Thomas Burke, 100-meter and 400-meter race. d, Thomas Curtis, 100-meter hurdles.
$10, Alfred Flatow, parallel bars.

2015, Dec. 21   Litho.   Perf. 14
1896 A467 $3.25 Sheet of 4, #a-
d   9.75 9.75

Souvenir Sheet
Perf. 12½
1897 A467 $10 multi   7.50 7.50
No. 1897 contains one 38x51mm stamp.

Dolphins
A468

No. 1898: a, Rough-toothed dolphin. b, Atlantic spotted dolphin. c, Striped dolphin. d, Common bottlenose dolphin. e, Risso's dolphin. f, Fraser's dolphin.
$10, Short-beaked common dolphin.

2016, Jan. 28   Litho.   Perf. 14
1898 A468 $4 Sheet of 6, #a-
f   18.00 18.00

Souvenir Sheet
Perf. 12
1899 A468 $10 multi   7.50 7.50
No. 1899 contains one 80x30mm stamp.

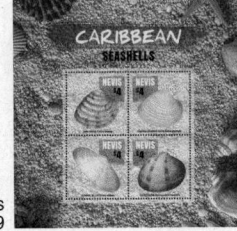

Shells
A469

No. 1900: a, King venus. b, Channeled duck clam. c, Sunrise tellin. d, Calico clam.
$10, Royal comb venus, horiz.

2016, Jan. 28   Litho.   Perf. 13¾
1900 A469 $4 Sheet of 4, #a-
d   12.00 12.00

Souvenir Sheet
Perf. 12½
1901 A469 $10 multi   7.50 7.50
No. 1901 contains one 51x38mm stamp.

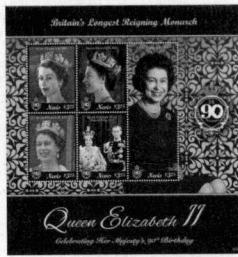

Queen Elizabeth II, 90th Birthday
A470

No. 1902: a, Queen Elizabeth II wearing pearl necklace (30x40mm). b, Queen Elizabeth II wearing long earring, looking left (30x40mm). c, Queen Elizabeth II wearing teardrop earrings (30x40mm). d, Queen Elizabeth II and Prince Philip (30x40mm). e, Queen Elizabeth II in 1970 (30x80mm).
$13, Queen Elizabeth II in 1987.

2016, Apr. 1   Litho.   Perf. 14
1902 A470 $3.25 Sheet of 5,
#a-e   12.00 12.00

Souvenir Sheet
Perf. 12
1903 A470 $13 multi   9.75 9.75
No. 1903 contains one 30x50mm stamp.

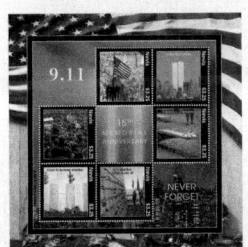

2016 World Stamp Show, New York
A471

No. 1904 — New York City landmarks: a, Central Park. b, Statue of Liberty. c, Grand Central Terminal. d, Brooklyn Bridge.
$8, New York skyline.

2016, Apr. 29   Litho.   Perf. 12
1904 A471 $4 Sheet of 4, #a-d 12.00 12.00

Souvenir Sheet
Perf. 14
1905 A471 $8 multi   6.00 6.00
No. 1905 contains one 60x80mm stamp.

September 11, 2001 Terrorist Attacks, 15th Anniv. — A472

No. 1906: a, Flag on World Trade Center rubble. b, World Trade Center. c, New York firefighters at World Trade Center. d, Pentagon 9/11 Memorial. e, Flight 93 National Memorial. f, 9/11 Memorial, Staten Island, New York.
No. 1907: a, Flag hanging from Pentagon. b, Pentagon. c, World Trade Center, diff. d, Tribute in Light.
$14, Tribute in Light, diff.

2016, May 26   Litho.   Perf. 13¾
1906 A472 $3.25 Sheet of 6,
#a-f   14.50 14.50
1907 A472 $3.50 Sheet of 4,
#a-d   10.50 10.50

Souvenir Sheet
1908 A472 $14 multi   10.50 10.50

William Shakespeare (1564-1616), Writer — A473

No. 1909: a, Shakespeare's birthplace, Stratford-on-Avon, England. b, Shakespeare,

c, Oberon, Titania and Puck with Fairies Dancing, painting by Henry Fuseli. d, Pity, painting by William Blake. e, Hamlet and His Father's Ghost, painting by Blake. f, Macbeth Consulting the Vision of the Armed Head, painting by Fuseli.
$12, Shakespeare, diff.

2016, June 1   Litho.   Perf. 12½
1909 A473 $3.15 Sheet of 6,
#a-f   14.00 14.00

Souvenir Sheet
Perf.
1910 A473 $12 multi   9.00 9.00
No. 1910 contains one 33x43mm oval stamp.

Pres. Barack Obama's Visit to Saudi Arabia
A474

No. 1911: a, Pres. Obama, U.S. flag (40x60mm). b, Pres. Obama behind microphone (80x30mm). c, King Salman of Saudi Arabia (40x60mm). d, Pres. Obama and King Salman standing in front of emblem (40x30mm). e, Pres. Obama and King Salman walking (40x30mm).
No. 1912: a, Pres. Obama, U.S. flag. b, King Salman, Saudi Arabia flag.

2016, Oct. 18   Litho.   Perf. 14
1911 A474 $4 Sheet of 5, #a-e 15.00 15.00

Souvenir Sheet
Perf. 12½
1912 A474 $7 Sheet of 2, #a-b 10.50 10.50
No. 1912 contains two 38x51mm stamps.

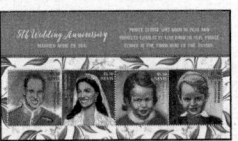

Duke and Duchess of Cambridge, 5th Wedding Anniversary — A475

No. 1913: a, Duke of Cambridge. b, Duchess of Cambridge. c, Princess Charlotte. d, Prince George.
$10, Duke and Duchess of Cambridge kissing at wedding, vert.

2017, Mar. 14   Litho.   Perf. 13¾
1913 A475 $5.50 Sheet of 4,
#a-d   16.50 16.50

Souvenir Sheet
Perf. 12½
1914 A475 $10 multi   7.50 7.50
No. 1914 contains one 38x51mm stamp.

Princess Diana (1961-97) — A476

No. 1915 — Princess Diana: a, With Princes William and Harry, horse. b, Carrying Prince Harry. c, With Princes William and Harry on fence. d, Leaning over Prince William's shoulder. e, With Princes William and Harry, wearing suits. f, With hands together talking to Prince William.
No. 1916 — Princess Diana, Princes Charles, William and Harry with: a, Building in background. b, Trees in background.

2017, Apr. 14   Litho.   Perf. 14
1915 A476 $3.50 Sheet of 6,
#a-f   15.50 15.50

Souvenir Sheet
1916 A476 $7.50 Sheet of 2,
#a-b   11.00 11.00

Star Trek Television Shows, 50th Anniv. (in 2016) — A477

No. 1917 — Scenes from Star Trek: The Next Generation episodes: a, The Pegasus. b, Unification II. c, Q Who. d, Deja Q. e, Rascals. f, All Good Things. . .
$12, Scene from Darmok episode.

2017, Apr. 24   Litho.   Perf. 12
1917 A477 $4 Sheet of 6, #a-
f   18.00 18.00

Souvenir Sheet
Perf. 12½
1918 A477 $12 multi   9.00 9.00
No. 1918 contains one 51x38mm stamp.

Ancient Ruins
A478

No. 1919: a, Stonehenge, England. b, Amphitheater of El Djem, Tunisia. c, Bagan, Burma. d, Petra, Jordan. e, Ellora Caves, India. f, Moai, Easter Island, Chile.
$10, Machu Picchu, Peru.

2017, June 7   Litho.   Perf. 12
1919 A478 $3.50 Sheet of 6,
#a-f   15.50 15.50

Souvenir Sheet
1920 A478 $10 multi   7.50 7.50

A479

A480

Pres. John F. Kennedy (1917-63) — A481

No. 1921: a, $5, Pres. Kennedy facing forward. b, $6, Pres. Kennedy facing right. c, $8, Pres. Kennedy facing left. d, $10, Pres. Kennedy and wife, Jacqueline.
No. 1922, vert. — Pres. Kennedy: a, Seated at desk. b, Pointing. c, Wearing Navy cap. d, Facing left.
No. 1923, Pres. Kennedy and U.S. flag, vert.

2017, June 7   Litho.   Perf. 13¾
1921 A479   Sheet of 4, #a-d   21.50 21.50
Perf. 14
1922 A480 $5.50 Sheet of 4, #a-b   16.50 16.50
Souvenir Sheet
1923 A481 $10 multi   7.50 7.50

Piping Plovers A482

No. 1924: a, Chick (entire bird). b, Adult (head).
$10, Two birds, vert.

2017, June 22   Litho.   Perf.
1924 A482 $7.50 Sheet of 2, #a-b   11.00 11.00
Souvenir Sheet
Perf. 12½
1925 A482 $10 multi   7.50 7.50
No. 1925 contains one 38x51mm stamp.

Animals A483

No. 1926: a, Naked mole rat. b, Cydno longwing butterfly. c, Saint Croix sheep. d, Asian garden dormouse.
$15, Cave cricket, vert.

2017, Apr. 14   Litho.   Perf. 12¾
1926 A483 $4 Sheet of 4, #a-d   12.00 12.00
Souvenir Sheet
1927 A483 $15 multi   11.00 11.00

Miniature Sheets

Tree Flowers A484

No. 1928, $5.50: a, Tulip tree. b, Royal poinciana. c, Shaving brush tree. d, Geiger tree.
No. 1929, $5.50: a, Golden shower tree. b, Jacaranda. c, Japanese cherry. d, Southern magnolia.

2017, June 22   Litho.   Perf. 14
Sheets of 4, #a-d
1928-1929 A484   Set of 2   32.50 32.50

Miniature Sheet

Brown Pelicans A485

No. 1930: a, One pelican in flight. b, Two pelicans in flight. c, Pelican on rock. denomination in black. d, Pelican, denomination in yellow. e, Juvenile pelican facing left. f, Pelican hatchling and egg.

2017, Sept. 28   Litho.   Perf. 13¾
1930 A485 $4 Sheet of 6, #a-f   18.00 18.00

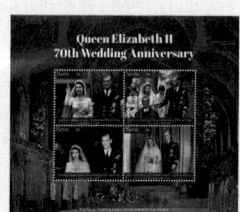

70th Wedding Anniversary of Queen Elizabeth II and Prince Philip — A486

No. 1931: a, Couple, bride waving. b, Couple with attendants. c, Couple passing line of people. d, Formal photograph of couple.
$12, Couple with family and attendants.

2017, Sept. 28   Litho.   Perf. 14
1931 A486 $6 Sheet of 4, #a-d   18.00 18.00
Souvenir Sheet
1932 A486 $12 multi   9.00 9.00
No. 1932 contains one 80x30mm stamp.

Inhabitants of Coral Reefs — A487

No. 1933: a, Diamond blenny. b, Caribbean reef shark. c, Green sea turtle. d, Flamingo tongue snail. e, Fairy basslet. f, Green moray eel.
No. 1934, $12, Longsnout seahorse, vert.
No. 1935, $12, Green sea turtle, vert.

2017, Dec. 4   Litho.   Perf. 14
1933 A487 $4 Sheet of 6, #a-f   18.00 18.00
Souvenir Sheets
1934-1935 A487   Set of 2   18.00 18.00

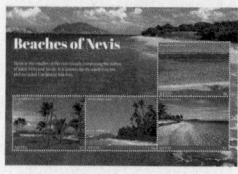

Nevis Beaches A488

No. 1936: a, $2, Long Haul Beach. b, $4, Pinney's Beach. c, $6, Nisbet Beach. d, $8, Newcastle Beach.
No. 1937: a, $7, Pinney's Beach, diff. b, $8, Oualie Beach.

2017, Dec. 22   Litho.   Perf. 13¼
1936 A488   Sheet of 4, #a-d   15.00 15.00
Souvenir Sheet
Perf. 12½x13¼
1937 A488   Sheet of 2, #a-b   11.00 11.00
No. 1937 contains two 40x30mm stamps.

Miniature Sheet

British Royalty A489

No. 1938: a, Queen Elizabeth II. b, Duke and Duchess of Cambridge. c, Prince George and Princess Charlotte of Cambridge. d, Prince Harry and fiancée Meghan Markle.

2018, Jan. 24   Litho.   Perf. 12½x13¼
1938 A489 $7 Sheet of 4, #a-d   21.00 21.00

Swans A490

No. 1939: a, $4, Black-necked swan. b, $5.50, Trumpeter swan. c, $6, Mute swan. d, $6.50, Black swan.
No. 1940, vert.: a, $7, Tundra swan. b, $9, Coscoroba swan.

2018, Apr. 23   Litho.   Perf. 14
1939 A490   Sheet of 4, #a-d   16.50 16.50
Souvenir Sheet
Perf. 12½
1940 A490   Sheet of 2, #a-b   12.00 12.00
No. 1940 contains two 38x51mm stamps.

Geckos A491

No. 1941: a, $4, Crested gecko. b, $5.50, Madagascar day gecko. c, $6, Tokay gecko. d, $6.50, Kuhl's flying gecko.
No. 1942: a, $7, William's dwarf gecko. b, $9, Leopard gecko.

2018, Apr. 23   Litho.   Perf. 14
1941 A491   Sheet of 4, #a-d   16.50 16.50
Souvenir Sheet
Perf. 12½
1942 A491   Sheet of 2, #a-b   12.00 12.00
No. 1942 contains two 51x38mm stamps.

Souvenir Sheet

Red Squirrel A492

No. 1943 — Various photographs of red squirrel: a, $4. b, $5. c, $6.

2018, May 4   Litho.   Perf.
1943 A492   Sheet of 3, #a-c   11.00 11.00

Coronation of Queen Elizabeth II, 65th Anniv. — A493

No. 1944 — Various photographs of Queen Elizabeth II wearing crown, as shown.
No. 1945 — Queen Elizabeth II: a, Sitting in coach. b, Waving.

2018, May 4   Litho.   Perf. 12
1944 A493 $5 Sheet of 3, #a-c   11.00 11.00
Souvenir Sheet
Perf. 12½
1945 A493 $7.50 Sheet of 2, #a-b   11.00 11.00
No. 1945 contains two 38x51mm stamps.

Planets and Moons A494

No. 1946, $5.50: a, Phobos. b, Mars. c, Deimos.
No. 1947: a, $5, Mercury, Venus, Earth. b, $6, Mars, Jupiter. c, $7, Saturn, Uranus, Neptune.
No. 1948: a, $8, Moon. b, $9, Earth.

2018, May 4   Litho.   Perf. 12½
Sheets of 3, #a-c
1946-1947 A494   Set of 2   25.50 25.50
Souvenir Sheet
1948 A494   Sheet of 2, #a-b   12.50 12.50

Miniature Sheet

Variegated Scallops — A495

Various shells, as shown.

2018, May 24   Litho.   Perf. 12
1949 A495 $4.50 Sheet of 4, #a-d   13.50 13.50

Miniature Sheet

Elvis Presley (1935-77) — A496

No. 1950 — Various photographs of Presley: a, Playing guitar, both hands visible, black background. b, Playing guitar, red background. c, Singing without guitar. d, Playing guitar, one arm visible, black background.

2018, May 24   Litho.   Perf. 14
1950 A496 $6.80 Sheet of 4,
#a-d   20.00 20.00

Whales
A497

No. 1951: a, Humpback whale. b, Sperm whale. c, Killer whale.
$10, Blue whale, vert.

2018, May 24   Litho.   Perf. 12½
1951 A497 $5.50 Sheet of 3,
#a-c   12.50 12.50
Souvenir Sheet
1952 A497 $10 multi   7.50 7.50

Souvenir Sheet

Pres. Donald Trump at G7 Meeting, Rome A498

No. 1953: a, Leaders of G7 nations standing in front of flags. b, Pres. Trump and Italian Pres. Sergio Mattarella. c, Leaders seated at table.

2018, June 5   Litho.   Perf. 14
1953 A498 $5.50 Sheet of 3,
#a-c   12.50 12.50

Miniature Sheet

Fish
A499

No. 1954: a, Moorish idol. b, Black tang. c, Flame angelfish. d, Northern red snapper. e,

Pelagic porcupine fish. f, Yellow longnose butterflyfish.

2018, June 5   Litho.   Perf. 12
1954 A499 $4 Sheet of 6, #a-f 18.00 18.00

Hummingbirds — A500

No. 1955: a, Antillean crested hummingbird. b, Green-throated carib. c, Blue-headed hummingbird. d, Purple-throated carib.
$10, White-bellied emerald hummingbird.

2018, June 5   Litho.   Perf. 12
1955 A500 $4 Sheet of 4, #a-d
                              12.00 12.00
Souvenir Sheet
Perf. 12½
1956 A500 $10 multi   7.50 7.50
No. 1956 contains one 38x51mm stamp.

Miniature Sheet

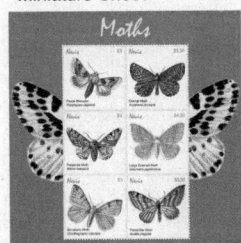

Moths
A501

No. 1957: a, $3, Pease blossom moth. b, $3.50, Orange moth. c, $4, Peppered moth. d, $4.50, Large emerald moth. e, $5, Brimstone moth. f, $5.50, Treble-bar moth.

2018, June 27   Litho.   Perf. 13¾
1957 A501   Sheet of 6, #a-f   19.00 19.00

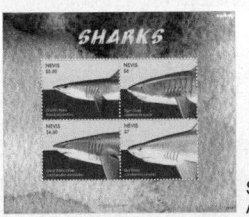

Sharks
A502

No. 1958: a, $5.50, Shortfin mako shark. b, $6, Tiger shark. c, $6.50, Great white shark. d, $7, Bull shark.
$10, Smooth hammerhead shark.

2018, June 29   Litho.   Perf. 12½x12
1958 A502   Sheet of 4, #a-d
                              18.50 18.50
Souvenir Sheet
Perf. 12½x13¼
1959 A502 $10 multi   7.50 7.50
No. 1959 contains one 80x30mm stamp.

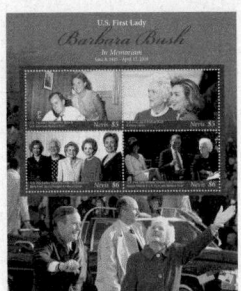

Barbara Bush (1925-2018), U.S. First Lady — A503

No. 1960 — Mrs. Bush and: a, $5, Her husband, Pres. George H. W. Bush. b, $5, First Lady Hillary Clinton. c, $6, First Ladies Rosalynn Carter, Betty Ford, Nancy Reagan and Hillary Clinton. d, $6, Pres. Barack Obama and his wife, Michelle.
$10, Mrs. Bush, vert.

2018, June 29   Litho.   Perf. 13½
1960 A503   Sheet of 4, #a-
d   16.50 16.50
Souvenir Sheet
Perf. 13½x12½
1961 A503 $10 multi   7.50 7.50
No. 1961 contains one 30x40mm stamp.

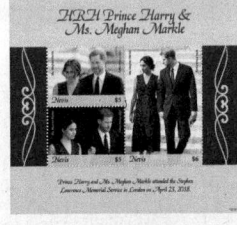

British Royalty and Their Newborn Children A504

No. 1962: a, Duke and Duchess of Cambridge with Prince Louis. b, Prince Charles and Princess Diana with Prince William. c, Queen Elizabeth II with Prince Charles. d, King George V and Queen Mother with Princess Elizabeth.

2018, June 29   Litho.   Perf. 12½
1962 A504 $5.50 Sheet of 4,
#a-d   16.50 16.50

Souvenir Sheet

Wedding of Prince Harry and Meghan Markle A505

No. 1963 — Couple with: a, $5, Steps in background (40x30mm). b, $5, Black background (40x30mm). c, $6, Steps in background (40x60mm).

2018, June 29   Litho.   Perf. 12½x12
1963 A505   Sheet of 3, #a-c   12.00 12.00

Concorde — A506

No. 1964: a, Air France Concorde, 1973. b, Two-person camera crew watching Air France Concorde take off, 1976. c, Five people watching Air France Concorde taking off, 1976. d, Air France Concorde, 2003.
$10, Queen Elizabeth II and Prince Philip on Concorde stairway, 1977.

2018, July 1   Litho.   Perf. 12½x12
1964 A506 $5 Sheet of 4, #a-
d   15.00 15.00
Souvenir Sheet
Perf. 12½x13¼
1965 A506 $10 multi   7.50 7.50
No. 1965 contains one 80x30mm stamp.

Prince George of Cambridge, 5th Birthday — A507

No. 1966: a, $4, Prince George as infant, with parents, Duke and Duchess of Cambridge. b, $5, Prince George. c, $6, Prince George in arms of his father.
No. 1967, horiz.: a, Prince George as infant, with parents and dog. b, Prince George with dog.

2018, July 1   Litho.   Perf. 13¼x12½
1966 A507   Sheet of 3, #a-c   11.00 11.00
Souvenir Sheet
Perf. 12½x13¼
1967 A507 $8 Sheet of 2, #a-b 12.00 12.00

A508

Wedding of Prince Harry and Meghan Markle A509

No. 1968: a, Couple in coach, waving. b, Couple kissing. c, Couple holding hands on steps. d, Couple with people in background.
No. 1969: a, Couple kissing. b, Couple waving.

2018, July 17   Litho.   Perf. 12
1968 A508 $5 Sheet of 4, #a-d 15.00 15.00
Souvenir Sheet
1969 A509 $8 Sheet of 2, #a-b 12.00 12.00

Miniature Sheet

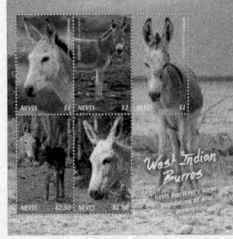

Donkeys
A510

No. 1970 — Various photographs: a, $1. b, $1.50. c, $2. d, $2.50. e, $3.

2018, Oct. 22　Litho.　　Perf. 12
1970　A510　Sheet of 5, #a-e　　　7.50　7.50

Miniature Sheet

Visit of Pres. Donald Trump to Windsor Castle A511

No. 1971: a, $4, Pres. Trump and Queen Elizabeth II inspecting troops. b, $5, Pres. Trump, his wife, Melania, and Queen Elizabeth II. c, $6, Pres. Trump, his wife, and Queen Elizabeth II, diff. d, $7, Pres. Trump, his wife, Queen Elizabeth II and Sir Andrew Ford.

2018, Oct. 22　Litho.　　Perf. 12
1971　A511　Sheet of 4, #a-d　16.50　16.50

Christmas — A512

Words from Christmas music: 30c, Deck The Halls With Boughs Of Holly. 90c, Sweet Chiming Christmas Bells. $2, Beautiful Star Of Bethlehem. $5, Oh Christmas Tree, Oh Christmas Tree, How Lovely Are Thy Branches. $10, Ho, Ho, Ho, How Will Santa Get Here.

2018, Dec. 5　Litho.　　Perf. 12½
1972-1975　A512　Set of 4　　　6.25　6.25
Souvenir Sheet
1976　A512　$10 multi　　　　　7.50　7.50

Souvenir Sheets

Butterflies — A513

No. 1977: a, $4, Jamaican ringlet butterfly (35x35mm). b, $5, Red-splashed sulphur butterfly (35x35mm). c, $6, Poey's black swallowtail butterflies (70x35mm).
No. 1978: a, $7, Cuban mimic butterfly (70x35mm). b, $8, Gundlach's swallowtail butterflies (70x35mm).

2018, Dec. 5　Litho.　　Perf. 13¾
1977　A513　Sheet of 3, #a-c　11.00　11.00
1978　A513　Sheet of 2, #a-b　11.00　11.00

Miniature Sheet

Mohandas K. Gandhi (1869-1948), Indian Nationalist Leader — A514

No. 1979 — Various photographs of Gandhi: a, $4. b, $5. c, $6. d, $7.

2018, Dec. 20　Litho.　　Perf. 14
1979　A514　Sheet of 4, #a-d　16.50　16.50

Red-Footed Tortoise — A515

No. 1980 — Various photographs of Red-footed tortoises: a, $4. b, $5. c, $6. d, $7. $10, Tortoise, diff.

2018, Dec. 20　Litho.　　Perf. 14
1980　A515　Sheet of 4, #a-d　16.50　16.50
Souvenir Sheet
Perf. 12½
1981　A515　$10 multi　　　　　7.50　7.50
No. 1981 contains one 51x38mm stamp.

Paintings by Leonardo da Vinci (1452-1519) — A516

No. 1982: a, $4, Ginevra de'Benci. b, $5, Lady with an Ermine. c, $6, La Belle Ferronnière.
$10, Mona Lisa.

2019, Feb. 11　Litho.　　Perf. 12
1982　A516　Sheet of 3, #a-c　11.00　11.00
Size: 80x130mm
Imperf
1983　A516　$10 multi　　　　　7.50　7.50

Miniature Sheet

Pigeons and Doves A517

No. 1984: a, $4, White-tipped dove. b, $5, Ruddy ground dove. c, $6, Pale-vented pigeon. d, $7, Rock pigeon.

2019, Mar. 16　Litho.　　Perf. 12½
1984　A517　Sheet of 4, #a-d　16.50　16.50

Royal Poinciana Flowers — A518

No. 1985: a, $4, Tree. b, $5, Blossom. c, $6, Cluster of flowers. d, $7, Cluster of flowers, diff.
$14, Tree, diff.

2019, Mar. 16　Litho.　　Perf. 14
1985　A518　Sheet of 4, #a-d　16.50　16.50
Souvenir Sheet
Perf. 12½
1986　A518　$14 multi　　　　10.50　10.50
No. 1986 contains one 51x38mm stamp.

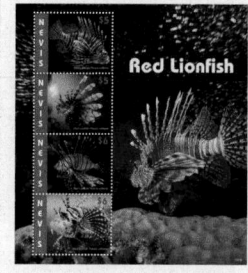

First Man on the Moon, 50th Anniv. A519

No. 1987: a, $4, Apollo 11 mission patch and itinerary. b, $5, Astronaut Edwin "Buzz" Aldrin on Moon. c, $6, Astronaut Neil Armstrong. d, $7, Apollo 11 astronauts in space suits.
$11, Sketches of heads of Apollo 11 astronauts.

2019, May 25　Litho.　　Perf. 14
1987　A519　Sheet of 4, #a-d　16.50　16.50
Souvenir Sheet
Perf. 12
1988　A519　$11 multi　　　　　8.25　8.25
No. 1988 contains one 50x30mm stamp.

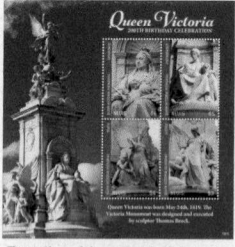

Red Lionfish A520

No. 1989 — Red lionfish facing: a, $5, Right. b, $5, Left. c, $6, Left, black background. d, $6, Left, blue background.
$14, Red lionfish, diff.

2019, July 1　Litho.　　Perf. 12
1989　A520　Sheet of 4, #a-d　16.50　16.50
Souvenir Sheet
Perf. 12¾
1990　A520　$14 multi　　　　10.50　10.50
No. 1990 contains one 51x38mm stamp.

Details of London's Victoria Monument, by Thomas Brock — A521

No. 1991: a, $3, Justice. b, $4, Truth. c, $5, Motherhood. d, $6, Queen Victoria Enthroned.
No. 1992: a, $3, Progress. b, $4, Agriculture. c, $5, Peace. d, $6, Manufacture.
$14, Winged Victory.

2019, July 1　Litho.　　Perf. 14
1991　A521　Sheet of 4, #a-d　13.50　13.50
1992　A521　Sheet of 4, #a-d　13.50　13.50
Souvenir Sheet
Perf. 12
1993　A521　$14 multi　　　　10.50　10.50

Miniature Sheet

Leonard Bernstein (1918-90), Conductor — A522

No. 1994 — Bernstein: a, Conducting orchestra. b, Wearing shirt with open collar. c, Writing. d, Wearing turtle-neck sweater.

2019, July 7　Litho.　　Perf. 14
1994　A522　$6 Sheet of 4, #a-d　18.00　18.00

Atlantic Spotted Dolphins A523

No. 1995: a, Two dolphins facing right. b, Head of dolphin facing left. c, One dolphin facing right. d, Two dolphins facing left.
$14, Head of dolphin facing right.

2019, July 7　Litho.　　Perf. 14
1995　A523　$4 Sheet of 4, #a-d　　　12.00　12.00
Souvenir Sheet
Perf. 12½
1996　A523　$14 multi　　　　10.50　10.50
No. 1996 contains one 51x38mm stamp.

Miniature Sheet

Birth of Archie Mountbatten-Windsor — A524

No. 1997: a, $4, Duke and Duchess of Sussex with infant. b, $5, Duke of Sussex. c, $6, Duke and Duchess of Sussex. d, $7, Duke and Duchess of Sussex with infant, diff.

2019, July 10　Litho.　　Perf. 12
1997　A524　Sheet of 4, #a-d　16.50　16.50

Orchids A525

No. 1998: a, $4, Guarianthe skinneri. b, $5, Papilionanthe Miss Joaquim. c, $6, Prosthechea cochleata. d, $7, Cattleya labiata.
$14, Unnamed orchids.

2019, July 31　Litho.　　Perf. 14
1998　A525　Sheet of 4, #a-d　16.50　16.50
Souvenir Sheet
Perf. 12½
1999　A525　$14 multi　　　　10.50　10.50
Singpex 2019 International Stamp Exhibition, Singapore. No. 1999 contains one 51x38mm stamp.

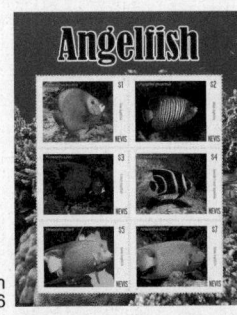

Angelfish
A526

No. 2000: a, $1, Gray angelfish. b, $2, Royal angelfish. c, $3, French angelfish. d, $4, Juvenile French angelfish. e, $5, Queen angelfish. f, $7, Queen angelfish, diff.
$14, Emperor angelfish, vert.

2020, Jan. 6 Litho. Perf. 12½
2000 A526 Sheet of 6, #a-f 16.50 16.50
Souvenir Sheet
Perf. 12
2001 A526 $14 multi 10.50 10.50
No. 2001 contains one 30x40mm stamp.

Sea Animals

Marine Life
A527

No. 2002: a, $2, Wolffish. b, $3, Equal sea star. c, $4, Purple sea urchin. d, $5, Mountain crab.
$14, Ornate butterflyfish, vert.

2020, Jan. 6 Litho. Perf. 14
2002 A527 Sheet of 4, #a-d 10.50 10.50
Souvenir Sheet
Perf. 12
2003 A527 $14 multi 10.50 10.50

Rabbits
A528

No. 2004: a, Pygmy rabbit facing right. b, Angora rabbit. c, Holland lop rabbit. d, Pygmy rabbit facing left.
$14, Angora rabbit, diff., vert.

2020, Jan. 6 Litho. Perf. 13¾
2004 A528 $5 Sheet of 4, #a-d 15.00 15.00
Souvenir Sheet
Perf. 12½
2005 A528 $14 multi 10.50 10.50
No. 2005 contains one 38x51mm stamp.

Arrival in Massachusetts of the Pilgrims, 400th Anniv. — A529

No. 2006: a, Myles Standish (c. 1584-1656), military adviser to Plymouth Colony. b, Pilgrim settlers. c, William Bradford (1590-1657), governor of Plymouth Colony. d, Landing of the Pilgrims. e, Embarkation of the Pilgrims. f, The Mayflower Compact.

$14, Mayflower in Plymouth Harbor, by William Halsall (1841-1919), vert.

2020, May 20 Litho. Perf. 14
2006 A529 $4 Sheet of 6, #a-f 18.00 18.00
Souvenir Sheet
Perf. 12
2007 A529 $14 multi 10.50 10.50

A530

Starfish
A531

No. 2008: a, Crown of thorns starfish. b, Granulated sea star. c, Ocher sea star. d, Giant spined star. e, Egyptian sea star.
$14, Blue starfish.

2020, Nov. 2 Litho. Perf. 14
2008 A530 $4.50 Sheet of 5, #a-e 17.00 17.00
Souvenir Sheet
Perf. 13¾
2009 A531 $14 multi 10.50 10.50

A532

Tree Frogs
A533

No. 2010: a, Squirrel tree frog. b, Cuban tree frog. c, Gray tree frog. d, Red-eyed tree frog.
$14, Two tree frogs.

2020, Nov. 2 Litho. Perf. 13¾
2010 A532 $5.50 Sheet of 4, #a-d 16.50 16.50
Souvenir Sheet
Perf. 14
2011 A533 $14 multi 10.50 10.50

Dorje Chang Buddha III, Religious Leader — A534

2020, Dec. 28 Litho. Perf. 13¼
2012 A534 $5 multi 3.75 3.75

Miniature Sheet

Tribute to Workers During the COVID-19 Pandemic — A535

No. 2013: a, Doctor holding globe. b, World map on computer, gloved hand. c, Hospital gurneys. d, Health care worker, hands holding vials of blood.

2020, Dec. 28 Litho. Perf. 14
2013 A535 $5 Sheet of 4, #a-d 15.00 15.00

Miniature Sheet

Victory in Europe in World War II (V-E Day), 75th Anniv.
A536

No. 2014: a, Alfred Jodl (1890-1946), chief of German Armed Forces High Command. b, Harry S. Truman (1884-1972), U.S. President. c, Soldiers at Arc de Triomphe, Paris. d, Franklin D. Roosevelt (1882-1945), U.S. President. e, Winston Churchill (1874-1965), British Prime Minister.

2020, Dec. 28 Litho. Perf. 12
2014 A536 $4.50 Sheet of 5, #a-e 17.00 17.00

Paintings by Raphael (1483-1520) — A537

No. 2015: a, Portrait of Elisabetta Gonzaga, c. 1504. b, Portrait of Pope Julius II, c. 1512. c, Portrait of Bindo Altoviti, c. 1514. d, Portrait of Baldassaare Castiglione, c. 1515.
$5, Self-portrait, c. 1504-06.

2020, Dec. 28 Litho. Perf. 14
2015 A537 $5.50 Sheet of 4, #a-d 16.50 16.50
Souvenir Sheet
Perf. 12½
2016 A537 $5 multi 3.75 3.75
No. 2016 contains one 38x51mm stamp that has the incorrect inscription of "Sistine Madonna, 1512."

Miniature Sheet

New Year 2021 (Year of the Ox)
A538

No. 2017: a, Red ox with raised leg facing right. b, Head of red ox. c, Red ox with raised leg facing left. d, White ox with raised leg facing right. e, Head of white ox. f, White ox with raised leg facing left.

2020, Dec. 28 Litho. Perf. 14
2017 A538 $3 Sheet of 6, #a-f 13.50 13.50

A539

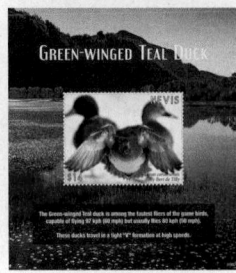

Anas Carolensis — A540

No. 2018 — Photograph of green-winged teal by: a, Unattributed photographer. b, Outriggr. c, Rudolphous. d, Trachemys.
$14, Three ducks.

2021, Jan. 20 Litho. Perf. 14
2018 A539 $5.50 Sheet of 4, #a-d 16.50 16.50
Souvenir Sheet
Perf. 12½
2019 A540 $14 multi 10.50 10.50

A541

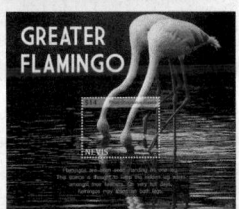

Phoenicopterus Roseus — A542

No. 2020 — Photograph of greater flamingo: a, Facing right, black background. b, Facing right, in water. c, Facing left. d, Facing left, photograph by Max Benningfield.
$14, Two greater flamingos with heads in water.

2021, Jan. 20 Litho. Perf. 14
2020 A541 $5.50 Sheet of 4, #a-d 16.50 16.50
Souvenir Sheet
2021 A542 $14 multi 10.50 10.50

A543

Sea Turtles
A544

No. 2022 — Drawings of sea turtles with: a, Head at right, denomination at LR. b, Denomination at UL. c, Denomination at LL. d, Head at center, denomination at LR.

No. 2023 — Drawings of sea turtles with head at: a, Right. b, Left.

2021, Jan. 20   Litho.   Perf. 14
2022 A543 $5.50 Sheet of 4,
        #a-d   16.50 16.50

Souvenir Sheet
2023 A544 $8 Sheet of 2,
        #a-b   12.00 12.00

A545

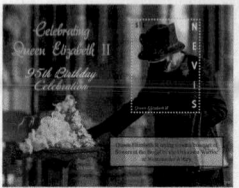

95th Birthday of Queen Elizabeth II A546

No. 2024 — Image of Queen Elizabeth II from: a, 2007 (30x40mm). b, 2006 (30x40mm). c, 1962 (30x80mm). d, 2012, wearing light blue jacket and hat (30x40mm). e, 2012, wearing tiara and ceremonial robe (30x40mm).

$14, Queen Elizabeth II wearing protective face mask.

2021, Mar. 14   Litho.   Perf. 14
2024 A545 $4.95 Sheet of 5,
        #a-e   18.50 18.50

Souvenir Sheet
Perf. 12½
2025 A546 $14 multi   10.50 10.50

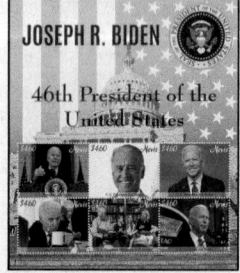

Joseph R. Biden, Jr., 46th President of the United States — A547

No. 2026 — Pres. Biden: a, Behind lectern with Presidential seal. b, With white background. c, With blue background. d, Holding mug. e, With wife, Jill and grandchildren Robert and Natalie. f, Behind microphones at the Pentagon.

$14.60, Pres. Biden behind microphones, vert.

2021   Litho.   Perf. 14
2026 A547 $4.60 Sheet of 6,
        #a-f   20.50 20.50

Souvenir Sheet
Perf. 12½
2027 A547 $14.60 multi   11.00 11.00

Issued: No. 2026, 3/15; No. 2027, 3/14. No. 2027 contains one 38x51mm stamp.

Prince Philip (1921-2021) — A548

No. 2028: a, Prince Philip and Princess Elizabeth on wedding day. b, Prince Philip and

Queen Elizabeth II. c, Prince Philip wearing hat. d, Prince Philip without hat.

$14, Pallbearers at coffin of Prince Philip.

2021   Litho.   Perf. 14
2028 A548 $5.50 Sheet of 4,
        #a-d   16.50 16.50

Souvenir Sheet
Perf. 12
2029 A548 $14 multi   10.50 10.50

The date of issue reported for Nos. 2028-2029 is April. 9, 2021, the date of Prince Philip's death. No. 2029 contains one 50x30mm stamp.

Miniature Sheet

Elvis Presley (1935-77) — A549

No. 2030 — Presley: a, Wearing blue and gray shirt. b, Looking left, one eye visible. c, Wearing white jacket. d, Singing. e, Looking left, both eyes visible.

2021, July 5   Litho.   Perf. 14
2030 A549 $4.50 Sheet of 5,
        #a-e   17.00 17.00

10th Wedding Anniversary of the Duke and Duchess of Cambridge — A550

No. 2031: a, Duke and Duchess of Cambridge, Duke with legs crossed. b, Duke and Duchess, Duchess wearing hat. c, Duke and Duchess, Duke holding umbrella. d, Queen Elizabeth II and Duchess of Cambridge.

$14, Duke and Duchess on wedding day.

2021, July 5   Litho.   Perf. 14
2031 A550 $5.50 Sheet of 4,
        #a-d   16.50 16.50

Souvenir Sheet
Perf. 12½
2032 A550 $14 multi   10.50 10.50

No. 2032 contains one 51x38mm stamp.

3rd Wedding Anniversary of the Duke and Duchess of Sussex — A551

No. 2031: a, $5, Duke and Duchess of Sussex, Duchess wearing striped dress. b, $5, Duke and Duchess, Duchess wearing hat. c, $6, Duke and Duchess, Duchess waving. d, $6, Queen Elizabeth II and Duchess of Sussex.

$14, Duke and Duchess looking skyward at Royal Air Force ceremony.

2021, July 5   Litho.   Perf. 14
2033 A551   Sheet of 4, #a-
        d   16.50 16.50

Souvenir Sheet
2034 A551 $14 multi   10.50 10.50

Miniature Sheet

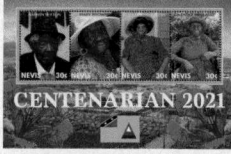

Centenarians — A552

No. 2035: a, Nathan Sutton. b, Mary Browne. c, Eliza Liburd Jeffers. d, Gwendolyn Clarke.

2021, Nov. 5   Litho.   Perf. 13¼x13½
2035 A552 30c Sheet of 4, #a-d   .90   .90

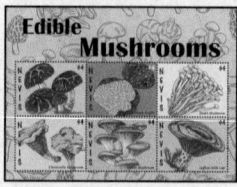

Edible Mushrooms — A553

No. 2036: a, Shiitake mushrooms. b, Black truffles. c, Enoki mushrooms. d, Chanterelle mushrooms. e, Oyster mushrooms. f, Saffron milk cap.

$14, Caesar's mushrooms, vert.

2021, Nov. 8   Litho.   Perf. 14
2036 A553 $4 Sheet of 6, #a-
        f   18.00 18.00

Souvenir Sheet
Perf. 12½
2037 A553 $14 multi   10.50 10.50

No. 2037 contains one 38x51mm stamp.

Macaws A554

No. 2038: a, Glaucous macaw. b, Blue and yellow macaw. c, Green-winged macaw. d, Red-shouldered macaw. e, Great green macaw. f, Lear's macaw.

No. 2039: a, Cuban macaw. b, Red-fronted macaw.

2021, Nov. 8   Litho.   Perf. 14
2038 A554 $3.50 Sheet of 6,
        #a-f   15.50 15.50

Souvenir Sheet
2039 A554 $8 Sheet of 2,
        #a-b   12.00 12.00

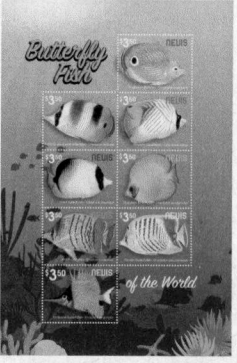

Butterflyfish — A555

No. 2040: a, Foureye butterflyfish. b, Pacific double-saddle butterflyfish. c, Threadfin butterflyfish. d, Lined butterflyfish. e, Bluecheek butterflyfish. f, Atoll butterflyfish. g, Eritrean butterflyfish. h, Longnose butterflyfish.

No. 2041: a, Millet butterflyfish. b, Fourspot butterflyfish.

2021, Nov. 8   Litho.   Perf. 14
2040 A555 $3.50 Sheet of 8,
        #a-h   21.00 21.00

Souvenir Sheet
2041 A555 $8 Sheet of 2,
        #a-b   12.00 15.50

Sharks A556

No. 2042: a, Caribbean reef shark. b, Bull shark. c, Blacktip reef shark. d, Silky shark. e, Pelagic thresher shark. f, Galapagos shark. g, Caribbean sharpnose shark. h, Night shark.

No. 2043: a, Australian sharpnose shark. b, Crocodile shark.

2021, Nov. 8   Litho.   Perf. 14
2042 A556 $3.50 Sheet of 8,
        #a-h   21.00 21.00

Souvenir Sheet
2043 A556 $8 Sheet of 2,
        #a-b   12.00 15.50

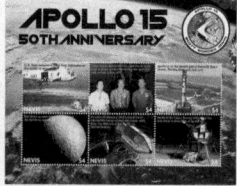

Flight of Apollo 15, 50th Anniv. A557

No. 2044: a, U.S. Navy divers leaving helicopter to secure Apollo 15 capsule in Pacific Ocean. b, Apollo 15 crew members James B. Irwin, Alfred M. Worden and David R. Scott. c, Apollo 15 on launch pad. d, Picture of Moon taken from Apollo 15. e, Drawing of deployment of Particles and Fields Subsatellite. f, Model of Apollo 15 Lunar Module on Moon.

$14, Scott's spacesuit on display at the Smithsonian Institution, vert.

2021, Dec. 1   Litho.   Perf. 14
2044 A557 $4 Sheet of 6, #a-
        f   18.00 18.00

Souvenir Sheet
Perf. 12½
2045 A557 $14 multi   10.50 10.50

No. 2045 contains one 38x51mm stamp.

Reign of Queen Elizabeth II (1926-2022), 70th Anniv. — A558

No. 2046 — Photograph of Queen Elizabeth II: a, Wearing tiara and sash. b, Wearing pink jacket and hat. c, Wearing light blue jacket and hat. d, Holding infant. e, Wearing white jacket and hat.

$12.70, Queen Elizabeth II wearing gown and tiara.

2022, Feb. 6   Litho.   Perf. 14
2046 A558 $3.70 Sheet of 5,
        #a-e   14.00 14,00

Souvenir Sheet
Perf. 12½
2047 A558 $12.70 multi   9.50   9.50

No. 2047 contains one 38x51mm stamp.

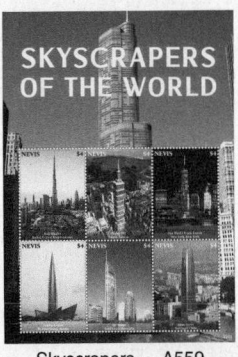

SKYSCRAPERS OF THE WORLD

Skyscrapers — A559

No. 2048: a, Burj Khalifa, Dubai, United Arab Emirates. b, Taipei 101, Taipei, Republic of China. c, One World Trade Center, New York City. d, Lakhta Center, St. Petersburg, Russia. e, Q1 Tower, Gold Coast, Australia. f, Gran Torre Santiago, Santiago, Chile. $14, Willis Tower, Chicago, Illinois.

2022, Mar. 7		**Litho.**		**Perf. 14**
2048	A559	$4 Sheet of 6, #a-f	18.00	18.00

Souvenir Sheet
Perf. 12

2049	A559	$14 multi	10.50	10.50

No. 2049 contains one 30x60mm stamp.

OFFICIAL STAMPS

> Catalogue values for unused stamps in this section are for Never Hinged items.

Nos. 103-112 Ovptd. "OFFICIAL"
Perf. 14½x14

1980, July 30		**Litho.**		**Wmk. 373**
O1	A61	15c multicolored	.25	.25
O2	A61	25c multicolored	.25	.25
O3	A61	30c multicolored	.25	.25
O4	A61	40c multicolored	.25	.25
O5	A61	45c multicolored	.25	.25
O6	A61	50c multicolored	.25	.25
O7	A61	55c multicolored	.25	.25
O8	A61	$1 multicolored	.30	.30
O9	A61	$5 multicolored	1.50	1.50
O10	A61	$10 multicolored	2.50	2.50
		Nos. O1-O10 (10)	6.05	6.05

Inverted or double overprints exist on some denominations.

Nos. 123-134 Ovptd. "OFFICIAL"

1981, Mar.				**Perf. 14**
O11	A9	15c multicolored	.25	.25
O12	A9	20c multicolored	.25	.25
O13	A9	25c multicolored	.25	.25
O14	A9	30c multicolored	.25	.25
O15	A9	40c multicolored	.25	.25
O16	A9	45c multicolored	.25	.25
O17	A9	50c multicolored	.25	.25
O18	A9	55c multicolored	.25	.25
O19	A9	$1 multicolored	.35	.35
O20	A9	$2.50 multicolored	.80	.80
O21	A9	$5 multicolored	1.50	1.50
O22	A9	$10 multicolored	2.50	2.50
		Nos. O11-O22 (12)	7.15	7.15

Nos. 135-140 Ovptd. or Surcharged "OFFICIAL" in Blue or Black

1983, Feb. 2				
O23	A9a	45c on $2 #137	.30	.30
O24	A9b	45c on $2 #138	.30	.30
O25	A9b	55c #135	.40	.40
O26	A9b	55c #136	.40	.40
O27	A9a	$1.10 on $5 #139 (Bk)	.80	.80
O28	A9b	$1.10 on $5 #140 (Bk)	.80	.80
		Nos. O23-O28 (6)	3.00	3.00

Inverted or double overprints exist on some denominations.

Nos. 367-378 Ovptd. "OFFICIAL"

1985, Jan. 2				**Wmk. 380**
O29	A24b	15c multicolored	.30	.30
O30	A24b	20c multicolored	.30	.30
O31	A24b	30c multicolored	.30	.30
O32	A24b	40c multicolored	.30	.30
O33	A24b	50c multicolored	.35	.35
O34	A24b	55c multicolored	.35	.35
O35	A24b	60c multicolored	.35	.35
O36	A24b	75c multicolored	.45	.45
O37	A24b	$1 multicolored	.65	.65
O38	A24b	$3 multicolored	1.90	1.90
O39	A24b	$5 multicolored	3.25	3.25
O40	A24b	$10 multicolored	6.50	6.50
		Nos. O29-O40 (12)	15.00	15.00

Nos. 640-646, 648-653 Ovptd. "OFFICIAL"

1993		**Litho.**		**Perf. 14**
O41	A71	5c multicolored	.30	.30
O42	A71	10c multicolored	.30	.30
O43	A71	15c multicolored	.30	.30
O44	A71	20c multicolored	.30	.30
O45	A71	25c multicolored	.30	.30
O46	A71	40c multicolored	.35	.35
O47	A71	50c multicolored	.50	.50
O48	A71	75c multicolored	.70	.70
O49	A71	80c multicolored	.75	.75
O50	A71	$1 multicolored	.95	.95
O51	A71	$3 multicolored	2.75	2.75
O52	A71	$5 multicolored	4.75	4.75
O53	A71	$10 multicolored	9.25	9.25
O54	A71	$20 multicolored	18.00	18.00
		Nos. O41-O54 (14)	39.50	39.50

Dated "1992."

Nos. 1055-1066 Ovptd. "OFFICIAL"

1999, Mar. 22		**Litho.**		**Perf. 14**
O55	A151	25c multicolored	.25	.25
O56	A151	30c multicolored	.25	.25
O57	A151	50c multicolored	.40	.40
O58	A151	60c multicolored	.45	.45
O59	A151	80c multicolored	.60	.60
O60	A151	90c multicolored	.70	.70
O61	A151	$1 multicolored	.75	.75
O62	A151	$1.80 multicolored	1.40	1.40
O63	A151	$3 multicolored	2.25	2.25
O64	A151	$5 multicolored	3.75	3.75
O65	A151	$10 multicolored	7.50	7.50
O66	A151	$20 multicolored	15.00	15.00
		Nos. O55-O66 (12)	33.30	33.30

NEW BRITAIN

'nü 'bri-tən

LOCATION — South Pacific Ocean, northeast of New Guinea
GOVT. — Australian military government
AREA — 13,000 sq. mi. (approx.)
POP. — 50,600 (approx.)
CAPITAL — Rabaul

The island Neu-Pommern, a part of former German New Guinea, was captured during World War I by Australian troops and named New Britain. Following the war it was mandated to Australia and designated a part of the Mandated Territory of New Guinea. See German New Guinea, North West Pacific Islands and New Guinea.

12 Pence = 1 Shilling

Stamps of German New Guinea, 1900, Surcharged

Kaiser's Yacht "The Hohenzollern"
A3   A4

First Setting
Surcharge lines spaced 6mm on 1p-8p, 4mm on 1sh-5sh
Unwmk.

		Perf. 14, 14½		
1	A3	1p on 3pf brown	750.00	875.00
2	A3	1p on 5pf green	95.00	200.00
3	A3	2p on 10pf car	100.00	260.00
4	A3	2p on 20pf ultra	100.00	200.00
a.		"2d." dbl., "G.R.I." omitted	6,000.	
b.		Inverted surcharge	16,500.	
5	A3	2½p on 10pf car	105.00	220.00
6	A3	2½p on 20pf ultra	120.00	250.00
a.		Inverted surcharge		
7	A3	3p on 25pf org & blk, yel	375.00	475.00
8	A3	3p on 30pf org & blk, sal	475.00	525.00
a.		Double surcharge	15,000.	15,000.
b.		Inverted surcharge	16,250.	
c.		"4d." omitted		
9	A3	4p on 40pf lake & black	475.00	625.00
a.		Double surcharge	4,100.	5,000.
b.		Inverted surcharge	16,250.	

10	A3	5p on 50pf pur & blk, sal	850.00	1,100.
a.		Double surcharge	16,250.	
11	A3	8p on 80pf lake & blk, rose	1,050.	1,650.
a.		No period after "8d"	4,600.	
b.		Surcharged "G.R.I. 4d" (error)	15,250.	
12	A4	1sh on 1m car	5,500.	4,750.
13	A4	2sh on 2m blue	3,750.	4,500.
a.		Surcharged "G.R.I. 5s" (error)	45,000.	
b.		Surcharged "G.R.I. 2d" corrected by hand-stamped "s"	55,000.	
14	A4	3sh on 3m blk vio	6,000.	7,750.
a.		No period after "I"	14,000.	14,000.
15	A4	5sh on 5m slate & car	14,000.	16,500.
a.		No period after "I"	18,500.	23,000.
b.		Surcharged "G.R.I. 1s" (error)	87,500.	

"G.R.I." stands for Georgius Rex Imperator.

Second Setting
Surcharge lines spaced 5mm on 1p-8p, 5½mm on 1sh-5sh

1914, Dec. 16				
16	A3	1p on 3pf brown	110.00	120.00
a.		Double surcharge	1,500.	1,850.
b.		"I" for "1"	825.00	
c.		"1" with straight top serif	160.00	190.00
d.		Inverted surcharge	6,000.	—
e.		"4" for "1"	17,500.	
f.		Small "1"	350.00	
g.		Double surcharge, one inverted	8,000.	
17	A3	1p on 5pf green	37.50	55.00
a.		Double surcharge	5,250.	
b.		"G. I. R."	13,000.	14,000.
c.		"d" inverted		3,750.
d.		No periods after "G R I"		11,000.
e.		Small "1"	140.00	210.00
f.		"1d" double		
g.		No period after "1d"		
h.		Triple surcharge		
18	A3	2p on 10pf car	50.00	65.00
a.		Double surcharge	16,250.	16,250.
b.		Dbl. surch., one inverted		13,000.
c.		Surcharged "G. I. R., 3d" (error)	13,000.	
d.		Surcharged "1d" (error)	12,500.	12,500.
e.		Period before "G"	11,000.	
f.		No period after "2d"	200.00	275.00
g.		Inverted surcharge		
h.		"2d" double, one inverted		
j.		Pair, #18, 20	30,000.	
19	A3	2p on 20pf ultra	50.00	75.00
a.		Double surcharge	3,500.	5,250.
b.		Double surch., one inverted	5,000.	6,500.
c.		"R" inverted		9,250.
d.		Surcharged "1d" (error)	13,000.	14,000.
f.		Inverted surcharge	11,500.	13,500.
h.		Pair, one without surcharge	25,000.	
i.		Vertical pair, #19, 21	20,000.	23,000.
20	A3	2½p on 10pf car	250.00	375.00
21	A3	2½p on 20pf ultra	2,100.	2,500.
a.		Double surcharge, one invtd.		
b.		"2½" triple		
c.		Surcharged "3d" in pair with normal	42,500.	
22	A3	3p on 25pf org & blk, yel	190.00	275.00
a.		Double surcharge	11,000.	13,000.
b.		Inverted surcharge	11,000.	13,000.
c.		"G. R. I." only		
d.		"G. I. R."		
e.		Pair, one without surcharge	15,000.	
f.		Surcharged "G. I. R., 5d" (error)		
g.		Surcharged "G" (error)	22,000.	
23	A3	3p on 30pf org & blk, sal	175.00	240.00
a.		Double surcharge	4,000.	4,600.
b.		Double surcharge, one invtd.	4,500.	5,500.
c.		"d" inverted		
d.		Surcharged "1d" (error)	12,000.	16,000.
e.		Triple surcharge		
g.		Double inverted surcharge	13,000.	14,000.
h.		Pair, one without surcharge	14,000.	
24	A3	4p on 40pf lake & blk	185.00	300.00
a.		Double surcharge	3,500.	—
b.		Double surcharge, both invtd.	13,000.	
c.		Double surcharge, one invtd.	5,250.	
d.		Inverted surcharge	9,250.	
e.		Surcharged "1d" (error)	9,000.	
f.		"1" on "4"		
g.		As "e," inverted	20,000.	
h.		Surcharge "G.R.I. 3d," double (error)	27,500.	
i.		No period after "I"	3,500.	
25	A3	5p on 50pf pur & blk, sal	350.00	400.00
a.		Double surcharge	4,500.	5,500.
b.		Double surcharge, one invtd.	10,500.	10,500.
c.		"5" omitted		
d.		Inverted surcharge	10,000.	10,000.
e.		Double inverted surcharge	13,000.	14,000.
f.		"G. I. R."		
g.		Surcharge "G.R.I. 3d" (error)	23,000.	
26	A3	8p on 80pf lake & blk, rose	475.00	650.00
a.		Double surcharge	7,000.	8,250.
b.		Double surcharge, one invtd.	7,000.	8,250.
d.		Triple surcharge	9,500.	10,000.
e.		No period after "8d"		
f.		Inverted surcharge	14,000.	14,000.
g.		Surcharged "3d" (error)	18,500.	18,500.
27	A4	1sh on 1m car	5,250.	8,250.
a.		No period after "I"	12,000.	

28	A4	2sh on 2m bl	5,500.	8,750.
a.		Surcharged "5s" (error)		
b.		Inverted surcharge		
c.		No period after "I"	13,000.	
29	A4	3sh on 3m blk vio	10,000.	16,250.
a.		No periods after "R I"		
b.		Surcharged "s"	45,000.	
29C	A4	5sh on 5m sl & car	42,500.	45,000.
d.		No period after "R I"		
e.		Surcharged "1s"		

Nos. 18-19 Surcharged with Large "1"

1915, Jan.				
29F	A3	1(p) on 2p on 10pf carmine	32,500.	30,000.
29G	A3	1(p) on 2p on 20pf ultramarine	30,000.	17,500.

Same Surcharge on Stamps of Marshall Islands

1914				
30	A3	1p on 3pf brn	110.00	170.00
a.		Inverted surcharge	9,250.	
31	A3	1p on 5pf green	90.00	130.00
a.		Double surcharge	3,800.	5,000.
b.		No period after "d"		
c.		Inverted surcharge	5,250.	
32	A3	2p on 10pf car	27.50	50.00
a.		Double surcharge	3,800.	
b.		Double surcharge, one invtd.	5,500.	
c.		Surcharge sideways	10,500.	
d.		No period after "2d"		
e.		No period after "G"	875.00	
f.		Inverted surcharge	7,000.	
33	A3	2p on 20 pf ultra	30.00	50.00
a.		No period after "d"	80.00	150.00
b.		Double surcharge	4,000.	5,000.
c.		Double surcharge, one invtd.	9,750.	10,500.
d.		Inverted surcharge	11,000.	11,000.
e.		"I" omitted		
34	A3	3p on 25pf org & blk, yel	475.00	600.00
a.		Double surcharge	4,250.	5,000.
b.		Double surcharge, one invtd.	4,700.	
c.		No period after "d"	925.00	1,250.
d.		Inverted surcharge	13,000.	
35	A3	3p on 30pf org & blk, sal	475.00	600.00
a.		No period after "d"	925.00	1,200.
b.		Inverted surcharge	9,000.	9,500.
c.		Double surcharge	7,000.	
d.		Double surcharge, one invtd.		
36	A3	4p on 40pf lake & blk	175.00	250.00
a.		No period after "d"	475.00	700.00
b.		Double surcharge	7,000.	8,000.
c.		"4d" omitted		
d.		"1d" on "4d"		
e.		No period after "R"		
f.		Inverted surcharge	11,000.	
g.		Surcharged "1d" (error)	17,500.	
h.		Surcharged "G.R.I. 3d" (error)		
37	A3	5p on 50pf pur & blk, sal	300.00	375.00
a.		"d" omitted	2,250.	
b.		Double surcharge	10,500.	
c.		"5d" double		
d.		Inverted surcharge	16,500.	
38	A3	8p on 80pf lake & blk, rose	525.00	775.00
a.		Inverted surcharge	11,500.	
b.		Double surcharge	10,000.	
c.		Double surcharge, one invtd.		
d.		Triple surcharge	16,500.	
e.		Double surcharge, both inverted	13,250.	14,000.
39	A4	1sh on 1m car	4,100.	5,500.
a.		Double surcharge	45,000.	
b.		Dbl. surch., one with "s1" for "1s"		
c.		No period after "I"	6,500.	9,250.
d.		Additional surcharge "1d"	50,000.	
40	A4	2sh on 2m blue	2,000.	4,500.
a.		Double surcharge, one invtd.	45,000.	45,000.
b.		No period after "I"	45,000.	45,000.
c.		Large "S"		
d.		No period after "I"	3,750.	6,500.
41	A4	3sh on 3m blk vio	6,500.	9,750.
a.		Double surcharge	42,500.	45,000.
b.		No period after "I"	8,750.	
c.		No period after "R I"		
d.		Inverted surcharge		
42	A4	5sh on 5m sl & car	14,000.	15,000.
a.		Double surcharge, one invtd.	75,000.	

See Nos. 44-45.

A5

Surcharged in Black on Registration Label
Town Name in Sans-Serif Letters

1914				**Perf. 12**
43	A5	3p black & red (Rabaul)	300.00	350.00
a.		Double surcharge (Rabaul)	5,500.	7,000.

44	A5 3p black & red (Friedrich Wilhelmshaven)	275.00	875.00
45	A5 3p black & red (Herbertshohe)	325.00	875.00
46	A5 3p black & red (Kawieng)	350.00	700.00
a.	Double surcharge		
47	A5 3p black & red (Kieta)	500.00	875.00
a.	Pair, one without surcharge	16,500.	
48	A5 3p black & red (Manus)	325.00	925.00
a.	Double surcharge	9,250.	
49	A5 3p black & red (Deulon)	27,500.	30,000.
50	A5 3p black & red (Stephansort)		4,500.

Nos. 44, 46 and 48 exist with town name in letters with serifs. The varieties Deutsch-Neuguinea, Deutsch Neu-Guinea, etc., are known. For detailed listings see the *Scott Classic Specialized Catalogue of Stamps and Covers*.

Nos. 32-33 Surcharged
with Large "1"

1915

51	A3 1p on 2p on 10pf	275.	300.
a.	"1" double	16,500.	
b.	"1" inverted	20,000.	20,000.
52	A3 1p on 2p on 20pf	4,000.	2,750.
a.	"1" inverted	20,000.	20,000.

The stamps of Marshall Islands surcharged "G. R. I." and new values in British currency were all used in New Britain and are therefore listed here.

Stamps of Marshall Islands Surcharged
Surcharge lines spaced 6mm apart

53	A3 1p on 3pf brown	3,750.	
a.	Inverted surcharge	16,000.	
54	A3 1p on 5pf green	3,750.	
a.	Inverted surcharge	16,500.	
55	A3 2p on 10pf car	4,750.	
56	A3 2p on 20pf ultra	4,250.	
a.	Inverted surcharge	17,000.	
57	A3 2½p on 10pf car	30,000.	
58	A3 2½p on 20pf ultra	45,000.	
59	A3 3p on 25pf org & blk, *yel*	7,000.	
60	A3 3p on 30pf org & blk, *sal*	7,000.	
61	A3 4p on 40pf lake	7,000.	
a.	Inverted surcharge	18,000.	
62	A3 5p on 50pf pur & blk, *sal*	6,500.	
63	A3 8p on 80pf lake & blk, *rose*	7,500.	
		20,000.	

Surcharge lines spaced 5½mm apart

64	A4 1sh on 1m car	17,500.	
a.	Large "S"	22,500.	
65	A4 2sh on 2m bl	14,500.	
a.	Large "S"	20,000.	
66	A4 3sh on 3m blk viol	30,000.	
a.	Large "S"	40,000.	
67	A4 5sh on 5m sl & car	45,000.	
a.	Large "S"	52,500.	

OFFICIAL STAMPS

O1

German New Guinea Nos. 7-8 Surcharged

1915   **Unwmk.**   **Perf. 14**

O1	O1 1p on 3pf brown	36.00	80.00
a.	Double surcharge	5,500.	
O2	O1 1p on 5pf green	110.00	150.00

NEW CALEDONIA

ˌnü ˌka-lə-ˈdō-nyə

LOCATION — Island in the South Pacific Ocean, east of Queensland, Australia

GOVT. — French Overseas Territory
AREA — 7,172 sq. mi.
POP. — 197,361 (1999 est.)
CAPITAL — Noumea

Dependencies of New Caledonia are the Loyalty Islands, Isle of Pines, Huon Islands and Chesterfield Islands.

100 Centimes = 1 Franc

> **Catalogue values for unused stamps in this country are for Never Hinged items, beginning with Scott 252 in the regular postage section, Scott B10 in the semipostal section, Scott C14 in the airpost section, Scott J32 in the postage due section, and Scott O1 in the official section.**

Watermark

TOR C
CARTO
TOR C
CARTO   Wmk. 385

Napoleon III — A1

1859   **Unwmk.**   **Litho.**   **Imperf.**
Without Gum

1	A1 10c black	250.00	250.00

Fifty varieties. Counterfeits abound. See No. 315.

Type of French Colonies, 1877 Surcharged in Black

Nos. 2-5   Nos. 6-7

1881-83

2	A8 5c on 40c red, *straw* ('82)	425.00	425.00
a.	Inverted surcharge	1,600.	1,600.
b.	Double surcharge	1,350.	
c.	Double surcharge, both inverted	1,900.	1,900.
3	A8 05c on 40c red, *straw* ('83)	40.00	40.00
4	A8 25c on 35c dp vio, *yel*	300.00	300.00
a.	Inverted surcharge	950.00	950.00
5	A8 25c on 75c rose car, *rose* ('82)	400.00	400.00
a.	Inverted surcharge	1,250.	1,250.

1883-84

6	A8 5c on 40c red, *straw* ('84)	26.50	26.50
a.	Inverted surcharge	26.50	26.50
7	A8 5c on 75c rose car, *rose* ('83)	52.50	52.50
a.	Inverted surcharge	75.00	75.00

In type "a" surcharge, the narrower-spaced letters measure 14½mm, and an early printing of No. 4 measures 13½mm. Type "b" letters measure 18mm.

French Colonies No. 59 Surcharged in Black

No. 8   Nos. 9-10

1886   **Perf. 14x13½**

8	A9 5c on 1fr	32.50	26.50
a.	Inverted surcharge	45.00	45.00
b.	Double surcharge	200.00	200.00
c.	Double surcharge, one inverted	225.00	225.00
9	A9 5c on 1fr	32.50	30.00
a.	Inverted surcharge	60.00	60.00
b.	Double surcharge	200.00	200.00
c.	Double surcharge, one inverted	225.00	225.00

French Colonies No. 29
Surcharged

Imperf

10	A8 5c on 1fr	10,000.	11,500.

Types of French Colonies, 1877-86, Surcharged in Black

Nos. 11, 13   No. 12

1891-92   **Imperf.**

11	A8 10c on 40c red, *straw* ('92)	45.00	40.00
a.	Inverted surcharge	42.50	37.50
b.	Double surcharge	100.00	100.00
c.	Double surcharge, one inverted	190.00	190.00
d.	No period after "10c"	125.00	125.00

Perf. 14x13½

12	A9 10c on 30c brn, *bis*	25.00	22.50
a.	Inverted surcharge	25.00	22.50
b.	Double surcharge	67.50	67.50
c.	Double surcharge, inverted	60.00	60.00
d.	Double surcharge, one inverted	100.00	100.00
13	A9 10c on 40c red, *straw* ('92)	26.00	26.00
a.	Inverted surcharge	26.00	26.00
b.	No period after "10c"	60.00	60.00
c.	Double surcharge	67.50	67.50
d.	Double surcharge, one inverted	110.00	100.00
	Nos. 11-13 (3)	96.00	88.50

Variety "double surcharge, one inverted" exists on Nos. 11-13. Value slightly higher than for "double surcharge."

Types of French Colonies, 1877-86, Handstamped in Black — g

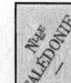

1892   **Imperf.**

16	A8 20c red, *grn*	350.00	400.00
a.	Inverted surcharge	850.00	900.00
17	A8 35c violet, *org*	75.00	75.00
a.	Pair, one stamp without surcharge	950.00	
18	A8 40c red, *straw*	1,500.	
19	A8 1fr bronz grn, *straw*	300.00	300.00

The 1c, 2c, 4c and 75c of type A8 are believed not to have been officially made or actually used.

1892   **Perf. 14x13½**

23	A9 5c green, *grnsh*	19.00	15.00
a.	Pair, one stamp without overprint	600.00	
24	A9 10c blk, *lavender*	140.00	82.50
25	A9 15c blue	110.00	60.00
a.	Pair, one stamp without surcharge	825.00	
26	A9 20c red, *grn*	110.00	60.00
27	A9 25c yellow, *straw*	30.00	22.50
28	A9 25c black, *rose*	110.00	37.50
29	A9 30c brown, *bis*	90.00	75.00
30	A9 35c violet, *org*	240.00	190.00
a.	Inverted overprint	650.00	
b.	Pair, one stamp without overprint	1,350.	
32	A9 75c carmine, *rose*	225.00	190.00
a.	Pair, one stamp without overprint	1,350.	
33	A9 1fr bronz grn, *straw*	190.00	175.00
	Nos. 23-33 (10)	1,264.	907.50

The note following No. 19 also applies to the 1c, 2c, 4c and 40c of type A9.

Surcharged in Blue or
Black — h

1892-93   **Imperf.**

34	A8 10c on 1fr brnz grn, *straw* (Bl)	5,250.	4,500.

Perf. 14x13½

35	A9 5c on 20c red, *grn* (Bk)	27.50	22.50
a.	Inverted surcharge	125.00	125.00
b.	Double surcharge	82.50	100.00
36	A9 5c on 75c car, *rose* (Bk)	22.50	16.50
a.	Inverted surcharge	125.00	125.00
b.	Double surcharge	82.50	82.50
37	A9 5c on 75c car, *rose* (Bl)	18.50	15.00
a.	Inverted surcharge	125.00	125.00
b.	Double surcharge	82.50	82.50
38	A9 10c on 1fr brnz grn, *straw* (Bk)	21.00	15.00
a.	Inverted surcharge	600.00	600.00
39	A9 10c on 1fr brnz grn, *straw* (Bl)	22.50	21.00
a.	Inverted surcharge	125.00	125.00
b.	Double surcharge	85.00	85.00
	Nos. 35-39 (5)	112.00	90.00

Navigation and
Commerce — A12

1892-1904   **Typo.**   **Perf. 14x13½**
Name of Colony in Blue or Carmine

40	A12 1c black, *blue*	1.10	1.10
41	A12 2c brown, *buff*	1.90	1.90
42	A12 4c claret, *lav*	2.50	2.25
43	A12 5c green, *grnsh*	4.00	1.90
44	A12 5c yellow green ('00)	2.25	1.50
45	A12 10c blk, *lavender*	9.00	5.25
46	A12 10c rose red ('00)	11.00	1.50
47	A12 15c bl, quadrille paper	30.00	3.50
48	A12 15c gray ('00)	20.00	1.50
49	A12 20c red, *grn*	20.00	10.50
50	A12 25c black, *rose*	25.00	6.75
51	A12 25c blue ('00)	22.00	10.50
52	A12 30c brown, *bis*	25.00	13.50
53	A12 40c red, *straw*	26.00	13.50
54	A12 50c carmine, *rose*	67.50	37.50
55	A12 50c brn, *az* (name in car) ('00)	125.00	85.00
56	A12 50c brn, *az* (name in bl) ('04)	65.00	42.50
57	A12 75c violet, *org*	37.50	26.50
58	A12 1fr bronz grn, *straw*	45.00	26.50
	Nos. 40-58 (19)	539.75	293.15

Perf. 13½x14 stamps are counterfeits. For overprints and surcharges see Nos. 59-87, 117-121.

Nos. 41-42, 52, 57-58 Surcharged in Black

j

1900-01

59	A12 (h) 5c on 2c ('01)	22.50	19.00
a.	Double surcharge	140.00	140.00
b.	Inverted surcharge	125.00	125.00
	Never hinged	210.00	
60	A12 (h) 5c on 4c	4.50	4.50
a.	Inverted surcharge	82.50	82.50
b.	Double surcharge	87.50	87.50
61	A12 (j) 15c on 30c	5.25	4.50
a.	Inverted surcharge	75.00	75.00
b.	Double surcharge	67.50	67.50
62	A12 (j) 15c on 75c ('01)	20.00	17.50
a.	Pair, one without surcharge	—	
b.	Inverted surcharge	130.00	130.00
c.	Double surcharge	140.00	140.00
63	A12 (j) 15c on 1fr ('01)	26.50	26.50
a.	Inverted surcharge	175.00	175.00
b.	Double surcharge	175.00	175.00
	Nos. 59-63 (5)	78.75	72.00

Nos. 52-53 Surcharged in Black

k

1902

64	A12 (k) 5c on 30c	10.50	9.00
a.	Inverted surcharge	52.50	52.50
65	A12 (k) 15c on 40c	10.50	8.25
a.	Inverted surcharge	52.50	52.50

Jubilee Issue

Stamps of 1892-1900
Overprinted in Blue, Red,
Black or Gold

1903

66	A12	1c blk, *lil bl* (Bl)	3.00	3.00
a.		Inverted overprint	290.00	290.00
67	A12	2c brown, *buff* (Bl)	5.25	4.50
68	A12	4c claret, *lav* (Bl)	7.50	6.00
a.		Double overprint	375.00	375.00
69	A12	5c dk grn, *grnsh* (R)	7.50	4.50
70	A12	5c yellow green (R)	10.00	9.00
71	A12	10c blk, *lav* (R)	19.00	16.00
72	A12	10c blk, *lav* (double G & Bk)	11.50	9.00
73	A12	15c gray (R)	15.00	11.50
74	A12	20c red, *grn* (Bl)	22.00	19.00
75	A12	25c blk, *rose* (Bl)	19.50	19.00
a.		Double overprint	325.00	
76	A12	30c brown, *bis* (R)	26.50	22.50
77	A12	40c red, *straw* (Bl)	34.00	30.00
78	A12	50c car, *rose* (Bl)	60.00	52.50
a.		Pair, one without overprint	300.00	
79	A12	75c vio, *org* (Bk)	77.50	72.50
a.		Dbl. ovpt. in blk and red	500.00	
80	A12	1fr brnz grn, *straw* (Bl)	120.00	115.00
a.		Dbl. ovpt., one in red	525.00	525.00
		Nos. 66-80 (15)	438.25	394.00

With Additional Surcharge of New Value in Blue

(a)   (b)

(c)

81	A12 (a)	1c on 2c #67	1.90	1.90
a.		Numeral double	115.00	115.00
b.		Numeral only	400.00	
82	A12 (b)	2c on 4c #68	3.50	3.50
83	A12 (a)	4c on 5c #69	2.25	2.25
a.		Small "4"	650.00	650.00
84	A12 (c)	4c on 5c #70	3.00	3.00
a.		Pair, one without numeral		
85	A12 (b)	10c on 15c #73	3.00	3.00
86	A12 (b)	15c on 20c #74	3.75	3.75
87	A12 (b)	20c on 25c #75	9.00	9.00
		Nos. 81-87 (7)	26.40	26.40

50 years of French occupation.

Surcharge on Nos. 81-83, 85-86 is horizontal, reading down.

There are three types of numeral on No. 83. The numeral on No. 84 is identical with that of No. 83a except that its position is upright.

Nos. 66-87 are known with "I" of "TENAIRE" missing.

Kagu
A16

Landscape
A17

Ship — A18

1905-28   Typo.   Perf. 14x13½

88	A16	1c blk, *green*	.30	.30
89	A16	2c red brown	.30	.30
90	A16	4c bl, *yel*	.45	.45
91	A16	5c pale green	.55	.55
92	A16	5c dl bl ('21)	.40	.40
93	A16	10c carmine	1.90	1.25
94	A16	10c green ('21)	.75	.75
95	A16	10c red, *pink* ('25)	.85	.85
96	A16	15c violet	.90	.85
97	A17	20c brown	.55	.55
98	A17	25c blue, *grn*	1.05	.60
99	A17	25c red, *yel* ('21)	.75	.75
100	A17	30c brn, *org*	1.40	.85
101	A17	30c dp rose ('21)	2.50	2.50
102	A17	30c org ('25)	.60	.60
103	A17	35c blk, *yellow*	.75	.75
104	A17	40c car, *org*	1.25	1.05
105	A17	45c vio brn, *lav*	.75	.75
106	A17	50c red, *org*	3.25	3.00
107	A17	50c dk bl ('21)	1.75	1.75
108	A17	50c gray ('25)	1.05	1.05
109	A17	65c dp bl ('28)	.90	.90
110	A17	75c ol grn, *straw*	.85	.70
111	A17	75c bl, *bluish* ('25)	.90	.90
112	A17	75c violet ('27)	1.15	1.15
113	A18	1fr bl, *yel grn*	1.30	1.05
114	A18	1fr dp bl ('25)	1.90	1.90

115	A18	2fr car, *bl*	3.50	2.25
116	A18	5fr blk, *straw*	6.75	6.75
		Nos. 88-116 (29)	39.30	35.50

See Nos. 311, 317a. For surcharges see Nos. 122-135, B1-B3, Q1-Q3.

Nos. 96, 98, 103, 106, 113 and 115, pasted on cardboard and handstamped "TRESORIER PAYEUR DE LA NOUVELLE CALEDONIE" were used as emergency currency in 1914.

Stamps of 1892-1904 Surcharged in Carmine or Black

1912

117	A12	5c on 15c gray (C)	1.50	*1.90*
a.		Inverted surcharge	210.00	210.00
118	A12	5c on 20c red, *grn* (C)	1.50	*1.90*
119	A12	5c on 30c brn, *bis* (C)	2.25	*3.00*
120	A12	10c on 40c red, *straw*	3.25	3.25
121	A12	10c on 50c brn, *az* (C)	3.25	*4.25*
		Nos. 117-121 (5)	11.75	14.30

Two spacings between the surcharged numerals are found on Nos. 117 to 121. For detailed listings, see the *Scott Classic Specialized Catalogue of Stamps and Covers.*

No. 96 Surcharged in Brown

1918

122	A16	5c on 15c violet	1.90	1.90
a.		Double surcharge	75.00	75.00
b.		Inverted surcharge	45.00	45.00

The color of the surcharge on No. 122 varies from red to dark brown.

No. 96 Surcharged

1922

123	A16	5c on 15c vio (R)	.60	.60
a.		Double surcharge	75.00	75.00

Stamps and Types of 1905-28 Surcharged in Red or Black

No. 124   No. 127

1924-27

124	A16	25c on 15c vio	.75	.75
a.		Double surcharge	75.00	
b.		Double surcharge, one inverted	110.00	
125	A18	25c on 2fr car, *bl*	.85	.85
126	A18	25c on 5fr blk, *straw*	.90	.90
a.		Double surcharge	125.00	125.00
b.		Triple surcharge	225.00	210.00
127	A17	60c on 75c grn (R)	.75	.75
128	A17	65c on 45c red brn	2.00	2.00
129	A17	85c on 45c red brn	2.00	2.00
130	A17	90c on 75c dp rose	1.05	1.05
131	A18	1.25fr on 1fr dp bl	.90	.90
132	A18	1.50fr on 1fr dp bl, *bl*	1.60	1.60
133	A18	3fr on 5fr red vio	2.10	2.10
134	A18	10fr on 5fr ol, *lav*	7.50	7.50
135	A18	20fr on 5fr vio rose, *org*	14.50	14.50
		Nos. 124-135 (12)	34.90	34.90

Issue years: Nos. 125-127, 1924. Nos. 124, 128-129, 1925. Nos. 131, 134, 1926. Nos. 130, 132-133, 135, 1927.

Bay of Palétuviers Point — A19

Landscape with Chief's House — A20

Admiral de Bougainville and Count de La Pérouse — A21

1928-40   Typo.

136	A19	1c brn vio & ind	.30	.25
137	A19	2c dk brn & yel grn	.30	.25
137B	A19	3c brn vio & ind	.30	.30
138	A19	4c org & Prus grn	.30	.30
139	A19	5c Prus bl & dp ol	.45	.45
140	A19	10c gray lil & dk brn	.30	.30
141	A19	15c yel brn & dp bl	.55	.55
142	A19	20c brn red & dk brn	.55	.55
143	A19	25c dk grn & brn	.70	.70
144	A20	30c ol grn & grn	.60	.60
145	A20	35c blk & brt vio	.90	.90
146	A20	40c brt red & olvn	.55	.55
147	A20	45c dp bl & red org	1.60	1.30
147A	A20	45c bl grn & dl grn	1.05	1.05
148	A20	50c vio & brn	.85	.85
149	A20	55c vio bl & car	3.50	2.25
150	A20	60c vio bl & car	.75	.75
151	A20	65c org brn & bl	1.30	1.15
152	A20	70c dp rose & brn	.60	.60
153	A20	75c Prus bl & ol gray	1.40	1.15
154	A20	80c red brn & grn	1.15	1.00
155	A20	85c grn & brn	2.00	1.30
156	A20	90c dp red & brt red	1.30	.90
157	A20	90c ol grn & rose red	1.05	1.05
158	A21	1fr dp ol & sal red	7.25	4.25
159	A21	1fr rose red & dk car	2.25	1.75
160	A21	1fr brn red & grn	1.05	1.05
161	A21	1.10fr grn & brn	12.00	12.00
162	A21	1.25fr brn red & grn	1.20	1.20
163	A21	1.25fr rose red & dk car	1.15	1.15
164	A21	1.40fr dk bl & red org	1.20	1.20
165	A21	1.50fr dp bl & bl	.90	.90
166	A21	1.60fr dp grn & bl	1.35	1.35
167	A21	1.75fr dk bl & red org	1.05	1.05
168	A21	1.75fr violet bl	1.50	1.05
169	A21	2fr red org & brn	.90	.75
170	A21	2.25fr vio bl	1.20	1.20
171	A21	2.50fr brn & lt brn	1.75	1.75
172	A21	3fr mag & brn	.75	.75
173	A21	5fr dk bl & brn	1.15	1.15
174	A21	10fr vio & brn, *pnksh*	1.30	1.30
175	A21	20fr red & brn, *yel*	2.75	2.75
		Nos. 136-175 (42)	63.05	55.45

The 35c in Prussian green and dark green without overprint is listed as Wallis and Futuna No. 53a.

Issue years: 35c, 70c, 85c, #162, 167, 1933; 55c, 80c, #159, 168, 1938; #157, 163, 2.25fr, 1939; 3c, 60c, 1.40fr, 1.60fr, 2.50fr, 147A, 160, 1940; others, 1928.

For overprints see #180-207, 217-251, Q4-Q6.

Common Design Types pictured following the introduction.

Colonial Exposition Issue
Common Design Types

1931   Engr.   Perf. 12½
Country Name Typo. in Black

176	CD70	40c dp green	6.00	6.00
177	CD71	50c violet	6.00	6.00
178	CD72	90c red orange	6.00	6.00
179	CD73	1.50fr dull blue	6.00	6.00
		Nos. 176-179 (4)	24.00	24.00

Paris-Nouméa Flight Issue
Regular Issue of 1928 Overprinted

1932   Perf. 14x13½

180	A20	40c brt red & ol	475.00	*500.00*
181	A20	50c vio & brn	475.00	*500.00*

Arrival on Apr. 5, 1932 at Nouméa, of the French aviators, Verneilh, Dévé and Munch. Excellent forgeries exist of #180-181.

Types of 1928-33 Overprinted in Black or Red

1933

182	A19	1c red vio & dl bl	6.50	*7.00*
183	A19	2c dk brn & yel grn	6.50	*7.00*
184	A19	4c dl org & Prus bl	6.50	*7.00*
185	A19	5c Prus grn & ol (R)	6.50	*7.00*
186	A19	10c gray lil & dk brn (R)	6.50	*7.00*
187	A19	15c yel brn & dp bl (R)	6.50	*7.00*
188	A19	20c brn red & dk brn	6.50	*7.00*
189	A19	25c dk grn & dk brn (R)	6.50	*7.00*
190	A20	30c gray grn & bl grn (R)	6.75	*7.50*
191	A20	35c blk & lt vio	6.75	*7.50*
192	A20	40c brt red & olvn	6.75	*7.00*
193	A20	45c dp bl & red org	6.75	*7.50*
194	A20	50c vio & brn	6.75	*7.00*
195	A20	70c dp rose & brn	7.50	*8.00*
196	A20	75c Prus bl & ol gray (R)	7.50	*8.00*
197	A20	85c grn & brn	7.50	*8.00*
198	A20	90c dp red & brt red	9.50	*10.00*
199	A21	1fr dp ol & sal red	9.50	*10.00*
200	A21	1.25fr brn red & grn	9.50	*10.00*
201	A21	1.50fr dp bl & bl (R)	9.50	*10.00*
202	A21	1.75fr dk bl & red org	9.50	*10.00*
203	A21	2fr red org & brn	9.50	*10.00*
204	A21	3fr mag & brn	9.50	*10.00*
205	A21	5fr dk bl & brn (R)	9.50	*10.00*
206	A21	10fr vio & brn, *pnksh*	10.00	*11.00*
207	A21	20fr red & brn, *yel*	10.00	*11.00*
		Nos. 182-207 (26)	204.25	218.50

1st anniv., Paris-Nouméa flight. Plane centered on Nos. 190-207.

Paris International Exposition Issue
Common Design Types

1937   Engr.   Perf. 13

208	CD74	20c dp vio	2.75	2.75
209	CD75	30c dk grn	2.75	2.75
210	CD76	40c car rose	2.75	2.75
211	CD77	50c dk brn & bl	2.75	2.75
212	CD78	90c red	2.75	2.75
213	CD79	1.50fr ultra	2.75	2.75
		Nos. 208-213 (6)	16.50	16.50

Colonial Arts Exhibition Issue
Souvenir Sheet
Common Design Type

1937   Imperf.

214	CD78	3fr sepia	22.50	*34.00*

New York World's Fair Issue
Common Design Type

1939			Perf. 12½x12	
215	CD82	1.25fr car lake	1.60	1.60
216	CD82	2.25fr ultra	1.75	1.75

Nouméa
Roadstead and
Marshal Pétain

1941		Engr.	Perf. 12½x12	
216A	A21a	1fr bluish green		.75
216B	A21a	2.50fr dark blue		.75

Nos. 216A-216B were issued by the Vichy government in France, but were not placed on sale in the colony.
For surcharges, see Nos. B12A-B12B.

Types of 1928-40 Overprinted in Black

1941			Perf. 14x13½	
217	A19	1c red vio & dl bl	13.50	13.50
218	A19	2c dk brn & yel grn	13.50	13.50
219	A19	3c brn vio & ind	13.50	13.50
220	A19	4c dl org & Prus bl	13.50	13.50
221	A19	5c Prus bl & dp ol	13.50	13.50
222	A19	10c gray lil & dk brn	13.50	13.50
223	A19	15c yel brn & dp bl	18.00	18.00
224	A19	20c brn red & dk brn	18.00	18.00
225	A19	25c dk grn & dk brn	18.00	18.00
226	A20	30c gray grn & bl grn	18.00	18.00
227	A20	35c blk & brt vio	18.00	18.00
228	A20	40c brt red & olvn	18.00	18.00
229	A20	45c bl grn & dl grn	18.00	18.00
230	A20	50c vio & brn	18.00	18.00
231	A20	55c vio bl & car	18.00	18.00
232	A20	60c vio bl & car	18.00	18.00
233	A20	65c org brn & bl	18.00	18.00
234	A20	70c dp rose & brn	18.00	18.00
235	A20	75c Prus bl & ol gray	18.00	18.00
236	A20	80c red brn & grn	18.00	18.00
237	A20	85c grn & brn	18.00	18.00
238	A20	90c dp red & brt red	18.00	18.00
239	A21	1fr rose red & dk car	18.00	18.00
240	A21	1.25fr brn red & grn	18.00	18.00
241	A21	1.40fr dk bl & red org	18.00	18.00
242	A21	1.50fr dp bl & bl	18.00	18.00
243	A21	1.60fr dp grn & brn	18.00	18.00
244	A21	1.75fr dk bl & red org	18.00	18.00
245	A21	2fr red org & brn	18.00	18.00
246	A21	2.25fr vio bl	18.00	18.00
247	A21	2.50fr brn & lt brn	22.00	19.50
248	A21	3fr mag & brn	22.00	19.50
249	A21	5fr dk bl & brn	22.00	19.50
250	A21	10fr vio & brn, pnksh	22.00	22.00
251	A21	20fr red & brn, yel	23.50	23.50
		Nos. 217-251 (35)	624.50	617.00
		Set, never hinged	875.00	

Issued to note this colony's affiliation with the "Free France" movement.

> Catalogue values for unused stamps in this section, from this point to the end of the section, are for Never Hinged items.

Kagu — A22

1942		Photo.	Perf. 14½x14	
252	A22	5c brown	.40	.25
253	A22	10c dk gray bl	.45	.30
254	A22	25c emerald	.70	.30
255	A22	30c red org	.70	.45
256	A22	40c dk slate grn	.70	.45
257	A22	80c dl red brn	.70	.45
258	A22	1fr rose vio	.90	.70
259	A22	1.50fr red	.90	.70
260	A22	2fr gray blk	1.30	1.10
261	A22	2.50fr brt ultra	1.30	1.10
262	A22	4fr dl vio	1.30	1.10
263	A22	5fr bister	1.30	1.10

264	A22	10fr dp brn	1.60	1.50
265	A22	20fr dp grn	2.50	2.25
		Nos. 252-265 (14)	14.75	11.75

Types of 1928 Without "RF"

1944		Typo.	Perf. 14x13½	
265A	A19	10c gray lil & dk brn		.75
265B	A20	60c vio bl & car		1.50

Nos. 265A-265B were issued by the Vichy government in France, but were not placed on sale in the colony.

Stamps of 1942 Surcharged in Carmine or Black

1945-46		Unwmk.	Perf. 14½x14	
266	A22	50c on 5c (C) ('46)	1.60	1.50
267	A22	60c on 5c (C)	1.60	1.50
268	A22	70c on 5c (C)	1.60	1.50
269	A22	1.20fr on 5c (C)	.85	.75
270	A22	2.40fr on 25c	.85	.75
271	A22	3fr on 25c ('46)	1.00	.75
272	A22	4.50fr on 25c	1.90	1.10
273	A22	15fr on 2.50fr (C)	2.60	2.00
		Nos. 266-273 (8)	12.00	9.85

Eboue Issue
Common Design Type

1945		Engr.	Perf. 13	
274	CD91	2fr black	.90	.90
275	CD91	25fr Prus grn	2.50	2.10

Kagus — A23

Ducos
Sanatorium
A24

Porcupine
Isle — A25

Nickel
Foundry — A26

"Towers of Notre Dame" A27

Chieftain's House A28

1948	Unwmk.	Photo.	Perf. 13½x13	
276	A23	10c yel & gray brn	.30	.30
277	A23	30c bl grn & gray brn	.30	.30
278	A23	40c org & gray brn	.30	.30
279	A24	50c pink & gray blk	.60	.45
280	A24	60c yel & brn	.60	.60
281	A24	80c pale bl grn & bl grn	.60	.60
282	A25	1fr brn, vio & org	.75	.60
283	A25	1.20fr brn & bl	.75	.60
284	A25	1.50fr dk bl & yel	.90	.70
285	A26	2fr turq grn & brnsh blk	.75	.60
286	A26	2.40fr car & peach	1.20	.85
287	A26	3fr pale org & vio	7.50	2.00
288	A26	4fr lt bl & dk bl	2.10	1.00
289	A27	5fr sal & dk vio	2.75	1.10
290	A27	6fr yel & brn	2.75	1.60
291	A27	10fr pale org & dk bl	2.75	1.60
292	A28	15fr red brn & bl gray	3.50	1.75
293	A28	20fr vio & yel	3.50	2.25
294	A28	25fr dk bl & pale org	4.50	3.50
		Nos. 276-294 (19)	36.40	20.70

Military Medal Issue
Common Design Type

1952		Engr. & Typo.	Perf. 13	
295	CD101	2fr multi	6.50	6.00

Admiral Bruni d'Entrecasteaux and his Two Frigates — A29

Designs: 2fr, Msgr. Douarre and Cathedral of Nouméa. 6fr, Admiral Dumont d'Urville and map. 13fr, Admiral Auguste Febvrier-Despointes and Nouméa roadstead.

1953, Sept. 24			Engr.	
296	A29	1.50fr org brn & dp claret	7.25	5.50
297	A29	2fr ind & aqua	6.00	3.50
298	A29	6fr dk brn, bl & car	11.00	6.00
299	A29	13fr bl grn & dk grnsh bl	12.50	7.00
		Nos. 296-299 (4)	36.75	22.00

Centenary of the presence of the French in New Caledonia.

"Towers of Notre Dame" A30

Coffee A31

1955, Nov. 21		Unwmk.	Perf. 13	
300	A30	2.50fr dk brn, ultra & grn	1.90	1.05
301	A30	3fr grn, ultra & red brn	8.25	4.00
302	A31	9fr vio bl & indigo	3.00	1.05
		Nos. 300-302 (3)	13.15	6.10

FIDES Issue
Common Design Type

Design: Dumbea Dam.

1956, Oct. 22		Engr.	Perf. 13x12½	
303	CD103	3fr grn & bl	1.90	1.10

Flower Issue
Common Design Type

Designs: 4fr, Xanthostemon. 15fr, Hibiscus.

1958, July 7		Photo.	Perf. 12x12½	
304	CD104	4fr multi	2.75	1.25
305	CD104	15fr grn, red & yel	5.25	1.75

Imperforates

Most stamps of New Caledonia from 1958 onward exist imperforate, in trial colors, or in small presentation sheets in which the stamps are printed in changed colors.

Human Rights Issue
Common Design Type

1958, Dec. 10		Engr.	Perf. 13	
306	CD105	7fr car & dk bl	2.00	1.50

Brachyrus Zebra A32

Lienardella Fasciata A33

Designs: 10fr, Glaucus and Spirographe. 26fr, Fluorescent corals.

1959, Mar. 21		Engr.	Perf. 13	
307	A32	1fr lil gray & red brn	.75	.55
308	A33	3fr bl, grn & red	1.75	.60
309	A32	10fr dk brn, Prus bl & org brn	2.50	1.00
310	A33	26fr multi	4.50	4.50
		Nos. 307-310 (4)	9.50	6.65

Types of 1859, 1905 and

Girl Operating Check Writer — A34

Telephone Receiver and Exchange — A35

Port-de-France (Nouméa) in 1859 — A36

Designs: 9fr, Wayside mailbox and mail bus, vert. 33fr, like 19fr without stamps.

		Perf. 13½x13, 13		
1960, May 20			Unwmk.	
311	A16	4fr red	1.00	.55
312	A34	5fr claret & org brn	1.20	.75
313	A36	9fr dk grn & brn	1.20	.75
314	A35	12fr bl & blk	1.50	.90
315	A1	13fr slate blue	3.75	2.00
316	A36	19fr bl grn, dl grn & red	3.75	1.25
317	A36	33fr Prus bl & dl red	4.00	2.75
a.		Souv. sheet of 3, #315, 311, 317 + label	12.50	12.50
		Nos. 311-317 (7)	16.40	8.95

Cent. of postal service and stamps in New Caledonia.
No. 317a has label between 4fr and 33fr stamps.

Melanesian Sailing Canoes — A37

Designs: 4fr, Spear fisherman, vert. 5fr, Sail Rock and sailboats, Noumea.

1962, July 2		Engr.	Perf. 13	
318	A37	2fr slate grn, ultra & brn	1.10	.55
319	A37	4fr brn, car & grn	1.40	.55
320	A37	5fr sepia, grn & bl	1.75	.75
		Nos. 318-320 (3)	4.25	1.85

See Nos. C29-C32.

Map of Australia and South Pacific A37a

1962, July 18		Photo.	Perf. 13x12	
321	A37a	15fr multi	3.00	1.90

Fifth South Pacific Conf., Pago Pago, 1962.

Air Currents over Map of New Caledonia and South Pacific, Barograph and Compass Rose — A38

1962, Nov. 5			Perf. 12x12½	
322	A38	50fr multi	7.50	6.00

3rd regional assembly of the World Meteorological Association, Noumea, November 1962.

Wheat Emblem and Globe — A38a

1963, Mar. 21		Engr.	Perf. 13	
323	A38a	17fr choc & dk bl	3.50	1.75

FAO "Freedom from Hunger" campaign.

Relay Race — A39

Perf. 12½
1963, Aug. 29   Unwmk.   Photo.
324 A39 1fr shown   1.20   .60
325 A39 7fr Tennis   1.75   .90
326 A39 10fr Soccer   2.40 1.50
327 A39 27fr Javelin   4.25 2.75
        Nos. 324-327 (4)   9.60 5.75
South Pacific Games, Suva, Aug. 29-Sept. 7.

Red Cross Centenary Issue
Common Design Type
1963 Sept. 2   Engr.   Perf. 13
328 CD113 37fr bl, gray & car 8.00 6.75

Human Rights Issue
Common Design Type
1963, Dec. 10   Engr.   Perf. 13
329 CD117 50fr sl grn & dp clar-
              et   7.00 6.00

Bikkia
Fritillarioides — A40

Flowers: 1fr, Freycinettia Sp. 3fr, Xanthostemon Francii. 4fr, Psidiomyrtus locellatus. 5fr,
Callistemon suberosum. 7fr, Montrouziera
sphaeroidea, horiz. 10fr, Ixora collina, horiz.
17fr, Deplanchea speciosa.

**Photogravure; Lithographed (2fr,
3fr)**
1964-65   Perf. 13x12½
330 A40 1fr multi   1.00   .55
331 A40 2fr multi   1.00   .60
332 A40 3fr multi   1.60   .75
333 A40 4fr multi   3.00   .90
334 A40 5fr multi ('65)   3.75 1.25
335 A40 7fr multi   4.75 1.60
336 A40 10fr multi   5.50 1.75
337 A40 17fr multi   8.50 4.25
        Nos. 330-337 (8)   29.10 11.65

Sea Squirts — A41

Design: 10fr, Alcyonium catalai. 17fr,
Shrimp (hymenocera elegans).

1964-65   Engr.   Perf. 13
338 A41 7fr dk bl, red org & brn 1.75 1.00
339 A41 10fr dk red & dk vio bl
              ('65)   2.75 1.10
340 A41 17fr dk bl, red brn & grn 4.75 2.50
        Nos. 338-340 (3)   9.25 4.60
Nouméa Aquarium. See Nos. C41-C43.

Philatec Issue
Common Design Type
1964, Apr. 9   Unwmk.   Perf. 13
341 CD118 40fr dk vio, grn &
              choc   6.50 6.50

De Gaulle's 1940
Poster "A Tous
les
Francais" — A42

1965, Sept. 20   Engr.   Perf. 13
342 A42 20fr red, bl & blk   12.50 8.25
25th anniv. of the rallying of the Free French.

Amedee
Lighthouse — A43

1965, Nov. 25
343 A43 8fr dk vio bl, bis & grn 2.60 1.00
Centenary of the Amedee lighthouse.

Games' Emblem — A44

1966, Mar. 1   Engr.   Perf. 13
344 A44 8fr dk red, brt bl & blk 1.50   .90
2nd So. Pacific Games, Nouméa, Dec. 1966.

Red-throated Parrot
Finch — A45

Design: 3fr, Giant imperial pigeon.

1966, Oct. 10   Litho.   Perf. 13x12½
                              Size: 22x37mm
345 A45 1fr green & multi   3.00 1.50
346 A45 3fr citron & multi   5.00 1.90
        See #361-366, 380-381, C48-C49A, C70-
    C71.

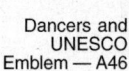

Dancers and
UNESCO
Emblem — A46

1966, Nov. 4   Engr.   Perf. 13
347 A46 16fr pur, ocher & grn 2.40 1.40
20th anniv. of UNESCO.

High Jump and
Games'
Emblem — A47

1966, Dec. 8   Engr.   Perf. 13
348 A47 17fr shown   3.00 1.25
349 A47 20fr Hurdling   4.25 2.10
350 A47 40fr Running   5.50 2.40
351 A47 100fr Swimming   9.50 6.25
a. Souv. sheet of 4, #348-351 +
        label   35.00 35.00
        Nos. 348-351 (4)   22.25 12.00
2nd So. Pacific Games, Nouméa, Dec. 8-18.

Lekine
Cliffs — A48

1967, Jan. 14   Engr.   Perf. 13
352 A48 17fr brt grn, ultra & sl
              grn   2.40 2.00

Magenta Stadium,
Nouméa — A49

Design: 20fr, Ouen Toro Municipal Swimming Pool, Nouméa.

1967, June 5   Photo.   Perf. 12x13
353 A49 10fr multi   1.50   .85
354 A49 20fr multi   3.50 1.60

ITY Emblem,
Beach at
Nouméa — A50

1967, June 19   Engr.   Perf. 13
355 A50 30fr multi   4.75 2.60
Issued for International Tourist Year, 1967.

19th Century
Mailman — A51

1967, July 12
356 A51 7fr dk car, bl grn & brn 3.00 1.40
Issued for Stamp Day.

Papilio
Montrouzieri
A52

Butterflies: 9fr, Polyura clitarchus. 13fr, 15fr,
Hypolimnas bolina, male and female
respectively.

1967-68   Engr.   Perf. 13
                    Size: 36x22mm
357 A52 7fr lt grn, blk & ultra 4.75 1.25
358 A52 9fr brn, lil & ind ('68) 5.75 1.50
359 A52 13fr vio bl, brn org &
              dk brn   7.00 2.50
360 A52 15fr dk brn, bl & yel 10.00 4.50
        Nos. 357-360,C51-C53 (7) 58.50 24.25
Issued: 9fr, 3/26/68; others, 8/10/67.

Bird Type of 1966
Birds: 1fr, New Caledonian grass warbler.
2fr, New Caledonia whistler. 3fr, New Caledonia white-throated pigeon. 4fr, Kagus. 5fr,
Crested parakeet. 10fr, Crow honey-eater.

1967-68   Photo.   Perf. 13x12½
                    Size: 22x37mm
361 A45 1fr multi   1.50 1.00
362 A45 2fr multi   2.00 1.25
363 A45 3fr multi   2.50 1.40
364 A45 4fr grn & multi   4.00 2.50
365 A45 5fr lt yel & multi   7.00 3.25
366 A45 10fr pink & multi   12.00 4.25
        Nos. 361-366 (6)   29.00 13.65
Issued: #364-366, 12/16/67; others 5/14/68.

WHO Anniversary Issue
Common Design Type
1968, May 4   Engr.   Perf. 13
367 CD126 20fr mar, vio & dk bl
              grn   4.00 2.25

Ferrying Mail
Truck Across
Tontouta River,
1900 — A53

1968, Sept. 2   Engr.   Perf. 13
368 A53 9fr dk red brn, grn & ul-
              tra   3.75 1.60
Issued for Stamp Day, 1968.

Human Rights Year Issue
Common Design Type
1968, Aug. 10   Engr.   Perf. 13
369 CD127 12fr sl grn, dp car &
              org yel   2.75 1.50

Conus
Geographus
A54

1968, Nov. 9   Engr.   Perf. 13
                    Size: 36x22mm
370 A54 10fr dk brn, brt bl &
              gray   4.25 2.25
        Nos. 370,C58-C60 (4)   37.75 13.50

Car on
Road — A55

1968, Dec. 26   Engr.   Perf. 13
371 A55 25fr dp bl, sl grn & hn
              brn   7.50 3.75
2nd Automobile Safari of New Caledonia.

Cattle Dip — A56

1969, May 10   Engr.   Perf. 13
                    Size: 36x22mm
372 A56 9fr shown   2.50 1.00
373 A56 25fr Cattle branding 3.50 1.75
        Nos. 372-373,C64 (3)   13.00 6.00
Cattle breeding in New Caledonia.

Murex Haustellum
A57

Sea Shells: 5fr, Venus comb. 15fr, Murex
ramosus.

1969, June 21   Engr.   Perf. 13
                    Size: 35½x22mm
374 A57 2fr ver, bl & brn   1.75   .90
375 A57 5fr dl red, pur &
              beige   3.75 1.20
376 A57 15fr ver, dl grn & gray 6.00 2.40
        Nos. 374-376,C65 (4)   35.50 16.00

Judo — A58

1969, Aug. 7   Engr.   Perf. 13
                    Size: 36x22mm
377 A58 19fr shown   3.75 1.90
378 A58 20fr Boxers   3.75 1.90
        Nos. 377-378,C66-C67 (4) 19.50 8.80
3rd South Pacific Games, Port Moresby,
Papua and New Guinea, Aug. 13-23.

ILO Issue
Common Design Type
1969, Nov. 24   Engr.   Perf. 13
379 CD131 12fr org, brn vio &
              brn   2.25 1.10

Bird Type of 1966
15fr, Friarbird. 30fr, Sacred kingfisher.

1970, Feb. 19   Photo.   Perf. 13
                    Size: 22x37mm
380 A45 15fr yel grn & multi   8.25 3.25
381 A45 30fr pale salmon &
              multi   12.00 5.50
        Nos. 380-381,C70-C71 (4) 59.75 22.75

UPU Headquarters Issue
Common Design Type
1970, May 20   Engr.   Perf. 13
382 CD133 12fr brn, gray & dk
              car   3.00 1.50

Porcelain Sieve
Shell — A59

Designs: 1fr, Strombus epidromis linne, vert. No. 385, Strombus variabilis swainson, vert. 21fr, Mole porcelain shell.

1970   Size: 22x36mm, 36x22mm
383 A59 1fr bl grn & multi   2.25   .75
384 A59 10fr car & multi   5.25   1.50
385 A59 10fr blk & multi   6.75   2.40
386 A59 21fr bl grn, red brn &
              dk brn   10.00   4.00
     Nos. 383-386,C73-C76 (8)   64.50 25.65
     See Nos. 395-396, C89-C90.

Packet Ship "Natal," 1883 — A60

1970, July 23   Engr.   Perf. 13
387 A60 9fr Prus bl, blk & brt grn 4.00 1.40
     Issued for Stamp Day.

Dumbea Railroad Post Office — A61

1971, Mar. 13   Engr.   Perf. 13
388 A61 10fr red, slate grn & blk   5.00 2.00
     Stamp Day, 1971.

Racing Yachts A62

1971, Apr. 17   Engr.   Perf. 13
389 A62 16fr bl, Prus bl & sl grn   5.00 3.00
     Third sailing cruise from Whangarei, New Zealand, to Nouméa.

Morse Recorder, Communications Satellite — A63

1971, May 17   Engr.   Perf. 13
390 A63 19fr red, lake & org   4.00 1.25
     3rd World Telecommunications Day.

Weight Lifting — A64

1971, June 24   Engr.   Perf. 13
391 A64 11fr shown   2.50 1.00
392 A64 23fr Basketball   3.75 1.50
     Nos. 391-392,C82-C83 (4)   18.00 8.75
     4th South Pacific Games, Papeete, French Polynesia, Sept. 8-19.

De Gaulle Issue
Common Design Type
Designs: 34fr, Pres. de Gaulle, 1970. 100fr, Gen. de Gaulle, 1940.

1971, Nov. 9
393 CD134 34fr dk pur & blk   8.00 3.75
394 CD134 100fr dk pur & blk   15.00 8.00

Sea Shell Type of 1970
Designs: 1fr, Scorpion conch, vert. 3fr, Common spider conch., vert.

1972, Mar. 4   Engr.   Perf. 13
          Size: 22x36mm
395 A59 1fr vio & dk brn   2.00   .70
396 A59 3fr grn & ocher   3.00   .80
     Nos. 395-396,C89-C90 (4)   19.50 8.50

Carved Wooden Pillow — A66

1fr, Doorpost, Goa. 5fr, Monstrance. 12fr, Tchamba mask.

1972-73   Photo.   Perf. 12½x13
397 A66 1fr multi ('73)   1.75   .40
398 A66 2fr shown   1.75   .65
399 A66 5fr multi   2.00   .80
400 A66 12fr multi   5.00 1.25
     Nos. 397-400,C102-C103 (6)   18.00 6.10
     Objects from Nouméa Museum.
     Issued: 2fr-15fr, 8/5.

Chamber of Commerce Emblem — A67

1972, Dec. 16   Perf. 13
401 A67 12fr blk, yel & brt bl   1.75   .90
     Junior Chamber of Commerce, 10th anniv.

Tchamba Mask — A68

1973, Mar. 15   Engr.   Perf. 13
402 A68 12fr lilac   8.25 2.00
  a.   Booklet pane of 5   200.00
     No. 402 issued in booklets only.
     See No. C99.

Black-back Butterflyfish (Day) — A69

1973, June 23   Photo.   Perf. 13x12½
403 A69 8fr shown   2.50 1.00
404 A69 14fr same fish (night)   3.75 1.50
     Nos. 403-404,C105 (3)   11.25 4.50
     Nouméa Aquarium.

Emblem — A70

1973, July 21   Perf. 13
405 A70 20fr grn, yel & vio bl   2.25   .80
     School Coordinating Office, 10th anniv.

"Nature Protection" A72

1974, June 22   Photo.   Perf. 13x12½
406 A72 7fr multi   1.50   .55

Scorched Landscape — A73

1975, Feb. 7   Photo.   Perf. 13
407 A73 20fr multi   2.25 1.10
     "Prevent brush fires."

Calanthe Veratrifolia — A74

Design: 11fr, Liperanthus gigas.

1975, May 30   Photo.   Perf. 13
408 A74 8fr pur & multi   3.00 1.00
409 A74 11fr dk bl & multi   3.50 1.00
     Nos. 408-409,C125 (3)   12.50 4.25
     Orchids. See Nos. 425-426.

Festival Emblem — A75

1975, Sept. 6   Photo.   Perf. 12½x13
410 A75 12fr ultra, org & yel   2.00   .70
     Melanesia 2000 Festival.

Birds in Flight — A76

1975, Oct. 18   Photo.   Perf. 13½x13
411 A76 5fr ocher, yel & blk   1.75   .55
     Nouméa Ornithological Society, 10th anniversary.

Georges Pompidou — A77

1975, Dec. 6   Engr.   Perf. 13
412 A77 26fr dk grn, blk & sl   3.25 1.25
     Pompidou (1911-74), president of France.

Sea Birds — A78

Perf. 13x12½, 12½x13
1976, Feb. 26   Photo.
413 A78 1fr Brown booby   1.25   .45
414 A78 2fr Blue-faced booby   1.75   .70
415 A78 8fr Red-footed booby,
              vert.   3.00 1.10
     Nos. 413-415 (3)   6.00 2.25

Festival Emblem — A79

1976, Mar. 13   Litho.   Perf. 12½
416 A79 27fr bl, org & blk   2.50   .90
     Rotorua 1976, South Pacific Arts Festival, New Zealand.

Lion and Lions Emblem — A80

1976, Mar. 13   Photo.   Perf. 12½x13
417 A80 49fr multi   5.00 2.00
     Lions Club of Nouméa, 15th anniversary.

Music Pavilion A81

Design: 30fr, Fountain, vert.

1976, July 3   Litho.   Perf. 12½
418 A81 25fr multi   1.75   .70
419 A81 30fr blue & multi   2.25 1.00
     Old Nouméa.

Polluted Shore A82

1976, Aug. 21   Photo.   Perf. 13
420 A82 20fr dp bl & multi   2.50   .90
     Nature protection.

South Pacific People — A83

1976, Oct. 23   Photo.   Perf. 13
421 A83 20fr bl & multi   2.25   .90
     16th South Pacific Commission Conference, Nouméa, Oct. 1976.

Giant Grasshopper A84

1977, Feb. 21   Engr.   Perf. 13
422 A84 26fr shown   2.00 1.25
423 A84 31fr Beetle and larvae   3.00 1.40

Ground Satellite Station, Nouméa A85

1977, Apr. 16   Litho.   *Perf. 13*
424 A85 29fr multi   2.75 1.10

Orchid Type of 1975

Designs: 22fr, Phajus daenikeri. 44fr, Dendrobium finetianum.

1977, May 23   Photo.   *Perf. 13*
425 A74 22fr brn & multi   3.75 1.25
426 A74 44fr bl & multi   4.25 1.90

Mask, Palms, "Stamps" A86

1977, June 25   Photo.   *Perf. 13*
427 A86 35fr multi   2.00 1.00

Philately in school, Philatelic Exhibition, La Perouse Lyceum, Nouméa.

Trees — A87

1977, July 23   Photo.   *Perf. 13*
428 A87 20fr multi   1.50 .75

Nature protection.

Congress Emblem A88

1977, Aug. 6   Photo.   *Perf. 13*
429 A88 200fr multi   9.25 5.50

French Junior Economic Chambers Congress, Nouméa.

Young Frigate Bird — A89

Black-naped Tern — A89a

Sooty Terns — A89b

1977-78   Photo.   *Perf. 13*
430 A89 16fr multi   5.75 1.00
431 A89a 22fr multi   2.25 1.10
432 A89b 40fr multi   3.75 1.50
    Nos. 430-432,C138 (4)   17.75 5.20

Issued: 16fr, 9/17/77; 22fr, 40fr, 2/11/78.

Mare and Foal — A90

1977, Nov. 19   Engr.   *Perf. 13*
433 A90 5fr multi   2.00 .55

10th anniversary of the Society for Promotion of Caledonian Horses.

Araucaria Montana — A91

1978, Mar. 17   Photo.   *Perf. 12½x13*
434 A91 16fr multi   1.25 .55

See No. C149.

Halityle Regularis — A92

1978, May 20   Photo.   *Perf. 13*
436 A92 10fr vio bl & multi   1.60 .45

Nouméa Aquarium.

Stylized Turtle and Globe — A93

1978, May 20
437 A93 30fr multi   3.00 1.10

Protection of the turtle.

Flying Fox — A94

1978, June 10
438 A94 20fr multi   4.50 1.50

Nature protection.

Maurice Leenhardt — A95

1978, Aug. 12   Engr.   *Perf. 13*
439 A95 37fr multi   2.00 1.25

Pastor Maurice Leenhardt (1878-1954).

Soccer Player, League Emblem — A96

1978, Nov. 4   Photo.   *Perf. 13*
440 A96 26fr multi   4.50 2.50

New Caledonia Soccer League, 50th anniversary.

Lifu Island — A97

1978, Dec. 9   Litho.   *Perf. 13*
441 A97 33fr multi   2.25 1.75

Petroglyph, Mère — A98

1979, Jan. 27   Engr.   *Perf. 13*
442 A98 10fr brick red   1.40 .55

Map of Ouvea — A99

Design: 31fr, Map of Mare Island, horiz.

Perf. 12½x13, 13x12½
1979, Feb. 17   Photo.
443 A99 11fr multi   1.25 .55
444 A99 31fr multi   1.75 .75

House at Artillery Point A100

1979, Apr. 28   Photo.   *Perf. 13*
445 A100 20fr multi   2.00 1.50

Auguste Escoffier — A101

1979, July 21   Engr.   *Perf. 12½x13*
446 A101 24fr multi   1.50 1.50

Auguste Escoffier Hotel School.

Regatta and Games Emblem — A102

1979, Aug. 11   Photo.   *Perf. 13*
447 A102 16fr multi   2.00 .70

6th South Pacific Games, Suva, Fiji, Aug. 27-Sept. 8.

Agathis Ovata — A103

Design: 34fr, Cyathea intermedia.

1979, Oct. 20   Photo.   *Perf. 13x12½*
448 A103 5fr shown   1.50 .35
449 A103 34fr multicolored   2.00 .75

Pouembout Rodeo — A104

1979, Oct. 27   Engr.   *Perf. 13x12½*
450 A104 12fr multi   1.75 .55

Bantamia Merleti — A105

1979, Dec. 1   Photo.   *Perf. 13x11½*
451 A105 23fr multi   1.75 .70

Fluorescent corals from Nouméa Aquarium.

Map of Pine Tree Island, Fishermen with Nets — A106

1980, Jan. 12   Photo.   *Perf. 13x12½*
452 A106 23fr multi   1.60 .45

Hibbertia Virotii — A107

Design: 12fr, Grevillea meisneri.

1980, Apr. 19   Photo.   *Perf. 13x12½*
453 A107 11fr multicolored   1.40 .65
454 A107 12fr multicolored   1.40 .65

Philately at School — A108

1980, May 10   Litho.   *Perf. 12½*
455 A108 30fr multi   1.75 .55

Prevention of Traffic Accidents — A109

1980, July 5   Photo.   *Perf. 13x12½*
456 A109 15fr multi   1.20 .35

Parribacus Caledonicus A110

Noumea Aquarium Crustacea: 8fr, Panulirus versicolor.

1980, Aug. 23   Litho.   *Perf. 13x13½*
457 A110 5fr multi   .75 .35
458 A110 8fr multi   1.00 .55

Solar Energy — A111

1980, Oct. 11   Photo.   *Perf. 13x12½*
459 A111 23fr multi   1.50 .70

Manta Birostris — A112

25fr, Carcharhinus amblyrhnchos.

1981, Feb. 18   Photo.   *Perf. 13x12½*
460 A112 23fr shown   2.50   .90
461 A112 25fr multicolored   2.50   .90

Belep Islands — A113

1981, Mar. 4
462 A113 26fr multi   1.25   .55

Cypraea Stolida — A114

1fr, Cymbiola rossiniana, vert. 2fr, Connus floccatus, vert.

1981, June 17   Photo.   *Perf. 13*
463 A114 1fr multicolored   .95   .50
464 A114 2fr multicolored   1.00   .65
465 A114 13fr shown   1.90   .75
       Nos. 463-465 (3)   3.85 1.90
              See Nos. 470-471.

Corvette Constantine, 1854 — A115

25fr, Aviso le Phoque, 1853.

1981, July 22   Engr.   *Perf. 13*
466 A115 10fr shown   1.40   .55
467 A115 25fr multicolored   2.10 1.10
              See Nos. 476-477.

Intl. Year of the Disabled — A116

1981, Sept. 2   Litho.   *Perf. 12½*
468 A116 45fr multicolored   1.90   .85

Nature Preservation — A117

1981, Nov. 7   Photo.   *Perf. 13*
469 A117 28fr multicolored   2.25   .90

Marine Life Type of 1981
1982, Jan. 20   Photo.   *Perf. 13x13½*
470 A114 13fr Calappa calappa   1.50   .80
471 A114 25fr Etisus splendidus 2.25 1.10

Chalcantite A118

1982, Mar. 17   Photo.   *Perf. 13x13½*
472 A118 15fr shown   2.25 1.10
473 A118 30fr Anorthosite   3.00 1.10

Melaleuca Quinquenervia A119

20fr, Savannah trees, vert.

1982, June 23   Photo.   *Perf. 13*
474 A119 20fr multicolored   1.25   .70
475 A119 29fr shown   1.50   .70

Ship Type of 1981
44fr, Barque Le Cher. 59fr, Naval dispatch vessel Kersaint.

1982, July 7   Engr.
476 A115 44fr multicolored   2.10 1.00
477 A115 59fr multicolored   2.75 1.00

Ateou Tribe Traditional House — A120

1982, Oct. 13   Photo.   *Perf. 13½x13*
478 A120 52fr multicolored   1.75   .90

Grey's Ptilope — A121

Design: 35fr, Caledonian loriquet.

1982, Nov. 6
479 A121 32fr shown   1.75   .70
480 A121 35fr multicolored   2.00   .90

Central Education Coordination Office — A122

1982, Nov. 27   Litho.   *Perf. 13½x13*
481 A122 48fr Boat   1.75   .75

Bernheim Library, Noumea A123

1982, Dec. 15   Engr.   *Perf. 13*
482 A123 36fr multicolored   1.10   .55

Caledonian Orchids — A123a

10fr, Dendrobium oppositifolium. 15fr, Dendrobium munificum. 29fr, Dendrobium fractiflexum.

1983, Feb. 16   Photo.   *Perf. 13x13½*
482A A123a 10fr multicolored   .75   .35
482B A123a 15fr multicolored   1.10   .45
482C A123a 29fr multicolored   1.75   .90
       Nos. 482A-482C (3)   3.60 1.70

Xanthostemon Aurantiacum A124

1fr, Crinum asiaticum. 2fr, Xanthostemon aurantiacum. 4fr, Metrosideros demonstrans, vert.

1983, Mar. 23   Litho.   *Perf. 13*
483 A124 1fr multicolored   .45   .35
484 A124 2fr multicolored   .45   .65
485 A124 4fr multicolored   .45   .35
       Nos. 483-485 (3)   1.35 1.35

25th Anniv. of Posts and Telecommunications Dept. — A125

Telephones and post offices.

1983, Apr. 30   Litho.   *Perf. 13*
486 A125 30fr multicolored   1.10   .45
487 A125 40fr multicolored   1.20   .75
488 A125 50fr multicolored   1.75   .80
   a.   Souvenir sheet of 3   11.00 10.00
   b.   Strip of 3, #486-488   5.50   5.50

No. 488a contains Nos. 486-488 with changed background colors.

Local Snakes — A126

Designs: 31fr, Laticauda laticauda. 33fr, Laticauda colubrina.

1983, June 22   Photo.   *Perf. 13*
489 A126 31fr multicolored   1.75   .75
490 A126 33fr multicolored   2.00   .85

A127

1983, Aug. 10   Engr.
491 A127 16fr Volleyball   1.25   .65
7th South Pacific Games, Sept.

Nature Protection — A128

1983, Oct. 12   Photo.   *Perf. 12½*
492 A128 56fr multi   2.00 1.00

Birds of Prey — A129

34fr, Tyto Alba Lifuensis, vert. 37fr, Pandion Haliaetus.

1983, Nov. 16   Litho.
493 A129 34fr multicolored   2.00   .95
494 A129 37fr multicolored   2.50 1.25

Local Shells — A130

5fr, Conus chenui. 15fr, Conus moluccensis. 20fr, Conus optimus.

1984, Jan. 11   Litho. & Engr.
495 A130 5fr multicolored   1.00   .60
496 A130 15fr multicolored   1.10   .60
497 A130 20fr multicolored   1.40   .80
       Nos. 495-497 (3)   3.50 2.00
              See Nos. 521-522.

Steamers — A131

1984, Feb. 8   Engr.
498 A131 18fr St. Joseph   1.00   .65
499 A131 31fr St. Antoine   1.50   .85

Arms of Noumea — A132

1984, Apr. 11   Litho.   *Perf. 12½x13*
500 A132 35fr multi   1.25   .65
              See No. 546, 607, C214.

Environmental Preservation — A133

1984, May 23   *Perf. 13*
501 A133 65fr Island scene   2.25   .90

Orchids A134

16fr, Diplocaulobium ou-hinnae. 38fr, Acianthus atepalus.

1984, July 18   Litho.   *Perf. 12*
502 A134 16fr multicolored   1.50   .75
503 A134 38fr multicolored   2.00 1.10

Cent. of Public Schooling A135

1984, Oct. 11   Litho.   *Perf. 13½x13*
504 A135 59fr Schoolhouse   2.00   .90

Kagu — A137

1985-86   Engr.   *Perf. 13*
511 A137 1fr brt bl   .60   .60
512 A137 2fr green   .60   .60
513 A137 3fr brt org   .60   .60
514 A137 4fr brt grn   .60   .60
515 A137 5fr dp rose lil   .60   .60
516 A137 35fr crimson   1.25   .90
517 A137 38fr vermilion   1.25 1.00
518 A137 40fr brt rose ('86) 1.40   .70
       Nos. 511-518 (8)   6.90 5.60

Issued: 1, 2, 5, 38fr, 5/22; 3, 4, 35fr, 2/13; 40fr, 7/30.
See types A179, A179a.

Sea Shell Type of 1984
Lithographed and Engraved
1985, Feb. 27   *Perf. 13*
521 A130 55fr Conus bullatus   1.50   .90
522 A130 72fr Conus lamberti   2.00 1.40

25th World Meteorological
Day — A138

17fr, Radio communication, storm.

1985, Mar. 20 Litho.
523 A138 17fr multicolored .85 .85

Red Cross,
Medicine
Without
Frontiers
A139

1985, Apr. 10 Perf. 12½
524 A139 41fr multicolored 1.50 .80

Telephone
Switching
Center
Inauguration
A140

1985, Apr. 24
525 A140 70fr E 10 B installation 1.75 1.00

Marguerite La
Foa Suspension
Bridge — A141

1985, May 10 Engr. Perf. 13
526 A141 44fr brt bl & red brn 1.75 .90

Historical Preservation Association.

Le Cagou
Philatelic
Society
A142

1985, June 15 Litho.
527 A142 220fr multicolored 5.75 4.00
a. Souvenir sheet, perf. 12½ 8.50 8.50

No. 527a sold for 230fr.

4th Pacific Arts
Festival — A143

1985, July 3 Perf. 13½
Black Overprint
528 A143 55fr multicolored 1.50 1.00
529 A143 75fr multicolored 2.25 1.40

Not issued without overprint. Festival was
transferred to French Polynesia.

Intl. Youth
Year
A144

1985, July 24 Litho. Perf. 13
530 A144 59fr multicolored 2.00 .80

Amedee
Lighthouse
Electrification
A145

1985, Aug. 13
531 A145 89fr multicolored 2.25 1.10

Environmental
Conservation — A146

1985, Sept. 18
532 A146 100fr Planting trees 2.50 1.10

Birds — A147

1985, Dec. 18 Perf. 12½
533 A147 50fr Poule sultane 1.75 1.00
534 A147 60fr Merle caledonien 2.75 1.10

Noumea
Aquarium — A148

10fr, Pomacanthus imperator. 17fr, Rhi-
nopias aphanes.

1986, Feb. 19 Litho. Perf. 12½x13
535 A148 10fr multicolored .55 .35
536 A148 17fr multicolored .75 .60

Kanumera
Bay, Isle of
Pines
A149

1986, Mar. 26 Litho. Perf. 12½
537 A149 50fr shown 1.25 .70
538 A149 55fr Inland village 1.40 .80

See Nos. 547-548, 617-618.

Geckos — A150

20fr, Bavayia sauvagii. 45fr, Rhacodactylus
leachianus.

1986, Apr. 16 Perf. 12½x13
539 A150 20fr multicolored 1.10 .75
540 A150 45fr multicolored 1.50 .85

1986 World Cup Soccer
Championships, Mexico — A151

1986, May 28 Perf. 13
541 A151 60fr multicolored 1.50 1.00

1st
Pharmacy
in New
Caledonia,
120th Anniv.
A152

1986, June 25 Litho. Perf. 13
542 A152 80fr multicolored 2.25 1.25

Orchids — A153

44fr, Coelogynae licastioides. 58fr,
Calanthe langei.

1986, July 16 Perf. 12½x13
543 A153 44fr multicolored 1.50 .80
544 A153 58fr multicolored 1.75 .90

STAMPEX
'86,
Adelaide
A154

1986, Aug. 4 Perf. 12½
545 A154 110fr Bird 3.00 1.40

Arms Type of 1984
1986, Oct. 11 Litho. Perf. 13½
546 A132 94fr Mont Dore 3.00 1.10

Landscape Type of 1986
40fr, West landscape, vert. 76fr, South
Landscape.

1986, Oct. 29 Litho. Perf. 12½
547 A149 40fr multicolored 1.10 .70
548 A149 76fr multicolored 1.75 .80

Flowers — A156

Niponthes vieillardi, Syzygium ngayense,
Archidendropsis Paivana, Scavola balansae.

1986, Nov. 12 Perf. 12½
549 A156 73fr multicolored 1.90 .90

Nature Protection Assoc.

A157

1986, Nov. 26 Perf. 13x12½
550 A157 350fr Emblem 8.00 4.25

Noumea Lions Club, 25th anniv.

A158

Paintings: 74fr, Moret Point, by A. Sisley.
140fr, Butterfly Chase, by B. Morisot.

1986, Dec. 23 Litho. Perf. 13
551 A158 74fr multicolored 2.25 1.40
552 A158 140fr multicolored 4.00 1.60

America's
Cup — A159

1987, Jan. 28 Perf. 13½
553 A159 30fr Challenge France 1.50 .90
554 A159 70fr French Kiss 1.90 1.10

Plants, Butterflies
A160

46fr, Anona squamosa, Graphium gelon.
54fr, Albizzia granulosa, Polyura gamma.

1987, Feb. 25 Litho. Perf. 13x12½
555 A160 46fr multicolored 2.50 .90
556 A160 54fr multicolored 3.00 1.50

Pirogues — A161

1987, May 13 Engr. Perf. 13x12½
557 A161 72fr from Isle of Pines 1.75 1.00
558 A161 90fr from Ouvea 2.25 1.25

New Town Hall,
Mont
Dore — A162

1987, May 23 Litho. Perf. 12½x13
559 A162 92fr multicolored 2.10 1.00

Seashells — A163

1987, June 24 Perf. 13
560 A163 28fr Cypraea moneta 1.00 .65
561 A163 36fr Cypraea martini 1.50 .70

8th South Pacific
Games — A164

1987, July 8 Perf. 12½x13
562 A164 40fr multicolored 1.25 .55

A165

1987, July 22 Perf. 13½
563 A165 270fr multicolored 5.75 2.75

Soroptimist Int'l. 13th Convention, Melbourne, July 26-31.

Birds — A166

18fr, Zosterops xanthochroa. 21fr, Falco
peregrinus nesiotes, vert.

1987, Aug. 26   *Perf. 13*
564 A166 18fr multicolored   .90 .35
565 A166 21fr multicolored   1.10 .35

South Pacific Commission, 40th
Anniv. — A167

1987, Oct. 14   Litho.   *Perf. 13*
566 A167 200fr multicolored   5.00 2.50

Philately at
School — A168

1987, Oct. 21   *Perf. 12½*
567 A168 15fr multicolored   .90 .50

8th South
Pacific
Games,
Noumea
A169

1987, Dec. 8   Litho.   *Perf. 12½*
568 A169 20fr Golf   1.25 .50
569 A169 30fr Rugby   1.75 1.20
570 A169 100fr Long jump   3.00 1.25
       Nos. 568-570 (3)   6.00 2.95

Map, Ships,
La Perouse
A170

1988, Feb. 10   Engr.   *Perf. 13*
571 A170 36fr dark rose lil   1.50 .70

Disappearance of La Perouse expedition,
200th anniv., and Jean-Francois de Galaup
(1741-1788), Comte de La Perouse.

A171

Design: French University of the South
Pacific at Noumea and Papeete.

1988, Feb. 24   Litho.   *Perf. 13x12½*
572 A171 400fr multicolored   9.25 4.25

Tropical
Fish — A172

30fr, Pomacanthus semicirculatus. 46fr,
Glyphidodontops cyaneus.

1988, Mar. 23   Litho.   *Perf. 13*
573 A172 30fr multicolored   1.10 .55
574 A172 46fr multicolored   1.50 .80

Intl. Red Cross
and Red Crescent
Organizations,
125th
Annivs. — A173

1988, Apr. 27
575 A173 300fr multicolored   7.50 3.75

Regional
Housing — A174

Designs: 19fr, Mwaringou, Canala Region,
vert. 21fr, Nathalo, Lifou.

1988, Apr. 13   Engr.   *Perf. 13*
576 A174 19fr emer grn, brt blue
               & red brn   .85 .50
577 A174 21fr brt blue, emer grn
               & red brn   .85 .50

Medicinal
Plants — A175

1988, May 18   Litho.   *Perf. 13x12½*
578 A175 28fr Ochrosia elliptica   1.10 .55
579 A175 64fr Rauvolfia levenetii   2.10 1.10
       No. 579 is airmail.

Living
Fossils
A176

51fr, Gymnocrinus richeri.

1988, June 11   *Perf. 13*
580 A176 51fr multicolored   2.25 .90

Bourail
Museum
and
Historical
Soc.
A177

1988, June 25   Litho.   *Perf. 13*
581 A177 120fr multi   3.00 1.60

SYDPEX
'88 — A178

Designs: No. 582, La Perouse aboard *La
Boussole*, gazing through spyglass at the First
Fleet in Botany Bay, Jan. 24, 1788. No. 583,
Capt. Phillip and crew ashore on Botany Bay
watching the approach of La Perouse's ships
La Boussole and *L'Astrolabe*.

1988, July 30   Litho.   *Perf. 13x12½*
582 A178 42fr multi   1.50 .90
583 A178 42fr multi   1.50 .90
  a.   Souvenir sheet of 2, #582-583,
       perf. 13x13½   4.75 4.25
  b.   Strip of 2, #582-583 + label 3.50 3.00
       No. 583a sold for 120fr.

Kagu — A179

1988-90   Engr.   *Perf. 13*
584 A179 1fr bright blue   .50 .25
585 A179 2fr green   .50 .25
586 A179 3fr bright orange   .75 .25
587 A179 4fr bright green   .75 .25

588 A179 5fr deep rose lilac   1.00 .25
589 A179 28fr orange   1.00 .25
590 A179 40fr bright rose   1.10 .25
       Nos. 584-590 (7)   5.60 1.75
  Issued: 40fr, 8/10/88; 1fr, 4fr, 1/25/89; 2fr,
3fr, 5fr, 4/19/89; 28fr, 1/15/90.
  See Type A137.

Kagu — A179a

1990-93   Engr.   *Perf. 13*
591 A179a 1fr dark blue   .25 .25
592 A179a 2fr bright green   .25 .25
593 A179a 3fr brt yel org   .30 .25
594 A179a 4fr dark green   .30 .25
595 A179a 5fr bright violet   .30 .25
596 A179a 9fr blue black   .35 .25
597 A179a 12fr orange   .40 .25
598 A179a 40fr lilac rose   1.00 .25
599 A179a 50fr red   1.40 .30
       Nos. 591-599 (9)   4.55 2.30
  Issued: 50fr, 9/5/90; 1fr-5fr, 1/9/91; 40fr,
1/15/92; 9fr, 12fr, 1/25/93.
  See Type A137 and Nos. 675, 683. For
surcharge see No. 685.

1988
Summer
Olympics,
Seoul
A180

1988, Sept. 14   *Perf. 12½x12*
600 A180 150fr multi   4.00 2.00

Pasteur Institute,
Noumea,
Cent. — A181

1988, Sept. 28   Engr.   *Perf. 13*
601 A181 100fr blk, brt ultra &
               dark red   2.50 1.25

Writers
A182

72fr, Georges Baudoux (1870-1949). 73fr,
Jean Mariotti (1901-1975).

1988, Oct. 15   Engr.   *Perf. 13*
602 A182 72fr multicolored   2.00 1.00
603 A182 73fr multicolored   2.00 1.00
       No. 603 is airmail.

WHO, 40th
Anniv. — A183

1988, Nov. 16   Litho.   *Perf. 13x12½*
604 A183 250fr multi   6.00 2.75

**Art Type of 1984 Without "ET
DEPENDANCES"**

Paintings by artists of the Pacific: 54fr, *Land
of Men*, by L. Bunckley. 92fr, *The Latin Quarter*, by Marik.

1988, Dec. 7
605 AP113 54fr multi   2.25 1.00
606 AP113 92fr multi   3.00 1.40

**Arms Type of 1984 Without "ET
DEPENDANCES"**

1989, Feb. 22   *Perf. 13½*
607 A132 200fr Koumac   4.50 2.00

Indigenous
Flora — A184

80fr, Parasitaxus ustus, vert. 90fr, Tristani-
opsis guillainii.

1989, Mar. 22   Litho.   *Perf. 13½*
608 A184 80fr multicolored   2.00 1.10
609 A184 90fr multicolored   2.50 1.40

Marine
Life — A185

1989, May 17   Litho.   *Perf. 12½x13*
610 A185 18fr Plesionika   1.10 .60
611 A185 66fr Ocosia apia   1.90 1.00
612 A185 110fr Latiaxis   2.75 1.60
       Nos. 610-612 (3)   5.75 3.20
       See Nos. 652-653.

French Revolution,
Bicent. — A186

40fr, Liberty. 58fr, Equality. 76fr, Fraternity.
180fr, Liberty, Equality, Fraternity.

1989, July 7   Litho.   *Perf. 13½*
613 A186 40fr multi   1.75 .60
614 A186 58fr multi   1.75 .75
615 A186 76fr multi   1.75 1.00
       Nos. 613-615 (3)   5.25 2.35
       Souvenir Sheet
616 A186 180fr multi   5.50 5.50
       Nos. 614-616 are airmail.

**Landscape Type of 1986 Without
"ET DEPENDANCES"**

64fr, La Poule rookery, Hienghene. 180fr,
Ouaieme ferry.

1989, Aug. 23   Litho.   *Perf. 13*
617 A149 64fr multicolored   1.50 .75
618 A149 180fr multicolored   4.00 1.60
       No. 617 is airmail.

Carved
Bamboo — A187

Litho. & Engr.

1989, Sept. 27   *Perf. 12½x13*
619 A187 70fr multicolored   1.75 .70
       See No. C216.

A188

1989, Oct. 25   Litho.   *Perf. 13*
620 A188 350fr multicolored   8.50 3.50

Hobie-Cat 14 10th World Championships,
Nov. 3, Noumea.

Natl. Historical Soc., 20th Anniv. A189

Cover of *Moeurs: Superstitions of New Caledonians*, cover of book on Melanesian oral literature and historians G. Pisier, R.P. Neyret and A. Surleau.

1989, Nov. 3   **Engr.**
621 A189 74fr brown & black   2.00 .80

Ft. Teremba A190

1989, Nov. 18   **Engr.**
622 A190 100fr bl grn & dk org   2.50 1.40

Marguerite Historical Preservation Soc.

Impressionist Paintings — A191

Designs: 130fr, The Escape of Rochefort, by Manet. 270fr, Self-portrait, by Courbet.

1989, Dec. 6   **Litho.**   **Perf. 13½**
623 A191 130fr multicolored   3.25 1.90
624 A191 270fr multicolored   7.50 4.00

Fr. Patrick O'Reilly (1900-1988), Writer — A192

1990, Jan. 24   **Engr.**   **Perf. 13x13½**
625 A192 170fr blk & plum   4.25 1.90

Grasses and Butterflies A193

Various Cyperacea costularia and Paratisiphone lyrnessa: 18fr, Female. 50fr, Female, diff. 94fr, Male.

1990, Feb. 21   **Litho.**   **Perf. 13½**
626 A193 18fr shown   1.90 .60
627 A193 50fr multicolored   .90 .50
628 A193 94fr multicolored   3.25 1.25
    Nos. 626-628 (3)   6.05 2.35

Nos. 626 and 628 are airmail.

A194

1990, Mar. 16   **Engr.**   **Perf. 12½x13**
629 A194 85fr Kanakan money   1.90 .80
630 A194 140fr money, diff.   3.50 1.40

A195

1990, Mar. 16   **Litho.**   **Perf. 13x13½**
631 A195 230fr multicolored   5.25 2.50

Jade and mother of pearl exhibition, New Caledonian Museum.

Noumea Aquarium — A196

10fr, Phyllidia ocellata. 42fr, Chromodoris kuniei, vert.

1990, Apr. 25   **Perf. 13x12½, 12½x13**
632 A196 10fr multicolored   .45 .45
633 A196 42fr multicolored   1.50 .70

Petroglyphs — A197

1990, July 11   **Engr.**   **Perf. 13**
634 A197 40fr Neounda   1.25 .55
635 A197 58fr Kassducou   1.75 .90

No. 635 is airmail.

Meeting Center of the Pacific A198

1990, July 25   **Litho.**   **Perf. 13**
636 A198 320fr multicolored   7.00 3.00

World Cup Soccer Championships, Italy — A199

1990, May 30   **Litho.**   **Perf. 13**
637 A199 240fr multicolored   6.00 3.00

Flowers — A200

105fr, Gardenia aubryi. 130fr, Hibbertia baudouinii.

1990, Nov. 7   **Perf. 13x12½**
638 A200 105fr multicolored   2.50 1.25
639 A200 130fr multicolored   3.00 2.00

La Maison Celieres by M. Petron — A201

365fr, Le Mont-Dore de Jade by C. Degroiselle.

1990, Dec. 5   **Perf. 12½**
640 A201 110fr multicolored   2.50 1.25
641 A201 365fr multicolored   9.00 2.75

No. 640 is airmail.

Writers — A202

Designs: #642, Louise Michel (1830-1905). #643, Charles B. Nething (1867-1947).

1991, Mar. 20   **Engr.**   **Perf. 13**
642   125fr rose lil & bl   3.00 1.50
643   125fr brn & bl   3.00 1.50
 a.   A202 Pair, #642-643 + label   6.50 6.00

Native Huts — A203

1991, May 15   **Litho.**   **Perf. 12**
644 A203 12fr Houailou   .75 .40
645 A203 35fr Hienghene   1.00 .60

Maps of the Provinces — A204

1991, June 17   **Litho.**   **Perf. 13½**
646 A204 45fr Northern   1.00 .45
647 A204 45fr Island   1.00 .45
648 A204 45fr Southern   1.00 .45
 a.   Strip of 3, #646-648   3.50 3.25

Orchids A205

55fr, Dendrobium biflorum. 70fr, Dendrobium closterium.

1991, July 24   **Litho.**   **Perf. 13**
649 A205 55fr multicolored   1.60 .80
650 A205 70fr multicolored   2.25 1.00

French Institute of Scientific Research A206

1991, Aug. 26
651 A206 170fr multicolored   3.75 1.75

Marine Life Type of 1989

60fr, Monocentris japonicus. 100fr, Tristigenys niphonia.

1991, Aug. 26   **Litho.**   **Perf. 12**
652 A185 60fr multicolored   1.50 .80
653 A185 100fr multicolored   2.50 1.10

9th South Pacific Games, Papua New Guinea — A207

1991, Sept. 6   **Perf. 12½**
654 A207 170fr multicolored   3.50 1.50

Vietnamese in New Caledonia, Cent. A208

1991, Sept. 8   **Engr.**   **Perf. 13x12½**
655 A208 300fr multicolored   6.50 2.50

Lions Club of New Caledonia, 30th Anniv. — A209

1991, Oct. 5   **Litho.**   **Perf. 12½**
656 A209 192fr multicolored   5.50 2.75

First Commercial Harvesting of Sandalwood, 150th Anniv. A210

1991, Oct. 23   **Engr.**   **Perf. 13**
657 A210 200fr multicolored   5.25 2.75

Phila Nippon '91 — A211

Plants and butterflies: 8fr, Phillantus, Eurema hecabe. 15fr, Pipturus incanus, Hypolimnas octocula. 20fr, Stachytarpheta urticaefolia, Precis villida. 26fr, Malaisia scandens, Cyrestis telamon.

Butterflies: No. 662a, Cyrestis telamon, vert. b, Hypolimnas octocula, vert. c, Eurema hecabe, vert. d, Precis villida, vert.

1991, Nov. 16   **Litho.**   **Perf. 12½**
658 A211 8fr multicolored   .30 .25
659 A211 15fr multicolored   .35 .35
660 A211 20fr multicolored   .45 .35
661 A211 26fr multicolored   .70 .45
 a.   Strip of 4, #658-661 + label   2.75 2.50

Souvenir Sheet

662 A211 75fr Sheet of 4, #a.-
         d.   12.00 12.00

Central Bank for Economic Cooperation, 50th Anniv. — A212

Designs: No. 663, Nickel processing plant, dam. No. 664, Private home, tourist hotels.

1991, Dec. 2   **Litho.**   **Perf. 13**
663   76fr multicolored   1.90 1.00
664   76fr multicolored   1.90 1.00
 a.   A212 Pair, #663-664 + label   4.00 4.00

Preservation of Nature A213

15fr, Madeleine waterfalls.

1992, Mar. 25   **Litho.**   **Perf. 13**
665 A213 15fr multicolored   .60 .45
 a.   Souv. sheet, perf. 12½   4.00 4.00

No. 665a sold for 150fr.

Immigration of First Japanese to New Caledonia, Cent. — A214

1992, June 11 Litho. Perf. 13x12½
666　95fr yellow & multi　　2.25 1.25
667　95fr gray & multi　　　2.25 1.25
　a.　A214 Pair, #666-667 + label　4.50 4.50

Arrival of American Armed Forces, 50th Anniv. A215

1992, Aug. 13
668　A215 50fr multicolored　　1.50 .60

Lagoon Protection A216

1993, Feb. 23 Litho. Perf. 13
669　A216 120fr multicolored　　2.75 1.25

Kagu Type of 1990
1993-94 Engr. Perf. 13
675　A179a 55fr red　　　2.00 1.25
676　A179a (60fr) claret　　1.50 .60

Self-Adhesive Litho.

Die Cut Perf. 10
681　A179a　5fr bright lilac　　1.40 1.40
　a.　Bklt. pane, 8+8, gutter btwn.　22.50
683　A179a　55fr red　　　3.50 3.50
　a.　Bklt. pane, 8+8, gutter btwn.　57.50

Issued: Nos. 675, 683, 4/7/93; No. 676, 1/27/94; No. 681, 2/94.
No. 676 sold for 60fr on day of issue.
By their nature, Nos. 681a, 683a are complete booklets. The peelable paper backing serves as a booklet cover.

No. 599 Surcharged

1993 Engr. Perf. 13
685　A179a 55fr on 50fr red　　1.40 .70

Philately in School — A217

1993, Apr. 7 Litho. Perf. 13½
686　A217 25fr multicolored　　.60 .30
For overprint see No. 690.

Miniature Sheet of 13

Town Coats of Arms — A218

Designs: a, Bourail. b, Noumea. c, Canala. d, Kone. e, Paita. f, Dumbea. g, Koumac. h, Ponerhouen. i, Kaamoo Hyehen. j, Mont Dore. k, Thio. l, Kaala-Gomen. m, Touho.

1993, Dec. 10 Litho. Perf. 13½
687　A218 70fr #a.-m., + 2 labels　40.00 40.00

Souvenir Sheet

Hong Kong '94 — A219

Wildlife: a, Panda. b, Kagu.

1994, Feb. 18 Litho. Perf. 13
688　A219 105fr Sheet of 2, #a.-b.　8.25 8.25

First Postal Delivery Route, 50th Anniv. A220

1994, Apr. 28 Engr. Perf. 13
689　A220 15fr multicolored　　.50 .25

No. 686 Ovptd. in Blue

1994, Apr. 22 Litho. Perf. 13½
690　A217 25fr multicolored　　.70 .35

Headquarters of New Caledonian Post Office — A222

1994, June 25 Litho. Perf. 13½x13
691　Strip of 4, #a.-d.　　8.00 8.00
　a.　A222 30fr 1859　　.75 .45
　b.　A222 60fr 1936　　1.50 .80
　c.　A222 90fr 1967　　2.10 1.40
　d.　A222 120fr 1993　　3.00 1.75

Pacific Sculpture — A223

1994, June 25 Litho. Perf. 13x13½
693　A223 60fr multicolored　　1.50 .70

Chambeyronia Macrocarpa — A224

1994, July 7 Litho. Perf. 13x13½
694　A224 90fr multicolored　　2.25 1.10

No. J46 Overprinted With Bar Over "Timbre Taxe"
1994, Aug. 8 Litho. Perf. 13
696　D5 5fr multicolored　　17.50 —

Stag — A227

1994, Aug. 14 Litho. Perf. 13½
697　A227 150fr multicolored　　3.50 1.60

Jacques Nervat, Writer — A228

1994, Sept. 15　　　　Perf. 13x13½
698　A228 175fr multicolored　　4.00 1.90

Frigate Nivose — A229

No. 699, 30fr, Ship at sea. No. 700, 30fr, Ship along shore. No. 701, 30fr, Ship docked. No. 702, 60fr, Painting of frigate, map of island, ship's crest. No. 703, 60fr, Ship's bell. No. 704, 60fr, Sailor looking at ship.

1994, Oct. 7 Litho. Perf. 13½
Booklet Stamps
699　A229 30fr multicolored　　1.10 .45
700　A229 30fr multicolored　　1.10 .45
701　A229 30fr multicolored　　1.10 .35
702　A229 60fr multicolored　　1.75 .80
703　A229 60fr multicolored　　1.75 .80
704　A229 60fr multicolored　　1.75 .80
　a.　Booklet pane, #699-704　9.00
　　　Booklet, 4 #704a　40.00

Philately at School — A230

1994, Nov. 4 Litho. Perf. 13½
705　A230 30fr multicolored　　.90 .35
For overprint see No. 749

Christmas — A231

Top of bell starts below: a, Second "o." b, Third "e." c, "a." d, "C." e, Second "e."

1994, Dec. 17
706　Strip of 5　　　4.75 4.25
　a.-e.　A231 30fr Any single　.85 .55
Nos. 706a-706e differ in location of the red ball, yellow bell and statue. No.706 is designed for stereoscopic viewing.

Le Monde Newspaper, 50th Anniv. — A232

1994, Dec. 17
707　A232 90fr multicolored　　2.75 1.60

Louis Pasteur (1822-95) A233

1995, Feb. 13 Litho. Perf. 13
708　A233 120fr No. 601　　2.75 1.40

Charles de Gaulle (1890-1970) A234

Litho. & Embossed
1995, Mar. 28　　　　Perf. 13
709　A234 1000fr blue & gold　18.00 15.00

Teacher's Training College for the French Territories in the Pacific — A235

1995, Apr. 24 Litho. Perf. 13
710　A235 100fr multicolored　　2.25 1.25
See French Polynesia No. 656 and Wallis & Futuna No. C182.

Sylviornis Neo-Caledonia, Fossil Bird — A236

1995, May 16 Litho. Perf. 13x13½
711　A236 60fr multicolored　　1.75 .70

10th Sunshine Triathlon A237

1995, May 26 Engr. Perf. 13x12½
712　A237 60fr multicolored　　1.50 .90

Creation of the CFP Franc, 1945 — A238

Top of tree at left points to: a, Second "e." b, Second "l." c, First "l." d, First "e."

1995, June 8 Litho. Perf. 13x13½
713　A238 10fr Strip of 4, #a.-d.　1.50 1.50
Nos. 713a-713d show coin rotating clockwise with trees, hut at different locations. No. 713 is designed for stereoscopic viewing.

1st New Caledonian Deputy in French Natl. Assembly, 50th Anniv. — A239

1995, June 8　　　　Perf. 13½
714　A239 60fr multicolored　　1.50 .70

End of World War II, 50th Anniv. — A240

1995, June 8　　　　Perf. 13x13½
715　A240 90fr multicolored　　1.50 .60

UN, 50th Anniv. — A241

1995, June 8
716　A241 90fr multicolored　　2.25 .90

Sebertia Acuminata A242

1995, July 28 Litho. Perf. 13x13½
717　A242 60fr multicolored　　1.50 .60

Singapore
'95 — A243

Sea birds: 5fr, Anous stolidus. 10fr, Larus novaehollandiae. 20fr, Sterna dougallii. 35fr, Pandion haliaetus. 65fr, Sula sula. 125fr, Fregata minor.

1995, Aug. 24   Litho.   Perf. 13x13½
718	A243	5fr multicolored	.30	.25
719	A243	10fr multicolored	.35	.25
720	A243	20fr multicolored	.40	.25
721	A243	35fr multicolored	.80	.55
722	A243	65fr multicolored	1.40	1.10
723	A243	125fr multicolored	3.00	1.60

a. Souvenir sheet, #718-723 + label   7.50 7.50
Nos. 718-723 (6)   6.25 4.00

10th South Pacific Games — A244

1995, Aug. 24
724 A244 90fr multicolored   2.10 1.10

Sculpture, The Lizard Man, by Dick Bone — A248

1995, Oct. 25   Litho.   Perf. 13
730 A248 65fr multicolored   1.25 .75

Gargariscus Prionocephalus A249

1995, Dec. 15   Litho.   Perf. 13
731 A249 100fr multicolored   2.25 1.00

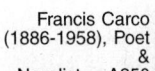

Francis Carco (1886-1958), Poet & Novelist — A250

1995, Nov. 15   Litho.   Perf. 13x13½
732 A250 95fr multicolored   2.25 1.25

Ancient Pottery — A251

1996, Apr. 12   Litho.   Perf. 13
733 A251 65fr multicolored   1.60 .90

Endemic Rubiaceous Plants — A252

Designs: 65fr, Captaincookia margaretae. 95fr, Ixora cauliflora.

1996, Apr. 17
734 A252 65fr multicolored   1.50 .60
735 A252 95fr multicolored   2.10 .90

7th Va'a (Outrigger Canoe) World Championship, Noumea, New Caledonia A253

Designs: a, 30fr, Islander standing on shore with early version of canoe. b, 65fr, Early single-hull canoe with islanders. c, 95fr, Early catamaran, people rowing. d, 125fr, Modern racing canoe.

1996, May 10   Litho.   Perf. 13
736 A253 Strip of 4, #a.-d.   6.50 6.50
No. 736 is a continuous design.

CHINA '96 — A254

Marine life: 25fr, Halieutaea stellata. 40fr, Perotrochus deforgesi. 65fr, Mursia musorstomia. 125fr, Metacrinus levii.

1996, May 18
737	A254	25fr multicolored	.55	.35
738	A254	40fr multicolored	.85	.65
739	A254	65fr multicolored	1.50	.90
740	A254	125fr multicolored	2.75	1.60

Nos. 737-740 (4)   5.65 3.50

Nos. 737-740 were each issued in sheets of 10 + 5 labels.
On Nos. 737-740 portions of the design were applied by a thermographic process producing a shiny, raised effect.

737a	Booklet pane of 6	5.00
738a	Booklet pane of 6	6.50
739a	Booklet pane of 6	12.50
740a	Booklet pane of 6	25.00
	Complete booklet, #737a-740a	49.00

CAPEX '96 — A255

Orchids: 5fr, Sarcochilus koghiensis. 10fr, Phaius robertsii. 25fr, Megastylis montana. 65fr, Dendrobium macrophyllum. 95fr, Dendrobium virotii. 125fr, Ephemerantha comata.

1996, June 25   Litho.   Perf. 13
741	A255	5fr multicolored	.30	.25
742	A255	10fr multicolored	.40	.25
743	A255	25fr multicolored	.65	.35
744	A255	65fr multicolored	1.40	.65
745	A255	95fr multicolored	2.25	1.00
746	A255	125fr multicolored	2.50	1.25

a. Booklet pane of 6, #741-746   7.75
Souvenir booklet, 4 #746a   38.00
Nos. 741-746 (6)   7.50 3.75

Nos. 741-746 were each issued in sheets of 10 + 5 labels.

No. 705 Ovptd. with UNICEF Emblem in Blue
1996, Sept. 12   Litho.   Perf. 13½
749 A230 30fr multicolored   .75 .45
UNICEF, 50th anniv.

Ordination of the First Melanesian Priests — A258

1996, Oct. 9   Litho.   Perf. 13
750 A258 160fr multicolored   3.50 1.90
Portions of the design on No. 750 were applied by a thermographic process producing a shiny, raised effect.

7th Festival of South Pacific Arts — A259

Designs: 100fr, Dancer, face carving. 105fr, Wood carvings of women. 200fr, Painting by Paula Boi. 500fr, Gaica Dance, Lifou.

1996, Oct. 9
751	A259	100fr multicolored	2.25	1.25
752	A259	105fr multicolored	2.25	1.25
753	A259	200fr multicolored	4.00	2.25
754	A259	500fr multicolored	9.00	5.75

Nos. 751-754 (4)   17.50 10.50
No. 751 is airmail.

French Pres. Francois Mitterrand (1916-96) A260

1997, Mar. 14   Litho.   Perf. 13
755 A260 1000fr multicolored   18.00 11.00

Alphonse Daudet (1840-97), Writer — A261

Designs: No. 756, "Letters from a Windmill." No. 757, "Le Petit Chose." No. 758, "Tartarin of Tarascon." No. 759, Daudet writing.

1997, May 14   Perf. 13
756	A261	65fr multicolored	1.50	1.50
757	A261	65fr multicolored	1.50	1.50
758	A261	65fr multicolored	1.50	1.50
759	A261	65fr multicolored	1.50	1.50

a. Souvenir sheet, #756-759   6.50 6.50

Henri La Fleur, First Senator of New Caledonia A262

1997, June 12   Litho.   Perf. 13
760 A262 105fr multicolored   2.40 1.25

Insects — A263

Designs: a, Tectocoris diophthalmus. b, Kanakia gigas. c, Aenetus cohici.

1997, June 25   Litho.   Perf. 13x12½
761 A263 65fr Strip of 3, #a.-c.   4.50 4.00

Jacques Iekawe (1946-92), First Melanesian Prefect A264

1997, July 23   Litho.   Perf. 13
762 A264 250fr multicolored   5.00 2.50

Kagu — A265

1997, Aug. 13   Engr.   Perf. 13
763 A265 95fr blue   2.10 1.25
See Nos. 772-773C, 878-879, 897.

Horse Racing — A266

No. 764, Harness racing. No. 765, Thoroughbred racing.

1997, Sept. 20   Litho.   Perf. 13
764 A266 65fr multicolored   1.75 .80
765 A266 65fr multicolored   1.75 .80

Early Engraving of "View of Port de France" (Noumea) A267

Photo. & Engr.
1997, Sept. 22   Perf. 13x12½
766 A267 95fr multicolored   2.00 1.25
See No. 802.

A268

1997, Sept. 22   Litho.   Perf. 13
767 A268 150fr multicolored   3.00 1.75
First Melanesian election, 50th anniv.

Hippocampus Bargibanti — A269

1997, Nov. 3   Litho.   Perf. 13½x13
768 A269 100fr multicolored   2.25 1.50
5th World Conf. on Fish of the Indo-Pacific. Issued in sheets of 10+5 labels.

South Pacific Arts — A270

Designs: a, Doka wood carvings. b, Beizam dance mask. c, Abstract painting of primative life by Yvette Bouquet.

1997, Nov. 3   Perf. 13
769 A270 100fr Strip of 3, #a.-c.   6.00 6.00

Christmas A271

Designs: 95fr, Santa on surfboard pulled by dolphins. 100fr, Dolphin with banner in mouth.

1997, Nov. 17
770 A271 95fr multicolored   2.00 1.00
771 A271 100fr multicolored   2.00 1.00

Nos. 770-771 issued in sheets of 10+5 labels.

Kagu Type of 1997
1997-98   Engr.   Perf. 13
772 A265 30fr orange   1.00 .35
773 A265 (70fr) red   1.60 .75

Booklet Stamps
Self-Adhesive
Litho.
Serpentine Die Cut 11
773A A265 (70fr) red   2.00 .45
b.   Booklet pane of 10   22.50

Engr.
Serpentine Die Cut 6¾ Vert.
773C A265 (70fr) red   — —
d.   Booklet pane of 10   —

The peelable paper backing of No. 773A serves as a booklet cover.

Issued: 30fr, 1997; No. 773A, 1/2/98; No. 773C, 2004.

A272

Mushrooms: #774, Lentinus tuber-regium. #775, Volvaria bombycina. #776, Morchella anteridiformis.

1998, Jan. 22   Litho.   Perf. 13
774 A272 70fr multicolored   1.40 .80
775 A272 70fr multicolored   1.40 .80
776 A272 70fr multicolored   1.40 .80
   Nos. 774-776 (3)   4.20 2.40

A273

Artifacts from Territorial Museum: 105fr, Mask, Northern Region. 110fr, "Dulon" door frame pillar, Central Region.

1998, Mar. 17   Litho.   Perf. 13
777 A273 105fr multicolored   2.00 1.10
778 A273 110fr multicolored   2.10 1.10

Paul Gauguin (1848-1903) A274

1998, May 15   Litho.   Perf. 13
779 A274 405fr multicolored   8.00 5.00

1998 World Cup Soccer Championships, France — A280

1998, June 5   Photo.   Perf. 12½
787 A280 100fr multicolored   2.00 1.25

A281

Jean-Marie Tjibaou Cultural Center — A282

Designs: 30fr, "Mitimitia," artwork by Fatu Feu'u. No. 789, Jean-Marie Tjibaou (1936-89), Melanesian political leader. No. 790, Exterior view of building, vert. 105fr, "Man Bird," painting by Mathias Kauage.

1998, June 21   Litho.   Perf. 13x13½
788 A281 30fr multicolored   .75 .35
a.   Booklet pane of 6   4.50
789 A281 70fr multicolored   1.50 .85
a.   Booklet pane of 6   9.00
790 A281 70fr multicolored   1.50 .85
a.   Booklet pane of 6   9.00
791 A282 105fr multicolored   2.25 1.25
a.   Booklet pane of 6   15.00
   Complete booklet, #788a, 789a, 790a, 791a   40.00
   Nos. 788-791 (4)   6.00 3.30

Abolition of Slavery, 150th Anniv. A283

1998, July 21   Engr.   Perf. 13
792 A283 130fr multicolored   2.50 1.50

Postman, Dogs — A284

1998, Aug. 20   Litho.   Perf. 13
793 A284 70fr multicolored   1.75 .85

Arab Presence in New Caledonia, Cent. — A285

1998, Sept. 4
794 A285 80fr multicolored   1.75 1.00

A286

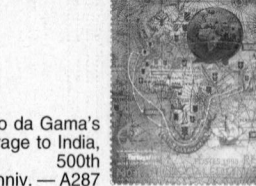

Vasco da Gama's Voyage to India, 500th Anniv. — A287

No. 795: a, Port in India. b, Da Gama at Cape of Good Hope, ships at sea. c, Da Gama meeting with Indians. d, Da Gama's picture in crest.
No. 796: a, Map of route. b, Vasco da Gama. c, Ship at anchor.

1998, Sept. 4
795 A286 100fr Strip of 4, #a.-d.   8.00 8.00

Souvenir Sheet
796 A287 70fr Sheet of 3, #a.-c.   5.00 5.00

Portugal '98 Intl. Philatelic Exhibition.

A288

Litho. & Engr.
1998, Sept. 25   Perf. 12½x13
797 A288 110fr multicolored   2.25 2.25

Vincent Bouquet (1893-1971), High Chief.

A289

World Wildlife Fund — Kagu: 5fr, Male. 10fr, Female. 15fr, Two in grass. 70fr, Two in dirt, one ruffling feathers.

1998, Oct. 20   Litho.   Perf. 13
798 A289 5fr multicolored   .30 .25
799 A289 10fr multicolored   .40 .25
800 A289 15fr multicolored   .60 .25
801 A289 70fr multicolored   1.75 1.25
   Nos. 798-801 (4)   3.05 2.00

Early Engraving Type of 1997
1998, Nov. 4   Engr.   Perf. 13x12½
802 A267 155fr Nou Island   3.00 2.00

Universal Declaration of Human Rights, 50th Anniv. — A290

1998, Nov. 4   Engr.   Perf. 13
803 A290 70fr blk, bl & bl grn   1.75 1.40

Columnar Pine — A291

1998, Nov. 5   Litho.   Perf. 13x13½
804 A291 100fr shown   2.25 2.00
805 A291 100fr Coast, forest   2.25 2.00

A292

Post and Telecommunications, 40th Anniv.: #806, Switchboard, bicycle, early post office. #807, Cell phone, microwave relay, motorcycle.

1998, Nov. 27   Litho.   Perf. 13½x13
806 A292 70fr multicolored   1.60 1.60
807 A292 70fr multicolored   1.60 1.60
a.   Pair, #806-807 + label   3.50 3.50

A293

Underwater scenes (Greetings Stamps): No. 808, Fish, coral forming flower, Happy Anniversary. No. 809, Fish up close, Happy New Year. No. 810, Open treasure chest, Best Wishes. No. 811, Fish, starfish forming Christmas tree, Merry Christmas.

1998, Dec. 1
808 A293 100fr multicolored   2.00 1.50
809 A293 100fr multicolored   2.00 1.50
810 A293 100fr multicolored   2.00 1.50
811 A293 100fr multicolored   2.00 1.50
   Nos. 808-811 (4)   8.00 6.00

Monument to the Disappearance of the Ship Monique, 20th Anniv. — A294

1998, Dec. 1   Perf. 13
812 A294 130fr multicolored   2.75 2.00

Arachnids A295

Designs: No. 813, Argiope aetherea. No. 814, Barycheloides alluvviophilus. No. 815, Latrodectus hasselti. No. 816, Crytophora moluccensis.

1999, Mar. 19   Litho.   Perf. 13x13½
813 A295 70fr multicolored   1.60 1.40
814 A295 70fr multicolored   1.60 1.40
815 A295 70fr multicolored   1.60 1.40
816 A295 70fr multicolored   1.60 1.40
   Nos. 813-816 (4)   6.40 5.60

Carcharodon Megalodon — A296

Designs: 100fr, Fossil tooth of megalodon. No. 818: a, Shark swimming with mouth open, vert. b, Comparison of shark to man and carcharodon carcharias. c, Fossil tooth on bottom of ocean.

1999, Mar. 19   Perf. 12½
817 A296 100fr multicolored   2.25 1.50

Souvenir Sheet
Perf. 13
818 A296 70fr Sheet of 3, #a.-c.   4.50 4.50

Nos. 818a is 30x40mm and 818b is 40x30mm.
Australia '99, World Stamp Expo (#818).

Paul Bloc (1883-1970), Writer — A297

1999, Apr. 23   Engr.   Perf. 13x12½
819 A297 105fr grn, bl grn & brn   2.25 1.50

Traditional Musical Instruments — A298

1999, May 20   Litho.   Perf. 13½x13
820 A298 30fr Bwanjep   .75 .60
821 A298 70fr Sonnailles   1.50 1.40
822 A298 100fr Flutes   2.25 2.00
   Nos. 820-822 (3)   4.50 4.00

11th South Pacific Games, Guam — A299

1999, May 20 Perf. 13x13¼
823 A299 5fr Track & field .30 .25
824 A299 10fr Tennis .30 .25
825 A299 30fr Karate .75 .60
826 A299 70fr Baseball 1.50 1.40
Nos. 823-826 (4) 2.85 2.50

Overseas Transport Squadron 52, Humanitarian Missions — A300

1999, June 18 Perf. 13
827 A300 135fr multicolored 2.75 1.75

Escoffier Hotel Catering and Business School, Noumea, 20th Anniv. — A301

Designs: No. 828, Building, computer. No. 829, Building, chef's hat.

1999, June 17 Litho. Perf. 13
828 A301 70fr multicolored 1.40 1.00
a. Pair + central label 3.00 2.50
829 A301 70fr multicolored 1.40 1.00
a. Pair + central label 3.00 2.50

New Caledonia's First Postage Stamp, 140th Anniv. — A302

Designs: No. 830, #1.
No. 831: a, Two #1. b, #1, diff. c, #1 up close. d, like #830. e, Design A265, image of Napolean III from #1, "1999."

1999, July 2 Photo. Perf. 13¼
830 A302 70fr multicolored 1.75 1.40
Souvenir Sheet
Perf. 12
831 Sheet of 5 27.50 27.50
a. A302 100fr Engraved 2.50 2.50
b. A302 100fr Litho., thermograph 2.50 2.50
c. A302 100fr Litho. 2.50 2.50
d. A302 100fr Litho. & embossed 2.50 2.50
e. A302 700fr Litho., hologram 15.00 15.00

Nos. 831a-831d are each 36x28mm. No. 831e is 44x35mm. Portions of the design on No. 831b were applied by a thermographic process producing a shiny, raised effect. No. 831e contains a holographic image. Soaking in water may affect the hologram.
PhilexFrance '99 (#831).

Tourism — A303

1999, Sept. 28 Litho. Perf. 13¼
832 A303 5fr Fish, vegetables .30 .25
833 A303 30fr Lobster dish .75 .55
834 A303 70fr Tourist huts 1.50 1.25
835 A303 100fr Hotel pool 2.25 1.90
Nos. 832-835 (4) 4.80 3.95

Ratification of Noumea Accord, 1998 — A304

1999, Nov. 10 Litho. Perf. 13x13½
836 A304 70fr multi 1.75 1.25

Aji Aboro Dance — A305

1999, Nov. 10
837 A305 70fr multi 1.50 1.25

Château Hagen A306

1999, Nov. 18 Perf. 13
838 A306 155fr multi 3.50 2.75

Nature Protection A307

1999, Dec. 7
839 A307 30fr multi .75 .50

Greetings A308

Designs: No. 840, "Joyeux Noel." No. 841, "Félicitations." No. 842, "Bon Anniversaire." No. 843, "Meilleurs Voeux 2000."

1999, Dec. 20
840 A308 100fr multi 2.00 1.50
841 A308 100fr multi 2.00 1.50
842 A308 100fr multi 2.00 1.50
843 A308 100fr multi 2.00 1.50
Nos. 840-843 (4) 8.00 6.00

Amédée Lighthouse — A309

2000, Mar. 7 Litho. Perf. 13½x12
844 A309 100fr multi 2.25 1.60

Ship Emile Renouf A310

2000, Apr. 19 Engr. Perf. 13x13¼
845 A310 135fr multi 3.50 2.25

Painting by Giles Subileau A311

2000, June 15 Litho. Perf. 13
846 A311 155fr multi 3.00 2.25

Souvenir Sheet

New Year 2000 (Year of the Dragon) A312

Denomination: a, at R. b, at L.

2000, June 15
847 A312 105fr Sheet of 2, #a-b 5.00 4.50

Antoine de Saint-Exupéry (1900-44), Aviator, Writer — A313

2000, July 7
848 A313 130fr multi 3.00 2.75
World Stamp Expo 2000, Anaheim.

Noumea Aquarium — A314

Designs: No. 849, Hymenocera elegans. No. 850, Fluorescent corals. No. 851, Chelinus undulatus.

2000, July 7 Perf. 13x13¼
849-851 A314 70fr Set of 3 5.50 3.50

Mangrove Heart — A315

2000, Aug. 10 Photo. Perf. 13
852 A315 100fr multi 2.50 1.40
Value is for copy with surrounding selvage.

2000 Summer Olympics, Sydney — A316

Designs: 10fr, Archery. 30fr, Boxing. 80fr, Cycling. 100fr, Fencing.

2000, Sept. 15 Litho. Perf. 13x13¼
853-856 A316 Set of 4 4.50 4.50

Lucien Bernheim (1856-1917), Library Founder, and Bernheim Library, Cent. — A317

2000, Oct. 24 Engr. Perf. 13
857 A317 500fr multi 11.00 7.25

A318

8th Pacific Arts Festival A319

Kanak money and background colors of: 90fr, Orange. 105fr, Dark blue.
Festival emblem and works of art — No. 860: a, White denomination at UL, "RF" at UR. b, White denomination and "RF" at UL. c, Yellow denomination. d, White denomination at UR.

2000, Oct. 24 Perf. 13x13¼
858-859 A318 Set of 2 4.50 3.00
Souvenir Sheet
860 A319 70fr Sheet of 4, #a-d 6.25 6.25

Red Cross — A320

2000, Nov. 9 Litho. Perf. 13¼x13
861 A320 100fr multi 2.25 2.00

Queen Hortense (1848-1900) — A321

2000, Nov. 9 Engr. Perf. 12½x13
862 A321 110fr multi 2.50 2.25

Northern Province Landscapes — A322

a, Fisherman in canoe. b, Motorboat near beach and cliffs. c, Fisherman on raft.

2000, Nov. 9 Litho. Perf. 13x13¼
863 A322 Horiz. strip of 3 6.50 6.50
a.-c. 100fr Any single 2.00 1.50

Philately in School — A323

Children's art by: a, Kévyn Pamoiloun. b, Lise-Marie Samanich. c, Alexandre Mandin.

2000, Nov. 14 Perf. 13¼x13
864 A323 Horiz. strip of 3 4.50 3.50
a.-c. 70fr Any single 1.40 1.10

Christmas, Holy Year 2000 — A324

2000, Dec. 19 **Perf. 13**
865 A324 100fr multi 2.00 1.60

Portions of the design were applied by a thermographic process producing a shiny, raised effect.

Greetings — A325

Kagu and: No. 866, "Meilleurs voeux de bonheur." No. 867, "Vive les vacances." No. 868, Félicitations.

2000, Dec. 19 **Perf. 13¼x13**
866-868 A325 100fr Set of 3 6.75 6.00

No. 868 printed se-tenant with two labels.

New Year 2001 (Year of the Snake) — A326

Designs: 100fr, Snake on beach, snake wearing robe.
No. 870: a, Snake in flowers. b, Snake in city.

2001, Feb. 15 **Litho.** **Perf. 13**
869 A326 100fr multi 2.50 2.00
Souvenir Sheet
Perf. 13½x13
870 A326 70fr Sheet of 2, #a-b 4.25 4.25
Size of Nos. 870a-870b: 30x40mm.

Sailing Ship France II — A327

2001, Apr. 18 Engr. Perf. 13x13¼
871 A327 110fr multi 2.50 2.25

Noumea Aquarium — A328

Nautilus macromphalus: a, Conjoined pair. b, Anatomical cross-section. c, Pair separated.

2001, May 22 **Litho.**
872 A328 Horiz. strip of 3 7.00 7.00
a.-c. 100fr Any single 2.25 1.50

Corvus Moneduliodes and Tools — A329

2001, June 14 **Perf. 13**
873 A329 70fr multi 1.60 1.50

Operation Cetacean — A330

No. 874: a, Pair of Megaptera novaeangliae underwater. b, Whales breaching surface.

2001, July 18 **Perf. 13x13¼**
874 A330 Horiz. pair with central label 5.00 5.00
a.-b. 100fr Any single 2.25 1.50
See Vanuatu Nos. 785-787.

The Keeper of Gaia, the Eden, by Ito Waia — A331

Vision From Oceania, by Jipé Le-Bars A332

2001, Aug. 22 **Perf. 13**
875 A331 70fr multi 1.60 1.25
876 A332 110fr multi 2.25 2.00

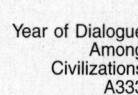

Year of Dialogue Among Civilizations A333

2001, Sept. 19 Litho. Perf. 13x13¼
877 A333 265fr multi 6.50 5.50

Kagu Type of 1997
2001 **Engr.** **Perf. 13**
878 A265 100fr bright blue 2.50 2.50
Self-Adhesive
Litho.
Serpentine Die Cut 11
879 A265 100fr bright blue 2.75 2.50
a. Booklet pane of 10 32.50
Issued: No. 878, 9/23; No. 879, 9/20.
For surcharge see No. 972.

The Lonely Boatman, by Marik A334

2001, Oct. 11 Litho. Perf. 13
880 A334 110fr multi 2.25 2.25

Underwater Observatory A335

2001, Oct. 11
881 A335 135fr multi 2.75 1.25

Qanono Church, Lifou A336

2001, Oct. 11
882 A336 500fr multi 10.00 8.00

Fernande Le Riche (1884-1967), Novelist — A337

2001, Nov. 8
883 A337 155fr brown & blue 3.00 3.00

First Olympic Gold Medal Won by a New Caledonian A338

2001, Nov. 8 **Perf. 13x13¼**
884 A338 265fr multi 5.50 5.00

Kitesurfing — A339

2001, Nov. 16 **Perf. 13**
885 A339 100fr multi 2.50 2.00

"The Book, My Friend" Literacy Campaign — A340

2001, Nov. 27 **Perf. 13x13¼**
886 A340 70fr multi 1.75 1.40

Lifou Scenes — A341

No. 887: a, Easo. b, Jokin.

2001, Nov. 27 **Perf. 13¼x13**
887 A341 100fr Vert. pair, #a-b 4.75 4.50

Greetings — A342

Flying fox and: No. 888, 100fr, Joyeux Noel (Merry Christmas). No. 889, 100fr, Meilleurs

voeux (Best wishes). No. 890, 100fr, Vive la fete (Long live the holiday).

2001, Dec. 7 **Perf. 13x13¼**
888-890 A342 Set of 3 6.50 6.00

New Year 2002 (Year of the Horse) A343

Designs: 100fr, Horse, other zodiac animals.
No. 892, vert.: a, Horse. b, Seahorse.

2002, Feb. 7 **Perf. 13**
891 A343 100fr multi 2.50 2.25
Souvenir Sheet
892 A343 70fr Sheet of 2, #a-b 3.50 3.25

Love — A344

2002, Feb. 13
893 A344 100fr multi 2.50 2.00
Value is for stamp with surrounding selvage.

Cricket A345

2002, Mar. 20 Litho. Perf. 13
894 A345 100fr multi 2.50 2.00

Ancient Hatchet — A346

2002, Mar. 20 **Litho.**
895 A346 505fr multi 11.00 10.00

Portions of the design were applied by a thermographic process producing a shiny, raised effect.

Hobie Cat 16 World Championships — A347

2002, Apr. 1 Litho. Perf. 13
896 A347 70fr multi 1.75 1.40

Kagu Type of 1997
2002, Apr. 15 Engr. Perf. 13
897 A265 5fr purple .30 .25

2002 World Cup Soccer Championships, Japan and Korea — A348

2002, May 15   Photo.
898 A348 100fr multi   2.75 2.00
Values are for stamp with surrounding selvage.

Souvenir Sheet

Turtles at Noumea Aquarium — A349

No. 899: a, 30fr, Caretta caretta. b, 70fr, Eretmochelys imbricat. c, 70fr, Dermochelys coriacea. d, 30fr, Chelonia mydas.

2002, May 15   Litho.   Perf. 13x13¼
899 A349   Sheet of 4, #a-d   4.75 4.75
   e.   As #899, with inscription added in margin   4.75 4.75
Issued: No. 899e, 10/24/03. Inscription in margin of No. 899e reads "Coupe du monde 2003 / Champion du monde."

Corvette Alcmene and Map — A350

2002, June 13   Engr.   Perf. 13x13¼
900 A350 210fr multi   4.75 4.00

Coffee — A351

No. 901: a, Coffee plant and beans. b, Bean roasters. c, Coffee makers, woman, cup of coffee.

2002, June 13   Litho.
901 A351   Horiz. strip of 3   5.00 5.00
   a.-c.   70fr Any single   1.50 1.40
No. 901 was impregnated with coffee scent.

Edmond Caillard (1912-91), Astronomer A352

2002, June 26   Engr.
902 A352 70fr multi   1.75 1.50

Statue of Emma Piffault (1861-77), by Michel Rocton — A353

2002, July 17   Litho.   Perf. 13¼x13
903 A353 10fr multi   .40 .25

Noumea Circus School — A354

2002, Aug. 30   Perf. 13
904 A354 70fr multi   1.75 1.40

Illustrations From Books by Jean Mariotti A355

2002, Sept. 18
905 A355 70fr multi   1.60 1.40

Operation Cetacean — A356

No. 906: a, Adult and young of Physeter macrocephalus. b, Physeter macrocephalus and squid.

2002, Sept. 18   Perf. 13x13¼
906 A356   Horiz. pair with central label   4.75 4.75
   a.-b.   100fr Either single   2.25 2.00
See Norfolk Island No. 783.

Intl. Year of Mountains A357

2002, Nov. 7   Litho.   Perf. 13
907 A357 100fr multi   2.50 2.00

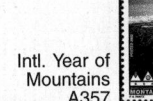

Christmas and New Year's Day — A358

2002, Nov. 7
908 A358 100fr multi   2.25 2.00

Bourail Fort Powder Magazine — A359

2002, Nov. 7   Engr.   Perf. 13x12½
909 A359 1000fr multi   20.00 18.00

Mel Me Mec, by Adrien Trohmae A360

2002, Nov. 28   Litho.   Perf. 13
910 A360 100fr multi   2.50 2.00

New Year 2003 (Year of the Ram) — A361

2003, Jan. 29
911 A361 100fr multi   2.50 2.00
Printed in sheets of 10 + 2 labels. See No. 1251h.

Valentine's Day — A362

2003, Jan. 29   Photo.   Perf. 13
912 A362 100fr multi   2.50 2.00
Values are for stamps with surrounding selvage.

Jubilee Issue, Cent. — A363

2003   Litho.   Perf. 13¼x13
913 A363 70fr No. 77   1.75 1.40
Booklet Stamp
Size: 19x25mm
913A A363 70fr No. 77   1.75 1.40
   b.   Booklet pane of 10   17.50 —
Issued: No. 913, 2/7. No. 913A, 8/20.

Kagu — A364

2003   Engr.   Perf. 13
914 A364 10fr green   .30 .25
915 A364 15fr brown   .35 .25
916 A364 30fr orange   .80 .60
917 A364 (70fr) red   1.50 1.40
  Nos. 914-917 (4)   2.95 2.50
Booklet Stamps
Litho. & Embossed
Perf. 13¼x13¾
918 A364   70fr gray & silver   1.75 1.40
   a.   Booklet pane of 10   17.50 —
   Complete booklet, #913Ab, 918a   35.00
Engr.
Serpentine Die Cut 6¾ Vert.
Self-Adhesive
919 A364 (70fr) red   1.90 1.40
   a.   Booklet pane of 10   20.00
Issued: Nos. 914-917, 2/7; No. 918, 8/20; No. 919, 5/15.
See Nos. 938, 965-966, 985-986, 1007, 1070.

Fish at Nouméa Aquarium — A365

No. 920: a, Epinephelus maculatus. b, Plectropomus leopardus. c, Cromileptes altivelis.

2003, Apr. 9   Photo.   Perf. 12¾
920 A365 70fr Horiz. strip of 3, #a-c   5.00 4.00

Greater Nouméa High School A366

2003, May 14   Litho.   Perf. 13
921 A366 70fr multi   1.50 1.40

Operation Cetacean — A367

No. 922: a, Dugong swimming (79x29mm). b, Dugong feeding (40x29mm).

2003, June 11   Perf. 13x13¼
922 A367 100fr Horiz. pair, #a-b   5.00 4.00

12th South Pacific Games, Suva, Fiji — A368

Designs: 5fr, Trapshooting. 30fr, Rugby. 70fr, Squash.

2003, June 11
923-925 A368 Set of 3   2.50 2.10

Man Picking Fruit From a Tree, by Paul Gauguin (1848-1903) A369

2003, June 25   Photo.   Perf. 13
926 A369 100fr multi   2.50 1.90

Aircalin, 20th Anniv. A370

2003, July 9   Litho.
927 A370 100fr multi   2.50 1.90

Governor Paul Feillet (1857-1903) — A371

2003, July 9   Engr.   Perf. 12½x13
928 A371 100fr dk blue & ol grn   2.00 1.50

Souvenir Sheet

Paintings by Paul Gauguin A372

No. 929: a, Study of Heads of Tahitian Women. b, Still Life with Maori Statuette.

2003, Aug. 20   Litho.   Perf. 13
929 A372 100fr Sheet of 2, #a-b   5.00 4.50

German
Shepherd
A373

2003, Oct. 8
930 A373 105fr multi   2.50 2.10

Le Phoque, Le Prony and Le Catinat
in Balade Roadstead, 1853
A374

2003, Oct. 8   Engr.   Perf. 13x12½
931 A374 110fr multi   2.75 2.10

Robert Tatin
d'Avesnières
(1925-82),
Painter
A375

2003, Oct. 8   Litho.   Perf. 13
932 A375 135fr multi   3.25 2.60

Souvenir Sheet

Geckos
A376

No. 933: a, 30fr, Bavayia cyclura. b, 30fr,
Rhacodactylus chahoua. c, 70fr, Rhacodactylus ciliatus. d, 70fr, Eurydactylodes vieillardi.

2003, Oct. 8   Perf. 13x13¼
933 A376   Sheet of 4, #a-d   5.50 5.50

Ouen Island
A377

2003, Nov. 6   Perf. 13
934 A377 100fr multi   2.50 1.90

Merry Christmas
and Happy New
Year — A378

2003, Nov. 6
935 A378 100fr multi   2.50 1.90

New Year
2004 (Year
of the
Monkey)
A379

Designs: 70fr, Monkeys, Hong Kong skyline.
No. 937: a, Tiger and woman. b, Monkey on
horse.

2004, Jan. 30   Litho.   Perf. 13
936 A379 70fr multi   1.75 1.50

Souvenir Sheet
Perf. 13¼x13
Litho. With Foil Application
937 A379 100fr Sheet of 2, #a-b   5.00 5.00
  2004 Hong Kong Stamp Expo. No. 937 contains two 30x40mm stamps.

Kagu Type of 2003
2004, Feb. 11   Engr.   Perf. 13
938 A364 100fr blue   2.50 2.10
  For surcharge see No. 973.

Love — A380

2004, Feb. 11   Photo.
939 A380 100fr multi   2.50 2.10
  Values are for stamps with surrounding
selvage.

Stamp Day
A381

2004, May 15   Litho.
940 A381 105fr multi   2.50 2.10

Railroads in
New
Caledonia
A382

2004, May 15   Engr.   Perf. 13x12½
941 A382 155fr multi   3.50 3.00

Rays — A383

No. 942: a, Dasyatis kuhlii. b, Aetobatus
narinari. c, Taeniura meyeni.

2004, May 15 Litho. Perf. 13x13¼
942   A383   Horiz. strip of 3   7.25 7.25
a.-c.   100fr Any single   2.25 2.00

Souvenir Sheet

Mesoplodon Densirostris — A384

No. 943: a, Male (79x29mm). b, Female
(40x29mm).

2004, May 15
943 A384 100fr Sheet of 2, #a-b   5.00 5.00
  Operation Cetacean.

Flowers — A385

No. 944: a, Oxera sulfurea. b, Turbina
inopinata. c, Gardenia urvillei.

2004, June 26
944   A385   Horiz. strip of 3   7.25 7.25
a.-c.   100fr Any single   2.25 2.00

Sandalwood
A386

Designs: 200fr, Sandalwood sculpture,
house. No. 946: a, Fruit and flowers. b, Sandalwood
oil extraction machinery. c, Flowerpot.

2004, June 26   Perf. 13
945 A386 200fr multi   4.75 4.25
Souvenir Sheet
Perf. 13x13¼
946 A386 100fr Sheet of 3, #a-c   7.25 7.25
  No. 946 contains three 40x29mm stamps.

Noumea,
150th
Anniv.
A387

2004, July 8   Litho.   Perf. 13
947 A387 70fr multi   1.60 1.50

Miniature Sheet

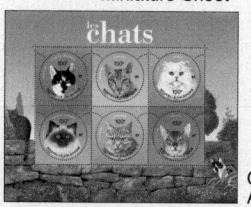

Cats
A388

No. 948: a, Mixed breed. b, Oriental. c, Persian. d, Birman. e, European. f, Abyssinian.

2004, July 25
948 A388 100fr Sheet of 6, #a-
  f   14.50 12.50

2004 Summer
Olympics,
Athens — A389

Designs: No. 949, 70fr, Women's rhythmic
gymnastics. No. 950, 70fr, Women's 4x400m
relay. No. 951, 70fr, Beach volleyball.

2004, Aug. 5   Perf. 13x13¼
949-951 A389   Set of 3   5.00 4.50

Symposium on French Research in
the Pacific — A390

No. 952: a, Butterfly, hut. b, Dolphin,
woman.

2004, Aug. 10   Perf. 13
952   A390   Pair   4.75 4.75
a.-b.   100fr Either single   2.25 2.00

Belep
Island and
Walla Bay
A391

2004, Nov. 10
953 A391 100fr multi   2.50 2.25

Tradimodernition, by Nathalie
Deschamps — A392

2004, Nov. 10
954 A392 505fr multi   12.00 11.00

Christmas
A393

2004, Dec. 8
955 A393 100fr multi   2.50 2.25

A394

New
Year
2005
(Year of
the
Rooster)
A395

No. 957: a, Rooster. b, Monkey.

2005, Feb. 9   Litho.   Perf. 13
956 A394 100fr multi   2.50 2.25
Souvenir Sheet
Perf. 13¼x13
957 A395 100fr Sheet of 2, #a-b   4.75 4.50

Rotary
International,
Cent. — A396

2005, Feb. 23   Photo.   Perf. 12½
958 A396 110fr multi   2.75 2.50
  Values are for stamps with surrounding
selvage.

Francophone
Week — A397

2005, Mar. 17   Litho.   Perf. 13x13¼
959 A397 135fr multi   3.25 3.00
  Printed in sheets of 10 + 5 labels. See Wallis & Futuna Islands No. 600.

20th
International
Triathlon,
Noumea
A398

2005, Apr. 22   Litho.   Perf. 13
960 A398 80fr multi   2.00 1.75

Coastal
Tour Ship
A399

2005, May 21
961 A399 75fr multi   1.90 1.60

New
Caledonian
Railways
A400

2005, May 21
962 A400 745fr multi   18.00 15.00

Dolphins
A401

No. 963: a, Stenella attenuata. b, Turciop
truncatus. c, Stenella longirostris.

2005, May 21   **Perf. 13x13¼**
963 A401   Horiz. strip of 3   7.75 7.75
 a.-c.   100fr Any single   2.25 2.00
For surcharge, see No. 971.

Souvenir Sheet

Sharks
A402

No. 964: a, Carcharinus melanopterus. b,
Nebrius ferrugineus.

2005, July 20   **Perf. 13**
964 A402 110fr Sheet of 2, #a-b   5.25 4.50

Kagu Type of 2003
2005, Aug. 10 **Engr.** **Perf. 13**
965 A364 1fr sky blue   .25 .25
966 A364 3fr brt yel green   .60 .25

Luengoni
Beach,
Lifou
A403

2005, Aug. 24   **Litho.**
967 A403 85fr multi   2.00 1.75

Parakeets
A404

Designs: No. 968, 75fr, Eunymphicus
uvaeensis. No. 969, 75fr, Eunymphicus
cornutus. No. 970, 75fr, Cyanoramphus
saisseti.

2005, Aug. 24   **Perf. 13x13¼**
968-970 A404   Set of 3   5.50 4.75

No. 963 Surcharged in Silver

and Nos. 878 and 938
Surcharged

Methods and Perfs as Before
2005
971   Horiz. strip of 3
          (#963)   7.00 7.00
 a.-c. A401 100fr +10fr Any single 2.25 2.25
972 A265 100fr +10fr bright
              blue (#878)   2.25 2.25
973 A364 100fr +10fr blue
              (#938)   2.25 2.25
 Nos. 971-973 (3)   11.50 11.50
Issued: No. 971, July. Nos. 972-973, Oct.

World Health Organization West
Pacific Region Conference,
Noumea — A405

2005, Sept. 14 **Litho.** **Perf. 13x13¼**
974 A405 150fr multi   3.75 3.00

World Peace
Day — A406

2005, Sept. 21   **Perf. 13¼x13**
975 A406 85fr multi   2.00 1.75

Governor Eugène du
Bouzet (1805-
67) — A407

2005, Nov. 10   **Engr.**
976 A407 500fr multi   12.50 10.00

Petroglyphs
A408

Designs: No. 977, 120fr, Enclosed crosses.
No. 978, 120fr, Petroglyph, Balade. No. 979,
120fr, Ouaré Petroglyph, Hienghène.

2005, Nov. 10   **Perf. 13x12¾**
977-979 A408   Set of 3   8.75 7.25

Common Destiny,
Artwork by Ito
Waia and
Adjé — A409

2005, Dec. 7   **Litho.**   **Perf. 13**
980 A409 190fr multi   4.75 4.00

Insects — A410

Designs: No. 981, 110fr, Bohumiljania
caledonica. No. 982, 110fr, Bohumiljania
humboldti. No. 983, 110fr, Cazeresia
montana.

2005, Dec. 7   **Perf. 13x13¼**
981-983 A410   Set of 3   8.00 6.75

Christmas — A411

2005, Dec. 8   **Perf. 13¼x13**
984 A411 110fr multi   2.75 2.25

Kagu Type of 2003
2006   **Engr.**   **Perf. 13**
985 A364 110fr dk blue gray   2.75 2.25
Booklet Stamp
Self-Adhesive
Serpentine Die Cut 6¾ Vert.
986 A364 110fr dk blue gray   2.75 2.25
 a.   Booklet pane of 10   30.00
Issued: No. 985, 1/18. No. 986, June.

Nokanhoui
Islet
A412

2006, Mar. 9   **Litho.**   **Perf. 13**
987 A412 110fr multi   2.75 2.25

Automobiles — A413

No. 988: a, 1903 Georges Richard. b, 1925
Renault NN. c, 1925 Citroen Tréfle.

2006, Mar. 23   **Perf. 13x13¼**
988 A413 Horiz. strip of 3   8.00 8.00
 a.-c.   110fr Any single   2.50 2.25

New Caledonian Red
Cross, 60th
Anniv. — A414

2006, Apr. 12 **Litho.** **Perf. 13¼x13**
989 A414 75fr red & black   1.90 1.60

Conus
Geographus — A415

2006, Apr. 12   **Litho.**   **Perf. 13**
990 A415 150fr multi   3.75 3.25

11th World Congress on Pain, New Caledonia, 2005. Portions of the design were applied
by a thermographic process producing a
shiny, raised effect.

Arrival of
French
Colonists,
80th Anniv.
A416

2006, May 23 **Engr.** **Perf. 13x12¾**
991 A416 180fr multi   4.50 3.75

2006 World Cup
Soccer
Championships,
Germany — A417

2006, June 8 **Litho.** **Perf. 13**
992 A417 110fr multi   2.75 2.25

BirdLife
International — A418

Designs: No. 993, 75fr, Charmosyna
diadema. No. 994, 75fr, Aegotheles savesi.
No. 995, 75fr, Gallirallus lafresnayanis.

2006, June 17   **Perf. 13¼x13**
993-995 A418   Set of 3   5.50 4.75

Souvenir Sheet

Endangered Birds — A419

No. 996: a, Charmosyna diadema. b,
Aegotheles savesi, vert. c, Gallirallus
lafresnayanis.

2006, June 17
996 A419 110fr Sheet of 3, #a-c 8.00 7.00

Creeper Flowers — A420

No. 997: a, Artia balansae. b, Oxera brevi-
calyx. c, Canavalia favieri.

2006, June 17   **Perf. 13x13¼**
997 A420 Horiz. strip of 3   8.00 8.00
 a.-c.   110fr Any single   2.50 2.25

Mobile Post
Office
A421

2006, Aug. 5 **Engr.** **Perf. 13x12¾**
998 A421 75fr multi   1.75 1.60
Stamp Day.

New Caledonian
Evacuee Voluntary Aid
Association, 25th
Anniv. — A422

2006, Aug. 5 **Litho.** **Perf. 13¼x13**
999 A422 85fr multi   2.00 1.90

NEW CALEDONIA

17th South Pacific Regional Environment Program Conference, Noumea — A423

2006, Sept. 11 Litho. *Perf. 13*
1000 A423 190fr multi 4.00 4.00

Nakale 7547 Locomotive of New Caledonia Railroad A424

2006, Sept. 19 Engr. *Perf. 13x13¼*
1001 A424 320fr multi 6.75 6.75

Kaneka Music, 20th Anniv. — A425

2006, Nov. 8 Litho. *Perf. 13x13½*
1002 A425 75fr multi 1.90 1.75

Mobilis Mobile Phone Service, 10th Anniv. A426

2006, Nov. 8 *Perf. 13*
1003 A426 75fr multi 1.90 1.75

Wooden Players Puppet Theater, 30th Anniv. A427

2006, Nov. 8
1004 A427 280fr multi 7.00 6.25

Christmas A428

Litho. & Engr.
2006, Nov. 9 *Perf. 13*
1005 A428 110fr multi 2.75 2.50

Lizard Man, Sculpture by Joseph Poukiou — A429

2006, Dec. 13 Litho.
1006 A429 110fr multi 2.75 2.40

Kagu Type of 2003
2007, Jan. 25 Engr. *Perf. 13*
1007 A364 5fr purple .35 .25

New Year 2007 (Year of the Pig) — A430

2007, Feb. 6 Litho. *Perf. 13*
1008 A430 110fr multi 2.50 2.50

Printed in sheets of 10 + central label. See No. 1251j.

General Secretariat of the South Pacific Community, 60th Anniv. — A431

2007, Feb. 6
1009 A431 120fr multi 2.75 2.75

Audit Office, Bicent. — A432

2007, Mar. 17 Engr. *Perf. 13¼*
1010 A432 110fr multi 2.50 2.50

Treaty of Rome, 50th Anniv. — A433

2007, May 10 Litho. *Perf. 13x13¼*
1011 A433 110fr multi 2.50 2.50

13th South Pacific Games, Samoa A434

2007, June 13 Litho. *Perf. 13*
1012 A434 75fr multi 1.75 1.75

Submarine Cable Between Noumea and Sydney A435

2007, June 13 Litho. & Engr.
1013 A435 280fr multi 6.50 6.50

Fish — A436

Designs: 35fr, Siganus lineatus. 75fr, Lutianus adetii. 110fr, Naso unicornis.

2007, June 13 Litho. *Perf. 13x13½*
1014-1016 A436 Set of 3 5.00 5.00

Natl. Sea Rescue Society, 40th Anniv. A437

2007, Aug. 3 *Perf. 13*
1017 A437 75fr multi 1.75 1.75

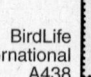

BirdLife International A438

Endangered birds: 35fr, Gymnomyza aubryana. 75fr, Coracina analis. 110fr, Rhynochetos jubatus.

2007, Aug. 3 *Perf. 13x13¼*
1018-1020 A438 Set of 3 5.00 5.00

A439 A440

A441 A442

A443

A444

A445

A446

A447

Mailboxes A448

2007, Aug. 3 *Perf. 13¼x13, 13x13¼*
1021 Booklet pane of 10 17.50 17.50
a. A439 75fr multi 1.75 1.75
b. A440 75fr multi 1.75 1.75
c. A441 75fr multi 1.75 1.75
d. A442 75fr multi 1.75 1.75
e. A443 75fr multi 1.75 1.75
f. A444 75fr multi 1.75 1.75
g. A445 75fr multi 1.75 1.75

h. A446 75fr multi 1.75 1.75
i. A447 75fr multi 1.75 1.75
j. A448 75fr multi 1.75 1.75
Complete booklet, #1021 17.50
Stamp Day.

Souvenir Sheet

Kagu Philatelic Club, 60th Anniv. A449

No. 1022: a, Magnifying glass over New Caledonia #262 on cover. b, Kagu.

Litho. & Silk Screened
2007, Aug. 3 *Perf. 13x13¼*
1022 A449 110fr Sheet of 2, #a-b 5.00 5.00

Season of New Hebrides Culture in New Zealand A450

2007, Aug. 16 Litho. *Perf. 13*
1023 A450 190fr multi 4.50 4.50

New Aquarium of New Caledonia — A451

No. 1024 — Entrance of new aquarium and: a, Gymnothorax polyranodon (40x30mm). b, Entrance of old aquarium. (80x30mm). c, Monodactylus argenteus (40x30mm). d, Negaprion brevirostris (40x30mm). e, Pseudanthias bicolor (40x30mm).

2007, Aug. 31 *Perf. 13x13¼*
1024 A451 110fr Booklet pane of 5, #a-e 13.00 13.00
Complete booklet, 2 #1024 26.00

2007 Rugby World Cup, France — A452

2007, Sept. 5 Photo. *Perf.*
1025 A452 110fr multi 2.60 2.60

Jules Repiquet (1874-1960), Governor of New Caledonia, 1914-23 — A453

2007, Oct. 10 Engr. *Perf. 13x13¼*
1026 A453 320fr multi 7.75 7.75

Tropical Fruits — A454

Designs: 35fr, Bananas and passion fruits. 75fr, Vanilla beans, vert. 110fr, Pineapples and lychees.

Perf. 13x13¼, 13¼x13
2007, Nov. 8   **Litho.**
1027-1029 A454   Set of 3   5.50 5.50

The banana, vanilla bean and pineapple portions of these stamps are covered with scratch-and-sniff coatings having those fragrances.

La Montagnarde Locomotive, New Caledonian Railways — A455

2007, Nov. 8   **Engr.**   **Perf. 13x13¼**
1030 A455 400fr multi   10.00 10.00

Tao Waterfall — A456

2007, Nov. 8   **Litho.**   **Perf. 13**
1031 A456 110fr multi   2.75 2.75

The Damned, Performance by Najib Guerfi Dance Company — A457

2007, Nov. 8
1032 A457 110fr multi   2.75 2.75

Birth Announcement A458

2007, Nov. 8   **Perf. 13x13¼**
1033 A458 110fr multi   2.75 2.75

New Year's Greetings A459

2007, Nov. 8
1034 A459 110fr multi   2.75 2.75

Rooftop Totem — A460

2007, Dec. 5   **Litho.**   **Perf. 13**
1035 A460 110fr multi   2.75 2.75

New Year 2008 (Year of the Rat) — A461

2008, Feb. 6   **Litho.**   **Perf. 13**
1036 A461 110fr multi   3.00 3.00

See No. 1251a.

Academic Palms, Bicent. A462

Litho. & Embossed
2008, Mar. 17   **Perf. 13x13¼**
1037 A462 110fr multi   3.00 3.00

Tjibaou Cultural Center, 10th Anniv. — A463

2008, June 14   **Litho.**   **Perf. 13**
1038 A463 120fr multi   3.25 3.25

Matignon Accords, 20th Anniv. A464

2008, June 14
1039 A464 430fr multi   11.50 11.50

Kanak Ax — A465

2008, June 14
1040 A465 500fr multi   13.50 13.50

BirdLife International A466

Endangered birds: No. 1041, 110fr, Pterodroma leucoptera. No. 1042, 110fr, Pseudobulweria rostrata. No. 1043, 110fr, Nesofregatta fuliginosa.

2008, June 14   **Perf. 13x13¼**
1041-1043 A466   Set of 3   8.75 8.75

Fruit — A467

Designs: No. 1044, 110fr, Citrus nobilis. No. 1045, 110fr, Mangifera indica. No. 1046, 110fr, Carica papaya.

2008, June 14
1044-1046 A467   Set of 3   8.75 8.75

2008 Summer Olympics, Beijing — A468

Designs: No. 1047, 75fr, Weight lifting. No. 1048, 75fr, Table tennis. No. 1049, 75fr, Taekwondo.

2008, July 31
1047-1049 A468   Set of 3   5.75 5.75

Office of Posts and Telecommunications, 50th Anniv. — A469

Designs: No. 1050, 75fr, New Caledonia #314, dish antennas, cable, map of South Pacific. No. 1051, 75fr, New Caledonia #311, savings card, person at computer. No. 1052, 75fr, New Caledonia #C106, mailbox, mail sorter.

2008, July 31
1050-1052 A469   Set of 3   5.75 5.75

Miniature Sheet

Telecommunications History — A470

No. 1053: a, Telegraph. b, Radio telephone. c, Satellite and antenna. d, Fiber-optic cables and flowers.

2008, July 31   **Perf. 13¼x13**
1053 A470 75fr Sheet of 4, #a-d   7.50 7.50

Kagu A471

Serpentine Die Cut 6¾x7¾
2008   **Self-Adhesive**   **Litho.**
1054 A471 (75fr) red & multi   4.50 4.50
1055 A471 110fr blue & multi   5.25 5.25

Nos. 1054 and 1055 each were issued in sheets of 20 and 25. Sheets of 20 of each stamp sold for 3800fr and 4500fr, respectively, and sheets of 25 sold for 4125fr and 5000fr, respectively. The left part of the stamp, which cannot be separated from the stamp, could be personalized if desired. The left part of the stamp shown has a generic image that was utilized if a customer did not provide an image for personalization.

Koné Fort A472

2008, Oct. 3   **Engr.**   **Perf. 13x12¾**
1056 A472 220fr multi   5.00 5.00

Fifth French Republic, 50th Anniv. A473

2008, Oct. 14   **Perf. 13x13¼**
1057 A473 290fr blue & red   6.25 6.25

Handicap Awareness A474

2008, Nov. 6   **Litho.**   **Perf. 13**
1058 A474 120fr multi   2.60 2.60

Diahot River — A475

No. 1059 — View of river with denomination color of: a, Green. b, Blue violet.

2008, Nov. 6
1059 A475   Horiz. pair + central label   5.00 5.00
a.-b.   110fr Either single   2.50 2.50

Christmas — A476

2008, Nov. 6   **Perf. 13¼x13**
1060 A476 110fr multi   2.50 2.50

14th Pacific Games, New Caledonia — A477

2008, Dec. 12   **Perf. 13**
1061 A477 110fr multi   2.50 2.50

Miniature Sheet

New Caledonia Lagoons UNESCO World Heritage Site — A478

No. 1062: a, Birds from Entrecasteaux Reefs Zone. b, Snake from Northeastern Coastal Zone, horiz. c, Sea turtles from Beautemps-Beaupré Zone, horiz. d, Fish from Great Northern Lagoon Zone. e, Dugong from Western Coastal Zone. f, Whale from Great Southern Lagoon Zone, horiz.

Perf. 13¼x13, 13x13¼ (horiz. stamps)
2008, Dec. 12
1062 A478 75fr Sheet of 6, #a-f   10.50 10.50

Fish — A479

No. 1063 — Fish sold at local fish markets: a, Lethrinus atkinsoni. b, Chlorurus microrhinos. c Lethrinus nebulosus.

2009, Mar. 25 Litho. Perf. 13x13¼
1063 A479 Horiz. strip of 3 5.00 5.00
a.-c. 75fr Any single 1.60 1.60

New Year 2009 (Year of the Ox) — A480

2009, Apr. 8 Perf. 13
1064 A480 75fr multi 1.75 1.75
See No. 1251b for stamp dated "2019."

Souvenir Sheet

New Year 2009 (Year of the Ox) A481

No. 1065 — Ox: a, Standing. b, Charging.

2009, Apr. 8 Litho. Perf. 13
1065 A481 110fr Sheet of 2, #a-b 5.00 5.00

The Turtle Bearer, Sculpture by Tein Thavouvace A482

2009, May 14 Litho. Perf. 13
1066 A482 180fr multi 4.25 4.25

BirdLife International — A483

No. 1067 — Terns: a, Sterna nereis. b, Sterna sumatrana. c, Sterna dougalli.

2009, June 10 Perf. 13x13¼
1067 A483 Horiz. strip of 3 5.25 5.25
a.-c. 75fr Any single 1.75 1.75

Jean-Pierre Jeunet Cinema, La Foa, 10th Anniv. — A484

2009, June 26 Perf. 13
1068 A484 75fr multi 1.75 1.75

Third France-Oceania Summit, Noumea — A485

No. 1069 — Earth in: a, Hands. b, Flower.

2009, July 16
1069 A485 110fr Pair, #a-b 5.25 5.25

Kagu Type of 2003
Serpentine Die Cut 7½ Vert.
2009, July Litho.
Booklet Stamp
Self-Adhesive
1070 A364 (75fr) red 1.75 1.75
a. Booklet pane of 10 17.50

A486   Kagu — A487

2009, Aug. 6 Engr. Perf. 13
1071 A486 5fr purple .30 .25
1072 A486 10fr green .30 .25
1073 A486 (75fr) red 1.75 1.75
a. Dated "2014" .30 .25
1074 A486 110fr dark blue 2.60 2.60

Litho. With Three-Dimensional Plastic Affixed
Perf. 16
Self-Adhesive
1075 A487 500fr multi 12.00 12.00

Litho.
Serpentine Die Cut 7½ Vert.
Booklet Stamp
1076 A486 (75fr) red 1.75 1.75
a. Booklet pane of 10 17.50
b. As #1076, serpentine die cut 6¾ vert., with "Phil@poste" printer's inscription at bottom 1.60 1.60
c. Booklet pane of 10 #1076b 16.00
d. As "b," dated "2014" 1.75 1.75
e. Booklet pane of 10 #1076d 17.50
f. As "b," dated "2016" 1.40 1.40
g. Booklet pane of 10 #1076f 14.00
Nos. 1071-1076 (6) 18.70 18.60

No. 1075 printed in sheets of 4.
Issued: Nos. 1076b, 1076c, June 2010; Nos. 1076d, 1076e, July 2014.
See No. 1131.

Intl. Year of Astronomy A488

2009, Aug. 6 Litho. Perf. 13
1077 A488 110fr multi 2.60 2.60

Miniature Sheet

New Caledonia Postal Service, 150th Anniv. — A489

No. 1078 — Modes of mail delivery: a, Coach. b, Horse, vert. c, Automobile. d, Mail deliverer on foot, vert.

2009, Aug. 6 Perf. 13¼
1078 A489 110fr Sheet of 4, #a-d 10.50 10.50

Society for Historical Research, 40th Anniv. A490

2009, Aug. 6 Engr. Perf. 13x13¼
1079 A490 75fr multi 1.75 1.75

Personalized Stamps — A490a

Serpentine Die Cut 6¾x8
2009, Sept. Litho.
Self-Adhesive
1079A A490a (75fr) red & multi — —
1079B A490a 110fr blue & multi — —

Nos. 1079A and 1079B were issued in sheets of 20 and 25. The personalized part of the stamp is at left. The illustration is that of a generic image used for both No. 1079A and 1079B. Sheets with other personalized images sold for more than the face value.

14th Pacific Games, New Caledonia — A491

2009, Nov. 5 Litho. Perf. 13
1080 A491 75fr multi 1.90 1.90

Western Coastal Zone of Lagoons of New Caledonia UNESCO World Heritage Site — A492

2009, Nov. 5
1081 A492 75fr multi 1.90 1.90

Christmas A493

2009, Nov. 5 Perf. 13x13¼
1082 A493 110fr multi 2.75 2.75

Canala Barracks A494

2009, Nov. 5 Engr.
1083 A494 120fr multi 3.00 3.00

Maritime History Museum, Noumea, 10th Anniv. A495

No. 1084: a, Ships and museum. b, Ship and map.

2009, Nov. 5 Litho.
1084 A495 75fr Horiz. pair, #a-b 3.75 3.75

A496

Tontouta River A497

2009, Nov. 5 Perf. 13
1085 Horiz. pair + central label 5.50 5.50
a. A496 110fr multi 2.75 2.75
b. A497 110fr multi 2.75 2.75

Women and Children, by Micheline Néporon — A498

2010, Mar. 8 Litho. Perf. 13
1086 A498 110fr multi 2.50 2.50
Intl. Women's Day.

Champlain Alliance, 25th Anniv. — A499

2010, Mar. 18 Perf. 13x13¼
1087 A499 110fr multi 2.50 2.50

Fish — A500

No. 1089 — Fish sold at local fish markets: a, Acanthocybium solandri. b, Thunnus albacares. c, Coryphaena hippurus.

2010, Mar. 18
1088 A500 Horiz. strip of 3 5.25 5.25
a.-c. 75fr multi 1.75 1.75

New Year 2010 (Year of the Tiger) — A501

2010, Mar. 18 Perf. 13
1089 A501 110fr multi 2.50 2.50
See No. 1251c.

Dumbea River — A502

No. 1090: a, River bends. b, Canoers on river, bridge.

2010, Mar. 18
1090 A502 Horiz. pair + central label 5.00 5.00
a.-b. 110fr Either single 2.50 2.50

14th Va'a (Outrigger Canoe) World Championships, Anse Vata Bay — A503

2010, May 3 Litho. Perf. 13x13¼
1091 A503 75fr multi 1.75 1.75

French Pavilion, Expo 2010, Shanghai A504

2010, June 14 Perf. 13
1092 A504 110fr multi 2.40 2.40

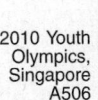

Mueo Fort A505

2010, Aug. 5 Engr. Perf. 13x13¼
1093 A505 75fr multi 1.75 1.75

2010 Youth Olympics, Singapore A506

2010, Aug. 5 Litho. Perf. 13
1094 A506 75fr multi 1.75 1.75

St. Joseph's Cathedral, Noumea — A507

2010, Aug. 5 Litho. & Engr.
1095 A507 1000fr multi 22.50 22.50

Nickel Mining A508

No. 1096: a, Open-pit mine. b, Smelter. c, Ship transport.

Litho. With Foil Application
2010, Aug. 5 Perf. 13x12¾
1096 A508 75fr Horiz. strip of 3, #a-c 5.00 5.00

Miniature Sheet

Flora and Fauna of Grandes Fougères Park A509

No. 1097: a, Pteropus ornatus. b, Ducula goliath. c, Cyathea sp. d, Calanthe langel.

2010, Aug. 5 Litho. Perf. 13¼x13
1097 A509 110fr Sheet of 4, #a-d 9.75 9.75

14th Pacific Games, New Caledonia A510

2010, Aug. 27 Perf. 13
1098 A510 75fr multi 1.60 1.60

Fourth Melanesian Arts Festival A511

2010, Sept. 8
1099 A511 180fr multi 4.00 4.00

Governor Henri Sautot (1885-1963) A512

2010, Sept. 16 Engr. Perf. 13x13¼
1100 A512 250fr multi 6.00 6.00
New Caledonia's alliance with Free France, 70th anniv.

Road Safety — A513

Designs: No. 1101, 75fr, Car with drunk driver. No. 1102, 75fr, Woman with baby stroller in crosswalk escaping speeding motorcyclist.

2010, Oct. 13 Litho. Perf. 13x13¼
1101-1102 A513 Set of 2 3.50 3.50

Great Northern Lagoon UNESCO World Heritage Site A514

2010, Nov. 3 Perf. 13
1103 A514 75fr multi 1.75 1.75

New Caledonia House, Paris A515

2010, Nov. 3
1104 A515 110fr multi 2.50 2.50

Intl. Year of Biodiversity — A516

2010, Nov. 3 Perf. 13¼
1105 A516 110fr multi 2.50 2.50

Christmas A517

2010, Nov. 3 Perf. 13x13¼
1106 A517 110fr multi 2.50 2.50

New Year 2011 (Year of the Rabbit) — A518

2011, Feb. 2 Perf. 13
1107 A518 110fr multi 2.50 2.50
Printed in sheets of 10 + central label. See No. 1251f.

Inauguration of Digital High Definition Television Transmission A519

2011, Feb. 2 Perf. 13x13¼
1108 A519 75fr multi 1.75 1.75

14th Pacific Games, New Caledonia — A520

2011, Mar. 17 Perf. 13
1109 A520 110fr multi 2.75 2.75

Rivers — A521

No. 1110: a, Pourina River. b, Ouinné River.

2011, Mar. 17 Litho.
1110 A521 Horiz. pair + central label 5.50 5.50
a.-b. 110fr Either single 2.75 2.75

Transcaledonian Adventure Race, 20th Anniv. — A522

2011, June 23 Perf. 13x13¼
1111 A522 75fr multi 1.75 1.75

Podoserpula Miranda — A523

2011, June 23 Perf. 13¼x13
1112 A523 110fr multi 2.60 2.60

Ouégoa Fort A524

2011, Aug. 5 Engr. Perf. 13x13¼
1113 A524 75fr multi 1.90 1.90

Ouvea and Beautemps-Beaupré Lagoon Area UNESCO World Heritage Site — A525

2011, Aug. 5 Litho. Perf. 13
1114 A525 75fr multi 1.90 1.90

Intl. Year of Forests A526

2011, Aug. 5
1115 A526 120fr multi 3.00 3.00

Miniature Sheet

Rivière Bleue Provincial Park — A527

No. 1116: a, Syzygium acre. b, Montrouziera gabriellae. c, Waterfall. d, Rhynochetos jubatus.

2011, Aug. 5 Photo. Perf. 13¼x13
1116 A527 110fr Sheet of 4, #a-d 11.00 11.00

Kanak Traditional Games — A528

2011, Aug. 27 Litho. Perf. 13x13¼
1117 A528 75fr multi 1.75 1.75

Souvenir Sheet

14th Pacific Games, Noumea A529

No. 1118 — Emblem and: a, Medal. b, Torch. c, Flame basin.

Photo. Photo & Embossed (#1118a)
2011, Aug. 27 Perf. 13¼x13
1118 A529 110fr Sheet of 3, #a-c 7.75 7.75

Ruins and Chimney of Nimba Sugar Factory, Dumbea A530

2011, Nov. 3 Engr. Perf. 13x13¼
1119 A530 450fr multi 10.50 10.50

Animals and Scenery — A531

Designs: No. 1120, 110fr, Cerf rusa (rusa deer). No. 1121, 110fr, Tricot rayé (striped jersey snake). No. 1122, 110fr, Lindéralique Cliffs. No. 1123, 110fr, Ilôt Canard, vert.

Perf. 13x13¼, 13¼x13
2011, Nov. 3   Litho.
1120-1123 A531   Set of 4   10.50 10.50

Christmas — A532

2011, Nov. 3   **Perf. 13¼x13**
1124 A532 110fr multi   2.60 2.60

Jacques Lafleur (1932-2010), Politician — A533

2011, Dec. 1   **Engr.**   **Perf. 12¼x13**
1125 A533 1000fr multi   22.50 22.50

New Year 2012 (Year of the Dragon) — A534

2012, Jan. 23   Litho.   **Perf. 13**
1126 A534 75fr multi   1.75 1.75
Printed in sheets of 10 + central label. See No. 1251e for stamp dated "2019."

St. Valentine's Day — A535

2012, Jan. 23
1127 A535 110fr multi   2.50 2.50
Values are for stamps with surrounding selvage.

Voh, 120th Anniv. A536

No. 1128: a, Coffee plantation. b, Mine.

2012, Jan. 23   **Perf. 13x13¼**
1128 A536 110fr Horiz. pair, #a-b 5.00 5.00

Southern Backpacking Trail — A537

2012, Mar. 5   **Perf. 13¼x13**
1129 A537 110fr multi   2.50 2.50

Ouaménie Sugar Works Chimney — A538

2012, May 4   **Engr.**   **Perf. 12¼x13**
1130 A538 750fr multi   16.00 16.00

Kagu Type of 2009
2012, June 5   **Engr.**   **Perf. 13**
1131 A486 30fr orange   .65 .65
   a.   Dated "2014"   .60 .60

Nudibranchs A539

Designs: 75fr, Glossodoris cruenta. 85fr, Halgerda sp., vert. 120fr, Noumea catalai.

Perf. 13x13¼, 13¼x13
2012, July 6   A539   Set of 3   Litho.
1132-1134 A539   Set of 3   5.75 5.75

Souvenir Sheet

Japanese Presence on New Caledonia, 120th Anniv. — A540

No. 1135: a, Memorial. b, Nickel miner with pick, horiz. c, Mine worker with ore cart, horiz.

Perf. 13¼x13, 13x13¼
2012, July 6   **Photo.**
1135 A540 110fr Sheet of 3, #a-c 6.75 6.75

Amborella Trichopoda — A541

2012, Aug. 6   Litho.   **Perf. 13¼x13**
1136 A541 180fr multi   4.00 4.00

2012 Paralympics, London — A542

Designs: No. 1137, 75fr, Wheelchair race. No. 1138, 75fr, Shot put.

2012, Aug. 6   **Perf. 13x13¼**
1137-1138 A542   Set of 2   3.25 3.25

Local Scenes A543

Designs: No. 1139, 110fr, Bonhomme de Bourail rock formation. No. 1140, 110fr, Hut made of coconut palm fronds, Maré. No. 1141, 110fr, Mouth of Koumac River. No. 1142, 110fr, Cowboys and cattle.

2012, Aug. 6   **Perf. 13**
1139-1142 A543   Set of 4   9.50 9.50

Souvenir Sheet

Michel Corbasson Zoo and Forest, Noumea, 50th Anniv. — A544

No. 1143: a, Rhacodactylus leachianus. b, Corvus moneduloides. c, Pittosporum tanianum.

2012, Sept. 25   **Perf. 13¼x13**
1143 A544 110fr Sheet of 3, #a-c 7.25 7.25

National Tree Planting Campaign A545

2012, Sept. 26   **Perf. 13**
1144 A545 75fr multi   1.60 1.60

3G Technology A546

2012, Sept. 26   **Perf. 13x13¼**
1145 A546 280fr multi   6.00 6.00

Whales in Great Southern Lagoon Zone A547

2012, Nov. 9   **Perf. 13**
1146 A547 75fr multi   1.60 1.60

Mangrove Forest — A548

2012, Nov. 9   **Litho.**
1147 A548 75fr multi   1.60 1.60

Christmas A549

2012, Nov. 9   **Perf. 13x13¼**
1148 A549 110fr multi   2.40 2.40

New Year 2013 (Year of the Snake) — A550

2013, Feb. 7   Litho.   **Perf. 13**
1149 A550 110fr multi   2.40 2.40
See No. 1251d.

Encastreaux Reefs Area A551

2013, Mar. 7
1150 A551 110fr multi   2.40 2.40

Opening of La Tontouta Intl. Airport, Noumea A552

2013, Mar. 19
1151 A552 110fr multi   2.40 2.40

Bacouya Sugar Factory Chimney A553

2013, May 13   **Engr.**   **Perf. 13x12¼**
1152 A553 120fr multi   2.75 2.75

Red Cross South Pacific Regional Intervention Platform — A554

2013, June 7   Litho.   **Perf. 13**
1153 A554 75fr multi   1.75 1.75

Opening of Calédoscope, New Philatelic Office — A555

2013, June 7   Litho.   **Perf. 14½**
1154 A555 75fr multi   1.75 1.75

Naso Unicornis — A556

2013, June 7   **Engr.**   **Perf. 13**
1155 A556 110fr blue   2.50 2.50

Marine Life in Lagoons — A557

No. 1156: a, Plectorpomus leopardus, Epinephelus polyphekadion. b, Carcharhinus amblyrhynchos. c, Scomberomorus commerson. d, Chelonia mydas. e, Caranx melampygus. f, Tridacna maxima, Forcipiger flavissimus. g, Chromis viridis. h, Panulirus penicillatus. i, Myripristis berndti. j, Lutjanus kasmira.

Serpentine Die Cut 11
2013, June 8   **Litho.**
    Self-Adhesive
1156   Booklet pane of 10   25.00
   a.-j.   A557 110fr Any single   2.50 2.50

Re-opening of Maritime History Museum A558

2013, June 28   Litho.   Perf. 13
1157 A558 110fr multi   2.40 2.40

Opening of Nouville Penitentiary Museum A559

2013, Aug. 7   Litho.   Perf. 13
1158 A559 280fr multi   6.25 6.25

Birth of a Girl — A560

Birth of a Boy — A561

2013, Aug. 8   Litho.   Perf. 13¼x13
1159 A560 110fr multi   2.50 2.50
1160 A561 110fr multi   2.50 2.50

World Swimming Championships for the Intellectually Disabled, Dumbea — A562

2013, Aug. 19   Litho.   Perf. 13
1161 A562 120fr multi   2.75 2.75

Captaincookia Tree — A563

2013, Sept. 9   Litho.   Perf. 13¼x13
1162 A563 85fr multi   1.90 1.90

Pouembout Dovecote — A564

2013, Sept. 9   Litho.   Perf. 13¼x13
1163 A564 180fr multi   4.00 4.00

Wildlife and Landscapes A565

Designs: 85fr, Fruit bat and bougainvillea flowers. 110fr, 500-Franc Note Beach, Hienghène. 190fr, Warrior's Leap, Maré Island, vert. 250fr, Thio and Bota Méré, vert.

Perf. 13x13¼, 13¼x13
2013, Nov. 6   Litho.
1164-1167 A565   Set of 4   14.50 14.50

Beekeeping — A566

No. 1168: a, Jars of honey, honeydipper, flower, beekeeper checking hives. b, Bees and hives.

2013, Nov. 6   Litho.   Perf. 13
1168 A566 110fr Horiz. pair, #a-b   5.00 5.00

Miniature Sheet

Orchids A567

No. 1169: a, Eria karicouyensis. b, Earina deplanchei, vert. c, Eriaxis rigida, vert. d, Dendrobium poissonianum.

Perf. 13x13¼, 13¼x13
2013, Sept. 10   Litho.
1169 A567 110fr Sheet of 4,
            #a-d   10.00 10.00

Christmas A568

2013, Nov. 6   Litho.   Perf. 13x13¼
1170 A568 110fr multi   2.50 2.50

Miniature Sheet

New Banknotes — A569

No. 1171: a, 75fr, 500-franc banknote. b, 75fr, 1000-franc banknote. c, 110fr, 5000-franc banknote. d, 110fr, 10,000-franc banknote.

Litho. & Silk-screened
2014, Jan. 20   Perf. 13x12¾
1171 A569   Sheet of 4, #a-d   8.50 8.50

New Year 2014 (Year of the Horse) — A570

2014, Feb. 3   Litho.   Perf. 13
1172 A570 110fr multi   2.50 2.50

No. 1172 was printed in sheets of 10 + central label. See No. 1251g.

Exhibition at Tjibaou Cultural Center of Kanak Art — A571

2014, Mar. 15   Litho.   Perf. 12¾x13
1173 A571 110fr multi   2.60 2.60

North and East Coastal Zone UNESCO World Heritage Site — A572

2014, Apr. 22   Litho.   Perf. 13¼x13
1174 A572 110fr multi   2.60 2.60

Veteran's Center, Noumea, 50th Anniv. — A573

2014, May 16   Litho.   Perf. 13x13¼
1175 A573 150fr multi   3.50 3.50

Cajoulle House, Koné A574

2014, May 16   Engr.   Perf. 13x13¼
1176 A574 750fr multi   17.00 17.00

World Blood Donor Day — A575

2014, June 6   Litho.   Perf. 13
1177 A575 110fr multi   2.50 2.50

Landscapes and Wildlife — A576

Designs: 75fr, Koné Coral Reef. 110fr, Golden damselfish (poisson-demoiselle), horiz. 120fr, Horned parakeet (perruche), horiz. 190fr, Drowned Forest (La Forêt Noyée).

Perf. 13¼x13, 13x13¼
2014, June 6   Litho.
1178-1181 A576   Set of 4   11.50 11.50

Marine Rescue Service, 10th Anniv. A577

Litho. & Engr.
2014, Sept. 8   Perf. 13
1182 A577 110fr multi   2.40 2.40

Souvenir Sheet

Flora and Fauna of the Mining Scrubland — A578

No. 1183: a, Red-throated parrotfinch (Diamant psittaculaire). b, Grevillea gillivrayi, vert. c, Deplanchea sessilifolia.

Perf. 13x13¼, 13¼x13
2014, Sept. 8   Photo.
1183 A578 110fr Sheet of 3, #a-c 7.00 7.00

Murraya Paniculata Bonsai, by Jean-Jacques Mahuteau — A579

2014, Oct. 6   Litho.   Perf. 13¼x13
1184 A579 150fr multi   3.25 3.25

Isle of Pines Penitentiary A580

2014, Oct. 6   Engr.   Perf. 13x12½
1185 A580 280fr multi   6.00 6.00

Papilio Montrouzieri A581

Litho. & Embossed With Foil Application
2014, Nov. 6   Perf. 13½
1186 A581 180fr multi   3.75 3.75

Niaouli Flowers and Oil Distillation A582

2014, Nov. 6   Litho.   Perf. 13
1187 A582 190fr multi   4.00 4.00

No. 1187 is impregnated with a niaouli scent.

Kanak Weaving — A583

Litho. & Embossed
2014, Nov. 6   Perf. 13
1188 A583 250fr multi   5.25 5.25

Christmas A584

2014, Nov. 6   Litho.   Perf. 13x13¼
1189 A584 110fr multi   2.40 2.40

New Year 2015 (Year of the Goat) — A585

2015, Feb. 19   Litho.   Perf. 13
1190 A585 110fr multi   2.10 2.10

No. 1190 was printed in sheets of 10 + central label.

Dick Ukeiwe (1928-2013), Senator — A586

2015, Feb. 19   **Engr.**   *Perf. 13¼*
1191 A586 500fr dark blue & brown   9.25 9.25

Pittosporum Tanianum — A587

2015, Mar. 19   **Litho.**   *Perf. 13x13¼*
1192 A587 120fr multi   2.25 2.25

Kô Salt Marshes, Poingam A588

2015, Apr. 22   **Litho.**   *Perf. 13*
1193 A588 450fr multi   8.50 8.50

Children's Art — A589

Designs: No. 1194, Wildlife, by Eliot-Louis Hatterer.
No. 1195, horiz.: a, Building, tree and Sun, by Emmanuelle Hnawang. b, Flower and snake, by Thomas Bodeouarou.

2015, June 5   **Litho.**   *Perf. 13¼x13*
1194 A589 75fr multi   1.40 1.40
   Perf. 13x13¼
1195   Horiz. pair + central label   2.80 2.80
  a.-b.   A589 75fr Either single   1.40 1.40

World War I, Cent. — A590

No. 1196 — Military medals and: a, Soldiers boarding the Sontay. b, Battle of the Serre. c, Soldiers returning home on the El Kantara.

2015, June 5   **Litho.**   *Perf. 13x13¼*
1196   Horiz. strip of 3   2.00 2.00
  a.-c.   A590 35fr Any single   .65 .65

Souvenir Sheet

Birds A591

No. 1197: a, Nycticorax caledonicus. b, Egretta sacra albolineata, horiz. c, Egretta novaehollandiae nana.

   Perf. 13¼x13, 13x13¼
2015, June 5   **Litho.**
1197 A591 110fr Sheet of 3, #a-c 6.25 6.25

Maxat, First Yam Farming Cycle A592

2015, July 20   **Litho.**   *Perf. 13*
1198 A592 110fr multi   2.10 2.10

New Caledonia Ornithological Society, 50th Anniv. — A593

2015, Aug. 5   **Litho.**   *Perf. 13*
1199 A593 180fr multi   3.50 3.50

Château Escande, Poya A594

2015, Sept. 15   **Engr.**   *Perf. 13x12½*
1200 A594 750fr multi   14.00 14.00

First Lighting of Amédée Lighthouse, 150th Anniv. — A595

2015, Nov. 5   **Litho.**   *Perf. 13*
1201 A595 110fr multi   2.00 2.00

Flowers — A596

No. 1202: a, Arthroclianthus deplanchei. b, Thiollierea campanulata. c, Xanthostemon aurantiacus. d, Deplanchea speciosa. e, Xanthostemon sulfureus. f, Deplanchea sessifolia. g, Boronella pancheri. h, Artia balansae. i, Virotia angustifolia. j, Arthroclianthus microbotrys.

Serpentine Die Cut 11
2015, Nov. 5   **Litho.**
   Self-Adhesive
1202   Booklet pane of 10   20.00
  a.-j.   A596 110fr Any single   2.00 2.00

Miniature Sheet

Turtles A597

No. 1203 — Inscriptions: a, Tortue bonne écaille. b, Tortue grosse tête. c, Tortue verte, horiz. d, Tortue luth, horiz.

2015, Nov. 5   **Photo.**   *Perf. 13½x13*
1203 A597 110fr Sheet of 4, #a-d 8.00 8.00

Christmas — A598

Litho. & Thermographed
2015, Nov. 5   *Perf. 13 on 3 Sides*
1204 A598 110fr multi   2.00 2.00

New Year 2016 (Year of the Monkey) — A599

2016, Feb. 8   **Litho.**   *Perf. 13*
1205 A599 110fr multi   2.00 2.00

No. 1205 was printed in sheets of 10 + central label. See No. 1251i.

Conifers and Palm Trees A600

2016, Mar. 14   **Litho.**   *Perf. 13*
1206 A600 120fr multi   2.40 2.40

Tiga Island A601

2016, Apr. 14   **Litho.**   *Perf. 13*
1207 A601 110fr multi   2.10 2.10

Marriage — A602

2016, May 12   **Litho.**   *Perf. 13x13¼*
1208 A602 75fr multi   1.40 1.40

Statue of Kanak Soldier of World War I — A603

2016, June 3   **Litho.**   *Perf. 13*
1209 A603 110fr multi   2.10 2.10

Shell Engraved by Convict — A604

Litho. & Silk-Screened
2016, June 10   *Perf. 13x13¼*
1210 A604 75fr multi   1.40 1.40

Fiber Optic Communications A605

2016, June 10   **Litho.**   *Perf. 13x13¼*
1211 A605 75fr multi   1.40 1.40

Natural Park of the Coral Sea — A606

2016, June 10   **Litho.**   *Perf. 13*
1212 A606 110fr multi   2.10 2.10

Astronomy in New Caledonia A607

2016, Aug. 5   **Litho.**   *Perf. 14¼x14*
1213 A607 450fr multi   8.50 8.50

Janisel House, Pouébo — A608

2016, Sept. 12   **Litho.**   *Perf. 13x13¼*
1214 A608 110fr multi   2.10 2.10

Dr. René Catala (1901-88), Biologist — A609

2016, Sept. 12   **Litho.**   *Perf. 13*
1215 A609 120fr multi + label   2.25 2.25

Horat, Second Yam Farming Cycle A610

2016, Oct. 10   **Litho.**   *Perf. 13*
1216 A610 120fr multi   2.25 2.25

Ocean Liner Le Calédonien A611

2016, Nov. 3   **Litho.**   *Perf. 13*
1217 A611 110fr multi   2.00 2.00

Miniature Sheet

Items With Spirals A612

No. 1218: a, Hippocampus kuda (seahorse). b, Spirobranchus giganteus (Christmas tree worms), horiz. c, Cyathea intermedia (tree fern). d, Nautilus macromphalus (nautilus), horiz.

2016, Nov. 3   **Litho.**   *Perf. 13¼*
1218 A612 110fr Sheet of 4, #a-d 8.00 8.00

Kagu — A613

2016, Nov. 3   **Litho.**   *Perf. 13*
   Background Color
1219 A613   5fr red lilac   .30 .25
  a.   Dated "2018"   .30 .25
  b.   Dated "2019"   .30 .25
1220 A613   10fr light green   .30 .25
  a.   Dated "2018"   .30 .25
  b.   Dated "2019"   .30 .25
1221 A613   30fr cerise   .55 .55
  a.   Dated "2018"   .60 .60
  b.   Dated "2019"   .55 .55
   Nos. 1219-1221 (3)   1.15 1.05

   Booklet Stamps
   Self-Adhesive
   Serpentine Die Cut 6¾ Vert.
1222 A613   (75fr) dark red   1.40 1.40
  a.   Booklet pane of 10   14.00
  b.   As No. 1222, dated "2018"   1.50 1.50
  c.   Booklet pane of 10 #1222b   15.00

d.	As #1222, dated "2019"	1.40	1.40
e.	Booklet pane of 10 #1222d	14.00	
1223	A613 (120fr) yel orange	2.25	2.25
a.	Booklet pane of 10	22.50	

Issued: No. 1219a, 4/5/18; Nos. 1220a, 1221a, 4/10/18; Nos. 1219b, 1220b, 1221b, 8/9/19; Nos. 1222b, 1222c, 4/18/18; Nos. 1222d, 1222e, 9/15/19.

Christmas and New Year's Day — A614

2016, Nov. 3   Litho.   Perf. 13x13¼
1224 A614 110fr multi   2.00 2.00

New Year 2017 (Year of the Rooster) — A615

2017, Feb. 1   Litho.   Perf. 13¼
1225 A615 75fr multi   1.40 1.40

No. 1225 was printed in sheets of 10 + central label. See No. 1251I for stamp dated "2019."

Roger Gervolino (1909-91), Politician A616

2017, Mar. 14   Engr.   Perf. 13
1226 A616 1000fr dk blue & dk brn   18.00 18.00

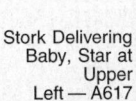

Stork Delivering Baby, Star at Upper Left — A617

Stork Delivering Baby, Heart at Upper Left — A618

2017, May 4   Litho.   Perf. 13x13¼
1227 A617 110fr multi, unscratched panel   2.10 2.10
  Scratched panel   1.75
1228 A618 110fr multi, unscratched panel   2.10 2.10
  Scratched panel   1.75

Gold scratch-off panels hide inscriptions "un garçon" (a boy) on No. 1227, and "une fille" (a girl) on No. 1228.

Mixed Battalion of the Pacific, Cent. — A619

2017, May 15   Litho.   Perf. 13
1229 A619 120fr multi   2.25 2.25

Lions Clubs International, Cent. — A620

2017, July 6   Litho.   Perf. 13¼x13
1230 A620 75fr multi   1.50 1.50

Steamer Natal — A621

2017, July 7   Litho.   Perf. 13
1231 A621 110fr multi   2.25 2.25

Buildings A622

No. 1232: a, Beaumont House, Moindou. b, Round houses, Isle of Pines.

2017, July 7   Litho.   Perf. 13x13¼
1232 A622 75fr Horiz. pair, #a-b, + central label   3.00 3.00

Noumea Carnival — A623

2017, Sept. 15   Litho.   Perf. 13x13¼
1233 A623 75fr multi   1.50 1.50

Miniature Sheet

Birds of Prey A624

No. 1234: a, Pandion cristatus. b, Circus approximans. c, Accipiter haplochrous. d, Haliastur sphenurus.

2017, Oct. 17   Photo.   Perf. 13¼x13
1234 A624 110fr Sheet of 4, #a-d 8.75 8.75

Kagu Philatelic Club, 70th Anniv. — A625

2017, Nov. 8   Litho.   Perf. 13x13¼
1235 A625 75fr multi   1.50 1.50

Wênit, Third Yam Farming Cycle — A626

2017, Nov. 9   Litho.   Perf. 13
1236 A626 75fr multi   1.50 1.50

Caves and Water Holes — A627

No. 1237 — Inscriptions: a, Grotte de Koumac. b, Pléiades du Nord. c, Trou Feuillet. d, Trou bleu. e, Trou d'eau à la Rivière Bleue. f, Trou d'eau d'Anawa. g, Grotte de la Reine Hortense. h, Aquarium naturel. i, Trou de Bone. j, Grotte du Diable.

Serpentine Die Cut 11
2017, Nov. 9   Litho.
Self-Adhesive
1237   Booklet pane of 10   22.50
  a.-j. A627 110fr Any single   2.25 2.25

Christmas — A628

2017, Nov. 9   Litho.   Perf. 13¼x13
1238 A628 110fr multi   2.25 2.25

New Year 2018 (Year of the Dog) — A629

2018, Feb. 16   Litho.   Perf. 13
1239 A629 75fr multi   1.60 1.60

No. 1239 was printed in sheets of 10 + central label. See No. 1251k for stamp dated "2019."

New Caledonian Battalion's Capture of Vesles-et-Caumont, France, Cent. — A630

2018, Apr. 10   Litho.   Perf. 13
1240 A630 75fr multi   1.50 1.50

Tjibaou Cultural Center, 20th Anniv. A631

2018, May 7   Litho.   Perf. 13
1241 A631 110fr multi   2.25 2.25

Kuyiuk Huuda, Fourth Yam Farming Cycle — A632

2018, June 8   Litho.   Perf. 13
1242 A632 110fr multi   2.25 2.25

Steamship Dupleix 1 — A633

2018, June 8   Litho.   Perf. 13
1243 A633 110fr multi   2.25 2.25

Buildings A634

No. 1244: a, Great Chief's hut, Poindimié. b, Albaret House, Canala.

2018, June 8   Litho.   Perf. 13x13¼
1244 A634 110fr Horiz. pair, #a-b, + central label   4.25 4.25

Bancoule Worm Eating Festival, Farino — A635

2018, Sept. 7   Litho.   Perf. 13x13¼
1245 A635 75fr multi   1.50 1.50

Horse Breeder's Promotion Unit (UPRA), 20th Anniv. — A636

2018, Sept. 13   Litho.   Perf. 13x13¼
1246 A636 75fr multi   1.50 1.50

Fauna — A637

No. 1247: a, Triops intermedius. b, Callismilax bouabouiensis. c, Tuba valkyrie.

2018, Nov. 7   Litho.   Perf. 13x13¼
1247   Horiz. strip of 3   4.50 4.50
  a.-c. A637 75fr Any single   1.50 1.50

Women's Handball Players A638

2018, Nov. 8   Litho.   Perf. 13
1248 A638 110fr multi   2.10 2.10

Miniature Sheet

Pollinators — A639

No. 1249: a, Gymnomyza aubryana. b. Pteropus ornatus, horiz. c, Apis mellifera mellifera, horiz. d, Eurema hecabe novaecalidoniae.

Perf. 13¼x13, 13x13¼ (horiz. stamps)

2018, Nov. 8   **Photo.**
1249 A639 110fr Sheet of 4, #a-d 8.50 8.50

Michel Rocard (1930-2016), Politician — A640

2018, Nov. 8   **Engr.**   **Perf. 13**
1250 A640 1000fr multi   19.00 19.00
Matignon-Oudinot Accords, 30th anniv.

New Year Types of 2003-17
Miniature Sheet
2019, Feb. 5   **Litho.**   **Perf. 13**
Dated "2019"
1251   Sheet of 12   18.00 18.00
a.   A461 75fr Rat   1.50 1.50
b.   A480 75fr Ox   1.50 1.50
c.   A501 75fr Tiger   1.50 1.50
d.   A550 75fr Snake   1.50 1.50
e.   A534 75fr Dragon   1.50 1.50
f.   A518 75fr Rabbit   1.50 1.50
g.   A570 75fr Horse   1.50 1.50
h.   A361 75fr Goat   1.50 1.50
i.   A599 75fr Monkey   1.50 1.50
j.   A430 75fr Pig   1.50 1.50
k.   A629 75fr Dog   1.50 1.50
l.   A615 75fr Rooster   1.50 1.50

Turtle in Lagoon — A641

2019, Mar. 14   **Litho.**   **Perf. 13¼x13**
1252 A641 110fr multi   2.10 2.10
Lagoons of New Caledonia as UNESCO World Heritage Site, 10th anniv.

Disabled Athletes A642

2019, June 7   **Litho.**   **Perf. 13**
1253 A642 120fr multi   2.40 2.40

Packet Boat Le Polynésie A643

2019, June 7   **Litho.**   **Perf. 13**
1254 A643 110fr multi   2.10 2.10

South Pacific Community Headquarters, Noumea — A644

2019, Aug. 9   **Litho.**   **Perf. 13**
1255 A644 75fr multi   1.40 1.40
South Pacific Community headquarters in Noumea, 70th anniv.

Return of New Caledonian World War I Soldiers, Cent. — A645

2019, Sept. 13   **Litho.**   **Perf. 13**
1256 A645 75fr multi   1.40 1.40

Avocado Festival, Maré — A646

2019, Oct. 10   **Litho.**   **Perf. 13¼x13**
1257 A646 110fr multi   2.10 2.10

Buildings A647

No. 1258: a, Roh hut, Maré. b, House of Samuel MacFarlane, Lifou.

2019, Oct. 10   **Litho.**   **Perf. 13x13¼**
1258 A647 110fr Horiz. pair, #a-b, + central label   4.25 4.25

Hand on Braille Book, Emma Meyer (1910-87), Founder of Valentin Haüy Association in New Caledonia A648

Litho. & Embossed
2019, Nov. 6   **Perf. 13**
1259 A648 75fr multi   1.40 1.40
Valentin Haüy Association in New Caledonia, 40th anniv.

Fort Constantine, Colonial Hospital, Gaston Bourret Hospital and Bourret (1875-1917), Microbiologist — A649

2019, Nov. 6   **Litho.**   **Perf. 13x13¼**
1260 A649 120fr multi   2.25 2.25

Pilou Mine Chimney — A650

2019, Nov. 6   **Engr.**   **Perf. 13**
1261 A650 1000fr multi   18.50 18.50

Famous Sites of New Caledonia — A651

No. 1262: a, University of New Caledonia. b, Church, Vao. c, Kanak hut. d, Chicken of Hienghène rock formation. e, Place Feillet Bandstand. f, Tjibaou Cultural Center.

Serpentine Die Cut 11
2020, Jan. 13   **Litho.**
Self-Adhesive
1262   Booklet pane of 6   12.00
a.-f.   A651 110fr Any single   2.00 2.00

10th Pacific Island Biodiversity Conservation Conference, Noumea — A652

2020, July 1   **Litho.**   **Perf. 13¼x13**
1263 A652 (210fr) multi   4.00 4.00

Love — A653

Design: Sea Fans Resembling People Kissing.

2020, July 1   **Litho.**   **Perf. 13x13¼**
1264 A653 (210fr) multi   4.00 4.00

Ship and Bernard Brou (1922-2009), Historian — A654

2020, July 17   **Litho.**   **Perf. 13**
1265 A654 140fr multi   2.75 2.75
New Caledonia Society for Historic Studies, 50th anniv.

Pôle Espoir Judo League — A655

2020, July 17   **Litho.**   **Perf. 13¼x13**
1266 A655 140fr multi   2.75 2.75

Aircalin Airbus A330neo — A656

2020, July 17   **Litho.**   **Perf. 13x13¼**
1267 A656 (140fr) multi   2.75 2.75

Mushrooms A657

No. 1268: a, Panus lecomtei. b, Ryvardenia campyla.

2020, Sept. 7   **Litho.**   **Perf. 13x13¼**
1268   Horiz. pair + central label   5.50 5.50
a.-b.   A657 140fr Either single   2.75 2.75

International Organization of La Francophonie, 50th Anniv. — A658

2020, Sept. 16   **Litho.**   **Perf. 13x13¼**
1269 A658 210fr multi   4.25 4.25

Pouembout Solar Farm A659

2020, Oct. 20   **Litho.**   **Perf. 13**
1270 A659 (210fr) multi   4.25 4.25

Jacques Chirac (1932-2019), President and Prime Minister of France — A660

2020, Nov. 4   **Litho.**   **Perf. 13**
1271 A660 840fr multi   17.00 17.00

Christmas A661

2020, Nov. 4   **Litho.**   **Perf. 13x13¼**
1272 A661 (210fr) multi   4.25 4.25

Kagu
A662   A663

2021, Mar. 22   **Litho.**   **Perf. 13**
1273 A662 (180fr) red & black   3.75 3.75
1274 A663 (260fr) violet & black 5.25 5.25

Mushrooms A664

No. 1275: a, Aseroe arachnoidea. b, Ophiocordyceps sp.

2021, May 3   **Litho.**   **Perf. 13x13¼**
1275   Horiz. pair + central label   7.50 7.50
a.-b.   A664 (180fr) Either single 3.75 3.75

New Caledonian Society for the Safeguarding of Nature, 50th Anniv. — A665

2021, May 6   **Litho.**   **Perf. 13**
1276 A665 260fr multi + label   5.50 5.50

Tabou Lighthouse — A666

2021, Aug. 17   **Litho.**   **Perf. 13¼x13**
1277 A666 (260fr) multi   5.25 5.25

New Pacific Franc Coins A667

Litho. & Embossed

2021, Sept. 1		**Perf. 13**
1278 A667 (180fr) multi	3.75	3.75

Mandarin Oranges — A668

2021, Sept. 14	**Litho.**	**Perf. 13x13¼**
1279 A668 (180fr) multi	3.50	3.50

Mandarin Orange Fair, Canala, 25th anniv.
No. 1279 is impregnated with a mandarin orange scent.

Environmental Protection A669

No. 1280: a, Hands and kauri tree. b, Hands, ship, sea cucumbers.

2021, Oct. 15	**Litho.**	**Perf. 13**
1280 A669 (260fr) Vert. pair, #a-b	10.00	10.00

Pan American Airways Boeing B-314 Clippers — A670

2021, Nov. 15	**Litho.**	**Perf. 13x13¼**
1281 A670 260fr multi	5.00	5.00

Mamie Fogliani (1939-2020), Restauranteur and Market Owner — A671

2021, Dec. 17	**Litho.**	**Perf. 13**
1282 A671 (180fr) multi	3.50	3.50

New Caledonia Youth Rugby Hope Academy A672

2022, Jan. 25	**Litho.**	**Perf. 13**
1283 A672 260fr multi	5.00	5.00

Mushrooms A673

No. 1284: a, Ileodictyon sp. b, Anthracophyllum archeri.

2022, Apr. 11	**Litho.**	**Perf. 13x13¼**
1284 Horiz. pair + central label	6.50	6.50
a.-b. A673 (180fr) Either single	3.25	3.25

Earth Day — A674

2022, Apr. 22	**Litho.**	**Perf. 13¼x13**
1285 A674 (180fr) multi	3.25	3.25

Cap N'Dua Lighthouse — A675

2022, July 22	**Litho.**	**Perf. 13¼x13**
1286 A675 (310fr) multi	5.50	5.50

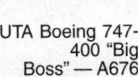

UTA Boeing 747-400 "Big Boss" — A676

2022, July 22	**Litho.**	**Perf. 13x13¼**
1287 A676 310fr multi	5.50	5.50

Peace Statue, Place de la Paix, Nouméa — A677

2022, Sept. 20	**Litho.**	**Perf. 13¼x13**
1288 A677 210fr multi	3.50	3.50

Miniature Sheet

Old Automobiles — A678

No. 1289: a, Willys Jeep. b, Cadillac Eldorado. c, Peugeot 504. d, Volkswagen Beetle Cabriolet.

2022, Sept. 20	**Litho.**	**Perf. 13x13¼**
1289 A678 (310fr) Sheet of 4, #a-d	20.00	20.00

Christmas — A679

2022, Nov. 15	**Litho.**	**Perf. 13¼x13**
1290 A679 (310fr) multi	5.50	5.50

Art by Camille Lincoln — A680

2022, Nov. 15	**Litho.**	**Perf. 13¼x13**
1291 A680 210fr multi	3.75	3.75

Kagu — A681

2022, Nov. 15	**Litho.**	**Perf. 13**
1292 A681 (210fr) red	3.75	3.75

Booklet Stamp
Self-Adhesive
Serpentine Die Cut 6¾ Vert.

1293 A681 (210fr) red	3.75	3.75
a. Booklet pane of 10	37.50	

Environmental Protection — A682

No. 1294: a, Giant crested gecko. b, Coral reef fauna.

2022, Dec. 6	**Litho.**	**Perf. 13¼x13**
1294 A682 (310fr) Pair, #a-b	11.00	11.00

SEMI-POSTAL STAMPS

No. 93 Surcharged

1915		**Unwmk.**	**Perf. 14x13½**	
B1	A16	10c + 5c carmine	1.50	1.50
a.		Inverted surcharge	75.00	75.00
b.		Cross omitted	100.00	—
c.		Double surcharge	160.00	160.00

Regular Issue of 1905 Surcharged

1917				
B2	A16	10c + 5c rose	1.50	1.30
a.		Double surcharge	130.00	
B3	A16	15c + 5c violet	1.50	1.40

Curie Issue
Common Design Type

1938, Oct. 24		**Perf. 13**	
B4	CD80	1.75fr + 50c brt ultra	16.50	17.50

French Revolution Issue
Common Design Type

1939, July 5		**Photo.**	
Name and Value Typo. in Black			
B5	CD83	45c + 25c green	13.50	13.50
B6	CD83	70c + 30c brown	13.50	13.50
B7	CD83	90c + 35c red org	13.50	13.50
B8	CD83	1.25fr + 1fr rose pink	13.50	13.50
B9	CD83	2.25fr + 2fr blue	13.50	13.50
		Nos. B5-B9 (5)	67.50	67.50

> Catalogue values for unused stamps in this section, from this point to the end of the section, are for Never Hinged items.

Common Design Type and

Dumont d'Urville's ship, "Zélée" SP2

New Caledonian Militiaman SP3

1941		**Photo.**	**Perf. 13½**
B10	SP2	1fr + 1fr red	2.25
B11	CD86	1.50fr + 3fr maroon	2.25
B12	SP3	2.50fr + 1fr dk blue	2.25
		Nos. B10-B12 (3)	6.75

Nos. B10-B12 were issued by the Vichy government in France, but were not placed on sale in New Caledonia.

Nos. 216A-216B Srchd. in Black or Red

1944		**Engr.**	**Perf. 12½x12**
B12A		50c + 1.50fr on 2.50fr deep blue (R)	1.00
B12B		+ 2.50fr on 1fr green	1.25

Colonial Development Fund.
Nos. B12A-B12B were issued by the Vichy government in France, but were not placed on sale in New Caledonia.

Red Cross Issue
Common Design Type

1944			**Perf. 14½x14**
B13	CD90	5fr + 20fr brt scar	1.50	1.50

The surtax was for the French Red Cross and national relief.

Tropical Medicine Issue
Common Design Type

1950, May 15		**Engr.**	**Perf. 13**
B14	CD100	10fr + 2fr red brn & sepia	6.75	5.25

The surtax was for charitable work.

AIR POST STAMPS

Seaplane Over Pacific Ocean — AP1

1938-40		**Unwmk. Engr.**	**Perf. 13**	
C1	AP1	65c deep violet	1.00	1.00
a.		"65c" omitted	225.00	
C2	AP1	4.50fr red	1.60	1.60
C3	AP1	7fr dk bl grn ('40)	1.15	.85
C4	AP1	9fr ultra	3.00	2.60
C5	AP1	20fr dk org ('40)	2.25	2.25
C6	AP1	50fr black ('40)	3.75	3.25
		Nos. C1-C6 (6)	12.75	11.55

Type of 1938-40 Without "RF"

1942-43				
C6A	AP1	65c deep violet	.30	
C6B	AP1	4.50fr red	.30	
C6C	AP1	5fr yellow brown	.55	
C6D	AP1	9fr ultramarine	.45	
C6E	AP1	10fr brown lilac	1.00	
C6F	AP1	20fr dark orange	1.60	
C6G	AP1	50fr black	1.75	
		Nos. C6A-C6G (7)	5.95	

Nos. C6A-C6G were issued by the Vichy government in France, but were not placed on sale in New Caledonia.

Common Design Type

1942		**Unwmk.**	**Perf. 14½x14**	
C7	CD87	1fr dk orange	.70	.70
C8	CD87	1.50fr brt red	.70	.70
C9	CD87	5fr brown red	.70	.70
C10	CD87	10fr black	1.10	.70
C11	CD87	25fr ultra	1.40	1.25

C12	CD87	50fr dk green	2.00	1.25
C13	CD87	100fr plum	2.25	2.00
		Nos. C7-C13 (7)	8.85	7.30

Eagle — AP1a

1944   *Perf. 13*
C13A   AP1a 100fr blue grn   1.50

No. C13A was issued by the Vichy government in France, but was not placed on sale in New Caledonia.

> **Catalogue values for unused stamps in this section, from this point to the end of the section, are for Never Hinged items.**

Victory Issue
Common Design Type

1946, May 8   **Engr.**   *Perf. 12½*
C14   CD92 8fr brt ultra   1.50   1.25

Chad to Rhine Issue
Common Design Types

1946, June 6
C15	CD93	5fr black	1.75	1.60
C16	CD94	10fr carmine	1.75	1.60
C17	CD95	15fr dk blue	1.75	1.60
C18	CD96	20fr orange brn	1.75	1.60
C19	CD97	25fr olive grn	2.40	2.00
C20	CD98	50fr dk rose vio	4.00	3.50
		Nos. C15-C20 (6)	13.40	11.90

St. Vincent
Bay — AP2

Planes over
Islands — AP3

View of
Nouméa
AP4

Perf. 13x12½, 12½x13
1948, Mar. 1   **Photo.**   **Unwmk.**
C21	AP2	50fr org & rose vio	6.00	4.00
C22	AP3	100fr bl grn & sl bl	10.50	4.50
C23	AP4	200fr brown & yel	16.50	8.50
		Nos. C21-C23 (3)	33.00	17.00

UPU Issue
Common Design Type

1949, Nov. 21   **Engr.**   *Perf. 13*
C24   CD99 10fr multicolored   7.50   5.00

Liberation Issue
Common Design Type

1954, June 6
C25   CD102 3fr indigo & ultra   7.50   5.00

Conveyor
for Nickel
Ore — AP5

1955, Nov. 21   **Unwmk.**   *Perf. 13*
C26   AP5 14fr indigo & sepia   4.00   1.50

Rock
Formations,
Bourail
AP6

1959, Mar. 21
C27   AP6 200fr lt bl, brn & grn   34.00   15.00

Yaté Dam — AP7

1959, Sept. 21   **Engr.**
C28   AP7 50fr grn, brt bl & sepia   7.50   4.50

Dedication of Yaté Dam.

Fisherman
with Throw-
net
AP8

Skin Diver
Shooting
Bumphead
Surgeonfish
AP9

20fr, Nautilus shell. 100fr, Yaté rock.

1962   **Unwmk.**   *Perf. 13*
C29	AP8	15fr red, Prus grn & sep	4.75	2.25
C30	AP9	20fr dk sl grn & org ver	9.50	3.75
C31	AP9	25fr red brn, gray & bl	9.50	4.50
C32	AP9	100fr dk brn, dk bl & sl grn	16.00	11.50
		Nos. C29-C32 (4)	39.75	22.00

Telstar Issue
Common Design Type

1962, Dec. 4   **Unwmk.**   *Perf. 13*
C33   CD111 200fr dk bl, choc & grnsh bl   25.00   18.50

Nickel
Mining,
Houailou
AP10

1964, May 14   **Photo.**
C34   AP10 30fr multi   4.00   2.50

Isle of Pines
AP11

1964, Dec. 7   **Engr.**   *Perf. 13*
C35   AP11 50fr dk bl, sl grn & choc   5.75   2.60

Marine
Life — AP12

Designs: 27fr, Paracanthurus teuthis (fish). 37fr, Phyllobranchus.

1964, Dec. 21   **Photo.**
| C36 | AP12 | 27fr multicolored | 7.50 | 3.50 |
| C37 | AP12 | 37fr multicolored | 9.00 | 5.00 |

Issued to publicize the Nouméa Aquarium.

Greco-Roman Wrestling — AP13

1964, Dec. 28   **Engr.**
C38   AP13 10fr brt grn, pink & blk   18.00   15.00

18th Olympic Games, Tokyo, Oct. 10-25.

Nimbus Weather
Satellite over New
Caledonia — AP14

1965, Mar. 23   **Photo.**   *Perf. 13x12½*
C39   AP14 9fr multi   3.75   3.00

Fifth World Meteorological Day.

ITU Issue
Common Design Type

1965, May 17   **Engr.**   *Perf. 13*
C40   CD120 40fr lt bl, lil rose & red brn   10.00   8.00

Coris
Angulata
(Young
Fish)
AP15

15fr, Adolescent fish. 25fr, Adult fish.

1965, Dec. 6   **Engr.**   *Perf. 13*
C41	AP15	13fr red org, ol bis & blk	4.00	1.50
C42	AP15	15fr ind, sl grn & bis	6.00	2.00
C43	AP15	25fr ind & yel grn	8.00	4.00
		Nos. C41-C43 (3)	18.00	7.50

Issued to publicize the Nouméa Aquarium.

French Satellite A-1 Issue
Common Design Type

Designs: 8fr, Diamant rocket and launching installations. 12fr, A-1 satellite.

1966, Jan. 10   **Engr.**   *Perf. 13*
C44	CD121	8fr rose brn, ultra & Prus bl	2.00	1.60
C45	CD121	12fr ultra, Prus bl & rose brn	3.00	3.00
a.		Strip of 2, #C44-C45 + label	7.00	7.00

French Satellite D-1 Issue
Common Design Type

1966, May 16   **Engr.**   *Perf. 13*
C46   CD122 10fr dl bl, ocher & sep   2.25   2.00

Port-de-France, 1866 — AP16

1966, June 2
C47   AP16 30fr dk red, bl & ind   4.25   3.00

Port-de-France changing name to Nouméa, cent.

Bird Type of Regular Issue

Designs: 27fr, Uvea crested parakeet. 37fr, Scarlet honey eater. 50fr, Two cloven-feathered doves.

1966-68   **Photo.**   *Perf. 13*
Size: 26x46mm
| C48 | A45 | 27fr pink & multi | 7.50 | 4.00 |
| C49 | A45 | 37fr grn & multi | 10.00 | 5.00 |

Size: 27x48mm
| C49A | A45 | 50fr multi ('68) | 13.00 | 7.50 |
| | | *Nos. C48-C49A (3)* | 30.50 | 16.50 |

Issued: 27fr, 37fr, Oct. 10; 50fr, May 14.

Sailboats and Map of New Caledonia-
New Zealand Route — AP17

1967, Apr. 15   **Engr.**   *Perf. 13*
C50   AP17 25fr brt grn, dp ultra & red   6.75   3.75

2nd sailboat race from Whangarei, New Zealand, to Nouméa, New Caledonia.

Butterfly Type of Regular Issue

Butterflies: 19fr, Danaus plexippus. 29fr, Hippotion celerio. 85fr, Delias elipsis.

1967-68   **Engr.**   *Perf. 13*
Size: 48x27mm
C51	A52	19fr multi ('68)	6.50	3.00
C52	A52	29fr multi ('68)	9.50	4.00
C53	A52	85fr red, dk brn & yel	15.00	7.50
		Nos. C51-C53 (3)	31.00	14.50

Issued: 85fr, Aug. 10; others, Mar. 26.

Jules
Garnier,
Garnierite
and Mine
AP18

1967, Oct. 9   **Engr.**   *Perf. 13*
C54   AP18 70fr bl gray, brn & yel grn   9.00   5.25

Discovery of garnierite (nickel ore), cent.

Lifu Island
AP19

1967, Oct. 28   **Photo.**   *Perf. 13*
C55   AP19 200fr multi   14.00   7.50

Skier,
Snowflake
and Olympic
Emblem
AP20

1967, Nov. 16   **Engr.**   *Perf. 13*
C56   AP20 100fr brn red, sl grn & brt bl   14.00   7.50

10th Winter Olympic Games, Grenoble, France, Feb. 6-18, 1968.

Sea Shell Type of Regular Issue

Designs: 39fr, Conus lienardi. 40fr, Conus cabriti. 70fr, Conus coccineus.

1968, Nov. 9   **Engr.**   *Perf. 13*
C58	A54	39fr bl grn, brn & gray	8.25	2.75
C59	A54	40fr blk, brn red & ol	8.25	3.00
C60	A54	70fr brn, pur & gray	17.00	5.50
		Nos. C58-C60 (3)	33.50	11.25

Maré Dancers — AP21

1968, Nov. 30   **Engr.**   *Perf. 13*
C61   AP21 60fr grn, ultra & hn brn   7.50   5.00

World Map and Caudron C 600 "Aiglon" AP22

1969, Mar. 24   Engr.   Perf. 13
C62 AP22 29fr lil, dk bl & dk car   5.00 2.25
Stamp Day and honoring the 1st flight from Nouméa to Paris of Henri Martinet & Paul Klein, Mar. 24, 1939.

Concorde Issue
Common Design Type
1969, Apr. 17   Engr.   Perf. 13
C63 CD129 100fr sl grn & brt grn   27.50 20.00

Cattle Type of Regular Issue
Design: 50fr, Cowboy and herd.
1969, May 10   Engr.   Perf. 13
Size: 48x27mm
C64 A56 50fr sl grn, dk brn & red brn   7.00 3.25

Sea Shell Type of Regular Issue, 1969
Design: 100fr, Black murex.
1969, June 21   Engr.   Perf. 13
Size: 48x27mm
C65 A57 100fr lake, bl & blk   24.00 11.50

Sports Type of 1969
30fr, Woman diver. 39fr, Shot put, vert.
1969, Aug. 7   Engr.   Perf. 13
Size: 48x27mm, 27x48mm
C66 A58 30fr dk brn, bl & blk   5.25 2.00
C67 A58 39fr dk ol, brt grn & ol   6.75 3.00

Napoleon in Coronation Robes, by François P. Gerard — AP23

1969, Oct. 2   Photo.   Perf. 12½x12
C68 AP23 40fr lil & multi   14.00 10.00
200th birth anniv. of Napoleon Bonaparte (1769-1821).

Air France Plane over Outrigger Canoe AP24

1969, Oct. 2   Engr.   Perf. 13
C69 AP24 50fr slate grn, sky bl & choc   5.50 3.25
20th anniversary of the inauguration of the Nouméa to Paris airline.

Bird Type of Regular Issue
39fr, Emerald doves. 100fr, Whistling kite.
1970, Feb. 19   Photo.   Perf. 13
Size: 27x48mm
C70 A45 39fr multi   13.50 4.00
C71 A45 100fr multi   26.00 10.00

Planes Circling Globe and Paris-Nouméa Route — AP25

1970, May 6   Engr.   Perf. 13
C72 AP25 200fr vio, org brn & grnsh bl   17.50 9.75
10th anniversary of the Paris to Nouméa flight: "French Wings Around the World."

Shell Type of Regular Issue, 1970
22fr, Strombus sinautus humphrey, vert. 33fr, Argus porcelain shell. 34fr, Strombus vomer, vert. 60fr, Card porcelain shell.
1970   Engr.   Perf. 13
Size: 27x48mm, 48x27mm
C73 A59 22fr lt bl & multi   7.25 3.00
C74 A59 33fr red brn & grnsh bl   9.00 4.50
C75 A59 34fr vio & multi   9.00 3.50
C76 A59 60fr emer & red brn   15.00 6.00
Nos. C73-C76 (4)   40.25 17.00
See Nos. C89-C90.

Bicyclists on Map of New Caledonia AP26

1970, Aug. 20   Engr.   Perf. 13
C77 AP26 40fr bl, ultra & choc   6.75 3.25
The 4th Bicycling Race of New Caledonia.

Mt. Fuji and Monorail Train AP27
45fr, Map of Japan and Buddha statue.
1970, Sept. 3   Photo.   Perf. 13x12½
C78 AP27 20fr blk, bl & yel grn   4.50 1.90
C79 AP27 45fr mar, lt bl & ol   6.00 3.25
EXPO '70 International Exposition, Osaka, Japan, Mar. 15-Sept. 13.

Racing Yachts — AP28

1971, Feb. 23   Engr.   Perf. 13
C80 AP28 20fr grn, blk & ver   3.75 1.25
First challenge in New Zealand waters for the One Ton Cup ocean race.

Lt. Col. Broche and Map of Mediterranean — AP29

1971, May 5   Photo.   Perf. 12½
C81 AP29 60fr multi   7.50 4.00
30th anniversary of Battalion of the Pacific.

Pole Vault AP30

1971, June 24   Engr.   Perf. 13
C82 AP30 25fr shown   3.75 2.00
C83 AP30 100fr Archery   8.00 4.25
4th South Pacific Games, Papeete, French Polynesia, Sept. 8-19.

Port de Plaisance, Nouméa AP31

1971, Sept. 27   Photo.   Perf. 13
C84 AP31 200fr multi   16.00 7.00

Golden Eagle and Pilot's Leaflet — AP32

1971, Nov. 20   Engr.   Perf. 13
C85 AP32 90fr dk brn, org & indigo   8.25 3.75
1st flight New Caledonia — Australia with Victor Roffey piloting the Golden Eagle, 40th anniv.

Skiing and Sapporo '72 Emblem AP33

1972, Jan. 22   Engr.   Perf. 13
C86 AP33 50fr brt bl, car & sl grn   6.00 2.75
11th Winter Olympic Games, Sapporo, Japan, Feb. 3-13.

South Pacific Commission Headquarters, Nouméa — AP34

1972, Feb. 5   Photo.
C87 AP34 18fr bl & multi   2.25 .85
South Pacific Commission, 25th anniv.

St. Mark's Basilica, Venice AP35

1972, Feb. 5   Engr.
C88 AP35 20fr lt grn, bl & grn   4.25 1.25
UNESCO campaign to save Venice.

Shell Type of Regular Issue, 1970
Designs: 25fr, Orange spider conch, vert. 50fr, Chiragra spider conch, vert.
1972, Mar. 4   Engr.   Perf. 13
Size: 27x48mm
C89 A59 25fr dp car & dk brn   6.50 3.00
C90 A59 50fr grn, brn & rose car   8.00 4.00

Breguet F-ALMV and Globe AP36

1972, Apr. 5   Engr.   Perf. 13
C91 AP36 110fr brt rose lil, bl & grn   8.00 6.00
40th anniversary of the first Paris-Nouméa flight, Mar. 9-Apr. 5, 1932.

Round House and Festival Emblem — AP37

1972, May 13
C92 AP37 24fr org, bl & brn   3.00 1.50
So. Pacific Festival of Arts, Fiji, May 6-20.

Hurdles and Olympic Rings AP38

1972, Sept. 2   Engr.   Perf. 13
C93 AP38 72fr vio, bl & red lil   7.50 3.75
20th Olympic Games, Munich, Aug. 26-Sept. 11.

New Post Office, Noumea AP39

1972, Nov. 25   Engr.   Perf. 13
C94 AP39 23fr brn, brt bl & grn   2.25 1.00

Molière and Scenes from Plays AP40

1973, Feb. 24   Engr.   Perf. 13
C95 AP40 50fr multi   7.50 2.75
300th anniversary of the death of Molière (Jean Baptiste Poquelin, 1622-1673), French actor and playwright.

Woodlands AP41
Designs: 18fr, Palm trees on coast, vert. 21fr, Waterfall, vert.
1973, Feb. 24   Photo.
C96 AP41 11fr gold & multi   2.00 1.00
C97 AP41 18fr gold & multi   3.00 1.50
C98 AP41 21fr gold & multi   4.00 1.50
Nos. C96-C98 (3)   9.00 4.00

Concorde — AP42

1973, Mar. 15   Engr.   Perf. 13
C99 AP42 23fr blue   12.50 5.00
a.   Booklet pane of 5   250.00
No. C99 issued in booklets only.

El Kantara in Panama Canal AP43

1973, Mar. 24   Engr.   Perf. 13
C100 AP43 60fr brn, yel grn &
      blk   7.50 3.25
50th anniversary of steamship connection Marseilles to Nouméa through Panama Canal.

Sun, Earth, Wind God and Satellite AP44

1973, Mar. 24
C101 AP44 80fr multi   7.00 2.75
Centenary of intl. meteorological cooperation and 13th World Meteorological Day.

Museum Type of Regular Issue
Designs: 16fr, Carved arrows and arrowhead. 40fr, Carved entrance to chief's house.

1973, Apr. 30 Photo.   Perf. 12½x13
C102 A66 16fr multi   3.00 1.00
C103 A66 40fr multi   4.50 2.00

DC-10 over Map of Route Paris to Nouméa AP45

1973, May 26   Engr.   Perf. 13
C104 AP45 100fr brn, ultra & sl
      grn   7.50 3.50
First direct flight by DC-10, Nouméa to Paris.

Fish Type of Regular Issue
32fr, Old and young olive surgeonfish.

1973, June 23 Photo.   Perf. 13x12½
C105 A69 32fr multi   5.00 2.00

Coach, 1880 — AP46

1973, Sept. 22   Engr.   Perf. 13
C106 AP46 15fr choc, bl & sl grn 2.50 1.25
Stamp Day 1973.

Landscape AP47

West Coast Landscapes: 8fr, Rocky path, vert. 26fr, Trees on shore.

1974, Feb. 23   Photo.   Perf. 13
C107 AP47 8fr gold & multi   1.60 .90
C108 AP47 22fr gold & multi   2.25 1.40
C109 AP47 26fr gold & multi   3.75 1.50
      Nos. C107-C109 (3)   7.60 3.80

Anse-Vata, Scientific Center, Nouméa AP48

1974, Mar. 23 Photo.   Perf. 13x12½
C110 AP48 50fr multi   3.25 2.00

Ovula Ovum — AP49

1974, Mar. 23
C111 AP49 3fr shown   1.50 .55
C112 AP49 32fr Hydatina   4.00 1.10
C113 AP49 37fr Dolium perdix 4.50 2.10
      Nos. C111-C113 (3)   10.00 3.75
Nouméa Aquarium.

Capt. Cook, Map of Grande Terre and "Endeavour" AP50

Designs: 25fr, Jean F. de la Perouse, his ship and map of Grande Terre. 28fr, French sailor, 18th century, on board ship, vert. 30fr, Antoine R. J. d'Entrecasteaux, ship and map. 36fr, Dumont d'Urville, ship and map of Loyalty Islands.

1974, Sept. 4   Engr.   Perf. 13
C114 AP50 20fr multi   2.00 1.00
C115 AP50 25fr multi   3.00 1.60
C116 AP50 28fr multi   4.00 1.60
C117 AP50 30fr multi   5.00 2.00
C118 AP50 36fr multi   9.00 2.50
      Nos. C114-C118 (5)   23.00 8.70
Discovery and exploration of New Caledonia and Loyalty Islands.

UPU Emblem and Symbolic Design AP51

1974, Oct. 9   Engr.   Perf. 13
C119 AP51 95fr multi   6.00 2.75
Centenary of Universal Postal Union.

Abstract Design AP52

1974, Oct. 26   Photo.   Perf. 13
C120 AP52 80fr bl, blk & org 5.00 2.00
ARPHILA 75, Philatelic Exhibition, Paris, June 6-16, 1975.

Hôtel Chateau-Royal, Nouméa — AP53

1975, Jan. 20   Photo.   Perf. 13
C121 AP53 22fr multi   2.25 1.25

Cricket AP54

Designs: 25fr, Bougna ceremony (food offering). 31fr, Pilou dance.

1975, Apr. 5   Photo.   Perf. 13
C122 AP54 3fr bl & multi   1.25 .45
C123 AP54 25fr olive grn & multi 2.50 .70
C124 AP54 31fr yel grn & multi 3.00 1.10
      Nos. C122-C124 (3)   6.75 2.25
Tourist publicity.

Orchid Type of 1975
Design: 42fr, Eriaxis rigida.

1975, May 30
C125 A74 42fr grn & multi   6.00 2.25

Globe as "Flower" with "Stamps" and leaves — AP55

1975, June 7   Engr.   Perf. 13
C126 AP55 105fr multi   7.00 2.75
ARPHILA 75 International Philatelic Exhibition, Paris, June 6-16.

Discus and Games' Emblem AP56

50fr, Volleyball and Games' emblem.

1975, Aug. 23 Photo.   Perf. 13x12½
C127 AP56 24fr emer, pur & dk
      bl   2.00 1.00
C128 AP56 50fr multi   3.50 2.00
5th South Pacific Games, Guam, Aug. 1-10.

Concorde AP57

1976, Jan. 21   Engr.   Perf. 13
C129 AP57 147fr car & ultra 12.00 7.00
First commercial flight of supersonic jet Concorde, Paris-Rio de Janeiro, Jan. 21. For surcharge see No. C141.

Telephones 1876 and 1976, Satellite — AP58

1976, Apr. 12   Photo.   Perf. 13
C130 AP58 36fr multi   3.50 1.25
Centenary of first telephone call by Alexander Graham Bell, Mar. 10, 1876.

Battle Scene AP59

1976, June 14   Engr.   Perf. 13
C131 AP59 24fr red brn & ver 2.75 1.25
American Bicentennial.

Runners and Maple Leaf — AP60

1976, July 24   Engr.   Perf. 13
C132 AP60 33fr car, vio & brn 2.25 1.25
21st Olympic Games, Montreal, Canada, July 17-Aug. 1.

Whimsical Bird as Student and Collector — AP61

1976, Aug. 21   Photo.
C133 AP61 42fr multi   3.50 1.50
Philately in School, Philatelic Exhibition in La Perouse Lyceum, Nouméa.

Old City Hall, Nouméa AP62

Design: 125fr, New City Hall, Nouméa.

1976, Oct. 22   Photo.   Perf. 13
C134 AP62 75fr multi   5.00 2.75
C135 AP62 125fr multi   7.25 3.25

Lagoon, Women and Festival Symbols — AP63

1977, Jan. 15 Photo.   Perf. 13x12½
C136 AP63 11fr multi   2.00 1.00
Summer Festival 1977, Nouméa.

Training Children in Toy Cars AP64

1977, Mar. 12   Litho.   Perf. 13
C137 AP64 50fr multi   3.00 1.60
Road safety training.

Bird Type of 1977
Design: 42fr, Male frigate bird, horiz.

1977, Sept. 17 Photo.   Perf. 13
C138 A89 42fr multi   6.00 1.60

Magenta Airport and Routes AP65

Design: 57fr, La Tontouta airport.

1977, Oct. 22   Litho.   Perf. 13
C139 AP65 24fr multi   1.75 1.00
C140 AP65 57fr multi   3.50 2.00

No. C129 Surcharged in Violet Blue

1977, Nov. 22   Engr.   Perf. 13
C141 AP57 147fr car & ultra 14.00 9.00
Concorde, 1st commercial flight Paris-NY.

Old Nouméa, by H. Didonna AP66

Valley of the Settlers, by Jean Kreber AP67

1977, Nov. 26   Photo.   Perf. 13
C142 AP66 41fr gold & multi   3.00 1.50
Engr.
C143 AP67 42fr red brn & dk brn 3.00 1.50

"Underwater Carnival," Aubusson Tapestry AP68

1978, June 17   Photo.   Perf. 13
C144 AP68 105fr multi   5.50 2.25

"The Hare and the Tortoise" AP69

1978, Aug. 19   Photo.   Perf. 13x13½
C145 AP69 35fr multi   4.50 1.50
School philately.

Bourail School Children, Map and Conus Shell AP70

1978, Sept. 30   Engr.   Perf. 13
C146 AP70 41fr multi   3.00 1.25
Promotion of topical philately in Bourail public schools.

Old and New Candles — AP71

1978, Oct. 28   Photo.   Perf. 13
C147 AP71 36fr multi   2.00 .75
Third Caledonian Senior Citizens' Day.

Faubourg Blanchot, by Lacouture AP72

1978, Nov. 25   Photo.   Perf. 13
C148 AP72 24fr multi   1.75 1.00

Type of 1978
Design: 42fr, Amyema scandens, horiz.

1978, Mar. 17   Perf. 13x12½
C149 A91 42fr multi   3.50 1.60

Orbiting Weather Satellites, WMO Emblem — AP73

1979, Mar. 24   Photo.   Perf. 13
C150 AP73 53fr multi   2.50 1.25
First world-wide satellite system in the atmosphere.

Ships and Emblem — AP74

1979, Mar. 31   Engr.
C151 AP74 49fr multi   2.10 1.10
Chamber of Commerce and Industry, centenary.

Child's Drawing, IYC Emblem — AP75

1979, Apr. 21   Photo.   Perf. 13
C152 AP75 35fr multi   2.10 1.10
International Year of the Child.

Surf Casting — AP76

Design: 30fr, Swordfish fishing.

1979, May 26   Litho.   Perf. 12½
C153 AP76 29fr multi   2.00 1.00
C154 AP76 30fr multi   2.00 1.00

Port-de-France, 1854, and de Montravel — AP77

1979, June 16   Engr.   Perf. 13
C155 AP77 75fr multi   4.25 2.25
125th anniversary of Noumea, formerly Port-de-France, founded by L. Tardy de Montravel.

The Eel Queen, Kanaka Legend — AP78

1979, July 7   Photo.   Perf. 13
C156 AP78 42fr multi   3.00 1.75
Nature protection.

Map of New Caledonia, Postmark, Five Races AP79

1979, Aug. 18   Photo.   Perf. 13
C157 AP79 27fr multi   1.75 .90
New Caledonian youth and philately.

Orstom Center, Noumea, Orstom Emblem AP80

1979, Sept. 17   Photo.   Perf. 13
C158 AP80 25fr multi   1.75 1.00

Old Post Office, Noumea, New Caledonia No. 1, Hill — AP81

1979, Nov. 17   Engr.
C159 AP81 150fr multi   5.25 2.00
Sir Rowland Hill (1795-1879), originator of penny postage.

Pirogue — AP82

1980, Jan. 26   Engr.   Perf. 13
C160 AP82 45fr multi   1.75 .90

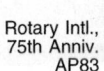

Rotary Intl., 75th Anniv. AP83

1980, Feb. 23   Photo.   Perf. 13
C161 AP83 100fr multi   4.50 1.60

Man Holding Dolphinfish AP84

39fr, Fishermen, sail fish, vert.

1980, Mar. 29   Photo.   Perf. 13x12½
C162 AP84 34fr shown   1.75 1.00
C163 AP84 39fr multicolored   2.50 1.25

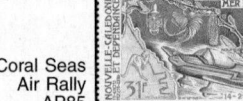

Coral Seas Air Rally AP85

1980, June 7   Engr.   Perf. 13
C164 AP85 31fr multi   1.75 .90

Carved Alligator, Boat AP86

1980, June 21   Photo.
C165 AP86 27fr multi   1.50 .55
South Pacific Arts Festival, Port Moresby, Papua New Guinea.

New Caledonian Kiwanis, 10th Anniversary AP87

1980, Sept. 10   Photo.   Perf. 13
C166 AP87 50fr multi   1.90 .90

View of Old Noumea AP88

1980, Oct. 25   Photo.   Perf. 13½
C167 AP88 33fr multi   1.60 .90

Charles de Gaulle, 10th Anniversary of Death — AP89

1980, Nov. 15   Engr.   Perf. 13
C168 AP89 120fr multi   6.00 3.50

Fluorescent Coral, Noumea Aquarium AP90

1980, Dec. 13   Photo.   Perf. 13x13½
C169 AP90 60fr multi   3.00 1.10

Xeronema Moorei — AP91

51fr, Geissois pruinosa.

1981, Mar. 18   Photo.   Perf. 13x12½
C170 AP91 38fr shown   1.50 1.25
C171 AP91 51fr multicolored   2.00 1.40

Yuri Gagarin and Vostok I — AP92

20th Anniversary of First Space Flights: 155fr, Alan B. Shepard, Freedom 7.

1981, Apr. 8   Engr.   Perf. 13
C172 AP92 64fr multi   2.75 1.10
C173 AP92 155fr multi   4.50 2.10
 a.   Souv. sheet of 2, #C172-
        C173   15.00 15.00

No. C173a sold for 225fr.

40th Anniv. of Departure of Pacific Batallion AP93

1981, May 5   Photo.   Perf. 13
C174 AP93 29fr multi   3.00 1.10

Ecinometra
Mathaei — AP94

51fr, Prionocidaris verticillata.

1981, Aug. 5   Photo.   *Perf. 13x13½*
C175 AP94 38fr shown   1.50   .80
C176 AP94 51fr multicolored   2.25   .95

No. 4, Post Office
Building — AP95

1981, Sept. 16   Photo.   *Perf. 13x13½*
C177 AP95 41fr multi   1.75   .90
Stamp Day.

Old Noumea Latin
Quarter — AP96

1981, Oct. 14   Photo.   *Perf. 13½*
C178 AP96 43fr multi   1.75   .75

New Caledonia to
Australia Airmail
Flight by Victor
Roffey, 50th
Anniv. — AP97

1981, Nov. 21   Engr.   *Perf. 13*
C179 AP97 37fr multi   1.50   .75

Rousette — AP98

1982, Feb. 24   Engr.   *Perf. 13*
C180 AP98 38fr shown   1.50   .75
C181 AP98 51fr Kagu   2.00   .85
See Nos. C188B-C188C.

50th Anniv. of Paris-Noumea
Flight — AP99

250fr, Pilots, map, plane.

1982, Apr. 5   Engr.   *Perf. 13*
C182 AP99 250fr multi   7.00 3.50

Scouting
Year — AP100

1982, Apr. 21   Photo.   *Perf. 13½x13*
C183 AP100 40fr multi   1.50   .80

PHILEXFRANCE '82 Intl. Stamp
Show, Paris, June 11-21 — AP101

1982, May 12   Engr.   *Perf. 13*
C184 AP101 150fr multi   3.25 2.00

1982 World
Cup — AP102

1982, June 9   Photo.   *Perf. 13x13½*
C185 AP102 74fr multi   2.10 1.00

French Overseas
Possessions
Week, Sept. 18-
25 — AP103

100fr, Map, kagu, citizens.

1982, Sept. 17   *Perf. 13x12½*
C186 AP103 100fr multicolored   2.75 1.00

Gypsum, Poya
Mines — AP104

59fr, Silica gel, Kone mine.

1983, Jan. 15   Photo.   *Perf. 13x13½*
C187 AP104 44fr shown   2.50 1.10
C188 AP104 59fr multicolored   3.50 1.40

World Communications
Year — AP104a

Design: WCY emblem, map, globe.

1983, Mar. 9   Litho.   *Perf. 13*
C188A AP104a 170fr multi   4.00 1.50

Aircraft Type of 1982

46fr, Pou-du-Ciel. 61fr, L'Aiglon Caudron.

1983, July 6   Engr.   *Perf. 13*
C188B AP98 46fr multi   1.50   .75
C188C AP98 61fr multi   2.50 1.25

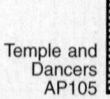

Temple and
Dancers
AP105

1983, July 20   Litho.   *Perf. 12½x12*
C189 AP105 47fr multi   1.50   .80
BANGKOK '83 Intl. Stamp Show, Aug. 4-13.

Oueholle
Tribe, Straw
Hut — AP106

1983, Sept. 7   Litho.   *Perf. 13*
C190 AP106 76fr multi   2.25 1.10

Loyalty Islander
by the Shore, by
R.
Mascart — AP107

Paintings: 350fr, The Guitarist from Mare
Island, by P. Neilly.

1983, Dec. 7   Photo.   *Perf. 13*
C191 AP107 100fr multi   3.75 1.75
C192 AP107 350fr multi   9.00 5.25

Noumea
Aquarium
Fish — AP108

46fr, Amphiprion clarkii. 61fr, Centropyge
bicolor.

1984, Mar. 7   Photo.   *Perf. 13*
C193 AP108 46fr multi   2.25   .90
C194 AP108 61fr multi   2.75 1.25

Local Plants — AP109

51fr, Araucaria columnaris. 67fr, Pritchardi-
opsis jeanneneyi.

1984, Apr. 25   Litho.   *Perf. 12½x13*
C195 AP109 51fr multi   2.00   .90
C196 AP109 67fr multi   2.75 1.25

1984
Summer
Olympics
AP110

1984, June 20   Photo.   *Perf. 13½x13*
C197 AP110 50fr Swimming   1.75 1.10
C198 AP110 83fr Wind surfing   3.50 1.60
C199 AP110 200fr Running   6.00 2.75
    Nos. C197-C199 (3)   11.25 5.45

Ausipex '84 — AP111

1984, Sept. 21   Engr.   *Perf. 13*
C200 AP111 150fr Exhibition Hall 4.50 2.25
  a.   Souvenir sheet   6.00 6.00
Se-tenant with label showing exhibition
emblem. No. C200a contains No. C200 in
changed colors.

Army Day — AP112

1984, Oct. 27   Litho.   *Perf. 13½x13*
C201 AP112 51fr multi   1.60 1.00

Woman
Fishing for
Crabs, by
Mme.
Bonnet de
Larbogne
AP113

Painting: 300fr, Cook Discovering New Caledonia, by Pilioko.

1984, Nov. 8   Litho.   *Perf. 13x12½*
C202 AP113 120fr multi   3.50 1.75
C203 AP113 300fr multi   8.00 4.50
See Nos. 605-606.

Transpac Dragon
Rapide,
Map — AP114

1985, Oct. 2   Litho.   *Perf. 13½*
C204 AP114 80fr multi   2.50 1.25
Internal air services, 30th anniv.

UN, 40th
Anniv. — AP115

Perf. 12½x13
1985, Oct. 25   Wmk. 385
C205 AP115 250fr multi   5.50 2.00

Jules Garnier
High
School — AP116

1985, Nov. 13   Unwmk.   *Perf. 13*
C206 AP116 400fr multi   10.00 4.25

Paris-Noumea
Scheduled Flights,
30th Anniv. — AP117

1986, Jan. 6
C207 AP117 72fr multi   2.25 1.25

Nou Island
Livestock
Warehouse
AP118

1986, June 14   Engr.   *Perf. 13*
C208 AP118 230fr Prus bl, sep &
              brn   5.25 2.75

ATR-42 Inaugural
Service — AP119

1986, Aug. 13   Litho.   *Perf. 12½x13*
C209 AP119 18fr multi   .90   .75

STOCKHOLMIA
'86 — AP120

1986, Aug. 29   Engr.   Perf. 13
C210 AP120 108fr No. 1   3.00 1.50

Natl. Assoc. of
Amateur Radio
Operators, 25th
Anniv. — AP121

1987, Jan. 7   Litho.   Perf. 12½
C211 AP121 64fr multi   1.75 .85

Nature
Conservation,
Fight Noise
Pollution
AP122

1987, Mar. 25   Litho.   Perf. 13x12½
C212 AP122 150fr multi   4.00 1.75

French Cricket
Federation
AP123

1987, Nov. 25   Litho.   Perf. 12½
C213 AP123 94fr multi   2.50 1.75

Arms Type of 1984
1988, Jan. 13   Perf. 12½x13
C214 A132 76fr Dumbea   2.50 1.00

Rotary Intl.
Anti-Polio
Campaign
AP124

1988, Oct. 26   Litho.   Perf. 13½
C215 AP124 220fr multi   5.25 2.75

Bamboo Type of 1989
Litho. & Engr.
1989, Sept. 27   Perf. 12½x13
C216 A187 44fr multi   1.25 .65

De Gaulle's Call
For French
Resistance, 50th
Anniv. — AP125

1990, June 20   Litho.   Perf. 12½
C217 AP125 160fr multicolored 4.00 1.75

Military Cemetery,
New Zealand —
AP126

Auckland 1990: #C219, Brigadier William
Walter Dove.

1990, Aug. 24   Perf. 13
C218 AP126 80fr multi   2.00 1.00
C219 AP126 80fr multi   2.00 1.00
  a.   Pair, #C218-C219 + label 4.50 4.50

Souvenir Sheet

New
Zealand
1990
AP126a

1990, Aug. 25   Litho.   Perf. 13x12½
C219B AP126a 150fr multi   6.00 5.00

Crustaceans — AP127

30fr, Munidopsis sp. Orstom. 60fr, Lyreidius
tridentatus.

1990, Oct. 17   Litho.   Perf. 12½x13
C220 AP127 30fr multi   1.00 .55
C221 AP127 60fr multi   2.00 1.10

30th South
Pacific
Conference
AP128

1990, Oct. 29   Litho.   Perf. 13
C222 AP128 85fr multicolored 2.10 1.10

Gen. Charles de
Gaulle (1890-
1970) — AP129

1990, Nov. 21   Engr.   Perf. 13
C223 AP129 410fr dk blue   9.00 3.50

Scenic
Views
AP130

1991, Feb. 13   Litho.   Perf. 13
C224 AP130 36fr Fayawa-Ouvea
             Bay   .90 .50
C225 AP130 90fr shown   2.40 1.25
       See No. C246.

New
Caledonian
Cricket
Players by
Marcel
Moutouh
AP131

Design: 435fr, Saint Louis by Janine Goetz.

1991, Dec. 18   Perf. 13x12½
C226 AP131 130fr multicolored 3.00 2.00
C227 AP131 435fr multicolored 10.00 5.00
       See Nos. C236, C242, C260.

Blue River Nature Park
AP132

1992, Feb. 6   Litho.   Perf. 12½
C228 AP132 400fr multicolored 9.25 4.75
  a.   Souvenir sheet of 1   10.50 10.50
No. C228a sold for 450fr and was issued
2/5/92.

Native
Pottery — AP133

Photo. & Engr.
1992, Apr. 9   Perf. 12½x13
C229 AP133 25fr black & orange .75 .30

Expo '92,
Seville — AP134

1992, Apr. 25   Litho.   Perf. 13
C230 AP134 10fr multicolored   .35 .25

Discovery of
America, 500th
Anniv. — AP135

#C234: a, Erik the Red, Viking longship. b,
Columbus, coat of arms. c, Amerigo Vespucci.

1992, May 22   Perf. 13½
C231 AP135 80fr Pinta   2.00 1.00
C232 AP135 80fr Santa Maria   2.00 1.00
C233 AP135 80fr Nina   2.00 1.00
  a.   Strip of 3, #C231-C233 6.00 6.00
  b.   Bklt. pane of 3, #C231-
         C233   10.00 10.00

Souvenir Sheet
Perf. 12½
C234 AP135 110fr Sheet of 3,
             #a.-c.   10.00 10.00
World Columbian Stamp Expo '92, Chicago.
No. C234 sold for 360fr.

1992
Summer
Olympics,
Barcelona
AP136

260fr, Synchronized swimming.

1992, July 25   Perf. 13
C235 AP136 260fr multi   6.75 3.25

Painters of the Pacific Type of 1991
Design: 205fr, Wahpa, by Paul Mascart

1992, Sept. 28   Litho.   Perf. 12½x13
C236 AP131 205fr multicolored 5.00 2.50

Australian
Bouvier — AP138

1992, Oct. 4   Perf. 12
C237 AP138 175fr multicolored 5.25 2.40

Exploration of New Caledonian Coast
by Chevalier d'Entrecasteaux,
Bicent. — AP139

1992, Nov. 18   Engr.   Perf. 13
C238 AP139 110fr bl grn, ocher
             & olive grn   3.00 1.25

Shells — AP140

30fr, Amalda fuscolingua. 50fr, Cassis
abbotti.

1992, Nov. 26   Litho.   Perf. 13½x13
C239 AP140 30fr multi   1.00 .35
C240 AP140 50fr multi   1.50 .75
The vignettes on Nos. C239-C240 were
applied by a thermographic process, produc-
ing a shiny, raised effect.

AP141

Comic Strip Characters from "La Brousse
en Folie," by Bernard Berger: a, Dede. b.
Torton Marcel in Mimine II. c, Tathan. d,
Joinville.

1992, Dec. 9   Litho.   Perf. 13½
C241 AP141 80fr Strip of 4, #a.-
             d.   8.50 8.50

Painters of the Pacific Type of 1991
Design: 150fr, Noumea, 1890, by Gaston
Roullet (1847-1925).

1993, Mar. 25   Litho.   Perf. 13x12½
C242 AP131 150fr multicolored 3.50 1.75

Extraction of Attar from Niaouli
Flowers (Melaleuca Quinquenervia),
Cent. — AP142

1993, Apr. 28   Perf. 13
C243 AP142 85fr multicolored 2.00 1.00

Nicolaus
Copernicus
(1473-1543)
AP143

1993, May 5   Engr.   Perf. 13
C244 AP143 110fr multicolored 3.00 1.25
       Polska '93.

Noumea Temple,
Cent. — AP144

1993, June 16   Litho.   Perf. 12½x13
C245 AP144 400fr multicolored 8.00 4.50

Scenic Views Type of 1991

1993, July 8   Litho.   *Perf. 13*
C246 AP130 85fr Malabou   2.00 1.00

Little Train
of Thio
AP145

1993, July 24   Engr.   *Perf. 13*
C247 AP145 115fr multicolored   3.00 1.40

AP146

1993, Aug. 18   Litho.
C248 AP146 100fr multicolored   2.50 1.10
Henri Rochefort (1831-1913), writer.

Bangkok '93 — AP147

No. C249, Vanda coerulea. No. C250,
Megastylis paradoxa. 140fr, Royal Palace,
Bangkok, horiz.

1993, Oct. 1   *Perf. 13½*
C249 AP147 30fr multicolored   1.00 .35
C250 AP147 30fr multicolored   1.00 .35
Souvenir Sheet
Perf. 13
C251 AP147 140fr multicolored   3.50 3.50
No. C251 contains one 52x40mm stamp.

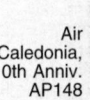

Air
Caledonia,
10th Anniv.
AP148

1993, Oct. 9   *Perf. 13*
C252 AP148 85fr multicolored   2.25 1.10

New Caledonia-Australia Telephone
Cable, Cent. — AP149

1993, Oct. 15   Engr.   *Perf. 13x12½*
C253 AP149 200fr blue & black   4.75 2.25

Oxpleurodon
Orbiculatus
AP150

1993, Oct. 15   Litho.   *Perf. 13½*
C254 AP150 250fr multicolored   6.00 2.75
  Portions of the design on No. C254 were
applied by a thermographic process producing
a shiny, raised effect.

Tontouta
Airport,
Noumea,
25th Anniv.
AP151

1993, Nov. 29   Litho.   *Perf. 13*
C255 AP151 90fr multicolored   2.25 1.00

Christmas
AP152

1993, Dec. 9   Litho.
C256 AP152 120fr multicolored   3.00 1.25
  Portions of the design on No. C256 were
applied by a thermographic process producing
a shiny, raised effect.

New Year 1994
(Year of the
Dog) — AP153

1994, Feb. 18   Litho.   *Perf. 13*
C257 AP153 60fr multicolored   1.75 .85
Hong Kong '94.

First Airbus A340 Flight, Paris-
Noumea — AP154

1994, Mar. 31   Litho.   *Die Cut 8*
Self-Adhesive
C258 AP154 90fr multicolored   2.75 1.25

South
Pacific
Geography
Day
AP155

1994, May 10   Litho.   *Perf. 13*
C259 AP155 70fr multicolored   1.75 .85
See Wallis and Futuna No. C177.

Painters of the Pacific Type of 1991
Design: 120fr, Legende du Poulpe, by
Micheline Neporon.

1994, June 24   Litho.   *Perf. 13*
C260 AP131 120fr multicolored   2.75 1.40

Pottery, Museum of
Noumea — AP156

1994, July 6   Litho.   *Perf. 12½x13*
C261 AP156 95fr multicolored   2.25 1.10

1994 World Cup Soccer
Championships, U.S. — AP156a

1994, July 12   Litho.   *Perf. 13*
C261A AP156a 105fr multicolored 2.50 1.50

Intl. Year of the
Family — AP157

PHILAKOREA
'94 — AP158

Korean cuisine: No. C263a, Rice, celery,
carrots, peppers. b, Lettuce, cabbage, garlic.
c, Onions. d, Shrimp, oysters.

1994, Aug. 17   *Perf. 13½x13*
C262 AP157 60fr multicolored   2.25 1.00
Souvenir Sheet
Perf. 12½
C263   Sheet of 4   4.75 4.75
  a.-d. AP158 35fr any single   1.10 1.00

Research
Ship
Atalante
AP159

1994, Aug. 26   *Perf. 13*
C264 AP159 120fr multicolored   2.75 1.50

Masons in
New
Caledonia,
125th Anniv.
AP160

1994, Sept. 16   *Perf. 13*
C265 AP160 350fr multicolored   8.00 3.75

Participation
in First
European
Stamp
Show
AP161

1994, Oct. 15   Litho.   *Perf. 13*
C266 AP161 90fr Island   2.00 1.00
C267 AP161 90fr Herding cattle   2.00 1.00
  a.   Pair, #C266-C267 + label 4.50 4.50

ORSTOM,
50th Anniv.
AP162

1994, Nov. 14   Photo.   *Perf. 13*
C268 AP162 95fr multicolored   2.50 1.25

Tiebaghi
Mine
AP163

1994, Nov. 24   Litho.
C269 AP163 90fr multicolored   2.75 1.00

South Pacific
Tourism
Year — AP164

1995, Mar. 15   Litho.   *Perf. 13½*
C270 AP164 90fr multicolored   3.00 1.00

35th South
Pacific
Conference,
Noumea
AP165

1995, Oct. 25   Litho.   *Perf. 13*
C271 AP165 500fr multicolored   9.00 5.00

Kanak
Dances — AP166

1995, Dec. 8   Litho.   *Perf. 13x13½*
C272 AP166 95fr Ouaré   2.25 1.00
C273 AP166 100fr Pothé   2.50 1.00

Mekosuchus
Inexpactatus
AP167

1996, Feb. 23   Litho.   *Perf. 13x13½*
C274 AP167 125fr multicolored   2.75 1.50

Indonesian
Centenary — AP168

1996, July 20
C275 AP168 130fr multicolored   3.00 3.00

Louis Brauquier (1900-
76), Writer — AP169

1996, Aug. 7   Litho.   *Perf. 12½*
C276 AP169 95fr multicolored   2.25 1.10

Ile Nou Ground
Station, 20th
Anniv. — AP170

125fr, Guglielmo Marconi, telegraph wires.

1996, Sept. 26   Litho.   *Perf. 13*
C277 AP170 95f multicolored   2.25 1.10
C278 AP170 125fr multicolored   2.75 1.50
  a.   Pair, #C277-C278 + label 5.00 5.00
Radio, cent. (#C278).

Regional Views AP171

1996, Nov. 7   Litho.   Perf. 13
C279 AP171 95fr Great reef   2.25 1.10
C280 AP171 95fr Mount Koghi   2.25 1.10
 a.   Pair, #C279-C280 + label   4.75 4.75

50th Autumn Philatelic Salon.

Christmas — AP172

1996, Nov. 25   Perf. 13½x13
C281 AP172 95fr multicolored   2.25 1.10

Horned Turtle Meiolania AP173

1997, Jan. 8   Litho.   Perf. 13
C282 AP173 95fr multicolored   2.25 1.25

Portions of the design were applied by a thermographic process producing a shiny, raised effect.

South Pacific Commission, 50th Anniv. — AP174

1997, Feb. 7   Litho.   Perf. 13X13½
C283 AP174 100fr multicolored   2.25 1.10

Hong Kong '97 — AP175

New Year 1997 (Year of the Ox) — #C285: a, Water buffalo pulling plow. b, Cattle in pasture.

1997, Feb. 12   Perf. 13
C284 AP175 95fr multicolored   2.50 1.10
Sheet of 2
Perf. 13x13½
C285 AP175 75fr #a.-b.   3.50 3.25

No. C285 contains two 40x30mm stamps.

Melanesian Pottery — AP176

Lapita pottery c. 1200-1000 B.C.: No. C286, With stylized faces. No. C287, With labyrinth pattern.

1997, May 14   Litho.   Perf. 13
C286 AP176 95fr multicolored   2.25 2.25
C287 AP176 95fr multicolored   2.25 2.25

TRAPAS, French Airlines in the South Pacific, 1947-50 AP177

Airplane, emblem, map showing: No. C288, Australia, New Herbrides, Suva, Tahiti, New Zealand. No. C289, Koumac, Poindimie, Noumea, Isle of Pines.

Photo. & Engr.   Perf. 13
1997, Aug. 12
C288 AP177 95fr multicolored   2.10 2.10
C289 AP177 95fr multicolored   2.10 2.10
 a.   Pair, #C288-C289   4.25 4.25

Regular Paris-Noumea Air Service, 50th Anniv. — AP178

1999, Sept. 29 Photo. Perf. 13x12½
C290 AP178 100fr multicolored   2.50 2.00

Inauguration of Noumea-Osaka Air Service — AP179

2001, Oct. 11   Litho.   Perf. 13
C291 AP179 110fr multi   2.25 2.25

AIR POST SEMI-POSTAL STAMPS

French Revolution Issue
Common Design Type
Unwmk.
1939, July 5   Photo.   Perf. 13
Name and Value Typo. in Orange
CB1 CD83 4.50fr + 4fr brn blk 34.00 34.00

Father & Child — SPAP1

1942, June 22   Engr.   Perf. 13
CB2 SPAP1 1.50fr + 3.50fr green   2.25
CB3 SPAP1 2fr + 6fr yel brn   2.25

Native children's welfare fund.
Nos. CB2-CB3 were issued by the Vichy government in France, but were not placed on sale in New Caledonia.

Colonial Education Fund
Common Design Type
1942, June 22
CB4 CD86a 1.20fr + 1.80fr blue
                        & red   2.25

No. CB4 was issued by the Vichy government in France, but was not placed on sale in New Caledonia.

POSTAGE DUE STAMPS

For a short time in 1894, 5, 10, 15, 20, 25 and 30c postage stamps (Nos. 43, 45, 47, 49, 50 and 52) were overprinted with a "T" in an inverted triangle and used as Postage Due stamps.

French Colonies Postage Due Stamps Overprinted in Carmine, Blue or Silver

1903   Unwmk.   Imperf.
J1 D1 5c blue (C)   3.75   3.75
J2 D1 10c brown (C)   11.50   11.50
J3 D1 15c yel grn (C)   22.50   11.50
J4 D1 30c carmine (Bl)   19.00   15.00
J5 D1 50c violet (Bl)   65.00   22.50
J6 D1 60c brn, buff (Bl)   260.00   95.00
J7 D1 1fr rose, buff (S)   42.50   26.00
 b.   Double overprint   225.00 225.00
J8 D1 2fr red brn (Bl)   1,300.   1,300.
    Nos. J1-J8 (8)   1,724.   1,485.

Nos. J1 to J8 are known with the "I" in "TENAIRE" missing.
Fifty years of French occupation.

Men Poling Boat — D2

1906   Typo.   Perf. 13½x14
J9 D2 5c ultra   .70   .75
J10 D2 10c vio brn, buff   .70   .75
J11 D2 15c greenish blue   1.00   1.10
J12 D2 20c blk, yellow   1.00   1.10
J13 D2 30c carmine   1.35   1.50
J14 D2 50c ultra, cream   2.25   2.25
J15 D2 60c olive brn, azure   1.50   1.90
J16 D2 1fr blue green   2.25   2.75
    Nos. J9-J16 (8)   10.75 12.10

Type of 1906 Issue Surcharged

1926-27
J17 D2 2fr on 1fr vio   5.75   6.25
J18 D2 3fr on 1fr org brn   5.75   6.25

Malayan Sambar — D3

1928   Typo.
J19 D3 2c sl bl & dp brn   .30   .40
J20 D3 4c brn red & bl grn   .45   .60
J21 D3 5c red org & bl blk   .60   .75
J22 D3 10c brt rose & Prus bl   .60   .75
J23 D3 15c dp gray grn &
               scar   .60   .75
J24 D3 20c mar & ol grn   1.05   1.10
J25 D3 25c bis brn & sl bl   .75   .90
J26 D3 30c bl grn & ol grn   1.05   1.10
J27 D3 50c lt brn & dk red   1.35   1.50
J28 D3 60c mag & brt rose   1.35   1.50
J29 D3 1fr dl bl & Prus bl   1.75   1.90
J30 D3 2fr dk red & ol grn   1.90   2.25
J31 D3 3fr violet & brn   2.75   3.00
    Nos. J19-J31 (13)   14.50 16.50

Catalogue values for unused stamps in this section, from this point to the end of the section, are for Never Hinged items.

D4

1948   Unwmk.   Photo.   Perf. 13
J32 D4 10c violet   .30   .30
J33 D4 30c brown   .40   .40
J34 D4 50c blue green   .60   .60
J35 D4 1fr orange   .60   .60
J36 D4 2fr red violet   .75   .75
J37 D4 3fr red brown   .75   .75
J38 D4 4fr dull blue   1.10   1.10
J39 D4 5fr henna brown   1.10   1.10
J40 D4 10fr slate green   1.75   1.75
J41 D4 20fr violet blue   2.40   2.40
    Nos. J32-J41 (10)   9.75   9.75

Bat — D5

1983   Litho.   Perf. 13
J42 D5 1fr multi   .30   .25
J43 D5 2fr multi   .30   .30
J44 D5 3fr multi   .30   .30
J45 D5 4fr multi   .45   .45
J46 D5 5fr multi   .55   .55
J47 D5 10fr multi   .75   .75
J48 D5 20fr multi   .90   .90
J49 D5 40fr multi   1.40   1.40
J50 D5 50fr multi   1.75   1.75
    Nos. J42-J50 (9)   6.70   6.65

For overprint see No. 696.

MILITARY STAMPS

Stamps of the above types, although issued by officials, were unauthorized and practically a private speculation.

OFFICIAL STAMPS

Catalogue values for unused stamps in this section are for Never Hinged items.

Ancestor Pole — O1

Various carved ancestor poles.

1959   Unwmk.   Typo.   Perf. 14x13
O1 O1 1fr org yel   .45   .45
O2 O1 3fr lt bl grn   .45   .45
O3 O1 4fr purple   .60   .60
O4 O1 5fr ultra   .75   .75
O5 O1 9fr black   1.00   1.00
O6 O1 10fr brt vio   1.40   1.40
O7 O1 13fr yel grn   1.50   1.50
O8 O1 15fr lt bl   2.00   2.00
O9 O1 24fr red lilac   2.40   2.40
O10 O1 26fr deep org   2.75   2.75
O11 O1 50fr green   5.75   5.75
O12 O1 100fr chocolate   11.00 11.00
O13 O1 200fr red   20.00 20.00
    Nos. O1-O13 (13)   50.05 50.05

Carved Wooden Pillow — O2

Vignette: Green, Red Brown (2, 29, 31, 35, 38, 65, 76fr), Brown (40fr), Blue (58fr)

1973-87   Photo.   Perf. 13
O14 O2 1fr yellow   .30   .30
O14A O2 2fr green ('87)   .30   .25
O15 O2 3fr tan   .45   .45
O16 O2 4fr pale violet   .60   .60
O17 O2 5fr lilac rose   .60   .60
O18 O2 9fr light blue   1.00   1.00
O19 O2 10fr orange   1.10   1.10
O20 O2 11fr bright lilac ('76) .60   .60
O21 O2 12fr bl grn ('73)   1.25   1.25
O22 O2 15fr green ('76)   .70   .70
O23 O2 20fr rose ('76)   .75   .75
O24 O2 23fr red ('80)   1.00   1.00
O25 O2 24fr Prus bl ('76)   1.00   1.00
O25A O2 25fr gray ('81)   1.30   1.30
O26 O2 26fr yellow ('76)   1.05   1.05
O26A O2 29fr dl grn ('83)   1.30   1.30
O26B O2 31fr yellow ('82)   1.40   1.40
O26C O2 35fr yellow ('84)   1.50   1.50
O27 O2 36fr dp lil rose ('76) 1.30   1.30
O27A O2 38fr tan   1.50   1.50
O27B O2 40fr blue ('87)   1.30   1.30
O28 O2 42fr bister ('76)   1.50   1.50
O29 O2 50fr blue ('76)   1.50   1.50
O29A O2 58fr blue grn ('87)   1.75   1.75
O29B O2 65fr lilac ('84)   1.90   1.90
O29C O2 76fr brt yel ('87)   2.25   2.25
O30 O2 100fr red ('76)   2.75   2.75
O31 O2 200fr orange ('76)   5.00   5.00
    Nos. O14-O31 (28)   36.95 36.90

PARCEL POST STAMPS

Type of Regular Issue of 1905-28 Srchd. or Ovptd.

1926		**Unwmk.**		**Perf. 14x13½**	
Q1	A18	50c on 5fr olive, *lav*		1.30	*1.90*
Q2	A18	1fr deep blue		1.75	*2.75*
Q3	A18	2fr car, *bluish*		2.10	*3.00*
		Nos. Q1-Q3 (3)		5.15	*7.65*

Regular Issue of 1928 Overprinted

1930					
Q4	A20	50c violet & brown		1.30	*1.90*
Q5	A21	1fr dp ol & sal red		1.75	*2.75*
Q6	A21	2fr red org & brn		2.10	*3.00*
		Nos. Q4-Q6 (3)		5.15	7.65

NEW GUINEA

'nü 'gi-nē

LOCATION — On an island of the same name in the South Pacific Ocean, north of Australia.

GOVT. — Mandate administered by Australia

AREA — 93,000 sq. mi.

POP. — 675,369 (1940)

CAPITAL — Rabaul

The territory occupies the northeastern part of the island and includes New Britain and other nearby islands. It was formerly a German possession and should not be confused with British New Guinea (Papua) which is in the southeastern part of the same island, nor Netherlands New Guinea. For previous issues see German New Guinea, New Britain, North West Pacific Islands. Issues for 1952 and later are listed under Papua.

12 Pence = 1 Shilling
20 Shillings = 1 Pound

Native Huts — A1

1925-28		**Engr.**		**Perf. 11**	
1	A1	½p orange		2.75	8.00
2	A1	1p yellow green		2.75	6.25
3	A1	1½p vermilion ('26)		3.75	3.00
4	A1	2p claret		7.25	5.00
5	A1	3p deep blue		8.00	4.50
6	A1	4p olive green		15.00	26.00
7	A1	6p yel bister ('28)		6.50	55.00
a.		6p light brown		22.50	55.00
b.		6p olive bister ('27)		15.00	52.50
8	A1	9p deep violet		15.00	55.00
9	A1	1sh gray green		17.50	30.00
10	A1	2sh red brown		35.00	55.00
11	A1	5sh olive bister		55.00	75.00
12	A1	10sh dull rose		120.00	200.00
13	A1	£1 grnsh gray		210.00	325.00
		Nos. 1-13 (13)		498.50	842.75

For overprints see Nos. C1-C13, O1-O9.

Bird of Paradise — A2

1931, Aug. 2					
18	A2	1p light green		4.50	7.50
19	A2	1½p red		5.75	11.50
20	A2	2p violet brown		5.75	2.50
21	A2	3p deep blue		5.75	5.50
22	A2	4p olive green		7.50	32.50
23	A2	5p slate green		9.00	24.00
24	A2	6p bister		8.00	25.00
25	A2	9p dull violet		9.50	21.00
26	A2	1sh bluish gray		7.00	17.00
27	A2	2sh red brown		11.50	50.00
28	A2	5sh olive brown		47.50	62.50
29	A2	10sh rose red		120.00	150.00
30	A2	£1 gray		250.00	300.00
		Nos. 18-30 (13)		491.75	709.00

10th anniversary of Australian Mandate. For overprints see #C14-C27, O12-O22.

Type of 1931 without date scrolls

A2a

1932-34				**Perf. 11**	
31	A2a	1p light green		8.00	.25
32	A2a	1½p violet brown		8.00	20.00
33	A2a	2p red		5.50	.25
34	A2a	2½p dp grn ('34)		7.50	27.50
35	A2a	3p gray blue		8.00	1.25
36	A2a	3½p magenta ('34)		15.00	22.50
37	A2a	4p olive green		7.00	7.00
38	A2a	5p slate green		7.25	.80
39	A2a	6p bister		7.50	5.50
40	A2a	9p dull violet		11.00	27.50
41	A2a	1sh bluish gray		7.00	11.50
42	A2a	2sh brown lake		5.00	19.00
43	A2a	5sh olive brown		32.50	50.00
44	A2a	10sh rose red		60.00	80.00
45	A2a	£1 gray		120.00	110.00
		Nos. 31-45 (15)		309.25	383.05

For overprints see #46-47, C28-C43, O23-O35. See footnote following C43.

Silver Jubilee Issue

Stamps of 1932-34 Overprinted

1935, June 27				**Glazed Paper**	
46	A2	1p green		1.10	.85
47	A2	2p red		3.25	.85
		Set, never hinged		6.50	

King George VI — A3

1937, May 18				**Engr.**	
48	A3	2p salmon rose		.30	1.60
49	A3	3p blue		.30	1.90
50	A3	5p green		.35	1.90
51	A3	1sh brown violet		.45	2.50
		Nos. 48-51 (4)		1.40	7.90
		Set, never hinged		2.50	

Coronation of George VI and Queen Elizabeth.

AIR POST STAMPS

Regular Issues of 1925-28 Overprinted

1931, June				**Perf. 11**	
C1	A1	½p orange		1.75	9.50
C2	A1	1p yellow green		1.75	5.75
C3	A1	1½p vermilion		1.40	8.50
C4	A1	2p claret		1.40	8.00
C5	A1	3p deep blue		2.00	15.00
C6	A1	4p olive green		1.40	10.00
C7	A1	6p light brown		2.00	16.00
C8	A1	9p deep violet		3.50	19.00
C9	A1	1sh gray green		3.50	19.00
C10	A1	2sh red brown		8.00	50.00
C11	A1	5sh ol bister		22.50	75.00
C12	A1	10sh light red		92.50	120.00
C13	A1	£1 grnsh gray		170.00	290.00
		Nos. C1-C13 (13)		311.70	645.75

Type of Regular Issue of 1931 and Nos. 18-30 Overprinted

1931, Aug.					
C14	A2	½p orange		3.75	3.75
C15	A2	1p light green		4.50	7.50
C16	A2	1½p red		4.25	11.50
C17	A2	2p violet brown		4.25	3.50
C18	A2	3p deep blue		7.00	7.00
C19	A2	4p olive green		7.00	7.00
C20	A2	5p slate green		7.00	12.50
C21	A2	6p bister		8.00	30.00
C22	A2	9p dull violet		9.00	17.00
C23	A2	1sh bluish gray		8.50	17.00
C24	A2	2sh red brown		18.00	55.00
C25	A2	5sh olive brown		47.50	80.00
C26	A2	10sh rose red		87.50	140.00
C27	A2	£1 gray		150.00	290.00
		Nos. C14-C27 (14)		366.25	681.75

10th anniversary of Australian Mandate.

Same Overprint on Type of Regular Issue of 1932-34 and Nos. 31-45

1932-34				**Perf. 11**	
C28	A2	½p orange		.65	1.75
C29	A2	1p light green		1.40	2.50
C30	A2	1½p violet brown		2.00	11.50
C31	A2	2p red		2.00	.35
C32	A2	2½p dp grn ('34)		8.75	2.75
C33	A2	3p gray blue		3.75	3.50
C34	A2	3½p mag ('34)		5.25	3.75
C35	A2	4p olive green		5.00	11.50
C36	A2	5p slate green		8.00	8.50
C37	A2	6p bister		5.00	17.00
C38	A2	9p dull violet		7.00	10.00
C39	A2	1sh bluish gray		7.00	12.50
C40	A2	2sh red brown		14.00	55.00
C41	A2	5sh olive brown		55.00	65.00
C42	A2	10sh rose red		100.00	92.50
C43	A2	£1 gray		87.50	62.50
		Nos. C28-C43 (16)		312.30	360.60

No. C28 exists without overprint, but is believed not to have been issued in this condition. Value $200.

Plane over Bulolo Goldfield — AP1

1935, May 1			**Engr.**	**Unwmk.**	
C44	AP1	£2 violet		350.00	160.00
C45	AP1	£5 green		750.00	550.00

AP2

1939, Mar. 1					
C46	AP2	½p orange		2.50	9.25
C47	AP2	1p green		2.00	7.00
C48	AP2	1½p vio brown		2.50	19.00
C49	AP2	2p red orange		5.00	4.00
C50	AP2	3p dark blue		11.00	21.00
C51	AP2	4p ol bister		9.00	9.75
C52	AP2	5p slate grn		8.50	4.50
C53	AP2	6p bister brn		25.00	30.00
C54	AP2	9p dl violet		27.50	45.00
C55	AP2	1sh sage grn		27.50	32.50
C56	AP2	2sh car lake		50.00	75.00
C57	AP2	5sh ol brown		110.00	160.00
C58	AP2	10sh rose red		350.00	425.00
C59	AP2	£1 grnsh gray		90.00	150.00
		Nos. C46-C59 (14)		720.50	990.00
		Set, never hinged		1,200.	

OFFICIAL STAMPS

Regular Issue of 1925 Overprinted

1925-29		**Unwmk.**		**Perf. 11**	
O1	A1	1p yellow green		5.00	5.00
O2	A1	1½p vermilion ('29)		6.25	19.00
O3	A1	2p claret		3.25	4.25
O4	A1	3p deep blue		6.00	10.00
O5	A1	4p olive green		5.00	9.75
O6	A1	6p yel bister ('29)		8.00	40.00
a.		6p olive bister		29.00	40.00
O7	A1	9p deep violet		4.50	40.00
O8	A1	1sh gray green		6.25	40.00
O9	A1	2sh red brown		42.50	70.00
		Nos. O1-O9 (9)		86.75	238.00

Nos. 18-28 Overprinted

1931, Aug. 2					
O12	A2	1p light green		12.00	14.00
O13	A2	1½p red		12.00	13.50
O14	A2	2p violet brown		12.00	8.00
O15	A2	3p deep blue		7.50	7.00
O16	A2	4p olive green		7.00	9.75
O17	A2	5p slate green		11.50	13.50
O18	A2	6p bister		16.00	19.00
O19	A2	9p dull violet		18.00	32.50
O20	A2	1sh bluish gray		18.00	32.50
O21	A2	2sh red brown		45.00	80.00
O22	A2	5sh olive brown		110.00	200.00
		Nos. O12-O22 (11)		269.00	429.75

10th anniversary of Australian Mandate.

Same Overprint on Nos. 31-43

1932-34					
O23	A2	1p light green		19.00	20.00
O24	A2	1½p violet brown		19.00	20.00
O25	A2	2p red		19.50	3.75
O26	A2	2½p dp green ('34)		10.00	12.50
O27	A2	3p gray blue		11.50	42.50
O28	A2	3½p magenta ('34)		8.00	10.00
O29	A2	4p olive green		21.00	32.50
O30	A2	5p slate green		10.00	30.00
O31	A2	6p bister		25.00	55.00
O32	A2	9p dull violet		16.00	50.00
O33	A2	1sh bluish gray		17.50	32.50
O34	A2	2sh red brown		40.00	85.00
O35	A2	5sh olive brown		140.00	190.00
		Nos. O23-O35 (13)		356.50	583.75

NEW HEBRIDES, BRITISH

'nü 'he-brə-ˌdēz

LOCATION — A group of islands in the South Pacific Ocean northeast of New Caledonia

GOVT. — Condominium under the joint administration of Great Britain and France

AREA — 5,790 sq. mi.

POP. — 100,000 (est. 1976)

CAPITAL — Vila (Port-Vila)

Stamps were issued by both Great Britain and France. In 1911 a joint issue bore the coats of arms of both countries. The British stamps bore the arms of Great Britain and the value in British currency on the right and the French arms and value at the left. On the French stamps the positions were reversed. After World War II when the franc dropped in value, both series were sold for their value in francs. New Hebrides became the independent state of Vanuatu in 1980.

12 Pence = 1 Shilling
100 Centimes = 1 Franc
100 Centimes = 1 New Hebrides Franc (FNH) (1977)

French issues (inscribed "Nouvelles Hebrides") follow after No. J20.

Catalogue values for unused stamps in this country are for Never Hinged items, beginning with Scott 62 in the regular postage section, Scott J11 in the postage due section.

British Issues

Stamps of Fiji, 1903- 06, Overprinted

		1908-09	Wmk. 2	Perf. 14

Colored Bar Covers "FIJI" on #2-6, 9

1	A22	½p grn & pale grn ('09)	60.00	87.50
2	A22	2p vio & orange	1.50	1.75
3	A22	2½p vio & ultra, bl	1.50	1.75
4	A22	5p vio & green	1.60	3.25
5	A22	6p vio & car rose	3.75	3.50
6	A22	1sh grn & car rose	145.00	300.00
		Nos. 1-6 (6)	213.35	397.75

Wmk. Multiple Crown and CA (3)

7	A22	½p gray green	1.00	5.00
8	A22	1p carmine	.80	1.00
a.		Pair, one without overprint	10,000.	
9	A22	1sh grn & car rose ('09)	25.00	4.25
		Nos. 7-9 (3)	26.80	10.25

Nos. 2-6, 9 are on chalk-surfaced paper.

Stamps of Fiji, 1904- 11, Overprinted in Black or Red

		1910, Dec. 15		
10	A22	½p green	3.50	25.00
11	A22	1p carmine	11.00	8.50
12	A22	2p gray	1.00	3.00
13	A22	2½p ultra	1.10	6.00
14	A22	5p violet & ol grn	2.25	5.50
15	A22	6p violet	2.50	7.50
16	A22	1sh black, grn (R)	3.00	7.50
		Nos. 10-16 (7)	24.35	63.00

Nos. 14-16 are on chalk-surfaced paper.

Native Idols — A1

		1911, July 25	Engr.	Wmk. 3
17	A1	½p pale green	1.00	1.75
18	A1	1p red	4.00	2.00
19	A1	2p gray	7.00	3.00
20	A1	2½p ultramarine	4.75	5.75
21	A1	5p olive green	4.50	6.00
22	A1	6p claret	3.00	5.00
23	A1	1sh black, green	2.75	12.00
24	A1	2sh violet, blue	22.50	20.00
25	A1	5sh green, yel	32.50	50.00
		Nos. 17-25 (9)	82.00	105.50

See Nos. 33-37. For surcharges see Nos. 26-29, 38-39, French Issues No. 36.

Surcharged

1920-21

26	A1	1p on 5p ol grn ('21)	10.00	60.00
a.		Inverted surcharge	4,500.	
27	A1	1p on 1sh blk, grn	4.00	13.00
28	A1	1p on 2sh vio, blue	1.50	10.00
29	A1	1p on 5sh grn, yel	1.25	10.00

On French Issue No. 16

| 30 | A2 | 2p on 40c red, yel ('21) | 2.00 | 22.00 |
| | | Nos. 26-30 (5) | 18.75 | 115.00 |

French Issue No. 27

Wmk. R F in Sheet

| 31 | A2 | 2p on 40c red, yel ('21) | 125.00 | 700.00 |

The letters "R.F." are the initials of "Republique Francaise." They are large double-lined Roman capitals, about 120mm high. About one-fourth of the stamps in each sheet show portions of the watermark, the other stamps are without watermark.

No. 26a is considered by some to be printers' waste.

Type of 1911 Issue

		1921, Oct.		Wmk. 4
33	A1	1p rose red	2.50	14.50
34	A1	2p gray	4.00	45.00
37	A1	6p claret	14.00	80.00
		Nos. 33-37 (3)	20.50	139.50

For surcharge see No. 40.

Stamps of 1911-21 Surcharged with New Values as in 1920-21

		1924, May 1		Wmk. 3
38	A1	1p on ½p pale green	4.00	22.50
39	A1	5p on 2½p ultra	7.50	27.50
a.		Inverted surcharge	3,500.	

Wmk. 4

| 40 | A1 | 3p on 1p rose red | 4.50 | 10.00 |
| | | Nos. 38-40 (3) | 16.00 | 60.00 |

No. 39a is considered by some to be printers' waste.

A3

The values at the lower right denote the currency and amount for which the stamps were to be sold. The English stamps could be bought at the French post office in French money.

		1925		Engr.
41	A3	½p (5c) black	1.25	20.00
42	A3	1p (10c) green	1.00	17.50
43	A3	2p (20c) grnsh gray	1.75	2.75
44	A3	2½p (25c) brown	1.00	14.00
45	A3	5p (50c) ultra	3.25	2.75
46	A3	6p (60c) claret	4.00	15.00
47	A3	1sh (1.25fr) blk, grn	3.50	18.00
48	A3	2sh (2.50fr) vio, bl	6.25	20.00
49	A3	5sh (6.25fr) grn, yel	6.25	27.50
		Nos. 41-49 (9)	28.25	137.50

Beach Scene — A5

		1938, June 1	Wmk. 4	Perf. 12
50	A5	5c green	1.75	4.00
51	A5	10c dark orange	2.00	2.00
52	A5	15c violet	2.50	3.00
53	A5	20c rose red	2.75	3.25
54	A5	25c brown	1.50	2.75
55	A5	30c dark blue	3.00	2.50
56	A5	40c olive green	3.25	5.50
57	A5	50c brown vio	1.25	1.50
58	A5	1fr car, emerald	6.50	9.00
59	A5	2fr dk blue, emer	22.50	22.00
60	A5	5fr red, yellow	40.00	50.00
61	A5	10fr violet, blue	125.00	80.00
		Nos. 50-61 (12)	212.00	186.00
		Set, never hinged	300.00	

Catalogue values for unused stamps in this section, from this point to the end of the section, are for Never Hinged items.

Common Design Types pictured following the introduction.

UPU Issue
Common Design Type

		1949, Oct. 10	Engr.	Perf. 13½
62	CD309	10c red orange	.35	.90
63	CD309	15c violet	.35	1.00
64	CD309	30c violet blue	.40	1.10
65	CD309	50c brown violet	.50	1.25
		Nos. 62-65 (4)	1.60	4.25

Outrigger Canoes with Sails — A6

Designs: 25c, 30c, 40c and 50c, Native Carving. 1fr, 2fr and 5fr, Island couple.

		1953, Apr. 30		Perf. 12½
66	A6	5c green	1.00	1.25
67	A6	10c red	1.10	.35
68	A6	15c yellow	1.10	.25
69	A6	20c ultramarine	1.10	.25
70	A6	25c olive	.90	.25
71	A6	30c light brown	.90	.25
72	A6	40c black brown	1.10	.40
73	A6	50c violet	1.40	.50
74	A6	1fr deep orange	5.75	1.75
75	A6	2fr red violet	6.00	9.00
76	A6	5fr scarlet	9.00	22.50
		Nos. 66-76 (11)	29.35	36.75

Coronation Issue
Common Design Type

		1953, June 2		Perf. 13½x13
77	CD312	10c car & black	.75	.60

Discovery of New Hebrides, 1606 — A7

20c, 50c, Britannia, Marianne, Flags & Mask.

		1956, Oct. 20	Photo.	Wmk. 4
78	A7	5c emerald	.25	.25
79	A7	10c scarlet	.25	.25
80	A7	20c dp ultra	.25	.25
81	A7	50c redsh pur	.25	.25
		Nos. 78-81 (4)	1.00	1.00

50th anniv. of the establishment of the Anglo-French Condominium.

Port Vila and Iririki Islet — A8

Designs: 25c, 30c, 40c, 50c, Tropical river and spear fisherman. 1fr, 2fr, 5fr, Woman drinking from coconut (inscribed: "Franco-British Alliance 4th March 1947").

		1957, Sept. 3	Engr.	Perf. 13½x13
82	A8	5c green	.45	1.00
83	A8	10c red	.40	.25
84	A8	15c orange yellow	.55	1.00
85	A8	20c ultramarine	.45	.25
86	A8	25c olive	.50	.25
87	A8	30c light brown	.50	.25
88	A8	40c sepia	.50	.25
89	A8	50c violet	.75	.25
90	A8	1fr orange	1.10	.25

91	A8	2fr rose lilac	4.50	2.75
92	A8	5fr black	10.00	5.50
		Nos. 82-92 (11)	19.70	12.85

Freedom from Hunger Issue
Common Design Type

			Perf. 14x14½
		1963, Sept. 2	Photo.	Wmk. 314
93	CD314	60c green	.60	.25

Red Cross Centenary Issue
Common Design Type with Royal Cipher and "RF" Replacing Queen's Portrait

		1963, Sept. 2	Litho.	Perf. 13
94	CD315	15c black & red	.40	.25
95	CD315	45c ultra & red	.60	.25

Copra Industry — A9

Designs: 5c, Manganese loading, Forari Wharf. 10c, Cacao. 20c, Map of New Hebrides, tuna, marlin, ships. 25c, Striped triggerfish. 30c, Pearly nautilus (mollusk). 40c, 60c, Turkeyfish. 50c, Lined tang (fish). 1fr, Cardinal honey-eater and hibiscus. 2fr, Buff-bellied flycatcher. 3fr, Thicket warbler. 5fr, White-collared kingfisher.

Wmk. 314 (10c, 20c, 40c, 60c, 3fr); Unwmkd. (others)
Perf. 12½ (10c, 20c, 40c, 60c); 14 (3fr); 13 (others)
Photo. (10c, 20c, 40c, 60c, 3fr); Engraved (others)

1963-67

96	A9	5c Prus bl, pur brn & cl ('66)	1.75	.50
a.		5c prus blue & claret ('72)	45.00	37.50
97	A9	10c brt grn, org brn & dk brn ('65)	.25	.25
98	A9	15c dk pur, yel & brn	.25	.25
99	A9	20c brt blue, gray & cit ('65)	.55	.25
100	A9	25c vio, rose lil & org brn ('66)	.75	.50
101	A9	30c lilac, brn & cit	1.00	.75
102	A9	40c dk bl & ver ('65)	1.25	1.50
103	A9	50c Prus bl, yel & green	1.10	.80
103A	A9	60c dk bl & ver ('67)	1.00	.50
104	A9	1fr blue grn, blk & red ('66)	3.00	3.50
105	A9	2fr ol, blk & brn	4.00	2.00
106	A9	3fr org grn, brt grn & blk ('65)	10.00	7.00
107	A9	5fr indigo, dp bl & gray ('67)	15.00	20.00
		Nos. 96-107 (13)	39.90	37.80

For surcharge see No. 141.

ITU Emblem CD317

			Perf. 11x11½
		1965, May 17	Litho.	Wmk. 314
108	CD317	15c ver & ol bister	.25	.25
109	CD317	60c ultra & ver	.40	.25

Intl. Cooperation Year Issue
Common Design Type with Royal Cipher and "RF" Replacing Queen's Portrait

		1965, Sept. 24		Perf. 14½
110	CD318	5c blue grn & claret	.25	.25
111	CD318	55c lt violet & green	.25	.25

Churchill Memorial Issue
Common Design Type with Royal Cipher and "RF" Replacing Queen's Portrait

		1966, Jan. 24	Photo.	Perf. 14
112	CD319	5c multicolored	.30	.25
113	CD319	15c multicolored	.50	.25
114	CD319	25c multicolored	.75	.25
115	CD319	30c multicolored	.75	.25
		Nos. 112-115 (4)	2.30	1.00

World Cup Soccer Issue
Common Design Type with Royal Cipher and "RF" Replacing Queen's Portrait

		1966, July 1	Litho.	Perf. 14
116	CD321	20c multicolored	.30	.30
117	CD321	40c multicolored	.70	.70

WHO Headquarters Issue
Common Design Type with Royal Cipher and "RF" Replacing Queen's Portrait

1966, Sept. 20   Litho.   Perf. 14
118 CD322 25c multicolored .25 .25
119 CD322 60c multicolored .50 .25

UNESCO Anniversary Issue
Common Design Type with Royal Cipher and "RF" Replacing Queen's Portrait

1966, Dec. 1   Litho.   Perf. 14
120 CD323 15c "Education" .35 .35
121 CD323 30c "Science" .60 .60
122 CD323 45c "Culture" .95 .95
Nos. 120-122 (3) 1.90 1.90

Coast Watchers A11

25c, Map of South Pacific war zone, US Marine and Australian soldier. 60c, Australian cruiser Canberra. 1fr, Flying fortress taking off from Bauer Field, & view of Vila.

Perf. 14x13
1967, Sept. 26   Photo.   Wmk. 314
123 A11 15c lt blue & multi .25 .25
124 A11 25c yellow & multi .30 .30
125 A11 60c multicolored .75 .75
126 A11 1fr pale salmon & multi 1.00 1.00
Nos. 123-126 (4) 2.30 2.30

25th anniv. of the Allied Forces' campaign in the South Pacific War Zone.

Globe and World Map — A12

Designs: 25c, Ships La Boudeuse and L'Etoile and map of Bougainville Strait. 60c, Louis Antoine de Bougainville, ship's figurehead and bougainvillaea.

1968, May 23   Engr.   Perf. 13
127 A12 15c ver, emer & dull vio .25 .25
128 A12 25c ultra, olive & brn .25 .25
129 A12 60c magenta, grn & brn .30 .25
Nos. 127-129 (3) .80 .75

200th anniv. of Louis Antoine de Bougainville's (1729-1811) voyage around the world.

Concorde Airliner — A13

Design: 60c, Concorde, sideview.

1968, Oct. 9   Litho.   Perf. 14x13½
130 A13 25c vio bl, red & lt bl .25 .25
131 A13 60c red, ultra & black .60 .50

Development of the Concorde supersonic airliner, a joint Anglo-French project to produce a high speed plane.

Kauri Pine — A14

Perf. 14x14½
1969, June 30   Wmk. 314
132 A14 20c brown & multi .30 .30

New Hebrides timber industry. Issued in sheets of 9 (3x3) on simulated wood grain background.

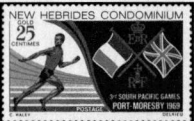

Relay Race, French and British Flags — A15

Design: 1fr, Runner at right.

Perf. 12½x13
1969, Aug. 13   Photo.   Unwmk.
133 A15 25c ultra, car, brn & gold .25 .25
134 A15 1fr brn, car, ultra & gold .25 .25

3rd South Pacific Games, Port Moresby, Papua and New Guinea, Aug. 13-23.

Land Diver, Pentecost Island — A16

Designs: 15c, Diver in starting position on tower. 1fr, Diver nearing ground.

Wmk. 314
1969, Oct. 15   Litho.   Perf. 12½
135 A16 15c yellow & multi .25 .25
136 A16 25c pink & multi .25 .25
137 A16 1fr gray & multi .25 .25
Nos. 135-137 (3) .75 .75

UPU Headquarters and Monument, Bern — A17

Unwmk.
1970, May 20   Engr.   Perf. 13
138 A17 1.05fr org, lilac & slate .30 .30

Opening of the new UPU Headquarters, Bern.

Charles de Gaulle — A18

1970, July 20   Photo.   Perf. 13
139 A18 65c brown & multi .25 .25
140 A18 1.10fr dp blue & multi .75 .75

30th anniv. of the rallying to the Free French. For overprints see Nos. 144-145.

No. 99 Surcharged

1970, Oct. 15   Wmk. 314   Perf. 12½
141 A9 35c on 20c multi .30 .30

Virgin and Child, by Giovanni Bellini — A19

Christmas: 50c, Virgin and Child, by Giovanni Cima.

Perf. 14½x14
1970, Nov. 30   Litho.   Wmk. 314
142 A19 15c tan & multi .25 .25
143 A19 50c lt green & multi .25 .25

Nos. 139-140 Overprinted in Black and Gold

Unwmk.
1971, Jan. 19   Photo.   Perf. 13
144 A18 65c brown & multi .25 .25
145 A18 1.10fr dp blue & multi .35 .35

In memory of Gen. Charles de Gaulle (1890-1970), President of France.

Soccer A20

Design: 65c, Basketball, vert.

1971, July 13   Photo.   Perf. 12½
146 A20 20c multicolored .25 .25
147 A20 65c multicolored .25 .25

4th South Pacific Games, Papeete, French Polynesia, Sept. 8-19.

Kauri Pine, Cone and Arms of Royal Society — A21

Perf. 14½x14
1971, Sept. 7   Litho.   Wmk. 314
148 A21 65c multicolored .30 .30

Royal Society of London for the Advancement of Science expedition to study vegetation and fauna, July 1-October.

Adoration of the Shepherds, by Louis Le Nain — A22

Design: 50c, Adoration of the Shepherds, by Jacopo Tintoretto.

1971, Nov. 23   Perf. 14x13½
149 A22 25c lt green & multi .25 .25
150 A22 50c lt blue & multi .25 .25

Christmas. See Nos. 167-168.

Drover Mk III — A23

Airplanes: 25c, Sandringham seaplane. 30c, Dragon Rapide. 65c, Caravelle.

Perf. 13½x13
1972, Feb. 29   Photo.   Unwmk.
151 A23 20c lt green & multi .25 .25
152 A23 25c ultra & multi .25 .25
153 A23 30c orange & multi .45 .45
154 A23 65c dk blue & multi .90 .90
Nos. 151-154 (4) 1.85 1.85

Headdress, South Malekula A24

Baker's Pigeon A25

Artifacts: 15c, Slit gong and carved figure, North Ambrym. 1fr, Carved figures, North Ambrym. 3fr, Ceremonial headdress, South Malekula.
Birds: 20c, Red-headed parrot-finch. 35c, Chestnut-bellied kingfisher. 2fr, Green palm lorikeet.
Sea shells: 25c, Cribraria fischeri. 30c, Oliva rubrolabiata. 65c, Strombus plicatus. 5fr, Turbo marmoratus.

1972, July 24   Photo.   Perf. 12½x13
155 A24 5c plum & multi .25 .25
156 A25 10c blue & multi .25 .25
157 A24 15c red & multi .30 .40
158 A25 20c org brown & multi .35 .50
159 A24 25c dp blue & multi .50 .80
160 A25 30c dk green & multi .65 .85
161 A25 35c gray bl & multi .70 1.10
162 A24 65c dk green & multi 1.25 3.75
163 A24 1fr orange & multi 2.00 3.00
164 A25 2fr multicolored 4.50 4.50
165 A24 3fr yellow & multi 5.75 6.75
166 A24 5fr pink & multi 9.00 13.50
Nos. 155-166 (12) 25.50 35.65

For overprints and surcharges see #181-182, 217-228.

Christmas Type of 1971
Designs: 25c, Adoration of the Magi (detail), by Bartholomaeus Spranger. 70c, Virgin and Child, by Jan Provoost.

Perf. 14x13½
1972, Sept. 25   Litho.   Wmk. 314
167 A22 25c lt green & multi .25 .25
168 A22 70c lt blue & multi .25 .25

Silver Wedding Issue, 1972
Common Design Type
Design: Elizabeth II and Prince Philip.

1972, Nov. 20   Photo.   Perf. 14x14½
169 CD324 35c vio black & multi .25 .25
170 CD324 65c olive & multi .25 .25

Dendrobium Teretifolium — A26

Orchids: 30c, Ephemerantha comata. 35c, Spathoglottis petri. 65c, Dendrobium mohlianum.

1973, Feb. 26   Litho.   Perf. 14
171 A26 25c blue vio & multi .40 .25
172 A26 30c multicolored .60 .35
173 A26 35c violet & multi .75 .45
174 A26 65c dk green & multi 1.25 .60
Nos. 171-174 (4) 3.00 1.65

New Wharf, Vila — A27

Design: 70c, New wharf, horiz.

1973, May 14   Wmk. 314
175 A27 25c multicolored .25 .25
176 A27 70c multicolored .30 .30

New wharf at Vila, finished Nov. 1972.

Wild Horses, Tanna Island — A28

70c, Yasur Volcano, Tanna.

Perf. 13x12½
1973, Aug. 13   Photo.   Unwmk.
177 A28 35c shown   .45   .45
178 A28 70c multicolored   1.25   .90

Mother and Child, by Marcel Moutouh — A29

Christmas: 70c, Star over Lagoon, by Tatin d'Avesnieres.

Perf. 14x13½
1973, Nov. 19   Litho.   Wmk. 314
179 A29 35c tan & multi   .25   .25
180 A29 70c lilac rose & multi   .25   .25

Nos. 161 and 164 Overprinted in Red or Black

Perf. 12½x13
1974, Feb. 11   Photo.   Unwmk.
181 A25 35c multicolored (R)   .35   .25
182 A25 2fr multicolored (B)   .75   .60

Visit of British Royal Family, Feb. 11-12.

Pacific Dove — A30

Designs: 35c, Night swallowtail. 70c, Green sea turtle. 1.15fr, Flying fox.

1974, Feb. 11   Perf. 13x12½
183 A30 25c gray & multi   .75   .25
184 A30 35c gray & multi   1.10   .25
185 A30 70c gray & multi   1.90 1.00
186 A30 1.15fr gray & multi 3.25 1.75
    Nos. 183-186 (4)   7.00 3.30

Nature conservation.

Old Post Office, Vila — A31

Design: 70c, New Post Office.

1974, May 6   Unwmk.   Perf. 12
187 A31 35c blue & multi   .25   .25
188 A31 70c red & multi   .25   .25
  a. Pair, #187-188   .50   .50

Opening of New Post Office, May, 1974.

Capt. Cook and Tanna Island — A32

#190, William Wales, & boat landing on island. #191, William Hodges painting islanders & landscape. 1.15fr, Capt. Cook, "Resolution" & map of New Hebrides.

Wmk. 314
1974, Aug. 1   Litho.   Perf. 13
Size: 40x25mm
189 A32 35c multicolored   1.50 1.00
190 A32 35c multicolored   1.50 1.00
191 A32 35c multicolored   1.50 1.00
  a. Strip of 3, #189-191 4.75 5.50

Perf. 11
Size: 58x34mm
192 A32 1.15fr lilac & multi 3.00 3.00
    Nos. 189-192 (4)   7.50 6.00

Bicentenary of the discovery of the New Hebrides by Capt. Cook. No. 191a has continuous design.

Exchange of Letters, UPU Emblem — A33

Perf. 13x12½
1974, Oct. 9   Photo.   Unwmk.
193 A33 70c multicolored   .30   .30

Centenary of Universal Postal Union.

Nativity, by Gerard van Honthorst A34

Christmas: 35c, Adoration of the Kings, by Velazquez, vert.

Wmk. 314
1974, Nov. 14   Litho.   Perf. 13½
194 A34 35c multicolored   .25   .25
195 A34 70c multicolored   .25   .25

Charolais Bull — A35

1975, Apr. 29   Engr.   Perf. 13
196 A35 10fr multicolored 10.00 20.00

For surcharge see No. 229.

A36

1975, Aug. 5   Litho.   Perf. 14x13½
197 A36 25c Kayak race   .25   .25
198 A36 35c Camp cooks   .25   .25
199 A36   1fr Map makers   .65   .65
200 A36   5fr Fishermen   4.50 4.50
    Nos. 197-200 (4)   5.65 5.65

Nordjamb 75, 14th Boy Scout Jamboree, Lillehammer, Norway, July 29-Aug. 7.

A37

Christmas (After Michelangelo): 35c, Pitti Madonna. 70c, Bruges Madonna. 2.50fr, Taddei Madonna.

Perf. 14½x14
1975, Nov. 11   Litho.   Wmk. 373
201 A37 35c ol green & multi .25   .25
202 A37 70c brown & multi   .45   .45
203 A37 2.50fr blue & multi   1.40 1.40
    Nos. 201-203 (3)   2.10 2.10

Concorde, British Airways Colors and Emblem A38

Unwmk.
1976, Jan. 30   Typo.   Perf. 13
204 A38 5fr blue & multi   7.50 7.50

First commercial flight of supersonic jet Concorde from London to Bahrain, Jan. 21.

Telephones, 1876 and 1976 — A39

Designs: 70c, Alexander Graham Bell. 1.15fr, Nouméa earth station and satellite.

1976, Mar. 31   Photo.   Perf. 13
205 A39 25c black, car & blue   .30   .30
206 A39 70c black & multi   .40   .40
207 A39 1.15fr black, org & vio bl 1.00 1.00
    Nos. 205-207 (3)   1.70 1.70

Centenary of first telephone call by Alexander Graham Bell, Mar. 10, 1876.

Map of New Hebrides — A40

View of Santo — A41

Design: 2fr, View of Vila.

1976, June 29   Photo.   Perf. 13
208 A40 25c blue & multi   .30   .30
209 A41   1fr multicolored   .70   .70
210 A41   2fr multicolored   1.50 1.50
    Nos. 208-210 (3)   2.50 2.50

Opening of First Representative Assembly, June 29 (25c); first Santo Municipal Council (1fr); first Vila Municipal Council (2fr).
See Nos. 263-264 for types of design A40 surcharged.

Flight into Egypt, by Francisco Vieira Lusitano — A42

Christmas (Portuguese 16th Cent. Paintings): 70c, Adoration of the Shepherds. 2.50fr, Adoration of the Kings.

Wmk. 373
1976, Nov. 8   Litho.   Perf. 14
211 A42 35c purple & multi   .25   .25
212 A42 70c blue & multi   .25   .25
213 A42 2.50fr lt green & multi .60   .60
    Nos. 211-213 (3)   1.10 1.10

Queen's Visit, 1974 — A43

70c, Imperial state crown. 2fr, The blessing.

1977, Feb. 7   Perf. 14x13½
214 A43 35c lt green & multi   .25   .25
215 A43 70c blue & multi   .25   .25
216 A43   2fr pink & multi   .25   .25
    Nos. 214-216 (3)   .75   .75

25th anniv. of the reign of Elizabeth II.

Nos. 155-166, 196 Surcharged

Paris Overprints
Perf. 12½x13
1977, July 1   Photo.   Unwmk.
217 A24   5fr on 5c multi   .50   .60
218 A25 10fr on 10c multi   .80   .40
219 A24 15fr on 15c multi   .65 1.75
220 A25 20fr on 20c multi   1.30   .60
221 A24 25fr on 25c multi   1.75 2.00
222 A24 30fr on 30c multi   1.75 1.25
223 A25 35fr on 35c multi   1.75 1.50
224 A24 40fr on 65c multi   1.50 1.50
225 A24 50fr on 1fr multi   1.10 2.00
226 A24 70fr on 2fr multi   6.75 1.00
227 A24 100fr on 3fr multi   1.20 4.00
228 A24 200fr on 5fr multi   5.50 14.00

Wmk. 314
Engr.   Perf. 13
229 A35 500fr on 10fr multi 15.00 17.50
    Nos. 217-229 (13)   39.55 48.10

Nos. 155//166, 196 Surcharged with New Value, "FNH" and Bars

Port Vila Overprints

Two settings of 35fr and 200fr surcharges: type 1, 1.4mm between new value and "FNH"; type 2, 2.1mm between value and "FNH".

Perf. 12½x13

1977-78		Photo.		Unwmk.
217a	A24	5fr on 5c (a)	.60	.25
218a	A24	10fr on 10c (b)	.85	.25
219a	A24	15fr on 15c (c)	2.00	1.00
221a	A24	25fr on 25c (d)	60.00	24.00
222a	A24	30fr on 30c (d)	275.00	75.00
223a	A25	35fr on 35c (d),		
		type 1	3.50	.90
b.		Type 2	6.00	1.20
224a	A24	40fr on 65c (d)	1.75	.65
225a	A24	50fr on 1fr (d)	50.00	30.00
227a	A24	100fr on (d)	50.00	30.00
228a	A24	200fr on 5fr (d), type		
		1	20.00	15.00
b.		Type 2		
229a	A35	500fr on 10fr (d)	22.50	16.00
		Nos. 217a-229a (11)	486.20	193.05

The 50fr and 100fr values were sold only through the philatelic bureau.

Issued: 10fr, 7/10; 15fr, 7/18; 5fr, 8/10; #228a, 8/22; 25fr, 30fr, #223a, 9/10; 40fr, 9/12; 500fr, 9/14; #223b, 1/6/78; #228b, 1/13/78.

Erromango and Kaori Tree — A44

Designs: 10fr, Archipelago and man making copra. 15fr, Espiritu Santo Island and cattle. 20fr, Efate Island and Post Office, Vila. 25fr, Malakula Island and headdresses. 30fr, Aoba and Maewo Islands and pig tusks. 35fr, Pentecost Island and land diving. 40fr, Tanna Island and Prophet John Frum's Red Cross. 50fr, Shepherd Island and canoe with sail. 70fr, Banks Island and dancers. 100fr, Ambrym Island and carvings. 200fr, Aneityum Island and decorated baskets. 500fr, Torres Islands and fishing with bow and arrow.

1977-78		Wmk. 373 Litho.	Perf. 14	
238	A44	5fr multicolored	.25	.25
239	A44	10fr multicolored	.25	.25
240	A44	15fr multicolored	.25	.25
241	A44	20fr multicolored	.30	.30
242	A44	25fr multicolored	.40	.40
243	A44	30fr multicolored	.50	.50
244	A44	35fr multicolored	.55	.55
245	A44	40fr multicolored	.60	.60
246	A44	50fr multicolored	1.25	.75
247	A44	70fr multicolored	1.50	2.00
248	A44	100fr multicolored	1.75	1.25
249	A44	200fr multicolored	2.50	2.50
250	A44	500fr multicolored	5.50	7.50
		Nos. 238-250 (13)	15.60	17.10

Issue dates: 5fr, 20fr, 50fr, 100fr, 200fr, Sept. 7; 15fr, 25fr, 30fr, 40fr, Nov. 23, 1977; 10fr, 35fr, 70fr, 500fr, May 9, 1978.

Tempi Madonna, by Raphael — A45

Christmas: 15fr, Virgin and Child, by Gerard David. 30fr, Virgin and Child, by Pompeo Batoni.

1977, Dec. 8		Litho.	Perf. 12	
251	A45	10fr multicolored	.25	.25
252	A45	15fr multicolored	.25	.25
253	A45	30fr multicolored	.30	.30
		Nos. 251-253 (3)	.80	.80

British Airways Concorde over New York City — A46

20fr, British Airways Concorde over London. 30fr, Air France Concorde over Washington. 40fr, Air France Concorde over Paris.

1978, May 9		Wmk. 373	Perf. 14	
254	A46	10fr multicolored	.85	.50
255	A46	20fr multicolored	1.10	1.10
256	A46	30fr multicolored	1.50	1.50
257	A46	40fr multicolored	1.75	1.75
		Nos. 254-257 (4)	5.20	4.85

Concorde, 1st commercial flight, Paris to NYC.

Elizabeth II Coronation Anniversary Issue
Common Design Types
Souvenir Sheet

1978, June 2	Unwmk.	Perf. 15	
258	Sheet of 6	1.75	1.75
a.	CD326 40fr White horse of Hanover	.25	.25
b.	CD327 40fr Elizabeth II	.25	.25
c.	CD328 40fr Gallic cock	.25	.25

No. 258 contains 2 se-tenant strips of Nos. 258a-258c, separated by horizontal gutter with commemorative and descriptive inscriptions and showing central part of coronation procession with coach.

Virgin and Child, by Dürer — A47

Dürer Paintings: 15fr, Virgin and Child with St. Anne. 30fr, Virgin and Child with Goldfinch. 40fr, Virgin and Child with Pear.

Perf. 14x13½

1978, Dec. 1		Litho.	Wmk. 373	
259	A47	10fr multicolored	.25	.25
260	A47	15fr multicolored	.25	.25
261	A47	30fr multicolored	.25	.25
262	A47	40fr multicolored	.25	.25
		Nos. 259-262 (4)	1.00	1.00

Christmas and 450th death anniv. of Albrecht Dürer (1471-1528), German painter.

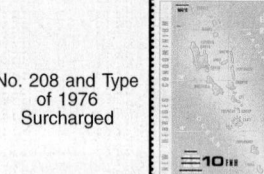

No. 208 and Type of 1976 Surcharged

Longitude changed to "166E."

1979, Jan. 11		Photo.	Perf. 13	
263	A40	10fr on 25c bl & multi	.25	.25
264	A40	40fr on 25c lt grn & multi	.25	.25

1st anniv. of Internal Self-Government.

New Hebrides No. 50 — A48

Rowland Hill and New Hebrides Stamps: 20fr, No. 136. 40fr, No. 43.

1979, Sept. 10		Litho.	Perf. 14	
265	A48	10fr multicolored	.25	.25
266	A48	20fr multicolored	.25	.25
a.		Souvenir sheet of 2	.90	.90
267	A48	40fr multicolored	.40	.40
		Nos. 265-267 (3)	.90	.90

Sir Rowland Hill (1795-1879), originator of penny postage. No. 266a contains New Hebrides, British, No. 266 and French, No. 286; margin shows Mulready envelope.

Arts Festival — A49

Designs: 10fr, Clubs and spears. 20fr, Ritual puppet. 40fr, Headdress.

1979, Nov. 16		Wmk. 373	Perf. 14	
268	A49	5fr multicolored	.25	.25
269	A49	10fr multicolored	.25	.25
270	A49	20fr multicolored	.25	.25
271	A49	40fr multicolored	.40	.40
		Nos. 268-271 (4)	1.15	1.15

Church, IYC Emblem — A50

IYC Emblem, Children's Drawings: 10fr, Father Christmas. 20fr, Cross and Bible, vert. 40fr, Stars, candle and Santa Claus, vert.

1979, Dec. 4			Perf. 13x13½	
272	A50	5fr multicolored	.25	.25
273	A50	10fr multicolored	.25	.25
274	A50	20fr multicolored	.25	.25
275	A50	40fr multicolored	.35	.35
		Nos. 272-275 (4)	1.10	1.10

Christmas; Intl. Year of the Child.

White-bellied Honeyeater A51

1980, Feb. 27		Litho.	Perf. 14	
276	A51	10fr shown	.85	.25
277	A51	20fr Scarlet robins	1.10	.45
278	A51	30fr Yellow white-eyes	1.50	.65
279	A51	40fr Fan-tailed brush cuckoo	1.75	.85
		Nos. 276-279 (4)	5.20	2.20

New Hebrides stamps were replaced in 1980 by those of Vanuatu.

POSTAGE DUE STAMPS

British Issues
Type of 1925 Overprinted

POSTAGE DUE

1925, June		Engr. Wmk. 4	Perf. 14	
J1	A3	1p (10c) green	37.50	1.25
J2	A3	2p (20c) gray	40.00	1.25
J3	A3	3p (30c) carmine	40.00	3.25
J4	A3	5p (50c) ultra	45.00	5.50
J5	A3	1fr (1fr) car, blue	52.50	6.50
		Nos. J1-J5 (5)	215.00	17.75

Values for Nos. J1-J5 are for toned stamps.

Regular Stamps of 1938 Overprinted in Black

POSTAGE DUE

1938, June 1			Perf. 12	
J6	A5	5c green	20.00	32.50
J7	A5	10c dark orange	20.00	32.50
J8	A5	20c rose red	22.50	50.00
J9	A5	40c olive green	27.50	57.50
J10	A5	1fr car, emerald	35.00	67.50
		Nos. J6-J10 (5)	125.00	240.00

Catalogue values for unused stamps in this section, from this point to the end of the section, are for Never Hinged items.

Regular Stamps of 1953 Overprinted in Black

POSTAGE DUE

1953, Apr. 30			Perf. 12½	
J11	A6	5c green	4.75	13.50
J12	A6	10c red	2.25	11.00
J13	A6	20c ultramarine	6.00	20.00
J14	A6	40c black brown	8.50	37.50
J15	A6	1fr deep orange	5.50	45.00
		Nos. J11-J15 (5)	27.00	127.00

Same on Nos. 82-83, 85, 88 and 90

1957, Sept. 3			Perf. 13½x13	
J16	A8	5c green	.25	1.00
J17	A8	10c red	.35	1.25
J18	A8	20c ultramarine	.75	1.50
J19	A8	40c sepia	1.00	2.50
J20	A8	1fr orange	2.00	3.50
		Nos. J16-J20 (5)	4.35	9.75

NEW HEBRIDES, FRENCH

'nü 'he-brə-ˌdēz

LOCATION — A group of islands in the South Pacific Ocean lying north of New Caledonia

GOVT. — Condominium under the joint administration of Great Britain and France

AREA — 5,790 sq. mi.

POP. — 100,000 (est. 1976)

CAPITAL — Port-Vila (Vila)

Postage stamps are issued by both Great Britain and France. In 1911 a joint issue was made bearing the coats of arms of both countries. The British stamps bore the coat of arms of Great Britain and the value in British currency on the right and the French coat of arms and values at the left. On the French stamps the positions were reversed. This resulted in some confusion when the value of the French franc decreased following World War I but the situation was corrected by arranging that both series of stamps be sold for their value as expressed in French currency.

12 Pence = 1 Shilling

100 Centimes = 1 Franc

New Hebrides Franc (FNH) — 1977

Catalogue values for unused stamps in this country are for Never Hinged items, beginning with Scott 79 in the regular postage section, Scott J16 in the postage due section.

French Issues
Stamps of New Caledonia, 1905, Overprinted in Black or Red

Nos. 1-4   No. 5

1908		Unwmk.	Perf. 14x13½	
1	A16	5c green	13.50	5.00
2	A16	10c rose	13.50	4.75
3	A17	25c blue, grnsh (R)	9.50	4.00
4	A17	50c carmine, org	8.50	6.50
5	A18	1fr bl, yel grn (R)	29.00	22.50
		Nos. 1-5 (5)	74.00	42.75

For overprints and surcharges see #6-10, 33-35.

Stamps of 1908 with Additional Overprint

1910				
6	A16	5c green	8.00	3.00
7	A16	10c rose	8.00	1.75
8	A17	25c blue, grnsh (R)	3.50	4.50
9	A17	50c red, org	12.00	27.50
10	A18	1fr bl, yel grn (R)	30.00	22.50
		Nos. 6-10 (5)	61.50	59.25

A2

		Perf. 14		
1911, July 12		Engr.	Wmk. 3	
11	A2	5c pale green	1.00	3.00
12	A2	10c red	.55	1.10
13	A2	20c gray	2.00	3.00

14	A2	25c ultramarine	2.75	7.00
15	A2	30c vio, *yellow*	6.50	6.50
16	A2	40c red, *yellow*	4.00	7.50
17	A2	50c olive green	4.00	7.50
18	A2	75c brn orange	7.00	30.00
19	A2	1fr brn red, *bl*	6.00	7.00
20	A2	2fr violet	12.00	22.50
21	A2	5fr brn red, *grn*	14.00	47.50
		Nos. 11-21 (11)	59.80	142.60

For surcharges see Nos. 36-37, 43 and British issue No. 30.

1912   **Wmk. R F in Sheet**

22	A2	5c pale green	1.75	5.50
23	A2	10c red	1.75	6.00
24	A2	20c gray	2.10	2.40
25	A2	25c ultramarine	2.50	5.00
26	A2	30c vio, *yellow*	2.50	17.00
27	A2	40c red, *yellow*	24.00	80.00
28	A2	50c olive green	18.00	35.00
29	A2	75c brn orange	9.00	42.50
30	A2	1fr brn red, *bl*	9.00	10.00
31	A2	2fr violet	9.25	50.00
32	A2	5fr brn red, *grn*	32.50	57.50
		Nos. 22-32 (11)	112.35	310.90

In the watermark, "R F" (République Française initials) are large double-lined Roman capitals, about 120mm high. About one-fourth of the stamps in each sheet show parts of the watermark. The other stamps are without watermark.

For surcharges see Nos. 38-42 and British issue No. 31.

No. 9 Surcharged

No. 8 Surcharged

1920   **Unwmk.**   **Perf. 14x13½**

33	A17	5c on 50c red, *org*	2.50	22.00
34	A17	10c on 25c bl, *grnsh*	.75	1.50

Same Surcharge on No. 4

35	A17	5c on 50c car, *org*	800.00	1,000.

British Issue No. 21 and French Issue No. 15 Surcharged

1921   **Wmk. 3**   **Perf. 14**

36	A1	10c on 5p ol grn	16.00	50.00
37	A2	20c on 30c vio, *yel*	15.00	65.00

Nos. 27 and 26 Surcharged

1921   **Wmk. R F in Sheet**

38	A2	5c on 40c red, *yel*	27.50	100.00
39	A2	20c on 30c vio, *yel*	11.50	80.00

Stamps of 1910-12 Surcharged with New Values as in 1920-21

1924

40	A2	10c on 5c pale grn	2.75	11.00
41	A2	30c on 10c red	2.75	3.00
42	A2	50c on 25c ultra	4.50	20.00
		Wmk. 3		
43	A2	50c on 25c ultra	45.00	110.00
		Nos. 40-43 (4)	55.00	144.00

A4

The values at the lower right denote the currency and amount for which the stamps were to be sold. The stamps could be purchased at the French post office and used to pay postage at the English rates.

1925   **Engr.**   **Wmk. R F in Sheet**

44	A4	5c (½p) black	.90	13.00
45	A4	10c (1p) green	1.00	9.00
46	A4	20c (2p) grnsh gray	4.25	3.75
47	A4	25c (2½p) brown	1.50	9.00
48	A4	30c (3p) carmine	1.75	18.00
49	A4	40c (4p) car, *org*	3.25	16.00
50	A4	50c (5p) ultra	2.00	11.00
51	A4	75c (7½p) bis brn	1.75	22.00
52	A4	1fr (10p) car, *blue*	3.00	14.50
53	A4	2fr (1sh 8p) gray vio	2.75	37.50
54	A4	5fr (4sh) car, *grnsh*	5.00	37.50
		Nos. 44-54 (11)	27.15	191.25

For overprints see Nos. J1-J5.

Beach Scene — A6

1938   **Perf. 12**

55	A6	5c green	3.00	9.75
56	A6	10c dark orange	3.25	3.25
57	A6	15c violet	3.25	8.00
58	A6	20c rose red	3.25	5.50
59	A6	25c brown	6.50	7.75
60	A6	30c dark blue	6.50	8.00
61	A6	40c olive grn	3.50	14.50
62	A6	50c brown violet	3.50	5.50
63	A6	1fr dk car, *grn*	4.00	8.50
64	A6	2fr blue, *grn*	27.50	42.50
65	A6	5fr red, *yellow*	40.00	67.50
66	A6	10fr vio, *blue*	87.50	145.00
		Nos. 55-66 (12)	191.75	325.75
		Set, never hinged	375.00	

For overprints see Nos. 67-78, J6-J15.

Stamps of 1938 Ovptd. in Black

1941

67	A6	5c green	1.25	25.00
68	A6	10c dark orange	3.50	24.00
69	A6	15c violet	5.50	40.00
70	A6	20c rose red	15.50	30.00
71	A6	25c brown	16.50	40.00
72	A6	30c dark blue	17.00	35.00
73	A6	40c olive green	17.00	40.00
74	A6	50c brn violet	14.50	35.00
75	A6	1fr dk car, *grn*	14.50	37.50
76	A6	2fr blue, *grn*	13.50	37.50
77	A6	5fr red, *yellow*	11.00	37.50
78	A6	10fr vio, *blue*	10.00	40.00
		Nos. 67-78 (12)	139.75	421.50
		Set, never hinged	245.00	

> **Catalogue values for unused stamps in this section, from this point to the end of the section, are for Never Hinged items.**

UPU Issue
Common Design Type
Wmk. RF in Sheet

1949   **Engr.**   **Perf. 13½x14**

79	CD309	10c red orange	1.90	2.75
80	CD309	15c violet	3.25	4.50
81	CD309	30c violet blue	3.50	5.00
82	CD309	50c brown violet	6.75	9.75
		Nos. 79-82 (4)	15.40	22.00

Some stamps in each sheet show part of the watermark; others show none.

Common Design Types
pictured following the introduction.

A8

5c, 10c, 15c, 20c, Canoes with sails. 25c, 30c, 40c, 50c, Native carving. 1fr, 2fr, 5fr, Natives.

1953   **Perf. 12½**

83	A8	5c green	.60	.75
84	A8	10c red	.60	.75
85	A8	15c yellow	.60	.75
86	A8	20c ultramarine	1.15	1.90

87	A8	25c olive	.80	1.25
88	A8	30c light brown	1.75	2.75
89	A8	40c black brown	2.00	3.25
90	A8	50c violet	2.25	3.75
91	A8	1fr deep orange	8.00	12.50
92	A8	2fr red violet	21.00	35.00
93	A8	5fr scarlet	37.50	60.00
		Nos. 83-93 (11)	76.25	122.65

For overprints see Nos. J16-J20.

Discovery of New Hebrides, 1606 — A9

20c, 50c, Britannia, Marianne, Flags and Mask.

Perf. 14½x14

1956, Oct. 20   **Unwmk.**   **Photo.**

94	A9	5c emerald	1.10	1.10
95	A9	10c crimson	1.25	1.25
96	A9	20c ultramarine	1.25	1.25
97	A9	50c purple	2.00	2.00
		Nos. 94-97 (4)	5.60	5.60

50th anniv. of the establishment of the Anglo-French Condominium.

Port Vila and Iririki Islet — A10

Designs: 25c, 30c, 40c, 50c, Tropical river and spear fisherman. 1fr, 2fr, 5fr, Woman drinking from coconut (inscribed: "Alliance Franco-Britannique 4 Mars 1947").

Wmk. RF in Sheet

1957   **Engr.**   **Perf. 13½x13**

98	A10	5c green	.60	1.25
99	A10	10c red	.90	.85
100	A10	15c orange yel	1.00	1.50
101	A10	20c ultramarine	1.25	1.50
102	A10	25c olive	1.25	1.25
103	A10	30c light brown	1.60	1.75
104	A10	40c sepia	1.90	2.25
105	A10	50c violet	2.40	3.25
106	A10	1fr orange	6.50	9.00
107	A10	2fr rose lilac	14.00	20.00
108	A10	5fr black	27.00	39.00
		Nos. 98-108 (11)	58.40	81.60

For overprints see Nos. J21-J25.

Wheat Emblem and Globe — A10a

1963, Sept. 2   **Unwmk.**   **Perf. 13**

109	A10a	60c org brn & slate grn	16.00	16.00

FAO "Freedom from Hunger" campaign.

Centenary Emblem — A11

1963, Sept. 2   **Unwmk.**

110	A11	15c org, gray & car	11.00	11.00
111	A11	45c bis, gray & car	16.50	16.50

Centenary of International Red Cross.

Copra Industry — A12

Designs: 5c, Manganese loading, Forari Wharf. 10c, Cacao. 20c, Map of New Hebrides, tuna, marlin and ships. 25c, Striped triggerfish. 30c, Nautilus. 40c, 60c, Turkeyfish (pterois volitans). 50c, Lined tang (fish). 1fr, Cardinal honeyeater and hibiscus. 2fr, Buff-bellied flycatcher. 3fr, Thicket warbler. 5fr, White-collared kingfisher.

Perf. 12½ (10c, 20c, 40c, 60c); 14 (3fr); 13 (others)
Photo. (10c, 20c, 40c, 60c, 3fr); Engr. (others)

1963-67   **Unwmk.**

112	A12	5c Prus bl, pur brn & cl ('66)	.60	.60
a.		5c prus blue & claret ('72)	57.50	60.00
113	A12	10c brt grn, org brn & "RF" at left) ('65)	1.75	1.75
114	A12	15c dk pur, yel & brn	.70	.70
115	A12	20c brt bl, gray & cit ("RF" at left) ('65)	2.60	2.60
116	A12	25c vio, rose lil & org brn ('66)	.70	.70
117	A12	30c lil, brn & citron	5.25	5.25
118	A12	40c dk bl & ver ('65)	4.75	4.75
119	A12	50c Prus bl, yel & grn	4.25	4.25
119A	A12	60c dk bl & ver ('67)	1.60	1.60
120	A12	1fr bl grn, blk & red ('66)	3.25	3.25
121	A12	2fr ol, blk & brn	15.00	15.00
122	A12	3fr org brn, brt grn & blk ("RF" at left) ('65)	14.00	14.00
123	A12	5fr ind, dp bl & gray ('67)	25.00	25.00
		Nos. 112-123 (13)	79.45	79.45

See #146-148. For surcharge see #160.

Telegraph, Syncom Satellite and ITU Emblem — A13

1965, May 17   **Unwmk.**   **Perf. 13**

124	A13	15c red brn, lt bl & bl grn	9.25	7.25
125	A13	60c dp bl grn, red & indigo	23.00	20.00

ITU, centenary.

Intl. Cooperation Year Issue
Common Design Type with Royal Cipher and "RF" Replacing Queen's Portrait

1965, Oct. 24   **Litho.**   **Perf. 14½**

126	CD318	5c blue grn & claret	4.00	4.00
127	CD318	55c lt violet & grn	8.00	8.00

International Cooperation Year.

Churchill Memorial Issue
Common Design Type with Royal Cipher and "RF" Replacing Queen's Portrait

1966, Jan. 24   **Photo.**   **Perf. 14**
Design in Black, Gold and Carmine Rose

128	CD319	5c brt blue	.80	.80
129	CD319	15c green	1.20	1.20
130	CD319	25c brown	2.60	2.60
131	CD319	30c violet	3.75	3.75
		Nos. 128-131 (4)	8.35	8.35

World Cup Soccer Issue
Common Design Type with Royal Cipher and "RF" Replacing Queen's Portrait

1966, July 1   **Litho.**   **Perf. 14**

132	CD321	20c multicolored	2.75	2.75
133	CD321	40c multicolored	4.25	4.25

WHO Headquarters Issue
Common Design Type with Royal Cipher and "RF" Replacing Queen's Portrait

1966, Sept. 20   **Litho.**   **Perf. 14**

134	CD322	25c multicolored	3.75	3.75
135	CD322	60c multicolored	4.75	4.75

UNESCO Anniversary Issue
Common Design Type with Royal Cipher and "RF" Replacing Queen's Portrait

1966, Dec. 1   **Litho.**   **Perf. 14**

136	CD323	15c "Education"	1.50	1.50
137	CD323	30c "Science"	3.00	3.00
138	CD323	45c "Culture"	3.25	3.25
		Nos. 136-138 (3)	7.75	7.75

US Marine, Australian Soldier and Map of South Pacific War Zone A19

Designs: 15c, The coast watchers. 60c, Australian cruiser Canberra. 1fr, Flying fortress taking off from Bauer Field, and view of Vila.

Perf. 14x13

1967, Sept. 26   Photo.   Unwmk.
139 A19 15c lt blue & multi   1.00 1.00
140 A19 25c yellow & multi   1.25 1.25
141 A19 60c multicolored   2.00 2.00
142 A19 1fr pale salmon & multi   2.50 2.50
    Nos. 139-142 (4)   6.75 6.75

25th anniv. of the Allied Forces' campaign in the South Pacific War Zone.

L. A. de Bougainville, Ship's Figurehead and Bougainvillea A20

15c, Globe & world map. 25c, Ships La Boudeuse & L'Etoile & map of Bougainville Strait.

1968, May 23   Engr.   Perf. 13
143 A20 15c ver, emer & dl vio   .45 .45
144 A20 25c ultra, ol & brn   .65 .65
145 A20 60c mag, grn & brn   1.15 1.15
    Nos. 143-145 (3)   2.25 2.25

200th anniv. of Louis Antoine de Bougainville's (1729-1811) voyage around the world.

Type of 1963-67 Redrawn, "E II R" at left, "RF" at Right

Designs as before.

1968, Aug. 5   Photo.   Perf. 12½
146 A12 10c brt grn, org brn &
        dk brn   1.00 1.00
147 A12 20c brt bl, gray & cit-
        ron   1.40 1.40

Perf. 14
148 A12 3fr org brn, brt grn &
        blk   9.50 9.50
    Nos. 146-148 (3)   11.90 11.90

On Nos. 113, 115 and 122 "RF" is at left and "E II R" is at right.
For surcharge see No. 160.

Concorde Supersonic Airliner — A21

Design: 25c, Concorde seen from above.

1968, Oct. 9   Litho.   Perf. 14x13½
149 A21 25c vio bl, red & lt bl   2.40 2.00
150 A21 60c red, ultra & blk   5.25 4.00

Development of the Concorde supersonic airliner, a joint Anglo-French project.

Kauri Pine — A22

1969, June 30   Perf. 14½x14
151 A22 20c brown & multi   .55 .55

New Hebrides timber industry. Issued in sheets of 9 (3x3) on simulated wood grain background.

Relay Race, British and French Flags — A23

1969, Aug. 13   Photo.   Perf. 12½x13
152 A23 25c shown   .75 .75
153 A23 1fr Runner at right   1.50 1.50

3rd South Pacific Games, Port Moresby, Papua and New Guinea, Aug. 13-23.

Land Diver at Start, Pentecost Island — A24

1969, Oct. 15   Litho.   Perf. 12½
154 A24 15c shown   .50 .50
155 A24 25c Diver in mid-air   .60 .60
156 A24 1fr Diver near ground   2.00 2.00
    Nos. 154-156 (3)   3.10 3.10

Land divers of Pentecost Island.

UPU Headquarters and Monument, Bern — A25

1970, May 20   Engr.   Perf. 13
157 A25 1.05fr org, lilac & slate   1.00 1.00

New UPU Headquarters, Bern.

Charles de Gaulle — A26

1970, July 20   Photo.   Perf. 13
158 A26 65c brown & multi   1.60 1.60
159 A26 1.10fr dp blue & multi   2.25 2.25

Rallying of the Free French, 30th anniv.
For overprints see Nos. 163-164.

No. 147 Surcharged

1970, Oct. 15   Photo.   Perf. 12½
160 A12 35c on 20c multi   .50 .60

Virgin and Child, by Giovanni Bellini — A27

50c, Virgin and Child, by Giovanni Cima.

1970, Nov. 30   Litho.   Perf. 14½x14
161 A27 15c tan & multi   .30 .25
162 A27 50c lt grn & multi   .65 .40

Christmas. See Nos. 186-187.

Nos. 158-159 Overprinted in Gold and Black

1971, Jan. 19   Photo.   Perf. 13
163 A26 65c brown & multi   .85 .85
164 A26 1.10c dp blue & multi   1.90 1.90

In memory of Gen. Charles de Gaulle (1890-1970), President of France.

Soccer A28

Design: 65c, Basketball, vert.

1971, July 13   Photo.   Perf. 12½
165 A28 20c multicolored   .75 .75
166 A28 65c multicolored   1.25 1.25

4th South Pacific Games, Papeete, French Polynesia, Sept. 8-19.

Breadfruit Tree and Fruit, Society Arms — A29

Perf. 14½x14

1971, Sept. 7   Litho.   Unwmk.
167 A29 65c multicolored   1.75 1.75

Expedition of the Royal Society of London for the Advancement of Science to study vegetation and fauna, July 1-October.

Adoration of the Shepherds, by Louis Le Nain — A30

Christmas: 50c, Adoration of the Shepherds, by Jacopo Tintoretto.

1971, Nov. 23   Perf. 14x13½
168 A30 25c lt green & multi   .60 .60
169 A30 50c lt blue & multi   .90 .90

Drover Mk III — A31

Airplanes: 25c, Sandringham seaplane. 30c, Dragon Rapide. 65c, Caravelle.

1972, Feb. 29   Photo.   Perf. 13½x13
170 A31 20c lt green & multi   .90 .90
171 A31 25c ultra & multi   1.00 1.00
172 A31 30c orange & multi   1.10 1.10
173 A31 65c dk blue & multi   3.25 3.25
    Nos. 170-173 (4)   6.25 6.25

Headdress, South Malekula A32

Baker's Pigeon A33

Artifacts: 15c, Slit gong and carved figure, North Ambrym. 1fr, Carved figures, North Ambrym. 3fr, Ceremonial headdress, South Malekula.
Birds: 20c, Red-headed parrot-finch. 35c, Chestnut-bellied kingfisher. 2fr, Green palm lorikeet.

Sea Shells: 25c, Cribraria fischeri. 30c, Oliva rubrolabiata. 65c, Strombus plicatus. 5fr, Turbo marmoratus.

1972, July 24   Photo.   Perf. 12½x13
174 A32 5c plum & multi   .30   .80
175 A33 10c blue & multi   1.75 1.40
176 A32 15c red & multi   .30   .80
177 A33 20c org brn & multi   2.00 1.20
178 A32 25c dp blue & multi   1.40 1.30
179 A32 30c dk green & multi   1.40 1.40
180 A33 35c gray bl & multi   2.40 2.00
181 A32 65c dk green & multi   3.00 2.40
182 A32 1fr orange & multi   2.25 3.50
183 A33 2fr multicolored   19.00 12.00
184 A32 3fr yellow & multi   8.00 14.00
185 A32 5fr pink & multi   20.00 24.00
    Nos. 174-185 (12)   61.80 64.80

For overprints see Nos. 200-201. For surcharges see Nos. 236-247.

Christmas Type of 1970

Christmas: 25c, Adoration of the Magi (detail), by Bartholomaeus Spranger. 70c, Virgin and Child, by Jan Provoost.

1972, Sept. 25   Litho.   Perf. 14x13½
186 A27 25c lt green & multi   .60 .60
187 A27 70c lt blue & multi   .90 .90

Silver Wedding Issue
Common Design Type With Royal Cipher and "RF" (at Right)

Design: Elizabeth II and Prince Philip.

Perf. 14x14½

1972, Nov. 20   Photo.   Wmk. 314
188 CD324 35c violet blk & multi   .50 .50
189 CD324 65c olive & multi   .75 .75

Dendrobium Teretifolium — A35

Orchids: 30c, Ephemerantha comata. 35c, Spathoglottis petri. 65c, Dendrobium mohlianum.

1973, Feb. 26   Unwmk.   Perf. 14
190 A35 25c blue vio & multi   1.75 1.75
191 A35 30c multicolored   1.75 1.75
192 A35 35c violet & multi   2.50 2.50
193 A35 65c dk green & multi   5.00 5.00
    Nos. 190-193 (4)   11.00 11.00

New Wharf, Vila — A36

1973, May 14   Litho.   Perf. 14
194 A36 25c shown   .90 .90
195 A36 70c New Wharf, horiz.   1.60 1.60

New wharf at Vila, completed Nov. 1972.

Wild Horses, Tanna — A37

Design: 70c, Yasur Volcano, Tanna.

1973, Aug. 13   Photo.   Perf. 13x13½
196 A37 35c multicolored   2.75 2.75
197 A37 70c multicolored   3.50 3.50

Christmas — A38

35c, Mother and Child, by Marcel Moutouh.
70c, Star over Lagoon, by Tatin D'Avesnieres.

1973, Nov. 19   Litho.   Perf. 14x13½
198 A38 35c tan & multi   .60   .60
199 A38 70c lil rose & multi   .90   .90

Nos. 180, 183
Overprinted in Red or
Black

1974, Feb. 11   Photo.   Perf. 12½x13
200 A33 35c multi (R)   2.40   .90
201 A33 2fr multi (B)   7.00 6.00

Visit of British Royal Family, Feb. 15-16.

Pacific
Dove — A39

Designs: 35c, Night swallowtail. 70c, Green
sea turtle. 1.15fr, Flying fox.

1974, Feb. 11   Perf. 13x12½
202 A39 25c gray & multi   3.75   2.40
203 A39 35c gray & multi   4.50   2.00
204 A39 70c gray & multi   5.50   4.00
205 A39 1.15fr gray & multi   6.25   7.75
     Nos. 202-205 (4)   20.00 16.15

Nature conservation.

Old Post
Office,
Vila
A40

Design: 70c, New Post Office.

Unwmk.
1974, May 6   Photo.   Perf. 12
206 A40 35c blue & multi   .60   .50
207 A40 70c red & multi   1.10   .90
  a.   Pair, #206-207   2.25   2.25

Opening of New Post Office, May, 1974.

Capt. Cook and
Tanna
Island — A41

Designs: No. 209, William Wales and boat
landing on island. No. 210, William Hodges
painting islanders and landscape. 1.15fr, Capt.
Cook, "Resolution" and map of New Hebrides.

1974, Aug. 1   Litho.   Perf. 13
Size: 40x25mm
208 A41 35c multicolored   3.75   2.25
209 A41 35c multicolored   3.75   2.25
210 A41 35c multicolored   3.75   2.25
  a.   Strip of 3, #208-210   14.50 14.50

Size: 58x34mm
Perf. 11
211 A41 1.15fr lilac & multi   6.00   6.00

Bicentenary of the discovery of the New
Hebrides by Capt. James Cook.
No. 210a has a continuous design.

Exchange of
Letters, UPU
Emblem — A42

1974, Oct. 9   Photo.   Perf. 13x12½
212 A42 70c multicolored   1.50   1.50

Centenary of Universal Postal Union.

Nativity, by
Gerard Van
Honthorst
A43

Christmas: 35c, Adoration of the Kings, by
Velazquez, vert.

1974, Nov. 14   Litho.   Perf. 13½
213 A43 35c multicolored   .50   .50
214 A43 70c multicolored   1.00 1.00

Charolais
Bull — A44

1975, Apr. 29   Engr.   Perf. 13
215 A44 10fr multicolored   22.00 24.00

For surcharge see No. 248.

Nordjamb Emblem,
Kayaks — A45

1975, Aug. 5   Litho.   Perf. 14x13½
216 A45 25c shown   .60   .50
217 A45 35c Camp cooks   .80   .70
218 A45 1fr Map makers   1.60 1.60
219 A45 5fr Fishermen   8.00 8.00
     Nos. 216-219 (4)   11.00 10.80

Nordjamb 75, 14th Boy Scout Jamboree, Lillehammer, Norway, July 29-Aug. 7.

Pitti Madonna, by
Michelangelo — A46

Christmas (After Michelangelo): 70c, Bruges Madonna. 2.50fr, Taddei Madonna.

1975, Nov. 11   Litho.   Perf. 14½x14
220 A46 35c multicolored   .50   .50
221 A46 70c brown & multi   .75   .75
222 A46 2.50fr blue & multi   3.25 3.25
     Nos. 220-222 (3)   4.50 4.50

Concorde,
Air France
Colors and
Emblem
A47

1976, Jan. 30   Typo.   Perf. 13
223 A47 5fr blue & multi   15.00 15.00

1st commercial flight of supersonic jet Concorde from Paris to Rio, Jan. 21.

Telephones, 1876 and
1976 — A48

Designs: 70c, Alexander Graham Bell.
1.15fr, Nouméa Earth Station and satellite.

1976, Mar. 31   Photo.   Perf. 13
224 A48 25c black, car & bl   .45   .45
225 A48 70c black & multi   1.40 1.40
226 A48 1.15fr blk, org & vio bl 1.90 1.90
     Nos. 224-226 (3)   3.75 3.75

Centenary of first telephone call by Alexander Graham Bell, Mar. 10, 1876.

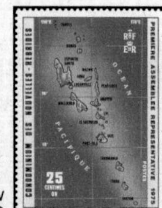

Map of New
Hebrides — A49

View of Luganville
(Santo) — A50

Design: 2fr, View of Vila.

1976, June 29   Unwmk.   Perf. 13
227 A49 25c blue & multi   .55   .45
228 A50 1fr multicolored   1.25 1.00
229 A50 2fr multicolored   3.00 3.00
     Nos. 227-229 (3)   4.80 4.45

Opening of first Representative Assembly,
June 29, 1976 (25c); first Luganville (Santo)
Municipal Council (1fr); first Vila Municipal
Council (2fr).
Nos. 228-229 exist with lower inscription
reading "Premiere Assemblée Representative
1975" instead of "Premiere Municipalite de
Luganville" on 1fr and "Premiere Municipalite
de Port-Vila" on 2fr.
For surcharges, see No. 283-284.

Flight into Egypt, by
Francisco Vieira
Lusitano — A51

Portuguese 16th Cent. Paintings: 70c, Adoration of the Shepherds. 2.50fr, Adoration of
the Kings.

1976, Nov. 8   Litho.   Perf. 14
230 A51 35c purple & multi   .60   .50
231 A51 70c blue & multi   .85   .75
232 A51 2.50fr multicolored   2.60 2.60
     Nos. 230-232 (3)   4.05 3.85

Christmas 1976.

Queen's Visit,
1974 — A52

70c, Imperial State crown. 2fr, The blessing.

1977, Feb. 7   Litho.   Perf. 14x13½
233 A52 35c lt green & multi   .45   .30
234 A52 70c blue & multi   .70   .65
235 A52 2fr pink & multi   1.35 1.35
     Nos. 233-235 (3)   2.50 2.30

Reign of Queen Elizabeth II, 25th anniv.

Nos. 174-185, 215 Surcharged

Paris Overprints

1977, July 1   Photo.   Perf. 12½x13
236 A32 5fr on 5c multi   2.10   1.75
237 A33 10fr on 10c multi   3.50   1.50
238 A32 15fr on 15c multi   1.75   1.50
239 A33 20fr on 20c multi   3.75   1.75
240 A32 25fr on 25c multi   3.50   2.00
241 A32 30fr on 30c multi   3.50   2.50
242 A33 35fr on 35c multi   5.50   4.00
243 A32 40fr on 65c multi   4.25   3.00
244 A32 50fr on 1fr multi   2.75   3.00
245 A33 70fr on 2fr multi   9.00   4.00
246 A32 100fr on 3fr multi   3.75   6.00
247 A32 200fr on 5fr multi   12.00 20.00

Engr.
Perf. 13
248 A44 500fr on 10fr multi   24.00 42.50
     Nos. 236-248 (13)   79.35 93.50

**Nos. 174/185, 215 Surcharged with
New Value, "FNH" and Bars**

a	b	c	d
FNH	FNH	FNH	25 FNH

Port Vila Overprints

Two settings of 35fr and 200fr surcharges:
type 1, 1.4mm between new value and "FNH";
type 2, 2.1mm between value and "FNH."

Perf. 12½x13
1977-78   Photo.   Unwmk.
236a A32 5fr on 5c (a)   1.00   1.00
237a A32 10fr on 10c (c)   1.25   1.25
238a A32 15fr on 15c (c)   2.50   2.50
240a A32 25fr on 25c (d)   190.00 190.00
241a A32 30fr on 30c (d)   210.00 210.00
242a A32 35fr on 35c (d),
            type 1   5.50   5.50
  b.   Type 2   37.50   22.50
243a A32 40fr on 65c (d)   7.00   7.00
244a A32 50fr on 1fr multi   16.00   16.00
245a A33 70fr on 2fr multi   26.00   26.00
246a A32 100fr on 3fr multi   32.50   32.50
247a A32 200fr on 5fr (d), type
            1   65.00   65.00
  b.   Type 2   75.00   75.00
248a A44 500fr on 10fr (d)   100.00 100.00
     Nos. 236a-248a (12)   656.75 656.75

The 50fr, 70fr and 100fr values were sold
only through the philatelic bureau.
Issued: 15fr, 7/18; 10fr, 7/20; 5fr,
8/10#247a, 8/22; 25fr, 30fr, #242a, 9/10; 40fr,
9/12; 500fr, 9/14; #242b, 1/6/78; #247b,
1/13/78.

Espiritu Santo and
Cattle — A53

Designs: 5fr, Erromango Island and Kaori tree. 10fr, Archipelago and man making copra. 20fr, Efate Island and Post Office, Vila. 25fr, Malakula Island and headdresses. 30fr, Aoba and Maewo Islands and pig tusks. 35fr, Pentecost Island and land diving. 40fr, Tanna Island and Prophet John Frum's Red Cross. 50fr, Shepherd Island and canoe with sail. 70fr, Banks Island and dancers. 100fr, Ambrym Island and carvings. 200fr, Aneityum Island and decorated baskets. 500fr, Torres Islands and fishing with bow and arrow.

1977-78		Litho.	Perf. 14	
258	A53	5fr multicolored	.30	.25
259	A53	10fr multicolored	.40	.40
260	A53	15fr multicolored	.50	.50
261	A53	20fr multicolored	.60	.60
262	A53	25fr multicolored	.75	.75
263	A53	30fr multicolored	1.00	1.00
264	A53	35fr multicolored	1.10	1.10
265	A53	40fr multicolored	1.25	1.25
266	A53	50fr multicolored	1.50	1.50
267	A53	70fr multicolored	2.40	3.25
268	A53	100fr multicolored	3.50	3.50
269	A53	200fr multicolored	6.75	6.75
270	A53	500fr multicolored	14.00	14.00
		Nos. 258-270 (13)	34.05	34.85

Issued: 5fr, 20fr, 50fr, 100fr, 200fr, 9/7/77; 15fr, 25fr, 30fr, 40fr, 11/23/77; 10fr, 35fr, 70fr, 500fr, 5/9/78.

Tempi Madonna, by Raphael — A54

Christmas: 15fr, Virgin and Child, by Gerard David. 30fr, Virgin and Child, by Pompeo Batoni.

1977, Dec. 8		Litho.	Perf. 12	
271	A54	10fr multicolored	.35	.35
272	A54	15fr multicolored	.50	.35
273	A54	30fr multicolored	.90	.90
		Nos. 271-273 (3)	1.75	1.60

British Airways Concorde over New York — A55

Designs: 20fr, British Airways Concorde over London. 30fr, Air France Concorde over Washington. 40fr, Air France Concorde over Paris.

1978, May 9		Litho.	Perf. 14	
274	A55	10fr multicolored	2.60	2.60
275	A55	20fr multicolored	2.60	2.60
276	A55	30fr multicolored	2.60	2.60
277	A55	40fr multicolored	2.60	2.60
		Nos. 274-277 (4)	10.40	10.40

Elizabeth II Coronation Anniversary Issue

Common Design Types

Souvenir Sheet

1978, June 2		Litho.	Perf. 15	
278		Sheet of 6	3.50	3.50
a.		CD326 40fr White Horse of Hanover	.25	.25
b.		CD327 40fr Elizabeth II	.25	.25
c.		CD328 40fr Gallic cock	.25	.25

No. 278 contains 2 se-tenant strips of Nos. 278a-278c, separated by horizontal gutter with commemorative and descriptive inscriptions and showing central part of coronation procession with coach.

Virgin and Child, by Dürer — A58

Christmas, Paintings by Albrecht Durer (1471-1528): 15fr, Virgin and Child with St. Anne. 30fr, Virgin and Child with Goldfinch. 40fr, Virgin and Child with Pear.

1978, Dec. 1		Litho.	Perf. 14x13½	
279	A58	10fr multicolored	.30	.25
280	A58	15fr multicolored	.50	.50
281	A58	30fr multicolored	.85	.85
282	A58	40fr multicolored	1.90	1.40
		Nos. 279-282 (4)	3.55	3.00

No. 227 and Type of 1976 Surcharged

1979, Jan. 11		Photo.	Perf. 13	
283	A49	10fr on 25c bl & multi	1.00	1.00
284	A49	40fr on 25c lt grn & multi	1.90	1.90

First anniv. of Internal Self-Government.

New Hebrides No. 155 and Hill Statue — A59

Rowland Hill and New Hebrides Stamps: 10fr, No. 55. 40fr, No. 46.

1979, Sept. 10		Litho.	Perf. 14	
285	A59	10fr multicolored	.30	.25
286	A59	20fr multicolored	.35	.25
287	A59	40fr multicolored	.75	.60
		Nos. 285-287 (3)	1.40	1.10

Sir Rowland Hill (1795-1879), originator of penny postage. A souvenir sheet containing No. 286 and British issue No. 266 is listed as No. 266a under New Hebrides, British issues.

Arts Festival — A60

Designs: 10fr, Clubs and spears. 20fr, Ritual puppet. 40fr, Headdress.

1979, Nov. 16		Litho.	Perf. 14	
288	A60	5fr multicolored	.55	.55
289	A60	10fr multicolored	.55	.55
290	A60	20fr multicolored	.55	.55
291	A60	40fr multicolored	.55	.55
		Nos. 288-291 (4)	2.20	2.20

Church, IYC Emblem — A61

IYC Emblem, Children's Drawings: 10fr, Father Christmas. 20fr, Cross and Bible, vert. 40fr, Stars, candle and Santa Claus, vert.

1979, Dec. 4		Litho.	Perf. 13x13½	
292	A61	5fr multicolored	.30	.30
293	A61	10fr multicolored	.50	.50
294	A61	20fr multicolored	1.00	1.00
295	A61	40fr multicolored	1.75	1.75
		Nos. 292-295 (4)	3.55	3.55

Christmas; Intl. Year of the Child.

White-bellied Honeyeater A62

20fr, Scarlet robins. 30fr, Yellow white-eyes. 40fr, Fan-tailed brush cuckoo.

1980, Feb. 27		Litho.	Perf. 14	
296	A62	10fr shown	.85	.85
297	A62	20fr multi	1.40	1.60
298	A62	30fr multi	2.60	2.60
299	A62	40fr multi	3.25	3.25
		Nos. 296-299 (4)	8.10	8.30

Stamps of Vanuatu replaced those of New Hebrides in 1980.

POSTAGE DUE STAMPS

French Issues

Nos. 45-46, 48, 50, 52 Overprinted

1925		Wmk. R F in Sheet	Perf. 14	
J1	A4	10c green	50.00	4.75
J2	A4	20c greenish gray	50.00	4.75
J3	A4	30c carmine	50.00	4.75
J4	A4	50c ultramarine	50.00	4.75
J5	A4	1fr carmine, blue	50.00	4.75
		Nos. J1-J5 (5)	250.00	23.75

Nos. 55-56, 58, 61, 63 Overprinted

1938			Perf. 12	
J6	A6	5c green	11.00	65.00
J7	A6	10c dark orange	12.50	65.00
J8	A6	20c rose red	14.50	70.00
J9	A6	40c olive green	30.00	140.00
J10	A6	1fr dark car, green	35.00	160.00
		Nos. J6-J10 (5)	103.00	500.00

Nos. J6-J10 Overprinted like Nos. 67-78

1941				
J11	A6	5c green	11.00	42.50
J12	A6	10c dark orange	11.00	42.50
J13	A6	20c rose red	11.00	42.50
J14	A6	40c olive green	13.00	42.50
J15	A6	1fr dk car, green	12.00	42.50
		Nos. J11-J15 (5)	58.00	212.50

> Catalogue values for unused stamps in this section, from this point to the end of the section, are for Never Hinged items.

Nos. 83-84, 86, 89, 91 Overprinted

1953		Unwmk.	Perf. 12½	
J16	A8	5c green	4.75	10.00
J17	A8	10c red	6.25	14.00
J18	A8	20c ultramarine	11.00	24.00
J19	A8	40c black brown	15.00	44.00
J20	A8	1fr deep orange	22.00	48.00
		Nos. J16-J20 (5)	59.00	140.00

Nos. 98-99, 101, 104, 106 Overprinted "TIMBRE-TAXE"

Wmk. R F in Sheet

1957		Engr.	Perf. 13½x13	
J21	A10	5c green	1.10	2.75
J22	A10	10c red	1.40	3.50
J23	A10	20c ultramarine	1.60	4.25
J24	A10	40c sepia	6.25	15.00
J25	A10	1fr orange	15.00	35.00
		Nos. J21-J25 (5)	25.35	60.50

NEW REPUBLIC

'nü ri-'pə-blik

LOCATION — In South Africa, located in the northern part of the present province of Natal
GOVT. — A former Republic
CAPITAL — Vryheid

New Republic was created in 1884 by Boer adventurers from Transvaal who proclaimed Dinizulu king of Zululand and claimed as their reward a large tract of country as their own, which they called New Republic. This area was excepted when Great Britain annexed Zululand in 1887, but New Republic became a part of Transvaal in 1888 and was included in the Union of South Africa.

12 Pence = 1 Shilling
20 Shillings = 1 Pound

New Republic stamps were individually handstamped on gummed and perforated sheets of paper. Naturally many of the impressions are misaligned and touch or intersect the perforations. Values are for stamps with good color and, for Nos. 37-64, sharp embossing. The alignment does not materially alter the value of the stamp.

A1

Handstamped

1886-87		Unwmk.	Perf. 11½	
1	A1	1p violet, yel	20.00	22.50
a.		"d" omitted, in pair with normal	2,750.	
1A	A1	1p black, yel		3,250.
2	A1	2p violet, yel	22.50	27.50
a.		"d" omitted	4,750.	
b.		Without date	42.50	50.00
c.		Tête-bêche pair		
3	A1	3p violet, yel	50.00	60.00
a.		Double impression		
b.		"d" omitted (Oct. 13 '86)	4,750.	
c.		Tete-beche pair		
4	A1	4p violet, yel	85.00	
a.		Without date		
b.		"4d" omitted, in pair with normal	3,000.	
5	A1	6p violet, yel	65.00	70.00
a.		Double impression		
b.		"6d" omitted in pair with normal		
6	A1	9p violet, yel	125.00	
7	A1	1sh violet, yel	125.00	
a.		"1/S"	800.00	
b.		"1s" omitted in pair with normal		
8	A1	1/6 violet, yel	120.00	
a.		Without date		
b.		"1s6d"	600.00	
c.		as "b", tete-beche pair		
d.		as "b," "d" omitted	150.00	
9	A1	2sh violet, yel	75.00	
a.		tete-beche pair	875.00	
10	A1	2sh6p violet, yel	190.00	
a.		Without date		
b.		"2/6"	190.00	
11	A1	4sh violet, yel	825.00	
a.		"4/s"		
12	A1	5sh violet, yel	55.00	65.00
a.		Without date		
b.		"s" omitted, in pair with normal	3,500.	
13	A1	5/6 violet, yel	300.00	
a.		"5s6d"	550.00	
14	A1	7sh6p violet, yel	175.00	
a.		"7/6"	250.00	
15	A1	10sh violet, yel	225.00	275.00
a.		Tete-beche pair		
16	A1	10sh6p violet, yel	250.00	
b.		"d" omitted	225.00	
16A	A1	13sh violet, yel	600.00	
17	A1	£1 violet, yel	150.00	
a.		Tete-beche pair	650.00	
18	A1	30sh violet, yel	150.00	
a.		tete-beche pair	750.00	

Granite Paper

19	A1	1p violet, gray	30.00	35.00
a.		"d" omitted	750.00	
b.		"1" omitted in pair with normal		
20	A1	2p violet, gray	22.50	25.00
a.		"ZUID AFRIKA" omitted		
b.		"d" omitted	1,350.	
c.		"2d." omitted in pair with normal		
21	A1	3p violet, gray	40.00	37.50
a.		tete-beche pair	375.00	
22	A1	4p violet, gray	55.00	60.00
23	A1	6p violet, gray	95.00	95.00
a.		"6" omitted in pair with normal	2,750.	
24	A1	9p violet, gray	150.00	
25	A1	1sh violet, gray	45.00	50.00
a.		tete-beche pair	425.00	
b.		"1s." omitted in pair with normal	2,750.	
26	A1	1sh6p violet, gray	125.00	
a.		tete-beche pair	750.00	
b.		"1/6"	190.00	
c.		"d" omitted		
27	A1	2sh violet, gray	150.00	
a.		"2s." omitted in pair with normal	3,250.	

28	A1	2sh6p violet, gray	3,500.	
a.		"2/6"	250.00	
29	A1	4sh violet, gray	525.00	
30	A1	5sh6p violet, gray	425.00	
b.		"5/6"	325.00	
c.		As "a," "/" omitted	4,500.	
31	A1	7/6 violet, gray	325.00	
a.		7s. 6d violet gray	450.00	
32	A1	10sh violet, gray	225.00	225.00
a.		tete-beche pair	525.00	
f.		"s" omitted	—	
32B	A1	10sh 6p vio, gray	275.00	
c.		Without date	—	
d.		tete-beche pair	—	
e.		"d" omitted	600.00	
33	A1	12sh violet, gray	450.00	
34	A1	14sh violet, gray	550.00	
35	A1	£1 violet, gray	375.00	
36	A1	30sh violet, gray	325.00	

Same with Embossed Arms

37	A1	1p violet, yel	22.50	25.00
a.		Arms inverted	30.00	35.00
b.		Arms tete-beche, pair	125.00	135.00
c.		tete-beche pair	950.00	
38	A1	2p violet, yel	27.50	30.00
a.		Arms inverted	30.00	35.00
39	A1	4p violet, yel	80.00	85.00
a.		Arms inverted	125.00	87.50
b.		Arms tete-beche, pair	350.00	
40	A1	6p violet, yel	375.00	

Granite Paper

41	A1	1p violet, gray	30.00	30.00
a.		Imperf. vert., pair	—	
b.		Arms inverted	40.00	45.00
c.		Arms tete-beche, pair	550.00	
42	A1	2p violet, gray	30.00	30.00
a.		Imperf. horiz., pair	—	
b.		Arms inverted	55.00	65.00
c.		Arms tete-beche, pair	550.00	

There were several printings of the above stamps and the date upon them varies from "JAN 86" and "7 JAN 86" to "20 JAN 87."

Nos. 7, 8, 10, 13, 14, 26, 28 and 30 have the denomination expressed in two ways. Example: "1s 6d" or "1/6."

A2

1887   Arms Embossed

43	A2	3p violet, yel	27.50	27.50
a.		Arms inverted	30.00	32.50
b.		tete-beche pair	375.00	450.00
c.		Imperf. vert., pair	—	
d.		Arms omitted	—	
e.		Arms tete-beche, pair	225.00	
f.		Arms sideways	375.00	
44	A2	4p violet, yel	20.00	20.00
a.		Arms inverted	25.00	25.00
45	A2	6p violet, yel	17.50	17.50
a.		Arms inverted	50.00	50.00
b.		Arms omitted	95.00	
c.		Arms tete-beche, pair	375.00	
46	A2	9p violet, yel	17.50	20.00
a.		Arms inverted	250.00	
b.		Arms tete-beche, pair	425.00	
47	A2	1sh violet, yel	20.00	20.00
a.		Arms inverted	75.00	
b.		Arms omitted	—	
48	A2	1sh6p violet, yel	55.00	45.00
49	A2	2sh violet, yel	42.50	45.00
a.		Arms inverted	65.00	60.00
b.		Arms omitted	150.00	
50	A2	2sh6p violet, yel	40.00	40.00
a.		Arms inverted	45.00	45.00
50B	A2	3sh violet, yel	65.00	65.00
c.		Arms tete-beche, pair	80.00	80.00
d.		Arms tete-beche, pair	600.00	
51	A2	4sh violet, yel	650.00	
a.		Arms omitted	—	
b.		"4/s"	65.00	65.00
c.		As "b," arms omitted	275.00	
51D	A2	4/s violet, yel	—	
a.		Arms omitted	—	
52	A2	5sh violet, yel	60.00	60.00
a.		Imperf. vert., pair	—	
b.		Arms omitted	—	175.00
53	A2	5sh6p violet, yel	30.00	35.00
54	A2	7sh6p violet, yel	35.00	37.50
a.		Arms inverted	125.00	
b.		Arms omitted	—	
55	A2	10sh violet, yel	32.50	35.00
a.		Arms inverted	40.00	
b.		Arms omitted	135.00	90.00
c.		Imperf. vert., pair	—	
d.		Arms tete-beche, pair	150.00	
56	A2	10sh6p violet, yel	30.00	32.50
a.		Imperf. vert., pair	—	
b.		Arms inverted	55.00	
c.		Arms omitted	—	
57	A2	£1 violet, yel	75.00	85.00
a.		Arms inverted	80.00	
b.		tete-beche pair	650.00	750.00
58	A2	30sh violet, yel	225.00	

Granite Paper

59	A2	1p violet, gray	32.50	20.00
a.		Arms inverted	150.00	150.00
b.		Arms omitted	30.00	30.00
c.		Imperf. vert., pair	—	
d.		tete-beche pair	650.00	
e.		Arms tete-beche, pair	—	
f.		Arms sideways	—	
60	A2	2p violet, gray	20.00	20.00
a.		Arms inverted	135.00	125.00
b.		Arms omitted	55.00	60.00
c.		tete-beche pair	425.00	
d.		Arms tete-beche, pair	—	

61	A2	3p violet, gray	35.00	35.00
a.		Arms inverted	65.00	65.00
b.		tete-beche pair	450.00	
c.		Arms tete-beche, pair	—	
62	A2	4p violet, gray	30.00	27.50
a.		Arms inverted	110.00	
b.		Tete-beche, pair	375.00	
c.		Arms tete-beche, pair	300.00	
63	A2	6p violet, gray	35.00	35.00
a.		Arms inverted	110.00	
64	A2	1sh6p violet, gray	50.00	42.50
a.		Arms inverted	175.00	
b.		Arms tete-beche, pair	475.00	
65	A2	2/6 violet, gray	—	1,150.
		Nos. 59-64 (6)	202.50	180.00

These stamps were valid only in New Republic.

All these stamps may have been valid for postage but bona-fide canceled examples of any but the 1p and 2p stamps are quite rare.

A £15 violet stamp on yellow paper exists with what is believed to be a fiscal cancel. Value, $50,000.

NEW ZEALAND

'nü 'zē-lənd

LOCATION — Group of islands in the south Pacific Ocean, southeast of Australia
GOVT. — Self-governing dominion of the British Commonwealth
AREA — 107,241 sq. mi.
POP. — 4,796,000 (2018 est.)
CAPITAL — Wellington

12 Pence = 1 Shilling
20 Shillings = 1 Pound
100 Cents = 1 Dollar (1967)

> **Catalogue values for unused stamps in this country are for Never Hinged items, beginning with Scott 246 in the regular postage section, Scott AR99 in the postal-fiscal section, Scott B9 in the semi-postal section, Scott J21 in the postage due section, Scott O92 in the officials section, Scott OY29 in the Life Insurance Department section, and Scott L1 in Ross Dependency.**

Watermarks

Wmk. 6 — Large Star

Wmk. 59 — N Z

Wmk. 60 — Lozenges

This watermark includes the vertical word "INVICTA" once in each quarter of the sheet.

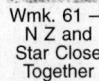

Wmk. 61 — N Z and Star Close Together

Wmk. 62 — N Z and Star Wide Apart

On watermark 61 the margins of the sheets are watermarked "NEW ZEALAND POSTAGE" and parts of the double-lined letters of

these words are frequently found on the stamps. It occasionally happens that a stamp shows no watermark whatever.

Wmk. 63 — Double-lined N Z and Star

Wmk. 64 — Small Star Only

Wmk. 253 — Multiple N Z and Star

Wmk. 387

Values for unused stamps are for examples with original gum as defined in the catalogue introduction.

Very fine examples of the perforated issues between Nos. 7a-69, AR1-AR30, J1-J11, OY1-OY9 and P1-P4 will have perforations touching the framelines or design on one or more sides due to the narrow spacing of the stamps on the plates and imperfect perforating methods.

The rouletted and serrate rouletted stamps of the same period rarely have complete roulettes and are valued as sound and showing partial roulettes. Stamps with complete roulettes range from very scarce to very rare, are seldom traded, and command great premiums.

Victoria — A1

London Print
Wmk. 6
1855, July 20   Engr.   Imperf.
White Paper

1	A1	1p dull carmine	85,000.	20,000.
2	A1	2p deep blue	40,000.	775.
3	A1	1sh yellow green	55,000.	6,000.
a.		Half used as 6p on cover		42,500.

The blueing of Nos. 2 and 3 was caused by chemical action in the printing process.

Auckland Print
1855-58   Blue Paper   Unwmk.

4	A1	1p orange red	14,000.	2,200.
5	Al	2p blue ('56)	4,000.	325.
6	Al	1sh green ('58)	50,000.	4,250.
a.		Half used as 6p on cover		27,500.

Nos. 4-6 may be found with parts of the papermaker's name in double-lined letters.

1857-61   Unwmk.
Thin Hard or Thick Soft White Paper

7	A1	1p orange ('58)	4,000.	825.
e.		1p org vermilion, Wmk. 6 ('56)		36,000.
8	A1	2p blue ('58)	1,450.	200.
9	A1	6p brown ('59)	3,000.	325.
e.		6p bister brown ('59)	4,250.	600.
f.		6p chestnut ('59)	5,000.	650.
h.		6p pale brown	2,850.	350.
10	A1	1sh blue grn ('61)	18,500.	2,250.
e.		1sh emerald ('58)	22,000.	1,850.

No. 7e is identical to a shade of No. 7. The only currently known example is a pair on a cover front. To qualify as No. 7e, a stamp must be on piece or on cover with a cancellation dated prior to 1862.

1859   Pin Rouletted 9-10

7a	A1	1p dull orange		6,000.
8a	A1	2p blue		3,800.
9a	A1	6p brown		4,600.
10a	A1	1sh greenish blue		8,250.

1859   Serrate Rouletted 16, 18

7b	A1	1p dull orange		5,500.
8b	A1	2p blue		4,100.
9b	A1	6p brown		3,800.
g.		6p chestnut		7,750.
10b	A1	1sh greenish blue		7,000.

Value for No. 10b is for a damaged stamp.

1859   Rouletted 7

7c	A1	1p dull orange	9,750.	5,500.
f.		Pair, imperf between		—
8c	A1	2p blue	8,250.	3,500.
9c	A1	6p brown	7,750.	4,750.
l.		Pair, imperf. between	27,500.	13,000.
10c	A1	1sh greenish blue		5,750.
10d	A1	1sh emerald green		7,000.

Roulettes are seldom complete or intact. Values for Nos. 7c to 10d are for stamps with partial roulettes.

1862   Perf. 13

7d	A1	1p orange vermilion		8,000.
8d	A1	2p blue	8,250.	3,800.
9d	A1	6p brown		7,000.

See No. 26.

1862-63 Wmk. 6 Imperf.

11	A1	1p orange ver	1,050.	275.00
d.		1p carmine vermilion ('63)	475.00	300.00
e.		1p vermilion	800.00	275.00
12	A1	2p deep blue	950.00	100.00
d.		2p slate blue	2,000.	200.00
f.		Double impression		4,250.
g.		2p blue, worn plate	950.00	95.00
13	A1	3p brn lil ('63)	750.00	95.00
14	A1	6p red brn ('63)	1,700.	115.00
d.		6p black brown	2,000.	130.00
e.		6p brown ('63)	2,100.	125.00
15	A1	1sh yellow green	2,500.	375.00
d.		1sh deep green	2,750.	650.00

See No. 7e.

1862 Pin Rouletted 9-10

12a	A1	2p deep blue	—	3,100.
14a	A1	6p black brown	—	4,250.

1862 Serrate Rouletted 16, 18

11b	A1	1p orange vermilion	11,500.	2,400.
12b	A1	2p blue	—	1,500.
13b	A1	3p brown lilac	6,000.	1,850.
14b	A1	6p black brown	—	2,250.
15b	A1	1sh yellow green	—	4,500.

1862 Rouletted 7

11c	A1	1p vermilion	4,750.	850.
12c	A1	2p blue	3,750.	500.
13c	A1	3p brown lilac	3,800.	900.
14c	A1	6p red brown	3,500.	525.
15c	A1	1sh yellow green	4,500.	950.

The 1p, 2p, 6p and 1sh come in two or more shades.

1863 Perf. 13

16	A1	1p carmine ver	2,500.	425.00
17	A1	2p blue, no plate wear	2,500.	450.00
18	A1	3p brown lilac	3,250.	525.00
19	A1	6p red brown	1,500.	120.00
c.		As "b," horiz. pair, imperf. btwn.		—
20	A1	1sh green	2,850.	375.00

The 1p, 2p, 6p and 1sh come in two or more shades. See the *Scott Classic Specialized Catalogue.*

1862 Unwmk. Imperf.
Pelure Paper

21	A1	1p vermilion	15,000.	2,750.
b.		Rouletted 7		6,500.
c.		Serrate perf.13		11,000.
22	A1	2p pale dull ultra	5,250.	1,000.
c.		2p gray blue	7,000.	1,000.
23	A1	3p brown lilac	50,000.	
24	A1	6p black brown	3,300.	400.
b.		Rouletted 7	4,250.	525.
c.		Serrate rouletted 15		6,000.
d.		Serrate rouletted 13		6,250.
25	A1	1sh dp yel grn	14,500.	1,100.
b.		1sh deep green	14,500.	1,250.
c.		Rouletted 7	15,000.	2,500.
d.		Serrate rouletted 15		5,000.
e.		"Y" rouletted 18		5,000.

No. 23 was never placed in use.

1863 Perf. 13

21a	A1	1p vermilion	15,000.	3,500.
22a	A1	2p gray blue	9,000.	1,100.
b.		2p pale dull ultramarine	8,000.	1,100.
24a	A1	6p black brown	8,000.	400.
25a	A1	1sh deep green	14,000.	2,100.

1863 Unwmk. Perf. 13
Thick White Paper

26	A1	2p dull dark blue	3,750.	900.
a.		Imperf.	2,000.	1,150.
b.		Pin Roulette 9-10		2,500.

Nos. 26 and 26a differ from 8 and 8d by a white patch of wear at right of head.

1864 Wmk. 59 Imperf.

27	A1	1p carmine ver	950.	325.
28	A1	2p blue	1,750.	275.
29	A1	6p red brown	5,250.	750.
30	A1	1sh green	3,250.	350.

1864 Rouletted 7

27a	A1	1p carmine vermilion	6,250.	4,000.
28a	A1	2p blue	2,500.	775.
29a	A1	6p deep red brown	7,250.	3,100.
30a	A1	1sh green	4,250.	1,150.

1864 Perf. 12½

27B	A1	1p carmine ver	12,000.	5,000.
28B	A1	2p blue	450.	80.
29B	A1	6p red brown	625.	70.
30B	A1	1sh dp yel green	7,750.	3,100.

1864 Perf. 13

27C	A1	1p carmine ver	11,500.	5,250.
d.		"Y" roulette 18		7,000.
28C	A1	2p blue	1,250.	210.
30C	A1	1sh yellow green	2,600.	800.
d.		Horiz. pair, imperf. btwn.		45,000.
e.		Perf. 6½x13		4,750.

1864-71 Wmk. 6 Perf. 12½

31	A1	1p vermilion	225.00	42.50
a.		1p orange ('71)	600.00	95.00
b.		1p pale org & ver	275.00	42.50
c.		1p Imperf. pair	4,500.	2,750.
d.		1p Vert. pair, imperf. btwn.		
32	A1	2p blue	225.00	22.00
a.		2p blue, worn plate	325.00	30.00
b.		Horiz. pair, imperf. btwn. (#32)		5,250.
c.		Perf. 10x12½		19,000.
d.		Imperf., pair (#32)	3,250.	2,250.
e.		indigo ('65), plate II	325.00	75.00
f.		As "e", horiz. pair, imperf. btwn.		
33	A1	3p lilac	165.00	35.00
a.		Imperf. pair (#33)	4,500.	2,000.
b.		As "a", imperf. pair	5,000.	2,000.
d.		3p brown lilac	2,600.	800.00
34	A1	4p deep rose ('65)	3,250.	275.00
35	A1	4p yellow ('65)	250.00	130.00
a.		4p orange yellow	2,350.	1,000.
36	A1	6p red brown	325.00	27.50
a.		6p brown	375.00	42.50
b.		Horiz. pair, imperf. btwn.	3,000.	3,000.
c.		Imperf. pair	2,250.	3,250.
37	A1	1sh yellow green	325.00	125.00
c.		Imperf., pair	5,500.	4,250.

The 1p, 2p and 6p come in two or more shades.

Imperforate examples of the 1p pale orange, worn plate; 2p dull blue and 6p dull chocolate brown are official reprints. Value, each $100.

1871 Wmk. 6 Perf. 10

38	A1	1p deep brown	950.00	130.00

1871 Perf. 12½

39	A1	1p brown	250.00	55.00
a.		Imperf., pair	3,500.	2,250.
b.		Vert. pair, imperf. horiz.	3,500.	5,750.
40	A1	2p orange	190.00	31.00
a.		2p vermilion	225.00	35.00
b.		Imperf., pair	3,000.	4,750.
41	A1	6p blue	500.00	75.00
		Nos. 39-41 (3)	940.00	161.00

1871 Perf. 10x12½

42	A1	1p brown	425.00	55.00
43	A1	2p orange	300.00	42.50
44	A1	6p blue	2,400.	575.00
c.		Vert. pair, imperf. btwn.		6,000.
d.		Horiz. pair, imperf. vert.		—
		Nos. 42-44 (3)	3,125.	672.50

1871 Wmk. 59 Perf. 12½

45	A1	1p brown		11,000.
46	A1	2p vermilion	1,600.	400.00
a.		Imperf., pair	4,750.	

1873 Unwmk. Perf. 12½

47	A1	1p brown	1,150.	260.00
48	A1	2p vermilion	160.00	60.00
49	A1	4p yellow orange	225.00	2,100.

The watermark "T.H. SAUNDERS" in double-line capitals falls on 32 of the 240 stamps in a sheet. The 1p and 2p also are known with script "WT & CO" watermark.

1873 Wmk. 60

50	A1	2p vermilion	3,500.	925.

A2

A3

A4

A5

A6

A7

1874 Typo. Wmk. 62 Perf. 12½

51	A2	1p violet	120.00	15.50
a.		Bluish paper	240.00	45.00
b.		Imperf. pair		1,750.
c.		Perf. 12x12½	1,650.	400.00
52	A3	2p rose	120.00	9.00
a.		Bluish paper	240.00	42.50
b.		Perf. 12	1,300.	210.00
c.		Perf. 12x12½	1,300.	350.00
53	A4	3p brown	210.00	85.00
a.		Bluish paper	400.00	110.00
54	A5	4p claret	315.00	75.00
a.		Bluish paper	625.00	125.00
55	A6	6p blue	275.00	13.50
a.		Bluish paper	475.00	60.00

56	A7	1sh green	625.00	40.00
a.		Bluish paper	1,150.	200.00
		Nos. 51-56 (6)	1,665.	238.00

1874 Perf. 12½, 10

51f	A2	1p violet	175.00	45.00
g.		Bluish paper	275.00	65.00
52f	A3	2p rose	250.00	95.00
g.		Bluish paper	600.00	110.00
53f	A4	3p brown	225.00	90.00
g.		Bluish paper	425.00	125.00
54f	A5	4p claret	850.00	165.00
g.		Bluish paper	425.00	125.00
55f	A6	6p blue	325.00	55.00
g.		Bluish paper	475.00	110.00
56f	A7	1sh green	700.00	150.00
g.		Bluish paper	1,200.	275.00
h.		Vert. pair, imperf. between		6,750.

1878 Perf. 12x11½

51i	A2	1p violet	65.00	9.00
52i	A3	2p rose	70.00	8.00
54i	A5	4p claret	210.00	60.00
55i	A6	6p blue	140.00	12.50
56i	A7	1sh green	225.00	50.00

1875 Wmk. 6 Perf. 12½

57	A2	1p violet	2,000.	310.00
58	A3	2p rose	775.00	45.00

A8

1878 Wmk. 62 Perf. 12x11½

59	A8	2sh deep rose	750.00	450.00
60	A8	5sh gray	800.00	500.00

No. 60 has numeral "5" in each of the four spandrels.

Beware of cleaned fiscally used examples of Nos. 59-60.

A9

A10

A11

A12

A13

A14

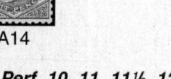
A15

Perf. 10, 11, 11½, 12, 12½ and Compound

1882-98

61	A9	1p rose	9.00	.25
a.		Vert. pair, imperf. horiz.	1,100.	
b.		Perf. 12x11½	55.00	7.50
c.		Perf. 12½	500.00	305.00
d.		Imperf., pair	1,100.	
62	A10	2p violet	16.00	1.00
a.		Vert. pair, imperf. btwn.	950.00	
b.		Perf. 12½	500.00	500.00
c.		Imperf., pair	1,000.	
63	A11	3p orange	60.00	9.50
a.		3p yellow ('99)	62.50	15.00
64	A12	4p blue grn ('97)	62.50	5.00
a.		Perf. 10x11 ('96)	110.00	13.50
65	A13	6p brown	82.50	8.50
b.		6p brown, thin coarse paper ('98)	140.00	14.50
66	A14	8p blue (''98)	85.00	65.00
67	A15	1sh red brown ('97)	120.00	14.00
d.		Vert. pair, imperf. btwn.		1,800.
		Nos. 61-67 (7)	435.00	103.25

See #87. For overprints see #O1-O2, O5, O7-O8.

A15a

A16

A17

1891-95

67A	A15a	½p black ('95)	9.00	.25
b.		Perf. 12x11½	45.00	90.00
68	A16	2½p ultramarine	57.50	4.25
a.		Perf. 12½	550.00	550.00
69	A17	5p olive gray ('99)	75.00	40.00
		Nos. 67A-69 (3)	141.50	44.50

In 1893 advertisements were printed on the backs of Nos. 61-67, 68-69. See #86C. For overprints see #O3-O4, O9.

Mt. Cook A18

Lake Taupo A19

Pembroke Peak A20

Mt. Earnslaw, Lake Wakatipu (Incorrect Spelling on Stamp) A21

Mt. Earnslaw, Lake Wakatipu (Correct Spelling on Stamp) A22

Huia, Sacred Birds A23

White Terrace, Rotomahana A24

Otira Gorge and Mt. Ruapehu A25

Kiwi A26

Maori Canoe A27

Pink Terrace, Rotomahana A28

Kea & Kaka (Hawk-billed Parrots) A29

Milford Sound A30

Mt. Cook A31

Perf. 12 to 16

1898, Apr. 5   Engr.   Unwmk.

70	A18	½p lilac gray	9.00	1.65
a.		Horiz. or vert. pair, im-		
		perf. btwn.	1,750.	1,450.
71	A19	1p yel brn & bl	6.00	.75
a.		Horiz. or vert. pair, im-		
		perf. btwn.	1,350.	1,350.
b.		Imperf. pair	950.00	850.00
72	A20	2p rose brown	57.50	.30
a.		Horiz. pair, imperf. vert.	650.00	
b.		Vert. pair, imperf. btwn.	1,300.	
73	A21	2½p bl (*Wakitipu*)	16.00	47.50
74	A22	2½p bl (*Wakatipu*)	50.00	9.00
75	A23	3p orange brn	35.00	9.00
76	A24	4p rose	17.00	21.00
77	A25	5p red brown	95.00	200.00
		5p violet brown	65.00	25.00
78	A26	6p green	85.00	50.00
79	A27	8p dull blue	75.00	50.00
80	A28	9p lilac	70.00	42.50
81	A29	1sh dull red	100.00	30.00
a.		Pair, imperf. between	5,250.	
82	A30	2sh blue green	275.00	160.00
a.		Vert. pair, imperf. btwn.	5,500.	5,250.
83	A31	5sh vermilion	375.00	525.00
		Nos. 70-83 (14)	1,266.	1,147.

The 5sh stamps are often found with revenue cancellations that are embossed or show a crown on the top of a circle. These are worth much less.

See Nos. 84, 88-89, 91-98, 99B, 102, 104, 106-107, 111-112, 114-121, 126-128, 1508-1521. For overprint see No. O10.

A32   A33

1900   Wmk. 63   Perf. 11

Thick Soft Wove Paper

84	A18	½p green	9.00	2.00
85	A32	1p carmine rose	14.00	.25
a.		1p lake	50.00	6.50
b.		1p crimson	14.00	.25
c.		As "b," pair, imperf. btwn.	1,650.	1,750.
d.		As "c," horiz. pair, imperf. vert.	650.00	
86	A33	2p red violet	15.00	.75
a.		Pair, imperf. btwn.	1,450.	
		Nos. 84-86 (3)	38.00	3.00

Nos. 84 and 86 are re-engravings of Nos. 70 and 72 and are slightly smaller.
See No. 110. For Handstamp see No. O18.

A34

1899-1900   Wmk. 63

86C	A15a	½p black ('00)	9.00	18.00
87	A10	2p violet ('00)	30.00	20.00

Unwmk.

88	A22	2½p blue	21.00	4.00
a.		Horiz. pair, imperf. vert.	1,500.	
b.		Vert. pair, imperf. btwn.	650.00	—
89	A23	3p org brown	27.50	2.50
a.		Horiz. pair, imperf.	700.00	
b.		Horiz. pair, imperf. btwn.	1,525.	
90	A34	4p yel brn & bl ('00)	6.50	4.00
91	A25	5p red brown	50.00	9.00
a.		5p violet brown	60.00	9.00
b.		Pair, imperf. between	3,250.	
92	A26	6p green	70.00	75.00
93	A26	6p rose ('00)	50.00	8.50
a.		6p carmine	50.00	8.00
d.		As #93, horiz. pair, imperf. vert.	600.00	
g.		As #93, horiz. pair, imperf. btwn.	1,400.	
94	A27	8p dark blue	50.00	20.00
95	A28	9p red lilac	60.00	37.50
96	A29	1sh red	70.00	11.00
97	A30	2sh blue green	215.00	60.00
98	A31	5sh vermilion	300.00	400.00
		Revenue cancel		27.50
		Nos. 86C-98 (13)	959.00	669.50

See #113. For overprints see #O11-O15.
The 5sh stamps are often found with revenue cancellations that are embossed or show a crown on the top of a circle. These are worth much less.

"Commerce" — A35

1901, Jan. 1 Unwmk. Perf. 12 to 16

99	A35 1p carmine		7.00	4.50

Universal Penny Postage.

See Nos. 100, 103, 105, 108, 129. For overprint see Nos. 121a, O16, O18, O24, O32, and Aitutaki No. 2. Compare design A35 with A42.

Boer War
Contingent — A36

1901   Wmk. 63   Perf. 11

Thick Soft Paper

99B	A18	½p green	14.00	7.50
c.		Pair, imperf. btwn.	650.00	
100	A35	1p carmine	10.00	.40
a.		Horiz. pair, imperf. vert.	425.00	350.00
101	A36	1½p brown org	10.00	4.00
a.		Vert. pair, imperf. horiz.	1,200.	
b.		As "d," imperf. pair	1,250.	
c.		Horiz. pair, imperf. vert.	1,300.	
		Nos. 99B-101 (3)	34.00	11.90

Perf. 14

99Bd	A18	½p green	24.00	7.00
100c	A35	1p carmine	70.00	23.00
d.		Horiz. pair, imperf. vert.	350.00	

Perf. 14x11

99Be	A18	½p green	12.00	16.50
100e	A35	1p carmine	300.00	125.00

Perf. 11x14

99Bf	A18	½p green	14.00	27.50
100f	A35	1p carmine	2,400.	925.00

Perf. 11, 14 mixed

99Bg	A18	½p green	60.00	90.00
100g	A35	1p carmine	300.00	125.00

No. 101 was issued to honor the New Zealand forces in the South African War.
See No. 109.

Thin Hard Paper

Perf. 14

102	A18	½p green	42.50	42.50
a.		Horiz. pair, imperf. vert.	400.00	
103	A35	1p carmine	18.00	8.00
a.		Horiz. pair, imperf. vert.	300.00	
b.		Vert. pair, imperf. horiz.	300.00	

Perf. 11

102c	A18	½p green	95.00	125.00
103c	A35	1p carmine	165.00	145.00

Perf. 14x11

102d	A18	½p green	50.00	70.00
103d	A35	1p carmine	35.00	20.00

Perf. 11x14

102e	A18	½p green	26.00	55.00
103e	A35	1p carmine	10.00	4.00

Perf. 11, 14 mixed

102f	A18	½p green	70.00	105.00
103f	A35	1p carmine	82.50	87.50

1902   Unwmk.   Perf. 14

104	A18	½p green	35.00	8.50
105	A35	1p carmine	12.50	4.25

Perf. 11

104a	A18	½p green	200.00	210.00

Perf. 14x11

104b	A18	½p green	145.00	210.00
105b	A35	1p carmine	125.00	145.00

Perf. 11x14

104c	A18	½p green	200.00	350.00
105c	A35	1p carmine	145.00	200.00

Perf. 11, 14 mixed

104d	A18	½p green	175.00	250.00
105d	A35	1p carmine	130.00	175.00

1902   Perf. 11

Thin White Wove Paper

106	A26	6p rose red	65.00	80.00
a.		Watermarked letters	120.00	130.00

The sheets of No. 106 are watermarked with the words "LISBON SUPERFINE" in two lines, covering 10 stamps. Value, block of 10 $4,000.

1902-07   Wmk. 61   Perf. 14

107	A18	½p green	9.00	2.75
a.		Horiz. pair, imperf. vert.	300.00	
108	A35	1p carmine	4.25	.25
d.		Horiz. pair, imperf. vert.	200.00	
e.		Vert. pair, imperf. horiz.	200.00	
f.		Booklet pane of 6	275.00	
109	A36	1½p brn org ('07)	25.00	55.00
110	A33	2p dull vio ('03)	12.00	2.75
111	A22	2½p blue	30.00	5.00
112	A23	3p org brown	32.50	8.00
a.		Horiz. pair, imperf. vert.	1,000.	
113	A34	4p yel brn & bl	10.00	4.50
a.		Horiz. pair, imperf. vert.	650.00	
b.		Vert. pair, imperf. horiz.	650.00	
114	A25	5p red brown	40.00	16.00
115	A26	6p rose red	60.00	9.00
116	A27	8p steel blue	45.00	11.50
117	A28	9p red violet	45.00	8.00
118	A29	1sh pale red	175.00	60.00
119	A30	2sh green	150.00	32.50
120	A31	5sh deep red	240.00	300.00
		Nos. 107-120 (14)	877.75	515.25

The unique example of No. 113 with inverted center is used and is in the New Zealand National Philatelic Collection.

1902-03   Perf. 11

107e	A18	½p green	70.00	120.00
108k	A35	1p carmine	800.00	800.00
111e	A22	2½p blue	35.00	11.00
112e	A23	3p yellow brown	37.50	3.50
113e	A34	4p yel brn & bl	6.00	75.00
f.		Horiz. pair, imperf. vert.	650.00	
114e	A25	5p deep brown	55.00	7.50
115e	A26	6p rose	40.00	8.00
h		Horiz. pair, imperf. vert.	850.00	
116e	A27	8p deep blue	55.00	11.50
g.		Horiz. pair, imperf. vert.	2,000.	
h.		Vert. pair, imperf. horiz.	2,000.	
117e	A28	9p red violet	70.00	11.00
118e	A29	1sh orange red	75.00	7.50
119e	A30	2sh blue green	190.00	42.50
120e	A31	5sh vermilion	275.00	375.00
		Nos. (12)	1,709.	1,473.

1902-07   Perf. compound 11 and 14

107i	A18	½p green, perf. 14x11 ('02)	30.00	125.00
j.		Perf 11x14	30.00	90.00
108l	A35	1p carmine, perf 14x11 ('02)	100.00	125.00
m.		Perf. 11x14	150.00	150.00
109i	A36	1½p chestnut ('07)	1,600.	
110i	A33	2p dull violet ('03)	500.00	400.00
112i	A23	3p orange brown	1,000.	750.00
113i	A34	4p yel brn & blue ('03)	450.00	450.00
114i	A25	5p red brown ('06)	1,800.	1,500.
115i	A26	6p rose carmine ('07)	450.00	450.00
116i	A27	8p steel blue ('07)	1,500.	1,500.
117i	A28	9p red violet ('06)	1,750.	1,600.
120i	A31	5sh deep red ('06)	3,500.	3,250.

1903-07   Perf. mixed 11 and 14

107k	A18	½p green	40.00	77.50
108o	A35	1p carmine	35.00	55.00
109k	A36	1½p chestnut ('07)	1,600.	
110k	A33	2p dull violet ('03)	450.00	325.00
112k	A23	3p orange brown ('06)	1,000.	750.00
113k	A34	4p yel brn & blue ('03)	425.00	450.00
114k	A25	5p red brown ('06)	1,400.	200.00
115k	A26	6p rose carmine ('03)	450.00	450.00
116k	A27	8p steel blue ('07)	1,500.	1,500.
117k	A28	9p red violet ('06)	1,650.	1,600.
119k	A30	2sh blue green ('06)	1,750.	1,800.
120k	A31	5sh deep red ('06)	3,500.	3,250.

Wmk. 61 is normally sideways on 3p, 5p, 6p, 8p and 1sh. The 6p exists with wmk. upright. The 1sh exists with wmk. upright and inverted.
See No. 129. For overprints see Nos. O17-O22.
The 5sh stamps are often found with revenue cancellations that are embossed or show a crown on the top of a circle. These are worth much less.

1903   Unwmk.   Perf. 11

Laid Paper

121	A30 2sh blue green		225.00	250.00

No. 108a Overprinted in Green:
"King Edward VII Land"
in Two Lines Reading Up

1908, Jan. 15   Wmk. 61   Perf. 14

121A	A35	1p rose carmine	600.00	67.50
b.		Double overprint		1,600.

In 1908 a quantity of the 1p carmine (A35) was overprinted "King Edward VII Land" and taken on a Shackleton expedition to the Antarctic. Because of the weather Shackleton landed at Victoria Land instead. The stamp was never sold to the public at face value.
Similar conditions prevailed for the 1909-12 ½p green and 1p carmine overprinted "VICTORIA LAND." See Nos. 130D, 131D.

Christchurch Exhibition Issue

Arrival of the Maoris — A37

Maori Art — A38

Landing of Capt. Cook — A39

Annexation of New Zealand — A40

Wmk. 61

1906, Nov.   Typo.   Perf. 14

122	A37	½p emerald	33.50	37.50
123	A38	1p vermilion	27.50	27.50
124	A39	3p blue & brown	100.00	120.00
125	A40	6p gray grn & rose	300.00	400.00
		Nos. 122-125 (4)	461.00	585.00

Designs of 1902-07 Issue, but smaller

1907-08   Engr.   Perf. 14x15

126	A23	3p orange brown	60.00	17.00
127	A26	6p carmine rose	70.00	15.00
128	A29	1sh orange red	250.00	35.00
		Nos. 126-128 (3)	380.00	67.00

Perf. 14x13, 13½ Compound

126a	A23	3p orange brown	72.50	47.50
127a	A26	6p carmine red	425.00	190.00
128a	A29	1sh orange red	190.00	85.00

Perf. 14

126b	A23	3p orange brown	120.00	40.00
127b	A26	6p carmine red	67.50	15.00

The small stamps are about 21mm high, those of 1898-1902 about 23mm.

Type of 1902 Redrawn

1908   **Typo.**   **Perf. 14x14½**
129 A35 1p carmine   40.00 1.00

REDRAWN, 1p: The lines of shading in the globe are diagonal and the other lines of the design are generally thicker than on No. 108.

Edward VII A41   "Commerce" A42

1909-16   **Perf. 14x14½**
130	A41	½p yellow green	7.50	.50
a.		Booklet pane of 6	250.00	
b.		Booklet pane 5 + label	900.00	
c.		Imperf., pair	300.00	
131	A42	1p carmine	2.25	.25
a.		Imperf., pair	375.00	
b.		Booklet pane of 6	225.00	

Perf. 14x14½
Engr.
Various Frames
132	A41	2p mauve	25.00	6.75
133	A41	3p orange brown	25.00	1.40
134	A41	4p red orange	30.00	26.00
135	A41	4p yellow ('12)	25.00	15.00
136	A41	5p red brown	22.00	3.75
137	A41	6p carmine rose ('10)	47.50	1.75
138	A41	8p deep blue	21.00	2.90
139	A41	1sh vermilion ('10)	85.00	9.50
		Nos. 130-139 (10)	290.25	67.80

Perf. 14
133a	A41	3p orange brown ('10)	65.00	25.00
134a	A41	4p red orange ('10)	27.50	18.00
136a	A41	5p red brown	32.50	5.00
137a	A41	6p carmine rose	55.00	12.00
138a	A41	8p deep blue ('16)	70.00	120.00
d.		No wmk.	150.00	240.00
139a	A41	1sh vermilion	85.00	17.50

Perf. 14x13½
133b	A41	3p orange brown	95.00	160.00
c.		Vert. pair, perf. 14x13½ and 14x14½	310.00	600.00
136b	A41	5p red brown	24.00	3.75
c.		Vert. pair, perf. 14x13½ and 14x14½	200.00	210.00
137b	A41	6p carmine rose	95.00	160.00
c.		Vert. pair, perf. 14x13½ and 14x14½	310.00	750.00
138b	A41	8p deep blue	62.50	4.00
c.		Vert. pair, perf. 14x13½ and 14x14½	200.00	200.00

See No. 177. For overprints see Nos. 130d-131d, 130e-137e, O33-O37, O49, O54; Cook Islands No. 49.

Nos. 130-131 Overprinted in Black in Two Lines

1911-13
130D	A41	½p yellow green ('13)	1,100.	1,100.
131D	A42	1p carmine	75.00	150.00

See note after No. 121A.
Issue dates: 1p, Feb. 9; ½p, Jan. 18, 1913.

Stamps of 1909 Overprinted in Black

1913
130E	A41	½p yellow green	30.00	40.00
131E	A42	1p carmine	35.00	45.00
133E	A41	3p orange brown	250.00	400.00
137E	A41	6p carmine rose	300.00	500.00
		Nos. 130E-137E (4)	615.00	985.00

This issue was valid only within New Zealand and to Australia from Dec. 1, 1913, to Feb. 28, 1914. The Auckland Stamp Collectors Club inspired this issue.

King George V — A43

1915, July 30   **Typo.**   **Perf. 14x15**
144	A43	½p yellow green	1.60	.25
a.		Perf. 14 ('27)	3.25	.40
b.		Booklet pane of 6	160.00	

See Nos. 163-164, 176, 178. For overprints see Nos. O41, O45-O46, MR1; Cook Islands No. 48.

A44   A45

1915-22   **Engr.**   **Perf. 14x13½**
145	A44	1½p gray	4.25	2.00
a.		Perf. 14x14½	5.50	2.00
b.		Vert. pair, both perfs	39.00	110.00
146	A45	2p purple	14.00	37.50
a.		Perf. 14x14½	7.75	55.00
b.		Vert. pair, both perfs	30.00	175.00
147	A45	2p org yel ('16)	8.75	30.00
a.		Perf. 14x14½	8.75	30.00
b.		Vert. pair, both perfs	23.00	275.00
148	A44	2½p dull blue	9.00	7.50
a.		Perf. 14x14½	10.00	35.00
b.		Vert. pair, both perfs	45.00	200.00
149	A45	3p violet brown	12.50	2.25
a.		Vert. pair, both perfs	55.00	150.00
b.		Perf. 14x14½	13.00	2.25
150	A45	4p org yel	7.00	47.50
a.		Vert. pair, both perfs	30.00	275.00
b.		Perf. 14x14½	7.00	47.50
151	A45	4p purple ('16)	17.50	.65
a.		Perf. 14x14½	9.25	.65
b.		Vert. pair, both perfs	65.00	165.00
c.		4p blackish violet ('26)	55.00	15.00
d.		Vert. pair, top stamp imperf., bottom stamp perf 3 sides	1,500.	
e.		As "c," perf. 14x14½	10.00	.55
f.		As "c," vert. pair, both perfs	10.00	.55
152	A44	4½p dark green	25.00	26.00
a.		Perf. 14x14½	15.00	60.00
b.		Vert. pair, both perfs	2,500.	190.00
153	A45	5p lt blue ('22)	19.00	2.25
a.		Imperf., pair	200.00	200.00
b.		Perf. 14x14½	13.00	17.50
c.		Vert. pair, both perfs	90.00	275.00
154	A45	6p carmine rose	12.00	.55
a.		Horiz. pair, imperf. vert.	1,500.	
b.		Perf. 14x14½	12.00	.65
c.		Vert. pair, both perfs	70.00	155.00
155	A44	7½p red brown	22.50	26.00
a.		Perf. 14x14½ ('20)	12.00	90.00
b.		Vert. pair, both perfs	55.00	250.00
156	A45	8p blue ('21)	21.50	45.00
a.		Perf. 14x14½	9.50	60.00
b.		Vert. pair, both perfs	42.50	200.00
157	A45	8p red brn ('22)	35.00	4.00
158	A45	9p olive green	30.00	5.00
a.		Imperf., pair	1,500.	
b.		Perf. 14x14½	16.50	32.50
c.		Vert. pair, both perfs	82.50	250.00
159	A45	1sh vermilion	30.00	2.25
a.		Imperf., pair	2,250.	
b.		Perf. 14x14½	15.00	.55
c.		Vert. pair, both perfs	82.50	300.00
		Nos. 145-159 (15)	268.00	238.45

Nos. 151c and 153 exist with the perf varieties reversed. These are rare. No. 157 only comes perf. 14x13½.
For overprints see Nos. O47-O48, O50-O53; Cook Islands Nos. 53-60.

A46   A47

No. 160   No. 161

The engr. stamps have a background of geometric lathe-work; the typo. stamps have a background of crossed dotted lines.
Type A43 has three diamonds at each side of the crown, type A46 has two, and type A47 has one.

1916-19   **Typo.**   **Perf. 14x15**
160	A46	1½p gray black	15.00	1.00
161	A47	1½p gray black	9.00	.60
162	A47	1½p brown org ('18)	4.00	.75
a.		Perf. 14 ('29)	10.00	45.00
163	A43	2p yellow	3.00	.25
a.		Perf. 14 ('29)	3.50	.25
164	A43	3p chocolate ('19)	12.00	1.60
a.		Perf. 14 ('29)	9.50	4.00
		Nos. 160-164 (5)	43.00	4.20

In 1916 the 1½, 2, 3 and 6p of the 1915-16 issue and the 8p of the 1909 issue were printed on paper intended for the long rectangular stamps of the 1902-07 issue. In this paper the watermarks are set wide apart, so that the smaller stamps often show only a

---

small part of the watermark or miss it altogether.
For overprints see Nos. O42-O44; Cook Islands Nos. 50-52.

Victory Issue

"Peace" and British Lion — A48   Peace and Lion — A49

Maori Chief — A50   British Lion — A51

"Victory" A52   King George V, Lion and Maori Fern at Sides A53

1920, Jan. 27   **Perf. 14**
165	A48	½p yellow green	5.00	3.00
166	A49	1p carmine	3.50	.65
167	A50	1½p brown orange	5.00	.55
168	A51	3p black brown	17.00	17.00
169	A52	6p purple	25.00	25.00
170	A53	1sh vermilion	35.00	55.00
		Nos. 165-170 (6)	90.50	101.20

No. 165 Surcharged in Red

1922, Mar.
174 A48 2p on ½p yellow green   6.00 1.75

Map of New Zealand — A54

1923   **Typo.**   **Perf. 14x15**
175 A54 1p carmine rose   3.00 .70

Restoration of Penny Postage. The paper varies from thin to thick.

Types of 1909-15
N Z and Star "watermark" printed on back, usually in blue

1925   **Unwmk.**   **Perf. 14x14½**
176	A43	½p yellow green	3.50	3.50
177	A42	1p carmine	3.50	.90
178	A43	2p yellow	20.00	62.50
		Nos. 176-178 (3)	27.00	66.90

Exhibition Buildings — A55

1925, Nov. 17   **Wmk. 61**
Surface Tinted Paper
179	A55	½p yel green, grnsh	4.50	7.50
180	A55	1p car rose, pink	4.75	6.75
181	A55	4p red violet, lilac	45.00	92.50
		Nos. 179-181 (3)	54.25	106.75

Dunedin Exhibition.

George V in Admiral's Uniform A56   In Field Marshal's Uniform A57

1926   **Perf. 14**
182	A56	2sh blue	72.50	35.00
a.		2sh dark blue	75.00	75.00
183	A56	3sh violet	175.00	170.00
a.		3sh deep violet	150.00	200.00
184	A57	1p rose red	2.40	.25
a.		Booklet pane of 6	150.00	
b.		Imperf., pair	275.00	
c.		Perf. 14x15	.85	.55
		Nos. 182-184 (3)	249.90	205.25

For overprints see Nos. O55-O56 and Cook Islands Nos. 74-75.

Pied Fantail and Clematis A58   Kiwi and Cabbage Palm A59

Maori Woman Cooking in Boiling Spring A60   Maori Council House (Whare) A61

Mt. Cook and Mountain Lilies A62   Maori Girl Wearing Tiki A63

Mitre Peak A64   Striped Marlin A65

Harvesting A66   Tuatara A67

Maori Panel from Door A68   Tui or Parson Bird A69

Capt. Cook Landing at Poverty Bay — A70

Mt. Egmont, North Island — A71

Perf. 13½-14x13½, 13-14x13½ (189, 192, 197, 198), 13½x14 (193), 14x14½ (195), 14 (191)

1935, May 1   Engr.   Wmk. 61

185	A58	½p bright green	.80	.60
186	A59	1p copper red	1.00	.90
c.		13½x14	85.00	55.00
186A	A59	1p copper red, re-engraved	9.00	3.25
b.		Booklet pane of 6 + ad labels	90.00	
187	A60	1½p red brown	8.25	13.00
a.		Perf. 13½x14	5.50	9.75
188	A61	2p red orange	2.50	1.40
189	A62	2½p dull blue & dk brown	10.00	21.50
a.		Perf. 13½x14	6.50	15.50
190	A63	3p chocolate	25.00	2.50
191	A64	4p blk brn & blk	7.50	2.50
192	A65	5p violet blue	31.00	25.00
a.		Perf. 13½x14	55.00	31.00
193	A66	6p red	17.00	7.50
194	A67	8p dark brown	10.00	13.00

Litho.

Size: 18x21½mm

195	A68	9p blk & scar	27.50	5.25

Engr.

196	A69	1sh dk sl green	23.00	13.00
197	A70	2sh olive green	50.00	31.00
a.		Perf. 13½x14	62.50	35.00
198	A71	3sh yel brn & brn black	42.50	42.50
a.		Perf. 13½x14	42.50	42.50
		Nos. 185-198 (15)	265.00	182.90
		Set, never hinged	575.00	

On No. 186A, the horizontal lines in the sky are much darker.

The 2½p, 5p, 2sh and 3sh are perf. 13½ vertically; perf. 13-14 horizontally on each stamp.

See Nos. 203-216, 244-245. For overprints see Nos. O58-O71, O90.

Silver Jubilee Issue

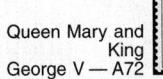

Queen Mary and King George V — A72

1935, May 7   Perf. 11x11½

199	A72	½p dp blue grn	.50	.50
200	A72	1p dark car rose	.50	.50
201	A72	6p scarlet	22.00	27.50
		Nos. 199-201 (3)	23.00	28.50
		Set, never hinged	35.00	

25th anniv. of the reign of King George V.

Types of 1935

Perf. 13½-14x13½

1936-42   Wmk. 253

203	A58	½p bright green	.80	.25
204	A59	1p copper red	1.00	.25
205	A60	1½p red brown	4.00	3.00
206	A61	2p red orange	.25	.25
a.		Perf. 14	13.00	13.00
b.		Perf. 14x14½-15	18.00	18.00
c.		Perf. 12½	2.00	.25
207	A62	2½p dull blue & dk brn	1.50	6.00
a.		Perf. 14	2.50	3.25
b.		Perf. 13-14x13½	5.25	13.00
208	A63	3p chocolate	23.50	1.50
209	A64	4p blk brn & blk	3.85	.65
a.		Perf. 12½	17.50	13.00
b.		Perf. 14	70.00	145.00
c.		Perf. 14x14¼	2.00	.35
210	A65	5p violet blue	3.25	.80
a.		Perf. 12½	22.00	5.25
b.		Perf. 13-14x13½	13.00	2.00
211	A66	6p red, perf. 13½x14	10.00	.80
a.		Perf. 12½	2.50	3.25
b.		Perf. 14x14½	2.00	.25
212	A67	8p dark brown	2.50	3.25
a.		Perf. 12½	2.50	1.50
b.		Perf. 14x14½	2.00	.80

Litho.

Size: 18x21½mm

213	A68	9p gray & scar, perf.14x15	4.00	4.00
a.		9p black & scarlet, perf. 14x14½	32.50	4.25

Engr.

214	A69	1sh dk sl grn	3.50	.25
a.		Perf. 12½	35.00	20.50
215	A70	2sh olive green	6.50	1.50
a.		Perf. 13½x14	225.00	4.00
b.		Perf. 12½	20.00	3.25
c.		Perf. 13-14x13½	42.50	5.25
216	A71	3sh yel brn & blk brn	7.25	4.00
a.		Perf. 12½ ('41)	45.00	50.00
b.		Perf. 13-14x13½	27.50	10.00
		Nos. 203-216 (14)	71.30	26.50
		Set, never hinged	135.00	

Perf. 13-14x13½ is perforated 13 on half of each horizontal side and 14 on the other half.

Wool Industry — A73

Butter Industry — A74

Sheep Farming — A75

Apple Industry — A76

Shipping — A77

1936, Oct. 1   Wmk. 61   Perf. 11

218	A73	½p emerald	.25	.30
219	A74	1p red	.25	.30
220	A75	2½p deep blue	2.50	3.25
221	A76	4p dark purple	2.50	3.25
222	A77	6p red brown	2.75	3.25
		Nos. 218-222 (5)	8.25	10.35
		Set, never hinged		13.25

Congress of the Chambers of Commerce of the British Empire held in New Zealand.

Queen Elizabeth and King George VI — A78

Perf. 13½x13

1937, May 13   Wmk. 253

223	A78	1p rose carmine	.25	.25
224	A78	2½p dark blue	.50	.65
225	A78	6p vermilion	1.00	1.35
		Nos. 223-225 (3)	1.75	2.25
		Set, never hinged		3.00

Coronation of George VI and Elizabeth.

A79   A80

1938-44   Engr.   Perf. 13½

226	A79	½p emerald	3.25	.25
226B	A79	½p brown org ('41)	.25	.25
227	A79	1p rose red	2.75	.25
227A	A79	1p lt blue grn ('41)	.25	.25
228	A80	1½p red brown	13.50	2.40
228B	A80	1½p red ('44)	.25	.25
228C	A80	3p blue ('41)	.25	.25
		Nos. 226-228C (7)	20.50	3.90
		Set, never hinged		39.00

See Nos. 258-264. For surcharges and overprints see Nos. 242-243, 279, 285, O72-O74, O88-O89, O92-O97.

Landing of the Maoris in 1350 — A81

Captain Cook, His Map of New Zealand, 1769, H.M.S. Endeavour — A82

Victoria, Edward VII, George V, Edward VIII and George VI — A83

Abel Tasman, Ship, and Chart of West Coast of New Zealand A84

Treaty of Waitangi, 1840 A85

Pioneer Settlers Landing on Petone Beach, 1840 — A86

The Progress of Transport A87

H.M.S. "Britomart" at Akaroa A88

Route of Ship Carrying First Shipment of Frozen Mutton to England — A89

Maori Council — A90

Gold Mining in 1861 and Modern Gold Dredge A91

Giant Kauri A92

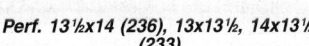

Perf. 13½x14 (236), 13x13½, 14x13½ (233)

1940, Jan. 2   Engr.   Wmk. 253

229	A81	½p dk blue green	.30	.25
230	A82	1p scarlet & sepia	.65	.25
231	A83	1½p brt vio & ultra	.40	.25
232	A84	2p blk brn & Prus grn	1.10	.25
233	A85	2½p dk bl & myr grn	1.10	.70
234	A86	3p dp plum & dk vio	3.25	.40
235	A87	4p dk red vio & vio brn	3.75	1.35
236	A88	5p brown & lt bl	3.25	2.40
237	A89	6p vio & brt grn	5.75	.70
238	A90	7p org red & black	3.75	6.50
239	A90	8p red & black	6.25	2.75
240	A91	9p dp org & olive	6.50	6.75
241	A92	1sh dk sl grn & ol	22.00	4.00
		Nos. 229-241 (13)	58.05	26.55
		Set, never hinged		110.00

Centenary of British sovereignty established by the treaty of Waitangi.

Imperfs of #229-241 exist. These probably are plate proofs.

For surcharge and overprints see Nos. 246, O76-O86.

Nos. 226 and 228 Surcharged in Black

1941   Wmk. 253   Perf. 13½

242	A79	1p on ½p emerald	.60	.25
243	A80	2p on 1½p red brn	.60	.25
		Set, never hinged		2.25

Type of 1935 Redrawn

1941   Typo.   Wmk. 61   Perf. 14x15

Size: 17½x20½mm

244	A68	9p int black & scarlet	75.00	35.00

Wmk. 253

245	A68	9p int black & scarlet	3.00	3.00
		Set, never hinged		156.00

> Catalogue values for unused stamps in this section, from this point to the end of the section, are for Never Hinged items.

No 231 Srchd. in Black

1944   Perf. 13½x13

246	A83	10p on 1½p brt vio & ultra	.45	1.00

Peace Issue

Lake Matheson A93

Parliament House, Wellington A94

St. Paul's Cathedral, London A95

The Royal Family A96

Badge of Royal New Zealand Air Force — A97

New Zealand Army Overseas Badge — A98

Badge of Royal Navy — A99

New Zealand Coat of Arms A100

Knight, Window of Wellington Boys' College A101

Natl. Memorial Campanile, Wellington A103

Southern Alps and Chapel Altar A102

Engr.; Photo. (1½p, 1sh)
Perf. 13x13½, 13½x13
1946, Apr. 1   **Wmk. 253**

247	A93	½p choc & grn	.25	.60
248	A94	1p emerald	.25	.25
249	A95	1½p scarlet	.25	.25
250	A96	2p rose violet	.25	.25
251	A97	3p dk grn & ultra	.25	.25
252	A98	4p brn org & ol grn	.30	.25
253	A99	5p ultra & grn	.25	.25
254	A100	6p org red & red brn	.35	.25
255	A101	8p brown lake & blk	.35	.25
256	A102	9p black & brt bl	.35	.60
257	A103	1sh gray black	.50	.45
		Nos. 247-257 (11)	3.35	3.65

Return to peace at the close of WWII.
Imperfs exist from the printer's archives.

George VI Type of 1938 and

King George VI — A104

1947   **Engr.**   **Perf. 13½**

258	A80	2p red org	.30	.25
260	A80	4p rose lilac	.65	.25
261	A80	5p gray	1.00	.25
262	A80	6p rose red	1.00	.25
263	A80	8p deep violet	1.30	.25
264	A80	9p sepia	1.90	.25

Perf. 14

265	A104	1sh rose car & chnt	1.90	.25
266	A104	1sh3p ultra & chnt	3.25	.40
267	A104	2sh gray grn & org brn	6.50	.60
268	A104	3sh gray blk & chnt	13.50	2.50
		Nos. 258-268 (10)	31.30	5.25

Nos. 265-267 have watermark either upright or sideways. On No. 268 watermark is always sideways.
For overprints see Nos. O98-O99.

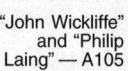

"John Wickliffe" and "Philip Laing" — A105

Cromwell, Otago A106

First Church, Dunedin A107

University of Otago — A108

1948, Feb. 23   **Perf. 13½**

269	A105	1p green & blue	.25	.25
270	A106	2p brown & green	.25	.25
271	A107	3p violet	.25	.25
272	A108	6p brt rose & gray blk	.35	.35
		Nos. 269-272 (4)	1.10	1.10

Otago Province settlement, cent.

> A Royal Visit set of four was prepared but not issued. Examples of the 3p have appeared in the stamp market.

A109

Black Surcharge
Wmk. 253
1950, July 28   **Typo.**   **Perf. 14**

273	A109	1½p rose red	.40	.40

No. 273 was not issued without surcharge.
See Nos. 367, 404A-404D, AR46-69.

Cathedral at Christchurch A110

"They Passed this Way" A111

3p, John Robert Godley. 6p, Canterbury University College. 1sh, View of Timaru.

1950, Nov. 20   **Engr.**   **Perf. 13x13½**

274	A110	1p dl gray grn & blue	.35	.35
275	A111	2p car & red org	.35	.35
276	A110	3p indigo & blue	.35	.35
277	A111	6p brown & blue	.50	.50
278	A111	1sh claret & blue	.70	.70
		Nos. 274-278 (5)	2.25	2.25

Centenary of the founding of Canterbury Provincial District.
Imperfs of #274-278 exist.

No. 227A Surcharged in Black
1952, Dec.   **Perf. 13½**

279	A79	3p on 1p lt blue green	.30	.25

Coronation Issue

Buckingham Palace and Elizabeth II A112

Queen Elizabeth II A113

Westminster Abbey — A114

Crown and royal scepter — A114a

Designs: 4p, Queen Elizabeth and state coach.

Perf. 13x12½, 14x14½ (3p, 8p)
Engr., Photo. (3p, 8p)
1953, May 25

280	A112	2p ultramarine	.30	.25
281	A113	3p brown	.30	.25
282	A112	4p carmine	.50	.70
283	A114	8p slate black	.85	1.35
284	A114a	1sh6p vio blue & pur	1.35	2.00
		Nos. 280-284 (5)	3.30	4.55

See Nos. 1869-1873.

No. 226B Surcharged in Black
1953, Sept.   **Perf. 13½**

285	A79	1p on ½p brown orange	.40	.25

Queen Elizabeth II A115

Queen Elizabeth II and Duke of Edinburgh A116

Perf. 12½x13½, 13½x13
1953, Dec. 9   **Engr.**

286	A115	3p lilac	.25	.25
287	A116	4p deep blue	.25	.25

Visit of Queen Elizabeth II and the Duke of Edinburgh.

A117

A118

A119

1953-57   **Perf. 13½**

288	A117	½p gray	.25	.30
289	A117	1p orange	.25	.25
290	A117	1½p rose brown	.25	.25
291	A117	2p blue green	.25	.25
292	A117	3p red	.25	.25
293	A117	4p blue	.35	.30
294	A117	6p rose violet	1.10	.75
295	A117	8p rose car	.80	.60
296	A118	9p emer & org brn	1.20	.30
297	A118	1sh car & blk	1.25	.30
298	A118	1sh6p blue & blk	2.40	.30
298A	A119	1sh9p org & blk	5.00	1.25
298B	A119	2sh6p redsh brn	37.50	5.25
299	A119	3sh blue green	16.00	.65
300	A119	5sh rose car	37.50	4.75
301	A119	10sh vio blue	75.00	25.00
		Nos. 288-301 (16)	179.35	40.70

The 1½p was issued in 1953; 1sh9p and 2sh6p in 1957; all others in 1954.
No. 298A exists on both ordinary and chalky paper.
Two dies of the 1sh differ in shading on the sleeve.
Imperfs of Nos. 298B-301 and tete-beche pairs of No. 301 and 312 exist from the printer's archives.
See Nos. 306-312. For surcharge see No. 320.

Maori Mailman A120

Queen Elizabeth II A121

Douglas DC-3 — A122

Perf. 13½ (2p), 14 (3p), 13 (4p)
1955, July 18   **Wmk. 253**

302	A120	2p deep grn & brn	.25	.25
303	A121	3p claret	.25	.25
304	A122	4p ultra & black	.30	.40
		Nos. 302-304 (3)	.80	.90

Cent. of New Zealand's 1st postage stamps.

Type of 1953-54 Redrawn
1955-59   **Wmk. 253**   **Perf. 13½**

306	A117	1p orange ('56)	.50	.25
307	A117	1½p rose brown	1.25	.45
308	A117	2p bl grn ('56)	.50	.25
309	A117	3p vermilion ('56)	.50	.25
310	A117	4p blue ('58)	3.00	.70
311	A117	6p purple	4.25	.25
312	A117	8p brown red ('59)	5.00	5.00
		Nos. 306-312 (7)	15.00	7.15

The numeral has been enlarged and the ornament in the lower right corner omitted.
Nos. 306, 308-310 exist on both ordinary and chalky paper.
Imperfs exist.
For surcharges see Nos. 319, 354.

Whalers of Foveaux Strait — A123

"Agriculture" with Cow and Sheep A124

Notornis (Takahe) A125

1956, Jan.   **Perf. 13x12½, 13 (8p)**

313	A123	2p deep green	.30	.25
314	A124	3p sepia	.25	.25
315	A125	8p car & blue vio	1.20	1.20
		Nos. 313-315 (3)	1.75	1.70

Southland centennial.

Lamb and Map of New Zealand A126

Lamb, S. S. "Dunedin" and Refrigeration Ship A127

Perf. 14x14½, 14½x14
1957, Feb. 15   **Photo.**

316	A126	4p bright blue	.80	.85
317	A127	8p vermilion	1.50	1.75

New Zealand Meat Export Trade, 75th anniv.

Sir Truby King — A128

1957, May 14   **Engr.**   **Perf. 13**

318	A128	3p rose red	.25	.25

Plunket Society, 50th anniversary.
Imperfs exist. These probably are plate proofs.

Nos. 307, 290 Surcharged

1958, Jan. 15   **Perf. 13½**

319	A117	2p on 1½p (#307)	.35	.25
a.		Small surcharge	.25	.25
320	A117	2p on 1½p (#290)	170.00	200.00
a.		Small surcharge		

Surcharge measures 9½mm vert. on Nos. 319-320; 9mm on No. 319a-320a. Diameter of dot 4½mm on Nos. 319-320; 3¾mm on No. 319a-320a.
Counterfeits exist.

Sir Charles Kingsford-Smith and "Southern Cross" — A129

Perf. 14x14½
1958, Aug. 27   **Engr.**   **Wmk. 253**

321	A129	6p brt violet blue	.45	.60

1st air crossing of the Tasman Sea, 30th anniv. See footnote under No. 2322.
See Australia No. 310.

Nelson Diocese Seal — A129a

1958, Sept. 29   **Perf. 13**

322	A129a	3p carmine rose	.25	.25

Centenary of Nelson City.
Imperfs exist. These probably are plate proofs.

Statue of
"Pania,"
Napier
A130

Gannet Sanctuary,
Cape Kidnappers
A131

Design: 8p, Maori shearing sheep.

Perf. 13½x14½, 14½x14
1958, Nov. 3   Photo.   Wmk. 253
323 A130 2p yellow green   .25 .25
324 A131 3p ultramarine   .25 .25
325 A130 8p red brown   1.40 1.60
    Nos. 323-325 (3)   1.90 2.10
Centenary of Hawkes Bay province.

Jamboree Kiwi
Badge — A132

1959, Jan. 5   Engr.   Perf. 13
326 A132 3p car rose & brown   .25 .25
Pan-Pacific Scout Jamboree, Auckland, Jan. 3-10.

"Endeavour" at
Ship
Cove — A133

Designs: 3p, Shipping wool at Wairau bar, 1857. 8p, Salt Industry, Grassmere.

1959, Mar. 2   Photo.   Perf. 14½x14
327 A133 2p green   .25 .25
328 A133 3p dark blue   .25 .25
329 A133 8p brown   1.40 1.60
    Nos. 327-329 (3)   1.90 2.10
Centenary of Marlborough Province.

The Explorer — A134

Westland Centennial: 3p, The Gold Digger. 8p, The Pioneer Woman.

1960, May 16   Perf. 14x14½
330 A134 2p green   .25 .25
331 A134 3p orange   .30 .25
332 A134 8p gray   2.00 2.75
    Nos. 330-332 (3)   2.55 3.25

Manuka
Flower
A135

Timber
Industry
A136

Tiki
A137

Maori Rock
Drawing
A138

Butter
Making — A139

Designs: 1p, Karaka flower. 2p, Kaka Beak Flower. 2½p, Titoki flower. 3p, Kowhai flower.

4p, Hibiscus. 5p, Mountain daisy. 6p, Clematis. 7p, Koromiko flower. 8p, Rata flower. 9p, Flag. 1sh3p, Rainbow trout. 1sh9p, Plane spraying farmland. 3sh, Ngauruhoe Volcano, Tongariro National Park. 5sh, Sutherland Falls. 10sh, Tasman Glacier, Mount Cook. £1, Pohutu Geyser.

Perf. 14½x14, 14x14½
1960-66   Photo.   Wmk. 253
333 A135 ½p dp car, grn
         & pale bl   .25   .25
  b. Green omitted   475.00
  c. Pale blue omitted   350.00 275.00
334 A135 1p brn, org &
         grn   .25   .25
  b. Orange omitted   675.00 400.00
  c. Perf. 14½x13, wmkd.
      sideways   1.50   2.75
335 A135 2p grn, rose
         car, blk &
         yel   .25   .25
  b. Black omitted   550.00
  c. Yellow omitted   600.00
336 A135 2½p blk, grn, red
         & brn   .25   .25
  a. Brown omitted   300.00
  b. Green & red omitted   950.00
  c. Green omitted   400.00
  d. Red omitted   850.00 850.00
337 A135 3p Prus bl, yel,
         brn & grn   .25   .25
  b. Yellow omitted   200.00
  c. Brown omitted   250.00
  d. Green omitted   350.00
  e. Perf. 14½x13, wmkd.
      sideways   1.50   2.75
338 A135 4p bl, grn, yel
         & lil   .25   .25
  a. Yellow omitted   900.00
  b. Lilac omitted   650.00 500.00
339 A135 5p pur, blk, yel
         & grn   .25   .25
  a. Yellow omitted   425.00 350.00
340 A135 6p bl grn, gray
         ol & lil   .25   .25
  a. Light green omitted   450.00 350.00
  b. Lilac omitted   450.00
340C A135 7p pink, red,
         grn & yel   .25   .85
341 A135 8p gray, grn,
         pink & yel   .50   .25
342 A136 9p ultra & car   .50   .25
  a. Carmine omitted   575.00
343 A136 1sh grn & brn   .60   .25
344 A137 1sh3p bl, brn &
         carmine   2.25   .25
  a. Carmine omitted   875.00
345 A137 1sh6p org brn &
         ol grn   1.90   .25
346 A136 1sh9p pale brn   7.00   .60
347 A138 2sh buff & blk   1.90   .25
348 A139 2sh6p red brn &
         yel   3.50   .50
  a. Yellow omitted   1,450.   825.00
349 A139 3sh gray brn   21.00   2.00
350 A138 5sh dk grn   7.00   1.60
351 A139 10sh lt blue   14.00   4.00
352 A138 £1 magenta   18.50   12.00
    Nos. 333-352 (21)   80.90   25.05

Nos. 334c and 337e were issued in coils.
Only on chalky paper: 2½p, 5p, 7p. On ordinary and chalky paper: 1p, 3p, 4p, 6p, 1sh9p, 2sh, 3sh, 5sh, 10sh. Others on ordinary paper only.
Issued: 2p, 4p, 1sh, 1sh3p, 1sh6p, 1sh9p, 2sh, 2sh6p, 3sh, 5sh, 10sh, £1, 7/11/60; 1p, 3p, 6p, 8p, 9p, 9/1/60; 2½p, 11/1/61; 5p, 5/14/62; 7p, 3/16/66; #334c, 11/63; #337e, 10/3/63.
See Nos. 360-361, 382-404.

Adoration of the
Shepherds, by
Rembrandt — A140

Perf. 11½x12
1960, Nov. 1   Wmk. 253
353 A140 2p dp brn & red,
         cream   .30   .25
  a. Red omitted   450.00 450.00
Christmas. See No. 355.

No. 309 Surcharged with New Value and Bars
Two types of surcharge:
Type I — "2½d" is 5½mm wide.
Type II — "2½d" is 5mm wide.

1961, Sept. 1   Engr.   Perf. 13½
354 A117 2½p on 3p vermilion, I   .40 .25
  a. Type II   .40 .25

Christmas Type of 1960
2½p, Adoration of the Magi, by Dürer.

1961, Oct. 16   Photo.   Perf. 14½x14
Size: 30x34mm
355 A140 2½p multicolored   .25 .25

Morse Key and
Port Hills,
Lyttelton,
1862 — A141

Design: 8p, Teleprinter and tape, 1962.

1962, June 1   Wmk. 253
356 A141 3p dk brn & grn   .25 .25
  a. Green omitted   3,000.
357 A141 8p dk red & gray   1.10 1.40
  a. Imperf., pair   2,600.
  b. Gray omitted   2,300.
Centenary of the New Zealand telegraph.

Madonna in Prayer by
Sassoferrato — A142

1962, Oct. 15   Perf. 14½x14
358 A142 2½p multicolored   .25 .25
Christmas.

Holy Family by
Titian — A143

1963, Oct. 14   Photo.   Perf. 12½
359 A143 2½p multicolored   .25 .25
  a. Imperf., pair   300.00
  b. Yellow omitted   500.00
Christmas.

Types of 1960-62
1sh9p, Plane spraying farmland. 3sh, Ngauruhoe volcano, Tongariro National Park.

1963-64   Perf. 14½x14
360 A136 1sh9p brt blue, grn &
         yel   2.75 .50
361 A139 3sh bl, grn & bis   4.50 1.50
Issued: 1sh9p, 11/4/63; 3sh, 4/1/64.

Old and New
Engines — A144

1sh9p, Express train and Mt. Ruapehu.

1963, Nov. 25   Perf. 14
362 A144 3p multicolored   .30 .25
  a. Blue (sky) omitted   550.00
363 A144 1sh9p bl, blk, yel &
         carmine   2.60 3.00
  a. Carmine (value) omitted 2,500.
Centenary of New Zealand Railways.

Cable Around
World and Under
Sea — A144a

1963, Dec. 3   Unwmk.   Perf. 13½
364 A144a 8p yel, car, blk & bl 1.90 2.75
Opening of the Commonwealth Pacific (telephone) cable service (COMPAC).
See Australia No. 381.

Map of New
Zealand and
Steering
Wheel — A145

Perf. 14½x14
1964, May 1   Wmk. 253
365 A145 3p multicolored   .25 .25
National Road Safety Campaign.

Rev. Samuel Marsden Conducting
First Christian Service, Rangihoua
Bay, Christmas 1814 — A146

1964, Oct. 12   Perf. 14x13½
366 A146 2½p multicolored   .25 .25
Christmas.

Postal-Fiscal Type of 1950
1964, Dec. 14   Typo.   Perf. 14
Black Surcharge
367 A109 7p rose red   .40 .70

ANZAC Issue

Anzac Cove,
Gallipoli — A147

Design: 5p, Anzac Cove and poppy.

Perf. 12½
1965, Apr. 14   Unwmk.   Photo.
368 A147 4p light brown   .25 .25
369 A147 5p green & red   .25 .40
50th anniv. of the landing of the Australian and New Zealand Army Corps, ANZAC, at Gallipoli, Turkey, Apr. 25, 1915.

ITU Emblem, Old
and New
Communication
Equipment
A148

Perf. 14½x14
1965, May 17   Photo.   Wmk. 253
370 A148 9p lt brown & dk blue .40 .90
Centenary of the ITU.

Sir Winston Spencer
Churchill (1874-
1965) — A148a

1965, May 24   Unwmk.   Perf. 13½
371 A148a 7p lt blue, gray & blk .25 .50
See Australia No. 389.

Provincial Council
Building,
Wellington
A149

Perf. 14½x14
1965, July 26   Photo.   Wmk. 253
372 A149 4p multicolored   .25 .25
Centenary of the establishment of Wellington as seat of government. The design is from a water color by L. B. Temple, 1867.

ICY
Emblem — A150

1965, Sept. 28   Litho.   Perf. 14
373 A150 4p ol bister & dk red .25 .25
International Cooperation Year.

"The Two Trinities" by
Murillo — A151

1965, Oct. 11   Photo.   Perf. 13½x14
374 A151 3p multicolored   .25   .25
a.   Gold omitted   1,500.

Christmas.

Parliament House, Wellington and
Commonwealth Parliamentary
Association Emblem — A152

Designs: 4p, Arms of New Zealand and
Queen Elizabeth II. 2sh, Wellington from Mt.
Victoria.

1965, Nov. 30   Unwmk.   Perf. 14
375 A152 4p multicolored   .25   .25
a.   Blue omitted   1,000.
376 A152 9p multicolored   1.20 1.20
377 A152 2sh multicolored   5.75 5.75
a.   Red omitted   950.00
      Nos. 375-377 (3)   7.20 7.20

11th Commonwealth Parliamentary Assoc.
Conf.

Scout Emblem, Maori
Pattern — A153

Perf. 14x14½
1966, Jan. 5   Photo.   Wmk. 253
378 A153 4p green & gold   .25   .25
a.   Gold omitted   1,100.

4th National Scout Jamboree, Trentham.

Virgin with Child, by
Carlo Maratta — A154

1966, Oct. 3   Wmk. 253   Perf. 14
379 A154 3p multicolored   .25   .25
a.   Red omitted   350.00

Christmas.

Queens Victoria and
Elizabeth II — A155

New Zealand PO Savings Bank cent.: 9p,
Reverse of half sovereign, 1867, and 1967
dollar.

Perf. 14x14½
1967, Feb. 3   Photo.   Wmk. 253
380 A155 4p plum, gold & black   .25   .25
381 A155 9p dk grn, bl, blk, sil &
         gold   .25   .35

Decimal Currency
Types of 1960-62

Designs: ½c, Manuka flower. 1c, Karaka
flower. 2c, Kaka beak flower. 2½c, Kowhai
flower. 3c, Hibiscus. 4c, Mountain daisy. 5c,
Clematis. 6c, Koromiko flower. 7c, Rata flower.
7½c, Brown trout. 8c, Flag. 10c, Timber
industry. 15c, Tiki. 20c, Maori rock drawing.
25c, Butter making. 28c, Fox Glacier, Westland National Park. 30c, Ngauruhoe Volcano,
Tongariro National Park. 50c, Sutherland

Falls. $1, Tasman Glacier, Mount Cook. $2,
Pohutu Geyser.

Wmk. 253, Unwmkd. (#400)
1967-70   Photo.   Various Perfs.
382 A135 ½c multicolored   .25   .25
a.   Pale blue omitted   325.00
383 A135 1c multicolored   .25   .25
a.   Booklet pane of 5 + label   2.25
384 A135 2c multicolored   .25   .25
385 A135 2½c multicolored   .25   .25
a.   Dark blue omitted   3,750.
386 A135 3c multicolored   .25   .25
387 A135 4c multicolored   .25   .25
388 A135 5c multicolored   .25   .25
389 A135 6c multicolored   .25   .25
390 A135 7c multicolored   .30   .25
391 A137 7½c multicolored   .25   .25
392 A136 8c ultra & car   .30   .25
a.   Red omitted   1,200.
393 A136 10c grn & brn   .40   .25
394 A137 15c org brn &
          slate grn   .50   .40
395 A137 15c grn, sl grn &
          red ('68)   .75   .25
396 A138 20c buff & black   1.25 .25
397 A139 25c brown & yel   1.25 1.25
398 A138 28c multi ('68)   .90   .30
399 A139 30c multicolored   2.90 .75
400 A139 30c multi ('70)   9.00 3.00
401 A138 50c dark green   2.90 .75
402 A139 $1 blue   12.00 4.25
403 A138 $2 magenta   12.00 12.00
404 A138 $2 multi ('68)   30.00 19.00
      Nos. 382-404 (23)   76.70 45.20

Perf. 13½x14: ½c to 3c, 5c, 7c. Perf.
14½x14: 4c, 6c, 8c, 10c, 25c, 30c, $1.
Perf. 13½: 7½c. Perf. 14x14½: 15c, 20c,
28c, 50c, $2.
Issued: 7½c, 8/29/67; No. 395, 3/19/68;
28c, 7/30/68; No. 404, 12/10/68; No. 400,
1970; others, 7/10/67.
The 7½c was issued to commemorate the
centenary of the brown trout's introduction to
New Zealand, and retained as part of the regular series.
No. 395 has been redrawn. The "c" on No.
395 lacks serif; No. 394 has serif.
No. 391 exists with watermarks either sideways or upright.

Coat of Arms — A155a

Decimal Currency
1967, July 10   Wmk. 253   Perf. 14
404A A155a $4 purple   6.00 2.00
404B A155a $6 green   6.00 4.00
a.   Unwmk. ('87)   9.00 4.50
404C A155a $8 light blue   8.00 4.75
a.   Unwmk. ('87)   9.50 12.00
404D A155a $10 dark blue   10.00 4.00
a.   Unwmk. ('87)   11.00 9.00
      Nos. 404A-404D (4)   30.00 14.75

See Nos. AR46-AR69.

Adoration of the
Shepherds, by
Poussin — A156

Perf. 13½x14
1967, Oct. 3   Photo.   Wmk. 253
405 A156 2½c multicolored   .25   .25

Christmas.

Sir James Hector — A157

Design: 4c, Mt. Aspiring, aurora australis
and Southern Cross.

1967, Oct. 10   Litho.   Perf. 14
406 A157 4c multicolored   .25   .25
407 A157 8c multicolored   .40   .55

Centenary of the Royal Society of New Zealand to Promote Science.

Maori Bible — A158

1968, Apr. 23   Litho.   Perf. 13½
408 A158 3c multicolored   .25   .25
a.   Gold omitted   160.00

Publication of the Bible in Maori, cent.

Soldiers of Two
Eras and
Tank — A159

10c, Airmen of two eras, insigne & plane.
28c, Sailors of two eras, insigne & battleships.

1968, May 7   Perf. 14x13½
409 A159 4c multicolored   .25   .25
410 A159 10c multicolored   .50   .50
411 A159 28c multicolored   1.50 1.50
      Nos. 409-411 (3)   2.25 2.25

Issued to honor the Armed Services.

"Universal   Human
Suffrage"   Rights
A160   Flame
                      A161

Perf. 13½
1968, Sept. 19   Photo.   Unwmk.
412 A160 3c ol grn, lt bl & grn   .25   .25
413 A161 10c dp grn, yel & red   .30   .30

75th anniv. of universal suffrage in New
Zealand; Intl. Human Rights Year.

Adoration of the Holy
Child, by Gerard van
Honthorst — A162

Perf. 14x14½
1968, Oct. 1   Wmk. 253
414 A162 2½c multicolored   .25   .25

Christmas.

Romney Marsh
Sheep and
Woolmark on
Carpet — A163

Designs: 7c, Trawler and catch. 8c, Apples
and orchard. 10c, Radiata pines and stacked
lumber. 20c, Cargo hoist and grazing cattle.
25c, Dairy farm in Taranaki, Mt. Egmont and
crated dairy products.

**Wmk. 253 (10c, 18c, 25c); others
Unwmkd.**
Perf. 13½; 14½x14 (10c, 25c)
1968-69   Litho.; Photo. (10c, 25c)
415 A163 7c multi ('69)   .50   .50
416 A163 8c multi ('69)   .80   .80
417 A163 10c multi   .50   .25
a.   Green omitted   950.00
418 A163 18c multi ('69)   1.40 .25
419 A163 20c multi ('69)   1.25 .25
420 A163 25c multi   3.50 .60
      Nos. 415-420 (6)   7.95 2.65

ILO
Emblem — A164

Perf. 14½x14
1969, Feb. 11   Photo.   Wmk. 253
421 A164 7c scarlet & black   .50   .50

50th anniv. of the ILO.

Law Society Coat of
Arms — A165

Designs: 3c, Supreme Court Building, Auckland, horiz. 18c, "Justice" from memorial window of the University of Canterbury Hall,
Christchurch.

1969, Apr. 8   Litho.   Perf. 13½
422 A165 3c multicolored   .25   .25
423 A165 10c multicolored   .40   .40
424 A165 18c multicolored   .70   .70
      Nos. 422-424 (3)   1.35 1.35

Centenary of New Zealand Law Society.

Otago University — A166

Design: 10c, Conferring degree and arms of
the University, horiz.

1969, June 3
425 A166 3c multicolored   .25   .25
426 A166 10c multicolored   .50   .50

Centenary of the University of Otago.

Oldest House in
New Zealand,
Kerikeri — A167

Design: 6c, Bay of Islands.

1969, Aug. 18   Litho.   Wmk. 253
427 A167 4c multicolored   .30   .30
428 A167 6c multicolored   .75   .75

Early European settlements in New Zealand
on the 150th anniv. of the founding of Kerikeri,
the oldest existing European settlement.

Nativity, by Federico
Fiori — A168

Perf. 13½x14
1969, Oct. 1   Photo.   Wmk. 253
429 A168 2½c multicolored   .25   .25

Unwmk.
430 A168 2½c multicolored   .25   .25

Christmas.

Capt. Cook,
Transit of Venus
and
Octant — A169

Designs: 6c, Joseph Banks and bark
Endeavour. 18c, Dr. Daniel Solander and
matata branch (rhabdothamnus solandri). 28c,
Queen Elizabeth II and map showing Cook's
chart of 1769.

1969, Oct. 9   Perf. 14½x14
431 A169 4c dk bl, blk & brt
          rose   .25   .25
a.   Imperf., pair   425.00
432 A169 6c sl grn & choc   1.40 1.40
433 A169 18c choc, sl grn &
          black   2.00 2.00
434 A169 28c dk ultra, blk &
          brt rose   3.75 3.75
a.   Souv. sheet of 4, #431-434 18.50 18.50
      Nos. 431-434 (4)   7.40 7.40

Cook's landing in New Zealand, bicent.

Child Drinking
Milk, and
Cattle — A170

7c, Wheat and child with empty bowl, vert.

1969, Nov. 18 Photo. Perf. 13
435 A170 7c multicolored   1.25 1.25
436 A170 8c multicolored   1.25 1.25

25th anniv. of CORSO (Council of Organizations for Relief Services Overseas).

Cardigan
Bay — A171

1970, Jan. 28 Unwmk. Perf. 11½
Granite Paper
437 A171 10c multicolored   .40 .40

Return to New Zealand from the US of Cardigan Bay, 1st standard bred light-harness race horse to win a million dollars in stake money.

Glade
Copper
Butterfly
A172

Scarlet
Parrotfish
A173

New Zealand
Coat of Arms and
Queen Elizabeth
II — A174

Maori
Fishhook — A175

Egmont National
Park
A176

Hauraki
Gulf
Maritime
Park
A177

Designs: 1c, Red admiral butterfly. 2c, Tussock butterfly. 2½c, Magpie moth. 3c, Lichen moth. 4c, Puriri moth. 6c, Sea horses. 7c, Leatherjackets (fish). 7½c, Garfish. 8c, John dory (fish). 18c, Maori club. 20c, Maori tattoo pattern. 30c, Mt. Cook National Park (chamois). 50c, Abel Tasman National Park. $1, Geothermal power plant. $2, Helicopter over field, molecule (agricultural technology).

1970-71 Wmk. 253 Perf. 13½x13
438 A172 ½c ultra & multi   .25 .25
439 A172 1c dp bis & multi   .25 .25
  a. Bklt. pane of 3 + 3 labels
       ('71)   2.50
  b. Red omitted   275.00
440 A172 2c ol grn & multi   .25 .25
  a. Black omitted   400.00
441 A172 2½c yel & multi   .25 .25
442 A172 3c brown & multi   .25 .25
443 A172 4c dk brown &
           multi   .25 .25
  a. Bright green omitted   250.00 110.00
444 A173 5c dk green &
           multi   .35 .25
445 A173 6c dp car & multi   .45 .25
446 A173 7c brn red &
           multi   .50 .25
447 A173 7½c dk vio & multi   .70 .50
448 A173 8c blue grn &
           multi   .50 .25

Perf. 14½x14
449 A174 10c dk bl, sil, red
           & ultra   .45 .25

Perf. 14x13, 13x14
450 A175 15c brick red, sal
           & blk   .45 .25
  a. Brick red omitted   700.00
451 A177 18c yel grn, blk &
           red brn   .55 .25
452 A175 20c yel brn & blk   .60 .25

Nos. 439, 442 and 443 exist with watermark either sideways or upright.

Perf. 13½x12½
Unwmk.
453 A176 23c bl, grn & blk   .60 .25

Litho.
Perf. 13½
454 A177 25c gray & multi   .70 .25
  a. Perf. 14 ('76)   .60 .25
455 A177 30c tan & multi   .70 .25
  a. Perf. 14 ('76)   2.75 2.00

Photo.
Perf. 13½x12½
456 A176 50c sl grn & multi   .80 .25
  a. Apple grn omitted   27.50
  b. Buff omitted   55.00
  c. Slate grn omitted   350.00

Perf. 11½
Granite Paper
457 A175 $1 lt ultra & multi   1.90 .40
458 A175 $2 ol & multi   3.75 1.60
  Nos. 438-458 (21)   14.50 7.00

The 10c for the visit of Queen Elizabeth II, Prince Philip and Princess Anne.
Issued: 10c, 3/12/70; ½c-4c, 9/2/70; 5c-8c, 11/4/70; 15c-20c, 1/20/71; 25c-50c, 9/1/71; $1-$2, 4/14/71; 23c, 12/1/71.
See Nos. 533-546. For surcharge see No. 480.

EXPO '70
Emblem, Geyser
Restaurant
A178

Designs: 8c, EXPO '70 emblem and New Zealand Pavilion. 18c, EXPO '70 emblem and bush walk (part of N.Z. exhibit).

Perf. 13x13½
1970, Apr. 8 Photo. Unwmk.
459 A178 7c multicolored   .75 .75
460 A178 8c multicolored   .75 .75
461 A178 18c multicolored   1.50 1.50
  Nos. 459-461 (3)   3.00 3.00

EXPO '70 Intl. Expo., Osaka, Japan.

UN Headquarters, New
York — A179

UN, 25th anniv.: 10c, Plowing toward the sun and "25" with laurel.

1970, June 24 Litho. Perf. 13½
462 A179 3c multicolored   .25 .25
463 A179 10c yellow & red   .50 .50

Adoration,
by
Correggio
A180

Tower, Catholic
Church, Sockburn
A181

Christmas: 3c, Holy Family, stained glass window, First Presbyterian Church, Invercargill.

1970, Oct. 1 Unwmk. Perf. 12½
464 A180 2½c multicolored   .25 .25
465 A180 3c multicolored   .25 .25
  a. Green omitted   275.00
466 A181 10c silver, org & blk .45 .45
  Nos. 464-466 (3)   .95 .95

Chatham Islands
Mollymawk
A182

1970, Dec. 2 Photo. Perf. 13x13½
467 A182 1c Chatham Islands lily .25 .25
468 A182 2c shown   .25 .25

G Clef, Emblem
and Spinning
Wheel — A183

Rotary Emblem
and Map of New
Zealand — A184

1971, Feb. 10 Photo. Perf. 13x13½
469 A183 4c multicolored   .25 .25
470 A184 10c lemon, dk blue &
           gold   .50 .50

50th anniv. of Country Women's Inst. (4c) and Rotary Intl. in New Zealand (10c).

Ocean
Racer — A185

8c, One Ton Cup and blueprint of racing yacht.

1971, Mar. 3 Litho. Perf. 13½x13
471 A185 5c blue, blk & red   .25 .25
472 A185 8c ultra & black   .70 .70

First challenge in New Zealand waters for the One Ton Cup ocean race.

Coats of
Arms — A186

1971, May 12 Photo. Perf. 13x13½
473 A186 3c Palmerston North   .25 .25
474 A186 4c Auckland   .25 .25
475 A186 5c Invercargill   .40 .40
  Nos. 473-475 (3)   .90 .90

Centenary of New Zealand cities.

Map of
Antarctica
A187

1971, June 9 Photo. Perf. 13x13½
476 A187 6c dk blue, pur & grn 1.05 .70

10th anniv. of the Antarctic Treaty pledging peaceful uses of and scientific cooperation in Antarctica.

Child on Swing — A188

1971, June 9 Perf. 13½x13
477 A188 7c yellow & multi   .75 .75

25th anniv. of UNICEF.

A189

1971, July 14 Perf. 11½
478 A189 8c Radar Station   .70 .70
479 A189 10c Satellite   .70 .70

Opening of New Zealand's 1st satellite Earth station near Warkworth.

No. 441 Surcharged

1971 Wmk. 253 Perf. 13½x13
480 A172 4c on 2½c multi   .40 .25
  a. Narrow bars   .25 .25

Surcharge typographed on No. 480, photogravure or typographed on No. 480a.

Holy Night, by Carlo
Maratta
A190

The Three
Kings
A191

Christmas: 4c, Annunciation, stained glass window, St. Luke's Anglican Church, Havelock North.

Perf. 13x13½
1971, Oct. 6 Photo. Unwmk.
481 A190 3c orange & multi   .25 .25
482 A191 4c multicolored   .25 .25
483 A191 10c dk blue & multi   .50 .50
  Nos. 481-483 (3)   1.00 1.00

World Rose
Convention — A192

1971, Nov. 3 Perf. 11½
484 A192 2c Tiffany rose   .25 .25
485 A192 5c Peace rose   .35 .35
486 A192 8c Chrysler Imperial
           rose   .75 .75
  Nos. 484-486 (3)   1.35 1.35

Rutherford and
Alpha Particles
Passing Atomic
Nucleus — A193

7c, Lord Rutherford, by Sir Oswald Birley, and formula of disintegration of nitrogen atom.

1971, Dec. 1 Litho. Perf. 13½x13
487 A193 1c gray & multi   .25 .25
488 A193 7c bister & multi   .75 .75

Centenary of the birth of Ernest Lord Rutherford (1871-1937), physicist.

Benz, 1895 — A194

Vintage Cars: 4c, Oldsmobile, 1904. 5c, Model T Ford, 1914. 6c, Cadillac service car, 1915. 8c, Chrysler, 1924. 10c, Austin 7, 1923.

1972, Feb. 2 Perf. 14x14½
489 A194 3c car rose & multi   .25 .25
490 A194 4c brt lilac & multi .25 .25
491 A194 5c brt pur & multi   .25 .25
492 A194 6c dl bl grn & multi .40 .40
493 A194 8c vio blue & multi   .60 .60
494 A194 10c sepia & multi   .70 .70
  Nos. 489-494 (6)   2.45 2.45

13th International Vintage Car Rally, New Zealand, Feb. 1972.

232 NEW ZEALAND

Asian-Oceanic Postal Union — A195

Designs: 3c, Wanganui City arms and Drurie Hill tower, vert. 5c, De Havilland DH89 and Boeing 737 planes, vert. 8c, French frigate and Maori palisade at Moturoa, vert. 10c, Stone cairn at Kaeo (site of first Methodist mission).

1972, Apr. 5   Perf. 13x14, 14x13
495 A195 3c gray & multi   .30 .30
496 A195 4c red org & multi   .30 .30
497 A195 5c dp turq bl & multi .45 .45
498 A195 8c dp olive & multi 1.20 1.20
499 A195 10c bister & multi   1.40 1.40
   Nos. 495-499 (5)   3.65 3.65

Cent. of Council government at Wanganui (3c); 10th anniv. of Asian-Oceanic Postal Union (4c); 25th anniv. of Nat. Airways Corp. (5c); bicent. of the landing by Marion du Fresne at the Bay of Islands (8c); 150th anniv. of the Methodist Church in New Zealand (10c).

Black Scree Cotula — A196

Alpine Plants: 6c, North Is. edelweiss. 8c, Haast's buttercup. 10c, Brown mountain daisy.

1972, June 7   Litho.   Perf. 13x14
500 A196 4c orange & multi   .40 .40
501 A196 6c dp blue & multi   .70 .70
502 A196 8c rose lilac & multi 1.10 1.10
503 A196 10c brt yel grn & multi 1.60 1.60
   Nos. 500-503 (4)   3.80 3.80

Madonna and Child, by Murillo — A197

Christmas: 5c, Resurrection, stained-glass window, St. John's Methodist Church, Levin. 10c, Pohutukawa (New Zealand's Christmas flower).

1972, Oct. 4   Photo.   Perf. 11½
504 A197 3c gray & multi   .25 .25
505 A197 5c gray & multi   .25 .25
506 A197 10c gray & multi   .65 .65
   Nos. 504-506 (3)   1.15 1.15

New Zealand Lakes — A198

1972, Dec. 6   Photo.   Unwmk.
507 A198 6c Waikaremoana   1.00 1.00
508 A198 8c Hayes   1.25 1.25
509 A198 18c Wakatipu   2.10 2.10
510 A198 23c Rotomahana   3.00 3.00
   Nos. 507-510 (4)   7.35 7.35

Old Pollen Street — A199

Coal Mining and Landscape A200

Cloister, University of Canterbury A201

Forest, Birds and Lake — A202

Rowing and Olympic Emblems — A203

Progress Chart — A204

1973, Feb. 7   Litho.   Perf. 13½x13
511 A199 3c ocher & multi   .25 .25
512 A200 4c blue & multi   .25 .25
513 A201 5c multicolored   .25 .25
514 A202 6c blue & multi   .50 .50
515 A203 8c multicolored   .60 .60
516 A204 10c blue & multi   .60 .60
   Nos. 511-516 (6)   2.45 2.45

Centenaries of Thames and Westport Boroughs (3c, 4c); centenary of the Univ. of Canterbury, Christchurch (5c); 50th anniv. of Royal Forest and Bird Protection Soc. (6c); success of New Zealand rowing team at 20th Olympic Games (8c); 25th anniv. of the Economic Commission for Asia and the Far East (ECAFE, 10c).

Class W Locomotive, 1889 — A205

New Zealand Steam Locomotives: 4c, Class X, 1908. 5c, "Passchendaele" Ab Class. 10c, Ja Class, last steam locomotive.

1973, Apr. 4   Litho.   Perf. 14½
517 A205 3c lt green & multi .25 .25
518 A205 4c lil rose & multi .25 .25
519 A205 5c lt blue & multi   .50 .50
520 A205 10c cream & multi   2.10 2.00
   Nos. 517-520 (4)   3.10 3.00

Maori Woman and Child, by Hodgkins — A206

Paintings by Frances Hodgkins: 8c, The Hill Top. 10c, Barn in Picardy. 18c, Self-portrait, Still Life.

1973, June 6   Photo.   Perf. 12x11½
521 A206 5c multicolored   .25 .25
522 A206 8c multicolored   .75 .75
523 A206 10c multicolored .75 .75
524 A206 18c multicolored 1.25 1.25
   Nos. 521-524 (4)   3.00 3.00

Christmas in New Zealand — A207

Christmas: 3c, Tempi Madonna, by Raphael. 5c, Three Kings, stained-glass window, St. Theresa's R.C. Church, Auckland.

1973, Oct. 3   Photo.   Perf. 12½x13½
525 A207 3c gold & multi   .25 .25
526 A207 5c gold & multi   .25 .25
527 A207 10c gold & multi .50 .50
   Nos. 525-527 (3)   1.00 1.00

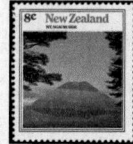

Mt. Ngauruhoe — A208

6c, Mitre Peak. 18c, Mt. Sefton, horiz. 23c, Burnett Range, horiz.

Perf. 13x13½, 13½x13
1973, Dec. 5   Photo.
528 A208 6c multi   .60 .60
529 A208 8c shown   .90 .90
530 A208 18c multi 1.60 1.60
531 A208 23c multi 1.90 1.90
   Nos. 528-531 (4)   5.00 5.00

Types of 1970-71
Designs as before.

Perf. 13½x13
1973-76   Photo.   Unwmk.
533 A172 1c multicolored   .60 1.00
a. Bklt. pane of 3 + 3 labels ('74)   2.50
534 A172 2c multicolored   .30 .25
536 A172 2c multicolored   .50 .50
537 A172 4c multicolored   .45 .25
538 A173 5c multicolored   .60 .60
539 A173 6c multicolored   1.50 1.50
540 A173 7c multicolored   4.00 2.75
542 A173 8c multicolored   4.75 3.50

Perf. 14x13½
543 A174 10c multicolored 1.25 .25

Perf. 13x14, 14x13
544 A175 15c multicolored   .50 .50
545 A177 18c multicolored 2.00 .60
546 A175 20c yel brn & blk .80 .80
   Nos. 533-546 (12)   17.25 12.50

Issued: 2c, 10c, 6/73; 1c, 4c, 6c, 9/7/73; 5c, 1973; 3c, 7c, 8c, 18c, 20c, 1974; 15c, 8/2/76. For surcharges see Nos. 630-631.

Hurdles and Games' Emblem — A209

Designs: 5c, Paraplegic ballplayer. 10c, Bicycling. 18c, Rifle shooting. 23c, Lawn bowling. 4c, 10c, 18c and 23c stamps also show Commonwealth Games' emblem.

1974, Jan. 9   Litho.   Perf. 13x13½
547 A209 4c yellow & multi   .25 .25
548 A209 5c violet & black   .25 .25
549 A209 10c brt red & multi .40 .40
550 A209 18c brown & multi   .60 .60
551 A209 23c yel green & multi .80 .80
   Nos. 547-551 (5)   2.30 2.30

10th British Commonwealth Games, Christchurch, 1/24-2/2. #548 for the 4th Paraplegic Games, Dunedin, 1/10-20.

Souvenir Sheet

New Zealand Day A210

1974, Feb. 6   Litho.   Perf. 13
552 A210 Sheet of 5   1.60 1.60
a. 4c Treaty House, Waitangi
b. 4c Parliament extension buildings   .25 .25
c. 4c Signing Treaty of Waitangi .25 .25
d. 4c Queen Elizabeth II   .25 .25
e. 4c Integrated school   .25 .25

New Zealand Day (Waitangi Day). No. 552 has marginal inscription and imprint.

"Spirit of Napier" Fountain A211

Clock Tower, Bern A212

Design: 8c, UPU emblem.

1974, Apr. 3   Photo.   Perf. 11½
553 A211 4c blue green & multi .25 .25
554 A212 5c brown & multi   .25 .25
555 A212 8c lemon & multi   .60 .60
   Nos. 553-555 (3)   1.10 1.10

Centenaries of Napier (4c); UPU (5c, 8c).

Boeing Seaplane, 1919 — A213

Designs: 4c, Lockheed Electra, 1937. 5c, Bristol freighter, 1958. 23c, Empire S30 flying boat, 1940.

1974, June 5   Litho.   Perf. 14x13
556 A213 3c multicolored   .25 .25
557 A213 4c multicolored   .30 .30
558 A213 5c multicolored   .30 .30
559 A213 23c multicolored 1.90 1.90
   Nos. 556-559 (4)   2.75 2.75

Development of New Zealand's air transport.

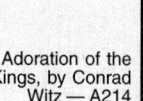

Adoration of the Kings, by Conrad Witz — A214

Christmas: 5c, Angels, stained glass window, St. Paul's Church, Wellington. 10c, Christmas lily (lilium candidum).

1974, Oct. 2   Photo.   Perf. 11½
Granite Paper
560 A214 3c olive & multi   .25 .25
561 A214 5c lilac & multi   .25 .25
562 A214 10c orange & multi .50 .50
   Nos. 560-562 (3)   1.00 1.00

Offshore Islands — A215

1974, Dec. 4   Photo.   Perf. 13½x13
563 A215 6c Great Barrier   .40 .40
564 A215 8c Stewart   .60 .60
565 A215 18c White   .85 .85
566 A215 23c The Brothers 1.00 1.00
   Nos. 563-566 (4)   2.85 2.85

Child Using Walker — A216

Farm Woman and Children — A217

IWY Symbol — A218

Otago Medical School — A219

567	A216	3c orange & multi	.25 .25
568	A217	5c green & multi	.25 .25
569	A218	10c blue & multi	.30 .30
570	A219	18c multicolored	.50 .50

1975, Feb. 5   Litho.   Perf. 13½x13

Nos. 567-570 (4)   1.30 1.30

New Zealand Crippled Children's Soc., 40th anniv. (3c); Women's Division Federated Farmers of N. Z., 50th anniv. (5c); IWY (10c); Otago Medical School cent. (18c).

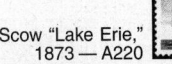

Scow "Lake Erie," 1873 — A220

Historic Sailing Ships: 5c, Schooner "Herald," 1826. 8c, Brigantine "New Zealander," 1828. 10c, Topsail schooner "Jessie Kelly," 1866. 18c, Barque "Tory," 1834. 23c, Clipper "Rangitiki," 1863.

1975, Apr. 2   Litho.   Perf. 13½x13

571	A220	4c vermilion & blk	.25 .25
572	A220	5c grnsh blue & blk	.25 .25
573	A220	8c yellow & black	.40 .40
574	A220	10c yellow grn & blk	.50 .50
575	A220	18c brown & black	.65 .65
576	A220	23c dull lilac & blk	.85 .85

Nos. 571-576 (6)   2.90 2.90

State Forest Parks — A221

1975, June 4   Photo.   Perf. 13½x13

577	A221	6c Lake Sumner	.50 .50
578	A221	8c North West Nelson	.75 .75
579	A221	18c Kaweka	.90 .90
580	A221	23c Coromandel	1.40 1.40

Nos. 577-580 (4)   3.55 3.55

Virgin and Child, by Zanobi Machiavelli (1418-1479) — A222

Stained Glass Window, Greendale Methodist/Presbyterian Church — A223

Christmas: 10c, Medieval ships and doves.

Perf. 13½x14, 14x13½

1975, Oct. 1   Photo.

581	A222	3c multicolored	.25 .25
582	A223	5c multicolored	.25 .25
583	A223	10c multicolored	.45 .45

Nos. 581-583 (3)   .95 .95

Sterling Silver — A224

Roses: 2c, Lilli Marlene. 3c, Queen Elizabeth. 4c, Super star. 5c, Diamond jubilee. 6c, Cresset. 7c, Michele Meilland. 8c, Josephine Bruce. 9c, Iceberg.

1975, Nov. 26   Photo.   Perf. 14½x14

584	A224	1c multicolored	.25 .25
585	A224	2c orange & multi	.25 .25
586	A224	3c ultra & multi	.25 .25
a.		Perf. 14½ ('79)	.25
587	A224	4c purple & multi	.25 .25
588	A224	5c brown & multi	.25 .25
589	A224	6c multicolored ('76)	.25 .25
a.		Perf. 14½	.50 .50
590	A224	7c multicolored ('76)	.25 .25
a.		Perf. 14½	.80 .50
591	A224	8c yellow & multi ('76)	.25 .25
a.		Perf. 14½	.80 .50
592	A224	9c blue & multi	.25 .25

Nos. 584-592 (9)   2.25 2.25

For surcharges see Nos. 693, 695, 718.

Family and Mothers' League Emblem — A225

Designs: 7c, "Weight, measure, temperature and capacity." 8c, 1st emigrant ship "William Bryan" and Mt. Egmont. 10c, Maori and Caucasian women and YWCA emblem. 25c, Telecommunications network on Goode's equal area projection.

1976, Feb. 4   Litho.   Perf. 14

593	A225	6c yel olive & multi	.25 .25
594	A225	7c reddsh pur & multi	.25 .25
595	A225	8c red & multi	.25 .25
596	A225	10c yellow & multi	.25 .25
597	A225	25c tan & multi	.50 .50

Nos. 593-597 (5)   1.50 1.50

League of Mothers of New Zealand, 50th anniv. (6c); Metric conversion, 1976 (7c); cent. of New Plymouth (8c); YWCA in New Zealand, 50th anniv. (10c); cent. of link into intl. telecommunications network (25c).

Gig — A226

Farm Vehicles: 7c, Thornycroft truck. 8c, Scandi wagon. 9c, Traction engine. 10c, Wool wagon. 25c, One-horse cart.

1976, Apr. 7   Litho.   Perf. 14x13½

598	A226	6c dk olive & multi	.25 .25
599	A226	7c gray & multi	.25 .25
600	A226	8c dk blue & multi	.50 .25
601	A226	9c maroon & multi	.40 .30
602	A226	10c brown & multi	.40 .30
603	A226	25c multicolored	.60 .60

Nos. 598-603 (6)   2.40 1.95

Purakaunui Falls — A227

Waterfalls: 14c, Marakopa Falls. 15c, Bridal Veil Falls. 16c, Papakorito Falls.

1976, June 2   Photo.   Perf. 11½

604	A227	10c blue & multi	.25 .25
605	A227	14c lilac & multi	.60 .60
606	A227	15c ocher & multi	.50 .50
607	A227	16c multicolored	.75 .75

Nos. 604-607 (4)   2.10 2.10

Nativity, Carved Ivory, Spain, 16th Century — A228

Christmas: 11c, Risen Christ, St. Joseph's Church, Grey Lynn, Auckland, horiz. 18c, "Hark the Herald Angels Sing," horiz.

Perf. 14x14½, 14½x14

1976, Oct. 6   Photo.

608	A228	7c ocher & multi	.25 .25
609	A228	11c ocher & multi	.35 .35
610	A228	18c ocher & multi	.45 .45

Nos. 608-610 (3)   1.05 1.05

Maripi (Carved Wooden Knife) — A229

Maori Artifacts: 12c, Putorino, carved flute. 13c, Wahaika, hardwood club. 14c, Kotiate, violin-shaped weapon.

1976, Nov. 24   Photo.   Perf. 11½
Granite Paper

611	A229	11c multicolored	.25 .25
612	A229	12c multicolored	.25 .25
613	A229	13c multicolored	.25 .25
614	A229	14c multicolored	.25 .25

Nos. 611-614 (4)   1.00 1.00

Arms of Hamilton A230

Automobile Assoc. Emblem A231

Designs: No. 616, Arms of Gisborne. No. 617, Arms of Masterton. No. 619, Emblem of Royal Australasian College of Surgeons.

1977, Jan. 19   Litho.   Perf. 13x13½

615	A230	8c multicolored	.25 .25
616	A230	8c multicolored	.25 .25
617	A230	8c multicolored	.25 .25
a.		Strip of 3, #615-617	.75 .75
618	A231	10c multicolored	.25 .35
619	A231	10c multicolored	.25 .35
a.		Pair, #618-619	.50 .70

Nos. 615-619 (5)   1.25 1.45

Centenaries of Hamilton, Gisborne and Masterton (cities); 75th anniv. of the New Zealand Automobile Assoc. and 50th anniv. of the Royal Australasian College of Surgeons.

Souvenir Sheet

Queen Elizabeth II, 1976 — A232

Designs: Various portraits.

1977, Feb.   Photo.   Perf. 14x14½

620	A232	Sheet of 5	1.25 1.40
a.-e.		8c single stamp	.25 .25
f.		Sheet imperf.	1,350.

25th anniv. of the reign of Elizabeth II.

Physical Education, Maori Culture A233

Education Dept., Geography, Science A234

#623, Special school for the deaf; kindergarten. #624, Language class. #625, Home economics, correspondence school, teacher training.

1977, Apr. 6   Litho.   Perf. 13x13½

621	A233	8c shown	.40 .40
622	A234	8c shown	.40 .40
623	A233	8c multicolored	.40 .40
624	A234	8c multicolored	.40 .40
625	A233	8c multicolored	.40 .40
a.		Strip of 5, #621-625	2.50 2.60

Nos. 621-625 (5)   2.00 2.00

Cent. of Education Act, establishing Dept. of Education.

Karitane Beach — A235

Seascapes and beach scenes: 16c, Ocean Beach, Mount Maunganui. 18c, Piha Beach. 30c, Kaikoura Coast.

1977, June 1   Photo.   Perf. 14½

626	A235	10c multicolored	.25 .25
627	A235	16c multicolored	.30 .30
628	A235	18c multicolored	.30 .30
629	A235	30c multicolored	.40 .35

Nos. 626-629 (4)   1.25 1.20

Nos. 536-537 Surcharged with New Value and Heavy Bar

1977   Unwmk.   Perf. 13½x13

630	A172	7c on 3c multicolored	.35 .35
631	A172	8c on 4c multicolored	.35 .35

Holy Family, by Correggio A236

Window, St. Michael's and All Angels Church A237

Partridge in a Pear Tree — A238

1977, Oct. 5   Photo.   Perf. 11½

632	A236	7c multicolored	.25 .25
633	A237	16c multicolored	.30 .30
634	A238	23c multicolored	.50 .50

Nos. 632-634 (3)   1.05 1.05

Christmas.

Merryweather Manual Pump, 1860 — A239

Fire Fighting Equipment: 11c, 2-wheel hose reel and ladder, 1880. 12c, Shand Mason Steam Fire Engine, 1873. 23c, Chemical fire engine, 1888.

1977, Dec. 7   Litho.   Perf. 14x13½

635	A239	10c multicolored	.25 .25
636	A239	11c multicolored	.25 .25
637	A239	12c multicolored	.25 .25
638	A239	23c multicolored	.30 .30

Nos. 635-638 (4)   1.05 1.05

A240

A240a

Parliament Building, Wellington — A241

1977-82   Photo.   Perf. 14½

648	A240	10c ultra & multi	.25 .25
a.		Perf. 14½x14	.75 .50

Perf. 14½x14

649	A240a	24c blue & lt green	.30 .25
a.		Perf. 13x12½	.45 .25

Perf. 13

650	A241	$5 multicolored	4.75 3.50

Nos. 648-650 (3)   5.30 4.00

Issued: No. 648, 2/79; No. 648a, 12/7/77; $5, 12/2/81; No. 649, 4/1/82; No. 649a, 12/13/82.

For surcharge see No. 694.

A242

Coil Stamps

1978   Photo.   Perf. 13½x13

651	A242	1c red lilac	.25 .25
652	A242	2c orange	.25 .25
653	A242	5c brown	.25 .25

Perf. 14½x14

654	A242	10c ultramarine	.25 .25

Nos. 651-654 (4)   1.00 1.00

Issue dates: 10c, May 3; others, June 9.

234 NEW ZEALAND

Ashburton
A244

Stratford
A245

Old
Telephone
A246

Bay of Islands
A247

1978, Feb. 1   Litho.   Perf. 14
656 A244 10c multicolored .25 .25
657 A245 10c multicolored .25 .25
a. Pair, #656-657 .50 .50
658 A246 12c multicolored .25 .25
659 A247 20c multicolored .30 .30
Nos. 656-659 (4) 1.05 1.05

Cent. of the cities of Ashburton, Stratford, the NZ Telephone Co. and Bay of Islands County.

Lincoln Univ. College of
Agriculture,
Cent. — A248

Designs: 10c, Students and Ivey Hall. 12c, Grazing sheep. 15c, Mechanical fertilization. 16c, Furrow, plow and tractor. 20c, Combine harvester. 30c, Grazing cattle.

1978, Apr. 26   Perf. 14½
660 A248 10c multicolored .25 .25
661 A248 12c multicolored .25 .25
662 A248 15c multicolored .25 .25
663 A248 16c multicolored .25 .25
664 A248 20c multicolored .25 .25
665 A248 30c multicolored .30 .30
Nos. 660-665 (6) 1.55 1.55

Maui Gas Drilling
Platform — A249

The sea and its resources: 15c, Fishing boat. 20c, Map of New Zealand and 200-mile limit. 23c, Whale and bottle-nosed dolphins. 35c, Kingfish, snapper, grouper and squid.

1978, June 7   Litho.   Perf. 13½x14
666 A249 12c multicolored .25 .25
667 A249 15c multicolored .25 .25
668 A249 20c multicolored .25 .25
669 A249 23c multicolored .30 .30
670 A249 35c multicolored .45 .45
Nos. 666-670 (5) 1.50 1.50

Christmas — A250

Designs: 7c, Holy Family, by El Greco, vert. 16c, All Saints Church, Howick. 23c, Beach scene.

1978, Oct. 4   Photo.   Perf. 11½
671 A250 7c gold & multi .25 .25
672 A250 16c gold & multi .30 .30
673 A250 23c gold & multi .35 .35
Nos. 671-673 (3) .90 .90

Sea Shells — A251

20c, Paua (Haliotis Iris). 30c, Toheroa (paphies ventricosa). 40c, Coarse dosinia (dosinia anus). 50c, Spiny murex (poirieria zelandica).

1978, Nov. 29   Photo.   Perf. 13x12½
674 A251 20c multicolored .25 .25
675 A251 30c multicolored .30 .25
676 A251 40c multicolored .45 .30
677 A251 50c multicolored .55 .40
Nos. 674-677 (4) 1.55 1.20
See Nos. 696-697.

Julius Vogel — A252

19th cent. NZ statesmen: No. 679, George Grey. No. 680, Richard John Seddon.

1979, Feb. 7   Litho.   Perf. 13x13½
678 A252 10c light & dark brown .25 .25
679 A252 10c light & dark brown .25 .25
680 A252 10c light & dark brown .25 .25
a. Strip of 3, #678-680 1.10 1.10

Riverlands
Cottage,
Blenheim
A253

Early NZ Architecture: 12c, Mission House, Waimate North, 1831-32. 15c, The Elms, Anglican Church Mission, Tauranga, 1847. 20c, Provincial Council Buildings, Christchurch, 1859.

1979, Apr. 4   Perf. 13½x13
681 A253 10c multicolored .25 .25
682 A253 12c multicolored .25 .25
683 A253 15c black & gray .25 .25
684 A253 20c multicolored .25 .25
Nos. 681-684 (4) 1.00 1.00

Whangaroa
Harbor — A254

Small Harbors: 20c, Kawau Island. 23c, Akaroa Harbor, vert. 35c, Picton Harbor, vert.

Perf. 13x13½, 13½x13
1979, June 6   Photo.
685 A254 15c multicolored .25 .25
686 A254 20c multicolored .25 .25
687 A254 23c multicolored .25 .25
688 A254 35c multicolored .40 .40
Nos. 685-688 (4) 1.15 1.15

IYC — A255

1979, June 6   Litho.   Perf. 14
689 A255 10c Children playing .25 .25

Virgin and Child, by
Lorenzo Ghiberti — A256

Christmas: 25c, Christ Church, Russell, 1835. 35c, Pohutukawa ("Christmas") tree.

1979, Oct. 3   Photo.   Perf. 11½
690 A256 10c multicolored .25 .25
691 A256 25c multicolored .35 .35
692 A256 35c multicolored .45 .45
Nos. 690-692 (3) 1.05 1.05

**Nos. 591a, 648 and 589a
Surcharged**
1979, Sept.   Perf. 14½, 14½x14 (14c)
693 A224 4c on 8c multi .25 .25
694 A240 14c on 10c multi .25 .25
695 A224 17c on 6c multi .25 .25
Nos. 693-695 (3) .75 .75

Shell Type of 1978
$1, Scallop (pecten novaezelandiae). $2, Circular saw (astraea heliotropium).

1979, Nov. 26   Photo.   Perf. 13x12½
696 A251 $1 multicolored 1.25 .25
697 A251 $2 multicolored 2.40 .75

Debating Chamber,
House of
Parliament — A257

1979, Nov. 26   Litho.   Perf. 14x13½
698 A257 14c shown .25 .25
699 A257 20c Mace, black rod .25 .25
700 A257 30c Wall hanging .40 .40
Nos. 698-700 (3) .90 .90

25th Commonwealth Parliamentary Conference, Wellington, Nov. 26-Dec. 2.

NZ No. 1 — A258

1980, Feb. 7   Litho.   Perf. 14x13½
701 A258 14c shown .25 .25
702 A258 14c No. 2 .25 .25
703 A258 14c No. 3 .25 .25
a. Souvenir sheet of 3, #701-703 2.00 2.00
b. Strip of 3, #701-703 .75 .75

NZ postage stamps, 125th anniv. No. 703a publicizes Zeapex '80 Intl. Stamp Exhib., Auckland, Aug. 23-31; it sold for 52c, of which 10c went to exhib. fund.

Maori Wood
Carving, Tudor
Towers — A259

Earina
Autumnalis and
Thelymitra
Venosa — A260

Tractor Plowing,
Golden Plow
Trophy — A261

1980, Feb. 7   Perf. 14½
704 A259 17c multicolored .25 .25
705 A260 25c multicolored .30 .30
706 A261 30c multicolored .30 .30
Nos. 704-706 (3) .85 .85

Rotorua cent.; Intl. Orchid Conf., Auckland, Oct.; World Plowing Championship, Christchurch, May.

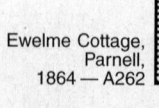

Ewelme Cottage,
Parnell,
1864 — A262

Early NZ Architecture: 17c, Broadgreen, Nelson, 1855. 25c, Courthouse, Oamaru, 1822, 30c, Government Buildings, Wellington, 1877.

1980, Apr. 2   Litho.   Perf. 13½x13
707 A262 14c multicolored .25 .25
708 A262 17c multicolored .25 .25
709 A262 25c multicolored .30 .30
710 A262 30c multicolored .30 .30
Nos. 707-710 (4) 1.10 1.10

Harbors — A263

1980, June 4   Photo.   Perf. 13x13½
711 A263 25c Auckland .30 .20
712 A263 30c Wellington .35 .35
713 A263 35c Lyttelton .40 .40
714 A263 50c Port Chalmers .65 .65
Nos. 711-714 (4) 1.70 1.60

Madonna and Child with
Cherubim, by Andrea
della Robbia — A264

25c, St. Mary's Church, New Plymouth. 35c, Picnic.

1980, Oct. 1   Photo.   Perf. 12
715 A264 10c shown .25 .25
716 A264 25c multi .30 .30
717 A264 35c multi .40 .40
Nos. 715-717 (3) .95 .95
Christmas.

No. 590 Surcharged
1980, Sept. 29   Photo.   Perf. 14½x14
718 A224 20c on 7c multicolored .25 .25

Te Heu Heu Tukino IV,
Ngati Tuwharetoa Tribal
Chief — A265

Maori Leaders: 25c, Te Hau-Takiri Wharepapa. 35c, Princess Te Puea Herangi. 45, Apirana Ngata. 60c, Hakopa Te Ata-o-tu.

1980, Nov. 26   Perf. 13
719 A265 15c multicolored .25 .25
720 A265 25c multicolored .25 .25
721 A265 35c multicolored .35 .35
722 A265 45c multicolored .55 .55
723 A265 60c multicolored .60 .60
Nos. 719-723 (5) 2.00 2.00

Henry A.
Feilding, Borough
Emblem — A266

1981, Feb. 4   Litho.   Perf. 14½
724 A266 20c multicolored .30 .25
Borough of Feilding centenary.

IYD — A267

1981, Feb. 4
725 A267 25c orange & black .35 .35

Family and
Dog — A268

25c, Grandparents. 30c, Parents reading to children. 35c, Family outing.

1981, Apr. 1   Litho.   Perf. 13
726 A268 20c shown .25 .25
727 A268 25c multi .30 .30
728 A268 30c multi .35 .35
729 A268 35c multi .40 .40
Nos. 726-729 (4) 1.30 1.30

Shotover
River — A269

30c, Kaiauai River, vert. 35c, Mangahao
River, vert. 60c, Cleddau River.

1981, June 3   Photo.   Perf. 13½
730 A269 30c multi   .35 .35
731 A269 35c multi   .40 .40
732 A269 40c shown   .50 .50
733 A269 60c multi   .65 .65
  Nos. 730-733 (4)   1.90 1.90

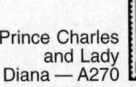

Prince Charles
and Lady
Diana — A270

No. 735, St. Paul's Cathedral.

1981, July 29   Litho.   Perf. 14½
734 A270 20c shown   .30 .25
735 A270 20c multi   .30 .25
  a. Pair, #734-735   .60 .60

Royal Wedding.

Golden Tainui — A271

Christmas: 14c, Madonna and Child, by
Marco d'Oggiono, 15th cent. 30c, St. John's
Church, Wakefield.

1981, Oct.   Photo.   Perf. 11½
Granite Paper
736 A271 14c multicolored   .25 .25
737 A271 30c multicolored   .30 .30
738 A271 40c multicolored   .45 .45
  Nos. 736-738 (3)   1.00 1.00

SPCA
Centenary
A272

Intl. Science
Year
A273

Centenaries: No. 739, Tauranga. No. 740,
Hawera. 30c, Frozen meat exports.

1982, Feb. 3   Litho.   Perf. 14½
739 A272 20c multicolored   .25 .25
740 A272 20c multicolored   .25 .25
  a. Pair, #739-740   .60 .60
741 A272 25c multicolored   .30 .30
742 A272 30c multicolored   .40 .40
743 A273 35c multicolored   .45 .45
  Nos. 739-743 (5)   1.65 1.65

Alberton
Farmhouse,
Auckland,
1867 — A274

25c, Caccia Birch, Palmerston North, 1893.
30c, Dunedin Railway Station, 1904. 35c, PO,
Ophir, 1886.

1982, Apr. 7   Litho.
744 A274 20c shown   .25 .25
745 A274 25c multicolored   .30 .30
746 A274 30c multicolored   .45 .45
747 A274 35c multicolored   .45 .45
  Nos. 744-747 (4)   1.45 1.45

Summer,
Kaiteriteri — A275

40c, Autumn, Queenstown. 45c, Winter, Mt.
Ngauruhoe. 70c, Spring, Wairarapa.

1982, June 2   Photo.   Perf. 13½
748 A275 35c shown   .40 .40
749 A275 40c multicolored   .45 .45
750 A275 45c multicolored   .50 .50
751 A275 70c multicolored   .85 .85
  Nos. 748-751 (4)   2.20 2.20

Madonna with Child and
Two Angels, by Piero di
Cosimo — A276

Christmas: 35c, Rangiatea Maori Church,
Otaki. 45c, Surf life-saving patrol.

1982, Oct. 6   Photo.   Perf. 14
752 A276 18c multicolored   .25 .25
753 A276 35c multicolored   .35 .35
754 A276 45c multicolored   .60 .60
  Nos. 752-754 (3)   1.20 1.20

Nephrite
A277

Fruit Export
A278

1982-83   Litho.
755 A277 1c shown   .25 .25
  a. Perf 13x12½   .40 .40
756 A277 2c Agate   .25 .25
  a. Perf 13x12½   1.25 1.25
757 A277 3c Iron pyrites   .25 .25
758 A277 4c Amethyst   .25 .25
759 A277 5c Carnelian   .25 .25
760 A277 9c Native sulphur   .25 .25
761 A278 10c Grapes   .25 .25
762 A278 20c Citrus fruit   .30 .25
763 A278 30c Nectarines   .40 .25
764 A278 40c Apples   .60 .25
765 A278 50c Kiwifruit   .70 .25
  Nos. 755-765 (11)   3.75 2.75

Issued: A277, Dec. 1; A278, Dec. 7, 1983.

Native Birds — A279

1985-89   Perf. 14½
766 A279 30c Kakapo   .50 .25
767 A279 45c Falcon   1.00 .50
768 A279 $1 Kokako   1.00 .45
769 A279 $2 Black Robin   2.50 .70
  a. Souvenir sheet of one   11.00 11.00
770 A279 $3 Stitchbird   4.00 2.75
770A A279 $4 Saddleback   4.75 3.25
  Nos. 766-770A (6)   13.75 7.90

No. 769a for PHILEXFRANCE '89 and has
margin picturing progressive proofs of No.
769. No. 769a sold for $3.50.
  Issued: $1, $2, 4/24; $3, $4, 4/23/86; 30c,
45c, 5/1/86; No. 769a, 7/7/89.
  See Nos. 830-835, 919-933.

Salvation
Army in NZ
Cent.
A280

Univ. of
Auckland
Cent.
A281

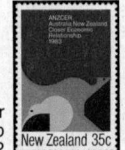

NZ-Australia Closer
Economic Relationship
Agreement — A282

Introduction
of Rainbow
Trout Cent.
A283

WCY
A284

Perf. 14, 14x13½ (35c)
1983, Feb. 2   Litho.
771 A280 24c multicolored   .30 .30
772 A281 30c multicolored   .40 .40
773 A282 35c multicolored   .50 .50
774 A283 40c multicolored   .60 .60
775 A284 45c multicolored   .60 .60
  Nos. 771-775 (5)   2.40 2.40

A285

24c, Queen Elizabeth II. 35c, Maori rock
painting. 40c, Wool industry logos. 45c, Arms.

1983, Mar. 14   Litho.   Perf. 14
776 A285 24c multicolored   .40 .40
777 A285 35c multicolored   .45 .45
778 A285 40c multicolored   .55 .55
779 A285 45c multicolored   .60 .60
  Nos. 776-779 (4)   2.00 2.00

Commonwealth Day.

Island Bay, by Rita
Angus (1908-
1970) — A286

Landscapes.

1983, Apr. 6   Litho.   Perf. 14½
780 A286 24c shown   .40 .40
781 A286 30c Central Otago   .40 .40
782 A286 35c Wanaka   .50 .50
783 A286 45c Tree, Greymouth   .60 .60
  Nos. 780-783 (4)   1.90 1.90

Lake
Matheson — A287

Perf. 13½x13, 13x13½
1983, June 1   Photo.
784 A287 35c Mt. Egmont, vert.   .40 .40
785 A287 40c Cooks Bay, vert.   .50 .50
786 A287 45c shown   .60 .60
787 A287 70c Lake Alexandrina   .95 .95
  Nos. 784-787 (4)   2.45 2.45

Christmas
1983 — A288

18c, Holy Family of the Oak Tree, by
Raphael. 35c, St. Patrick's Church,
Greymouth. 45c, Star, poinsettias.

1983, Oct. 5   Photo.   Perf. 12
788 A288 18c multicolored   .25 .25
789 A288 35c multicolored   .45 .45
790 A288 45c multicolored   .70 .70
  Nos. 788-790 (3)   1.40 1.40

Antarctic
Research
A289

1984, Feb. 1   Litho.   Perf. 13½x13
791 A289 24c Geology   .35 .35
792 A289 40c Biology   .55 .55
793 A289 58c Glaciology   .90 .90
794 A289 70c Meteorology   1.00 1.00
  a. Souvenir sheet of 4, #791-794 3.00 3.00
  Nos. 791-794 (4)   2.80 2.80

Ferry
Mountaineer,
Lake Wakatipu,
1879 — A290

40c, Waikana, Otago Harbor, 1909. 58c,
Britannia, Waitemata Harbor, 1885. 70c,
Wakatere, Firth of Thames, 1896.

1984, Apr. 4   Litho.   Perf. 13½
795 A290 24c multicolored   .40 .40
796 A290 40c multicolored   .60 .60
797 A290 58c multicolored   .80 .80
798 A290 70c multicolored   1.00 1.00
  Nos. 795-798 (4)   2.80 2.80

Skier, Mount
Hutt — A291

1984, June 6   Litho.   Perf. 13½x13
799 A291 35c shown   .50 .50
800 A291 40c Coronet Peak   .60 .60
801 A291 45c Turoa   .60 .60
802 A291 70c Whakapapa   1.00 1.00
  Nos. 799-802 (4)   2.70 2.70

Hamilton's
Frog — A292

1984, July 11   Perf. 13½
803 A292 24c shown   .35 .25
804 A292 24c Great barrier skink .35 .25
  a. Pair, #803-804   .80 .60
805 A292 30c Harlequin gecko   .40 .40
806 A292 58c Otago skink   .90 .90
807 A292 70c Gold-striped gecko 1.00 1.00
  Nos. 803-807 (5)   3.00 2.80

No. 804a has continuous design.

Christmas
A293

Designs: 18c, Adoration of the Shepherds,
by Lorenzo Di Credi. 35c, Old St. Paul's
Church, Wellington. 45c, Bell, vert.

Perf. 13½x14, 14x13½
1984, Sept. 26   Photo.
808 A293 18c multicolored   .25 .25
809 A293 35c multicolored   .35 .35
810 A293 45c multicolored   .50 .50
  Nos. 808-810 (3)   1.10 1.10

Military
History — A294

24c, South Africa, 1901. 40c, France, 1917.
58c, North Africa, 1942. 70c, Korea & Southeast Asia, 1950-72.

1984, Nov. 7   Litho.   Perf. 15x14
811 A294 24c multi   .40 .40
812 A294 40c multi   .60 .60
813 A294 58c multi   .80 .80
814 A294 70c multi   1.00 1.00
  a. Souvenir sheet of 4, #811-814 3.00 3.00
  Nos. 811-814 (4)   2.80 2.80

St. John
Ambulance
Assoc. Cent. in
NZ — A295

1985, Jan. 16 Litho.   Perf. 14
815	A295	24c multicolored	.40 .40
816	A295	30c multicolored	.40 .40
817	A295	40c multicolored	.60 .60
		Nos. 815-817 (3)	1.40 1.40

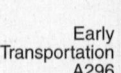

Early Transportation A296

24c, Nelson Horse Tram, 1862. 30c, Graham's Town-Steam, 1871. 35c, Dunedin Cable Car, 1881. 40c, Auckland Electric, 1902. 45c, Wellington Electric, 1904. 58c, Christchurch Electric, 1905.

1985, Mar. 6 Litho.   Perf. 13½
818	A296	24c multicolored	.40 .25
819	A296	30c multicolored	.40 .40
820	A296	35c multicolored	.50 .50
821	A296	40c multicolored	.60 .60
822	A296	45c multicolored	.60 .60
823	A296	58c multicolored	.80 .80
		Nos. 818-823 (6)	3.30 3.15

Bridges — A297

35c, Shotover. 40c, Alexandra. 45c, South Rangitikei, vert. 70c, Twin Bridges, vert.

1985, June 12 Photo.   Perf. 11½
824	A297	35c multicolored	.45 .45
825	A297	40c multicolored	.50 .50
826	A297	45c multicolored	.65 .65
827	A297	70c multicolored	.90 .90
		Nos. 824-827 (4)	2.50 2.50

Bird Type of 1985 and

Elizabeth II — A298

1985-89 Litho.   Perf. 14½x14
828	A298	25c multicolored	.50 .40
829	A298	35c multicolored	.70 .60

Perf. 14½
830	A279	40c Blue duck	.65 .25
		Complete booklet, 10 #830	6.50
831	A279	60c Brown teal	1.00 .65
832	A279	70c Paradise shelduck	1.05 .75
a.		Souvenir sheet of 1	10.00 10.00
835	A279	$5 Takahe	7.00 6.00
		Nos. 828-835 (6)	10.90 8.65

Size of 70c, 22x27mm.
No. 832a for World Stamp Expo '89. Sold for $1.50.
Issued: 25c, 35c, 7/1/85; 40c, 60c, 2/2/87; 70c, 6/7/88; $5, 4/20/88; #832a, 11/17/89.

Christmas — A301

Carol "Silent Night, Holy Night," by Joseph Mohr (1792-1848), Austrian clergyman.

Perf. 13½x12½
836	A301	18c Stable	.25 .25
837	A301	40c Shepherds	.55 .55
838	A301	50c Angels	.60 .60
		Nos. 836-838 (3)	1.40 1.40

Navy Ships — A302

25c, Philomel, 1914-1947. 45c, Achilles, 1936-1946. 60c, Rotoiti, 1949-1965. 75c, Canterbury, 1971-.

1985, Nov. 6 Litho.   Perf. 13½
839	A302	25c multicolored	.40 .25
840	A302	45c multicolored	.75 .75
841	A302	60c multicolored	1.00 1.00
842	A302	75c multicolored	1.25 1.25
a.		Souvenir sheet of 4, #839-842	4.00 4.00
		Nos. 839-842 (4)	3.40 3.25

Police Force Act, Cent. — A303

Designs: a, Radio operators, 1940-1985. b, Mounted policeman, 1890, forensic specialist in mobile lab, 1985. c, Police station, 1895, policewoman and badge, 1985. d, 1920 motorcycle, 1940s car, modern patrol cars and graphologist. e, Original Mt. Cook Training Center and modern Police College, Poriria.

1986, Jan. 15   Perf. 14½x14
843		Strip of 5	2.40 1.90
a.-e.	A303 25c any single		.40 .25

Intl. Peace Year — A304

1986, Mar. 5   Perf. 13½x13
844		25c Tree	.35 .25
845		25c Dove	.35 .25
a.		A304 Pair, #844-845	.80 .70

Motorcycles A305

35c, 1920 Indian Power Plus. 45c, 1927 Norton CS1. 60c, 1930 BSA Sloper. 75c, 1915 Triumph Model H.

1986, Mar. 5
846	A305	35c multicolored	.50 .50
847	A305	45c multicolored	.60 .60
848	A305	60c multicolored	.80 .80
849	A305	75c multicolored	1.00 1.00
		Nos. 846-849 (4)	2.90 2.90

Knight's Point — A306

1986, June 11 Litho.   Perf. 14
850	A306	55c shown	.65 .65
851	A306	60c Beck's Bay	.70 .70
852	A306	65c Doubtless Bay	.75 .75
853	A306	80c Wainui Bay	.80 .80
a.		Miniature sheet of one	1.90 1.90
		Nos. 850-853 (4)	2.90 2.90

No. 853a sold for $1.20. Surtax benefited the "NZ 1990" executive committee.
No. 853a exists with Stockholmia '86 emblem. This sheet was sold only at the exhibition.

The Twelve Days of Christmas — A307

1986, Sept. 17 Photo.   Perf. 14½
854	A307	25c First day	.35 .35
855	A307	55c Second	.55 .55
856	A307	65c Third	.90 .90
		Nos. 854-856 (3)	1.80 1.70

Music — A308

1986, Nov. 5 Litho.   Perf. 14½x14
857	A308	30c Conductor	.45 .30
858	A308	60c Brass band	.70 .70
859	A308	80c Highland pipe band	.95 .95
860	A308	$1 Country music	1.20 1.20
		Nos. 857-860 (4)	3.30 3.15

Tourism — A309

60c, Boating. 70c, Aviation. 80c, Camping. 85c, Windsurfing. $1.05, Mountain climbing. $1.30, White water rafting.

1987, Jan. 14   Perf. 14½x14
861	A309	60c multi	.75 .75
862	A309	70c multi	.90 .90
863	A309	80c multi	1.00 1.00
864	A309	85c multi	1.10 1.10
865	A309	$1.05 multi	1.25 1.25
866	A309	$1.30 multi	1.50 1.50
		Nos. 861-866 (6)	6.50 6.50

Blue Water Classics — A310

40c, Southern Cross Cup. 80c, Admiral's Cup. $1.05, Kenwood Cup. $1.30, America's Cup.

1987, Feb. 2   Perf. 14x14½
867	A310	40c multi	.60 .35
868	A310	80c multi	1.00 1.00
869	A310	$1.05 multi	1.25 1.25
870	A310	$1.30 multi	1.50 1.50
		Nos. 867-870 (4)	4.35 4.10

Vesting Day — A311

a, Motor vehicles, plane. b, Train, bicycle.

1987, Apr. 1 Litho.   Perf. 13½
871	A311	Pair	1.35 1.35
a.-b.	40c any single		.50 .40

Establishment of NZ Post Ltd., Apr. 1, replacing the NZ PO.

Royal NZ Air Force, 50th Anniv. — A312

Designs: 40c, Avro 626, Wigram Airfield, c. 1937. 70c, P-40 Kittyhawks. 80c, Sunderland seaplane. 85c, A4 Skyhawks.

1987, Apr. 15   Perf. 14x14½
872	A312	40c multicolored	.60 .60
873	A312	70c multicolored	1.00 1.00
874	A312	80c multicolored	1.10 1.10
875	A312	85c multicolored	1.25 1.25
a.		Souvenir sheet of 4, #872-875	4.75 4.75
b.		As "a," ovptd. with CAPEX '87 emblem in margin	13.00 15.00
		Nos. 872-875 (4)	3.95 3.95

Natl. Parks System, Cent. — A313

1987, June 17 Litho.   Perf. 14½
876	A313	70c Urewera	.85 .85
877	A313	80c Mt. Cook	.90 .90
878	A313	85c Fiordland	1.00 1.00
879	A313	$1.30 Tongariro	1.75 1.75
a.		Souvenir sheet of one	3.75 3.75
b.		As "a," ovptd. with CAPEX '87 emblem in margin	13.00 15.00
		Nos. 876-879 (4)	4.50 4.50

No. 879a sold for $1.70 to benefit the NZ 1990 World Phil. Exhib., Auckland.

Christmas Carols — A314

35c, Hark! The Herald Angels Sing. 70c, Away in a Manger. 85c, We Three Kings of Orient Are.

1987, Sept. 16 Litho.   Perf. 14x14½
880	A314	35c multi	.50 .40
881	A314	70c multi	.90 .90
882	A314	85c multi	1.25 1.25
		Nos. 880-882 (3)	2.65 2.55

Maori Fiber Art — A315

1987, Nov. 4 Litho.   Perf. 12
883	A315	40c Knot	.55 .45
884	A315	60c Binding	.75 .75
885	A315	80c Plait	.95 .95
886	A315	85c Flax fiber	1.00 1.00
		Nos. 883-886 (4)	3.25 3.15

Royal Phil. Soc. of NZ, Cent. A316   Portrait of Queen Victoria by Chalon A317

Queen Elizabeth II and: No. 887, No. 61 (blue background). No. 888, No. 62 (red background).

1988, Jan. 13   Perf. 14x14½
887	A316	40c multicolored	.55 .55
888	A316	40c multicolored	.55 .55
a.		Pair, #887-888	1.25 1.25

Souvenir Sheet
889	A317	$1 multicolored	2.75 2.75
a.		Overprinted with SYDPEX '88 emblem in margin	30.00 30.00

NZ Electrification, Cent. — A318

1988, Jan. 13   Perf. 14x14½
890	A318	40c Geothermal	.45 .45
891	A318	60c Thermal	.60 .60
892	A318	70c Plait	.75 .75
893	A318	80c Hydroelectric	1.00 1.00
		Nos. 890-893 (4)	2.80 2.80

Maori Rafter Paintings — A319

1988, Mar. 2 Litho.   Perf. 14½
894	A319	40c Mangopare	.65 .65
895	A319	40c Koru	.65 .65
896	A319	40c Raupunga	.65 .65
897	A319	60c Koiri	.95 .95
		Nos. 894-897 (4)	2.90 2.90

Greetings Messages — A320

1988, May 18   Litho.   *Perf. 13½x13*
Booklet Stamps
898	A320	40c Good luck	.75	.75
899	A320	40c Keeping in touch	.75	.75
900	A320	40c Happy birthday	.75	.75

Size: 41x27mm
901	A320	40c Congratulations	.75	.75
902	A320	40c Get well soon	.75	.75
a.		Bklt. pane of 5, #898-902	4.25	

Landscapes — A321

1988, June 8   *Perf. 14½*
903	A321	70c Milford Track	.80	.80
904	A321	80c Heaphy Track	.85	.85
905	A321	85c Copland Track	.95	.95
906	A321	$1.30 Routeburn Track	*1.50*	1.50
a.		Miniature sheet of one	3.00	3.00
		Nos. 903-906 (4)	4.10	4.10

No. 906a sold for $1.70 to benefit the exhibition.

NEW ZEALAND 1990 Souvenir Sheets
Four souvenir sheets were sold by the New Zealand post to benefit NEW ZEALAND 1990 World Stamp Exhibition. They each contain three $1 and one $2 "stamps" picturing antarctic scenes. They are not valid for postage.

Australia Bicentennial A322

Caricature: Kiwi and koala around campfire.

1988, June 21
907	A322	40c multicolored	.55	.55

See Australia No. 1086.

Christmas Carols — A323

Illuminated manuscripts: 35c, O, Come All Ye Faithful, by John Francis Wade, 1742. 70c, Hark! the Herald Angels Sing. 80c, Ding Dong! Merrily on High. 85c, The First Noel, first published in Davies & Gilbert's Some Ancient Christmas Carols, 1832.

1988, Sept. 14   Litho.   *Perf. 14½*
908	A323	35c multicolored	.55	.40
909	A323	70c multicolored	.95	.95
910	A323	80c multicolored	1.00	1.00
911	A323	85c multicolored	1.10	1.10
		Nos. 908-911 (4)	3.60	3.45

New Zealand Heritage — A324

The Land. Paintings by 19th cent. artists: 40c, Lake Pukaki, 1862, by John Gully. 60c, On the Grass Plain Below Lake Arthur, 1846, by William Fox. 70c, View of Auckland, 1873, by John Hoyte. 80c, Mt. Egmont from the Southward, 1840, by Charles Heaphy. $1.05, Anakiwa, Queen Charlotte Sound, 1871, by John Kinder. $1.30, White Terraces, Lake Rotomahana, 1880, by Charles Barraud.

1988, Oct. 5   Litho.   *Perf. 14x14½*
912	A324	40c multicolored	.50	.50
913	A324	60c multicolored	.70	.70
914	A324	70c multicolored	.90	.90
915	A324	80c multicolored	1.00	1.00
916	A324	$1.05 multicolored	1.20	1.20
917	A324	$1.30 multicolored	1.40	1.40
		Nos. 912-917 (6)	5.70	5.45

Kiwi — A325

1988, Oct. 19   Engr.   *Perf. 14½*
918	A325	$1 green	2.50	2.50
a.		Booklet pane of 6	15.00	
b.		Litho.	2.50	2.50

Value is for stamp with surrounding selvage. No. 918 issued in booklets only.
No. 918b is from No. 1161a.
See Nos. 1027, 1161, 1445, 1635, 1787, 2368-2370.

Bird Type of 1985
5c, Spotless crake. 10c, Banded dotterel. 20c, Yellowhead. 30c, Silvereye. 40c, Brown kiwi. 45c, Rock wren. 50c, Kingfisher. 60c, Spotted shag. No. 927, Fiordland crested penguin. No. 928, New Zealand falcon. 90c, South Island robin. $10, Little spotted kiwi.

1988-95   Litho.   *Perf. 14½x14*
Sizes: $10, 26x31½mm, Others, 22x27mm
919	A279	5c multi	.25	.25
920	A279	10c multi	.25	.25
921	A279	20c multi	.30	.25
a.		Perf. 13½	.75	.75
922	A279	30c multi	.45	.25
923	A279	40c multi	.60	.25
		Complete booklet, 10 #923	6.50	
c.		Perf. 13½x13	2.50	2.50
924	A279	45c multi	.70	.25
b.		Booklet pane of 10	7.00	
925	A279	50c multi	.70	.35
926	A279	60c multi	.85	.60
a.		Sheet of 8, #919-926	5.00	5.00
b.		Perf. 13½	7.00	7.00
927	A279	80c multi	1.10	.70
		Complete booklet, 10 #927 + 10 etiquettes	11.00	
928	A279	80c multi	1.10	.70
		Complete booklet, 10 #928	11.00	
c.		Perf. 12 on 3 sides	4.00	4.00
d.		As "c," booklet pane of 10	45.00	
		Complete booklet, #928d	47.50	
929	A279	90c multi	1.40	1.25
930	A279	$10 multi	9.50	6.75
a.		Souv. sheet of 1	20.00	20.00

Self-Adhesive
Die Cut Perf 11½
931	A279	40c like #923	.80	.50
932	A279	45c like #924	.70	.55

Die Cut Perf 10½x11
933	A279	45c like #924	.70	.55
		Nos. 919-933 (15)	19.40	13.45

No. 933 has a darker blue background than No. 932 and has perf "teeth" at the corners while No. 932 does not. Perf "teeth" on the top and left side are staggered to line up with perf "holes" on the bottom and right on No. 933. "Teeth" line up with "teeth" on No. 932.
PHILAKOREA '94 (#926a). POST'X '95 Postal Exhibition (#930d).
Issued: $10, 4/19/89; #931, 4/17/91; 5c, #924, 932, 7/1/91; #933, 1991; #928, 3/31/93; #926a, 8/16/94; #930d, 2/3/95; #921a, 926b, 9/22/95; #923c, 11/8/89; others, 11/2/88.

Whales of the Southern Oceans — A326

60c, Humpback. 70c, Killer. 80c, Southern right. 85c, Blue. $1.05, Southern bottlenose. $1.30, Sperm.

1988, Nov. 2   Litho.   *Perf. 13½*
936	A326	60c multi	.95	.95
937	A326	70c multi	1.00	1.00
938	A326	80c multi	1.10	1.10
939	A326	85c multi	1.25	1.25
940	A326	$1.05 multi	1.50	1.50
941	A326	$1.30 multi	1.90	1.90
		Nos. 936-941 (6)	7.70	7.70

Wildflowers — A327

1989, Jan. 18   Litho.   *Perf. 14½*
942	A327	40c Clover	.55	.55
943	A327	60c Lotus	.80	.80
944	A327	70c Montbretia	1.00	1.00
945	A327	80c Wild ginger	1.20	1.20
		Nos. 942-945 (4)	3.55	3.55

Authors — A328

Portraits: 40c, Katherine Mansfield (1888-1923). 60c, James K. Baxter (1926-1972). 70c, Bruce Mason (1921-1982). 80c, Ngaio Marsh (1899-1982).

1989, Mar. 1   Litho.   *Perf. 12½*
946	A328	40c multicolored	.45	.45
947	A328	60c multicolored	.65	.65
948	A328	70c multicolored	.70	.70
949	A328	80c multicolored	.80	.80
		Nos. 946-949 (4)	2.60	2.60

New Zealand Heritage — A329

The people.

1989, May 17   *Perf. 14x14½*
950	A329	40c Moriori	.60	.35
951	A329	60c Prospectors	.85	.85
952	A329	70c Land settlers	.70	.70
953	A329	80c Whalers	.85	.85
954	A329	$1.05 Missionaries	.95	.95
955	A329	$1.30 Maori	1.25	1.25
		Nos. 950-955 (6)	5.20	4.95

Trees — A330

1989, June 7
956	A330	80c Kahikatea	.90	.90
957	A330	85c Rimu	1.00	1.00
958	A330	$1.05 Totara	1.25	1.25
959	A330	$1.30 Kauri	1.50	1.50
a.		Miniature sheet of one	3.50	3.50
		Nos. 956-959 (4)	4.65	4.65

No. 959a sold for $1.80. Surtax benefited the "NZ 1990" executive committee.

Christmas — A331

Star of Bethlehem illuminating settings: 35c, View of One Tree Hill from a bedroom window. 65c, A shepherd overlooking snow-capped mountains. 80c, Boats in harbor. $1, Earth.

1989, Sept. 13   Litho.   *Perf. 14½*
960	A331	35c multicolored	.40	.25
a.		Booklet pane of 10	5.50	
961	A331	65c multicolored	.75	.75
962	A331	80c multicolored	.95	.95
963	A331	$1 multicolored	1.10	1.10
		Nos. 960-963 (4)	3.20	3.05

New Zealand Heritage — A332

The sea.

1989, Oct. 11   Litho.   *Perf. 14x14½*
964	A332	40c Windsurfing	.50	.25
965	A332	60c Fishing	.70	.70
966	A332	65c Swordfish	.90	.90
967	A332	80c Harbor	1.00	1.00
968	A332	$1 Gulls over coast	1.25	1.25
969	A332	$1.50 Container ship	1.90	1.90
		Nos. 964-969 (6)	6.25	6.00

14th Commonwealth Games, Auckland, Jan. 24-Feb. 3, 1990 — A333

No. 970, Emblem. No. 971, Goldie character trademark. No. 972, Gymnastics. No. 973, Weight lifting. No. 974, Swimming. No. 975, Cycling. No. 976, Lawn bowling. No. 977, Hurdles.

1989, Nov. 8   *Perf. 14½*
970	A333	40c multi	.50	.50
971	A333	40c multi	.50	.50
a.		Souvenir sheet of 2, #970-971, sailboats ('90)	2.75	2.75
b.		As "a," stadium ('90)	2.75	2.75
972	A333	40c multi	.50	.50
973	A333	50c multi	.60	.60
974	A333	65c multi	.75	.75
975	A333	80c multi	.95	.95
976	A333	$1 multi	1.10	1.10
977	A333	$1.80 multi	1.90	1.90
		Nos. 970-977 (8)	6.80	6.80

Air New Zealand, 50th Anniv. — A334

1990, Jan. 17   *Perf. 13½x14½*
978	A334	80c multicolored	1.00	.80

Souvenir Sheet

Treaty of Waitangi, 150th Anniv. A335

Painting by Leonard Mitchell: a, Maori chief signing the treaty. b, Chief Hone Heke shaking hand of Lt.-Gov. William Hobson.

1990, Jan. 17   *Perf. 13½*
979	A335	Sheet of 2	3.00	3.00
a.-b.		40c any single	1.10	1.10

New Zealand Heritage — A336

The Ships: No. 980, Polynesian double-hulled canoe, c. 1000. No. 981, Endeavour. No. 982, Tory. No. 983, Crusader. No. 984, Edwin Fox. No. 985, Arawa.

1990, Mar. 7   Litho.   *Perf. 14x14½*
980	A336	40c multi	.60	.25
981	A336	50c multi	.75	.75
a.		Souvenir sheet of 1	20.00	20.00
982	A336	60c multi	.90	.90
983	A336	80c multi	1.40	1.40
984	A336	$1 multi	1.50	1.50
985	A336	$1.50 multi	2.00	2.00
		Nos. 980-985 (6)	7.15	6.80

No. 981a for Stamp World London '90. Sold for $1.30. Issued May 3.

Miniature Sheet

Orchids — A337

Designs: a, Sun. b, Spider. c, Winika. d, Greenhood. e, Odd-leaved orchid.

1990, Apr. 18   Litho.   Perf. 14½
986	Sheet of 5	7.50	7.50
a.-d.	A337 40c any single	1.00	1.00
e.	A337 80c multicolored	2.00	2.00

No. 986 sold for $4.90. Surcharge for the intl. stamp exhibition, Auckland, Aug. 24-Sept 2. Imperf. sheets were available only in season tickets which were sold for $25. Value, $42.50.

New Zealand
Heritage — A338

The Achievers: 40c, Grace Neill (1846-1926), nurse, journalist. 50c, Jean Batten (1909-1982), aviator. 60c, Katherine Sheppard (1848-1934), social worker. 80c, Richard Pearse (1877-1953), inventor. $1, Gov.-Gen. Bernard Freyberg (1889-1963). $1.50, Peter Buck (1877-1951), cabinet minister.

1990, May 16   Litho.   Perf. 14x14½
987	A338	40c multicolored	.65	.30
988	A338	50c multicolored	.80	.80
989	A338	60c multicolored	.95	.95
990	A338	80c multicolored	1.25	1.25
991	A338	$1 multicolored	1.50	1.50
992	A338	$1.50 multicolored	1.75	1.75
	Nos. 987-992 (6)		6.90	6.55

Akaroa Harbor — A339

Early Settlements: $1, Durie Hill, Wanganui River. $1.50, Mt. Victoria, Wellington. $1.80, Rangitoto Island, Takapuna Beach, Auckland.

1990, June 13   Litho.   Perf. 14½
993	A339	80c multicolored	1.00	1.00
994	A339	$1 multicolored	1.40	1.40
995	A339	$1.50 multicolored	2.25	2.25
996	A339	$1.80 multicolored	2.50	2.50
a.	Souvenir sheet of 1		4.25	4.25
	Nos. 993-996 (4)		7.15	7.15

No. 996a sold for $2.30. Surtax for world philatelic expo, New Zealand '90.

New Zealand
Heritage — A340

The Maori: 40c, Legend of Rangi and Papa. 50c, Maori feather cloak. 60c, Song. 80c, Maori tattoo. $1, War canoe prow. $1.50, Maori war dance.

1990, Aug. 24   Litho.   Perf. 14
997	A340	40c multicolored	.55	.30
998	A340	50c multicolored	.65	.65
999	A340	60c multicolored	.75	.75
1000	A340	80c multicolored	.85	.85
1001	A340	$1 multicolored	1.25	1.25
1002	A340	$1.50 multicolored	1.75	1.75
	Nos. 997-1002 (6)		5.80	5.55

Souvenir Sheet

First Postage Stamps, 150th Anniv.
A341

Designs: a, Victoria. b, Edward VII. c, George V. d, Edward VIII. e, George VI. f, Elizabeth II.

1990, Aug. 29   Engr.   Perf. 14½x14
1003	A341	40c Sheet of 6	5.25	5.25
a.-f.	any single		.75	.75

Christmas — A342

Various angels.

1990, Sept. 12   Litho.   Perf. 14
1004	A342	40c multicolored	.55	.40
1005	A342	$1 multicolored	1.25	.25
1006	A342	$1.50 multicolored	2.00	1.25
1007	A342	$1.80 multicolored	2.25	2.00
	Nos. 1004-1007 (4)		6.05	3.90

Antarctic
Petrel — A343

50c, Wilson's storm petrel. 60c, Snow petrel. 80c, Antarctic fulmar. $1, Chinstrap penguin. $1.50, Emperor penguin.

1990, Nov. 7   Perf. 13½x13
1008	A343	40c shown	.65	.35
1009	A343	50c multicolored	.80	.70
1010	A343	60c multicolored	.95	.85
1011	A343	80c multicolored	1.25	1.10
1012	A343	$1 multicolored	1.60	1.60
1013	A343	$1.50 multicolored	2.40	2.25
	Nos. 1008-1013 (6)		7.65	6.85

Sheep — A344

1991, Jan. 23   Litho.   Perf. 14½
1014	A344	40c Coopworth	.55	.25
1015	A344	60c Perendale	.80	.80
1016	A344	80c Corriedale	1.00	1.00
1017	A344	$1 Drysdale	1.25	1.25
1018	A344	$1.50 South Suffolk	1.75	1.75
1019	A344	$1.80 Romney	2.00	2.00
	Nos. 1014-1019 (6)		7.35	7.05

Map, Royal Albatross, Designs from Moriori House, Moriori Man, Nikau Palm, Tree Carving — A345

Design: 80c, Map, sailing ship, carving, petroglyph, Moriori house, Tommy Solomon, last full-blooded Moriori.

1991, Mar. 6   Litho.   Perf. 13½
1020	A345	40c shown	.65	.55
1021	A345	80c multicolored	1.25	1.10

Discovery of the Chatham Islands, Bicent.

New Zealand
Football (Soccer)
Assoc.,
Cent. — A346

Designs: a, Goal. b, 5 players, referee.

1991, Mar. 6
1022		Pair	2.50	2.50
a.-b.	A346 80c any single		1.25	1.25

Tuatara — A347

Designs: No. 1023, Juvenile. No. 1024, In burrow. No. 1025, Female. No. 1026, Male.

1991, Apr. 17   Litho.   Perf. 14½
Denomination Color
1023	A347	40c gray blue	.80	.80
1024	A347	40c dark brown	.80	.80
1025	A347	40c olive green	.80	.80
1026	A347	40c orange brown	.80	.80
	Nos. 1023-1026 (4)		3.20	3.20

Kiwi Type of 1988

1991, Apr. 17   Engr.   Perf. 14½
1027	A325	$1 red	1.60	1.25
a.	Litho.		1.75	1.50

Value is for stamp with surrounding selvage. No. 1027a is from Nos.1161a, 1635a.

Happy	Thinking of
Birthday	You
A348	A349

No. 1028, Clown face. No. 1029, Balloons. No. 1030, Birthday hat. No. 1031, Present. No. 1032, Cake & candles. No. 1033 Cat, front paws on window sill. No. 1034, Cat, slippers. No. 1035, Cat, alarm clock. No. 1036, Cat sitting on window sill. No. 1037, Cat walking by door.

1991, May 15   Litho.   Perf. 14x13½
Size of Nos. 1031-1032, 1036-1037:
41x27mm
1028	A348	40c multi	.90	.90
1029	A348	40c multi	.90	.90
1030	A348	40c multi	.90	.90
1031	A348	40c multi	.90	.90
1032	A348	40c multi	.90	.90
a.	Bklt. pane of 5, #1028-1032		6.00	
1033	A349	40c shown	.90	.90
1034	A349	40c multi	.90	.90
1035	A349	40c multi	.90	.90
1036	A349	40c multi	.90	.90
1037	A349	40c multi	.90	.90
a.	Bklt. pane of 5, #1033-1037		6.00	
	Nos. 1028-1037 (10)		9.00	9.00

See Nos. 1044-1053.

Rock
Formations — A350

40c, Punakaiki Rocks. 50c, Moeraki Boulders. 80c, Organ Pipes. $1, Castle Hill. $1.50, Te Kaukau Point. $1.80, Ahuriri River Clay Cliffs.

1991, June 12   Litho.   Perf. 14½
1038	A350	40c multicolored	.60	.35
1039	A350	50c multicolored	.75	.75
1040	A350	80c multicolored	1.10	1.10
1041	A350	$1 multicolored	1.25	1.25
1042	A350	$1.50 multicolored	2.00	2.00
1043	A350	$1.80 multicolored	2.25	2.25
	Nos. 1038-1043 (6)		7.95	7.70

Greetings Types

1991, July 1   Litho.   Perf. 14x13½
Size of Nos. 1047-1048, 1052-1053:
41x27mm
1044	A348	45c like #1028	.80	.80
1045	A348	45c like #1029	.80	.80
1046	A348	45c like #1030	.80	.80
1047	A348	45c like #1031	.80	.80
1048	A348	45c like #1032	.80	.80
a.	Bklt. pane of 5, #1044-1048		5.00	
1049	A349	45c like #1033	.80	.80
1050	A349	45c like #1034	.80	.80
1051	A349	45c like #1035	.80	.80
1052	A349	45c like #1036	.80	.80
1053	A349	45c like #1037	.80	.80
a.	Bklt. pane of 5, #1049-1053		5.00	
	Nos. 1044-1053 (10)		8.00	8.00

1991 Rugby World
Cup — A351

1991, Aug. 21   Litho.   Perf. 14½x14
1054	A351	80c Children's	1.00	1.00
1055	A351	$1 Women's	1.25	1.25
1056	A351	$1.50 Senior	2.00	2.00
1057	A351	$1.80 All Blacks	2.25	2.25
a.	Souvenir sheet of 1		4.00	4.00
b.	As "a," with Phila Nippon '91 emblem in margin		15.00	15.00
	Nos. 1054-1057 (4)		6.50	6.50

No. 1057a sold for $2.40 to benefit philatelic trust for hobby support.

Christmas — A352

No. 1058, Shepherds. No. 1059, Wise men, camels. No. 1060, Mary, Baby Jesus. No. 1061, Wise man, gift. No. 1062, Star. No. 1063, Crown. No. 1064, Angel.

1991, Sept. 18   Litho.   Perf. 13½x14
1058	A352	45c multi	.55	.55
1059	A352	45c multi	.55	.55
1060	A352	45c multi	.55	.55
1061	A352	45c multi	.55	.55
a.	Block of 4, #1058-1061		3.00	3.00
1062	A352	65c multi	.90	.90
1063	A352	$1 multi	1.50	1.50
1064	A352	$1.50 multi	2.00	2.00
	Nos. 1058-1064 (7)		6.60	6.60

Butterflies — A354

$1, Forest ringlet. $2, Southern blue. $3, Yellow admiral. $4, Common copper. $5, Red admiral.

1991-2008   Litho.   Perf. 14¼
1075	A354	$1 multi	1.40	1.10
a.	Perf. 14x14½ on 3 sides		5.00	5.00
b.	Booklet pane of 5 + 5 labels Perf. 14x14½ on 3 sides		25.00	
	Complete booklet, #1075b		25.00	
c.	Perf. 13¾x14¼		2.00	2.00
1076	A354	$2 multi	3.00	2.25
a.	Perf. 13¾x14¼		12.00	12.00
1077	A354	$3 multi	4.00	3.50
a.	Souvenir sheet of 1		10.00	10.00
b.	Perf. 13¾x14¼		12.00	12.00
1078	A354	$4 multi	5.00	3.00
a.	Perf. 13¾x14¼		7.00	5.25
b.	Perf. 14 ('08)		6.25	4.50
1079	A354	$5 multi	6.50	5.00
a.	Perf. 13¾x14¼		8.50	6.00
	Nos. 1075-1079 (5)		19.90	14.85

No. 1077a issued later for Phila Nippon '91. Issued: #1075, 1075a, 1076, 1077, 11/6/91; $4-$5, 1/25/95; #1075b, 9/1/95; #1078a, 10/97; #1079a, 10/9/96; #1075c, 1076a, 11/6/96; #1077b, Aug. 1996.

Mount
Cook
A356

Engraved with Foil Application
Perf. 14½x15

1994, Feb. 18   Wmk. 387
1084	A356	$20 gold & blue	22.50	15.00

1992 America's
Cup Competition
A357

45c, KZ7 Kiwi Magic, 1987. 80c, KZ1 New Zealand, 1988. $1, America, 1851. $1.50, New Zealand, 1992.

Perf. 14x14½

1992, Jan. 22   Litho.   Unwmk.
1085	A357	45c multicolored	.60	.25
1086	A357	80c multicolored	.95	.95
1087	A357	$1 multicolored	1.25	1.25
1088	A357	$1.50 multicolored	1.90	1.90
	Nos. 1085-1088 (4)		4.70	4.35

Sighting of New
Zealand by Abel
Tasman, 350th
Anniv. — A358

1992, Mar. 12   *Perf. 13½x14½*
1089	A358	45c Heemskerck	.60	.30
1090	A358	80c Zeehaen	1.00	1.00
1091	A358	$1 Santa Maria	1.40	1.40
1092	A358	$1.50 Pinta and Nina	1.90	1.90
a.		Souvenir sheet of 2, #1091-1092, Perf. 14x14½	8.00	8.00
		Nos. 1089-1092 (4)	4.90	4.60

Discovery of America, 500th anniv. (#1091-1092).

Issue date: No. 1092a, May 22. World Columbian Stamp Expo (#1092a).

1992 Summer Olympics, Barcelona A359

1992, Apr. 3   **Litho.**   *Perf. 13½*
1093	A359	45c Runners	.70	.60

Antarctic Seals — A360

45c, Weddell seal. 50c, Crabeater seal. 65c, Leopard seal. 80c, Ross seal. $1, Southern elephant seal. $1.80, Hooker's sea lion.

1992, Apr. 8   *Perf. 14x13½*
1094	A360	45c multi	.70	.60
1095	A360	50c multi	.80	.70
1096	A360	65c multi	1.00	.85
1097	A360	80c multi	1.25	1.00
1098	A360	$1 multi	1.60	1.40
1099	A360	$1.80 multi	2.75	2.50
		Nos. 1094-1099 (6)	8.10	7.05

1992 Summer Olympics, Barcelona A361

1992, May 13   **Litho.**   *Perf. 13½*
1100	A361	45c Cycling	.65	.40
1101	A361	80c Archery	1.00	1.00
1102	A361	$1 Equestrian	1.25	1.25
1103	A361	$1.50 Board sailing	1.90	1.90
a.		Souvenir sheet of 4, #1100-1103, perf 14x14½	5.75	5.75
b.		No. 1103a overprinted	11.50	11.50
		Nos. 1100-1103 (4)	4.80	4.55

No. 1103b overprint consists of World Columbian Stamp Expo emblem in sheet margin. Issue date: No. 1103b, May 22.

Glaciers — A362

45c, Glacier ice. 50c, Tasman glacier. 80c, Snowball glacier. $1, Brewster glacier. $1.50, Fox glacier. $1.80, Franz Josef glacier.

1992, June 12
1104	A362	45c multicolored	.60	.30
1105	A362	50c multicolored	.70	.70
1106	A362	80c multicolored	.85	.85
1107	A362	$1 multicolored	1.25	1.25
1108	A362	$1.50 multicolored	1.90	1.90
1109	A362	$1.80 multicolored	2.10	2.10
		Nos. 1104-1109 (6)	7.40	7.10

Camellias — A363

45c, Grand finale. 50c, Showa-no-sakae. 80c, Sugar dream. $1, Night rider. $1.50, E.G. Waterhouse. $1.80, Dr. Clifford Parks.

1992, July 8   *Perf. 14½*
1110	A363	45c multicolored	.60	.30
1111	A363	50c multicolored	.70	.70
1112	A363	80c multicolored	.90	.90
1113	A363	$1 multicolored	1.25	1.25
1114	A363	$1.50 multicolored	1.90	1.90
1115	A363	$1.80 multicolored	2.10	2.10
		Nos. 1110-1115 (6)	7.45	7.15

Scenic Views of New Zealand — A364

No. 1116, Tree, hills. No. 1117, Hills, stream. No. 1118, Hills, mountain tops. No. 1119, Glacier. No. 1120, Trees, green hills. No. 1121, Tree branch, rapids. No. 1122, Rocky shoreline. No. 1123, Fjord. No. 1124, Glacial runoff. No. 1125, Vegetation, stream.

1992, Sept. 1   **Litho.**   *Perf. 14x14½*
Booklet Stamps
1116	A364	45c multicolored	.65	.65
1117	A364	45c multicolored	.65	.65
1118	A364	45c multicolored	.65	.65
1119	A364	45c multicolored	.65	.65
1120	A364	45c multicolored	.65	.65
1121	A364	45c multicolored	.65	.65
1122	A364	45c multicolored	.65	.65
1123	A364	45c multicolored	.65	.65
1124	A364	45c multicolored	.65	.65
1125	A364	45c multicolored	.65	.65
a.		Bkt. pane of 10, #1116-1125	8.75	
		Nos. 1116-1125 (10)	6.50	6.50

No. 1125a has continous design.

Christmas — A365

No. 1126, Two reindeer over village. No. 1127, Two reindeer pulling Santa's sleigh. No. 1128, Christmas tree in window. No. 1129, Two children looking out window. 65c, Fireplace, stockings. $1, Church. $1.50, People beneath pohutukawa tree at beach.

1992, Sept. 16   *Perf. 14½*
1126	A365	45c multicolored	.50	.50
1127	A365	45c multicolored	.50	.50
1128	A365	45c multicolored	.50	.50
1129	A365	45c multicolored	.50	.50
a.		Block of 4, #1126-1129	2.50	2.50
1130	A365	65c multicolored	.75	.75
1131	A365	$1 multicolored	1.00	1.00
1132	A365	$1.50 multicolored	1.75	1.75
		Nos. 1126-1132 (7)	5.50	5.50

No. 1129a has continous design.

A366

The Emerging Years: The 1920s: 45c, Flaming youth. 50c, Birth of broadcasting. 80c, All Blacks rugby player. $1, The swaggie. $1.50, Motorcar brings freedom. $1.80, Arrival of the air age.

1992, Nov. 4   **Litho.**   *Perf. 13½*
1133	A366	45c multicolored	.50	.25
1134	A366	50c multicolored	.55	.35
1135	A366	80c multicolored	.85	.85
1136	A366	$1 multicolored	1.10	1.10
1137	A366	$1.50 multicolored	1.75	1.75
1138	A366	$1.80 multicolored	2.00	2.00
		Nos. 1133-1138 (6)	6.75	6.30

Royal Doulton Ceramics — A367

45c, Character jug, "Old Charley." 50c, Plate from "Bunnykins" series. 80c, Maori art tea ware. $1, Hand painted "Ophelia" plate. $1.50, Burslem figurine of St. George. $1.80, Salt glazed vase.

1993, Jan. 20   **Litho.**   *Perf. 13*
1139	A367	45c multicolored	.50	.25
1140	A367	50c multicolored	.55	.55
1141	A367	80c multicolored	.85	.85
1142	A367	$1 multicolored	1.10	1.10
1143	A367	$1.50 multicolored	1.60	1.60
1144	A367	$1.80 multicolored	1.90	1.90
a.		Souvenir sheet of 1	2.50	2.50
		Nos. 1139-1144 (6)	6.50	6.25

A368

The Emerging Years: The 1930's: 45c, Buttons and bows, the new femininity. 50c, The Great Depression. 80c, Race horse, Phar Lap. $1, State housing. $1.50, Free milk for schools. $1.80, The talkies.

1993, Feb. 17   **Litho.**   *Perf. 14½x14*
1145	A368	45c multicolored	.55	.25
1146	A368	50c multicolored	.60	.60
1147	A368	80c multicolored	.95	.95
1148	A368	$1 multicolored	1.10	1.10
1149	A368	$1.50 multicolored	1.60	1.60
1150	A368	$1.80 multicolored	1.90	1.90
		Nos. 1145-1150 (6)	6.70	6.40

Woman Suffrage, Cent. — A369

45c, First vote. 80c, War work. $1, Child care. $1.50, Contemporary women.

1993, Mar. 31   **Litho.**   *Perf. 13½*
1151	A369	45c multicolored	.55	.25
1152	A369	80c multicolored	.85	.85
1153	A369	$1 multicolored	1.10	1.10
1154	A369	$1.50 multicolored	2.25	2.25
		Nos. 1151-1154 (4)	4.75	4.45

Thermal Wonders — A370

45c, Champagne Pool. 50c, Boiling mud, Rotorua. 80c, Emerald Pool. $1, Hakereteke Falls. $1.50, Warbrick Terrace. $1.80, Pohutu Geyser.

1993, May 5   **Litho.**   *Perf. 12*
1155	A370	45c multicolored	.55	.25
1156	A370	50c multicolored	.65	.65
1157	A370	80c multicolored	1.00	1.00
1158	A370	$1 multicolored	1.10	1.10
1159	A370	$1.50 multicolored	1.50	1.50
1160	A370	$1.80 multicolored	2.00	2.00
a.		Souvenir sheet of 1	3.50	3.50
		Nos. 1155-1160 (6)	6.80	6.50

No. 1160a inscribed with Bangkok '93 emblem in sheet margin. Issue date: No. 1160a, Oct. 1.

Kiwi Type of 1988
1993, June 9   **Engr.**   *Perf. 14½*
1161	A325	$1 blue	1.40	1.40
a.		Souv. sheet of 3, #918b, 1027a, 1161	8.50	8.50
b.		Litho.	2.25	1.75
c.		Souv. sheet of 3, #918b, 1027a, 1161b	6.00	6.00

Taipei '93, Asian Intl. Stamp Exhibition (#1161a), Hong Kong '94 (#1161c).
Value is for stamp with surrounding selvage. Issued: #1161a, 8/14/93; #1161c, 2/18/94. See No. 1635a.

Species Unique to New Zealand — A371

Designs: No. 1162, Yellow-eyed penguin, Hector's dolphin, New Zealand fur seal. 1162A, Taiko, Mt. Cook lily, blue duck. 1162B, Giant snail, rock wren, Hamilton's frog. 1162C, Kaka, Chatham Island pigeon, giant weta. No. 1163, Tusked weta.

1993, June 9   **Litho.**   *Perf. 14x14½*
1162	A371	45c multicolored	.80	.80
1162A	A371	45c multicolored	.80	.80
1162B	A371	45c multicolored	.80	.80
1162C	A371	45c multicolored	.80	.80
d.		As #1162-1162C, block of 4	4.00	4.00

1163	A371	45c multicolored	.80	.80
a.		Booklet pane of 10	8.00	—
		Complete booklet	8.50	
		Nos. 1162-1163 (5)	4.00	4.00

World Wildlife Fund.
Nos. 1162-1162C were issued both in sheets containing individual designs and in sheets containing the four values setenant (#1162d).

Christmas — A372

Christmas designs: No. 1164, Flowers from pohutukawa tree, denomination at UL. No. 1165, Like #1164, denomination at UR. No. 1166, Present with yellow ribbon, denomination at LL. No. 1167, Present with red ribbon, denomination at LR. $1.00, Ornaments, cracker, sailboats. $1.50, Wreath, sailboats, present.

1993, Sept. 1   **Litho.**   *Perf. 14½x14*
1164	A372	45c multicolored	.60	.60
1165	A372	45c multicolored	.60	.60
1166	A372	45c multicolored	.60	.60
1167	A372	45c multicolored	.60	.60
a.		Block of 4, #1164-1167	2.50	2.50
1168	A372	$1 multicolored	1.25	1.10
1169	A372	$1.50 multicolored	2.00	1.75
		Nos. 1164-1169 (6)	5.65	5.25

Booklet Stamps
Perf. 12
1164a	A372	45c multicolored	1.00	1.00
1165a	A372	45c multicolored	1.00	1.00
1166a	A372	45c multicolored	1.00	1.00
1167b	A372	45c multicolored	1.00	1.00
c.		Bkt. pane, 2 ea #1166a, 1167b, 3 ea #1164a-1165a	17.00	

At least one edge of No. 1167c is guillotined.

Fish — A373

Designs: No. 1170, Paua (#1175). No. 1171, Greenshell mussels. No. 1172, Terakihi (#1171). No. 1173, Salmon (#1172). No. 1174, Southern bluefin tuna, albacore tuna, kahawai (#1173). No. 1175, Rock lobster (#1171). No. 1176, Snapper (#1177). No. 1177, Grouper ("Groper," #1178). No. 1178, Orange roughy (#1179). No. 1179, Squid, hoki, oreo dory (#1173, #1174, #1178).

1993, Sept. 1   *Perf. 13½*
Booklet Stamps
1170	A373	45c multicolored	.90	.90
1171	A373	45c multicolored	.90	.90
1172	A373	45c multicolored	.90	.90
1173	A373	45c multicolored	.90	.90
1174	A373	45c multicolored	.90	.90
1175	A373	45c multicolored	.90	.90
1176	A373	45c multicolored	.90	.90
1177	A373	45c multicolored	.90	.90
1178	A373	45c multicolored	.90	.90
1179	A373	45c multicolored	.90	.90
a.		Booklet pane of 10, #1170-1179 + 2 labels	11.00	
		Nos. 1170-1179 (10)	9.00	9.00

Nos. 1179a has continuous design.

Dinosaurs — A374

1993, Oct. 1
1180	A374	45c Sauropod	.60	.50
1181	A374	80c Pterosaur	1.10	1.10
1182	A374	$1 Ankylosaur	1.25	1.25
1183	A374	$1.20 Mauisaurus	1.50	1.50
1184	A374	$1.50 Carnosaur	1.60	1.60
a.		Souvenir sheet of 1, perf. 14½x14	2.00	2.00
b.		As "a," inscribed with Bangkok '93 emblem	3.00	2.75
		Nos. 1180-1184 (5)	6.05	5.95

Booklet Stamp
Size: 25½x23½mm
Perf. 12
1185	A374	45c Carnosaur, sauropod	.70	.55
a.		Booklet pane of 10 + 2 labels	7.00	7.00

The 1940s — A375

Designs: 45c, New Zealand at war. 50c, Crop dusting. 80c, State produces hydroelectricity. $1, New Zealand Marching Assoc. $1.50, The American invasion. $1.80, Victory.

		1993, Nov. 3	**Litho.**	**Perf. 14**	
1186	A375	45c multicolored		.65	.30
1187	A375	50c multicolored		.75	.75
1188	A375	80c multicolored		1.10	1.10
1189	A375	$1 multicolored		1.40	1.40
1190	A375	$1.50 multicolored		2.00	2.00
1191	A375	$1.80 multicolored		2.25	2.25
		Nos. 1186-1191 (6)		8.15	7.80

Outdoor Adventure Sports — A376

45c, Bungy jumping. 80c, Trout fishing. $1, Jet boating, horiz. $1.50, Tramping. $1.80, Heli-skiing.

		1994, Jan. 19	**Litho.**	**Perf. 12**	
1192	A376	45c multicolored		.60	.30
1193	A376	80c multicolored		.95	.95
1194	A376	$1 multicolored		1.25	1.25
1195	A376	$1.50 multicolored		1.75	1.75
1196	A376	$1.80 multicolored		2.00	2.00
a.		Souvenir sheet of 1		3.75	3.75
		Nos. 1192-1196 (5)		6.55	6.25

No. 1196a inscribed in sheet margin with Hong Kong '94 emblem and text in English and Chinese. Issue date: No. 1196a, Feb. 18.

White Water Rafting — A377

	1994, Jan. 19	**Litho.**	**Perf. 12**	
		Booklet Stamp		
1197	A377	45c multicolored	.55	.55
a.	Booklet pane of 10 + 4 labels	6.00		

Whitbread Trans-Global Yacht Race — A378

	1994, Jan. 19		**Perf. 15**	
1198	A378	$1 Endeavour	1.40	1.40

Used value is for stamp with complete selvage.

The 1950's — A379

Designs: 45c, Rock and roll. 80c, Conquest of Mt. Everest. $1, Aunt Daisy, "Good Morning Everybody." $1.20, Royal visit, 1953. $1.50, Opo, the Friendly Dolphin. $1.80, The Coat Hanger (Auckland Harbor Bridge.)

		1994, Mar. 24	**Litho.**	**Perf. 14**	
1199	A379	45c multicolored		.60	.30
1200	A379	80c multicolored		.95	.95
1201	A379	$1 multicolored		1.25	1.25
1202	A379	$1.20 multicolored		1.50	1.50

1203	A379	$1.50 multicolored		1.75	1.75
1204	A379	$1.80 multicolored		2.25	2.25
		Nos. 1199-1204 (6)		8.30	8.00

Scenic Views of the Four Seasons A380

Designs: 45c, Winter, Mt. Cook, Mt. Cook lily. 70c, Spring, Lake Hawea, kowhai flower. $1.50, Summer, Opononi, pohutukawa flower. $1.80, Autumn, Mt. Cook, Lake Pukaki, puriri flower.

		1994, Apr. 27		**Perf. 12**	
1205	A380	45c multicolored		.50	.30
1206	A380	70c multicolored		.85	.85
1207	A380	$1.50 multicolored		1.25	1.25
1208	A380	$1.80 multicolored		1.75	1.75
a.		Strip of 4, #1205-1208		5.00	5.00
		Nos. 1205-1208 (4)		4.35	4.15

 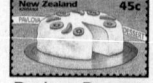

Paua Shell A381 | **Pavlova Dessert A382**

Jandals A383 | **Bush Shirt A384**

Buzzy Bee Toy — A385 | **Kiwi Fruit — A386**

Kiwiana: #1211, Hokey pokey ice cream. #1212, Fish and chips. #1216, Black singlet, gumboots. #1217, Rugby shoes, ball.

	1994, Apr. 27	**Litho.**	**Perf. 12**	
		Booklet Stamps		
1209	A381	45c shown	.80	.80
1210	A382	45c shown	.80	.80
1211	A381	45c multicolored	.80	.80
1212	A382	45c multicolored	.80	.80
1213	A383	45c shown	.80	.80
1214	A384	45c shown	.80	.80
1215	A385	45c shown	.65	.80
1216	A383	45c multicolored	.80	.80
1217	A384	45c multicolored	.80	.80
1218	A386	45c shown	.80	.80
a.	Booklet pane of 10, #1209-1218	10.00		
	Nos. 1209-1218 (10)	8.00	8.00	

Maori Myths — A387

Designs: 45c, Maui pulls up Te Ika (the fish). 80c, Rona is snatched up by Marama (moon). $1, Maui attacks Tuna (eel). $1.20, Tane separates Rangi (sky) and Papa (earth). $1.50, Matakauri slays Giant of Wakatipu. $1.80, Panenehu shows Koura (crayfish) to Tangaroa.

	1994, June 8		**Perf. 13**	
1219	A387	45c multicolored	.65	.35
1220	A387	80c multicolored	.95	.95
1221	A387	$1 multicolored	1.25	1.25
1222	A387	$1.20 multicolored	1.50	1.50
1223	A387	$1.50 multicolored	1.90	1.90
1224	A387	$1.80 multicolored	2.25	2.25
	Nos. 1219-1224 (6)		8.50	8.20

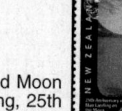

First Manned Moon Landing, 25th Anniv. — A388

	1994, July 20	**Litho.**	**Perf. 12**	
1225	A388	$1.50 multicolored	2.25	2.25

No. 1225 has a holographic image. Soaking in water may affect the hologram.

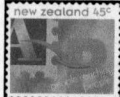

People Reaching People — A389

Serpentine Die Cut 11

	1994, July 20		**Photo.**	
		Self-Adhesive		
1226	A389	45c multicolored	.60	.50
a.	Arrow partially covering hole in "B," serpentine die cut 11 ¼	2.00		.75

No. 1226a issued Aug. 1995.
See No. 1311.

Wild Animals — A390

No. 1227, Hippopotamus. No. 1228, Spider monkey. No. 1229, Giant panda. No. 1230, Polar bear. No. 1231, African elephant. No. 1232, White rhinoceros. No. 1233, African lion. No. 1234, Plains zebra. No. 1235, Giraffe. No. 1236, Siberian tiger.

		1994, Aug. 16	**Litho.**	**Perf. 14**	
1227	A390	45c multicolored		.80	.80
1228	A390	45c multicolored		.80	.80
1229	A390	45c multicolored		.80	.80
1230	A390	45c multicolored		.80	.80
1231	A390	45c multicolored		.80	.80
1232	A390	45c multicolored		.80	.80
1233	A390	45c multicolored		.80	.80
1234	A390	45c multicolored		.80	.80
1235	A390	45c multicolored		.80	.80
1236	A390	45c multicolored		.80	.80
a.		Block of 10, #1227-1236		10.00	10.00
b.		Souvenir sheet of 6, #1229-1231, 1233, 1235-1236		4.50	4.50
		Nos. 1227-1236 (10)		8.00	8.00

PHILAKOREA '94 (#1236b). Nos. 1227-1236 printed in sheets of 100. Because of the design of these sheets, blocks or strips of Nos. 1227-1236 exist in 10 different arrangements. Value assigned to No. 1236a applies to all arrangements.

Christmas — A391

Designs: No. 1237, Children, Nativity scene. 70c, Magi, father, child. 80c, Carolers, stained glass window. $1, Carolers, Christmas tree. $1.50, Children, candles. $1.80, Father, mother, infant. No. 1243, Children, Christmas tree, Santa.

		1994, Sept. 21	**Litho.**	**Perf. 14**	
1237	A391	45c multicolored		.60	.50
1238	A391	70c multicolored		.90	.90
1239	A391	80c multicolored		1.10	1.10
1240	A391	$1 multicolored		1.25	1.25
a.		Souv. sheet, 1 ea #1237-1240		4.00	4.00
1241	A391	$1.50 multicolored		1.50	1.50
1242	A391	$1.80 multicolored		1.75	1.75
		Nos. 1237-1242 (6)		7.10	7.00

Booklet Stamp
Size: 30x25mm

	1994			
1243	A391	45c multicolored	.55	.55
a.	Booklet pane of 10	7.00		

Cricket in New Zealand, Cent. A392

Beach Cricket A393

No. 1248: a, Woman with striped bathing suit in ocean. b, Person on bodyboard in ocean. c, Child holding float toy at water's edge. d, Boy with beach ball. e, Man holding ice cream cone. f, Beach umbrella at LL. g, Man in blue and red shorts holding cricket bat. h, Woman with cap holding cricket bat. i, Child with pail and shovel. j, Sunbather reading newspaper.

		1994, Nov. 2		**Perf. 13½**	
1244	A392	45c Batting		.60	.40
1245	A392	80c Bowling		1.10	.80
1246	A392	$1 Wicketkeeping		1.25	1.25
1247	A392	$1.80 Fielding		2.00	2.00
		Nos. 1244-1247 (4)		4.95	4.45
				Perf. 12	
1248		45c Bklt. pane of 10		8.00	8.00
a.-j.	A393 Any single			.70	.55

New Zealand at Night — A394

		1995, Feb. 22	**Litho.**	**Perf. 12**	
1249	A394	45c Auckland		.65	.35
1250	A394	80c Wellington		1.00	.60
1251	A394	$1 Christchurch		1.40	1.00
1252	A394	$1.20 Dunedin		1.60	1.60
1253	A394	$1.50 Rotorua		1.75	1.75
1254	A394	$1.80 Queenstown		2.00	2.00
a.		Souv. sheet of 6, #1249-1254		25.00	25.00
		Nos. 1249-1254 (6)		8.40	7.25

Singapore '95, Jakarta '95 (#1254a). Issued: No. 1254a, 9/1/95.

Golf Courses — A395

		1995, Mar. 22	**Litho.**	**Perf. 14**	
1255	A395	45c Waitangi		.65	.35
1256	A395	80c New Plymouth		1.00	1.00
1257	A395	$1.20 Rotorua		1.50	1.50
1258	A395	$1.80 Queenstown		2.50	2.50
		Nos. 1255-1258 (4)		5.65	5.35

Environmental Protection — A396

No. 1259, Native fauna, flora. No. 1260, Plant native trees, shrubs. No. 1261, Protect marine mammals. No. 1262, Conserve power, water. No. 1263, Enjoy natural environment. No. 1264, Control animal pests. No. 1265, Eliminate noxious plants. No. 1266, Return undersized catches. No. 1267, Control air, water quality. No. 1268, Dispose of trash properly.

		1995, Mar. 22			
1259	A396	45c multicolored		.65	.65
1260	A396	45c multicolored		.65	.65
1261	A396	45c multicolored		.65	.65
1262	A396	45c multicolored		.65	.65
1263	A396	45c multicolored		.65	.65
1264	A396	45c multicolored		.65	.65
1265	A396	45c multicolored		.65	.65
1266	A396	45c multicolored		.65	.65
1267	A396	45c multicolored		.65	.65
1268	A396	45c multicolored		.65	.65
a.		Booklet pane, #1259-1268		7.50	
		Complete booklet, #1268a		8.00	
		Nos. 1259-1268 (10)		6.50	6.50

Maori Language — A397

Designs: 45c, Treasured Language Nest. 70c, Sing to awaken the spirit. 80c, Acquire knowledge through stories. $1, The welcoming call. $1.50, Recite the genealogies that link people. $1.80, Tell the lore of the people.

1995, May 3   Litho.   Perf. 13½
1269	A397	45c multicolored	.60	.25
1270	A397	70c multicolored	.90	.90
1271	A397	80c multicolored	1.10	1.10
1272	A397	$1 multicolored	1.25	1.25
1273	A397	$1.50 multicolored	2.00	2.00
1274	A397	$1.80 multicolored	2.25	2.25
		Nos. 1269-1274 (6)	8.10	7.75

Asian Development Bank, 28th Meeting of the Board of Governors, Auckland — A398

Design: $1.50, Pacific Basin Economic Council, 28th Intl. Meeting, Auckland.

1995, May 3
1275	A398	$1 Map shown	1.25	1.25
1276	A398	$1.50 Map of Pacific	2.00	2.00

Team New Zealand, 1995 America's Cup Winner — A399

1995, May 16   Perf. 12
1277	A399	45c Black Magic yacht	.70	.60

Rugby League, Cent. — A400

Designs: No. 1278, Club Rugby League, Lion Red Cup. No. 1282, Trans Tasman. $1, Mini League. $1.50, George Smith, Albert Baskerville, Early Rugby League. $1.80, Intl. Rugby League, Courtney Intl. Goodwill Trophy.

1995, July 26   Litho.   Perf. 14
1278	A400	45c multicolored	.65	.25
1279	A400	$1 multicolored	1.40	1.40
1280	A400	$1.50 multicolored	2.10	2.10
1281	A400	$1.80 multicolored	2.50	2.50
a.		Souvenir sheet of 1	3.00	3.00
		Nos. 1278-1281 (4)	6.65	6.25

Booklet Stamp
Perf. 12 on 3 Sides
1282	A400	45c multicolored	.60	.60
a.		Booklet pane of 10	7.00	
		Complete booklet, #1282a	7.00	

#1281a exists imperf from a "Limited Edition" album.

From 1995 onward, New Zealand Post has released a series of "Limited Edition" albums in editions of 2,000. Some contain souvenir sheets unique to these albums.

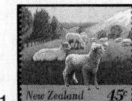

Farm Animals — A401

1995   Litho.   Perf. 14x14½
Booklet Stamps
1283	A401	40c Sheep	.50	.50
1284	A401	40c Deer	.50	.50
1285	A401	40c Horses	.50	.50
1286	A401	40c Cattle	.50	.50
1287	A401	40c Goats	.50	.50
1288	A401	40c Turkey	.50	.50

1289	A401	40c Ducks	.50	.50
1290	A401	40c Chickens	.50	.50
1291	A401	40c Pigs	.50	.50
1292	A401	40c Border collie	.50	.50
a.		Bklt. pane of 10, #1283-1292	6.25	
		Complete booklet	6.75	
1293	A401	45c Sheep	.75	.75
1294	A401	45c Deer	.75	.75
1295	A401	45c Horses	.75	.75
1296	A401	45c Cattle	.75	.75
1297	A401	45c Goats	.75	.75
1298	A401	45c Turkey	.75	.75
1299	A401	45c Ducks	.75	.75
1300	A401	45c Chickens	.75	.75
1301	A401	45c Pigs	.75	.75
1302	A401	45c Border collie	.75	.75
a.		Bklt. pane of 10, #1293-1302	8.25	
		Complete booklet, #1302a	8.75	
b.		Souvenir sheet of 5, #1298-1302, perf. 12	4.25	4.25
		Nos. 1283-1302 (20)	12.50	12.50

Singapore '95 (#1302b).
#1302b exists imperf.
Issued: #1302a, 9/1/95; #1292a, 10/2/95.

Christmas — A402

Stained glass windows: 40c, 45c, Archangel Gabriel. No. 1309A, Angel with trumpet. 70c, Mary. 80c, Shepherds. $1, Madonna and Child. $1.50, Two wise men. $1.80, One wise man.

1995   Perf. 12
1303	A402	40c multi	.60	.25
1304	A402	45c multi	.65	.35
1305	A402	70c multi	.95	.95
1306	A402	80c multi	1.00	1.00
1307	A402	$1 multi	1.25	1.25
1308	A402	$1.50 multi	2.25	2.25
1309	A402	$1.80 multi	2.50	2.50
		Nos. 1303-1309 (7)	9.20	8.55

Booklet Stamp
Size: 25x30mm
Perf. 14½x14
1309A	A402	40c multi	.55	.55
b.		Booklet pane of 10	6.50	
		Complete booklet, #1309b	6.50	

Issued: 45c-$1.80, 9/1; #1303, 10/2; #1309A, 11/9.
Nos. 1303-1309 exist in a souvenir sheet from a "Limited Edition" pack.

Nuclear Disarmament — A403

1995, Sept. 1   Litho.   Perf. 13½
1310	A403	$1 multicolored	1.40	1.40

People Reaching People Type of 1994
Serpentine Die Cut 11
1995, Oct. 2   Photo.
Self-Adhesive
1311	A389	40c multicolored	2.00	1.00
a.		Arrow partially covering hole in "B," serpentine die cut 11¼	1.00	1.00

No. 1311a, Nov. 1995.

Scenic Views

Mitre Peak — A404

1995, Oct. 2   Litho.   Perf. 13½
1312	A404	40c multicolored	.65	.55
a.		Perf 12	1.25	.90
b.		As "a," miniature sheet of 10	12.50	

Southpex '96 Stamp Show (No. 1312a).
See Nos. 1345-1360, 1405, 1412, 1636-1640, 1679-1680, 1909, 1929.

UN, 50th Anniv. — A405

1995, Oct. 4   Perf. 14½
1313	A405	$1.80 multicolored	2.50	2.50

Famous Living New Zealanders A406

Person, career field: 40c, Dame Kiri Te Kanawa, performing arts. 80c, Charles Upham, service, business, development. $1, Barry Crump, fine arts, literature. $1.20, Sir Brian Barratt-Boyes, science, medicine, education. $1.50, Dame Whina Cooper, community leader, social campaigner. $1.80, Sir Richard Hadlee, sports.

1995, Oct. 4   Perf. 12
1314	A406	40c multicolored	.90	.45
1315	A406	80c multicolored	1.10	.85
1316	A406	$1 multicolored	1.25	1.25
1317	A406	$1.20 multicolored	1.50	1.50
1318	A406	$1.50 multicolored	2.00	2.00
1319	A406	$1.80 multicolored	2.50	2.50
		Nos. 1314-1319 (6)	9.25	8.55

Nos. 1314-1319 issued with se-tenant tab inscribed "STAMP / MONTH / OCTOBER / 1995."

Commonwealth Heads of Government Meeting, Auckland — A407

Designs: 40c, Fern, sky, globe. $1.80, Fern, sea, national flag.

1995, Nov. 9   Litho.   Perf. 14
1320	A407	40c multicolored	.65	.50
1321	A407	$1.80 multicolored	2.75	2.50

Racehorses A408

40c, Kiwi. 80c, Rough Habit. $1, Blossom Lady. $1.20, Il Vicolo. $1.50, Horlicks. $1.80, Bonecrusher.

1996, Jan. 24   Litho.   Perf. 13½x14
1322	A408	40c multi	.75	.25
1323	A408	80c multi	1.00	1.00
1324	A408	$1 multi	1.25	1.25
1325	A408	$1.20 multi	1.75	1.75
1326	A408	$1.50 multi	2.00	2.00
1327	A408	$1.80 multi	2.50	2.50
		Nos. 1322-1327 (6)	9.25	8.75

Souvenir Booklet
1328	A408	multicolored	19.00	

No. 1328 contains one booklet pane of Nos. 1322-1327, perf. 14, and individual panes of 1 each Nos. 1322-1327.

Maori Crafts — A409

1996, Feb. 21   Litho.   Perf. 14x13½
1329	A409	40c Basket	.45	.25
1330	A409	80c Weapon	.85	.85
1331	A409	$1 Embroidery	1.10	1.10
1332	A409	$1.20 Greenstone	1.50	1.50

1333	A409	$1.50 Gourd	1.75	1.75
a.		Souvenir sheet of 3, #1329, 1330, 1333, perf. 13	5.50	5.50
1334	A409	$1.80 Cloak	2.00	2.00
		Nos. 1329-1334 (6)	7.65	7.45

No. 1333a for Hong Kong '97. Issued 2/12/97.

Seashore — A410

Designs: No. 1335, Black-backed gull. No. 1336, Sea cucumber, spiny starfish. No. 1337, Common shrimp. No. 1338, Gaudy nudibranch. No. 1339, Large rock crab, clingfish. No. 1340, Snake skin chiton, red rock crab. No. 1341, Estuarine triplefin, cat's eye shell. No. 1342, Cushion star, sea horse. No. 1343, Blue-eyed triplefin, yaldwyn's triplefin. No. 1344, Common octopus.

1996, Feb. 21   Perf. 14x14½
Booklet Stamps
1335	A410	40c multicolored	.55	.55
1336	A410	40c multicolored	.55	.55
1337	A410	40c multicolored	.55	.55
1338	A410	40c multicolored	.55	.55
1339	A410	40c multicolored	.55	.55
1340	A410	40c multicolored	.55	.55
1341	A410	40c multicolored	.55	.55
1342	A410	40c multicolored	.55	.55
1343	A410	40c multicolored	.55	.55
1344	A410	40c multicolored	.55	.55
a.		Booklet pane, #1335-1344	6.50	
		Complete booklet, No. 1344a	6.75	
		Nos. 1335-1344 (10)	5.50	5.50

No. 1344a has a continuous design.

Serpentine Die Cut 11½
1996, Aug. 7   Litho.
Booklet Stamps
Self-Adhesive
1344B	A410	40c like #1335	2.10	2.10
1344C	A410	40c like #1336	2.10	2.10
1344D	A410	40c like #1337	2.10	2.10
1344E	A410	40c like #1338	2.10	2.10
1344F	A410	40c like #1339	2.10	2.10
1344G	A410	40c like #1340	2.10	2.10
1344H	A410	40c like #1341	2.10	2.10
1344I	A410	40c like #1342	2.10	2.10
1344J	A410	40c like #1343	2.10	2.10
1344K	A410	40c like #1344	2.10	2.10
l.		Bklt. pane, #1344B-1344K	24.00	
		Nos. 1344B-1344K (10)	21.00	21.00

No. 1344Kl is a complete booklet. The peelable paper backing serves as a booklet cover.

Scenic Views Type of 1995

5c, Mt. Cook, horiz. 10c, Champagne Pool, horiz. 20c, Cape Reinga, horiz. 30c, Mackenzie Country, horiz. 50c, Mt. Ngauruhoe, horiz. 60c, Lake Wanaka. 70c, Giant Kauri-Tane Mahuta. 80c, Doubtful Sound. 90c, Waitomo Limestone Cave.

No. 1354, Tory Channel, Marlborough Sounds. No. 1355, Lake Wakatipu. No. 1356, Lake Matheson. No. 1357, Fox Glacier. No. 1358, Mt. Egmont, Taranaki. No. 1359, Piercy Island, Bay of Islands. No. 1354-1359 horiz.

1996, Mar. 27   Litho.   Perf. 13½
1345	A404	5c multicolored	.25	.25
1346	A404	10c multicolored	.25	.25
1347	A404	20c multicolored	.25	.25
1348	A404	30c multicolored	.35	.35
1349	A404	50c multicolored	.50	.50
a.		Souv. sheet of 4, #1346-1349	3.00	3.00
1350	A404	60c multicolored	.70	.70
1351	A404	70c multicolored	.80	.80
1352	A404	80c multicolored	1.00	1.00
1353	A404	90c multicolored	1.25	1.25
a.		Souv. sheet of 4, #1350-1353	6.50	6.50
		Nos. 1345-1353 (9)	5.35	5.35

CHINA '96 (#1349a). CAPEX '96 (#1353a). See No. 1405.

Serpentine Die Cut 11¼
1996, May 1   Photo.
Size: 26x21mm
Self-Adhesive
1354	A404	40c multicolored	.55	.55
1355	A404	40c multicolored	.55	.55
1356	A404	40c multicolored	.55	.55
1357	A404	40c multicolored	.55	.55
1358	A404	40c multicolored	.55	.55
1359	A404	40c multicolored	.55	.55
a.		Strip of 6, Nos. 1354-1359	3.50	3.50
k.		Sheet of 10, #1356, 1359, 2 each #1354-1355, 1357-1358	27.50	
l.		Sheet of 10, #1355, 1358, 2 each #1354, 1356-1357, 1359	27.50	

m. Sheet of 10, #1354, 1357, 2
each #1355-1356, 1358-
1359   27.50
Nos. 1354-1359 (6)   3.30   3.30

Serpentine Die Cut 10x9¾
1998, Jan. 14   Litho.

Booklet Stamps
Size: 26x21mm
Self-Adhesive

1359B	A404	40c like #1358	.55	.55
1359C	A404	40c like #1357	.55	.55
1359D	A404	40c like #1359	.55	.55
1359E	A404	40c like #1356	.55	.55
1359F	A404	40c like #1354	.55	.55
h.		"Marlborough Sounds" omitted	17.50	
1359G	A404	40c like #1355	.55	.55
i.		Booklet pane, #1359D, 1359F, 1359Fh, 1359G, 2 #1359B-1359C, 1359E	19.00	
j.		Booklet pane, #1359D, 1359G, 2 each #1359B, 1359C, 1359E, 1359F	5.50	
n.		Coil strip of 6, #1359B-1359G	3.60	
		Nos. 1359B-1359G (6)	3.30	3.30

No. 1359Gi is a complete booklet.

Serpentine Die Cut 11½
1996, Aug. 7   Litho.
Size: 33x22mm
Self-Adhesive

Design: $1, Pohutukawa tree, horiz.

1360	A404	$1 multicolored	1.40	1.40
a.		Booklet pane of 5	7.00	

By its nature No. 1360a is a complete booklet. The peelable paper backing serves as a
booklet cover. The outside of the cover contains 5 peelable international airpost labels.

Rescue Services — A411

40c, Fire service, ambulance. 80c, Civil
defense. $1, Air sea rescue. $1.50, Air ambulance, rescue helicopter. $1.80, Mountain res-
cue, Red Cross.

1996, Mar. 27   Perf. 14½x15

1361	A411	40c multicolored	.60	.45
1362	A411	80c multicolored	1.00	1.00
1363	A411	$1 multicolored	1.25	1.25
1364	A411	$1.50 multicolored	2.00	2.00
1365	A411	$1.80 multicolored	2.50	2.50
		Nos. 1361-1365 (5)	7.35	7.20

Wildlife — A412

Designs: 40c, Yellow-eyed penguin, vert.
80c, Royal albatross. $1, White heron. $1.20,
Sperm whale. $1.50, Fur seal, vert. $1.80,
Bottlenose dolphin, vert.

1996, May 1   Litho.   Perf. 14

1366	A412	40c multicolored	.70	.50
1367	A412	80c multicolored	1.25	.90
1368	A412	$1 multicolored	1.40	1.40
1369	A412	$1.20 multicolored	1.50	1.50
1370	A412	$1.50 multicolored	1.75	1.75
a.		Sheet of 2, #1368, 1370	6.50	6.50
1371	A412	$1.80 multicolored	2.00	2.00
a.		Sheet of 2, #1367, 1371	5.00	5.00
b.		Block, #1366-1371, + 2 labels	9.50	9.50
		Nos. 1366-1371 (6)	8.60	8.05

No. 1370a for CHINA '96. Issued May 18.
No. 1371a for Taipei '96. Issued Oct. 2.

New Zealand
Symphony
Orchestra,
50th Anniv.
A413

1996, July 10   Litho.   Perf. 15x14½

1372	A413	40c Violin	.60	.50
1373	A413	80c French horn	1.10	1.10

1996 Summer
Olympics,
Atlanta — A414

1996, July 10   Perf. 14½

1374	A414	40c Swimming	.75	.30
1375	A414	80c Cycling	1.40	1.40
1376	A414	$1 Athletics	1.50	1.50
1377	A414	$1.50 Rowing	1.75	1.75
1378	A414	$1.80 Yachting	2.00	2.00
a.		Sheet of 5, #1374-1378	8.00	8.00
		Nos. 1374-1378 (5)	7.40	6.95

Used value is for stamp with complete
selvage.
A miniature sheet containing #1374-1378,
both perf and imperf within the sheet, exists.
This comes from a "Limited Edition" collectors'
pack.
See No. 1383.

A415

Motion pictures, cent.: 40c, Hinemoa. 80c,
Broken Barrier. $1.50, Goodbye Pork Pie.
$1.80, Once Were Warriors.

1996, Aug. 7   Litho.   Perf. 14½x15

1379	A415	40c multicolored	.60	.35
1380	A415	80c multicolored	1.10	1.10
1381	A415	$1.50 multicolored	1.75	1.75
1382	A415	$1.80 multicolored	2.00	2.00
		Nos. 1379-1382 (4)	5.45	5.20

Nos. 1379-1382 are printed se-tenant with
scratch and win labels for a contest available
to New Zealand residents. Values 25% more
with unscratched labels attached.

1996 Summer Olympics Type

Design: Danyon Loader, swimmer, Blyth
Tait, horseman, 1996 gold medalists from New
Zealand.

1996, Aug. 28   Litho.   Perf. 14½

1383	A414	40c multicolored	.65	.65

Used value is for stamp with complete
selvage.
Leaves in selvage printed in six different
patterns.

Beehive Ballot
Box — A416

1996, Sept. 4   Perf. 12

1384	A416	40c multicolored	.65	.50

Mixed member proportional election, 1966.
No. 1384 was issued in sheets of 10.

Christmas — A417

Scenes from the Christmas story: No. 1385,
Following the star. 70c, Shepherd finding baby
in manger. 80c, Angel's announcement to
shepherd. $1, The Nativity. $1.50, Journey to
Bethlehem. $1.80, The annunciation.
No. 1391, Adoration of the Magi. No. 1392,
Heavenly host praising God.

1996, Sept. 4   Perf. 14

1385	A417	40c multicolored	.60	.30
1386	A417	70c multicolored	1.00	1.00
1387	A417	80c multicolored	1.10	1.10
1388	A417	$1 multicolored	1.25	1.25

1389	A417	$1.50 multicolored	1.75	1.75
1390	A417	$1.80 multicolored	2.00	2.00
		Nos. 1385-1390 (6)	7.70	7.40

Size: 29x24mm
Self-Adhesive
Serpentine Die Cut 11½

1391	A417	40c multicolored	.65	.55
a.		Booklet pane 10	6.50	
1392	A417	40c multicolored	.65	.55

By its nature No. 1391a is a complete booklet. The peelable paper backing serves as a
booklet cover.

Extinct
Birds — A418

No. 1393, 40c, Adzebill. 80c, Laughing owl.
$1, Piopio. $1.20, Huia. $1.50, Giant eagle.
$1.80, Giant moa. No. 1399, 40c, Stout-
legged wren.

1996, Oct. 2   Litho.   Perf. 13½

1393	A418	40c multi	.60	.45
1394	A418	80c multi	1.10	1.10
1395	A418	$1 multi	1.50	1.50
1396	A418	$1.20 multi	1.60	1.60
1397	A418	$1.50 multi	2.00	2.00
1398	A418	$1.80 multi	2.25	2.25
a.		Souvenir sheet	3.00	3.00
b.		As "a," with added inscription	4.50	4.50
		Nos. 1393-1398 (6)	9.05	8.90

Size: 29x24mm
Self-Adhesive
Serpentine Die Cut 11½

1399	A418	40c multi	.65	.55
a.		Booklet pane of 10	6.50	

Inscriptions on backs of Nos. 1393-1398
describe each species. By its nature No.
1399a is a complete booklet. The peelable
backing serves as a booklet cover.
No. 1398b contains Taipei '96 exhibition
emblem in sheet margin.

Scenic
Gardens — A419

Designs: 40c, Seymour Square Gardens,
Blenheim. 80c, Pukekura Park Gardens, New
Plymouth. $1, Wintergarden, Auckland. $1.50,
Botanic Gardens, Christchurch. $1.80, Marine
Parade Gardens, Napier.

1996, Nov. 13   Litho.   Perf. 13½

1400	A419	40c multicolored	.55	.45
1401	A419	80c multicolored	1.00	1.00
1402	A419	$1 multicolored	1.25	1.25
1403	A419	$1.50 multicolored	1.75	1.75
1404	A419	$1.80 multicolored	2.25	2.25
		Nos. 1400-1404 (5)	6.80	6.70

New Zealand Post produced and distributed three souvenir sheets as
rewards for purchases made from the
post office during 1996. The sheets
were not available through normal philatelic channels. The sheets are
inscribed "NEW ZEALAND POST / Best
of 1996" and the Stamp Points emblem.
Each sheet contains 3 stamps; #1327,
1365, 1334; #1378, 1382, 1371; #1390,
1404, 1398.

Scenic Views Type of 1995
Serpentine Die Cut 11½
1996, Nov. 1   Litho.
Size: 21x26mm
Self-Adhesive

1405	A404	80c like #1352	1.10	1.10
a.		Booklet pane of 10	12.50	

By its nature No. 1405a is a complete booklet. The peelable paper backing serves as a
booklet cover. The outside of the cover contains 10 peelable international airpost labels.

Cattle — A420

40c, Holstein-Friesian. 80c, Jersey. $1, Sim-
mental. $1.20, Ayrshire. $1.50, Angus. $1.80,
Hereford.

1997, Jan. 15   Perf. 14x14½

1406	A420	40c multi	.65	.30
1407	A420	80c multi	1.10	1.10
1408	A420	$1 multi	1.50	1.40
1409	A420	$1.20 multi	1.60	1.60
1410	A420	$1.50 multi	1.90	1.90
a.		Souvenir sheet of 3, #1407, 1408, 1410	8.50	8.50
1411	A420	$1.80 multi	2.10	2.10
		Nos. 1406-1411 (6)	8.85	8.40

No. 1410a for Hong Kong '97. Issued
2/12/97.

Souvenir Sheets
The 1997 sheets contain: Nos. 1411,
1418, 1434; Nos. 1440, 1444, 1451;
Nos. 1445, 1457, 1475.
See note following No. 1404.

Scenic Views Type of 1995
1997, Feb. 12   Litho.   Perf. 13½
Size: 37x32mm

1412	A404	$10 Mt. Ruapehu	10.00	8.00

Discoverers
A421

40c, James Cook. 80c, Kupe. $1, Maui, vert.
$1.20, Jean de Surville, vert. $1.50, Dumont
d'Urville. $1.80, Abel Tasman.

1997, Feb. 12   Perf. 14

1413	A421	40c multicolored	.75	.50
1414	A421	80c multicolored	1.10	1.10
1415	A421	$1 multicolored	1.40	1.40
1416	A421	$1.20 multicolored	1.75	1.75
1417	A421	$1.50 multicolored	2.25	2.25
1418	A421	$1.80 multicolored	2.50	2.50
		Nos. 1413-1418 (6)	9.75	9.50

#1413-1418 exist in sheet of 6 created for a
hard-bound millennium book that sold for
$129.

"Wackiest
Letterboxes" — A422

Serpentine Die Cut 11¼
1997, Mar. 19   Litho.
Self-Adhesive
Booklet Stamps

1419	A422	40c Log house	.55	.55
1420	A422	40c Owl	.55	.55
1421	A422	40c Whale	.55	.55
1422	A422	40c "Kilroy is Back"	.55	.55
1423	A422	40c House of twigs	.55	.55
1424	A422	40c Scottish piper	.55	.55
1425	A422	40c Diving helmet	.55	.55
1426	A422	40c Airplane	.55	.55
1427	A422	40c Water faucet	.55	.55
1428	A422	40c Painted buildings	.55	.55
a.		Bklt. pane of 10, #1419-1428	7.00	
b.		Sheet of 10, #1419-1428	17.00	
		Nos. 1419-1428 (10)	5.50	5.50

By its nature No. 1428a is a complete booklet. The peelable paper backing serves as a
booklet cover.

Vineyards
A423

40c, Central Otago. 80c, Hawke's Bay. $1,
Marlborough. $1.20, Canterbury, Waipara.
$1.50, Gisborne. $1.80, Auckland, Waiheke.

1997, Mar. 19 — Perf. 14

1429	A423	40c multicolored	.50 .30
a.	Booklet pane of 1		.65
1430	A423	80c multicolored	1.10 1.10
a.	Booklet pane of 1		1.10
1431	A423	$1 multicolored	1.40 1.40
a.	Booklet pane of 1		1.40
1432	A423	$1.20 multicolored	1.60 1.60
a.	Booklet pane of 1		1.60
1433	A423	$1.50 multicolored	2.00 2.00
a.	Booklet pane of 1		2.00
b.	Souvenir sheet of 3, #1429, 1431, 1433		9.25 9.25
1434	A423	$1.80 multicolored	2.40 2.40
a.	Booklet pane of 1		2.40
b.	Bkt. pane of 6, #1429-1434		9.25
	Complete booklet, #1429a, 1430a, 1431a, 1432a, 1433a, 1434a, 1434b		19.00
	Nos. 1429-1434 (6)		9.00 8.80

No. 1433b for PACIFIC 97. Issued: 5/29.

Pigeon Mail Service, Cent. — A424

Design: 1899 local stamp.

1997, May 7 — Litho. — Perf. 14

1435	A424	40c red	.65 .65
1436	A424	80c blue	1.25 1.25
a.	Souv. sheet of 2, #1435-1436		10.50 10.50
b.	As "a," diff. inscription		6.00 6.00

No. 1436a for PACIFIC 97. Issued: 5/29.
No. 1436b was inscribed in sheet margin for AUPEX '97 National Stamp Exhibition, Auckland. Issued 11/13.

Paintings by Colin McCahon (1919-87) A425

Designs: 40c, The Promised Land, 1948. $1, Six Days in Nelson and Canterbury, 1950. $1.50, Northland Panels, 1958. $1.80, Moby Dick is sighted off Muriwai Beach, 1972.

1997, May 7

1437	A425	40c multicolored	.65 .30
1438	A425	$1 multicolored	1.25 1.25
1439	A425	$1.50 multicolored	2.00 2.00
1440	A425	$1.80 multicolored	2.25 2.25
	Nos. 1437-1440 (4)		6.15 5.80

See Nos. 1597-1600.

Fly Fishing — A426

Designs: 40c, Red setter fly, rainbow trout. $1, Grey ghost fly, sea-run brown trout. $1.50, Twilight beauty fly, brook trout. $1.80, Hare & copper fly, brown trout.

1997, June 18 — Litho. — Perf. 13

1441	A426	40c multicolored	.60 .40
1442	A426	$1 multicolored	1.50 1.50
1443	A426	$1.50 multicolored	2.00 2.00
1444	A426	$1.80 multicolored	2.25 2.25
a.	Souv. sheet of 2, #1441, 1444		6.00 6.00
	Nos. 1441-1444 (4)		6.35 6.15

No.1444a issued 5/13/98 for Israel '98 World Stamp Exhibition, Tel Aviv.

Kiwi Type of 1988

1997, Aug. 6 — Litho. — Perf. 14½

1445	A325	$1 violet	1.25 1.25

Value is for stamp with surrounding selvage. Selvage comes with and without gold sunbursts.
See No. 1635a.

Scenic Trains — A426a

Name of train, area scene, map of train route: 40c, Overlander, Paremata, Wellington,

Wellington-Auckland. 80c, Trans-Alpine, Southern Alps, Christchurch-Greymouth. $1, Southerner, Canterbury, Invercargill-Christchurch. $1.20, Coastal Pacific, Kaikoura Coast, Christchurch-Picton. $1.50, Bay Express, Central Hawke's Bay, Wellington-Napier. $1.80, Kaimai Express, Tauranga Harbor, Tauranga-Auckland.

1997, Aug. 6 — Perf. 14x14½

1446	A426a	40c multicolored	.60 .40
1447	A426a	80c multicolored	1.10 1.00
1448	A426a	$1 multicolored	1.25 1.25
1449	A426a	$1.20 multicolored	1.50 1.50
1450	A426a	$1.50 multicolored	2.00 2.00
a.	Sheet of 3, #1447-1448, 1450		7.50 7.50
1451	A426a	$1.80 multicolored	2.25 2.25
	Nos. 1446-1451 (6)		8.70 8.40

No. 1450a issued 5/13/98 for Israel '98 World Stamp Exhibition, Tel Aviv.
Nos. 1446-1451 exist in a sheet of 6 from a "Limited Edition" album.

Christmas — A427

Scenes from first Christian service, Rangihoua Bay, and words from Christmas carol, "Te Harinui:" No. 1452, Samuel Marsden's ship, Active. 70c, Marsden preaching from pulpit. 80c, Marsden extending hand to local chiefs. $1, Mother, children from Rangihoua. $1.50, Maori and Pakeha hands, Marsden's memorial cross. $1.80, Pohutukawa flowers, Rangihoua Bay. No. 1458, Cross marking spot of service, flowers, bay.

1997, Sept. 3 — Litho. — Perf. 14

1452	A427	40c multicolored	.60 .25
1453	A427	70c multicolored	.90 .90
1454	A427	80c multicolored	1.00 1.00
1455	A427	$1 multicolored	1.25 1.25
1456	A427	$1.50 multicolored	1.75 1.75
1457	A427	$1.80 multicolored	2.00 2.00
a.	Block of 6, #1452-1457		10.00 10.00
	Nos. 1452-1457 (6)		7.50 7.15

Self-Adhesive
Size: 30x24mm
Serpentine Die Cut 10

1458	A427	40c multicolored	.50 .50
a.	Booklet pane of 10		6.50

By its nature No. 1458a is a complete booklet. The peelable paper backing serves as a booklet cover.

"Creepy Crawlies" — A428

Serpentine Die Cut 11¼

1997, Oct. 1 — Litho.
Booklet Stamps

1459	A428	40c Huhu beetle	.55 .55
1460	A428	40c Giant land snail	.55 .55
1461	A428	40c Giant weta	.55 .55
1462	A428	40c Giant dragonfly	.55 .55
1463	A428	40c Peripatus	.55 .55
1464	A428	40c Cicada	.55 .55
1465	A428	40c Puriri moth	.55 .55
1466	A428	40c Veined slug	.55 .55
1467	A428	40c Katipo	.55 .55
1468	A428	40c Flaxweevil	.55 .55
a.	Booklet pane, #1459-1468		6.25
b.	Sheet of 10, #1459-1468		10.00
	Nos. 1459-1468 (10)		5.50 5.50

By its nature No. 1468a is a complete booklet. The peelable paper backing serves as a booklet cover.

China-New Zealand Stamp Expo — A429

1997, Oct. 9 — Perf. 14

1469	40c Rosa rugosa		.65 .50
1470	40c Aotearoa-New Zealand		.65 .50
a.	A429 Pair, #1469-1470		1.40 1.10
b.	Souvenir sheet, #1470a		2.00 2.00
c.	As "b," diff. inscription		2.00 2.00

No. 1470c inscribed in gold and black in sheet margin for Shanghai 1997 Intl. Stamp & Coin Expo. Issued: 11/19/97.
See People's Republic of China Nos. 2797-2798.

Queen Elizabeth II and Prince Philip, 50th Wedding Anniv. — A430

1997, Nov. 12 — Litho. — Perf. 12

1471	A430	40c multicolored	.65 .45

Issued in sheets of 10.

Cartoonists A431

"Kiwis Taking on the World:" 40c, Kiwi flying on bee, by Garrick Tremain. $1, Kiwi using world as egg and having it for breakfast, by Jim Hubbard. $1.50, Kiwi in yacht race against the world, by Eric Heath. $1.80, Man with chain saw, trees on mountainside cut as peace symbol, by Burton Silver.

1997, Nov. 12 — Perf. 14

1472	A431	40c multicolored	.65 .30
1473	A431	$1 multicolored	1.25 1.25
1474	A431	$1.50 multicolored	1.75 1.75
1475	A431	$1.80 multicolored	2.50 2.50
	Nos. 1472-1475 (4)		6.15 5.80

Performing Arts — A432

1998, Jan. 14 — Litho. — Perf. 13½

1476	A432	40c Modern dance	.60 .35
a.	Booklet pane of 1		.60
1477	A432	80c Music	1.00 .95
a.	Booklet pane of 1		1.00
b.	Perf 14		2.50 2.50
1478	A432	$1 Opera	1.25 1.25
a.	Booklet pane of 1		1.25
1479	A432	$1.20 Theater	1.50 1.50
a.	Booklet pane of 1		1.50
1480	A432	$1.50 Song	2.00 2.00
a.	Booklet pane of 1		2.00
1481	A432	$1.80 Ballet	2.25 2.25
a.	Booklet pane of 1		2.25
b.	Bkt. pane of 6, #1476-1481		11.00
	Complete booklet, 1 each #1476a-1481a, 1481b		22.50
c.	Perf 14		5.50 5.50
	Nos. 1476-1481 (6)		8.60 8.30

Museum of New Zealand Te Papa Tongarewa A433

40c, People at entrance. $1.80, Waterfront location.

1998, Feb. 11 — Litho. — Perf. 14

1482	A433	40c multicolored	.50 .45
1483	A433	$1.80 multicolored	2.00 2.00

Souvenir Sheets
The 1998 sheets contain: Nos. 1489, 1483, 1481; Nos. 1491, 1521, 1525; Nos. 1531, 1537, 1562.
See note following No. 1404.

Domestic Cat — A434

1998, Feb. 11 — Perf. 13½

1484	A434	40c Moggy	.55 .30
1485	A434	80c Burmese	1.00 1.00
1486	A434	$1 Birman	1.10 1.10
1487	A434	$1.20 British blue	1.25 1.25
1488	A434	$1.50 Persian	1.75 1.75
1489	A434	$1.80 Siamese	2.25 2.25
a.	Souvenir sheet of 3, #1484, #1486, #1489		6.00 6.00
	Nos. 1484-1489 (6)		7.90 7.65

Memorial Statues — A435

40c, "With Great Respect to the Mehmetcik, Gallipoli" (Turkish soldier carrying wounded ANZAC). $1.80, "Mother with Children," Natl. War Memorial, Wellington.

1998, Mar. 18 — Litho. — Perf. 13½

1490	A435	40c multicolored	.50 .40
1491	A435	$1.80 multicolored	2.00 2.00

See Turkey Nos. 2695-2696.

New Zealand's Multi-cultural Society — A436

Designs: 40c, The Maori. 80c, British/European settlers, 1840-1914. $1, Fortune seekers, 1800-1920. $1.20, Post-war British/European migrants, 1945-70. $1.50, Pacific Islanders, from 1960. $1.80, Asian arrivals, 1980s-90s.

1998, Mar. 18 — Perf. 14

1492	A436	40c multicolored	.55 .25
1493	A436	80c multicolored	1.10 .90
1494	A436	$1 multicolored	1.40 1.10
1495	A436	$1.20 multicolored	1.50 1.50
1496	A436	$1.50 multicolored	1.75 1.75
1497	A436	$1.80 multicolored	2.00 2.00
	Nos. 1492-1497 (6)		8.30 7.50

Nos. 1492-1497 exist in sheet of 6 created for a hard-bound millennium book that sold for $129.

"Stay in Touch" Greetings Stamps — A437

Designs: No. 1498, Young and older person hugging, vert. No. 1499, Middle-aged couple wading in water at beach, vert. No. 1500, Characters giving "high five," vert. No. 1501, Stylized boy pointing way to old woman, vert. No. 1502, Cartoon of woman with tears embracing man. No. 1503, Couple kissing. No. 1504, Older couple with faces together. No. 1505, Two boys arm in arm in swimming pool. No. 1506, Stylized couple, clouds. No. 1507, Stylized couple seated on sofa.

Die Cut Perf. 10x10¼, 10¼x10
1998, Apr. 15 — Litho.
Booklet Stamps
Self-Adhesive

1498	A437	40c multicolored	.80 .80
1499	A437	40c multicolored	.80 .80
1500	A437	40c multicolored	.80 .80
1501	A437	40c multicolored	.80 .80
a.	Sheet of 4, #1498-1501		5.00
1502	A437	40c multicolored	.80 .80
1503	A437	40c multicolored	.80 .80
1504	A437	40c multicolored	.80 .80
1505	A437	40c multicolored	.80 .80
1506	A437	40c multicolored	.80 .80

1507	A437	40c multicolored	.80	.80
a.		Booklet pane, #1498-1507	10.00	
b.		Sheet of 6, #1502-1507	8.00	
		Nos. 1498-1507 (10)	8.00	8.00

The peelable paper backing of No. 1507a serves as a booklet cover.

Types of 1898

1998, May 20   Litho.   Perf. 14x14½

1508	A18	40c Mt. Cook	.55	.55
1509	A19	40c Lake Taupo	.55	.55
1510	A20	40c Pembroke Peak	.55	.55
1511	A23	40c Huia	.55	.55
1512	A24	40c White Terrace	.55	.55
1513	A26	40c Kiwi	.55	.55
1514	A27	40c Maori canoe	.55	.55
1515	A29	40c Hawk-billed parrots	.55	.55

Perf. 14½

1516	A21	80c Wakatipu	1.00	1.00
1517	A22	80c Wakatipu	1.00	1.00
a.		Souvenir sheet of 2, 1516-1517	4.75	4.75
1518	A25	$1 Otira Gorge	1.25	1.25
1519	A28	$1.20 Pink Terrace	1.50	1.50
1520	A30	$1.50 Milford Sound	1.75	1.75
a.		Sheet of 2, #1517, 1520	4.00	4.00
1521	A31	$1.80 Mt. Cook	2.00	2.00
		Nos. 1508-1521 (14)	12.90	12.90

No. 1517a issued 8/7/98 for Tarapex '98, Natl. Stamp Exhibition.
No. 1520a issued 10/23/98 for Italia '98.

Paintings by
Peter McIntyre
A438

Designs: 40c, Wounded at Cassino, 1944. $1, The Cliffs of Rangitikei, c. 1958. $1.50, Maori Children, King Country, 1963. $1.80, The Anglican Church, Kakahi, 1972.

1998, June 24   Litho.   Perf. 13½

1522	A438	40c multicolored	.45	.30
1523	A438	$1 multicolored	1.10	1.10
1524	A438	$1.50 multicolored	1.60	1.60
1525	A438	$1.80 multicolored	1.90	1.90
a.		Souvenir sheet, #1524-1525, perf 14	6.00	6.00
		Nos. 1522-1525 (4)	5.05	4.90

No. 1525a issued 10/23/98 for Italia '98.
Nos. 1524-1525 exist in an imperf souvenir sheet from a "Limited Edition" album.

Scenic Skies
A439

40c, Cambridge. 80c, Lake Wanaka. $1, Mt. Maunganui. $1.20, Kaikoura. $1.50, Whakatane. $1.80, Lindis Pass.

1998, July 29   Litho.   Perf. 14½

1526	A439	40c multi	.60	.25
1527	A439	80c multi	1.10	.90
1528	A439	$1 multi	1.25	1.10
1529	A439	$1.20 multi	1.40	1.40
1530	A439	$1.50 multi	2.00	2.00
1531	A439	$1.80 multi	2.25	2.25
a.		Souv. sheet of 2, #1526, 1531	3.75	3.75
		Nos. 1526-1531 (6)	8.60	7.90

No. 1531a issued 3/19/99 for Australia '99 World Stamp Expo.

Christmas — A440

Designs: 40c, Madonna and Child. 70c, Shepherds approaching nativity scene. 80c, Joseph, Mary, Christ Child. $1, Magus. $1.50, Magi with gifts. $1.80, Angel telling shepherds about Messiah.

1998, Sept. 2   Litho.   Perf. 13x14

1532	A440	40c multicolored	.55	.25
1533	A440	70c multicolored	.90	.80
1534	A440	80c multicolored	1.10	.90
1535	A440	$1 multicolored	1.25	1.25
1536	A440	$1.50 multicolored	1.75	1.75
1537	A440	$1.80 multicolored	2.00	2.00
		Nos. 1532-1537 (6)	7.55	6.95

Self-adhesive
Size: 24x30mm
Serpentine Die Cut 11½

| 1538 | A440 | 40c multicolored | .50 | .40 |
| a. | | Booklet pane of 10 | 6.50 | |

No. 1538a is a complete booklet. The peelable paper backing serves as a booklet cover.

Marine Life — A441

1998, Oct. 7   Litho.   Perf. 14

1539	A441	40c Moonfish	.45	.45
1540	A441	40c Mako shark	.45	.45
1541	A441	40c Yellowfin tuna	.45	.45
1542	A441	40c Giant squid	.45	.45
a.		Block of 4, #1539-1542	2.50	2.50
1543	A441	80c Striped marlin	.90	.90
1544	A441	80c Porcupine fish	.90	.90
a.		Souvenir sheet of 4, #1539-1540, #1543-1544	5.25	5.25
1545	A441	80c Eagle ray	.90	.90
1546	A441	80c Sandager's wrasse	.90	.90
a.		Block of 4, #1543-1546	4.75	4.75
b.		Souvenir sheet of 4, #1541-1542, 1545-1546	8.00	8.00
		Nos. 1539-1546 (8)	5.40	5.40

No. 1544a issued 3/19/99 for Australia '99, World Stamp Expo. No. 1546b was issued 7/2/99 for PhilexFrance '99, World Philatelic Exhibition.
#1539-1546 exist in sheets of 8 from a "Limited Edition" album.

Famous Town Icons
A442   A443

Designs: No. 1547, L&P bottle, Paeroa. No. 1548, Carrot, Ohakune. No. 1549, Brown trout, Gore. No. 1550, Crayfish, Kaikoura. No. 1551, Sheep shearer, Te Kuiti. No. 1552, Pania of the Reef, Napier. No. 1553, Paua shell, Riverton. No. 1554, Kiwifruit, Te Puke. No. 1555, Border collie, Tekapo. No. 1556, Cow, Hawera.

Serpentine Die Cut 11½

1998, Oct. 7   Litho.
Self-Adhesive

1547	A442	40c multicolored	.50	.25
1548	A442	40c multicolored	.50	.25
1549	A443	40c multicolored	.50	.25
1550	A443	40c multicolored	.50	.25
1551	A443	40c multicolored	.50	.25
1552	A443	40c multicolored	.50	.25

Size: 25x30mm

1553	A443	40c multicolored	.50	.25
1554	A443	40c multicolored	.50	.25
1555	A443	40c multicolored	.50	.25
1556	A443	40c multicolored	.50	.25
a.		Sheet of 10, #1547-1556	11.50	
b.		Booklet pane, #1547-1556	6.00	
		Nos. 1547-1556 (10)	5.00	2.50

No. 1556b is a complete booklet. The peelable paper backing serves as a booklet cover.

Urban
Transformation
A444

1998, Nov. 11   Litho.   Perf. 14x14½

1557	A444	40c Wellington	.60	.35
1558	A444	80c Auckland	1.00	.65
1559	A444	$1 Christchurch	1.10	1.10
1560	A444	$1.20 Westport	1.40	1.40
1561	A444	$1.50 Tauranga	1.75	1.75
1562	A444	$1.80 Dunedin	2.25	2.25
		Nos. 1557-1562 (6)	8.10	7.50

#1557-1562 exist in sheet of 6 created for a hard-bound Millennium book that sold for $129.

Native Tree
Flowers — A445

40c, Kotukutuku. 80c, Poroporo. $1, Kowhai. $1.20, Weeping broom. $1.50, Teteaweka. $1.80, Southern rata.

1999, Jan. 13   Litho.   Perf. 14½x14

1563	A445	40c multi	.50	.50
1564	A445	80c multi	.85	.85
a.		Souv. sheet of 2, #1563-1564	3.75	3.75
1565	A445	$1 multi	1.10	1.10
1566	A445	$1.20 multi	1.30	1.30
1567	A445	$1.50 multi	1.60	1.60
1568	A445	$1.80 multi	2.00	2.00
		Nos. 1563-1568 (6)	7.35	7.10

No. 1564a was issued 8/21/99 for China 1999 Philatelic Exhibition.
Nos. 1567-1568 exist in a souvenir sheet from a "Limited Edition" album.

Souvenir Sheets

The 1999 sheets contain: Nos. 1568, 1572, 1578; Nos. 1584, 1600, 1607; Nos. 1613, 1620, 1627.
See note following No. 1404.

Art Deco
Buildings — A446

40c, Civic Theatre, Auckland. $1, Masonic Hotel, Napier. $1.50, Medical and Dental Offices, Hastings. $1.80, Buller County Offices, Westport.

1999, Feb. 10   Litho.   Perf. 14

1569	A446	40c multicolored	.70	.25
1570	A446	$1 multicolored	1.75	1.00
1571	A446	$1.50 multicolored	1.75	1.75
1572	A446	$1.80 multicolored	2.00	2.00
		Nos. 1569-1572 (4)	6.20	5.00

Popular Pets — A447

Designs: 40c, Labrador puppy. 80c, Netherland dwarf rabbit. $1, Rabbit, tabby kitten. $1.20, Lamb. $1.50, Welsh pony. $1.80, Budgies.

1999, Feb. 10

1573	A447	40c multicolored	.50	.35
1574	A447	80c multicolored	1.00	.60
1575	A447	$1 multicolored	1.25	1.25
a.		Souvenir sheet, #1573-1575	4.25	4.25
b.		Souvenir sheet, #1573, 1575	5.50	5.50
1576	A447	$1.20 multicolored	1.50	1.50
1577	A447	$1.50 multicolored	1.75	1.75
1578	A447	$1.80 multicolored	2.25	2.25
		Nos. 1573-1578 (6)	8.25	7.70

New Year 1999, Year of the Rabbit (#1575a).
No. 1575b was issued 8/21/99 for China 1999 World Philatelic Exhibition.

Nostalgia
A448

1999, Mar. 10   Litho.   Perf. 14

1579	A448	40c Toys	.70	.25
1580	A448	80c Food	1.00	1.00
1581	A448	$1 Transport	1.25	1.25
1582	A448	$1.20 Household	1.50	1.50

1583	A448	$1.50 Collectibles	1.75	1.75
1584	A448	$1.80 Garden	2.00	2.00
		Nos. 1579-1584 (6)	8.20	7.75

#1579-1584 exist in sheet of 6 created for a hard-bound Millennium book that sold for $129.

Victoria University
of Wellington,
Cent. — A449

1999, Apr. 7   Litho.   Perf. 14

| 1585 | A449 | 40c multicolored | .55 | .45 |

1999 New Zealand U-Bix Rugby Super
12 — A450

Auckland Blues: a, Kicking ball. b, Running with ball.
Chiefs: c, Being tackled. d, Catching ball.
Wellington Hurricanes: e, Being tackled. f, Passing.
Canterbury Crusaders: g, Catching ball. h, Kicking ball.
Otago Highlanders: i, Falling down with ball. j, Running with ball.

1999, Apr. 7   Perf. 14½

| 1586 | A450 | 40c Sheet of 10, #a.-j. | 13.50 | 13.50 |

Booklet Stamps
Self-Adhesive
Die Cut Perf. 12

1587	A450	40c like #1586a	.60	.45
1588	A450	40c like #1586b	.60	.45
a.		Bklt. pane, 5 ea #1587-1588	6.50	
1589	A450	40c like #1586c	.60	.45
1590	A450	40c like #1586d	.60	.45
a.		Bklt. pane, 5 ea #1589-1590	6.50	
1591	A450	40c like #1586e	.60	.45
1592	A450	40c like #1586f	.60	.45
a.		Bklt. pane, 5 ea #1591-1592	6.50	
1593	A450	40c like #1586g	.60	.45
1594	A450	40c like #1586h	.60	.45
a.		Bklt. pane, 5 ea #1593-1594	6.50	
1595	A450	40c like #1586i	.60	.45
1596	A450	40c like #1586j	.60	.45
a.		Bklt. pane, 5 ea #1595-1596	6.50	

Nos. 1587-1588, 1589-1590, 1591-1592, 1593-1594, 1595-1596 were also issued as pairs without surrounding selvage.
Nos. 1588a, 1590a, 1592a, 1594a and 1596a are all complete booklets.

Paintings Type of 1997

Paintings by Doris Lusk: 40c, The Lake, Tuai, 1948. $1, The Pumping Station, 1958. $1.50, Arcade Awning, St. Mark's Square, Venice (2), 1976. $1.80, Tuan St. II, 1982.

1999, June 16   Litho.   Perf. 14

1597	A425	40c multicolored	.60	.25
1598	A425	$1 multicolored	1.25	1.25
1599	A425	$1.50 multicolored	1.60	1.60
1600	A425	$1.80 multicolored	2.25	2.25
a.		Souv. sheet of 2, #1597, 1600	5.00	5.00
		Nos. 1597-1600 (4)	5.70	5.35

No. 1600a was issued 7/2/99 for Philex-France '99, World Philatelic Exhibition.

Asia-Pacific Economic
Cooperation
(APEC) — A451

1999, July 21   Litho.   Perf. 14
1601 A451 40c multicolored   .50   .45

Scenic
Walks — A452

Designs: 40c, West Ruggedy Beach, Stewart Island. 80c, Ice Lake, Butler Valley, Westland. $1, Tonga Bay, Abel Tasman Natl. Park. $1.20, East Matakitaki Valley, Nelson Lakes Natl. Park. $1.50, Great Barrier Island. $1.80, Mt. Taranaki/Egmont.

1999, July 28
1602 A452 40c multicolored   .50   .25
a.   Booklet pane of 1   .55
1603 A452 80c multicolored   .85   .85
a.   Booklet pane of 1   .95
1604 A452 $1 multicolored   1.10 1.10
a.   Booklet pane of 1   1.20
1605 A452 $1.20 multicolored   1.40 1.40
a.   Booklet pane of 1   1.50
1606 A452 $1.50 multicolored   2.00 2.00
a.   Booklet pane of 1   2.25
1607 A452 $1.80 multicolored   2.25 2.25
a.   Booklet pane of 1   2.50
b.   Bkt. pane of 6, #1602-1607 11.00
     Complete booklet, 1 each
     #1602a-1607a, 1607b   22.50
c.   Souvenir sheet of 1   3.50 3.50
     Nos. 1602-1607 (6)   8.10 7.85
Issued: No. 1607c, 10/1.

Christmas — A453

40c, Baby in manger. 80c, Virgin Mary. $1.10, Joseph and Mary. $1.20, Angel with harp. $1.50, Shepherds. $1.80, Three Magi. No. 1614, Baby in manger.

1999, Sept. 8   Litho.   Perf. 13
1608 A453 40c multicolored   .50   .25
1609 A453 80c multicolored   1.00 1.00
1610 A453 $1.10 multicolored   1.40 1.40
1611 A453 $1.20 multicolored   1.50 1.50
1612 A453 $1.50 multicolored   1.75 1.75
1613 A453 $1.80 multicolored   2.00 2.00
     Nos. 1608-1613 (6)   8.15 7.90

Self-Adhesive
Size: 23x27mm
Die Cut Perf. 9½x10
1614 A453 40c multicolored   .50   .25
a.   Booklet pane of 10   6.00
No. 1614a is a complete booklet.

Yachting — A454

1999, Oct. 20   Litho.   Perf. 14
1615 A454 40c P Class   .60   .25
1616 A454 80c Laser   1.00   .85
1617 A454 $1.10 18-foot skiff 1.25 1.25
1618 A454 $1.20 Hobie Cat   1.40 1.40
1619 A454 $1.50 Racing yacht   1.60 1.60
1620 A454 $1.80 Cruising
           yacht   1.90 1.90
a.   Souvenir sheet of 6, #1615-
     1620   8.50 8.50
     Nos. 1615-1620 (6)   7.75 7.25
Nos. 1615-1620 exist in an imperf souvenir sheet from a "Limited Edition" album.

Self-Adhesive
Size: 25x30mm
Die Cut Perf. 9½x10
1621 A454 40c Optimist   .45   .40
a.   Booklet pane of 10   6.00
No. 1621a is a complete booklet.

Millennium
A455

New Zealanders Leading the Way: 40c, Women, ballot box. 80c, Airplane of Richard Pearse, pioneer aviator. $1.10, Lord Ernest Rutherford, physicist. $1.20, Jet boat. $1.50, Sir Edmund Hillary, Mt. Everest. $1.80, Anti-nuclear protesters.

1999, Nov. 17   Litho.   Perf. 14x14¼
1622 A455 40c multicolored   .60   .25
1623 A455 80c multicolored   1.10   .60
1624 A455 $1.10 multicolored   1.50 1.50
1625 A455 $1.20 multicolored   1.60 1.60
1626 A455 $1.50 multicolored   1.75 1.75
1627 A455 $1.80 multicolored   2.00 2.00
     Nos. 1622-1627 (6)   8.55 7.70
Nos. 1622-1627 exist in sheet of 6 created for a hard-bound millennium book that sold for $129.

Year
2000 — A456

2000, Jan. 1   Litho.   Perf. 14¼
1628 A456 40c multi   .65   .45
a.   Miniature sheet of 10   6.50 4.50
No. 1628 exists in a sheet of 6 created for a hard-bound Millennium book that sold for $129.
The third stamp in the left column on No. 1628a is missing the map and sun emblem between the time and country name.

New Year 2000 (Year
of the Dragon) — A457

Spirits and guardians: 40c, Araiteuru. 80c, Kurangaituku. $1.10, Te Hoata and Te Pupu. $1.20, Patupaiarehe. $1.50, Te Ngarara-huarau. $1.80, Tuhirangi.

2000, Feb. 9   Litho.   Perf. 14
1629 A457 40c multi   .60   .25
1630 A457 80c multi   .90   .45
1631 A457 $1.10 multi   1.25 1.25
1632 A457 $1.20 multi   1.50 1.50
1633 A457 $1.50 multi   1.75 1.75
1634 A457 $1.80 multi   2.25 2.25
a.   Souv. sheet of 2, #1633-
     1634   5.25 5.25
     Nos. 1629-1634 (6)   8.25 7.45
Nos. 1631-1632 exist in a souvenir sheet from a "Limited Edition" album.

Kiwi Type of 1988
2000, Mar. 6   Litho.   Perf. 14½
1635 A325 $1.10 gold   1.50 1.50
a.   Souv. sheet, #918b, 1027a,
     1161b, 1445, 1635   8.25 8.25
Used value is for stamp with complete selvage.
#1635a issued 7/7 for World Stamp Expo 2000, Anaheim.

The 2000 sheets contain: #1694, 1635, 1671; #1662, 1634, 1638; #1677, 1665, 1656. See note following #1404.

Scenic Views Type of 1995
$1, Taiaroa Head. $1.10, Kaikoura Coast. $2, Great Barrier Is. $3, Cape Kidnappers.

2000   Litho.   Perf. 13¼x13½
Size: 27x22mm
1636 A404 $1 multi   1.50 1.00
1637 A404 $1.10 multi   1.60 1.10
1638 A404 $2 multi   2.25 1.75
1639 A404 $3 multi   2.75 2.50
a.   Souv. sheet, #1636, 1638-
     1639   9.00 9.00
     Nos. 1636-1639 (4)   8.10 6.35

Self-Adhesive
Booklet Stamp
Die Cut Perf 10x9¾
1640 A404 $1.10 Like #1637   1.50 1.10
a.   Booklet, 5 #1640 + 5 eti-
     quettes   8.75
The Stamp Show 2000, London (No. 1639a). Issued: #1639a, 5/22; #1640, 4/3; others, 3/6.

New Zealand Popular
Culture — A458

Kiwi with: #1641, Insulated cooler. #1642, Pipis. #1643, Inflatable beach cushion. #1644, Chocolate fish. #1645, Beach house and surf board. #1646, Barbecue. #1647, Ug boots. #1648, Anzac biscuit. #1649, Hot dog. #1650, Meat pie.

Die Cut Perf. 9¾x10
2000, Apr. 3   Litho.
Booklet Stamps
Self-Adhesive
1641 A458 40c multi   .50   .25
1642 A458 40c multi   .50   .25
1643 A458 40c multi   .50   .25
1644 A458 40c multi   .50   .25
1645 A458 40c multi   .50   .25
1646 A458 40c multi   .50   .25
1647 A458 40c multi   .50   .25
1648 A458 40c multi   .50   .25
1649 A458 40c multi   .50   .25
1650 A458 40c multi   .50   .25
a.   Booklet, #1641-1650   5.75
b.   Sheet, #1641-1650   5.75
     Nos. 1641-1650 (10)   5.00 2.50
No. 1650b has plain backing paper.

Automobiles — A459

40c, Volkswagen Beetle. 80c, Ford Zephyr MK I. $1.10, Morris Mini MK II. $1.20, Holden HQ Kingswood. $1.50, Honda Civic EB2. $1.80, Toyota Corolla.

2000, June 1   Perf. 14
1651 A459 40c claret   .55   .35
a.   Booklet pane of 1   .55
1652 A459 80c blue   .90   .65
a.   Booklet pane of 1   .90
1653 A459 $1.10 brown   1.25 1.25
a.   Booklet pane of 1   1.25
1654 A459 $1.20 green   1.50 1.50
a.   Booklet pane of 1   1.50
1655 A459 $1.50 olive grn   2.00 2.00
a.   Booklet pane of 1   2.00
1656 A459 $1.80 violet   2.25 2.25
a.   Booklet pane of 1   2.25
b.   Booklet, #1651-1656   9.00
     Booklet, #1651a-1656a,
     1656b   18.00
     Nos. 1651-1656 (6)   8.45 8.00
A miniature sheet containing #1651-1656, both perf and imperf within the sheet, exists. This comes from a "Limited Edition" album.

Scenic
Reflections
A460

Designs: 40c, Lake Lyndon. 80c, Lake Wakatipu. $1.10, Mt. Ruapehu. $1.20, Rainbow Mountain Scenic Reserve. $1.50, Tairua Harbor. $1.80, Lake Alexandrina.

2000, July 7   Litho.   Perf. 14
1657 A460 40c multi   .60   .35
1658 A460 80c multi   1.10   .55
1659 A460 $1.10 multi   1.25 1.00
1660 A460 $1.20 multi   1.50 1.50
1661 A460 $1.50 multi   1.75 1.75
1662 A460 $1.80 multi   2.00 2.00
a.   Souvenir Sheet, #1657,
     1662   4.00 4.00
     Nos. 1657-1662 (6)   8.20 7.15
No. 1662a issued 10/5/00 for Canpex 2000 Stamp Exhibition, Christchurch.

Queen Mother's
100th
Birthday — A461

Queen Mother in: 40c, 1907. $1.10, 1966. $1.80, 1997.

2000, Aug. 4
1663 A461 40c multi   .60   .35
1664 A461 $1.10 multi   1.25 1.00
1665 A461 $1.80 multi   2.50 2.00
     Nos. 1663-1665 (3)   4.35 3.35

Sports — A462

2000, Aug. 4   Perf. 14x14¼
1666 A462 40c Rowing   .60   .35
1667 A462 80c Equestrian   1.00   .55
1668 A462 $1.10 Cycling   1.50 1.00
1669 A462 $1.20 Triathlon   1.50 1.50
1670 A462 $1.50 Lawn bowling   1.75 1.75
1671 A462 $1.80 Netball   2.00 2.25
     Nos. 1666-1671 (6)   8.35 7.40
2000 Summer Olympics, Sydney (Nos. 1666-1669).

Christmas
A463

Designs: 40c, Madonna and child. 80c, Mary, Joseph and donkey. $1.10, Baby Jesus, cow, lamb. $1.20, Archangel. $1.50, Shepherd and lamb. $1.80, Magi.

2000, Sept. 6   Perf. 14
1672 A463 40c multi   .60   .25
1673 A463 80c multi   1.00   .60
1674 A463 $1.10 multi   1.40 1.40
1675 A463 $1.20 multi   1.60 1.60
1676 A463 $1.50 multi   1.75 1.75
1677 A463 $1.80 multi   2.00 2.00
     Nos. 1672-1677 (6)   8.35 7.60

Self-Adhesive
Size: 30x25mm
Serpentine Die Cut 11¼x11
1678 A463 40c multi   .60   .25
a.   Booklet of 10   6.50
Issued: No. 1678a, 11/1/00.

Scenic Views Type of 1995
Designs: 90c, Rangitoto Island. $1.30, Lake Camp, South Canterbury.

2000   Litho.   Perf. 13¼x13½
Size: 27x22mm
1679 A404 90c multi   1.25   .75
1680 A404 $1.30 multi   1.75 1.10
a.   Souvenir sheet, #1636-1637,
     1679-1680   6.00 6.00
Issued: Nos. 1679-1680, 10/2/00; No. 1680a, 3/16/01. 2001: A Stamp Odyssey Philatelic Exhibition, Invercargill (#1680a).

Teddy Bears and
Dolls — A464

Designs: 40c+5c, Teddy bear "Geronimo," by Rose Hill. 80c+5c, Antique French and wooden Schoenhut dolls. $1.10, Chad Valley bear. $1.20, Doll "Poppy," by Debbie Pointon. $1.50, Teddy bears "Swanni," by Robin Rive, and "Dear John," by Rose Hill. $1.80, Doll "Lia," by Gloria Young, and teddy bear.

2000, Oct. 5   Perf. 14½x14¾
1681 A464 40c +5c multi   .65   .40
1682 A464 80c +5c multi   1.25   .70
a.   Souvenir sheet, #1681-1682 2.75 2.75
1683 A464 $1.10 multi   1.40 1.40
1684 A464 $1.20 multi   1.60 1.60
1685 A464 $1.50 multi   1.75 1.75
1686 A464 $1.80 multi   2.00 2.00
a.   Block of 6, #1681-1686   9.50 9.50

Coil Stamp
Size: 30x25mm
Self-Adhesive
Serpentine Die Cut 11¼

| 1687 | A464 | 40c +5c multi | .55 | .40 |

Endangered Birds — A465

Designs: No. 1688, Lesser kestrel. No. 1689, Orange fronted parakeet. 80c, Black stilt. $1.10, Stewart Island fernbird. $1.20, Kakapo. $1.50, North Island weka. $1.80, Okarito brown kiwi.

2000, Nov. 4   Perf. 14
1688	A465	40c multi	.60	.35
1689	A465	40c multi	.60	.35
a.		Pair, #1688-1689	1.75	1.75
1690	A465	80c multi	1.25	.90
1691	A465	$1.10 multi	1.40	1.40
1692	A465	$1.20 multi	1.50	1.50
1693	A465	$1.50 multi	1.75	1.75
1694	A465	$1.80 multi	2.00	2.00
a.		Souvenir sheet, #1693-1694	5.75	5.75
		Nos. 1688-1694 (7)	9.10	8.25

Nos. 1689-1690 exist in a souvenir sheet from a "Limited Edition" album.
Issued: No. 1694a, 2/1/01. Hong Kong 2001 Stamp Exhibition (#1694a). See France Nos. 2790-2791.

Penny Universal Postage, Cent. — A466

Methods of mail delivery: a, Steamship. b, Horse-drawn coach. c, Early mail truck. d, Paddle steamer. e, Railway traveling post office. f, Airplane with front cargo hatch. g, Bicycle. h, Tractor trailer. i, Airplane with side cargo hatch. j, Computer mouse.

2001, Jan. 1
1695		Sheet of 10	7.00	7.00
a.-j.		A466 40c Any single	.60	.60
k.		As No. 1695, with Belgica 2001 sheet margin	7.00	7.00

No. 1695k has no perforations running through sheet margin.

Marine Reptiles — A467

Designs: 40c, Green turtle. 80c, Leathery turtle. 90c, Loggerhead turtle. $1.30, Hawksbill turtle. $1.50, Banded sea snake. $2, Yellow-bellied sea snake.

2001, Feb. 1
1696	A467	40c multi	.75	.25
1697	A467	80c multi	1.10	.65
1698	A467	90c multi	1.25	1.25
1699	A467	$1.30 multi	1.75	1.75
1700	A467	$1.50 multi	2.00	2.00
1701	A467	$2 multi	2.25	2.25
a.		Souvenir sheet, #1700-1701	5.00	5.00
		Nos. 1696-1701 (6)	9.10	8.15

New Year 2001 (Year of the snake) (#1701a).

Flowers — A468

2001, Mar. 7
1702	A468	40c Camellia	.55	.35
1703	A468	80c Siberian iris	.90	.55
1704	A468	90c Daffodil	1.10	1.10
1705	A468	$1.30 Chrysanthemum	1.50	1.50
1706	A468	$1.50 Sweet pea	1.75	1.75
1707	A468	$2 Petunia	2.50	2.50
a.		Souvenir sheet, #1702-1707	8.25	8.25
		Nos. 1702-1707 (6)	8.30	7.75

No. 1707a exists imperf from a "Limited Edition" album.

Art From Nature — A469

2001, Apr. 4   Litho.   Perf. 14¼
1708	A469	40c Greenstone	.55	.35
1709	A469	80c Oamaru stone	.90	.55
1710	A469	90c Paua	1.10	1.10
1711	A469	$1.30 Kauri gum	1.50	1.50
1712	A469	$1.50 Flax	1.75	1.75
1713	A469	$2 Fern	2.50	2.50
		Nos. 1708-1713 (6)	8.30	7.75

Within sheets of 25 printed for each stamp are four blocks of four showing a circular design, made by rotating each stamp design 90 degrees.

Aircraft — A470

Designs: 40c, Douglas DC-3. 80c, Fletcher FU24 Topdresser. 90c, De Havilland DH82A Tiger Moth. $1.30, Fokker FVIIb/3m. $1.50, De Havilland DH100 Vampire. $2, Boeing & Westervelt Seaplane.

2001, May 2   Perf. 14x14¼
1714	A470	40c multi	.60	.35
a.		Booklet pane of 1	.60	
1715	A470	80c multi	.90	.65
a.		Booklet pane of 1	.90	
1716	A470	90c multi	1.25	1.25
a.		Booklet pane of 1	1.25	
1717	A470	$1.30 multi	1.50	1.50
a.		Booklet pane of 1	1.50	
1718	A470	$1.50 multi	1.75	1.75
a.		Booklet pane of 1	1.75	
1719	A470	$2 multi	2.50	2.50
a.		Booklet pane of 1	2.50	
b.		Booklet, #1714-1719	10.00	
		Booklet, #1714a-1719a, 1719b	20.00	
		Nos. 1714-1719 (6)	8.50	8.00

Greetings A471

No. 1720: a, Heart. b, Balloons. c, Flower. d, Gift. e, Trumpet.
No. 1721: a, Candles. b, Stars. c, Roses and candle. d, Picture frame. e, Letter and fountain pen.

2001, June 6   Perf. 14½x14
1720		Vert. strip of 5 + 5 labels	2.75	2.75
a.-e.		A471 40c Any single + label	.50	.50
1721		Vert. strip of 5 + 5 labels	5.75	5.75
a.-e.		A471 90c Any single + label	.90	.90

Labels could be personalized on sheets that sold for $15.95 and $27.95 respectively.

Government Tourist Office, Cent. — A472

Designs: 40c, Bungee jumper, Queenstown. 80c, Canoeing on Lake Rotoiti. 90c, Sightseers on Mt. Alfred. $1.30, Fishing in Glenorchy River. $1.50, Kayakers in Abel Tasman Natl. Park. $2, Hiker in Fiordland Natl. Park.

2001   Litho.   Perf. 14¼
1722	A472	40c multi	.50	.25
1723	A472	80c multi	.90	.90
1724	A472	90c multi	1.10	1.10
1725	A472	$1.30 multi	1.50	1.50
1726	A472	$1.50 multi	1.75	1.75
1727	A472	$2 multi	2.25	2.25
a.		Souvenir sheet, #1726-1727	6.00	6.00

Size: 26x21mm
Serpentine Die Cut 11¼x11
Self-Adhesive
| 1728 | A472 | 40c multi | .60 | .50 |
| a. | | Booklet of 10 + 10 etiquettes | 6.50 | |

1729	A472	90c multi	1.25	1.25
a.		Booklet of 10 + 10 etiquettes	14.00	
1730	A472	$1.50 multi	2.25	2.25
a.		Horiz. strip, #1728-1730	4.50	
b.		Booklet of 5 + 5 etiquettes	12.00	

Coil Stamp
Size: 26x21mm
Self-Adhesive
Serpentine Die Cut 10x9¾
| 1730C | A472 | 40c Like #1722 | .55 | .35 |
| | | Nos. 1722-1730C (10) | 12.65 | 12.10 |

Phila Nippon '01, Japan (No. 1727a). Issued: No. 1727a, 8/1; others, 7/4.
A sheet containing 3 each of Nos. 1722-1727 was included in a book that sold for $69.95.

Christmas — A473

Designs: 40c, In Excelsis Gloria. 80c, Away in the Manger. 90c, Joy to the World. $1.30, Angels We Have Heard on High. $1.50, O Holy Night. $2, While Shepherds Watched Their Flocks.

2001, Sept. 5   Perf. 13¼x13¾
1731	A473	40c multi	.60	.25
1732	A473	80c multi	1.10	.50
1733	A473	90c multi	1.25	1.25
1734	A473	$1.30 multi	1.50	1.50
1735	A473	$1.50 multi	1.75	1.75
1736	A473	$2 multi	2.00	2.00

Size: 21x26mm
Serpentine Die Cut 9¾x10
Self-Adhesive
1737	A473	40c multi	.65	.25
a.		Booklet of 10	6.50	
		Nos. 1731-1737 (7)	8.85	7.50

Issued: No. 1737a, 11/7/01.

Visit of Queen Elizabeth II, Oct. 2001 — A474

Queen in past visits: 40c, Arriving for opening of Parliament, 1953. 80c, With crowd, 1970. 90c, With crowd, 1977. $1.30, With crowd, 1986. $1.50, At Commonwealth Games, 1990. $2, 2001 portrait.

2001, Oct. 3   Litho.   Perf. 14
1738	A474	40c multi	.65	.35
1739	A474	80c multi	1.10	.60
1740	A474	90c multi	1.25	1.25
1741	A474	$1.30 multi	1.50	1.50
1742	A474	$1.50 multi	1.75	1.75
1743	A474	$2 multi	2.25	2.25
a.		Horiz. strip, #1738-1743	8.50	8.50
		Nos. 1738-1743 (6)	8.50	7.70

Nos. 1738-1743 exist in a souvenir sheet from a "Limited Edition" album. Nos. 1738-1743 also exist imperf.

Penguins — A475

Designs: 40c, Rockhopper. 80c, Little blue. 90c, Snares crested. $1.30, Erect-crested. $1.50, Fiordland crested. $2, Yellow-eyed.

2001, Nov. 7   Perf. 14¼
1744	A475	40c multi	.75	.40
1745	A475	80c multi	1.10	.60
1746	A475	90c multi	1.25	1.25
1747	A475	$1.30 multi	1.75	1.75
1748	A475	$1.50 multi	2.00	2.00
1749	A475	$2 multi	2.25	2.25
		Nos. 1744-1749 (6)	9.10	8.25

Filming in New Zealand of The Lord of the Rings Trilogy A476

Scenes from "The Lord of the Rings: The Fellowship of the Ring:" 40c, Gandalf the Gray and Saruman the White, vert. 80c, Lady Galadriel, vert. 90c, Sam Gamgee and Frodo Baggins. $1.30, Guardian of Rivendell, vert. $1.50, Strider, vert. $2, Boromir, son of Denethor.

Perf. 14½x14, 14x14½
2001, Dec. 4   Litho.
1750	A476	40c multi	.75	.50
a.		Souvenir sheet of 1	2.25	1.75
b.		Sheet of 10 #1750	7.50	—
1751	A476	80c multi	1.75	1.75
a.		Souvenir sheet of 1	4.00	3.50
1752	A476	90c multi	2.00	2.00
a.		Souvenir sheet of 1	4.75	4.00
1753	A476	$1.30 multi	2.75	2.75
a.		Souvenir sheet of 1	6.50	5.75
1754	A476	$1.50 multi	3.00	3.00
a.		Souvenir sheet of 1	7.50	6.50
1755	A476	$2 multi	4.00	4.00
a.		Souvenir sheet of 1	11.00	8.75
b.		Souvenir sheet, #1754-1755	8.00	8.00
c.		Souvenir sheet, #1750, 1753, 1755	9.50	9.50

Self-Adhesive
Serpentine Die Cut 10x10¼, 10¼x10
Size: 22x33mm, 33x22mm
1756	A476	40c multi	.85	.85
1757	A476	80c multi	2.00	2.00
1758	A476	90c multi	2.25	2.25
1759	A476	$1.30 multi	3.00	3.00
1760	A476	$1.50 multi	3.25	3.25
1761	A476	$2 multi	4.25	4.25
a.		Pane, #1756-1761	16.00	
b.		Booklet pane, #1757, 1759-1761, 4 #1756, 2 #1758	35.00	
		Nos. 1750-1761 (12)	29.85	29.60

Issued: No. 1755b, 8/30/02; No. 1755c, 4/5/02. Other values, 12/4/01.
No. 1755b issued for Amphilex 2002 World Stamp Exhibition, Amsterdam; No. 1755c issued for Northpex 2002.
See Nos. 1835-1846, 1897-1908.

New Year 2002 (Year of the Horse) — A477

Champion race horses: 40c, Christian Cullen. 80c, Lyell Creek. 90c, Yulestar. $1.30, Sunline. $1.50, Ethereal. $2, Zabeel.

2002, Feb. 7   Perf. 14
1762	A477	40c multi	.55	.35
1763	A477	80c multi	.90	.90
1764	A477	90c multi	1.10	1.10
1765	A477	$1.30 multi	1.50	1.50
1766	A477	$1.50 multi	1.75	1.75
a.		Souvenir sheet, #1765-1766	4.50	4.50
1767	A477	$2 multi	2.50	2.50
		Nos. 1762-1767 (6)	8.30	8.10

Fungi — A478

Designs: 40c, Hygrocybe rubrocarnosa. 80c, Entoloma hochstetteri. 90c, Aseroe rubra. $1.30, Hericium coralloides. $1.50, Thaxterogaster porphyreus. $2, Ramaria aureorhiza.

2002, Mar. 6   Litho.   Perf. 14
1768	A478	40c multi	.60	.40
1769	A478	80c multi	1.10	.60
1770	A478	90c multi	1.25	1.25
1771	A478	$1.30 multi	1.75	1.75
1772	A478	$1.50 multi	2.00	2.00
1773	A478	$2 multi	2.25	2.25
a.		Souvenir sheet, #1768-1773	9.00	9.00
		Nos. 1768-1773 (6)	8.95	8.25

No. 1773a exists as an imperforate souvenir sheet from a "Limited Edition" album.

A479

A480

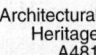

Architectural Heritage
A481

Designs: 40c, War Memorial Museum, Auckland. 80c, Stone Store, Kerikeri. 90c, Arts Center, Christchurch. $1.30, Government buildings, Wellington. $1.50, Railway Station, Dunedin. $2, Sky Tower, Auckland.

2002, Apr. 3   Litho.   Perf. 14½x14

1774	A479	40c multi	.65	.30
a.		Booklet pane of 1	.65	
1775	A480	80c multi	1.10	.75
a.		Booklet pane of 1	1.10	
1776	A481	90c multi	1.25	1.00
a.		Booklet pane of 1	1.25	
1777	A481	$1.30 multi	1.50	1.50
a.		Booklet pane of 1	1.50	
1778	A480	$1.50 multi	1.75	1.75
a.		Booklet pane of 1	1.75	
1779	A479	$2 multi	2.00	2.00
a.		Booklet pane of 1	2.00	
b.		Block of 6, #1774-1779	10.00	10.00
c.		Booklet pane, #1774a-1779a, 1779c	11.00	
		Booklet, #1774a-1779a, 1779c	20.00	
		Nos. 1774-1779 (6)	8.25	7.30

Booklet containing Nos. 1774a-1779a, 1779c sold for $16.95.

Art from Sweden and New Zealand — A482

Designs: No. 1780, Maori basket, by Willa Rogers, New Zealand. No. 1781, Starfish Vessel, by Graeme Priddle, New Zealand. 80c, Catch II, by Raewyn Atkinson, New Zealand. 90c, Silver brooch, by Gavin Hithings, New Zealand. $1.30, Glass towers, by Emma Camden, New Zealand. $1.50, Pacific Rim, by Merilyn Wiseman, New Zealand. $2, Rain Forest, glass vase by Ola Höglund, Sweden.

Litho. & Engr. (#1780, 1786), Litho.
Perf. 12½x12¾ (#1780, 1786), 14

2002, May 2

1780	A482	40c multi	.60	.35
1781	A482	40c multi	.60	.35
1782	A482	80c multi	1.10	.65
1783	A482	90c multi	1.25	1.25
1784	A482	$1.30 multi	1.50	1.50
1785	A482	$1.50 multi	1.75	1.75
1786	A482	$2 multi	2.00	2.00
		Nos. 1780-1786 (7)	8.80	7.85

See Sweden No. 2440.
Nos. 1780-1786 exist in a souvenir sheet from a "Limited Edition" album.

Kiwi Type of 1988

2002, June 5   Litho.   Perf. 14½

1787	A325	$1.50 brown	2.00	1.50
a.		Souvenir sheet of 3	7.00	7.00

Used value is for stamp with complete selvage.

Issued: No. 1787a, 11/12/10. Palmpex 2010 Stamp Show, Palmerston North (No. 1787a).

Queen Mother Elizabeth (1900-2002) — A483

2002, June 5   Perf. 14¼

1788	A483	$2 multi		2.25	2.00

Children's Book Festival Stamp Design Contest Winners — A484

Art by: No. 1789, Anna Poland, Cardinal McKeefry School, Wellington. No. 1790, Hee Su Kim, Glendowie Primary School, Auckland. No. 1791, Jayne Bruce, Rangiora Borough School, Rangiora. No. 1792, Teigan Stafford-Bush (bird), Ararimu School, Auckland. No. 1793, Hazel Gilbert, Gonville School, Wanganui. No. 1794, Gerard Mackle, Temuka High School, Temuka. No. 1795, Maria Rodgers, Salford School, Invercargill. No. 1796, Paul Read (hand and ball), Ararimu School, Auckland. No. 1797, Four students, Glendene Primary School, Auckland. No. 1798, Olivia Duncan, Takapuna Normal Intermediate School, Auckland.

2002, June 5   Perf. 14

1789	A484	40c multi	.80	.80
1790	A484	40c multi	.80	.80
1791	A484	40c multi	.80	.80
1792	A484	40c multi	.80	.80
1793	A484	40c multi	.80	.80
1794	A484	40c multi	.80	.80
1795	A484	40c multi	.80	.80
1796	A484	40c multi	.80	.80
1797	A484	40c multi	.80	.80
1798	A484	40c multi	.80	.80
a.		Block of 10, #1789-1798	10.00	10.00
b.		Sheet of 10, #1789-1798	11.00	11.00
		Nos. 1789-1798 (10)	8.00	8.00

Scenic Coastlines — A485

Designs: 40c, Tongaporutu Cliffs, Taranaki. 80c, Lottin Point, East Cape. 90c, Curio Bay, Catlins. $1.30, Kaikoura Coast. $1.50, Meybille Bay, West Coast. $2, Papanui Point, Raglan.

2002, July 3   Perf. 14

1799	A485	40c multi	.50	.30
1800	A485	80c multi	1.00	.60
1801	A485	90c multi	1.25	1.25
1802	A485	$1.30 multi	1.50	1.50
1803	A485	$1.50 multi	1.75	1.75
1804	A485	$2 multi	2.10	2.10

Size: 28x22mm
Self-Adhesive
Serpentine Die Cut 10x9¾

1805	A485	40c multi	.55	.55
a.		Booklet pane of 10	6.50	
b.		Serpentine die cut 11	.70	.70
c.		Booklet pane of 10 #1805b	7.50	
1806	A485	90c multi	1.25	1.25
a.		Booklet pane of 10	14.00	
1807	A485	$1.50 multi	2.40	1.50
a.		Booklet pane of 5	12.00	
b.		Coil strip of 3, #1805-1807	4.50	

Coil Stamp
Size: 28x22mm
Self-Adhesive
Die Cut Perf. 12¾

1808	A485	40c multi	.55	.40
		Nos. 1799-1808 (10)	12.85	11.20

Christmas — A487

Church interiors: 40c, Saint Werenfried Catholic Church, Waihi Village, Tokaannu. 80c, St. David's Anglican Church, Christchurch. 90c, Orthodox Church of the Transfiguration of Our Lord, Masterton. $1.30, Cathedral of the Holy Spirit, Palmerston North. $1.50, Cathedral of St. Paul, Wellington. $2, Cathedral of the Blessed Sacrament, Christchurch.

2002, Sept. 4   Perf. 14¼

1812	A487	40c multi	.50	.25
1813	A487	80c multi	1.00	.45
1814	A487	90c multi	1.25	1.00
1815	A487	$1.30 multi	1.75	1.75
1816	A487	$1.50 multi	2.00	2.00
1817	A487	$2 multi	2.25	2.25

Coil Stamp
Size: 21x26mm
Self-Adhesive
Die Cut Perf. 13x12¾

1818	A487	40c multi	.55	.25

Booklet Stamp
Size: 21x26mm
Self-Adhesive
Die Cut Perf 9¾x10

1818A	A487	40c Like No. 1818	.55	.25
b.		Booklet pane of 10	6.50	
		Nos. 1812-1818A (8)	9.85	8.20

Issued: No. 1818A, 11/6/02.

Boats — A488

Designs: 40c, KZ1. 80c, High 5. 90c, Gentle Spirit. $1.30, NorthStar. $1.50, OceanRunner. $2, Salperton.

2002, Oct. 2   Litho.   Perf. 14

1819	A488	40c multi	.60	.35
1820	A488	80c multi	1.00	.65
1821	A488	90c multi	1.10	1.10
1822	A488	$1.30 multi	1.50	1.50
1823	A488	$1.50 multi	2.00	2.00
1824	A488	$2 multi	2.25	2.25
a.		Souvenir sheet, #1819-1824	9.00	9.00
		Nos. 1819-1824 (6)	8.45	7.85

No. 1824a exists an an imperforate souvenir sheet from a "Limited Edition" album.

2003 America's Cup Yacht Races — A489

Scenes from 2000 America's Cup finals: $1.30, Black Magic next to Luna Rossa. $1.50, Aerial view. $2, Black Magic passing Luna Rossa.

2002

1825	A489	$1.30 multi	1.75	1.50
1826	A489	$1.50 multi	2.00	2.00
1827	A489	$2 multi	2.25	2.25
a.		Souvenir sheet, #1825-1827	7.50	7.50
b.		As "a," with Stampshow Melbourne 02 ovpt. in margin	7.00	7.00
		Nos. 1825-1827 (3)	6.00	5.75

Issued: No. 1827b, 10/4; others 10/2.

Vacation Homes — A490

Various vacation homes with denominations over: No. 1828, Paua shell. No. 1829, Sunflower. No. 1830, Life preserver. No. 1831, Fish hook. No. 1832, Fish. No. 1833, Flower bouquet.

2002, Nov. 6   Litho.   Perf. 14

1828	A490	40c multi	.70	.55
1829	A490	40c multi	.70	.55
1830	A490	40c multi	.70	.55
1831	A490	40c multi	.70	.55
1832	A490	40c multi	.70	.55
1833	A490	40c multi	.70	.55
		Nos. 1828-1833 (6)	4.20	3.30

Nativity, by Pseudo Ambrogio di Baldese A491

2002, Nov. 21   Perf. 14¼x14

1834	A491	$1.50 multi	2.10	1.75

See Vatican City No. 1232.

The Lord of the Rings Type of 2001

Scenes from The Lord of the Rings: The Two Towers: 40c, Aragorn and Eowyn. 80c, Orc raider. 90c, Gandalf the White, vert. $1.30, The Easterlings. $1.50, Frodo captured, vert. $2, Shield Maiden of Rohan.

2002, Dec. 4   Perf. 14x14½, 14½x14

1835	A476	40c multi	.65	.40
a.		Souvenir sheet of 1	1.00	.65
1836	A476	80c multi	1.40	1.40
a.		Souvenir sheet of 1	2.00	2.00
1837	A476	90c multi	1.50	1.50
a.		Souvenir sheet of 1	2.25	2.25
1838	A476	$1.30 multi	2.25	2.25
a.		Souvenir sheet of 1	3.25	3.25
1839	A476	$1.50 multi	2.50	2.50
a.		Souvenir sheet of 1	3.75	3.75
1840	A476	$2 multi	3.25	3.25
a.		Souvenir sheet of 1	4.25	4.25
		Set of 6 souvenir sheets of 1 each, #1835a//1840a	16.50	

Self-Adhesive
Size: 34x23mm, 23x34mm
Serpentine Die Cut 10¼x10, 10x10¼

1841	A476	40c multi	.65	.40
1842	A476	80c multi	1.25	1.25
1843	A476	90c multi	1.40	1.40
1844	A476	$1.30 multi	2.10	2.10
1845	A476	$1.50 multi	2.40	2.40
1846	A476	$2 multi	3.25	3.25
a.		Pane, #1841-1846	11.00	
b.		Booklet pane, #1842, 1844-1846, 2 #1843, 4 #1841	14.50	
		Nos. 1835-1846 (12)	22.60	22.10

The 2002 sheets contain: #1767, 1773, 1779, 1785, 1787, 1804, 1817, 1830, B170. See note following #1404.

2003 America's Cup Yacht Races — A492

Designs: 40c, Yacht and sail with sponsor's advertisements. 80c, Yachts circling. 90c, Yachts racing.

2003, Jan. 8   Litho.   Perf. 14

1847	A492	40c multi	.50	.35
1848	A492	80c multi	1.10	1.10
1849	A492	90c multi	1.25	1.25
a.		Souvenir sheet of 3, #1847-1849	3.25	3.25
		Nos. 1847-1849 (3)	2.85	2.70

New Year 2003 (Year of the Ram) — A493

Designs: 40c, Sheep in high country. 90c, Sheep leaving pen. $1.30, Sheepdog and sheep. $1.50, Shearer. $2, Shearing gang.

2003, Feb. 5   Litho.   Perf. 14

1850	A493	40c multi	.55	.35
1851	A493	90c multi	1.00	.65
1852	A493	$1.30 multi	1.50	1.50
1853	A493	$1.50 multi	2.00	2.00
1854	A493	$2 multi	2.50	2.50
a.		Souvenir sheet of 2, #1852, 1854	4.00	4.00
		Nos. 1850-1854 (5)	7.55	7.00

Royal New Zealand Ballet, 50th Anniv. — A494

Scenes from productions of: 40c, Carmina Burana, 1971, vert. 90c, Papillon, 1989. $1.30, Cinderella, 2000, vert. $1.50, FrENZy, 2001, vert. $2, Swan lake, 2002.

2003, Mar. 5   Litho.   Perf. 14

1855	A494	40c multi	.55	.40
1856	A494	90c multi	1.10	.75
1857	A494	$1.30 multi	1.50	1.50
1858	A494	$1.50 multi	2.00	2.00
1859	A494	$2 multi	2.50	2.50
a.		Souvenir sheet, #1855, 1856, 1859	6.50	6.50
		Nos. 1855-1859 (5)	7.65	7.15

No. 1859a issued for Bangkok 2003 World Philatelic Exhibition.
Nos. 1855-1859 exist in a souvenir sheet from a "Limited Edition" album.

Military Uniforms, Medals and Insignia — A495

No. 1860: a, Forest ranger, 1860s. b, Napier naval artillery volunteer officer, 1890s. c, Amuri mounted rifles officer, 1900-10. d, Mounted Rifles, South Africa, 1898-1902. e, Staff officer, France, 1918. f, Petty officer, 1914-18. g, Infantry, France, 1916-18. h, Engineer, 1939-45. i, Matron, RNZN Hospital, 1940s. j, WAAC, Egypt, 1942. k, Bomber pilot, Europe, 1943. l, Fighter pilot, Pacific, 1943. m, WAAF driver, 1943. n, Gunner, Korea, 1950-53. o, Petty officer, 1950s. p, SAS, Malaya, 1955-57. q, Canberra Pilot, 1960. r, Infantry, Viet Nam, 1960s. s, UN Peacekeeper, East Timor, 2000. t, Peace Monitor, Bougainville, 2001.

2003, Apr. 2   Litho.   Perf. 14

1860		Sheet of 20	20.00	20.00
a.-t.		A495 40c Any single	.65	.45
u.		Booklet pane, 2 each #a-d	6.00	—
v.		Booklet pane, 2 each #e-h	6.00	—
w.		Booklet pane, 2 each #i-l	6.00	—
x.		Booklet pane, 2 each #m-p	6.00	—
y.		Booklet pane, 2 each #q-t	6.00	—
		Complete booklet, #u-y	30.00	

Tourist Attractions — A496

Designs: 50c, Ailsa Mountains. $1, Coromandel Peninsula. $1.50, Arrowtown. $2, Tongariro National Park. $5, Castlepoint.

2003, May 7   Litho.   Perf. 13¼x13½

1861	A496	50c multi	.65	.40
1862	A496	$1 multi	1.30	.90
1863	A496	$1.50 multi	1.75	1.40
1863A	A496	$1.50 multi	1.75	1.40
1864	A496	$2 multi	2.75	2.00
1865	A496	$5 multi	5.75	4.75

Self-Adhesive

Serpentine Die Cut 10x9½

1866	A496	$1.50 multi	2.00	1.50
a.		Booklet pane of 5	11.00	
1866B	A496	$1.50 As #1866, vignette 26mm wide	2.10	2.00
c.		Booklet pane of 5 #1866b + 10 etiquettes	12.00	
		Nos. 1861-1866 (7)	15.95	12.35

Nos. 1861-1865 exist with silver fern leaf overprints from a limited printing.
Nos. 1866b, 1866c issued 3/27/07. Vignette of No. 1866 is 27mm wide. No. 1863A issued 2007.
Nos. 1863A and 1866B show a person on the sidewalk in front of the door of the house in the foreground (above the zero in the denomination). The person is not found on Nos. 1863 and 1866.
See Nos. 1926-1928B, 1972-1977, 2062-2067, 2129-2137, 2222, 2238, 2257-2263, 2316-2322, 2392, 2405-2409.

Ascent of Mt. Everest, 50th Anniv. — A497

Designs: No. 1867, Sir Edmund Hillary, Mt. Everest. No. 1868, Tenzing Norgay, climbers on mountain.

2003, May 29   Perf. 14

1867	A497	40c multi	.95	.95
1868	A497	40c multi	.95	.95
a.		Pair, #1867-1868	2.00	2.00

Nos. 1867-1868 exist in a miniature sheet of 10. Value, $15.

Coronation Type of 1953
Perf. 14x14½, 14½x14

2003, June 4   Litho.

1869	A112	40c Like #280	.60	.30
1870	A113	90c Like #281	1.10	.75
1871	A112	$1.30 Like #282	1.75	1.75
1872	A114	$1.50 Like #283	2.00	2.00
1873	A112	$2 Like #284	2.25	2.25
		Nos. 1869-1873 (5)	7.70	7.05

Nos. 1869-1873 exist in a souvenir sheet from a "Limited Edition" album.

Test Rugby, Cent. — A498

Designs: 40c, New Zealand vs. South Africa, 1937. 90c, New Zealand vs. Wales, 1963. $1.30, New Zealand vs. Australia, 1985. No.1877, New Zealand vs. France, 1986. No. 1878, All Blacks jersey. $2, New Zealand vs. England, 1997.

2003, July 2   Perf. 14

1874	A498	40c multi	.65	.35
1875	A498	90c multi	1.25	.80
1876	A498	$1.30 multi	1.75	1.75
1877	A498	$1.50 multi	2.00	2.00
1878	A498	$1.50 multi	2.00	2.00
1879	A498	$2 multi	2.25	2.25
a.		Souvenir sheet, #1874-1879	10.00	10.00
b.		Sheet, #1877-1879	7.00	7.00
c.		Souvenir sheet, #1878-1879	6.00	6.00
		Nos. 1874-1879 (6)	9.90	9.15

No. 1879b issued 11/7 for Welpex 2003 Stampshow, Wellington. No. 1879b sold for $6.
No. 1879c issued 1/30/04 for 2004 Hong Kong Stamp Expo (#1879c).

Waterways A499

Designs: 40c, Papaaroha, Coromandel Peninsula. 90c, Waimahana Creek, Chatham Islands. $1.30, Blue Lake, Central Otago. $1.50, Waikato River, Waikato. $2, Hooker River, Canterbury.

2003, Aug. 6   Litho.   Perf. 14¼

1880	A499	40c multi	.55	.35
1881	A499	90c multi	1.00	.90
1882	A499	$1.30 multi	1.75	1.75
1883	A499	$1.50 multi	2.00	2.00
1884	A499	$2 multi	2.25	2.25
		Nos. 1880-1884 (5)	7.55	7.25

Antique Automobiles A500

Designs: 40c, 1895 Benz Velo. 90c, 1903 Oldsmobile. $1.30, 1911 Wolseley. $1.50, 1915 Talbot. $2, 1915 Ford Model T.

2003, Sept. 3   Litho.   Perf. 13x13¼

1885	A500	40c multi	.60	.40
1886	A500	90c multi	1.10	.95
1887	A500	$1.30 multi	1.75	1.75
1888	A500	$1.50 multi	2.00	2.00
1889	A500	$2 multi	2.25	2.25
		Nos. 1885-1889 (5)	7.70	7.35

Christmas — A501

Tree decorations: 40c, Christ child. 90c, Dove. $1.30, Geometric (candles). $1.50, Bells. $2, Angel.
$1, Geometric (fleur-de-lis).

2003, Oct. 1   Perf. 13½

1890	A501	40c multi	.60	.25
1891	A501	90c multi	1.10	.75
1892	A501	$1.30 multi	1.75	1.75
1893	A501	$1.50 multi	2.00	2.00
1894	A501	$2 multi	2.25	2.25

Self-Adhesive

Serpentine Die Cut 9½x10
Size: 21x26mm

1895	A501	40c multi	.60	.40
a.		Booklet pane of 10	6.50	
1896	A501	$1 multi	1.25	1.25
a.		Booklet pane of 8 + 8 etiquettes	13.00	
		Nos. 1890-1896 (7)	9.55	8.65

The Lord of the Rings Type of 2001

Scenes from *The Lord of the Rings: The Return of the King:* 40c, Legolas, vert. 80c, Frodo, vert. 90c, Merry and Pippin. $1.30,

Aragorn, vert. $1.50, Gandalf the White, vert. $2, Gollum.

2003, Nov. 5   Perf. 14½x14, 14x14½

1897	A476	40c multi	.65	.40
a.		Souvenir sheet of 1	.90	.90
1898	A476	80c multi	1.10	1.10
a.		Souvenir sheet of 1	1.50	1.50
1899	A476	90c multi	1.25	1.25
a.		Souvenir sheet of 1	2.00	2.00
1900	A476	$1.30 multi	2.00	2.00
a.		Souvenir sheet of 1	2.25	2.25
1901	A476	$1.50 multi	2.25	2.25
a.		Souvenir sheet of 1	2.75	2.75
1902	A476	$2 multi	2.50	2.50
a.		Souvenir sheet of 1	3.75	3.75
		Set of 6 souvenir sheets of 1 each, #1897a-1902a	13.25	

Self-Adhesive
Size: 23x34mm, 34x23mm
Serpentine Die Cut 10x10¼, 10¼x10

1903	A476	40c multi	.65	.45
1904	A476	80c multi	1.10	1.00
1905	A476	90c multi	1.40	1.10
1906	A476	$1.30 multi	2.00	2.00
1907	A476	$1.50 multi	2.25	2.25
1908	A476	$2 multi	2.50	2.50
a.		Pane, #1903-1908	10.00	
b.		Booklet pane, #1904, 1906-1908, 2 #1905, 4 #1903	14.00	
		Nos. 1897-1908 (12)	19.65	18.80

The 2003 sheets contain: #1854, 1859, 1864, 1873, 1879, 1884, 1889, 1894, 1902. See note following #1404.

Scenic Views Type of 1995
Serpentine Die Cut 10x9¾

2004, Jan. 28   Litho.
Booklet Stamp
Size: 26x21mm
Self-Adhesive

1909	A404	10c Like #1346	.40	.40
a.		Booklet pane, 10 #1359F, 4 #1909	8.00	

Zoo Animals — A502

Designs: 40c, Hamadryas baboon. 90c, Malayan sun bear. $1.30, Red panda. $1.50, Ring-tailed lemur. $2, Spider monkey.

2004, Jan. 28   Litho.   Perf. 13¼x13

1910	A502	40c multi	.60	.50
1911	A502	90c multi	1.25	1.25
1912	A502	$1.30 multi	2.00	2.00
1913	A502	$1.50 multi	2.25	2.25
1914	A502	$2 multi	2.50	2.50
a.		Souvenir sheet, #1913-1914	5.00	5.00

Nos. 1910-1914 exist in a souvenir sheet from a "Limited Edition" album.

Self-Adhesive
Size: 21x26mm
Coil Stamp
Die Cut Perf. 12¾x12½

1915	A502	40c multi	.60	.55

Booklet Stamp
Serpentine Die Cut 11¼

1916	A502	40c multi	.60	.55
a.		Booklet pane of 10	6.50	
		Nos. 1910-1916 (7)	9.80	9.60

New Year 2004 (Year of the Monkey) (#1914a).

Rugby Sevens — A503

Designs: 40c, New Zealand Sevens. 90c, Hong Kong Sevens. $1.50, Hong Kong Stadium. $2, Westpac Stadium, Wellington.

2004, Feb. 25   Litho.   Perf. 14x14¼

1917	A503	40c multi	.60	.45
1918	A503	90c multi	1.25	1.25
1919	A503	$1.50 multi	1.75	1.75
1920	A503	$2 multi	2.75	2.75
a.		Souvenir sheet, #1917-1920	7.00	7.00
b.		Souvenir sheet, #1877, 1878, 1920	7.00	7.00
		Nos. 1917-1920 (4)	6.35	6.20

No. 1920b issued 6/26 for Le Salon du Timbre 2004, Paris.

See Hong Kong Nos. 1084-1087.

Parliament, 150th Anniv. — A504

Designs: 40c, Parliament Building, Auckland, 1854. 90c, Parliament Buildings, Wellington (Provincial Chambers), 1865. $1.30, Parliament Buildings, Wellington, 1899. $1.50, Parliament House, Wellington, 1918. $2, Beehive, Wellington, 1977.

2004, Mar. 3   Perf. 14½x14¼

1921	A504	40c blk & purple	.60	.45
1922	A504	90c blk & violet	1.25	1.10
1923	A504	$1.30 blk & gray	1.75	1.75
1924	A504	$1.50 blk & blue	2.00	2.00
1925	A504	$2 blk & green	2.50	2.50
a.		Souvenir sheet, #1921-1925	9.75	9.75
		Nos. 1921-1925 (5)	8.10	7.80

See No. 1935.

Tourist Attractions Type of 2003

Designs: 45c, Kaikoura. $1.35, Church of the Good Shepherd, Lake Tekapo.

Perf. 13¼x13½

1926	A496	45c multi	.60	.60

Perf. 14x14½

1927	A496	$1.35 multi	2.00	2.00
a.		Perf. 13½ ('06)	2.10	2.10

Self-Adhesive
Serpentine Die Cut 11¼x11

1928	A496	45c multi	.70	.70
a.		Booklet pane of 10	7.00	

Coil Stamp

1928B	A496	45c multi	.70	.70
		Nos. 1926-1928B (4)	4.00	4.00

Country name on No. 1928B has an unserifed font, with horizontal bars in "e," and a symmetrical "w."
No. 1927a issued 8/2006.

Scenic Views Type of 1995

2004, Apr. 5   Die Cut Perf. 10x9½
Size: 27x22mm
Self-Adhesive

1929	A404	90c Like #1679	1.10	1.10
a.		Booklet pane of 10	11.00	

Historic Farm Equipment A505

Designs: 45c, Kinnard Haines tractor. 90c, Fordson F tractor with plow. $1.35, Burrell traction engine. $1.50, Threshing mill. $2, Duncan's seed drill.

2004, Apr. 5   Perf. 14

1930	A505	45c multi	.65	.40
a.		Booklet pane of 1, perf. 14x13¼	.90	
1931	A505	90c multi	1.25	.75
a.		Booklet pane of 1, perf. 14x13¼	1.75	—
1932	A505	$1.35 multi	2.00	2.00
a.		Booklet pane of 1, perf. 14x13¼	2.75	—
1933	A505	$1.50 multi	2.25	2.25
a.		Booklet pane of 1, perf. 14x13¼	3.00	—
1934	A505	$2 multi	2.50	2.50
a.		Booklet pane of 1, perf. 14x13¼	4.00	—
b.		Booklet pane of 5, #1930-1934, perf. 14x13¼	10.00	—
		Complete booklet, #1930a, 1931a, 1932a, 1933a, 1934a, 1934b	25.00	
		Nos. 1930-1934 (5)	8.65	7.90

The complete booklet sold for $19.95.

Parliament Type of 2004

2004, May 5   Perf. 14½x14¼

1935	A504	45c Like #1921	.65	.65

World of Wearable Art Awards Show — A506

Designs: 45c, Dragon Fish. 90c, Persephone's Descent. $1.35, Meridian. $1.50, Taunga Ika. $2, Cailleach Na Mara (Sea Witch).

2004, May 5				Perf. 14
1936	A506	45c multi	.65	.35
1937	A506	90c multi	1.10	.85
1938	A506	$1.35 multi	1.75	1.75
1939	A506	$1.50 multi	2.00	2.00
1940	A506	$2 multi	2.50	2.50
	Nos. 1936-1940 (5)		8.00	7.45

Strips of 5 exist from a special sheet.. Exists imperf. Value, strip with tabs, $32.50

New Zealanders A507

Designs: No. 1941, Man outside of Pungarehu Post Office. No. 1942, Children on horse. No. 1943, Elderly man and woman in front of house.

2004, Feb.	Litho.	Die Cut Perf. 13½
Booklet Stamps
Self-Adhesive
1941	A507	$1.50 multi	5.00	5.00
1942	A507	$1.50 multi	5.00	5.00
1943	A507	$1.50 multi	5.00	5.00
a.	Booklet pane, 2 each # 1941-1943, 6 etiquettes and 10 stickers		30.00	
	Complete booklet, #1943a		30.00	
	Nos. 1941-1943 (3)		15.00	15.00

Wild Food A508

Designs: No. 1944, Mountain oysters. No. 1945, Huhu grubs. No. 1946, Possum paté.

2004, Feb.		Booklet Stamps
Self-Adhesive
1944	A508	$1.50 multi	5.00	5.00
1945	A508	$1.50 multi	5.00	5.00
1946	A508	$1.50 multi	5.00	5.00
a.	Booklet pane, 2 each # 1944-1946, 6 etiquettes and 6 stickers		30.00	
	Complete booklet, #1946a		30.00	
	Nos. 1944-1946 (3)		15.00	15.00

New Zealand Post Emblem A509

2004, Feb.		Booklet Stamps
Self-Adhesive
1947	A509	$1.50 blue & red	6.00	6.00
1948	A509	$1.50 red	6.00	6.00
1949	A509	$1.50 green & red	6.00	6.00
a.	Booklet pane, 2 each # 1947-1949, 6 etiquettes		35.00	
	Complete booklet, #1949a		35.00	
	Nos. 1947-1949 (3)		18.00	18.00

Country name is at bottom on No. 1948. A pane of eight stamps containing two each of Nos. 1947-1949 and two $1.50 purple and red stamps similar to No. 1948 came unattached in a folder together with a set of four markers, a sheet of decorative magnets and two sheets of self-adhesive plastic stickers. The pane of eight was not available without purchasing the other non-stamp items, which sold as a package for $19.95.

Flowers — A510

Designs: 45c, Magnolia "Vulcan." 90c, Helleborus "Unnamed Hybrid." $1.35, Nerine "Anzac." $1.50, Rhododendron "Charisma." $2, Delphinium "Sarita."

2004, June 2			Perf. 13¼x13¾
1950	A510	45c multi	.65	.35
1951	A510	90c multi	1.25	.75
1952	A510	$1.35 multi	1.75	1.75
1953	A510	$1.50 multi	2.00	2.00
1954	A510	$2 multi	2.25	2.25
a.	Souvenir sheet, #1950-1954		8.75	8.75
	Nos. 1950-1954 (5)		7.90	7.10

The 45c stamp in the souvenir sheet was impregnated with a floral scent.

Numeral — A511

Serpentine Die Cut 5¾

2004, June 28		Litho.
Booklet Stamp
Self-Adhesive
1955	A511	5c multi	1.40	1.40
a.	Booklet pane of 10		14.00	

Postage Advertising Labels

In 2004, New Zealand Post began issuing "Postage Advertising Labels," which have the New Zealand Post emblem and curved side panel found on type A511. These stamps have various vignettes and denominations and were designed in conjunction with various private parties who contracted for and purchased the entire print run of these stamps. Though valid for domestic postage only as most of these stamps lack a country name, none of these stamps were made available to the general public by New Zealand Post.

In 2006, a limited number of Postal Advertising Labels began to be sold at face value by New Zealand Post when new contracts with the private parties were written. These agreements allowed New Zealand Post to print more items than the private party desired and to sell the overage to collectors.

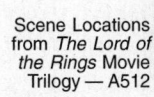

Scene Locations from The Lord of the Rings Movie Trilogy — A512

Designs: Nos. 1956, 1965, Skippers Canyon. Nos. 1957, 1964, Skippers Canyon (Ford of Bruinden) with actors. Nos. 1958, 1967, Mount Olympus. No. 1959, 1966, Mount Olympus (South of Rivendell) with actors. No. 1960, Erewhon. No. 1961, Erewhon (Edoras) with actors. No. 1962, Tongariro National Park. No. 1963, Tongariro National Park (Emyn Muil) with actors.

2004, July 7			Perf. 14
1956	A512	45c multi	.65	.65
1957	A512	45c multi	.65	.65
a.	Vert. pair, #1956-1957		1.40	1.40
1958	A512	90c multi	1.25	1.25
1959	A512	90c multi	1.25	1.25
a.	Vert. pair, #1958-1959		2.75	2.75
1960	A512	$1.50 multi	2.25	2.25
1961	A512	$1.50 multi	2.25	2.25
a.	Vert. pair, #1960-1961		4.75	4.75
b.	Souvenir sheet, #1958-1961		7.25	7.25
1962	A512	$2 multi	3.00	3.00
1963	A512	$2 multi	3.00	3.00
a.	Vert. pair, #1962-1963		6.50	6.50
b.	Horiz. block of 8, #1956-1963		15.50	15.50
c.	Souvenir sheet, #1956-1963		15.50	15.50

No. 1963c exists imperf from a "Limited Edition" album.

Self-Adhesive
Serpentine Die Cut 11¼
Size: 30x25mm

1964	A512	45c multi	.60	.60
1965	A512	45c multi	.60	.60
1966	A512	90c multi	1.25	1.25
1967	A512	90c multi	1.25	1.25
a.	Block of 4, #1964-1967		4.00	
b.	Booklet pane, 3 each #1964-1965, 2 each #1966-1967		9.25	
	Nos. 1956-1967 (12)		18.00	18.00

No. 1961b issued 8/28. World Stamp Championship (No. 1961b).

2004 Summer Olympics, Athens — A513

Gold medalists: 45c, John Walker, 1500 meters, Montreal, 1976. 90c, Yvette Williams, long jump, Helsinki, 1952. $1.50, Ian Ferguson and Paul MacDonald, 500 meters kayak doubles, Seoul, 1988. $2, Peter Snell, 800 meters, Rome, 1960.

Litho. with 3-Dimensional Plastic Affixed
Serpentine Die Cut 10¾

2004, Aug. 2		Self-Adhesive
1968	A513	45c multi	.65	.50
1969	A513	90c multi	1.00	.80
1970	A513	$1.50 multi	1.75	1.75
1971	A513	$2 multi	2.25	2.25
a.	Horiz. strip of 4, #1968-1971		7.00	
	Nos. 1968-1971 (4)		5.65	5.30

Tourist Attractions Type of 2003

Designs: No. 1972, Lake Wakatipu, Queenstown. No. 1973, Kaikoura. No. 1974, Bath House, Rotorua. No. 1975, Pohutu Geyser, Rotorua. No. 1976, Mitre Peak, Milford Sound. No. 1977, Hawke's Bay.

2004-05		Litho.	Perf. 13¼x13½
1972	A496	$1.50 multi	1.90	1.90
a.	Perf. 14x14¼		1.90	1.90
1973	A496	$1.50 multi	1.90	1.90
1974	A496	$1.50 multi	1.90	1.90
1975	A496	$1.50 multi	1.90	1.90
a.	Souvenir sheet, #1973, 1975		5.00	5.00
1976	A496	$1.50 multi	1.90	1.90
a.	Perf. 14x14¼		1.90	1.90
b.	Souvenir sheet, #1972a, 1976a		4.50	4.50
1977	A496	$1.50 multi	1.90	1.90
a.	Souvenir sheet, #1639, 1977		7.25	7.25
	Nos. 1972-1977 (6)		11.40	11.40

Issued: Nos. 1972-1977, 8/28; No. 1977a, 10/29 for Baypex 2004; No. 1975a, 8/18/05 for Taipei 2005 Stamp Exhibition; Nos. 1972a, 1976a, 1976b, 8/3/07. Bangkok 2007 Asian International Stamp Exhibition (#1976b).

A514

Christmas — A515

Designs: 45c, Candle, wine bottle, turkey, ham. 90c, Hangi. $1, Christmas cards, fruit cake. $1.35, Barbecued shrimp. $1.50, Wine bottle, pie and salad. $2, Candelabra, pavlova and plum pudding.

2004, Oct. 4			Perf. 14¼
1978	A514	45c multi	.60	.25
1979	A514	90c multi	1.25	.50
1980	A514	$1.35 multi	1.50	1.50
1981	A514	$1.50 multi	1.75	1.75
1982	A514	$2 multi	2.50	2.50
	Nos. 1978-1982 (5)		7.60	6.50

Self-Adhesive
Serpentine Die Cut 9½x10

1983	A515	45c multi	.60	.40
a.	Booklet pane of 10		7.00	

1984	A515	90c multi	1.10	1.00
1985	A515	$1 multi	1.40	1.40
a.	Booklet pane of 8 + 8 etiquettes		13.00	
b.	Horiz. strip, #1983-1985		3.75	3.75
	Nos. 1983-1985 (3)		3.10	2.80

Extreme Sports — A516

Designs: 45c, Whitewater rafting. 90c, Snow sports. $1.35, Skydiving. $1.50, Jet boating. $2, Bungy jumping.

2004, Dec. 1			Perf. 14
1986	A516	45c multi	.55	.25
a.	Booklet pane of 1		.75	
1987	A516	90c multi	1.00	.65
a.	Booklet pane of 1		1.50	
1988	A516	$1.35 multi	1.50	1.50
a.	Booklet pane of 1		2.00	
1989	A516	$1.50 multi	1.75	1.75
a.	Booklet pane of 1		2.50	
1990	A516	$2 multi	2.75	2.75
a.	Booklet pane of 1		3.25	
b.	Booklet pane, #1986-1990		12.00	—
	Complete booklet, #1986a, 1987a, 1988a, 1989a, 1990a, 1990b		24.00	
	Nos. 1986-1990 (5)		7.55	6.90

Complete booklet sold for $14.95.

The 2004 sheets contain: #1914, 1920, 1925, 1934, 1940, 1954, 1962, 1982, 1990. See note following #1404.

Farm Animals — A517

Designs: 45c, Ewe (with horns) and lambs. 90c, Scottish border collies. $1.35, Pigs. $1.50, Rooster and chicken. $2, Rooster and chicken, diff.

2005, Jan. 12			Perf. 14
1991	A517	45c multi	.60	.45
1992	A517	90c multi	1.25	.75
1993	A517	$1.35 multi	1.50	1.50
1994	A517	$1.50 multi	1.75	1.75
1995	A517	$2 multi	2.75	2.75
a.	Horiz. strip, #1991-1995		10.00	10.00
b.	Souvenir sheet, #1994-1995		5.25	5.25
	Nos. 1991-1995 (5)		7.85	7.20

Nos. 1991-1995 exist in a souvenir sheet from a "Limited Edition" album.

Self-Adhesive
Size: 22x27mm
Serpentine Die Cut 11x11¼

1996	A517	45c multi	.50	.60
a.	Booklet pane of 10		6.50	

New Year 2005 (Year of the Cock) (No. 1995b).

Community Groups — A518

Designs: No. 1997, Canoeists, YMCA emblem. No. 1998, Three people holding cement, Rotary International emblem. No. 1999, People building track bed, Lions International emblem. No. 2000, Four people jumping, YMCA emblem. No. 2001, People building wall, Rotary International emblem. No. 2002, Miniature train, Lions International emblem.

2005, Feb. 2		Litho.	Perf. 14
1997	A518	45c multi	.50	.40
1998	A518	45c multi	.50	.40
1999	A518	45c multi	.50	.40
2000	A518	$1.50 multi	2.00	2.00
a.	Horiz. pair, #1997, 2000, + central label		3.00	3.00
b.	Miniature sheet, 3 #2000a		8.00	8.00
2001	A518	$1.50 multi	2.00	2.00
a.	Horiz. pair, #1998, 2001, + central label		3.00	3.00
b.	Miniature sheet, 3 #2001a		8.00	8.00
2002	A518	$1.50 multi	2.00	2.00
a.	Horiz. pair, #1999, 2002, + central label		3.00	3.00

b.	Miniature sheet, #2000a, 2001a, 2002a			8.00	8.00
c.	Miniature sheet, 3 #2002a			8.25	8.25
	Nos. 1997-2002 (6)			7.50	7.20

New Zealand Postage Stamps, 150th Anniv. — A519

2005, Mar. 2		Litho.	*Perf. 14*		
2003	A519	45c No. 1		.60	.35
2004	A519	90c No. P1		1.10	.75
2005	A519	$1.35 No. OY5		1.50	1.50
2006	A519	$1.50 No. 83		1.75	1.75
2007	A519	$2 No. 99		2.75	2.75
a.		Souvenir sheet, #2003-2007		8.75	8.75
		Nos. 2003-2007 (5)		7.70	7.10

2005, Apr. 6		Litho.	*Perf. 14*		
2008	A519	45c No. 123a		.60	.60
2009	A519	90c No. B3		1.10	.75
2010	A519	$1.35 No. C7		1.50	1.50
2011	A519	$1.50 No. 256		1.75	1.75
2012	A519	$2 No. 301		2.75	2.75
a.		Souvenir sheet, #2008-2012		8.75	8.75
b.		Souvenir sheet, #2007, 2012		6.50	6.50
		Nos. 2008-2012 (5)		7.70	7.35

No. 2012b issued 4/21 for Pacific Explorer 2005 World Stamp Expo, Sydney.

Size: 25x30mm
Self-Adhesive
Coil Stamps
Serpentine Die Cut 12¾

2013	A519	45c No. 123a	.55	.55
2014	A519	90c No. B3	1.00	1.00
a.		Horiz. pair, #2013-2014	2.25	

Booklet Stamps
Serpentine Die Cut 11x11¼

2015	A519	45c No. 123a	.60	.50
a.		Booklet pane of 10	7.00	
2016	A519	90c No. B3	1.10	1.10
a.		Booklet pane of 10	12.00	
		Nos. 2013-2016 (4)	3.25	3.15

2005, June 1		Litho.	*Perf. 14*		
2017	A519	45c No. 369		.60	.25
2018	A519	90c No. 918		1.10	.75
2019	A519	$1.35 No. 989		1.50	1.50
2020	A519	$1.50 No. 1219		1.75	1.75
a.		Souvenir sheet, #2006, 2011, 2020		7.25	7.25
2021	A519	$2 No. 1878		2.75	2.75
a.		Souvenir sheet, #2017-2021		10.00	10.00
		Nos. 2017-2021 (5)		7.70	7.00

No. 2020a issued 11/17 for New Zealand 2005 National Stamp Show, Auckland.

A miniature sheet containing Nos. 2003-2012 and 2017-2021 was sold only with a commemorative book.

Cafés — A520

2005, May 4		Litho.	*Die Cut*
		Self-Adhesive	
2022	A520	45c 1910s	.60	.35
2023	A520	90c 1940s	1.25	.75
2024	A520	$1.35 1970s	1.50	1.50
2025	A520	$1.50 1990s	2.00	2.00
2026	A520	$2 2005	2.75	2.75
a.		Horiz. strip, #2022-2026	10.00	
		Nos. 2022-2026 (5)	8.10	7.35

Rugby Team Shirts — A521

Shirts of: Nos. 2027, 2029, All Blacks. Nos. 2028, 2030, British & Irish Lions.

2005, June 1			*Die Cut*
		Self-Adhesive	
2027	A521	45c multi	.55	.55
2028	A521	45c multi	.55	.55
a.		Horiz. pair, #2027-2028	1.30	

2029	A521	$1.50 multi		2.00	2.00
2030	A521	$1.50 multi		2.00	2.00
a.		Horiz. pair, #2029-2030		4.50	
		Nos. 2027-2030 (4)		5.10	5.10

Miniature Sheet

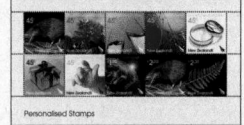

Greetings Stamps — A522

No. 2031: a, Kiwi. b, Pohutukawa flower. c, Champagne flutes. d, Balloons. e, Wedding rings. f, Gift. g, Baby's hand. h, New Zealand on globe. i, Kiwi. j, Fern.

2005, July 6			*Perf. 14*	
2031	A522	Sheet of 10	12.50	12.50
a.-g.		45c Any single	.60	.50
h.		$1.50 multi	2.10	1.75
i.-j.		$2 Either single	3.00	3.00
k.		Sheet of 20 #2031a + 20 labels	25.00	—
l.		Sheet of 20 #2031b + 20 labels	25.00	—
m.		Sheet of 20 #2031c + 20 labels	25.00	—
n.		Sheet of 20 #2031d + 20 labels	25.00	—
o.		Sheet of 20 #2031e + 20 labels	25.00	—
p.		Sheet of 20 #2031f + 20 labels	25.00	—
q.		Sheet of 20 #2031g + 20 labels	25.00	—
r.		Sheet of 20 #2031h + 20 labels	50.00	—
s.		Sheet of 20 #2031i + 20 labels	70.00	—
t.		Sheet of 20 #2031j + 20 labels	70.00	—

Nos. 2031k-2031q each sold for $19.95; No. 2031r sold for $44.95; Nos. 2031s-2031t each sold for $54.95.

Examples of Nos. 2031a and 2031h without the "2005" year date were produced in sheets of 20 stamps + 20 labels for the Washington 2006 World Philatelic Exhibition and sold only at that show.

See Nos. 2070, 2120.

Worldwide Fund for Nature (WWF) — A523

Kakapo and text: No. 2032, "Nocturnal bird living on the forest floor." No. 2033, "Endangered — only 86 known surviving." No. 2034, "Relies heavily on camouflage for defence." No. 2035, "Night Parrot unique to New Zealand."

2005, Aug. 3				
2032	A523	45c multi	.70	.70
2033	A523	45c multi	.70	.70
2034	A523	45c multi	.70	.70
2035	A523	45c multi	.70	.70
a.		Strip of 4, #2032-2035	2.75	2.75
		Nos. 2032-2035 (4)	2.80	2.80

Christmas — A525

Designs: 45c, Baby Jesus. 90c, Mary and Joseph. $1.35, Shepherd and sheep. $1.50, Magi. $2, Star of Bethlehem.

2005		Litho.	*Perf. 14¼*	
2036	A524	45c multi	.60	.30
2037	A524	90c multi	1.10	.90
2038	A524	$1.35 multi	1.50	1.50
2039	A524	$1.50 multi	1.75	1.75
2040	A524	$2 multi	2.75	2.75
a.		Horiz. strip, #2036-2040	9.50	9.50
		Nos. 2036-2040 (5)	7.70	7.00

Booklet Stamps
Size: 22x27mm
Self-Adhesive
Serpentine Die Cut 11x11¼

2041	A524	45c multi	.65	.55
a.		Booklet pane of 10	7.00	
2042	A525	$1 multi	1.40	1.40
a.		Booklet pane of 10	14.00	

Issued: $1, 10/5; Nos. 2036-2041, 11/2.

Premiere of Movie, *King Kong* — A526

Characters: 45c, King Kong. 90c, Carl Denham. $1.35, Ann Darrow. $1.50, Jack Driscoll. $2, Darrow and Driscoll.

2005, Oct. 19			*Perf. 14¾*	
2043	A526	45c multi	.70	.70
2044	A526	90c multi	1.40	1.40
2045	A526	$1.35 multi	2.10	2.10
2046	A526	$1.50 multi	2.40	2.40
2047	A526	$2 multi	3.25	3.25
a.		Horiz. pair, #2043-2047	10.00	10.00
b.		Souvenir sheet, #2047a	10.00	10.00
		Nos. 2043-2047 (5)	9.85	9.85

Premiere of Film *Narnia: The Lion, The Witch and the Wardrobe* — A527

Designs: 45c, Lucy and the Wardrobe. 90c, Lucy, Edmund, Peter and Susan, horiz. $1.35, White Witch and Edmund, horiz. $1.50, Frozen Army. $2, Aslan and Lucy, horiz.

		Perf. 14x14¼, 14¼x14		
2005, Dec. 1			**Litho.**	
2048	A527	45c multi	.70	.70
a.		Souvenir sheet of 1	1.00	1.00
2049	A527	90c multi	1.40	1.40
a.		Souvenir sheet of 1	1.90	1.90
2050	A527	$1.35 multi	2.10	2.10
a.		Souvenir sheet of 1	3.00	3.00
2051	A527	$1.50 multi	2.40	2.40
a.		Souvenir sheet of 1	3.25	3.25
2052	A527	$2 multi	3.25	3.25
a.		Souvenir sheet of 1	4.25	4.25
		Nos. 2048-2052 (5)	9.85	9.85
		Set of 5 souvenir sheets of 1 each, #2048a//2052a	13.40	13.40

Self-Adhesive
Serpentine Die Cut 12½x12, 12x12½

2053		Sheet of 5	10.00		
a.		A527 45c multi, 26x37mm		.70	.70
b.		A527 90c multi, 37x26mm		1.40	1.40
c.		A527 $1.35 multi, 37x26mm		2.10	2.10
d.		A527 $1.50 multi, 26x37mm		2.40	2.40
e.		A527 $2 multi, 37x26mm		3.25	3.25

Nos. 2048a-2052a sold as a set for $8.70.

The 2005 sheets contain: #2003, 2006, 2007, 2008, 2011, 2012, 2017, 2020, 2021. See note following #1404.

New Year 2006 (Year of the Dog) — A528

Designs: 45c, Labrador retriever. 90c, German shepherd. $1.35, Jack Russell terrier. $1.50, Golden retriever. $2, Huntaway.

Litho. & Embossed

2006, Jan. 4			*Perf. 14*	
2054	A528	45c multi	.60	.30

			Litho.	
2055	A528	90c multi	1.10	1.10
2056	A528	$1.35 multi	1.50	1.50
2057	A528	$1.50 multi	2.00	2.00

2058	A528	$2 multi	2.75	2.75
a.		Souvenir sheet, #2057-2058	5.75	5.75
		Nos. 2054-2058 (5)	7.95	7.65

No. 2058a exists imperf in a limited edition album.

Self-Adhesive
Size: 25x30mm Coil Stamp
Coil Stamp
Die Cut Perf. 12¾

2059	A528	45c multi	.65	.55

Booklet Stamp
Serpentine Die Cut 11x11¼

2060	A528	45c multi	.65	.55
a.		Booklet pane of 10	7.00	

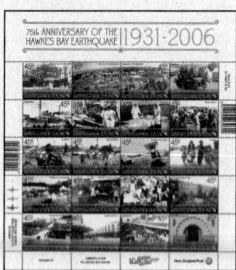

Hawke's Bay Earthquake, 75th Anniv. — A529

No. 2061: a, Napier before the earthquake. b, Aerial view of the devastation (denomination at left). c, Aerial view of the devastation (denomination at right). d, Fire service. e, HMS Veronica. f, HMS Veronica sailors. g, Red Cross. h, Rescue services. i, Devastation. j, Medical services. k, Emergency mail flights. l, Refugees. m, Emergency accommodation. n, Makeshift cooking facilities. o, Community spirit. p, Refugees evacuated by train. q, Building industry. r, A new Art Deco city. s, Celebrations. t, Hawke's Bay region today.

2006, Feb. 3			Litho.	*Perf. 14*	
2061	A529	Sheet of 20		14.00	14.00
a.-t.		45c Any single		.70	.70
u.		Booklet pane, 2 each #2061a-2061t		4.75	
v.		Booklet pane, 2 each #2061r-2061t		4.75	
w.		Booklet pane, 2 each #2061d-2061f		4.75	
x.		Booklet pane, 2 each #2061g-2061h + 2 labels		3.25	
y.		Booklet pane, 2 each #2061i, 2061k, 2061p		4.75	
z.		Booklet pane, 2 each #2061j, 2061l, 2061m		4.75	
aa.		Booklet pane, 2 each #2061n, 2061o, 2061q		4.75	
		Complete booklet, #2061u-2061aa		32.50	

Complete booklet sold for $19.95.

Tourist Attractions Type of 2003

Designs: No. 2062, Franz Josef Glacier, West Coast. No. 2063, Halfmoon Bay, Stewart Island. No. 2064, Cathedral Cove, Coromandel. No. 2065, Mount Taranaki. No. 2066, Huka Falls, Taupo. No. 2067, Lake Wanaka.

2006, Mar. 1			*Perf. 13¼x13½*	
2062	A496	$1.50 multi	2.00	2.00
2063	A496	$1.50 multi	2.00	2.00
2064	A496	$1.50 multi	2.00	2.00
2065	A496	$1.50 multi	2.00	2.00
2066	A496	$1.50 multi	2.00	2.00
2067	A496	$1.50 multi	2.00	2.00
		Nos. 2062-2067 (6)	12.00	12.00

Queen Elizabeth II, 80th Birthday — A530

Litho. & Embossed with Foil Application

2006, Apr. 21			*Perf. 13½*	
2068	A530	$5 dk bl & multi	8.00	8.00
a.		$5 Prussian blue & multi	8.00	8.00
b.		Souvenir sheet, #2068a, Jersey #1215a	27.50	27.50

Printed in sheets of 4.
No. 2068b sold for $17.50. See Jersey No. 1215.

Miniature Sheet

Greetings Stamps — A531

No. 2069: a, Champagne flutes. b, Child's toy. c, Fern. d, Pohutukawa flower. e, Stars. f, Wedding and engagement rings. g, Rose. h, Fern. i, Pohutukawa flower. j, Stars.

2006, May 3	Litho.		Perf. 14	
2069	A531	Sheet of 10 + 5 labels	14.00	14.00
a.-g.		45c Any single	.70	.70
h.		$1.50 multi	2.40	2.40
i.-j.		$2 Either single	3.25	3.25
k.		Souvenir sheet, #2069i, 2 #2069h	8.00	8.00
l.		Sheet of 20 #2069h + 20 labels	67.50	
m.		Sheet of 20 #2069i + 20 labels	82.50	
n.		Sheet of 20 #2069j + 20 labels	82.50	

No. 2069k issued 11/16. Belgica'06 World Philatelic Exhibition, Brussels (#2069k).
Nos. 2069i-2069n issued 2007. No. 2069l sold for $44.90; Nos. 2069m and 2069n, each sold for $54.90. Labels could be personalized
A sheet of 20 #2069c + 20 labels depicting New Zealand's America's Cup Emirates Team yacht sold for $19.90. Labels on this sheet could not be personalized.
See Nos. 2138, 2292, 2326-2327, 2412.

Greetings Type of 2005 Redrawn
Souvenir Sheet

No. 2070: a, Like #2031i, without "2005" year date. b, Like #2031j, without "2005" year date.

2006, May 27	Litho.		Perf. 14	
2070		Sheet of 2 + central label	6.50	6.50
a.-b.	A522	$2 Either single	3.25	3.25
c.		Souvenir sheet, #2070a-2070b	6.75	6.75

Washington 2006 World Philatelic Exhibition.
No. 2070c issued 11/2. Kiwipex 2006 National Stamp Exhibition, Christchurch (#2070c). No. 2070c lacks label, and sold for $5, with the extra $1 going to the NZ Philatelic Foundation.

A set of five gummed stamps, a self-adhesive coil stamp and a self-adhesive booklet stamp depicting Traditional Maori Performing Arts was prepared for release on June 7, 2006 but was withdrawn on June 2. Some mail orders for these stamps were fulfilled and shipped out inadvertently prior to the June 7 issue date, but apparently no examples were sold over post office counters. Used examples are also known, but there is no evidence of sale of any of these stamps over post office counters.

Renewable Energy — A532

Designs: 45c, Wind farm, Tararua. 90c, Roxburgh Hydroelectric Dam. $1.35, Biogas facility, Waikato. $1.50, Geothermal Power Station, Wairakei. $2, Solar panels on Cape Reinga Lighthouse, vert.

2006, July 5				
2071	A532	45c multi	.70	.70
2072	A532	90c multi	1.40	1.40
2073	A532	$1.35 multi	2.10	2.10
2074	A532	$1.50 multi	2.40	2.40
2075	A532	$2 multi	3.25	3.25
		Nos. 2071-2075 (5)	9.85	9.85

Fruits and Vegetables — A533

Slogan "5 + a day," and: 45c+5c, Tomatoes and "5." 90c+10c, Oranges and "+." $1.35,

Onions and "a" (30x30mm). $1.50, Kiwi fruit and "Day," horiz. $2, Radicchio and hand.

2006, Aug. 2	Litho.		Perf. 14	
2076	A533	45c +5c multi	.70	.70
2077	A533	90c +10c multi	1.40	1.40
2078	A533	$1.35 multi	2.10	2.10
2079	A533	$1.50 multi	2.40	2.40
2080	A533	$2 multi	3.25	3.25
a.		Souvenir sheet, #2076-2080	10.00	10.00
		Nos. 2076-2080 (5)	9.85	9.85

Self-Adhesive
Size: 24x29mm
Serpentine Die Cut 9¾x10

2081	A533	45c +5c multi	.70	.70

New Zealand Gold Rush — A534

Designs: 45c, Gold panner, c. 1880. 90c, Miners, Kuranui Creek, c. 1868, horiz. $1.35, Chinese miners, Tuapeka, c. 1900, horiz. $1.50, Gold escort coach, Roxburgh, 1901, horiz. $2, Dunedin harbor, c. 1900, horiz.

2006, Sept. 9			Perf. 14	
2082	A534	45c multi	.70	.70
2083	A534	90c multi	1.40	1.40
2084	A534	$1.35 multi	2.10	2.10
2085	A534	$1.50 multi	2.40	2.40
2086	A534	$2 multi	3.25	3.25
		Nos. 2082-2086 (5)	9.85	9.85

Souvenir Sheet
Litho. With Foil Application

2087		Sheet of 5	10.00	10.00
a.		A534 45c gold & multi	.70	.70
b.		A534 90c gold & multi	1.40	1.40
c.		A534 $1.35 gold & multi	2.10	2.10
d.		A534 $1.50 gold & multi	2.40	2.40
e.		A534 $2 gold & multi	3.25	3.25

Portions of the design of Nos. 2082 and 2087a are printed with a thermochromic ink that changes color when warmed that is applied by a thermographic process producing a shiny, raised effect.
No. 2087 exists imperf in a limited edition album.

Christmas — A535

Children's art by: Nos. 2088, 2098, Hanna McLachlan. No. 2089, Isla Hewitt. No. 2090, Caitlin Davidson. No. 2091, Maria Petersen. No. 2092, Deborah Yoon. No. 2093, Hannah Webster. 90c, Pierce Higginson. $1.35, Rosa Tucker. $1.50, Sylvie Webby. $2, Gemma Baldock.

2006, Oct. 4	Litho.		Perf. 14¼	
2088	A535	45c multi	.70	.70
2089	A535	45c multi	.70	.70
2090	A535	45c multi	.70	.70
2091	A535	45c multi	.70	.70
2092	A535	45c multi	.70	.70
2093	A535	45c multi	.70	.70
a.		Miniature sheet, #2088-2093	4.25	4.25
b.		Horiz. strip of 5, #2089-2093	3.50	3.50
2094	A535	90c multi	1.40	1.40
2095	A535	$1.35 multi	2.10	2.10
2096	A535	$1.50 multi	2.40	2.40
2097	A535	$2 multi	3.25	3.25
		Nos. 2088-2097 (10)	13.35	13.35

Self-Adhesive
Size: 21x26mm
Serpentine Die Cut 9¾x10

2098	A535	45c multi	.70	.70
a.		Booklet pane of 10	7.00	
2099	A535	$1.50 multi	2.40	2.40
a.		Horiz. pair, #2098-2099	3.00	
b.		Booklet pane of 10	24.00	

No. 2099b sold for $13.50.

Summer Festivals — A536

Designs: 45c, Dragon boat racing. 90c, Race day. $1.35, Teddy Bears' Picnic. $1.50, Outdoor concerts. $2, Jazz festivals.

2006, Nov. 1			Perf. 14¼	
2100	A536	45c multi	.70	.70
2101	A536	90c multi	1.40	1.40
2102	A536	$1.35 multi	2.10	2.10
2103	A536	$1.50 multi	2.40	2.40
2104	A536	$2 multi	3.25	3.25
a.		Horiz. strip of 5, #2100-2104	10.00	10.00
b.		Miniature sheet, #2104a	10.00	10.00
		Nos. 2100-2104 (5)	9.85	9.85

The 2006 sheets contain: #2058, 2061e, 2066, 2069i, 2075, 2080, 2086, 2097, 2104. See note following #1404.

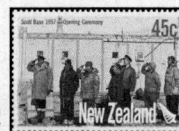

Scott Base, Antarctica, 50th Anniv. — A537

Designs: 45c, Opening ceremony, 1957. 90c, Scott Base, 1990. $1.35, Aerial view, 2000. $1.50, Sign, 2003-04. $2, Aerial view, 2005.

2007, Jan. 20			Perf. 14¼x14	
2105	A537	45c multi	.70	.70
a.		Souvenir sheet of 1	1.00	1.00
2106	A537	90c multi	1.40	1.40
a.		Souvenir sheet of 1	1.90	1.90
2107	A537	$1.35 multi	2.10	2.10
a.		Souvenir sheet of 1	2.75	2.75
2108	A537	$1.50 multi	2.40	2.40
a.		Souvenir sheet of 1	3.50	3.50
2109	A537	$2 multi	3.25	3.25
a.		Souvenir sheet of 1	4.50	4.50
		Nos. 2105-2109 (5)	9.85	9.85

Nos. 2105a-2109a sold as a set for $8.70. The souvenir sheets exist overprinted in a limited edition album.

New Year 2007 (Year of the Pig) — A538

Pig breeds: 45c, Kunekune. 90c, Kunekune, diff. $1.35, Arapawa. $1.50, Auckland Island. $2, Kunekune, diff.

2007, Feb. 7			Perf. 14½x14	
2110	A538	45c multi	.70	.70
2111	A538	90c multi	1.40	1.40
2112	A538	$1.35 multi	2.10	2.10
2113	A538	$1.50 multi	2.40	2.40
2114	A538	$2 multi	3.25	3.25
a.		Souvenir sheet, #2113-2114	5.75	5.75

Nos. 2111-2112 exist in a souvenir sheet in a limited edition album.

Indigenous Animals — A539

Designs: 45c, Tuatara. 90c, Kiwi. $1.35, Hamilton's frog. $1.50, Yellow-eyed penguin. $2, Hector's dolphin.

Serpentine Die Cut
2007, Mar. 7			Litho.	

Self-Adhesive

2115	A539	45c multi	.65	.65
2116	A539	90c multi	1.25	1.25
2117	A539	$1.35 multi	1.90	1.90
2118	A539	$1.50 multi	2.10	2.10
2119	A539	$2 multi	2.75	2.75
a.		Horiz. strip of 5, #2115-2119	8.65	

Greetings Type of 2005 Redrawn
Souvenir Sheet

2007, Mar. 30	Litho.		Perf. 14	
2120		Sheet , #2075, 2120a	6.00	6.00
a.		A531 $2 Like #2069i, without "2006" year date	3.00	3.00

Northland 2007 National Stamp Exhibition, Whangarei.

Centenaries A540

Designs: No. 2121, Scouts and Lieutenant Colonel David Cossgrove, founder of scouting movement in New Zealand. No. 2122, Infant, nurse, Dr. Frederic Truby King, founder of Plunket Society. No. 2123, Rugby players, Hercules "Bumper" Wright, first team captain. No. 2124, Sister of Compassion teaching children, Suzanne Aubert, founder of Sisters of Compassion. $1, Plunket Society emblem, family. $1.50, Sisters of Compassion emblem, women reading book. No. 2127, New Zealand Rugby League emblem, rugby players. No. 2128, Scouting emblem, scouts.

2007, Apr. 24			Perf. 14	
2121	A540	50c multi	.75	.75
2122	A540	50c multi	.75	.75
2123	A540	50c multi	.75	.75
2124	A540	50c multi	.75	.75
a.		Horiz. strip of 4, #2121-2124	4.00	4.00
2125	A540	$1 multi	1.50	1.50
2126	A540	$1.50 multi	2.25	2.25
2127	A540	$2 multi	3.00	3.00
2128	A540	$2 multi	3.00	3.00
a.		Block of 8, #2121-2128	12.75	12.75
b.		Horiz. pair, #2127-2128	9.00	9.00

Tourist Attractions Type of 2003

Designs: 5c, Whakarewarewa geothermal area. 10c, Central Otago. 20c, Rainbow Falls, Northland. 50c, Lake Coleridge. $1, Rangitoto Island. $2.50, Abel Tasman National Park. $3, Tongaporutu, Taranaki.

2007, May 9			Perf. 13¼x13½	
2129	A496	5c multi	.25	.25
2130	A496	10c multi	.25	.25
2131	A496	20c multi	.30	.30
2132	A496	50c multi	.75	.75
2133	A496	$1 multi	1.50	1.50
2134	A496	$2.50 multi	3.75	3.75
2135	A496	$3 multi	4.50	4.50
		Nos. 2129-2135 (7)	11.30	11.30

Self-Adhesive
Serpentine Die Cut 10x9½

2136	A496	50c multi	.75	.75
a.		Booklet pane of 10	7.50	
2137	A496	$1 multi	1.50	1.50
a.		Horiz. pair, #2136-2137	2.25	2.25
b.		Booklet pane of 10	15.00	

Greetings Type of 2006 Redrawn

No. 2138: a, Child's toy. b, Pohutukawa flower. c, Wedding and engagement rings. d, Fern. e, Champagne flutes. f, Rose. g, Stars.

2007, May 9			Perf. 14	
2138	A531	Sheet of 7 + 8 labels	5.25	5.25
a.-g.		50c Any single	.75	.75
h.		Sheet of 20 #2138a + 20 labels	32.50	—
i.		Sheet of 20 #2138b + 20 labels	32.50	—
j.		Sheet of 20 #2138c + 20 labels	32.50	—
k.		Sheet of 20 #2138d + 20 labels	32.50	—
l.		Sheet of 20 #2138e + 20 labels	32.50	—
m.		Sheet of 20 #2138f + 20 labels	32.50	—
n.		Sheet of 20 #2138g + 20 labels	32.50	—

Nos. 2138h-2138n each sold for $20.90.

Southern Skies and Observatories A541

Designs: 50c, Southern Cross, Stardome Observatory. $1, Pleiades, McLellan Mt. John Observatory. 50c, Trifid Nebula, Ward Observatory. $2, Southern Pinwheel, MOA telescope, Mt. John Observatory. $2.50, Large Magellanic Cloud, Southern African Large Telescope.

2007, June 6			Perf. 13x13¼	
2139	A541	50c multi	.80	.80
a.		Perf. 14	1.00	1.00
b.		Booklet pane of 1 #2139a	1.00	
2140	A541	$1 multi	1.60	1.60
a.		Perf. 14	2.00	2.00
b.		Booklet pane of 1 #2140a	2.00	
2141	A541	$1.50 multi	2.40	2.40
a.		Perf. 14	3.00	3.00
b.		Booklet pane of 1 #2141a	3.00	
2142	A541	$2 multi	3.00	3.00
a.		Perf. 14	4.25	4.25
b.		Booklet pane of 1 #2142a	4.25	
2143	A541	$2.50 multi	3.75	3.75
a.		Perf. 14	5.25	5.25
b.		Booklet pane of 1 #2143a	5.25	

c.　Booklet pane of 5, #2139a-
　　2143a　　　　　　　15.50
　　Complete booklet, #2139b,
　　2140b, 2141b, 2142b,
　　2143b, 2143c　　　　31.00
d.　Souvenir sheet, #2142a,
　　2143a　　　　　　6.75　6.75
　　Nos. 2139-2143 (5)　11.55 11.55

No. 2143d issued 8/31. Huttpex 2007
Stampshow (#2143d).

Miniature Sheet

New
Zealand
Slang
A542

No. 2144 — Designs: a, "Good as gold,"
gold nugget. b, "Sweet as," kiwi fruit. c, "She'll
be right," hand with thumb up. d, "Hissy fit,"
insect. e, "Sparrow fart," sun in sky. f, "Cuz,"
kiwi bird. g, "Away laughing," sandals. h, "Tiki
tour," road sign. i, "Away with the fairies,"
cookies. j, "Wop-wops," house. k, "Hard
yakka," shirt. l, "Cods wollop," fish. m, "Boots
and all," rugby ball and athletic shoes. n,
"Shark and taties," fish and chips. o, "Knack-
ered," boots. p, "Laughing gear," mug. q,
"Everyman and his dog," dog. r, "Bit of a dag,"
sheep. s, "Dreaded lurgy," box of tissues. t,
"Rark up," hand pointing.

2007, July 4　　　　　　***Perf. 14***
2144　A542　Sheet of 20　16.00 16.00
a.-t.　50c Any single　　　.80　.80

Portions of the design were covered with a
thermographic ink that allowed printing below
(definitinons of the slang phrases) to appear
when the ink was warmed.

Technical
Innovations by
New Zealanders
A543

Designs: 50c, Gallagher electric fence. $1,
Spreadable butter. $1.50, Mountain buggy. $2,
Hamilton jet boat. $2.50, Tranquilizer gun.

2007, Aug. 1
2145　A543　50c multi　　　.75　.75
2146　A543　$1 multi　　　1.50　1.50
2147　A543　$1.50 multi　　2.25　2.25
2148　A543　$2 multi　　　3.00　3.00
2149　A543　$2.50 multi　　3.75　3.75
　　Nos. 2145-2149 (5)　11.25 11.25

Nos. 2145-2149 exist in a souvenir sheet in
a limited edition album.

Wedding of Queen
Elizabeth II and
Prince Philip, 60th
Anniv. — A544

Queen and Prince: 50c, In 2007. $2, On
wedding day, 1947.

2007, Sept. 5　***Litho.***　***Perf. 14***
2150　A544　50c multi　　　.70　.70
2151　A544　$2 multi　　　2.75　2.75
　　a.　Souvenir sheet, #2150-2151　3.50　3.50

Christmas — A545

Children's art by: 50c, Sione Vao. $1, Reece
Cateley. $1.50, Emily Wang. $2, Alexandra
Eathorne. $2.50, Jake Hooper.

2007, Oct. 3　　　　　***Perf. 14¼***
2152　A545　50c multi　　　.80　.80
2153　A545　$1 multi　　　1.50　1.50
2154　A545　$1.50 multi　　2.40　2.40
2155　A545　$2 multi　　　3.00　3.00
2156　A545　$2.50 multi　　4.00　4.00
　　Nos. 2152-2156 (5)　11.70 11.70

Size: 25x30mm
Self-Adhesive
Coil Stamps
Die Cut Perf. 13x12¾
2157　A545　50c multi　　　.80　.80
2158　A545　$1.50 multi　　2.40　2.40
　　a.　Horiz. pair, #2157-2158　3.25

Booklet Stamps
Serpentine Die Cut 11x11¼
2159　A545　50c multi　　　.80　.80
　　a.　Booklet pane of 10　8.00
2160　A545　$1.50 multi　　2.10　2.10
　　a.　Booklet pane of 10　21.00

No. 2160a sold for $13.50.

Miniature Sheet

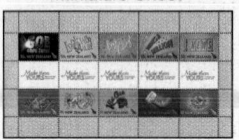

Greetings Stamps — A546

No. 2161: a, "Go You Good Thing." b, "Look
Who It Is." c, "Love Always." d, "Thanks a Mil-
lion." e, "We've Got News." f, "Wish You Were
Here." g, "Time to Celebrate." h, "Kia Ora." i,
"You Gotta Love Christmas." j, Chinese
characters.

2007, Nov. 7　　　　　***Perf. 14***
2161　A546　Sheet of 10 + 5
　　　　labels　　　　13.00 13.00
a.-f.　50c Any single　　　.75　.75
g.-h.　$1 Either single　　1.50　1.50
i.　$1.50 multi　　　2.40　2.40
j.　$2 multi　　　3.00　3.00
k.　Sheet of 20 #2161c + 20
　　labels　　　　32.50　—
l.　Sheet of 20 #2161d + 20
　　labels　　　　32.50　—
m.　Sheet of 20 #2161e + 20
　　labels　　　　32.50　—
n.　Sheet of 20 #2161f + 20 la-
　　bels　　　　32.50　—
o.　Sheet of 20 #2161g + 20
　　labels　　　　47.50　—
p.　Sheet of 20 #2161h + 20
　　labels　　　　47.50　—
q.　Sheet of 20 #2161i + 20 la-
　　bels　　　　70.00　—
r.　Sheet of 20 #2161j + 20 la-
　　bels　　　　85.00　—
s.　As #2161h, perf 13¼x13½
　　(2224b)　　　1.25　1.25
t.　As #2161j, perf 13¼x13½
　　(2224b)　　　2.40　2.40

Nos. 2161k-2161n each sold for $20.90;
Nos. 2161o-2161p, for $30.90; No. 2161q, for
$44.90; No. 2161r, for $54.90. Labels were
personalizable on demand. Nos. 2161k-2161r. Issued:
Nos. 2161s, 2161t, 4/1/09.

The 2007 sheets contain: #2114,
2109, 2142; #2127, 2128, 2148; #2155,
2151, 2161j. See note following #1404.

Reefs — A547

Marine life from: 50c, Dusky Sound, Fiord-
land. $1, Mayor Island, Bay of Plenty. $1.50,
Fiordland. $2, Volkner Rocks, White Island,
Bay of Plenty.

2008, Jan. 9　***Litho.***　***Perf. 13x13¼***
2162　A547　50c multi　　　.80　.80
2163　A547　$1 multi　　　1.60　1.60
2164　A547　$1.50 multi　　2.40　2.40
2165　A547　$2 multi　　　3.25　3.25
　　a.　Souvenir sheet, #2162-2165　8.25　8.25
　　Nos. 2162-2165 (4)　8.05　8.05

Self-Adhesive
Size: 26x21mm
Serpentine Die Cut 11¼
2166　A547　50c multi　　　.80　.80
　　a.　Booklet pane of 10　8.00
2167　A547　$1 multi　　　1.60　1.60
　　a.　Horiz. pair, #2166-2167　2.40
　　b.　Booklet pane of 10 #2167　16.00

Pocket
Pets — A548

2008, Feb. 7　　　　　***Perf. 14***
2168　A548　50c Rabbits　　.80　.80
2169　A548　$1 Guinea pigs　1.60　1.60
2170　A548　$1.50 Rats　　2.40　2.40
2171　A548　$2 Mice　　　3.25　3.25
　　a.　Souvenir sheet, #2170-2171　5.75　5.75
　　b.　As #2171, perf. 13½x13¼　3.25　3.25
　　c.　Souvenir sheet, #2161j, 2171b　6.50　6.50

New Year 2008 (Year of the Rat), No. 2171a.
Nos. 2171b, 2171c issued 3/7. Taipei 2008
International Stamp Exhibition (#2171c).

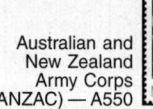

Weather
Extremes — A549

Designs: No. 2172, Drought, Gisborne,
1998. No. 2173, Wind, Auckland, 2007. $1,
Storm, Wellington, 2001. $1.50, Flooding,
Hikurangi, 2007. $2, Snow storm, Southland,
2001. $2.50, Heat, Matarangi, 2005.

2008, Mar. 5　***Litho.***　***Perf. 14***
2172　A549　50c multi　　　.80　.80
2173　A549　50c multi　　　.80　.80
2174　A549　$1 multi　　　1.60　1.60
2175　A549　$1.50 multi　　2.40　2.40
2176　A549　$2 multi　　　3.25　3.25
2177　A549　$2.50 multi　　4.00　4.00
　　Nos. 2172-2177 (6)　12.85 12.85

Nos. 2172-2177 exist in a souvenir sheet in
a limited edition album.

Australian and
New Zealand
Army Corps
(ANZAC) — A550

Designs: No. 2178, Dawn Parade. No. 2179,
Soldiers at Gallipoli, 1915. $1, Soldiers at
Western Front, 1916-18. $1.50, Chalk kiwi
made by soldiers, England, 1919. $2, Soldier's
Haka dance, Egypt, 1941. $2.50, Soldiers in
Viet Nam, 1965-71.

2008, Apr. 2
2178　A550　50c multi　　　.80　.80
　　a.　Booklet pane of 1　1.00　—
2179　A550　50c multi　　　.80　.80
　　a.　Booklet pane of 1　1.00　—
2180　A550　$1 multi　　　1.60　1.60
　　a.　Booklet pane of 1　2.00　—
2181　A550　$1.50 multi　　2.40　2.40
　　a.　Booklet pane of 1　3.00　—
　　b.　Souvenir sheet, #2179-2181　3.50　3.50
2182　A550　$2 multi　　　3.25　3.25
　　a.　Booklet pane of 1　4.00　—
2183　A550　$2.50 multi　　4.00　4.00
　　a.　Booklet pane of 1　5.00　—
　　b.　Booklet pane of 6, #2178-
　　　2183　　　　　16.00　—
　　Complete booklet, #2178a,
　　2179a, 2180a, 2181a,
　　2182a, 2183a, 2183b　32.00
　　Nos. 2178-2183 (6)　12.85 12.85

No. 2181b issued 10/20. End of World War
I, 90th anniv. (#2181b).

Maori King Movement,
150th Anniv. — A551

Various unnamed artworks by Fred Graham
and English text: 50c, "There is but one eye of
the needle. . ." $1.50, "Taupiri is the moun-
tain. . ." $2.50, "After I am gone. . .," horiz.

2008, May 2　***Litho.***　***Perf. 14***
2184　A551　50c multi　　　.80　.80
2185　A551　$1.50 multi　　2.40　2.40
2186　A551　$2.50 multi　　4.00　4.00
　　Nos. 2184-2186 (3)　7.20　7.20

Premiere of
Film, *The
Chronicles of
Narnia: Prince
Caspian*
A552

Designs: 50c, The Pevensie children. $1,
Queen Susan. $1.50, High King Peter. $2,
Prince Caspian.

2008, May 7　　　　***Perf. 14½x14***
2187　A552　50c multi　　　.80　.80
　　a.　Souvenir sheet of 1　1.10　1.10
2188　A552　$1 multi　　　1.60　1.60
　　a.　Souvenir sheet of 1　2.25　2.25
2189　A552　$1.50 multi　　2.40　2.40
　　a.　Souvenir sheet of 1　3.25　3.25
2190　A552　$2 multi　　　3.25　3.25
　　a.　Souvenir sheet of 1　4.50　4.50
　　Nos. 2187-2190 (4)　8.05　8.05

Nos. 2187a-2190a were sold as a set for $7.

Matariki (Maori
New
Year) — A553

Inscriptions: No. 2191, Ranginui. No. 2192,
Te Moana nui a Kiwa. $1, Papatuanuku. $1.50,
Whakapapa. $2, Takoha. $2.50, Te Tau Hou.

2008, June 5　***Litho.***　***Perf. 14***
2191　A553　50c multi　　　.80　.80
2192　A553　50c multi　　　.80　.80
2193　A553　$1 multi　　　1.60　1.60
2194　A553　$1.50 multi　　2.40　2.40
2195　A553　$2 multi　　　3.25　3.25
　　a.　Souvenir sheet, #2192,
　　　2194, 2195　　　6.50　6.50
2196　A553　$2.50 multi　　4.00　4.00
　　a.　Miniature sheet of 6, #2191-
　　　2196, perf. 13½x13¼　13.00 13.00
　　Nos. 2191-2196 (6)　12.85 12.85

No. 2195a issued 9/18. Vienna Intl. Postage
Stamp Exhibition (#2195a).
No. 2196a exists as an imperf miniature
sheet from a limited edition album.

2008 Summer
Olympics,
Beijing
A554

2008, July 2　　　　　***Perf. 14¼***
2197　A554　50c Rowing　　.80　.80
2198　A554　50c Cycling　　.80　.80
2199　A554　$1 Kayaking　1.60　1.60
2200　A554　$2 Running　3.00　3.00
　　Nos. 2197-2200 (4)　6.20　6.20

Compare with Type SP82.

Miniature Sheet

Alphabet
A555

No. 2201 — Inscriptions: a, A is for
Aotearoa (Maori name for New Zealand). b, B
is for Beehive (Parliament Building). c, C is for
Cook (Capt. James Cook). d, D is for Dog
(comic strip character). e, E is for Edmonds
(Thomas J. Edmonds, cookbook producer). f,
F is for Fantail (bird). g, G is for Goodnight Kiwi
(cartoon). h, H is for Haka (Maori dance). i, I is
for Interislander (ferry). j, J is for Jelly tip (ice
cream bar). k, K is for Kia ora. l, L is for Log
O'Wood (rugby trophy). m, M is for Mudpools.
n, N is for Nuclear free. o, O is for O.E. (overseas experience). p, P is for Pinetree (Colin
"Pinetree" Meads, rugby player). q, Q is for
Quake. r, R is for Rutherford (Sir Ernest Rutherford, chemist and physicist). s, S is for
Southern Cross (constellation). t, T is for Tiki
(rock carving). u, U is for Upham (Capt.
Charles Upham, war hero). v, V is for Vote. w,

W is for Weta (insect). x, X is for X-treme sports. y, Y is for Yarn. z, Z is for Zeeland (Dutch province for which New Zealand was named).

2008, Aug. 6		Perf. 14¼	
2201	A555	Sheet of 26	18.50 18.50
a.-z.		50c Any single	.70 .70

North Island Main Trunk Line, Cent. — A556

Designs: 50c, Last spike ceremony, Manganui-o-te-Ao, 1908. $1, Locomotive at Taumarunui Station, 1958. $1.50, Train on Makatote Viaduct, 1963. $2, Train on Raurimi Spiral, 1964. $2.50, Train on Hapuawhenua Viaduct, 2003.

2008, Sept. 3	Litho.	Perf. 14	
2202	A556	50c multi	.70 .70
2203	A556	$1 multi	1.40 1.40
2204	A556	$1.50 multi	2.00 2.00
2205	A556	$2 multi	2.75 2.75
2206	A556	$2.50 multi	3.50 3.50
		Nos. 2202-2206 (5)	10.35 10.35

Christmas — A557

Winning art in children's stamp design competition: 50c, Sheep With Stocking Cap, by Kirsten Fisher-Marsters. $2, Pohutukawa and Koru, by Tamara Jenkin. $2.50, Kiwi and Pohutukawa, by Molly Bruhns.

2008, Oct. 1		Perf. 14¼	
2207	A557	50c multi	.70 .70
2208	A557	$2 multi	2.75 2.75
2209	A557	$2.50 multi	3.25 3.25
		Nos. 2207-2209 (3)	6.70 6.70

Christmas — A558

Designs: 50c, Nativity. $1, Holy Family. $1.50, Madonna and Child.

2008, Oct. 1		Perf. 14¼	
2210	A558	50c multi	.70 .70
2211	A558	$1 multi	1.40 1.40
2212	A558	$1.50 multi	2.00 2.00
		Nos. 2210-2212 (3)	4.10 4.10

Size: 21x26mm
Self-Adhesive
Coil Stamps
Die Cut Perf. 12¾

2213	A558	50c multi	.70 .70
2214	A558	$1.50 multi	2.00 2.00
a.		Horiz. pair, #2213-2214	2.75

Booklet Stamps
Serpentine Die Cut 11¼

2215	A558	50c multi	.70 .70
a.		Booklet pane of 10	7.00
2216	A558	$1.50 multi	2.00 2.00
a.		Booklet pane of 10	20.00
		Nos. 2213-2216 (4)	5.40 5.40

Sir Edmund Hillary (1919-2008), Mountaineer — A559

New Zealand flag and: 50c, Hillary. $1, Hillary and Tenzing Norgay on Mt. Everest, 1953. $1.50, Hillary on Trans-Antarctic Expedition, 1958. $2, Hillary with Nepalese people, 1964. $2.50, Hillary at Order of the Garter ceremony, 1995.

2008, Nov. 5	Litho.	Perf. 14¾	
2217	A559	50c multi	.60 .60
a.		Perf. 14	.75 .75
2218	A559	$1 multi	1.25 1.25
a.		Perf. 14	1.50 1.50
2219	A559	$1.50 multi	1.75 1.75
2220	A559	$2 multi	2.40 2.40
2221	A559	$2.50 multi	3.00 3.00
a.		Perf. 14	3.75 3.75
b.		Souvenir sheet, #2217a, 2218a, 2221a, + specimen of #1084	6.00 6.00
		Nos. 2217-2221 (5)	9.00 9.00

Timpex 2009 National Stamp Exhibition, Timaru (Nos. 2217a, 2218a, 2221a-b); Issued 10/16/09.

Tourist Attractions Type of 2003
Souvenir Sheet

No. 2222: a, Like #2065, without year date. b, Like #2135, without year date.

2008, Nov. 7		Perf. 13¼x13½	
2222		Sheet of 2	5.50 5.50
a.	A496	$1.50 multi	1.75 1.75
b.	A496	$3 multi	3.75 3.75

Tarapex 2008 Philatelic Exhibition, New Plymouth.

The 2008 sheets contain: #2165, 2171, 2177; #2183, 2186, 2196; #2206, 2212, 2221. See note following #1404.

New Year 2009 (Year of the Ox) — A560

Designs: 50c, Chinese character for "ox." $1, Ox. $2, Chinese lanterns and Auckland Harbor Bridge.

2009, Jan. 7		Perf. 13¼x13	
2223	A560	50c multi	.60 .60
2224	A560	$1 multi	1.25 1.25
a.		Perf. 13¼x13½	1.25 1.25
b.		Souvenir sheet, #2161s, 2161t, 2224a	5.00 5.00
2225	A560	$2 multi	2.40 2.40
a.		Souvenir sheet, #2223-2225	4.25 4.25
		Nos. 2223-2225 (3)	4.25 4.25

China 2009 World Stamp Exhibition, Luoyand (#2224b). Issued: Nos. 2224a, 2224b, 4/1.

Lighthouses A561

Designs: 50c, Pencarrow Lighthouse. $1, Dog Island Lighthouse. $1.50, Cape Brett Lighthouse. $2, Cape Egmont Lighthouse. $2.50, Cape Reinga Lighthouse.

2009, Jan. 7		Perf. 13x13¼	
2226	A561	50c multi	.60 .60
2227	A561	$1 multi	1.25 1.25
2228	A561	$1.50 multi	1.75 1.75
2229	A561	$2 multi	2.40 2.40
2230	A561	$2.50 multi	3.00 3.00
		Nos. 2226-2230 (5)	9.00 9.00

Motor Sports Champions A562

Designs: 50c, Scott Dixon. $1, Bruce McLaren. $1.50, Ivan Mauger. $2, Denny Hulme. $2.50, Hugh Anderson.

2009, Feb. 4	Litho.	Perf. 14	
2231	A562	50c multi	.50 .50
2232	A562	$1 multi	1.00 1.00
2233	A562	$1.50 multi	1.50 1.50
2234	A562	$2 multi	2.10 2.10
2235	A562	$2.50 multi	2.60 2.60
a.		Sheet, #2231-2235	7.75 7.75
		Nos. 2231-2235 (5)	7.70 7.70

Self-Adhesive
Size: 26x21mm
Serpentine Die Cut 10x9¾

2236	A562	50c multi	.50 .50
a.		Booklet pane of 10	5.00
2237	A562	$1 multi	1.00 1.00
a.		Booklet pane of 10	10.00
b.		Horiz. pair, #2236-2237	1.50

Tourist Attractions Type of 2003

2009, Mar. 4	Litho.	Perf. 13¼x13½	
2238		Sheet of 2 #2238a	3.00 3.00
a.	A496	$1.50 Like #2062, without year date	1.50 1.50

Intl. Polar Year.

Giants of New Zealand A563

Designs: 50c, Giant moa. $1, Colossal squid. $1.50 Southern right whale. $2, Giant eagle. $2.50, Giant weta.

2009, Mar. 4		Perf. 14½	
2239	A563	50c multi	.75 .75
2240	A563	$1 multi	1.50 1.50
2241	A563	$1.50 multi	2.00 2.00
2242	A563	$2 multi	2.50 2.50
2243	A563	$2.50 multi	3.00 3.00
a.		Miniature sheet, #2239-2243	8.00 8.00
		Nos. 2239-2243 (5)	9.75 9.75

Australian and New Zealand Army Corps (ANZAC) — A564

Poppy and: No. 2244, Funeral procession of the Unknown Warrior. No. 2245, New Zealand Maori Pioneer Battalion, World War I. $1, New Zealand No. 75 Squadron of the Royal Air Force, World War II. $1.50, HMS Achilles, World War II. $2, Kayforce soldiers, Korean War. $2.50, ANZAC Battalion, Vietnam War.

2009, Apr. 1	Litho.	Perf. 13½x13¼	
2244	A564	50c multi	.60 .60
a.		Perf. 14	.70 .70
b.		Booklet pane of 1 #2244a	.70
2245	A564	50c multi	.60 .60
a.		Perf. 14	.70 .70
b.		Booklet pane of 1 #2245a	.70
2246	A564	$1 multi	1.25 1.25
a.		Perf. 14	1.50 1.50
b.		Booklet pane of 1 #2246a	1.50
2247	A564	$1.50 multi	1.75 1.75
a.		Perf. 14	2.25 2.25
b.		Booklet pane of 1 #2247a	2.25
2248	A564	$2 multi	2.40 2.40
a.		Perf. 14	3.00 3.00
b.		Booklet pane of 1 #2248a	3.00
2249	A564	$2.50 multi	3.00 3.00
a.		Perf. 14	3.75 3.75
b.		Booklet pane of 1 #2249a	3.75
c.		Booklet pane of 6, #2244a, 2245a, 2246a, 2247a, 2248a, 2249a	12.00
		Complete booklet #2244b, 2245b, 2246b, 2247b, 2248b, 2249b, 2249c	24.00
		Nos. 2244-2249 (6)	9.60 9.60

Complete booklet sold for $19.90.

Auckland Harbour Bridge, 50th Anniv. — A565

Various views of bridge with inscription: 50c, Opening Day 1959. $1, Our Bridge 2009. $1.50, Our Icon 1961. $2, Our Link 2009.

2009, May 1		Perf. 13½x13¼	
2250	A565	50c multi	.60 .60
2251	A565	$1 multi	1.25 1.25
2252	A565	$1.50 multi	1.75 1.75
2253	A565	$2 multi	2.25 2.25
		Nos. 2250-2253 (4)	5.85 5.85

Self-Adhesive
Serpentine Die Cut 9½x10

2254	A565	50c multi	.60 .60

Miniature Sheets

Matariki (Maori New Year) A566

Nos. 2255 and 2256 — Various heitikis: a, Heitiki in Te Maori Exhibition. b, Heitiki carved by Raponi. c, Corian heitiki carved by Rangi Kipa. d, Female greenstone heitiki. e, Heitiki in Museum of New Zealand. f, Whalebone heitiki carved by Rangi Hetet.

Perf. 13¼x13½

2009, June 24		Litho.	
2255	A566	Sheet of 6	11.50 11.50
a.		50c multi	.60 .60
b.		$1 multi	1.25 1.25
c.		$1.50 multi	1.90 1.90
d.		$1.80 multi	2.25 2.25
e.		$2 multi	2.50 2.50
f.		$2.30 multi	3.00 3.00

Self-Adhesive
Serpentine Die Cut 10x9½

2256	A566	Sheet of 6	11.50 11.50
a.		50c multi	.60 .60
b.		$1 multi	1.25 1.25
c.		$1.50 multi	1.90 1.90
d.		$1.80 multi	2.25 2.25
e.		$2 multi	2.50 2.50
f.		$2.30 multi	3.00 3.00

Tourist Attractions Type of 2003

Designs: 30c, Tolaga Bay. $1.80, Russell. $2.30, Lake Wanaka. $2.80, Auckland. $3.30, Rakaia River. $4, Wellington.

2009, July 1		Perf. 13¼x13½	
2257	A496	30c multi	.40 .40
2258	A496	$1.80 multi	2.25 2.25
2259	A496	$2.30 multi	3.00 3.00
2260	A496	$2.80 multi	3.50 3.50
2261	A496	$3.30 multi	4.25 4.25
2262	A496	$4 multi	5.00 5.00
		Nos. 2257-2262 (6)	18.40 18.40

Self-Adhesive
Serpentine Die Cut 10x9½

2263	A496	$1.80 multi	2.25 2.25
a.		Booklet pane of 5	11.50

Miniature Sheet

Tiki Tour of New Zealand A567

No. 2264 — Parts of map of New Zealand and: a, Signpost and lighthouse, Cape Reinga, fisherman and red snapper, Tane Mahuta, quill pen, Stone Store, Kerikeri. b, Bird, boat on Hole in the Rock tour, dolphin. c, White heron, Maori snaring the Sun. d, Bird, airplane, yachts. e, Rangitoto Island volcano, Sky tower, Auckland, L&P Bottle, Paeroa, bird, surf boat, hibiscus, car and trailer. f, Fishing boat and marlin. g, Balloons, Maori canoe, bull playing rugby. h, Balloon, rower, statue of sheep shearer, Te Kuiti, trout, kiwifruit, Maori carving, Rotorua Mud Pools. i, Pohutukawa tree blossom, meeting house, surfer, horse and rider. j, Maui gas rig, Mt. Taranaki, hang glider, Wind Wand sculpture. k, Rubber boot, apple, pear, windmills, Waimarie River cruise boat, highway sign, Viking helmet, giant kiwi. l, Tractor and wagon, gannet, Pania of the Reef, Napier. m, Westport Municipal Building, statue, Greymouth, Pancake Rocks, Punakaiki. n, Mussel, fisherman, grapes, glass blowers and bottle. o, Birds, statue of Richard Seddon, daffodil, windsurfer, Cook Strait ferry, Golden Shears, Masterton, Westpac Stadium, Wellington. p, Mount Cook lily, bulldozer lifting coal, statue of Mackenzie sheep dog, Lake Tekapo. q, Red deer, punt on Avon River, trailer for selling crayfish, French flags, Chalice, sculpture by Neil Dawson, Christchurch. r, Birds, boat, whale, fish. s, Crayfish, black robin, fishing boat. t, Kayakers, skier, mountains, jetboat on Shotover River. u, Kea, biplane, clams, Museum, Oamaru, clock, Alexandra. v, Kakapo, Museum, Invercargill, Burt Munro motorcycle, musician at Country and Western Festival, Gore. w, Moeraki Boulders, Larnach Castle, Dunedin, curler, seal. x, Stewart Island shag, blue cod, Chain sculpture, Oban.

2009, Aug. 5		Perf. 14¼	
2264	A567	Sheet of 24 + label	16.00 16.00
a.-x.		50c Any single	.65 .65

Kiwistamps — A568

Designs: No. 2265, Cricket ball, bails and wickets. No. 2266, Kiwi fruit. No. 2267, Highway route sign. No. 2268, Wind turbine and man with broken umbrella. No. 2269, Rotary lawn mower. No. 2270, Trailer. No. 2271, Wall decorations (three birds). No. 2272, Fish and chips. No. 2273, Jacket on barbed-wire fence. No. 2274, Hot dog and barbecue.

Serpentine Die Cut 9¾x10

2009, Sept. 7   **Litho.**

Self-Adhesive

2265	A568	(50c) multi	.75 .75
a.		Serpentine die cut 11x11¼	.75 .75
b.		As "a," with silver text	.75 .75
c.		Serpentine die cut 10x9¾	.75 .75
d.		As "c," with silver text	.75 .75
2266	A568	(50c) multi	.75 .75
a.		Serpentine die cut 11x11¼	.75 .75
b.		As "a," with silver text	.75 .75
c.		Serpentine die cut 10x9¾	.75 .75
d.		As "c," with silver text	.75 .75
2267	A568	(50c) multi	.75 .75
a.		Serpentine die cut 11x11¼	.75 .75
b.		As "a," with silver text	.75 .75
c.		Serpentine die cut 10x9¾	.75 .75
d.		As "c," with silver text	.75 .75
2268	A568	(50c) multi	.75 .75
a.		Serpentine die cut 11x11¼	.75 .75
b.		As "a," with silver text	.75 .75
c.		Serpentine die cut 10x9¾	.75 .75
d.		As "c," with silver text	.75 .75
2269	A568	(50c) multi	.75 .75
a.		Serpentine die cut 11x11¼	.75 .75
b.		As "a," with silver text	.75 .75
c.		Serpentine die cut 10x9¾	.75 .75
d.		As "c," with silver text	.75 .75
2270	A568	(50c) multi	.75 .75
a.		Serpentine die cut 11x11¼	.75 .75
b.		As "a," with silver text	.75 .75
c.		Serpentine die cut 10x9¾	.75 .75
d.		As "c," with silver text	.75 .75
2271	A568	(50c) multi	.75 .75
a.		Serpentine die cut 11x11¼	.75 .75
b.		As "a," with silver text	.75 .75
c.		Serpentine die cut 10x9¾	.75 .75
d.		As "c," with silver text	.75 .75
2272	A568	(50c) multi	.75 .75
a.		Serpentine die cut 11x11¼	.75 .75
b.		As "a," with silver text	.75 .75
c.		Serpentine die cut 10x9¾	.75 .75
d.		As "c," with silver text	.75 .75
2273	A568	(50c) multi	.75 .75
a.		Serpentine die cut 11x11¼	.75 .75
b.		As "a," with silver text	.75 .75
c.		Serpentine die cut 10x9¾	.75 .75
d.		As "c," with silver text	.75 .75
2274	A568	(50c) multi	.75 .75
a.		Serpentine die cut 11x11¼	.75 .75
b.		As "a," with silver text	.75 .75
c.		Serpentine die cut 10x9¾	.75 .75
d.		As "c," with silver text	.75 .75
e.		Block of 10, #2265-2274	7.50
f.		Booklet pane of 10, #2265a-2274a	7.50
g.		Booklet pane of 10, #2265b-2274b	7.50
h.		Vert. coil strip of 10, #2265-2274	7.50
		Nos. 2265-2274 (10)	7.50 7.50

A569

A570

Christmas — A571

Designs: Nos. 2275, 2281, Adoration of the Shepherds. No. 2276, Chair and Pohutukawa Tree, by Felix Wang. $1, Holy Family. $1.80, Adoration of the Magi. $2.30, New Zealand Pigeon, by Dannielle Aldworth. $2.80, Child, Gifts and Christmas Tree, by Apurv Bakshi.

2009, Oct. 7   **Litho.**   **Perf. 14¼**

2275	A569	50c multi	.75 .75
2276	A570	50c multi	.75 .75
2277	A569	$1 multi	1.50 1.50
2278	A569	$1.80 multi	2.60 2.60
2279	A570	$2.30 multi	3.50 3.50
2280	A570	$2.80 multi	4.00 4.00
		Nos. 2275-2280 (6)	13.10 13.10

Self-Adhesive

Serpentine Die Cut 10x9½

2281	A571	50c multi	.75 .75
a.		Booklet pane of 10	7.50
2282	A571	$1.80 multi	2.60 2.60
a.		Booklet pane of 10	26.00
b.		Horiz. pair, #2281-2282	3.50

No. 2282a sold for $15.

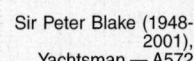

Sir Peter Blake (1948-2001), Yachtsman — A572

Photograph of Blake and New Zealand flag with inscription at lower right: 50c, Inspirational leader. $1, Yachtsman. $1.80, Record breaker. $2.30, Passionate Kiwi. $2.80, Environmentalist.

2009, Nov. 25   **Perf. 13¼x13½**

2283	A572	50c multi	.75 .75
2284	A572	$1 multi	1.50 1.50
2285	A572	$1.80 multi	2.60 2.60
2286	A572	$2.30 multi	3.25 3.25
2287	A572	$2.80 multi	4.00 4.00
a.		Souvenir sheet, #2283-2287	12.50 12.50
		Nos. 2283-2287 (5)	12.10 12.10

The 2009 sheets contain: #2230, 2225, 2235; #2249, 2243, 2253; #2256f, 2278, 2287. See note following #1404.

New Year 2010 (Year of the Tiger) — A573

Designs: 50c, Chinese character for "tiger." $1, Tiger. $1.80, Tiger's head. $2.30, Bird and Wellington Beehive.

2010, Jan. 6   **Perf. 14**

2288	A573	50c multi	.70 .70
a.		Perf. 13½	.70 .70
2289	A573	$1 multi	1.40 1.40
a.		Perf. 13½	1.40 1.40
2290	A573	$1.80 multi	2.60 2.60
a.		Perf. 13½	2.60 2.60
2291	A573	$2.30 multi	3.25 3.25
a.		Perf. 13½	3.25 3.25
b.		Souvenir sheet, #2288a-2291a	8.00 8.00
		Nos. 2288-2291 (4)	7.95 7.95

Greetings Type of 2006 Redrawn Without Silver Frames

No. 2292: a, Heitiki. b, Champagne flutes. c, Wedding and engagement rings. d, Pohutukawa flower.

2010, Feb. 10   **Litho.**   **Perf. 15x14½**

2292		Sheet of 4 + 2 labels	12.50 12.50
a.	A531	$1.80 multi	2.60 2.60
b.-d.		$2.30 Any single	3.25 3.25
e.		Sheet of 20 #2292a + 20 labels	72.50 72.50
f.		Sheet of 20 #2292b + 20 labels	85.00 85.00
g.		Sheet of 20 #2292c + 20 labels	85.00 85.00
h.		Sheet of 20 #2292d + 20 labels	85.00 85.00

Labels are not personalizable on No. 2292. No. 2292e sold for $56.90. Nos. 2292f-2292h each sold for $60.90. Labels could ber personalized on Nos. 2292e-2292h.

Prehistoric Animals — A574

Designs: 50c, Allosaurus. $1, Anhanguera. $1.80, Titanosaurus. $2.30, Moanasaurus. $2.80, Mauisaurus.

2010, Mar. 3   **Litho.**   **Perf. 14¾**

2293	A574	50c multi	.70 .70
2294	A574	$1 multi	1.40 1.40
2295	A574	$1.80 multi	2.50 2.50
2296	A574	$2.30 multi	3.25 3.25
2297	A574	$2.80 multi	4.00 4.00
		Nos. 2293-2297 (5)	11.85 11.85

Self-Adhesive

Serpentine Die Cut 10x9¾

2298		Sheet of 5	12.00
a.	A574	50c multi	.70 .70
b.	A574	$1 multi	1.40 1.40
c.	A574	$1.80 multi	2.50 2.50
d.	A574	$2.30 multi	3.25 3.25
e.	A574	$2.80 multi	4.00 4.00

ANZAC Remembrance A575

Designs: No. 2299, Silhouette of soldier. No. 2300, Gallipoli veterans marching on ANZAC Day, 1958. $1, Posthumous Victoria Cross ceremony for Te Moana-nui-a-Kiwa, 1943. $1.80, Nurses placing wreath in Cairo cemetery on ANZAC Day, 1940. $2.30, Unveiling of ANZAC War Memorial, Port Said, Egypt, 1932. $2.80, Veteran visiting Sangro War Cemetery, Italy, 2004.

2010, Apr. 7   **Litho.**   **Perf. 13½x13¼**

2299	A575	50c multi	.75 .75
a.		Perf. 14	.80 .80
b.		Booklet pane of 1, perf. 14	.80
2300	A575	50c multi	.75 .75
a.		Perf. 14	.80 .80
b.		Booklet pane of 1, perf. 14	.80
2301	A575	$1 multi	1.50 1.50
a.		Perf. 14	1.60 1.60
b.		Booklet pane of 1, perf. 14	1.60
2302	A575	$1.80 multi	2.60 2.60
a.		Perf. 14	3.00 3.00
b.		Booklet pane of 1, perf. 14	3.00
2303	A575	$2.30 multi	3.25 3.25
a.		Perf. 14	3.75 3.75
b.		Booklet pane of 1, perf. 14	3.75
2304	A575	$2.80 multi	4.00 4.00
a.		Perf. 14	4.50 4.50
b.		Booklet pane of 1, perf. 14	4.50
c.		Booklet pane of 6, #2299a-2304a	14.50
		Complete booklet, #2299b-2304b, 2304c	29.00
d.		Souvenir sheet of 3, #2299a, 2303a, 2304a	9.25 9.25
		Nos. 2299-2304 (6)	12.85 12.85

Complete booklet sold for $19.90.
Issued: No. 2304d, 4/30. London 2010 Festival of Stamps (No. 2304d).

Expo 2010, Shanghai — A576

Designs: 50c, Pohutukawas and peonies. $1, Kaitiaki and Fu Dog. $1.80, Tane and Pan Gu. $2.30, Auckland and Shanghai. $2.80, Heitiki and Cong.

2010, Apr. 30   **Litho.**   **Perf. 14**

2305	A576	50c multi	.75 .75
2306	A576	$1 multi	1.50 1.50
2307	A576	$1.80 multi	2.60 2.60
2308	A576	$2.30 multi	3.50 3.50
2309	A576	$2.80 multi	4.25 4.25
a.		Horiz. strip of 5, #2305-2309	13.00 13.00
b.		Sheet of 5, #2305-2309, without back printing	13.00 13.00
		Nos. 2305-2309 (5)	12.60 12.60

Maori Rugby, Cent. — A577

Designs: 50c, Centenary jersey. $1.80, Centenary emblem.

2010, June 9

2310	A577	50c multi	.70 .70
2311	A577	$1.80 multi	2.50 2.50
a.		Souvenir sheet of 2, #2310-2311	3.25 3.25

Traditional Maori Kites — A578

Designs: 50c, Manu Aute. $1, Manu Patiki, vert. $1.80, Manu Taratahi, vert. $2.30, Upoko Tangata.

2010, June 9

2312	A578	50c multi	.70 .70
2313	A578	$1 multi	1.40 1.40
2314	A578	$1.80 multi	2.50 2.50
2315	A578	$2.30 multi	3.25 3.25
a.		Souvenir sheet of 4, #2312-2315	8.00 8.00
		Nos. 2312-2315 (4)	7.85 7.85

Tourist Attractions Type of 2003

Designs: $1.20, Mitre Peak, Milford Sound. $1.90, Queenstown. $2.40, Lake Rotorua. $2.90, Kaikoura. $3.40, Christchurch.

2010, Aug. 4   **Perf. 13¼x13½**

2316	A496	$1.20 multi	1.75 1.75
2317	A496	$1.90 multi	2.75 2.75
2318	A496	$2.40 multi	3.50 3.50
a.		Souvenir sheet of 3, #2316-2318	8.50 8.50
2319	A496	$2.90 multi	4.25 4.25
2320	A496	$3.40 multi	5.00 5.00
a.		Souvenir sheet of 2, #2319-2320, #321	9.00 9.00
		Nos. 2316-2320 (5)	17.25 17.25

Self-Adhesive

Serpentine Die Cut 10x9½

2321	A496	$1.20 multi	1.75 1.75
a.		Booklet pane of 10	17.50
2322	A496	$1.90 multi	2.75 2.75
a.		Booklet pane of 5	14.00

Issued: No. 2318a, 2/12/11. Indipex 2011 (#2318a). Christchurch 2016 Stamp & Postcard Exhibition (No. 2320a). Issued: No. 2320a, 11/18/16. No. 2320a contains a lithographed perf. 14½ reproduction of No. 321 that is not valid for postage.

Emblem of All Blacks Rugby Team — A579

2010, Aug. 4   **Perf. 13½x13¼**

2323	A579	60c black	.90 .90
2324	A579	$1.90 black	2.75 2.75
a.		Miniature sheet of 6	60.00 60.00

Souvenir Sheet

2325		Sheet of 4, #2323, 2324, 2325a, 2325b	7.50 7.50
a.		A579 60c black, 32x17mm, perf. 15x14½	.90 .90
b.		A579 $1.90 black, 32x17mm, perf. 15x14½	.90 .90
c.		Sheet of 20 #2325a + 20 labels	34.00 34.00
d.		Sheet of 20 #2325b + 20 labels	77.50 77.50

2011 Rugby World Cup victory of New Zealand rugby team (No. 2324a). Issued: No. 2324a, 10/28/11. No. 2324a sold for $19.90.

No. 2325c sold for $22.90. No. 2325d sold for $52.90. Labels could be personalized on Nos. 2325c-2325d. In 2011, No. 2325c was made available for the same price with labels that could not be personalized.

See Nos. 2410-2411, 2519-2521.

Greetings Stamps Type of 2006 Without Silver Frames

No. 2326: a, Champagne flutes. b, Child's toy. c, Fern. d, Pohutukawa flower. e, Wedding and engagement rings. f, Rose. g, Heitiki. h, Teddy bear.

No. 2327: a, Heitiki. b, Champagne flutes. c, Wedding and engagement rings. d, Pohutukawa flower.

2010, Sept. 9   **Perf. 15x14½**

2326	A531	Sheet of 8 + 4 labels	7.25 7.25
a.-h.		60c Any single	.90 .90
i.		Sheet of 20 #2326a + 20 labels	34.00 34.00
j.		Sheet of 20 #2326b + 20 labels	34.00 34.00
k.		Sheet of 20 #2326c + 20 labels	34.00 34.00
l.		Sheet of 20 #2326d + 20 labels	34.00 34.00
m.		Sheet of 20 #2326e + 20 labels	34.00 34.00
n.		Sheet of 20 #2326f + 20 labels	34.00 34.00
o.		Sheet of 20 #2326g + 20 labels	34.00 34.00
p.		Sheet of 20 #2326h + 20 labels	34.00 34.00
2327	A531	Sheet of 4 + 2 labels	13.50 13.50
a.		$1.90 multi	2.75 2.75
b.-d.		$2.40 Any single	3.50 3.50
e.		Sheet of 20 #2327a + 20 labels	77.50 77.50
f.		Sheet of 20 #2327b + 20 labels	92.50 92.50

g. Sheet of 20 #2327c + 20 labels   92.50   92.50
h. Sheet of 20 #2327d + 20 labels   92.50   92.50

Nos. 2326i-2326p each sold for $22.90. No. 2327e sold for $52.90. Nos. 2327f-2327h each sold for $62.90. Labels could be personalized on Nos. 2326i-2326p, 2327e-2327h.

Emblem of 2011
Rugby World
Cup — A580

2010, Sept. 9   **Perf. 13½x13¼**
2328 A580   60c multi   .90   .90
2329 A580 $1.90 multi   2.75   2.75

Souvenir Sheet
2330   Sheet of 4, #2328, 2329, 2330a, 2330b   7.50   7.50
a. A580 60c multi, 32x17mm, perf. 15x14½   .90   .90
b. A580 $1.90 multi, 32x17mm, perf. 15x14½   .90   .90
c. Sheet of 20 #2330a + 20 labels   34.00   34.00
d. Sheet of 20 #2330b + 20 labels   77.50   77.50

No. 2330c sold for $22.90. No. 2330d sold for $52.90. Labels could be personalized on Nos. 2330c-2330d. In 2011, No. 2330c was made available for the same price with labels that could not be personalized.

Miniature Sheet

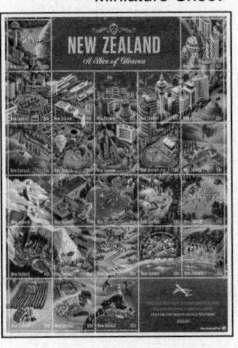

"A Slice
of
Heaven"
A581

No. 2331: a, Tane Mahuta kauri tree, Stone Store, Kerikeri, Waitangi Treaty Grounds, boat at dock. b, Carter Fountain, Oriental Bay, buildings. c, The Octagon, St. Paul's Cathedral, Dunedin. d, Cruise ship, Princes Wharf, Auckland. e, The Beehive, Wellington. f, Sky Tower, Auckland Ferry Terminal. g, Rugby field, Mount Ruapehu (volcano), punts on Avon River, Christchurch. i, Fairfield Bridge, hot-air balloons over Basin Reserve Cricket Grounds, Wellington. j, Christchurch Cathedral, Bridge of Remembrance. k, Horse racing track. l, Road, small town, war memorial, sheep in field. m, Mountain climbers with flag on Mt. Cook, ski plane, helicopter. n, Farm house, storage shed, plowed field, cows in pasture, shore of Lake Taupo. o, Lake Taupo, Huka Falls. p, Champagne Pool, geyser, mud pool. q, Rugby field. r, TSS Earnslaw on Lake Wakatipu, parasailers, Queenstown. s, Biplane and glider over ski and golf resort. t, Suspension bridge over river, river mouth. u, Trailer park near beach, Moeraki Boulders. v, Line of boatsheds, Tihati Bay. w, Farmhouse, barn, tractor, silos. x, House, sheep pens, truck. y, Nugget Point Lighthouse, whale.

2010, Oct. 6   **Perf. 14¼**
2331 A581   Sheet of 25   22.50   22.50
a.-y. 60c Any single   .90   .90

Christmas — A582

New Zealand Christmas stamps of the past: 60c, #353. $1.20, #465. $1.90, #692. $2.40, #790. $2.90, #1672.

2010, Oct. 20   **Perf. 13¼x13½**
Stamps Without White Frames
2332 A582   60c multi   .95   .95
2333 A582 $1.20 multi   1.90   1.90
2334 A582 $1.90 multi   3.00   3.00

2335 A582 $2.40 multi   4.00   4.00
2336 A582 $2.90 multi   4.75   4.75
   Nos. 2332-2336 (5)   14.60   14.60

Stamps With White Frames
Coil Stamps
Self-Adhesive
Size: 21x26mm
Die Cut Perf. 12¾
2337 A582   60c multi   .95   .95
2338 A582 $1.90 multi   3.00   3.00
a. Horiz. pair, #2337-2338   4.00

Booklet Stamps
Serpentine Die Cut 11¼
2339 A582   60c multi   .95   .95
a. Booklet pane of 10   9.50
2340 A582 $1.90 multi   3.00   3.00
a. Booklet pane of 10   30.00
   Nos. 2337-2340 (4)   7.90   7.90

New Zealand Christmas stamps, 50th anniv. No. 2339a sold for $5.40 and No. 2340a sold for $16.

Volunteer
Lifeguard Clubs,
Cent. — A583

Designs: 60c, Surf lifeguard and beach flag. $1.20, Lifeguards on inflatable rescue boat. $1.90, Lifeguards on ski paddlers. $2.40, Lifeguards on surf boat. $2.90, Lifeguards marching on beach.

2010, Nov. 3   **Perf. 13x13¼**
2341 A583   60c multi   .95   .95
2342 A583 $1.20 multi   1.90   1.90
2343 A583 $1.90 multi   3.00   3.00
2344 A583 $2.40 multi   4.00   4.00
2345 A583 $2.90 multi   4.75   4.75
   Nos. 2341-2345 (5)   14.60   14.60

The 2010 sheets contain: #2291, 2297, 2304; #2309, 2315, B198; #2319, 2336, 2345. See note following #1404.

New Year 2011 (Year
of the Rabbit) — A584

Designs: 60c, Chinese character for "rabbit." $1.20, Paper-cut rabbit. $1.90, Rabbit. $2.40, Kite, Christchurch Cathedral.

2011, Jan. 12   **Litho.**   **Perf. 13½x13**
2346 A584   60c multi   .95   .95
2347 A584 $1.20 multi   1.90   1.90
2348 A584 $1.90 multi   3.00   3.00
2349 A584 $2.40 multi   3.75   3.75
a. Souvenir sheet of 4, #2346-2349   9.75   9.75
   Nos. 2346-2349 (4)   9.60   9.60

Miniature Sheets

Kapa
Haka
A585

Nos. 2350 and 2351: a, Whakaeke. b, Poi. c, Waiata-a-ringa. d, Haka. e, Whakawatea. f, Moteatea.

2011, Feb. 17   **Perf. 13¼x13½**
2350 A585   Sheet of 6   15.00   15.00
a.-b. 60c Either single   .90   .90
c. $1.20 multi   1.90   1.90
d. $1.90 multi   3.00   3.00
e. $2.40 multi   3.75   3.75
f. $2.90 multi   4.50   4.50

Self-Adhesive
Serpentine Die Cut 10x9½
2351 A585   Sheet of 6   15.00   15.00
a.-b. 60c Either single   .90   .90
c. $1.20 multi   1.90   1.90
d. $1.90 multi   3.00   3.00
e. $2.40 multi   3.75   3.75
f. $2.90 multi   4.50   4.50

Kiwistamps — A586

Designs: Nos. 2352, 2357, Hokey pokey ice cream cone. Nos. 2353, 2358, Kiwi crossing road sign. Nos. 2354, 2359, People on beach. Nos. 2355, 2360, Trout fisherman. Nos. 2356, 2361, Mountain biking.

Serpentine Die Cut 10x9¾
2011, Mar. 23   **Litho.**
Self-Adhesive
Coil Stamps
2352 A586   (60c) multi   .95   .95
2353 A586   (60c) multi   .95   .95
2354 A586   (60c) multi   .95   .95
2355 A586   (60c) multi   .95   .95
2356 A586   (60c) multi   .95   .95
a. Horiz. strip of 5, #2352-2356   4.75
   Nos. 2352-2356 (5)   4.75   4.75

Booklet Stamps
Serpentine Die Cut 11
2357 A586   (60c) multi   .95   .95
2358 A586   (60c) multi   .95   .95
2359 A586   (60c) multi   .95   .95
2360 A586   (60c) multi   .95   .95
2361 A586   (60c) multi   .95   .95
a. Booklet pane of 10, 2 each #2357-2361   9.50
   Nos. 2357-2361 (5)   4.75   4.75

Wedding of Prince
William and
Catherine
Middleton — A587

Prince William and Catherine Middleton with Prince William wearing: No. 2362, Suit and tie. No. 2363, Sweater.

2011, Mar. 23   **Perf. 14½x14¾**
2362 A587 $2.40 multi   3.75   3.75
2363 A587 $2.40 multi   3.75   3.75
a. Horiz. pair, #2362-2363   7.50   7.50
b. Souvenir sheet of 2, #2362-2363   7.50   7.50

New Zealand's
Victoria Cross
Recipients — A588

No. 2364: a, Charles Heaphy. b, William James Hardham. c, Cyril Royston Guyton Bassett. d, Donald Forrester Brown. e, Samuel Frickleton. f, Leslie Wilton Andrew. g, Henry James Nicholas. h, Richard Charles Travis. i, Samuel Forsyth. j, Reginald Stanley Judson. k, Harry John Laurent. l, James Crichton. m, John Gildroy Grant. n, James Edward Allen Ward. o, Charles Hazlitt Upham. p, Alfred Clive Hulme. q, John Daniel Hinton. r, Keith Elliott. s, Moana-nui-a-Kiwa Ngarimu. t, Lloyd Allen Trigg. u, Leonard Henry Trent. v, Bill Henry Apiata (medal only).

2011, Apr. 14   **Perf. 13¼x13½**
2364   Miniature sheet of 22   22.00   22.00
a.-v. A588 60c Any single   1.00   1.00

Miniature Sheet

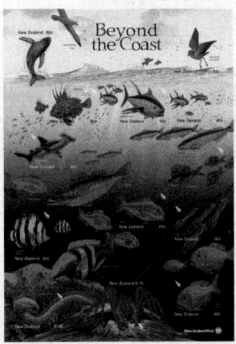

Life
Beyond
the
Coast
A589

No. 2365: a, Humpback whale. b, White-faced storm petrel, horiz. c, John Dory, horiz. d, Yellowfin tuna, horiz. e, Kingfish, horiz. f, Hammerhead shark, horiz. g, Snapper, horiz. h, Arrow squid, horiz. i, Lord Howe coralfish. j, Orange roughy, horiz. k, Yellow moray eel, horiz. l, King crab.

Serpentine Die Cut 10x9½, 9½x10
2011, May 4   **Self-Adhesive**
2365 A589   Sheet of 12   15.50
a.-j. 60c Any single   .95   .95
k.-l. $1.90 Either single   3.00   3.00

Miniature Sheet

Matariki
(Maori
New
Year)
A590

Nos. 2366 and 2367 — Various hei mataus (decorative fish hooks): a, Green pounamu fish hook by Lewis Gardiner. b, White whalebone fish hook, c. 1500-1800, in Museum of New Zealand. c, Inanga fish hook, c. 1800, in Museum of New Zealand. d, Pounamu, whalebone, feathers and flax fiber fish hook by Gardiner. e, Wooden fish hook, c. 1800, in Auckland War Memorial Museum. f, Whalebone fish hook, c. 1750-1850, in Museum of New Zealand.

2011, June 1   **Litho.**   **Perf. 13¼x13½**
2366 A590   Sheet of 6   16.00   16.00
a.-b. 60c Either single   1.00   1.00
c. $1.20 multi   2.00   2.00
d. $1.90 multi   3.25   3.25
e. $2.40 multi   4.00   4.00
f. $2.90 multi   4.75   4.75

Self-Adhesive
Serpentine Die Cut 10x9½
2367 A590   Sheet of 6   16.00   16.00
a.-b. 60c Either single   1.00   1.00
c. $1.20 multi   2.00   2.00
d. $1.90 multi   3.25   3.25
e. $2.40 multi   4.00   4.00
f. $2.90 multi   4.75   4.75

Kiwi Type of 1988
2011   **Litho.**   **Perf. 14½**
2368 A325 $1.20 black   2.00   2.00
2369 A325 $1.90 silver   3.25   3.25
a. Souvenir sheet, #2369, 2 #2324   9.75   9.75
2370 A325 $2.40 blue   4.00   4.00
a. Horiz. strip of 3, #2368-2370   9.25   9.25
b. Souvenir sheet of 3, #2368-2370   8.75   8.75
   Nos. 2368-2370 (3)   9.25   9.25

Issued: Nos. 2368-2370, 7/6; No. 2369a, 7/28. No. 2370b, 11/11. Philanippon 2011 World Stamp Exhibition, Yokohama (#2369a). China 2011 Intl. Stamp Exhibition, Wuxi, China (#2370b).
Values for Nos. 2368-2370 are for stamps with surrounding selvage.

Miniature Sheet

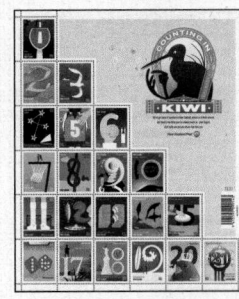

Numbers
A591

No. 2371 — Maori words for numbers and stylized numbers: a, 1 (State Highway 1 sign). b, 2 (2 beach sandals). c, 3 (sea gull, Cook Strait ferry). d, 4 (stars in Southern Cross, sailboat). e, 5 (child with backpack). f, 6 (hand, cricket umpire). g, 7 (netball goal and players). h, 8 (barbed wire, tractor). i, 9 (woman in fancy clothes, race horse). j, 10 (guitar). k, 11 (legs of soccer player). l, 12 (oyster shell, tongue, plate of oysters). m, 13 (Lamington cakes). n, 14 (dolphins, outrigger canoes in national parks). o, 15 (hand on rugby ball). p, 16 (dice hanging from rear-view mirror). q, 17 (Capt. James Cook and year of his arrival in New Zealand). r, 18 (bird on statue, ballot circles, Parliament building). s, 19 (surf board and wave). t, 20 (parrot with crown). u, 21 (key and streamers).

2011, Aug. 10   **Perf. 14**
2371 A591   Sheet of 21   21.00   21.00
a.-u. 60c Any single   1.00   1.00

Webb Ellis Cup, Trophy of Rugby World Cup — A592

Litho. With 3-Dimensional Plastic Affixed

Serpentine Die Cut 10¼

2011, Sept. 7 Self-Adhesive

2372 A592 $15 multi 25.00 25.00

The New Zealand Experience — A593

Designs: No. 2373, Backpacker, paraglider, camp, hikers, mountains. No. 2374, Sailboaters, motor boat, sailboarder. $1.20, Fisherman and fish. $1.90, Maoris. $2.40, Skier, helicopter. $2.90, Bungee jumper, whitewater raft, hot air balloon.

2011, Sept. 7 Litho. *Perf. 14*

2373 A593 60c multi .95 .95
2374 A593 60c multi .95 .95
2375 A593 $1.20 multi 1.90 1.90
2376 A593 $1.90 multi 3.00 3.00
2377 A593 $2.40 multi 3.75 3.75
2378 A593 $2.90 multi 4.50 4.50
a. Souvenir sheet of 6, #2373-2378 15.50 15.50
Nos. 2373-2378 (6) 15.05 15.05

A594

Christmas — A595

Star of Bethlehem and: 60c, Baby Jesus and livestock. $1.20, Angel appearing to shepherds. $1.90, Holy Family. $2.40, Adoration of the Shepherds. $2.90, Adoration of the Magi.

2011, Nov. 2 Litho. *Perf. 14¼*

2379 A594 60c multi .95 .95
2380 A594 $1.20 multi 1.90 1.90
2381 A594 $1.90 multi 3.00 3.00
2382 A594 $2.40 multi 4.00 4.00
2383 A594 $2.90 multi 4.75 4.75
Nos. 2379-2383 (5) 14.60 14.60

Self-Adhesive

Serpentine Die Cut 9¾x10

2384 A595 60c multi .95 .95
2385 A595 $1.90 multi 3.00 3.00
a. Booklet pane of 10 30.00
2386 A595 $2.40 multi 4.00 4.00
a. Horiz. sheet of 3, #2384-2386 8.00
b. Booklet pane of 10 40.00

Booklet Stamp

Serpentine Die Cut 11¼

2387 A595 60c multi .95 .95
a. Booklet pane of 10 9.50
Nos. 2384-2387 (4) 8.90 8.90

Nos. 2385a and 2386b sold for $17.10 and $21.60, respectively. A se-tenant strip of Nos. 2379-2383 was not put on sale but was a reward for standing order customers.

The 2011 sheets contain: #2349, 2362, 2350f; #2364v, B202, 2366f; #2378, 2370, 2383. See note following #1404.

New Year 2012 (Year of the Dragon) — A596

Designs: 60c, Chinese character for "dragon." $1.20, Dragon. $1.90, Dragon lantern. $2.40, Dunedin Railroad Station, swallows.

2012, Jan. 5 Litho. *Perf. 13¼x13½*

2388 A596 60c multi 1.00 1.00
2389 A596 $1.20 multi 2.00 2.00
2390 A596 $1.90 multi 3.25 3.25
2391 A596 $2.40 multi 4.00 4.00
a. Souvenir sheet of 4, #2388-2391 10.50 10.50
b. Souvenir sheet of 3, #2388, 2390, 2391 8.25 8.25
Nos. 2388-2391 (4) 10.25 10.25

Issued: No. 2391b, 11/2. 2012 Beijing Intl. Stamp and Coin Expo (#2391b).

Tourist Attractions Type of 2003

Serpentine Die Cut 10x9½

2012, Feb. 1 Litho.

Self-Adhesive

2392 A496 $2.40 Lake Rotorua 4.00 4.00
a. Booklet pane of 5 + 2 etiquettes 20.00
b. Dated "2010" 3.25 3.25
c. Booklet pane of 5 #2392b + 2 etiquettes 16.50

Issued: Nos. 2392b, 2392c, 2015.

Native Trees — A597

Designs: 60c, Pohutukawa. $1.20, Cabbage tree. $1.90, Kowhai. $2.40, Nikau. $2.90, Manuka.

2012, Feb. 1 *Perf. 13¼x13½*

2393 A597 60c multi 1.00 1.00
2394 A597 $1.20 multi 2.00 2.00
2395 A597 $1.90 multi 3.25 3.25
2396 A597 $2.40 multi 4.00 4.00
a. Souvenir sheet of 3, #2393, 2395, 2396 8.25 8.25
2397 A597 $2.90 multi 5.00 5.00
a. Souvenir sheet of 5, #2393-2397 15.50 15.50
Nos. 2393-2397 (5) 15.25 15.25

Issued: No. 2396a, 6/18. Indonesia 2012 World Stamp Championship and Exhibition, Jakarta (#2396a).

Miniature Sheet

Royal New Zealand Air Force, 75th Anniv. A598

No. 2398 — Inscriptions: a, The Beginning. b, Air Training corps. c, WWII Europe. d, Women's Auxiliary Air Force. e, WWII Pacific. f, Aerial Topdressing. g, Territorial Air Force. h, Sout East Asia. i, ANZAC. j, Naval Support. k, Transport. l, Peacekeeping. m, Search and Rescue. n, Remembrance. o, The Future.

2012, Mar. 15 *Perf. 14½*

2398 A598 Sheet of 15 15.00 15.00
a.-o. 60c Any single 1.00 1.00
p. Booklet pane of 4, 2 each #2398a-2398b 4.50 —
q. Booklet pane of 4, 2 each #2398c-2398d 4.50 —
r. Booklet pane of 4, 2 each #2398e-2398f 4.50 —
s. Booklet pane of 4, 2 each #2398g-2398h 4.50 —
t. Booklet pane of 4, 2 each #2398i-2398j 4.50 —
u. Booklet pane of 4, 2 each #2398k-2398l 4.50 —
v. Booklet pane of 4, 2 each #2398m, 2398o 4.50 —
w. Booklet pane of 2 #2398n 2.25 —
Complete booklet, #2398p-2398w 34.00

Complete booklet sold for $19.90.

Reign of Queen Elizabeth II, 60th Anniv. — A599

Photographs of: No. 2399, Queen, 2012. No. 2400, Queen and Prince Philip, 2012. $1.40, Queen and Prince Philip, 1986. $1.90, Queen and Prince Philip, 1981. $2.40, Queen and Prince Philip, 1977. $2.90, Queen, 1953.

Litho. With Foil Application

2012, May 9 *Perf. 13¼x13½*

2399 A599 70c multi 1.10 1.10
2400 A599 70c multi 1.10 1.10
2401 A599 $1.40 multi 2.25 2.25
2402 A599 $1.90 multi 3.00 3.00
2403 A599 $2.40 multi 3.75 3.75
2404 A599 $2.90 multi 4.50 4.50
a. Souvenir sheet of 6, #2399-2404 16.00 16.00
b. Souvenir sheet of 3, #2399, 2402, 2404 9.25 9.25
Nos. 2399-2404 (6) 15.70 15.70

Issued: No. 2404b, 10/12. 2012 New Zealand National Stamp Exhibition, Blenheim (#2404b).

Tourist Attractions Type of 2003

Designs: $1.40, Cape Reinga Lighthouse. $2.10, Stewart Island. $3.50, Lake Matheson.

2012, May 23 Litho. *Perf. 13¼x13½*

2405 A496 $1.40 multi 2.25 2.25
2406 A496 $2.10 multi 3.25 3.25
2407 A496 $3.50 multi 5.50 5.50
Nos. 2405-2407 (3) 11.00 11.00

Self-Adhesive

Serpentine Die Cut 10x9½

2408 A496 $1.40 multi 2.25 2.25
a. Booklet pane of 10 22.50
2409 A496 $2.10 multi 3.25 3.25
a. Booklet pane of 5 16.50
b. Horiz. pair, #2408-2409 5.50

All Blacks Type of 2010

2012, May 23 *Perf. 13½x13¼*

2410 A579 70c black 1.10 1.10

Souvenir Sheet

2411 Sheet of 2, #2410, 2411a 2.25 2.25
a. A579 70c black, 32x17mm, perf. 15x14½ 1.10 1.10

Greetings Stamps Type of 2006 Without Silver Frames

No. 2412: a, Champagne flutes. b, Child's toy. c, Fern. d, Pohutukawa flower. e, Wedding and engagement rings. f, Rose. g, Heitiki. h, Tedddy bear.

2012, June 6 *Perf. 15x14½*

2412 A531 Sheet of 8 + 4 labels 9.00 9.00
a.-h. 70c Any single 1.10 1.10

Miniature Sheets

Maori Rock Art A600

Nos. 2413 and 2414: a, Pouakai, Pareora. b, Tiki, Maerewhenua. c, Mohiki, Opihi. d, Te Puawaitanga, Waitaki. e, Tiki, Te Ana a Wai. f, Taniwha, Opihi.

2012, June 6 *Perf. 13½x13¼*

2413 A600 Sheet of 6 16.00 16.00
a.-b. 70c Either single 1.10 1.10
c. $1.40 multi 2.25 2.25
d. $1.90 multi 3.00 3.00
e. $2.40 multi 3.75 3.75
f. $2.90 multi 4.50 4.50

Self-Adhesive

Serpentine Die Cut 9½x10

2414 A600 Sheet of 6 16.00 16.00
a.-b. 70c Either single 1.10 1.10
c. $1.40 multi 2.25 2.25
d. $1.90 multi 3.00 3.00
e. $2.40 multi 3.75 3.75
f. $2.90 multi 4.50 4.50

Miniature Sheet

Tiki Tour of New Zealand A601

No. 2415 — Places named on map of New Zealand: a, Cape Reinga, Ninety Mile Beach, Kaitaia. b, Whangarei, Bay of Islands. c, Cape Brett. d, Lion Rock. e, Auckland, Hamilton, Tauranga. f, White Island, East Cape. g, Mt. Taranaki, New Plymouth, Hawera. h, Rotorua, Taupo, Palmerston North. i, Gisborne, Napier. j, No place names (fish, boat, waves). k, Westport, Greymouth. l, Golden Bay, Nelson, Cook Strait, Kaikoura. m, Wellington, Castlepoint. n, Chatham Islands. o, Mitre Peak, Milford Sound. p, Queenstown, Aoraki (Mount Cook), Timaru. q, Christchurch, Ashburton. r, Gore, Invercargill, Foveaux Strait, Stewart Island. s, Dunedin. t, Taiaroa Head.

2012, July 4 *Perf. 14¼*

2415 A601 Sheet of 20 22.00 22.00
a.-t. 70c Any single 1.10 1.10

Samoan Head Combs — A602

Designs: 70c, Fu'a. $1.40, Niu. $1.90, Maota. $2.40, Tatau. $2.90, Malumalu.

2012, Aug. 1 *Perf. 14*

2416 A602 70c multi 1.25 1.25
2417 A602 $1.40 multi 2.40 2.40
2418 A602 $1.90 multi 3.25 3.25
2419 A602 $2.40 multi 4.00 4.00
2420 A602 $2.90 multi 4.75 4.75
a. Souvenir sheet of 5, #2416-2420 16.00 16.00
Nos. 2416-2420 (5) 15.65 15.65

Ships — A603

Designs: 70c, Aramoana. $1.40, Waka. $1.90, Earnslaw. $2.40, Dunedin. $2.90, Rotomahana.

2012, Sept. 5

2421 A603 70c multi 1.25 1.25
2422 A603 $1.40 multi 2.25 2.25
2423 A603 $1.90 multi 3.25 3.25
2424 A603 $2.40 multi 4.00 4.00
2425 A603 $2.90 multi 4.75 4.75
a. Souvenir sheet of 5, #2421-2425 15.50 15.50
Nos. 2421-2425 (5) 15.50 15.50

A604

Christmas — A605

Designs: 70c, Holy Family. $1.40, Adoration of the Shepherds. $1.90, Angel. $2.40 Adoration of the Magi. $2.90, Magi and camels.

2012, Oct. 3   **Perf. 14**

2426	A604	70c multi	1.25	1.25
2427	A604	$1.40 multi	2.25	2.25
2428	A604	$1.90 multi	3.25	3.25
2429	A604	$2.40 multi	4.00	4.00
2430	A604	$2.90 multi	4.75	4.75
	Nos. 2426-2430 (5)		15.50	15.50

Self-Adhesive

Serpentine Die Cut 11x11¼

2431	A605		1.25	1.25
a.	Booklet pane of 10		12.50	
2432	A605	$1.90 multi	3.25	3.25
a.	Booklet pane of 10 + 10 etiquettes		32.50	
2433	A605	$2.40 multi	4.00	4.00
a.	Booklet pane of 10 + 10 etiquettes		40.00	
b.	Horiz. sheet of 3, #2431-2433		8.50	
	Nos. 2431-2433 (3)		8.50	8.50

Nos. 2432 and 2433 are air mail. No. 2432a sold for $17.10. No. 2433a sold for $21.60.

Premiere of Movie *The Hobbit: An Unexpected Journey*
A606   A607

Characters: 70c, Bilbo Baggins. $1.40, Gollum. $1.90, Gandalf, horiz. $2.10, Thorin Oakenshield, horiz. $2.40, Radagast. $2.90, Elrond.

2012, Nov. 1   **Perf. 14½x14, 14x14½**

2434	A606	70c multi	1.25	1.25
a.	Souvenir sheet of 1		1.50	1.50
2435	A606	$1.40 multi	2.40	2.40
a.	Souvenir sheet of 1		3.00	3.00
2436	A606	$1.90 multi	3.25	3.25
a.	Souvenir sheet of 1		4.00	4.00
2437	A606	$2.10 multi	3.50	3.50
a.	Souvenir sheet of 1		4.50	4.50
2438	A606	$2.40 multi	4.00	4.00
a.	Souvenir sheet of 1		5.00	5.00
2439	A606	$2.90 multi	4.75	4.75
a.	Souvenir sheet of 1		6.25	6.25
	Nos. 2434-2439 (6)		19.15	19.15

Self-Adhesive

Serpentine Die Cut 11¼

2440	Sheet of 6		19.50	
a.	A607 70c multi		1.25	1.25
b.	A607 $1.40 multi		2.40	2.40
c.	A607 $1.90 multi		3.25	3.25
d.	A607 $2.10 multi		3.50	3.50
e.	A607 $2.40 multi		4.00	4.00
f.	A607 $2.90 multi		4.75	4.75
g.	Booklet pane of 10, #2440c-2440f, 4 #2440a, 2 #2440b		25.50	

Nos. 2434a-2439a sold as a set of 6 sheets for $14.40.

New Year 2013 (Year of the Snake) — A608

Designs: 70c, Chinese character for "snake." $1.40, Snake. $1.90, Snake on lantern. $2.40, Lanterns and Skyline Gondola, Queenstown.

2013, Jan. 9   **Perf. 13¼x13**

2441	A608	70c multi	1.25	1.25
2442	A608	$1.40 multi	2.40	2.40
2443	A608	$1.90 multi	3.25	3.25
2444	A608	$2.40 multi	4.00	4.00
a.	Souvenir sheet of 4, #2441-2444		11.00	11.00
	Nos. 2441-2444 (4)		10.90	10.90

Ferns — A609

Designs: 70c, Hen and chickens fern. $1.40, Kidney fern. $1.90, Colenso's hard fern. $2.40, Umbrella fern. $2.90, Silver fern.

2013, Feb. 7   **Perf. 13x13¼**

2445	A609	70c multi	1.25	1.25
2446	A609	$1.40 multi	2.40	2.40
2447	A609	$1.90 multi	3.25	3.25
2448	A609	$2.40 multi	4.00	4.00
2449	A609	$2.90 multi	5.00	5.00
a.	Souvenir sheet of 5, #2445-2449		16.00	16.00
b.	Souvenir sheet of 2, #2448-2449, perf. 13½		13.00	13.00
	Nos. 2445-2449 (5)		15.90	15.90

Issued: No. 2449b, 9/13. Upper Hutt 2013 National Stamp Show (#2449b). No. 2449b sold for $7.80, with $2.50 of that amount going to the Philatelic Trust.

Children's Books by Margaret Mahy (1936-2012) A610

Designs: 70c, A Lion in the Meadow. $1.40, A Summery Saturday Morning. $1.90, The Word Witch. $2.40, The Great White Man-Eating Shark. $2.90, The Changeover.

2013, Mar. 13   **Perf. 14**

2450	A610	70c multi	1.25	1.25
2451	A610	$1.40 multi	2.40	2.40
2452	A610	$1.90 multi	3.25	3.25
2453	A610	$2.40 multi	4.00	4.00
2454	A610	$2.90 multi	4.75	4.75
a.	Souvenir sheet of 5, #2450-2454		16.00	16.00
	Nos. 2450-2454 (5)		15.65	15.65

New Zealand Defense Force Missions Abroad — A611

Mission in: No. 2455, Afghanistan. No. 2456, Timor. 140c, Solomon Islands. 190c, Bosnia and Herzegovina. 240c, Antarctica. 290c, Korea.

2013, Apr. 10

2455	A611	70c multi	1.25	1.25
a.	Booklet pane of 1		1.25	1.25
2456	A611	70c multi	1.25	1.25
a.	Booklet pane of 1		1.25	1.25
2457	A611	140c multi	2.40	2.40
a.	Booklet pane of 1		2.40	2.40
2458	A611	190c multi	3.25	3.25
a.	Booklet pane of 1		3.25	3.25
2459	A611	240c multi	4.00	4.00
a.	Booklet pane of 1		4.00	4.00
2460	A611	290c multi	5.00	5.00
a.	Booklet pane of 1		5.00	5.00
b.	Booklet pane of 6, #2455-2460		17.50	—
	Complete booklet, #2455a, 2456a, 2457a, 2458a, 2459a, 2460a, 2460b		35.00	
	Nos. 2455-2460 (6)		17.15	17.15

Complete booklet sold for $19.90.

Coronation of Queen Elizabeth II, 60th Anniv. — A612

Depictions of Queen Elizabeth II used on New Zealand currency by: No. 2461, Mary Gillick, 1953. No. 2462, Gillick, re-engraved in 1956. $1.40, Arnold Machin, 1967. $1.90, James Berry, 1979. $2.40, Raphael Maklouf, 1986. $2.90, Ian Rank-Broadley, 1999.

Litho. & Embossed With Foil Application

2013

2461	A612	70c multi	1.25	1.25
2462	A612	70c multi	1.25	1.25
2463	A612	$1.40 multi	2.25	2.25
2464	A612	$1.90 multi	3.00	3.00
2465	A612	$2.40 multi	4.00	4.00
2466	A612	$2.90 multi	4.75	4.75
a.	Souvenir sheet of 6, #2461-2466		16.50	16.50
b.	Souvenir sheet of 3, #2461, 2463, 2466		8.25	8.25
	Nos. 2461-2466 (6)		16.50	16.50

Australia 2013 World Stamp Exhibition, Melbourne (#2466b). Issued: Nos. 2461-2466, 2466a, 5/8; No. 2466b, 5/10.

Miniature Sheets

Matariki (Maori New Year) A613

Nos. 2467 and 2468 — Koru patterns: a, Piko. b, Manu Tukutuku. c, Nguru. d, Pataka. e, Kotiate. f, Patiki.

2013, June 5   **Litho.**   **Perf. 13¾x13½**

2467	A613	Sheet of 6	16.50	16.50
a.-b.	70c Either single		1.25	1.25
c.	$1.40 multi		2.25	2.25
d.	$1.90 multi		3.00	3.00
e.	$2.40 multi		4.00	4.00
f.	$2.90 multi		4.75	4.75

Self-Adhesive

Serpentine Die Cut 9½x10

2468	A613	Sheet of 6	16.50	16.50
a.-b.	70c Either single		1.25	1.25
c.	$1.40 multi		2.25	2.25
d.	$1.90 multi		3.00	3.00
e.	$2.40 multi		4.00	4.00
f.	$2.90 multi		4.75	4.75

Honey Bees — A614

Designs: 70c, Bee collecting nectar. 140c, Bees at hive entrance. 190c, Bees on honeycomb. 240c, Apiarist collecting honey. 290c, Harvested honeycomb.

2013, July 3   **Perf. 14**

2469	A614	70c multi	1.25	1.25
2470	A614	140c multi	2.25	2.25
2471	A614	190c multi	3.00	3.00
2472	A614	240c multi	4.00	4.00
2473	A614	290c multi	4.75	4.75
a.	Souvenir sheet of 5, #2469-2473		15.50	15.50
	Nos. 2469-2473 (5)		15.25	15.25

Classic Travel Posters — A615

No. 2474 — Travel poster depicting: a, Woman in bathing suit, Napier Carnival. b, Fishing boat and fish. c, Tree fern. d, Rata blossom, Franz Josef Glacier. e, Fisherman in river. f, Wellington. g, Contrail of TEAL Airlines emblem going through mouth of Maori carving, mountains. h, Queenstown. i, Timaru by the Sea. j, Lake and mountains. k, Man reaching for hand, Tauranga. l, Kea. m, Bus touring the Southern Alps. n, Marlborough Sounds. o, Sheep drover on horse, sheep herd, dog. p, Basket weaver. q, Skier at Mt. Cook. r, Mt. Egmont. s, Maori statues, mountains, geyser. t, Swimmers at Blue Baths, Rotorua.

2013, Aug. 7   **Perf. 14x14½**

2474	A615	Sheet of 20	22.00	22.00
a.-t.	70c Any single		1.10	1.10

Coastlines and Lighthouses — A616

Designs: 70c, Castlepoint. $1.40, Nugget Point. $1.90, East Cape. $2.40, Pencarrow Head. $2.90, Cape Campbell.

2013, Sept. 4   **Perf. 13¼x13½**

2475	A616	70c multi	1.10	1.10
2476	A616	$1.40 multi	2.25	2.25
2477	A616	$1.90 multi	3.00	3.00
2478	A616	$2.40 multi	4.00	4.00

2479	A616	$2.90 multi	4.75	4.75
a.	Souvenir sheet of 5, #2475-2479		15.50	15.50
	Nos. 2475-2479 (5)		15.10	15.10

Birth of Prince George of Cambridge — A617

Designs: 70c, Duke, Duchess of Cambridge, Prince George. $1.90, Duke of Cambridge holding Prince George. $2.40, Duke, Duchess of Cambridge, Prince George, diff. $2.90, Duchess of Cambridge holding Prince George.

2013, Sept. 11   **Perf. 14¾**

2480	A617	70c multi	1.25	1.25
2481	A617	$1.90 multi	3.25	3.25
2482	A617	$2.40 multi	4.00	4.00
2483	A617	$2.90 multi	4.75	4.75
a.	Horiz. strip of 4, #2480-2483		13.50	13.50
	Nos. 2480-2483 (4)		13.25	13.25

A618

Christmas — A619

Designs: 70c, Child receiving gift. $1.40, Christmas lunch. $1.90, Children decorating Christmas tree. $2.40, Children playing cricket on beach. $2.90, People singing Christmas carols.

2013, Oct. 2   **Perf. 14¼**

2484	A618	70c multi	1.25	1.25
2485	A618	$1.40 multi	2.40	2.40
2486	A618	$1.90 multi	3.25	3.25
2487	A618	$2.40 multi	4.00	4.00
2488	A618	$2.90 multi	5.00	5.00
	Nos. 2484-2488 (5)		15.90	15.90

Self-Adhesive

Serpentine Die Cut 9½x10¼

2489	Sheet of 3		8.50	
a.	A619 70c multi		1.25	1.25
b.	A619 $1.90 multi		3.25	3.25
c.	A619 $2.40 multi		4.00	4.00
d.	Booklet pane of 10 #2489a		12.50	
e.	Booklet pane of 10 #2489b		32.50	
f.	Booklet pane of 10 #2489c		40.00	

No. 2489a does not have a blue airmail panel at the bottom of the stamp. No. 2489e sold for $17.10. No. 2489f sold for $21.60.

Premiere of Movie *The Hobbit: The Desolation of Smaug*
A620   A621

Designs: 70c, Thorin Oakenshield. $1.40, Gandalf. $1.90, Tauriel, horiz. $2.10, Bilbo Baggins, horiz. $2.40, Legolas Greenleaf. $2.90, Bard the Bowman.

2013, Nov. 1   **Perf. 14½x14, 14x14½**

2490	A620	70c multi	1.25	1.25
a.	Souvenir sheet of 1		1.50	1.50
2491	A620	$1.40 multi	2.40	2.40
a.	Souvenir sheet of 1		3.00	3.00
2492	A620	$1.90 multi	3.25	3.25
a.	Souvenir sheet of 1		4.00	4.00
2493	A620	$2.10 multi	3.50	3.50
a.	Souvenir sheet of 1		4.50	4.50
2494	A620	$2.40 multi	4.00	4.00
a.	Souvenir sheet of 1		5.00	5.00

2495	A620	$2.90 multi	5.00	5.00
a.		Souvenir sheet of 1	6.25	6.25

Nos. 2490-2495 (6)   19.40   19.40

Self-Adhesive

Serpentine Die Cut 10¼x10, 10x10¼

2496		Sheet of 6	19.50	
a.	A621	70c multi	1.25	1.25
b.	A621	$1.40 multi	2.40	2.40
c.	A621	$1.90 multi	3.25	3.25
d.	A621	$2.10 multi	3.50	3.50
e.	A621	$2.40 multi	4.00	4.00
f.	A621	$2.90 multi	5.00	5.00
g.		Booklet pane of 10, #2496c- 2496f, 4 #2496a, 2 #2496b	26.00	

Nos. 2490a-2495a were sold as a set for $14.40.

New Year 2014 (Year of the Horse) — A622

Designs: 70c, Chinese character for "horse." $1.40, Horse. $1.90, Horse jumping over hurdle. $2.40, Rotorua Museum, Chinese lantern.

2014, Jan. 8   Litho.   Perf. 13½x13

2497	A622	70c multi	1.25	1.25
2498	A622	$1.40 multi	2.40	2.40
2499	A622	$1.90 multi	3.25	3.25
2500	A000	$2.40 multi	4.00	4.00
a.		Souvenir sheet of 4, #2497- 2500	11.00	11.00

Nos. 2497-2500 (4)   10.90   10.90

Seaweeds — A623

Map of New Zealand and: 70c, Hormosira banksii. $1.40, Landsburgia quercifolia. $1.90, Caulerpa brownii. $2.40, Marginariella boryana. $2.90, Pterocladia lucida.

2014, Feb. 5   Litho.   Perf. 14

2501	A623	70c multi	1.25	1.25
a.		Perf. 13¼x13½	1.25	1.25
2502	A623	$1.40 multi	2.40	2.40
a.		Perf. 13¼x13½	2.40	2.40
2503	A623	$1.90 multi	3.25	3.25
a.		Perf. 13¼x13½	3.25	3.25
2504	A623	$2.40 multi	4.00	4.00
a.		Perf. 13¼x13½	4.00	4.00
2505	A623	$2.90 multi	5.00	5.00
a.		Perf. 13¼x13½	5.00	5.00
b.		Souvenir sheet of 5, #2501a-2505a	16.00	16.00

Nos. 2501-2505 (5)   15.90   15.90

Houses — A624

Designs: 70c, Colonial cottage. $1.40, Villa. $1.90, Californian bungalow. $2.40, Art Deco. $2.90, State house.

2014, Mar. 5   Litho.   Perf. 14

2506	A624	70c multi	1.25	1.25
2507	A624	$1.40 multi	2.40	2.40
2508	A624	$1.90 multi	3.25	3.25
2509	A624	$2.40 multi	4.00	4.00
2510	A624	$2.90 multi	5.00	5.00
a.		Souvenir sheet of 5, #2506- 2510	15.90	5.00

Nos. 2506-2510 (5)   15.90   15.90

World War II Poster Art — A625

Posters inscribed: No. 2511, Duty Calls the Youth of New Zealand. No. 2512, Help Farm for Victory. $1.40, The Air Force Needs Men! $1.90, Navy Week. $2.40, Army Week. $2.90, Taringa Whakarongo!

2014, Apr. 2   Litho.   Perf. 14¾

2511	A625	70c multi	1.25	1.25
a.		Perf. 13	1.25	1.25
b.		Booklet pane of 1, #2511a	1.25	—
2512	A625	70c multi	1.25	1.25
a.		Perf. 13	1.25	1.25
b.		Booklet pane of 1, #2512a	1.25	—
2513	A625	$1.40 multi	2.40	2.40
a.		Perf. 13	2.40	2.40
b.		Booklet pane of 1, #2513a	2.40	—
2514	A625	$1.90 multi	3.25	3.25
a.		Perf. 13	3.25	3.25
b.		Booklet pane of 1, #2514a	3.25	—
2515	A625	$2.40 multi	4.00	4.00
a.		Perf. 13	4.00	4.00
b.		Booklet pane of 1, #2515a	4.00	—
2516	A625	$2.90 multi	5.00	5.00
a.		Perf. 13	5.00	5.00
b.		Booklet pane of 1, #2516a	5.00	—
c.		Booklet pane of 6, #2511a- 2516a	17.50	
		Complete booklet, #2511b, 2512b, 2513b, 2514b, 2515b, 2516b, 2516c	35.00	

Nos. 2511-2516 (6)   17.15   17.15

Complete booklet sold for $19.90.

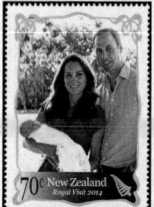

Visit to New Zealand of Duke and Duchess of Cambridge and Prince George — A626

Various photos of Duke, Duchess and Prince.

2014, Apr. 7   Litho.   Perf. 14½

2517	A626	70c multi	1.25	1.25
2518	A626	$2.40 multi	4.25	4.25

All Blacks Type of 2010

2014, May 7   Litho.   Perf. 13½x13¼

2519	A579	80c black	1.40	1.40
2520	A579	$2.50 black	4.25	4.25

Souvenir Sheet

2521		Sheet of 4, #2519, 2520, 2521a, 2521b	11.50	11.50
a.		A579 80c black, 32x17mm, perf. 15x14½	1.40	1.40
b.		A579 $2.50 black, 32x17mm, perf. 15x14½	4.25	4.25

Tourist Attractions — A627

Designs: 60c, Franz Josef Glacier. $1.60, Moeraki Boulders. $2, Mount Taranaki. $2.50, Pancake Rocks. $3.60, Waikato River.

2014, May 7   Litho.   Perf. 13¼

2522	A627	60c multi	1.00	1.00
2523	A627	$1.60 multi	2.75	2.75
2524	A627	$2.50 multi	4.25	4.25
2525	A627	$3.60 multi	6.25	6.25

Nos. 2522-2525 (4)   14.25   14.25

Self-Adhesive

Serpentine Die Cut 10x9½

2526	A627	$2 multi	3.50	3.50
a.		Booklet pane of 5	17.50	
2527	A627	$2.50 multi	4.25	4.25
a.		Pair, #2526-2527	7.75	
b.		Booklet pane of 5	21.50	

See Nos. 2644-2651, 2729-2730, 2800-2803, 2863-2867, 3026. Compare types A627 and A738.

Miniature Sheets

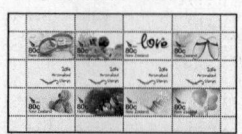

Personalized Stamps — A628

No. 2528: a, Wedding rings. b, Fern fiddlehead. c, "Love." d, Champagne flutes. e, Teddy bear. f, Pohutukawa flowers. g, Cupcake with birthday candles. h, Bunch of balloons.

No. 2529: a, Wedding rings. b, Fern fiddlehead. c, Champagne flutes. d, Pohutukawa flowers.

2014, May 7   Litho.   Perf. 15x14½

2528	A628	Sheet of 8 + 4 labels	11.50	11.50
a.-h.		80c Any single	1.40	1.40

2529	A628	Sheet of 4 + 2 labels	15.50	15.50
a.-b.		$2 Either single	3.50	3.50
c.-d.		$2.50 Either single	4.25	4.25

Miniature Sheets

Matariki A629

Nos. 2530 and 2531 — Maori art depicting the story of Papatuanuku and Ranginui: a, Te Wehenga o Rangi Raua ko Papa, by Cliff Whiting. b, Rangi and Papa, by Phil Mokaraka Berry. c, Te Whakamamae o te Wehenga, by Kura Te Waru Rewiri. d, The Separtation of Rangi and Papa, by Fred Graham, horiz. e, The Children of Rangi and Papa, by Pauline Kahurangi Yearbury, horiz. f, The Ranginui Doorway, by Robert Jahnke, horiz.

2014, June 4   Litho.   Perf. 13½

2530	A629	Sheet of 6	18.50	18.50
a.-b.		80c Either single	1.40	1.40
c.		$1.40 multi	2.40	2.40
d.		$2 multi	3.50	3.50
e.		$2.50 multi	4.25	4.25
f.		$3 multi	5.25	5.25

Self-Adhesive

Serpentine Die Cut 10x9½ (vert. stamps), 9½x10 (horiz. stamps)

2531	A629	Sheet of 6	18.50	
a.-b.		80c Either single	1.40	1.40
c.		$1.40 multi	2.40	2.40
d.		$2 multi	3.50	3.50
e.		$2.50 multi	4.25	4.25
f.		$3 multi	5.25	5.25

Miniature Sheet

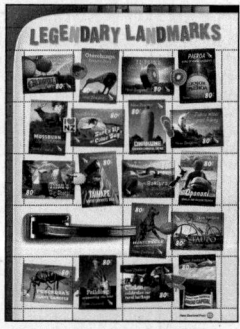

Landmarks — A630

No. 2532: a, Sculptures of peaches, Cromwell. b, Kiwi statue, Otorohanga. c, Kiwi fruit slice statue, Te Puke. d, Lemon and Paeroa bottle statue, Paeroa. e, Deer statue, Mossburn. f, Surfer statue, Colac Bay. g, Carrot statue, Ohakune. h, Fish statue, Rakaia. i, Sheep building, Tirau. j, Gumboot sculpture, Taihape. k, Chain sculpture, Raikura. l, Statue of boy and bottlenose dolphin, Opononi. m, Dog statue, Hunterville. n, Bicycle sculpture, Taupo. o, Sandfly sculpture, Pukekura. p, Sculpture of man and dog, Feilding. q, Clydesdale horses sculptures, Clinton. r, Sculpture of bread loaves, Manaia.

2014, July 2   Litho.   Perf. 14½

2532	A630	Sheet of 18 + la- bel	25.50	25.50
a.-r.		80c Any single	1.40	1.40

World War I, Cent. — A631

Designs: No. 2533, Lord Kitchener. No. 2534, Poster for military training. No. 2535, Announcement of war. No. 2536, Melville Mirfin in military uniform. No. 2537, Photograph of Mirfin family. No. 2538, Departure of troop ships. No. 2539, Training camp. No. 2540, Street scene, Karaka Bay. No. 2541, Letter from Mirfin from Samoa. No. 2542, New Zealand soldiers in Egypt.

2014, July 29   Litho.   Perf. 14½

2533	A631	80c multi	1.40	1.40
a.		Booklet pane of 1	2.00	—
2534	A631	80c multi	1.40	1.40
a.		Booklet pane of 1	2.00	—
2535	A631	80c multi	1.40	1.40
a.		Booklet pane of 1	2.00	—

2536	A631	80c multi	1.40	1.40
a.		Booklet pane of 1	2.00	—
2537	A631	80c multi	1.40	1.40
a.		Booklet pane of 1	2.00	—
2538	A631	80c multi	1.40	1.40
a.		Booklet pane of 1	2.00	—
b.		Booklet pane of 6, #2533- 2538	12.00	
c.		Block of 6, #2533-2538	8.50	8.50
d.		Souvenir sheet of #2533-2538	8.50	8.50
2539	A631	$2 multi	3.50	3.50
a.		Booklet pane of 1	5.00	—
2540	A631	$2 multi	3.50	3.50
a.		Booklet pane of 1	5.00	—
b.		Horiz. pair, #2539-2540	7.00	7.00
2541	A631	$2.50 multi	4.25	4.25
a.		Booklet pane of 1	6.25	—
2542	A631	$2.50 multi	4.25	4.25
b.		Booklet pane of 4, #2539- 2542	22.50	
		Complete booklet, #2533a, 2534a, 2535a, 2536a, 2537a. 2538a, 2538b, 2539a, 2540a, 2541a, 2542a, 2542b	69.00	
d.		Horiz. pair, #2541-2542	8.50	8.50
c.		Souvenir sheet of 4, #2539- 2542	15.50	15.50
e.		Souvenir sheet of 10, #2533-2542	24.00	24.00
f.		Souvenir sheet of 3, #2538, 2539, 2542	12.50	12.50

Nos. 2533-2542 (10)   23.90   23.90

Issued: No. 2542f, 11/14. Baypex 2014 National Stamp Exhibition, Hawke's Bay (No. 2542f). No. 2542f sold for $7.80 with surtax going to the Philatelic Trust. Complete booklet sold for $39.90. See Nos. 2574-2683, 2633-2642, 2715-2724, 2782-2791.

Endangered Seabirds — A632

Designs: 80c, Antipodean albatross. $1.40, New Zealand fairy tern. $2, Chatham Island shag. $2.50, Black-billed gull. $3, Chatham Island taiko.

2014, Sept. 3   Litho.   Perf. 14

2543	A632	80c multi	1.25	1.25
a.		Perf. 13½x13¼	1.25	1.25
2544	A632	$1.40 multi	2.25	2.25
a.		Perf. 13½x13¼	2.25	2.25
2545	A632	$2 multi	3.25	3.25
a.		Perf. 13½x13¼	3.25	3.25
2546	A632	$2.50 multi	4.00	4.00
a.		Perf. 13½x13¼	4.00	4.00
2547	A632	$3 multi	4.75	4.75
a.		Perf. 13½x13¼	4.75	4.75
b.		Souvenir sheet of 5, #2543a, 2544a, 2545a, 2546a, 2547a	15.50	15.50

Nos. 2543-2547 (5)   15.50   15.50

The silhouettes of birds were printed with thermochromic ink, which disappeared when warmed.

A633

Christmas — A634

Children in Nativity play depicting: 80c, Mary and Jesus. $1.40, Joseph. $2, Wise Man. $2.50, Angel. $3, Shepherd.

2014, Oct. 1   Litho.   Perf. 14

2548	A633	80c multi	1.25	1.25
2549	A633	$1.40 multi	2.25	2.25
2550	A633	$2 multi	3.25	3.25
2551	A633	$2.50 multi	4.00	4.00
2552	A633	$3 multi	4.75	4.75

Nos. 2548-2552 (5)   15.50   15.50

Self-Adhesive

Serpentine Die Cut 10x9½

2553		Sheet of 3	8.50	
a.		A634 80c multi	1.25	1.25
b.		A634 $2 multi	3.25	3.25
c.		A634 $2.50 multi	4.00	4.00
d.		Booklet pane of 10 #2553a	12.50	
e.		Booklet pane of 10 #2553b	32.50	
f.		Booklet pane of 10 #2553c	40.00	

Nos. 2553b and 2553c are airmail. No. 2553e sold for $18. No. 2553f sold for $22.50.

Souvenir Sheet

Premiere of Movie *The Hobbit: The Battle of the Five Armies*
A635

Design: Characters from movie in costume.

2014, Oct. 15   Litho.   Perf. 14¾x14½
2554	A635	Sheet of 2	5.25	5.25
a.		80c multi	1.25	1.25
b.		$2.50 multi	4.00	4.00

Nos. 2554a and 2554b were each available in sheets of 20 + 20 personalizable labels.

Premiere of Movie *The Hobbit: The Battle of the Five Armies*
A636   A637

Designs: 80c, Smaug. $1.40, Bilbo Baggins. $2, Gandalf, horiz. $2.10, Thranduil, horiz. Nos. 2559, 2562e, Bard the Bowman. $3, Tauriel. No. 2561, Door to Bag End.

Perf. 14½x14, 14x14½
2014, Nov. 12   Litho.
2555	A636	80c multi	1.25	1.25
a.		Souvenir sheet of 1	1.60	1.60
2556	A636	$1.40 multi	2.25	2.25
a.		Souvenir sheet of 1	2.75	2.75
2557	A636	$2 multi	3.00	3.00
a.		Souvenir sheet of 1	4.00	4.00
2558	A636	$2.10 multi	3.25	3.25
a.		Souvenir sheet of 1	4.25	4.25
2559	A636	$2.50 multi	4.00	4.00
a.		Souvenir sheet of 1	5.00	5.00
2560	A636	$3 multi	4.75	4.75
a.		Souvenir sheet of 1	5.75	5.75

Litho. & Thermography
2561	A636	$2.50 multi	4.00	4.00
a.		Souvenir sheet of 1	5.00	5.00
		Nos. 2555-2561 (7)	22.50	22.50

Self-Adhesive
Litho.
Serpentine Die Cut 10¼x10, 10x10¼
2562		Sheet of 6	18.50	
a.	A637	80c multi	1.25	1.25
b.	A637	$1.40 multi	2.25	2.25
c.	A637	$2 multi	3.00	3.00
d.	A637	$2.10 multi	3.25	3.25
e.	A637	$2.50 multi	4.00	4.00
f.	A637	$3 multi	4.75	4.75
g.		Booklet pane of 10, #2562c-2562f, 4 #2562a, 2 #2562b	24.50	

Particles of wood from the movie set are embedded in the thermographic ink on No. 2561. Nos. 2555a-2561a sold as a set for $17.80.

New Year 2015 (Year of the Sheep) — A638

Designs: 80c, Chinese character for "sheep." $1.40, Sheep in paper-cut design. $2, Sheep and fence, New Zealand. $2.50, Church of the Good Shepherd, Tekapo, and Chinese kite.

2015, Jan. 14   Litho.   Perf. 14
2563	A638	80c multi	1.25	1.25
a.		Perf. 13¼x13½	1.25	1.25
2564	A638	$1.40 multi	2.10	2.10
a.		Perf. 13¼x13½	2.10	2.10
2565	A638	$2 multi	3.00	3.00
a.		Perf. 13¼x13½	3.00	3.00
2566	A638	$2.50 multi	3.75	3.75
a.		Perf. 13¼x13½	3.75	3.75
b.		Souvenir sheet of 4, #2563a-2566a	10.50	10.50
		Nos. 2563-2566 (4)	10.10	10.10

Air New Zealand, 75th Anniv.
A639

Designs: 80c, Short S-30 Flying Boat on first Auckland-Sydney flight, 1940. $1.40, Airplanes, Stewardess Margaret Gould, child, pilot, 1948. $2, Tasman Empire Airways Ltd. 1951-60 Coral Route baggage label. $2.50, Children and flight attendant, 1977. $3, Air New Zealand Boeing 787-9 taking off.

2015, Jan. 14   Litho.   Perf. 14¾
2567	A639	80c multi	1.25	1.25
2568	A639	$1.40 multi	2.10	2.10
2569	A639	$2 multi	3.00	3.00
2570	A639	$2.50 multi	3.75	3.75
2571	A639	$3 multi	4.50	4.50
a.		Souvenir sheet of 5, #2567-2571	15.00	15.00
		Nos. 2567-2571 (5)	14.60	14.60

Souvenir Sheet

Treaty of Waitangi, 175th Anniv. — A640

Perf. 14x14½
2015, Feb. 4   Litho.   Wmk. 387
2572	A640	$2.50 multi	3.75	3.75

Miniature Sheet

2015 ICC Cricket World Cup Tournament, Australia and New Zealand — A641

No. 2573 — Tournament emblem on cricket ball with flag of competing team: a, India (dark blue ball, red stitching). b, England (white ball, red stitching). c, South Africa (green ball, orange stitching). d, Pakistan (yellow green ball, yellow stitching). e, United Arab Emirates (gray ball, red stitching). f, Sri Lanka (dark blue ball, yellow stitching). g, West Indies (red violet ball, orange stitching). h, Afghanistan (blue ball, red stitching). i, Ireland (green ball, blue stitching). j, Bangladesh (red ball, green stitching). k, Australia (yellow ball, black stitching). l, New Zealand (gray ball, black stitching). m, Zimbabwe (red ball, white stitching). n, Scotland (deep blue ball, blue stitching).

Unwmk.
2015, Feb. 4   Litho.   Die Cut
Self-Adhesive
2573	A641	Sheet of 14	17.50	
a.-n.		80c Any single	1.25	1.25

World War I, Cent. Type of 2014

Designs: No. 2574, Evelyn Brooke, nurse. No. 2575, Postcard from Egypt. No. 2576, Landing at Anzac Cove. No. 2577, Chunuk Bair. No. 2578, Casualties return. No. 2579, Marquette Memorial. No. 2580, The Sapper and His Donkey, painting by Horace Moore-Jones. No. 2581, War census poster. No. 2582, Hospital ship Maheno. No. 2583, An Enduting Bond, poster by Otho Hewett.

2015, Mar. 23   Litho.   Perf. 14½
2574	A631	80c multi	1.25	1.25
a.		Booklet pane of 1	1.75	—
2575	A631	80c multi	1.25	1.25
a.		Booklet pane of 1	1.75	—
2576	A631	80c multi	1.25	1.25
a.		Booklet pane of 1	1.75	—
2577	A631	80c multi	1.25	1.25
a.		Booklet pane of 1	1.75	—
2578	A631	80c multi	1.25	1.25
a.		Booklet pane of 1	1.75	—
2579	A631	80c multi	1.25	1.25
a.		Booklet pane of 1	1.75	
b.		Booklet pane of 6, #2574-2579	10.50	
c.		Block of 6, #2574-2579	7.50	7.50
d.		Souvenir sheet of 6, #2574-2579	7.50	7.50
2580	A631	$2 multi	3.00	3.00
a.		Booklet pane of 1	4.50	
2581	A631	$2 multi	3.00	3.00
a.		Booklet pane of 1	4.50	
b.		Horiz. pair, #2580-2581	6.00	6.00

2582	A631	$2.50 multi	3.75	3.75
a.		Booklet pane of 1	5.50	
b.		Souvenir sheet of 3, #2576, 2580, 2582	7.25	7.25
2583	A631	$2.50 multi	3.75	3.75
a.		Booklet pane of 1	5.50	
b.		Booklet pane of 4, #2580-2583	20.00	
		Complete booklet, #2574a, 2575a, 2576a, 2577a, 2578a, 2579a, 2579b, 2580a, 2581a, 2582a, 2583a, 2583b	61.00	
c.		Horiz. pair, #2582-2583	7.50	7.50
d.		Souvenir sheet of 4, #2580-2583	13.50	13.50
e.		Souvenir sheet of 10, #2574-2583	21.00	21.00
		Nos. 2574-2583 (10)	21.00	21.00

Complete booklet sold for $39.90.
Issued: No. 2582b, 10/23/15. 2015, Capital Stamp Show, Wellington, (No. 2582b).

Australian and New Zealand Army Corps, Cent. — A642

Soldier and bugler with bugler facing: 80c, Right. $2, Left.

2015, Apr. 7   Litho.   Perf. 14½x14
2584	A642	80c multi	1.25	1.25
2585	A642	$2 multi	3.00	3.00
a.		Souvenir sheet of 2, #2584-2585	4.25	4.25

See Australia Nos. 4271-4274.

Shells — A643

Designs: 80c, Silver paua. $1.40, Scott's murex. $2, Golden volute. $2.50, Fan shell. $3, Opal top shell.

2015, May 6   Litho.   Perf. 14
2586	A643	80c multi	1.25	1.25
a.		Perf. 13¼x13½	1.25	1.25
2587	A643	$1.40 multi	2.10	2.10
a.		Perf. 13¼x13½	2.10	2.10
2588	A643	$2 multi	3.00	3.00
a.		Perf. 13¼x13½	3.00	3.00
2589	A643	$2.50 multi	3.75	3.75
a.		Perf. 13¼x13½	3.75	3.75
2590	A643	$3 multi	4.50	4.50
a.		Perf. 13¼x13½	4.50	4.50
b.		Souvenir sheet of 5, #2586a-2590a	15.00	15.00
		Nos. 2586-2590 (5)	14.60	14.60

Miniature Sheets

Matariki (Maori New Year) A644

Nos. 2591 and 2592 — Kowhaiwhai: a, Digiwhaiwhai, by Johnson Witehira. b, Tenei Au Tenei Au, by Kura Te Waru Rewiri. c, Haki, by Kylie Tiuka. d, Banner Moon, by Buck Nin, horiz. e, Part of Te Hatete o Te Reo Series, by Ngatai Taepa, horiz. f, Taona Marama, by Sandy Adsett, horiz.

2015, June 3   Litho.   Perf. 14
2591	A644	Sheet of 6	14.50	14.50
a.-b.		80c Either single	1.10	1.10
c.		$1.40 multi	1.90	1.90
d.		$2 multi	2.75	2.75
e.		$2.50 multi	3.50	3.50
f.		$3 multi	4.00	4.00

Self-Adhesive
Serpentine Die Cut 10x9½ (vert. stamps), 9½x10 (horiz. stamps)
2592	A644	Sheet of 6	14.50	14.50
a.-b.		80c Either single	1.10	1.10
c.		$1.40 multi	1.90	1.90
d.		$2 multi	2.75	2.75
e.		$2.50 multi	3.50	3.50
f.		$3 multi	4.00	4.00

Miniature Sheet

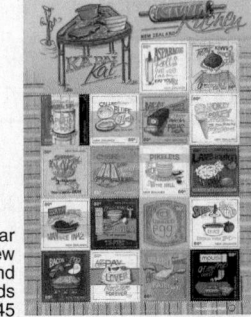

Popular New Zealand Foods A645

No. 2593: a, Aspargaus rolls. b, Kiwi onion dip. c, Puha and pork. d, Bluff oyster. e, Meat loaf. f, Hokey pokey ice cream. g, Shrimp cocktail. h, Cheese rolls. i, Pikelets. j, Lamington cake. k, Mince on toast. l, Whitebait fritters. m, Curried egg. n, Saveloy sausage and sauce. o, Bacon and egg pie. p, Pavlova. q, Fairy bread. r, Mouse trap.

2015, July 1   Litho.   Perf. 14¼x13¾
2593	A645	Sheet of 18	20.00	20.00
a.-r.		80c Any single	1.10	1.10

UNESCO World Heritage Sites — A646

Designs: 80c, Emerald Lakes, Tongariro National Park. $1.40, Franz Josef Glacier, Te Wahipounamu-South West New Zealand. $2, Enderby Island, New Zealand Sub-Antarctic Islands. $2.20, Mount Ngauruhoe, Tongariro National Park. $2.50, Lake Mackenzie, Te Wahipounamu-South West New Zealand. $3, Campbell Island, New Zealand Sub-Antarctic Islands.

2015, Aug. 5   Litho.   Perf. 14
2594	A646	80c multi	1.00	1.00
2595	A646	$1.40 multi	1.75	1.75
2596	A646	$2 multi	2.50	2.50
2597	A646	$2.20 multi	2.75	2.75
2598	A646	$2.50 multi	3.25	3.25
2599	A646	$3 multi	3.75	3.75
a.		Souvenir sheet of 6, #2594-2599	15.00	15.00
		Nos. 2594-2599 (6)	15.00	15.00

Parliament House, Wellington — A647

2015, Aug. 14   Litho.   Perf. 14¼
2600	A647	$2.50 multi	3.25	3.25
a.		Souvenir sheet of 3, #2600, Australia #4331, Singapore #1743	5.75	5.75

See Australia Nos. 4331-4333, Singapore Nos. 1743-1745.
No. 2600a sold for $4.50 and was released for Singapore 2015 International Stamp Exhibition.

All Blacks Rugby Team Uniform Shirt A648

Litho. With Fabric Affixed
2015, Sept. 2   Perf. 13¼x13½
2601	A648	$15 multi	19.00	19.00

No. 2601 was sold individually in a folder.

Queen Elizabeth II, Longest-Reigning British Monarch — A649

Photograph of Queen Elizabeth II from: No. 2602, 1950s. No. 2603, 1960s. $1.40, 1970s. $2, 1980s. $2.20, 1990s. $2.50, 2000s. $3, 2010s.

2015, Oct. 7 Litho. Perf. 14¾x14¼

2602	A649	80c multi	1.10	1.10
2603	A649	80c multi	1.10	1.10
2604	A649	$1.40 multi	1.90	1.90
2605	A649	$2 multi	2.75	2.75
2606	A649	$2.20 multi	3.00	3.00
2607	A649	$2.50 multi	3.50	3.50
2608	A649	$3 multi	4.00	4.00
a.		Souvenir sheet of 7, #2602-2608	17.50	17.50
		Nos. 2602-2608 (7)	17.35	17.35

A650

Christmas — A651

Stained-glass windows: 80c, Angel, St. Mark's Church, Carterton. $1.40, Dove, St. Aidan's Anglican Church, Remuera. $2, Madonna and Child, St. Mary's-in-Holy Trinity Cathedral, Parnell. $2.50, Pohutukawa flower, Christchurch Hospital Nurses Memorial Chapel. $3, Wise Men, St. Benedict's Church, Auckland.

2015, Nov. 4 Litho. Perf. 14

2609	A650	80c multi	1.10	1.10
2610	A650	$1.40 multi	1.90	1.90
2611	A650	$2 multi	2.75	2.75
2612	A650	$2.50 multi	3.50	3.50
2613	A650	$3 multi	4.00	4.00
		Nos. 2609-2613 (5)	13.25	13.25

Miniature Sheet
Translucent Paper

2614		Sheet of 5	13.50	13.50
a.	A650	80c multi	1.10	1.10
b.	A650	$1.40 multi	1.90	1.90
c.	A650	$2 multi	2.75	2.75
d.	A650	$2.50 multi	3.50	3.50
e.	A650	$3 multi	4.00	4.00

Self-Adhesive
Serpentine Die Cut 9½x10

2615	A651	80c multi	1.10	1.10
a.		Booklet pane of 10	9.00	
2616	A651	$2 multi	2.75	2.75
a.		Booklet pane of 10 + 10 etiquettes	27.50	
2617	A651	$2.50 multi	3.50	3.50
a.		Booklet pane of 10 + 10 etiquettes	35.00	
b.		Horiz. strip of 3, #2615-2617	7.50	
		Nos. 2615-2617 (3)	7.35	7.35

No. 2616a sold for $18. No. 2617a sold for $22.50.

New Year 2016 (Year of the Monkey) — A652

Designs: 80c, Chinese character for "monkey." $1.40, Monkey in paper-cut design. $2, Monkey hanging from branch. $2.50, Bartailed godwit and Monkey Island.

2016, Jan. 13 Litho. Perf. 14

2618	A652	80c multi	1.10	1.10
a.		Perf. 13¼x13½	1.10	1.10
2619	A652	$1.40 multi	1.90	1.90
a.		Perf. 13¼x13½	1.90	1.90
2620	A652	$2 multi	2.60	2.60
a.		Perf. 13¼x13½	2.60	2.60
2621	A652	$2.50 multi	3.25	3.25
a.		Perf. 13¼x13½	3.25	3.25
b.		Souvenir sheet of 4, #2618-2621a	9.00	9.00
		Nos. 2618-2621 (4)	8.85	8.85

Returned and Services' Association, Cent. — A653

Inscription: 80c, The returned. $1.40, The poppy. $2, Supporting those who served. $2.20, At the RSA. $2.50, The badge. $3, We will remember them.

2016, Feb. 3 Litho. Perf. 14¼x14¾

2622	A653	80c multi	1.10	1.10
2623	A653	$1.40 multi	1.90	1.90
2624	A653	$2 multi	2.75	2.75
2625	A653	$2.20 multi	3.00	3.00
2626	A653	$2.50 multi	3.50	3.50
2627	A653	$3 multi	4.00	4.00
a.		Souvenir sheet of 6, #2622-2627	16.50	16.50
		Nos. 2622-2627 (6)	16.25	16.25

A654

Glowworms — A655

Glowworms from: 80c, Mangawhitikau Cave. $1.40, Nikau Cave. $2, Ruakuri Cave. $2.50, Waipu Cave.

2016, Mar. 2 Litho. Perf. 14½x14

2628	A654	80c multi	1.10	1.10
2629	A654	$1.40 multi	1.90	1.90
2630	A654	$2 multi	2.75	2.75
2631	A654	$2.50 multi	3.50	3.50
a.		Souvenir sheet of 4, #2628-2631	9.25	9.25
		Nos. 2628-2631 (4)	9.25	9.25

Self-Adhesive
Serpentine Die Cut 10x9½

2632	A655	$2 multi	2.75	2.75
a.		Booklet pane of 10	27.50	

No. 2632 was issued with backing paper with and without printing on the reverse.

World War I, Cent. Type of 2014

Designs: No. 2633, Solomon Isaacs, member of New Zealand Expeditionary Force. No. 2634, Pioneer Battalion. No. 2635, Inscriptions in Arras Tunnels. No. 2636, Newspaper story announcing introduction of conscription. No. 2637, New Zealand troops in the Middle East. No. 2638, Troops in trenches during the Somme Offensive. No. 2639, First ANZAC Day. No. 2640, Soldiers away from the front at Bloomsbury Square headquarters of New Zealand Expeditionary Force. No. 2641, Battle of Jutland. No. 2642, The home front (Kaikoura, New Zealand Post Office).

2016, Apr. 6 Litho. Perf. 14½

2633	A631	80c multi	1.10	1.10
a.		Booklet pane of 1	1.60	—
2634	A631	80c multi	1.10	1.10
a.		Booklet pane of 1	1.60	—
2635	A631	80c multi	1.10	1.10
a.		Booklet pane of 1	1.60	—
2636	A631	80c multi	1.10	1.10
a.		Booklet pane of 1	1.60	—
2637	A631	80c multi	1.10	1.10
a.		Booklet pane of 1	1.60	—
2638	A631	80c multi	1.10	1.10
a.		Booklet pane of 1	1.60	—
b.		Booklet pane of 6, #2633-2638	9.50	—
c.		Block of 6, #2633-2638	6.60	6.60
d.		Souvenir sheet of 6, #2633-2638	6.60	6.60
2639	A631	$2 multi	2.75	2.75
a.		Booklet pane of 1	4.00	—
2640	A631	$2 multi	2.75	2.75
a.		Booklet pane of 1	4.00	—
b.		Horiz. pair, #2639-2640	5.50	5.50
2641	A631	$2.50 multi	3.50	3.50
a.		Booklet pane of 1	5.00	—
2642	A631	$2.50 multi	3.50	3.50
a.		Booklet pane of 1	5.00	—
b.		Booklet pane of 4, #2639-2642	17.50	
		Complete booklet, #2633a, 2634a, 2635a, 2636a, 2637a, 2638a, 2638b, 2639a, 2640a, 2641a, 2642a, 2642b	55.00	
c.		Horiz. pair, #2641-2642	7.00	7.00
d.		Souvenir sheet of 4, #2639-2642	12.50	12.50
e.		Souvenir sheet of 10, #2633-2642	19.50	19.50
		Nos. 2633-2642 (10)	19.10	19.10

Complete booklet sold for $39.90.

Souvenir Sheet

Queen Elizabeth II, 90th Birthday A656

No. 2643: a, Infant Princess Elizabeth with King George VI and Queen Mother Elizabeth, 1926, Princess Elizabeth with infant Prince Charles, 1949, Queen Elizabeth II on visit to New Zealand, 1995. b, Princess Elizabeth as young girl, 1936, Queen Elizabeth II opening New Zealand's Parliament, 1963, Queen Elizabeth II on visit to New Zealand, 2002. d, Princess Elizabeth in wedding dress, 1947, Queen Elizabeth II on visit to New Zealand, 1977, Queen Elizabeth II attending ANZAC centenary commemorations, 2015.

Litho. With 3-Dimensional Plastic Affixed

2016, May 4 Die Cut
Self-Adhesive

2643	A656	Sheet of 3	21.00	21.00
a.-c.		$5 Any single	7.00	7.00

Tourist Attractions Type of 2014

Designs: 40c, Church of the Good Shepherd, Lake Tekapo. 80c, Chatham Islands. $2.20, Awaroa Bay, Abel Tasman Scenic Reserve. $2.70, Vineyard, Marlborough. $3.30, Dunedin Railway Station. $3.80, Te Mata Peak, Hawke's Bay.

2016, May 18 Litho. Perf. 13¼x13½

2644	A627	40c multi	.55	.55
2645	A627	80c multi	1.10	1.10
2646	A627	$2.20 multi	3.00	3.00
2647	A627	$2.70 multi	3.75	3.75
2648	A627	$3.30 multi	4.50	4.50
2649	A627	$3.80 multi	5.25	5.25
		Nos. 2644-2649 (6)	18.15	18.15

Self-Adhesive
Serpentine Die Cut 10x9½

2650	A627	$2.20 multi	3.00	3.00
a.		Booklet pane of 5	15.00	
2651	A627	$2.70 multi	3.75	3.75
a.		Horiz. pair, #2650-2651	6.75	
b.		Booklet pane of 5	19.00	

For self-adhesive version of $3.80 stamp, see No. 3026.

Miniature Sheets

Matariki (Maori New Year) A657

Nos. 2652 and 2653 — Kete woven by: a, Cori Marsters. b, Pip Devonshire. c, Te Atiwei Ririnui. d, Audra Potaka, horiz. e, Matthew McIntyre Wilson, horiz. f, Sonia Snowden, horiz.

2016, June 1 Litho. Perf. 13½

2652	A657	Sheet of 6	17.00	17.00
a.-b.		$1 Either single	1.40	1.40
c.		$1.80 multi	2.50	2.50
d.		$2.20 multi	3.00	3.00
e.		$2.70 multi	3.75	3.75
f.		$3.30 multi	4.50	4.50

Self-Adhesive
Serpentine Die Cut 10x9½ (vert. stamps), 9½x10 (horiz. stamps)

2653	A657	Sheet of 6	17.00	17.00
a.-b.		$1 Either single	1.40	1.40
c.		$1.80 multi	2.50	2.50
d.		$2.20 multi	3.00	3.00
e.		$2.70 multi	3.75	3.75
f.		$3.30 multi	4.50	4.50

Miniature Sheet

Personalized Stamps — A658

No. 2654: a and i, Wedding rings. b and h, Fern fiddlehead. c, "Love." d, Champagne flutes. e, Teddy bear. f and j, Pohutukawa flowers. g, Bunch of balloons.

2016, June 22 Litho. Perf. 15x14½

2654	A658	Sheet of 10 + 5 labels	21.00	21.00
a.-g.		$1 Any single	1.50	1.50
h.-i.		$2.20 Either single	3.25	3.25
j.		$2.70 multi	4.00	4.00

See No. 2799.

Track — A659

Boxing A660

Canoeing A661

Swimming A662

Equestrian A663

Field Hockey A664

Triathlon A665

Cycling A666

Rowing A667

Sailing A668

2016, July 6 Litho. Perf. 14¼

2655	A659	$1 multi	1.50	1.50
2656	A660	$1 multi	1.50	1.50
2657	A661	$1 multi	1.50	1.50
2658	A662	$1 multi	1.50	1.50
2659	A663	$1 multi	1.50	1.50
2660	A664	$1 multi	1.50	1.50
2661	A665	$1 multi	1.50	1.50
2662	A666	$1 multi	1.50	1.50
2663	A667	$1 multi	1.50	1.50
2664	A668	$1 multi	1.50	1.50
a.		Block of 10, #2655-2664	15.00	15.00
b.		Souvenir sheet of 10, #2655-2664	15.00	15.00

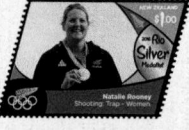

A669

Designs: No. 2665, Natalie Rooney, women's trap shooting silver medalist. No. 2666, Women's rugby sevens team, silver medalist. No. 2667, Eric Murray and Hamish Bond, men's rowing pair gold medalists. No. 2668, Luuka Jones, women's kayaking single slalom silver medalist. No. 2669, Ethan Mitchell, Sam Webster and Eddie Dawkins, men's team sprint track cycling silver medalists. No. 2670, Genevieve Behrent and Rebecca Scown, women's rowing pair silver medalists. No. 2671, Valerie Adams, women's shot put silver medalist. No. 2672, Mahe Drysdale, men's single scull rowing gold medalist. No. 2673, Lisa Carrington, women's 200-meter single kayaking sprint gold medalist. No. 2674, Sam Meech, men's Laser class sailing bronze medalist. No. 2675, Lisa Carrington, women's 500-meter single kayaking sprint bronze medalist. No. 2676, Jo Aleh and Polly Powrie, women's 470 class sailing silver medalists. No. 2677, Peter Burling and Blair Tuke, men's 49er class sailing gold medalists. No. 2678, Molly Meech and Alex Maloney, women's 49erFX class sailing silver medalists. No. 2679, Tomas Walsh, men's shot put bronze medalist. No. 2680, Eliza McCartney, women's pole vault bronze medalist. No. 2681, Lydia Ko, women's golf silver medalist. No. 2682, Nick Willis, men's 1500-meter race bronze medalist.

2016 **Litho.** *Perf. 14¼*

2665	A669	$1 multi	1.50	1.50
2666	A669	$1 multi	1.50	1.50
2667	A669	$1 multi	1.50	1.50
2668	A669	$1 multi	1.50	1.50
2669	A669	$1 multi	1.50	1.50
2670	A669	$1 multi	1.50	1.50
2671	A669	$1 multi	1.50	1.50
2672	A669	$1 multi	1.50	1.50
2673	A669	$1 multi	1.50	1.50
2674	A669	$1 multi	1.50	1.50
2675	A669	$1 multi	1.50	1.50
2676	A669	$1 multi	1.50	1.50
2677	A669	$1 multi	1.50	1.50
2678	A669	$1 multi	1.50	1.50
2679	A669	$1 multi	1.50	1.50
2680	A669	$1 multi	1.50	1.50
2681	A669	$1 multi	1.50	1.50
2682	A669	$1 multi	1.50	1.50
a.		Souvenir sheet of 18, #2665-2682	27.00	27.00
Nos. 2665-2682 (18)			*27.00*	*27.00*

New Zealand medalists at the 2016 Summer Olympics, Rio de Janeiro.

Issued: No. 2665, 8/8; Nos. 2666-2669, 8/12; Nos. 2670-2672, 8/15; Nos. 2673-2674, 8/18; Nos. 2675-2679, 8/19; Nos. 2680-2682, 2682a, 8/22.

Miniature Sheet

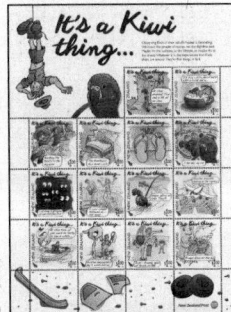

"It's a Kiwi Thing" A670

No. 2683 — Inscriptions: a, At that moment Trev had a bit of an idea. b, I'll have a trim decaf latte with a twist and a . . . c, Breaking the tackle in the big game. d, The traditional Kiwi sand-wich. e, Gone but not forgotten 2011-2014. f, A kea ate my car. g, Catching a glimpse of our national bird. h, A cool splash followed by a hot dash. i, Water skiing on Lake Taupo. j, Another smooth landing in the capital. k, At this time of year we'd be lucky to see a whale . . . l, Another successful day's whitebaiting. m, Just a friendly game of beach cricket. n, Always blow on the pie.

2016, Sept. 7 **Litho.** *Perf. 14¼x14½*

2683	A670	Sheet of 14	21.00	21.00
a.-n.		$1 Any single	1.50	1.50

Royal New Zealand Navy, 75th Anniv. A671

Designs: No. 2684, Sailors from HMS Neptune. No. 2685, Ship in Korean conflict. $1.80, Woman sailor using sextant. $2.20, Ship and helicopter supporting United Nations peacekeepers. $2.70, Sailor in Christchurch disaster relief efforts. $3.30, Sailor with his children.

2016, Oct. 5 **Litho.** *Perf. 14½x14¼*

2684	A671	$1 multi	1.50	1.50
2685	A671	$1 multi	1.50	1.50
2686	A671	$1.80 multi	2.75	2.75
2687	A671	$2.20 multi	3.25	3.25
2688	A671	$2.70 multi	4.00	4.00
2689	A671	$3.30 multi	5.00	5.00
a.		Souvenir sheet of 6, #2684-2689	18.00	18.00
Nos. 2684-2689 (6)			*18.00*	*18.00*

Souvenir Sheet

The One Ring From *The Lord of the Rings* A672

Litho. & Embossed With Foil Application

2016, Oct. 19 **Perf.**

2690	A672	$10 multi	15.50	15.50

No. 2690 sold for $10.50.

Christmas — A674

Designs: $1, Infant Jesus. $1.80, Joseph. $2.20, Shepherd. $2.70, Virgin Mary. $3.30, Magus.

2016, Nov. 2 **Litho.** *Perf. 14x14¼*

2691	A673	$1 multi	1.50	1.50
2692	A673	$1.80 multi	2.75	2.75
2693	A673	$2.20 multi	3.25	3.25
2694	A673	$2.70 multi	4.00	4.00
2695	A673	$3.30 multi	5.00	5.00
a.		Souvenir sheet of 5, #2691-2695	16.50	16.50
Nos. 2691-2695 (5)			*16.50*	*16.50*

Self-Adhesive

Serpentine Die Cut 9½x10

2696	A674	$1 multi	1.50	1.50
a.		Booklet pane of 10	15.00	
2697	A674	$2.20 multi	3.25	3.25
a.		Booklet pane of 10 + 10 labels	32.50	
2698	A674	$2.70 multi	4.00	4.00
a.		Booklet pane of 10 + 10 labels	40.00	
b.		Horiz. strip of 3, #2696-2698	11.50	
Nos. 2696-2698 (3)			*8.75*	*8.75*

No. 2697a sold for $19.80, No. 2698a, for $24.30.

New Year 2017 (Year of the Rooster) — A675

Designs: $1, Chinese character for "rooster." $1.80, Paper-cut rooster. $2.20, Rooster. $2.70, Auckland War Memorial Museum, Chinese lantern.

2017, Jan. 11 **Litho.** *Perf. 13¼x13*

2699	A675	$1 multi	1.50	1.50
2700	A675	$1.80 multi	2.60	2.60
2701	A675	$2.20 multi	3.25	3.25
2702	A675	$2.70 multi	4.00	4.00
a.		Souvenir sheet of 4, #2699-2702	11.50	11.50
Nos. 2699-2702 (4)			*11.35*	*11.35*

Southern Lights — A676

Various depictions of Southern Lights (Aurora Australis) from Mackenzie Basin.

2017, Feb. 8 **Litho.** *Perf. 14½x14*

2703	A676	$1 multi	1.40	1.40
2704	A676	$1.80 multi	2.60	2.60
2705	A676	$2 multi	3.00	3.00
2706	A676	$2.20 multi	3.25	3.25
2707	A676	$2.70 multi	4.00	4.00
2708	A676	$3.30 multi	4.75	4.75
Nos. 2703-2708 (6)			*19.00*	*19.00*

Miniature Sheet

Litho. With Foil Application

2709		Sheet of 6	19.00	19.00
a.	A676	$1 Like #2703	1.40	1.40
b.	A676	$1.80 Like #2704	2.60	2.60
c.	A676	$2 Like #2705	3.00	3.00
d.	A676	$2.20 Like #2706	3.25	3.25
e.	A676	$2.70 Like #2707	4.00	4.00
f.	A676	$3.30 Like #2708	4.75	4.75

Freshwater Fish — A677

Designs: $1, Lowland longjaw galaxias. $1.80, Redfin bully. $2.20, Longfin eel. $2.70, Lamprey. $3.30, Torrentfish.

2017, Mar. 1 **Litho.** *Perf. 14x14½*

2710	A677	$1 multi	1.40	1.40
2711	A677	$1.80 multi	2.60	2.60
2712	A677	$2.20 multi	3.25	3.25
2713	A677	$2.70 multi	4.00	4.00
2714	A677	$3.30 multi	4.75	4.75
a.		Souvenir sheet of 5, #2710-2714	16.00	16.00
Nos. 2710-2714 (5)			*16.00*	*16.00*

World War I, Cent. Type of 2014

Designs: No. 2715, Ellen Knight, mother who lost three sons in World War I. No. 2716, New Zealand officers near Beersheba mosque. No. 2717, Postmarks of Sling Camp, England. No. 2718, Tank at Battle of Messines. No. 2719, Hospital staffers in plastic surgery operating room. No. 2720, People looking at graves at Passchendaele battlefield. No. 2721, Soldiers marching at Battle of Messines. No. 2722, Notice of closing of New Zealand bars at 6 o'clock. No. 2723, SS Port Kembla, sunk off New Zealand coast. No. 2724, Women working at Census and Statistics Office Military Service Section.

2017, Apr. 5 **Litho.** *Perf. 14½*

2715	A631	$1 multi	1.40	1.40
a.		Booklet pane of 1	1.75	
2716	A631	$1 multi	1.40	1.40
a.		Booklet pane of 1	1.75	
2717	A631	$1 multi	1.40	1.40
a.		Booklet pane of 1	1.75	
2718	A631	$1 multi	1.40	1.40
a.		Booklet pane of 1	1.75	
2719	A631	$1 multi	1.40	1.40
a.		Booklet pane of 1	1.75	
2720	A631	$1 multi	1.40	1.40
a.		Booklet pane of 1	1.75	
b.		Booklet pane of 6, #2715-2720	11.00	
c.		Block of 6, #2715-2720	8.50	8.50
d.		Souvenir sheet, #2715-2720	8.50	8.50
2721	A631	$2.20 multi	3.25	3.25
a.		Booklet pane of 1	4.00	
2722	A631	$2.20 multi	3.25	3.25
a.		Booklet pane of 1	4.00	
b.		Vert. pair, #2721-2722	6.50	6.50
2723	A631	$2.70 multi	3.75	3.75
a.		Booklet pane of 1	4.75	
2724	A631	$2.70 multi	3.75	3.75
a.		Booklet pane of 1	4.75	
b.		Booklet pane of 4, #2721-2724	17.50	
		Complete booklet, #2715a, 2716a, 2717a, 2718a, 2719a, 2720a, 2720b, 2721a, 2722a, 2723a, 2724a, 2724b	57.00	
c.		Vert. pair, #2723-2724	7.50	7.50
d.		Souvenir sheet of 4, #2721-2724	14.00	14.00
e.		Souvenir sheet of 10, #2715-2724	22.50	22.50
Nos. 2715-2724 (10)			*22.40*	*22.40*

Complete booklet sold for $39.90.

Miniature Sheet

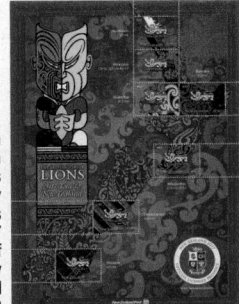

British and Irish Lions Rugby Team's 2017 Tour of New Zealand A678

No. 2725 — Lion from team emblem and parts of map of New Zealand showing: a, Whangarei area. b, Auckland area. c, Hamilton area. d, Rotorua area. e, Wellington area. f, Christchurch area. g, Dunedin area.

2017, May 3 **Litho.** *Perf. 14x14¼*

2725	A678	Sheet of 7	28.00	28.00
a.-g.		$2.70 Any single	4.00	4.00

Opening of He Tohu Exhibition at National Library, Wellington A679

Historic and modern people and text: $1, Declaration of Independence of the United Tribes of New Zealand, 1835. $2, Treaty of Waitangi, 1840. $2.20, Women's Suffrage Petition, 1893.

2017, May 17 **Litho.** *Perf. 14x14¼*

2726	A679	$1 multi	1.40	1.40
2727	A679	$2 multi	3.00	3.00
2728	A679	$2.20 multi	3.25	3.25
Nos. 2726-2728 (3)			*7.65*	*7.65*

Tourist Attractions Type of 2014

Designs: $2.30, Mangamaunu, Kaikoura. $4.30, Manu Bay, Raglan.

2017, June 7 **Litho.** *Perf. 13¼x13½*

2729	A627	$2.30 multi	3.50	3.50
2730	A627	$4.30 multi	6.25	6.25

Surfing Areas A681

Designs: $1, Piha Bar, Piha. $2.20, Manu Bay, Raglan. $2.30, Surf Highway 45, Taranaki. $2.70, Mangamaunu, Kaikoura. $3.30, Aramoana Spit, Dunedin.

2017, June 7 **Litho.** *Perf. 14x14½*

2731	A681	$1 multi	1.50	1.50
2732	A681	$2.20 multi	3.25	3.25
2733	A681	$2.30 multi	3.50	3.50
2734	A681	$2.70 multi	4.00	4.00
2735	A681	$3.30 multi	5.00	5.00
a.		Souvenir sheet of 5, #2731-2735	17.50	17.50
Nos. 2731-2735 (5)			*17.25*	*17.25*

A682

A683

A684

A685

A686

Victory of Emirates Team New Zealand in 2017 America's Cup Yacht Race — A687

2017, July 3   Litho.   Perf. 13½x13¼

2736	Sheet of 6	29.00	29.00
a.	A682 $2.70 multi	4.75	4.75
b.	A683 $2.70 multi	4.75	4.75
c.	A684 $2.70 multi	4.75	4.75
d.	A685 $2.70 multi	4.75	4.75
e.	A686 $2.70 multi	4.75	4.75
f.	A687 $2.70 multi	4.75	4.75

No. 2736 sold for $19.90.

Miniature Sheet

Great Kiwi Road Trip A688

No. 2737 — Tourists and: a, Lighthouse and seven directional signs. b, Directional sign for 90 Mile Beach. c, Three directional signs for Sheep. d, "Welcome to Rotovegas" sign. e, Directional sign for Auckland. f, Directional sign for Taumatawhakatangihangakoauauotamateaturipukakapikimaungahoronukupokaiwhenuakitanatahu. g, Directional sign for Dessert Road. h, Directional signs for Wellington and Picton. i, Three directional signs for Sumner Beach, Togs and Undies. j, "Welcome to the West Coast" sign. k, Kaikoura sign. l, Directional sign for Baldwin Street. m, Waterfalls and four directional signs. n, Directional sign for best oysters.

2017, July 12   Litho.   Perf. 14½x14

2737	A688 Sheet of 14	21.00	21.00
a.-n.	$1 Any single	1.50	1.50

Native Birds — A689

Designs: $1, Campbell Island teal. $2.20, Black stilt. $2.30, North Island kaka. $2.70, South Island saddleback. $3.30, Northern New Zealand dotterel.

2017, Aug. 2   Litho.   Perf. 14½x14

2738	A689 $1 multi	1.50	1.50
a.	Perf. 14¼x14	1.50	1.50
2739	A689 $2.20 multi	3.25	3.25
a.	Perf. 14¼x14	3.25	
2740	A689 $2.30 multi	3.50	3.50
a.	Perf. 14¼x14	3.50	
b.	Souvenir sheet of 3, #2738-2740	7.75	7.75
2741	A689 $2.70 multi	4.00	4.00
a.	Perf. 14¼x14	4.00	
2742	A689 $3.30 multi	4.75	4.75
a.	Perf. 14¼x14	4.75	
b.	Souvenir sheet of 5, #2738a-2742a	17.00	17.00
	Nos. 2738-2742 (5)	17.00	17.00

Royalpex 2017 National Stamp Exhibition, Hamilton (No. 2740b). Issued: No. 2740b, 11/24.

Miniature Sheet

Maori Language — A690

No. 2743 — English and Maori words for modern objects: a, Mobile phone. b, Text. c, Computer. d, Flash drive. e, Passport. f, Airport. g, Global positioning system. h, Skyscraper. i, Wifi. j, Electric car.

Herbs and Vegetables — A691

Designs: Nos. 2744, 2750a, Basil. Nos. 2745, 2750b, Carrots. $2.20, Parsley. $2.30, Chives. $2.70, Broccoli. $3.30, Lettuce.

Perf. 14x14¼ on 3 sides, Rouletted 9½ on diagonal sides

2017, Oct. 4   Litho.

2744	A691 $1 multi	1.40	1.40
2745	A691 $1 multi	1.40	1.40
2746	A691 $2.20 multi	3.25	3.25
2747	A691 $2.30 multi	3.50	3.50
2748	A691 $2.70 multi	4.00	4.00
2749	A691 $3.30 multi	4.75	4.75
	Nos. 2744-2749 (6)	18.30	18.30

Miniature Sheet
Stamps With Circle and "Plant Me" at Bottom

2750	Sheet of 6	18.50	18.50
a.-b.	A691 $1 Either single	1.40	1.40
c.	A691 $2.20 multi	3.25	3.25
d.	A691 $2.30 multi	3.50	3.50
e.	A691 $2.70 multi	4.00	4.00
f.	A691 $3.30 multi	4.75	4.75

Examples of No. 2750 sold in New Zealand had seeds affixed to the bottom of each stamp. The stamps could be planted so the seeds could sprout. Inthernational purchasers of No. 2750 were only sent examples without seeds affixed.

70th Wedding Anniversary of Queen Elizabeth II and Prince Philip — A692

Designs: $1, Engagement photograph. $2, Wedding photograph. $2.20, Queen Elizabeth II, Prince Philip and their children. $2.30, Queen Elizabeth II and Prince Philip. $2.70, Queen Elizabeth II, Princes, Philip, Charles, William, Harry, Duchess of Cambridge and Princess Charlotte. $3.30, Queen Elizabeth II and Prince Philip, diff.

Litho. With Foil Application

2017, Nov. 20   Perf. 14¼

2751	A692 $1 sil & multi	1.40	1.40
2752	A692 $2 sil & multi	2.75	2.75
2753	A692 $2.20 sil & multi	3.00	3.00
2754	A692 $2.30 sil & multi	3.25	3.25
2755	A692 $2.70 sil & multi	3.75	3.75
2756	A692 $3.30 sil & multi	4.50	4.50
a.	Souvenir sheet of 6, #2751-2756	19.00	19.00
	Nos. 2751-2756 (6)	18.65	18.65

A693

Christmas — A694

Quilled: $1, Angel. $2.20, Christmas ornament. $2.30, Star. $2.70, Bell. $3.30, Wreath.

2017, Dec. 6   Litho.   Perf. 14¼

2757	A693 $1 multi	1.50	1.50
2758	A693 $2.20 multi	3.25	3.25
2759	A693 $2.30 multi	3.25	3.25

2760	A693 $2.70 multi	4.00	4.00
2761	A693 $3.30 multi	4.75	4.75
a.	Souvenir sheet of 5, #2757-2761	17.00	17.00
	Nos. 2757-2761 (5)	16.75	16.75

Self-Adhesive
Serpentine Die Cut 9½x10

2762	A694 $1 multi	1.50	1.50
a.	Booklet pane of 10	15.00	
2763	A694 $2.20 multi	3.25	3.25
a.	Booklet pane of 10	32.50	
2764	A694 $2.70 multi	4.00	4.00
a.	Booklet pane of 10	40.00	
b.	Horiz. strip of 3, #2762-2764	8.75	

Nos. 2763 and 2764 are airmail. No. 2763a sold for $19.80. No. 2764a sold for $24.30.

New Year 2018 (Year of the Dog) — A695

Designs: $1, Chinese character for "dog." $2.20, Paper-cut dog. $2.70, Dog and sheep. $3.30, Sheepdog Memorial, Lake Tekapo and birds.

2018, Jan. 10   Litho.   Perf. 13¼x13

2765	A695 $1 multi	1.50	1.50
2766	A695 $2.20 multi	3.25	3.25
2767	A695 $2.70 multi	4.00	4.00
2768	A695 $3.30 multi	5.00	5.00
a.	Souvenir sheet of 4, #2765-2768	14.00	14.00
	Nos. 2765-2768 (4)	13.75	13.75

New Zealand in Space — A696

No. 2769: a, Electron rocket being delivered to launch pad. b, Rocket on launch pad. c, Humanity Star satellite. d, Aerial view of launch facility. e, Rocket launch. f, Satellite in space.

2018, Jan. 25   Litho.   Perf. 13½x13¼

2769	Sheet of 6	29.50	29.50
a.	A696 $1 multi	2.00	2.00
b.	A696 $2 multi	4.25	4.25
c.	A696 $2.20 multi	4.50	4.50
d.	A696 $2.70 multi	5.75	5.75
e.	A696 $3 multi	6.25	6.25
f.	A696 $3.30 multi	6.75	6.75

No. 2769 sold for $19.90.

Bicycle Trails — A697

Designs: No. 2770, $1, Alps 2 Ocean Trail. No. 2771, $1, Mountains to Sea Trail. $2, Otago Central Rail Trail. $2.20, Old Ghost Road. $2.70, Queen Charlotte Track. $3.30, Timber Trail.

2018, Feb. 7   Litho.   Perf. 14x14½

2770	A697 $1 multi	1.50	1.50
2771	A697 $1 multi	1.50	1.50
2772	A697 $2 multi	3.00	3.00
2773	A697 $2.20 multi	3.25	3.25
2774	A697 $2.70 multi	4.00	4.00
2775	A697 $3.30 multi	4.75	4.75
a.	Souvenir sheet of 6, #2770-2775	18.00	18.00
	Nos. 2770-2775 (6)	18.00	18.00

Wahine Ferry Disaster, 50th Anniv. — A698

Inscription: No. 2776, $1, World's Finest Drive-on Vessel. No. 2777, $1, Wahine in Trouble. $2, Waiting to Abandon Ship. $2.20, Lifeboats Make Land. $2.70, Hundreds Rescued From Wellington Harbor. $3.30, Aranui Passes Wahine Wreck.

2018, Mar. 7   Litho.   Perf. 14½x14

2776	A698 $1 multi	1.50	1.50
2777	A698 $1 multi	1.50	1.50
2778	A698 $2 multi	3.00	3.00

2779	A698 $2.20 multi	3.25	3.25
2780	A698 $2.70 multi	4.00	4.00
2781	A698 $3.30 multi	4.75	4.75
a.	Souvenir sheet of 6, #2776-2781	18.00	18.00
	Nos. 2776-2781 (6)	18.00	18.00

World War I, Cent. Type of 2014

Designs: No. 2782, Private Arthur Gordon (1895-1978), advocate for disabled veterans. No. 2783, Hundred Days Offensive. No. 2784, Medicine Depot for treating victims of influenza pandemic. No. 2785, Demobilized soldier in New Zealand with family. No. 2786, Resettlement of veterans. No. 2787, Sopwith Camel biplane in air battle. No. 2788, Auckland Town Hall with lights celebrating armistice. No. 2789, Return of Maori Battalion. No. 2790, New Zealand soldiersat Le Quesnoy on stained-glass window of St. Andrew's Anglican Church, Cambridge, England. No. 2791, Emblem of War Amputees' Association.

2018, Apr. 4   Litho.   Perf. 14½

2782	A631 $1 multi	1.50	1.50
a.	Booklet pane of 1	1.90	—
2783	A631 $1 multi	1.50	1.50
a.	Booklet pane of 1	1.90	—
2784	A631 $1 multi	1.50	1.50
a.	Booklet pane of 1	1.90	—
2785	A631 $1 multi	1.50	1.50
a.	Booklet pane of 1	1.90	—
2786	A631 $1 multi	1.50	1.50
a.	Booklet pane of 1	1.90	—
2787	A631 $1 multi	1.50	1.50
a.	Booklet pane of 1	1.90	—
b.	Block of 6, #2782-2787	9.00	9.00
c.	Souvenir sheet of 6, #2782-2787	9.00	9.00
2788	A631 $2.20 multi	3.25	3.25
a.	Booklet pane of 1	4.00	—
b.	Booklet pane of 6, #2782-2786, 2788	13.00	
2789	A631 $2.20 multi	3.25	3.25
a.	Booklet pane of 1	4.00	—
b.	Horiz. pair, #2788-2789	6.50	6.50
2790	A631 $2.70 multi	4.00	4.00
a.	Booklet pane of 1	5.00	—
2791	A631 $2.70 multi	4.00	4.00
a.	Booklet pane of 1	5.00	—
b.	Booklet pane of 4, #2787, 2789-2791	16.00	
	Complete booklet, #2782a, 2783a, 2784a, 2785a, 2786a. 2787a, 2788a, 2788b, 2789a, 2790a, 2791a, 2791b	58.50	
c.	Horiz. pair, #2790-2791	8.00	8.00
d.	Souvenir sheet of 4, #2788-2791	14.50	14.50
e.	Souvenir sheet of 10, #2782-2791	23.50	23.50
	Nos. 2782-2791 (10)	23.50	23.50

Complete booklet sold for $39.90.

Earthquake Reconstruction — A699

Designs: No. 2792, Construction on a seaside road. No. 2793, Helicopter above worker on hillside. $2, Dumptruck and excavator at construction site. $2.70, Construction of wall. $3.30, Finished rail bridge. $3.30, Freight train.

2018, May 2   Litho.   Perf. 14½x14

2792	A699 $1 multi	1.40	1.40
2793	A699 $1 multi	1.40	1.40
2794	A699 $2 multi	2.75	2.75
2795	A699 $2.20 multi	3.25	3.25
2796	A699 $2.70 multi	3.75	3.75
2797	A699 $3.30 multi	4.75	4.75
a.	Souvenir sheet of 6, #2792-2797	17.50	17.50
	Nos. 2792-2797 (6)	17.30	17.30

Miniature Sheet

Wedding of Prince Harry and Meghan Markle A700

No. 2798: a, Color engagement photograph. b, Couple in wedding attire holding hands. c, Black-and-white engagement photograph. d, Couple kissing. e, Couple at wedding ceremony with Archbishop of Canterbury. f, Couple waving.

2018, May 21   Litho.   Perf. 14¼

2798	A700 Sheet of 6	28.00	28.00
a.-f.	$2.70 Any single	4.50	4.50

No. 2798 sold for $19.90.

Personalized Stamps Type of 2016
Miniature Sheet

No. 2799: a and i, Wedding rings. b and h, Fern fiddlehead. c, "Love." d, Champagne flutes. e, Teddy bear. f and j, Pohutukawa flowers. g, Bunch of balloons.

2018, June 6   Litho.   Perf. 15x14½
2799	A658	Sheet of 10 + 5 labels	21.00 21.00
a.-g.		$1.20 Any single	1.60 1.60
h.-i.		$2.40 Either single	3.25 3.25
j.		$3 multi	4.00 4.00

Tourist Attractions Type of 2014

Designs: $2.40, Mount Maunganui, Tauranga. $3, Tongaporutu, Taranaki. $4.40, Lake Te Anau, Fiordland.

2018, June 6   Litho.   Perf. 13¼x13½
2800	A627	$2.40 multi	3.25 3.25
2801	A627	$4.40 multi	6.00 6.00

Self-Adhesive
Serpentine Die Cut 10x9½
2802	A627	$2.40 multi	3.25 3.25
a.		Booklet pane of 5	16.50
2803	A627	$3 multi	4.00 4.00
a.		Booklet pane of 5 + 2 etiquettes	20.00
b.		Horiz. pair, #2802-2803	7.25
c.		Dated "2022"	4.00 4.00
d.		Booklet pane of 5 #2803c + 2 etiquettes	20.00

Issued: No. 2803c, 6/1/22.

Miniature Sheets

Legend of Maui and the Fish
A702

Nos. 2804 and 2805: a, Eyes. b, Prow of waka. c, Hand holding jawbone. d, Fish. e, Curved triangles over land. f, Map of New Zealand.

2018, June 6   Litho.   Perf. 13¼x13½
2804	A702	Sheet of 6	17.00 17.00
a.-c.		$1.20 Any single	1.60 1.60
d.		$2.40 multi	3.25 3.25
e.		$3 multi	4.00 4.00
f.		$3.60 multi	4.75 4.75

Self-Adhesive
Serpentine Die Cut 10x9½
2805	A702	Sheet of 6	17.00 17.00
a.-c.		$1.20 Any single	1.60 1.60
d.		$2.40 multi	3.25 3.25
e.		$3 multi	4.00 4.00
f.		$3.60 multi	4.75 4.75

Kiwis — A703

Designs: No. 2806, Brown kiwi. No. 2807, Great spotted kiwi. $2.40, Little spotted kiwi. $3, Tokoeka. $3.60, Rowi.

2018, July 4   Litho.   Perf. 14¾
2806	A703	$1.20 multi	1.75 1.75
a.		Booklet pane of 6	10.50
		Complete booklet, #2806a	10.50
2807	A703	$1.20 multi	1.75 1.75
2808	A703	$2.40 multi	3.25 3.25
a.		Souvenir sheet of 3, #2806-2808, with Asian International Stamp Exhibition emblem in sheet margin	7.75 7.75
b.		As "a," with Thailand 2018 World Stamp Expo emblem in sheet margin	8.00 8.00
2809	A703	$3 multi	4.25 4.25
2810	A703	$3.60 multi	5.00 5.00
a.		Souvenir sheet of 5, #2806-2810	16.00 16.00
		Nos. 2806-2810 (5)	16.00 16.00

Values are for stamps with surrounding selvage.

Issued: No. 2808a, 9/21; No. 2808b, 12/3. 2018 Asian International Stamp Exhibition, Macao (#2808a); Thailand 2018 World Stamp Expo (#2808b). Nos. 2808a, 2808b each sold for $5.80.

Animals Native to New Zealand Threatened by Predators
A704

Designs: No. 2811, Tui, stitchbird, saddleback, building, car, couple in beach chairs. No. 2812, White herons, blue ducks, kingfisher, Hochstetter's frog, couple on bicycles. $2.40, Tuatara, jewelled gecko, red admiral butterfly, weka, family on picnic. $3, Whitehead, tomtit, North Island robin, Forbes' parakeet, people at outdoor tables. $3.60, Owl, giant snail, kiwi, giant weta, people in house.

2018, Aug. 1   Litho.   Perf. 14½x14
2811	A704	$1.20 multi	1.75 1.75
a.		Perf. 14	2.00 2.00
2812	A704	$1.20 multi	1.75 1.75
a.		Perf. 14	2.00 2.00
2813	A704	$2.40 multi	3.25 3.25
a.		Perf. 14	3.75 3.75
b.		Souvenir sheet of 3, #2811a, 2812a, 2813a	7.75 7.75
2814	A704	$3 multi	4.25 4.25
a.		Souvenir sheet of 3, #2811, 2812, 2814	9.00 9.00
2815	A704	$3.60 multi	5.00 5.00
a.		Souvenir sheet of 5, #2811-2815	16.00 16.00
		Nos. 2811-2815 (5)	16.00 16.00

Issued: No. 2813b, 9/21; No. 2814a, 12/3. 2018 Asian International Stamp Exhibition, Macao (#2813b); Thailand 2018 World Stamp Expo (#2814a). No. 2813b sold for $5.80; No. 2814a sold for $6.40.

Woman Suffrage, 125th Anniv.
A705

Designs: No. 2816, Kate Sheppard (1848-1934), suffragette. No. 2817, Camellia.

2018, Sept. 5   Litho.   Perf. 14¼x14
2816		$3 multi	4.00 4.00
2817		$3 multi	4.00 4.00
a.		A705 Horiz. pair, #2816-2817	8.00 8.00
b.		Souvenir sheet of 2, #2816-2817	8.00 8.00

Miniature Sheet

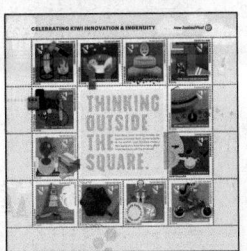

Innovations by New Zealanders — A706

No. 2818: a, Log splitter, invented by Ayla Hutchinson. b, Lifepod incubator, invented by Sir Ray Avery. c, Instant coffee, invented by David Strang. d, Jogging movement, popularized by Arthur Lydard. e, Self-resetting traps, invented by Stu Barr, Robbie van Dam and Craig Bond. f, Retractable boat wheels, invented by Maurice Bryham. g, Automatic chicken feeder, invented by Bill Kirkham. h, Referee's whistle, invented by William Harrington Atack. i, Land yacht, invented by Paul Beckett. j, Wind-resistant umbrella, invented by Greig Brebner. k, Child-proof medicine bottle caps, invented by Claudio Petronelli. l, 3-stage bike, invented by Rich Latham.

2018, Sept. 5   Perf. 14½
2818	A706	Sheet of 12 + central label	19.50 19.50
a.-l.		$1.20 Any single	1.60 1.60

End of World War I, Cent. — A707

Designs: No. 2819, Old and modern Air Force aviators. No. 2820, Medical Corps nurse from World War I and modern doctor. $2.40,

---

Old and modern Army soldiers. $3, Old and modern Navy sailors. $3.60, Poppy.

2018, Oct. 1   Litho.   Perf. 14¼
2819	A707	$1.20 multi	1.60 1.60
2820	A707	$1.20 multi	1.60 1.60
2821	A707	$2.40 multi	3.25 3.25
2822	A707	$3 multi	4.00 4.00
a.		Souvenir sheet of 3, #2819, 2821, 2822	13.00 13.00
2823	A707	$3.60 multi	4.75 4.75
a.		Souvenir sheet of 5, #2819-2823	15.50 15.50
		Nos. 2819-2823 (5)	15.20 15.20

Issued: No. 2822a, 11/9. Armistice Stamp Show, Dunedin (No. 2822a). No. 2822a sold for $9.10 with $2.50 going to the Philatelic Trust.

Miniature Sheet

Royal Visit of the Duke and Duchess of Sussex
A708

No. 2824: a, Duchess of Sussex touching heads with New Zealand man at welcoming ceremony. b, Black-and-white photograph of Duke and Duchess of Sussex. c, Duke of Sussex holding child's toy. d, Duke of Sussex reviewing troops. e, Duke and Duchess of Sussex with crowd in background. f, Duke and Duchess of Sussex with building pillar in background.

2018, Oct. 30   Litho.   Perf. 14¼x14½
2824	A708	Sheet of 6	27.00 27.00
a.-f.		$3 Any single	4.50 4.50

No. 2824 sold for $19.90.

Christmas — A709

Designs: Nos. 2825, 2830a, 2831, Virgin Mary. Nos. 2826, 2830b, 2832, Holy Family. $2.40, Christmas angel. $3, Magi with infant Jesus. $3.60, Shepherd.

2018, Nov. 7   Litho.   Perf. 14
2825	A709	$1.20 multi	1.75 1.75
2826	A709	$1.20 multi	1.75 1.75
a.		Horiz. pair, #2825-2826	3.50 3.50
2827	A709	$2.40 multi	3.50 3.50
2828	A709	$3 multi	4.25 4.25
2829	A709	$3.60 multi	5.00 5.00
		Nos. 2825-2829 (5)	16.25 16.25

Miniature Sheet
Litho. With Foil Application
2830		Sheet of 5	16.50 16.50
a.-b.		A709 $1.75 Either single	1.75 1.75
c.		A709 $2.40 gold & multi	3.50 3.50
d.		A709 $3 gold & multi	4.25 4.25
e.		A709 $3.60 gold & multi	5.00 5.00

Self-Adhesive
Size: 25x30mm
Litho.
Serpentine Die Cut 9¾x10¼
2831	A709	$1.20 multi	1.75 1.75
2832	A709	$1.20 multi	1.75 1.75
a.		Booklet pane of 10, 5 each #2831-2832	17.50

With Added Blue International Air Inscription
2833	A709	$2.40 multi	3.50 3.50
a.		Booklet pane of 10 + 10 stickers	35.00
2834	A709	$3 multi	4.25 4.25
a.		Booklet pane of 10 + 10 stickers	42.50
b.		Horiz. strip of 4, #2831-2834	11.50
		Nos. 2831-2834 (4)	11.25 11.25

No. 2833a sold for $21.60. No. 2834a sold for $27.

New Year 2019 (Year of the Pig) — A710

Designs: $1.20, Chinese character for "pig." $2.40, Paper-cut pig. $3, Arapawa pig. $3.60, State Highway 85, the "Pig Route".

2019, Jan. 16   Litho.   Perf. 13¼x13
2835	A710	$1.20 multi	1.75 1.75
2836	A710	$2.40 multi	3.50 3.50
2837	A710	$3 multi	4.25 4.25
2838	A710	$3.60 multi	5.00 5.00
a.		Souvenir sheet of 4, #2835-2838	14.50 14.50
		Nos. 2835-2838 (4)	14.50 14.50

Native Alpine Flowers — A711

Designs: No. 2839, Mountain buttercups. No. 2840, Penwiper plant. No. 2841, Black scree button daisies. $2.40, Woollyheads. $3, Mount Cook lilies. $3.60, Moss-dwelling forget-me-nots.

2019, Feb. 13   Litho.   Perf. 14
2839	A711	$1.20 multi	1.75 1.75
a.		Perf. 13½	2.25 2.25
2840	A711	$1.20 multi	1.75 1.75
2841	A711	$1.20 multi	1.75 1.75
a.		Perf. 13½	2.25 2.25
2842	A711	$2.40 multi	3.25 3.25
a.		Perf. 13½	4.50 4.50
b.		Souvenir sheet of 3, #2839a, 2841a, 2842a	9.00 9.00
2843	A711	$3 multi	4.25 4.25
2844	A711	$3.60 multi	5.00 5.00
a.		Souvenir sheet of 6, #2839-2844	18.00 18.00
		Nos. 2839-2844 (6)	17.75 17.75

China 2019 World Stamp Exhibition, Wuhan (No. 2842b). Issued; No. 2842b, 6/11. No. 2842b sold for $6.80. On each of the seven days of the China 2019 World Stamp Exhibition, 300 examples were offered for sale of No. 2842b with an overprint added in the sheet margin at lower right noting the day of the show on which it was sold and a serial number.

Views From Lighthouses
A712

Drawing of and view from: No. 2845, Pouto Lighthouse. No. 2846, Manukau Heads Lighthouse. No. 2847, Baring Head Lighthouse. $2.40, French Pass Lighthouse. $3, Nugget Point Lighthouse. $3.60, Puysegur Point Lighthouse.

2019, Mar. 6   Litho.   Perf. 14¼x14
2845	A712	$1.20 multi	1.75 1.75
2846	A712	$1.20 multi	1.75 1.75
2847	A712	$1.20 multi	1.75 1.75
a.		Souvenir sheet of 3, #2845-2847	4.25 4.25
2848	A712	$2.40 multi	3.25 3.25
2849	A712	$3 multi	4.25 4.25
2850	A712	$3.60 multi	5.00 5.00
a.		Souvenir sheet of 6, #2845-2850	18.00 18.00
		Nos. 2845-2850 (6)	17.75 17.75

Issued: No. 2847a, 3/19/20. New Zealand 2020 International Stamp Exhibition, Auckland (No. 2847a).

ANZAC Day Dawn Service
A713

Dawn service at: No. 2851, Auckland. No. 2852, Kaikoura. No. 2853, Stewart Island. $2.40, Scott Base, Antarctica. $3, Whangarei. $3.60, Dannevirke.

2019, Apr. 3   Litho.   Perf. 14x14½
2851	A713	$1.20 multi	1.75 1.75
2852	A713	$1.20 multi	1.75 1.75
2853	A713	$1.20 multi	1.75 1.75
2854	A713	$2.40 multi	3.25 3.25
2855	A713	$3 multi	4.25 4.25
2856	A713	$3.60 multi	5.00 5.00
a.		Souvenir sheet of 6, #2851-2856	18.00 18.00
		Nos. 2851-2856 (6)	17.75 17.75

Space
Pioneers — A714

Space
Missions
A715

Designs: No. 2857, Beatrice Hill Tinsley (1941-81), cosmologist. No. 2858, Alan Gilmore and Pamela Kilmartin, astronomers. $2.40, Charles Gifford (1861-1948), astronomer. $3, Albert Jones (1920-2013), visual astronomer. $3.60, Sir William Pickering (1910-2004), rocket scientist.

No. 2862: a, Space probe and stars. b, Space Shuttle. c, Astronaut on Moon. d, Lunar Module lifting off from Moon.

2019, May 1	Litho.	Perf. 14½		
2857	A714	$1.20 multi	1.60	1.60
2858	A714	$1.20 multi	1.60	1.60
2859	A714	$2.40 multi	3.25	3.25
2860	A714	$3 multi	4.00	4.00
2861	A714	$3.60 multi	4.75	4.75
a.		Vert. strip of 5, #2857-2861	15.50	15.50
Nos. 2857-2861 (5)			15.20	15.20

Miniature Sheet
Litho. With Lenticular Lens Affixed
Perf. 14x14¼

2862	A715	Sheet of 4	21.00	21.00
a.-d.		$4 Any single	5.25	5.25

Crushed meteorites were added to the ink used to print the circle around the portraits on Nos. 2857-2861.

Tourist Attractions Type of 2014

Designs: $2.60, Escarpment Walkway, Paekakariki. $3.30, Dunedin Railway Station. $3.90, Banks Peninsula, Canterbury. $4.50, Shotover River Valley, Otago.

2019, June 5	Litho.	Perf. 13¼x13½		
2863	A627	$2.60 multi	3.50	3.50
2864	A627	$3.90 multi	5.25	5.25
2865	A627	$4.50 multi	6.00	6.00
Nos. 2863-2865 (3)			14.75	14.75

Self-Adhesive
Serpentine Die Cut 10x9¾

2866	A627	$2.60 multi	3.50	3.50
a.		Booklet pane of 5 + 2 etiquettes	17.50	
2867	A627	$3.30 multi	4.50	4.50
a.		Booklet pane of 5 + 2 etiquettes	22.50	
b.		Horiz. pair, #2866-2867 on paper without back printing	8.00	

A716

A717

A718

A719

A720

A721

A722

Legend of
Kupe, the
Great
Navigator
A723

2019, June 5		Litho.	Perf. 14¼	
2868		Block of 8	14.00	14.00
a.	A716	$1.30 multi	1.75	1.75
b.	A717	$1.30 multi	1.75	1.75
c.	A718	$1.30 multi	1.75	1.75
d.	A719	$1.30 multi	1.75	1.75
e.	A720	$1.30 multi	1.75	1.75
f.	A721	$1.30 multi	1.75	1.75
g.	A722	$1.30 multi	1.75	1.75
h.	A723	$1.30 multi	1.75	1.75
i.		Sheet of 8, #2868a-2868h	14.00	14.00
j.		Souvenir sheet of 4, #2868a, 2868b, 2868c, 2868e	6.25	6.25

Issued: No. 2868j, 3/19/20. New Zealand 2020 International Stamp Exhibition, Auckland (No. 2868j).

Paintings by
Colin McCahon
(1919-87)
A724

Paintings: No. 2869, I Am, 1954. No. 2870, Titirangi Landscape, 1954. $2.60, The Angel of the Annunciation, 1947, vert. $3.30, Red and Black Landscape, 1959, vert. $4, The First Waterfall, 1964, vert.

2019, July 3	Litho.	Perf. 14¼		
2869	A724	$1.30 multi	1.75	1.75
2870	A724	$1.30 multi	1.75	1.75
2871	A724	$2.60 multi	3.50	3.50
2872	A724	$3.30 multi	4.50	4.50
2873	A724	$4 multi	5.25	5.25
a.		Souvenir sheet of 5, #2869-2873	17.00	17.00
Nos. 2869-2873 (5)			16.75	16.75

Sir Edmund
Hillary (1919-
2008),
Mountaineer
A725

No. 2874 — Various images of Hillary and inscription: a. Hillary Ridge, Aoraki/Mount Cook. b. Mount Everest. c, South Pole Expedition. d, Himalayan Trust. e, Ocean to Sky, India.

2019, July 23	Litho.	Perf. 14¼		
2874		Horiz. strip of 5	8.75	8.75
a.-e.	A725 $1.30 Any single		1.75	1.75

Miniature Sheet

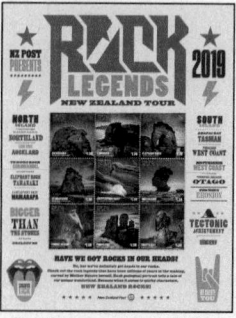

Rock Formations — A726

No. 2875: a, Kaiaraara. b, Lion Rock. c, Elephant Rock. d, Te Hoho Rock. e, Castlepoint Reef. f, Motukiekie. g, Tunnel Beach. h, Punakaiki. i, Anapai Bay.

2019, Aug. 7	Litho.	Perf. 14¼		
2875	A726	Sheet of 9	15.00	15.00
a.-i.		$1.30 Any single	1.60	1.60

Te Araroa
Trail — A727

Designs: No. 2876, Ninety Mile Beach, Northland. No. 2877, Karamu Walkway, Waikato. No. 2878, Tongariro Alpine Crossing, Manawatu. $2.60, Nelson Lakes, Tasman. $3.30, Stag Saddle, Canterbury. $4, Lake Hawea, Otago.

2019, Sept. 4	Litho.	Perf. 14¼		
2876	A727	$1.30 multi	1.60	1.60
2877	A727	$1.30 multi	1.60	1.60
2878	A727	$1.30 multi	1.60	1.60
2879	A727	$2.60 multi	3.25	3.25
2880	A727	$3.30 multi	4.25	4.25
2881	A727	$4 multi	5.00	5.00
a.		Souvenir sheet of 6, #2876-2881	17.50	17.50
Nos. 2876-2881 (6)			17.30	17.30

Emblems
of All
Blacks
Rugby
Team
A728

No. 2882 — Emblem from: a, 1905. b, 1921. c, 1924. d, 1967. e, 1986. f, 2003.

Perf. 13¾x13¼
2019, Sept. 20		Litho.		
2882	A728	Sheet of 6	19.50	19.50
a.-f.		$2.60 Any single	3.25	3.25

Paintings by Michel
Tuffery on 250th Anniv.
of Encounter of the
Maori and British
Explorers — A729

Designs: No. 2883, Birds and Maori boats. No. 2884, British sailor on ship and Maori on shore. $2.60, Daniel Solander (1733-82), naturalist, and Te Maro. $3.30, Maori and British ship in harbor. $4, Captain James Cook (1728-79).

2019, Oct. 2	Litho.	Perf. 14		
2883	A729	$1.30 multi	1.75	1.75
2884	A729	$1.30 multi	1.75	1.75
2885	A729	$2.60 multi	3.50	3.50
2886	A729	$3.30 multi	4.25	4.25
2887	A729	$4 multi	5.25	5.25
a.		Souvenir sheet of 5, #2883-2887	16.50	16.50
Nos. 2883-2887 (5)			16.50	16.50

A730

Christmas — A731

Designs: Nos. 2888, 2893, Madonna and Child. Nos. 2889, 2894, St. Joseph. Nos. 2890, 2895, Shepherd playing flute. Nos. 2891, 2896, Magi. No. 2892, $4, Angel.

2019, Nov. 6	Litho.	Perf. 14¼x14		
2888	A730	$1.30 multi	1.75	1.75
2889	A730	$1.30 multi	1.75	1.75
a.		Horiz. pair, #2888-2889	3.50	3.50
2890	A730	$2.60 multi	3.50	3.50
2891	A730	$3.30 multi	4.25	4.25
2892	A730	$4 multi	5.25	5.25
a.		Souvenir sheet of 5, #2888-2892	16.50	16.50

Self-Adhesive
Serpentine Die Cut 9½x10

2893	A731	$1.30 multi	1.75	1.75
2894	A731	$1.30 multi	1.75	1.75
a.		Booklet pane of 10, 5 each #2893-2894	17.50	
2895	A731	$2.60 multi	3.50	3.50
a.		Booklet pane of 10 + 10 etiquettes	35.00	
2896	A731	$3.30 multi	4.25	4.25
a.		Booklet pane of 10 + 10 etiquettes	42.50	
b.		Horiz. strip of 4, #2893-2896	11.50	
Nos. 2893-2896 (4)			11.25	11.25

Nos. 2895-2896 are airmail. No. 2895a sold for $23.40 and No. 2896a sold for $29.70.

Miniature Sheet

Visit to New Zealand of Prince Charles
and Duchess of Cornwall
A732

No. 2897: a, Prince Charles. b, Prince Charles reviewing troops. c, Prince Charles and Duchess of Cornwall at wreath-laying ceremony. d, Duchess of Cornwall and Prince Charles. e, Prince Charles and Duchess of Cornwall wearing ceremonial robes. f, Duchess of Cornwall.

2019, Nov. 22	Litho.	Perf. 14½x15		
2897	A732	Sheet of 6	26.50	26.50
a.-b.		$1.30 Either single	2.40	2.40
c.-d.		$2.60 Either single	4.75	4.75
e.-f.		$3.30 Either single	6.00	6.00

No. 2897 sold for $19.90.

New Year 2020 (Year
of the Rat) — A733

Designs: $1.30, Chinese character for "rat." $2.60, Paper-cut rat. $3.30, Rat and ship. $4, Sky Tower, Auckland.

2019-20	Litho.	Perf. 13¼x13		
2898	A733	$1.30 multi	1.75	1.75
a.		Perf. 13¼x13½	1.50	1.50
2899	A733	$2.60 multi	3.50	3.50
a.		Perf. 13¼x13½	3.00	3.00
2900	A733	$3.30 multi	4.50	4.50
a.		Perf. 13¼x13½	4.00	4.00
b.		Souvenir sheet of 3, #2898a, 2899a, 2900a	8.50	8.50
2901	A733	$4 multi	5.50	5.50
a.		Souvenir sheet of 4, #2898-2901	15.50	15.50
Nos. 2898-2901 (4)			15.25	15.25

Issued: Nos. 2898-2901, 2901a, 12/4; Nos. 2898a, 2899a, 2900a, 2900b, 3/19/20. New Zealand 2020 International Stamp Exhibition, Auckland (No. 2900b).

Moths — A734

Designs: No. 2902, Notoreas blax. No. 2903, Notoreas casanova. No. 2904, Notoreas edwardsi. $2.60, Notoreas mechanitis. $3.30, Notoreas "Wellington Coast." $4, Notoreas "Kaitorete Spit."

2020, Feb. 5   Litho.   Perf. 14
Background Color

2902	A734	$1.30 bright blue	1.60	1.60
2903	A734	$1.30 bright green	1.60	1.60
2904	A734	$1.30 bright yellow	1.60	1.60
2905	A734	$2.60 bright orange	3.25	3.25
2906	A734	$3.30 bright pink	4.25	4.25
2907	A734	$4 bright lilac	5.00	5.00
a.		Souvenir sheet of 6, #2902-2907	17.50	17.50
		Nos. 2902-2907 (6)	17.30	17.30

Parakeets — A735

Designs: No. 2908, Yellow-crowned parakeet. No. 2909, Orange-fronted parakeet. $2.60, Red-crowned parakeet. $3.30, Forbes' parakeet. $4, Antipodes Island parakeet.

2020, Mar. 4   Litho.   Perf. 14½x14

2908	A735	$1.30 multi	1.50	1.50
2909	A735	$1.30 multi	1.50	1.50
2910	A735	$2.60 multi	3.00	3.00
2911	A735	$3.30 multi	4.00	4.00
2912	A735	$4 multi	4.75	4.75
a.		Souvenir sheet of 5, #2908-2912	15.00	15.00
		Nos. 2908-2912 (5)	14.75	14.75

Souvenir Sheet

New Zealand 2020 International Stamp Exhibition, Auckland — A736

No. 2913 — Exhibition emblem, lifebuoy, and: a, Auckland Harbour Bridge, sailboats in distance. b, Auckland Harbour Bridge, sailboats in foreground. c, Auckland skyline.

2020, Mar. 19   Litho.   Perf. 14

2913	A736	Sheet of 3	6.00	6.00
a.-b.		$1.30 Either single	1.50	1.50
c.		$2.60 multi	3.00	3.00

End of World War II, 75th Anniv. A737

No. 2914 — Inscriptions: a, Mobilizing the nation. b, HMS Achilles. c, Fighter pilots. d, Retreat from Crete. e, 28th (Maori) Battalion. f, Women's War Service Auxiliary. g, Railway construction in Africa. h, At rest in the Pacific. i, American servicemen in Wellington. j, Merchant Marine. k, Bomber Command. l, Air raid drill in Auckland. m, Home Guard. n, Monte Cassino. o, Peace celebration in Wellington.

2020, May 18   Litho.   Perf. 14¼x14

2914		Miniature sheet of 15	24.00	24.00
a.-o.	A737	$1.30 Any single	1.60	1.60
p.		Booklet pane of 2 #2914a	3.25	—
q.		Booklet pane of 2 #2914b	3.25	—
r.		Booklet pane of 2 #2914c	3.25	—
s.		Booklet pane of 2 #2914d	3.25	—
t.		Booklet pane of 2 #2914e	3.25	—
u.		Booklet pane of 2 #2914f	3.25	—
v.		Booklet pane of 2 #2914g	3.25	—
w.		Booklet pane of 2 #2914h	3.25	—
x.		Booklet pane of 2 #2914i	3.25	—
y.		Booklet pane of 2 #2914j	3.25	—
z.		Booklet pane of 2 #2914k	3.25	—
aa.		Booklet pane of 2 #2914l	3.25	—
ab.		Booklet pane of 2 #2914m	3.25	—
ac.		Booklet pane of 2 #2914n	3.25	—
ad.		Booklet pane of 2 #2914o	3.25	—
		Complete bookleet, #2914p-2914ad	49.00	

Complete booklet sold for $39.90.

Scenery — A738

Designs: $4, Island Bay, Wellington. $10, Aoraki Mount Cook.

2020, June 3   Litho.   Perf. 13¼x13½

2915	A738	$4 multi	5.25	5.25
2916	A738	$10 multi	13.00	13.00

Compare types A627 and A738. See Nos. 2922-2925, 2966, 2968-2969, 3024-3025.

The Four Winds — A739

Various designs.

2020, June 3   Litho.   Perf. 14¼x14

2917	A739	$1.40 multi	1.90	1.90
2918	A739	$2.70 multi	3.50	3.50
2919	A739	$3.30 multi	4.25	4.25
2920	A739	$4 multi	5.25	5.25
a.		Souvenir sheet of 4, #2917-2920	15.00	15.00
		Nos. 2917-2920 (4)	14.90	14.90

Baked Goods — A740

No. 2921: a, Anzac biscuits. b, Pavlova. c, Churchill slices. d, Cheese rolls. e, Lolly cakes. f, Neenish tarts. g, Lamingtons. h, Cheese scones. i, Custard squares. j, Chocolate crackles. k, Ginger biscuits. l, Melting moments. m, Louise cakes. n, Afghans. o, Banana cake.

2020, July 1   Litho.   Perf. 13¾x14¼

2921		Miniature sheet of 15	28.50	28.50
a.-o.	A740	$1.40 Any single	1.90	1.90

Scenery Type of 2020

Designs: $3.50, Fitzroy Bay, Marlborough Sounds. $4.40, Waterfall on Whanganui River. $4.70, Mount Ngauruhoe.

2020, Aug. 5   Litho.   Perf. 13¼x13½

2922	A738	$3.50 multi	4.75	4.75
2923	A738	$4.20 multi	5.75	5.75
2924	A738	$4.70 multi	6.50	6.50
		Nos. 2922-2924 (3)	17.00	17.00

Booklet Stamp
Self-Adhesive
Serpentine Die Cut 10x9¾

2925	A738	$3.50 multi	4.75	4.75
a.		Booklet pane of 5 + 2 etiquettes	24.00	
b.		Single stamp on backing paper without back printing	4.75	

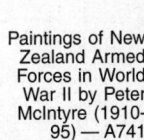

Paintings of New Zealand Armed Forces in World War II by Peter McIntyre (1910-95) — A741

Artwork: $1.40, General Hospital, Crete, 1941. $2.70, Building the Railway to Tobruk, 1941. $3.50, The Grant Tanks Go Into Action, El Alamein, 1942. $4, Medical Officer Attending Wounded Germans After Final Surrender in Tunisia, 1943.

2020, Aug. 5   Litho.   Perf. 14½

2926	A741	$1.40 multi	1.90	1.90
2927	A741	$2.70 multi	3.75	3.75
2928	A741	$3.50 multi	4.75	4.75

2929	A741	$4 multi	5.50	5.50
a.		Souvenir sheet of 4, #2926-2929	16.00	16.00
		Nos. 2926-2929 (4)	15.90	15.90

Maori Language Week — A742

Maori words: $1.40, Aroha (love). $2.70, Whanau (family). $3.50, Tane (man). $4, Wahine (woman).

2020, Sept. 2   Litho.   Perf. 14x14¼

2930	A742	$1.40 multi	1.90	1.90
2931	A742	$2.70 multi	3.50	3.50
2932	A742	$3.50 multi	4.75	4.75
2933	A742	$4 multi	5.25	5.25
a.		Souvenir sheet of 4, #2930-2933	15.50	15.50
		Nos. 2930-2933 (4)	15.40	15.40

2020 Summer Olympics, Tokyo — A743

Designs: No. 2934, Track. No. 2935, Surfing. No. 2936, Pole vault, horiz. $2.70, Field hockey, horiz. $3.50, Rugby sevens. $4, Shot put.

Perf. 14½x14, 14x14½
2020, Oct. 7   Litho.

2934	A743	$1.40 multi	1.90	1.90
2935	A743	$1.40 multi	1.90	1.90
2936	A743	$1.40 multi	1.90	1.90
2937	A743	$2.70 multi	3.75	3.75
2938	A743	$3.50 multi	4.75	4.75
2939	A743	$4 multi	5.25	5.25
a.		Souvenir sheet of 6, #2934-2939	19.50	19.50
		Nos. 2934-2939 (6)	19.45	19.45

First appearance of a New Zealand team at Summer Olympics, cent. The 2020 Summer Olympics was postponed to 2021 because of the coronavirus pandemic.

A744

Christmas — A745

Stained-glass windows depicting: $1.40, Angel. $2.70, Madonna and Child. $3.50, Star. $4, Magus.

2020, Nov. 4   Litho.   Perf. 14¼x14

2940	A744	$1.40 multi	2.00	2.00
2941	A744	$2.70 multi	3.75	3.75
2942	A744	$3.50 multi	5.00	5.00
2943	A744	$4 multi	5.75	5.75
a.		Souvenir sheet of 4, #2940-2943	16.50	16.50
		Nos. 2940-2943 (4)	16.50	16.50

Self-Adhesive
Serpentine Die Cut 9¾x10

2944	A745	$1.40 multi	2.00	2.00
a.		Booklet pane of 10	20.00	
2945	A745	$2.70 multi	3.75	3.75
a.		Booklet pane of 10 + 10 etiquettes	37.50	
2946	A745	$3.50 multi	5.00	5.00
a.		Booklet pane of 10 + 10 etiquettes	50.00	
b.		Horiz. strip of 3, #2944-2946	11.00	
		Nos. 2944-2946 (3)	10.75	10.75

New Year 2020 (Year of the Ox) — A746

Designs: $1.40, Faces of child and ox. $2.70, Ox and two children. $3.50, Child with toy ox. $4, Ox, child and apples.

2020, Dec. 2   Litho.   Perf. 13¼x13½

2947	A746	$1.40 dp ultra & pink	2.00	2.00
2948	A746	$2.70 red & pink	4.00	4.00
2949	A746	$3.50 dp ultra & pink	5.00	5.00
2950	A746	$4 red & pink	5.75	5.75
a.		Souvenir sheet of 4, #2947-2950	17.00	17.00
		Nos. 2947-2950 (4)	16.75	16.75

Passage of Homosexual Law Reform Bill, 35th Anniv. — A747

2021, Feb. 3   Litho.   Perf. 14

2951	A747	$1.40 multi	2.10	2.10

Miniature Sheet

Holiday at Home A748

No. 2952: a, Surfer and Mount Taranaki. b, Hiker and kiwis, Stewart Island. c, Telescope and Church of the Good Shepherd, Tekapo. d, Dolphins and building, Akaroa. e, Snorkelers and Treaty House, Treaty Grounds, Waitangi. f, Castlepoint Lighthouse, Wairarapa. g, Automobile, woman at Hamilton Gardens, Hamilton. h, Canoers and Bridge to Nowhere, Whanganui. i, Boats, fisherman on pier, Marlborough Sounds.

2021, Feb. 3   Litho.   Perf. 14¼x14

2952	A748	Sheet of 9	19.00	19.00
a.-i.		$1.40 Any single	2.10	2.10

Royal New Zealand Yacht Squadron, 150th Anniv. — A749

New Zealand yachts victorious in international competitions: $1.40, Te Rehutai, 2020. $2.70, Steinlager II, 1989. $3.50, Rainbow II, 1969. $4, Rainbow I, 1898.

2021, Mar. 3   Litho.   Perf. 14x14½

2953	A749	$1.40 multi	2.10	2.10
2954	A749	$2.70 multi	4.00	4.00
2955	A749	$3.50 multi	5.25	5.25
2956	A749	$4 multi	6.00	6.00
a.		Souvenir sheet of 4, #2953-2956	17.50	17.50
		Nos. 2953-2956 (4)	17.35	17.35

America's Cup — A750   Aerial View of Te Rehutai — A751

Te Rehutai — A752

Top of Te Rehutai Sails — A753

Te Rehutai and Auckland Skyline — A754

Te Rehutai — A755

Perf. 14¼x13¾

2021, Mar. 17		Litho.		
2957	Sheet of 6		29.00	29.00
a.	A750 $2.70 multi		4.75	4.75
b.	A751 $2.70 multi		4.75	4.75
c.	A752 $2.70 multi		4.75	4.75
d.	A753 $2.70 multi		4.75	4.75
e.	A754 $2.70 multi		4.75	4.75
f.	A755 $2.70 multi		4.75	4.75

Victory of Te Rehutai in 2021 America's Cup Yacht Race. No. 2957 sold for $19.90.

Queen Elizabeth II, 95th Birthday — A756

Designs: Manuka flower and various photographs of Queen Elizabeth II.

2021, Apr. 7		Litho.	**Perf. 14**	
2958	A756 $1.40 multi		2.00	2.00
2959	A756 $2.70 multi		3.75	3.75
2960	A756 $3.50 multi		5.00	5.00
2961	A756 $4 multi		5.75	5.75
a.	Souvenir sheet of 4, #2958-2961		16.50	16.50
	Nos. 2958-2961 (4)		16.50	16.50

Botanical Art by Sarah Featon (1848-1927) — A757

Designs: $1.40, Clematis paniculata. $2.70, Corynocarpus laevigatus. $3.50, Clianthus puniceus. $4, Pleurophyllum speciosum.

2021, May 5		Litho.	**Perf. 13¼x13½**	
2962	A757 $1.40 multi		2.00	2.00
2963	A757 $2.70 multi		4.00	4.00
2964	A757 $3.50 multi		5.25	5.25
2965	A757 $4 multi		5.75	5.75
a.	Souvenir sheet of 4, #2962-2965		17.00	17.00
	Nos. 2962-2965 (4)		17.00	17.00

Scenery Type of 2020

Designs: $2.80, Auckland. $3.60, Bridge over Waikato River. $4.10, Castle Hill, Canterbury.

2021, June 2		Litho.	**Perf. 13¼x13½**	
2966	A738 $4.10 multi		5.75	5.75

Self-Adhesive

Serpentine Die Cut 10x9¾

2968	A738 $2.80 multi		4.00	4.00
a.	Booklet pane of 5 + 2 eti-quettes		20.00	
2969	A738 $3.60 multi		5.00	5.00
a.	Booklet pane of 5 + 2 eti-quettes		25.00	
b.	Horiz. pair, #2968-2969 on backing paper without back printing		9.00	

Kayaking A758

Cycling A759

Skiing A760

Hiking A761

Camping with Recreational Vehicle — A762

Serpentine Die Cut 10x9¾

2021, June 2			**Litho.**	
	Self-Adhesive			
2970	A758 ($1.50) multi		2.10	2.10
2971	A759 ($1.50) multi		2.10	2.10
2972	A760 ($1.50) multi		2.10	2.10
2973	A761 ($1.50) multi		2.10	2.10
2974	A762 ($1.50) multi		2.10	2.10
a.	Horiz. coil strip of 5, #2970-2974		10.50	
b.	Booklet pane of 10, 2 each #2970-2974		21.00	
	Nos. 2970-2974 (5)		10.50	10.50

Family of Light — A763

Various designs.

2021, June 2		Litho.	**Perf. 14x14¼**	
2975	A763 $1.50 multi		2.10	2.10
2976	A763 $2.80 multi		4.00	4.00
2977	A763 $3.60 multi		5.00	5.00
2978	A763 $4.10 multi		5.75	5.75
a.	Souvenir sheet of 4, #2975-2978		17.00	17.00
	Nos. 2975-2978 (4)		16.85	16.85

Matariki (Maori New Year).

A764   A765

A766

A767

A768

Curved Lines — A769

2021, July 2		Litho.	**Perf. 14¼**	
2979	Sheet of 6		21.50	21.50
a.	A764 $1.50 multi		2.10	2.10
b.	A765 $1.50 multi		2.10	2.10
c.	A766 $1.50 multi		2.10	2.10
d.	A767 $2.80 multi		4.00	4.00
e.	A768 $3.60 multi		5.00	5.00
f.	A769 $4.10 multi		5.75	5.75

Rebranding and new emblem of NZPost.

Souvenir Sheet

Prince Philip (1921-2021) — A770

2021, Aug. 4		Litho.	**Perf. 14x14¼**	
2980	A770 $3.60 multi		5.25	5.25

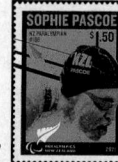
2020 Paralympics, Tokyo — A771

Designs: $1.50, Sophie Pascoe. $2.80, Cameron Leslie. $3.60, Emma Foy and Hannah Van Kampen. $4.10, "Spirit of Gold."

2021, Aug. 4		Litho.	**Perf. 14**	
2981	A771 $1.50 black & gold		2.10	2.10
2982	A771 $2.80 black & gold		4.00	4.00
2983	A771 $3.60 black & gold		5.25	5.25
2984	A771 $4.10 black & gold		5.75	5.75
a.	Souvenir sheet of 4, #2981-2984		17.50	17.50
	Nos. 2981-2984 (4)		17.10	17.10

The 2020 Paralympics were postponed until 2021 because of the COVID-19 pandemic.

Home of Bilbo and Frodo Baggins — A772

Frodo and Samwise Gamgee Hiding From Black Rider — A773

Frodo, Samwise and Aragorn Elessar II at the Prancing Pony A774

Arwen Undómiel A775

Balrog — A776

The Fellowship at the Gates of Argonath — A777

2021		Litho.	**Perf. 14x14½**	
2985	A772 $1.50 multi		2.10	2.10
a.	Souvenir sheet of 1		2.10	2.10
2986	A773 $1.50 multi		2.10	2.10
a.	Souvenir sheet of 1		2.10	2.10
2987	A774 $1.50 multi		2.10	2.10
a.	Souvenir sheet of 1		2.10	2.10
2988	A775 $2.80 multi		4.00	4.00
a.	Souvenir sheet of 1		4.00	4.00
2989	A776 $3.60 multi		5.25	5.25
a.	Souvenir sheet of 1		5.25	5.25
2990	A777 $4.10 multi		5.75	5.75
a.	Souvenir sheet of 1		5.75	5.75
b.	Souvenir sheet of 2, #2989-2990		11.00	11.00
	Nos. 2985-2990 (6)		21.30	21.30

Movie *The Lord of the Rings: The Fellowship of the Ring*, 20th anniv.; Royalpex 2021, (No. 2990b). Issued: Nos. 2985-2990, 2985a-2990a, 9/1. No. 2990b, 9/10.

Diwali A778

2021, Aug. 4		Litho.	**Perf. 14x14¼**	

Designs: $1.50, Oil lamp. $2.80, Sparkler. $3.60, Woman's hands holding plate of laddus. $4.10, Lotus flower.

2021, Oct. 7		Litho.	**Perf. 14x14¼**	
2991	A778 $1.50 multi		2.25	2.25
2992	A778 $2.80 multi		4.00	4.00
2993	A778 $3.60 multi		5.25	5.25
2994	A778 $4.10 multi		6.00	6.00
a.	Souvenir sheet of 4, #2991-2994		17.50	17.50
	Nos. 2991-2994 (4)		17.10	17.10

The New Zealand Post Philatelic Bureau sent out se-tenant blocks of 4 of Nos. 2991-2994 that were removed from a rejected printing of No. 2994a rather than sending out singles from sheets of 25 of each stamp.

A779

Christmas — A780

Designs: $1.50, Angel. $2.80, Baby Jesus. $3.60, Shepherd. $4.10, Magus.

2021, Nov. 3		Litho.	**Perf. 14¼x14**	
2995	A779 $1.50 multi		2.10	2.10
2996	A779 $2.80 multi		4.00	4.00
2997	A779 $3.60 multi		5.00	5.00
2998	A779 $4.10 multi		5.75	5.75
a.	Souvenir sheet of 4, #2995-2998		17.00	17.00
	Nos. 2995-2998 (4)		16.85	16.85

Self-Adhesive

Serpentine Die Cut 9¾x10

2999	A780 $1.50 multi		2.10	2.10
a.	Booklet pane of 10		21.00	
3000	A780 $2.80 multi		4.00	4.00
a.	Booklet pane of 10 + 10 eti-quettes		40.00	
3001	A780 $3.60 multi		5.00	5.00
a.	Booklet pane of 10 + 10 eti-quettes		50.00	
b.	Strip of 3, #2999-3001		11.50	
	Nos. 2999-3001 (3)		11.10	11.10

New Year 2022 (Year of the Tiger) — A781

Chinese child with: $1.50, Tiger, coins, bowls. $2.80, Tiger, Chinese lanterns. $3.60, Tiger, bowls, bamboo. $4.10, Tiger mask, firecrackers.

2021, Dec. 1		Litho.	**Perf. 14x14¼**	
3002	A781 $1.50 green & pink		2.10	2.10
3003	A781 $2.80 red & pink		4.00	4.00
3004	A781 $3.60 green & pink		5.00	5.00
3005	A781 $4.10 red & pink		5.75	5.75
a.	Souvenir sheet of 4, #3002-3005		16.85	16.85
	Nos. 3002-3005 (4)		16.85	16.85

19th Century Ships — A782

Designs: $1.50, European ships trading with Maori and Pakeha at Tata Beach, 1843. $2.80, Whalers from the Charles W. Morgan whaling in Cloudy Bay, 1852. $3.60, The Mataura sailing from England to New Zealand, 1879. $4.10, The Felicity and the Blind Bay hookers, at Nelson, 1889.

2022, Feb. 2		Litho.	**Perf. 14¼x14**	
3006	A782 $1.50 multi		2.10	2.10
3007	A782 $2.80 multi		3.75	3.75
3008	A782 $3.60 multi		5.00	5.00
3009	A782 $4.10 multi		5.50	5.50
a.	Souvenir sheet of 4, #3006-3009		16.50	16.50
	Nos. 3006-3009 (4)		16.35	16.35

Armistice Day Poppy Appeal, Cent. — A783

Armistice Day poppies to support veterans from: $1.50, 1922. $2.80, 1960s or 1970s. $3.60, 1978. $4.10, 2015. $4.90, 2020.

2022, Mar. 2   Litho.   Perf. 13¼x13½

3010	A783	$1.50 multi	2.10	2.10
3011	A783	$2.80 multi	4.00	4.00
3012	A783	$3.60 multi	5.00	5.00
3013	A783	$4.10 multi	5.75	5.75
3014	A783	$4.90 multi	6.75	6.75
a.		Souvenir sheet of 5, #3010-3014	24.00	24.00
		Nos. 3010-3014 (5)	23.60	23.60

Souvenir Sheet

New Zealand Symphony Orchestra, 75th Anniv. — A784

2022, Mar. 2   Litho.   Perf. 13¼x13½

3015	A784	Sheet of 2	8.00	8.00
a.		$1.50 Harp	2.10	2.10
b.		$4.10 French horn	5.75	5.75

Eid — A785

Various Arabic inscriptions.

2022, Apr. 6   Litho.   Perf. 14¼x14

3016	A785	$1.50 gold & green	2.00	2.00
3017	A785	$2.80 gold & blue	4.00	4.00
3018	A785	$3.60 gold & purple	5.00	5.00
3019	A785	$6.50 gold & green	9.00	9.00
a.		Souvenir sheet of 4, #3016-3019	20.00	20.00
		Nos. 3016-3019 (4)	20.00	20.00

Matariki (Maori New Year) — A786

Designs: $1.50, Tawhirimatea throwing his eyes into the sky. $2.80, Head of Tawhirimatea. $3.60, Stars of the Pleiades in sky, horiz. $4.10, Tawhirimatea in sky with stars, horiz.

2022, May 4   Litho.   Perf. 14

3020	A786	$1.50 multi	2.00	2.00
3021	A786	$2.80 multi	3.75	3.75
3022	A786	$3.60 multi	4.75	4.75
3023	A786	$4.10 multi	5.50	5.50
a.		Souvenir sheet of 4, #3020-3023	16.00	16.00
		Nos. 3020-3023 (4)	16.00	16.00

Tourist Attractions and Scenery Types of 2014-20

Designs: $3.80, Te Mata Oeak, Hawke's Bay. $5.10, Sarjeant Gallery, Whanganui. $6.70, Whanganui.

2022, June 1   Litho.   Perf. 13¼x13½

3024	A738	$5.10 multi	6.75	6.75
3025	A738	$6.10 multi	8.75	8.75

Self-Adhesive
Serpentine Die Cut 10x9½

3026	A627	$3.80 multi	5.00	5.00
a.		Booklet pane of 5 + 2 etiquettes on backing paper with back printing	25.00	

No. 3026 was printed in the booklet pane and also was made available on a translucent backing paper without back printing.

Te Aho o Te Kura Pounamu (The Correspondence School), Wellington, Cent. — A787

Designs: $1.70, Early students, Wairarapa, 1930s. $3, Rider on horse collecting mail bag, Aoraki Mt. Cook, 1950s. $3.80, Boy receiving schoolwork, Arapito, 1960s. $6.70, Lighthouse lessons, Tiritiri Matangi, 1970s.

2022, June 1   Litho.   Perf. 14¼x14

3027	A787	$1.70 multi	2.25	2.25
3028	A787	$3 multi	4.00	4.00
3029	A787	$3.80 multi	5.00	5.00
3030	A787	$6.70 multi	8.75	8.75
a.		Souvenir sheet of 4, #3027-3030	20.00	20.00
		Nos. 3027-3030 (4)	20.00	20.00

Tiaki Care for New Zealand Promise — A788

No. 3031 — Inscription at lower right: a, Protect nature. b, Keep NZ clean. c, Drive carefully. d, Be prepared. e, Show respect. f, Tiaki care for New Zealand.

2022, June 1   Litho.   Perf. 13½x13¼

3031		Sheet of 6	25.00	25.00
a.-b.	A788	$1.70 Either single	2.25	2.25
c.	A788	$3 black	4.00	4.00
d.	A788	$3.80 black	5.00	5.00
e.	A788	$4.30 black	5.50	5.50
f.	A788	$4.50 black	6.00	6.00

IHC Art Award-Winning Works by New Zealanders with Intellectual Disabilities — A789

Designs: $1.70, Aeroplane, by 2021 winner, Matthew Tonkin. $3, Colorful Unicorn, by 2020 winner, Katie McMillan. $3.80, My Nani as a Maori Girl, by 2019 winner, Malachi Oldridge. $5.10, Looking Out from the Inside, by 2018 winner, Charlize Wilson.

2022, July 6   Litho.   Perf. 14

3032	A789	$1.70 multi	2.25	2.25
3033	A789	$3 multi	3.75	3.75
3034	A789	$3.90 multi	5.00	5.00
3035	A789	$5.10 multi	6.50	6.50
a.		Souvenir sheet of 4, #3032-3035	17.50	17.50
		Nos. 3032-3035 (4)	17.50	17.50

Gandalf, the White Wizard — A790

Attack of the Warg Riders — A791

Gollum at the Forbidden Pool — A792

Battle of Helm's Deep — A793

Last March of the Ents — A794

The Tales That Really Mattered — A795

2022   Litho.   Perf. 14x14½

3036	A790	$1.70 multi	2.00	2.00
a.		Souvenir sheet of 1	2.00	2.00
3037	A791	$1.70 multi	2.00	2.00
a.		Souvenir sheet of 1	2.00	2.00
3038	A792	$3 multi	3.50	3.50
a.		Souvenir sheet of 1	3.50	3.50
3039	A793	$3.80 multi	4.50	4.50
a.		Souvenir sheet of 1	4.50	4.50
3040	A794	$4.30 multi	5.00	5.00
a.		Souvenir sheet of 1	5.00	5.00
3041	A795	$4.50 multi	5.25	5.25
a.		Souvenir sheet of 1	5.25	5.25
b.		Souvenir sheet of 2, #3040-3041	10.50	10.50
		Nos. 3036-3041 (6)	22.25	22.25

Movie *The Lord of the Rings: The Two Towers*, 20th anniv., Wellington Philatelic Society 100 Stamp Show (No. 3041b). Issued: Nos. 3036-3041, 3036a-3041a, 9/7; No. 3041b, 11/11.

Emblem of the Black Ferns, New Zealand's National Women's Rugby Team — A796

2022, Oct. 5   Litho.   Perf. 14¼x14½

3042		Sheet of 6, #3042b-3042e, 2 #3042a	22.50	22.50
a.	A796	$1.70 multi	2.00	2.00
b.	A796	$3 multi	3.50	3.50
c.	A796	$3.80 multi	4.50	4.50
d.	A796	$4.30 multi	5.00	5.00
e.	A796	$4.50 multi	5.25	5.25

Christmas
A797   A798

Designs: $1.70, Christmas star and kakabeak flowers. $3, Christmas candle, toetoe and raupo. $3.80, New Zealand fantail, poroporo flowers and berries. $4.30, Christmas bell and manuka flowers. $4.50, New Zealand pigeon, kowhai flowers.

2022, Oct. 5   Litho.   Perf. 14

3043	A797	$1.70 sil & multi	2.00	2.00
3044	A797	$3 sil & multi	3.50	3.50
3045	A797	$3.80 sil & multi	4.50	4.50
3046	A797	$4.30 sil & multi	5.00	5.00
3047	A797	$4.50 sil & multi	5.25	5.25
a.		Souvenir sheet of 5, #3043-3047	20.50	20.50
		Nos. 3043-3047 (5)	20.25	20.25

Self-Adhesive
Serpentine Die Cut 9¾x10

3048	A798	$1.70 sil & multi	2.00	2.00
a.		Booklet pane of 10	20.00	
3049	A798	$3 sil & multi	3.50	3.50
a.		Booklet pane of 10 + 10 etiquettes	35.00	
3050	A798	$3.80 sil & multi	4.50	4.50
a.		Booklet pane of 10 + 10 etiquettes	45.00	
b.		Strip of 3, #3048-3050	10.00	
		Nos. 3048-3050 (3)	10.00	10.00

Women in Science — A799

Designs: $1.70, Lucy Moore (1906-87), botanist. $3, Joan Wiffen (1922-2009), paleontologist. $3.80, Beatrice Hill Tinsley (1941-81), astronomer and cosmologist. $4.30, Makereti Papakura (1873-1930), ethnographer.

2022, Nov. 2   Litho.   Perf. 13½x13¾

3051	A799	$1.70 multi	2.10	2.10
3052	A799	$3 multi	3.75	3.75
3053	A799	$3.80 multi	4.75	4.75
3054	A799	$4.30 multi	5.50	5.50
a.		Souvenir sheet of 4, #3051-3054	16.50	16.50
		Nos. 3051-3054 (4)	16.10	16.10

New Year 2023 (Year of the Rabbit) — A800

Chinese child with: $1.70, Head of rabbit, cherries. $3, Another child, rabbit and ball. $3.80, Platter, peaches, rabbit and incense sticks. $6.70, Another child, rabbit, tree in pot.

2022, Dec. 7   Litho.   Perf. 13¼x13½

3055	A800	$1.70 multi	2.25	2.25
3056	A800	$3 multi	3.75	3.75
3057	A800	$3.80 multi	4.75	4.75
3058	A800	$6.70 multi	8.50	8.50
a.		Souvenir sheet of 4, #3055-3058	19.50	19.50
		Nos. 3055-3058 (4)	19.25	19.25

Katherine Mansfield (1888-1923), Writer — A801

Mansfield and: $1.70, Typewriter, and "I'm a writer first and a woman after." $3, Fan, and "I want to be all that I am capable of becoming." $3.80, Plant, and "To be alive and . . . a writer is enough." $4.30, House, and "Risk! Risk anything! Care no more for the opinions of others."

2023, Feb. 1   Litho.   Perf. 14¼

3059	A801	$1.70 multi	2.25	2.25
3060	A801	$3 multi	4.00	4.00
3061	A801	$3.80 multi	5.00	5.00
3062	A801	$4.30 multi	5.50	5.50
a.		Souvenir sheet of 4, #3059-3062	17.00	17.00
		Nos. 3059-3062 (4)	16.75	16.75

Premiere of Movie *Avatar: The Way of Water* A802

Designs: No. 3063, Tulkun breaching surface of water. No. 3064, Rider on skimwing. $3, Woodsprite and riders on mountain banshees. $3.80, Ilus. $4.30, Neytiri. $4.50, Rider on mountain banshee.

2023, Mar. 1   Litho.   Perf. 14¼x14

3063	A802	$1.70 multi	2.25	2.25
a.		Souvenir sheet of 1	2.25	2.25
3064	A802	$1.70 multi	2.25	2.25
a.		Souvenir sheet of 1	2.25	2.25
3065	A802	$3 multi	3.75	3.75
a.		Souvenir sheet of 1	3.75	3.75
3066	A802	$3.80 multi	4.75	4.75
a.		Souvenir sheet of 1	4.75	4.75
3067	A802	$4.30 multi	5.50	5.50
a.		Souvenir sheet of 1	5.50	5.50
3068	A802	$4.50 multi	5.75	5.75
a.		Souvenir sheet of 1	5.75	5.75
		Nos. 3063-3068 (6)	24.25	24.25

Characters From Children's Book, *Hairy Maclary From Donaldson's Dairy*, by Lynley Dodd — A803

Designs: No. 3069, Hairy Maclary. No. 3070, Hercules Morse. $3, Bottomley Potts. $3.80, Muffin McLay. $4.30, Bitzer Maloney. 4.50, Schnitzel von Krumm.

2023, Mar. 1   Litho.   Perf. 14¼x14

3069	A803	$1.70 multi	2.25	2.25
3070	A803	$1.70 multi	2.25	2.25
3071	A803	$3 multi	3.75	3.75
3072	A803	$3.80 multi	4.75	4.75
3073	A803	$4.30 multi	5.50	5.50

3074 A803 $4.50 multi 5.75 5.75
a. Souvenir sheet of 6, #3069-3074 24.50 24.50
Nos. 3069-3074 (6) 24.25 24.25

POSTAL-FISCAL STAMPS

In 1881 fiscal stamps of New Zealand of denominations over one shilling were made acceptable for postal duty. Values for canceled stamps are for postal cancellations. Denominations above £5 appear to have been used primarily for fiscal purposes.

Queen Victoria
PF1   PF2
Perf. 11, 12, 12½

1882 Typo. **Wmk. 62**
AR1 PF1 2sh blue 125.00 20.00
AR2 PF1 2sh6p dk brown 125.00 20.00
AR3 PF1 3sh violet 225.00 25.00
AR4 PF1 4sh brown vio 325.00 40.00
AR5 PF1 4sh red brn 275.00 40.00
AR6 PF1 5sh green 325.00 40.00
AR7 PF1 6sh rose 500.00 65.00
AR8 PF1 7sh ultra 550.00 150.00
AR9 PF1 7sh6p ol gray 1,500. 500.00
AR10 PF1 8sh dull blue 525.00 125.00
AR11 PF1 9sh org red 900.00 300.00
AR12 PF1 10sh red brn 350.00 75.00

1882-90
AR13 PF2 15sh dk grn 1,500. 400.00
AR15 PF2 £1 rose 700.00 150.00
AR16 PF2 25sh blue —
AR17 PF2 30sh brown —
AR18 PF2 £1 15sh yellow —
AR19 PF2 £2 purple —

PF3   PF4
AR20 PF3 £2 10sh red brn —
AR21 PF3 £3 yel green —
AR22 PF3 £3 10sh rose —
AR23 PF3 £4 ultra —
AR24 PF3 £4 10sh ol brn —
AR25 PF3 £5 dark blue —
AR26 PF4 £6 org red —
AR27 PF4 £7 brn red —
AR28 PF4 £8 green —
AR29 PF4 £9 rose —
AR30 PF4 £10 blue —
AR30A PF4 £20 yellow —

No. AR31

With "COUNTERPART" at Bottom
1901
AR31 PF1 2sh6p brown 300.00 400.00

Perf. 11, 14, 14½x14
1903-15 **Wmk. 61**
AR32 PF1 2sh blue ('07) 80.00 12.00
AR33 PF1 2sh6p brown 80.00 12.00
AR34 PF1 3sh violet 175.00 14.00
AR35 PF1 4sh brn red 200.00 30.00
AR36 PF1 5sh grn ('06) 225.00 30.00
AR37 PF1 6sh rose 375.00 50.00
AR38 PF1 7sh dull blue 400.00 80.00
AR39 PF1 7sh6p ol gray ('06) 1,500. 400.00
AR40 PF1 8sh dk blue 450.00 75.00
AR41 PF1 9sh dl org ('06) 600.00 200.00
AR42 PF1 10sh dp clar 250.00 50.00
AR43 PF2 15sh blue grn 1,350. 350.00

AR44 PF2 £1 rose 500.00 150.00
Perf. 14½
AR45 PF2 £2 dp vio ('25) 600.00 150.00
a. Perf. 14 700.00 150.00
Nos. AR32-AR45 (14) 6,785. 1,603.

For overprints see Cook Islands Nos. 67-71.

Coat of Arms — PF5

1931-39 **Wmk. 61** *Perf. 14*
Type PF5 (Various Frames)
AR46 1sh3p lemon 30.00 40.00
AR47 1sh3p org ('32) 8.00 9.00
AR48 2sh6p brown 16.00 5.25
AR49 4sh dull red ('32) 17.00 7.50
AR50 5sh green 21.00 12.50
AR51 6sh brt rose ('32) 37.50 15.00
AR52 7sh gray blue 32.50 25.00
AR53 7sh6p olive gray ('32) 75.00 92.50
AR54 8sh dark blue 50.00 37.50
AR55 9sh dull ver 52.50 32.50
AR56 10sh dark car 27.50 10.50
AR57 12sh6p brn vio ('35) 250.00 250.00
AR58 15sh ol grn ('32) 70.00 42.50
AR59 £1 pink ('32) 75.00 22.50
AR60 25sh turq bl ('38) 550.00 600.00
AR61 30sh dk brn ('36) 300.00 200.00
AR62 35sh yel ('37) 6,000. 7,500.
AR63 £2 vio ('33) 400.00 70.00
AR64 £2 10sh dk red ('36) 400.00 550.00
AR65 £3 lt grn ('32) 400.00 210.00
AR66 £3 10sh rose ('39) 2,250. 2,250.
AR67 £4 light brn 400.00 175.00
AR68 £4 10sh dk ol gray ('39) 2,500. 2,500.
AR69 £5 dk blue ('32) 400.00 100.00

For overprints see Cook Islands Nos. 80-83.

No. AR62 Surcharged in Black
35/-

1939 *Perf. 14*
AR70 PF5 35sh on 35sh yel 500.00 350.00

Type PF5 Surcharged in Black
1940
AR71 3sh6p on 3sh6p dl green 28.50 21.00
AR72 5sh6p on 5sh6p rose lilac 60.00 57.50
AR73 11sh on 11sh pale yellow 125.00 150.00
AR74 22sh on 22sh scar 275.00 350.00
Nos. AR71-AR74 (4) 488.50 578.50

Type of 1931
1940-58 **Wmk. 253** *Perf. 14*
Type PF5 (Various Frames)
AR75 1sh3p orange 5.75 .60
AR76 2sh6p brown 5.75 .60
AR77 4sh dull red 6.75 .60
AR78 5sh green 11.50 .90
AR79 6sh brt rose 20.00 4.00
AR80 7sh gray bl 20.00 6.75
AR81 7sh6p ol gray ('50) 70.00 70.00
AR82 8sh dk blue 45.00 25.00
AR83 9sh orange ('46) 50.00 30.00
AR84 10sh dk carmine 25.00 3.25
AR85 15sh olive ('45) 55.00 20.00
AR86 £1 pink('45) 29.00 8.50
a. Perf. 14x13½ ('58) 32.50 15.00
AR87 25sh blue ('46) 500.00 550.00
AR88 30sh choc ('46) 250.00 200.00
AR89 £2 violet ('46) 100.00 60.00
AR90 £2 10sh dk red ('51) 400.00 525.00
AR91 £3 lt grn ('46) 150.00 125.00
AR92 £3 10sh rose ('48) 2,300. 2,500.
AR93 £4 lt blue ('52) 150.00 160.00
AR94 £5 dk blue ('40) 175.00 150.00

Type PF5 Surcharged in Black
1942-45 **Wmk. 253**
AR95 3sh6p on 3sh6p grn 12.50 8.00
AR96 5sh6p on 5sh6p rose lil ('44) 26.00 8.50
AR97 11sh on 11sh yel 67.50 52.50

AR98 22sh on 22sh car ('45) 325.00 275.00
Nos. AR95-AR98 (4) 431.00 344.00

> **Catalogue values for unused stamps in this section, from this point to the end of the section, are for Never Hinged items.**

Type of 1931 Redrawn Surcharged in Black
1953 Typo.
AR99 PF5 3sh6p on 3sh6p green 32.50 35.00

Denomination of basic stamp is in small, sans-serif capitals without period after "sixpence."

Type of 1931
1955 **Wmk. 253** *Perf. 14*
Denomination in Black
AR100 PF5 1sh3p orange 2.75 .90

1956 **Denomination in Blue**
AR101 PF5 1sh3p orange yel 17.50 14.50

For decimal-currency postage stamps of design No. PF5, see Nos. 404A-404D, 404Ba, 404Ca, 404Da.

1967, July 10 *Perf. 14*
AR102 PF5 $4 purple 10.00 2.50
AR103 PF5 $6 green 9.00 4.00
AR104 PF5 $8 light blue 12.00 5.50
AR105 PF5 $10 dark blue 17.00 6.50
Nos. AR102-AR105 (4) 48.00 18.50

1987 **Unwmk.**
AR103a PF5 $6 green 9.00 9.00
AR104a PF5 $8 light blue 12.00 12.00
AR105a PF5 $10 dark blue 15.00 15.00
Nos. AR103a-AR105a (3) 36.00 36.00

SEMI-POSTAL STAMPS

Nurse — SP1

Inscribed: "Help Stamp out Tuberculosis, 1929"
Wmk. 61
1929, Dec. 11 Typo. *Perf. 14*
B1 SP1 1p + 1p scarlet 12.50 20.00

Nurse — SP2

Inscribed: "Help Promote Health, 1930"
1930, Oct. 29
B2 SP2 1p + 1p scarlet 30.00 45.00

Boy — SP3

1931, Oct. 31 *Perf. 14½x14*
B3 SP3 1p + 1p scarlet 100.00 90.00
B4 SP3 2p + 1p dark blue 100.00 75.00

Hygeia, Goddess of Health — SP4

1932, Nov. 18 Engr. *Perf. 14*
B5 SP4 1p + 1p carmine 22.50 30.00
Never hinged 55.00

Road to Health — SP5

1933, Nov. 8
B6 SP5 1p + 1p carmine 15.00 20.00
Never hinged 35.00

Crusader — SP6

1934, Oct. 25 *Perf. 14x13½*
B7 SP6 1p + 1p dark carmine 12.50 20.00
Never hinged 25.00

Child at Bathing Beach — SP7

1935, Sept. 30 *Perf. 11*
B8 SP7 1p + 1p scarlet 3.00 3.25
Never hinged 5.00

> **Catalogue values for unused stamps in this section, from this point to the end of the section, are for Never Hinged items.**

Anzac — SP8

1936, Apr. 27
B9 SP8 ½p + ½p green .70 2.00
B10 SP8 1p + 1p red .70 1.60

21st anniv. of Anzac landing at Gallipoli.

"Health" — SP9

1936, Nov. 2
B11 SP9 1p + 1p red 2.00 4.25

Boy Hiker — SP10

1937, Oct. 1
B12 SP10 1p + 1p red 3.00 4.00

Children at Play — SP11

Perf. 14x13½
1938, Oct. 1 **Wmk. 253**
B13 SP11 1p + 1p red 6.25 3.25

Children at Play — SP12

Black Surcharge

1939, Oct. 16   Wmk. 61   Perf. 11½
B14 SP12 1p on ½p + ½p grn   5.00 5.00
B15 SP12 2p on 1p + 1p scar   5.00 5.00

Children at Play — SP12a

1940, Oct. 1
B16 SP12a 1p + ½p green   16.00 17.50
B17 SP12a 2p + 1p org brown   16.00 17.50

The surtax was used to help maintain children's health camps.

Nos. B16-B17 Overprinted in Black

1941, Oct. 4   Perf. 11½
B18 SP12a 1p + ½p green   3.00 3.50
B19 SP12a 2p + 1p org brown   3.00 3.50

Children in Swing — SP13

1942, Oct. 1   Engr.
B20 SP13 1p + ½p green   .35 1.10
B21 SP13 2p + 1p dp org brown   .35 1.10

Imperf plate proofs on card exist for #B22-B27, B32-B33, B38-B39, B46-B48, B59-B60. Imperfs exist for B44-B45, B49-B51. These are from the printer's archives.

Princess Elizabeth SP14

Design: 1p+1/2p, Princess Margaret Rose.

1943, Oct. 1   Wmk. 253   Perf. 12
B22 SP14 1p + ½p dark green   .25 .40
  a.   Vert. pair, imperf. between   12,500.
B23 SP14 2p + 1p red brown   .25 .40
  a.   Vert. pair, imperf. between   12,500.

Princesses Margaret Rose and Elizabeth — SP16

1944, Oct. 9   Perf. 13½
B24 SP16 1p + ½p dp bl grn   .35 .45
B25 SP16 2p + 1p chalky blue   .35 .35

Peter Pan Statue, London — SP17

1945, Oct. 1
B26 SP17 1p + ½p gray grn & bis brn   .25 .35
B27 SP17 2p + 1p car & ol bis   .25 .35

Soldier Helping Child over Stile — SP18

1946, Oct. 24   Perf. 13½x13
B28 SP18 1p + ½p dk grn & org brn   .25 .35
B29 SP18 2p + 1p dk brn & org brn   .25 .35

Statue of Eros, London — SP19

1947, Oct. 1   Engr.   Perf. 13x13½
B30 SP19 1p + ½p deep green   .25 .35
B31 SP19 2p + 1p scarlet   .25 .35

Children's Health Camp — SP20

1948, Oct. 1   Perf. 13½x13
B32 SP20 1p + ½p blue grn & ultra   .25 .35
B33 SP20 2p + 1p red & dk brn   .25 .35

Nurse and Child — SP21

1949, Oct. 3   Photo.   Perf. 14x14½
B34 SP21 1p + ½p deep green   .30 .35
B35 SP21 2p + 1p ultramarine   .30 .35

Princess Elizabeth and Prince Charles — SP22

1950, Oct. 2
B36 SP22 1p + ½p green   .25 .35
B37 SP22 2p + 1p violet brown   .25 .35

Racing Yachts — SP23

Perf. 13½x13

1951, Nov. 1   Engr.   Wmk. 253
B38 SP23 1½p + ½p red & yel   .25 .35
B39 SP23 2p + 1p dp grn & yel   .25 .35

Princess Anne SP24

Prince Charles SP25

Perf. 14x14½

1952, Oct. 1   Wmk. 253   Photo.
B40 SP24 1½p + ½p crimson   .25 .35
B41 SP25 2p + 1p brown   .25 .35

Girl Guides Marching SP26

Boy Scouts at Camp SP27

1953, Oct. 7
B42 SP26 1½p + ½p bright blue   .25 .35
B43 SP27 2p + 1p deep green   .25 .35

The border of No. B43 consists of Morse code reading "Health" at top and bottom and "New Zealand" on each side. On No. B42 the top border line is replaced by "Health" in Morse code.

Young Mountain Climber Studying Map — SP28

1954, Oct. 4   Engr.   Perf. 13½
B44 SP28 1½p + ½p pur & brn   .25 .35
B45 SP28 2p + 1p vio gray & brn   .25 .35

Child's Head — SP29

1955, Oct. 3   Wmk. 253   Perf. 13
B46 SP29 1½p + ½p brn org & sep   .25 .35
B47 SP29 2p + 1p grn & org brn   .25 .35
B48 SP29 3p + 1p car & sepia   .25 .35
    Nos. B46-B48 (3)   .75 1.05

Children Picking Apples — SP30

1956, Sept. 24
B49 SP30 1½p + ½p chocolate   .25 .35
B50 SP30 2p + 1p blue green   .25 .35
B51 SP30 3p + 1p dk car   .25 .35
    Nos. B49-B51 (3)   .75 1.05

Life-Saving Team — SP31

3p+1p, Children playing and boy in canoe.

1957, Sept. 25   Perf. 13½
B52 SP31 2p + 1p emer & blk   .25 .35
  a.   Miniature sheet of 6   7.25 25.00
B53 SP31 3p + 1p car & ultra   .25 .35
  a.   Miniature sheet of 6   7.25 25.00

The watermark is sideways on Nos. B52a and B53a. In a second printing, the watermark is upright; values double.

Girls' Life Brigade Cadet — SP32

Design: 3p+1p, Bugler, Boys' Brigade.

1958, Aug. 20   Photo.   Perf. 14x14½
B54 SP32 2p + 1p green   .25 .45
  a.   Miniature sheet of 6   5.00 25.00
B55 SP32 3p + 1p dl ultra   .25 .45
  a.   Miniature sheet of 6   5.00 25.00

75th anniv. of the founding of the Boys' Brigade.

The surtax on this and other preceding semi-postals was for the maintenance of children's health camps.

Globes and Red Cross Flag — SP33

1959, June 3   Perf. 14½x14
B56 SP33 3p + 1p ultra & car   .25 .25
  a.   Red Cross omitted   2,000.

The surtax was for the Red Cross.

Gray Teal (Tete) — SP34

Design: 3p+1p, Pied stilt (Poaka).

1959, Sept. 16   Perf. 14x14½
B57 SP34 2p + 1p pink, blk, yel & gray   .60 .75
  a.   Miniature sheet of 6   6.00 20.00
B58 SP34 3p + 1p blue, black & pink   .60 .75
  a.   Miniature sheet of 6   6.00 20.00
  b.   Pink omitted   160.00

Sacred Kingfisher (Kotare) — SP35

Design: 3p+1p, NZ pigeon (Kereru).

1960, Aug. 10   Engr.   Perf. 13x13½
B59 SP35 2p + 1p grnsh blue & sepia   .60 .85
  a.   Min. sheet of 6, perf. 11½x11   13.00 22.50
B60 SP35 3p + 1p org & sepia   .60 .85
  a.   Min. sheet of 6, perf. 11½x11   13.00 22.50

Type of 1959

Birds: 2p+1p, Great white egret (Kotuku). 3p+1p, New Zealand falcon (Keararea).

1961, Aug. 2   Wmk. 253
B61 SP34 2p + 1p pale lil & blk   .60 .80
  a.   Miniature sheet of 6   13.00 22.50
B62 SP34 3p + 1p yel grn & blk brn   .60 .80
  a.   Miniature sheet of 6   13.00 22.50

Type of 1959

Birds: 2½p+1p, Red-fronted parakeet (Kakariki). 3p+1p, Saddleback (Tieke).

1962, Oct. 3   Photo.   Perf. 15x14
B63 SP34 2½p + 1p lt bl, grn & org   .60 .80
  a.   Miniature sheet of 6   20.00 27.50
B64 SP34 3p + 1p salmon, blk, grn & org   .60 .80
  a.   Miniature sheet of 6   20.00 27.50
  b.   Orange omitted   2,750.

Prince Andrew — SP36

Design: 3p+1p, Prince without book.

1963, Aug. 7   Engr.   Perf. 14
B65 SP36 2½p + 1p ultra   .35   .80
  a. Miniature sheet of 6   13.00 22.50
B66 SP36 3p + 1p rose car   .35   .25
  a. Miniature sheet of 6   13.00 22.50

Red-billed Gull
(Tarapunga)
SP37

Design: 3p+1p, Blue penguin (Korora).

1964, Aug. 5   Photo.   Perf. 14
B67 SP37 2½p + 1p lt bl,
              pale yel,
              red & blk   .45   .75
  a. Miniature sheet of 8   22.50 35.00
  b. Red omitted   325.00 225.00
  c. Yellow omitted
B68 SP37 3p + 1p blue,
             yel & blk   .45   .75
  a. Miniature sheet of 8   22.50 35.00

Kaka — SP38

Design: 4p+1p, Fantail (Piwakawaka).

1965, Aug. 4   Perf. 14x14½
B69 SP38 3p + 1p gray, red,
             brn & yellow   .60   .85
  a. Miniature sheet of 6   11.00 27.50
B70 SP38 4p + 1p yel, blk,
             emer & brn   .60   .85
  a. Miniature sheet of 6   11.00 27.50
  b. As No. B70, green omitted 2,000. 2,000.

Bellbird & Bough of
Kowhai Tree — SP39

4p+1p, Flightless rail (Weka) and fern.

1966, Aug. 3   Photo.   Wmk. 253
B71 SP39 3p + 1p lt bl &
             multi   .60   .85
  a. Miniature sheet of 6   9.00 25.00
B72 SP39 4p + 1p lt grn &
             multi   .60   .85
  a. Miniature sheet of 6   9.00 25.00
  b. Brown omitted   2,250.

National Team Rugby
Player and Boy — SP40

Design: 3c+1c, Man and boy placing ball for
place kick, horiz.

1967, Aug. 2   Perf. 14½x14, 14x14½
B73 SP40 2½c + 1c multi   .25   .25
  a. Miniature sheet of 6   10.00 20.00
B74 SP40 3c + 1c multi   .25   .25
  a. Miniature sheet of 6   10.00 20.00

Boy Running and
Olympic
Rings — SP41

3c+1c, Girl swimming and Olympic rings.

1968, Aug. 7   Perf. 14½x14
B75 SP41 2½c + 1c multi   .25   .25
  a. Miniature sheet of 6   9.50 22.50
  b. As No. B75, blue omitted   400.00
B76 SP41 3c + 1c multi   .25   .25
  a. Miniature sheet of 6   9.50 22.50
  b. Red omitted, from No.
      B76a   3,350. 2,000.
  c. Dark blue omitted, from
      No. B76a   2,250.

Boys Playing   Dr. Elizabeth
Cricket   Gunn
SP42   SP43

Design: 3c+1c, playing cricket.

Perf. 13½x13, 13x13½
1969, Aug. 6   Litho.   Unwmk.
B77 SP42 2½c + 1c multi   .45   .75
  a. Miniature sheet of 6   10.00 25.00
B78 SP42 3c + 1c multi   .45   .75
  a. Miniature sheet of 6   10.00 25.00
B79 SP43 4c + 1c multi   .45   2.50
    Nos. B77-B79 (3)   1.35   4.00

50th anniv. of Children's Health Camps,
founded by Dr. Elizabeth Gunn.

Boys Playing
Soccer — SP44

2½c+1c, Girls playing basketball, vert.

1970, Aug. 5   Unwmk.   Perf. 13½
B80 SP44 2½c + 1c multi   .30   .80
  a. Miniature sheet of 6   10.00 26.00
B81 SP44 3c + 1c multi   .30   .80
  a. Miniature sheet of 6   10.00 26.00

Hygienist and
Child — SP45

Designs: 3c+1c, Girls playing hockey.
4c+1c, Boys playing hockey.

1971, Aug. 4   Litho.   Perf. 13½
B82 SP45 3c + 1c multicolored   .50   .75
  a. Miniature sheet of 6   10.00 22.50
B83 SP45 4c + 1c multicolored   .50   .75
  a. Miniature sheet of 6   10.00 22.50
B84 SP45 5c + 1c multicolored   1.00   2.25
    Nos. B82-B84 (3)   2.00   3.75

50th anniv. of School Dental Service (No.
B84).

Boy Playing
Tennis — SP46

Design: 4c+1c, Girl playing tennis.

1972, Aug. 2   Litho.   Perf. 13x13½
B85 SP46 3c + 1c gray & lt
             brn   .35   .60
  a. Miniature sheet of 6   9.50 20.00
B86 SP46 4c + 1c red brn, yel
            & gray   .35   .60
  a. Miniature sheet of 6   9.50 20.00

Prince Edward — SP47

1973, Aug. 1   Photo.
B87 SP47 3c + 1c grn & brn   .35   .60
  a. Miniature sheet of 6   9.00 20.00
B88 SP47 4c + 1c dk red & blk   .35   .60
  a. Miniature sheet of 6   9.00 20.00

Children with Cat and
Dog — SP48

Designs: 4c+1c, Girl with dogs and cat.
5c+1c, Children and dogs.

1974, Aug. 7   Litho.   Perf. 13½x14
B89 SP48 3c + 1c multicolored   .25   .60
B90 SP48 4c + 1c multicolored   .30   .60
  a. Miniature sheet of 10   20.00 40.00
B91 SP48 5c + 1c multicolored   1.10   1.75
    Nos. B89-B91 (3)   1.65   2.95

Girl Feeding
Lamb — SP49

Designs: 4c+1c, Boy with hen and chicks.
5c+1c, Boy with duck and duckling.

1975, Aug. 6   Litho.   Perf. 14x13½
B92 SP49 3c + 1c multicolored   .25   .35
B93 SP49 4c + 1c multicolored   .25   .35
  a. Miniature sheet of 10   15.00 40.00
B94 SP49 5c + 1c multicolored   .75   1.75
    Nos. B92-B94 (3)   1.25   2.45

Boy and Piebald
Pony — SP50

Designs: 8c+1c, Farm girl and calf. 10c+1c,
2 girls watching nest-bound thrush.

1976, Aug. 4   Litho.   Perf. 13½x14
B95 SP50 7c + 1c multicolored   .25   .35
B96 SP50 8c + 1c multicolored   .25   .35
B97 SP50 10c + 1c multicolored   .45   .90
  a. Min. sheet, 2 each #B95-B97 4.25 6.00
    Nos. B95-B97 (3)   .95   1.60

Girl and Bluebird — SP51

8c+2c, Boy & frog. 10c+2c, Girl & butterfly.

1977, Aug. 3   Litho.   Perf. 13½x14
B98 SP51 7c + 2c multi   .25   .60
B99 SP51 8c + 2c multi   .25   .65
B100 SP51 10c + 2c multi   .50   1.10
  a. Miniature sheet of 6   2.50   6.50
    Nos. B98-B100 (3)   1.00   2.35

No. B100a contains 2 each of Nos. B98-
B100 in 2 strips of continuous design.

NZ No. B1   Heart
SP52   Surgery
                     SP53

1978, Aug. 2   Litho.   Perf. 13½x14
B101 SP52 10c + 2c multi   .35   .40
B102 SP53 12c + 2c multi   .35   .45
  a. Min. sheet, 3 ea #B101-B102 1.40 4.00

50th Health Stamp issue (No. B101) and
National Heart Foundation (No. B102).
No. B102a exists in two printings: with
"HARRISON & SONS LTD., LONDON" imprint
at bottom left margin (valued) and with imprint
more centered across three bottom stamps
(apparently very scarce). Both varieties are
known on first day covers.

Demoiselle
Fish — SP54

Designs: No. B104, Sea urchin. 12c+2c,
Underwater photographer and red mullet, vert.

1979, July 25   Perf. 13½x13, 13x13½
B103 SP54 10c + 2c multi   .35   .70
B104 SP54 10c + 2c multi   .35   .70
  a. Pair, #B103-B104   .70   1.25
B105 SP54 12c + 2c multi   .35   .70
  a. Min. sheet, 2 ea #B103-B105 1.50 2.75
    Nos. B103-B105 (3)   1.05   2.10

Children Surf
Casting — SP55

No. B107, Wharf Fishing. B108, Underwater
fishing.

1980, Aug. 6   Litho.   Perf. 13½x13
B106 SP55 14c + 2c shown   .35   .95
B107 SP55 14c + 2c multi   .35   .95
  a. Pair, #B106-B107   .70   1.75
B108 SP55 17c + 2c multi   .35   .65
  a. Min. sheet, 2 ea #B106-B108 1.90 3.25
    Nos. B106-B108 (3)   1.05   2.55

Boy and Girl at Rock
Pool — SP56

1981, Aug. 5   Litho.   Perf. 14½
B109 SP56 20c + 2c Girl, starfish .30   .75
B110 SP56 20c + 2c Boy fishing   .30   .75
  a. Pair, #B109-B110   .60   1.50
B111 SP56 25c + 2c shown   .30   .40
  a. Min. sheet, 2 ea #B109-B111 1.50 3.50
    Nos. B109-B111 (3)   .90   1.90

Cocker Spaniel — SP57

1982, Aug. 4   Litho.   Perf. 13x13½
B112 SP57 24c + 2c Labrador   .90   1.10
B113 SP57 24c + 2c Border col-
             lie   .90   1.10
  a. Pair, #B112-B113   1.90   2.25
B114 SP57 30c + 2c shown   .90   1.10
  a. Min. sheet, 2 each #B112-
      B114, perf. 14x13½   5.00   7.50
    Nos. B112-B114 (3)   2.70   3.30

Persian Cat — SP58

1983, Aug. 3   Litho.   Perf. 14½
B115 SP58 24 + 2c Tabby   .70   .85
B116 SP58 24 + 2c Siamese   .70   .85
  a. Pair, #B115-B116   1.40   1.75
B117 SP58 30 + 2c shown   .95   1.10
  a. Min. sheet, 2 ea #B115-B117 3.00 3.50
    Nos. B115-B117 (3)   2.35   2.80

Thoroughbreds
SP59

1984, Aug. 1   Litho.   Perf. 13½x13
B118 SP59 24c + 2c Clydesdales   .60   .85
B119 SP59 24c + 2c Shetlands   .60   .85
  a. Pair, #B118-B119   1.25   1.75
B120 SP59 30c + 2c shown   .60   .85
  a. Min. sheet, 2 ea #B118-B120 2.50 3.75
    Nos. B118-B120 (3)   1.80   2.55

Health — SP60

Princess Diana and: No. B121, Prince William. No. B122, Prince Henry. No. B123, Princes Charles, William and Henry.

1985, July 31   Litho.   Perf. 13½
B121 SP60 25c + 2c multi   1.00 1.50
B122 SP60 25c + 2c multi   1.00 1.50
  a. Pair, #B121-B122   2.10 3.00
B123 SP60 35c + 2c multi   1.00 1.50
  a. Min. sheet, 2 ea #B121-B123   4.75 7.00
    Nos. B121-B123 (3)   3.00 4.50

Surtax for children's health camps.

Children's
Drawings — SP61

No. B125, Children playing. No. B126, Skipping rope, horiz.

1986, July 30   Litho.   Perf. 14½x14
B124 SP61 30c + 3c shown   .50 .75
B125 SP61 30c + 3c multi   .50 .75
  a. Pair, #B124-B125   1.00 1.50
B126 SP61 45c + 3c multi   .75 .90
  a. Min. sheet, 2 ea #B124-B126   3.50 4.00
    Nos. B124-B126 (3)   1.75 2.40

Surtax for children's health camps. No. B126a exists with Stockholmia '86 emblem. This sheet was sold only at the exhibition.

Children's
Drawings — SP62

1987, July 29   Litho.   Perf. 14½
B127 SP62 40c + 3c shown   .90 1.75
B128 SP62 40c + 3c Swimming   .90 1.75
  a. Pair, #B127-B128   1.90 3.50
B129 SP62 60c + 3c Riding
    horse, vert.   1.50 7.75
  a. Min. sheet, 2 ea #B127-
    B129   6.50 11.00
    Nos. B127-B129 (3)   3.30 11.25

Surtax benefited children's health camps.

1988 Summer
Olympics,
Seoul — SP63

1988, July 27   Litho.   Perf. 14½
B130 SP63 40c + 3c Swimming   .70 .80
B131 SP63 60c + 3c Running   .95 1.25
B132 SP63 70c + 3c Rowing   1.10 1.25
B133 SP63 80c + 3c Equestrian   1.25 1.60
  a. Souv. sheet of 4, #B130-B133   4.00 5.00
    Nos. B130-B133 (4)   4.00 4.90

Children's
Health — SP64

Designs: No. B134, Duke and Duchess of York, Princess Beatrice. No. B135, Duchess, princess. No. B136, Princess.

1989, July 23
B134 SP64 40c + 3c multi   .90 1.75
B135 SP64 40c + 3c multi   .90 1.75
  a. Pair, #B134-B135   1.90 3.50
B136 SP64 80c + 3c multi   1.60 2.00
  a. Min. sheet, 2 ea #B134-
    B136   6.75 8.75
  b. As "a," overprinted with
    World Stamp Expo '89
    emblem in margin   17.50 17.50
    Nos. B134-B136 (3)   3.40 5.50

Athletes — SP65

40c+5c, Jack Lovelock (1910-1949), runner. 80c+5c, George Nepia (1905-1986), rugby player.

1990, July 25   Litho.   Perf. 14½x14
B137 SP65 40c +5c multi   .60 .95
B138 SP65 80c +5c multi   1.25 1.60
  a. Min. sheet, 2 ea #B137-B138   3.75 4.25

Hector's
Dolphin — SP66

1991, July 24   Litho.   Perf. 14½
B139 SP66 45c +5c 3 Swimming   1.00 1.40
B140 SP66 80c +5c 2 Jumping   1.40 2.25
  a. Souv. sheet, 2 ea #B139-B140   5.75 7.50

Surtax benefited children's health camps.

Anthony F. Wilding
(1883-1915), Tennis
Player — SP67

Design: No. B142, C.S. "Stewie" Dempster (1903-1974), cricket player.

1992, Aug. 12   Litho.   Perf. 14x13½
B141 SP67 45c +5c multi   1.10 1.40
B142 SP67 80c +5c multi   1.40 1.75
  a. Souv. sheet, 2 each #B141-
    B142, perf. 14½   4.50 6.25

Surtax for children's health camps.

SP68

1993, July 21   Litho.   Perf. 13½x14
B143 SP68 45c +5c Boy, puppy   .80 1.00
B144 SP68 80c +5c Girl, kitten   1.40 1.75
  a. Souvenir sheet, 2 each #B143-
    B144, perf. 14½   4.50 5.00
  b. As "a," inscribed in sheet mar-
    gin   7.00 7.00

Surtax for children's health camps. No. B144b inscribed with "TAIPEI '93" emblem.
Issue date: No. B144b, Aug. 14.

SP69

Children's Health Camps, 75th Anniv.: No. B145, #B15, Children playing with ball. No. B146, #B34, Nurse holding child. No. B147, #B79, Children reading. 80c+5c, #B4, Boy.

1994, July 20   Litho.   Perf. 14
B145 SP69 45c +5c multi   .80 .90
B146 SP69 45c +5c multi   .80 .90
B147 SP69 45c +5c multi   .80 .90
B148 SP69 80c +5c multi   1.40 1.40
  a. Souv. sheet of 4, #B145-B148   4.50 5.00
    Nos. B145-B148 (4)   3.80 4.10

Surtax for children's health camps.

Children's
Health
Camps — SP70

Designs: 45c+5c, Boy on skateboard. 80c+5c, Child on bicycle.

1995, June 21   Litho.   Perf. 14½
B149 SP70 45c +5c multi   .85 1.25
B150 SP70 80c +5c multi   2.10 2.10
  a. Souv. sheet, 2 ea #B149-B150   4.75 5.75
  b. As "a," with added inscription   8.00 8.00

No. B150b inscribed with Stampex '95 emblem in sheet margin.
Surtax for children's health camps.

SP71

Children's Health: Nos. B151, B153, Infant buckled into child safety seat. 80c, Child holding adult's hand on pedestrian crossing.

1996, June 5   Litho.   Perf. 14x13½
B151 SP71 40c +5c multi   .80 .95
B152 SP71 80c +5c multi   1.40 1.50
  a. Souvenir sheet, 2 each Nos.
    B151-B152, perf. 14x14½   4.00 4.00
  b. As "a" with added inscription   5.50 5.50

Self-Adhesive
Serpentine Die Cut 11½
B153 SP71 40c +5c multi   .60 .85

No. B152b inscribed with CAPEX '96 emblem in sheet margin.

SP72

Original Design
1996, June 5   Litho.   Perf. 14x13½
B154 SP72 40c +5c multi   *1,000.* 1,200.
Self-Adhesive
Serpentine Die Cut 11½
B155 SP72 40c +5c multi   1,750. 1,750.

Nos. B154 and B155 were withdrawn before issue by New Zealand Post. Slightly over 1,000 examples of No. B154 and 500 examples of No. B155 were sold in error by two post offices within three days of June 5. A total of 402 examples of the souvenir sheet containing No. B154 were made available by the printer, but none were sold at post offices.

The stamps were withdrawn because the inclusion of the stuffed animal indicated that the infant was improperly belted into the vehicle.

Children's
Health — SP73

Children's designs of "Healthy Living:" No. B156, Child on beach. 80c+5c, Child riding horse on waterfront. No. B158, Mosaic of person collecting fruit from tree, vert.

1997, June 18   Litho.   Perf. 14
B156 SP73 40c +5c multi   .80 .85
B157 SP73 80c +5c multi   1.40 1.40
Souvenir Sheet
B157A Sheet of 3, #B156-B157,
    B157Ab   3.50 3.50
  b. SP73 40c +5c like #B158   2.00 2.00
Size: 25x36mm
Self-Adhesive
Serpentine Die Cut 10½
B158 SP73 40c +5c multi   .75 .70

Children's Water
Safety — SP74

Designs: 40c+5c, Child in life jacket. 80c+5c, Child learning to swim.

1998, June 24   Litho.   Perf. 13½
B159 SP74 40c +5c multicolored   .75 .60
B160 SP74 80c +5c multicolored   1.40 1.40
  a. Sheet, 2 each #B159-B160   4.25 4.25
Size: 25x38mm
Self-Adhesive
Serpentine Die Cut 11½
B161 SP74 40c +5c multicolored   .75 .45

Children's
Health — SP75

Scenes from children's books: #B162, Hairy Maclary's Bone, by Lynley Dodd. #B163, Lion in the Meadow, by Margaret Mahy. 80c+5c, Greedy Cat, by Joy Cowley.

Serpentine Die Cut 10¼
1999, June 16   Litho.
Self-Adhesive (#B162)
B162 SP75 40c +5c multi   .75 .60
Perf. 14¼
B163 SP75 40c +5c multi   .75 .60
B164 SP75 80c +5c multi   1.40 1.40
Souvenir Sheet
B165 Sheet of 3, #B163-B164,
    B165a   3.50 3.50
  a. SP75 40c +5c like #B162   2.00 2.00
Nos. B162, B165a are 37x26mm.

For 2000 semi-postals, see Nos. 1681, 1682, 1682a and 1687.

Children's
Health — SP76

Designs: No. B166, Four cyclists. 90c+5c, Cyclist in air. No. B168, Cyclist riding through puddle.

2001, Aug. 1   Litho.   Perf. 14
B166 SP76 40c +5c multi   .75 .60
  a. Sheet of 10   7.50 7.50
B167 SP76 90c +5c multi   1.50 1.40
  a. Souvenir sheet, #B166-B167   2.10 2.10
Size: 30x25mm
Serpentine Die Cut 10x9¾
Self-Adhesive
B168 SP76 40c +5c multi   .60 .60
    Nos. B166-B168 (3)   2.85 2.60

Healthy
Living — SP77

Designs: B169, 40c+5c, Fruits. 90c+5c, Vegetables.
No. B171a, Fruits, diff. B172, Fruits diff. (like B171a).

2002, Aug. 7   Perf. 14¼x14
B169 SP77 40c +5c multi   .75 .60
B170 SP77 90c +5c multi   1.50 1.50
Souvenir Sheet
B171 Sheet, #B169-B170,
    B171a   3.50 3.50
  a. SP77 40c +5c multi (21x26mm)   2.00 2.00
Coil Stamp
Size: 21x26mm
Self-Adhesive
Serpentine Die Cut 9¾x10
B172 SP77 40c +5c multi   .75 .50

Children's
Health — SP78

Designs: No. B173, 40c+5c, Children on swings. 90c+5c, Child with ball, girl playing hopscotch. Nos. B175a, B176, 40c+ 5c, Girl on monkey bars.

2003, Aug. 6 — Litho. — Perf. 14
B173 SP78 40c +5c multi .75 .55
B174 SP78 90c +5c multi 1.50 1.50

Souvenir Sheet
B175 Sheet, #B173-B174, B175a 3.50 3.50
a. SP78 40c +5c multi (21x26mm), perf. 14½x14 2.00 2.00

Coil Stamp
Size: 21x26mm
Self-Adhesive
Serpentine Die Cut 9¾x10
B176 SP78 40c +5c multi .75 .55

Children's Health — SP79

Designs: No. B177, Children playing with beach ball in water. No. B178, People in boat. Nos. B179a, B180, People fishing.

2004, Sept. 1 — Litho. — Perf. 14
B177 SP79 45c +5c multi .75 .65
B178 SP79 90c +5c multi 1.50 1.50

Souvenir Sheet
B179 Sheet, #B177-B178, B179a 3.50 3.50
a. SP79 45c +5c multi (22x27mm), perf. 14¼x14 2.00 2.00

Self-Adhesive
Size: 22x27mm
Serpentine Die Cut 9½x10
B180 SP79 45c +5c multi .75 .65

Children's Health — SP80

Designs: No. B181, Girl and horse. 90c+5c, Boy and rabbit. Nos. B183a, B184, Children and dog.

2005, Aug. 3 — Litho. — Perf. 14
B181 SP80 45c +5c multi .75 .65
B182 SP80 90c +5c multi 1.50 1.50
B183 Souvenir sheet, #B181-B182, B183a 3.50 3.50
a. SP80 45c +5c multi, 20x25mm, perf. 14½x14 2.00 2.00

Self-Adhesive
Size: 20x25mm
Serpentine Die Cut 9½x10
B184 SP80 45c +5c multi .75 .65

Children's Health — SP81

Designs: No. B185, Girl releasing dove. $1+10c, Boy with origami bird. Nos. B187a, B188, Two children, peace lily (25x30mm).

2007, Sept. 5 — Litho. — Perf. 14
B185 SP81 50c +10c multi .85 .85
a. Perf. 13½ .85 .85
B186 SP81 $1 +10c multi 1.50 1.50
a. Perf. 13½ 1.50 1.50

Souvenir Sheet
B187 Sheet, #B185-B186, B187a 3.75 3.75
a. SP81 50c +10c multi, perf. 14½x14 2.50 2.50
b. As "a," perf. 14½x13½x14½x14 2.00 2.00
c. Souvenir sheet, #B185a, B186a, B187b 3.25 3.25

Self-Adhesive
Serpentine Die Cut 9½x10
B188 SP81 50c +10c multi .85 .85

Surtax for Children's Health Camps.

Children's Health SP82

Child: No. B189, Cycling. $1+10c, Kayaking. Nos. B191a, B192, Running.

2008, July 2 — Litho. — Perf. 14¼
B189 SP82 50c +10c multi .75 .75
B190 SP82 $1 +10c multi 1.50 1.50

Souvenir Sheet
B191 Sheet, #B189-B190, B191a 4.00 4.00
a. SP82 50c +10c multi (36x36mm), perf. 14x14½ 1.75 1.75

Self-Adhesive
Serpentine Die Cut 9¾
Size: 34x34mm
B192 SP82 50c +10c multi .95 .95

Surtax for Children's Health Camps.

Children's Health Stamps, 80th Anniv. — SP83

Stamps in color: No. B193, #B151. $1+10c, #B5. Nos. B195a, B196, #B23.

2009, Sept. 7 — Litho. — Perf. 13¼x13½
B193 SP83 50c +10c multi .90 .90
a. Perf. 14 1.00 1.00
B194 SP83 $1 +10c multi 1.60 1.60
a. Perf. 14 1.75 1.75

Souvenir Sheet
B195 Sheet, #B193a, B194a, B195a 3.75 3.50
a. SP83 50c+10c multi, perf. 14½x14, 22x27mm 2.00 2.00

Self-Adhesive
Serpentine Die Cut 9½x10
Size: 21x26mm
B196 SP83 50c +10c multi .90 .90

Surtax for Children's Health Camps.

Butterflies SP84

Designs: No. B197, Monarch butterfly. $1+10c, Tussock butterfly. Nos. B199a, B200, Boulder copper butterfly, vert. (25x30mm).

2010, July 7 — Litho. — Perf. 14
B197 SP84 50c + 10c multi .75 .75
B198 SP84 $1 +10c multi 1.50 1.50

Souvenir Sheet
B199 Sheet of 3, #B197-B198, B199a 3.75 3.75
a. SP84 50c +10c multi 1.50 1.50

Self-Adhesive
Serpentine Die Cut 9½x10
B200 SP84 50c +10c multi 1.00 1.00

Surtax for Children's Health Camps.

Flightless Birds — SP85

Designs: No. B201, Kiwi. $1.20+10c, Kakapo. Nos. B203a, B204, Takahe, vert. (25x30mm).

2011, July 6 — Litho. — Perf. 14
B201 SP85 60c + 10c multi 1.10 1.10
B202 SP85 $1.20 +10c multi 2.25 2.25

Souvenir Sheet
B203 Sheet of 3, #B201-B202, B203a 5.00 5.00
a. SP85 60c +10c multi 1.60 1.60

Self-Adhesive
Serpentine Die Cut 9½x10
B204 SP85 60c +10c multi 1.25 1.25

Surtax for Children's Health Camps.

New Zealand Sea Lions — SP86

Designs: No. B205, Sea lion pup. $1.40+10c, Adolescent male sea lion. Nos. B207a, B208, Head of sea lion pup, vert. (23x27mm).

2012, Aug. 1 — Perf. 14
B205 SP86 70c + 10c multi 1.25 1.25
B206 SP86 $1.40 +10c multi 2.50 2.50

Souvenir Sheet
B207 Sheet of 3, #B205-B206, B207a 5.75 5.75
a. SP86 70c +10c multi 2.00 2.00

Self-Adhesive
Serpentine Die Cut 9½x10
B208 SP86 70c +10c multi 1.40 1.40

Surtax for New Zealand Foundation for Child and Family Health and Development.

Children and Farm Pets — SP87

Designs: No. B209, Boy and lamb. $1.40 + 10c, Girl and piglets. Nos. B211a, B212, Boy and goat (22x27mm).

2013, Sept. 4 — Perf. 14
B209 SP87 70c +10c multi 1.25 1.25
a. Perf. 13½ 1.25 1.25
B210 SP87 $1.40 +10c multi 2.40 2.40
a. Perf. 13½ 2.40 2.40

Souvenir Sheet
Perf. 13½
B211 Sheet of 3, #B209a, B210a, B211a 5.00 5.00
a. SP87 70c +10c multi 1.25 1.25

Self-Adhesive
Serpentine Die Cut 9½x10
B212 SP87 70c +10c multi 1.25 1.25

Surtax for Stand Children's Services.

Children and Vegetables — SP88

Designs: No. B213, Girl and carrots. $1.40 + 10c, Boy and apples. Nos. B215a, B216, Boy and pumpkin.

2014, Sept. 3 — Litho. — Perf. 14
B213 SP88 80c +10c multi 1.40 1.40
a. Perf. 13½ 1.40 1.40
B214 SP88 $1.40 +10c multi 2.40 2.40
a. Perf. 13½ 2.40 2.40

Souvenir Sheet
B215 Sheet of 3, #B213a, B214a, B215a 5.25 5.25
a. SP88 80c +10c multi (22x27mm) 1.40 1.40

Self-Adhesive
Size: 21x26mm
B216 SP88 80c +10c multi 1.40 1.40

Surtax for Stand Children's Services Tu Maia Whanau.

Children and Sun Protection — SP89

Designs: No. B217, Girl under beach umbrella. $1.40+10c, Girl wearing hat with ear flaps putting sun screen on hands. $2+10c, Girl with large hat over head. Nos. B220a, B221, Boy, large pair of sunglasses.

2015, Sept. 2 — Litho. — Perf. 14
B217 SP89 80c +10c multi 1.25 1.25
a. Perf. 13¼x13½ 1.25 1.25
B218 SP89 $1.40 +10c multi 1.90 1.90
a. Perf. 13¼x13½ 1.90 1.90
B219 SP89 $2 +10c multi 2.75 2.75
a. Perf. 13¼x13½ 2.75 2.75
Nos. B217-B219 (3) 5.90 5.90

Miniature Sheet
B220 Sheet of 4, #B217a, B218a, B219a, B220a 7.25 7.25
a. SP89 80c+10c multi, perf. 13¾x13½, 25x30mm 1.25 1.25

Self-Adhesive
Size: 25x30mm
Serpentine Die Cut 9½x10
B221 SP89 80c +10c multi 1.25 1.25

Surtax for Stand Children's Services Tu Maia Whanau.

Children's Health — SP90

Designs: $1+10c, Child with rugby ball, child holding end of rope. $1.80+10c, Children playing tug-of-war. $2.20+10c, Child holding end of rope, children stretching.

2016, Sept. 7 — Litho. — Perf. 14¼
B222 SP90 $1 +10c multi 1.60 1.60
B223 SP90 $1.80 +10c multi 2.75 2.75
B224 SP90 $2.20 +10c multi 3.50 3.50
a. Horiz. strip of 3, #B222-B224 8.00 8.00
b. Souvenir sheet of 3, #B222-B224 8.00 8.00
Nos. B222-B224 (3) 7.85 7.85

Surtax for Stand Children's Services Tu Maia Whanau.

Theodore Bear on Ladder — SP91
Hay Hay Teddy Bear — SP92

Lubert Bear Wearing Sweater — SP93
Teddy Bear in Mailbox — SP94

Little Ted Bear Wearing Poppy — SP95
Frontliner Bear With Face Mask — SP96

2020, May 20 — Litho. — Perf. 14¼x14½
B225 Miniature sheet of 6 19.00 19.00
a. SP91 $1.30 multi 2.00 2.00
b. SP92 $1.30 multi 2.00 2.00
c. SP93 $1.30 multi 2.00 2.00

d.	SP94 $2.60 multi	4.25	4.25
e.	SP95 $2.60 multi	4.25	4.25
f.	SP96 $2.60 multi	4.25	4.25

No. B225 sold for $14.70, with $3 going to the Red Cross.

AIR POST STAMPS

Plane over Lake Manapouri — AP1

Perf. 14x14½

1931, Nov. 10   Typo.   Wmk. 61

C1	AP1	3p chocolate	27.50	22.50
a.		Perf. 14x15	150.00	500.00
C2	AP1	4p dark violet	27.50	27.50
C3	AP1	7p orange	30.00	27.50
		Nos. C1-C3 (3)	85.00	77.50

Most examples of No. C1a are poorly centered.

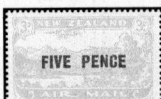

Type of 1931 Surcharged in Red

1931, Dec. 18   Perf. 14x14½

C4	AP1	5p on 3p yel green	20.00	25.00

Type of 1931 Overprinted in Dark Blue

1934, Jan. 17

C5	AP1	7p bright blue	50.00	55.00

1st official air mail flight between NZ and Australia.

Airplane over Landing Field — AP2

1935, May 4   Engr.   Perf. 14

C6	AP2	1p rose carmine	1.10	.80
C7	AP2	3p dark violet	5.75	3.75
C8	AP2	6p gray blue	11.50	5.75
		Nos. C6-C8 (3)	18.35	10.30
		Set, never hinged	40.00	

SPECIAL DELIVERY STAMPS

SD1

Perf. 14x14½,14x15

1903-26   Typo.   Wmk. 61

E1	SD1	6p purple & red ('26)	60.00	40.00
a.		6p violet & red, perf. 11	70.00	50.00

Mail Car — SD2

1939, Aug. 16   Engr.   Perf. 14

E2	SD2	6p violet gray	1.75	6.00

POSTAGE DUE STAMPS

D1

Wmk. 62

1899, Dec. 1   Typo.   Perf. 11

J1	D1	½p green & red	8.00	19.00
a.		No period after "D"	75.00	60.00
J2	D1	1p green & red	12.50	2.10
J3	D1	2p green & red	40.00	6.25
J4	D1	3p green & red	20.00	6.00
J5	D1	4p green & red	42.50	25.00
J6	D1	5p green & red	45.00	60.00
J7	D1	6p green & red	45.00	60.00
J8	D1	8p green & red	110.00	150.00
J9	D1	10p green & red	175.00	225.00
J10	D1	1sh green & red	140.00	100.00
J11	D1	2sh green & red	225.00	300.00
		Nos. J1-J11 (11)	863.00	953.35
		Set, never hinged	1,650.	

Nos. J1-J11 may be found with N. Z. and D. varying in size.

D2

1902, Feb. 28   Unwmk.

J12	D2	½p gray grn & red	3.00	7.50

Wmk. 61

J13	D2	½p gray grn & red	3.00	2.10
J14	D2	1p gray grn & red	12.00	4.00
J15	D2	2p gray grn & red	150.00	150.00

1904-28   Perf. 14, 14x14½

J16	D2	½p green & car	3.75	4.25
J17	D2	1p green & car	7.00	1.00
J18	D2	2p green & car	9.00	3.50
J19	D2	3p grn & rose ('28)	50.00	25.00
		Nos. J16-J19 (4)	69.75	33.75

N Z and Star printed on the back in Blue

1925   Unwmk.   Perf. 14x14½, 14x15

J20	D2	½p green & rose	4.00	26.00
J21	D2	2p green & rose	9.00	35.00

> Catalogue values for unused stamps in this section, from this point to the end of the section, are for Never Hinged items.

D3

1939   Wmk. 61   Typo.   Perf. 15x14

J22	D3	½p turquoise green	13.00	9.00
J23	D3	1p rose pink	5.00	.60
J24	D3	2p ultramarine	9.00	1.75
J25	D3	3p brown orange	26.00	29.00
		Nos. J22-J25 (4)	53.00	40.35

1945-49   Wmk. 253

J27	D3	1p rose pink ('49)	5.00	25.00
J28	D3	2p ultramarine ('47)	7.00	9.00
J29	D3	3p brown orange	15.00	5.75
		Nos. J27-J29 (3)	27.00	39.75

The use of postage due stamps was discontinued in Sept., 1951.

WAR TAX STAMP

No. 144 Overprinted in Black

Perf. 14x14½

1915, Sept. 24   Wmk. 61

MR1	A43	½p green	2.10	.60

OFFICIAL STAMPS

Regular Issues of 1882-92 Overprinted & Handstamped

1892   Wmk. 62   Perf as Before
Rose or Magenta Handstamp

O1	A9	1p rose	600.
O2	A10	2p violet	800.
O3	A16	2½p ultramarine	700.
O4	A17	5p olive gray	1,000.
O5	A13	6p brown	1,200.

Violet Handstamp

O6	N1	½p rose	1,000.
O7	A9	1p rose	600.
O8	A10	2p violet	

Handstamped on No. 67A in Rose

1899   Perf. 10, 10x11

O9	A15a	½p black	600.

Handstamped on No. 79 in Violet
Unwmk.   Perf. 14, 15

O10	A27	8p dull blue	1,200.

Hstmpd. on Stamps of 1899-1900 in Violet

1902   Perf. 11

O11	A22	2½p blue	650.
O12	A23	3p org brown	1,000.
O13	A25	5p red brown	900.
O14	A27	8p dark blue	1,000.

Green Handstamp

O15	A25	5p red brown	900.

Handstamped on Stamp of 1901 in Violet
Wmk. 63   Perf. 11

O16	A35	1p carmine	600.

Handstamped on Stamps of 1902-07 in Violet or Magenta

1905-07   Wmk. 61   Perf. 11, 14

O17	A18	½p green	600.
O18	A35	1p carmine	600.
O19	A22	2½p blue	700.
O20	A25	5p red brown	
O21	A27	8p deep blue	
O22	A30	2sh blue green	5,000.

The "O. P. S. O." handstamp is usually struck diagonally, reading up, but on No. O19 it also occurs horizontally. The letters stand for "On Public Service Only."

Overprinted in Black

On Stamps of 1902-07

1907   Perf. 14, 14x13, 14x14½

O23	A18	½p green	12.00	2.00
O24	A35	1p carmine	12.00	1.00
a.		Booklet pane of 6	110.00	
O25	A33	2p violet	20.00	2.00
O26	A23	3p orange brn	60.00	6.00
O27	A26	6p carmine rose	250.00	40.00
a.		Horiz. pair, imperf. vert.	925.00	
O28	A29	1sh brown red	125.00	25.00
O29	A30	2sh blue green	175.00	150.00
a.		Horiz. pair, imperf. vert.	1,400.	
O30	A31	5sh vermilion	350.00	350.00
		Nos. O23-O30 (8)	1,004.	576.00

On No. 127

Perf. 14x13, 14x14½

O31	A26	6p carmine rose	325.00	65.00

On No. 129

1909   Perf. 14x14½

O32	A35	1p car (redrawn)	90.00	3.00

On Nos. 130-131, 133, 137, 139

1910   Perf. 14, 14x13½, 14x14½

O33	A41	½p yel grn	10.00	1.00
a.		Inverted overprint		1,600.
O34	A42	1p carmine	3.75	.25
O35	A41	3p org brn	20.00	2.00
O36	A41	6p car rose	30.00	10.00
O37	A41	1sh vermilion	70.00	40.00
		Nos. O33-O37 (5)	133.75	53.25

For 3p see note on perf varieties following No. 139.

On Postal-Fiscal Stamps Nos. AR32, AR36, AR44

1911-14

O38	PF1	2sh blue ('14)	75.00	52.50
O39	PF1	5sh green ('13)	125.00	200.00
O40	PF2	£1 rose	1,000.	625.00
		Nos. O38-O40 (3)	1,200.	877.50

On Stamps of 1909-19

Perf. 14x13½, 14x14½, 14x15]

1915-19   Typo.

O41	A43	½p green	1.60	.25
O42	A46	1½p gray black ('16)	8.00	3.00
O43	A47	1½p gray black ('16)	5.75	.25
O44	A47	1½p brown org ('19)	.60	.60
O45	A43	2p yellow ('17)	5.75	.50
O46	A43	3p chocolate ('19)	16.00	1.50

Engr.

O47	A45	3p vio brn ('16)	8.00	1.50
O48	A45	6p car rose ('16)	12.00	1.00
O49	A41	8p dp bl (R) ('16)	20.00	30.00
O50	A45	1sh vermilion ('16)	7.50	2.25
a.		1sh orange	15.00	20.00
		Nos. O41-O50 (10)	90.35	41.60

For 8p see note on perf varieties following No. 139.

1922   On No. 157

O51	A45	8p red brown	125.00	200.00

1925   On Nos. 151, 158

O52	A45	4p purple	20.00	4.25
O53	A45	9p olive green	45.00	42.50

On No. 177

1925   Perf. 14x14½

O54	A42	1p carmine	5.00	5.00

On Nos. 184, 182

1927-28   Wmk. 61   Perf. 14, 14½x14

O55	A57	1p rose red	2.50	.25
O56	A56	2sh blue	125.00	140.00

On No. AR50

1933   Perf. 14

O57	PF5	5sh green	450.00	450.00

Nos. 186, 187, 196 Overprinted in Black

1936   Perf. 14x13½, 13½x14, 14

O58	A59	1p copper red	2.00	1.40
O59	A60	1½p red brown	14.00	30.00
O60	A61	1sh dark slate grn	30.00	52.50
		Nos. O58-O60 (3)	46.00	83.90
		Set, never hinged	120.00	

Same Overprint Horizontally in Black or Green on Stamps of 1936
Perf. 12½, 13½, 13x13½, 14x13½, 13½x14, 14

1936-42   Wmk. 253

O61	A58	½p brt grn ('37)	1.50	5.25
O62	A59	1p copper red	3.00	.60
O63	A60	1½p red brown	4.00	5.25
O64	A61	2p red org ('38)	1.00	.25
		Never hinged	250.00	
O65	A62	2½p dk gray & dk brown	8.00	24.00
O66	A63	3p choc ('38)	27.50	4.00
O67	A64	4p blk brn & blk	5.00	1.10
O68	A66	6p red ('37)	5.75	.35
O68B	A67	8p dp brn ('42)	8.50	20.00
O69	A68	9p blk & scar (G) ('38)	80.00	45.00
O70	A69	1sh dk slate grn	14.00	1.60
a.		Perf. 12½ ('42)	27.50	1.75

Overprint Vertical

O71	A70	2sh ol grn ('37)	24.00	8.50
a.		Perf. 12½ ('42)	90.00	25.00
		Nos. O61-O71 (12)	182.25	115.90
		Set, never hinged	550.00	

Same Overprint Horizontally in Black on Nos. 226, 227, 228

1938

O72	A79	½p emerald	5.75	1.75
O73	A79	1p rose red	7.25	.30
O74	A80	1½p red brn	37.50	10.50
	Nos. O72-O74 (3)		50.50	12.55
	Set, never hinged		95.00	

Same Overprint on No. AR50

1938   Wmk. 61   Perf. 14

O75	PF5	5sh green	75.00	47.50

Nos. 229-235, 237, 239-241 Overprinted in Red or Black

Perf. 13½x13, 13x13½, 14x13½

1940   Wmk. 253

O76	A81	½p dk bl grn (R)	.60	.75
a.	"ff" joined		29.00	70.00
O77	A82	1p scar & sepia	2.25	.30
a.	"ff" joined		29.00	70.00
O78	A83	1½p brt vio & ultra	1.10	4.25
O79	A84	2p blk brn & Prus grn	2.25	.30
a.	"ff" joined		35.00	70.00
O80	A85	2½p dk bl & myr grn	1.40	4.50
a.	"ff" joined		29.00	77.50
O81	A86	3p dp plum & dk vio (R)	5.75	.95
a.	"ff" joined		24.00	55.00
O82	A87	4p dk red vio & vio brn	14.50	1.60
a.	"ff" joined		70.00	92.50
O83	A89	6p vio & brt grn	14.50	1.60
a.	"ff" joined		40.00	80.00
O84	A90	8p org red & blk	14.50	13.00
a.	"ff" joined		40.00	110.00
O85	A91	9p dp org & olive	5.75	5.75
O86	A92	1sh dk sl grn & ol	35.00	5.25
	Nos. O76-O86 (11)		97.60	38.25
	Set, never hinged		190.00	

Nos. 227A, 228C Overprinted in Black

1941   Wmk. 253   Perf. 13½

O88	A79	1p light blue green	.30	.30
O89	A80	3p blue	.75	.30
	Set, never hinged		2.25	

Same Overprint on No. 245

1944   Perf. 14x15

Size: 17¼x20¼mm

O90	A68	9p int black & scar	20.00	17.00
			60.00	

Same Overprint on No. AR78

Perf. 14

O91	PF5	5sh green	12.00	7.00
			20.00	

Catalogue values for unused stamps in this section, from this point to the end of the section, are for Never Hinged items.

Same Ovpt. on Stamps of 1941-47

1946-51   Perf. 13½, 14

O92	A79	½p brn org ('46)	1.75	1.25
O92B	A80	1½p red	5.75	1.25
O93	A80	2p orange	.90	.30
O94	A80	4p rose lilac	4.00	1.25
O95	A80	6p rose carmine	5.75	1.25
O96	A80	8p deep violet	10.00	4.50
O97	A80	9p chocolate	11.50	5.75
O98	A104	1sh dk car rose & chestnut	11.50	1.75
O99	A104	2sh dk grn & brn org	26.00	8.50
	Nos. O92-O99 (9)		77.15	25.80

Queen Elizabeth II — O1

1954, Mar. 1   Engr.   Wmk. 253

Perf. 13½x13

O100	O1	1p orange	1.10	.90
O101	O1	1½p rose brown	4.25	5.75
O102	O1	2p green	.45	.95
O103	O1	3p red	.45	.25
O104	O1	4p blue	1.10	.60

O105	O1	9p rose carmine	10.50	2.50
O106	O1	1sh rose violet	1.10	.25
	Nos. O100-O106 (7)		18.95	10.10

Exist imperf.

Nos. O102, O101 Surcharged

1959-61

O107	O1	2½p on 2p green ('61)	1.10	1.75
O108	O1	6p on 1½p rose brn	.60	1.25

Exist imperf.

1963, Mar. 1

O109	O1	2½p dark olive	4.00	1.75
O111	O1	3sh slate	47.50	57.50

Exist imperf.

LIFE INSURANCE

Lighthouses — LI1

Perf. 10, 11, 10x11, 12x11½

1891, Jan. 2   Typo.   Wmk. 62

OY1	LI1	½p purple	110.00	7.00
OY2	LI1	1p blue	80.00	2.00
OY3	LI1	2p red brown	150.00	4.25
OY4	LI1	3p chocolate	425.00	22.50
OY5	LI1	6p green	550.00	70.00
OY6	LI1	1sh rose pink	800.00	140.00
	Nos. OY1-OY6 (6)		2,115.	245.75

Stamps from outside rows of the sheets sometimes lack watermark.

1903-04   Wmk. 61   Perf. 11, 14x11

OY7	LI1	½p purple	120.00	7.00
OY8	LI1	1p blue	75.00	1.10
OY9	LI1	2p red brown	200.00	10.00
	Nos. OY7-OY9 (3)		395.00	18.10

Lighthouses — LI2

1905-32   Perf. 11, 14, 14x14½

OY10	LI2	½p yel grn ('13)	1.40	.90
OY11	LI2	½p green ('32)	5.75	2.75
OY12	LI2	1p blue ('06)	375.00	29.00
OY13	LI2	1p dp rose ('13)	9.75	1.10
OY14	LI2	1p scarlet ('31)	4.25	2.00
OY15	LI2	1½p brn org ('19)	1.75	1.40
OY16	LI2	1½p gray ('17)	14.00	4.25
OY17	LI2	2p red brown	2,750.	200.00
OY18	LI2	2p violet ('13)	20.00	17.00
OY19	LI2	2p yellow ('21)	6.00	6.00
OY20	LI2	3p ocher ('13)	29.00	20.00
OY21	LI2	3p choc ('31)	11.00	26.00
OY22	LI2	6p car rose ('13)	20.00	26.00
OY23	LI2	6p pink ('31)	20.00	45.00
	Nos. OY10-OY23 (14)		3,268.	381.40

#OY15, OY16 have "POSTAGE" at each side. Stamps from outside rows of the sheets sometimes lack watermark.

1946-47   Wmk. 253   Perf. 14x15

OY24	LI2	½p yel grn ('47)	1.90	1.90
OY25	LI2	1p scarlet	1.40	1.25
OY26	LI2	2p yellow	2.25	15.00
OY27	LI2	3p chocolate	10.50	30.00
OY28	LI2	6p pink ('47)	8.50	25.00
	Nos. OY24-OY28 (5)		24.55	73.15
	Set, never hinged		42.50	

Catalogue values for unused stamps in this section, from this point to the end of the section, are for Never Hinged items.

New Zealand Lighthouses

Castlepoint — LI3   Taiaroa — LI4

Cape Palliser LI5   Cape Campbell LI6

Eddystone (England) LI7   Stephens Island LI8

The Brothers LI9   Cape Brett LI10

Perf. 13½x13, 13x13½

1947-65   Engr.   Wmk. 253

OY29	LI3	½p dk grn & red orange	1.75	1.70
OY30	LI4	1p ol brn & blue	1.75	1.10
OY31	LI5	2p int bl & gray	.90	.90
OY32	LI6	2½p ultra & blk ('63)	11.00	15.00
OY33	LI7	3p red vio & bl	3.50	.75
OY34	LI8	4p dk brn & org	4.50	1.75
a.	Wmkd. sideways ('65)		4.50	16.00
OY35	LI9	6p dk brn & bl	4.25	2.50
OY36	LI10	1sh red brn & bl	4.25	3.50
	Nos. OY29-OY36 (8)		31.90	27.20

Set first issued Aug. 1, 1947. Exist imperf.

Nos. OY30, OY32-OY33, OY34a, OY35-OY36 and Types Surcharged

No. OY37   No. OY38

Perf. 13½x13, 13x13½

1967-68   Engr.   Wmk. 253

OY37	LI4	1c on 1p	2.50	4.75
a.	Wmkd. upright ('68)		1.10	4.75
OY38	LI6	2c on 2½p	11.00	16.00
OY39	LI7	2½c on 3p, wmkd. upright	1.75	5.50
a.	Watermarked sideways ('68)		2.75	5.50
OY40	LI8	3c on 4p	5.25	6.25
OY41	LI9	5c on 6p	.85	7.00
OY42	LI10	10c on 1sh, wmkd. sideways	.85	4.75
a.	Watermarked upright		2.40	11.50
	Nos. OY37-OY42 (6)		22.20	44.25

The surcharge is different on each stamp and is adjusted to obliterate old denomination. One dot only on 2½c. Set first issued July 10, 1967.

Moeraki Point Lighthouse — LI11

Lighthouses: 2½c, Puysegur Point, horiz. 3c, Baring Head. 4c, Cape Egmont, horiz. 8c, East Cape. 10c, Farewell Spit. 15c, Dog Island.

Perf. 13x13½, 13½x13, 14 (8c, 10c)

1969-76   Litho.   Unwmk.

OY43	LI11	½c pur, bl & yel	.75	2.00
OY44	LI11	2½c yel, ultra & grn	.60	1.40
OY45	LI11	3c org brn & brn	.60	.85
OY46	LI11	4c lt ultra, org & ol brn	.60	1.10
OY47	LI11	8c multicolored	.60	3.25
OY48	LI11	10c multicolored	.40	3.25
OY49	LI11	15c multicolored	.40	2.40
a.	Perf. 14 ('78)		1.00	2.00
	Nos. OY43-OY49 (7)		3.95	14.25

Cent. of Government Life Insurance Office. Issued: #OY47-OY48, 11/17/76; others 3/27/69.

No. OY44 Srchd.

Perf. 13½x13

1978, Mar. 8   Litho.   Wmk. 253

OY50	LI11	25c on 2½c multi	.85	2.00

Lighthouse LI12

1981, June 3   Litho.   Perf. 14½

OY51	LI12	5c multicolored	.25	.25
OY52	LI12	10c multicolored	.25	.25
OY53	LI12	20c multicolored	.25	.25
OY54	LI12	30c multicolored	.30	.30
OY55	LI12	40c multicolored	.35	.35
OY56	LI12	50c multicolored	.35	.50
	Nos. OY51-OY56 (6)		1.75	1.90

Government Life Insurance Stamps have been discontinued.

NEWSPAPER STAMPS

Queen Victoria — N1

Wmk. 59

1873, Jan. 1   Typo.   Perf. 10

P1	N1	½p rose	140.00	47.50
a.	Perf. 12½x10		160.00	75.00
b.	Perf. 12½		210.00	75.00

The "N Z" watermark is widely spaced and intended for larger stamps. About a third of the stamps in each sheet are unwatermarked. They are worth a slight premium.
For overprint, see No. O6.

1875, Jan.   Wmk. 64   Perf. 12½

P3	N1	½p rose	25.00	5.00
a.	Pair, imperf. between		800.00	500.00
b.	Perf. 12		70.00	12.50

1892   Wmk. 62   Perf. 12½

P4	N1	½p bright rose	11.00	1.50
a.	Unwatermarked		20.00	10.00

ROSS DEPENDENCY

Catalogue values for unused stamps in this section are for Never Hinged items.

H.M.S. Erebus and Mount Erebus — A1

Ernest H.
Shackleton and
Robert F. Scott
A2

Map
Showing
Location of
Ross
Dependency
A3

Queen Elizabeth II — A4

Perf. 14, 13 (A4)
1957, Jan. 11   Engr.   Wmk. 253

L1	A1	3p dark blue	3.00	1.25
L2	A2	4p dark carmine	3.00	1.25
L3	A3	8p ultra & car rose	3.00	1.25
L4	A4	1sh6p dull violet	3.00	1.25
		Nos. L1-L4 (4)	12.00	5.00

1967, July 10

L5	A1	2c dark blue	21.00	15.00
L6	A2	3c dark carmine	12.00	10.00
L7	A3	7c ultra & car rose	12.00	10.00
L8	A4	15c dull violet	12.00	10.00
		Nos. L5-L8 (4)	57.00	45.00

Skua — A5   Scott Base — A6

Designs: 4c, Hercules plane unloading at Williams Field. 5c, Shackleton's hut, Cape Royds. 8c, Naval supply ship Endeavour unloading. 18c, Tabular ice floe.

Perf. 13x13½
1972, Jan. 18   Litho.   Unwmk.

L9	A5	3c lt bl, blk & gray	1.00	1.75
L10	A5	4c black & violet	.25	1.75
L11	A5	5c rose lil, blk & gray	.25	1.75
L12	A5	8c blk, dk gray & brn	.25	1.75

Perf. 14½x14

L13	A6	10c slate grn, brt grn & blk	.25	1.90
a.		Perf. 14½x13½ ('79)	.70	1.75
L14	A6	18c pur & black	.25	1.90
a.		Perf. 14½x13½ ('79)	1.60	3.00
		Nos. L9-L14 (6)	2.25	10.80

25th Anniv. of
Scott Base — A7

5c, Adelie penguins. 10c, Tracked vehicles. 30c, Field party, Upper Taylor Valley. 40c, Vanda Station. 50c, Scott's hut, Cape Evans, 1911.

1982, Jan. 20   Litho.   Perf. 15½

L15	A7	5c multicolored	1.40	1.60
L16	A7	10c multicolored	.25	.75
L17	A7	20c shown	.25	.75
L18	A7	30c multicolored	.25	.45
L19	A7	40c multicolored	.25	.45
L20	A7	50c multicolored	.25	.45
		Nos. L15-L20 (6)	2.65	4.45

Wildlife — A8

5c, South polar skua. 10c, Snow petrel chick. 20c, Black-browed albatross. 45c, Emperor penguins. 50c, Chinstrap penguins. 70c, Adelie penguins. 80c, Elephant seals. $1, Leopard seal. $2, Weddell seal. $3, Crabeater seal pup.

1994-95   Litho.   Perf. 13½

L21	A8	5c multicolored	.25	.25
L22	A8	10c multicolored	.25	.25
L23	A8	20c multicolored	.30	.30
L23A	A8	40c like No. 24	.65	.65
L24	A8	45c multicolored	.70	.70

L25	A8	50c multicolored	.80	.80
L26	A8	70c multicolored	1.10	1.10
L27	A8	80c multicolored	1.25	1.25
L28	A8	$1 multicolored	1.60	1.60
L29	A8	$2 multicolored	3.25	3.25
L30	A8	$3 multicolored	4.75	4.75
		Nos. L21-L30 (11)	14.90	14.90

Issued: 40c, 10/2/95; others, 11/2/94.

Antarctic
Explorers — A9

Explorer, ships: 40c, James Cook, Resolution & Adventure. 80c, James Clark Ross, Erebus & Terror. $1, Roald Amundsen, Fram. $1.20, Robert Falcon Scott, Terra Nova. $1.50, Ernest Henry Shackleton, Endurance. $1.80, Richard Evelyn Byrd, Floyd Bennett (airplane).

1995, Nov. 9   Litho.   Perf. 14½

L31	A9	40c multicolored	.65	.65
L32	A9	80c multicolored	1.25	1.25
L33	A9	$1 multicolored	1.60	1.60
L34	A9	$1.20 multicolored	1.90	1.90
L35	A9	$1.50 multicolored	2.40	2.40
L36	A9	$1.80 multicolored	2.75	2.75
		Nos. L31-L36 (6)	10.55	10.55

Antarctic
Landscapes — A10

Designs: 40c, Inside ice cave, vert. 80c, Base of glacier, vert. $1, Glacier ice fall, vert. $1.20, Climbers on crater rim. $1.50, Pressure ridges. $1.80, Fumarole ice tower.

1996, Nov. 13   Litho.   Perf. 14

L37	A10	40c multicolored	.65	.65
L38	A10	80c multicolored	1.25	1.25
L39	A10	$1 multicolored	1.60	1.60
L40	A10	$1.20 multicolored	1.90	1.90
L41	A10	$1.50 multicolored	2.40	2.40
L42	A10	$1.80 multicolored	2.75	2.75
		Nos. L37-L42 (6)	10.55	10.55

Antarctic Sea
Birds — A11

40c, Snow petrel. 80c, Cape petrel. $1, Antarctic prion. $1.20, Antarctic fulmar. $1.50, Antarctic petrel. $1.80, Antarctic tern.

1997, Nov. 12   Litho.   Perf. 14

L43	A11	40c multi	.65	.65
L44	A11	80c multi	1.25	1.25
L45	A11	$1 multi	1.75	1.50
L46	A11	$1.20 multi	2.25	2.00
L47	A11	$1.50 multi	2.50	2.25
L48	A11	$1.80 multi	3.00	15.00
		Nos. L43-L48 (6)	11.40	22.65
L48A		Block of 6, #L45, L48, L48b-L48e	20.00	20.00
b.		A11 40c As #L43, without WWF emblem	.90	.90
c.		A11 80c As #L44, without WWF emblem	1.75	1.75
d.		A11 $1.20 As #L46, without WWF emblem	2.75	2.75
e.		A11 $1.50 As #L47, without WWF emblem	3.50	3.50

World Wildlife Fund. Nos. L43-L44, L46-L47 have WWF emblem. Nos. L45 and L48 do not have emblem.

Ice
Formations — A12

Designs: 40c, Sculptured sea ice. 80c, Glacial tongue. $1, Stranded tabular iceberg. $1.20, Autumn at Cape Evans. $1.50, Sea ice in summer thaw. $1.80, Sunset on tabular icebergs.

1998, Nov. 11   Litho.   Perf. 14

L49	A12	40c multicolored	.65	.65
L50	A12	80c multicolored	1.25	1.25
L51	A12	$1 multicolored	1.60	1.60
L52	A12	$1.20 multicolored	1.90	1.90
L53	A12	$1.50 multicolored	2.40	2.40
L54	A12	$1.80 multicolored	2.75	2.75
a.		Block of 6, #L49-L54	15.00	15.00
		Nos. L49-L54 (6)	10.55	10.55

Night
Skies — A13

Designs: 40c, Sea smoke, McMurdo Sound. 80c, Alpenglow, Mt. Erebus. $1.10, Sunset, Black Island. $1.20, Pressure ridges, Ross Sea. $1.50, Evening light, Ross Island. $1.80, Mother of pearl clouds, Ross Island.

1999, Nov. 17   Litho.   Perf. 14

L55	A13	40c multicolored	.65	.65
L56	A13	80c multicolored	1.25	1.25
L57	A13	$1.10 multicolored	1.75	1.75
L58	A13	$1.20 multicolored	1.90	1.90
L59	A13	$1.50 multicolored	2.40	2.40
L60	A13	$1.80 multicolored	2.75	2.75
		Nos. L55-L60 (6)	10.70	10.70

Antarctic
Transportation
A14

Designs: 40c, RNZAF C130 Hercules. 80c, Hagglunds BV206 All-terrain carrier. $1.10, Tracked 4x4 motorbike. $1.20, ASV Track truck. $1.50, Squirrel helicopter. $1.80, Elan Skidoo.

2000, Nov. 4   Litho.   Perf. 14

L61	A14	40c multi	.65	.65
L62	A14	80c multi	1.25	1.25
L63	A14	$1.10 multi	1.75	1.75
L64	A14	$1.20 multi	1.90	1.90
L65	A14	$1.50 multi	2.40	2.40
L66	A14	$1.80 multi	2.75	2.75
		Nos. L61-L66 (6)	10.70	10.70

Penguins Type of 2001 of New Zealand

Designs: 40c, Emperor. 80c, Adelie. 90c, Emperor, diff. $1.30, Adelie, diff. $1.50, Emperor, diff. $2, Adelie, diff.

2001, Nov. 7   Perf. 14¼

L67	A475	40c multi	.65	.65
L68	A475	80c multi	1.25	1.25
L69	A475	90c multi	1.40	1.40
L70	A475	$1.30 multi	2.10	2.10
L71	A475	$1.50 multi	2.40	2.40
L72	A475	$2 multi	3.25	3.25
		Nos. L67-L72 (6)	11.05	11.05

Discovery
Expedition of Capt.
Robert Falcon
Scott, 1901-
04 — A15

Designs: 40c, Three men with sleds. 80c, HMS Discovery. 90c, HMS Discovery trapped in ice. $1.30, Edward Wilson, Ernest Shackleton and sleds. $1.50, Explorers with flags and dog. $2, Base hut.

2002, Nov. 6   Litho.   Perf. 14

L73	A15	40c multi	.65	.65
L74	A15	80c multi	1.25	1.25
L75	A15	90c multi	1.40	1.40
L76	A15	$1.30 multi	2.10	2.10
L77	A15	$1.50 multi	2.40	2.40
L78	A15	$2 multi	3.25	3.25
		Nos. L73-L78 (6)	11.05	11.05

Marine Life — A16

Designs: 40c, Odontaster validus. 90c, Beroe cucumis. $1.30, Macroptychaster accrescens. $1.50, Sterechinus neumayeri. $2, Perkinsiana littoralis.

2003, Oct. 1   Litho.   Perf. 13x13¼

L79	A16	40c multi	.65	.65
L80	A16	90c multi	1.40	1.40
L81	A16	$1.30 multi	2.10	2.10
L82	A16	$1.50 multi	2.40	2.40
L83	A16	$2 multi	3.25	3.25
		Nos. L79-L83 (5)	9.80	9.80

Emperor Penguins
and Map of
Antarctica — A17

Various pictures of penguins.

2004, Nov. 3   Litho.   Perf. 13¼x14
Color of Denomination

L84	A17	45c yellow orange	.70	.70
L85	A17	90c dark brown	1.40	1.40
L86	A17	$1.35 lilac	2.10	2.10
L87	A17	$1.50 red brown	2.40	2.40
L88	A17	$2 gray blue	3.25	3.25
		Nos. L84-L88 (5)	9.85	9.85

Photographs
A18

Designs: 45c, Dry Valleys, by Craig Potton. 90c, Emperor Penguins, by Andris Apse. $1.35, Fur Seal, by Mark Mitchell. $1.50, Captain Scott's Hut, by Colin Monteath. $2. Minke Whale, by Kim Westerskov.

2005, Nov. 2   Litho.   Perf. 13¼

L89	A18	45c multi	.70	.70
L90	A18	90c multi	1.40	1.40
L91	A18	$1.35 multi	2.10	2.10
L92	A18	$1.50 multi	2.40	2.40
L93	A18	$2 multi	3.25	3.25
		Nos. L89-L93 (5)	9.85	9.85

A sheet containing Nos. L89-L93 was in a limited edition album.

New Zealand
Antarctic
Program, 50th
Anniv. — A19

Designs: 45c, Biologist. 90c, Hydrologist. $1.35, Geologist. $1.50, Meteorologist. $2, Marine biologist.

2006, Nov. 1   Litho.   Perf. 14

L94	A19	45c multi	.70	.70
L95	A19	90c multi	1.40	1.40
L96	A19	$1.35 multi	2.10	2.10
L97	A19	$1.50 multi	2.40	2.40
L98	A19	$2 multi	3.25	3.25
		Nos. L94-L98 (5)	9.85	9.85

Commonwealth
Trans-Antarctic
Expedition, 50th
Anniv. — A20

Designs: 50c, Man and Beaver airplane. $1, Man and sled. $1.50, Sled dogs. $2, TE20 Ferguson tractor. $2.50, HMNZS Endeavour.

2007, Nov. 7   Litho.   Perf. 14

L99	A20	50c multi	.80	.80
L100	A20	$1 multi	1.50	1.50
L101	A20	$1.50 multi	2.40	2.40
L102	A20	$2 multi	3.25	3.25
L103	A20	$2.50 multi	4.00	4.00
a.		Souvenir sheet, #L102-L103	7.25	7.25
		Nos. L99-L103 (5)	11.95	11.95

1907-09 British
Antarctic
Expedition — A21

Designs: 50c, Departure of Nimrod from Lyttleton. $1, Expedition Hut, Cape Royds. $1.50, First vehicle on Antarctica. $2, First men to reach South Magnetic Pole. $2.50, First ascent of Mt. Erebus.

2008, Nov. 5   Litho.   Perf. 13½x13¼
L104	A21	50c multi	.80	.80
L105	A21	$1 multi	1.50	1.50
L106	A21	$1.50 multi	2.40	2.40
L107	A21	$2 multi	3.25	3.25
L108	A21	$2.50 multi	4.00	4.00
	Nos. L104-L108 (5)		11.95	11.95

Signing of Antarctic
Treaty, 50th
Anniv. — A22

Mountains and: 50c, Map of Antarctica. $1, Penguins. $1.80, Scientist and equipment. $2.30, Flags. $2.80, Seal.

**   Perf. 13¼x13½**
2009, Nov. 25   Litho.
L109	A22	50c multi	.75	.75
L110	A22	$1 multi	1.50	1.50
L111	A22	$1.80 multi	2.60	2.60
L112	A22	$2.30 multi	3.25	3.25
L113	A22	$2.80 multi	4.00	4.00
	Nos. L109-L113 (5)		12.10	12.10

Whales
A23

Designs: 60c, Sperm whale. $1.20, Minke whale. $1.90, Sei whale. $2.40, Killer whale. $2.90, Humpback whale.

2010, Nov. 17   Litho.   Perf. 15x14¾
L114	A23	60c multi	.95	.95
L115	A23	$1.20 multi	1.90	1.90
L116	A23	$1.90 multi	3.00	3.00
L117	A23	$2.40 multi	3.75	3.75
L118	A23	$2.90 multi	4.50	4.50
a.	Souvenir sheet of 5, #L114-L118		14.50	14.50
	Nos. L114-L118 (5)		14.10	14.10

Race to the
South
Pole — A24

Map of Antarctica and: 60c, Roald Amundsen and ship, Fram. $1.20, Men of Amundsen's expedition. $1.90, Robert Falcon Scott and ship Terra Nova. $2.40, Men of Scott expedition, cross on cairn. $2.90, Flags of United Kingdom and Norway.

2011, Nov. 2   Perf. 13½x13¼
L119	A24	60c multi	.95	.95
L120	A24	$1.20 multi	1.90	1.90
L121	A24	$1.90 multi	3.00	3.00
L122	A24	$2.40 multi	4.00	4.00
a.	Souvenir sheet of 2, #L121-L122		10.00	10.00
L123	A24	$2.90 multi	4.75	4.75
a.	Souvenir sheet of 5, #L119-L123		15.00	15.00
	Nos. L119-L123 (5)		14.60	14.60

Issued: No. L122a, 1/14/12. Christchurch Philatelic Society Centennial Stamp and Postcard Exhibition (#L122a).

Antarctic
Landscapes
A25

Designs: 70c, Mount Erebus. $1.40, Beardmore Glacier. $1.90, Lake Vanda. $2.40, Cape Adare. $2.90, Ross Ice Shelf.

2012, Nov. 21
L124	A25	70c multi	1.25	1.25
L125	A25	$1.40 multi	2.40	2.40
L126	A25	$1.90 multi	3.25	3.25
L127	A25	$2.40 multi	4.00	4.00
L128	A25	$2.90 multi	4.75	4.75
a.	Souvenir sheet of 5, #L124-L128		16.00	16.00
	Nos. L124-L128 (5)		15.65	15.65

Antarctic Food
Web — A26

Designs: 70c, Antarctic krill. $1.40, Lesser snow petrel. $1.90, Adélie penguin. $2.40, Crabeater seal. $2.90, Blue whale.

2013, Nov. 20   Litho.   Perf. 14
L129	A26	70c multi	1.25	1.25
L130	A26	$1.40 multi	2.40	2.40
L131	A26	$1.90 multi	3.25	3.25
L132	A26	$2.40 multi	4.00	4.00
L133	A26	$2.90 multi	4.75	4.75
a.	Souvenir sheet of 5, #L129-L133		16.00	16.00
	Nos. L129-L133 (5)		15.65	15.65

Penguins — A27

Designs: 80c, Emperor penguins. $1.40, Adélie penguin. $2, Macaroni penguins. $2.50, Gentoo penguin and eggs. $3, Chinstrap penguin.

2014, Nov. 19   Litho.   Perf. 14½
L134	A27	80c multi	1.25	1.25
L135	A27	$1.40 multi	2.25	2.25
L136	A27	$2 multi	3.25	3.25
L137	A27	$2.50 multi	4.00	4.00
L138	A27	$3 multi	4.75	4.75
a.	Souvenir sheet of 1 + label		4.75	4.75
b.	Souvenir sheet of 5, #L134-L138		15.50	15.50
	Nos. L134-L138 (5)		15.50	15.50

Values for Nos. L134-L138 are for stamps with surrounding selvage. See Greenland No. 679a.

Imperial Trans-Antarctic Expedition,
Cent. — A28

Designs: No. L139, S.Y. Endurance. No. L140, Ocean Camp. $1.40, Expedition members in boat going from Elephant Island to South Georgia. $2, S.Y. Aurora. $2.50, Expedition members laying depots. $3, Rescue of the Ross Sea Party.

2015, Nov. 4   Litho.   Perf. 14x14½
L139	A28	80c multi	1.10	1.10
L140	A28	80c multi	1.10	1.10
L141	A28	$1.40 multi	1.90	1.90
a.	Souvenir sheet of 3, #L139-L141		4.25	4.25
L142	A28	$2 multi	2.75	2.75
L143	A28	$2.50 multi	3.50	3.50
L144	A28	$3 multi	4.00	4.00
a.	Souvenir sheet of 3, #L142-L144		10.50	10.50
	Nos. L139-L144 (6)		14.35	14.35

Creatures of the Antarctic
Sea Floor — A29

Designs: $1, Stalked crinoid. $1.80, Sea star. $2.20, Sponge. $2.70, Hydroid. $3.30, Sea spider.

2016, Nov. 16   Litho.   Perf. 14½x14
L145	A29	$1 multi	1.40	1.40
L146	A29	$1.80 multi	2.60	2.60
L147	A29	$2.20 multi	3.25	3.25
L148	A29	$2.70 multi	4.00	4.00
L149	A29	$3.30 multi	4.75	4.75
a.	Souvenir sheet of 5, #L145-L149		16.00	16.00
	Nos. L145-L149 (5)		16.00	16.00

Historic Huts and
Items Found In
Them — A30

Designs: $1, Captain Robert Falcon Scott's Discovery Hut. $2, Box, bottle, kettle and crate in Discovery Hut. $2.20, Sir Ernest Shackleton's Nimrod Hut. $2.30, Stove, kettles and canister in Nimrod Hut. $2.70, Scott's Terra Nova Hut. $3.30, Letter, bottles and pencils in Terra Nova Hut.

2017, Sept. 20   Litho.   Perf. 14½
L150	A30	$1 multi	1.40	1.40
L151	A30	$2 multi	3.00	3.00
L152	A30	$2.20 multi	3.25	3.25
L153	A30	$2.30 multi	3.50	3.50
L154	A30	$2.70 multi	4.00	4.00
L155	A30	$3.30 multi	4.75	4.75
a.	Souvenir sheet of 6, #L150-L155		20.00	20.00
	Nos. L150-L155 (6)		19.90	19.90

Aircraft
A31

Designs: No. L156, Royal New Zealand Air Force Auster T7C. No. L157, Royal New Zealand Air Force DHC-2 Beaver. No. L158, Royal New Zealand Air Force C130 Hercules. $2.40, Royal New Zealand Air Force Boeing 757. $3, Southern Lakes Helicopters AS350 B3 Squirrel. $3.60, Kenn Borek Air DHC6 Twin Otter.

2018, Nov. 7   Litho.   Perf. 14¼x14
L156	A31	$1.20 multi	1.75	1.75
L157	A31	$1.20 multi	1.75	1.75
L158	A31	$1.20 multi	1.75	1.75
L159	A31	$2.40 multi	3.50	3.50
L160	A31	$3 multi	4.25	4.25
L161	A31	$3.60 multi	5.00	5.00
a.	Souvenir sheet of 6, #L156-L161		18.00	18.00
	Nos. L156-L161 (6)		18.00	18.00

Ship and
Carsten
Borchgrevink
(1864-1934),
Explorer
A32

Fruitcake and
Cape Adare
Cabin — A33

Toothbrush
and Men in
Cape Adare
Cabin — A34

Primus Stove
and Penguins
Near Cape
Adare
Cabin — A35

Artist and
Watercolor of
Dead
Bird — A36

2019, Sept. 18   Litho.   Perf. 14½x14
L162	A32	$1.30 multi	1.60	1.60
L163	A33	$1.30 multi	1.60	1.60
L164	A34	$2.60 multi	3.25	3.25
L165	A35	$3.30 multi	4.25	4.25
L166	A36	$4 multi	5.00	5.00
a.	Souvenir sheet of 5, #L162-L166		16.00	16.00
	Nos. L162-L166 (5)		15.70	15.70

The fern emblem and "Ross Dependency" inscription on Nos. L162-L166 and L166a were printed in a clear ink that is difficult to see.

Seasonal Views
of Scott
Base — A37

Designs: $1.40, Aurora Australis over Scott Base in winter. $2.70, Sunrise at Scott Base in spring. $3.50, Sunset at Scott Base in summer. $4, Twilight at Scott Base in autumn.

2020, Oct. 7   Litho.   Perf. 13½x13¼
L167	A37	$1.40 multi	1.90	1.90
L168	A37	$2.70 multi	3.75	3.75
L169	A37	$3.50 multi	4.75	4.75
L170	A37	$4 multi	5.25	5.25
a.	Souvenir sheet of 4, #L167-L170		16.00	16.00
	Nos. L167-L170 (4)		15.65	15.65

Portions of the designs of Nos. L167-L170 and L170a were covered with thermochromic ink, which changes color when warmed.

Megafauna — A38

Designs: $1.50, Weddell seal. $2.80, Minke whale. $3.60, Skua. $4.10, Emperor penguins.

2021, Sept. 1   Litho.   Perf. 13¼x13½
L171	A38	$1.50 multi	2.10	2.10
L172	A38	$2.80 multi	4.00	4.00
L173	A38	$3.60 multi	5.25	5.25
L174	A38	$4.10 multi	5.75	5.75
a.	Souvenir sheet of 4, #L171-L174		17.50	17.50
	Nos. L171-L174 (4)		17.10	17.10

Ice Science — A39

Designs: $1.70, Scientist studying microbial communities in sea ice. $3, Chart of supercool measurements. $3.80, Helicopter with ice and snow thickness measuring device. $4.30, Platelet ice research.

2022, Nov. 2   Litho.   Perf. 14
L175	A39	$1.70 multi	2.10	2.10
L176	A39	$3 multi	3.75	3.75
L177	A39	$3.80 multi	4.75	4.75
L178	A39	$4.30 multi	5.50	5.50
a.	Souvenir sheet of 4, #L175-L178		16.50	16.50
	Nos. L175-L178 (4)		16.10	16.10

NICARAGUA

ˌni-kə-ˈrä-gwə

LOCATION — Central America, between Honduras and Costa Rica
GOVT. — Republic
AREA — 50,439 sq. mi.
POP. — 4,384,400 (1997 est.)
CAPITAL — Managua

100 Centavos = 1 Peso
100 Centavos = 1 Córdoba (1913)

> **Catalogue values for unused stamps in this country are for Never Hinged items, beginning with Scott 689 in the regular postage section, Scott C261 in the airpost section, Scott CO37 in the airpost official section, and Scott RA60 in the postal tax section.**

ISSUES OF THE REPUBLIC
Watermarks

Wmk. 117 —
Liberty Cap

Wmk. 209 —
Multiple Ovals

Liberty Cap on Mountain Peak; From Seal of Country — A1

Unwmk.

1862, Dec. 2		Engr.		Perf. 12

Yellowish Paper

| 1 | A1 | 2c dark blue | 75.00 | 20.00 |
| 2 | A1 | 5c black | 150.00 | 60.00 |

Designs of Nos. 1-2 measure 22½x18½mm. Perforations are invariably rough.

Values are for stamps without gum. Examples with gum sell for more. Nos. 1-2 were canceled only by pen.

There is one reported cover of No. 1, two of No. 2.

See No. C509.

A2   A3

1869-71			**White Paper**	
3	A1	1c bister ('71)	3.00	1.25
4	A1	2c blue	3.00	1.25
5	A1	5c black	100.00	1.00
6	A2	10c vermilion	4.00	1.75
7	A3	25c green	7.50	4.00
		Nos. 3-7 (5)	117.50	9.25

Designs of Nos. 3-7 measure 22½x19mm. Perforations are clean cut.

There are two reported covers of No. 5, five of No. 7.

1878-80			**Rouletted 8½**	
8	A1	1c brown	2.00	1.25
9	A1	2c blue	2.00	1.25
10	A1	5c black	50.00	1.00
11	A2	10c ver ('80)	2.50	1.50
12	A3	25c green ('79)	2.50	4.00
		Nos. 8-12 (5)	59.00	9.00

Most values exist on thicker soft paper. Stamps with letter/numeral cancellations other than "3 G," "6 M," "9 C" sell for more.

Nos. 3-12 were reprinted in 1892. The corresponding values of the two series are printed in the same shades which is not usually true of the originals. They are, however, similar to some of the original shades and the only certain test is comparison. Originals have thin white gum; reprints have rather thick yellowish gum. Value 50c each. Unused examples of Nos. 3-12 without gum should be presumed to be reprints. Nos. 5 and 10 unused are extremely scarce and should be purchased with original gum and should be expertized.

Seal of Nicaragua — A4

1882, Aug.-1888			Engr.		Perf. 12
13	A4	1c green	.25	.25
14	A4	2c carmine	.25	.25
15	A4	5c blue	.30	.25
16	A4	10c dull violet	.40	.75
17	A4	15c yellow	.80	25.00
18	A4	20c slate gray	1.60	5.00
19	A4	50c dull violet ('88)	2.25	25.00
		Nos. 13-19 (7)	5.85	56.50

Used Values of Nos. 13-120 are for stamps with genuine cancellations applied while the stamps were valid. Various counterfeit cancellations exist.

Locomotive and Telegraph Key — A5

1890			Engr.	
20	A5	1c yellow brown	.25	.30
21	A5	2c vermilion	.25	.30
22	A5	5c deep blue	.25	.30
23	A5	10c lilac gray	.25	.30
24	A5	20c red	.25	.30
25	A5	50c purple	.25	.30
26	A5	1p brown	.25	.40
27	A5	2p dark green	.25	.40
28	A5	5p lake	.25	.50
29	A5	10p orange	.25	.50
		Nos. 20-29 (10)	2.50	

The issues of 1890-1899 were printed by the Hamilton Bank Note Co., New York, to the order of N. F. Seebeck who held a contract for stamps with the government of Nicaragua. Reprints were made, for sale to collectors, of the 1896, 1897 and 1898 issues, postage, postage due and official stamps. See notes following those issues.

For overprints see Nos. O1-O10.

Perforation Varieties

Imperfs and part perfs of all the Seebeck issues, Nos. 20-120, exist for all except originals of the 1898 issue, Nos. 99-109M.

Goddess of Plenty — A6

1891			Engr.	
30	A6	1c yellow brn	.25	.35
31	A6	2c red	.25	.35
32	A6	5c dk blue	.25	.25
33	A6	10c slate	.25	.50
34	A6	20c plum	.25	2.00
35	A6	50c purple	.25	5.00
36	A6	1p black brn	.25	5.00
37	A6	2p green	.25	8.50
38	A6	5p brown red	.25	
39	A6	10p orange	.25	
		Nos. 30-39 (10)	2.50	

For overprints see Nos. O11-O20.

Columbus Sighting Land — A7

1892			Engr.	
40	A7	1c yellow brn	.25	.25
41	A7	2c vermilion	.25	.25
42	A7	5c dk blue	.25	.25
43	A7	10c slate	.25	.25
44	A7	20c plum	.25	2.00
45	A7	50c purple	.25	7.00
46	A7	1p brown	.25	7.00
47	A7	2p blue grn	.25	8.50
48	A7	5p rose lake	.25	
49	A7	10p orange	.25	
		Nos. 40-49 (10)	2.50	

Commemorative of the 400th anniversary of the discovery of America by Columbus.

Stamps of the 1892 design were printed in other colors than those listed and overprinted "Telegrafos". The 1c blue, 10c orange, 20c slate, 50c plum and 2p vermilion are telegraph stamps which did not receive the overprint.

For overprints see Nos. O21-O30.

Arms — A8

1893			Engr.	
51	A8	1c yellow brn	.35	.25
52	A8	2c vermilion	.35	.25
53	A8	5c dk blue	.35	.25
54	A8	10c slate	.35	.25
55	A8	20c dull red	.35	1.50
56	A8	50c violet	.35	4.00
57	A8	1p dk brown	.35	7.00
58	A8	2p blue green	.35	8.50
59	A8	5p rose lake	.35	
60	A8	10p orange	.35	
		Nos. 51-60 (10)	3.50	

The 1c blue and 2c dark brown are telegraph stamps which did not receive the "Telegrafos" overprint.

For overprints see Nos. O31-O41.

"Victory" — A9

1894			Engr.	
61	A9	1c yellow brn	.30	.30
62	A9	2c vermilion	.30	.30
63	A9	5c dp blue	.30	.30
64	A9	10c slate	.30	.30
65	A9	20c lake	.30	2.00
66	A9	50c purple	.30	5.00
67	A9	1p brown	.40	9.50
68	A9	2p green	.40	17.50
69	A9	5p brown red	.50	45.00
70	A9	10p orange	.50	45.00
		Nos. 61-70 (10)	3.60	125.20

There were three printings of this issue. Only the first is known postally used. Unused values are for the third printing.

Used values are for stamps with "DIRECCION" cancels in black that were removed from post office new year cards.

Specialists believe the 25c yellow green, type A9, is a telegraph denomination never issued for postal purposes. Stamps in other colors are telegraph stamps without the usual "Telegrafos" overprint.

For overprints see Nos. O42-O51.

Coat of Arms — A10

1895			Engr.	
71	A10	1c yellow brn	.25	.30
72	A10	2c vermilion	.25	.30
73	A10	5c deep blue	.25	.25
74	A10	10c slate	.25	.25
75	A10	20c claret	.25	.75
76	A10	50c light violet	50.00	5.00
77	A10	1p dark brown	.25	5.00
78	A10	2p deep green	.25	8.00
79	A10	5p brown red	.25	11.00
80	A10	10p orange	.25	
		Nos. 71-80 (10)	52.25	

Frames of Nos. 71-80 differ for each denomination.

A 50c violet blue exists. Its status is questioned. Value 25c.

There was little proper use of No. 80. Canceled examples are almost always c-t-o or have faked cancels.

For overprints see Nos. O52-O71.

Map of Nicaragua — A11

1896				Engr.
81	A11	1c violet	.30	1.00
82	A11	2c blue grn	.30	.50
83	A11	5c brt rose	.30	.30
84	A11	10c blue	.50	.50
85	A11	20c bister brn	3.00	4.00
86	A11	50c blue gray	.60	8.00
87	A11	1p black	.75	11.00
88	A11	2p claret	.75	15.00
89	A11	5p deep blue	.75	15.00
		Nos. 81-89 (9)	7.25	55.30

There were two printings of this issue. Only the first is known postally used. Unused values are for the second printing.

See italic note after No. 109M.

For overprints see Nos. O82-O117.

Wmk. 117

89A	A11	1c violet	3.75	.90
89B	A11	2c bl grn	3.75	1.25
89C	A11	5c brt rose	15.00	.30
89D	A11	10c blue	25.00	.90
89E	A11	20c bis brn	22.50	4.25
89F	A11	50c bl gray	42.50	9.00
89G	A11	1p black	37.50	12.50
89H	A11	2p claret		18.00
89I	A11	5p dp bl		40.00

Same, dated 1897

1897			Engr.	Unwmk.
90	A11	1c violet	.50	.50
91	A11	2c bl grn	.50	.60
92	A11	5c brt rose	.50	.30
93	A11	10c blue	6.25	.75
94	A11	20c bis brn	2.50	3.75
95	A11	50c bl gray	9.00	9.50
96	A11	1p black	9.00	15.00
97	A11	2p claret	20.00	19.00
98	A11	5p dp bl	20.00	42.50
		Nos. 90-98 (9)	68.25	91.90

See italic note after No. 109M.

Wmk. 117

98A	A11	1c violet	14.00	.50
98B	A11	2c bl grn	14.00	.50
98C	A11	5c brt rose	20.00	.40
98D	A11	10c blue	22.50	.90
98E	A11	20c bis brn	22.50	4.25
98F	A11	50c bl gray	22.50	8.00
98G	A11	1p black	25.00	16.00
98H	A11	2p claret	25.00	25.00
98I	A11	5p dp bl	125.00	50.00
		Nos. 98A-98I (9)	290.50	105.55

Coat of Arms of "Republic of Central America" — A12

1898			Engr.	Wmk. 117
99	A12	1c brown	.25	.40
100	A12	2c slate	.25	.40
101	A12	4c red brown	.25	.50
102	A12	5c olive green	40.00	22.50
103	A12	10c violet	15.00	.60
104	A12	15c ultra	.40	1.50
105	A12	20c blue	10.00	2.00
106	A12	50c yellow	10.00	9.50
107	A12	1p violet blue	.40	16.00
108	A12	2p brown	19.00	22.50
109	A12	5p orange	25.00	32.50
		Nos. 99-109 (11)	120.55	108.40

Unwmk.

109A	A12	1c brown	1.25	.30
109B	A12	2c slate	1.25	
109D	A12	4c red brown	2.25	.60
109E	A12	5c olive green	25.00	.25
109G	A12	10c violet	25.00	.60
109H	A12	15c ultra	25.00	
109I	A12	20c blue	25.00	
109J	A12	50c yellow	25.00	
109K	A12	1p deep ultra	25.00	
109L	A12	2p olive brown	25.00	
109M	A12	5p orange	25.00	
		Nos. 109A-109M (11)	204.75	

The paper of Nos. 109A to 109M is slightly thicker and more opaque than that of Nos. 81 to 89 and 90 to 98. The 5c and 10c also exist on very thin, semi-transparent paper.

Many reprints of Nos. 81-98, 98F-98H, 99-109M are on thick, porous paper, with and without watermark. The watermark is sideways. Paper of the originals is thinner for Nos. 81-109 but thicker for Nos. 109A-109M. Value 25c each.

In addition, reprints of Nos. 81-89 and 90-98 exist on thin paper, but with shades differing slightly from those of originals.

For overprints see Nos. O118-O128.

"Justice" — A13

1899   **Litho.**

110	A13	1c gray grn	.25	.35
111	A13	2c brown	.25	.25
112	A13	4c dp rose	.35	.40
113	A13	5c dp bl	.25	.25
114	A13	10c buff	.25	.30
115	A13	15c chocolate	.25	.65
116	A13	20c dk grn	.35	.75
117	A13	50c brt rose	.25	3.00
118	A13	1p red	.25	8.50
119	A13	2p violet	.25	20.00
120	A13	5p lt bl	.25	25.00
		Nos. 110-120 (11)	2.95	59.45

Nos. 110-120 exist imperf. and in horizontal pairs imperf. between.
Nos. 110-111, 113 exist perf 6x12 due to defective perforating equipment.
For overprints see Nos. O129-O139.

Mt. Momotombo — A14

Imprint: "American Bank Note Co. NY"

1900, Jan. 1   **Engr.**

121	A14	1c plum	.65	.25
122	A14	2c vermilion	.65	.25
123	A14	3c green	.90	.25
124	A14	4c ol grn	1.25	.25
125	A14	5c dk bl	4.00	.25
126	A14	6c car rose	14.00	5.00
127	A14	10c violet	7.00	.25
128	A14	15c ultra	8.00	.65
129	A14	20c brown	8.00	.65
130	A14	50c lake	7.00	1.10
131	A14	1p yellow	12.00	4.00
132	A14	2p salmon	10.00	2.25
133	A14	5p black	10.00	3.00
		Nos. 121-133 (13)	83.45	18.15

Used values for #123, 126, 130-133 are for canceled to order examples.

See Nos. 159-161. For overprints and surcharges see Nos. 134-136, 144-151, 162-163, 175-178, O150-O154, 1L1-1L13, 1L16-1L19, 1L20, 2L1-2L10, 2L16-2L24, 2L36-2L39.

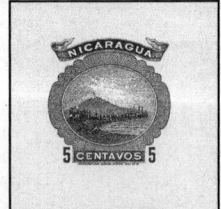

Mt. Momotombo — A14a

1902   **White Wove Paper**   *Imperf.*
Size: 55x52mm

133A	A14a	5c blue
133B	A14a	10c red violet
133C	A14a	20c brown
133D	A14a	30c black green
133E	A14a	50c red

51x51mm

133F	A14a	2c dk red, *buff*
133G	A14a	4c red brown, *buff*

Nos. 133A-133G are documented on covers postmarked from 1902-04. Specimen pairs and blocks are from sheets of 35 (Nos. 133A-133E) or 28 (Nos. 133F-133G) sold in the 1990 American Bank Note Company archives sale. Nos. 133A-133G are not cutouts from similar postal envelopes issued in 1900. They can be distinguished from postal stationery cutouts by their size, and unlike postal staationery cutouts, the stamps are square in which the image is centered. The mesh is perpendicular with the sides.

Nos. 131-133 Surcharged in Black or Red

1901, Mar. 5

134	A14	2c on 1p yel org	5.00	4.50
a.		Bar below date	16.00	9.00
b.		Inverted surcharge		50.00
c.		Double surcharge		50.00
135	A14	10c on 5p blk (R)	12.00	4.50
a.		Bar below date	17.50	8.00
136	A14	20c on 2p salmon	7.50	7.50
a.		Bar below date	14.00	10.00
		Nos. 134-136 (3)	24.50	16.50

A 2c surcharge on No. 121, the 1c plum, was not put on sale, though some are known

used from a few sheets distributed by the post office to "government friends." Value, $250.
The 2c on 1p yellow without ornaments is a reprint.

Postage Due Stamps of 1900 Overprinted in Black or Gold

1901, Mar.

137	D3	1c plum	4.50	3.50
138	D3	2c vermilion	4.50	3.50
139	D3	5c dk bl	6.00	3.50
140	D3	10c pur (G)	8.50	8.50
a.		Double overprint	14.00	14.00
141	D3	20c org brn	10.00	10.00
142	D3	30c dk grn	10.00	6.50
143	D3	50c lake	8.50	4.00
a.		"1091" for "1901"	35.00	35.00
b.		"Correo"	37.50	
		Nos. 137-143 (7)	52.00	39.50

In 1904 an imitation of this overprint was made to fill a dealer's order. The date is at top and "Correos" at bottom. The overprint is printed in black, sideways on the 1c and 2c and upright on the 5c and 10c. Some examples of the 2c were further surcharged "1 Centavo." None of these stamps was ever regularly used.

Nos. 126, 131-133 Surcharged

1901, Oct. 20   **Black Surcharge**

144	A14	3c on 6c rose	12.00	5.00
a.		Bar below value	13.00	5.50
b.		Inverted surcharge	14.00	8.00
c.		Double surcharge	14.00	8.00
d.		Double surch., one inverted	25.00	25.00
145	A14	4c on 6c rose	8.00	4.00
a.		Bar below value	9.00	4.50
b.		"1 cent" instead of "4 cent"	11.00	8.00
c.		Double surcharge	20.00	20.00
146	A14	5c on 1p yellow	6.00	4.00
a.		Three bars below value	7.00	4.50
b.		Ornaments at each side of "1901"	30.00	4.50
c.		Double surcharge, one in red	17.50	15.00
147	A14	10c on 2p salmon	6.50	4.00
a.		Inverted surcharge	30.00	27.50
b.		Double surcharge		

Blue Surcharge

148	A14	3c on 6c rose	9.00	4.50
a.		Bar below value	10.00	5.50
b.		Double surcharge	11.00	8.00
149	A14	4c on 6c rose	12.00	5.00
a.		Bar below value	13.00	7.50
b.		"1 cent" instead of "4 cent"	20.00	10.00
c.		Inverted surcharge	25.00	20.00

Red Surcharge

150	A14	5c on 1p yel org	8.00	6.50
a.		Three bars below value	10.00	7.00
b.		Ornaments at each side of "1901"	10.00	7.00
c.		Inverted surcharge	20.00	12.00
d.		Double surcharge, inverted	22.50	17.50
151	A14	20c on 5p black	5.50	3.50
a.		Inverted surcharge	20.00	16.00
b.		Double surcharge	22.50	22.50
c.		Triple surcharge		
		Nos. 144-151 (8)	67.00	36.50

In 1904 a series was surcharged as above, but with "Centavos" spelled out. About the same time No. 122 was surcharged "1 cent." and "1901," "1902" or "1904." All of these surcharges were made to fill a dealer's order and none of the stamps was regularly issued or used.

Postage Due Stamps of 1900 Overprinted in Black

1901, Oct.

152	D3	1c red violet	1.00	.40
a.		Ornaments at each side of the stamp	10.00	.65
b.		Ornaments at each side of "1901"	1.10	.65
c.		"Correos" in italics	1.50	1.50
d.		Double overprint	14.00	14.00
153	D3	2c vermilion	.75	.40
a.		Double overprint	8.50	5.50
154	D3	5c dark blue	1.00	.60
a.		Double overprint, one inverted		
b.		Double overprint	7.00	7.00
155	D3	10c purple	1.00	.60
b.		Double overprint	10.00	10.00
c.		Double overprint, one inverted	12.00	12.00
156	D3	20c org brn	1.50	1.25
b.		Double overprint	7.00	7.00
157	D3	30c dk grn	1.00	1.10
a.		Double overprint	9.00	9.00
b.		Inverted overprint	19.00	19.00
158	D3	50c lake	1.00	1.10
a.		Triple overprint	25.00	25.00
b.		Double overprint	16.00	16.00
		Nos. 152-158 (7)	7.25	5.45

One stamp in each group of 25 has the 2nd "o" of "Correos" italic. Value twice normal.

Momotombo Type of 1900
Without Imprint

1902   **Litho.**   **Perf. 14**

159	A14	5c blue	.50	.25
a.		Imperf., pair	3.75	
160	A14	5c carmine	.50	.25
a.		Imperf., pair	3.75	
161	A14	10c violet	1.50	.25
a.		Imperf., pair	3.75	
		Nos. 159-161 (3)	2.50	.75

No. 161 was privately surcharged 6c, 1p and 5p in black in 1903. Not fully authorized but known postally used. Value of c-t-o peso denominations, $5 each.

Nos. 121 and 122 Surcharged in Black

1902, Oct.   **Perf. 12**

162	A14	15c on 2c ver	4.00	.75
a.		Double surcharge	32.50	
b.		Blue surcharge	90.00	
163	A14	30c on 1c plum	3.00	2.25
a.		Double surcharge	12.00	
b.		Inverted surcharge	27.50	

Counterfeits of No. 163 exist in slightly smaller type.

President José Santos Zelaya — A15

1903, Jan.   **Engr.**

167	A15	1c emer & blk	.45	.50
168	A15	2c rose & blk	1.00	.50
169	A15	5c ultra & blk	.50	.50
170	A15	10c yel & blk	.50	.85
171	A15	15c lake & blk	1.75	2.00
172	A15	20c vio & blk	1.75	2.00
173	A15	50c ol & blk	1.75	5.00
174	A15	1p red brn & blk	2.00	6.00
		Nos. 167-174 (8)	9.70	17.35

10th anniv. of 1st election of Pres. Zelaya.
The so-called color errors-1c orange yellow and black, 2c ultramarine and black, 5c lake and black and 10c emerald and black-were also delivered to postal authorities. They were intended for official use though not issued as such. Value, $4 each.

No. 161 Surcharged in Blue

Nos. 175-176   No. 177

1904-05

175	A14	5c on 10c vio ('05)	1.75	.25
a.		Inverted surcharge	5.50	3.00
b.		Without ornaments	2.00	.70
c.		Character for "cents" inverted	1.75	.40
d.		As "b," inverted		
e.		As "c," inverted	2.75	2.75
f.		Double surcharge	25.00	8.00
g.		"5" omitted	2.75	2.75
176	A14	15c on 10c vio ('05)	.90	.30
a.		Inverted surcharge	4.00	1.40
b.		Without ornaments	2.00	1.40
c.		Character for "cents" inverted	2.50	1.10
d.		As "b," inverted		
e.		As "c," inverted	5.00	1.75
f.		Imperf.	7.00	
h.		As "a," imperf.	10.00	9.00
i.		Double surcharge	16.00	14.00

177	A14	15c on 10c vio	4.50	2.75
a.		Inverted surcharge	7.00	6.00
b.		"Centcvos"	7.00	4.50
c.		"5" of "15" omitted	12.50	
d.		As "b," inverted	8.50	8.50
e.		Double surcharge	11.00	11.00
f.		Double surcharge, inverted	13.00	13.00
g.		Imperf., pair	9.00	9.00
		Nos. 175-177 (3)	7.15	3.30

There are two settings of the surcharge on No. 175. In the 1st the character for "cents" and the figure "5" are 2mm apart and in the 2nd 4mm.

The 2c vermilion, No. 122, with surcharge "1 cent. / 1904" was not issued.

No. 161 Surcharged in Black

1905, June

178	A14	5c on 10c violet	.60	.35
a.		Inverted surcharge	13.50	10.00
b.		Double surcharge	4.50	4.50
c.		Surcharge in blue	75.00	

Coat of Arms — A18

Imprint: "American Bank Note Co. NY"

1905, July 25   **Engr.**   **Perf. 12**

179	A18	1c green	.30	.25
180	A18	2c car rose	.30	.25
181	A18	3c violet	.45	.25
182	A18	4c org red	.45	.25
183	A18	5c blue	.45	.25
184	A18	6c slate	.60	.40
185	A18	10c yel brn	.85	.25
186	A18	15c brn olive	.75	.35
187	A18	20c lake	.60	.40
188	A18	50c orange	3.00	1.50
189	A18	1p black	1.50	1.50
190	A18	2p dk grn	1.50	2.00
191	A18	5p violet	1.75	2.50
		Nos. 179-191 (13)	12.50	10.15

See Nos. 202-208, 237-248. For overprints and surcharges see Nos. 193-201, 212-216, 235-236, 249-265, O187-O198, O210-O222, 1L21-1L62, 1L73-1L95, 1LO1-1LO3, 2L26-2L35, 2L42-2L46, 2L48-2L72, 2LO1-2LO4.

Nos. 179-184 and 191 Surcharged in Black or Red Reading Up or Down

1906-08

193	A18	10c on 2c car rose (up)	7.00	4.50
a.		Surcharge reading down	13.00	13.00
194	A18	10c on 3c vio (up)	.80	.25
a.		"c" normal	2.75	1.35
b.		Double surcharge	4.50	4.50
c.		Double surch., up and down	7.00	5.00
d.		Pair, one without surcharge	9.50	
e.		Surcharge reading down	.30	.30
195	A18	10c on 4c org red (up) ('08)	35.00	15.00
a.		Surcharge reading down	32.50	26.00
196	A18	10c on 1c grn (up)	.60	.30
a.		Double surcharge	7.50	7.50
b.		Dbl. surch., one reading down	11.00	11.00
c.		Surcharge reading down	.70	.35
197	A18	20c on 2c car rose (down) ('07)	.50	.30
a.		Double surcharge	13.00	13.00
b.		Surcharge reading up	37.50	32.50
c.		"V" omitted	10.00	10.00
198	A18	20c on 5c bl (down)	.90	.50
a.		Surcharge reading up	35.00	
199	A18	50c on 6c sl (R) (down)	.80	.50
a.		Double surcharge		
b.		Surcharge reading up	30.00	30.00
c.		Yellow brown surcharge	80.00	.40
200	A18	1p on 5p vio (down) ('07)	42.50	18.00
		Nos. 193-200 (8)	88.10	39.35

There are several settings of these surcharges and many varieties in the shapes of the figures, the spacing, etc.

Surcharged in Red Vertically Reading Up

1908, May
201	A18	35c on 6c slate	3.50	2.25
a.		Double surcharge (R)	25.00	
b.		Double surcharge (R + Bk)	65.00	
c.		Carmine surcharge	3.50	2.25

Arms Type of 1905
Imprint: "Waterlow & Sons, Ltd."

1907, Feb.   **Perf. 14 to 15**
202	A18	1c green	.70	.40
203	A18	2c rose	.80	.25
204	A18	4c brn org	2.00	.30
205	A18	10c yel brn	3.00	.95
206	A18	15c brn olive	4.50	.90
207	A18	20c lake	8.00	1.25
208	A18	50c orange	20.00	4.25
		Nos. 202-208 (7)	39.00	7.60

Nos. 202-204, 207-208
Surcharged in Black or
Blue (Bl) Reading Down

1907-08
212	A18	10c on 2c rose	1.50	.50
a.		Double surcharge		10.00
b.		"Vale" only		22.50
c.		Surcharge reading up	14.00	6.50
213	A18	10c on 4c brn org (up) ('08)	2.25	.85
a.		Double surcharge		10.00
b.		Surcharge reading up		80.00
214	A18	10c on 20c lake ('08)	3.25	1.40
b.		Surcharge reading up		80.00
215	A18	10c on 50c org (Bl) ('08)	2.00	.60
216	A18	15c on 1c grn ('08)	32.50	4.00
		Nos. 212-216 (5)	41.50	7.35

Several settings of this surcharge provide varieties of numeral font, spacing, etc.

Revenue Stamps
Overprinted "CORREO-
1908" — A19

1908, June
217	A19	5c yel & blk	.60	.40
a.		"CORROE"	2.75	2.75
b.		Overprint reading down		7.00
c.		Double overprint		13.00
218	A19	10c lt bl & blk	.50	.25
a.		Double overprint	4.50	4.50
b.		Overprint reading down	.50	.25
c.		Double overprint, up and down	13.00	13.00
219	A19	1p yel brn & blk	.50	2.00
a.		"CORROE"	10.00	12.00
220	A19	2p pearl gray & blk	.50	2.50
a.		"CORROE"	10.00	10.00
		Nos. 217-220 (4)	2.10	5.15

The overprint exists on a 5p in green (value $200) and on a 50p in black (value $300).

Revenue Stamps
Surcharged Vertically
Reading Up in Red (1c,
15c), Blue (2c), Green (4c,
5c) or Orange (35c)

221	A19	1c on 5c yel & blk	.40	.25
a.		"1008"	2.00	3.00
b.		"8908"	2.00	3.00
c.		Surcharge reading down	4.00	4.00
d.		Double surcharge	4.00	4.00
222	A19	2c on 5c yel & blk	.50	.30
b.		"ORREO"	1.75	1.75
c.		"1008"	1.75	1.75
d.		"8908"	2.50	5.50
f.		Double surcharge	7.00	7.00
g.		Double surcharge, one inverted	7.00	7.00
h.		Surcharge reading down	9.00	9.00
223	A19	4c on 5c yel & blk	.65	.35
a.		"ORREO"	3.50	7.50
b.		"1008"	2.00	2.00
c.		"8908"	2.00	2.00
224	A19	15c on 50c ol & blk	.60	.40
a.		"1008"	7.50	11.50
b.		"8908"	4.00	4.00
c.		Surcharge reading down	10.00	10.00
225	A19	35c on 50c ol & blk	4.00	1.00
a.		Double surcharge, one inverted	12.00	12.00
b.		Surcharge reading down	12.00	12.00
c.		Double surcharge, one in black		
		Nos. 221-225 (5)	6.15	2.30

For surcharges and overprints see Nos. 225D-225H, 230-234, 266-278, 1L63-1L72A, 1L96-1L106, 2L47.

Revenue Stamps
Surcharged Vertically
Reading Up in Blue, Black
or Orange

1908, Nov.
225D	A19	2c on 5c yel org & blk (Bl)	20.00	12.50
e.		"9c" instead of "2c"	75.00	75.00
225F	A19	10c on 50c ol & blk (Bk)	850.00	325.00
g.		Double surcharge	425.00	
225H	A19	35c on 50c ol & blk (O)	17.50	10.00

In this setting there are three types of the character for "cents."

Revenue Stamps Overprinted or Surcharged in Various Colors

No. 226   No. 227

1908, Dec.
226		2c org (Bk)	3.50	2.00
a.		Double overprint	6.00	6.00
b.		Overprint reading up	5.00	5.00
227		4c on 2c org (Bk)	1.75	.90
a.		Surcharge reading up	5.00	5.00
b.		Blue surcharge	80.00	80.00
228		5c 2c org (Bl)	1.50	.60
a.		Surcharge reading up	6.00	6.00
229		10c on 2c org (G)	1.50	.30
a.		"1988" for "1908"	4.00	3.00
b.		Surcharge reading up	5.00	5.00
c.		"c" inverted	4.00	4.00
d.		Double surcharge	7.50	
		Nos. 226-229 (4)	8.25	3.80

Two printings of No. 229 exist. In the first, the initial of "VALE" is a small capital, and in the second a large capital.

The overprint "Correo-1908," 35mm long, handstamped on 1c blue revenue stamp of type A20, is private and fraudulent.

Revenue Stamps
Surcharged in Various
Colors

1909, Feb.   **Color: Olive & Black**
230	A19	1c on 50c (V)	4.00	1.60
231	A19	2c on 50c (Br)	7.00	3.00
232	A19	4c on 50c (G)	7.00	3.00
233	A19	5c on 50c (C)	4.00	1.75
a.		Double surcharge	12.50	12.50
234	A19	10c on 50c (Bk)	1.10	.75
		Nos. 230-234 (5)	23.10	10.10

Nos. 230 to 234 are found with three types of the character for "cents."

Nos. 190 and 191
Surcharged in Black

1909, Mar.   **Perf. 12**
235	A18	10c on 2p dk grn	20.00	12.00
236	A18	10c on 5p vio	100.00	70.00

There are three types of the character for "cents."

Arms Type of 1905
Imprint: "American Bank Note Co. NY"

1909, Mar.
237	A18	1c yel grn	.35	.25
238	A18	2c vermilion	.35	.25
239	A18	3c red org	.35	.25
240	A18	4c violet	.35	.25
241	A18	5c dp bl	.35	.25
242	A18	6c gray brn	3.00	1.50
243	A18	10c lake	.85	.25
244	A18	15c black	.85	.25
245	A18	20c brn olive	.85	.25
246	A18	50c dp grn	1.25	.40

247	A18	1p yellow	1.25	.40
248	A18	2p car rose	1.00	.40
		Nos. 237-248 (12)	10.80	4.70

Nos. 239 and 244,
Surcharged in Black or
Red

1910, July
249	A18	2c on 3c red org	2.75	1.10
250	A18	10c on 15c blk (R)	1.25	.30
a.		"VLEA"	3.50	2.00
b.		Double surcharge	17.50	17.50

There are two types of the character for "cents."

Nos. 239, 244, 245
Surcharged in Black or
Red

1910
252	A18	2c on 3c (Bk)	1.50	1.25
a.		Double surcharge	6.00	6.00
b.		Pair, one without surcharge		
c.		"Vale" omitted	10.00	10.00
254	A18	5c on 20c (R)	.40	.30
a.		Double surcharge (R)	6.00	5.00
b.		Inverted surcharge (R)	10.00	32.50
c.		Black surcharge		100.00
d.		Double surcharge (Bk)	140.00	
e.		Inverted surcharge (Bk)	110.00	
255	A18	10c on 15c (Bk)	.90	.30
a.		"c" omitted	2.00	1.10
b.		"10c" omitted	2.50	1.50
c.		Inverted surcharge	4.00	4.00
d.		Double surcharge	6.00	6.00
e.		Double surch., one inverted	14.00	18.50
		Nos. 252-255 (3)	2.80	1.85

There are several minor varieties in this setting, such as italic "L" and "E" and fancy "V" in "VALE," small italic "C," and italic "I" for "1" in "10."

Nos. 239, 244, 246 and
247, Surcharged in
Black

1910, Dec. 10
256	A18	2c on 3c red org	.85	.45
a.		Without period	1.00	.75
b.		Inverted surcharge	6.00	6.00
c.		Double surcharge	6.00	6.00
257	A18	10c on 15c blk	2.00	.75
a.		Without period	3.50	1.25
b.		Double surcharge	6.00	6.00
c.		Inverted surcharge	10.00	18.00
258	A18	10c on 50c dp grn	1.25	.40
a.		Without period	1.50	.75
b.		Double surcharge	10.00	26.00
c.		Inverted surcharge	3.00	3.00
259	A18	10c on 1p yel	.90	.40
a.		Without period	1.25	.75
b.		Double surcharge	3.00	3.00
		Nos. 256-259 (4)	5.00	2.00

The 15c on 50c deep green is a telegraph stamp from which the "Telegrafos" overprint was omitted. It appears to have been pressed into postal service, as all examples are used with postal cancels. Value $450.

Nos. 240, 244-248
Surcharged in Black

Surcharge as on Nos. 256-259 but lines wider apart.

1911, Mar.
260	A18	2c on 4c vio	.30	.25
a.		Without period	.35	.30
b.		Double surcharge	3.50	3.00
c.		Double surcharge, inverted	4.00	4.00
d.		Double surcharge, one invtd.	9.00	17.50
e.		Inverted surcharge	10.00	18.50
261	A18	5c on 20c brn ol	.30	.25
a.		Without period	.60	.50
b.		Double surcharge	2.50	2.50
c.		Inverted surcharge	2.50	2.00
d.		Double surcharge, one invtd.	6.00	6.00
262	A18	10c on 15c blk	.40	.25
a.		Without period	1.00	.50
b.		"Yale"	12.00	12.00
c.		Double surcharge	3.00	3.00
d.		Inverted surcharge	3.00	3.00
e.		Double surch., one inverted	5.00	4.00
f.		Double surch., both inverted	12.00	12.00
263	A18	10c on 50c dp grn	.25	.25
a.		Without period	1.00	1.00
b.		Double surcharge	3.00	2.50

c.		Double surcharge, one invtd.	5.00	4.00
d.		Inverted surcharge	5.00	5.00
264	A18	10c on 1p yel	1.50	.40
a.		Without period	2.00	1.50
b.		Double surcharge	4.00	4.00
c.		Double surcharge, one invtd.	7.50	
265	A18	10c on 2p car rose	.60	.50
a.		Without period	2.00	1.50
b.		Double surcharge	2.50	2.50
c.		Double surcharge, one invtd.	6.00	6.00
d.		Inverted surcharge	6.00	6.00
		Nos. 260-265 (6)	3.35	1.90

Revenue Stamps
Surcharged in Black

1911, Apr. 10   **Perf. 14 to 15**
266	A19	2c on 5p dl bl	1.00	1.25
a.		Without period	1.25	1.50
b.		Double surcharge	2.50	2.00
267	A19	2c on 5p ultra	.35	.40
a.		Without period	.75	1.25
b.		Double surcharge	3.50	
268	A19	5c on 10p pink	.75	.40
a.		Without period	1.50	1.00
b.		"cte" for "cts"	1.50	1.00
c.		Double surcharge	4.00	4.00
d.		Inverted surcharge	2.50	2.50
269	A19	10c on 25c lilac	.40	.25
a.		Without period	1.00	.75
b.		"cte" for "cts"	1.25	1.00
c.		Inverted surcharge	4.00	4.00
d.		Double surcharge, one inverted	4.00	4.00
270	A19	10c on 2p gray	.40	.25
a.		Without period	1.00	.75
b.		"cte" for "cts"	1.25	1.00
c.		Double surcharge	5.00	5.00
d.		Double surcharge, one inverted	4.00	3.00
271	A19	35c on 1p brown	.40	.30
a.		Without period	1.00	.75
b.		"cte" for "cts"	1.25	1.00
c.		"Corre"	1.50	1.50
d.		Double surcharge	2.50	2.50
e.		Double surcharge, one inverted	2.50	2.50
f.		Double surcharge inverted	3.00	3.00
g.		Inverted surcharge	5.00	
		Nos. 266-271 (6)	3.30	2.85

These surcharges are in settings of twenty-five. One stamp in each setting has a large square period after "cts" and two have no period. One of the 2c has no space between "02" and "cts" and one 5c has a small thin "s" in "Correos."

Surcharged in Black

1911, June
272	A19	5c on 2p gray	1.50	1.00
a.		Inverted surcharge	6.00	5.00

In this setting one stamp has a large square period and another has a thick up-right "c" in "cts."

Surcharged in Black

1911, June 12
273	A19	5c on 25c lilac	1.50	1.25
274	A19	5c on 50c ol grn	5.00	5.00
275	A19	5c on 5p blue	7.00	7.00
276	A19	5c on 5p ultra	7.50	6.00
a.		Inverted surcharge	45.00	
277	A19	5c on 50p ver	6.25	5.00
278	A19	10c on 50c dp grn	1.50	.50
		Nos. 273-278 (6)	28.75	24.75

This setting has the large square period and the thick "c" in "cts." Many of the stamps have no period after "cts." Owing to broken type and defective impressions letters sometimes appear to be omitted.

A21

Revenue Stamps Surcharged on the Back in Black

vale 05 cts. CORREO DE 1911	Vale 05 cts. CORREO DE 1911
a	b

Railroad coupon tax stamps (1st class red and 2nd class blue) are the basic stamps of Nos. 279-294. They were first surcharged for revenue use in 1903 in two types: I — "Timbre Fiscal" and "ctvs." II — "TIMBRE FISCAL" and "cents" (originally intended for use in Bluefields).

1911, July
279	A21 (a)	2c on 5c on 2c bl	.25	.30
a.		New value in yellow on face	6.00	6.00
b.		New value in black on face	10.00	5.00
c.		New value in red on face	100.00	
d.		Inverted surcharge	.75	
e.		Double surch., one inverted	7.50	7.50
f.		"TIMBRE FISCAL" in black	.75	.75
280	A21 (b)	2c on 5c on 2c bl	.25	.30
a.		New value in yellow on face	3.00	3.00
b.		New value in black on face	9.00	4.00
c.		New value in red on face	100.00	
d.		Inverted surcharge	.90	1.00
e.		Double surch., one inverted	7.50	7.50
f.		"TIMBRE FISCAL" in black	1.00	1.00
281	A21 (a)	5c on 5c on 2c bl	.25	.25
a.		Inverted surcharge	.50	.35
b.		"TIMBRE FISCAL" in black	1.00	1.00
c.		New value in yellow on face		
282	A21 (b)	5c on 5c on 2c bl	.25	.25
a.		Inverted surcharge	.40	.35
b.		"TIMBRE FISCAL" in black	1.00	1.00
c.		New value in yellow on face		
283	A21 (a)	10c on 5c on 2c bl	.25	.25
a.		Inverted surcharge	.75	.50
b.		"TIMBRE FISCAL" in black	1.00	1.00
c.		New value in yellow on face	100.00	
d.		Double surcharge	6.00	6.00
284	A21 (b)	10c on 5c on 2c bl	.25	.25
a.		Inverted surcharge	.75	.50
b.		"TIMBRE FISCAL" in black	1.00	1.00
c.		Double surcharge	6.00	6.00
d.		New value in yellow on face	110.00	
285	A21 (a)	15c on 10c on 1c red	.25	.25
a.		Inverted surcharge	1.00	1.25
b.		"Timbre Fiscal" double	5.00	
286	A21 (b)	15c on 10c on 1c red	.40	.35
a.		Inverted surcharge	1.00	1.00
b.		"Timbre Fiscal" double	5.00	
		Nos. 279-286 (8)	2.15	2.20

These surcharges are in settings of 20. For listing, they are separated into small and large figures, but there are many other varieties due to type and arrangement.

The colored surcharges on the face of the stamps were trial printings. These were then surcharged in black on the reverse. The olive yellow surcharge on the face of the 2c was later applied to prevent use as a 5c revenue stamps. Other colors known on the face are orange and green. Forgeries exist.

For overprints and surcharges see Nos. 287-294, O223-O244, 1L107-1L108.

Surcharged on the Face in Black

CORREO 02 centavos

1911, Oct.
287	A21	2c on 10c on 1c red	6.50	6.50
a.		Inverted surcharge	1.40	1.40
b.		Double surcharge	10.00	10.00
288	A21	20c on 10c on 1c red	4.50	4.50
a.		Inverted surcharge	5.25	5.00
289	A21	50c on 10c on 1c red	5.25	4.50
a.		Inverted surcharge	10.00	10.00
		Nos. 287-289 (3)	16.25	15.50

There are two varieties of the figures "2" and "5" in this setting.

Surcharged on the Back in Black

Vale 5 cts. CORREO DE 1911

1911, Nov.
289B	A21	5c on 10c on 1c red	37.50	
c.		Inverted surcharge	20.00	
289D	A21	10c on 10c on 1c red	12.50	
e.		Inverted surcharge	24.00	

Surcharged on the Face

Correo Vale 2 cts. 1911

1911, Dec.
Dark Blue Postal Surcharge
290	A21	2c on 10c on 1c red	.25	.25
a.		Inverted surcharge	2.50	2.50
b.		Double surcharge	5.00	5.00
291	A21	2c on 10c on 1c red	.30	.25
a.		Double surcharge	2.50	2.50
b.		Inverted surcharge	2.50	2.50
292	A21	10c on 10c on 1c red	.35	.25
a.		Inverted surcharge	2.50	2.50
b.		Double surcharge	2.50	2.50
c.		"TIMBRE FISCAL" on back	3.50	3.50

Black Postal Surcharge
293	A21	10c on 10c on 1c red	1.50	1.00
a.		Inverted surcharge	7.00	7.00
b.		New value surch. on back	12.00	12.00

Red Postal Surcharge
293C	A21	5c on 5c on 2c blue	1.40	1.25
d.		"TIMBRE FISCAL" in black	2.50	1.75
e.		"5" omitted	3.75	3.75
f.		Inverted surcharge	4.75	4.75
		Nos. 290-293C (5)	3.80	3.00

Bar Overprinted on No. O234 in Dark Blue

Correo Vale 10 cts. 1911

294	A21	10c on 10c on 1c red	1.25	1.00
a.		Inverted surcharge	2.50	2.50
b.		Bar at foot of stamp	5.00	5.00

Nos. 290-294 each have three varieties of the numerals in the surcharge.

"Liberty" — A22   Coat of Arms — A23

1912, Jan.   Engr.   Perf. 14, 15
295	A22	1c yel grn	.30	.25
296	A22	2c carmine	.40	.25
297	A22	3c yel brn	.30	.25
298	A22	4c brn vio	.30	.25
299	A22	5c blue & blk	.25	.25
300	A22	6c olive bister	.30	.80
301	A22	10c red brn	.25	.25
302	A22	15c vio	.25	.25
303	A22	20c red	.25	.25
304	A22	25c blue grn & blk	.30	.25
305	A23	35c grn & chnt	2.00	1.50
306	A22	50c lt blue	1.00	.40
307	A22	1p org	1.40	2.00
308	A22	2p dark blue grn	1.50	2.25
309	A22	5p blk	3.50	3.50
		Nos. 295-309 (15)	12.30	12.70

For overprints and surcharges see Nos. 310-324, 337A-348, 395-396, O245-O259.

No. 305 Surcharged in Violet

Vale 15 cts. Carreos-1913

1913, Mar.
310	A23	15c on 35c	.40	.25
a.		"ats" for "cts"	7.50	6.00

Stamps of 1912 Surcharged in Red or Black

VALE medio centavo de córdoba 1913

1913-14
311	A22	½c on 3c yel brn (R)	.40	.35
a.		"Corooba"	2.50	2.50
b.		"do" for "de"	2.50	2.50
c.		Inverted surcharge	22.50	

312	A22	½c on 15c vio (R)	.25	.25
a.		"Coroba"	1.00	1.00
b.		"do" for "de"	1.25	1.25
313	A22	½c on 1p org	.75	.25
a.		"VALB"	3.00	5.00
b.		"ALE"	4.00	3.50
c.		"LE"	5.00	5.00
d.		"VALE" omitted	3.50	3.50
314	A22	1c on 3c yel brn	.95	.60
315	A22	1c on 4c brn vio	.75	.25
316	A22	1c on 50c lt blue	.25	.25
317	A22	1c on 5p blk	.25	.25
318	A22	2c on 4c brn vio	.35	.25
a.		"do" for "de"	3.00	12.00
319	A22	2c on 20c red	3.50	4.50
a.		"do" for "de"	17.50	12.50
320	A22	2c on 25c blue grn & blk	.35	.25
a.		"do" for "de"	3.50	2.50
321	A23	2c on 35c grn & chnt	.25	.40
a.		"9131"	4.00	7.50
b.		"do" for "de"	2.50	2.50
322	A22	2c on 50c lt blue	.25	.25
a.		"do" for "de"	2.00	4.00
323	A22	2c on 2p dark blue grn	.25	.25
a.		"VALB"	1.25	1.25
b.		"ALE"	2.50	1.25
c.		"VALE" omitted	6.00	
d.		"VALE" and "dos" omitted	6.00	
324	A22	3c on 6c olive bis	.25	
a.		"VALB"	35.00	
		Nos. 311-324 (14)	8.80	8.35

Nos. 311, 312 surcharged in black were not regularly issued.

Surcharged on Zelaya Issue of 1912
325	Z2	½c on 2c ver	.60	1.25
a.		"Corooba"	1.25	1.25
b.		"do" for "de"	1.25	1.25
326	Z2	1c on 3c org brn	.50	.25
327	Z2	1c on 4c car	.50	.25
328	Z2	1c on 6c red brn	.40	.25
329	Z2	1c on 20c dark vio	.50	.25
330	Z2	1c on 25c grn & blk	.50	.25
331	Z2	1c on 1c yel grn ('14)	6.75	1.25
a.		"Centavos"	7.50	1.50
332	Z2	2c on 25c grn & blk	2.25	3.00
333	Z2	5c on 35c brn & blk	.40	.25
334	Z2	5c on 50c ol grn	.40	.25
a.		Double surcharge	22.50	
335	Z2	6c on 1p org	.50	.25
336	Z2	10c on 2p org brn	.90	.25
337	Z2	1p on 5p dk bl grn	1.00	.40
		Nos. 325-337 (13)	15.20	8.15

On No. 331 the surcharge has a space of 2 ½mm between "Vale" and "dos."

Space between "Vale" and "dos" 2 ½mm instead of 1mm, "de Cordoba" in different type.

1914, Feb.
337A	A22	2c on 4c brn vio	27.50	4.00
a.		"Ccntavos"		12.00
337C	A22	2c on 20c red	13.00	3.75
d.		"Ccntavos"		12.00
337E	A22	2c on 25c bl grn & blk		6.00
f.		"Ccntavos"		12.00
337G	A23	2c on 35c grn & chnt		8.50
h.		"Ccntavos"		15.00
337I	A22	2c on 50c lt bl	22.50	4.00
j.		"Ccntavos"		10.00

No. 310 with Additional Surcharge

REPUBLICA NICARAGUA medio cvo. Córdoba

1913, Dec.
337K	A23	½c on 15c on 35c	300.00	

The word "Medio" is usually in heavy-faced, shaded letters. It is also in thinner, unshaded letters and in letters from both fonts mixed.

No. 310 Surcharged in Black and Violet

¼ ct. Cordoba Correos-1913

338	A23	½c on 15c on 35c	.50	.25
a.		Double surcharge	3.50	
b.		Inverted surcharge	3.50	
c.		Surcharged on No. 305	12.00	
339	A23	1c on 15c on 35c	.25	.25
a.		Double surcharge	4.00	

Official Stamps of 1912 Surcharged

VALE c 0.01

1914, Feb.
340	A22	1c on 25c lt bl	.40	.25
a.		Double surcharge	9.00	
341	A23	1c on 35c lt bl	.40	.25
a.		"0.10" for "0.01"	10.00	10.00

341B	A22	1c on 50c lt bl	200.00	
342	A22	1c on 1p lt bl	.25	.25
342A	A22	2c on 20c lt bl	200.00	150.00
b.		"0.12" for "0.02"		
343	A22	2c on 50c lt bl	.40	.25
a.		"0.12" for "0.02"		150.00
344	A22	2c on 2p lt bl	.40	.25
345	A22	2c on 5p lt bl	250.00	
346	A22	5c on 5p lt bl	.25	.25

Red Surcharge
347	A22	5c on 5p lt bl	140.00	
348	A22	5c on 5p lt bl		500.00

National Palace, Managua A24   León Cathedral A25

Various Frames
1914, May 13   Engr.   Perf. 12
349	A24	½c lt blue	.85	.25
350	A24	1c dk green	.85	.25
351	A24	2c red orange	.85	.25
352	A24	3c red brown	1.25	.30
353	A25	4c scarlet	1.25	.40
354	A24	5c gray black	.45	.25
355	A25	6c black brn	9.00	5.50
356	A25	10c orange yel	.85	.25
357	A24	15c dp violet	5.75	2.00
358	A25	20c slate	11.00	5.50
359	A24	25c orange	1.50	.45
360	A25	50c pale blue	1.40	.40
		Nos. 349-360 (12)	35.00	15.80

In 1924 the 5c, 10c, 25c, 50c were issued in slightly larger size, 27x22¾mm. The original set was 26x22½mm.

No. 356 with overprint "Union Panamericana 1890-1940" in green is of private origin.

See Nos. 408-415, 483-495, 513-523, 652-664. For overprints and surcharges see Nos. 361-394, 397-400, 416-419, 427-479, 500, 540-548, 580-586, 600-648, 671-673, 684-685, C1-C3, C9-C13, C49-C66, C92-C105, C121-C134, C147-C149, C155-C163, C174-C185, CO1-CO24, O260-O294, O296-O319, O332-O376, RA1-RA5, RA10-RA11, RA26-RA35, RA39-RA40, RA44, RA47, RA52.

No. 355 Surcharged in Black

VALE 5 cts. de Córdoba 1915

1915, Sept.
361	A25	5c on 6c blk brn	1.50	.40
a.		Double surcharge	7.00	7.00

Stamps of 1914 Surcharged in Black or Red

Vale dos centavos de córdoba

1918-19   New Value in Figures
362	A24	1c on 3c red brn	6.50	2.25
a.		Double surch., one invtd		12.50
363	A25	2c on 4c scarlet	32.50	22.50
364	A24	5c on 15c dp vio (R)	7.50	1.50
a.		Double surcharge		12.00
364C	A24	5c on 15c dp vio		350.00

Surcharged in Black

VALE por 2 centavos de Córdoba

365	A25	2c on 20c slate	110.00	60.00
a.		"ppr" for "por"	500.00	300.00
b.		Double surcharge		300.00
c.		"Cordoba"	500.00	300.00
365D	A25	5c on 20c slate	—	200.00
e.		Double surcharge (Bk + R)		300.00
f.		"Cordoba"		300.00

The surcharge on No. 365 is in blue black, and that on No. 365D usually has an admixture of red.

Used only at Bluefields and Rama.

Surcharged in Black, Red or Violet

Vale medio centavo de córdoba

New Value in Words

366	A25	½c on 6c blk brn	4.00	1.50
a.		"Meio"		15.00
b.		Double surcharge		12.00
367	A25	½c on 10c yellow	2.50	.30
a.		"Val" for "Vale"		3.00
b.		"Codoba"		3.00
c.		Inverted surcharge		6.00
d.		Double surch., one inverted		10.00
368	A24	½c on 15c dp vio	2.50	.60
a.		Double surcharge		7.50
b.		"Codoba"		4.00
c.		"Meio"		6.00
369	A24	½c on 25c orange	5.00	2.00
a.		Double surcharge		8.00
b.		Double surch., one inverted		6.00
370	A25	½c on 50c pale bl	2.50	.30
a.		"Meio"		6.00
b.		Double surcharge		5.00
c.		Double surch., one inverted		7.00
371	A25	½c on 50c pale bl (R)	4.50	1.50
a.		Double surcharge		10.00
372	A24	1c on 3c red brn	3.00	.30
a.		Double surcharge		3.50
373	A25	1c on 6c blk brn	12.50	3.50
a.		Double surcharge		9.00
374	A25	1c on 10c yellow	24.00	8.00
a.		"nu" for "un"		22.50
375	A24	1c on 15c dp vio	4.50	.75
a.		Double surcharge		10.00
b.		"Codoba"		6.00
376	A25	1c on 20c slate	200.00	100.00
a.		Black surch. normal and red surch. invtd.		150.00
b.		Double surch., red & black		150.00
c.		Blue surcharge		200.00
377	A25	1c on 20c sl (V)	110.00	70.00
a.		Double surcharge (V + Bk)		150.00
378	A25	1c on 20c sl (R)	2.50	.30
a.		Double surch., one inverted		
b.		"Val" for "Vale"		3.50 3.00
379	A24	1c on 25c orange	4.50	1.00
a.		Double surcharge		11.00
380	A25	1c on 50c pale bl	14.00	4.50
a.		Double surcharge		17.50
381	A25	2c on 4c scarlet	3.50	.30
a.		Double surcharge		10.00
b.		"centavo"		5.00
c.		"Val" for "Vale"		
382	A25	2c on 6c blk brn	24.00	8.00
a.		"Centavoes"		
b.		"Cordobas"		
383	A25	2c on 10c yellow	24.00	4.50
a.		"centavo"		
384	A25	2c on 20c sl (R)	13.00	3.25
a.		"pe" for "de"		15.00
b.		Double surch., red & blk		27.50
c.		"centavo"		12.00
d.		Double surcharge (R)		17.50
385	A24	2c on 25c orange	5.50	.40
a.		"Vle" for "Vale"		7.50
b.		"Codoba"		7.50
c.		Inverted surcharge		10.00
386	A25	5c on 6c blk brn	10.00	4.25
a.		Double surcharge		13.50
387	A24	5c on 15c dp vio	3.50	.60
a.		"cincoun" for "cinco"		15.00
b.		"Vle" for "Vale"		12.50
c.		"Codoba"		12.50
	Nos. 366-387 (22)		*479.50*	*215.85*

No. 378 is surcharged in light red and brown red: the latter color is frequently offered as the violet surcharge (No. 377).

Official Stamps of 1915 Surcharged in Black or Blue

1919-21

388	A24	1c on 25c lt blue	1.50	.25
a.		Double surcharge		10.00
b.		Inverted surcharge		12.00
389	A25	2c on 50c lt blue	1.50	.25
a.		"centavo"		4.00 4.00
b.		Double surcharge		12.00
390	A25	10c on 20c lt blue	1.40	.40
a.		"centovos"		5.00 5.00
b.		Double surcharge		8.00
390F	A25	10c on 20c lt bl (Bl)	65.00	
	Nos. 388-390 (3)		*4.40*	*.90*

There are numerous varieties of omitted, inverted and italic letters in the foregoing surcharges.

No. 358 Surcharged in Black

Types of the numerals

1919, May

391	A25	2c on 20c (I)	200.00	150.00
a.		Type II		
b.		Type III		
c.		Type IV		
d.		Type VI		
e.		Type VIII		
392	A25	5c on 20c (I)	110.00	50.00
a.		Type II	110.00	45.00
b.		Type III	125.00	55.00
c.		Type IV	125.00	50.00
d.		Type V	140.00	60.00
e.		Type VI	140.00	60.00
f.		Type VII	400.00	250.00
h.		Double surch., one inverted		

No. 358 Surcharged in Black

393	A25	2 Cents on 20c (I)	200.00	150.00
a.		Type II		
b.		Type III		
c.		Type IV		
d.		Type V		
e.		Type VI		
f.		Type VII		
393G	A25	5 Cents on 20c sl, (VIII)	140.00	55.00

Nos. 391-393G used only at Bluefields and Rama.

No. 351 Surcharged in Black

1920, Jan.

394	A25	1c on 2c red org	1.50	.25
a.		Inverted surcharge		
b.		Double surcharge		

No. 394 stamps with uppercase "VALE" in surcharge are believed to be unauthorized surcharges.

Official Stamps of 1912 Overprinted in Carmine

1921, Mar.

395	A22	1c lt blue	1.50	.60
a.		"Parricular"	5.00	5.00
b.		Inverted overprint		10.00
396	A22	5c lt blue	1.50	.40
a.		"Parricular"	5.00	5.00

Official Stamps of 1915 Surcharged in Carmine

1921, May

397	A25	½c on 2c light blue	.50	.25
a.		"Mddio"	2.50	2.50
398	A25	½c on 4c light blue	1.25	.25
a.		"Mddio"	2.50	2.50
399	A24	1c on 3c light blue	1.25	.30
	Nos. 397-399 (3)		*3.00*	*.80*

No. 354 Surcharged in Red

1921, Aug.

400	A24	½c on 5c gray blk	.75	.75

Trial printings of this stamp were surcharged in yellow, black and red, and yellow and red. Some of these were used for postage.

Gen. Manuel José Arce — A26

Miguel Larreinaga A28

Gen. Máximo Jérez A30

José Cecilio del Valle — A27

Gen. Fernando Chamorro A29

Gen. Pedro Joaquín Chamorro A31

Rubén Darío — A32

1921, Sept.   Engr.

401	A26	½c lt bl & blk	1.60	1.60
402	A27	1c grn & blk	1.60	1.60
403	A28	2c rose red & blk	1.60	1.60
404	A29	5c ultra & blk	1.60	1.60
405	A30	10c org & blk	1.60	1.60
406	A31	25c yel & blk	1.60	1.60
407	A32	50c vio & blk	1.60	1.60
	Nos. 401-407 (7)		*11.20*	*11.20*

Centenary of independence.
For overprints and surcharges see Nos. 420-421, RA12-RA16, RA19-RA23.

Types of 1914 Issue

1922   Various Frames

408	A24	½c green	.25	.25
409	A24	1c violet	.25	.25
410	A25	2c car rose	.25	.25
411	A24	3c ol gray	.30	.25
411A	A24	4c vermilion	.35	.25
412	A25	6c red brn	.25	.25
413	A24	15c brown	.35	.25
414	A25	20c bis brn	.50	.25
415	A25	1cor blk brn	.90	.50
	Nos. 408-415 (9)		*3.40*	*2.50*

In 1924 Nos. 408-415 were issued in slightly larger size, 27x22¾mm. The original set was 26x22½mm.
Nos. 408, 410 exist with signature controls. See note before No. 600. Same values.

No. 356 Surcharged in Black

1922, Nov.

416	A25	1c on 10c org yel	1.00	.35
417	A25	2c on 10c org yel	1.00	.25

Nos. 354 and 356 Surcharged in Red

1923, Jan.

418	A24	1c on 5c gray blk	1.25	.25
419	A25	2c on 10c org yel	1.25	.25
a.		Inverted surcharge		

Nos. 401 and 402 Overprinted in Red

1923

420	A26	½c lt blue & blk	7.50	7.50
421	A27	1c green & blk	2.50	.85
a.		Double overprint		7.50

Francisco Hernández de Córdoba — A33

1924   Engr.

422	A33	1c deep green	2.50	.30
423	A33	2c carmine rose	2.50	.30
424	A33	5c deep blue	2.00	.30
425	A33	10c bister brn	2.00	.60
	Nos. 422-425 (4)		*9.00*	*1.50*

Founding of León & Granada, 400th anniv. For overprint & surcharges see #499, 536, O295.

Stamps of 1914-22 Overprinted

Black, Red or Blue Overprint

1927, May 3

427	A24	½c green (Bk)	.25	.25
428	A24	1c violet (R)	.25	.25
a.		Double overprint		3.00
428B	A24	1c violet (Bk)	85.00	55.00
429	A25	2c car rose (Bk)	.25	.25
a.		Inverted overprint		5.00
b.		Double overprint		5.00
430	A24	3c ol gray (Bk)	1.25	1.25
a.		Inverted overprint		5.00
b.		Double overprint		6.00
c.		Double ovpt., one inverted		9.00 7.00
430D	A24	3c ol gray (Bl)	8.00	3.25
431	A25	4c ver (Bk)	16.00	13.00
a.		Inverted overprint		30.00
432	A24	5c gray blk (R)	1.25	.25
a.		Inverted overprint		7.50
432B	A24	5c gray blk (Bk)	.75	.25
c.		Double ovpt., one inverted		8.00
d.		Double overprint		8.00
433	A25	6c red brn (Bk)	13.00	11.00
a.		Inverted overprint		17.50
b.		Double overprint		
c.		"1297" for "1927"		250.00
434	A25	10c yellow (Bl)	.65	.40
a.		Double overprint		12.50
b.		Double ovpt., one inverted		10.00
435	A24	15c brown (Bk)	6.00	2.50
436	A24	20c bis brn (Bk)	6.00	2.50
a.		Double overprint		17.50
437	A24	25c orange (Bk)	27.50	5.00
438	A25	50c pale bl (Bk)	7.50	3.00
439	A25	1cor blk brn (Bk)	15.00	9.00
	Nos. 427-439 (16)		*188.65*	*107.15*

Most stamps of this group exist with tall "1" in "1927." Counterfeits exist of normal stamps and errors of Nos. 427-478.

1927, May 19   Violet Overprint

440	A24	½c green	.25	.25
a.		Inverted overprint	2.00	2.00
b.		Double overprint	2.00	2.00
441	A24	1c violet	.25	.25
a.		Double overprint	2.00	2.00
442	A25	2c car rose	.25	.25
a.		Double overprint	2.00	2.00
b.		"1927" double	5.00	
c.		Double ovpt., one inverted	2.00	2.00
443	A24	3c ol gray	.25	.25
a.		Inverted overprint	6.00	
b.		Overprinted "1927" only	12.00	
c.		Double ovpt., one inverted	9.00	
444	A25	4c vermilion	37.50	27.50
a.		Inverted overprint	75.00	
445	A24	5c gray blk	1.00	.25
a.		Double overprint, one inverted	6.00	
446	A25	6c red brn	37.50	27.50
a.		Inverted overprint	75.00	
447	A25	10c yellow	.35	.25
a.		Double overprint	2.00	2.00
448	A24	15c brown	.75	.30
a.		Double overprint	8.00	
b.		Double overprint, one inverted	8.00	
449	A25	20c bis brn	.35	.25
a.		Double overprint		
450	A24	25c orange	.40	.25
451	A25	50c pale bl	.40	.25
a.		Double overprint, one inverted	4.00	4.00
452	A25	1cor blk brn	.75	.25
a.		Double overprint	3.00	
b.		"1927" double	5.00	
c.		Double overprint, one inverted	5.00	
	Nos. 440-452 (13)		*80.00*	*57.80*

Stamps of 1914-22
Overprinted in Violet

1928, Jan. 3

453	A24	½c green	.25	.25
a.		Double overprint	3.00	
b.		Double overprint, one inverted	4.00	
454	A24	1c violet	.25	.25
a.		Inverted overprint	2.00	
b.		Double overprint	2.00	
c.		Double overprint, one inverted	2.00	
d.		"928" for "1928"	2.50	
455	A25	2c car rose	.25	.25
a.		Inverted overprint	2.00	
b.		Double overprint	2.00	
c.		"1928" omitted	5.00	
d.		"928" for "1928"	2.50	
e.		As "d," inverted		
f.		"19" for "1928"		
456	A24	3c ol gray	.40	.25
457	A25	4c vermilion	.25	.25
458	A24	5c gray blk	.25	.25
a.		Double overprint	5.00	
b.		Double overprint, one inverted	5.00	
459	A25	6c red brn	.25	.25
460	A25	10c yellow	.25	.25
a.		Double overprint	2.50	
c.		Inverted overprint		
461	A24	15c brown	.35	.25
462	A25	20c bis brn	.50	.25
463	A24	25c orange	.75	.25
a.		Double overprint, one inverted	4.00	
464	A25	50c pale bl	1.25	.25
465	A25	1cor blk brn	1.25	.35
		Nos. 453-465 (13)	6.25	3.35

Stamps of 1914-22
Overprinted in Violet

1928, June 11

466	A24	½c green	.25	.25
467	A24	1c violet	.25	.25
a.		"928" omitted		
469	A24	3c ol gray	.75	.25
a.		Double overprint	6.00	
470	A25	4c vermilion	.35	.25
471	A25	5c gray blk	.25	.25
a.		Double overprint	4.00	
472	A25	6c red brn	.40	.25
a.		Double overprint	5.00	
473	A25	10c yellow	.50	.25
474	A24	15c brown	1.75	.25
a.		Double overprint		
475	A25	20c bis brn	2.00	.25
476	A24	25c orange	2.00	.25
a.		Double overprint, one inverted	6.00	
477	A25	50c pale bl	2.00	.25
478	A25	1cor blk brn	5.00	2.50
a.		Double overprint	10.00	
		Nos. 466-478 (12)	15.50	5.25

No. 410 with above overprint in black was
not regularly issued.

No. 470 with
Additional Surcharge
in Violet

1928

479	A25	2c on 4c ver	1.25	.35
a.		Double surcharge	9.00	

A34

Inscribed: "Timbre Telegrafico"

1928   Red Surcharge

480	A34	1c on 5c bl & blk	.30	.25
a.		Double surcharge	5.00	
b.		Double surcharge, one inverted		
481	A34	2c on 5c bl & blk	.30	.25
a.		Double surcharge	5.00	
482	A34	3c on 5c bl & blk	.30	.25
		Nos. 480-482 (3)	.90	.75

Stamps similar to Nos. 481-482, but with
surcharge in black and with basic stamp
inscribed "Timbre Fiscal," are of private origin.
See designs A36, A37, A44, PT1, PT4, PT6,
PT7.

Types of 1914 Issue

1928   **Various Frames**

483	A24	½c org red	.40	.25
484	A24	1c orange	.40	.25
485	A25	2c green	.40	.25

486	A24	3c dp vio	.40	.25
487	A25	4c brown	.40	.25
488	A24	5c yellow	.40	.25
489	A25	6c lt bl	.40	.25
490	A25	10c dk bl	.90	.25
491	A24	15c car rose	1.40	.50
492	A25	20c dk grn	1.40	.50
493	A24	25c blk brn	27.50	6.00
494	A25	50c bis brn	3.25	1.00
495	A25	1cor dl vio	6.25	3.00
		Nos. 483-495 (13)	43.50	13.00

No. 425 Overprinted in
Violet

1929

499	A33	10c bis brn	.75	.60

No. 408 Overprinted in
Red

1929

500	A24	½c green (R)	.25	.25
a.		Inverted overprint	5.50	
b.		Double overprint	5.00	
c.		Double overprint, one inverted	5.00	

A36

**Telegraph Tax Stamp Surcharged
Vertically in Red**

1929

504	A36	1c on 5c bl & blk (R)	.25	.25
a.		Inverted surcharge	3.00	
b.		Surcharged "0.10" for "0.01"	3.00	
c.		"0.0" instead of "0.01"	5.00	
509	A36	2c on 5c bl & blk (R)	.25	.25
a.		Double surcharge	2.50	
b.		Double surcharge, one inverted	3.50	
c.		Inverted surcharge	5.00	

**Telegraph Tax Stamp Surcharged
Vertically in Red**

510	A36	2c on 5c bl & blk (R)	22.50	1.25
a.		Dbl. surcharge, one inverted	25.00	

A37

Surcharged in Red

511	A37	1c on 10c dk grn & blk (R)	.25	.25
a.		Double surcharge		
512	A37	2c on 5c bl & blk (R)	.25	.25
		Nos. 504-512 (5)	23.50	2.25

The varieties tall "1" in "0.01" and "O$" for
"C$" are found in this surcharge.

Nos. 500, 504, 509-512 and RA38 were
surcharged in red and sold in large quantities
to the public. Surcharges in various other colors were distributed only to a favored few and
not regularly sold at the post offices.

Types of 1914 Issue

1929-31   **Various Frames**

513	A24	1c ol grn	.25	.25
514	A24	3c lt bl	.30	.25
515	A25	4c dk bl ('31)	.30	.25
516	A24	5c ol brn	.40	.25
517	A25	6c bis brn ('31)	.50	.30
518	A25	10c lt brn ('31)	.60	.25
519	A24	15c org red ('31)	.90	.25
520	A25	20c org ('31)	1.25	.35
521	A24	25c dk vio	.25	.25
522	A25	50c grn ('31)	.50	.25
523	A25	1cor yel ('31)	4.50	1.25
		Nos. 513-523 (11)	9.75	3.90

Nos. 513-523 exist with signature controls.
See note before No. 600. Same values.

New Post Office at
Managua — A38

1930, Sept. 15   **Engr.**

525	A38	½c olive gray	1.25	1.25
526	A38	1c carmine	1.25	1.25
527	A38	2c red org	.90	.90
528	A38	3c orange	1.75	1.75
529	A38	4c yellow	1.75	1.75
530	A38	5c ol grn	2.25	2.25
531	A38	6c bl grn	2.25	2.25
532	A38	10c black	2.75	2.75
533	A38	25c dp bl	5.50	5.50
534	A38	50c ultra	9.00	9.00
535	A38	1cor dp vio	25.00	25.00
		Nos. 525-535 (11)	53.65	53.65

Opening of the new general post office at
Managua. The stamps were on sale on day of
issuance and for an emergency in April, 1931.

No. 499 Surcharged in
Black and Red

1931, May 29

536	A33	2c on 10c bis brn	.50	1.60
a.		Red surcharge omitted	2.50	
b.		Red surcharge double	5.00	
c.		Red surcharge inverted	6.00	
d.		Red surcharge double, one invtd.		

Surcharge exists in brown.

Types of 1914-31
Issue Overprinted

1931, June 11

540	A24	½c green	.35	.25
a.		Double overprint	.80	
b.		Double ovpt., one inverted	1.40	
c.		Inverted overprint	.80	
541	A24	1c ol grn	.35	.25
a.		Double overprint	.80	
b.		Double ovpt., one inverted	1.40	
c.		Inverted overprint		
542	A25	2c car rose	.35	.25
a.		Double overprint	.80	
b.		Double ovpt., both inverted	2.50	
c.		Inverted overprint	1.40	
543	A24	3c lt bl	.35	.25
a.		Double overprint	.80	
b.		Double ovpt., one inverted	1.40	
c.		Inverted overprint	1.40	
544	A24	5c yellow	4.00	2.25
545	A24	5c ol brn	1.25	.25
a.		Double overprint	4.50	
b.		Inverted overprint	4.50	
546	A24	15c org red	1.50	.40
a.		Double overprint	3.50	
547	A24	25c blk brn	12.00	6.50
a.		Double overprint	13.00	7.00
b.		Inverted overprint	13.00	7.00
548	A24	25c dk vio	4.50	2.50
a.		Double overprint	10.00	
		Nos. 540-548 (9)	24.65	12.90

Counterfeits exist of the scarcer values. The
4c brown and 6c light blue with this overprint
are bogus.

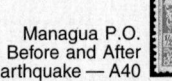

Managua P.O.
Before and After
Earthquake — A40

1932, Jan. 1   Litho.   Perf. 11½
Soft porous paper, Without gum

556	A40	½c emerald	1.50	
557	A40	1c yel brn	1.90	
558	A40	2c dp car	1.50	
559	A40	3c ultra	1.50	
560	A40	4c dp ultra	1.50	
561	A40	5c yel brn	1.60	
562	A40	6c gray brn	1.60	
563	A40	10c yel brn	2.50	
564	A40	15c dl rose	3.75	
565	A40	20c orange	3.50	
566	A40	25c dk vio	2.50	
567	A40	50c emerald	2.50	
568	A40	1cor yellow	6.25	
		Nos. 556-568 (13)	32.10	

Issued in commemoration of the earthquake
at Managua, Mar. 31, 1931. The stamps were
on sale on Jan. 1, 1932, only. The money
received from this sale was for the reconstruction of the Post Office building and for the
improvement of the postal service. Many
shades exist.
Sheets of 10.

Reprints are on thin hard paper and do not
have the faint horiz. ribbing that is on the front
or back of the originals. Fake cancels abound.
Value 75 cents each.
See Nos. C20-C24. For overprints and
surcharges see Nos. C32-C43, C47-C48.

Rivas Railroad Issue

"Fill" at El Nacascolo — A41

1c, Wharf at San Jorge. 5c, Rivas Station.
10c, San Juan del Sur. 15c, Train at Rivas
Station.

1932, Dec. 17   Litho.   Perf. 12
Soft porous paper

570	A41	1c yellow	16.00	
a.		1c ocher	18.00	
571	A41	2c carmine	16.00	
572	A41	5c blk brn	16.00	
573	A41	10c olive brown	16.00	
574	A41	15c yellow	16.00	
a.		15c deep orange	18.00	
		Nos. 570-574 (5)	80.00	

Inauguration of the railroad from San Jorge
to San Juan del Sur. On sale only on Dec. 17,
1932.
Sheets of 4, without gum. See #C67-C71.
Reprints exist on five different papers rang-
ing from thick soft light cream to thin very hard
paper and do not have the faint horiz. ribbing
that is normally on the front or back of the
originals. Originals are on very white paper.
Value of reprints, $5 each.

Leon-Sauce Railroad Issue

Bridge No. 2
at Santa
Lucia — A42

Designs: 1c, Environs of El Sauce. 5c,
Santa Lucia. 10c, Works at Km. 64. 15c, Rock
cut at Santa Lucia.

1932, Dec. 30   Perf. 12
Soft porous paper

575	A42	1c orange	16.00	
576	A42	2c carmine	16.00	
577	A42	5c blk brn	16.00	
578	A42	10c olive brown	16.00	
579	A42	15c orange	16.00	
		Nos. 575-579 (5)	80.00	

Inauguration of the railroad from Leon to El
Sauce. On sale only on Dec. 30, 1932.
Sheets of 4, without gum. See #C72-C76.
Reprints exist on thin hard paper and do not
have the faint horiz. ribbing that is on the front
or back of the originals. Value $5 each.

Nos. 514-515, 543
Surcharged in Red

1932, Dec. 10

580	A24	1c on 3c lt bl (514)	.35	.25
a.		Double surcharge	3.50	
581	A24	1c on 3c lt bl (543)	4.00	3.50
582	A25	2c on 4c dk bl (515)	.25	.25
a.		Double surcharge	2.50	
		Nos. 580-582 (3)	4.60	4.00

Nos. 514, 516, 545
and 518 Surcharged in
Black or Red

1933

583	A24	1c on 3c lt bl (Bk) (514)	.25	.25
a.		"Censavo"	4.00	2.25
b.		Double surcharge, one inverted	4.00	
584	A24	1c on 5c ol brn (R) (516)	.25	.25
a.		Inverted surcharge		
b.		Double surcharge		

585 A24 1c on 5c ol brn (R)
(545) 6.50 5.00
a. Red surcharge double 12.00
586 A25 2c on 10c lt brn (Bk)
(518) .25 .25
a. Double surcharge 7.00 2.50
b. Inverted surcharge 6.00 1.30
c. Double surcharge, one inverted 7.00 2.50
Nos. 583-586 (4) 7.25 5.75

On No. 586 "Vale Dos" measures 13mm and 14mm.
No. 583 with green surcharge and No. 586 with red surcharge are bogus.

Flag of the Race Issue

Flag with Three Crosses for Three Ships of Columbus — A43

1933, Aug. 3   Litho.   Rouletted 9
Without gum
587 A43 ½c emerald 1.75 1.75
588 A43 1c green 1.50 1.50
589 A43 2c red 1.50 1.50
590 A43 3c dp rose 1.50 1.50
591 A43 4c orange 1.50 1.50
592 A43 5c yellow 1.75 1.75
593 A43 10c dp brn 1.75 1.75
594 A43 15c dk brn 1.75 1.75
595 A43 20c vio bl 1.75 1.75
596 A43 25c dl bl 1.75 1.75
597 A43 30c violet 4.50 4.50
598 A43 50c red vio 4.50 4.50
599 A43 1cor ol brn 4.50 4.50
Nos. 587-599 (13) 30.00 30.00

Commemorating the raising of the symbolical "Flag of the Race"; also the 441st anniversary of the sailing of Columbus for the New World, Aug. 3, 1492. Printed in sheets of 10.
See Nos. C77-C87, O320-O331.

In October, 1933, various postage, airmail and official stamps of current issues were overprinted with facsimile signatures of the Minister of Public Works and the Postmaster-General. These overprints are control marks.

Nos. 410 and 513 Overprinted in Black

1935   Perf. 12
600 A24 1c ol grn .25 .25
a. Inverted overprint 1.40 1.60
b. Double overprint 1.40 1.60
c. Double overprint, one inverted 1.60 1.60
601 A25 2c car rose .25 .25
a. Inverted overprint 1.60
b. Double overprint 1.60
c. Double overprint, one inverted 1.60
d. Double overprint, both inverted 2.50 2.25

No. 517 Surcharged in Red as in 1932

1936, June
602 A25 2c on 6c bis brn .35 .25
a. "Ccentavo" .80 .80
b. Double surcharge 3.50 3.50

Regular Issues of 1929-35 Overprinted in Blue

1935, Dec.
603 A25 ½c on 6c bis brn .65 .25
604 A24 1c ol grn (#600) .80 .25
605 A25 2c car rose (#601) .80 .25
a. Black overprint inverted 6.00
606 A24 3c lt bl .80 .25
607 A24 5c ol brn 1.00 .25
608 A25 10c lt brn 1.60 .80
Nos. 603-608 (6) 5.65 2.05

Nos. 606-608 have signature control overprint. See note before No. 600.

Same Overprint in Red

1936, Jan.
609 A24 ½c dk grn .25 .25
610 A25 ½c on 6c bis brn
(602) .25 .25
a. Double surch., one inverted 6.00 6.00
611 A24 1c ol grn (513) .25 .25
612 A24 1c ol grn (600) .25 .25
613 A25 2c car rose (410) .50 .25
614 A25 2c car rose (601) .25 .25
a. Black overprint inverted 12.00 2.50
b. Black ovpt. double, one invtd. 12.00 3.50

---

615 A24 3c lt bl .25 .25
616 A25 4c dk bl .25 .25
617 A24 5c ol brn .25 .25
618 A25 6c bis brn .25 .25
619 A25 10c lt brn .50 .25
620 A24 15c org red .25 .25
621 A25 20c orange .80 .25
622 A24 25c dk vio .25 .25
623 A25 50c green .35 .25
624 A25 1cor yellow .40 .25
Nos. 609-624 (16) 5.30 4.00

Red or blue "Resello 1935" overprint may be found inverted or double. Red and blue overprints on same stamp are bogus.
Nos. 615-624 have signature control overprint. See note before No. 600.

Regular Issues of 1922-29 Overprinted in Carmine

1936, May
625 A24 ½c green .25 .25
626 A24 1c olive green .25 .25
627 A25 2c carmine rose .50 .25
628 A24 3c light blue .25 .25
Nos. 625-628 (4) 1.25 1.00

No. 628 has signature control overprint. See note before No. 600.

Nos. 514, 516 Surcharged in Black

1936, June
629 A24 1c on 3c lt bl .25 .25
a. "1396" for "1936" 1.00 1.00
b. "Un" omitted 4.50 1.40
c. Inverted surcharge 1.60 1.60
d. Double surcharge 1.60 1.60
630 A24 2c on 5c ol brn .25 .25
a. "1396" for "1936" 1.40 1.40
b. Double surcharge 3.50 3.50

Regular Issues of 1929-31 Surcharged in Black or Red

1936
631 A24 ½c on 15c org red (R) .25 .25
a. Double surcharge 5.00
632 A25 1c on 4c dk bl (Bk) .25 .25
633 A24 1c on 5c ol brn (Bk) .25 .25
634 A25 1c on 6c bis brn (Bk) .40 .25
a. "1939" instead of "1936" 2.50 1.60
635 A24 1c on 15c org red (Bk) .25 .25
a. "1939" instead of "1936" 2.50 1.60
636 A24 1c on 20c org (Bk) .25 .25
a. "1939" instead of "1936" 2.50 1.60
b. Double surcharge 4.00
637 A25 1c on 20c org (R) .25 .25
638 A25 2c on 10c lt brn (Bk) .25 .25
639 A24 2c on 15c org red (Bk) 1.00 .80
640 A25 2c on 20c org (Bk) .50 .25
641 A24 2c on 25c dk vio (R) .35 .25
642 A24 2c on 25c dk vio (Bk) .35 .25
a. "1939" instead of "1936" 2.50 1.60
643 A25 2c on 50c grn (Bk) .35 .25
a. "1939" instead of "1936" 2.50 1.60
644 A25 2c on 1 cor yel (Bk) .35 .25
a. "1939" instead of "1936" 2.50 1.60
645 A24 3c on 4c dk bl (Bk) .65 .50
a. "1939" instead of "1936" 2.50 1.60
b. "s" of "Centavos" omitted and "r" of "Tres" inverted 2.50
Nos. 631-645 (15) 5.70 4.55

Nos. 634, 639, 643-644 exist with and without signature controls. Same values, except for No. 639, which is rare without the signature control. Nos. 635-636, 642, 645 do not have signature controls. Others have signature controls only. See note before No. 600.

Regular Issues of 1929-31 Overprinted in Black

No. 646

No. 648, Script Control Mark

1936, Aug.
646 A24 3c lt bl .35 .25
647 A24 5c ol brn .25 .25
648 A25 10c lt brn .50 .35
Nos. 646-648 (3) 1.10 .85

A44

1936, Oct. 19   Red Surcharge
649 A44 1c on 5c grn & blk .25 .25
650 A44 2c on 5c grn & blk .25 .25

Types of 1914

1937, Jan. 1   Engr.
652 A24 ½c black .25 .25
653 A24 1c car rose .25 .25
654 A25 2c dp bl .25 .25
655 A24 3c chocolate .25 .25
656 A25 4c yellow .25 .25
657 A24 5c org red .25 .25
658 A25 6c dl vio .25 .25
659 A24 10c ol grn .25 .25
660 A25 15c green .25 .25
661 A24 20c red brn .35 .25
663 A25 50c brown .35 .25
664 A25 1cor ultra .60 .25
Nos. 652-664 (12) 3.45 3.00

See note after No. 360.

Mail Carrier — A45

Designs: 1c, Mule carrying mail. 2c, Mail coach. 3c, Sailboat. 5c, Steamship. 7½c, Train.

1937, Dec.   Litho.   Perf. 11
665 A45 ½c green .25 .25
666 A45 1c magenta .25 .25
667 A45 2c brown .25 .25
668 A45 3c purple .25 .25
669 A45 5c blue .25 .25
670 A45 7½c red org .55 .35
Nos. 665-670 (6) 1.80 1.60

75th anniv. of the postal service in Nicaragua.
Nos. 665-670 exists printed on several different kinds of paper: medium thick porous white paper, a thinner whitish toned paper, and a thin hard brownish tone paper.
Nos. 665-670 were also issued in sheets of 4. Value, set of sheets $20.
The miniature sheets are ungummed, and also exist imperf. and part-perf.

Nos. 359, 663 and 664 Surcharged in Red

1938   Perf. 12
671 A24 3c on 25c org .25 .25
672 A25 5c on 50c brn .25 .25
a. "e" of "Vale" omitted 1.60 1.00
673 A25 6c on 1cor ultra .25 .25
Nos. 671-673 (3) .75 .75

No. 672 has a script signature control and the surcharge is in three lines.

Dario Park — A46

1939, Jan.   Engr.   Perf. 12½
674 A46 1½c yel grn .25 .25
675 A46 2c dp rose .25 .25
676 A46 3c brt bl .25 .25
677 A46 6c brn org .25 .25
678 A46 7½c dp grn .25 .25
679 A46 10c blk brn .25 .25
680 A46 15c orange .25 .25
681 A46 5t vio .25 .25
682 A46 50c brt yel grn .25 .25
683 A46 1cor yellow .65 .40
Nos. 674-683 (10) 2.90 2.65

Nos. 660 and 661 Surcharged in Red

1939   Perf. 12
684 A24 1c on 15c grn .25 .25
a. Inverted surcharge 2.00 2.00
685 A25 1c on 20c red brn .25 .25

No. C236 Surcharged in Carmine

1941   Unwmk.   Perf. 12
686 AP14 10c on 1c brt grn .65 .40
a. Double surcharge 10.00 2.50
b. Inverted surcharge 10.00 2.50

Rubén Darío — A47

1941, Dec.   Engr.   Perf. 12½
687 A47 10c red .80 .40
Nos. 687,C257-C260 (5) 4.00 2.00

25th anniversary of the death of Rubén Darío, poet and writer.

No. C236 Surcharged in Carmine

1943   Perf. 12
688 AP14 10c on 1c brt grn 4.00 .40
a. Inverted surcharge 10.00
b. Double surcharge 10.00

Catalogue values for unused stamps in this section, from this point to the end of the section, are for Never Hinged items.

"Victory" — A48

1943, Dec. 8   Engr.
689 A48 10c vio & cerise .40 .40
690 A48 30c org brn & cerise .50 .40

2nd anniv. of Nicaragua's declaration of war against the Axis. See Nos. C261-C262.

Columbus and Lighthouse — A49

1945, Sept. 1   Unwmk.   Perf. 12½
691 A49 4c dk grn & blk .40 .30
692 A49 6c org & blk .40 .30
693 A49 8c dp rose & blk .50 .35
694 A49 10c bl & blk .55 .40
Nos. 691-694,C266-C271 (10) 8.00 5.70

Issued in honor of the discovery of America by Columbus and the Columbus Lighthouse near Ciudad Trujillo, Dominican Republic.

Franklin D.
Roosevelt,
Philatelist
A50

Roosevelt
Signing
Declaration
of War
Against
Japan
A51

8c, F. D. Roosevelt, Winston Churchill. 16c, Gen. Henri Giraud, Roosevelt, de Gaulle & Churchill. 32c, Stalin, Roosevelt, Churchill. 50c, Sculptured head of Roosevelt.

Engraved, Center Photogravure
1946, June 15   Unwmk.   Perf. 12½
Frame in Black

695	A50	4c sl grn	.40	.30
696	A50	8c violet	.40	.30
697	A50	10c ultra	.40	.30
698	A50	16c rose red	.55	.30
699	A50	32c org brn	.40	.30
700	A51	50c gray	.40	.30
		Nos. 695-700,C272-C276 (11)	15.30	11.55

Issued to honor US Pres. Franklin D. Roosevelt (1882-1945). See Nos. C272-C276.

Buildings
A56

Designs: 4c, Metropolitan Cathedral, Managua. 5c, Sanitation Building. 6c, Municipal Building.10c, Projected Provincial Seminary. 75c, Communications Building.

1947, Jan. 10   Frame in Black

701	A56	4c carmine	.45	.30
702	A56	5c blue	.45	.30
703	A56	6c green	.45	.30
704	A56	10c olive	.45	.30
705	A56	75c golden brn	.55	.30
		Nos. 701-705,C277-C282 (11)	8.40	4.65

Centenary of the founding of the city of Managua. See Nos. C277-C282.

San Cristóbal
Volcano — A61

Designs: 3c, Tomb of Rubén Dario. 4c, Grandstand. 5c, Soldiers' monument. 6c, Sugar cane. 8c, Tropical fruit. 10c, Cotton industry. 20c, Horse race. 30c, Nicaraguan coffee. 50c, Steer. 1cor, Agriculture.

Engraved, Center Photogravure
1947, Aug. 29   Frame in Black

706	A61	2c orange	.35	.30
707	A61	3c violet	.35	.30
708	A61	4c gray	.35	.30
709	A61	5c rose car	.75	.30
710	A61	6c green	.40	.30
711	A61	8c org brn	.55	.30
712	A61	10c red	.75	.30
713	A61	20c brt ultra	2.60	.50
714	A61	30c rose lilac	2.00	.50
715	A61	50c dp claret	4.25	.95
716	A61	1cor brn org	1.50	.50
		Nos. 706-716,C283-C295 (24)	43.45	29.55

The frames differ for each denomination.
For surcharge see No. 769.

Softball — A62

Boy Scout,
Badge and
Flag — A63

Designs: 3c, Pole vault. 4c, Diving. 5c, Bicycling. 10c, Proposed stadium. 15c, Baseball. 25c, Boxing. 35c, Basketball. 40c, Regatta. 60c, Table tennis. 1 cor, Soccer. 2 cor, Tennis.

1949, July 15   Photo.   Perf. 12

717	A62	1c henna brn	.50	.25
718	A63	2c ultra	.90	.25
719	A63	3c bl grn	.50	.25
720	A62	4c dp claret	.35	.25
721	A63	5c orange	.70	.25
722	A62	10c emerald	.70	.25
723	A62	15c cerise	1.00	.25
724	A63	25c brt bl	1.00	.25
725	A63	35c olive grn	1.90	.25
726	A62	40c violet	2.75	.30
727	A62	60c olive gray	3.25	.40
728	A62	1cor scarlet	4.50	1.25
729	A62	2cor red vio	7.25	2.50
		Nos. 717-729 (13)	25.30	6.70
		Nos. 717-729,C296-C308 (26)	62.75	17.25

10th World Series of Amateur Baseball, 1948.
Each denomination was also issued in a souvenir sheet containing four stamps and marginal inscriptions. Value, set of 13 sheets, $395.

Rowland Hill — A64

Designs: 25c, Heinrich von Stephan. 75c, UPU Monument. 80c, Congress medal, obverse. 4cor, as 80c, reverse.

1950, Nov. 23   Engr.   Perf. 13
Frame in Black

730	A64	20c car lake	.35	.25
731	A64	25c yel grn	.35	.25
732	A64	75c ultra	.70	.25
733	A64	80c green	.35	.25
734	A64	4cor blue	1.40	.80
		Nos. 730-734 (5)	3.15	1.80
		Nos. 730-734,C309-C315,CO45-CO50 (18)	17.30	9.45

75th anniv. (in 1949) of the UPU.
Each denomination was also issued in a souvenir sheet containing 4 stamps. Size: 115x123mm. Value, set of 5 sheets, $30.
For surcharge see #771.

Queen
Isabella I
A65

Ships of
Columbus
A66

Designs: 98c, Santa Maria. 1.20cor, Map. 1.76cor, Portrait facing left.

1952, June 25   Perf. 11½

735	A65	10c lilac rose	.30	.25
736	A66	96c deep ultra	.90	.75
737	A65	98c carmine	.95	.75
738	A65	1.20cor brown	1.10	.90
739	A65	1.76cor red violet	1.50	1.25
a.		Souvenir sheet of 5, #735-739	12.00	8.00
		Nos. 735-739 (5)	4.75	3.90
		Nos. 735-739,C316-C320 (10)	19.75	13.90

Queen Isabella I of Spain, 500th birth anniv.

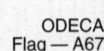

ODECA
Flag — A67

Designs: 5c, Map of Central America. 6c, Arms of ODECA. 15c, Presidents of Five Central American Republics. 50c, ODECA Charter and Flags.

1953, Apr. 15   Perf. 13½x14

740	A67	4c dk bl	.40	.40
741	A67	5c emerald	.40	.40
742	A67	6c lt brn	.40	.40
743	A67	15c lt ol grn	.40	.40
744	A67	50c blk brn	.40	.40
		Nos. 740-744,C321-C325 (10)	7.85	5.85

Founding of the Organization of the Central American States (ODECA).
For surcharge see #767.

Pres. Carlos
Solorzano — A68

Presidents: 6c, Diego Manuel Chamorro. 8c, Adolfo Diaz. 15c, Gen. Anastasio Somoza. 50c, Gen. Emiliano Chamorro.

Heads in Gray Black
Engr. (frames); Photo. (heads)
1953, June 25   Perf. 12½

745	A68	4c dk car rose	.40	.40
746	A68	6c dp ultra	.40	.40
747	A68	8c brown	.40	.40
748	A68	15c car rose	.40	.40
749	A68	50c bl grn	.40	.40
		Nos. 745-749,C326-C338 (18)	13.80	7.30

For surcharges see Nos. 768, 853.

Sculptor and UN
Emblem — A69

4c, Arms of Nicaragua. 5c, Globe. 15c, Candle & Charter. 1cor, Flags of Nicaragua & UN.

Perf. 13½
1954, Apr. 30   Engr.   Unwmk.

750	A69	3c olive	.30	.25
751	A69	4c olive green	.30	.25
752	A69	5c emerald	.30	.25
753	A69	15c deep green	1.20	.25
754	A69	1cor blue green	1.40	.30
		Nos. 750-754,C339-C345 (12)	17.40	7.30

UN Organization.

Capt. Dean L. Ray,
USAF — A70

Designs: 2c, Sabre jet plane. 3c, Plane, type A-20. 4c, B-24 bomber. 5c, Plane, type AT-6. 15c, Gen. Anastasio Somoza. 1cor, Air Force emblem.

Frame in Black
Engraved; Center Photogravure
1954, Nov. 5   Perf. 13

755	A70	1c gray	.45	.25
756	A70	2c gray	.45	.25
757	A70	3c dk gray grn	.45	.25
758	A70	4c orange	.45	.25
759	A70	5c emerald	.45	.25
760	A70	15c aqua	.45	.25
761	A70	1cor purple	.45	.25
		Nos. 755-761,C346-C352 (14)	11.10	4.10

National Air Force.

Rotary
Slogans and
Wreath
A71

Map of the World
and Rotary
Emblem
A72

20c, Handclasp, Rotary emblem & globe. 35c, Flags of Nicaragua & Rotary. 90c, Paul P. Harris.

1955, Aug. 30   Photo.   Perf. 11½
Granite Paper.

762	A71	15c dp orange	.60	.35
763	A71	20c dk olive grn	.60	.35
764	A71	35c red violet	.60	.35
765	A72	40c carmine	.60	.35

766	A71	90c black & gray	1.10	.35
a.		Souvenir sheet of 5, #762-766	6.50	4.25
		Nos. 762-766,C353-C362 (15)	8.90	5.25

50th anniversary of Rotary International.
For surcharges see Nos. 770, 772, 876.

Issues of 1947-55
Surcharged in
Various Colors

Perf. 13½x14, 12½, 11½, 13
Engraved, Photogravure
1956, Feb. 4   Unwmk.

767	A67	5c on 6c lt brn	.40	.35
768	A68	5c on 6c ultra & gray blk (Ult)	.40	.35
769	A61	5c on 8c blk & org brn	.40	.35
770	A71	15c on 35c red vio (G)	.40	.35
771	A64	15c on 80c blk & grn	.40	.35
772	A71	15c on 90c blk & gray (Bl)	.40	.35
		Nos. 767-772,C363-C366 (10)	9.15	4.65

Spacing of surcharge varies to fit shape of stamps.
National Exhibition, Feb. 4-16, 1956.

Gen.
Máximo
Jerez — A73

Battle of San
Jacinto — A74

10c, Gen. Fernando Chamorro. 25c, Burning of Granada. 50c, Gen. José Dolores Estrada.

Perf. 12½x12, 12, 12½
1956, Sept. 14   Engr.

773	A73	5c brown	.40	.35
774	A73	10c dk car rose	.40	.35
775	A74	15c blue gray	.40	.35
776	A74	25c brt red	.40	.35
777	A73	50c brt red vio	.80	.35
		Nos. 773-777,C367-C371 (10)	9.45	5.20

National War, cent.

Boy Scout — A75

Designs: 15c, Cub Scout. 20c, Boy Scout. 25c, Lord Baden-Powell. 50c, Joseph A. Harrison.

Perf. 13½x14
1957, Apr. 9   Photo.   Unwmk.

778	A75	10c violet & ol	.50	.35
779	A75	15c dp plum & gray blk	.50	.35
780	A75	20c ultra & brn	.50	.35
781	A75	25c dl red brn & dp bluish grn	.50	.35
782	A75	50c red & olive	.50	.35
a.		Souvenir sheet of 5, #778-782, imperf.	7.00	4.00
		Nos. 778-782,C377-C386 (15)	11.15	5.50

Centenary of the birth of Lord Baden-Powell, founder of the Boy Scouts.
For surcharge see #C754.

Pres. Luis A.
Somoza — A76

Portrait in Dark Brown
1957, July 2   Perf. 14x13½

783	A76	10c brt red	.35	.25
784	A76	15c deep blue	.35	.25
785	A76	35c rose violet	.35	.25
786	A76	50c brown	.40	.25
787	A76	75c gray green	.90	.55
		Nos. 783-787,C387-C391 (10)	8.40	5.55

President Luis A. Somoza.

Leon Cathedral
A77

Bishop Pereira
y Castellon
A78

Designs: 5c, Managua Cathedral. 15c, Archbishop Lezcano and Ortega. 50c, De la Merced Church, Granada. 1cor, Father Mariano Dubon.

Centers in Olive Gray

1957, July 12   Perf. 13½x14, 14x13½
788	A77	5c dull green	.35 .25
789	A78	10c dk purple	.35 .25
790	A78	15c dk blue	.40 .25
791	A77	20c dk brown	.50 .25
792	A77	50c dk slate grn	.55 .25
793	A78	1cor dk violet	1.40 .30

Nos. 788-793,C392-C397 (12) 10.20 3.60

Honoring the Catholic Church in Nicaragua.

M. S.
Honduras — A79

5c, Gen. Anastasio Somoza & freighter. 6c, M. S. Guatemala. 10c, M. S. Salvador. 15c, Ship between globes. 50c, Globes & ship.

1957, Oct. 15   Litho.   Perf. 14
794	A79	4c green, bl & blk	.65 .25
795	A79	5c multi	.65 .25
796	A79	6c red, bl & blk	.65 .25
797	A79	10c brn, bl grn & blk	.65 .25
798	A79	15c dk car, ultra & ol brn	.65 .25
799	A79	50c violet, bl & mar	1.90 .75

Nos. 794-799,C398-C403 (12) 14.15 6.10

Issued to honor Nicaragua's Merchant Marine. For surcharge see No. C691.

Melvin Jones and Lions Emblem — A80

Designs: 5c, Arms of Central American Republics. 20c, Dr. Teodoro A. Arias. 50c, Edward G. Barry. 75c, Motto and emblem. 1.50 cor, Map of Central America.

Emblem in Yellow, Red and Blue

1958, May 8   Unwmk.   Perf. 14
800	A80	5c blue & multi	.40 .25
801	A80	10c blue & org	.40 .25
802	A80	20c blue & olive	.40 .25
803	A80	50c blue & lilac	.40 .25
804	A80	75c blue & pink	.55 .25
805	A80	1.50cor blue, gray ol & sal	.90 .45
a.		Souvenir sheet of 6, #800-805	4.50 2.50

Nos. 800-805,C410-C415 (12) 9.90 4.70

17th convention of Lions Intl. of Central America, May, 1958.
For overprnts and surchargse see Nos. 1104H, C686.

St. Jean Baptiste De La Salle — A81

Christian Brothers: 5c, Arms of La Salle. 10c, School, Managua, horiz. 20c, Bro. Carlos. 50c, Bro. Antonio. 75c, Bro. Julio. 1cor, Bro. Argeo.

1958, July 13   Photo.   Perf. 14
806	A81	5c car, bl & yel	.35 .25
807	A81	10c emer, blk & ultra	.35 .25
808	A81	15c red brn, bis & blk	.35 .25
809	A81	20c car, bis & blk	.35 .25
810	A81	50c org, bis & brn blk	.35 .25
811	A81	75c bl, lt grn & dk brn	.35 .25

812	A81	1cor vio, bis & grnsh blk	.55 .30

Nos. 806-812,C416-C423 (15) 13.55 5.65

For surcharges see Nos. C539A, C755-C756.

UN Emblem and Globe — A82

15c, UNESCO building. 25c, 45c, "UNESCO." 40c, UNESCO building and Eiffel tower.

1958, Dec. 15   Litho.   Perf. 11½
813	A82	10c brt pink & bl	.40 .25
814	A82	15c blue & brt pink	.40 .25
815	A82	25c green & brn	.40 .25
816	A82	40c red org & blk	.40 .25
817	A82	45c dk bl & rose lil	.40 .25
818	A82	50c brown & grn	.40 .25
a.		Miniature sheet of 6, #813-818	2.00 .75

Nos. 813-818,C424-C429 (12) 11.35 5.00

UNESCO Headquarters in Paris opening, Nov. 3.

Pope John XXIII and Cardinal Spellman — A83

Designs: 10c, Spellman coat of arms. 15c, Cardinal Spellman. 20c, Human rosary and Cardinal, horiz. 25c, Cardinal with Ruben Dario order.

1959, Nov. 26   Unwmk.   Perf. 12½
819	A83	5c grnsh bl & brn	.40 .25
820	A83	10c yel, bl & car	.40 .25
821	A83	15c dk grn, blk & dk car	.40 .25
822	A83	20c yel, dk bl & grn	.40 .25
823	A83	25c ultra, vio & mag	.40 .25
a.		Min. sheet of 5, #819-823, perf. or imperf.	4.00 2.00

Nos. 819-823,C430-C436 (12) 8.95 4.65

Cardinal Spellman's visit to Managua, Feb. 1958.
For surcharges see #C638, C747, C752.

Abraham Lincoln — A84

Center in Black

1960, Jan.   Engr.   Perf. 13x13½
824	A84	5c car ver	.45 .30
825	A84	10c green	.45 .30
826	A84	15c dp orange	.45 .30
827	A84	1cor plum	.45 .30
828	A84	2cor ultra	.45 .30
a.		Souv. sheet of 5, #824-828, imperf.	1.50 1.00

Nos. 824-828,C437-C442 (11) 8.65 4.60

150th anniv. of the birth of Abraham Lincoln.
For surcharges see Nos. C500, C539, C637, C680, C753.

Nos. 824-828 Overprinted in Red

1960, Sept. 19   Center in Black
829	A84	5c deep carmine	.40 .30
830	A84	10c green	.40 .30
831	A84	15c deep orange	.40 .30
832	A84	1cor plum	.40 .30
833	A84	2cor ultra	.40 .30

Nos. 829-833,C446-C451 (11) 12.80 6.10

Issued for the Red Cross to aid earthquake victims in Chile.

Gen. Tomas Martinez and Pres. Luis A. Somoza — A85

5c, Official decrees. 10c, Two envelopes.

Perf. 13½
1961, Aug. 29   Unwmk.   Litho.
834	A85	5c grnsh bl & lt brn	.80 .40
835	A85	10c green & lt brn	.80 .40
836	A85	15c pink & brn	.80 .40

Nos. 834-836 (3) 2.40 1.20

Cent. (in 1960) of the postal rates regulation.

Arms of Nueva Segovia — A86

Coats of Arms: 3c, León. 4c, Managua. 5c, Granada. 6c, Rivas.

Arms in Original Colors;
Black Inscriptions

1962, Nov. 22   Perf. 12½x13
837	A86	2c pink	.45 .40
838	A86	3c lt blue	.45 .40
839	A86	4c pale lilac	.45 .40
840	A86	5c yellow	.45 .40
841	A86	6c buff	.45 .40

Nos. 837-841,C510-C514 (10) 7.20 4.60

For surcharge see #854.

No. RA73 Overprinted in Red:
"CORREOS"

1964   Photo.   Perf. 11½
842	PT13	5c gray, red & org	.75 .40
a.		Inverted overprint	

Nos. RA66-RA75 Overprinted

1965   Photo.   Perf. 11½
Orchids in Natural Colors
843	PT13	5c pale lilac & grn	1.10 .45
844	PT13	5c yellow & grn	1.10 .45
845	PT13	5c pink & grn	1.10 .45
846	PT13	5c pale vio & grn	1.10 .45
847	PT13	5c lt grnsh bl & red	1.10 .45
848	PT13	5c buff & lil	1.10 .45
849	PT13	5c yel grn & brn	1.10 .45
850	PT13	5c gray & red	1.10 .45
851	PT13	5c lt blue & dk bl	1.10 .45
852	PT13	5c lt green & brn	1.10 .45

Nos. 843-852 (10) 11.00 4.50

Seventh Central American Scout Camporee at El Coyotete. This overprint was also applied to each stamp on souvenir sheet No. C386a. Value, $15.
Use of Nos. 843-852 for postage was authorized by official decree.

Nos. 746 and 841 Surcharged with New Value and "RESELLO"

1968, May   Engr.   Perf. 12½
853	A68	5c on 6c dp ultra & gray blk	1.00 1.00

Litho.   Perf. 12½x13
854	A86	5c on 6c multi	1.00 1.00

Nos. RA66-RA67, RA69 and RA71 Overprinted

1969   Photo.   Perf. 11½
Orchids in Natural Colors
855	PT13	5c pale lil & grn	1.25 .75
856	PT13	5c yellow & grn	1.25 .75
857	PT13	5c pale vio & grn	1.25 .75
858	PT13	5c buff & lilac	1.25 .75

Nos. 855-858 (4) 5.00 3.00

Nos. RA66-RA75 Overprinted

O.I.T.
1919 - 1969

1969   Photo.   Perf. 11½
Orchids in Natural Colors
859	PT13	5c pale lil & grn	1.00 .45
860	PT13	5c yellow & grn	1.00 .45
861	PT13	5c pink & grn	1.00 .45
862	PT13	5c pale vio & grn	1.00 .45
863	PT13	5c lt grnsh bl & red	1.00 .45
864	PT13	5c buff & lil	1.00 .45
865	PT13	5c yel grn & brn	1.00 .45
866	PT13	5c gray & red	1.00 .45
867	PT13	5c lt & dk blue	1.00 .45
868	PT13	5c lt grn & brn	1.00 .45

Nos. 859-868 (10) 10.00 4.50

International Labor Organization, 50th anniv.

Pelé, Brazil — A87

Soccer Players: 10c, Ferenc Puskás, Hungary. 15c, Sir Stanley Matthews, England. 40c, Alfredo di Stefano, Argentina. 2cor, Giacinto Facchetti, Italy. 3cor, Lev Yashin, USSR. 5cor, Franz Beckenbauer, West Germany.

1970, May 11   Litho.   Perf. 13½
869	A87	5c multicolored	.40 .40
870	A87	10c multicolored	.40 .40
871	A87	15c multicolored	.40 .40
872	A87	40c multicolored	.40 .40
873	A87	2cor multicolored	1.25 .75
874	A87	3cor multicolored	1.60 .90
875	A87	5cor multicolored	2.40 1.25

Nos. 869-875,C712-C716 (12) 15.55 10.15

Issued to honor the winners of the 1970 poll for the International Soccer Hall of Fame. Names of players and their achievements printed in black on back of stamps.
For surcharges and overprint see Nos. 899-900, C786-C788.

No. 766 Surcharged & Overprinted in Black

1971, Mar.   Photo.   Perf. 11
876	A71	30c on 90c blk & gray	210.00 100.00

Egyptian Using Fingers to Count — A88

Symbolic Designs of Scientific Formulas: 15c, Newton's law (gravity). 20c, Einstein's theory (relativity). 1cor, Tsiolkovski's law (speed of rockets). 2cor, Maxwell's law (electromagnetism).

1971, May 15   Litho.   Perf. 13½
877	A88	10c lt bl & multi	.95 .40
878	A88	15c lt bl & multi	.95 .40
879	A88	20c lt bl & multi	1.10 .50
880	A88	1cor lt bl & multi	3.50 1.10
881	A88	2cor lt bl & multi	7.75 2.25

Nos. 877-881,C761-C765 (10) 26.50 9.75

Mathematical equations which changed the world. On the back of each stamp is a descriptive paragraph.
See Nos. C761-C765.

Symbols of Civilization, Peace Emblem with Globe — A89

1971, Sept. 6   Litho.   *Perf. 14*

882	A89	10c blk & bl	.45	.40
883	A89	15c vio bl, bl & blk	.45	.40
884	A89	20c brn bl & blk	.45	.40
885	A89	40c emer, bl & blk	.55	.40
886	A89	50c mag, bl & blk	.80	.45
887	A89	80c org, bl & blk	1.10	.60
888	A89	1cor ol, bl & blk	1.40	.75
889	A89	2cor vio, bl & blk	3.00	1.75
	Nos. 882-889 (8)		8.20	5.15

"Is there a formula for peace?" issue.

Moses with Tablets of the Law, by Rembrandt — A90

The Ten Commandments (Paintings): 15c, Moses and the Burning Bush, by Botticelli (I). 20c, Jephthah's Daughter, by Degas, (II), horiz. 30c, St. Vincent Ferrer Preaching in Verona, by Domenico Morone (III). 35c, The Nakedness of Noah, by Michelangelo (IV), horiz. 40c, Cain and Abel, by Francesco Trevisani (V), horiz. 50c, Potiphar's wife, by Rembrandt (VI). 60c, Isaac Blessing Jacob, by Gerbrand van den Eeckhout (VII), horiz. 75c, Susanna and the Elders, by Rubens (VIII), horiz.

1971, Nov. 1   *Perf. 11*

890	A90	10c yel brn & multi	.35	.35
891	A90	15c yel brn & multi	.35	.35
892	A90	20c yel brn & multi	.35	.35
893	A90	30c yel brn & multi	.35	.35
894	A90	35c yel brn & multi	.35	.35
895	A90	40c yel brn & multi	.35	.35
896	A90	50c yel brn & multi	.45	.45
897	A90	60c yel brn & multi	.85	.65
898	A90	75c yel brn & multi	1.80	1.00
	Nos. 890-898,C776-C777 (11)		10.45	5.80

Descriptive inscriptions printed in gray on back of stamps.

Nos. 873-874 Surcharged

1972, Mar. 20   Litho.   *Perf. 13½*

899	A87	40c on 2cor multi	.40	.25
900	A87	50c on 3cor multi	.45	.25
	Nos. 899-900,C786-C788 (5)		4.40	2.70

20th Olympic Games, Munich, 8/26-9/10.

Nos. RA66-RA69, RA71-RA74 Overprinted in Blue

1972, July 29   Photo.   *Perf. 11½*
Granite Paper

901	PT13	5c (#RA66)	1.10	.40
902	PT13	5c (#RA67)	1.10	.40
903	PT13	5c (#RA68)	1.10	.40
904	PT13	5c (#RA69)	1.10	.40
905	PT13	5c (#RA71)	1.10	.40
906	PT13	5c (#RA72)	1.10	.40
907	PT13	5c (#RA73)	1.10	.40
908	PT13	5c (#RA74)	1.10	.40
	Nos. 901-908 (8)		8.80	3.20

Gown by Givenchy, Paris — A91

1973, July 26   Litho.   *Perf. 13½*

909	A91	1cor shown	.50	.25
910	A91	2cor Hartnell, London	.80	.50
911	A91	5cor Balmain, Paris	2.00	1.20
	Nos. 909-911,C839-C844 (9)		8.10	3.45

Gowns by famous designers, modeled by Nicaraguan women. Inscriptions on back printed on top of gum give description of gown in Spanish and English.
Nos. 909-911 in perf. 11, see No. C844a.

Christmas — A92

2c, 5c, Virginia O'Hanlon writing letter, father. 3c, 15c, letter. 4c, 20c, Virginia, father reading letter.

1973, Nov. 15   Litho.   *Perf. 15*

912	A92	2c multicolored	.40	.25
913	A92	3c multicolored	.40	.25
914	A92	4c multicolored	.40	.25
915	A92	5c multicolored	.40	.25
916	A92	15c multicolored	.40	.25
917	A92	20c multicolored	.40	.25
	Nos. 912-917,C846-C848 (9)		7.95	4.35

Sir Winston Churchill (1874-1965) — A93

Designs: 2c, Churchill speaking. 3c, Military planning. 4c, Cigar, lamp. 5c, Churchill with Roosevert and Stalin. 10c, Churchill walking ashore from landing craft.

1974, Apr. 30   *Perf. 14½*

918	A93	2c multicolored	.40	.25
919	A93	3c multicolored	.40	.25
920	A93	4c multicolored	.40	.25
921	A93	5c multicolored	.40	.25
922	A93	10c multicolored	.40	.25
	Nos. 918-922,C849-C850 (7)		7.85	4.40

World Cup Soccer Championships, Munich — A94

Scenes from previous World Cup Championships with flags and scores of finalists.

1974, May 8   *Perf. 14½*

923	A94	1c 1930	.40	.25
924	A94	2c 1934	.40	.25
925	A94	3c 1938	.40	.25
926	A94	4c 1950	.40	.25
927	A94	5c 1954	.40	.25
928	A94	10c 1958	.40	.25
929	A94	15c 1962	.40	.25
930	A94	20c 1966	.40	.25
931	A94	25c 1970	.40	.25
	Nos. 923-931,C853 (10)		9.85	8.50

For overprint see No. C856.

A95

Wild Flowers and Cacti: 2c, Hollyhocks. 3c, Paguira insignis. 4c, Morning glory. 5c, Pereschia autumnalis. 10c, Cultivated morning glory. 15c, Hibiscus. 20c, Pagoda tree blossoms.

1974, June 11   Litho.   *Perf. 14*

932	A95	2c grn & multi	.40	.25
933	A95	3c grn & multi	.40	.25
934	A95	4c grn & multi	.40	.25
935	A95	5c grn & multi	.40	.25
936	A95	10c grn & multi	.40	.25
937	A95	15c grn & multi	.40	.25
938	A95	20c grn & multi	.40	.25
	Nos. 932-938,C854-C855 (9)		9.30	5.25

Nicaraguan Stamps — A96

1974, July 10   *Perf. 14½*

939	A96	2c No. 670	.35	.25
940	A96	3c No. 669	.35	.25
941	A96	4c No. C110, horiz.	.35	.25
942	A96	5c No. 667	.35	.25
943	A96	10c No. 666	.35	.25
944	A96	20c No. 665	.35	.25
	Nos. 939-944,C855A-C855C (9)		8.90	5.40

UPU, Cent.

Four-toed Anteater — A97

Designs: 2c, Puma. 3c, Raccoon. 4c, Ocelot. 5c, Kinkajou. 10c, Coypu. 15c, Peccary. 20c, Tapir.

1974, Sept. 10   Litho.   *Perf. 14½*

946	A97	1c multi	.35	.25
947	A97	2c multi	.35	.25
948	A97	3c multi	.35	.25
949	A97	4c multi	.35	.25
950	A97	5c multi	.35	.25
951	A97	10c multi	.35	.25
952	A97	15c multi	.35	.25
953	A97	20c multi	.35	.25
	Nos. 946-953,C857-C858 (10)		8.55	5.50

Wild animals from San Diego and London Zoos.

Prophet Zacharias, by Michelangelo — A98

Works of Michelangelo: 2c, The Last Judgment. 3c, The Creation of Adam, horiz. 4c, Sistine Chapel. 5c, Moses. 10c, Mouscron Madonna. 15c, David. 20c, Doni Madonna.

1974, Dec. 15

954	A98	1c dp rose & multi	.60	.30
955	A98	2c yellow & multi	.60	.30
956	A98	3c sal & multi	.60	.30
957	A98	4c blue & multi	.60	.30
958	A98	5c tan & multi	.60	.30
959	A98	10c multicolored	.60	.30
960	A98	15c multicolored	.60	.30
961	A98	20c blue & multi	.60	.30
	Nos. 954-961,C859-C862 (12)		16.50	7.65

Christmas 1974 and 500th birth anniversary of Michelangelo Buonarroti (1475-1564), Italian painter, sculptor and architect.

Giovanni Martinelli, Othello — A99

Opera Singers and Scores: 2c, Tito Gobbi, Simone Boccanegra. 3c, Lotte Lehmann, Der Rosenkavalier. 4c, Lauritz Melchior, Parsifal. 5c, Nellie Melba, La Traviata. 15c, Jussi Bjoerling, La Bohème. 20c, Birgit Nilsson, Turandot.

1975, Jan. 22   *Perf. 14x13½*

962	A99	1c rose lil & multi	.45	.25
963	A99	2c brt bl & multi	.45	.25
964	A99	3c yel & multi	.45	.25
965	A99	4c dl bl & multi	.45	.25
966	A99	5c org & multi	.45	.25
967	A99	15c lake & multi	.45	.25
968	A99	20c gray & multi	.45	.25
	Nos. 962-968,C863-C870 (15)		13.85	5.20

Famous opera singers.

Jesus Condemned — A100

Stations of the Cross: 2c, Jesus Carries the Cross. 3c, Jesus falls the first time. 4c, Jesus meets his mother. 5c, Simon of Cyrene carries the Cross. 15c, St. Veronica wipes Jesus' face. 20c, Jesus falls the second time. 25c, Jesus meets the women of Jerusalem. 35c, Jesus falls the third time. Designs from Leon Cathedral.

1975, Mar. 20   *Perf. 14½*

969	A100	1c ultra & multi	.50	.25
970	A100	2c ultra & multi	.50	.25
971	A100	3c ultra & multi	.50	.25
972	A100	4c ultra & multi	.50	.25
973	A100	5c ultra & multi	.50	.25
974	A100	15c ultra & multi	.50	.25
975	A100	20c ultra & multi	.50	.25
976	A100	25c ultra & multi	.50	.25
977	A100	35c ultra & multi	.50	.25
	Nos. 969-977,C871-C875 (14)		11.20	4.65

Easter 1975.

The Spirit of 76, by Archibald M. Willard — A101

Designs: 2c, Pitt Addressing Parliament, by K. A. Hickel. 3c, The Midnight Ride of Paul Revere, horiz. 4c, Statue of George III Demolished, by W. Walcutt, horiz. 5c, Boston Massacre. 10c, Colonial coin and seal, horiz. 15c, Boston Tea Party, horiz. 20c, Thomas Jefferson, by Rembrandt Peale. 25c, Benjamin Franklin, by Charles Willson Peale. 30c, Signing Declaration of Independence, by John Trumbull, horiz. 35c, Surrender of Cornwallis, by Trumbull, horiz.

1975, Apr. 16   *Perf. 14*

978	A101	1c buff & multi	.40	.25
979	A101	2c buff & multi	.30	.25
980	A101	3c buff & multi	.40	.25
981	A101	4c buff & multi	.40	.25
982	A101	5c buff & multi	.40	.25
983	A101	10c buff & multi	.40	.25
984	A101	15c buff & multi	.40	.25
985	A101	20c buff & multi	.40	.25
986	A101	25c buff & multi	.40	.25
987	A101	30c buff & multi	.40	.25
988	A101	35c buff & multi	.40	.25
	Nos. 978-988,C876-C879 (15)		13.40	7.15

American Bicentennial. See Nos. C876-C879.

Scouts Saluting Flag, Scout Emblems A102

2c, Two-men canoe. 3c, Scouts of various races shaking hands. 4c, Scout cooking. 5c, Entrance to Camp Nicaragua. 20c, Group discussion.

1975, Aug. 15   *Perf. 14½*

989	A102	1c multi	.40	.25
990	A102	2c multi	.40	.25
991	A102	3c multi	.40	.25
992	A102	4c multi	.40	.25
993	A102	5c multi	.40	.25
994	A102	20c multi	.40	.25
	Nos. 989-994,C880-C883 (10)		8.45	4.30

Nordjamb 75, 14th World Boy Scout Jamboree, Lillehammer, Norway, July 29-Aug. 7.

Pres. Somoza, Map and Arms of Nicaragua — A103

1975, Sept. 10 — *Perf. 14*
995 A103 20c multi .55 .30
996 A103 40c org & multi .55 .30
Nos. 995-996,C884-C886 (5) 13.70 6.10

Reelection of Pres. Anastasio Somoza D.

King's College Choir, Cambridge A104

Famous Choirs: 2c, Einsiedeln Abbey. 3c, Regensburg. 4c, Vienna Choir Boys. 5c, Sistine Chapel. 15c, Westminster Cathedral. 20c, Mormon Tabernacle.

1975, Nov. 15 — *Perf. 14½*
997 A104 1c silver & multi .45 .25
998 A104 2c silver & multi .45 .25
999 A104 3c silver & multi .45 .25
1000 A104 4c silver & multi .45 .25
1001 A104 5c silver & multi .45 .25
1002 A104 15c silver & multi .45 .25
1003 A104 20c silver & multi .45 .25
Nos. 997-1003,C887-C890 (11) 8.75 3.90

Christmas 1975.

The Chess Players, by Ludovico Carracci — A105

History of Chess: 2c, Arabs Playing Chess, by Delacroix. 3c, Cardinals Playing Chess, by Victor Marais-Milton. 4c, Albrecht V of Bavaria and Anne of Austria Playing Chess, by Hans Muelich, vert. 5c, Chess Players, Persian manuscript, 14th century. 10c, Origin of Chess, Indian miniature, 17th century. 15c, Napoleon Playing Chess at Schönbrunn, by Antoni Uniechowski, vert. 20c, The Chess Game, by J. E. Hummel.

1976, Jan. 8 — *Perf. 14½*
1004 A105 1c brn & multi .40 .25
1005 A105 2c lt vio & multi .40 .25
1006 A105 3c ocher & multi .40 .25
1007 A105 4c multi .40 .25
1008 A105 5c multi .40 .25
1009 A105 10c multi .40 .25
1010 A105 15c blue & multi .40 .25
1011 A105 20c ocher & multi .40 .25
Nos. 1004-1011,C891-C893 (11) 9.70 5.00

Olympic Rings, Danish Crew A107

Winners, Rowing and Sculling Events: 2c, East Germany, 1972. 3c, Italy, 1968. 4c, Great Britain, 1936. 5c, France, 1952. 35c, US, 1920, vert.

1976, Sept. 7 — Litho. — *Perf. 14*
1022 A107 1c blue & multi .30 .25
1023 A107 2c blue & multi .30 .25
1024 A107 3c blue & multi .30 .25
1025 A107 4c blue & multi .30 .25
1026 A107 5c blue & multi .30 .25
1027 A107 35c blue & multi .30 .25
Nos. 1022-1027,C902-C905 (10) 13.85 8.25

Candlelight A108

#1028, The Smoke Signal, by Frederic Remington. #1029, Space Signal Monitoring Center. #1031, Edison's laboratory & light bulb. #1032, Agriculture, 1776. #1033, Agriculture, 1976. #1034, Harvard College, 1726. #1035, Harvard University, 1976. #1036, Horse-drawn carriage. #1037, Boeing 747.

1976, May 25 — Litho. — *Perf. 13½*
1028 A108 1c gray & multi .25 .25
1029 A108 1c gray & multi .25 .25
a. Pair, #1028-1029 .60 .45
1030 A108 2c gray & multi .25 .25
1031 A108 2c gray & multi .25 .25
a. Pair, #1030-1031 .60 .45
1032 A108 3c gray & multi .25 .25
1033 A108 3c gray & multi .25 .25
a. Pair, #1032-1033 .60 .45

1034 A108 4c gray & multi .25 .25
1035 A108 4c gray & multi .25 .25
a. Pair, #1034-1035 .60 .45
1036 A108 5c gray & multi .25 .25
1037 A108 5c gray & multi .25 .25
a. Pair, #1036-1037 .60 .45
Nos. 1028-1037,C907-C912 (16) 5.60 4.80

American Bicentennial, 200 years of progress.

Mauritius No. 2 — A109

Rare Stamps: 2c, Western Australia #3a. 3c, Mauritius #1. 4c, Jamaica #83a. 5c, US #C3a. 10c, Basel #3L1. 25c, Canada #387a.

1976, Dec. — *Perf. 14*
1038 A109 1c multi .40 .25
1039 A109 2c multi .40 .25
1040 A109 3c multi .40 .25
1041 A109 4c multi .40 .25
1042 A109 5c multi .40 .25
1043 A109 10c multi .40 .25
1044 A109 20c multi .40 .25
Nos. 1038-1044,C913-C917 (12) 10.30 4.40

Back inscriptions printed on top of gum describe illustrated stamp.

Zeppelin in Flight — A110

1c, Zeppelin in hangar. 3c, Giffard's dirigible airship, 1852. 4c, Zeppelin on raising stilts coming out of hangar. 5c, Zeppelin ready for take-off.

1977, Oct. 31 — Litho. — *Perf. 14½*
1045 A110 1c multi .40 .25
1046 A110 2c multi .40 .25
1047 A110 3c multi .40 .25
1048 A110 4c multi .40 .25
1049 A110 5c multi .40 .25
Nos. 1045-1049,C921-C924 (9) 10.95 6.00

75th anniversary of Zeppelin.

Lindbergh, Map of Nicaragua A111

2c, Spirit of St. Louis, map of Nicaragua. 3c, Lindbergh, vert. 4c, Spirit of St. Louis & NYC-Paris route. 5c, Lindbergh & Spirit of St. Louis. 20c, Lindbergh, NYC-Paris route & plane.

1977, Nov. 30
1050 A111 1c multi .40 .25
1051 A111 2c multi .40 .25
1052 A111 3c multi .40 .25
1053 A111 4c multi .40 .25
1054 A111 5c multi .40 .25
1055 A111 20c multi .40 .25
Nos. 1050-1055,C926-C929 (10) 11.00 4.95

Charles A. Lindbergh's solo transatlantic flight from NYC to Paris, 50th anniv.

Nutcracker Suite — A112

1c, Christmas party. 2c, Dancing dolls. 3c, Clara and Snowflakes. 4c, Snowflake and prince. 5c, Snowflake dance. 15c, Sugarplum fairy and prince. 40c, Waltz of the flowers. 90c, Chinese tea dance. 1cor, Bonbonnière. 10cor, Arabian coffee dance.

1977, Dec. 12
1056 A112 1c multi .40 .25
1057 A112 2c multi .40 .25
1058 A112 3c multi .40 .25
1059 A112 4c multi .40 .25
1060 A112 5c multi .40 .25
1061 A112 15c multi .40 .25
1062 A112 40c multi .40 .25
1063 A112 90c multi .40 .25

1064 A112 1cor multi .60 .30
1065 A112 10cor multi 6.00 3.00
Nos. 1056-1065 (10) 9.80 5.30

Christmas 1977. See No. C931.

Mr. and Mrs. Andrews, by Gainsborough A113

Paintings: 2c, Giovanna Bacelli, by Gainsborough. 3c, Blue Boy by Gainsborough. 4c, Francis I, by Titian. 5c, Charles V in Battle of Muhlberg, by Titian. 25c, Sacred Love, by Titian.

1978, Jan. 11 — Litho. — *Perf. 14½*
1066 A113 1c multi .35 .25
1067 A113 2c multi .35 .25
1068 A113 3c multi .35 .25
1069 A113 4c multi .35 .25
1070 A113 5c multi .35 .25
1071 A113 25c multi .35 .25
Nos. 1066-1071,C932-C933 (8) 10.10 5.75

Thomas Gainsborough (1727-1788), 250th birth anniv.; Titian (1477-1576), 500th birth anniv.

Gothic Portal, Lower Church, Assisi — A114

Designs: 2c, St. Francis preaching to the birds. 3c, St. Francis, painting. 4c, St. Francis and Franciscan saints, 15th century tapestry. 5c, Portiuncola, cell of St. Francis, now in church of St. Mary of the Angels, Assisi. 15c, Blessing of St. Francis for Brother Leo (parchment). 25c, Stained-glass window, Upper Church of St. Francis, Assisi.

1978, Feb. 23 — Litho. — *Perf. 14½*
1072 A114 1c red & multi .40 .25
1073 A114 2c brt grn & multi .40 .25
1074 A114 3c bl grn & multi .40 .25
1075 A114 4c ultra & multi .40 .25
1076 A114 5c rose & multi .40 .25
1077 A114 15c yel & multi .40 .25
1078 A114 25c ocher & multi .40 .25
Nos. 1072-1078,C935-C936 (9) 8.15 3.75

St. Francis of Assisi (1182-1266), 750th anniversary of his canonization, and in honor of Our Lady of the Immaculate Conception, patron saint of Nicaragua.

Passenger and Freight Locomotives A115

Locomotives: 2c, Lightweight freight. 3c, American. 4c, Heavy freight Baldwin. 5c, Light freight and passenger Baldwin. 15c, Presidential coach.

1978, Apr. 7 — Litho. — *Perf. 14½*
1079 A115 1c lil & multi .30 .25
1080 A115 2c rose lil & multi .30 .25
1081 A115 3c lt bl & multi .30 .25
1082 A115 4c ol & multi .45 .25
1083 A115 5c yel & multi .45 .25
1084 A115 15c dp org & multi .45 .25
Nos. 1079-1084,C938-C940 (9) 11.25 5.90

Centenary of Nicaraguan railroads.

Michael Strogoff, by Jules Verne — A116

Jules Verne Books: 2c, The Mysterious Island. 3c, Journey to the Center of the Earth (battle of the sea monsters). 4c, Five Weeks in a Balloon.

1978, Aug. — Litho. — *Perf. 14½*
1085 A116 1c multi .35 .25
1086 A116 2c multi .35 .25
1087 A116 3c multi .35 .25
1088 A116 4c multi .35 .25
Nos. 1085-1088,C942-C943 (6) 7.30 4.35

Jules Verne (1828-1905), science fiction writer.

Montgolfier Balloon — A117

1c, Icarus. 3c, Wright Brothers' Flyer A. 4c, Orville Wright at control of Flyer, 1908.

Perf. 14½, horiz.
1978, Sept. 29 — Litho.
1089 A117 1c multi, horiz. .40 .25
1090 A117 2c multi, horiz. .40 .25
1091 A117 3c multi, horiz. .40 .25
1092 A117 4c multi .40 .25
Nos. 1089-1092,C945-C946 (6) 6.00 3.30

History of aviation & 75th anniv. of 1st powered flight.

Ernst Ocwirk and Alfredo Di Stefano — A118

Soccer Players: 25c, Ralf Edstroem and Oswaldo Piazza.

1978, Oct. 25 — Litho. — *Perf. 13½x14*
1093 A118 20c multicolored .40 .25
1094 A118 25c multicolored .40 .25
Nos. 1093-1094,C948-C949 (4) 4.20 2.50

11th World Soccer Cup Championship, Argentina, June 1-25. See No. C950.

St. Peter, by Goya — A119

Paintings: 15c, St. Gregory, by Goya.

1978, Dec. 12 — Litho. — *Perf. 13½x14*
1095 A119 10c multi .35 .25
1096 A119 15c multi .35 .25
Nos. 1095-1096,C951-C952 (4) 5.35 2.95

Christmas 1978. See No. C953.

San Cristobal Volcano and Map — A120

Designs: No. 1098, Lake Cosigüina. No. 1099, Telica Volcano. No. 1100, Lake Jiloa.

1978, Dec. 29 — *Perf. 14x13½*
1097 A120 5c multi .40 .25
1098 A120 5c multi .40 .25
a. Pair, #1097-1098 .95 .50
1099 A120 20c multi .40 .25
1100 A120 20c multi .40 .25
a. Pair, #1099-1100 .95 .50
Nos. 1097-1100,C954-C961 (12) 7.80 5.30

Volcanos, lakes and their locations.

Overprinted in Silver or
Red — A120a

Overprint reads: 1979 / ANO DE LA
LIBERACION / OLYMPIC RINGS /
PARTICIPACION NICARAGUA /
OLIMPIADAS 1980 / Litografia
Nacional, Portugal symbol

International Year of the Child: 20c, Carousel. 90c, Playing soccer. 2cor, Collecting stamps. 2.20cor, Playing with model train, plane. 10cor, Playing baseball.

1980, Apr. 7   Litho.   Perf. 13¾x14¼
Overprinted in Silver

1101	A120a	20c multi	10.00	10.00
e.		Red ovpt.	10.00	10.00
1101A	A120a	90c multi	10.00	10.00
f.		Red ovpt.	10.00	10.00
1101B	A120a	2cor multi	10.00	10.00
g.		Red ovpt.	10.00	10.00
1101C	A120a	2.20cor multi	10.00	10.00
h.		Red ovpt.	10.00	10.00
1101D	A120a	10cor multi	10.00	10.00
		Red ovpt.	10.00	10.00
	Nos. 1101-1101D (5)		50.00	50.00

Overprinted for Year of Liberation and 1980 Olympic Games.
Nos. 1101-1101D, 1101e-1101i were not issued without overprint.
Nos. 1101A-1101D are airmail.

Overprinted in Red or
Silver — A120b

Overprint reads like Nos. 1101-1101D

Designs: 20c, North American Indian messenger. 35c, Post rider on horse. 1cor, Prestamp cover to London, horiz. 1.80cor, Sir Rowland Hill (1795-1897), postal reformer. 2.20cor, Block of six of Great Britain #1, horiz. 5cor, Nicaragua Zeppelin cover to Germany, horiz.

1980, Apr. 7   Litho.   Perf. 14½
Overprinted in Red

1102	A120b	20c multi	11.00	11.00
f.		Silver overprint	11.00	11.00
1102A	A120b	35c multi	11.00	11.00
g.		Silver overprint	11.00	11.00
1102B	A120b	1cor multi	11.00	11.00
h.		Silver overprint	11.00	11.00
1102C	A120b	1.80cor multi	11.00	11.00
i.		Silver overprint	11.00	11.00
1102D	A120b	2.20cor multi	11.00	11.00
j.		Silver overprint	11.00	11.00
1102E	A120b	5cor multi	11.00	11.00
k.		Silver overprint	11.00	11.00
	Nos. 1102-1102E (6)		66.00	66.00

Overprinted for Year of Liberation and 1980 Olympic Games. Nos. 1102-1102E, 1102f-1102k were not issued without overprint. Nos. 1102C-1102E are airmail.

**Stamps of Type A120b With
Different Overprints**

Overprinted in   Overprinted in
Red — A120c   Silver —
                        A120d

Designs of unoverprinted stamps as Nos. 1102-1102E.

1980   Litho.   Perf. 14½
Overprinted in Red

1102L	A120c	20c multi	—	—
1102M	A120c	35c multi	—	—
1102N	A120c	1cor multi	—	—

Overprinted in Silver

1102O	A120d	1.80cor multi	—	—
1102P	A120d	2.20cor multi	—	—
1102Q	A120d	5cor multi	—	—

Issued: Nos. 1102L-1102Q, 9/30/80. Nos. 1102L-1102Q were not issued without overprint. Nos. 1102O-1102Q are airmail.

Overprinted in Silver or Red — A120c

Overprint reads: 1979 / ANO DE LA
LIBERACION / OLYMPIC RINGS /
PARTICIPACION NICARAGUA /
OLIMPIADAS 1980 / Litografia
Nacional, Portugal symbol

Albert Einstein and: 5c, Albert Schweitzer. 10c, Theory of Relativity: 15c, Trylon & Perisphere, NY World's Fair, 1939. 20c, J. Robert Oppenheimer. 25c, Wailing Wall, Jerusalem. 1cor, Nobel Prize Medal. 2.75cor, Spaceship, radio telescope antenna. 10cor, Mohandas K. Gandhi and Taj Mahal.

1980, Apr. 7   Litho.   Perf. 14¾
Overprinted in Silver

1103	A120c	5c multi		
h.		Red ovpt.	5.75	5.75
1103A	A120c	10c multi		
i.		Red ovpt.	5.75	5.75
1103B	A120c	15c multi		
j.		Red ovpt.	5.75	5.75
1103C	A120c	20c multi		
k.		Red ovpt.	5.75	5.75
1103D	A120c	25c multi		
l.		Red ovpt.	5.75	5.75
1103E	A120c	1cor multi		
m.		Red ovpt.	5.75	5.75
1103F	A120c	2.75cor multi		
n.		Red ovpt.	5.75	5.75
	Nos. 1103-1103F (7)		5.50	5.50

Overprinted in Red

1103G	A120c	10cor multi		

Overprinted for Intl. Year of the Child, Year of Liberation and 1980 Olympic Games.
Nos. 1103-1103F were not issued without overprint. Nos. 1103E-1103G are airmail. No. 1103G was only issued with red overprint.

1st Anniv. of
the
Revolution —
A120d

Sandino portrait and: 40c, Rigoberto Lopez Perez. 75c, Street fighters. 1cor, Literacy Logo, Intl. Solidarity with Nicaragua, vert. 1.25cor, German Pomares Ordonez, jungle fighters. 1.85cor, Crowd celebrating, vert. 2.50cor, Carlos Fonseca, campfire, FSLN. 5cor, Map of Central America, Flag of Nicaragua, vert. 10cor, Literacy statement, rural scene.

1980, July 19   Litho.   Perf. 14

1104	A120d	40c multi	1.20	1.20
1104A	A120d	75c multi	1.20	1.20
1104B	A120d	1cor multi	1.20	1.20
1104C	A120d	1.25cor multi	1.20	1.20
1104D	A120d	1.85cor multi	1.20	1.20
1104E	A120d	2.50cor multi	1.20	1.20
1104F	A120d	5cor multi	1.20	1.20
	Nos. 1104-1104F (7)		8.40	8.40

Souvenir Sheet
Perf. 14½x14¼

1104G	A120d	10cor multi	8.50	8.50

**No. 805a Overprinted in Black and
Silver**

A120e

Methods and Perfs. As Before
1980, Sept. 30

1104H	A120e	Sheet of 6	105.00	
i.		5c multi		
j.		10c multi		
k.		20c multi		
l.		50c multi		
m.		75c multi		
n.		1.50cor multi		

Intl. Year of the Child
Type of 1980
Overprinted in Black —
A120f

Overprint reads: 1980 ANO DE LA
ALFABETIZACION and Litografia
Nacional, Portugal symbol

Perf. 13¾x14¼
1980, Dec. 20   Litho.

1106	A120f	20c like #1101	7.50	7.50
1106A	A120f	90c like #1101A	7.50	7.50
1106B	A120f	2cor like #1101B	7.50	7.50
1106C	A120f	2.20cor like #1101C	7.50	7.50
1106D	A120f	10cor like #1101D	7.50	7.50
	Nos. 1106-1106D (5)		37.50	37.50

Souvenir Sheet

1106E	A120f	10cor ovn on 15cor, like #C970b	7.25	7.25

Nos. 1106-1106D were not issued without overprint. Nos. 1106A-1106D are airmail.
No. 1106E was not issued without the surcharge, however it does not have an overprint.

Einstein Type of 1980
Overprinted in Gold and Black: 1980
ANO DE LA ALFABETIZACION,
Litografia Nacional, Portugal symbol
and

A120g

Additional overprints read: No. 1107, YURI GAGARIN / 12/IV/1961 / LER HOMBRE EN EL ESPACIO. No. 1107A, Space Shuttle and LUNABA 1981. No. 1107B, Space Shuttle. Nos. 1107C, 1107E, 1107F, 1980 ANO DE LA ALFABETIZACION and Litografia Nacional, Portugal symbol. No. 1107D, Apollo XI / 16/VIII/1969 / LER HONBRE A LA LUNA. No. 1107G, Einstin and Gandhi, with LUNOJOD 1 Overprint. No. 1107H, Einstin holding clipboard, with Space Shuttle, LUNABA 1981, PLANETA SATURNO 1980 and VOYAGER overprints.

1981, May 15   Litho.   Perf. 14½

1107	A120g	5c like #1103	—	—
1107A	A120g	10c like #1103A	—	—
1107B	A120g	15c like #1103B	—	—
1107C	A120g	20c like #1103C	—	—
1107D	A120g	25c like #1103D	—	—
1107E	A120g	1cor like #1103E	—	—
1107F	A120g	2.75cor like #1103F		
1107G	A120g	10cor multi		
	Nos. 1107-1107G (10)		100.00	

Souvenir Sheet
Perf. 14¾

1107H	A120g	10cor on 20cor multi	100.00	

Nos. 1107-1107H were not issued without overprint. Nos. 1107E-1107H are airmail.

Souvenir Sheet

Quetzal
A121

1981, May 18   Litho.   Perf. 13

1108	A121	10cor multi	2.50	1.25

WIPA 1981 Phil. Exhib., Vienna, May 22-31.

1982 World
Cup — A122

Various soccer players and stadiums.

1981, June 25   Perf. 12x12½

1109	A122	5c multi	.45	.25
1109A	A122	20c multi	.45	.25
1109B	A122	25c multi	.45	.25
1109C	A122	30c multi	.45	.25
1109D	A122	50c multi	.45	.25
1109E	A122	4cor multi	.95	.25
1109F	A122	5cor multi	1.20	.30
1109G	A122	10cor multi	2.25	.80
	Nos. 1109-1109G (8)		6.65	2.60

Souvenir Sheet
Perf. 13

1109H	A122	10cor multi	3.50	1.50

2nd Anniv. of
Revolution
A123

1981, July 19   Perf. 12½x12

1110	A123	50c Adult education	.55	.25
	Nos. 1110,C975E-C975G (4)		10.55	1.20

20th Anniv. of
the
FSLN — A124

1981, July 23

1111	A124	50c Armed citizen	.60	.40

See No. C976.

Postal Union
of Spain and
the Americas,
12th
Congress,
Managua
A125

1981, Aug. 10

1112	A125	50c Mailman	.60	.40
	Nos. 1112,C977-C979 (4)		3.00	1.70

Natl. Literacy
Campaign,
1st Anniv. —
A125a

Designs: 5c, "S"ahino, man counting on fingers. 20c, "A"rmadillo, children marching. 30c, "N"utria, teacher with 2 women. 40c, "D"anto, teacher with 5 people.60c, "I"guana, teacher with 3 adults, hut. 6cor, "N"icaragua, map of Nicaragua with graph. 9cor, "O"so hormiguera, UNESCO Krupskaya medal.

1981, August   Litho.   Perf. 14

1113	A125a	5c multi		
1113A	A125a	10c multi		
1113B	A125a	30c multi		
1113C	A125a	40c multi		
1113D	A125a	60c multi		
1113E	A125a	6cor multi		
1113F	A125a	9cor multi		
	Nos. 1113-1113F (7)		29.00	5.00

Aquatic Flowers
(Nymphaea...)
A126

1981, Sept. 15 — Perf. 12½

1114	A126	50c Capensis	.35	.25
1115	A126	1cor Daubenyana	.35	.25
1116	A126	1.20cor Marliacea	.35	.25
1117	A126	1.80cor GT Moore	.50	.25
1118	A126	2cor Lotus	.55	.25
1119	A126	2.50cor BG Berry	.75	.30
		Nos. 1114-1119,C981 (7)	9.35	2.45

Tropical Fish — A127

50c, Cheirodon axelrodi. 1cor, Poecilia reticulata. 1.85cor, Anostomus anostomus. 2.10cor, Corydoras arcuatus. 2.50cor, Cynolebias nigripinnis.

1981, Oct. 19

1120	A127	50c multicolored	.35	.25
1121	A127	1cor multicolored	.35	.25
1122	A127	1.85cor multicolored	.70	.25
1123	A127	2.10cor multicolored	.95	.25
1124	A127	2.50cor multicolored	1.20	.30
		Nos. 1120-1124,C983-C984 (7)	9.30	1.90

Dryocopus Lineatus — A128

1.20cor, Ramphastos sulfuratus, horiz. 1.80cor, Aratinga finschi, horiz. 2cor, Ara macao.

1981, Nov. 30 — Perf. 12½

1125	A128	50c multi	.50	.25
1126	A128	1.20cor multi	.70	.25
1127	A128	1.80cor multi	.90	.25
1128	A128	2cor multi	1.10	.25
		Nos. 1125-1128,C986-C988 (7)	8.20	2.45

Space Communications A129

Various communications satellites.

1981, Dec. 15 — Perf. 13x12½

1129	A129	50c multi	.40	.25
1130	A129	1cor multi	.40	.25
1131	A129	1.50cor multi	.40	.25
1132	A129	2cor multi	.75	.25
		Nos. 1129-1132,C989-C991 (7)	8.55	1.90

Vaporcito 93 — A130

1cor, Vulcan Iron Works, 1946. 1.20cor, 1911. 1.80cor, Hoist & Derrick, 1909. 2cor, U-10B, 1956. 2.50cor, Ferrobus, 1945.

1981, Dec. 30 — Perf. 12½

1133	A130	50c multi	.30	.25
1134	A130	1cor multi	.35	.25
1135	A130	1.20cor multi	.40	.25
1136	A130	1.80cor multi	.65	.25
1137	A130	2cor multi	.75	.25
1138	A130	2.50cor multi	1.00	.30
		Nos. 1133-1138,C992 (7)	9.70	2.30

No. 1136 is inscribed "Hoist & Derriel."

1982 World Cup — A131

Designs: Various soccer players. 3.50cor horiz.

1982, Jan. 25

1139	A131	5c multi	.35	.25
1140	A131	20c multi	.35	.25
1141	A131	25c multi	.35	.25
1142	A131	2.50cor multi	.55	.35
1143	A131	3.50cor multi	.75	.35
		Nos. 1139-1143,C993-C994 (7)	9.45	2.55

Cocker Spaniels A132

20c, German shepherds. 25c, English setters. 2.50cor, Brittany spaniels.

1982, Feb. 18

1144	A132	5c multi	.40	.25
1145	A132	20c multi	.40	.25
1146	A132	25c multi	.40	.25
1147	A132	2.50cor multi	1.25	.40
		Nos. 1144-1147,C996-C998 (7)	8.60	2.25

Dynamine Myrrhina — A133

1.20cor, Eunica alcmena. 1.50cor, Callizona acesta. 2cor, Adelpha leuceria.

1982, Mar. 26

1148	A133	50c multi	.40	.25
1149	A133	1.20cor multi	.50	.25
1150	A133	1.50cor multi	.65	.25
1151	A133	2cor multi	.70	.25
		Nos. 1148-1151,C1000-C1002 (7)	8.50	2.00

Satellite — A134

Designs: Various satellites. 5c, 50c, 1.50cor, 2.50cor horiz.

1982, Apr. 12

1152	A134	5c multi	.40	.25
1153	A134	15c multi	.40	.25
1154	A134	25c multi	.40	.25
1155	A134	1.50cor multi	.40	.25
1156	A134	2.50cor multi	.60	.25
		Nos. 1152-1156,C1003-C1004 (7)	6.60	2.15

UPU Membership Centenary A135

1982, May 1 — Litho. — Perf. 13

1157	A135	50c Mail coach	.65	.25
1158	A135	1.20cor Ship	.65	.25
		Nos. 1157-1158,C1005-C1006 (4)	4.40	1.45

14th Central American and Caribbean Games (Cuba '82) — A136

1982, May 13

1159	A136	10c Bicycling	.45	.25
1160	A136	15c Swimming, horiz.	.45	.25
1161	A136	25c Basketball	.45	.25
1162	A136	50c Weight lifting	.45	.25
		Nos. 1159-1162,C1007-C1009 (7)	7.30	2.35

3rd Anniv. of Revolution A137

1982, July 19

1163	A137	50c multi	.60	.25
		Nos. 1163,C1012-C1014 (4)	6.05	1.55

George Washington (1732-1799) — A138

19th Century Paintings. 50c, Mount Vernon. 1cor, Signing the Constitution, horiz. 2cor, Riding through Trenton.
Size of 50c: 45x35mm.

Perf. 13x12½, 12½x13
1982, June 20 — Litho.

1164	A138	50c multicolored	.40	.25
1165	A138	1cor multicolored	.40	.25
1166	A138	2cor multicolored	.85	.25
		Nos. 1164-1166,C1015-C1018 (7)	8.35	2.40

Flower Arrangement, by R. Penalba — A139

Paintings: 50c, Masked Dancers, by M. Garcia, horiz. 1cor, The Couple, by R. Perez. 1.20cor, Canales Valley, by A. Mejias, horiz. 1.85cor, Portrait of Mrs. Castellon, by T. Jerez. 2cor, Street Vendors, by L. Cerrato. 10cor, Cock Fight, by Gallos P. Ortiz.

1982, Aug. 17 — Perf. 13

1167	A139	25c multi	.40	.25
1168	A139	50c multi	.40	.25
1169	A139	1cor multi	.40	.25
1170	A139	1.20cor multi	.40	.25
1171	A139	1.85cor multi	.45	.25
1172	A139	2cor multi	.45	.25
		Nos. 1167-1172,C1019 (7)	8.50	2.30

Souvenir Sheet

1173	A139	10cor multi	2.25	1.00

No. 1173 contains one 36x28mm stamp.

George Dimitrov, First Pres. of Bulgaria A140

50c, Lenin, Dimitrov, 1921.

1982, Sept. 9

1174	A140	50c multicolored	.70	.25
		Nos. 1174,C1020-C1021 (3)	2.70	.95

26th Anniv. of End of Dictatorship A141

50c, Ausberto Narvaez. 2.50cor, Cornelio Silva.

1982, Sept. 21 — Perf. 13x12½

1175	A141	50c multi	.40	.25
1176	A141	2.50cor multi	.90	.30
		Nos. 1175-1176,C1022-C1023 (4)	4.45	1.55

Ruins, Leon Viejo — A142

1cor, Ruben Dario Theater and Park. 1.20cor, Independence Plaza, Granada. 1.80cor, Corn Island. 2cor, Santiago Volcano crater, Masaya.

1982, Sept. 25 — Perf. 13

1177	A142	50c multi	.40	.25
1178	A142	1cor multi	.40	.25
1179	A142	1.20cor multi	.40	.25
1180	A142	1.80cor multi	.45	.25
1181	A142	2cor multi	.45	.25
		Nos. 1177-1181,C1024-C1025 (7)	7.35	1.85

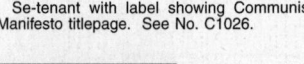

Karl Marx (1818-1883) — A143

1982, Oct. 4 — Perf. 12½

1182	A143	1cor Marx, birthplace	.35	.25

Se-tenant with label showing Communist Manifesto titlepage. See No. C1026.

World Food Day (Oct. 16) — A144

50c, Picking fruit. 1cor, Farm workers, vert. 2cor, Cutting sugar cane. 10cor, Emblems.

1982, Oct. 10 — Perf. 13

1183	A144	50c multicolored	.35	.25
1184	A144	1cor multicolored	.35	.25
1185	A144	2cor multicolored	.80	.25
1186	A144	10cor multicolored	4.25	1.25
		Nos. 1183-1186 (4)	5.75	2.00

Discovery of America, 490th Anniv. — A145

50c, Santa Maria. 1cor, Nina. 1.50cor, Pinta. 2cor, Columbus, fleet.

1982, Oct. 12 — Perf. 12½x13

1187	A145	50c multi	.40	.25
1188	A145	1cor multi	.40	.25
1189	A145	1.50cor multi	.75	.25
1190	A145	2cor multi	1.00	.30
		Nos. 1187-1190,C1027-C1029 (7)	8.70	2.40

A146

50c, Lobelia laxiflora. 1.20cor, Bombacopsis quinata. 1.80cor, Mimosa albida. 2cor, Epidendrum alatum.

1982, Nov. 13 — Perf. 12½

1191	A146	50c multi	.40	.25
1192	A146	1.20cor multi	.40	.25
1193	A146	1.80cor multi	.50	.25
1194	A146	2cor multi	.50	.25
		Nos. 1191-1194,C1031-C1033 (7)	8.10	2.00

A147

10c, Coral snake. 50c, Iguana, horiz. 2cor, Lachesis muta, horiz.

1982, Dec. 10   *Perf. 13*
1195	A147	10c multi	.35	.25
1196	A147	50c multi	.35	.25
1197	A147	2cor multi	1.10	.25

Nos. 1195-1197,C1034-C1037
(7)   10.60   2.05

Telecommunications Day — A148

50c, Radio transmission station. 1cor, Telcor building, Managua.

1982, Dec. 12   **Litho.**   *Perf. 12½*
| 1198 | A148 | 50c multicolored | .75 | .25 |
| 1199 | A148 | 1cor multicolored | .75 | .25 |

50c airmail.

Jose Marti, Cuban Independence Hero, 130th Birth Anniv. — A149

1983, Jan. 28   *Perf. 13*
| 1200 | A149 | 1cor multi | .90 | .25 |

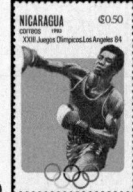

Boxing — A150

1cor, Gymnast. 1.50cor, Running. 2cor, Weightlifting. 4cor, Women's discus. 5cor, Basketball. 6cor, Bicycling. 15cor, Sailing.

1983, Jan. 31   *Perf. 12½*
1201	A150	50c shown	.40	.25
1202	A150	1cor multi	.40	.25
1203	A150	1.50cor multi	.40	.25
1204	A150	2cor multi	.90	.25
1205	A150	4cor multi	1.75	.30
1206	A150	5cor multi	2.40	.40
1207	A150	6cor multi	2.75	.50

Nos. 1201-1207 (7)   9.00   2.20

Souvenir Sheet
Perf. 13
| 1208 | A150 | 15cor multi | 4.25 | 2.00 |

23rd Olympic Games, Los Angeles, July 28-Aug. 12, 1984. Nos. 1205-1208 airmail. No. 1208 contains one 31x39mm stamp.

Local Flowers — A151

No. 1209, Bixa orellana. No. 1210, Brassavola nodosa. No. 1211, Cattleya lueddemanniana. No. 1212, Cochlospermum spec. No. 1213, Hibiscus rosa-sinensis. No. 1214, Laella spec. No. 1215, Malvaviscus arboreus. No. 1216, Neomarica coerulea. No. 1217, Plumeria rubra. No. 1218, Senecio spec. No. 1219, Sobralla macrantha. No. 1220, Stachytarpheta indica. No. 1221, Tabebula ochraceae. No. 1222, Tagetes erecta. No. 1223, Tecoma stans. No. 1224, Thumbergia alata.

1983, Feb. 5   *Perf. 12½*
1209	A151	1cor black	.75	.25
1210	A151	1cor olive green	.75	.25
1211	A151	1cor olive grey	.75	.25
1212	A151	1cor apple green	.75	.25
1213	A151	1cor brown rose	.75	.25
1214	A151	1cor deep magenta	.75	.25
1215	A151	1cor blue green	.75	.25
1216	A151	1cor ultramarine	.75	.25
1217	A151	1cor dull vermilion	.75	.25
1218	A151	1cor brown ochre	.75	.25
1219	A151	1cor deep purple	.75	.25
1220	A151	1cor light blue	.75	.25
1221	A151	1cor bluish violet	.75	.25
1222	A151	1cor orange yellow	.75	.25
1223	A151	1cor bright magenta	.75	.25
1224	A151	1cor dp turq grn	.75	.25

Nos. 1209-1224 (16)   12.00   4.00

See #1515-1530, 1592-1607, 1828-1843.

Visit of Pope John Paul II — A152

50c, Peace banner. 1cor, Map, girl picking coffee beans. 4cor, Pres. Rafael Rivas, Pope. 7cor, Pope, Managua Cathedral. 15cor, Pope, vert.

1983, Mar. 4   *Perf. 13*
1225	A152	50c multicolored	.35	.25
1226	A152	1cor multicolored	.35	.25
1227	A152	4cor multicolored	2.00	.60
1228	A152	7cor multicolored	3.75	1.00

Nos. 1225-1228 (4)   6.45   2.10

Souvenir Sheet
| 1229 | A152 | 15cor multicolored | 6.75 | 2.50 |

Nos. 1227-1229 airmail. No. 1229 contains one 31x39mm stamp.

Nocturnal Moths — A153

15c, Xilophanes chiron. 50c, Protoparce ochus. 65c, Pholus lasbruscae. 1cor, Amphypterus gannascus. 1.50cor, Pholus licaon. 2cor, Agrius cingulata. 10cor, Rothschildia jurulla, vert.

1983, Mar. 10
1230	A153	15c multi	.35	.25
1231	A153	50c multi	.35	.25
1232	A153	65c multi	.70	.25
1233	A153	1cor multi	.80	.25
1234	A153	1.50cor multi	.95	.25
1235	A153	2cor multi	1.00	.25
1236	A153	10cor multi	4.25	.80

Nos. 1230-1236 (7)   8.40   2.30

No. 1236 airmail.

26th Anniv. of the Anti-Somoza Movement A154

Various monuments and churches — 50c, Church of Subtiava, Leon. 1cor, La Immaculata Castle, Rio San Juan. 2cor, La Recoleccion Church, Leon, vert. 4cor, Ruben Dario monument, Managua, vert.

1983, Mar. 25   *Perf. 12½*
1237	A154	50c multi	.40	.25
1238	A154	1cor multi	.40	.25
1239	A154	2cor multi	1.10	.25
1240	A154	4cor multi	2.10	.40

Nos. 1237-1240 (4)   4.00   1.15

Nos. 1237-1239 has "correos" above date. No. 1240 has "aereo" above date.

Railroad Cars — A155

15c, Passenger. 65c, Freight. 1cor, Tank. 1.50cor, Ore. 4cor, Rail bus. 5cor, Dump truck. 7cor, Rail bus, diff.

1983, Apr. 15
1241	A155	15c multi	.40	.25
1242	A155	65c multi	.40	.25
1243	A155	1cor multi	.40	.25
1244	A155	1.50cor multi	.40	.25
1245	A155	4cor multi	1.30	.30
1246	A155	5cor multi	1.60	.40
1247	A155	7cor multi	2.25	.50

Nos. 1241-1247 (7)   6.75   2.20

Nos. 1245-1247 airmail.

Red Cross Flood Rescue A156

1cor, Putting patient in ambulance. 4cor, 1972 earthquake & fire rescue. 5cor, Nurse examining soldier, 1979 Liberation War.

1983, May 8   *Perf. 13*
1248	A156	50c multi	.40	.25
1249	A156	1cor multi	.40	.25
1250	A156	4cor multi	2.00	.40
1251	A156	5cor multi	2.25	.40

Nos. 1248-1251 (4)   5.05   1.30

4cor, 5cor airmail. 4cor vert.

World Communications Year — A157

1983, May 17
| 1252 | A157 | 1cor multi | .90 | .40 |

9th Pan-American Games, Aug. — A158

15c, Baseball. 50c, Water polo. 65c, Running. 1cor, Women's basketball, vert. 2cor, Weightlifting, vert. 7cor, Fencing. 8cor, Gymnastics. 15cor, Boxing.

1983, May 30   **Litho.**   *Perf. 13*
1253	A158	15c multi	.35	.25
1254	A158	50c multi	.35	.25
1255	A158	65c multi	.35	.25
1256	A158	1cor multi	.35	.25
1257	A158	2cor multi	1.00	.25
1258	A158	7cor multi	3.25	.55
1259	A158	8cor multi	3.75	.65

Nos. 1253-1259 (7)   9.40   2.45

Souvenir Sheet
| 1260 | A158 | 15cor multi | 3.50 | 1.50 |

Nos. 1258-1260 airmail. No. 1260 contains one 39x31mm stamp.

4th Anniv. of Revolution A159

1cor, Port of Corinto. 2cor, Telecommunications Bldg., Leon.

1983, July 19   **Litho.**   *Perf. 12½*
| 1261 | A159 | 1cor multicolored | .55 | .25 |
| 1262 | A159 | 2cor multicolored | 1.10 | .25 |

Founders of FSLN (Sandinista Party) — A160

1983, July 23   **Litho.**   *Perf. 13*
1263	A160	50c multi	.40	.25
1264	A160	1cor multi	.45	.25
1265	A160	4cor multi, vert.	2.00	.35

Nos. 1263-1265 (3)   2.85   .85

No. 1265, airmail, 33x44mm.

Simon Bolivar, 200th Birth Anniv. — A161

50c, Bolivar and Sandino. 1cor, Bolivar on horseback, vert.

1983, July 24   **Litho.**   *Perf. 12½*
| 1266 | A161 | 50c multicolored | .40 | .25 |
| 1267 | A161 | 1cor multicolored | 1.40 | .25 |

14th Winter Olympic Games, Sarajevo, Yugoslavia, Feb. 8-19, 1984 — A162

50c, Speed skating. 1cor, Slalom. 1.50cor, Luge. 2cor, Ski jumping. 4cor, Ice dancing. 5cor, Skiing. 6cor, Biathlon.

1983, Aug. 5   **Litho.**   *Perf. 13*
1268	A162	50c multi	.40	.40
1269	A162	1cor multi	.40	.40
1270	A162	1.50cor multi	.40	.40
1271	A162	2cor multi	1.10	.40
1272	A162	4cor multi	1.30	.40
1273	A162	5cor multi	1.60	.40
1274	A162	6cor multi	2.10	.50

Nos. 1268-1274 (7)   7.30   2.90

Souvenir Sheet
1983, Aug. 25   **Litho.**   *Perf. 13*
| 1275 | A162 | 15cor Hockey | 5.25 | 2.50 |

No. 1275 contains one 39x32mm stamp. Nos. 1272-1275 airmail.

Chess Moves — A163

1983, Aug. 20   **Litho.**   *Perf. 13*
1276	A163	15c Pawn	.40	.40
1277	A163	65c Knight	.40	.40
1278	A163	1cor Bishop	.40	.40
1279	A163	2cor Castle	1.20	.40
1280	A163	4cor Queen	2.00	.40
1281	A163	5cor King	2.40	.40
1282	A163	7cor Player	2.75	.55

Nos. 1276-1282 (7)   9.55   2.95

Nos. 1280-1282 airmail.

Archaeological Finds — A164

1983, Aug. 20   *Perf. 13x12½*
1283	A164	50c Stone figurine	.40	.40
1284	A164	1cor Covered dish	.40	.40
1285	A164	2cor Vase	1.20	.40
1286	A164	4cor Platter	2.00	.40

Nos. 1283-1286 (4)   4.00   1.60

No. 1286 airmail.

Madonna of the Chair, by Raphael (1483-1517) — A165

Paintings: 1cor, The Eszterhazy Madonna. 1.50cor, Sistine Madonna. 2cor, Madonna of the Linnet. 4cor, Madonna of the Meadow. 5cor, La Belle Jardiniere. 6cor, Adoration of the Kings. 15cor, Madonna de Foligno. 4, 5, 6, 15cor airmail.

1983, Sept. 15
1287	A165	50c multi	.40	.25
1288	A165	1cor multi	.40	.25
1289	A165	1.50cor multi	.40	.25
1290	A165	2cor multi	1.00	.25
1291	A165	4cor multi	1.75	.35
1292	A165	5cor multi	2.00	.40
1293	A165	6cor multi	2.50	.45

Nos. 1287-1293 (7)   8.45   2.20

Souvenir Sheet

1984, Sept. 15   Litho.   *Perf. 13*
1293A A165 15cor multi   5.00 2.25

Mining Industry
Nationalization
A166

1cor, Pouring molten metal. 4cor, Mine headstock, workers.

1983, Oct. 2   *Perf. 13*
1294 A166 1cor multicolored   .40 .25
1295 A166 4cor multicolored   1.10 .40

4cor airmail.

Ship-to-Shore
Communications — A167

1983, Oct. 7   *Perf. 12½*
1296 A167 1cor shown   .40 .25
1297 A167 4cor Radio tower,
              view   3.00 .40

FRACAP '83, Federation of Central American and Panamanian Radio Amateurs Cong., Oct. 7-9.

Agrarian
Reform — A168

1983, Oct. 16
1298 A168 1cor Tobacco   .40 .25
1299 A168 2cor Cotton   .90 .25
1300 A168 4cor Corn   1.60 .25
1301 A168 5cor Sugar cane   1.80 .35
1302 A168 6cor Cattle   2.50 .40
1303 A168 7cor Rice paddy   2.75 .45
1304 A168 8cor Coffee beans 3.00 .55
1305 A168 10cor Bananas   3.75 .65
    Nos. 1298-1305 (8)   16.70 3.15

See Nos. 1531-1538, 1608-1615.

Fire
Engine — A169

Various Fire Engines.

1983, Oct. 17   *Perf. 13*
1306 A169 50c multi   .35 .25
1307 A169 1cor multi   .35 .25
1308 A169 1.50cor multi   .35 .25
1309 A169 2cor multi   1.20 .25
1310 A169 4cor multi   2.00 .35
1311 A169 5cor multi   2.40 .40
1312 A169 6cor multi   2.75 .45
    Nos. 1306-1312 (7)   9.40 2.20

Nos. 1308-1311 airmail.

Nicaraguan-Cuban Solidarity — A170

1cor, José Marti, Gen. Sandino. 4cor, Education, health, industry.

1983, Oct. 24
1313 A170 1cor multicolored   .45 .25
1314 A170 4cor multicolored 1.40 .40

4cor airmail.

A171

Christmas (Adoration of the Kings Paintings by): 50c, Hugo van der Goes. 1 cor, Ghirlandaio. 2cor, El Greco. 7cor, Konrad von Soest. 7cor airmail.

1983, Dec. 1
1315 A171 50c multi   .40 .25
1316 A171 1cor multi   .40 .25
1317 A171 2cor multi   .65 .25
1318 A171 7cor multi   2.60 .40
    Nos. 1315-1318 (4)   4.05 1.15

A172

1984, Jan. 10
1319 A172 50c Biathlon   .40 .25
1320 A172 50c Bobsledding   .40 .25
1321 A172 1cor Speed skating   .40 .25
1322 A172 1cor Slalom   .40 .25
1323 A172 4cor Downhill skiing 1.90 .35
1324 A172 5cor Ice dancing   2.10 .40
1325 A172 10cor Ski jumping   3.75 .75
    Nos. 1319-1325 (7)   9.35 2.50

Souvenir Sheet

1326 A172 15cor Hockey   4.00 1.75

1984 Winter Olympics. No. 1326 contains one 31x39mm stamp. Nos. 1323-1326 airmail.

Domestic
Cats — A173

No. 1327, Chinchilla. No. 1328, Long-haired Angel. No. 1329, Red tabby. No. 1330, Tortoiseshell. No. 1331, Siamese. No. 1332, Blue Burmese. No. 1333, Silver long-haired.

1984, Feb. 15   *Perf. 12½*
1327 A173 50c multicolored   .35 .25
1328 A173 50c multicolored   .35 .25
1329 A173 1cor multicolored   .90 .25
1330 A173 2cor multicolored   1.50 .25
1331 A173 3cor multicolored   1.30 .30
1332 A173 4cor multicolored   2.10 .40
1333 A173 7cor multicolored   4.25 .60
    Nos. 1327-1333 (7)   10.75 2.30

Nos. 1331, 1333 airmail.

Augusto Cesar
Sandino (d.
1934) — A174

1984, Feb. 21
1334 A174 1cor Arms   .40 .25
1335 A174 4cor Portrait   2.00 .40

4cor airmail.

Intl. Women's
Day — A175

1984, Mar. 8
1336 A175 1cor Blanca Arauz   .90 .25

Bee-pollinated
Flowers — A176

No. 1337, Poinsettia. No. 1338, Sunflower. No. 1339, Antigonan leptopus. No. 1340, Cassia alata. No. 1341, Bidens pilosa. No. 1342, Althea rosea. No. 1343, Rivea corymbosa.

1984, Mar. 20
1337 A176 50c multicolored   .40 .25
1338 A176 50c multicolored   .40 .25
1339 A176 1cor multicolored   .40 .25
1340 A176 1cor multicolored   .40 .25
1341 A176 3cor multicolored 1.60 .25
1342 A176 4cor multicolored 2.40 .35
1343 A176 5cor multicolored 2.75 .40
    Nos. 1337-1343 (7)   8.35 2.00

Nos. 1341-1343 airmail.

Space
Annivs. — A177

No. 1344, Soyuz 6,7,8, 1969. No. 1345, Soyuz 6,7,8, diff. No. 1346, Apollo 11, 1969. No. 1347, Luna 1, 1959. No. 1348, Luna 2, 1959. No. 1349, Luna 3, 1959. No. 1350, Painting by Koroliov, 1934.

1984, Apr. 20
1344 A177 50c multicolored   .40 .25
1345 A177 50c multicolored   .40 .25
1346 A177 1cor multicolored   .40 .25
1347 A177 2cor multicolored 1.00 .25
1348 A177 3cor multicolored 1.40 .25
1349 A177 4cor multicolored 1.75 .35
1350 A177 9cor multicolored 3.75 .50
    Nos. 1344-1350 (7)   9.10 2.10

Nos. 1348-1350 airmail.

Noli Me Tangere, by
Correggio — A178

No. 1352, Madonna of San Girolamo. No. 1353, Allegory of the Virtues. No. 1354, Allegory of Placer. No. 1355, Ganimedes. No. 1356, Danae. No. 1357, Leda. No. 1358, St. John the Evangelist.

1984, May 17   Litho.   *Perf. 12½*
1351 A178 50c shown   .40 .25
1352 A178 50c multicolored   .40 .25
1353 A178 1cor multicolored   .40 .25
1354 A178 2cor multicolored   .70 .25
1355 A178 3cor multicolored 1.00 .25
1356 A178 5cor multicolored 1.60 .40
1357 A178 8cor multicolored 2.60 .65
    Nos. 1351-1357 (7)   7.10 2.30

Souvenir Sheet

1358 A178 15cor multicolored 4.50 1.75

No. 1358 contains one 31x39mm stamp. Nos. 1355-1358 airmail.

Vintage
Cars — A179

No. 1359, Abadal, 1914. No. 1360, Daimler, 1886, vert. No. 1361, Ford, 1903, vert. No. 1362, Renault, 1899, vert. No. 1363, Rolls Royce, 1910. No. 1364, Metallurgique, 1907. No. 1365, Bugatti Mode 40.

1984, May 18
1359 A179 1cor multicolored   .35 .25
1360 A179 1cor multicolored   .35 .25
1361 A179 2cor multicolored 1.10 .25
1362 A179 2cor multicolored 1.10 .25
1363 A179 3cor multicolored 1.50 .25
1364 A179 4cor multicolored 1.80 .35
1365 A179 7cor multicolored 3.00 .60
    Nos. 1359-1365 (7)   9.20 2.20

Birth sesquicentennial of Gottlieb Daimler. Nos. 1363-1365 airmail.

1984 Summer
Olympics — A180

1984, July 6
1366 A180 50c Volleyball   .35 .25
1367 A180 50c Basketball   .35 .25
1368 A180 1cor Field hockey   .35 .25
1369 A180 2cor Tennis   1.00 .25
1370 A180 3cor Soccer   1.50 .25
1371 A180 4cor Water polo   1.90 .35
1372 A180 9cor Net ball   4.25 .70
    Nos. 1366-1372 (7)   9.70 2.30

Souvenir Sheet
Perf. 13

1373 A180 15cor Baseball   5.50 2.00

No. 1373 contains one 40x31mm stamp. Nos. 1370-1373 airmail and horiz.

5th Anniv. of
Revolution
A181

1984, July 19
1374 A181 50c Construction   .40 .25
1375 A181 1cor Transportation .40 .25
1376 A181 4cor Agriculture   1.25 .35
1377 A181 7cor Govt. building 2.45 .55
    Nos. 1374-1377 (4)   4.50 1.40

Nos. 1376-1377 airmail.

UNESCO Nature
Conservation
Campaign
A182

50c, Children dependent on nature. 1cor, Forest. 2cor, River. 10cor, Seedlings, field, vert.

1984, Aug. 3   *Perf. 12½x13, 13x12½*
1378 A182 50c multicolored   .40 .25
1379 A182 1cor multicolored   .40 .25
1380 A182 2cor multicolored   .65 .25
1381 A182 10cor multicolored 2.75 .80
    Nos. 1378-1381 (4)   4.20 1.55

No. 1381 airmail.

Nicaraguan
Red Cross,
50th Anniv.
A183

1984, Sept. 16   *Perf. 12½x12*
1382 A183 1cor Air ambulance .40 .25
1383 A183 7cor Battle field 3.60 .55

No. 1383 airmail.

History of
Baseball
A184

Portraits and national colors: #1384, Ventura Escalante, Dominican Republic. #1385, Daniel Herrera, Mexico. #1386, Adalberto Herrera, Venezuela. #1387, Roberto Clemente, Puerto Rico. #1388, Carlos Colas, Cuba. #1389, Stanley Cayasso, Nicaragua. #1390, Babe Ruth, US.

1984, Oct. 25   Litho.   Perf. 12½
1384	A184	50c multi	.40	.25
1385	A184	50c multi	.40	.25
1386	A184	1cor multi	.60	.25
1387	A184	1cor multi	.60	.25
1388	A184	3cor multi	1.50	.25
1389	A184	4cor multi	2.25	.25
1390	A184	5cor multi	2.75	.35
		Nos. 1384-1390 (7)	8.50	1.85

Nos. 1388-1390 are airmail.

Tapirus
Bairdii — A185

1984, Dec. 28   Perf. 13
1391	A185	25c In water	.65	.25
1392	A185	25c In field	.65	.25
1393	A185	3cor Baring teeth	1.40	.25
1394	A185	4cor Female and young	1.90	.25
		Nos. 1391-1394 (4)	4.60	1.00

Wildlife conservation. Nos. 1393-1394 are airmail. Compare with type A202.

1986 World Cup Soccer Championships, Mexico — A186

Evolution of soccer.

1985, Jan. 20
1395	A186	50c 1314	.40	.25
1396	A186	50c 1500	.40	.25
1397	A186	1cor 1846	.40	.25
1398	A186	1cor 1872	.40	.25
1399	A186	2cor 1883	.40	.25
1400	A186	4cor 1890	1.75	.25
1401	A186	6cor 1953	2.60	.30
		Nos. 1395-1401 (7)	6.35	1.80

Souvenir Sheet   Perf. 12½
1402	A186	10cor 1985	5.00	2.25

Nos. 1399-1402 are airmail. No. 1402 contains one 40x32mm stamp.

Mushrooms — A187

No. 1403, Boletus calopus. No. 1404, Strobilomyces retisporus. No. 1405, Boletus luridus. No. 1406, Xerocomus illudens. No. 1407, Gyrodon merulioides. No. 1408, Tylopilus plumbeoviolaceus. No. 1409, Gyroporus castaneus.

1985, Feb. 20
1403	A187	50c multicolored	.40	.25
1404	A187	50c multicolored	.40	.25
1405	A187	1cor multicolored	.40	.25
1406	A187	1cor multicolored	.40	.25
1407	A187	4cor multicolored	1.90	.25
1408	A187	5cor multicolored	2.10	.25
1409	A187	8cor multicolored	3.75	.40
		Nos. 1403-1409 (7)	9.35	1.90

Nos. 1406-1409 are airmail.

Postal Union of the Americas and Spain, 13th Congress — A188

UPAE emblem and: 1cor, Chasqui, mail runner and map of Realejo-Nicaragua route. 7cor, Monoplane and Nicaraguan air network.

1985, Mar. 11   Perf. 12½x13
1410	A188	1cor multi	1.00	.25
1411	A188	7cor multi	3.50	.40

No. 1411 is airmail.

Locomotives A189

1985, Apr. 5   Perf. 12½
1412	A189	1cor Electric	.35	.25
1413	A189	1cor Steam	.35	.25
1414	A189	9cor Steam, diff.	1.60	.25
1415	A189	9cor Tram	1.60	.25
1416	A189	15cor Steam, diff.	2.75	.40
1417	A189	21cor Steam, diff.	4.00	.35
		Nos. 1412-1417 (6)	10.65	1.75

Souvenir Sheet   Perf. 13
1418	A189	42cor Steam, diff.	8.00	5.75

German Railroads, 150th Anniv. #1418 also for 100th anniv. of Nicaraguan railroads. #1418 contains one 40x32mm stamp. #1414-1418 are airmail.

Motorcycle Cent. — A190

1985, Apr. 30   Litho.   Perf. 12½
1419	A190	50c F.N., 1928	.35	.35
1420	A190	50c Douglas, 1928	.35	.35
1421	A190	1cor Puch, 1938	.75	.25
1422	A190	2cor Wanderer, 1939	1.00	.40
1423	A190	4cor Honda, 1949	2.10	.40
1424	A190	5cor BMW, 1984	2.90	.40
1425	A190	7cor Honda, 1984	3.50	.40
		Nos. 1419-1425 (7)	10.95	2.70

Nos. 1419-1425 se-tenant with labels picturing manufacturers' trademarks. Nos. 1422-1425 are airmail.

Flowers — A194

No. 1454, Metelea quirosii. No. 1455, Ipomea nil. No. 1456, Lysichitum americanum. No. 1457, Clusia sp. No. 1458, Vanilla planifolia. No. 1459, Stemmadenia obovata.

1985, May 20   Litho.   Perf. 13
1454	A194	50c multicolored	.35	.25
1455	A194	50c multicolored	.35	.25
1456	A194	1cor multicolored	.75	.25
1457	A194	2cor multicolored	1.40	.25
1458	A194	4cor multicolored	2.75	.35
1459	A194	5cor multicolored	5.00	.60
a.		Miniature sheet of 6, #1454-1459	10.50	
		Nos. 1454-1459 (6)	10.60	1.95

Nos. 1457-1459 are airmail. Stamps in No. 1459a do not have white border.

End of World War II, 40th Anniv. — A195

9.50cor, German army surrenders. 28cor, Nuremberg trials, horiz.

1985, May   Perf. 12x12½, 12½x12
1460	A195	9.50cor multi	1.25	.35
1461	A195	28cor multi	2.75	1.00

No. 1461 is airmail.

Lenin, 115th Birth Anniv. — A196

Design: 21cor, Lenin speaking to workers.

1985, June   Litho.   Perf. 12x12½
1462	A196	4cor multicolored	.75	.25
1463	A196	21cor multicolored	3.75	1.10

Souvenir Sheet

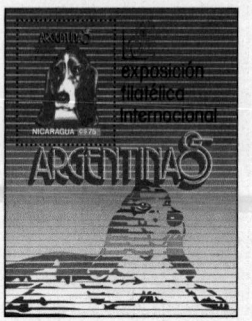

Argentina '85 — A197

1985, June 5   Litho.   Perf. 13
1464	A197	75cor multicolored	15.00	5.00

World Stamp Exposition.

Birds — A198

No. 1465, Ring-neck pheasant. No. 1466, Chicken. No. 1467, Guinea hen. No. 1468, Goose. No. 1469, Turkey. No. 1470, Duck.

1985, Aug. 25
1465	A198	50c multi	.35	.25
1466	A198	50c multi	.35	.25
1467	A198	1cor multi	.60	.25
1468	A198	2cor multi	1.10	.25
1469	A198	6cor multi	3.50	.60
1470	A198	8cor multi	4.25	.80
		Nos. 1465-1470 (6)	10.15	2.40

Intl. Music Year — A199

No. 1471, Luis A. Delgadillo, vert. No. 1473, Parade. No. 1474, Managua Cathedral. No. 1475, Masked dancer. No. 1476, Parade, diff.

1985, Sept. 1
1471	A199	1cor multicolored	.35	.25
1472	A199	1cor shown	.35	.25
1473	A199	9cor multicolored	1.75	.35
1474	A199	9cor multicolored	1.75	.35
1475	A199	15cor multicolored	2.60	.55
1476	A199	21cor multicolored	3.50	.75
		Nos. 1471-1476 (6)	10.30	2.50

Nos. 1473-1476 are airmail.

Natl. Fire Brigade, 6th Anniv. — A200

No. 1477, Fire station. No. 1478, Fire truck. No. 1480, Ambulance. No. 1481, Airport fire truck. No. 1482, Waterfront fire. No. 1483, Hose team, fire.

1985, Oct. 18
1477	A200	1cor multi	.35	.30
1478	A200	1cor multi	.35	.30
1479	A200	1cor shown	.35	.30
1480	A200	3cor multi	.35	.30
1481	A200	9cor multi	1.90	.35
1482	A200	15cor multi	3.00	.50
1483	A200	21cor multi	4.50	.75
a.		Min. sheet of 7, #1474-1483 + 2 labels	12.00	
		Nos. 1477-1483 (7)	10.80	2.80

Stamps from No. 1483a have orange borders. Nos. 1480-1483 are airmail. Nos. 1477-1483 exist imperf, Value, $140.

Halley's Comet — A201

No. 1484, Edmond Halley. No. 1485, Map of comet's track, 1910. No. 1486, Tycho Brahe's observatory. No. 1487, Astrolabe, map. No. 1488, Telescopes. No. 1489, Telescope designs.

1985, Nov. 26
1484	A201	1cor multicolored	.35	.25
1485	A201	3cor multicolored	.70	.25
1486	A201	3cor multicolored	.70	.25
1487	A201	9cor multicolored	1.75	.25
1488	A201	15cor multicolored	2.90	.40
1489	A201	21cor multicolored	4.00	.60
		Nos. 1484-1489 (6)	10.40	2.00

Nos. 1487-1489 are airmail.

Tapirus Bairdii — A202

1985, Dec. 30
1490	A202	1cor Eating	.65	.40
1491	A202	3cor Drinking	1.00	.40
1492	A202	5cor Grazing in field	1.60	.40
1493	A202	9cor With young	3.25	.40
		Nos. 1490-1493 (4)	6.50	1.60

Nos. 1491-1493 are airmail.

Roses A203

1986, Jan. 15   Perf. 12½
1494	A203	1cor Spinosissima	.35	.25
1495	A203	1cor Canina	.35	.25
1496	A203	3cor Eglanteria	.75	.25
1497	A203	3cor Rubrifolia	.75	.25
1498	A203	9cor Foetida	.75	.25
1499	A203	100cor Rugosa	7.50	1.10
		Nos. 1494-1499 (6)	10.45	2.35

Nos. 1497-1499 are airmail.

Birds — A204

No. 1500, Colibri topacio. No. 1501, Paraulata picodorado. No. 1502, Troupial. No. 1503, Vereron pintado. No. 1504, Tordo ruisenor. No. 1505, Buho real. No. 1506, Gran kiskadee.

1986, Feb. 10   Perf. 13x12½
1500	A204	1cor multi	.35	.25
1501	A204	3cor multi	.60	.25
1502	A204	3cor multi	.60	.25
1503	A204	5cor multi	.60	.25

1504	A204	10cor multi	.90	.25
1505	A204	21cor multi	1.75	.25
1506	A204	75cor multi	6.00	1.10
	Nos. 1500-1506 (7)		10.80	2.60

Nos. 1504-1506 are airmail.

A205

World Cup Soccer Championships, Mexico: Soccer players and pre-Columbian artifacts. No. 1514, Player's foot, ball.

1986, Mar. 20   **Perf. 12½**
Shirt Colors

1507	A205	1cor blue & yel	.35	.25
1508	A205	1cor yel & green	.35	.25
1509	A205	3cor blue & white	.35	.25
1510	A205	3cor red & white	.35	.25
1511	A205	5cor red	.35	.25
1512	A205	9cor blk & yel	.35	.25
1513	A205	100cor red & grn	5.50	1.10
	Nos. 1507-1513 (7)		7.60	2.60

Souvenir Sheet
Perf. 13

1514	A205	100cor multicolored	4.25	1.25

Nos. 1509-1514 are airmail.

Flower Type of 1983

1986, Mar.		**Litho.**	**Perf. 12½**	
1515	A151	5cor like #1209	.90	.40
1516	A151	5cor like #1210	.90	.40
1517	A151	5cor like #1211	.90	.40
1518	A151	5cor like #1212	.90	.40
1519	A151	5cor like #1213	.90	.40
1520	A151	5cor like #1214	.90	.40
1521	A151	5cor like #1215	.90	.40
1522	A151	5cor like #1216	.90	.40
1523	A151	5cor like #1217	.90	.40
1524	A151	5cor like #1218	.90	.40
1525	A151	5cor like #1219	.90	.40
1526	A151	5cor like #1220	.90	.40
1527	A151	5cor like #1221	.90	.40
1528	A151	5cor like #1222	.90	.40
1529	A151	5cor like #1223	.90	.40
1530	A151	5cor like #1224	.90	.40
	Nos. 1515-1530 (16)		14.40	6.40

Agrarian Reform Type of 1983

1986, Apr. 15			**Perf. 12½**	
1531	A168	1cor dk brown	.35	.25
1532	A168	9cor purple	.35	.25
1533	A168	15cor rose violet	.65	.25
1534	A168	21cor dk car rose	1.00	.25
1535	A168	33cor orange	1.60	.35
1536	A168	42cor green	2.00	.45
1537	A168	50cor brown	2.50	.55
1538	A168	100cor blue	5.00	1.10
	Nos. 1531-1538 (8)		13.45	3.45

Writers — A207

No. 1539, Alfonso Cortes. No. 1540, Salomon de la Selva. No. 1541, Azarias H. Pallais. No. 1542, Ruben Dario. No. 1543, Pablo Neruda. No. 1544, Alfonso Reyes. No. 1545, Pedro Henriquez Urena.

1986, Apr. 23			**Perf. 12½x13**	
1539	A207	1cor multicolored	.35	.25
1540	A207	3cor multicolored	.35	.25
1541	A207	3cor multicolored	.35	.25
1542	A207	5cor multicolored	.35	.25
1543	A207	9cor multicolored	.55	.25
1544	A207	15cor multicolored	.75	.25
1545	A207	100cor multicolored	6.00	1.10
	Nos. 1539-1545 (7)		8.70	2.60

Nos. 1544-1545 are airmail.

Nuts & Fruits — A208

No. 1546, Maranon (cashew). No. 1547, Zapote. No. 1548, Pitahaya. No. 1549, Granadilla. No. 1550, Anona. No. 1551, Melocoton (starfruit). No. 1552, Mamey.

1986, June 20			**Perf. 12x12½**	
1546	A208	1cor multicolored	.35	.25
1547	A208	1cor multicolored	.35	.25
1548	A208	3cor multicolored	.60	.25
1549	A208	3cor multicolored	.60	.25
1550	A208	5cor multicolored	.60	.25
1551	A208	21cor multicolored	1.50	.25
1552	A208	100cor multicolored	6.75	1.10
	Nos. 1546-1552 (7)		10.75	2.60

FAO, 40th Anniv. Nos. 1550-1552 are airmail.

Lockheed L-1011 Tristar — A209

Airplanes: No. 1554, YAK 40. No. 1555, BAC 1-11. No. 1556, Boeing 747. 9cor, A-300. 15cor, TU-154. No. 1559, Concorde, vert. No. 1560, Fairchild 340.

1986, Aug. 22			**Perf. 12½**	
1553	A209	1cor multicolored	.35	.25
1554	A209	1cor multicolored	.35	.25
1555	A209	3cor multicolored	.35	.25
1556	A209	3cor multicolored	.65	.25
1557	A209	9cor multicolored	.80	.25
1558	A209	15cor multicolored	1.00	.25
1559	A209	100cor multicolored	7.50	1.10
	Nos. 1553-1559 (7)		11.00	2.60

Souvenir Sheet
Perf. 13

1560	A209	100cor multicolored	5.50	3.75

Stockholmia '86. No. 1560 contains one 40x32mm stamp. Nos. 1557-1560 airmail.

A210

A210a

Discovery of America, 500th Anniv. (in 1992) — A210b

No. 1561, 1 of Columbus' ships. No. 1562, 2 of Columbus' ships. No. 1563, Juan de la Cosa. No. 1564, Columbus. No. 1565, Ferdinand, Isabella. No. 1566, Columbus before throne.

1986, Oct. 12			**Perf. 12½x12**	
1561	A210	1cor multi	.30	.25
1562	A210	1cor multi	.30	.25
a.		Pair, #1561-1562	.80	.60
b.		Souv. sheet of 2, #1561-1562	1.25	.50
		Perf. 12x12½		
1563	A210a	9cor multi	.45	.25
1564	A210a	9cor multi	.45	.25
a.		Pair, #1563-1564	1.10	.75
1565	A210b	21cor multi	1.20	.25
1566	A210b	100cor multi	5.00	1.10
a.		Pair, #1565-1566	8.00	4.00
b.		Souv. sheet of 4, #1563-1566	14.00	7.00
	Nos. 1561-1566 (6)		7.70	2.35

Nos. 1563-1566 are airmail. Nos. 1564a, 1566a have continuous design.

Butterflies — A211

No. 1567, Theritas coronata. No. 1568, Charayes nitebis. No. 1569, Salamis cacta. No. 1570, Papilio maacki. No. 1571, Euphaedro cyparissa. No. 1572, Palaeochrysophonus hippothoe. No. 1573, Ritra aurea.

1986, Dec. 12			**Perf. 12½**	
1567	A211	10cor multi	.75	.25
1568	A211	15cor multi	1.20	.25
1569	A211	15cor multi	1.20	.25
1570	A211	15cor multi	1.20	.25
1571	A211	25cor multi	1.90	.30
1572	A211	25cor multi	1.90	.30
1573	A211	30cor multi	2.60	.35
	Nos. 1567-1573 (7)		10.75	1.95

Nos. 1568-1573 are airmail.

Ruben Dario Order of Cultural Independence A212

Dario Order Winning Writers: No. 1574, Ernesto Mejia Sanchez. No. 1575, Fernando Gordillo C. No. 1576, Francisco Perez Estrada. 30cor, Julio Cortazar. 60cor, Enrique Fernandez Morales.

1987, Jan. 18		**Litho.**	**Perf. 13**	
1574	A212	10cor multicolored	.30	.25
1575	A212	10cor multicolored	.30	.25
1576	A212	15cor multicolored	.30	.25
1577	A212	15cor multicolored	.40	.25
1578	A212	30cor multicolored	.80	.30
1579	A212	60cor multicolored	1.75	.65
a.		Strip of 6, #1574-1579	5.25	2.50
b.		Min. sheet of 6, #1574-1579	6.25	3.50

1988 Winter Olympics, Calgary — A213

#1580, Speed skating. #1581, Ice hockey. #1582, Women's figure skating. #1583, Ski jumping. 20cor, Biathalon. 30cor, Slalom skiing. 40cor, Downhill skiing. 110cor, Ice hockey, diff., horiz.

1987, Feb. 3			**Perf. 13**	
1580	A213	10cor multi	.90	.25
1581	A213	10cor multi	.90	.25
1582	A213	15cor multi	1.20	.25
1583	A213	15cor multi	1.20	.25
1584	A213	20cor multi	1.50	.25
1585	A213	30cor multi	2.10	.30
1586	A213	40cor multi	3.25	.40
	Nos. 1580-1586 (7)		11.05	1.95

Souvenir Sheet
Perf. 12½

1587	A213	110cor multi	5.50	3.75

Nos. 1582-1587 are airmail. No. 1587 contains one 40x32mm stamp.

Children's Welfare Campaign — A214

No. 1588, Growth & development. No. 1589, Vaccination. No. 1590, Rehydration. No. 1591, Breastfeeding.

1987, Mar. 18   **Perf. 13**

1588	A214	10cor multi	.35	.25
1589	A214	25cor multi	.65	.30
1590	A214	30cor multi	1.90	.35
1591	A214	50cor multi	6.50	.60
	Nos. 1588-1591 (4)		9.40	1.50

Nos. 1589-1591 are airmail. For surcharges, see Nos. 1674A-1674D.

Flower Type of 1983

No. 1592, Bixa orellana. No. 1593, Brassavola nodosa. No. 1594, Cattleya lueddemanniana. No. 1595, Cochlospermum spec. No. 1596, Hibiscus rosa-sinensis. No. 1597, Laella spec. No. 1598, Malvaviscus arboreus. No. 1599, Neomarica coerulea. No. 1600, Plumeria rubra. No. 1601, Senecio spec. No. 1602, Sobralla macrantha. No. 1603, Stachytarpheta indica. No. 1604, Tabebula ochraceae. No. 1605, Tagetes erecta. No. 1606, Tecoma stans. No. 1607, Thumbergia alata.

1987, Mar. 25			**Perf. 12½**	
1592	A151	10cor black	.70	.30
1593	A151	10cor olive green	.70	.30
1594	A151	10cor olive grey	.70	.30
1595	A151	10cor apple green	.70	.30
1596	A151	10cor brown rose	.70	.30
1597	A151	10cor deep magenta	.70	.30
1598	A151	10cor blue green	.70	.30
1599	A151	10cor ultramarine	.70	.30
1600	A151	10cor dull vermilion	.70	.30
1601	A151	10cor brown ochre	.70	.30
1602	A151	10cor deep purple	.70	.30
1603	A151	10cor light blue	.70	.30
1604	A151	10cor bluish violet	.70	.30
1605	A151	10cor orange yellow	.70	.30
1606	A151	10cor bright magenta	.70	.30
1607	A151	10cor dp turq grn	.70	.30
	Nos. 1592-1607 (16)		11.20	4.80

Agrarian Reform Type of 1983 Inscribed "1987"

Designs: No. 1608, Tobacco. No. 1609, Cotton. 15cor, Corn. 25cor, Sugar. 30cor, Cattle. 50cor, Coffee Beans. 60cor, Rice. 100cor, Bananas.

1987, Mar. 25			**Perf. 12½**	
1608	A168	10cor dk brown	.60	.30
1609	A168	10cor purple	.60	.30
1610	A168	15cor rose violet	.90	.30
1611	A168	25cor dk car rose	1.40	.35
1612	A168	30cor orange	1.75	.45
1613	A168	50cor brown	2.75	.65
1614	A168	60cor green	3.50	.90
1615	A168	100cor blue	5.50	1.40
	Nos. 1608-1615 (8)		17.00	4.65

77th Interparliamentary Conf., Managua — A215

1987, Apr. 27

1616	A215	10cor multicolored	.80	.30

Prehistoric Creatures A216

1987, May 25			**Perf. 13**	
1617	A216	10cor Mammoth	.65	.30
1618	A216	10cor Dimetrodon	.65	.30
1619	A216	10cor Triceratops	.65	.30
1620	A216	15cor Dinichthys	1.00	.30
1621	A216	15cor Uintaterium	1.00	.30
1622	A216	30cor Pteranodon	2.25	.30
1623	A216	40cor Tilosaurus	3.00	.30
	Nos. 1617-1623 (7)		9.20	2.10

Nos. 1620-1623 are airmail.

CAPEX '87 — A217

Various tennis players in action: No. 1624, Male player. No. 1625, Female player serving. No. 1626, Male player at net. No. 1627, Female player at line, racquet at left side. No. 1628, Female player, racquet behind her ready to hit ball. No. 1629, Female player, both hands on racquet above head. No. 1630, Male player, one hand hold racquet above head. No. 1631, Doubles partners, vert.

1987, June 2			**Perf. 13**	
1624	A217	10cor multi	.55	.30
1625	A217	10cor multi	.55	.30
1626	A217	15cor multi	1.00	.30
1627	A217	15cor multi	1.00	.30
1628	A217	20cor multi	1.10	.30
1629	A217	30cor multi	2.00	.30
1630	A217	40cor multi	3.00	.40
		Nos. 1624-1630 (7)	9.20	2.20

Souvenir Sheet
Perf. 12½

1631	A217	110cor multi	5.50	3.75

Nos. 1626-1631 are airmail. No. 1631 contains one 32x40mm stamp.

Dogs — A218

No. 1632, Doberman pinscher. No. 1633, Bull Mastiff. No. 1634, Japanese Spaniel. No. 1635, Keeshond. No. 1636, Chihuahua. No. 1637, St. Bernard. No. 1638, West Gotha spitz.

1987, June 25			**Perf. 13**	
1632	A218	10cor multicolored	.50	.30
1633	A218	10cor multicolored	.50	.30
1634	A218	15cor multicolored	1.00	.30
1635	A218	15cor multicolored	1.00	.30
1636	A218	20cor multicolored	1.40	.30
1637	A218	30cor multicolored	2.00	.30
1638	A218	40cor multicolored	3.00	.40
		Nos. 1632-1638 (7)	9.40	2.20

Nos. 1634-1638 are airmail.

Cacti — A219

No. 1639, Lophocereus schottii. No. 1640, Opuntia acanthocarpa. No. 1641, Echinocereus engelmanii. No. 1642, Lemaireocereus thurberi. No. 1643, Saguaros. No. 1644, Opuntia fulgida. No. 1645, Opuntia ficus.

1987, July 25			**Perf. 12½**	
1639	A219	10cor multicolored	.70	.30
1640	A219	10cor multicolored	.70	.30
1641	A219	10cor multicolored	.70	.30
1642	A219	20cor multicolored	1.50	.30
1643	A219	20cor multicolored	1.50	.30
1644	A219	30cor multicolored	2.40	.30
1645	A219	50cor multicolored	3.75	.50
		Nos. 1639-1645 (7)	11.25	2.30

Nos. 1642-1645 are airmail.

10th Pan American Games, Indianapolis A220

No. 1646, High jump. No. 1647, Volleyball. No. 1648, Sprinter. No. 1649, Gymnastics. No. 1650, Baseball. No. 1651, Synchronized swimming. No. 1652, Weightlifting. 110cor, Rhythmic gymnastics.

1987, Aug. 7			**Perf. 13**	
1646	A220	10cor multi	.65	.30
1647	A220	10cor multi	.65	.30
1648	A220	15cor multi	1.20	.30
1649	A220	15cor multi	1.20	.30
1650	A220	20cor multi	1.50	.30

1651	A220	30cor multi	2.40	.45
1652	A220	40cor multi	3.25	.60
		Nos. 1646-1652 (7)	10.85	2.55

Souvenir Sheet

1653	A220	110cor multi	5.25	3.50

Nos. 1648-1653 are airmail. No. 1653 contains one 32x40mm stamp. Nos. 1651-1653 are vert.

Satellites A221

1987, Oct. 4				
1654	A221	10cor Sputnik	.70	.35
1655	A221	10cor Cosmos	.70	.35
1656	A221	15cor Proton	1.00	.35
1657	A221	25cor Meteor	1.75	.35
1658	A221	25cor Luna	1.75	.35
1659	A221	30cor Electron	1.90	.35
1660	A221	50cor Mars 1	3.25	.60
		Nos. 1654-1660 (7)	11.05	2.70

Cosmonauts' Day. Nos. 1656-1660 are airmail.

Fish — A222

Designs: No. 1661, Tarpon atlanticus. No. 1662, Cichlasoma managuense. No. 1663, Atractoteus tropicus. No. 1664, Astyana fasciatus. No. 1665, Cichlasoma citrimellum. 20cor, Cichlasoma dowi. 50cor, Caracharhinus nicaraguensis.

1987, Oct. 18			**Perf. 12½**	
1661	A222	10cor multicolored	.70	.40
1662	A222	10cor multicolored	.70	.40
1663	A222	10cor multicolored	.70	.40
1664	A222	15cor multicolored	1.20	.40
1665	A222	15cor multicolored	1.20	.40
1666	A222	20cor multicolored	1.60	.40
1667	A222	50cor multicolored	4.25	.40
		Nos. 1661-1667 (7)	10.35	2.80

Nos. 1663-1667 are airmail.

October Revolution, 70th Anniv. — A223

Designs: 30cor, Cruiser Aurora, horiz. 50cor, USSR natl. arms.

1987, Nov. 7			**Perf. 13**	
1668	A223	10cor multicolored	.60	.40
1669	A223	30cor multicolored	1.40	.40
1670	A223	50cor multicolored	2.40	.60
		Nos. 1668-1670 (3)	4.40	1.40

Nos. 1669-1670 are airmail.

Christmas Paintings by L. Saenz — A224

10cor, Nativity. 20cor, Adoration of the Magi. 25cor, Adoration of the Magi, diff. 50cor, Nativity, diff.

1987, Nov. 15			**Perf. 13**	
1671	A224	10cor multicolored	1.00	.40
1672	A224	20cor multicolored	1.40	.40
1673	A224	25cor multicolored	1.60	.40
1674	A224	50cor multicolored	3.25	.40
		Nos. 1671-1674 (4)	7.25	1.60

Nos. 1588-1591 Surcharged

Methods and Perfs As Before

1987, Dec. 26				
1674A	A214	400cor on 10cor #1588	—	5.00
1674B	A214	600cor on 50cor #1591	—	—
1674C	A214	1000cor on 25cor #1589	—	—
1674D	A214	5000cor on 30cor #1590	—	—
		Nos. 1674A-1674D (4)	80.00	80.00

1988 Winter Olymmpics, Calgary — A225

No. 1675, Biathlon. No. 1676, Cross-country skiing, vert. No. 1677, Hockey, vert. No. 1678, Women's figure skating, vert. No. 1679, Slalom skiing, vert. No. 1680, Ski jumping. No. 1681, Men's downhill skiing, vert. No. 1682, Pairs figure skating.

1988, Jan. 30		**Litho.**	**Perf. 12½**	
1675	A225	10cor multicolored	.45	.30
1676	A225	10cor multicolored	.45	.30
1677	A225	15cor multicolored	1.00	.30
1678	A225	20cor multicolored	1.50	.30
1679	A225	25cor multicolored	2.00	.30
1680	A225	30cor multicolored	2.25	.40
1681	A225	40cor multicolored	3.00	.50
		Nos. 1675-1681 (7)	10.65	2.40

Souvenir Sheet
Perf. 13

1682	A225	100cor multicolored	5.50	3.75

Nos. 1675-1681 printed with se-tenant label showing Canadian flag and wildlife. No. 1682 contains one 40x32mm stamp.

Nicaraguan Journalists Assoc., 10th Anniv. — A226

Design: 5cor, Churches of St. Francis Xavier and Fatima, and speaker addressing journalists, horiz.

1988, Feb. 10				
1683	A226	1cor shown	1.25	.25
1684	A226	5cor multicolored	3.75	.40

No. 1684 is airmail.

1988 Summer Olympics, Seoul — A227

1988, Feb. 28				
1685	A227	10cor Gymnastics	.50	.30
1686	A227	10cor Basketball	.50	.30
1687	A227	15cor Volleyball	.95	.30
1688	A227	20cor Long jump	1.50	.30
1689	A227	25cor Soccer	1.90	.30
1690	A227	30cor Water polo	2.00	.40
1691	A227	40cor Boxing	3.50	.55
		Nos. 1685-1691 (7)	10.85	2.45

Souvenir Sheet

1692	A227	100cor Baseball	5.50	3.75

No. 1692 contains one 40x32mm stamp.

European Soccer Championships, Essen — A228

Designs: Various soccer players in action.

1988, Apr. 14		**Perf. 13x12½, 12½x13**		
1693	A228	50c multicolored	.70	.25
1694	A228	1cor multicolored	.70	.25
1695	A228	2cor multi, vert.	.80	.25
1696	A228	3cor multi, vert.	1.40	.25
1697	A228	4cor multi, vert.	1.90	.25
1698	A228	5cor multi, vert.	2.50	.35
1699	A228	6cor multicolored	3.00	.40
		Nos. 1693-1699 (7)	11.00	2.00

Souvenir Sheet
Perf. 13

1700	A228	15cor multi, vert.	5.50	3.75

Nos. 1695-1700 are airmail. No. 1700 contains one 32x40mm stamp.

Sandinista Revolution, 9th Anniv. — A229

1988, July 19			**Perf. 13**	
1701	A229	1cor shown	.60	.25
1702	A229	5cor Volcanoes, dove	2.40	.30

No. 1702 is airmail.

Animals A230

10c, Bear, cub. 15c, Lion, cubs. 25c, Spaniel, pups. 50c, Wild boars. 4cor, Cheetah, cubs. 7cor, Hyenas. 8cor, Fox, kit. 15cor, House cat, kittens, vert.

1988, Mar. 3			**Perf. 13x12½**	
1703	A230	10c multi	.40	.25
1704	A230	15c multi	.40	.25
1705	A230	25c multi	.40	.25
1706	A230	50c multi	.40	.25
1707	A230	4cor multi	1.90	.35
1708	A230	7cor multi	2.75	.70
1709	A230	8cor multi	3.50	.80
		Nos. 1703-1709 (7)	9.75	2.85

Souvenir Sheet
Perf. 12½

1710	A230	15cor multi	5.50	3.75

Nos. 1707-1710 are airmail. No. 1710 contains one 32x40mm stamp.

Helicopters — A231

1988, June 1			**Perf. 12½x12**	
1711	A231	4cor B-206B-JRIII	.50	.25
1712	A231	12cor BK-117A-3	.50	.25
1713	A231	16cor B-360	1.10	.25
1714	A231	20cor 109-MRII	1.25	.25
1715	A231	24cor S-61	1.75	.25
1716	A231	28cor SA-365N-D2	2.00	.25
1717	A231	56cor S-76	2.60	.50
		Nos. 1711-1717 (7)	9.70	2.00

Souvenir Sheet
Perf. 13

1718	A231	120cor NH-90	5.50	3.75

Nos. 1712-1718 are airmail. No. 1718 contains one 40x32mm stamp.

Shells — A232

4cor, Strombus pugilis. 12cor, Polymita picta. 16cor, Architectonica maximum. 20cor, Pectens laqueatus. 24cor, Guildfordia triumphans. 28cor, Ranella pustulosa. 50cor, Trochus maculatus.

1988, Sept. 20   *Perf. 13*
1719	A232	4cor multicolored	.50	.40
1720	A232	12cor multicolored	.60	.40
1721	A232	16cor multicolored	1.00	.40
1722	A232	20cor multicolored	1.40	.40
1723	A232	24cor multicolored	1.75	.40
1724	A232	28cor multicolored	1.90	.40
1725	A232	50cor multicolored	3.50	.40

Nos. 1719-1725 (7)   10.65 2.80

Nos. 1720-1725 are airmail.

Insects — A233

4cor, Chrysina macropus. 12cor, Plusiotis victoriana. 16cor, Ceratotrupes bolivari. 20cor, Gymnetosoma stellata. 24cor, Euphoria lineoligera. 28cor, Euphoria candezei. 50cor, Sulcophanaeus chryseicollis.

1988, Nov. 10
1726	A233	4cor multicolored	.50	.40
1727	A233	12cor multicolored	.75	.40
1728	A233	16cor multicolored	1.00	.40
1729	A233	20cor multicolored	1.50	.40
1730	A233	24cor multicolored	1.75	.40
1731	A233	28cor multicolored	2.00	.40
1732	A233	50cor multicolored	3.25	.40

Nos. 1726-1732 (7)   10.75 2.80

Nos. 1727-1732 are airmail.

Heroes of the Revolution — A234

Designs: 4cor, Casimiro Sotelo Montenegro. 12cor, Ricardo Morales Aviles. 16cor, Silvio Mayorga Delgado. 20cor, Pedro Arauz Palacios. 24cor, Oscar A. Turcios Chavarrias. 28cor, Julio C. Buitrago Urroz. 50cor, Jose B. Escobar Perez. 100cor, Eduardo E. Contreras Escobar.

1988, Aug. 27   *Perf. 12½x12*
1733	A234	4cor sky blue	.60	.40
1734	A234	12cor red lilac	.60	.40
1735	A234	16cor yel grn	.70	.40
1736	A234	20cor org brown	1.00	.40
1737	A234	24cor brown	1.10	.40
1738	A234	28cor purple	1.30	.40
1739	A234	50cor henna brn	2.40	.50
1740	A234	100cor plum	4.75	.95

Nos. 1733-1740 (8)   12.45 3.85

Nos. 1734-1740 are airmail.

Flowers — A235

Designs: 4cor, Acacia baileyana. 12cor, Anigozanthos manglesii. 16cor, Telopia speciosissima. 20cor, Eucalyptus ficifolia. 24cor, Boronia heterophylla. 28cor, Callistemon speciosus. 30cor, Nymphaea caerulea, horiz. 50cor, Clianthus formosus.

1988, Aug. 30   *Perf. 13*
1741	A235	4cor multicolored	.60	.40
1742	A235	12cor multicolored	.85	.40
1743	A235	16cor multicolored	1.10	.40
1744	A235	20cor multicolored	1.40	.40
1745	A235	24cor multicolored	1.75	.40
1746	A235	28cor multicolored	1.90	.40
1747	A235	30cor multicolored	2.10	.40
1748	A235	50cor multicolored	1.80	.40

Nos. 1741-1748 (8)   11.50 3.20

Nos. 1742-1748 are airmail.

Pre-Columbian Art — A236

Designs: 4cor, Zapotec funeral urn. 12cor, Mochica ceramic kneeling man. 16cor, Mochica ceramic head. 20cor, Taina ceramic vase. 28cor, Nazca cup, horiz. 100cor, Inca pipe, horiz.
120cor, Aztec ceramic vessel, horiz.

1988, Oct. 12   *Perf. 12x12½, 12½x12*
1749	A236	4cor multi + label	.55	.35
1750	A236	12cor multi + label	.75	.35
1751	A236	16cor multi + label	1.00	.35
1752	A236	20cor multi + label	1.25	.35
1753	A236	28cor multi + label	1.75	.35
1754	A236	100cor multi + label	6.00	1.00

Nos. 1749-1754 (6)   11.30 2.75

Souvenir Sheet
Perf. 13x13½
1755	A236	120cor multicolored	5.50	3.75

Discovery of America, 500th anniv. (in 1992). Nos. 1750-1755 are airmail. No. 1755 contains one 40x32mm stamp.

Publication of Blue, by Ruben Dario, Cent. — A237

1988, Oct. 12   *Perf. 12x12½*
1756	A237	25cor multi + label	3.00	.40

No. 1756 is airmail.

Tourism A238

4cor, Pochomil. 12cor, Granada. 20cor, Olof Palme Convention Center. 24cor, Masaya Volcano Natl. Park. 28cor, La Boquita. 30cor, Xiloa. 50cor, Hotels of Managua. 160cor, Montelimar.

1989, Feb. 5   *Perf. 12½x12*
1757	A238	4cor multicolored	.50	.40
1758	A238	12cor multicolored	.70	.40
1759	A238	20cor multicolored	1.30	.40
1760	A238	24cor multicolored	1.30	.40
1761	A238	28cor multicolored	1.80	.40
1762	A238	30cor multicolored	1.90	.40
1763	A238	50cor multicolored	3.50	.40

Nos. 1757-1763 (7)   11.00 2.80

Souvenir Sheet
Perf. 13
1764	A238	160cor multicolored	6.50	3.75

Nos. 1758-1764 are airmail. No. 1764 contains one 40x32mm stamp.

French Revolution, Bicentennial A240

Designs: 50cor, Procession of the Estates General, Versailles. 300cor, Oath of the Tennis Court. 600cor, 14th of July, vert. 1000cor, Dancing Around the Liberty Tree. 2000cor, Liberty Guiding the People, vert. 3000cor, Storming the Bastille. 5000cor, Lafayette Swearing Allegiance to the Constitution, vert. 9000cor, La Marseillaise, vert.

Perf. 12½x13 (50cor), 13x12½ (600, 2000cor), 12½
1989, July 14
Sizes: 50cor, 40x25mm
600cor, 2000cor, 33x44mm
1773	A240	50cor multicolored	.45	.30
1774	A240	300cor shown	.45	.30
1775	A240	600cor multicolored	.60	.30
1776	A240	1000cor multicolored	.90	.30
1777	A240	2000cor multicolored	1.60	.30
1778	A240	3000cor multicolored	2.60	.40
1779	A240	5000cor multicolored	4.00	.65

Nos. 1773-1779 (7)   10.60 2.55

Souvenir Sheet
Perf. 12½
1780	A240	9000cor multicolored	6.25	4.50

Philexfrance '89. #1774-1780 are airmail. #1780 contains one 32x40mm stamp.

Currency Reform
Currency reform took place Mar. 4, 1990. Until stamps in the new currency were issued, mail was to be hand-stamped "Franqueo Pagado," (Postage Paid). Stamps were not used again until Apr. 25, 1991. Nos. 1781-1812 were prepared but not issued prior to the currency reform and were sold by the post office without postal validity. Used values are for CTO stamps.

Ships — A241

Stamp World London '90: 500cor, Director. 1000cor, Independence. 3000cor, Orizaba. 5000cor, SS Lewis. 10,000cor, Golden Rule. 30,000cor, Santiago de Cuba. 100,000cor, North Star.
75,000cor, Bahia de Corinto.

1990, Apr. 3   *Perf. 12½x12*
1781	A241	500cor shown	.40	.30
1782	A241	1000cor multi	.40	.30
1783	A241	3000cor multi	.50	.30
1784	A241	5000cor multi	.75	.30
1785	A241	10,000cor multi	1.25	.40
1786	A241	30,000cor multi	2.40	.50
1787	A241	100,000cor multi	3.50	.65

Nos. 1781-1787 (7)   9.20 2.75

Souvenir Sheet
Perf. 12½
1788		75,000cor multi	6.00	4.00

World Cup Soccer Championships, Italy — A242

Designs: Various soccer players in action.

1990, Apr. 30   *Perf. 13*
1789	A242	500cor shown	.35	.25
1790	A242	1000cor multi	.35	.25
1791	A242	3000cor multi	.50	.30
1792	A242	5000cor multi	.85	.35
1793	A242	10,000cor multi	1.40	.50
1794	A242	30,000cor multi	2.40	.60
1795	A242	100,000cor multi	3.50	.70

Nos. 1789-1795 (7)   9.35 3.00

Souvenir Sheet
Perf. 12½
1796	A242	75,000cor multi	5.00	2.50

1992 Winter Olympics, Albertville A243

Designs: 500cor, Ski jumping. 1000cor, Downhill skiing. 3000cor, Figure skating, vert. 5000cor, Speed skating, vert. 10,000cor, Biathlon, vert. 30,000cor, Cross country skiing, vert. 100,000cor, Ice hockey, vert. 75,000cor, Two-man bobsled, vert.

1990, July 25   *Perf. 13*
1797	A243	500cor shown	.70	.55
1798	A243	1000cor multi	.70	.55
1799	A243	3000cor multi	.90	.75
1800	A243	5000cor multi	1.90	.85
1801	A243	10,000cor multi	2.50	1.30
1802	A243	30,000cor multi	4.50	1.65
1803	A243	100,000cor multi	7.00	1.85

Nos. 1797-1803 (7)   18.20 7.50

Souvenir Sheet
Perf. 12½
1804	A243	75,000cor multi	5.50	2.50

1992 Summer Olympics, Barcelona — A244

Designs: 500cor, Javelin. 1000cor, Steeplechase. 3000cor, Handball. 5000cor, Basketball. 10,000cor, Gymnastics. 30,000cor, Cycling. 100,000cor, Boxing, horiz. 75,000cor, Soccer.

1990, Aug. 10   *Perf. 13*
1805	A244	500cor shown	.70	.55
1806	A244	1000cor multi	.70	.55
1807	A244	3000cor multi	.90	.75
1808	A244	5000cor multi	1.90	.85
1809	A244	10,000cor multi	2.50	1.30
1810	A244	30,000cor multi	4.50	1.65
1811	A244	100,000cor multi	7.00	1.85

Nos. 1805-1811 (7)   18.20 7.50

Souvenir Sheet
1812		75,000cor multi	5.50	2.50

Birds — A245

Designs: No. 1813, Apteryx owenii. No. 1814, Notornis mantelli. 10c, Cyanoramphus novaezelandiae. 20c, Gallirallus australis. 30c, Rhynochetos jubatus, vert. 60c, Nestor notabilis. 70c, Strigops habroptilus.
1.50cor, Cygnus atratus.

1990, Aug. 14   Litho.   *Perf. 12½*
1813	A245	5c multicolored	.40	.25
1814	A245	5c multicolored	.40	.25
1815	A245	10c multicolored	.40	.25
1816	A245	20c multicolored	1.00	.25
1817	A245	30c multicolored	1.50	.30
1818	A245	60c multicolored	3.00	.65
1819	A245	70c multicolored	3.50	.75

Nos. 1813-1819 (7)   10.20 2.70

Souvenir Sheet
1820	A245	1.50cor multicolored	5.25	3.75

New Zealand '90, Intl. Philatelic Exhibition.

Fauna A246

No. 1821, Panthera onca. No. 1822, Felis pardalis, vert. No. 1823, Atelles geoffrogi, vert. No. 1824, Tapirus bairdi, vert. No. 1825, Dasypus novencintus. No. 1826, Canis latrans. No. 1827, Choloepus hoffmanni.

1990, Oct. 10
1821	A246	5c multicolored	.45	.25
1822	A246	5c multicolored	.45	.25
1823	A246	10c multicolored	.45	.25
1824	A246	20c multicolored	.95	.25
1825	A246	30c multicolored	1.60	.30

1826	A246	60c multicolored	3.00	.65
1827	A246	70c multicolored	3.75	.75
		Nos. 1821-1827 (7)	10.65	2.70

FAO, 45th anniv.

Flower Type of 1983 Redrawn
Without Date
1991, Apr. 24   Litho.   Perf. 14x13½
Size: 19x22mm

1828	A151	1cor like #1220	.65	.25
1829	A151	2cor like #1212	1.25	.25
1830	A151	3cor like #1218	1.60	.25
1831	A151	4cor like #1219	2.50	.25
1832	A151	5cor like #1217	3.10	.25
1833	A151	6cor like #1210	3.60	.25
1834	A151	7cor like #1216	4.25	.25
1835	A151	8cor like #1215	5.00	.25
1836	A151	9cor like #1211	5.50	.25
1837	A151	10cor like #1221	8.25	.25
1838	A151	11cor like #1214	7.00	.25
1839	A151	12cor like #1222	7.25	.25
1840	A151	13cor like #1213	8.00	.25
1841	A151	14cor like #1224	8.50	.25
1842	A151	15cor like #1223	9.50	.25
1843	A151	16cor like #1209	10.25	.25
		Nos. 1828-1843 (16)	86.20	4.00

Dr. Pedro Joaquin
Chamorro — A247

1991, Apr. 25   Perf. 14½x14
1844	A247	2.25cor multicolored	1.90	.45

1990 World Cup
Soccer
Championships,
Italy — A248

Designs: No. 1845, Two players. No. 1846,
Four players, vert. 50c, Two players, referee.
1cor, Germany, five players, vert. 1.50cor,
One player, vert. 3cor, Argentina, five players,
vert. 3.50cor, Italian players.
7.50cor, German team with trophy.

1991, July 16   Perf. 14x14½, 14½x14
1845	A248	25c multicolored	.60	.25
1846	A248	25c multicolored	.60	.25
1847	A248	50c multicolored	.60	.25
1848	A248	1cor multicolored	.95	.25
1849	A248	1.50cor multicolored	1.30	.25
1850	A248	3cor multicolored	3.00	.60
1851	A248	3.50cor multicolored	3.25	.70
		Nos. 1845-1851 (7)	10.30	2.60

Souvenir Sheet
1852	A248	7.50cor multicolored	5.00	1.50
a.		Overprinted in sheet margin ('93)	5.00	1.60

No. 1852a overprint reads "COPA DE
FOOTBALL / U.S.A. '94."

Butterflies — A249

Designs: No. 1853, Prepona praeneste. No.
1854, Anartia fatima. 50c, Eryphanis aesacus.
1cor, Heliconius melpomene. 1.50cor,
Chlosyne janais. 3cor, Marpesia iole. 3.50cor,
Metamorpha epaphus.
7.50cor, Morpho peleides.

1991, July 16   Perf. 14½x14
1853	A249	25c multicolored	.35	.25
1854	A249	25c multicolored	.35	.25
1855	A249	50c multicolored	.60	.25
1856	A249	1cor multicolored	.90	.30
1857	A249	1.50cor multicolored	1.30	.45
1858	A249	3cor multicolored	2.90	.95
1859	A249	3.50cor multicolored	3.00	1.05
		Nos. 1853-1859 (7)	9.40	3.50

Souvenir Sheet
1860	A249	7.50cor multicolored	5.00	2.10

Fauna of Rainforest — A250

No. 1861 a, Yellow-headed amazon. b, Toucan. c, Scarlet macaw (lapa roja). d, Quetzal.
e, Spider monkey (mono arana). f, Capuchin
monkey. g, Sloth (cucala). h, Oropendola. i,
Violet sabrewing (colibri violeta). j, Tamandua.
k, Jaguarundi. l, Boa constrictor. m, Iguana. n,
Jaguar. o, White-necked jacobin. p, Doxocopa
clothilda. q, Dismorphia deione. r, Golden
arrow-poison frog (rana venenosa). s, Cal-
lithomia hezia. t, Chameleon.

1991, Aug. 7   Litho.   Perf. 14x14½
1861	A250	2.25cor Sheet of 20, #a.-t.	35.00	15.00

America Issue — A251

2.25cor, Concepcion volcano.

1990, Oct. 12   Perf. 14½x14
1862	A251	2.25cor multi	2.00	.55

Orchids — A252

Designs: No. 1863, Isochilus major. No.
1864, Cycnoches ventricosum. 50c, Vanilla
odorata. 1cor, Helleriella nicaraguensis.
1.50cor, Barkeria spectabilis. 3cor, Maxillaria
hedwigae. 3.50cor, Cattleya aurantiaca.
7.50cor, Psygmorchis pusilla, vert.

1991   Litho.   Perf. 14x14½
1863	A252	25c multicolored	.55	.25
1864	A252	25c multicolored	.55	.25
1865	A252	50c multicolored	.55	.25
1866	A252	1cor multicolored	.80	.25
1867	A252	1.50cor multicolored	1.30	.25
1868	A252	3cor multicolored	2.40	.50
1869	A252	3.50cor multicolored	3.00	.55
		Nos. 1863-1869 (7)	9.15	2.30

Souvenir Sheet
Perf. 14½x14
1870	A252	7.50cor multicolored	4.75	1.50

Locomotives of South
America — A253

Various steam locomotives.

1991, Apr. 21   Perf. 14½x14
1871	A253	25c Bolivia	.55	.25
1872	A253	25c Peru	.55	.25
1873	A253	50c Argentina	.55	.25
1874	A253	1.50cor Chile	1.30	.25
1875	A253	2cor Colombia	1.75	.30
1876	A253	3cor Brazil	2.40	.50
1877	A253	3.50cor Paraguay	2.90	.55
		Nos. 1871-1877 (7)	10.00	2.35

Souvenir Sheets
1878	A253	7.50cor Nicaragua	5.00	3.00
1879	A253	7.50cor Guatemala	5.00	3.00

Birds — A254

Designs: 50c, Eumomota supercilliosa. 75c,
Trogon collaris. 1cor, Electron platyrhynchum.
1.50cor, Teleonema filicauda. 1.75cor, Tangara chilensis, horiz. No. 1885, Pharomachrus
mocino. No. 1886, Phlegopsis nigromaculata.
No. 1887, Hylophylax naevioides, horiz. No.
1888, Aulacorhynchus haematopygius, horiz.

1991   Perf. 14½x14, 14x14½
1880	A254	50c multicolored	.55	.25
1881	A254	75c multicolored	.65	.25
1882	A254	1cor multicolored	.80	.25
1883	A254	1.50cor multicolored	1.40	.25
1884	A254	1.75cor multicolored	1.50	.30
1885	A254	2.25cor multicolored	2.00	.35
1886	A254	2.25cor multicolored	2.00	.35
		Nos. 1880-1886 (7)	8.90	2.00

Souvenir Sheets
1887	A254	7.50cor multicolored	4.50	3.00
1888	A254	7.50cor multicolored	4.50	3.00

Paintings by
Vincent Van
Gogh — A255

Designs: No. 1889, Head of a Peasant
Woman Wearing a Bonnet. No. 1890, One-
Eyed Man. 50c, Self-Portrait. 1cor, Vase with
Carnations and Other Flowers. 1.50cor, Vase
with Zinnias and Geraniums. 3cor, Portrait of
Pere Tanguy. 3.50cor, Portrait of a Man, horiz.
7.50cor, Path Lined with Poplars, horiz.

1991   Perf. 14x13½, 13½x14
1889	A255	25c multicolored	.50	.25
1890	A255	25c multicolored	.50	.25
1891	A255	50c multicolored	.60	.25
1892	A255	1cor multicolored	.80	.25
1893	A255	1.50cor multicolored	1.25	.25
1894	A255	3cor multicolored	2.50	.50
1895	A255	3.50cor multicolored	2.60	.55
		Nos. 1889-1895 (7)	8.75	2.30

Souvenir Sheet
Size: 128x102mm
Imperf
1896	A255	7.50cor multicolored	4.75	1.25

Phila Nippon
'91 — A256

Designs: 25c, Golden Hall. 50c, Phoenix
Hall. 1cor, Bunraku puppet head. 1.50cor,
Japanese cranes. 2.50cor, Himeji Castle.
3cor, Statue of the Guardian. 3.50cor, Kabuki
warrior. 7.50cor, Vase.

1991   Perf. 14x14½
1897	A256	25c multicolored	.50	.25
1898	A256	50c multicolored	.50	.25
1899	A256	1cor multicolored	.90	.25
1900	A256	1.50cor multicolored	1.30	.25
1901	A256	2.50cor multicolored	1.90	.40
1902	A256	3cor multicolored	2.40	.50
1903	A256	3.50cor multicolored	2.75	.55
		Nos. 1897-1903 (7)	10.25	2.45

Souvenir Sheet
1904	A256	7.50cor multicolored	5.00	3.00

Inscriptions are switched on 50c and 2.50cor.

Child's
Drawing — A257

1991
1905	A257	2.25cor multicolored	1.75	.45

Central American Bank of Economic
Integration, 30th Anniv. — A258

1991, Aug. 1   Litho.   Perf. 14
1906	A258	1.50cor multicolored	1.50	.50

No. 1906 printed with se-tenant label.

Discovery of America,
500th Anniv. (in
1992) — A259

1991, Oct. 12   Perf. 14½x14
1907	A259	2.25cor Columbus' fleet	2.00	.75

Swiss
Confederation,
700th Anniv. (in
1991) — A260

1992, Aug. 1   Litho.   Perf. 14x14½
1908	A260	2.25cor black & red	2.00	.75

Contemporary
Art — A261

Designs: No. 1909, Pitcher, by Jose Ortiz.
No. 1910, Black jar, by Lorenza Pineda Cooperative, vert. 50c, Vase, by Elio Gutierrez, vert.
1cor, Christ on Cross, by Jose de Los Santos,
vert. 1.50cor, Sculpture of family, by Erasmo
Moya, vert. 3cor, Bird and fish, by Silvio
Chavarria Cooperative. 3.50cor, Filigree jar, by
Maria de Los Angeles Bermudez, vert.
7.50cor, Masks by Jose Flores.

Perf. 14x14½, 14½x14
1992, Sept. 17   Litho.
1909	A261	25c multicolored	.50	.25
1910	A261	25c multicolored	.50	.25
1911	A261	50c multicolored	.50	.25
1912	A261	1cor multicolored	.85	.25
1913	A261	1.50cor multicolored	1.25	.30
1914	A261	3cor multicolored	2.50	.65
1915	A261	3.50cor multicolored	3.00	.75
		Nos. 1909-1915 (7)	9.10	2.70

Imperf
Size: 100x70mm
1916	A261	7.50cor multicolored	5.00	1.60

Miniature Sheet

Fauna and Flora of
Rainforest — A262

No. 1917: a, Colibri magnifico (b). b, Aguila
arpia (f). c, Orchids. d, Toucan, Mariposa
morpho. e, Quetzal (i). f, Guardabarranco (g,
k). g, Mono aullador (howler monkey). h, Perezoso (sloth). i, Mono ardilla (squirrel monkey). j, Guacamaya (macaw) (n). k, Boa
esmeralda, Tanagra escarlata (emerald boa,
scarlet tanager). l, Rana flecha venenosa
(arrow frog). m, Jaguar. n, Oso hormiguero
(anteater) (o). o, Ocelot. p, Coati.

1992, Nov. 12   Perf. 14½x14
1917	A262	1.50cor Sheet of 16, #a.-p.	21.50	6.00

1992 Winter
Olympics,
Albertville
A263

No. 1918, Ice hockey. No. 1919, 4-man bob-sled. No. 1920, Combined slalom, vert. No. 1921, Speed skating. No. 1922, Cross-country skiing. No. 1923, Double luge. No. 1924, Ski jumping, vert. No. 1925, Slalom.

Perf. 14x14½, 14½x14
1992, Sept. 17

1918	A263	25c multi	.55	.25
1919	A263	25c multi	.55	.25
1920	A263	50c multi	.55	.25
1921	A263	1cor multi	.60	.25
1922	A263	1.50cor multi	1.30	.30
1923	A263	3cor multi	3.00	.65
1924	A263	3.50cor multi	3.10	.75
		Nos. 1918-1924 (7)	9.65	2.70

Imperf
Size: 100x70mm

1925	A263	7.50cor multi	4.75	1.60
a.		Overprinted ('93)	4.75	1.60

No. 1925a overprint reads "JUEGOS PRE OLIMPICOS DE INVIERNO / LILLEHAMMER, NORUEGA."

1992 Summer Olympics, Barcelona A264

No. 1926, Javelin. No. 1927, Fencing. No. 1928, Basketball. No. 1929, 1500-meter race. No. 1930, Long jump. No. 1931, Women's 10,000-meter race. No. 1932, Equestrian. No. 1933, Canoeing

Perf. 14x14½, 14½x14
1992, Sept. 17   Litho.

1926	A264	25c multi	.50	.25
1927	A264	25c multi	.50	.25
1928	A264	25c multi	.50	.25
1929	A264	1.50cor multi	1.30	.30
1930	A264	2cor multi	1.75	.40
1931	A264	3cor multi	2.50	.65
1932	A264	3.50cor multi	3.00	.75
		Nos. 1926-1932 (7)	10.05	2.85

Imperf
Size: 100x70mm

1933	A264	7.50cor multi	5.00	1.60
a.		Overprinted ('93)	4.75	1.60

Nos. 1927-1932 are vert. Dated 1991.
No. 1933a overprint reads "JUEGOS OLIMPICOS DE VERANO / ATLANTA, GA. / ESTADOS UNIDOS DE AMERICA."

Father R. M. Fabretto and Children — A265

1992, Nov. 12   Litho.   Perf. 14x14½

1934	A265	2.25cor multicolored	1.75	.50

Nicaraguan Natives, by Claudia Gordillo — A266

1992, Nov. 12

1935	A266	2.25cor black & brn	1.75	.50

Nicaraguan Caciques, by Milton Jose Cruz — A267

1992, Nov. 12

1936	A267	2.25cor multicolored	1.60	.50

Contemporary Paintings A268

Paintings by: No. 1937, Alberto Ycaza, vert. No. 1938, Alejandro Arostegui, vert. 50c, Bernard Dreyfus. 1.50cor, Orlando Sobalvarro. 2cor, Hugo Palma. 3cor, Omar D'Leon. 3.50cor, Carlos Montenegro, vert. 7.50cor, Federico Nordalm.

Perf. 14½x14, 14x14½
1992, Nov. 12

1937	A268	25c multicolored	.50	.25
1938	A268	25c multicolored	.50	.25
1939	A268	50c multicolored	.50	.25
1940	A268	1.50cor multicolored	1.20	.30
1941	A268	2cor multicolored	1.75	.40
1942	A268	3cor multicolored	2.40	.65
1943	A268	3.50cor multicolored	2.90	.75
		Nos. 1937-1943 (7)	9.75	2.85

Imperf
Size: 100x70mm

1944	A268	7.50cor multicolored	4.75	1.60

Monument to Columbus, Rivas — A269

1993, Mar. 22   Perf. 14½x14

1945	A269	2.25cor multicolored	1.75	.50

UPAEP issue. Dated 1992.

Catholic Religion in Nicaragua, 460th Anniv. — A270

Designs: 25c, Eucharistic gonfalon. 50c, Statue of Virgin Mary. 1cor, Document, 1792-93. 1.50cor, Baptismal font. 2cor, Statue of Madonna and Child. 2.25cor, Monsignor Diego Alvarez Osario. 3cor, Christ on cross.

1993, Mar. 22

1946	A270	25c multicolored	.50	.25
1947	A270	50c multicolored	.50	.25
1948	A270	1cor multicolored	.80	.25
1949	A270	1.50cor multicolored	1.30	.30
1950	A270	2cor multicolored	1.75	.40
1951	A270	2.25cor multicolored	1.95	.50
1952	A270	3cor multicolored	2.60	.65
		Nos. 1946-1952 (7)	9.40	2.60

Dated 1992.

A271

Archdiocese of Managua: a, 3cor, Cathedral of the Immaculate Conception. b, 4cor, Cross, map.

1993, Apr. 30

1953	A271	Pair, #a.-b.	5.00	1.75

Dated 1992.

A272

Player, country: 50c, Brolin, Sweden. No. 1955, Karas, Poland; Costa, Brazil. No. 1956, Bossis, Platini, France. 1.50cor, Schumacher, Germany. 2cor, Zubizarreta, Spain. 2.50cor, Matthaeus, Germany; Maradona, Argentina. 3.50cor, Robson, England; Santos, Portugal. 10cor, Biyik, Cameroun; Valderrama, Colombia.

1994, Jan. 28   Litho.   Perf. 14

1954	A272	50c multicolored	.50	.25
1955	A272	1cor multicolored	.75	.25
1956	A272	1cor multicolored	.75	.25
1957	A272	1.50cor multicolored	1.30	.30
1958	A272	2cor multicolored	1.60	.40
1959	A272	2.50cor multicolored	2.10	.55
1960	A272	3.50cor multicolored	3.00	.75
		Nos. 1954-1960 (7)	10.00	2.75

Souvenir Sheet

1961	A272	10cor multicolored	6.25	2.00

1994 World Cup Soccer Championships, US.

Sonatina, by Alma Iris Prez A272a

1993, Oct. 29   Litho.   Perf. 13½x14

1961A	A272a	3cor multicolored	1.90	1.00

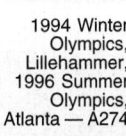

Butterflyfish — A273

No. 1962: a, Chaetodon lunula. b, Chaetodon rainfordi. c, Chaetodon reticulatus. d, Chaetodon auriga. e, Heniochus acuminatus. f, Coradion fulvocinctus. g, Chaetodon speculum. h, Chaetodon lineolatus. i, Chaetodon bennetti. j, Chaetodon melanotus. k, Chaetodon aureus. l, Chaetodon ephippium. m, Hemitaurichthys polylepis. n, Chaetodon semeion. o, Chaetodon kleinii. p, Chelmon rostratus.

1993, Nov. 18   Litho.   Perf. 14

1962		Sheet of 16	21.50	7.50
a.-p.		A273 1.50cor Any single	.75	.30
q.		Inscribed with Bangkok '93 emblem in sheet margin	19.50	7.50
r.		Inscribed with Indopex '93 emblem in sheet margin	19.50	7.50
s.		Inscribed with Taipei '93 emblem in sheet margin	19.50	7.50

Issue date: No. 1962, Nov. 1, 1993.
No. 1962 is without any show emblem in sheet margin.

1994 Winter Olympics, Lillehammer, 1996 Summer Olympics, Atlanta — A274

No. 1963, Downhill skiing. No. 1964, Four-man bobsled. No. 1965, Swimming. No. 1966, Diving. No. 1967, Speed skating. No. 1968, Race walking. No. 1969, Hurdles. No. 1970, Ski jumping. No. 1971, Women's gymnastics. No. 1972, Women's figure skating. No. 1973, Pairs figure skating. No. 1974, Javelin. No. 1975, Biathlon. No. 1976, Running. No. 1977, Torch, hands. No. 1978, Flags.

1993, Nov. 18

1963	A274	25c multicolored	.45	.25
1964	A274	25c multicolored	.45	.25
1965	A274	25c multicolored	.45	.25
1966	A274	25c multicolored	.45	.25
1967	A274	50c multicolored	.45	.25
1968	A274	50c multicolored	.45	.25
1969	A274	1cor multicolored	.75	.25
1970	A274	1.50cor multicolored	1.25	.30
1971	A274	1.50cor multicolored	1.25	.30
1972	A274	2cor multicolored	1.50	.40
1973	A274	3cor multicolored	2.40	.65
1974	A274	3cor multicolored	2.40	.65
1975	A274	3.50cor multicolored	2.75	.75
1976	A274	3.50cor multicolored	2.75	.75
		Nos. 1963-1976 (14)	17.75	5.55

Souvenir Sheets

1977	A274	7.50cor multicolored	4.75	1.50
1978	A274	7.50cor multicolored	4.75	1.50

1994 Winter Olympics (#1963-1964, 1967, 1970, 1972-1973, 1975, 1978). Others, 1996 Summer Olympics.

Pan-American Health Organization, 90th Anniv. — A275

1993, June 16   Perf. 14½

1979	A275	3cor multicolored	2.25	.65

Organization of American States, 23rd General Assembly A276

1993, June 7   Perf. 13½x14

1980	A276	3cor multicolored	2.25	.65

Christmas A276a

Paintings: 1cor, Holy Family, by unknown painter. 4cor, Birth of Christ, by Lezamon.

1994, Feb. 23   Litho.   Perf. 13½x14

1980A	A276a	1cor multicolored	.70	.25
1980B	A276a	4cor multicolored	2.60	.70

Fauna and Flora of Rainforest — A277

No. 1981: a, Bromeliacae. b, Tilmatura dupontii. c, Anolis biporcatus (b). d, Fulgara laternaria. e, Bradypus. f, Spizaetus ornatus. g, Cotinga amabilis. h, Bothrops schlegelii. i, Odontoglossum. j, Agalychnis callidryas. k, Heliconius spaho. l, Passiflora vitifolia.
No. 1982, Dasyprocta punctata. No. 1983, Melinaea lilis.

1994, Jan. 20   Perf. 14

1981	A277	2cor Sheet of 12, #a.-l.	20.00	7.50

Souvenir Sheets

1982	A277	10cor multicolored	5.25	1.75
1983	A277	10cor multicolored	5.25	1.75

Hong Kong '94 — A278

No. 1984 — Butterflies: a, Callicore patelina. b, Chlosyne narva. c, Anteos maerula. d, Marpesia petreus. e, Pierella helvetia. f, Eurytides epidaus. g, Heliconius doris. h, Smyrna blomfildia. i, Eueides lybia. j, Adelpha heraclea. k, Heliconius hecale. l, Parides montezuma. m, Morpho polyphemus. n, Eresia alsina. o, Prepona omphale. p, Morpho granadensis.

1994, Feb. 18   Litho.   Perf. 14

1984	A278	1.50cor Sheet of 16, #a.-p.	20.00	6.00

Astronomers A279

No. 1985 — Copernicus and: a, Satellite. b, Tycho Brahe (1546-1601), making observations. c, Galileo probe, Galileo. d, Isaac Newton, Newton telescope. e, Giotto probe to Halley's comet, Edmund Halley. f, James Bradley (1693-1762), Grenwich Observatory.

g, 1793 telescope, William Herschel (1738-1822). h, John Goodricke (1764-86), stellar eclipse. i, Gottingen observatory, Karl Fredrich Gauss (1777-1855). j, Friedrich Bessell (1784-1846), astronomical instrument. k, Harvard College Observatory, William Granch (1783-1859). l, George B. Airy (1801-92), stellar disc. m, Lowell Observatory, Flagstaff, Arizona, Percival Lowell (1855-1916). n, George A. Halle (1868-1938), solar spectrograph. o, Space telescope, Edwin Hubble (1889-1953). p, Gerard Kuiper (1905-73), Uranus' moon Miranda.

10cor, Nicolas Copernicus, interstellar probe.

1994, Apr. 4
1985 A279 1.50cor Sheet of 16,
    #a.-p.   19.00 4.50
Souvenir Sheet
1986 A279 10cor multicolored   5.50 2.00

Automotive Anniversaries — A280

No. 1987: a, 1886 Benz three-wheel car. b, 1909 Benz Blitzen. c, 1923 Mercedes Benz 24/100/140. d, 1928 Mercedes Benz SSK. e, 1934 Mercedes Benz Cabriolet 500k. f, 1949 Mercedes Benz 170S. g, 1954 Mercedes Benz W196. h, 1954 Mercedes Benz 300SL. i, 1896 Ford four-wheel car. j, 1920 Ford taxi. k, 1928 Ford Roadster. l, 1932 Ford V-8. m, 1937 Ford 78 (V-8). n, 1939 Ford 91 Deluxe Tudor Sedan. o, 1946 Ford V-8 Sedan Coupe. p, 1958 Ford Custom 300.

10cor, Henry Ford (1863-1947), 1903 Ford Model A; Karl Benz (1844-1929), 1897 Benz 5CH.

1994, Apr. 5
1987 A280 1.50cor Sheet of 16,
    #a.-p.   19.00 4.50
Souvenir Sheet
1988 A280 10cor multicolored   5.25 2.00

First Benz four-wheeled vehicle, cent. (Nos. 1987a-1987h). First Ford gasoline engine, cent. (Nos. 1987i-1987p).

Graf Zeppelin — A281

No. 1989 — Graf Zeppelin and: a, Dr. Hugo Eckener, Count Zeppelin (inside cabin). b, New York City, 1928. c, Tokyo, 1929. d, San Simeon, California, 1929. e, Col. Charles Lindbergh, Dr. Hugo Eckener, 1929. f, Moscow, 1930. g, Paris, 1930. h, Cairo, 1931. i, Arctic waters. j, Rio de Janeiro, 1932. k, London, 1935. l, St. Peter's Basilica, Vatican City. m, Swiss Alps. n, Brandenburg Gate. o, Eckener in control room. p, Ernest A. Lehman, DO-X.

No. 1990, Graf Zeppelin, Count Zeppelin. No. 1991, Zeppelin, Eckener.

1994, Apr. 6
1989 A281 1.50cor Sheet of 16.
    #a.-p.   19.00 4.50
Souvenir Sheets
1990 A281 10cor multicolored   5.25 1.75
1991 A281 10cor multicolored   5.25 1.75

Dr. Hugo Eckener (1868-1954) (#1991).

Contemporary Crafts — A282

Designs: No. 1992, 50c, Basket weaving, by Rosalia Sevilla, horiz. No. 1993, 50c, Wood carving, by Julio Lopez. No. 1994, 1cor, Woman carrying sack, by Indiana Robleto. No. 1995, 1cor, Church, by Auxiliadora Bush. 2.50cor, Carving, by Jose de Los Santos. 3cor, Costumed doll with horse's head, by

Ines Gutierrez de Chong. 4cor, Ceramic container, by Elio Gutierrez.
10cor, Metate, by Saul Carballo.

Perf. 13½x14, 14x13½
1994, Feb. 15   **Litho.**
1992-1998 A282 Set of 7   9.25 2.00
Imperf
Size: 96x66mm
1999 A282 10cor multicolored   5.25 1.60
    Dated 1993.

Stone Carvings, Chontal Culture — A283

Color of inscription tablet: No. 2000, 50c, Yellow. No. 2001, 50c, Yellow brown. No. 2002, 1cor, Green. No. 2003, 1cor, Yellow green. 2.50cor, Greenish blue. 3cor, Blue. 4cor, Grey green.
10cor, Two stone totems seen against landscape painting.

1994, Feb. 23   **Perf. 14**
2000-2006 A283 Set of 7   9.25 2.00
Imperf
Size: 96x66mm
2007 A283 10cor multicolored   5.25 1.60
    Dated 1993.

Contemporary Art — A284

Designs: No. 2008, 50c, Lady Embroidering, by Guillermo Rivas Navas. No. 2009, 50c, Virgin of Nicaragua, by Cella Lacayo. No. 2010, 1cor, The Dance, by June Beer. No. 2011, 1cor, Song of Peace, by Alejandro Canales. 2.50cor, Fruits, by Genaro Lugo, horiz. 3cor, Figures and Fragments, by Leonel Vanegas. 4cor, Eruption of Volcano of Water, by Asilia Guillen, horiz.
10cor, Still life, by Alejandro Alonso Rochi.

1994, Mar. 15 Perf. 14x13½, 13½x14
2008-2014 A284 Set of 7   9.25 2.00
Imperf
Size: 96x66mm
2015 A284 10cor multicolored   5.25 1.60
    Dated 1993.

Prominent Nicaraguan Philatelists — A285

Designs: 1cor, Gabriel Horvilleur (1907-91). 3cor, Jose S. Cuadra A. (1932-92). 4cor, Alfredo Pertz (1864-1948).

1994, Apr. 18   Litho.   Perf. 14
2016-2018 A285 Set of 3   5.25 1.40
    Dated 1993.

First Tree Conference of Nicaragua A286

1994, June 5   Perf. 14x13½
2019 A286 4cor multicolored   2.40 .70

Souvenir Sheets

Reported Alien Sightings A287

Date and location of sighting: No. 2020, 60cor, July 21, 1991, Missouri. No. 2021, 60cor, July 28, 1965, Argentina. No. 2022, 60cor, Aug. 21, 1955, Kentucky. No. 2023, 60cor, Oct. 25, 1973, Pennsylvania. No. 2024, 60cor, Sept. 19, 1961, New Hampshire. No. 2025, 60cor, Nov. 7, 1989, Kansas. No. 2026, 60cor, Sept. 26, 1976, Grand Canary Island. No. 2027, 60cor, May 8, 1973, Texas.

1994, May 25   Litho.   Perf. 14
2020-2027 A287 Set of 8   225.00 75.00

Sacred Art — A288

Designs: No. 2028, 50c, Pulpit, Cathedral of Leon. No. 2029, 50c, Statue of Saint Ann, Chinandega Parish. No. 2030, 1cor, Statue of St. Joseph, San Pedro Parish, Rivas. No. 2031, 1cor, Statue of St. James, Jinotepe Parish. 2.50cor, Chalice, Subtiava Temple, Leon. 3cor, Processional cross, Nequinohoma Parish, Masaya. 4cor, Crucifix, Temple of Miracles, Managua.
10cor, Silver frontal, San Pedro Parish, Rivas.

1994, July 11   Litho.   Perf. 14
2028-2034 A288 Set of 7   9.25 2.25
Size: 96x66mm
Imperf
2036 A288 10cor multicolored   5.00 1.75
    No. 2035 is unassigned.

A289

1994, July 4   Litho.   Perf. 14
2037 A289 3cor multicolored   1.90 1.00
Intl. Conference of New or Restored Democracies.

A290

1994, Aug. 2
2038 A290 4cor multicolored   2.40 1.50
32nd World Amateur Baseball Championships.

PHILAKOREA '94 — A291

No. 2039: a, Soraksan. b, Statue of Kim Yu-Shin. c, Solitary Rock. d, Waterfall, Hallasan Valley. e, Mirukpong and Pisondae. f, Chonbuldong Valley. g, Bridge of the Seven Nymphs. h, Piryong Falls.
No. 2040, Boy on first birthday, gifts of fruit.

1994, Aug. 16
2039 A291 1.50cor Sheet of 8,
    #a.-h.   9.50 4.00
Souvenir Sheet
2040 A291 10cor multicolored   4.75 3.00

Dinosaurs A292

No. 2041: a, Tyrannosaurus rex. b, Plateosaurus (f-g). c, Pteranodon (b). d, Camarasaurus (c). e, Euplocephalus. f, Sacuanjoche. g, Deinonychus (h). h, Chasmosaurus (d). i, Dimorphodon. j, Ametriorhynchids (i). k, Ichthyosaurus (j). l, Pterapsis, Compsognathus. m, Cephalopod. n, Archelon (o). o, Griphognatus, Gyroptychius. p, Plesiosaur (o), Navtiloid.

1994, Sept. 1
2041 A292 1.50cor Sheet of 16,
    #a.-p.   20.00 8.50

1994 World Cup Soccer Championships, US — A293

Players: a, Rai. b, Freddy Rincon. c, Luis Garcia. d, Thomas Dooley. e, Tony Meola. f, Tony Meola. g, Enzo Francescoli. h, Roy Wegerle.
No. 2043, 10cor, Faustino Asprilla. No. 2044, 10cor, Adolfo Valencia, horiz.

1994, Sept. 19
2042 A293 3cor Sheet of 8, #a.-
    h.   14.00 7.50
Souvenir Sheets
2043-2044 A293 Set of 2   10.50 6.00

D-Day, 50th Anniv. — A294

No. 2045: a, British fighter plane. b, C-47 transports dropping paratroopers. c, HMS Mauritius bombards Houlgate. d, Mulberry artificial harbor. e, Churchill tank. f, Landing craft approaching beach.

1994, Sept. 26
2045 A294 3cor Sheet of 6, #a.-
    f.   10.00 6.00

Ruben Dario National Theater, 25th Anniv. — A295

1994, Sept. 30
2046 A295 3cor multicolored   1.60 1.00

A296

Intl. Olympic Committee, Cent. — A297

Gold Medalists: No. 2047, Cassius Clay (Muhammad Ali), boxing, 1960. No. 2048, Renate Stecher, track, 1972, 1976. 10cor, Claudia Pechstein, speed skating, 1994.

1994, Oct. 3
2047 A296 3.50cor multicolored ... 2.25 1.25
2048 A296 3.50cor multicolored ... 2.25 1.25

Souvenir Sheet
2049 A297 10cor multicolored ... 5.25 3.25

La Carreta Nagua, by Erick Joanello Montoya — A298

1994, Oct. 19
2050 A298 4cor multicolored ... 2.40 1.25

Motion Pictures, Cent. — A299

No. 2051 — Film and director: a, The Kid, Charlie Chaplin. b, Citizen Kane, Orson Welles. c, Lawrence of Arabia, David Lean. d, Ivan the Terrible, Sergei Eisenstein. e, Metropolis, Fritz Lang. f, The Ten Commandments, Cecil B. DeMille. g, Gandhi, Richard Attenborough. h, Casablanca, Michael Curtis. i, Platoon, Oliver Stone. j, The Godfather, Francis Ford Coppola. k, 2001: A Space Odyssey, Stanley Kubrick. l, The Ocean Depths, Jean Renoir.
No. 2052, Gone With the Wind, Victor Fleming.

1994, Nov. 14
2051 A299 2cor Sheet of 12, #a.-l. ... 17.00 8.00

Souvenir Sheet
2052 A299 15cor multicolored ... 8.00 5.00

Wildlife — A300

No. 2053: a, Nyticorax nyticorax. b, Ara macao. c, Bulbulcus ibis. d, Coragyps atratus. e, Epicrates cenchria. f, Cyanerpes cyaneus. g, Ortalis vetula. h, Bradypus griseus. i, Felis onca. j, Anhinga anhinga. k, Tapirus bairdi. l, Myrmecophaga jubata. m, Iguana iguana. n, Chelydra serpentina. o, Dendrocygna autumnalis. p, Felis paradalis.

1994, Oct. 31
2053 A300 2cor Sheet of 16, #a.-p. ... 23.00 10.00

First Manned Moon Landing, 25th Anniv. A301

No. 2054: a, Docking command, lunar modules. b, Lift-off. c, Entering lunar orbit. d, Footprint on moon. e, Separation of first stage. f, Trans-lunar insertion. g, Lander descending toward moon. h, Astronaut on moon.
No. 2055, 10cor, Astronaut saluting, flag. No. 2056, 10cor, Astronauts in quarantine, horiz.

1994, Oct. 17
2054 A301 3cor Sheet of 8, #a.-h. ... 14.00 8.00

Souvenir Sheets
2055-2056 A301 Set of 2 ... 9.50 6.50
Nos. 2055-2056 each contain one 29x47mm stamp.

Contemporary Paintings by Rodrigo Penalba — A302

Designs: 50c, Discovery of America. 1cor, Portrait of Maurice. 1.50cor, Portrait of Franco. 2cor, Portrait of Mimi Hammer. 2.50cor, Seated Woman. 3cor, Still Life, horiz. 4cor, Portrait of Maria Augusta. 15cor, Entrance to Anticoli.

1994, Nov. 15
2057-2063 A302 Set of 7 ... 9.75 4.75
Size: 66x96mm
Imperf
2064 A302 15cor multicolored ... 6.75 4.75

Domestic Cats — A303

No. 2065: a, Chocolate point Himalayan. b, Red Somalian. c, American long hair. d, Russian blue. e, Scottish folded ear. f, Persian chinchilla. g, Egyptian mau. h, Manx blue cream. i, Burmese blue Malaysian. j, Balinesian seal point. k, Oriental long-haired blue. l, Persian chinchilla cameo. m, Angora. n, Siamese. o, Burmese seal point. p, Mixed red. 15cor, Golden shoulder Persian.

1994, Dec. 20 Litho. Perf. 14
2065 A303 1.50cor Sheet of 16, #a.-p. ... 18.00 8.00

Souvenir Sheet
2066 A303 15cor multicolored ... 6.75 5.00
No. 2066 contains one 38x51mm stamp.

Wild Fowl — A304

No. 2067 — Penelopina nigra: a, 50c, Male, female on tree branch. b, 1cor, Head of male, male on tree branch. c, 2.50cor, Head of female, female on tree branch. d, 3cor, Male spreading wings, female.
No. 2068, Heads of male and female Penelopina nigra. No. 2069, Anhinga anhinga.

1994, Dec. 20 Litho. Perf. 14
2067 A304 Vert. strip of 4, #a.-d. ... 13.00 2.25

Souvenir Sheets
2068 A304 15cor multi ... 6.75 7.00
2069 A304 15cor multi ... 6.75 5.50
World Wildlife Fund (#2067).
No. 2067 was issued in miniature sheets of 3 strips.

Sculpture — A305

Designs: 50c, Truth, by Aparicio Arthola. 1cor, Owl, by Orlando Sobalvarro. 1.50cor, Small Music Player, by Noel Flores Castro. 2cor, Exodus II, by Miguel Angel Abarca. 2.50cor, Raza, by Fernando Saravia. 3cor, Dolor Incognito, by Edith Gron. 4cor, Heron, by Ernesto Cardenal.
No. 2077, 15cor, Atlante, by Jorge Navas Cordonero. No. 2078, 15cor, Motherhood, by Rodrigo Penalba.

1995, Feb. 23 Litho. Perf. 14½
2070-2076 A305 Set of 7 ... 9.75 4.50
Size: 66x96mm
Imperf
2077-2078 A305 Set of 2 ... 13.50 9.00

Historic Landmarks A306

Designs: 50c, Animas Chapel, Granada, vert. 1cor, San Francisco Convent, Granada. 1.50cor, Santiago Tower, Leon, vert. 2cor, Santa Ana Church, Nindiri. 2.50cor, Santa Ana Church, Nandaime, vert. 3cor, Lion Gate, Granada. 4cor, Castle of the Immaculate Conception, Rio San Juan.
15cor, Hacienda San Jacinto, Managua.

1995 Litho. Perf. 14
2079-2085 A306 Set of 7 ... 9.75 4.50
Size: 96x66mm
2086 A306 15cor multicolored ... 6.75 4.50

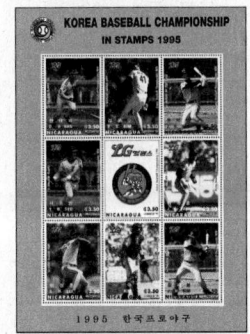

Korean Baseball Championships — A307

No. 2087, 3.50cor — LG Twins: No. 2087a, D.H. Han. b, Y.S. Kim. c, J.H. Yoo. d, Y.B. Seo. e, Team logo. f, J.H. Park. g, S.H. Lee. h, D.S. Kim. i, J.H. Kim.
No. 2088, 3.50cor — Samsung Lions: a, J.L. Ryu. b, S.Y. Kim. c, S.R. Kim. d, B.C. Dong. e, Team logo. f, K.W. Kang. g, C.S. Park. h, J.H. Yang. i, T.H. Kim.
No. 2089, 3.50cor — SBW Raiders: a, H.J. Park. b, K.J. Cho. c, K.T. Kim. d, W.H. Kim. e, Team logo. f, I.H. Baik. g, S.K. Park. h, K.L. Kim. i, J.S. Park.
No. 2090, 3.50cor — Doosan OB Bears: a, M.S. Lee. b, C.S. Park. c, H.S. Lim. d, K.W. Kim. e, Team logo. f, J.S. Kim. g, T.H. Kim. h, H.S. Kim. i, S.J. Kim.
No. 2091, 3.50cor — Pacific Dolphins: a, M.W. Jung. b, K.K. Kim. c, H.J. Kim. d, M.T. Chung. e, Team logo. f, B.W. An. g, D.G. Yoon. h, S.D. Choi. i, D.K. Kim.
No. 2092, 3.50cor — Hanwha Eagles: a, J.H. Jang. b, Y.D. Han. c, K.D. Lee. d, J.S. Park. e, Team logo. f, M.C. Jeong. g, J.W. Song. h, J.G. Kang. i, D.S. Koo.
No. 2093, 3.50cor — Lotte Giants: a, H.K. Yoon. b, D.H. Park. c, H.K. Joo. d, E.G. Kim. e, Team logo. f, J.T. Park. g, P.S. Kong. h, J.S. Yeom. i, M.H. Kim.
No. 2094, 3.50cor — Haitai Tigers: a, D.Y. Sun. b, J.B. Lee. c, J.S. Kim. d, S.H. Kim. e, Team logo. f, G.C. Lee. g, G.H. Cho. h, S.H. Kim. i, S.C. Lee.

1995, Mar. 25 Litho. Perf. 14
Sheets of 9, #a-i
2087-2094 A307 Set of 8 ... 140.00 77.50

Nature Paintings — A308

Designs: 1cor, Advancing Forward, by Maria Jose Zamora. 2cor, Natural Death, by Rafael Castellon. 4cor, Captives of Water, by Alvaro Gutierrez.

1995, Apr. 4 Litho. Perf. 14
2095-2097 A308 Set of 3 ... 4.50 2.25

British-Nicaragua Expedition, San Juan River — A309

1995, May 5
2098 A309 4cor multicolored ... 2.25 1.25

Boaco Festival A310

1995, May 10
2099 A310 4cor multicolored ... 2.25 1.25
Printed with se-tenant label.

Contemporary Paintings, by Armando Morales — A311

Designs: 50c, Ferry Boat. 1cor, Oliverio Castañeda, vert. 1.50cor, Sitting Nude, vert. 2cor, Señoritas at the Port of Cabeza. 2.50cor, The Automobile and Company, vert. 3cor, Bullfight, vert. 4cor, Still life.
15cor, Woman Sleeping.

1995, Oct. 31 Litho. Perf. 14
2100-2106 A311 Set of 7 ... 10.00 4.50
Size: 96x66mm
2107 A311 15cor multicolored ... 7.25 4.50

Louis Pasteur (1822-95) — A312

1995, Sept. 28 Litho. Perf. 14
2108 A312 4cor multicolored ... 2.25 1.25

First Place in Childrens' Painting Contest — A313

Nature scene, by Brenda Jarquin Gutierrez.

1995, Oct. 9
2109 A313 3cor multicolored ... 1.90 .90

Animals — A314

No. 2110: a, Crocodile. b, Opossum. c, Zahina. d, Guardatinale. e, Frog. f, Iguana. g, Macaw. h, Capybara. i, Vampire bat.
No. 2111, 15cor, Jaguar, vert. No. 2112, 15cor, Eagle, vert.

1995, Oct. 9
2110 A314 2.50cor Sheet of 9,
 #a.-i. 15.00 6.75
Souvenir Sheets
2111-2112 A314 Set of 2 14.50 9.00
 Issued: #2112, 4/15; #2110-2111, 10/9.

FAO, 50th
Anniv. — A315

1995, Oct. 16
2113 A315 4cor multicolored 2.25 1.25

UN, 50th
Anniv. — A316

No. 2114: a, 3cor, UN flag, doves, rainbow. b, 4cor, Rainbow, lion, lamb. c, 5cor, Rainbow, dove on soldier's helmet.
No. 2115, Children holding hands under sun, dove.

1995, Oct. 31
2114 A316 Strip of 3, #a.-c. 7.00 3.75
Souvenir Sheet
2115 A316 10cor multicolored 5.00 3.00
 No. 2114 is a continuous design.

Rotary Intl., 90th
Anniv. — A317

1995, Nov. 17
2116 A317 15cor Paul Harris,
 logo 7.25 4.50
Souvenir Sheet
2117 A317 25cor Old, new logos 11.50 7.50

Butterflies,
Moths — A318

No. 2118: a, Cyrestis camillus. b, Salamis cacta. c, Charaxes castor. d, Danaus formosa. e, Graphium ridleyanus. f, Hewitsonia boisduvali. g, Charaxes zoolina. h, Kallima cymodoce i, Precis westermanni. j, Papilo antimachus. k, Cymothoe sangaris. l, Papillo zalmoxis.
No. 2119, Danaus formosa, vert.

1995, Nov. 17
2118 A318 2.50cor Sheet of 12,
 #a.-l. 19.00 9.00
Souvenir Sheet
2119 A318 15cor multicolored 7.25 4.50

1996 Summer
Olympics,
Atlanta — A319

No. 2120: a, Michael Jordan. b, Heike Henkel. c, Linford Christie. d, Vitaly Chtcherbo. e, Heike Drechsler. f, Mark Tewksbury.
Pierre de Coubertin and: No. 2121, 20cor, Javelin thrower, horiz. No. 2122, 20cor, Runner.

1995, Dec. 1 **Litho.** *Perf. 14*
2120 A319 5cor Sheet of 6,
 #a.-f. 16.00 9.00
Souvenir Sheets
2121-2122 A319 Set of 2 19.00 12.00

John Lennon (1940-
80) — A320

1995, Dec. 8
2123 A320 2cor multicolored 1.75 .60
 Issued in sheets of 16.

Trains — A321

Designs: No. 2124, 2cor, Mombasa mail train, Uganda. No. 2125, 2cor, Steam locomotive, East Africa. No. 2126, 2cor, Electric locomotive, South Africa. No. 2127, 2cor, Beyer-Garrat steam locomotive, South Africa. No. 2128, 2cor, Beyer-Garrat steam locomotive, Rhodesia. No. 2129, 2cor, Class 30 steam locomotive, East Africa.
No. 2130: a, New York Central & Hudson River RR 4-4-0, #999, US. b, Australian Class 638, 4-6-2, Pacific. c, Baldwin 2-10-2, Bolivia. d, Vulcan 4-8-4, China. e, Paris-Orleans 4-6-2 Pacific, France. f, Class 062, 4-6-4, Japan.
No. 2131, 15cor, Siberian cargo train. No. 2132, 15cor, Midland 4-4-0 train, Great Britain. No. 2133, 15cor, Soviet steam locomotive.

1995, Dec. 11
2124-2129 A321 Set of 6 8.50 3.75
Miniature Sheet
2130 A321 4cor Sheet of 6,
 #a.-f. 14.00 7.25
Souvenir Sheets
2131-2133 A321 Set of 3 21.00 13.50
 #2131-2133 each contain one 85x28mm stamp.

Establishment of Nobel
Prize Fund,
Cent. — A322

No. 2134: a, Otto Meyerhof, medicine, 1922. b, Léon Bourgeois, peace, 1920. c, James Franck, physics, 1925. d, Leo Esaki, physics, 1973. e, Miguel Angel Asturias, literature, 1967. f, Henri Bergson, literature, 1927. g, Friedrich Bergius, chemistry, 1931. h, Klaus von Klitzing, physics, 1985. i, Eisaku Sato, Japan, peace, 1974.
No. 2135: a, Wilhelm C. Roentgen, physics, 1901. b, Theodor Mommsen, literature, 1902. c, Philipp E.A. von Lenard, physics, 1905. d, Walther H. Nernst, chemistry, 1920. e, Hans Spemann, medicine, 1935. f, Jean Paul Sartre, literature, 1964. g, T.S. Eliot, literature, 1948. h, Albert Camus, literature, 1957. i, Ludwig Quidde, peace, 1927. j, Werner Heisenberg, physics, 1932. k, Joseph Brodsky, literature, 1987. l, Carl von Ossietzky, peace, 1935.
No. 2136, 15cor, Sin-itiro Tomonaga, physics, 1965. No. 2137, 15cor, Johannes Stark, physics, 1919. No. 2138, 15cor, Oscar Arias Sánchez, peace, 1987.

1995, Dec. 11
2134 A322 2.50cor Sheet of 9,
 #a.-i. 14.50 6.75
2135 A322 2.50cor Sheet of
 12, #a.-l. 1.90 9.00
Souvenir Sheets
2136-2138 A322 Set of 3 21.00 13.50

Orchids — A323

No. 2139: a, Cattleya dowinana. b, Odontoglossum maculatum. c, Barkeria lindleyana. d, Rossioglossum grnde. e, Brassavpia digbyana. f, Miltonia schroederiana. g, Ondidium ornithorhynchum. h, Odontoglossum cervantesii. i, Chysis tricostata.
No. 2140: a, Lycaste auburn. b, Lembglossum cordatum. c, Cyrtochilum macranthum. d, Miltassia Aztec "Nalo." e, Masdevaltia ignea. f, Oncidium sniffen "Jennifer Dauro." g, Brassolaeliocattleya Alma Kee. h, Ascocenda blue boy. i, Phalaenopsis.
15cor, Odontogiossum uro-skinneri.

1995, Dec. 15
2139 A323 2.50cor Sheet of 9,
 #a.-i. 15.00 6.75
2140 A323 3cor Sheet of 9,
 #a.-i. 16.00 8.25
Souvenir Sheet
2141 A323 15cor multicolored 7.25 4.50

World War II,
50th
Anniv. — A324

No. 2142: a, Patton's troops crossing the Rhine. b, Churchill, Roosevelt, and Stalin at Yalta. c, US flag being raised at Iwo Jima. d, Marine infantry taking possession of Okinawa. e, US troops greeting Russian troops at Torgau. f, Liberation of concentration camps. g, Signing UN Charter, June 1945. h, Ships arriving at Tokyo after war's end.
10cor, German Bf-109 fighter plane.

1996, Jan. 24 **Litho.** *Perf. 14*
2142 A324 3cor Sheet of 8,
 #a.-h. + label 15.00 7.25
Souvenir Sheet
2143 A324 10cor multicolored 5.00 3.00

Miniature Sheet

Exotic Birds — A325

No. 2144: a, Paradisiaea apoda. b, Dryocopus galeatus. c, Psarisomus dalhousiae (g). d, Psarocolius montezuma. e, Halcyon pileata. f, Calocitta formosa. g, Ara chloroptera. h, Platycercus eximius. i, Polyplectron emphanum. j, Cariama cristata. k, Opisthocomus hoatzin. l, Coracias cyanogaster.
10cor, Dryocopus galeatus.

1996, Feb. 1
2144 A325 2cor Sheet of 12,
 #a.-l. 17.00 7.25
Souvenir Sheet
2145 A325 10cor multicolored 5.00 3.00

Town of
Rivas,
275th
Anniv.
A326

1995, Sept. 23 **Litho.** *Perf. 14*
2146 A326 3cor multi +label 1.80 .90

Christmas
A327

1995, Dec. 8
2147 A327 4cor multicolored 2.25 1.25

20th Century
Writers — A328

No. 2148 — Writer, country flag: a, C. Drummond de Andrade (1902-87), Brazil. b, Cesar Vallejo (1892-1938), Peru. c, J. Luis Borges (1899-1986), Argentina. d, James Joyce (1882-1941), Italy. e, Marcel Proust (1871-1922), France. f, William Faulkner (1897-1962), US. g, Vladmir Maiakovski (1893-1930), Russia. h, Ezra Pound (1885-1972), US. i, Franz Kafka (1883-1924), Czechoslovakia. j, T.S. Eliot (188-1965), United Kingdom. k, Rainer Rilke (1875-1926), Austria. l, Federico G. Lorca (1898-1936), Spain.

1995, Oct. 15 *Perf. 14½x14*
2148 A328 3cor Sheet of 12,
 #a.-l. 22.00 12.50

Classic Sailing
Ships — A329

No. 2149, 2.50cor: a, Mayflower, England. b, Young America, US. c, Preussen, Germany. d, Lateen-rigged pirate ship, Caribbean Sea. e, Cutty Sark, England. f, Square-rigged pirate ship, Caribbean Sea. g, Galeón, Spain. h, The Sun King, France. i, Santa Maria, Spain.
No. 2150, 2.50cor: a, HMS Bounty, England. b, The President, US. c, Prince William, Holland. d, Flying Cloud, US. e, Markab, Nile River, Egypt. f, Europa, Holland. g, Vasa, Sweden. h, Foochow junk, China. i, San Gabriel, Portugal.
No. 2151, 15cor, Passat, Germany. No. 2152, 15cor, Japanese junk, vert.

1996, Jan. 10 **Litho.** *Perf. 14*
Sheets of 9, #a-i
2149-2150 A329 Set of 2 29.00 13.50
Souvenir Sheets
2151-2152 A329 Set of 2 14.50 9.00

Visit of Pope
John Paul
II — A330

1996, Feb. 7
2153 A330 5cor multicolored 2.75 1.50

Puppies — A331

Various breeds: No. 2154, 1cor, Holding red leash in mouth. No. 2155, 1cor, With red bandanna around neck. No. 2156, 2cor, Spaniel playing with ball. No. 2157, 2cor, With dog biscuit in mouth. No. 2158, 3cor, Akita. No. 2159, 3cor, Bull dog. No. 2160, 4cor, With newspaper in mouth. No. 2161, 4cor, Dalmatian with cat.
No. 2162, 16cor, Bending down on front paws. No. 2163, 16cor, Poodle.

1996, Mar. 6
2154-2161 A331 Set of 8 13.00 7.25
Souvenir Sheets
2162-2163 A331 Set of 2 15.00 9.50

Famous
Women
A332

No. 2164: a, Indira Gandhi. b, Mme. Chiang Kai-shek. c, Mother Teresa. d, Marie Curie. e, Margaret Thatcher. f, Eleanor Roosevelt. g,

Eva Perón. h, Golda Meir. i, Violeta Barrios de Chamorro.
No. 2165, 15cor, Jacqueline Kennedy Onassis, vert. No. 2166, 15cor, Aung San Suu Kyi, vert. No. 2167, 15cor, Valentina Tereshkova, vert.

1996, Mar. 8   *Perf. 14x13½*
2164 A332 2.50cor Sheet of 9,
          #a.-i.   14.50 7.25
Souvenir Sheets
Perf. 13½x14
2165-2167 A332 Set of 3   22.00 13.50

Members of Baseball's Hall of Fame — A333

No. 2168 — Player, year inducted: a, Lou Gehrig, 1944. b, Rogers Hornsby, 1946. c, Mike Schmidt, 1995. d, Honus Wagner, 1936. e, Ty Cobb, 1936. f, Roberto Clemente, 1973. g, Babe Ruth, 1936. h, Johnny Bench, 1987. i, Tom Seaver, 1993.
10cor, Reggie Jackson, 1993.

1996, Mar. 15 Litho. Perf. 13½x14
2168 A333 4cor Sheet of 9,
          #a.-i.   21.00 14.00
Souvenir Sheet
2169 A333 10cor multicolored   9.75 9.25

1996 Summer Olympics, Atlanta — A334

Designs: 1cor, Takehide Nakatani, Japan. 2cor, Olympic Stadium, Tokyo, 1964. 3cor, Al Oerter, US, vert. 10cor, Discus thrower from ancient games.
No. 2174, 2.50cor, vert. — Gold medal winners in boxing: a, Andrew Maynard, U.S. b, Rudi Fink, Germany. c, Peter Lessov, Bulgaria. d, Angel Herrera, Cuba. e, Patrizio Oliva, Italy. f, Armando Martinez, Cuba. g, Slobodan Kacar, Yugoslavia. h, Teofilo Stevenson, Cuba. i, George Foreman, U.S.
No. 2175, 2.50cor — Events: a, Basketball. b, Baseball. c, Boxing. d, Long jump. e, Judo. f, Team handball. g, Volleyball. h, Water polo. i, Tennis.
25cor, Cassius Clay (Muhammad Ali), US.

1996, Mar. 28   *Perf. 14*
2170-2173 A334 Set of 4   9.25 7.25
Sheets of 9, #a-i
2174-2175 A334 Set of 2   29.00 20.00
Souvenir Sheet
2176 A334 25cor multicolored   12.00 11.00

Race Horses — A335

Carousel Horses A336

Race horses: 1cor, "Wave." 2cor, "Charming Traveler." 2.50cor, "Noble Vagabond." No. 2180, 3cor, "Golden Dancer," vert. No. 2181, 3cor, "Wave Runner." No. 2182, 4cor, "Ebony Champion." No. 2183, 4cor, "Wave Tamer."

Antique carousel horses: No. 2184a, Persian light infantry horse, 18th cent. b, Italian parade horse, 15th cent. c, German armored horse, 15th cent. d, Turkish light infantry horse, 17th cent.
16cor, "Proud Heart." 25cor, German armored horse, 16th cent.

1996, Apr. 15
2177-2183 A335 Set of 7   12.00 6.00
2184 A336 2cor Sheet of 4,
          #a.-d.   6.75 2.50
Souvenir Sheets
2185 A335 16cor multi   7.75 6.50
2186 A336 25cor multi   10.75 7.50

Marine Life — A337

No. 2187, 2.50cor: a, Butterflyfish (d). b, Barracuda (a). c, Manatee. d, Jellyfish. e, Octopus (b, d, f, g, h). f, Small yellow-striped fish. g, Lemon shark. h, Striped fish. i, Red fish.
No. 2188, 2.50cor: a, Reef shark. b, Diver, hammerhead shark (c, e). c, Moray eel (f). d, Macrela ojos de caballo (a, b, e). e, Hammerhead shark. f, Butterflyfish. g, Mediterranean grouper. h, Octopus, diff. i, Manta ray.
No. 2189, 20cor, Angelfish. No. 2190, 20cor, Saddleback butterflyfish.

1996, Apr. 29 Litho. Perf. 14
Sheets of 9, #a-i
2187-2188 A337 Set of 2   29.00 14.50
Souvenir Sheets
2189-2190 A337 Set of 2   19.00 13.00

Chinese Lunar Calendar A338

Year signs: a, Rat. b, Ox. c, Tiger. d, Hare. e, Dragon. f, Snake. g, Horse. h, Sheep. i, Monkey. j, Rooster. k, Dog. l, Boar.

1996, May 6
2191 A338 2cor Sheet of 12,
          #a.-l.   15.00 6.50
China'96.

Central American Integration System (SICA) — A339

1996, May 8   *Perf. 14½*
2192 A339 5cor multicolored   2.75 1.60

20th Century Events — A340

No. 2193: a, Russian revolution, 1917. b, Chinese revolution, 1945. c, Creation of the UN, 1945. d, Tearing down the Berlin Wall, 1989. e, World War I, vert. f, Creation of the State of Israel, 1948, vert. g, World War II, vert. h, 2nd Vatican Council, 1962-65, vert. i, Atom bombing of Hiroshima, 1945. j, Viet Nam War, 1962-73. k, Persian Gulf War, 1991. l, End of Apartheid, 1991.

1996   *Perf. 14*
2193 A340 3cor Sheet of 12,
          #a.-l. + label 22.00 11.50
Souvenir Sheet

New Year 1997 (Year of the Ox) A341

1996   **Litho.**   *Perf. 15x14*
2194 A341 10cor multicolored   5.00 3.00

Wuhan Huanghelou A342

1996, May 20 Litho. Perf. 14
2195 A342 4cor multicolored   2.25 1.50
China '96. No. 2195 was not available until March 1997. No. 2195 comes in a souvenir sheet of 1.

Red Parrot, by Ernesto Cardenal — A343

1996, June 5 Litho. Perf. 14½x14
2196 A343 4cor multicolored   1.75 1.25

Friendship Between Nicaragua and Republic of China — A344

Designs: 10cor, Painting, "Landscape with Bags," by Fredrico Nordalm, vert. 20cor, Dr. Lee Teng-Hui, Pres. of Republic of China and Violeta Barrios de Chamorro, President of Nicaragua.

Perf. 14½x14, 14x14½
1996, June 26   **Litho.**
2197 A344 10cor multicolored   3.25 1.75
2198 A344 20cor multicolored   5.75 3.50

Violeta Barrios de Chamorro, President, 1990-96 — A345

Serpentine Die Cut
1997, Jan. 27   **Litho.**
Self-Adhesive
2199 A345 3cor multicolored   1.25 .90
a.   Booklet pane of 9 + 2 labels 11.50
The peelable paper backing serves as a booklet cover.

"Plan International," Intl. Children's Organization, 60th Anniv. — A346

1997, Feb. 24 Serpentine Die Cut
Self-Adhesive
2200 A346 7.50cor multicolored   2.50 2.25
a.   Booklet pane of 12   31.00
The peelable paper backing serves as a booklet cover.

"Iberoamerica," Spanish-America Art Exhibition — A347

Painting, "Night with Two Figures," by Alejandro Aróstegui.

1998, May 8   *Perf. 13½*
2201 A347 7.50cor multicolored   2.60 2.00

Butterflies A348

No. 2202: a, Metamorpha stelenes. b, Erateina staudingeri. c, Premolis semirufa. d, Heliconius eisini. e, Phoebis phlea. f, Dione juno. g, Helicopis cupido. h, Catonephele numili. i, Anteos clorinde.
No. 2203, 25cor, Thecla coronata. No. 2204, 25cor, Ufefheisa bela.

1999, Mar. 15 Litho. Perf. 14
2202 A348 2.50cor Sheet of 9,
          #a.-i.   10.75 5.00
Souvenir Sheets
2203-2204 A348 Set of 2   17.00 15.50
Dated 1996.

Fauna of Central America — A349

No. 2205, 2cor: a, Red banded parrot. b, Sloth. c, Porcupine. d, Toucan. e, Howler monkey. f, Anteater. g, Kinkajou. h, Owl monkey. i, Red-footed land turtle. j, Red deer. k, Armadillo. l, Paca.
No. 2206, 2cor: a, Vulture. b, Tarantula. c, Palm viper. d, Ocelot. e, Fighting spider. f, Large fruit bat. g, Jaguar. h, Venomous tree frog. i, Viper. j, Grison. k, Rattlesnake. l, Puma.
No. 2207, 25cor, Tapir. No. 2208, 25cor, Caiman.

1999, Mar. 15 Sheets of 12, #a-l
2205-2206 A349 Set of 2   20.00 9.00
Souvenir Sheets
2207-2208 A349 Set of 2   14.50 9.00
Dated 1996.

Endangered Species — A350

No. 2209, 2.50cor: a, Owls, gorilla. b, Cheetahs. c, Giraffes. d, Gazelle, elephants. e, Elephants. f, Lion, okapi. g, Rhinoceros. h, Hippopotamus. i, Lion.
No. 2210, 2.50cor, vert: a, Lemurs. b, Blue gliding parrot. c, Toucan. d, Boa. e, Jaguar. f, Margay. g, Loris. h, White egret. i, Armadillo.
No. 2211, 2.50cor, vert: a, Prezwalski horse. b, Red deer. c, Zebra. d, Golden lion monkey. e, African elephant. f, Black bear. g, Tiger. h, Orangutan. i, Snow leopard.
25cor, Chimpanzee. 25.50cor, Panda, vert.

1999, Mar. 15 Sheets of 9, #a-i
2209-2211 A350 Set of 3   26.00 14.00
Souvenir Sheets
2212 A350 25cor multi   6.75 4.50
2213 A350 25.50cor multi   7.75 4.75
Dated 1996.

India's Independence, 50th Anniv. — A351

1998, Aug. 13 Litho. Perf. 14½
2214 A351 3cor blue & multi   1.00 .50
2215 A351 9cor brn yel & multi   2.00 1.50
Dated 1997.

Nature Reserves and Natl. Parks — A352

Designs: 1.50cor, Mombacho Volcano Nature Reserve. 2.50cor, La Flor Wildlife Refuge. 3cor, Zapatera Archipelago Natl. Park. 3.50cor, Miraflor Nature Reserve. 5cor, Cosigüina Volcano Natl. Park. 6.50cor, Masaya Volcano Natl. Park. 7.50cor, Juan Venado Island Nature Reserve. 8cor, Escalante Chacocente River Wildlife Refuge. 10cor, Protected Areas, Natl. Park System. 12cor, Trees, first Biosphere Reserve.

1998, Aug. 20		Perf. 10½	
2216 A352	1.50cor multicolored	.50	.25
2217 A352	2.50cor multicolored	.10	.45
2218 A352	3cor multicolored	1.00	.50
2219 A352	3.50cor multicolored	1.25	.60
2220 A352	5cor multicolored	1.75	.85
2221 A352	6.50cor multicolored	2.25	1.10
2222 A352	7.50cor multicolored	2.60	1.25
2223 A352	8cor multicolored	2.90	1.40
2224 A352	10cor multicolored	3.75	1.75
Nos. 2216-2224 (9)		16.10	8.15

Size: 65x95mm
Imperf

2225 A352	12cor multicolored	3.75	2.00

National Museum, Cent — A353

1998, Aug. 25
2226 A353 3.50cor Footprints	1.50	.60

Paintings by Rodrigo Peñalba (1908-1979) — A354

Designs: 2.50cor, "Descendimiento." 3.50cor, "Victoria y Piere With Child." 5cor, "Motherhood." 10cor, "El Güegüense."

1998, Aug. 26		Perf. 10½	
2227 A354	2.50cor multicolored	1.10	.45
2228 A354	3.50cor multicolored	1.40	.60
2229 A354	5cor multicolored	2.10	.85
Nos. 2227-2229 (3)		4.60	1.90

Size: 95x65mm
Imperf

2230 A354	10cor multicolored	3.25	1.75

Child's Painting, "Children Love Peace" — A355

1998, Aug. 28		Perf. 14½	
2231 A355	50c multicolored	1.50	.25

Dated 1997.

Publishing of "Profane Prose and Other Poems," by Rubén Darío (1867-1916), Cent. — A356

1998, Sept. 11		Perf. 10½	
2232 A356	3.50cor shown	1.40	.60
2233 A356	5cor Portrait	1.95	.85

Naturaleza '98 — A357

Painting by Bayron Gómez Chavarría.

1998, Sept. 25
2234 A357 3.50cor multicolored	1.50	.60

World Stamp Day — A358

1998, Oct. 9
2235 A358 6.50cor multicolored	2.25	1.10

Dialogue of Nicaragua — A359

1998, Oct. 12
2236 A359 5cor multicolored	1.80	.85

Famous Nicaraguan Women — A360

America issue: 3.50cor, Lolita Soriano de Guerrero (b. 1922), writer. 7.50cor, Violeta Barrios de Chamorro (b. 1929), former president.

1998, Oct. 16
2237 A360	3.50cor multicolored	1.25	.60
2238 A360	7.50cor multicolored	2.75	1.25

Universal Declaration of Human Rights, 50th Anniv. — A361

1998, Dec. 10		Perf. 13½	
2239 A361	12cor multicolored	3.75	2.10

Christmas A362

Nativity scenes: 50c, Molded miniature, vert. 1cor, Drawing on pottery, vert. 2cor, Adoration of the Magi. 3cor, Painting. 7.50cor, Painting of angel over modern village.

1998, Dec. 14		Perf. 14	
2240 A362	50c multicolored	.70	.25
2241 A362	1cor multicolored	.70	.25
2242 A362	2cor multicolored	.95	.35
2243 A362	3cor multicolored	1.40	.50
Nos. 2240-2243 (4)		3.75	1.35

Size: 95x64mm
Imperf

2244 A362	7.50cor multicolored	2.60	1.25

Dated 1997.

Managua Earthquake, 25th Anniv. (in 1997) — A363

Designs: 3cor, Managua in 1997, vert. 7.50cor, Devastation after earthquake in 1972. 10.50cor, Buildings toppling, clock, vert.

1998, Dec. 23
2245 A363	3cor multicolored	1.25	.50
2246 A363	7.50cor multicolored	2.75	1.25

Souvenir Sheet
2247 A363	10.50cor multicolored	3.75	1.75

Dated 1997.

Diana, Princess of Wales (1961-97) — A364

Designs: 5cor, Wearing hat. 7.50cor, Wearing tiara. 10cor, Wearing white dress.

1999, Apr. 29	Litho.	Perf. 13½	
2248-2250 A364	Set of 3	7.25	3.75

Nos. 2248-2250 were each issued in sheets of 6.

Butterflies A365

Designs: 3.50cor, Papilionidae ornithoptera. 8cor, Nymphalidae cepheuptychia. 12.50cor, Pieridae phoebis.

No. 2254: a, Nymphalidae eryphanis. b, Nymphalidae callicore. c, Nymphalidae hypolimmas. d, Nymphalidae precis. e, Papilionidae troides. f, Nymphalidae cithaerias. g, Papilionidae parides. h, Nymphalidae heliconius. i, Nymphalidae morpho. 15cor, Papilionidae papilio.

1999, Apr. 30		Perf. 14	
2251-2253 A365	Set of 3	8.00	4.25
2254 A365	9cor Sheet of 9, #a.-i.	26.00	14.00

Souvenir Sheet
2255 A365	15cor multicolored	4.50	3.25

Sailing Ships A366

Paintings: 2cor, Eagle, 1851, US. 4cor, Contest, 1800, US. 5cor, Architect, 1847, US. 10cor, Edward O'Brien, 1863, UK.

No. 2260, vert: a, HMS Rodney, 1830, UK. b, Boyne, 1700's, Great Britain. c, Castor, 1800's, UK. d, Mutin, 1800's, UK. e, Britainnia, 1820, UK. f, Gouden Leeuw, 1600, Holland. g, Hercules, 1600, Holland. h, Resolution, 1667, Great Britain. i, Royal George, 1756, Great Britain. j, Vanguard, 1700's, Great Britain. k, Prince Royal, 1600, Great Britain. l, Zeven Provincien, 1600, Holland.

No. 2261, 15cor, Pamir, 1905, US. No. 2262, 15cor, Great Expedition, 1700's, Great Britain.

1999, May 31	Litho.	Perf. 14x13½	
2256-2259 A366	Set of 4	7.75	3.75
		Perf. 14½x14¼	
2260 A366	3cor Sheet of 12, #a.-l.	15.00	6.50

Souvenir Sheets
Perf. 13½x14
2261-2262 A366	Set of 2	9.25	5.50

No. 2260 contains twelve 28x36mm stamps.

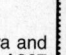

Flora and Fauna — A367

Designs: 5cor, Anteos clorinde. 6cor, Coereba flaveola. No. 2265, 7.50cor, Rynchops niger. No. 2266, 7.50cor, Chaetodon striatus. No. 2267, vert: a, Palm tree. b, Phaethon lepturus. c, Cinclocerthia ruficauda. d, Myadestes genibarbis. e, Rosa sinesis. f, Cyanophala bicolor. g, Delphinus delphis. h, Anolis carolinensis (I). i, Dynastes tityus. j, Heliconia psittacorum. k, Iguana iguana (j). l, Propona meander.

No. 2268, 10cor, Ceryle torquata, vert. No. 2269, 10cor, Anisotremus virginicus.

1999, June 14		Perf. 14x14¼	
2263-2266 A367	Set of 4	10.00	4.75
		Perf. 14¼x14	
2267 A367	5cor Sheet of 12, #a.-l.	22.00	11.00

Souvenir Sheet
2268-2269 A367	Set of 2	6.50	4.50

No. 2267 I is inscribed 3cor, but the editors believe the sheet was sold as sheet of 5cor stamps.

Birds — A368

Designs: 5cor, Eudyptes chrysocome. 5.50cor, Spheniscus magellanious. 6cor, Pygoscelis antarctica. 7.50cor, Magadyptes antipodes.

No. 2274, horiz.: a, Phalacrocorax punctatus featherstoni. b, Phalacrocorax bougainvillii. c, Anhinga anhinga. d, Phalacrocorax punctatus punctatus. e, Phalacrocorax sulcirostris. f, Pelecanus occidentalis.

No. 2275, 12cor, Aptenodytes forsteri, horiz. No. 2276, 12cor, Pygoscelis papua.

1999, May 25	Litho.	Perf. 14	
2270-2273 A368	Set of 4	6.00	4.00
2274 A368	6cor Sheet of 6, #a.- f.	13.00	6.00

Souvenir Sheets
2275-2276 A368	Set of 2	12.00	4.00

Dated 1998.

Dinosaurs A369

No. 2277: a, Sordes. b, Dimorphodon. c, Anurognathus. d, Rhamphorhynchus. e, Pterodaustro. f, Pteranodon.

No. 2278: a, Macroplata. b, Coelurus. c, "Stegosaurus." d, "Corythosaurus." e, Thadeosaurus. f, "Brachisaurus."

No. 2279, 12cor, Platecarpus. No. 2280, 12cor, Pterodactylus.

1999, June 1	Litho.	Perf. 14	
2277 A369	5cor Sheet of 6, #a.-f.	11.50	5.00
2278 A369	6cor Sheet of 6, #a.-f.	12.50	6.00

Souvenir Sheets
2279-2280 A369	Set of 2	7.50	5.25

Dated 1998. Stamp inscriptions on Nos. 2278c, 2278d and 2278f, and perhaps others, are incorrect or misspelled.

Trains — A370

Designs: 1cor, U25B, Rock Island Line. 5cor, C-630 Santa Fe Railroad. 6.50cor, Class D. D. 40 AX, Union Pacific Railroad. 7.50cor, F Series B. B. EMD, Maryland Department of Transportation.

No. 2285: a, CR Alco RS11. b, Metra EMD F40. c, British Columbia Railways GF6C. d,

Amtrak AEM7. e, C-40-9, Norfolk Southern. f, C-630, Reading Railroad.

No. 2286: a, British Columbia Railways GF6C, diff. b, Indian Railways WDM C-C. c, Class 421, Australia. d, Class M821, Australia. e, LRC B.B., Via Canada. f, GM Class X, Victorian Railways, Australia.

No. 2287, 15cor, Queen Victoria. No. 2288, 15cor, Donald Smith driving last spike of Trans-Canada Railway, vert.

1999, June 28 Litho. Perf. 14
2281-2284 A370 Set of 4 7.50 3.25
2285 A370 5cor Sheet of 6, #a.-
         f. 11.50 5.00
2286 A370 6cor Sheet of 6, #a.-
         f. 12.50 6.00
Souvenir Sheets
2287-2288 A370 Set of 2 9.25 5.00

Dated 1998. Stamp inscription on No. 2284, and perhaps others, is misspelled.

Mushrooms and Insects — A371

No. 2289: a, Tricholoma ustaloides, leaf beetle. b, Tricholoma pardinum, grasshopper. c, Amanita echinocephala, crickets. d, Tricholoma saponaceum, red-tipped clearwing moth. e, Amanita inaurata, hanging scorpionfly. f, Amanita rubescens, assassin bug.

No. 2290: a, Amanita citrina, banded agrion. b, Cryptotrama asprata, clouded yellow butterfly. c, Amanita gemmata, mayfly. d, Catathelasma imperiale, variable reed beetle. e, Collybia fusipes, black swallowtail caterpillar. f, Collybia butyracea, South African savannah grasshopper.

No. 2291, 12.50cor, Tricholomopsis rutilans, lesser cloverleaf weevil. No. 2292, 12.50cor, Tricholoma virgatum, rose weevil.

1999, Oct. 27 Litho. Perf. 13¼x13½
2289 A371 5.50cor Sheet of 6,
         #a.-f. 11.00 9.00
2290 A371 7.50cor Sheet of 6,
         #a.-f. 16.00 12.50
Souvenir Sheets
2291-2292 A371 Set of 2 8.00 7.50

Dated 1998.

Ballooning — A372

No. 2293, 12cor: a, Solo Spirit 3. b, Emblem of Breitling Orbiter 3, first balloon to make nonstop circumnavigation, 1999. c, ICO Global.

No. 2294, 12cor: a, Breitling Orbiter 3 over mountains. b, Leonardo da Vinci. c, Brian Jones and Bertrand Piccard, pilots of Breitling Orbiter 3.

No. 2295, 12cor: a, Tiberius Cavallo. b, Breitling Orbiter 3 on ground. c, Piccard and Jones, diff.

No. 2296, 12cor: a, Jones. b, Breitling Orbiter 3 in flight. c, Piccard.

No. 2297, 25cor, Jean-Francois Pilatre de Rozier. No. 2298, 25cor, Jean-Pierre Blanchard. No. 2299, 25cor, Madame Thible. No. 2300, 25cor, J. A. C. Charles.

1999, Nov. 12 Perf. 13½x13¼
Sheets of 3, #a-c
2293-2296 A372 Set of 4 42.50 24.00
Souvenir Sheets
2297-2300 A372 Set of 4 37.50 16.00

Dated 1998.

Orchids — A373

Designs: 2cor, Cattleya, skinneri. 4cor, Lycaste aromatica. 5cor, Odontoglossum cervantesii. 10cor, Brassia verrucosa.

No. 2305, 3cor: a, Odontoglossum rossii. b, Cattleya aurantiaca. c, Encyclia cordigera. d, Phragmipedium bessae. e, Brassavola nodosa. f, Cattleya forbesii.

No. 2306, 3cor: a, Barkeria spectabilis. b, Dracula erythrochaete. c, Cochleanthes discolor. d, Encyclia cochleata. e, Lycaste aromatica. f, Brassia maculata.

No. 2307, 25cor, Odontoglossum rossii, diff. No. 2308, 25cor, Phragmipedium longifolium.

1999, Nov. 10
2301-2304 A373 Set of 4 7.75 4.25
Sheets of 6, #a.-f.
2305-2306 A373 Set of 2 16.00 7.25
Souvenir Sheets
2307-2308 A373 Set of 2 14.50 8.00

Rubén Darío Natl. Theater, 30th Anniv. — A374

1999, Dec. 6 Perf. 13¼x13½
2309 A374 7.50cor multi 2.60 1.50

Inter-American Development Bank, 40th Anniv. — A375

1999, Nov. 18 Perf. 13¼
2310 A375 7.50cor multi 2.60 1.50

America Issue, A New Millennium Without Arms — A376

1999, Nov. 25 Perf. 13½
2311 A376 7.50cor multi 2.60 1.50

Japanese-Nicaraguan Friendship — A377

Designs: a, 3.50cor, Fishing boats, Puertos Cabezas. b, 9cor, Hospital. c, 5cor, Combine in field. d, 6cor, Japanese school. e, 7.50cor, Bridge on Pan-American Highway. f, 8cor, Aqueduct.

1999, Nov. 12 Perf. 13x13¼
2312 A377 Sheet of 6, #a.-f. 12.50 10.00

UPU, 125th Anniv. — A378

1999, Dec. 20 Litho. Perf. 13½
2313 A378 7.50cor multi 2.50 1.40

Cities of Granada and León, 475th Anniv. — A379

No. 2314 — Granada: a, City Hall. b, Guadalupe Church. c, Buildings on central square. d, Houses with porches. e, House of the Leones. f, El Consulado Street.

No. 2315 — León: a, Cathedral. b, Municipal theater. c, La Recolección Church. d, Rubén Dario Museum. e, Post and Telegraph office. f, Cural de Subtiava house.

1999, Dec. 13 Perf. 13x13½
2314 A379 3.50cor Sheet of 6,
         #a.-f. 8.00 6.00
2315 A379 7.50cor Sheet of 6,
         #a.-f. 16.00 12.00

Dogs and Cats — A380

Designs: 1cor, Azawakh. 2cor, Chihuahua. 2.50cor, Chocolate colorpoint Birman, horiz. 3cor, Norwegian Forest cat, horiz.

No. 2320: a, Clumber spaniel. b, Australian shepherd. c, German wire-haired pointer. d, Unnnamed. e, Ibizan hound. f, Norwegian elkhound.

No. 2321, horiz.: a, Blue European Shorthair. b, Turkish Angora. c, Red Tiffany. d, Persian. e, Calico Shorthair. f, Russian Blue.

No. 2322, 12cor, Braque du Bourbonnais. No. 2323, 12cor, Burmese, horiz.

Perf. 13¾x13½, 13½x13¾
2316-2319 A380 Set of 4 4.25 2.40
2320 A380 6cor Sheet of 6,
         #a-f 8.50 6.25
2321 A380 6.50cor Sheet of 6,
         #a-f 10.50 6.75
Souvenir Sheets
2322-2323 A380 Set of 2 7.50 6.50

No. 2322 contains one 42x56mm stamp; No. 2323 contains one 56x42mm stamp.

Trains — A381

Designs: 3cor, Class 470 APT-P, Great Britain. 4cor, X-2000, Sweden. 5cor, XPT, Australia. 10cor, High speed train, Great Britain.

No. 2328: a, Metro North B-25-7. b, Long Island Railroad EMD DE30. c, EMD F40 PHM-2C. d, Pennsylvania Railroad GG1. e, New Jersey Transit MK GP40 FH-2. f, Amtrak EMD F59 PHI.

No. 2329: a, DM-3, Sweden. b, EW 165, New Zealand. c, Class 87, Great Britain. d, Class 40, Great Britain. e, GE 6/6, Switzerland. f, Class 277, Spain.

No. 2330, Metra EMD P69PN-AC. No. 2331, Class 44, Great Britain.

2000, Aug. 21 Litho. Perf. 14
2324-2327 A381 Set of 4 8.00 6.00
Sheets of 6, #a-f
2328-2329 A381 3cor Set of
         2 16.00 10.00
Souvenir Sheets
2330-2331 A381 25cor Set of
         2 14.50 14.00

Marine Life — A382

Designs: 3.50cor, Great white shark. 5cor, Humpback whale. 6cor, Sea turtle. 9cor, Sperm whale.

No. 2336, 7.50cor: a, Puffer fish. b, Manta ray. c, Black grouper. d, Tiger grouper. e, Golden-tailed eel. f, Atlantic squid.

No. 2337, 7.50cor: a, Hawksbill turtle. b, Moon jellyfish. c, Caribbean reef shark. d, Turtle. e, Spotted dolphin. f, Southern sting ray.

No. 2338, Tiger shark. No. 2339, Spotted dolphins.

2000, Aug. 22 Perf. 14
2332-2335 A382 Set of 4 8.25 6.25
Sheets of 6, #a-f
2336-2337 A382 Set of 2 23.00 17.50
Souvenir Sheets
2338-2339 A382 25cor Set of
         2 14.50 14.00

Queen Mother, 100th Birthday A383

No. 2340: a, As young woman. b, In 1970. c, With King George VI. d, As old woman.

Litho. (Margin Embossed)
2000, July 25 Perf. 14
2340 A383 10cor Sheet of 4,
         #a-d + label 12.00 11.00
Souvenir Sheet
Perf. 13¾
2341 A383 25cor In 1948 7.50 7.50

No. 2341 contains one 38x51mm stamp.

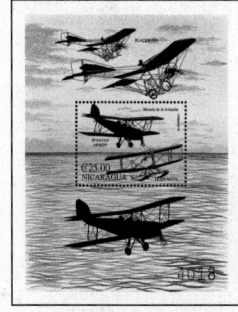

History of Aviation A384

No. 2342, 7.50cor: a, Montgolfier balloon (blue background), vert. b, Hawker Hart. c, Lysander. d, Bleriot and Fox Moth, vert. e, Harrier. f, VC10.

No. 2343, 7.50cor: a, Montgolfier balloon (tan background), vert. b, Bristol F2B. c, Jet Provost. d, Avro 504K and Redwing II trainer, vert. e, Hunter. f, Wessex.

No. 2344, 25cor, Spartan Arrow (top) and Tiger Moth. No. 2345, 25cor, Tiger Moth (top) and Spartan Arrow.

2000, July 27 Litho. Perf. 14½x14
Sheets of 6, #a-d
2342-2343 A384 Set of 2 30.00 25.00
Souvenir Sheets
2344-2345 A384 Set of 2 14.50 14.00

Size of Nos. 2342a, 2342d, 2343a, 2343d: 41x60mm.

Birds — A385

Designs: 5cor, Cotinga amabilis. 7.50cor, Galbula ruficauda. 10cor, Guiraca caerulea. 12.50cor, Momotus momota.

No. 2350: a, Ara macao. b, Amazona ochrocephala. c, Chloroceryle americana. d, Archilocus colubris. e, Pharamachrus mocinno. f, Ramphastos sulfuratus. g, Coereba flaveola. h, Piculus rubiginosus. i, Passerina ciris. j, Busarellus nigricollis.

No. 2351, 25cor, Aulacorhynchus prasinus. No. 2352, 25cor, Ceryle alcyon.

2000, Aug. 23   *Perf. 14*
2346-2349 A385   Set of 4   10.25   8.25
2350 A385 3cor Sheet of 10,
    #a-j   13.00   8.25
Souvenir Sheets
2351-2352 A385   Set of 2   14.50   14.00

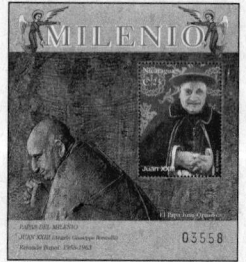

Space Exploration — A386

No. 2353, 5cor: a, Donald K. Slayton. b, M. Scott Carpenter. c, Walter M. Schirra. d, John H. Glenn, Jr. e, L. Gordon Cooper. f, Virgil I. Grissom. g, Mercury Redsone 3 rocket. h, Alan B. Shepard.
No. 2354, 5cor, horiz.: a, Recovery of Mercury 8. b, View of Earth from space. c, Carpenter in life raft. d, Shepard in water. e, USS Intrepid. f, Friendship 7. g, Mercury 9 splashdown. h, Recovery of Mercury 6.
No. 2355, 25cor, Glenn, diff. No. 2356, 25cor, Shepard, horiz.

2000, Aug. 25   Litho.
Sheets of 8, #a-h
2353-2354 A386   Set of 2   29.00   20.00
Souvenir Sheets
2355-2356 A386   Set of 2   14.50   13.50

Millennium — A387

No. 2357: a, Pope Leo XIII. b, Rerum Novarum. c, Pope Pius X. d, Revision of ecclesiatic music. e, Pope Benedict XV. f, Canonization of Joan of Arc. g, Pope Pius XI. h, Establishment of Radio Vatican. i, Pope John XXIII. j, Peace symbol. k, Pope Paul VI. l, Arms of Paul VI. m, Pope John Paul I. n, Lamb and cross. o, Pope John Paul II. p, Globe, hands holding dove.
No. 2358, 25cor, John XXIII. No. 2359, 25cor, John Paul II.

2000, Sept. 7   *Perf. 13¼*
2357 A387 3cor Sheet of 16,
    #a-p + label   21.00   16.00
Souvenir Sheets
2358-2359 A387   Set of 2   14.50   14.00
No. 2357 contains sixteen 30x40mm stamps.

Butterflies — A388

No. 2360, 8cor: a, Catonephele numilla esite. b, Marpesia marcella. c, Heliconius hecalesia. d, Actinote thalia anteas. e, Doxocopa larentia cherubina. f, Napeogenes tolosa mombachoensis.
No. 2361, 9cor: a, Heliconius cydno galanthus. b, Nessaea agiaura. c, Godyris zavaleta sosunga. d, Caligo atreus dionysos. e, Morpho amatonte. f, Eryphanis polyxena lycomedon.
No. 2362, 25cor, Papilio garamas. No. 2363, 25cor, Cithaerias menander.

2000, Sept. 27   *Perf. 14*
Sheets of 6, #a-f
2360-2361 A388   Set of 2   33.00   27.50
Souvenir Sheets
2362-2363 A388   Set of 2   14.50   14.00

20th Century National Leaders A389

No. 2364, 5cor: a, Kemal Ataturk, dam. b, Ataturk, Turkish flag, horiz. c, John F. Kennedy, wife Jacqueline, Soviet missiles, horiz. d, John F. Kennedy, rocket. e, Winston Churchill, bomb explosion. f, Churchill, airplane, horiz. g, Jomo Kenyatta, tribesman, animals, horiz. h, Kenyatta, Mt. Kenya.
No. 2365, 5cor: a, Indira Gandhi. b, Indira Gandhi, soldier, elephant, horiz. c, Ronald Reagan, airplanes, horiz. d, Reagan, American flags. e, Lenin. f, Lenin, hammer and sickle, horiz. g, Charles de Gaulle, Eiffel Tower, horiz. h, De Gaulle, monument.
No. 2366, 25cor, Chiang Kai-shek. No. 2367, 25cor, Theodore Roosevelt.

2000, Oct. 5   *Perf. 14*
Sheets of 8, #a-h
2364-2365 A389   Set of 2   29.00   21.00
Souvenir Sheets
2366-2367 A389   Set of 2   14.50   13.50
Horizontal stamps are 56x42mm.

Lions Intl. A390

No. 2368, horiz.: a, Melvin Jones and other founding members, Chicago, 1917. b, Old headquarters building, Chicago. c, Helen Keller and dog. d, UN Secretary General Kofi Annan greeting Lions Intl. Pres. Kajit Hadananda. e, Jones and globe. f, André de Villiers, winner of 1998-99 Peace Poster contest.

2000, Oct. 26   Litho.
2368 A390   5cor Sheet of 6,
    #a-f   14.50   11.50
Souvenir Sheet
2369 A390 25cor Melvin Jones   7.25   6.75

Rotary Intl. A391

No. 2370: a, Clowns and child in Great Britain. b, Polio vaccination in Egypt. c, Burkina Faso natives at well. d, School for girls in Nepal. e, Assisting the disabled in Australia. f, Discussing problem of urban violence.

2000, Oct. 26   *Perf. 14*
2370 A391   7cor Sheet of 6,
    #a-f   11.00   8.25
Souvenir Sheet
2371 A391 25cor Rotary emblem   7.25   7.00

Campaign Against AIDS — A392

2000, Dec. 1   Litho.   *Perf. 13¼*
2372 A392 7.50cor multi   2.10   1.60

Third Conference of States Signing Ottawa Convention A393

Designs: 7.50cor, People, world map. 10cor, People opposing land mines on globe.

2001, Sept. 18   *Perf. 13x13½*
2373-2374 A393   Set of 2   4.25   3.25

Miniature Sheet

Bridges Built With Japanese Assistance — A394

No. 2375: a, 6.50cor, Tamarindo Bridge. b, 7.50cor, Ochomogo Bridge. c, 9cor, Gil González Bridge. d, 10cor, Las Lajas Bridge. e, 12cor, Río Negro Bridge.

2001, Oct. 23   *Perf. 13x13¼*
2375 A394   Sheet of 5, #a-e, +
    label   9.50   8.25

World Post Day — A395

2001, Nov. 21   *Perf. 13½*
2376 A395 6.50cor multi   1.80   1.40
Dated 2000.

America Issue — Old Léon Ruins, UNESCO World Heritage Site — A396

2001, Nov. 23   *Perf. 13½*
2377 A396 10cor multi   2.40   2.00

Order of Piarists in Nicaragua, 50th Anniv. — A397

       Perf. 13¼x13½
2001, Nov. 27   Litho.
2378 A397 7cor multi   1.75   1.40
Dated 2000.

Miniature Sheet

Endangered Wildlife — A398

No. 2379: a, 5cor, Rhamphastos swaisonii. b, 6.50cor, Amazona auropalliata. c, 8cor, Buteo magnirostris. d, 9cor, Atteles geoffroyi. 10cor, Leopardus wiedii. 12cor, Puma concolor.

2001, Nov. 27   *Perf. 13¼x13*
2379 A398   Sheet of 6, #a-f   9.75   7.50
Dated 2000.

SOS Children's Villages, 50th Anniv. — A399

2001, Dec. 6   *Perf. 13¼x13½*
2380 A399 5.50cor multi   1.50   1.00
Dated 2000.

Miguel Cardinal Obando Bravo — A400

2002, Jan. 3   Litho.   *Perf. 13½*
2381 A400 6.50cor multi   1.75   1.25

Souvenir Sheet

Friendship Between Nicaragua and People's Republic of China — A401

No. 2382: a, 3cor, President's House, Managua. b, 7.50cor, Ministry of Foreign Affairs Building, Managua.

2002, Jan. 4   Litho.   *Perf. 13x13¼*
2382 A401   Sheet of 2, #a-b   2.50   2.00

Visit of UN Secretary General Kofi Annan to Nicaragua — A402

2002, Mar. 15   Litho.   *Perf. 13¼*
2383 A402 14cor multi   2.75   2.50

Sister Maria Romero — A403

2002, Apr. 9   *Perf. 13x13¼*
2384 A403 7.50cor multi   2.00   1.50

Discovery of Nicaragua, 500th Anniv. — A404

Design: 12cor, Natives watching ships on horizon, vert.

2002, Sept. 12   Litho.   Perf. 13x13¼
2385 A404 7.50cor shown   2.00 1.50

Souvenir Sheet
Perf. 13¼x13
2386 A404 12cor multi   3.25 2.00

America Issue - Youth, Education and Literacy — A405

2002, Nov. 29   Litho.   Perf. 13¼x13
2387 A405 7.50cor multi   2.00 1.75

Canonization of St. Josemaría Escrivá de Balaguer — A406

2002, Nov. 28   Perf. 13x13¼
2388 A406 2.50cor multi   1.00 .50

Port of Corinto — A407

2002, Dec. 10
2389 A407 5cor multi   1.50 1.00

Managua Earthquake, 30th Anniv. — A408

Pictures of earthquake damage: 3.50cor, Avenida del Mercado Central. 7.50cor, Managua Cathedral, vert.

Perf. 13¼x13½, 13½x13¼
2002, Dec. 13
2390-2391 A408 Set of 2   3.25 2.50

Visit of Grand Duke Henri and Princess Maria Teresa of Luxembourg — A409

2003, Feb. 5   Perf. 13¼x13
2392 A409 12cor multi   3.00 2.50

Paintings — A410

Designs: 3cor, En Diriamba de Nicaragua, Capturaronme Amigo, by Roger Pérez de la Rocha. 5cor, San Gabriel Arcangel, by Orlando Sobalvarro. 6.50cor, Ava Fénix, by Alejandro Aróstegui. 7.50cor, Abstracción de Frutas, by Leonel Vanegas. 8cor, Suite en Turquesa y Azules, by Bernard Dreyfus, horiz. 9cor, Ana III, by Armando Morales, horiz. 10cor, Coloso IV, by Arnoldo Guillén, horiz.

Perf. 14x13½, 13½x14
2003, Oct. 23   Litho.
2393-2399 A410 Set of 7   11.50 10.00

Souvenir Sheet

Pontificate of Pope John Paul II, 25th Anniv. — A411

No. 2400: a, 3cor, Pope wearing zucchetto. b, 10cor, Pope wearing miter.

2003, Oct. 28   Litho.   Perf. 13¼x13
2400 A411 Sheet of 2, #a-b   3.25 2.50

Christian Brothers (La Salle Order) in Nicaragua, Cent. — A412

Designs: 3cor, San Juan de Dios Hospice, horiz. 5cor, Brother Octavio de Jesús. 6.50cor, Brother Bodrán Marie. 7.50cor, Brother Agustin Hervé. 9cor, Brother Vauthier de Jesús. 10cor, Father Mariano Dubón. 12cor, St. Jean-Baptiste de la Salle.

Perf. 13½x14, 14x13½
2003, Nov. 14   Litho.
2401-2406 A412 Set of 6   9.50 7.00

Souvenir Sheet
2407 A412 12cor multi   2.75 2.50

Insects — A413

No. 2408, 6.50cor: a, Fulgora laternaria. b, Acraephia perspicillata. c, Copidocephala guttata. d, Pterodictya reticularis. e, Phrictus quinquepartitus. f, Odontoptera carrenoi.
No. 2409, 8cor: a, Golofa pizarro. b, Phaneus pyrois. c, Plusiotis aurigans. d, Polyphylla concurrens. e, Dynastes hercules septentrionalis. f, Phaneus demon excelsus.

2003, Nov. 19   Perf. 13x13½
Sheets of 6, #a-f
2408-2409 A413 Set of 2   20.00 16.00

Contemporary Crafts — A414

Designs: 3cor, Marble sculpture, vert. 5cor, Dolls. 6.50cor, Balsa wood fish and birds. 7.50cor, Cord and jipijapa hats. 8cor, Ceramics. 9cor, Saddle. 10cor, Clay rendition of Léon Cathedral.

Perf. 14x13½, 13½x14
2003, Nov. 20
2410-2416 A414 Set of 7   11.50 8.50

Lake and River Mail Steamships — A415

Designs: 3cor, Victoria. 5cor, Irma. 6.50cor, Hollenbeck. 7.50cor, Managua.

2003, Nov. 28   Perf. 13½x14
2417-2420 A415 Set of 4   5.50 4.00

America Issue - Flora and Fauna — A416

Designs: 10cor, Corytophanes cristatus. 12.50cor, Guaiacum sanctum.

2003, Dec. 4   Perf. 13x13¼
2421-2422 A416 Set of 2   4.75 4.00

San Juan del Sur, 150th Anniv. — A417

2003, Dec. 9   Litho.
2423 A417 10cor multi   2.25 1.75

Miniature Sheet

Toyota Motor Vehicles — A418

No. 2424: a, 1936 Model AA. b, 1936 Model AB Phaeton. c, 1947 Model SA. d, 1951 Model BJ. e, 1955 Model Crown RSD. f, 1958 Model FJ28VA.

2003, Dec. 11
2424 A418 7.50cor Sheet of 6, #a-f   9.00 6.75

Publication of Tierras Solares, by Rubén Darío, Cent. — A419

2004, June 22   Perf. 13x13¼
2425 A419 10cor multi   2.25 1.75

Flora — A420

Designs: 3cor, Tabebuia rosea. 5cor, Cassia fistula. 6.50cor, Delonix regia.

2004, June 24
2426-2428 A420 Set of 3   4.00 3.25

America Issue - Environmental Protection — A421

Designs: No. 2429, 7.50cor, Bosawas Río Bocay Biosphere Reserve. No. 2430, 7.50cor, Cerro Kilambé Nature Reserve.

2004, June 30
2429-2430 A421 Set of 2   3.75 3.25

2004 Summer Olympics, Athens — A422

Designs: 7.50cor, Track athletes. 10cor, Swimmers. 12cor, Rifleman.

2004, Aug. 13   Perf. 13¼x13
2431-2433 A422 Set of 3   6.25 5.00

Central American Student's Games, Managua — A423

Designs: 3cor, Judo. 5cor, Soccer, baseball. 6.50cor, High jump, swimming.

2004, Sept. 17
2434-2436 A423 Set of 3   4.25 3.00

Birds — A424

Designs: 5cor, Selenidera spectabilis. 6.50cor, Nycticorax nycticorax. 7.50cor, Caracara plancus. 10cor, Myiozetetes similis.

2004, Sept. 28   Litho.
2437-2440 A424 Set of 4   7.00 5.00

Granada Railroad Station — A425

2004, Oct. 8   Perf. 13x13¼
2441 A425 3cor multi   1.00 .50

Tourist Attractions A426

Designs: No. 2442, 7.50cor, Río Tapou, Río San Juan Forest Refuge. No. 2443, 7.50cor, Mombacho Volcano Natural Reserve.

2004, Oct. 12
2442-2443 A426 Set of 2   3.50 2.50

Contemporary Paintings — A427

Designs: 3cor, Frutas Ocultas, by Federico Nordalm. 7.50cor, Nicaraguapa, by Efrén Medina, vert. 10cor, Bambues, by Genaro Lugo.

2004, Nov. 4   Perf. 13x13¼, 13¼x13
2444-2446 A427 Set of 3   5.00 3.75

Dogma of the Immaculate Conception, 150th Anniv. — A428

2004, Dec. 6   *Perf. 13¼x13*
2447 A428 3cor multi   1.30 1.00

Pablo Neruda (1904-73), Poet — A429

2004, Dec. 16
2448 A429 7.50cor multi   1.75 1.25

Publication of *Songs of Life and Hope,* by Rubén Darío, Cent. — A430

2005, Feb. 7   Litho.   *Perf. 13¼x13½*
2449 A430 7.50col multi + label   1.80 1.40

Souvenir Sheet

Nicaragua — Japan Diplomatic Relations, 70th Anniv. — A431

No. 2450: a, 3col, Adult volunteer teaching student. b, 7.50col, Momotombo Volcano. c, 10col, Vado Bridge, Bocana de Paiwas. d, 12col, Flowers.

2005, Feb. 21   *Perf. 13x13¼*
2450 A431   Sheet of 4, #a-d   7.00 5.50

Orchids — A432

Designs: 3.50cor, Eleanthus hymeniformis. 5cor, Laelia superbens. 6.50cor, Cattleya aurentiaca. 7.50cor, Bletia roezlii. 10cor, Dimerandra emarginata. 12cor, Epidendrum werckleii.
25cor, Cyhysis tricostata.

2005   Litho.   *Perf. 13¼x13*
2451-2456 A432   Set of 6   9.25 6.75
Souvenir Sheet
2457 A432 25cor multi   4.25 3.75

Endangered Reptiles and Amphibians A433

Designs: 3cor, Dendrobates pumilio. 6.50cor, Drymodius melanotropis. 7.50cor, Cochranella granulosa. 10cor, Bolitoglossa mombachoensis. 12cor, Caiman crocodilus. 15cor, Polychrus gutturosus.
25cor, Lepidochelys olivacea.

2005   Litho.   *Perf. 13x13¼*
2458-2463 A433   Set of 6   10.50 8.50
Souvenir Sheet
2464 A433 25cor multi   4.25 3.75

Intl. Year of Microcredit — A434

2005   Litho.   *Perf. 13¼x13*
2465 A434 3.50cor multi   1.10 .45

Europa Stamps, 50th Anniv. — A435

Designs: Nos. 2466, 2470a, 14cor, Morpho peleides. Nos. 2467, 2470b, 14cor, Amazona autumnalis. Nos. 2468, 2470c, 15cor, Rubén Darío Monument. Nos. 2469, 2470d, 25cor, Antigua Cathedral, Managua.

2005, Dec. 12   *Perf. 13⅜x13½*
2466-2469 A435   Set of 4   12.00 10.00
Souvenir Sheet
Imperf
2470 A435   Sheet of 4, #a-d   14.50 13.50
No. 2470 contains four 40x30mm stamps.

Souvenir Sheet

Second Intl. Poetry Festival, Granada A436

No. 2471: a, 4.50cor, Jose Coronel Urtecho (1906-94), poet. b, 7cor, Guadalupe Church, 1856. c, 10cor, Church of St. Francis. d, 12cor, Joaquin Pasos (1914-47), poet.

2006   Litho.   *Perf. 14*
2471 A436   Sheet of 4, #a-d   6.75 5.25

Environmental Protection A437

Designs: 4.50cor, Casmerodius albus. 11.50cor, Amazilia tzacatl. 13.50cor, Jacana spinosa. 14.50cor, Mico River.

2007   Litho.   *Perf. 13x13¼*
2472-2475 A437   Set of 4   8.50 7.00

Gen. Augusto C. Sandino (1893-1934) — A438

Various photographs of Sandino: 8.50cor, 10.50cor, 12.50cor.

2007   *Perf. 13¼x13*
2476-2478 A438   Set of 3   6.50 5.25

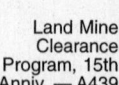

Land Mine Clearance Program, 15th Anniv. — A439

2007   Litho.   *Perf. 13x13¼*
2479 A439 19cor multi   3.75 3.25

Literacy Campaign, 27th Anniv. — A440

Various literacy campaign workers and students: 1cor, 2cor, 2.50cor, 4.50cor.

2007   *Perf. 13¼x13*
2480-2483 A440   Set of 4   3.75 2.10

Second Edition of "Cantos de Vida y Esperanza," by Rubén Darío — A441

Designs: 4cor, Baptismal font, León Cathedral. 10cor, Photograph of Darío at age 5. 13.50cor, Birthplace of Darío, monument. 16cor, Portrait of Darío as diplomat in Spain.

2007, May 4   Litho.   *Perf. 13¼x13*
2484-2487 A441   Set of 4   8.50 7.00

Port Facilities — A442

Designs: 1cor, Port of Corinto. 2cor, Port of Rama. 5cor, Port of Granada. 10cor, Port of San Juan del Sur. 15cor, Port of Sandino. 25cor, Salvador Allende Port.

2009, Apr. 28   Litho.   *Perf. 10½*
2488-2493 A442   Set of 6   10.50 8.25

Gen. Augusto C. Sandino (1895-1934) — A443

Designs: No. 2494, 10cor, Sandino and wife, Blanca Aráuz. No. 2495, 10cor, Statue of Sandino.

2009, May 18   Litho.   *Perf. 10½*
2494-2495 A443   Set of 2   4.25 3.50

Víctor Raúl Haya de la Torre (1895-1979), President of Peruvian Constitutional Assembly — A444

2009, May 27   Litho.   *Perf. 10½*
2496 A444 12cor multi   2.40 1.90

Nicaraguan Social Security Institute, 50th Anniv. — A445

50th anniversary emblem and: 4cor, Nurse examining child. 14cor, Hands, map of Nicaragua. 16cor, Elderly women. 25cor, Workman wearing air filter.

2009, July 30   Litho.   *Perf. 10½*
2497-2500 A445   Set of 4   11.50 9.00

A446

Sandinista Revolution, 30th Anniv. — A447

Designs: 4cor, General Augusto C. Sandino. 5cor, Victory celebration, July 19, 1979. 60cor, Soldier.

2009, July 30
2501 A446   4cor multi   .75   .75
2502 A446   5cor multi   1.50 1.00
2503 A447 60cor multi   10.50 9.75
   Nos. 2501-2503 (3)   12.75 11.50

Caribbean Coast Autonomy Law, 22nd Anniv. — A448

Designs: 6.50cor, Creole children. 10cor, Map and Mayagna people. 14cor, Garifuna people, vert. 60cor, Dancers wrapping ribbons around pole.

2009, Oct. 9   Litho.   *Perf. 10½*
2504-2507 A448   Set of 4   16.00 14.00

Central American Court of Justice, 17th Anniv. — A449

2009
2508 A449 25cor multi   3.25 2.75

Central Bank of Nicaragua, 50th Anniv. — A450

Designs: No. 2509, 15cor, 50th anniversary emblem. No. 2510, 15cor, Nicaraguan banknotes.

2010, Jan. 6
2509-2510 A450   Set of 2   4.25 3.25

National Assembly, 25th Anniv. — A451

2010, Jan. 9
2511 A451 60cor multi   9.75 9.25

Venezuelan Independence, Bicent. — A452

2010
2512 A452 60cor multi   4.25 4.00

Mexican Revolution, Cent. — A453

Mexican Independence, Bicent. — A454

2010   *Imperf.*
2513 A453   10cor multi   2.00 1.75
2514 A454   13.50cor multi   3.00 2.60

Miniature Sheet

Ecuadoran Independence, Bicent. — A455

No. 2515: a, 50c, Manuel Rodríguez de Quiroga. b, 4cor, Eugenio de Santa Cruz y Espejo. c, 5cor, Juan Salinas. d, 6.50cor, José Joaquín Olmedo. e, 10cor, Juan Pio Montufar.

2010   *Perf. 10½*
2515 A455   Sheet of 5, #a-e, + label   5.25 3.00

Postal Union of the Americas, Spain and Portugal (UPAEP), Cent. — A456

2011, Sept. 1
2516 A456   12cor multi   2.50 1.90

Bernardo O'Higgins (1778-1842), Chilean General — A457

2011
2517 A457   15cor multi   2.10 1.75

José de San Martín (1778-1850), Argentine General — A458

2011
2518 A458   25cor multi   3.25 2.75
Argentine independence, bicent.

Souvenir Sheet

Preservation of Polar Regions and Glaciers — A459

2011   **Litho.**
2519 A459   50.50cor multi   8.75 8.00

Miniature Sheet

Solidarity Hospital, Managua A460

No. 2520: a, 4cor, Woman in chair holding infant in neo-natal unit. b, 6.50cor, Nurse's station. c, 7.50cor, Woman in chair receiving chemotherapy. d, 8cor, Pediatrician, mother and child. e, 12cor, Woman sitting on hospital bed holding infant. f, 25cor, Pediatrics unit equipment.

2011   *Perf. 10½*
2520 A460   Sheet of 6, #a-f   13.50 10.50

Central American Parliament, 20th Anniv. — A461

2011, Aug. 9   **Litho.**   *Perf. 10½*
2521 A461   16cor multi   3.00 3.00

Colombian Independence, Bicent. (in 2010) — A462

2012, Feb. 29   **Litho.**   *Perf. 10½*
2522 A462   50.50cor multi   5.50 5.25
Dated 2011.

Paintings — A463

Designs: No. 2523, 50c, La Embarcación, by Leonel Vanegas. No. 2524, 50c, La Princesa Está Triste, by Vanegas. No. 2525, 1cor, La Montaña Mágica, by Leoncio Sáenz. No. 2426, 1cor, La Gigantona I, by Sáenz. No. 2527, 2cor, No Olvides Monimbó, by Roger Pérez de la Rocha. No. 2528, 2cor, Campesinas, by Pérez de la Rocha. 10cor, Amanecer, by Arnoldo Guillén. 13.50cor, Esta Tierra ni se Vende, ni se Rinde, Guillén. 15cor, Metamorfosis de las Mujeres del Cua, by

Orlando Sobalvarro. 16cor, Verano, by Sobalvarro.
2012, Sept. 6
2523-2532 A463   Set of 10   10.75 7.25

Miniature Sheet

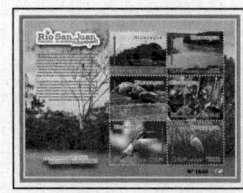

San Juan River A464

No. 2533: a, 1cor, El Castillo. b, 4cor, River and its shores. c, 5cor, Crocodylus acutus. d, 10cor, Ctenosaura similis. e, 14cor, Mellisuga helenae. f, 50cor, Egretta alba.

2012, Sept. 6
2533 A464   Sheet of 6, #a-f   12.50 10.00

Miniature Sheet

Diplomatic Relations Between Nicaragua and South Korea, 50th Anniv. — A465

No. 2534: a, 4cor, Solar panels. b, 5cor, Water pump, Juigalpa. c, 13.50cor, Machinery in factory. d, 25cor, Building in free trade zone.

2012, Sept. 30
2534 A465   Sheet of 4, #a-d   6.50 5.50

Souvenir Sheet

Cádiz Constitution (First Spanish Constitution), Bicent. — A466

2012, Oct. 16
2535 A466   100cor multi   12.50 12.00

Souvenir Sheet

Spanish Agency for Intl. Development Cooperation, 25th Anniv. — A467

2013, Nov. 21   **Litho.**   *Perf. 10½*
2536 A467   25cor multi   3.25 2.75

America Issue — A468

Flags and Hugo Chávez (1954-2013), President of Venezuela: 5cor, Waving. 10cor, Holding map of South America.

2014, Mar. 5   **Litho.**   *Perf. 10½*
2537-2538 A468   Set of 2   3.50 2.25

Miniature Sheet

International Day of Older Persons — A469

No. 2539: a, 50c, Man using computer. b, 1cor, Man and woman with guitars. c, 4cor, Teacher and students in classroom. d, 7cor, Dancers. e, 13.50cor, Women holding greeting cards. f, 20cor, People exercising.

2015, Oct. 1   **Litho.**   *Perf. 10½*
2539 A469   Sheet of 6, #a-f   7.00 3.50

Rubén Darío (1867-1916), Poet — A470

2015, Oct. 15   **Litho.**   *Perf. 13½*
2540 A470   60cor multi   5.75 4.50

Tourism — A471

Designs: 50c, Icon of St. Dominic de Guzmán (1170-1221), patron saint of Managua. 1cor, Icon of St. Geronimo, patron saint of Masaya. 2cor, Nacatamal. 3cor, Baho. 4cor, Black ceramics of Jinotega. 5cor, Carved balsa wood birds. 6.50cor, Palo de Mayo dancers. 13.50cor, El Güegüense street theater performance.

2017, Oct. 1   **Litho.**   *Perf. 11¾*
2541-2548 A471   Set of 8   *18.00 16.00*

Miniature Sheet

Managua, 200th Anniv. — A472

No. 2549: a, 1cor, Nicaraguan Institute of Social Security Building, 2019. b, 1.50cor, Nicaraguan Institute of Social Security Building, 1956. c, 3cor, National Stadium, 2017. d, 5cor, National Stadium, 1948. e, 6cor, Rubén Darío National Theater, 2019. f, 10cor, Rubén Darío National Theater, 1969. g, 20cor, Communications Building, 2019. h, 30cor, Communications Building, 1931.

2019, May 21   **Litho.**   *Perf. 13½x13*
2549 A472   Sheet of 8, #a-h   14.00 8.25

Central Bank of Nicaragua, 60th Anniv. — A473

Denominations: 5cor, 10cor, 20cor, 60cor.

2020, Feb. 29		**Litho.**	**Perf. 13x13¼**	
2550-2553	A473	Set of 4	5.75	5.75

Miniature Sheet

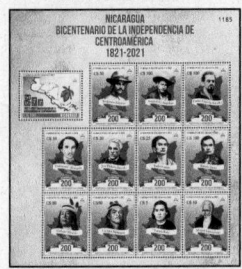

Central American Independence, 200th Anniv. — A474

No. 2554 — Nicaraguan coat of arms and: a, 5cor, Tomás Ruiz (1777-1819), priest and lawyer. b, 10cor, Enmanuel Mongalo (1834-72), teacher and military hero. c, 10cor, Miguel Larreynaga (1772-1847), judge and minister of finance. d, 20cor, José Dolores Estrada (1792-1869), military hero. e, 25cor, Andrés Castro (1831-82), military hero. f, 50cor, Benjamín Zeladón (1879-1912), general and President of Nicaragua. g, 50cor, Cacique Diriangén (c. 1497-c. 1524), leader of rebellions against Spanish colonizers. h, 80cor, Cacique Nicarao (fl. 16th century), chief of the Niquiranos. i, 100cor, Augusto C. Sandino (1895-1934), leader of rebellion against United States occupation of Nicaragua. j, 100cor, Carlos Fonseca Amador (1936-76), founder of Sandinista National Liberation Front. k, 100cor, Rubén Darío (1867-1916), poet. l, 100cor, Map of Central America, cacao pod, horiz.

Perf. 13¼x13, 13x13¼ (#2554l)

2021, Sept. 30			**Litho.**	
2554	A474	Sheet of 12, #a-l	37.00	37.00

AIR POST STAMPS

Counterfeits exist of almost all scarce surcharges among Nos. C1-C66.

Regular Issues of 1914-28 Overprinted in Red

1929		**Unwmk.**		**Perf. 12**	
C1	A24	25c orange		1.75	1.75
a.		Double overprint, one inverted		50.00	
b.		Inverted overprint		50.00	
c.		Double overprint		50.00	
C2	A24	25c blk brn		2.25	2.25
a.		Double overprint, one inverted		50.00	
b.		Inverted overprint		50.00	
c.		Inverted overprint		30.00	

Issued: No. C1, July 17; No. C2, May 12 (used on May 15 first-flight covers).

There are numerous varieties in the setting of the overprint. The most important are: Large "1" in "1929" and large "A" in "Aereo" and "P. A. A."

Similar Overprint on Regular Issue of 1929 in Red

1929, Sept. 1				
C3	A24	25c dk vio	1.25	.75
a.		Double overprint	50.00	
b.		Inverted overprint	50.00	
c.		Double overprint, one inverted	50.00	
		Nos. C1-C3 (3)	5.25	4.75

The stamps in the bottom row of the sheet have the letters "P. A. A." larger than usual.

Similar overprints, some including an airplane, have been applied to postage issues of 1914-20, officials of 1926 and Nos. 401-407. These are, at best, essays.

Airplanes over Mt. Momotombo — AP1

1929, Dec. 15			**Engr.**	
C4	AP1	25c olive blk	.50	.40
C5	AP1	50c blk brn	.75	.75
C6	AP1	1cor org red	1.00	1.00
		Nos. C4-C6 (3)	2.25	2.15

See Nos. C18-C19, C164-C168. For surcharges and overprints see Nos. C7-C8, C14-C17, C25-C31, C106-C120, C135-C146, C150-C154, C169-C173, CO25-CO29.

No. C4 Surcharged in Red or Black

1930, May 15				
C7	AP1	15c on 25c ol blk (R)	.50	.40
a.		"$" inverted	3.50	
b.		Double surcharge (R + Bk)	7.00	
c.		As "b," red normal, blk invtd.	7.00	
d.		Double red surch., one inverted	7.00	
C8	AP1	20c on 25c ol blk (Bk)	.75	.60
a.		"$" inverted	7.00	
b.		Inverted surcharge	15.00	

Nos. C1, C2 and C3 Surcharged in Green

1931, June 7				
C9	A24	15c on 25c org	70.00	50.00
C10	A24	15c on 25c blk		
		brn	100.00	100.00
C11	A24	15c on 25c dk vio	15.00	15.00
c.		Inverted surcharge	47.50	
C12	A24	20c on 25c dk vio	10.00	10.00
c.		Inverted surcharge	100.00	
d.		Double surcharge	100.00	
C13	A24	20c on 25c blk		
		brn	375.00	

No. C13 was not regularly issued.

"1391"

C9a	A24	15c on 25c		
C10a	A24	15c on 25c		
C11a	A24	15c on 25c	60.00	
d.		As "a," inverted	400.00	
C12a	A24	20c on 25c	75.00	
e.		As "a," inverted	400.00	
g.		As "a," double	400.00	
C13a	A24	20c on 25c		

"1921"

C9b	A24	15c on 25c	400.00	
C10b	A24	15c on 25c	60.00	
C11b	A24	15c on 25c	400.00	
e.		As "b," inverted	400.00	
C12b	A24	20c on 25c	100.00	
f.		As "b," inverted	400.00	
h.		As "b," double	400.00	
C13b	A24	20c on 25c		

Nos. C8, C4-C6 Surcharged in Blue

1931, June				
C14	AP1	15c on 20c on		
		25c	26.00	9.00
b.		Blue surcharge inverted	37.50	
c.		"$" in blk, surch. inverted	50.00	
d.		Blue surch. dbl., one		
		invtd.	30.00	
C15	AP1	15c on 25c	5.50	5.50
b.		Blue surcharge inverted	100.00	
c.		Double surch., one invtd.	25.00	
C16	AP1	15c on 50c	40.00	40.00
C17	AP1	15c on 1cor	100.00	100.00
		Nos. C14-C17 (4)	171.50	154.50

"1391"

C14a	AP1	15c on 20c on 25c	50.00	
C15a	AP1	15c on 25c	30.00	
C16a	AP1	15c on 50c	80.00	
C17a	AP1	15c on 1cor	225.00	
		Nos. C14a-C17a (4)	385.00	

Momotombo Type of 1929

1931, July 8				
C18	AP1	15c deep violet	.25	.25
C19	AP1	20c deep green	.40	.40

Managua Post Office Before and After Earthquake — AP2

Without gum, Soft porous paper

1932, Jan. 1			**Litho.**	**Perf. 11**
C20	AP2	15c lilac	1.50	*1.25*
a.		15c violet	22.50	
b.		Vert. pair, imperf. btwn.	35.00	

C21	AP2	20c emerald	2.00	
b.		Horizontal pair, imperf. between	35.00	
C22	AP2	25c yel brn	6.50	
b.		Vertical pair, imperf. between	60.00	
C23	AP2	50c yel brn	8.00	
C24	AP2	1cor dp car	12.00	
a.		Vert. or horiz. pair, imperf.		
		btwn.	80.00	
		Nos. C20-C24 (5)	30.00	

Sheets of 10. See note after No. 568. For overprint and surcharges see #C44-C46.

Reprints: see note following No. 568. Value $1 each.

Nos. C5 and C6 Surcharged in Red or Black

1932, July 12			**Perf. 12**	
C25	AP1	30c on 50c (Bk)	1.50	1.50
a.		"Valc"	25.00	
b.		Double surcharge	15.00	
c.		Double surch., one inverted	15.00	
d.		Period omitted after "0"	25.00	
e.		As "a," double	300.00	
C26	AP1	35c on 50c (R)	1.50	1.50
a.		"Valc"	30.00	
b.		Double surcharge	12.00	
c.		Double surch., one inverted	12.00	
d.		As "a," double	300.00	
C27	AP1	35c on 50c (Bk)	35.00	35.00
a.		"Valc"	250.00	
C28	AP1	40c on 1cor (Bk)	1.75	1.75
a.		"Valc"	25.00	
b.		Double surcharge	15.00	
c.		Double surch., one inverted	15.00	
d.		Inverted surcharge	15.00	
e.		As "a," inverted	300.00	
f.		As "a," double	300.00	
C29	AP1	55c on 1cor (R)	1.75	1.75
a.		"Valc"	25.00	
b.		Double surcharge	12.00	
c.		Double surch., one inverted	12.00	
d.		Inverted surcharge	12.00	
e.		As "a," inverted	300.00	
f.		As "a," double	300.00	
		Nos. C25-C29 (5)	41.50	41.50

No. C18 Overprinted in Red

1932, Sept. 11				
C30	AP1	15c dp vio	70.00	70.00
a.		"Aerreo"	150.00	150.00
b.		Invtd. "m" in "Septiembre"	150.00	

International Air Mail Week.

No. C6 Surcharged

1932, Oct. 12				
C31	AP1	8c on 1 cor org red	20.00	20.00
a.		"1232"	30.00	30.00
b.		2nd "u" of "Inauguracion" is		
		an "n"	30.00	30.00

Inauguration of airmail service to the interior.

Regular Issue of 1932 Overprinted in Red

1932, Oct. 24			**Perf. 11½**	
		Without Gum		
C32	A40	1c yel brn	20.00	20.00
a.		Inverted overprint	125.00	125.00
C33	A40	2c carmine	20.00	20.00
a.		Inverted overprint	125.00	125.00
b.		Double overprint	100.00	100.00
C34	A40	3c ultra	9.50	9.50
a.		Inverted overprint	150.00	150.00
b.		As "a," vert. pair, imperf.		
		btwn.	500.00	
C35	A40	4c dp ultra	9.50	9.50
a.		Inverted overprint	125.00	125.00
b.		Double overprint	100.00	100.00
c.		Vert. or horiz. pair, imperf.		
		btwn.	300.00	
C36	A40	5c yel brn	9.50	9.50
a.		Inverted overprint	125.00	125.00
b.		Vert. pair, imperf. btwn.	75.00	
C37	A40	6c gray brn	9.50	9.50
a.		Inverted overprint	100.00	100.00
C38	A40	50c green	9.00	9.00
a.		Inverted overprint	125.00	125.00

C39	A40	1cor yellow	9.50	9.50
a.		Inverted overprint	125.00	125.00
b.		Horiz. pair, imperf. btwn.	200.00	
		Nos. C32-C39 (8)	96.50	96.50

Nos. 564, C20-C21 exist overprinted as C32-C39. The editors believe they were not regularly issued.

Surcharged in Red

1932, Oct. 24				
C40	A40	8c on 10c yel brn	9.00	9.00
a.		Inverted surcharge	125.00	125.00
C41	A40	16c on 20c org	9.00	9.00
a.		Inverted surcharge	125.00	125.00
C42	A40	24c on 25c dp vio	9.00	9.00
a.		Inverted surcharge	125.00	125.00
b.		Horiz. pair, imperf. vert.	300.00	

Surcharged in Red as No. C40 but without the word "Vale"

C43	A40	8c on 10c yel brn	45.00	45.00
a.		Inverted surcharge	125.00	125.00
b.		Horiz. pair, imperf. vert.	300.00	

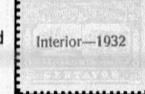

No. C22 Overprinted in Red

1932, Oct. 24				
C44	AP2	25c yel brn	8.00	8.00
a.		Inverted overprint	125.00	125.00

Nos. C23 and C24 Surcharged in Red

1932, Oct. 24				
C45	AP2	32c on 50c yel brn	9.50	9.50
a.		Inverted surcharge	125.00	125.00
b.		"Interior-1932" inverted	150.00	150.00
c.		"Vale $0.32" inverted	150.00	150.00
d.		Horiz. pair, imperf. btwn.	200.00	
C46	AP2	40c on 1cor car	7.00	7.00
a.		Inverted surcharge	125.00	125.00
b.		"Vale $0.40" inverted	200.00	200.00

Nos. 557-558 Overprinted in Black

1932, Nov. 16				
C47	A40	1c yel brn	25.00	22.50
a.		"1232"	45.00	45.00
b.		Inverted overprint	125.00	125.00
c.		Double ovpt., one invtd.	125.00	125.00
d.		As "a," inverted	500.00	
C48	A40	2c dp car	20.00	17.50
a.		"1232"	45.00	45.00
b.		Inverted overprint	125.00	125.00
c.		As "a," inverted	500.00	

Excellent counterfeits exist of Nos. C27, C30-C48. Forged overprints and surcharges as on Nos. C32-C48 exist on reprints of Nos. C20-C24.

Regular Issue of 1914-32 Surcharged in Black

1932			**Perf. 12**	
C49	A25	1c on 2c brt rose	.65	.30
C50	A24	2c on 3c lt bl	.65	.30
C51	A25	3c on 4c dk bl	.65	.30
C52	A24	4c on 5c gray brn	.65	.30
C53	A25	5c on 6c ol brn	.65	.30
C54	A25	6c on 10c lt brn	.65	.30
a.		Double surcharge	25.00	
C55	A24	8c on 15c org red	.65	.30
C56	A25	16c on 20c org	.65	.35
C57	A24	24c on 25c dk vio	2.50	1.00
C58	A24	25c on 25c dk vio	2.50	1.00
a.		Double surcharge	25.00	
C59	A25	32c on 50c grn	2.50	1.25
C60	A25	40c on 50c grn	3.00	1.40
C61	A25	50c on 1cor yel	4.25	1.25
C62	A25	1cor on 1cor yel	6.50	3.00
		Nos. C49-C62 (14)	26.45	12.35

Nos. C49-C62 exist with inverted surcharge.

In addition to C49 to C62, four other stamps, Type A25, exist with this surcharge:
40c on 50c bister brown, black surcharge.
1cor on 2c bright rose, black surcharge.
1cor on 1cor yellow, red surcharge.

1cor on 1cor dull violet, black surcharge.
The editors believe they were not regularly
issued.

Surcharged on Nos. 548, 547
1932
C65	A24	24c on 25c dk vio	45.00	45.00
C66	A24	25c on 25c blk brn	50.00	50.00

Counterfeits of Nos. C65 and C66 are
plentiful.

Rivas Railroad Issue

La Chocolata
Cut — AP3

El Nacascola — AP4

Designs: 25c, Cuesta cut. 50c, Mole of San
Juan del Sur. 1cor, View of El Estero.

1932, Dec.   **Litho.**
Soft porous paper
C67	AP3	15c dk vio	20.00
C68	AP4	20c grn	20.00
C69	AP4	25c dk brn	20.00
C70	AP4	50c blk brn	20.00
C71	AP4	1cor rose red	20.00
		Nos. C67-C71 (5)	100.00

Inauguration of the railroad from San Jorge
to San Juan del Sur, Dec. 18, 1932. Printed in
sheets of 4, without gum.
*Reprints: see note following No. 574. Value,
$6 each.*

Leon-Sauce Railroad Issue

"Fill" at
Santa Lucia
River
AP5

Designs: 15c, Bridge at Santa Lucia. 25c,
Malpaicillo Station. 50c, Panoramic view. 1cor,
San Andres.

1932, Dec. 30   **Soft porous paper**
C72	AP5	15c purple	20.00
C73	AP5	20c bl grn	20.00
C74	AP5	25c lt brn	20.00
C75	AP5	50c dk brn	20.00
C76	AP5	1cor ver	20.00
		Nos. C72-C76 (5)	100.00

Inauguration of the railroad from Leon to El
Sauce, 12/30/32. Sheets of 4, without gum.
*Reprints: see note following No. 579. Value,
$6 each.*

Flag of the Race Issue
1933, Aug. 3   **Litho.**   ***Rouletted 9***
Without gum
C77	A43	1c dk brn	1.50	1.50
C78	A43	2c red vio	1.50	1.50
C79	A43	4c violet	2.50	2.25
C80	A43	5c dl bl	2.25	2.25
C81	A43	6c vio bl	2.25	2.25
C82	A43	8c dp brn	.70	.70
C83	A43	15c ol brn	.70	.70
C84	A43	20c yellow	2.25	2.25
a.		Horiz. pair, imperf. btwn.	15.00	
b.		Horiz. pair, imperf. vert.	15.00	
C85	A43	25c orange	2.25	2.25
C86	A43	50c rose	2.25	2.25
C87	A43	1cor green	11.00	11.00
		Nos. C77-C87 (11)	29.15	28.90

See note after No. 599. Printed in sheets of
10.
*Reprints exist, shades differ from postage
and official stamps.*

Imperf., Pairs
C78a	A43	2c	14.00
C79a	A43	4c	10.00
C81a	A43	6c	10.00
C82a	A43	8c	10.00
C83a	A43	15c	10.00
C87a	A43	1cor	30.00

AP7

1933, Nov.   ***Perf. 12***
C88	AP7	10c bis brn	1.60	1.60
a.		Vert. pair, imperf. between	35.00	
C89	AP7	15c violet	1.25	1.25
a.		Vert. pair, imperf. between	37.50	
C90	AP7	25c red	1.50	1.50
a.		Horiz. pair, imperf. between	22.50	
C91	AP7	50c dp bl	1.60	1.60
		Nos. C88-C91 (4)	5.95	5.95

Intl. Air Post Week, Nov. 6-11, 1933. Printed
in sheets of 4. Counterfeits exist.

Stamps and Types of 1928-31 Surcharged in Black

1933, Nov. 3
C92	A25	1c on 2c grn	.25	.25
C93	A24	2c on 3c ol gray	.25	.25
C94	A25	3c on 4c car rose	.25	.25
C95	A24	4c on 5c lt bl	.25	.25
C96	A25	5c on 6c dk bl	.25	.25
C97	A25	6c on 10c ol brn	.25	.25
C98	A24	8c on 15c bis brn	.25	.25
C99	A25	16c on 20c brn	.25	.25
C100	A24	24c on 25c ver	.25	.25
C101	A24	25c on 25c org	.25	.25
C102	A25	32c on 50c vio	.25	.25
C103	A24	40c on 50c grn	.30	.30
C104	A25	50c on 1cor yel	.40	.40
C105	A25	1cor on 1cor org red	.75	.80
		Nos. C92-C105 (14)	4.20	4.25

Nos. C100, C102-C105 exist without script
control overprint. Value, each $1.50.

Type of Air Post Stamps of 1929 Surcharged in Black

1933, Oct. 28
C106	AP1	30c on 50c org red	2.00	.25
C107	AP1	35c on 50c lt bl	2.00	.25
C108	AP1	40c on 1cor yel	5.00	.25
C109	AP1	55c on 1cor grn	4.00	.25
		Nos. C106-C109 (4)	13.00	1.00

No. C19 Surcharged in Red

1934, Mar. 31
C110	AP1	10c on 20c grn	.30	.25
a.		Inverted surcharge	15.00	
b.		Double surcharge, one invert-ed	15.00	
c.		"Ceutroamericano"	10.00	

No. C110 with black surcharge is believed to
be of private origin.

No. C4 Surcharged in Red

1935, Aug.
C111	AP1	10c on 25c ol blk	.25	.25
a.		Small "v" in "vale" (R)	5.00	
b.		"centrvos" (R)	5.00	
c.		Double surcharge (R)	25.00	
d.		Inverted surcharge (R)	25.00	
g.		As "a," inverted	400.00	
h.		As "a," double	400.00	

No. C111 with blue surcharge is believed to
be of private origin.

The editors do not recognize the Nicaraguan air post stamps overprinted in
red "VALIDO 1935" in two lines and with
or without script control marks as having been issued primarily for postal
purposes.

Nos C4-C6, C18-C19 Overprinted Vertically in Blue, Reading Up:

1935-36
C112	AP1	15c dp vio	1.00	1.00
C113	AP1	20c dp grn	1.75	1.75
C114	AP1	25c ol blk	2.25	2.25
C115	AP1	50c blk brn	5.00	5.00
C116	AP1	1cor org red	40.00	40.00
		Nos. C112-C116 (5)	50.00	50.00

Same Overprint on Nos. C106-C109 Reading Up or Down
C117	AP1	30c on 50c org red	1.50	1.40
C118	AP1	35c on 50c lt bl	6.50	6.50
C119	AP1	40c on 1cor yel	6.50	6.50
C120	AP1	55c on 1cor grn	6.50	6.50
		Nos. C117-C120 (4)	21.00	20.90
		Nos. C112-C120 (9)	71.00	70.90

Same Overprint in Red on Nos. C92-C105
1936
C121	A25	1c on 2c grn	.25	.25
C122	A24	2c on 3c ol gray	.25	.25
C123	A25	3c on 4c car rose	.25	.25
C124	A24	4c on 5c lt bl	.25	.25
C125	A25	5c on 6c dk bl	.25	.25
C126	A25	6c on 10c ol brn	.25	.25
C127	A24	8c on 15c bis brn	.25	.25
C128	A25	16c on 20c brn	.30	.25
C129	A24	24c on 25c ver	.50	.30
C130	A24	25c on 25c org	.35	.25
C131	A25	32c on 50c vio	.35	.25
C132	A25	40c on 50c grn	1.00	.50
C133	A25	50c on 1cor yel	.85	.25
C134	A25	1cor on 1cor org red	3.50	.65
		Nos. C121-C134 (14)	8.60	4.20

Nos. C121 to C134 are handstamped with
script control mark.

Overprint Reading Down on No. C110
C135	AP1	10c on 20c grn	*350.00*	

This stamp has been extensively
counterfeited.

Overprinted in Red on Nos. C4 to C6, C18 and C19
C136	AP1	15c dp vio	1.00	.25
C137	AP1	20c dp grn	1.25	.60
C138	AP1	25c ol blk	1.25	.55
C139	AP1	50c blk brn	1.00	.55
C140	AP1	1cor org red	3.25	.55

On Nos. C106 to C109
C141	AP1	30c on 50c org red	2.25	.60
C142	AP1	35c on 50c lt bl	2.25	.40
C143	AP1	40c on 1cor yel	2.25	.55
C144	AP1	55c on 1cor grn	2.25	.50

Same Overprint in Red or Blue on No. C111 Reading Up or Down
C145	AP1	10c on 25c, down	3.00	.45
a.		"Centrvos"	25.00	
C146	AP1	10c on 25c (Bl), up	6.00	1.00
a.		"Centrvos"	25.00	
		Nos. C136-C146 (11)	25.75	6.00

Overprint on No. C145 is at right, on No.
C146 in center.

Nos. C92, C93 and C98 Overprinted in Black

1936
C147	A25	1c on 2c grn	2.00	.25
C148	A24	2c on 3c ol gray	2.00	.25
a.		"Resello 1936" dbl., one invtd.	7.50	
C149	A24	8c on 15c bis brn	2.00	.25
		Nos. C147-C149 (3)	6.00	.75

With script control handstamp.

Nos. C5 and C6 Surcharged in Red

1936, Nov. 26
C150	AP1	15c on 50c blk brn	.40	.25
C151	AP1	15c on 1cor org red	.40	.25

Nos. C18 and C19 Overprinted in Carmine

1936, July 2
C152	AP1	15c dp vio	.60	.25
C153	AP1	20c dp grn	.60	.25

Overprint reading up or down.

No. C4 Surcharged and Overprinted in Red

C154	AP1	10c on 25c olive blk	.50	.30
a.		Surch. and ovpt. inverted	3.50	

Same Overprint in Carmine on Nos. C92 to C99
C155	A25	1c on 2c green	.75	.25
C156	A24	2c on 3c olive gray	4.00	2.00
C157	A24	3c on 4c car rose	.75	.25
C158	A24	4c on 5c light blue	.75	.25
C159	A24	5c on 6c dark blue	.75	.25
C160	A25	6c on 10c olive brn	.75	.25
C161	A24	8c on 15c bister brn	.75	.25
C162	A25	16c on 20c brown	.75	.25
		Nos. C154-C162 (9)	9.75	4.05

No. 518 Overprinted in Black

C163	A25	10c lt brn	.75	.25
a.		Overprint inverted	3.50	
b.		Double overprint	3.50	

Two fonts are found in the sheet of #C163.

Momotombo Type of 1929
1937
C164	AP1	15c yel org	1.00	.25
C165	AP1	20c org red	1.00	.25
C166	AP1	25c black	1.00	.25
C167	AP1	50c violet	1.00	.25
C168	AP1	1cor orange	4.50	.25
		Nos. C164-C168 (5)	8.50	1.25

Surcharged in Black

1937
C169	AP1	30c on 50c car rose	1.25	.25
C170	AP1	35c on 50c olive grn	1.25	.25
C171	AP1	40c on 1cor green	1.25	.25
C172	AP1	55c on 1cor blue	1.25	.25
		Nos. C169-C172 (4)	5.00	1.00

No. C168 Surcharged in Violet

1937   **Unwmk.**   ***Perf. 12***
C173	AP1	10c on 1cor org	.45	.25
a.		"Centavos"	10.00	

No. C98 with Additional Overprint "1937"
C174	A24	8c on 15c bis brn	.65	.25
a.		"1937" double	6.50	

Nos. C92-C102 with Additional Overprint in Blue reading "HABILITADO 1937"

C175	A25	1c on 2c grn	.90	.25
a.		Blue overprint double	3.50	
C176	A24	2c on 3c ol gray	.90	.25
a.		Double surch., one inverted	3.50	
C177	A25	3c on 4c car rose	.90	.25
C178	A24	4c on 5c lt bl	.90	.25
C179	A25	5c on 6c dk bl	.90	.25
C180	A25	6c on 10c ol brn	.90	.25
C181	A24	8c on 15c bis brn	.90	.25
a.		"Habilitado 1937" double	4.50	
C182	A24	16c on 20c brn	.90	.25
a.		Double surcharge	3.50	
C183	A24	24c on 25c ver	.90	.25
C184	A24	25c on 25c org	.90	.25
C185	A25	32c on 50c vio	.90	.25
		Nos. C175-C185 (11)	9.90	2.75

Map of Nicaragua AP8

For Foreign Postage

1937, July 30   **Engr.**

C186	AP8	10c green	.40	.25
C187	AP8	15c dp bl	.40	.25
C188	AP8	20c yellow	.40	.25
C189	AP8	25c bl vio	.40	.25
C190	AP8	30c rose car	.40	.25
C191	AP8	50c org yel	.50	.25
C192	AP8	1cor ol grn	1.00	.55
		Nos. C186-C192 (7)	3.50	2.05

Presidential Palace — AP9

For Domestic Postage

C193	AP9	1c rose car	.40	.25
C194	AP9	2c dp bl	.40	.25
C195	AP9	3c ol grn	.40	.25
C196	AP9	4c black	.40	.25
C197	AP9	5c dk vio	.40	.25
C198	AP9	6c chocolate	.40	.55
C199	AP9	8c bl vio	.40	.25
C200	AP9	16c org yel	.40	.25
C201	AP9	24c yellow	.40	.25
C202	AP9	25c yel grn	.40	.25
		Nos. C193-C202 (10)	4.00	2.50

No. C201 with green overprint "Union Panamericana 1890-1940" is of private origin.

Managua — AP10

Designs: 15c, Presidential Palace. 20c, Map of South America. 25c, Map of Central America. 30c, Map of North America. 35c, Lagoon of Tiscapa, Managua. 40c, Road Scene. 45c, Park. 50c, Another park. 55c, Scene in San Juan del Sur. 75c, Tipitapa River. 1cor, Landscape.

Wmk. 209
1937, Sept. 17   **Perf. 11**
Center in Dark Blue

C203	AP10	10c yel grn	2.25	1.20
C204	AP10	15c orange	2.25	1.40
C205	AP10	20c red	1.75	1.00
C206	AP10	25c vio brn	1.75	1.00
a.		Center, double impression	—	
C207	AP10	30c bl grn	1.75	1.00
a.		Great Lakes omitted	40.00	40.00
C208	AP10	35c lemon	.75	.45
C209	AP10	40c green	.75	.40
C210	AP10	45c brt vio	.75	.35
C211	AP10	50c rose lil	.75	.35
a.		Vert. pair, imperf. btwn.	140.00	
C212	AP10	55c lt bl	.75	.35
C213	AP10	75c gray grn	.75	.35

Center in Brown Red

C214	AP10	1cor dk bl	1.75	.50
		Nos. C203-C214 (12)	16.00	8.35

150th anniv. of the Constitution of the US.

Diriangen AP11

Designs: 4c, 10c, Nicarao. 5c, 15c, Bartolomé de Las Casas. 8c, 20c, Columbus.

For Domestic Postage
Without gum
1937, Oct. 12   **Unwmk.**   **Perf. 11**

C215	AP11	1c green	.25	.25
C216	AP11	4c brn car	.25	.25
C217	AP11	5c dk vio	.25	.25
a.		Without imprint	.40	
C218	AP11	8c dp bl	.25	.25
a.		Without imprint	.50	

For Foreign Postage
Wmk. 209
With Gum

C219	AP11	10c lt brn	.25	.25
C220	AP11	15c pale bl	.25	.25
a.		Without imprint	1.00	
C221	AP11	20c pale rose	.25	.25
		Nos. C215-C221 (7)	1.75	1.75

Nos. C215-C221 printed in sheets of 4.

Imperf., Pairs

C215a	AP11	1c	.25	.25
C216a	AP11	4c	.25	.25
C217b	AP11	5c	.25	.25
C217c	AP11	5c Without imprint		
C218b	AP11	8c	.25	
C218c	AP11	8c Without imprint		
C219a	AP11	10c	.25	.25
C220b	AP11	15c	.25	.25
C220c	AP11	15c Without imprint		
C221a	AP11	20c	.35	.35

Gen. Tomas Martinez AP11a

Design: 10c-50c, Gen. Anastasio Somoza.

For Domestic Postage
Without Gum
Perf. 11½, Imperf.
1938, Jan. 18   **Typo.**   **Unwmk.**
Center in Black

C221B	AP11a	1c orange	.25	.25
C221C	AP11a	5c red vio	.25	.25
C221D	AP11a	8c dk bl	.25	.25
C221E	AP11a	16c brown	.25	.25
f.		Sheet of 4, 1c, 5c, 8c, 16c	3.50	3.50

For Foreign Postage

C221G	AP11a	10c green	.25	.25
C221H	AP11a	15c dk bl	.25	.25
C221J	AP11a	25c violet	.40	.40
C221K	AP11a	50c carmine	.50	.45
m.		Sheet of 4, 10c, 15c, 25c, 50c	3.50	3.50
		Nos. C221B-C221K (8)	2.40	2.35

75th anniv. of postal service in Nicaragua. Printed in sheets of four.

Stamps of type AP11a exist in changed colors and with inverted centers, double centers and frames printed on the back. These varieties were private fabrications.

Lake Managua AP12

President Anastasio Somoza AP13

For Domestic Postage
1939   **Unwmk.**   **Engr.**   **Perf. 12½**

C222	AP12	2c dp bl	.25	.25
C223	AP12	3c green	.25	.25
C224	AP12	8c pale lil	.25	.25
C225	AP12	16c orange	.25	.25
C226	AP12	24c yellow	.25	.25
C227	AP12	32c dk grn	.25	.25
C228	AP12	50c dp rose	.25	.25

For Foreign Postage

C229	AP13	10c brown	.25	.25
C230	AP13	15c dk bl	.25	.25
C231	AP13	20c org yel	.25	.25
C232	AP13	25c dk pur	.25	.25
C233	AP13	30c lake	.25	.25
C234	AP13	50c dp org	.25	.25
C235	AP13	1cor dk ol grn	.25	.25
		Nos. C222-C235 (14)	3.60	3.65

For Domestic Postage

Will Rogers and View of Managua AP14

Designs: 2c, Rogers standing beside plane. 3c, Leaving airport office. 4c, Rogers and US Marines. 5c, Managua after earthquake.

1939, Mar. 31   **Engr.**   **Perf. 12**

C236	AP14	1c brt grn	.25	.25
C237	AP14	2c org red	.25	.25
C238	AP14	3c lt ultra	.25	.25
C239	AP14	4c dk bl	.25	.25
C240	AP14	5c rose car	.25	.25
		Nos. C236-C240 (5)	1.25	1.25

Will Rogers' flight to Managua after the earthquake, Mar. 31, 1931.
For surcharges see Nos. 686, 688.

Pres. Anastasio Somoza in US House of Representatives AP19

President Somoza and US Capitol AP20

President Somoza, Tower of the Sun and Trylon and Perisphere AP21

For Domestic Postage
1940, Feb. 1

C241	AP19	4c red brn	.25	.25
C242	AP20	8c blk brn	.25	.25
C243	AP19	16c grnsh bl	.25	.25
C244	AP20	20c brt plum	.50	.30
C245	AP21	32c scarlet	.25	.25

For Foreign Postage

C246	AP19	25c dp bl	.25	.25
C247	AP19	30c black	.25	.25
C248	AP20	50c rose pink	.45	.40
C249	AP21	60c green	.50	.30
C250	AP19	65c dk vio brn	.50	.25
C251	AP19	90c ol grn	.65	.30
C252	AP21	1cor violet	1.00	.55
		Nos. C241-C252 (12)	5.10	3.60

Visit of Pres. Somoza to US in 1939.
For surcharge see No. C636.

L. S. Rowe, Statue of Liberty, Nicaraguan Coastline, Flags of 21 American Republics, US Shield and Arms of Nicaragua — AP22

1940, Aug. 2   **Engr.**   **Perf. 12½**

C253	AP22	1.25cor multi	2.00	1.00

50th anniversary of Pan American Union.
For overprint see No. C493.

First Nicaraguan Postage Stamp and Sir Rowland Hill — AP23

1941, Apr. 4

C254	AP23	2cor brown	2.50	.80
C255	AP23	3cor dk bl	8.25	1.40
C256	AP23	5cor carmine	22.50	3.50
		Nos. C254-C256 (3)	33.25	5.70

Centenary of the first postage stamp.
Nos. C254-C256 imperf. are proofs.

Rubén Darío — AP24

1941, Dec. 23

C257	AP24	20c pale lil	.50	.40
C258	AP24	35c yel grn	.60	.40
C259	AP24	40c org yel	.80	.40
C260	AP24	60c lt bl	1.30	.40
		Nos. C257-C260 (4)	3.20	1.60

25th anniversary of the death of Rubén Dario, poet and writer.

> Catalogue values for unused stamps in this section, from this point to the end of the section, are for Never Hinged items.

Victory Type
1943, Dec. 8   **Perf. 12**

C261	A48	40c dk bl grn & cer	.75	.40
C262	A48	60c lt bl & cer	.95	.40

Red Cross AP26

Cross and Globes AP27

Red Cross Workers — AP28

1944, Oct. 12   **Engr.**

C263	AP26	25c red lil & car	.80	.30
C264	AP27	50c ol brn & car	1.20	.55
C265	AP28	1cor dk bl grn & car	2.40	2.00
		Nos. C263-C265 (3)	4.40	2.85

International Red Cross Society, 80th anniv.

Caravels of Columbus and Columbus Lighthouse AP29

Landing of Columbus AP30

1945, Sept. 1   **Perf. 12½**

C266	AP29	20c dp grn & gray	.35	.35
C267	AP29	35c dk car & blk	.50	.30
C268	AP29	75c ol grn & rose pink	.70	.40
C269	AP29	90c brick red & aqua	1.10	.75
C270	AP29	1cor blk & pale bl	1.25	.30
C271	AP30	2.50cor dk bl & car rose	2.25	2.25
		Nos. C266-C271 (6)	6.15	4.35

Issued in honor of the discovery of America by Columbus and the Columbus Lighthouse near Ciudad Trujillo, Dominican Republic.

Roosevelt Types

Designs: 25c, Franklin D. Roosevelt and Winston Churchill. 75c, Roosevelt signing declaration of war against Japan. 1cor, Gen. Henri Giraud, Roosevelt, Gen. Charles de Gaulle and Churchill. 3cor, Stalin, Roosevelt and Churchill. 5cor, Sculptured head of Roosevelt.

Engraved, Center Photogravure
1946, June 15   **Perf. 12½**
Frame in Black

C272	A50	25c orange	.35	.30
a.		Horiz. pair, imperf. btwn.	225.00	
b.		Imperf., pair	175.00	
C273	A51	75c carmine	.35	.30
a.		Imperf., pair	175.00	
C274	A50	1cor dark green	.55	.40
C275	A50	3cor violet	5.00	5.00
C276	A51	5cor greenish blue	6.50	5.00
		Nos. C272-C276 (5)	12.75	9.75

Issued to honor Franklin D. Roosevelt.

Projected Provincial Seminary — AP36

Designs: 20c, Communications Building. 35c, Sanitation Building. 90c, National Bank. 1cor, Municipal Building. 2.50cor, National Palace.

1947, Jan. 10   Frame in Black

C277	AP36	5c violet	.45	.30
a.		Imperf., pair	125.00	
C278	AP36	20c gray grn	.45	.30
C279	AP36	35c orange	.45	.30
C280	AP36	90c red lil	.70	.30
C281	AP36	1cor brown	1.00	.45
C282	AP36	2.50cor rose lil	3.00	1.50
	Nos. C277-C282 (6)		6.05	3.15

City of Managua centenary.

Rubén Darío Monument AP42

Designs: 6c, Tapir. 8c, Stone Highway. 10c, Genizaro Dam. 20c, Detail of Dario Monument. 25c, Sulphurous Lake of Nejapa. 35c, Mercedes Airport. 50c, Prinzapolka River delta. 1cor, Tipitapa Spa. 1.50cor, Tipitapa River. 5cor, United States Embassy. 10cor, Indian fruit vendor. 25cor, Franklin D. Roosevelt Monument.

Engraved, Center Photogravure

1947, Aug. 29   Unwmk.   Perf. 12½

C283	AP42	5c dk bl grn & rose car	.30	.25
C284	AP42	6c blk & yel	.30	.25
C285	AP42	8c car & ol	.30	.25
C286	AP42	10c brn & bl	.30	.25
C287	AP42	20c bl vio & org	.35	.30
C288	AP42	25c brn red & emer	.40	.35
C289	AP42	35c gray & bis	.35	.30
C290	AP42	50c pur & sep	.30	.25
C291	AP42	1cor blk & lil rose	.90	.75
C292	AP42	1.50cor red brn & aqua	.60	.80
C293	AP42	5cor choc & car rose	7.50	6.25
C294	AP42	10cor vio & dk brn	6.00	5.00
C295	AP42	25cor dk bl grn & yel	12.00	10.00
	Nos. C283-C295 (13)		29.60	25.00

The frames differ for each denomination.
For surcharge see No. C750.

Tennis — AP43

Designs: 2c, Soccer. 3c, Table tennis. 4c, Proposed stadium. 5c, Regatta. 15c, Basketball. 25c, Boxing. 30c, Baseball. 40c, Bicycling. 75c, Diving. 1cor, Pole vault. 2cor, Boy Scouts. 5cor, Softball.

1949, July   Photo.   Perf. 12

C296	AP43	1c cerise	.40	.25
C297	AP43	2c ol gray	.40	.25
C298	AP43	3c scarlet	.40	.25
C299	AP43	4c dk bl gray	.40	.25
C300	AP43	5c aqua	.40	.25
C301	AP43	15c bl grn	.40	.25
C302	AP43	25c red vio	3.25	.30
C303	AP43	30c red brn	3.00	.25
C304	AP43	40c violet	.80	.30
C305	AP43	75c magenta	8.25	2.75
C306	AP43	1cor lt bl	10.00	1.40
C307	AP43	2cor brn ol	4.25	1.75
C308	AP43	5cor lt grn	5.50	2.25
a.		Set of 13 souv. sheets of 4	475.00	450.00
	Nos. C296-C308 (13)		37.45	10.55

10th World Series of Amateur Baseball, 1948.

Rowland Hill — AP44

Designs: 20c, Heinrich von Stephan. 25c, First UPU Bldg. 30c, UPU Bldg., Bern. 85c, UPU Monument. 1.10cor, Congress medal, obverse. 2.14cor, as 1.10cor, reverse.

1950, Nov. 23   Engr.   Perf. 13
Frames in Black

C309	AP44	16c cerise	.35	.25
C310	AP44	20c orange	.35	.25
C311	AP44	25c gray	.35	.25
C312	AP44	30c cerise	.55	.25
C313	AP44	85c dk bl grn	1.00	.65
C314	AP44	1.10cor chnt brn	2.00	.45
C315	AP44	2.14cor ol grn	3.00	2.25
	Nos. C309-C315 (7)		7.60	4.35

75th anniv. (in 1949) of the UPU.
Each denomination was also issued in a souvenir sheet containing four stamps and marginal inscriptions. Size: 126x114mm. Value, set of 7 sheets, $35.
For surcharges see Nos. C501, C758.

Queen Isabela I Type

Designs: 2.30cor, Portrait facing left. 2.80cor, Map. 3cor, Santa Maria. 3.30cor, Columbus' ships. 3.60cor, Portrait facing right.

1952, June 25   Unwmk.   Perf. 11½

C316	A65	2.30cor rose car	3.00	2.00
C317	A65	2.80cor red org	2.75	1.75
C318	A65	3cor green	3.00	2.00
C319	A66	3.30cor lt bl	3.00	2.00
C320	A65	3.60cor yel grn	3.25	2.25
a.		Souv. sheet of 5, #C316-C320	14.00	14.00
	Nos. C316-C320 (5)		15.00	10.00

For overprint see No. C445.

Arms of ODECA — AP47

Designs: 25c, ODECA Flag. 30c, Presidents of five Central American countries. 60c, ODECA Charter and Flags. 1cor, Map of Central America.

1953, Apr. 15   Perf. 13½x14

C321	AP47	20c red lil	.90	.40
C322	AP47	25c lt bl	.90	.40
C323	AP47	30c sepia	.90	.40
C324	AP47	60c dk bl grn	.90	.40
C325	AP47	1cor dk vio	2.25	2.25
	Nos. C321-C325 (5)		5.85	3.85

Founding of the Organization of Central American States (ODECA).

Leonardo Arguello — AP48

Presidents: 5c, Gen. Jose Maria Moncada. 20c, Juan Bautista Sacasa. 25c, Gen. Jose Santos Zelaya. 30c, Gen. Anastasio Somoza. 35c, Gen. Tomas Martinez. 40c, Fernando Guzman. 45c, Vicente Cuadra. 50c, Pedro Joaquin Chamorro. 60c, Gen. Joaquin Zavala. 85c, Adan Cardenas. 1.10cor, Evaristo Carazo. 1.20cor, Roberto Sacasa.

Engraved (frames); Photogravure (heads)

1953, June 25   Perf. 12½
Heads in Gray Black

C326	AP48	4c dp car	.75	.40
C327	AP48	5c dp org	.75	.40
C328	AP48	20c dk Prus bl	.75	.40
C329	AP48	25c blue	.75	.40
C330	AP48	30c red brn	.75	.40
C331	AP48	35c dp grn	.75	.40
C332	AP48	40c dk vio brn	.75	.40
C333	AP48	45c olive	.75	.40
C334	AP48	50c carmine	.90	.40
C335	AP48	60c ultra	.90	.40
C336	AP48	85c brown	1.20	.40
C337	AP48	1.10cor purple	1.40	.45
C338	AP48	1.20cor ol bis	1.40	.45
	Nos. C326-C338 (13)		11.80	5.30

For surcharges see Nos. C363-C364, C757.

Torch and UN Emblem — AP49

Designs: 4c, Raised hands. 5c, Candle and charter. 30c, Flags of Nicaragua and UN. 2cor, Globe. 3cor, Arms of Nicaragua. 5cor, Type A69 inscribed "Aereo."

1954, Apr. 30   Engr.   Perf. 13½

C339	AP49	3c rose pink	.30	.25
C340	AP49	4c dp org	.30	.25
C341	AP49	5c red	.30	.25
C342	AP49	30c cerise	1.60	.25
C343	AP49	2cor magenta	2.40	1.00
C344	AP49	3cor org brn	4.25	1.75
C345	AP49	5cor brn vio	4.75	2.25
	Nos. C339-C345 (7)		13.90	6.00

Honoring the United Nations.
For overprint & surcharge see #C366, C443.

Capt. Dean L. Ray, USAF — AP50

Designs: 15c, Sabre jet plane. 20c, Air Force emblem. 25c, National Air Force hangars. 30c, Gen. A. Somoza. 50c, AT-6's in formation. 1cor, Plane, type P-38.

Frame in Black
Engraved; Center Photogravure

1954, Nov. 5   Perf. 13

C346	AP50	10c gray	.95	.25
C347	AP50	15c gray	.95	.25
C348	AP50	20c claret	.95	.25
C349	AP50	25c red	.95	.25
C350	AP50	30c ultra	.95	.25
C351	AP50	50c blue	1.80	.60
C352	AP50	1cor green	1.40	.50
	Nos. C346-C352 (7)		7.95	2.35

Issued to honor the National Air Force.

Rotary Intl. Type

Designs: 1c, 1cor, Paul P. Harris. 2c, 50c, Handclasp, Rotary emblem and globe. 3c, 45c, Map of world and Rotary emblem. 4c, 30c, Rotary slogans and wreath. 5c, 25c, Flags of Nicaragua and Rotary.

Perf. 11½

1955, Aug. 30   Unwmk.   Photo.
Granite Paper

C353	A71	1c vermilion	.50	.35
C354	A71	2c ultra	.50	.35
C355	A72	3c pck grn	.50	.35
C356	A71	4c violet	.50	.35
C357	A71	5c org brn	.50	.35
C358	A71	25c brt grnsh bl	.50	.35
C359	A71	30c dl pur	.50	.35
C360	A72	45c lil rose	.70	.35
C361	A71	50c lt bl grn	.50	.35
C362	A71	1cor ultra	.70	.35
a.		Souv. sheet of 5, #C358-C362	11.00	11.00
	Nos. C353-C362 (10)		5.40	3.50

For surcharge see No. C365.

Nos. C331, C333, C360, C345 Surcharged in Green or Black

Engraved, Photogravure

1956, Feb. 4   Perf. 13½x13, 11½

C363	AP48	30c on 35c (G)	1.00	.35
C364	AP48	30c on 45c (G)	1.00	.35
C365	A72	30c on 45c	1.00	.35
C366	AP49	2cor on 5cor	3.75	1.50
	Nos. C363-C366 (4)		6.75	2.55

National Exhibition, Feb. 4-16, 1956.
See note after No. 772.

Gen. Jose D. Estrada AP53

The Stoning of Andres Castro AP54

1.50 cor, Emanuel Mongalo. 2.50 cor, Battle of Rivas. 10 cor, Com. Hiram Paulding.

1956, Sept. 14   Engr.   Perf. 12½

C367	AP53	30c dk car rose	.40	.35
C368	AP54	60c chocolate	.40	.35
C369	AP53	1.50cor green	.40	.35
C370	AP54	2.50cor dk ultra	.85	.40
C371	AP53	10cor red org	5.00	2.00
	Nos. C367-C371 (5)		7.05	3.45

Centenary of the National War.
For overprint and surcharge see #C444, C751.

President Somoza — AP55

1957, Feb. 1   Photo.   Perf. 14x13½
Various Frames: Centers in Black

C372	AP55	15c gray blk	.35	.25
C373	AP55	30c indigo	.35	.25
C374	AP55	2cor purple	1.40	1.00
C375	AP55	3cor dk grn	2.75	2.00
C376	AP55	5cor dk brn	4.25	3.25
	Nos. C372-C376 (5)		9.10	6.75

President Anastasio Somoza, 1896-1956.

Type of Regular Issue and

Handshake and Globe — AP56

Designs: 4c, Scout emblem, globe and Lord Baden-Powell. 5c, Cub Scout. 6c, Crossed flags and Scout emblem. 8c, Scout symbols. 30c, Joseph A. Harrison. 40c, Pres. Somoza receiving decoration at first Central American Camporee. 75c, Explorer Scout. 85c, Boy Scout. 1cor, Lord Baden-Powell.

1957, Apr. 9   Unwmk.   Perf. 13½x14

C377	AP56	3c red org & ol	.85	.35
C378	A75	4c dk brn & dk Prus grn	.85	.35
C379	A75	5c grn & brn	.85	.35
C380	A75	6c pur & ol	.85	.35
C381	A75	8c grnsh blk & red	.85	.35
C382	AP56	30c Prus grn & gray	.85	.35
C383	AP56	40c dk bl & grysh blk	.85	.35
C384	A75	75c mar & brn	.85	.35
C385	A75	85c red & gray	.85	.35
C386	A75	1cor dl red brn & sl grn	1.00	.60
a.		Souv. sheet of 5, #C382-C386, imperf.	4.00	4.00
	Nos. C377-C386 (10)		8.65	3.75

Centenary of the birth of Lord Baden-Powell, founder of the Boy Scouts.
No. C386a with each stamp overprinted "CAMPOREE SCOUT 1965" was issued in 1965 along with Nos. 843-852. Value, sheet $10.
For surcharge see No. C754.

Pres. Luis A. Somoza — AP57

1957, July 2   Perf. 14x13½
Portrait in Dark Brown

C387	AP57	20c dp bl	.45	.25
C388	AP57	25c lil rose	.45	.25
C389	AP57	30c blk brn	.45	.25
C390	AP57	40c grnsh bl	.45	.25
C391	AP57	2cor brt vio	4.25	3.00
	Nos. C387-C391 (5)		6.05	4.00

Issued to honor President Luis A. Somoza.

Church Types of Regular Issue

Designs: 30c, Archbishop Lezcano y Ortega. 60c, Managua Cathedral. 75c, Bishop Pereira y Castellon. 90c, Leon Cathedral. 1.50cor, De la Merced Church, Granada. 2cor, Father Mariano Dubon.

1957, July 16 — Unwmk.
Centers in Olive Gray

C392	A78	30c dk grn	.55	.25
C393	A77	60c chocolate	.55	.25
C394	A78	75c dk bl	.55	.25
C395	A77	90c brt red	.85	.30
C396	A77	1.50cor Prus grn	1.75	.40
C397	A78	2cor brt pur	2.40	.60
	Nos. C392-C397 (6)		6.65	2.05

Merchant Marine Type of 1957

Designs: 25c, M. S. Managua. 30c, Ship's wheel and map. 50c, Pennants. 60c, M. S. Costa Rica. 1 cor, M. S. Nicarao. 2.50 cor, Flag, globe & ship.

1957, Oct. 24 — Litho. — Perf. 14

C398	A79	25c ultra grysh bl & gray	.65	.25
C399	A79	30c red brn, gray & yel	.65	.25
C400	A79	50c vio, ol gray & bl	.75	.30
C401	A79	60c lake, grnsh bl & blk	.95	.35
C402	A79	1cor crim, brt bl & blk	1.25	.45
C403	A79	2.50cor blk, bl & red brn	4.75	2.50
	Nos. C398-C403 (6)		9.00	4.10

For surcharge see No. C691.

Fair Emblem — AP58

Designs: 30c, 2cor, Arms of Nicaragua. 45c, 10cor, Pavilion of Nicaragua, Brussels.

1958, Apr. 17 — Unwmk. — Perf. 14

C404	AP58	25c bluish grn, blk & yel	.40	.25
C405	AP58	30c multi	.40	.25
C406	AP58	45c bis, bl & blk	.40	.25
C407	AP58	1cor pale brn, lt bl & blk	.40	.25
C408	AP58	2cor multi	.75	.30
C409	AP58	10cor pale brn, lil & brn	2.60	1.60
a.		Souv. sheet of 6, #C404-C409	13.50	12.00
	Nos. C404-C409 (6)		4.95	2.90

World's Fair, Brussels, Apr. 17-Oct. 19.

Lions Type of Regular Issue

Designs: 30c, Dr. Teodoro A. Arias. 60c, Arms of Central American Republics. 90c, Edward G. Barry. 1.25cor, Melvin Jones. 2cor, Motto and emblem. 3cor, Map of Central America.

1958, May 8 — Litho.
Emblem in Yellow, Red and Blue

C410	A80	30c bl & org	.40	.25
C411	A80	60c multi	.40	.25
C412	A80	90c blue	.70	.30
C413	A80	1.25cor bl & ol	1.00	.40
C414	A80	2cor bl & grn	1.75	.70
C415	A80	3cor bl, lil & pink	2.60	1.10
a.		Souv. sheet of 6, #C410-C415	6.50	4.25
	Nos. C410-C415 (6)		6.85	3.00

For overprints and surcharges see Nos. C686, C971P.

Christian Brothers Type of 1958

Designs: 30c, Arms of La Salle. 60c, School, Managua, horiz. 85c, St. Jean Baptiste De La Salle. 90c, Bro. Carlos. 1.25cor, Bro. Julio. 1.50cor, Bro. Antonio. 1.75cor, Bro. Argeo. 2cor, Bro. Eugenio.

1958, July 13 — Photo. — Perf. 14

C416	A81	30c bl, car & yel	.40	.25
C417	A81	60c gray, brn & lil	.75	.25
C418	A81	85c red, bl & grnsh blk	.75	.30
C419	A81	90c ol grn, ocher & blk	1.10	.35
C420	A81	1.25cor car, ocher & blk	1.50	.50
C421	A81	1.50cor lt grn, gray & vio blk	1.75	.55
C422	A81	1.75cor brn, bl & grnsh blk	1.90	.65
C423	A81	2cor ol grn, gray & vio blk	2.75	1.00
	Nos. C416-C423 (8)		10.90	3.85

For surcharges see Nos. C539A, C755-C756.

UNESCO Building, Paris — AP59

75c, 5cor, "UNESCO." 90c, 3cor, UNESCO building, Eiffel tower. 1cor, Emblem, globe.

1958, Dec. 15 — Unwmk. — Litho.
Perf. 11½

C424	AP59	60c magenta & bl	.70	.25
C425	AP59	75c bl grn & org brn	.70	.25
C426	AP59	90c lt brn & blue grn	.70	.25
C427	AP59	1cor ultra & magenta	.70	.25
C428	AP59	3cor blk & org	2.40	1.00
C429	AP59	5cor rose lil & dk bl	3.75	1.50
a.		Min. sheet of 6, #C424-C429	7.00	4.50
	Nos. C424-C429 (6)		8.95	3.50

UNESCO Headquarters Opening in Paris, Nov. 3.
For overprints see Nos. C494-C499.

Type of Regular Issue, 1959 and

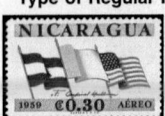

Nicaraguan, Papal and US Flags — AP60

Designs: 35c, Pope John XXIII and Cardinal Spellman. 1cor, Spellman coat of arms. 1.05cor, Cardinal Spellman. 1.50cor, Human rosary and Cardinal, horiz. 2cor, Cardinal with Ruben Dario order.

1959, Nov. 26 — Perf. 12½

C430	AP60	30c vio bl, yel & red	.40	.25
C431	A83	35c dp org & grnsh blk	.40	.25
C432	A83	1cor yel, bl & car	.40	.25
C433	A83	1.05cor red, blk & dk car	1.00	.40
C434	A83	1.50cor dk bl & yel	1.00	.40
C435	A83	2cor multi	1.25	.60
C436	AP60	5cor multi	2.50	1.25
a.		Min. sheet of 7, #C430-C436, perf. or imperf.	8.00	5.00
	Nos. C430-C436 (7)		6.95	3.40

Visit of Cardinal Spellman to Managua, Feb. 1958.
For overprints and surcharges see #C538, C638, C747, C752, C971.

Type of Lincoln Regular Issue and

AP61

Perf. 13x13½, 13½x13
1960, Jan. 21 — Engr. — Unwmk.
Portrait in Black

C437	A84	30c indigo	.45	.30
C438	A84	35c brt car	.45	.30
C439	A84	70c plum	.45	.30
C440	A84	1.05cor emerald	.45	.30
C441	A84	1.50cor violet	1.10	.40
C442	AP61	5cor int blk & bis	3.50	1.50
a.		Souv. sheet of 6, #C437-C442, imperf.	6.50	4.50
	Nos. C437-C442 (6)		6.40	3.10

150th anniv. of the birth of Abraham Lincoln.
For overprints and surcharges see Nos. C446-C451, C500, C539, C637, C680, C753, C971W.

Nos. C343, C370 and C318 Overprinted

1960, July 4 — Engr.

C443	AP49	2cor magenta	1.30	.70
C444	AP54	2.50cor dk ultra	1.30	.75
C445	A65	3cor green	1.90	1.10
	Nos. C443-C445 (3)		4.50	2.55

10th anniversary of the Philatelic Club of San Jose, Costa Rica.

Nos. C437-C442 Overprinted in Red

Perf. 13x13½, 13½x13
1960, Sept. 19 — Unwmk.
Center in Black

C446	A84	30c indigo	.65	.30
C447	A84	35c brt car	.65	.30
C448	A84	70c purple	.65	.30
C449	A84	1.05cor emerald	.95	.30
C450	A84	1.50cor violet	1.90	.80
C451	AP61	5cor int blk & bis	5.75	2.50
	Nos. C446-C451 (6)		10.55	4.50

Issued for the Red Cross to aid earthquake victims in Chile. The overprint on No. C451 is horizontal and always inverted.

People and World Refugee Year Emblem — AP62

5cor, Crosses, globe and WRY emblem.

1961, Dec. 30 — Litho. — Perf. 11x11½

C452	AP62	2cor multi	.75	.30
C453	AP62	5cor multi	1.25	.65
a.		Souv. sheet of 2, #C452-C453	3.00	2.50

World Refugee Year, July 1, 1959-June 30, 1960.

Consular Service Stamps Surcharged in Red, Black or Blue — AP63

Unwmk.
1961, Feb. 21 — Engr. — Perf. 12
Red Marginal Number

C454	AP63	20c on 50c dp bl (R)	.80	.40
C455	AP63	20c on 1cor grnsh blk (R)	.80	.40
C456	AP63	20c on 2cor grn (R)	.80	.40
C457	AP63	20c on 3cor dk car	.80	.40
C458	AP63	20c on 5cor org (Bl)	.80	.40
C459	AP63	20c on 10cor vio (R)	.80	.40
C460	AP63	20c on 20cor red brn (R)	.80	.40
C461	AP63	20c on 50cor brn (R)	.80	.40
C462	AP63	20c on 100cor mag (R)	.80	.40
	Nos. C454-C462 (9)		7.20	3.60

See Nos. CO51-CO59, RA63-RA64.

Charles L. Mullins, Anastasio Somoza and Franklin D. Roosevelt AP64

Standard Bearers with Flags of Nicaragua and Academy AP65

Designs: 25c, 70c, Flags of Nicaragua and Academy. 30c, 1.05cor, Directors of Academy: Fred T. Cruse, LeRoy Bartlett, Jr., John F. Greco, Anastasio Somoza Debayle, Francisco Boza, Elias Monge. 40c, 2cor, Academy Emblem. 45c, 5cor, Anastasio Somoza Debayle and Luis Somoza Debayle.

Perf. 11x11½, 11½x11
1961, Feb. 24 — Litho. — Unwmk.

C463	AP64	20c rose, gray & buff	.60	.40
C464	AP65	25c bl, red & blk	.60	.40
C465	AP64	30c bl, gray & yel	.60	.40
C466	AP65	35c multi	.60	.40
C467	AP65	40c multi	.60	.40
C468	AP64	45c pink, gray & buff	.60	.40
a.		Min. sheet of 6, #C463-C468, imperf.	1.50	1.00
C469	AP64	60c brn, gray & buff	.60	.40
C470	AP65	70c multi	.60	.40
C471	AP64	1.05cor clar, gray & yel	.60	.40
C472	AP65	1.50cor multi	.60	.40
C473	AP65	2cor multi	.75	.40

C474	AP64	5cor gray & buff	1.75	.40
a.		Min. sheet of 6, #C469-C474, imperf.	6.50	4.00
	Nos. C463-C474 (12)		8.50	4.80

20th anniversary (in 1959) of the founding of the Military Academy of Nicaragua.
In 1977, Nos. C468a and C474a were overprinted in black: "1927-1977 50 ANIVERSARIO / Guardia Nacional de Nicaragua." Value, $7.50 for both.
For surcharges see Nos. C692, C748, C759.

Emblem of Junior Chamber of Commerce — AP66

Designs: 2c, 15c, Globe showing map of Americas, horiz. 4c, 35c, Globe and initials, horiz. 5c, 70c, Chamber credo. 6c, 1.05cor, Handclasp. 10c, 5cor, Regional map.

Perf. 11x11½, 11½x11
1961, May 16 — Unwmk.

C475	AP66	2c multi	.65	.40
C476	AP66	3c yel & blk	.65	.40
C477	AP66	4c multi	.65	.40
C478	AP66	5c crim & blk	.65	.40
C479	AP66	6c brn, yel & blk	.65	.40
C480	AP66	10c org, blk & lt bl	.65	.40
C481	AP66	15c bl, blk & grn	.65	.40
C482	AP66	30c bl & blk	.65	.40
C483	AP66	35c multi	.65	.40
C484	AP66	70c yel, blk & crim	.65	.40
C485	AP66	1.05cor multi	.65	.40
C486	AP66	5cor multi	1.50	.40
	Nos. C475-C486 (12)		8.65	4.80

13th Regional Congress of the Junior Chamber of Commerce of Nicaragua and the Intl. Junior Chamber of Commerce.
The imperforates of Nos. C475-C486 were not authorized.
For overprints and surcharges see Nos. C504-C508, C537, C634, C687, C749.

Rigoberto Cabezas AP67

Map of Costa Rica and View of Cartago AP68

Designs: 45c, Newspaper. 70c, Building. 2cor, Cabezas quotation. 10cor, Map of lower Nicaragua with Masaya area.

1961, Aug. 29 — Litho. — Perf. 13½

C487	AP67	20c org & dk bl	.60	.40
C488	AP68	40c lt bl & claret	.60	.40
C489	AP68	45c citron & brn	.60	.40
C490	AP68	70c beige & grn	.60	.40
C491	AP68	2cor pink & dk bl	1.80	.40
C492	AP68	10cor grnsh bl & cl	3.50	1.10
	Nos. C487-C492 (6)		7.70	3.10

Centenary of the birth of Rigoberto Cabezas, who acquired the Mosquito Territory (Atlantic Littoral) for Nicaragua.

No. C253 Overprinted in Red:
"Convención Filatélica-Centro-América-Panama-San Salvador-27 Julio 1961"

1961, Aug. 23 — Engr. — Perf. 12½

C493	AP22	1.25cor multi	.90	.65
a.		Inverted overprint	75.00	

Central American Philatelic Convention, San Salvador, July 27.

Nos. C424-C429 Overprinted in Red

1961 — Litho. — Perf. 11½

C494	AP59	60c magenta & bl	.40	.40
C495	AP59	75c bl grn & org brn	.50	.40
C496	AP59	90c lt brn & blue grn	.50	.40

C497 AP59 1cor ultra & magenta .50 .40
C498 AP59 3cor blk & org 1.10 .65
C499 AP59 5cor rose lil & dk bl 4.50 1.75
Nos. C494-C499 (6) 7.50 4.00

Issued in memory of Dag Hammarskjold, Secretary General of the United Nations, 1953-61.

Nos. C314 and C440
Surcharged in Red

Perf. 13x13½, 13
1962, Jan. 20 Engr.
C500 A84 1cor on 1.05cor .80 .40
C501 AP44 1cor on 1.10cor .80 .40

UNESCO Emblem and
Crowd — AP69

Design: 5cor, UNESCO and UN Emblems.

Unwmk.
1962, Feb. 26 Photo. **Perf. 12**
C502 AP69 2cor multi .75 .25
C503 AP69 5cor multi 1.50 .70
　a.　Souv. sheet of 2, #C502-
　　　C503, imperf. 2.00 1.50

15th anniv. (in 1961) of UNESCO. For overprint, see No. C971H, C971K.

Nos. C480 and C483-
C486 Overprinted

Perf. 11x11½, 11½x11
1962, July Litho.
C504 AP66 10c multi .50 .25
C505 AP66 35c multi .70 .25
C506 AP66 70c multi .90 .30
C507 AP66 1.05cor multi 1.20 .45
C508 AP66 5cor multi 1.90 1.40
Nos. C504-C508 (5) 5.20 2.65

WHO drive to eradicate malaria.

Souvenir Sheet

Stamps and Postmarks of
1862 — AP69a

1962, Sept. 9 Litho. Imperf.
C509 AP69a 7cor multi 3.25 2.75

Cent. of Nicaraguan postage stamps. For overprint, see Nos. C971Y-C971Z.

Arms Type of Regular Issue, 1962

30c, Nueva Segovia. 50c, León. 1cor, Managua. 2cor, Granada. 5cor, Rivas.

1962, Nov. 22 **Perf. 12½x13**
Arms in Original Colors; Black
Inscriptions
C510 A86 30c rose .75 .40
C511 A86 50c salmon .75 .40
C512 A86 1cor lt grn .75 .40
C513 A86 2cor gray .90 .40
C514 A86 5cor lt bl 1.80 1.00
Nos. C510-C514 (5) 4.95 2.60

Liberty
Bell — AP70

1963, May 15 Litho. **Perf. 13x12**
C515 AP70 30c lt bl, blk & ol bis .80 .40

Sesquicentennial of the 1st Nicaraguan declaration of Independence (in 1961).

Paulist Brother
Comforting
Boy — AP71

60c, Nun comforting girl. 2cor, St. Vincent de Paul and St. Louisa de Marillac, horiz.

1963, May 15 Photo. **Perf. 13½**
C516 AP71 60c gray & ocher .55 .40
C517 AP71 1cor salmon & blk .70 .40
C518 AP71 2cor crimson & blk 1.20 .40
Nos. C516-C518 (3) 2.45 1.20

300th anniv. of the deaths of St. Vincent de Paul and St. Louisa de Marillac (in 1960).

Map of Central
America — AP72

Lithographed and Engraved
1963, Aug. 2 Unwmk. **Perf. 12**
C519 AP72 1cor bl & yel .80 .40

Issued to honor the Federation of Central American Philatelic Societies.

Cross over
World — AP73

1963, Aug. 6
C520 AP73 20c yel & red .80 .40

Vatican II, the 21st Ecumenical Council of the Roman Catholic Church.

Wheat and Map of
Nicaragua — AP74

Design: 25c, Dead tree on parched earth.

1963, Aug. 6
C521 AP74 10c lt grn & grn .80 .40
C522 AP74 25c yel & dk brn .80 .40

FAO "Freedom from Hunger" campaign.

Boxing — AP75

Lithographed and Engraved
1963, Dec. 12 Unwmk. **Perf. 12**
C523 AP75 2c shown .65 .25
C524 AP75 3c Running .65 .25
C525 AP75 4c Underwater .65 .25
C526 AP75 5c Soccer .65 .25
C527 AP75 6c Baseball .65 .25

C528 AP75 10c Tennis .65 .25
C529 AP75 15c Bicycling .65 .25
C530 AP75 20c Motorcycling .65 .25
C531 AP75 35c Chess .65 .25
C532 AP75 60c Deep-sea fish-
　　　　　　ing .75 .30
C533 AP75 1cor Table tennis 1.00 .40
C534 AP75 2cor Basketball 2.00 .80
C535 AP75 5cor Golf 5.00 2.00
Nos. C523-C535 (13) 14.60 5.75

Publicizing the 1964 Olympic Games.
For overprints and surcharge see Nos. C553-C558, C635.

**Central American Independence
Issue**

Flags of Central
American States —
AP75a

1964, Sept. 15 Litho. **Perf. 13x13½**
Size: 27x43mm
C536 AP75a 40c multi .80 .40

**Nos. C479, C430, C437 and C416
Surcharged in Black or Red**

a　　　　　　　b

1964 Litho. **Perf. 11½x11**
C537 AP66 (a) 5c on 6c .90 .40
Perf. 12½
C538 AP60 (a) 10c on 30c 1.80 .40
Engr.
Perf. 13x13½
C539 A84 (a) 15c on 30c (R) 2.25 .40
Photo.
Perf. 14
C539A A81 (b) 20c on 30c .90 .40
Nos. C537-C539A (4) 5.85 1.60

Floating Red Cross
Station — AP76

Designs: 5c, Alliance for Progress emblem, vert. 15c, Highway. 20c, Plowing with tractors, and sun. 25c, Housing development. 30c, Presidents Somoza and Kennedy and World Bank Chairman Eugene Black. 35c, Adult education. 40c, Smokestacks.

1964, Oct. 15 Litho. **Perf. 12**
C540 AP76 5c yel, brt bl, grn &
　　　　　　gray .40 .40
C541 AP76 10c multi .40 .40
C542 AP76 15c multi .40 .40
C543 AP76 20c org brn, yel & blk .40 .40
C544 AP76 25c multi .40 .40
C545 AP76 30c dk bl, blk & brn .40 .40
C546 AP76 35c lil rose, dk red &
　　　　　　blk .40 .40
C547 AP76 40c dp car, blk & yel 4.00 .40
Nos. C540-C547 (8) 6.80 3.20

Alliance for Progress.
For surcharges see Nos. C677, C693.

Map of Central
America and
Central American
States — AP77

Designs (Map of Central America and): 25c, Grain. 40c, Cogwheels. 50c, Heads of cattle.

1964, Nov. 30 Litho. **Perf. 12**
C548 AP77 15c ultra & multi .80 .40
C549 AP77 25c multi .80 .40
C550 AP77 40c multi .80 .40
C551 AP77 50c multi .80 .40
Nos. C548-C551 (4) 3.20 1.60

Central American Common Market.
For surcharge see No. C678.

**Nos. C523-C525, C527 and C533-
C534 Overprinted: "OLIMPIADAS /
TOKYO-1964"**

Lithographed and Engraved
1964, Dec. 19 Unwmk. **Perf. 12**
C553 AP75 2c multi .40 .25
C554 AP75 3c multi .40 .25
C555 AP75 4c multi .40 .25
C556 AP75 6c multi .40 .25
C557 AP75 1cor multi 3.75 2.00
C558 AP75 2cor multi 5.00 2.50
Nos. C553-C558 (6) 10.35 5.50

18th Olympic Games, Tokyo, Oct. 10-25.

Blood
Transfusion — AP78

Designs: 20c, Volunteers and priest rescuing wounded man. 40c, Landscape during storm. 10cor, Red Cross over map of Nicaragua.

1965, Jan. 28 Litho. **Perf. 12**
C559 AP78 20c yel, blk & red .50 .40
C560 AP78 25c red, blk & ol
　　　　　　bis .50 .40
C561 AP78 40c grn, blk & red .50 .40
C562 AP78 10cor multi 3.50 1.10
Nos. C559-C562 (4) 5.00 2.30

Centenary (in 1963) of the Intl. Red Cross.

Stele — AP79

Antique Indian artifacts: 5c, Three jadeite statuettes, horiz. 15c, Dog, horiz. 20c, Talamanca pendant. 25c, Decorated pottery bowl and vase, horiz. 30c, Stone pestle and mortar on animal base. 35c, Three statuettes, horiz. 40c, Idol on animal pedestal. 50c, Decorated pottery bowl and vase. 60c, Vase and metate (tripod bowl), horiz. 1cor, Metate.

Perf. 13½x13, 13x13½
1965, Mar. 24 Litho. Unwmk.
Black Margin and Inscription
C563 AP79 5c yel & multi .75 .40
C564 AP79 10c multi .75 .40
C565 AP79 15c multi .75 .40
C566 AP79 20c sal & dk brn .75 .40
C567 AP79 25c lil & multi .75 .40
C568 AP79 30c lt grn & multi .75 .40
C569 AP79 35c multi .75 .40
C570 AP79 40c cit & multi .75 .40
C571 AP79 50c ocher & multi .75 .40
C572 AP79 60c multi .75 .40
C573 AP79 1cor car & multi 1.00 .40
Nos. C563-C573 (11) 8.50 4.40

For surcharges see Nos. C596-597, C679, C688-C690.

Pres. John F. Kennedy
(1917-63) — AP80

Photogravure & Lithographed
1965, Apr. 28 **Perf. 12½x13½**
C574 AP80 35c blk & brt
　　　　　　grn .45 .25
C575 AP80 75c blk & brt
　　　　　　pink .65 .25
C576 AP80 1.10cor blk & dk bl .90 .40

C577 AP80 2cor blk & yel
brn   2.25   1.00
Nos. C574-C577 (4)   4.25   1.90
Set of 4 souvenir sheets   17.00   12.00

Nos. C574-C577 each exist in souvenir sheets containing one imperf. block of 4. For surcharge see No. C760.

Andrés Bello — AP81

1965, Oct. 15   **Litho.**   *Perf. 14*
C578 AP81 10c dk brn & red
brn   .75   .25
C579 AP81 15c ind & lt bl   .75   .25
C580 AP81 45c blk & dl lil   .75   .25
C581 AP81 80c blk & yel grn   .75   .25
C582 AP81 1cor dk brn & yel   .75   .25
C583 AP81 2cor blk & gray   .85   .30
Nos. C578-C583 (6)   4.60   1.55

Centenary of the death of Andrés Bello (1780?-1864), Venezuelan writer and educator.

Winston Churchill — AP82

Winston Churchill: 35c, 1cor, Broadcasting, horiz. 60c, 3cor, On military inspection. 75c, As young officer.

1966, Feb. 7   **Unwmk.**   *Perf. 14*
C584 AP82 20c cer & blk   .40   .40
C585 AP82 35c dk ol grn & blk   .40   .40
C586 AP82 60c brn & blk   .40   .40
C587 AP82 75c rose red   .50   .40
C588 AP82 1cor vio blk   .75   .40
C589 AP82 2cor lil & blk   1.40   .40
  a.   Souv. sheet of 4   2.75   1.40
C590 AP82 3cor ind & blk   2.10   .40
Nos. C584-C590 (7)   5.95   2.80

Sir Winston Spencer Churchill (1874-1965), statesman and World War II leader.

No. C589a contains four imperf. stamps similar to Nos. C586-C589 with simulated perforations.

Pope John XXIII — AP83

35c, Pope Paul VI. 1cor, Archbishop Gonzalez y Robleto. 2cor, St. Peter's, Rome. 3cor, Arms of Pope John XXIII & St. Peter's.

1966, Dec. 15   **Litho.**   *Perf. 13*
C591 AP83 20c multi   .65   .40
C592 AP83 35c multi   .65   .40
C593 AP83 1cor multi   .65   .40
C594 AP83 2cor multi   1.10   .40
C595 AP83 3cor multi   1.60   .50
Nos. C591-C595 (5)   4.65   2.10

Closing of the Ecumenical Council, Vatican II.

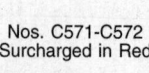

Nos. C571-C572 Surcharged in Red

1967   *Perf. 13x13½, 13½x13*
C596 AP79 10c on 50c multi   .80   .40
C597 AP79 15c on 60c multi   .80   .40

Rubén Dario and Birthplace AP84

Portrait and: 10c, Monument, Managua. 20c, Leon Cathedral, site of Dario's tomb. 40c, Centaurs. 75c, Swans. 1cor, Roman triumphal march. 2cor, St. Francis and the Wolf. 5cor, "Faith" defeating "Death."

1967, Jan. 18   **Litho.**   *Perf. 13*
C598 AP84 5c lt brn, tan & blk   .65   .40
C599 AP84 10c org, pale org &
blk   .65   .40
C600 AP84 20c vio, lt bl & blk   .65   .40
C601 AP84 40c grn, dk grn &
blk   .65   .40
  a.   Souv. sheet of 4, #C598-C601   1.75   1.75
C602 AP84 75c ultra, pale bl &
blk   .65   .40
C603 AP84 1cor red, pale red &
blk   .65   .40
C604 AP84 2cor rose pink, car &
blk   .80   .40
C605 AP84 5cor dp ultra, vio bl,
& blk   1.80   .40
  a.   Souv. sheet of 4, #C602-C605   6.75   6.75
Nos. C598-C605 (8)   6.50   3.20

Rubén Dario (pen name of Felix Rubén Garcia Sarmiento, 1867-1916), poet, newspaper correspondent and diplomat.
Sheets were issued perf. and imperf.

Megalura Peleus — AP85

Designs: Various butterflies. 5c, 10c, 30c, 35c, 50c and 1cor are vertical.

1967, Apr. 20   **Litho.**   *Perf. 14*
C606 AP85 5c multi   .40   .40
C607 AP85 10c multi   .40   .40
C608 AP85 15c multi   .45   .40
C609 AP85 20c multi   .80   .40
C610 AP85 25c multi   1.00   .40
C611 AP85 30c multi   1.20   .40
C612 AP85 35c multi   1.25   .40
C613 AP85 40c multi   1.50   .40
C614 AP85 50c multi   1.60   .40
C615 AP85 60c multi   2.00   .80
C616 AP85 1cor multi   3.25   .80
C617 AP85 2cor multi   7.00   4.00
Nos. C606-C617 (12)   20.85   9.20

Com. James McDivitt and Maj. Edward H. White — AP86

Gemini 4 Space Flight: 10c, 40c, Rocket launching and astronauts. 15c, 75c, Edward H. White walking in space. 20c, 1cor, Recovery of capsule.

1967, Sept. 20   **Litho.**   *Perf. 13*
C618 AP86 5c red & multi   .80   .40
C619 AP86 10c org & multi   .80   .40
C620 AP86 15c multi   .80   .40
C621 AP86 20c multi   .80   .40
C622 AP86 35c ol & multi   .80   .40
C623 AP86 40c ultra & multi   .80   .40
C624 AP86 75c brn & multi   .80   .40
C625 AP86 1cor multi   .80   .40
Nos. C618-C625 (8)   6.40   3.20

Saquanjoche, National Flower of Nicaragua — AP87

National Flowers: No. C626, White nun orchid, Guatemala. No. C627, Rose, Honduras. No. C629, Maquilishuat, Salvador. No. C630, Purple guaria orchid, Costa Rica.

1967, Nov. 22   **Litho.**   *Perf. 13½*
C626 AP87 40c multi   1.25   .40
C627 AP87 40c multi   1.25   .40
C628 AP87 40c multi   1.25   .40
C629 AP87 40c multi   1.25   .40
C630 AP87 40c multi   1.25   .40
  a.   Strip of 5, #C626-C630   6.75   2.00

5th anniversary of the General Treaty for Central American Economic Integration.

Presidents of Nicaragua and Mexico — AP88

Designs: 40c Pres. Gustavo Díaz Ordaz of Mexico and Pres. René Schick of Nicaragua signing statement, horiz. 1cor, President Díaz.

1968, Feb. 28   **Litho.**   *Perf. 12½*
C631 AP88 20c black   .80   .40
C632 AP88 40c slate grn   .80   .40
C633 AP88 1cor dp brn   .80   .40
Nos. C631-C633 (3)   2.40   1.20

Issued to commemorate the visit of the President of Mexico, Gustavo Díaz Ordaz.

Nos. C479, C527, C242, C440 and C434 Surcharged in Black, Red (#C637) or Yellow (#C638)

1968, May   **Litho.; Engr.**
C634 AP66 5c on 6c multi   .80   .40
C635 AP75 5c on 6c multi   .80   .40
C636 AP20 5c on 8c blk brn   .80   .40
C637 A84 1cor on 1.05cor emer
& blk   .80   .40
C638 A83 1cor on 1.50cor dk bl
& yel   .80   .40
Nos. C634-C638 (5)   4.00   2.00

Mangos — AP89

1968, May 15   **Litho.**   *Perf. 14*
C639 AP89 5c shown   .45   .40
C640 AP89 10c Pineapples   .45   .40
C641 AP89 15c Orange   .45   .40
C642 AP89 20c Papaya   .50   .40
C643 AP89 30c Bananas   .50   .40
C644 AP89 35c Avocado   .95   .40
C645 AP89 50c Watermelon   .95   .40
C646 AP89 75c Cashews   .95   .40
C647 AP89 1cor Sapodilla   .95   .40
C648 AP89 2cor Cacao   1.80   .40
Nos. C639-C648 (10)   7.95   4.00

The Last Judgment, by Michelangelo AP90

Paintings: 10c, The Crucifixion, by Fra Angelo, horiz. 35c, Madonna with Child and St. John, by Raphael. 2cor, The Disrobing of Christ, by El Greco. 3cor, The Immaculate Conception, by Murillo. 5cor, Christ of St. John of the Cross, by Salvador Dali.

1968, July 22   **Litho.**   *Perf. 12½*
C649 AP90 10c gold & multi   .55   .40
C650 AP90 15c gold & multi   .55   .40
C651 AP90 35c gold & multi   .55   .40
C652 AP90 2cor gold & multi   1.00   .40
C653 AP90 3cor gold & multi   1.50   .55
Nos. C649-C653 (5)   4.15   2.15

Miniature Sheet
C654 AP90 5cor gold & multi   3.25   2.75

Nos. C649-C652 Overprinted: "Visita de S.S. Paulo VI C.E. de Bogota 1968"

1968, Oct. 25   **Litho.**   *Perf. 12½*
C655 AP90 10c gold & multi   .60   .40
C656 AP90 15c gold & multi   .60   .40
C657 AP90 35c gold & multi   .60   .40
C658 AP90 2cor gold & multi   1.20   .40
Nos. C655-C658 (4)   3.00   1.60

Visit of Pope Paul VI to Bogota, Colombia, Aug. 22-24. The overprint has 3 lines on the 10c stamp and 5 lines on others.

Basketball — AP91

Sports: 15c, Fencing, horiz. 20c, Diving. 35c, Running. 50c, Hurdling, horiz. 75c, Weight lifting. 1cor, Boxing, horiz. 2cor, Soccer.

1968, Nov. 28   **Litho.**   *Perf. 14*
C659 AP91 10c multi   .65   .40
C660 AP91 15c org red, blk &
gray   .65   .40
C661 AP91 20c multi   .65   .40
C662 AP91 35c multi   .65   .40
C663 AP91 50c multi   .65   .40
C664 AP91 75c multi   .65   .40
C665 AP91 1cor yel & multi   .75   .40
C666 AP91 2cor gray & multi   2.10   .80
  a.   Souv. sheet of 4, #C663-C666   3.75   2.50
Nos. C659-C666 (8)   6.75   3.60

19th Olympic Games, Mexico City, 10/12-27.

Cichlasoma Citrinellum AP92

Fish: 15c, Cichlasoma nicaraguensis. 20c, Carp. 30c, Gar (lepisosteus tropicus). 35c, Swordfish. 50c, Phylipnus dormitor, vert. 75c, Tarpon atlanticus, vert. 1cor, Eulamia nicaraguensis, vert. 2cor, Sailfish, vert. 3cor, Sawfish, vert.

Perf. 13½x13, 13x13½
1969, Mar. 12   **Litho.**
C667 AP92 10c vio bl & multi   1.00   .40
C668 AP92 15c org & multi   1.00   .40
C669 AP92 20c grn & multi   1.00   .40
C670 AP92 30c pur & multi   1.00   .40
C671 AP92 35c yel & multi   1.00   .40
C672 AP92 50c brn & multi   1.00   .40
C673 AP92 75c ultra & multi   1.00   .40
C674 AP92 1cor org & multi   1.00   .40
C675 AP92 2cor dk bl & multi   1.75   .40
C676 AP92 3cor multi   2.60   .40
  a.   Min. sheet of 4, #C673-C676   6.25   5.00
Nos. C667-C676 (10)   12.35   4.00

Nos. C544, C549, C567 and C439 Srchd. in Black or Red

No. C678   No. C680

1969, Mar.   **Litho.**   *Perf. 12, 13½x13*
C677 AP76 10c on 25c multi   .80   .40
C678 AP77 10c on 25c multi   .80   .40
C679 AP79 15c on 25c multi   .80   .40

Engr.
C680 A84 50c on 70c (R)   .80   .40
Nos. C677-C680 (4)   3.20   1.60

Size of 50c surcharge: 11½x9mm.

View, Exhibition Tower and Emblem — AP93

1969, May 30   **Litho.**   *Perf. 13½x13*
C681 AP93 30c dk vio bl & red   .60   .40
C682 AP93 35c blk & red   .60   .40
C683 AP93 75c car rose & vio bl   .60   .40
C684 AP93 1cor dp plum & blk   .60   .40
C685 AP93 2cor dk brn & blk   1.50   .40
  a.   Souv. sheet of 4, #C681-
C682, C684-C685   4.00   2.50
Nos. C681-C685 (5)   3.90   2.00

HEMISFAIR 1968 Exhibition.

Nos. C410, C482,
C567-C569, C399,
C465, C546 Srchd.
in Black or Red

1969   Litho.   Perfs. as before
C686	A80	10c on 30c multi	1.00	.40
C687	AP66	10c on 30c bl & blk		
		(R)	1.00	.40
C688	AP79	10c on 25c multi	1.00	.40
C689	AP79	10c on 30c multi	1.00	.40
C690	AP79	15c on 35c multi (R)	1.00	.40
C691	A79	20c on 30c multi	1.00	.40
C692	AP64	20c on 30c multi	1.00	.40
C693	AP76	20c on 35c multi	1.00	.40
		Nos. C686-C693 (8)	8.00	3.20

Products of
Nicaragua
AP94

5c, Minerals (miner). 10c, Fishing. 15c, Bananas. 20c, Timber (truck). 35c, Coffee. 40c, Sugar cane. 60c, Cotton. 75c, Rice and corn. 1cor, Tobacco. 2cor, Meat.

1969, Sept. 22   Litho.   Perf. 13x13½
C694	AP94	5c gold & multi	.80	.40
C695	AP94	10c gold & multi	.80	.40
C696	AP94	15c gold & multi	.80	.40
C697	AP94	20c gold & multi	.80	.40
C698	AP94	35c gold & multi	.80	.40
C699	AP94	40c gold & multi	.80	.40
C700	AP94	60c gold & multi	.80	.40
C701	AP94	75c gold & multi	.80	.40
C702	AP94	1cor gold & multi	.80	.40
C703	AP94	2cor gold & multi	1.00	.40
		Nos. C694-C703 (10)	8.20	4.00

Woman Carrying Jar,
Conference
Emblem — AP95

1970, Feb. 26   Litho.   Perf. 13½x14
C704	AP95	10c multi	.65	.40
C705	AP95	15c grn & multi	.65	.40
C706	AP95	20c ultra & multi	.65	.40
C707	AP95	35c multi	.65	.40
C708	AP95	50c multi	.65	.40
C709	AP95	75c multi	.65	.40
C710	AP95	1cor lil & multi	1.10	.40
C711	AP95	2cor multi	2.00	.50
		Nos. C704-C711 (8)	7.00	3.30

8th Inter-American Conf. on Savings & Loans.

Soccer Type of Regular Issue and

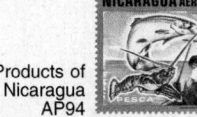

Flags of Participating
Nations, World Cup,
1970 — AP96

Soccer Players: 20c, Djalma Santos, Brazil. 80c, Billy Wright, England. 4cor, Jozef Bozsik, Hungary. 5cor, Bobby Charlton, England.

1970, May 11   Litho.   Perf. 13½
C712	A87	20c multi	.55	.40
C713	A87	80c multi	.70	.40
C714	AP96	1cor multi	.95	.60
C715	A87	4cor multi	3.00	2.00
C716	A87	5cor multi	3.50	2.25
		Nos. C712-C716 (5)	8.70	5.65

Issued to honor the winners of the 1970 poll for the International Soccer Hall of Fame. No. C714 also publicizes the 9th World Soccer Championships for the Jules Rimet Cup, Mexico City, May 30-June 21, 1970.

Names of players and their achievements printed in black on back of stamps.

For overprint and surcharges see Nos. C786-788.

EXPO Emblem, Mt.
Fuji and Torii — AP97

1970, July 5   Litho.   Perf. 13½x14
C717	AP97	25c multi	.45	.40
C718	AP97	30c multi	.45	.40
C719	AP97	35c multi	.45	.40
C720	AP97	75c multi	.70	.45
C721	AP97	1.50cor multi	1.00	.65
C722	AP97	3cor multi	2.10	1.25
	a.	Souv. sheet of 3, #C720-C722, imperf.	2.00	1.25
		Nos. C717-C722 (6)	5.15	3.55

EXPO '70 International Exhibition, Osaka, Japan, Mar. 15-Sept. 13, 1970. For overprint, see No. C972.

Moon Landing,
Apollo 11
Emblem and
Nicaragua
Flag — AP98

Apollo 11 Emblem, Nicaragua Flag and: 40c, 75c, Moon surface and landing capsule. 60c, 1cor, Astronaut planting US flag.

1970, Aug. 12   Litho.   Perf. 14
C723	AP98	35c multi	.65	.40
C724	AP98	40c multi	.65	.40
C725	AP98	60c pink & multi	.65	.40
C726	AP98	75c yel & multi	.65	.40
C727	AP98	1cor vio & multi	1.00	.40
C728	AP98	2cor org & multi	1.50	.40
		Nos. C723-C728 (6)	5.10	2.40

Man's 1st landing on the moon, July 20, 1969. See note after US No. C76.

Franklin D.
Roosevelt — AP99

Roosevelt Portraits: 15c, 1cor, as stamp collector. 20c, 50c, 2cor, Full face.

1970, Oct. 12
C729	AP99	10c blk & bluish blk	.75	.40
C730	AP99	15c blk & brn vio	.75	.40
C731	AP99	20c blk & ol grn	.75	.40
C732	AP99	35c blk & brn vio	.75	.40
C733	AP99	50c brown	.75	.40
C734	AP99	75c blue	.75	.40
C735	AP99	1cor rose red	.75	.40
C736	AP99	2cor black	.75	.40
		Nos. C729-C736 (8)	6.00	3.20

Franklin Delano Roosevelt (1882-1945).

Christmas
1970 — AP100

Paintings: Nos. C737, C742, Annunciation, by Matthias Grunewald. Nos. C738, C743, Nativity, by El Greco. Nos. C739, C744, Adoration of the Magi, by Albrecht Dürer. Nos. C740, C745, Virgin and Child, by J. van Hemessen. Nos. C741, C746, Holy Shepherd, Portuguese School, 16th century.

1970, Dec. 1   Litho.   Perf. 14
C737	AP100	10c multi	.80	.40
C738	AP100	10c multi	.80	.40
C739	AP100	10c multi	.80	.40
C740	AP100	10c multi	.80	.40
C741	AP100	10c multi	.80	.40
C742	AP100	15c multi	.80	.40
C743	AP100	20c multi	.80	.40
C744	AP100	35c multi	.80	.40
C745	AP100	75c multi	.80	.40
C746	AP100	1cor multi	.80	.40
		Nos. C737-C746 (10)	8.00	4.00

Nos. C737-C741 printed se-tenant.

Issues of 1947-67
Surcharged

1971, Mar.
C747	A83	10c on 1.05cor, #C433	.55	.40
C748	AP64	10c on 1.05cor, #C471	.55	.40
C749	AP66	10c on 1.05cor, #C485	.55	.40
C750	AP42	15c on 1.50cor, #C292	.80	.40
C751	AP53	15c on 1.50cor, #C369	.80	.40
C752	A83	15c on 1.50cor, #C434	.80	.40
C753	A84	15c on 1.50cor, #C441	.80	.40
C754	A75	20c on 85c, #C385	1.00	.50
C755	A81	20c on 85c, #C418	1.00	.50
C756	A81	25c on 90c, #C419	1.40	.70
C757	AP48	30c on 1.10cor, #C337	1.50	.85
C758	AP44	40c on 1.10cor, #C314	2.25	1.10
C759	AP65	40c on 1.50cor, #C472	2.25	1.10
C760	AP80	1cor on 1.10cor, #C576	5.50	2.75
		Nos. C747-C760 (14)	19.75	10.30

The arrangement of the surcharge differs on each stamp.

Mathematics Type of Regular Issue

Symbolic Designs of Scientific Formulae: 25c, Napier's law (logarithms). 30c, Pythagorean theorem (length of sides of right-angled triangle). 40c, Boltzman's equation (movement of gases). 1cor, Broglie's law (motion of particles of matter). 2cor, Archimedes' principle (displacement of mass).

1971, May 15   Litho.   Perf. 13½
C761	A88	25c lt bl & multi	.95	.40
C762	A88	30c lt bl & multi	1.10	.50
C763	A88	40c lt bl & multi	1.60	.55
C764	A88	1cor lt bl & multi	1.60	1.40
C765	A88	2cor lt bl & multi	7.00	2.25
		Nos. C761-C765 (5)	12.25	5.10

On the back of each stamp is a descriptive paragraph.

Montezuma
Oropendola — AP101

Birds: 15c, Turquoise-browed motmot. 20c, Magpie-jay. 25c, Scissor-tailed flycatchers. 30c, Spot-breasted oriole, horiz. 35c, Rufous-naped wren. 40c, Great kiskadee. 75c, Red-legged honeycreeper, horiz. 1cor, Great-tailed grackle, horiz. 2cor, Belted kingfisher.

1971, Oct. 15   Litho.   Perf. 14
C766	AP101	10c multi	1.25	.40
C767	AP101	15c multi	1.25	.40
C768	AP101	20c gray & multi	1.25	.40
C769	AP101	25c multi	1.25	.40
C770	AP101	30c multi	1.25	.40
C771	AP101	35c multi	1.50	.40
C772	AP101	40c multi	1.50	.40
C773	AP101	75c yel & multi	1.75	.40
C774	AP101	1cor org & multi	2.25	.40
C775	AP101	2cor org & multi	3.75	.40
		Nos. C766-C775 (10)	17.00	4.00

Ten Commandments Type of Regular Issue

Designs: 1cor, Bathsheba at her Bath, by Rembrandt (IX). 2cor, Naboth's Vineyard, by James Smetham (X).

1971, Nov. 1   Perf. 11
C776	A90	1cor yel brn & multi	2.00	.60
C777	A90	2cor yel brn & multi	3.25	1.00

Descriptive inscriptions printed in gray on back of stamps.

U Thant,
Anastasio
Somoza, UN
Emblem — AP102

1972, Feb. 15   Perf. 14x13½
C778	AP102	10c pink & mar	.70	.40
C779	AP102	15c green	.70	.40
C780	AP102	20c blue	.70	.40
C781	AP102	25c rose claret	.70	.40
C782	AP102	30c org & brn	.70	.40
C783	AP102	40c gray & sl grn	.70	.40
C784	AP102	1cor ol grn	.70	.40
C785	AP102	2cor brown	1.40	.40
		Nos. C778-C785 (8)	6.30	3.20

25th anniv. of the United Nations (in 1970).

Nos. C713, C715, C716 Surcharged or Overprinted Like Nos. 899-900

1972, Mar. 20   Litho.   Perf. 13½
C786	A87	20c on 80c multi	.65	.35
C787	A87	60c on 4cor multi	.65	.35
C788	A87	5cor multi	2.25	1.50
		Nos. C786-C788 (3)	3.55	2.20

20th Olympic Games, Munich, 8/26-9/11.

Ceramic
Figure, Map
of Nicaragua
AP103

Pre-Columbian ceramics (700-1200 A.D.) found at sites indicated on map of Nicaragua.

1972, Sept. 16   Litho.   Perf. 14x13½
C789	AP103	10c blue & multi	.75	.40
C790	AP103	15c blue & multi	.75	.40
C791	AP103	20c blue & multi	.75	.40
C792	AP103	25c blue & multi	.75	.40
C793	AP103	30c blue & multi	.75	.40
C794	AP103	35c blue & multi	.75	.40
C795	AP103	40c blue & multi	.75	.40
C796	AP103	50c blue & multi	.75	.40
C797	AP103	60c blue & multi	.75	.40
C798	AP103	80c blue & multi	.75	.40
C799	AP103	1cor blue & multi	.75	.40
C800	AP103	2cor blue & multi	1.10	.40
		Nos. C789-C800 (12)	9.35	4.80

Lord Peter
Wimsey, by
Dorothy L.
Sayers — AP104

Designs (Book and): 10c, Philip Marlowe, by Raymond Chandler. 15c, Sam Spade, by Dashiell Hammett. 20c, Perry Mason, by Erle S. Gardner. 25c, Nero Wolfe, by Rex Stout. 35c, Auguste Dupin, by Edgar Allan Poe. 40c, Ellery Queen, by Frederick Dannay and Manfred B. Lee. 50c, Father Brown, by G. K. Chesterton. 60c, Charlie Chan, by Earl Derr Biggers. 80c, Inspector Maigret, by Georges Simenon. 1cor, Hercule Poirot, by Agatha Christie. 2cor, Sherlock Holmes, by A. Conan Doyle.

1972, Nov. 13   Litho.   Perf. 14x13½
C801	AP104	5c blue & multi	.70	.25
C802	AP104	10c blue & multi	.70	.25
C803	AP104	15c blue & multi	.70	.25
C804	AP104	20c blue & multi	.70	.25
C805	AP104	25c blue & multi	.70	.25
C806	AP104	35c blue & multi	1.00	.25
C807	AP104	40c blue & multi	1.00	.25
C808	AP104	50c blue & multi	1.20	.30
C809	AP104	60c blue & multi	1.60	.40
C810	AP104	80c blue & multi	2.10	.50
C811	AP104	1cor blue & multi	2.75	.65
C812	AP104	2cor blue & multi	5.50	1.25
		Nos. C801-C812 (12)	18.65	4.85

50th anniv. of INTERPOL, intl. police organization. Designs show famous fictional detectives. Inscriptions on back, printed on top of gum, give thumbnail sketch of character and author.

Shepherds
Following
Star — AP105

Legend of the Christmas Rose: 15c, Adoration of the kings and shepherds. 20c, Shepherd girl alone crying. 35c, Angel appears to girl. 40c, Christmas rose (Helleborus niger). 60c, Girl thanks angel. 80c, Girl and Holy Family. 1cor, Girl presents rose to Christ Child. 2cor, Adoration.

1972, Dec. 20
C813	AP105	10c multi	.70	.25
C814	AP105	15c multi	.70	.25
C815	AP105	20c multi	.70	.25
C816	AP105	35c multi	.70	.25

C817	AP105	40c multi	.70	.25
C818	AP105	60c multi	.70	.25
C819	AP105	80c multi	.70	.25
C820	AP105	1cor multi	.70	.25
C821	AP105	2cor multi	1.40	.30
a.		Souv. sheet of 9, #C813-C821	7.00	1.75
		Nos. C813-C821 (9)	7.00	2.30

Christmas 1972.

No. C821a exists with red marginal overprint, "TERREMOTO DESASTRE," for the Managua earthquake of Dec. 22-23, 1972. It was sold abroad, starting in Jan. 1973. Value, $7.

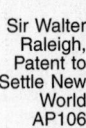

Sir Walter Raleigh, Patent to Settle New World
AP106

Events and Quotations from Contemporary Illustrations: 15c, Mayflower Compact, 1620. 20c, Acquittal of Peter Zenger, 1735, vert. 25c, William Pitt, 1766, vert. 30c, British revenue stamp for use in America No. RM31, vert. 35c, "Join or Die" serpent, 1768. 40c, Boston Massacre and State House, 1770, vert. 50c, Boston Tea Party and 3p coin, 1774. 60c, Patrick Henry, 1775, vert. 75c, Battle scene ("Our cause is just, our union is perfect," 1775). 80c, Declaration of Independence, 1776. 1cor, Liberty Bell, Philadelphia. 2cor, Seal of US, 1782, vert.

1973, Feb. 22		Photo.	Perf. 13½	
C822	AP106	10c olive & multi	.65	.25
C823	AP106	15c olive & multi	.65	.25
C824	AP106	20c olive & multi	.65	.25
C825	AP106	25c olive & multi	.65	.25
C826	AP106	30c olive & multi	.65	.25
C827	AP106	35c ol, gold & blk	.85	.25
C828	AP106	40c olive & multi	.85	.25
C829	AP106	50c olive & multi	.85	.35
C830	AP106	60c olive & multi	.95	.35
C831	AP106	75c olive & multi	1.20	.40
C832	AP106	80c olive & multi	1.20	.40
C833	AP106	1cor olive & multi	1.90	.50
C834	AP106	2cor olive & multi	3.50	1.00
		Nos. C822-C834 (13)	14.55	4.75

Inscriptions on back, printed on top of gum, give brief description of subject and event.

Baseball, Player and Map of Nicaragua — AP107

1973, May 25		Litho.	Perf. 13½x14	
C835	AP107	15c multi	.70	.25
C836	AP107	20c multi	.70	.25
C837	AP107	40c multi	.70	.25
C838	AP107	10cor multi	5.00	1.50
a.		Souvenir sheet of 4	16.50	15.00
		Nos. C835-C838 (4)	7.10	2.25

20th International Baseball Championships, Managua, Nov. 15-Dec. 5, 1972. No. C838a contains 4 stamps similar to Nos. C835-C838 with changed background colors (15c, olive; 20c, gray; 40c, lt. green; 10cor, lilac), and 5 labels.

Fashion Type of 1973

10c, Lourdes Nicaragua. 15c, Halston, New York. 20c, Pino Lancetti, Rome. 35c, Madame Ges, Paris. 40c, Irene Galitzine, Rome. 80c, Pedro Rodriguez, Barcelona.

1973, July 26		Litho.	Perf. 13½	
C839	A91	10c multicolored	.80	.25
C840	A91	15c multicolored	.80	.25
C841	A91	20c multicolored	.80	.25
C842	A91	35c multicolored	.80	.25
C843	A91	40c multicolored	.80	.25
C844	A91	80c multicolored	.80	.25
a.		Souv. sheet of 9, #909-911, C839-C844, perf. 11 + 3 labels	2.40	5.50
		Nos. C839-C844 (6)	4.80	1.50

Inscriptions on back printed on top of gum give description of gown in Spanish and English.

Type of Air Post Semi-Postal Issue

Design: 2cor, Pediatric surgery.

1973, Sept. 25				
C845	SPAP1	2cor multi	2.75	.40
		Nos. C845,CB1-CB11 (12)	7.80	3.60

Planned Children's Hospital. Inscription on back, printed on top of gum gives brief description of subject shown.
See Nos. CB1-CB11.

Christmas Type

1cor, Virginia O'Hanlon writing letter, father. 2cor, Letter. 4cor, Virginia, father reading letter.

1973, Nov. 15		Litho.	Perf. 15	
C846	A92	1cor multicolored	.80	.45
C847	A92	2cor multicolored	1.75	.90
C848	A92	4cor multicolored	3.00	1.50
a.		Souvenir sheet of 3, #C846-C848, perf. 14½	3.50	4.00
		Nos. C846-C848 (3)	5.55	2.85

Churchill Type

No. C851, Silhouette, Parliament. No. C852, Silhouette, #10 Downing St. 5cor, Showing "V" sign. 6cor, "Bulldog" Churchill protecting England.

1974, Apr. 30			Perf. 14½	
C849	A93	2cor multicolored	2.60	1.40
C850	A93	6cor multicolored	3.25	1.75

Souvenir Sheets
Perf. 15

C851	A93	4cor blk, org & bl	2.90	1.40
C852	A93	4cor blk, org, & grn	2.90	1.40

Nos. C851-C852 contain one 28x42mm stamp.

World Cup Type

Scenes from previous World Cup Championships with flags and scores of finalists.

1974, May 8			Perf. 14½	
C853	A94	10cor Flags of participants	6.25	6.25

Souvenir Sheets

C853A	A94	4cor like No. 928	4.00	1.10
C853B	A94	5cor like No. 930	5.00	1.40

For overprint see No. C856.

Flower Type of 1974

Wild Flowers and Cacti: 1 cor, Centrosema. 3 cor, Night-blooming cereus.

1974, June 11		Litho.	Perf. 14	
C854	A95	1cor green & multi	2.00	1.00
C855	A95	3cor green & multi	4.50	2.50

Nicaraguan Stamps Type

1974, July 10			Perf. 14½	
C855A	A96	40c #835	.65	.40
C855B	A96	3cor #C313, horiz.	2.40	1.25
C855C	A96	5cor #734	3.75	2.25
		Nos. C855A-C855C (3)	6.80	3.90

Souvenir Sheet
Imperf

C855D		Sheet of 3	15.00	
e.		A96 1cor #665	1.50	
f.		A96 2cor #C110, horiz.	2.75	
g.		A96 4cor Globe, stars	7.00	

UPU, Cent.

No. C853
Ovptd.

1974, July 12				
C856	A94	10cor Flags	3.25	2.25

Animal Type of 1974

3cor, Colorado deer. 5cor, Jaguar.

1974, Sept. 10		Litho.	Perf. 14½	
C857	A97	3cor multi	1.75	1.00
C858	A97	5cor multi	4.00	2.50

Christmas Type of 1974

Works of Michelangelo: 40c, Madonna of the Stairs. 80c, Pitti Madonna. 2cor, Pietà. 5cor, Self-portrait.

1974, Dec. 15				
C859	A98	40c multi	1.90	.50
C860	A98	80c multi	1.90	.50
C861	A98	2cor multi	2.40	1.25
C862	A98	5cor multi	5.50	3.00
		Nos. C859-C862 (4)	11.70	5.25

An imperf. souvenir sheet with simulated perfs exists containing 2cor and 5cor stamps.

Value, $4. This imperforate sheet was overprinted with Literacy Year and 1980 Summer Olympic inscriptions and illustrations on 9/26/80.

Opera Type of 1975

Opera Singers and Scores: 25c, Rosa Ponselle, Norma. 35c, Giuseppe de Luca, Rigoletto. 40c, Joan Sutherland, La Figlia del Reggimento. 50c, Ezio Pinza, Don Giovanni. 60c, Kirsten Flagstad, Tristan und Isolde. 80c, Maria Callas, Tosca. 2cor, Fyodor Chaliapin, Boris Godunov. 5cor, Enrico Caruso, La Juive.

1975, Jan. 22			Perf. 14x13½	
C863	A99	25c grn & multi	.65	.35
C864	A99	35c multi	.65	.35
C865	A99	40c multi	.65	.35
C866	A99	50c org & multi	.65	.35
C867	A99	60c rose & multi	.65	.35
C868	A99	80c lake & multi	.80	.35
C869	A99	2cor sep & multi	1.90	.35
C870	A99	5cor multi	4.75	1.00
a.		Souvenir sheet of 3	13.50	10.00
		Nos. C863-C870 (8)	10.70	3.45

No. C870a contains one each of Nos. C869-C870 and a 1cor with design and colors of No. C868. Exists imperf.

Easter Type of 1975

Stations of the Cross: 40c, Jesus stripped of his clothes. 50c, Jesus nailed to the Cross. 80c, Jesus dies on the Cross. 1cor, Descent from the Cross. 5cor, Jesus laid in the tomb.

1975, Mar. 20			Perf. 14½	
C871	A100	40c ultra & multi	.50	.25
C872	A100	50c ultra & multi	.50	.25
C873	A100	80c ultra & multi	.70	.25
C874	A100	1cor ultra & multi	1.00	.25
C875	A100	5cor ultra & multi	4.00	1.40
		Nos. C871-C875 (5)	6.70	2.40

American Bicentennal Type of 1975

Designs: 40c, Washington's Farewell, 1783. 50c, Washington Addressing Continental Congress by J. B. Stearns. 2cor, Washington Arriving for Inauguration. 5cor, Statue of Liberty and flags of 1776 and 1976. 40c, 50c, 2cor, horiz.

1975, Apr. 16			Perf. 14	
C876	A101	40c tan & multi	.65	.25
C877	A101	50c tan & multi	.80	.30
C878	A101	2cor tan & multi	2.40	.85
C879	A101	5cor tan & multi	5.25	3.00
		Nos. C876-C879 (4)	9.10	4.40

Perf. and imperf. 7cor souvenir sheets exist. Value, $8. These sheets were overprinted with Literacy Year and 1980 Winter Olympic inscriptions and illustrations on 9/26/80.
See Nos. 978-988.

Nordjamb 75 Type of 1975

Designs (Scout and Nordjamb Emblems and): 35c, Camp. 40c, Scout musicians. 1cor, Campfire. 10cor, Lord Baden-Powell.

1975, Aug. 15			Perf. 14½	
C880	A102	35c multi	.55	.25
C881	A102	40c multi	.55	.25
C882	A102	1cor multi	.70	.30
C883	A102	10cor multi	4.25	2.00
		Nos. C880-C883 (4)	6.05	2.80

Two airmail souvenir sheets of 2 exist. One, perf., contains 2cor and 3cor with designs of Nos. 992 and 990. The other, imperf., contains 2cor and 3cor with designs of Nos. 993 and C882. Size: 125x101mm. Value, pair $19. These sheets were overprinted with Literacy Year and International Year of the Child inscriptions and illustrations on 9/26/80.

Pres. Somoza Type of 1975

1975, Sept. 10			Perf. 14	
C884	A103	1cor vio & multi	.35	.25
C885	A103	10cor bl & multi	4.00	1.75
C886	A103	20cor multi	8.25	3.50
		Nos. C884-C886 (3)	12.60	5.50

Choir Type of 1975

Famous Choirs: 50c, Montserrat Abbey. 1cor, St. Florian Choir Boys. 2cor, Choir Boys of the Wooden Cross, vert. 5cor, Boys and Pope Paul VI (Pueri Cantores International Federation).

1975, Nov. 15			Perf. 14½	
C887	A104	50c sil & multi	.45	.25
C888	A104	1cor sil & multi	.45	.25
C889	A104	2cor sil & multi	.95	.40
C890	A104	5cor sil & multi	3.75	1.25
		Nos. C887-C890 (4)	5.60	2.15

A 10cor imperf. souvenir sheet exists (Oberndorf Memorial Chapel Choir and score of "Holy Night-Silent Night"). Value, $12.50.

Chess Type of 1976

Designs: 40c, The Chess Players, by Thomas Eakins. 2cor, Bobby Fischer and Boris Spasski in Reykjavik, 1972. 5cor, Shakespeare and Ben Johnson Playing Chess, by Karel van Mander.

1976, Jan. 8			Perf. 14½	
C891	A105	40c multi	.40	.25
C892	A105	2cor vio & multi	2.10	.75
C893	A105	5cor multi	4.00	2.00
		Nos. C891-C893 (3)	6.50	3.00

A souvenir sheet contains one each of Nos. C892-C893, perf. and imperf. Size: 143x67mm. Value, pair $11.

Olympic Winner Type 1976

Winners, Rowing and Sculling Events: 55c, USSR, 1956, 1960, 1964, vert. 70c, New Zealand, 1972, vert. 90c, New Zealand, 1968. 10cor, Women's rowing crew, US, 1976, vert. 20cor, US, 1956.

1976, Sept. 7		Litho.	Perf. 14	
C902	A107	55c bl & multi	.35	.25
C903	A107	70c bl & multi	.35	.25
C904	A107	90c bl & multi	.35	.25
C905	A107	20cor bl & multi	11.00	6.00
		Nos. C902-C905 (4)	12.05	6.75

Souvenir Sheet

C906	A107	10cor multi	8.50	5.00

No. C906 for the 1st participation of women in Olympic rowing events, size of stamp: 37x50mm.
The overprint "Republica Democratica Alemana Vencedor en 1976" was applied in 1976 to No. C905 in black in 3 lines and to the margin of No. C906 in gold in 2 lines.

Bicentennial Type of 1976

American Bicentennial Emblem and: #C907, Philadelphia, 1776. #C908, Washington, 1976. #C909, John Paul Jones' ships. #C910, Atomic submarine. #C911, Wagon train. #C912, Diesel train.

1976, May 25		Litho.	Perf. 13½	
C907	A108	80c multi	.25	.25
C908	A108	80c multi	.25	.25
a.		Pair, #C907-C908	.75	.60
C909	A108	2.75cor multi	.50	.40
C910	A108	2.75cor multi	.50	.40
a.		Pair, #C909-C910	2.25	1.75
C911	A108	4cor multi	.80	.50
C912	A108	4cor multi	.80	.50
a.		Pair, #C911-C912	4.00	3.00
		Nos. C907-C912 (6)	13.10	2.30

A souvenir sheet contains two 10cor stamps showing George Washington and Gerald R. Ford with their families. Size: 140x111mm. Value, $9.50.

Rare Stamps Type of 1976

Rare Stamps: 40c, Hawaii #1. 1cor, Great Britain #1. 2cor, British Guiana #13. 5cor, Honduras #C12. 10cor, Newfoundland #C1.

1976, Dec.			Perf. 14	
C913	A109	40c multi	.40	.25
C914	A109	1cor multi	.55	.25
C915	A109	2cor multi	.80	.25
C916	A109	5cor multi	2.25	.65
C917	A109	10cor multi	3.50	1.25
		Nos. C913-C917 (5)	7.50	2.65

Inscriptions on back printed on top of gum give description of illustrated stamp.
A 4cor imperf. souvenir sheet shows 1881 Great Britain-Nicaragua combination cover. Size: 140x101mm. Value, $2.50. This sheet was overprinted with Literacy Year and International Year of the Child inscriptions and illustrations on 9/26/80.

Olga Nuñez de Saballos
AP108

Designs: 1cor, Josefa Toledo de Aguerri. 10cor, Hope Portocarrero de Somoza.

1977, Feb.		Litho.	Perf. 13½	
C918	AP108	35c multi	.35	.25
C919	AP108	1cor red & multi	.85	.25
C920	AP108	10cor multi	3.25	1.75
		Nos. C918-C920 (3)	3.95	2.25

Famous Nicaraguan women and for International Women's Year (in 1975).

Zeppelin Type of 1977

Designs: 35c, Ville de Paris airship. 70c, Zeppelin "Schwaben." 3cor, Zeppelin in flight. 10cor, Vickers "Mayfly" before take-off. 20cor, Zeppelin with leadlines extended.

1977, Oct. 31   Litho.   Perf. 14½

C921	A110	35c multi	.40	.25
C922	A110	70c multi	.40	.25
C923	A110	3cor multi	1.90	.75
C924	A110	10cor multi	6.25	3.50
	Nos. C921-C924 (4)		8.95	4.75

Souvenir Sheet

C925	A110	20cor multi	15.00	7.50

No. C925 exists imperf.
For overprints, see Nos. C974-C974A,

Lindbergh Type of 1977

Designs: 55c, Lindbergh's plane approaching Nicaraguan airfield, 1928. 80c, Spirit of St. Louis and map of New York-Paris route. 2cor, Plane flying off Nicaragua's Pacific Coast. 10cor, Lindbergh flying past Momotombo Volcano on way to Managua. 20cor, Spirit of St. Louis.

1977, Nov. 30

C926	A111	55c multi	.40	.25
C927	A111	80c multi	.40	.25
C928	A111	2cor multi	1.30	.45
C929	A111	10cor multi	6.50	2.50
	Nos. C926-C929 (4)		8.60	3.45

Souvenir Sheet

C930	A111	20cor multi	15.00	7.50

For overprint, see Nos. C973-C973A.

Christmas Type of 1977
Souvenir Sheet

Design: 20cor, Finale of Nutcracker Suite.

1977, Dec. 12

C931	A112	20cor multi	9.00	4.50

Painting Type of 1978

Rubens Paintings: 5cor, Hippopotamus and Crocodile Hunt. 10cor, Duke de Lerma on Horseback. 20cor, Self-portrait.

1978, Jan. 11   Litho.   Perf. 14½

C932	A113	5cor multi	2.75	1.25
C933	A113	10cor multi	5.25	3.00

Souvenir Sheet

C934	A113	20cor multi	10.00	5.00

Peter Paul Rubens (1577-1640), 400th birth anniversary.

St. Francis Type of 1978

Designs: 80c, St. Francis and the wolf. 10cor, St. Francis, painting. 20cor, Our Lady of Conception, statue in Church of El Viejo.

1978, Feb. 23   Litho.   Perf. 14½

C935	A114	80c lt brn & multi	.60	.25
C936	A114	10cor bl & multi	4.75	1.75

Souvenir Sheet

C937	A114	20cor multi	10.00	5.00

For overprint, see No, C971N-C971O.

Railroad Type of 1978

Locomotives: 35c, Light-weight American. 4cor, Heavy Baldwin. 10cor, Juniata, 13-ton. 20cor, Map of route system.

1978, Apr. 7   Litho.   Perf. 14½

C938	A115	35c lt grn & multi	.95	.40
C939	A115	4cor dp org & multi	2.90	1.50
C940	A115	10cor cit & multi	5.00	2.50
	Nos. C938-C940 (3)		8.85	4.40

Souvenir Sheet

C941	A115	20cor multi	16.00	8.00

Jules Verne Type of 1978

Designs: 90c, 20,000 Leagues under the Sea. 10cor, Around the World in 80 Days. 20cor, From the Earth to the Moon.

1978, Aug.   Litho.   Perf. 14½

C942	A116	90c multi	.65	.35
C943	A116	10cor multi	5.25	3.00

Souvenir Sheet

C944	A116	20cor multi	9.75	5.00

Aviation History Type of 1978

Designs: 55c, Igor Sikorsky in his helicopter, 1913, horiz. 10cor, Space shuttle, horiz. 20cor, Flyer III, horiz.

1978, Sept. 29   Litho.   Perf. 14½

C945	A117	55c multi	.65	.30
C946	A117	10cor multi	3.75	2.00

Souvenir Sheet

C947	A117	20cor multi	40.00	20.00

Soccer Type of 1978

Soccer Players: 50c, Denis Law and Franz Beckenbauer. 5cor, Dino Zoff and Pelé.

20cor, Dominique Rocheteau and Johan Neeskens.

1978, Oct. 25   Litho.   Perf. 13½x14

C948	A118	50c multi	.40	.25
C949	A118	5cor multi	3.00	1.75

Souvenir Sheet

C950	A118	20cor multi	10.00	5.00

Christmas Type of 1978

Paintings: 3cor, Apostles John and Peter, by Dürer. 10cor, Apostles Paul and Mark, by Dürer. 20cor, Virgin and Child with Garlands, by Dürer.

1978, Dec. 12   Litho.   Perf. 13½x14

C951	A119	3cor multi	.90	.45
C952	A119	10cor multi	3.75	2.00

Souvenir Sheet

C953	A119	20cor multi	8.00	4.00

Volcano Type of 1978

Designs: No. C954, Cerro Negro Volcano. No. C955, Lake Masaya. No. C956, Momotombo Volcano. No. C957, Lake Asososca. No. C958, Mombacho Volcano. No. C959, Lake Apoyo. No. C960, Concepcion Volcano. No. C961, Lake Tiscapa.

1978, Dec. 29   Perf. 14x13½

C954	A120	35c multi	.40	.25
C955	A120	35c multi	.40	.25
a.	Pair, #C549-C955		.80	.40
C956	A120	90c multi	.40	.25
C957	A120	90c multi	.40	.25
a.	Pair, #C956-C957		.90	.45
C958	A120	1cor multi	.40	.25
C959	A120	1cor multi	.40	.25
a.	Pair, #C958-C959		1.00	.50
C960	A120	10cor multi	1.90	1.40
C961	A120	10cor multi	1.90	1.40
a.	Pair, #C960-C961		6.50	5.00
	Nos. C954-C961 (8)		6.20	4.30

Bernardo O'Higgins — AP109

1979, Mar. 7   Litho.   Perf. 14

C962	AP109	20cor multi	4.75	3.25

Bernardo O'Higgins (1778-1842), Chilean soldier and statesman.

Red Ginger and Rubythroated Hummingbird AP110

Designs: 55c, Orchid. 70c, Poinsettia. 80c, Flower and bees. 2cor, Lignum vitae and blue morpho butterfly. 4cor, Cattleya.

1979, Apr. 6   Litho.   Perf. 14x13½

C963	AP110	50c multi	.65	.25
C964	AP110	55c multi	.65	.25
C965	AP110	70c multi	.65	.25
C966	AP110	80c multi	.65	.25
C967	AP110	2cor multi	1.75	.30
C968	AP110	4cor multi	6.50	.50
	Nos. C963-C968 (6)		10.85	1.80

Endangered Turtles Overprinted in Red — AP110a

Overprint reads: 1979 / ANO DE LA LIBERACION / OLYMPIC RINGS / PARTICIPACION NICARAGUA / OLIMPIADAS 1980 / Litografia Nacional, Portugal symbol

Turtles: 90c, Loggerhead. 2cor, Correoso. 2.20cor, Ridley. 10cor, Pico Halcón.

1980, Apr. 7   Litho.   Perf. 14¼x13¾

C969	AP110a	90c multi	19.00	19.00
C969A	AP110a	2cor multi	19.00	19.00
C969B	AP110a	2.20cor multi	19.00	19.00
C969C	AP110a	10cor multi	19.00	19.00
	Nos. C969-C969C (4)		76.00	76.00

Overprinted for Year of Liberation and 1980 Olympic Games.

Nos. C969-C969C were not issued without overprints.

Souvenir Sheet

Intl. Year of the Child — AP110b

Designs: a, 5cor, like #1101C. b, 15cor, Dr. Hermann Gmeiner.

1980, May 3   Litho.   Perf. 14½

C970	AP110b	Sheet of 2, #a-		
	b.		85.00	—

No. C970 exists imperf.

Souvenir Sheet

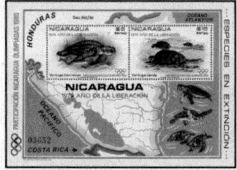

Endangered Turtles Overprinted in Red and Blue — AP110c

No. C970C: d, 5cor, Correoso turtle. e, 15cor, Green (verde) turtle.

1980, May 3   Litho.   Perf. 13¼x13

C970C	AP110c	Sheet of 2, #d-		
	e		—	—

Overprinted for Year of Liberation and 1980 Olympic Games. No. C970C was not issued without overprints.

Souvenir Sheet

AP110d

No. C970F: g, 6cor, Albert Einstein (1879-1955), physicist. h, 15cor, Einstein and Mohandas K, Gandhi (1869-1948), Indian nationalist leader.

1980, May 3   Litho.   Perf. 13½

C970F	AP110d	Sheet of 2, #g-h		

Souvenir Sheet

Sir Rowland Hill and Nicaragua No. 1 — AP110e

1980, May 3   Litho.   Imperf.

C970I	AP110e	20cor multi	—	—

Souvenir Sheet

Sir Rowland Hill and Indigenous Messenger — AP110f

1980, May 3   Litho.   Perf. 14½

C970J	AP110f	20cor multi	—	—

No. C436a Overprinted in Black and Silver

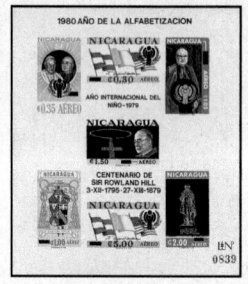

AP110g

Methods and Perfs. As Before
1980, Sept. 26

C971	AP110g	Sheet of 7	—	—
a.		30c multi	—	—
b.		35c multi	—	—
c.		1cor multi	—	—
d.		1.05cor multi	—	—
e.		1.50cor multi	—	—
f.		2cor multi	—	—
g.		5cor multi	—	—

No. C503a Overprinted

AP110h

Methods and Perfs. As Before
1980, Sept. 26
Black and Silver Overprint in Sheet Margin

C971H	AP110h	Sheet of 2	—	—
i.		2col multi	—	—
j.		5col multi	—	—

Dark Blue and Gold Overprint in Sheet Margin

C971K	AP110h	Sheet of 2	—	—
l.		2col multi	—	—
m.		5col multi	—	—

No. C937 Overprinted
Souvenir Sheet

AP110i

1980, Sept. 26   Litho.   Perf. 14½
Overprinted in Black and Silver

C971N	AP110i	20cor multi		

Overprnted in Black, Gold and Silver

C971O	AP110i	20cor multi	—	—

No. C415a Overprinted in Blue and Silver

AP110j

Methods and Perfs. As Before
1980, Sept. 30
C971P	AP110j	Sheet of 6	—	—
q.		30c multi	—	—
r.		60c multi	—	—
s.		90c multi	—	—
t.		1.25cor multi	—	—
u.		2cor multi	—	—
v.		3cor multi	—	—

No. C442a Overprinted in Black and Red

AP110k

Methods and Perfs. As Before
1980, Sept. 30
C971W	AP110k	Sheet of 6,		
		#C437-C441,		
		C971Lm	—	—
x.		5cor multi with overprint	—	—

No. C509 Overprinted in Red, Black and Silver

AP110l

Methods and Perfs. As Before
1980, Sept. 30
Overprinted in Red, Black and Silver, With Vostok 1 at Left
C971Y	AP110l	7cor multi	—	—

Overprinted in Red, Black and Silver, With Apollo 11 at Left
C971Z	AP110l	7cor multi	—	—

No. C722a Overprinted in Black, Red and Silver

AP110m

Methods and Perfs. As Before
1980, Sept. 30
C972	AP110m	Sheet of 3	—	—
a.		75c multi	—	—
b.		1.50cor multi	—	—
c.		3cor multi	—	—

No. C930 Overprinted in Gold, Purple and Green, Blue & Orange Brown

A111

1980, Sept. 30   Perf. 14½
C973	A111	20cor multi	44.00	

No. C930 Overprinted in Silver, Black and Green, Blue & Orange Brown
C973A	A111	20cor multi	—	—

No. C925 Overprinted

AP111a

Methods and Perfs. As Before
1980, Sept. 30
Overprinted in Dark Blue and Silver
C974	AP111a	20cor multi	—	—

Overprinted in Dark Blue and Gold
C974A	AP111a	20cor multi	—	—

Nos. C974 and C974A exist imperforate.

Souvenir Sheet

AP111d

Overprint reads: 1980 ANO DE LA ALFABETIZACION / 1980 MOSCU and Litografia Nacional, Portugal symbol

1980, Dec. 20   Litho.   Perf. 14½
Overprinted & Surcharged in Black & Silver
C974F	AP111d	10cor on 20cor multi	22.00	—

Overprinted & surcharged for Literacy Year. No. 974F was not issued without surcharge. Numbers have been reserved for 6 additional stamps in this set. The editors would like to examine these stamps.

Endangered Turtles Type of 1980 Overprinted in Red — AP111e

Overprint reads: 1980 ANO DE LA ALFABETIZACION and Litografia Nacional, Portugal symbol

No. C975D, Green (Verde) turtle.

1981, May 15   Litho.   Perf. 14¼x13¾
C975	AP111e	90c like #C969	8.00	—
C975A	AP111e	2cor like #C969A	8.00	—
C975B	AP111e	2.20cor like #C969B	8.00	—
C975C	AP111e	10cor like #C969C	8.00	—
		Nos. C975-C975C (4)	32.00	

Souvenir Sheet
C975D	AP111e	5cor on 20cor multi	100.00	—

Overprinted for Literacy Year. Nos. C975-C975D were not issued without overprints and surcharge.

Revolution Type of 1981
1981, July 19   Litho.   Perf. 12½x12
C975E	A123	2.10cor March	1.50	.25
C975F	A123	3cor Construction	2.50	.25
C975G	A123	6cor Health programs	6.00	.45
		Nos. C975E-C975G (3)	10.00	.95

FSLN Type of 1981
1981, July 23
C976	A124	4cor Founder	2.40	.40

Postal Union Type of 1981
1981, Aug. 10
C977	A125	2.10cor Pony express	.60	.40
C978	A125	3cor Headquarters	.70	.40
C979	A125	6cor Members' flags	1.10	.50
		Nos. C977-C979 (3)	2.40	1.30

1300th Anniv. of Bulgaria AP112

1981, Sept. 2   Imperf.
C980	AP112	10cor multi	3.00	1.00
		Size: 96x70mm.		

Aquatic Flower Type of 1981
10cor, Nymphaea gladstoniana.

1981, Sept. 15   Perf. 12½
C981	A126	10cor multi	6.50	.90

Souvenir Sheet

Panda Bear AP113

1981, Oct. 9   Perf. 13
C982	AP113	10cor multi	5.50	2.00

Philatokyo Stamp Exhibition, Tokyo.

Tropical Fish Type of 1981
3.50cor, Pterolebias longipinnis. 4cor, Xiphophorus helleri.

1981, Oct. 19   Perf. 12½
C983	A127	3.50cor multi	2.50	.30
C984	A127	4cor multi	3.25	.30

Souvenir Sheet

Frigate AP114

1981, Nov. 2   Perf. 13
C985	AP114	10cor multi	3.50	1.00

Espamer '81 Stamp Exhibition, Buenos Aires, Nov. 13-22.

Bird Type of 1981
3cor, Trogon massena. 4cor, Campylopterus hemileucurus, horiz. 6cor, Momotus momota.

1981, Nov. 30   Perf. 12½
C986	A128	3cor multicolored	1.00	.30
C987	A128	4cor multicolored	1.25	.40
C988	A128	6cor multicolored	2.75	.75
		Nos. C986-C988 (3)	5.00	1.45

Satellite Type of 1981
1981, Dec. 15   Perf. 13x12½
C989	A129	3cor multi	1.60	.25
C990	A129	4cor multi	2.25	.30
C991	A129	5cor multi	2.75	.35
		Nos. C989-C991 (3)	6.60	.90

Railroad Type of 1981
1981, Dec. 30   Perf. 12½
C992	A130	6cor Ferrobus, 1967	6.25	.75

World Cup Type of 1982
1982, Jan. 25
C993	A131	4cor multi	2.10	.30
C994	A131	10cor multi, horiz.	4.00	.80

Souvenir Sheet
Perf. 13
C995	A131	10cor multi	4.00	1.60

No. C995 contains one 39x31mm stamp.

Dog Type of 1982
1982, Feb. 18
C996	A132	3cor Boxers	1.50	.30
C997	A132	3.50cor Pointers	1.90	.30
C998	A132	6cor Collies	2.75	.50
		Nos. C996-C998 (3)	6.15	1.10

Intl. ITU Congress AP115

1982, Mar. 12
C999	AP115	25cor multi	4.00	2.25

Butterfly Type of 1982
3cor, Parides iphidamas. 3.50cor, Consul hippona. 4cor, Morpho peleides.

1982, Mar. 26
C1000	A133	3cor multi	1.75	.30
C1001	A133	3.50cor multi	2.00	.30
C1002	A133	4cor multi	2.50	.40
		Nos. C1000-C1002 (3)	6.25	1.00

Satellite Type of 1982
1982, Apr. 12
C1003	A134	5cor multi, horiz.	2.00	.40
C1004	A134	6cor multi	2.40	.50

UPU Type of 1982
1982, May 1   Litho.   Perf. 13
C1005	A135	3.50cor Train	.85	.25
C1006	A135	10cor Jet	2.25	.70

Sports Type of 1982
2.50cor, Women's volleyball, vert. 3cor, Boxing. 9cor, Soccer. 10cor, Baseball, vert.

1982, May 13
C1007	A136	2.50cor multi	.90	.25
C1008	A136	3cor multi	1.10	.30
C1009	A136	9cor multi	3.50	.80
		Nos. C1007-C1009 (3)	5.50	1.35

Souvenir Sheet
C1010	A136	10cor multi	5.50	2.50

No. C1010 contains one 29x36mm stamp.

Souvenir Sheet

PHILEXFRANCE '82 Intl. Stamp Exhibition, Paris, June 11-21 — AP116

1982, June 9   Perf. 13x12½
C1011	AP116	15cor multi	5.50	1.25

Revolution Type of 1982
Symbolic doves. 2.50cor, 4cor vert.

1982, July 19   Perf. 13
C1012	A137	2.50cor multi	1.10	.30
C1013	A137	4cor multi	1.75	.40
C1014	A137	6cor multi	2.60	.60
		Nos. C1012-C1014 (3)	5.45	1.30

Washington Type of 1982
2.50cor, Crossing the Delaware. 3.50cor, At Valley Forge. 4cor, Battle of Trenton. 6cor, Washington in Princeton.

Perf. 12½x13, 13x12½
1982, June 20   Litho.
C1015	A138	2.50cor multi, horiz.	1.10	.30
C1016	A138	3.50cor multi, horiz.	1.40	.35

C1017 A138 4cor multi 1.60 .40
C1018 A138 6cor multi 2.60 .60
Nos. C1015-C1018 (4) 6.70 1.65

Painting Type of 1982

9cor, Seated Woman, by A. Morales.

1982, Aug. 17 *Perf. 13*
C1019 A139 9cor multi 6.00 .80

Dimitrov Type of 1982

2.50cor, Dimitrov, Yikov, Sofia, 1946. 4cor, Portrait, flag.

1982, Sept. 9
C1020 A140 2.50cor multi .90 .30
C1021 A140 4cor multi 1.10 .40

Dictatorship Type of 1982

4cor, Rigoberto Lopez Perez. 6cor, Edwin Castro.

1982, Sept. 21 *Perf. 13x12½*
C1022 A141 4cor multi 1.25 .40
C1023 A141 6cor multi 1.90 .60

Tourism Type of 1982

2.50cor, Coyotepe Fortress, Masaya. 3.50cor, Velazquez Park, Managua.

1982, Sept. 25 *Perf. 13*
C1024 A142 2.50cor multi 2.25 .30
C1025 A142 3.50cor multi 3.00 .30

Marx Type of 1982

4cor, Marx, Highgate Monument.

1982, Oct. 4 *Perf. 12½*
C1026 A143 4cor multi 1.75 .35

Discovery of America Type of 1982

2.50cor, Trans-atlantic voyage. 4cor, Landing of Columbus. 7cor, Death of Columbus. 10cor, Columbus' fleet.

1982, Oct. 12 *Perf. 12½x13*
C1027 A145 2.50cor multi 1.25 .25
C1028 A145 4cor multi 1.90 .40
C1029 A145 7cor multi 3.00 .70
a. Sheet, 2 each #1187-1190,
C1027-C1029, + 2 labels 16.00 —
Nos. C1027-C1029 (3) 6.15 1.35

Souvenir Sheet
Perf. 13

C1030 A145 10cor multi 5.50 1.10

No. C1030 contains one 31x39mm stamp.

Flower Type of 1982

2.50cor, Pasiflora foetida. 3.50cor, Clitoria sp. 5cor, Russelia sarmentosa.

1982, Nov. 13 *Perf. 12½*
C1031 A146 2.50cor multi 1.80 .25
C1032 A146 3.50cor multi 2.00 .30
C1033 A146 5cor multi 2.50 .45
Nos. C1031-C1033 (3) 6.30 1.00

Reptile Type of 1982

2.50cor, Turtle, horiz. 3cor, Boa constrictor. 3.50cor, Crocodile, horiz. 5cor, Sistrurus catenatus, horiz.

1982, Dec. 10 *Perf. 13*
C1034 A147 2.50cor multi 1.80 .25
C1035 A147 3cor multi 1.90 .30
C1036 A147 3.50cor multi 2.10 .30
C1037 A147 5cor multi 3.00 .45
Nos. C1034-C1037 (4) 8.80 1.30

Non-aligned States Conference, Jan. 12-14 — AP117

1983, Jan. 10 *Litho.* *Perf. 12½x13*
C1038 AP117 4cor multi 1.40 .40

Geothermal Electricity Generating Plant, Momotombo Volcano AP118

1983, Feb. 25 *Perf. 13*
C1039 AP118 2.50cor multi .90 .40

Souvenir Sheet

TEMBAL '83 Philatelic Exhibition, Basel, Switzerland — AP119

1983, May 21 *Litho.* *Perf. 13*
C1040 AP119 15cor Chamoix 3.50 1.40

Souvenir Sheet

1st Nicaraguan Philatelic Exhibition — AP120

10cor, Nicaragua Airlines jet.

1983, July 17 *Litho.* *Perf. 13*
C1041 AP120 10cor multi 3.00 1.40

Armed Forces — AP121

4cor, Frontier guards, watch dog.

1983, Sept. 2 *Litho.* *Perf. 13*
C1042 AP121 4cor multi 1.10 .40

Souvenir Sheet

BRASILIANA '83 Intl. Stamp Show, Rio de Janeiro, July 29-Aug. 7 — AP122

1983
C1043 AP122 15cor Jaguar 5.50 1.75

Cuban Revolution, 25th Anniv. — AP122a

6cor, Castro, Guevara, flag.

1984, Jan. 1 *Litho.* *Perf. 13*
C1043A AP122a 4cor shown 1.25 .40
C1043B AP122a 6cor multi 1.75 .60

Souvenir Sheet

Cardinal Infante Don Fernando, by Diego Velazquez — AP123

1984, May 2 *Litho.* *Perf. 13*
C1044 AP123 15cor multi 4.25 1.25
ESPANA '84.

Souvenir Sheet

Hamburg '84 AP124

1984, June 19 *Litho.* *Perf. 13*
C1045 AP124 15cor Dirigible 4.25 1.25

1984 UPU Congress AP125

15cor, Mail transport.

1984, June 24 *Perf. 12½*
C1046 AP125 15cor multi 6.25 1.00

Souvenir Sheet

Expofilnic '84 (2nd Natl. Stamp Exhibition) — AP126

15cor, Communications Museum.

1984, July 15
C1047 AP126 15cor multi 3.00 1.00

Souvenir Sheet

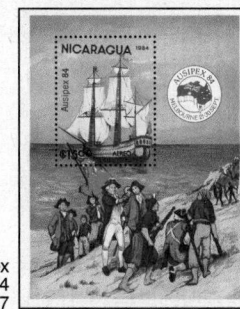

Ausipex '84 AP127

1984, Sept. 21
C1048 AP127 15cor Explorer ship 3.00 1.00

Souvenir Sheet

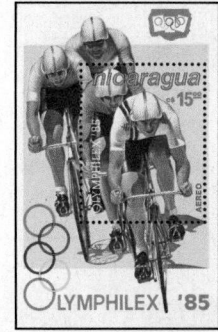

OLYMPHILEX '85 — AP128

1985, Mar. 18 *Litho.* *Perf. 12½*
C1049 AP128 15cor Bicycle race 2.50 .75

Souvenir Sheet

ESPAMER '85, Havana, Mar. 19-24 — AP129

10cor, Crocodylus rhombifer.

1985, Mar. 19
C1050 AP129 10cor multi 5.50 .75

Victory of Sandanista Revolution, 6th Anniv. — AP134

1985, July 19 *Litho.* *Perf. 12½*
C1125 AP134 9cor Soldier, flag 1.40 .60
C1126 AP134 9cor Sugar mill 1.40 .60

Benjamin Zeledon, Birth Cent. — AP135

1985, Oct. 4 *Litho.* *Perf. 12½*
C1127 AP135 15cor multicolored 3.00 .40

Henri Dunant (1828-1910), Founder of Red Cross AP136

15cor, Dunant, air ambulance.

1985, Oct. 10 *Perf. 12½x12*
C1128 AP136 3cor shown .40 .25
C1129 AP136 15cor multi 1.40 .45
a. Pair, #C1128-C1129 + label 3.10 1.50

Nicaraguan Stamps, 125th Anniv. — AP137

1986, May 22 *Perf. 12½x13*
C1130 AP137 30cor No. C1 1.25 .30
C1131 AP137 40cor No. 174 1.60 .40
C1132 AP137 50cor No. 48 2.00 .50
C1133 AP137 100cor No. 1 3.50 1.10
Nos. C1130-C1133 (4) 8.35 2.30

Intl. Peace
Year — AP138

1986, July 19   *Perf. 12½*
C1134 AP138 5cor shown   .85 .25
C1135 AP138 10cor Globe, dove .85 .25

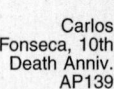

Carlos
Fonseca, 10th
Death Anniv.
AP139

1986, Aug. 11   Litho.   Perf. 12½
C1136 AP139 15cor multicolored .95 .40
  Formation of the Sandinista Front, 25th
anniv.

AP140

1986, Nov. 20   *Perf. 13*
C1137 AP140 15cor Rhinoceros 1.00 .35
C1138 AP140 15cor Zebra   1.00 .35
C1139 AP140 25cor Elephant   1.40 .50
C1140 AP140 25cor Giraffe   1.40 .50
C1141 AP140 50cor Mandrill   2.90 1.00
C1142 AP140 50cor Tiger   2.90 1.00
  Nos. C1137-C1142 (6)   10.60 3.70

AP141

World Cup Soccer Championships, Mexico:
Various soccer players and natl. flags.

1986, Dec. 20   *Perf. 13*
Shirt Colors
C1143 AP141 10cor blue   .85 .25
C1144 AP141 10cor blk &
                  white   .85 .25
C1145 AP141 10cor blue &
                  white   .85 .25
C1146 AP141 15cor pink &
                  white   1.20 .25
C1147 AP141 15cor grn & blk   1.20 .25
C1148 AP141 25cor blk &
                  white,
                  red   1.90 .30
C1149 AP141 50cor grn & yel,
                  red,
                  horiz.   2.10 .55
  Nos. C1143-C1149 (7)   8.95 2.10
Souvenir Sheet
Perf. 12½
C1150 AP141 100cor blk &
                  white, bl
                  & white   5.50 1.10

Vassil Levski, 150th
Birth Anniv. — AP142

1987, Apr. 18   *Perf. 13*
C1151 AP142 30cor multicolored 1.50 .40

Intl. Year of
Shelter for the
Homeless
AP143

Design: 30cor, Housing, diff.

1987, Aug. 2
C1152 AP143 20cor multicolored 1.00 .25
C1153 AP143 30cor multicolored 1.80 .35
  For surcharges, see Nos. C1160B-C1160C.

Souvenir Sheet

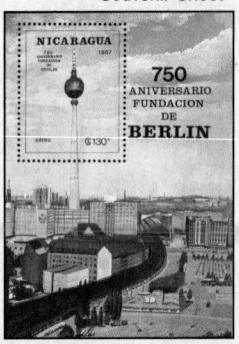

Berlin,
750th
Anniv.
AP144

1987, Sept. 25   Litho.   Perf. 13
C1154 AP144 130cor multi 4.50 1.00

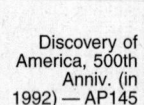

Discovery of
America, 500th
Anniv. (in
1992) — AP145

No. C1155, Indian village. No. C1156, Sailing ships. No. C1157, Battle in village. No.
C1158, Battle, prisoners. No. C1159, Spanish
town. No. C1160, Cathedral.

1987, Oct. 12   *Perf. 13*
C1155 AP145 15cor mul-
                  ticolored   1.10 .25
C1156 AP145 15cor mul-
                  ticolored   1.10 .25
C1157 AP145 20cor mul-
                  ticolored   1.40 .25
C1158 AP145 30cor mul-
                  ticolored   2.10 .30
C1159 AP145 40cor mul-
                  ticolored   3.00 .40
C1160 AP145 50cor mul-
                  ticolored   3.50 .50
  a.   Min. sheet of 6, #C1155-
            C1160   12.50 7.00
  Nos. C1155-C1160 (6)   12.20 1.95

Nos. C1152-C1153 Surcharged

Methods and Perfs As Before
1987, Dec. 26
C1160B AP143 200cor on
                  20cor   250.00 250.00
C1160C AP143 3000cor on
                  30cor   250.00 250.00
  Nos. C1160B-C1160C (2)   500.00

Cuban
Revolution, 30th
Anniv. — AP146

1989, Jan. 1   *Perf. 13*
C1161 AP146 20cor multicolored 1.75 .40

AP147

Designs: Various soccer players in action.

1989, Feb. 20   *Perf. 13x12½*
C1162 AP147 100cor multi   .55 .25
C1163 AP147 200cor multi   .55 .25
C1164 AP147 600cor multi   .55 .25
C1165 AP147 1000cor multi   .90 .25
C1166 AP147 2000cor multi 1.60 .45
C1167 AP147 3000cor multi 2.75 .40
C1168 AP147 5000cor multi 4.00 .65
  Nos. C1162-C1168 (7)   10.90 2.50
Souvenir Sheet
Perf. 13
C1169 AP147 9000cor multi 5.50 2.25
  World Cup Soccer Championships, Italy.
No. C1169 contains one 32x40mm stamp.

AP148

Design: 9000cor, Concepcion Volcano.

1989, July 19   *Perf. 13*
C1170 AP148 300cor multi   .80 .40
Souvenir Sheet
C1171 AP148 9000cor multi 7.75 2.25
  Sandinista Revolution, 10th Anniv.
No. C1171 contains one 40x32mm stamp.

AP149

Birds: 100cor, Anhinga anhinga. 200cor,
Elanoides forficatus. 600cor, Eumomota
superciliosa. 1000cor, Setophaga picta.
2000cor, Taraba major, horiz. 3000cor,
Onychorhynchus mexicanus. 5000cor,
Myrmotherula axillaris, horiz. 9000cor,
Amazona ochrocephala.

1989, July 18   Perf. 13x12½, 12½x13
C1172 AP149 100cor multi   .45 .25
C1173 AP149 200cor multi   .45 .25
C1174 AP149 600cor multi   .45 .25
C1175 AP149 1000cor multi   .75 .25
C1176 AP149 2000cor multi 1.60 .30
C1177 AP149 3000cor multi 2.60 .45
C1178 AP149 5000cor multi 4.50 .75
  Nos. C1172-C1178 (7)   10.80 2.50
Souvenir Sheet
Perf. 13
C1179 AP149 9000cor multi 5.50 2.00
  Brasiliana '89. No. C1179 contains one
32x40mm stamp.

AP150

Designs: 50cor, Downhill skiing. 300cor, Ice
hockey. 600cor, Ski jumping. 1000cor, Pairs
figure skating. 2000cor, Biathalon. 3000cor,
Slalom skiing. 5000cor, Cross country skiing.
9000cor, Two-man luge.

1989, Mar. 25   *Perf. 13*
C1180 AP150 50cor multi   1.10 .25
C1181 AP150 300cor multi   1.10 .25
C1182 AP150 600cor multi   1.10 .25

C1183 AP150 1000cor multi 1.10 .25
C1184 AP150 2000cor multi 1.90 .25
C1185 AP150 3000cor multi 2.10 .25
C1186 AP150 5000cor multi 2.40 .25
  Nos. C1180-C1186 (7)   10.80 1.75
Souvenir Sheet
C1187 AP150 9000cor multi 5.50 2.00
  1992 Winter Olympics, Albertville.
No. C1187 contains one 32x40mm stamp.

AP151

Designs: 100cor, Water polo. 200cor, Running. 600cor, Diving. 1000cor, Gymnastics.
2000cor, Weight lifting. 3000cor, Volleyball.
5000cor, Wrestling. 9000cor, Field hockey.

1989, Apr. 23
C1188 AP151 100cor multi   1.10 .25
C1189 AP151 200cor multi   1.10 .25
C1190 AP151 600cor multi   1.10 .25
C1191 AP151 1000cor multi 1.10 .25
C1192 AP151 2000cor multi 1.90 .25
C1193 AP151 3000cor multi 2.10 .25
C1194 AP151 5000cor multi 2.40 .25
  Nos. C1188-C1194 (7)   10.80 1.75
Souvenir Sheet
C1195 AP151 9000cor multi 5.50 .45
  1992 Summer Olympics, Barcelona.
No. C1195 contains one 32x40mm stamp.

AP152

1989, Oct. 12
C1196 AP152 2000cor Vase   1.50 .30
  Discovery of America, 500th Anniv. (in 1992).

Currency Reform
  Currency reform took place Mar. 4,
1990. Until stamps in the new currency
were issued, mail was to be handstamped "Franqueo Pagado," (Postage
Paid). Stamps were not used again until
Apr. 25, 1991. Nos. C1197-C1203 were
prepared but not issued prior to the currency reform and were sold by the post
office without postal validity. Used values are for CTO stamps.

Mushrooms — AP153

Designs: 500cor, Morchella esculenta.
1000cor, Boletus edulis. 5000cor, Lactarius
deliciosus. 10,000cor, Panellus stipticus.
20,000cor, Craterellus cornucopioides.
40,000cor, Cantharellus cibarius. 50,000cor,
Armillariella mellea.

1990, July 15   *Perf. 13*
C1197 AP153 500cor multi   .45 .25
C1198 AP153 1000cor multi   .65 .25
C1199 AP153 5000cor multi   1.00 .25
C1200 AP153 10,000cor multi 1.60 .25
C1201 AP153 20,000cor multi 1.90 .40
C1202 AP153 40,000cor multi 2.40 .50
C1203 AP153 50,000cor multi 2.90 .60
  Nos. C1197-C1203 (7)   10.90 2.50

AIR POST SEMI-POSTAL STAMPS

Mrs. Somoza and Children's Hospital SPAP1

Designs: 5c+5c, Children and weight chart. 15c+5c, Incubator and Da Vinci's "Child in Womb." 20c+5c, Smallpox vaccination. 30c+5c, Water purification. 35c+5c, 1cor+50c, like 10c+5c. 50c+10c, Antibiotics. 60c+15c, Malaria control. 70c+10c, Laboratory. 80c+20c, Gastroenteritis (sick and well babies).

1973, Sept. 25   Litho.   Perf. 13½x14

CB1	SPAP1	5c + 5c multi	.25	.25
CB2	SPAP1	10c + 5c multi	.25	.25
CB3	SPAP1	15c + 5c multi	.30	.25
CB4	SPAP1	20c + 5c multi	.30	.25
CB5	SPAP1	30c + 5c multi	.30	.25
CB6	SPAP1	35c + 5c multi	.30	.25
CB7	SPAP1	50c + 10c multi	.30	.25
CB8	SPAP1	60c + 15c multi	.50	.30
CB9	SPAP1	70c + 10c multi	.75	.30
CB10	SPAP1	80c + 20c multi	.85	.40
CB11	SPAP1	1cor + 50c multi	.95	.45
		Nos. CB1-CB11 (11)	5.05	3.20

The surtax was for hospital building fund.
See No. C845. Inscriptions on back, printed on top of gum give brief description of subjects shown.

AIR POST OFFICIAL STAMPS

OA1

"Typewritten" Overprint on #O293

1929, Aug.   Unwmk.   Perf. 12

CO1	OA1	25c orange	50.00	45.00

Excellent counterfeits of No. CO1 are plentiful.

Official Stamps of 1926 Ovptd. in Dark Blue

1929, Sept. 15

CO2	A24	25c orange	.50	.50
a.		Inverted overprint	25.00	
b.		Double overprint	25.00	
CO3	A25	50c pale blue	.75	.75
a.		Inverted overprint	25.00	
b.		Double overprint	25.00	
c.		Double overprint, one inverted	25.00	

Nos. 519-523 Overprinted in Black

1932, Feb.

CO4	A24	15c org red	.40	.40
a.		Inverted overprint	25.00	
b.		Double overprint	25.00	
c.		Double overprint, one invtd.	25.00	
CO5	A25	20c orange	.45	.45
a.		Double overprint	25.00	
CO6	A24	25c dk vio	.45	.45
CO7	A25	50c green	.55	.55
CO8	A25	1cor yellow	1.00	1.00
		Nos. CO4-CO8 (5)	2.85	2.85

Nos. CO4-CO5, CO7-CO8 exist with signature control overprint. Value, each, $2.50.

No. 547 Overprinted

CO9 A24 25c blk brn   42.50 42.50

The varieties "OFICAL", "OFIAIAL" and "CORROE" occur in the setting and are found on each stamp of the series.
Counterfeits of No. CO9 are plentiful.

Stamp No. CO4 with overprint "1931" in addition is believed to be of private origin.

Type of Regular Issue of 1914 Overprinted

1933

CO10	A24	25c olive	.25	.25
CO11	A25	50c ol grn	.25	.25
CO12	A25	1cor org red	.40	.40

On Stamps of 1914-28

CO13	A24	15c dp vio	.25	.25
CO14	A25	20c dp grn	.25	.25
		Nos. CO10-CO14 (5)	1.40	1.40

Nos. CO10-CO14 exist without signature control mark. Value, each $2.50.

Air Post Official Stamps of 1932-33 Ovptd. in Blue

1935

CO15	A24	15c dp vio	1.00	.80
CO16	A25	20c dp grn	2.00	1.60
CO17	A24	25c olive	3.00	2.50
CO18	A25	50c ol grn	35.00	30.00
CO19	A25	1cor org red	40.00	37.50
		Nos. CO15-CO19 (5)	81.00	72.40

Overprinted in Red

CO20	A24	15c dp vio	.50	.25
CO21	A25	20c dp grn	.50	.25
CO22	A24	25c olive	.50	.25
CO23	A25	50c ol grn	1.60	.80
CO24	A25	1cor org red	1.60	.80
		Nos. CO20-CO24 (5)	4.70	2.35

Nos. CO15 to CO24 are handstamped with script control mark. Counterfeits of blue overprint are plentiful.

The editors do not recognize the Nicaraguan air post Official stamps overprinted in red "VALIDO 1935" in two lines and with or without script control marks as having been issued primarily for postal purposes.

Nos. C164-C168 Overprinted in Black

1937

CO25	AP1	15c yel org	1.00	.55
CO26	AP1	20c org red	1.00	.60
CO27	AP1	25c black	1.00	.70
CO28	AP1	50c violet	1.00	.70
CO29	AP1	1cor orange	1.00	.70
		Nos. CO25-CO29 (5)	5.00	3.25

Pres. Anastasio Somoza — OA2

1939, Feb. 7   Engr.   Perf. 12½

CO30	OA2	10c brown	.30	.25
CO31	OA2	15c dk bl	.30	.25
CO32	OA2	20c yellow	.30	.25
CO33	OA2	25c dk pur	.30	.25
CO34	OA2	30c lake	.30	.25
CO35	OA2	50c dp org	1.00	.65
CO36	OA2	1cor dk ol grn	2.00	1.25
		Nos. CO30-CO36 (7)	4.50	3.15

Catalogue values for unused stamps in this section, from this point to the end of the section, are for Never Hinged items.

Mercedes Airport OA3

Designs: 10c, Sulphurous Lake of Nejapa. 15c, Ruben Dario Monument. 20c, Tapir. 25c, Genizaro Dam. 50c, Tipitapa Spa. 1cor, Stone Highway. 2.50cor, Franklin D. Roosevelt Monument.

Engraved, Center Photogravure
1947, Aug. 29
Various Frames in Black

CO37	OA3	5c org brn	.80	.25
CO38	OA3	10c blue	.80	.25
CO39	OA3	15c violet	.80	.25
CO40	OA3	20c red org	.80	.25
CO41	OA3	25c blue	.80	.25
CO42	OA3	50c car rose	.80	.25
CO43	OA3	1cor slate	1.20	.45
CO44	OA3	2.50cor red brn	3.50	1.25
		Nos. CO37-CO44 (8)	9.50	3.20

Rowland Hill — OA4

Designs: 10c, Heinrich von Stephan. 25c, 1st UPU Bldg. 50c, UPU Bldg., Bern. 1cor, UPU Monument. 2.60cor, Congress medal, reverse.

1950, Nov. 23   Engr.   Perf. 13
Frames in Black

CO45	OA4	5c rose vio	.50	.25
CO46	OA4	10c dp grn	.50	.25
CO47	OA4	25c rose vio	.50	.25
CO48	OA4	50c dp org	.50	.25
CO49	OA4	1cor ultra	.55	.30
CO50	OA4	2.60cor gray blk	4.00	2.00
		Nos. CO45-CO50 (6)	6.55	3.30

75th anniv. (in 1949) of the UPU.
Each denomination was also issued in a souvenir sheet containing four stamps and marginal inscriptions. Size: 121x96mm. Value, set of 6 sheets, $35.

Consular Service Stamps
Surcharged "Oficial Aéreo" and New Denomination in Red, Black or Blue
1961, Nov.   Unwmk.   Engr.   Perf. 12
Red Marginal Number

CO51	AP63	10c on 1cor grnsh blk (R)	.60	.25
CO52	AP63	15c on 20cor red brn (R)	.60	.25
CO53	AP63	20c on 100cor mag	.60	.25
CO54	AP63	25c on 50c dp bl (R)	.60	.25
CO55	AP63	35c on 50cor brn	.60	.25
CO56	AP63	50c on 3cor dk car	.60	.25
CO57	AP63	1cor on 2cor grn (R)	.60	.25
CO58	AP63	2cor on 5cor org (Bl)	1.00	.40
CO59	AP63	5cor on 10cor vio (R)	2.75	1.00
		Nos. CO51-CO59 (9)	7.95	3.15

POSTAGE DUE STAMPS

D1

1896   Unwmk.   Engr.   Perf. 12

J1	D1	1c orange	.50	1.25
J2	D1	2c orange	.50	1.25
J3	D1	5c orange	.50	1.25
J4	D1	10c orange	.50	1.25
J5	D1	20c orange	.50	1.25
J6	D1	30c orange	.50	1.25
J7	D1	50c orange	.50	1.50
		Nos. J1-J7 (7)	3.50	9.00

Wmk. 117

J8	D1	1c orange	1.00	1.50
J9	D1	2c orange	1.00	1.50
J10	D1	5c orange	1.00	1.50
J11	D1	10c orange	1.00	1.50
J12	D1	20c orange	1.25	1.50
J13	D1	30c orange	1.00	1.50
J14	D1	50c orange	1.00	1.50
		Nos. J8-J14 (7)	7.25	10.50

1897   Unwmk.

J15	D1	1c violet	.50	1.50
J16	D1	2c violet	.50	1.50
J17	D1	5c violet	.50	1.50
J18	D1	10c violet	.50	1.50
J19	D1	20c violet	1.25	2.00
J20	D1	30c violet	.50	1.50
J21	D1	50c violet	.50	1.50
		Nos. J15-J21 (7)	4.25	11.00

Wmk. 117

J22	D1	1c violet	.50	1.50
J23	D1	2c violet	.50	1.50
J24	D1	5c violet	.50	1.50
J25	D1	10c violet	.50	1.50
J26	D1	20c violet	1.00	2.00
J27	D1	30c violet	.50	1.50
J28	D1	50c violet	.50	1.50
		Nos. J22-J28 (7)	4.00	11.00

Reprints of Nos. J8-J28 are on thick, porous paper. Color of 1896 reprints, reddish orange; or 1897 reprints, reddish violet. On watermarked reprints, liberty cap is sideways. Value 25c each.

D2

1898   Litho.   Unwmk.

J29	D2	1c blue green	.30	2.00
J30	D2	2c blue green	.30	2.00
J31	D2	5c blue green	.30	2.00
J32	D2	10c blue green	.30	4.00
J33	D2	20c blue green	.30	2.00
J34	D2	30c blue green	.30	2.00
J35	D2	50c blue green	.30	2.00
		Nos. J29-J35 (7)	2.10	14.00

1899

J36	D2	1c carmine	.30	2.00
J37	D2	2c carmine	.30	2.00
J38	D2	5c carmine	.30	2.00
J39	D2	10c carmine	.30	2.00
J40	D2	20c carmine	.30	2.00
J41	D2	50c carmine	.30	2.00
		Nos. J36-J41 (6)	1.80	12.00

Some denominations are found in se-tenant pairs.
Various counterfeit cancellations exist on #J1-J41.

D3

1900   Engr.

J42	D3	1c plum	.75	
J43	D3	2c vermilion	.75	
J44	D3	5c dk bl	.75	
J45	D3	10c purple	.75	
J46	D3	20c org brn	.75	
J47	D3	30c dk grn	1.50	
J48	D3	50c lake	1.50	
		Nos. J42-J48 (7)	6.75	

Nos. J42-J48 were not placed in use as postage due stamps. They were only issued with "Postage" overprints. See Nos. 137-143, 152-158, O72-O81, 2L11-2L15, 2L25, 2L40-2L41.

OFFICIAL STAMPS

Types of Postage Stamps Overprinted in Red Diagonally Reading up

1890   Unwmk.   Engr.   Perf. 12

O1	A5	1c ultra	.30	.30
O2	A5	2c ultra	.30	.30
O3	A5	5c ultra	.30	.30
O4	A5	10c ultra	.30	.40
O5	A5	20c ultra	.30	.45
O6	A5	50c ultra	.30	.75
O7	A5	1p ultra	.30	1.25
O8	A5	2p ultra	.30	1.60
O9	A5	5p ultra	.30	2.40
O10	A5	10p ultra	.30	4.00
		Nos. O1-O10 (10)	3.00	11.75

All values of the 1890 issue are known without overprint and most of them with inverted or double overprint, or without overprint and imperforate. There is no evidence that they were issued in these forms.
Official stamps of 1890-1899 are scarce with genuine cancellations. Forged cancellations are plentiful.

Overprinted Vertically Reading Up

1891				**Litho.**
O11	A6	1c green	.25	.30
O12	A6	2c green	.25	.30
O13	A6	5c green	.25	.30
O14	A6	10c green	.25	.30
O15	A6	20c green	.25	.50
O16	A6	50c green	.25	1.10
O17	A6	1p green	.25	1.25
O18	A6	2p green	.25	1.30
O19	A6	5p green	.40	2.40
O20	A6	10p green	.60	4.00
	Nos. O11-O20 (10)		.60	11.75

All values of this issue except the 2c and 5p exist without overprint and several with double overprint. They are not known to have been issued in this form.

Many of the denominations may be found in se-tenant pairs.

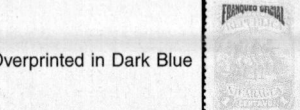

Overprinted in Dark Blue

1892				**Engr.**
O21	A7	1c yellow brown	.30	.30
O22	A7	2c yellow brown	.30	.30
O23	A7	5c yellow brown	.30	.30
O24	A7	10c yellow brown	.30	.30
O25	A7	20c yellow brown	.30	.50
O26	A7	50c yellow brown	.30	1.00
O27	A7	1p yellow brown	.30	1.25
O28	A7	2p yellow brown	.30	1.60
O29	A7	5p yellow brown	.30	2.40
O30	A7	10p yellow brown	.30	4.00
	Nos. O21-O30 (10)		3.00	11.95

The 2c and 1p are known without overprint and several values exist with double or inverted overprint. These probably were not regularly issued.

Commemorative of the 400th anniversary of the discovery of America by Christopher Columbus.

Overprinted in Red

1893				**Engr.**
O31	A8	1c slate	.30	.30
O32	A8	2c slate	.30	.30
O33	A8	5c slate	.30	.30
O34	A8	10c slate	.30	.30
O35	A8	20c slate	.30	.50
O36	A8	25c slate	.30	.75
O37	A8	50c slate	.30	.85
O38	A8	1p slate	.30	1.00
O39	A8	2p slate	.30	2.00
O40	A8	5p slate	.30	2.50
O41	A8	10p slate	.30	5.50
	Nos. O31-O41 (11)		3.30	14.30

The 2, 5, 10, 20, 25, 50c and 5p are known without overprint but probably were not regularly issued. Some values exist with double or inverted overprints.

Overprinted in Black

1894				
O42	A9	1c orange	.30	.35
O43	A9	2c orange	.30	.35
O44	A9	5c orange	.30	.35
O45	A9	10c orange	.30	.35
O46	A9	20c orange	.30	.50
O47	A9	50c orange	.30	.75
O48	A9	1p orange	.30	1.50
O49	A9	2p orange	.30	2.00
O50	A9	5p orange	2.00	3.00
O51	A9	10p orange	2.00	4.00
	Nos. O42-O51 (10)		6.40	13.15

Reprints are yellow.

Overprinted in Dark Blue

1895				
O52	A10	1c green	.30	.35
O53	A10	2c green	.30	.35
O54	A10	5c green	.30	.35
O55	A10	10c green	.30	.35
O56	A10	20c green	.30	.50
O57	A10	50c green	.30	1.00
O58	A10	1p green	.30	1.50
O59	A10	2p green	.30	2.00
O60	A10	5p green	.30	3.00
O61	A10	10p green	.30	4.00
	Nos. O52-O61 (10)		3.00	13.40

Wmk. 117

O62	A10	1c green	
O63	A10	2c green	
O64	A10	5c green	
O65	A10	10c green	
O66	A10	20c green	
O67	A10	50c green	
O68	A10	1p green	
O69	A10	2p green	
O70	A10	5p green	
O71	A10	10p green	

Nos. O62-O71 probably exist only as reprints. Value, each 30¢.

Postage Due Stamps of Same Date Handstamped in Violet

1896			**Unwmk.**
O72	D1	1c orange	7.00
O73	D1	2c orange	7.00
O74	D1	5c orange	5.00
O75	D1	10c orange	5.00
O76	D1	20c orange	10.00
	Nos. O72-O76 (5)		34.00

Wmk. 117

O77	D1	1c orange	7.00
O78	D1	2c orange	7.00
O79	D1	5c orange	4.00
O80	D1	10c orange	4.00
O81	D1	20c orange	4.00
	Nos. O77-O81 (5)		26.00

Nos. O72-O81 were handstamped in rows of five. Several handstamps were used, one of which had the variety "Oftcial." Most varieties are known inverted and double. Forgeries exist.

Types of Postage Stamps Overprinted in Red

1896				**Unwmk.**
O82	A11	1c red	2.50	3.00
O83	A11	2c red	2.50	3.00
O84	A11	5c red	2.50	3.00
O85	A11	10c red	2.50	3.00
O86	A11	20c red	3.00	3.00
O87	A11	50c red	5.00	5.00
O88	A11	1p red	12.00	12.00
O89	A11	2p red	12.00	12.00
O90	A11	5p red	16.00	16.00
	Nos. O82-O90 (9)		58.00	60.00

Wmk. 117

O91	A11	1c red	3.00	3.50
O92	A11	2c red	3.00	3.50
O93	A11	5c red	3.00	3.50
O94	A11	10c red	3.00	3.50
O95	A11	20c red	5.00	5.00
O96	A11	50c red	3.00	5.00
O97	A11	1p red	14.00	14.00
O98	A11	2p red	16.00	16.00
O99	A11	5p red	25.00	25.00
	Nos. O91-O99 (9)		75.00	79.00

Used values for Nos. O88-O90, O97-O99 are for CTO examples. Postally used examples are not known.

Same, Dated 1897

1897				**Unwmk.**
O100	A11	1c red	3.00	3.00
O101	A11	2c red	3.00	3.00
O102	A11	5c red	3.00	2.50
O103	A11	10c red	3.00	3.00
O104	A11	20c red	4.00	4.00
O105	A11	50c red	5.00	5.00
O106	A11	1p red	12.00	12.00
O107	A11	2p red	12.00	12.00
O108	A11	5p red	16.00	16.00
	Nos. O100-O108 (9)		60.00	60.50

Wmk. 117

O109	A11	1c red	5.00	5.00
O110	A11	2c red	5.00	5.00
O111	A11	5c red	5.00	5.00
O112	A11	10c red	10.00	10.00
O113	A11	20c red	10.00	10.00
O114	A11	50c red	12.00	12.00
O115	A11	1p red	20.00	20.00
O116	A11	2p red	20.00	20.00
O117	A11	5p red	20.00	20.00
	Nos. O109-O117 (9)		107.00	107.00

Reprints of Nos. O82-O117 are described in notes after No. 109M. Value 30¢ each.

Used values for Nos. O106-O108, O115-O117 are for CTO examples. Postally used examples are not known.

Overprinted in Blue

1898				**Unwmk.**
O118	A12	1c carmine	3.25	3.25
O119	A12	2c carmine	3.25	3.25
O120	A12	4c carmine	3.25	3.25
O121	A12	5c carmine	2.50	2.50
O122	A12	10c carmine	4.00	4.00
O123	A12	15c carmine	6.00	6.00
O124	A12	20c carmine	6.00	6.00
O125	A12	50c carmine	8.50	8.50
O126	A12	1p carmine	11.00	11.00
O127	A12	2p carmine	11.00	11.00
O128	A12	5p carmine	11.00	11.00
	Nos. O118-O128 (11)		69.75	69.75

Stamps of this set with sideways watermark 117 or with black overprint are reprints. Value 30¢ each.

Used values for Nos. O126-O128 are for CTO examples. Postally used examples are not known.

"Justice" — O5

1900				**Engr.**
O140	O5	1c plum	.60	.60
O141	O5	2c vermilion	.50	.50
O142	O5	4c ol grn	.60	.60
O143	O5	5c dk bl	1.25	.45
O144	O5	10c purple	1.25	.35
O145	O5	20c brown	.90	.35
O146	O5	50c lake	1.25	.50
O147	O5	1p ultra	3.50	2.50
O148	O5	2p red org	4.00	4.00
O149	O5	5p grnsh blk	3.00	3.00
	Nos. O140-O149 (10)		18.85	14.85

For surcharges see Nos. O155-O157.

Nos. 123, 161 Surcharged in Black

1903				**Perf. 12, 14**
O150	A14	1c on 10c violet	.25	.30
a.		"Centovo"	1.00	
b.		"Contavo"	1.00	
c.		With ornaments	.30	
d.		Inverted surcharge	1.00	
e.		"1" omitted at upper left	2.00	
O151	A14	2c on 3c green	.30	.40
a.		"Centovos"	1.00	
b.		"Contavos"	1.00	
c.		With ornaments	.35	
d.		Inverted surcharge	1.00	

Overprinted in Dark Blue

1899				
O129	A13	1c gray grn	.35	1.00
O130	A13	2c bis brn	.35	1.00
O131	A13	4c lake	.35	1.00
O132	A13	5c dk bl	.35	1.00
O133	A13	10c buff	.35	1.00
O134	A13	15c chocolate	.35	2.00
O135	A13	20c dk grn	.35	3.00
O136	A13	50c car rose	.35	6.00
O137	A13	1p red	.35	10.00
O138	A13	2p violet	.35	10.00
O139	A13	5p lt bl	.35	15.00
	Nos. O129-O139 (11)		3.85	47.50

Counterfeit cancellations on Nos. O129-O139 are plentiful.

O152	A14	4c on 3c green	1.25	1.25
a.		"Centovos"	2.50	
b.		"Contavos"	2.50	
c.		With ornaments	2.50	
d.		Inverted surcharge	2.50	
O153	A14	4c on 10c violet	1.25	1.25
a.		"Centovos"	2.50	
b.		"Contavos"	2.50	
c.		With ornaments	2.00	
d.		Inverted surcharge		
O154	A14	4c on 3c green	.35	.30
a.		"Centovos"	1.00	
b.		"Contavos"	1.00	
c.		With ornaments	.30	
d.		Double surcharge	1.00	
e.		Inverted surcharge		
	Nos. O150-O154 (5)		3.40	3.50

These surcharges are set up to cover 25 stamps. Some of the settings have bars or pieces of fancy border type below "OFICIAL." There are 5 varieties on #O150, 3 on #O151, 1 each on #O152, O153, O154.

In 1904 #O151 was reprinted to fill a dealer's order. This printing lacks the small figure at the upper right. It includes the variety "OFICILA." At the same time the same setting was printed in carmine on official stamps of 1900, 1c on 10c violet and 2c on 1p ultramarine. Also the 1, 2 and 5p official stamps of 1900 were surcharged with new values and the dates 1901 or 1902 in various colors, inverted, etc. It is doubtful if any of these varieties were ever in Nicaragua and certain that none of them ever did legitimate postal duty.

No. O145 Surcharged in Black

1904				**Perf. 12**
O155	O5	10c on 20c brn	.25	.25
a.		No period after "Ctvs"	1.00	.75
O156	O5	30c on 20c brn	.25	.25
O157	O5	50c on 20c brn	.50	.35
a.		Lower "50" omitted	2.50	2.50
b.		Upper figures omitted	2.50	2.50
c.		Top left and lower figures omitted	3.50	3.50
	Nos. O155-O157 (3)		1.00	.85

Coat of Arms — O6

1905, July 25				**Engr.**
O158	O6	1c green	.30	.25
O159	O6	2c rose	.30	.25
O160	O6	5c blue	.30	.25
O161	O6	10c yel brn	.30	.25
O162	O6	20c orange	.30	.25
O163	O6	50c brn ol	.30	.25
O164	O6	1p lake	.30	.25
O165	O6	2p violet	.30	.25
O166	O6	5p gray blk	.30	.25
	Nos. O158-O166 (9)		2.70	2.25

Surcharged Vertically Up or Down

1907				
O167	O6	10c on 1c grn	.75	.75
O168	O6	10c on 2c rose	25.00	22.50
O169	O6	20c on 2c rose	22.50	26.00
O170	O6	50c on 1c grn	1.50	1.50
O171	O6	50c on 2c rose	22.50	23.00

Surcharged

O172	O6	1p on 2c rose	1.50	1.50
O173	O6	2p on 2c rose	1.50	1.50
O174	O6	3p on 2c rose	1.50	1.50
O175	O6	4p on 2c rose		
O176	O6	4p on 5c blue	2.25	2.25

The setting for this surcharge includes various letters from wrong fonts, the figure "1" for "I" in "Vale" and an "I" for "1" in "$1.00."

Surcharged

O177	O6	20c on 1c green	1.00	1.00
a.		Double surcharge	5.00	5.00
Nos. O167-O174,O176-O177				
(10)			80.00	81.50

The preceding surcharges are vertical, reading both up and down.

Revenue Stamps Surcharged

O7

1907   *Perf. 14 to 15*

O178	O7	10c on 2c org (Bk)	.30	.25
O179	O7	35c on 1c bl (R)	.30	.25
a.		Inverted surcharge	3.00	3.00
O180	O7	70c on 1c bl (V)	.30	.25
a.		Inverted surcharge	3.00	3.00
O181	O7	70c on 1c bl (O)	.30	.25
a.		Inverted surcharge	3.00	3.00
O182	O7	1p on 2c org (G)	.30	.25
a.		Inverted surcharge	14.00	14.00
O183	O7	2p on 2c org (Br)	.30	.25
O184	O7	3p on 5c brn (Bl)	.30	.25
O185	O7	4p on 5c brn (G)	.30	.25
a.		Double surcharge	3.00	3.00
O186	O7	5p on 5c brn (G)	.30	.25
a.		Inverted surcharge	3.50	3.50
Nos. O178-O186 (9)			2.70	2.25

Letters and figures from several fonts were mixed in these surcharges.
See Nos. O199-O209.

No. 202 Surcharged

1907, Nov.
Black or Blue Black Surcharge

O187	A18	10c on 1c grn	15.00	15.00
O188	A18	15c on 1c grn	15.00	20.00
O189	A18	20c on 1c grn	15.00	15.00
O190	A18	50c on 1c grn	15.00	20.00

Red Surcharge

O191	A18	1(un)p on 1c grn	14.00	15.00
O192	A18	2(dos)p on 1c grn	14.00	15.00
Nos. O187-O192 (6)			88.00	100.00

No. 181 Surcharged

1908   Yellow Surcharge *Perf. 12*

O193	A18	10c on 3c vio	15.00	15.00
O194	A18	15c on 3c vio	15.00	15.00
O195	A18	20c on 3c vio	15.00	15.00
O196	A18	35c on 3c vio	15.00	15.00
O197	A18	50c on 3c vio	15.00	15.00
Nos. O193-O197 (5)			75.00	75.00

Black Surcharge

O198	A18	35c on 3c vio	210.00	210.00

Revenue Stamps Surcharged like 1907 Issue Dated "1908"

1908   *Perf. 14 to 15*

O199	O7	10c on 1c bl (V)	.75	.50
a.		Inverted surcharge	3.50	3.50
O200	O7	35c on 1c bl (Bk)	.75	.50
a.		Inverted surcharge	3.50	3.50
b.		Double surcharge	4.00	4.00
O201	O7	50c on 1c bl (R)	.75	.50
O202	O7	1p on 1c bl (Br)	40.00	40.00
a.		Inverted surcharge	65.00	65.00
O203	O7	2p on 1c bl (G)	.90	.75
O204	O7	10c on 2c org (Bk)	1.10	.65
O205	O7	35c on 2c org (R)	1.10	.65
a.		Inverted surcharge	3.50	
O206	O7	50c on 2c org (Bk)	1.10	.65
O207	O7	70c on 2c org (Bl)	1.10	.65

O208	O7	1p on 2c org (G)	1.10	.65
O209	O7	2p on 2c org (Br)	1.10	.65
Nos. O199-O209 (11)			49.75	46.15

There are several minor varieties in the figures, etc., in these surcharges.

Nos. 243-248 Overprinted in Black

1909   *Perf. 12*

O210	A18	10c lake	.25	.25
a.		Double overprint	2.50	2.50
O211	A18	15c black	.60	.50
O212	A18	20c brn ol	1.00	.75
O213	A18	50c dp grn	1.50	1.00
O214	A18	1p yellow	1.75	1.25
O215	A18	2p car rose	6.50	2.00
Nos. O210-O215 (6)			11.60	5.75

Overprinted in Black

1910

O216	A18	15c black	1.50	1.25
a.		Double overprint	4.00	4.00
O217	A18	20c brn ol	2.50	2.00
O218	A18	50c dp grn	2.50	2.00
O219	A18	1p yellow	2.75	2.50
a.		Inverted overprint	16.00	7.50
O220	A18	2p car rose	4.00	3.00
Nos. O216-O220 (5)			13.25	10.75

Nos. 239-240 Surcharged in Black

No. O221   No. O222

1911

O221	A18	5c on 3c red org	10.00	6.00
O222	A18	10c on 4c vio	12.00	5.00
a.		Double surcharge	24.00	24.00
b.		Pair, one without new value	35.00	

Revenue Stamps Surcharged in Black

1911, Nov.   *Perf. 14 to 15*

O223	A21	10c on 10c on 1 red		
		org	3.00	3.00
a.		Inverted surcharge	4.50	
b.		Double surcharge	4.50	
O224	A21	15c on 10c on 1 red		
		org	3.00	3.00
a.		Inverted surcharge	5.00	
b.		Double surcharge	4.50	
O225	A21	20c on 10c on 1 red		
		org	3.00	3.00
a.		Inverted surcharge	5.00	
O226	A21	50c on 10c on 1 red		
		org	3.75	3.75
a.		Inverted surcharge	4.50	
O227	A21	1p on 10c on 1 red		
		org	5.00	7.00
a.		Inverted surcharge	6.00	
O228	A21	2p on 10c on 1 red		
		org	5.50	10.00
a.		Inverted surcharge	7.50	
b.		Double surcharge	7.50	
Nos. O223-O228 (6)			23.25	29.75

Surcharged in Black

1911, Nov.

O229	A21	10c on 10c on 1 red		
		org	22.50	
O230	A21	15c on 10c on 1 red		
		org	22.50	
O231	A21	20c on 10c on 1 red		
		org	22.50	
O232	A21	50c on 10c on 1 red		
		org	16.00	
Nos. O229-O232 (4)			83.50	

Surcharged in Black

1911, Dec.

O233	A21	5c on 10c on 1 red		
		org	4.50	6.00
a.		Double surcharge	7.50	
b.		Inverted surcharge	7.50	
c.		"5" omitted	6.00	
O234	A21	10c on 10c on 1 red		
		org	5.50	7.00
O235	A21	15c on 10c on 1 red		
		org	6.00	7.50
O236	A21	20c on 10c on 1 red		
		org	6.50	8.50
O237	A21	50c on 10c on 1 red		
		org	7.50	10.00
Nos. O233-O237 (5)			30.00	39.00

Nos. O233 to O237 have a surcharge on the back like Nos. 285 and 286 with "15 cts" obliterated by a heavy horizontal bar.

Surcharged Vertically in Black

1912

O238	A21	5c on 10c on 1 red		
		org	10.00	10.00
O239	A21	10c on 10c on 1 red		
		org	10.00	10.00
O240	A21	15c on 10c on 1 red		
		org	10.00	10.00
O241	A21	20c on 10c on 1 red		
		org	10.00	10.00
O242	A21	35c on 10c on 1 red		
		org	10.00	10.00
O243	A21	50c on 10c on 1 red		
		org	10.00	10.00
O244	A21	1p on 10c on 1 red		
		org	10.00	10.00
Nos. O238-O244 (7)			70.00	70.00

Nos. O238 to O244 are printed on Nos. 285 and 286 but the surcharge on the back is obliterated by a vertical bar.

Types of Regular Issue of 1912 Overprinted in Black

1912   *Perf. 12*

O245	A22	1c light blue	.25	.25
O246	A22	2c light blue	.25	.25
O247	A22	3c light blue	.25	.25
O248	A22	4c light blue	.25	.25
O249	A22	5c light blue	.25	.25
O250	A22	6c light blue	.35	.25
O251	A22	10c light blue	.35	.25
O252	A22	15c light blue	.35	.25
O253	A22	20c light blue	.35	.25
O254	A22	25c light blue	.35	.25
O255	A23	35c light blue	.40	.25
O256	A22	50c light blue	3.75	2.00
O257	A22	1p light blue	.65	.45
O258	A22	2p light blue	.75	.55
O259	A22	5p light blue	1.00	.75
Nos. O245-O259 (15)			9.55	6.50

On the 35c the overprint is 15½mm wide, on the other values it is 13mm.

Types of Regular Issue of 1914 Overprinted in Black

1915, May

O260	A24	1c light blue	.25	.25
O261	A25	2c light blue	.25	.25
O262	A25	3c light blue	.25	.25
O263	A25	4c light blue	.25	.25
O264	A24	5c light blue	.25	.25
O265	A25	6c light blue	.25	.25
O266	A25	10c light blue	.25	.25
O267	A24	15c light blue	.25	.25
O268	A25	20c light blue	.25	.25
O269	A24	25c light blue	.30	.25
O270	A25	50c light blue	.60	.60
Nos. O260-O270 (11)			3.15	3.15

Regular Issues of 1914-22 Overprinted in Red

1925

O271	A24	½c dp grn	.25	.25
a.		Double overprint	2.50	2.50
O272	A24	1c violet	.25	.25
O273	A25	2c car rose	.25	.25
O274	A25	3c ol grn	.25	.25
O275	A25	4c vermilion	.25	.25
a.		Double overprint	4.00	4.00
O276	A24	5c black	.25	.25
a.		Double overprint	4.00	4.00
O277	A25	6c red brn	.25	.25
O278	A25	10c yellow	.30	.30
a.		Double overprint	4.25	4.25
O279	A24	15c red brn	.40	.40
O280	A25	20c bis brn	.50	.50
O281	A24	25c orange	.60	.60
a.		Inverted overprint	60.00	40.00
O282	A25	50c pale bl	.75	.75
a.		Double overprint	20.00	20.00
Nos. O271-O282 (12)			4.30	4.30

Type II overprint has "f" and "i" separated. Comes on Nos. O272-O274 and O276.

Regular Issues of 1914-22 Overprinted in Black

1926

O283	A24	½c dk grn	.25	.25
O284	A24	1c dp vio	.25	.25
O285	A25	2c car rose	.25	.25
O286	A24	3c ol gray	.25	.25
O287	A24	4c vermilion	.25	.25
O288	A24	5c gray blk	.25	.25
O289	A25	6c red brn	.25	.25
O290	A25	10c yellow	.25	.25
O291	A24	15c dp brn	.25	.25
O292	A25	20c bis brn	.25	.25
O293	A25	25c orange	.25	.25
O294	A25	50c pale bl	.25	.25
Nos. O283-O294 (12)			3.00	3.00

No. 499 Surcharged in Red & Black

1931

O295	A33	5c on 10c bis brn	.50	.30

Nos. 517-518 Overprinted in Red

1931

O296	A25	6c bis brn	.50	.30
O297	A25	10c lt brn	.50	.30

Nos. 541, 543, 545 With Additional Overprint in Red

O298	A24	1c ol grn	.25	.25
O299	A24	3c lt bl	.25	.25
a.		"OFICIAL" inverted	.80	.80
O300	A24	5c gray brn	.25	.25
a.		"1931" double	.80	.80
Nos. O298-O300 (3)			.75	.75

Regular Issues of 1914-31 Overprinted in Black

1932, Feb. 6

O301	A24	1c ol grn	.25	.25
a.		Double overprint	1.40	1.40
O302	A25	2c brt rose	.25	.25
a.		Double overprint	1.40	1.40
O303	A24	3c lt bl	.25	.25
a.		Double overprint	.50	.50
O304	A25	4c dk bl	.25	.25
O305	A24	5c ol brn	.25	.25
O306	A25	6c bis brn	.25	.25
a.		Double overprint	2.00	2.00
O307	A25	10c lt brn	.30	.25
O308	A24	15c org red	.40	.25
a.		Double overprint	2.25	2.25
O309	A25	20c orange	.70	.35
O310	A24	25c dk vio	2.00	.50
O311	A25	50c green	.25	.25
O312	A25	1cor yellow	.25	.25
Nos. O301-O312 (12)			5.40	3.35

With Additional Overprint in Black

1932, Feb. 6

O313	A24	1c ol grn	5.50	5.50
O314	A25	2c brt rose	6.50	6.50
a.		Double overprint	8.25	8.25
O315	A24	3c lt bl	5.00	5.00
O316	A24	5c ol brn	5.00	5.00
O317	A24	15c org red	.65	.65
O318	A24	25c blk brn	.65	.65
O319	A24	25c dk vio	1.50	1.50
		Nos. O313-O319 (7)	24.80	24.80

The variety "OFIAIAL" occurs once in each sheet of Nos. O301 to O319 inclusive. Despite the 1932 release date, the "1931" overprint on Nos. O313-O319 is correct.

Flag of the Race Issue

1933, Aug. 9　　Litho.　　Rouletted 9
Without gum

O320	A43	1c orange	1.25	1.25
O321	A43	2c yellow	1.25	1.25
O322	A43	3c dk brn	1.25	1.25
O323	A43	4c dp brn	1.25	1.25
O324	A43	5c gray brn	1.25	1.25
O325	A43	6c dp ultra	1.50	1.50
O326	A43	10c dp vio	1.50	1.50
O327	A43	15c red vio	1.50	1.50
O328	A43	20c dp grn	1.50	1.50
O329	A43	25c green	2.50	2.50
O330	A43	50c carmine	3.00	3.00
O331	A43	1cor red	5.00	5.00
		Nos. O320-O331 (12)	22.75	22.75

See note after No. 599.
Reprints of Nos. O320-O331 exist.
A 25c dull blue exists. Its status is questioned.

Regular Issue of 1914-31 Overprinted in Red

1933, Nov.　　　　Perf. 12

O332	A24	1c ol grn	.30	.30
O333	A25	2c brt rose	.30	.30
O334	A24	3c lt bl	.30	.30
O335	A25	4c dk bl	.30	.30
O336	A24	5c ol brn	.30	.30
O337	A25	6c bis brn	.30	.30
O338	A25	10c lt brn	.30	.30
O339	A25	15c red org	.30	.30
O340	A25	20c orange	.30	.30
O341	A24	25c dk vio	.30	.30
O342	A25	50c green	.30	.30
O343	A25	1cor yellow	.30	.30
		Nos. O332-O343 (12)	3.60	3.60

Nos. O332-O343 exist with or without signature control overprint. Values are the same.

Nos. O332-O343 Overprinted in Blue

1935, Dec.

O344	A24	1c ol grn	.65	.40
O345	A25	2c brt rose	.65	.50
O346	A24	3c lt bl	1.60	.50
O347	A25	4c dk bl	1.60	1.60
O348	A24	5c ol brn	1.60	1.60
O349	A25	6c bis brn	2.00	2.00
O350	A25	10c lt brn	2.00	2.00
O351	A24	15c org red	27.50	27.50
O352	A25	20c orange	27.50	27.50
O353	A24	25c dk vio	27.50	27.50
O354	A25	50c green	27.50	27.50
O355	A25	1cor yellow	27.50	27.50
		Nos. O344-O355 (12)	147.60	146.10

Nos. O344-O355 have signature control overprints. Counterfeits of overprint abound.

Nos. O332-O343 Overprinted in Red

1936, Jan.

O356	A24	1c ol grn	.30	.30
O357	A25	2c brt rose	.30	.30
O358	A25	3c lt bl	.30	.30
a.		Double overprint		
O359	A25	4c dk bl	.30	.30
O360	A25	5c ol brn	.30	.30
O361	A25	6c bis brn	.30	.30

O362	A25	10c lt brn	.30	.30
O363	A24	15c org red	.30	.30
O364	A24	20c orange	.30	.30
O365	A24	25c dk vio	.30	.30
O366	A25	50c green	.30	.30
O367	A25	1cor yellow	.55	.55
		Nos. O356-O367 (12)	3.85	3.85

Nos. O356-O367 have signature control overprints.

Nos. 653 to 655, 657, 659 660, 662 to 664 Overprinted in Black

1937

O368	A24	1c car rose	.65	.55
O369	A25	2c dp bl	.65	.55
O370	A24	3c chocolate	.65	.55
O371	A24	5c org red	.95	.55
O372	A24	10c ol grn	1.75	.90
O373	A24	15c green	2.10	1.10
O374	A24	25c orange	2.60	1.40
O375	A25	50c brown	3.75	1.75
O376	A25	1cor ultra	7.00	2.75
		Nos. O368-O376 (9)	20.10	10.10

Islands of the Great Lake — O9

1939, Jan.　　Engr.　　Perf. 12½

O377	O9	2c rose red	.65	.25
O378	O9	3c lt bl	.65	.25
O379	O9	6c brn org	.65	.25
O380	O9	7½c dp grn	.65	.25
O381	O9	10c blk brn	.65	.25
O382	O9	15c orange	.65	.25
O383	O9	25c dk vio	1.00	.25
O384	O9	50c brt yel grn	2.60	.75
		Nos. O377-O384 (8)	7.50	2.50

POSTAL TAX STAMPS

Official Stamps of 1915 Surcharged in Black

1921, July　　Unwmk.　　Perf. 12

RA1	A24	1c on 5c lt bl	1.50	.60
RA2	A25	1c on 6c lt bl	.65	.25
a.		Double surcharge, one inverted		
RA3	A25	1c on 10c lt bl	1.00	.25
a.		Double surcharge	3.50	3.50
RA4	A24	1c on 15c lt bl	1.50	.25
a.		Double surcharge, one inverted	5.00	5.00
		Nos. RA1-RA4 (4)	4.65	1.35

"R de C" signifies "Reconstruccion de Comunicaciones." The stamps were intended to provide a fund for rebuilding the General Post Office which was burned in April, 1921. One stamp was required on each letter or parcel, in addition to the regular postage. In the setting of one hundred there are five stamps with antique "C" and twenty-one with "R" and "C" smaller than in the illustration. One or more stamps in the setting have a dotted bar, as illustrated over No. 388, instead of the double bar.

The use of the "R de C" stamps for the payment of regular postage was not permitted.

Official Stamp of 1915 Overprinted in Black

1921, July

RA5	A24	1c light blue	6.00	1.75

This stamp is known with the dotted bar as illustrated over No. 388, instead of the double bar.

Coat of Arms — PT1

1921, Sept.　　　Red Surcharge

RA6	PT1	1c on 1c ver & blk	.30	.30
RA7	PT1	1c on 2c grn & blk	.30	.30
a.		Double surcharge	3.00	3.00
b.		Double surcharge, one inverted	4.00	4.00
RA8	PT1	1c on 4c org & blk	.30	.30
a.		Double surcharge	4.00	4.00
RA9	PT1	1c on 15c dk bl & blk	.30	.30
a.		Double surcharge	3.00	3.00
		Nos. RA6-RA9 (4)	1.20	1.20

PT2

1922, Feb.　　　Black Surcharge

RA10	PT2	1c on 10c yellow	.30	.30
a.		Period after "de"	.50	.40
b.		Double surcharge	2.00	2.00
c.		Double inverted surcharge	3.75	3.75
d.		Inverted surcharge	3.00	3.00
e.		Without period after "C"	1.00	1.00

No. 409 Overprinted in Black

1922

RA11	A24	1c violet	.30	.30
a.		Double overprint	2.00	2.00

This stamp with the overprint in red is a trial printing.

Nos. 402, 404-407 Surcharged in Black

1922, June

RA12	A27	1c on 1c grn & blk	.75	.75
RA13	A29	1c on 5c ultra & blk	.75	.75
RA14	A30	1c on 10c org & blk	.75	.40
RA15	A31	1c on 25c yel & blk	.75	.30
a.		Inverted surcharge	5.00	5.00
RA16	A32	1c on 50c vio & blk	.30	.25
a.		Double surcharge	4.00	4.00
		Nos. RA12-RA16 (5)	3.30	2.45

PT3

Surcharge in Red or Dark Blue

1922, Oct.　　　　Perf. 11½

RA17	PT3	1c yellow (R)	.30	.30
a.		No period after "C"	1.00	1.00
RA18	PT3	1c violet (DBl)	.30	.30
a.		No period after "C"	1.00	1.00

Surcharge is inverted on 22 out of 50 of No. RA17, 23 out of 50 of No. RA18.
See No. RA24.

Nos. 403-407 Surcharged in Black

1923　　　　　Perf. 12

RA19	A28	1c on 2c rose red & black	.50	.45
RA20	A29	1c on 5c ultra & blk	.55	.25
RA21	A30	1c on 10c org & blk	.25	.25
RA22	A31	1c on 25c yel & blk	.35	.30
RA23	A32	1c on 50c vio & blk	.25	.25
		Nos. RA19-RA23 (5)	1.90	1.50

The variety no period after "R" occurs twice on each sheet.

Red Surcharge
Wmk. Coat of Arms in Sheet
Perf. 11½

RA24	PT3	1c pale blue	.30	.30

Type of 1921 Issue

Without Surcharge of New Value

Unwmk.

RA25	PT1	1c ver & blk	.30	.30
a.		Double overprint, one inverted	3.00	3.00

No. 409 Overprinted in Blue

1924

RA26	A24	1c violet	.30	.30
a.		Double overprint	8.00	8.00

There are two settings of the overprint on No. RA26, with "1924" 5½mm or 6½mm wide.

No. 409 Overprinted in Blue

1925

RA27	A24	1c violet	.30	.30

No. 409 Overprinted in Blue

1926

RA28	A24	1c violet	.30	.30

No. RA28 Overprinted in Various Colors

1927

RA29	A24	1c vio (R)	.30	.30
a.		Double overprint (R)	2.50	2.50
b.		Inverted overprint (R)	3.00	3.00
RA30	A24	1c vio (V)	.30	.30
a.		Double overprint	2.50	2.50
b.		Inverted overprint	2.50	2.50
RA31	A24	1c vio (Bl)	.30	.30
a.		Double overprint	5.00	5.00
RA32	A24	1c vio (Bk)	.30	.30
a.		Double ovpt., one invtd.	4.25	4.25
b.		Inverted overprint	4.25	4.25

Same Overprint on No. RA27

RA33	A24	1c vio (Bk)	25.00	25.00
		Nos. RA29-RA33 (5)	26.20	26.20

No. RA28 Overprinted in Violet

1928

RA34	A24	1c violet	.30	.30
a.		Double overprint	2.00	2.00
b.		"928"	1.00	1.00

Similar to No. RA34 but 8mm space between "Resello" and "1928"
Black Overprint

RA35	A24	1c violet	.40	.30
a.		"1828"	2.00	2.00

PT4

Inscribed "Timbre Telegrafico"
Horiz. Srch. in Black, Vert. Srch. in Red

RA36	PT4	1c on 5c bl & blk	.60	.30
a.		Comma after "R"	1.25	1.25
b.		No period after "R"	1.25	1.25
c.		No periods after "R" and "C"	1.25	1.25

("CORREOS" at right) — PT5

1928 **Engr.** **Perf. 12**
RA37 PT5 1c plum .30 .30

See Nos. RA41-RA43. For overprints see Nos. RA45-RA46, RA48-RA51.

PT6

1929 **Red Surcharge**
RA38 PT6 1c on 5c bl & blk .30 .30
a. Inverted surcharge 3.00 3.00
b. Double surcharge 2.00 2.00
c. Double surcharge, one inverted 2.00 2.00
d. Period after "de" 1.25 1.25
e. Comma after "R" 1.25 1.25

See note after No. 512.

Regular Issue of 1928 Overprinted in Blue

RA39 A24 1c red orange .30 .30

No. RA39 exists both with and without signature control overprint.
An additional overprint, "1929" in black or blue on No. RA39, is fraudulent.

No. 513 Overprinted in Red

1929
RA40 A24 1c ol grn .30 .30
a. Double overprint .75 .75

No. RA40 is known with overprint in black, and with overprint inverted. These varieties were not regularly issued, but copies have been canceled by favor.

Type of 1928 Issue Inscribed at right "COMUNICACIONES"
1930-37
RA41 PT5 1c carmine .30 .30
RA42 PT5 1c orange ('33) .30 .30
RA43 PT5 1c green ('37) .30 .30
Nos. RA41-RA43 (3) .90 .90

No. RA42 has signature control. See note before No. 600.

No. RA39 Overprinted in Black

1931
RA44 A24 1c red orange .30 .30
a. "1931" double overprint .35 .35
b. "1931" double ovpt., one invtd. .40 .40

No. RA44 exists with signature control overprint. See note before No. 600. Value is the same.

No. RA42 Overprinted Vertically, up or down, in Black

1935
RA45 PT5 1c orange .30 .30
a. Double overprint 1.00 1.00
b. Double ovpt., one inverted

No. RA45 and RA45a Overprinted Vertically, Reading Down, in Blue

RA46 PT5 1c orange .50 .30
a. Black overprint double 2.00 2.00

Same Overprint in Red on Nos. RA39, RA42 and RA45
RA47 A24 1c red org (#RA39) 50.00 50.00
RA48 PT5 1c org (#RA42) .30 .30
RA49 PT5 1c org (#RA45) .30 .30
a. Black overprint double .80 .80

Overprint is horizontal on No. RA47 and vertical, reading down, on Nos. RA48-RA49.
No. RA48 exists with signature control overprint. See note before No. 600. Same values.

No. RA42 Overprinted Vertically, Reading Down, in Carmine

1935 **Unwmk.** **Perf. 12**
RA50 PT5 1c orange .30 .30

No. RA45 with Additional Overprint "1936", Vertically, Reading Down, in Red
1936
RA51 PT5 1c orange .50 .30

No. RA39 with Additional Overprint "1936" in Red
RA52 A24 1c red orange 1.00 .30

No. RA52 exists only with script control mark.

PT7

1936 **Vertical Surcharge in Red**
RA53 PT7 1c on 5c grn & blk .30 .30
a. "Cenavo" 1.40 1.40
b. "Centavos" 1.40 1.40

Horizontal Surcharge in Red
RA54 PT7 1c on 5c grn & blk .30 .30
a. Double surcharge 1.40 1.40

Baseball Player — PT8

1937 **Typo.** **Perf. 11**
RA55 PT8 1c carmine .60 .25
RA56 PT8 1c yellow .60 .25
RA57 PT8 1c blue .60 .25
RA58 PT8 1c green .60 .25
b. Sheet of 4, #RA55-RA58 8.00 3.00
Nos. RA55-RA58 (4) 2.40 1.00

Issued for the benefit of the Central American Caribbean Games of February 1938 in Panama City, Panama.
Control mark in red is variously placed. See dark oval below "OLIMPICO" in illustration.

Tête bêche Pairs
RA55a PT8 1c 1.25 1.25
RA56a PT8 1c 1.25 1.25
RA57a PT8 1c 1.25 1.25
RA58a PT8 1c 1.25 1.25
Nos. RA55a-RA58a (4) 5.00 5.00

Catalogue values for unused stamps in this section, from this point to the end of the section, are for Never Hinged items.

Proposed Natl. Stadium, Managua — PT9

1949 **Photo.** **Perf. 12**
RA60 PT9 5c greenish blue .80 .40
a. Souvenir sheet of 4 5.00 5.00

10th World Series of Amateur Baseball, 1948. The tax was used toward the erection of a national stadium at Managua.

Type Similar to 1949, with "Correos" omitted
1952
RA61 PT9 5c magenta .80 .40

The tax was used toward the erection of a national stadium at Managua.

PT10

1956 **Engr.** **Perf. 12½x12**
RA62 PT10 5c deep ultra .80 .40

The tax was used for social welfare.

PT11 PT11a

Surcharged in Red or Black
1959 **Unwmk.** **Perf. 12**
Red Marginal Number
RA63 PT11 5c on 50c vio bl (R) .80 .40
RA64 PT11a 5c on 50c vio bl (B) .80 .40

Nos. RA63-RA64 are surcharged on consular revenue stamps. Surcharge reads "Sobre Tasa Postal CO.O5." Vertical surcharge on No. RA63, horizontal on No. RA64.

Jesus and Children — PT12

1959 **Photo.** **Perf. 16**
RA65 PT12 5c ultra .80 .40

Hexisia Bidentata — PT13

Orchids: No. RA67, Schomburgkia tibicinus. No. RA68, Stanhopea ecornuta. No. RA69, Lycaste macrophylla. No. RA70, Maxillaria tenuifolia. No. RA71, Cattleya skinneri. No. RA72, Cycnoches egertonianum. No. RA73, Bletia roezlii. No. RA74, Sobralia pleiantha. No. RA75, Oncidium cebolleta and ascendens.

1962, Feb. **Photo.** **Perf. 11½**
Granite Paper
Orchids in Natural Colors
RA66 PT13 5c rose lil & grn .65 .40
RA67 PT13 5c yel & gray bl .65 .40
RA68 PT13 5c pink & bl grn .65 .40
RA69 PT13 5c lil & brn ol .65 .40
RA70 PT13 5c turq bl & red .65 .40
RA71 PT13 5c pale sal & vio .65 .40
RA72 PT13 5c yel grn & dk brn .65 .40
RA73 PT13 5c gray & red .65 .40
RA74 PT13 5c lt bl & indigo .65 .40
RA75 PT13 5c turq grn & red brn .65 .40
Nos. RA66-RA75 (10) 6.50 4.00

For overprints see #842-852, 855-868, 901-908.
Exist imperf. Value, each pair $100.

PROVINCE OF ZELAYA

(Bluefields)

A province of Nicaragua lying along the eastern coast. Special postage stamps for this section were made necessary because for a period two currencies, which differed materially in value, were in use in Nicaragua. Silver money

was used in Zelaya and Cabo Gracias a Dios while the rest of Nicaragua used paper money. Later the money of the entire country was placed on a gold basis.

Dangerous counterfeits exist of most of the Bluefields overprints.

Regular Issues of 1900-05 Handstamped in Black (4 or more types)

1904-05 **Unwmk.** **Perf. 12, 14**
On Engraved Stamps of 1900
1L1 A14 1c plum 1.50 .75
1L2 A14 2c vermilion 1.50 .75
1L3 A14 3c green 1.90 1.50
1L4 A14 4c ol grn 11.00 9.00
1L5 A14 15c ultra 3.00 1.90
1L6 A14 20c brown 3.00 1.90
1L7 A14 50c lake 10.50 9.00
1L8 A14 1p yellow 21.00
1L9 A14 2p salmon 30.00
1L10 A14 5p black 37.50
Nos. 1L1-1L10 (10) 120.90
Nos. 1L1-1L7 (7) 24.80

On Lithographed Stamps of 1902
1L11 A14 5c blue 3.00 .75
1L12 A14 5c carmine 1.90 .90
1L13 A14 10c violet 1.50 .75
Nos. 1L11-1L13 (3) 6.40 2.40

On Postage Due Stamps Overprinted "1901 Correos"
1L14 D3 20c brn (No. 156) 4.50 1.90
1L15 D3 50c lake (No. 158) 1.50 1.50

On Surcharged Stamps of 1904-05
1L16 A14 5c on 10c (#175) 1.50 1.10
1L17 A14 5c on 10c (#178) 3.00 1.50
1L18 A14 15c on 10c vio (#176) 1.50 1.50
1L19 A14 15c on 10c vio (#177) 14.00 4.50
Nos. 1L16-1L19 (4) 20.00 8.60

On Surcharged Stamp of 1901
1L20 A14 20c on 5p blk 18.00 3.00

On Regular Issue of 1905
1906-07 **Perf. 12**
1L21 A18 1c green .30 .30
1L22 A18 2c car rose .30 .30
1L23 A18 3c violet .30 .30
1L24 A18 4c org red .45 .45
1L25 A18 5c blue .25 .25
1L26 A18 10c yel brn 3.00 1.50
1L27 A18 15c brn ol 4.50 1.75
1L28 A18 20c lake 9.00 7.50
1L29 A18 50c orange 35.00 30.00
1L30 A18 1p black 30.00 27.50
1L31 A18 2p dk grn 37.50
1L32 A18 5p violet 45.00
Nos. 1L21-1L32 (12) 165.60
Nos. 1L21-1L30 (10) 69.85

On Surcharged Stamps of 1906-08
1L33 A18 10c on 3c vio .40 .40
1L34 A18 15c on 1c grn .50 .50
1L35 A18 20c on 2c rose 3.50 3.50
1L36 A18 20c on 5c bl 1.50 1.50
1L37 A18 50c on 6c sl (R) 1.50 3.00
Nos. 1L33-1L37 (5) 7.40 8.90

Handstamped

Stamps with the above overprints were made to fill dealers' orders but were never regularly issued or used. Stamps with similar overprints handstamped are bogus.

Surcharged Stamps of 1906 Overprinted in Red, Black or Blue

1L38	A18	15c on 1c grn (R)	2.75 2.75
a.	Red overprint inverted		
1L39	A18	20c on 2c rose (Bk)	1.90 1.90
1L40	A18	20c on 5c bl (R)	3.00 3.00
1L41	A18	50c on 6c sl (Bl)	14.00 14.00
	Nos. 1L38-1L41 (4)		21.65 21.65

Stamps of the 1905 issue overprinted as above No. 1L38 or similarly overprinted but with only 2¼mm space between "B" and "Dpto. Zelaya" were made to fill dealers' orders but not placed in use.

No. 205 Handstamped in Black

Perf. 14 to 15

1L42	A18	10c yel brn	24.00 24.00

Stamps of 1907 Overprinted in Red or Black

1L43	A18	15c brn ol (R)	3.00 3.00
1L44	A18	20c lake	.90 .90
a.	Inverted overprint		11.00 11.00

With Additional Surcharge

1L45	A18	5c brn org	.50 .45
a.	Inverted surcharge		7.50 7.50

With Additional Surcharge

1L46	A18	5c on 4c brn org	12.00 12.00

On Provisional Postage Stamps of 1907-08 in Black or Blue

1L47	A18	10c on 2c rose (Bl)	4.50 4.50
1L48	A18	10c on 2c rose	300.00
1L48A	A18	10c on 4c brn org	300.00
1L49	A18	10c on 20c lake	3.00 3.00
1L50	A18	10c on 50c org (Bl)	3.00 2.25

Arms Type of 1907 Overprinted in Black or Violet

"COSTA ATLANTICA" B.

1907

1L51	A18	1c green	.30 .25
1L52	A18	2c rose	.30 .25
1L53	A18	3c violet	.40 .40
1L54	A18	4c brn org	.45 .45
1L55	A18	5c blue	4.50 2.25
1L56	A18	10c yel brn	.40 .30
1L57	A18	15c brn ol	.75 .40
1L58	A18	20c lake	.75 .45
1L59	A18	50c orange	2.25 1.50
1L60	A18	1p blk (V)	2.25 1.50
1L61	A18	2p dk grn	2.25 1.90
1L62	A18	5p violet	3.75 2.25
	Nos. 1L51-1L62 (12)		18.35 11.90

Nos. 217-225 Overprinted in Green

1908

1L63	A19	1c on 5c yel & blk (R)	.45 .40
1L64	A19	2c on 5c yel & blk (Bl)	.45 .40
1L65	A19	4c on 5c yel & blk	.45 .40
a.	Overprint reading down		11.00 11.00
b.	Double overprint, reading up and down		18.00 18.00
1L66	A19	5c yel & blk	.45 .45
a.	"CORROE"		4.50
b.	Double overprint		11.00 11.00
c.	Double overprint, reading up and down		19.00 19.00
d.	"CORREO 1908" double		15.00 15.00
1L67	A19	10c lt bl & blk	.45 .45
a.	Ovpt. reading down		.50
b.	"CORREO 1908" triple		37.50
1L68	A19	15c on 50c ol & blk (R)	.90 .90
a.	"1008"		4.50
b.	"8908"		4.50
1L69	A19	35c on 50c ol & blk	1.40 1.40
a.	"CORROE"		12.00 12.00
1L70	A19	1p yel brn & blk	1.90 1.90
a.	"CORROE"		15.00 15.00
1L71	A19	2p pearl gray & blk	2.25 2.25
a.	"CORROE"		15.00 15.00
	Nos. 1L63-1L71 (9)		8.70 8.55

Overprinted Horizontally in Black or Green

1L72	A19	5c yel & blk	9.00 7.50
1L72A	A19	2p pearl gray & blk (G)	300.00

On Nos. 1L72-1L72A, space between "B" and "Dpto. Zelaya" is 13mm.

Nos. 237-248 Overprinted in Black

Imprint: "American Bank Note Co. NY"

1909			***Perf. 12***
1L73	A18	1c yel grn	.25 .25
1L74	A18	2c vermilion	.25 .25
a.	Inverted overprint		
1L75	A18	3c red org	.25 .25
1L76	A18	4c violet	.25 .25
1L77	A18	5c dp bl	.30 .25
a.	Inverted overprint		9.00 9.00
b.	"B" inverted		7.50 7.50
c.	Double overprint		12.00 12.00
1L78	A18	6c gray brn	4.50 3.00
1L79	A18	10c lake	.30 .30
a.	"B" inverted		9.00 9.00
1L80	A18	15c black	.45 .40
a.	"B" inverted		11.00 11.00
b.	Inverted overprint		12.00 12.00
c.	Double overprint		14.00 14.00
1L81	A18	20c brn ol	.50 .50
a.	"B" inverted		19.00 19.00
1L82	A18	50c dp grn	1.50 1.50
1L83	A18	1p yellow	5.00 2.25
1L84	A18	2p car rose	6.00 3.00
a.	Double overprint		27.50 27.50
	Nos. 1L73-1L84 (12)		19.55 12.20

One stamp in each sheet has the "o" of "Dpto." sideways.

Overprinted in Black

1910

1L85	A18	3c red org	.40 .40
1L86	A18	4c violet	.40 .40
a.	Inverted overprint		14.00 14.00
1L87	A18	15c black	4.50 2.25
1L88	A18	20c brn ol	.25 .30
1L89	A18	50c dp grn	.30 .40
1L90	A18	1p yellow	.30 .45
a.	Inverted overprint		7.50
1L91	A18	2p car rose	.40 .75
	Nos. 1L85-1L91 (7)		6.55 4.95

No. 243 Overprinted and Surcharged in Black, Green & Carmine

1910

1L92	A18	5c on 10c lake	3.75 3.00

There are three types of the letter "B". It is stated that this stamp was used exclusively for postal purposes and not for telegrams.

No. 247 Surcharged in Black

1911

1L93	A18	5c on 1p yellow	.75 .75
a.	Double surcharge		14.00
1L94	A18	10c on 1p yellow	1.50 1.50
1L95	A18	15c on 1p yellow	.75 .75
a.	Inverted surcharge		9.00
b.	Double surcharge		9.00
c.	Double surcharge, one invtd.		9.00
	Nos. 1L93-1L95 (3)		3.00 3.00

Revenue Stamps Surcharged in Black

Perf. 14 to 15

1L96	A19	5c on 25c lilac	.75 1.10
a.	Without period		1.50 1.50
b.	Inverted surcharge		9.00 9.00
1L97	A19	10c on 1p yel brn	1.10 .75
a.	Without period		1.90 1.90
b.	"01" for "10"		9.00 7.50
c.	Inverted surcharge		13.00 13.00

Surcharged in Black

1L98	A19	5c on 1p yel brn	1.50 1.50
a.	Without period		2.25
b.	"50" for "05"		14.00 14.00
c.	Inverted surcharge		15.00 15.00
1L99	A19	5c on 10p pink	1.50 1.50
a.	Without period		2.25 2.25
b.	"50" for "05"		11.00 11.00
1L100	A19	10c on 1p yel brn	82.50 82.50
a.	Without period		95.00 95.00
1L101	A19	10c on 25p grn	.75 .75
a.	Without period		2.25 2.25
b.	"1" for "10"		7.50
1L102	A19	10c on 50p ver	11.00 11.00
a.	Without period		16.00
b.	"1" for "10"		22.50
	Nos. 1L98-1L102 (5)		97.25 97.25

With Additional Overprint "1904"

1L103	A19	5c on 10p pink	14.00 14.00
a.	Without period		24.00 24.00
b.	"50" for "05"		110.00 110.00
1L104	A19	10c on 2p gray	.75 .75
a.	Without period		1.90
b.	"1" for "10"		6.50
1L105	A19	10c on 25p grn	92.50
a.	Without period		100.00
1L106	A19	10c on 50p ver	7.50 7.50
a.	Without period		14.00
b.	"1" for "10"		18.00
c.	Inverted surcharge		

The surcharges on Nos. 1L96 to 1L106 are in settings of twenty-five. One stamp in each setting has a large square period after "cts" and another has a thick upright "c" in that word. There are two types of "1904".

No. 293C Overprinted

1911

1L107	A21	5c on 5c on 2 bl (R)	32.50
a.	"5" omitted		37.50
b.	Red overprint inverted		40.00
c.	As "a" and "b"		47.50

Same Overprint On Nos. 290, 291, 292 and 289D with Lines of Surcharge spaced 2½mm apart Reading Down

1L107D	A21	2c on 10c on 1 red	250.00
e.	Overprint reading up		250.00
1L107F	A21	5c on 10c on 1 red	150.00
1L107G	A21	10c on 10c on 1 red (#292)	200.00
1L108	A21	10c on 10c on 1 red (#289D)	200.00

Locomotive — Z2

1912		**Engr.**	***Perf. 14***
1L109	Z2	1c yel grn	1.50 .50
1L110	Z2	2c vermilion	1.25 .25
1L111	Z2	3c org brn	1.50 .45
1L112	Z2	4c carmine	1.50 .30
1L113	Z2	5c dp bl	1.50 .45
1L114	Z2	6c red brn	9.00 3.50
1L115	Z2	10c slate	1.50 .30
1L116	Z2	15c dl lil	1.50 .60
1L117	Z2	20c bl vio	1.50 .60
1L118	Z2	25c grn & blk	2.25 .80
1L119	Z2	35c brn & blk	3.00 1.25
1L120	Z2	50c ol grn	3.00 1.25
1L121	Z2	1p orange	4.00 1.75
1L122	Z2	2p org brn	7.50 3.25
1L123	Z2	5p dk bl grn	18.00 7.50
	Nos. 1L109-1L123 (15)		58.50 22.75

The stamps of this issue were for use in all places on the Atlantic Coast of Nicaragua where the currency was on a silver basis. For surcharges see Nos. 325-337.

OFFICIAL STAMPS

Regular Issue of 1909 Overprinted in Black

1909		**Unwmk.**	***Perf. 12***
1LO1	A18	20c brn ol	15.00 12.00
a.	Double overprint		30.00

No. O216 Overprinted in Black

1LO2	A18	15c black	15.00 10.00

Same Overprint on Official Stamp of 1911

1911

1LO3	A18	5c on 3c red org	22.50 17.50

CABO GRACIAS A DIOS

A cape and seaport town in the extreme northeast of Nicaragua. The name was coined by Spanish explorers who had great difficulty finding a landing place along the Nicaraguan coast and when eventually locating this harbor expressed their relief by designating the point "Cape Thanks to God." Special postage stamps came into use for the same reasons as the Zelaya issues. See Zelaya.

Dangerous counterfeits exist of most of the Cabo Gracias a Dios overprints. Special caution should be taken with double and inverted handstamps of Nos. 2L1-2L25, as most are counterfeits. Expert opinion is required.

Regular Issues of
1900-04
Handstamped in
Violet

On Engraved Stamps of 1900

		1904-05	Unwmk.	Perf. 12, 14	
2L1	A14	1c plum		2.25	1.10
2L2	A14	2c vermilion		4.50	1.25
2L3	A14	3c green		6.00	4.50
2L4	A14	4c ol grn		9.75	9.75
2L5	A14	15c ultra		35.00	22.50
2L6	A14	20c brown		3.00	2.25
		Nos. 2L1-2L6 (6)		60.50	41.35

On Lithographed Stamps of 1902

2L7	A14	5c green	24.00	24.00
2L8	A14	10c violet	24.00	24.00

On Surcharged Stamps of 1904

2L9	A14	5c on 10c vio	22.50	22.50
2L10	A14	5c on 10c vio		

On Postage Due Stamps

Violet Handstamp

2L11	D3	20c org brn (#141)	5.00	1.25
2L12	D3	20c org brn (#156)	3.50	1.25
2L13	D3	30c dk grn (#157)	14.00	14.00
2L14	D3	50c lake (#158)	3.75	.75
		Nos. 2L11-2L14 (4)	26.25	17.25

Black Handstamp

2L15	D3	30c dk grn (#157)	24.00	24.00

Stamps of 1900-05
Handstamped in
Violet

On Engraved Stamps of 1900

2L16	A14	1c plum	2.75	2.25
2L17	A14	2c vermilion	27.50	27.50
2L18	A14	3c green	37.50	27.50
2L19	A14	4c ol grn	40.00	37.50
2L20	A14	15c ultra	45.00	45.00
		Nos. 2L16-2L20 (5)	152.75	136.25

On Lithographed Stamps of 1902

2L22	A14	5c dk bl	95.00	50.00
2L23	A14	10c violet	27.50	24.00

On Surcharged Stamp of 1904

2L24	A14	5c on 10c vio		

On Postage Due Stamp

2L25	D3	20c org brn (#141)		

The editors have no evidence that
stamps with this handstamp were
issued. Examples were sent to the UPU
and covers are known.

Stamps of 1900-08
Handstamped in Violet

		1905	On Stamps of 1905	
2L26	A18	1c green	1.10	1.10
2L27	A18	2c car rose	1.50	1.50
2L28	A18	3c violet	1.50	1.50
2L29	A18	4c org red	3.75	3.75
2L30	A18	5c blue	1.50	1.10
2L31	A18	6c slate	3.75	3.75
2L32	A18	10c yel brn	3.00	1.90
2L33	A18	15c brn ol	4.50	4.50
2L34	A18	1p black	20.00	20.00
2L35	A18	2p dk grn	35.00	35.00
		Nos. 2L26-2L35 (10)	75.60	74.10

Magenta Handstamp

2L26a	A18	1c	3.75	3.00
2L27a	A18	2c	3.00	2.75
2L28a	A18	3c	3.75	3.00
2L30a	A18	5c	7.50	6.00
2L33a	A18	15c	13.50	11.00
		Nos. 2L26a-2L33a (5)	31.50	25.75

On Stamps of 1900-04

2L36	A14	5c on 10c vio	14.00	14.00
2L37	A14	10c violet		
2L38	A14	20c brown	12.00	12.00
2L39	A14	20c on 5p blk		95.00

On Postage Due Stamps Overprinted "Correos"

2L40	D3	20c org brn (#141)	9.00	9.00
2L41	D3	20c org brn (#156)	5.00	4.50

On Surcharged Stamps of 1906-08

2L42	A18	10c on 3c slate		250.00
2L43	A18	20c on 5c blue	9.00	9.00
2L44	A18	50c on 6c slate	24.00	24.00

On Stamps of 1907
Perf. 14 to 15

2L44A	A18	2c rose		250.00
2L45	A18	10c yel brn	100.00	75.00
2L46	A18	15c brn ol	90.00	75.00

On Provisional Stamp of 1908 in Magenta

2L47	A19	5c yel & blk	7.50	7.50

Stamps with the above large handstamp in
black instead of violet, are bogus. There are
also excellent counterfeits in violet.

The foregoing overprints being handstamped are found in various positions, especially the last type.

Stamps of 1907 Type
A18, Overprinted in
Black or Violet

1907

2L48	A18	1c green	.35	.30
a.		Vert. pair, imperf. btwn.	—	
2L49	A18	2c rose	.35	.30
2L50	A18	3c violet	.35	.30
a.		Vert. pair, imperf. btwn.	350.00	
2L51	A18	4c brn org	.50	.40
2L52	A18	5c blue	.60	.50
2L53	A18	10c yel brn	.50	.40
2L54	A18	15c brn ol	.85	.75
2L55	A18	20c lake	.85	.75
2L56	A18	50c orange	2.25	1.50
2L57	A18	1p blk (V)	2.50	1.90
2L58	A18	2p dk grn	3.50	2.25
2L59	A18	5p violet	5.00	3.75
		Nos. 2L48-2L59 (12)	17.60	13.10

Nos. 237-248
Overprinted in Black

Imprint: American Bank Note Co.

		1909		Perf. 12	
2L60	A18	1c yel grn		.35	.40
2L61	A18	2c vermilion		.35	.40
2L62	A18	3c red org		.35	.40
2L63	A18	4c violet		.35	.40
2L64	A18	5c dp bl		.35	.60
2L65	A18	6c gray brn		6.00	6.00
2L66	A18	10c lake		.60	.70
2L67	A18	15c black		.90	.90
2L68	A18	20c brn ol		1.00	4.00
2L69	A18	50c dp grn		2.50	2.50
2L70	A18	1p yellow		4.00	4.00
2L71	A18	2p car rose		5.75	5.75
		Nos. 2L60-2L71 (12)		22.50	26.10

No. 199 Overprinted
Vertically

2L72	A18	50c on 6c slate (R)	7.50	7.50

CABO GRACIAS A DIOS OFFICIAL STAMPS

Official Stamps of 1907
Overprinted in Red or
Violet

1907

2LO1	A18	10c on 1c green	60.00
2LO2	A18	15c on 1c green	75.00
2LO3	A18	20c on 1c green	100.00
2LO4	A18	50c on 1c green	125.00

NIGER

'nī-jər

LOCATION — Northern Africa, directly
north of Nigeria
GOVT. — Republic
AREA — 458,075 sq. mi.
POP. — 9,962,242 (1999 est.)
CAPITAL — Niamey

The colony, formed in 1922, was originally a military territory. The Republic
of the Niger was proclaimed December
18, 1958. In the period between issues
of the colony and the republic, stamps
of French West Africa were used. Full
independence from France was proclaimed August 3, 1960.

100 Centimes = 1 Franc

Catalogue values for unused
stamps in this country are for
Never Hinged items, beginning
with Scott 91 in the regular postage section, Scott B14 in the semi-
postal section, Scott C14 in the
airpost section, Scott J22 in the
postage due section, and Scott O1
in the official section.

Watermark

TOR C
CART
TOR C
CART   Wmk. 385

Stamps of Upper
Senegal and Niger Type
of 1914, Overprinted

In the overprint, normal spacing between
the words "DU" and "NIGER" is 2½mm. In one
position (72) of all sheets in the first printing,
the space between the two words is 3mm.

		1921-26	Unwmk.	Perf. 13½x14	
1	A4	1c brn vio & vio		.25	.40
2	A4	2c dk gray & dl vio		.25	.40
3	A4	4c black & blue		.35	.50
4	A4	5c ol brn & dk brn		.30	.50
5	A4	10c yel grn & bl grn		1.60	2.00
6	A4	10c mag, *bluish* ('26)		.95	1.20
7	A4	15c red brn & org		.40	.55
8	A4	20c brn vio & blk		.35	.50
9	A4	25c blk & bl grn		.80	.80
10	A4	30c red org & rose		2.75	3.50
11	A4	30c bl grn & red org ('26)		.80	.80
12	A4	35c rose & violet		.95	1.20
13	A4	40c gray & rose		.95	1.20
14	A4	45c blue & ol brn		1.40	1.40
15	A4	50c ultra & bl		.80	1.20
16	A4	50c dk gray & bl vio ('25)		1.60	1.60
17	A4	60c org red ('26)		1.40	2.00
18	A4	75c yel & ol brn		1.40	1.60
19	A4	1fr dk brn & dl vio		1.60	2.00
20	A4	2fr green & blue		1.60	2.00
21	A4	5fr violet & blk		2.75	4.00
		Nos. 1-21 (21)		23.25	29.35

Types of 1921
Surcharged in Black or
Red

1922-26

22	A4	25c on 15c red brn & org ('25)		.95	.80
a.		Multiple surcharge		260.00	
b.		"25c" inverted		140.00	
23	A4	25c on 2fr grn & bl (R) ('24)		.90	.80
24	A4	25c on 5fr vio & blk (R) ('24)		.95	.80
a.		Double surcharge		225.00	
25	A4	60c on 75c vio,*pnksh*		.90	1.20
26	A4	65c on 45c bl & ol brn ('25)		2.75	3.50
27	A4	85c on 75c yel & ol brn ('25)		2.75	3.50
28	A4	1.25fr on 1fr dp bl & lt bl (R) ('26)		1.10	1.20
a.		Surcharge omitted		260.00	
b.		As "a," in pair with un-surcharged stamp		1,700.	
		Nos. 22-28 (7)		10.30	11.80

Nos. 22-24 are surcharged "25c," No. 28,
"1f25." Nos. 25-27 are surcharged like
illustration.

Drawing
Water from
Well
A2

Zinder
Fortress
A4

Boat on Niger
River — A3

Perf. 13x14, 13½x14, 14x13, 14x13½

		1926-40			Typo.
29	A2	1c lil rose & ol		.25	.40
30	A2	2c dk gray & dl red		.25	.40
31	A2	3c red vio & ol gray ('40)		.25	.40
32	A2	4c amber & gray		.25	.40
33	A2	5c ver & yel grn		.25	.40
34	A2	10c dp bl & Prus bl		.25	.40
35	A2	15c gray grn & yel grn		.55	.80
36	A2	15c gray lil & lt red ('28)		.40	.40
37	A3	20c Prus grn & ol brn		.40	.55
38	A3	25c black & dl red		.40	.50
39	A3	30c bl grn & yel grn		.80	1.20
40	A3	30c yel & red vio ('40)		.30	.50
41	A3	35c brn org & turq bl, *bluish*		.80	.80
42	A3	35c bl grn & dl grn ('38)		1.20	1.60
43	A3	40c red brn & slate		.40	.50
44	A3	45c yel & red vio		1.60	1.90
45	A3	45c bl grn & dl grn ('40)		.30	.50
46	A3	50c scar & grn, *grnsh*		.40	.40
47	A3	55c dk car & brn ('38)		2.00	2.00
48	A3	60c dk car & brn ('40)		.55	.70
49	A3	65c ol grn & rose		.40	.55
50	A3	70c ol grn & rose ('40)		2.00	2.50
51	A3	75c grn & vio, *pink*		2.00	2.25
a.		Center and value double		225.00	
52	A3	80c cl & ol grn ('38)		1.60	2.00
53	A3	90c brn red & ver		1.60	1.90
54	A3	90c brt rose & yel grn ('39)		2.00	2.40
55	A4	1fr rose & yel grn		8.00	8.75
56	A4	1fr dk red & red org ('38)		2.00	2.40
57	A4	1fr grn & red ('40)		.80	.80
58	A4	1.10fr ol brn & grn		4.00	6.50
59	A4	1.25fr red & red ('33)		2.40	2.40
60	A4	1.25fr dk red & red org ('39)		.80	1.20
61	A4	1.40fr red vio & dk brn ('40)		.80	1.50
62	A4	1.50fr dp bl & pale bl		.55	.70
63	A4	1.60fr ol brn & grn ('40)		1.75	2.00
64	A4	1.75fr red vio & dk brn ('33)		1.60	2.40
65	A4	1.75fr dk bl & vio bl ('38)		1.25	1.60
66	A4	2fr red org & ol brn		.30	.50
67	A4	2.25fr dk bl & vio bl ('39)		1.20	1.60
68	A4	2.50fr blk brn ('40)		1.20	1.60
69	A4	3fr dl vio & blk ('27)		.55	.80

70	A4	5fr vio brn & blk,		
		pink	.80	1.20
71	A4	10fr chlky bl & mag	1.60	2.00
72	A4	20fr yel grn & red		
		org	1.60	2.00
		Nos. 29-72 (44)	52.40	66.70

For surcharges see Nos. B7-B10.

Common Design Types
pictured following the introduction.

Colonial Exposition Issue
Common Design Types

1931　　Typo.　　Perf. 12½
Name of Country in Black

73	CD70	40c deep green	4.75	4.75
74	CD71	50c violet	4.75	4.75
75	CD72	90c red orange	5.50	5.50
76	CD73	1.50fr dull blue	5.50	5.50
		Nos. 73-76 (4)	20.50	20.50

Paris International Exposition Issue
Common Design Types

1937　　　　　　　　　Perf. 13

77	CD74	20c deep violet	1.90	1.90
78	CD75	30c dark green	1.90	1.90
79	CD76	40c car rose	1.90	1.90
80	CD77	50c dark brown	1.50	1.50
81	CD78	90c red	1.50	1.50
82	CD79	1.50fr ultra	1.90	1.90
		Nos. 77-82 (6)	10.60	10.60

Colonial Arts Exhibition Issue
Souvenir Sheet
Common Design Type

1937　　　　　　　　　Imperf.

83	CD74	3fr magenta	9.50	14.00

Caillie Issue
Common Design Type

1939　　　　　　　　Perf. 12½x12

84	CD81	90c org brn & org	.35	.35
85	CD81	2fr brt violet	1.00	1.00
86	CD81	2.25fr ultra & dk bl	1.00	1.00
		Nos. 84-86 (3)	2.35	2.35

New York World's Fair Issue
Common Design Type

1939, May 10

87	CD82	1.25fr car lake	.80	1.40
88	CD82	2.25fr ultra	.80	1.40

Zinder Fortress and
Marshal Pétain — A5

1941　Unwmk.　Engr.　Perf. 12x12½

89	A5	1fr green	.35	
90	A5	2.50fr dark blue	.35	
		Set, never hinged	1.75	

Nos. 89-90 were issued by the Vichy government in France, but were not placed on sale in Niger.
For surcharges, see Nos. B13A-B13B.

See French West Africa No. 68 for additional stamp inscribed "Niger" and "Afrique Occidentale Francaise."

Catalogue values for unused stamps in this section, from this point to the end of the section, are for Never Hinged items.

Republic of the Niger

Giraffes — A6

1fr, 2fr, Crested cranes. 5fr, 7fr, Saddle-billed storks. 15fr, 20fr, Barbary sheep. 25fr, 30fr, Giraffes. 50fr, 60fr, Ostriches. 85fr, 100fr, Lion.

1959-60　Unwmk.　Engr.　Perf. 13

91	A6	1fr multi	.35	.25
92	A6	2fr multi	.35	.25
93	A6	5fr blk, car & ol	.55	.25
94	A6	7fr grn, blk & red	.65	.25
95	A6	15fr grnsh bl & dk brn	.25	.25
96	A6	20fr vio, blk & ind	.25	.25
97	A6	25fr multi	.35	.25
98	A6	30fr multi	.45	.30
99	A6	50fr ind & org brn	5.00	.65
100	A6	60fr dk brn & emer	7.00	.90
101	A6	85fr org brn & bis	2.50	.80
102	A6	100fr bis & yel grn	3.25	1.10
		Nos. 91-102 (12)	20.95	5.50

Issue years: #97, 1959; others, 1960.
For surcharge see No. 103.

Imperforates

Most stamps of the republic exist imperforate in issued and trial colors, and also in small presentation sheets in issued color.

No. 102 Surcharged

1960

103	A6	200fr on 100fr	15.00	15.00

Niger's independence.

C.C.T.A. Issue
Common Design Type

1960　　Engr.　　Perf. 13

104	CD106	25fr buff & red brn	.85	.45

Emblem of the Entente — A6a

1960, May 29　Photo.　Perf. 13x13½

105	A6a	25fr multi	.85	.55

1st anniversary of the Entente (Dahomey, Ivory Coast, Niger and Upper Volta).

Pres. Diori
Hamani — A7

1960, Dec. 18　　Engr.　　Perf. 13

106	A7	25fr ol bis & blk	.60	.35

2nd anniversary of the proclamation of the Republic of the Niger.

Manatee — A8

1962, Jan. 29　Unwmk.　Perf. 13

107	A8	50c grn & dk sl grn	.40	.25
108	A8	10fr red brn & dk grn	.65	.25

Abidjan Games Issue
Common Design Type

25fr, Basketball & Soccer. 85fr, Track, horiz.

1962, May 26　Photo.　Perf. 12x12½

109	CD109	15fr multi	.40	.25
110	CD109	25fr multi	.60	.30
111	CD109	85fr multi	1.60	.70
		Nos. 109-111 (3)	2.60	1.25

African-Malgache Union Issue
Common Design Type

1962, Sept. 8　　　　Perf. 12½x12

112	CD110	30fr multi	.80	.50

Pres. Diori
Hamani and Map
of Niger in
Africa — A10

1962, Dec. 18　Photo.　Perf. 12½x12

113	A10	25fr multi	.60	.30

Woman Runner — A11

15fr, Swimming, horiz. 45fr, Volleyball.

Unwmk.
1963, Apr. 11　Engr.　Perf. 13

114	A11	15fr brt bl & dk brn	.40	.25
115	A11	25fr dk brn & red	.60	.30
116	A11	45fr grn & blk	1.10	.50
		Nos. 114-116 (3)	2.10	1.05

Friendship Games, Dakar, Apr. 11-21.

Woodworker — A12

10fr, Tanners, horiz. 25fr, Goldsmith. 30fr, Mat makers, horiz. 85fr, Decoy maker.

Perf. 12x12½, 12½x12
1963, Aug. 30　　　　Photo.

117	A12	5fr brn & multi	.25	.25
118	A12	10fr dk grn & multi	.35	.25
119	A12	25fr blk & multi	.60	.30
120	A12	30fr vio & multi	.90	.35
121	A12	85fr dk bl & multi	2.00	.90
		Nos. 117-121,C26 (6)	7.10	3.65

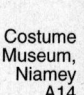

Berberi (Nuba)
Woman's
Costume — A13

Costume
Museum,
Niamey
A14

Costumes: 20fr, Hausa woman. 25fr, Tuareg woman. 30fr, Tuareg man. 60fr, Djerma woman.

Perf. 12x12½, 12½x12
1963, Oct. 15　　　　Photo.

122	A13	15fr multi	.35	.25
123	A13	20fr blk & bl	.50	.25
124	A13	25fr multi	.70	.30
125	A13	30fr multi	.75	.30
126	A13	60fr multi	1.75	.70
127	A14	85fr multi	2.00	.80
		Nos. 122-127 (6)	6.05	2.60

Man, Globe and
Scales — A15

Unwmk.
1963, Dec. 10　Engr.　Perf. 13

128	A15	25fr lt ol grn, ultra & brn org	.80	.30

15th anniversary of the Universal Declaration of Human Rights.

Parkinsonia
Aculeata — A16

Plumeria Rubra — A16a

Flowers: 10fr, Russelia equisetiformis. 15fr, Red sage (lantana). 20fr, Argyreia nervosa. 25fr, Luffa cylindrica. 30fr, Hibiscus rosa sinensis. 50fr, Catharanthus roseus. 60fr, Caesalpinia pulcherrima.

1964-65　　Photo.　　Perf. 13½x13

129	A16	5fr dk red, grn & yel	.75	.35
130	A16	10fr multi	.60	.35
131	A16	15fr multi	1.00	.50
132	A16	20fr multi	1.00	.50
133	A16	25fr multi	1.00	.50
134	A16	30fr multi	1.25	.55
135	A16a	45fr multi ('65)	2.25	.95
136	A16a	50fr dk red, brt pink & grn ('65)	2.25	.95
137	A16a	60fr multi ('65)	4.00	1.25
		Nos. 129-137 (9)	14.10	5.90

On No. 135 "PLUMERIA" is spelled incorrectly.

Solar Flares and IQSY
Emblem — A17

1964, May 12　Engr.　Perf. 13

138	A17	30fr dp org, vio & blk	.70	.45

International Quiet Sun Year, 1964-65.

Mobile Medical
Unit — A18

30fr, Mobile children's clinic. 50fr, Mobile women's clinic. 60fr, Outdoor medical laboratory.

1964, May 26

139	A18	25fr bl, org & ol	.45	.25
140	A18	30fr multi	.55	.25
141	A18	50fr vio, org & bl	.85	.30
142	A18	60fr grnsh bl, org & dk brn	.95	.40
		Nos. 139-142 (4)	2.80	1.20

Nigerian mobile health education organization, OMNES (Organisation Médicale Mobile Nigérienne d'Education Sanitaire).

Cooperation Issue
Common Design Type

1964, Nov. 7　Unwmk.　Perf. 13

143	CD119	50fr vio, dk brn & org	.80	.40

Tuareg Tent of
Azawak — A19

Designs: 20fr, Songhai house. 25fr, Wogo and Kourtey tents. 30fr, Djerma house. 60fr, Huts of Sorkawa fishermen. 85fr, Hausa town house.

1964-65　　　　　　　Engr.

144	A19	15fr ultra, dl grn & red brn	.25	.25
145	A19	20fr multi	.30	.25
146	A19	25fr Prus bl, dk brn & org brn	.40	.25
147	A19	30fr multi ('65)	.50	.30
148	A19	60fr red, grn & bis ('65)	1.10	.30
149	A19	85fr multi ('65)	1.60	.50
		Nos. 144-149 (6)	4.15	1.85

Leprosy
Examination — A20

1964, Dec. 15 Photo. Perf. 13x12½
150 A20 50fr multi .80 .50
Issued to publicize the fight against leprosy.

Abraham Lincoln — A21

1965, Apr. 3 Perf. 13x12½
151 A21 50fr vio bl, blk, & ocher .80 .50
Centenary of death of Abraham Lincoln.

Teaching
with Radio
and Pictures
A22

Designs: 25fr, Woman studying arithmetic: "A better life through knowledge." 30fr, Adult education class. 50fr, Map of Niger and 5 tribesmen, "Literacy for adults."

1965, Apr. 16 Engr. Perf. 13
152 A22 20fr dk bl, dk brn & ocher .40 .25
153 A22 25fr sl grn, brn & ol brn .50 .25
154 A22 30fr red, sl grn & vio brn .60 .30
155 A22 50fr dp bl, brn & vio brn .85 .40
Nos. 152-155 (4) 2.35 1.20

Issued to promote adult education and "a better life through knowledge."

Ader Portable
Telephone — A23

Designs: 30fr, Wheatstone telegraph interrupter. 50fr, Early telewriter.

1965, May 17 Unwmk. Perf. 13
156 A23 25fr red brn, dk grn & ind .60 .30
157 A23 30fr lil, slate grn & red .70 .30
158 A23 50fr red, slate grn & pur 1.00 .50
Nos. 156-158 (3) 2.30 1.10

International Telecommunication Union, cent.

Runner — A24

Designs: 10fr, Hurdler, horiz. 20fr, Pole vaulter, horiz. 30fr, Long jumper.

1965, July 1 Engr. Perf. 13
159 A24 10fr brn, ocher & blk .25 .25
160 A24 15fr gray, brn & red .45 .25
161 A24 20fr dk grn, brn & vio bl .60 .25
162 A24 30fr maroon, brn & grn .70 .30
Nos. 159-162 (4) 2.00 1.05

African Games, Brazzaville, July 18-25.

Radio Interview
and Club
Emblem — A25

45fr, Recording folk music, vert. 50fr, Group listening to broadcast, vert. 60fr, Public debate.

1965, Oct. 1 Engr. Perf. 13
163 A25 30fr brt vio, emer & red brn .40 .25
164 A25 45fr blk, car & buff .55 .25
165 A25 50fr dk car, bl & lt brn .70 .30
166 A25 60fr bis, ultra & brn .80 .35
Nos. 163-166 (4) 2.45 1.15

Issued to promote radio clubs.

Water
Cycle — A26

1966, Feb. 28 Engr. Perf. 13
167 A26 50fr vio, ocher & bl .90 .40
Hydrological Decade, 1965-74.

Carvings, Mask
and Headdresses
A27

50fr, Carvings and wall decorations. 60fr, Carvings and arch. 100fr, Architecture and handicraft.

1966, Apr. 12 Engr.
168 A27 30fr red brn, blk & brt grn .55 .40
169 A27 50fr brt bl, ocher & pur .80 .40
170 A27 60fr car lake, dl pur & yel brn .90 .55
171 A27 100fr brt red, bl & blk 1.75 .95
Nos. 168-171 (4) 4.00 2.30

Intl. Negro Arts Festival, Dakar, Senegal, Apr. 1-24.

Soccer Player — A28

50fr, Goalkeeper, horiz. 60fr, Player kicking ball.

1966, June 17 Engr. Perf. 13
172 A28 30fr dk brn, brt bl & rose red .65 .30
173 A28 50fr bl, choc & emer .80 .40
174 A28 60fr bl, lil & brn .95 .50
Nos. 172-174 (3) 2.40 1.20

8th World Soccer Cup Championship, Wembley, England, July 11-30.

Color Guard — A29

20fr, Parachutist, horiz. 45fr, Tanks, horiz.

Perf. 12½x13, 13x12½
1966, Aug. 23 Photo.
175 A29 20fr multi .40 .25
176 A29 30fr multi .50 .25
177 A29 45fr multi .70 .35
Nos. 175-177 (3) 1.60 .85

5th anniv. of the National Armed Forces.

Cow Receiving
Injection — A30

1966, Sept. 26 Litho. Perf. 12½x13
178 A30 45fr org brn, bl & blk 1.25 .60
Campaign against cattle plague.

UNESCO
Emblem — A31

1966, Nov. 4 Litho. Perf. 13x12½
179 A31 50fr multi .70 .40
20th anniversary of UNESCO.

Cement Works
Malbaza — A32

Designs: 10fr, Furnace, vert. 20fr, Electric center. 50fr, Handling of raw material.

1966, Dec. 17 Engr. Perf. 13
180 A32 10fr ind, brn & org .30 .25
181 A32 20fr dk ol grn & dl bl .50 .25
182 A32 30fr bl, gray & red brn .50 .25
183 A32 50fr ind, bl & brn .70 .35
Nos. 180-183 (4) 2.00 1.10

Redbilled
Hornbill — A33

Birds: 2fr, Pied kingfisher. 30fr, Barbary shrike. 45fr, 65fr, Little weaver and nest. 70fr, Chestnut-bellied sand grouse.

1967-81 Engr. Perf. 13
184 A33 1fr red, sl grn & dk brn .70 .35
185 A33 2fr brn, brt grn & blk .70 .35
186 A33 30fr multi 4.00 .70
187 A33 45fr multi 1.90 .40
188 A33 65fr multi ('81) 3.25 .85
189 A33 70fr multi 3.25 .70
Nos. 184-189 (6) 13.80 3.35

Issued: 1fr, 2fr, 30fr, 2/8; 45fr, 70fr, 11/18; 65fr, 9/81. See #237.

Villard-de-Lans and
Olympic Emblem — A34

Olympic Emblem and Mountains: 45fr, Autrans and ski jump. 60fr, Saint Nizier du Moucherotte and ski jump. 90fr, Chamrousse and course for downhill and slalom races.

1967, Feb. 24
190 A34 30fr grn, ultra & brn .50 .25
191 A34 45fr grn, ultra & brn .70 .40
192 A34 60fr grn, ultra & brn .95 .50
193 A34 90fr grn, ultra & brn 1.40 .75
Nos. 190-193 (4) 3.55 1.90

10th Winter Olympic Games, Grenoble, 1968.

Lions Emblem and
Family — A35

1967, Mar. 4
194 A35 50fr dk grn, brn red & ultra 1.00 .40
Lions International, 50th anniversary.

ITY Emblem,
Views, Globe and
Plane — A36

1967, Apr. 28 Engr. Perf. 13
195 A36 45fr vio, brt grn & red lil .70 .35
International Tourist Year, 1967.

1967 Jamboree Emblem
and Scouts — A37

Designs (Jamboree Emblem and): 45fr, Scouts gathering from all directions, horiz. 80fr, Campfire.

1967, May 25 Engr. Perf. 13
196 A37 30fr mar, Prus bl & ol .55 .25
197 A37 45fr org, vio bl & brn ol .75 .30
198 A37 80fr multi 1.50 .75
Nos. 196-198 (3) 2.80 1.30

12th Boy Scout World Jamboree, Farragut State Park, Idaho, Aug. 1-9.

Red Cross Aides
Carrying Sick
Man — A38

Designs: 50fr, Nurse, mother and infant. 60fr, Physician examining woman.

1967, July 13 Engr. Perf. 13
199 A38 45fr blk, grn & car .65 .30
200 A38 50fr grn, blk & car .90 .50
201 A38 60fr blk, grn & car 1.25 .55
Nos. 199-201 (3) 2.80 1.35

Issued for the Red Cross.

Europafrica Issue

Map of Europe
and Africa — A39

1967, July 20 Photo. Perf. 12½x12
202 A39 50fr multi .80 .35

Women and UN
Emblem — A40

1967, Oct. 21 Engr. Perf. 13
203 A40 50fr brn, brt bl & yel .80 .40
UN Commission on Status of Women.

Monetary Union Issue
Common Design Type
1967, Nov. 4 Engr. Perf. 13
204 CD125 30fr grn & dk gray .55 .25

A41

Design: Human Rights Flame, Globe, People and Statue of Liberty.

1968, Feb. 19 Engr. Perf. 13
205 A41 50fr brn, indigo & brt bl .80 .40
International Human Rights Year.

Woman Dancing and
WHO Emblem — A42

1968, Apr. 8   Engr.   Perf. 13
206 A42 50fr brt bl, blk & red brn 1.00 .40
20th anniv. of WHO.

Gray
Hornbill — A43

Birds: 10fr, Woodland kingfisher. 15fr, Senegalese coucal. 20fr, Rose-ringed parakeets.
25fr, Abyssinian roller. 50fr, Cattle egret.

Dated "1968"

1968, Nov. 15 Photo. Perf. 12½x13
207 A43 5fr dk grn & multi   .60 .40
208 A43 10fr grn & multi   .70 .40
209 A43 15fr bl vio & multi   1.25 .40
210 A43 20fr pink & multi   1.25 .50
211 A43 25fr ol & multi   2.00 .60
212 A43 50fr pur & multi   2.75 1.50
       Nos. 207-212 (6)   8.55 3.80
     See Nos. 233-236, 316.

ILO Emblem and
"Labor Supporting
the World" — A44

1969, Apr. 22   Engr.   Perf. 13
213 A44 30fr yel grn & dk car   .50 .25
214 A44 50fr dk car & yel grn   .65 .40
50th anniv. of the World Labor Organization.

Red Crosses, Mother
and Child — A45

Designs: 50fr, People, globe, red crosses,
horiz. 70fr, Man with gift parcel and red
crosses.

1969, May 5   Engr.   Perf. 13
215 A45 45fr bl, red & brn ol   .80 .25
216 A45 50fr dk grn, red & gray   .80 .40
217 A45 70fr ocher, red & dk brn 1.25 .60
       Nos. 215-217 (3)   2.85 1.25
50th anniv. of the League of Red Cross
Societies.

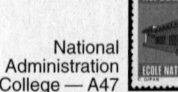

Mouth and
Ear — A46

1969, May 20 Photo. Perf. 12½x12
218 A46 100fr multi   1.25 .60
First (cultural) Conference of French-speaking Community at Niamey.

National
Administration
College — A47

1969, July 8 Photo. Perf. 12½x12
219 A47 30fr emer & dp org   .70 .30

Development Bank Issue
Common Design Type
1969, Sept. 10   Engr.   Perf. 13
220 CD130 30fr pur, grn & ocher   .70 .30

ASECNA Issue
Common Design Type
1969, Dec. 12   Engr.   Perf. 12
221 CD132 100fr car rose   1.40 .70

Classical Pavilion,
National
Museum — A48

Pavilions, National Museum: 45fr, Tempo-
rary exhibitions. 50fr, Audio-visual. 70fr,
Nigerian musical instruments. 100fr,
Craftsmanship.

1970, Feb. 23   Engr.   Perf. 13
222 A48 30fr brt bl, sl grn & brn   .40 .25
223 A48 45fr emer, Prus bl &
            brn   .60 .25
224 A48 50fr sl grn, vio bl & brn   .65 .25
225 A48 70fr brn, sl grn & lt bl   .95 .45
226 A48 100fr sl grn, vio bl & brn 1.40 .60
       Nos. 222-226 (5)   4.00 1.80

Map of Africa and
Vaccination Gun — A49

1970, Mar. 31   Engr.   Perf. 13
227 A49 50fr ultra, dp yel grn &
            mag   .80 .40
Issued to commemorate the 100 millionth
smallpox vaccination in West Africa.

Mexican Figurine
and Soccer
Player — A50

Designs: 70fr, Figurine, globe and soccer
ball. 90fr, Figurine and 2 soccer players.

1970, Apr. 25   Engr.   Perf. 13
228 A50 40fr dk brn, red lil & em-
            er   .75 .35
229 A50 70fr red brn, bl & plum   1.05 .50
230 A50 90fr blk & red   1.40 .70
       Nos. 228-230 (3)   3.20 1.55
9th World Soccer Championship for the
Jules Rimet Cup, Mexico City, 5/29-6/21.

UPU Headquarters Issue
Common Design Type
1970, May 20   Engr.   Perf. 13
231 CD133 30fr brn, dk gray &
              dk red   .50 .25
232 CD133 60fr vio bl, dk car &
              vio   1.00 .35

Bird Types of 1967-68
Birds: 5fr, Gray hornbill. 10fr, Woodland
kingfisher. 15fr, Senegalese coucal. 20fr,
Rose-ringed parakeets. 40fr, Red bishop.

Dated "1970"

1970-71   Photo.   Perf. 13
233 A43 5fr multi ('71)   .45 .25
234 A43 10fr multi ('71)   .45 .25
235 A43 15fr multi ('71)   .75 .25
236 A43 20fr multi ('71)   1.00 .30
                 Engr.
237 A33 40fr multi   3.25 1.00
       Nos. 233-237 (5)   5.90 2.05
Issue dates: 40fr, Dec. 9; others Jan. 4.

World Map with
Niamey in
Center — A51

1971, Mar. 3 Photo. Perf. 12½x12
238 A51 40fr brn & multi   .90 .40
First anniversary of founding of the cooperative agency of French-speaking countries.
For overprint see No. 289.

Scout Emblem,
Merit Badges, Mt.
Fuji, Japanese
Flag — A52

Designs: 40fr, Boy Scouts and flags, vert.
45fr, Map of Japan, Boy Scouts and compass
rose, vert. 50fr, Tent and "Jamboree."

1971, July 5   Engr.   Perf. 13
239 A52 35fr rose lil, dp car &
            org   .55 .25
240 A52 40fr dk pur, grn & mar   .60 .25
241 A52 45fr ultra, cop red & grn   .80 .30
242 A52 50fr ultra   .90 .35
       Nos. 239-242 (4)   2.85 1.15
13th Boy Scout World Jamboree, Asagiri
Plain, Japan, Aug. 2-10.

Maps of
Europe and
Africa — A53

1971, July 29 Photo. Perf. 13x12
243 A53 50fr lt bl & multi   .90 .40
Renewal of the agreement on economic
association between Europe and Africa, 2nd
anniv.

Broad-tailed
Whydah — A54

1971, Aug. 17   Perf. 12½x12
244 A54 35fr yel grn & multi   4.00 1.25
             See No. 443.

Garaya, Haoussa — A55

Stringed Instruments of Niger: 25fr,
Gouroumi, Haoussa. 30fr, Molo, Djerma. 40fr,
Godjie, Djerma-Sonrai. 45fr, Inzad, Tuareg.
50fr, Kountigui, Sonrai.

1971-72   Engr.   Perf. 13
245 A55 25fr red, emer & brn   .50 .25
246 A55 30fr emer, pur & brn   .55 .25
247 A55 35fr brn red, emer & ind .60 .40
248 A55 40fr emer, org & dk brn .70 .45
249 A55 45fr Prus bl, grn & bis .95 .50
250 A55 50fr blk, red & brn   1.25 .60
       Nos. 245-250 (6)   4.55 2.45
Issued: 35, 40, 45fr, 10/13/71; others,
6/16/72.

UNICEF Emblem,
Children of 4
Races — A56

1971, Dec. 11 Photo. Perf. 11
251 A56 50fr multi   .80 .50
25th anniversary of UNICEF.

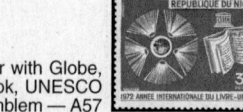

Star with Globe,
Book, UNESCO
Emblem — A57

Design: 40fr, Boy reading, UNESCO
emblem, sailing ship, plane, mosque.

1972, Mar. 27   Engr.   Perf. 13
252 A57 35fr mag & emer   .25 .25
253 A57 40fr dk car & Prus bl   .75 .30
International Book Year 1972.

Cattle
Egret — A58

1972, July 31 Photo. Perf. 12½x12
254 A58 50fr tan & multi   5.25 2.75
             See No. 425.

Cattle at Salt
Pond of In-
Gall — A59

40fr, Cattle wading in pond.

1972, Aug. 25   Engr.   Perf. 13
255 A59 35fr shown   .85 .40
256 A59 40fr multicolored   1.25 .45
         Salt cure for cattle.
For surcharge see No. 282.

Lottery Drum — A60

1972, Sept. 18
257 A60 35fr multi   .80 .40
6th anniversary of the national lottery.

West African Monetary Union Issue
Common Design Type
Design: 40fr, African couple, city, village
and commemorative coin.

1972, Nov. 2   Engr.   Perf. 13
258 CD136 40fr brn, lil & gray   .65 .30

Dromedary
Race — A61

Design: 40fr, Horse race.

1972, Dec. 15   Engr.   Perf. 13
259 A61 35fr brt bl, dk red & brn .90 .50
260 A61 40fr sl grn, mar & brn   1.25 .70

Pole Vault, Map of
Africa — A62

Map of Africa and: 40fr, Basketball. 45fr,
Boxing. 75fr, Soccer.

1973, Jan. 15   Engr.   Perf. 13
261 A62 35fr claret & multi   .40 .25
262 A62 40fr grn & multi   .45 .25
263 A62 45fr red & multi   .55 .30
264 A62 75fr dk bl & multi   .90 .40
       Nos. 261-264 (4)   2.30 1.20
2nd African Games, Lagos, Nigeria, 1/7-18.

Knight, Pawn,
Chessboard — A63

1973, Feb. 16   Engr.   Perf. 13
265 A63 100fr dl red, sl grn & bl   4.00 1.25

World Chess Championship, Reykjavik, Iceland, July-Sept. 1972.

Abutilon
Pannosum — A64

Rare African Flowers: 45fr, Crotalaria barkae. 60fr, Dichrostachys cinerea. 80fr, Caralluma decaisneana.

1973, Feb. 26   Photo.   Perf. 12x12½
266 A64 30fr dk vio & multi   .75 .40
267 A64 45fr red & multi   .90 .40
268 A64 60fr ultra & multi   1.25 .50
269 A64 80fr ocher & multi   1.75 .65
    Nos. 266-269 (4)   4.65 1.95

Interpol Emblem — A65

1973, Mar. 13   Typo.   Perf. 13x12½
270 A65 50fr brt grn & multi   .90 .40

50th anniversary of International Criminal Police Organization (INTERPOL).

Dr. Hansen,
Microscope and Petri
Dish — A66

1973, Mar. 29   Engr.   Perf. 13
271 A66 50fr vio bl, sl grn & dk brn   1.25 .50

Centenary of the discovery by Dr. Armauer G. Hansen of the Hansen bacillus, the cause of leprosy.

Nurse Treating Infant,
UN and Red Cross
Emblems — A67

1973, Apr. 3   Engr.   Perf. 13
272 A67 50fr red, bl & brn   .80 .30

25th anniversary of WHO.

Crocodile — A68

Animals from W National Park: 35fr, Elephant. 40fr, Hippopotamus. 80fr, Wart hog.

1973, June 5   Typo.   Perf. 12½x13
273 A68 25fr gray & blk   .90 .25
274 A68 35fr blk, gold & gray   1.25 .30
275 A68 40fr red, lt bl & blk   1.25 .35
276 A68 80fr multi   2.50 .50
    Nos. 273-276 (4)   5.90 1.40

Eclipse over
Mountains — A69

1973, June 21   Engr.   Perf. 13
277 A69 40fr dk vio bl   .75 .40

Solar eclipse, June 30, 1973.

Palominos
A70

Horses: 75fr, French trotters. 80fr, English thoroughbreds. 100fr, Arabian thoroughbreds.

1973, Aug. 1   Photo.   Perf. 13x12½
278 A70 50fr ultra & multi   1.00 .45
279 A70 75fr gray & multi   1.40 .55
280 A70 80fr emer & multi   1.75 .70
281 A70 100fr ocher & multi   2.25 .90
    Nos. 278-281 (4)   6.40 2.60

No. 255 Srchd. and Ovptd. in Ultramarine

1973, Aug. 16   Perf. 13
282 A59 100fr on 35fr multi   1.75 1.10

African solidarity in drought emergency.

Diesel Engine and
Rudolf
Diesel — A71

Designs: Various Diesel locomotives.

1973, Sept. 7   Perf. 13x12½
283 A71 25fr gray, choc & Prus bl   .75 .25
284 A71 50fr sl bl, gray & dk grn   1.40 .45
285 A71 75fr red lil, sl bl & gray   1.75 .65
286 A71 125fr brt grn, vio bl & car   3.00 1.20
    Nos. 283-286 (4)   6.90 2.55

Rudolf Diesel (1858-1913), inventor of an internal combustion engine, later called Diesel engine.

African Postal Union Issue
Common Design Type

1973, Sept. 12   Engr.   Perf. 13
287 CD137 100fr ol, dk car & sl grn   .90 .60

TV Set, Map of
Niger,
Children — A72

1973, Oct. 1   Engr.   Perf. 13
288 A72 50fr car, ultra & brn   .90 .40

Educational television.

Type of 1971 Overprinted

1973, Oct. 12   Photo.   Perf. 13
289 A51 40fr red & multi   .90 .30

3rd Conference of French-speaking countries, Liège, Sept. 15-Oct. 14.

Apollo of
Belvedère — A73

Classic Sculpture: No. 291, Venus of Milo. No. 292, Hercules. No. 293, Atlas.

1973, Oct. 15   Engr.
290 A73 50fr brn & sl grn   1.25 .50
291 A73 50fr rose car & pur   1.25 .50
292 A73 50fr red brn & dk brn   1.25 .50
293 A73 50fr red brn & blk   1.25 .50
    Nos. 290-293 (4)   5.00 2.00

Beehive, Bees
and
Globes — A74

1973, Oct. 31   Engr.   Perf. 13
294 A74 40fr dl red, ocher & dl bl   .75 .30

World Savings Day.

Tcherka
Songhai
Blanket
A75

Design: 35fr, Kounta Songhai blanket, vert.

Perf. 12½x13, 13x12½
1973, Dec. 17   Photo.
295 A75 35fr brn & multi   .80 .40
296 A75 40fr brn & multi   .80 .45

Textiles of Niger.

WPY Emblem,
Infant and
Globe — A76

1974, Mar. 4   Engr.   Perf. 13
297 A76 50fr multi   .70 .35

World Population Year 1974.

Locomotives, 1938 and 1948 — A77

75fr, Locomotive, 1893. 100fr, Locomotives, 1866 and 1939. 150fr, Locomotives, 1829.

1974, May 24   Engr.   Perf. 13
298 A77 50fr shown   .95 .40
299 A77 75fr multicolored   1.50 .55
300 A77 100fr multicolored   2.10 .85
301 A77 150fr multicolored   3.25 1.40
    Nos. 298-301 (4)   7.80 3.20

Map and Flags of
Members — A78

1974, May 29   Photo.   Perf. 13x12½
302 A78 40fr bl & multi   .80 .40

15th anniversary of the Council of Accord.

Marconi
Sending
Radio
Signals to
Australia
A79

1974, July 1   Engr.   Perf. 13
303 A79 50fr pur, bl & dk brn   .80 .40

Centenary of the birth of Guglielmo Marconi (1874-1937), Italian inventor and physicist.

Hand Holding
Sapling — A80

1974, Aug. 2   Engr.   Perf. 13
304 A80 35fr multi   .75 .40

National Tree Week.

Camel Saddle — A81

Design: 50fr, 3 sculptured horses, horiz.

1974, Aug. 20   Engr.   Perf. 13
305 A81 40fr ol brn, bl & red   .65 .30
306 A81 50fr ol brn, bl & red   .80 .40

Chopin and Polish
Eagle — A82

Design: No. 308, Ludwig van Beethoven and allegory of Ninth Symphony.

1974
307 A82 100fr multi   2.10 .80
308 A82 100fr multi   2.10 .80

125th anniversary of the death of Frederic Chopin (1810-1849), composer and 150th anniversary of Beethoven's Ninth Symphony, composed 1823.
    Issue dates: #307, Sept. 4; #308, Sept. 19.

Don-Don Drum — A83

1974, Nov. 12   Engr.   Perf. 13
309 A83 60fr multi   1.25 .55

Tenere Tree,
Compass
Rose and
Caravan
A84

1974, Nov. 24   Engr.   Perf. 13
310 A84 50fr multi   2.50 1.25

Tenere tree, a landmark in Sahara Desert, first death anniversary.

Satellite over World Weather Map — A85

1975, Mar. 23   Litho.   *Perf. 13*
311 A85 40fr bl, blk & red   .65   .30

World Meteorological Day, Mar. 23, 1975.

"City of Truro," English, 1903 — A86

Locomotives and Flags: 75fr, "5.003," Germany, 1937. 100fr, "The General," United States, 1863. 125fr, "Electric BB 15.000," France, 1971.

1975, Apr. 24   Typo.   *Perf. 13*
312 A86 50fr org & multi   1.40   .35
313 A86 75fr yel grn & multi   1.75   .50
314 A86 100fr lt bl & multi   2.40   .80
315 A86 125fr multi   3.00   1.00
    Nos. 312-315 (4)   8.55   2.65

Bird Type of 1968 Dated "1975"
1975, Apr.   Photo.   *Perf. 13*
316 A43 25fr ol & multi   2.00   .65

Zabira Leather Bag — A87

Handicrafts: 40fr, Damier tapestry. 45fr, Vase. 60fr, Gourd flask.

1975, May 28   Litho.   *Perf. 12½*
317 A87 35fr dp bl & multi   .35   .25
318 A87 40fr dp grn & multi   .50   .30
319 A87 45fr brn & multi   .70   .40
320 A87 60fr dp org & multi   1.00   .45
    Nos. 317-320 (4)   2.55   1.40

Mother and Child, IWY Emblem — A88

1975, June 9   Engr.   *Perf. 13*
321 A88 50fr claret, brn & bl   .80   .40

International Women's Year 1975.

Dr. Schweitzer and Lambarene Hospital A89

1975, June 23   Engr.   *Perf. 13*
322 A89 100fr brn, grn & blk   1.75   .80

Dr. Albert Schweitzer (1875-1965), medical missionary.

Peugeot, 1892 — A90

Early Autos: 75fr, Daimler, 1895. 100fr, Fiat, 1899. 125fr, Cadillac, 1903.

1975, July 16   Engr.   *Perf. 13*
323 A90 50fr rose & vio bl   1.05   .40
324 A90 75fr bl & vio brn   1.60   .50
325 A90 100fr brt grn & mag   2.25   .80
326 A90 125fr brick red & brt grn 2.75   .90
    Nos. 323-326 (4)   7.65   2.60

Sun, Tree and Earth — A91

1975, Aug. 2   Engr.   *Perf. 13*
327 A91 40fr multi   .80   .40

National Tree Week.

Boxing — A92

Designs: 35fr, Boxing, horiz. 45fr, Wrestling, horiz. 50fr, Wrestling.

1975, Aug. 25   Engr.   *Perf. 13*
328 A92 35fr blk, org & brn   .45   .25
329 A92 40fr bl grn, brn & blk .50   .30
330 A92 45fr blk, brt bl & brn .75   .40
331 A92 50fr red, brn & blk   .80   .45
    Nos. 328-331 (4)   2.50   1.40

Lion's Head Tetradrachm, Leontini, 460 B.C. — A93

Greek Coins: 75fr, Owl tetradrachm, Athens, 500 B.C. 100fr, Crab didrachm, Himera, 480 B.C. 125fr, Minotaur tetradrachm, Gela, 460 B.C.

1975, Sept. 12   Engr.   *Perf. 13*
332 A93 50fr red, dl bl & blk   1.00   .30
333 A93 75fr lil, brt bl & blk 1.40   .40
334 A93 100fr bl, org & blk   1.75   .60
335 A93 125fr grn, pur & blk   2.50   .80
    Nos. 332-335 (4)   6.65   2.10

Starving Family — A94

45fr, Animal skeletons. 60fr, Truck bringing food.

1975, Oct. 21   Engr.   *Perf. 13x12½*
336 A94 40fr multi   .80   .35
337 A94 45fr ultra & brn   .80   .35
338 A94 60fr grn, org & dk bl .85   .45
    Nos. 336-338 (3)   2.45   1.15

Fight against drought.

Niger River Crossing A95

Designs: 45fr, Entrance to Boubon camp. 50fr, Camp building.

1975, Nov. 10   Litho.   *Perf. 12½*
339 A95 40fr multi   .70   .30
340 A95 45fr multi   .75   .30
341 A95 50fr multi   .80   .40
    Nos. 339-341 (3)   2.25   1.00

Tourist publicity.

Teacher and Pupils — A96

Each stamp has different inscription in center.

1976, Jan. 12   Photo.   *Perf. 13*
342 A96 25fr ol & multi   .25   .25
343 A96 30fr vio bl & multi   .25   .25
344 A96 40fr multi   .25   .25
345 A96 50fr multi   .40   .25
346 A96 60fr multi   .50   .25
    Nos. 342-346 (5)   1.65   1.25

Literacy campaign 1976.
For overprints see Nos. 371-375.

12th Winter Olympic Games, Innsbruck A97

1976, Feb. 20   Litho.   *Perf. 14x13½*
347 A97 40fr Ice hockey   .40   .25
348 A97 50fr Luge   .55   .30
349 A97 150fr Ski jump   1.35   .65
    Nos. 347-349,C266-C267 (5) 6.30   3.20

Satellite, Telephone, ITU Emblem — A98

1976, Mar. 10   Litho.   *Perf. 13*
350 A98 100fr org, bl & vio bl 1.25   .65

Centenary of first telephone call by Alexander Graham Bell, Mar. 10, 1876.

WHO Emblem, Red Cross Truck, Infant — A99

1976, Apr. 7   Engr.   *Perf. 13*
351 A99 50fr multi   .75   .30

World Health Day 1976.

Statue of Liberty and Washington Crossing the Delaware A100

50fr, Statue of Liberty and call to arms.

1976, Apr. 8   Litho.   *Perf. 14x13½*
352 A100 40fr multi   .30   .25
353 A100 50fr multi   .40   .25
    Nos. 352-353,C269-C271 (5) 6.05   2.45

American Bicentennial.

The Army Helping in Development — A101

Design: 50fr, Food distribution, vert.

Perf. 12½x13, 13x12½
1976, Apr. 15   Litho.
354 A101 50fr multi   .45   .25
355 A101 100fr multi   .90   .45

National Armed Forces, 2nd anniv. of take-over.

Europafrica Issue

Maps, Concorde, Ship and Grain — A102

1976, June 9   Litho.   *Perf. 13*
356 A102 100fr multi   1.25   .55

Road Building — A103

Design: 30fr, Rice cultivation.

1976, June 26   *Perf. 12½*
357 A103 25fr multi   .25   .25
358 A103 30fr multi   .40   .25

Community labor.

Motobecane 125, France A104

Motorcycles: 75fr, Norton Challenge, England. 100fr, BMW 90 S, Germany. 125fr, Kawasaki 1000, Japan.

1976, July 16   Engr.   *Perf. 13*
359 A104 50fr vio bl & multi   .70   .30
360 A104 75fr dp grn & multi   1.00   .40
361 A104 100fr dk brn & multi 1.50   .70
362 A104 125fr slate & multi   1.75   .90
    Nos. 359-362 (4)   4.95   2.30

Boxing — A105

Designs: 50fr, Basketball. 60fr, Soccer. 80fr, Cycling, horiz. 100fr, Judo, horiz.

1976, July 17   Litho.   *Perf. 14*
363 A105 40fr multi   .50   .30
364 A105 50fr multi   .60   .30
365 A105 60fr multi   .70   .30
366 A105 80fr multi   .80   .30
367 A105 100fr multi   1.10   .35
    Nos. 363-367 (5)   3.70   1.55

21st Summer Olympic games, Montreal. See No. C279.

Map of Niger, Planting Seedlings A106

Designs: 50fr, Woman watering seedling, vert. 60fr, Women planting seedlings, vert.

1976, Aug. 1   Litho.   *Perf. 12½x13*
368 A106 40fr org & multi   .45   .25
369 A106 50fr yel & multi   .55   .30
370 A106 60fr grn & multi   .70   .40
    Nos. 368-370 (3)   1.70   .95

Reclamation of Sahel Region.

Nos. 342-346 Overprinted: "JOURNEE / INTERNATIONALE / DE L'ALPHABETISATION"

1976, Sept. 8   Photo.   *Perf. 13*
371	A96	25fr ol & multi	.25	.25
372	A96	30fr vio bl & multi	.25	.25
373	A96	40fr multi	.35	.25
374	A96	50fr multi	.45	.25
375	A96	60fr multi	.45	.30
		Nos. 371-375 (5)	1.75	1.30

Literacy campaign.

Hairdresser A107

Designs: 40fr, Woman weaving straw, vert. 50fr, Women potters, vert.

1976, Oct. 6   *Perf. 13*
376	A107	40fr buff & multi	.45	.25
377	A107	45fr bl & multi	.50	.25
378	A107	50fr red & multi	.70	.30
		Nos. 376-378 (3)	1.65	.80

Niger Women's Association.

Rock Carvings — A108

Archaeology: 50fr, Neolithic sculptures. 60fr, Dinosaur skeleton.

1976, Nov. 15   Photo.   *Perf. 13x12½*
379	A108	40fr blk, sl & yel	2.50	.55
380	A108	50fr blk, red & bis	2.75	.55
381	A108	60fr buff, blk & org brn	5.50	.80
		Nos. 379-381 (3)	10.75	1.90

Benin Head — A109

Weaver, Dancers and Musicians A110

1977, Jan. 15   Engr.   *Perf. 13*
382	A109	40fr dk brn	.45	.25
383	A110	50fr gray bl	1.00	.40

2nd World Black and African Festival, Lagos, Nigeria, Jan. 15-Feb. 12.

First Aid, Student, Blackboard and Plow — A111

Designs: Inscriptions on blackboard differ on each denomination.

1977, Jan. 23   Photo.   *Perf. 12½x13*
384	A111	40fr multi	.40	.25
385	A111	50fr multi	.50	.30
386	A111	60fr multi	.70	.40
		Nos. 384-386 (3)	1.60	.95

Literacy campaign.

Midwife — A112

Design: 50fr, Midwife examining newborn.

1977, Feb. 23   Litho.   *Perf. 13*
387	A112	40fr multi	.45	.25
388	A112	50fr multi	.75	.35

Village health service.

Titan Rocket Launch — A113

80fr, Viking orbiter near Mars, horiz.

1977, Mar. 15   Litho.   *Perf. 14*
389	A113	50fr multi	.45	.25
390	A113	80fr multi	.75	.30
		Nos. 389-390,C283-C285 (5)	4.70	1.85

Viking Mars project. For overprints see #497-498, C295-C297.

Marabous A114

Design: 90fr, Harnessed antelopes.

1977, Mar. 18   Engr.   *Perf. 13*
391	A114	80fr multi	2.00	1.00
392	A114	90fr multi	2.25	1.00

Nature protection.

Weather Map, Satellite, WMO Emblem — A115

1977, Mar. 23
393	A115	100fr multi	1.25	.65

World Meteorological Day.

Group Gymnastics A116

50fr, High jump. 80fr, Folk singers.

1977, Apr. 7   Litho.   *Perf. 13x12½*
394	A116	40fr dl yel & multi	.45	.25
395	A116	50fr bl & multi	.60	.30
396	A116	80fr org & multi	.75	.35
		Nos. 394-396 (3)	1.80	.90

2nd Tahoua Youth Festival, Apr. 7-14.

Red Cross, WHO Emblems and Children A117

1977, Apr. 25   Engr.   *Perf. 13*
397	A117	80fr lil, org & red	.85	.40

World Health Day: "Immunization means protection of your children."

Eye with WHO Emblem, and Sword Killing Fly — A118

1977, May 7
398	A118	100fr ver, lt bl & bluish blk	1.25	.65

Fight against onchocerciasis, a roundworm infection, transmitted by flies, causing blindness.

Guirka Tahoua Dance — A119

50fr, Mailfilafili Gaya. 80fr, Naguihinayan Loga.

1977, June 7   Photo.   *Perf. 13x12½*
399	A119	40fr multi	.55	.30
400	A119	50fr multi	.75	.40
401	A119	80fr multi	1.10	.55
		Nos. 399-401 (3)	2.40	1.25

Popular arts and traditions.

Cavalry A120

Traditional chief's cavalry, different groups.

1977, July 7   Litho.   *Perf. 13x12½*
402	A120	40fr multi	.70	.40
403	A120	50fr multi	.80	.45
404	A120	60fr multi	1.20	.60
		Nos. 402-404 (3)	2.70	1.45

Planting and Cultivating A121

1977, Aug. 10
405	A121	40fr multi	.65	.30

Reclamation of Sahel Region.

Albert John Luthuli Peace A122

Designs: 80fr, Maurice Maeterlinck, literature. 100fr, Allan L. Hodgkin, medicine. 150fr, Albert Camus, literature. 200fr, Paul Ehrlich, medicine.

1977, Aug. 20   Litho.   *Perf. 14*
406	A122	50fr multi	.40	.25
407	A122	80fr multi	.50	.25
408	A122	100fr multi	.75	.25
409	A122	150fr multi	1.25	.40
410	A122	200fr multi	1.60	.55
		Nos. 406-410 (5)	4.50	1.70

Nobel prize winners. See No. C287.

Mao Tse-tung — A123

1977, Sept. 9   Engr.   *Perf. 13*
411	A123	100fr blk & red	3.75	1.75

Argentina '78 Emblem, Soccer Players and Coach, Vittorio Pozzo, Italy — A124

Designs (Argentina '78 emblem, soccer players and coach): 50fr, Vincente Feola, Spain. 80fr, Aymore Moreira, Portugal. 100fr, Sir Alf Ramsey, England. 200fr, Helmut Schoen, Germany. 500fr, Sepp Herberger, Germany.

1977, Oct. 12   Litho.   *Perf. 13½*
412	A124	40fr multi	.40	.25
413	A124	50fr multi	.50	.25
414	A124	80fr multi	.65	.25
415	A124	100fr multi	1.10	.35
416	A124	200fr multi	1.75	.65
		Nos. 412-416 (5)	4.40	1.75

Souvenir Sheet
417	A124	500fr multi	4.25	1.75

World Cup Soccer championship, Argentina '78. For overprints see Nos. 453-458.

Horse's Head, Parthenon and UNESCO Emblem A125

1977, Nov. 12   Engr.   *Perf. 13*
418	A125	100fr multi	1.75	.80

Woman Carrying Water Pots — A126

Design: 50fr, Women pounding corn.

1977, Nov. 23   Photo.   *Perf. 12½x13*
419	A126	40fr multi	.50	.25
420	A126	50fr red & multi	.65	.30

Niger Women's Association.

Crocodile's Skull, 100 Million Years Old — A127

Design: 80fr, Neolithic flint tools.

1977, Dec. 14   *Perf. 13*
421	A127	50fr multi	1.50	.65
422	A127	80fr multi	2.00	.90

Raoul Follereau and Lepers — A128

40fr, Raoul Follereau and woman leper, vert.

1978, Jan. 28   Engr.   Perf. 13
423   A128 40fr multi   .45   .25
424   A128 50fr multi   .65   .40

25th anniversary of Leprosy Day. Follereau (1903-1977) was "Apostle to the Lepers" and educator of the blind.

Bird Type of 1972 Redrawn
1978, Feb.   Photo.
425   A58 50fr tan & multi   2.50 1.00

No. 425 is dated "1978" and has only designer's name in imprint. No. 254 has printer's name also.

Assumption, by
Rubens — A129

Rubens Paintings: 70fr, Rubens and Friends, horiz. 100fr, History of Marie de Medici. 150fr, Alathea Talbot and Family. 200fr, Marquise de Spinola. 500fr, Virgin and St. Ildefonso.

1978, Feb. 25   Litho.   Perf. 14
426   A129 50fr multi   .40   .25
427   A129 70fr multi   .45   .25
428   A129 100fr multi   .85   .30
429   A129 150fr multi   1.25   .40
430   A129 200fr multi   1.80   .50
      Nos. 426-430 (5)   4.75 1.70

Souvenir Sheet
Perf. 13½
431   A129 500fr gold & multi   5.00 1.60

Peter Paul Rubens (1577-1640), 400th birth anniversary.

Shot Put — A130

1978, Mar. 22   Photo.   Perf. 13
432   A130 40fr shown   .30   .25
433   A130 50fr Volleyball   .40   .25
434   A130 60fr Long jump   .45   .30
435   A130 100fr Javelin   .80   .40
      Nos. 432-435 (4)   1.95 1.20

Natl. University Games' Championships.

First Aid and Red
Crosses — A131

1978, May 13   Litho.
436   A131 40fr red & multi   .40   .25

Niger Red Cross.

Goudel Earth
Station — A132

1978, May 23
437   A132 100fr multi   .85   .40

Soccer Ball, Flags
of Participants
A133

Argentina '78 Emblem and: 50fr, Ball in net. 100fr, Globe with South America, Soccer field. 200fr, Two players, horiz. 300fr, Player and globe.

1978, June 18   Litho.   Perf. 13½
438   A133   40fr multi   .30   .25
439   A133   50fr multi   .50   .25
440   A133 100fr multi   .75   .35
441   A133 200fr multi   1.50   .70
      Nos. 438-441 (4)   3.05 1.55

Souvenir Sheet
442   A133 300fr multi   2.50 1.25

11th World Cup Soccer Championship, Argentina, June 1-25.

Bird Type of 1971 Redrawn
1978, June   Photo.   Perf. 13
443   A54 35fr bl & multi   3.25   .90

No. 443 has no year date, nor Delrieu imprint.

Post Office,
Niamey
A134

Design: 60fr, Post Office, different view.

1978, Aug. 12   Litho.
444   A134 40fr multi   .40   .25
445   A134 60fr multi   .60   .30

Goudel Water
Works — A135

1978, Sept. 25   Photo.   Perf. 13
446   A135 100fr multi   1.00   .55

Giraffe — A136

Animals and Wildlife Fund Emblem: 50fr, Ostrich. 70fr, Cheetah. 150fr, Oryx, horiz. 200fr, Addax, horiz. 300fr, Hartebeest, horiz.

1978, Nov. 20   Litho.   Perf. 15
447   A136 40fr multi   1.10   .50
448   A136 50fr multi   2.00   .60
449   A136 70fr multi   2.75   .80
450   A136 150fr multi   5.75 1.40
451   A136 200fr multi   9.00 2.00
452   A136 300fr multi   12.00 2.75
      Nos. 447-452 (6)   32.60 8.05

Endangered species.

Nos. 412-417 Overprinted in Silver

a

---

b

c

d

e

1978, Dec. 1   Perf. 13½
453   A124(a)   40fr multi   .40   .25
454   A124(b)   50fr multi   .55   .25
455   A124(c)   80fr multi   .85   .30
456   A124(d) 100fr multi   1.00   .40
457   A124(e) 200fr multi   2.10 1.00
      Nos. 453-457 (5)   4.90 2.20

Souvenir Sheet
458   A124(e) 500fr multi   4.50 1.75

Winners, World Soccer Cup Championship, Argentina, June 1-25.

Tinguizi — A137

Musicians: No. 460, Dan Gourmou. No. 461, Chetima Ganga, horiz.

1978, Dec. 11   Litho.   Perf. 13
459   A137 100fr multi   1.10   .55
460   A137 100fr multi   1.10   .55
461   A137 100fr multi   1.10   .55
      Nos. 459-461 (3)   3.30 1.65

Virgin Mary, by
Dürer — A138

50fr, The Homecoming, by Honoré Daumier (1808-79). 150fr, 200fr, 500fr, Virgin and Child, by Albrecht Dürer (1471-1528), diff.

1979, Jan. 31   Litho.   Perf. 13½
462   A138   50fr multi   .70   .25
463   A138 100fr multi   .75   .30
464   A138 150fr multi   1.25   .40
465   A138 200fr multi   1.75   .60
      Nos. 462-465 (4)   4.45 1.55

Souvenir Sheet
466   A138 500fr multi   4.75 1.60

Solar
Panels and
Tank
A139

Design: 40fr, Tank and panels on roof, vert.

1979, Feb. 28   Perf. 12½x12, 12x12½
467   A139 40fr multi   .45   .25
468   A139 50fr multi   .55   .30

Hot water from solar heat.

Children with
Building
Blocks
A140

Children and IYC Emblem: 100fr, Reading books. 150fr, With model plane.

1979, Apr. 10   Litho.   Perf. 13½
469   A140   40fr multi   .40   .25
470   A140 100fr multi   .80   .30
471   A140 150fr multi   1.60   .50
      Nos. 469-471 (3)   2.80 1.05

International Year of the Child.

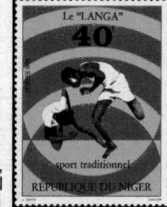

The Langa,
Traditional
Sport — A141

Design: 50fr, The langa, diff.

1979, Apr. 10   Litho.   Perf. 12½x12
472   A141 40fr multi   .45   .25
473   A141 50fr multi   .55   .30

Rowland Hill,
Mail Truck
and France
No.
8 — A142

Designs (Hill and): 100fr, Canoes and Austria #P4. 150fr, Air Niger plane and US #122. 200fr, Streamlined mail train and Canada type A6. 400fr, Electric train and Niger #51.

1979, June 6   Litho.   Perf. 14
474   A142   40fr multi   .50   .25
475   A142 100fr multi   1.00   .30
476   A142 150fr multi   1.50   .40
477   A142 200fr multi   1.80   .55
      Nos. 474-477 (4)   4.80 1.50

Souvenir Sheet
478   A142 400fr multi   4.00 1.50

Sir Rowland Hill (1795-1879), originator of penny postage.

Zabira
Handbag
and Niger
No.
135 — A143

Design: 150fr, Heads with communications waves, world map, UPU emblem and satellite.

1979, June 8   Litho.   Perf. 12x12½
479 A143 50fr multi   1.25 .60

Engr.   Perf. 13
480 A143 150fr brt red & ultra   3.25 1.60

Philexafrique II, Libreville, Gabon, June 8-17. Nos. 479, 480 each printed in sheets of 10 and 5 labels showing exhibition emblem.

Djermakoye Palace
A144

1979, Sept. 26   Litho.   Perf. 13x12½
481 A144 100fr multi   .90 .50

Bororo Festive Headdress
A145

60fr, Bororo women's traditional costumes.

Perf. 13x12½, 12½x13
1979, Sept. 26
482 A145 45fr multi   .45 .30
483 A145 60fr multi, vert.   .55 .35

Annual Bororo Festival.

Olympic Emblem, Flame and Boxers
A146

Designs: 100fr, 150fr, 250fr, 500fr, Olympic emblem, flame and boxers, diff.

1979, Oct. 6   Perf. 13½
484 A146 45fr multi   .40 .25
485 A146 100fr multi   .85 .30
486 A146 150fr multi   1.30 .40
487 A146 250fr multi   2.25 .65
      Nos. 484-487 (4)   4.80 1.60
Souvenir Sheet
488 A146 500fr multi   4.00 1.75

Pre-Olympic Year.

John Alcock, Arthur Whitten Brown, Vickers-Vimy Biplane
A147

1979, Sept. 3   Perf. 13½
489 A147 100fr multi   1.25 .50

First Transatlantic flight, 60th anniversary.

Road and Traffic Safety
A148

1979, Nov. 20   Litho.   Perf. 12½
490 A148 45fr multi   .45 .30

Four-Man Bobsledding, Lake Placid '80 Emblem
A149

Lake Placid '80 Emblem and: 60fr, Downhill skiing. 100fr, Speed skating. 150fr, Two-man bobsledding. 200fr, Figure skating. 300fr, Cross-country skiing.

1979, Dec. 10   Perf. 14½
491 A149 40fr multi   .30 .25
492 A149 60fr multi   .45 .25
493 A149 100fr multi   .80 .30
494 A149 150fr multi   1.25 .45
495 A149 200fr multi   1.75 .75
      Nos. 491-495 (5)   4.55 2.00
Souvenir Sheet
496 A149 300fr multi   2.75 1.10

13th Winter Olympic Games, Lake Placid, NY, Feb. 12-24, 1980.
For overprints see Nos. 501-506.

Nos. 389, 390 Overprinted in Silver or Black

1979, Dec. 20   Litho.   Perf. 14
497 A113 50fr multi (S)   .40 .25
498 A113 80fr multi   .70 .30
      Nos. 497-498,C295-C296 (4) 3.95 2.10

Apollo 11 moon landing, 10th anniv. See #C297.

Court of Sultan of Zinder
A150

1980, Mar. 25   Litho.   Perf. 13x12½
499 A150 45fr shown   .40 .25
500 A150 60fr Sultan's court, diff.   .50 .25

Nos. 491-496 Overprinted

(a)

(b)

(c)

(d)

(e)

(f)

1980, Mar. 31   Litho.   Perf. 14½
501 A149 (a) 40fr multi   .30 .25
502 A149 (b) 60fr multi   .45 .25
503 A149 (c) 100fr multi   .85 .40
504 A149 (d) 150fr multi   1.25 .45
505 A149 (e) 200fr multi   1.75 .70
      Nos. 501-505 (5)   4.60 2.10
Souvenir Sheet
506 A149 (f) 300fr multi   2.50 1.50

Javelin, Olympic Rings — A151

90fr, Walking. 100fr, High jump, horiz. 300fr, Marathon runners, horiz. 500fr, High jump, horiz.

1980, Apr. 17
507 A151 60fr shown   .55 .25
508 A151 90fr multi   .85 .25
509 A151 100fr multi   .95 .30
510 A151 300fr multi   2.50 .80
      Nos. 507-510 (4)   4.85 1.60
Souvenir Sheet
511 A151 500fr multi   4.00 1.50

22nd Summer Olympic Games, Moscow, July 19-Aug. 3.
For overprints see Nos. 527-531.

Man Smoking Cigarette, Runner — A152

1980, Apr. 7   Perf. 13
512 A152 100fr multi   1.00 .50

World Health Day; fight against cigarette smoking.

Health Year — A153

1980, May 15   Photo.   Perf. 13x12½
513 A153 150fr multi   1.25 .65

Shimbashi-Yokohama Locomotive — A154

60fr, American type. 90fr, German Reichsbahn series 61. 100fr, Prussian Staatsbahn P2. 130fr, L'Aigle. 425fr, Stephenson's Rocket.

1980, June   Litho.   Perf. 12½
514 A154 45fr shown   .55 .30
515 A154 60fr multicolored   .80 .35
516 A154 90fr multicolored   1.05 .50
517 A154 100fr multicolored 1.40 .65
518 A154 130fr multicolored 1.75 .85
      Nos. 514-518 (5)   5.55 2.65
Souvenir Sheet
519 A154 425fr multicolored 7.50 2.25

For overprint see No. 674.

Steve Biko, 4th Anniversary of Death — A155

1980, Sept. 12   Litho.   Perf. 13
520 A155 150fr org & blk   1.40 .70

Soccer Players
A156

Designs: Various soccer scenes.

1980, Oct. 15   Perf. 12½
521 A156 45fr multi   .30 .25
522 A156 60fr multi   .40 .25
523 A156 90fr multi   .70 .25
524 A156 100fr multi   .80 .30
525 A156 130fr multi   .90 .35
      Nos. 521-525 (5)   3.10 1.40
Souvenir Sheet
526 A156 425fr multi   4.00 1.25

World Soccer Cup 1982.

Nos. 507-511 Overprinted in Gold with Winner's Name and Country
1980, Sept. 27   Litho.   Perf. 14½
527 A151 60fr multi   .45 .25
528 A151 90fr multi   .70 .30
529 A151 100fr multi   .80 .35
530 A151 300fr multi   2.40 1.10
      Nos. 527-530 (4)   4.35 2.00
Souvenir Sheet
531 A151 500fr multi, horiz.   4.00 2.50

African Postal Union, 5th Anniversary — A157

1980, Dec. 24   Photo.   Perf. 13½
532 A157 100fr multi   .90 .50

Terra Cotta Kareygorou Head — A158

Designs: Terra Cotta Kareygorou Statues, 5th-12th cent. 45fr, 150fr, horiz.

1981, Jan. 23   Litho.   Perf. 13
533 A158 45fr multi   .35 .25
534 A158 60fr multi   .55 .25
535 A158 90fr multi   .70 .35
536 A158 150fr multi   1.30 .60
      Nos. 533-536 (4)   2.90 1.45

Ostrich — A159

1981, Mar. 17   Litho.   Perf. 12½
537 A159 10fr shown   1.20 .30
538 A159 20fr Oryx   .45 .30
539 A159 25fr Gazelle   .45 .30
540 A159 30fr Great bustard 2.00 .60
541 A159 60fr Giraffe   .85 .40
542 A159 150fr Addax   2.00 .80
      Nos. 537-542 (6)   6.95 2.70

7th Anniv. of the
F.A.N. — A160

1981, Apr. 14   Litho.   *Perf. 13*
543 A160 100fr multi   .90   .45

One-armed
Archer — A161

1981, Apr. 24   Engr.
544 A161 50fr shown   .70   .30
545 A161 100fr Draftsman   1.25   .60

Intl. Year of the Disabled.

Scene from
Mahalba Ballet,
1980 Youth
Festival,
Dosso — A162

1981, May 17   Litho.
546 A162 100fr shown   .80   .40
547 A162 100fr Ballet, diff. .80   .40

Prince Charles
and Lady
Diana,
Coach — A163

Designs: Couple and coaches.

1981, July 15   Litho.   *Perf. 14½*
548 A163 150fr multi   1.10   .45
549 A163 200fr multi   1.40   .65
550 A163 300fr multi   2.00   .80
    Nos. 548-550 (3)   4.50 1.90
Souvenir Sheet
551 A163 400fr multi   3.25 1.50

Royal wedding.
For overprints see Nos. 595-598.

Hegira 1500th
Anniv. — A164

1981, July 15   *Perf. 13½x13*
552 A164 100fr multi   .90   .45

Alexander Fleming
(1881-1955) — A165

1981, Aug. 6   Engr.   *Perf. 13*
553 A165 150fr multi   2.10   .95

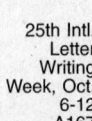

25th Intl.
Letter
Writing
Week, Oct.
6-12
A167

1981, Oct. 9   Surcharged in Black
554 A167 65fr on 40fr multi   .55   .30
555 A167 85fr on 60fr multi   .75   .50

Nos. 554-555 not issued without surcharge.

World Food
Day — A168

1981, Oct. 16   Litho.
556 A168 100fr multi   .90   .45

Espana '82
World Cup
Soccer
A169

Designs: Various soccer players.

1981, Nov. 18   Litho.   *Perf. 14x13½*
557 A169 40fr multi   .30   .25
558 A169 65fr multi   .50   .25
559 A169 85fr multi   .60   .25
560 A169 150fr multi   1.10   .45
561 A169 300fr multi   2.00   .90
    Nos. 557-561 (5)   4.50 2.10
Souvenir Sheet
562 A169 500fr multi   4.00 1.75

For overprints see Nos. 603-608.

75th Anniv.
of Grand
Prix — A170

Designs: Winners and their cars — 20fr,
Peugeot, 1912. 40fr, Bugatti, 1924. 65fr,
Lotus-Climax, 1962. 85fr, Georges Boillot,
1912. 150fr, Phil Hill, 1960.
450fr, Race.

1981, Nov. 30   *Perf. 14*
563 A170 20fr multicolored   .40   .25
564 A170 40fr multicolored   .55   .25
565 A170 65fr multicolored   .80   .25
566 A170 85fr multicolored 1.00   .50
567 A170 150fr multicolored 1.60   .80
    Nos. 563-567 (5)   4.35 2.05
Souvenir Sheet
568 A170 450fr multicolored 5.25 1.75

For overprint see No. 675.

Christmas
1981 — A171

Designs: Virgin and Child paintings.

1981, Dec. 24
569 A171 100fr Botticelli   .80   .35
570 A171 200fr Botticini   1.40   .75
571 A171 300fr Botticelli, diff. 2.40 1.00
    Nos. 569-571 (3)   4.60 2.10

School
Gardens — A172

1982, Feb. 19   Litho.   *Perf. 13x13½*
572 A172 65fr shown   .55   .30
573 A172 85fr Garden, diff.   .70   .45

L'Estaque,
by Georges
Braque
(1882-1963)
A173

Anniversaries: 120fr, Arturo Toscanini
(1867-1957), vert. 140fr, Fruit on a Table, by
Edouard Manet (1832-1883). 300fr, George
Washington (1732-99), vert. 400fr, Goethe
(1749-1832), vert. Nos. 579-580, 21st birthday
of Diana, Princess of Wales (portraits), vert.

1982, Mar. 8   Litho.   *Perf. 13*
574 A173 120fr multi   1.15   .45
575 A173 140fr multi   1.60   .50
576 A173 200fr multi   2.75   .75
577 A173 300fr multi   3.25 1.15
578 A173 400fr multi   4.00 1.50
579 A173 500fr multi   5.00 2.00
    Nos. 574-579 (6)   17.75 6.35
Souvenir Sheet
580 A173 500fr multi   4.00 1.75

Palace of
Congress
A174

1982, Mar. 17
581 A174 150fr multi   1.25   .70

7th Youth Festival,
Agadez — A175

65fr, Martial arts, horiz. 100fr, Wrestling.

1982, Apr. 7   *Perf. 12½*
582 A175 65fr multicolored   .50   .30
583 A175 100fr multicolored   .90   .50

Reafforestation
Campaign — A176

1982, Apr. 16   *Perf. 13*
584 A176 150fr Tree planting 1.20   .50
585 A176 200fr Trees, Desert 1.60   .80

For overprints see Nos. 668-669.

Scouting
Year — A177

65fr, Canoeing, two boys sitting. 85fr,
Scouts in rubber boat. 130fr, Canoeing, two
boys standing. 200fr, Rafting.
400fr, Beach scene.

1982, May 13
586 A177 65fr multi   .60   .25
587 A177 85fr multi   .85   .30
588 A177 130fr multi   1.25   .45
589 A177 200fr multi   1.75   .75
    Nos. 586-589 (4)   4.45 1.75
Souvenir Sheet
590 A177 400fr multi   3.25 1.75

For overprint see No. 673.

A178

1982, June 6
591 A178 100fr multi   .90   .45

13th Meeting of Islamic Countries Foreign
Affairs Ministers, Niamey, Aug. 20-27.

West African Economic
Community — A179

1982, June 28
592 A179 200fr Map   1.40   .85

Fishermen in
Canoe — A180

1982, July 18   *Perf. 13x12½*
593 A180 65fr shown   .60   .35
594 A180 85fr Bringing in nets .80 .40

**Nos. 548-551 Overprinted in Blue:
"NAISSANCE ROYALE 1982"**
1982, Aug. 4   *Perf. 14½*
595 A163 150fr multi   .95   .50
596 A163 200fr multi   1.20   .70
597 A163 300fr multi   2.10 1.00
    Nos. 595-597 (3)   4.25 2.20
Souvenir Sheet
598 A163 400fr multi   2.75 1.50

Flautist, by Norman
Rockwell — A181

85fr, Clerk. 110fr, Teacher and Pupil. 150fr,
Girl Shopper.

1982, Sept. 10   Litho.   *Perf. 14*
599 A181 65fr shown   .50   .30
600 A181 85fr multi   .70   .30
601 A181 110fr multi   .90   .40
602 A181 150fr multi   1.25   .55
    Nos. 599-602 (4)   3.35 1.55

**Nos. 557-562 Overprinted with Past
and Present Winners in Black on
Silver**
1982, Sept. 28   *Perf. 14x13½*
603 A169 40fr multi   .30   .25
604 A169 65fr multi   .45   .25
605 A169 85fr multi   .55   .30
606 A169 150fr multi   1.20   .45
607 A169 300fr multi   2.25 1.10
    Nos. 603-607 (5)   4.75 2.35
Souvenir Sheet
608 A169 500fr multi   4.00 2.75

Italy's victory in 1982 World Cup.

ITU
Plenipotentiaries
Conference,
Nairobi,
Sept. — A182

1982, Sept. 28   *Perf. 13*
609 A182 130fr black & blue 1.00   .50

Laboratory
Workers — A183

Various laboratory workers.

1982, Nov. 9   Litho.   Perf. 13
610 A183 65fr multi   .65   .35
611 A183 115fr multi   .90   .55

Self-sufficiency in
Food
Production — A184

1983, Feb. 16   Litho.   Perf. 13½x13
612 A184 65fr Rice harvest   .70   .35
613 A184 85fr Planting rice, vert.   .95   .45

Grand Ducal
Madonna, by
Raphael — A185

Raphael Paintings: 65fr, Miraculous Catch
of Fishes. 100fr, Deliverance of St. Peter.
150fr, Sistine Madonna. 200fr, Christ on the
Way to Calvary. 300fr, Deposition. 400fr,
Transfiguration. 500fr, St. Michael Slaying the
Dragon.

1983, Mar. 30   Litho.   Perf. 14
614 A185 65fr multi, vert.   .50   .25
615 A185 85fr multi   .60   .25
616 A185 100fr multi, vert.   .80   .25
617 A185 150fr multi   1.10   .40
618 A185 200fr multi   1.40   .55
619 A185 300fr multi, vert.   2.00   .80
620 A185 400fr multi   3.00 1.10
621 A185 500fr multi   4.00 1.25
      Nos. 614-621 (8)   13.40 4.85

African Economic
Commission, 25th
Anniv. — A186

1983, Mar. 18   Perf. 12½x13
622 A186 120fr multi   .95   .45
623 A186 200fr multi   1.50   .85

Army
Surveyors — A187

1983, Apr. 14   Perf. 13x12½
624 A187 85fr shown   .35   .40
625 A187 150fr Road building .65   .75

Agadez
Court — A188

1983, Apr. 26   Litho.   Perf. 13x12½
626 A188 65fr multi   .45   .25

Mail Van — A189

1983, June 25   Litho.
627 A189 65fr Van   .45   .40
628 A189 100fr Van, map   .80   .45

Palestine
Solidarity — A190

1983, Aug. 21   Litho.   Perf. 12½
629 A190 65fr multi   .65   .30

Intl. Literacy
Year — A191

Various adult education classes. 65fr, 150fr
vert.

Perf. 13½x14½, 14½x13½
1983, Sept. 8   Litho.
630 A191 40fr multi   .35   .25
631 A191 65fr multi   .45   .25
632 A191 85fr multi   .60   .30
633 A191 100fr multi   .75   .40
634 A191 150fr multi   1.25   .80
      Nos. 630-634 (5)   3.40 2.00

7th Ballet Festival
of Dosso
Dept. — A192

Various dancers.

1983, Oct. 7   Perf. 14½x13½
635 A192 65fr multi   .50   .35
636 A192 85fr multi   .70   .45
637 A192 120fr multi   1.10   .60
      Nos. 635-637 (3)   2.30 1.40

World Communications
Year — A193

80fr, Post Office, mail van. 120fr, Sorting
mail. 150fr, Emblem, vert.

1983, Oct. 18 Perf. 13x12½, 12½x13
638 A193 80fr multi   .60   .45
639 A193 120fr multi   .85   .50
640 A193 150fr multi   1.25   .60
      Nos. 638-640 (3)   2.70 1.55

Solar Energy For
Television — A194

1983, Nov. 26   Perf. 13
641 A194 85fr Antenna   .60   .40
642 A194 130fr Car   1.00   .45

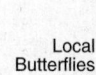

Local
Butterflies
A195

75fr, Hypolimnas misippus. 120fr, Papilio
demodocus. 250fr, Vanessa antiopa. 350fr,
Charesex jasius. 500fr, Danaus chrisippus.

1983, Dec. 9   Perf. 12½
643 A195 75fr multicolored   .90   .40
644 A195 120fr multicolored   1.25   .50
645 A195 250fr multicolored   2.25   .90
646 A195 350fr multicolored   3.00 1.25
647 A195 500fr multicolored   4.75 1.60
      Nos. 643-647 (5)   12.15 4.65

SAMARIYA Natl.
Development
Movement — A196

1984, Jan. 18   Litho.   Perf. 13x13½
648 A196 80fr multi   .60   .40

Alestes
Bouboni — A197

1984, Mar. 28   Litho.   Perf. 13
649 A197 120fr multi   3.25   .80

Military
Pentathlon — A198

1984, Apr. 10
650 A198 120fr Hurdles   .85   .45
651 A198 140fr Shooting 1.00   .65

Radio Broadcasting
Building
Opening — A199

1984, May 14   Litho.   Perf. 13
652 A199 120fr multi   .90   .45

25th Anniv. of Council
of Unity — A200

1984, May 29   Perf. 12½
653 A200 65fr multi   .55   .35
654 A200 85fr multi   .75   .45

Renault,
1902 — A201

80fr, Paris. 100fr, Gottlieb Daimler. 120fr,
Three-master Jacques Coeur. 150fr, Barque
Bosphorus. 250fr, Delage D8. 300fr, Three-
master Comet. 400fr, Maybach Zeppelin.
  Vintage cars (#656, 658, 660, 662) & ships.

1984, June 12   Perf. 12½
655 A201 80fr multicolored   .60   .30
656 A201 100fr multicolored   .75   .40
657 A201 120fr multicolored   .75   .40
658 A201 140fr shown   1.00   .50
659 A201 150fr multicolored   1.10   .60
660 A201 250fr multicolored   1.90   .90
661 A201 300fr multicolored   2.00   .75
662 A201 400fr multicolored   3.00 1.00
      Nos. 655-662 (8)   11.10 4.70

1984 UPU
Congress — A202

1984, June 20   Engr.   Perf. 13x12½
663 A202 300fr Ship, emblems 3.00 1.75

Ayerou Market
Place — A203

1984, July 18   Litho.   Perf. 12½
664 A203 80fr shown   .80   .55
665 A203 120fr River scene 1.25   .70

Vipere Echis
Leucogaster
A204

1984, Aug. 16   Perf. 13x12½
666 A204 80fr multi   1.05   .55

West African
Union, CEAO,
10th
Anniv. — A205

1984, Oct. 26   Litho.   Perf. 13½
667 A205 80fr multi   .65   .40

UN Disarmament
Campaign, 20th
Anniv. — A205a

1984, Oct. 31   Perf. 13
667A A205a 400fr brt grn & blk 2.75 1.50
667B A205a 500fr brt bl & blk   3.25 2.00

**Nos. 584-585 Overprinted "Aide au
Sahel 84"**
1984   Litho.   Perf. 13
668 A176 150fr multi   1.40   .75
669 A176 200fr multi   1.60 1.10

World Tourism
Organization,
10th
Anniv. — A206

1985, Jan. 2   Litho.   Perf. 12½
670 A206 110fr WTO emblem .90   .45

Infant Survival
Campaign — A207

85fr, Breastfeeding. 110fr, Weighing child,
giving liquids.

1985, Jan. 28   Litho.   Perf. 12½
671 A207 85fr multi   .70   .35
672 A207 110fr multi   .90   .50

**Nos. 590, 519 and 568 Overprinted
with Exhibitions in Red**
Souvenir Sheets
Perf. 13, 12½, 14
1985, Mar. 11   Litho.
673 A177 400fr MOPHILA '85 /
           HAMBOURG   4.50 4.50
674 A154 425fr TSUKUBA EXPO
           '85   4.50 4.50
675 A170 450fr ROME, ITALIA
           '85 emblem   4.50 4.50

      See Nos. C356-C357.

Technical & Cultural
Cooperation Agency,
15th Anniv. — A208

1985, Mar. 20   **Perf. 13**
676 A208 110fr vio, brn & car
      rose   .80   .45

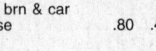

8th Niamey
Festival — A209

Gaya Ballet Troupe. No. 678 vert.

1985, Apr. 8   **Perf. 12½x13, 13x12½**
677 A209 85fr multi   .60   .40
678 A209 110fr multi   .75   .55
679 A209 150fr multi   1.10   .70
     Nos. 677-679 (3)   2.45 1.65

Intl. Youth
Year
A210

Authors and scenes from novels: 85fr, Jack
London (1876-1916). 105fr, Joseph Kessel
(1898-1979). 250fr, Herman Melville. 450fr,
Rudyard Kipling.

1985, Apr. 29   **Perf. 13**
680 A210 85fr multi   .75   .35
681 A210 105fr multi   .80   .40
682 A210 250fr multi   2.00 1.00
683 A210 450fr multi   3.50 1.75
     Nos. 680-683 (4)   7.05 3.50

PHILEXAFRICA '85, Lome,
Togo — A211

1985, May 6   **Perf. 13x12½**
684 A211 200fr Tree planting   1.50 1.10
685 A211 200fr Industry   1.50 1.10
  a.   Pair, Nos. 684-685 + label   4.25 4.25

Victor Hugo and His
Son Francois, by A. de
Chatillon — A212

1985, May 22   **Perf. 12½**
686 A212 500fr multi   4.00 2.00

Europafrica
A213

1985, June 3   **Perf. 13**
687 A213 110fr multi   1.00   .50

World
Wildlife
Fund
A214

50fr, 60fr, Addax. 85fr, 110fr, Oryx.

1985, June 15
688 A214 50fr Head, vert.   3.25   .65
689 A214 60fr Grazing   4.25   .85
690 A214 85fr Two adults   5.00 1.05
691 A214 110fr Head, vert.   6.50 1.25
     Nos. 688-691 (4)   19.00 3.80

Environ-destroying Species — A215

85fr, Oedaleus sp. 110fr, Dysdercus volkeri.
150fr, Tolyposporium ehrenbergii, Sclerospora
graminicola, horiz. 210fr, Passer luteus. 390fr,
Quelea quelea.

1985, July 1   **Perf. 13x12½, 12½x13**
692 A215 85fr multi   1.00   .40
693 A215 110fr multi   1.10   .45
694 A215 150fr multi   1.75   .65
695 A215 210fr multi   2.50 1.00
696 A215 390fr multi   4.75 1.90
     Nos. 692-696 (5)   11.10 4.40

Official Type of 1988 and

Cross of Agadez — A216

1985-94   **Engr.**   **Perf. 13**
697 A216 85fr green   .75   .40
698 O2 110fr brown   1.00   .50
699 A216 125fr blue green   —
700 A216 175fr emerald   —
701 A216 210fr orange   —   —

    Issued: 85fr, 110fr, 7/85; 125fr, 175fr, 210fr,
5/15/94.

Natl. Independence, 25th
Anniv. — A217

1985, Aug. 3   **Litho.**   **Perf. 13x12½**
707 A217 110fr multi   1.00   .50

Protected
Trees — A218

Designs: 30fr, No. 711, Adansonia digitata
and pod, vert. 85fr, 210fr, Acacia albida. No.
710, 390fr, Adansonia digitata, diff. Nos. 708-
710 inscribed "DES ARBRES POUR LE
NIGER."

1985   **Perf. 13x12½, 12½x13**
708 A218 30fr grn & multi   .55   .40
709 A218 85fr brn & multi   .85   .50
710 A218 110fr mag & multi   1.20   .60
711 A218 110fr blk & multi   1.05   .55
712 A218 210fr blk & multi   1.75 1.10
713 A218 390fr blk & multi   3.75 1.75
     Nos. 708-713 (6)   9.15 4.90

    Issued: #708-710, 10/1; #711-713, 8/19.

Niamey-Bamako
Motorboat
Race — A219

110fr, Boats on Niger River. 150fr, Helicopter, competitor. 250fr, Motorboat, map.

1985, Sept. 16   **Perf. 13½**
714 A219 110fr multicolored   .80   .40
715 A219 150fr multicolored   1.10   .60
716 A219 250fr multicolored   2.00 1.00
     Nos. 714-716 (3)   3.90 2.00

Mushrooms
A220

85fr, Boletus. 110fr, Hypholoma fasciculare.
200fr, Coprinus comatus. 300fr, Agaricus
arvensis. 400fr, Geastrum fimbriatum.

1985, Oct. 3
717 A220   85fr multicolored   .80   .35
718 A220 110fr multicolored   1.10   .40
719 A220 200fr multicolored   1.90   .75
720 A220 300fr multicolored   3.25 1.25
721 A220 400fr multicolored   4.25 1.75
     Nos. 717-721 (5)   11.30 4.50

     Nos. 717-719 vert.

PHILEXAFRICA '85, Lome,
Togo — A221

No. 722, Village water pump. No. 723, Children playing dili.

1985, Oct. 21   **Perf. 13x12½**
722 A221 250fr multicolored   2.00 1.25
723 A221 250fr multicolored   2.00 1.25
  a.   Pair, Nos. 722-723   4.50 4.50

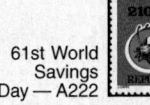

61st World
Savings
Day — A222

1985, Oct. 31   **Perf. 12½x13**
724 A222 210fr multi   1.50   .90

European Music
Year — A223

Traditional instruments.

1985, Nov. 4   **Perf. 13½**
725 A223 150fr Gouroumi, vert.   1.25   .80
726 A223 210fr Gassou   1.75 1.25
727 A223 390fr Algaita, vert.   3.00 1.75
     Nos. 725-727 (3)   6.00 3.80

Souvenir Sheet
Perf. 12½
728 A223 500fr Biti   4.00 4.00

Civil Statutes
Reform — A224

1986, Jan. 2   **Litho.**   **Perf. 13x12½**
729 A224 85fr Natl. identity card   .65   .40
730 A224 110fr Family services   .85   .50

Traffic Safety — A225

1986, Mar. 26   **Litho.**   **Perf. 12½x13**
731 A225 85fr Obey signs   .65   .40
732 A225 110fr Speed restriction   .85   .50

Artists — A226

60fr, Oumarou Ganda, filmmaker. 85fr, Ida
Na Dadaou, entertainer. 100fr, Dan Gourmou,
entertainer. 130fr, Koungoui, comedian.

1986, Apr. 11   **Perf. 12½**
733 A226 60fr multi   .45   .30
734 A226 85fr multi   .60   .40
735 A226 100fr multi   .75   .50
736 A226 130fr multi   1.00   .55
     Nos. 733-736 (4)   2.80 1.75

Hunger
Relief
Campaign,
Trucks of
Hope
A227

85fr, Relief supply truck. 110fr, Mother,
child, vert.

1986, Aug. 27   **Litho.**   **Perf. 12½**
737 A227 85fr multicolored   .75   .40
738 A227 110fr multicolored   1.00   .50

Intl. Solidarity
Day — A228

200fr, Nelson Mandela and Walter Sisulu,
Robben Island prison camp. 300fr, Mandela.

1986, Oct. 8   **Perf. 13½**
739 A228 200fr multi   1.80   .90
740 A228 300fr multi   2.75 1.40

FAO, 40th
Anniv. — A229

50fr, Cooperative peanut farm. 60fr, Fight
desert encroachment. 85fr, Irrigation management. 100fr, Breeding livestock. 110fr,
Afforestation.

1986, Oct. 16   **Perf. 13**
741 A229 50fr multicolored   .40   .30
742 A229 60fr multicolored   .45   .30
743 A229 85fr multicolored   .60   .40
744 A229 100fr multicolored   .75   .40
745 A229 110fr multicolored   1.00   .40
     Nos. 741-745 (5)   3.20 1.80

Improved Housing for
a Healthier
Niger — A230

1987, Feb. 26   **Litho.**   **Perf. 13½**
746 A230 85fr Albarka   .75   .30
747 A230 110fr Mai Sauki   .95   .50

Insects Protecting
Growing
Crops — A231

1987, Mar. 26   *Perf. 13x12½*
748 A231 85fr Sphodromantis   1.00 .50
749 A231 110fr Delta   1.50 .60
750 A231 120fr Cicindela   1.75 .85
    Nos. 748-750 (3)   4.25 1.95

Liptako-Gourma Telecommunications
Link Inauguration — A232

1987, Apr. 10   *Perf. 13½*
751 A232 110fr multi   .85 .55

Samuel
Morse — A233

120fr, Telegraph key, operator, horiz. 350fr,
Receiver, horiz.

1987, May 21   *Litho.*   *Perf. 12x12½*
752 A233 120fr multicolored   .75 .40
753 A233 200fr shown   1.50 .75
754 A233 350fr multicolored   3.00 1.50
    Nos. 752-754 (3)   5.25 2.65

Invention of the telegraph, 150th anniv.

1988 Seoul Summer
Olympics — A234

1987, July 15
755 A234 85fr Tennis   .55 .40
756 A234 110fr Pole vault   .85 .40
757 A234 250fr Soccer   2.00 .85
    Nos. 755-757 (3)   3.40 1.65
    Souvenir Sheet
758 A234 500fr Running   4.00 2.75

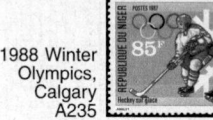

1988 Winter
Olympics,
Calgary
A235

85fr, Ice hockey. 110fr, Speed skating.
250fr, Pairs figure skating.
500fr, Downhill skiing.

1987, July 28   *Litho.*   *Perf. 12½*
759 A235 85fr multi   .60 .35
760 A235 110fr multi   .85 .40
761 A235 250fr multi   2.00 .85
    Nos. 759-761 (3)   3.45 1.60
    Souvenir Sheet
762 A235 500fr multi   4.00 2.75

For overprints see Nos. 783-785.

African
Games,
Nairobi
A236

1987, Aug. 5   *Perf. 13*
763 A236 85fr Runners   .60 .35
764 A236 110fr High jump   .75 .40
765 A236 200fr Hurdles   1.50 .75
766 A236 400fr Javelin   3.00 1.50
    Nos. 763-766 (4)   5.85 3.00

Natl. Tourism
Office, 10th
Anniv. — A237

85fr, Chief's stool, scepter, vert. 110fr,
Nomad, caravan, scepter. 120fr, Moslem village. 200fr, Bridge over Niger River.

1987, Sept. 10   *Perf. 13½*
767 A237 85fr multicolored   .50 .40
768 A237 110fr multicolored   1.00 .45
769 A237 120fr multicolored   1.00 .45
770 A237 200fr multicolored   1.75 .85
    Nos. 767-770 (4)   4.25 2.15

Aga Khan
Architecture
Prize, 1986
A238

85fr, Yaama Mosque, dawn. 110fr, At night.
250fr, In daylight.

1987, Oct. 7   *Perf. 13*
771 A238 85fr multi   .60 .30
772 A238 110fr multi   .80 .40
773 A238 250fr multi   2.00 1.00
    Nos. 771-773 (3)   3.40 1.70

Niamey Court of
Appeal — A239

1987, Nov. 17   *Perf. 13x12½*
774 A239 85fr multi   .60 .30
775 A239 110fr multi   .80 .40
776 A239 140fr multi   1.10 .55
    Nos. 774-776 (3)   2.50 1.25

Christmas
1987 — A240

Paintings: 110fr, The Holy Family with
Lamb, by Raphael. 500fr, The Adoration of the
Magi, by Hans Memling (c. 1430-1494).

    Wmk. 385
1987, Dec. 24   *Litho.*   *Perf. 12½*
777 A240 110fr multi   1.00 .50
    Souvenir Sheet
778 A240 500fr multi   4.00 2.50

No. 778 is airmail.

Modern
Services for
a Healthy
Community
A241

1988, Jan. 21   *Perf. 13*
779 A241 85fr Water drainage   .95 .55
780 A241 110fr Sewage   1.10 .70
781 A241 165fr Garbage removal   1.90 .95
    Nos. 779-781 (3)   3.95 2.20

Dan-Gourmou
Prize — A242

1988, Feb. 16   *Litho.*   *Perf. 13½*
782 A242 85fr multi   1.25 .70

Natl. modern music competition.

**Nos. 759-761 Ovptd. "Medaille d'or"
and Name of Winner in Gold**
1988, Mar. 29   *Perf. 12½*
783 A235 85fr USSR   .60 .40
784 A235 110fr Gusafson, Swe-
     den   .80 .50
785 A235 250fr Gordeeva and
     Grinkov, USSR   2.00 1.20
    Nos. 783-785 (3)   3.40 2.10

New Market
Building,
Niamey — A243

1988, Apr. 9   *Litho.*   *Perf. 13x12½*
786 A243 85fr multi   .80 .40

WHO 40th Anniv.,
Universal
Immunization
Campaign
A244

1988, May 26   *Litho.*   *Perf. 12½x13*
787 A244 85fr Mother and child   .65 .40
788 A244 110fr Visiting doctor   .90 .45

Organization for
African Unity (OAU),
25th Anniv. — A245

1988, June 28   *Perf. 12½*
789 A245 85fr multi   .70 .35

Construction of a
Sand Break to
Arrest Desert
Encroachment
A246

1988, Sept. 27   *Litho.*   *Perf. 12½x13*
790 A246 85fr multi   1.10 .55

 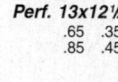

Intl. Red Cross and
Red Crescent
Organizations, 125th
Annivs. — A247

1988, Oct. 26   *Perf. 13x12½*
791 A247 85fr multi   .65 .35
792 A247 110fr multi   .85 .45

Niger Press
Agency — A248

1989, Jan. 31   *Litho.*   *Perf. 12½*
793 A248 85fr blk, org & grn   .70 .35

Fight Against
AIDS — A249

1989, Feb. 28   *Perf. 13½*
794 A249 85fr multi   .70 .40
795 A249 110fr multi   .90 .50

Intl. Maritime
Organization,
30th
Anniv. — A250

1989, Mar. 29   *Litho.*   *Perf. 12½x13*
796 A250 100fr multi   .90 .45
797 A250 120fr multi   1.20 .55

FAN Seizure of
Government, 15th
Anniv. — A251

85fr, Gen. Ali Saibou. 110fr, Raising of the
flag.

1989, Apr. 14
798 A251 85fr multi   .60 .30
799 A251 110fr multi   .80 .40

PHILEXFRANCE '89 — A252

100fr, Eiffel Tower. 200fr, Simulated stamps.

1989, July 1   *Litho.*   *Perf. 13*
800 A252 100fr multi   .80 .45
801 A252 200fr multi   1.60 .80

French
Revolution,
Bicent.
A253

250fr, Planting a tree for liberty.

1989, July 1
802 A253 250fr multicolored   2.25 1.10

Zinder Regional
Museum —
A253a

    Perf. 14¾x14¼
1989, Aug. 23   *Litho.*
802A A253a 85fr multicolored   20.00 20.00

African Development
Bank, 25th
Anniv. — A254

1989, Aug. 30   *Litho.*   *Perf. 13½*
803 A254 100fr multicolored   .80 .40

Communication and Postal Organization of West Africa (CAPTEAO), 30th Anniv. — A255

1989, July 3   Litho.   Perf. 13½
804 A255 85fr multicolored   .70   .35

Verdant Field, Field After Locust Plague A256

1989, Oct. 1   Litho.   Perf. 13
805 A256 85fr multicolored   1.25   .60

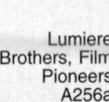

Lumiere Brothers, Film Pioneers A256a

Designs: 150fr, Auguste Lumiere (1862-1954). 250fr, Louis Lumiere (1864-1948).

1989, Nov. 21   Litho.   Perf. 13½
805A A256a 150fr multicolored   1.50   .75
805B A256a 250fr multicolored   2.25 1.00
805C A256a 400fr multicolored   3.75 1.75
   Nos. 805A-805C (3)   7.50 3.50

Rural Development Council, 30th Anniv. — A256b

1989   Litho.   Perf. 15x14
805D A256b 75fr multicolored   20.00

Flora — A257

10fr, Russelia equisetiformis. 20fr, Argyreia nervosa. 30fr, Hibiscus rosa-sinensis. 50fr, Catharanthus roseus. 100fr, Cymothoe sangaris, horiz.

1989, Dec. 12   Litho.   Perf. 13
806 A257 10fr multicolored   .25   .25
807 A257 20fr multicolored   .25   .25
808 A257 30fr multicolored   .25   .25
809 A257 50fr multicolored   .45   .25
810 A257 100fr multicolored   1.00   .40
   Nos. 806-810 (5)   2.20 1.40

Dunes of Temet — A257a

1989   Litho.   Perf. 15x14
810A A257a 145fr Caravan   55.00 45.00
810B A257a 165fr shown   55.00 45.00

Pan-African Postal Union, 10th Anniv. — A258

1990, Jan. 18   Perf. 12½
811 A258 120fr multicolored   1.00   .50

Intl. Literacy Year — A259

1990, Feb. 27   Perf. 13½x13
812 A259 85fr shown   .65   .35
813 A259 110fr Class, diff.   .95   .45

Islamic Conference Organization, 20th anniv. — A260

1990, Mar. 15   Perf. 13x12½
814 A260 85fr OCI emblem   .70   .35

U.S. Congressman Mickey Leland — A261

1990, Mar. 29   Litho.   Perf. 13½
815 A261 300fr multicolored   2.40 1.25
816 A261 500fr multicolored   4.00 2.00

Leland died Aug. 7, 1989 in a plane crash on a humanitarian mission.

Natl. Development Society, 1st Anniv. — A262

1990, May 15   Litho.   Perf. 13½
817 A262 85fr multicolored   .70   .35

Multinational Postal School, 20th Anniv. — A263

1990, May 31   Perf. 13x12½
818 A263 85fr multicolored   .80   .40

1992 Summer Olympics, Barcelona A263a

1990, June 4   Litho.   Perf. 13½
818A A263a 85fr Gymnastics   .65   .30
818B A263a 110fr Hurdles   .85   .40
818C A263a 250fr Running   2.00 1.00
818D A263a 400fr Equestrian   3.00 1.50
818E A263a 500fr Long jump   4.00 2.00
   Nos. 818A-818E (5)   10.50 5.20
Souvenir Sheet
818F A263a 600fr Cycling   4.75 2.75

Nos. 818D-818F are airmail.

Independence, 30th Anniv. — A264

1990, Aug. 3   Perf. 12½
819 A264 85fr gray grn & multi   .65   .35
820 A264 110fr buff & multi   .95   .50

UN Development Program, 40th Anniv. — A265

1990, Oct. 24   Litho.   Perf. 13½
821 A265 100fr multicolored   .80   .40

A266

Butterflies and Mushrooms — A266a

Designs: 85fr, Amanita rubescens. 110fr, Graphum pylades. 200fr, Pseudacraea hostilia. 250fr, Russula virescens. 400fr, Boletus impolitus. 500fr, Precis octavia. 600fr, Cantharellus cibarius & pseudacraea boisduvali.

1991, Jan. 15   Litho.   Perf. 13½
822 A266 85fr multicolored   .65   .30
823 A266 110fr multicolored   .75   .40
824 A266 200fr multicolored   1.20   .80
825 A266 250fr multicolored   2.25 1.00
826 A266 400fr multicolored   3.25 1.50
827 A266 500fr multicolored   3.50 1.60
   Nos. 822-827 (6)   11.60 5.60
Souvenir Sheet
828 A266a 600fr multicolored   5.00 5.00

Nos. 826-828 are airmail. No. 828 contains one 30x38mm stamp.

Palestinian Uprising — A267

1991, Mar. 30   Litho.   Perf. 12½
829 A267 110fr multicolored   1.00   .45

Christopher Columbus (1451-1506) — A268

Hypothetical portraits and: 85fr, Santa Maria. 110fr, Frigata, Portuguese caravel, 15th cent. 200fr, Four-masted caravel, 16th cent. 250fr, Estremadura, Spanish caravel, 1511. 400fr, Vija, Portuguese caravel, 1600. 500fr, Pinta. 600fr, Nina.

1991, Mar. 19   Litho.   Perf. 13½
830 A268 85fr multicolored   .75   .35
831 A268 110fr multicolored   .90   .40
832 A268 200fr multicolored   1.60   .70
833 A268 250fr multicolored   2.00   .90

834 A268 400fr multicolored   3.25 1.25
835 A268 500fr multicolored   3.75 1.60
   Nos. 830-835 (6)   12.25 5.20
Souvenir Sheet
835A A268 600fr multicolored   5.00 5.00

Nos. 834-835A are airmail.

Timia Falls — A269   African Tourism Year — A270

Designs: 85fr, Boubon Market, horiz. 130fr, Ruins of Assode, horiz.

1991, July 10
836 A269 85fr multicolored   .70   .30
837 A269 110fr multicolored   .95   .45
838 A269 130fr multicolored   1.10   .50
839 A270 200fr multicolored   1.75   .85
   Nos. 836-839 (4)   4.50 2.10

Anniversaries and Events — A270a

85fr, Chess players Anatoly Karpov and Garry Kasparov. 110fr, Race car drivers Ayrton Senna and Alain Prost. 200fr, An official swears allegiance to the constitution, Honoré-Gabriel Riqueti (Comte de Mirabeau). 250fr, Gen. Dwight D. Eisenhower, Winston Churchill, Field Marshal Bernard Montgomery and Republic P-4D Thunderbolt. 400fr, Charles de Gaulle and Konrad Adenauer. 500fr, German Chancellor Helmut Kohl, Brandenburg Gate. 600fr, Pope John Paul II's visit to Africa.

1991, July 15   Litho.   Perf. 13½
839A A270a 85fr multicolored   .45   .25
839B A270a 110fr multicolored   .60   .25
839C A270a 200fr multicolored   1.10   .35
839D A270a 250fr multicolored   6.00 1.25
839E A270a 400fr multicolored   2.25   .80
839F A270a 500fr multicolored   2.75   .90
839G A270a 600fr multicolored   5.00 5.00
   Nos. 839A-839G (7)   18.15 8.80

French Revolution, bicent. (#839C). Franco-German Cooperation Agreement, 28th anniv. (#839E). #839E is airmail & exists in a souvenir sheet of 1. German reunification (#839F). Nos. 839F and 839G are airmail and exist in souvenir sheets of 1.
For surcharge see No. 865.

Women's Hairstyles — A271

1991
840 A271 85fr multicolored   .95   .35
841 A271 110fr multicolored   1.25   .45
842 A271 165fr multicolored   1.90   .70
843 A271 200fr multicolored   2.10   .85
   Nos. 840-843 (4)   6.20 2.35

Transportation — A271a

Design: 85fr, Earth Resources Satellite, ERS-1, Japan; 110fr, EXOS-D satellite for observation of the Aurora Borealis, Japan; 200fr, Louis Favre (1826-1879), Congo-Ocean locomotive BB 415; 250fr, Congo-Ocean locomotive BB.BB.301; 400fr, Locomotive BB BB 302; 500fr, Anglo-French Concorde,   F117

NIGER

341

stealth fighter, US. 600fr, George
Nagelmacker (1845-1905), Orient Express.

1991, Oct. 15 Litho.   Perf. 13½x13¼
843A A271a 85fr multi   .45   .25
843B A271a 110fr multi   .60   .25
843C A271a 200fr multi   2.25   .35
843D A271a 250fr multi   2.75   .40
843E A271a 400fr multi   4.00   .55
843F A271a 500fr multi   2.75   .50
    Nos. 843A-843F (6)   12.80 2.30
Souvenir Sheet
843G A271a 600fr multi   4.75 4.75
Nos. 843E-843G are airmail. Nos. 843A-
843F exist in souvenir sheets of one. A souvenir sheet of 3 containing Nos. 843A-843B,
843F exists.

Natl. Conference of
Niger — A272

1991, Dec. 17   Litho.   Perf. 12½
844 A272 85fr multicolored   .70   .35

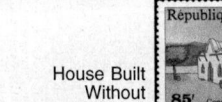

House Built
Without
Wood — A273

1992, May 25   Litho.   Perf. 12½
845 A273 85fr multicolored   .75   .40

World Population
Day — A274

Designs: 85fr, Assembling world puzzle.
110fr, Globe on a kite string.

1992, July 11   Litho.   Perf. 12½
846 A274 85fr multicolored   .70   .40
847 A274 110fr multicolored .90   .50

Discovery of
America,
500th Anniv.
A275

1992, Sept. 16   Perf. 13
848 A275 250fr multicolored 2.25 1.10

Hadjia Haoua
Issa (1927-1990),
Singer — A276

1992, Sept. 23   Perf. 12½x13
849 A276 150fr multicolored 1.25   .65

Intl. Conference on
Nutrition,
Rome — A277

1992   Litho.   Perf. 12½
850 A277 145fr tan & multi   1.40   .60
851 A277 350fr blue & multi 3.00 1.50

African School of
Meteorology and Civil
Aviation, 30th
Anniv. — A278

1993, Feb. 7   Perf. 13½
852 A278 110fr bl, grn & blk .90   .45

Environmental
Protection — A279

1993, June 26 Litho.   Perf. 12½
853 A279 85fr salmon & multi .75   .40
854 A279 165fr green & multi 1.50   .75

World Population
Day — A280

110fr, Buildings, person with globe as head,
tree.

1993, July 11 Litho.   Perf. 13½
855 A280 85fr multicolored   .70   .35
856 A280 110fr multicolored .90   .45

Holy City of
Jerusalem
A281

1993, Nov. 8 Litho.   Perf. 13x12½
857 A281 110fr multicolored 1.00   .45

Artisans at Work
— A282b

1994   Litho.   Perf. 13x13¼
857D A282b 125fr Tailor   20.00 —
857E A282b 175fr Weaver, vert. 20.00 —

Nelson Mandela, F.W.
De Klerk, Winners of
1993 Nobel Peace
Prize — A282

1994, Feb. 11   Litho.   Perf. 13
858 A282 270fr multicolored 1.10   .55

A282a

A282b

Landscapes —
A282c

1994   Litho.   Perf. 12½
858A A282a 85fr multi   —
858B A282b 110fr multi   —
858C A282c 165fr multi   —

Cultural Cooperation &
Technique Agency,
25th Anniv. — A283

1995   Litho.   Perf. 13½x13
859 A283 100fr multicolored .50   .25

Animals Used for
Transportation
A284

500fr, Donkey cart. 1000fr, Man, saddled
horse.

1995   Perf. 13x13½
860 A284 500fr multi   1.60   .95
861 A284 1000fr multi   4.00 2.25

Economic Community
of West African States
(ECOWAS), 20th
Anniv. — A285

1995   Litho.   Perf. 13½
862 A285 125fr multicolored .70   .35

Cattle
Ranching — A286

Design: 300fr, Irrigating fields.

1995   Litho.   Perf. 13½x13
863 A286 125fr shown   .60   .35
864 A286 300fr multicolored 1.20 .65

Souvenir Sheet of No. 839E Ovptd.

1995, Nov. 8   Litho.   Perf. 13½
865 A270a 400fr multicolored 6.75 5.00

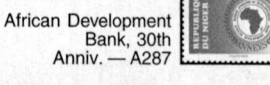

African Development
Bank, 30th
Anniv. — A287

1995   Litho.   Perf. 14
866 A287 300fr green & red 1.25   .70

Boy Scouts — A288

350fr, Robert Baden-Powell. 500fr, Scout
saluting.

1996   Perf. 13½
867 A288 350fr multicolored 1.25   .75
868 A288 500fr multicolored 1.75 1.20
Nos. 867-868 exist imperf. and in souvenir
sheets of 1 both perf. and imperf.

UN, UNICEF, 50th
Anniv. — A289

Designs: 150fr, Child with head bandaged,
UNICEF emblem. 225fr, Boy carrying bowl of
food on head, dove, globes. 475fr, Woman,
boy playing on artillery piece, space station
Mir. 550fr, Boy, race car driver Michael Schumacher, UNICEF emblem.

1996
869 A289 150fr multicolored .70   .35
870 A289 225fr multicolored 1.00   .50
871 A289 475fr multicolored 2.25 1.10
a.   Sheet of 2, #870-871 + label 11.00 5.50
872 A289 550fr multicolored 2.50 1.25
a.   Sheet of 2, #869, 872 + label 11.00 5.50
    Nos. 869-872 (4)   6.45 3.20

Entertainers
A290

No. 873, Bob Marley. No. 874, Janis Joplin.
No. 874A, Madonna. No. 875, Jerry Garcia.
No. 876, Elvis Presley. No. 877, Marilyn
Monroe. No. 878, John Lennon. No. 879,
Monroe, diff. No. 880, Presley, diff.
No. 881, Presley, diff. No. 882, Monroe, diff.

1996
873 A290 175fr multicolored .65   .45
874 A290 300fr multicolored 1.00   .90
874A A290 400fr multicolored 1.40 1.20
875 A290 600fr multicolored 2.25 1.75
876 A290 700fr multicolored 2.50 2.10
877 A290 700fr multicolored 2.50 2.10
878 A290 750fr multicolored 3.00 2.25
879 A290 800fr multicolored 3.00 2.40
880 A290 800fr multicolored 3.00 2.40
    Nos. 873-880 (9)   19.30 15.55
Souvenir Sheets
881 A290 2000fr multicolored 6.75 6.00
882 A290 2000fr multicolored 6.75 6.00
Nos. 873-882 exist imperf. and in souvenir
sheets of 1 both perf. and imperf.
No. 874A exists in a souvenir sheet of 1.

Butterflies — A291

Boy Scout Jamboree emblem and: 150fr,
Chrysiridia riphearia. 200fr, Palla ussheri.
750fr, Mylothris chloris. 800fr, Papilo
dardanus.

1996   Litho.   Perf. 13½
883 A291 150fr multicolored .60   .35
884 A291 200fr multicolored .80   .50
885 A291 750fr multicolored 2.60 2.25
886 A291 800fr multicolored 2.75 2.40
    Nos. 883-886 (4)   6.75 5.50
Nos. 883-886 exist imperf. and in souvenir
sheets of 1 both perf. and imperf.

Wild Animals — A292

Boy Scout Jamboree emblem, Rotary emblem and: 150fr, Erythrocebus patas. 200fr, Panthera pardus. 900fr, Balearica regulorum. 1000fr, Alcelaphus buselaphus.
2000fr, Panthera leo.

1996
887	A292	150fr multicolored	.55	.35
888	A292	200fr multicolored	.70	.55
889	A292	900fr multicolored	2.75	2.50
890	A292	1000fr multicolored	3.25	2.75
	Nos. 887-890 (4)		7.25	6.15

Souvenir Sheet
891	A292	2000fr multicolored	6.75	5.75

Nos. 887-890 exist in souvenir sheets of 1.

Rotary International — A292a

Designs: 200fr, Boy holding fruits and vegetables. 700fr, Girl holding sheaves of grain.

1996   Litho.   Perf. 13½
891A	A292a	200fr multicolored	.70	.55
891B	A292a	700fr multicolored	2.75	1.90

Intl. Red Cross and Lions Intl. — A293

Designs: 250fr, Jean-Henri Dunant as young man. 300fr, Lions Intl. emblems, boy with books. 400fr, Dunant as old man. 600fr, Older boy carrying younger boy, Lions Intl. emblems.

1996   Litho.   Perf. 13½
892	A293	250fr multicolored	.90	.60
893	A293	300fr multicolored	1.05	.55
894	A293	400fr multicolored	1.50	1.25
895	A293	600fr multicolored	2.25	1.75
	Nos. 892-895 (4)		5.70	4.15

Traditional Musical Instruments — A294

1996   Litho.   Perf. 13½
896	A294	125fr violet & multi	.50	.30
897	A294	175fr pink & multi	.70	.45

Sports — A295

1996
898	A295	300fr Golf	1.05	.70
899	A295	500fr Tennis	1.75	1.40
900	A295	700fr Table tennis	2.60	1.80
	Nos. 898-900 (3)		5.40	3.90

Nos. 898-900 exist in souvenir sheets of one.

1996 Summer Olympic Games, Atlanta — A296

Designs: 250fr, Track & field. 350fr, Women's gymnastics, table tennis. 400fr, Tennis, swimming. 600fr, Hurdles, pole vault. 1500fr, Men's track and field.

1996   Litho.   Perf. 13½
901	A296	250fr multicolored	.90	.60
902	A296	350fr multicolored	1.25	1.05
903	A296	400fr multicolored	1.50	1.25
904	A296	600fr multicolored	2.10	1.80
	Nos. 901-904 (4)		5.75	4.70

Souvenir Sheet
904A	A296	1500fr multicolored	5.75	5.75

Souvenir Sheet

CHINA '96 A297

Statues from Yunguang Grottoes, Datong, China: a, Head of Buddha. b, Side view.

1996
905	A297	140fr Sheet of 2, #a.-b.	1.75	1.75

1998 Winter Olympic Games, Nagano — A298

1996
906	A298	85fr Hockey	.40	.30
907	A298	200fr Downhill skiing	.90	.50
908	A298	400fr Slalom skiing	1.75	1.00
909	A298	500fr Pairs figure skating	2.25	1.25
	Nos. 906-909 (4)		5.30	3.05

Nos. 906-909 were not issued without metallic blue overprint on stamps dated 1991. Nos. 908-909 are airmail.
Nos. 906-909 exist with red metallic overprint. A 600fr souvenir sheet with red metallic overprint exists in limited quantities.

Formula I Race Car Drivers — A299

Designs: 450fr, Jacques Villeneuve. 2000fr, Ayrton Senna (1960-94).

1996
910	A299	450fr multicolored	1.60	1.00

Souvenir Sheet
911	A299	2000fr multicolored	6.75	6.00

No. 910 exists in souvenir sheet of 1. No. 911 contains one 39x57mm stamp.

Tockus Nasutus — A300

Coracias Abyssinica A301

Designs: 15fr, Psittacula krameri. 25fr, Coracias abyssinica. 35fr, Bulbucus ibis.

1996   Litho.   Perf. 13½x13
912	A300	5fr multi	6.75	2.50
912A	A300	15fr multi	6.75	2.50
912B	A300	25fr multi	10.00	5.00
912C	A300	35fr multi	6.75	2.50

Perf. 13
913	A301	25fr multi		
914	A301	35fr multi		

Compare type A300 to types A301 and A309.

1998 Winter Olympic Games, Nagano, Japan — A302

1996   Litho.   Perf. 13x13½
915	A302	125fr Ice hockey	.90	.30
916	A302	175fr Slalom skiing	.65	.35
917	A302	700fr Pairs figure skating	2.75	1.50
918	A302	800fr Speed skating	3.00	1.75
	Nos. 915-918 (4)		7.30	3.90

Souvenir Sheet
919	A302	1500fr Downhill skiing	6.00	6.00

No. 919 contains one 57x51mm stamp. Nos. 915-918 exist in souvenir sheets of 1.

Minerals — A303

No. 920: a, Brookite. b, Elbaite indicolite. c. Elbaite rubellite verdelite. d, Olivine.
No. 921: a, Topaz. b, Autunite. c, Leucite. d, Struvite.

1996   Litho.   Perf. 13½
920	A303	375fr Sheet of 4, #a.-d.	5.25	5.25
921	A303	500fr Sheet of 4, #a.-d.	6.50	6.50

Souvenir Sheet
922	A303	2000fr Pyrargyrite	6.50	6.50

No. 922 contains one 42x39mm stamp.

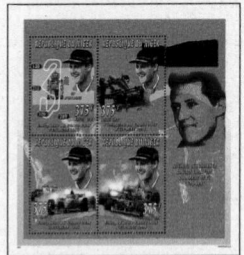

World Driving Champion Michael Schumacher — A304

Schumacher: a, Grand Prix of Spain. b, In race car in pit. c, Ahead of another car. d, Behind another car.

1996   Litho.   Perf. 13½
923	A304	375fr Sheet of 4, #a.-d.	5.50	5.50

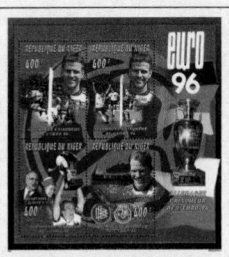

German Soccer Team, Euro '96 Champions — A305

No. 924: a, Oliver Bierhoff, player jumping up. b, Bierhoff, player holding up arms. c, ChancellorHelmut Kohl, Queen Elizabeth II, Klinsmann. d, Stadium, Mathias Sammer. logos.

1996   Litho.   Perf. 13½
924	A305	400fr Sheet of 4, #a.-d.	5.75	5.75

Dinosaurs — A306

No. 925: a, Ouranosaurus. b, Spinosaurus. c, Polacanthus. d, Deinonychus.
No. 926: a, Camptosaurus. b, Allosaurus. c, Nodosaurus. d, Kritosaurus.
2000fr, Protoceratops, oviraptor, horiz.

1996
925	A306	300fr Sheet of 4, #a.-d.	7.00	7.00
926	A306	450fr Sheet of 4, #a.-d.	11.00	11.00

Souvenir Sheet
927	A306	2000fr multicolored	7.00	7.00

France '98, World Soccer Cup Championships A307

World Cup Trophy and: 125fr, American player. 175fr, Brazilian player. 750fr, Italian player. 1000fr, German player.
1500fr, Player in action scene.

1996
928	A307	125fr multicolored	.45	.35
929	A307	175fr multicolored	.60	.50
930	A307	750fr multicolored	2.60	2.10
931	A307	1000fr multicolored	3.50	2.75
	Nos. 928-931 (4)		7.15	5.70

Souvenir Sheet
932	A307	1500fr multicolored	5.75	5.75

No. 932 contains one 57x51mm stamp.

New Year 1997 (Year of the Ox) A308

1997   Litho.   Perf. 13½
933	A308	500fr shown	2.00	1.00
934	A308	500fr Riding three oxen	2.00	1.00

Nos. 933-934 exist in souvenir sheets of 1, design extending to perfs on No. 933.

Birds — A309

5fr, Tockus nasutus. 15fr, Psittacula kramer. 25fr, Coracias abyssinica. 35fr, Bulbucus ibis.

1997   Litho.   Perf. 13½
935 A309 5fr multicolored   .30   .25
936 A309 15fr multicolored   .30   .25
937 A309 25fr multicolored   .30   .25
938 A309 35fr multicolored   .30   .25
    Nos. 935-938 (4)   1.20   1.00
          See No. 1050.

19th Dakar-Agades-Dakar
Rally — A310

Designs: 125fr, Truck, child in traditional dress. 175fr, Ostrich, three-wheel vehicle. 300fr, Camel, heavy-duty support truck. 500fr, Motorcycles.

1997
939 A310 125fr multicolored   .55   .30
940 A310 175fr multicolored   .80   .40
941 A310 300fr multicolored   1.20   .75
942 A310 500fr multicolored   1.90   1.25
 a.   Souvenir sheet, #939-942   4.50   4.50
 b.   Strip of 4, #939-942   4.50   4.50

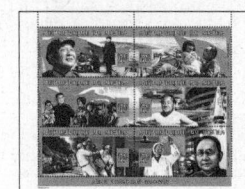

Deng Xiaoping (1904-97), Chinese
Leader — A311

Designs: a, Deng, flag, eating at table, Deng as young man. b, Farming with oxen, Deng holding girl, flag. c, Flag, Deng with soldiers, camp. d, Deng bathing, ships in port, combining grain, launching space vehicle. e, Huts, heavy equipment vehicle, men working. f, Airplane, man holding up flask, operating room, Deng.

1997
943 A311 150fr Sheet of 6, #a.-f. 3.25 3.25

Diana, Princess of Wales (1961-
97) — A312

No. 944: Various portraits performing humanitarin deeds, on world tours, with various figures.
No. 945: Various portraits in designer dresses.
No. 946: With Mother Teresa (in margin).

1997, Sept. 30   Litho.   Perf. 13½
944 A312 180fr Sheet of 9,
          #a.-i.   6.50   4.00
945 A312 180fr Sheet of 9,
          #a.-i.   6.50   4.00

Souvenir Sheets
946 A312 2000fr multicolored   7.25   5.00
947 A312 4000fr multicolored   14.00 14.00

No. 947 contains one 40x46mm stamp depicting Princess Diana in red coat, holding bouquet.
A number of other stamps and souvenir sheets having similar type fonts depicting Princess Diana exist. These were declared to be not authorized by Niger postal authorites.

Famous Americans — A313

No. 948 — Various portraits: a-b, John F. Kennedy. c-d, Pres. Bill Clinton.
No. 949 — Various pprtraits: a, Kennedy. b, Dr. Martin Luther King (1929-68). c-d, Clinton. 2000fr, John F. Kennedy.

1997   Litho.   Perf. 13½
948 A313 350fr Sheet of 4, #a.-
          d.   4.75   3.00
949 A313 400fr Sheet of 4, #a.-
          d.   5.75   5.75

Souvenir Sheet
950 A313 2000fr multicolored   6.75   6.75

No. 950 contains one 42x60mm stamp.

Stars of American Cinema — A314

No. 951: a, Eddie Murphy. b, Elizabeth Taylor. c, Bruce Willis. d, James Dean. e, Clint Eastwood. f, Elvis Presley. g, Michelle Pfeiffer. h, Marilyn Monroe. i, Robert Redford.

1997   Litho.   Perf. 13½
951 A314 300fr Sheet of 9,
          #a.-i.   9.50   9.50

Communications — A315

No. 952: a, 80fr, Satellite transmission, radios. b, 100fr, Computers. c, 60fr, Cellular phone transmission around world. d, 120fr, Hand holding car phone. e, 180fr, Satellite, earth. f, 50fr, Transmission tower, cellular phone.

1997
952 A315   Sheet of 6, #a.-f.   2.25   2.25

Prof. Abdou
Moumouni
Dioffo — A316

1997   Litho.   Perf. 13½x13
953 A316 125fr multicolored

Methods of Transportation — A317

Bicycles, motorcycles: No. 954: a, Jan Ullrich, 1997 Tour de France winner, Eiffel Tower. b, Diana 250, Harley Davidson. c, MK VIII motorcycle, bicycles of 1819, 1875. d, Brands Match Motorcycle Race, Great Britain.
Modern locomotives, country flags: No. 955: a, Pendolino ETR 470, Italy. b, Rame TGV 112, France. c, Eurostar, France, Belgium, UK. d, Intercity Express ICE train, Germany.
Early locomotives, country flags: No. 956: a, Trevithick, UK. b, Pacific North Chapelon, France. c, Buddicom, UK, France. d, PLM "C", France.
Trains of Switzerland: No. 957: a, Crocodile, St. Gothard. b, RE 460. c, Red Streak, RAE 2/4 1001. d, Limmat.
Classic cars, modern sports cars: No. 958: a, Mercedes 300 SL Gullwing, Mercedes E320 Cabriolet. b, Aston Martin V8, Aston Martin DBR2. c. Ferrari F50, Ferrari 250 GT Berlinette. d, Ford Thunderbird, Ford GT40.
Air flight: No. 959: a, Clement Ader's Avion 111, dirigible R101. b, Concorde jet, X36 NASA/MCDD prototype. c, Aile volante FW900, Airbus A340. d, Gaudron GIII, Montgolfier's balloon.
Space travel: No. 960: a, HII rocket, Japan, Copernicus. b, Galileo, Ariane rocket. c, Space shuttle, Neil Armstrong. d, Yuri Gagarin, orbital space station, Soyuz.
1500fr, Swiss train, RE 4/4 II 11349, vert. No. 962, Hubble Space Telescope, Concorde jet. No. 963, TGV mail train, 1958 Chevrolet Corvette.

1997   Litho.   Perf. 13½
954 A317 300fr Sheet of 4, #a.-d. 4.00   4.00
955 A317 350fr Sheet of 4, #a.-d. 4.75   4.75
956 A317 375fr Sheet of 4, #a.-d. 4.75   4.75
957 A317 400fr Sheet of 4, #a.-d. 5.75   5.75
958 A317 450fr Sheet of 4, #a.-d. 5.75   5.75
959 A317 500fr Sheet of 4, #a.-d. 6.50   6.50
960 A317 600fr Sheet of 4, #a.-d. 7.25   7.25

Souvenir Sheets
961 A317 1500fr multicolored   5.75   5.75
962 A317 2000fr multicolored   6.75   6.75
963 A317 2000fr multicolored   6.75   6.75

Swiss Railroad, 150th anniv. (#957, #961). Nos. 961-963 each contain one 50x60mm stamp.

Diana, Princess of Wales (1961-
97) — A318

Various portraits.
1500fr, Wearing red dress. No. 966, Wearing blue dress.

1997   Litho.   Perf. 13½
964 A318 250fr Sheet of 9,
           #a.-i.   8.00   8.00
964J A318 300fr Sheet of 9,
           #k.-s.   9.50   9.50

Souvenir Sheets
965 A318 1500fr multicolored   5.25   5.25
966 A318 2000fr multicolored   7.00   7.00

Nos. 965-966 contain one 42x60mm stamp.

Man in
Space
A319

No. 967: a, John Glenn, Mercury capsule. b, Cassini/Huygens satellite. c, Laika, first dog in space, Sputnik 2. d, Valentina Tereshkova, first woman in space, Vostok 6. e. Edward White, first American to walk in space, Gemini 4. f, Alexi Leonov, first Soviet to walk in space. g, Luna 9. h, Gemini capsule docked to Agena.
No. 968: a, Skylab space station. b, Pioneer 13, Venus 2. c, Giotto probe, Halley's Comet. d, Apollo-Soyuz mission. e, Mariner 10. f, Viking 1. g, Venera 11. h, Surveyor 1.
No. 969: a, Yuri Gagarin, first man in space, Sergei Korolev, RD107 rocket. No. 970, 2000fr, John F. Kennedy, Apollo 11, Neil Armstrong, first man to set foot on the moon.

1997   Litho.   Perf. 13½
967 A319 375fr Sheet of 8 +
          label   8.00   8.00
968 A319 450fr Sheet of 8 +
          label   9.00   9.00

Souvenir Sheets
969-970 A319 Set of 2   12.00 12.00

Nos. 969-970 each contain one 42x60mm stamp.

Pres. Ibrahim
Mainassara-Bare
A320

1997 Litho. & Embossed   Perf. 13½
971 A320 500fr gold & multi   1.75   1.75

Scouting, Intl., 90th Anniv. (in
1997) — A321

No. 972 — Scout and: a, Lion. b, Rhinoceros. c, Giraffe. d, Elephant.
No. 972E — Girl Scout: f, Building bird house. g, Examining flower with magnifying glass. h, Identifying flower from book. i, Playing with bird.
No. 973: a, Butterfly. b, Bird with berries in mouth. c, Bird. d, Brown & white butterfly.
No. 974: a, Holding up rock to light. b, Using magnifying glass. c, Looking at rock. d, On hands and knees.
No. 975 — Scout, mushroom, with background color of: a, Yellow. b, White. c, Pink. d, Green.
2000fr, Robert Baden-Powell, Scouts chasing butterflies, mushroom.

1998   Litho.
972 A321 350fr Sheet of 4,
           #a.-d.   4.75   4.75
972E A321 400fr Sheet of 4, #f.-
           i.   5.50   5.50
973 A321 450fr Sheet of 4,
           #a.-d.   6.50   6.50
974 A321 500fr Sheet of 4,
           #a.-d.   7.00   7.00

975 A321 600fr Sheet of 4,
　　　#a.-d. 　　　8.00 8.00
　　　Souvenir Sheet
975E A321 2000fr multicolored　7.00 7.00

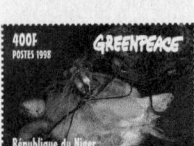

Greenpeace
A322

No. 976 — Turtles: a, Being caught in net. b, One swimming right. c, Mating. d, One swimming left.

1998
976 A322 400fr Block of 4, #a-
　　　d 　　　8.00 8.00
e. 　Souvenir sheet, #976 　16.00 16.00
Sheets overprinted "CHINA 99 World Philatelic Exhibition" are not authorized.

A323

No. 977 — Turtles: a, Pelomedusa subruta. b, Megacephalum shiui. c, Eretmochelus imbricata. d, Platycephala platycephala. e, Spinifera spinifera. f, Malayemys subtrijuga.
No. 978 — Raptors: a, Aquila uerreauxii. b, Asia otus. c, Bubo bubo. d, Surnia ulula. e, Asio flammeus. f, Falco biarnicus.
No. 979 — Orchids: a, Oeceoclades saundersiana. b, Paphiopedilum venustum. c, Maxillaria picta. d, Masdevallia triangularis. e, Zugopetalum. f, Encyllia nemoralis.
No. 980 — Butterflies: a, Danaus plexippus. b, Leto venus. c, Callioratis millari. d, Hippotion celerio. e, Euchloron megaera. f, Teracotona euprepia.
No. 981 — Mushrooms: a, Phaeolepotia aurea. b, Disciotis venosa. c, Gomphidius glutinosus. d, Amanita vaginata. e, Tremellodon gelatinosum. f, Voluariella voluacea.

1998, Sept. 29　Litho.　Perf. 13½
977 A323 250fr Sheet of 6, #a.-f.　5.50 5.50
978 A323 300fr Sheet of 6, #a.-f.　6.50 6.50
979 A323 350fr Sheet of 6, #a.-f.　7.25 7.25
980 A323 400fr Sheet of 6, #a.-f.　8.00 8.00
981 A323 450fr Sheet of 6, #a.-f.　9.75 8.75

Marine
Life
A324

No. 982: a, Tursiops truncatus. b, Phocoenoides dalli. c, Sousa teuszii. d, Stegostoma fasciatum. e, Delphinus delphis, balaenoptera musculus. f, Carcharodon carcharias. g, Argonauta argo, heterodontus portusjacksoni. h, Mitsukurina owstoni. j, Sphyrna mokarran. j, Homarus gammarus, prosthecereaus vittatus. k, Glossodoris valenciennesi, cephalopodes decapodes. l, Nemertien anople, elysia viridis.

1998, Sept. 29　Litho.　Perf. 13½
982 A324 175fr Sheet of 12, #a-l　8.00 8.00

World Wildlife
Fund — A325

Gazella dorcas: No. 983, Doe, fawn. No. 984, Adult lying down. No. 985, Two adults standing still. No. 986 Adult walking.

1998
983 A325 250fr multicolored　1.40　.85
984 A325 250fr multicolored　1.40　.85
985 A325 250fr multicolored　1.40　.85

---

986 A325 250fr multicolored　1.40　.85
a. 　Se-tenant block of 4 　8.00 8.00
b. 　Souvenir sheet #983-986　40.00 40.00
　　　Nos. 983-986 (4) 　5.60 3.40
Similar items without WWF emblem are not authorized.

Pope John Paul II — A326

Various portraits of pontiff thoughout his life.

1998, Sept. 29　Litho.　Perf. 13½
987 A326 250fr Sheet of 9, #a.-
　　　i. 　　　8.00 8.00
　　　Souvenir Sheet
988 A326 2000fr multicolored　7.25 7.25
No. 988 contains one 57x51mm stamp.

Frank Sinatra (1915-98) — A327

Various portraits.

1998
989 A327 300fr Sheet of 9, #a.-
　　　i. 　　　9.75 9.75

Explorers — A328

No. 990: a, Juan Sebastian del Cano (1476-1526), commander of vessel that completed circumnavigation of globe. b, Globe, sailing ships. c, Ferdinand Magellan (1480-1521).
No. 991 — Vasco da Gama (1469-1524): a. Portrait. b, Angels, explorers, soldiers, flag. c, Sailing ship, da Gama's tomb, Lisbon.
No. 992 — Aviator Roland Garros (1888-1918): a, Arriving at Utrecht. b, Flying across Mediterranean, 1913. c, Portrait.

1998, Sept. 29
990 A328 350fr Sheet of 3, #a.-c.　3.75 3.75
991 A328 400fr Sheet of 3, #a.-c.　4.50 4.50
992 A328 450fr Sheet of 3, #a.-c.　4.75 4.75
Nos. 990b, 991b, 992b are 60x51mm.

Jacques-Yves Cousteau (1910-97),
Environmentalist — A329

No. 993: a, Whales. b, Fish, diver, whales, sled dog team. c, Portrait of Cousteau surrounded by ship, explorers in polar region, whale, fish.
No. 994: a, Cousteau, children, bird. b, Ship, marine life. c, Cousteau in diving gear, fish.

1998, Sept. 29
993 A329 500fr Sheet of 3, #a.-c. 5.75 5.75
994 A329 600fr Sheet of 3, #a.-c. 6.50 6.50
Nos. 993b and 994b are 60x51mm.

1998 World Cup Soccer
Championships, France — A330

No. 995: a, Emmanuel Petit. b, Zinedine Zidane. c, Fabien Barthez. d, Lilian Thuram. e, Didier Deschamps. f, Youri Djorkaeff. g, Marcel Desailly, Christian Karembeu. h, Bixente Lizarazu. i, Frank Leboeuf, Stephane Guivarc'h.

1998
995 A330 250fr Sheet of 9, #a.-i.　8.50 8.50

A331

FIMA Niger '98 African
Fashion
Festival — A332

1998　　Litho.　　Perf. 13½x13
996 A331 175fr multi　　1.20　.75
997 A332 225fr multi　　1.50　.75

Flowers — A333

Designs: 10fr, Roses and anemone. 20fr, Asystasia vogeliana, horiz. 30fr, Agrumes, horiz. 40fr, Angraecum sesquipedale. 45fr, Dissotis rotundifolia. 50fr, Hibiscus rosa-sinensis. 100fr, Datura.

1998　　Litho.　　Perf. 13¼x13½
997A A333 10fr multi
997B A333 20fr multi　　　—　8.00
997C A333 30fr multi　　　—　8.00
997D A333 40fr multi
997E A333 45fr multi　　　—　8.00
998 　A333 50fr multi
999 　A333 100fr multi　24.00 8.00

A number of items inscribed "Republique du Niger" were not authorized by Niger postal authorities. These include:
Dated 1996: Overprinted 500fr souvenir sheet for 20th anniv. first commercial flight of the Concorde.
Dated 1998: Martin Luther King, Jr., 2000fr souvenir sheet;
Ferrari automobile, 2000fr stamp and souvenir sheet;
Trains, 650fr sheet of 4, 2500fr souvenir sheet, two 3000fr souvenir sheets;
Titanic, 650fr sheet of 4, four 650fr souvenir sheets, 2500fr souvenir sheet;
Paintings by Toulouse-Lautrec, Gauguin, Renoir, Matisse, Delacroix, Van Gogh, sheets of nine 250fr, 300fr, 375fr 400fr, 425fr, 500fr stamps, sheet of three 725fr Matisse stamps, 200fr, Delacroix souvenir sheet;
French and Italian performers, sheet of nine 675fr stamps;
Sailing vessels, sheets of four 525fr, 875fr stamps;
Events of the 20th Century, 3 sheets of nine 225fr stamps, 2 sheets of nine 375fr stamps, 3 sheets of nine 500fr stamps, fourteen 225fr souvenir sheets, three 2000fr souvenir sheets;
Space events of the 20th Century, two 2000fr souvenir sheets;
Papal visits, sheet of nine 500fr stamps, sheet of two 1500fr stamps;
Cats, sheetlet of 5 stamps, various denominations, 500fr souvenir sheet;
African Music, sheet of nine 225fr stamps;
Pinocchio, sheet of nine 200fr stamps;
Dated 1999: History of the Cinema (Marilyn Monroe), sheet of nine 275fr stamps, 2000fr souvenir sheet;
History of American Cinema (various actors), sheet of nine 400fr stamps;
John F. Kennedy, Jr., sheet of nine 500fr stamps;
Sheets of nine stamps of various denominations depicting Cats, Panda, Dinosaurs, Kennedy Space Center, Mushrooms, Butterflies, Eagles, Tiger Woods, Chess Pieces (2 different sheets);
Sheets of six stamps of various denominations depicting Butterflies, Cartoon Network Cartoon Characters.
Additional issues may be added to this list.

Wildlife — A334

Designs: No. 1000, 180fr, Tiger, Rotary emblem, vert. No. 1001, 250fr, Tigers, Lions emblem. No. 1002, 375fr, Tiger, Scouting, scouting jamboree emblems. 500fr, Owl, vert.
No. 1003, vert. — Rotary emblem and: a, Lions. b, Leopard. c, Red-headed cranes. d, Owl. e, Buzzards. f, Gazelles (long horns). g, Elands (twisted horns). h, Antelope (short horns).
No. 1004 — Lions emblem and: a, Lion, looking left. b, Lion, lioness. c, Lion reclining. d, Leopards. e, Leopard on rock. f, Lion, looking right. g, Lion in grass. h, Lion cub.
No. 1005 — Scouting and scouting jamboree emblems and: a, Leopard, mouth open. b, Leopard overlooking plains. c, Leopard looking right. d, Cat. e, Pair of leopards. f, Leopard and trees. g, Leopard reclining. h, Leopard standing on rock.
1000fr, Tiger in water, horiz. 2500fr, Leopards.

1998　　Litho.　　Perf. 13½
1000-1002 A334　Set of 3
1003 A334 180fr Sheet of 9, #a-
　　　h, 1000
1004 A334 250fr Sheet of 9, #a-
　　　h, 1001
1005 A334 375fr Sheet of 9, #a-
　　　h, 1002

Souvenir Sheets

1005I A334 500fr multi — —
1006 A334 1000fr mutli
1007 A334 2500fr multi

New Year 1998, Year of the Tiger, Nos. 1000-1002, 1006. Nos. 1006-1007 each contain one 46x40mm stamp.
No. 1005I contains one 40x46mm stamp. Italia '98 Intl. Philatelic Exhibition (No. 1005I).

Jerry Garcia A335

No. 1008: a, In brown shirt. b. In blue shirt, with flower. c. In yellow shirt. d, in green shirt. e, With fists clenched. f, In blue shirt. g, In black jacket. h, Holding glasses. i, In black shirt, with black guitar strap.

1998
1008 A335 350fr Sheet of 9,
   #a-i   10.00 10.00

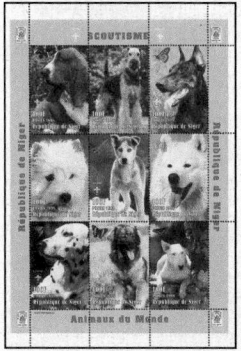

Dogs and Birds A336

No. 1009, 100fr — Scouting emblem and: a, Beagle, butterfly. b, Airedale terrier, Italia 98 emblem. c, Doberman pinscher, butterfly. d, Small white dog, Italia emblem. e, Husky pup, Concorde. f, White Eskimo dog, Italia emblem. g, Dalmatian, butterfly. h, Retriever, butterfly. i, Pit bull, butterfly.
No. 1010, 300fr — a-i, Scouting jamboree emblem and various penguins.
No. 1011, 500fr — a-i, Various parrots.

1999 Sheets of 9, #a-i
1009-1011 A336 Set of 3   15.00 15.00

Intl. Year of the Ocean (No. 1010). Dated 1998.

Sailing A337

No. 1012: a, Sailboat, lighthouse. b, Man, woman in sailboat. c, Sailor, large waves. d, Yachts racing.

1999
1012 A337 750fr Sheet of 4, #a-d

Dated 1998. Sheets of four 525fr and 875fr stamps were not authorized by Niger Post.

Trains A338

Various trains. Sheets of 4, each stamp denominated: 225fr, 325fr, 375fr, 500fr.

1999 Sheets of 4, #a-d
1013-1017 A338 Set of 5

Dated 1998. PhilexFrance 99 (#1017). A sheet of four similar stamps with 650fr denominations, 750fr souvenir sheet, 2500fr souvenir sheet, and two 3000fr souvenir sheets were not authorized by Niger Post.

Astronauts — A339

No. 1018, 450fr: a, James Lovell. b, Alan Shepard. c, David Scott. d, John Young.
No. 1019, 500fr: a, Neil Armstrong. b, Michael Collins. c, Edwin Aldrin. d, Alan Bean.
No. 1020, 600fr: a, Walter Schirra. b, Robert Crippen. c, Thomas Stafford. d, Owen Garriott.
No. 1021, 750fr: a, John Glenn. b, Gordon Cooper. c, Scott Carpenter. d, Virgil Grissom.
2000fr, Collins, Armstrong and Aldrin.

1999 Sheets of 4, #a-d
1018-1021 A339 Set of 4   35.00 35.00
Souvenir Sheet
1022 A339 2000fr multi   8.00 8.00

No. 1022 contains one 56x51mm stamp.

Chess A340

No. 1023, 350fr: a, Tigran Petrosian. b, Robert Fischer. c, Boris Spassky. d, Viktor Korchnoi. e, Garry Kasparov. f, Anatoly Karpov.
No. 1024, 400fr: a, Richard Reti. b, Alexander Alekhine. c, Max Euwe. d, Paul Keres. e, Mikhail Botvinnik. f, Mikhail Tal.
No. 1025, 500fr: a, Philidor. b, Adolf Anderssen. c, Joseph Henry Blackburne. d, Emanuel Lasker. e, Frank Marshall. f, José Raul Capablanca.
2000fr, head of Kasparov, Leo Tolstoy playing chess.

1999 Sheets of 6, #a-f
1023-1025 A340 Set of 3   30.00 30.00
Souvenir Sheet
1026 A340 2000fr multi   9.00 9.00

Nos. 1023-1025 each contain six 51x36mm stamps. Dated 1998.

Baseball Players A341

No. 1027, 200fr, Various views of Lou Gehrig.
No. 1028, 250fr, Various views of Ty Cobb.
Nos. 1029, 1031, Gehrig, diff. Nos. 1030, 1032, Cobb, diff.

1999 Sheets of 9, #a-i
1027-1028 A341 Set of 2   19.00 19.00
Souvenir Sheets
1029-1030 A341 1500fr Set of
   2   15.00 15.00
1031-1032 A341 2000fr Set of
   2   15.00 15.00

Animals and Mushrooms — A342

No. 1033, 300fr: a, Snake. b, Tortoise. c, Scorpion. d, Lizard.
No. 1034, 400fr: a, Vulture. b, Gray cuckoo. c, Jackdaw. d, Turtle dove.
No. 1035, 600fr: a, Ham the chimpanzee. b, Laika the dog. c, Cat. d, Spider.
No. 1036, 750fr: a, Nymphalidae palla. b, Nymphalidae perle. c, Nymphalidae diademe-bleu. d, Nymphalidae pirate.
No. 1037, 1000fr: a, Cliotcybe rouge brique. b, Lactaire a odeur de camphre. c, Strophaire vert-de-gris. d, Lepiote a ecailles aigues.
Illustration reduced.

1999, Nov. 23 Sheets of 4, #a-d
1033-1037 A342 Set of 5   50.00 50.00

Council of the Entente, 40th Anniv. — A343

1999, May 29 Litho. Perf. 13x13¼
1039 A343 175fr multi   1.75 1.75

An additional stamp was issued in this set. The editors would like to examine any examples.

First French Stamps, 150th Anniv. — A344

Litho. With Hologram Applied
1999, Oct. 7 Perf. 13
1040 A344 200fr France Type A1 1.50 1.50

Fire Fighting Equipment — A345

No. 1041 — Automobiles: a, Bugatti Type 37. b, Chevrolet Corvette. c, Lotus Elise. d, Ferrari 550 Maranello.
No. 1042: a, Canadair airplane. b, Hook and ladder truck. c, Water pumper of middle ages. d, 1914 pumper.
No. 1043 — Trains: a, Union Pacific, 1869. b, Prussian State Railway P8, 1905. c, Pennsylvania Railroad T1, 1942. d, German Railways Series 015, 1962.
No. 1044 — Airplanes: a, De Havilland Comet. b, Airbus A340. c, Boeing 747. d, Concorde.
No. 1045 — Trains: a, Diesel-electric locomotive. b, Bullet train, Japan. c, Thalys. d, X2000, China.
No. 1046 — Spacecraft: a, Atlas rocket, Mercury capsule. b, RD-107 Soyuz. c, Saturn V rocket, Apollo capsule. d, Space shuttle.

1999, Nov. 23 Litho. Perf. 13½
1041 A345 450fr Sheet of 4,
   #a-d   10.00 10.00
1042 A345 500fr Sheet of 4,
   #a-d   11.50 11.50
1043 A345 600fr Sheet of 4,
   #a-d   13.00 13.00

1044 A345 650fr Sheet of 4,
   #a-d   14.50 14.50
1045 A345 750fr Sheet of 4,
   #a-d   16.00 16.00
1046 A345 800fr Sheet of 4,
   #a-d   12.50 12.50

Intl. Anti-Desertification Day — A346

Designs: 150fr, Trenches. 200fr, Men in field. 225fr, Trees in desert.

2000, June 17 Litho. Perf. 13½
1047-1049 A346 Set of 3   — —

Bird Type of 1997

2000, June 20 Perf. 13¼
1050 A309 150fr Psittacula
   krameri   1.25 1.25

2000 Summer Olympics, Sydney — A347

No. 1051: a, 50fr, Men's singles, badminton. b, 50fr, Men's doubles, badminton. c, 50fr, Softball. d, 50fr, Men's floor exercises. e, 50fr, Women's singles, badminton. f, 50fr, Women's doubles, badminton. g, 50fr, Baseball. h, 50fr, Men's long horse vault. i, 50fr, Women's cycling. j, 50fr, Women's pursuit cycling. k, 50fr, Women's road race cycling. l, 50fr, Women's shot put. m, 900fr, Men's singles, table tennis. n, 900fr, Men's doubles, table tennis. o, 900fr, Women's singles, table tennis. p, 900fr, Women's doubles, table tennis.
No. 1052: a, 100fr, Women's freestyle swimming. b, 100fr, Women's butterfly. c, 100fr, Men's prone rifle. d, 100fr, Women's sport pistol. e, 100fr, Women's 3-meter diving. f, 100fr, Women's 10-meter diving. g, 100fr, Women's three-position rifle. h, 100fr, Women's double trap. i, 100fr, Women's beach volleyball. j, 100fr, Women's volleyball. k, 100fr, Women's handball. l, 100fr, Men's sailboarding. m, 700fr, Women's kayak singles. n, 700fr, Women's kayak pairs. o, 700fr, Women's kayak fours. p, 700fr, Women's eight-oared shell with coxswain.

2000, July 27 Litho.
Sheets of 16, #a-p
1051-1052 A347 Set of 2   70.00 70.00

Modern and Prehistoric Fauna — A348

No. 1053, 200fr — Butterflies: a, Epiphora bauhiniae. b, Cymothoe sangaris. c, Cyrestris camillus. d, Precis clelia. e, Precis octavia amestris. f, Nudaurelia zambesina.
No. 1054, 200fr — Insects: a, Stenocara eburnea. b, Chalcocoris anchorago. c, Scarabaeus aeratus. d, Pseudocreobotra wahlbergi. e, Schistocera gregaria. f, Anopheles gambiae.
No. 1055, 225fr — Prehistoric winged animals: a, Sordes pilosus. b, Quetzalcoatlus. c, Dimorphodon. d, Podopteryx. e, Archaeopteryx. f, Pteranodon.
No. 1056, 225fr — Birds: a, Bec-en-sabot. b, Euplecte ingnicolore. c, Spreo royal. d, Calao trompette. e, Pseudocanari parasite. f, Gonolek rouge et noir.
No. 1057, 400fr — Cats: a, Egyptian mau. b, Domestic. c, African wildcat. d, Chat dore. e, Chat a pieds noirs. f, Chat des sables.
No. 1058, 400fr — Dogs: a, Chien du pharaon. b, Saluki. c, Rhodesian ridgeback. d, Beagle. e, Spitz. f, Basenji.
No. 1059, 450fr — Modern and prehistoric African animals: a, Proconsul africanus. b, Chimpanzee. c, Metamynodon planifrons. d,

Black rhinoceros. e, Hyrachius eximus. f, White rhinoceros.

No. 1060, 450fr — Modern and prehistoric African animals: a, Canis familiaris. b, Black and white basenji. c, Hipparion mediterraneum. d, Burchell zebra. e, Moeritherium. f, African elephant.

No. 1061, 475fr — Modern and prehistoric reptiles: a, Palaeobatrachus. b, African frog. c, Metoposaurus. d, Salamander. e, Tylosaurus. f, Varan du Nil.

No. 1062, 475fr — Modern and prehistoric African animals: a, Basilosaurus. b, Solalie du Cameroun. c, Mesosaurus. d, Cordylus giganteus. e, Sarcosuchus. f, Nile crocodile.

2000, Oct. 27   *Perf. 13¼*
Sheets of 6, #a-f
1053-1062 A348   Set of 10   120.00 120.00

2002 World Cup Soccer Championships, Japan and Korea — A349

No. 1063, 400fr: a, Castro. b, Orsi. c, Piola. d, Ghiggia.
No. 1064, 400fr: a, Morlock. b, Pele. c, Amarildo. d, Hurst.
No. 1065, 400fr: a, Jairzinho. b, Müller. c, Kempes. d, Rossi.
No. 1066, 400fr: a, Burruchaga. b, Brehme. c, Dunga. d, Petit.

2001, Jan. 16   **Sheets of 4, #a-d**
1063-1066 A349   Set of 4   24.00 24.00
Dated 2000.

Universal Postal Union, 125th Anniv. (in 1999) A350

No. 1067, 150fr — Ships: a, Transat, Citta di Catania. b, Great Eastern, Julius Caesar. c, Caledonia, Mercury. d, Braganza, Westland.
No. 1068, 225fr — Vehicles: a, Horse-drawn omnibus, postal bus. b, 1899 automobile, rural omnibus. c, 1904 van, postal automobile and bicycle. d, 1906 automobile, Swiss postal bus.
No. 1069, 450fr — Trains: a, 25NC Modder Kimberley locomotive, CDJR diesel. b, Pacific Karoo, Budd diesel. c, 141 Maghreb locomotive, EAR Diesel-electric locomotive. d, 230 Series 6 C.G.A., Postal TGV train.
No. 1070, 500fr — Airplanes: a, Late-28, Super Constellation. b, Douglas DC-4, Nord Atlas. c, Boeing 707, Concorde. d, Boeing 747, Airbus A3XX.
No. 1071, 550fr — Spacecraft: a, 1934 postal rocket, Asian telecommunications satellite. b, Space capsules. c, Apollo 15, Astra 1 H telecommunications satellite. d, Voyager, Space Station and shuttle.
No. 1072, 700fr — Trains: a, 230 locomotive, Senegal, 141 locomotive, Tanganyika. b, 141 locomotive, Niger. 242 locomotive, South Africa. c, 130+031 locomotive, Ivory Coast, Garrat 242+242. d, 040 locomotive, Cameroun, 14R locomotive.

2001, Jan. 16   *Perf. 13¼*
Sheets of 4, #a-d
1067-1072 A350   Set of 6   47.50 47.50
Dated 2000.

Zeppelins and Satellites — A351

No. 1073, 430fr — Zeppelins: a, LZ-1. b, LZ-10 Schwaben. c, LZ II Viktoria Luise. d, L-30. e, L-11. f, L-59.
No. 1074, 460fr — Zeppelins: a, LZ-120 Bodensee. b, L-72 Dixmude. c, LZ-127 Graf Zeppelin. d, LZ-129 Hindenburg. e, LZ-130. f, D-LZFN.
No. 1075, 750fr, vert. — Satellites: a, Meteosat. b, GOMS. c, GMS. d, Insat 1A. e, GOES. f, FY-2.

2001, June 20   Litho.
Sheets of 6, #a-f
1073-1075 A351   Set of 3   40.00 40.00

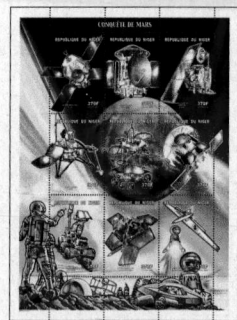

Space Exploration — A352

No. 1076, 370fr — Conquest of Mars: a, Mariner 9. b, Mars 3. c, Mars Climate Orbiter. d, Mars Lander. e, Mars Rover. f, Netlander. g, Robot on Mars. h, Beagle 2. i, Ames Research plane for Mars.
No. 1077, 390fr — Orbital and Lunar Exploration: a, Yuri Gagarin, Vostok capsule. b, John Glenn, Mercury capsule. c, Space shuttle. d, Alan Shepard, Apollo 14. e, Neil Armstrong, Apollo 11. f, Charles Conrad, Apollo 12. g, Edward White, Gemini 4. h, James Irwin, Apollo 15. i, Lunar base and shuttle.
No. 1078, 490fr — Planetary and Interstellar Exploration: a, Pioneer 10. b, Mariner 10. c, Venera 13. d, Pioneer 13, Venus 2. e, Probe for detecting "Big Bang." f, Interstellar spacecraft. g, Inhabited space station. h, Giotto probe, Astronaut on comet. i, Galileo probe.

2001, June 20   Litho.
Sheets of 9, #a-i
1076-1078 A352   Set of 3   45.00 45.00

African History A353

No. 1079, 390fr: a, Gahna Empire, 10th cent. b, Kankou Moussa, Emperor of Mali, 1324. c, Sankore, University of Tombouctou, 15th cent. d, Sonni Ali Ber, Songhai Emperor. e, Bantu migrations, 15th and 16th cents. f, Slave trade, 1513.
No. 1080, 490fr: a, Ramses II, 1301-1235 B.C., Battle of Qadesh. b, Mummification. c, Religion. d, Instruction. e, Justice. f, Artisans.
No. 1081, 530fr: a, Djoser, Third Dynasty, 2650 B.C. b, Rahotep and wife, Fourth Dynasty, 2570 B.C. c, Cheops and Pyramid, Fourth Dynasty, 2600 B.C. d, Chephren, Fourth Dynasty, 2500 B.C. e, Akhenaton and Nefertiti, 18th Dynasty, 1372-1354 B.C. f, Tutankhamen, 18th Dynasty, 1354-1346 B.C.

2001, July 24   Litho.
Sheets of 6, #a-f
1079-1081 A353   Set of 3   35.00 35.00

Air Chiriet A354

2001   *Perf. 13x13¼*
1082 A354 150fr multi   1.00 1.00

Intl. Volunteers Year — A355

2001
1083 A355 150fr multi   1.00 1.00

Birds, Butterflies, Meteorites, and Mushrooms — A356

No. 1084, 530fr — Birds: a, Falco peregrinus. b, Falco biarmicus. c, Vultur gryphus.
No. 1085, 575fr — Butterflies: a, Junonia orithya. b, Salamis parhassus. c, Amauris echeria.
No. 1086, 750fr — Meteorites: a, P. Pallas, 1772. b, Iron meteorite. c, Bouvante rock.
No. 1087, 825fr — Mushrooms: a, Otidea onotica. b, Lentinus sajor-caju. c, Pleurotus luteoalbus.

2002, Apr. 24   *Perf. 13¼*
Sheets of 3, #a-c
1084-1087 A356   Set of 4   26.00 26.00
Souvenir sheets of 1 of each of the individual stamps exist.

Cow's Head — A357

2002, Sept. 17   Litho.   *Perf. 13¼*
1088 A357 50fr multi   .50 .50

Toubou Spears — A358

2002, Sept. 17   Litho.   *Perf. 13x12½*
1089 A358 100fr multi   7.50 7.50

Birds A359

2002, Sept. 17   Litho.   *Perf. 13*
1090 A359 225fr multi   1.10 1.10

Hippopotamus in Captivity — A360

Boudouma Cow — A361   Boudouma Calf — A362

2003, Dec. 3   Litho.   *Perf. 13x13¼*
1091 A360 100fr multi   .60 .60
     Perf. 13
1092 A361 150fr multi   .80 .80
     Perf. 13¼
1093 A362 225fr multi   1.10 1.10
   Nos. 1091-1093 (3)   2.50 2.50
Values for No. 1092 are for stamps with surrounding selvage.

Pottery A363

Camel and Rider — A364

2004   *Perf. 13x13¼*
1094 A363 150fr multi   10.00 10.00
     Perf. 13
1095 A364 1000fr multi   5.00 5.00
Values for No. 1095 are for stamps with surrounding selvage.

In Universal Postal Union Circular 388, issued Nov. 28, 2005, Niger postal officials declared illegal additional items bearing the inscription "Republique du Niger." As this circular contains a somewhat unintelligible list of items which lacks specifics as to denominations found on the illegal items or the sizes of sheets, some of the items may be duplicative of items mentioned in the note on illegal stamps following No. 999. Also, because of the lack of clarity of the list, some catalogued items may now be items cited as "illegal" in Circular 388. The text of this circular can be seen on the UPU's WNS website.

Emblem of 2005 Francophone Games — A365

2005, May 12   Litho.   *Perf. 13x13¼*
1096 A365 150fr multi   4.00 4.00

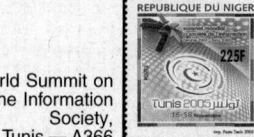

World Summit on the Information Society, Tunis — A366

2005, May 26   *Perf. 13¼*
1097 A366 225fr multi   7.50 7.50

Mascot of 2005 Francophone Games
A367

2005, Aug. 22   *Perf. 13*
1098 A367 225fr multi   4.00 4.00

Léopold Sédar Senghor (1906-2001), First President of Senegal — A368

2006, Apr. 6   Litho.   *Perf. 12¾*
1099 A368 175fr multi   2.50 2.50

Pres. Tandja Mamadou — A369

2006, July 14
1100 A369 750fr multi   3.50 3.50

Boubou Hama (1906-82), Writer — A370

Background colors: 150fr, Green. 175fr, Orange brown. 325fr, Light blue.

2006, Sept. 23   Litho.   *Perf. 13x12¾*
1101-1103 A370   Set of 3   10.00 10.00

Messenger From Madaoua — A371

2006, Nov. 6   Litho.   *Perf. 13x12¾*
1104 A371 25fr multi   —

Dated 2004.

24th UPU Congress, Geneva, Switzerland A373

2007, Nov. 9   Litho.   *Perf. 13*
1106 A373 500fr multi   3.50 3.50

Values are for stamps with surrounding selvage. UPU Congress was moved to Geneva after political violence in Nairobi, Kenya.

Wildlife — A374

Designs: 200fr, Giraffes. 400fr, Addax. 600fr, Ostriches.

2007, Nov. 9   *Perf. 12¾*
1107-1109 A374   Set of 3   5.50 5.50

Grain Grinding — A375

Bororo Dance — A376

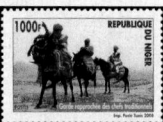

Chief's Guard — A377

2008, Aug. 8   *Perf. 12¾*
1110 A375 100fr multi   .45 .45
1111 A376 350fr multi   1.60 1.60
1112 A377 1000fr multi   4.75 4.75
    Nos. 1110-1112 (3)   6.80 6.80

Women At Well — A378

Hunters A379

2009, Nov. 20   *Perf. 13*
1113 A378 300fr multi   1.40 1.40
1114 A379 450fr multi   2.10 2.10

Baobab Tree — A380

Téra-téra Blanket — A381

Women's Hairstyles — A382

2010, June 4   *Perf. 12¾*
1115 A380 500fr multi   1.90 1.90
    Perf. 13
1116 A381 700fr multi   2.60 2.60
    Perf. 13¼
1117 A382 1500fr multi   5.50 5.50
    Nos. 1115-1117 (3)   10.00 10.00

Values for No. 1116 are for stamps with surrounding selvage.

Independence, 50th Anniv. — A383

2010, June 30   *Perf. 13*
1118 A383 1000fr multi   4.00 4.00

Hut of Sultan Usman Dan Fodio (1754-1817) A384

Lété Island — A385

2011, May 30   *Perf. 12¾*
1119 A384 175fr multi   .80 .80
1120 A385 320fr multi   1.40 1.40

Violet de Galmi Onions — A386

Djado Ruins — A387

Gen. Salou Djibo, Head of State of Niger — A388

2011, Oct. 19
1121 A386 500fr multi   2.10 2.10
1122 A387 735fr multi   3.25 3.25
1123 A388 1000fr multi   4.25 4.25
    Nos. 1121-1123 (3)   9.60 9.60

Worldwide Fund for Nature (WWF) — A389

Wildlife A390

No. 1124 — Giraffa camelopardalis peralta with: a, WWF emblem at LR, animal name at UR. b, WWF emblem at UL, animal name at bottom. c, WWF emblem at LR, animal name at UL. d, WWF emblem at UR, animal name at bottom.

No. 1125, 750fr — Hippopotamus amphibius: a, Denomination at UR, head down, facing right. b, Denomination at UL. c, Denomination at UR, head up at right. d, Denomination at UR, head up at left.

No. 1126, 750fr — Syncerus caffer: a, Denomination at UR, animal name at UL. b, Denomination at UL, animal name at top, animal facing right. c, Denomination at UL, animal name at top, animal facing left. d, Denomination at UR, animal name at LL.

No. 1127, 750fr — Foxes: a, Vulpes rueppellii, animal name at UL. b, Vulpes zerda, animal name at UL, end of name even with top of denomination. c, Vulpes zerda, animal name at left, end of name lower than denomination. d, Vulpes rueppellii, animal name at LR.

No. 1128, 750fr — Hyenas: a, Crocuta crocuta, animal name at LL. b, Hyaena hyaena, animal name at UR. c, Hyaena hyaena, animal name at UL. d, Crocuta crocuta, animal name at top.

No. 1129, 750fr — Antelopes: a, Oryx dammah. b, Ammotragus lervia. c, Nanger dama. d, Tragelaphus eurycerus.

No. 1130, 750fr — Primates: a, Galago senegalensis. b, Chlorocebus tantalus. c, Erythrocebus patas. d, Papio anubis.

No. 1131, 750fr — Bats: a, Eidolon helvum. b, Micropteropus pusillus. c, Lavia frons. d, Nycteris thebaica.

No. 1132, 750fr — Lions and leopards: a, Male Panthera leo. b, One Panthera pardus. c, Two Panthera pardus. d, Two female Panthera leo.

No. 1133, 750fr — Wildcats: a, Felis silvestris lybica. b, Felis margarita. c, Leptailurus serval. d, Felis margarita airensis.

No. 1134, 750fr — Lycaon pictus: a, Denomination at UR, animal name at UL. b, Denomination at UL, animal name at UR. c, Denomination at UL, animal name at top center. d, Denomination at UR, animal name at top center.

No. 1135, 750fr — Loxodonta africana: a, Denomination at right center, animal name at UL. b, Denomination at UR, animal name at UL. c, Denomination at UL, animal name at left. d, Denomination at UR, animal name at right center.

No. 1136, 750fr — Trichechus senegalensis: a, Animal name at UL, left flipper above "b" in "République." b, Animal name at UL, right flipper above "d" in "du." c, Animal name at UL, right fin above space between "République" and "du." d, Animal name at LL.

No. 1137, 750fr — Owls: a, Scotopelia peli. b, Glaucidium perlatum. c, Otus senegalensis. d, Ptilopsis leucotis.

No. 1138, 750fr — Doves: a, Colombar waalia. b, Oena capensis. c, Columba guinea. d, Columba arquatrix.

No. 1139, 750fr — Parrots: a, Poicephalus robustus. b, Psittacula krameri, animal name below denomination. c, Psittacula krameri, animal name to left of denomination. d, Psittacus erithacus, Psittacula krameri.

No. 1140, 750fr — Birds: a, Chalcomitra senegalensis. b, Hedydipna platurus. c, Cinnyris pulchella. d, Cinnyris cupreus.

No. 1141, 750fr — Water birds: a, Ardea cinerea in flight. b, Ardeola rufiventris. c, Ardea cinerea with fish. d, Ardea goliath.

No. 1142, 750fr — Birds of prey: a, Circaetus cinereus. b, Hieraaetus pennatus. c, Aquila rapax. d, Aquila pomarina.

No. 1143, 750fr — Butterflies: a, Pinacopteryx eriphia. b, Colotis antevippe with orange wing tips. c, Colotis antevippe with yellow and black coloratiion. d, Zizeeria knysna.

No. 1144, 750fr — Butterflies: a, Catopsilia florella. b, Coeliades forestan. c, Acraea neobule. d, Hypolimnas misippus.

No. 1145, 750fr — Fish: a, Hemichromis fasciatus. b, Fundulosoma thierryi. c, Aphyosemion bitaeniatum. d, Arnoldichthys spilopterus.

No. 1146, 750fr — Turtles: a, Psammobates geometricus. b, Pelomedusa subrufa. c, Pelusios niger. d, Astrochelys yniphora.

No. 1147, 750fr — Crocodiles: a, Crocodylus niloticus, animal name at UL. b, Crocodylus cataphractus, denomination at UL. c, Crocodylus cataphractus, denomination at UR. d, Crocodylus niloticus, animal name at LL.

No. 1148, 750fr — Snakes: a, Dasypeltis sahelensis. b, Dromophis praeornatus. c, Dromophis lineatus. d, Dasypeltis gansi.

No. 1149, 2500fr, Giraffa camelopardalis peralta, diff. No. 1150, 2500fr, Hippopotamus amphibius, diff. No. 1151, 2500fr, Syncerus caffer, diff. No. 1152, 2500fr, Vulpes rueppellii, diff. No. 1153, 2500fr, Crocuta crocuta, diff. No. 1154, 2500fr, Ammotragus lervia, diff. No. 1155, 2500fr, Papio anubis, diff. No. 1156, 2500fr, Micropteropus pusillus, diff. No. 1157, 2500fr, Panthera pardus, diff. No. 1158, 2500fr, Caracal caracal. No. 1159, 2500fr, Lycaon pictus, diff. No. 1160, 2500fr, Loxodonta africana, diff. No. 1161, 2500fr, Trichechus senegalensis, diff. No. 1162, 2500fr, Bubo ascalaphus. No. 1163, 2500fr, Colombar waalia, diff. No. 1164, 2500fr, Psittacus erithacus, diff. No. 1165, 2500fr, Cinnyris coccinigastrus. No. 1166, 2500fr, Ardea cinerea, diff. No. 1167, 2500fr, Falco naumanii. No. 1168, 2500fr, Spialia spio. No. 1169, 2500fr, Danaus chysippus. No. 1170, 2500fr, Oreochromis aureus. No. 1171, 2500fr, Pelusios sinuatus. No. 1172, 2500fr, Crocodylus niloticus, diff. No. 1173, 2500fr, Atracaspis microlepidota.

2013, Mar. 1   **Perf. 13¼x13**
1124   Strip of 4   12.00   12.00
   a.-d.   A389 750fr Any single   3.00   3.00
   e.   Souvenir sheet of 8, 2
     each #1124a-1124d, + 2
     labels   24.00   24.00

Sheets of 4, #a-d
Perf. 13¼
1125-1148 A390   Set of 24   285.00 285.00
Souvenir Sheets
1149-1173 A390   Set of 25   250.00 250.00

Pres. Issoufou
Mahamadou
A391

2013, Mar. 8   **Perf. 13¼x13**
1174 A391 500fr multi   2.00 2.00

A392

No. 1175, 500fr — Mahatma Gandhi (1869-1948), Indian independence leader: a, On Russia #3639, denomination at LR. b, On cover of *Time* magazine, denomination at LL. c, Denomination at UR. d, With hands together, denomination at UL.
No. 1176, 500fr — Yang Liwei, Chinese astronaut, and Shenzhou 5 with: a, Denomination at LR. b, Denomination at LL. c, Denomination at UR. d, Denomination at UL.
No. 1177, 675fr — Pope Benedict XVI with: a, Denomination at LR. b, Denomination at LL. c, Denomination at UR. d, Denomination at UL.
No. 1178, 675fr — Garry Kasparov, chess champion, and chess pieces with: a, Denomination at LR. b, Denomination at LL. c, Denomination at UR. d, Denomination at UL.
No. 1179, 675fr — Cat breeds: a, Cymric. b, Maine coon cat. c, Persian. d, Oriental.
No. 1180, 675fr — Small dog breeds: a, Chihuahua. b, Spitz. c, Russian toy terrier. d, Yorkshire terrier.
No. 1181, 750fr — Paintings by Albrecht Dürer (1471-1528): a, Portrait of Barbara Dürer, denomination at LR. b, Nativity, denomination at LL. c, Young Hare, denomination at UR. d, Feast of the Rosary, denomination at UL.
No. 1182, 750fr — Paintings by Paul Signac (1863-1935): a, Calvados, denomination at LR. b, Road to Gennevilliers, denomination at LL. c, The Gas Tanks at Clichy, denomination at UR. d, The Railroad at Bois Colombes, denomination at UL.
No. 1183, 750fr — Paintings by Joan Miró (1893-1983): a, Carneval d'Arlequin, denomination at LR. b, Catalan Landscape (The Hunter), denomination at LL. c, Circus, denomination at UR. d, The Poetess, denomination at UL.
No. 1184, 750fr — Bobby Fischer (1943-2008), chess champion: a, On Iceland #1203, denomination at LR. b, On cover of *Life* magazine, denomination at LL. c, With chess pieces, denomination at UR. d, With chess pieces, denomination at UL.
No. 1185, 750fr — Audrey Hepburn (1929-93), actress: a, Wearing red dress. b, With Peter O'Toole. c, With Cary Grant. d, With Gregory Peck.
No. 1186, 750fr — Ancient Egyptian monuments: a, Sculpted head of Amenhotep III. Temple of Horus. b, Bust of Nefertiti. c, Sphinx and Pyramids. d, Pyramids.
No. 1187, 750fr — Lighthouses: a, Biloxi Lighthouse, U.S. b, Rotesand Lighthouse, Germany. c, Execution Rocks Lighthouse, U.S. d, Coney Island Lighthouse, U.S.
No. 1188, 750fr — Cessation of Concorde flights, 10th anniv.: a, Concorde, Buckingham Palace, Queen Elizabeth II, Prince Philip. b, Concorde, Heathrow Airport, Brian Trubshaw, pilot. c, Concorde, Tower Bridge, British flag. d, Concorde, Arc de Triomphe, French flag.
No. 1189, 750fr — Space Shuttle Columbia disaster, 10th anniv.: a, Explosion. b, Columbia, map of U.S.. c, Memorial to Columbia astronauts. d, Columbia on launch pad.

No. 1190, 750fr — Tour de France bicycle race, cent.: a, Lucien Petit-Breton. b, Philippe Thys. c, Greg LeMond. d, Cadel Evans.
No. 1191, 750fr — 2013 African Cup of Nations soccer tournament: a, Two players, denomination at LR. b, One player, denomination at LL. c, One player, denomination at UR. d, Two players, denomination at UL.
No. 1192, 750fr — 2014 Winter Olympics, Sochi: a, Luge. b, Figure skating. c, Ice hockey. d, Speed skating.
No. 1193, 750fr — Dinosaurs: a, Jobaria tiguidensis. b, Afrovenator abakensis. c, Spinophorosaurus nigerensis. d, Suchomimus tenerensis.
No. 1194, 825fr — Paintings by Vincent van Gogh (1853-90): a, Portrait of Postman Joseph Roulin, denomination at LR. b, Self-portrait, Agostina Segatori Sitting in the Cafe du Tambourin, denomination at LL. c, Self-portrait, Olive Trees, denomination at UR. d, The Drinkers, denomination at UL.
No. 1195, 825fr — Hamadou Djibo Issaka, Nigerien rower at 2012 Summer Olympics: a, Denomination at LR. b, Denomination at LL. c, Denomination at UR. d, Denomination at UL.
No. 1196, 825fr — Scouting: a, Scouts building bridge, denomination at LR. b, Scout at campfire, denomination at LL. c, Map, Scout with pocket watch. d, Scouts erecting tents, denomination at UL.
No. 1197, 825fr — Rotary International Flood Aid to Niger: a, Denomination at LR. b, Denomination at LL. c, Denomination at UR. d, Denomination at UL.
No. 1198, 825fr — Scenes from the Djado Plateau: a, Denomination at LR. b, Denomination at LL. c, Denomination at UR. d, Denomination at UL.
No. 1199, 825fr — Minerals of Niger: a, Diamond, denomination at LR. b, Gold, denomination at LL. c, Tin, denomination at UR. d, Silver, denomination at UL.
No. 1200, 2000fr, Gandhi, diff. No. 1201, 2000fr, Yang Liwei and Shenzhou 5, diff. No. 1202, 2000fr, Pope Benedict XVI, diff. No. 1203, 2000fr, Kasparov, diff. No. 1204, 2000fr, Cymric cat, diff. No. 1205, 2000fr, Papillon. No. 1206, 2500fr, Adoration of the Magi, by Dürer. No. 1207, 2500fr, Evening Calm, Concarneau, by Signac. No. 1208, 2500fr, Women and Birds at Sunrise, by Miró. No. 1209, 2500fr, Fischer, diff. No. 1210, 2500fr, Hepburn and husband, Mel Ferrer. No. 1211, 2500fr, Bust of Nefertiti, diff. No. 1212, 2500fr, Mohegan Lighthouse, U.S. No. 1213, 2500fr, Concorde and London. No. 1214, 2500fr, Crew of Space Shuttle Columbia flight STS-107. No. 1215, 2500fr, Bradley Wiggins, cyclist. No. 1216, 2500fr, Two soccer players, diff. No. 1217, 2500fr, Freestyle skiing. No. 1218, 2500fr, Kryptops palaios. No. 1219, 3000fr, Pietà, by van Gogh. No. 1220, 3000fr, Issaka, diff. No. 1221, 3000fr, Scouts and tent. No. 1222, 3000fr, Map of Niger, Rotary International emblem, child and Gaston Kaba, Niamey Rotary president. No. 1223, 3000fr, Djado Plateau rock painting. No. 1224, 3000fr, Salt, map of Niger.

2013, Apr. 15   **Perf. 13¼**
Sheets of 4, #a-d
1175-1199 A392   Set of 25   290.00 290.00
Souvenir Sheets
1200-1224 A392   Set of 25   250.00 250.00

A393

No. 1225, 750fr — Yuri Gagarin (1934-68), first man in space: a, Blue panel, Gagarin without cap at left. b, Red panel, Gagarin wearing space helmet at left. c, Red panel, Gagarin wearing military cap at left. d, Blue panel, Gagarin wearing military cap.
No. 1226, 750fr — Space tourism: a, International Space Station, XCOR Lynx Mark II. b, WhiteKnightTwo, SpaceShipOne. c, SpaceShipTwo. d, International Space Station, Astrium Suborbital Space Plane.
No. 1227, 750fr — Steam trains: a, South African Class 26. b, LNER Peppercorn Class A1 60163 Tornado. c, LB&SCR Class B4. d, Reading Blue Mountain & Northern Railway 425.
No. 1228, 750fr — High-speed trains: a, Acela Express, New York City skyline. b, Chinese CRH380A UEM, Yongdinghe Bridge, Beijing. c, Maglev train, Shanghai. d, Alfa train, Lisbon, Portugal skyline.
No. 1229, 750fr — Ships and lighthouses: a, Barque Europa, 2007. b, Mahatao Lighthouse, Philippines. c, Amerigo Vespucci, 1976. d, Isle of May Lighthouse, Scotland.
No. 1230, 750fr — French airplanes: a, Concorde. b, Dassault Rafale. c, Breguet 14. d, Dassault Mirage F1.

No. 1231, 750fr — Fire trucks: a, SACFS Isuzu 800. b, Atego Mercedes-Benz LF 10/6 Ziegler. c, Valdosta, Georgia Airport E-7 fire truck. d, Kronenburg MAC 11.
No. 1232, 750fr — Motorcycles and actors: a, 1953 Triumph Thunderbird, Marlon Brando. b, 1955 Triumph TR5, James Dean, Marilyn Monroe. c, 1934 Harley-Davidson RL, Clark Gable. d, 1940 Indian Four Cylinder, Steve McQueen.
No. 1233, 750fr — Elvis Presley (1935-77), with panel color of: a, Blue. b, Purple. c, Olive green. d, Red.
No. 1234, 750fr — Marilyn Monroe (1926-62), with panel color of: a, Prussian blue. b, Red. c, Violet. d, Brown orange.
No. 1235, 750fr — 60th anniv. of coronation of Queen Elizabeth II, with panel color of: a, Blue. b, Red. c, Green. d, Brown orange.
No. 1236, 750fr — Pope Francis, with panel color of: a, Blue. b, Brown orange. c, Green. d, Red.
No. 1237, 750fr — Dr. Albert Schweitzer (1875-1965), 1952 Nobel Peace laureate, with panel color of: a, Dark brown. b, Prussian blue. c, Dark blue. d, Brown orange.
No. 1238, 750fr — Louis Pasteur (1822-95), microbiologist, with panel colors of: a, Brown. b, Prussian blue. c, Dark blue. d, Brown orange.
No. 1239, 750fr — Mao Zedong (1893-1976), Chinese Communist leader: a, Holding book at right, gray panel. b, Clapping at right, brown orange panel. c, Holding book at right, brown orange panel. d, With raised arm at right, gray panel.
No. 1240, 750fr — Table tennis players: a, Zhang Jike. b, Ding Ning. c, Ma Long. d, Xu Xin.
No. 1241, 750fr — Paul Cézanne (1839-1906), painter, and: a, Compotier, Pitcher and Fruit, 1894. b, Mont Saint-Victoire and Chateau Noir, 1904-06. c, Lac d'Annecy, 1896. d, Apples and Oranges, 1899.
No. 1242, 750fr — Pierre-Auguste Renoir (1841-1919), painter, and: a, Luncheon of the Boating Party, 1881. b, La Grenouillère, 1869. c, Chestnut Tree in Bloom, 1881. d, Madame Georges Charpentier and Her Children, 1878.
No. 1243, 750fr — Volcanoes and minerals: a, Chaitén Volcano, Chile, Vanadinite. b, Popocatépetl, Mexico, Calcite. c, Tungurahua, Ecuador, Hemimorphite. d, Redoubt Volcano, Alaska, Calcite and hematite.
No. 1244, 750fr — Dolphins and shells: a, Lagenorhynchus obscurus. b, Turbinella pyrum. c, Cymbiola vespertilio. d, Tursiops truncatus.
No. 1245, 750fr — Owls and mushrooms: a, Tyto alba, unnamed mushrooms. b, Gomphidus glutinosus, unnamed owl. c, Bubo virginianus, unnamed mushrooms. d, Sarcodon imbricatus, unnamed owl.
No. 1246, 750fr — Orchids and butterflies: a, Encyclia vitellina, unnamed butterflies. b, Papilio maackii, unnamed orchid. c, Vanda sanderiana, unnamed butterflies. d, Bhutanitis lidderdalii, unnamed orchid.
No. 1247, 750fr — Year of the Horse: a, Horse, brown orange panel. b, Two horses, blue panel. c, Two horses, purple panel. d, Horse, black panel.
No. 1248, 2500fr, Gagarin, diff. No. 1249, 2500fr, Richard Branson, SpaceShip Two. No. 1250, 2500fr, Southern Railway Class Ps-4. No. 1251, 2500fr, Shinkansen Series 800, Japan. No. 1252, 2500fr, Fastnet Lighthouse, Ireland, and ship. No. 1253, 2500fr, Blériot XI. No. 1254, 2500fr, Oshkosh Striker T-3000. No. 1255, 2500fr, 1964 Triumph Tiger 100, Bob Dylan. No. 1256, 2500fr, Presley, diff. No. 1257, 2500fr, Monroe, diff. No. 1258, 2500fr, Queen Elizabeth II, diff. No. 1259, 2500fr, Pope Francis, diff. No. 1260, 2500fr, Schweitzer, diff. No. 1261, 2500fr, Pasteur, diff. No. 1262, 2500fr, Mao Zedong, diff. No. 1263, 2500fr, Timo Boll, table tennis player. No. 1264, 2500fr, Cézanne, Mont Sainte-Victoire, 1885-87. No. 1265, 2500fr, Renoir, Ball at the Moulin de la Galette, 1876. No. 1266, 2500fr, Mount Etna, Italy, Pyrite. No. 1267, 2500fr, Stenella coeruleoalba. No. 1268, 2500fr, Strix aluco, unnamed mushrooms. No. 1269, 2500fr, Atrophaneura hector, unnamed orchid. No. 1270, 2500fr, Horse, diff.

2013, July 1   **Litho.**   **Perf. 13¼**
Sheets of 4, #a-d
1225-1247 A393   Set of 23   275.00 275.00
Souvenir Sheets
1248-1270 A393   Set of 23   230.00 230.00
2013 China International Collection Expo (Nos. 1239, 1262).

Photography by Sergey Tkachenko
and Russian Philatelic Items — A394

No. 1271 — Photograph and: a, Post card depicting Graf Zeppelin. b, Russia #C24. c, Russia #C21. d, Russia #C20.
2500fr, Photograph and Russia #6016.

2013, July 1 Litho.   **Perf. 12¾x13¼**
1271 A394   750fr Sheet of 4,
        #a-d   12.00 12.00
Souvenir Sheet
1272 A394 2500fr multi   10.00 10.00

Souvenir Sheet

Mao Zedong (1893-1976), Chinese
Communist Leader — A395

2013, July 1   Litho.   Perf. 12¾x13¼
On Wood Veneer
Self-Adhesive
1273 A395 6500fr multi   26.00 26.00

Souvenir Sheet

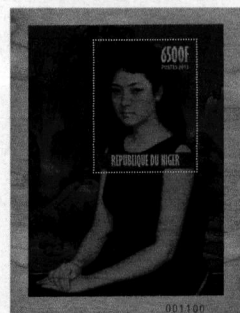

Peng Liyuan, Singer and Wife of Xi
Jinping, President of People's Republic
of China — A396

2013, July 1   Litho.   Perf. 12¾x13¼
On Wood Veneer
Self-Adhesive
1274 A396 6500fr multi   26.00 26.00

Cooperation
Between
Niger and
Algeria
A397

Perf. 12¾x13¼
2013, Sept. 10   **Litho.**
1275 A397 1060fr multi   4.50 4.50

A398

No. 1276, 500fr — Chinese high-speed trains: a, Maglev. b, CRH5. c, Bombardier. d, CRH6A.

No. 1277, 500fr — Shenzhou 10: a, Astronaut Wang Yaping, Shenzhou 10. b, Astronaut Nie Haisheng, Shenzhou 10. c, Astronaut Zhang Xiaoguang, rocket on launch pad. d, Shenzhou 10 and emblem.

No. 1278, 675fr — Nanger Dama: a, Head of gazelle facing left, gazelle in background. b, Gazelle leaping. c, Gazelle resting. d, Adult and juvenile gazelles.

No. 1279, 675fr — African mammals: a, Equus burchelli. b, Phacochoerus africanus. c, Hippopotamus amphibius. d, Alcelaphus buselaphus caama.

No. 1280, 675fr — Wildcats: a, Caracal caracal. b, Leptailurus serval. c, Acinonyx jubatus. d, Panthera pardus.

No. 1281, 750fr — Whales: a, Megaptera novaeangliae. b, Balaenoptera borealis. c, Balaenoptera musculus. d, Eschrichtius robustus.

No. 1282, 750fr — Apis mellifera and flowers: a, Chaenomeles japonica. b, Tanacetum parthenium. c, Paeonia cambessedesii. d, Odontoglossum rossii.

No. 1283, 750fr — Birds: a, Halcyon malimbica. b, Caprimulgus eximius. c, Scopus umbretta. d, Musophaga violacea.

No. 1284, 750fr — Reptiles: a, Python regius. b, Crocodylus niloticus. c, Varanus griseus. d, Trionyx triunguis.

No. 1285, 750fr — Campaign against malaria: a, Red Cross worker feeling head of sick child. b, Children under mosquito netting, mosquito at right. c, Children under mosquito netting, mosquito at left. d, Red Cross worker wearing gloves treating sick child.

No. 1286, 750fr — Prehistoric man: a, Homo georgicus. b, Homo neanderthalensis. c, Homo tyrolensis. d, Homo erectus.

No. 1287, 750fr — Military aircraft: a, Argentine Air Force Douglas A-4 Skyhawk. b, Iranian Air Force F14 Tomcat. c, U.S. Air Force Northrop Grumman RQ-4 Global Hawk. d, U.S. Air Force Lockheed Martin F35B Stealth fighter.

No. 1288, 750fr — Special transportation: a, BMW R1200RT police motorcycle. b, Agusta A-109 K2 helicopter ambulance. c, Pierce Arrow 105-foot X-ladder fire truck. d, Chevrolet C4500 ambulance.

No. 1289, 750fr — Famous cricket players: a, Inzamam-ul-Haq. b, Malcolm Marshall. c, Sanath Jayasuriya. d, Sachin Tendulkar.

No. 1290, 750fr — Pierre de Coubertin (1863-1937), founder of International Olympic Committee, and: a, Runner. b, High jumper. c, Wrestlers. d, Gymnast.

No. 1291, 750fr — Giuseppe Verdi (1813-1901), composer, and performers from opera: a, Rigoletto. b, Hermani. c, Macbeth. d, La Pucelle d'Orléans (Giovanna d'Arco).

No. 1292, 750fr — Richard Wagner (1813-83), composer, and performers from opera: a, Lohengrin. b, Tristan and Isolde. c, The Mastersingers of Nuremberg (Les Maîtres Chanteurs de Nuremberg). d, The Flying Dutchman (Le Vaisseau Fantôme).

No. 1293, 750fr — Nelson Mandela (1918-2013), President of South Africa, and: a, Princess Diana. b, Dove. c, Michael Jackson. d, Bill Gates.

No. 1294, 750fr — Pope John Paul II (1920-2005): a, Waving. b, Seated. c, Seated holding crucifix. d, Standing and praying.

No. 1295, 750fr — Grace Kelly (1929-82), actress and Princess of Monaco: a, Wearing red dress in background. b, In scene from To Catch a Thief, 1955. c, In scene from Dial M for Murder, 1954. d, Wearing blue dress in background.

No. 1296, 750fr — Paintings by Francisco Goya (1746-1828): a, Witches' Sabbath, 1798. b, The Grape Harvest, 1787. c, The Parasol, 1777. d, Gaspar Melchor de Jovellanos, 1798.

No. 1297, 750fr — Paintings by American Impressionists: a, The Hammock, by Joseph DeCamp. b, Five O'Clock, by Guy Rose. c, Madonna of the Apples, by Joseph Kleitsch. d, Marjorie and Little Edmund, by Edmund C. Tarbell.

No. 1298, 750fr — Paintings by Pablo Picasso (1881-1973): a, Woman at Fountain, 1901. b, Still Life with a Bull's Skull, 1939. c, Science and Charity, 1897. d, The Red Armchair, 1931 (incorrect inscription).

No. 1299, 750fr — Birth of Prince George of Cambridge: a, Prince Charles, Princess Diana and Prince William. b, Duke and Duchess of Cambridge with Prince George outside hospital. c, Duke and Duchess of Cambridge with

Prince George in nursery. d, Princess Diana, Princes William and Harry.

No. 1300, 875fr — Rotary International emblem and: a, Paul P. Harris (1868-1947), founder of Rotary International, Acraea neobule. b, Polio virus. c, Rotarians giving baby polio vaccine, Hypolimnas misippus. d, Hands touching, Colotis danae.

No. 1301, 2000fr, CRH3 train. No. 1302, 2000fr, Nanger dama, diff. No. 1303, 2000fr, Ceratotherium simum. No. 1304, 2000fr, Panthera leo. No. 1305, 2500fr, Wang Yaping, Shenzhou 10, diff. No. 1306, 2500fr, Orcinus orca. No. 1307, 2500fr, Apis mellifera, Raphanus sativus. No. 1308, 2500fr, Halcyon chelicuti. No. 1309, 2500fr, Geochelone sulcata. No. 1310, 2500fr, Red Cross emblem, medical worker giving child an injection. No. 1311, 2500fr, Homo neanderthalensis, cave drawing. No. 1312, 2500fr, Russian Air Force Sukhoi PAK FA. No. 1313, 2500fr, Ford F150 fire truck. No. 1314, 2500fr, Cricket player Andrew Flintoff. No. 1315, 2500fr, Coubertin, meeting of International Olympic Committee. No. 1316, 2500fr, Verdi. No. 1317, 2500fr, Wagner. No. 1318, 2500fr, Mandela and Queen Elizabeth II. No. 1319, 2500fr, Popes John Paul II and Benedict XVI. No. 1320, 2500fr, Kelly. No. 1321, 2500fr, Two Boys with a Giant Mastiff, by Goya. No. 1322, 2500fr, Spring on the Riviera, by Rose. No. 1323, 2500fr, Bullfight, by Picasso. No. 1324, 2500fr, Duke and Duchess of Cambridge, Prince George, vert. No. 1325, 3000fr, Harris, Rotary International emblem, Charaxes jasius.

2013, Sept. 30   Litho.   Perf. 13¼

Sheets of 4, #a-d

1276-1300 A398 Set of 25   300.00 300.00

Souvenir Sheets

1301-1325 A398 Set of 25   255.00 255.00

A399

A400

A401

Chinese Chang'e 3 Mission to the Moon
A402

Perf. 12¾x13¼

2013, Dec. 20				**Litho.**
1326		Horiz. strip of 4	13.00	13.00
a.	A399	750fr multi	3.25	3.25
b.	A400	750fr multi	3.25	3.25
c.	A401	750fr multi	3.25	3.25
d.	A402	750fr multi	3.25	3.25

Polo
A403

No. 1327 — Polo players on horses: a, Adolfo Cambiaso. b, Mariano Aguerre. c, Bartolomé Castagnola. d, Facundo Pieres. 2500fr, Polo player on horse.

2013, Dec. 20		**Litho.**		**Perf.**
1327	A403	750fr Sheet of 4,		
		#a-d	13.00	13.00

Souvenir Sheet

1328 A403 2500fr multi   10.50 10.50

Les chimpanzés

A404

No. 1329, 750fr — Pan troglodytes: a, Sitting on rock. b, Sitting next to tree, looking forward. c, Adult and juvenile. d, Sitting on branch looking left.

No. 1330, 750fr — Dugong dugon with Latin name: a, At LL, animal facing left. b, At UR, animal facing forward. c, At UR, with animal's head touching sea floor. d, At LL, with animal looking forward.

No. 1331, 750fr — Dolphins: a, Tursiops truncatus, Latin name at LR. b, Two Tursiops truncatus, Latin name at LL. c, Two Tursiops truncatus, Latin name at UR. d, Two Delphinus delphi.

No. 1332, 750fr — Tropical fish: a, Chelmon rostratus. b, Pygoplites diacanthus. c, Chaetodon auriga. d, Amphiprion ocellaris.

No. 1333, 750fr — Turtles: a, Geochelone sulcata. b, Chelonoidis denticulata. c, Geochelone nigra. d, Trachemys scripta elegans.

No. 1334, 750fr — Dinosaurs: a, Diceratops. b, Dicraeosaurus. c, Diplodocus. d, Tyrannosaurus.

No. 1335, 750fr — Endangered animals: a, Eretmochelys imbricata. b, Ailuropoda melanoleuca. c, Loxodonta cyclotis. d, Panthera pardus orientalis.

No. 1336, 750fr — Climate change: a, Arctocephalus gazella on shore. b, Ursus maritimus in water. c, Giraffa camelopardalis in water. d, Odobenus rosmarus on ice.

No. 1337, 750fr — Orchids: a, Paphiopedilum callosum. b, Cattleya auera. c, Cattleya labiata. d, Miltonia spectabilis.

No. 1338, 750fr — Mushrooms: a, Macrolepiota procera. b, Sarcodon imbricatus. c, Cantharellus cibarius. d, Leccinum aurantiacum.

No. 1339, 750fr — Minerals: a, Jasper. b, Amethyst. c, Malachite. d, Smoky quartz.

No. 1340, 750fr — Lighthouses: a, Rubjerg Knude Lighthouse, Denmark. b, Green Cape Lighthouse, Australia (incorrect inscription on stamp). c, Fingal Head Lighthouse, Australia (incorrect inscription on stamp). d, Hov Fyr Lighthouse, Denmark.

No. 1341, 750fr — Windmills in: a, Campo de Criptana, Spain. b, Kuzelov, Czech Republic. c, Kinderdijk, Netherlands. d, Volendam, Netherlands.

No. 1342, 750fr — Japanese high-speed trains: a, E3 Series Shinkansen. b, 700 Series Shinkansen. c, E2 Series Shinkansen. d, E3 R1 Akita Shinkansen.

No. 1343, 750fr — Fire trucks: a, Ural. b, 1938 Quad. c, Magirus-Deutz LF 16-TS. d, Steam-driven wagon.

No. 1344, 750fr — Ferrari automobiles: a, F40. b, 458. c, FF. d, "Enzo Ferrari".

No. 1345, 750fr — Chess: a, White piece tilting wooden king on white square. b, White and black queens. c, Timer. d, Player holding white piece tilting wooden king on black square.

No. 1346, 750fr — Campaign against AIDS: a, Women wearing head covering, child. b, Mother and infant meeting with doctor. c, Woman. d, Doctor examining infant held in woman's arms.

No. 1347, 750fr — Niger culture: a, Aerial view of desert village. b, Buildings in Agadez. c, Mural. d, Mountains in desert.

No. 1348, 750fr — Composers: a, Joseph Haydn (1732-1809). b, Johann Sebastian Bach (1685-1750). c, Robert Schumann (1810-56). d, Wolfgang Amadeus Mozart (1756-91).

No. 1349, 750fr — Paintings by Eugène Delacroix (1798-1863): a, Combat of Horsemen in the Countryside, 1824. b, The Dying Turk, 1825-30. c, Horse Frightened by a Storm, 1824. d, A Mortally Wounded Brigand Quenches His Thirst, 1825.

No. 1350, 750fr — Pope Benedix XVI with top inscription: a, In white on one line. b, In black on two lines. c, In white on two lines. d, In black on three lines.

No. 1351, 750fr — Nelson Mandela (1918-2013), President of South Africa: a, With hand

clenched at LL. b, Waving. c, Saluting. d, With flag of South Africa.

No. 1352, 2500fr, Adult and juvenile Pan troglodytes, diff. No. 1353, 2500fr, Dugong dugon, diff. No. 1354, 2500fr, Tursiops truncatus, diff. No. 1355, 2500fr, Heniochus acuminatus. No. 1356, 2500fr, Chelonia mydas. No. 1357, 2500fr, Spinosaurus. No. 1358, 2500fr, Diceros bicornis. No. 1359, 2500fr, Pygoscelis papua. No. 1360, 2500fr, Oncidium altissimum. No. 1361, 2500fr, Boletus edulis. No. 1362, 2500fr, Chalcedony. No. 1363, 2500fr, Michigan City East Lighthouse, Michigan City, Indiana. No. 1364, 2500fr, Windmill at Lithuanian Ethnographic Museum. No. 1365, 2500fr, E3-2000 Series Shinkansen. No. 1366, 2500fr, Mercedes-Benz Zetros fire truck. No. 1367, 2500fr, Enzo Ferrari (1898-1988), automobile manufacturer. No. 1368, 2500fr, Chess board and timer. No. 1369, 2500fr, Two women, infant, red cross. No. 1370, 2500fr, Sahara Desert rock paintings. No. 1371, 2500fr, Ludwig van Beethoven (1770-1827), composer. No. 1372, 2500fr, The Combat of the Giaour and Hassan, by Delacroix. No. 1373, 2500fr, Pope Benedict XVI, diff. No. 1374, 2500fr, Mandela with fist raised. No. 1375, 2500fr, Mandela and flag of South Africa, diff.

2013, Dec. 20   Litho.   Perf. 13¼

Sheets of 4, #a-d

1329-1351 A404 Set of 23   290.00 290.00

Souvenir Sheets

1352-1375 A404 Set of 24   250.00 250.00

Millet — A405

2014, Apr. 25   Litho.   Perf. 13¼x13

1376 A405 35fr multi   .25 .25

A406

No. 1377, 500fr — Jawaharlal Nehru (1889-1964), First Prime Minister of India, and: a, Panthera tigris tigris. b, Mahatma Gandhi (1869-1948), Indian nationalist leader (Nehru wearing hat). c, Pavo cristatus. d, Gandhi (Nehru without hat).

No. 1378, 500fr — Diplomatic relations between Niger and People's Republic of China, 40th anniv.: a, Flags of Niger and People's Republic of China, Great Wall of China, ruins of Djado, Niger. b, Flags, Niger Prime Minister Senyi Oumarou and Chinese President Hu Jintao shaking hands. c, Flags, Cheiffou Amadou and Wang Gang shaking hands. d, Flags, 2012 meeting of Presidents of Niger and People's Republic of China.

No. 1379, 675fr — Charles Lindbergh (1902-74), aviator, and airplane: a, Lindbergh wearing cap. b, Lindbergh wearing headgear and goggles, standing. c, Lindbergh without hat. d, Lindbergh wearing headgear and goggles, in cockpit.

No. 1380, 675fr — Louis Renault (1877-1944), automobile manufacturer: a, At right of car. b, Driving car. c, With head above car roof. d, At left of car.

No. 1381, 675fr — Giacomo Puccini (1858-1924), opera composer: a, Theater in background. b, Poster for Tosca in background. c, With Giuseppe Verdi (1813-1901). d, With character from Turandot in background.

No. 1382, 750fr — Jean-Philippe Rameau (1683-1764), composer, and: a, Cathedral of St. Benignus, Dijon, France. b, Dulcimer. c, Baroque lute. d, Harpsichord.

No. 1383, 750fr — Joséphine de Beauharnais (1763-1814), first wife of Napoleon Bonaparte: a, With head on chair, Napoleon standing. b, In her Malmaison bedroom. c, Standing, with Napoleon. d, Seated, her portrait in background.

No. 1384, 750fr — Charlie Chaplin (1889-1977), actor: a, Holding hat. b, With legs above head, holding cane. c, Reading. d, Touching bottom of shoe.

No. 1385, 750fr — Yuri Gagarin (1934-68), first man in space: a, Receiving flowers from girl. b, Wearing space helmet. c, Wearing military uniform, Vostok 1 in flight. d, Wearing space suit, no helmet.

No. 1386, 750fr — Pope Francis: a, Wearing miter, dove flying in background. b, With cardinals in background. c, Standing on platform, cardinals in background. d, Wearing zucchetto, dove flying in background.

No. 1387, 750fr — Joe DiMaggio (1914-99), baseball player, and his wife, Marilyn Monroe (1926-62), actress: a, DiMaggio wearing brown suit. b, DiMaggio wearing baseball uniform. c, Monroe alone. d, DiMaggio wearing green suit.

No. 1388, 750fr — Ayrton Senna (1960-94), race car driver: a, Driving blue race car. b, Holding trophy. c, Flag of Brazil in background. d, Driving yellow car.

No. 1389, 750fr — 2014 Winter Olympics, Sochi, Russia: a, Ski jumper. b, Figure skater. c, Ice hockey player. d, Snowboarder.

No. 1390, 750fr — 2014 World Cup Soccer Championships, Brazil: a, Player in blue shirt and player in green shirt. b, Player in yellow orange shirt. c, Player in light yellow shirt. d, Player in light blue shirt and player in light yellow shirt.

No. 1391, 750fr — Start of World War I, cent.: a, Carrier pigeon. b, Fokker Dr.I airplane of Manfred von Richtofen c, Renault Ft tank. d, German soldiers wearing gas masks.

No. 1392, 750fr — USS Nautilus, 60th anniv.: a, Entire ship at surface. b, Submarine submerging. c, Fore of submarine at surface. d, Submarine and wake.

No. 1393, 750fr — English Channel Tunnel, 20th anniv.: a, British Rail Class 92, flags of Great Britain and France. b, Eurotunnel Class 9, Eiffel Tower, flag of France. c, ICE3, Tower Bridge, flag of Great Britain. d, Eurostar Class 373, flags of Great Britain and France.

No. 1394, 750fr — Red List of Endangered Animals, 50th anniv.: a, Procolobus kirkii. b, Onychogalea fraenata. c, Gyps rueppellii. d, Balearica regulorum.

No. 1395, 2000fr, Nehru, Gandhi, flag of India. No. 1396, 2000fr, Prime Minister Oumarou shaking hands with Chinese Premier Wen Jiabao, flags of Niger and People's Republic of China. No. 1397, 2000fr, Lindbergh, map of transatlantic flight. No. 1398, 2000fr, Renault and tank. No. 1399, 2000fr, Puccini and poster for La Bohàme. No. 1400, 2500fr, Rameau and Baroque guitar. No. 1401, 2500fr, Napoleon Bonaparte and Josàphine de Beauharnais, diff. No. 1402, 2500fr, Chaplin in and out of stage makeup. No. 1403, 2500fr, Gagarin and Vostok 1, diff. No. 1404, 2500fr, Pope Francis and two cardinals. No. 1405, 2500fr, DiMaggio in baseball uniform. No. 1406, 2500fr, Senna and race car, diff. No. 1407, 2500fr, Biathlon. No. 1408, 2500fr, Two soccer players, diff. No. 1409, 2500fr, Assassination of Archduke Franz Ferdinand. No. 1410, 2500fr, Launch of USS Nautilus. No. 1411, 2500fr, Eurostar Class 320, map of English Channel Tunnel, flags of Great Britain and France. No. 1412, 2500fr, Panthera tigris sumatrae.

2014, Apr. 25   Litho.   Perf. 13¼
Sheets of 4, #a-d
1377-1394 A406 Set of 18 215.00 215.00
Souvenir Sheets
1395-1412 A406 Set of 18 180.00 180.00

Works of Famous Artists
A407

No. 1413, 750fr — Alphonse Mucha (1860-1939): a, Poster for F. Champenois, 1897. b, The Precious Stones Series, 1900. c, The Celebration of Svantovit on Rügen, 1912. d, Fate, 1920.

No. 1414, 750fr — Edvard Munch (1863-1944): a, Self-portrait with a Bottle of Wine, 1906. b, The Girls on the Bridge, 1901. c, Two Human Beings: The Lonely Ones, 1933-35. d, Separation, 1896.

No. 1415, 750fr — Frida Kahlo (1907-54): a, The Wounded Deer, 1946. b, Self-portrait Along the Border of Mexico and the United States, 1932. c, The Bride Frightened at Seeing Life Opened, 1944. d, The Two Fridas, 1939.

No. 1416, 750fr — Henri de Toulouse-Lautrec (1864-1901): a, Self-portrait in Front of a Mirror, 1883. b, Count Alphonse de Toulouse-Lautrec Driving a Four Horse Hitch, 1881. c,

Portrait of Suzanne Valadon, 1888. d, In Bed, 1893.

No. 1417, 750fr — Salvador Dalí (1904-89): a, Apparition of a Face and Fruit Dish on a Beach, 1938. b, Atavism at Twilight, 1934. c, Metamorphosis of Narcissus, 1937. d, Paranoiac-Critical Solitude, 1935.

No. 1418, 750fr — Wassily Kandinsky (1866-1944): a, Autumn Landscape, 1911. b, Transverse Line, 1923. c, Green Emptyness, 1930. d, In Blue, 1925.

No. 1419, 750fr — William Hogarth (1697-1764): a, The Distrest Poet, 1729. b, The Life of a Libertine, 1732-35. c, The Graham Children, 1742. d, Marriage à la Mode: The Toilette, 1743-45.

No. 1420, 2500fr, Spring, by Mucha, 1896. No. 1421, 2500fr, Cendres, by Munch, 1924. No. 1422, 2500fr, Without Hope, by Kahlo, 1945. No. 1423, 2500fr, At the Moulin Rouge, by Toulouse-Lautrec, 1892-95. No. 1424, 2500fr, The Persistence of Memory, by Dalí, 1931. No. 1425, 2500fr, Murnau, A Village Street, by Kandinsky, 1908. No. 1426, 2500fr, Columbus Breaking the Egg, 1752.

2014, Apr. 25   Litho.   Perf. 13¼
Sheets of 4, #a-d
1413-1419 A407 Set of 7 90.00 90.00
Souvenir Sheets
1420-1426 A407 Set of 7 75.00 75.00

A408

No. 1427, 750fr — St. John Paul II (1920-2005), and: a, St. Peter's Basilica, holding crucifix. b, Castel Sant'Angelo. c, St. Peter's Basilica, waving. d, Pope Francis.

No. 1428, 750fr — Deng Xiaoping (1904-97), paramount leader of People's Republic of China, and: a, Mao Zedong (1893-1976) and other Chinese leaders. b, City Skyline, flag of People's Republic of China. c, Chinese temple, flag of People's Republic of China. d, Mao Zedong.

No. 1429, 750fr — Postage stamps of various countries: a, Russia #6178, Tokelau #389. b, Australia #3563, Falkland Islands #1031. c, Australia #3562, Russia #7302. d, Australia #3561, Jamaica #1057.

No. 1430, 2500fr, St. John Paul II and his papal coat of arms. No. 1431, 2500fr, Deng Xiaoping, Mao Zedong, flowers, map of People's Republic of China. No. 1432, 2500fr, Australia #3564, Christmas Island #487a.

Litho. With Foil Application (#1427, 1430), Litho.
2014, June 25   Perf. 13¼
Sheets of 4, #a-d
1427-1429 A408 Set of 3 37.50 37.50
Souvenir Sheets
1430-1432 A408 Set of 3 32.00 32.00

Animals
A409

No. 1433, 750fr — Ursus maritimus: a, Cub on adult polar bear. b, Adult polar bear on ice. c, Adult polar bear crossing gap in ice. d, Two polar bear cubs.

No. 1434, 750fr — Ailuropoda melanoleuca: a, Head and paws of giant panda. b, Giant panda sitting and eating. c, Giant panda reclining and eating. d, Giant panda climbing rock.

No. 1435, 750fr — Gorillas: a, Gorilla gorilla diehli. b, Gorilla gorilla gorilla. c, Gorilla beringei graueri. d, Gorilla gorilla.

No. 1436, 750fr — Rhinoceroses: a, Diceros bicornis. b, Rhinoceros unicornis. c, Dicerorhinus sumatrensis. d, Rhinoceros sondaicus.

No. 1437, 750fr — Bovids: a, Bubalus bubalis. b, Bos primigenius indicus. c, Ovis aries. d, Gazella dorcas.

No. 1438, 750fr — Sea lions: a, Otaria flavescens. b, Phocarctos hookeri. c, Adult and juvenile Zalophus californianus. d, One Zalophus californianus.

No. 1439, 750fr — Wild cats: a, Panthera leo. b, Panthera tigris tigris. c, Panthera onca. d, Acinonyx jubatus.

No. 1440, 750fr — Domesticated cats: a, Japanese bobtail. b, Himalayan. c, Munchkin. d, Singapura.

No. 1441, 750fr — Dogs: a, West Highland white terriers. b, Field spaniel. c, Parson Russell terriers. d, Basset hounds.

No. 1442, 750fr — Elephants: a, Three juvenile Loxodonta africana. b, Two adult Loxodonta africana. c, One Loxodonta africana. d, Elephas maximus.

No. 1443, 750fr — Horses: a, Bavarian Warmblood. b, East Bulgarian. c, Icelandic. d, Gypsy Cob.

No. 1444, 750fr — Dolphins: a, Delphinus delphis. b, Sotalia guianensis. c, Tursiops aduncus. d, Sousa chinensis.

No. 1445, 750fr — Orcinas orca: a, Dorsal fin at UR. b, Dorsal fin at UL. c, Backflipping. d, With open mouth.

No. 1446, 750fr — Fish: a, Parambassis ranga. b, Pterapogon kauderni. c, Centropyge loricula. d, Pterophyllum scalare.

No. 1447, 750fr — Owls: a, Megascops asio. b, Strix occidentalis. c, Bubo virginianus. d, Strix nebulosa.

No. 1448, 750fr — Birds of prey: a, Pithecophaga jefferyi. b, Accipiter soloensis. c, Elanus leucurus. d, Gypaetus barbatus.

No. 1449, 750fr — Water birds: a, Fratercula arctica. b, Ardea herodias. c, Aethia cristatella. d, Podiceps nigricollis nigricollis.

No. 1450, 750fr — Butterflies: a, Danaus plexippus. b, Siproeta epaphus. c, Talicada nyseus. d, Diaethria neglecta.

No. 1451, 750fr — Turtles: a, Chelydra serpentina. b, Terrapene carolina. c, Stigmochelys pardalis. d, Clemmys guttata.

No. 1452, 750fr — Varanus komodensis: a, Komodo dragon facing left. b, Komodo dragon, head and tail facing right, tongue extended. c, Komodo dragon, head facing right, tongue extended. d, Komodo dragon facing left, mouth open.

No. 1453, 750fr — Extinct animals: a, Megaladapis. b, Macrotis leucura. c, Pinguinus impennis. d, Diceros bicornis longipes.

No. 1454, 2500fr, Ursus maritimus, diff. No. 1455, 2500fr, Adult and juvenile Ailuropoda melanoleuca. No. 1456, 2500fr, Three Gorilla gorilla. No. 1457, 2500fr, Ceratotherium simum simum. No. 1458, 2500fr, Antilope cervicapra. No. 1459, 2500fr, Phocarctos hookeri and bird. No. 1460, 2500fr, Neofelis nebulosa. No. 1461, 2500fr, Abyssinian cat. No. 1462, 2500fr, Russian toy dogs. No. 1463, 2500fr, Loxodonta africana, diff. No. 1464, 2500fr, Marwari horse. No. 1465, 2500fr, Delphinus delphis, diff. No. 1466, 2500fr, Orcinus orca, diff. No. 1467, 2500fr, Pomacanthus annularis. No. 1468, 2500fr, Tyto alba. No. 1469, 2500fr, Harpia harpyja. No. 1470, 2500fr, Aix galericulata. No. 1471, 2500fr, Danaus plexippus, diff. No. 1472, 2500fr, Chelonia mydas. No. 1473, 2500fr, Varanus komodoensis, diff. No. 1474, 2500fr, Palaeopropithecus.

2014, June 25   Litho.   Perf. 13¼
Sheets of 4, #a-d
1433-1453 A409 Set of 21 260.00 260.00
Souvenir Sheets
1454-1474 A409 Set of 21 220.00 220.00

Souvenir Sheet

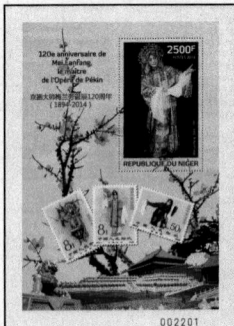
Mei Lanfang (1894-1961), Chinese Opera Actor — A410

Perf. 12¾x13¼
2014, June 25   Litho.
Self-Adhesive On Silk
1475 A410 2500fr multi 10.50 10.50

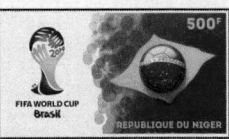
2014 World Cup Soccer Championships, Brazil — A411

No. 1476: a, Emblem of 2014 World Cup, flag of Brazil with soccer ball in place of constellation in sky (150x80mm). b, World Cup (150x240mm). c, Flag of Brazil with soccer ball in place of constellation in sky, mascot of 2014 World Cup (150x80mm).

2014, June 25   Litho.   Perf. 13¼x13
1476 Sheet of 3 + 40 labels 6.50 6.50
a.-c. A411 500fr Any single 2.10 2.10

SEMI-POSTAL STAMPS

Curie Issue
Common Design Type
1938   Unwmk.   Engr.   Perf. 13
B1 CD80 1.75fr + 50c brt ultra 16.50 16.50

French Revolution Issue
Common Design Type
1939   Photo.   Perf. 13
Name and Value Typo. in Black
B2 CD83 45c + 25c grn 12.00 12.00
B3 CD83 70c + 30c brn 12.00 12.00
B4 CD83 90c + 35c red org 12.00 12.00
B5 CD83 1.25fr + 1fr rose pink 12.00 12.00
B6 CD83 2.25fr + 2fr blue 12.00 12.00
Nos. B2-B6 (5) 60.00 60.00

Stamps of 1926-38, Surcharged in Black

1941   Perf. 14x13½, 13½x14
B7 A3 50c + 1fr scar & grn, grnsh 3.25 3.25
B8 A3 80c + 2fr cl & ol grn 8.00 8.00
B9 A4 1.50fr + 2fr dp bl & pale bl 8.00 8.00
B10 A4 2fr + 3fr red org & ol brn 8.00 8.00
Nos. B7-B10 (4) 27.25 27.25

Common Design Type and

Colonial Cavalry SP1

Soldiers and Tank SP2

1941   Unwmk.   Photo.   Perf. 13½
B11 SP2 1fr + 1fr red 1.10
B12 CD86 1.50fr + 3fr claret 1.10
B13 SP1 2.50fr + 1fr blue 1.10
Nos. B11-B13 (3) 3.30
Set, never hinged 5.25

Nos. B11-B13 were issued by the Vichy government in France, but were not placed on sale in Niger.

Nos. 89-90 Surcharged in Black or Red

1944   Engr.   Perf. 12x12½
B13A 50c + 1.50fr on 2.50fr deep blue (R) .45
B13B + 2.50fr on 1fr green .45
Set, never hinged 1.75

Colonial Development Fund.

Nos. B13A-B13B were issued by the Vichy government in France, but were not placed on sale in Niger.

Republic of the Niger
Anti-Malaria Issue
Common Design Type

Perf. 12½x12

1962, Apr. 7   Engr.   Unwmk.
B14 CD108 25fr + 5fr brn   .75 .75

Freedom from Hunger Issue
Common Design Type

1963, Mar. 21   Perf. 13
B15 CD112 25fr + 5fr gray ol, red
      lil & brn   .75 .75

Dome of the
Rock — SP3

1978, Dec. 11   Litho.   Perf. 12½
B16 SP3 40fr + 5fr multi   .45 .30

Surtax was for Palestinian fighters and their families.

AIR POST STAMPS

Common Design Type

1940 Unwmk.   Engr.   Perf. 12½x12
C1 CD85 1.90fr ultra   .35 .35
C2 CD85 2.90fr dk red   .35 .35
C3 CD85 4.50fr dk gray grn   .70 .70
C4 CD85 4.90fr yel bis   .70 .70
C5 CD85 6.90fr dp org   1.40 1.40
    Nos. C1-C5 (5)   3.50 3.50

Common Design Types

1942
C6 CD88 50c car & bl   .30
C7 CD88 1fr brn & blk   .35
C8 CD88 2fr multi   .60
C9 CD88 3fr multi   .60
C10 CD88 5fr vio & brn red   .60

Frame Engraved, Center Typographed

C11 CD89 10fr multi   .90
C12 CD89 20fr multi   1.25
C13 CD89 50fr multi   1.60
    Nos. C6-C13 (8)   6.20
    Set, never hinged   9.00

There is doubt whether Nos. C6-C13 were officially placed in use. They were issued by the Vichy government.

Republic of the Niger

Wild Animals, W
National Park — AP1

1960, Apr. 11   Engr.   Perf. 13
C14 AP1 500fr multi   19.00 8.00

For overprint see No. C112.

Nubian
Carmine
Bee-eater
AP2

1961, Dec. 18   Unwmk.   Perf. 13
C15 AP2 200fr multi   8.50 3.25

UN Headquarters and Emblem, Niger
Flag and Map — AP3

1961, Dec. 16
C20 AP3 25fr multi   .60 .40
C21 AP3 100fr multi   2.00 1.35

Niger's admission to the United Nations.
For overprints see Nos. C28-C29.

Air Afrique Issue
Common Design Type

1962, Feb. 17   Unwmk.   Perf. 13
C22 CD107 100fr multi   1.75 .90

Mosque at
Agadez and
UPU Emblem
AP4

Designs: 85fr, Gaya Bridge. 100fr, Presidential Palace, Niamey.

1963, June 12   Photo.   Perf. 12½
C23 AP4 50fr multi   1.00 .55
C24 AP4 85fr multi   1.75 .75
C25 AP4 100fr multi   1.75 .90
    Nos. C23-C25 (3)   4.50 2.20

2nd anniv. of Niger's admission to the UPU.

Type of Regular Issue, 1963
Design: 100fr, Building boats (kadei), horiz.

1963, Aug. 30   Perf. 12½x12
              Size: 47x27mm
C26 A12 100fr multi   3.00 1.60

African Postal Union Issue
Common Design Type

1963, Sept. 8   Perf. 12½
C27 CD114 85fr multi   1.25 .90

Nos. C20-C21 Overprinted in Red

1963, Sept. 30   Engr.   Perf. 13
C28 AP3 25fr multi   .80 .50
C29 AP3 100fr multi   1.90 .90

Centenary of International Red Cross.

White and Black before
Rising Sun — AP5

1963, Oct. 25   Photo.   Perf. 12x13
C30 AP5 50fr multi   3.50 2.50

See note after Mauritania No. C28.

Peanut
Cultivation
AP6

Designs: 45fr, Camels transporting peanuts to market. 85fr, Men closing bags. 100fr, Loading bags on truck.

1963, Nov. 5   Engr.   Perf. 13
C31 AP6 20fr grn, bl & red brn   .60 .25
C32 AP6 45fr red brn, bl & grn   1.00 .40
C33 AP6 85fr multi   2.00 .70
C34 AP6 100fr red brn, ol bis &
            bl   2.25 1.00
    a. Souv. sheet of 4, #C31-C34   6.00 6.00
    Nos. C31-C34 (4)   5.85 2.35

To publicize Niger's peanut industry.

1963 Air Afrique Issue
Common Design Type

1963, Nov. 19   Photo.   Perf. 13x12
C35 CD115 50fr multi   1.00 .55

Telstar and Capricornus and
Sagittarius Constellations — AP7

100fr, Relay satellite, Leo & Virgo constellations.

1964, Feb. 11   Engr.   Perf. 13
C36 AP7 25fr ol brn & bluish vio   .50 .30
C37 AP7 100fr grn & dp claret   1.40 .85

Ramses II Holding
Crook and Flail, Abu
Simbel — AP8

1964, Mar. 9
C38 AP8 25fr bis brn & dl bl grn   .80 .50
C39 AP8 30fr dk bl & org brn   1.25 .65
C40 AP8 50fr dp claret & dk bl   2.25 1.25
    Nos. C38-C40 (3)   4.30 2.40

Issued to publicize the UNESCO world campaign to save historic monuments in Nubia.

Tiros I Weather Satellite over Globe
and WMO Emblem
AP9

1964, Mar. 23   Unwmk.   Perf. 13
C41 AP9 50fr emer, dk bl & choc 1.50 .75

4th World Meteorological Day, Mar. 23.

Rocket,
Stars and
"Stamp"
AP10

1964, June 5   Engr.
C42 AP10 50fr dk bl & car red 1.25 .65

"PHILATEC," International Philatelic and Postal Techniques Exhibition, Paris, June 5-21, 1964.

Europafrica Issue, 1963
Common Design Type

50fr, European & African shaking hands, emblems of industry & agriculture.

1964, July 20   Photo.   Perf. 12x13
C43 CD116 50fr multi   .85 .50

John F.
Kennedy — AP11

Perf. 12½

1964, Sept. 25   Unwmk.   Photo.
C44 AP11 100fr multi   1.90 1.25
    a. Souvenir sheet of 4   8.50 8.50

President John F. Kennedy (1917-1963).

Discobolus and Discus
Thrower — AP12

60fr, Water polo, horiz. 85fr, Relay race, horiz. 250fr, Torch bearer & Pierre de Coubertin.

1964, Oct. 10   Engr.   Perf. 13
C45 AP12 60fr red brn & sl
              grn   1.00 .50
C46 AP12 85fr ultra & red brn   1.50 .60
C47 AP12 100fr brt grn, dk red
              & sl   1.50 .70
C48 AP12 250fr yel brn, brt
              grn & sl   3.50 1.75
    a. Min. sheet of 4, #C45-C48   10.50 10.50
    Nos. C45-C48 (4)   7.50 3.55

18th Olympic Games, Tokyo, Oct. 10-25.

Pope John XXIII
(1881-1963)
AP13

1965, June 3   Photo.   Perf. 12½x13
C49 AP13 100fr multi   1.75 .80

Hand Crushing
Crab — AP14

1965, July 15   Engr.   Perf. 13
C50 AP14 100fr yel grn, blk &
              brn   1.50 .85

Issued to publicize the fight against cancer.

Sir Winston
Churchill — AP15

Perf. 12½x13

1965, Sept. 3   Photo.   Unwmk.
C51 AP15 100fr multi   1.40 .85

Symbols of Agriculture, Industry, Education — AP16

1965, Oct. 24   **Engr.**   *Perf. 13*
C52 AP16 50fr henna brn, blk & ol   .90 .50

International Cooperation Year, 1965.

Flags and Niamey Fair — AP17

1965, Dec. 10   **Photo.**   *Perf. 13x12½*
C53 AP17 100fr multi   1.40 .85

International Fair at Niamey.

Dr. Schweitzer, Crippled Hands and Symbols of Medicine, Religion and Music AP18

1966, Jan. 4   **Photo.**   *Perf. 12½x13*
C54 AP18 50fr multi   1.10 .55

Weather Survey Frigate and WMO Emblem AP19

1966, Mar. 23   **Engr.**   *Perf. 13*
C55 AP19 50fr brt rose lil, dl grn & dk vio bl   1.50 .60

6th World Meteorological Day, Mar. 23.

Edward H. White Floating in Space and Gemini IV — AP20

#C57, Alexei A. Leonov & Voskhod II.

1966, Mar. 30
C56 AP20 50fr dk red brn, blk & brt grn   1.00 .50
C57 AP20 50fr pur, slate & org   1.00 .50

Issued to honor astronauts Edward H. White and Alexei A. Leonov.

A-1 Satellite and Earth AP21

45fr, Diamant rocket and launching pad. 90fr, FR-1 satellite. 100fr, D-1 satellite.

1966, May 12   **Photo.**   *Perf. 13*
C58 AP21 45fr multi, vert.   .75 .45
C59 AP21 60fr multi   .90 .55
C60 AP21 90fr multi   1.10 .80
C61 AP21 100fr multi   1.75 1.00
   Nos. C58-C61 (4)   4.50 2.80

French achievements in space.

Maps of Europe and Africa and Symbols of Industry — AP22

1966, July 20   **Photo.**   *Perf. 12x13*
C62 AP22 50fr multi   .90 .45

Third anniversary of economic agreement between the European Economic Community and the African and Malgache Union.

Air Afrique Issue, 1966
Common Design Type

1966, Aug. 31   **Photo.**   *Perf. 13*
C63 CD123 30fr gray, yel grn & blk   .70 .35

Voskhod 1 — AP23

Design: 100fr, Gemini 6 and 7.

1966, Oct. 14   **Engr.**   *Perf. 13*
C64 AP23 50fr multi   .80 .45
C65 AP23 100fr multi   1.60 .80

Russian & American achievements in space.

Torii and Atom Destroying Crab — AP24

1966, Dec. 2   **Photo.**   *Perf. 13*
C66 AP24 100fr dp claret, brn, vio & bl grn   1.60 .80

9th Intl. Anticancer Cong., Tokyo, Oct. 23-29.

New Mosque, Niamey AP25

1967, Jan. 11   **Engr.**   *Perf. 13*
C67 AP25 100fr grn & brt bl   1.60 .80

Albrecht Dürer, Self-portrait AP26

Self-portraits: 100fr, Jacques Louis David. 250fr, Ferdinand Delacroix.

1967, Jan. 27   **Photo.**   *Perf. 12½*
C68 AP26 50fr multi   1.10 .70
C69 AP26 100fr multi   2.00 1.00
C70 AP26 250fr multi   4.50 2.25
   Nos. C68-C70 (3)   7.60 3.95
   See No. C98.

Maritime Weather Station — AP27

1967, Mar. 23   **Engr.**   *Perf. 13*
C71 AP27 50fr brt bl, dk car rose & blk   1.50 .75

7th World Meteorological Day.

View of EXPO '67, Montreal AP28

1967, Apr. 28   **Engr.**   *Perf. 13*
C72 AP28 100fr lil, brt bl & blk   1.25 .70

Issued for EXPO '67, International Exhibition, Montreal, Apr. 28-Oct. 27, 1967.

Audio-visual Center, Stylized Eye and People AP29

1967, June 22   **Engr.**   *Perf. 13*
C73 AP29 100fr brt bl, pur & grn   1.25 .60

National Audio-Visual Center.

Konrad Adenauer (1876-1967), Chancellor of West Germany (1949-63) — AP30

1967, Aug. 11   **Photo.**   *Perf. 12½*
C74 AP30 100fr dk bl, gray & sep   1.75 .70
   a. Souv. sheet of 4   7.75 7.75

African Postal Union Issue, 1967
Common Design Type

1967, Sept. 9   **Engr.**   *Perf. 13*
C75 CD124 100fr emer, red & brt lil   1.40 .60

Jesus Teaching in the Temple, by Ingres AP31

Design: 150fr, Jesus Giving the Keys to St. Peter, by Ingres, vert.

1967, Oct. 2   **Photo.**   *Perf. 12½*
C76 AP31 100fr multi   2.50 1.25
C77 AP31 150fr multi   3.50 1.75

Jean Dominique Ingres (1780-1867), French painter.

Children and UNICEF Emblem — AP32

1967, Dec. 11   **Engr.**   *Perf. 13*
C78 AP32 100fr bl, brn & grn   1.50 1.00

21st anniv. of UNICEF.

O.C.A.M. Emblem AP33

1968, Jan. 12   **Engr.**   *Perf. 13*
C79 AP33 100fr brt bl, grn & org   1.25 .55

Conf. of the Organization Communitée Afrique et Malgache (OCAM), Niamey, Jan. 1968.

Vincent van Gogh, Self-portrait AP34

Self-portraits: 50fr, Jean Baptiste Camille Corot. 150fr, Francisco de Goya.

1968, Jan. 29   **Photo.**   *Perf. 12½*
C80 AP34 50fr multi   1.00 .45
C81 AP34 150fr multi   2.75 1.10
C82 AP34 200fr multi   4.50 1.75
   Nos. C80-C82 (3)   8.25 3.30
   See No. C98.

Breguet 27 — AP35

Planes: 80fr, Potez 25 on the ground. 100fr, Potez 25 in the air.

1968, Mar. 14   **Engr.**   *Perf. 13*
C83 AP35 45fr ind, car & dk grn   1.00 .40
C84 AP35 80fr indigo, bl & brn   1.50 .75
C85 AP35 100fr sky bl, brn blk & dk grn   2.50 .90
   Nos. C83-C85 (3)   5.00 2.05

25th anniversary of air mail service between France and Niger.

Splendid Glossy Starling AP36

Design: 100fr, Amethyst starling, vert.

1968-69   **Photo.**   *Perf. 13*
C86 AP36 100fr gold & multi ('69)   5.50 1.10
Engr.
C87 AP36 250fr mag, sl grn & brt bl   3.25 1.40
   See No. C255.

Dandy Horse, 1818, and Racer, 1968 AP37

1968, May 17   **Engr.**   *Perf. 13*
C88 AP37 100fr bl grn & red   2.40 .80

150th anniversary of the invention of the bicycle.

Sheet Bend Knot AP37a

1968, July 20   **Photo.**   *Perf. 13*
C89 AP37a 50fr gray, blk, red & grn   .90 .45

Fifth anniversary of economic agreement between the European Economic Community and the African and Malgache Union.

Fencing
AP38

Designs: 100fr, Jackknife dive, vert. 150fr, Weight lifting, vert. 200fr, Equestrian.

1968, Sept. 10   Engr.   Perf. 13
C90 AP38 50fr pur & blk   .60   .40
C91 AP38 100fr choc, ultra & blk 1.10   .60
C92 AP38 150fr choc & org   1.60   .75
C93 AP38 200fr brn, emer & ind   2.25 1.50
  a. Min. sheet of 4, #C90-C93   8.00 8.00
   Nos. C90-C93 (4)   5.55 3.25

19th Olympic Games, Mexico City, 10/12-27.
No. C93a is folded down the vertical gutter separating Nos. C90-C91 se-tenant at left and Nos. C92-C93 se-tenant at right.

Robert F.
Kennedy — AP39

#C95, John F. Kennedy. #C96, Rev. Dr. Martin Luther King, Jr. #C97, Mahatma Gandhi.

1968, Oct. 4   Photo.   Perf. 12½
C94 AP39 100fr blk & pale org   1.25   .70
C95 AP39 100fr blk & aqua   1.40   .70
C96 AP39 100fr blk & bluish gray 1.25   .70
C97 AP39 100fr blk & yel   1.25   .70
  a. Souv. sheet of 4, #C94-C97   6.75 6.75
   Nos. C94-C97 (4)   5.15 2.80

Issued to honor proponents of non-violence.

PHILEXAFRIQUE Issue
Painting Type of 1968

Design: 100fr, Interior Minister Paré, by J. L. La Neuville (1748-1826).

1968, Oct. 25   Photo.   Perf. 12½
C98 AP34 100fr multi   2.75 2.75

Issued to publicize PHILEXAFRIQUE, Philatelic Exhibition in Abidjan, Feb. 14-23, 1969. Printed with alternating light blue label.

Arms and
Flags of
Niger
AP40

1968, Dec. 17   Litho.   Perf. 13
C99 AP40 100fr multi   1.50   .70

10th anniv. of the proclamation of the Republic.

Bonaparte as First
Consul, by
Ingres — AP41

Paintings: 100fr, Napoleon Visiting the Plague House in Jaffa, by Antoine Jean Gros. 150fr, Napoleon on the Imperial Throne, by Jean Auguste Dominique Ingres. 200fr, Napoleon's March Through France, by Jean Louis Ernest Meissonier, horiz.

Perf. 12½x12, 12x12½
1969, Jan. 20   Photo.
C100 AP41 50fr multi   1.90   .95
C101 AP41 100fr grn & multi   3.00 1.50
C102 AP41 150fr pur & multi   4.00 1.75
C103 AP41 200fr brn & multi   6.00 3.00
   Nos. C100-C103 (4)   14.90 7.20

Napoleon Bonaparte (1769-1821).

2nd PHILEXAFRIQUE Issue
Common Design Type

Designs: 50fr, Niger No. 41 and giraffes.

1969, Feb. 14   Engr.   Perf. 13
C104 CD128 50fr slate, brn & org 3.00 1.90

Weather Observation Plane in Storm
and Anemometer — AP42

1969, Mar. 23   Engr.   Perf. 13
C105 AP42 50fr blk, brt bl & grn .90   .45

9th World Meteorological Day.

Panhard
Levassor,
1900
AP43

Early Automobiles: 45fr, De Dion Bouton 8, 1904. 50fr, Opel, 1909. 70fr, Daimler, 1910. 100fr, Vermorel 12/16, 1912.

1969, Apr. 15   Engr.   Perf. 13
C106 AP43 25fr gray, lt grn & bl grn   .55   .30
C107 AP43 45fr gray, bl & vio   .70   .30
C108 AP43 50fr gray, yel bis & brn   1.60   .40
C109 AP43 70fr gray, brt pink & brt lil 2.00 .65
C110 AP43 100fr gray, lem & sl grn   2.25   .90
   Nos. C106-C110 (5)   7.10 2.55

Apollo 8 Trip
around
Moon — AP44

Embossed on Gold Foil
1969, Mar. 31   Die-cut Perf. 10½
C111 AP44 1000fr gold   18.50 18.50

US Apollo 8 mission, which put the 1st men into orbit around the moon, Dec. 21-27, 1968.

No. C14 Overprinted
in Red

1969, July 25   Engr.   Perf. 13
C112 AP1 500fr multi   7.50 7.50

See note after Mali No. C80.

Toys
AP45

1969, Oct. 13   Engr.   Perf. 13
C113 AP45 100fr bl, red brn & grn 1.40 .60

International Nuremberg Toy Fair.

Europafrica Issue

Links
AP46

1969, Oct. 30   Photo.
C114 AP46 50fr vio, yel & blk   .90   .50

Camels and
Motor
Caravan
Crossing
Desert
AP47

100fr, Motor caravan crossing mountainous region. 150fr, Motor caravan in African village. 200fr, Map of Africa showing tour, Citroen B-2 tractor, African & European men shaking hands.

1969, Nov. 22   Engr.   Perf. 13
C115 AP47 50fr lil, pink & brn   .95   .40
C116 AP47 100fr dk car rose, lt bl & vio bl 2.00 .75
C117 AP47 150fr multi   2.50 1.25
C118 AP47 200fr sl grn, bl & blk 4.00 1.75
   Nos. C115-C118 (4)   9.45 4.15

Black Tour across Africa from Colomb-Bechar, Algeria, to Mombassa, Dar es Salaam, Mozambique, Tananarive and the Cape of Good Hope.

EXPO '70 at
Osaka — AP48

1970, Mar. 25   Photo.   Perf. 12½
C119 AP48 100fr multi   1.50   .60

Issued to publicize EXPO '70 International Exhibition, Osaka, Japan, Mar. 15-Sept. 13.

Education
Year
Emblem and
Education
Symbols
AP49

1970, Apr. 6   Engr.   Perf. 13
C120 AP49 100fr plum, red & gray 1.25 .60

Issued for International Education Year.

Rotary
Emblem,
Globe and
Niamey Club
Emblem
AP50

1970, Apr. 30   Photo.   Perf. 12½
C121 AP50 100fr gold & multi   1.60   .80

65th anniversary of Rotary International.

Modern Plane, Clement Ader and his
Flying Machine
AP51

Designs: 100fr, Joseph and Jacques Montgolfier, rocket and balloon. 150fr, Isaac Newton, planetary system and trajectories. 200fr, Galileo Galilei, spaceship and trajectories. 250fr, Leonardo da Vinci, his flying machine, and plane.

1970, May 11   Engr.   Perf. 13
C122 AP51 50fr bl, cop red & sl   1.00   .40
C123 AP51 100fr cop red, bl & sl 1.75   .80
C124 AP51 150fr brn, grn & ocher 1.90 1.00
C125 AP51 200fr dk car rose, dp vio & bis 2.60 1.40
C126 AP51 250fr cop red, gray & pur 4.00 1.75
   Nos. C122-C126 (5)   11.25 5.35

Pioneers of space research.
For overprints and surcharges see Nos. C129-C130, C141-C142.

Bay of
Naples,
Buildings, Mt.
Vesuvius and
Niger No.
97 — AP52

1970, May 5   Photo.   Perf. 12½
C127 AP52 100fr multi   1.40   .60

Issued to publicize the 10th Europa Philatelic Exhibition, Naples, Italy, May 2-10.

TV Tube,
Books,
Microscope,
Globe and
ITU Emblem
AP53

1970, May 16   Engr.   Perf. 13
C128 AP53 100fr grn, brn & red   1.40   .70

Issued for World Telecommunications Day.

Nos. C123 and C125 Overprinted:
"Solidarité Spatiale / Apollo XIII /
11-17 Avril 1970"

1970, June 6   Engr.   Perf. 13
C129 AP51 100fr multi   1.25   .60
C130 AP51 200fr multi   2.25   .80

Abortive flight of Apollo 13, 4/11-17/70.

UN Emblem,
Man, Woman
and Doves
AP54

1970, June 26   Photo.   Perf. 12½
C131 AP54 100fr brt bl, dk bl & org 1.25 .60
C132 AP54 150fr multi   1.75   .90

25th anniversary of the United Nations.

European and African Men, Globe and
Fleur-de-lis — AP55

Lithographed; Embossed on Gold
Foil
1970, July 22   Perf. 12½
C133 AP55 250fr gold & ultra   4.00 4.00

French Language Cong., Niamey, Mar. 1970.

Europafrica Issue

European
and African
Women
AP56

1970, July 29   Engr.   Perf. 13
C134 AP56 50fr slate grn & dl red .85 .40

EXPO Emblem, Geisha and Torii — AP57

Design: 150fr, EXPO emblem, exhibition at night and character from Noh play.

1970, Sept. 16　Engr.　Perf. 13
C135 AP57 100fr multi　　　1.10 .55
C136 AP57 150fr bl, dk brn & grn 1.60 .75

EXPO '70 International Exhibition, Osaka, Japan, Mar. 15-Sept. 13.

Gymnast on Parallel Bars — AP58

Sports: 100fr, Vaulting, horiz. 150fr, Flying jump, horiz. 200fr, Rings.

1970, Oct. 26　Engr.　Perf. 13
C137 AP58 50fr brt bl　　　.65 .40
C138 AP58 100fr brt grn　　1.40 .70
C139 AP58 150fr brt rose lil 2.25 .95
C140 AP58 200fr red org　　2.75 1.25
　Nos. C137-C140 (4)　7.05 3.30

17th World Gymnastics Championships, Ljubljana, Oct. 22-27.

Nos. C124 and C126 Surcharged and Overprinted: "LUNA 16 - Sept. 1970 / PREMIERS PRELEVEMENTS / AUTOMATIQUES SUR LA LUNE"

1970, Nov. 5
C141 AP51 100fr on 150fr multi 1.50 .70
C142 AP51 200fr on 250fr multi 3.00 1.40

Unmanned moon probe of the Russian space ship Luna 16, Sept. 12-24.

Beethoven and Piano — AP59

Design: 150fr, Beethoven and dancers with dove, symbolic of Ode to Joy.

1970, Nov. 18　Photo.　Perf. 12½
C143 AP59 100fr multi　　1.60 .60
C144 AP59 150fr multi　　2.40 .90

Ludwig van Beethoven (1770-1827), composer.

John F. Kennedy Bridge, Niamey AP60

1970, Dec. 18　Photo.　Perf. 12½
C145 AP60 100fr multicolored 1.50 .65

Proclamation of the Republic, 12th anniv.

Gamal Abdel Nasser (1918-70), President of Egypt — AP61

Design: 200fr, Nasser with raised arm.

1971, Jan. 5　Photo.　Perf. 12½
C146 AP61 100fr blk, org brn & grn 1.00 .50
C147 AP61 200fr grn, org & blk brn 1.75 .85

Charles de Gaulle — AP62

Embossed on Gold Foil
1971, Jan. 22　Die-cut Perf. 10
C148 AP62 1000fr gold　65.00 65.00

In memory of Gen. Charles de Gaulle (1890-1970), President of France.

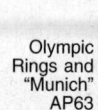

Olympic Rings and "Munich" AP63

1971, Jan. 29　Engr.　Perf. 13
C149 AP63 150fr dk bl, rose lil & grn 1.90 .90

1972 Summer Olympic Games, Munich.

Landing Module over Moon — AP64

1971, Feb. 5　Engr.　Perf. 13
C150 AP64 250fr ultra, sl grn & org 3.00 1.75

Apollo 14 mission, Jan. 31-Feb. 9.

Masks of Hate — AP65

200fr, People & 4-leaf clover (symbol of unity).

1971, Mar. 20　Engr.　Perf. 13
C151 AP65 100fr red, sl & brt bl 1.10 .45
C152 AP65 200fr slate, red & grn 2.25 .85

Intl. Year against Racial Discrimination.

Map of Africa and Telecommunications System — AP66

1971, Apr. 6　Photo.　Perf. 12½
C153 AP66 100fr grn & multi　.90 .45

Pan-African telecommunications system.

African Mask and Japan No. 580 — AP67

Design: 100fr, Japanese actors, stamps of Niger, No. 95 on cover and No. 170.

1971, Apr. 23　Engr.　Perf. 13
C154 AP67 50fr choc, brt grn & blk .90 .45
C155 AP67 100fr red brn & multi 1.50 .60

Philatokyo 71, Tokyo Philatelic Exposition, Apr. 19-29.

Longwood, St. Helena, by Carle Vernet AP68

Napoleon Bonaparte: 200fr, Napoleon's body on camp bed, by Marryat.

1971, May 5　Photo.　Perf. 13
C156 AP68 150fr gold & multi 2.50 .75
C157 AP68 200fr gold & multi 3.50 1.25

Satellite, Waves and Earth — AP69

1971, May 17　Engr.　Perf. 13
C158 AP69 100fr org, ultra & dk brn 1.50 .70

3rd World Telecommunications Day.

Olympic Rings, Athletes and Torch — AP70

Designs: 50fr, Pierre de Coubertin, discus throwers, horiz. 150fr, Runners, horiz.

1971, June 10
C159 AP70 50fr red & slate　.80 .35
C160 AP70 100fr sl, brn & grn 1.25 .60
C161 AP70 150fr plum, bl & rose lil 2.10 1.10
　Nos. C159-C161 (3)　4.15 2.05

75th anniv. of modern Olympic Games.

Astronauts and Landing Module on Moon — AP71

1971, July 26　Engr.　Perf. 13
C162 AP71 150fr scar, pur & sl 1.90 1.00

US Apollo 15 moon mission, 7/26-8/7/71.

Charles de Gaulle — AP72

1971, Nov. 9　Photo.　Perf. 12½x12
C163 AP72 250r multi　8.50 5.50

First anniversary of the death of Charles de Gaulle (1890-1970), president of France.

African Postal Union Issue, 1971
Common Design Type

Design: 100fr, Water carrier, cattle and UAMPT headquarters, Brazzaville, Congo.

1971, Nov. 13　Photo.　Perf. 13x13½
C164 CD135 100fr blue & multi 1.25 .60

Al Hariri Holding Audience, Baghdad, 1237 AP73

Designs from Mohammedan Miniatures: 150fr, Archangel Israfil, late 14th century, vert. 200fr, Horsemen, 1210.

1971, Nov. 25　　　　Perf. 13
C165 AP73 100fr multi　1.40 .60
C166 AP73 150fr multi　2.25 .95
C167 AP73 200fr multi　3.25 1.75
　Nos. C165-C167 (3)　6.90 3.30

Louis Armstrong — AP74

Design: 150fr, Armstrong with trumpet.

1971, Dec. 6
C168 AP74 100fr multi　2.10 .75
C169 AP74 150fr multi　3.25 1.00

Armstrong (1900-71), American jazz musician.

Adoration of the Kings, by Di Bartolo AP75

Christmas (Paintings): 150fr, Nativity, by Domenico Ghirlandaio, vert. 200fr, Adoration of the Shepherds, by Il Perugino.

1971, Dec. 24　Photo.　Perf. 13
C170 AP75 100fr blk & multi 1.25 .55
C171 AP75 150fr blk & multi 2.00 .80
C172 AP75 200fr blk & multi 2.50 1.20
　Nos. C170-C172 (3)　5.75 2.55

See Nos. C210-C212, C232-C234.

Presidents Pompidou and Diori Hamani, Flags of Niger and France AP76

1972, Jan. 22
C173 AP76 250fr multi　6.75 4.00

Visit of President Georges Pompidou of France, Jan. 1972.

Snowflakes, Olympic Torch and Emblem AP77

Design: 100fr, Torii made of ski poles and skis, and dwarf tree, vert.

1972, Jan. 27　　　　Engr.
C174 AP77 100fr dk vio, grn & car 1.25 .55
C175 AP77 150fr dk vio, lil & red 1.90 .75
　a.　Souv. sheet of 2, #C174-C175 3.25 3.25

11th Winter Olympic Games, Sapporo, Japan, Feb. 3-13.

The Masked Ball, by Guardi AP78

50fr, 100fr, 150fr, Details from "The Masked Ball," by Francesco Guardi (1712-93); all vert.

1972, Feb. 7   **Photo.**
C176 AP78 50fr gold & multi   1.10   .50
C177 AP78 100fr gold & multi   1.75   .85
C178 AP78 150fr gold & multi   2.75 1.10
C179 AP78 200fr gold & multi   3.25 1.40
    Nos. C176-C179 (4)   8.85 3.85

UNESCO campaign to save Venice. See Nos. C215-C216.

Johannes Brahms and "Lullaby" — AP79

1972, Mar. 17   **Engr.**   *Perf. 13*
C180 AP79 100fr multicolored   2.10   .75

75th anniversary of death of Johannes Brahms (1833-1897), German composer.

Scout Sign and Tents — AP80

1972, Mar. 22
C181 AP80 150fr pur, org & slate bl   1.75   .75

World Boy Scout Seminar, Cotonou, Dahomey, March 1972.

Surgical Team, Heart-shaped Globe and Emblem — AP81

1972   **Engr.**   *Perf. 13*
C182 AP81 100fr dp brn & car   1.40   .60

"Your heart is your health," World Health Day.

Famous Aircraft AP82

50fr, Bleriot XI Crossing English Channel. 75fr, Spirit of St. Louis crossing Atlantic. 100fr, 1st flight of Concorde supersonic jet.

1972, Apr. 24
C183 AP82 50fr shown   1.00   .40
C184 AP82 75fr multicolored   1.60   .55
C185 AP82 100fr multicolored   3.00 1.40
    Nos. C183-C185 (3)   5.60 2.35

ITU Emblem, Satellite, Stars and Earth AP83

1972, May 17   **Engr.**   *Perf. 13*
C186 AP83 100fr pur, car & blk   1.50   .60

4th World Telecommunications Day.

20th Olympic Games, Munich — AP84

50fr, Boxing and Opera House. 100fr, Broad jump & City Hall. 150fr, Soccer & Church of the Theatines, vert. 200fr, Running and Propylaeum.

1972, May 26
C187 AP84 50fr blue & grn   .70   .30
C188 AP84 100fr yel grn & dk brn   1.00   .50
C189 AP84 150fr org red & dk brn   1.60   .70
C190 AP84 200fr violet & dk brn   2.10   .90
  a.   Min. sheet of 4. #C187-C190   5.75 5.75
    Nos. C187-C190 (4)   5.40 2.40

For overprints see Nos. C196-C199.

"Alexander Graham Bell," Telephone AP85

1972, July 7
C191 AP85 100fr car, dk pur & slate   1.75   .60

Alexander Graham Bell (1847-1922), inventor of the telephone. Stamp pictures Samuel F. B. Morse.

Europafrica Issue

Stylized Maps of Africa and Europe — AP86

1972, July 29   **Engr.**   *Perf. 13*
C192 AP86 50fr red brn, bl & grn   .60   .25

Mail Runner, UPU Emblem AP87

Designs: 100fr, Mail truck, UPU emblem. 150fr, Mail plane, UPU emblem.

1972, Oct. 9   **Engr.**   *Perf. 13*
C193 AP87 50fr multicolored   .80   .40
C194 AP87 100fr multicolored   1.25   .65
C195 AP87 150fr multicolored   2.00   .95
    Nos. C193-C195 (3)   4.05 2.00

Universal Postal Union Day.

Nos. C187-C190 Overprinted in Red or Violet Blue

(a)

(b)

(c)

(d)

1972, Nov. 10
C196 AP84(a) 50fr multi (R)   .70   .40
C197 AP84(b) 100fr multi (R)   1.10   .55
C198 AP84(c) 150fr multi (VBl)   2.10   .90
C199 AP84(d) 200fr multi (R)   2.60 1.10
    Nos. C196-C199 (4)   6.50 2.95

Gold medal winners in 20th Olympic Games: Emilio Correa, Cuba, welterweight boxing; Victor Saneev, USSR, triple jump; Poland, soccer; Frank Shorter, US, marathon.

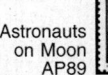

Fables AP88

25fr, The Crow and The Fox. 50fr, The Lion and the Mouse. 75fr, The Monkey and the Leopard.

1972, Nov. 23
C200 AP88 25fr emer, blk & brn   1.25   .40
C201 AP88 50fr brt pink, bl grn & brn   1.75   .50
C202 AP88 75fr lt brn, grn & dk brn   2.75   .80
    Nos. C200-C202 (3)   5.75 1.70

Jean de La Fontaine (1621-1695), French fabulist.

Astronauts on Moon AP89

1972, Dec. 12   **Photo.**   *Perf. 13*
C203 AP89 250fr multi   3.25 1.75

Apollo 17 US moon mission, Dec. 7-19.

Young Athlete — AP90

Design: 100fr, Head of Hermes.

1973, Feb. 7   **Engr.**   *Perf. 13*
C204 AP90 50fr dk car   .60   .35
C205 AP90 100fr purple   1.25   .50

Treasures of antiquity.

Boy Scouts and Radio Transmission — AP91

Niger Boy Scouts: 50fr, Red Cross, first aid. 100fr, Scout and gazelle. 150fr, Scouts with gazelle and bird.

1973, Mar. 21   **Engr.**   *Perf. 13*
C206 AP91 25fr multicolored   .40   .30
C207 AP91 50fr multicolored   .75   .35
C208 AP91 100fr multicolored   1.25   .60
C209 AP91 150fr multicolored   1.60   .80
    Nos. C206-C209 (4)   4.00 2.05

For overprints see Nos. C217-C218.

Christmas Type of 1971

Paintings: 50fr, Crucifixion, by Hugo van der Goes, vert. 100fr, Burial of Christ, by Cima da Conegliano. 150fr, Pietà, by Giovanni Bellini.

1973, Apr. 20   **Photo.**   *Perf. 13*
C210 AP75 50fr gold & multi   .70   .30
C211 AP75 100fr gold & multi   1.40   .55
C212 AP75 150fr gold & multi   2.00   .80
    Nos. C210-C212 (3)   4.10 1.65

Easter 1973.

Air Afrique Plane and Mail Truck AP92

1973, Apr. 30   **Engr.**   *Perf. 13*
C213 AP92 100fr brt grn, choc & car   1.60   .70

Stamp Day 1973.

WMO Emblem, Pyramids with Weather Symbols, Satellite — AP93

1973, May 7
C214 AP93 100fr multicolored   1.25   .55

Cent. of intl. meteorological cooperation.

Painting Type of 1972

Paintings by Delacroix: 150fr, Prowling lioness. 200fr, Tigress and cub.

1973, May 22   **Photo.**   *Perf. 13x12½*
C215 AP78 150fr blk & multi   2.75 1.40
C216 AP78 200fr blk & multi   4.50 2.25

175th anniversary of the birth of Ferdinand Delacroix (1798-1863), French painter.

Nos. C208-C209 Overprinted

1973, July 19   Engr.   Perf. 13
C217 AP91 100fr multi   1.25   .55
C218 AP91 150fr multi   1.75   .80
    Boy Scout 24th World Jamboree, Nairobi,
Kenya, July 16-21.

Head and City Hall,
Brussels — AP93a

1973, Sept. 17   Engr.   Perf. 13
C219 AP93a 100fr multicolored   1.25   .80
    Africa Weeks, Brussels, Sept. 15-30, 1973.

Men Emptying
Cornucopia, FAO
Emblem,
People — AP94

1973, Nov. 2   Engr.   Perf. 13
C220 AP94 50fr ultra, pur & ver   .90   .40
    10th anniversary of the World Food Program.

AP95

Copernicus, Sputnik 1, Heliocentric System.

1973, Nov. 12
C221 AP95 150fr rose red, vio bl
              & brn   2.00   .90

AP96

1973, Nov. 22   Photo.   Perf. 12½
C222 AP96 100fr reddsh brn &
              multi   1.25   .60

Souvenir Sheet
Perf. 13
C223 AP96 200fr dp ultra & multi 2.40 2.40
    10th anniv. of the death of Pres. John F.
Kennedy.

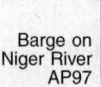

Barge on
Niger River
AP97

Design: 75fr, Tug Baban Maza.

1974, Jan. 18   Engr.   Perf. 13
C224 AP97 50fr mar, vio bl & grn 1.00   .50
C225 AP97 75fr yel grn, bl & lil
              rose   1.40   .50
    1st anniv. of the upstream voyage of the
Flotilla of Hope.

Lenin — AP98

1974, Jan. 21
C226 AP98 50fr dk red brn   2.10   .60

Skiers — AP99

1974, Feb. 8   Engr.   Perf. 11½x11
C227 AP99 200fr bl, sepia & car   3.00 1.20
    50th anniversary of the first Winter Olympic
Games, Chamonix, France.

Soccer and
Emblem
AP100

Designs: Various views of soccer game.

1974, Apr. 8   Engr.   Perf. 13
C228 AP100 75fr vio & blk   .85   .40
C229 AP100 150fr brn, lt & sl grn 1.75   .75
C230 AP100 200fr Prus bl, grn &
                   brn   2.40 1.25
    Nos. C228-C230 (3)   5.00 2.40
Souvenir Sheet
C231 AP100 250fr yel grn, brn &
                   ol brn   3.25 3.25
    World Soccer Championship, Munich, June
13-July 7.
    For overprint see No. C239.

Christmas Type of 1971
    Paintings: 50fr, Crucifixion, by Matthias Gru-
newald. 75fr, Avignon Pietà, attributed to
Enguerrand Quarton. 125fr, Burial of Christ,
by G. Isenmann.

1974, Apr. 12   Litho.   Perf. 13x12½
C232 AP75 50fr blk & multi   .70   .35
C233 AP75 75fr blk & multi   .95   .45
C234 AP75 125r blk & multi   1.60   .75
    Nos. C232-C234 (3)   3.25 1.55
    Easter 1974.

21st Chess Olympiad,
Nice, June 6-
30 — AP101

1974, June 3   Engr.   Perf. 13
C235 AP101 50fr Knights   2.10   .70
C236 AP101 75fr Kings   2.60 1.10

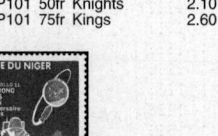

Astronaut and
Apollo 11
Badge — AP102

1974, July 20   Engr.   Perf. 13
C237 AP102 150fr multi   1.60   .80
    5th anniversary of the first manned moon
landing.

Europafrica Issue

The Rhinoceros, by Pietro
Longhi — AP103

1974, Aug. 10   Photo.   Perf. 12½x13
C238 AP103 250fr multi   7.25 4.00

No. C231 Overprinted in Red

Souvenir Sheet
1974, Sept. 27   Engr.   Perf. 13
C239 AP100 250fr multi   3.25 3.25
    World Cup Soccer Championship, Munich,
1974, victory of German Federal Republic.

Caucasian Woman,
Envelope, UPU
Emblem and
Jets — AP104

Designs (UPU emblem, Envelope and):
100fr, Oriental woman and trains. 150fr, Indian
woman and ships. 200fr, Black woman and
buses.

1974, Oct. 9   Engr.   Perf. 13
C240 AP104 50fr multi   .75   .35
C241 AP104 100fr multi   1.40   .45
C242 AP104 150fr bl & multi   2.00   .75
C243 AP104 200fr multi   2.75 1.20
    Nos. C240-C243 (4)   6.90 2.75
    Centenary of Universal Postal Union.

Skylab over
Africa — AP105

1974, Nov. 4   Engr.   Perf. 13
C244 AP105 100fr multi   1.25   .55

Virgin and Child,
by Correggio
AP106

    150fr, Virgin and Child with St. Hilary, by
Filippo Lippi. 200fr, Virgin and Child, by
Murillo.

1974, Dec. 24   Litho.   Perf. 12½x13
C245 AP106 100fr multi   1.25   .45
C246 AP106 150fr multi   2.00   .70
C247 AP106 200fr multi   2.50 1.10
    Nos. C245-C247 (3)   5.75 2.25
    Christmas 1974. See Nos. C252-C254,
C260-C262, C280-C282.

Apollo and
Emblem — AP107

    Designs (Emblem of Soyuz-Apollo Space
Docking): 100fr, Docking in space over earth.
150fr, Soyuz in space.

1975, Jan. 31   Engr.   Perf. 13
C248 AP107 50fr bl & multi   .55   .35
C249 AP107 100fr multi   1.10   .50
C250 AP107 150fr multi   1.90   .70
    Nos. C248-C250 (3)   3.55 1.55
    Russo-American space cooperation.
For overprints see Nos. C263-C265.

Europafrica Issue

European and African
Women,
Globe — AP108

1975, Feb. 28   Engr.   Perf. 13
C251 AP108 250fr brn, lil & red   3.25 1.75

Painting Type of 1974
    Easter: 75fr, Jesus in Garden of Olives, by
Delacroix, horiz. 125fr, Crucifixion, by El
Greco. 150fr, Resurrection, by Leonard
Limosin.

Perf. 13x12½, 12½x13
1975, Mar. 27   Litho.
C252 AP106 75fr multi   .85   .35
C253 AP106 125fr multi   1.60   .50
C254 AP106 150fr multi   2.00   .70
    Nos. C252-C254 (3)   4.45 1.60

Bird Type of 1968-69 Dated "1975"
    100fr, Cinnyricinclus leucogaster, vert.

1975, Apr.   Photo.   Perf. 13
C255 AP36 100fr gold & multi   4.00 1.30

Lt. Col. Seyni
Kountche
AP109

1975, Apr. 15   Litho.   Perf. 12½x13
C256 AP109 100fr multi   1.40   .70
    Military Government, first anniversary.

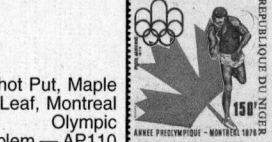

Shot Put, Maple
Leaf, Montreal
Olympic
Emblem — AP110

    Design: 200fr, Gymnast on rings, Canadian
flag, Montreal Olympic emblem.

1975, Oct. 6   Engr.   Perf. 13
C257 AP110 150fr blk & red   1.40   .70
C258 AP110 200fr red & blk   2.00 1.00
    Pre-Olympic Year 1975.

UN Emblem
and Dove
AP111

1975, Nov. 26   Engr.   Perf. 13
C259 AP111 100fr grn & bl   1.25 .50
United Nations, 30th anniversary.

Painting Type of 1974
50fr, Virgin of Seville, by Murillo. 75fr, Adoration of the Shepherds, by Tintoretto, horiz. 125fr, Virgin with Angels, Florentine, 15th cent.

1975, Dec. 24   Litho.   Perf. 12½x13
C260 AP106 50fr multi   .65 .35
C261 AP106 75fr multi   1.00 .45
C262 AP106 125fr multi   1.60 .80
    Nos. C260-C262 (3)   3.25 1.60
Christmas 1975.

Nos. C248-C250
Ovptd.

1975, Dec. 30   Engr.   Perf. 13
C263 AP107 50fr bl & multi   .70 .25
C264 AP107 100fr multi   .90 .55
C265 AP107 150fr multi   1.60 .90
    Nos. C263-C265 (3)   3.20 1.70
Apollo-Soyuz link-up in space, July 17, 1975.

12th Winter Olympic Games Type, 1976
Designs: 200fr, Women's figure skating. 300fr, Biathlon. 500fr, Speed skating.

1976, Feb. 20   Litho.   Perf. 14x13½
C266 A97 200fr multi   1.60 .80
C267 A97 300fr multi   2.40 1.20

Souvenir Sheet
C268 A97 500fr multi   4.50 2.00

American Bicentennial Type, 1976
Design (Statue of Liberty and): 150fr, Joseph Warren, martyr at Bunker Hill. 200fr, John Paul Jones on the bridge of the "Bonhomme Richard." 300fr, Molly Pitcher, Monmouth battle heroine. 500fr, Start of the fighting.

1976, Apr. 8
C269 A100 150fr multi   1.20 .40
C270 A100 200fr multi   1.75 .70
C271 A100 300fr multi   2.40 .85
    Nos. C269-C271 (3)   4.95 1.85

Souvenir Sheet
C272 A100 500fr multi   4.75 1.60

LZ-129 over Lake Constance — AP112

Designs: 50fr, LZ-3 over Würzburg. 150fr, LZ-9 over Friedrichshafen. 200fr, LZ-2 over Rothenburg, vert. 300fr, LZ-130 over Essen. 500fr, LZ-127 over the Swiss Alps.

1976, May 18   Litho.   Perf. 11
C273 AP112 40fr multi   .50 .25
C274 AP112 50fr multi   .60 .25
C275 AP112 150fr multi   1.75 .50
C276 AP112 200fr multi   2.00 .55
C277 AP112 300fr multi   3.00 .70
    Nos. C273-C277 (5)   7.85 2.25

Souvenir Sheet
C278 AP112 500fr multi   5.00 2.00
75th anniversary of the Zeppelin.

Olympic Games Issue
Souvenir Sheet
1976, July 17   Litho.   Perf. 14
C279 A105 150fr Sprint   1.75 .80

Christmas Type of 1974
Paintings: 50fr, Nativity, by Rubens. 100fr, Virgin and Child, by Correggio. 150fr, Adoration of the Kings, by Gerard David, horiz.

1976, Dec. 24   Litho.   Perf. 12½
C280 AP106 50fr multi   .60 .25
C281 AP106 100fr multi   1.25 .50
C282 AP106 150fr multi   2.00 .85
    Nos. C280-C282 (3)   3.85 1.60
Christmas 1976.

Viking Mars Project Issue
100fr, Viking lander & nprobe, horiz. 150fr, Descent phases of Viking lander. 200fr, Titan rocket start for Mars. 400fr, Viking orbiter in flight.

1977, Mar. 15   Litho.   Perf. 14
C283 A113 100fr multi   .80 .25
C284 A113 150fr multi   1.10 .45
C285 A113 200fr multi   1.60 .60
    Nos. C283-C285 (3)   3.50 1.10

Souvenir Sheet
C286 A113 400fr multi   3.25 1.25
For overprints see Nos. C295-C297.

Nobel Prize Issue
Souvenir Sheet
Design: 500fr, Theodore Roosevelt, peace.

1977, Aug. 20   Litho.   Perf. 14
C287 A122 500fr multi   4.75 1.40

Games' Emblem,
Wheels and
Colors — AP113

150fr, Rings, colors and Games' emblem.

1978, July 13   Litho.   Perf. 12½x13
C288 AP113 40fr multi   .40 .30
C289 AP113 150fr multi   1.40 .70
Third African Games, Algiers, July 13-28.

Emblem — AP114

1978, Oct. 6   Litho.   Perf. 13
C290 AP114 150fr multi   1.25 .70
Niger Broadcasting Company, 20th anniversary.

Philexafrique II — Essen Issue
Common Design Types
Designs: No. C291, Giraffes and Niger No. 92. No. C292, Eagle and Oldenburg No. 7.

1978, Nov. 1   Litho.   Perf. 13x12½
C291 CD138 100fr multi   2.25 1.40
C292 CD139 100fr multi   2.25 1.40
    a.   Pair, #C291-C292 + label   6.00 6.00

View of
Campus and
Laying
Cornerstone
AP115

1978, Dec. 11   Litho.   Perf. 12½
C293 AP115 100fr multi   2.00 .40
Islamic University of Niger.

Control Tower,
Emblem, Plane,
Map of
Niger — AP116

1979, Dec. 12   Litho.   Perf. 12½
C294 AP116 150fr multi   1.50 .80
ASECNA (Air Safety Board), 20th anniversary.

Nos. C284-C286
Overprinted in
Silver or Black

1979, Dec. 20   Litho.   Perf. 14
C295 A113 150fr multi   1.25 .70
C296 A113 200fr multi (S)   1.60 .85

Souvenir Sheet
C297 A113 400fr multi   3.50 3.50
Apollo 11 moon landing, 10th anniversary.

Gaweye
Hotel — AP117

1980, Jan. 10   Litho.   Perf. 13
C298 AP117 100fr multi   .90 .45

Self-portrait, by
Rembrandt
AP118

Rembrandt Portraits: 90fr, Hendrickje at the Window. 100fr, Old Man. 130fr, Maria Trip. 200fr, Self-portrait, diff. 400fr, Saskia.

1981, Feb. 12   Litho.   Perf. 12½
C299 AP118 60fr multi   .45 .25
C300 AP118 90fr multi   .70 .25
C301 AP118 100fr multi   .80 .30
C302 AP118 130fr multi   1.10 .40
C303 AP118 200fr multi   1.60 .40
C304 AP118 400fr multi   3.25 1.00
    Nos. C299-C304 (6)   7.90 2.60

Apollo 11,
1969
AP119

Space Conquest: Views of Columbia space shuttle, 1981.

1981, Mar. 30   Litho.   Perf. 12½
C305 AP119 100fr multi   .80 .30
C306 AP119 150fr multi   1.25 .35
C307 AP119 200fr multi   1.40 .45
C308 AP119 300fr multi   2.25 .75
    Nos. C305-C308 (4)   5.70 1.85

Souvenir Sheet
C309 AP119 500fr multi   4.25 1.60
For overprint see No. C356.

Girl in a
Room, by
Picasso
AP120

Picasso Birth Centenary: 60fr, Olga in an Armchair. 90fr, Family of Acrobats. 120fr, Three Musicians. 200fr, Paul on a Donkey. All vert.

1981, June 25   Litho.   Perf. 12½
C310 AP120 60fr multi   .50 .25
C311 AP120 90fr multi   .80 .30
C312 AP120 120fr multi   1.00 .40
C313 AP120 200fr multi   1.75 .60
C314 AP120 400fr multi   3.50 1.10
    Nos. C310-C314 (5)   7.55 2.65

Christmas
1982 — AP121

Rubens Paintings — 200fr, Adoration of the Kings. 300fr, Mystical Marriage of St. Catherine. 400fr, Virgin and Child.

1982, Dec. 24   Litho.   Perf. 14
C315 AP121 200fr multi   1.50 .40
C316 AP121 300fr multi   2.25 .65
C317 AP121 400fr multi   3.00 .90
    Nos. C315-C317 (3)   6.75 1.95

Manned Flight
Bicentenary
AP122

65fr, Montgolfiere balloon, 1783, vert. 85fr, Hydrogen balloon, 1783, vert. 200fr, Zeppelin. 250fr, Farman plane. 300fr, Concorde. 500fr, Apollo 11, vert.

1983, Jan. 24
C318 AP122 65fr multi   .50 .25
C319 AP122 85fr multi   .75 .25
C320 AP122 200fr multi   1.50 .40
C321 AP122 250fr multi   2.00 .60
C322 AP122 300fr multi   2.25 .70
C323 AP122 500fr multi   4.00 1.10
    Nos. C318-C323 (6)   11.00 3.30

Pre-Olympic
Year
AP123

1983, May 25   Litho.   Perf. 13
C324 AP123 85fr Javelin   .60 .25
C325 AP123 200fr Shot put   1.60 .55
C326 AP123 250fr Hammer, vert.   1.90 .70
C327 AP123 300fr Discus   2.40 .80
    Nos. C324-C327 (4)   6.50 2.30

Souvenir Sheet
C328 AP123 500fr Shot put, diff.   4.00 1.50
For overprint see No. C357.

Christmas
1983
AP124

Botticelli Paintings — 120fr, Virgin and Child with Angels, vert. 350fr, Adoration of the Kings. 500fr, Virgin of the Pomegranate, vert.

Wmk. 385 Cartor
1983   Litho.   Perf. 13
C329 AP124 120fr multi   .90 .35
C330 AP124 350fr multi   2.75 .75
C331 AP124 500fr multi   3.75 1.10
    Nos. C329-C331 (3)   7.40 2.20

1984 Summer
Olympics
AP125

80fr, Sprint. 120fr, Pole vault. 140fr, High
jump. 200fr, Triple jump, vert. 350fr, Long
jump, vert.
500fr, 110-meter hurdles.

Unwmk.

1984, Feb. 22		**Litho.**		**Perf. 13**
C332	AP125	80fr multi	.55	.25
C333	AP125	120fr multi	.80	.25
C334	AP125	140fr multi	1.25	.40
C335	AP125	200fr multi	1.75	.40
C336	AP125	350fr multi	2.75	.90
	Nos. C332-C336 (5)		7.10	2.20

Souvenir Sheet

C337	AP125	500fr multi	3.75	1.25

1984, Oct. 8 — **Litho.**

Designs: Winners of various track events:
80fr, Carl Lewis, vert. 120fr, J. Cruz, vert.
140fr, A. Cova, vert. 300fr, Al Joyner, vert.
500fr, D. Mogenburg, high jump.

C338	AP125	80fr multi	.55	.30
C339	AP125	120fr multi	.90	.45
C340	AP125	140fr multi	1.00	.50
C341	AP125	300fr multi	2.10	1.10
	Nos. C338-C341 (4)		4.55	2.40

Souvenir Sheet

C342	AP125	500fr multi	3.75	2.25

World Soccer
Cup
AP126

1984, Nov. 19		**Litho.**		**Perf. 13**
C345	AP126	150fr multi	.90	.60
C346	AP126	250fr multi	1.60	1.05
C347	AP126	450fr multi	3.00	1.60
C348	AP126	500fr multi	3.25	1.90
	Nos. C345-C348 (4)		8.75	5.15

Christmas
1984 — AP127

Paintings: 100fr, The Visitation, by Ghir-
landajo. 200fr, Virgin and Child, by the Master
of Santa Verdiana. 400fr, Virgin and Child, by
J. Koning.

1984, Dec. 24		**Litho.**		**Perf. 13**
C349	AP127	100fr multi	.80	.45
C350	AP127	200fr multi	1.60	.95
C351	AP127	400fr multi	3.25	1.40
	Nos. C349-C351 (3)		5.65	2.80

Audubon
Birth
Bicentennial
AP128

110fr, Himantopus mexicanus. 140fr,
Phoenicopterus ruber, vert. 200fr, Fratercula
arctica. 350fr, Sterna paradisaea, vert.

1985, Feb. 6		**Litho.**		**Perf. 13**
C352	AP128	110fr multi	.90	.50
C353	AP128	140fr multi	1.40	.55
C354	AP128	200fr multi	1.75	.85
C355	AP128	350fr multi	3.25	1.40
	Nos. C352-C355 (4)		7.30	3.30

**Nos. C309, C328 Ovptd. in Silver
with Exhibition Emblems**

1985, Mar. 11 Litho. Perf. 12½, 13
C356 AP119 500fr ARGENTINA
'85 BUENOS
AIRES 4.75 4.75

C357 AP123 500fr OLYMPHILEX
'85 LAU-
SANNE 4.75 4.75

Religious
Paintings by
Bartolome Murillo
(1617-1682)
AP129

110fr, Virgin of the Rosary. 250fr, The
Immaculate Conception. 390fr, Virgin of
Seville.

1985, Dec. 19		**Litho.**		**Perf. 13**
C358	AP129	110fr multi	.80	.45
C359	AP129	250fr multi	2.10	1.00
C360	AP129	390fr multi	3.50	1.60
	Nos. C358-C360 (3)		6.40	3.05

Christmas 1985.

Halley's
Comet
AP130

110fr, Over Paris, 1910. 130fr, Over New
York. 200fr, Giotto space probe. 300fr, Vega
probe. 390fr, Planet A probe.

1985, Dec. 26				
C361	AP130	110fr multi	.80	.40
C362	AP130	130fr multi	.90	.55
C363	AP130	200fr multi	1.60	.80
C364	AP130	300fr multi	2.25	1.20
C365	AP130	390fr multi	3.00	1.60
	Nos. C361-C365 (5)		8.55	4.55

Martin Luther King,
Jr. (1929-1968), Civil
Rights
Activist — AP131

1986, Apr. 28 Litho. Perf. 13½
C366 AP131 500fr multi 4.00 2.00

1986 World Cup Soccer
Championships, Mexico — AP132

Various soccer plays, stamps and labels.

1986, May 21				**Perf. 13**
C367	AP132	130fr No. 228	.90	.40
C368	AP132	210fr No. 229	1.40	.70
C369	AP132	390fr No. 230	2.75	1.25
C370	AP132	400fr Aztec drawing	2.75	1.25
	Nos. C367-C370 (4)		7.80	3.60

Souvenir Sheet

C371	AP132	500fr World Cup	3.75	2.25

Statue of Liberty,
Cent. — AP133

300fr, Bartholdi, statue.

1986, June 19
C372 AP133 300fr multi 2.60 1.35

1988 Summer
Olympics,
Seoul — AP134

Olympic Rings, Pierre de Coubertin and:
85fr, One-man kayak, vert. 165fr, Crew racing.
200fr, Two-man kayak. 600fr, One-man kayak,
diff., vert. 750fr, One-man kayak, diff., vert.

1988, June 22		**Litho.**		**Perf. 13**
C373	AP134	85fr multi	.60	.30
C374	AP134	165fr multi	1.15	.60
C375	AP134	200fr multi	1.50	.80
C376	AP134	600fr multi	4.25	2.25
	Nos. C373-C376 (4)		7.50	3.95

Souvenir Sheet

C377	AP134	750fr multi	5.75	4.50

First Moon
Landing, 20th
Anniv. — AP135

200fr, Launch. 300fr, Crew. 350fr, Lunar
experiments. 400fr, Raising flag.

1989, July 27		**Litho.**		**Perf. 13**
C378	AP135	200fr multi	1.60	.75
C379	AP135	300fr multi	2.40	1.25
C380	AP135	350fr multi	2.75	1.40
C381	AP135	400fr multi	3.25	1.50
	Nos. C378-C381 (4)		10.00	4.90

1990 World Cup Soccer
Championships, Italy — AP136

Athletes & views or symbols of Italian cities.

1990, Mar. 6		**Litho.**		**Perf. 13**
C382	AP136	130fr Florence	.90	.45
C383	AP136	210fr Verona	1.50	.85
C384	AP136	500fr Bari	3.25	2.00
C385	AP136	600fr Rome	4.00	2.40
	Nos. C382-C385 (4)		9.65	5.70

1992 Winter
Olympics,
Albertville
AP138

110fr, Speed skating. 300fr, Ice hockey.
500fr, Downhill skiing. 600fr, Luge.

1991, Mar. 28		**Litho.**		**Perf. 13**
C392	AP138	110fr multicolored	.70	.35
C393	AP138	300fr multicolored	2.10	1.25
C394	AP138	500fr multicolored	3.50	2.00
C395	AP138	600fr multicolored	4.25	2.40
	Nos. C392-C395 (4)		10.55	6.00

AIR POST SEMI-POSTAL STAMPS

**Dahomey types SPAP1-SPAP3
inscribed Niger**
Perf. 13½x12½, 13 (#CB3)
Photo, Engr. (#CB3)
1942, June 22

CB1	SPAP1	1.50fr + 3.50fr		
		green	.35	5.00
CB2	SPAP2	2fr + 6fr brown	.35	5.00
CB3	SPAP3	3fr + 9fr car red	.35	5.00
	Nos. CB1-CB3 (3)		1.05	15.00
Set, never hinged			3.00	

Native children's welfare fund.

Colonial Education Fund
Common Design Type
Perf. 12½x13½
1942, June 22 — **Engr.**

CB4	CD86a	1.20fr + 1.80fr blue		
		& red	.35	5.00
Never hinged			.90	

POSTAGE DUE STAMPS

1914 Upper Senegal and
Niger Postage Due Stamps
Ovptd.

1921		**Unwmk.**		**Perf. 14x13½**
J1	D1	5c green	.75	.95
J2	D1	10c rose	.75	.95
J3	D1	15c gray	.75	1.05
J4	D1	20c brown	.75	1.05
J5	D1	30c blue	.75	1.20
J6	D1	50c black	.75	1.20
J7	D1	60c orange	1.60	2.00
J8	D1	1fr violet	1.60	2.00
	Nos. J1-J8 (8)		7.70	10.40

Caravansary Near
Timbuktu — D2

1927				**Typo.**
J9	D2	2c dk bl & red	.35	.35
J10	D2	4c ver & blk	.35	.35
J11	D2	5c org & vio	.35	.35
J12	D2	10c red brn & blk vio	.35	.35
J13	D2	15c grn & org	.35	.35
J14	D2	20c cer & ol brn	.35	.70
J15	D2	25c blk & ol brn	.35	.70
J16	D2	30c dl vio & blk	1.40	1.40
J17	D2	50c dp red, *grnsh*	.70	1.10
J18	D2	60c gray vio & org,		
		bluish	.70	.70
J19	D2	1fr ind & ultra, *bluish*	1.00	1.20
J20	D2	2fr rose red & vio	1.10	1.40
J21	D2	3fr org brn & ultra	1.75	2.00
	Nos. J9-J21 (13)		9.10	10.95

> **Catalogue values for unused
> stamps in this section, from this
> point to the end of the section, are
> for Never Hinged items.**

Republic of the Niger

Cross of
Agadez — D3

Native Metalcraft: 3fr, 5fr, 10fr, Cross of Ifer-
ouane. 15fr, 20fr, 50fr, Cross of Tahoua.

Perf. 12½

1962, July 1		**Unwmk.**		**Photo.**
J22	D3	50c emerald	.25	.25
J23	D3	1fr violet	.25	.25
J24	D3	2fr slate green	.25	.25
J25	D3	3fr lilac rose	.25	.25
J26	D3	5fr green	.25	.25
J27	D3	10fr orange	.25	.25
J28	D3	15fr deep blue	.25	.25
J29	D3	20fr carmine	.25	.25
J30	D3	50fr chocolate	.35	.35
	Nos. J22-J30 (9)		2.35	2.35

1993   Litho.   Perf. 12½
Designs as Before
Size: 50x50mm

J31	D3	5fr green	.25	.25
J32	D3	10fr orange	.25	.25
J33	D3	15fr blue	.25	.25
J34	D3	20fr red	.25	.25
J35	D3	50fr chocolate	.40	.40
		Nos. J31-J35 (5)	1.40	1.40

Imprint on Nos. J31-J35 is in black.

OFFICIAL STAMPS

> Catalogue values for unused stamps in this section are for Never Hinged items.

Djerma Girl Carrying Jug — O1

Denomination in Black

Perf. 14x13½

1962-71		Typo.	Unwmk.	
O1	O1	1fr dark purple	.25	.25
O2	O1	2fr yel grn	.25	.25
O3	O1	5fr brt blue	.25	.25
O4	O1	10fr deep red	.25	.25
O5	O1	20fr vio blue	.25	.25
O6	O1	25fr orange	.25	.25
O7	O1	30fr light blue ('65)	.30	.25
O8	O1	35fr pale grn ('71)	.40	.30
O9	O1	40fr brown ('71)	.40	.30
O10	O1	50fr black	.40	.30
O11	O1	60fr rose red	.60	.35
O12	O1	85fr blue green	.90	.35
O13	O1	100fr red lilac	.95	.35
O14	O1	200fr dark blue	2.00	.75
		Nos. O1-O14 (14)	7.45	4.45

Djerma Girl Carrying Jug — O2

Denomination Same Color As Design

1988, Nov.   Photo. & Typo.   Perf. 13

O15	O2	5fr brt blue	.25	.25
O16	O2	10fr henna brn	.25	.25
O17	O2	20fr vio blue	.25	.25
O18	O2	50fr greenish blk	.55	.30

1989-96(?)

O19	O2	15fr bright yellow	.25	.25
O20	O2	45fr orange	.30	.25
O21	O2	85fr blue green	—	—
O22	O2	100fr red lilac	—	—

Issued: 15, 45fr, 3/89; 85, 100fr, 1996(?).
See No. 698.

Djerma Girl Carrying Jug Type of 1988

1995 ?   Litho.   Perf. 13
Denomination in Black

O24	O2	35fr dull green	—	—

Three additional stamps were issued in this set. The editors would like to examine any examples.

NIGER COAST PROTECTORATE

'nī-jər 'kōst prə-'tek-t͟ə-rət

(Oil Rivers Protectorate)

LOCATION — West coast of Africa on Gulf of Guinea
GOVT. — British Protectorate

This territory was originally known as the Oil Rivers Protectorate, and its affairs were conducted by the British Royal Niger Company. The Company surrendered its charter to the Crown in 1899. In 1900 all of the territories formerly controlled by the Royal Niger Company were incorporated into the two protectorates of Northern and

Southern Nigeria, the latter absorbing the area formerly known as Niger Coast Protectorate. In 1914 Northern and Southern Nigeria joined to form the Crown Colony of Nigeria. (See Nigeria, Northern Nigeria, Southern Nigeria and Lagos.)

12 Pence = 1 Shilling

Stamps of Great Britain, 1881-87, Overprinted in Black

1892		Wmk. 30	Perf. 14	
1	A54	½p vermilion	22.50	13.00
2	A40	1p lilac	13.00	11.00
a.		"OIL RIVERS" at top	10,000.	
b.		Half used as ½p on cover		2,750.
3	A56	2p green & car	40.00	9.50
		Half used as 1p on cover		2,500.
4	A57	2½p violet, bl	10.00	2.75
5	A61	5p lilac & blue	20.00	7.25
6	A65	1sh green	77.50	100.00
		Nos. 1-6 (6)	183.00	143.50

For surcharges see Nos. 7-36, 50.

Dangerous forgeries exist of all surcharges.

No. 2 Surcharged in Red or Violet

1893

7	A40	½p on half of 1p (R)	175.	160.
c.		Unsevered pair	550.	500.
d.		As "c," surcharge inverted and dividing line reversed		27,500.
e.		"½" omitted		
f.		Straight top to "1" in "½"	390.	400.
g.		Double surcharge in pair with normal		2,100.
7A	A40	½p on half of 1p (V)	7,750.	5,500.
b.		Surcharge double	27,500.	
c.		Unsevered pair	20,000.	17,500.

Nos. 3-6 Handstamp Srchd. in Violet, Red, Carmine, Bluish Black, Deep Blue, Green or Black

1893		Wmk. 30	Perf. 14	
8	A56	½p on 2p (V)	525.	325.
a.		Surcharge inverted	19,000.	
b.		Surcharge diagonal, inverted	18,500.	
9	A57	½p on 2½p (V)	14,000.	
10	A57	½p on 2½p (R)	425.	275.
a.		Surcharge inverted	12,500.	
b.		Surcharge diagonal, inverted	14,500.	
11	A57	½p on 2½p (C)	25,000.	24,500.
12	A57	½p on 2½p (B)	40,000.	—
13	A57	½p on 2½p (G)	550.	

14	A56	½p on 2p (V)	500.	375.
15	A56	½p on 2p (Bl)	2,200.	825.
16	A57	½p on 2½p (V)	7,750.	
17	A57	½p on 2½p (R)	650.	775.
18	A57	½p on 2½p (Bl)	475.	450.
19	A57	½p on 2½p (G)	500.	550.

20	A56	½p on 2p (V)	550.	775.
a.		Surcharge inverted	17,500.	
21	A57	½p on 2½p (R)	600.	475.
a.		Surcharge inverted	20,000.	
b.		Surcharge diagonal, inverted	8,250.	
22	A57	½p on 2½p (C)	475.	500.
23	A57	½p on 2½p (Bl Bk)	5,500.	
24	A57	½p on 2½p (Bl)	475.	525.
25	A57	½p on 2½p (G)	325.	275.
a.		Surcharge diagonal, inverted		

26	A57	½p on 2½p (Bk)	4,750.	
a.		Surcharge inverted	15,500.	
b.		Surcharge diagonal, inverted	13,500.	

27	A57	½p on 2½p (R)	10,000.	
28	A57	½p on 2½p (G)	550.	500.

29	A56	1sh on 2p (V)	500.	425.
a.		Surcharge inverted	13,500.	
b.		Surcharge diagonal, inverted	12,500.	
30	A56	1sh on 2p (R)	825.	4,500.
a.		Surcharge inverted	18,000.	
31	A56	1sh on 2p (Bk)	6,500.	
a.		Surcharge inverted	21,000.	

32	A56	5sh on 2d (V)	10,000.	11,500.
a.		Surcharge inverted	55,000.	
33	A61	10sh on 5p (R)	7,250.	11,000.
a.		Surcharge inverted	55,000.	
34	A65	20sh on 1sh (V)	165,000.	
a.		Surcharge inverted	190,000.	
35	A65	20sh on 1sh (R)	145,000.	
36	A65	20sh on 1sh (Bk)	145,000.	

The handstamped 1893 surcharges are known inverted, vertical, etc.

Queen Victoria
A8   A9

A10   A11

A12   A13

1893		Unwmk.	Perf. 12 to 15	
37	A8	½p vermilion	9.00	11.00
38	A9	1p light blue	5.75	5.25
a.		Half used as ½p on cover		825.00
39	A10	2p green	22.00	20.00
a.		Half used as 1p on cover		1,000.
b.		Horiz. pair, imperf. between		17,500.
40	A11	2½p car lake	20.00	4.50
41	A12	5p gray lilac	24.00	15.00
a.		5p lilac	16.50	24.00
42	A13	1sh black	15.50	16.00
		Nos. 37-42 (6)	96.25	71.75

For surcharge see No. 49.

A15   A16

A17   A18

A19   A20

1894				Engr.
43	A15	½p yel green	5.50	5.50
44	A16	1p vermilion	15.00	9.50
a.		1p orange vermilion	25.00	17.50
b.		Diagonal half, used as ½p on cover		875.00
45	A17	2p car lake	35.00	7.25
a.		Half used as 1p on cover		
46	A18	2½p blue	10.00	4.50
47	A19	5p dp violet	14.00	6.00
48	A20	1sh black	70.00	8.50
		Nos. 43-48 (6)	149.50	41.25

See #55-59, 61. For surcharges see #51-54.

Halves of Nos. 38, 3 & 44 Srchd. in Red, Blue, Violet or Black

No. 49

No. 50

Nos. 51-53

1894

49	A9	½p on half of 1p (R)	1,300.	425.
a.		Inverted surcharge	15,500.	

Perf. 14
Wmk. 30

50	A56	1p on half of 2p (R)	1,950.	425.
a.		Double surcharge	7,250.	1,350.
b.		Inverted surcharge		2,250.

Perf. 12 to 15
Unwmk.

51	A16	½p on half of 1p (Bl)	3,850.	550.
a.		Double surcharge		
52	A16	½p on half of 1p (V)	4,400.	775.
53	A16	½p on half of 1p (Bk)	6,000.	1,100.

This surcharge is found on both vertical and diagonal halves of the 1p.

No. 46 Surcharged in Black

1894

54	A18	½p on 2½p blue	475.	275.
a.		Double surcharge	8,750.	2,500.

The surcharge is found in eight types. The "OIE" variety is broken type.

A27   A28

A29

1897-98   Wmk. 2

55	A15	½p yel green	3.50	3.00
56	A16	1p vermilion	9.00	1.60
a.		1p orange-vermilion	3.00	1.50
57	A17	2p car lake	4.75	2.50
58	A18	2½p blue	17.50	3.25
a.		2½p slate blue	7.50	3.00
59	A19	5p dp violet	22.50	90.00
a.		5p purple	13.00	95.00
60	A27	6p yel brn ('98)	8.00	10.00
61	A20	1sh black	17.50	32.50
62	A28	2sh6p olive bister	24.00	90.00
63	A29	10sh dp pur ('98)	140.00	250.00
a.		10sh bright purple	135.00	225.00
		Nos. 55-63 (9)	246.75	482.85

The stamps of Niger Coast Protectorate were superseded in Jan. 1900, by those of Northern and Southern Nigeria.

NIGERIA

nī-'jir-ē-ə

LOCATION — West coast of Africa, bordering on the Gulf of Guinea
GOVT. — Republic
AREA — 356,669 sq. mi.
POP. — 113,828,587 (1999 est.)
CAPITAL — Abuja

The colony and protectorate were formed in 1914 by the union of Northern and Southern Nigeria. The mandated territory of Cameroons (British) was also attached for administrative purposes. The Federation of Nigeria was formed in 1960. It became a republic in 1963. See Niger Coast Protectorate, Lagos, Northern Nigeria and Southern Nigeria.

12 Pence = 1 Shilling
20 Shillings = 1 Pound
100 Kobo = 1 Naira (1973)

Catalogue values for unused stamps in this country are for Never Hinged items, beginning with Scott 71 in the regular postage section, Scott B1 in the semipostal section and Scott J1 in the postage due section.

Watermarks

Wmk. 335 — FN Multiple

Wmk. 379 — NIGERIA in Continuous Wavy Lines

King George V — A1

Numerals of 3p, 4p, 6p, 5sh and £1 of type A1 are in color on plain tablet.
Dies I and II are described at front of this volume.

Die I
Ordinary Paper

Wmk. Multiple Crown and CA (3)

1914-27   Typo.   Perf. 14

1	A1	½p green	5.50	.70
a.		Booklet pane of 6		
2	A1	1p carmine	5.25	.25
a.		Booklet pane of 6		
b.		1p scarlet ('16)	16.00	.25
3	A1	2p gray	9.00	2.00
a.		2p slate gray ('18)	10.00	.85
4	A1	2½p ultramarine	10.00	8.00
a.		2½p dull blue	225.00	

Chalky Paper

5	A1	3p violet, yel	1.60	3.00
6	A1	4p blk & red, yel	1.25	6.00
7	A1	6p dull vio & red vio	10.00	11.00
8	A1	1sh black, green, white back	2.25	22.50
a.		1sh black, yel grn (white back) ('15)	1.40	15.00
b.		1sh As "a," yellow green back ('15)	60.00	60.00
c.		As "a," blue green back ('15)	4.00	9.50
d.		As "c," ovpt. "SPECIMEN"	40.00	
e.		1sh black, "bl grn," pale olive back ('17)	42.50	52.50
f.		1sh black, "emerald," pale olive back ('20)	8.00	50.00
g.		1sh black, "emerald," emerald back ('20)	1.75	15.00
9	A1	2sh6p blk & red, bl	17.50	6.75
10	A1	5sh grn & red, yel, white back	25.00	65.00
11	A1	10sh grn & red, bl grn, white back	60.00	175.00
a.		10sh bl grn & red, bl grnr, bl grn back ('15)	75.00	100.00
b.		As "a," ovpt. "SPECIMEN"	55.00	
c.		10sh grn & red, blue grn, pale olive back ('17)	11.00	17.50
d.		10sh grn & red, emerald, pale olive back ('20)	160.00	250.00
e.		10sh grn & red, emerald, emerald back ('20)	40.00	120.00
12	A1	£1 vio & blk, red	190.00	260.00
a.		Die II ('27)	275.00	350.00
		Nos. 1-12 (12)	337.35	560.20

Surface-colored Paper

13	A1	3p violet, yel	3.50	12.00
14	A1	4p black & red, yel	1.60	11.50
15	A1	1sh black, green	1.60	25.00
a.		1sh black, emerald	225.00	
16	A1	5sh grn & red, yel	21.00	55.00
17	A1	10sh grn & red, grn	50.00	180.00
		Nos. 13-17 (5)	77.70	283.50

Die II

1921-33   Ordinary Paper   Wmk. 4

18	A1	½p green	6.50	.90
a.		Die I	1.25	.75
19	A1	1p carmine	1.75	.55
a.		Booklet pane of 6	27.50	
b.		Die I	3.25	.35
c.		Booklet pane of 6, Die I	37.50	
20	A1	1½p orange ('31)	9.25	.25
21	A1	2p gray	10.00	.40
a.		Die I	2.25	8.00
b.		Booklet pane of 6, Die I	55.00	
22	A1	2p red brown ('27)	5.00	1.00
a.		Booklet pane of 6	60.00	
23	A1	2p dk brown ('28)	5.50	.25
a.		Booklet pane of 6	50.00	
b.		Die I ('32)	6.50	.75
24	A1	2½p ultra (die I)	1.50	15.00
25	A1	3p dp violet	11.00	1.10
a.		Die I ('24)	6.00	5.00
26	A1	3p ultra ('31)	12.00	1.25

Chalky Paper

27	A1	4p blk & red, yel	1.10	.60
a.		Die I ('32)	4.00	5.00
28	A1	6p dull vio & red vio	8.00	9.00
a.		Die I	14.00	42.50
29	A1	1sh black, emerald	8.00	2.25
30	A1	2sh6p blk & red, bl	10.00	52.50
a.		Die I ('32)	50.00	85.00
31	A1	5sh green & red, yel ('26)	20.00	80.00
a.		Die I ('32)	75.00	250.00
32	A1	10sh green & red, emer	75.00	225.00
a.		Die I ('32)	140.00	500.00
		Nos. 18-32 (15)	184.60	390.05

Silver Jubilee Issue
Common Design Type

1935, May 6   Engr.   Perf. 11x12

34	CD301	1½p black & ultra	1.00	1.50
35	CD301	2p indigo & green	2.00	2.00
36	CD301	3p ultra & brown	3.50	22.00
37	CD301	1sh brown vio & ind	11.00	47.50
		Nos. 34-37 (4)	17.50	73.00
		Set, never hinged	24.00	
		Set, perf "SPECIMEN"	125.00	

Wharf at Apapa — A2

Dredging for Tin A4

Fishing Village A6

Minaret at Habe — A8

Victoria-Buea Road — A10

View of Niger at Jebba — A12

Picking Cacao Pods — A3

Timber A5

Ginning Cotton A7

Fulani Cattle — A9

Oil Palms — A11

Nigerian Canoe — A13

1936, Feb. 1   Perf. 11½x13

38	A2	½p green	1.50	1.40
39	A3	1p rose car	.60	.40
40	A4	1½p brown	2.00	.40
a.		Perf. 12½x13½	85.00	5.00
41	A5	2p black	.60	.80
42	A6	3p dark blue	2.00	1.50
a.		Perf. 12½x13½	150.00	27.50
43	A7	4p red brown	2.50	2.00
44	A8	6p dull violet	.75	.75
45	A9	1sh olive green	1.75	5.00

Perf. 14

46	A10	2sh6p ultra & blk	10.00	45.00
47	A11	5sh ol grn & blk	25.00	65.00
48	A12	10sh slate & blk	90.00	150.00
49	A13	£1 orange & blk	150.00	225.00
		Nos. 38-49 (12)	286.70	497.25
		Set, never hinged	400.00	
		Set, perf "SPECIMEN"	300.00	

Common Design Types pictured following the introduction.

Coronation Issue
Common Design Type

1937, May 12   Perf. 11x11½

50	CD302	1p dark carmine	.50	2.00
51	CD302	1½p dark brown	1.25	2.50
52	CD302	3p deep ultra	1.50	4.00
		Nos. 50-52 (3)	3.25	8.50
		Set, never hinged		6.50

George VI — A14

Victoria-Buea Road — A15

Niger at Jebba — A16

1938-51   Wmk. 4   Perf. 12

53	A14	½p deep green	.25	.25
a.		Perf. 11 ½ ('50)	1.40	1.75
54	A14	1p dk carmine	.40	.30
55	A14	1½p red brown	.25	.25
a.		Perf. 11 ½ ('50)	.25	.25
56	A14	2p black	.25	3.00
57	A14	2½p orange ('41)	.25	3.00
58	A14	3p deep blue	.25	.25
59	A14	4p orange	32.50	4.00
60	A14	6p brown violet	.30	.25
a.		Perf. 11 ½ ('51)	1.40	.60
61	A14	1sh olive green	.40	.25
a.		Perf. 11 ½ ('50)	.90	.25
62	A14	1sh3p turq blue ('40)	.60	.70
a.		Perf. 11 ½ ('50)	2.10	.70
63	A15	2sh6p ultra & blk ('51)	1.50	4.50
a.		Perf. 13 ½ ('42)	2.25	7.00
b.		Perf. 14 ('42)	2.00	3.50
c.		Perf. 13x11½	37.50	24.00
64	A16	5sh org & blk, perf. 13 ½ ('42)	4.50	4.50
a.		Perf. 12 ('49)	5.50	4.00
b.		Perf. 14 ('48)	6.75	3.00
c.		Perf. 13x11 ½	67.50	21.00

1944, Dec. 1   Perf. 12

65	A14	1p red violet	.25	.30
a.		Perf. 11 ½ ('50)	.60	.60
66	A14	2p deep red	.25	3.00
a.		Perf. 11 ½ ('50)	.35	.70
67	A14	3p black	.25	3.50
68	A14	4p dark blue	.25	4.00
		Nos. 53-68 (16)	42.45	32.05
		Set, never hinged	75.00	

Issue date: Nos. 65a, 66a, Feb. 15.

Catalogue values for unused stamps in this section, from this point to the end of the section, are for Never Hinged items.

Peace Issue
Common Design Type

1946, Oct. 21   Engr.   Perf. 13½x14

71	CD303	1½p brown	.35	.25
72	CD303	4p deep blue	.35	2.50

Silver Wedding Issue
Common Design Types

1948, Dec. 20   Photo.   Perf. 14x14½

73	CD304	1p brt red violet	.35	.30

Perf. 11½x11
Engraved; Name Typographed

74	CD305	5sh brown orange	17.50	22.50

UPU Issue
Common Design Types
Engr.; Name Typo. on 3p, 6p
Perf. 13½, 11x11½

1949, Oct. 10   Wmk. 4

75	CD306	1p red violet	.25	.25
76	CD307	3p indigo	.35	3.50
77	CD308	6p rose violet	.80	3.50
78	CD309	1sh olive	1.40	2.00
		Nos. 75-78 (4)	2.80	9.25

Coronation Issue
Common Design Type

1953, June 2   Engr.   Perf. 13½x13

79	CD312	1½p brt grn & blk	.40	.25

Manilla (Bracelet) Currency — A17

Olokun Head, Ife — A18

Designs: 1p, Bornu horsemen. 1½p, Peanuts, Kano City. 2p, Mining tin. 3p, Jebba Bridge over Niger River. 4p, Cocoa industry. 1sh, Logging. 2sh6p, Victoria harbor. 5sh, Loading palm oil. 10sh, Goats and Fulani cattle. £1, Lagos waterfront, 19th and 20th centuries.

1953, Sept. 1   Perf. 14
Size: 35½x22½mm

80	A17	½p red org & blk	.25	.25
81	A17	1p ol gray & blk	.25	.25
82	A17	1½p blue green	.50	.25
83	A17	2p bister & blk	4.00	.30
84	A17	3p purple & blk	.50	.30
85	A17	4p ultra & black	2.50	.25
86	A18	6p blk & org brn	.30	.25
87	A17	1sh brn vio & blk	.50	.25

Size: 40½x24½mm

88	A17	2sh6p green & black	16.00	1.25
89	A17	5sh ver & black	5.50	1.40
90	A17	10sh red brn & blk	24.00	3.25

Size: 42x31½mm

91	A17	£1 violet & black	32.50	16.00
		Nos. 80-91 (12)	86.80	24.00

Booklet panes of 4 of Nos. 80, 81, 84, 87 were issued in 1957. They are identical to margin blocks of 4 from sheets.
See No. 93.

No. 83
Overprinted in
Black

1956, Jan. 28   Wmk. 4   Perf. 13½
92	A17	2p bister & black	.40	.30

Visit of Queen Elizabeth II to Nigeria, Jan.-Feb., 1956.

Mining Tin Type of 1953

Two types:
I — Broken row of dots between "G" and miner's head.
II — Complete row of dots.

1956-57
93	A17	2p bluish gray (shades)		
		(I)	3.25	2.00
b.		2p gray (shades) (II)	4.75	.40

Booklet pane of 4 of No. 93 was issued in 1957. See note after No. 91.

Ambas Bay,
Victoria
Harbor — A19

Wmk. 314
1958, Dec. 1   Engr.   Perf. 13½
94	A19	3p purple & black	.40	.30

Cent. of the founding of Victoria, Southern Cameroons.

1959, Mar. 14

3p, Lugard Hall, Kaduna. 1sh, Kano Mosque.

95	A19	3p purple & black	.30	.25
96	A19	1sh green & black	.75	.50

Attainment of self-government by the Northern Region, Mar. 15, 1959.

Federation of Nigeria

Federal
Legislature — A20

3p, Man Paddling Canoe. 6p, Federal Supreme Court. 1sh3p, Map of Africa, dove and torch.

Wmk. 335
1960, Oct. 1   Photo.   Perf. 13½
Size: 35x22mm
97	A20	1p carmine & black	.25	.25
98	A20	3p blue & black	.25	.25
99	A20	6p dk red brn & emer	.25	.25

Size: 39½x23½mm
100	A20	1sh3p ultra & yellow	.25	.25
		Nos. 97-100 (4)	1.00	1.00

Nigeria's independence, Oct. 1, 1960.

Peanuts
A21

Central Bank, Lagos
A22

Designs: 1p, Coal miner. 1½p, Adult education. 2p, Potter. 3p, Oyo carver. 4p, Weaver. 6p, Benin mask. 1sh, Yellow-casqued hornbill. 1sh3p, Camel train and map. 5sh, Nigeria museum and sculpture. £1, Lagos terminal.

Perf. 14½x14
1961, Jan. 1   Wmk. 335
101	A21	½p emerald	.30	.60
102	A21	1p purple	.80	.30
a.		Booklet pane of 6	5.00	
103	A21	1½p rose red	.80	2.25
104	A21	2p ultra	.30	.30
105	A21	3p dk grn	.40	.30
a.		Booklet pane of 6	2.50	
106	A21	4p blue	.30	2.00
107	A21	6p blk & yel	.80	.30
a.		Booklet pane of 6	5.00	
b.		Yellow omitted	2,750.	1,300.
108	A21	1sh yel grn	4.00	.30
109	A21	1sh3p orange	1.50	.30
a.		Booklet pane of 6	9.00	
110	A22	2sh6p yellow & blk	2.75	.30
111	A22	5sh emer & blk	1.25	1.25
112	A22	10sh dp ultra & blk	3.75	3.75
113	A22	£1 dp car & blk	13.00	14.00
		Nos. 101-113 (13)	29.95	25.95

For overprint see No. 198.

Globe and
Train — A23

1961, July 25   Wmk. 335
114	A23	1p shown	.25	.25
115	A23	3p Truck	.25	.25
116	A23	1sh3p Plane	.35	.35
117	A23	2sh6p Ship	.80	.80
		Nos. 114-117 (4)	1.65	1.65

Nigeria's admission to the UPU.

Coat of
Arms — A24

Map and Natural
Resources — A25

Designs: 6p, Eagle carrying banner. 1sh3p, Flying eagles forming flag. 2sh6p, Young couple looking at flag and government building.

Perf. 14½x14, 14x14½
1961, Oct. 1   Photo.   Wmk. 335
118	A24	3p multicolored	.25	.25
119	A25	4p org, yel grn & dk red	.25	.25
120	A25	6p emerald	.25	.25
121	A25	1sh3p ultra, emer & gray	.25	.25
122	A25	2sh6p blue, emer & sep	.50	.50
		Nos. 118-122 (5)	1.50	1.50

First anniversary of independence.

Map of Africa and Staff
of Aesculapius — A26

Map of Africa and: 3p, Lyre, book and scroll. 6p, Cogwheel. 1sh, Radio beacon. 1sh3p, Hands holding globe.

1962, Jan. 25   Perf. 14x14½
123	A26	1p bister	.25	.25
124	A26	3p deep magenta	.25	.25
125	A26	6p blue green	.25	.25

126	A26	1sh chestnut	.25	.25
127	A26	1sh3p bright blue	.25	.25
		Nos. 123-127 (5)	1.25	1.25

Issued to honor the conference of heads of state of African and Malagasy Governments.

Malaria
Eradication
Emblem and
Larvae — A27

Emblem and: 6p, Man with spray gun. 1sh3p, Plane spraying insecticide. 2sh6p, Microscope, retort and patient.

1962, Apr. 7   Perf. 14½
128	A27	3p emer, brn & ver	.25	.25
129	A27	6p lil rose & dk blue	.25	.25
130	A27	1sh3p dk blue & lil rose	.25	.25
131	A27	2sh6p yel brown & blue	.30	.80
		Nos. 128-131 (4)	1.05	1.55

WHO drive to eradicate malaria.

National
Monument,
Lagos — A28

Ife Bronze
Head and
Flag — A29

Perf. 14½x14, 14x14½
1962, Oct. 1   Wmk. 335   Photo.
132	A28	3p lt ultra & emer	.25	.25
a.		Emerald omitted	800.00	475.00
133	A29	5sh vio, emer & org red	1.25	1.25

Second anniversary of independence.

Fair Emblem — A30

Designs (horizontal): 6p, "Wheels of Industry." 1sh, Cornucopia, goods and trucks. 2sh6p, Oil derricks and tanker.

1962, Oct. 27   Wmk. 335
134	A30	1p brown olive & org	.25	.25
135	A30	6p crimson & blk	.25	.25
136	A30	1sh dp orange & blk	.25	.25
137	A30	2sh6p dk ultra, yel & blk	.30	.25
		Nos. 134-137 (4)	1.05	1.00

Lagos Intl. Trade Fair, Oct. 27-Nov. 8.

Globe and
Arrows — A31

4p, Natl. Hall & Commonwealth emblem, horiz. 1sh3p, Palm tree, emblem & doves.

1962, Nov. 5
138	A31	2½p sky blue	.25	1.00
139	A31	4p dp rose & slate bl	.25	.25
140	A31	1sh3p gray & yellow	.25	.25
		Nos. 138-140 (3)	.75	1.50

8th Commonwealth Parliamentary Conf., Lagos.

Herdsman with
Cattle — A32

Design: 6p, Tractor and corn, horiz.

1963, Mar. 21   Photo.   Perf. 14½
141	A32	3p olive green	1.10	.25
142	A32	6p brt lilac rose	1.40	.25

FAO "Freedom from Hunger" campaign.

US Mercury Capsule
over Kano Tracking
Station — A33

Design: 1sh3p, Syncom II satellite and US tracking ship "Kingsport," Lagos harbor.

1963, June 21   Perf. 14½
143	A33	6p dk blue & yel grn	.25	.25
144	A33	1sh3p black & dp green	.30	.30

Peaceful uses of outer space.
Printed in sheets of 12 (4x3) with ornamental borders and inscriptions.

Nigerian and Greek Scouts Shaking
Hands and Jamboree Emblem — A34

1sh, Scouts dancing around campfire.

1963, Aug. 1   Photo.   Perf. 14
145	A34	3p gray olive & red	.30	.25
146	A34	1sh red & black	.60	.60
a.		Souvenir sheet of 2, #145-146	1.60	1.60

11th Boy Scout Jamboree, Marathon, Greece, Aug. 1963.

Republic

First Aid — A35

Designs: 6p, Blood donors and ambulances. 1sh3p, Helping the needy.

1963, Sept. 1   Wmk. 335   Perf. 14½
147	A35	3p dk blue & red	.35	.25
148	A35	6p dk green & red	.55	.30
149	A35	1sh3p black & red	1.50	1.00
a.		Souvenir sheet of 4, #149	12.00	12.00
		Nos. 147-149 (3)	2.40	1.55

Cent. of the Intl. Red Cross.

Pres. Nnamdi Azikiwe
and State House — A36

Designs: 1sh3p, President and Federal Supreme Court. 2sh6p, President and Parliament Building.

1963, Oct. 1   Unwmk.   Perf. 14x13
150	A36	3p dull grn & yel grn	.25	.25
151	A36	6p brown & bister	.25	.25
a.		Bister (head) omitted		
152	A36	2sh6p vio bl & brt grnsh bl	.25	.25
		Nos. 150-152 (3)	.75	.75

Independence Day, Oct. 1, 1963.

"Freedom of
Worship" — A37

3p, Charter & broken whip, horiz. 1sh3p, "Freedom from Want." 2sh6p, "Freedom of Speech."

1963, Dec. 10   Wmk. 335   Perf. 13
153	A37	3p vermilion	.25	.25
154	A37	6p green	.25	.25
155	A37	1sh3p deep ultra	.25	.25
156	A37	2sh6p red lilac	.30	.30
		Nos. 153-156 (4)	1.05	1.05

15th anniv. of the Universal Declaration of Human Rights.

Queen Nefertari — A38

1964, Mar. 8   Photo.   Perf. 14
157	A38	6p shown	.90	.35
158	A38	2sh6p Ramses II	1.75	2.25

UNESCO world campaign to save historic monuments in Nubia.

John F. Kennedy, US and Nigerian Flags — A39

1sh3p, Kennedy bust & laurel. 5sh, Kennedy coin (US), flags of US & Nigeria at half-mast.

1964, Aug. 20   Unwmk.   Perf. 13x14
159	A39	1sh3p black & lt vio	.25	.25
160	A39	2sh6p multicolored	.50	.50
161	A39	5sh multicolored	.75	1.75
a.		Souvenir sheet of 4	7.50	7.50
		Nos. 159-161 (3)	1.50	2.50

Pres. John F. Kennedy (1917-63). No. 161a contains 4 imperf. stamps similar to No. 161 with simulated perforations.

Pres. Nnamdi Azikiwe A40

Herbert Macaulay A41

Design: 2sh6p, King Jaja of Opobo.

Perf. 14x13, 14
1964, Oct. 1   Photo.   Unwmk.
162	A40	3p red brown	.25	.25
163	A41	1sh3p green	.25	.25
164	A41	2sh6p slate green	.60	.60
		Nos. 162-164 (3)	1.10	1.10

First anniversary of the Republic.

Boxing Gloves and Torch — A42

Hurdling A43

6p, High jump. 1sh3p, Woman runner, vert.

1964, Oct.   Perf. 14½
165	A42	3p olive grn & sepia	.25	.25
166	A42	6p dk blue & emer	.35	.35
167	A42	1sh3p olive & brown	.55	.55

Perf. 14
168	A43	2sh6p orange red & brn	1.50	1.50
a.		Souvenir sheet of 4	4.25	4.25
		Nos. 165-168 (4)	2.65	2.65

18th Olympic Games, Tokyo, Oct. 10-25. No. 168a contains 4 imperf. stamps similar to No. 168 with simulated perforations.

Mountain Climbing Scouts — A44

3p, Golden Jubilee emblem. 6p, Nigeria's Scout emblem & merit badges. 1sh3p, Lord Baden-Powell & Nigerian Boy Scout.

1965, Jan.   Photo.   Perf. 14½
169	A44	1p brown	.25	.25
170	A44	3p emer, blk & red	.25	.25
171	A44	6p yel grn, red & blk	.25	.25
172	A44	1sh3p sep, yel & dk grn	.35	.75
a.		Souvenir sheet of 4	6.50	6.50
		Nos. 169-172 (4)	1.10	1.50

Founding of the Nigerian Boy Scouts, 50th anniv.
No. 172a contains four imperf. stamps similar to No. 172 with simulated perforation.

IQSY Emblem and Telstar, Map of Africa — A45

1sh3p, Explorer XII over map of Africa.

1965, Apr. 1   Unwmk.   Perf. 14x13
173	A45	6p grnsh bl & vio	.25	.25
174	A45	1sh3p lilac & green	.30	.30

Intl. Quiet Sun Year, 1964-65. Printed in sheets of 12 (4x3) with ornamental borders and inscriptions.

ITU Emblem, Drummer, Man at Desk and Telephone — A46

Cent. of the ITU: 1sh3p, ITU emblem and telecommunication tower, vert. 5sh, ITU emblem, Syncom satellite and map of Africa showing Nigeria.

Perf. 11x11½, 11½x11
1965, Aug. 2   Photo.   Unwmk.
175	A46	3p ocher, red & blk	.30	.25
176	A46	1sh3p ultra, grn & blk	1.50	1.50
177	A46	5sh multicolored	6.00	6.00
		Nos. 175-177 (3)	7.80	7.75

ICY Emblem, Diesel Locomotive and Camel Caravan — A47

ICY Emblem and: 1sh, Students and hospital, Lagos. 2sh6p, Kainji Dam, Niger River.

Perf. 14x15
1965, Sept. 1   Wmk. 335
178	A47	3p orange, grn & car	3.50	.35
179	A47	1sh ultra, blk & yel	3.00	.50
180	A47	2sh6p ultra, yel & grn	10.00	7.50
		Nos. 178-180 (3)	16.50	8.35

Intl. Cooperation Year and 20th anniv. of the UN.

Stone Images, Ikom — A48

Designs: 3p, Carved frieze, horiz. 5sh, Seated man, Taba bronze.

Perf. 14x15, 15x14
1965, Oct. 1   Photo.   Unwmk.
181	A48	3p ocher, blk & red	.25	.25
182	A48	1sh3p lt ultra, grn & reddish brn	.25	.25

183	A48	5sh emer, dk brn & reddish brn	.50	1.25
		Nos. 181-183 (3)	1.00	1.75

Second anniversary of the Republic.

Elephants — A49

Designs: ½p, Lioness and cubs, vert. 1½p, Splendid sunbird. 2p, Weaverbirds. 3p, Cheetah. 4p, Leopard and cubs. 6p, Saddle-billed storks, vert. 9p, Gray parrots. 1sh, Kingfishers. 1sh3p, Crowned cranes. 2sh6p, Buffon's kobs (antelopes). 5sh, Giraffes. 10sh, Hippopotami, vert. £1, Buffalos.

"MAURICE FIEVET" below Design
Perf. 12x12½, 12½x12, 14x13½ (1p, 2p, 3p, 4p, 9p)
1965-66   Photo.
Size: 23x38mm, 38x23mm
184	A49	½p multicolored	1.00	2.50
185	A49	1p red & multi	.50	.25
186	A49	1½p lt blue & multi	8.00	9.50
187	A49	2p brt red & multi	3.75	.25
a.		White "2d" ('70)	4.50	2.50
188	A49	3p brt grn, yel & dl brn	1.25	.30
189	A49	4p lilac & multi	.30	.25
a.		Perf 12½x12	.60	3.00
b.		"4" 5mm wide ('71)	60.00	8.00
190	A49	6p violet & multi	2.10	.40
191	A49	9p blue & orange	3.00	.60

Perf. 12½
Size: 45x26mm, 26x45mm
192	A49	1sh gray & multi	5.00	.60
a.		Red omitted		
193	A49	1sh3p brt bl & multi	9.00	2.00
194	A49	2sh6p dk brn, yel & ocher	1.00	2.00
195	A49	5sh brn, yel & red brown	2.25	3.50
196	A49	10sh grnsh bl & multi	7.00	3.25
197	A49	£1 brt grn & multi	18.50	9.00
		Nos. 184-197 (14)	62.65	34.40

The designer's name, Maurice Fievet, appears at right or left, in small or large capitals. Nos. 187a and 189b have "MAURICE FIEVET" at right, 5mm wide. No. 187a has "2d" in white instead of yellow. No. 189b has "REPUBLIC" and "4d" larger, bolder.
Issued: ½p, 1p, 11/1/65; 2p, 4/1/66; 1½p, #189a, 6p, 1sh, 1sh3p, 2sh6p, 5sh, 10sh, 1£, 5/2/66; 3p, 9p, 10/17/66; 4p, 1966.
Nine values were overprinted "F. G. N./ F. G. N." (Federal Government of Nigeria) in 1968. They were not issued, but some were sold by accident in 1968. Later the Nigerian Philatelic Service sold examples, stating they were not postally valid. However, some were used by government agencies in 1969.
See Nos. 258-267.

No. 110 Overprinted in Red: "COMMONWEALTH / P.M. MEETING / 11. Jan. 1966"
Perf. 14½x14
1966, Jan. 11   Photo.   Wmk. 335
198	A22	2sh6p yellow & black	.35	.35

Conf. of British Commonwealth Prime Ministers, Lagos.

YWCA Building, Lagos — A50

Unwmk.
1966, Sept. 1   Litho.   Perf. 14
199	A50	4p yel, green & multi	.25	.25
200	A50	9p brt green & multi	.25	.50

60th anniv. of the Nigerian YWCA.

Lineman and Telephone — A51

Designs: 4p, Flag and letter carrying pigeon, vert. 2sh6p, Niger Bridge.

Perf. 14½x14, 14x14½
1966, Oct. 1   Photo.   Wmk. 335
201	A51	4p green	.25	.25
202	A51	1sh6p lilac, blk & sep	.30	.50
203	A51	2sh6p multicolored	.70	1.75
		Nos. 201-203 (3)	1.25	2.50

Third anniversary of the Republic.

Book, Chemical Apparatus, Carved Head and UNESCO Emblem — A52

1966, Nov. 4   Perf. 14½x14
204	A52	4p dl org, mar & blk	.45	.25
205	A52	1sh6p bl grn, plum & blk	2.10	2.50
206	A52	2sh6p pink, plum & blk	2.90	6.00
		Nos. 204-206 (3)	5.45	8.75

20th anniv. of UNESCO.

Surveyors and Hydrological Decade Emblem — A53

Design: 2sh6p, Water depth gauge on dam and Hydrological Decade emblem, vert.

Perf. 14½x14, 14x14½
1967, Feb. 1   Photo.   Wmk. 335
207	A53	4p multicolored	.25	.25
208	A53	1sh6p multicolored	.50	1.25

Hydrological Decade (UNESCO), 1965-74.

Weather Satellite Orbiting Earth — A54

1sh6p, Storm over land & sea & World Meteorological Organization emblem.

1967, Mar. 23   Photo.   Perf. 14½x14
209	A54	4p dp ultra & brt rose	.25	.25
210	A54	1sh6p ultra & yellow	.65	.90

World Meteorological Day, March 23.

Eyo Masqueraders A55

1sh6p, Acrobat. 2sh6p, Stilt dancer, vert.

Perf. 11x11½, 11½x11
1967, Oct. 1   Photo.   Unwmk.
211	A55	4p multicolored	.25	.25
212	A55	1sh6p turq bl & multi	.50	1.25
213	A55	2sh6p pale grn & multi	.75	2.50
		Nos. 211-213 (3)	1.50	4.00

4th anniversary of the Federal Republic.

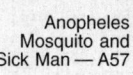

Vaccination of Cattle — A56

1967, Dec. 1   Perf. 14½x14
214	A56	4p maroon & multi	.25	.25
215	A56	1sh6p ultra & multi	.70	1.25

Campaign to eradicate cattle plague.

Anopheles Mosquito and Sick Man — A57

20th anniv. of the WHO: 4p, WHO emblem and vaccination.

1968, Apr. 7   Litho.   Perf. 14
216	A57	4p dp lil rose & blk	.25	.25
217	A57	1sh6p org yel & blk	.55	.80

Shackled Hands, Map of Nigeria and Human Rights Flame — A58

Design: 1sh6p, Flag of Nigeria and human rights flame, vert.

1968, July 1   Photo.   Perf. 14
218 A58 4p dp blue, yel & blk   .25 .25
219 A58 1sh6p green, blk & red   .45 .80

International Human Rights Year.

Hand and Doves — A59

1968, Oct. 1   Unwmk.   Perf. 14
220 A59 4p brt blue & multi   .25 .25
221 A59 1sh6p black & multi   .25 .25

5th anniversary of the Federal Republic.

Olympic Rings, Nigerian Flag and Athletes — A60

4p, Map of Nigeria and Olympic rings.

1968, Oct. 14   Photo.   Perf. 14
222 A60 4p red, blk & emer   .25 .25
223 A60 1sh6p multicolored   .50 .35

19th Olympic Games, Mexico City, 10/12-27.

G.P.O., Lagos — A61

1969, Apr. 11   Unwmk.   Perf. 14
224 A61 4p emerald & black   .25 .25
225 A61 1sh6p dk blue & black   .25 .40

Opening of the Nigerian Philatelic Service of the GPO, Lagos.

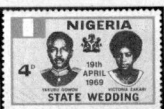

Gen. Yakubu Gowon and Victoria Zakari — A62

Perf. 13x13½
1969, Sept. 20   Litho.   Unwmk.
226 A62 4p emerald & choc   .30 .25
227 A62 1sh6p emerald & black   .70 .45

Wedding of Yakubu Gowon, head of state of Nigeria, and Miss Victoria Zakari, Apr. 19, 1969.

Development Bank Emblem and "5" — A63

Design: 1sh6p, Emblem and rays.

1969, Oct. 18   Litho.   Perf. 14
228 A63 4p dk bl, blk & org   .25 .25
229 A63 1sh6p dk pur, yel & blk   .35 1.00

African Development Bank, 5th anniv.

ILO Emblem — A64

50th anniv. of the ILO: 1sh6p, ILO emblem and world map.

1969, Nov. 15   Photo.
230 A64 4p purple & black   .25 .25
231 A64 1sh6p green & black   .65 1.25

Tourist Year Emblem and Musicians — A65

Designs: 4p, Olumo Rock and Tourist Year emblem, horiz. 1sh6p, Assob Falls.

1969, Dec. 30   Photo.   Perf. 14
232 A65 4p blue & multi   .25 .25
233 A65 1sh emerald & black   .30 .30
234 A65 1sh6p multicolored   1.00 .85
      Nos. 232-234 (3)   1.55 1.40

International Year of African Tourism.

12-Spoke Wheel and Arms of Nigeria — A66

Designs: 4p, Map of Nigeria and tree with 12 fruits representing 12 tribes. 1sh6p, People bound by common destiny and map of Nigeria. 2sh, Torch with 12 flames and map of Africa, horiz.

Perf. 11½x11, 11x11½
1970, May 28   Photo.   Unwmk.
235 A66 4p gold, blue & blk   .25 .25
236 A66 1sh gold & multi   .25 .25
237 A66 1sh6p green & black   .25 .25
238 A66 2sh bl, org, gold & black   .25 .25
      Nos. 235-238 (4)   1.00 1.00

Establishment of a 12-state administrative structure in Nigeria.

Opening of New UPU Headquarters, Bern — A67

1970, June 29   Unwmk.   Perf. 14
239 A67 4p purple & yellow   .30 .25
240 A67 1sh6p blue & vio blue   .45 .35

UN Emblem and Charter — A68

25th anniv. of the UN: 1sh6p, UN emblem and headquarters, New York.

1970, Sept. 1   Photo.   Perf. 14
241 A68 4p brn org, buff & blk   .25 .25
242 A68 1sh6p dk bl, gold & bis brn   .25 .25

Student — A69

Designs: 2p, Oil drilling platform. 6p, Durbar horsemen. 9p, Soldier and sailors raising flag. 1sh, Soccer player. 1sh6p, Parliament Building. 2sh, Kainji Dam. 2sh6p, Export products: Timber, rubber, peanuts, cocoa and palm produce.

1970, Sept. 30   Litho.   Perf. 14x13½
243 A69 2p blue & multi   .25 .25
244 A69 4p blue & multi   .25 .25
245 A69 6p blue & multi   .30 .25
246 A69 9p blue & multi   .40 .25

---

247 A69 1sh blue & multi   .40 .25
248 A69 1sh6p blue & multi   .40 .40
249 A69 2sh blue & multi   .50 .90
250 A69 2sh6p blue & multi   .50 1.00
      Nos. 243-250 (8)   3.00 3.55

Ten years of independence.

Black and White Men Uprooting Racism — A70

Designs: 4p, Black and white school children and globe, horiz. 1sh6p, World map with black and white stripes. 2sh, Black and white men, shoulder to shoulder, horiz.

Perf. 13½x14, 14x13½
1971, Mar. 22   Photo.   Unwmk.
251 A70 4p multicolored   .25 .25
252 A70 1sh yellow & multi   .25 .25
253 A70 1sh6p blue, yel & blk   .25 .65
254 A70 2sh multicolored   .25 1.25
      Nos. 251-254 (4)   1.00 2.40

Intl. year against racial discrimination.

Ibibio Mask, c. 1900 — A71

Nigerian Antiquities: 1sh3p, Bronze mask of a King of Benin, c. 1700. 1sh9p, Bronze figure of a King of Ife.

1971, Sept. 30   Perf. 13½x14
255 A71 4p lt blue & black   .25 .25
256 A71 1sh3p yellow bis & blk   .25 .35
257 A71 1sh9p apple grn, dp grn & blk   .25 1.00
      Nos. 255-257 (3)   .75 1.60

Type of 1965-66 Redrawn
Imprint: "N.S.P. & M. Co. Ltd."
Added to "MAURICE FIEVET"
Perf. 13x13½; 14x13½ (6p)
1969-72   Photo.
                        Size: 38x23mm
258 A49 1p red & multi   3.00 2.25
259 A49 2p brt red & multi   4.00 1.50
260 A49 3p multi ('71)   .75 2.00
261 A49 4p lilac & multi   8.50 .25
262 A49 6p brt vio & multi ('71)   2.25 .25
263 A49 9p dl bl & dp org ('70)   7.00 .50
                        Size: 45x26mm
264 A49 1sh multi ('71)   3.00 .25
265 A49 1sh3p multi ('71)   11.00 3.50
266 A49 2sh6p multi ('71)   15.00 7.00
267 A49 5sh multi ('72)   3.50 17.50
      Nos. 258-267 (10)   58.00 35.00

"Maurice Fievet" imprint on No. 259 exists in two lengths, 5mm and 5½mm.
"Maurice Fievet" imprint on No. 260 exists in two lengths, 5½mm and 8½mm.

UNICEF Emblem and Children — A72

UNICEF 25th anniv.: 1sh3p, Mother and child. 1sh9p, African mother carrying child on back.

1971, Dec. 11   Perf. 14
270 A72 4p purple & yellow   .25 .25
271 A72 1sh3p org, pur & plum   .25 .45
272 A72 1sh9p blue & dk blue   .25 .90
      Nos. 270-272 (3)   .75 1.60

Satellite Earth Station — A73

Various views of satellite communications earth station, Lanlate, Nigeria. All horiz.

1971, Dec. 30   Photo.   Perf. 14
273 A73 4p multicolored   .25 .25
274 A73 1sh3p blue, blk & grn   .25 .65
275 A73 1sh9p orange & blk   .30 .95
276 A73 3sh brt pink & blk   .55 1.75
      Nos. 273-276 (4)   1.35 3.60

Satellite communications earth station, Lanlate, Nigeria.

Fair Emblem — A74

Fair Emblem and: 1sh3p, Map of Africa, horiz. 1sh9p, Globe with map of Africa.

Perf. 13½x13, 13x13½
1972, Feb. 23   Litho.
277 A74 4p multicolored   .25 .25
278 A74 1sh3p dull pur, yel & gold   .25 .40
279 A74 1sh9p orange, yel & blk   .25 1.25
      Nos. 277-279 (3)   .75 1.90

First All-Africa Trade Fair, Nairobi, Kenya, Feb. 23-Mar. 5.

Traffic — A75

Designs: 1sh3p, Traffic flow at circle. 1sh9p, Car and truck on road. 3sh, Intersection with lights and pedestrians.

1972, June 23   Photo.   Perf. 13x13½
280 A75 4p orange & blk   .45 .25
281 A75 1sh3p lt blue & multi   1.40 .85
282 A75 1sh9p emerald & multi   1.50 1.10
283 A75 3sh yellow & multi   2.60 3.00
      Nos. 280-283 (4)   5.95 5.20

Introduction of right-hand driving in Nigeria, Apr. 2, 1972.

Nok Style Terra-cotta Head, Katsina Ala — A76

1sh3p, Roped bronze vessel, Igbo Ukwu. 1sh9p, Bone harpoon, Daima, horiz.

Perf. 13½x13, 13x13½
1972, Sept. 1   Litho.
284 A76 4p dk blue & multi   .25 .25
285 A76 1sh3p gold & multi   .40 .50
286 A76 1sh9p dp blue & multi   .50 1.50
      Nos. 284-286 (3)   1.15 2.25

All-Nigeria Festival of the Arts, Kaduna, Dec. 9.

Games Emblem and Soccer — A77

Designs: 5k, Running. 18k, Table tennis. 25k, Stadium, vert.

1973, Jan. 8　Litho.　*Perf. 13x13½*

287	A77	5k lilac, blue & blk	.25	.25
288	A77	12k multicolored	.35	.55
289	A77	18k yellow & multi	.60	1.10
290	A77	25k brown & multi	1.00	1.50
		Nos. 287-290 (4)	2.20	3.40

2nd All-Africa Games, Lagos, Jan. 7-18.

Hides and Skins — A78

Designs: 2k, Natural gas tanks. 3k, Cement works. 5k, Cattle ranching. 7k, Lumbermill. 8k, Oil refinery. 10k, Leopards, Yankari Game Reserve. 12k, New civic building. 15k, Sugar cane harvesting. 18k, Palm oil production, vert. 20k, Vaccine production. 25k, Modern docks. 30k, Argungu Fishing Festival, vert. 35k, Textile industry. 50k, Pottery, vert. 1n, Eko Bridge. 2n, Teaching Hospital, Lagos.

Imprint at left: "N S P & M Co Ltd"
6mm on Litho. Stamps, 5¼ mm on Photo. Stamps

1973-74　Litho.; Photo. (50k)　Unwmk.　*Perf. 14*

291	A78	1k multi, buff imprint	.25	.25
292	A78	2k multi ('74)	4.00	.90
293	A78	3k multi ('74)	.25	.25
294	A78	5k grn & multi ('74)	6.00	.90
295	A78	7k multicolored	.35	1.25
296	A78	8k multicolored	.40	.25
297	A78	10k multicolored	6.00	.25
298	A78	12k multicolored	.50	2.00
299	A78	15k multicolored	.35	.60
300	A78	18k multicolored	.55	.30
301	A78	20k multicolored	.65	.30
302	A78	25k multicolored	.85	.45
303	A78	30k multicolored	.50	1.50
304	A78	35k black background	6.00	4.00
305	A78	50k black background	2.00	2.50
306	A78	1n multicolored	1.00	.90
307	A78	2n multicolored	1.00	2.25
		Nos. 291-307 (17)	30.65	18.85

Imprint on 35k has periods.

Imprint at left: "N S P & M Co Ltd"

1973　Photo., Imprint 5¼mm

291a	A78	1k multi, dk grn foliage	1.00	.75
291b	A78	1k multi, brt grn foliage	.25	.25
292a	A78	2k multicolored	.35	.25
294a	A78	5k multi, emer fields	.60	.75
294b	A78	5k multi, yel grn fields	.50	.25
297a	A78	10k multicolored	.75	.80
298a	A78	12k multicolored	12.00	10.00
300a	A78	18k multicolored	12.00	2.00
301a	A78	20k multicolored	13.00	3.00
303a	A78	30k multicolored	12.00	7.50
305a	A78	50k dk brn background	.75	.90
306a	A78	1n multicolored	2.00	4.00
		Nos. 291a-306a (12)	55.20	30.45

Nos. 300a, 305a and 306a have periods in the imprint. The liquid in the flasks is gray on No. 301, black on No. 301a, and blue on No. 301b.

1975-80　Wmk. 379

291c	A78	1k multi, dk grn foliage	1.50	2.00
292b	A78	2k multi ('75)	1.75	.25
293a	A78	3k multi ('75)	.25	.25
294c	A78	5k emerald fields ('76)	2.25	.25
295a	A78	7k multi ('80)	3.50	3.50
296a	A78	8k multi ('76)	1.75	2.00
297b	A78	10k multi ('76)	2.00	.25
299a	A78	15k multicolored		3.00
300b	A78	18k multi ('78)	4.25	4.00
301b	A78	20k multi, pale pink table, door, windows ('79)	3.25	3.50
302a	A78	25k multi, pur barges	3.25	.25
302b	A78	25k multi, brn barges	3.25	.25
305b	A78	50k dk brn background, grn imprint	3.50	3.75
307a	A78	2n multicolored	5.50	6.50

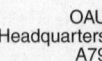

OAU Headquarters A79

Designs: 18k, OAU flag, vert. 30k, Stairs leading to OAU emblem, vert.

1973, May 25　Litho.　*Perf. 14*

308	A79	5k blue & multi	.25	.25
309	A79	18k olive grn & multi	.35	.50
310	A79	30k lilac & multi	.55	.80
		Nos. 308-310 (3)	1.15	1.55

Org. for African Unity, 10th anniv.

WMO Emblem, Weather Vane — A80

1973, Sept. 4　Litho.　*Perf. 13*

311	A80	5k multicolored	.30	.25
312	A80	30k multicolored	1.50	2.25

Cent. of intl. meteorological cooperation.

View of Ibadan University — A81

Designs: 12k, Campus, crest and graph showing growth, vert. 18k, Campus, students and crest. 30k, Teaching hospital.

1973, Nov. 17　*Perf. 14*

313	A81	5k lt blue & multi	.25	.25
314	A81	12k lilac & multi	.25	.30
315	A81	18k orange & multi	.45	.40
316	A81	30k blue, org & blk	.65	.80
		Nos. 313-316 (4)	1.60	1.75

University of Ibadan, 25th anniversary.

Growth of Mail, 1874-1974 — A82

12k, Nigerian Post emblem & Northern Nigeria #18A. 18k, Postal emblem & Lagos #1. 30k, Map of Nigeria &means of transportation.

1974, June 10　Litho.　*Perf. 14*

317	A82	5k green, black & org	.25	.25
318	A82	12k green & multi	.55	.55
319	A82	18k green, lilac & blk	.90	.90
320	A82	30k black & multi	1.60	1.60
		Nos. 317-320 (4)	3.30	3.30

Centenary of first Nigerian postage stamps.

Globe and UPU Emblem — A83

UPU cent.: 18k, World map and means of transportation. 30k, Letters.

1974, Oct. 9

321	A83	5k blue & multi	.25	.25
322	A83	18k orange & multi	2.50	.60
323	A83	30k brown & multi	2.00	1.75
		Nos. 321-323 (3)	4.75	2.60

Hungry and Well-fed Children — A84

Designs: 12k, Chicken farm, horiz. 30k, Irrigation project.

1974, Nov. 25　Litho.　*Perf. 14*

324	A84	5k orange, blk & grn	.25	.25
325	A84	12k multicolored	.35	.50
326	A84	30k multicolored	.80	1.50
		Nos. 324-326 (3)	1.40	2.25

Freedom from Hunger.

A85

Map of Nigeria with Telex Network, Teleprinter — A86

1975, July 3　Litho.　*Perf. 14*

327	A85	5k multicolored	.25	.25
328	A85	12k multicolored	.25	.25
329	A86	18k multicolored	.30	.30
330	A86	30k multicolored	.55	.55
		Nos. 327-330 (4)	1.35	1.35

Inauguration of Nigeria Telex Network.

Queen Amina of Zaria (1536-1566) — A87

1975, Aug. 18　Litho.　*Perf. 14*

331	A87	5k multicolored	.25	.25
332	A87	18k multicolored	1.10	.90
333	A87	30k multicolored	1.40	1.75
		Nos. 331-333 (3)	2.75	2.90

International Women's Year.

Alexander Graham Bell — A88

Designs: 18k, Hands beating gong, modern telephone operator, horiz. 25k, Telephones, 1876, 1976.

1976, Mar. 10　Wmk. 379

334	A88	5k pink, black & ocher	.25	.25
335	A88	18k deep lilac & multi	.45	.55
336	A88	25k lt bl, vio bl & blk	.90	1.10
		Nos. 334-336 (3)	1.60	1.90

Centenary of first telephone call by Alexander Graham Bell, Mar. 10, 1876.

Children Going to School — A89

Designs: 5k, Child learning to write, horiz. 25k, Classroom.

1976, Sept. 20　Litho.　*Perf. 14*

337	A89	5k multicolored	.25	.25
338	A89	18k multicolored	.55	.75
339	A89	25k multicolored	.70	1.00
		Nos. 337-339 (3)	1.50	2.00

Launching of universal primary education in 1976.

Traditional Musical Instruments A90

5k, Carved mask (festival emblem). 10k, Natl. Arts Theater, Lagos. 12k, Nigerian & African women's hair styles. 30k, Nigerian carvings.

1976-77　Wmk. 379

340	A90	5k black, gold & grn	.25	.25
341	A90	10k multicolored	.40	.40
342	A90	12k multicolored	.75	.75
343	A90	18k brown, ocher & blk	.90	.90
344	A90	30k multicolored	1.10	1.25
		Nos. 340-344 (5)	3.40	3.55

2nd World Black and African Festival of Arts and Culture, Lagos, Jan. 15-Feb. 12, 1977. Issued: 5k, 18k, 11/1; others 1/15/77.

Gen. Muhammed Broadcasting and Map of Nigeria — A91

Designs: 18k, Gen. Muhammed as Commander in Chief, vert. 30k, in battle dress, vert.

1977, Feb. 13　Litho.　*Perf. 14*

345	A91	5k multicolored	.25	.25
346	A91	18k multicolored	.40	.40
347	A91	30k multicolored	.70	.70
		Nos. 345-347 (3)	1.35	1.35

Gen. Murtala Ramat Muhammed, Head of State and Commander in Chief, 1st death anniversary.

Scouts Clearing Street — A92

5k, Senior and Junior Boy Scouts saluting, vert. 25k, Scouts working on farm. 30k, African Scout Jamboree emblem, map of Africa.

1977, Apr. 1　Wmk. 379

348	A92	5k multicolored	.30	.30
349	A92	18k multicolored	.65	.65
350	A92	25k multicolored	.80	1.00
351	A92	30k multicolored	1.10	1.60
		Nos. 348-351 (4)	2.85	3.55

First All-Africa Boy Scout Jamboree, Sherehills, Jos, Nigeria, Apr. 2-8, 1977.

Trade Fair Emblem — A93

Emblem and: 5k, View of Fair grounds. 30k, Weaver and potter.

1977, Nov. 27　Litho.　*Perf. 13*

352	A93	5k multicolored	.25	.25
353	A93	18k multicolored	.30	.30
354	A93	30k multicolored	.60	.60
		Nos. 352-354 (3)	1.15	1.15

1st Lagos Intl. Trade Fair, Nov. 27-Dec. 11.

Nigeria's 13 Universities A94

12k, Map of West African highways and telecommunications network. 18k, Training of technicians, and cogwheel. 30k, World map and map of Argentina with Buenos Aires.

1978, Apr. 28　Wmk. 379

355	A94	5k multicolored	.25	.25
356	A94	12k multicolored	.25	.25
357	A94	18k multicolored	.25	.25
358	A94	30k multicolored	.60	.60
		Nos. 355-358 (4)	1.35	1.35

Global Conf. on Technical Cooperation among Developing Countries, Buenos Aires.

Antenna and ITU Emblem — A95

1978, May 17　Litho.　*Perf. 14*

359	A95	30k multicolored	.75	.75

10th World Telecommunications Day.

Students on Cassava Plantation — A96

"Operation Feed the Nation": 18k, Woman working in backyard vegetable garden. 30k, Plantain harvest, vert.

1978, July 7　Litho.　*Perf. 14*

360	A96	5k multicolored	.25	.25
361	A96	18k multicolored	.30	.30
362	A96	30k multicolored	.50	.50
		Nos. 360-362 (3)	1.05	1.05

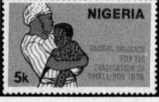

Mother Holding Sick Child — A97

Designs: 12k, Sick boy at health station. 18k, Vaccination of children. 30k, Syringe and WHO emblem, vert.

1978, Aug. 31   **Wmk. 379**
363 A97 5k multicolored   .25   .25
364 A97 12k multicolored   .30   .30
365 A97 18k multicolored   .45   .45
366 A97 30k multicolored   .75   .75
   Nos. 363-366 (4)   1.75 1.75
   Global eradication of smallpox.

Bronze Horseman from Benin — A98

Nigerian antiquities: 5k, Nok terracotta figure from Bwari. 12k, Bronze snail and animal from Igbo-Ukwu. 18k, Bronze statue of a king of Ife.

1978, Oct. 27   **Litho.**   **Perf. 14**
367 A98 5k multicolored   .25   .25
368 A98 12k multicolored, horiz.   .25   .25
369 A98 18k multicolored   .30   .30
370 A98 30k multicolored   .50   .50
   Nos. 367-370 (4)   1.30 1.30

Anti-Apartheid Emblem — A99

1978, Dec. 10   **Perf. 14**
371 A99 18k red, yellow & black   .35   .35
   Anti-Apartheid Year.

Wright Brothers, Flyer A — A100

18k, Nigerian Air Force fighters in formation.

1978, Dec. 28
372 A100 5k multicolored   .30   .30
373 A100 18k multicolored   .60   .60
   75th anniversary of powered flight.

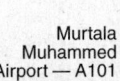

Murtala Muhammed Airport — A101

1979, Mar. 15   **Litho.**   **Perf. 14**
374 A101 5k bright blue & black   .50   .30
   Inauguration of Murtala Muhammed Airport.

Young Stamp Collector — A102

1979, Apr. 11
375 A102 5k multicolored   .35   .25
   Philatelic Week; Natl. Philatelic Service, 10th anniv.

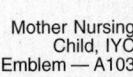

Mother Nursing Child, IYC Emblem — A103

18k, Children at study. 25k, Children at play, vert.

1979, June 28   **Wmk. 379**   **Perf. 14**
376 A103 5k multicolored   .25   .25
377 A103 18k multicolored   .30   .30
378 A103 25k multicolored   .35   .35
   Nos. 376-378 (3)   .90   .90
   International Year of the Child.

A104

Design: 10k, Preparation of audio-visual material. 30k, Adult education class.

1979, July 25   **Photo. & Engr.**
379 A104 10k multicolored   .25   .25
380 A104 30k multicolored   .40   .40
   Intl. Bureau of Education, Geneva, 50th anniv.

Necom House, Lagos — A105

1979, Sept. 20   Litho.   Perf. 13½x14
381 A105 10k multicolored   .30   .30
   Intl. Radio Consultative Committee (CCIR) of the ITU, 50th anniv.

Trainees and Survey Equipment A106

1979, Dec. 12   **Photo.**   **Perf. 14**
382 A106 10k multicolored   .30   .30
   Economic Commission for Africa, 21st anniv.

Soccer Cup and Ball on Map of Nigeria — A107

1980, Mar. 8
383 A107 10k shown   .25   .25
384 A107 30k Player, vert.   .60   .60
   12th African Cup of Nations Soccer Championship, Lagos and Ibadan, Mar.

Swimming, Moscow '80 Emblem — A108

10k, Wrestling, vert. 20k, Long jump, vert. 45k, Women's basketball, vert.

Litho. & Engr.
1980, July 19   **Perf. 14**
385 A108 10k multi   .25   .25
386 A108 20k multi   .25   .25
387 A108 30k shown   .30   .30
388 A108 45k multi   .35   .35
   Nos. 385-388 (4)   1.15 1.15
   22nd Summer Olympic Games, Moscow, July 19-Aug. 3.

Men Holding OPEC Emblem — A109

45k, Anniversary emblem, vert.

1980, Sept. 15   **Litho. & Engr.**
389 A109 10k shown   .25   .25
390 A109 45k multi   .75   .75
   OPEC, 20th anniversary.

First Steam Locomotive in Nigeria — A110

20k, Unloading freight car. 30k, Freight train.

1980, Oct. 2   **Wmk. 379**   **Perf. 14**
391 A110 10k shown   .50   .50
392 A110 20k multi   1.40 1.40
393 A110 30k multi   2.10 2.10
   Nos. 391-393 (3)   4.00 4.00
   Nigerian Railway Corp., 75th anniv.

Technician Performing Quality Control Test — A111

1980, Oct. 14
394 A111 10k Scale, ruler, vert.   .25   .25
395 A111 30k shown   .45   .45
   World Standards Day.

A112

Designs: 10k, Map of West Africa showing ECOWAS Members, Modes of Communication. 25k, Transportation. 30k, Map, cow, cocoa. 45k, Map, industrial symbols.

1980, Nov. 5   **Litho. & Engr.**
396 A112 10k multicolored   .25   .25
396A A112 25k multicolored   .30   .30
397 A112 30k multicolored   .40   .40
398 A112 45k multicolored   .55   .55
   Nos. 396-398 (4)   1.50 1.50

Woman with Cane Sweeping — A113

30k, Amputee photographer.

Wmk. 379
1981, June 25   **Litho.**   **Perf. 14**
399 A113 10k shown   .25   .25
400 A113 30k multicolored   .50   .50
   Intl. Year of the Disabled.

World Food Day — A114

10k, Pres. Shenu Shagari. 25k, Produce, vert. 30k, Tomato crop, vert. 45k, Pig farm.

1981, Oct. 16   **Litho. & Engr.**
401 A114 10k multicolored   .25   .25
402 A114 25k multicolored   .30   .30
403 A114 30k multicolored   .35   .35
404 A114 45k multicolored   .50   .50
   Nos. 401-404 (4)   1.40 1.40

Anti-apartheid Year — A115

30k, Soweto riot. 45k, Police hitting man, vert.

1981, Dec. 10   **Litho.**
405 A115 30k multicolored   .40   .55
406 A115 45k multicolored   .60 1.00

Scouting Year — A116

30k, Animal first aid. 45k, Baden-Powell, scouts.

1982, Feb. 22   **Litho.**   **Perf. 14**
407 A116 30k multicolored   .60   .65
408 A116 45k multicolored   1.10 1.25

TB Bacillus Centenary A117

10k, Inoculation. 30k, Research. 45k, Patient being x-rayed, vert.

1982, Mar. 24   **Litho.**   **Perf. 14**
409 A117 10k multicolored   .30   .30
410 A117 30k multicolored   .50   .60
411 A117 45k multicolored   .80 1.40
   Nos. 409-411 (3)   1.60 2.30

10th Anniv. of UN Conference on Human Environment A118

10k, Keep your environment clean. 20k, Check air pollution. 30k, Preserve natural environment. 45k, Reafforestation concerns all.

1982, June 10   **Litho.**
412 A118 10k multicolored   .25   .25
413 A118 20k multicolored   .25   .35
414 A118 30k multicolored   .35   .50
415 A118 45k multicolored   .60   .80
   Nos. 412-415 (4)   1.45 1.90

Salamis Parnassus A119

20k, Papilio zalmoxis. 30k, Pachylophus beckeri. 45k, Papilio hesperus.

1982, Sept. 15   **Litho.**
416 A119 10k shown   .35   .25
417 A119 20k multicolored   .65   .55
418 A119 30k multicolored   1.00 1.00
419 A119 45k multicolored   1.50 1.40
   Nos. 416-419 (4)   3.50 3.20

25th Anniv. of Natl. Museum — A120

10k, Statuettes, vert. 20k, Bronze leopard. 30k, Soapstone seated figure, vert. 45k, Wooden helmet mask.

1982, Nov. 18   **Wmk. 379**
420 A120 10k multicolored   .25   .25
421 A120 20k multicolored   .35   .35
422 A120 30k multicolored   .40   .40
423 A120 45k multicolored   .60   .60
   Nos. 420-423 (4)   1.60 1.60

Family Day — A121

10k, Extended family, house, horiz. 30k, Family.

1983, Mar. 8   **Litho.**   **Perf. 14**
424 A121 10k multicolored   .25   .25
425 A121 30k multicolored   .50   .50

Commonwealth Day — A122

10k, Satellite view, horiz. 25k, Natl. Assembly buildings, horiz. 30k, Oil exploration. 45k, Runners.

1983, Mar. 14
426 A122 10k multicolored   .25   .25
427 A122 25k multicolored   .35   .35
428 A122 30k multicolored   .45   .45
429 A122 45k multicolored   .55   .55
   Nos. 426-429 (4)   1.60 1.60

10th Anniv. of Natl. Youth Service Corps — A123

1983, May 25   Litho.   Perf. 14
430 A123 10k Construction   .25   .25
431 A123 25k Climbing wall, vert.   .45   .45
432 A123 30k Marching, vert.   .65   .65
Nos. 430-432 (3)   1.35   1.35

World Communications Year — A124

10k, Mailman, vert. 25k, Newspaper stand. 30k, Traditional horn messenger. 45k, TV news broadcast.

Wmk. 379
1983, July 22   Litho.   Perf. 14
433 A124 10k multicolored   .25   .25
434 A124 25k multicolored   .35   .35
435 A124 30k multicolored   .55   .55
436 A124 45k multicolored   .45   .45
Nos. 433-436 (4)   1.60   1.60

World Fishery — A125

1983, Sept. 22   Litho.   Wmk. 379
437 A125 10k Pink shrimp   .30   .30
438 A125 25k Long neck croaker   .40   .40
439 A125 30k Barracuda   .50   .50
440 A125 45k Fishing technique   .60   .60
Nos. 437-440 (4)   1.80   1.80

Boys' Brigade, 75th Anniv. — A126

10k, Boys, emblem, vert. 30k, Food production. 45k, Skill training.

1983, Oct. 14   Perf. 14
441 A126 10k multicolored   .30   .30
442 A126 30k multicolored   1.50   1.50
443 A126 45k multicolored   2.25   2.25
Nos. 441-443 (3)   4.05   4.05

Fight Against Polio Campaign A127

1984, Feb. 29   Litho.   Perf. 14
444 A127 10k Crippled boy, vert.   .25   .25
445 A127 25k Vaccination   .60   .60
446 A127 30k Healthy child, vert.   .80   .80
Nos. 444-446 (3)   1.65   1.65

Hartebeests A128

10k, Waterbuck, vert. 30k, Buffalo. 45k, African golden monkey.

1984, May 25   Wmk. 379   Perf. 14
447 A128 10k multicolored   .50   .30
448 A128 25k shown   .45   .45
449 A128 30k multicolored   .65   .65
450 A128 45k multicolored   1.00   1.00
Nos. 447-450 (4)   2.60   2.40

Central Bank of Nigeria, 25th Anniv. — A129

1984, July 2   Wmk. 379
451 A129 10k £1 note, 1968   .25   .25
452 A129 25k Bank   .55   .55
453 A129 30k £5 note, 1959   .70   .70
Nos. 451-453 (3)   1.50   1.50

1984 Summer Olympics, Los Angeles — A130

Wmk. 379
1984, Aug. 9   Litho.   Perf. 14
454 A130 10k Boxing   .25   .25
455 A130 25k Discus   .40   .40
456 A130 30k Weight lifting   .50   .50
457 A130 45k Bicycling   .75   .75
Nos. 454-457 (4)   1.90   1.90

African Development Bank, 20th Anniv. — A131

10k, Irrigation project, Lesotho. 25k, Bomi Hills roadway, Liberia. 30k, Education development, Seychelles. 45k, Coal mining & transportation, Niger. #459-461 horiz.

1984, Sept. 10
458 A131 10k multicolored   .30   .30
459 A131 25k multicolored   .55   .55
460 A131 30k multicolored   .75   .75
461 A131 45k multicolored   1.20   1.20
Nos. 458-461 (4)   2.80   2.80

A132   A132a

A132b   A132c

Rare bird species: 10k, Pin-tailed whydah. 25k, Spur-winged plover. 30k, Red bishop. 45k, Francolin.

1984, Oct. 24
462 A132   10k multicolored   .75   .75
463 A132a 25k multicolored   1.25   1.25
464 A132b 30k multicolored   1.75   1.75
465 A132c 45k multicolored   2.75   2.75
Nos. 462-465 (4)   6.50   6.50

Intl. Civil Aviation Organization, 40th Anniv. — A132d

45k, Jet circling Earth.

1984, Dec. 7   Litho.   Perf. 14
465A A132d 10k shown   .50   .50
465B A132d 45k multicolored   2.00   2.00

Fight Against Indiscipline A133

20k, Encourage punctuality. 50k, Discourage bribery.

1985, Feb. 27
466 A133 20k multicolored   .30   .30
467 A133 50k multicolored   .90   .90

Intl. Youth Year — A134

20k, Sports, horiz. 50k, Nationalism. 55k, Service organizations.

1985, June 5
468 A134 20k multi   .25   .25
469 A134 50k multi   .60   .60
470 A134 55k multi   .70   .70
Nos. 468-470 (3)   1.55   1.55

OPEC, 25th Anniv. — A135

1985, Sept. 15
471 A135 20k shown   .90   .90
472 A135 50k World map, horiz.   1.75   1.75

Natl. Independence, 25th Anniv. — A136

20k, Oil refinery. 50k, Map of states. 55k, Monument. 60k, Eleme Oil Refinery.

1985, Sept. 25
473 A136 20k multi   .25   .25
474 A136 50k multi   .60   .60
475 A136 55k multi   .65   .65
476 A136 60k multi   .75   .75
  a.   Souvenir sheet of 4, #473-476   5.50   5.50
Nos. 473-476 (4)   2.25   2.25

World Tourism Day — A137

20k, Waterfalls. 50k, Crafts, horiz. 55k, Carved calabashes, flag. 60k, Leather goods, rug.

1985, Sept. 27
477 A137 20k multi   .25   .25
478 A137 50k multi   .55   .55
479 A137 55k multi   .60   .60
480 A137 60k multi   .65   .65
Nos. 477-480 (4)   2.05   2.05

UN, 40th Anniv. — A138

1985, Oct. 7
481 A138 20k Emblem, map, flag   .30   .30
482 A138 50k UN building, horiz.   .50   .50
483 A138 55k Emblem, horiz.   .80   .80
Nos. 481-483 (3)   1.60   1.60

Admission of Nigeria to UN, 25th anniv.

African Reptiles — A139

1986, Apr. 15   Wmk. 379   Perf. 14
484 A139 10k Python   .30   .30
485 A139 20k Crocodile   .50   .50
486 A139 25k Gopher tortoise   .60   .60
487 A139 30k Chameleon   .70   .70
Nos. 484-487 (4)   2.10   2.10

Volkswagen Automobile Assembly Factory — A140

Designs: 1k, Social worker with children, vert. 5k, Modern housing development. 10k, Modern method of harvesting coconuts, vert. 15k, Port activities. 20k, Tecoma stans, flower, vert. 25k, Medical care. 30k, Birom folk dancers. 35k, Telephone operators. 40k, Nkpokiti dancers, vert. 45k, Hibiscus. 50k, Modern p.o. 1n, Stone quarry. 2n, Technical education.

1986, June 16   Wmk. 379   Perf. 14
488 A140   1k multicolored   .45   .45
489 A140   2k multicolored   .45   .45
490 A140   5k multicolored   .30   .25
491 A140 10k multicolored   .30   .25
492 A140 15k multicolored   1.00   .25
493 A140 20k multicolored   .30   .25
494 A140 25k multicolored   .35   .45
494A A140 30k multicolored   .55   .55
495 A140 35k multicolored   .35   .25
496 A140 40k multicolored   .35   .25
497 A140 45k multicolored   .35   .25
498 A140 50k multicolored   1.00   .60
499 A140   1n multicolored   .45   .40
500 A140   2n multicolored   .45   .45
Nos. 488-500 (14)   6.65   5.10

Use of some denominations began as early as 1984. Date of issue of the 30k is not definite.
See Nos. 560A-560D, 615C.

Intl. Peace Year — A141

10k, Emblem. 20k, Hands touching globe.

1986, June 20   Litho.   Perf. 14
501 A141 10k multi   .30   .30
502 A141 20k multi   .50   .50

Insects — A142

1986, July 14
503 A142 10k Goliath beetle   .35   .35
504 A142 20k Wasp   .80   .80
505 A142 25k Cricket   1.00   1.00
506 A142 30k Carpet beetle   1.25   1.25
  a.   Souvenir sheet of 4, #503-506   5.75   5.75
Nos. 503-506 (4)   3.40   3.40

Nos. 503-506 and 506a exist imperf. Values: 503-506, set $6; 506a, $12.

UNICEF, 40th Anniv. — A143

10k, Oral rehydration. 20k, Immunization. 25k, Breast-feeding. 30k, Mother playing with child.

1986, Nov. 11
507 A143 10k multicolored   .25   .25
508 A143 20k multicolored   .35   .35
509 A143 25k multicolored   .70   .70
510 A143 30k multicolored   .80   .80
Nos. 507-510 (4)   2.10   2.10

UN Child Survival Campaign.

Institute of Intl. Affairs, 25th Anniv. — A144

20k, Intl. understanding, horiz.

1986, Dec. 13
511 A144 20k multi   .70   .70
512 A144 30k shown   .90   .90

Nos. 511-512 exist imperf. Value, set $2.50.

Seashells — A145

1987, Mar. 31
513 A145 10k Freshwater clam 1.25 1.25
514 A145 20k Periwinkle 1.50 1.50
515 A145 25k Bloddy cockle 1.75 1.75
516 A145 30k Mangrove oyster 2.00 2.00
Nos. 513-516 (4) 6.50 6.50

A146

A147

10k, Blue pea but. 20k, Hibiscus. 25k, Acanthus montanus. 30k, Combretum racemosum.

1987, May 28
517 A146 10k multicolored .25 .25
518 A146 20k multicolored .25 .25
519 A147 25k multicolored .25 .25
520 A147 30k multicolored .25 .25
Nos. 517-520 (4) 1.00 1.00

Hair Styles — A148

1987, Sept. 15 Wmk. 379 ***Perf. 14***
521 A148 10k Doka .30 .30
522 A148 20k Eting .30 .30
523 A148 25k Agogo .30 .30
524 A148 30k Goto .30 .30
Nos. 521-524 (4) 1.20 1.20

Intl. Year of Shelter for the Homeless — A149

20k, Homeless family. 30k, Moving to new home.

1987, Dec. 10 **Litho.**
525 A149 20k multicolored .30 .25
526 A149 30k multicolored .30 .25

A150

1988, Feb. 17 Litho. ***Perf. 14***
527 A150 20k Help the Needy .70 .50
528 A150 30k Care for the sick 1.10 .90

Intl. Red Cross and Red Crescent Organizations, 125th annivs.

A151

10k, Immunization. 20k, Map, globe, emblem. 30k, Mobile hospital.

1988, Apr. 7 Wmk. 379 ***Perf. 14***
529 A151 10k multicolored .30 .25
530 A151 20k multicolored .60 .60
531 A151 30k multicolored .70 .70
Nos. 529-531 (3) 1.60 1.55

WHO, 40th anniv.

A152

20k, Emblem, map, 4 men.

1988, May 25
532 A152 10k shown .30 .25
533 A152 20k multicolored .30 .25

Organization of African Unity, 25th anniv.

Shrimp — A153

10k, Pink shrimp. 20k, Tiger shrimp. 25k, Deepwater roseshrimp. 30k, Estuarine prawn.

1988, June 2
534 A153 10k multicolored .30 .30
535 A153 20k multicolored .50 .50
536 A153 25k multicolored .60 .60
537 A153 30k multicolored .70 .70
a. Miniature sheet of 4, #534-537 2.50 2.50
Nos. 534-537 (4) 2.10 2.10

1988 Summer Olympics, Seoul — A154

1988, Sept. 6 Wmk. 379 ***Perf. 14***
538 A154 10k Weight lifting .30 .30
539 A154 20k Boxing .30 .30
540 A154 30k Running, vert. .30 .30
Nos. 538-540 (3) .90 .90

A155

A156

Nigerian Security Printing and Minting Co., Ltd., 25th Anniv. — A157

10k, Bank note production. 20k, Coin production. 25k, Products. 30k, Anniv. emblem.

1988, Oct. 28
541 A155 10k multicolored .35 .35
542 A155 20k multicolored .35 .35
543 A156 25k multicolored .35 .35
544 A157 30k multicolored .35 .35
Nos. 541-544 (4) 1.40 1.40

Traditional Musical Instruments A158

Wmk. 379
1989, June 29 Litho. ***Perf. 14***
545 A158 10k Tambari .40 .40
546 A158 20k Kundung .40 .40
547 A158 25k Ibid .40 .40
548 A158 30k Dundun .40 .40
Nos. 545-548 (4) 1.60 1.60

African Development Bank, 25th Anniv. — A159

10k, Reservoir, Mali. 20k, Irrigation project, Gambia. 25k, Bank headquarters.

1989, Sept. 10
549 A159 10k multicolored .30 .25
550 A159 20k multicolored .30 .25
551 A159 25k multicolored .30 .25
552 A159 30k shown .30 .25
Nos. 549-552 (4) 1.20 1.00

Nos. 549-551 horiz.

Nigerian Girl Guides Assoc., 70th Anniv. — A160

1989, Sept. 16
553 A160 10k Campfire, horiz. .50 .50
554 A160 20k shown .50 .50

Traditional Costumes — A161

1989, Oct. 26
555 A161 10k Etubom .40 .40
556 A161 20k Fulfulde .40 .40
557 A161 25k Aso-ofi .40 .40
558 A161 30k Fuska Kura .40 .40
Nos. 555-558 (4) 1.60 1.60

Pan-African Postal Union, 10th Anniv. — A162

1990, Jan. 18
559 A162 10k shown .35 .35
560 A162 20k Map, delivery .40 .40

National Theater — A162a

20n, Ancient wall, Kano. 50n, Rock bridge. 100n, Ekpe masquerade, vert.

1990, May 23 Litho. ***Perf. 14***
560A A162a 20n multicolored *13.00* *2.00*
560B A162a 50n multicolored *9.00* *4.00*
560C A162a 100n multicolored *7.00* *7.00*
560D A162a 500n multicolored *37.50* *25.00*
e. Perf. 13, unwatermarked (NSPMPLC inscription at LL) — —
Nos. 560A-560D (4) *66.50* *38.00*

Postal counterfeits are known of No. 560B.
Issued: No. 560De, 2010.

Pottery — A163

1990, May 24
561 A163 10k Oil lamp .25 .25
562 A163 20k Water pot .25 .25
563 A163 25k Musical pots .25 .25
564 A163 30k Water jug .25 .25
a. Sheet of 4, #561-564 with yellow frames, + 4 labels 1.75 1.75
Nos. 561-564 (4) 1.00 1.00

Inscriptions, including country name, denomination and descriptions vary widely in size and style.

Intl. Literacy Year — A164

1990, Aug. 8
565 A164 20k multicolored .30 .25
566 A164 30k multicolored .30 .25

A165

A166

1990, Sept. 14
567 A165 10k shown .25 .25
568 A166 20k Flags .25 .25
569 A165 25k Globe .25 .25
570 A166 30k shown .25 .25
Nos. 567-570 (4) 1.00 1.00

Organization of Petroleum Exporting Countries (OPEC), 30th anniv.

Wildlife — A167

20k, Grey parrot. 30k, Roan antelope. 1.50n, Grey-necked rock fowl. 2.50n, Mountain gorilla.

1990, Nov. 8
571 A167 20k multi .30 .30
572 A167 30k multi .40 .40
573 A167 1.50n multi 1.25 1.25
574 A167 2.50n multi 1.75 1.75
a. Souvenir sheet of 4, #571-574 4.25 4.25
Nos. 571-574 (4) 3.70 3.70

Inscriptions vary widely in size and style.

A168

A169

1991, Mar. 20
575 A168 10k Eradication .25 .25
576 A169 20k shown .25 .25
577 A168 30k Prevention .25 .25
Nos. 575-577 (3) .75 .75

Natl. Guineaworm Eradication Day.

A170

1991, May 26
578 A170 20k Progress .25 .25
579 A170 30k Unity .25 .25
580 A170 50k Freedom .25 .25
Nos. 578-580 (3) .75 .75

OAU Heads of State Meeting, Abiya.

ECOWAS Summit, Abuja — A171

1991, July 4
581 A171 20k Flags   .45 .40
582 A171 50k Map of West Africa   .45 .40
Economic Community of West African States.

Fish — A172

1991, July 10
583 A172 10k Electric catfish   .30 .30
584 A172 20k Niger perch   .45 .45
585 A172 30k Talapia   .50 .50
586 A172 50k African catfish   .60 .60
a.   Souvenir sheet of 4, #583-586   2.75 2.75
      Nos. 583-586 (4)   1.85 1.85

Telecom '91 — A173

1991, Oct. 7
587 A173 20k shown   .25 .25
588 A173 50k multi, vert.   .45 .45
Sixth World Forum and Exposition on Tele-communications, Geneva, Switzerland.

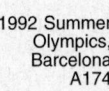

1992 Summer Olympics, Barcelona A174

1992, Jan. 24   Unwmk.
589 A174 50k Boxing   .30 .30
590 A174 1n Running   .30 .30
591 A174 1.50n Table tennis   .40 .40
592 A174 2n Taekwondo   .50 .50
a.   Souvenir sheet of 4, #589-592,
      wmk. 379   3.50 3.50
      Nos. 589-592 (4)   1.50 1.50

1992 Summer Olympics, Barcelona — A175

Wmk. 379
1992, Apr. 3   Litho.   Perf. 14
593 A175 1.50n multicolored   .55 .55

World Health Day — A176

Designs: 50k, Heart and blood pressure gauge. 1n, Globe and blood pressure guage. 1.50n, Heart in rib cage. 2n, Cross-section of heart.

1992, Apr. 7   Unwmk.
594 A176 50k multicolored   .25 .25
595 A176 1n multicolored   .25 .25
596 A176 1.50n multicolored   .30 .30
597 A176 2n multicolored   .40 .40
a.   Souvenir sheet of 4, #594-597   1.50 1.50
      Nos. 594-597 (4)   1.20 1.20

Intl. Institute of Tropical Agriculture, 25th Anniv. — A177

Designs: 50k, Plantain, vert. 1n, Food products. 1.50n, Harvesting cassava tubers, vert. 2n, Yam barn, vert.

1992, July 17
598 A177 50k multicolored   .25 .25
599 A177 1n multicolored   .25 .25
600 A177 1.50n grn, blk & brown   .25 .25
601 A177 2n multicolored   .30 .30
a.   Souvenir sheet of 4, #598-601   2.40 2.40
      Nos. 598-601 (4)   1.05 1.05

Olymphilex '92 — A178

1.50n, Stamp under magnifying glass.

Wmk. 379
1992, July 3   Litho.   Perf. 14
602 A178 50k multicolored   .25 .25
603 A178 1.50n multicolored   .45 .45
a.   Souvenir sheet of 2, #602-603 +
      4 labels, unwmkd.   2.25 2.25

Maryam Babangida, Natl. Center for Women's Development
A179   A180

A180a

Designs: 50k, Emblem of Better Life Program. 1n, Women harvesting corn. 1.50n, Natl. Center, horiz. 2n, Woman using loom.

1992, Oct. 16
604 A179 50k multicolored   .25 .25
605 A180 1n multicolored   .25 .25
606 A180 1.50n multicolored   .30 .30
607 A180a 2n multicolored   .35 .35
      Nos. 604-607 (4)   1.15 1.15

Traditional Dances — A181

Unwmk.
1992, Dec. 15   Litho.   Perf. 14
608 A181 50k Sabada   .25 .25
609 A181 1n Sato   .25 .25
610 A181 1.50n Asian Ubo Ikpa   .30 .30
611 A181 2n Dundun   .35 .35
a.   Souvenir sheet of 4, #608-611   2.25 2.25
      Nos. 608-611 (4)   1.15 1.15

Intl. Conference on Nutrition, Rome — A182

1992, Dec. 1   Litho.   Perf. 14
612 A182 50k Vegetables   .25 .25
613 A182 1n Child eating   .25 .25
614 A182 1.50n Fruits, vert.   .30 .30
615 A182 2n Vegetables, diff.   .35 .35
a.   Souvenir sheet of 4, #611-615   2.75 2.75
      Nos. 612-615 (4)   1.15 1.15

African Elephant — A182a

Stanley Crane — A182b

Lekki Beach — A182c

Roan Antelopes — A182d

Lion — A182e

1992-93   Litho.   Perf. 14
615A A182a 1.50n multi   4.25 1.50
615B A182b 5n multi   5.00 1.00
615C A182c 10n multi   2.50 1.00
615D A182d 20n multi   9.00 4.00
615E A182e 30n multi   12.00 6.00
      Nos. 615A-615E (5)   32.75 13.50

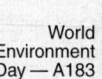

World Environment Day — A183

Designs: 1n, Clean environment ensures good health. 1.50n, Check water polution. 5n, Preserve your environment. 10n, Environment and nature.

1993, June 4   Litho.   Perf. 14
616 A183 1n multicolored   .25 .25
617 A183 1.50n multicolored   .30 .30
618 A183 5n multicolored   .80 .80
619 A183 10n multicolored   1.00 1.00
      Nos. 616-619 (4)   2.35 2.35

Natl. Commission for Museums and Monuments, 50th Anniv. — A184

1n, Oni figure, vert. 1.50n, Queen Mother head, vert. 5n, Pendant. 10n, Nok head, vert.

1993, July 28   Litho.   Perf. 14
620 A184 1n multi   .25 .25
621 A184 1.50n multi   .30 .30
622 A184 5n multi   .45 .45
623 A184 10n multi   .75 .75
      Nos. 620-623 (4)   1.75 1.75

Orchids — A185

1n, Bulbophyllum distans. 1.50n, Eulophia cristata. 5n, Eulophia horsfalli. 10n, Eulophia quartiniana.

1993, Oct. 28   Litho.   Perf. 14
624 A185 1n multicolored   .30 .30
625 A185 1.50n multicolored   .35 .35
626 A185 5n multicolored   .60 .60
627 A185 10n multicolored   1.25 1.25
a.   Souv. sheet of 4, #624-627   3.50 3.50
      Nos. 624-627 (4)   2.50 2.50

No. 627a exists with perforations through either the bottom or top margins.

Intl. Year of the Family — A186

1.50n, Child abuse, classroom scene. 10n, Fending for the family, market scene.

1994, Mar. 30   Litho.   Perf. 14
628 A186 1.50n multicolored   .50 .50
629 A186 10n multicolored   1.10 1.10

Nigerian Philatelic Service, 25th Anniv. — A187

1n, #224. 1.50n, Bureau building. 5n, Map made of stamps. 10n, Counter staff, customers.

1994, Apr. 11
630 A187 1n multicolored   .25 .25
631 A187 1.50n multicolored   .30 .30
632 A187 5n multicolored   .50 .50
633 A187 10n multicolored   1.20 1.20
      Nos. 630-633 (4)   2.25 2.25

First Nigerian Postage Stamps, 120th Anniv. — A188

Designs: 1n, "I love stamps." 1.50n, "I collect stamps." 5n, Methods of transporting mail. 10n, Lagos type A1 on airmail envelope.

1994, June 10   Litho.   Perf. 14
634 A188 1n multicolored   .25 .25
635 A188 1.50n multicolored   .30 .30
636 A188 5n multicolored   .50 .50
637 A188 10n multicolored   1.20 1.20
      Nos. 634-637 (4)   2.25 2.25

PHILAKOREA '94 — A189

1994, Aug. 16   Litho.   Perf. 14
638 A189 30n multicolored   3.00 3.00
a.   Souvenir sheet of 1, #638   5.50 5.50

Crabs — A190

1n, Geryon quinquedens. 1.50n, Spider crab. 5n, Red spider. 10n, Geryon maritae.

1994, Aug. 12   Litho.   Perf. 14
639 A190 1n multi   .25 .25
640 A190 1.50n multi   .35 .35
641 A190 5n multi   .75 .75
642 A190 10n multi   1.50 1.50
      Nos. 639-642 (4)   2.85 2.85

African Development Bank, 30th Anniv. — A191

1.50n, Water treatment plant. 30n, Emblem, field.

1994, Sept. 16
643 A191 1.50n multi   .25 .25
644 A191 30n multi   2.75 2.75

NIPOST/NITEL, 10th Anniv. — A192

Designs: 1n, Putting letter into mailbox, vert. 1.50n, Airmail letter. 5n, NIPOST, NITEL logos. 10n, Telephones, vert.

1995, Jan. 1 Litho. Perf. 14
645 A192 1n multicolored .25 .25
646 A192 1.50n multicolored .25 .25
647 A192 5n multicolored .40 .40
648 A192 10n multicolored .80 .80
  Nos. 645-648 (4) 1.70 1.70

Family Support
Program — A194

Designs: 1n, Feed the family. 1.50n, Monitoring child education. 5n, Caring for the family. 10n, Support agriculture.

1995, July 20 Litho. Perf. 14
653 A194 1n multicolored .25 .25
654 A194 1.50n multicolored .25 .25
655 A194 5n multicolored .40 .40
656 A194 10n multicolored .80 .80
  Nos. 653-656 (4) 1.70 1.70

First Telephone in
Nigeria, Cent. — A195

Designs: 1.50n, Dial telephone, c. 1919. 10n, Crank telephone, c. 1885.

1995, Oct. 9 Litho. Perf. 14
657 A195 1.50n multicolored .30 .30
658 A195 10n multicolored 1.10 1.10

FAO, 50th
Anniv. — A196

1995, Oct. 16
659 A196 1.50n shown .25 .25
660 A196 30n Fishing boats 3.00 3.00

UN, 50th
Anniv. — A197

Designs: 1n, Emblem of justice, vert. 1.50n, Against illegal dumping of toxic chemicals. 5n, Tourism. 10n, Peace-keeping soldiers.

1995, Oct. 24
661 A197 1n multicolored .25 .25
662 A197 1.50n multicolored .25 .25
663 A197 5n multicolored .40 .40
664 A197 10n multicolored .80 .80
  Nos. 661-664 (4) 1.70 1.70

Niger Dock, 10th
Anniv. — A198

5n, Overall view of dock. 10n, Boat being lifted. 20n, Boats in dock area. 30n, Boat on water.

1996, Apr. 29 Litho. Perf. 14
665 A198 5n multicolored .40 .40
666 A198 10n multicolored 1.00 1.00
667 A198 20n multicolored 1.75 1.75
668 A198 30n multicolored 2.50 2.50
  Nos. 665-668 (4) 5.65 5.65

Economic Community of West African
States (ECOWAS), 21st
Anniv. — A199

5n, Developing agriculture and scientific research. 30n, Free movement of people.

1996, May 5 Litho. Perf. 14
669 A199 5n multicolored .50 .50
670 A199 30n multicolored 2.50 2.50

A200

1996, June 28
671 A200 5n Judo .40 .40
672 A200 10n Tennis 1.00 1.00
673 A200 20n Relay race 1.75 1.75
674 A200 30n Soccer 2.50 2.50
  Nos. 671-674 (4) 5.65 5.65

1996 Summer Olympic Games, Atlanta.

Natl. Flag, Logo — A201

1996, Oct. 10 Litho. Perf. 14
675 A201 30n multicolored 3.00 3.00

Istanbul '96.

Mushrooms
A202

Designs: 5n, Volvariella esculenta. 10n, Lentinus subnudus. 20n, Tricholoma lobayensis. 30n, Pleurotus tuber-regium.

1996, Nov. 19
676 A202 5n multicolored .50 .50
677 A202 10n multicolored .90 .90
678 A202 20n multicolored 2.10 2.10
679 A202 30n multicolored 3.00 3.00
  Nos. 676-679 (4) 6.50 6.50

UNICEF, 50th
Anniv. — A203

Designs: 5n, "Child's right to play," vert. 30n, "Educate the girl child."

1996, Dec. 10
680 A203 5n multicolored .50 .50
681 A203 30n multicolored 2.50 2.50

Mass Literacy
Commission, 5th
Anniv. — A204

Designs: 5n, "Teach one to teach one." 30n, "Education through co-operation."

1996, Dec. 30
682 A204 5n grn, blk & dk grn .45 .45
683 A204 30n grn, blk & dk grn 2.40 2.40

1998 World Cup
Soccer
Championships,
France — A205

1998, June 10 Litho. Perf. 13
684 A205 5n shown .45 .45
685 A205 10n Player, vert. .90 .90
686 A205 20n Player, diff., vert. 1.60 1.60
687 A205 30n Two players 2.50 2.50
  Nos. 684-687 (4) 5.45 5.45

ECOMOG
(Military Co-
operation
Organization), 8th
Anniv. — A206

Designs: 5n, Silhouette of ship. 30n, Flag colors of Gambia, Ghana, Guinea, Mali, Nigeria, Senegal, Sierra Leone. 50n, Flag colors of

Gambia, Ghana, Nigeria, Guinea, Mali, Senegal, Sierra Leone, Niger, Ivory Coast, Benin, Burkina Faso.

1998, Nov. 30 Litho. Perf. 14
688 A206 5n multicolored .40 .40
689 A206 30n multicolored 2.40 2.40
690 A206 50n multicolored 4.00 4.00
  Nos. 688-690 (3) 6.80 6.80

Nigerian Railroad,
Cent. — A207

5n, Caged locomotive. 10n, Iddo Terminal. 20n, Locomotive. 30n, Passenger tram.

1999, Jan. 20 Litho. Perf. 13
691 A207 5n multicolored .40 .40
692 A207 10n multicolored .85 .85
693 A207 20n multicolored 1.75 1.75
694 A207 30n multicolored 2.50 2.50
  Nos. 691-694 (4) 5.50 5.50

Rain Forest — A207a

1999, May 10 Litho. Perf. 13
694A A207a 10n multi — —

University of
Ibadan, 50th
Anniv. — A208

1998, Nov. 17 Litho. Perf. 14
695 A208 5n University building .50 .50
696 A208 30n "50," Crest 2.25 2.25

Federal
Environmental
Protection
Agency, 10th
Anniv. — A209

5n, Water resources. 10n, Natural resources. 20n, Endangered species. 30n, One earth, one family.

1999, June 8 Litho. Perf. 13
697 A209 5n multicolored .50 .50
698 A209 10n multicolored .75 .75
699 A209 20n multicolored 1.75 1.75
700 A209 30n multicolored 2.50 2.50
  Nos. 697-700 (4) 5.50 5.50

NICON Insurance
Corp., 30th
Anniv. — A210

Emblem and: 5n, Airplane, ship, oil refinery, vert. 30n, Building.

Perf. 12¾x13, 13x12¾
1999, Aug. 31 Litho.
701 A210 5n multi .40 .40
702 A210 30n multi 2.00 2.00

Millennium
A211

Designs: 10n, Map of Northern and Southern Protectorates, 1900-14. 20n, Map of Nigeria, 1914. 30n, Coat of arms. 40n, Map of 36 states, 1996.

2000 Litho. Perf. 13
703-706 A211 Set of 4 2.10 2.10

World
Meteorological
Organization,
50th
Anniv. — A212

Designs: 10n, Sunshine hour recorder, vert. 30n, Meteorological station.

2000 Perf. 12¾x13, 13x12¾
707-708 A212 Set of 2 1.00 1.00

Return to
Democracy
A213

Designs: 10n, Flag, "Freedom of the press," vert. 20n, Scales of justice. 30n, Legislative mace, vert. 40n, Pres. Olusegun Obasanjo, flag, vert.

2000 Perf. 14¾
709-712 A213 Set of 4 3.25 3.25
712a Souvenir sheet, #709-712 5.00 5.00

2000 Summer
Olympics,
Sydney — A214

Designs: 10n, Boxing. 20n, Weight lifting. 30n, Soccer. 40n, Soccer, diff.

2000, Sept. 7 Litho. Perf. 13x12¾
713-716 A214 Set of 4 3.25 3.25
716a Souvenir sheet, #713-716 + 4 labels 5.00 5.00

A215

Independence, 40th anniv.: 10n, Obafemi Awolowo (1909-87), promoter of federal constitution. 20n, Prime Minister Abubakar Tafawa Balewa (1912-66). 30n, Pres. Nnamdi Azikiwe (1904-96). 40n, Liquified gas refinery, horiz. 50n, Ship carrying exports, horiz.

Perf. 12¾x13, 13x12¾
2000, Sept. 27 Litho.
717-721 A215 Set of 5 3.75 3.75

A216

Fruit: 20n, Hug plum. 30n, White star apple. 40n, African breadfruit. 50n, Akee apple.

2001, Jan. 16 Perf. 14
722-725 A216 Set of 4 3.00 3.00

Nigeria Daily
Times Newspaper,
75th
Anniv. — A217

Designs: 20n, Corporate headquarters, Lagos. 30n, First issue. 40n, Daily Times complex, Lagos. 50n, Masthead.

2001, June 1 Litho. Perf. 13x12¾
726-729 A217 Set of 4 3.25 3.25

Fauna — A218

Designs: 10n, Broad-tailed paradise whydahs, vert. 15n, Fire-bellied woodpeckers, vert. 20n, Grant's zebras. 25n, Aardvark. 30n, Preuss's guenon, vert. 40n, Giant ground pangolin. 50n, Bonobo. 100n, Red-eared guenon, vert.

2001, June 15   *Perf. 14*
730	A218	10n multi	.40	.25
731	A218	15n multi	.50	.25
732	A218	20n multi	.60	.35
a.		Thinner inscriptions, perf. 13x13¼ ('05)	.30	.30
733	A218	25n multi	.70	.45
734	A218	30n multi	.80	.60
735	A218	40n multi	.90	.80
736	A218	50n multi	1.00	.90
a.		Thinner inscriptions, perf. 13x13¼ ('05)	.80	.80
737	A218	100n multi	2.50	2.00
a.		Perf. 13¼x13		
		Nos. 730-737 (8)	7.40	5.60

Inscriptions vary widely in size and style.
Issued: Nos. 732a, 736a, 737a, 2005.

Year of Dialogue Among
Civilizations — A219

2001, Oct. 9   *Litho.*   *Perf. 13*
738	A219	20n multi	.90	.90

New Millennium
A220

Designs: 20n, Peace. 30n, Age of globaliza-
tion. 40n, Reconciliation. 50n, Love.

2002, Feb. 13   *Litho.*   *Perf. 13x12¾*
739-742	A220	Set of 4	3.00	3.00

Crops — A221

Designs: 20n, Kola nuts. 30n, Oil palm. 40n,
Cassava. 50n, Corn, vert.

2002, May 10   *Perf. 13x12¾, 12¾x13*
743-746	A221	Set of 4	2.60	2.60

2002 World Cup
Soccer
Championships,
Japan and
Korea — A222

Emblem and: 20n, Nigerian player and
opponent, vert. 30n, Globe and soccer balls,
vert. 40n, Player's legs and ball. 50n, World
Cup trophy, vert.

Perf. 12¾x13, 13x12¾
2002, June 14
747-750	A222	Set of 4	2.75	2.75

World AIDS
Day — A223

Designs: 20n, Nurse, patient, flowers. 50n,
AIDS counseling.

2003, May 3   *Litho.*   *Perf. 13x12¾*
751-752	A223	Set of 2	1.70	1.70
752a		Souvenir sheet, #751-752	3.50	3.50

A224

Universal basic education: 20n, Students.
50n, Student writing, horiz.

Perf. 12¾x13, 13x12¾
2003, Sept. 22   *Litho.*
753-754	A224	Set of 2	2.00	2.00

A225

Eighth All Africa Games: 20n, Runner. 30n,
High jump, horiz. 40n, Taekwondo, horiz. 50n,
Long jump.

2003, Oct. 4
755-758	A225	Set of 4	2.50	2.50
758a		Souvenir sheet, #755-758 + 4 labels	3.00	3.00

Worldwide Fund for
Nature
(WWF) — A226

Side-striped jackal: 20n, Adult and pups.
40n, Adult in grass. 80n, Two adults. 100n,
Adult in grass, diff.

2003, Dec. 12   *Perf. 13x12¾*
759-762	A226	Set of 4	4.25	3.75
762a		Block of 4, #759-762	4.75	4.75

Commonwealth
Heads of
Government
Meeting,
Abuja — A227

Emblem and: 20n, Map of Nigeria. 50n, Flag
of Nigeria, vert.

Perf. 13x12¾, 12¾x13
2003, Dec. 7   *Litho.*
763-764	A227	Set of 2	2.00	2.00

2004 Summer Olympics,
Athens — A228

Designs: 50n, Runners. 120n, Basketball.

2004, Aug. 18   *Litho.*   *Perf. 12¾x13*
765-766	A228	Set of 2	3.00	3.00
766a		Souvenir sheet of 2, #765-766, + 4 labels	25.00	25.00

No. 766a sold for 150n.

A229   A232

A230

Winning Children's Stamp Art Contest
Designs — A231

Perf. 12¾x13, 13x12¾
2004, Oct. 29   *Litho.*
767	A229	50n multi	.75	.75
768	A230	90n multi	1.50	1.50
769	A231	120n multi	2.00	2.00
770	A232	150n multi	2.50	2.50
a.		Souvenir sheet, #767-770, + 12 labels	7.00	7.00
		Nos. 767-770 (4)	6.75	6.75

Rotary International, Cent. — A233

Designs: 50n, "100" with Rotary emblems
for zeroes. 120n, Rotary emblem and world
map.

2005, Aug. 9   *Litho.*   *Perf. 13x12¾*
771-772		Set of 2	3.50	3.50
772a	A233	Horiz. pair, #771-772	3.50	3.50

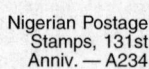

Nigerian Postage
Stamps, 131st
Anniv. — A234

Designs: 50n, Text in simulated stamp. 90n,
Map of Nigeria, simulated stamp. 120n, Map
of Nigeria, years "1874" and "2005." 150n,
Nigeria #118, 746, vert.

2005, Oct. 9   *Perf. 13x12¾, 12¾x13*
773-776	A234	Set of 4	6.50	6.50

World Summit on
the Information
Society,
Tunis — A235

Summit emblems, globe and: 20n, Nigeria
Post emblem. 50n, Postman on motorcycle,
vert. 120n, Like 20n.

Perf. 13x12¾, 12¾x13
2005, Nov. 4   *Litho.*
777-779	A235	Set of 3	3.50	3.50

Writers — A236

Designs: 20n, Prof. Chinua Achebe. 40n,
Dr. Abubakar Imam (1911-81). 50n, Prof.
Wole Soyinka.

2006, Jan. 18   *Perf. 13x12¾*
780-782	A236	Set of 3	1.75	1.75

Scholars — A237

Designs: No. 783, 50n, No. 786, 100n, Prof.
Ayodele Awojobi (1937-84), engineer. No.
784, 50n, No. 787, 120n, Prof. Gabriel Oyibo,
mathematician. No. 785, 50n, No. 788, 150n,
Philip Emeagwali, computer scientist.

2006, Jan. 18   *Perf. 12¾x13*
783-788	A237	Set of 6	8.25	8.25

Dated 2005.

52nd
Commonwealth
Parliamentary
Conference,
Abuja — A238

Designs: No. 789, International Conference
Center. No. 790, National Assembly Building.
No. 791: a, 20n, Like No. 789 with smaller-
sized denomination in green and white. b, 50n,
Like No. 790 with denomination in green.

2006, Sept. 4   *Litho.*   *Perf. 13x12¾*
789	A238	20n multi	—	—
790	A238	50n multi	—	—

Souvenir Sheet
Imperf
791	A238	Sheet of 2, #a-b		

Queen Elizabeth
II, 80th
Birthday — A239

2006, Oct. 9   *Litho.*   *Perf. 13*
792-793	A239	Set of 2	1.40	1.40

Agbani Darego, 2001
Miss World — A240

Darego and: 20n, Map of Nigeria. 50n, Map
of world, horiz.

2006, Nov. 9
794-795	A240	Set of 2	1.10	1.10

Abuja, 30th
Anniv. — A241

Designs: 20n, Gate, fireworks, palm trees,
map of Nigeria. 50n, Emblem, hands beating
drum, vert.

2006, Dec. 13
796-797	A241	Set of 2	1.10	1.10

143rd
Extraordinary
Conference of
OPEC,
Abuja — A242

2006, Dec. 14
798	A242	50n multi	.80	.80

The editors have been shown numerous examples of this stamp on cover,
but Nigerian postal authorities state that
it was issued "strictly for the validation
of documents, and not for postage," and
that use of the stamp on mail was probably done out of ignorance.

Mungo Park (1771-
1806), Explorer — A243

Park and: 20n, Monument. 50n, River, horiz.

2007, Mar. 29   *Litho.*   *Perf. 13*
799-800	A243	Set of 2	1.10	1.10

A244

2007, Mar. 29   *Litho.*   *Perf. 13*
801	A244	50n multi	.80	.80
h.		Sheet of 2 #801, imperf.		

Second World Black and African festival of
arts and culture, 30th Anniv.

24th UPU Congress —
A244a

Ceremonial costumes: No. 801A, Fulani man. No. 801B, Igbo man and woman. No. 801C, South Zone man and woman. No. 801D, Tiv man and woman, horiz. No. 801E, 50n, Yoruba man and woman. No. 801F, North East Zone women.

Perf. 13x12¾, 12¾x13

2007, Oct. 9			Litho.
801A	A244a	20n multi	— —
801B	A244a	20n multi	— —
801C	A244a	30n multi	— —
801D	A244a	30n multi	—
801E	A244a	30n multi	—
801F	A244a	50n multi	—
	g.	Souvenir sheet of 6, #801A-801F, imperf.	—

The 24th UPU Congress, scheduled to be held in Nairobi, was moved to Geneva, Switzerland, because of political unrest in Kenya.

A245

Cross river gorilla: 20n, Adult. 50n, Two adults, horiz. 100n, Adult and juvenile, horiz. 150n, Head.

2008, Mar. 26	Litho.		**Perf. 13**
802-805	A245	Set of 4	5.00 5.00

Worldwide Fund for Nature (WWF).

A246

Designs: 20n, Hands, money. 50n, Campaign to end violation of 419 law. 100n, Clasped hands.

2008, Apr. 10			
806-808	A246	Set of 3	3.00 3.00
808a		Souvenir sheet of 3, #806-808, imperf.	— —

Economic & Financial Crimes Commission anti-corruption campaign.
Nos. 806-809 exist without printer's imprint. Their issue status is uncertain. Value, set $110.

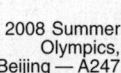

2008 Summer Olympics, Beijing — A247

Designs: 20n, Runners at finish line. 50n, Soccer. 100n, Wrestling, vert.

2008, Aug. 8			
809-811	A247	Set of 3	3.00 3.00

Federal Road Safety Commission, 20th Anniv. — A247a — 811A

2008, Nov. 13	Litho.		**Perf. 13**
811A	A247a	50n multi	1.25 1.00

Nigerian Institute of Advanced Legal Studies — A248

2009, Sept. 4	Litho.		**Perf. 13**
812	A248	50n multi	.65 .65

Pan-African Postal Union, 30th Anniv. — A248a

2010, Jan. 8	Litho.	**Perf. 13x12¾**
812A	A248a	50n multi	1.00 1.00

Dated 2009.

Return to Democracy, 10th Anniv. — A249

Designs: No. 813, 50n, Nigerian flag, Pres. Umaru Musa Yar'Adua. No. 814, 50n, Mace, scales of justice, barrister's wig, vert.

Perf. 13x12¾, 12¾x13

2010, Apr. 6		Litho.
813-814	A249	Set of 2	1.75 1.75

Dated 2009.

GT Bank, 20th Anniv. — A250

Woman, globe, 20th anniversary emblem, bank emblem and background color of: 20n, Red. 50n, Gray. 100n, Pale yellow. 120n, Gray green.

2010, July 14	Litho.	**Perf. 13x12¾**
815-818	A250	Set of 4	5.50 5.50

Organization of Petroleum Exporting Countries, 50th Anniv. — A251

Designs: 50n, Oil droplet, 50th anniversary emblem. 120n, 50th anniversary emblem.

2010, Aug. 12	Litho.	**Perf. 12¾x13**
819-820	A251	Set of 2	3.00 3.00

A252   A252a

2010 World Cup Soccer Championships, South Africa — A252b

Design: 20n, Two soccer players and ball. 30n, Soccer ball, globe, World Cup, vert. 50n, Soccer players and stadium.

2010		**Perf. 13x12¾, 12¾x13**
821	A252	20n multi	.50
821A	A252a	30n multi	1.00 —
821B	A252b	50n multi	1.75 —

Terracotta Head — A253

Terracotta Head — A253a

Terracotta Head — A253b

Bronze Bowl — A254

Igbo-Ukwu Bronze Bowl — A254a

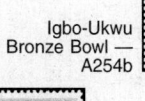

Igbo-Ukwu Bronze Bowl — A254b

Slave Chain A255

Lander Brothers Anchorage A256

Lander Brothers Anchorage — A256a

Nok Terracotta Head A257

Monkey Colony, Lagwa-Mbaise A258

Lander Brothers Anchorage — A258a

Elephants, Yankari Game Reserve — A258b

Argungu Fishing Festival, Kebbi State A259

Seated Human Figurine A260

Lander Brothers Anchorage — A260a

Perf. 12¼x12½, 13 (Nos. 822A, 823A, 825A, 826, 827, 828), 12½x12¼ (Nos. 823B, 827A)
Litho. With Hologram Applied

2010-11			
822	A253	20n multi	.75 —
822A	A253a	20n multi	— —
822B	A253b	20n multi	— —
823	A254	30n multi	— —
823A	A254a	30n multi	— —
823B	A254b	30n multi	— —
824	A255	50n multi	— —
825	A256	50n multi	— —
825A	A256a	50n multi	— —
826	A257	50n multi	— —
827	A258	50n multi	— —
827A	A258a	50n multi (round hologram)	— —
827B	A258b	90n multi	— —
828	A259	100n multi	4.00
829	A260	120n multi	3.50 —

Litho.
Perf. 12¾x13

829A	A260a	50n multi	20.00 20.00

Issued: No. 822A, 823A, 825A, 2011; No. 829A, 2010; others, 10/9/2010. No. 822A is dated 2010. No. 829A is dated 2009. Nos. 822B and 823B are dated 2010.

Independence, 50th Anniv. — A261

Nigerian arms and: 20n, Nigerian flag on pole, man holding pole with British flag, 50th anniv. emblem. 30n, Map and symbols of Nigeria. No. 832, 50n, Four men and Nigerian flag, 50th anniv. emblem, horiz. (77x22mm). No. 833, 50n, Photographs of Nigerian crops and industries, 50th anniv. emblem, horiz. (53x37mm).

Perf. 13, 13¼ (#832), 13¼x13 (#833)

2010			Litho.
830-833	A261	Set of 4	3.50 3.50

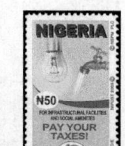

Federal Inland Revenue Service — A262

Emblem of Federal Inland Revenue Service and: 20n, Heart, map of Nigeria. 50n, Light bulb, water faucet. 100n, Taxcard.

2011		Litho.	**Perf. 13**
834	A262	20n multi	.75 —
835	A262	50n multi	1.25 —
836	A262	100n multi	2.50 —

Dated 2009.

Benue State — A263

Map of Benue State and: 20n, Gugur Waterfall. 30n, Food basket. 50n, Senator Joseph Sawuan Tarka (1932-80). 100n, Benue Bridge.

2011		Litho.	**Perf. 13**
837-840	A263	Set of 4	4.50 4.50
840a		Souvenir sheet of 4, #837-840, imperf.	14.00 14.00

Nigerian Institute of Management, 50th Anniv. — A264

2011, Sept. 27
841   A264   50n multi   1.00   1.00
   a.   Souvenir sheet of 1, imperf.   —   —

Phila Africa 2012 Stamp
Exhibition — A265

2012, Jan. 31
842   A265   50n multi   1.00   1.00

An imperforate souvenir sheet of 1 sold for
400n.

Enugu, Cent. (in
2009) — A266

2012, Sept. 27   Litho.   Perf. 12¾x13
843   A266   50n multi   —   —

Ahmadu Bello University,
Zaria, 50th
Anniv. — A267

50th Anniv. emblem and: Nos. 844, 848, Sir
Ahmadu Bello (1910-66), Premier of Northern
Nigeria. Nos. 845, 849, Ahmadu Bello University Senate Building, horiz. 90n, University
crest. 120n, Shika brown chickens, horiz.

Litho. With Hologram Applied
2012, Nov. 24   Perf. 13
844   A267   50n multi   —   —
845   A267   50n multi   —   —
846   A267   90n multi   —   —
847   A267   120n multi   —   —

Litho.
Perf. 13¼x14
Booklet Stamps
848   A267   50n multi   —   —
849   A267   50n multi   —   —
850   A267   90n multi   —   —
851   A267   120n multi   —   —
   a.   Booklet pane of 4, #848-851   —   —
      Complete booklet, 3 #851a

Diplomatic Relations Between Nigeria
and Philippines, 50th Anniv. — A268

Flags of Philippines and Nigeria and: 50n,
Coat of arms of Nigeria, daisy. 120n, Coat of
arms of Philippines, sampaguita.

Litho. With Hologram Applied
2013, Dec. 24   Perf. 12¾x13¼
853   A268   50n multi   —   —
854   A268   120n multi   —   —

See Philippines No. 3511.

Civilian Leaders
of Nigerians
A269

Designs: Nos. 855, 862a, 50n, Nnamdi
Azikwe (1904-96), President and Governor-
General. Nos. 856, 862b, 50n, Sir Abubakar
Tafawa Balewa (1912-96), Prime Minister.
Nos. 857, 862c, 50n, Alhajlaliyu Shehu Sha-
gari, President. Nos. 858, 862d, 50n, Good-
luck Ebele Jonathan, President. Nos. 859,
862e, 50n, Ernest Shonekan, President. Nos.

860, 862f, 50n, Olusegun Obasanjo, President. Nos. 861, 862g, 50n, Umaru Musa
Yar'Adua (1951-2010), President.

Litho. With Hologram
2014, Nov. 27   Perf. 13½
855-861   A269   Set of 7   —   —
Souvenir Sheet
Litho.
Imperf
862   A269   Sheet of 7, #a-g   —   —

Nigeria,
Cent. — A270

Designs: Nos. 863, 867a, 50n, Fist, map of
Nigeria. Nos. 864, 867b, 50n, People lifting
map of Nigeria. Nos. 865, 867c, 100n, Chief
Obafemi Awolowo (1909-87), Sir Ahmadu
Bello (1910-66), Dr. Nnamdi Azikwe (1904-
96). Nos. 866, 867d, 120n, Sir Frederick Lord
Lugard (1858-1945), colonial administrator.

Litho. With Hologram
2014   Perf. 14
863-866   A270   Set of 4   —   —
Souvenir Sheet
Litho.
Imperf
867   A270   Sheet of 4, #a-d   —   —

Famous Nigerian
Buildings — A271

Designs: Nos. 868, 874a, 50n, Amalgama-
tion House, Calabar. Nos. 869, 874b, 50n,
Lord Lugard Court, Lokoja. Nos. 870, 874c,
50n, Seat of Administration of Lord Lugar
(now Kogi State Government House), Lokoja.
Nos. 871, 874d, 50n, National Assembly,
Abuja, Nigeria #97. Nos. 872, 874e, 50n,
Supreme Court, Abuja, Nigeria #98. Nos. 873,
874f, 50n, State House, Marina, Lagos, Presidential Villa, Abuja.

Litho. With Hologram
2014   Perf. 13½x13¾
868-873   A271   Set of 6   —   —
Souvenir Sheet
Litho.
Imperf
874   A271   Sheet of 6, #a-f   —   —
     Nigeria, cent.

Economic
Community of
West African
States
(ECOWAS), 40th
Anniv. — A272

2015, May 28   Litho.   Perf. 13x13¼
875   A272   50n multi   —   —

No. 875 comes in sheets of 25.

University of
Nigeria, 55th
Anniv. — A273

Designs: No. 876, 50n, University crest,
emblem of West African University Games.
No. 877, 50n, Prof. Benjamin C. Ozumba, University Vice-Chancellor, university crest and
games emblem. 100n, Dr. George M. Johnson, first Vice-Chancellor, university crest and
games emblem. 120n, Dr. Nnamdi Azikwe,
founder, university crest and games emblem.

2015, Oct. 23   Litho.   Perf. 14x13½
876-879   A273   Set of 4   —   —
879a   Souvenir sheet of 4, #876-   —   —
      879, imperf.

University of Nigeria, host of 2015 West African University Games.

University of Nigeria Type of 2015

Designs: No. 879B, 50n, Like #876. No.
879C, 50n, Like #877. No. 879D, 100n, Like
#878. No. 879E, 120n, Like #879.

Litho. With Hologram Affixed
2015, Oct. 23   Perf. 14x13½
879B-879E   A273   Set of 4   —   —

Anti-Corruption
Campaign
A274

Inscriptions: No. 880, 50n, Say no to theft.
No. 881, 50n, Say no to bunkering. No. 882,
50n, Say no to fraud. No. 883, 50n, Say no to
bribery.

Litho. With Hologram
2016, Nov. 7   Perf. 12½x13¼
880-883   A274   Set of 4   —   —
883a   Souvenir sheet of 4, #880-   —   —
      883

Rivers State,
50th
Anniv. — A275

Designs: Nos. 884, 888, 50n, Old Brick
House, Port Harcourt. Nos. 885, 889, 50n,
Aquatic resources of Rivers State. Nos. 886,
890, 50n, Point Block, Port Harcourt. Nos.
887, 891, 50n, Woman carrying basket on
head, vert.

2018   Litho.   Rouletted 6¾
884-887   A275   Set of 4   —   —
Perf. 13
888-891   A275   Set of 4   —   —

Issued: Nos. 884-887, 5/29; No. 890, 12/6;
Nos. 888-889, 891, 12/13.

African Drum
Festival,
Abeokuta — A276

Emblem and denomination in: 50n, Red (in
LL). 100n, Green (in UR).

2019, Apr. 25   Litho.   Perf. 13
892-893   A276   Set of 2   —   —

Mohandas K.
Gandhi (1869-
1948), Indian
Nationalist
Leader — A277

Litho. With Hologram Affixed
2019, Oct. 2   Perf. 13
894   A277   100n multi   —   —
Litho.
Size: 45x33mm
Without Hologram
Perf. 10¾
895   A277   100n multi   —   —
Souvenir Sheet
Without Gum
896   A277   100n multi   —   —
   a.   Imperf.

No. 896 contains one 71x47mm stamp. No.
896a has simulated perforations. On Nos. 895
and 896, "N" in denomination lacks horizontal
lines.

Sheikh Mujibur
Rahman (1920-
75), First
President of
Bangladesh
A278

Litho. With Hologram Affixed
2020, Aug. 27   Perf. 13½x14
897   A278   100n multi   —   —
Without Hologram
897A   A278   100n multi   —   —

Souvenir Sheet
Without Gum
Litho.
Imperf
898   A278   100n multi   —   —
   a.   As #898, with windblown flags   —   —
      in sheet margin
   b.   As #898a, perf. 10½   —   —

Nos. 898 and 898a contain one 65x47mm
stamp with simulated perforations. Flags on
sheet margin of No. 898 are not windblown.

Nigerian postal officials have
declared as "illegal" items bearing the
country name of Nigeria:
Sheets of five stamps depicting
Mushrooms, Pope John Paul II.
Sheets of four stamps depicting the
500th anniversary of the Reformation.
30 sheets of four stamps, two stamps
or one stamp with Space themes.
24 sheets of four stamps, two stamps
or one stamp with Soccer and Olympic
themes.
10 sheets of nine stamps depicting
2013 Formula 1 racing cars and drivers.

A279

Independence,
60th
Anniv. — A280

2020, Dec. 30   Litho.   Perf. 13
899   A279   100n multi   —   —
900   A280   500n multi   —   —

Law Making
Abuja Capital of
Nigeria, 45th
Anniv. — A281

2021, Mar. 18   Litho.   Perf. 13
901   A281   100n multi   —   —

Special Agro-
Industrial
Processing Zones
Program — A282

2022, Oct. 24   Litho.   Perf. 13
902   A282   250n multi   —   —

SEMI-POSTAL STAMPS

Catalogue values for unused
stamps in this section are for
Never Hinged items.

Children Drinking
Milk at
Orphanage
SP1

Designs: 1sh6p+3p, Civilian first aid, vert.
2sh6p+3p, Military first aid.

1966, Dec. 1   Photo.   Perf. 14½x14
B1   SP1   4p + 1p pur, blk &
      red   .35   .35
B2   SP1   1sh6p + 3p multi   .80   .80
B3   SP1   2sh6p + 3p multi   1.25   1.25
     Nos. B1-B3 (3)   2.40   2.40

The surtax was for the Nigerian Red Cross.

Dr. Armauer G.
Hansen — SP2

1973, July 30   Litho.   Perf. 14
B4 SP2 5k + 2k blk, brn & buff   .50 *1.00*
  Centenary of the discovery of the Hansen bacillus, the cause of leprosy. The surtax was for the Nigerian Anti-Leprosy Association.

Nigeria '99, FIFA
World Youth
Championships
SP3

  5n+5n, Soccer ball, FIFA emblem. 10n+5n, Throwing ball. 20n+5n, Kicking ball into goal. 30n+5n, Map of Nigeria. 40n+5n, FIFA emblem, eagle, soccer ball. 50n+5n, Tackling.

1999, Mar. 31   Litho.   Perf. 13x14
B5   SP3 5n +5n multi   .25   .25
B6   SP3 10n +5n multi   .30   .30
B7   SP3 20n +5n multi   .55   .55
B8   SP3 30n +5n multi   .65   .65
B9   SP3 40n +5n multi   .90   .90
B10 SP3 50n +5n multi   1.20 1.20
  a. Souvenir sheet of 6, #B5-B10   3.75 3.75
    Nos. B5-B10 (6)   3.85 3.85

POSTAGE DUE STAMPS

> Catalogue values for unused stamps in this section are for Never Hinged items.

D1

Perf. 14½x14
1959, Jan. 4   Wmk. 4   Litho.
J1   D1 1p orange   .25   1.00
J2   D1 2p orange   .25   1.25
J3   D1 3p orange   .25   1.75
J4   D1 6p orange   .80   6.25
J5   D1 1sh black   1.25 11.00
  Nos. J1-J5 (5)   2.80 21.25

1961, Aug. 1   Wmk. 335
J6   D1 1p red   .25   .40
J7   D1 2p blue   .25   .50
J8   D1 3p emerald   .25   .75
J9   D1 6p yellow   .25 2.00
J10 D1 1sh dark blue .40 4.00
  Nos. J6-J10 (5) 1.40 7.65

D2

Perf. 12½x13½
1973, May 3   Litho.   Unwmk.
J11 D2 2k red   .25   .25
J12 D2 3k blue   .25   .25
J13 D2 5k orange   .25   .25
J14 D2 10k yellow green .25   .25
  Nos. J11-J14 (4) 1.00 1.00

1987-94   Rouletted 9
J15 D2 2k red   1.75   2.50
J16 D2 5k yellow   4.50   5.00
J17 D2 10k green   9.00 10.00
  Nos. J15-J17 (3) 15.25 17.50

D3

2004   Litho.   Perf. 12¾
J18 D3 20n yel green   .75   —
J19 D3 40n red   .95   —

NIUE

nē-'ü-ˌā

LOCATION — Island in the south Pacific Ocean, northeast of New Zealand

GOVT. — Self-government, in free association with New Zealand

AREA — 100 sq. mi.

POP. — 1,708 (1997 est.)

CAPITAL — Alofi

Niue, also known as Savage Island, was annexed to New Zealand in 1901 with the Cook Islands. Niue achieved internal self-government in 1974.

12 Pence = 1 Shilling
20 Shillings = 1 Pound
100 Cents = 1 Dollar (1967)

Catalogue values for unused stamps in this country are for Never Hinged items, beginning with Scott 90 in the regular postage section, Scott B1 in the semi-postal section, Scott C1 in the air post section, and Scott O1 in the officials section.

Watermarks

Wmk. 61 — Single-lined NZ and Star Close Together

Wmk. 253 — NZ and Star

New Zealand No. 100 Handstamped in Green

1902	**Wmk. 63**		**Perf. 11**

Thick Soft Paper

1	A35	1p carmine	350.00	350.00

Stamps of New Zealand Surcharged in Carmine, Vermilion or Blue

1/2p   1p

2 1/2p

Perf. 14
Thin Hard Paper

3	A18	½p green (C)	8.50	11.00
a.		Inverted surcharge	375.00	700.00
b.		Double surcharge	1,400.	
4	A35	1p carmine (Bl), perf. 11x14	2.00	5.00
a.		No period after "PENI"	62.50	80.00
b.		Perf. 14	57.50	62.50
c.		As "a," perf. 14	600.00	700.00

Perf. 14
Wmk. 61

6	A18	½p green (V)	2.00	2.00
7	A35	1p carmine (Bl)	1.25	2.00
a.		No period after "PENI"	10.00	21.00
b.		Double surcharge	2,000.	2,300.

Perf. 11
Unwmk.

8	A22	2½p blue (C)	2.20	7.00
a.		No period after "PENI"	35.00	75.00
b.		Double surcharge	2,000.	2,300.

The surcharge on the ½ & 1p stamps is printed in blocks of 60. Two stamps in each block have a space between the "U" and "E" of "NIUE" and one of the 1p stamps has a broken "E" like an "F."

The 2½p blue stamp with surcharge in vermilion, formerly listed as No. 9, has been deleted, along with Nos. 9a and 9b. The editors are seeking evidence of its existence.

Blue Surcharge on Stamps of New Zealand, Types of 1898

e   f

g   h

1903	**Wmk. 61**		**Perf. 11**	
10	A23(e)	3p yellow brown	11.00	5.50
11	A26(f)	6p rose	15.00	12.50
13	A29(g)	1sh brown red	40.00	50.00
a.		1sh scarlet	40.00	50.00
b.		1sh orange red	50.00	52.50
c.		As "b," surcharge "h" (error)	750.00	
		Nos. 10-13 (3)	66.00	68.00

Surcharged in Carmine or Blue on Stamps of New Zealand — j

1911-12			**Perf. 14, 14x14½**	
14	A41(j)	½p yellow grn (C)	1.00	1.00
15	A41(f)	6p car rose (Bl)	2.50	7.50
16	A41(g)	1sh vermilion (Bl)	8.00	55.00
		Nos. 14-16 (3)	11.50	63.50

1915			**Perf. 14**	
18	A22(d)	2½p dark blue (C)	26.00	55.00

Surcharged in Brown or Dark Blue on Stamps of New Zealand

1917			**Perf. 14x15**	
19	A42	1p carmine (Br)	24.00	6.25
a.		No period after "PENI"	950.00	

			Perf. 14x14½	
20	A45(e)	3p violet brn (Bl)	55.00	125.00
a.		No period after "Pene"	950.00	
b.		Perf. 14x13½	75.00	150.00
c.		Vert. pair, #20 & 20b	225.00	

New Zealand Stamps of 1909-19 Overprinted in Dark Blue or Red — k

1917-20	**Typo.**		**Perf. 14x15**	
21	A43	½p yellow grn (R)	.80	3.25
22	A42	1p carmine (Bl)	11.00	17.50
23	A47	1½p gray black (R)	1.10	3.25
24	A47	1½p brown org (R)	1.00	10.00
25	A43	3p chocolate (Bl)	1.60	40.00

Engr.
Perf. 14x14½

26	A44	2½p dull blue (R)	1.50	19.00
a.		Perf. 14x13½	5.75	22.50
b.		Vert. pair, #26-26a	19.00	72.50
27	A45	3p violet brown (Bl)	1.75	3.00
a.		Perf. 14x13½	4.25	3.00
b.		Vert. pair, #27-27a	25.00	50.00
28	A45	6p car rose (Bl)	6.00	26.00
a.		Perf. 14x13½	12.50	25.00
b.		Vert. pair, #28-28a	32.50	125.00
29	A45	1sh vermilion (Bl)	6.00	30.00
a.		Perf. 14x13½	20.00	42.50
b.		Vert. pair, #29-29a	47.50	135.00
		Nos. 21-29 (9)	30.75	152.00

Same Overprint On Postal-Fiscal Stamps of New Zealand, 1906-15
Perf. 14, 14½ and Compound

1918-23				
30	PF1	2sh blue (R)	18.00	35.00
31	PF1	2sh6p bn (Bl) ('23)	24.00	55.00
32	PF1	5sh green (R)	32.50	67.50
a.		Perf. 14	115.00	125.00
b.		Perf. 14½x14 ('29)	27.50	60.00
33	PF1	10sh red brn (Bl) ('23)	150.00	185.00
a.		Perf. 14½x14 ('27)	100.00	165.00
34	PF2	£1 rose (Bl) ('23)	185.00	275.00
a.		Perf. 14½x14 ('28)	165.00	300.00
		Nos. 30-34 (5)	409.50	617.50

Nos. 32b, 33a and 34a come on thick paper and in different color varieties.

Landing of Captain Cook A16   Avarua Waterfront A17

Capt. James Cook A18   Coconut Palm A19

Arorangi Village — A20   Avarua Harbor — A21

Unwmk.

1920, Aug. 23	**Engr.**		**Perf. 14**	
35	A16	½p yel grn & blk	4.25	4.75
36	A17	1p car & black	2.25	1.40
37	A18	1½p red & black	3.50	18.00
38	A19	3p pale blue & blk	2.50	17.50
39	A20	6p dp grn & red brn	6.25	19.00
a.		Center inverted	1,000.	
40	A21	1sh blk brn & blk	9.00	19.00
		Nos. 35-40 (6)	27.75	79.65

See Nos. 41-42. For surcharge see No. 48.

Types of 1920 Issue and

Rarotongan Chief (Te Po) — A22   Avarua Harbor — A23

1925-27			**Wmk. 61**	
41	A16	½p yel grn & blk ('26)	4.00	13.00
42	A17	1p car & black	1.75	1.00
43	A22	3p dk blue & blk ('27)	6.50	16.00
44	A23	4p dull vio & blk ('27)	12.50	22.50
		Nos. 41-44 (4)	24.75	52.50

New Zealand No. 182 Overprinted Type "k" in Red

1927				
47	A56	2sh blue	18.00	35.00
		2sh dark blue	17.00	50.00

No. 37 Surcharged

1931	**Unwmk.**		**Perf. 14**	
48	A18	2p on 1½p red & blk	5.25	1.50

New Zealand Postal-Fiscal Stamps of 1931-32 Overprinted Type "k" in Blue or Red

1931, Nov. 12			**Wmk. 61**	
49	PF5	2sh6p deep brown	4.50	12.00
50	PF5	5sh green (R)	40.00	80.00
51	PF5	10sh dark car	45.00	130.00
52	PF5	£1 pink ('32)	90.00	180.00
		Nos. 49-52 (4)	179.50	402.00

See Nos. 86-89D, 116-119.

Landing of Captain Cook A24   Capt. James Cook A25

Polynesian Migratory Canoe — A26   Islanders Unloading Ship — A27

View of Avarua Harbor A28   R.M.S. Monowai A29

King George V — A30

Perf. 13, 14 (4p, 1sh)

1932, Mar. 16	**Engr.**		**Unwmk.**	
53	A24	½p yel grn & blk	14.00	25.00
		Perf. 13x14x13x13	275.00	
54	A25	1p dp red & blk	1.10	1.25
55	A26	2p org brn & blk	8.50	5.75
a.		Perf. 14x13x13x13	150.00	210.00
56	A27	2½p indigo & blk	8.50	80.00
a.		Center inverted	325.00	
57	A28	4p Prus blue & blk	40.00	70.00
a.		Perf. 13	17.00	72.50
58	A29	6p dp org & blk	3.25	2.50
59	A30	1sh dull vio & blk	4.75	7.25
		Nos. 53-59 (7)	59.10	191.75

For types overprinted see Nos. 67-69.

1932-36	**Wmk. 61**		**Perf. 14**	
60	A24	½p yel grn & blk	.50	3.50
61	A25	1p deep red & blk	.50	2.25
62	A26	2p brown & blk ('36)	.75	1.75
63	A27	2½p indigo & blk	.75	4.50
64	A28	4p Prus blue & blk	1.75	4.50
65	A29	6p org & blk ('36)	1.50	.75
66	A30	1sh dk vio & blk ('36)	12.50	27.50
		Nos. 60-66 (7)	18.25	44.75

See Nos. 77-82.

Silver Jubilee Issue

Types of 1932 Overprinted in Black or Red

1935, May 7			**Perf. 14**	
67	A25	1p car & brown red	1.00	3.50
68	A27	2½p indigo & bl (R)	5.75	15.00
a.		Vert. pair, imperf. horiz.	200.00	
69	A29	6p dull org & dark grn	12.50	12.50
		Nos. 67-69 (3)	19.25	31.00
		Set, never hinged	22.50	

The vertical spacing of the overprint is wider on No. 69.

No. 68a is from proof sheets.

Coronation Issue

New Zealand Stamps of 1937 Overprinted in Black

Perf. 13½x13

1937, May 13   **Wmk. 253**
70	A78	1p rose carmine	.30	.25
71	A78	2½p dark blue	.30	1.50
72	A78	6p vermilion	.30	.30
		Nos. 70-72 (3)	.90	2.05
		Set, never hinged	1.00	

George VI
A31

Village Scene A32

Coastal Scene with Canoe — A33

1938, May 2   Wmk. 61   Perf. 14
73	A31	1sh dp violet & blk	6.00	10.00
74	A32	2sh dk red brown & blk	7.75	22.50
75	A33	3sh yel green & blue	22.50	22.50
		Nos. 73-75 (3)	36.25	55.00
		Set, never hinged	67.50	

See Nos. 83-85.

Mt. Ikurangi behind Avarua — A34

Perf. 13½x14

1940, Sept. 2   Engr.   Wmk. 253
76	A34	3p on 1½p rose vio & blk	.45	.75
		Never hinged		.75

Examples without surcharge are from printer's archives. Value, $250 unused. See Cook Islands No. 115.

Types of 1932-38

1944-46   Wmk. 253   Perf. 14
77	A24	½p yel grn & blk	.40	6.50
78	A25	1p dp red & blk ('45)	.40	4.75
79	A26	2p org brn & blk ('46)	3.75	15.00
80	A27	2½p dk bl & blk ('45)	.50	3.75
81	A28	4p Prus blue & blk	2.75	1.25
82	A29	6p orange & blk	1.40	1.75
83	A31	1sh dp vio & blk	.85	2.00
84	A32	2sh brn car & blk ('45)	8.50	6.75
85	A33	3sh yel grn & bl ('45)	11.00	15.00
		Nos. 77-85 (9)	29.55	56.75
		Set, never hinged	45.00	

New Zealand Postal-Fiscal Stamps Overprinted (narrow "E") in Blue or Red

1941-45   Wmk. 61   Perf. 14
86	PF5	2sh6p brown	65.00	125.00
87	PF5	5sh green (R)	140.00	450.00
88	PF5	10sh rose	85.00	600.00
89	PF5	£1 pink	125.00	750.00
		Nos. 86-89 (4)	415.00	1,925.
		Set, never hinged	850.00	

Wmk. 253
89A	PF5	2sh6p brown	2.75	11.00
89B	PF5	5sh brt grn (R)	5.50	19.00
e.		5sh light yellow green, wmkd. sideways ('67)	10.00	80.00
89C	PF5	10sh rose	37.50	135.00
89D	PF5	£1 pink	40.00	90.00
		Nos. 89A-89D (4)	85.75	255.00
		Set, never hinged	150.00	

No. 89Be exists in both line and comb perf.

> Catalogue values for unused stamps in this section, from this point to the end of the section, are for Never Hinged items.

Peace Issue

New Zealand Nos. 248, 250, 254 and 255 Overprinted in Black or Blue

p   q

1946, June 4   Perf. 13x13½, 13½x13
90	A94 (p)	1p emerald	.40	.35
91	A96 (q)	2p rose violet (Bl)	.40	.35
92	A100 (p)	6p org red & red brn	.40	.75
93	A101 (p)	8p brn lake & blk (Bl)	.50	.75
		Nos. 90-93 (4)	1.70	2.20

Map of Niue A35

H.M.S. Resolution A36

Designs: 2p, Alofi landing. 3p, Thatched Dwelling. 4p, Arch at Hikutavake. 6p, Alofi bay. 9p, Fisherman. 1sh, Cave at Makefu. 2sh, Gathering bananas. 3sh, Matapa Chasm.

Perf. 14x13½, 13½x14

1950, July 3   Engr.   Wmk. 253
94	A35	½p red orange & bl	.30	2.25
95	A36	1p green & brown	2.25	3.25
96	A36	2p red & blk	1.25	3.25
97	A36	3p blue vio & blue	.30	.25
98	A36	4p brn vio & ol grn	.30	.25
99	A36	6p brn org & bl grn	1.00	1.25
100	A35	9p dk brn & brn org	.30	1.40
101	A36	1sh black & purple	.30	.25
102	A35	2sh dp grn & brn org	7.50	6.25
103	A35	3sh black & dp blue	6.50	7.50
		Nos. 94-103 (10)	20.00	25.90

For surcharges see Nos. 106-115.

Coronation Issue

Queen Elizabeth II — A36a

Westminster Abbey — A36b

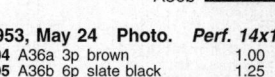

1953, May 24   Photo.   Perf. 14x14½
104	A36a	3p brown	1.00	.75
105	A36b	6p slate black	1.25	.75

Nos. 94-103 Surcharged

Perf. 14x13½, 13½x14

1967, July 10   Engr.   Wmk. 253
106	A35	½c on ½p red org & blue	.30	.25
107	A36	1c on 1p green & brn	1.00	.25
108	A36	2c on 2p rose car & blk	.30	.25
109	A36	2½c on 3p bl vio & bl	.30	.25
110	A36	3c on 4p brn vio & ol grn	.30	.25
111	A36	5c on 6p brn org & grn	.30	.25
112	A35	8c on 9p dk brn & brn org	.30	.25
113	A36	10c on 1sh blk & pur	.30	.25
114	A35	20c on 2sh dp grn & brn org	.40	1.25
115	A35	30c on 3sh blk & dp bl	.75	1.25
		Nos. 106-115 (10)	4.25	4.50

The position of the numeral varies on each denomination. The surcharge on the ½c, 2½c, 8c, 10c and 20c contains one dot only.

New Zealand Arms — A37

Wmk. 253

1967, July 10   Typo.   Perf. 14

Black Surcharge
116	A37	25c yellow brown	.30	.60
117	A37	50c green	.75	.85
118	A37	$1 cerise	.50	1.25
119	A37	$2 pale pink	.50	2.00
		Nos. 116-119 (4)	2.05	4.70

1967   Perf. 11
116a	A37	25c	6.50	18.50
117a	A37	50c	6.50	19.50
118a	A37	$1	8.00	13.50
119a	A37	$2	9.00	14.50
		Nos. 116a-119a (4)	30.00	66.00

The perf. 11 stamps were produced when a normal perforating machine broke down and 2,500 of each denomination were perforated on a treadle machine first used by the N.Z. Post Office in 1899.

Christmas Issues

Adoration of the Shepherds, by Poussin — A37a

Perf. 13½x14

1967, Oct. 3   Photo.   Wmk. 253
120	A37a	2½c multicolored	.30	.25

Nativity, by Federico Fiori — A37b

1969, Oct. 1   Photo.   Wmk. 253
121	A37b	2½c multicolored	.30	.25

Pua — A38

Flowers (except 20c): 1c, Golden shower. 2c, Flamboyant. 2½c, Frangipani. 3c, Niue crocus. 5c, Hibiscus. 8c, Passion fruit. 10c, Kamapui. 20c, Queen Elizabeth II. 30c, Tapeu orchid.

Perf. 12½x13

1969, Nov. 27   Litho.   Unwmk.
122	A38	½c green & multi	.30	.25
123	A38	1c orange & multi	.30	.25
124	A38	2c gray & multi	.30	.25
125	A38	2½c bister & multi	.30	.25
126	A38	3c blue & multi	.30	.25
127	A38	5c ver & multi	.30	.25
128	A38	8c violet & multi	.30	.25
129	A38	10c yellow & multi	.30	.25
130	A38	20c dk blue & multi	1.00	1.75
131	A38	30c olive grn & multi	2.00	2.25
		Nos. 122-131 (10)	5.40	6.00

See Nos. 678.

Edible Crab — A39

Perf. 13½x12½

1969, Aug. 19   Litho.
132	A39	3c Kalahimu	.30	.25
133	A39	5c Kalavi	.30	.25
134	A39	30c Unga	.40	.40
		Nos. 132-134 (3)	1.00	.90

Christmas Issue

Adoration, by Correggio — A39a

1970, Oct. 1   Litho.   Perf. 12½
135	A39a	2½c multicolored	.30	.25

Plane over Outrigger Canoe — A40

Designs: 5c, Plane over ships in harbor. 8c, Civair plane over island.

1970, Dec. 9   Litho.   Perf. 13½
136	A40	3c multicolored	.30	.25
137	A40	5c multicolored	.30	.25
138	A40	8c multicolored	.30	.30
		Nos. 136-138 (3)	.90	.80

Opening of Niue Airport.

Polynesian Triller (Heahea) — A41

Birds: 10c, Crimson-crowned fruit pigeon (kulukulu). 20c, Blue-crowned lory (henga).

1971, June 23   Litho.   Perf. 13½x13
139	A41	5c multicolored	.30	.25
140	A41	10c multicolored	.50	.25
141	A41	20c multicolored	.85	.25
		Nos. 139-141 (3)	1.65	.75

Christmas Issue

Holy Night, by Carlo Maratta A41a

1971, Oct. 6   Photo.   Perf. 13x13½
142	A41a	3c orange & multi	.35	.25

People of Niue — A42

1971, Nov. 17
143	A42	4c Boy	.30	.25
144	A42	6c Girl	.30	.25
145	A42	9c Man	.30	.35
146	A42	14c Woman	.30	.70
		Nos. 143-146 (4)	1.20	1.55

Octopus Lure and Octopus — A43

5c, Warrior and weapons. 10c, Sika (spear) throwing, horiz. 25c, Vivi dance, horiz.

1972, May 3   Litho.   Perf. 13x13½
147	A43	3c blue & multi	.30	.25
148	A43	5c rose & multi	.30	.25
149	A43	10c blue & multi	.30	.25
150	A43	25c yellow & multi	.30	.25
		Nos. 147-150 (4)	1.20	1.00

So. Pacific Festival of Arts, Fiji, May 6-20.

Alofi
Wharf — A44

South Pacific Commission Emblem and: 5c, Health service. 6c, School children. 18c, Cattle and dwarf palms.

1972, Sept. 6   Litho.   Perf. 13½x14
151	A44	4c blue & multi	.30	.25
152	A44	5c blue & multi	.30	.25
153	A44	6c blue & multi	.30	.25
154	A44	18c blue & multi	.30	.25
		Nos. 151-154 (4)	1.20	1.00

So. Pacific Commission, 25th anniv.

Christmas Issue

Madonna and Child, by
Murillo — A44a

1972, Oct. 4   Photo.   Perf. 11½
155	A44a	3c gray & multi	.30	.25

Pempheris
Oualensis — A45

Designs: Various fish.

Perf. 13½x13
1973, June 27   Litho.   Unwmk.
156	A45	8c shown	.35	.35
157	A45	10c Cephalopholis	.35	.35
158	A45	15c Variola louti	.40	.40
159	A45	20c Etelis carbunculus	.45	.45
		Nos. 156-159 (4)	1.55	1.55

Flowers, by Jan
Breughel — A46

Paintings of Flowers: 5c, by Hans Bollongier. 10c, by Rachel Ruysch.

1973, Nov. 21   Litho.   Perf. 13½x13
160	A46	4c bister & multi	.30	.25
161	A46	5c orange brn & multi	.30	.25
162	A46	10c emerald & multi	.30	.25
		Nos. 160-162 (3)	.90	.75

Christmas.

Capt. Cook and
"Resolution"
A47

Capt. Cook and: 3c, Cook's landing place and ship. 8c, Map of Niue. 20c, Administration Building and flag of 1774.

1974, June 20   Litho.   Perf. 13½x14
163	A47	2c multicolored	.30	.25
164	A47	3c multicolored	.30	.25
165	A47	8c multicolored	.30	.30
166	A47	20c multicolored	.35	.55
		Nos. 163-166 (4)	1.25	1.35

Bicentenary of Cook's landing on Niue.

King
Fataaiki
A48

Annexation
Day, Oct.
19, 1900
A49

Village
Meeting — A50

Design: 10c, Legislative Assembly Building.

Perf. 14x13½, 13½x14
1974, Oct. 19   Litho.
167	A48	4c multicolored	.30	.25
168	A49	8c multicolored	.30	.25
169	A50	10c multicolored	.30	.25
170	A50	20c multicolored	.30	.25
		Nos. 167-170 (4)	1.20	1.00

Referendum for Self-government, 9/3/74.

Decorated Bicycle — A51

Christmas: 10c, Decorated motorcycle. 20c, Going to church by truck.

1974, Nov. 13   Litho.   Perf. 12½
171	A51	3c green & multi	.30	.25
172	A51	10c dull blue & multi	.30	.25
173	A51	20c brown & multi	.30	.25
		Nos. 171-173 (3)	.90	.75

Children Going to
Church — A52

Children's Drawings: 5c, Child on bicycle trailing balloons. 10c, Balloons and gifts hanging from tree.

1975, Oct. 29   Litho.   Perf. 14½
174	A52	4c multicolored	.30	.25
175	A52	5c multicolored	.30	.25
176	A52	10c multicolored	.30	.25
		Nos. 174-176 (3)	.90	.75

Christmas.

Opening of
Tourist
Hotel — A53

Design: 20c, Hotel, building and floor plan.

1975, Nov. 19   Litho.   Perf. 14x13½
177	A53	8c multicolored	.30	.25
178	A53	20c multicolored	.30	.25

Preparing Ground
for Taro — A54

2c, Planting taro (root vegetable). 3c, Banana harvest. 4c, Bush plantation. 5c, Shellfish gathering. 10c, Reef fishing. 20c, Luku (fern) harvest. 50c, Canoe fishing. $1, Husking coconuts. $2, Hunting uga (land crab).

1976, Mar. 3   Litho.   Perf. 13½x14
179	A54	1c multicolored	.30	.25
180	A54	2c multicolored	.30	.25
181	A54	3c multicolored	.30	.25
182	A54	4c multicolored	.30	.25
183	A54	5c multicolored	.30	.25
184	A54	10c multicolored	.30	.25
185	A54	20c multicolored	.30	.25
186	A54	50c multicolored	.30	.50
187	A54	$1 multicolored	.30	.75
188	A54	$2 multicolored	.75	1.00
		Nos. 179-188 (10)	3.45	4.00

See #222-231. For surcharges see #203-210.

Water Tower, Girl
Drawing Water — A55

15c, Teleprinter & Niue radio station. 20c, Instrument panel, generator & power station.

1976, July 7   Litho.   Perf. 14x14½
189	A55	10c multicolored	.30	.25
190	A55	15c multicolored	.30	.25
191	A55	20c multicolored	.30	.25
		Nos. 189-191 (3)	.90	.75

Technical achievements.

Christmas Tree
(Flamboyant)
and
Administration
Building — A56

Christmas: 15c, Avatele Church, interior.

1976, Sept. 15   Litho.   Perf. 14½
192	A56	9c orange & multi	.30	.25
193	A56	15c orange & multi	.30	.25

Elizabeth II,
Coronation
Portrait, and
Westminster
Abbey
A57

Design: $2, Coronation regalia.

1977, June 7   Photo.   Perf. 13½
194	A57	$1 multicolored	.50	.50
195	A57	$2 multicolored	1.25	.75
a.		Souvenir sheet of 2, #194-195	2.00	2.00

25th anniv. of reign of Elizabeth II. Nos. 194-195 each printed in sheets of 5 stamps and label showing Niue flag and Union Jack. For surcharge see No. 213.

Mothers and
Infants — A58

Designs: 15c, Mobile school dental clinic. 20c, Elderly couple and home.

1977, June 29   Litho.   Perf. 14½
196	A58	10c multicolored	.30	.25
197	A58	15c multicolored	.30	.25
198	A58	20c multicolored	.30	.25
		Nos. 196-198 (3)	.90	.75

Personal (social) services.
For surcharges see Nos. 211-212.

Annunciation, by
Rubens — A59

Rubens Paintings (details, Virgin and Child): 12c, Adoration of the Kings. 20c, Virgin with Garland. 35c, Holy Family.

1977, Nov. 15   Photo.   Perf. 13x13½
199	A59	10c multicolored	.30	.25
200	A59	15c multicolored	.30	.25
201	A59	20c multicolored	.35	.50
202	A59	35c multicolored	.40	.80
a.		Souvenir sheet of 4, #199-202	1.75	1.75
		Nos. 199-202 (4)	1.35	1.80

Christmas and 400th birth anniversary of Peter Paul Rubens (1577-1640). Nos. 199-202 each printed in sheets of 6 stamps.

Stamps of 1976-77 Surcharged with New Value and 4 Bars in Black or Gold
Printing and Perforations as Before

1977, Nov. 15
203	A54	12c on 1c (#179)	.45	.25
204	A54	16c on 2c (#180)	.50	.30
205	A54	30c on 3c (#181)	.50	.40
206	A54	35c on 4c (#182)	.50	.45
207	A54	40c on 5c (#183)	.50	.50
208	A54	60c on 20c (#185)	.50	.50
209	A54	70c on $1 (#187)	.50	.50
210	A54	85c on $2 (#188)	.50	.60
211	A58	$1.10 on 10c (#196)	.50	.60
212	A58	$2.60 on 20c (#198)	.85	.65
213	A57	$3.20 on $2 (#195, G)	1.05	.75
		Nos. 203-213 (11)	6.35	5.50

"An Inland
View in
Atooi," by
John Webber
A60

Scenes in Hawaii, by John Webber: 16c, A View of Karakooa in Owyhee. 20c, An Offering Before Capt. Cook in the Sandwich Islands. 30c, Tereoboo, King of Owyhee, bringing presents (boats). 35c, Masked rowers in boat.

1978, Jan. 18   Photo.   Perf. 13½
214	A60	12c gold & multi	.70	.35
215	A60	16c gold & multi	.75	.40
216	A60	20c gold & multi	.75	.50
217	A60	30c gold & multi	.85	.60
218	A60	35c gold & multi	.90	.65
a.		Souv. sheet, #214-218 + label	4.50	2.75
		Nos. 214-218 (5)	3.95	2.50

Bicentenary of Capt. Cook's arrival in Hawaii. Nos. 214-218 printed in sheets of 5 stamps and one label showing flags of Hawaii and Niue.

Descent from the
Cross, by
Caravaggio — A61

Easter: 20c, Burial of Christ, by Bellini.

1978, Mar. 15   Photo.   Perf. 13x13½
219	A61	10c multicolored	.30	.25
220	A61	20c multicolored	.35	.25
a.		Souv. sheet, #219-220, perf. 13½	1.00	1.00

Nos. 219-220 issued in sheets of 8.
See Nos. B1-B2.

Souvenir Sheet

Elizabeth II — A62

1978, June 26   Photo.   Perf. 13
221	A62	Sheet of 6	3.00	3.00
a.		$1.10 Niue and UK flags	.50	.75
b.		$1.10 shown	.50	.75
c.		$1.10 Queen's New Zealand flag	.50	.75
d.		Souvenir sheet of 3	2.25	2.25

25th anniv. of coronation of Elizabeth II. No. 221 contains 2 horizontal se-tenant strips of Nos. 221a-221c, separated by horizontal gutter showing coronation coach. No. 221d contains a vertical se-tenant strip of Nos. 221a-221c.

Type of 1977

12c, Preparing ground for taro. 16c, Planting taro. 30c, Banana harvest. 35c, Bush plantation. 40c, Shellfish gathering. 60c, Reef fishing. 75c, Luku (fern) harvest. $1.10, Canoe fishing. $3.20, Husking coconuts. $4.20, Hunting uga (land crab).

1978, Oct. 27   Litho.   Perf. 14
222	A54	12c multicolored	.30	.25
223	A54	16c multicolored	.30	.25
224	A54	30c multicolored	.30	.25
225	A54	35c multicolored	.30	.25
226	A54	40c multicolored	.30	.25
227	A54	60c multicolored	.30	.35
228	A54	75c multicolored	.35	.40

229 A54	$1.10 multicolored	.45	.50
230 A54	$3.20 multicolored	1.25	1.50
231 A54	$4.20 multicolored	1.90	2.25
	Nos. 222-231 (10)	5.75	6.25

Celebration of the Rosary, by Dürer — A63

Designs: 30c, Nativity, by Dürer. 35c, Adoration of the Kings, by Dürer.

1978, Nov. 30   Photo.   Perf. 13

232 A63	20c multicolored	.30	.30
233 A63	30c multicolored	.45	.45
234 A63	35c multicolored	.50	.50
a.	Souv. sheet, #232-234 + label	1.60	1.60
	Nos. 232-234 (3)	1.25	1.25

Christmas and 450th death anniversary of Albrecht Dürer (1471-1528). Nos. 232-234 each printed in sheets of 5 stamps and descriptive label.
See Nos. B3-B5.

Pietà, by Gregorio Fernandez A64

Easter: 35c, Burial of Christ, by Pedro Roldan.

1979, Apr. 2

235 A64	30c multicolored	.35	.35
236 A64	35c multicolored	.40	.40
a.	Souvenir sheet of 2, #235-236	1.50	1.50

See Nos. B6-B7.

Child, by Franz Hals — A65

IYC (Emblem and Details from Paintings): 16c, Nurse and Child. 20c, Child of the Duke of Osuna, by Goya. 30c, Daughter of Robert Strozzi, by Titian. 35c, Children Eating Fruit, by Murillo.

1979, May 31   Photo.   Perf. 14

237 A65	16c multicolored	.30	.25
238 A65	20c multicolored	.35	.35
239 A65	30c multicolored	.40	.40
240 A65	35c multicolored	.50	.50
a.	Souvenir sheet of 4, #237-240	2.10	2.10
	Nos. 237-240 (4)	1.55	1.50

See Nos. B8-B11.

Penny Black, Bath Mail Coach, Rowland Hill A66

30c, Basel #3L1 & Alpine village coach. 35c, US #1 & 1st US transatlantic mail ship. 50c, France #3 & French railroad mail car, 1849. 60c, Bavaria #1 & Bavarian mail coach.

1979, July 3   Photo.   Perf. 14

241 A66	20c Pair, #a.-b.	.40	.40
242 A66	30c Pair, #a.-b.	.55	.55
243 A66	35c Pair, #a.-b.	.65	.65
244 A66	50c Pair, #a.-b.	1.00	1.00
245 A66	60c Pair, #a.-b.	1.10	1.10
c.	Souv. sheet of 10, #241-245 + 2 labels	4.25	4.25
	Nos. 241-245 (5)	3.70	3.70

Sir Rowland Hill (1795-1879), originator of penny postage.
For overprints and surcharges see Nos. 281-285, B16, B21, B26, B30, B33, B41.

Cook's Landing at Botany Bay — A68

18th Century Paintings: 30c, Cook's Men during a Landing on Erromanga. 35c, Resolution and Discovery in Queen Charlotte's Sound. 75c, Death of Capt. Cook on Hawaii, by Johann Zoffany.

1979, July 30   Photo.   Perf. 14

251 A68	20c multicolored	.65	.30
252 A68	30c multicolored	.85	.45
253 A68	35c multicolored	1.10	.50
254 A68	75c multicolored	1.10	.90
a.	Souv. sheet, #251-254, perf. 13½	3.75	3.75
	Nos. 251-254 (4)	3.70	2.10

200th death anniv. of Capt. James Cook.
For surcharges see Nos. B18, B23, B28, B36.

Apollo 11 Lift-off — A69

1979, Sept. 27   Photo.   Perf. 13½

255 A69	30c shown	.35	.35
256 A69	35c Lunar module	.40	.40
257 A69	60c Splashdown	.70	.70
a.	Souvenir sheet of 3	1.90	1.90
	Nos. 255-257 (3)	1.45	1.45

Apollo 11 moon landing, 10th anniversary. No. 257a contains Nos. 255-257 in changed colors.
For surcharges see Nos. B24, B29, B35.

Virgin and Child, by P. Serra — A70

Virgin and Child by: 25c, R. di Mur. 30c, S. diG. Sasseta. 50c, J. Huguet.

1979, Nov. 29   Photo.   Perf. 13

258 A70	20c multicolored	.30	.25
259 A70	25c multicolored	.30	.25
260 A70	30c multicolored	.30	.25
261 A70	50c multicolored	.30	.25
a.	Souvenir sheet of 4, #258-261	1.40	1.40
	Nos. 258-261 (4)	1.20	1.00

Christmas. See Nos. B12-B15. For surcharges see Nos. B19-B20, B25, B32.

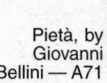

Pietà, by Giovanni Bellini — A71

Easter (Pietà, Paintings by): 30c, Botticelli. 35c, Anthony Van Dyck.

1980, Apr. 2   Photo.   Perf. 13

262 A71	25c multicolored	.30	.30
263 A71	30c multicolored	.35	.35
264 A71	35c multicolored	.40	.40
	Nos. 262-264 (3)	1.05	1.05

See Nos. B37-B40.

A72

#265a, Ceremonial Stool, New Guinea (shown). #265b, Ku-Tagwa plaque. #265c, Suspension hook. #265d, Ancestral board.

#266a, Platform post. #266b, Canoe ornament. #266c, Carved figure. #266d, Woman and child. #267a, God A'a, statue. #267b, Tangaroa, statue. #267c, Ivory pendant. #267d, Tapa cloth. #268a, Maori feather box. #268b, Hei-tiki. #268c, House post. #268d, God Ku, feather image.

1980, July 30   Photo.   Perf. 13

265 A72	20c Strip of 4, #a.-d.	.65	.65
266 A72	25c Strip of 4, #a.-d.	.80	.80
267 A72	30c Strip of 4, #a.-d.	.95	.95
268 A72	35c Strip of 4, #a.-d.	1.10	1.10

Souvenir Sheets of 4

e.	#265a, 266a, 267a, 268a	1.10	1.10
f.	#265b, 266b, 267b, 268b	1.10	1.10
g.	#265c, 266c, 267c, 268c	1.10	1.10
h.	#265d, 266d, 267d, 268d	1.10	1.10
	Nos. 265-268 (4)	3.50	3.50

3rd South Pacific Festival of Arts, Port Moresby, Papua New Guinea, June 30-July 12. Stamps in souvenir sheets have 2c surtax.
For surcharges see Nos. 626-629.

Nos. 241-250, Overprinted in Black on Silver

1980, Aug. 22   Perf. 14

281 A66	20c Pair, #a.-b.	.50	.50
282 A66	30c Pair, #a.-b.	.70	.70
283 A66	35c Pair, #a.-b.	.80	.80
284 A66	50c Pair, #a.-b.	1.10	1.10
285 A66	60c Pair, #a.-b.	1.40	1.40
	Nos. 281-285 (5)	4.50	4.50

ZEAPEX '80, New Zealand International Stamp Exhibition, Auckland, Aug. 23-31.

Queen Mother Elizabeth, 80th Birthday — A73

1980, Sept. 15 Photo. Perf. 13x13½

| 291 A73 | $1.10 multicolored | .90 | 1.40 |

Souvenir Sheet

| 292 A73 | $3 multicolored | 2.00 | 2.00 |

No. 291 issued in sheets of 5 and label showing coad of arms.

A74

#293a, 100-meter dash. #293b, Allen Wells, England. #294a, 400-Meter freestyle. #294b, Ines Diers, DDR. #295a, Soling class yachting. #295b, Denmark. #296a, Soccer. #296b, Czechoslovakia.

1980, Oct. 30   Photo.   Perf. 14

293 A74	20c Pair, #a.-b.	.45	.45
294 A74	25c Pair, #a.-b.	.50	.50
295 A74	60c Pair, #a.-b.	.60	.60
296 A74	35c Pair, #a.-b.	.70	.70
	Nos. 293-296 (4)	2.25	2.25

22nd Summer Olympic Games, Moscow, July 19-Aug. 3.
See No. B42.

Virgin and Child, by del Sarto — A76

Paintings of Virgin & Child, by Andrea del Sarto.

1980, Nov. 28 Photo. Perf. 13x13½

301 A76	20c multicolored	.25	.25
302 A76	25c multicolored	.25	.25
303 A76	30c multicolored	.25	.25
304 A76	35c multicolored	.25	.25
a.	Souvenir sheet of 4, #301-304	1.00	1.25
	Nos. 301-304 (4)	1.00	1.00

Christmas and 450th death anniversary of Andrea del Sarto.
See Nos. B43-B46.

A77

Golden Shower Tree — A77a

#317a, Phalaenopsis sp. #317b, Moth Orchid. #318a, Euphorbia pulcherrima. #318b, Poinsettia. #319a, Thunbergia alata. #319b, Black-eyed Susan. #320a, Cochlospermum hibiscoides. #320b, Buttercup tree. #321a, Begonia sp. #321b, Begonia. #322a, Plumeria sp. #322b, Frangipani. #323a, Sterlitzia reginae. #323b, Bird of paradise. #324a, Hibiscus syriacus. #324b, Rose of Sharon. #325a, Nymphaea sp. #325b, Water lily. #326a, Tibouchina sp. #326b, Princess flower. #327a, Nelumbo sp. #327b, Lotus. #328a, Hybrid hibiscus. #328b, Yellow hibiscus.

1981-82   Photo.   Perf. 13x13½

317 A77	2c Pair, #a.-b.	.25	.25
318 A77	5c Pair, #a.-b.	.25	.25
319 A77	10c Pair, #a.-b.	.25	.25
320 A77	15c Pair, #a.-b.	.30	.30
321 A77	20c Pair, #a.-b.	.40	.40
322 A77	25c Pair, #a.-b.	.50	.50
323 A77	30c Pair, #a.-b.	.55	.55
324 A77	35c Pair, #a.-b.	.65	.65
325 A77	40c Pair, #a.-b.	.70	.70
326 A77	50c Pair, #a.-b.	1.00	1.00
327 A77	60c Pair, #a.-b.	1.10	1.10
328 A77	80c Pair, #a.-b.	1.60	1.60

Perf. 13½

329 A77a	$1 shown	1.00	1.00
330 A77a	$2 Orchid var.	2.00	2.00
331 A77a	$3 Orchid sp.	2.75	2.75
332 A77a	$4 Poinsettia	4.00	4.00
333 A77a	$6 Hybrid hibiscus	5.75	5.75
334 A77a	$10 Hibiscus rosa-sinensis	10.00	10.00
	Nos. 317-334 (18)	33.05	33.05

Issued: 2c, 5c, 10c, 15c, 20c, 25c, Apr. 2; 30c, 35c, 40c, 50c, 60c, 80c, May 26; $1, $2, $3, Dec. 9, 1981; $4, $6, $10, Jan. 15, 1982.
For surcharges and overprints see Nos. 406-409, 413E, 594-595, O14, O16, O19.

Jesus Defiled, by El Greco — A78

Easter (Paintings): 50c, Pieta, by Fernando Gallego. 60c, The Supper of Emaus, by Jacopo da Pontormo.

1981, Apr. 10   Perf. 14

337 A78	35c multicolored	.40	.40
338 A78	50c multicolored	.65	.65
339 A78	60c multicolored	.75	.75
	Nos. 337-339 (3)	1.80	1.80

See Nos. B47-B50.

Prince Charles and Lady Diana — A79

1981, June 26   Photo.   Perf. 14

340 A79	75c Charles	.50	.50
341 A79	95c Lady Diana	.65	.65
342 A79	$1.20 shown	.90	.90
a.	Souvenir sheet of 3, #340-342	2.50	2.50
	Nos. 340-342 (3)	2.05	2.05

Royal Wedding. Nos. 340-342 each printed in sheets of 5 plus label showing St. Paul's Cathedral.

For overprints and surcharges see Nos. 357-359, 410, 412, 455, 596-598, B52-B55.

1982 World Cup Soccer — A80

No. 343: Players dribbling ball. No. 344, Players kicking ball (#a, b.), heading ball (#c.). No. 345, Players kicking ball (#a, b.), goalie (#c.).

			1981, Oct. 16	Photo.		Perf. 13
343			Strip of 3		.80	.80
a.-c.	A80	30c any single			.30	.25
344			Strip of 3		1.05	1.05
a.-c.	A80	35c any single			.35	.35
345			Strip of 3		1.20	1.20
a.-c.	A80	40c any single			.40	.40
		Nos. 343-345 (3)			3.05	3.05

See No. B51.

Christmas 1981 — A81

Rembrandt Paintings: 20c, Holy Family with Angels, 1645. 35c, Presentation in the Temple, 1631. 50c, Virgin and Child in Temple, 1629. 60c, Holy Family, 1640.

		1981-82	Photo.		Perf. 14x13
346	A81	20c multicolored		.35	.35
347	A81	35c multicolored		.80	.80
348	A81	50c multicolored		1.10	1.10
349	A81	60c multicolored		1.25	1.25
a.	Souvenir sheet of 4, #346-349			3.50	3.50
	Nos. 346-349 (4)			3.50	3.50

Souvenir Sheets

350	A81 80c + 5c like #346	.80	.80
351	A81 80c + 5c like #347	.80	.80
352	A81 80c + 5c like #348	.80	.80
353	A81 80c + 5c like #349	.80	.80

Surtax was for school children. Issued: #346-349, 12/11; others, 1/22/82.

21st Birthday of Princess Diana — A82

		1982, July 1		Perf. 14
354	A82	50c Charles	.50	.50
355	A82	$1.25 Wedding	1.25	1.25
356	A82	$2.50 Diana	2.25	2.25
a.	Souvenir sheet of 3, #354-356		6.00	6.00
	Nos. 354-356 (3)		4.00	4.00

Nos. 354-356 each printed in sheets of 5 plus label showing wedding day picture. For overprints and surcharges see Nos. 359B-359D, 411, 413, 456.

Nos. 340-342a Overprinted

Type I   Type II

Type III

		1982, July 23		Perf. 14
357	A79	75c multi (I)	1.40	1.40
357A	A79	75c multi (II)	1.40	1.40
358	A79	95c multi (I)	1.75	1.75
358A	A79	95c multi (II)	1.75	1.75
359	A79	$1.20 multi (I)	2.25	2.25
359A	A79	$1.20 multi (II)	2.25	2.25
	Nos. 357-359A (6)		10.80	10.80

Souvenir Sheet

359B	A79	Sheet of 3, #a.-c.	7.50	7.50
a.		75c multi (III)	2.00	2.00
b.		95c multi (III)	2.00	2.00
c.		$1.20 multi (III)	2.00	2.00

Nos. 357/357A, 358/358A and 359/359A were printed in small sheets containing three stamps overprinted Type I, two overprinted type II and one label.

Birthday Type of 1982 Inscribed in Silver

		1982	Photo.		Perf. 14
359C	A82	50c like #354		.70	.70
359D	A82	$1.25 like #355		1.75	1.75
359E	A82	$2.50 like #356		3.25	3.25
a.	Souvenir sheet of 3			7.00	7.00
	Nos. 359C-359E (3)			5.70	5.70

Christmas A83

Princess Diana Holding Prince William and Paintings of Infants by: 40c, Bronzino (1502-1572). 52c, Murillo (1617-1682). 83c, Murillo, diff. $1.05, Boucher (1703-1770). Singles in No. 363a: 34x30mm, showing paintings only.

		1982, Dec. 3	Photo.		Perf. 13½x14½
360	A83	40c multicolored		1.20	1.20
361	A83	52c multicolored		1.40	1.40
362	A83	83c multicolored		2.40	2.40
363	A83	$1.05 multicolored		3.50	3.50
a.	Souvenir sheet of 4, #364-367			6.75	6.75
	Nos. 360-363 (4)			8.50	8.50

Souvenir Sheets

364	A83	80c + 5c like #360	2.40	2.40
365	A83	80c + 5c like #361	2.40	2.40
366	A83	80c + 5c like #362	2.40	2.40
367	A83	80c + 5c like #363	2.40	2.40

Nos. 364-367 each contain one 30x42mm stamp showing Royal family. Surtax was for children's funds.

Commonwealth Day — A84

No. 368, Flag, Premier Robert R. Rex. No. 369, Resolution, Adventurer. No. 370, Passion flower. No. 371, Lime branch.

		1983, Mar. 14	Photo.		Perf. 13
368	A84	70c multi		.75	.75
369	A84	70c multi		.75	.75
370	A84	70c multi		.75	.75
371	A84	70c multi		.75	.75
a.	Block of 4, #368-371			3.00	3.00

For overprints see Nos. 484-487.

Scouting Year — A85

		1983, Apr. 28	Photo.		Perf. 13
372	A85	40c Flag signals		.70	.70
373	A85	50c Tree planting		.80	.80
374	A85	83c Map reading		1.50	1.50
	Nos. 372-374 (3)			3.00	3.00

Souvenir Sheet

375		Sheet of 3	3.00	3.00
a.	A85	40c + 3c like 40c	.75	.75
b.	A85	50c + 3c like 50c	.80	.80
c.	A85	83c + 3c like 83c	1.30	1.30

Nos. 372-375 Overprinted in Black on Silver: "XV WORLD JAMBOREE CANADA"

		1983, July 14		Photo.
376	A85	40c multicolored	.60	.60
377	A85	50c multicolored	.75	.75
378	A85	83c multicolored	1.15	1.15
	Nos. 376-378 (3)		2.50	2.50

Souvenir Sheet

379		Sheet of 3	2.75	2.75
a.	A85	40c + 3c multicolored	.60	.60
b.	A85	50c + 3c multicolored	.70	.70
c.	A85	83c + 3c multicolored	1.40	1.40

Save the Whales Campaign A86

		1983, Aug. 15		Perf. 13x14
380	A86	12c Right whale	.90	.50
381	A86	25c Fin whale	1.30	.60
382	A86	35c Sei whale	1.75	.95
383	A86	40c Blue whale	2.00	1.10
384	A86	58c Bowhead whale	2.25	1.25
385	A86	70c Sperm whale	2.75	1.25
386	A86	83c Humpback whale	3.00	1.75
387	A86	$1.05 Lesser rorqual	3.75	1.90
388	A86	$2.50 Gray whale	5.00	3.25
	Nos. 380-388 (9)		22.70	12.55

Manned Flight Bicentenary A87

25c, Montgolfier, 1783. 40c, Wright Bros. Flyer, 1903. 58c, Graf Zeppelin, 1928. 70c, Boeing 247, 1933. 83c, Apollo VIII, 1968. $1.05, Columbia space shuttle.

		1983, Oct. 14		Photo.		Perf. 14
389	A87	25c multicolored			.50	.50
390	A87	40c multicolored			.75	.75
391	A87	58c multicolored			1.25	1.25
392	A87	70c multicolored			1.75	1.75
393	A87	83c multicolored			2.10	2.10
394	A87	$1.05 multicolored			2.40	2.40
a.	Souvenir sheet of 6				5.50	5.50
	Nos. 389-394 (6)				8.75	8.75

No. 394a contains Nos. 389-394 inscribed "AIRMAIL."

Christmas — A87a

Paintings by Raphael (1483-1520): 30c, Garvagh Madonna, National Gallery, London. 40c, Granduca Madonna, Pitti Gallery, Florence. 58c, Goldfinch Madonna, Uffizi Gallery, Florence. 70c, Holy Family of Francis I, Louvre, Paris. 83c, Holy Family with Saints, Alte Pinakothek, Munich.

		1983		Photo.		Perf. 14
395	A87a	30c multicolored			.60	.60
396	A87a	40c multicolored			.80	.80
397	A87a	58c multicolored			1.20	1.20
398	A87a	70c multicolored			1.30	1.30
399	A87a	83c multicolored			1.60	1.60
	Nos. 395-399 (5)				5.50	5.50

Souvenir Sheets
Perf. 13½

400		Sheet of 5	4.00	4.00
a.	A87a	30c + 3c like #395	.40	.40
b.	A87a	40c + 3c like #396	.55	.55
c.	A87a	58c + 3c like #397	.80	.80
d.	A87a	70c + 3c like #398	.90	.90
e.	A87a	83c + 3c like #399	1.10	1.10
401	A87a	85c + 5c like #395	1.20	1.20
402	A87a	85c + 5c like #396	1.20	1.20
403	A87a	85c + 5c like #397	1.20	1.20
404	A87a	85c + 5c like #398	1.20	1.20
405	A87a	85c + 5c like #399	1.20	1.20

500th birth anniv. of Raphael. Issued: #395-400, 11/25; #401-405, 12/29.

Nos. 323, 326-328, 341, 355, 342, 356 and 331 Surcharged in Black or Gold with One or Two Bars

		1983, Nov. 30			Photo.
		Pairs, #a.-b. (#406-409)			
406	A77	52c on 30c		1.60	1.60
407	A77	58c on 50c		1.75	1.75
408	A77	70c on 60c		2.25	2.25
409	A77	83c on 80c		2.75	2.75
410	A79	$1.10 on 95c #341		1.60	1.60
411	A82	$1.10 on $1.25 #355 (G)		1.60	1.60
412	A79	$2.60 on $1.20 #342		4.00	4.00
413	A82	$2.60 on $2.50 #356 (G)		4.00	4.00
413A	A77a	$3.70 on $3 #331		5.50	5.50
	Nos. 406-413A (9)			25.05	25.05

World Communications Year — A88

		1984, Jan. 23	Photo.		Perf. 13x13½
414	A88	40c Telegraph sender		.45	.45
415	A88	52c Early telephone		.65	.65
416	A88	83c Satellite		1.10	1.10
a.	Souvenir sheet of 3, #414-416			2.00	2.00
	Nos. 414-416 (3)			2.20	2.20

Moth Orchid — A89   Golden Shower Tree — A90

25c, Poinsettia. 30c, Buttercup tree. 35c, Begonia. 40c, Frangipani. 52c, Bird of paradise. 58c, Rose of Sharon. 70c, Princess flower. 83c, Lotus. $1.05, Yellow hibiscus. $2.30, Orchid var. $3.90, Orchid sp. $5, Poinsettia, diff. $6.60, Hybrid hibiscus. $8.30, Hibiscus rosasinensis.

		1984		Perf. 13x13½
417	A89	12c shown	.25	.25
418	A89	25c multicolored	.35	.35
419	A89	30c multicolored	.50	.50
420	A89	35c multicolored	.50	.50
421	A89	40c multicolored	.55	.55
422	A89	52c multicolored	.70	.70
423	A89	58c multicolored	.80	.80
424	A89	70c multicolored	1.00	1.00
425	A89	83c multicolored	1.10	1.10
426	A89	$1.05 multicolored	1.60	1.60
427	A90	$1.75 shown	1.60	1.60
428	A90	$2.30 multicolored	2.25	2.25
429	A90	$3.90 multicolored	3.50	3.50
430	A90	$5 multicolored	4.50	4.50
431	A90	$6.60 multicolored	6.00	6.00
431A	A90	$8.30 multicolored	8.00	8.00
	Nos. 417-431A (16)		33.20	33.20

Issued: #417-426, 2/20; #427-429, 5/10; others 6/18. For overprints see #O1-O13, O15, O17-O18.

1984 Summer Olympics — A91

Designs: Greek pottery designs, 3rd cent. BC. 30c, 70c vert.

		1984, Mar. 15	Photo.		Perf. 14
432	A91	30c Discus		.45	.45
433	A91	35c Running		.50	.50
434	A91	40c Equestrian		.55	.55
435	A91	58c Boxing		.80	.80
436	A91	70c Javelin		.95	.95
	Nos. 432-436 (5)			3.25	3.25

For overprints and surcharges see #446-450, 480-483.

AUSIPEX '84, Australian Animals — A92

25c, Koala on gray branch. 35c, Koala sitting in curve of branch. 40c, Koala on green branch (yellow background). 58c, Koala on branch, arms stretched out in front. 70c, Koala on green branch (lt. blue green background). 83c, Kangaroo with joey, facing right. $1.05, Kangaroo with joey, facing left. $2.50, Kangaroo, tail in LR corner.

		1984	**Photo.**	**Perf. 14**	
437	A92	25c gold & multi		.30	.30
438	A92	35c gold & multi		.40	.40
439	A92	40c gold & multi		.65	.65
440	A92	58c gold & multi		1.00	1.00
441	A92	70c gold & multi		1.30	1.30
442	A92	83c gold & multi		1.50	1.50
443	A92	$1.05 gold & multi		1.75	1.75
444	A92	$2.50 gold & multi		4.00	4.00
		Nos. 437-444 (8)		10.90	10.90

Souvenir Sheets

445		Sheet of 2 + label	5.00	5.00
a.	A92	$1.75 Wallaby	2.50	2.50
b.	A92	$1.75 Koala, diff.	2.50	2.50
c.		Sheet, #437-441, 445b, perf 13½	4.50	4.50
d.		Sheet, #442-444, 445a, perf 13½	6.50	6.50

Nos. 442-444 airmail.
Issued: #437-444, Aug. 24; $445, Sept. 20.

Nos. 432-436 Ovptd. with Event, Names of Gold Medalists, Country in Gold or Red

		1984, Sept. 7	**Perf. 14**	
446	A91	30c Danneberg	.40	.40
447	A91	35c Coe (R)	.50	.50
448	A91	40c Todd	.55	.55
449	A91	58c Biggs	.80	.80
450	A91	70c Haerkoenen	1.00	1.00
		Nos. 446-450 (5)	3.25	3.25

10th Anniv. of Self Government A93

		1984, Oct. 19	**Photo.**	**Perf. 13**	
451	A93	40c Niue flag		.55	.55
452	A93	58c Niue map		1.00	1.00
453	A93	70c Ceremony		1.15	1.15
a.		Souvenir sheet of 3, #451-453		2.50	2.50
		Nos. 451-453 (3)		2.70	2.70

Souvenir Sheet

454	A93	$2.50 like 70c	2.50	2.50

For overprints and surcharges see Nos. 655-660.

Nos. 340, 354 Surcharged "Prince Henry / 15.9.84" and Bars and New Values in Red or Silver

		1984, Oct. 22	**Photo.**	**Perf. 14**	
455	A79	$2 on 75c multi (R)		2.25	2.25
456	A82	$2 on 50c multi (S)		2.25	2.25

Nos. 455-456 issued in sheets of 5 + label.

Christmas — A94

Paintings: 40c, The Nativity, by A. Vaccaro. 58c, Virgin with Fly, anonymous. 70c, Adoration of the Shepherds, by B. Murillo. 83c, Flight into Egypt, by B. Murillo.

		1984, Oct. 19	**Photo.**	**Perf. 13x13½**	
457	A94	40c multicolored		.55	.55
458	A94	58c multicolored		.80	.80
459	A94	70c multicolored		1.00	1.00
460	A94	83c multicolored		1.10	1.10
		Nos. 457-460 (4)		3.45	3.45

Souvenir Sheets

461		Sheet of 4	3.25	3.25
a.	A94	40c + 5c Like 40c	.55	.55
b.	A94	58c + 5c Like 58c	.70	.70
c.	A94	70c + 5c Like 70c	.90	.90

d.		A94 83c + 5c Like 83c	1.00	1.00
		Perf. 13½		
462	A94	95c + 10c Like 40c	1.25	1.25
463	A94	95c + 10c Like 58c	1.25	1.25
464	A94	95c + 10c Like 70c	1.25	1.25
465	A94	95c + 10c Like 83c	1.25	1.25

Audubon Birth Bicentenary — A95

Illustrations of North American bird species by artist/naturalist John J. Audubon: 40c, House wren. 70c, Veery. 83c, Grasshopper sparrow. $1.05, Henslow's sparrow. $2.50, Vesper sparrow.

		1985, Apr. 15	**Photo.**	**Perf. 14½**	
466	A95	40c multicolored		1.50	1.50
467	A95	70c multicolored		2.00	2.00
468	A95	83c multicolored		2.75	2.75
469	A95	$1.05 multicolored		3.25	3.25
470	A95	$2.50 multicolored		7.50	7.50
		Nos. 466-470 (5)		17.00	17.00

Souvenir Sheets
Perf. 14

471	A95	$1.75 like #466	2.50	2.50
472	A95	$1.75 like #467	2.50	2.50
473	A95	$1.75 like #468	2.50	2.50
474	A95	$1.75 like #469	2.50	2.50
475	A95	$1.75 like #470	2.50	2.50
		Nos. 471-475 (5)	12.50	12.50

Queen Mother, 85th Birthday — A96

Designs: 70c, Wearing mantle of the Order of the Garter. $1.15, With Queen Elizabeth II. $1.50, With Prince Charles. $3, Writing letter.

		1985, June 14	**Perf. 13½x13**	
476	A96	70c multicolored	1.00	1.00
477	A96	$1.15 multicolored	1.25	1.25
478	A96	$1.50 multicolored	1.75	1.75
a.		Souvenir sheet of 3 + label, #476-478	8.00	8.00
		Nos. 476-478 (3)	4.00	4.00

Souvenir Sheet
Perf. 13½

479	A96	$3 multicolored	4.25	4.25

Nos. 476-478 issued in sheets of 5 plus label. No. 479 contains one 39x36mm stamp. No. 478a issued 8/4/86, for 86th birthday.

Nos. 432-433, 435-436 Overprinted "Mini South Pacific Games, Rarotonga" and Surcharged with Gold Bar and New Value in Black

		1985, July 26	**Perf. 14**	
480	A91	52c on 95c multi	.55	.55
481	A91	83c on 58c multi	1.15	1.15
482	A91	95c on 35c multi	1.30	1.30
483	A91	$2 on 30c multi	2.50	2.50
		Nos. 480-483 (4)	5.50	5.50

Nos. 368-371 Overprinted with Conference Emblem and: "Pacific Islands Conference, Rarotonga"

		1985, July 26	**Perf. 13½x13**	
484	A84	70c on #368	.75	.75
485	A84	70c on #369	.75	.75
486	A84	70c on #370	.75	.75
487	A84	70c on #371	.75	.75
a.		Block of 4, #484-487	3.00	3.00

A97

Paintings of children: 58c, Portrait of R. Strozzi's Daughter, by Titian. 70c, The Fifer, by Manet. $1.15, Portrait of a Young Girl, by Renoir. $1.50, Portrait of M. Berard, by Renoir.

		1985, Oct. 11	**Perf. 13**	
488	A97	58c multicolored	1.75	1.75
489	A97	70c multicolored	2.00	2.00
490	A97	$1.15 multicolored	3.50	3.50
491	A97	$1.50 multicolored	4.50	4.50
		Nos. 488-491 (4)	11.75	11.75

Souvenir Sheets
Perf. 13x13½

492	A97	$1.75 + 10c like #488	5.00	5.00
493	A97	$1.75 + 10c like #489	5.00	5.00
494	A97	$1.75 + 10c like #490	5.00	5.00
495	A97	$1.75 + 10c like #491	5.00	5.00

Intl. Youth Year.

A98

Christmas, Paintings (details) by Correggio: 58c, No. 500a, Virgin and Child. 85c, No. 500b, Adoration of the Magi. $1.05, No. 500c, Virgin and Child, diff. $1.45, No. 500d, Virgin and Child with St. Catherine.

		1985, Nov. 29	**Photo.**	**Perf. 13x13½**	
496	A98	58c multicolored		1.25	1.25
497	A98	85c multicolored		2.25	2.25
498	A98	$1.05 multicolored		2.75	2.75
499	A98	$1.45 multicolored		3.75	3.75
		Nos. 496-499 (4)		10.00	10.00

Souvenir Sheets

500		Sheet of 4	5.50	5.50
a.-d.	A98	60c + 10c, any single	1.30	1.30
		Imperf		
501	A98	65c like #496	1.25	1.25
502	A98	95c like #497	1.75	1.75
503	A98	$1.20 like #498	2.50	2.50
504	A98	$1.75 like #499	3.75	3.75
		Nos. 500-504 (5)	14.50	14.50

Nos. 501-504 each contain one 61x71mm stamp.

Halley's Comet A99

The Constellations, fresco by Giovanni De Vecchi, Farnesio Palace, Caprarola, Italy.

		1986, Jan. 24	**Perf. 13½**	
505	A99	60c multicolored	.90	.90
506	A99	75c multicolored	1.10	1.00
507	A99	$1.10 multicolored	1.50	1.50
508	A99	$1.50 multicolored	2.40	2.40
		Nos. 505-508 (4)	5.90	5.80

Souvenir Sheet

509		Sheet of 4	8.00	8.00
a.	A99	95c like #505	2.00	2.00
b.	A99	95c like #506	2.00	2.00
c.	A99	95c like #507	2.00	2.00
d.	A99	95c like #508	2.00	2.00

A100

Elizabeth II, 60th Birthday: $1.10, No. 513a, Elizabeth and Prince Philip at Windsor Castle. $1.50, No. 513b, At Balmoral. $2, No. 513c, Elizabeth at Buckingham Palace. $3, Elizabeth seated and Prince Philip.

		1986, Apr. 28	**Perf. 14½x13½**	
510	A100	$1.10 multicolored	1.00	1.00
511	A100	$1.50 multicolored	1.50	1.50
512	A100	$2 multicolored	2.00	2.00
		Nos. 510-512 (3)	4.50	4.50

Souvenir Sheets

513		Sheet of 3	2.75	2.75
a.-c.	A100	75c any single	.90	.90
514	A100	$3 multicolored	3.50	3.50

For surcharges see Nos. 546-547.

A101

AMERIPEX '86: #515a, Washington, US #1. #515b, Jefferson, Roosevelt, Lincoln.

		1986, May 22	**Photo.**	**Perf. 14**	
515	A101	$1 Pair, #a.-b.		7.75	7.75

A102

Paintings: $1, Statue under construction, 1883, by Victor Dargaud. $2.50, Unveiling the Statue of Liberty, 1886, by Edmund Morand (1829-1901).

		1986, July 4	**Perf. 13x13½**	
517	A102	$1 multicolored	2.25	2.25
518	A102	$2.50 multicolored	5.50	5.50

Souvenir Sheet

519		Sheet of 2	4.00	4.00
a.	A102	$1.25 like #517	2.00	2.00
b.	A102	$1.25 like #518	2.00	2.00

Statue of Liberty, cent.

Wedding of Prince Andrew and Sarah Ferguson A103

Designs: $2.50, Portraits, Westminster Abbey. $5, Portraits.

		1986, July 23	**Perf. 13½x13**	
520	A103	$2.50 multicolored	4.00	4.00

Souvenir Sheet

521	A103	$5 Portraits	8.25	8.25

No. 520 printed in sheets of 4. No. 521 contains one 45x32mm stamp.

STAMPEX '86, Adelaide, Aug. 4-10 — A104

Birds — 40c, Egretta alba, vert. 60c, Emblema picta. 75c, Aprosmictus scapularis, vert. 80c, Malurus lamberti. $1, Falco peregrinus, vert. $1.65, Halcyon azurea. $2.20, Melopsittacus undulatus, vert. $4.25,

Perf. 13x13½, 13½x13

		1986, Aug. 4	**Photo.**	
522	A104	40c multi	1.10	1.10
523	A104	60c multi	1.60	1.60
524	A104	75c multi	2.25	2.25
525	A104	80c multi	2.50	2.50
526	A104	$1 multi	3.00	3.00
527	A104	$1.65 multi	4.75	4.75
528	A104	$2.20 multi	7.00	7.00
529	A104	$4.25 multi	13.00	13.00
		Nos. 522-529 (8)	35.20	35.20

Christmas — A105

Paintings in the Vatican Museum: 80c, No. 534a, Virgin and Child, by Perugino (1446-1523). $1.15, No. 534b, Virgin of St. N. dei Frari, by Titian. $1.80, No. 534c, Virgin with Milk, by Lorenzo di Credi (1459-1537). $2.60,

$7.50, No. 534d, Foligno Madonna, by Raphael.

1986, Nov. 14   Litho.   Perf. 14
530	A105	80c multi	1.60	1.60
531	A105	$1.15 multi	2.25	2.25
532	A105	$1.80 multi	4.00	4.00
533	A105	$2.60 multi	6.00	6.00
		Nos. 530-533 (4)	13.85	13.85

Souvenir Sheets
Perf. 13½
| 534 | | Sheet of 4 | 11.00 | 11.00 |
| a.-d. | A105 | $1.50 any single | 2.75 | 2.75 |

Perf. 14½x13½
| 535 | A105 | $7.50 multi | 12.00 | 12.00 |

For surcharges see Nos. B56-B61.

Souvenir Sheets

Statue of Liberty, Cent. — A106

Photographs: No. 536a, Tall ship, bridge. No. 536b, Workmen, flame from torch. No. 536c, Workman, flame, diff. No. 536d, Ships, New York City. No. 536e, Tall ship, sailboat, bridge. No. 537a, Statue, front. No. 537b, Statue, left side. No. 537c, Torch dismantled. No. 537d, Statue, right side. No. 537e, Welder.

1987, May 20
536	A106	Sheet of 5 + label	3.75	3.75
a.-e.		75c any single	.75	.75
537	A106	Sheet of 5 + label	3.75	3.75
a.-e.		75c any single, vert.	.75	.75

Tennis Champions A107

Olympic emblem, coin and: 80c, $1.15, $1.40, $1.80, Boris Becker. 85c, $1.05, $1.30, $1.75, Steffi Graf. Various action scenes.

1987
538	A107	80c multi	2.50	2.50
539	A107	85c multi	2.10	2.10
540	A107	$1.05 multi	2.50	2.50
541	A107	$1.15 multi	2.60	2.60
542	A107	$1.30 multi	2.50	2.50
543	A107	$1.40 multi	3.00	3.00
544	A107	$1.75 multi	3.00	3.00
545	A107	$1.80 multi	3.75	3.75
		Nos. 538-545 (8)	21.95	21.95

Issued: 80c, $1.15, $1.40, $1.80, 9/25; others, 10/20.
For overprints see Nos. 560-563.

Nos. 511-512 Surcharged "40th /WEDDING / ANNIV." with Denomination in Black on Gold
Perf. 14½x13½
1987, Nov. 20   Photo.
| 546 | A100 | $4.85 on $1.50 #511 | 6.00 | 6.00 |
| 547 | A100 | $4.85 on $2 #512 | 6.00 | 6.00 |

40th Wedding anniv. of Queen Elizabeth II and Prince Philip, Duke of Edinburgh.

Christmas A108

Paintings (details) by Albrecht Durer (Angel with Lute on 80c, $1.05, $2.80): 80c, No. 551a, The Nativity. $1.05, No. 551b, Adoration of the Magi. $2.80, No. 551c, Celebration of the Rosary.

1987, Dec. 4   Photo.   Perf. 13½
548	A108	80c multi	1.75	1.75
549	A108	$1.05 multi	2.25	2.25
550	A108	$2.80 multi	5.00	5.00
		Nos. 548-550 (3)	9.00	9.00

Souvenir Sheets
551		Sheet of 3	9.00	9.00
a.-c.	A108	$1.30 any single	3.00	3.00
552	A108	$7.50 multi	11.00	11.00

Size of Nos. 551a-551c: 49½x38½mm. No. 552 contains one 51x33mm stamp.

European Soccer Championships — A109

Highlights from Franz Beckenbauer's career: 20c, Match scene. 40c, German all-star team. 60c, Brussels, 1974. 80c, England, 1966. $1.05, Mexico, 1970. $1.30, Munich, 1974. $1.80, FC Bayern Munchen vs. Athletico Madrid.

1988, June 20   Litho.   Perf. 14
553	A109	20c multi	.40	.40
554	A109	40c multi	.80	.80
555	A109	60c multi	1.25	1.25
556	A109	80c multi	1.60	1.60
557	A109	$1.05 multi	2.25	2.25
558	A109	$1.30 multi	3.00	3.00
559	A109	$1.80 multi	3.75	3.75
		Nos. 553-559 (7)	13.05	13.05

Nos. 539-540, 542 and 543 Ovptd.
a. "AUSTRALIA 24 JAN 88 / FRENCH OPEN 4 JUNE 88"
b. "WIMBLEDON 2 JULY 88 / U S OPEN 10 SEPT. 88"
c. "WOMEN'S TENNIS GRAND / SLAM: 10 SEPTEMBER 88"
d. "SEOUL OLYMPIC GAMES / GOLD MEDAL WINNER"

1988, Oct. 14   Litho.   Perf. 13½x14
560	A107(a)	85c on No. 539	1.75	1.75
561	A107(b)	$1.05 on No. 540	2.25	2.25
562	A107(c)	$1.30 on No. 542	2.75	2.75
563	A107(d)	$1.75 on No. 543	3.75	3.75
		Nos. 560-563 (4)	10.50	10.50

Steffi Graf, 1988 Olympic gold medalist; opportunities for youth in sports.

Christmas — A110

Adoration of the Shepherds, by Rubens: 60c, Angels. 80c, Joseph and witness. $1.05, Madonna. $1.30, Christ child. $7.20, Entire painting.

1988, Oct. 28   Photo.   Perf. 13½
564	A110	60c multi	1.40	1.40
565	A110	80c multi	2.40	2.40
566	A110	$1.05 multi	3.50	3.50
567	A110	$1.30 multi	4.00	4.00
		Nos. 564-567 (4)	11.30	11.30

Souvenir Sheet
| 568 | A110 | $7.20 multi | 10.00 | 10.00 |

No. 568 contains one 40x50mm stamp.

First Moon Landing, 20th Anniv. — A111

Apollo 11: #a, Mission emblem and astronaut. #b, Earth, Moon and simplified flight plan. #c, Olive branch, Apollo 1 mission emblem and astronaut on Moon. Printed in continuous design.

1989, July 20   Photo.   Perf. 14
| 571 | A111 | $1.50 Strip of 3, #a.-c. | 14.50 | 14.50 |

Souvenir Sheet of 3
Perf. 13½x13
| 572 | A111 | $1.15 #a.-c. | 8.00 | 8.00 |

Christmas A112

Details of Presentation in the Temple, 1631, by Rembrandt, Royal Cabinet of Paintings, The Hague: 70c, Priests. 80c, Madonna. $1.05, Joseph. $1.30, Christ child. $7.20, Entire painting.

1989, Nov. 22   Photo.   Perf. 13x13½
573	A112	70c gold & multi	2.60	2.60
574	A112	80c gold & multi	2.75	2.75
575	A112	$1.05 gold & multi	3.50	3.50
576	A112	$1.30 gold & multi	4.50	4.50
		Nos. 573-576 (4)	13.35	13.35

Souvenir Sheet
Perf. 13½
| 577 | A112 | $7.20 gold & multi | 13.50 | 13.50 |

No. 577 contains one 39x50mm stamp.

Emblem of the German Natl. Soccer Team and Signatures A113

Former team captains: 80c, Fritz Walter. $1.15, Franz Beckenbauer. $1.40, Uwe Seeler.

1990, Feb. 5   Photo.   Perf. 13½
578	A113	80c multicolored	2.25	2.25
579	A113	$1.15 multicolored	2.60	2.60
580	A113	$1.40 multicolored	4.50	4.50
581	A113	$1.80 shown	5.25	5.25
		Nos. 578-581 (4)	14.60	14.60

1990 World Cup Soccer Championships, Italy.

First Postage Stamp, 150th Anniv. — A114

Paintings by Rembrandt showing letters: 80c, No. 586d, Merchant Maarten Looten (1632). $1.05, No. 586c, Rembrandt's son Titus holding pen (1655). $1.30, No. 586b, The Shipbuilder and his Wife (1633). $1.80, No. 586a, Bathsheba with King David's letter (1654).

1990, May 2   Photo.   Perf. 13½
582	A114	80c multicolored	2.25	2.25
583	A114	$1.05 multicolored	3.00	3.00
584	A114	$1.30 multicolored	4.50	4.50
585	A114	$1.80 multicolored	6.00	6.00
		Nos. 582-585 (4)	15.75	15.75

Souvenir Sheet
| 586 | | Sheet of 4 | 11.00 | 11.00 |
| a.-d. | A114 | $1.50 any single | 2.75 | 2.75 |

A115

1990, July 23   Perf. 13½x13½
| 587 | A115 | $1.25 multicolored | 5.00 | 5.00 |

Souvenir Sheet
| 588 | A115 | $7 multicolored | 16.00 | 16.00 |

Queen Mother, 90th birthday.

A116

Christmas (Paintings): 70c, Adoration of the Magi by Bouts. 80c, Holy Family by Fra Bartolomeo. $1.05, The Nativity by Memling. $1.30, Adoration of the King by Pieter Bruegel, the Elder. $7.20, Virgin and Child Enthroned by Cosimo Tura.

1990, Nov. 27   Litho.   Perf. 14
589	A116	70c multicolored	2.25	2.25
590	A116	80c multicolored	3.00	3.00
591	A116	$1.05 multicolored	3.50	3.50
592	A116	$1.30 multicolored	4.25	4.25
		Nos. 589-592 (4)	13.00	13.00

Souvenir Sheet
| 593 | A116 | $7.20 multicolored | 13.00 | 13.00 |

No. 334 Overprinted in Silver

1990, Dec. 5   Perf. 13x13½
| 594 | A77a | $10 multicolored | 16.00 | 16.00 |

Birdpex '90, 20th Intl. Ornithological Congress, New Zealand.

No. 333 Overprinted "SIXTY FIFTH BIRTHDAY QUEEN ELIZABETH II"
1991, Apr. 22   Litho.   Perf. 13x13½
| 595 | A77a | $6 multicolored | 8.00 | 8.00 |

Nos. 340-342 Overprinted in Black or Silver

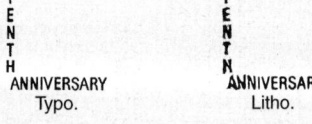

TENTH ANNIVERSARY   TENTH ANNIVERSARY
Typo.   Litho.

1991, June 26   Photo.   Perf. 14
596	A79	75c on #340 (S)	1.50	1.50
a.		Litho. overprint	1.50	1.50
597	A79	95c on #341	2.25	2.25
a.		Litho. overprint	2.25	2.25
598	A79	$1.20 on #342	3.25	3.25
a.		Litho. overprint	3.25	3.25
		Nos. 596-598 (3)	7.00	7.00
		Nos. 596a-598a (3)	7.00	7.00

Nos. 596-598 issued in miniature sheets of 5 with typo. overprint. Nos. 596a-598a issued in uncut panes of 4 miniature sheets of 5. Letters of typo. overprint are taller and thinner than litho. overprint.

Christmas — A117

Paintings: 20c, The Virgin and Child with Saints Jerome and Dominic, by Filippino Lippi. 50c, The Isenheim Altarpiece, The Virgin and Child, by Grunewald. $1, The Nativity, by Pittoni. $2, Adoration of the Kings, by Jan Brueghel, the Elder. $7, The Adoration of the Shepherds, by Reni.

1991, Nov. 11   Litho.   Perf. 14
599	A117	20c multicolored	.50	.50
600	A117	50c multicolored	1.40	1.40
601	A117	$1 multicolored	3.00	3.00
602	A117	$2 multicolored	5.50	5.50
		Nos. 599-602 (4)	10.40	10.40

Souvenir Sheet
| 603 | A117 | $7 multicolored | 11.00 | 11.00 |

Birds — A118

20c, Banded rail. 50c, Red-tailed tropicbird. 70c, Purple swamphen. $1, Pacific pigeon. $1.50, White-collared kingfisher. $2, Blue-crowned lory. $3, Crimson-crowned fruit dove. $5, Barn owl. $7, Longtailed cockoo. $10, Reef heron. $15, Polynesian triller.

1992-93   Litho.   Perf. 14x13½
604	A118	20c multicolored	.30	.30
605	A118	50c multicolored	.70	.70
606	A118	70c multicolored	1.00	1.00
607	A118	$1 multicolored	1.50	1.50
608	A118	$1.50 multicolored	2.00	2.00
609	A118	$2 multicolored	2.75	2.75
610	A118	$3 multicolored	4.25	4.25
611	A118	$5 multicolored	6.50	6.50

Perf. 13
Size: 51x38mm
612	A118	$7 multicolored	8.50	8.50

Size: 49x35mm
613	A118	$10 multicolored	11.50	11.50
614	A118	$15 multicolored	18.00	18.00
		Nos. 604-614 (11)	57.00	57.00

Issued $1.50, $2, 3/20; $3, 4/16; $5, 5/15; $7, 3/26/93; $10, 4/16/93; $15, 8/10/93; others, 2/92.
For overprints & surcharges see Nos. O20-O25, 676-677.

Discovery of America, 500th Anniv. A119

$2, Queen Isabella supports Columbus. $3, Columbus' fleet. $5, Columbus landing in America.

1992   Litho.   Perf. 13
621	A119	$2 multicolored	2.55	2.55
622	A119	$3 multicolored	4.50	4.50
623	A119	$5 multicolored	7.50	7.50
		Nos. 621-623 (3)	14.55	14.55

1992 Summer Olympics, Barcelona A120

No. 624: a, $10 coin, tennis player. b, Flags, torch. c, Gymnast, $10 coin. $5, Water polo player.

1992, July 22   Litho.   Perf. 13½x13
624	A120	$2.50 Strip of 3, #a.-c.	17.00	17.00

Souvenir Sheet
625	A120	$5 multicolored	10.50	10.50

Nos. 265-268 Surcharged

1992, Sept. 30   Photo.   Perf. 13
Strips of 4, #a.-d.
626	A72	$1 on 20c	4.75	4.75
627	A72	$1 on 25c	4.75	4.75
628	A72	$1 on 30c	4.75	4.75
629	A72	$1 on 35c	4.75	4.75
		Nos. 626-629 (4)	19.00	19.00

6th South Pacific Festival of the Arts.

Christmas — A121

Design: Different details from St. Catherine's Mystic Marriage, by Hans Memling.

1992, Nov. 18   Litho.   Perf. 13½
642	A121	20c multicolored	.35	.35
643	A121	50c multicolored	1.00	1.00
644	A121	$1 multicolored	2.40	2.40
645	A121	$2 multicolored	4.00	4.00
		Nos. 642-645 (4)	7.75	7.75

Souvenir Sheet
646	A121	$7 like #643	11.50	11.50

No. 646 contains one 39x48mm stamp.

Queen Elizabeth II's Accession to the Throne, 40th Anniv. — A122

Various portraits of Queen Elizabeth II.

1992, Dec. 7   Perf. 14
647	A122	70c multicolored	.60	.60
648	A122	$1 multicolored	1.75	1.75
649	A122	$1.50 multicolored	3.50	3.50
650	A122	$2 multicolored	4.25	4.25
		Nos. 647-650 (4)	10.10	10.10

Dolphins — A123

Designs: 20c, Rough-toothed dolphin. 50c, Fraser's dolphin. 75c, Pantropical spotted dolphin. $1, Risso's dolphin.

1993, Jan. 13   Litho.   Perf. 14
651	A123	20c multicolored	1.25	.75
652	A123	50c multicolored	3.50	1.50
653	A123	75c multicolored	4.75	2.50
654	A123	$1 multicolored	6.00	4.50
		Nos. 651-654 (4)	15.50	9.25

World Wildlife Fund.

Nos. 451-453 Ovptd.

1993, Mar. 15   Photo.   Perf. 13
655	A93	40c on #451 multi	.65	.65
656	A93	58c on #452 multi	1.25	1.25
657	A93	70c on #453 multi	1.75	1.75

Nos. 655-657 Surcharged
1993, Mar. 15
658	A93	$1 on 40c #655	3.25	3.25
659	A93	$1 on 58c #656	3.25	3.25
660	A93	$1 on 70c #657	3.25	3.25
		Nos. 655-660 (6)	13.40	13.40

Queen Elizabeth II, 40th Anniv. of Coronation A124

1993, June 2   Litho.   Perf. 14
661	A124	$5 multicolored	10.50	10.50

Christmas — A125

Details from Virgin of the Rosary, by Guido Reni: 20c, Infant Jesus. 70c, Cherubs. $1, Two men, one pointing upward. $1.50, Two men looking upward. $3, Madonna and child.

1993, Oct. 29   Litho.   Perf. 14
662	A125	20c multicolored	.30	.30
663	A125	70c multicolored	1.20	1.20
664	A125	$1 multicolored	1.75	1.75
665	A125	$1.50 multicolored	3.25	3.25

Size: 32x47mm
Perf. 13½
666	A125	$3 multicolored	6.00	6.00
		Nos. 662-666 (5)	12.50	12.50

1994 World Cup Soccer Championships, U.S. — A126

1994, June 17   Litho.   Perf. 14
667	A126	$4 multicolored	8.00	8.00

First Manned Moon Landing, 25th Anniv. A127

Designs: a, Flight to Moon, astronaut opening solar wind experiment lunar surface. b, Astronaut holding flag. c, Astronaut standing by lunar experiment package.

1994, July 20   Litho.   Perf. 14
668	A127	$2.50 Tryptic, #a.-c.	20.00	20.00

Christmas A128

Entire paintings or details: No. 669a, The Adoration of the Kings, by Jan Gossaert. b, Madonna & Child with Saints John & Catherine, by Titian. c, The Holy Family and Shepherd, by Titian. d, Virgin & Child with Saints, by Gerard David.
No. 670: a-b, Adoration of the Shepherds, by N. Poussin. c, Madonna & Child with Saints Joseph & John, by Sebastiano. d, Adoration of the Kings, by Veronese.

1994, Nov. 28   Litho.   Perf. 14
669	A128	70c Block of 4, #a.-d.	4.50	4.50
670	A128	$1 Block of 4, #a.-d.	7.00	7.00

Robert Louis Stevenson (1850-94), Writer — A129

a, Treasure Island. b, Dr. Jekyll and Mr. Hyde. c, Kidnapped. d, Stevenson, tomb, inscription.

1994, Dec. 14   Perf. 15x14
671	A129	$1.75 Block of 4, #a.-d.	15.00	15.00

Flowers — A130

1996, May 10   Litho.   Perf. 14½x14
672	A130	70c Tapeu orchid	.90	.90
673	A130	$1 Frangipani	1.40	1.40
674	A130	$1.20 Golden shower	1.60	1.60
675	A130	$1.50 Pua	2.10	2.10
		Nos. 672-675 (4)	6.00	6.00

Nos. 606, 608 Surcharged

1996, Feb. 19   Litho.   Perf. 14x13½
676	A118	50c on 70c #606	11.50	8.50
677	A118	$1 on $1.50 #608	13.50	10.50

Flower Type of 1969 Redrawn
Design: 20c, Hibiscus.

1996, Aug. 22   Litho.   Rouletted 7
678	A38	20c red & green	.45	.45

Yachting — A131

1996   Litho.   Perf. 14½
679	A131	70c Jackfish	1.00	1.00
680	A131	$1 S/V Jennifer	1.40	1.40
681	A131	$1.20 Mikeva	2.00	2.00
682	A131	$2 Eye of the Wind	3.50	3.50
		Nos. 679-682 (4)	7.90	7.90

Souvenir Sheet
Perf. 14
683	A131	$1.50 Desert Star	2.50	2.50

Issued: Nos. 679-682, 9/30/96. No. 683, 10/96 (Taipei '96). No. 683 contains one 30x30mm stamp.

Coral — A132

20c, Acropora gemmifera. 50c, Acropora nobilis. 70c, Goniopora lobata. $1, Stylaster. $1.20, Alveopora catalai. $1.50, Fungia scutaria. $2, Porites solida. $3, Millepora. $4, Pocillopora eydouxi. $5, Platygyra pini.

1996, Dec. 20   Litho.   Perf. 14
684-693	A132	Set of 10	26.00	26.00

Souvenir Sheet

New Year 1997 (Year of the Ox) A133

1997, Feb. 10   Litho.   Perf. 13
694	A133	$1.50 multicolored	2.50	2.50

Hong Kong '97.

Humpback Whale A134

20c, Whale in water. 50c, Killer whale. 70c, Minke whale. $1, Adult, young whale swimming upward. $1.20, Sperm whale. $1.50, Whale breaching.

1997		Litho.		Perf. 14	
695	A134	20c multi		.40	.40
696	A134	50c multi, vert.		1.05	1.05
697	A134	70c multi, vert.		1.40	1.40
698	A134	$1 multi, vert.		2.25	2.25
699	A134	$1.20 multi, vert.		2.60	2.60
700	A134	$1.50 multi, vert.		3.50	3.50
a.		Souvenir sheet, #695, 698, 700		4.25	4.25
		Nos. 695-700 (6)		11.20	11.20

Pacific '97 (#700a).
Issued: 20c, $1, $1.50, 5/29; others, 9/3.

Island Scenes — A135

Designs: a, Steps leading over island along inlet. b, Island, vegetagion, sky. c, Coral reef, undersea vegetation. d, Reef, vegetation, diff.

1997, Apr. 18		Litho.	Perf. 13½x14	
701	A135	$1 Block of 4, #a.-d.	5.50	5.50

Christmas — A136

Bouquets of various flowers.

1997, Nov. 26		Litho.	Perf. 14	
702	A136	20c deep plum & multi	.30	.30
703	A136	50c green & multi	.70	.70
704	A136	70c blue & multi	1.00	1.00
705	A136	$1 red & multi	1.50	1.50
		Nos. 702-705 (4)	3.50	3.50

Diana, Princess of Wales (1961-97)
Common Design Type

Various portraits: a, 20c. b, 50c. c, $1. d, $2.

1998, Apr. 29		Litho.	Perf. 14½x14	
706	CD355	Sheet of 4, #a.-d.	5.50	5.50

No. 706 sold for $3.70 + 50c, with surtax from international sales being donated to the Princess of Wales Memorial fund and surtax from national sales being donated to designated local charity.

Diving — A137

Designs: 20c, Two snorkeling beneath water's surface. 70c, One diver, coral. $1, Diving into underwater canyon, vert. $1.20, Two divers, coral. $1.50, Divers exploring underwater cavern.

Wmk. Triangles

1998, May 20		Litho.	Perf. 14½	
707	A137	20c multicolored	.40	.40
708	A137	70c multicolored	1.00	1.00
709	A137	$1 multicolored	1.40	1.40
710	A137	$1.20 multicolored	1.75	1.75
711	A137	$1.50 multicolored	2.40	2.40
		Nos. 707-711 (5)	6.95	6.95

Sea Birds — A138

Designs: 20c, Pacific black duck. 70c, Fairy tern. $1, Great frigatebird, vert. $1.20, Lesser golden plover. $2, Brown noddy.

Perf. 14½x14, 14x14½
Wmk. Triangles

1998, July 23		Litho.	
712	A138	20c multicolored	.55 .55
713	A138	70c multicolored	1.20 1.20
714	A138	$1 multicolored	2.10 2.10
715	A138	$1.20 multicolored	2.40 2.40
716	A138	$2 multicolored	3.50 3.50
		Nos. 712-716 (5)	9.75 9.75

Shells — A139

Two views of various shells from the Pacific Ocean.

Perf. 14½

1998, Sept. 23		Litho.	Unwmk.	
717	A139	20c multicolored	.50	.50
718	A139	70c multicolored	1.15	1.15
719	A139	$1 multicolored	2.40	2.40
720	A139	$5 multicolored	7.50	7.50
		Nos. 717-720 (4)	11.55	11.55

Ancient Weapons A140

Perf. 14x14½

1998, Nov. 18		Litho.	Unwmk.	
721	A140	20c Clubs	.50	.50
722	A140	$1.20 Spears	1.50	1.50
723	A140	$1.50 Spears, diff.	1.90	1.90
724	A140	$2 Throwing stones	2.60	2.60
		Nos. 721-724 (4)	6.50	6.50

Nos. 722-723 are each 60x23mm.

Maritime Heritage A141

Designs: 70c, First migration of Niue Fekai. $1, Crew of Resolution discover Niue. $1.20, LMS John Williams. $1.50, Captain James Cook (1728-79).

1999, Feb. 24		Litho.	Perf. 14½x14	
725	A141	70c bright violet blue	.90	.90
726	A141	$1 bright violet blue	1.40	1.40
727	A141	$1.20 bright violet blue	1.75	1.75
728	A141	$1.50 bright violet blue	2.10	2.10
		Nos. 725-728 (4)	6.15	6.15

Nudibranchs A142

World Wide Fund for Nature: 20c, Risbecia tryoni. $1, Chromodoris lochi. $1.20, Chromodoris elizabethina. $1.50, Chromodoris bullocki.

1999, Mar. 17		Litho.	Perf. 14½	
729	A142	20c multicolored	.40	.40
730	A142	$1 multicolored	1.40	1.40
731	A142	$1.20 multicolored	1.50	1.50
732	A142	$1.50 multicolored	2.25	2.25
a.		Souv. sheet, 2 ea #729-732	11.50	11.50
		Nos. 729-732 (4)	5.55	5.55

Scenic Views — A143

$1, Togo Chasm, vert. $1.20, Matapa Chasm, vert. $1.50, Tufukia. $2, Talava Arches.

1999, June 16		Litho.	Perf. 14	
734	A143	$1 multicolored	1.40	1.40
735	A143	$1.20 multicolored	1.50	1.50
736	A143	$1.50 multicolored	1.90	1.90
737	A143	$2 multicolored	2.75	2.75
		Nos. 734-737 (4)	7.55	7.55

Woven Baskets — A144

Various styles and patterns: #738a, 20c. #738b, $1. #739a, 70c. #739b, $3.

1999, Sept. 18		Litho.	Perf. 12	
738	A144	Pair, a.-b.	2.00	2.00
739	A144	Pair, a.-b.	4.00	4.00

Nos. 738b, 739b are each 45x35mm.

Souvenir Sheet

Self-Government, 25th Anniv. — A145

Designs: a, 20c, Natives, boats. b, $5, Fish, tree, diver, child.

Litho. with Foil application

1999, Dec. 1			Perf. 15x14¾	
740	A145	Sheet of 2, #a.-b	6.00	6.00

Millennium — A146

a, 20c, Man in outrigger canoe. b, 70c, Women pointing up. c, $4, Swimmers, bird, fish.

1999, Dec. 31		Litho.	Perf. 14¼x15	
741	A146	Strip of 3, #a.-c.	6.50	6.50

Birds and Flora — A147

20c, Purple-capped fruit dove, mamane. $1, Purple swamphen, fig. $1.20, Barn owl, koa. $2, Blue-crowned lory, ohia lehua.

2000, Apr. 5		Litho.	Perf. 13x13¼	
742-745	A147	Set of 4	6.50	6.50

Royal Birthdays — A148

Designs: $1.50, Queen Mother, 100th birthday, vert. $3, Prince William, 18th birthday, and Queen Mother.

2000, May 22		Perf. 13¼x13, 13x13¼		
746-747	A148	Set of 2	4.50	4.50

2000 Summer Olympics, Sydney — A149

Designs: 50c, Pole vault. 70c, Diving. $1, Hurdles. $3, Gymnastics.

Perf. 13½x13¼

2000, Sept. 16			Litho.	
748-751	A149	Set of 4	5.00	5.00

Dancers — A150

No. 752: a, Couple. b, Woman with red garments. c, Woman with white garments. d, Child with garments made of leaves.

2000, Nov. 22		Litho.	Perf. 13¼x13	
752		Horiz. strip of 4	5.00	5.00
a.	A150	20c multi	.30	.30
b.	A150	70c multi	.65	.65
c.	A150	$1.50 multi	1.30	1.30
d.	A150	$3 multi	2.75	2.75

Niue Postage Stamps, Cent. (in 2002) — A151

Designs: 70c, #1. $3, #34.

2001, Jan. 31				
753-754	A151	Set of 2	3.25	3.25

Butterflies — A152

No. 755: a, Large green-banded blue. b, Leafwing. c, Cairns birdwing. d, Meadow argus.

2001, Mar. 22			Perf. 13½x13¼	
755		Horiz. strip of 4	4.00	4.00
a.	A152	20c multi	.25	.25
b.	A152	70c multi	.60	.60
c.	A152	$1.50 multi	1.40	1.40
d.	A152	$2 multi	1.75	1.75

Turtles — A153

Designs: 50c, Green turtle hatching. $1, Hawksbill turtle. $3, Green turtle on beach.

2001, May 10				
756-758	A153	Set of 3	4.00	4.00

Coconut Crabs — A154

Crab: 20c, In water. 70c, On beach. $1.50, Climbing tree. $3, With coconut.

2001, July 7			Perf. 14	
759-762	A154	Set of 4	5.00	5.00

Annexation by New Zealand, Cent. — A155

Designs: $1.50, Building. $2, Man and woman.

2001, Oct. 19		Litho.	Perf. 13½x13¼	
763-764	A155	Set of 2	3.25	3.25

Christmas — A156

Designs: 20c, Magi. 70c, Dove. $1, Angel. $2, Star.

2001, Dec. 13   **Perf. 13x13¼**
765-768 A156   Set of 4   3.50 3.50
768a   Horiz. strip, #765-768   3.50 3.50

No. 729 Surcharged

2002, July 7   **Litho.**   **Perf. 14½**
769 A142 $10 on 20c multi   75.00 65.00

Worldwide Fund for Nature (WWF) — A156a

Various depictions of small giant clam.

2002, Nov. 7   **Litho.**   **Perf. 13¼x13**
769A   Horiz. strip of 4   4.50 4.50
  b.   A156a 50c multi   .60 .60
  c.   A156a 70c multi   .75 .70
  d.   A156a $1 multi   1.10 1.10
  e.   A156a $1.50 multi   1.60 1.60
  f.   As #769Ab, without emblem   — —
  g.   As #760Ac, without emblem   — —
  h.   As #769Ad, without emblem   — —
  i.   As #769Ae, without emblem   — —
  j.   Souvenir sheet of 4, #769Ab-769Ae   — —
  k.   Souvenir sheet of 4, #769Af-769Ai   10.00

A limited quantity of No. 769Ab received a $10 surcharge. Value, $145.

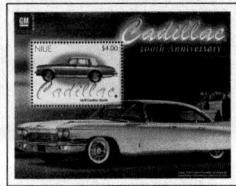

General Motors Automobiles — A157

No. 770, $1.50 — Cadillacs: a, 1953 Eldorado. b, 2002 Eldorado. c, 1967 Eldorado. d, 1961 Sedan de Ville.
No. 771, $1.50 — Corvettes: a, 1954 convertible. b, 1979. c, 1956 convertible. d, 1964 Stingray.
No. 772, $4, 1978 Cadillac Seville. No. 773, $4, 1979 Corvette.

2003   **Litho.**   **Perf. 14**
Sheets of 4, #a-d
770-771 A157   Set of 2   24.00 24.00
Souvenir Sheets
772-773 A157   Set of 2   22.00 22.00
Issued: Nos. 770, 772, 8/25; Nos. 771, 773, 9/2.

Coronation of Queen Elizabeth II, 50th Anniv. — A158

No. 774: a, Wearing crown as younger woman. b, Wearing tiara. c, Wearing crown as older woman.
$4, Wearing hat.

2003, Sept. 2
774 A158 $1.50 Sheet of 3, #a-c   9.00 9.00
Souvenir Sheet
775 A158 $4 multi   9.00 9.00

Prince William, 21st Birthday A159

No. 776: a, Wearing blue checked tie. b, Wearing shirt and jacket. c, Wearing striped shirt and tie.
$4, Wearing shirt.

2003, Sept. 2
776 A159 $1.50 Sheet of 3, #a-c   9.00 9.00
Souvenir Sheet
777 A159 $4 multi   8.50 8.50

Tour de France Bicycle Race, Cent. A160

No. 778: a, Nicholas Frantz, 1927. b, Frantz, 1928. c, Maurice de Waele, 1929. d, André Leducq, 1930.
$4, Leducq, 1930, diff.

2003, Sept. 2   **Perf. 13½x13¼**
778 A160 $1.50 Sheet of 4, #a-d   10.50 10.50
Souvenir Sheet
779 A160 $4 multi   8.75 8.75

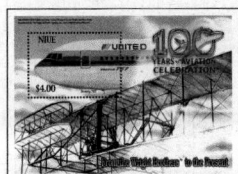

Powered Flight, Cent. A161

No. 780: a, Boeing 737-200. b, Boeing Stratocruiser. c, Boeing Model SA-307B. d, Douglas DC-2. e, Wright Flyer I. f, De Havilland D.H.4A.
$4, Boeing 767.

2003, Sept. 2   **Perf. 14**
780 A161 80c Sheet of 6, #a-f   9.00 9.00
Souvenir Sheet
781 A161 $4 multi   9.00 9.00

Birds, Butterflies and Fish A162

No. 782, $1.50, vert. — Birds: a, Wrinkled hornbill. b, Toco toucan. c, Roseate spoonbill. d, Blue and gold macaw.
No. 783, $1.50 — Butterflies: a, Agrias beata. b, Papilio blumei. c, Cethosia bibbis. d, Cressida cressida.
No. 784, $1.50 — Fish: a, Garibaldi fish. b, Golden damselfish. c, Squarespot anthias. d, Orange-fin anemonefish.
No. 785, $3, Green-wing macaw. No. 786, $3, Blue morpho butterfly. No. 787, $3, Maculosus angelfish.

Perf. 13½x13¼, 13¼x13½
2004, Aug. 16   **Litho.**
Sheets of 4, #a-d
782-784 A162   Set of 3   24.00 24.00
Souvenir Sheets
785-787 A162   Set of 3   12.00 12.00

Miniature Sheet

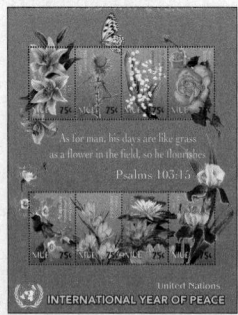

Intl. Year of Peace A163

No. 788: a, Lily. b, Thistle. c, Lily of the valley. d, Rose. e, Garland flower. f, Crocus. g, Lotus. h, Iris.

2004, Oct. 13   **Perf. 13½x13¼**
788 A163 75c Sheet of 8, #a-h   8.50 8.50

Miniature Sheet

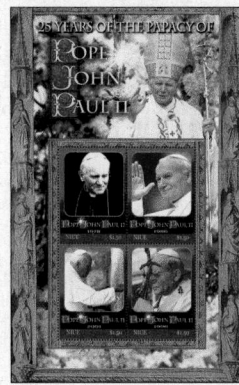

Election of Pope John Paul II, 25th Anniv. (in 2003) A164

No. 789 — Pope in: a, 1978. b, 1986. c, 2001. d, 1996.

2004, Oct. 13   **Perf. 13¼**
789 A164 $1.50 Sheet of 4, #a-d   8.50 8.50

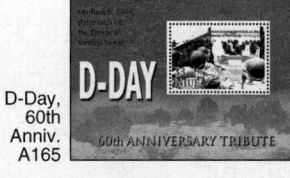

D-Day, 60th Anniv. A165

No. 790: a, Allied Air Forces begin bombing German coastal batteries. b, Allied naval guns pound Atlantic Wall. c, Paratroopers drop over Normandy. d, Allies advance and the Germans begin to surrender.
$3, Assault troops disembark on the shores of Normandy.

2004, Oct. 13   **Perf. 13¼x13½**
790 A165 $1.50 Sheet of 4, #a-d   8.50 8.50
Souvenir Sheet
791 A165 $3 multi   4.50 4.50

Locomotives, 200th Anniv. — A166

No. 792: a, 520 Class 4-8-4, Australia. b, FEF-2 Class 4-8-4, US. c, Royal Scot Class 4-6-0, Great Britain. d, A4 Class 4-6-2, Great Britain.
$3, Class GS-4 4-8-4, US.

2004, Oct. 13
792 A166 $1.50 Sheet of 4, #a-d   8.50 8.50
Souvenir Sheet
793 A166 $3 multi   4.50 4.50

Pope John Paul II (1920-2005) A167

2005, Dec. 13   **Litho.**   **Perf. 13¼**
794 A167 $2 multi   3.00 3.00
Printed in sheets of 4.

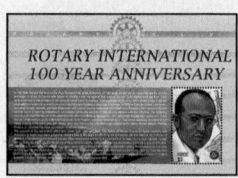

Rotary International, Cent. — A168

No. 795: a, Children. b, Paul P. Harris, Rotary founder. c, Carlo Ravizza, 1999-2000 Rotary International President.
$3, Dr. Jonas Salk, polio vaccine pioneer.

2005, Dec. 22
795 A168 $1.50 Sheet of 3, #a-c   6.50 6.50
Souvenir Sheet
796 A168 $3 multi   4.50 4.50

Pope Benedict XVI — A169

2005, Dec. 27
797 A169 $1.50 multi   2.25 2.25
Printed in sheets of 4.

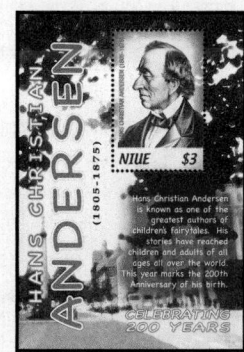

Hans Christian Andersen (1805-75), Author — A170

No. 798 — Andersen and country name and denomination in: a, Lilac. b, Ocher. c, Red.
$3, Andersen facing left.

2005, Dec. 27
798 A170 $1.50 Sheet of 3, #a-c   6.50 6.50
Souvenir Sheet
799 A170 $3 multi   4.50 4.50

World Cup Soccer Championships, 75th Anniv. — A171

No. 800: a, Frank Bauman. b, Marcus Babbel. c, Dietmar Hamann.

$3, Christian Worns.

2005, Dec. 27
800 A171 $1.50 Sheet of 3, #a-c   6.50 6.50

Souvenir Sheet
801 A171 $3 multi   4.50 4.50

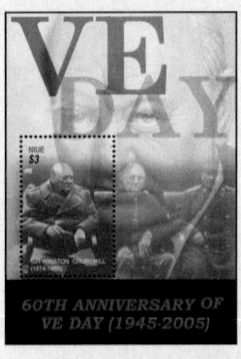

End of World War II, 60th Anniv. A172

No. 802, horiz.: a, Entertaining the troops in the Pacific. b, USS Argonaut sailors reading letters from home. c, Japan surrenders on USS Missouri. d, A toast to peace. e, Entertainment at sea. f, Welcoming peace.
No. 803: a, D-Day invasion, Normandy, France. b, Lt. Meyrick Clifton-James, double for Field Marshal Bernard Montgomery. c, RAF Hawker Typhoon over French coast. d, Allied war cemetery, St. Laurent-sur-Mer, France.
No. 804, $3, Sir Winston Churchill. No. 805, $3, Pres. Franklin D. Roosevelt.

2005, Dec. 27
802 A172   75c Sheet of 6, #a-f   6.75 6.75
803 A172 $1.25 Sheet of 4, #a-d   7.50 7.50

Souvenir Sheets
804-805 A172   Set of 2   9.00 9.00

Souvenir Sheets

National Basketball Association Players and Team Emblems — A173

No. 806, $4.50: a, LeBron James. b, Cleveland Cavaliers emblem.
No. 807, $4.50: a, Tim Duncan. b, San Antonio Spurs emblem.
No. 808, $4.50: a, Allen Iverson. b, Denver Nuggets emblem.
No. 809, $4.50: a, Kobe Bryant. b, Los Angeles Lakers emblem.
No. 810, $4.50: a, Tracy McGrady. b, Houston Rockets emblem.
No. 811, $4.50: a, Jermaine O'Neal. b, Indiana Pacers emblem.

Litho. & Embossed
2007, Feb. 4   *Imperf.*
Without Gum
Sheets of 2, #a-b
806-811 A173   Set of 6   77.50 77.50

Miniature Sheet

Elvis Presley (1935-77) — A174

No. 812 — Presley: a, With hands resting on guitar. b, In green shirt, playing guitar. c, In brown red shirt, playing guitar. d, Holding guitar by neck.

2007, Feb. 15   Litho.   Perf. 12¾
812 A174 $1.50 Sheet of 4, #a-d   8.50 8.50

Miniature Sheets

Space Achievements — A175

No. 813: a, Stardust probe at Kennedy Space Center. b, Stardust dust collector with aerogel. c, Stardust navigational camera. d, Stardust Whipple shield. e, Cometary and interstellar dust analyzer. f, Stardust and Comet Wild 2.
No. 814, horiz. — Artist's rendition of future projects: a, Astrobiology field laboratory. b, Deep-drill lander. c, Mars science laboratory. d, Phoenix lander.

2007, Feb. 15
813 A175 $1 Sheet of 6, #a-f   8.50 8.50
814 A175 $1.50 Sheet of 4, #a-d   8.50 8.50

Queen Elizabeth II, 80th Birthday (in 2006) A176

No. 815 — Dress color: a, Brown. b, Pink. c, Red. d, White.
$3, Purple.

2007, Feb. 15   Perf. 12¼x12
815 A176 $1.50 Sheet of 4, #a-d   8.50 8.50

Souvenir Sheet
Perf. 13¼
816 A176 $3 multi   4.50 4.50

Rembrandt (1606-69), Painter — A177

Designs: 75c, Life Study of a Young Man Pulling a Rope. $1.25, Self-portrait. $1.50, Joseph Telling His Dreams. $2, The Blindness of Tobit.
$3, Christ in the Storm on the Lake of Galilee.

2007, Feb. 15   Perf. 12¼x12
817-820 A177   Set of 4   8.25 8.25
Imperf
Size: 70x100mm
821 A177 $3 multi   4.75 4.75

Princess Diana (1961-97) — A178

No. 822 — Diana wearing: a, Purple dress. b, Tiara and black dress. c, Green dress, close-up. d, Purple dress, close-up. e, Tiara, close-up. f, Green dress.
$3, Diana with head on hand.

2007, May 3   Perf. 13½x13¼
822 A178 $1 Sheet of 6, #a-f   9.50 9.50

Souvenir Sheet
823 A178 $3 multi   4.75 4.75

Local Attractions, Flora and Fauna — A179

Designs: 20c, Palaha Cave. 70c, White pua flower. $1, Talava Natural Arch. $1.20, Avaiki Pool. $1.50, Coral rock spears. $2, Humpback whale. $3, Spinner dolphins.

2007, July 9   Litho.   Perf. 14x14¾
824 A179   20c multi   .35 .35
825 A179   70c multi   1.20 1.20
826 A179 $1 multi   1.60 1.60
827 A179 $1.20 multi   2.00 2.00
828 A179 $1.50 multi   2.40 2.40
829 A179 $2 multi   3.25 3.25
830 A179 $3 multi   4.75 4.75
    Nos. 824-830 (7)   15.55 15.55

Miniature Sheets

Concorde — A180

No. 831, $1: a, Concorde and hangar, blue tint. b, Concorde in air, normal tint. c, Concorde and hangar, red tint. d, Concorde in air, pink tint. e, Concorde and hangar, normal tint. f, Concorde in air, blue tint.
No. 832, $1: a, Concorde landing, yellow green frame. b, Concorde being towed, gray frame. c, Concorde landing, green gray frame. d, Concorde being towed, brown frame. e, Concorde landing, gray frame. f, Concorde being towed, blue frame.

2007, July 21   Perf. 13¼
Sheets of 6, #a-f
831-832 A180   Set of 2   19.00 19.00

Wedding of Queen Elizabeth II and Prince Philip, 60th Anniv. A181

No. 833, vert.: a, Queen and Prince, "N" of "Niue" and denomination over white area, parts of flag in faded area between country name and denomination. b, Queen, "N" of "Niue" and denomination over white and blue areas. c, Queen, flower buds in faded area between country name and denomination. d, Queen and Prince, "N" of "Niue" and denomination over gray area, parts of flag in faded area between country name and denomination. e, Queen and Prince, country name and denomination over solid gray area. f, Queen, country name and denomination over solid gray area.
$3, Queen and Prince.

2007, July 21   Perf. 13¼
833 A181 $1 Sheet of 6, #a-f   9.25 9.25

Souvenir Sheet
834 A181 $3 multi   4.25 4.25

Miniature Sheets

A182

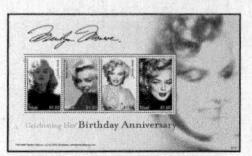

Marilyn Monroe (1926-62), Actress — A183

Various portraits.

2007, Aug. 21
835 A182 $1.50 Sheet of 4, #a-d   8.50 8.50
836 A183 $1.50 Sheet of 4, #a-d   8.50 8.50

Jamestown, Virginia, 400th Anniv. — A184

No. 837: a, Marriage of John Rolfe to Pocahontas. b, First settlers reach Jamestown. c, Tobacco plant. d, Capt. John Smith. e, Jamestown Tercentenary Monument. f, Map of Jamestown.
$3, Queen Elizabeth II and Prince Philip at Jamestown.

2007, Aug. 21
837 A184 $1 Sheet of 6, #a-f   9.00 9.00

Souvenir Sheet
838 A184 $3 multi   4.50 4.50

Pope Benedict XVI — A185

2007, Dec. 3   Litho.   Perf. 13¼
839 A185   70c multi   1.25 1.25
    Printed in sheets of 8.

Miniature Sheet

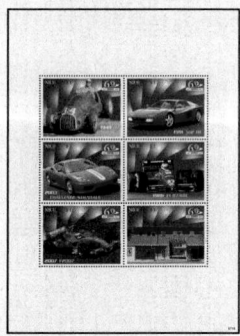

Ferrari Automobiles, 60th Anniv. — A186

No. 840: a, 1949 166 FL. b, 1991 512 TR. c, 2003 Challenge Stradale. d, 1988 F1 87/88C. e, 2007 F2007. f, Building with Ferrari sign.

2007, Dec. 10
840 A186 $1 Sheet of 6, #a-f   10.50 10.50

Tourism — A187

Designs: 10c, Coconut palm. 20c, Tropical sunset. 30c, Humpback whale. 50c, Rainbow over rainforest. $1, Hio Beach. $1.20, Talava Arches. $1.40, Limu Pools. $1.70, Limestone caves. $2, Snorkeling in Limu Pools. $3, Panoramic coastline. $5, Liku Caves.

Perf. 13½x13¼
2009, Sept. 14   Litho.
841 A187   10c multi   .25 .25
842 A187   20c multi   .30 .30
843 A187   30c multi   .45 .45
844 A187   50c multi   .75 .75
845 A187 $1 multi   1.50 1.50
846 A187 $1.20 multi   1.75 1.75
    a.   Miniature sheet of 6, #841-846, perf. 14   5.00 5.00
847 A187 $1.40 multi   2.00 2.00
848 A187 $1.70 multi   2.50 2.50
849 A187 $2 multi   3.00 3.00
850 A187 $3 multi   4.50 4.50

851	A187	$5 multi	7.25	7.25
a.	Miniature sheet of 5, #847-851, perf. 14		19.50	19.50
	Nos. 841-851 (11)		24.25	24.25

Christmas — A188

Stained-glass window depicting: 30c, Man facing right, Ekalesia Millennium Hall. 80c, Dove, Lakepa Ekalesia Church. $1.20, Chalice and bread, Lakepa Ekalesia Church. $1.40, Man facing left, Ekalesia Millennium Hall.

Perf. 13¼x13½

2009, Nov. 25   **Litho.**
| 852-855 | A188 | Set of 4 | 5.50 | 5.50 |
| 855a | | Souvenir sheet, #852-855 | 5.50 | 5.50 |

Butterflies A189

Designs: $1.40, Hypolimnas bolina. $1.70, Junonia villida, vert. (22x26mm). $2.40, Hypolimnas antilope.

2010, July 7   **Litho.**   **Perf. 14**
| 856-858 | A189 | Set of 3 | 8.00 | 8.00 |
| 858a | | Souvenir sheet of 3, #856-858 | 8.00 | 8.00 |

Christmas — A190

Designs: a, Annunciation. b, Journey to Bethlehem. c, Nativity. d, Adoration of the Shepherds.

2010, Oct. 20   **Perf. 13¼x13½**
859		Horiz. strip of 4	12.00	12.00
a.	A190 30c multicolored		.45	.45
b.	A190 $1.40 multicolored		2.10	2.10
c.	A190 $2 multicolored		3.00	3.00
d.	A190 $4 multicolored		6.00	6.00

Whales — A191

Designs: 80c, Whale's flukes. $1.20, Two whales raising heads out of water. $1.40, Calf breaching surface. $2, Mother and calf playing.

2010, Nov. 17   **Litho.**   **Perf. 14**
| 860-863 | A191 | Set of 4 | 8.50 | 8.50 |
| 863a | | Souvenir sheet, #860-863 | 8.50 | 8.50 |

Wedding of Prince William and Catherine Middleton — A192

No. 864: a, $2.40, Catherine Middleton. b, $3.40, Prince William.

2011, Mar. 23
| 864 | A192 | Horiz. pair, #a-b | 9.25 | 9.25 |
| c. | | Souvenir sheet, #864a-864b | 9.25 | 9.25 |

Birds — A193

Designs: $1.70, Aplonis tabuensis. $2, Lalage maculosa, vert. (25x30mm). $2.40, Ptilinopus porphyraceus.

2011, July 6
| 865-867 | A193 | Set of 3 | 10.50 | 10.50 |
| 867a | | Souvenir sheet of 3, #865-867 | | 10.50 | 10.50 |

Christmas — A194

Designs: 30c, Pacific sunset. $1.40, Matapa Chasm. $2, Coconut palms. $4, Centennial Church, Alofi.

2011, Nov. 16   **Perf. 13¼x13½**
| 868-871 | A194 | Set of 4 | 12.00 | 12.00 |
| 871a | | Souvenir sheet of 4, #868-871 | | 12.00 | 12.00 |

Shells — A195

Designs: $1.20, Map cowrie. $1.40, Geography cone. $1.70, Partridge tun. $2, Tiger cowrie.

2012, Apr. 11   **Perf. 13½x13¼**
| 872-875 | A195 | Set of 4 | 10.50 | 10.50 |
| 875a | | Souvenir sheet of 4, #872-875 | | 10.50 | 10.50 |

Reign of Queen Elizabeth II, 60th Anniv. — A196

Hibiscus flowers and photograph of Queen Elizabeth II from: $2.40, 1953. $3.40, 2012.

2012, May 23   **Perf. 13¼x13½**
876-877	A196	Set of 2	9.00	9.00
877a		Souvenir sheet of 2, #876-877		9.00	9.00
877b		Horiz. pair, #876-877		9.00	9.00

Worldwide Fund For Nature (WWF) — A197

Various depictions of Giant sea fan: $1.20, $1.40, $1.70, $2.

2012, Sept. 5   **Perf. 13½x13¼**
| 878-881 | A197 | Set of 4 | 10.50 | 10.50 |
| 881a | | Souvenir sheet of 4, #878-881 | | 10.50 | 10.50 |

Christmas — A198

Designs: 30c, Angel and infant Jesus. $1.40, Holy Family. $2, Magi. $4, Shepherds.

2012, Nov. 21
| 882-885 | A198 | Set of 4 | 13.00 | 13.00 |

Niue Blue Butterfly — A199

Designs: $1.20, Male underside. $1.40, Male upperside. $1.70, Female underside. $2, Female upperside.

2013, Apr. 10   **Perf. 13½**
| 886-889 | A199 | Set of 4 | 10.50 | 10.50 |
| 889a | | Souvenir sheet of 4, #886-889 | | 10.50 | 10.50 |

Coronation of Queen Elizabeth II, 60th Anniv. — A200

Designs: $2.40, Queen Elizabeth II. $3.40, Queen Elizabeth II, Prince Philip, Princess Margaret, Queen Mother.

2013, May 8   **Perf. 13¼x13½**
| 890-891 | A200 | Set of 2 | 9.25 | 9.25 |
| 891a | | Souvenir sheet of 2, #890-891 | | 9.25 | 9.25 |

Christmas — A201

Designs: 30c, Dove. $1.40, Angel. $2, Star of Bethlehem. $4, Bells.

Perf. 13¼x13¾

2013, Nov. 20   **Litho.**
| 892-895 | A201 | Set of 4 | 13.00 | 13.00 |
| 895a | | Souvenir sheet of 4, #892-895 | | 13.00 | 13.00 |

Traditional Dress — A202

Designs: 30c, Pulou (hat). $1.40, Pipi (belt). $2, Tiputa (poncho). $4, Patutiti (skirt).

2014, Apr. 23   **Litho.**   **Perf. 13½x13¼**
| 896-899 | A202 | Set of 4 | 13.50 | 13.50 |
| 899a | | Souvenir sheet of 4 #896-899 | | 13.50 | 13.50 |

Fish — A203

Designs: 30c, Whitemouth moray. $1.40, Orangefin anemonefish. $2, Fire dartfish. $4, Longnose butterflyfish.

Perf. 13½x13¼

2014, June 18   **Litho.**
| 900-903 | A203 | Set of 4 #900-903 | 13.50 | 13.50 |
| 903a | | Souvenir sheet of 4 #900-903 | | 13.50 | 13.50 |

Island Views A204

Designs: 20c, Talava Arches. 30c, Mutalau. $1, Avaiki Caves. $1.20, Lakepa Village Church. $1.40, Golf course. $1.70, Huvalu Forest. $2, Tepa Point. $4, Togo Chasm.

2014, Oct. 18   **Litho.**   **Perf. 14x14¼**
904	A204	20c multi	.35	.35
905	A204	30c multi	.50	.50
906	A204	$1 multi	1.60	1.60
907	A204	$1.20 multi	1.90	1.90
908	A204	$1.40 multi	2.25	2.25

909	A204	$1.70 multi	2.75	2.75
910	A204	$2 multi	3.25	3.25
911	A204	$4 multi	6.25	6.25
		Nos. 904-911 (8)	18.85	18.85

Christmas — A205

Various Christmas ornaments in: 30c Blue. $1.40, Red. $2, Green. $4, Purple.

Perf. 13¼x13½

2014, Dec. 10   **Litho.**
| 912-915 | A205 | Set of 4 | 12.00 | 12.00 |
| 915a | | Souvenir sheet of 4, #912-915 | | 12.00 | 12.00 |

Haipo (Tapa Cloths) — A206

Various haipo designs: 30c, $1.40, $2, $4.

2015, Apr. 7   **Litho.**   **Perf. 13½**
| 916-919 | A206 | Set of 4 | 12.00 | 12.00 |
| 919a | | Souvenir sheet of 4, #916-919 | | 12.00 | 12.00 |

Flora — A207

Designs: 30c, Hibiscus tiliaceus. $1.40, Fagraea Berteroana. $2, Alphitonia zizyphoides. $4, Cordyline fruticosa.

2015, June 3   **Litho.**   **Perf. 13½**
| 920-923 | A207 | Set of 4 | 10.50 | 10.50 |
| 923a | | Souvenir sheet of 4, #920-923 | | 10.50 | 10.50 |

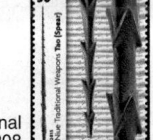

Traditional Weapons — A208

Designs: 30c, Spear. $1.40, Club. $3, Spear, diff. $4, Club, diff.

2015, Aug. 5   **Litho.**   **Perf. 13½**
| 924-927 | A208 | Set of 4 | 11.00 | 11.00 |
| 927a | | Souvenir sheet of 4, #924-927 | | 11.00 | 11.00 |

Miniature Sheet

World War I, Cent. A209

No. 928: a, 20c, Life in Niue, pre-war. b, 30c, Soldiers at Narrow Neck Camp, Auckland. c, $1, Troops departing for war from Auckland. d, $1.20, Badge of New Zealand Pioneer Battalion, map of Egypt. e, $1.40, Trench in Armentières, France. f, $1.70, New Zealand Convalescent Hospital, Hornchurch, England. g, $2, Soldiers and nurses recovering in Auckland. h, $4, War Memorial, Niue.

2015, Oct. 13   **Litho.**   **Perf. 14x14½**
| 928 | A209 | Sheet of 8, #a-h | 16.00 | 16.00 |

Christmas — A210

Carols: 30c, Silent Night. $1.40, Joy to the World. $2, Away in the Manger. $4, Deck the Halls.

2015, Nov. 25   Litho.   Perf. 14½
929-932 A210   Set of 4   10.50 10.50
932a   Souvenir sheet of 4, #929-
                932   10.50 10.50

Queen Elizabeth II,
90th Birthday — A211

Queen Elizabeth II: $2.40, As young child. $3.40, In 2016.

2016, May 4   Litho.   Perf. 13¼x13½
933-934 A211   Set of 2   8.00 8.00
934a   Souvenir sheet of 2, #933-
                934   8.00 8.00

Humpback
Whale — A212

Designs: 30c, Whale with flukes above water. $1.40, Two whales exhaling. $2, Whale with head above water. $4, Whale breaching surface of water.

2016, Aug. 3   Litho.   Perf. 14x14¼
935-938 A212   Set of 4   11.50 11.50
938a   Souvenir sheet of 4,
                #935-938   11.50 11.50

Language
Week — A213

Niuean phrases for: 30c, "Hello." $1.40, "How are you?" $2, "Nice to meet you." $4, "Goodbye."

2016, Oct. 5   Litho.   Perf. 13¼x13½
939-942 A213   Set of 4   11.50 11.50
942a   Souvenir sheet of 4,
                #939-942   11.50 11.50

Christmas — A214

Winning children's art in stamp design contest: 30c, Golden grouper, by Bailey Pasisi. $1.40, Family arriving for Christmas feast, by Bentley Poihenga. $2, Gift box, by Iva Tanevesi. $4, Family at Christmas, by Flornie R. Malinao.

2016, Dec. 7   Litho.   Perf. 14x14¼
943-946 A214   Set of 4   11.00 11.00
946a   Souvenir sheet of 4,
                #943-946   11.00 11.00

Awarding of Knight
Companion of the New
Zealand Order of Merit
to Niue Premier Sir
Toke Talagi — A215

Designs: $2.40, Talagi and Niue flag. $3.40, Talagi.

2017, Mar. 21   Litho.   Perf. 13½
947-948 A215   Set of 2   8.25 8.25

Reptiles — A216

Designs: 30c, Mourning gecko. $1.40, Flat-tail sea snake. $2, Snake-eyed skink. $4, Pacific slender-toed gecko.

2017, Apr. 5   Litho.   Perf. 13½
949-952 A216   Set of 4   11.00 11.00
952a   Souvenir sheet of 4,
                #949-952   11.00 11.00

Walkways — A217

Designs: 30c, Matapa Chasm. $1.40, Avaiki Cave. $2, Anapala Chasm. $4, Talava Arches.

2017, July 12   Litho.   Perf. 13½
953-956 A217   Set of 4   11.50 11.50
956a   Souvenir sheet of 4,
                #953-956   11.50 11.50

Butterflyfish
A218

Designs: 30c, Reticulate butterflyfish. $1.40, Bennett's butterflyfish. $2, Lined butterflyfish. $4, Acropora butterflyfish.

2017, Sept. 20   Litho.   Perf. 13½
957-960 A218   Set of 4   11.00 11.00
960a   Souvenir sheet of 4,
                #957-960   11.00 11.00

70th Wedding
Anniversary of Queen
Elizabeth II and Prince
Philip — A219

Photographs of Queen Elizabeth II and Prince Philip: 30c, On wedding day, 1947. $1.40, With their children, 1960. $2, On vacation, 1972. $4, With family of Duke and Duchess of Cambridge at Trooping the Colors ceremony, 2017.

2017, Nov. 20   Litho.   Perf. 13¼
961-964 A219   Set of 4   10.50 10.50
964a   Souvenir sheet of 4,
                #961-964   10.50 10.50

Christmas — A220

Flowers: 30c, Frangipani. $1.40, Guava. $2, Hibiscus. $4, Papaya.

2017, Dec. 6   Litho.   Perf. 14x14¼
965-968 A220   Set of 4   11.00 11.00
968a   Souvenir sheet of 4,
                #965-968   11.00 11.00

Fruit Trees — A221

Designs: 30c, Lime. $1.40, Mango. $2, Avocado. $4, Coconut.

2018, Mar. 7   Litho.   Perf. 13¼x13½
969-972 A221   Set of 4   11.50 11.50
972a   Souvenir sheet of 4,
                #969-972   11.50 11.50

Wedding of Prince
Harry and Meghan
Markle — A222

Couple: 30c, Walking down steps. $1.40, Looking at each other. $2, Kissing on wedding day. $4, Holding hands on wedding day.

2018, May 21   Litho.   Perf. 13¼x13½
973-976 A222   Set of 4   11.00 11.00
976a   Souvenir sheet of 4,
                #973-976   11.00 11.00

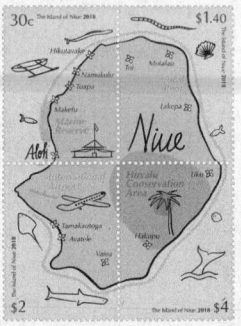

Map of
Niue
A223

No. 977 — Map of Niue highlighting: a, 30c, Marine Reserve. b, $1.40, Coral reef. c, $2, International Airport. d, $4, Huvalu Conservation Area.

2018, Sept. 5   Litho.   Perf. 13¼x13½
977 A223   Block of 4, #a-d   10.50 10.50
e.   Souvenir sheet of 4, #977a-
                977d   10.50 10.50

Items From Taoga
Niue Museum — A224

Designs: 30c, Woven tray. $1.40, Walking stick. $2, Close combat club. $4, Arrowroot grater.

2018, Oct. 19   Litho.   Perf. 13¼x13½
978-981 A224   Set of 4   10.50 10.50
981a   Souvenir sheet of 4,
                #978-981   10.50 10.50

Paintings by John
Pule — A225

Paintings: 30c, Pia. $1.40, Hafata. $2, First Time Outside. $4, Kavaka.

2019, June 5   Litho.   Perf. 14x14¼
982-985 A225   Set of 4   10.50 10.50
985a   Souvenir sheet of 4,
                #982-985   10.50 10.50

First Man on the
Moon, 50th
Anniv. — A226

Designs: 30c, Apollo 11 on launchpad. $1.40, Launch of Apollo 11. $2, Astronaut on Moon. $4, Apollo 11 capsule in ocean.

2019, July 5   Litho.   Perf. 13¼x13½
986-989 A226   Set of 4   10.00 10.00
989a   Souvenir sheet of 4,
                #986-989   10.00 10.00

Queen Victoria
(1819-1901) — A227

Roses and various depictions of Queen Victoria: 30c, $1.40, $2, $4.

2019, Oct. 16   Litho.   Perf. 14x14½
990-993 A227   Set of 4   10.00 10.00
993a   Souvenir sheet of 4,
                #990-993   10.00 10.00

Christmas — A228

Star of Bethlehem and: 30c, Angel, Mary and infant Jesus. $1.40, Magus. $2, Angel and shepherd. $4, Magus, shepherd, Mary and infant Jesus.

2019, Dec. 4   Litho.   Perf. 13¼x13½
994-997 A228   Set of 4   10.50 10.50
997a   Souvenir sheet of 4,
                #994-997   10.50 10.50

Woven Items — A229

Designs: 30c, Potu. $1.40, Kato with cover and straps. $2, Kato with strap. $4, Iliili.

2020, Apr. 16   Litho.   Perf. 13¼x13½
998-1001 A229   Set of 4   9.50 9.50
1001a   Souvenir sheet of 4, #998-
                1001   9.50 9.50

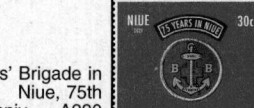

Boys' Brigade in
Niue, 75th
Anniv. — A230

Designs: 30c, Brigade emblem. $1.40, Emblem and 38 people. $2, Emblem and 13 people. $4, Emblem and 49 people.

2021, Apr. 7   Litho.   Perf. 13½
1002-1005 A230 Set of 4   11.00 11.00
1005a   Souvenir sheet of 4,
                #1002-1005   11.00 11.00

SEMI-POSTAL STAMPS

Catalogue values for unused stamps in this section are for Never Hinged items.

Easter Type of 1978
Souvenir Sheets

Designs: No. B1, Descent from the Cross, by Caravaggio. No. B2, Burial of Christ, by Bellini. Sheets show paintings from which stamp designs were taken.

1978, Mar. 15   Photo.   Perf. 13½
B1 A61 70c + 5c multi   1.00 1.00
B2 A61 70c + 5c multi   1.00 1.00

Surtax was for school children in Niue.

Christmas Type of 1978
Souvenir Sheets

1978, Nov. 30   Photo.   Perf. 13
B3	A63	60c + 5c like #232	.90	.90
B4	A63	60c + 5c like #233	.90	.90
B5	A63	60c + 5c like #234	.90	.90
	Nos. B3-B5 (3)		2.70	2.70

Surtax was for school children of Niue. The sheets show paintings from which designs of stamps were taken.

Easter Type of 1979
Souvenir Sheets

1979, Apr. 2
B6	A64	70c + 5c like #235	1.10	1.10
B7	A64	70c + 5c like #236	1.10	1.10

Surtax was for school children of Niue. The sheets show altarpiece from which designs of stamps were taken.

IYC Type of 1979
Souvenir Sheets

1979, May 31   Photo.   Perf. 13
B8	A65	70c + 5c like #237	.85	.85
B9	A65	70c + 5c like #238	.85	.85
B10	A65	70c + 5c like #239	.85	.85
B11	A65	70c + 5c like #240	.85	.85
	Nos. B8-B11 (4)		3.40	3.40

Sheets show paintings from which designs of stamps were taken.

Christmas Type of 1979
Souvenir Sheets

1979, Nov. 29   Photo.   Perf. 13
B12	A70	85c + 5c like #258	.80	.80
B13	A70	85c + 5c like #259	.80	.80
B14	A70	85c + 5c like #260	.80	.80
B15	A70	85c + 5c like #261	.80	.80
	Nos. B12-B15 (4)		3.20	3.20

Multicolored margins show entire paintings.

Nos. 241-245, 251-254, 255-257, 258-261 Srchd. in Black (2 lines) or Silver (3 lines)

1980, Jan. 25   Photo.   Perf. 14, 13½
B16	A66	20c + 2c Pair, #a-b	.55	.55
B18	A68	20c + 2c multi (S)	.30	.30
B19	A70	20c + 2c multi (S)	.30	.30
B20	A70	25c + 2c multi (S)	.40	.40
B21	A66	30c + 2c Pair, #a-b	.80	.80
B23	A68	30c + 2c multi (S)	.45	.45
B24	A69	30c+ 2c multi (S)	.45	.45
B25	A70	30c + 2c multi (S)	.45	.45
B26	A66	35c + 2c Pair, #a-b	1.00	1.00
B28	A68	35c + 2c multi (S)	.55	.55
B29	A69	35c + 2c multi (S)	.55	.55
B30	A66	50c + 2c Pair, #a-b	1.20	1.20
B32	A70	50c + 2c multi (S)	.65	.65
B33	A66	60c + 2c Pair, #a-b	1.40	1.40
B35	A69	60c + 2c multi (S)	.80	.80
B36	A68	75c + 2c multi (S)	1.00	1.00
	Nos. B16-B36 (16)		10.85	10.85

Easter Type of 1980
Souvenir Sheets

1980, Apr. 2   Photo.   Perf. 13½
B37		Sheet of 3	1.05	1.05
a.	A71	25c + 2c like #262	.30	.30
b.	A71	30c + 2c like #263	.35	.35
c.	A71	35c + 2c like #264	.40	.40

1980, Apr. 2
B38	A71	85c + 5c like #262	.75	.75
B39	A71	85c + 5c like #263	.75	.75
B40	A71	85c + 5c like #264	.75	.75
	Nos. B38-B40 (3)		2.25	2.25

Surtax was for hurricane relief.

No. 245c Overprinted and Surcharged
Souvenir Sheet

1980, Aug. 22   Photo.   Perf. 14
B41		Sheet of 10	5.00	5.00
a.	A66	20c + 2c pair	.50	.50
b.	A66	30c + 2c pair	.65	.65
c.	A66	35c + 2c pair	.80	.80
d.	A66	50c + 2c pair	1.25	1.25
e.	A66	60c + 2c pair	1.60	1.60

ZEAPEX '80, New Zealand Intl. Stamp Exhib., Auckland, Aug. 23-31.

Nos. 293-296 Surcharged in Black
Souvenir Sheet

1980, Oct. 30   Photo.   Perf. 14
B42	Sheet of 8, #a.-h.	2.50	2.50

22nd Summer Olympic Games, Moscow, July 19-Aug. 3.

Christmas Type of 1980
Souvenir Sheets

1980, Nov. 28   Photo.   Perf. 13½x13
B43	A76	80c + 5c like #301	.75	.75
B44	A76	80c + 5c like #302	.75	.75
B45	A76	80c + 5c like #303	.75	.75
B46	A76	80c + 5c like #304	.75	.75
	Nos. B43-B46 (4)		3.00	3.00

Nos. B43-B46 each contain one 31x39mm stamp.

Easter Type of 1981
Souvenir Sheets

1981, Apr. 10   Photo.   Perf. 13½
B47		Sheet of 3	1.75	1.75
a.	A78	35c + 2c like #337	.40	.40
b.	A78	50c + 2c like #338	.50	.50
c.	A78	60c + 2c like #339	.60	.60
B48	A78	80c + 5c like #337	.75	.75
B49	A78	80c + 5c like #338	.75	.75
B50	A78	80c + 5c like #339	.75	.75
	Nos. B47-B50 (4)		4.00	4.00

Soccer Type of 1981

1981, Oct. 16   Photo.   Perf. 13
B51	A80	Sheet of 9	3.25	3.25

#B51 contains #343-345 each with 3c surtax.

Nos. 340-342a Surcharged

1981, Nov. 3   Photo.   Perf. 14
B52	A79	75c + 5c like #340	1.00	1.00
B53	A79	95c + 5c like #341	1.25	1.25
B54	A79	$1.20 + 5c like #342	1.50	1.50
	Nos. B52-B54 (3)		3.75	3.75

Souvenir Sheet
B55		Sheet of 3	4.50	4.50
a.	A79	75c + 10c like #340	1.20	1.20
b.	A79	95c + 10c like #341	1.40	1.40
c.	A79	$1.20 + 10c like #342	1.75	1.75

Intl. Year of the Disabled. Surtax was for disabled.

Nos. 530-535 Surcharged in Black on Silver

1986, Nov. 21   Litho.   Perf. 14
B56	A105	80c + 10c multi	2.75	2.75
B57	A105	$1.15 + 10c multi	3.75	3.75
B58	A105	$1.80 + 10c multi	5.50	5.50
B59	A105	$2.60 + 10c multi	8.00	8.00
	Nos. B56-B59 (4)		20.00	20.00

Souvenir Sheets
Perf. 13½
B60		Sheet of 4	18.00	18.00
a.-d.	A105	$1.50 + 10c on #534a-534d	4.50	4.50

Perf. 14½x13½
B61	A105	$7.50 + 10c	18.00	18.00

No. B60 ovptd. "FIRST VISIT OF A POPE TO SOUTH PACIFIC" and "HIS HOLINESS POPE JOHN PAUL II" on margin. No. B61 ovptd. on margin only "Visit of Pope John Paul II, Nov 21-24 1986 / First Papal Visit to the South Pacific."

Souvenir Sheets

Aupex '97 Stamp Exhibition — SP1

1997, June 9   Litho.   Perf. 14x15
B62	SP1	$2 +20c like #1	3.75	3.75

Perf. 14½x15
B63	SP1	$2 +20c like #34	3.25	3.25

No. B63 contains one 31x60mm stamp.

AIR POST STAMPS

Catalogue values for unused stamps in this section are for Never Hinged items.

Type of 1977

Designs: 15c, Preparing ground for taro. 20c, Banana harvest. 23c, Bush plantation. 50c, Canoe fishing. 90c, Reef fishing. $1.35, Preparing ground for taro. $2.10, Shellfish gathering. $2.60, Luku harvest.

1979   Litho.   Perf. 14
C1	A54	15c gold & multi	.30	.25
C2	A54	20c gold & multi	.30	.25
C3	A54	23c gold & multi	.30	.30
C4	A54	50c gold & multi	.45	.45
C5	A54	90c gold & multi	.70	.70
C6	A54	$1.35 gold & multi	1.10	1.10
C7	A54	$2.10 gold & multi	1.75	1.75
C8	A54	$2.60 gold & multi	2.25	2.25
C9	A54	$5.10 like #187	4.25	4.25
C10	A54	$6.35 like #188	5.50	5.50
	Nos. C1-C10 (10)		16.90	16.80

Issue dates: Nos. C1-C5, Feb. 26. Nos. C6-C8, Mar. 30. C9-C10, May 28.

OFFICIAL STAMPS

Catalogue values for unused stamps in this section are for Never Hinged items.

Nos. 417-430, 332-334, 431-431A Ovptd. in Metallic Blue or Gold

Perf. 13½, 13½x13, 13x13½, 13
1985-87   Photo.
O1	A89	12c multi	.30	.25
O2	A89	25c multi	.30	.25
O3	A89	30c multi	.30	.25
O4	A89	35c multi	.30	.25
O5	A89	40c multi	.30	.30
O6	A89	52c multi	.40	.40
O7	A89	58c multi	.50	.50
O8	A89	70c multi	.55	.55
O9	A89	83c multi	.65	.65
O10	A89	$1.05 multi	.75	.75
O11	A90	$1.75 multi	1.50	1.50
O12	A90	$2.30 multi	2.50	2.50
O13	A90	$3.90 multi	4.75	4.75
O14	A77a	$4 multi (G)	4.50	4.50
O15	A90	$5 multi	5.50	5.50
O16	A77a	$6 multi ('87) (G)	10.00	10.00
O17	A90	$6.60 multi ('86)	7.00	7.00
O18	A90	$8.30 multi ('86)	9.00	9.00
O19	A77a	$10 multi ('87) (G)	16.00	16.00
	Nos. O1-O19 (19)		65.10	64.90

Nos. 604-613 Ovptd. in Gold

1993-94   Litho.   Perf. 14x13½
O20	A118	20c multicolored	.30	.30
O21	A118	50c multicolored	.55	.55
O22	A118	70c multicolored	.80	.80
O23	A118	$1 multicolored	1.25	1.25
O24	A118	$1.50 multicolored	2.00	2.00
O25	A118	$2 multicolored	3.50	3.50
O26	A118	$3 multicolored	4.25	4.25
O27	A118	$5 multicolored	6.50	6.50
O28	A118	$7 multicolored	9.00	9.00
O29	A118	$10 multicolored	13.00	13.00
O30	A118	$15 multicolored	20.00	20.00
	Nos. O20-O30 (11)		61.15	61.15

Nos. O20-O30 were not sold unused to local customers.

Issued: 20c-$2, 12/10/93; $3, $5, 4/27/94; $7, $10, 9/1/94; $15, 9/30/94.

NORFOLK ISLAND

'nor-fək 'ī-lənd

LOCATION — Island in the south Pacific Ocean, 900 miles east of Australia
GOVT. — Territory of Australia
AREA — 13½ sq. mi.
POP. — 1,905 (1999 est.)

12 Pence = 1 Shilling
100 Cents = 1 Dollar (1966)

Catalogue values for all unused stamps in this country are for Never Hinged items.

Watermark

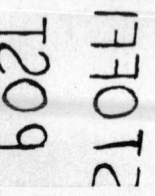

Wmk. 380 — "POST OFFICE"

View of Ball Bay — A1

Unwmk.
1947, June 10　Engr.　Perf. 14
On Toned Paper

1	A1	½p deep orange	1.35	.40
2	A1	1p violet	.80	.40
3	A1	1½p bright green	.80	.60
4	A1	2p red violet	.90	.50
5	A1	2½p red	1.25	.50
6	A1	3p brown orange	1.10	.70
7	A1	4p rose lake	2.75	.70
8	A1	5½p slate	1.10	.70
9	A1	6p sepia	1.10	1.10
10	A1	9p lilac rose	2.00	1.25
11	A1	1sh gray green	1.10	1.10
12	A1	2sh olive bister	2.00	2.75
		Nos. 1-12 (12)	16.25	10.70

Nos. 1-4 were reprinted in 1956-59 on white paper. Values, set: never hinged $125; used $200.
See Nos. 23-24.
The ½p, 1p, 1½p, 6p, and 1sh exist perf. 11 in different colors. These were not officially issued.

Warder's Tower A2

Airfield A3

Designs: 7½p, First Governor's Residence. 8½p, Barracks entrance. 10p, Salt House. 5sh, Bloody Bridge.

1953, June 10　　　Perf. 14½

13	A2	3½p rose brown	1.40	2.75
14	A3	6½p dark green	3.25	3.50
15	A3	7½p deep ultra	2.00	3.50
16	A2	8½p chocolate	2.40	4.75
17	A2	10p rose lilac	1.40	.75
18	A3	5sh dark brown	47.50	14.50
		Nos. 13-18 (6)	57.95	29.75

See Nos. 35, 40. For surcharges see Nos. 21-22, 27. For types surcharged see Nos. 26, 28.

Original Norfolk Seal and First Settlers — A4

1956, June 8

19	A4	3p bluish green	2.00	1.40
20	A4	2sh violet	3.75	2.50

Cent. of the landing of the Pitcairn Islanders on Norfolk Island.

Two types of No. 20 exist on alternating stamps in each row: with and without a dot in the lower right corner.

Nos. 15 and 16 Surcharged with New Value and Bars
1958, July 1

21	A3	7p on 7½p dp ultra	1.75	1.10
22	A2	8p on 8½p choc	2.25	1.40

Ball Bay Type of 1947
1959, July 6　Engr.　Perf. 14

23	A1	3p green	12.50	7.75
24	A1	2sh dark blue	13.00	8.25

A5

Australia #332 Surcharged in Red
1959, Dec. 7

25	A5	5p on 4p dk gray blue	1.75	1.25

No. 14 and Types of 1953 Surcharged with New Values and Bars
1960, Sept. 26　　　Perf. 14½

26	A2	1sh1p on 3½p dk bl	5.25	3.25
27	A3	2sh5p on 6½p dk grn	7.00	4.75
28	A3	2sh8p on 7½p dk brn	9.25	6.50
		Nos. 26-28 (3)	21.50	14.50

Types of 1953 and

Island Hibiscus A6

Fairy Tern A7

Red-Tailed Tropic Bird — A8

Designs: 2p, Lagunaria patersonii (flowers). 5p, Lantana. 8p, Red hibiscus. 9p, Cereus and Fringed hibiscus. 2sh, Providence petrel, vert. 2sh5p, Passion flower. 2sh8p, Rose apple. 5sh, Bloody Bridge.

1960-62　Unwmk.　Engr.　Perf. 14½

29	A6	1p blue green	.25	.25
30	A6	2p gray grn & brt pink	.30	.25
31	A7	3p brt green ('61)	1.00	.25
32	A6	5p lilac	.85	.25
33	A6	8p vermilion	1.20	.40
34	A6	9p ultramarine	1.20	.40
35	A2	10p pale pur & brn ('61)	3.75	.80
36	A6	1sh1p dark red ('61)	1.20	.30
37	A6	2sh sepia ('61)	6.00	.80
38	A6	2sh5p dk purple ('62)	1.50	.35
39	A6	2sh8p green & sal ('62)	3.50	.45
40	A3	5sh green & gray ('61)	4.50	.60

Perf. 14½x14

41	A8	10sh green ('61)	40.00	30.00
		Nos. 29-41 (13)	65.25	35.10

See #585-586. For surcharges see #71-82.

Map of Norfolk Island — A9

1960, Oct. 24　Engr.　Perf. 14

42	A9	2sh8p rose violet	19.00	15.00

Introduction of local government for Norfolk Island.

Open Bible and Candle — A9a

1960, Nov. 21　　　Perf. 14½

43	A9a	5p bright lilac rose	4.00	4.00

Christmas.

Page from Book of Hours, 15th Century — A9b

1961, Nov. 20　　　Perf. 14½x14

44	A9b	5p slate blue	2.00	2.00

Nos. 43-44 were issued to mark the beginning and the end of the 350th anniversary year of the publication of the King James translation of the Bible.

Madonna and Child — A9c

1962, Nov. 19　　　Perf. 14½

45	A9c	5p blue	2.00	2.00

Christmas.

Overlooking Kingston A10

Dreamfish A11

Designs: 6p, Tweed trousers (fish). 8p, Kingston scene. 9p, "The Arches." 10p, Slaughter Bay. 11p, Trumpeter fish. 1sh, Po'ov (wrasse). 1sh6p, Queensland grouper. 2sh3p, Ophie (carangidae).

Perf. 14½x14

			Unwmk.	Photo.
1962-64				
49	A10	5p multi ('64)	.45	.35
50	A11	6p multi	.60	.45
51	A10	8p multi ('64)	.75	.50
52	A10	9p multi ('64)	1.00	.75
53	A10	10p multi ('64)	1.25	.95
54	A11	11p multi ('63)	1.75	.95
55	A11	1sh olive, bl & pink	2.00	1.30
57	A11	1sh3p bl, mar & grn ('63)	2.25	1.60
58	A11	1sh6p bl, brn & lil ('63)	2.50	2.00
60	A11	2sh3p dl bl, yel & red ('63)	3.00	2.25
		Nos. 49-60 (10)	15.55	11.10

Star of Bethlehem — A11a

1963, Nov. 11　Engr.　Perf. 14½

65	A11a	5p vermilion	1.50	1.25

Christmas.

Symbolic Pine Tree — A12

1964, July 1　Photo.　Perf. 13½x13

66	A12	5p orange, blk & red	1.10	.85
67	A12	8p gray green, blk & red	1.40	1.15

50th anniv. of Norfolk Island as an Australian Territory.

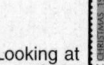

Child Looking at Nativity Scene — A12a

1964, Nov. 9　　　Perf. 13½

68	A12a	5p multicolored	1.40	1.20

Christmas.

"Simpson and His Donkey" by Wallace Anderson — A12b

1965, Apr. 14　Photo.　Perf. 13½x13

69	A12b	5p brt grn, sepia & blk	.65	.55

ANZAC issue. See note after Australia No. 387.

Nativity — A12c

1965, Oct. 25　Unwmk.　Perf. 13½

70	A12c	5p gold, blk, ultra & redsh brn	.45	.45

Christmas. No. 70 is luminescent. See note after Australia No. 331.

Nos. 29-33 and 35-41 Surcharged in Black on Overprinted Metallic Rectangles

No. 74

Type IV

Two types of 1c on 1p:
I. Silver rectangle 4x5 ½mm.
II. Silver rectangle 5 ½x5 ¼mm.
Two types of $1 on 10sh:
III. Silver rectangle 7x6 ½mm.
IV. Silver rectangle 6x4mm.

Perf. 14½, 14½x14

			Engr.	
1966, Feb. 14				
71	A6	1c on 1p bl grn (I)	.25	.25
a.		Type II	.35	.25
72	A6	2c on 2p gray grn & brt pink	.25	.25
73	A7	3c on 3p brt green	.35	.35
74	A6	4c on 5p purple	.25	.25
75	A6	5c on 8p vermilion	.25	.25
76	A2	10c on 10p pale pur & brn	.70	.70
77	A6	15c on 1sh1p dark red	.30	.30
78	A6	20c on 2sh sepia	2.75	2.75
79	A6	25c on 2sh5p de pur	1.10	1.10
80	A6	30c on 2sh8p grn & sal	.75	.75
81	A3	50c on 5sh grn & gray	2.75	2.75
82	A8	$1 on 10sh green (III)	2.50	2.50
a.		Type IV	5.25	2.50
		Nos. 71-82 (12)	12.20	12.20

Headstone Bridge — A13

1966, June 27　Photo.　Perf. 14½

88	A13	7c shown	.25	.25
89	A13	9c Cemetery road	.45	.40

St. Barnabas Chapel — A14

Design: 4c, Interior of St. Barnabas Chapel.

Perf. 14x14½

1966, Aug. 23   Photo.   Unwmk.
97 A14 4c multicolored   .25 .25
98 A14 25c multicolored   .45 .30
Centenary of the Melanesian Mission.

Star over Philip
Island — A15

1966, Oct. 24   Photo.   Perf. 14½
99 A15 4c violet, grn, blue & sil   .35 .25
Christmas.

H.M.S. Resolution,
1774 — A16

Ships: 2c, La Boussole and Astrolabe,
1788. 3c, Brig Supply, 1788. 4c, Sirius, 1790.
5c, The Norfolk, 1798. 7c, Survey cutter Mermaid, 1825. 9c, The Lady Franklin, 1853. 10c
The Morayshire, 1856. 15c, Southern Cross,
1866. 20c, The Pitcairn, 1891. 25c, Norfolk
Island whaleboat, 1895. 30c, Cable ship Iris,
1907. 50c, The Resolution, 1926. $1, S.S.
Morinda, 1931.

1967-68   Photo.   Perf. 14x14½
100 A16 1c multicolored   .25 .25
101 A16 2c multicolored   .25 .25
102 A16 3c multicolored   .25 .25
103 A16 4c multicolored   .40 .25
104 A16 5c multicolored   .25 .25
105 A16 7c multicolored   .25 .25
106 A16 9c multicolored   .30 .25
107 A16 10c multicolored   .40 .35
108 A16 15c multicolored   .60 .55
109 A16 20c multicolored   .90 .80
110 A16 25c multicolored   1.40 1.25
111 A16 30c multicolored   1.75 1.50
112 A16 50c multicolored   2.25 2.00
113 A16 $1 multicolored   3.50 3.25
    Nos. 100-113 (14)   12.75 11.45

Issued: #100-103, 4/17; #104-107, 8/19;
#108-110, 3/18/68; #111-113, 6/18/68.

Lions Intl., 50th
Anniv. — A16a

1967, June 7   Photo.   Perf. 13½
114 A16a 4c citron, blk & bl grn   .30 .25
Printed on luminescent paper; see note
after Australia No. 331.

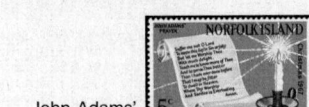

John Adams'
Prayer — A17

1967, Oct. 16   Photo.   Perf. 14x14½
115 A17 5c brick red, blk & buff   .40 .40
Christmas.

**Queen Elizabeth II Type of Australia,
1966-67**
Coil Stamps
Perf. 15 Horizontally

1968-71   Photo.   Unwmk.
116 A157 3c brn org, blk & buff   .25 .25
117 A157 4c blue grn, blk &
            buff   .25 .25
118 A157 5c brt purple, blk &
            buff   .25 .25
118A A157 6c dk red, brn, blk &
            buff   .25 .25
    Nos. 116-118A (4)   1.00 1.00

Issued: 6c, 8/2/71; others, 8/5/68.

DC-4 Skymaster
and Lancastrian
Plane — A18

1968, Sept. 25   Perf. 14½x14
119 A18 5c dk car, sky bl & ind   .25 .25
120 A18 7c dk car, bl grn & sep   .25 .25
21st anniv. of the Sydney to Norfolk Island
air service by Qantas Airways.

Star and Hibiscus
Wreath — A19

Photo.; Silver Impressed (Star)
1968, Oct. 24   Perf. 14½x14
121 A19 5c sky blue & multi   .25 .25
Christmas.

Map of Pacific,
Transit of Venus
before Sun, Capt.
Cook and
Quadrant — A20

1969, June 3   Photo.   Perf. 14x14½
122 A20 10c brn, ol, pale brn &
            yel   .35 .25
Bicent. of the observation at Tahiti by Capt.
James Cook of the transit of the planet Venus
across the sun.

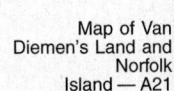

Map of Van
Diemen's Land and
Norfolk
Island — A21

1969, Sept. 29   Perf. 14x14½
123 A21 5c multicolored   .25 .25
124 A21 30c multicolored   .45 .45
125th anniv. of the annexation of Norfolk
Island by Van Diemen's Land (Tasmania).

Nativity (Mother-of-Pearl
carving) — A22

1969, Oct. 27   Photo.   Perf. 14½x14
125 A22 5c brown & multi   .30 .25
Christmas.

Gerygone
Modesta — A23

Birds of Norfolk Island from Book by Gregory Mathews: 1c, Petroica multicolor, vert. 2c,
Pachycephala xanthoprocta, vert. 4c,
Urodynamis taitensis. 5c, Cyanoramphus verticalis, vert. 7c, Diaphoropterus leucopygus,
vert. 9c, Turdus poliocephalus. 10c, Ninox
boobook royana, vert. 15c, Hemiphaga argetraea (extinct), vert. 20c, Zosterops albogularis. 25c, Nestor productus (extinct), vert.
30c, Rhipidura pelzelni. 45c, Aplonis fuscus.
50c, Platycercus elegans, vert. $1, Halcyon
sanctus norfolkiensis.

Perf. 14x14½, 14½x14

1970-71   Photo.   Unwmk.
126 A23 1c multicolored   .25 .25
127 A23 2c multicolored   .25 .30
128 A23 3c multicolored   .25 .25
129 A23 4c multicolored   .45 .30
130 A23 5c multicolored   1.15 .75
131 A23 7c multicolored   .35 .25
132 A23 9c multicolored   .50 .30
133 A23 10c multicolored   1.30 1.45
134 A23 15c multicolored   1.15 .70

135 A23 20c multicolored   5.25 3.25
136 A23 25c multicolored   1.75 1.15
137 A23 30c multicolored   5.25 2.60
138 A23 45c multicolored   2.25 1.25
139 A23 50c multicolored   2.75 2.00
140 A23 $1 multicolored   7.50 6.25
    Nos. 126-140 (15)   30.40 21.05

Issued: 3c, 4c, 9c, 45c, 2/25; 1c, 7c, 10c,
25c, 7/22; 2c, 2c, 5c, 15c, 50c, 2/24/71; 20c,
30c, $1, 6/16/71.

Map of
Australia, James
Cook and
Southern
Cross — A24

Design: 10c, "Endeavour" entering Botany
Bay, Apr. 29, 1770, and aborigine with spear.
The 1776 portrait of James Cook on the 5c is
by John Webber.

1970, Apr. 29   Photo.   Perf. 14x14½
141 A24 5c multicolored   .25 .25
142 A24 10c multicolored   .25 .25
200th anniv. of Cook's discovery and exploration of the eastern coast of Australia.

First Christmas, Sydney
Bay, 1788 — A25

1970, Oct. 15   Photo.   Perf. 14x14½
143 A25 5c multicolored   .25 .25
Christmas.

Bishop Patteson,
Open Bible — A26

#145, Bible opened to Acts Chap. 7, martyrdom of St. Stephen, & knotted palm fronds.
#146, Bishop Patteson, rose window of Melanesian Mission Chapel on Norfolk Island.
#147, Cross erected at Nukapu where Patteson died & his arms.

1971, Sept. 20
144 A26 6c brown & multi   .25 .25
145 A26 6c brown & multi   .25 .25
  a. Pair, #144-145   .55 .55
146 A26 10c purple & multi .25 .25
147 A26 10c purple & multi .25 .25
  a. Pair, #146-147   .65 .65
    Nos. 144-147 (4)   1.00 1.00

Centenary of the death of Bishop John
Coleridge Patteson (1827-1871), head of the
Melanesian mission.

Rose Window, St.
Barnabas Chapel,
Norfolk Island — A27

1971, Oct. 25   Perf. 14x13½
148 A27 6c dk vio blue & multi   .25 .25
Christmas.

Map of South
Pacific and
Commission
Flag — A28

1972, Feb. 7   Perf. 14x14½
149 A28 7c multicolored   .30 .30
So. Pacific Commission, 25th anniv.

Stained-glass
Window — A29

1972, Oct. 16   Photo.   Perf. 14x14½
150 A29 7c dark olive & multi   .25 .25
Christmas. The stained-glass window by
Edward Coley Burne-Jones is in All Saints
Church, Norfolk Island.

Cross, Church,
Pines — A30

1972, Nov. 20
151 A30 12c multicolored   .40 .40
  a. Purple omitted   1,600.
Centenary of All Saints Church, first built by
Pitcairners on Norfolk Island.

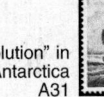

"Resolution" in
Antarctica
A31

1973, Jan. 17   Photo.   Perf. 14½x14
152 A31 35c multicolored   2.10 1.75
200th anniv. of the 1st crossing of the
Antarctic Circle by Cook, Jan. 17, 1773.

Sleeping Child, and
Christmas Tree — A32

Christmas: 35c, Star over lagoon.

1973, Oct. 22   Photo.   Perf. 14x14½
153 A32 7c black & multi   .30 .25
154 A32 12c black & multi   .50 .30
155 A32 35c black & multi 1.60 1.10
    Nos. 153-155 (3)   2.40 1.65

Protestant
Clergyman's
House — A33

Designs: 2c, Royal Engineer Office. 3c,
Double quarters for free overseers. 4c, Guard
House. 5c, Pentagonal Gaol entrance. 7c,
Pentagonal Gaol, aerial view. 8c, Convict barracks. 10c, Officers' quarters, New Military
Barracks. 12c, New Military Barracks. 14c,
Beach stores. 15c, Magazine. 20c, Old Military
Barracks, entrance. 25c, Old Military Barracks.
30c, Old stores, Crankmill. 50c, Commissariat
stores. $1, Government House.

1973-75   Photo.   Perf. 14x14½
156 A33 1c multicolored   .25 .25
157 A33 2c multicolored   .25 .25
158 A33 3c multicolored   .30 .30
159 A33 4c multicolored   .25 .25
160 A33 5c multicolored   .25 .25
161 A33 7c multicolored   .30 .30
162 A33 8c multicolored   1.20 1.20
163 A33 10c multicolored   .45 .45
164 A33 12c multicolored   .45 .45
165 A33 14c multicolored   .45 .45
166 A33 15c multicolored   1.10 1.10
167 A33 20c multicolored   .45 .45
168 A33 25c multicolored   1.10 1.10
169 A33 30c multicolored   .45 .45

170	A33	50c multicolored	.50	.50
171	A33	$1 multicolored	.95	.95
		Nos. 156-171 (16)	8.70	8.70

Issued: 1c, 5c, 10c, 50c, 11/19/73; 2c, 7c, 12c, 30c, 5/1/74; 4c, 14c, 20c, $1, 7/12/74; 3c, 8c, 15c, 25c, 2/19/75.

Map of Norfolk Island — A34

1974, Feb. 8   Photo.   Perf. 14x14½

172	A34	7c red lilac & multi	.50	.35
173	A34	25c dull blue & multi	1.10	1.00

Visit of Queen Elizabeth II and the Duke of Edinburgh, Feb. 11-12.

Gipsy Moth over Norfolk Island — A35

1974, Mar. 28   Litho.   Perf. 14x14½

174	A35	14c multicolored	1.60	1.35

1st aircraft to visit Norfolk, Sir Francis Chichester's "Mme. Elijah," Mar. 28, 1931.

Capt. Cook — A36

Designs: 10c, "Resolution," by Henry Roberts. 14c, Norfolk Island pine, cone and seedling. 25c, Norfolk Island flax, by George Raper, 1790. Portrait of Cook on 7c by William Hodges, 1770.

1974, Oct. 8   Litho.   Perf. 14

175	A36	7c multicolored	.60	.60
176	A36	10c multicolored	1.50	1.50
177	A36	14c multicolored	1.25	1.25
178	A36	25c multicolored	1.25	1.25
		Nos. 175-178 (4)	4.60	4.60

Bicentenary of the discovery of Norfolk Island by Capt. James Cook.

Nativity — A37

1974, Oct. 18   Photo.   Perf. 14

179	A37	7c rose & multi	.25	.25
180	A37	30c violet & multi	1.00	1.00

Christmas.

Norfolk Island Pine A38

15c, Off-shore islands. 35c, Crimson rosella and sacred kingfisher. 40c, Map showing Norfolk's location. Stamps in shape of Norfolk Island.

1974, Dec. 16   Litho.   Imperf.
Self-adhesive

181	A38	10c brown & multi	.35	.30
182	A38	15c dk blue & multi	.50	.40
183	A38	35c dk purple & multi	1.25	1.05

184	A38	40c dk blue grn & multi	1.50	2.10
a.		Souvenir sheet of 4	24.00	24.00
		Nos. 181-184 (4)	3.60	3.85

Cent. of UPU. Stamps printed on peelable paper backing. No. 184a contains 4 imperf. stamps similar to Nos. 181-184 in reduced size on a background of map of Norfolk Island. Peelable paper backing shows beach scene on Norfolk Island.

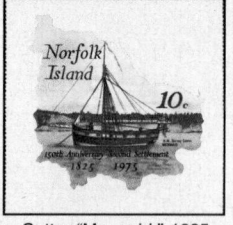

Survey Cutter "Mermaid," 1825 — A39

Design: 35c, Kingston, 1835, after painting by Thomas Seller. Stamps outlined in shape of Norfolk Island map.

1975, Aug. 18   Litho.   Imperf.
Self-adhesive

185	A39	10c multicolored	.35	.30
186	A39	35c multicolored	.70	.55

Sesquicentennial of 2nd settlement of Norfolk Island. Printed on peelable paper backing with green and black design and inscription.

Star over Norfolk Island Pine and Map — A40

1975, Oct. 6   Photo.   Perf. 14½x14

187	A40	10c lt blue & multi	.35	.30
188	A40	15c lt brown & multi	.55	.45
189	A40	35c lilac & multi	.75	.60
		Nos. 187-189 (3)	1.65	1.35

Christmas.

Brass Memorial Cross — A41

Design: 60c, Laying foundation stone, 1875, and chapel, 1975, horiz.

Perf. 14½x14, 14x14½

1975, Nov. 24   Photo.

190	A41	30c multicolored	.35	.35
191	A41	60c multicolored	1.00	.90

St. Barnabas Chapel, centenary.

Launching "Resolution" — A42

Design: 45c, "Resolution" under sail.

1975, Dec. 1   Perf. 14x14½

192	A42	25c multicolored	.50	.45
193	A42	45c multicolored	1.25	.90

50th anniversary of launching of schooner "Resolution."

Bedford Flag, Charles W. Morgan Whaler — A43

Designs: 25c, Grand Union Flag, church interior. 40c, 15-stari flag, 1795, and plane over island, WWII. 45c, 13-star flag and California quail.

1976, July 5   Photo.   Perf. 14

194	A43	18c multicolored	.40	.35
195	A43	25c multicolored	.40	.30
196	A43	40c multicolored	.80	.75
197	A43	45c multicolored	.90	.85
		Nos. 194-197 (4)	2.50	2.25

American Bicentennial.

Bird in Flight, Brilliant Sun — A44

1976, Oct. 4   Photo.   Perf. 14

198	A44	18c blue grn & multi	.40	.30
199	A44	25c dp blue & multi	.60	.50
200	A44	45c violet & multi	1.00	.80
		Nos. 198-200 (3)	2.00	1.60

Christmas.

Bassaris Itea — A45

Butterflies and Moths: 2c, Utetheisa pulchelloides vaga. 3c, Agathia asterias jowettorum. 4c, Cynthia kershawi. 5c, Leucania loreyimima. 10c, Hypolimnas bolina nerina. 15c, Pyrrhorachis pyrrhogona. 16c, Austrocarea iocephala millsi. 17c, Pseudocoremia christiani. 18c, Cleora idiocrossa. 19c, Simplicia caeneusalis buffetti. 20c, Austrocidaria ralstonae. 30c, Hippotion scrofa. 40c, Papilio ilioneus. 50c, Tiracola plagiata. $1, Precis vilida. $2, Cepora perimale.

1976-77   Photo.   Perf. 14

201	A45	1c multicolored	.25	.25
202	A45	2c multicolored	.25	.25
203	A45	3c multicolored	.25	.25
204	A45	4c multicolored	.25	.25
205	A45	5c multicolored	.25	.25
206	A45	10c multicolored	.25	.25
207	A45	15c multicolored	.25	.25
208	A45	16c multicolored	.25	.25
209	A45	17c multicolored	.30	.30
210	A45	18c multicolored	.30	.30
211	A45	19c multicolored	.30	.30
212	A45	20c multicolored	.35	.35
213	A45	30c multicolored	.45	.45
214	A45	40c multicolored	.50	.50
215	A45	50c multicolored	.65	.65
216	A45	$1 multicolored	.70	.70
217	A45	$2 multicolored	1.10	1.10
		Nos. 201-217 (17)	6.65	6.65

Issued: 1c, 5c, 10c, 16c, 18c, $1, 11/17; others, 1977.

View of Kingston — A46

1977, June 10

218	A46	25c multicolored	.60	.50

25th anniv. of reign of Elizabeth II.

Hibiscus and 19th Century Whaler's Lamp — A47

1977, Oct. 4   Photo.   Perf. 14½

219	A47	18c multicolored	.25	.25
220	A47	35c multicolored	.35	.25
221	A47	45c multicolored	.65	.40
		Nos. 219-221 (3)	1.25	.90

Christmas.

Capt. Cook, by Nathaniel Dance — A48

Designs: 25c, Discovery of Northern Hawaiian Islands (Cook aboard ship), horiz. 80c, British flag and Island, horiz.

1978, Jan. 18   Photo.   Perf. 14½

222	A48	18c multicolored	.35	.35
223	A48	25c multicolored	.45	.35
224	A48	80c multicolored	.85	.70
		Nos. 222-224 (3)	1.65	1.40

Bicentenary of Capt. Cook's arrival in Hawaiian Islands.

World Guides Flag and Globe A49

Designs: 25c, Norfolk Guides' scarf badge and trefoil. 35c, Elizabeth II and trefoil. 45c, FAO Ceres medal with portrait of Lady Olive Baden-Powell, and trefoil. Stamps outlined in shape of Norfolk Island map.

1978, Feb. 22   Litho.   Imperf.
Self-adhesive

225	A49	18c lt ultra & multi	.35	.30
226	A49	25c yellow & multi	.35	.30
227	A49	35c lt green & multi	.45	.35
228	A49	45c yellow grn & multi	.55	.45
		Nos. 225-228 (4)	1.70	1.40

50th anniversary of Norfolk Island Girl Guides. Printed on peelable paper backing with green multiple pines and tourist publicity inscription.

St. Edward's Crown — A50

Design: 70c, Coronation regalia.

1978, June 29   Photo.   Perf. 14½

229	A50	25c multicolored	.45	.45
230	A50	70c multicolored	.90	.90

25th anniv. of coronation of Elizabeth II.

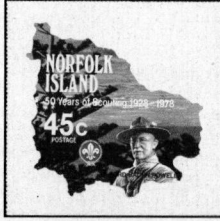

Norfolk Island Boy Scouts, 50th Anniv. A51

Designs: 20c, Cliffs, Duncombe Bay, Scout Making Fire. 25c, Emily Bay, Philip and Nepean Islands from Kingston. 35c, Anson Bay, Cub and Boy Scouts. 45c, Sunset and Lord Baden-Powell. Stamps outlined in shape of Norfolk Island map.

1978, Aug. 22   Litho.   Imperf.
Self-adhesive

231	A51	20c multicolored	.40	.40
232	A51	25c multicolored	.45	.45
233	A51	35c multicolored	.65	.65
234	A51	45c multicolored	.70	.70
		Nos. 231-234 (4)	2.20	2.20

Printed on peelable paper backing with green multiple pines and tourist publicity inscription and picture.

Map of Bering Sea and Pacific Ocean, Routes of Discovery and Resolution A52

Design: 90c, Discovery and Resolution trapped in ice, by John Webber.

1978, Aug. 29   Photo.   Perf. 14½

235	A52	25c multicolored	.40	.40
236	A52	90c multicolored	1.00	1.00

Northernmost point of Cook's voyages.

Poinsettia and Bible — A53

Christmas: 30c, Native oak (flowers) and Bible. 55c, Hibiscus and Bible.

1978, Oct. 3   Photo.   Perf. 14½
237 A53 20c multicolored .30 .30
238 A53 30c multicolored .40 .40
239 A53 55c multicolored .75 .75
Nos. 237-239 (3) 1.45 1.45

Capt. Cook, View of Staithes — A54

80c, Capt. Cook and view of Whitby harbor.

1978, Oct. 27
240 A54 20c multicolored .40 .50
241 A54 80c multicolored 1.10 1.25

Resolution, Map of Asia and Australia — A55

Designs: No. 243, Map of Hawaii and Americas, Cook's route and statue. No. 244, Capt. Cook's death. No. 245, Ships off Hawaii.

1979, Feb. 14   Photo.   Perf. 14½
242 20c multicolored .25 .25
243 20c multicolored .25 .25
  a. A55 Pair, #242-243 .60 .60
244 40c multicolored .60 .60
245 40c multicolored .60 .60
  a. A55 Pair, #244-245 1.30 1.30
  Nos. 242-245 (4) 1.70 1.70

Bicentenary of Capt. Cook's death.

Rowland Hill and Tasmania No. 1 — A56

Rowland Hill and: 30c, Great Britain No. 8. 55c, Norfolk Island No. 2.

1979, Aug. 27   Perf. 14x14½
246 A56 20c multicolored .30 .30
247 A56 30c multicolored .35 .35
248 A56 55c multicolored .45 .45
  a. Souvenir sheet of 1 1.10 1.10
  Nos. 246-248 (3) 1.10 1.10

Sir Rowland Hill (1795-1879), originator of penny postage.

Legislative Assembly — A57

1979, Aug.   Photo.   Perf. 14½x14
249 A57 $1 multicolored 1.10 1.10

First session of Legislative Assembly.

Map of Pacific Ocean, IYC Emblem — A58

1979, Sept. 25   Litho.   Perf. 15
250 A58 80c multicolored .95 .95

International Year of the Child.

Emily Bay Beach A59

1979, Oct. 2   Photo.   Perf. 12½x13
251 15c Beach .25 .25
252 20c Emily Bay .25 .25
253 30c Salt House .30 .30
  a. Souv. sheet of 3, #251-253, perf. 14x14½ 1.50 2.00
  b. A59 Strip of 3, #251-253 .80 .80

Christmas. #253b has continuous design.

Lions District Convention 1980 — A60

1980, Jan. 25   Litho.   Perf. 15
254 A60 50c multicolored .70 .70

Rotary International, 75th Anniversary A61

1980, Feb. 21
255 A61 50c multicolored .60 .60
  a. Black omitted 11,000.

No. 255a is unique.

DH-60 "Gypsy Moth" — A62

1c, Hawker Siddeley HS-748. 3c, Curtiss P-40 Kittyhawk. 4c, Chance Vought Corsair. 5c, Grumman Avenger. 15c, Douglas Dauntless. 20c, Cessna 172. 25c, Lockheed Hudson. 30c, Lockheed PV-1 Ventura. 40c, Avro York. 50c, DC-3. 60c, Avro 691 Lancastrian. 80c, DC-4. $1, Beechcraft Super King Air. $2, Fokker Friendship. $5, Lockheed C-130 Hercules.

1980-81   Litho.   Perf. 14½
256 A62 1c multicolored .25 .25
257 A62 2c multicolored .25 .25
258 A62 3c multicolored .25 .25
259 A62 4c multicolored .25 .25
260 A62 5c multicolored .25 .25
261 A62 15c multicolored .25 .25
262 A62 20c multicolored .30 .25
262A A62 25c multicolored .40 .35
263 A62 30c multicolored .50 .45
264 A62 40c multicolored .60 .50
265 A62 50c multicolored .75 .65
266 A62 60c multicolored .80 .70
267 A62 80c multicolored 1.25 1.10
268 A62 $1 multicolored 1.45 1.25
269 A62 $2 multicolored 1.75 1.60
270 A62 $5 multicolored 4.75 4.25
  Nos. 256-270 (16) 14.05 12.60

Issued: 2, 3, 20c, $5, 3/25; 4, 5, 15c, $2, 8/19; 30, 50, 60, 80c, 1/13/81; 1, 25, 40c, $1, 3/3/81.

Queen Mother Elizabeth, 80th Birthday — A63

1980, Aug. 4   Litho.   Perf. 14½
271 A63 22c multicolored .30 .30
272 A63 60c multicolored .70 .70

Red-tailed Tropic Birds — A64

22c, Adult and juvenile white terns. 35c, White-capped noddys. 60c, Two adult white terns.

1980, Oct. 28   Litho.   Perf. 14x14½
273 A64 15c shown .25 .25
274 A64 22c multicolored .25 .25
275 A64 35c multicolored .40 .40
  a. Strip of 3, #273-275 1.00 1.00
276 A64 60c multicolored .75 .75
  Nos. 273-276 (4) 1.65 1.65

Christmas. No. 275a has continuous design.

Citizens Arriving at Norfolk Island — A65

1981, June 5   Litho.   Perf. 14½
277 A65 5c Departure .25 .25
278 A65 35c shown .40 .40
279 A65 60c Settlement .70 .70
  a. Souvenir sheet of 3, #277-279 1.50 1.50
  Nos. 277-279 (3) 1.35 1.35

Pitcairn migration to Norfolk Island, 125th anniv.

Common Design Types pictured following the introduction.

Royal Wedding Issue
Common Design Type
1981, July 22   Litho.   Perf. 14
280 CD331 35c Bouquet .40 .40
281 CD331 55c Charles .65 .65
282 CD331 60c Couple .70 .70
  Nos. 280-282 (3) 1.75 1.75

Nos. 280-282 each se-tenant with decorative label.

Uniting Church of Australia — A66

24c, Seventh Day Adventist Church. 30c, Church of the Sacred Heart. $1, St. Barnabas Church.

1981, Sept. 15   Litho.   Perf. 14½
283 A66 18c shown .25 .25
284 A66 24c multicolored .30 .30
285 A66 30c multicolored .35 .35
286 A66 $1 multicolored 1.10 1.10
  Nos. 283-286 (4) 2.00 2.00

Christmas.

White-breasted Silvereye — A67

1981, Nov. 10   Litho.   Perf. 14½
287 Strip of 5 2.75 2.75
  a.-e. A67 35c any single .50 .50

Philip Island — A68

Views, Flora and Fauna: No. 288, Philip Isld. No. 289, Nepean Island.

1982, Jan. 12   Litho.   Perf. 14
288 Strip of 5 1.50 1.50
  a.-e. A68 24c any single .25 .25
289 Strip of 5 2.25 2.25
  a.-e. A68 35c any single .40 .40

Sperm Whale — A69

55c, Southern right whale. 80c, Humpback whale.

1982, Feb. 23   Litho.   Perf. 14½
290 A69 24c shown .50 .50
291 A69 55c multicolored 1.00 1.00
292 A69 80c multicolored 1.75 1.75
  Nos. 290-292 (3) 3.25 3.25

Shipwrecks A70

1982   Litho.   Perf. 14½
293 A70 24c Sirius, 1790 .40 .35
294 A70 27c Diocet, 1873 .40 .35
295 A70 35c Friendship, 1835 .65 .60
296 A70 40c Mary Hamilton, 1873 .70 .65
297 A70 55c Fairlie, 1840 .85 .75
298 A70 65c Warrigal, 1918 1.10 .95
  Nos. 293-298 (6) 4.10 3.65

Christmas and 40th Anniv. of Aircraft Landing — A71

1982, Sept. 7   Perf. 14
299 A71 27c Supplies drop .35 .35
300 A71 40c Landing .60 .60
301 A71 75c Sharing supplies 1.15 1.15
  Nos. 299-301 (3) 2.10 2.10

A72

British Army Uniforms, Second Settlement, 1839-1848: 27c, Battalion Company Officer, 50th Regiment, 1835-1842. 40c, Light Company Officer, 58th Reg., 1845. 55c, Private, 80th Bat., 1838. 65c, Bat. Company Officer, 11th Reg., 1847.

1982, Nov. 9   Perf. 14½
302 A72 27c multicolored .30 .30
303 A72 40c multicolored .55 .50
304 A72 55c multicolored .60 .55
305 A72 65c multicolored .80 .70
  Nos. 302-305 (4) 2.25 2.05

Local Mushrooms — A73

Designs: 27c, Panaeolus papilonaceus. 40c, Coprinus domesticus. 55c, Marasmius niveus. 65c, Cymatoderma elegans.

1983, Mar. 29   Litho.   Perf. 14x13½
306 A73 27c multicolored .40 .35
307 A73 40c multicolored .65 .55
308 A73 55c multicolored .80 .70
309 A73 65c multicolored 1.00 .90
  Nos. 306-309 (4) 2.85 2.50

Manned Flight Bicentenary — A74

10c, Beech 18, aerial mapping. 27c, Fokker F-28. 45c, DC4. 75c, Sikorsky helicopter.

1983, July 12   Litho.   Perf. 14½x14
310 A74 10c multicolored .25 .25
311 A74 27c multicolored .35 .30
312 A74 45c multicolored .75 .65
313 A74 75c multicolored 1.10 1.00
  a. Souvenir sheet of 4, #310-313 2.75 2.50
  Nos. 310-313 (4) 2.45 2.20

Christmas — A75

Stained-glass Windows by Edward Burne-Jones (1833-1898), St. Barnabas Chapel.

1983, Oct. 4   Litho.   Perf. 14
314	A75	5c multicolored	.25	.25
315	A75	24c multicolored	.30	.30
316	A75	30c multicolored	.35	.35
317	A75	45c multicolored	.45	.45
318	A75	85c multicolored	.90	.90
		Nos. 314-318 (5)	2.25	2.25

World Communications Year — A76

ANZCAN Cable Station: 30c, Chantik, Cable laying Ship. 45c, Shore end. 75c, Cable Ship Mercury. 85c, Map of cable route.

1983, Nov. 15   Litho.   Perf. 14½x14
319	A76	30c multicolored	.30	.30
320	A76	45c multicolored	.50	.50
321	A76	75c multicolored	.90	.90
322	A76	85c multicolored	1.00	1.00
		Nos. 319-322 (4)	2.70	2.70

Local Flowers — A77

1c, Myoporum obscurum. 2c, Ipomoea pes-caprae. 3c, Phreatia crassiuscula. 4c, Streblorrhiza speciosa. 5c, Rhopalostylis baueri. 10c, Alyxia gynopogon. 15c, Ungeria floribunda. 20c, Capparis nobilis. 25c, Lagunaria patersonia. 30c, Cordyline obtecta. 35c, Hibiscus insularis. 40c, Millettia australis. 50c, Jasminum volubile. $1, Passiflora aurantia. $3, Oberonia titania. $5, Araucaria heterophylla.

1984   Litho.   Perf. 14
323	A77	1c multicolored	.25	.25
324	A77	2c multicolored	.25	.25
325	A77	3c multicolored	.25	.25
326	A77	4c multicolored	.25	.25
327	A77	5c multicolored	.25	.25
328	A77	10c multicolored	.25	.25
329	A77	15c multicolored	.25	.25
330	A77	20c multicolored	.30	.30
331	A77	25c multicolored	.35	.35
332	A77	30c multicolored	.45	.45
333	A77	35c multicolored	.50	.50
334	A77	40c multicolored	.55	.55
335	A77	50c multicolored	.65	.65
336	A77	$1 multicolored	1.25	1.25
337	A77	$3 multicolored	4.00	4.00
338	A77	$5 multicolored	6.00	6.00
		Nos. 323-338 (16)	15.80	15.80

Issued: 2-3, 10, 20-25, 40-50c, $5, 1/10; others 3/27.

Reef Fish — A78

30c, Painted morwong. 45c, Black-spot goatfish. 75c, Ring-tailed surgeon fish. 85c, Three-striped butterfly fish.

Perf. 13½x14
1984, Apr. 17   Litho.   Wmk. 373
339	A78	30c multicolored	.50	.50
340	A78	45c multicolored	.65	.65
341	A78	75c multicolored	1.15	1.15
342	A78	85c multicolored	1.30	1.30
		Nos. 339-342 (4)	3.60	3.60

Boobook Owl — A79

Designs: a, Laying eggs. b, Standing at treehole. c, Sitting on branch looking sideways. d, Looking head on. e, Flying.

Wmk. 373
1984, July 17   Litho.   Perf. 14
343		Strip of 5	6.00	6.00
a.-e.	A79 30c any single		1.20	1.20

AUSIPEX '84
A80

1984, Sept. 18   Litho.   Perf. 14½
344	A80	30c Nos. 15 and 176	.40	.40
345	A80	45c First day cover	.65	.65
346	A80	75c Presentation pack	1.25	1.25
a.	Souvenir sheet of 3, #344-346		4.00	4.00
		Nos. 344-346 (3)	2.30	2.30

Christmas — A81

5c, The Font. 24c, Church at Kingston, interior. 30c, Pastor and Mrs. Phelps. 45c, Phelps, Church of Chester. 85c, Phelps, Methodist Church, modern interior.

1984, Oct. 9   Litho.   Perf. 13½
347	A81	5c multicolored	.25	.25
348	A81	24c multicolored	.40	.35
349	A81	30c multicolored	.45	.40
350	A81	45c multicolored	.70	.60
351	A81	85c multicolored	1.25	1.10
		Nos. 347-351 (5)	3.05	2.70

Rev. George Hunn Nobbs, Death Cent. — A82

30c, As teacher. 45c, As minister. 75c, As chaplain. 85c, As community leader.

1984, Nov. 6   Litho.   Perf. 14x15
352	A82	30c multicolored	.40	.40
353	A82	45c multicolored	.50	.50
354	A82	75c multicolored	.90	.90
355	A82	85c multicolored	1.20	1.20
		Nos. 352-355 (4)	3.00	3.00

Whaling Ships — A83

1985   Litho.   Perf. 13½x14
356	A83	5c Fanny Fisher	.25	.25
357	A83	15c Waterwitch	.30	.30
358	A83	20c Canton	.35	.35
359	A83	33c Costa Rica Packet	.55	.55
360	A83	50c Splendid	.80	.80
361	A83	60c Aladin	1.25	1.25
362	A83	80c California	1.50	1.50
363	A83	90c Onward	1.90	1.90
		Nos. 356-363 (8)	6.90	6.90

Issued: 5c, 33c, 50c, 90c, 2/19; others 4/30.

Queen Mother 85th Birthday
Common Design Type

5c, Portrait, 1926. 33c, With Princess Anne. 50c, Photograph by N. Parkinson. 90c, Holding Prince Henry. $1, With Princess Anne, Ascot Races.

Perf. 14½x14
1985, June 6   Litho.   Wmk. 384
364	CD336	5c multicolored	.25	.25
365	CD336	33c multicolored	.45	.45
366	CD336	50c multicolored	.65	.65
367	CD336	90c multicolored	1.40	1.40
		Nos. 364-367 (4)	2.75	2.75
		Souvenir Sheet		
368	CD336	$1 multicolored	2.25	2.25

Intl. Youth Year — A84

Children's drawings.

1985, July 9   Litho.   Perf. 13½x14
369	A84	33c Swimming	.55	.50
370	A84	50c Nature walk	.90	.85

Girl, Prize-winning Cow — A85

Designs: 90c, Embroidery, jam-making, baking, animal husbandry.

1985, Sept. 10   Litho.   Perf. 13½x14
371	A85	80c multicolored	1.00	1.00
372	A85	90c multicolored	1.10	1.10
a.	Souvenir sheet of 2, #371-372		3.00	3.00

Royal Norfolk Island Agricultural & Horticultural Show, 125th anniv.

Christmas — A86

27c, Three Shepherds. 33c, Journey to Bethlehem. 50c, Three Wise Men. 90c, Nativity.

1985, Oct. 3   Perf. 13½
373	A86	27c multicolored	.35	.35
374	A86	33c multicolored	.50	.50
375	A86	50c multicolored	.65	.65
376	A86	90c multicolored	1.25	1.25
		Nos. 373-376 (4)	2.75	2.75

Marine Life — A87

5c, Long-spined sea urchin. 33c, Blue starfish. 55c, Eagle ray. 75c, Moray eel.

1986, Jan. 14   Perf. 13½x14
377	A87	5c multicolored	.25	.25
378	A87	33c multicolored	.55	.55
379	A87	55c multicolored	.95	.95
380	A87	75c multicolored	1.25	1.25
a.	Souvenir sheet of 4, #377-380		4.00	4.00
		Nos. 377-380 (4)	3.00	3.00

Halley's Comet A88

Designs: a, Giotto space probe. b, Comet.

1986, Mar. 11   Perf. 15
381	A88	Pair	3.25	3.25
a.-b.	$1 any single		1.60	1.60

Se-tenant in continuous design.

AMERIPEX '86
A89

Designs: 33c, Isaac Robinson, US consul in Norfolk, 1887-1908, vert. 50c, Ford Model-T. 80c, Statue of Liberty.

1986, May 22   Litho.   Perf. 13½
382	A89	33c multicolored	.45	.45
383	A89	50c multicolored	.70	.70
384	A89	80c multicolored	1.10	1.10
a.	Souvenir sheet of #382-384		3.00	3.00
		Nos. 382-384 (3)	2.25	2.25

Queen Elizabeth II, 60th Birthday — A90

Various portraits — 5c, As Princess. 33c, Contemporary photograph. 80c, Opening N.I. Golf Club. 90c, With Prince Philip.

1986, June 12
385	A90	5c multicolored	.25	.25
386	A90	33c multicolored	.60	.60
387	A90	80c multicolored	1.30	1.30
388	A90	90c multicolored	1.60	1.60
		Nos. 385-388 (4)	3.75	3.75

Christmas — A91

1986, Sept. 23   Litho.   Perf. 13½x14
389	A91	30c multicolored	.50	.50
390	A91	40c multicolored	.60	.60
391	A91	$1 multicolored	1.50	1.50
		Nos. 389-391 (3)	2.60	2.60

Commission of Gov. Phillip, Bicent. — A92

36c, British prison, 1787. 55c, Transportation, Court of Assize. No. 394, Gov. meeting Home Society. No. 395, Gov. meeting Home Secretary. $1, Gov. Phillip, 1738-1814.

1986   Litho.   Perf. 14x13½
392	A92	36c multicolored	.80	.80
393	A92	55c multicolored	1.35	1.35
394	A92	90c multicolored	2.25	2.25
395	A92	90c multicolored	2.25	2.25
396	A92	$1 multicolored	3.25	3.25
		Nos. 392-396 (5)	9.90	9.90

No. 395 was issued because No. 394 is incorrectly inscribed.
Issued: #395, Dec. 16; others, Oct. 14.
See #417-420, 426-436.

Commission of Gov. Phillip, Bicent. A93

1986, Dec. 16   Perf. 13½
397	A93	36c Maori chief	.95	.95
398	A93	36c Bananas, taro	.95	.95
399	A93	36c Stone tools	.95	.95
400	A93	36c Polynesian outrigger	.95	.95
		Nos. 397-400 (4)	3.80	3.80

Pre-European occupation of the Island.

Island Scenery — A94

1c, Cockpit Creek Bridge. 2c, Cemetery Bay Beach. 3c, Guesthouse. 5c, Philip Island from Point Ross. 15c, Cattle grazing. 30c, Rock fishing. 37c, Old home. 40c, Shopping center. 50c, Emily Bay. 60c, Bloody Bridge. 80c, Pitcairner-style shop. 90c, Government House. $1, Melanesian Memorial Chapel. $2, Kingston convict settlement. $3, Ball Bay. $5, Northerly cliffs.

1987-88   Litho.   Perf. 13½

401	A94	1c multicolored	.25	.25
402	A94	2c multicolored	.25	.25
403	A94	3c multicolored	.25	.25
404	A94	5c multicolored	.25	.25
405	A94	15c multicolored	.25	.25
406	A94	30c multicolored	.40	.40
407	A94	37c multicolored	.50	.50
408	A94	40c multicolored	.55	.55
409	A94	50c multicolored	.65	.65
410	A94	60c multicolored	.75	.75
411	A94	80c multicolored	.95	.95
412	A94	90c multicolored	1.10	1.10
413	A94	$1 multicolored	1.25	1.25
414	A94	$2 multicolored	2.60	2.60
415	A94	$3 multicolored	4.00	4.00
416	A94	$5 multicolored	8.75	8.75
		Nos. 401-416 (16)	22.75	22.75

Issued: 5c, 50c, 90c, $1, 2/17; 30c, 40c, 80c, $2, 4/17; 15c, 37c, 60c, $3, 7/27; 1c, 2c, 3c, $5, 5/17/88.

Bicentennial Type of 1986

Designs: 5c, Loading supplies at Deptford, England, 1787. No. 418, First Fleet sailing from Spithead (buoy in water). No. 419, Sailing from Spithead (ship flying British merchant flag). $1, Convicts below deck.

1987, May 13   Litho.   Perf. 14x13½

417	A92	5c multicolored	.45	.45
418	A92	55c multicolored	1.40	1.40
419	A92	55c multicolored	1.40	1.40
a.		Pair, #418-419	3.00	3.00
420	A92	$1 multicolored	2.10	2.10
		Nos. 417-420 (4)	5.35	5.35

No. 419a has a continuous design.

A96

World Wildlife Fund: Green parrot.

1987, Sept. 16   Unwmk.

421		Strip of 4	14.00	14.00
a.	A96	5c Parrot facing right	2.25	2.25
b.	A96	15c Parrot, chick, egg	2.75	2.75
c.	A96	36c Parrots	3.75	3.75
d.	A96	55c Parrot facing left	5.00	5.00

Christmas — A97

Children's party: 30c, Norfolk Island pine tree, restored convicts' settlement. 42c, Santa Claus, children opening packages. 58c, Santa, children, gifts in fire engine. 63c, Meal.

Perf. 13½x14

1987, Oct. 13   Litho.   Wmk. 384

422	A97	30c multicolored	.55	.55
423	A97	42c multicolored	.80	.80
424	A97	58c multicolored	1.05	1.05
425	A97	63c multicolored	1.15	1.15
		Nos. 422-425 (4)	3.55	3.55

Bicentennial Type of 1986

Designs: 5c, Lt. Philip Gidley King. No. 427, La Perouse and Louis XVI of France. No. 428, Gov. Phillip sailing in ship's cutter from Botany Bay to Port Jackson. No. 429, Flag raising on Norfolk Is. 55c, Lt. King and search party exploring the island. 70c, Landfall, Sydney Bay. No. 432, L'Astrolabe and La Boussole off coast of Norfolk. No. 433, HMS Supply. No. 434, Wrecking of L'Astrolabe off the Solomon Isls. No. 435, First Fleet landing at Sydney Cove. No. 436, First settlement, Sydney Bay, 1788.

1987-88   Litho.   Perf. 14x13½

426	A92	5c multicolored	.25	.25
427	A92	37c multicolored	.80	.80
428	A92	37c multicolored	.80	.80
429	A92	37c multicolored	.80	.80
430	A92	55c multicolored	1.60	1.60
431	A92	70c multicolored	1.40	1.40
432	A92	90c multicolored	2.50	2.50
433	A92	90c multicolored	2.00	2.00
434	A92	$1 multicolored	2.50	2.50
435	A92	$1 multicolored	2.25	2.25
436	A92	$1 multicolored	2.25	2.25
		Nos. 426-436 (11)	17.15	17.15

Visit of Jean La Perouse (1741-88), French navigator, to Norfolk Is. (Nos. 427, 432, 434); arrival of the First Fleet at Sydney Cove (Nos. 428, 435); founding of Norfolk Is. (Nos. 426, 429-431, 433, 436).

Issued: #427, 432, 434, Dec. 8, 1987; #428, 435, Jan. 25, 1988; others, Mar. 4, 1988.

SYDPEX '88, July 30-Aug. 7 — A98

Sydney-Norfolk transportation and communication links — No. 437, Air and sea transports, vert. No. 439, Telecommunications, vert.

Perf. 14x13½ 13½x14

1988, July 30   Litho.

437	A98	37c multicolored	1.15	1.15
438	A98	37c shown	1.15	1.15
439	A98	37c multicolored	1.15	1.15
a.		Souvenir sheet of 3, #437-439	7.00	7.00
		Nos. 437-439 (3)	3.45	3.45

No. 438 exists perf. 13½ within No. 439a.

Christmas — A99

1988, Sept. 27   Litho.   Perf. 14x13½

440	A99	30c shown	.60	.60
441	A99	42c Flowers, diff.	.85	.85
442	A99	58c Trees, fish	1.20	1.20
443	A99	63c Trees, sailboats	1.20	1.20
		Nos. 440-443 (4)	3.85	3.85

Convict Era Georgian Architecture, c. 1825-1850 — A100

Designs: 39c, Waterfront shop and boat shed. 55c, Royal Engineers' Building. 90c, Old military barracks. $1, Commissary and new barracks.

1988, Dec. 6   Litho.   Perf. 13½x14

444	A100	39c multicolored	.65	.65
445	A100	55c multicolored	.95	.95
446	A100	90c multicolored	1.50	1.50
447	A100	$1 multicolored	1.75	1.75
		Nos. 444-447 (4)	4.85	4.85

Indigenous Insects — A101

39c, Lamprima aenea. 55c, Insulascirtus nythos. 90c, Caedicia araucariae. $1, Thrincophora aridela.

Perf. 13½x14

1989, Feb. 14   Litho.   Unwmk.

448	A101	39c multicolored	.85	.85
449	A101	55c multicolored	1.15	1.15
450	A101	90c multicolored	1.75	1.75
451	A101	$1 multicolored	2.40	2.40
		Nos. 448-451 (4)	6.15	6.15

Mutiny on the Bounty — A102

Designs: 5c, Bounty's landfall, Adventure Bay, Tasmania. 39c, Mutineers and Polynesian maidens, c. 1790. 55c, Cumbria, Christian's home county. $1.10, Capt. Bligh and crewmen cast adrift.

Perf. 13½

1989, Apr. 28   Litho.   Unwmk.

452	A102	5c multicolored	.60	.60
453	A102	39c multicolored	2.00	2.00
454	A102	55c multicolored	2.60	2.60
455	A102	$1.10 multicolored	4.00	4.00
		Nos. 452-455 (4)	9.20	9.20

Souvenir Sheet

456		Sheet of 3 + label (#453, 456a-456b)	10.00	10.00
a.	A102	90c Isle of Man No. 393	3.25	3.25
b.	A102	$1 Pitcairn Isls. No. 321d	3.50	3.50

See Isle of Man Nos. 389-394 and Pitcairn Isls. Nos. 320-322.

Self-Government, 10th Anniv. — A103

41c, Flag. 55c, Ballot box. $1, Norfolk Is. Act of 1979. $1.10, Norfolk Island crest.

Perf. 14x13½

1989, Aug. 10   Litho.   Unwmk.

457	A103	41c multicolored	.80	.80
458	A103	55c multicolored	.90	.90
459	A103	$1 multicolored	1.90	1.90
460	A103	$1.10 multicolored	2.00	2.00
		Nos. 457-460 (4)	5.60	5.60

Natl. Red Cross, 75th Anniv. — A104

Perf. 13½x13

1989, Sept. 25   Litho.   Unwmk.

461	A104	$1 dk ultra & dk red	3.50	3.50

Bounty Hymns — A105

Designs: 36c, "While nature was sinking in stillness to rest, The last beams of daylight show dim in the west." 60c, "There's a land that is fairer than day, And by faith we can see it afar." 75c, "Let the lower lights be burning, Send a gleam across the wave." 80c, "Oh, have you not heard of that beautiful stream That flows through our father's lands."

1989, Oct. 9   Perf. 13½x14

462	A105	36c multicolored	.75	.75
463	A105	60c multicolored	1.50	1.50
464	A105	75c multicolored	2.10	2.10
465	A105	80c multicolored	2.10	2.10
		Nos. 462-465 (4)	6.45	6.45

Radio Australia, 50th Anniv. — A106

41c, Announcer John Royle. 65c, Sound waves on map. $1.10, Jacko, the laughing kookaburra.

1989, Nov. 21   Perf. 14x13½

466	A106	41c multicolored	1.25	1.25
467	A106	65c multicolored	1.75	1.75
468	A106	$1.10 multicolored	2.60	2.60
		Nos. 466-468 (3)	5.60	5.60

A107

Settlement of Pitcairn (The Norfolk Islanders): 70c, The Bounty on fire. $1.10, Armorial ensign of Norfolk.

Perf. 15x14½

1990, Jan. 23   Litho.   Unwmk.

469	A107	70c multicolored	2.75	2.75
470	A107	$1.10 multicolored	3.00	3.00

Salvage Team at Work — A108

Designs: No. 471, HMS Sirius striking reef. No. 472, HMS Supply clearing reef. $1, Map of salvage sites, artifacts.

1990, Mar. 19   Perf. 14x13½
Size of Nos. 471-472: 40x27

471	A108	41c multicolored	1.60	1.60
472	A108	41c multicolored	1.60	1.60
a.		Pair, #471-472	3.50	3.50
473	A108	65c shown	2.40	2.40
474	A108	$1 multicolored	2.60	2.60
		Nos. 471-474 (4)	8.20	8.20

Wreck of HMS Sirius, 200th anniv. No. 472a has continuous design.

Lightering Cargo Ashore, Kingston A109

MV Ile de Lumiere A110

45c, La Dunkerquoise. 50c, Dmitri Mendeleev. 65c, Pacific Rover. 75c, Norfolk Trader. 80c, Roseville. 90c, Kalia. $1, HMS Bounty. $2, HMAS Success. $5, HMAS Whyalia.

1990-91   Litho.   Perf. 14x14½

479	A109	5c shown	.35	.35
480	A109	10c like #479	.35	.35

Perf. 14½

481	A110	45c multicolored	.75	.75
482	A110	50c multicolored	.85	.85
483	A110	65c multicolored	1.10	1.10
484	A110	70c shown	1.15	1.15
485	A110	75c multicolored	1.25	1.25
486	A110	80c multicolored	1.25	1.25
487	A110	90c multicolored	1.50	1.50
488	A110	$1 multicolored	1.60	1.60
489	A110	$2 multicolored	3.50	3.50
490	A110	$5 multicolored	8.75	8.75
		Nos. 479-490 (12)	22.40	22.40

Issued: 5c, 10c, 70c, $2, 7/17/90; 45c, 50c, 65c, $5, 2/19/91; 75c, 80c, 90c, $1, 8/13/91.

Christmas — A111

38c, Island home. 43c, New post office. 65c, Sydney Bay, Kingston, horiz. 85c, Officers' Quarters, 1836, horiz.

1990, Sept. 25   Litho.   Perf. 14½

491	A111	38c multicolored	.70	.70
492	A111	43c multicolored	.75	.75
493	A111	65c multicolored	1.75	1.75
494	A111	85c multicolored	1.90	1.90
		Nos. 491-494 (4)	5.10	5.10

A112

Designs: 70c, William Charles Wentworth (1790-1872), Australian politician. $1.20, Thursday October Christian (1790-1831).

1990, Oct. 11 Litho. *Perf. 15x14½*
495 A112 70c brown   1.60 1.60
496 A112 $1.20 brown   2.50 2.50

Norfolk Island Robin
A113   A114

1990, Dec. 3 Litho. *Perf. 14½*
497 A113 65c multicolored   1.25 1.25
498 A113 $1 shown   2.00 2.00
499 A113 $1.20 multi, diff.   2.50 2.50
      Nos. 497-499 (3)   5.75 5.75

Souvenir Sheet
500   Sheet of 2   6.50 6.50
  a.   A114 $1 shown   2.75 2.75
  b.   A114 $1 Two robins   2.75 2.75

Birdpex '90, 20th Intl. Ornithological Congress, New Zealand.

Ham Radio — A115

1991, Apr. 9 Litho. *Perf. 14½*
501 A115 43c Island map   1.25 1.25
502 A115 $1 World map   2.75 2.75
503 A115 $1.20 Regional location   2.75 2.75
      Nos. 501-503 (3)   6.75 6.75

Museum
Displays — A116

43c, Ship's bow, Sirius Museum, vert. 70c, House Museum. $1, Carronade, Sirius Museum. $1.20, Pottery, Archaeology Museum, vert.

1991, May 16 Litho. *Perf. 14½*
504 A116 43c multicolored   1.00 1.00
505 A116 70c multicolored   1.75 1.75
506 A116 $1 multicolored   1.90 1.90
507 A116 $1.20 multicolored   2.25 2.25
      Nos. 504-507 (4)   6.90 6.90

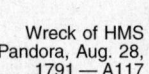

Wreck of HMS
Pandora, Aug. 28,
1791 — A117

Design: $1.20, HMS Pandora searching for Bounty mutineers.

1991, July 2 Litho. *Perf. 13½x14*
508 A117 $1 shown   3.25 3.25
509 A117 $1.20 multicolored   3.75 3.75

Christmas — A118

1991, Sept. 23 Litho. *Perf. 14½*
510 A118 38c multicolored   .65   .65
511 A118 43c multicolored   .90   .90
512 A118 65c multicolored   1.40 1.40
513 A118 85c multicolored   1.75 1.75
      Nos. 510-513 (4)   4.70 4.70

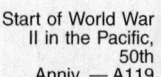

Start of World War
II in the Pacific,
50th
Anniv. — A119

1991, Dec. 9 Litho. *Perf. 14½*
514 A119 43c Tank and soldier   1.25 1.25
515 A119 70c B-17   2.25 2.25
516 A119 $1 War ships   3.00 3.00
      Nos. 514-516 (3)   6.50 6.50

Discovery of America,
500th Anniv. — A120

45c, Columbus' Coat of Arms. $1.05, Santa Maria. $1.20, Columbus at globe.

1992, Feb. 11 Litho. *Perf. 14½*
517 A120 45c multicolored   .85   .85
518 A120 $1.05 multicolored   2.00 2.00
519 A120 $1.20 multicolored   2.50 2.50
      Nos. 517-519 (3)   5.35 5.35

A121

Designs: No. 520, Map of Coral Sea Battle area. No. 521, Battle area, Midway. No. 522, HMAS Australia. No. 523, Catalina PBY5. No. 524, USS Yorktown. No. 525, Dauntless dive bomber.

1992, May 4 Litho. *Perf. 14½*
520 A121 45c multicolored   1.00 1.00
521 A121 45c multicolored   1.00 1.00
522 A121 70c multicolored   1.75 1.75
523 A121 70c multicolored   1.75 1.75
524 A121 $1.05 multicolored   2.75 2.75
525 A121 $1.05 multicolored   2.75 2.75
      Nos. 520-525 (6)   11.00 11.00

Battles of the Coral Sea and Midway, 50th anniv.

US Invasion of
Guadalcanal, 50th
Anniv. — A122

Designs: 45c, Troops landing on beach. 70c, Troops in battle. $1.05, Map, flags.

1992, Aug. 6 Litho. *Perf. 14½*
526 A122 45c multicolored   1.10 1.10
527 A122 70c multicolored   1.90 1.90
528 A122 $1.05 multicolored   3.25 3.25
      Nos. 526-528 (3)   6.25 6.25

Christmas — A123

Scenes of Norfolk Island: 40c, Ball Bay, looking over Point Blackbourne. 45c, Headstone Creek. 75c, Ball Bay. $1.20, Rocky Point Reserve.

1992, Oct. 29 Litho. *Perf. 15x14½*
529 A123 40c multicolored   .75   .75
530 A123 45c multicolored   .85   .85
531 A123 75c multicolored   1.75 1.75
532 A123 $1.20 multicolored   2.50 2.50
      Nos. 529-532 (4)   5.85 5.85

Tourism — A124

Tourist sites at Kingston: a, Boat shed, flaghouses. b, Old military barracks. c, All Saints Church. d, Officers quarters. e, Quality row.

1993, Feb. 23 Litho. *Perf. 14½*
533 A124 45c Strip of 5, #a.-e.   5.00 5.00

Emergency
Services — A125

45c, Volunteer fire service. 70c, Rescue squad. 75c, St. John ambulance. $1.20, Police service.

1993, May 18 Litho. *Perf. 14½*
534 A125 45c multicolored   1.00 1.00
535 A125 70c multicolored   1.25 1.25
536 A125 75c multicolored   1.50 1.50
537 A125 $1.20 multicolored   2.75 2.75
      Nos. 534-537 (4)   6.50 6.50

Nudibranchs
A126

No. 538, Phyllidia ocellata. No. 539, Glaucus atlanticus. 75c, Bornella sp. 85c, Glossodoris rubroannolata. 95c, Halgerda willeyi. $1.05, Chromodoris amoena.

1993, July 7 Litho. *Perf. 14½*
538 A126 45c multicolored   1.00 1.00
539 A126 45c multicolored   1.25 1.25
540 A126 75c multicolored   1.40 1.40
541 A126 85c multicolored   1.60 1.60
542 A126 95c multicolored   1.75 1.75
543 A126 $1.05 multicolored   2.00 2.00
      Nos. 538-543 (6)   9.00 9.00

No. 539 identified as "glauc."

A127

Designs: 70c, Maori patus. $1.20, First Maori map of New Zealand on paper, 1793.

1993, Oct. 28 Litho. *Perf. 14½*
544 A127 70c tan, buff & black   1.40 1.40
545 A127 $1.20 tan, buff & black   2.60 2.60

Cultural contact with New Zealand, bicent.

A128

1993, Oct. 28
546 A128 40c blue & multi   .75   .75
547 A128 45c red & multi   .85   .85
548 A128 75c green & multi   1.40 1.40
549 A128 $1.20 black & multi   2.25 2.25
      Nos. 546-549 (4)   5.25 5.25

Early Pacific
Explorers — A129

Explorer, ship: 5c, Vasco Nunez de Balboa, Barbara. 10c, Ferdinand Magellan, Victoria. 20c, Juan Sebastian de Elcano, Victoria. 50c, Alvaro de Saavedra, Florida. 70c, Ruy Lopez de Villalobos, San Juan. 75c, Miguel Lopez de Legaspi, San Lesmes. 80c, Sir Frances Drake, Golden Hinde. 85c, Alvaro de Mendana, Santiago. 90c, Pedro Fernandes de Quiros, San Pedro Paulo. $1, Luis Baez de Torres, San Perico. $2, Abel Tasman, Heemskerk. $5, William Dampier, Cygnet. No. 562, Golden Hinde (Francis Drake).

1994 Litho. *Perf. 14½*
550 A129 5c multicolored   .30   .30
551 A129 10c multicolored   .35   .35
552 A129 20c multicolored   .60   .60
554 A129 50c multicolored   .90   .90
556 A129 70c multicolored   1.10 1.10
557 A129 75c multicolored   1.25 1.25
558 A129 80c multicolored   1.25 1.25
559 A129 85c multicolored   1.40 1.40
560 A129 90c multicolored   1.60 1.60
560A A129 $1 multicolored   1.75 1.75
561 A129 $2 multicolored   3.50 3.50
561A A129 $5 multicolored   8.00 8.00
      Nos. 550-561A (12)   22.00 22.00

Souvenir Sheet
Perf. 13
562 A129 $1.20 multicolored   3.75 3.75

No. 562 contains one 32x52mm stamp.

Issued: 50c, 70c, 75c, $2, No. 562, 2/8/94; 5c, 10c, 20c, $5, 5/3/94. 80c, 85c, 90c, $1, 7/26/94.

A130

Seabirds: a, Sooty tern. b, Red-tailed tropic bird. c, Australasian gannet. d, Wedge-tail shearwater. e, Masked booby.

1994, Aug. 17 Litho. *Perf. 14½x14*
565 A130 45c Strip of 5, #a.-e.   6.50 6.50
      Booklet, 2 #565   14.00

A131

Christmas: 45c, Church, flowers, words from Pitcairn anthem. 75c, Stained glass windows, "To God be the glory." $1.20, Rainbow, ship, "Ship of Fame."

1994, Oct. 27 Litho. *Die Cut*
Self-Adhesive
566 A131 45c multicolored   1.20 1.20
567 A131 75c multicolored   1.40 1.40
568 A131 $1.20 multicolored   2.40 2.40
      Nos. 566-568 (3)   5.00 5.00

Vintage
Cars — A132

45c, 1926 Chevrolet. 75c, 1928 Model A Ford. $1.05, 1929 Model A A/C Ford truck. $1.20, 1930 Model A Ford.

1995, Feb. 7 Litho. *Perf. 14x14½*
569 A132 45c multicolored   .65   .65
570 A132 75c multicolored   1.25 1.25
571 A132 $1.05 multicolored   1.75 1.75
572 A132 $1.20 multicolored   2.50 2.50
      Nos. 569-572 (4)   6.15 6.15

Humpback
Whales — A133

Perf. 14x14½, 14½x14
1995, May 9   Litho.
573 A133 45c Tail fluke   1.15 1.15
574 A133 75c Mother & calf   1.60 1.60
575 A133 $1.05 Breaching, vert.   2.25 2.25
      Nos. 573-575 (3)   5.00 5.00

Souvenir Sheet
Perf. 14½x14
576 A133 $1.20 Bubble netting,
                vert.   4.00 4.00
  a.   Overprinted in gold & black   7.50 7.50

No. 576 contains one 30x50mm stamp and is a continuous design.
Overprint in margin of No. 576a has "Selamat Hari Merdeka" and JAKARTA '95 exhibition emblem.

Butterfly Fish — A134

Chaetodon: 5c, pelewensis. 45c, plebeius. $1.20, tricinctus. $1.50, auriga.

1995, June 15   Litho.   Perf. 14
577	A134	5c multicolored	.90	.90
578	A134	45c multicolored	1.40	1.40
579	A134	$1.20 multicolored	2.75	2.75
580	A134	$1.50 multicolored	3.25	3.25
		Nos. 577-580 (4)	8.30	8.30

World War II
Vehicles — A135

Designs: 5c, 1942 Intl. 4x4 refueler. 45c, 1942 Ford 5 passenger sedan. $1.20, 1942 Ford 3-ton tipper. $2, D8 Caterpillar with scraper.

1995, Aug. 8   Litho.   Perf. 14x15
Black Vignettes
581	A135	5c brown & tan	.50	.50
582	A135	45c blue & red lil	1.25	1.25
583	A135	$1.20 grn & org	2.60	2.60
584	A135	$2 red & gray	4.25	4.25
		Nos. 581-584 (4)	8.60	8.60

Island Flower Type of 1960
1995, Sept. 1   Litho.   Rouletted 7
Booklet Stamps
585	A6	5c like No. 30	.25	.25
a.		Booklet pane of 18 + 3 labels	4.25	
586	A6	5c like No. 33	.25	.25
a.		Booklet pane of 18 + 3 labels	4.25	
		Complete booklet, 1 each #585a-586a	8.75	

A136

Victory in the Pacific Day, 50th Anniv.
A136a

Designs: 5c, Fighter plane en route. 45c, Sgt. T.C. Derrick, VC, vert. 75c, Gen. MacArthur, vert. $1.05, Girls at victory party.

1995, Sept. 1   Litho.   Perf. 12
587	A136	5c multicolored	.35	.35
588	A136	45c multicolored	.80	.80
589	A136	75c multicolored	1.30	1.30
590	A136	$1.05 multicolored	2.00	2.00
		Nos. 587-590 (4)	4.45	4.45

Litho. & Embossed
591	A136a	$10 Medals	23.00	23.00

Singapore '95.

UN, 50th Anniv. — A137

45c, Dove. 75c, Christmas star. $1.05, Christmas candles. $1.20, Olive branch.

1995, Nov. 7   Litho.   Perf. 14½x14
592	A137	45c multicolored	.85	.85
593	A137	75c multicolored	1.20	1.20
594	A137	$1.05 multicolored	1.60	1.60
595	A137	$1.20 multicolored	2.10	2.10
		Nos. 592-595 (4)	5.75	5.75

Christmas (#593-594).

Skinks and
Geckos — A138

World Wildlife Fund: a, 5c, Skink crawling left. b, 45c, Skink crawling right. c, 5c, Gecko crawling right. d, 45c, Gecko crawling left, flower.

1996, Feb. 7   Litho.   Perf. 14½x15
596	A138	Strip of 4, #a.-d.	3.00	3.00

No. 596 was issued in sheets of 4 strips with stamps in each strip in different order.

Royal Australian Air
Force, 75th
Anniv. — A139

1996, Apr. 22   Litho.   Perf. 14
597	A139	45c Sopwith pup	.85	.85
598	A139	45c Wirraway	.85	.85
599	A139	75c F-111C	1.40	1.40
600	A139	85c F/A-18 Hornet	1.60	1.60
		Nos. 597-600 (4)	4.70	4.70

Souvenir Sheet

New
Year
1996
(Year
of
the Rat)
A140

1996, May 17   Litho.   Perf. 12
601	A140	$1 multicolored	2.60	2.60
a.		With addl. inscription in sheet margin	5.00	5.00

No. 601a is inscribed in sheet margin with China '96 exhibition emblem.

Shells — A141

Designs: No. 602, Argonauta nodosa. No. 603, Janthina janthina. No. 604, Naticarius oncus. No. 605, Cypraea caputserpentis.

1996, July 2   Litho.   Perf. 14
602	A141	45c multicolored	.90	.90
603	A141	45c multicolored	.90	.90
604	A141	45c multicolored	.90	.90
605	A141	45c multicolored	.90	.90
		Nos. 602-605 (4)	3.60	3.60

Tourism — A142

1996, Sept. 17   Litho.   Perf. 13½x14
606	A142	45c Shopping	.70	.70
607	A142	75c Bounty day	1.10	1.10
608	A142	$2.50 Horse riding	3.50	3.50
609	A142	$3.70 Working the ship	5.25	5.25
		Nos. 606-609 (4)	10.55	10.55

A143

Christmas: Cow, star, Bible verse, and: No. 610, Nativity scene. No. 611, Boats, boathouses. 75c, House, trees. 85c, Flowers, fruits.

1996, Nov. 5   Litho.   Perf. 15
610	A143	45c multicolored	.75	.75
611	A143	45c multicolored	.75	.75
612	A143	75c multicolored	1.25	1.25
613	A143	85c multicolored	1.40	1.40
		Nos. 610-613 (4)	4.15	4.15

A144

No. 614, Natl. Arms. No. 615, Natl. Seal.

1997, Jan. 22   Litho.   Roulette 7
614	A144	5c yellow & green	.35	.35
a.		Booklet pane of 10	3.50	

615	A144	5c tan & brown	.35	.35
a.		Booklet pane of 10	3.50	
		Complete booklet, 2 each #614a-615a	7.00	

Souvenir Sheet

Beef
Cattle
A145

1997, Feb. 11   Perf. 13½x13
616	A145	$1.20 multicolored	2.75	2.75
a.		Inscribed in sheet margin	30.00	25.00

No. 616a is inscribed with Hong Kong '97 exhibition emblem.

Butterflies — A146

Designs: 75c, Cepora perimale perimale. 90c, Danaus chrysippus petilia. $1, Danaus bamata bamata. $1.20, Danaus plexippus.

1997, Mar. 28   Perf. 14½
617	A146	75c multicolored	1.50	1.50
a.		Black omitted, denomination and country name are missing	10,000.	
618	A146	90c multicolored	1.75	1.75
619	A146	$1 multicolored	2.00	2.00
620	A146	$1.20 multicolored	2.50	2.50
		Nos. 617-620 (4)	7.75	7.75

On No. 617a the denomination and country name are missing.

Dolphins
A147

1997, May 29   Litho.   Perf. 14
621	A147	45c Dusky dolphin	1.00	1.00
622	A147	75c Common dolphin	2.00	2.00

Souvenir Sheet
623	A147	$1.05 Dolphin, diff.	2.75	2.75
a.		Inscribed in sheet margin	5.25	5.25

No. 623a is inscribed in sheet margin with PACIFIC 97 exhibition emblem.

First Norfolk Island Stamp, 50th Anniv.
A148

Designs: $1, View of Ball Bay. $1.50, #4. $8, #12, view of Ball Bay.

1997, June 10   Perf. 12
624		$1.00 multicolored	1.25	1.25
625		$1.50 multicolored	2.00	2.00
a.		A148 Pair, #624-625	3.50	3.50

Size: 90x45mm
626	A148	$8 multicolored	10.00	10.00

Queen Elizabeth II &
Prince Philip, 50th
Wedding
Anniv. — A149

Designs: 20c, Queen. No. 628, Prince guiding 4-in-hand team. No. 629, Prince in formal suit, hat. 50c, Queen riding in royal coach. $1.50, Younger picture of Queen, Prince riding in carriage.

1997, Aug. 12   Litho.   Perf. 14½
627	A149	20c multicolored	.45	.45
628	A149	25c multicolored	.50	.50
a.		Pair, #627-628	1.00	1.00
629	A149	25c multicolored	.50	.50
630	A149	50c multicolored	1.00	1.00
a.		Pair, #629-630	1.60	1.60

Souvenir Sheet
631	A149	$1.50 multicolored	3.25	3.25

Souvenir Sheet

Return of
Hong
Kong to
China
A150

1997, Sept. 16   Litho.   Perf. 14
632	A150	45c Royal Yacht Britannia	2.75	2.75

Greetings
Stamps — A151

1997, Nov. 4   Litho.   Perf. 13x13½
633	A151	45c Christmas	.75	.75
634	A151	75c New Year's Eve	1.10	1.10
635	A151	$1.20 Valentine's Day	1.90	1.90
		Nos. 633-635 (3)	3.75	3.75

Souvenir Sheet

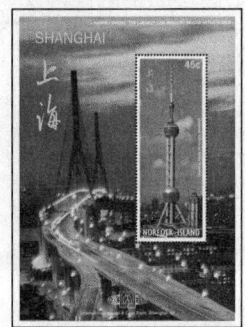

Oriental Pearl TV Tower,
Shanghai — A152

1997, Nov. 18   Perf. 14½
636	A152	45c multicolored	2.25	2.25

Shanghai '97, Intl. Stamp & Coin Expo.

Souvenir Sheet

New
Year
1998
(Year of
the
Tiger)
A153

1998, Feb. 12   Litho.   Perf. 12
637	A153	45c multicolored	2.00	2.00

Paintings of
Cats — A154

1998, Feb. 26								*Perf. 14½*
638	A154	45c "Pepper"				.65	.65
639	A154	45c "Tabitha"				.65	.65
640	A154	75c "Midnight"				1.10	1.10
641	A154	$1.20 "Rainbow"				1.75	1.75
		Nos. 638-641 (4)			4.15	4.15

Island Scenes, by
Brent Hilder — A155

Designs: No. 642, Penal Settlement, 1825-
56. No. 643, First settlement, 1788-1814.

1998, Feb. 27								*Rouletted 7*
642	A155	5c blue & black				.30	.30
	a.	Booklet pane of 10				3.00
643	A155	5c blue green & black			.30	.30
	a.	Booklet pane of 10				3.00
		Complete booklet, 2 each
		1642a-1643a				6.00

Diana, Princess of Wales (1961-97)
Common Design Type

#645: a, Wearing blue & white dress. b,
Wearing pearl pendant earrings. c, In striped
dress.

**1998, Apr. 28	Litho.			*Perf. 14½x14***
644	CD355	45c multicolored			1.10	1.10
Sheet of 4
645	CD355	45c #a.-c., #644			4.50	4.50

No. 644 sold for $1.80 + 45c, with surtax
from international sales being donated to the
Princess Diana Memorial fund and surtax from
national sales being dontated to designated
local charity.

Reef Fish — A156

Designs: 10c, Tweed trousers. 20c, Con-
spicuous angelfish. 30c, Moon wrasse. 45c,
Wide-stiped clownfish. 50c, Raccoon butterfly
fish. 70c, Artooti. 75c, Splendid hawkfish. 85c,
Scorpion fish. 90c, Orange fairy basslet. $1,
Sweetlip. $3, Moorish idol. $4, Gold ribbon
soapfish.
$1.20, Shark.

**1998	Litho.			*Perf. 14½***
646	A156	10c multicolored			.25	.25
647	A156	20c multicolored			.30	.30
648	A156	30c multicolored			.45	.45
649	A156	45c multicolored			.60	.60
650	A156	50c multicolored			.70	.70
651	A156	70c multicolored			.95	.95
652	A156	75c multicolored			1.05	1.05
653	A156	85c multicolored			1.20	1.20
654	A156	90c multicolored			1.20	1.20
655	A156	$1 multicolored				1.40	1.40
656	A156	$3 multicolored				4.25	4.25
657	A156	$4 multicolored				5.75	5.75
		Nos. 646-657 (12)		18.10	18.10

Souvenir Sheet
Perf. 14x14½
658	A156	$1.20 multicolored			2.50	2.50

No. 658 contains 30x40mm stamp.
Issued: 10c, 30c, 50c, 75c, 90c, $1.20, $4,
5/5; others, 6/29.

16th Commonwealth
Games, Kuala
Lumpur — A157

Designs: 75c, Hammer throw, vert. 95c,
Trap shooting. $1.05, Lawn bowling, vert.
85c, Flag bearer, vert.

**1998, July 23	Litho.			*Perf. 14½***
659	A157	75c black & red				1.10	1.10
660	A157	95c black & violet
		blue					1.35	1.35
661	A157	$1.05 black & red lilac			1.40	1.40
		Nos. 659-661 (3)			3.85	3.85
Souvenir Sheet
662	A157	85c black & greenish
		blue					2.40	2.40

The Norfolk,
Bicent. — A158

**1998, Sept. 24	Litho.			*Perf. 13***
663	A158	45c multicolored			1.90	1.90
Souvenir Sheet
664	A158	$1.20 multicolored			3.00	3.00

Souvenir Sheet

Whales
A159

**1998, Oct. 23	Litho.		*Perf. 13½x14***
665	A159	$1.50 multicolored			4.25	4.25
		See Namibia No. 919, South Africa No.
1095.

Christmas
A160

Designs: 45c, "Peace on earth." 75c, "Joy to
the World." $1.05, Doves, "A season of love."
$1.20, Candle, "Light of the World."

**1998, Nov. 10				*Perf. 13x13½***
666	A160	45c multicolored			.65	.65
667	A160	75c multicolored			1.10	1.10
668	A160	$1.05 multicolored			1.50	1.50
669	A160	$1.20 multicolored			1.60	1.60
		Nos. 666-669 (4)			4.85	4.85

Airplanes — A161

No. 670, S23 Sandringham. No. 671, DC4
"Norfolk Trader."

**1999, Jan. 28	Litho.			*Roulette 7***
Booklet Stamps
670	A161	5c dk grn & lake			.50	.50
	a.	Booklet pane of 10			5.00
671	A161	5c lake & dk grn			.50	.50
	a.	Booklet pane of 10			5.00
		Complete booklet, 2 ea #670a-
		671a					10.00

Souvenir Sheet

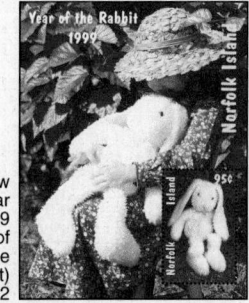

New
Year
1999
(Year of
the
Rabbit)
A162

**1999, Feb. 9	Litho.			*Perf. 14***
672	A162	95c multicolored			2.40	2.40
	a.	With additional sheet margin in-
		scription				4.00	4.00

No. 672a is inscribed in sheet margin with
China '99 exhibition emblem. Issued: 8/23/99.

Trading Ship
Resolution
A163

Designs: No. 673, Under construction. No.
674, Launch day. No. 675, Emily Bay. No.
676, Cascade. No. 677, Docked at Auckland.

**1999, Mar. 19				*Perf. 13x13½***
Booklet Stamps
673	A163	45c multicolored			2.00	2.00
674	A163	45c multicolored			2.00	2.00
675	A163	45c multicolored			2.00	2.00
676	A163	45c multicolored			2.00	2.00
677	A163	45c multicolored			2.00	2.00
	a.	Booklet pane, #673-677 + label		10.00
		Complete booklet, #677a			10.00

Australia '99, World Stamp Expo.

Souvenir Sheet

Pacific
Black
Duck
A164

**1999, Apr. 27	Litho.			*Perf. 14***
678	A164	$2.50 multicolored			4.75	4.75
IBRA '99, Intl. Philatelic Exhibition, Nuremberg, Germany.

Providence
Petrel — A165

**1999, May 27	Litho.			*Perf. 14½***
679	A165	75c In flight, vert.			1.90	1.90
680	A165	$1.05 Up close				2.75	2.75
681	A165	$1.20 Adult, young			3.00	3.00
		Nos. 679-681 (3)			7.65	7.65
Souvenir Sheet
Perf. 13
682	A165	$4.50 In flight				7.75	7.75

No. 682 contains one 35x51mm stamp.
See No. 710.

Roses — A166

**1999, July 30	Litho.			*Perf. 14½x14***
683	A166	45c Cecile Brunner			.90	.90
684	A166	75c Green				1.25	1.25
685	A166	$1.05 David Buffett			2.00	2.00
		Nos. 683-685 (3)			4.15	4.15
Souvenir Sheet
686	A166	$1.20 A Country Wo-
		man					2.75	2.75

Handicrafts — A167

Designs: a, 45c, Pottery. b, 45c, Woodcarv-
ing. c, 75c, Quilting. d, $1.05, Weaving.

**1999, Sept. 16				*Perf. 14¼x14¾***
687	A167	Strip of 4, #a.-d.			4.25	4.25

Queen Mother's Century
Common Design Type

Queen Mother: No. 688, Inspecting bomb
damage at Buckingham Palace, 1940. No.
689, With royal family at Abergeldy Castle,
1955. 75c, With Queen Elizabeth, Prince William, 94th birthday. $1.20, As colonel-in-chief
of King's Regiment.
$3, With Amy Johnson, pilot of 1930 flight to
Australia.

Wmk. 384
**1999, Oct. 12	Litho.			*Perf. 13½***
688	CD358	45c multicolored			.70	.70
689	CD358	45c multicolored			.70	.70
690	CD358	75c multicolored			1.10	1.10
691	CD358	$1.20 multicolored			1.75	1.75
		Nos. 688-691 (4)			4.25	4.25
Souvenir Sheet
692	CD358	$3 multicolored				5.25	5.25

Melanesian Mission, 150th
Anniv. — A168

Christmas: a, 45c, Bishop George Augustus
Selwyndd. b, 45c, Bishop John Coleridge Patteson. c, 75c, Text. d, $1.05, Stained glass. e,
$1.20, Southern Cross.

**1999, Nov. 10	Litho.			*Perf. 14***
693	A168	Strip of 5, #a.-e.			7.50	7.50
See Solomon Islands No. 890.

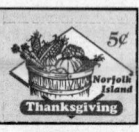

Festivals — A169

No. 694, Thanksgiving. No. 695, Country
music festival.

**2000, Jan. 31	Litho.			*Roulette 5¾***
Booklet Stamps
694	A169	5c lav & blk				.25	.25
695	A169	5c blue & blk				.25	.25
	a.	Booklet pane, 5 each #694-695		1.75
		Complete booklet, 4 #695a		7.00

Souvenir Sheet

New Year
2000
(Year of
the
Dragon)
A170

**2000, Feb. 7	Litho.			*Perf. 13¼***
696	A170	$2 multi				3.25	3.25

Fowl — A171

Designs: 45c, Domestic goose. 75c, Pacific
black duck. $1.05, Mallard drake. $1.20, Ayles-
bury duck.

**2000, Feb. 18	Litho.			*Perf. 14¼***
697	A171	45c multi				.85	.85
698	A171	75c multi				1.25	1.25
699	A171	$1.05 multi				1.75	1.75
700	A171	$1.20 multi				2.25	2.25
		Nos. 697-700 (4)			6.10	6.10

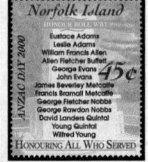

Anzac Day — A172

Monument and lists of war dead from: 45c,
WWI. 75c, WWII and Korean War.

**2000, Apr. 25	Litho.			*Perf. 14x14¾***
701-702	A172	Set of 2			2.40	2.40

Souvenir Sheets

Whaler Project A173

Designs: No. 703, shown. No. 704, As #703, with gold overprints for The Stamp Show 2000, London, and Crown Agents.

Perf. 14¼, Imperf. (#704)
2000, May 1
703-704 A173 $4 Set of 2   14.00 14.00

Bounty Day — A174

Designs: 45c, Capt. William Bligh. 75c, Fletcher Christian.

2000, June 8   **Perf. 14¼**
705-706 A174 Set of 2   3.25 3.25

Eighth Festival of Pacific Arts, New Caledonia — A175

Designs: 45c, Pot and broom.
No. 708: a, 75c, Turtle and shells. $1.05, Paintings. $1.20, Spear, mask. $2, Decorated gourds.

2000, June 19   **Die cut 9x9½**
Self-Adhesive
707 A175 45c multi   1.75 1.75
Souvenir Sheet
Perf. 13¾
Water-Activated Gum
708 A175 Sheet of 4, #a-d   9.00 9.00
No. 708 contains four 30x38mm stamps.

Souvenir Sheet

Malcolm Eadie Champion, 1912 Olympic Gold Medalist — A176

2000, Sept. 15 Litho. Perf. 14x14¼
709 A176 $3 multi   5.75 5.75
Olymphilex 2000 Stamp Exhibition, Sydney.

Providence Petrel Type of 1999
Souvenir Sheet
2000, Oct. 5   **Perf. 14½x14¾**
710 Sheet of 2 #710a   6.00 6.00
  a. A165 $1.20 Like #681, 32x22mm, with white frame   3.75 3.75
Canpex 2000 Stamp Exhibition, Christchurch, New Zealand.

Christmas — A177

Words from "Silent Night" and: 45c, Sun. 75c, Candle. $1.05, Moon. $1.20, Stars.

2000, Oct. 20   **Perf. 13¼x13**
711-714 A177 Set of 4   7.25 7.25

Millennium — A178

Children's art by: No. 715, 45c, Jessica Wong and Mardi Pye. No. 716, 45c, Roxanne Spreag. No. 717, 75c, Tara Grube. No. 718, 75c, Tom Greenwood.

2000, Nov. 26   **Perf. 14¾x14½**
715-718 A178 Set of 4   7.50 7.50

Green Parrot — A179

2001, Jan. 26   **Rouletted 5½**
Booklet Stamp
719 A179 5c green & red   .25 .25
  a. Booklet pane of 10   2.25
      Booklet, 4 #719a   9.00

Tarler Bird — A180

Designs: $2.30, Norfolk island eel and tarler bird.

2001, Feb. 1   **Perf. 13¼**
720 A180 45c multi   1.75 1.75
Imperf
Size: 110x70mm
721 A180 $2.30 multi   7.00 7.00
No. 720 issued in sheet of 5 + label. New Year 2001 (Year of the snake), Hong Kong 2001 Stamp Exhibition (#721).

Australian Federation, Cent. — A181

Pre-federation political cartoons from The Bulletin Magazine: No. 722, 45c, Promises, Promises! No. 723, 45c, The Gout of Federation. No. 724, 45c, The Political Garotters. No. 725, 45c, Tower of Babel. No. 726, 45c, Old Clothes. No. 727, 45c, The Federal Spirit. 75c, Australia Faces the Dawn. $1.05, The Federal Capital Question. $1.20, The Imperial Fowl Yard.

2001, Mar. 12 Litho. Perf. 14x14¾
722-730 A181 Set of 9   8.50 8.50

Souvenir Sheet

2001 A Stamp Odyssey Stamp Show, Invercargill, New Zealand — A182

Blue portion of background at: a, Right. b, Left. c, Top.

2001, Mar. 16   **Perf. 13**
731 A182 75c Sheet of 3, #a-c, + 3 labels   3.75 3.75

Bounty Day — A183

2001, June 8   **Rouletted 6**
732 A183 5c green & black   .25 .25
  a. Booklet pane of 10   1.50
      Booklet, 4 #732a   6.00

Tourism — A184

Perfume bottle and: 45c, Jasminium simplicifolium. 75c, Woman's face in perfume bottle. $1.05, Woman with roses. $1.20, Taylors Road. $1.50, Couple shopping for perfume. $3, Woman and Norfolk pine trees.

2001, June 9   **Perf. 13¼**
733 A184 45c multi   1.00 1.00
734 A184 75c multi   2.00 2.00
  a. Booklet pane, #733-734   3.00
735 A184 $1.05 multi   2.00 2.00
736 A184 $1.20 multi   2.25 2.25
  a. Booklet pane, #735-736   4.25
737 A184 $1.50 multi   3.25 2.75
  a. Booklet pane of 1   3.25
Souvenir Sheet
738 A184 $3 multi   5.50 5.50
Booklet Stamp
Size: 154x97mm
Microrouletted at Left
739 A184 $3 Like #738   5.50 5.50
  a. Booklet pane of 1   5.50 5.50
      Booklet, #734a, 736a, 737a, 739a   16.00
Nos. 733-739 are impregnated with jasmine perfume. No. 738 contains one 60x72mm stamp.
No. 739 has perfume bottle at LR, country name moved on one line at UL, and is impregnated with jasmine perfume. No. 739a has binding stub at left. Booklet sold for $10 and includes postal card.
For overprint see No. 824.

Boats — A185

Designs: 45c, Whaler, vert. No. 741, $1, Rowers in boat. No. 742, $1, Motorboat, vert. $1.50, Men in cutter.

Perf. 14½x14¼, 14¼x14½
2001, Aug. 1   **Litho.**
740-743 A185 Set of 4   6.00 6.00
Coil Stamp
Self-Adhesive
Die Cut Perf. 14¼x14¾
744 A185 45c multi   .90 .90

Peace Keepers in Japan — A186

No. 745: a, Australian soldiers playing cards. b, Soldiers with birthday cake.
No. 746: a, Soldiers on Christmas float. b, Soldiers controlling traffic.

2001, Sept. 9   **Perf. 14½x14¾**
745 Pair with central label   3.00 3.00
  a. A186 45c multi   .90 .90
  b. A186 $1 multi   2.10 2.10
746 Pair with central label   3.00 3.00
  a. A186 45c multi   .90 .90
  b. A186 $1 multi   2.10 2.10

6th South Pacific Mini Games — A187

2001, Oct. 1   **Rouletted 6**
747 A187 10c green & brown   .30 .30
  a. Booklet pane of 10   3.00
      Booklet, 2 #747a   6.00

Two souvenir sheets publicizing the 6th South Pacific Mini-Games, featuring four 45c and four $1 values, respectively, were scheduled for release but were withdrawn from sale upon arrival in Norfolk, when serious design errors were discovered. A small quantity had previously been sold by Crown Agents. Value for pair of sheets, $150.

Christmas — A188

Christmas carols and flora: No. 748, 45c, Hark, the Herald Angels Sing, strawberry guava. No. 749, 45c, Deck the Halls, poinsettia. No., 750, $1, The First Noel, hibiscus. No. 751, $1, Joy to the World, Christmas croton. $1.50, We Wish You a Merry Christmas, Indian shot.

2001, Oct. 26   **Perf. 12½**
748-752 A188 Set of 5   7.25 7.25

Sacred Kingfisher — A189

2002, Jan. 15 Litho. Rouletted 5¾
Booklet Stamp
753 A189 10c aqua & dk bl   .25 .25
  a. Booklet pane of 10   2.50
      Booklet, 2 #753a   5.00

Cliff Ecology — A190

Designs: 45c, Red-tailed tropicbird. No. 755, $1, White oak tree. No. 756, $1, White oak flower. $1.50, Eagle ray.

2002, Jan. 21 Unwmk. Perf. 13
754-757 A190 Set of 4   7.25 7.25

Reign Of Queen Elizabeth II, 50th Anniv. Issue
Common Design Type
Designs: Nos. 758, 762a, 45c, Queen Mother with Princesses Elizabeth and Margaret, 1930. Nos. 759, 762b, 75c, Wearing scarf, 1977. Nos. 760, 762c, $1, Wearing crown, 1953. Nos. 761, 762d, $1.50, Wearing yellow hat, 2000. No. 762e, $3, 1955 portrait by Annigoni (38x50mm).

Perf. 14¼x14½, 13¾ (#762e)
2002, Feb. 6 Litho. Wmk. 373
With Gold Frames
758 CD360 45c multicolored   .75 .75
759 CD360 75c multicolored   1.25 1.25
760 CD360 $1 multicolored   1.75 1.75
761 CD360 $1.50 multicolored   2.40 2.40
    Nos. 758-761 (4)   6.15 6.15
Souvenir Sheet
Without Gold Frames
762 CD360 Sheet of 5, #a-e   9.75 9.75

The Age of Steam — A191

Perf. 14½x14¾
2002, Mar. 21 Litho. Unwmk.
763 A191 $4.50 multi   7.25 7.25

South Pacific Mini Games — A192

Designs: 50c, Track and field. $1.50, Tennis.

2002, Mar. 21   *Perf. 13¾x14¼*
764-765 A192   Set of 2   3.50 3.50

2002 Bounty Bowls Tournament — A193

2002, May 6   *Rouletted 6*
Booklet Stamp
766 A193 10c multi   .25 .25
  a.   Booklet pane of 10   2.00 —
     Booklet, 2 #766a   4.00

Phillip Island Flowers — A194

Designs: 10c, Streblorrhiza specioca. 20c, Plumbago zeylanica. 30c, Canavalia rosea. 40c, Ipomoea pes-caprae. 45c, Hibiscus insularis. 50c, Solanum laciniatum. 95c, Phormium tenax. $1, Lobelia anceps. $1.50, Carpobrotus glaucescens. $2, Abutilon julianae. $3, Wollastonia biflora. $5, Oxalis corniculata.

2002   *Perf. 14½*
767 A194 10c multi   .25 .25
768 A194 20c multi   .30 .30
769 A194 30c multi   .45 .45
770 A194 40c multi   .55 .55
771 A194 45c multi   .60 .60
772 A194 50c multi   .70 .70
773 A194 95c multi   1.50 1.50
774 A194 $1 multi   1.60 1.60
775 A194 $1.50 multi   2.25 2.25
776 A194 $2 multi   3.25 3.25
777 A194 $3 multi   4.75 4.75
778 A194 $5 multi   7.50 7.50
   Nos. 767-778 (12)   23.70 23.70

Issued: 20c, 40c, 45c, 95c, $2, $5, 5/21; others 9/18.

2002 Commonwealth Games, Manchester, England — A195

Designs: 10c, Track and field, vert. 45c, Cycling. $1, Lawn bowling, vert. $1.50, Shooting.

2002, July 25
779-782 A195   Set of 4   6.00 6.00

Operation Cetacean — A196

No. 783: a, Sperm whale and calf. b, Sperm whale and squid.

2002, Sept. 18   *Perf. 14*
783 A196   Horiz. pair with central label   6.50 6.50
  a.-b. $1 Either single   3.25 3.25
    See New Caledonia No. 906.

Christmas — A197

White tern: No. 784, 45c, Hatchling. No. 785, 45c, Bird on egg in nest. $1, Pair in flight. $1.50, One in flight.

2002, Nov. 12   *Litho.*   *Perf. 14*
784-787 A197   Set of 4   6.50 6.50

Horses on Norfolk Island — A198

No. 788: a, Horses with riders near stable. b, Horses grazing. c, Show jumping. d, Horse racing. e, Horses pulling carriage.

2003, Jan. 14
788   Horiz. strip of 5   6.50 6.50
  a.-c.   A198 45c Any single   .80 .80
  d.-e.   A198 75c Either single   1.75 1.75
    Year of the horse (in 2002).

Island Scenes A199

Photographs by Mary Butterfield: 50c, Buildings. 95c, Boat on beach. $1.10 Cattle grazing. $1.65 Tree near water.

2003, Mar. 18   *Perf. 14x14¼*
789-792 A199   Set of 4   7.50 7.50
    See Nos. 805-808.

Day Lilies — A200

No. 793: a, Southern Prize. b, Becky Stone. c, Cameroons. d, Chinese Autumn. e, Scarlet Orbit. f, Ocean Rain. g, Gingerbread man. h, Pink Corduroy. i, Elizabeth Hinrichsen. j, Simply Pretty.

2003, June 10   *Litho.*   *Perf. 14¼*
793   Block of 10   8.50 8.50
  a.-j.   A200 50c Any single   .85 .85
    Complete booklet, #793   9.50

Island Views A201

No. 794: a, Large trees at left, ocean. b, Beach. c, Rocks at shoreline. d, Cattle grazing.

2003, July 21   *Perf. 14*
794   Horiz. strip of 4 + 4 labels   6.25 6.25
  a.-d.   A201 50c Any single + label   .95 .95
No. 794 was issued in sheets of five strips that had labels that could be personalized for an additional fee.

First Norfolk Island Writer's Festival — A202

No. 795: a, Maeve and Gil Hitch. b, Alice Buffett. c, Nan Smith. d, Archie Bigg. e, Colleen McCullough. f, Peter Clarke. g, Bob Tofts. h, Merval Hoare.

2003, July 21   *Perf. 14½*
795   Block of 8 + 2 labels   5.50 5.50
  a.-d.   A202 10c Any single   .25 .25
  e.-h.   A202 50c Any single   .75 .75

Souvenir Sheet

Coronation of Queen Elizabeth II, 50th Anniv. — A203

No. 796: a, 10c, Queen wearing crown. b, $3, Queen wearing hat.

2003, July 29   *Perf. 14½*
796 A203   Sheet of 2, #a-b   5.75 5.75

Christmas — A204

Designs: No. 797, 50c, Dove, rainbow, "Joy to the World." No. 798, 50c, Earth, "Peace on Earth." $1.10, Heart, "Give the gift of Love." $1.65, Candle, "Trust in Faith."

2003, Oct. 21   *Perf. 14¼x14*
797-800 A204   Set of 4   7.25 7.25

Powered Flight, Cent. — A205

Designs: 50c, Seaplane. $1.10, QANTAS airliner in flight. No. 803, $1.65, QANTAS airliner on ground.
No. 804, $1.65, Wright Flyer.

2003, Dec. 2   *Perf. 14x14¼*
801-803 A205   Set of 3   8.00 8.00
Souvenir Sheet
Perf. 14½x14
804 A205 $1.65 multi   8.25 8.25
No. 804 contains one 48x30mm stamp. Limited quantities of No. 804 exist with an 85c surcharge and a 2004 Hong Kong Stamp Expo emblem in the margin. These were sold only at the exhibition. Value, mint never hinged or cto, $60.

Island Scenes Type of 2003

Designs: 50c, Houses, boat prow with foliage, vert. 95c, Waterfall, vert. $1.10, Cattle, vert. $1.65, Sea shore, vert.

2004, Feb. 10   *Litho.*   *Perf. 14¼x14*
805-808 A199   Set of 4   8.00 8.00

Sharks A206

Designs: 10c, Whale shark. 50c, Hammerhead shark. $1.10, Tiger shark. $1.65, Bronze whaler shark.

2004, Apr. 6   *Perf. 14¾*
809-812 A206   Set of 4   8.75 8.75

Spiders — A207

Designs: No. 813, 50c, Golden orb spider. No. 814, 50c, Community spider. $1, St. Andrew's cross spider. $1.65, Red-horned spider.
$1.50, Red-horned spider, diff.

2004, June 1   *Perf. 14½*
813-816 A207   Set of 4   6.75 6.75
Souvenir Sheet
Perf. 14½x14
817 A207 $1.50 multi   3.50 3.50
No. 817 contains one 47x40mm stamp.

Unloading of Ship Cargo A208

Designs: 50c, Men climbing on cargo nets. $1.10, Small boat with men and cargo. No. 820, $1.65, Two small boats. No. 821, $1.65, Two small boats at dock.

2004, July 13   *Litho.*   *Perf. 14¾*
818-820 A208   Set of 3   5.75 5.75
Souvenir Sheet
821 A208 $1.65 multi   3.50 3.50

Souvenir Sheet

Quota International, 25th Anniv. on Norfolk Island — A209

No. 822: a, 50c, Three children. b, $1.10, "We Care" on feet. c, $1.65, Child drawing "Quota" in sand.

2004, Aug. 16   *Perf. 14¼*
822 A209   Sheet of 3, #a-c   9.00 9.00

Day Lilies — A210

No. 823 — Hippeastrum varieties: a, Apple Blossom. b, Carnival. c, Cherry Blossom. d, Lilac Wonder. e, Millenium Star. f, Cocktail. g, Milady. h, Pacific Sunset. i, Geisha Girl. j, Lady Jane.

2004, Aug. 16   *Perf. 14½*
823   Block of 10   9.75 9.75
  a.-j.   A210 50c Any single   .95 .95
    Complete booklet, #823   10.50

No. 738 Overprinted in Silver

Souvenir Sheet

2004, Aug.   *Litho.*   *Perf. 13¼*
824 A184 $3 multi   12.00 12.00
No. 824 is impregnated with jasmine perfume.

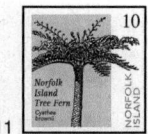

Flora — A211

Designs: No. 825, Norfolk Island tree fern. No. 826, Norfolk Island palm.

2004, Sept. 28   *Rouletted 6*
Booklet Stamps
825 A211 10c bl grn & blk   .40 .30
  a.   Booklet pane of 10   4.00
826 A211 10c yel & blk   .40 .25
  a.   Booklet pane of 10   4.00
    Complete booklet, #825a, 826a   8.00

Christmas — A212

Norfolk pine and words from: No. 827, 50c, Silent Night. No. 828, 50c, 'Twas the Night Before Christmas. $1.10, On the First Day of Christmas. $1.65, Oh, Holy Night.

2004, Oct. 26   *Perf. 14¼*
827-830 A212   Set of 4   6.25 6.25

Legislative Assembly, 25th Anniv. — A213

2004, Dec. 14   *Perf. 14*
831 A213 $5 multi   8.50 8.50

Worldwide Fund for Nature (WWF) — A214

Sacred kingfisher: No. 832, 50c, Two birds on tree branch. No. 833, 50c, Bird in flight with insect in beak. $1, Bird on branch. $2, Bird on branch, vert.

2004, Dec. 14
832-835 A214 Set of 4   7.25 7.25
835a   Miniature sheet, 2 each
           #832-835   14.00 14.00

Rotary International, Cent. — A215

Emblem and: No. 836, 50c, Beach Carnival. No. 837, 50c, Tree planting, vert. $1.20, Paul Harris. $1.80, Rotary Youth Leadership Awards, vert. $2, District 9910 ceremony.

2005, Feb. 23   Litho.   Perf. 14½
836-839 A215 Set of 4   6.50 6.50
Souvenir Sheet
840 A215 $2 multi   4.00 4.00
No. 840 contains one 40x30mm stamp.

Items From Norfolk Island Museum — A216

Designs: No. 841, 50c, Teacup, 1856. No. 842, 50c, Salt cellar from HMAV Bounty, 1856. $1.10, Medicine cups, 1825-55. $1.65, Stoneware jar, 1825-55.

2005, Apr. 5
841-844 A216 Set of 4   7.25 7.25

Pacific Explorers — A217

Designs: 50c, Polynesian explorer, boat and fish. $1.20, Magellan's ship and bird. $1.80, Captain James Cook, ship and flower. $2, Old map of world, horiz.

2005, Apr. 21   Perf. 14
845-847 A217 Set of 3   6.00 6.00
Souvenir Sheet
Perf. 14¾
848 A217 $2 multi   4.00 4.00
Pacific Explorer 2005 World Stamp Expo, Sydney. No. 848 contains one 46x32mm stamp.

Old Houses — A218

Designs: No. 849, 50c, Greenacres. No. 850, 50c, Branka House. $1.20, Ma Annas. $1.80, Naumai.

2005, June 16   Litho.   Perf. 14½
849-852 A218 Set of 4   6.50 6.50

Sea Birds — A219

Designs: 10c, Red-tailed tropicbird. 50c, Australasian gannet. $1.50 Gray ternlet. $2, Masked booby. $5, White-necked petrel.

$4, Red-tailed tropicbird, horiz.

2005, Aug. 9
853-857 A219 Set of 5   17.00 17.00
Souvenir Sheet
858 A219 $4 multi   7.75 7.75
See Nos. 883-888. For surcharge, see No. 1044.

Hibiscus Varieties — A220

No. 859: a, Marjory Brown. b, Aloha. c, Pulau Tree. d, Ann Miller. e, Surfrider. f, Philip Island. g, Rose of Sharon. h, D. J. O'Brien. i, Elaine's Pride. j, Castle White. k, Skeleton Hibiscus. l, Pink Sunset.

2005, Aug. 30   Perf. 14¼x14
859   Block of 12   9.75 9.75
a.-l.   A220 50c Any single   .80 .80
        Complete booklet, #859 12.00

Christmas A221

Designs: 50c, Anson Bay. $1.20, Cascade Bay. $1.80, Ball Bay.

2005, Oct. 25   Litho.   Perf. 14¼x14
860-862 A221 Set of 3   5.75 5.75

Jazz Festival — A222

Designs: 50c, Drummer. $1.20, Saxophonist. $1.80, Guitarist.

2005, Dec. 6   Perf. 14x14¼
863-865 A222 Set of 3   5.75 5.75

Queen's Baton Relay for 2006 Commonwealth Games — A223

No. 866: a, 50c, Baton relay runner, boat's prow. b, $1.50, Baton.

2006, Jan. 16   Litho.   Perf. 14½x14¾
866 A223 Horiz. pair, #a-b   3.50 3.50

2006 Commonwealth Games, Melbourne — A224

Norfolk Island flag and: 50c, Shooting. $1.50, Lawn bowling. $2, Squash.

2006, Mar. 14   Litho.   Perf. 14½
867-869 A224 Set of 3   6.00 6.00

Pitcairn Migration, 150th Anniv. A225

Pitcairn Island history: No. 870, 50c, The Bounty at Portsmouth. No. 871, 50c, Collecting breadfruit at Tahiti. $1.20, The mutiny. $1.50, Burning of the Bounty at Pitcairn Island.

$1.80, Pitcairners arrive at Norfolk Island, 1856.

2006, May 4   Perf. 14x14½
870-874 A225 Set of 5   8.75 8.75

Bounty Anniversary Day — A226

Designs: 10c, Re-enactment procession. 30c, Remembering old soldiers. No. 877, 50c, Honoring ancestors. No. 878, 50c, Community picnic. $4, Bounty Ball.

2006, June 7
875-879 A226 Set of 5   8.50 8.50
See Pitcairn Islands No. 643.

Traditional Hat Making A227

No. 880, 50c — Purple panel: a, Hat with flowers on brim. b, Hat with no flowers.
No. 881, 50c — Blue green panel: a, Hat with flowers on brim. b, Hat with feather at right.
No. 882, 50c — Green panel: a, Hat with flowers on brim. b, Hat with no flowers.

2006, June 7   Perf. 15¼x14¾
Horiz. Pairs, #a-b
880-882 A227 Set of 3   5.00 5.00

Sea Birds Type of 2005
Designs: 25c, White tern. 40c, Sooty tern. 70c, Black-winged petrel. $1, Black noddy. $3, Wedge-tailed shearwater. $2.50, Sooty tern, diff.

2006, Aug. 9   Perf. 14½
883-887 A219 Set of 5   8.00 8.00
Souvenir Sheet
888 A219 $2.50 multi   5.50 5.50

Dogs — A228

Dogs named: 10c, Wal. 50c, Axel. $1, Wag. $2.65, Gemma.

2006, Sept. 12   Perf. 14½
889-892 A228 Set of 4   7.25 7.25

Norfolk Island Central School, Middlegate, Cent. A229

Designs: No. 893, $2, Sepia-toned photograph. No. 894, $2, Color photograph.

2006, Oct. 3
893-894 A229 Set of 2   7.00 7.00

Christmas A230

Ornaments showing: No. 895, 50c, Birds. No. 896, 50c, House. $1.20, Building. $1.80, Flower.

2006, Nov. 21   Litho.
Stamp + Label
895-898 A230 Set of 4   11.00 11.00

Weeds — A231

Designs: No. 899, 50c, Ageratina riparia. No. 900, 50c, Lantana camara. $1.20, Ipomoea cairica. $1.80, Solanum mauritianum.

2007, Feb. 6   Perf. 14¼
899-902 A231 Set of 4   6.00 6.00

Adventure Sports — A232

Designs: No. 903, 50c, Wind surfing. No. 904, 50c, Sea kayaking. $1.20, Mountain biking. $1.80, Surfing.

2007, Apr. 3   Litho.   Perf. 14½
903-906 A232 Set of 4   6.50 6.50

Souvenir Sheet

Kentia Palm Seed Harvest A233

No. 907: a, Ladder and trees, vert. b, Dog and buckets of seeds. c, Man pouring seeds into box. d, Seeds on tree, vert.

Perf. 14 (14½ on Short Side Not Adjacent to Another Stamp)
2007, May 29
907 A233 50c Sheet of 4, #a-d, +
           central label   4.00 4.00

Ghosts — A234

Designs: 10c, Violinist, musical notes, building. 50c, Graveyard. $1, Female ghost on dock steps. $1.80, Ghosts on building steps.

2007, June 26   Perf. 14½
908-911 A234 Set of 4   6.00 6.00

Queen Victoria — A235

2007, July 31   Die Cut
Self-Adhesive
Booklet Stamp (10c)
912 A235 10c multi   .30 .30
a.   Booklet pane of 10   3.00
Size: 21x28mm
913 A235 $5 multi   10.00 10.00
Queen Victoria Scholarship, 120th anniv.

13th South Pacific Games, Samoa — A236

Designs: 50c, Squash. $1, Golf. $1.20, Netball. $1.80, Running. $2, Games emblem.

400

NORFOLK ISLAND

2007, Aug. 28   *Perf. 14¼*
914-917 A236   Set of 4   7.50 7.50
Souvenir Sheet
918 A236 $2 multi   3.50 3.50

Closure of First Convict Settlement, Bicent. — A237

Designs: 10c, HMS Sirius and Supply off Kingston. 50c, Shipping signal, Kingston. $1.20, First settlement, Kingston. $1.80, Ship Lady Nelson leaving for Tasmania.

2007, Nov. 13
919-922 A237   Set of 4   6.25 6.25

Banyan Park Play Center — A238

Children and slogans: 50c, "Friendship." $1, "Community." $1.20, "Play, learn, grow together." $1.80, "Read books."

2007, Nov. 27   Litho.   *Perf. 14x14¼*
923-926 A238   Set of 4   7.00 7.00

Christmas A239

Items with Christmas lights: 50c, Christmas tree. $1.20, Building. $1.80, Rowboat.

2007, Nov. 27
927-929 A239   Set of 3   5.50 5.50

Automobiles A240

Designs: 50c, 1965 Ford Falcon XP. $1, 1952 Chevrolet Styleline. $1.20, 1953 Pontiac Silver Arrow. $1.80, 1971 Rolls Royce Silver Shadow.

2008, Feb. 5
930-933 A240   Set of 4   6.75 6.75

Norfolk Islanders With Pitcairn Islands Heritage — A241

Designs: 50c, Andre Nobbs. $1, Darlene Buffett. $1.20, Colin "Boonie" Lindsay Buffett. $1.80, Tania Grube.

2008, Apr. 4   Litho.   *Perf. 14½*
934-937 A241   Set of 4   6.75 6.75

Jewish Gravestones — A242

Gravestone of: 50c, Carl Hans Nathan Strauss. $1.20, Meta Kienhuize. $1.80, Johan Jacobus Kienhuize. $2, Sally Kadesh.

2008, May 14   *Perf. 14½*
938-940 A242   Set of 3   5.50 5.50
Souvenir Sheet
Perf. 13½
941 A242 $2 multi   3.50 3.50
2008 World Stamp Championship, Israel (#941). No. 941 contains one 30x40mm stamp.

Calves — A243

Designs: 50c, Limousin Cross. $1, Murray Grey. $1.20, Poll Hereford. $1.80, Brahman Cross.

2008, May 30   *Perf. 14¼*
942-945 A243   Set of 4   7.00 7.00

St. John Ambulance, 25th Anniv. on Norfolk Island — A244

Designs: 30c, Past and present members. 40c, Re-enactment of treatment of accident victim at scene. 95c, Accident victim being placed in ambulance. $4, Accident victim entering hospital.

2008, June 27   *Perf. 14½*
946-949 A244   Set of 4   8.75 8.75

Ferns A245

No. 950, 20c: a, Netted brakefern. b, Pteris zahlbruckneriana.
No. 951, 50c: a, Robinsonia. b, Asplenium australasicum.
No. 952, 80c: a, Hanging fork fern. b, Tmesipteris norfolkensis.
No. 953, $2: a, King fern. b, Marattia salicina.

2008, Aug. 1   Litho.   *Perf. 14¼*
Horiz. Pairs, #a-b
950-953 A245   Set of 4   10.50 10.50

Ships Built On Norfolk Island — A246

Designs: 50c, Sloop Norfolk, 1798. $1.20, Schooner Resolution, 1925. $1.80, Schooner Endeavour, 1808.

2008, Sept. 2
954-956 A246   Set of 3   5.00 5.00

A247

Designs: 25c, Prison buildings. 55c, Gate and prison buildings. $1.75, Graveyard. $2.50, Building and walls.

2008, Oct. 27   Litho.   *Perf. 14½*
957-960 A247   Set of 4   7.00 7.00
Isles of Exile Conference, Norfolk Island.

A248

Christmas: 55c, Adoration of the Shepherds. $1.40, Madonna and Child. $2.05, Adoration of the Magi.

2008, Nov. 7   *Perf. 14¼*
961-963 A248   Set of 3   5.50 5.50

Mosaics — A249

Designs: 5c, Fish. No. 965, 15c, Flower. 55c, Bird. $1.40, Tree. No. 968, 15c, Turtle. No. 969, 15c, Starfish.

2009, Feb. 16   *Perf. 14x14¼*
964-967 A249   Set of 4   3.00 3.00
Booklet Stamps
Self-Adhesive
Serpentine Die Cut 9½x10
968-969 A249   Set of 2   .75 .75
969a   Booklet pane of 12, 6 each #968-969   4.25 4.25

Cattle Breeds — A250

Designs: 15c, Shorthorn. 55c, South Devon. $1.40, Norfolk Blue. $2.05, Lincoln Red. $5.00, Three calves.

2009, Apr. 24   Litho.   *Perf. 14x14¼*
970-973 A250   Set of 4   6.00 6.00
Souvenir Sheet
Perf. 14¼
974 A250 $5 multi   7.25 7.25

Mushrooms — A251

Designs: 15c, Gyrodon sp. 55c, Stereum ostrea. $1.40, Cymatoderma elegans. $2.05, Chlorophyllum molybdites.

2009, May 29   Litho.   *Perf. 14½x14*
975-978 A251   Set of 4   6.75 6.75
978a   Souvenir sheet, #975-978   6.75 6.75
978b   As "a," overprinted with Intl. Stamp & Coin Expo emblem and text in sheet margin in gold   8.25 8.25
Issued: No. 978b, 11/7/10.

Endangered Wildlife — A252

Designs: No. 979, Bridled nailtail wallaby. No. 980, Norfolk Island green parrot. No. 981, Subarctic fur seal. No. 982, Christmas Island blue-tailed skink. No. 983, Green turtle.

2009, Aug. 4   Litho.   *Perf. 14¾x14*
"Norfolk Island" Above Denomination
979 A252 55c multi   .95 .95
980 A252 55c multi   .95 .95
981 A252 55c multi   .95 .95
982 A252 55c multi   .95 .95
983 A252 55c multi   .95 .95
  a.   Horiz. strip of 5, #979-983   4.75 4.75
   Nos. 979-983 (5)   4.75 4.75
Miniature Sheet
984 A252 55c Sheet of 5, #980, Australia #3126, 3128-3130   5.00 5.00
See Australia Nos. 3126-3136. No. 984 is identical to Australia No. 3131. Australia No. 3127 is similar to No. 980, but has "Australia" above denomination.

Birds — A253

Designs: 15c, Gray fantail. 55c, Pacific robin, vert. $1.40, Golden whistler, vert. $2.05, Sacred kingfisher.

2009, Aug. 19   *Perf. 14½*
985 A253 15c multi   .25 .25
986 A253 55c multi   .95 .95
   Complete booklet, 10 #986   9.50
987 A253 $1.40 multi   2.40 2.40
988 A253 $2.05 multi   3.50 3.50
   Nos. 985-988 (4)   7.10 7.10

Self-government, 30th Anniv. — A254

2009, Aug. 19   *Perf. 14*
989 A254 $10 multi   15.00 15.00

Christmas — A255

Stained-glass windows depicting: 15c, St. Matthew. 50c, Roses. $1.45, Christ in Glory. $2.10, Saint with Chalice.

2009, Nov. 2   Litho.   *Perf. 14¼*
990-993 A255   Set of 4   7.75 7.75

Historical Artifacts — A256

Designs: 5c, China from second convict settlement, drawing of man and woman. 55c, Polynesian ivory fish hook, drawing of fishing boat. $1.10, Regimental badge, painting of soldiers. $1.45, Brass wall fitting from HMS Sirius shipwreck, drawing of shipwreck. $1.65, Bottles from convict settlement's Civil Hospital, drawing of treatment of an ill woman. $2.10, Bounty wedding ring, painting of the Bounty.

2010, Feb. 22   Litho.   *Perf. 14½*
994 A256   5c multi   .25 .25
995 A256   55c multi   1.00 1.00
996 A256 $1.10 multi   1.10 1.10
997 A256 $1.45 multi   2.60 2.60
998 A256 $1.65 multi   3.00 3.00
999 A256 $2.10 multi   3.75 3.75
   Nos. 994-999 (6)   11.70 11.70
   See Nos. 1021-1026.

Cruise Ships — A257

Designs: 55c, Pacific Jewel. $1.45, Pacific Sun. $1.65, Pacific Pearl. $1.75, Pacific Dawn. $2.10, RMS Strathaird.

2010, Mar. 26   Litho.   *Perf. 14x14½*
1000-1004 A257   Set of 5   14.00 14.00

1856 Emigration of Pitcairn Islanders to Norfolk Island — A258

Ship Morayshire and: 55c, Pitcairn Island girls on Norfolk Island, 1857. $1.10, Passengers aboard ship, 1856. $1.45, Pitcairn Island men on Norfolk Island, 1861. $2.75, Naomi and Jane Nobbs.

2010, June 15   *Perf. 13½x13¼*
1005-1008 A258   Set of 4   10.00 10.00

History of Whaling — A259

Designs: No. 1009, 60c, Blessing of the fleet. No. 1010, 60c, Launching of boats. $1.20, Cliff top navigational fires. $3, Products made from whales.

2010, Aug. 16   Litho.   Perf. 14x14¼
1009-1012 A259   Set of 4   10.00 10.00

Christmas — A260

Parrots and: 15c, Bells. 55c, Conifer sprig. 60c, Gift. $1.30, Christmas ornament.

2010, Oct. 18   Litho.   Perf. 13¼x13½
1013-1016 A260   Set of 4   5.25 5.25

2010 World Bowls Champion of Champions Lawn Bowling Tournament, Norfolk Island — A261

Designs: 60c, Woman holding trophy. $1.50, Man bowling. $2.20, Bowling balls.

2010, Nov. 23   Litho.   Perf. 14
1017-1019 A261   Set of 3   8.75 8.75

Souvenir Sheet

St. Barnabas Chapel, 130th Anniv. — A262

No. 1020: a, Chapel under construction. b, Congregation in front of chapel. c, Two men in front of chapel.

2010, Dec. 7   Perf. 14½x14
1020 A262 60c Sheet of 3, #a-c   3.75 3.75

Historical Artifacts Type of 2010

Designs: 15c, Women, iron. 60c, Thursday October Christian and his mug. $1.20, Soldiers, bone dominoes. $1.50, Soldier in front of Civil Hospital, clay pipe and ceramic shards. $1.80, Woman and child, doll and doll's head. $3, People at Melanesian Mission, wooden and shell hair items.

2011, Feb. 22   Perf. 14½
1021 A256 15c multi   .30 .30
1022 A256 60c multi   1.25 1.25
1023 A256 $1.20 multi   2.50 2.50
1024 A256 $1.50 multi   3.00 3.00
1025 A256 $1.80 multi   3.75 3.75
1026 A256 $3 multi   6.25 6.25
Nos. 1021-1026 (6)   17.05 17.05

Shells — A263

Designs: 15c, Cirostrema zelebori, Canarium labiatum. 60c, Janthina janthina, Spirula spirula. $1.50, Conus capitaneus, Conus ebraeus. $1.80, Cypraea vitellus, Cypraea caputserpentis. $3, Nerita atramentosa, Neritina turrita.

2011, Apr. 21   Litho.   Perf. 14½
1027-1031 A263   Set of 5   15.00 15.00

Norfolk Island National Park, 25th Anniv. — A264

Park emblem and: 25c, Abutilon julianae. 60c, Hibiscus insularis. $1.55, Myoporum obscurum. $2.25, Meryta latifolia.

2011, June 24   Perf. 13½x13¼
1032-1035 A264   Set of 4   10.00 10.00

Kingston and Arthur's Vale UNESCO World Heritage Site — A265

No. 1036: a, Guard House, 1796-1826. b, Graveyard, 1790s-1825. c, Government House, 1804-28. d, Pier Store, 1825. e, Crank Mill, 1827. f, Bloody Bridge, 1835. g, Commissariat Store, 1835. h, Kingston Pier, 1839. i, No. 9 Quality Row, 1839. j, Flaghouses, 1840s. k, New Jail, 1847. l, Royal Engineers Office, 1851.

2011, Aug. 1   Die Cut Perf. 9¾x10
Self-Adhesive
1036   Booklet pane of 12   15.00
a.-l.   A265 60c Any single   1.25 1.25

Norfolk Island Police Force, 80th Anniv. — A266

Designs: 60c, Mounted policeman on Bounty Day, c. 1933. $1.55, 1970s police car. $2.25, Policeman observing ship.

2011, Oct. 14   Litho.   Perf. 13x13¼
1037-1039 A266   Set of 3   9.25 9.25

Christmas — A267

Various flowers: 15c, 55c, 60c, $1.35.

2011, Oct. 14   Perf. 14½
1040-1043 A267   Set of 4   5.50 5.50

No. 853 Surcharged in Brown and Black

Methods and Perfs As Before
2012, Feb. 13
1044 A219 $4 on 10c #853   8.75 8.75

Iconic Activities — A268

Designs: 60c, Collecting hi hi shells. 75c, Collecting whale bird eggs. $1.55, Fishing off the rocks. $2.75, Clifftop barbecue.

2012, Apr. 10   Litho.   Die Cut
Self-Adhesive
1045-1048 A268   Set of 4   11.50 11.50

Souvenir Sheet

Reign of Queen Elizabeth II, 60th Anniv. — A269

No. 1049: a, Commemorative plaque on Queen Elizabeth Avenue. b, Beacon at Queen Elizabeth Lookout. c, Decorated pine tree at Government House.

Litho. With Foil Application
2012, Aug. 20   Perf. 14½
1049 A269 $1.60 Sheet of 3, #a-c   10.00 10.00

Sunshine Club, 51st Anniv. — A270

Designs: 60c, Baked goods. $1.60, Basket with bananas, flour and sugar. $1.65, Cook book and pie ingredients. $2.35, Hands.

2012, Oct. 19   Litho.   Perf. 14
1050-1053 A270   Set of 4   13.00 13.00

Christmas — A271

Various pearl inlays from pews in St. Barnabas Chapel and lyrics from Christmas carols: 15c, 55c, $1.55, $2.35.

2012, Nov. 1
1054-1057 A271   Set of 4   9.75 9.75

Airplanes Landing on Norfolk Island, 70th Anniv. — A272

No. 1058: a, Royal New Zealand Air Force Hudson Bomber. b, DC-3. c, Lancastrian. d, DC-4 Skymaster. e, Fokker F27 Friendship. f, Beechcraft Super King Air 200. g, Fokker F28 Fellowship. h, C-130 Hercules. i, BAe 146. j, Boeing 737-300. k, F/A-18 Hornet. l, Airbus A320.

Serpentine Die Cut 9¾x10
2012, Dec. 24
1058   Booklet pane of 12   15.00
a.-l.   A272 60c Any single   1.25 1.25

Bell, All Saints Church, Kingston — A273

2013, Apr. 9   Perf. 14
1059 A273 $5 multi   10.50 10.50

Norfolk Island Country Music Festival, 20th Anniv. — A274

Designs: 15c, Boots, Emily Bay Beach. 60c, Adam Harvey with guitar. $1.60, Guitar. $1.65, Dennis Marsh with guitar. $2.35, Street performer with guitar.

2013, May 20
1060-1064 A274   Set of 5   12.00 12.00

Shorelines A275

Designs: 15c, Ball Bay. 60c, Second Sands. 95c, Anson Bay. $1.20, Slaughter Bay. $1.70, Bumboras. $1.85, Emily Bay.

2013, Sept. 30   Litho.   Perf. 13½
1065 A275 15c multi   .30 .30
1066 A275 60c multi   1.10 1.10
1067 A275 95c multi   1.90 1.90
1068 A275 $1.20 multi   2.25 2.25
1069 A275 $1.70 multi   3.25 3.25
1070 A275 $1.85 multi   3.50 3.50
Nos. 1065-1070 (6)   12.30 12.30
See Nos. 1079-1084.

Christmas — A276

Locally-made Christmas ornamentation: 15c, Wreath. 55c, Christmas tree made of driftwood. $1.10, Bird made of driftwood. $1.65, Three stars.

2013, Nov. 1   Litho.   Perf. 14½
1071-1074 A276   Set of 4   6.50 6.50

Trans-Tasman Freestyle Motocross Challenge A277

Flag of Norfolk Island and New Zealand motorcyclists performing stunts on motorcycle: 50c, Joe McNaughton. $1, McNaughton, diff. $1.50, McNaughton, diff. $1.60, Callum Shaw.

2013, Dec. 18   Litho.   Perf. 13½
1075-1078 A277   Set of 4   8.25 8.25

Shorelines Type of 2013

Designs: 5c, Cemetery Beach. 10c, Beefsteak. 25c, Crystal Pool. 70c, Cascade Bay. $1.75, Garnet Point. $2.60, Duncombe Bay.

2014, May 7   Litho.   Perf. 13½
1079 A275 5c multi   .25 .25
1080 A275 10c multi   .25 .25
1081 A275 25c multi   .50 .50
1082 A275 70c multi   1.40 1.40
1083 A275 $1.75 multi   3.25 3.25
1084 A275 $2.60 multi   4.75 4.75
Nos. 1079-1084 (6)   10.40 10.40

Wearable Art — A278

Designs: 15c, Fishing for the Groom, by Wayne Boniface. 70c, Pasta Bella, by Boniface. $1.40, Flora Abunda Metallica, by Tony Gazzard., $1.50, Romeo and Julieta, by Julie Paris. $3.50, Bamboo Princess Warrior, by Robyn Butterfield.

2014, May 26   Litho.   Perf. 14
1085-1089 A278   Set of 5   13.50 13.50

Norfolk Island Pine — A279

Norfolk Island Pine and: 20c, Cottesloe Beach, Western Australia. 70c, Old Military Barracks, Kingston, Norfolk Island.

2014, July 22   Litho.   Perf. 14x14¾
1090-1091 A279   Set of 2   1.75 1.75

   See Australia Nos. 4145-4146.

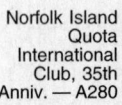

Norfolk Island Quota International Club, 35th Anniv. — A280

Designs: 15c, Picnic table near Emily Bay. 70c, Telescope on Queen Elizabeth Lookout. $3.20, Family on bench overlooking ocean.

2014, Aug. 15   Litho.   Perf. 14
1092-1094 A280   Set of 3   7.50 7.50

Souvenir Sheet

Red Cross on Norfolk Island, Cent. A281

2014, Sept. 29   Litho.   Perf. 14
1095 A281 $3.50 multi   6.25 6.25

Tip of Norfolk Island Pine A282

Developing Norfolk Island Pine Cone A283

Norfolk Island Pine Seedling A284

Norfolk Island Pine Forest A285

Norfolk Island Pine Seeds A286

Norfolk Island Pine Branches A287

Shed Norfolk Island Pine Needles A288

Hollowed-out Norfolk Island Pine A289

Norfolk Island Pines A290

Norfolk Island Pine A291

Serpentine Die Cut 10¾x10
2014, Sept. 29   Litho.
Self-Adhesive
1096   Booklet pane of 10   12.50
  a. A282 70c multi   1.25 1.25
  b. A283 70c multi   1.25 1.25
  c. A284 70c multi   1.25 1.25
  d. A285 70c multi   1.25 1.25
  e. A286 70c multi   1.25 1.25
  f. A287 70c multi   1.25 1.25
  g. A288 70c multi   1.25 1.25
  h. A289 70c multi   1.25 1.25
  i. A290 70c multi   1.25 1.25
  j. A291 70c multi   1.25 1.25

   See No. 1109.

Quilts — A292

Designs: 15c, Memory Quilt, by Julie South. 70c, Sampler Quilt, by Kay Greenbury, Raewyn Maxwell, Rowena Massicks and Barbara Solomon. $1.40, Sunset at Puppy's Point, by Greenbury. $1.50, Southern Cross Shared, by Greenbury. $3.50, Storm at Sea, by Massicks.

2014, Oct. 17   Litho.   Perf. 14½
1097-1101 A292   Set of 5   12.50 12.50

Christmas A293

Fabric designs by Sue Pearson depicting: 15c, Breadfruit leaves. 65c, Passion fruit flowers. $1.70, Turtles. $1.80, Taro leaves. $2.55, Hibiscus flowers.

2014, Nov. 3   Litho.   Perf. 14¼x14
1102-1106 A293   Set of 5   12.00 12.00

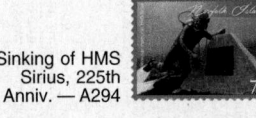

Sinking of HMS Sirius, 225th Anniv. — A294

No. 1107: a, Diver at underwater memorial. b, HMS Sirius, painting by John Allcott. c, The Melancholy Loss of HMS Sirius, painting by George Rapet. d, Cross belt plate from HMS Sirius. e, Capt. John Hunter of the HMS Sirius. f, Anchor of HMS Sirius. g, HMS Sirius, painting by Francis J. Bayldon. h, Carronades of HMS Sirius. i, Bronze shackle from HMS Sirius. j, Pantograph from HMS Sirius.

Serpentine Die Cut 10x10¾
2015, Mar. 19   Litho.
Self-Adhesive
1107   Booklet pane of 10   11.00
  a.-j. A294 70c Any single   1.10 1.10

Souvenir Sheet

Battle of Gallipoli, Cent. — A295

Litho. With Foil Application
2015, Apr. 24   Perf. 13½
1108 A295 $5 multi   8.00 8.00

Norfolk Island Pine Types of 2014
Designs as before.

Serpentine Die Cut 10¾x10
2015, June 1   Litho.
Self-Adhesive
1109   Booklet pane of 10   2.50
  a. A282 15c multi   .25   .25
  b. A283 15c multi   .25   .25
  c. A284 15c multi   .25   .25
  d. A285 15c multi   .25   .25
  e. A286 15c multi   .25   .25
  f. A287 15c multi   .25   .25
  g. A288 15c multi   .25   .25
  h. A289 15c multi   .25   .25
  i. A290 15c multi   .25   .25
  j. A291 15c multi   .25   .25

Celebrities at Christmas in July Festival — A296

Designs: 25c, John Rowles, singer. 35c, Suzanne Prentice, singer. 45c, Normie Rowe, singer. $1.40, Glenn A. Baker, journalist and 2015 festival master of ceremonies. $1.95, Colleen McCullough (1937-2015), writer.

2015, July 13   Litho.   Perf. 14¼x14
1110-1114 A296   Set of 5   6.50 6.50

Christmas — A297

Ornaments made from plant fibers: 15c, Bird. 65c, Star. $1.30, Fish. $1.70, Rings around glass balls, candle. $2.55, Netting around glass ball.

2015, Oct. 1   Litho.   Perf. 14½x14¾
1115-1119 A297   Set of 5   9.00 9.00

Norfolk's Ocean Challenge Canoe Races A298

Various participants with panel color of: No. 1120, $1, Cerise. No. 1121, $1, Cobalt. $1.85, Green. $2.75, Gray blue.

2016, Jan. 14   Litho.   Perf. 14x14½
1120-1123 A298   Set of 4   9.50 9.50

Phillip Island — A299

Designs: 15c, Building. 20c, Building, diff. No. 1126, $1, Building, diff. No. 1127, $1, Man, woman and building. $1.85, Building, diff. $2, Tree near cliff.

2016, Feb. 22   Litho.   Perf. 14½
1124-1129 A299   Set of 6   9.00 9.00

Souvenir Sheet

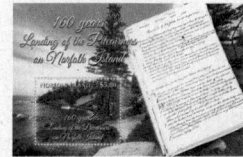

Landing of Pitcairn Islanders on Norfolk Island, 160th Anniv. A300

2016, June 7   Litho.   Perf. 13½
1130 A300 $5 multi   7.50 7.50

Sea Birds — A301

Designs: $1, Red-tailed tropicbird. $2, Masked booby.

2016, Sept. 20   Litho.   Perf. 14x14¾
1131-1132 A301   Set of 2   4.75 4.75
  1132a   Souvenir sheet of 2,
    #1131-1132   4.75 4.75

Waterfalls — A302

Designs: $1, Cockpit Waterfall. $2, Cascade Creek Falls.

2017, Jan. 17   Litho.   Perf. 14¾x14
1133-1134 A302   Set of 2   4.50 4.50
  1134a   Souvenir sheet of 2,
    #1133-1134   4.50 4.50

Flowers — A303

Designs: $1, Hibiscus insularis. $2, Lagunaria patersonia.

2017, July 18   Litho.   Perf. 14x14¾
1135-1136 A303   Set of 2   5.00 5.00
  1136a   Souvenir sheet of 2,
    #1135-1136   5.00 5.00

UNESCO World Heritage Sites on Norfolk Island — A304

Designs: $1, New Jail. $2, Prisoners Barracks.

2017, Sept. 19   Litho.   Perf. 14¾x14
1137-1138 A304   Set of 2   4.75 4.75
  1138a   Souvenir sheet of 2,
    #1137-1138   4.75 4.75

Norfolk Island Golf Club — A305

2018, Feb. 27   Litho.   Perf. 13¾x14
1139 A305 $5 multi   7.75 7.75
  a.   Souvenir sheet of 1   7.75 7.75

Wrasses — A306

Designs: $1, Surge wrasse. $2, Luculent wrasse.

2018, Apr. 30   Litho.   Perf. 14x14¾
1140-1141 A306   Set of 2   4.50 4.50
  1141a   Souvenir sheet of 2,
    #1140-1141   4.50 4.50

Crystal Pool — A307

Pool at: $1, High tide. $2, Low tide.

2018, July 17   Litho.   Perf. 14x14¾
1142-1143 A307   Set of 2   4.50 4.50
  1143a   Souvenir sheet of 2,
    #1142-1143   4.50 4.50

Cruise Ships — A308

Designs: $1, Seven Seas Mariner. $2, Pacific Explorer.

2018, Sept. 18 Litho. Perf. 14x14¾
1144-1145 A308 Set of 2 4.50 4.50
1145a Souvenir sheet of 2,
#1144-1145 4.50 4.50

Pitcairn Settlement
on Norfolk
Island — A309

Pitcairn settlement on Norfolk Island and:
$1, George Hunn Nobbs (1799-1884), missionary. $2, Queen Victoria (1819-1901).

2019, Jan. 22 Litho. Perf. 14x14¾
1146-1147 A309 Set of 2 4.50 4.50
1147a Souvenir sheet of 2,
#1146-1147 4.50 4.50

Cyathea
Brownii — A310

Designs: $1, Curled frond tip. $2, Opened frond.

2019, Apr. 2 Litho. Perf. 14x14¾
1148-1149 A310 Set of 2 4.25 4.25
1149a Souvenir sheet of 2,
#1148-1149 4.25 4.25

Phillip Island
Landscapes
A311

Designs: $1, Boulders on hillside. $2, Forest.

2019, July 9 Litho. Perf. 14x14¾
1150-1151 A311 Set of 2 4.25 4.25
1151a Souvenir sheet of 2,
#1150-1151 4.25 4.25

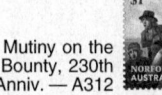

Mutiny on the
Bounty, 230th
Anniv. — A312

Designs: $1, Captain William Bligh set adrift. $2, Mutineers (38x52mm).

2019, Sept. 24 Litho. Perf. 14x14¾
1152-1153 A312 Set of 2 4.00 4.00
1153a Souvenir sheet of 2,
#1152-1153 4.00 4.00

Botanical Art of the
1790s Attributed to John
Doody — A313

Designs: $1.10, Lagunaria patersonia.
$2.20, Ungeria floribunda.

2020, Jan. 14 Litho. Perf. 14¾x14
1154-1155 A313 Set of 2 4.50 4.50
1155a Souvenir sheet of 2,
#1154-1155 4.50 4.50

Norfolk Blue
Cattle — A314

Designs: $1.10, Bull. $2.20, Cow and calf.

2020, June 2 Litho. Perf. 14¾x14
1156-1157 A314 Set of 2 4.75 4.75
1157a Souvenir sheet of 2,
#1156-1157 4.75 4.75

Fish — A315

Designs: $1.10, Bump-head sunfish. $2.20, Oarfish.

2020, July 14 Litho. Perf. 14¾x14
1158-1159 A315 Set of 2 4.75 4.75
1159a Souvenir sheet of 2,
#1158-1159 4.75 4.75

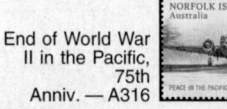

End of World War
II in the Pacific,
75th
Anniv. — A316

Designs: $1.10, Airplane. $2.20, Soldiers.

2020, Sept. 1 Litho. Perf. 14x14¾
1160-1161 A316 Set of 2 5.00 5.00
1161a Souvenir sheet of 2,
#1160-1161 5.00 5.00

Lizards — A317

Designs: $1.10, Lord Howe Island skink.
$2.20, Lord Howe Island gecko.

2021, Feb. 9 Litho. Perf. 14x14¾
1162-1163 A317 Set of 2 5.25 5.25
1163a Souvenir sheet of 2,
#1162-1163 5.25 5.25

Land
Snails — A318

Designs: $1.10, Greenwoodoconcha nux.
$2.20, Duritropis albocarinata.

2021, June 22 Litho. Perf. 14x14¾
1164-1165 A318 Set of 2 5.00 5.00
1165a Souvenir sheet of 2,
#1164-1165 5.00 5.00

Model Ships Displayed
at HMS Sirius Museum
Site — A319

Model of: $1.10, HMS Sirius. $2.20, HMAT Supply.

2021, July 13 Litho. Perf. 14¾x14
1166-1167 A319 Set of 2 5.00 5.00
1167a Souvenir sheet of 2,
#1166-1167 5.00 5.00

Butterflies — A320

Designs: $1.10, Norfolk swallowtail butterfly.
$2.20, Norfolk Island gull butterfly.

2021, Sept. 21 Litho. Perf. 14x14¾
1168-1169 A320 Set of 2 5.00 5.00
1169a Souvenir sheet of 2,
#1168-1169 5.00 5.00

Watercolors of
Norfolk Island by
John Eyre — A321

View of: $1.10, Sydney (now Kingston), c. 1805. $2.20, Queenborough, 1804.

2022, Jan. 19 Litho. Perf. 14x14¾
1170-1171 A321 Set of 2 4.75 4.75
1171a Souvenir sheet of 2,
#1170-1171 4.75 4.75

Norfolk Island
Morepork — A322

Norfolk Island morepork: $1.10, On branch.
$2.20, Head.

2022, June 21 Litho. Perf. 14¾x14
1172-1173 A322 Set of 2 4.50 4.50
1173a Souvenir sheet of 2,
#1172-1173 4.50 4.50

Art of George
Raper (1769-
96) — A323

Designs: $1.10, Map of south coast of Norfolk Island. $2.20, Snapper of Norfolk Island and map of Phillip Island.

2022, Sept. 13 Litho. Perf. 14x14¾
1174-1175 A323 Set of 2 4.25 4.25
1175a Souvenir sheet of 2,
#1174-1175 4.25 4.25

NORTH BORNEO

'north 'bor-nē-ˌō

LOCATION — Northeast part of island
of Borneo, Malay archipelago
GOVT. — British colony
AREA — 29,388 sq. mi.
POP. — 470,000 (est. 1962)
CAPITAL — Jesselton

The British North Borneo Company administered North Borneo, under a royal charter granted in 1881, until 1946 when it became a British colony. Labuan (q.v.) became part of the new colony. As "Sabah," North Borneo joined with Singapore, Sarawak and Malaya to form the Federation of Malaysia on Sept. 16, 1963.

100 Cents = 1 Dollar

Quantities of most North Borneo stamps through 1912 have been canceled to order with an oval of bars. Values given for used stamps beginning with No. 6 are for those with this form of cancellation. Stamps from No. 6 through Nos. 159 and J31 that do not exist CTO have used values in italics. Stamps with dated town cancellations sell for much higher prices.

> **Catalogue values for unused stamps in this country are for Never Hinged items, beginning with Scott 238.**

North Borneo

Coat of Arms — A1

1883-84 Unwmk. Litho. Perf. 12
1 A1 2c brown 47.50 75.00
a. Horiz. pair, imperf. btwn. 20,000.
2 A1 4c rose ('84) 65.00 70.00
3 A1 8c green ('84) 90.00 60.00
Nos. 1-3 (3) 202.50 205.00

For surcharges see Nos. 4, 19-21.

No. 1 Surcharged in Black

4 A1 8c on 2c brown 500.00 210.00
a. Double surcharge 6,000.

Coat of Arms with
Supporters

A4 A5

Perf. 14
6 A4 50c violet 225.00 40.00
7 A5 $1 red 185.00 19.00

1886 Perf. 14
8 A1 ½c magenta 120.00 200.00
9 A1 1c orange 210.00 350.00
a. Imperf., pair 300.00
b. Vert. pair, imperf horiz. 1,500.
10 A1 2c brown 47.50 42.50
a. Horiz. pair, imperf. between 700.00
11 A1 4c rose 20.00 55.00
a. Horiz. pair, imperf. between — 1,700.
12 A1 8c green 22.50 50.00
a. Horiz. pair, imperf. between 900.00
13 A1 10c blue 55.00 65.00
a. Imperf., pair 375.00
Nos. 8-13 (6) 475.00 762.50

Nos. 8, 11, 12 and 13 Surcharged or
Overprinted in Black

b c

d

1886
14 A1 (b) ½c magenta 225.00 325.00
15 A1 (c) 3c on 4c rose 130.00 150.00
16 A1 (d) 3c on 4c rose 1,800.
17 A1 (c) 5c on 8c green 140.00 150.00
a. Inverted surcharge 2,750.
18 A1 (b) 10c blue 300.00 375.00

On Nos. 2 and 3
Perf. 12
19 A1 (c) 3c on 4c rose 325.00 375.00
20 A1 (d) 3c on 4c rose — 16,000.
a. Double surcharge, both types of "3" —
21 A1 (c) 5c on 8c green 325.00 375.00

British North Borneo

A9

1886 Unwmk. Litho. Perf. 12
22 A9 ½c lilac rose 400.00 700.00
23 A9 1c orange 250.00 400.00

Perf. 14
25 A9 ½c rose 4.75 21.00
a. ½c lilac rose 21.00 50.00
b. Imperf., pair 70.00
26 A9 1c orange 2.25 16.00
a. Imperf., pair 80.00
b. Vert. pair, imperf. btwn. 425.00
27 A9 2c brown 2.25 16.00
a. Imperf., pair 50.00
28 A9 4c rose 6.50 19.00
a. Cliché of 1c in plate of 4c 350.00 1,300.
b. Imperf., pair 65.00
c. As "a," imperf. in pair with #28 7,500.
d. Horiz. pair, imperf vert. 425.00
29 A9 8c green 30.00 28.00
a. Imperf., pair 55.00 55.00
30 A9 10c blue 15.00 45.00
a. Imperf., pair 55.00
b. Vert. pair, imperf btwn. 425.00
Nos. 25-30 (6) 60.75 145.00

For surcharges see Nos. 54-55.

A10

A11

A13

A12

31	A10	25c slate blue	475.00	25.00
a.		Imperf., pair	475.00	50.00
32	A11	50c violet	475.00	25.00
a.		Imperf., pair	550.00	50.00
33	A12	$1 red	400.00	24.00
a.		Imperf., pair	600.00	55.00
34	A13	$2 sage green	700.00	30.00
a.		Imperf., pair	600.00	55.00
		Nos. 31-34 (4)	2,050.	104.00
		Nos. 22-34 (12)	2,761.	1,349.

See Nos. 44-47.

A14

1887-92   Perf. 14

35	A14	½c rose	1.50	.60
a.		½c magenta	4.00	3.00
36	A14	1c orange	6.50	.50
37	A14	2c red brown	7.50	.50
b.		As "a," horiz. pair imperf. between		425.00
38	A14	3c violet	2.75	.50
39	A14	4c rose	14.50	.50
a.		Horiz. pair, imperf. vert.		250.00
40	A14	5c slate	3.00	.50
41	A14	6c lake ('92)	20.00	.50
42	A14	8c green	32.50	1.00
a.		Horiz. pair, imperf. between		
43	A14	10c blue	7.25	.50
		Nos. 35-43 (9)	95.50	5.10

Exist imperf. Value $20 each, unused, $4.50 used. Forgeries exist, perf. 11½.
For surcharges see Nos. 52-53, 56-57.

Redrawn

25c. The letters of "BRITISH NORTH BORNEO" are 2mm high instead of 1½mm.
50c. The club of the native at left does not touch the frame. The 0's of "50" are flat at top and bottom instead of being oval.
$1.00. The spear of the native at right does not touch the frame. There are 14 pearls at each side of the frame instead of 13.
$2.00. "BRITISH" is 11mm long instead of 12mm. There are only six oars at the side of the dhow.

1888

44	A10	25c slate blue	115.00	.75
b.		Horiz. pair, imperf. between		300.00
c.		Imperf., pair	500.00	22.50
45	A11	50c violet	135.00	.75
a.		Imperf., pair	600.00	22.50
46	A12	$1 red	67.50	.75
a.		Imperf., pair	450.00	22.50
47	A13	$2 sage green	250.00	1.50
a.		Imperf., pair	750.00	25.00
		Nos. 44-47 (4)	567.50	3.75

For surcharges see Nos. 50-51, 58.

A15

A16

1889

48	A15	$5 red violet	400.00	9.00
a.		Imperf., pair	1,100.	80.00
49	A16	$10 brown	400.00	12.50
b.		Imperf., pair	1,300.	90.00

No. 44 Surcharged in Red — e

1890

50	A10	2c on 25c slate blue	87.50	100.00
a.		Inverted surcharge	450.00	450.00
b.		With additional surcharge "2 cents" in black		
51	A10	8c on 25c slate blue	135.00	145.00

Surcharged in Black On #42-43 — f

1891-92

52	A14	6c on 8c green	25.00	11.00
a.		"c" of "cents" inverted	700.00	750.00
b.		"cetns"	700.00	750.00
c.		Inverted surcharge	500.00	500.00
53	A14	6c on 10c blue	210.00	27.50

On Nos. 29 and 30

54	A9	6c on 8c green	9,000.	4,750.
55	A9	6c on 10c blue	67.50	22.50
a.		Inverted surcharge	300.00	300.00
b.		Double surcharge	1,500.	
c.		Triple surcharge	550.00	

Nos. 39, 40 and 44 Surcharged in Red

1892

56	A14	1c on 4c rose	27.50	15.00
a.		Double surcharge	1,650.	
b.		Surcharged on face & back		675.00
57	A14	1c on 5c slate	8.00	6.50
58	A10	8c on 25c blue	185.00	200.00
		Nos. 56-58 (3)	220.50	221.50

North Borneo

Dyak Chief — A21

Malayan Sambar
A22

Malay Dhow
A26

Sago Palm
A23

Saltwater Crocodile
A27

Argus Pheasant
A24

Mt. Kinabalu
A28

Coat of Arms
A25

Coat of Arms with Supporters
A29

A30

A31

A32

A33

A34

A35

Perf. 12 to 15 and Compound

1894		Engr.	Unwmk.	
59	A21	1c bis brn & blk	1.40	.50
a.		Vert. pair, imperf. btwn.	950.00	
60	A22	2c rose & black	5.50	.75
a.		Horiz. pair, imperf. btwn.	950.00	950.00
b.		Vert. pair, imperf. btwn.	950.00	950.00
61	A23	3c vio & ol green	4.00	.55
a.		Horiz. pair, imperf. btwn.	—	850.00
b.		Vert. pair, imperf. btwn.	1,350.	
62	A24	5c org red & blk	14.00	.75
a.		Horiz. pair, imperf. btwn.	850.00	
63	A25	6c brn ol & blk	4.50	.60
64	A26	8c lilac & black	6.50	.75
a.		Vert. pair, imperf. btwn.	550.00	350.00
b.		Horiz. pair, imperf. btwn.	750.00	
65	A27	12c ultra & black	47.50	3.00
a.		12c blue & black	30.00	2.75
66	A28	18c green & black	30.00	2.00
67	A29	24c claret & blue	25.00	2.00

			Litho.	Perf. 14
68	A30	25c slate blue	10.00	1.00
a.		Imperf., pair	60.00	12.00
69	A31	50c violet	50.00	2.00
a.		Imperf., pair		12.00
70	A32	$1 red	14.50	1.25
a.		Perf. 14x11	300.00	
b.		Imperf., pair	47.50	12.00
71	A33	$2 gray green	27.50	2.75
a.		Imperf., pair		18.00
72	A34	$5 red violet	275.00	17.50
a.		Imperf., pair	925.00	65.00
73	A35	$10 brown	325.00	16.00
a.		Imperf., pair	950.00	60.00
		Nos. 59-73 (15)	840.40	51.40

For #68-70 in other colors see Labuan #63b-65b.
For surcharges & overprints see #74-78, 91-94, 97-102, 115-119, 130-135, 115-119, 150-151, 158-159, J1-J8. In other colors see Labuan #63-65, 93-95, 116-118, and 120.

No. 70 Surcharged in Black

1895, June

74	A32	4c on $1 red	7.00	1.25
a.		Double surcharge	1,000.	
75	A32	10c on $1 red	27.50	.60
76	A32	20c on $1 red	57.50	.60
77	A32	30c on $1 red	52.50	2.00
78	A32	40c on $1 red	65.00	2.00
		Nos. 74-78 (5)	209.50	6.45

See No. 99.

A37

A38

A39

A40

A41

A42

A43

"Postal Revenue"
A44

No "Postal Revenue"
A45

Perf. 13 to 16 and Compound

1897-1900		Engr.		
79	A37	1c bis brn & blk	12.00	.55
a.		Horiz. pair, imperf. btwn.		600.00
80	A38	2c dp rose & blk	25.00	.55
81	A38	2c grn & blk ('00)	72.50	.60
82	A39	3c lilac & ol green	36.00	.55
83	A40	5c orange & black	125.00	.85
84	A41	6c ol brown & blk	57.50	.50
85	A42	8c brn lilac & blk	16.50	.75
86	A43	12c blue & black	160.00	1.50
87	A44	18c green & black	40.00	4.50
a.		Vert. pair, imperf. btwn.		350.00
b.		Horiz. pair, imperf. vert.		95.00
c.		Imperf., pair		200.00
88	A45	24c claret & blue	40.00	4.25
		Nos. 79-88 (10)	584.50	14.60

For overprints and surcharges see Nos. 105-107, 109-112, 124-127, J9-J17, J20-J22, J24-J26, J28.

"Postage & Revenue"
A46   A47

1897

89	A46	18c green & black	135.00	1.75
90	A47	24c claret & blue	62.50	2.10

For surcharges & overprints see #95-96, 128-129, 113-114, J18-J19, J30-J31.

Stamps of 1894-97 Surcharged in Black

1899

91	A40	4c on 5c org & blk	40.00	12.50
92	A41	4c on 6c ol brn & blk	20.00	25.00
93	A42	4c on 8c brn lil & blk	16.00	13.00
94	A43	4c on 12c bl & blk	29.00	15.00
a.		Horiz. pair, imperf. btwn.	850.00	
b.		Vert. pair, imperf. btwn.		950.00
95	A46	4c on 18c grn & blk	16.00	18.00
96	A47	4c on 24c cl & blue	25.00	20.00
a.		Perf. 16	55.00	55.00
97	A30	4c on 25c sl blue	6.00	10.00
98	A31	4c on 50c violet	18.00	18.00
99	A32	4c on $1 red	6.25	14.00
100	A33	4c on $2 gray grn	6.25	19.00

"CENTS" 8½mm below "4"

101	A34	4c on $5 red vio	7.25	18.00
a.		Normal spacing	170.00	250.00

102 A35 4c on $10 brown 7.25 18.00
a. Normal spacing 130.00 250.00
Nos. 91-102 (12) 197.00 200.50

No. 99 differs from No. 74 in the distance between "4" and "cents" which is 4¾mm on No. 99 and 3¾mm on No. 74.

Orangutan — A48

1899-1900 **Engr.**
103 A48 4c green & black 10.00 1.75
104 A48 4c dp rose & blk ('00) 40.00 .75

For overprints see Nos. 108, J13, J23.

Stamps of 1894-1900 Overprinted in Red, Black, Green or Blue — m

1901-05
105 A37 1c bis brn & blk (R) 4.00 .35
106 A38 2c grn & blk (R) 3.50 .35
107 A39 3c lil & ol grn (Bk) 2.00 .35
108 A48 4c dp rose & blk (G) 10.00 .35
109 A40 5c org & blk (G) 16.00 .35
110 A41 6c ol brn & blk (R) 4.50 .75
111 A42 8c brn & blk (Bl) 4.25 .55
a. Vert. pair, imperf. btwn. 425.00
112 A43 12c blue & blk (R) 60.00 1.50
113 A46 18c grn & blk (R) 15.00 1.40
114 A47 24c red & blue (Bk) 18.00 1.75
115 A30 25c slate blue (R) 3.00 .60
a. Inverted overprint 700.00
116 A31 50c violet (R) 3.00 .70
117 A32 $1 red (R) 20.00 3.75
118 A32 $1 red (Bk) 10.00 2.75
a. Double overprint 425.00
119 A33 $2 gray grn (R) 37.50 4.00
a. Double overprint 1,600.
Nos. 105-119 (15) 210.75 19.50

Nos. 110, 111 and 122 are known without period after "PROTECTORATE."
See Nos. 122-123, 150-151.

Bruang (Sun Bear) — A49
Railroad Train — A50

1902 **Engr.**
120 A49 10c slate & dk brn 130.00 3.25
a. Vertical pair, imperf. between 575.00
121 A50 16c yel brn & grn 150.00 3.75

Overprinted type "m" in Red or Black
122 A49 10c sl & dk brn (R) 75.00 1.10
a. Double overprint 900.00 350.00
123 A50 16c yel brn & grn (Bk) 150.00 2.50
Nos. 120-123 (4) 505.00 10.60

For overprints see Nos. J27, J29.

Stamps of 1894-97 Surcharged in Black

1904
124 A40 4c on 5c org & blk 50.00 14.00
125 A41 4c on 6c ol brn & blk 8.00 14.00
a. Inverted surcharge 350.00
126 A42 4c on 8c brn lil & blk 15.00 14.00
a. Inverted surcharge 350.00
127 A43 4c on 12c blue & blk 40.00 14.00
128 A46 4c on 18c grn & blk 16.00 14.00
129 A47 4c on 24c cl & bl 20.00 14.00
130 A30 4c on 25c sl blue 5.00 14.00
131 A31 4c on 50c violet 5.50 14.00
132 A32 4c on $1 red 7.00 14.00
133 A33 4c on $2 gray grn 10.50 14.00
134 A34 4c on $5 red vio 14.00 14.00

135 A35 4c on $10 brown 14.00 14.00
a. Inverted surcharge 2,750.
Nos. 124-135 (12) 205.00 168.00

Malayan Tapir A51
Traveler's Palm A52

Railroad Station A53
Meeting of the Assembly A54

Elephant and Mahout A55
Sumatran Rhinoceros A56

Natives Plowing — A57
Wild Boar — A58

Palm Cockatoo A59
Rhinoceros Hornbill A60

Banteng (Wild Ox)
A61 A62

Cassowary — A63

1909-22 **Unwmk.** **Engr.** **Perf. 14**
Center in Black
136 A51 1c chocolate 7.00 .30
b. Perf. 13½
c. Perf. 15 47.50 .40
137 A52 2c green 1.00 .30
b. Perf. 15 3.25 .30
138 A53 3c deep rose 3.25 .30
b. Perf. 15 42.50 .55
139 A53 3c green ('22) 42.50 .40
140 A54 4c dull red 2.75 .30
b. Perf. 13½ 11.00 10.50
c. Perf. 15 21.00 .40
141 A55 5c yellow brn 16.00 .40
b. Perf. 15
142 A56 6c olive green 13.00 .30
b. Perf. 15 80.00 1.00
143 A57 8c rose 4.00 .60
b. Perf 15 12.00
144 A58 10c blue 45.00 2.00
b. Perf. 13½
c. Perf. 15 70.00 6.50
145 A59 12c deep blue 42.50 1.00
c. Perf. 15 12.00
146 A60 16c red brown 26.00 1.25
b. Perf. 15 30.00 6.50
147 A61 18c blue green 120.00 1.25
148 A62 20c on 18c bl grn (R) 7.00 .55
b. Perf. 15 250.00 75.00
149 A63 24c violet 28.00 1.75
Nos. 136-149 (14) 358.00 10.70

Issued: No. 139, 1922; others, July 1, 1909.
See No. 167-178.
For surcharges and overprints, see Nos. 160-162, 166, B1-B12, B14-B24, B31-B41, J32-J49. Nos. 136a-149a follow No. 162.

Nos. 72-73 Overprinted type "m" in Red
1910
150 A34 $5 red violet 325.00 9.00
151 A35 $10 brown 550.00 11.00
a. Double overprint
b. Inverted overprint 2,700. 450.00

A64
A65

1911 **Engr.** **Perf. 14**
Center in Black
152 A64 25c yellow green 18.00 2.00
a. Perf. 15 19.00
b. Imperf., pair 55.00
153 A64 50c slate blue 18.00 2.25
a. Perf. 15 24.00 22.50
b. Imperf., pair 90.00
154 A64 $1 brown 18.00 4.00
a. Perf. 15 60.00 8.00
c. Imperf., pair 180.00
155 A64 $2 dk violet 75.00 5.00
156 A65 $5 claret 150.00 32.50
a. Perf. 13½ 150.00
b. Imperf., pair 200.00
157 A65 $10 vermilion 500.00 90.00
a. Imperf., pair 475.00
Nos. 152-157 (6) 779.00 135.75

See #179-184. #152c-153c follow #162.
For overprint and surcharges see Nos. B13, B25-B30, B42-B47.

Nos. 72-73 Overprinted in Red

1912
158 A34 $5 red violet 1,500. 9.25
159 A35 $10 brown 1,800. 9.25
Nos. 158 and 159 were prepared for use but not regularly issued.

Nos. 138, 142 and 145 Surcharged in Black or Red

1916 **Center in Black** **Perf. 14**
160 A53 2c on 3c dp rose 30.00 15.00
a. Inverted "S" 110.00 95.00
161 A56 4c on 6c ol grn (R) 30.00 20.00
a. Inverted "S" 110.00 100.00
162 A59 10c on 12c bl (R) 60.00 70.00
a. Inverted "S" 180.00 190.00
Nos. 160-162 (3) 120.00 105.00

Stamps and Types of 1909-11 Overprinted in Red or Blue

1922 **Center in Black**
136a A51 1c brown 20.00 70.00
137a A52 2c green 2.50 25.00
138a A53 3c deep rose (B) 16.00 65.00
140a A54 4c dull red (B) 3.75 45.00
141a A55 5c yel brown (B) 9.50 65.00
142a A56 6c olive green 9.50 70.00
143a A57 8c rose (B) 8.50 42.50
144a A58 10c gray blue 20.00 65.00
145a A59 12c deep blue 12.00 45.00
146a A60 16c red brown (B) 26.00 75.00
148a A62 20c on 18c bl grn 27.50 90.00
149a A63 24c violet 50.00 75.00
152c A64 25c yel green 12.00 65.00
153c A64 50c slate blue 17.50 70.00
Nos. 136a-153c (14) 234.75 867.50

Industrial fair, Singapore, 3/31-4/15/22.

No. 140 Surcharged in Black

1923
166 A54 3c on 4c dull red & blk 2.75 6.00
a. Double surcharge 1,300.

Types of 1909-22 Issues
1926-28 **Engr.** **Perf. 12½**
Center in Black
167 A51 1c chocolate 1.00 .70
168 A52 2c lake .85 .60
169 A53 3c green 3.00 .75
170 A54 4c dull red .50 .25
171 A55 5c yellow brown 6.00 3.50
172 A56 6c yellow green 10.00 .90
173 A57 8c rose 4.75 .50
174 A58 10c bright blue 4.25 .90
175 A59 12c deep blue 24.00 .80
176 A60 16c orange brn 37.50 225.00
177 A62 20c on 18c bl grn (R) 16.00 4.00
178 A63 24c dull violet 60.00 170.00
179 A64 25c yellow grn 16.00 5.50
180 A64 50c slate blue 25.00 14.00
181 A64 $1 brown 25.00 500.00
182 A64 $2 dark violet 85.00 650.00
183 A65 $5 deep rose 200.00 1,300.
184 A65 $10 dull vermilion 550.00 1,500.
Nos. 167-184 (18) 1,069. 4,377.

Murut A66
Orangutan A67

Dyak — A68
Mt. Kinabalu — A69

Clouded Leopard — A70
Coat of Arms — A71

Arms with Supporters and Motto A72
Arms with Supporters A73

1931, Jan. 1 **Engr.** **Perf. 12½**
Center in Black
185 A66 3c blue green 1.50 1.50
186 A67 6c orange red 17.50 4.75
187 A68 10c carmine 4.50 13.00
188 A69 12c ultra 4.75 8.00
189 A70 25c deep violet 40.00 35.00
190 A71 $1 yellow green 27.50 110.00
191 A72 $2 red brown 47.50 110.00
192 A73 $5 red violet 160.00 500.00
Nos. 185-192 (8) 303.25 782.25

50th anniv. of the North Borneo Co.

Buffalo Transport A74
Palm Cockatoo A75

Murut
A76

Proboscis
Monkey
A77

Bajaus
A78

Map of North
Borneo and
Surrounding
Lands
A79

Orangutan
A80

Murut with
Blowgun
A81

Dyak — A82

River
Scene — A83

Proa — A84   Mt.
                          Kinabalu — A85

Coat of Arms
A86

Arms with
Supporters
A87

1939, Jan. 1   **Perf. 12½**

193	A74	1c red brn & dk grn	2.75	2.25
194	A75	2c Prus bl & red vio	3.25	2.25
195	A76	3c dk grn & sl blue	3.50	2.50
196	A77	4c rose vio & ol grn	8.50	.50
197	A78	6c dp cl & dk blue	7.75	14.00
198	A79	8c red	11.00	2.00
199	A80	10c olive grn & vio	26.00	7.00
200	A81	12c ultra & grn	27.50	8.00
201	A82	15c bis brn & brt bl grn	21.00	13.00
202	A83	20c ind & rose vio	14.50	7.00
203	A84	25c dk brn & bl grn	21.00	15.00
204	A85	50c purple & brn	22.50	14.00
205	A86	$1 car & brown	72.50	22.50
206	A86	$2 ol grn & pur	120.00	150.00
207	A87	$5 blue & indigo	350.00	375.00
		Nos. 193-207 (15)	711.75	635.00
		Set, never hinged	1,200.	

For overprints see #208-237, MR1-MR2, N1-N15, N16-N31.

Nos. 193 to 207
Overprinted in Black

1945, Dec. 17   **Unwmk.**   **Perf. 12½**

208	A74	1c red brn & dk grn	9.50	2.25
209	A75	2c Prus bl & red vio	10.00	2.00

210	A76	3c dk grn & sl bl	.90	1.25
211	A77	4c rose vio & ol grn	12.00	16.00
212	A78	6c dp cl & dk bl	.90	1.25
213	A79	8c red	2.10	.75
214	A80	10c ol green & vio	2.10	.40
215	A81	12c ultra & green	4.25	3.50
216	A82	15c bis brn & brt bl grn	1.20	1.10
217	A83	20c ind & rose vio	4.25	2.50
218	A84	25c dk brn & bl grn	4.75	1.50
219	A85	50c purple & brn	3.00	2.50
220	A86	$1 carmine & brn	35.00	40.00
221	A86	$2 ol green & pur	35.00	42.50
a.		Double overprint	4,000.	
222	A87	$5 blue & indigo	18.00	18.00
		Nos. 208-222 (15)	142.95	135.50
		Set, never hinged	235.00	

"BMA" stands for British Military Administration.

Nos. 193 to 207 Ovptd.
in Black or Carmine

1947

223	A74	1c red brn & dk grn	.25	1.00
224	A75	2c Prus bl & red vio	1.25	.80
225	A76	3c dk grn & sl bl (C)	.25	.80
226	A77	4c rose vio & ol grn	.50	.80
227	A78	6c dp cl & dk bl (C)	.25	.25
228	A79	8c red	.25	.25
229	A80	10c olive grn & vio	1.10	.35
230	A81	12c ultra & grn	2.40	2.75
231	A82	15c bis brn & brt bl grn	1.75	.30
232	A83	20c ind & rose vio	2.40	.85
233	A84	25c dk brn & bl grn	2.40	.50
234	A85	50c purple & brn	2.00	.85
235	A86	$1 carmine & brn	8.50	1.75
236	A86	$2 ol green & pur	11.50	18.00
237	A87	$5 blue & ind (C)	19.00	25.00
		Nos. 223-237 (15)	53.80	54.25
		Set, never hinged	80.00	

The bars obliterate "The State of" and "British Protectorate."

> **Catalogue values for unused stamps in this section, from this point to the end of the section, are for Never Hinged items.**

Silver Wedding Issue
Common Design Types
Perf. 14x14½
1948, Nov. 1   **Wmk. 4**   **Photo.**

238	CD304	8c scarlet	.30	.75

Perf. 11½x11
Engraved; Name Typographed

239	CD305	$10 purple	35.00	45.00

Common Design Types pictured following the introduction.

UPU Issue
Common Design Types
Engr.; Name Typo. on 10c and 30c
1949, Oct. 10   **Perf. 13½, 11x11½**

240	CD306	8c rose carmine	.65	.25
241	CD307	10c chocolate	3.25	1.75
242	CD308	30c deep orange	1.50	1.75
243	CD309	55c blue	1.75	2.75
		Nos. 240-243 (4)	7.15	6.50

Mount
Kinabalu — A88

Coconut
Grove — A89

Designs: 2c, Musician. 4c, Hemp drying. 5c, Cattle at Kota Belud. 8c, Map. 10c, Logging. 15c, Proa at Sandakan. 20c, Bajau Chief. 30c, Suluk Craft. 50c, Clock tower. $1, Bajau horsemen. $2, Murut with blowgun. $5, Net fishing. $10, Arms.

Perf. 13½x14½, 14½x13½
1950, July 1   **Photo.**

244	A88	1c red brown	.25	1.25
245	A88	2c blue	.25	.50
246	A89	3c green	.25	.25
247	A89	4c red violet	.25	.25
248	A89	5c purple	.25	.25

249	A88	8c red	1.35	.85
250	A88	10c violet brn	1.90	.25
251	A88	15c brt ultra	2.10	.65
252	A88	20c dk brown	2.40	.25
253	A88	30c brown	6.00	.25
254	A89	50c cer (Jesselton)	1.90	4.75
255	A89	$1 red orange	6.50	1.75
256	A88	$2 dark green	16.00	20.00
257	A88	$5 emerald	26.00	30.00
258	A88	$10 gray blue	70.00	90.00
		Nos. 244-258 (15)	135.40	151.25

Redrawn

1952, May 1   **Perf. 14½x13½**

259	A89	50c cerise (Jesselton)	16.00	3.25

Coronation Issue
Common Design Type
1953, June 3   **Engr.**   **Perf. 13½x13**

260	CD312	10c carmine & black	1.75	1.00

Types of 1950 with Portrait of Queen Elizabeth II
Perf. 13½x14½, 14½x13½
1954-57   **Photo.**

261	A88	1c red brown	.25	.30
262	A88	2c Prus blue ('56)	1.25	.25
263	A89	3c green ('57)	4.00	2.00
264	A89	4c magenta ('55)	1.75	.25
265	A89	5c purple	1.00	.25
266	A88	8c red	1.25	.30
267	A88	10c violet brown	.40	.25
268	A89	15c brt ultra ('55)	1.00	.25
269	A88	20c dk brown	.50	.25
270	A89	30c brown	3.25	.25
271	A88	50c cerise ('56)	6.25	.25
272	A89	$1 red orange ('55)	7.50	.25
273	A88	$2 dk green ('55)	15.00	1.25
274	A88	$5 emerald ('57)	12.50	32.50
275	A88	$10 gray blue ('57)	29.00	35.00
		Nos. 261-275 (15)	84.90	73.60

Issued: 10c, 3/1; 5c, 7/1; 20c, 30c, 8/3; 1c, 8c, 10/1; $1, 4/1/55; 4c, 15c, 5/16/55; $2, 10/1/55; 50c, 2/10/56; 2c, 6/1/56; 3c, $5, $10, 2/1/57.

In 1960, the 30c plate was remade, using a finer, smaller-dot (250) screen instead of the 200 screen. The background appears smoother. Value, $2.75 unused.

Borneo Railway,
1902 — A90

Comp.
Arms — A91

15c, Proa (sailboat). 35c, Mount Kinabalu.

Perf. 13x13½, 13½x13
1956, Nov. 1   **Engr.**   **Wmk. 4**

276	A90	10c rose car & blk	1.50	.40
277	A90	15c red brown & blk	.80	.30
278	A90	35c green & blk	.80	1.50
279	A91	$1 slate & blk	1.90	2.50
		Nos. 276-279 (4)	5.00	4.70

75th anniv. of the founding of the Chartered Company of North Borneo.

Malayan Sambar
A92

Orangutan
A93

Designs: 4c, Honey bear. 5c, Clouded leopard. 6c, Dusun woman with gong. 10c, Map of Borneo. 12c, Banteng (wild ox). 20c, Butterfly orchid. 25c, Rhinoceros. 30c, Murut with blowgun. 35c, Mount Kinabalu. 50c, Dusun with buffalo transport. 75c, Bajau horsemen. $2, Rhinoceros hornbill. $5, Crested wood partridge. $10, Coat of arms.

Perf. 13x12½, 12½x13
1961, Feb. 1   **Wmk. 314**   **Engr.**

280	A92	1c lt red brn & grn	.25	.25
281	A92	4c orange & olive	.90	.90
282	A92	5c violet & sepia	.30	.25
283	A92	6c bluish grn & sl	.75	.40
284	A92	10c rose red & lt grn	1.25	.25
285	A92	12c dull grn & brn	.50	.25
286	A92	20c ultra & bl grn	4.00	.25
287	A92	25c rose red & gray	1.25	1.50
288	A92	30c gray ol & sep	1.25	.25
289	A92	35c redsh brn & stl bl	2.50	2.25

290	A92	50c brn org & bl grn	2.25	.25
291	A92	75c red vio & sl bl	16.00	.90
292	A93	$1 yel grn & brn	14.00	.80
293	A93	$2 slate & brown	35.00	3.75
294	A93	$5 brn vio & grn	37.50	22.50
295	A93	$10 blue & car	50.00	50.00
		Nos. 280-295 (16)	167.70	84.75

Freedom from Hunger Issue
Common Design Type
1963, June 4   **Photo.**   **Perf. 14x14½**

296	CD314	12c ultramarine	1.90	.75

SEMI-POSTAL STAMPS

Nos. 136-138, 140-146, 148-149, 152
Ovptd. in Carmine or Vermilion

1916   **Unwmk.**   **Perf. 14**
Center in Black

B1	A51	1c chocolate	7.50	35.00
B2	A52	2c green	30.00	80.00
a.		Perf. 15	35.00	80.00
B3	A53	3c deep rose	27.50	50.00
B4	A54	4c dull red	7.25	32.50
a.		Perf. 15	275.00	180.00
B5	A55	5c yellow brown	50.00	55.00
B6	A56	6c olive green	70.00	75.00
a.		Perf. 15	225.00	225.00
B7	A57	8c rose	24.00	60.00
B8	A58	10c brt blue	55.00	70.00
B9	A59	12c deep blue	100.00	100.00
B10	A60	16c red brown	110.00	110.00
B11	A62	20c on 18c bl grn	55.00	100.00
B12	A63	24c violet	130.00	130.00

Perf. 15

B13	A64	25c yellow green	375.00	425.00
		Nos. B1-B13 (13)	1,041.	1,323.

All values exist with the vermilion overprint and all but the 4c with the carmine.

Of the total overprinting, a third was given to the National Philatelic War Fund Committee in London to be auctioned for the benefit of the wounded and veterans' survivors. The balance was lost en route from London to Sandakan when a submarine sank the ship. Very few were postally used.

Nos. 136-138, 140-146, 149, 152-157
Surcharged

1918   **Center in Black**   **Perf. 14**

B14	A51	1c + 2c choc	3.50	14.00
B15	A52	2c + 2c green	1.00	8.50
B16	A53	3c + 2c dp rose	14.00	19.00
a.		Perf. 15	30.00	65.00
B17	A54	4c + 2c dull red	.70	5.00
a.		Inverted surcharge	450.00	
B18	A55	5c + 2c yel brn	8.00	29.00
B19	A56	6c + 2c olive grn	5.00	29.00
a.		Perf. 15	225.00	250.00
B20	A57	8c + 2c rose	5.50	11.00
B21	A58	10c + 2c brt blue	8.00	27.50
B22	A59	12c + 2c deep bl	21.00	55.00
a.		Inverted surcharge	700.00	
B23	A60	16c + 2c red brn	22.50	45.00
B24	A63	24c + 2c violet	22.50	45.00
B25	A64	25c + 2c yel grn	12.00	42.50
B26	A64	50c + 2c sl blue	14.00	42.50
B27	A64	$1 + 2c brown	50.00	55.00
B28	A64	$2 + 2c dk vio	75.00	95.00
B29	A65	$5 + 2c claret	425.00	650.00
B30	A65	$10 + 2c ver	475.00	700.00
		Nos. B14-B30 (17)	1,163.	1,873.

On Nos. B14-B24 the surcharge is 15mm high, on Nos. B25-B30 it is 19mm high.

Nos. 136-138, 140-146, 149, 152-157
Surcharged in Red

1918   **Center in Black**

B31	A51	1c + 4c choc	.60	5.00
B32	A52	2c + 4c green	.65	8.00
B33	A53	3c + 4c dp rose	1.00	3.75
B34	A54	4c + 4c dull red	.40	4.75
B35	A55	5c + 4c yel brn	2.00	22.50
B36	A56	6c + 4c olive grn	2.00	12.00
a.		Vert. pair, imperf. between	2,500.	
B37	A57	8c + 4c rose	1.25	9.50
B38	A58	10c + 4c brt blue	3.75	12.00
B39	A59	12c + 4c dp blue	14.00	14.00
B40	A60	16c + 4c red brn	8.00	16.00
B41	A63	24c + 4c violet	11.00	20.00

B42	A64	25c + 4c yel grn		9.00	50.00
B43	A64	50c + 4c sl blue		15.00	45.00
a.		Perf. 15		60.00	
B44	A64	$1 + 4c brown		22.50	60.00
a.		Perf. 15		180.00	
B45	A64	$2 + 4c dk vio		55.00	80.00
B46	A65	$5 + 4c claret		300.00	400.00
B47	A65	$10 + 4c ver		375.00	450.00
		Nos. B31-B47 (17)		821.15	1,213.

POSTAGE DUE STAMPS

Regular Issues
Overprinted

On Nos. 60 to 67
Reading Up Vert. (V), or Horiz. (H)

1895, Aug. 1		**Unwmk.**	**Perf. 14, 15**	
J1	A22	2c rose & blk (V)	30.00	2.50
J2	A23	3c vio & ol grn (V)	6.00	1.25
J3	A24	5c org red & blk (V)	60.00	3.25
a.		Period after "DUE" (V)	275.00	
J4	A25	6c ol brn & blk (V)	20.00	2.75
J5	A26	8c lilac & blk (H)	50.00	3.00
a.		Double ovpt. (H)		400.00
J6	A27	12c blue & blk (H)	70.00	3.00
a.		Double overprint (H)		325.00
J7	A28	18c green & blk (V)	70.00	4.25
a.		Ovpt. reading down	600.00	350.00
b.		Overprinted horizontally	70.00	4.25
c.		Same as "b" inverted	375.00	400.00
J8	A29	24c claret & bl (H)	40.00	4.00
		Nos. J1-J8 (8)	346.00	24.00

1897		**On Nos. 80 and 85**		
J9	A38	2c dp rose & blk (V)	8.50	1.50
a.		Overprinted horizontally	23.00	15.00
J10	A42	8c brn lil & blk (H)	65.00	80.00
a.		Period after "DUE"	30.00	75.00

On Nos. 81-88 and 104 Vertically reading up

1901				
J11	A38	2c green & blk	75.00	.70
a.		Overprinted horizontally	225.00	
J12	A39	3c lilac & ol grn	32.00	.50
a.		Period after "DUE"	70.00	70.00
J13	A48	4c dp rose & blk	70.00	.50
J14	A40	5c orange & blk	28.00	.90
a.		Period after "DUE"	90.00	
J15	A41	6c olive brn & blk	7.00	.50
J16	A42	8c brown & blk	9.00	.50
a.		Overprinted horizontally	30.00	
b.		Period after "DUE" (H)	23.00	75.00
J17	A43	12c blue & blk	150.00	4.00
J18	A46	18c green & blk	80.00	4.00
J19	A47	24c red & blue	50.00	2.50
		Nos. J11-J19 (9)	501.00	14.10

On Nos. 105-114, 122-123 Horizontally

1903-11			**Perf. 14**	
J20	A37	1c bis brn & blk, period after "DUE"	4.50	55.00
a.		Period omitted		
J21	A38	2c green & blk	27.50	.30
a.		Ovpt. vert., perf. 16	550.00	275.00
b.		Perf 15 (ovpt. horiz.)	55.00	55.00
J22	A39	3c lilac & ol grn	7.00	.35
a.		Ovpt. vert.	140.00	140.00
b.		Perf. 15 (ovpt. horiz.)	50.00	45.00
J23	A48	4c dp rose & blk, perf. 15	11.00	2.00
a.		"Postage Due" double	550.00	170.00
b.		Perf. 14	21.00	1.00
J24	A40	5c orange & blk	45.00	.45
a.		Ovpt. vert., perf. 15	250.00	160.00
b.		Perf. 13½ (ovpt. horiz.)		
c.		Perf. 15 (ovpt. horiz.)	85.00	35.00
J25	A41	6c olive brn & blk	24.00	.40
a.		"Postage Due" double	750.00	
b.		"Postage Due" inverted	500.00	125.00
c.		Perf. 16	90.00	37.50
J26	A42	8c brown & blk	27.50	.50
a.		Overprint vertical	200.00	125.00
J27	A49	10c slate & brn	130.00	1.60
J28	A43	12c blue & blk	42.50	3.75
J29	A50	16c yel brn & grn	85.00	3.75
J30	A46	18c green & blk	17.50	1.50
a.		"Postage Due" double	500.00	100.00
J31	A47	24c claret & blue	17.50	3.75
a.		"Postage Due" double	350.00	125.00
b.		Overprint vertical	325.00	140.00
		Nos. J20-J31 (12)	439.00	73.35

On Nos. 137 and 139-146

1921-31			**Perf. 14, 15**	
J32	A52	2c green & blk	27.50	80.00
a.		Perf. 13½	11.00	75.00
J33	A53	3c green & blk	5.25	50.00
J34	A54	4c dull red & blk	1.25	1.25
J35	A55	5c yel brn & blk	9.50	30.00
J36	A56	6c olive grn & blk	17.00	17.00
J37	A57	8c rose & blk	2.00	5.00
J38	A58	10c blue & blk	16.00	19.00
a.		Perf. 15	120.00	200.00

J39	A59	12c dp vio & blk		70.00	55.00
J40	A60	16c red brn & blk		26.00	65.00
		Nos. J32-J40 (9)		174.50	319.25

On Nos. 168 to 176

1926-28			**Perf. 12½**	
J41	A52	2c lake & blk	.75	2.00
J42	A53	3c green & blk	10.00	32.50
J43	A54	4c dull red & blk	3.25	2.00
J44	A55	5c yel brown & blk	8.50	90.00
J45	A56	6c yel green & blk	14.00	3.00
J46	A57	8c rose & black	11.00	22.50
J47	A58	10c brt blue & blk	12.00	90.00
J48	A59	12c dp blue & blk	32.50	160.00
J49	A60	16c org brn & blk	75.00	225.00
		Nos. J41-J49 (9)	167.00	627.00

Crest of British North Borneo Company — D1

1939, Jan. 1			**Engr.**	**Perf. 12½**	
J50	D1	2c brown		4.25	80.00
J51	D1	4c carmine		4.75	110.00
J52	D1	6c dp rose violet		17.50	150.00
J53	D1	8c dk blue green		22.50	300.00
J54	D1	10c deep ultra		50.00	450.00
		Nos. J50-J54 (5)		99.00	1,090.
		Set, never hinged		160.00	

WAR TAX STAMPS

Nos. 193-194 Overprinted

No. MR1   No. MR2

1941, Feb. 24			**Unwmk.**	**Perf. 12½**	
MR1	A74	1c red brn & dk grn		2.75	4.50
MR2	A75	2c Prus blue & red violet		11.00	4.75

For overprints see Nos. N15A-N15B.

OCCUPATION STAMPS

Issued under Japanese Occupation

Nos. 193-207 Handstamped in Violet or Black

On Nos. N1-N15B, the violet overprint is attributed to Jesselton, the black to Sandakan. Nos. N1-N15 are generally found with violet overprint, Nos. N15A-N15B with black.

1942			**Unwmk.**	**Perf. 12½**	
N1	A74	1c		200.00	250.00
N2	A75	2c		220.00	300.00
N3	A76	3c		175.00	300.00
N4	A77	4c		175.00	300.00
N5	A78	6c		200.00	355.00
N6	A79	8c		275.00	210.00
N7	A80	10c		250.00	360.00
N8	A81	12c		275.00	525.00
N9	A82	15c		220.00	525.00
N10	A83	20c		300.00	650.00
N11	A84	25c		300.00	700.00
N12	A85	50c		400.00	775.00
N13	A86	$1		440.00	925.00
N14	A86	$2		650.00	1,250.
N15	A87	$5		775.00	1,350.
		Nos. N1-N15 (15)		4,855.	8,775.

For overprints see Nos. N22a, N31a.

Same Overprint on Nos. MR1-MR2 in Black or Violet

1942					
N15A	A74	1c		750.00	325.00
N15B	A75	2c		1,900.	650.00

Nos. 193 to 207
Overprinted in Black

1944, Sept. 30			**Unwmk.**	**Perf. 12½**	
N16	A74	1c		8.25	13.00
N17	A75	2c		8.25	10.00
a.		On No. N2		300.00	
N18	A76	3c		8.25	11.00
a.		On No. N3		400.00	
N19	A77	4c		15.00	25.00
N20	A78	6c		12.00	7.00
N21	A79	8c		11.00	18.50
a.		On No. N6		375.00	
N22	A80	10c		9.25	14.50
a.		On No. N7		425.00	
N23	A81	12c		17.50	14.50
a.		On No. N8		400.00	
N24	A82	15c		17.50	17.50
a.		On No. N9		450.00	
N25	A83	20c		40.00	60.00
N26	A84	25c		40.00	60.00
N27	A85	50c		100.00	130.00
N28	A86	$1		150.00	150.00
		Nos. N16-N28 (13)		437.00	531.00

Nos. N1 and 205 Surcharged in Black

No. N30   No. N31

1944, May					
N30	A74	$2 on 1c		*7,500.*	*5,000.*
N31	A86	$5 on $1		*7,000.*	*4,500.*
a.		On No. N13		*10,000.*	*6,000.*

Mt. Kinabalu   Boat and
OS1   Traveler's Palm
          OS2

1943, Apr. 29			**Litho.**	
N32	OS1	4c dull rose red	30.00	60.00
N33	OS2	8c dark blue	25.00	55.00

Stamps of Japan, 1938-43, Overprinted in Black

1s, War factory girl. 2s, Gen. Maresuke Nogi. 3s, Power plant. 4s, Hyuga Monument and Mt. Fuji. 5s, Adm. Heihachiro Togo. 6s, Garambi Lighthouse, Formosa. 8s, Meiji Shrine, Tokyo. 10s, Palms and map of "Greater East Asia." 15s, Aviator saluting and Japanese flag. 20s, Mt. Fuji and cherry blossoms. 25s, Horyu Temple, Nara. 30s, Miyajima Torii, Itsukushima shrine. 50s, Golden Pavilion, Kyoto. 1y, Great Buddha, Kamakura. See Burma, Vol. 1, for illustrations of 2s, 3s, 5s, 8s, 20s and watermark. For others, see Japan.

Wmk. Curved Wavy Lines (257)

1944, Sept. 30			**Perf. 13**	
N34	A144	1s orange brown	10.00	35.00
N35	A84	2s vermilion	9.00	30.00
N36	A85	3s green	10.00	35.00
N37	A146	4s emerald	17.00	27.50
N38	A86	5s brown lake	12.50	30.00
N39	A88	6s orange	15.00	32.50
N40	A90	8s dk purple & pale vio	11.00	32.50
N41	A148	10s crim & dull rose	15.00	35.00
N42	A150	15s dull blue	15.00	32.50
N43	A94	20s ultra	100.00	125.00
N44	A95	25s brown	80.00	110.00
N45	A96	30s peacock blue	200.00	200.00
N46	A97	50s olive	100.00	100.00
N47	A98	1y lt brown	100.00	100.00
		Nos. N34-N47 (14)	694.50	945.00

The overprint translates "North Borneo."

OCCUPATION POSTAGE DUE STAMPS

Nos. J50-J51, J53
Handstamped in Black

1942, Sept. 30				
NJ1	D1	2c brown	600.	—
NJ2	D1	4c carmine	600.	—
NJ3	D1	8c dk blue green	600.	—

NORTHERN NIGERIA

'nor-thə ṛ n nī-'jir-ē-ə

LOCATION — Western Africa
GOVT. — British Protectorate
AREA — 281,703 sq. mi.
POP. — 11,866,250
CAPITAL — Zungeru

In 1914 Northern Nigeria united with Southern Nigeria to form the Colony and Protectorate of Nigeria.

12 Pence = 1 Shilling
20 Shillings = 1 Pound

Victoria — A1

Numerals of 5p and 6p, types A1 and A2, are in color on plain tablet.

Wmk. Crown and C A (2)

1900, Mar.   **Typo.**   **Perf. 14**

1	A1	½p lilac & grn	8.75	22.00
2	A1	1p lilac & rose	5.75	5.50
3	A1	2p lilac & yel	16.00	60.00
4	A1	2½p lilac & blue	13.00	45.00
5	A1	5p lilac & brn	30.00	70.00
6	A1	6p vio & blk	30.00	50.00
7	A1	1sh green & blk	32.50	85.00
8	A1	2sh6p green & blue	180.00	550.00
9	A1	10sh green & brn	325.00	900.00
		Nos. 1-9 (9)	641.00	1,788.

Edward VII — A2

1902, July 1

10	A2	½p violet & green	2.25	2.00
11	A2	1p vio & car rose	5.00	1.00
12	A2	2p violet & grn	2.50	3.00
13	A2	2½p violet & ultra	2.00	13.00
14	A2	5p vio & org brn	7.00	7.50
15	A2	6p violet & pur	20.00	8.00
16	A2	1sh green & black	8.50	8.50
17	A2	2sh6p green & ultra	19.00	75.00
18	A2	10sh green & brown	55.00	60.00
		Nos. 10-18 (9)	121.25	178.00

1904, Apr.   **Wmk. 3**

18A   A2   £25 green & car   *60,000.*

No. 18A was available for postage but probably was used only for fiscal purposes.

1905

19a	A2	½p violet & grn	6.00	5.50
20a	A2	1p violet & car rose	6.00	1.25
21	A2	2p violet & org	19.00	32.50
22	A2	2½p violet & ultra	7.25	10.00
23	A2	5p violet & org brn	32.50	85.00
24	A2	6p violet & pur	29.00	65.00
25a	A2	1sh green & black	24.00	55.00
26a	A2	2sh6p green & ultra	45.00	60.00
		Nos. 19a-26a (8)	166.25	314.25

All values except the 2½p exist on ordinary and chalky papers. The less expensive values are given above. For detailed listings, see the *Scott Classic Specialized Catalogue of Stamps and Covers 1840-1940.*

1910-11   **Ordinary Paper**

28	A2	½p green	2.25	1.25
29	A2	1p carmine	5.75	1.00
30	A2	2p gray	9.50	6.50
31	A2	2½p ultra	4.25	11.00

Chalky Paper

32	A2	3p violet	4.50	1.00
33	A2	5p vio & ol grn	6.00	19.00
34	A2	6p vio & red vio ('11)	6.00	6.00
a.		6p violet & deep violet	7.50	28.00
35	A2	1sh black, *green*	5.25	.75
36	A2	2sh6p blk & red, *bl*	19.00	50.00
37	A2	5sh grn & red, *yel*	29.00	75.00
38	A2	10sh grn & red, *grn*	55.00	50.00
		Nos. 28-38 (11)	146.50	221.75

George V — A3

For description of dies I and II, see A pages in front section of catalogue.

Die I

1912   **Ordinary Paper**

40	A3	½p green	4.50	1.00
41	A3	1p carmine	4.50	.60
42	A3	2p gray	6.75	17.00

Chalky Paper

43	A3	3p violet, *yel*	2.25	1.25
44	A3	4p blk & red, *yel*	4.25	2.25
45	A3	5p vio & ol grn	4.50	20.00
46	A3	6p vio & red vio	4.25	4.50
47	A3	9p violet & scar	2.25	12.00
48	A3	1sh blk, *green*	5.00	2.25
49	A3	2sh6p blk & red, *bl*	10.00	55.00
50	A3	5sh grn & red, *yel*	25.00	90.00
51	A3	10sh grn & red, *grn*	45.00	50.00
52	A3	£1 vio & blk, *red*	200.00	120.00
		Nos. 40-52 (13)	315.25	375.85

Numerals of 3p, 4p, 5p and 6p, type A3, are in color on plain tablet.
Stamps of Northern Nigeria were replaced in 1914 by those of Nigeria.

NORTHERN RHODESIA

'nor-thə ṛ n rō-'dē-zhē-ə

LOCATION — In southern Africa, east of Angola and separated from Southern Rhodesia by the Zambezi River.
GOVT. — British Protectorate
AREA — 287,640 sq. mi.
POP. — 2,550,000 (est. 1962)
CAPITAL — Lusaka

Prior to April 1, 1924, Northern Rhodesia was administered by the British South Africa Company. It joined the Federation of Rhodesia and Nyasaland in 1953 and issued its stamps in 1954-63. It resumed issuing its own stamps in December, 1963, after the Federation was dissolved. On Oct. 24, 1964, Northern Rhodesia became the independent republic of Zambia. See Rhodesia, Southern Rhodesia, Rhodesia and Nyasaland, Zambia.

12 Pence = 1 Shilling
20 Shillings = 1 Pound

> **Catalogue values for unused stamps in this country are for Never Hinged items, beginning with Scott 46 in the regular postage section and Scott J5 in the postage due section.**

King George V
A1   A2

1925-29   **Engr.**   **Wmk. 4**   **Perf. 12½**

1	A1	½p dk green	1.75	.80
2	A1	1p dk brown	1.75	.25
3	A1	1½p carmine	4.25	.30
4	A1	2p brown org	4.50	.25
5	A1	3p ultra	4.50	1.30
6	A1	4p dk violet	7.50	.50
7	A1	6p gray	9.00	.40
8	A1	8p rose lilac	9.00	60.00
9	A1	10p olive drn	9.00	50.00
10	A1	1sh black & org	4.75	2.25
11	A2	2p ultra & brn	32.50	50.00
12	A2	2sh6p green & blk	26.00	15.00
13	A2	3sh indigo & vio	50.00	28.00
14	A2	5sh dk vio & gray	57.50	22.50
15	A2	7sh6p blk & lil rose	200.00	325.00
16	A2	10sh black & green	125.00	100.00
17	A2	20sh rose lil & red	375.00	400.00
		Nos. 1-17 (17)	922.00	1,057.

High values with revenue cancellations are inexpensive.
Issue dates: 3sh, 1929; others, Apr. 1.

Common Design Types pictured following the introduction.

Silver Jubilee Issue
Common Design Type

1935, May 6   **Perf. 13½x14**

18	CD301	1p olive grn & ultra	1.50	1.50
19	CD301	2p indigo & grn	2.75	2.00
20	CD301	3p blue & brown	4.25	9.00
21	CD301	6p brt vio & indigo	8.50	2.50
		Nos. 18-21 (4)	17.00	15.00
		Set, never hinged	26.00	

Coronation Issue
Common Design Type

1937, May 12   **Perf. 11x11½**

22	CD302	1½p dark carmine	.25	.25
23	CD302	2p yellow brown	.30	.75
24	CD302	3p deep ultra	.40	1.25
		Nos. 22-24 (3)	.95	2.25
		Set, never hinged	1.50	

King George VI — A3

1938-52   **Wmk. 4**   **Perf. 12½**
Size: 19x24mm

25	A3	½p green	.25	.25
26	A3	½p dk brn ('51)	1.40	1.50
a.		Perf. 12½x14	1.00	6.00
27	A3	1p dk brown	.25	.25
28	A3	1p green ('51)	.90	2.25
29	A3	1½p carmine	27.50	.75
a.		Horiz. pair, imperf. between	30,000.	
30	A3	1½p brn org ('41)	.30	.25
31	A3	2p brown org	27.50	1.75
32	A3	2p carmine ('41)	1.00	.50
33	A3	2p rose lilac ('51)	.40	1.50
34	A3	3p ultra	.45	.30
35	A3	3p red ('51)	.30	3.00
36	A3	4p dk violet	.30	.40
37	A3	4½p dp blue ('52)	1.75	12.00
38	A3	6p dark gray	.30	.25
39	A3	9p violet ('52)	1.75	12.00

Size: 21½x26¾mm

40	A3	1sh blk & brn org	2.50	.60
41	A3	2sh6p green & blk	8.00	7.00
42	A3	3sh ind & dk vio	14.00	16.00
43	A3	5sh violet & gray	14.50	17.00
44	A3	10sh black & green	16.00	32.50
45	A3	20sh rose lil & red	37.50	75.00
		Nos. 25-45 (21)	156.85	185.05
		Set, never hinged	275.00	

> **Catalogue values for unused stamps in this section, from this point to the end of the section, are for Never Hinged items.**

Peace Issue
Common Design Type

1946, Nov. 26   **Engr.**   **Perf. 13½x14**

46	CD303	1½p deep orange	1.00	1.50
a.		Perf. 13½	14.00	13.00
47	CD303	2p carmine	.25	.50

Silver Wedding Issue
Common Design Types

1948, Dec. 1   **Photo.**   **Perf. 14x14½**

48	CD304	1½p orange	.30	.25

Perf. 11½x11
Engr.

49	CD305	20sh rose brown	100.00	90.00

UPU Issue
Common Design Types
Engr.; Name Typo. on 3p, 6p
Perf. 13½, 11x11½

1949, Oct. 10   **Wmk. 4**

50	CD306	2p rose carmine	.50	.50
51	CD307	3p indigo	2.00	3.00
52	CD308	6p gray	1.50	1.50
53	CD309	1sh red orange	1.00	1.50
		Nos. 50-53 (4)	5.00	6.50

A4

Designs: Victoria Falls and Railway Bridge, Cecil Rhodes and Elizabeth II.

1953, May 30   **Engr.**   **Perf. 12x11**

54	A4	½p brown	.55	1.25
55	A4	1p green	.45	1.25
56	A4	2p deep claret	.80	1.25
57	A4	4½p deep blue	.55	4.00
58	A4	1sh gray & orange	1.25	4.25
		Nos. 54-58 (5)	3.60	11.15

Cecil Rhodes (1853-1902).

Exhibition Seal — A5

1953, May 30   **Perf. 14x13½**

59	A5	6p purple	.70	1.25

Central African Rhodes Centenary Exhib.

Coronation Issue
Common Design Type

1953, June 2   **Perf. 13½x13**

60	CD312	1½p orange & black	.70	.25

Elizabeth II — A6

Perf. 12½x13½

1953, Sept. 15   **Engr.**
Size: 19x23mm

61	A6	½p dark brown	.65	.25
62	A6	1p green	.75	.25
63	A6	1½p brown orange	1.25	.25
64	A6	2p rose lilac	1.40	.25
65	A6	3p red	.80	.25
66	A6	4p dark violet	1.25	2.00
67	A6	4½p deep blue	1.50	4.25
68	A6	6p dark gray	1.25	.40
69	A6	9p violet	1.25	4.25

Size: 21x27mm

70	A6	1sh black & brn org	1.00	.25
71	A6	2sh6p green & blk	15.00	8.00
72	A6	5sh violet & gray	16.00	15.00
73	A6	10sh black & green	12.00	32.50
74	A6	20sh rose lilac & red	30.00	37.50
		Nos. 61-74 (14)	84.10	105.40

Coat of Arms — A7

Size: 23x19mm

Perf. 14½

1963, Dec. 1   **Unwmk.**   **Photo.**
Arms in Black, Blue and Orange

75	A7	½p redsh lil & blk	.70	1.00
a.		Value omitted	1,100.	
b.		Orange (eagle) omitted	1,400.	
76	A7	1p turq bl & blk	1.50	.25
a.		Value omitted	12.50	
77	A7	2p red brn & blk	.70	.25
78	A7	3p orange & blk	.25	.25
a.		Bkt. pane of 4	1.00	
b.		Value omitted	120.00	
c.		Orange (eagle) omitted	1,200.	—
d.		Value and orange (eagle) omitted	325.00	
79	A7	4p green & blk	.70	.30
a.		Value omitted	130.00	
80	A7	6p ol grn & blk	1.00	.25
a.		Value omitted	800.00	
81	A7	9p dl org & blk	.70	1.60
a.		Value omitted	600.00	
b.		Value and orange (eagle) omitted	600.00	
82	A7	1sh dk gray & blk	.50	.25
83	A7	1sh3p mag & blk	2.25	.25

Perf. 13
Size: 27x23mm

84	A7	2sh ver & blk	2.50	5.25
85	A7	2sh6p claret & blk	2.25	2.25
86	A7	5sh blk dk car rose & blk	10.00	8.00
a.		Value omitted	2,750.	
87	A7	10sh brt pink & blk	17.00	22.50
88	A7	20sh Prus bl & blk	22.00	40.00
a.		Value omitted	1,100.	
		Nos. 75-88 (14)	62.30	82.40

Stamps of Northern Rhodesia were replaced by those of Zambia, starting Oct. 24, 1964.

POSTAGE DUE STAMPS

D1

1929   Typo.   Wmk. 4   Perf. 14
J1	D1	1p black	3.00	2.75
a.		Wmk. 4a (error)	7,000.	
J2	D1	2p black	8.00	3.50
a.		Bisected, used as 1d, on cover		850.00
J3	D1	3p black	3.00	27.50
a.		Crown in watermark missing	700.00	
b.		Wmk. 4a (error)	425.00	
J4	D1	4p black	11.00	42.50
		Nos. J1-J4 (4)	25.00	76.25

> **Catalogue values for unused stamps in this section, from this point to the end of the section, are for Never Hinged items.**

D2

1964   Unwmk.   Litho.   Perf. 12½
J5	D2	1p orange	3.00	5.50
J6	D2	2p dark blue	3.00	4.50
J7	D2	3p rose claret	3.00	7.50
J8	D2	4p violet blue	3.00	13.00
J9	D2	6p purple	9.50	10.00
J10	D2	1sh emerald	11.00	30.00
		Nos. J5-J10 (6)	32.50	70.50

NORTH INGERMANLAND

'north 'iŋ-gər-mən-ˌland

LOCATION — In Northern Russia lying between the River Neva and Finland
CAPITAL — Kirjasalo

In 1920 the residents of this territory revolted from Russian rule and set up a provisional government. The new State existed only a short period as the revolution was quickly quelled by Soviet troops.

100 Pennia = 1 Markka

Arms — A1

Perf. 11½
1920, Mar. 21   Unwmk.   Litho.
1	A1	5p green	2.75	3.50
2	A1	10p rose red	2.75	3.50
b.		Horiz. pair, imperf. btwn.	50.00	
3	A1	25p bister	2.75	3.50
b.		Horiz. pair, imperf. btwn.	50.00	
c.		Vert. pair, imperf. btwn.	50.00	
4	A1	50p dark blue	2.50	3.50
b.		Horiz. pair, imperf. btwn.	75.00	
5	A1	1m car & black	30.00	42.50
6	A1	5m lilac & black	175.00	160.00
7	A1	10m brown & blk	200.00	200.00
		Nos. 1-7 (7)	415.75	416.50
		Set, never hinged	1,100.	

Well centered examples sell for twice the values shown.

Imperf., Pairs
1a	A1	5p	45.00
2a	A1	10p	100.00
3a	A1	25p	50.00
4a	A1	50p	50.00
5a	A1	1m	65.00
6a	A1	5m	200.00
7a	A1	10m	350.00

Arms — A2

Peasant — A3

Plowing — A4

Milking — A5

Planting — A6

Ruins of Church — A7

Peasants Playing Zithers — A8

1920, Aug. 2
8	A2	10p gray grn & ultra	3.50	7.00
9	A3	30p buff & gray grn	3.50	7.00
a.		Horiz. pair, imperf. btwn.	100.00	
10	A4	50p ultra & red brn	3.50	7.00
11	A5	80p claret & slate	3.50	7.00
12	A6	1m red & slate	20.00	45.00
13	A7	5m dk vio & dl rose	8.25	18.00
14	A8	10m brn & violet	8.25	18.00
a.		Center inverted	1,000.	
		Nos. 8-14 (7)	50.50	109.00
		Set, never hinged	120.00	

Counterfeits abound.
Nos. 8-14 exist imperf. Value for set in pairs, $200.

NORTH WEST PACIFIC ISLANDS

'north 'west pə-'si-fik 'ī-lənds

LOCATION — Group of islands in the West Pacific Ocean including a part of New Guinea and adjacent islands of the Bismarck Archipelago
GOVT. — Australian military government
AREA — 96,160 sq. mi.
POP. — 636,563

Stamps of Australia were overprinted for use in the former German possessions of Nauru and German New Guinea which Australian troops had captured. Following the League of Nations' decision which placed these territories under mandate to Australia, these provisional issues were discontinued. See German New Guinea, New Britain, Nauru and New Guinea.

12 Pence = 1 Shilling
20 Shillings = 1 Pound

Watermarks

Wmk. 8 — Wide Crown and Wide A   Wmk. 9 — Wide Crown and Narrow A

Wmk. 10 — Narrow Crown and Narrow A   Wmk. 11 — Multiple Crown and A

Stamps of Australia Overprinted — a

Type a: "P" of "PACIFIC" above "S" of "ISLANDS."

There are two varieties of the letter "S" in the Type "a" overprint. These occur in three combinations:1. both normal "S"; 2. 1st "S" with small head and long bottom stroke, 2nd "S" normal; 3.. both "S" with small head and long bottom stroke.

DESIGN A1
Die I — The inside frameline has a break at left, even with the top of the letters of the denomination.
Die II — The frameline does not show a break.
Die IV — As Die III, with a break in the top outside frameline above the "ST" of "AUSTRALIA." The upper right inside frameline has an incomplete corner.
Dies are only indicated when there are more than one for any denomination.

1915-16   Wmk. 8   Perf. 12
1	A1(a)	2p gray	25.00	75.00
2	A1(a)	2½p dark blue	5.00	22.50
3	A1(a)	3p ol bis, die I	25.00	65.00
a.		Die II	385.00	600.00
b.		Pair, #3, 3a	825.00	1,200.
c.		Pair, die I and die II	2,500.	
4	A1(a)	6p ultra	120.00	130.00
5	A1(a)	9p violet	60.00	72.50
6	A1(a)	1sh blue green	75.00	77.50
8	A1(a)	5sh yel & gray ('16)	2,750.	3,850.
9	A1(a)	10sh pink & gray	170.00	200.00
		Revenue cancel		
10	A1(a)	£1 ultra & brown	600.00	775.00
		Nos. 1-6,8-10 (9)	3,830.	5,268.

For surcharge see No. 27.

Wmk. Wide Crown and Narrow A (9)
Perf. 12, 14

ONE PENNY
Die I — Normal die, having outside the oval band with "AUSTRALIA" a white line and a heavy colored line.
Die Ia — As die I with a small white spur below the right serif at foot of the "1" in left tablet.
Dies are only indicated when there are more than one for any denomination.

11	A4(a)	½p emerald	3.25	10.00
a.		Double overprint		
12	A4(a)	1p car (Die I)	7.75	7.25
a.		1p carmine rose (Die I)	120.00	150.00
b.		1p carmine (Die Ia)	110.00	145.00
13	A1(a)	2p gray	20.00	50.00
14	A1(a)	2½p dk bl ('16)	30,000.	30,000.
16	A4(a)	4p orange	4.50	17.50
17	A4(a)	5p org brown	3.25	19.00
18	A1(a)	6p ultra	11.00	13.00
19	A1(a)	9p violet	17.50	24.00
20	A1(a)	1sh blue green	12.50	27.50
21	A1(a)	2sh brown	110.00	130.00

22	A1(a)	5sh yel & gray	82.50	120.00
		Nos. 11-13,16-22 (10)	272.25	418.25

For surcharge see No. 28.

1915-16   Wmk. 10   Perf. 12
23	A1(a)	2p gray, die I	9.00	32.50
24	A1(a)	3p ol bis, die I	7.00	15.00
a.		Die II	125.00	190.00
b.		Pair, #24, 24a	350.00	
25	A1(a)	2sh brown ('16)	45.00	65.00
26	A1(a)	£1 ultra & brn ('16)	400.00	525.00
		Nos. 23-26 (4)	461.00	637.50

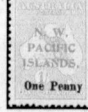

Nos. 6 and 17 Surcharged

1918, May 23   Wmk. 8   Perf. 12
27	A1	1p on 1sh bl grn	125.00	100.00

Wmk. 9   Perf. 14
28	A4	1p on 5p org brn	110.00	100.00

Stamps of Australia Overprinted — b

Type "b": "P" of "PACIFIC" above space between "I" and "S" of "ISLANDS."

1918-23   Wmk. 10   Perf. 12
29	A1(b)	2p gray	8.50	30.00
a.		Die II	13.50	57.50
30	A1(b)	2½p dk bl ('19)	6.50	19.00
a.		"1" of fraction omitted	14,000.	16,500.
31	A1(b)	3p ol bis, die I	27.50	30.00
a.		Die II	80.00	100.00
b.		Pair, #31, 31a	500.00	650.00
32	A1(b)	6p ultra ('19)	7.50	16.50
a.		6p chalky blue	50.00	75.00
33	A1(b)	9p violet ('19)	11.50	60.00
34	A1(b)	1sh bl grn ('18)	16.50	37.50
a.		1sh emerald green	7.00	32.50
35	A1(b)	2sh brown	25.00	42.50
36	A1(b)	5sh yel & gray ('19)	75.00	80.00
37	A1(b)	10sh pink & gray ('19)	200.00	275.00
38	A1(b)	£1 ultra & brn	4,500.	5,500.
		Nos. 29-37 (9)	378.00	590.50

1919   Wmk. 11   Perf. 14
39	A4(b)	½p emerald	5.00	6.00

1918-23   Wmk. 9
40	A4(b)	½p emerald	2.00	4.00
41	A4(b)	1p car red, die I	4.25	1.75
a.		1p carmine red, die Ia	125.00	90.00
42	A4(b)	1p scar, die I, rough paper	1,000.	675.00
a.		1p rose red, die Ia, rough paper	1,000.	675.00
43	A4(b)	1p violet ('22)	2.75	7.25
44	A4(b)	2p orange	8.75	2.75
45	A4(b)	2p red ('22)	10.50	2.25
46	A4(b)	4p yel org	4.00	17.50
47	A4(b)	4p violet ('22)	22.50	45.00
a.		"Four Penc" in thinner letters	900.00	1,550.
48	A4(b)	4p light ultra ('22)	12.50	65.00
a.		"Four Penc" in thinner letters	1,000.	2,000.
49	A4(b)	5p brown	4.25	13.50
		Nos. 40-41,43-49 (9)	71.50	159.00

North West Pacific Islands stamps were largely used in New Britain. Some were used in Nauru. They were intended to serve the Bismarck Archipelago and other places.

NORWAY
'nor-ˌwā

LOCATION — Western half of the Scandinavian Peninsula in northern Europe
GOVT. — Kingdom
AREA — 125,051 sq. mi.
POP. — 4,644,457 (2008 est.)
CAPITAL — Oslo

120 Skilling = 1 Specie Daler
100 Ore = 1 Krone (1877)

Catalogue values for unused stamps in this country are for Never Hinged items, beginning with Scott 275 in the regular postage section, Scott B27 in the semi-postal section, and Scott O65 in the official section.

Watermarks

Wmk. 159 — Lion

Wmk. 160 — Post Horn

Coat of Arms — A1

Wmk. 159

1855, Jan. 1   Typo.   Imperf.

1	A1	4s blue	4,250.	165.
a.		Double foot on right hind leg of lion		3,000.

Only a few genuine unused examples of No. 1 exist. Stamps often offered have had pen-markings removed. The unused catalogue value is for a stamp without gum. Stamps with original gum sell for much more.
No. 1 was reprinted in 1914 and 1924 unwatermarked. Lowest value reprint, $125.

ROULETTED REPRINTS
1963: No. 1, value $25; Nos. 2-5, 15, value each $15.
1966: Nos. 57, 70a, 100, 152, J1, O1. Value each $12.
1969: Nos. 69, 92, 107, 114, 128, J12. Value each $12.

King Oscar I — A2

1856-57   Unwmk.   Perf. 13

2	A2	2s yellow ('57)	600.00	150.00
3	A2	3s lilac ('57)	250.00	50.00
4	A2	4s blue	240.00	13.00
a.		Imperf.		7,500.
b.		Half used as 2s on cover		—
5	A2	8s dull lake	1,450.	—

Nos. 2-5 were reprinted in 1914 and 1924, perf. 13½. Lowest valued reprint, $45 each.

Background of Crisscrossed Lines

A3

1863   Litho.   Perf. 14½x13½

6	A3	2s yellow	750.00	250.00
7	A3	3s gray lilac	400.00	300.00
8	A3	4s blue	240.00	14.00
9	A3	8s rose	850.00	60.00
10	A3	24s brown	45.00	125.00
		Nos. 6-10 (5)	2,285.	749.00

There are four types of the 2, 3, 8 and 24 skilling and eight types of the 4 skilling. See note on used value of No. 10 following No. 21. No. 8 exists imperf. Value, unused $1,200.

Background of Vertical Lines

A4

1867-68   Typo.

11	A4	1s black, coarse impression ('68)	85.00	55.00
12	A4	2s orange	22.50	55.00
b.		Vert. pair, imperf between		
13	A4	3s dl lil, coarse impression ('68)	450.00	160.00
14	A4	4s blue, thin paper	175.00	11.00
15	A4	4s car rose	600.00	55.00
a.		8s rose, clear impression	1,500.	425.00
		Nos. 11-15 (5)	1,333.	336.00

See note on used value of #12 following #21. For surcharges see Nos. 59-61, 149.
No. 15 was reprinted in 1914 and 1924, perf. 13½. Lowest valued reprint, $45.

Post Horn and Crown — A5

1872-75   Wmk. 160

16	A5	1s yel grn ('75)	12.00	40.00
a.		1s deep green ('73)	250.00	75.00
b.		"E.EN"	25.00	75.00
d.		Vert. pair, imperf between		
17	A5	2s ultra ('74)	14.00	85.00
a.		2s Prussian blue ('74)	15,000.	4,750.
b.		2s gray blue	11.00	75.00
18	A5	3s rose	60.00	12.00
a.		3s carmine	110.00	42.50
b.		3s carmine, *bluish thin paper*	240.00	30.00
19	A5	4s lilac, thin paper ('75)	15.00	72.50
a.		4s dark violet, *bluish, thin paper*	450.00	160.00
b.		4s brown violet, *bluish, thin paper* ('73)	500.00	190.00
c.		4s violet, *white, thick paper* ('73)	110.00	72.50

20	A5	6s org brn ('75)	500.00	72.50
21	A5	7s red brn ('73)	50.00	72.50
		Nos. 16-21 (6)	651.00	354.50

In this issue there are 12 types each of Nos. 16, 17, 18 and 19; 12 types of No. 20 and 20 types of No. 21. The differences are in the words of value.
Nos. 10, 12, 16, 17, 19 and 21 were re-released in 1888 and used until March 31, 1908. Used values of these stamps are for examples canceled in this later period, usually with a two-ring cancellation. Examples bearing clear dated cancellations before 1888 are worth considerably more, as follows: No. 10 $300, No. 12 $140, No. 16 $125, No. 17 $175, No. 17b $350, No. 19 $300, No. 21 $140.
No. 21 exists imperf. Value, unused without gum $800.
No. 19 comes on thin and thick paper.
For surcharges see Nos. 62-63.

Post Horn   King
A6   Oscar II
             A7

"NORGE" in Sans-serif Capitals, Ring of Post Horn Shaded

1877-78

22	A6	1o drab	7.25	8.00
23	A6	3o orange	90.00	35.00
24	A6	5o ultra	30.00	12.00
a.		5o dull blue	500.00	125.00
b.		5o bright blue	300.00	60.00
c.		No period after "Postfrim"	45.00	18.00
d.		Retouched plate	150.00	25.00
e.		As "c," retouched plate	225.00	27.50
25	A6	10o rose	120.00	3.50
b.		Retouched plate	120.00	3.75
26	A6	12o lt green	120.00	24.00
27	A6	20o orange brn	350.00	12.00
28	A6	25o lilac	500.00	150.00
29	A6	35o bl grn ('78)	24.00	15.00
a.		Retouched plate	250.00	110.00
30	A6	50o maroon	50.00	12.50
31	A6	60o dk bl ('78)	50.00	11.00
32	A7	1k gray grn & org ('78)	30.00	12.50
33	A7	1.50k ultra & bl ('78)	60.00	50.00
34	A7	2k rose & mar ('78)	45.00	25.00
		Nos. 22-34 (13)	1,476.	370.50

There are 6 types each of Nos. 22, 26 and 28 to 34; 12 types each of Nos. 23, 24, 25 and 27. The differences are in the numerals.
A 2nd plate of the 5o ultramarine has 100 types, the 10o, 200 types.
The retouch on 5o, 10o and 35o shows as a thin white line between crown and post horn.

Post Horn — A8

"NORGE" in Sans-serif Capitals, Ring of Horn Unshaded

1882-93   Wmk. 160   Perf. 14½x13½

35	A8	1o blk brn ('86)	17.50	24.00
a.		No period after "Post-frim"	60.00	60.00
b.		Small "N" in "NORGE"	60.00	60.00
36	A8	1o gray ('93)	15.00	30.00
37	A8	2o brown ('90)	4.50	10.00
38	A8	3o yellow ('89)	90.00	8.50
a.		3o orange ('83)	150.00	20.00
b.		Perf. 13½x12½ ('93)	8,500.	2,500.
39	A8	5o bl grn ('89)	60.00	2.50
a.		5o gray green ('86)	85.00	5.00
b.		5o emerald ('88)	200.00	7.50
c.		5o yellow green ('91)	70.00	6.00
d.		Perf. 13½x12½ ('93)	3,000.	1,200.
40	A8	10o rose	60.00	1.75
a.		10o rose red ('86)	60.00	1.75
b.		10o carmine ('91)	60.00	1.75
c.		As "b," imperf. ('91)	3,000.	2,750.
41	A8	12o green ('84)	1,600.	400.00
42	A8	12o org brn ('84)	24.00	27.00
a.		12o bister brown ('83)	70.00	60.00
43	A8	20o brown	160.00	20.00
44	A8	20o blue ('86)	125.00	6.00
a.		20o ultramarine ('83)	600.00	30.00
b.		No period after "Post-frim" ('85)	600.00	24.00
c.		As "a," imperf. ('90)	2,500.	3,000.
d.		20o Prussian blue	225.00	21.00
45	A8	25o dull vio ('84)	15.00	16.00

Dies vary from 20 to 21mm high. Numerous types exist due to different production methods, including separate handmade dies for value figures. Many shades exist.

No. 42 and 42a Surcharged in Black

1888   Perf. 14½x13½

46	A8	2o on 12o org brn	3.00	3.00
a.		2o on 12o bister brown	3.00	3.00

Post Horn — A10

"NORGE" in Roman instead of Sans-serif capitals
Perf. 14½x13½

1893-1908   Wmk. 160
Size: 16x20mm

47	A10	1o gray ('99)	2.50	2.50
48	A10	2o pale brn ('99)	2.50	1.75
49	A10	3o orange yel	1.75	.25
50	A10	5o dp green ('98)	6.00	.25
b.		Booklet pane of 6	800.00	
51	A10	10o carmine ('98)	12.00	.25
b.		Booklet pane of 6	1,100.	
d.		10o rose ('94)	250.00	2.50
e.		Imperf		4,000.
52	A10	15o brown ('08)	50.00	12.00
53	A10	20o dp ultra	24.00	.25
b.		Booklet pane of 6		
54	A10	25o red vio ('01)	55.00	3.00
55	A10	30o sl gray ('07)	45.00	3.50
56	A10	35o dk bl grn ('98)	11.00	8.50
57	A10	50o maroon ('94)	50.00	2.50
58	A10	60o dk blue ('00)	60.00	13.00
		Nos. 47-58 (12)	319.75	47.75

Two dies exist of 3, 10 and 20o.
See Nos. 74-95, 162-166, 187-191, 193, 307-309, 325-326, 416-419, 606, 709-714, 960-968, 1141-1145.
For overprints and surcharge see Nos. 99, 207-211, 220-224, 226, 329.

1893-98   Wmk. 160   Perf. 13½x12½

47a	A10	1o gray ('95)	15.00	30.00
49a	A10	3o orange ('95)	30.00	6.00
50a	A10	5o green	42.50	6.00
51a	A10	10o carmine ('96)	27.50	1.50
c.		10o rose ('95)	75.00	1.75
53a	A10	20o dull ultra ('95)	110.00	4.25
54a	A10	25o red violet ('98)	90.00	30.00
56a	A10	35o dark blue green ('95)	90.00	30.00
57a	A10	50o maroon ('97)	400.00	25.00
		Nos. 47a-57a (8)	805.00	132.75

Two dies exist of each except 25o and 35o.

No. 12 Surcharged in Green, Blue or Carmine

1905   Unwmk.   Perf. 14½x13½

59	A4	1k on 2s org (G)	42.50	35.00
60	A4	1.50k on 2s org (Bl)	75.00	95.00
61	A4	2k on 2s org (C)	85.00	100.00
		Nos. 59-61 (3)	202.50	230.00

Used values are for stamps canceled before 1910. Stamps used before that sell for twice as much.

Nos. 19 and 21 Surcharged in Black

1906-08   Wmk. 160   Perf. 14½x13½

62	A5	15o on 4s lilac ('08)	4.50	5.50
a.		15o on 4s violet ('08)	11.00	13.00
63	A5	30o on 7s red brn	7.50	11.00
a.		Inverted overprint		9,000.

Used values are for stamps canceled after 1914. Stamps used before that sell for twice as much.

King Haakon VII — A11

Die A   Die B

Die C

Die A — Background of ruled lines. The coils at the sides are ornamented with fine cross-lines and small dots. Stamps 20¼mm high.

Die B — Background of ruled lines. The coils are ornamented with large white dots and dashes. Stamps 21¼mm high.

Die C — Solid background. The coils are without ornamental marks. Stamps 20¾mm high.

Die A

1907		**Typo.**	**Perf. 14½x13½**	
64	A11	1k yellow grn	45.00	35.00
65	A11	1.50k ultra	85.00	85.00
66	A11	2k rose	130.00	130.00
		Nos. 64-66 (3)	260.00	250.00

Used values are for stamps postmarked 1910-14. Stamps postmarked before that sell for twice as much. Stamps postmarked after 1914 sell for one-half the values listed. See note after No. 180.

1909-10				**Die B**
67	A11	1k green	175.00	130.00
68	A11	1.50k ultra	210.00	425.00
69	A11	2k rose	150.00	9.00
		Nos. 67-69 (3)	535.00	564.00

Used values for Nos. 67-68 are for stamps canceled through 1914.

1911-18				**Die C**
70	A11	1k light green	.75	.25
a.		1k dark green	85.00	4.00
71	A11	1.50k ultra	1.75	1.50
72	A11	2k rose ('15)	2.50	1.50
73	A11	5k dk violet ('18)	5.00	6.00
		Nos. 70-73 (4)	10.00	9.25
		Set, never hinged	32.50	

See note following No. 180.

Post Horn Type Redrawn

Original   Redrawn

In the redrawn stamps the white ring of the post horn is continuous instead of being broken by a spot of color below the crown. On the 3 and 30 ore the top of the figure "3" in the oval band is rounded instead of flattened.

1910-29			**Perf. 14½x13½**	
74	A10	1o pale olive	.60	.75
75	A10	2o pale brown	.75	.60
76	A10	3o orange	.75	.25
77	A10	5o green	4.50	.25
a.		Booklet pane of 6	150.00	
		Complete booklet, 4 #77a	2,500.	
78	A10	5o magenta ('22)	.75	.25
79	A10	7o green ('29)	.75	.25
80	A10	10o car rose	5.00	.25
a.		Booklet pane of 6	80.00	
		Complete booklet, 2 #80a	400.00	
81	A10	10o green ('22)	6.00	.85
82	A10	12o purple ('17)	1.00	1.75
83	A10	15o brown	5.00	.35
a.		Booklet pane of 6	12.50	
		Complete booklet, 2 #83a	50.00	
84	A10	15o indigo ('20)	5.00	.25
85	A10	20o deep ultra	6.00	.25
a.		Booklet pane of 6	300.00	
		Complete booklet, 2 #85a	3,000.	
86	A10	20o ol grn ('21)	6.00	.25
87	A10	25o red lilac	45.00	.35
88	A10	25o car rose ('22)	5.50	.95
89	A10	30o slate gray	8.50	.50
90	A10	30o lt blue ('27)	7.50	8.00
91	A10	35o dk olive ('20)	8.50	.35
92	A10	40o ol grn ('17)	6.00	.75
93	A10	40o dp ultra ('22)	24.00	.30
94	A10	50o claret	18.00	.35
95	A10	60o deep blue	24.00	.50
		Nos. 74-95 (22)	189.10	18.35
		Set, never hinged	750.00	

Constitutional
Assembly of
1814 — A12

1914, May 10		**Engr.**	**Perf. 13½**	
96	A12	5o green	.75	.75
97	A12	10o car rose	1.75	.75
98	A12	20o deep blue	9.00	9.50
		Nos. 96-98 (3)	11.50	11.00
		Set, never hinged	72.50	

Norway's Constitution of May 17, 1814.

No. 87 Surcharged

1922, Mar. 1			**Perf. 14½x13½**	
99	A10	5o on 25o red lilac	.50	.75
		Never hinged	1.50	

Lion Rampant — A13

"NORGE" in Roman capitals, Line below "Ore"

1922-24		**Typo.**	**Perf. 14½x13½**	
100	A13	10o dp grn ('24)	9.00	.85
101	A13	20o dp vio	13.00	.25
102	A13	25o scarlet ('24)	25.00	.75
103	A13	45o blue ('24)	1.25	1.50
		Nos. 100-103 (4)	48.25	3.35
		Set, never hinged	190.00	

For surcharge see No. 129.

Polar Bear and
Airplane — A14

1925, Apr. 1				
104	A14	2o yellow brn	2.25	3.50
105	A14	3o orange	4.50	5.50
106	A14	5o magenta	11.00	18.00
107	A14	10o yellow grn	15.00	32.50
108	A14	15o dark blue	15.00	30.00
109	A14	20o plum	21.00	35.00
110	A14	25o scarlet	5.00	7.00
		Nos. 104-110 (7)	73.75	131.50
		Set, never hinged	150.00	

Issued to help finance Roald Amundsen's attempted flight to the North Pole.

A15

1925, Aug. 19				
111	A15	10o yellow green	7.00	15.00
112	A15	15o indigo	5.00	6.50
113	A15	20o plum	7.00	2.50
114	A15	45o dark blue	6.00	7.00
		Nos. 111-114 (4)	25.00	31.00
		Set, never hinged	80.00	

Annexation of Spitsbergen (Svalbard). For surcharge see No. 130.

A16

"NORGE" in Sans-serif Capitals, No Line below "Ore"

1926-34			**Wmk. 160**	
		Size: 16x19½mm		
115	A16	10o yel grn	.60	.25
116	A16	14o dp org ('29)	1.50	3.00
117	A16	15o olive brown	.60	.25
118	A16	20o plum	22.50	.60
119	A16	20o scar ('27)	.60	.25
a.		Booklet pane of 6	65.00	
		Complete booklet, 2 #119a	300.00	
120	A16	25o red	10.00	3.00
121	A16	25o org brn ('27)	1.00	.25
122	A16	30o dull bl ('28)	1.00	.25
123	A16	35o ol brn ('27)	70.00	.25
124	A16	35o red vio ('34)	2.00	.25
125	A16	40o dull blue	5.00	1.50
126	A16	40o slate ('27)	2.00	.25

127	A16	50o claret ('27)	2.00	.25
128	A16	60o Prus bl ('27)	2.00	.25
		Nos. 115-128 (14)	120.80	10.60
		Set, never hinged	650.00	

See Nos. 167-176, 192, 194-202A. For overprints and surcharges see Nos. 131, 212-219, 225, 227-234, 302-303.

Nos. 103 and 114 Surcharged

1927, June 13

129	A13	30o on 45o blue	11.00	3.00
130	A15	30o on 45o dk blue	4.00	10.00
		Set, never hinged	45.00	

No. 120 Surcharged

1928

131	A16	20o on 25o red	1.75	2.50
		Never hinged	12.00	

See Nos. 302-303.

Henrik Ibsen — A17

1928, Mar. 20 Litho.

132	A17	10o yellow grn	6.00	3.00
133	A17	15o chnt brown	3.50	4.25
134	A17	20o carmine	3.00	.75
135	A17	30o dp ultra	4.25	4.25
		Nos. 132-135 (4)	16.75	12.25
		Set, never hinged	70.00	

Ibsen (1828-1906), dramatist.

Postage Due Stamps of 1889-1923 Overprinted

a   b

1929, Jan.

136	D1 (a)	1o gray	.50	1.25
137	D1 (a)	4o lilac rose	.50	.75
138	D1 (a)	10o green	2.25	5.00
139	D1 (b)	15o brown	3.00	6.50
140	D1 (b)	20o dull vio	1.25	.75
141	D1 (b)	40o deep ultra	2.50	1.00
142	D1 (b)	50o maroon	8.50	9.50
143	D1 (a)	100o orange yel	3.50	3.50
144	D1 (b)	200o dk violet	5.00	4.25
		Nos. 136-144 (9)	27.00	32.50
		Set, never hinged	65.00	

Niels Henrik Abel — A18

1929, Apr. 6 Litho. Perf. 14½x13½

145	A18	10o green	3.25	1.00
146	A18	15o red brown	3.25	1.75
147	A18	20o rose red	1.00	.50
148	A18	30o deep ultra	3.25	3.00
		Nos. 145-148 (4)	10.75	6.25
		Set, never hinged	45.00	

Abel (1802-1829), mathematician.

No. 12 Surcharged

Perf. 14½x13½

1929, July 1 Unwmk.

149	A4	14o on 2s orange	3.50	6.00
		Never hinged	6.00	

Saint Olaf
A19

Trondheim
Cathedral
A20

Death of Olaf in
Battle of
Stiklestad — A21

Typo.; Litho. (15o)
Perf. 14½x13½

1930, Apr. 1 Wmk. 160

150	A19	10o yellow grn	11.00	.60
151	A20	15o brn & blk	1.40	.85
152	A19	20o scarlet	1.00	.50

Engr.
Perf. 13½

153	A21	30o deep blue	3.50	5.00
		Nos. 150-153 (4)	16.90	6.95
		Set, never hinged	75.00	

King Olaf Haraldsson (995-1030), patron saint of Norway.

Björnson — A22

1932, Dec. 8 Perf. 14½x13½

154	A22	10o yellow grn	9.00	.75
155	A22	15o black brn	1.50	1.50
156	A22	20o rose red	1.00	.50
157	A22	30o ultra	3.00	3.00
		Nos. 154-157 (4)	14.50	5.75
		Set, never hinged	50.00	

Björnstjerne Björnson (1832-1910), novelist, poet and dramatist.

Holberg — A23

1934, Nov. 23

158	A23	10o yellow grn	2.00	.85
159	A23	15o brown	.65	1.25
160	A23	20o rose red	11.00	.50
161	A23	30o ultra	3.00	3.50
		Nos. 158-161 (4)	16.65	6.10
		Set, never hinged	70.00	

Ludvig Holberg (1684-1754), Danish man of letters.

Types of 1893-1900, 1926-34
Second Redrawing
Perf. 13x13½

1937   **Wmk. 160**   **Photo.**
Size: 17x21mm

162	A10	1o olive	.70	2.00
163	A10	2o yellow brn	.60	1.50
164	A10	3o deep orange	1.75	4.00
165	A10	5o rose lilac	.50	.50
166	A10	7o brt green	.50	.50
167	A16	10o brt green	.50	.25
		Complete booklet, 2 panes of 6 #167	675.00	
168	A16	14o dp orange	3.00	5.00
169	A16	15o olive bis	1.25	.25
170	A16	20o scarlet	1.00	.25
		Complete booklet, 2 panes of 6 #170	1,250.	
171	A16	25o dk org brn	5.00	.55
172	A16	30o ultra	2.75	.75
173	A16	35o brt vio	2.00	.50
174	A16	40o dk slate grn	3.00	.50
175	A16	50o deep claret	3.00	.75
176	A16	60o Prussian bl	1.50	.50
		Nos. 162-176 (15)	27.05	17.80
		Set, never hinged	110.00	

Nos. 162 to 166 have a solid background inside oval. Nos. 74, 75, 76, 78, 79 have background of vertical lines.

King Haakon VII — A24

1937-38

177	A24	1k dark green	.25	.50
178	A24	1.50k sapphire ('38)	1.00	4.00
179	A24	2k rose red ('38)	.75	2.50
180	A24	5k dl vio ('38)	6.00	10.00
		Nos. 177-180 (4)	8.00	17.00

Nos. 64-66, 67-69, 70-73, 177-180 and B11-B14 were demonitized and banned on Sept. 30, 1940. Nos. 267, B19, B32-B34 and B38-B41 were demonitized on May 15, 1945. All of these stamps became valid again Sept. 1, 1981. Nos. 64-66, 67-69 and 70-73 rarely were used after 1981, and values represent stamps used in the earlier period. Values for Nos. B11-B14 used are for stamps used in the earlier period, and used examples in the later period are the same as mint stamps. Values for the other stamps used are for examples used in the later period, and stamps with dated cancellations prior to May 15, 1945 sell for more. False cancellations exist.

Reindeer
A25

Borgund
Church
A26

Jolster in
Sunnfiord — A27

Perf. 13x13½, 13½x13

1938, Apr. 20 Wmk. 160

181	A25	15o olive brn	1.00	1.25
182	A26	20o copper red	4.50	.55
183	A27	30o brt ultra	4.00	2.50
		Nos. 181-183 (3)	9.50	4.30
		Set, never hinged	30.00	

1939, Jan. 16 Unwmk.

184	A25	15o olive brn	.50	.75
185	A26	20o copper red	.50	.25
186	A27	30o brt ultra	.50	.75
		Nos. 184-186 (3)	1.50	1.75
		Set, never hinged	3.00	

Types of 1937
Perf. 13x13½

1940-49   **Unwmk.**   **Photo.**
Size: 17x21mm

187	A10	1o olive grn ('41)	.25	.25
188	A10	2o yel brn ('41)	.25	.25
189	A10	3o dp org ('41)	.25	.25
190	A10	5o rose lilac ('41)	.25	.25
191	A10	7o brt green ('41)	.25	.25
192	A16	10o brt green	.25	.25
		Complete booklet, 2 panes of 6 #192	50.00	
193	A10	12o brt vio	.50	2.00
194	A16	14o dp org ('41)	1.00	4.00
195	A16	15o olive bister	.50	.35
196	A16	20o red	.25	.25
		Complete booklet, 2 panes of 6 #196	60.00	
		Complete booklet, pane of 6 ea of #190, 192, 196	200.00	
		Complete booklet, pane of 10 ea of #190, 192, 196	125.00	
197	A16	25o dk org brn	1.25	.25
197A	A16	25o scarlet ('46)	.25	.25
		Complete booklet, pane of 10 ea of #190, 192, 197A	110.00	
		Complete booklet, pane of 10 ea of #192, 195, 197A	100.00	
198	A16	30o brt ultra ('41)	1.75	.40
198A	A16	30o gray ('49)	4.00	.25
199	A16	35o brt vio ('41)	1.75	.25
200	A16	40o dk sl grn ('41)	1.00	.25
200A	A16	40o dp ultra ('46)	2.50	.45
201	A16	50o dp claret ('41)	1.20	.25
201A	A16	50o dp org ('46)	10.00	.45
202	A16	60o Prus bl ('41)	1.25	.25
202A	A16	80o dk org brn ('46)	10.00	.45
		Nos. 187-202A (21)	38.70	11.60
		Set, never hinged	150.00	

Lion Rampant — A28

1940   **Unwmk. Photo.**   *Perf. 13x13½*

203	A28	1k brt green	1.00	.25
204	A28	1½k deep blue	1.50	.30
205	A28	2k bright red	2.50	1.25
206	A28	5k dull purple	3.50	6.00
		Nos. 203-206 (4)	8.50	7.80
		Set, never hinged	30.00	

For overprints see Nos. 235-238.

Stamps of 1937-41, Types A10, A16, A28, Overprinted in Black

1941   **Wmk. 160**   *Perf. 13x13½*

207	A10	1o olive	.50	8.00
208	A10	2o yellow brn	.50	12.00
209	A10	3o orange	1.75	25.00
210	A10	5o rose lilac	.50	2.50
211	A10	7o brt green	.50	6.00
212	A16	10o brt green	6.00	40.00
213	A16	14o dp orange	1.00	22.50
214	A16	15o olive bis	.50	1.25
215	A16	30o ultra	1.25	4.50
216	A16	35o brt violet	1.00	1.00
217	A16	40o dk slate grn	7.50	11.00
218	A16	50o dp claret	200.00	600.00
		Never hinged	500.00	
219	A16	60o Prus blue	.85	2.50
		Nos. 207-217,219 (12)	21.85	136.25
		Set, never hinged	55.00	

The "V" overprint exists on Nos. 170-171, but these were not regularly issued.

Unwmk.

220	A10	1o olive	.25	6.00
221	A10	2o yellow brn	.25	10.00
222	A10	3o deep orange	.25	6.50
223	A10	5o rose lilac	.35	.65
224	A10	7o brt green	1.00	8.50
225	A16	10o brt green	.25	.25
226	A16	12o brt violet	.75	20.00
227	A16	15o olive bis	1.40	18.00
228	A16	20o red	.25	.25
a.		Inverted overprint	1,100.	1,500.
229	A16	25o dk orange brn	.50	.50
230	A16	30o brt ultra	.75	5.00
231	A16	35o brt violet	1.00	1.00
232	A16	40o dk slate grn	.70	.90
233	A16	50o dp claret	1.00	3.50
234	A16	60o Prus blue	3.00	1.75
235	A28	1k brt green	.75	1.00
236	A28	1½k dp blue	3.00	18.00
237	A28	2k bright red	9.00	60.00
238	A28	5k dull purple	18.00	150.00

Lion Rampant with
"V" — A29

Coil Stamp

239	A29	10o brt green	1.00	15.00
		Nos. 220-239 (20)	43.45	326.80
		Set, never hinged	110.00	

No. 239 has a white "V" incorporated into design, rather than an overprint. Nos. 207-239 were demonitized March 29, 1944. Used values are for stamps with postmarks dated prior to March 29, 1944. Forged cancellations exist.

Dream of
Queen
Ragnhild
A30

Snorri
Sturluson
A32

Einar
Tambarskjelve in
Fight at
Svolder — A31

Designs: 30o, King Olaf sailing in wedding procession to Landmerket. 50o, Syipdag's sons and followers going to Hall of Seven Kings. 60o, Before Battle of Stiklestad.

1941   *Perf. 13½x13, 13x13½*

240	A30	10o bright green	.25	.25
241	A31	15o olive brown	.25	.75
242	A32	20o dark red	.50	.25
243	A31	30o blue	.85	2.50

244 A31 50o dull violet .75 1.75
245 A31 60o Prus blue 1.10 2.25
Nos. 240-245 (6) 3.70 7.75
Set, never hinged 15.00

700th anniversary of the death of Snorri Sturluson, writer and historian. Issued: 10o, 30o, 60o, 9/23; others, 10/23.

University of Oslo — A36

1941, Sept. 2 **Perf. 13x13½**
246 A36 1k dk olive grn 30.00 65.00
Never hinged 65.00

Centenary of cornerstone laying of University of Oslo building.

Richard (Rikard) Nordraak (1842-66), Composer A37

"Broad Sails Go over the North Sea" A38

View of Coast and Lines of National Anthem — A39

1942, June 12 **Perf. 13**
247 A37 10o dp green 1.40 3.00
248 A38 15o dp brown 1.20 3.00
249 A37 20o rose red 1.20 3.50
250 A39 30o sapphire 1.20 3.00
Nos. 247-250 (4) 5.00 12.50
Set, never hinged 12.00

Johan Herman Wessel (1742-1785), Author — A40

1942, Oct. 6
251 A40 15o dull brown .25 .50
252 A40 20o henna .25 .50
Set, never hinged 1.00

Designs of 1942 and 1855 Stamps of Norway — A41

1942, Oct. 12
253 A41 20o henna .25 1.75
254 A41 30o sapphire .35 2.75
Set, never hinged 1.25

European Postal Congress at Vienna, October, 1942.

Nos. 253-254, B24-B27, B31 and B35-B37 were demonitized May 15, 1945. Used values are for stamps with postmarks dated prior to May 15, 1945. Forged cancellations exist.

Edvard Grieg (1843-1907), Composer — A42

1943, June 15
255 A42 10o deep green .25 .35
256 A42 20o henna .25 .35
257 A42 40o grnsh black .25 .50
258 A42 60o dk grnsh blue .25 .50
Nos. 255-258 (4) 1.00 1.70
Set, never hinged 1.90

Destroyer Sleipner — A43

5o, 10o, "Sleipner." 7o, 30o, Convoy under midnight sun. 15o, Plane and pilot. 20o, "We will win." 40o, Ski troops. 60o, King Haakon VII.

1943-45 **Unwmk. Engr.** **Perf. 12½**
259 A43 5o rose vio ('45) .25 .25
260 A43 7o grnsh blk ('45) .25 .50
261 A43 10o dk blue grn .25 .25
262 A43 15o dk olive grn .50 1.75
263 A43 20o rose red .25 .25
264 A43 30o dp ultra .60 2.00
265 A43 40o olive black .60 1.75
266 A43 60o dark blue .60 1.75
Nos. 259-266 (8) 3.30 8.50
Set, never hinged 8.50

Nos. 261-266 were used for correspondence carried on Norwegian ships until after the liberation of Norway, when they became regular postage stamps.
Nos. 261-266 exist with overprint "London 17-5-43" and serial number. Value for set, unused, $700; canceled $1,100.

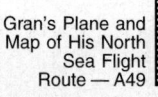

Gran's Plane and Map of His North Sea Flight Route — A49

1944, July 30 **Perf. 13**
267 A49 40o dk grnsh blue .25 .50
Never hinged .75

20th anniv. of the 1st flight over the North Sea, made by Tryggve Gran on July 30, 1914. Value for used stamp postmarked before May 15, 1945, $6. See note following No. 180.

New National Arms of 1943 — A50

1945, Feb. 15 **Typo.** **Perf. 13**
268 A50 1½k dark blue 1.25 .60
Never hinged 4.00

Henrik Wergeland — A51

1945, July 12 **Photo.**
269 A51 10o dk olive green .25 .35
270 A51 15o dark brown .50 1.25
271 A51 20o dark red .25 .30
Nos. 269-271 (3) 1.00 1.90
Set, never hinged 1.50

Wergeland, poet & playwright, death cent.

Lion Rampant — A52

1945, Dec. 19
272 A52 10o dk olive green .50 .50
273 A52 20o red .50 .50
Set, never hinged 3.00

Norwegian Folklore Museum, 50th anniv.

Pilot and Mechanic — A53

1946, Mar. 22 **Engr.** **Perf. 12**
274 A53 15o brown rose .40 1.50
Never hinged .85

Issued in honor of Little Norway, training center in Canada for Norwegian pilots.

┌─────────────────────────────────────┐
│ **Catalogue values for unused** │
│ **stamps in this section, from this** │
│ **point to the end of the section, are** │
│ **for Never Hinged items.** │
└─────────────────────────────────────┘

King Haakon VII — A54

1946, June 7 **Photo.** **Perf. 13**
275 A54 1k bright green 2.75 .25
276 A54 1½k Prus blue 7.00 .25
277 A54 2k henna brown 45.00 .25
278 A54 5k violet 35.00 .50
Nos. 275-278 (4) 89.75 1.25

Hannibal Sehested — A55

Designs: 10o, Letter carrier, 1700. 15o, Adm. Peter W. Tordenskjold. 25o, Christian Magnus Falsen. 30o, Cleng Peerson and "Restaurationen." 40o, Post ship "Constitution." 45o, First Norwegian locomotive. 50o, Sven Foyn and whaler. 55o, Fridtjof Nansen and Roald Amundsen. 60o, Coronation of King Haakon VII and Queen Maud, 1906. 80o, Return of King Haakon, June 7, 1945.

1947, Apr. 15 **Photo.** **Perf. 13**
279 A55 5o red lilac .70 .25
280 A55 10o green .70 .25
281 A55 15o brown 1.25 .25
282 A55 25o orange red 1.00 .25
283 A55 30o gray 2.25 .25
284 A55 40o blue 5.00 .25
285 A55 45o violet 2.50 .75
286 A55 50o orange brn 4.75 .35
287 A55 55o orange 6.50 .35
288 A55 60o slate gray 7.00 2.00
289 A55 80o dk brown 6.50 .35
Nos. 279-289 (11) 38.15 5.30

Establishment of the Norwegian Post Office, 300th anniv.

Petter Dass — A66

1947, July 1 **Unwmk.**
290 A66 25o bright red 1.50 1.25

300th birth anniv. of Petter Dass, poet.

King Haakon VII — A67

1947, Aug. 2
291 A67 25o orange red .80 .80

75th birthday of King Haakon.

Axel Heiberg — A68

1948, June 15
292 A68 25o deep carmine 1.00 .50
293 A68 80o dp red brown 2.50 .30

50th anniv. of the Norwegian Society of Forestry; birth cent. of Axel Heiberg, its founder.

Alexander L. Kielland — A69

1949, May 9
295 A69 25o rose brown 1.50 .50
296 A69 40o greenish blue 1.90 .75
297 A69 80o orange brown 2.50 1.00
Nos. 295-297 (3) 5.90 2.25

Birth cent. of Alexander L. Kielland, author.

Symbols of UPU Members A70

Stylized Pigeons and Globe A71

Symbolical of the UPU — A72

1949, Oct. 8 — Perf. 13
299	A70	10o dk green & blk	.50	.60
300	A71	25o scarlet	.70	.50
301	A72	40o dull blue	.70	.50
		Nos. 299-301 (3)	1.90	1.60

75th anniv. of the formation of the UPU.

Nos. 196 and 200A Surcharged with New Value and Bar in Black
1949 — Perf. 13x13½
302	A16	25o on 20o red	.75	.25
303	A16	45o on 40o dp ultra	3.00	.65

King Harald Haardraade and Oslo City Hall — A73

1950, May 15 Photo. Perf. 13
304	A73	15o green	.90	.90
305	A73	25o red	.90	.50
306	A73	45o ultramarine	.90	.90
		Nos. 304-306 (3)	2.70	2.30

900th anniversary of Oslo.

Redrawn Post Horn Type of 1937
1950-51 Photo. Perf. 13x13½
Size: 17x21mm
307	A10	10o grnsh gray	1.00	.25
		Complete booklet, pane of 10 #307	250.00	
308	A10	15o dark green	2.50	.50
309	A10	20o chnt brn ('51)	5.00	3.00
		Nos. 307-309 (3)	8.50	3.75

King Haakon VII — A74

1950-51 Photo. Perf. 13x13½
310	A74	25o dk grn ('50)	.90	.25
		Complete booklet, pane of 10 ea of #307, 308, 310	85.00	
311	A74	30o gray	9.00	.75
312	A74	35o red brn	18.00	.35
313	A74	45o brt blue	1.75	2.50
314	A74	50o olive brn	5.00	.25
315	A74	55o orange	2.25	1.25
316	A74	60o gray blue	15.00	.25
317	A74	80o chnt brn	3.00	.35
		Nos. 310-317 (8)	54.90	5.95

See Nos. 322-324, 345-352. For surcharge see No. 321.

Arne Garborg — A75

1951, Jan. 25 — Perf. 13
318	A75	25o red	1.00	.50
319	A75	45o dull blue	3.75	4.00
320	A75	80o brown	3.75	2.00
		Nos. 318-320 (3)	8.50	6.50

Birth cent. of Arne Garborg, poet.

No. 310 Surcharged with New Value in Black
1951 — Perf. 13x13½
321	A74	30o on 25o dk red	.90	.30

Haakon Type of 1950-51
1951-52 — Photo.
322	A74	25o gray	20.00	.25
323	A74	30o dk red ('52)	.90	.25
		Complete booklet, pane of 10 ea of #307, 308, 323	225.00	
		Complete booklet, pane of 10 ea of #307, 325, 323	110.00	
324	A74	55o blue ('52)	2.00	.40
		Nos. 322-324 (3)	22.90	.90

Redrawn Post Horn Type of 1937
1952, June 3 — Perf. 13x13½
325	A10	15o org brn	.70	.25
326	A10	20o dark green	.70	.25

King Haakon VII — A76

1952, Aug. 3 Unwmk. Perf. 13
327	A76	30o red	.50	.50
328	A76	55o deep blue	1.50	1.50

80th birthday of King Haakon VII.

No. 308 Surcharged with New Value
1952, Nov. 18 — Perf. 13x13½
329	A10	20o on 15o dk grn	.70	.25

Medieval Sculpture, Nidaros Cathedral — A77

1953, July 15 — Perf. 13
330	A77	30o henna brn	1.40	.75

800th anniv. of the creation of the Norwegian Archbishopric of Nidaros.

Train of 1854 and Horse-drawn Sled — A78

Designs: 30o, Diesel train. 55o, Engineer.

1954, Apr. 30 — Photo.
331	A78	20o green	1.10	.50
332	A78	30o red	1.25	.35
333	A78	55o ultra	1.75	1.25
		Nos. 331-333 (3)	4.10	2.10

Inauguration of the first Norwegian railway, cent.

Carsten T. Nielsen — A79

Designs: 30o, Government radio towers. 55o, Lineman and telegraph poles in snow.

1954, Dec. 10
334	A79	20o ol grn & blk	.55	.50
335	A79	30o brt red	.55	.35
336	A79	55o blue	1.40	1.10
		Nos. 334-336 (3)	2.50	1.95

Centenary (in 1955) of the inauguration of the first Norwegian public telegraph line.

Norway No. 1 — A80

Stamp Reproductions: 30o, Post horn type A5. 55o, Lion type A13.

1955, Jan. 3 — Perf. 13
337	A80	20o dp grn & gray bl	.45	.45
338	A80	30o red & carmine	.40	.40
339	A80	55o gray bl & dp bl	.75	.50
		Nos. 337-339 (3)	1.60	1.35

Centenary of Norway's first postage stamp.

Nos. 337-339 Overprinted in Black

1955, June 4
340	A80	20o dp grn & gray bl	12.50	12.50
341	A80	30o red & carmine	12.50	12.50
342	A80	55o gray bl & dp bl	12.50	12.50
		Nos. 340-342 (3)	37.50	37.50

Norway Philatelic Exhibition, Oslo, 1955. Sold at exhibition post office for face value plus 1kr admission fee.

King Haakon VII and Queen Maud in Coronation Robes — A81

1955, Nov. 25 Photo. Perf. 13
343	A81	30o rose red	.40	.40
344	A81	55o ultra	.75	.75

Haakon's 50th anniv. as King of Norway.

Haakon Type of 1950-51
1955-57 Unwmk. Perf. 13x13½
345	A74	25o dk grn ('56)	1.20	.25
346	A74	35o brn red ('56)	4.75	.25
		Complete booklet, pane of 10 ea of #307, 325, 346	100.00	
347	A74	40o pale pur	2.00	.25
		Complete booklet, pane of 10 ea of #307, 325, 347	80.00	
348	A74	50o bister ('57)	4.75	.25
349	A74	65o ultra ('56)	1.20	.40
350	A74	70o brn ol ('56)	20.00	.25
351	A74	75o mar ('57)	2.75	.25
352	A74	90o dp org	1.60	.25
		Nos. 345-352 (8)	38.25	2.15

Northern Countries Issue

Whooper Swans — A81a

1956, Oct. 30 Engr. Perf. 12½
353	A81a	35o rose red	.70	.60
354	A81a	65o ultra	.70	.70

Close bonds connecting the northern countries: Denmark, Finland, Iceland, Norway and Sweden.

Jan Mayen Island A82 — Map of Spitsbergen A83

Design: 65o, Map of South Pole with Queen Maud Land.

Perf. 12½x13, 13x12½
1957, July 1 Photo. Unwmk.
355	A82	25o slate green	.70	.60
356	A83	35o dk red & gray	.70	.40
357	A83	65o dk grn & bl	.70	.60
		Nos. 355-357 (3)	2.10	1.60

Intl. Geophysical Year, 1957-58.

King Haakon VII — A84

1957, Aug. 3 — Perf. 13
358	A84	35o dark red	.60	.40
359	A84	65o ultra	1.20	1.20

85th birthday of King Haakon VII.

King Olav V — A85

1958-60 Photo. Perf. 13x13½
360	A85	25o emerald	1.10	.25
		Complete booklet, pane of 4 of #360	125.00	
361	A85	30o purple ('59)	2.00	.25
361A	A85	35o brown car ('60)	.95	.25
362	A85	40o dark red	.95	.25
		Complete booklet, pane of 10 of ea #307, 325, 362	100.00	
363	A85	45o scarlet	1.40	.25
		Complete booklet, pane of 10 of #363	65.00	
		Complete booklet, pane of 10 ea of #307, 325, 363	85.00	
364	A85	50o bister ('59)	6.00	.25
365	A85	55o dk gray ('59)	1.75	.75
366	A85	65o blue	2.00	.40
367	A85	80o org brn ('60)	11.00	.85
368	A85	85o olive brn ('59)	2.00	.25
369	A85	90o orange ('59)	1.50	.25
		Nos. 360-369 (11)	30.65	4.00

See Nos. 408-412.

King Olav V — A86

1959, Jan. 12
370	A86	1k green	1.50	.25
371	A86	1.50k dark blue	4.00	.25
372	A86	2k crimson	4.00	.25
373	A86	5k lilac	50.00	.25
374	A86	10k dp orange	7.50	.25
		Nos. 370-374 (5)	67.00	1.25

See Phosphorescence note following No. 430.

Asbjörn Kloster — A87

1959, Feb. 2
375	A87	45o violet brown	.50	.35

Centenary of the founding of the Norwegian Temperance Movement; Asbjörn Kloster, its founder.

Agricultural Society Medal — A88

1959, May 26
376	A88	45o red & ocher	.60	.60
377	A88	90o blue & gray	2.00	2.00

150th anniversary of the Royal Agricultural Society of Norway.

Sower — A89

Design: 90o, Grain, vert.

1959, Oct. 1 Photo. Perf. 13
378	A89	45o ocher & blk	.75	.60
379	A89	90o blue & blk	1.50	1.50

Agricultural College of Norway, cent.

Society Seal — A90

1960, Feb. 26 — Unwmk.
380	A90	45o carmine	.55	.50
381	A90	90o dark blue	1.60	1.60

Bicentenary of the Royal Norwegian Society of Sciences, Trondheim.

Viking Ship — A91

25o, Caravel & fish. 45o, Sailing ship & nautical knot. 55o, Freighter & oil derricks. 90o, Passenger ship & Statue of Liberty.

1960, Aug. 27   **Perf. 12½x13**
382 A91 20o gray & blk   1.60   1.40
383 A91 25o yel grn & blk   1.00   1.00
384 A91 45o ver & blk   1.00   .40
385 A91 55o ocher & blk   2.75   2.75
386 A91 90o Prus bl & blk   3.25   2.25
    Nos. 382-386 (5)   9.60   7.80

Norwegian shipping industry.

Common Design Types pictured following the introduction.

Europa Issue
Common Design Type
1960, Sept. 19   **Perf. 13**
Size: 27x21mm
387 CD3 90o blue   1.00   .80

DC-8 Airliner — A91a

1961, Feb. 24   **Photo.**   **Perf. 13**
388 A91a 90o dark blue   .80   .80
Scandinavian Airlines System, SAS, 10th anniv.

Javelin Thrower — A92

1961, Mar. 15
389 A92 20o shown   1.10   1.00
390 A92 25o Skater   1.00   .90
391 A92 45o Ski jumper   .75   .40
392 A92 90o Sailboat   1.25   1.25
    Nos. 389-392 (4)   4.10   3.55

Norwegian Sports Federation centenary.

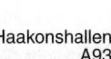

Haakonshallen A93

1961, May 25   **Perf. 12½x13**
393 A93 45o maroon & gray   .70   .50
394 A93 1k gray green & gray   1.00   .40

700th anniv. of Haakonshallen, castle in Bergen.

Domus Media, Oslo University — A94

1961, Sept. 2   **Photo.**   **Perf. 12½x13**
395 A94 45o dark red   .70   .50
396 A94 1.50k Prus blue   1.00   .40

150th anniversary of Oslo University.

Fridtjof Nansen — A95

1961, Oct. 10   **Perf. 13**
397 A95 45o orange red & gray   .80   .40
398 A95 90o chlky blue & gray   1.50   1.50

Birth centenary of Fridtjof Nansen, explorer.

Roald Amundsen — A96

Design: 90o, Explorers and tent at Pole.

1961, Nov. 10   **Unwmk.**   **Perf. 13**
399 A96 45o dl red brn & gray   1.00   .60
400 A96 90o dk & lt blue   1.75   1.75

50th anniversary of Roald Amundsen's arrival at the South Pole.

Frederic Passy, Henri Dunant — A97

1961, Dec. 9   **Photo.**
401 A97 45o henna brown   .50   .50
402 A97 1k yellow green   1.25   .50

Winners of the first Nobel Peace prize. Frederic Passy, a founder of the Interparliamentary Union, and Henri Dunant, founder of the International Red Cross.

Vilhelm Bjerknes — A98

1962, Mar. 14   **Perf. 13**
403 A98 45o dk red & gray   .50   .40
404 A98 1.50k dk blue & gray   1.00   .50

Vilhelm Bjerknes (1862-1951), physicist, mathematician, meteorologist, etc.

German Rumpler Taube over Oslo Fjord — A99

1962, June 1   **Photo.**
405 A99 1.50k dl bl & blk   3.50   .70

50th anniversary of Norwegian aviation.

Fir Branch and Cone — A100

1962, June 15
406 A100 45o salmon & blk   .60   .60
407 A100 1k pale grn & blk   6.00   .40

State Forest Administration, centenary.

Olav Type of 1958-60
1962   **Unwmk.**   **Perf. 13x13½**
408 A85 25o slate grn   1.25   .25
    Complete booklet, pane of 4
      of #408   125.00
    Complete booklet, pane of 10
      ea of #190, 307, 408   35.00
409 A85 35o emerald   5.00   .25
410 A85 40o gray   3.50   1.75
411 A85 50o scarlet   8.00   .25
    Complete booklet, pane of 10
      of #411   175.00
412 A85 60o violet   5.50   .50
    Nos. 408-412 (5)   23.25   3.00

Europa Issue
Common Design Type
1962, Sept. 17   **Photo.**   **Perf. 13**
Size: 37x21mm
414 CD5 50o dp rose & maroon   .55   .50
415 CD5 90o blue & dk blue   1.20   1.20

Post Horn Type of 1893-1908
Redrawn and

Rock Carvings A101   Boatswain's Knot A102

Designs: 30o, 55o, 85o, Rye and fish. 65o, 80o, Stave church and northern lights.

1962-63   **Engr.**   **Perf. 13x13½**
416 A10 5o rose cl   .25   .25
417 A10 10o slate   .25   .25
    Complete booklet, pane of
      10 of #417   40.00

418 A10 15o orange brn   .25   .25
419 A10 20o green   .25   .25
    Complete booklet, pane of 4
      ea of #416, 419   20.00
420 A101 25o gray grn ('63)   1.25   .25
    Complete booklet, pane of 4
      of #420   20.00
    Complete booklet, pane of
      10 ea of #416, 417, 420   45.00
421 A101 30o olive brn ('63)   4.00   4.00
422 A102 35o brt green ('63)   .30   .25
423 A101 40o lake ('63)   3.00   .25
424 A102 50o vermilion   4.25   .25
    Complete booklet, pane of
      10 of #424   90.00
425 A101 55o orange brn
      ('63)   .45   .45
426 A102 60o dk grnsh gray
      ('63)   12.50   .25
427 A102 65o dk blue ('63)   3.00   .35
    Complete booklet, pane of
      10 of #427   100.00
428 A102 80o rose lake ('63)   2.25   2.25
429 A101 85o sepia ('63)   .45   .25
430 A101 90o blue ('63)   .30   .25
    Nos. 416-430 (15)   32.75   9.80

Nos. 416-419 have been redrawn and are similar to 1910-29 issue, with vertical lines inside oval and horizontal lines in oval frame. See Nos. 462-470, 608-615.

Phosphorescence
Nos. 370-372, 416-419, 423, 425, 428, 430, 462, 466, O65-O68, O75, O78-O82, O83-O84 and O88 have been issued on both ordinary and phosphorescent paper.

Camilla Collett (1813-1895), Author — A103

1963, Jan. 23   **Photo.**   **Perf. 13**
431 A103 50o red brn & tan   .60   .40
432 A103 90o slate & gray   1.40   1.25

Girl in Boat Loaded with Grain A104   Still Life A105

1963, Mar. 21   **Unwmk.**   **Perf. 13**
433 A104 25o yellow brown   .50   .40
434 A104 35o dark green   .75   .75
435 A105 50o dark red   .75   .50
436 A105 90o dark blue   1.40   1.10
    Nos. 433-436 (4)   3.40   2.75

FAO "Freedom from Hunger" campaign.

River Boat — A106

Design: 90o, Northern sailboat.

1963, May 20   **Unwmk.**   **Perf. 13**
437 A106 50o brown red   1.00   1.00
438 A106 90o blue   3.00   3.00

Tercentenary of regular postal service between Northern and Southern Norway.

Ivar Aasen — A107

1963, Aug. 5   **Photo.**
439 A107 50o dk red & gray   .60   .40
440 A107 90o dk blue & gray   1.75   1.75

150th birth anniv. of Ivar Aasen, poet and philologist.

Europa Issue
Common Design Type
1963, Sept. 14   **Unwmk.**   **Perf. 13**
Size: 27x21½mm
441 CD6 50o dull rose & org   .60   .40
442 CD6 90o blue & yel grn   2.00   2.00

Patterned Fabric — A108

1963, Sept. 24
443 A108 25o olive & ol grn   .75   .75
444 A108 35o Prus bl & dk bl   1.40   1.40
445 A108 50o dk car rose &
      plum   .60   .60
    Nos. 443-445 (3)   2.75   2.75

Norwegian textile industry, 150th anniv.

"Loneliness" A109

Paintings by Edvard Munch (1863-1944): 25o, Self-portrait, vert. 35o, "Fertility." 90o, "Girls on Bridge," vert.

1963, Dec. 12   **Litho.**   **Perf. 13**
446 A109 25o black   .40   .40
447 A109 35o dark green   .40   .40
448 A109 50o deep claret   .60   .40
449 A109 90o gray bl & dk bl   1.00   1.00
    Nos. 446-449 (4)   2.40   2.20

Eilert Sundt — A110

50o, Beehive, Workers' Society emblem.

1964, Feb. 17   **Photo.**
450 A110 25o dark green   .60   .60
451 A110 50o dk red brown   .60   .25

Centenary of the Oslo Workers' Society.

Cato M. Guldberg and Peter Waage by Stinius Fredriksen — A111

1964, Mar. 11   **Unwmk.**   **Perf. 13**
452 A111 35o olive green   .70   .70
453 A111 55o bister   1.50   1.50

Centenary of the presentation of the Law of Mass Action (chemistry) by Professors Cato M. Guldberg and Peter Waage in the Oslo Scientific Society.

Eidsvoll Building — A112

Design: 90o, Storting (Parliament House).

1964, May 11   **Photo.**
454 A112 50o hn brn & blk   1.00   .50
455 A112 90o Prus bl & dk bl   2.25   2.00

150th anniv. of Norway's constitution.

Church and Ships in Harbor — A113

1964, Aug. 17   **Perf. 13**
456 A113 25o dk sl grn & buff   .60   .60
457 A113 90o dk bl & gray   2.00   2.00

Centenary of the Norwegian Seamen's Mission, which operates 32 stations around the world.

Europa Issue
Common Design Type
1964, Sept. 14   **Photo.**   **Perf. 13**
458 CD7 90o dark blue   3.50   3.50

Herman Anker and Olaus Arvesen — A114

1964, Oct. 31   Litho.   Unwmk.
459 A114 50o rose   .80 .50
460 A114 90o blue   2.50 2.50

Centenary of the founding of Norwegian schools of higher education (Folk High Schools).

Types of Regular Issue, 1962-63

Type I

Type II

Two types of 60o:
I — Four twists across bottom of knot.
II — Five twists.

Designs: 30o, 45o, Rye and fish. 40o, 100o, Rock carvings. 50o, 60o, 65o, 70o, Boatswain's knot.

1964-70   Engr.   Perf. 13x13½
462 A101 30o dull green   .40 .25
463 A101 40o lt bl grn ('68)   .30 .25
464 A101 45o lt yel grn ('68)   .60 .60
465 A102 50o indigo ('68)   .25 .25
466 A102 60o brick red, II ('75)   1.50 .50
a.   Type I   1.25 .30
    Complete booklet, pane of 10
    of #466a   80.00
467 A102 65o lake ('68)   .50 .25
    Complete booklet, pane of 10
    of #467   35.00
468 A102 70o brown ('70)   .25 .25
    Complete booklet, pane of 10
    of #468   30.00
469 A101 100o violet bl ('70)   .60 .25
    Complete booklet, pane of 4 ea
    of #416, 419, 469   8.00
    Nos. 462-469 (8)   4.40 2.60

See Phosphorescence note following #430.

Coil Stamp

1965   Perf. 13½ Horiz.
470 A101 30o dull green   3.50 3.50

Telephone Dial and Waves — A115

Design: 90o, Television mast and antenna.

1965, Apr. 1   Engr.   Perf. 13
471 A115 60o redsh brown   .60 .40
472 A115 90o slate   1.60 1.60

ITU, centenary.

Mountain Scene — A116

Design: 90o, Coastal view.

1965, June 4   Unwmk.   Perf. 13
473 A116 60o brn blk & car   .80 .60
474 A116 90o slate bl & car   3.50 3.50

Centenary of the Norwegian Red Cross.

Europa Issue
Common Design Type

1965, Sept. 25   Photo.   Perf. 13
Size: 27x21mm
475 CD8 60o brick red   .90 .40
476 CD8 90o blue   1.50 1.50

St. Sunniva and Buildings of Bergen — A117

90o, St. Sunniva and stylized view of Bergen.

1965, Oct. 25   Perf. 13
477 A117 30o dk green & blk   .50 .40
478 A117 90o blue & blk, horiz.   1.75 1.75

Bicentenary of Bergen's philharmonic society "Harmonien."

Rondane Mountains by Harold Sohlberg — A118

1965, Nov. 29   Photo.   Perf. 13
484 A118 1.50k dark blue   2.50 .30

Rock Carving of Skier, Rodoy Island, c. 2000 B.C. — A120

Designs: 55o, Ski jumper. 60o, Cross country skier. 90o, Holmenkollen ski jump, vert.

1966, Feb. 8   Engr.   Perf. 13
486 A120 40o sepia   1.40 1.20
487 A120 55o dull green   1.60 1.60
488 A120 60o dull red   .80 .40
489 A120 90o blue   1.50 1.50
    Nos. 486-489 (4)   5.30 4.70

World Ski Championships, Oslo, Feb. 17-27.

Open Bible and Chrismon — A121

1966, May 20   Photo.   Perf. 13
490 A121 60o dull red   .60 .40
491 A121 90o slate blue   1.40 1.40

150th anniv. of the Norwegian Bible Society.

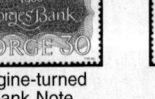

Engine-turned Bank Note Design A122

Bank of Norway A123

1966, June 14   Engr.
492 A122 30o green   .70 .70
493 A123 60o dk carmine rose   .50 .30

150th anniversary of Bank of Norway.

Johan Sverdrup — A124

1966, July 30   Photo.   Perf. 13
494 A124 30o green   .45 .45
495 A124 60o rose lake   .45 .40

Johan Sverdrup (1816-92), Prime Minister of Norway (1884-89).

Canceled to Order
The Norwegian philatelic agency began in 1966 to sell commemorative and definitive issues canceled to order at face value.

Europa Issue
Common Design Type

1966, Sept. 26   Engr.   Perf. 13
Size: 21x27mm
496 CD9 60o dark carmine   .60 .40
497 CD9 90o blue gray   1.75 1.75

Nitrogen Molecule in Test Tube — A125

Design: 55o, Wheat and laboratory bottle.

1966, Oct. 29   Photo.   Perf. 13x12½
498 A125 40o bl & dp bl   1.50 1.50
499 A125 55o red, org & lil rose   2.00 2.00

Centenary of the birth of Kristian Birkeland (1867-1917), and of Sam Eyde (1866-1940), who together developed the production of nitrates.

EFTA Emblem — A126

1967, Jan. 16   Engr.   Perf. 13
500 A126 60o rose red   .50 .35
501 A126 90o dark blue   2.00 2.00

European Free Trade Association. Tariffs were abolished Dec. 31, 1966, among EFTA members: Austria, Denmark, Finland, Great Britain, Norway, Portugal, Sweden, Switzerland.

Sabers, Owl and Oak Leaves — A127

1967, Feb. 16   Engr.   Perf. 13
502 A127 60o chocolate   .80 .80
503 A127 90o black   3.00 3.00

Higher military training in Norway, 150th anniv.

Europa Issue
Common Design Type

1967, May 2   Photo.   Perf. 13
Size: 21x27mm
504 CD10 60o magenta & plum   .60 .40
505 CD10 90o bl & dk vio bl   1.40 1.40

Johanne Dybwad, by Per Ung — A128

1967, Aug. 2   Photo.   Perf. 13
506 A128 40o slate blue   .50 .45
507 A128 60o dk carmine rose   .50 .40

Johanne Dybwad (1867-1950), actress.

Missionary L.O. Skrefsrud A129

Ebenezer Church, Benagaria, Santal A130

1967, Sept. 26   Engr.   Perf. 13
508 A129 60o red brown   .55 .45
509 A130 90o blue gray   1.25 1.25

Norwegian Santal (India) mission, cent.

Mountaineers A131

Designs: 60o, Mountain view. 90o, Glitretind mountain peak.

1968, Jan. 22   Engr.   Perf. 13
510 A131 40o sepia   1.25 1.25
511 A131 60o brown red   .75 .30
512 A131 90o slate blue   1.25 1.25
    Nos. 510-512 (3)   3.25 2.80

Centenary of the Norwegian Mountain Touring Association.

Two Smiths — A132

1968, Mar. 30   Photo.   Perf. 12½x13
513 A132 65o dk car rose & brn   .45 .25
514 A132 90o blue & brown   1.20 1.20

Issued to honor Norwegian craftsmen.

A. O. Vinje — A133

1968, May 21   Engr.   Perf. 13
515 A133 50o sepia   .60 .50
516 A133 65o maroon   .50 .30

Aasmund Olafsson Vinje (1818-1870), poet, journalist and language reformer.

Cross and Heart — A134

1968, Sept. 16   Photo.
517 A134 40o brt grn & brn red   2.25 2.25
518 A134 65o brn red & vio bl   .50 .25

Centenary of the Norwegian Lutheran Home Mission Society.

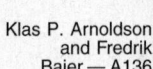

Cathinka Guldberg — A135

1968, Oct. 31   Engr.   Perf. 13
519 A135 50o bright blue   .50 .45
520 A135 65o dull red   .50 .25

Nursing profession; centenary of Deaconess House in Oslo. Cathinka Guldberg was a pioneer of Norwegian nursing and the first deaconess.

Klas P. Arnoldson and Fredrik Bajer — A136

1968, Dec. 10   Engr.   Perf. 13
521 A136 65o red brown   .50 .30
522 A136 90o dark blue   1.50 1.50

60th anniv. of the awarding of the Nobel Peace prize to Klas P. Arnoldson (1844-1916), Swedish writer and statesman, and to Fredrik Bajer (1837-1922), Danish writer and statesman.

Nordic Cooperation Issue

Five Ancient Ships — A136a

1969, Feb. 28   Engr.   Perf. 13
523 A136a 65o red   .35 .30
524 A136a 90o blue   1.40 1.40

50th anniv. of the Nordic Society and centenary of postal cooperation among the northern countries. The design is taken from a coin found on the site of Birka, an ancient Swedish town.

See Demark Nos. 454-455, Finland No. 481, Iceland Nos. 404-405 and Sweden Nos. 808-810.

Ornament from Urnes Stave Church A137

Traena Island A138

1969   **Engr.**   *Perf. 13*
526 A137 1.15k sepia   1.00 .45
529 A138 3.50k bluish blk   1.60 .25
Issue dates: 1.15k, Jan. 23, 3.50k, June 18.

Plane, Train, Ship and Bus — A139

Child Crossing Street — A140

1969, Mar. 24   **Photo.**   *Perf. 13*
531 A139 50o green   1.00 1.00
532 A140 65o slate grn & dk red   .50 .25
No. 531 for the centenary of the publication of "Rutebok of Norway" (Communications of Norway); No. 532 publicizes traffic safety.

Europa Issue
Common Design Type
1969, Apr. 28   **Size: 37x21mm**
533 CD12 65o dk red & gray   .60 .35
534 CD12 90o chalky bl & gray   1.60 1.60

Johan Hjort — A141

Design: 90o, different emblem.

1969, May 30   **Engr.**   *Perf. 13*
535 A141 40o brn & bl   1.00 1.00
536 A141 90o bl & grn   1.75 1.75
Zoologist and oceanographer (1869-1948).

King Olav V — A142

1969-83   **Engr.**   *Perf. 13*
537 A142   1k lt ol grn ('70)   .60 .25
538 A142   1.50k dk blue ('70)   .70 .25
539 A142   2k dk red ('70)   .75 .25
540 A142   5k vio bl ('70)   2.00 .25
541 A142   10k org brn ('70)   5.00 .25
542 A142   20k brown   9.00 .25
543 A142   50k dk ol grn ('83)   16.00 1.50
    Nos. 537-543 (7)   34.05 3.00

Man, Woman and Child, by Vigeland — A143

65o, Mother and Child, by Gustav Vigeland.

1969, Sept. 8   **Photo.**   *Perf. 13*
545 A143 65o car rose & blk   .50 .35
546 A143 90o blue & black   1.25 1.25
Gustav Vigeland (1869-1943), sculptor.

People — A144

1969, Oct. 10
547 A144 65o Punched card   .50 .35
548 A144 90o shown   1.25 1.25
1st Norwegian census, 200th anniv.

Queen Maud — A145

1969, Nov. 26   **Engr.**   *Perf. 13*
549 A145 65o dk carmine   .50 .35
550 A145 90o violet blue   1.25 1.25
Queen Maud (1869-1938), wife of King Haakon VII.

Pulsatilla Vernalis — A146

European Nature Conservation Year: 40o, Wolf. 70o, Voringsfossen (waterfall). 100o, White-tailed sea eagle, horiz.

1970, Apr. 10   **Photo.**   *Perf. 13*
551 A146 40o sep & pale bl   1.25 1.25
552 A146 60o lt brn & gray   2.50 2.50
553 A146 70o pale bl & brn   1.25 .60
554 A146 100o pale bl & brn   1.75 1.75
    Nos. 551-554 (4)   6.75 6.10

"V" for Victory — A147

Design: 100o, Convoy, horiz.

Perf. 13x12½, 12½x13
1970, May 8   **Photo.**
555 A147 70o red & lilac   2.00 .60
556 A147 100o vio bl & brt grn   2.00 1.75
Norway's liberation from the Germans, 25th anniv.

"Citizens" — A148

Designs: 70o, "The City and the Mountains." 100o, "Ships."

1970, June 23   **Engr.**   *Perf. 13*
557 A148 40o green   1.75 1.25
558 A148 70o rose claret   2.50 .40
559 A148 100o violet blue   2.00 2.00
    Nos. 557-559 (3)   6.25 3.65
City of Bergen, 900th anniversary.

Olive Wreath and Hands Upholding Globe — A149

1970, Sept. 15   **Engr.**   *Perf. 13*
560 A149 70o dk car rose   2.50 .50
561 A149 100o steel blue   1.50 1.50
25th anniversary of the United Nations.

Georg Ossian Sars (1837-1927) — A150

Portraits: 50o, Hans Strom (1726-1797). 70o, Johan Ernst Gunnerus (1718-1773). 100o, Michael Sars (1805-1869).

1970, Oct. 15   **Engr.**   *Perf. 13*
562 A150 40o brown   1.25 1.25
563 A150 50o dull purple   1.25 .90
564 A150 70o brown red   1.25 .50
565 A150 100o bright blue   1.25 1.25
    Nos. 562-565 (4)   5.00 3.90
Issued to honor Norwegian zoologists.

Central School of Gymnastics, Oslo, Cent. — A151

50o, Ball game, vert. 70o, Leapfrog.

1970, Nov. 17   **Photo.**   *Perf. 13*
566 A151 50o dk blue, brn   .80 .40
567 A151 70o red, brn, blk   1.00 .30

Seal of Tonsberg — A152

1971, Jan. 20   **Photo.**   *Perf. 13*
568 A152 70o dark red   .85 .30
569 A152 100o blue black   1.25 1.25
City of Tonsberg, 1,100th anniversary.

Parliament A153

1971, Feb. 23
570 A153 70o red brn & lil   .60 .30
571 A153 100o dk bl & sl grn   1.25 1.25
Centenary of annual sessions of Norwegian Parliament.

Hand, Heart and Eye — A154

1971, Mar. 26   **Photo.**   *Perf. 13*
572 A154 50o emerald & blk   .60 .50
573 A154 70o scarlet & blk   .60 .30
Joint northern campaign for the benefit of refugees.

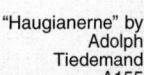
"Haugianerne" by Adolph Tiedemand A155

1971, Apr. 27   **Photo.**   *Perf. 13*
574 A155 60o dark gray   .65 .65
575 A155 70o brown   .50 .30
Hans Nielsen Hauge (1771-1824), church reformer.

Worshippers Coming to Church — A156

Design: 70o, Building first church, vert.

1971, May 21
576 A156 70o black & dk red   .40 .35
577 A156 1k black & blue   1.60 1.60
900th anniversary of the Bishopric of Oslo.

Roald Amundsen, Antarctic Treaty Emblem — A157

1971, June 23   **Engr.**   *Perf. 13*
578 A157 100o blue & org red   3.50 2.50
Antarctic Treaty pledging peaceful uses of and scientific cooperation in Antarctica, 10th anniv.

The Farmer and the Woman — A158

Designs: 50o, The Preacher and the King, horiz. 70o, The Troll and the Girl. Illustrations for legends and folk tales by Erik Werenskiold.

1971, Nov. 17   **Photo.**   *Perf. 13*
579 A158 40o olive & blk   .80 .50
580 A158 50o blue & blk   .80 .30
581 A158 70o magenta & blk   .50 .25
    Nos. 579-581 (3)   2.10 1.05

Engine Turning — A159

1972, Apr. 10   **Photo.**   *Perf. 13*
582 A159 80o red & gold   .60 .30
583 A159 1.20k ultra & gold   1.25 1.25
Norwegian Savings Bank sesquicentennial.

Norway #18 — A160

Engr. & Photo.
1972, May 6   *Perf. 12*
584 A160 80o shown   1.25 .30
585 A160 1k Norway #17   1.25 1.25
    a.   Souvenir sheet of 2, #584-585   6.00 7.50
Centenary of the post horn stamps. No. 585a sold for 2.50k.

Dragon's Head, Oseberg Viking Ship — A161

Ancient Artifacts: 50o, Horseman from Stone of Alstad. 60o, Horseman, wood carving, stave church, Hemsedal. 1.20k, Sword hilt, found at Lodingen.

1972, June 7   **Engr.**   *Perf. 13*
586 A161 50o yellow grn   .60 .60
587 A161 60o brown   1.40 1.40
588 A161 80o dull red   1.40 .45
589 A161 1.20k ultra   1.60 1.60
    Nos. 586-589 (4)   5.00 4.05
1,100th anniversary of unification.

King Haakon VII (1872-1957) — A162

1972, Aug. 3   **Engr.**   *Perf. 13*
590 A162 80o brown orange   2.75 .35
591 A162 1.20k Prussian bl   1.75 1.60

"Joy" — A163

Design: 1.20k, "Solidarity."

1972, Aug. 15   **Photo.**   *Perf. 13x13½*
592 A163 80o brt magenta   .75 .30
593 A163 1.20k Prussian blue   1.25 1.25
2nd Intl. Youth Stamp Exhib., INTERJUNEX 72, Kristiansand, Aug. 25-Sept. 3.

Nos. 592-593 Overprinted "INTERJUNEX 72"
1972, Aug. 25
594 A163 80o brt magenta   2.50 2.50
595 A163 1.20k Prussian blue   2.50 2.50
Opening of INTERJUNEX 72. Sold at exhibition only together with 3k entrance ticket.

"Fram." — A164

Polar Exploration Ships: 60o, "Maud." 1.20k, "Gjoa."

1972, Sept. 20   Perf. 13½x13
596 A164   60o olive & green   1.40 1.00
597 A164   80o red & black   2.50 .35
598 A164   1.20k blue & red brn   2.10 1.60
     Nos. 596-598 (3)   6.00 2.95

"Little Man" — A165

Illustrations for folk tales by Theodor Kittelsen (1857-1914): 60o, The Troll who wondered how old he was. 80o, The princess riding the polar bear.

1972, Nov. 15   Litho.   Perf. 13½x13
599 A165   50o green & blk   .85 .25
600 A165   60o blue & blk   1.00 .75
601 A165   80o pink & blk   .85 .25
     Nos. 599-601 (3)   2.70 1.25

Dr. Armauer G. Hansen and Leprosy Bacillus Drawing — A166

Design: 1.40k, Dr. Hansen and leprosy bacillus, microscopic view.

1973, Feb. 28   Engr.   Perf. 13x13½
602 A166   1k henna brn & bl   .50 .25
603 A166   1.40k dk bl & dp org   1.25 1.25
Centenary of the discovery of the Hansen bacillus, the cause of leprosy.

Europa Issue
Common Design Type
1973, Apr. 30   Photo.   Perf. 12½x13
Size: 37x20mm
604 CD16   1k red, org & lil   2.50 .30
605 CD16   1.40k dk grn, grn & bl 1.50 1.50

Types of 1893 and 1962-63

Designs: 75o, 85o, Rye and fish. 80o, 140o, Stave church. 100o, 110o, 120o, 125o, Rock carvings.

1972-75   Engr.   Perf. 13x13½
606 A10   25o ultra ('74)   .25 .25
   Complete booklet, pane of 4 of
   #606   2.00
608 A101   75o green ('73)   .30 .25
609 A102   80o red brown   .40 .35
   Complete booklet, pane of 10
   of #609   50.00
610 A101   85o bister ('74)   .30 .25
611 A101   100o red ('73)   .75 .25
   Complete booklet, pane of 10
   of #611   40.00
612 A101   110o rose car ('74)   .50 .25
613 A101   120o gray blue   .60 .50
614 A101   125o red ('75)   .75 .25
   Complete booklet, pane of 10
   of #614   17.50
615 A102   140o dk blue ('73)   .60 .40
     Nos. 606-615 (9)   4.45 2.75

Nordic Cooperation Issue

Nordic House, Reykjavik — A167

1973, June 26   Engr.   Perf. 12½
617 A167   1k multi   1.00 .40
618 A167   1.40k multi   1.25 1.25
A century of postal cooperation among Denmark, Finland, Iceland, Norway and Sweden; Nordic Postal Conference, Reykjavik, Iceland.

King Olav V — A168

1973, July 2   Engr.   Perf. 13
619 A168   1k car & org brn   1.25 .30
620 A168   1.40k blue & org brn   1.25 1.25
70th birthday of King Olav V.

Jacob Aall — A169

1973, Aug. 22   Engr.   Perf. 13
621 A169   1k deep claret   .60 .30
622 A169   1.40k dk blue gray   1.25 1.25
Jacob Aall (1773-1844), mill owner and industrial pioneer.

Blade Decoration — A170

Handicraft from Lapland: 1k, Textile pattern. 1.40k, Decoration made of tin.

1973, Oct. 9   Photo.   Perf. 13x12½
623 A170   75o blk brn & buff   .60 .50
624 A170   1k dp car & buff   1.00 .30
625 A170   1.40k blk & dl bl   1.25 1.25
     Nos. 623-625 (3)   2.85 2.05

Viola Biflora — A171

70o, Veronica Fruticans. 1k, Phyllodoce corrulea.

1973, Nov. 15   Litho.   Perf. 13
626 A171   65o shown   .60 .50
627 A171   70o multicolored   .60 .60
628 A171   1k multicolored   .60 .30
     Nos. 626-628 (3)   1.80 1.40
See Nos. 754-756, 770-771.

Surveyor in Northern Norway, 1907 — A172

1.40k, South Norway Mountains map, 1851.

1973, Dec. 14   Engr.   Perf. 13
629 A172   1k red orange   .60 .30
630 A172   1.40k slate blue   1.25 1.25
Geographical Survey of Norway, bicent.

Lindesnes — A173

Design: 1.40k, North Cape.

1974, Apr. 25   Photo.   Perf. 13
631 A173   1k olive   1.00 .50
632 A173   1.40k dark blue   2.50 2.50

Ferry in Hardanger Fjord, by A. Tidemand and H. Gude — A174

Classical Norwegian paintings: 1.40k, Stugunoset from Filefjell, by Johan Christian Dahl.

1974, May 21   Litho.   Perf. 13
633 A174   1k multi   .65 .30
634 A174   1.40k multi   1.10 1.10

Gulating Law Manuscript, 1325 A175

King Magnus VI Lagaböter A176

1974, June 21   Engr.
635 A175   1k red & brn   .65 .30
636 A176   1.40k red & brn   1.40 1.40
700th anniv. of the National Code given by King Magnus VI Lagaböter (1238-80).

Saw Blade and Pines — A177

Design: 1k, Cog wheel and guard.

1974, Aug. 12   Photo.   Perf. 13
637 A177   85o grn, ol & dk grn   2.00 2.00
638 A177   1k org, plum & dk red 1.25 .40
Safe working conditions.

J.H.L. Vogt — A178

Geologists: 85o, V. M. Goldschmidt. 1k, Theodor Kjerulf. 1.40k, Waldemar C. Brogger.

1974, Sept. 4   Engr.
639 A178   65o olive & red brn   .40 .30
640 A178   85o mag & red brn   1.75 1.75
641 A178   1k org & red brn   .75 .25
642 A178   1.40k blue & red brn   1.25 1.25
     Nos. 639-642 (4)   4.15 3.55

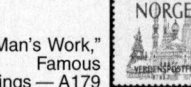

"Man's Work," Famous Buildings — A179

Design: 1.40k, "Men, our brethren," people of various races.

1974, Oct. 9   Photo.   Perf. 13
643 A179   1k green & brn   .65 .30
644 A179   1.40k brn & grnsh bl   1.25 1.25
Centenary of Universal Postal Union.

Horseback Rider A180

Flowers A181

1974, Nov. 15   Litho.   Perf. 13
645 A180   85o multicolored   .50 .50
646 A181   1k multicolored   .50 .25
Norwegian folk art, rose paintings from furniture decorations.

Woman Skier, c. 1900 — A182

1975, Jan. 15   Litho.   Perf. 13
647 A182   1k shown   .75 .30
648 A182   1.40k Telemark turn   1.00 1.00
"Norway, homeland of skiing."

Women — A183

Design: Detail from wrought iron gates of Vigeland Park, Oslo.

1975, Mar. 7   Litho.   Perf. 13
649 A183   1.25k brt rose lil & dk
           bl   .65 .25
650 A183   1.40k bl & dk bl   1.00 1.00
International Women's Year.

Nusfjord Fishing Harbor — A184

1.25k, Street in Stavanger. 1.40k, View of Roros.

1975, Apr. 17   Litho.   Perf. 13
651 A184   1k yellow green   .95 .60
652 A184   1.25k dull red   .65 .25
653 A184   1.40k blue   1.00 1.00
     Nos. 651-653 (3)   2.60 1.85
European Architectural Heritage Year.

Norwegian Krone, 1875 — A185

Ole Jacob Broch — A186

1975, May 20   Engr.   Perf. 13
654 A185   1.25k dark carmine   .90 .25
655 A186   1.40k blue   1.00 1.00
Centenary of Monetary Convention of Norway, Sweden and Denmark (1.25k); and of Intl. Meter Convention, Paris, 1875. Ole Jacob Broch (1818-1889) was first director of Intl. Bureau of Weights and Measures.

Scouting in Summer — A187

Design: 1.40k, Scouting in winter (skiers).

1975, June 19   Litho.   Perf. 13
656 A187   1.25k multicolored   .90 .25
657 A187   1.40k multicolored   1.25 1.25
Nordjamb 75, 14th Boy Scout Jamboree, Lillehammer, July 29-Aug. 7.

Sod Hut and Settlers — A188

Cleng Peerson and Letter from America, 1874 — A189

1975, July 4   Engr.
658 A188   1.25k red brown   .85 .25
659 A189   1.40k bluish blk   1.10 1.10
Sesquicentennial of Norwegian emigration to America.

Templet, Tempelfjord, Spitsbergen A190

Miners Leaving Coal Pit A191

Design: 1.40k, Polar bear.

1975, Aug. 14　Engr.　Perf. 13
660	A190	1k olive black	.90	.50
661	A191	1.25k maroon	.90	.25
662	A191	1.40k Prus blue	1.90	1.90
		Nos. 660-662 (3)	3.70	2.65

50th anniversary of union of Spitsbergen (Svalbard) with Norway.

Microphone with Ear Phones A192　　　Radio Tower and Houses A193

Designs after children's drawings.

1975, Oct. 9　Litho.　Perf. 13
663	A192	1.25k multi	.60	.25
664	A193	1.40k multi	.80	.80

50 years of broadcasting in Norway.

Annunciation A194　　　Nativity A195

Painted vault of stave church of Al, 13th cent: 1k, Visitation. 1.40k, Adoration of the Kings.

1975, Nov. 14
665	A194	80o red & multi	.40	.30
666	A194	1k red & multi	.50	.50
667	A195	1.25k red & multi	.60	.25
668	A195	1.40k red & multi	.90	.80
		Nos. 665-668 (4)	2.40	1.85

Sigurd and Regin — A196

1976, Jan. 20　Engr.　Perf. 13
669	A196	7.50k brown	3.25	.25

Norwegian folk tale, Sigurd the Dragon-killer. Design from portal of Hylestad stave church, 13th century.

Halling, Hallingdal Dance — A197

Folk Dances: 1k, Springar, Hordaland region. 1.25k, Gangar, Setesdal.

1976, Feb. 25　Litho.　Perf. 13
670	A197	80o black & multi	.80	.50
671	A197	1k black & multi	.80	.30
672	A197	1.25k black & multi	.60	.25
		Nos. 670-672 (3)	2.20	1.05

Silver Sugar Shaker, Stavanger, c. 1770 — A198

1.40k, Goblet, Nostetangen glass, c. 1770.

1976, Mar. 25　Engr.　Perf. 13
673	A198	1.25k multicolored	.60	.30
674	A198	1.40k multicolored	.80	.80

Oslo Museum of Applied Art, centenary.

Ceramic Bowl Shaped Like Bishop's Mitre — A199

Europa: 1.40k, Plate and CEPT emblem. Both designs after faience works from Herrebo Potteries, c. 1760.

1976, May 3　Litho.　Perf. 13
675	A199	1.25k rose mag & brn	.60	.40
676	A199	1.40k brt bl & vio bl	.85	.85

The Pulpit, Lyse Fjord A200　　　Gulleplet (Peak), Sogne Fjord A201

Perf. 13 on 3 Sides

1976, May 20　　　Litho.
677	A200	1k multi	.60	.25
a.		Booklet pane of 10	6.50	
		Complete booklet, #677a	7.50	
678	A201	1.25k multi	1.00	.25
a.		Booklet pane of 10	10.00	
		Complete booklet, #678a	12.00	

Nos. 677-678 issued only in booklets.

Graph Paper, Old and New Subjects — A202

Design: 2k, Graph of national product.

1976, July 1　Engr.　Perf. 13
679	A202	1.25k red brown	.50	.25
680	A202	2k dark blue	.90	.35

Central Bureau of Statistics, centenary.

Olav Duun on Dun Mountain — A203

1976, Sept. 10　Engr.　Perf. 13
681	A203	1.25k multi	.50	.25
682	A203	1.40k multi	.80	.80

Olav Duun (1876-1939), novelist.

"Birches" by Th. Fearnley (1802-1842) A204

Design: 1.40k, "Gamle Furutraer" (trees), by L. Hertervig (1830-1902).

1976, Oct. 8　Litho.　Perf. 13
683	A204	1.25k multi	.55	.30
684	A204	1.40k multi	1.00	1.00

"April" A205　　　"May" A206

Baldishol Tapestry A207

80o, 1k, Details from 13th cent. Baldishol tapestry, found in Baldishol stave church.

1976, Nov. 5　Litho.　Perf. 13
685	A205	80o multi	.40	.30
686	A206	1k multi	.50	.25
687	A207	1.25k multi	.60	.25
		Nos. 685-687 (3)	1.50	.85

Five Water Lilies — A208

Photo. & Engr.

1977, Feb. 2　　　Perf. 12½
688	A208	1.25k multi	.75	.30
689	A208	1.40k multi	.75	.75

Nordic countries cooperation for protection of the environment and 25th Session of Nordic Council, Helsinki, Feb. 19.

Akershus Castle, Oslo — A209

Steinviksholm Fort, Asen Fjord — A210

Torungen Lighthouses, Arendal — A211

1977, Feb. 24　Engr.　Perf. 13
690	A209	1.25k red	.50	.25
		Complete booklet pane of 10 #690	6.00	
		Complete booklet pane of 8 #690	8.50	
691	A210	1.30k olive brown	.60	.25
692	A211	1.80k blue	.75	.30
		Nos. 690-692 (3)	1.85	.80

See Nos. 715-724, 772-774.

Europa Issue

Hamnoy, Lofoten, Fishing Village A212　　　Huldre Falls, Loen A213

Perf. 13 on 3 Sides

1977, May 2　　　Litho.
693	A212	1.25k multi	1.00	.25
a.		Booklet pane of 10	10.00	
		Complete booklet, #693a	12.00	
694	A213	1.80k multi	.75	.75
a.		Booklet pane of 10	8.00	
		Complete booklet, #694a	9.00	

Nos. 693-694 issued only in booklets.

Norwegian Trees — A214

1977, June 1　Engr.　Perf. 13
695	A214	1k Spruce	.50	.30
696	A214	1.25k Fir	.75	.30
697	A214	1.80k Birch	.90	.90
		Nos. 695-697 (3)	2.15	1.50

"Constitutionen," Norway's 1st Steamship, at Arendal — A215

Designs: 1.25k, "Vesteraalen" off Bodo, 1893. 1.30k, "Kong Haakon," 1904 and "Dronningen," 1893, off Stavanger. 1.80k, "Nordstjernen" and "Harald Jarl" at pier, 1970.

1977, June 22
698	A215	1k brown	.50	.25
699	A215	1.25k red	.80	.25
700	A215	1.30k green	1.50	1.50
701	A215	1.80k blue	1.00	.90
		Nos. 698-701 (4)	3.80	2.90

Norwegian ships serving coastal routes.

Fishermen and Boats A216　　　Fish and Fishhooks A217

1977, Sept. 22　Engr.　Perf. 13
702	A216	1.25k buff, lt brn & dk brn	.80	.25
703	A217	1.80k lt bl, bl & dk bl	.90	.90

Men, by Halfdan Egedius — A218　　　Landscape, by August Cappelen — A219

1977, Oct. 7　Litho.　Perf. 13
704	A218	1.25k multi	.45	.25
705	A219	1.80k multi	1.00	1.00

Norwegian classical painting.

David with the Bells — A220

Christmas: 1k, Singing Friars. 1.25k, Virgin and Child, horiz. Designs from Bible of Bishop Aslak Bolt, 13th century.

1977, Nov. 10　Litho.　Perf. 13

Size: 21x27mm
706	A220	80o multi	.40	.30
707	A220	1k multi	.50	.25

Size: 34x27mm
708	A220	1.25k multi	.50	.25
		Nos. 706-708 (3)	1.40	.80

Post Horn Type of 1893 and Scenic Types of 1977

Designs: 1k, Austrat Manor, 1650. 1.10k, Trondenes Chruch, early 13th Cent. 1.40k, Ruins of Hamar Cathedral, 12th Cent. 1.75k, Seamen's Hall, Stavern, 1926, vert. 2k, Tofte Estate, Dovre, 16-17th cent., vert. 2.25k, Oscarhall, Oslofijord, 1847, vert. 2.50k, Log house, Breiland, 1785. 2.75k, Damsgard Building, Lakesvag, 1770. 3k, Selje Monastery, 11th cent. 3.50k, Lighthouse, Lindesnes, 1655.

Perf. 13x13½, 13½x13

1978-83　　　Engr.
709	A10	40o olive	.25	.25
710	A10	50o dull purple	.25	.25
711	A10	60o vermilion	.25	.25
712	A10	70o orange	.40	.30
713	A10	80o red brown	.40	.35
714	A10	90o brown	.40	.40
715	A209	1k green	.40	.25
		Complete booklet, pane of 4 ea #416, 419, 715	12.00	
716	A209	1.10k rose mag	.50	.25
717	A209	1.40k dark purple	.60	.25
718	A211	1.75k green ('82)	.60	.25
719	A211	2k brown red ('82)	.60	.25
720	A211	2.25k dp vio ('82)	.80	.35
721	A209	2.50k brn red ('83)	.80	.25
722	A209	2.75k dp mag ('82)	1.25	1.00
723	A209	3k dk bl ('82)	.80	.25
724	A209	3.50k dp vio ('83)	1.25	.30
		Nos. 709-724 (16)	9.55	5.20

See Nos. 772-774.

Peer Gynt, and Reindeer by Per Krogh A222

Henrik Ibsen, by Erik Werenskiold, 1895 A223

1978, Mar. 10   **Litho.**   **Perf. 13**
725 A222 1.25k buff & blk   .50   .25
726 A223 1.80k multicolored   1.00   .90

Ibsen (1828-1906), poet and dramatist.

Heddal Stave Church, c. 1250 — A224

Europa: 1.80k, Borgund stave church.

1978, May 2   **Engr.**   **Perf. 13**
727 A224 1.25k redsh brn & org   1.00   .25
728 A224 1.80k sl grn & bl   1.25   1.25

Lenangstindene and Jaegervasstindene A225

1.25k, Gaustatoppen, mountain, Telemark.

Perf. 13 on 3 Sides
1978, June 1   **Litho.**
729 A225 1k multi   .60 .25
   a.   Booklet pane of 10   6.50
     Complete booklet, #729a   8.00
730 A225 1.25k multi   .90 .25
   a.   Booklet pane of 10   9.00
     Complete booklet, #730a   10.00

Nos. 729-730 issued only in booklets.

Olav V Sailing — A226

Design: 1.80k, King Olav delivering royal address in Parliament, vert.

1978, June 30   **Engr.**   **Perf. 13**
731 A226 1.25k red brown   .80 .25
732 A226 1.80k violet blue   1.00 .70

75th birthday of King Olav V.

Norway No. 107 — A227

Stamps: b, #108. c, #109. d, #110. e, #111. f, #112. g, #113. h, #114.

Perf. 13 on 3 Sides
1978, Sept. 19   **Litho.**
733   Booklet pane of 8   8.00 8.00
   a.-h.   A227 1.25k, any single   1.00 1.00
     Complete booklet, #733   8.00

NORWEX '80 Philatelic Exhibition, Oslo, June 13-22, 1980. Booklet sold for 15k; the additional 5k went for financing the exhibition.

Willow Pipe Player — A228

Musical Instruments: 1.25k, Norwegian violin. 1.80k, Norwegian zither. 7.50k, Ram's horn.

1978, Oct. 6   **Engr.**   **Perf. 13**
734 A228 1k deep green   .35 .25
735 A228 1.25k dk rose car   .55 .25
736 A228 1.80k dk violet blue   .90 .75
737 A228 7.50k gray   4.00 .25
   Nos. 734-737 (4)   5.80 1.50

Wooden Doll, 1830 — A229

Christmas: 1k, Toy town 1896-97. 1.25k, Wooden horse from Torpo in Hallingdal.

1978, Nov. 10   **Litho.**
738 A229 80o multi   .40 .25
739 A229 1k multi   .50 .25
740 A229 1.25k multi   .50 .25
   Nos. 738-740 (3)   1.40 .75

Ski Jump, Huseby Hill, c. 1900 — A230

1.25k, Crown Prince Olav, Holmenkollen ski jump competition, 1922. 1.80k, Cross-country race, Holmenkollen, 1976.

1979, Mar. 2   **Engr.**   **Perf. 13**
741 A230 1k green   .60 .35
742 A230 1.25k red   .60 .25
743 A230 1.80k blue   1.00 .90
   Nos. 741-743 (3)   2.20 1.50

Huseby Hills and Holmenkollen ski competitions, centenary.

Girl, by Mathias Stoltenberg — A231

1.80k, Boy, by H. C. F. Hosenfelder.

1979, Apr. 26   **Litho.**   **Perf. 13**
744 A231 1.25k multi   .50 .25
745 A231 1.80k multi   .80 .80

International Year of the Child.

Road to Briksdal Glacier — A232

1.25k, Boat on Skjernoysund, near Mandal.

1979, June 13   **Perf. 13 on 3 Sides**
746 A232 1k multi   .60 .25
   a.   Booklet pane of 10   6.00
     Complete booklet, #746a   7.00
747 A232 1.25k multi   .75 .25
   a.   Booklet pane of 10   7.50
     Complete booklet, #747a   9.00

Nos. 746-747 issued only in booklets.

Johan Falkberget, by Harald Dal — A233

1.80k, "Ann-Magritt and the Hovi Bullock" (by Falkberget), monument by Kristofer Leirdal.

1979, Sept. 4   **Engr.**   **Perf. 13**
748 A233 1.25k deep claret   .50 .25
749 A233 1.80k Prus blue   .90 .90

Johan Falkberget (1879-1967), novelist.

Kylling Bridge, Verma, 1923 — A234

Norwegian Engineering: 2k, Vessingsjo Dam, Nea, 1960. 10k, Stratfjord A, oil drilling platform in North Sea.

1979, Oct. 5
750 A234 1.25k black & brown   .50 .25
751 A234   2k dk blue & blue   .80 .25
752 A234 10k brown & bister   4.00 .45
   Nos. 750-752 (3)   5.30 .95

Souvenir Sheet

Dornier Wal over Polar Map — A235

Arctic Aviation and Polar Maps: 2k, Dirigible Norge. 2.80k, Loening air yacht amphibian. 4k, Reidar Viking DC-7C.

1979, Oct. 5   **Litho.**   **Perf. 13**
753   Sheet of 4   5.50 5.00
   a.   A235 1.25k multi   1.25 1.25
   b.   A235 2k multi   1.25 1.25
   c.   A235 2.80k multi   1.25 1.25
   d.   A235 4k multi   1.25 1.25

Norwex '80 Intl. Phil. Exhib., Oslo, June 13-22, 1980. No. 753 sold for 15k.

Mountain Flower Type of 1973

80o, Ranunculus glacialis. 1k, Potentilla crantzii. 1.25k, Saxiflora oppositifolia.

1979, Nov. 22   **Litho.**   **Perf. 13½**
754 A171 80o multicolored   .40 .25
755 A171 1k multicolored   .40 .25
756 A171 1.25k multicolored   .50 .25
   Nos. 754-756 (3)   1.30 .75

Norwegian Christian Youth Assn. Centenary A237

180o, Emblems and doves.

1980, Feb. 26   **Litho.**   **Perf. 13**
757 A237 100o shown   .50 .25
758 A237 180o multicolored   .80 .80

Oyster Catcher — A238

Perf. 13 on 3 Sides
1980, Apr. 18   **Litho.**
759 A238 100o shown   .35 .25
760 A238 100o Mallard   .35 .25
   a.   Bkt. pane, 5 #759, 5 #760   4.00
     Complete booklet, #760a   5.00
761 A238 125o Dipper   .55 .25
762 A238 125o Great tit   .55 .25
   a.   Bkt. pane, 5 #761, 5 #762   5.50
     Complete booklet, #762a   6.00
   Nos. 759-762 (4)   1.80 1.00

Nos. 759-762 issued in booklets only. See Nos. 775-778, 800-801, 821-822.

Dish Antenna, Old Phone — A239

National Telephone Service Centenary: 1.80k, Erecting telephone pole.

1980, May 9   **Litho.**   **Perf. 13½**
763 A239 1.25k multi   .50 .25
764 A239 1.80k multi   .80 .80

Souvenir Sheet

NORWEX '80 Stamp Exhibition — A240

1980, June 13
765 A240 Sheet of 4   5.00 5.00
   a.   1.25k Paddle Steamer "Bergen"   1.25 1.25
   b.   2k Train, 1900   1.25 1.25
   c.   2.80k Bus, 1940   1.25 1.25
   d.   4k Boeing 737   1.25 1.25

NORWEX '80 Stamp Exhibition, Oslo, June 13-22. Sold for 15k.

Nordic Cooperation Issue

Vulcan as an Armourer, by Henrich Bech, 1761 — A241

Henrich Bech Cast Iron Stove Ornament: 1.80k, Hercules at a Burning Altar, 1769.

1980, Sept. 9   **Engr.**   **Perf. 13**
766 A241 1.25k dk vio brn   .50 .25
767 A241 1.80k dark blue   .80 .80

Self-Portrait, by Christian Skredsvig (1854-1924) A242

Paintings: 1.25k, Fire, by Nikolai Astrup.

1980, Nov. 14   **Litho.**   **Perf. 13½x13**
768 A242 1.25k multi   .50 .25
769 A242 1.80k multi   1.00 .80

Mountain Flower Type of 1973

1980, Nov. 14   **Perf. 13**
770 A171 80o Sorbus aucuparia   .40 .25
771 A171 1k Rosa canina   .40 .25

Scenic Type of 1977

1.50k, Stavanger Cathedral, 13th cent. 1.70k, Rosenkrantz Tower, Bergen, 13th-16th cent. 2.20k, Church of Tromsdalen (Arctic Cathedral), 1965.

Perf. 13x13½, 13½x13
1981, Feb. 26   **Engr.**
772 A211 1.50k brown red   .60 .25
773 A211 1.70k olive green   .80 .60
774 A209 2.20k dark blue   1.00 .60
   Nos. 772-774 (3)   2.40 1.45

Bird Type of 1980
Perf. 13 on 3 Sides
1981, Feb. 26   **Litho.**
775 A238 1.30k Anser erythropus   .50 .50
776 A238 1.30k Peregrine falcon   .50 .50
   a.   Booklet pane of 10 (5 each)   5.50
     Complete booklet, #776a   6.50
777 A238 1.50k Black guillemot   .65 .25
778 A238 1.50k Puffin   .65 .25
   a.   Booklet pane of 10 (5 each)   6.50
     Complete booklet, #778a   7.50
   Nos. 775-778 (4)   2.30 1.50

Nos. 775-778 issued in booklets. See Nos. 800-801, 821-822.

Nat'l Milk Producers Assn. Centenary — A244

1981, Mar. 24   **Litho.**   **Perf. 13x13½**
779 A244 1.10k Cow   .50 .35
780 A244 1.50k Goat   .60 .25

A245

Europa: 1.50k, The Mermaid, painted dish, Hol. 2.20k, The Proposal, painted box, Nes.

1981, May 4 **Litho.** **Perf. 13**
781 A245 1.50k multi .75 .25
782 A245 2.20k multi 1.00 .75

A246

Designs: 1.30k, Weighing anchor. 1.50k, Climbing rigging, vert. 2.20k, Training Ship Christian Radich.

1981, May 4 **Engr.**
783 A246 1.30k dk olive grn .60 .35
784 A246 1.50k orange red .60 .25
785 A246 2.20k dark blue 1.00 .75
Nos. 783-785 (3) 2.20 1.35

Paddle Steamer
Skibladner, 1856,
Mjosa
Lake — A247

Lake Transportation: 1.30k, Victoria, 1882, Bandak Channel. 1.50k, Faemund II, 1905, Fermund Lake. 2.30k, Storegut, 1956, Tinnsjo Lake.

1981, June 11 **Engr.** **Perf. 13**
786 A247 1.10k dark brown .60 .25
787 A247 1.30k green .75 .50
788 A247 1.50k red .75 .25
789 A247 2.30k dark blue 1.00 .50
Nos. 786-789 (4) 3.10 1.50

Group Walking Arm
in Arm — A248

1981, Aug. 25 **Engr.**
790 A248 1.50k shown .60 .25
791 A248 2.20k Group, diff. .90 .90

Intl. Year of the Disabled.

Paintings — A249

1.50k, Interior in Blue, by Harriet Backer (1845-1932). 1.70k, Peat Moor on Jaeren, by Kitty Lange Kielland (1843-1914).

1981, Oct. 9 **Litho.** **Perf. 13**
792 A249 1.50k multi .60 .25
793 A249 1.70k multi .75 .75

Tapestries — A250

1.10k, One of the Three Kings, Skjak, 1625. 1.30k, Adoration of the Infant Christ, tapestry, Skjak, 1625. 1.50k, The Marriage in Cana, Storen, 18th cent.

1981, Nov. 25 **Litho.** **Perf. 13½**
794 A250 1.10k multi .40 .25
795 A250 1.30k multi .50 .35

Size: 29x37mm
796 A250 1.50k multi .55 .25
Nos. 794-796 (3) 1.45 .85

1921 Nobel Prize
Winners — A251

5k, Christian L. Lange (1869-1938) and Hjalmar Branting (1860-1925).

1981, Nov. 25 **Engr.** **Perf. 13**
797 A251 5k black 2.25 .25

World Skiing
Championship,
Oslo — A252

1982, Feb. 16 **Perf. 13½**
798 A252 2k Poles .65 .25
799 A252 3k Skis .90 .50

Bird Type of 1980
Perf. 13 on 3 Sides
1982, Apr. 1 **Litho.**
Booklet Stamps
800 A238 2k Blue-throat .75 .25
801 A238 2k Robin .75 .25
  a. Bklt. pane, 5 each #800-801 7.50
    Complete booklet, #801a 8.50

Fight Against
Tuberculosis — A253

1982, Apr. 1 **Perf. 13**
802 A253 2k Nurse .50 .25
803 A253 3k Microscope .90 .85

Mouth
Harp — A254

1982, May 3 **Engr.** **Perf. 13**
804 A254 15k sepia 6.00 .35

Europa
1982 — A255

2k, Haakon VII, 1905. 3k, Prince Olav, King Haakon VII, 1945.

1982, May 3
805 A255 2k brown red 1.75 .25
806 A255 3k indigo 1.50 .60

Girls from
Telemark, by Erik
Werenskiold (1855-
1938)
A256

Design: 2k, Tone Veli at the Fence, by Henrik Sorensen (1882-1962), vert.

1982, June 23 **Litho.** **Perf. 13**
807 A256 1.75k multi .60 .50
808 A256 2k multi .60 .25

Consecration
Ceremony, Nidaros
Cathedral,
Trondheim — A257

1982, Sept. 2 **Engr.** **Perf. 13x13½**
809 A257 3k blue 1.75 1.00

Reign of King Olav, 25th anniv.

Sigrid Undset (1882-
1949), Writer, by A.C.
Svarstad — A258

Painting: 1.75k, Bjornstjerne Bjornson (1832-1910), writer, by Erik Werenskiold, horiz.

1982, Oct. 1 **Litho.** **Perf. 13**
810 A258 1.75k multi .75 .35
811 A258 2k multi .75 .25

A souvenir sheet containing Nos. 810-811 was prepared by the Norwegian Philatelic Association.

Graphical Union of
Norway
Centenary — A259

1982, Oct. 1
812 A259 2k "A" .65 .25
813 A259 3k Type 1.00 .60

Fridtjof Nansen — A260

1982, Nov. 15 **Engr.** **Perf. 13½x13**
814 A260 3k dark blue 1.50 .60
Fridtjof Nansen (1861-1930) polar explorer, 1922 Nobel Peace Prize winner.

Christmas — A261

Painting: Christmas Tradition, by Adolf Tidemand (1814-1876).

Perf. 13 on 3 Sides
1982, Nov. 15 **Litho.**
815 A261 1.75k multi .50 .25
  a. Booklet pane of 10 6.00
    Complete booklet, #815a 6.75

Farm Dog — A262

1983, Feb. 16 **Litho.** **Perf. 13x13½**
816 A262 2k shown 1.00 .50
817 A262 2.50k Elk hound 1.25 .25
818 A262 3.50k Hunting dog .75 1.00
Nos. 816-818 (3) 3.00 1.75

Nordic Cooperation
Issue — A263

1983, Mar. 24 **Litho.** **Perf. 13**
819 A263 2.50k Mountains .90 .25
820 A263 3.50k Fjord 1.25 .80

Bird Type of 1980
1983, Apr. 14 **Perf. 13 on 3 Sides**
821 A238 2.50k Goose 1.10 .25
822 A238 2.50k Little auk 1.10 .25
  a. Bklt. pane, 5 each #821-822 11.00
    Complete booklet, #822a 12.00

Nos. 821-822 issued only in booklets.

Europa — A264

Designs: 2.50k, Edvard Grieg (1843-1907), composer and his Piano Concerto in A-minor. 3.50k, Niels Henrik Abel (1802-1829), mathematician, by Gustav Vigeland, vert.

1983, May 3 **Engr.** **Perf. 13**
823 A264 2.50k red orange 1.75 .25
824 A264 3.50k dk bl & grn 1.75 .75

World
Communications
Year — A265

Symbolic arrow designs.

1983, May 3 **Litho.**
825 A265 2.50k multi .90 .25
826 A265 3.50k multi 1.25 .75

80th Birthday of King
Olav V, July 2 — A266

1983, June 22 **Engr.** **Perf. 13x13½**
827 A266 5k green 2.50 .40

Jonas Lie (1833-1908),
Writer — A267

1983, Oct. 7 **Engr.** **Perf. 13½x13**
828 A267 2.50k red 1.00 .25

Northern Ships — A268

1983, Oct. 7 **Litho.**
829 A268 2k Nordlandsfemboring 1.00 .50
830 A268 3k Nordlandsjekt 1.50 .75

Christmas
1983 — A269

Paintings: 2k, The Sleigh Ride by Axel Ender (1853-1920). 2.50k, The Guests are Arriving by Gustav Wenzel (1859-1927).

Perf. 13 on 3 sides
1983, Nov. 17 **Litho.**
831 A269 2k multi 1.00 .25
  a. Booklet pane of 10 10.00
    Complete booklet, #831a 11.00
832 A269 2.50k multi 1.00 .25
  a. Booklet pane of 10 10.00
    Complete booklet, #832a 11.00

Postal
Services — A270

1984, Feb. 24 **Litho.** **Perf. 13½x13**
833 A270 2k Counter service 1.00 .40
834 A270 2.50k Sorting 1.10 .25
835 A270 3.50k Delivery 1.50 .60
Nos. 833-835 (3) 3.60 1.25

Freshwater Fishing — A271

1984, Apr. 10   Engr.   Perf. 13
836 A271 2.50k shown   1.00   .25
837 A271 3k Salmon fishing   1.00   .50
838 A271 3.50k Ocean fishing 1.50   .50
    Nos. 836-838 (3)   3.50 1.25

Christopher Hansteen (1784-1873), Astronomer — A272

3.50k, Magnetic meridians, parallels, horiz.

1984, Apr. 10
839 A272 3.50k multicolored   1.40   .50
840 A272 5k multicolored   2.00   .40

Europa (1959-84) — A273

1984, June 4   Litho.   Perf. 13
841 A273 2.50k multi   1.50   .25
842 A273 3k multi   1.60   .80

Produce, Spices — A274

1984, June 4   Perf. 13
843 A274 2k shown   .80   .40
844 A274 2.50k Flowers   .90   .25

Horticultural Society centenary.

A275

1984, June 4
845 A275 2.50k Worker bees   .85   .25
846 A275 2.50k Rooster   .85   .25

Centenaries: Beekeeping Society (No. 845); Poultry-breeding Society (No. 846).

A276

1984, Oct. 5   Engr.   Perf. 13
847 A276 2.50k lake   1.10   .25

Ludvig Holberg (1684-1754), writer, by J.M. Bernigeroth.

A277

1984, Oct. 5   Litho. & Engr.
848 A277 2.50k Children reading .75   .25
849 A277 3.50k First edition   1.00 .50

Norwegian Weekly Press sesquicentennial.

A278

Illustrations from Children's Stories by Thorbjorn Egner: No. 850, Karius & Baktus. No. 851, Tree Shrew. No. 852, Cardamom Rovers. No. 853, Chief Constable Bastian.

Perf. 13½x13 on 3 sides
1984, Nov. 15   Litho.
Booklet Stamps
850 A278 2k multi   1.75   .50
851 A278 2k multi   1.75   .50
  a. Bklt. pane, 5 each #850-851 17.50
      Complete booklet, #851a   24.00
852 A278 2.50k multi   1.75   .25
853 A278 2.50k multi   1.75   .25
  a. Bklt. pane, 5 each #852-853 22.50
      Complete booklet, #853a   25.00
    Nos. 850-853 (4)   7.00 1.50

Parliament Centenary A279

7.50k, Sverdrup Govt. parliament, 1884.

1984, Nov. 15   Engr.   Perf. 13½x13
854 A279 7.50k multicolored   4.00 1.00

Antarctic Mountains — A280

2.50k, The Saw Blade. 3.50k, The Chopping Block.

1985, Apr. 18   Litho.   Perf. 13
855 A280 2.50k multi   1.50   .25
856 A280 3.50k multi   2.00   .80

Liberation from the German Occupation Forces, 40th Anniv. — A281

1985, May 8   Engr.   Perf. 13x13½
857 A281 3.50k dk bl & red   1.75   .60

Norwegian Artillery — A282

Anniv.: 3k, Norwegian Artillery, 300th. 4k, Artillery Officers Training School, 200th.

1985, May 22   Litho.   Perf. 13½x13
858 A282 3k multi   1.50   .80
859 A282 4k multi   2.00   .50

Kongsten Fort, 300th Anniv. — A283

1985, May 22
860 A283 2.50k multi   1.50   .25

Europa — A284

Designs: 2.50k, Torgeir Augundsson (1801-1872), fiddler. 3.50k, Ole Bull (1810-1880), composer, violinist.

1985, June 19   Engr.
861 A284 2.50k brown lake   1.75   .25
862 A284 3.50k dark blue   2.00   .60

Intl. Youth Year — A285

Stone and bronze sculptures: 2k, Boy and Girl, detail, Vigeland Museum, Oslo. 3.50k, Fountain, detail, Vigeland Park, Oslo.

1985, June 19   Litho.
863 A285 2k multi   1.00   .40
864 A285 3.50k multi   1.60   .90

Electrification of Norway, Cent. — A286

2.50k, Glomfjord Dam penstock. 4k, Linemen.

1985, Sept. 6   Engr.   Perf. 13½x13
865 A286 2.50k dp car & scar 1.00   .25
866 A286 4k ultra & bl grn   1.75   .40

Public Libraries, 200th Anniv. — A287

Designs; 2.50k, Carl Deichman (1705-1780), Public Libraries System founder. 10k, Modern library interior, horiz.

1985, Oct. 4
867 A287 2.50k hn brn & yel brn 1.25   .25
868 A287 10k dark green   5.00   .60

Ship Navigation — A288

2.50k, Dredger Berghavn, 1980. 5k, Sextant and chart, 1791.

Lithographed & Engraved
1985, Nov. 14   Perf. 13x13½
869 A288 2.50k multicolored   1.00   .25
870 A288 5k multicolored   2.50   .50

Port Authorities, 250th anniv., Hydrographic Services, bicent.

Christmas Wreath A289

Bullfinches A290

Booklet Stamps
Perf. 13½ on 3 Sides
1985, Nov. 14   Litho.
871 A289 2k multi   2.00   .25
  a. Booklet pane of 10   20.00
      Complete booklet, #871a   22.50
872 A290 2.50k multi   2.00   .25
  a. Booklet pane of 10   20.00
      Complete booklet, #872a   22.50

World Biathlon Championships, Feb. 18-23 — A290a

3.50k, Shooting upright.

1986, Feb. 18   Perf. 13x13½
873 A290a 2.50k shown   1.00   .25
874 A291 3.50k multicolored   1.50 1.00

Ornaments A291

Fauna A292

Litho. & Engr.
1986-90   Perf. 13½x13
875 A291 2.10k Sun   1.00   .25
876 A291 2.30k Fish   1.00   .25
877 A292 2.60k Fox   1.10   .25
878 A291 2.70k Flowers, wheat 1.25   .25
879 A292 2.90k Capercaillie   1.50   .25
880 A292 3k Ermine   1.40   .25
881 A292 3.20k Mute swan   1.40   .25
882 A292 3.80k Reindeer   2.00   .25
883 A291 4k Stars   1.50   .30
883A A292 4k Squirrel   1.75   .25
883B A292 4.50k Beaver   1.75   .25
    Nos. 875-883B (11)   15.65 2.80

Issued: 2.10k, #883, 2/18/86; 2.30k, 2.70k, 2/12/87; 2.90k, 3.80k, 2/18/88; 2.60k, 3k, #883A, 2/20/89; 3.20k, 4.50k, 2/23/90.
See Nos. 958-959.

Mushrooms — A293

No. 884, Cantharellus tubaeformis. No. 885, Rozites caperata. No. 886, Lepista nuda. No. 887, Lactarius deterrimus. No. 888, Cantharellus cibarius. No. 889, Suillus luteus.

Booklet Stamps
Perf. 13½x13 on 3 Sides
1987-89   Litho.
884 A293 2.70k multi   1.25   .25
885 A293 2.70k multi   1.25   .25
  a. Bklt. pane, 5 #884, 5 #885 12.50
      Complete booklet, #885a   15.00
886 A293 2.90k multi   1.25   .25
887 A293 2.90k multi   1.25   .25
  a. Bklt. pane, 5 #886, 5 #887 12.50
      Complete booklet, #887a   15.00
888 A293 3k multi   1.25   .25
889 A293 3k multi   1.25   .25
  a. Bklt. pane, 5 #888, 5 #889 12.50
      Complete booklet, #889a   16.00
    Nos. 884-889 (6)   7.50 1.50

Issued: 2.70k, 5/8; 2.90k, 4/26/88; 3k, 2/20/89.

Natl. Federation of Craftsmen, Cent. — A294

1986, Apr. 11   Engr.
890 A294 2.50k Stone cutter   1.00   .25
891 A294 7k Carpenter   3.50   .80

Europa — A295

1986, Apr. 11   Litho.   Perf. 13
892 A295 2.50k Bird, industry 1.25   .40
893 A295 3.50k Acid rain   1.75 1.25

Nordic Cooperation Issue — A296

Sister towns.

1986, May 27   Perf. 13½x13
894 A296 2.50k Moss   1.25   .25
895 A296 4k Alesund   1.75   .50

Famous Men — A297

Designs: 2.10k, Hans Poulson Egede (1686-1758), missionary, and map of Norway and Greenland. 2.50k, Herman Wildenvey (1886-1959), poet, and poem carved in Seaman's Commemoration Hall, Stavern. 3k, Tore Orjasaeter (1886-1968), poet, and antique cupboard, Skjak. 4k, Engebret Soot, engineer, and canal lock, Orje.

Engr., Litho. & Engr. (#897)
1986, Oct. 17   *Perf. 13x13½*
896 A297 2.10k multi .90 .90
897 A297 2.50k multi 1.00 .25
898 A297 3k multi 1.25 .50
899 A297 4k multi 1.50 .50
   Nos. 896-899 (4) 4.65 2.15

Christmas — A298

Stained glass windows by Gabriel Kielland, Nidaros Cathedral, Trondheim: 2.10k, Olav Kyrre Founding The Diocese in Nidaros. 2.50k, The King and the Peasant at Sul.

Perf. 13½ on 3 Sides
1986, Nov. 26   Litho.
Booklet Stamps
900 A298 1.50k multi 1.50 .40
 a. Booklet pane of 10 17.50
  Complete booklet, #900a 20.00
901 A298 2.50k multi 1.50 .25
 a. Booklet pane of 10 17.50
  Complete booklet, #901a 20.00

Intl. Peace Year — A299

Lithographed & Engraved
1986, Nov. 26   *Perf. 13½x13*
902 A299 15k brt grn, org & lt bl 8.00 .75

A300

1987, Feb. 12   Litho.   *Perf. 13½*
903 A300 3.50k red, yel & dk bl 1.75 .80
904 A300 4.50k bl, yel & grn 2.00 .50

Europa — A301

Modern architecture: 2.70k, Wood. 4.50k, Glass and stone.

1987, Apr. 3   Litho.   *Perf. 13½x13*
905 A301 2.70k multi 1.25 .25
906 A301 4.50k multi 2.50 .75

A302

1987, Apr. 3   Engr.   *Perf. 13x13½*
907 A302 12k dark green 6.00 .55

Odelsting (Norwegian Assembly) voting on Law Administering Local Councils, 150th anniv.

Miniature Sheet

Red Crescent-Red Cross Rehabilitation Center, Mogadishu, Somalia — A303

1987, May 8   Litho.   *Perf. 13½x13*
908 A303 4.50k multi 2.50 2.00
  See Somalia Nos. 576-577.

Sandvig Collection, Maihaugen Open-air Museum — A305

2.70k, Bjornstad Farm, Vaga. 3.50k, Horse and Rider, by Christen E. Listad.

1987, June 10   Engr.   *Perf. 13x13½*
911 A305 2.70k multi .90 .25
912 A305 3.50k multi 1.60 .80

Churchyard, Inspiration for Valen's Churchyard by the Sea A306   **Fartein Valen (1887-1952), Composer A306a**

Perf. 13x13½, 13½x13
1987, Aug. 25   Engr.
913 A306 2.30k emer grn & dark blue .90 .90
914 A306a 4.50k dark brown 1.75 .40

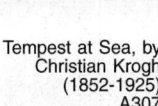

Tempest at Sea, by Christian Krogh (1852-1925) A307

Painting: 5k, The Farm, by Gerhard Munthe (1849-1929).

1987, Oct. 9   Litho.   *Perf. 13½x13*
915 A307 2.70k multi 1.25 .25
916 A307 5k multi 2.50 .50

Norwegian Horse Breeds — A308

Litho. & Engr.
1987, Nov. 12   *Perf. 13x13½*
917 A308 2.30k Dales 1.25 1.00
918 A308 2.70k Fjord 1.25 .25
919 A308 4.50k Nordland 2.10 .60
   Nos. 917-919 (3) 4.60 1.85

Christmas — A309

2.30k, Children making tree ornaments. 2.70k, Baking gingersnaps.

Booklet Stamps
Perf. 13½x13 on 3 sides
1987, Nov. 12   Litho.
920 A309 2.30k multi 1.40 .40
 a. Booklet pane of 10 14.00
  Complete booklet, #920a 16.00

921 A309 2.70k multi 1.25 .25
 a. Booklet pane of 10 12.50
  Complete booklet, #921a 16.00

Salvation Army in Norway, Cent. — A310

4.80k, Othilie Tonning, early Salvation Army worker in Norway.

1988, Feb. 18   *Perf. 13½*
922 A310 2.90k multi 1.25 .25
923 A310 4.80k multi 2.25 .90

European North-South Solidarity Campaign — A311

1988, Apr. 26   *Perf. 13x13½*
924 A311 25k multi 10.00 1.00

Defense Forces Activities — A312

Defense Forces, 300th anniv.: 2.50k, Fortress construction. 2.90k, Army Signal Corps on duty. 4.60k, Pontoon bridge under construction, Corps of Engineers.

1988, Apr. 26   Engr.
925 A312 2.50k dark green 1.00 .40
926 A312 2.90k carmine lake 1.25 .25
927 A312 4.60k dark blue 2.00 .60
   Nos. 925-927 (3) 4.25 1.25

Europa — A313

Transport: 2.90k, *Prinds Gustav* passing Lofoten Isls., 1st passenger steamer in northern Norway, sesquicent. 3.80k, Heroybrua Bridge, between Leinoy and Blankholm, 1976.

Litho. & Engr.
1988, July 1   *Perf. 13x13½*
928 A313 2.90k multi 2.00 .25
929 A313 3.80k multi 2.25 1.50

85th Birthday of King Olav V — A314

Designs: No. 930, Portrait, c. 1988. No. 931a, Arrival in 1905 after Norway declared independence from Sweden. No. 931b, Olav in snowstorm at Holmenkollen.

1988, July 1   Litho.   *Perf. 13½x13*
930 A314 2.90k multi 1.50 1.00

Souvenir Sheet
931 Sheet of 3 5.00 5.00
 a. A314 2.90k org red, black & ultra 1.50 1.50
 b. A314 2.90k multi 1.25 .25
 c. A314 2.90k like No. 930, no date 1.50 1.50

Reign of King Christian IV (1577-1648), 400th Anniv. — A315

Designs: 10k, Reverse of a rixdaler struck in Christiania (Oslo), 1628, and excerpt of a mining decree issued by Christian IV.

Litho. & Engr.
1988, Oct. 7   *Perf. 13½x13*
932 A315 2.50k black & buff 1.50 .25
933 A315 10k multi 5.00 .50

Miniature Sheet

Handball — A316

Ball sports: b, Soccer. c, Basketball. d, Volleyball.

1988, Oct. 7   Litho.   *Perf. 13½x13*
934 Sheet of 4 10.00 10.00
 a.-d. A316 2.90k any single 2.00 2.00
  Stamp Day. No. 934 sold for 15k.

Christmas — A317

Ludvig, a cartoon character created by Kjell Aukrust: No. 935, With ski pole. No. 936, Reading letter.

Perf. 13½x13 on 3 sides
1988, Nov. 15   Litho.
Booklet Stamps
935 A317 2.90k multi 1.50 .25
936 A317 2.90k multi 1.50 .25
 a. Bklt. pane, 5 #935, 5 #936 15.00
  Complete booklet, #936a 17.00

World Cross-Country Running Championships, Stavanger, Mar. 19 — A318

1989, Feb. 20   Litho.   *Perf. 13x13½*
937 A318 5k multi 2.00 .30

Port City Bicentennials — A319

Litho. & Engr.
1989, Apr. 20   *Perf. 13½x13*
938 A319 3k Vardo 1.25 .25
939 A319 4k Hammerfest 2.00 .80

Nordic Cooperation Issue — A320

Folk costumes.

1989, Apr. 20   Litho.   *Perf. 13x13½*
940 A320 3k Setesdal (woman) 1.25 .25
941 A320 4k Kautokeino (man) 2.00 .80

Europa 1989 — A321

Children's games: 3.70k, Building snowman. 5k, Cat's cradle.

1989, June 7   Litho.   *Perf. 13x13½*
942 A321 3.70k multi 1.75 .75
943 A321 5k multi 2.50 .90

Public Primary Schools, 250th Anniv. — A322

3k, Child learning to write.

424 — NORWAY

Litho. & Engr.

1989, June 7   Perf. 13½x13
944 A322 2.60k shown   1.25 .60

Engr.
945 A322 3k multi   1.25 .25

Souvenir Sheet

Winter Olympic Gold Medalists from Norway — A323

Portraits: a, Bjoerg Eva Jensen, women's 3000-meter speed skating, 1980. b, Eirik Kvalfoss, 10k biathlon, 1984. c, Tom Sandberg, combined cross-country and ski jumping, 1984. d, Women's Nordic ski team, 20k relay, 1984.

1989, Oct. 6   Litho.   Perf. 13½x13
946   Sheet of 4   7.50 7.50
a.-d.   4k any single   1.75 1.75

Sold for 20k to benefit Olympic sports promotion.
See Nos. 984, 997, 1021, 1035.

Souvenir Sheet

Impression of the Countryside, 1982, by Jakob Weidemann — A324

1989, Oct. 6
947 A324 Sheet of 4   8.50 8.50
a.-d.   3k any single   2.00 2.00

Stamp Day. Sold for 15k to benefit philatelic promotion.

Writers — A325

3k, Arnulf Overland (1889-1968), poet. 25k, Hanna Winsnes (1789-1872), author.

Litho. & Engr.

1989, Nov. 24   Perf. 13x13½
948 A325 3k dk red & brt bl   1.25 .25
949 A325 25k multicolored   11.00 1.00

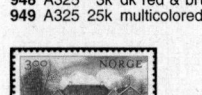

Manors — A326

1989, Nov. 24   Engr.   Perf. 13
950 A326 3k Manor at Larvik   1.25 .25
951 A326 3k Rosendal Barony   1.25 .25

Christmas Decorations — A327

Perf. 13 on 3 sides
1989, Nov. 24   Litho.
Booklet Stamps
952 A327 3k Star   1.25 .25
953 A327 3k Round ornament   1.25 .25
a.   Bklt. pane of 10, 5 #952, 5 #953   12.50
  Complete booklet, #953a   15.00

Winter City Events, Tromso — A328

1990, Feb. 23   Litho.   Perf. 13½
954 A328 5k multicolored   2.25 .35

Fauna Type of 1988 and

Scenes of Norway — A329

Designs: 4k, Cable cars. 4.50k, Goat Mountain. 5.50k, Top of the World outpost.

1991-94   Litho.   Perf. 13
955 A329 4k multicolored   2.00 .60
956 A329 4.50k multicolored   2.50 .60
957 A329 5.50k multicolored   2.50 .50

Litho. & Engr.
958 A292 5.50k Lynx   2.50 .25
959 A292 6.40k Owl   2.50 .40
  Nos. 955-959 (5)   12.00 2.35

Issued: #958-959, 2/21/91; #955-957, 4/19/94.

Posthorn Type of 1893
1991-92   Engr.   Perf. 12½x13
960 A10 1k orange & black   .50 .25
961 A10 2k emerald & lake   .60 .25
962 A10 3k blue & green   1.00 .25
963 A10 4k org & henna brn   1.20 .25
964 A10 5k green & dark blue   1.40 .25
965 A10 6k grn & red vio   1.75 .60
966 A10 7k red brn & bl   2.00 .60
967 A10 8k red vio & bl grn   2.50 .35
968 A10 9k ultra & red brn   3.00 .50
  Nos. 960-968 (9)   13.95 3.30

Issued: 1k-5k, 11/23/92; others, 11/22/91.

Orchids — A332

No. 970, Dactylorhiza fuchsii. No. 971, Epipactis atrorubens. No. 972, Cypripedium calceolus. No. 973, Ophrys insectifera.

Perf. 13½x13 on 3 Sides
1990-92   Litho.   Booklet Stamps
970 A332 3.20k multi   1.25 .25
971 A332 3.20k multi   1.25 .25
a.   Bklt. pane, 5 #970, 5 #971   12.50
  Complete booklet, #971a   14.00
972 A332 3.30k multi   1.25 .25
973 A332 3.30k multi   1.25 .25
a.   Bklt. pane, 5 each #972-973   13.00
  Complete booklet, #973a   17.50
  Nos. 970-973 (4)   5.00 1.00

Issued: #970-971, 2/23; #972-973, 2/21/92.

A334

German Invasion of Norway, 50th Anniv.: 3.20k, King Haakon VII's monogram, merchant navy, air force, Norwegian Home Guard and cannon Moses. 4k, Recapture of Narvik, May 28, 1940, by the Polish, British, Norwegian and French forces.

1990, Apr. 9   Litho.   Perf. 13x13½
975 A334 3.20k shown   2.10 .25
976 A334 4k multicolored   2.50 .50

Souvenir Sheet

A335

Stamps on stamps: b, Norway #1.

1990, Apr. 9   Perf. 13½x13
977   Sheet of 2   9.00 9.00
a.-b. A335 5k any single   3.00 3.00

Penny Black, 150th anniv. Sold for 15k.

A336

1990, June 14   Litho. & Engr.
978 A336 3.20k Portrait   1.75 .25
979 A336 5k Coat of arms   2.10 .50

Tordenskiold (Peter Wessel, 1690-1720), naval hero.

A337

Europa: Post offices.

1990, June 14   Litho.   Perf. 13x13½
980 A337 3.20k Trondheim   1.75 .25
981 A337 4k Longyearbyen   2.25 .80

A338

2.70k, Svendsen. 15k, Monument by Fredriksen.

1990, Oct. 5   Litho. & Engr.   Perf. 13
982 A338 2.70k multicolored   1.40 .60
983 A338 15k multicolored   7.00 .60

Johan Severin Svendsen (1840-1911), composer.

Winter Olympic Type of 1989
Souvenir Sheet

Gold medal winners: a, Thorleif Haug, skier, 1924. b, Sonja Henie, figure skater, 1928, 1932, 1936. c, Ivar Ballangrud, speed skater, 1928, 1936. d, Hjalmar Andersen, speed skater, 1952.

1990, Oct. 5   Litho.   Perf. 13½x13
984   Sheet of 4   8.50 8.50
a.-d. A323 4k any single   1.90 1.90

Sold for 20k to benefit Olympic sports promotion.

A339

Litho & Engr.
1990, Nov. 23   Perf. 13
985 A339 30k bl, brn & car rose   15.00 1.00

Lars Olof Jonathan Soderblom (1866-1931), 1930 Nobel Peace Prize winner.

A340

Christmas (Children's drawings): No. 987, Church, stars, and Christmas tree.

Perf. 13 on 3 sides
1990, Nov. 23   Litho.
986 A340 3.20k multicolored   1.25 .25
987 A340 3.20k multicolored   1.25 .25
a.   Bklt. pane, 5 each #986-987   12.50
  Complete booklet, #987a   15.00

Ship Building Industry — A341

1991, Feb. 21   Litho.   Perf. 13½x13
988 A341 5k multicolored   2.50 .85

Europa — A342

3.20k, ERS-1. 4k, Andoya rocket range.

1991, Apr. 16   Litho.   Perf. 13
989 A342 3.20k multi   1.75 .40
990 A342 4k multi   2.50 .75

City of Christiansand, 350th Anniv. — A343

Litho. & Engr.

1991, Apr. 16   Perf. 13
991 A343 3.20k Early view   1.50 .25
992 A343 5.50k Modern view   2.50 .40

Lifeboat Service, Cent. — A344

Designs: 3.20k, Rescue boat, Skomvaer III, horiz. 27k, Sailboat Colin Archer.

Litho & Engr.

1991, June 7   Perf. 13
993 A344 3.20k multicolored   1.75 .25
994 A344 27k multicolored   12.00 1.50

Tourism — A345

Designs: 3.20k, Fountain, Vigeland Park. 4k, Globe, North Cape.

1991, June 7   Litho.   Perf. 13½x13
995 A345 3.20k multicolored   1.75 .25
996 A345 4k multicolored   3.00 1.50

Winter Olympic Type of 1989
Souvenir Sheet

Gold medal winners: a, Birger Ruud, ski jumping. b, Johan Grottumsbraten, cross country skiing. c, Knut Johannesen, speed skating. d, Magnar Solberg, biathlon.

1991, Oct. 11   Litho.   Perf. 13½x13
997   Sheet of 4   8.50 8.50
a.-d. A323 4k any single   1.75 1.75

Sold for 20k to benefit Olympic sports promotion.

A346

Natl. Stamp Day: a, Hands engraving. b, Magnifying glass above hands. c, View of hands through magnifying glass. d, Printed label being removed from plate.

1991, Oct. 11   Perf. 13x13½
Souvenir Sheet
998	Sheet of 4	9.00	9.00
a.	A346 2.70k multicolored	1.75	1.75
b.	A346 3.20k multicolored	1.75	1.75
c.	A346 4k multicolored	1.75	1.75
d.	A346 5k multicolored	1.75	1.75

Sold for 20k.

A347

Christmas: No. 1000, People with lantern.

Perf. 13½x13 on 3 Sides
1991, Nov. 22   Litho.
Booklet Stamps
999	A347 3.20k multicolored	1.25	.25
1000	A347 3.20k multicolored	1.25	.25
a.	Bklt. pane, 5 each #999-1000	12.50	
	Complete booklet, #1000a	14.00	

Queen Sonja A348 — King Harald A349

A349a

Perf. 13x13½, 12½x13½ (6.50k)
1992-2002   Litho. & Engr.
1004	A348	2.80k multi	1.40	.25
1005	A348	3k multi	1.25	.25
1007	A349	3.30k multi	1.75	.25
1008	A349	3.50k multi	1.40	.25
1009	A349	4.50k carmine	1.75	.40
1011	A349	5.50k multi	2.00	.30
1012	A349	5.60k multi	2.50	.25
1014	A349	6.50k green	1.75	.70
1015	A349	6.60k multi	3.00	.40
1016	A349	7.50k violet	2.75	2.00
1016A	A349	8.50k brown	3.00	2.00

Perf. 13½x13
1017	A349a	10k dark grn	3.00	.25
a.		Perf. 13½x13¾	.75	
1019	A349a	20k deep vio	6.00	.50
b.		Perf. 13½x13¾	8.00	1.20
1019A	A349a	30k dark blue	9.00	.50
1020	A349a	50k olive black	15.00	1.75
a.		Perf. 13½x13¾	15.00	2.50
	Nos. 1004-1020 (15)	55.55	10.05

Issued: 2.80k, 3.30k, 5.60k, 6.60k, 2/21/92; 50k, 6/12/92; 3k, 3.50k, 5.50k, 2/23/93; 10k, 20k, 6/17/93; 6.50k, 2/12/94; 30k, 11/18/94; 4.50k, 7.50k, 8.50k, 11/24/95; Nos. 1019b, 1020a, Dec. 2001. No. 1017a, 2002.

Winter Olympic Type of 1989
Souvenir Sheet
Gold Medal winners: a, Hallgeir Brenden, cross-country skiing. b, Arnfinn Bergmann, ski jumping. c, Stein Eriksen, giant slalom. d, Simon Slattvik, Nordic combined.

1992, Feb. 21   Litho.   Perf. 13½x13
1021	Sheet of 4	8.50	8.50
a.-d.	A323 4k any single	1.75	1.75

Sold for 20k to benefit Olympic sports promotion.

Expo '92, Seville — A350

Designs: 3.30k, Norwegian pavilion, ship. 5.20k, Mountains, boat and fish.

1992, Apr. 20   Perf. 13x13½
1022	A350 3.30k multicolored	1.25	.25
1023	A350 5.20k multicolored	2.00	.50

Discovery of America, 500th Anniv. — A351

Europa: 3.30k, Sailing ship Restauration at sea, 1825. 4,20k, Stavangerfjord in New York Harbor, 1918.

Litho. & Engr.
1992, Apr. 21   Perf. 13x13½
1024	A351 3.30k multicolored	1.90	.25
1025	A351 4.20k multicolored	2.50	.80

Kristiansund, 250th Anniv. — A352

Litho. & Engr.
1992, June 12   Perf. 13
1026	A352 3.30k brn, bl & blk	1.50	.25
1027	A352 3.30k View of Molde	1.50	.25

Molde, 250th anniv. (#1027).

Souvenir Sheet

Glass A353

Stamp Day: a, Decorated vase. b, Carafe with gold design. c, Cut glass salad bowl. d, Decorated cup.

1992, Oct. 9   Litho.   Perf. 13x13½
1028	A353 Sheet of 4	10.00	10.00
a.	2.80k multicolored	2.00	2.00
b.	3.30k multicolored	2.00	2.00
c.	4.20k multicolored	2.00	2.00
d.	5.20k multicolored	2.00	2.00

No. 1028 sold for 20k.

A354

Designs: 3.30k, Flags, buildings in Lillehammer. 4.20k, Flag.

1992, Oct. 9   Litho.   Perf. 13x13½
1029	A354 3.30k multicolored	1.40	.25
1030	A354 4.20k multicolored	1.90	.75

1994 Winter Olympics, Lillehammer. See Nos. 1047-1048, 1053-1058.

A355

Christmas: No. 1031, Elves in front of mailbox. No. 1032, One elf holding other on shoulders to mail letters.

Perf. 13 on 3 Sides
1992, Nov. 23   Litho.
Booklet Stamps
1031	A355 3.30k multicolored	.90	.25
1032	A355 3.30k multicolored	.90	.25
b.	Booklet pane, 5 each #1031-1032	12.00	
	Complete booklet, #1032b	15.00	

Butterflies — A356

Designs: No. 1033, Anthocharis cardamines. No. 1034, Aglais urticae.

Perf. 13½x13 on 3 Sides
1993, Feb. 23   Litho.
Booklet Stamps
1033	A356 3.50k multicolored	1.00	.25
1034	A356 3.50k multicolored	1.00	.25
b.	Booklet pane, 5 each #1033-1034	12.50	
	Complete booklet, #1034b	15.00	

See Nos. 1051-1052.

Winter Olympic Type of 1989
Souvenir Sheet
1992 Gold Medal winners: a, Finn Christian Jagge, slalom. b, Bjorn Daehlie, cross-country skiing. c, Geir Karlstad, speed skating. d, Vegard Ulvang, cross-country skiing.

1993, Feb. 23   Perf. 13½x13
1035	Sheet of 4	8.50	8.50
a.-d.	A323 4.50k any single	1.75	1.75

No. 1035 sold for 22k to benefit Olympic sports promotion.

Norden — A357

1993, Apr. 23   Litho.   Perf. 13½x13
1036	A357 4k Canoe on lake	2.00	.40
1037	A357 4.50k River rafting	2.25	.50

Edvard Grieg — A358

Litho. & Engr.
1993, Apr. 23   Perf. 13½x13½
1038	A358 3.50k Portrait	1.50	.25
1039	A358 5.50k Landscape	2.25	.50

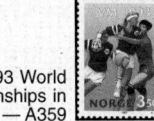

1993 World Championships in Norway — A359

1993, June 17   Litho.   Perf. 13½x13
1040	A359 3.50k Team handball	1.50	.25
1041	A359 5.50k Cycling	2.50	.50

Hurtigruten Shipping Line, Cent. — A360

3.50k, Richard With, ship. 4.50k, Ship, officers.

Litho. & Engr.
1993, June 17   Perf. 12½x13
1042	A360 3.50k multicolored	1.75	.25
1043	A360 4.50k multicolored	2.25	.75

Worker's Organization, Cent. — A361

1993, Sept. 24   Engr.   Perf. 13x13½
1044	A361 3.50k Johan Castberg	1.75	.25
1045	A361 12k Betzy Kjelsberg	5.00	.50

Souvenir Sheet

Carvings A362

Stamp Day: a, Spiral leaf scroll. b, Interlocking scroll. c, "1754" surrounded by scroll. d, Face with scroll above.

1993, Sept. 24   Litho.   Perf. 13½x13
1046	A362 Sheet of 4, #a.-d.	10.00	10.00
a.	3k multicolored	1.75	1.75
b.	3.50k multicolored	1.75	1.75
c.	4.50k multicolored	1.75	1.75
d.	5.50k multicolored	1.75	1.75

No. 1046 sold for 21k.
See No. 1069.

1994 Winter Olympic Type of 1992
#1047, Flags, cross country skiier. #1048, Flags, buildings in Lillehammer.

1993, Nov. 27   Litho.   Perf. 13x13½
1047	A354 3.50k multicolored	1.10	.25
1048	A354 3.50k multicolored	1.10	.25
a.	Pair, #1047-1048	2.50	2.50

No. 1048a has a continuous design.

Christmas — A363

Designs: No. 1049, Store Mangen Chapel. No. 1050, Church of Stamnes, Sandnes.

Perf. 13½x13 on 3 Sides
1993, Nov. 27   Booklet Stamps
1049	A363 3.50k shown	1.00	.25
1050	A363 3.50k multicolored	1.00	.25
b.	Booklet pane, 5 each #1049-1050	10.00	
	Complete booklet, #1050b	12.50	

Butterfly Type of 1993
No. 1051, Colias hecla. No. 1052, Clossiana freija.

Perf. 13½x13 on 3 Sides
1994, Feb. 12   Litho.
Booklet Stamps
1051	A356 3.50k multi	1.10	.25
1052	A356 3.50k multi	1.10	.25
b.	Booklet pane, 5 each #1051-1052	12.50	
	Complete booklet, #1052b	15.00	

1994 Winter Olympic Type of 1992
Designs: No. 1053, Stylized Norwegian flag, Olympic rings UR. No. 1054, Stylized Norwegian flag, Olympic rings, UL. No. 1055, Olympic rings, buildings in Lillehammer. No. 1056, Olympic rings, ski jump. 4.50k, Flags of Norway, Belgium, Greece, Switzerland, Sweden, Germany, United Kingdom. 5.50k, Flags of Australia, New Zealand, Brazil, Canada, US, Japan, Mexico, South Korea.

1994, Feb. 12   Perf. 13x13½
1053	A354 3.50k multicolored	1.25	.25
1054	A354 3.50k multicolored	1.25	.25
1055	A354 3.50k multicolored	1.25	.25
1056	A354 3.50k multicolored	1.25	.25
a.	Block of 4, #1053-1056	6.00	6.00
1057	A354 4.50k multicolored	1.75	.50
1058	A354 5.50k multicolored	2.10	.40
	Nos. 1053-1058 (6)	8.85	1.90

1994 Paralympics — A365

1994, Mar. 10   Litho.   Perf. 13
1059	A365 4.50k Skier	1.75	.60
1060	A365 5.50k Skier, diff.	1.50	.50

Tromso Charter, Bicent. — A366

Litho. & Engr.
1994, Apr. 19   Perf. 13
1061	A366 3.50k Royal seal	1.50	.25
1062	A366 4.50k Cathedral	2.00	.60

Norwegian Folk Museum, Cent. — A367

Designs: 3k, Log buildings, Osterdal Valley. 3.50k, Sled, 1750.

Litho. & Engr.

1994, June 14   **Perf. 12½x13**
| 1063 | A367 | 3k multicolored | 1.25 | .40 |
| 1064 | A367 | 3.50k multicolored | 1.50 | .25 |

Research in Norway — A368

Abstract designs with various formulas, microchips, glass flasks.

1994, June 14   **Litho.**
| 1065 | A368 | 4k multicolored | 1.50 | .50 |
| 1066 | A368 | 4.50k multicolored | 2.00 | .50 |

Electric Tram Lines, Cent. — A369

3.50k, Early tram, map. 12k, Modern tram, map.

Litho. & Engr.

1994, Sept. 23   **Perf. 13x13½**
| 1067 | A369 | 3.50k multi | 1.50 | .25 |
| 1068 | A369 | 12k multi | 5.00 | .50 |

Stamp Day Type of 1993

Ornamental broaches: a, Gold, embossed designs. b, Silver, embossed designs. c, Silver, circular designs. d, Gold, jeweled center.

1994, Sept. 23   **Litho.**   **Perf. 13½x13**
1069		Sheet of 4, #a.-d.	9.00	9.00
a.	A362	3k multicolored	1.75	1.75
b.	A362	3.50k multicolored	1.75	1.75
c.	A362	4.50k multicolored	1.75	1.75
d.	A362	5.50k multicolored	1.75	1.75

No. 1069 sold for 21k.

Christmas — A370

Perf. 13½x13 on 3 Sides

1994, Nov. 18   **Litho.**

Booklet Stamps
1070	A370	3.50k Sled	1.25	.25
1071	A370	3.50k Kick sled	1.25	.25
a.		Booklet pane, 5 each	12.50	
		Complete booklet, #1071a	13.50	

Berries — A371

No. 1086, Vaccinium vitis. No. 1087, Vaccinium myrtillus. No. 1088, Fragaria vesca. No. 1089, Rubus chamaemorus.

Booklet Stamps

1995-96   **Litho.**   **Perf. 13½x13**
1086	A371	3.50k multi	1.10	.25
1087	A371	3.50k multi	1.10	.25
a.		Bklt. pane, 4 ea #1086-1087	9.00	
		Complete booklet, #1087a	11.00	
1088	A371	3.50k multi	1.10	.25
1089	A371	3.50k multi	1.10	.25
a.		Bklt. pane, 4 ea #1088-1089	9.00	
		Complete booklet, #1089a	11.00	
		Nos. 1086-1089 (4)	4.40	1.00

Issued: #1086-1087, 2/23/95; #1088-1089, 2/22/96.

A372

Apothecary Shops, 400th Anniv.: 3.50k, Swan Pharmacy, Bergen. 25k, Apothecary's tools.

Litho. & Engr.

1995, Feb. 23   **Perf. 13½x13**
| 1090 | A372 | 3.50k multicolored | 1.75 | .25 |
| 1091 | A372 | 25k multicolored | 11.00 | 1.00 |

Tourism — A373

4k, Skudeneshavn Harbor. 4.50k, Torghatten mountain, Helgeland coastline.

1995, May 8   **Litho.**   **Perf. 13½x13**

Booklet Stamps
1092	A373	4k multicolored	1.25	.40
a.		Booklet pane of 8	10.00	
		Complete booklet, #1092a	12.00	
1093	A373	4.50k multicolored	1.25	.40
a.		Booklet pane of 8	12.00	
		Complete booklet, #1093a	14.00	

Christianity in Norway — A374

3.50k, Old Moster Church, c. 1100. 15k, Slettebakken Church, Bergen, 1970.

Litho. & Engr.

1995, May 8   **Perf. 13x13½**
| 1094 | A374 | 3.50k multicolored | 1.75 | .25 |
| 1095 | A374 | 15k multicolored | 6.00 | .60 |

End of World War II, 50th Anniv. — A375

Designs: 3.50k, German commander saluting Terje Rollem in 1945, German forces marching down Karl Johans Gate from Royal Palace, 1940. 4.50k, King Haakon VII, Crown Prince leaving Norway in 1940, King saluting upon return in 1945. 5.50k, Children waving Norwegian flags, 1945.

1995, May 8   **Litho.**   **Perf. 13½x13**
1096	A375	3.50k multicolored	1.75	.25
1097	A375	4.50k multicolored	2.25	.50
1098	A375	5.50k multicolored	2.50	.40
		Nos. 1096-1098 (3)	6.50	1.15

Kirsten Flagstad (1895-1962), Opera Singer — A376

Design: 5.50k, In Lohengrin.

1995, June 26   **Litho.**   **Perf. 13**
| 1099 | A376 | 3.50k multicolored | 1.75 | .25 |
| 1100 | A376 | 5.50k multicolored | 2.50 | .40 |

Conciliation Boards, Bicent. — A377

Designs: 7k, Three-man board between two people facing away from each other. 12k, Seated board member, two people talking to each other.

1995, June 26   **Perf. 13½**
| 1101 | A377 | 7k multicolored | 2.75 | .40 |
| 1102 | A377 | 12k multicolored | 4.75 | .50 |

UN, 50th Anniv. — A378

UN emblem and: 3.50k, Trygve Lie, Secretary General 1946-53. 5.50k, Woman drinking from clean water supply.

Litho. & Engr.

1995, Sept. 22   **Perf. 13**
| 1103 | A378 | 3.50k multicolored | 1.75 | .25 |
| 1104 | A378 | 5.50k multicolored | 2.50 | .40 |

Norway Post, 350th Anniv. — A379

No. 1105, Signature, portrait of Hannibal Sehested, letter post, 1647. No. 1106, Wax seal, registered letters, 1745. No. 1107, Christiania, etc. postmarks. No. 1108, Funds transfer, coins, canceled envelopes, 1883. No. 1109, "Norske Intelligenz-Seddeler," first newspaper, newspapers, magazines, 1660. No. 1110, Postmarks, label, parcel post, 1827. No. 1111, No. 1, Type A5, stamps, 1855. No. 1112, Savings book stamps, bank services, 1950.

Booklet Stamps

1995, Sept. 22   **Litho.**
1105	A379	3.50k multicolored	1.25	.30
1106	A379	3.50k multicolored	1.25	.30
1107	A379	3.50k multicolored	1.25	.30
1108	A379	3.50k multicolored	1.25	.30
1109	A379	3.50k multicolored	1.25	.30
1110	A379	3.50k multicolored	1.25	.30
1111	A379	3.50k multicolored	1.25	.30
a.		Missing gray stamp at LR	12.50	5.00
1112	A379	3.50k multicolored	1.25	.30
a.		Booklet pane, #1105-1112	12.50	18.00
		Complete booklet, #1112a	15.00	
b.		Booklet pane, #1105-1110, #1111a, 1112	25.00	25.00
		Complete booklet, #1112b	27.50	

Christmas — A380

Booklet Stamps

Perf. 13 on 3 Sides

1995, Nov. 24   **Litho.**
1113	A380	3.50k Knitted cap	1.10	.25
1114	A380	3.50k Knitted mitten	1.10	.25
a.		Bklt. pane, 4 ea #1113-1114	9.00	
		Complete booklet, #1114a	11.00	

Svalbard Islands — A381

1996, Feb. 22   **Litho.**   **Perf. 13**
| 1115 | A381 | 10k Advent Bay | 4.25 | .50 |
| 1116 | A381 | 20k Polar bear | 9.00 | .75 |

Olympic Games, Cent. — A382

Children's drawings: 3.50k, Cross country skier. 5.50k, Runner.

1996, Apr. 18   **Litho.**   **Perf. 13½**
| 1117 | A382 | 3.50k multicolored | 1.75 | .25 |
| 1118 | A382 | 5.50k multicolored | 2.50 | .40 |

Tourism — A383

4k, Besseggen. 4.50k, Urnes Stave Church. 5.50k, Alta Rock Carvings.

1996, Apr. 18   **Perf. 13 on 3 Sides**
1119	A383	4k multi	1.00	.60
a.		Booklet pane of 8	8.00	
		Complete booklet, #1119a	10.00	
1120	A383	4.50k multi	1.25	.50
a.		Booklet pane of 8	10.00	
		Complete booklet, #1120a	12.00	
1121	A383	5.50k multi	1.50	.60
a.		Booklet pane of 8	12.00	
		Complete booklet, #1121a	14.00	
		Nos. 1119-1121 (3)	3.75	1.70

See Nos. 1155-1157.

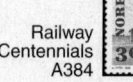

Railway Centennials A384

Litho. & Engr.

1996, June 19   **Perf. 13**
| 1122 | A384 | 3k Urskog-Holand | 1.25 | .40 |
| 1123 | A384 | 4.50k Setesdal | 1.75 | .75 |

The Troll Offshore Gasfield — A385

3.50k, Size of Troll platform compared to Eiffel Tower. 25k, Troll platform, map of gas pipelines.

1996, June 19   **Litho.**
| 1124 | A385 | 3.50k multicolored | 1.50 | .25 |
| 1125 | A385 | 25k multicolored | 9.00 | 1.00 |

Norway Post, 350th Anniv. — A386

#1126, Postal courier on skis. #1127, Fjord boat, SS "Framnaes," 1920's. #1128, Mail truck, Oslo, 1920's. #1129, Early airmail service. #1130, Unloading mail, East Railroad Station, Oslo, 1950's. #1131, Using bicycle for rural mail delivery, 1970's. #1132, Customer, mail clerk, Elverum post office. #1133, Computer, globe, E-mail service.

Booklet Stamps

1996, Sept. 20   **Litho.**   **Perf. 13**
1126	A386	3.50k multicolored	1.00	.60
1127	A386	3.50k multicolored	1.00	.60
1128	A386	3.50k multicolored	1.00	.60
1129	A386	3.50k multicolored	1.00	.60
1130	A386	3.50k multicolored	1.00	.60
1131	A386	3.50k multicolored	1.00	.60
1132	A386	3.50k multicolored	1.00	.60
1133	A386	3.50k multicolored	1.00	.60
a.		Booklet pane, #1126-1133	10.00	10.00
		Complete booklet, #1133a	11.00	

Motion Pictures, Cent. — A387

Film strips showing: 3.50k, Leif Juster, Sean Connery, Liv Ullmann, The Olsen Gang Films, Il Temp Gigante. 5.50k, Wenche Foss, Jack Fjeldstad, Marilyn Monroe, murder, blood, shooting. 7k, Charlie Chaplin, Ottar Gladvedt, Laurel & Hardy, Marlene Dietrich.

1996, Sept. 20
1134	A387	3.50k multicolored	1.40	.25
1135	A387	5.50k multicolored	1.75	.40
1136	A387	7k multicolored	2.75	.40
		Nos. 1134-1136 (3)	5.90	1.05

A388

Christmas (Embroidered motif from Norwegian folk costume): Denomination at UL (#1137), UR (#1138).

Perf. 13 on 3 Sides

1996, Nov. 21   **Litho.**
1137	A388	3.50k multicolored	1.10	.25
1138	A388	3.50k multicolored	1.10	.25
a.		Bklt. pane, 4 ea #1137-1138	9.00	
		Complete booklet, #1138a	10.00	

A389

Amalie Skram (1846-1905), Novelist: 3.50k, Portrait. 15k, Scene from performance of Skram's "People of Hellemyr."

1996, Nov. 21   **Engr.**
1139	A389	3.50k claret	1.50	.35
1140	A389	15k claret & dk blue	6.00	1.25

Posthorn Type of 1893 Redrawn

1997, Jan. 2   **Litho.**   **Perf. 13x13½**
Color of Oval
1141	A10	10o red	.25	.25
1142	A10	20o blue	.25	.25
a.		Perf. 13¾x13¼	.40	.40
1143	A10	30o orange	.25	.25
1144	A10	40o gray	.25	.25
1145	A10	50o bl grn, bl grn numeral	.25	.25
		Nos. 1141-1145 (5)	1.25	1.25

Numerous design differences exist in the vertical shading lines, the size and shading of the posthorn, and in the corner wings.
See No. 1282A for stamp similar to No. 1145 but with blue numeral.
Issued: No. 1142a, Dec. 2000.

Insects — A390

1997, Jan. 2   **Perf. 13 on 3 Sides**
1146	A390	3.70k Bumblebee	1.10	.25
1147	A390	3.70k Ladybug	1.10	.25
a.		Bklt. pane, 4 ea #1146-1147	9.00	
		Complete booklet	10.00	

See Nos. 1180-1181.

Flowers — A391

3.20k, Red clover. 3.70k, Coltsfoot. 4.30k, Lily of the Valley. 5k, Harebell. 6k, Oxeye daisy.

1997, Jan. 2   **Perf. 13**
1148	A391	3.20k multi	1.25	.40
1149	A391	3.70k multi	1.40	.25
1150	A391	4.30k multi	1.75	.40
1151	A391	5k multi	1.75	.40
1152	A391	6k multi	2.10	.40
		Nos. 1148-1152 (5)	8.25	1.85

See #1182-1187, 1210-1212, 1244-1247.

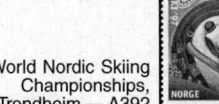

World Nordic Skiing Championships, Trondheim — A392

3.70k, Ski jumping. 5k, Cross-country skiing.

1997, Feb. 20
1153	A392	3.70k multi	1.50	.40
1154	A392	5k multi	2.00	.60

Tourism Type of 1996

4.30k, Roros. 5k, Faerder Lighthouse. 6k, Nusfjord.

Perf. 13 on 3 Sides

1997, Apr. 16   **Litho.**
Booklet Stamps
1155	A383	4.30k multi	1.50	.75
a.		Booklet pane of 8	12.00	
		Complete booklet, #1155a	14.00	

1156	A383	5k multi	1.75	.60
a.		Booklet pane of 8	14.00	
		Complete booklet, #1156a	16.00	
1157	A383	6k multi	2.00	.60
a.		Booklet pane of 8	16.00	
		Complete booklet, #1157a	18.00	

King Harald, Queen Sonja, 60th Birthdays — A393

No. 1159, King Harald, vert.

1997, Apr. 16   **Litho.**   **Perf. 13**
1158	A393	3.70k shown	1.50	.25
1159	A393	3.70k multi	1.50	.25

Norway Post, 350th Anniv. — A394

Post-World War II development: No. 1160, Tools for construction, 1945. No. 1161, Kon-Tiki Expedition, 1947. No. 1162, Environmental protection, establishing national parks, 1962. No. 1163, Welfare, help for the elderly, 1967. No. 1164, Off-shore oil drilling, 1969. No. 1165, Grete Waitz, marathon winner, 1983. No. 1166, Askoy Bridge, 1992. No. 1167, Winter Olympic Games, Lillehammer, 1994.

1997, Apr. 16   **Booklet Stamps**
1160	A394	3.70k multicolored	1.10	.60
1161	A394	3.70k multicolored	1.10	.60
1162	A394	3.70k multicolored	1.10	.60
1163	A394	3.70k multicolored	1.10	.60
1164	A394	3.70k multicolored	1.10	.60
1165	A394	3.70k multicolored	1.10	.60
1166	A394	3.70k multicolored	1.10	.60
1167	A394	3.70k multicolored	1.10	.60
a.		Booklet pane, #1160-1167	12.00	12.00
		Complete booklet, #1167a	14.00	14.00

City of Trondheim, Millenium — A395

Stylized designs: 3.70k, New Trondheim. 12k, Ships entering harbor, King, early settlements in Old Nidaros.

1997, June 6   **Litho.**   **Perf. 13½x13**
1168	A395	3.70k multicolored	1.50	.40
1169	A395	12k multicolored	5.00	.80

Einar Gerhardsen (1897-1987), Prime Minister — A396

Caricatures: 3.70k, In front on government buildings. 25k, Scenes of Norway.

1997, June 6   **Perf. 13½**
1170	A396	3.70k multicolored	1.50	.40
1171	A396	25k multicolored	11.00	1.25

Junior Stamp Club — A397

Topics found on stamps: No. 1172, Insect, butterfly (silhouette of person's face), cartoon character, fish, flag, hand holding pen, heart, tiger, horn, boy with dog, globe. No. 1173, Flag, hand holding pen, tree, butterfly (silhouette of person's face), ladybug, cartoon character, antique postal vehicle, soccer ball, stylized bird, man on bicycle, lighthouse.

1997, Sept. 29   **Litho.**   **Perf. 13**
1172	A397	3.70k multicolored	1.50	.40
1173	A397	3.70k multicolored	1.50	.40

Harald Saeverud (1897-1992), Composer — A398

15k, Tarjei Vesaas (1897-1970), writer.

Litho. & Engr.
1997, Sept. 19   **Perf. 13½x13**
1174	A398	10k blue	4.25	.80
1175	A398	15k green	6.50	1.50

Petter Dass (1647-1706), Poet, Priest — A399

Designs: 3.20k, Dass standing in rowboat, verse. 3.70k, Dass, church on island of Alsten.

Litho. & Engr.
1997, Nov. 26   **Perf. 13**
1176	A399	3.20k multicolored	1.25	.75
1177	A399	3.70k multicolored	1.50	.40

Christmas — A400

Various designs from Norwgian calendar stick, medieval forerunner of modern day calendar.

Serpentine Die Cut 13½ on 3 Sides
1997, Nov. 26   **Litho.**
Self-Adhesive
Booklet Stamps
1178	A400	3.70k yellow & multi	1.10	.25
1179	A400	3.70k blue & multi	1.10	.25
a.		Bklt. pane, 2 ea #1178-1179	5.00	
		Complete booklet, 2 #1179a	10.00	

Insect Type of 1997

1998, Jan. 2   **Perf. 13½ on 3 Sides**
Booklet Stamps
1180	A390	3.80k Dragonfly	1.25	.25
1181	A390	3.80k Grasshopper	1.25	.25
a.		Bklt. pane, 4 ea #1180-1181	10.00	
		Complete booklet, #1181a	12.00	

Flower Type of 1997

3.40k, Marsh marigold. 3.80k, Wild pansy. 4.50k, White clover. 5.50k, Hepatica. 7.50k, Pale pasqueflower. 13k, Purple saxifrage.

1998, Jan. 2   **Litho.**   **Perf. 13**
1182	A391	3.40k multi	1.00	.50
1183	A391	3.80k multi	1.25	.25
1184	A391	4.50k multi	1.50	.40
1185	A391	5.50k multi	1.75	.45
1186	A391	7.50k multi	2.25	.45
1187	A391	13k multi	4.00	.55
		Nos. 1182-1187 (6)	11.75	2.60

Valentine's Day — A401

1998, Feb. 9   **Die Cut Perf. 14x13**
Self-Adhesive
1188	A401	3.80k multicolored	1.00	.50

No. 1188 was issued in sheets of 3 + 4 labels.

A402

Coastal Shipping: 3.80k, Mail boat, SS Hornelen. 4.50k, Catamaran, Kommandoren.

Litho. & Engr.
1998, Apr. 20   **Perf. 13x13½**
1189	A402	3.80k dark bl & grn	1.50	.30
1190	A402	4.50k bl & dark grn	2.00	1.00

A403

Tourism: 3.80k, Holmenkollen ski jump, Oslo. 4.50k, Fisherman, city of Alesund. 5.50k, Summit of Hamaroyskaftet Mountain.

Perf. 13 on 3 Sides

1998, Apr. 20   **Litho.**
1191	A403	3.80k multicolored	1.25	.35
a.		Booklet pane of 8	10.00	
		Complete booklet, #1191a	10.00	
1192	A403	4.50k multicolored	1.50	1.00
a.		Booklet pane of 8	12.00	
		Complete booklet, #1192a	12.00	
1193	A403	5.50k multicolored	1.75	.75
a.		Booklet pane of 8	14.00	
		Complete booklet, #1193a	14.00	
		Nos. 1191-1193 (3)	4.50	2.10

Town of Egersund, Bicent. — A404

Designs: 3.80k, Port, herring boats. 6k, Pottery, white stoneware.

Litho. & Engr.
1998, Apr. 20   **Perf. 13**
1194	A404	3.80k dk blue & pink	1.25	.30
1195	A404	6k mag & dp bl	2.00	.60

Minerals — A405

1998, June 18   **Litho.**   **Perf. 13**
1196	A405	3.40k Silver	1.00	.70
1197	A405	5.20k Cobaltite	2.00	.75

Contemporary Art — A406

Designs: 6k, "Water Rider," painting by Frans Widerberg. 7.50k, "Red Moon," tapestry by Synnove Anker Aurdal. 13k, "King Haakon VII," sculpture by Nils Aas.

1998, June 18
1198	A406	6k multicolored	2.00	.40
1199	A406	7.50k multicolored	2.25	.80
1200	A406	13k multicolored	4.50	1.25
		Nos. 1198-1200 (3)	8.75	2.45

Children's Games — A407

1998, Sept. 18   **Litho.**   **Perf. 13**
1201	A407	3.80k Hopscotch	1.10	.40
1202	A407	5.50k Pitching coins	1.75	.80

New Airport, Gardermoen A408

1998, Sept. 18   **Perf. 13½**
1203	A408	3.80k DC-3	1.50	.50
1204	A408	6k Boeing 737	2.25	.75
1205	A408	24k New airport	9.00	1.50
		Nos. 1203-1205 (3)	12.75	2.75

The Royal Palace — A409

1998, Nov. 20   **Engr.**   **Perf. 13x13½**
1206	A409	3.40k Royal Guard	1.25	.75
1207	A409	3.80k Facade	1.40	.75

Christmas — A410

Serpentine Die Cut 14x13 on 3 Sides
1998, Nov. 20   Photo.
Self-Adhesive
Booklet Stamps
1208	A410	3.80k red & multi	1.25	.30
1209	A410	3.80k blue & multi	1.25	.30
a.		Bkt. pane, 2 ea #1208-1209	5.00	
		Complete booklet, 2 #1209a	10.00	

Flower Type of 1997
3.60k, Red campion. 4k, Wood anemone. 7k, Yellow wood violet.

1999, Jan. 2   Litho.   Perf. 13
1210	A391	3.60k multi	1.25	.40
1211	A391	4k multi	1.50	.50
1212	A391	7k multi	2.50	.40
		Nos. 1210-1212 (3)	5.25	1.05

Norwegian
Inventions — A411

Designs: 3.60k, Cheese slicer, by Thor Bjorklund. 4k, Paper clip, by Johan Vaaler.

Die Cut Perf. 13
1999, Jan. 2   Photo.
Self-Adhesive
1213	A411	3.60k blue & black	1.00	.40
1214	A411	4k red & gray	1.40	.25
		See No. 1260.		

Salmon	Cod
A412	A413

Die Cut Perf. 14x13
1999, Jan. 2   Litho. & Photo.
Self-Adhesive
Booklet Stamps
1215	A412	4k multicolored	1.25	.25
1216	A413	4k multicolored	1.25	.25
a.		Bkt. pane, 2 ea #1215-1216	5.00	
		Complete booklet, 2 #1216a	10.00	

St. Valentine's
Day — A414

1999, Feb. 14   Litho.   Perf. 13x13½
1217	A414	4k multicolored	1.50	.40

A415

Litho. & Engr.
1999, Apr. 12   Perf. 13
1218	A415	4k multicolored	1.40	.40

Norwegian Confederation of Trade Unions, Cent.

A416

Tourism: 4k, Swans on lake. 5k, Hamar Cathedral. 6k, Man in traditional attire.

1999, Apr. 12   Litho.   Perf. 13
Booklet Stamps
1219	A416	4k multicolored	1.25	.40
a.		Booklet pane of 8	10.00	
		Complete booklet, #1219a	10.00	
1220	A416	5k multicolored	1.25	.50
a.		Booklet pane of 8	12.50	
		Complete booklet, #1220a	12.50	
1221	A416	6k multicolored	1.75	.75
a.		Booklet pane of 8	15.00	
		Complete booklet, #1221a	15.00	

Ice Hockey World
Championships
A417

Designs: 4k, Poland vs Norway, 1998 Class B Championships. 7k, Sweden vs Switzerland, 1998 Class A Championships.

1999, Apr. 12   Perf. 13½
1222	A417	4k multicolored	1.25	.40
1223	A417	7k multicolored	2.25	.75

Millennium
Stamps — A418

Events from 1000-1899: 4k, Family leaving Sejestad Station, emigration period, 1800's. 6k, Statue of St. Olav (995-1030), Christian III Bible, 1550, Christianization period. 14k, King Christian IV speciedaler, miners, union period, 1380-1814. 26k, Textile factory, paper mill on Aker River, Oslo, 1850's, industrialization period.

Litho. & Engr.
1999, June 11   Perf. 12¾x13
1224	A418	4k multicolored	1.40	.50
1225	A418	6k multicolored	2.00	.75
1226	A418	14k multicolored	4.75	1.25
1227	A418	26k multicolored	8.00	1.75
		Nos. 1224-1227 (4)	16.15	4.25

Pictures of
Everyday
Life — A419

No. 1228, Carriage on ferry. No. 1229, Men with hammers. No. 1230, Pumping gasoline. No. 1231, Milking cow. No. 1232, Rakers. No. 1233, Skier. No. 1234, Boat captain. No. 1235, Soccer player.

1999, Sept. 9   Litho.   Perf. 13
1228	A419	4k multicolored	1.50	.50
1229	A419	4k multicolored	1.50	.50
1230	A419	4k multicolored	1.50	.50
1231	A419	4k multicolored	1.50	.50
1232	A419	4k multicolored	1.50	.50
1233	A419	4k multicolored	1.50	.50
1234	A419	4k multicolored	1.50	.50
1235	A419	4k multicolored	1.50	.50
a.		Souv. sheet of 8, #1228-1235	12.50	12.50

Children's
Games — A420

1999, Sept. 9   Litho.   Perf. 13¼
1236	A420	4k Skateboarder	1.25	.50
1237	A420	6k Roller skater	2.00	.75

National Theater,
Cent. — A421

Designs: 3.60k, Scene from "An Ideal Husband." 4k, Scene from "Peer Gynt."

1999, Nov. 19 Engr. Perf. 12¾x13¼
1238	A421	3.60k claret & org yel	1.50	1.50
1239	A421	4k dk bl & royal bl	1.25	.50

Christmas — A422

Designs: No. 1240, Mother, children at door. No. 1241, Mother, children at window.

Die Cut Perf. 14x13 on 3 sides
1999, Nov. 19   Litho.
Self-Adhesive
1240	A422	4k multi	1.25	.25
1241	A422	4k multi	1.25	.25
a.		Bkt. pane, 2 ea #1240-1241	5.00	
		Complete booklet, 2 #1241a	12.00	

Millennium — A423

Winners of photo competition: No. 1242, "Winter Night." No. 1243, "Sunset."

Die Cut Perf. 13¼x13
1999, Dec. 31   Litho. & Photo.
Self-Adhesive
1242	A423	4k multi	1.40	.50
1243	A423	4k multi	1.40	.50
a.		Bkt. pane of 2, #1242-1243	4.00	
		Complete booklet, #1243a	5.00	
b.		Bkt. pane, 2 ea #1242-1243	7.50	
		Complete booklet, 2 #1243b	15.00	

One complete booklet containing No. 1243a was given free to each Norwegian household in January 2000.

Flower Type of 1997
Designs: 5.40k, Oeder's lousewort. 8k, White water lily. 14k, Globe flower. 25k, Melancholy thistle.

2000, Feb. 9 Litho. Perf. 12¾x13¼
1244	A391	5.40k multi	1.75	.60
1245	A391	8k multi	2.50	.75
1246	A391	14k multi	4.25	1.00
1247	A391	25k multi	8.00	1.25
		Nos. 1244-1247 (4)	16.50	3.60

Love — A424

2000, Feb. 9   Perf. 13x13¼
1248	A424	4k multi	1.25	.40

Oslo, 1000th
Anniv. — A425

4k, Angry Child sculpture, Frogner Park. 6k, Statue of King Christian IV, by C. L. Jacobsen. 8k, Oslo City Hall. 27k, Oslo Stock Exchange.

2000, Apr. 7   Litho.   Perf. 13¼
1249	A425	4k multi	1.25	.40
1250	A425	6k multi	1.75	.75
1251	A425	8k multi	2.50	.80
1252	A426	27k multi	8.00	1.50
		Nos. 1249-1252 (4)	13.50	3.45

Fauna — A426

2000, Apr. 7   Perf. 13¼ on 3 sides
Booklet Stamps
1253	A426	5k Golden eagle	1.40	.75
a.		Booklet pane of 8	12.00	
		Booklet, #1253a	12.50	
1254	A426	6k Elk	1.75	.75
a.		Booklet pane of 8	14.00	
		Booklet, #1254a	15.00	
1255	A426	7k Whale	2.00	1.00
a.		Booklet pane of 8	16.00	
		Complete booklet, #1255a	17.00	
		Nos. 1253-1255 (3)	5.15	2.50

Expo 2000,
Hanover — A427

Artwork of Marianne Heske: 4.20k, The Quiet Room. 6.30k, Power and Energy.

2000, June 1   Perf. 13¼
1256	A427	4.20k multi	1.75	.75
1257	A427	6.30k multi	2.40	.65

Royal Norwegian
Military Academy,
250th Anniv. — A428

Litho. & Engr.
2000, June 2   Perf. 13¼x13¼
1258	A428	3.60k 1750 Cadets	1.25	.80
1259	A428	8k 2000 Cadets	2.50	1.00

Inventions Type of 1999
4.20k, Aerosol container, by Erik Rotheim.

Die Cut Perf. 12¾
2000, June 2   Photo.
Self-Adhesive
1260	A411	4.20k green & black	1.25	.25

Mackerel	Herring
A429	A430

Die Cut Perf. 14x13 on 3 sides
2000, June 2   Photo. & Litho.
Self-Adhesive
Booklet Stamps
1261	A429	4.20k multi	1.25	.25
1262	A430	4.20k multi	1.25	.25
a.		Booklet pane, 2 each #1261-1262	5.00	
		Complete booklet, 2#1262a	10.00	

A431

Litho. & Engr.
2000, Sept. 15   Perf. 13¼x13
1263	A431	5k multi	1.75	.75

Lars Levi Laestadius (1800-61), botanist.

A432

Intl. Museum of Children's Art, Oslo: 4.20k, Astronaut, by May-Therese Vorland. 6.30k, Rocket, by Jann Fredrik Ronning.

**   Perf. 13¼x13¾**
2000, Sept. 15   Litho.
1264	A432	4.20k multi	1.25	.40
1265	A432	6.30k multi	1.75	.60

Skien, 1000th
Anniv. — A433

Designs: 4.20k, Monument to loggers. 15k, Skien Church.

2000, Sept. 15   Perf. 13¼x13
1266	A433	4.20k multi	1.25	.75
1267	A433	15k multi	4.75	1.25

Church Altar
Pieces — A434

3.60k, Hamaroy Church. 4.20k, Ski Church.

2000, Nov. 17 Litho. Perf. 13x13¼
1268	A434	3.60k multi	1.25	1.25
1269	A434	4.20k multi	1.25	.60

Comic Strips — A435

Designs: No. 1270, Nils og Blamman, by Sigurd Winsnes and Ivar Mauritz-Hansen. No. 1271, Nr. 91 Stomperud, by Ernst Garvin and Torbjorn Wen.

Die Cut Perf. 14x13 on 3 sides
2000, Nov. 17 Photo. & Litho.
Booklet Stamps
Self-Adhesive
1270	A435	4.20k multi	1.25	.25
1271	A435	4.20k multi	1.25	.25
a.		Booklet pane, 2 each #1270-1271	5.00	
		Complete booklet, 2 #1271a	14.00	

Rose Varieties — A436

Designs: No. 1272, Sekel (green denomination). No. 1273, Namdal (brown denomination).

Die Cut Perf. 13¼ on 3 sides
2001, Jan. 2 Photo.
Booklet Stamps
Self-Adhesive
1272	A436	4.50k multi	1.25	.25
1273	A436	4.50k multi	1.25	.25
a.		Booklet pane, 2 each #1272-1273	5.00	
		Complete booklet, 2 #1273a	10.00	

See Nos. 1303-1304.

Crafts — A437

Designs: 4k, Mat of bound birch roots. 4.50k, Birch bark basket. 7k, Embroidered bunad.

2001, Jan. 2 Die Cut Perf. 12¾
Coil Stamps
Self-Adhesive
1274	A437	4k multi	1.25	.30
1275	A437	4.50k multi	1.50	.25
1276	A437	7k multi	2.25	.50
		Nos. 1274-1276 (3)	5.00	1.05

See Nos. 1305-1307, 1354.

Actors and Actresses — A438

Designs: 4k, Aase Bye (1904-91). 4.50k, Per Aabel (1902-99). 5.50k, Alfred Maurstad (1896-1967). 7k, Lillebil Ibsen (1899-1989). 8k, Tore Segelcke (1901-79).

2001, Jan. 2 Litho. Perf. 14x12¾
1277	A438	4k brn & blk	1.25	.75
1278	A438	4.50k bl & blk	1.50	.40
1279	A438	5.50k gold & blk	1.75	.75
1280	A438	7k pur & blk	2.10	.80
1281	A438	8k bl gray & blk	2.50	1.00
		Nos. 1277-1281 (5)	9.10	3.70

Ties That Bind, by Magne Furuholmen A439

2001, Feb. 7 Litho. Perf. 14¾x14
1282	A439	4.50k multi	1.50 .40

Redrawn Posthorn — A439a

2001-06 Litho. Perf. 13¾x13¼
Color of Oval
1282A	A439a	50o green, blue denomination	.25	.25
1283	A439a	1k green	.50	.25
a.		Horiz. rows of dots between vert. lines	.50	.25
1284	A439a	2k Prus blue	.60	.40
a.		Horiz. rows of dots between vert. lines	.60	.40
1285	A439a	3k blue	1.00	.60
1287	A439a	5k purple	1.50	.60
a.		Horiz. rows of dots between vert. lines	1.50	.25
1288	A439a	6k purple	1.75	.50
1289	A439a	7k brown	2.25	.70
1291	A439a	9k orange brn	2.75	.90
a.		Horiz. rows of dots between vert. lines	2.75	.90
		Nos. 1282A-1291 (8)	10.60	4.20

Numerous design differences exist between types A10 and A439a in the vertical shading lines, the size and shading of the posthorn and in the corner wings.

No. 1282A has no dots between vertical lines. Dots between vertical lines on Nos. 1283-1284, 1287-1288 and 1291 are arranged diagonally. Nos. 1285 and 1289 have horizontal rows of dots between vertical lines.

Issued: Nos.1283, 1284, 6k, 2/7/01; 50o, 3/01; 5k, 9k, 2/11/02; Nos. 1283a, 1284a, 1291a, 2003; 3k, 7k, 4/15/05; No. 1287a, 2006.

See No. 1145 for green 50o stamp with green denomination. See Nos. 1628-1630, 1661, 1690, 1723-1724, 1749-1752, 1783, 1802B, 1822-1824, 1872, 1911, 1945, 1947.

School Bands, Cent. — A440

Designs: 4.50k, Tuba player. 9k, Drum majorette.

2001, Apr. 20 Litho. Perf. 14¾x14
1292	A440	4.50k multi	1.40 .50
1293	A440	9k multi	3.00 1.50

Adventure Sports — A441

Designs: 4.50k, Kayaking. 7k, Rock climbing.

Serpentine Die Cut 14x13 on 3 Sides
2001, Apr. 20 Photo. & Litho.
Booklet Stamps
Self-Adhesive
1294	A441	4.50k multi	1.75	.50
a.		Booklet of 8	15.00	
1295	A441	7k multi	2.50	.75
a.		Booklet of 8	20.00	

Norwegian Architecture A442

Designs: 5.50k, Bank of Norway, Oslo, by Christian Heinrich Grosch. 8.50k, Ivar Aasen Center, Orsta, by Sverre Fehn.

2001, June 22 Litho. Perf. 14¾x14
1296	A442	5.50k multi	1.75 .75
1297	A442	8.50k multi	3.00 1.00

Actors and Actresses — A443

Designs: 5k, Lalla Carlsen (1889-1967). 5.50k, Leif Juster (1910-95). 7k, Kari Diesen (1914-87). 9k, Arvid Nilssen (1913-76). 10k, Einar Rose (1898-1979).

2001, June 22 Perf. 13x14
1298	A443	5k multi	1.40	1.00
1299	A443	5.50k multi	1.50	.60
1300	A443	7k multi	2.00	1.00
1301	A443	9k multi	2.50	2.50
1302	A443	10k multi	2.75	1.50
		Nos. 1298-1302 (5)	10.15	6.60

Rose Type of 2001
Die Cut Perf. 13¼x13 on 3 Sides
2001, June 22 Photo. & Litho.
Booklet Stamps
Self-Adhesive
1303	A436	5.50k Red roses	1.75	.30
1304	A436	5.50k Pink roses	1.75	.30
a.		Booklet pane, 2 each #1303-1304	7.00	
		Booklet, 2 #1304a	16.00	

Nos. 1303-1304 are impregnated with a rose scent.

Roses on No. 1303 have white centers. Compare with Illustration A460.

Crafts Type of 2001

Designs: 5k, Carved bird-shaped drinking vessel. 5.50k, Doll with crocheted clothing. 8.50k, Knitted cap.

Die Cut Perf. 14½
2001, June 22 Photo.
Coil Stamps
Self-Adhesive
1305	A437	5k multi	2.50	2.50
1306	A437	5.50k multi	2.50	2.50
1307	A437	8.50k multi	4.25	4.25
		Nos. 1305-1307 (3)	9.25	9.25

2001, June 22 Photo.
Coil Stamps
Self-Adhesive
1305a		Die cut perf. 12¾	1.75	.30
1306a		Die cut perf. 12¾	1.75	.30
1307a		Die cut perf. 12¾	3.00	.30

Nobel Peace Prize, Cent. — A444

Designs: No. 1308, 1991 winner Aung San Suu Kyi. No. 1309, 1993 winner Nelson Mandela. No. 1310, Alfred Nobel. No. 1311, 1901 winner Henri Dunant. No. 1312, 1922 winner Fridjof Nansen. No. 1313, 1990 winner, Mikhail S. Gorbachev. No. 1314, 1964 winner, Dr. Martin Luther King, Jr. No. 1315, 1992 winner Dr. Rigoberta Menchú Tum.

Perf. 13¼x13¾
2001, Sept. 14 Litho. & Engr.
1308	A444	5.50k multi	1.75	.75
1309	A444	5.50k multi	1.75	.75
a.		Vert. pair, #1308-1309	3.50	3.00
1310	A444	7k multi	2.50	1.25
a.		Souvenir sheet of 1	3.50	2.75
1311	A444	7k multi	2.50	1.25
a.		Vert. pair, #1310-1311	5.00	4.50
1312	A444	9k multi	2.75	1.50
1313	A444	9k multi	2.75	1.50
a.		Vert. pair, #1312-1313	5.50	5.00
1314	A444	10k multi	3.00	2.00
1315	A444	10k multi	3.00	2.00
a.		Vert. pair, #1314-1315	6.00	5.00
		Nos. 1308-1315 (8)	20.00	11.00

Pets — A445

2001, Sept. 14 Litho. Perf. 14x13¼
1316	A445	5.50k Kittens	1.75 .50
1317	A445	7.50k Goat	2.10 1.25

Aurora Borealis — A446

2001, Nov. 15
1318	A446	5k Trees	1.50 1.25
1319	A446	5.50k Reindeer	1.75 1.00

Christmas — A447

Gingerbread: No. 1320, Man. No. 1321, House.

Serp. Die Cut 14x13 on 3 Sides
2001, Nov. 15 Photo. & Litho.
Booklet Stamps
Self-Adhesive
1320	A447	5.50k multi	1.50	.30
1321	A447	5.50k multi	1.50	.30
a.		Booklet pane, 2 each #1320-1321	6.00	
		Complete booklet, 2 #1321a	12.00	

Actors and Actresses — A448

Designs: 5k, Tordis Maurstad (1901-97). 5.50k, Rolf Just Nilsen (1931-81). 7k, Lars Tvinde (1886-1973). 9k, Henry Gleditsch (1902-42). 10k, Norma Balean (1907-89).

2002, Feb. 11 Litho. Perf. 13x14
Background Color
1322	A448	5k rose lilac	1.40	1.25
1323	A448	5.50k lilac	1.40	.60
1324	A448	7k beige	2.00	.80
1325	A448	9k light green	2.50	2.50
1326	A448	10k dull rose	2.75	1.75
		Nos. 1322-1326 (5)	10.05	6.90

Contemporary Sculpture — A449

Designs: 7.50k, Monument to Whaling, by Sivert Donali. 8.50k, Throw, by Kare Groven.

2002, Apr. 12 Litho. Perf. 13¼x13¾
1327	A449	7.50k multi	2.00	.80
1328	A449	8.50k multi	2.50	1.25

Fairy Tales
A450   A451

Designs: No. 1329, Askeladden and the Good Helpers, by Ivo Caprino. No. 1330, Giant Troll on Karl Johan, by Theodor Kittelsen.

Serpentine Die Cut 13x14 on 3 Sides
2002, Apr. 12 Photo. & Litho.
Booklet Stamps
Self-Adhesive
1329	A450	5.50k multi	1.50	.25
a.		Booklet pane of 4	6.00	
		Booklet, 2 #1329a	12.00	
1330	A451	9k multi	2.50	1.25
a.		Booklet pane of 4	10.00	
		Booklet, 2 #1330a	20.00	

Norwegian Soccer Association, Cent. — A452

No. 1331: a, Boys playing soccer. b, Referee pointing, player. c, Girls playing soccer. d, Boy kicking ball.

2002, Apr. 12 Die Cut Perf.
Self-Adhesive
1331		Booklet pane of 4	6.00
a.-d.	A452	5.50k Any single	1.60 .70
		Booklet, 2 #1331	12.50

The margins of the two panes in the booklet differ.

Niels Henrik Abel (1802-29), Mathematician A453

Designs: 5.50k, Abel, formula and curves. 22k, Formula, front page of book by Abel, curve.

Perf. 13¼x13¾
2002, June 5   **Litho. & Engr.**
1332 A453 5.50k multi   1.50 1.50
1333 A453 22k multi   6.00 3.00

For overprints, see No. 1346-1347.

City Charter Anniversaries A454

Designs: No. 1334, Holmestrand, 250th anniv. No. 1335, Kongsberg, 200th anniv.

2002, June 5   **Litho.**
1334 A454 5.50k multi   1.50 .60
1335 A454 5.50k multi   1.50 .60

Authors — A455

Designs: 11k, Johan Collett Muller Borgen (1902-79). 20k, Nordahl Grieg (1902-43).

2002, June 5   **Perf. 14¼x14**
1336 A455 11k multi   3.00 2.00
1337 A455 20k multi   5.50 3.00

Europa — A456

Designs: 5.50k, Clown juggling balls. 8.50k, Elephant, monkey on rocking horse.

2002, Sept. 20   **Perf. 14x14¾**
1338 A456 5.50k multi   1.75 .75
1339 A456 8.50k multi   2.50 1.25

Great Moments in Norwegian Soccer — A457

Players involved in: 5k, Victory against Germany in 1936 Olympics. No. 1341, Victory against Brazil in 1998 World Cup tournament. No. 1342, Victory of women's team against US in 2000 Olympics. 7k, Victory against Sweden, 1960. 9k, Victory against England, 1981. 10k, Rosenborg's victory against Milan, in Champions League tournament, 1996.

2002, Sept. 20   **Perf. 13¼x13¾**
1340 A457 5k multi   1.60 .70
1341 A457 5.50k multi   1.75 .70
1342 A457 5.50k multi   1.75 .70
1343 A457 7k multi   2.00 1.25
1344 A457 9k multi   2.50 1.25
1345 A457 10k multi   2.00 1.40
a.   Souvenir sheet, #1340-1345 + 6 labels   12.50 12.50
Nos. 1340-1345 (6)   12.20 6.00

Norwegian Soccer Association, cent.

Nos. 1332-1333 Overprinted

Perf. 13¼x13¾
2002, Oct. 10   **Litho. & Engr.**
1346 A453 5.50k multi   2.50 2.50
1347 A453 22k multi   10.00 10.00

Pastor Magnus B. Landstad (1802-80), Hymn Writer and Folk Song Collector — A458

Designs: 5k, Landstad on horse, front page of 1853 book of folk songs. 5.50k, Church's hymn board, front page of 1870 hymn book, portrait of Landstad.

2002, Nov. 20
1348 A458 5k multi   1.50 1.00
1349 A458 5.50k multi   1.75 .75

Christmas Ornaments — A459

Die Cut Perf. 13½x13 on 3 Sides
2002, Nov. 20   **Photo.**
Booklet Stamps
Self-Adhesive
1350 A459 5.50k Hearts   1.50 .30
1351 A459 5.50k Star   1.50 .30
a.   Booklet pane, 2 each #1350-1351   6.00
Booklet, 2 #1351a   12.00

Rose Type of 2001 and

Grand Prix Rose — A460

Design: No. 1353, Champagne roses (light yellow).

Die Cut Perf. 13¼x13 on 3 Sides
2003, Feb. 10   **Photo. & Litho.**
Booklet Stamps
Self-Adhseive
1352 A460 5.50k multi   2.00 .25
1353 A436 5.50k multi   2.00 .25
a.   Booklet pane, 2 each #1352-1353   8.00
Booklet, 2 #1353a   16.00

Roses on No. 1303 have white centers, while those on No. 1352 do not.

Crafts Type of 2001
2003, Feb. 10   **Die Cut Perf. 12¾**
Self-Adhesive
1354 A437 5.50k Duodji knife handle   1.75 .25

No. 1354 was printed in sheets and coils.

Graphic Arts — A461

Designs: 5k, Nordmandens Krone, by Kaare Espolin Johnson. 8.50k, Bla Hester, by Else Hagen. 9k, Dirigent og Solist, by Niclas Gulbrandsen. 11k, Olympia, by Svein Strand. 22k, Still Life XVII, by Rigmor Hansen.

Perf. 13¼x12¾
2003, Feb. 10   **Litho.**
1355 A461 5k multi   1.40 1.00
1356 A461 8.50k multi   2.75 1.50
1357 A461 9k multi   2.75 1.75
1358 A461 11k multi   3.25 1.50
1359 A461 22k multi   6.00 2.00
a.   Perf. 14x12¾   6.00 2.25
Nos. 1355-1359 (5)   16.15 7.75

St. Valentine's Day — A462

Inscriptions beneath scratch-off heart: b, Elsker deg! c, Jusen kyss! d, Glad i dag! e, Klem fra meg! f, Du er sot! g, Min beste venn! h, Yndlings-bror. i, Yndlings-soster. j, Verdens beste far. k, Verdens beste mor.

2003, Feb. 10   **Perf. 14¾x14**
1360   Sheet of 10   18.00 18.00
a.   A462 5.50k Any single, unscrached   1.75 1.00
b.-k.   A462 5.50k Any single, scratched   .65

Unused value for No. 1360a is for stamp with attached selvage. Inscriptions are shown in selvage next to each stamp.

Fairy Tale Illustrations by Theodor Kittelsen (1857-1914)
A463   A464

Serpentine Die Cut 13x14 on 3 Sides
2003, May 22   **Photo. & Litho.**
Booklet Stamps
Self-Adhesive
1361 A463 5.50k Forest troll   1.40 .45
a.   Booklet pane of 4   7.00
Complete booklet, 2 #1361a   14.00

Serpentine Die Cut 14x13 on 3 Sides
1362 A464 9k Water sprite   2.50 1.25
a.   Booklet pane of 4   10.00
Complete booklet, 2 #1362a   20.00

Bergen Intl. Music Festival, 50th Anniv. — A465

Musical score and: 5.50k, Violinist. 10k, Children.

2003, May 22   **Litho.**   **Perf. 13¼x14**
1363 A465 5.50k multi   1.75 1.00
1364 A465 10k multi   3.00 2.00

Public Health Service, 400th Anniv. — A466

Designs: 5.50k, Heart transplant operation. 7k, Infant welfare clinic.

2003, May 22
1365 A466 5.50k multi   1.75 1.00
1366 A466 7k multi   2.10 1.75

Norwegian Refugee Council, 50th Anniv. — A467

Designs: 5.50k, Child with bread. 10k, Line of refugees.

2003, June 20
1367 A467 5.50k multi   1.75 1.00
1368 A467 10k multi   3.00 1.10

King Olav V (1903-91) — A468

Designs: 5.50k, As child, with parents. 8.50k, With Crown Princess Märtha. 11k, In uniform.

Litho. & Engr.
2003, June 20   **Perf. 14x13¼**
1369 A468 5.50k multi   1.75 1.00
1370 A468 8.50k multi   2.50 1.50
1371 A468 11k multi   3.00 2.00
a.   Souvenir sheet, #1369-1371   11.00 11.00
Nos. 1369-1371 (3)   7.25 4.50

Norwegian Nobel Laureates A469

Designs: 11k, Bjornsterne Bjornson, Literature, 1903. 22k, Lars Onsager, Chemistry, 1968.

Perf. 13¼x13¾
2003, Sept. 19   **Litho. & Engr.**
1372 A469 11k multi   3.50 1.75
1373 A469 22k multi   6.75 2.50

See nos. 1414-1415.

Europa — A470

Poster art: 8.50k, Dagbladet newspaper poster, by Per Krohg. 9k, Travel poster, by Knut Yran. 10k, 1985 North of Norway Music Festival poster, by Willibald Storn.

2003, Sept. 19   **Litho.**   **Perf. 13¾**
1374 A470 8.50k multi   2.50 1.75
1375 A470 9k multi   2.60 1.75
1376 A470 10k multi   3.00 1.75
Nos. 1374-1376 (3)   8.10 5.25

Special Occasions — A471

Designs: No. 1377, Baby, children's names. No. 1378, Children, birthday cake, toys. No. 1379, Man and woman at party, musical notes. No. 1380, Hands, Cupid. No. 1381, Lily.

Die Cut Perf. 13x13½
2003, Sept. 19   **Photo.**
Self-Adhesive
1377 A471 5.50k multi   1.75 1.00
1378 A471 5.50k multi   1.75 1.00
1379 A471 5.50k multi   1.75 1.00
1380 A471 5.50k multi   1.75 1.00
1381 A471 5.50k multi   1.75 1.00
Nos. 1377-1381 (5)   8.75 5.00

Graphic Arts — A472

Designs: 5k, Winter Landscape, woodcut by Terje Grostad. 5.50k, Goatherd and Goats, by Rolf Nesch.

Perf. 13¾x12¾
2003, Nov. 21   **Litho.**
1382 A472 5k multi   1.60 1.00
1383 A472 5.50k multi   1.75 1.00

Christmas — A473

Serpentine Die Cut 13¼x13 on 3 Sides
2003, Nov. 21   **Photo.**
Booklet Stamps
Self-Adhesive
1384 A473 5.50k Santa Claus   1.40 .30
1385 A473 5.50k Gift   1.40 .30
a.   Booklet pane, 2 each #1384-1385   6.00
Complete booklet, 2 #1385a   12.00

Paintings — A474

Designs: 6k, Idyll, by Christian Skredsvig. 9.50k, Stetind in Fog, by Peder Balke. 10.50k, Worker's Protest, by Reidar Aulie.

2004, Jan. 2   Litho.   Perf. 13x14

1386	A474	6k multi	1.75	.85
1387	A474	9.50k multi	2.75	1.75
1388	A474	10.50k multi	3.00	2.00
		Nos. 1386-1388 (3)	7.50	4.60

Marine Life — A475

Designs: 5.50k, Periphylla periphylla. 6k, Anarhichas lupus. 9k, Sepiola atlantica.

Die Cut Perf. 15½x14¼

2004, Jan. 2   Photo.

Self-Adhesive

1389	A475	5.50k multi	1.75	.30
1390	A475	6k multi	2.00	.25
1391	A475	9k multi	2.60	.50
		Nos. 1389-1391 (3)	6.35	1.05

See Nos. 1440-1441.

"Person to Person" — A476

Stylized: No. 1392, Man and woman. No. 1393, Globe.

Serpentine Die Cut 13¼x13 on 3 Sides

2004, Jan. 2   Photo. & Litho.

Self-Adhesive

Booklet Stamps

1392	A476	6k multi	1.75	.25
1393	A476	6k multi	1.75	.25
a.		Booklet pane, 2 each #1392-1393	7.00	
		Complete booklet, 2 #1393a	14.00	

Sunflower Heart — A477

2004, Feb. 6   Litho.   Perf. 14x13¼

1394	A477	6k multi	1.75	.75

Printed in sheets of 6 stamps and 3 labels.

Europa — A478

Designs: 6k, Bicyclist in Moskenes. 7.50k, Kayaker on Oslo Fjord. 9.50k, Hikers crossing Stygge Glacier.

Die Cut Perf. 13½x13 on 3 Sides

2004, Mar. 26   Photo. & Litho.

Self-Adhesive

Booklet Stamps

1395	A478	6k multi	1.75	.50
a.		Booklet pane of 4	7.00	
		Complete booklet, 2 #1395a	14.00	
1396	A478	7.50k multi	2.10	1.00
a.		Booklet pane of 4	8.50	
		Complete booklet, 2 #1396a	17.00	
1397	A478	9.50k multi	2.75	1.25
a.		Booklet pane of 4	11.00	
		Complete booklet, 2 #1397a	22.00	
		Nos. 1395-1397 (3)	6.60	2.75

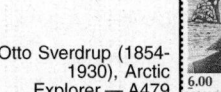

Otto Sverdrup (1854-1930), Arctic Explorer — A479

Litho. & Engr.

2004, Mar. 26   Perf. 13¼

1398	A479	6k shown	2.00	1.25
1399	A479	9.50k Ship "Fram"	2.75	2.10
a.		Souvenir sheet, #1398-1399 + label	7.50	7.50

See Canada Nos. 2026-2027, Greenland No. 426.

Norse Mythology — A480

Designs: 7.50k, Njord, god of wind, sea and fire and ship. 10.50k, Nanna, wife of Balder, Balder's horse, ship.

Perf. 14¼x13¾

2004, Mar. 26   Litho.

1400	A480	7.50k multi	2.50	1.75
1401	A480	10.50k multi	3.00	2.25
a.		Souvenir sheet, #1400-1401	7.50	6.00

Souvenir Sheet

Birth of Princess Ingrid Alexandra — A481

2004, Apr. 17   Perf. 13¾

1402	A481	6k multi	2.50	2.50

King Haakon IV Haakonson (1204-63) — A482

Designs: 12k, Silhouette of King Haakon IV Haakonson, bows of Viking ships. 22k, Sword and Haakon's Hall, Bergen.

2004, June 18   Perf. 14¼x14¾

1403	A482	12k multi	3.50	1.90
1404	A482	22k multi	9.00	2.50

Railways in Norway, 150th Anniv. — A483

Designs: 6k, Koppang Station. 7.50k, Dovre Station. 9.50k, Locomotive, Kylling Bridge. 10.50k, Airport Express train.

2004, June 18   Perf. 13¼

1405	A483	6k multi	1.75	.65
1406	A483	7.50k multi	2.10	1.50
1407	A483	9.50k multi	2.90	1.75
1408	A483	10.50k multi	3.25	2.25
		Nos. 1405-1408 (4)	10.00	6.15

A484

Children's Stamps — A485

2004, Sept. 17   Perf. 13¼x14

1409	A484	6k multi	1.75	.75
1410	A485	9k multi	3.00	1.50

Oseberg Excavations, Cent. A486

Designs: 7.50k, Archaeologists uncovering ship's stern, excavated containers. 9.50k, Textile fragment, ceremonial sleigh. 12k, Bed and rattle.

Litho. & Engr.

2004, Sept. 17   Perf. 13x13¼

1411	A486	7.50k multi	2.25	1.75
1412	A486	9.50k multi	2.60	1.75
1413	A486	12k multi	3.50	1.75
		Nos. 1411-1413 (3)	8.35	5.25

Norwegian Nobel Laureates Type of 2003

Designs: 5.50k, Odd Hassel, Chemistry, 1969. 6k, Christian Lous Lange, Peace, 1921.

Perf. 13¼x13¾

2004, Nov. 19   Litho. & Engr.

1414	A469	5.50k multi	1.40	1.40
1415	A469	6k multi	1.75	1.00

Christmas — A487

Winning art in UNICEF children's stamp design contest: No. 1416, Children and sun, by Hanne Soteland. No. 1417, Child on woman's lap, by Synne Amalie Lund Kallak.

Serpentine Die Cut 13x13¼ on 3 Sides

2004, Nov. 19   Photo. & Litho.

Self-Adhesive

Booklet Stamps

1416	A487	6k multi	1.75	.30
1417	A487	6k multi	1.75	.30
a.		Booklet pane, 2 each #1416-1417	7.00	
		Complete booklet, 2 #1417a	14.00	

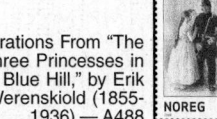

Illustrations From "The Three Princesses in the Blue Hill," by Erik Werenskiold (1855-1936) — A488

Designs: 7.50k, Princesses and guard. 9.50k, Baby in cradle.

2005, Jan. 7   Litho.   Perf. 14¼x14

1418	A488	7.50k multi	2.00	1.25
1419	A488	9.50k multi	2.60	2.00

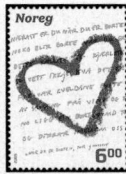

St. Valentine's Day — A489

2005, Feb. 4   Perf. 13¼x13¾

1420	A489	6k red & silver	1.75	.90

Church City Missions, 150th Anniv. — A490

Designs: 5.50k, Soup kitchen. 6k, Ministers administering communion.

2005, Feb. 4   Perf. 13¾x14¼

1421	A490	5.50k multi	1.75	1.25
1422	A490	6k multi	2.00	1.00

Children's Mental Health Pioneers — A491

Designs: 12k, Nic Waal (1905-60), first Norwegian child psychiatrist. 22k, Aase Gruda

---

Skard (1905-85), first Norwegian child psychologist.

2005, Feb. 4   Perf. 14¼x14¾

1423	A491	12k multi	3.25	2.00
1424	A491	22k multi	6.50	2.00

A492

Children's Drawings of Norway in 2105 — A493

2005, Apr. 15   Litho.   Perf. 14x12¾

1425	A492	6k multi	1.75	1.00
1426	A493	7.50k multi	2.25	1.50

Tourism — A494

Designs: 6k, Geiranger Fjord. 9.50k, Kjofossen Waterfall, Flam. 10.50k, Polar bear, Svalbard.

Die Cut Perf. 13x13¼ on 3 Sides

2005, Apr. 15   Photo. & Litho.

Booklet Stamps

Self-Adhesive

1427	A494	6k multi	1.75	.30
a.		Booklet pane of 4	7.00	
		Complete booklet, 2 #1427a	14.00	
1428	A494	9.50k multi	3.00	1.50
a.		Booklet pane of 4	12.00	
		Complete booklet, 2 #1428a	24.00	
1429	A494	10.50k multi	3.25	1.75
a.		Booklet pane of 4	13.00	
		Complete booklet, 2 #1429a	26.00	
		Nos. 1427-1429 (3)	8.00	3.55

Dissolution of Union with Sweden, Cent. — A495

Designs: 6k, Norwegian Prime Minister Christian Michelsen, Norwegian negotiators and signatures. 7.50k, King Haakon VII, ships.

Perf. 12½x12¾

2005, May 27   Litho. & Engr.

1430	A495	6k multi	1.75	1.00
1431	A495	7.50k multi	2.25	1.25
a.		Souvenir sheet, #1430-1431	4.00	4.00

See Sweden No. 2514.

Historic Events Since Dissolution of Union with Sweden — A496

Designs: No. 1432, King Haakon VII taking oath of allegiance, 1905. No. 1433, Crown Prince Olav celebrating end of World War II, 1945. No. 1434, King Olav V at inauguration of Norwegian television broadcasting, 1960. No. 1435, Prime Minister Trygve Bratteli opening Ekofisk oil field, 1971. No. 1436, Victory of Norwegian World Cup soccer team over Brazil, 1998.

2005, June 7   Litho.   Perf. 13¾

1432	A496	6k multi	1.75	1.00
1433	A496	6k multi	1.75	1.00
1434	A496	6k multi	1.75	1.00
1435	A496	6k multi	1.75	1.00
1436	A496	9k multi	2.75	1.50
		Nos. 1432-1436 (5)	9.75	5.50

Tall Ships — A497

Designs: 6k, Christian Radich. 9.50k, Sorlandet. 10.50k, Statsraad Lehmkuhl.

2005, June 7   *Perf. 13¾x13½*
1437	A497	6k multi	1.75 1.00
1438	A497	9.50k multi	2.75 1.75
1439	A497	10.50k multi	3.00 2.40
	Nos. 1437-1439 (3)		7.50 5.15

Marine Life Type of 2004

Designs: B, Orcinus orca. A, Urticina eques.

Die Cut Perf. 15½x14¼
2005, Sept. 1   **Photo.**
Self-Adhesive
1440	A475	B multi	1.75 .30
1441	A475	A multi	2.00 .30

No. 1440 sold for 5.50k and No. 1441 sold for 6k on day of issue.

Lighthouses — A498

Designs: No. 1442, Jomfruland (white lighthouse). No. 1443, Tranoy (red and white lighthouse).

Die Cut Perf. 13¼x13 on 3 Sides
2005, Sept. 1   **Photo. & Litho.**
Self-Adhesive
Booklet Stamps
1442	A498	A multi	2.00 .30
1443	A498	A multi	2.00 .30
a.	Booklet pane, 2 each #1442-1443		8.00
	Complete booklet, 2 #1443a		16.00

Nos. 1442-1443 each sold for 6k on day of issue.

Europa — A499

2005, Sept. 16   **Litho.**   *Perf. 14¾x14*
1444	A499	9.50k Fish	2.75 1.75
1445	A499	10.50k Table	3.00 1.75

Norwegian Telegraph Service, 150th Anniv. — A500

Designs: 6k, Telegraph key and poles. 10.50k, Woman and symbols of modern communication.

Perf. 13½x13¾
2005, Sept. 16   **Litho. & Engr.**
1446	A500	6k multi	2.00 1.40
1447	A500	10.50k multi	3.00 2.00

Geological Society of Norway, Cent. — A501

Designs: 5.50k, Thortveitite and feldspar. 6k, Oil rig, ship, map of Norway, microfossil and stylized rock layers.

2005, Sept. 16   **Litho.**   *Perf. 13¾*
1448	A501	5.50k multi	1.75 1.40
1449	A501	6k multi	2.00 1.25

Norwegian Postage Stamps, 150th Anniv. — A502

Designs: A, Eye, vignette and spandrels of Norway #1. 12k, Norway #1, woman writing letter.

Litho., Engr. & Silk Screened
2005, Nov. 17   *Perf. 14x14¼*
1450	A502	A multi	2.00 1.00

Souvenir Sheet
1451		Sheet, #1450, 1451a	5.50 5.50
a.	A502 12k multi		3.50 3.50

No. 1450 sold for 6k on day of issue.

Royal House, Cent. A503

Designs: No. 1452, Norwegian Prime Minister greeting King Haakon VII and Crown Prince Olav, 1905. No. 1453, Royal coat of arms, King Haakon VII, Queen Maud and Crown Prince Olav, 1945, King Harald V, Crown Prince Haakon, and Princess Ingrid Alexandra, 2004.

2005, Nov. 18   **Litho.**   *Perf. 14x13½*
1452	A503	6k multi	2.00 1.00
1453	A503	6k multi	2.00 1.00

Christmas — A504

Designs: No. 1454, Gingerbread Christmas tree. No. 1455, Oranges studded with cloves on bed of nuts.

Serpentine Die Cut 13x13¼ on 3 Sides
2005, Nov. 19   **Photo. & Litho.**
Booklet Stamps
Self-Adhesive
1454	A504	A multi	1.75 .30
1455	A504	A multi	1.75 .30
a.	Booklet pane, 2 each #1454-1455		7.00
	Complete booklet, 2, #1455a		14.00

Nos. 1454-1455 each sold for 6k on day of issue and are impregnated with a cinnamon scent.

Norwegian Language Society, Cent. — A505

2006, Feb. 3   **Litho.**   *Perf. 13¼x13¾*
1456	A505	6k multi	1.75 1.40

St. Valentine's Day — A506

2006, Feb. 3   *Perf. 13¾x14¼*
1457	A506	A multi	1.75 1.40

Sold for 6k on day of issue.

2006 Winter Olympics, Turin — A507

Designs: 6k, Kari Traa, freestyle skier. 22k, Ole Einar Bjorndalen, biathlon.

2006, Feb. 3   *Perf. 14¼x14¾*
1458	A507	6k multi	2.00 1.00
1459	A507	22k multi	7.25 2.00

Norwegian Lifesaving Society, Cent. — A508

Designs: 10k, Lifeguard carrying man. 10.50k, Child swimming.

2006, Feb. 24   *Perf. 13¾*
1460	A508	10k multi	3.00 2.50
1461	A508	10.50k multi	3.00 2.75

Greetings — A509

Designs: No. 1462, Baby and spoon. No. 1463, Birthday cake. No. 1464, Heart and wedding rings. No. 1465, Flower.

2006, Feb. 24   ***Die Cut Perf. 13¼***
Self-Adhesive
1462	A509	A multi	2.00 1.00
1463	A509	A multi	2.00 1.00
1464	A509	A multi	2.00 1.00
1465	A509	A multi	2.00 1.00
	Nos. 1462-1465 (4)		8.00 4.00

Each stamp sold for 6k on day of issue. Each stamp was issued on a white paper backing with surrounding selvage and in coils on a translucent paper backing without surrounding selvage.

Polycera Quadrilineata A510

Die Cut Perf. 15½x14½
2006, Mar. 29   **Photo.**
Coil Stamp
1466	A510	10k multi	3.00 .50

Wildlife — A511

6.50k, Lynx. 8.50k, Capercaillie. 10k, Golden eagle. 10.50k, Arctic fox. 13k, Arctic hare.

2006, Mar. 29   **Litho.**   *Perf. 13¼x14*
1467	A511	6.50k multi	2.00 .50
1468	A511	8.50k multi	2.00 2.00
1469	A511	10k multi	3.00 2.00
1470	A511	10.50k multi	3.00 2.50
1471	A511	13k multi	3.50 2.50
	Nos. 1467-1471 (5)		13.50 9.50

See Nos. 1498-1499, 1531-1533, 1565-1567, 1600-1602, 1636-1637, 1726C-1728, 1756, 1763, 1825.

Souvenir Sheet

Norse Mythology — A512

No. 1472: a, Design on Sami shaman's drum. b, Carved door post from Hylestad Stave Church depicting dragon and dragon slayer.

2006, Mar. 29   *Perf. 14x14¼*
1472	A512	Sheet of 2	7.50 8.00
a.	A multi		2.75 2.75
b.	10.50k multi		3.25 3.25

No. 1472a sold for 6k on day of issue.

Norwegian Arctic Expeditions, Cent. — A513

Designs: 6.50k, Gunnar Isachsen and assistant surveying terrain. 8.50k, Coal cable car terminal, Store Norske Spitzbergen mines. 22k, Longyearbyen.

2006, June 9   **Litho. & Engr.**   *Perf. 13½x14*
1473	A513	6.50k multi	2.25 .75
1474	A513	8.50k multi	2.75 2.00

Litho.
1475	A513	22k multi	4.25 4.25
a.	Souvenir sheet, #1473-1475		10.00 10.00
	Nos. 1473-1475 (3)		9.25 7.00

Tourism — A514

Designs: No. 1476, Paddle steamer Skibladner. No. 1477, Maihaugen Museum, Lillehammer. No. 1478, Kirkeporten natural arch. No. 1479, North Cape. No. 1480, Bryggen UNESCO World Heritage Site. No. 1481, Storeseisundet Bridge on Atlantic Road.

Die Cut Perf. 13¼x13½
2006, June 9   **Photo.**
Self-Adhesive
Booklet Stamps
1476	A514	6.50k multi	2.00 .50
1477	A514	6.50k multi	2.00 .50
a.	Booklet pane, 5 each #1476-1477		20.00
1478	A514	8.50k multi	2.50 2.00
1479	A514	8.50k multi	2.50 2.00
a.	Booklet pane, 5 each #1478-1479		25.00
1480	A514	10.50k multi	3.00 2.50
1481	A514	10.50k multi	3.00 2.50
a.	Booklet pane, 5 each #1480-1481		30.00
	Nos. 1476-1481 (6)		15.00 10.00

Consumer Cooperatives, Cent. — A515

2006, June 9   **Litho.**   *Perf. 13½x14*
1482	A515	6.50k multi	2.00 1.00

Personalized Stamp — A516

Serpentine Die Cut 11¾ Syncopated
2006, Aug. 22   **Self-Adhesive**
1483	A516	A multi	2.00 2.00

No. 1483 sold for 6.50k on the day of issue. The image shown is the generic image sold at face value. Stamps could be personalized, presumably for an extra fee.

Marine Life — A517

Designs: B, Strongylocentrotus droebachiensis. A, Labrus bimaculatus.

Die Cut Perf. 15½x14½
2006, Sept. 15   **Photo.**
Self-Adhesive
Coil Stamps
1484	A517	B multi	1.75 .50
1485	A517	A multi	2.00 .30

On day of issue, No. 1484 sold for 6k; No. 1485 for 6.50k.

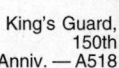

King's Guard, 150th Anniv. — A518

Designs: 6.50k, King's Guard in dress uniforms. 13k, In field uniforms, with helicopter.

2006, Sept. 15   Litho.   Perf. 14x13¼
1486 A518 6.50k multi   2.00 1.25
1487 A518 13k multi   3.50 3.00
a.   Souvenir sheet, #1486-1487   7.00 7.00

Europa — A519

Designs: 8.50k, Five children. 13k, Three children playing soccer.

2006, Nov. 17   Perf. 13¾
1488 A519 8.50k multi   2.50 2.00
1489 A519 13k multi   3.50 3.00

Christmas — A520

Designs: No. 1490, Children and Christmas tree. No. 1491, Child and snowman.

Die Cut Perf. 13¼x13½
2006, Nov. 17   Photo. & Litho.
Self-Adhesive
Booklet Stamps
1490 A520 A multi   2.00 .50
1491 A520 A multi   2.00 .50
a.   Booklet pane, 5 each #1490-1491   20.00

On day of issue each stamp sold for 6.50k.

Personalized Stamp — A521

Serpentine Die Cut 11¾ Syncopated
2006, Nov. 17   Litho.
Self-Adhesive
1492 A521 A multi   2.00 2.00

No. 1492 sold for 6.50k on the day of issue. The image shown is the generic image sold at face value. Stamps could be personalized, presumably for an extra fee.

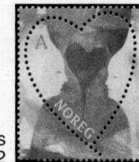

St. Valentine's Day — A522

2007, Feb. 6   Litho.   Perf. 13¼
1493 A522 A multi   2.00 1.50

Sold for 6.50k on day of issue. Values are for stamps with surrounding selvage.

Winter Rally Race Cars — A523

Designs: No. 1494, Petter Solberg's Subaru Impreza. No. 1495, Henning Solberg's Peugeot 307. No. 1496, Thomas Schie's Ford Focus.

Litho. With Foil Application
2007, Feb. 6   Perf. 13¼x13¾
1494 A523 A Innland multi   2.00 1.50
1495 A523 A Europa multi   2.50 2.25
1496 A523 A Verden multi   3.00 3.00
a.   Souvenir sheet, #1494-1496   7.50 7.50
    Nos. 1494-1496 (3)   7.50 6.75

On day of issue, No. 1494 sold for 6.50k; No. 1495, for 8.50k; No. 1496, for 10.50k.

King Harald V, 70th Birthday — A524

Perf. 13¾x13¼
2007, Feb. 21   Litho.
1497 A524 6.50k multi   2.00 1.50

Wildlife Type of 2006
2007, Feb. 21   Perf. 13¼x13¾
1498 A511 12k Hedgehog   3.50 1.75
1499 A511 22k Red squirrel   6.50 2.50

Souvenir Sheet

Intl. Polar Year A526

No. 1500: a, Ice core, oceanographic equipment. b, K/V Svalbard, dish antenna.

2007, Feb. 21
1500 A526   Sheet of 2   7.50 7.50
a.   10.50k multi   3.00 3.00
b.   13k multi   4.00 4.00

Porsgrunn, Bicent. A527

2007, Apr. 27
1501 A527 A Innland multi   2.00 1.50

Sold for 7k on day of issue.

Illustrations by Theodor Kittelsen (1857-1914) — A528

Designs: No. 1502, An Attack (grasshoppers, mosquito, flower). No. 1503, Premature Delivery (frogs, hatched bird).

2007, Apr. 27   Perf. 14x13½
1502 A528 A Europa multi   2.75 2.00
1503 A528 A Verden multi   3.25 2.75

On day of issue, No. 1502 sold for 9k; No. 1503, for 11k.

Skydivers A529

Cyclists A530

Buildings, Roros A531

Bridge, Fredrikstad A532

Pilot House, Portor — A533

Reine Harbor — A534

Die Cut Perf. 13¼x13¾
2007, Apr. 27
Self-Adhesive
Booklet Stamps
1504 A529 A Innland multi   2.00 .50
1505 A530 A Innland multi   2.00 .50
a.   Booklet pane, 5 each #1504-1505   20.00
1506 A531 A Europa multi   2.75 1.00
1507 A532 A Europa multi   2.75 1.00
a.   Booklet pane, 5 each #1506-1507   27.50
1508 A533 A Verden multi   3.25 1.00
1509 A534 A Verden multi   3.25 1.00
a.   Booklet pane, 5 each #1508-1509   32.50
    Nos. 1504-1509 (6)   16.00 5.00

On day of issue, Nos. 1504-1505 each sold for 7k; Nos. 1506-1507 each sold for 9k; Nos. 1508-1509 each sold for 11k.

Marine Life — A535

Designs: No. 1510, Pandalus montagui. No. 1511, Homarus gammarus. No. 1512, Cancer pagurus. No. 1513, Galathea strigosa. 11k, Scomber scombrus.

2007   Die Cut Perf. 15½x14½
Self-Adhesive
Coil Stamps
1510 A535   A Innland multi   2.00 .50
1511 A535   A Innland multi   2.00 .50
1512 A535   A Innland multi   2.00 .50
1513 A535   A Innland multi   2.00 .50
a.   Horiz. strip of 4, #1510-1513   8.50
1514 A535 11k multi   2.75 .90
    Nos. 1510-1514 (5)   10.75 2.90

Issued; Nos. 1510-1513, 9/21; No. 1514, 5/2. On day of issue, Nos. 1510-1513 each sold for 7k.

Europa — A536

Designs: 9k, Scouts, knots. 11k, Hitch diagrams, camp gateway.

Perf. 13¼x13¾
2007, May 11   Litho. & Engr.
1515 A536 9k multi   2.75 2.00
1516 A536 11k multi   3.00 2.50

Scouting, cent.

Building Anniversaries A537

Designs: 14k, Church of Our Lady, Trondheim, 800th anniv. 23k, Vardohus Fortress, 700th anniv.

2007, May 11
1517 A537 14k multi   3.25 3.00
1518 A537 23k multi   6.50 5.00

Riksmaal Society, Cent. — A538

2007, June 15   Litho.
1519 A538 7k multi   2.00 1.25

Personalized Stamp — A539

Serpentine Die Cut 11½ Syncopated
2007, June 15
1520 A539 A Innland multi   2.00 2.00

No. 1520 sold for 7k on day of issue. The image shown is the generic image sold at face value. Stamps could be personalized, presumably for an extra fee.

Ona Lighthouse, Romsdal A540

Tungeneset Lighthouse, Ersfjorden A541

Die Cut Perf. 13¼x13¾
2007, June 15
1521 A540 A Innland multi   2.00 .50
1522 A541 A Innland multi   2.00 .50
a.   Booklet pane, 5 each #1521-1522   20.00

Nos. 1521-1522 each sold for 7k on day of issue.

Haldis Moren Vesaas (1907-95), Poet — A542

Litho. With Foil Application
2007, Sept. 21   Perf. 14x13½
1523 A542 23k multi   7.00 3.00

Mining Academy, Kongsberg, 250th Anniv. — A543

Norwegian Academy of Science and Letters, 150th Anniv. — A544

Perf. 13¼x13¾
2007, Nov. 23   Litho. & Engr.
1524 A543 14k multi   4.00 2.25
1525 A544 14k multi   4.00 2.25

Personalized Stamp — A545

Booklet Stamp

Serpentine Die Cut 10¼ Syncopated
2007, Nov. 23   Self-Adhesive
1526 A545 A Innland multi   2.25 1.00
a.   Booklet pane of 8   18.00

No. 1526 sold for 7k on day of issue. The image shown is the generic image sold at face value. Stamps could be personalized, presumably for an extra fee.

Christmas Star — A546

Adoration of the Magi — A547

Die Cut Perf. 13¼x13¾

2007, Nov. 23   Photo.

Self-Adhesive
Booklet Stamps

1527	A546 A Innland multi	2.25	.50
1528	A547 A Innland multi	2.25	.50
a.	Booklet pane, 5 each #1527-1528	22.50	

On day of issue, Nos. 1527-1528 each sold for 7k.

A548

St. Valentine's Day — A549

2008, Feb. 8   Litho.   *Perf. 13¼x13¾*

1529	A548 A Innland multi	1.75	.75
1530	A549 A Europa multi	2.60	1.25

On day of issue, Nos. 1529-1530 sold for 7k and 9k, respectively.

Wildlife Type of 2006

2008, Feb. 21

1531	A511 11k Elk	3.25	1.25
1532	A511 14k Bear	4.25	2.25
1533	A511 23k Wolf	7.00	3.00
	Nos. 1531-1533 (3)	14.50	6.50

Thorleif Haug, 1924 Olympic Cross-country Skiing Gold Medalist — A551

Espen Bredesen, 1994 Olympic Ski Jumping Gold Medalist — A552

Children Skiing — A553

Kjetil André Aamodt, 1992, 2002, and 2006 Olympic Alpine Skiing Gold Medalist — A554

Die Cut Perf. 15½x14½

2008, Mar. 14   Photo.

Coil Stamps
Self-Adhesive

1534	A551 A Innland multi	2.10	.70
1535	A552 A Innland multi	2.10	.70
1536	A553 A Innland multi	2.10	.70
1537	A554 A Innland multi	2.10	.70
a.	Horiz. strip of 4, #1534-1537	8.50	4.00

On day of issue, Nos. 1534-1537 each sold for 7k. Norwegian Ski Federation, cent.

Souvenir Sheet

Norse Mythology — A555

No. 1538: a, Harald Fairhair meeting Snofrid. b, Snohetta Mountain.

2008, Mar. 27   Litho.   *Perf. 14x14¼*

1538	A555 Sheet of 2	5.00	5.00
a.	A Innland multi	2.10	2.10
b.	A Europa multi	2.40	2.40

On day of issue, No. 1538a sold for 7k, and No. 1538b sold for 9k.

Opera House, Oslo — A556

Litho. With Foil Application

2008, Apr. 12   *Perf. 14x13½*

1539	A556 A Innland multi	2.10	.95

Sold for 7k on day of issue.

Famous Men — A557

Designs: No. 1540, Frederik Stang (1808-84), Interior Minister. No. 1541, Henrik Wergeland (1808-45), lyricist.

Perf. 13¼x13¾

2008, Apr. 12   Litho. & Engr.

1540	A557 A Innland multi	4.25	2.10
1541	A557 A Innland multi	4.25	2.10

On day of issue, Nos. 1540-1541 each sold for 7k.

Oslo Harbor — A558

Divers, Sculpture, by Ola Enstad, Oslo — A559

The Blade, Sunnmore Alps — A560

Kjerag Boulder — A561

Sailboat and Lyngor Lighthouse A562

Lyngor A563

Die Cut Perf. 13¼x13¾

2008, Apr. 12   Photo.

Booklet Stamps
Self-Adhesive

1542	A558 A Innland multi	2.10	.70
1543	A559 A Innland multi	2.10	.70
a.	Booklet pane of 10, 5 each #1542-1543	21.00	
1544	A560 A Europa multi	2.75	1.40
1545	A561 A Europa multi	2.75	1.40
a.	Booklet pane of 10, 5 each #1544-1545	27.50	
1546	A562 A Varden multi	3.25	1.75
1547	A563 A Varden multi	3.25	1.75
a.	Booklet pane of 10, 5 each #1546-1547	32.50	
	Nos. 1542-1547 (6)	16.20	7.70

On day of issue, Nos. 1542-1543 each sold for 7k; Nos. 1544-1545, for 9k; Nos. 1546-1547, for 11k.

Stavanger, 2008 European Cultural Capital A564

Designs: 7k, Dancer in a Cultural Landscape, photograph by Marcel Lelienhof. 14k, Swords in Rock, sculpture by Fritz Roed. 23k, Scene from musical, The Thousandth Heart, vert.

Perf. 14x13½, 13½x14

2008, June 6   Litho.

1548	A564 7k multi	2.10	.95
1549	A564 14k multi	4.00	1.90
1550	A564 23k multi	7.00	2.60
a.	Souvenir sheet, #1548-1550	15.00	15.00
	Nos. 1548-1550 (3)	13.10	5.45

No. 1550a issue 10/23. Nordia 2008 Philatelic Exhibition, Stavenger (#1550a).

Transportation Centenaries A565

Designs: 7k, SS Boroysund. 9k, SS Oster. 25k, Automobile used on first bus route. 30k, Train on Thamshavn electric railroad line.

Perf. 13¼x13¾

2008, June 6   Litho. & Engr.

1551	A565 7k ocher & green	2.10	.95
1552	A565 9k rose pink & blue	2.75	1.40
1553	A565 25k lt bl & brown	7.25	3.00
1554	A565 30k pur & green	9.00	4.25
	Nos. 1551-1554 (4)	21.10	9.60

2008 Summer Olympics, Beijing — A566

Designs: 9k, Andreas Thorkildsen, javelin thrower. 23k, Women's handball player, Gro Hammerseng.

2008, Aug. 8   Litho.   *Perf. 14¾x14¼*

1555	A566 9k multi	2.75	1.75
1556	A566 23k multi	6.75	3.00

Personalized Stamp — A567

No. 1558: a, Like No. 1557, but with line of post horns running through middle of top line of "E" in "Norge." b, "Bring."

Serpentine Die Cut 11¾ Syncopated

2008, Sept. 5   Litho.

Self-Adhesive

1557	A567 A Innland multi	2.10	2.10

Souvenir Sheet

1558	Sheet of 2	32.50	
a.	A567 A Innland red & gray	16.00	16.00
b.	A567 A Innland green & gray	16.00	16.00

No. 1557 sold for 7k on day of issue. The image shown is the generic image sold at face value. Stamps could be personalized for an extra fee.

No. 1557 has line of post horn running through the right side of the top line of the "E" in "Norge."

About 375,000 examples of No. 1558 were distributed free of charge by Norway Post to the general public at post offices throughout Norway and through their agents abroad in a campaign to promote the sale of personalized stamps. The sheet was never offered for sale by Norway Post or their agents. Nos. 1558a and 1558b each had a franking value of 7k, and could not be personalized.

Art — A568

Designs: No. 1559, In the Forecourt of the Revolution, by Arne Ekeland. No. 1560, Svalbard Motif, by Kare Tveter. No. 1561, Composition in Red, by Inger Sitter. No. 1562, From Sagorsk, c. 1985, by Terje Bergstad.

Die Cut Perf. 15½x14½

2008, Oct. 24   Photo.

Coil Stamps
Self-Adhesive

1559	A568 A Innland multi	2.10	.70
1560	A568 A Innland multi	2.10	.70
1561	A568 A Innland multi	2.10	.70
1562	A568 A Innland multi	2.10	.70
a.	Horiz. strip of 4, #1559-1562	8.50	8.50
	Nos. 1559-1562 (4)	8.40	2.80

On day of issue, Nos. 1559-1562 each sold for 7k.

Gnomes, Amperhaugen Farm, Stor-Elvdal A569

Gnome, Nordre Lien Farm, Stor-Elvdal A570

Booklet Stamps

Die Cut Perf. 13¼x13¾

2008, Nov. 17   Self-Adhesive

1563	A569 A Innland multi	2.10	.50
1564	A570 A Innland multi	2.10	.50
a.	Booklet pane of 10, 5 each #1563-1564	21.00	

Christmas. On day of issue, Nos. 1563-1564 each sold for 7k.

Wildlife Type of 2006

2009, Jan. 2   Litho.   *Perf. 13¼x13¾*

1565	A511 11.50k Roe deer	3.50	1.25
1566	A511 15.50k Reindeer	4.50	2.50
1567	A511 25k Willow grouse	7.25	3.50
	Nos. 1565-1567 (3)	15.25	7.25

Art — A572

Designs: B, Summer Night, a Tribute to E. M., by Kjell Nupen. 12k, Light at Whitsuntide, by Irma Salo Jaeger.

Die Cut Perf. 15½x14½

2009, Jan. 2   Photo.

Coil Stamps
Self-Adhesive

1568	A572 B Innland multi	1.75	.75
1569	A572 12k multi	3.50	1.00

No. 1568 sold for 7.50k on day of issue.

Souvenir Sheet

Global Warming A573

No. 1570: a, Warm globe. b, Globe with melting ice at meridians.

Litho. (#1570a), Litho and Embossed (#1570b)

2009, Feb. 20   *Perf. 13½*

1570	A573 Sheet of 2	5.00	5.00
a.-b.	8k Either single	2.50	2.50

Personalized Stamp — A574

Serpentine Die Cut 10x10¼
Syncopated
2009, Mar. 2 — Litho.
Booklet Stamp
Self-Adhesive
1571 A574 A Innland gray 1.75 .95
a. Booklet pane of 8 17.00

No. 1571 sold for 8k on day of issue. The image shown is the generic image sold at face value. Stamps could be personalized for an extra fee.

National Anthem by Bjornestjerne Bjornson, 150th Anniv. A575

Litho. & Engr.
2009, Apr. 17 Perf. 13½x14
1572 A575 12k multi 3.50 2.10

Bergen Line Train in Mountains A576

Bergen Line Train Leaving Tunnel A577

Stotta Fjord A578

Rocky Shore, Revtangen A579

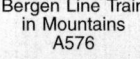
Aurora Borealis — A580
Pot Rock, Vagsoy — A581

Die Cut Perf. 13¼x13½
2009, Apr. 17 Photo.
Booklet Stamps
Self-Adhesive
1573 A576 A Innland multi 2.10 .95
1574 A577 A Innland multi 2.10 .95
a. Booklet pane of 10, 5 each #1573-1574 21.00
1575 A578 A Europa multi 2.60 1.25
1576 A579 A Europa multi 2.60 1.25
a. Booklet pane of 10, 5 each #1575-1576 26.00
1577 A580 A Verden multi 3.25 1.75
1578 A581 A Verden multi 3.25 1.75
a. Booklet pane of 10, 5 each #1577-1578 32.50
Nos. 1573-1578 (6) 15.90 7.90

On day of issue, Nos. 1573-1574 each sold for 8k, Nos. 1575-1576 each sold for 10k, and Nos. 1577-1578 each sold for 12k.

Royal Norwegian Society for Development, Bicent. A582

Perf. 13¼x13¾
2009, June 12 Litho.
1579 A582 12k multi 3.50 2.10

Submarine Branch of Norwegian Navy, Cent. — A583

Designs: 14.50k, The Kobben. 15.50k, Ula Class submarine.

Litho. & Engr.
2009, June 12 Perf. 13¼x14
1580 A583 14.50k multi 4.25 2.50
1581 A583 15.50k multi 4.50 2.60

Norwegian Year of Cultural Heritage — A584

Designs: No. 1582, Kurér radio, 1950. No. 1583, Telephone booth, 1932.

Die Cut Perf. 15½x14½
2009, June 12 Litho.
Coil Stamps
Self-Adhesive
1582 A584 A Innland multi 2.10 .95
1583 A584 A Innland multi 2.10 .95
a. Horiz. pair, #1582-1583 4.25 4.25

On day of issue, Nos. 1582-1583 each sold for 8k.

Europa — A585

Designs: 10k, Solar explosion. 12k, Moon.

2009, June 12 Perf. 14¼x13¾
1584 A585 10k multi 3.00 3.00
1585 A585 12k multi 3.50 3.00
a. Souvenir sheet of 2, #1584-1585 6.50 6.50

Intl. Year of Astronomy.

Knut Hamsun (1859-1952), 1920 Nobel Literature Laureate — A586

Litho. & Engr.
2009, Aug. 4 Perf. 14¼
1586 A586 25k multi 7.25 4.25

Rock 'n' Roll Pioneers — A587

Designs: No. 1587, Per "Elvis" Granberg (1941-80). No. 1588, Roald Stensby. No. 1589, Rocke-Pelle (Per Hartvig) (1938-80). No. 1590, Jan Rohde (1942-2005).

Die Cut Perf. 15½x14½
2009. Aug. 21 Photo.
Coil Stamps
Self-Adhesive
1587 A587 A Innland multi 2.10 .95
1588 A587 A Innland multi 2.10 .95
1589 A587 A Innland multi 2.10 .95
1590 A587 A Innland multi 2.10 .95
a. Horiz. strip of 4, #1587-1590 8.50 8.50

On day of issue, Nos. 1587-1590 each sold for 8k.

Norwegian Shipowners' Association, Cent. — A588

Perf. 13¾x13¼
2009, Sept. 15 Litho.
1591 A588 15.50k multi 4.50 2.75

Norwegian Association of the Blind, Cent. — A589

Litho. & Embossed
2009, Oct. 8 Perf. 13¼x14
1592 A589 8k red 2.10 .95

Sculptures — A590

Designs: No. 1593, Woman on a Man's Lap, by Gustav Vigeland. No. 1594, Crow, by Nils Aas. No. 1595, Birds in Flight, by Arnold Haukeland. No. 1596, Granite Head Lying on its Side, by Kristian Blystad.

Die Cut Perf. 15½x14½
2009, Nov. 16 Photo.
Coil Stamps
Self-Adhesive
1593 A590 A Innland multi 2.10 .95
1594 A590 A Innland multi 2.10 .95
1595 A590 A Innland multi 2.10 .95
1596 A590 A Innland multi 2.10 .95
a. Horiz. strip of 4, #1593-1596 8.50 4.25
Nos. 1593-1596 (4) 8.40 3.80

Nos. 1593-1596 each sold for 8k on day of issue.

Christmas — A591

Text and: No. 1597, Apple and snowflakes. No. 1598, Stars.

Die Cut Perf. 13¼x13¾
2009, Nov. 16 Photo.
Booklet Stamps
Self-Adhesive
1597 A591 A Innland multi 2.10 .95
1598 A591 A Innland multi 2.10 .95
a. Booklet pane of 10, 5 each #1597-1598 21.00

Nos. 1597-1598 each sold for 8k on day of issue.

Man Drinking, Sculpture bu Per Palle Storm — A592

Die Cut Perf. 15½x14½
2010, Jan. 2 Litho.
Coil Stamp
Self-Adhesive
1599 A592 13k multi 3.50 2.10

Wildlife Type of 2006
2010, Jan. 2 Perf. 13¼x13¾
1600 A511 15k European otter 4.50 2.50
1601 A511 16k Lemming 4.75 2.50
1602 A511 26k Wolverine 7.25 3.75
Nos. 1600-1602 (3) 16.50 8.75

Famous Men — A595

Designs: No. 1603, Peter Andreas Munch (1810-63), historian, and illuminated text. No. 1604, Ole Bull (1810-80), violinist.

2010, Feb. 5 Die Cut Perf. 15½x14½
Coil Stamps
Self-Adhesive
1603 A595 A Innland multi 2.10 .95
1604 A595 A Innland multi 2.10 .95
a. Horiz. pair, #1603-1604 4.25 2.50

On day of issue, Nos. 1603-1604 each sold for 8.50k.

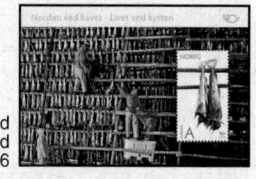
Souvenir Sheet
Dried Cod A596

Perf. 13¼x13¾
2010, Mar. 24 Litho.
1605 A596 A Europa multi 3.25 3.25

No. 1605 sold for 11k on day of issue.

Personalized Stamp — A597

Serpentine Die Cut 10x10¼
Syncopated
2010, Apr. 16 Self-Adhesive
1606 A597 A Europa gray 3.25 3.25

No. 1606 sold for 11k on day of issue. The image shown is the generic image sold at face value. Stamps could be personalized for an additional fee.

Valdresflya Road — A598

Gamle Strynefjellsvegen Road — A599

Sognefjellet Road — A600

Trollstigen Road — A601

Helgelandskysten Nord Road — A602
Lofoten National Tourist Road — A603

Booklet Stamps
Die Cut Perf. 13¼x13½
2010, Apr. 16 Self-Adhesive
1607 A598 A Innland multi 2.10 .95
1608 A599 A Innland multi 2.10 .95
a. Booklet pane of 10, 5 each #1607-1608 21.00
1609 A600 A Europa multi 2.60 1.25
1610 A601 A Europa multi 2.60 1.25
a. Booklet pane of 10, 5 each #1609-1610 26.00
1611 A602 A Verda multi 3.25 1.75
1612 A603 A Verda multi 3.25 1.75
a. Booklet pane of 10, 5 each #1611-1612 32.50
Nos. 1607-1612 (6) 15.90 7.90

On day of issue, Nos. 1607-1608 each sold for 8.50k, Nos. 1609-1610 each sold for 11k, and Nos. 1611-1612 each sold for 13k.

Norwegian Eurovision Song Contest Contestants A604

Designs: No. 1613, Bobbysocks, 1985 winner. No. 1614, Secret Garden, 1995 winner. No. 1615, Alexander Rybak, 2009 winner. No. 1616, Jahn Teigen, 1978 finalist.

Coil Stamps
Die Cut Perf. 15½x14½
2010, May 18 Self-Adhesive
1613 A604 A Innland multi 2.10 .95
1614 A604 A Innland multi 2.10 .95
1615 A604 A Innland multi 2.10 .95

1616 A604 A Innland multi 2.10 .95
　a. 　Horiz. strip of 4, #1613-
　　　1616 8.50 4.50
　Nos. 1613-1616 (4) 8.40 3.80
　On day of issue, Nos. 1613-1616 each sold
for 8.50k.

Molde Jazz
Festival, 50th
Anniv.
A605

2010, June 18 　Perf. 13¼x13¾
1617 A605 13k gray & blue 4.00 2.10

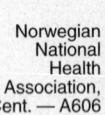

Norwegian
National
Health
Association,
Cent. — A606

2010, June 18 　Litho. & Engr.
1618 A606 26k multi 8.00 4.25

A607　　　　A608

A609　　　Television in
　　　　　Norway, 50th
　　　　　Anniv. — A610

　Designs: Nos. 1619a, 1620, Children's tele-
vision characters Bjornen Teodor,
Kometkameratene, Pompel & Pilt, Titten Tei.
No. 1621, Comedy stars Trond Kirkvag, Rob-
ert Stoltenberg, Rolv Wesenlund and Trond-
Viggo Torgersen. Nos. 1619b, 1622, Erik
Diesen, Dan Borge Akero, Ivar Dyrhaug and
Anne Grosvold. No. 1623, Arne Scheie, Ingrid
Espelid Hovig, Erik Bye and Ragnhild
Saelthun Fjortoft.

2010, Aug. 20 　Litho. 　Perf. 13¼x13
1619 　Sheet of 2 5.00 5.00
　a. A607 A Innland multi 2.25 2.25
　b. A609 A Innland multi 2.25 2.25

Coil Stamps
Self-Adhesive
Die Cut Perf. 15½x14½
1620 A607 A Innland multi 2.10 .95
1621 A608 A Innland multi 2.10 .95
1622 A609 A Innland multi 2.10 .95
1623 A610 A Innland multi 2.10 .95
　a. 　Horiz. strip of 4, #1620-
　　　1623 8.50 4.50
　Nos. 1620-1623 (4) 8.40 3.80
　On day of issue, Nos. 1619a-1619b, 1620-
1623 each sold for 8.50k.

Norwegian Press Association,
Norwegian Media Businesses
Association, Cent. — A611

2010, Sept. 15 　Perf. 13¼x13¾
1624 A611 11k multi 3.50 1.75

Norwegian Seafarers'
Union, Cent. — A612

2010, Sept. 15 　Perf. 13¾x13¼
1625 A612 16k multi 4.50 2.50

Norwegian
University of
Technology
and Science,
Cent. — A613

Royal Norwegian Society of Science
and Letters, 250th Anniv.
A614

Perf. 13¼x13¾
2010, Sept. 15 　Litho. & Engr.
1626 A613 8.50k multi 2.10 .95
1627 A614 13k multi 3.50 1.75

Redrawn Posthorn Type of 2001-06
Perf. 13¾x13¼
2010, Nov. 15 　Litho.
Color of Oval
1628 A439a 4k blue 1.25 .60
1629 A439a 8k brown 2.50 .95
1630 A439a 30k dull violet 8.50 1.75
　Nos. 1628-1630 (3) 12.25 3.30
　No. 1630 has a silver frame. See No. 1802B
for self-adhesive example of No. 1628.

A615　　　Europa — A616

　Illustrations from children's books by Anne-
Cath. Vestly (1920-2008): A Innland, Marte
and Grandma and Grandma and Morten. A
Europa, The House in the Woods — A New
Home.

Litho. With Foil Application
2010, Nov. 15 　Perf. 13¼
1631 A615 A Innland multi 2.10 .95
1632 A616 A Europa multi 2.75 1.40
　On day of issue, No. 1631 sold for 8.50k and
No. 1632 sold for 11k.

Christmas — A617

　Designs from embroidered Christmas table-
cloth: No. 1633, Straw billy goat. No. 1634,
Candlesticks and mistletoe.

Die Cut Perf. 13¼x13¾
2010, Nov. 15 　Litho.
Booklet Stamps
Self-Adhesive
1633 A617 A Innland multi 2.10 .95
1634 A617 A Innland multi 2.10 .95
　a. 　Booklet pane of 10, 5 each
　　　#1633-1634 21.00
　On day of issue, Nos. 1633-1634 each sold
for 8.50k.

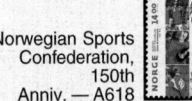

Norwegian Sports
Confederation,
150th
Anniv. — A618

Die Cut Perf. 15½x15
2011, Jan. 3 　Coil Stamp 　Litho.
Self-Adhesive
1635 A618 14k multi 4.00 2.50

Wildlife Type of 2006
2011, Jan. 3 　Litho. 　Perf. 13¼x13¾
1636 A511 17k Polar bear 4.75 2.40
　a. 　Perf. 14¼x13¾ 9.50 5.00
1637 A511 27k Musk ox 7.25 3.00

2011 World Nordic
Skiing
Championships,
Oslo — A619

　Designs: 9k, Holmenkollen ski jump. 12k,
Skiers, Holmenkollen Ski Stadium.

2011, Feb. 23 　Perf. 13½x13¼
1638 A619 9k multi 2.75 1.40
1639 A619 12k multi 3.50 2.00
　a. 　Souvenir sheet of 2, #1638-
　　　1639 6.50 6.50

Fridtjof Nansen
(1861-1930),
Explorer and
Statesman
A620

2011, Apr. 15 　Litho. 　Perf. 14x13¼
1640 A620 12k multi 3.50 2.10

Amnesty
International, 50th
Anniv. — A621

Perf. 14¼x14½
2011, Apr. 15 　Litho. & Engr.
1641 A621 A Innland multi 2.10 .95
　No. 1641 sold for 9k on day of issue.

Roald
Amundsen
Expedition to
South Pole,
Cent.
A622

　Designs: 14k, Amundsen (1872-1928), men
on expedition, Norwegian flag. 17k, Polar ship
Fram and sled dogs.

2011, Apr. 15 　Litho. 　Perf. 14x13¼
1642 A622 14k multi 4.00 2.50
1643 A622 17k multi 5.00 3.00

Buildings — A623

　Designs: No. 1644, Global Seed Vault, Svalbard. No. 1645, Visitor's Center, Borgund. No.
1646, Preikestolen Mountain Lodge,
Lysefjorden.

Booklet Stamps
Die Cut Perf. 13¼x13½
2011, Apr. 15 　Self-Adhesive
1644 A623 A Innland multi 2.10 .95
　a. 　Booklet pane of 10 21.00
1645 A623 A Europa multi 2.75 1.40
　a. 　Booklet pane of 10 27.50
1646 A623 A Verden multi 3.25 1.75
　a. 　Booklet pane of 10 32.50
　Nos. 1644-1646 (3) 8.10 4.10
　On day of issue, Nos. 1644-1646 sold for
9k, 12k and 14k, respectively.

Drammen,
Bicent.
A624

2011, May 20 　Perf. 14x13¼
1647 A624 9k multi 2.75 1.40

Fire and Rescue
Services, 150th
Anniv. — A625

　Designs: 9k, Firemen and fire truck from
Sagene Fire Station, Oslo. 27k, Firemen
training.

2011, June 3 　Perf. 13¼x13¾
1648 A625 9k multi 2.75 1.40
1649 A625 27k multi 8.00 4.50

Europa
A626

　Designs: 12k, Logging, Bjornsasen. 14k,
Forest, Farrisvannet.

2011, June 10 　Litho.
1650 A626 12k multi 3.50 2.10
1651 A626 14k multi 4.00 2.50
　Intl. Year of Forests.

University of
Oslo, Bicent.
A627

2011, Sept. 2 　Litho. & Engr.
1652 A627 9k ver & brn 2.75 1.40

Comic Strip
Art — A628

　Designs: 9k, Bird in nest, by John Arne
Saeteroy. 14k, Hold Brillan (man opening
envelope), by Cristopher Nielsen. 17k, Nemi
(women with index finger and pinkie raised),
by Lise Myhre. 20k, Pondus (soccer player),
by Frode Overli.

2011, Sept. 16 　Litho.
1653 A628 9k multi 2.75 1.40
1654 A628 14k multi 4.00 2.50
1655 A628 17k multi 4.75 2.50
1656 A628 20k multi 6.50 3.50
　Nos. 1653-1656 (4) 18.00 9.90

Female
Singers — A629

　Designs: No. 1657, Wenche Myhre. No.
1658, Inger Lise Rypdal. No. 1659, Mari
Boine. No. 1660, Sissel Kyrkjebo.

Coil Stamps
Die Cut Perf. 15½x14½
2011, Sept. 16 　Self-Adhesive
1657 A629 A Innland multi 2.10 .95
1658 A629 A Innland multi 2.10 .95
1659 A629 A Innland multi 2.10 .95
1660 A629 A Innland multi 2.10 .95
　a. 　Horiz. coil strip of 4, #1657-
　　　1660 8.50 5.00
　Nos. 1657-1660 (4) 8.40 3.80
　On day of issue, Nos. 1657-1660 each sold
for 9k.

Redrawn Posthorn Type of 2001-06
Perf. 13¾x13¼
2011, Nov. 11 　Litho.
Color of Oval
1661 A439a 50k blue gray 15.00 4.00
　No. 1661 has a silver frame. See No. 1751
for similar self-adhesive stamp.

Christmas — A630

Designs: No. 1662, Boy holding letter. No. 1663, Girl holding gifts.

Die Cut Perf. 13½x13¼

2011, Nov. 11 **Litho.**
Self-Adhesive
1662 A630 A Innland multi 2.10 .95
1663 A630 A Innland multi 2.10 .95
a. Horiz. pair, #1662-1663, on tan backing paper 4.50
b. Booklet pane of 10, 5 each #1662-1663 21.00

On day of issue, Nos. 1662-1663 each sold for 9k. On No. 1663b, Nos. 1662 and 1663 are arranged in vertical pairs.

Personalized Stamp — A631

Serpentine Die Cut 10x10¼ Syncopated

2012, Feb. 21 **Self-Adhesive**
1664 A631 A Innland multi 2.10 1.25

No. 1664 sold for 9.50k on day of issue. The image shown is the generic image sold at face value. Stamps could be personalized for an additional fee.

75th Birthdays of King and Queen — A632

Designs: 9.50k, Queen Sonja. 13k, King Harald V.

Perf. 14¼x14½

2012, Feb. 21 **Litho. & Engr.**
1665 A632 9.50k multi 2.75 1.25
1666 A632 13k multi 3.75 2.50

A booklet containing booklet panes of 2 No. 1665, 2 No. 1666 and 1 each of Nos. 1665-1666 sold for 99k. Value $30.

Griffin From Roof Of National Gallery Oslo, Sculpture by Lars Utne A633

Branntomt, by Hakon Stenstadvold A634

Die Cut Perf. 15½x14½

2012, Feb. 21 **Litho.**
Coil Stamps
Self-Adhesive
1667 A633 B Innland multi 1.75 .95
1668 A634 14k multi 4.00 2.50

No. 1667 sold for 9k on day of issue. An etiquette alternates with No. 1667 on rolls produced for sale to the public. On later printings, the etiquette is not present on the rolls.

Souvenir Sheet

Rescue Helicopter — A635

2012, Mar. 21 **Perf. 14x13½**
1669 A635 A Europa multi 3.50 3.50

No. 1669 sold for 13k on day of issue.

Famous People — A636

Designs: No. 1670, Sonja Henie (1912-69), figure skater. No. 1671, Close-up of Henie. No. 1672, Thorbjorn Egner (1912-90), writer of children's books. No. 1673, Egner's illustration of Kardemomme Town.

Coil Stamps

Die Cut Perf. 15½x14½

2012, Apr. 13 **Self-Adhesive**
1670 A636 A Innland multi 2.25 .95
1671 A636 A Innland multi 2.25 .95
1672 A636 A Innland multi 2.25 .95
1673 A636 A Innland multi 2.25 .95
a. Horiz. strip of 4, #1670-1673 9.00
Nos. 1670-1673 (4) 9.00 3.80

On day of issue, Nos. 1670-1673 each sold for 9.50k. No. 1673a was made available with stamps on the strip in a different order and having a different distance between stamps.

Nidaros Cathedral, Trondheim A637

Abbey Ruins, Selja Island A638

Pilgrims on Path Near Fokstugu — A639

Die Cut Perf. 13¼x13½

2012, Apr. 13 **Self-Adhesive**
1674 A637 A Innland multi 2.25 1.00
a. Booklet pane of 10 on white backing paper 22.50
1675 A638 A Europa multi 3.25 1.60
a. Booklet pane of 10 on white backing paper 32.50
1676 A639 A Verden multi 4.00 2.25
a. Booklet pane of 10 on white backing paper 40.00
Nos. 1674-1676 (3) 9.50 4.85

Europa. On day of issue Nos. 1674-1676 each sold for 9.50k, 13k and 15k, respectively. Values for unused examples of Nos. 1674-1676 are for copies either on white backing paper (from booklet panes) or tan backing paper (single stamps).

Norwegian Aviation, Cent. — A640

Designs: 14k, Start (Rumpler Taube), first airplane of Navy Air Service. 15k, Douglas DC-3 Dakota. 27k, Glider.

2012, May 18 **Litho.** **Perf. 13¼**
1677 A640 14k multi 4.00 2.50
1678 A640 15k multi 4.75 2.50
1679 A640 27k multi 8.00 4.50
a. Souvenir sheet of 3, #1677-1679 17.00 17.00
Nos. 1677-1679 (3) 16.75 9.50

Hadeland Glassworks, 250th Anniv. A641

Perf. 13¼x13¾
2012, June 15 **Litho. & Engr.**
1680 A641 13k multi 3.75 1.75

Kavringen Lighthouse A642

Medfjordbaen Lighthouse A643

Die Cut Perf. 13½x13¼

2012, June 15 **Litho.**
Self-Adhesive
1681 A642 A Innland multi 2.25 1.00
1682 A643 A Innland multi 2.25 1.00
a. Horiz. pair, #1681-1682, on tan backing paper 4.50
b. Booklet pane of 10, 5 each # 1681-1682 22.50

On day of issue, Nos. 1681-1682 each sold for 9.50k. On No. 1682b, Nos. 1681 and 1682 are arranged in vertical pairs.

Norwegian Nurses Organization, Cent. — A644

2012, Sept. 14 **Perf. 13¼x13¾**
1683 A644 13k multi 3.75 1.75

Famous Men — A645

Designs: 14k, Knud Knudsen (1812-95), linguist. 15k, Peter Christen Asbjornsen (1812-85) and Jorgen Moe (1813-82), collectors of Norwegian folklore.

2012, Sept. 14 **Perf. 14x13¼**
1684 A645 14k multi 2.50 1.25
1685 A645 15k multi 2.50 1.25

Popular Musicians — A646

Designs: No. 1686, Sondre Lerche. No. 1687, Ole Paus. No. 1688, Age Aleksandersen. No. 1689, Morten Abel.

Coil Stamps

Die Cut Perf. 15½x14½

2012, Sept. 14 **Self-Adhesive**
1686 A646 A Innland multi 2.50 1.25
1687 A646 A Innland multi 2.50 1.25
1688 A646 A Innland multi 2.50 1.25
1689 A646 A Innland multi 2.50 1.25
a. Horiz. strip of 4, #1686-1689 10.00
Nos. 1686-1689 (4) 10.00 5.00

Redrawn Posthorn Type of 2001-06

Perf. 13¾x13¼

2012, Nov. 12 **Litho.**
Color of Oval
1690 A439a 40k gray 12.00 2.50

No. 1690 has a silver frame. See No. 1824 for similar self-adhesive stamp.

Ruins of Hamar Cathedral A647

2012, Nov. 12 **Litho.**
1691 A647 15k multi 5.00 2.25

Directorate for Cultural Heritage, cent.

Santa Claus and Carpenter Andersen A648

Mrs. Claus and Children A649

Die Cut Perf. 13¼x13¾

2012, Nov. 12 **Self-Adhesive**
1692 A648 A Innland multi 2.50 1.25
1693 A649 A Innland multi 2.50 1.25
a. Booklet pane of 10, 5 each #1692-1693, on white backing paper 25.00

Nos. 1692-1693 each sold for 9.50k on day of issue. Horizontal pairs of Nos. 1692-1693 are on white backing paper, which are from No. 1693a, and a tan backing paper, which were prepared for philatelic sale. The stamps on the tan backing paper were only made available as pairs, and were not available in coil rolls.

Fashion — A650

Fashion designs by: No. 1694, Nina Skarras. No. 1695, Camilla Bruerberg.

2013, Jan. 2 **Die Cut Perf. 15½x14½**
Coil Stamps
Self-Adhesive
1694 A650 15k multi 5.00 2.50
1695 A650 15k multi 5.00 2.50
a. Horiz. pair, #1694-1695 10.00

Paintings by Edvard Munch (1863-1944) A651

Details from: 13k, Self-Portrait in Front of the House Wall, 1926. 15k, The Sick Child, 1898. 17k, Madonna, 1895. No. 1699, The Scream, 1893. No. 1700, The Sun, 1911.

2013, Feb. 15 **Perf. 14x13¼**
1696 A651 13k multi 4.00 2.50
a. Booklet pane of 1 8.50
1697 A651 15k multi 5.00 2.75
a. Booklet pane of 1 8.50
1698 A651 17k multi 5.50 3.50
a. Booklet pane of 1 8.50
1699 A651 20k multi 6.00 4.25
a. Booklet pane of 1 8.50
Nos. 1696-1699 (4) 20.50 13.00

Souvenir Sheet

1700 A651 20k multi 7.00 7.00
a. Booklet pane of 1 8.50
Complete booklet, #1696a, 1697a, 1698a, 1699a, 1700a 42.50

Complete booklet sold for 139k.

Statue of King Karl Johan, by Brynjulv Bergslien — A652

Perf. 14¼x14½

2013, Apr. 19 **Litho. & Engr.**
1701 A652 30k multi 10.50 7.00

King Karl Johan (1763-1844).

Ice Climber, Jostedal Glacier — A653

Boya Glacier — A654

Hikers at
Gaustatoppen
A655

Hikers at
Gaustatoppen
A656

Rafters, Sjoa
River — A657

Riverboarder,
Sjoa
River — A658

Die Cut Perf. 13¼x13½
2013, Apr. 19   **Litho.**
Booklet Stamps
Self-Adhesive

1702	A653	A Innland multi	2.50	1.25
1703	A654	A Innland multi	2.50	1.25
a.		Booklet pane of 10, 5 each #1702-1703	25.00	
1704	A655	A Europa multi	3.00	1.50
1705	A656	A Europa multi	3.00	1.50
a.		Booklet pane of 10, 5 each #1704-1705	30.00	
1706	A657	A Verden multi	4.00	2.50
1707	A658	A Verden multi	4.00	2.50
a.		Booklet pane of 10, 5 each #1706-1707	40.00	
		Nos. 1702-1707 (6)	26.00	26.00

On day of issue, Nos. 1702-1703 each sold for 9.50k, Nos. 1704-1705 each sold for 13k, and Nos. 1706-1707 each sold for 15k.

Norwegian
Student
Society, 200th
Anniv. — A659

2013, June 10   **Litho.**   **Perf. 13¼**

1708	A659	17k multi	5.25	3.00

Europa
A660

Postal vehicles: 13k, 1932 Harley-Davidson motorcycles and sidecars. 15k, Ford electric vans.

2013, June 10   **Litho.**   **Perf. 14x13½**

1709	A660	13k multi	4.25	2.50
1710	A660	15k multi	4.75	2.75

Crown Prince
Haakon
A661

Crown Princess
Mette-Marit
A662

Crown Prince
Haakon, Crown
Princess Mette-
Marit and Their
Children
A663

King Harald V,
Crown Prince
Haakon,
Princess Ingrid
Alexandra
A664

Die Cut Perf. 15½x14½
2013, June 10   **Litho.**
Coil Stamps
Self-Adhesive

1711	A661	A Innland multi	2.50	1.25
1712	A662	A Innland multi	2.50	1.25
1713	A663	A Innland multi	2.50	1.25
1714	A664	A Innland multi	2.50	1.25
a.		Horiz. strip of 4, #1711-1714	10.00	
		Nos. 1711-1714 (4)	10.00	5.00

Fortieth birthdays of Crown Prince Haakon and Crown Princess Mette-Marit. On day of issue, Nos. 1711-1714 each sold for 9.50k.

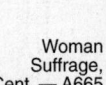

Woman
Suffrage,
Cent. — A665

Designs: 17k, Camilla Collett (1813-95), feminist writer, front page of *Amtmandens Dottre*. 30k, Anna Rogstad (1854-1938), first female in Parliament, Parliament Building.

Perf. 13¼x13¾
2013, Sept. 9   **Litho. & Engr.**

1715	A665	17k multi	4.25	2.50
1716	A665	30k multi	9.00	4.25

National Language
Year — A666

Designs: No. 1717, Lasse Kolstad (1922-2012), actor. No. 1718, Ivar Aasen (1813-96), writer and lexicographer.

Die Cut Perf. 15½x14½
2013, Sept. 9   **Litho.**
Coil Stamps
Self-Adhesive

1717	A666	A Innland multi	2.50	1.25
1718	A666	A Innland multi	2.50	1.25
a.		Horiz. pair, #1717-1718	5.00	

Nos. 1717-1718 each sold for 9.50k on day of issue.

Rock Bands — A667

Designs: No. 1719, The Pussycats. No. 1720, DumDum Boys. No. 1721, Turbonegro. No. 1722, DeLillos.

Die Cut Perf. 15½x14½
2013, Oct. 4   **Litho.**
Coil Stamps
Self-Adhesive

1719	A667	A Innland multi	2.50	1.25
1720	A667	A Innland multi	2.50	1.25
1721	A667	A Innland multi	2.50	1.25
1722	A667	A Innland multi	2.50	1.25
a.		Horiz. strip of 4, #1719-1722	10.00	
		Nos. 1719-1722 (4)	10.00	5.00

Nos. 1719-1722 each sold for 9.50k on day of issue.

Redrawn Posthorn Type of 2001-06
Perf. 13¾x13¼
2013, Nov. 11   **Litho.**
Color of Oval

1723	A439a	10k brown	3.00	1.25
1724	A439a	20k brown	5.50	1.50

See No. 1872 for self-adhesive example of No. 1723.

Solan
Gundersen
A668

Nabonissen
House
A669

Die Cut Perf. 13½x13¼
2013, Nov. 11   **Litho.**
Self-Adhesive

1725	A668	A Innland multi	2.50	1.25
1726	A669	A Innland multi	2.50	1.25
a.		Horiz. pair, #1725-1726, on tan backing paper	5.00	
b.		Booklet pane of 10, 5 each #1725-1726, on white backing paper	25.00	

Christmas. Nos. 1725-1726 each sold for 9.50k on day of issue.

Wildlife Type of 2006
2014   **Litho.**   **Perf. 14¼x13¾**
Self-Adhesive

1726C	A511	16k Lemming	4.00	2.00
1727	A511	19k Red deer	5.00	1.75
1728	A511	35k Badger	9.00	2.75
		Nos. 1726C-1728 (3)	18.00	6.50

Issued: Nos 1727-1728, 1/2; 1726C, 1/22.

Norwegian Church
Abroad, 150th
Anniv. — A670

Die Cut Perf. 14½x15½
2014, Jan. 2   **Litho.**
Coil Stamp
Self-Adhesive

1729	A670	15k multi	4.00	1.75

Marit
Bjorgen — A671

Tora
Berger — A672

Petter Northug
A673

Aksel Lund
Svindal — A674

Die Cut Perf. 13¼x13½
2014, Feb. 7   **Litho.**
Coil Stamps
Self-Adhesive

1730	A671	A Innland multi	2.50	1.25
1731	A672	A Innland multi	2.50	1.25
1732	A673	A Innland multi	2.50	1.25
1733	A674	A Innland multi	2.50	1.25
a.		Horiz. strip of 4, #1730-1733	10.00	
		Nos. 1730-1733 (4)	10.00	5.00

2014 Winter Olympics, Sochi, Russia. Nos. 1730-1733 each sold for 10k on day of issue.

Souvenir Sheet

Supply
Ship MS
Normand
Arctic
A675

2014, Mar. 17   **Litho.**   **Perf. 14x13¼**

1734	A675	A Europe multi	3.50	3.50

No. 1734 sold for 13k on day of issue.

Viking Buckle,
Longhouse and
Woman in Viking
Costume
Sewing — A676

Viking Helmet,
Actors
Recreating Viking
Fight — A677

Draken Harald
Harfagre, Dragon
Figurehead — A678

Die Cut Perf. 13¼x13½
2014, Apr.   **Litho.**
Self-Adhesive

1735	A676	A Innland multi	2.50	1.25
a.		Booklet pane of 10	25.00	
1736	A677	A Europa multi	3.50	1.75
a.		Booklet pane of 10	35.00	
1737	A678	A Verda multi	4.00	2.50
a.		Booklet pane of 10	40.00	
		Nos. 1735-1737 (3)	10.00	5.50

On day of issue, No. 1735 sold for 10k; No. 1736, for 13k; No. 1737, for 16k. Nos. 1735-1737 are on brownish translucent paper (single stamps for sale to collectors) and white translucent paper (stamps in booklet panes).

Thor
Heyerdahl
(1914-2002),
Ethnographer
A679

Kon-Tiki
A680

Easter Island
Moai — A681

Ra
II — A682

2014, Apr. 28   **Litho.**   **Perf. 13¾x14**
Booklet Stamps

1737B	A679	A Innland multi	5.50	5.50
f.		Booklet pane of 1	5.50	—
1737C	A680	A Innland multi	5.50	5.50
g.		Booklet pane of 1	5.50	—
1737D	A681	A Innland multi	5.50	5.50
h.		Booklet pane of 1	5.50	—
1737E	A682	A Innland multi	5.50	5.50
i.		Booklet pane of 1	5.50	—
j.		Booklet pane of 4, #1737B-1737E	22.00	—
		Complete booklet, #1737Bf, 1737Cg, 1737Dh, 1737Ei, 1737Ej	44.00	
		Nos. 1737B-1737E (4)	22.00	22.00

Coil Stamps
Self-Adhesive
Die Cut Perf. 13x13½

1738	A679	A Innland multi	2.75	2.75
1739	A680	A Innland multi	2.75	2.75
1740	A681	A Innland multi	2.75	2.75
1741	A682	A Innland multi	2.75	2.75
a.		Horiz. strip of 4, #1738-1741	11.00	
		Nos. 1738-1741 (4)	11.00	11.00

Nos. 1737B-1737E each had a franking value of 10k on day of issue. Complete booklet sold for 139k. Nos. 1738-1741 each sold for 10k on day of issue.

Norwegian
Constitution,
200th Anniv.
A683

Designs: 13k, Constituent Assembly meeting at Eidsvoll, 1814. 16k, Prince Christian Frederik and 1814 Constitution. 19k, Lion statue at Parliament, May 17 parade. 30k, Hands forming heart, 1814 Constitution.

Litho. & Engr.
2014, May 16   **Perf. 14x13¼**

1742	A683	13k multi	3.50	1.75
1743	A683	16k multi	4.00	2.25
1744	A683	19k multi	5.00	2.75
1745	A683	30k multi	9.00	4.00
		Nos. 1742-1745 (4)	21.50	10.75

See No. B71.

Personalized
Stamp — A684

Serpentine Die Cut 10¼x10 Syncopated
2014, May 16   **Litho.**
Self-Adhesive
1746 A684 A Verden multi   3.75 2.00

No. 1746 sold for 16k on day of issue. The image shown, depicting the Aurora Borealis, is the generic image sold at face value. Stamps could be personalized for an additional fee.

Alf Proysen (1914-70), Writer, and Radio — A685

Mrs. Pepperpot and Mouse — A686

Die Cut Perf. 15½x14½
2014, June 13   Coil Stamps   Litho.
Self-Adhesive
1747 A685 A Innland multi   2.75 2.00
1748 A686 A Innland multi   2.75 2.00
   a.   Horiz. pair, #1747-1748   5.50

Nos. 1747-1748 each sold for 10k on day of issue.

Redrawn Posthorn Type of 2001-06
2014-15   Litho.   Perf. 13¾x13¼
Self-Adhesive
Color of Oval
1749 A439a 1k green   .55
   a.   Die cut perf. 13¾x13¼   .30   .30
1750 A439a 5k purple   1.60
   a.   Die cut perf. 13¾x13¼   1.25   1.25
1751 A439a 50k blue gray   16.00
   a.   Die cut perf. 13¾x13¼   11.00   11.00
1752 A439a 70k gray grn   22.00   5.50
   Nos. 1749-1752 (4)   40.15

Issued: No. 1749, 1/7/15; No. 1749a, 11/19/18; No. 1750, 9/9; No. 1750a, 4/5/18; No. 1751, 7/17/14; No. 1751a, 11/15/21; No. 1752, 9/12. Used examples of Nos. 1749-1751 off the backing paper are identical to used examples of Nos. 1283, 1287 and 1661, respectively. Nos. 1749-1751 have ragged-ended perforation tips, while Nos. 1749a, 1750a and 1751a have clean-cut straight perforation tips.

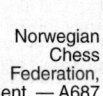

Norwegian Chess Federation, Cent. — A687

Litho. & Engr.
2014, Aug. 1   Perf. 13¼
1753 A687 15k multi   5.00 2.75

Solvguttene Boys' Choir — A688

Characters From Production of *Putti Plutti Pott* — A689

Die Cut Perf. 13¼x13½
2014, Nov. 10   Litho.
Self-Adhesive
1754 A688 A Innland multi   2.50 1.25
1755 A689 A Innland multi   2.50 1.25
   a.   Horiz. pair, #1754-1755, on tan backing paper   5.00
   b.   Booklet pane of 10, 5 each #1754-1755   25.00

Christmas. Nos. 1754-1755 both sold for 10k on day of issue.

Wildlife Type of 2006
Design: 31k, Eurasian eagle owl.
2015, Jan. 2   Litho.   Perf. 14¼x13¾
Self-Adhesive
1756 A511 31k multicolored   8.25 3.50

Birds — A690

Designs: No. 1757, Cyanistes caeruleus. No. 1758, Lophophanes cristatus.

Die Cut Perf. 15½x14½
2015, Jan. 2   Litho.   Coil Stamps
Self-Adhesive
1757 A690 16k multi   4.25 1.75
1758 A690 16k multi   4.25 1.75
   a.   Horiz. pair, #1757-1758   8.50

Norwegian Red Cross, 150th Anniv. — A691

Designs: No. 1759, Rescue team members in snow. No. 1760, Visitor service representative meeting with elderly woman. No. 1761, Emergency aid worker with Philippine children. No. 1762, Attempt to create world's largest human cross, 2010.

Die Cut Perf. 15½x14½
2015, Feb. 20   Litho.
Coil Stamps
Self-Adhesive
1759 A691 A Innland multi   2.50 1.25
1760 A691 A Innland multi   2.50 1.25
1761 A691 A Innland multi   2.50 1.25
1762 A691 A Innland multi   2.50 1.25
   a.   Horiz. strip of 4, #1759-1762   10.00
   Nos. 1759-1762 (4)   10.00   5.00

On day of issue, Nos. 1759-1762 each sold for 10.50k.

Wildlife Type of 2006
2015, Mar. 4   Litho.   Perf. 14¼x13¾
Self-Adhesive
1763 A511 14k Bear   3.75 2.25

Halden, 350th Anniv. — A692

Litho. & Engr.
2015, Apr. 10   Perf. 14½
1764 A692 20k multi   6.00 2.00

Photographs by Anders Beer Wilse (1865-1949) A693

Design: A Innland, Street View of Oslo, 1924. 14k, Kyrkja Mountain, 1933. 16k, Three Large Cod, 1910. 20k, Setesdal on the Way to Church, 1934.

2015, Apr. 16   Litho.   Perf. 14x13½
1765 A693 A Innland multi   2.50 1.25
1766 A693 14k multi   3.75 1.75
1767 A693 16k multi   4.25 2.50
   Nos. 1765-1767 (3)   10.50   5.50

Souvenir Sheet
1768 A693 20k multi   6.00 6.00

No. 1765 sold for 10.50k on day of issue. No. 1768 contains one 70x30mm stamp. A booklet containing panes of 1 of each of Nos. 1765-1768 sold for 139k.

Europa — A694

Old toys: 14k, Anne dolls. 17k Tomte Ford F-100 truck and firetruck.

2015, June 5   Litho.   Perf. 14¼x14½
1769 A694 14k multi   3.50 1.75
1770 A694 17k multi   4.25 2.50

Halfdan Kjerulf (1815-68), Composer A695

Agnar Mykle (1915-94), Writer A696

Die Cut Perf. 15½x14½
2015, June 5   Litho.
Coil Stamps
Self-Adhesive
1771 A695 A Innland multi   2.60 1.25
1772 A696 A Innland multi   2.60 1.25
   a.   Horiz. pair, #1771-1772   5.20

Nos. 1771-1772 each sold for 10.50k on day of issue.

Lighthouses — A697

Designs: No. 1773, Kvitsoy Lighthouse. No. 1774, Slatteroy Lighthouse. No. 1775, Lindesnes Lighthouse. No. 1776, Kjeungskjaeret Lighthouse.

Die Cut Perf. 13¾x13¼
2015, June 5   Litho.
Self-Adhesive
1773 A697 A Europa multi   2.75 1.50
1774 A697 A Europa multi   2.75 1.50
   a.   Booklet pane of 10, 5 each #1773-1774   27.50
1775 A697 A Verda multi   3.25 1.75
1776 A697 A Verda multi   3.25 1.75
   a.   Horiz. strip of 4, #1773-1776, on tan backing paper   12.00
   b.   Booklet pane of 10, 5 each #1773-1774   27.50
   Nos. 1773-1776 (4)   12.00   6.50

On day of issue, Nos. 1773-1774 each sold for 14k and Nos. 1775-1776 each sold for 17k.

Bergen Philharmonic Orchestra, 250th Anniv. A698

2015, Aug. 20   Litho.   Perf. 14x13½
1777 A698 31k multi   7.50 3.00

Supreme Court of Norway, 200th Anniv. A699

Litho. & Engr.
2015, Oct. 3   Perf. 13½x14
1778 A699 20k multi   4.75 2.40

Birds — A700

Designs: No. 1779, Somateria spectabilis. No. 1780, Somateria mollissima. No. 1781, Motacilla alba. No. 1782, Oenanthe oenanthe.

Die Cut Perf. 15½x14½
2015, Oct. 3   Litho.
Coil Stamps
Self-Adhesive
1779 A700 B Innland   1.75 1.25
1780 A700 B Innland   1.75 1.25
1781 A700 A Innland   2.10 1.25
1782 A700 A Innland   2.10 1.25
   a.   Horiz. strip of 4, #1779-1782   8.50
   Nos. 1779-1782 (4)   7.70   5.00

On day of issue, Nos. 1779-1780 each sold for 9.50k and Nos. 1781-1782 each sold for 10.50k.

Redrawn Posthorn Type of 2001-06
Perf. 13¾x13¼
2015, Nov. 13   Litho.
Self-Adhesive
Color of Oval
1783 A439a 60k dull bl grn   15.00   3.50

Christmas — A702

Serpentine Die Cut 11
2015, Nov. 13   Litho.
Booklet Stamps
Self-Adhesive
1784 A701 A Innland   2.25 1.00
1785 A702 A Innland   2.25 1.00
   a.   Booklet pane of 8, 4 each #1784-1785   18.00

Reign of King Harald V, 25th Anniv. — A703

Die Cut Perf. 14½x15½
2016, Jan. 11   Coil Stamp   Litho.
Self-Adhesive
1786 A703 17k multi   4.50 1.50

Youth Winter Olympic Games, Lillehammer A704

Designs: No. 1787, Skier. No. 1788, Person on mountain top.

Die Cut Perf. 13½x13¼
2016, Jan. 11   Litho.
Self-Adhesive
1787 A704 A Innland multi   2.25 1.00
1788 A704 A Innland multi   2.25 1.00
   a.   Horiz. pair, #1787-1788, on tan backing paper   4.50
   b.   Booklet pane of 10, 5 each #1787-1788   22.50

World Biathlon Championships, Oslo — A705

Two competitors: 21k, Skiing. 33k, Shooting.

Litho. With Foil Application
2016, Feb. 19   Perf. 14x13½
1789 A705 21k blue & multi   5.00 1.75
1790 A705 33k sil & multi   8.00 3.00

Cities — A706

Designs: 11k, Harbor of Grimstad, statue of fisherman by Terje Vigen. 17k, Cannons of Nyholmd Skandse, Bodo, Bishop Mathias Bonsach Krogh, city founder. 18k, Cannons near Kragero, *Winter, Kragero*, by Edvard Munch. 21k, Waterfall, Sarpsborg, statue of St. Olav by Finn Eirik Modahl.

2016, Apr. 15 Litho. Perf. 13½x13¾
1791	A706	11k multi	2.75	1.25
1792	A706	17k multi	4.25	1.50
1793	A706	18k multi	4.50	1.50
1794	A706	21k multi	5.00	1.75
	Nos. 1791-1794 (4)		16.50	6.00

Grimstad, 200th anniv.; Bodo, 200th anniv.; Kragero, 350th anniv.; Sarpsborg, 1000th anniv.

Nordic Food Culture — A707

Designs: No. 1795, Glazed langoustines, by Chef Espen Holmboe Bang. No. 1796, Beetroot barley risotto with Atlantic cod and kale, by Chef Freddy Storaker Bruu.

2016, Apr. 15 Litho. Perf. 14x13½
1795	A707	14k multi	4.00	4.00
1796	A707	14k multi	4.00	4.00
a.	Souvenir sheet of 2, #1795-1796		8.00	8.00

A708

Europa — A709

2016, May 9 Litho. Perf. 13½x13¾
| 1797 | A708 | 14k multi | 4.00 | 4.00 |
| 1798 | A709 | 18k multi | 4.50 | 1.50 |

Think Green Issue.

Norwegian Meteorological Institute, 150th Anniv. — A710

Clouds and: 17k, Lightning. 33k, Tree

2016, June 10 Litho. Perf. 14x13½
| 1799 | A710 | 17k multi | 4.25 | 1.50 |
| 1800 | A710 | 33k multi | 8.00 | 3.00 |

A booklet containing a pane of 1 of No. 1799 and a pane of 1 of No. 1800 sold for 149k and was printed in limited quantities.

Captain Sabertooth A711 — Julius the Chimpanzee A712

Die Cut Perf. 14½x15½
2016, June 10 Coil Stamps Self-Adhesive Litho.
1801	A711	A Innland multi	2.75	1.25
1802	A712	A Innland multi	2.75	1.25
a.	Horiz. pair, #1801-1802		5.50	

Kristiansand Zoo, 50th anniv. Nos. 1801-1802 each sold for 11k on day of issue.

Redrawn Posthorn Type of 2001-06
2016, Sept. 1 Litho. Perf. 13¾x13¼ Self-Adhesive Color of Oval
| 1802B | A439a | 4k dp ultra | | 1.00 |

A used example of No. 1802B off the backing paper is identical to a used example of No. 1628.

Central Bank of Norway, 200th Anniv. A713

Designs: 21k, 1819 Speciedaler coin, various banknotes. 50k, Bank headquarters, Oslo.

Litho. & Engr.
2016, Oct. 1 Perf. 14x13½
| 1803 | A713 | 21k multi | 5.25 | 1.75 |
| 1804 | A713 | 50k multi | 12.50 | 6.25 |

Lighthouses — A714

Designs: No. 1805, Sandvigodden Lighthouse. No. 1806, Sklinna Lighthouse.

Die Cut Perf. 13¾x13¼
2016, Oct. 1 Litho. Self-Adhesive
1805	A714	A Innland multi	2.75	1.25
1806	A714	A Innland multi	2.75	1.25
a.	Horiz. pair on tan backing paper		5.50	
b.	Booklet pane of 10, 5 each #1805-1806		27.50	

Nos. 1805-1806 each sold for 11k on day of issue.

Famous Men — A715

Designs: 20k, Tor Jonsson (1916-51), writer. 30k, Johan Sverdrup (1816-92), Prime Minister.

Perf. 14¼x14½
2016, Nov. 11 Litho. & Engr.
| 1807 | A715 | 20k multi | 4.75 | 1.90 |
| 1808 | A715 | 30k multi | 12.00 | 6.00 |

A716

Christmas — A717

Die Cut Perf. 13¼x13½
2016, Nov. 11 Litho. Self-Adhesive
1809	A716	A Innland multi	2.60	1.00
1810	A717	A Innland multi	2.60	1.00
a.	Horiz. pair, #1809-1810, on tan backing paper		5.20	
b.	Booklet pane of 10, 5 each #1809-1810		26.00	

On day of issue, Nos. 1809-1810 each sold for 11k.

Falcons — A718

Designs: No. 1811, Falco columbarius. No. 1812, Falco subbuteo.

Die Cut Perf. 15½x14¼
2017, Jan. 2 Litho. Coil Stamps Self-Adhesive
1811	A718	20k multi	4.75	1.75
1812	A718	20k multi	4.75	1.75
a.	Horiz. pair, #1811-1812		9.50	

Sami Culture — A719

Sami flag and: No. 1813, Triangles (Sami Parliament). No. 1814, Elsa Laula Renberg (1877-1931), Sami politician.

Die Cut Perf. 13½
2017, Feb. 6 Litho. Self-Adhesive
1813	A719	A Innland multi	2.75	1.00
1814	A719	A Innland multi	2.75	1.00
a.	Horiz. pair, #1813-1814, on tan backing paper		5.50	
b.	Booklet pane of 10, 5 each #1813-1814		27.50	

On day of issue, Nos. 1813-1814 each sold for 13k.

Royalty A720

80th birthday of: 23k, Queen Sonja. 36k, King Harald V.

2017, Feb. 21 Litho. Perf. 13½x14 Self-Adhesive
| 1815 | A720 | 23k gold & multi | 5.50 | 2.50 |
| 1816 | A720 | 36k gold & multi | 8.50 | 3.00 |

Viking Ship Excavated Near Tune and Drawing of Reconstructed Ship — A721 — Viking Ship at Sea — A722

Die Cut Perf. 15½x14½
2017, Apr. 21 Litho. Coil Stamps Self-Adhesive
1817	A721	A Innland multi	2.75	1.00
1818	A722	A Innland multi	2.75	1.00
a.	Horiz. pair, #1817-1818		5.50	

Nos. 1817-1818 each sold for 13k on day of issue.

National Archives, 200th Anniv. — A723

2017, Apr. 21 Litho. Perf. 13¼
| 1819 | A723 | 36k multi | 8.50 | 4.25 |

Europa A724

Designs: 17k, Akershus Castle. 21k, Royal Palace.

2017, Apr. 21 Litho. Perf. 14x13¼
| 1820 | A724 | 17k multi | 4.00 | 1.50 |
| 1821 | A724 | 21k multi | 5.00 | 1.75 |

Redrawn Posthorn Type of 2001-06
2017 Litho. Perf. 13¾x13¼ Self-Adhesive Color of Oval
1822	A439a	2k Prus blue		.60
1823	A439a	3k blue		—
1824	A439a	40k gray		—

Issued: 2k, 11/30; 3k, 3/2; 40k, 2/7. No. 1824 has a silver frame. Used examples of Nos. 1822-1824 off the backing paper areidentical to used examples of Nos. 1284,1285, and 1690, respectively,

---

Wildlife Type of 2006
Perf. 14¼x13¾
2017, Mar. 29 Litho. Self-Adhesive
| 1825 | A511 | 11.50k Roe deer | | — |

Statue of King Frederik II, Frederikstad — A725

Perf. 13¾x13¼
2017, June 16 Litho.
| 1826 | A725 | 23k multi | 5.50 | 2.50 |

Frederikstad, 450th anniv.

International Cycling Union 2017 Road World Championships, Norway — A726

Designs: No. 1827, Six cyclists. No. 1828, Two cyclists, vert.

Die Cut Perf. 13¼x13½
2017, June 16 Litho. Self-Adhesive
| 1827 | A726 | A Innland multi | 2.75 | 1.00 |

Die Cut Perf. 13½x13¼
1828	A726	A Innland multi	2.75	1.00
a.	Pair, #1827-1828, on translucent paper without back printing		5.50	
b.	Booklet pane of 10, 5 each #1827-1828		27.50	

On day of issue, Nos. 1827-1828 each sold for 13k.

Famous Men — A727

Designs: 23k: Marcus Thrane (1817-90), labor union leader, red flags and union newspaper. 30k, Eilert Sundt (1817-75), sociologist, buildings, and painting by Johannes Flintoe.

Perf. 13¼x13¾
2017, June 16 Litho. & Engr.
| 1829 | A727 | 23k multi | 5.50 | 2.50 |
| 1830 | A727 | 30k multi | 7.25 | 3.75 |

Automobiles A728

Designs: Nos. 1831a, 1832, 1917 Mustad Giant. Nos. 1831b, 1833, 1921 Bjering. Nos. 1831c, 1834, 1956 Troll. Nos. 1831d, 1835, 1998 Think City A266.

2017, Oct. 7 Litho. Perf. 13¼x13
Miniature Sheet
| 1831 | | Sheet of 4 | 13.00 | 13.00 |
| a.-d. | A728 A Innland Any single | | 3.25 | 3.25 |

Coil Stamps Self-Adhesive
Die Cut Perf. 15½x14½
1832	A728	A Innland multi	3.25	3.25
1833	A728	A Innland multi	3.25	3.25
1834	A728	A Innland multi	3.25	3.25
1835	A728	A Innland multi	3.25	3.25
a.	Horiz. strip of 4, #1832-1835		13.00	
	Nos. 1832-1835 (4)		13.00	13.00

On day of issue, Nos. 1831a-1831d, 1832-1835 each sold for 13k. A booklet containing four panes of one of Nos. 1831a-1831d sold for 169k.

National Federation for the Deaf and Hard of Hearing, Cent. — A729

National Association of the Deaf, Cent. (in 2018) — A730

2017, Nov. 10 Litho. Perf. 13¼x14
1836 A729 20k multi 5.00 5.00
1837 A730 20k multi 5.00 5.00

A731

Christmas — A732

A INNLAND

Die Cut Perf. 13¼x13½
2017, Nov. 10 Litho.
Self-Adhesive
1838 A731 A Innland 3.25 3.25
1839 A732 A Innland 3.25 3.25
a. Pair, #1838-1839, on translucent backing paper with numerals only or without printing on reverse 6.50
b. Booklet pane of 10, 5 each #1838-1839 32.50

On day of issue, Nos. 1838-1839 each sold for 13k.

Birds — A733

Designs: (14k), Strix nebulosa. 21k, Bubo scandiacus. 48k, Buteo lagopus.

Die Cut Perf. 15½x14½
2018, Jan. 2 Litho.
Coil Stamps
Self-Adhesive
1840 A733 (14k) multi 3.50 3.50
1841 A733 21k multi 5.25 5.25
1842 A733 48k multi 12.00 12.00
a. Horiz. strip of 3, #1840-1842 21.00
Nos. 1840-1842 (3) 20.75 20.75

No. 1840 is inscribed "Innland."

Wildlife of Bouvet Island — A734

Designs: 24k, Arctocephalus gazella. 38k, Pygoscelis antarcticus.

Die Cut Perf. 13½x13¼
2018, Feb. 16 Litho.
Self-Adhesive
1843 A734 24k multi 6.25 6.25
1844 A734 38k multi 9.75 9.75
a. Pair, #1843-1844, on translucent backing paper without printing on back 16.00

Perca Fluviatilis — A735

Die Cut Perf. 13¼
2018, Apr. 20 Litho.
Self-Adhesive
1845 A735 18k multi 4.50 4.50

Personalized Stamps — A736

Die Cut Perf. 11½
2018, Apr. 20 Litho.
Self-Adhesive
Inscrbed "Innland"
1846 A736 (14k) multi 3.50 3.50
Inscribed "Europa"
1847 A736 (18k) multi 4.50 4.50

Vignette portions of Nos. 1846-1847 could be personalized for an additional fee. A generic image of twelve Instagram photographs is shown in the A736 illustration, and a generic image of twelve different Instagram photographs was used for No. 1847.

Spjelkavik School Band — A737

Kampen Marching Band — A738

Die Cut Perf. 21
2018, Apr. 20 Litho.
Self-Adhesive
1848 A737 (14k) multi 3.50 3.50
1849 A738 (14k) multi 3.50 3.50
a. Horiz. pair on translucent paper 7.00
b. Booklet pane of 10, 5 each #1848-1849 35.00

Norwegian Marching Band Association, cent.

Souvenir Sheet

Hardanger Bridge — A739

2018, Apr. 20 Litho. Perf. 13¼
1850 A739 18k multi 4.50 4.50

Europa.

Gunnar Sonsteby (1918-2012), Hero of World War II Resistance Against Nazis, and War Cross Medal with Three Swords A740

Perf. 13¾x13½
2018, June 15 Litho. & Engr.
1851 A740 24k multi 6.00 6.00

Rochette Car of Floibanen Funicular A741

Blamann Car of Floibanen Funicular A742

Die Cut Perf. 15½x14½
2018, June 15 Litho.
Coil Stamps
Self-Adhesive
1852 A741 (14k) multi 3.50 3.50
1853 A742 (14k) multi 3.50 3.50
a. Horiz. pair, #1852-1853 7.00

Floibanen Funicular, Bergen, cent.

Kayaking in Vesteralen A743

Hikers A744

Sun Over Grahogda A745

Svartvassbu Mountain Lodge and Skier A746

Die Cut Perf. 13¼x13
2018, June 15 Litho.
Booklet Stamps
Self-Adhesive
1854 A743 (14k) multi 3.50 3.50
1855 A744 (14k) multi 3.50 3.50
a. Booklet pane of 10, 5 each #1854-1855 35.00
1856 A745 (18k) multi 4.50 4.50
1857 A746 (18k) multi 4.50 4.50
a. Booklet pane of 10, 5 each #1856-1857 45.00
Nos. 1854-1857 (4) 16.00 16.00

Norwegian Trekking Association, 150th anniv. A booklet containing perf. 13¼x12¾ water-activated gum booklet panes of one of stamps like Nos. 1854-1857 sold for 179k.

Souvenir Sheet

50th Wedding Anniversary of King Harald V and Queen Sonja — A747

Litho. & Engr.
2018, Aug. 29 Perf. 14¼
1858 A747 50k multi 12.00 12.00

Norwegian Postal Codes, 50th Anniv. — A748

Litho. With Foil Application
2018, Oct. 6 Die Cut Perf. 13¼x13¾
Self-Adhesive
1859 A748 24k multi 5.75 5.75

Writers — A749

Designs: 21k, André Bjerke (1918-85). 38k, Hans Borli (1918-89).

Die Cut Perf. 13¾x13¼
2018, Nov. 9 Litho.
Self-Adhesive
1860 A749 21k multi 5.00 5.00
1861 A749 38k multi 9.00 9.00

A750

Christmas — A751

Die Cut Perf. 21
2018, Nov. 9 Litho.
Booklet Stamps
Self-Adhesive
1862 A750 (14k) multi 3.25 3.25
1863 A751 (14k) multi 3.25 3.25
a. Horiz. pair, #1862-1863, on backing paper without image on reverse 6.50
b. Booklet pane of 10, 5 each #1862-1863 32.50

Oslo, 2019 European Green Capital — A752

Die Cut Perf. 14¼x15½
2019, Jan. 4 Litho.
Coil Stamp
Self-Adhesive
1864 A752 23k multi 5.50 5.50

Holtanna Peak, Antarctica A753

Carsten Borchgrevink (1864-1934), Antarctic Explorer A754

Die Cut Perf. 13x13½
2019, Jan. 4 Litho.
Self-Adhesive
1865 A753 26k multi 6.25 6.25
Die Cut Perf. 13½x13
1866 A754 42k multi 10.00 10.00
a. Horiz. pair, #1865-1866, on white backing paper —

See No. 1877A.

Discovery of Ekofisk Oil Field, 50th Anniv. — A755

Die Cut Perf. 13¼x13
2019, Feb. 15 Litho.
Self-Adhesive
1867 A755 (16k) multi 3.75 3.75
a. On white backing paper without bar code on back —

Cinclus Cinclus — A756

Serpentine Die Cut 12
2019, Apr. 11 Litho.
Self-Adhesive
1868 A756 (21k) multi + label, no perpendicular corners, on backing paper without back printing 5.00 5.00
a. multi + label, serpentine die cut 12, with 3 perpendicular corners 5.00 5.00
b. multi + label, serpentine die cut 12 ¼x12, with 3 perpendicular corners 5.00 5.00

c. multi + label, serpentine die
cut 12, with 2 perpendicular
corners　5.00 5.00
d. Booklet pane of 10, 4 each
#1868a, 1868b, 2 #1868c　50.00

Europa. The perpendicular corners can be at the lower left and lower right corners of the label, because the horizontal die cutting separating the stamp from the label does not touch the die cutting on the sides of the stamps.

Sinnataggen
A757

The Kiss
A758

Die Cut Perf. 11¼
2019, Apr. 11　　　　Litho.
Self-Adhesive
1869 A757 (21k) sil & multi　5.00 5.00
1870 A758 (24k) sil & multi　5.50 5.50
Sculptures by Gustav Vigeland (1869-1943).

Oslo Stock
Exchange, 200th
Anniv. — A759

Die Cut Perf. 13¼
2019, Apr. 11　　　　Litho.
Self-Adhesive
1871 A759 50k multi　11.50 11.50

Redrawn Posthorn Type of 2001-06
Die Cut Perf. 13¾x13¼
2019, May 16　　　　Litho.
Self-Adhesive
Color of Oval
1872 A439a 10k brown lake　2.40
A used example of No. 1872 off the backing paper is identical to a used example of No. 1723.

Egon Olsen Leaving
Prison — A760

Dynamite Harry, Egon Olsen, Benny
Fransen, Kjell and Valborg Jensen
A761

Die Cut Perf. 13¼
2019, June 8　　　　Litho.
Self-Adhesive
1873 A760 (16k) multi　3.75 3.75
1874 A761 23k multi　5.50 5.50
a. Horiz. pair, #1873-1874 on
white backing paper　—
Olsen Gang Movies, 50th anniv. A booklet containing two booklet panes containing one perf. 13 ¼ example with water-activated gum of types A760 and A761, respectively, sold for 179k.

2019 Orienteering World
Cup Competition,
Norway — A762

Die Cut Perf. 14¼x15½
2019, June 14　　　　Litho.
Booklet Stamp
Self-Adhesive
1875 A762 (16k) multi　3.75 3.75
1875b　Booklet pane of 10　37.50
　　Single on white
　　backing paper
　　without back
　　printing　—

Paintings by
Harald
Sohlberg
(1869-1935)
A763
Designs: 26k, Self-portrait, 1896, and Gate in Roros, 1902. 45k, Gate in Roros, 1903.

Die Cut Perf. 11¼
2019, June 14　　　　Litho.
Self-Adhesive
1876 A763 26k multi　6.25 6.25
1877 A763 45k multi　10.50 10.50
b. Horiz. pair, #1876-1877 on
white backing paper　—

Borchgrevink Type of 2019
Souvenir Sheet
2019, Aug. 23　Litho.　Perf. 14
1877A A754 42k multi　11.00 11.00
Nordia 2019 Stamp Exhibition, Gralum. No. 1877A sold for 50k.

Bicycles — A764
Designs: No. 1878, 1933 Diamond cross-country bicycle. No. 1879, 1936 Ideal commuter bicycle. No. 1880, 1972 DBS Kombi Butterfly bicycle. No. 1881, 1975 DBS Apache bicycle.

Die Cut Perf. 15½x14¼
2019, Aug. 23　　　　Litho.
Coil Stamps
Self-Adhesive
Panel Color
1878 A764 (16k) light brown　3.50 3.50
1879 A764 (16k) yellow　3.50 3.50
1880 A764 (16k) light green　3.50 3.50
1881 A764 (16k) orange　3.50 3.50
a. Horiz. strip of 4, #1878-
1881　14.00
Nos. 1878-1881 (4)　14.00 14.00
Nos. 1878-1881 are each inscribed "Innland."

Pets — A765
Designs: No. 1882, Puppy. No. 1883, Kitten.

Die Cut Perf. 13¼x13½
2019, Oct. 6　　　　Litho.
Booklet Stamps
Self-Adhesive
1882 A765 (16k) multi　3.50 3.50
1883 A765 (16k) multi　3.50 3.50
a. Booklet pane of 10, 5 each
#1882-1883　35.00
Nos. 1882-1883 are both inscribed "Innland."

Souvenir Sheet

Queen Maud (1869-1938) — A766

Litho. & Engr.
2019, Nov. 8　　　Perf. 14x13¼
1884 A766 16k copper & multi　3.50 3.50

Cobbler and
Talking
Shoe — A767

Children — A768

Die Cut Perf. 21
2019, Nov. 8　　　　Litho.
Booklet Stamps
Self-Adhesive
1885 A767 (16k) multi　3.50 3.50
1886 A768 (16k) multi　3.50 3.50
a. Booklet pane of 10, 5 each
#1885-1886　35.00
b. Horiz. pair, #1885-1886 on
white backing paper without
back printing　—
Characters from Norwegian Broadcasting Corporation Christmas programs.

Personalized
Stamp — A769

Die Cut Perf. 11½
2020, Feb. 21　　　　Litho.
Self-Adhesive
Inscribed "Verden"
1887 A769 (32k) multi　7.00 7.00
Vignette portion of No. 1887 could be personalized for an additional fee. A generic image of twelve Instagram photographs is shown in the A769 illustration.

Jan Mayen
Island — A770
Designs: 27k, Beerenberg Volcano. 45k, Meteorologist with weather balloon.

Die Cut Perf. 13x13½
2020, Feb. 21　　　　Litho.
Self-Adhesive
1888 A770 27k multi　5.75 5.75
1889 A770 45k multi　9.75 9.75
a. Horiz. pair, #1888-1889 on
backing paper without back
printing　—

Bergen, 950th
Anniv. — A771

Moss, 300th
Anniv. — A772

Die Cut Perf. 13¼x13¾
2020, Feb. 21　　　　Litho.
Coil Stamps
Self-Adhesive
1890 A771 (24k) multi　5.25 5.25
1891 A772 (24k) multi　5.25 5.25
a. Horiz. pair, #1890-1891　10.50

Kjell Aukrust
(1920-2002),
Writer — A773

Anne-Cath
Vestly (1920-
2008),
Writer — A774

Jens Bjorneboe
(1920-76),
Writer — A775

Die Cut Perf. 13¼
2020, Mar. 19　　　　Litho.
Self-Adhesive
1892 A773 (17k) multi　3.25 3.25
1893 A774 (24k) multi　4.50 4.50
1894 A775 27k multi　5.25 5.25
a. Horiz. strip of 3, #1892-
1894 on backing paper
without back printing　—
Nos. 1892-1894 (3)　13.00 13.00

Souvenir Sheet

Old Post
Road
A776

Litho. with Foil Application
2020, Apr. 17　　　Perf. 13¼x14
1895 A776 (26k) multi　5.00 5.00
Europa.

Ship and Orcinus
Orca — A777

Die Cut Perf. 13¼x13
2020, Apr. 17　　　　Litho.
Self-Adhesive
1896 A777 (26k) multi　5.00 5.00
a. On backing paper without back
printing　—

End of World War II,
75th Anniv. — A778

Litho. & Engr.
2020, May 8　　　Perf. 14¼
1897 A778 (17k) multi　3.50 3.50
a. Souvenir sheet of 1　3.50 3.50

Opening of
New Edvard
Munch
Museum,
Oslo — A779

Die Cut Perf. 13¼
2020, June 12　　　　Litho.
Self-Adhesive
1898 A779 (26k) multi　5.50 5.50

Dogs — A780
Designs: No. 1899, Norwegian lundehund named Zkipper. No. 1900, Belgian Malinois named Altea. No. 1901, Whippet named Flint. No. 1902, Great Dane named Milo.

Die Cut Perf. 13¼x13½
2020, June 12　　　　Litho.
Coil Stamps
Self-Adhesive
1899 A780 (17k) multi　3.50 3.50
1900 A780 (17k) multi　3.50 3.50
1901 A780 (17k) multi　3.50 3.50
1902 A780 (17k) multi　3.50 3.50
a. Horiz. coil strip of 4, #1899-
1902　14.00
Nos. 1899-1902 (4)　14.00 14.00

85th
Birthday of
King Harald
V
A812

85th
Birthday of
Queen
Sonja
A813

King
Haakon VII
(1872-1957)
A814

18th
Birthday of
Princess
Ingrid
Alexandra
A815

Die Cut Perf. 14½x15¾
2022, Apr. 22   Litho.

Coil Stamps
Self-Adhesive

1941 A812 (19k) multi   4.00   4.00
1942 A813 (19k) multi   4.00   4.00
   a.   Vert. coil pair, #1941-1942   8.00
1943 A814 (25k) multi   5.25   5.25
1944 A815 (25k) multi   5.25   5.25
   a.   Vert. coil pair, #1943-1944   10.50
    Nos. 1941-1944 (4)   18.50   18.50

A booklet containing four panes, each containing one perf. 12¾x13¼ water-activated gum stamp having the designs of Nos. 1941-1944 was printed in limited quantities and sold for 199k.

Redrawn Posthorn Type of 2001-06
Die Cut Perf. 13¾x13¼
2022, June 17   Litho.

Self-Adhesive
Color of Oval

1945 A439a 90k brown   18.00   18.00
   a.   On translucent paper without barcode on back   18.00

Rainbow Flag and
Heart — A816

Die Cut Perf. 13¾
2022, June 17   Litho.

Self-Adhesive

1946 A816 (25k) multi   5.00   5.00
   a.   On translucent paper, without surrounding selvage   5.00

Redrawn Posthorn Type of 2001-06
Souvenir Sheet
2022, Oct. 1   Litho.   **Perf. 13¾x13¼**
Color of Oval

1947 A439a 19k purple   3.50   3.50
Posthorn stamp design, 150th anniv. No. 1947 is dated "2022."

Souvenir Sheet

Arctic University Museum of Norway,
150th Anniv. — A817

No. 1948: a, Sailboat near shore. b, Sami with sled and reindeer.

Litho. & Engr.
2022, Oct. 1   **Perf. 14¼x14**
1948 A817   Sheet of 2   7.00   7.00
   a.-b.   19k Either single   3.50   3.50

Equinor
Offshore
Floating
Wind
Generator
A818

Stingray
Laser Sea
Lice
Removal
Method
A819

Die Cut Perf. 13¾x13¼
2022, Oct. 1   Litho.

Booklet Stamps
Self-Adhesive

1949 A818 (34k) multi   6.25   6.25
1950 A819 (34k) multi   6.25   6.25
   a.   Booklet pane of 10, 5 each #1949-1950   62.50

Voluntarism
A820

Die Cut Perf. 13¼x13½
2022, Nov. 11   Litho.

Coil Stamp
Self-Adhesive

1951 A820 (19k) multi   4.00   4.00

Gingerbread
House
Made by
Elin
Vatnar
Nilsen
A821

Gingerbread
House
Made by
Maren
Baxter
A822

Gingerbread House Made
by Maren
Vollestad — A823

Gingerbread Man Made by
Margrethe Lim — A824

Die Cut Perf. 13½
2022, Nov. 11   Litho.

Booklet Stamps
Self-Adhesive

1952 A821 (19k) multi   4.00   4.00
1953 A822 (19k) multi   4.00   4.00
1954 A823 (19k) multi   4.00   4.00
1955 A824 (19k) multi   4.00   4.00
   a.   Booklet pane of 10, 3 each # 1952, 1954, 2 each #1953, 1955   40.00
    Nos. 1952-1955 (4)   16.00   16.00

Christmas.

SEMI-POSTAL STAMPS

North Cape Issue

North Cape — SP1

Perf. 13½x14
1930, June 28   **Wmk. 160**   **Photo.**
Size: 33¼x21½mm

B1 SP1 15o + 25o blk brn   3.00   4.25
B2 SP1 20o + 25o car   35.00   55.00
B3 SP1 30o + 25o ultra   90.00   100.00
    Nos. B1-B3 (3)   128.00   159.25
   Set, never hinged   210.00

The surtax was given to the Tourist Association. See Nos. B9-B10, B28-B30, B54-B56, B59-B61.

Radium
Hospital — SP2

1931, Apr. 1   **Perf. 14½x13½**
B4 SP2 20o +10o carmine   10.00   7.50
   Never hinged   50.00

The surtax aided the Norwegian Radium Hospital.

Fridtjof Nansen — SP3

1935, Dec. 13   **Perf. 13½**
B5 SP3 10o + 10o green   3.50   4.75
B6 SP3 15o + 10o red brn   9.50   13.00
B7 SP3 20o + 10o crimson   2.50   3.00
B8 SP3 30o + 10o brt ultra   8.50   13.00
    Nos. B5-B8 (4)   24.00   33.75
   Set, never hinged   45.00

The surtax aided the International Nansen Office for Refugees.

North Cape Type of 1930
1938, June 20   **Perf. 13x13½**
Size: 27x21mm

B9 SP1 20o + 25o brn car   1.75   7.00
B10 SP1 30o + 25o dp ultra   8.50   29.00
   Set, never hinged   25.00

Surtax given to the Tourist Assoc.

Queen Maud — SP4

Perf. 13x13½
1939, July 24   **Photo.**   **Unwmk.**
B11 SP4 10o + 5o brt grn   .50   10.00
B12 SP4 15o + 5o red brn   .50   10.00
B13 SP4 20o + 5o scarlet   .50   7.50
B14 SP4 30o + 5o brt ultra   .50   12.00
    Nos. B11-B14 (4)   2.00   39.50
   Set, never hinged   3.00

The surtax was used for charities.

Fridtjof Nansen — SP5

1940, Oct. 21
B15 SP5 10o + 10o dk grn   1.50   4.50
B16 SP5 15o + 10o henna brn   1.75   6.00
B17 SP5 20o + 10o dark red   .60   1.50
B18 SP5 30o + 10o ultra   1.25   4.50
    Nos. B15-B18 (4)   5.10   16.50
   Set, never hinged   15.00

The surtax was used for war relief work.

SP6

Ancient Sailing Craft off Lofoten Islands.

1941, May 16
B19 SP6 15o + 10o deep blue   1.25   1.50
   Never hinged   3.50

Haalogaland Exposition. Surtax for relief fund for families of lost fishermen.
   Value for used stamp postmarked before May 15, 1945, $9.50. See note following No. 180.

Nos. 70-73, 177-180, 267, B19, B32-B34 and B38-B41 were demonetized from May 15, 1945 until Sept. 1, 1981. Used values are for stamps canceled after this period. Stamps with dated cancellations prior to May 15, 1945 sell for more. False cancellations exist.

Colin Archer
and Lifeboat
SP7

Lifeboat
SP8

1941, July 9   **Perf. 13x13½, 13½x13**
B20 SP7 10o + 10o yel grn   1.00   2.50
B21 SP7 15o + 10o dk ol brn   1.20   3.50
B22 SP8 20o + 10o brt red   .25   1.00
B23 SP8 30o + 10o ultra   2.50   8.00
    Nos. B20-B23 (4)   4.95   15.00
   Set, never hinged   15.00

Norwegian Lifeboat Society, 50th anniv.

Legionary, Norwegian
and Finnish Flags — SP9

1941, Aug. 1   **Perf. 13½x13**
B24 SP9 20o + 80o scar ver   30.00   100.00
   Never hinged   100.00

The surtax was for the Norwegian Legion.

Vidkun Quisling — SP10

1942, Feb. 1
B25 SP10 20o + 30o henna   3.00   25.00
   Never hinged   11.00

Overprinted in Red

B26 SP10 20o + 30o henna   3.00   30.00
   Never hinged   12.00

Inauguration of Quisling as prime minister.

> **Catalogue values for unused stamps in this section, from this point to the end of the section, are for Never Hinged items.**

Vidkun Quisling — SP11

1942, Sept. 26   **Perf. 13**
B27 SP11 20o + 30o henna   .85   7.50

8th annual meeting of Nasjonal Samling, Quisling's party. The surtax aided relatives of soldiers killed in action.

North Cape Type of 1930
1943, Apr. 1   Size: 27x21mm
B28 SP1 15o + 25o olive brn   1.75   2.00
B29 SP1 20o + 25o dark car   3.50   3.50
B30 SP1 30o + 25o chalky
     blue   3.50   3.50
   Nos. B28-B30 (3)   8.75   9.00

The surtax aided the Tourist Association.

Frontier Guardsmen
Emblem — SP12

1943, Aug. 2   Unwmk.
B31 SP12 20o + 30o henna   .75   9.00

The surtax aided the Frontier Guardsmen
(Norwegian Nazi Volunteers).

Fishing Village
SP13

Drying Grain
SP14

Barn in
Winter — SP15

1943, Nov. 10
B32 SP13 10o + 10o gray green   1.75   5.00
B33 SP14 20o + 10o henna   1.75   5.00
B34 SP15 40o + 10o grnsh blk   1.75   5.00
   Nos. B32-B34 (3)   5.25   15.00

The surtax was for winter relief.
Value, set postmarked before May 15, 1945,
$15. See note following No. B19.

The Baroy
Sinking
SP16

Sanct Svithun
Aflame
SP17

Design: 20o+10o, "Irma" sinking.

1944, May 20
B35 SP16 10o + 10o gray grn   1.25   5.00
B36 SP17 15o + 10o dk olive   1.25   5.00
B37 SP16 20o + 10o henna   1.25   5.00
   Nos. B35-B37 (3)   3.75   15.00

The surtax aided victims of wartime ship
sinkings, and their families.

Spinning
SP19

Plowing
SP20

Tree Felling
SP21

Child Care
SP22

1944, Dec. 1
B38 SP19 5o + 10o deep mag   1.00   .50
B39 SP20 10o + 10o dark yel grn   1.00   .50
B40 SP21 15o + 10o chocolate   1.00   .50
B41 SP22 20o + 10o henna   1.00   .50
   Nos. B38-B41 (4)   4.00   2.00

The surtax was for National Welfare.
Value, set postmarked before May 15, 1945,
$20. See note following No. B19.

Red Cross
Nurse — SP23

1945, Sept. 22
B42 SP23 20o + 10o red   1.00   1.40

80th anniv. of the founding of the Norwegian
Red Cross. The surtax was for that institution.
For surcharge see No. B47.

Crown Prince
Olav — SP24

1946, Mar. 4   Unwmk.
B43 SP24 10o + 10o ol grn   .75   .60
B44 SP24 15o + 10o ol brn   .75   .60
B45 SP24 20o + 10o dk red   1.00   .60
B46 SP24 30o + 10o brt bl   2.50   2.50
   Nos. B43-B46 (4)   5.00   4.30

The surtax was for war victims.

No. B42 Surcharged in
Black

1948, Dec. 1
B47 SP23 25o + 5o on 20o+10o   1.00   1.25

The surtax was for Red Cross relief work.

Child Picking
Flowers — SP25

1950, Aug. 15   Photo.   *Perf. 13*
B48 SP25 20o + 5o brt red   2.00   1.40
B49 SP25 45o + 5o dp bl   7.00   7.00

The surtax was for poliomyelitis victims.

Skater
SP26

Winter Scene
SP27

Design: 30o+10o, Ski jumper.

1951, Oct. 1
B50 SP26 15o + 5o olive grn   1.90   2.50
B51 SP26 30o + 10o red   2.75   2.75
B52 SP27 55o + 20o blue   10.00   10.00
   Nos. B50-B52 (3)   14.65   15.25

Olympic Winter Games, Oslo, 2/14-29/52.

Kneeling Woman — SP28

1953, June 1   Photo. & Litho.
B53 SP28 30o + 10o red & cr   2.00   2.00

The surtax was for cancer research.

North Cape Type of 1930
1953, June 15   Photo.
   Size: 27x21mm
B54 SP1 20o + 10o green   11.50   11.50
B55 SP1 30o + 15o red   13.00   13.00
B56 SP1 55o + 25o gray blue   15.00   15.00
   Nos. B54-B56 (3)   39.50   39.50

The surtax aided the Tourist Association.

Crown Princess
Martha — SP29

1956, Mar. 28   *Perf. 13*
B57 SP29 35o + 10o dark red   1.40   1.40
B58 SP29 65o + 10o dark blue   4.50   4.50

The surtax was for the Crown Princess
Martha Memorial Fund.

North Cape Type of 1930
1957, May 6   Size: 27x21mm
B59 SP1 25o + 10o green   6.25   6.25
B60 SP1 35o + 15o red   7.50   7.50
B61 SP1 65o + 25o gray blue   3.25   2.75
   Nos. B59-B61 (3)   17.00   16.50

The surtax aided the Tourist Association.

White Anemone — SP30

Design: 90o+10o, Hepatica.

1960, Jan. 12   Litho.   *Perf. 13*
B62 SP30 45o + 10o brt red &
     grn   2.75   2.75
B63 SP30 90o + 10o bl, org &
     grn   8.25   8.25

The surtax was for anti-tuberculosis work.

Mother, Child, WRY
Emblem — SP31

1960, Apr. 7   Photo.   Unwmk.
B64 SP31 45o + 25o rose &
     blk   6.00   6.00
B65 SP31 90o + 25o bl & blk   11.00   11.00

World Refugee Year, July 1, 1959-June 30,
1960. The surtax was for aid to refugees.

Severed Chain
and
Dove — SP32

Design: 60o+10o, Norwegian flags.

1965, May 8   Photo.   *Perf. 13*
B66 SP32 30o + 10o grn, blk &
     tan   .50   .50
B67 SP32 60o + 10o red & dk bl   .90   .60

20th anniversary of liberation from the
Germans. The surtax was for war cripples.

Souvenir Sheet

Offshore Oil Drilling — SP33

Designs: a, Ekofisk Center. b, Treasure
Scout drilling rig and Odin Viking supply vessel at Tromsoflaket, 1982. c, Statfjord C oil
platform, 1984. d, Men working on deck of
Neptune Nordraug.

1985, Oct. 4   Litho.   *Perf. 13½x13*
B68 SP33 Sheet of 4   8.00   10.00
  a.-d.   2k + 1k, any single   1.75   2.50

Stamp Day 1985. Surtax for philatelic
promotion.

Souvenir Sheet

Paper Industry — SP34

Paper mill: a, Wood aging containers. b,
Boiling plant. c, Paper-making machine. d,
Paper dryer.

1986, Oct. 17   Litho.   *Perf. 13½*
B69 SP34 Sheet of 4   12.50   12.50
  a.-d.   2.50k + 1k, any single   3.00   3.00

Surtax for philatelic promotion. Nos. B69a-
B69b and B69c-B69d printed in continuous
designs.

Souvenir Sheet

Salmon Industry — SP35

Designs: a, Eggs and milt pressed out of
fish by hand. b, Cultivation of eggs in tanks. c,
Outdoor hatchery. d, Market.

1987, Oct. 9   Litho.   *Perf. 13½x13*
B70 SP35 Sheet of 4   14.00   15.00
  a.   2.30k +50o multi   3.00   3.00
  b.   2.70k +50o multi   3.00   3.00
  c.   3.50k +50o multi   3.00   3.00
  d.   4.50k +50o multi   3.00   3.00

Souvenir Sheet

Norwegian Constituent Assembly,
200th Anniv. — SP36

No. B71: a, Prince Christian Frederik, Constitution of 1814. b, Parliament Lion sculpture,
parade.

2014, Nov. 21   Litho.   *Perf. 14x13¼*
B71 SP36 Sheet of 2   10.00   10.00
  a.   16k multi   4.25   4.25
  b.   19k multi   5.50   5.50

Nordia 2014 Stamp Exhibition, Oslo. No.
B71 sold for 41k, with 6k defraying the costs of
the exhibition.

AIR POST STAMPS

Airplane over Akershus
Castle — AP1

   Perf. 13½x14½
1927-34   Typo.   Wmk. 160
C1 AP1 45o lt bl, strong frame
    line ('34)   4.50   5.00
    Never hinged   22.50
  a.   Faint or broken frame line   15.00   8.00
    Never hinged   160.00

Airplane over Akershus
Castle — AP2

1937, Aug. 18   Photo.   *Perf. 13*
C2 AP2 45o Prussian blue   1.20   .70
    Never hinged   3.50

1941, Nov. 10   **Unwmk.**
C3   AP2 45o indigo   .50   .25
   Never hinged   1.75

POSTAGE DUE STAMPS

Numeral of Value — D1

Inscribed "at betale"

Perf. 14½x13½

1889-1914   **Typo.**   **Wmk. 160**
J1   D1   1o olive green ('15)   .75   1.75
   Never hinged   2.25
J2   D1   4o magenta ('11)   1.50   1.00
   Never hinged   12.00
J3   D1   10o carmine rose
     ('99)   3.00   .75
   Never hinged   21.00
  a.   10o rose red ('89)   75.00   25.00
J4   D1   15o brown ('14)   1.50   1.25
   Never hinged   20.00
J5   D1   20o ultra ('99)   2.50   .65
   Never hinged   20.00
  a.   Perf. 13½x12½ ('95)   210.00   100.00
J6   D1   50o maroon ('89)   5.00   2.50
   Never hinged   40.00
   Nos. J1-J6 (6)   14.25   7.90

See #J7-J12. For overprint see #136-144.

1922-23   **Inscribed "a betale"**
J7   D1   4o lilac rose   5.00   11.00
   Never hinged   22.50
J8   D1   10o green   2.50   2.50
   Never hinged   17.50
J9   D1   20o dull violet   3.00   5.50
   Never hinged   25.00
J10   D1   40o deep ultra   6.00   1.25
   Never hinged   35.00
J11   D1   100o orange yel   22.50   12.50
   Never hinged   130.00
J12   D1   200o dark violet   55.00   25.00
   Never hinged   130.00
   Nos. J7-J12 (6)   94.00   57.75

OFFICIAL STAMPS

Coat of Arms — O1

Perf. 14½x13½

1926   **Typo.**   **Wmk. 160**
O1   O1   5o rose lilac   .75   1.75
O2   O1   10o yellow green   .50   .50
O3   O1   15o indigo   2.00   4.25
O4   O1   20o plum   .50   .50
O5   O1   30o slate   3.00   8.00
O6   O1   40o deep blue   1.25   2.50
O7   O1   60o Prussian blue   3.00   10.00
   Nos. O1-O7 (7)   11.00   27.50
   Set, never hinged   35.00

Official Stamp of 1926
Surcharged

1929, July 1
O8   O1   2o on 5o magenta   .80   1.50
   Never hinged   1.50

Coat of
Arms — O2

Perf. 14½x13½

1933-34   **Litho.**   **Wmk. 160**
     Size: 35x19¼mm
O9   O2   2o ocher   .55   1.60
O10   O2   5o rose lilac   4.00   6.25
O11   O2   7o orange   4.00   9.00
O12   O2   10o green   27.50   1.10
O13   O2   15o olive   .55   1.10
O14   O2   20o vermilion   27.50   .55
O15   O2   25o yellow brn   .55   .90
O16   O2   30o ultra   .80   1.10
O18   O2   40o slate   27.50   1.10
O19   O2   60o blue   16.00   1.75

O20   O2   70o olive brn   1.25   3.50
O21   O2   100o violet   1.75   3.00
   Nos. O9-O16,O18-O21 (12)   111.95   30.95
   Same, never hinged   550.00

On the lithographed stamps, the lion's left
leg is shaded.

Typo.
     Size: 34x18¾mm
O10a   O2   5o rose lilac   1.25   3.50
O11a   O2   7o orange   7.25   22.50
O12a   O2   10o green   .50   .50
O13a   O2   15o olive   3.50   18.00
O14a   O2   20o vermilion   .60   .60
O17   O2   35o red violet ('34)   .60   .60
O18a   O2   40o slate   .85   .85
O19a   O2   60o blue   .85   1.00
   Nos. O10a-O14a,O17,O18a-O19a (8)   15.40   47.45
   Same, never hinged   55.00

Coat of Arms — O3

1937-38   **Photo.**   **Perf. 13½x13**
O22   O3   5o rose lilac ('38)   .60   1.50
O23   O3   7o dp orange   .60   3.75
O24   O3   10o brt green   .25   .25
O25   O3   15o olive bister   .55   1.40
O26   O3   20o carmine ('38)   1.75   4.25
O27   O3   25o red brown ('38)   .75   .50
O28   O3   30o ultra   .75   .50
O29   O3   35o red vio ('38)   .75   .75
O30   O3   40o Prus grn ('38)   .60   .60
O31   O3   60o Prus bl ('38)   .75   1.40
O32   O3   100o dk vio ('38)   1.50   2.50
   Nos. O22-O32 (11)   8.85   18.40
   Set, never hinged   35.00

See Nos. O33-O43, O55-O56. For
surcharge see No. O57.

1939-47   **Unwmk.**
O33   O3   5o dp red lil ('41)   .25   .25
O34   O3   7o dp orange ('41)   .25   1.50
O35   O3   10o brt green ('41)   .25   .25
O36   O3   15o olive ('45)   .25   .45
O37   O3   20o carmine   .25   .25
O38   O3   25o red brown   3.00   7.50
O38A   O3   25o scarlet ('46)   .25   .25
O39   O3   30o ultra   2.50   3.00
O39A   O3   30o dk gray ('47)   .60   .60
O40   O3   35o brt lilac ('41)   .75   .60
O41   O3   40o grnsh blk ('41)   .55   .50
O41A   O3   40o dp ultra ('46)   2.50   .50
O42   O3   60o Prus blue ('41)   .50   .50
O43   O3   100o dk violet ('41)   1.00   .50
   Nos. O33-O43 (14)   12.90   16.65
   Set, never hinged   40.00

Norwegian Nazi Party
Emblem — O4

1942-44
O44   O4   5o magenta   .25   2.00
O45   O4   7o yellow org   .25   2.00
O46   O4   10o emerald   .25   .40
O47   O4   15o olive ('44)   1.50   30.00
O48   O4   20o bright red   .25   .40
O49   O4   25o red brn ('43)   2.50   35.00
O50   O4   30o brt ultra ('44)   1.75   35.00
O51   O4   35o brt pur ('43)   1.75   15.00
O52   O4   40o grnsh blk ('43)   .25   .50
O53   O4   60o indigo ('43)   1.50   17.50
O54   O4   1k blue vio ('43)   1.50   25.00
   Nos. O44-O54 (11)   11.75   162.80
   Set, never hinged   25.00

Type of 1937

1947, Nov. 1
O55   O3   50o deep magenta   .50   1.00
O56   O3   200o orange   1.75   .50
   Set, never hinged   5.00

No. O37 Surcharged
in Black

1949, Mar. 15
O57   O3   25o on 20o carmine   .25   .50
   Never hinged   .50

Norway Coat of
Arms — O5

1951-52   **Unwmk.**   **Photo.**   **Perf. 13**
O58   O5   5o rose lilac   .75   .50
O59   O5   10o dk gray   .75   .25
O60   O5   15o dp org brn ('52)   1.00   .90
O61   O5   30o scarlet   .35   .25
O62   O5   35o red brn ('52)   1.25   .90
O63   O5   60o blue gray   .90   .25
O64   O5   100o vio bl ('52)   1.25   .75
   Set O58-O64 (7)   6.25   3.80
   Set, never hinged   15.00

> Catalogue values for unused
> stamps in this section, from this
> point to the end of the section, are
> for Never Hinged items.

Norway Coat of
Arms — O6

1955-61
O65   O6   5o rose lilac   .25   .25
O66   O6   10o slate   .25   .25
O67   O6   15o orange brn   .50   2.50
O68   O6   20o bl grn ('57)   .50   .25
O69   O6   25o emer ('59)   .70   .25
O70   O6   30o scarlet   3.00   .75
O71   O6   35o brown red   .55   .25
O72   O6   40o blue lilac   1.10   .25
O73   O6   45o scar ('58)   1.10   .25
O74   O6   50o gldn brn ('57)   3.00   .25
O75   O6   60o blue   12.00   .55
O76   O6   70o brn olive ('56)   5.25   1.00
O77   O6   75o maroon ('57)   20.00   13.50
O78   O6   80o org brn ('57)   6.75   1.00
O79   O6   90o org ('58)   1.00   .25
O80   O6   1k vio ('57)   1.75   .25
O81   O6   2k gray grn ('60)   3.00   .25
O82   O6   5k red lil ('61)   6.75   .65
   Nos. O65-O82 (18)   67.45   22.70

See Phosphorescence note after No. 430.

1962-74   **Photo.**
O83   O6   30o green ('64)   2.00   .25
O84   O6   40o ol grn ('68)   2.00   .50
O85   O6   50o scarlet   2.50   .25
O86   O6   50o slate ('69)   .70   .40
O87   O6   60o dk red ('64)   1.10   .25
O87A   O6   60o grnsh bl ('72)   4.25   8.25
O88   O6   65o dk red ('68)   1.75   .25
O89   O6   70o dk red ('70)   .50   .40
O90   O6   75o lt grn ('73)   1.25   1.25
O90A   O6   80o red brn ('72)   1.25   .40
O91   O6   85o ocher ('74)   .95   3.00
O92   O6   1k dp org ('73)   .50   .40
O93   O6   1.10k car lake ('74)   1.00   1.25
   Nos. O83-O93 (13)   19.75   16.85

Shades exist of several values of type O6.
Nos O87A, O90A are on phosphored paper.

1975-82   **Litho.**
O94   O6   5o rose lil ('80)   .40   1.75
O95   O6   10o bluish gray
     ('82)   .70   3.50
O96   O6   15o henna brn   1.00   4.00
O97   O6   20o green ('82)   6.00   5.50
O98   O6   25o yellow grn   .40   .40
O99   O6   40o ol grn ('79)   2.25   10.00
O100   O6   50o grnsh gray
     ('76)   .50   .25
O101   O6   60o dk grnsh bl   2.25   8.00
O102   O6   70o dk red ('82)   5.50   12.50
O103   O6   80o org brn ('76)   .60   .25
O104   O6   1k vio ('80)   2.50   .50
O105   O6   1.10k red ('80)   2.00   3.50
O106   O6   1.25k dull red   .70   .25
O107   O6   1.30k lilac ('81)   1.75   3.00
O108   O6   1.50k red ('81)   .70   .40
O109   O6   1.75k dl bl grn ('82)   1.75   1.75
O110   O6   2k dk gray grn   1.00   .25
O111   O6   2k cerise ('82)   1.40   .40
O112   O6   3k purple ('82)   1.75   .25
O113   O6   5k lt vio   30.00   3.00
O114   O6   5k blue ('77)   1.75   .25
   Nos. O94-O114 (21)   64.90   59.95

In lithographed set, shield's background is
dotted; on photogravure stamps it is solid
color.
Official stamps invalid as of Apr. 1, 1985.

NOSSI-BE

ˌno-sē-ˈbā

LOCATION — Island in the Indian
Ocean, off the northwest coast of
Madagascar
GOVT. — French Protectorate
AREA — 130 sq. mi.
POP. — 9,000 (approx. 1900)

CAPITAL — Hellville

In 1896 the island was placed under
the authority of the Governor-General
of Madagascar and postage stamps of
Madagascar were placed in use.

100 Centimes = 1 Franc

Stamps of French Colonies
Surcharged in Blue

   a   b   c

On the following issues the colors of the
French Colonies stamps, type A9, are: 5c,
green, *greenish*; 10c, black, *lavender*; 15c,
blue; 20c, red, *green*; 30c, brown, *bister*; 40c,
vermilion, *straw*; 75c, carmine, *rose*; 1fr,
bronze green, *straw*.

1889   **Unwmk.**   *Imperf.*
1   A8(a)   25 on 40c red,
     straw   2,600.   1,100.
  a.   Double surcharge   3,400.
  b.   Inverted surcharge   3,750.   1,600.
2   A8(b)   25c on 40c red,
     straw   3,100.   2,000.
  a.   Double surcharge   5,500.   2,800.
  b.   Inverted surcharge   5,500.   2,800.
  c.   Pair, "a" and "c"

     Perf. 14x13½
3   A9(b)   5c on 10c   3,750.   1,450.
  a.   Double surcharge   3,500.
  b.   Inverted surcharge   5,000.   3,100.
4   A9(b)   5c on 20c   4,000.   1,600.
  a.   Inverted surcharge   5,000.   3,100.
5   A9(c)   5c on 10c   3,100.   1,100.
  a.   Inverted surcharge   5,600.
6   A9(c)   5c on 20c   3,600.   2,400.
7   A9(a)   15 on 20c   2,800.   1,100.
  a.   Double surcharge   2,400.
  b.   Inverted surcharge   4,250.   1,750.
  c.   15 on 30c (error)   32,000.   28,000.
8   A9(a)   15 on 30c   2,800.   950.
  a.   Double surcharge   2,200.
  b.   Inverted surcharge   3,600.   1,600.
9   A9(a)   15 on 40c   2,400.   1,100.
  a.   Double surcharge   2,000.
  b.   Inverted surcharge   3,600.   1,600.

   d   e

     f

1890   **Black Surcharge**
10   A9(d)   25c on 20c   425.00   300.00
11   A9(e)   0.25 on 20c   425.00   300.00
12   A9(f)   25 on 20c   1,000.   675.00
13   A9(d)   25c on 75c   425.00   300.00
14   A9(e)   0.25 on 75c   425.00   300.00
15   A9(f)   25 on 75c   1,000.   675.00
16   A9(d)   25c on 1fr   425.00   300.00
17   A9(e)   0.25 on 1fr   425.00   300.00
18   A9(f)   25 on 1fr   1,000.   675.00

The 25c on 20c with surcharge composed of
"25 c." as in "d," "N S B" as in "e," and frame as
in "f" is an essay.

Surcharged or Overprinted in Black,
Carmine, Vermilion or Blue

   j   k

     m

1893
23   A9(j)   25 on 20c (Bk)   52.50   45.00
24   A9(j)   25 on 20c (Bk)   67.50   47.50
  a.   Inverted surcharge   400.00   260.00
25   A9(j)   75 on 20c (Bk)   300.00   240.00
26   A9(j)   1fr on 5c (Bk)   150.00   110.00
  a.   Inverted surcharge   400.00   275.00
27   A9(k)   10c (C)   28.00   24.00
  a.   Inverted overprint   130.00   120.00
28   A9(k)   10c (V)   27.50   24.00
29   A9(k)   15c (Bk)   32.50   32.50
  a.   Inverted overprint   140.00   130.00

30	A9(k)	20c (Bk)	500.00	75.00
31	A9(m)	20c (Bl)	130.00	67.50
a.		Inverted overprint	190.00	180.00

Counterfeits exist of surcharges and overprints of Nos. 1-31.

Navigation and Commerce — A14

1894 **Typo.** **Perf. 14x13½**
Name of Colony in Blue or Carmine

32	A14	1c blk, *lil bl*	1.60	1.60
33	A14	2c brn, *buff*	2.00	2.00
34	A14	4c claret, *lav*	2.75	2.00
35	A14	5c grn, *greenish*	4.00	3.25
36	A14	10c blk, *lav*	9.50	6.50
37	A14	15c blue, quadrille paper	13.50	6.50
38	A14	20c red, *grn*	9.50	6.50
39	A14	25c blk, *rose*	16.00	9.50
40	A14	30c brn, *bister*	16.00	14.50
41	A14	40c red, *straw*	22.50	16.00
42	A14	50c carmine, *rose*	22.50	16.00
43	A14	75c dp vio, *orange*	37.50	37.50
44	A14	1fr brnz grn, *straw*	27.50	27.50
		Nos. 32-44 (13)	184.85	149.35

Perf. 13½x14 stamps are counterfeits.

POSTAGE DUE STAMPS

Stamps of French Colonies Surcharged in Black

n   o

1891 **Unwmk.** **Perf. 14x13½**

J1	A9(n)	20 on 1c blk, *lil bl*	425.00	300.00
a.		Inverted surcharge	925.00	675.00
b.		Surcharged vertically	1,200.	1,400.
c.		Surcharge on back	1,050.	1,050.
J2	A9(n)	30 on 2c brn, *buff*	400.00	300.00
a.		Inverted surcharge	875.00	675.00
b.		Surcharge on back	1,000.	1,200.
J3	A9(n)	50 on 30c brn, *bister*	120.00	105.00
a.		Inverted surcharge	925.00	675.00
b.		Surcharge on back	1,050.	1,300.
J4	A9(o)	35 on 4c cl, *lav*	450.00	325.00
a.		Inverted surcharge	925.00	675.00
b.		Surcharge on back	1,100.	1,300.
c.		Pair, one without surcharge		
J5	A9(o)	35 on 20c red, *green*	450.00	325.00
a.		Inverted surcharge	925.00	675.00
J6	A9(o)	1fr on 35c vio, *orange*	325.00	240.00
a.		Inverted surcharge	925.00	625.00

p   q

r

1891

J7	A9(p)	5c on 20c	225.00	225.00
J8	A9(q)	5c on 20c	275.00	275.00
b.		In se-tenant pair with #J7	725.00	
J9	A9(r)	0.10c on 5c	27.50	24.00
J10	A9(q)	10c on 15c	225.00	225.00
J11	A9(q)	10c on 15c	275.00	275.00
b.		In se-tenant pair with #J10	725.00	
J12	A9(p)	15c on 10c	200.00	200.00
J13	A9(q)	15c on 10c	210.00	210.00
b.		In se-tenant pair with #J12	725.00	
J14	A9(r)	0.15c on 20c	32.50	32.50
a.		25c on 20c (error)	40,000.	35,000.
J15	A9(q)	25c on 5c	180.00	180.00
J16	A9(q)	25c on 5c	200.00	200.00
b.		In se-tenant pair with #J15	700.00	
J17	A9(r)	0.25c on 75c	650.00	575.00

Inverted Surcharge

J7a	A9(p)	5c on 20c	425.00	425.00
J8a	A9(q)	5c on 20c	425.00	425.00
J10a	A9(p)	10c on 15c	425.00	425.00
J11a	A9(q)	10c on 15c	425.00	425.00
J12a	A9(q)	15c on 10c	425.00	425.00
J13a	A9(q)	15c on 10c	425.00	425.00
J15a	A9(p)	25c on 5c	425.00	425.00
J16a	A9(q)	25c on 5c	425.00	425.00
J17a	A9(r)	0.25c on 75c	1,800.	1,500.

Stamps of Nossi-Be were superseded by those of Madagascar.
Counterfeits exist of surcharges on #J1-J17.

NYASALAND PROTECTORATE

nĭ-'a-sə-ˌland prə-'tek-tˌə-ˌrət

LOCATION — In southern Africa, bordering on Lake Nyasa
GOVT. — British Protectorate
AREA — 49,000 sq. mi.
POP. — 2,950,000 (est. 1962)
CAPITAL — Zomba

For previous issues, see British Central Africa.

Nyasaland joined the Federation of Rhodesia and Nyasaland in 1953, using its stamps until 1963. As the Federation began to dissolve in 1963, Nyasaland withdrew its postal services and issued provisional stamps. On July 6, 1964, Nyasaland became the independent state of Malawi.

12 Pence = 1 Shilling
20 Shillings = 1 Pound

Catalogue values for unused stamps in this country are for Never Hinged items, beginning with Scott 68 in the regular postage section and Scott J1 in the postage due section.

A1   King Edward VII — A2

Wmk. Crown and C A (2)
1908, July 22 **Typo.** **Perf. 14**
Chalky Paper

1	A1	1sh black, *green*	7.00	19.00

Wmk. Multiple Crown and C A (3)
Ordinary Paper

2	A1	½p green	2.00	2.25
3	A1	1p carmine	10.00	1.10

Chalky Paper

4	A1	3p violet, *yel*	2.00	4.75
5	A1	4p scar & blk, *yel*	2.25	1.75
6	A1	6p red vio & vio	7.00	12.50
7	A2	2sh6p car & blk, *bl*	80.00	110.00
8	A2	4sh black & car	120.00	180.00
9	A2	10sh red & grn, *grn*	225.00	325.00
10	A2	£1 blk & vio, *red*	650.00	750.00
11	A2	£10 ultra & lilac	12,000.	8,000.
		Nos. 1-10 (10)	1,105.	1,406.

A3   King George V — A4

1913-19 **Ordinary Paper**

12	A3	½p green	1.75	2.25
13	A3	1p scarlet	8.25	1.00
a.		1p carmine	4.25	2.00
14	A3	2p gray	11.00	1.00
15	A3	2½p ultra	2.75	9.00

Chalky Paper

16	A3	3p violet, *yel*	8.50	4.50
a.		3p violet, *pale yel*	6.50	10.00
17	A3	4p scar & blk, *yel*	2.00	2.50
a.		4p scar & blk, *pale yel*	6.50	8.50

18	A3	6p red vio & dull vio	6.00	8.50
19	A3	1sh black, *green*	2.50	9.00
a.		1sh black, emerald	5.50	7.00
b.		1sh blk, *bl grn*, olive back	6.00	1.75
20	A4	2sh6p red & blk, *bl*		
		('18)	14.00	30.00
21	A4	4sh blk & red ('18)	55.00	100.00
22	A4	10sh red & grn, *grn*	130.00	160.00
23	A4	£1 blk & vio, *red*		
		('18)	200.00	190.00
24	A4	£10 brt ultra & slate ('19)	4,500.	2,250.
		Revenue cancel		275.00
a.		£10 pale ultra & dull vio ('14)	8,500.	
		Revenue cancel		300.00
		Nos. 12-23 (12)	441.75	517.75

Stamps of Nyasaland Protectorate overprinted "N. F." are listed under German East Africa.

1921-30 **Wmk. 4** **Ordinary Paper**

25	A3	½p green	3.25	.50
26	A3	1p rose red	4.00	.50
27	A3	1½p orange	4.00	17.50
28	A3	2p gray	4.00	.50

Chalky Paper

29	A3	3p violet, *yel*	22.00	3.25
30	A3	4p scar & blk, *yel*	7.00	11.00
31	A3	6p red vio & dl vio	7.00	3.50
32	A3	1sh blk, *grn* ('30)	14.50	4.50
33	A4	2sh ultra & dl vio, *bl*	22.50	15.00
34	A4	2sh6p red & blk, *bl* ('24)	27.50	42.50
35	A4	4sh black & car	30.00	50.00
36	A4	5sh red & grn, *yel* ('29)	55.00	85.00
37	A4	10sh red & grn, *em-er*	120.00	120.00
		Nos. 25-37 (13)	320.75	353.75

George V and Leopard — A5

1934-35 **Engr.** **Perf. 12½**

38	A5	½p green	.75	.75
39	A5	1p dark brown	.75	.75
40	A5	1½p rose	.90	3.00
41	A5	2p gray	1.25	1.25
42	A5	3p dark blue	3.00	2.00
43	A5	4p rose lilac ('35)	10.00	4.00
44	A5	6p dk violet	3.50	.50
45	A5	9p olive bis ('35)	10.00	16.00
46	A5	1sh orange & blk	24.00	15.00
		Nos. 38-46 (9)	54.15	43.75

Common Design Types pictured following the introduction.

Silver Jubilee Issue
Common Design Type

1935, May 6 **Perf. 11x12**

47	CD301	1p gray blk & ultra	1.25	2.50
48	CD301	2p indigo & grn	1.25	2.50
49	CD301	3p ultra & brn	12.00	22.50
50	CD301	1sh brown vio & ind	29.00	55.00
		Nos. 47-50 (4)	43.50	82.50
		Set, never hinged	60.00	

Coronation Issue
Common Design Type

1937, May 12 **Perf. 11x11½**

51	CD302	½p deep green	.25	.30
52	CD302	1p dark brown	.40	.40
53	CD302	2p gray black	.40	.60
		Nos. 51-53 (3)	1.05	1.30
		Set, never hinged	1.75	

A6

Canoe on Lake Nyasa — A8   Soldier of King's African Rifles — A9

 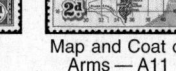

Tea Estate, Mlanje Mountain — A10   Map and Coat of Arms — A11

Fishing Village, Lake Nyasa A12   Tobacco Estate A13

King George VI — A7

1938-44 **Engr.** **Perf. 12½**

54	A6	½p green	.25	2.00
54A	A6	½p dk brown ('42)	.25	2.25
55	A6	1p dark brown	2.50	.35
55A	A6	1p green ('42)	.25	1.75
56	A6	1½p dark carmine	5.00	6.00
56A	A6	1½p gray ('42)	.25	5.75
57	A6	2p gray	5.00	1.25
57A	A6	2p dark car ('42)	.25	1.00

58	A6	3p blue	.60	1.00
59	A6	4p rose lilac	1.75	2.00
60	A6	6p dark violet	2.00	2.00
61	A6	9p olive bister	2.00	5.25
62	A6	1sh orange & blk	2.10	3.25
		Nos. 54-62 (13)	22.20	34.85

Typo. **Perf. 14**
Chalky Paper

63	A7	2sh ultra & dl vio, *bl*	7.00	17.50
64	A7	2sh6p red & blk, *bl*	9.00	24.00
65	A7	5sh red & grn, *yel*	35.00	30.00
a.		5sh dk red & dp grn, *yel* ('44)	55.00	140.00
66	A7	10sh red & grn, *grn*	35.00	70.00

Wmk. 3

67	A7	£1 blk & vio, *red*	30.00	52.50
		Nos. 63-67 (5)	116.00	194.00
		Nos. 54-67 (18)	138.20	228.85
		Set, never hinged	220.00	

Catalogue values for unused stamps in this section, from this point to the end of the section, are for Never Hinged items.

Arms of Nyasaland and George VI — A14

1945, Sept. 1 **Engr.** **Perf. 12**

68	A8	½p brn vio & blk	.50	.25
69	A9	1p dp green & blk	.25	.75
70	A10	1½p gray grn & blk	.35	.45
71	A11	2p scarlet & blk	1.50	.90
72	A12	3p blue & blk	.60	.30
73	A13	4p rose vio & blk	2.50	.80
74	A10	6p violet & blk	4.00	.90
75	A8	9p ol grn & blk	4.50	3.00
76	A11	1sh myr grn & ind	4.00	.25
77	A12	2sh dl red brn & grn	9.50	5.50
78	A13	2sh6p ultra & green	11.00	7.50
79	A14	5sh ultra & lt vio	7.50	10.00
80	A11	10sh green & lake	25.00	18.00
81	A14	20sh black & scar	30.00	45.00
		Nos. 68-81 (14)	101.20	93.60

Peace Issue
Common Design Type

Perf. 13½x14

1946, Dec. 16 **Wmk. 4**

82	CD303	1p bright green	.25	.30
83	CD303	2p red orange	.30	.30

A15

1947, Oct. 20   **Perf. 12**
84 A15 1p emerald & org brn   .75   .50

Silver Wedding Issue
Common Design Types
1948, Dec. 15 Photo.   Perf. 14x14½
85 CD304 1p dark green   .25   .25
Engr.; Name Typo.
Perf. 11½x11
86 CD305 10sh purple   18.00   35.00

UPU Issue
Common Design Types
Engr.; Name Typo. on 3p, 6p
Perf. 13½, 11x11½
1949, Nov. 21   **Wmk. 4**
87 CD306 1p blue green   .35   .35
88 CD307 3p Prus blue   3.00   4.00
89 CD308 6p rose violet   .85   1.25
90 CD309 1sh violet blue   .35   1.00
    Nos. 87-90 (4)   4.55   6.60

Arms of British
Central Africa
and Nyasaland
Protectorate
A16

1951, May 15   Engr.   Perf. 11x12
Arms in Black
91 A16 2p rose   1.25   1.25
92 A16 3p blue   1.25   1.25
93 A16 6p purple   1.50   2.25
94 A16 5sh deep blue   10.00   12.00
    Nos. 91-94 (4)   14.00   16.75
60th anniv. of the Protectorate, originally British Central Africa.

Exhibition
Seal — A17

1953, May 30   **Perf. 14x13½**
95 A17 6p purple   .65   .50
Central African Rhodes Cent. Exhib.

Coronation Issue
Common Design Type
1953, June 2   **Perf. 13½x13**
96 CD312 2p orange & black   .75   .75

Types of 1945-47 with Portrait of Queen Elizabeth II and

Grading
Cotton — A18

1953, Sept. 1   **Perf. 12**
97 A8 ½p red brn & blk   .25   1.25
  a. Booklet pane of 4   3.75
  b. Perf. 12x12½ ('54)   .25   1.25
98 A15 1p emer & org brn   .65   .25
  a. Booklet pane of 4   3.75
99 A10 1½p gray grn & blk   .25   1.75
100 A11 2p orange & blk   .85   .30
  a. Booklet pane of 4   4.25
  b. Perf. 12x12½ ('54)   .40   .30
101 A18 2½p blk & brt grn   .30   .50
102 A13 3p scarlet & blk   .30   .30
103 A12 4½p blue & blk   .90   .45
104 A10 6p violet & blk   1.25   1.25
  a. Booklet pane of 4   11.50
  b. Perf. 12x12½ ('54)   2.00   .90
105 A8 9p olive & blk   1.25   2.75
106 A11 1sh myr grn & ind   3.75   .50
107 A12 2sh rose brn & grn   3.50   3.75
108 A13 2sh6p ultra & grn   4.25   6.75
109 A14 5sh Prus bl & rose lil   10.00   7.00
110 A11 10sh green & lake   11.00   17.50
111 A14 20sh black & scar   25.00   32.50
    Nos. 97-111 (15)   63.50   76.80
Issue date: Nos. 97b, 100b, 104b, Mar. 8.

Revenue Stamps Overprinted in Black

Arms of
Nyasaland — A19

Perf. 11½x12
1963, Nov. 1   Engr.   Unwmk.
112 A19 ½p on 1p blue   .30   .30
113 A19 1p green   .30   .25
114 A19 2p rose red   .30   .30
115 A19 3p dark blue   .30   .25
116 A19 6p rose lake   .30   .25
117 A19 9p on 1sh car rose   .40   .40
118 A19 1sh purple   .45   2.75
119 A19 2sh6p black   1.25   2.00
120 A19 5sh brown   3.00   3.00
121 A19 10sh gray olive   5.25   8.00
122 A19 £1 violet   5.75   6.50
    Nos. 112-122 (11)   17.60   26.50
Nos. 112, 117 have 3 bars over old value.

Mother and Child — A20

Designs: 1p, Chambo fish. 2p, Zebu bull. 3p, Peanuts. 4p, Fishermen in boat. 6p, Harvesting tea. 1sh, Lumber and tropical pine branch. 1sh3p, Tobacco industry. 2sh6p, Cotton industry. 5sh, Monkey Bay, Lake Nyasa. 10sh, Afzelia tree (pod mahogany). £1, Nyala antelope, vert.

Perf. 14½
1964, Jan. 1   Unwmk.   Photo.
Size: 23x19mm
123 A20 ½p lilac   .25   .35
124 A20 1p green & blk   .25   .25
125 A20 2p red brown   .25   .25
126 A20 3p pale brn, brn red & grn   .25   .25
127 A20 4p org yel & indigo   .30   .35
Size: 41½x25mm, 25x41½mm
128 A20 6p bl pur & brt yel grn   .70   .70
129 A20 1sh yel brn & dk grn   .50   .30
130 A20 1sh3p red brn & olive   3.75   .30
131 A20 2sh6p blue & brn   3.25   .50
132 A20 5sh grn, bl, sep & yel   1.50   1.50
133 A20 10sh brn grn & gray   2.75   3.25
134 A20 £1 yel & dk brn   8.00   11.00
    Nos. 123-134 (12)   21.75   19.00

POSTAGE DUE STAMPS

Catalogue values for unused stamps in this section are for Never Hinged items.

D1

Perf. 14
1950, July 1   Wmk. 4   Typo.
J1 D1 1p rose red   4.00   32.50
J2 D1 2p ultramarine   21.00   32.50
J3 D1 3p green   17.50   8.00
J4 D1 4p claret   30.00   60.00
J5 D1 6p ocher   42.50   170.00
    Nos. J1-J5 (5)   115.00   303.00

NYASSA

nī-'a-sə

LOCATION — In the northern part of Mozambique in southeast Africa
AREA — 73,292 sq. mi.
POP. — 3,000,000 (estimated)
CAPITAL — Porto Amelia

The district formerly administered by the Nyassa Company is now a part of Mozambique.

    1000 Reis = 1 Milreis
    100 Centavos = 1 Escudo (1919)

Mozambique Nos. 24-35 Overprinted in Black

Perf. 11½, 12½ (Nos. 5, 7, 10, 12)
1898   **Unwmk.**
1 A3 5r yellow   3.75   3.50
2 A3 10r redsh violet   3.75   3.50
3 A3 15r chocolate   3.75   3.50
4 A3 20r gray violet   3.75   3.50
5 A3 25r blue green   3.75   3.50
6 A3 50r light blue   3.75   3.50
  a. Inverted overprint   67.50
  b. Perf. 12½   12.00   7.50
7 A3 75r rose   4.75   4.25
8 A3 80r yellow grn   4.75   4.25
9 A3 100r brown, *buff*   4.75   4.25
10 A3 150r car, *rose*   14.00   13.00
11 A3 200r dk blue, *blue*   8.25   7.50
12 A3 300r dk blue, *salmon*   8.25   7.50
    Nos. 1-12 (12)   67.25   61.75
Reprints of Nos. 1, 5, 8, 9, 10 and 12 have white gum and clean-cut perforation 13½. Value of No. 9, $15; others $3 each.

Same Overprint on Mozambique Issue of 1898
1898   **Perf. 11½**
13 A4 2½r gray   2.90   2.70
14 A4 5r orange   2.90   2.70
15 A4 10r light green   2.90   2.70
16 A4 15r brown   4.00   2.90
17 A4 20r gray violet   4.00   2.90
18 A4 25r sea green   4.00   2.90
19 A4 50r blue   4.00   2.90
20 A4 75r rose   4.00   3.25
21 A4 80r violet   3.75   2.75
22 A4 100r dk bl, *bl*   3.75   2.75
23 A4 150r brown, *straw*   3.75   2.75
24 A4 200r red lilac, *pnksh*   5.00   2.75
25 A4 300r dk blue, *rose*   6.00   2.75
    Nos. 13-25 (13)   50.95   36.70

Giraffe — A5

Camels — A6

1901   **Engr.   Perf. 14**
26 A5 2½r blk & red brn   2.60   1.20
27 A5 5r blk & violet   2.60   1.20
28 A5 10r blk & dp grn   2.60   1.20
29 A5 15r blk & org brn   2.60   1.20
30 A5 20r blk & org red   2.60   1.70
31 A5 25r blk & orange   2.60   1.70
32 A5 50r blk & dl bl   2.60   1.70
33 A5 75r blk & car lake   2.75   2.00
34 A6 80r blk & lilac   2.75   2.00
35 A6 100r blk & brn bis   3.00   2.00
36 A6 150r blk & dp org   3.25   2.25
37 A6 200r blk & grnsh bl   3.50   2.25
38 A6 300r blk & yel grn   3.50   2.25
    Nos. 26-38 (13)   36.95   22.65
Nos. 26 to 38 are known with inverted centers but are believed to be purely speculative and never regularly issued. Value $80 each.
Perf 13½, 14½, 15½ & compound also exist. For overprints and surcharges see Nos. 39-50, 63-80.

Nos. 34, 36, 38 Surcharged

1903
39 A6 65r on 80r   1.90   1.50
40 A6 115r on 150r   1.90   1.50
41 A6 130r on 300r   1.90   1.50
    Nos. 39-41 (3)   5.70   4.50

Nos. 29, 31 Overprinted

1903
42 A5 15r black & org brn   1.90   1.50
43 A5 25r black & orange   1.90   1.50

Nos. 34, 36, 38 Surcharged

1903
44 A6 65r on 80r   57.50   47.50
45 A6 115r on 150r   57.50   47.50
46 A6 130r on 300r   57.50   47.50
    Nos. 44-46 (3)   172.50   142.50

Nos. 29, 31 Overprinted

1903
47 A5 15r black & org brn   375.00   180.00
48 A5 25r black & orange   250.00   170.00
    Forgeries exist of Nos. 44-48.

Nos. 26, 35 Surcharged

1910
49 A5 5r on 2½r   2.00   1.75
50 A6 50r on 100r   2.00   1.75
  a. "50 REIS" omitted   350.00
Reprints of Nos. 49-50, made in 1921, have 2mm space between surcharge lines, instead of 1½mm. Value, each 25 cents.

Zebra A7

Vasco da Gama's Flagship "San Gabriel" A8

Designs: Nos. 51-53, Camels. Nos. 57-59, Giraffe and palms.

1911   **Red Overprint**
51 A7 2½r blk & dl vio   2.00   1.20
52 A7 5r black   2.00   1.20
53 A7 10r blk & gray grn   2.00   1.20
54 A7 20r blk & car lake   2.00   1.20
55 A7 25r blk & vio brn   2.00   1.20
56 A7 50r blk & dp bl   2.00   1.20
57 A8 75r blk & brn   2.00   1.20
58 A8 100r blk & brn, *grn*   2.00   1.20
59 A8 200r blk & dp grn, *sal*   2.00   1.90
60 A8 300r blk, *blue*   4.75   3.75
61 A8 400r blk & dk brn   5.50   3.75
62 A8 500r ol & vio brn   7.50   6.00
    Nos. 51-62 (12)   35.75   25.00
Nos. 51-62 exist without overprint but were not issued in that condition. Value $7.50 each. For surcharges see Nos. 81-105.

Stamps of 1901-03 Surcharged

1918

			On Nos. 26-38	
63	A5	¼c on 2½r	250.00	180.00
64	A5	½c on 5r	250.00	180.00
65	A5	1c on 10r	250.00	180.00
66	A5	1½c on 15r	4.00	2.25
67	A5	2c on 20r	2.75	2.25
68	A5	3½c on 25r	2.90	2.20
69	A5	5c on 50r	2.50	2.20
70	A6	7½c on 75r	2.50	2.20
71	A6	8c on 80r	2.50	2.20
72	A6	10c on 100r	2.50	2.20
73	A6	15c on 150r	4.00	4.00
74	A6	20c on 200r	4.00	4.00
75	A6	30c on 300r	6.50	5.50

On Nos. 39-41

76	A6	40c on 65r on 80r	35.00	34.00
77	A6	50c on 115r on 150r	5.00	4.25
78	A6	1e on 130r on 300r	5.50	4.25

On Nos. 42-43

79	A5	1½c on 15r	8.50	6.50
80	A5	3½c on 25r	3.25	2.20
		Nos. 63-80 (18)	841.40	620.20

On Nos. 70-78 there is less space between "REPUBLICA" and the new value than on the other stamps of this issue.

On Nos. 76-78 the 1903 surcharge is canceled by a bar.

The surcharge exists inverted on #64, 66-70, 72, 76, 78-80, and double on #64, 67, 69.

Nos. 51-62 Surcharged
in Black or Red

Numerals: The "1" (large or small) is thin, sharp-pointed, and has thin serifs. The "2" is italic, with the tail thin and only slightly wavy. The "3" has a flat top. The "4" is open at the top. The "7" has thin strokes.

Centavos: The letters are shaded, i.e., they are thicker in some parts than in others. The "t" has a thin cross bar ending in a downward stroke at the right. The "s" is flat at the bottom and wider than in the next group.

1921 — Lisbon Surcharges

81	A7	¼c on 2½r	5.00	4.00
83	A7	½c on 5r (R)	5.00	4.00
a.		½c on 2½r (R) (error)	330.00	310.00
84	A7	1c on 10r	5.00	4.00
85	A8	1½c on 300r (R)	5.00	4.00
86	A7	2c on 20r	5.00	4.00
87	A7	2½c on 25r	5.00	4.00
88	A8	3c on 400r	5.00	4.00
a.		"Republica" omitted		
89	A7	5c on 50r	5.00	4.00
90	A7	7½c on 75r	5.00	4.00
91	A8	10c on 100r	5.00	4.00
92	A8	12c on 500r	5.00	4.00
93	A8	20c on 200r	5.00	4.00
		Nos. 81-93 (12)	60.00	48.00

Forgeries exist of Nos. 81-93.

London Surcharges

Numerals — The "1" has the vertical stroke and serifs thicker than in the Lisbon printing. The "2" is upright and has a strong wave in the tail. The small "2" is heavily shaded. The "3" has a rounded top. The "4" is closed at the top. The "7" has thick strokes.

Centavos — The letters are heavier than in the Lisbon printing and are of even thickness throughout. The "t" has a thick cross bar with scarcely any down stroke at the end. The "s" is rounded at the bottom and narrower than in the Lisbon printing.

94	A7	¼c on 2½r	3.75	3.50
95	A7	½c on 5r (R)	3.75	3.50
96	A7	1c on 10r	3.75	3.50
97	A8	1½c on 300r (R)	3.75	3.50
98	A7	2c on 20r	3.75	3.50
99	A7	2½c on 25r	3.75	3.50
100	A8	3c on 400r	3.75	3.50
101	A7	5c on 50r	3.75	3.50
102	A8	7½c on 75r	3.75	3.50
103	A8	10c on 100r	3.75	3.50
104	A8	12c on 500r	3.75	3.50
105	A8	20c on 200r	3.75	3.50
		Nos. 94-105 (12)	45.00	42.00

A9

Zebra and
Warrior — A10

Designs: 2c-6c, Vasco da Gama. 7½c-20c, "San Gabriel." 2e-5e, Dhow and warrior.

Perf. 12½, 13½-15 & Compound

1921-23			Engr.	
106	A9	¼c claret	1.75	1.10
107	A9	½c steel blue	1.75	1.10
108	A9	1c grn & blk	1.75	1.10
109	A9	1½c blk & ocher	1.75	1.10
110	A9	2c red & blk	1.75	1.10
111	A9	2½c blk & ol grn	1.75	1.10
112	A9	4c blk & org	1.75	1.10
113	A9	5c ultra & blk	1.75	1.10
114	A9	6c blk & vio	1.75	1.10
115	A9	7½c blk & blk brn	1.75	1.10
116	A9	8c blk & ol grn	1.75	1.10
117	A9	10c blk & red brn	1.75	1.10
118	A9	15c blk & carmine	1.75	1.10
119	A9	20c blk & pale bl	1.75	1.10
120	A10	30c blk & bister	1.75	1.10
121	A10	40c blk & gray bl	1.75	1.10
122	A10	50c blk & green	1.75	1.40
123	A10	1e blk & red brn	1.90	1.40
124	A10	2e red brn & blk		
		('23)	6.00	5.25
125	A10	5e ultra & red brn		
		('23)	5.50	4.00
		Nos. 106-125 (20)	43.15	29.65

1921 — Perf. 13½-15 & Compound

108a	A9	1c grn & blk	1.60	1.00
109a	A9	1½c blk & ocher	1.60	1.00
110a	A9	2c red & blk	1.60	1.00
111a	A9	2½c blk & ol grn	1.60	1.00
112a	A9	4c blk & org	1.60	1.00
113a	A9	5c ultra & blk	1.60	1.00
114a	A9	6c blk & vio	1.60	1.00
115a	A9	7½c blk & blk brn	1.60	1.00
116a	A9	8c blk & red brn	1.60	1.00
117a	A9	10c blk & carmine	1.60	1.00
118a	A9	15c blk & car	1.60	1.00
119a	A9	20c blk & pale bl	1.60	1.00
120a	A10	30c blk & bister	1.60	1.00
121a	A10	40c blk & gray bl	1.60	1.00
122a	A10	50c blk & green	1.60	1.00
123a	A10	1e blk & red brn	1.60	1.00
		Nos. 108a-123a (16)	25.60	16.00

POSTAGE DUE STAMPS

Giraffe
D1

½c, 1c, Giraffe. 2c, 3c, Zebra. 5c, 6c, 10c, "San Gabriel." 20c, 50c, Vasco da Gama.

1924		Unwmk. Engr.	Perf. 14	
J1	D1	½c deep green	4.00	3.00
J2	D1	1c gray	4.00	3.00
J3	D1	2c red	4.00	3.00
J4	D1	3c red orange	4.00	3.00
J5	D1	5c dark brown	4.00	3.00
J6	D1	6c orange brown	4.00	3.00
J7	D1	10c brown violet	4.00	3.00
J8	D1	20c carmine	4.00	3.00
J9	D1	50c lilac gray	4.00	3.00
		Nos. J1-J9 (9)	36.00	27.00

Used values are for c-t-o copies.

NEWSPAPER STAMP

Mozambique No. P6
Ovptd. Like Nos. 1-25 in
Black

1898		Unwmk.	Perf. 13½	
P1	N3	2½r brown	3.75	3.50

Reprints have white gum and clean-cut perf. 13½. Value $1.

POSTAL TAX STAMPS

Pombal Issue
Mozambique Nos. RA1-RA3
Overprinted "NYASSA" in Red

1925		Unwmk.	Perf. 12½	
RA1	CD28	15c brown & blk	11.50	10.50
RA2	CD29	15c brown & blk	11.50	10.50
RA3	CD30	15c brown & blk	11.50	10.50
		Nos. RA1-RA3 (3)	34.50	31.50

POSTAL TAX DUE STAMPS

Pombal Issue
Mozambique Nos. RAJ1-RAJ3
Overprinted "NYASSA" in Red

1925		Unwmk.	Perf. 12½	
RAJ1	CD28	30c brown & blk	17.00	15.00
RAJ2	CD29	30c brown & blk	17.00	15.00
RAJ3	CD30	30c brown & blk	17.00	15.00
		Nos. RAJ1-RAJ3 (3)	51.00	45.00

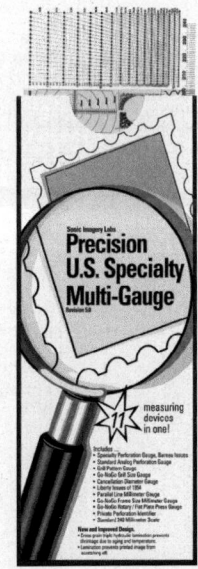

OBOCK

'ō-ˌbäk

LOCATION — A seaport in eastern Africa on the Gulf of Aden, directly opposite Aden.

Obock was the point of entrance from which French Somaliland was formed. The port was acquired by the French in 1862 but was not actively occupied until 1884 when Sagallo and Tadjoura were ceded to France. In 1888 Djibouti was made into a port and the seat of government moved from Obock to the latter city. In 1902 the name Somali Coast was adopted on the postage stamps of Djibouti, these stamps superseding the individual issues of Obock.

100 Centimes = 1 Franc

Counterfeits exist of Nos. 1-31.

Stamps of French Colonies Handstamped in Black

Nos. 1-11

Nos. 12-20

1892   Unwmk.   Perf. 14x13½

1	A9	1c blk, *lil bl*		45.00	45.00
2	A9	2c brn, *buff*		45.00	45.00
3	A9	4c claret, *lav*		450.00	475.00
4	A9	5c grn, *grnsh*		40.00	32.50
5	A9	10c blk, *lavender*		80.00	47.50
6	A9	15c blue		72.50	50.00
7	A9	25c blk, *rose*		110.00	80.00
8	A9	35c vio, *org*		450.00	450.00
9	A9	40c red, *straw*		400.00	425.00
10	A9	75c car, *rose*		450.00	475.00
11	A9	1fr brnz grn, *straw*		500.00	550.00
		Nos. 1-11 (11)		2,643.	2,675.

No. 3 has been reprinted. On the reprints the second "O" of "OBOCK" is 4mm high instead of 3½mm. Value $32.50.

1892

12	A9	4c claret, *lav*		27.50	27.50
13	A9	5c grn, *grnsh*		27.50	27.50
14	A9	10c blk, *lavender*		27.50	27.50
15	A9	15c blue		27.50	27.50
16	A9	20c red, *grn*		47.50	45.00
17	A9	25c blk, *rose*		35.00	27.50
18	A9	40c red, *straw*		60.00	52.50
19	A9	75c car, *rose*		325.00	275.00
20	A9	1fr brnz grn, *straw*		87.50	80.00
		Nos. 12-20 (9)		665.00	590.00

Exists inverted or double on all denominations.

Nos. 14, 15, 17, 20 with Additional Surcharge Handstamped in Red, Violet or Black

Nos. 21-30

No. 31

1892

21	A9	1c on 25c blk, *rose*		20.00	20.00
22	A9	2c on 10c blk, *lav*		72.50	60.00
23	A9	2c on 15c blue		22.50	20.00
24	A9	4c on 15c bl (Bk)		20.00	20.00
25	A9	4c on 25c blk, *rose* (Bk)		20.00	20.00
26	A9	5c on 25c blk, *rose*		27.50	27.50
27	A9	20c on 10c blk, *lav*		95.00	95.00
28	A9	30c on 10c blk, *lav*		120.00	110.00
29	A9	35c on 25c blk, *rose*		100.00	92.50
a.		"3" instead of "35"		950.00	
30	A9	75c on 1fr brnz grn, *straw*		110.00	110.00
b.		"57" instead of "75"		8,750.	9,250.
c.		"55" instead of "75"		8,750.	9,250.

31	A9	5fr on 1fr brnz grn, *straw* (V)		775.00	700.00
		Nos. 21-31 (11)		1,383.	1,275.

Exists inverted on most denominations.

Navigation and Commerce — A4

Obock in Red (1c, 5c, 15c, 25c, 75c, 1fr) or Blue

1892   Typo.   Perf. 14x13½

32	A4	1c blk, *lil bl*		2.75	2.75
33	A4	2c brn, *buff*		2.00	2.00
34	A4	4c claret, *lav*		2.75	2.75
35	A4	5c grn, *grnsh*		6.25	4.00
36	A4	10c blk, *lavender*		8.00	5.25
37	A4	15c bl, quadrille paper		19.50	11.50
38	A4	20c red, *grn*		27.50	27.50
39	A4	25c blk, *rose*		27.50	24.00
40	A4	30c brn, *bis*		24.00	20.00
41	A4	40c red, *straw*		24.00	20.00
42	A4	50c car, *rose*		28.00	24.00
43	A4	75c vio, *org*		32.50	24.00
a.		Name double		350.00	350.00
b.		Name inverted		5,500.	5,500.
44	A4	1fr brnz grn, *straw*		47.50	40.00
		Nos. 32-44 (13)		252.25	207.75

Perf. 13½x14 stamps are counterfeits.

Camel and Rider — A5

Quadrille Lines Printed on Paper

1893   Size: 32mm at base   Imperf.

44A	A5	2fr slate		65.00	55.00

Size: 45mm at base

45	A5	5fr red		140.00	125.00

Somali Warriors — A7

A8

1894   Imperf.

Quadrille Lines Printed on Paper

46	A7	1c blk & rose		2.75	2.75
47	A7	2c vio brn & grn		2.75	2.75
48	A7	4c brn vio & org		2.75	2.75
49	A7	5c bl grn & brn		3.50	3.50
50	A7	10c blk & org		9.50	8.00
a.		Half used as 5c on cover ('01)			350.00
51	A7	15c bl & rose		9.50	7.25
52	A7	20c brn org & mar		9.50	8.00
a.		Half used as 10c on cover ('01)			325.00
53	A7	25c blk & bl		10.50	6.50
a.		Right half used as 5c on cover ('01)			300.00
b.		Left half used as 2c on cover ('03)			300.00
54	A7	30c bis & yel grn		20.00	14.50
a.		Half used as 15c on cover ('01)			2,200.
55	A7	40c red & bl grn		17.00	13.00
56	A7	50c rose & bl		15.00	12.00
a.		Half used as 25c on cover			3,400.
57	A7	75c gray lil & org		20.00	13.00
58	A7	1fr ol grn & mar		17.00	10.50

Size: 37mm at base

60	A8	2fr vio & org		120.00	120.00

Size: 42mm at base

61	A8	5fr rose & bl		95.00	95.00

Size: 46mm at base

62	A8	10fr org & red vio		160.00	160.00
63	A8	25fr brn & bl		875.00	875.00
64	A8	50fr red vio & grn		1,000.	1,000.

Counterfeits exist of Nos. 63-64.
Stamps of Obock were replaced in 1901 by those of Somali Coast. The 5c on 75c, 5c on

25fr and 10c on 50fr of 1902 are listed under Somali Coast.

POSTAGE DUE STAMPS

Postage Due Stamps of French Colonies Handstamped Like #1-20

Nos. J1-J4

Nos. J5-J18

1892   Unwmk.   Imperf.

J1	D1	5c black	11,000.		
J2	D1	10c black	240.00	275.00	
J3	D1	30c black	375.00	450.00	
J4	D1	60c black	475.00	550.00	
J5	D1	1c black	55.00	55.00	
J6	D1	2c black	45.00	45.00	
J7	D1	3c black	52.50	52.50	
J8	D1	4c black	45.00	45.00	
J9	D1	5c black	16.00	16.00	
J10	D1	10c black	35.00	35.00	
J11	D1	15c black	24.00	24.00	
J12	D1	20c black	32.50	32.50	
J13	D1	30c black	32.50	32.50	
J14	D1	40c black	60.00	60.00	
J15	D1	60c black	80.00	80.00	
J16	D1	1fr brown	225.00	225.00	
J17	D1	2fr brown	240.00	240.00	
J18	D1	5fr brown	525.00	525.00	
		Nos. J2-J18 (17)	2,558.	2,743.	

Overprint Inverted

J5a	D1	1c black	200.00	200.00
J6a	D1	2c black	200.00	200.00
J7a	D1	3c black	200.00	200.00
J8a	D1	4c black	200.00	200.00
J9a	D1	5c black	200.00	200.00
J10a	D1	10c black	250.00	250.00
J11a	D1	15c black	200.00	200.00
J15a	D1	60c black	275.00	275.00
J16a	D1	1fr brown	550.00	550.00
J17a	D1	2fr brown	550.00	550.00

Double Overprint

J5b	D1	1c black	200.00	200.00
J6b	D1	2c black	200.00	200.00
J9b	D1	5c black	250.00	250.00
J10b	D1	10c black	300.00	300.00
J11b	D1	15c black	250.00	250.00
J12b	D1	20c black	250.00	250.00
J13b	D1	30c black	300.00	300.00

These handstamped overprints may be found double on some values. Counterfeits exist of Nos. J1-J18.

No. J1 has been reprinted. The overprint on the original measures 12½x3¾mm and on the reprint 12x3¼mm. Value, $325.

OLTRE GIUBA

ˌōl-trä-'jü-bə

(Italian Jubaland)

LOCATION — A strip of land, 50 to 100 miles in width, west of and parallel to the Juba River in East Africa
GOVT. — Former Italian Protectorate
AREA — 33,000 sq. mi.
POP. — 12,000
CAPITAL — Kismayu

Oltre Giuba was ceded to Italy by Great Britain in 1924 and in 1926 was incorporated with Italian Somaliland. In 1936 it became part of Italian East Africa.

100 Centesimi = 1 Lira

Watermark

Wmk. 140 — Crown

Italian Stamps of 1901-26 Overprinted

On #1-15

On #16-20

1925, July 29   Wmk. 140   Perf. 14

1	A42	1c brown		5.50	30.00
a.		Inverted overprint		475.00	
2	A43	2c yel brown		4.25	30.00
3	A48	5c green		4.25	12.50
4	A48	10c claret		4.25	12.50
5	A48	15c slate		4.25	17.50
6	A50	20c brn orange		4.25	17.50
7	A49	25c blue		4.25	17.50
8	A49	30c org brown		5.50	22.50
9	A49	40c brown		11.00	17.50
10	A49	50c violet		11.00	17.50
11	A49	60c carmine		11.00	22.50
12	A45	1 l brn & green		16.00	30.00
13	A46	2 l dk grn & org		85.00	60.00
14	A46	5 l blue & rose		110.00	87.50
15	A51	10 l gray grn & red		21.00	95.00
		Nos. 1-15 (15)		301.50	490.00

1925-26

16	A49	20c green		7.00	17.50
17	A49	30c gray		10.00	22.50
18	A46	75c dk red & rose		42.50	95.00
19	A46	1.25 l bl & ultra		87.50	160.00
20	A46	2.50 l dk grn & org		120.00	275.00
		Nos. 16-20 (5)		267.00	570.00

Issue years: #18-20, 1926; others 1925.

Victor Emmanuel Issue

Italian Stamps of 1925 Overprinted

1925-26   Unwmk.   Perf. 11

21	A78	60c brown car		1.60	16.00
a.		Perf. 13½		12,000.	
22	A78	1 l dark blue		1.60	25.00
a.		Perf. 13½		650.00	2,400.
23	A78	1.25 l dk bl ('26)		6.50	40.00
a.		Perf. 13½		6.50	40.00
		Nos. 21-23 (3)		9.70	81.00

Saint Francis of Assisi Issue

Italian Stamps and Type of 1926 Overprinted

1926, Apr. 12   Wmk. 140   Perf. 14

24	A79	20c gray green		2.50	45.00
25	A80	40c dark violet		2.50	45.00
26	A81	60c red brown		2.50	65.00

Overprinted in Red

Unwmk.

27	A82	1.25 l dk bl, perf. 11		2.50	87.50
28	A83	5 l + 2.50 l ol grn, perf. 13½		8.00	135.00
		Nos. 24-28 (5)		18.00	377.50

Map of Oltre Giuba — A1

1926, Apr. 21   Typo.   Wmk. 140

29	A1	5c yellow brown		1.60	35.00
30	A1	20c blue green		1.60	35.00
31	A1	25c olive brown		1.60	35.00
32	A1	40c dull red		1.60	35.00

33	A1	60c brown violet	1.60	35.00
34	A1	1 l blue	1.60	35.00
35	A1	2 l dark green	1.60	35.00
		Nos. 29-35 (7)	11.20	245.00

Oltre Giuba was incorporated with Italian Somaliland on July 1, 1926, and stamps inscribed "Oltre Giuba" were discontinued.

SEMI-POSTAL STAMPS

Note preceding Italy semi-postals applies to No. 28.

Colonial Institute Issue

"Peace" Substituting
Spade for Sword — SP1

Wmk. 140

1926, June 1		Typo.	Perf. 14	
B1	SP1	5c + 5c brown	1.20	9.50
B2	SP1	10c + 5c ol grn	1.20	9.50
B3	SP1	20c + 5c blue grn	1.20	9.50
B4	SP1	40c + 5c brn red	1.20	9.50
B5	SP1	60c + 5c orange	1.20	9.50
B6	SP1	1 l + 5c blue	1.20	20.00
		Nos. B1-B6 (6)	7.20	67.50

Surtax for Italian Colonial Institute.

SPECIAL DELIVERY STAMPS

Special Delivery
Stamps of Italy
Ovptd.

1926	Wmk. 140		Perf. 14	
E1	SD1	70c dull red	32.50	65.00
E2	SD2	2.50 l blue & red	67.50	180.00

POSTAGE DUE STAMPS

Italian Postage Due Stamps of 1870-1903 Ovptd. Like Nos. E1-E2

1925, July 29	Wmk. 140		Perf. 14	
J1	D3	5c buff & magenta	24.00	24.00
J2	D3	10c buff & magenta	24.00	24.00
J3	D3	20c buff & magenta	24.00	40.00
J4	D3	30c buff & magenta	24.00	40.00
J5	D3	40c buff & magenta	24.00	45.00
J6	D3	50c buff & magenta	32.50	55.00
J7	D3	60c buff & brown	32.50	65.00
J8	D3	1 l blue & magenta	35.00	80.00
J9	D3	2 l blue & magenta	175.00	275.00
J10	D3	5 l blue & magenta	225.00	275.00
		Nos. J1-J10 (10)	620.00	923.00

PARCEL POST STAMPS

These stamps were used by affixing them to the waybill so that one half remained on it following the parcel, the other half staying on the receipt given the sender. Most used halves are right halves. Complete stamps were obtainable canceled, probably to order. Both unused and used values are for complete stamps.

Italian Parcel Post Stamps of 1914-22 Overprinted

1925, July 29	Wmk. 140		Perf. 13½	
Q1	PP2	5c brown	21.00	45.00
Q2	PP2	10c blue	17.50	45.00
Q3	PP2	20c black	17.50	45.00
Q4	PP2	25c red	17.50	45.00
Q5	PP2	50c orange	21.00	45.00
Q6	PP2	1 l violet	17.50	100.00
a.		Double overprint	550.00	

Q7	PP2	2 l green	28.00	100.00
Q8	PP2	3 l bister	65.00	130.00
Q9	PP2	4 l slate	29.00	130.00
Q10	PP2	10 l rose lilac	95.00	225.00
Q11	PP2	12 l red brown	175.00	350.00
Q12	PP2	15 l olive green	160.00	350.00
Q13	PP2	20 l brown violet	160.00	350.00
		Nos. Q1-Q13 (13)	824.00	1,960.

Halves Used

Q1-Q4		1.75
Q5-Q7		3.00
Q8-Q9		4.75
Q10		9.25
Q11		15.00
Q12-Q13		10.00

OMAN

'ō-,män

Muscat and Oman

LOCATION — Southeastern corner of the Arabian Peninsula
GOVT. — Sultanate
AREA — 105,000 sq. mi.
POP. — 2,446,645 (1999 est.)
CAPITAL — Muscat

Nos. 16-93, the stamps with "value only" surcharges, were used not only in Muscat, but also in Dubai (Apr. 1, 1948 - Jan. 6, 1961), Qatar (Aug. 1950 - Mar. 31, 1957), and Abu Dhabi (Mar. 30, 1963 - Mar. 29, 1964). Occasionally they were also used in Bahrain and Kuwait.

The Sultanate of Muscat and Oman changed its name to Oman in 1970.

12 Pies = 1 Anna
16 Annas = 1 Rupee
100 Naye Paise = 1 Rupee (1957)
64 Baizas = 1 Rupee (1966)
1000 Baizas = 1 Rial Saidi (1970)

Watermarks

Wmk. 196 —
— Multiple
Stars

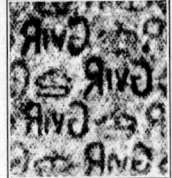

Wmk. 251 —
Crown and GviR
Multiple

Wmk. 259 —
Crown and Large
G VI R

Wmk. 298 —
Tudor Crown
and E 2 R
Multiple

Wmk. 308 —
St. Edward's
Crown and E
2 R Multiple

Wmk. 322 —
St. Edward's
Crown Multiple

Catalogue values for all unused stamps in this country are for Never Hinged items, beginning with No. 16.

Muscat

Stamps of India 1937-43
Overprinted in Black

On Nos. 1-13 the overprint is smaller — 13x6mm.

Perf. 13½x14				
1944, Nov. 20			**Wmk. 196**	
1	A83	3p slate	.40	8.00
2	A83	½a rose violet	.40	8.00
3	A83	9p lt green	.40	8.00
4	A84	1a carmine rose	.40	8.00
5	A84	1½a dark purple	.40	8.00
a.		Double overprint	325.00	
6	A84	2a scarlet	.50	8.00
7	A84	3a violet	1.00	8.00
8	A84	3½a ultra	1.00	8.00
9	A85	4a chocolate	1.10	8.00
10	A85	6a pck blue	1.25	8.00
11	A85	8a blue violet	1.40	8.50
12	A85	12a car lake	1.50	8.50
13	A81	14a rose violet	2.75	13.50
14	A82	1r brown & slate	1.75	12.50
15	A82	2r dk brn & dk vio	2.00	45.00
		Nos. 1-15 (15)	19.25	145.50

200th anniv. of Al Busaid Dynasty.
Used values for Nos. 1-15 are for stamps canceled with contemporaneous postmarks of the Indian postal administration. Examples with later British post office cancellations are worth much less.

Great Britain Nos. 258 to 263, 243, 248, 249A Surcharged

No. 16   No. 24

Perf. 14½x14				
1948, Apr. 1			**Wmk. 251**	
16	A101	½a on ½p green	3.00	8.00
17	A101	1a on 1p vermilion	3.25	.30
18	A101	1½a on 1½p lt red brn	15.00	4.25
19	A101	2a on 2p lt org	2.25	3.50
20	A101	2½a on 2½p ultra	4.25	8.50
21	A101	3a on 3p violet	4.00	.25
22	A102	6a on 6p rose lilac	4.50	.25
23	A103	1r on 1sh brown	5.00	.75
		Wmk. 259	**Perf. 14**	
24	A104	2r on 2sh6p yel grn	15.00	55.00
		Nos. 16-24 (9)	56.25	80.80

Silver Wedding Issue

Great Britain Nos. 267-268 Surcharged in Black

Perf. 14½x14, 14x14½				
1948, Apr. 26			**Wmk. 251**	
25	A109	2½a on 2½p brt ultra	3.50	5.00
26	A110	15r on £1 dp chlky bl	37.50	37.50

Three bars obliterate the original denomination on No. 26.

Olympic Games Issue

Great Britain, Nos. 271 to 274, Surcharged with New Value in Black

1948, July 29			**Perf. 14½x14**	
27	A113	2½a on 2½p brt ultra	1.00	3.00
28	A114	3a on 3p dp violet	1.15	3.00
29	A115	6a on 6p red violet	1.25	3.50
30	A116	1r on 1sh dk brn	3.00	4.75
a.		Double surcharge	1,500.	
		Nos. 27-30 (4)	6.40	14.25

A square of dots obliterates the original denomination on Nos. 28-30.

UPU Issue

Great Britain Nos. 276 to 279 Surcharged with New Value and Square of Dots in Black

1949, Oct. 10				**Photo.**
31	A117	2½a on 2½p brt ultra	1.10	3.00
32	A118	3a on 3p brt violet	1.40	4.25
33	A119	6a on 6p red violet	1.50	2.75
34	A120	1r on 1sh brown	4.00	7.50
		Nos. 31-34 (4)	8.00	17.50

Great Britain Nos. 280-286 Surcharged in Black

1951				
35	A101	½a on ½p lt org	1.00	9.50
36	A101	1a on 1p ultra	.60	8.00
37	A101	1½a on 1½p green	17.00	35.00
38	A101	2a on 2p lt red brn	.85	9.00
39	A101	2½a on 2½p vermilion	1.50	16.00
40	A102	4a on 4p ultra	1.25	3.75

		Perf. 11x12		
		Wmk. 259		
41	A121	2r on 2sh6p green	45.00	8.00
		Nos. 35-41 (7)	67.20	89.25

Two types of surcharge on No. 41.

Great Britain 1952-54
Stamps Srchd. in Black
and Dark Blue

1952-54	**Wmk. 298**		**Perf. 14½x14**	
42	A126	½a on ½p red org ('53)	.35	2.00
43	A126	1a on 1p ultra ('53)	.35	2.00
44	A126	1½a on 1½p grn ('52)	.40	2.00
45	A126	2a on 2p red brn ('53)	.50	.25
46	A127	2½a on 2½p scar ('52)	.35	.25
47	A127	3a on 3p dk pur (dk bl)	.50	1.00
48	A128	4a on 4p ultra ('53)	2.10	3.75
49	A129	6a on 6p lilac rose	.60	.45
50	A132	12a on 1sh3p dk grn ('53)	7.75	.90
51	A131	1r on 1sh6p dk bl ('53)	3.00	.75
		Nos. 42-51 (10)	15.90	13.35

Coronation Issue

Great Britain Nos. 313-316 Surcharged

1953, June 10				
52	A134	2½a on 2½p scarlet	2.25	3.00
53	A135	4a on 4p brt ultra	2.25	1.25
54	A136	12a on 1sh3p dk grn	4.25	1.25
55	A137	1r on 1sh6p dk blue	5.50	1.00
		Nos. 52-55 (4)	14.25	6.50

Squares of dots obliterate the original denominations on Nos. 54-55.

Great Britain Stamps of 1955-56 Surcharged

1955-57	**Wmk. 308**			**Photo.**
56	A126	1a on 1p ultra	.50	.60
56A	A126	1½a on 1½p grn	6,000.	950.00
57	A126	2a on 2p red brn	.85	2.00
58	A127	2½a on 2½p scar	1.00	3.00
59	A127	3a on 3p dk pur	1.10	7.50
60	A128	4a on 4p ultra	6.50	19.00
61	A129	6a on 6p lilac rose	1.40	6.50
62	A131	1r on 1sh6p dk bl	8.00	.50
		Engr.		**Perf. 11x12**
63	A133	2r on 2sh6p dk brown	10.00	1.50
64	A133	5r on 5sh crimson	14.00	3.50
		Nos. 56,57-64 (9)	41.35	44.10

Surcharge on No. 63 exists in three types, on No. 64 in two types.
Issued: 2r, 9/23/55; 2a, 2½a, 6/8/56; 1r, 8/2/56; 4a, 12/9/56; 1½a, 1956; 3a, 2/3/57; 6a, 2/10/57; 5r, 3/1/57; 1a, 3/4/57.

Great Britain Nos. 317-325, 328, 332 Surcharged

1957, Apr. 1   **Perf. 14½x14**

65	A129	1np on 5p lt brown	.25	.90
66	A126	3np on ½p red org	.35	2.00
67	A126	6np on 1p ultra	.40	2.25
68	A126	9np on 1½p green	.50	1.50
69	A126	12np on 2p red brown	.55	1.75
70	A127	15np on 2½p scar, I	.65	.50
a.		Type II	.55	3.00
71	A127	20np on 3p dk pur	.40	.30
72	A128	25np on 4p ultra	1.20	6.00
73	A129	40np on 6p lilac rose	.90	.60
74	A130	50np on 9p dp ol grn	1.75	2.50
75	A132	75np on 1sh3p dk grn	3.50	.75
		Nos. 65-75 (11)	10.45	19.05

The arrangement of the surcharge varies on different values; there are three bars through value on No. 74.

Jubilee Jamboree Issue
Great Britain Nos. 334-336 Surcharged with New Value and Square of Dots

Perf. 14½x14

1957, Aug. 1   **Wmk. 308**

76	A138	15np on 2½p scar	1.75	1.75
77	A138	25np on 4p ultra	1.75	1.75
78	A138	75np on 1sh3p dk grn	1.75	1.75
		Nos. 76-78 (3)	5.25	5.25

50th anniv. of the Boy Scout movement and the World Scout Jubilee Jamboree, Aug. 1-12.

Great Britain Stamps of 1958-60 Surcharged

Perf. 14½x14

1960-61   **Wmk. 322**   **Photo.**

79	A129	1np on 5p lt brn	.25	.30
80	A126	3np on ½p red org	1.00	1.25
81	A126	5np on 1p ultra	1.75	3.00
82	A126	6np on 1p ultra	1.25	1.00
83	A126	10np on 1½p green	1.00	2.50
84	A126	12np on 2p red brn	3.00	3.00
85	A127	15np on 2½p scar	.50	.25
86	A127	20np on 3p dk pur	.50	.25
87	A128	30np on 4½p hn brn	.75	1.10
88	A129	on 6p lil rose	.85	.30
89	A130	50np on 9p dp ol grn	1.50	2.25
90	A132	75np on 1sh3p dk grn	4.00	1.75
91	A131	1r on 1sh6p dk blue	30.00	6.50
92	A133	2r on 2sh6p dk blue	15.00	37.50
93	A133	5r on 5sh crim	35.00	55.00
		Nos. 79-93 (15)	96.35	115.95

Issued: 15np, 4/26; 3np, 6np, 12np, 6/21; 1np, 8/8; 20np, 40np, 9/28; 5np, 10np, 30np, 50np-5r, 4/8/61.

Muscat and Oman

Crest A1

View of Harbor A2

Nakhal Fort — A3

Crest and: 50b, Samail Fort. 1r, Sohar Fort. 2r, Nizwa Fort. 5r, Matrah Fort. 10r, Mirani Fort.

Perf. 14½x14 (A1), 14x14½ (A2), 14x13½ (A3)

1966, Apr. 29   **Photo.**   **Unwmk.**

94	A1	3b dp claret	.25	.25
95	A1	5b brown	.25	.25
96	A1	10b red brown	.25	.25
97	A2	15b black & violet	.90	.25
98	A2	20b black & ultra	1.35	.25
99	A2	25b black & orange	2.00	.60
100	A3	30b dk blue & lil rose	2.40	.65
101	A3	50b red brn & brt grn	3.50	1.50
a.		Value in "baizas" in Arabic	225.00	100.00
102	A3	1r org & dk bl	6.75	1.75
103	A3	2r grn & brn org	12.50	5.00
104	A3	5r dp car & vio	26.00	17.00
105	A3	10r dk vio & car rose	52.50	35.00
		Nos. 94-105 (12)	108.65	62.75

No. 101 has value in rupees in Arabic. See Nos. 110-121. For overprints & surcharges see Nos. 122-133C.

Mina al Fahal Harbor — A4

Designs: 25b, Oil tanks. 40b, Oil installation in the desert. 1r, View of Arabian Peninsula from Gemini IV.

Perf. 13½x13

1969, Jan. 1   **Litho.**   **Unwmk.**

106	A4	20b multicolored	4.50	.90
107	A4	25b multicolored	6.25	1.35
108	A4	40b multicolored	9.00	2.00
109	A4	1r multicolored	23.00	5.00
		Nos. 106-109 (4)	42.75	9.25

1st oil shipment from Muscat & Oman, July, 1967.

Types of 1966

Designs: 50b, Nakhal Fort. 75b, Samail Fort. 100b, Sohar Fort. ¼r, Nizwa Fort. ½r, Matrah Fort. 1r, Mirani Fort.

Perf. 14½x14 (A1), 14x14½ (A2), 14x13½ (A3)

1970, June 27   **Photo.**   **Unwmk.**

110	A1	5b plum	1.00	.25
111	A1	10b brown	2.00	.40
112	A1	20b red brown	2.25	.45
113	A2	25b black & vio	4.00	.60
114	A2	30b black & ultra	5.00	1.00
115	A2	40b black & org	6.00	1.25
116	A3	50b dk blue & lil rose	8.00	1.50
117	A3	75b red brn & brt grn	9.50	2.00
118	A3	100b orange & dk bl	11.00	2.25
119	A3	¼r grn & brn org	27.50	5.50
120	A3	½r brn car & vio	52.50	17.50
121	A3	1r dk vio & car rose	95.00	30.00
		Nos. 110-121 (12)	223.75	62.70

Sultanate of Oman
Nos. 110-121 Overprinted

a   b

c

Type 1

Type 2

5b, 10b 20b:
Type 1 — Lower bars 15¼mm long; letter "A" has low, thick crossbar.
Type 2 — Lower bars 14¾mm; "A" crossbar high, thin.

Perf. 14½x14, 14x14½, 14x13½

1971, Jan. 16   **Photo.**   **Unwmk.**

122	A1 (a)	5b plum	11.50	.60
a.	Type 2		65.00	25.00
123	A1 (a)	10b brown	32.00	17.50
a.	Type 2		70.00	30.00
124	A1 (a)	20b red brown	15.00	.80
a.	Type 2		75.00	30.00
125	A2 (b)	25b black & vio	2.10	.50
126	A2 (b)	30b black & ultra	3.00	.80
127	A2 (b)	40b black & org	3.75	1.00
128	A3 (c)	50b dk bl & lil rose	5.25	1.25
129	A3 (c)	75b red brn & brt grn	7.75	2.00
130	A3 (c)	100b org & dk bl	10.25	3.50
131	A3 (c)	¼r grn & brn org	25.00	8.50
132	A3 (c)	½r brn car & vio	57.50	15.00
133	A3 (c)	1r dk vio & car rose	120.00	30.00
		Nos. 122-133 (12)	293.10	81.45

For surcharge see No. 133B.

No. 94 Surcharged Nos. 127, 102 Surcharged

Perf. 14½x14, 14x14½, 14½x13½

1971-72

133A	A1	5b on 3b	170.00	20.00
133B	A2	25b on 40b	180.00	120.00
133C	A3	25b on 1r	200.00	140.00
		Nos. 133A-133C (3)	550.00	280.00

No. 133C surcharge resembles type "c" with "Sultanate of Oman" omitted and bars of criss-cross lines.
No. 133A exists with inverted surchagre and in pair, one with surcharge omitted. No. 133C exists with Arabic "2" or "5" omitted.
Issued: 5b, 11/1/71; #133C, 6/6/72; #133B, 7/1/72.

Sultan Qaboos bin Said and New Buildings A5

National Day: 40b, Sultan Qaboos and freedom symbols. 50b, Crest of Oman and health clinic. 100b, Crest of Oman, classrooms and school.

1971, July 23   **Litho.**   **Perf. 13½x14**

134	A5	10b multicolored	3.25	.45
135	A5	40b multicolored	12.00	.90
136	A5	50b multicolored	15.00	1.50
137	A5	100b multicolored	30.00	5.00
		Nos. 134-137 (4)	60.25	7.85

Open Book — A6

1972, Jan. 3   **Perf. 14x14½**

138	A6	25b ap grn, dk bl & dk red	27.50	5.00

International Book Year, 1972.

View of Muscat, 1809 — A7

Designs: 5, 10, 20, 25b, View of Matrah, 1809. 30, 40, 50, 75b, View of Shinas, 1809.

Wmk. 314 Sideways

1972, July 23   **Litho.**   **Perf. 14x14½**

Size: 21x17mm

139	A7	5b tan & multi	1.00	.30
140	A7	10b blue & multi	1.75	.30
141	A7	20b gray grn & multi	2.00	.30
142	A7	25b violet & multi	2.75	.30

Perf. 14½x14

Size: 25x21mm

143	A7	30b tan & multi	3.50	.35
144	A7	40b gray blue & multi	3.50	.40
145	A7	50b rose brn & multi	4.50	.50
146	A7	75b olive & multi	10.00	.90

Perf. 14
Size: 41x25mm

147	A7	100b lilac & multi	13.50	1.50
148	A7	¼r green & multi	30.00	3.00
149	A7	½r bister & multi	55.00	8.00
150	A7	1r dull bl grn & multi	85.00	17.00
		Nos. 139-150 (12)	212.50	32.85

Perf. 14x14½, 14½x14

1972-75   **Wmk. 314 Upright**

139a	A7	5b tan & multi ('75)	.45	.25
140a	A7	10b blue & multi ('75)	1.25	.35
141a	A7	20b gray grn & multi ('75)	2.50	.65
142a	A7	25b violet & multi ('75)	3.50	.90
143a	A7	30b tan & multi	4.75	1.20
144a	A7	40b blue & multi	7.50	1.50
145a	A7	50b rose brn & multi	8.00	1.75
146a	A7	75b olive & multi	13.50	5.00
		Nos. 139a-146a (8)	41.45	11.60

Issue dates: Nov. 17, 1972, Sept. 11, 1975.

Perf. 14x14½, 14½x14, 14

1976-82   **Wmk. 373**

139b	A7	5b tan & multi ('78)	.80	.60
140b	A7	10b blue & multi ('78)	1.25	.50
141b	A7	20b gray grn & multi ('82)	2.00	.55
142b	A7	25b vio & multi ('78)	2.50	.60
143b	A7	30b tan & multi	3.00	.85
144b	A7	40b blue & multi	4.00	1.25
145b	A7	50b rose brn & multi	5.00	1.40
146b	A7	75b olive & multi	8.75	1.60
147b	A7	100b lilac & multi	9.00	2.25
148a	A7	¼r grn & multi ('78)	25.00	6.50
149a	A7	½r bister & multi	35.00	11.00
150a	A7	1r dull bl grn & multi	85.00	22.50
		Nos. 139b-150a (12)	181.30	49.60

Issued: 4/12/76; 1/27/78; 3/15/82.

Ministerial Complex A8

Litho.; Date Typo.

1973, Sept. 20   **Unwmk.**   **Perf. 13**

151	A8	25b emerald & multi	4.25	1.25
152	A8	100b brown org & multi	15.00	3.00

Opening of ministerial complex.
Nos. 151-152 exist with date omitted and hyphen omitted.

Dhows — A9

Perf. 12½x12

1973, Nov. 18   **Litho.**   **Wmk. 314**

153	A9	15b shown	2.25	.55
154	A9	50b Seeb Airport	10.00	2.25
155	A9	65b Dhow and tanker	11.00	2.50
156	A9	100b Camel rider	17.50	3.00
		Nos. 153-156 (4)	40.75	8.30

National Day.

Port Qaboos A10

1974, July 30   **Litho.**   **Perf. 13**

157	A10	100b multicolored	18.00	4.00

Opening of Port Qaboos.

Open Book, Map of Arab World — A11

100b, Hands reaching for book, vert.

1974, Sept. 8   **Wmk. 314**   **Perf. 14½**

158	A11	25b multicolored	4.25	.55
159	A11	100b multicolored	14.00	3.25

International Literacy Day, Sept. 8.

Sultan Qaboos, UPU and Arab Postal Union Emblems A12

1974, Oct. 29   Litho.   Perf. 13½
160 A12 100b multicolored   5.00 2.00
Centenary of Universal Postal Union.

Arab Scribe — A13

1975, May 8   Photo.   Perf. 13x14
161 A13 25b multicolored   12.00 3.00
Eradication of illiteracy.

New Harbor at Mina Raysoot A14

Designs: 50b, Stadium and map of Oman. 75b, Water desalination plant. 100b, Oman color television station. 150b, Satellite earth station and map. 250b, Telephone, radar, cable and map.

Perf. 14x13½
1975, Nov. 18   Litho.   Wmk. 373
162 A14 30b multicolored   1.50   .65
163 A14 50b multicolored   3.00   .75
164 A14 75b multicolored   4.00 1.25
165 A14 100b multicolored   5.50 2.25
166 A14 150b multicolored   7.50 3.25
167 A14 250b multicolored   14.00 5.00
      Nos. 162-167 (6)   35.50 13.15
National Day 1975.
For surcharges see Nos. 190A, 190C.

Mother with Child, Nurse, Globe, Red Crescent, IWY Emblem A15

Design: 150b, Hand shielding mother and children, Omani flag, IWY emblem, vert.

Perf. 13½x14, 14x13½
1975, Dec. 27   Litho.
168 A15 75b citron & multi   3.75 1.25
169 A15 150b ultra & multi   6.25 2.25
International Women's Year 1975.
For surcharge see No. 190B.

Sultan Presenting Colors and Opening Seeb-Nizwa Road — A16

National Day: 40b, Paratroopers bailing out from plane and mechanized harvester. 75b, Helicopter squadron and Victory Day procession. 150b, Army building road and Salalah television station.

1976, Nov. 15   Litho.   Perf. 14½
173 A16 25b multicolored   1.50   .50
174 A16 40b multicolored   4.00   .75
175 A16 75b multicolored   8.00 1.75
176 A16 150b multicolored   10.00 2.00
      Nos. 173-176 (4)   23.50 5.00

Great Bath at Mohenjo-Daro A17

1977, Jan. 6   Wmk. 373   Perf. 13½
177 A17 125b multicolored   9.00 3.50
UNESCO campaign to save Mohenjo-Daro excavations in Pakistan.

APU Emblem, Members' Flags — A18

1977, Apr. 4   Litho.   Perf. 12
178 A18 30b emerald & multi   4.50 1.10
179 A18 75b blue & multi   8.75 3.25
Arab Postal Union, 25th anniversary.

Coffeepots — A19

Designs: 75b, Earthenware. 100b, Stone tablet, Khor Rori, 100 B.C. 150b, Jewelry.

1977, Nov. 18   Litho.   Perf. 13½
180 A19 40b multicolored   2.00   .60
181 A19 75b multicolored   4.00 1.10
182 A19 100b multicolored   6.00 1.75
183 A19 150b multicolored   10.00 2.25
      Nos. 180-183 (4)   22.00 5.70
National Day 1977.

Forts — A20

Wmk. 373
1978, Nov. 18   Litho.   Perf. 14
184 A20 20b Jalali   1.25   .30
185 A20 25b Nizwa   1.50   .40
186 A20 40b Rostaq   3.50   .80
187 A20 50b Sohar   4.00   .90
188 A20 75b Bahla   4.50 1.50
189 A20 100b Jibrin   7.50 2.00
      Nos. 184-189 (6)   22.25 5.90
National Day 1978.

Pilgrims, Mt. Arafat, Holy Kaaba — A21

1978, Nov. 1   Litho.   Perf. 13½
190 A21 40b multicolored   7.25 2.75
Pilgrimage to Mecca.

Nos. 166, 169 and 167 Surcharged
Perf. 14x13½
1978, July 30   Litho.   Wmk. 373
190A A14 40b on 150b   450.00 250.00
190B A15 50b on 150b   475.00 475.00
190C A14 75b on 250b   2,500.   750.00
      Nos. 190A-190C (3)   3,425. 1,475.

World Map, Book, Symbols of Learning — A22

1979, Mar. 22   Litho.   Perf. 14x13½
191 A22 40b multicolored   3.25   .60
192 A22 100b multicolored   6.25 1.50
Cultural achievements of the Arabs.

Girl on Swing, IYC Emblem — A23

1979, Oct. 28   Litho.   Perf. 14
193 A23 40b multicolored   5.00 2.50
International Year of the Child.

Gas Plant — A24

National Day: 75b, Fisheries.

1979, Nov. 18   Photo.   Perf. 11½
194 A24 25b multicolored   3.50   .85
195 A24 75b multicolored   9.00 2.75

Sultan on Horseback, Military Symbols A25

Design: 100b, Soldier, parachutes, tank.

1979, Dec. 11
196 A25 40b multicolored   8.50 1.75
197 A25 100b multicolored   14.00 4.00
Armed Forces Day.

Hegira (Pilgrimage Year) — A26

1980, Nov. 9   Photo.   Perf. 11½
198 A26 50b shown   7.00 1.10
199 A26 150b Hegira emblem   11.00 3.75

Omani Women A27

75b, Bab Alkabir. 100b, Corniche Highway. 250b, Polo match.

1980, Nov. 18   Granite Paper
200 A27 75b multi   2.75 1.10
201 A27 100b multi   4.00 2.00
202 A27 250b multi   7.25 4.75
203 A27 500b shown   14.50 8.75
      Nos. 200-203 (4)   28.50 16.60
10th National Day.
For surcharges see Nos. 212-213.

Sultan and Patrol Boat — A28

750b, Sultan, mounted troops.

1980, Dec. 11   Granite Paper
204 A28 150b shown   7.00 3.00
205 A28 750b multi   35.00 16.00
Armed Forces Day.
For surcharges see Nos. 210-211.

Policewoman and Children Crossing Street — A29

100b, Marching band. 150b, Mounted police on beach. ½r, Headquarters.

1981, Feb. 7   Litho.   Perf. 13½x14
206 A29 50b shown   4.50 1.00
207 A29 100b multi   5.50 2.00
208 A29 150b multi   6.50 3.00
209 A29 ½r multi   16.50 9.50
      Nos. 206-209 (4)   33.00 15.50
First National Police Day.

Nos. 204-205, 200, 203 Surcharged
in Black on Silver
1981, Apr. 8   Photo.   Perf. 11½
210 A28 20b on 150b multi   6.50 1.00
211 A28 30b on 750b multi   8.00 1.25
212 A27 50b on 75b multi   9.00 2.25
213 A27 100b on 500b multi   15.00 3.75
      Nos. 210-213 (4)   38.50 8.25

Welfare of the Blind — A30

1981, Oct. 14   Photo.   Perf. 11½
214 A30 10b multicolored   27.50 2.75

World Food Day — A31

1981, Oct. 16   Photo.   Perf. 12
215 A31 50b multicolored   7.50 2.50

Hegira (Pilgrimage Year) — A32

1981, Oct. 25   Litho.   Perf. 14½
216 A32 50b multicolored   8.25 3.25

11th Natl. Day — A32a

160b, Al-Razha match (sword vs. stick). 300b, Sultan, map, vert.

1981, Nov. 18   Photo.   Perf. 12
216A A32a 160b multicolored   6.00 3.25
216B A32a 300b multicolored   10.00 5.00

Voyage of Sinbad — A33

50b, Muscat Port, 1981. 100b, Dhow Shohar. 130b, Map. 200b, Muscat Harbor, 1650.

1981, Nov. 23   Litho.   Perf. 14½x14
217 A33 50b multicolored   2.50 1.10
218 A33 100b multicolored   5.25 3.00
219 A33 130b multicolored   6.25 4.00
220 A33 200b multicolored   8.75 5.50
  a. Souvenir sheet of 4, #217-220 57.50 57.50
      Nos. 217-220 (4)   22.75 13.60

Armed Forces Day — A34

1981, Dec. 11   Photo.   Perf. 11½
221 A34 100b Sultan, planes   7.00 3.25
222 A34 400b Patrol boats   18.00 8.75

Natl. Police Day — A35

1982, Jan. 5   Litho.   Perf. 14½
223 A35 50b Patrol launch   3.75 1.50
224 A35 100b Band, vert.   6.50 3.00

Nerium Mascatense A36

Red-legged Partridge A37

10b, Dionysia mira. 20b, Teucrium mascatense. 25b, Geranium mascatense. 30b, Cymatium boschi, horiz. 40b, Acteon eloiseae, horiz. 50b, Cypraea teulerei, horiz. 75b, Cypraea pulchra, horiz. ¼r, Hoopoe. ½r, Tahr. 1r, Arabian oryx.

1982, July 7 Photo. Perf. 12½, 11½
Granite Paper
225 A36   5b multicolored   .35 .25
226 A36 10b multicolored   .35 .25
227 A36 20b multicolored   .65 .25
228 A36 25b multicolored   .65 .30
229 A36 30b multicolored   1.00 .45
230 A36 40b multicolored   1.00 .55
231 A36 50b multicolored   1.25 .65
232 A36 75b multicolored,
             perf. 11½   1.50 .95
233 A37 100b multicolored   5.00 1.25
234 A37 ¼r multicolored   11.50 5.75
Size: 25x38mm
235 A37 ½r multicolored   14.00 8.25
236 A37 1r multicolored   22.50 15.50
     Nos. 225-236 (12)   59.75 34.40

2nd Municipalities Week (1981) A38

1982, Oct. 28 Litho. Perf. 13½x14½
237 A38 40b multicolored   8.50 3.00

ITU Plenipotentiaries Conference, Nairobi, Sept. — A39

1982, Nov. 6   Perf. 14½x13½
238 A39 100b multicolored   12.00 4.00

12th Natl. Day — A40

40b, State Consultative Council inaugural session. 100b, Oil refinery.

1982, Nov. 18   Perf. 12
239 A40 40b multicolored   5.00 2.00
240 A40 100b multicolored   9.50 3.50

Armed Forces Day — A41

1982, Dec. 11   Perf. 13½x14
241 A41 50b Soldiers   5.00 2.00
242 A41 100b Mounted band   9.50 4.00

Arab Palm Tree Day — A42

Perf. 13½x14½
1982, Sept. 19   Litho.
243 A42 40b Picking coconuts 5.50 2.25
244 A42 100b Dates   11.00 3.50

Natl. Police Day — A43

1983, Jan. 5 Litho. Perf. 14x13½
245 A43 50b multicolored   8.50 2.50

World Communications Year — A44

1983, May 17   Perf. 13½x14
246 A44 50b multicolored   6.75 2.50

Bees A45

Designs: a, Beehive. b, Bee, flower.

1983, Aug. 15   Litho.   Perf. 13½
247 A45   Pair   22.50 22.50
  a.-b.   50b any single   5.00 3.25

Hegira (Pilgrimage Year) — A46

1983, Sept. 14 Photo. Perf. 13½
248 A46 40b multicolored   11.50 3.25

Youth Year — A47

Perf. 12½x13½
1983, Nov. 15   Litho.
249 A47 50b multicolored   7.75 2.75

National Day 1983 — A48

50b, Sohar Copper Factory. 100b, Sultan Qaboos University.

1983, Nov. 18 Litho. Perf. 13½x14
250 A48 50b multicolored   5.25 2.25
251 A48 100b multicolored   9.25 4.50

Armed Forces Day — A49

1983, Dec. 11 Litho. Perf. 13½x14
252 A49 100b multicolored   10.00 4.00

Police Day — A50

1984, Jan. 5 Litho. Perf. 13½x14
253 A50 100b multicolored   11.00 3.50

7th Arabian Gulf Soccer Tournament, Muscat, Mar. 9-26 — A51

1984, Mar. 9   Litho.   Perf. 13½
254 A51 40b Players, cup, vert. 3.75 1.60
255 A51 50b Emblem   6.25 2.50

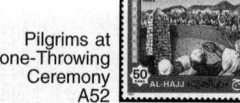

Pilgrims at Stone-Throwing Ceremony A52

1984, Sept. 5 Litho. Perf. 13½x14
256 A52 50b multicolored   7.50 2.75
Pilgrimage to Mecca.

National Day 1984 — A53

130b, Mail sorting, new p.o. 160b, Map, vert.

Perf. 13½x14, 14x13½
1984, Nov. 18   Litho.
257 A53 130b multicolored   7.50 3.25
258 A53 160b multicolored   9.50 4.00
Inauguration of the new Central P.O., development of telecommunications.

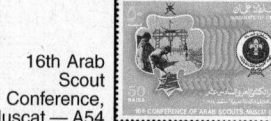

16th Arab Scout Conference, Muscat — A54

No. 259, Setting-up camp. No. 260, Map reading. No. 261, Saluting natl. flag. No. 262, Scouts and girl guides.

1984, Dec. 5   Litho.   Perf. 14½
259 A54 50b multicolored   2.25 .75
260 A54 50b multicolored   2.25 .75
  a.   Pair, #259-260   9.50 9.50

261 A54 130b multicolored   7.00 2.25
262 A54 130b multicolored   7.00 2.25
  a.   Pair, #261-262   22.50 22.50
     Nos. 259-262 (4)   18.50 6.00

Armed Forces Day — A55

1984, Dec. 11   Perf. 13½x14
263 A55 100b multicolored   11.50 4.50

Police Day — A56

1985, Jan. 5   Perf. 14x13½
264 A56 100b multicolored   11.50 4.00

Hegira (Pilgrimage Year) — A57

50b, Al-Khaif Mosque, Mina.

1985, Aug. 20 Litho. Perf. 13½x14
265 A57 50b multicolored   6.75 2.00

Intl. Youth Year — A58

50b, Emblems. 100b, Emblem, youth activities.

1985, Sept. 22 Litho. Perf. 13½x14
266 A58 50b multicolored   3.75 1.00
267 A58 100b multicolored   6.75 2.25

Jabrin Palace Restoration A59

1985, Sept. 22 Litho. Perf. 13½x14
268 A59 100b Interior   3.50 2.00
269 A59 250b Restored ceiling 8.75 5.75

Intl. Symposium on Traditional Music — A60

1985, Oct. 6 Litho. Perf. 13½x14
270 A60 50b multicolored   6.50 2.00

UN Child Survival Campaign A61

1985, Oct. 25 Litho. Perf. 13½x14
271 A61 50b multicolored   5.25 1.50

Flags, Map and Sultan Qaboos A62

50b, Supreme Council, vert.

1985, Nov. 3   Litho.   Perf. 12½
272 A62 40b shown   3.25 1.25
273 A62 50b multi   4.25 1.50

6th Session of Arab Gulf States Supreme Council, Muscat.

Natl. Day 1985 — A63

Progress and development. 20b, Sultan Qaboos University. 50b, Date picking, plowing field. 100b, Port Qaboos Cement Factory. 200b, Post, transportation and communications. 250b, Sultan Qaboos, vert.

1985, Nov. 18
274 A63 20b multicolored   1.10 1.00
275 A63 50b multicolored   2.75 2.00
276 A63 100b multicolored   5.00 3.00
277 A63 200b multicolored   8.25 5.25
278 A63 250b multicolored   9.75 6.00
Nos. 274-278 (5)   26.85 17.25

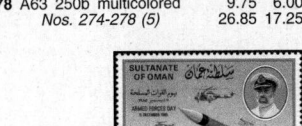

Armed Forces Day — A64

1985, Dec. 11   Perf. 13½x14
279 A64 100b multicolored   10.50 2.25

Fish and Crustaceans — A65

20b, Chaetodon collaris. 50b, Chaetodon melapterus. 100b, Chaetodon gardineri. 150b, Scomberomorus commerson. 200b, Panulirus homarus.

Perf. 11½x12, 12x11½
1985, Dec. 15   Photo.
280 A65 20b multicolored   .65 .25
281 A65 50b multicolored   1.25 .45
282 A65 100b multicolored   2.00 1.00
283 A65 150b multicolored   3.00 2.10
284 A65 200b multicolored   4.25 2.75
Nos. 280-284 (5)   11.15 6.55

Nos. 280-282, vert.

Frankincense Trees in Oman — A66

1985, Dec. 15   Litho.   Perf. 13½x14
285 A66 100b multicolored   1.75 1.25
286 A66 3r multicolored   47.50 32.50

Police Day — A67

50b, Camel Corps, Muscat.

1986, Jan. 5   Litho.   Perf. 13½x14
287 A67 50b multi   6.00 1.75

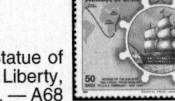

Statue of Liberty, Cent. — A68

Maps and: 50b, Sultanah, voyage from Muscat to US 1840. 100b, Statue, Shabab Oman voyage from Oman to US, 1986, and fortress.

1986, July 4   Perf. 14½
288 A68 50b multicolored   4.75 1.75
289 A68 100b multicolored   8.00 3.00
a. Souvenir sheet of 2, #288-289   32.50 22.50

No. 289a sold for 250b.

Pilgrimage to Mecca — A69

1986, Aug. 9
290 A69 50b Holy Kaaba   4.75 1.50

17th Arab Scout Camp — A70

1986, Aug. 20
291 A70 50b Erecting tent   3.50 1.25
292 A70 100b Surveying   5.50 2.50

Sultan Qaboos Sports Complex Inauguration A71

1986, Oct. 18   Litho.   Perf. 14½
293 A71 100b multicolored   4.50 2.00

Intl. Peace Year — A72

1986, Oct. 24   Perf. 13½x13
294 A72 130b multicolored   4.25 1.75

A73

A74

Natl. Day 1986 A75

1986, Nov. 18   Perf. 14½
295 A73 50b mutticolored   1.75 1.00
296 A74 100b multicolored   4.25 2.10
Perf. 13½x13
297 A75 130b multicolored   5.00 2.50
Nos. 295-297 (3)   11.00 5.60

Police Day — A76

1987, Jan. 5   Perf. 13½x14
298 A76 50b multicolored   4.50 1.75

Second Arab Gulf Week for Social Work, Bahrain — A77

1987, Mar. 21   Perf. 13½x13
299 A77 50b multicolored   3.50 1.25

Intl. Environment Day — A78

50b, Flamingos in flight. 130b, Irrigation canal, vert.

Perf. 13½x13, 13x13½
1987, June 5   Litho.
300 A78 50b multi   3.50 1.00
301 A78 130b multi   6.00 1.50

Pilgrimage to Mecca — A79

Stages of Pilgrimage (not in consecutive order): a, Pilgrims walking the tawaf, circling the Holy Kaaba 7 times. b, Tent City, Mina. c, Symbolic stoning of Satan. d, Pilgrims in Muzdalifah at dusk, picking up stones. e, Veneration of the prophet (pilgrims praying), Medina. f, Pilgrims wearing ihram, Pilgrim's Village, Jeddah.

1987, July 29   Litho.   Perf. 13½
302   Strip of 6   25.00 25.00
a.-f. A79 50b any single   1.75 1.75

Third Municipalities Month — A80

1987, Oct. 1   Perf. 13x13½
303 A80 50b multicolored   2.75 1.10

Natl. Day — A81

Designs: 50b, Marine Biology and Fisheries Center. 130b, Royal Hospital.

1987, Nov. 18   Litho.   Perf. 13½x13
304 A81 50b multicolored   1.25 .75
305 A81 130b multicolored   3.50 2.00

Royal Omani Amateur Radio Soc., 15th Anniv. — A82

1987, Dec. 23   Litho.   Perf. 13½x13
306 A82 130b multicolored   4.25 1.75

Traditional Handicrafts A83

1988, June 1   Photo.   Perf. 12x11½
Granite Paper
307 A83 50b Weaver   1.40 .75
308 A83 100b Potter   2.10 1.00
309 A83 150b Halwa maker   2.75 1.75
310 A83 200b Silversmith   3.25 2.25
a. Souvenir sheet of 4, #307-310   23.00 17.50
Nos. 307-310 (4)   9.50 5.75

No. 310a sold for 600b.

1988 Summer Olympics, Seoul — A84

1988, Sept. 17   Litho.   Perf. 14½
311 A84 100b Equestrian   1.50 .80
312 A84 100b Field hockey   1.50 .80
313 A84 100b Soccer   1.50 .80
314 A84 100b Running   1.50 .80
315 A84 100b Swimming   1.50 .80
316 A84 100b Shooting   1.50 .80
a. Block of 6, #311-316   20.00 20.00
b. Souvenir sheet of 6, #311-316   32.50 25.00

WHO, 40th Anniv. — A85

1988, Nov. 1   Litho.   Perf. 13½
317 A85 100b multicolored   2.00 1.50

Natl. Day, Agriculture Year — A86

1988, Nov. 18   Perf. 14½x13½
318 A86 100b Tending crops   1.90 1.40
319 A86 100b Animal husbandry   1.90 1.40
a. Pair, #318-319   8.50 8.50

No. 319a has a continuous design.

Women Wearing Regional Folk Costume — A87

Designs: 200b-1r, Men wearing regional folk costumes.

1989   Photo.   Perf. 11½x12
Granite Paper
320 A87 30b Dhahira   1.40 .25
321 A87 40b Eastern   1.75 .40
322 A87 50b Batinah   2.00 .50
323 A87 100b Interior   4.25 .90
324 A87 130b Southern   5.25 1.75
325 A87 150b Muscat   6.25 2.00
a. Souvenir sheet of 6, #320-325   37.50 37.50
326 A87 200b Dhahira   3.25 1.40
327 A87 ¼r Eastern   3.75 1.60
328 A87 ½r Southern   7.00 2.00
329 A87 1r Muscat   14.00 3.50
a. Souvenir sheet of 4, #326-329   37.50 37.50
Nos. 320-329 (10)   48.90 13.80

No. 325a sold for 700b, No. 329a for 2r.
Issued: 30b-150b, 8/26; 200b-1r, 11/11.

National Day, Agriculture Year — A88

1989, Nov. 18   *Perf. 12½x13*
330 A88 100b Fishing   2.00 1.00
331 A88 100b Farming   2.00 1.00
   a.   Pair, #330-331   5.00 4.50

Printed se-tenant in a continuous design.

10th Session of Supreme Council of the Cooperation Council for Arab Gulf States — A89

No. 332, Flags, Omani crest. No. 333, Sultan Qaboos, council emblem.

1989, Dec. 18   Litho.   *Perf. 13x12*
332 A89 50b multi   1.75 .75
333 A89 50b multi   1.75 .75
   a.   Pair, #332-333   4.50 4.00

No. 333a has a continuous design.

Gulf Investment Corp., 5th Anniv. (in 1989) — A90

1990, Jan. 1   Litho.   *Perf. 13x12*
334 A90 50b multicolored   2.50 1.00
335 A90 130b multicolored   3.25 1.75

Gulf Air, 40th Anniv. — A91

1990, Mar. 24   *Perf. 13x13½*
336 A91 80b multicolored   6.00 2.00

Symposium on the Oman Ophiolite — A92

1990, Apr. 22   Photo.   *Perf. 11½*
Granite Paper
337 A92 80b shown   1.75 1.00
338 A92 150b multicolored   3.50 2.00

First Omani Envoy to the U.S., 150th Anniv. — A93

1990, Apr. 30   Litho.   *Perf. 13*
339 A93 200b multicolored   3.50 2.00

Sultan Qaboos Rose — A94

1990, May 5   Photo.   *Perf. 11½*
Granite Paper
340 A94 200b multicolored   3.25 2.00

20th National Day — A95

100b, Natl. Day emblem. 200b, Sultan Qaboos.

Litho. & Embossed
1990, Nov. 18   *Perf. 12x11½*
Granite Paper
341 A95 100b gold, red & green   2.10 1.00
342 A95 200b gold, green & red   4.25 2.10
   a.   Souvenir sheet of 2, #341-342   12.50 12.50

No. 342a sold for 500b.

Blood Donors — A96

1991, Apr. 22   Litho.   *Perf. 13½x13*
343 A96 50b multicolored   .80 .60
344 A96 200b multicolored   4.25 2.00
   a.   Pair, #343-344   40.00 40.00

National Day A97

1991, Nov. 18   Photo.   *Perf. 13½*
345 A97 100b shown   3.50 1.10
346 A97 200b Sultan Qaboos   5.75 2.25
   a.   Souvenir sheet of 2, #345-346   10.00 8.00

No. 346a sold for 400b.

Armed Forces Day — A98

1991, Dec. 11   Litho.   *Perf. 14½*
347 A98 100b multicolored   3.50 1.25

A99

1992, Jan. 29   Litho.   *Perf. 13½x14*
348 A99 100b multicolored   3.25 1.25
   a.   Sheet of 1, perf. 13x13½   16.00 9.00

Inauguration of Omani-French Museum, Muscat. No. 348a sold for 300b.

A100

1992, Mar. 23   Litho.   *Perf. 14½*
349 A100 200b multicolored   4.25 1.75

World Meteorological Day.

A101

1992, June 5   Litho.   *Perf. 13x13½*
350 A101 100b multicolored   2.50 1.25

World Environment Day.

A102

1992, Sept. 26   Litho.   *Perf. 13½x14*
351 A102 70b multicolored   2.25 .75

Welfare of Handicapped Children.

Sultan Qaboos Encyclopedia of Arab Names — A103

1992, Oct. 10   *Perf. 14½*
352 A103 100b gold & multi   2.75 1.25

National Day A104

Sultan Qaboos and emblems of: 100b, Year of Industry. 200b, Majlis As'shura.

1992, Nov. 18   Litho.   *Perf. 14x13½*
353 A104 100b multicolored   3.00 1.75
354 A104 200b multicolored   4.25 2.50

Royal Oman Police Day — A105

1993, Jan. 5   Litho.   *Perf. 13½x14*
355 A105 80b multicolored   3.00 1.10

1993 Census A106

1993, Sept. 4   Litho.   *Perf. 14x13½*
356 A106 100b multicolored   3.00 1.25

Royal Navy Day — A107

1993, Nov. 3   Litho.   *Perf. 13*
357 A107 100b multicolored   3.25 1.50

23rd National Day — A108

1993, Nov. 18   Photo.   *Perf. 12*
Granite Paper
358 A108 100b Year of Youth emblem   2.25 1.50
359 A108 200b Sultan Qaboos   3.50 2.00

Scouting A109

#360, Emblem of Scouts & Guides, Scout Headquarters. #361, Scout camp, Sultan Qaboos.

1993, Nov. 20   Litho.   *Perf. 13x13½*
360 A109 100b multicolored   1.75 1.25
361 A109 100b multicolored   1.75 1.25
   a.   Pair, #360-361   5.00 5.00

Scouting movement in Oman, 61st anniv. (#360). Installation of Sultan Qaboos as chief scout, 10th anniv. (#361).

Whales and Dolphins A110

#362, Dolphins, humpback whale. #363, Dolphins, sperm whale.

1993, Dec. 8   *Perf. 14½*
362 100b multicolored   3.75 1.75
363 100b multicolored   3.75 1.75
   a.   A110 Pair, #362-363   12.00 12.00
   b.   Souvenir sheet of 2, #362-363   45.00 45.00

No. 363a has a continuous design. No. 363b sold for 400b and has a white border surrounding the stamps.

World Day for Water — A111

1994, Mar. 22   Litho.   *Perf. 13½*
364 A111 50b multicolored   2.25 .75

Muscat Municipality, 70th Anniv. — A112

1994, Apr. 16
365 A112 50b multicolored   2.25 1.00

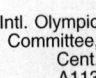

Intl. Olympic Committee, Cent. A113

1994, Aug. 29   Litho.   Perf. 13½
366 A113 100b multicolored   16.00 8.25

Al Busaid Dynasty, 250th Anniv. — A114

Natl. arms or sultan, dates: a, 1744-75. b, 1775-79. c, 1779-92. d, 1792-1804. e, 1804-7. f, Sa'id ibn Sultan, 1807-56. g, 1856-65. h, 1866-68. i, 1868-71. j, Sultan, 1871-88. k, Sultan, 1888-1913. l, Sultan Taymur ibn Faysal, 1913-32. m, Sultan Qaboos, laurel tree. n, Sultan Sa'id ibn Taymur, 1932-70. o, Sultan Qaboos, 1970-.
200b, Sultan Qaboos atop family "tree," Arabic listing of former Sultans, years in power.

Litho. & Embossed
1994, Dec. 28   Perf. 11½
367 A114 50b Block of 15, #a.-o.   60.00 60.00
Litho. & Typo.
Imperf
Size: 140x110mm
367P A114 200b gold & multi   9.50 7.50
Nos. 367f, 367j-367o contain portraits of sultans.

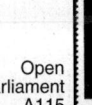

Open Parliament A115

1995, Jan. 7   Litho.   Perf. 14
Granite Paper
368 A115 50b silver & multi   2.40 1.00

24th National Day, Year of the Heritage A116

1994, Nov. 18   Litho.   Perf. 13½
369 A116 50b Emblem   1.00 .75
370 A116 50b Sultan Qaboos   1.00 .75
a.   Pair, #369-370   8.25 8.25

ICAO, 50th Anniv. — A117

1994, Dec. 7   Perf. 13½x14
371 A117 100b multicolored   6.50 3.00

Arab League, 50th Anniv. — A118

1995, Mar. 22   Litho.   Perf. 13
372 A118 100b multicolored   2.50 1.00

UN, 50th Anniv. — A119

1995, Sept. 2   Perf. 13½
373 A119 100b multicolored   4.50 1.50

16th Session of Supreme Council of the Co-operative Council for Arab Gulf States — A120

Designs: 100b, Emblem. 200b, Flags of Arab Gulf States, map, Sultan Qaboos.

1995, Dec. 4   Perf. 12
Granite Paper
374 A120 100b multicolored   3.00 1.25
375 A120 200b multicolored   4.00 1.75
a.   Pair, #374-375   34.00 22.00

25th National Day — A121

Portraits of Sultan Qaboos: 50b, In traditional attire. 100b, In military uniform.

Litho. & Embossed
1995, Nov. 18   Perf. 11½
Granite Paper
376 A121 50b multicolored   1.75 .80
377 A121 100b multicolored   3.25 1.00
a.   Souvenir sheet of 2, #376-377   7.50 5.50
No. 377a sold for 300b.

1996 Summer Olympic Games, Atlanta — A122

a, Shooting. b, Swimming. c, Cycling. d, Running.

1996, July 19   Litho.   Perf. 14½
378 A122 100b Strip of 4, #a.-d.   30.00 22.50

13th Arabian Gulf Cup Soccer Tournament A123

1996, Oct. 15   Perf. 13½
379 A123 100b multicolored   10.00 2.50

UN Decade Against Drug Abuse A124

1996, June 26   Perf. 13½x14
380 A124 100b multicolored   45.00 25.00

UNICEF, 50th Anniv. — A125

1996, Dec. 11   Litho.   Perf. 14½
381 A125 100b multicolored   2.75 1.10

26th National Day — A126

Designs: No. 382, Sultan Qaboos waving, boats in harbor. No. 383, Boats in harbor, Sultan Qaboos.

1996, Nov. 26   Perf. 13½
382   50b multicolored   1.50 .90
383   50b multicolored   1.50 .90
a.   A126 Pair, #382-383   4.75 4.75
No. 383a is a continuous design.

Traditional Boats A127

1996, Apr. 15   Photo.   Perf. 13½x14
384 A127   50b Ash'Shashah   .30 .25
385 A127   100b Al-Battil   .80 .60
386 A127   200b Al-Boum   1.50 1.10
387 A127   250b Al-Badan   1.90 1.40
388 A127   350b As'Sanbuq   2.75 2.00
389 A127   450b Al-Galbout   3.25 2.50
390 A127   650b Al-Baghlah   4.50 3.50
391 A127   1r Al-Ghanjah   7.75 5.50
Nos. 384-391 (8)   22.75 16.85
Souvenir Sheet
Imperf
392 A127 600b Designs of #384-391   15.00 11.00
No. 392 has simulated perfs. and individual stamps are defaced and not valid for postage.

Tourism — A128

a, Oasis fort among palm trees. b, Small waterfalls, trees. c, Highway, coastline, castle on hilltop. d, Lake, mountains. e, Ruins of ancient fort on cliff. f, Waterfall, mountain stream.

1997, Oct. 26   Litho.   Perf. 13½x14
393 A128 100b Block of 6, #a.-f.   13.50 13.50

27th National Day — A129

Waterfall, Sultan Qaboos wearing: No. 394, Multicolored outfit. No. 395, Wearing white outfit.

1997, Nov. 18   Litho.   Perf. 13½
394   100b multicolored   2.00 1.25
395   100b multicolored   2.00 1.25
a.   A129 Pair, #394-395   7.00 7.00

Girl Guides in Oman, 25th Anniv. — A130

1997, Nov. 30   Perf. 14½
396 A130 100b multicolored   2.75 1.50

Amateur Radio Society, 25th Anniv. A131

1997, Dec. 23   Perf. 13½
397 A131 100b multicolored   3.50 2.00

Al-Khanjar Assaidi — A132

1997, Mar. 22   Perf. 11½
Granite Paper
398 A132   50b red & multi   .85 .70
399 A132   50b green & multi   .85 .70
400 A132 100b purple & multi   2.25 1.50
401 A132 200b brown & multi   3.25 2.25
Nos. 398-401 (4)   7.20 5.15
See No. 418.

Traffic Week — A133

1998, Apr. 25   Perf. 13½
402 A133 100b multicolored   8.00 4.00

Tourism A134

Designs: a, Fort. b, Rocky mountainside, lake. c, City. d, Men raising swords, drummers. e, Stream running through countryside. f, Girls standing beside stream, trees.

1998, July 23   Perf. 13½x13
403 A134 100b Block of 6, #a.-f.   14.00 14.00

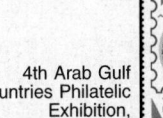

4th Arab Gulf Countries Philatelic Exhibition, Muscat — A135

1998, Sept. 5   Litho.   Perf. 13½
404 A135 50b multicolored   2.00 .80

Sultan Qaboos, Recipient of Intl. Peace Award — A136

1998, Dec. 7
405 A136 500b multicolored   19.00 14.00

28th National Day
A137

1998, Nov. 18   *Perf. 12½*
406 A137 100b Sultan Qaboos   2.25   1.00
407 A137 100b Emblem, map   2.25   1.00
   a.   Pair, #406-407   6.50   6.50
   b.   Souvenir sheet, #406-407   45.00   45.00

Opening of Raysut Port-Salalah Container Terminal — A138

1998, Dec. 1   *Perf. 13x13½*
408 A138 50b multicolored   5.50   2.25

World Stamp Day — A139

1998, Oct. 9   *Perf. 13½*
409 A139 100b multicolored   2.00   1.50

Royal Air Force of Oman, 40th Anniv. A140

       Perf. 13½x13¾
1999, June 20   Litho.
410 A140 100b multicolored   4.00   1.75

Butterflies — A141

Designs: a, Danaus chrysippus. b, Papilio demoleus. c, Precis orithya. d, Precis hierta.

1999, July 23   Litho.   *Perf. 13¼*
411 A141 100b Block of 4, #a.-
        d   13.00   13.00
   e.   Souvenir sheet of 4, #a.-d.   25.00   25.00

See No. 421.

Marine Life A142

Designs: a, Parupeneus macronema. b, Etrumeus teres. c, Epinephelus chlorostigma. d, Lethrinus lentjan. e, Lutjanus erythropterus. f, Acanthocybium solandri. g, Thunnus tongol. h, Pristipomoides filamentosus. i, Thunnus albacares. j, Penaeus indicus. k, Sepia pharaonis. l, Panulirus homarus.

1999, Aug. 21   Litho.   *Perf. 13½x13*
412 A142 100b Sheet of 12,
      #a.-l.   21.00   21.00

Wildlife A143

Designs: a, Sand cat. b, Genet. c, Leopard. d, Sand fox. e, Caracal lynx. f, Hyena.

1999, Sept. 18   Litho.   *Perf. 13½x13*
413   100b Block of 6, #a.-f.   10.00   10.00
   g.   A143 Souvenir sheet, #a.-f.   35.00   35.00

UPU, 125th Anniv. — A144

1999, Oct. 9   *Perf. 11*
414 A144 200b multi   2.75   2.25

29th National Day A145

1999, Nov. 18   Litho.   *Perf. 13½*
415   100b Sultan in black   2.25   1.25
416   100b Sultan in white   2.25   1.25
   a.   A145 Pair, #415-416   6.00   6.00

Souvenir Sheet

Millennium — A146

Litho. & Embossed with Foil Application
2000, Jan. 1   *Perf. 13¼*
417 A146 500b multi   14.00   14.00

Al-Khanjar Assaidi Type of 1997
2000, Feb. 12   Litho.   *Perf. 11½*
     Granite Paper
418 A132 80b orange & multi   1.75   1.25

GCC Water Week — A147

2000, Mar. 22   Litho.   *Perf. 13¼*
419 A147 100b multi   2.00   1.10

Gulf Air, 50th Anniv. A148

2000, Mar. 24   *Perf. 13½*
420 A148 100b multi   2.00   1.10

Butterfly Type of 1999
No. 421: a, Colotis danae. b, Anaphaeis aurota. c, Tarucus rosaceus. d, Lampides boeticus.

2000, Apr. 24   Litho.   *Perf. 13½*
421   Block of 4   12.00   12.00
   a.-d.   A141 100b Any single   2.50   1.25
   e.   Souvenir sheet, #421   27.50   27.50

Fish — A148a

No. 421F: g, Hippocampus kuda. h, Ostracion cubicus. i, Monocentris japonicus. j, Pterois antennata. k, Phinecanthus assasi. l, Taenura lymma.

       Perf. 13½x13¾
2000, June 12   Litho.
421F A148a 100b Block of 6,
       #g-l   22.50   17.50
   m.   Souvenir sheet, #421F   24.00   17.50

2000 Summer Olympics, Sydney — A149

Designs: a, Shooting. b, Emblem of Sydney Games. c, Running. d, Swimming.

2000, Sept. 15   *Perf. 13½x13¾*
422 A149 100b Block of 4, #a-
      d   10.00   10.00
   e.   Souvenir sheet, #422   27.50   27.50

Coup by Sultan Qaboos, 30th Anniv. A150

No. 423: a, Emblem, Sultan in blue hat. b, Emblem, Sultan seated. c, Emblem, Sultan in red beret. d, Emblem, Sultan in white hat. e, Emblem. f, Emblem, Sultan in black hat.

Litho. & Embossed
2000, Nov. 18   *Perf. 13½*
423   Block of 6   12.00   12.00
   a.-f.   A150 100b Any single   1.75   1.25
   g.   Souvenir sheet, #423   15.00   15.00

Wildlife A151

No. 424: a, Arabian tahr. b, Nubian ibex. c, Arabian oryx. d, Arabian gazelle.

2000, July 23   Litho.   *Perf. 13½x13*
424 A151 100b Block of 4, #a-
      d   12.00   9.00
   e.   Souvenir sheet, #424   22.50   13.00

Souvenir Sheet

Environment Day — A152

2001, Jan. 8   Litho.   *Perf. 13¾x14¼*
425 A152 200b multi   14.00   10.00

Souvenir Sheet

Palestinian Uprising in Jerusalem — A153

Litho. & Embossed
2001, July 31   *Perf. 13½x13*
426 A153 100b multi   19.00   19.00

Al-Khanjar A'Suri — A154

      Perf. 14½x13¾
2001, Mar. 19   Litho.
427 A154 50b red & multi   .75   .50
428 A154 80b yel org & multi   1.25   1.00
      Size: 26x34mm
      Perf. 13¼x13
429 A154 100b blue & multi   1.50   1.25
430 A154 200b multi   3.00   2.50
   a.   Miniature sheet, #427-430   9.00   7.50

See Nos. 474-476.

Souvenir Sheets

Jewelry A155

Litho., Typo. & Embossed
2001, Dec. 29   *Perf. 12¾x12½*
431 A155 100b Hair plait deco-
       ration   4.75   3.00
     Stamp Size: 62x27mm
      Perf. 13¼x13¾
432 A155 100b Pendant   4.75   3.00
     Stamp Size: 44x44mm
      Perf. 12¾
433 A155 100b Necklace   4.75   3.00
   Stamp Size: 38mm Diameter
      Perf.
434 A155 100b Mazrad   4.75   3.00
     Nos. 431-434 (4)   19.00   12.00

Supreme Council of Arab Gulf Cooperation Council States, 22nd Session — A156

Designs: 50b, Map. 100b, Sultan Qaboos.

Litho. & Typo.

2001, Dec. 30   *Perf. 14x14¼*
435-436   A156   Set of 2   3.25   2.00

Year of Dialogue Among Civilizations — A157

2001, Oct. 9   Litho.   *Perf. 13¾x13¼*
437   A157   200b multi   13.50   9.00

Shells A157a

No. 437A: b, Nassarius coronatus. c, Epitoneum pallasii d, Cerithium caeruleum. e, Cerithidea cingulata.

2001, Dec. 26   Litho.   *Perf. 13¼*
437A   A157a   100b Block of 4, #b-e   7.00   5.75

31st National Day A158

No. 438: a, Map of Oman, tree. b, Sultan Qaboos.

2001, Nov. 18   *Perf. 13¼*
438   A158   100b Horiz. pair, #a-b   4.75   4.75

Turtles A159

No. 439: a, Olive Ridley. b, Green. c, Hawksbill. d, Loggerhead.

2002, Aug. 12   Litho.   *Perf. 13¼x13*
439   A159   100b Block of 4, #a-d   8.25   7.00
  e.   Souvenir sheet, #439a-439d   12.00   7.00

Sultan Qaboos Grand Mosque A160

No. 440: a, Interior view of dome and chandelier. b, Exterior view of mosque and minaret. c, Exterior view of archway. d, Interior view of corner arches. 100b, Aerial view of mosque.

Litho. With Foil Application

2002, May 25   *Perf. 13¼*
440   A160   50b Block of 4, #a-d   6.00   4.75

Size: 120x90mm

Imperf
441   A160   100b multi   7.50   4.75

Souvenir Sheet

32nd National Day A160a

Design: 100b, Sultan Qaboos, flowers in corners.

Litho. With Foil Application

2002, Nov. 18   *Perf. 13x13¼*
441A   A160a   100b multi   5.25   3.00
441B   A160a   200b shown   3.50   2.75

Birds A161

No. 442: a, Streptopelia decaocto. b, Tchagra senegala. c, Ploceus galbula. d, Hieraaetus fasciatus. e, Pycnonotus xanthopygos. f, Bubo bubo. g, Eremalauda dunni. h, Burhinus capensis. i, Prinia gracilis. j, Francolinus pondicerianus. k, Onychognathus tristramii. l, Hoplopterus indicus. m, Corvus splendens. n, Chlamydotis undulata. o, Halcyon chloris. p, Pterocles coronatus.

2002, Dec. 15   *Perf. 13x13¼*
442   A161   50b Sheet of 16, #a-p   22.50   17.50

Early Intervention for Children With Special Needs — A161a

2002, Oct. 30   Litho.   *Perf. 13x13¼*
442Q   A161a   100b multi   3.50   1.75

Booklet Stamp
Self-Adhesive
Perf. 12¾
442R   A161a   100b multi   4.75   2.50
  s.   Booklet pane of 10   47.50   —

Muscat Festival 2003 — A162

2003, Jan. 8   *Perf. 14½*
443   A162   100b multi   2.00   1.00

Oman - People's Republic of China Diplomatic Relations, 25th Anniv. — A163

2003, May 25   Litho.   *Perf. 12*
444   A163   70b multi   2.50   1.25

Souvenir Sheets

A164

Arabian Horses A165

2003, Apr. 8   *Perf. 13¼x12¾*
445   A164   100b shown   4.00   3.00
446   A165   100b shown   4.00   3.00
447   A165   100b White horse facing left   4.00   3.00
448   A165   100b Brown horse   4.00   3.00
    Nos. 445-448 (4)   16.00   12.00

Census A166

No. 449: a, Emblem, buildings. b, Emblem, blue circle.

2003, Sept. 16   Litho.   *Perf. 13*
449   A166   50b Horiz. pair, #a-b   2.25   1.25

Intl. Day of Peace — A167

2003, Sept. 21   *Perf. 13¼x12¾*
450   A167   200b multi   2.75   2.50

Organization of the Islamic Conference A168

Litho. & Embossed

2003, Sept. 25   *Perf. 13*
451   A168   100b multi   2.00   1.50

Self-Employment and National Autonomous Development Program — A169

2003, Oct. 6   Litho.   *Perf. 13¼*
Souvenir Sheet
452   A169   100b multi   2.00   2.00

Booklet Stamp
Self-Adhesive
Serpentine Die Cut 12½
453   A169   100b multi   1.90   1.10
  a.   Booklet pane of 4   7.75
    Complete booklet, 3 #453a   23.50

A170

Manuscripts — A171

No. 454: a, Denomination at lower left. b, Denomination at lower right. c, Denomination at left center. d, Denomination at right center. No. 455: a, Illustrations of ships. b, Illustration of connected circles. c, Illustration of concentric circles. d, Text in large red circle.

2003, Oct. 14   Litho.   *Perf. 13½x13¼*
454   A170   100b Block of 4, #a-d   5.00   5.00
Miniature Sheet
Litho. With Foil Application
Perf. 13¼
455   A171   50b Sheet of 4, #a-d   4.75   4.00

33rd National Day A172

No. 456 — Sultan Qaboos and background color of: a, Light green. b, Light blue. c, Buff. d, Light red violet.

Litho. & Embossed

2003, Nov. 18   *Perf. 13x13¼*
456   A172   50b Block or strip of 4, #a-d   3.50   3.50

Flowers — A173

No. 457: a, Anogeissus dhofarica. b, Tecomella undulata. c, Euryops pinifolius. d, Aloe dhufarensis. e, Cleome glaucescens. f, Cassia italica. g, Cibirhiza dhofarensis. h, Ipomoea nil. i, Viola cinerea. j, Dyschoriste dalyi. k, Calotropis procera. l, Lavandula dhofarensis. m, Teucrium mascatense. n, Capparis mucronifolia. o, Geranium mascatense. p, Convolvulus arvensis.

2004, Jan. 24   Litho.   *Perf. 14½*
457   Sheet of 16   11.50   11.50
  a.-p.   A173 50b Any single   .60   .50

FIFA (Fédération Internationale de Football Association), Cent. — A174

Litho. & Embossed

2004, May 21   *Perf. 13¾*
458   A174   250b multi   4.25   3.75

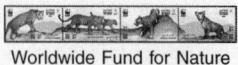

Worldwide Fund for Nature
(WWF) — A175

No. 459 — Arabian leopard: a, Front feet on mound. b, Pair of leopards. c, Rear feet on mound. d, Feet in depression.

2004, June 5 Litho. Perf. 13¾x13½
459 A175 Horiz. strip of 4 5.00 5.00
a.-d. 50b Any single .85 .75

Corals — A176

No. 460: a, Montipora. b, Porites. c, Acropora. d, Cycloseris.

2004, Aug. 1 Perf. 13¾
460 Horiz. strip of 4 7.00 7.00
a.-d. A176 100b Any single .90 .75

Intl. Day of
Peace — A177

Designs: 50b, Dove and green circle. 100b, Doves and Earth.

2004, Sept. 21 Perf. 13½x13¾
461-462 A177 Set of 2 1.50 1.50

Souvenir Sheet

Intl.
White
Cane
Day
A178

2004 Litho. Perf. 14x13¼
463 A178 100b black 5.50 5.50

Braille text was applied by a thermographic process producing a shiny, raised effect.

34th
National
Day
A179

No. 464 — Sultan Qaboos with kaffiyah in: a, Red. b, Blue green. c, Gray and white. d, Black and white.

**Litho. & Embossed With Foil
Application**
2004, Nov. 18 Perf. 13¾x13½
464 A179 100b Block of 4, #a-d 3.50 3.50

Water
Supply
Projects
A180

No. 465: a, Al Massarat. b, Ash'Sharqiyah.

2004, Dec. 1 Litho. Perf. 14
465 A180 50b Horiz. pair, #a-b 12.00 12.00

10th Gulf
Cooperation
Council
Stamp
Exhibition
A181

2004, Dec. 4 Perf. 13½
466 A181 50b multi 1.75 1.75

**Self-Adhesive
Booklet Stamp**
Serpentine Die Cut 12½

467 A181 50b multi 1.40 1.00
a. Booklet pane of 4 5.50
Complete booklet, 3 #467a 17.00

Civil
Defense
A182

Designs: 50b, Civil defense workers, Omani people. 100b, Rescue workers in action.

2005, May 14 Litho. Perf. 14
468-469 A182 Set of 2 2.10 2.10

World Blood Donor
Day — A183

2005, June 14 Litho. Perf. 13¾x14
470 A183 100b multi 1.50 1.50

Agricultural Census — A184

No. 471 — Census taker and: a, Herder and livestock. b, Farmer and crops.

2005, July 18 Perf. 14x13¼
471 A184 100b Horiz. pair, #a-b 3.25 3.25

World Summit on the Information
Society, Tunis — A185

2005, Nov. 16 Perf. 14
472 A185 100b multi 1.75 1.75

Miniature Sheet

35th
National
Day
A186

No. 473: a, Airplane, dish antennas. b, Helicopter, mounted soldiers. c, Sultan Qaboos. d, People in costumes. e, Military aircraft, ship, vehicle. f, Tower, highway. g, Tower, people at computers. h, Emblem of 35th National Day. i, Man at oasis. j, Petroleum facility.

**Litho., Litho. & Embossed With Foil
Application (#473c)**
2005, Nov. 18 Perf. 13¼x13½
473 A186 100b Sheet of 10,
#a-j 14.00 14.00

Al-Khanjar A'Suri Type of 2001
2005, Dec. 7 Litho. Perf. 13¼x13
Size: 26x34mm
474 A154 250b bl grn & multi 2.50 1.40
475 A154 300b red vio & multi 3.25 1.60
476 A154 400b yel brn & multi 4.25 2.10
Nos. 474-476 (3) 10.00 5.10

A187

Gulf Cooperation Council, 25th
Anniv. — A188

Litho. With Foil Application
2006, May 25 Perf. 14
477 A187 100b multi 6.00 6.00

Imperf
Size: 165x100mm
478 A188 500b multi 24.00 24.00

See Bahrain Nos. 628-629, Kuwait Nos. 1646-1647, Qatar Nos. 1007-1008, Saudi Arabia No. 1378, and United Arab Emirates Nos. 831-832.

Souvenir Sheet

Muscat,
2006
Capital
of Arab
Culture
A189

2006, Aug. 26 Litho. Perf. 14
479 A189 100b multi 4.50 4.50

Tourism
A190

No. 480: a, Man picking flowers, houses on mountain. b, Six men, building. c, Scuba diver, turtle on beach. d, Women with clothing on line, camels.

2006, Sept. 27 Litho. Perf. 14
480 A190 100b Block of 4, #a-d 6.00 6.00

Oman Post
Emblem
A191

Text in: 100b, Blue. 250b, White.

Litho. With Foil Application
2006, Nov. 6 Perf. 13¾x13½
481-482 A191 Set of 2 4.75 4.75

36th National
Day — A192

2006, Nov. 18 Perf. 13x13½
483 A192 100b multi 1.50 1.50

Sultan Qaboos
Prize for
Cultural
Innovation
A193

2006, Dec. 24 Litho. Perf. 13¼x13
484 A193 250b multi 4.00 4.00

Exportation of Crude Oil, 40th
Anniv. — A194

No. 485: a, Oil tanker and oil storage facility. b, Oil storage facility and oil well.

2007, July 27 Litho. Perf. 13¾
485 A194 100b Horiz. pair, #a-b 1.75 1.75

Symposium on
Agricultrual
Development — A195

2007, Oct. 1 Litho. Perf. 13¾x14
486 A195 100b multi 1.25 1.25

37th National
Day — A196

2008, Nov. 18 Perf. 13
487 A196 100b multi 2.25 2.25

Khasab
Castle
A197

No. 488: a, Exterior of castle. b, Man behind table. c, People reading. d, Men and cannons near door.

2007, Dec. 1 Perf. 13¼x13
488 A197 100b Block of 4, #a-d 4.50 4.50

Scouting,
Cent., and
Scouting in
Oman, 75th
Anniv.
A198

2007, Dec. 20 Perf. 13¾x13¼
489 A198 250b multi 2.50 2.50

19th Arabian
Gulf Cup
Soccer
Tournament
A199

2009, Jan. 4   Litho.   Perf. 12¾x13¼
490 A199 100b multi   1.25 1.25

38th National
Day — A200

**Litho. & Embossed With Foil
Application**
2008, Nov. 18   Perf. 13¾
491 A200 200b multi   2.00 2.00

Souvenir Sheet

Arab
Postal
Day
A201

No. 492 — Emblem and: a, World map, pigeon. b, Camel caravan.

Perf. 14½x13¾
2008, Dec. 21   Litho.
492 A201 200b Sheet of 2, #a-
b   12.00 12.00

Supreme Council of Gulf Cooperation
Council, 29th Session — A202

Emblem and: 100b, Flags. 300b, Rulers of
Council states.

Litho. With Foil Application
2008, Dec. 29   Perf. 13¼x13
493 A202 100b multi   3.00 3.00

Size: 162x81mm
Imperf
494 A202 300b multi   4.75 4.75

Jerusalem,
2009 Capital
of Arab
Culture
A203

2009, Nov. 10   Litho.   Perf. 13¾
495 A203 250b multi   2.75 2.75

Souvenir Sheet
With White Frame Around Stamp
496 A203 250b multi   20.00 20.00

15th Gulf
Cooperation
Council Stamps
Exhibition,
Oman — A204

No. 497: a, Part of Bahrain flag at right. b,
Part of Bahrain flag at left, part of United Arab
Emirates flag at right. c, Part of United Arab
Emirates flag at left. d, Part of Oman flag at
right. e, Part of Oman flag at left, part of Saudi
Arabia flag at right. f, Part of Saudi Arabia flag
at left, part of Kuwait flag at right. h, Part of
Kuwait flag at left, part of Qatar flag at right. i,
Part of Qatar flag at left.
50b, No flag in background.

2009, Nov. 15   Litho.   Perf. 13
497   Sheet of 9 + 6 labels 14.00 14.00
a.-i. A204 200b Any single   1.40 1.40

Booklet Stamp
Self-Adhesive
Serpentine Die Cut 12¾
498 A204 50b multi   .50   .50
a.   Booklet pane of 12   7.50 7.50

39th National
Day — A205

Litho. & Embossed
2009, Nov. 18   Perf. 13¼
499 A205 200b multi   1.75 1.75

Oman, Champions of
19th Arabian Gulf Cup
Soccer
Tournament — A206

2009, Dec. 19   Litho.   Perf. 13¼
500 A206 200b multi   2.00 2.00

Censuses — A207

Emblem of: No. 502, 50b, Third census of
Oman. No. 503, 50b, Joint Gulf Cooperation
Council census.

2010, Feb. 2   Litho.   Perf. 13¼
502-503 A207   Set of 2   1.00 1.00

Arab Water
Day — A209

2010, Mar. 3   Litho.   Perf. 14¼
506 A209 100b multi   .90   .90

A210

Expo 2010,
Shanghai — A211

2010, May 1   Perf. 12¾x13¼
Souvenir Sheet
507 A210 100b multi   2.75 2.75

Self-Adhesive
Serpentine Die Cut
508 A211 50b multi   .50   .50

Souvenir Sheet

Jewel of
Muscat
A212

2010, July 3   Perf. 13¾x13¼
509 A212 100b multi   2.75 2.75

Miniature Sheet

Renaissance Day — A213

No. 510 — Sultan Qaboos in: a, Blue uniform. b, Brown uniform, red brown background. c, White uniform. d, Beige uniform. e,
Brown uniform, gray brown background.

Litho. & Embossed
2010, July 23   Perf. 13¼
510 A213 50b Sheet of 5, #a-e   2.75 2.75

Souvenir Sheet

40th
National
Day
A214

No. 511 — Doves and: a, 100b, Map of
Oman. b, 150b, Sultan Qaboos.

2010, Oct. 18   Perf.
511 A214   Sheet of 2, #a-b   3.25 3.25

Traffic
Safety
Day
A215

2010, Oct. 18   Litho.   Perf. 13¼
Souvenir Sheet
512 A215 100b multi   2.50 2.50

Self-Adhesive
Serpentine Die Cut 13¼
513 A215 50b white & multi   .75   .75

Miniature Sheet

Second
Asian
Beach
Games,
Muscat
A216

No. 514: a, Handball. b, Sepak takraw
(player kicking ball in air). c, Soccer player
dribbling ball. d, Triathlon. e, Volleyball. f,
Water polo. g, Swimming. h, Sailing. i, Jet skiing. j, Woodball (player with mallet and ball). k,
Water skiing. l, Tent pegging (rider on horse).
m, Kabbadi (two athletes wrestling). n, Body
building.

2010, Dec. 8   Litho.   Perf. 13¼
514 A216 50b Sheet of 14, #a-n 5.50 5.50

Miniature Sheet

Children's Art — A217

No. 515: a, Cell phone with palette and
brush painting Earth on easel. b, Satellite, satellite dish, electronic devices, scissors cutting
cables. c, Car on road near buildings and
mountains with satellite dishes. d, Cell phone,
hand pointing at electronic options, telephone
handset. e, Electronic devices, film strip, people circling Earth. f, Spider web, satellite dish,
cell phones, antenna towers. g, Children and
boxes with colored squares. h, Boy using cell
phone. i, Flag of Oman, Sun, cell phones.

2010, Dec. 19   Perf. 14¼x14
515 A217 50b Sheet of 9, #a-i, +
        9 labels   4.00 4.00

Sultan Qaboos
University, 25th
Anniv. — A218

Emblems, tower, and: 50b, Symbols of science and industry. 100b, Sultan Qaboos,
horiz.

2011, Nov. 9   Perf. 13¾x13¼
516 A218 50b multi   .50   .50
Size: 90x65mm
Imperf
517 A218 100b multi   1.00 1.00

41st
National
Day
A219

Sultan Qaboos, Royal Opera House, Muscat, and scenes from various productions:
50b, 100b, 150b.

2011, Nov. 18
518-520 A219   Set of 3   3.50 3.50

Intl. Year of
Chemistry — A220

2011, Dec. 27   Perf. 14¼x14
521 A220 100b multi   .75   .75

Friendship With Japan, 40th
Anniv. — A221

2012, May 7   Perf. 14x13¼
522 A221 100b multi   .75   .75

Frankincense and Incense
Burner — A222

2012, June 21   Litho.   Perf. 13¼x14
523 A222 250b multi   3.00 3.00
Salalah Tourism Festival. Portions of No.
523 have a scratch-and-sniff covering with a
frankincese aroma.

Miniature Sheet

Muscat,
2012
Arab
Tourism
Capital
A223

No. 524: a, Old Muscat. b, Sultan Qaboos
Grand Mosque. c, Matrah and port. d, Royal
Opera House at night. e, Matrah Corniche with
docked ships. f, Barr al Jissah Resort.

2012, July 23   Litho.   Perf. 14¼x14
524 A223 50b Sheet of 6, #a-f, +
      6 labels   6.00 6.00

Arab Postal
Day — A224

Litho. & Embossed
2012, Aug. 3   Perf. 13½
525 A224 100b multi   .70   .70

Sultan Qaboos
Sailing
Trophy — A225

Litho. & Embossed With Foil Application
2012, Nov. 3   Perf. 14x13½
526 A225 250b multi   1.75 1.75

42nd
National
Day
A226

Sultan Qaboos and various ships at Oman
Drydock Company: 50b, 100b, 150b.

Perf. 13½x13¼
2012, Nov. 18   Litho.
527-529 A226 Set of 3   3.75 3.75

Miniature Sheets

Arabian
Horses
A227

No. 530, 100b — Horse named Dorar: a,
Facing right, black background. b, Facing left,
outdoors. c, Head, facing right, and hindquar-
ters, black background, vert. d, Facing left,

black background. e, Standing, facing right,
outdoors.
No. 531, 100b — Horse named: a, Ajlad,
standing and facing right. b, Psymamon, vert.
c, Ajlad, head only, vert. d, Modheeah. e,
Sadeed, vert.

2012, Dec. 12   Litho.   Perf. 13¼
Sheets of 5, #a-e
530-531 A227 Set of 2   7.00 7.00

Omani
Environment
Day — A228

Designs: 50b, Adenium obesum. 100b, Cis-
tanche tubulosa. 200b, Amygdalus arabica.
250b, Aegopordon berardoides.

2013, Jan. 8   Litho.   Perf. 14
532-535 A228 Set of 4   —   —

Miniature Sheet

Omani
Crafts
Day
A229

No. 536: a, Woven bowl and lid. b, Silver
sphere on pedestal. c, Teapot, bowl and cups.
d, Copper plate. e, Jewel box and string of
pearls. f, Bowl with lid showing emblem of
Oman. g, Carpet with tassels. h, Basket.

Litho. & Embossed
2013, Mar. 3   Perf. 13½
536 A229 150b Sheet of 8, #a-h,
      + central label   —   —

Diplomatic Relations Between Oman
and People's Republic of China, 35th
Anniv. — A230

2013, May 25   Litho.   Perf. 13
537 A230 200b multi   —   —

Girl Guides 20th Arab Regional
Conference — A231

2013, Aug. 24   Litho.   Perf. 14¼x14
538 A231 100b multi   .70   .70

Oman Boy Scouts 16th Intl. Youth
Gathering for Cultural
Exchange — A232

2013, Sept. 4   Litho.   Perf. 14¼x14
539 A232 200b multi   1.40 1.40

A233   Omani
               Women's
              Day — A234

Litho. & Embossed
2013, Oct. 17   Perf. 14
540 A233 100b multi   1.25 1.25
541 A234 100b multi   1.25 1.25

Traffic Safety
Day — A235

2013, Oct. 18   Litho.   Perf. 14
542 A235 50b multi   1.00 1.00

A236   A237

Sultan
Qaboos — A238

2013, Nov. 18   Litho.   Perf. 13½x13
543 A236 200b multi   1.50 1.50
544 A237 200b multi   1.50 1.50
545 A238 200b multi   1.50 1.50
      Nos. 543-545 (3)   4.50 4.50
43rd National Day. Nos. 543-545 each were
printed in sheets of 4.

Sultan's Armed
Forces Museum,
25th
Anniv. — A239

Designs: 50b, Museum exterior. 100b, Sultan Qaboos in museum.

2013, Dec. 11   Litho.   Perf. 13½
546-547 A239 Set of 2   1.75 1.75

Establishment of
Omani Philatelic
Association
A240

Designs: 100b, Association emblem. 150b,
Cancels and canceler. 200b, Various Oman
stamps.

2014, May 21   Litho.   Perf. 13x13¼
548-550 A240 Set of 3   3.25 3.25
550a   Souvenir sheet of 3, #548-
             550   3.25 3.25

Salalah
Festival — A241

Emblem and: 100b, People, raised hands,
flag.
150b, Building, vert.

2014, July 30   Litho.   Perf. 13¼
551 A241 100b multi   .70   .70

Souvenir Sheet
Perf. 13½x13
552 A241 150b multi   1.10 1.10
No. 552 contains one 30x40mm stamp.

Muscat
Festival — A242

2014, Aug. 14   Litho.   Perf. 13x13½
553 A242 100b multi   .70   .70

Souvenir Sheet

Tour of
Oman
Bicycle
Race
A243

2014, Aug. 14   Litho.   Perf. 13x13½
554 A243 250b multi   1.75 1.75

Architectural Details From Castles and
Forts — A244

No. 555: a, Jabreen Castle. b, Nizwa Fort. c,
Bahla Fort. d, Al Hazm Castle.
No. 556, 250b, Like #555a. No. 557, 250b,
Like #555b. No. 558, 250b, Like #555c. No.
559, 250b, Like #555d.

2014, Sept. 29   Litho.   Perf. 13½x13
555 A244 150b Sheet of 4, #a-d   4.25 4.25
Souvenir Sheets
556-559 A244 Set of 4   7.00 7.00

44th
National
Day
A245

No. 560 — Sultan Qaboos with background
color of: a, Purple brown. b, Blue. c, Green. d,
Purple.
200b, Sultan Qaboos, diff.

2014, Nov. 18   Litho.   Perf. 13½x13
560 A245 100b Sheet of 4, #a-d   4.00 4.00

Souvenir Sheet
Litho. With Foil Application
Imperf

561 A245 200b gold & multi   2.40 2.40

Sultan Qaboos Award for Volunteer Work — A246

2014, Dec. 5   **Litho.**   *Perf. 13¼*
562 A246 250b multi

Souvenir Sheets

Souq Muttrah A247

Designs: 200b, Entrance. 250b, Souq Muttrah, diff.

2014, Dec. 12   **Litho.**   *Perf. 14x14¼*
563-564 A247   Set of 2   3.25 3.25

Miniature Sheet

Oman Post Mascot A248

No. 565 — Inscription: a, Delivery items. b, Kids corner. c, Deposit boxes. d, Post boxes.

2014, Dec. 14   **Litho.**   *Perf. 13¼*
565 A248 100b Sheet of 4, #a-d 2.75 2.75

Wildlife A249

No. 566 — Arabian gazelles: a, 100b, One gazelle and tail of another gazelle. b, 150b, Two gazelles. c, 200b, Two gazelles, diff.
No. 567 — Butterflies: a, Papilio demoleus. b, Stone hamia varanes. c, Precis hierta. d, Belenois aurota.
No. 568 — Merops persicus facing: a, Right. b, Left.
No. 569, 150b, Ploceus galbula. No. 570, 200b, Treron waalia. No. 571, 200b, Coracias benghalensis. No. 572, 200b, Falco concolor. No. 573, 200b, Arabian owls.

Litho. & Embossed
            Perf. 14
566 A249   Sheet of 3, #a-c   —   —
567 A249 150b Sheet of 4, #a-d 4.25 4.25
568 A249 150b Sheet of 2, #a-b 2.10 2.10
Souvenir Sheets
569-573 A249   Set of 5   6.75 6.75

Souvenir Sheets

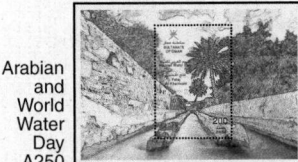

Arabian and World Water Day A250

Designs: No. 574, 200b, Falaj Al-Khatmeen. No. 575. 200b, Falaj Dares.

2015, Mar. 3   **Litho.**   *Perf. 14¼x14½*
574-575 A250   Set of 2   2.75 2.75

Nizwa, Capital of Islamic Culture A251

No. 576: a, Old door. b, Emblem, white backround. c, Siaal Mosque. d, Arrazha dance art. e, Emblem light brown background. f, Falaj Daris.
No. 577, 250b: a, Like #576e. b, Like #576a. c, Like #576c.
No. 578, 250b: a, Like #576d. b, Like #576b. c, Like #576f.

2015, Mar. 15   **Litho.**   *Perf. 13¼x13*
576 A251 200b Sheet of 6, #a-
            f   8.50 8.50
Souvenir Sheets of 3, #a-c
577-578 A251   Set of 2 10.50 10.50

Gulf Cooperation Council Stamp Exhibition, Nizwa — A252

2015, Oct. 15   **Litho.**   *Perf. 13½*
579 A252 200b multi   —   —

Nizwa, 2015 Capital of Islamic Culture.

International Telecommunication Union, 150th Anniv. — A253

2015, Nov. 30   **Litho.**   *Perf. 14*
580 A253 100b multi   —   —

A254

A255

45th National Day A256

No. 581: a, 100b, 45th National Day emblem (40x40mm). b, 200b, Royal Opera House, Muscat, at night (40x40mm). c, 200b, Daytime view of Royal Opera House (40x40mm). d, 200b, Interior of Royal Opera House (40x40mm). e, 200b, Sultan Qaboos (40x70mm).
No. 582, 200b, New Salalah Airport. 250b, Sultan Qaboos and Royal Opera House at night.

Litho., Litho. With Foil Application
(#582)

2015, Nov. 18   *Perf. 14*
581 A254   Sheet of 5, #a-e, +
        label   —   —
Souvenir Sheet
Size: 70x35mm
Perf. 14¼
582 A255 200b sil & multi   —   —
Size: 90x60mm
Imperf
583 A256 250b multi   —   —

Diplomatic Relations Between Oman and India, 60th Anniv. — A257

2015, Dec. 31   **Litho.**   *Perf. 14¼*
584 A257 200b multi   —   —

No. 584 was printed in sheets of 6 + 3 central labels.

Souvenir Sheets

Omani Postal Service, 50th Anniv. A258

No. 585, 250b: a, Post office and mail sorters. b, Oman #105, 129, 137, horiz. c, Red pillar box.
No. 586, 250b: a, Mail trucks. b, Oman #99, horiz. c, Yellow mail box.

Litho., Sheet Margin Litho. With Foil Application
Perf. 13¼x13 (vert. stamps), 13x13¼
2016, Apr. 30   Sheets of 3, #a-c
585-586 A258   Set of 2 10.50 10.50

Arab Postal Day A259

No. 587: a, Blue background, denomination at LR. b, Green background, denomination at LL.

2016, Aug. 3   **Litho.**   *Perf. 14*
587 A259 150b Horiz. pair, #a-b 2.10 2.10

Fourth Festival of Omani Dates — A260

2016, Oct. 23   **Litho.**   *Perf. 13*
588 A260 100b multi   .70 .70

National Oncology Center A261

2016, Nov. 2   **Litho.**   *Perf. 13*
589 A261 100b multi   .70 .70

46th National Day — A262

Litho. & Embossed With Foil Application
2016, Nov. 18   *Perf. 13x13¼*
590 A262 300b multi   2.10 2.10

Wildlife A263

No. 591, 200b — Oryx leucoryx with: a, Head down. b, Head up.
No. 592, 200b — Bubo ascalaphus: a, Feet visible. b, Feet not visible.
No. 593, 200b: a, Neophron pcnopterus. b, Alectoris chukar.
No. 594, 200b: a, Byblia ilithyia ilithyia. b, Hypolimnas misippus.
No. 595, 400b, Paraechinus aethiopicus, horiz. No. 596, 400b, Pterocles exustus, horiz.

Litho. & Embossed
2016, Dec. 20   *Perf. 13*
       Sheets of 2, #a-b
591-594 A263   Set of 4 11.50 11.50
Souvenir Sheets
595-596 A263   Set of 2 5.75 5.75

A264

A265

A266

A267

A268

A269

A270

A271

A272

Arches in Sultan Qaboos Grand Mosque — A273

2016, Dec. 21   Litho.   Perf. 13x13¼
597		Booklet pane of 5	7.00	—
	a.	A264 200b multi	1.40	1.40
	b.	A265 200b multi	1.40	1.40
	c.	A266 200b multi	1.40	1.40
	d.	A267 200b multi	1.40	1.40
	e.	A268 200b multi	1.40	1.40
		Complete booklet, #597	7.00	—
598		Booklet pane of 5	7.00	—
	a.	A269 200b multi	1.40	1.40
	b.	A270 200b multi	1.40	1.40
	c.	A271 200b multi	1.40	1.40
	d.	A272 200b multi	1.40	1.40
	e.	A273 200b multi	1.40	1.40
		Complete booklet, #598	7.00	—

Souvenir Sheet

2nd International Military Sports
Council World Cup Soccer
Tournament, Muscat — A274

No. 599: a, Tournament emblem. b, Mascot.

Litho. With Foil Application
2017, Jan. 15   Perf. 13
599	A274 250b Sheet of 2, #a-b,		
	+ central label	3.50	3.50

Miniature Sheet

Children
A275

No. 600: a, Girl with magnifying glass (56x33mm). b, Two girls (56x66mm). c, Five children reading (56x33mm). d, Two children

---

reading (56x33mm). e, Three children playing with toys (56x33mm).

Litho. With Foil Application
2017, Apr. 3   Perf. 13½x13¼
600	A275 250b Sheet of 5, #a-e	8.75	8.75

Miniature Sheet

Salalah
Tourism
Festival
A276

No. 601: a, Camel facing right. b, Clouds in canyon. c, Yellow flower. d, River and lake. e, Swimmers. f, Small tree. g, Waves hitting rocks, mountain in background. h, Pink flower. i, Waves and rocky shore. j, Flowering plants and tree, valley in background. k, Dry river bed in valley. l, Small tree, road in background. m, Field of red violet flowers. n, Camel facing left. o, White flower.

2017, July 8   Litho.   Perf. 14
601	A276 150b Sheet of 15,		
	#a-o	16.00	16.00

National
Day
A277

No. 602 — Sultan Qaboos and: a, Ships and cranes at Duqm Special Economic Zone. b, Aerial view of Duqm Special Economic Zone.

Litho. & Embossed
2017, Nov. 18   Perf. 14¼x14
602		Horiz. pair	3.75	3.75
	a.	A277 200b multi	1.10	1.10
	b.	A277 500b multi	2.60	2.60

Oman
Soccer
Team,
Winner of
23rd Arabian
Gulf Cup
Tournament
A278

Designs: 200b, Goaltender diving for ball. No. 604, 500b, Players, soccer ball, trophy. No. 605, 500b, Players and trophy in rowboat on shore. No. 606, 500b, Trophy, players in stadium, flag of Oman.

2018, Mar. 4   Litho.   Perf. 13
603-606	A278 Set of 4	9.00	9.00
606a	Souvenir sheet of 4, #603-606	9.00	9.00

2018 World Cup
Soccer
Championships,
Russia — A279

2018, July 1   Litho.   Perf. 13
607	A279 500b gold & multi	3.50	3.50
	a. Miniature sheet of 5	17.50	17.50

Values for No. 607 are for stamps with surrounding selvage.

Arab Document
Day — A280

Designs: 400b, Cover of *L'Univers Illustré* depicting 1875 visit to Paris of Sultan of Zanzibar. 600b, 1947 photograph of Muscat.

2018, Oct. 17   Litho.   Perf. 14¼
608-609	A280 Set of 2	7.00	7.00
609a	Souvenir sheet of 2, #608-609, perf. 13	7.00	7.00

Adolescent and
Youth
Health — A281

2018, Oct. 21   Litho.   Perf.
610	A281 400b multi	2.75	2.75
	a. Souvenir sheet of 4	11.00	11.00

48th National
Day — A282

Designs: 200b, "48." 400b, Sultan Qaboos.

Litho. With Foil Application
2018, Nov. 18   Perf. 13
611-612	A282 Set of 2	4.25	4.25
612a	Souvenir sheet of 2, #611-612	4.25	4.25

Airports of
Oman
A283

Designs: 200b, Interior of airport. 600b, Aerial view of Muscat International Airport.

2018, Dec. 5   Litho.   Perf. 13x12¾
613-614	A283 Set of 2	5.75	5.75
614a	Souvenir sheet of 2, #613-614	5.75	5.75

Shell Oman Marketing Company, 60th
Anniv. — A284

Designs: 200b, Modern Shell gas station. 500b, Modern and old Shell gas stations. 600b, Shell gas station sign, children holding solar panel. 800b, Building with solar panels on roof.

Perf. 14x13x14x14
2018, Dec. 12   Litho.
615-618	A284 Set of 4	15.00	15.00
618a	Souvenir sheet of 4, #615-618, perf. 14	15.00	15.00

Oman's
Chairmanship of
the Arab Women
Organization
A285

Litho. With Foil Application
2018, Dec. 18   Perf. 13
619	A285 200b gold & multi	1.40	1.40
	a. Souvenir sheet of 4	5.75	5.75

A286

Call of Peace
from Children of
the World — A287

2019, Feb. 19   Litho.   Perf. 13x13¼
620	A286 400b multi	2.75	2.75
621	A287 400b multi	2.75	2.75
	a. Souvenir sheet of 2, #620-621	5.50	5.50

Khanjars — A288

Designs: No. 622, 200b, Al Batenia or Al Sahelia khanjar. No. 623, 200b, Al Janbiya khanjar. No. 624, 500b, Al Saidia khanjar. No. 625, 500b, Al Suria khanjar. No. 626, 500b, Al Nizwania khanjar.

Litho. & Embossed
2019, Mar. 3   Perf. 14
622-626	A288 Set of 5	13.50	13.50
626a	Souvenir sheet of 5, #622-626	13.50	13.50

Musical
Instruments
A289

Designs: No. 627, 100b, Al-Rauwah (drums). No. 628, 100b, Kasir and Rahmani (drums). No. 629, 500b, Azi (drums). No. 630, 500b, Barghum (animal horn).

2019, Mar. 4   Litho.   Perf. 14
627-630	A289 Set of 4	8.50	8.50
630a	Souvenir sheet of 4, #627-630	8.50	8.50

Tourism — A289a

Designs: No. 630B, 50b, A'Rustaq Fort. No. 630C, 200b, Musandam. No. 630D, 500b, Balad Sayt. No. 630E, 800b, Al Ayjah.

2019   Litho.   Perf. 13
630B-630E	A289a Set of 4	11.00	11.00
630Ef	Souvenir sheet of 4, #630B-630E	11.00	11.00

Turtles — A290

Designs: Nois. 631, 636a, 100b, Leatherback turtle. Nos. 632, 636b, 100b, Green turtle. Nos. 633, 636c, 100b, Hawksbill turtle. Nos. 634, 636d, 100b, Loggerhead turtle. Nos. 635, 636e, 500b, Olive ridley turtle.

2019, Sept. 29   Litho.   Perf. 13¼
Stamps With Dark Blue Frames
631-635	A290 Set of 5	6.50	6.50

Souvenir Sheet
Stamps With Marine Life in Frames
636	A290 Sheet of 5, #a-e	6.50	6.50

Oman's Message of
Islam — A291

Designs: 200b, Emblem. No. 638, 250b, Emblem and the prophet's 629 letter to the people of Oman. No. 639, 250b, Emblem and map of Oman inscribed with word for "peace" in various languages. 300b, Emblem and Muslim men at entrance to mosque.

2019, Nov. 16   Litho.   Perf. 14

637-640	A291	Set of 4	7.00 7.00
640a		Souvenir sheet of 4, #637-640	7.00 7.00

49th National Day — A292

Sultan Qaboos and: 200b, Highway cloverleaf. 300b, Highway cloverleaf, horiz.

Litho. With Foil Application

2019, Nov. 18   Perf. 14x14¼

641	A292	200b gold & multi	1.40 1.40
a.		Perf. 13½	1.40 1.40

Perf. 14¼x14

642	A292	300b gold & multi	2.10 2.10
a.		Perf. 13½	2.10 2.10
b.		Souvenir sheet of 2, #641a, 642a	3.50 3.50

United Nations Convention on the Rights of the Child, 30th Anniv. — A293

2019, Nov. 24   Litho.   Perf. 14

643	A293	500b multi	3.50 3.50
a.		Souvenir sheet of 1	3.50 3.50

A294

A295

A296

A297

Aflaj Irrigation Systems UNESCO World Heritage Sites — A298

2019, Dec. 30   Litho.   Perf. 13¼x13

644	A294	100b multi	.70 .70
645	A295	100b multi	.70 .70
646	A296	100b multi	.70 .70
647	A297	500b multi	3.50 3.50
648	A298	500b multi	3.50 3.50
a.		Souvenir sheet of 5, #644-648	9.25 9.25
		Nos. 644-648 (5)	9.10 9.10

Doves, Flag of the Palestinian Authority, Dome of the Rock, Jerusalem — A299

2020, Feb. 9   Litho.   Perf. 14¼

649	A299	250b multi	1.75 1.75
a.		Souvenir sheet of 1, perf. 13¼	1.75 1.75

A300

A301

Achievements of Sultan Qaboos (1940-2020) — A302

2020, Mar. 3   Litho.   Perf. 14¼

650	A300	400b multi	2.75 2.75
651	A301	400b multi	2.75 2.75
652	A302	400b multi	2.75 2.75
a.		Souvenir sheet of 3, #650-652, perf. 13¼	8.25 8.25

Campaign Against COVID-19 A303

2020, June 22   Litho.   Perf. 14

653	A303	500b multi	3.50 3.50
a.		Souvenir sheet of 2	7.00 7.00

Arab League, 75th Anniv. — A304

Litho. With Foil Application

2020, June 28   Perf. 13¼x12¾

654	A304	500b gold & multi	3.50 3.50
a.		Souvenir sheet of 2	7.00 7.00

Oman Center for Traditional Music — A305

Designs: 100b, Drummers and dancers. 200b, Drummers and man blowing sea shell. 300b, Drummers and dancers, diff. 400b, Drummer and singer.

Litho. With Foil Application

2020, July 5   Perf. 13

655-658	A305	Set of 4	7.00 7.00
658a		Souvenir sheet of 4, #655-658	7.00 7.00

Diplomatic Relations Between Oman and People's Republic of China, 40th Anniv. A306

2020, Oct. 20   Litho.   Perf. 12¾x13¼

659	A306	200b multi	1.40 1.40

A souvenir sheet containing one example of No. 659 sold for 600b.

United Nations, 75th Anniv. — A307

2020, Oct. 24   Litho.   Perf. 14

660	A307	500b multi	3.50 3.50
a.		Souvenir sheet of 1	3.50 3.50

Camel Ardhah, UNESCO Intangible Cultural Heritage — A308

Litho. With Foil Application

2020, Nov. 11   Perf. 14

661		Horiz. strip of 4	8.50 8.50
a.	A308	100b Camel Ardhah	.70 .70
b.	A308	200b Camel Ardhah, diff.	1.40 1.40
c.	A308	400b Camel Ardhah, diff.	2.80 2.80
d.	A308	500b Camel Hambal	3.50 3.50
e.		Souvenir sheet of 4, #661a-661d	8.50 8.50

Horse Ardhah, UNESCO Intangible Cultural Heritage — A309

No. 662: a, 100b, Two men riding horses, one standing on horse's back, inscribed "Horse Ardhah." b, 200b, Two men with arms touching riding horses, inscribed "Horse Ardhah." c, 400b, Line of mounted horses, inscribed "Horse Hambal." d, 500b, Mounted horses and mosque, inscribed "Horse Hambal."

Litho. With Foil Application

2020, Nov. 11   Perf. 14

662		Horiz. strip of 4	8.50 8.50
a.	A309	100b gold & multi	.70 .70
b.	A309	200b gold & multi	1.40 1.40
c.	A309	400b gold & multi	2.75 2.75
d.	A309	500b gold & multi	3.50 3.50
e.		Souvenir sheet of 4, #662a-662d	8.50 8.50

Adventure Tourism Locations — A310

No. 663: a, Wadi Qa'sha. b, Wadi Umq Bir. c, Saab Bani Khamis. d, Wadi Bani Auf.

2020, Dec. 1   Litho.   Perf. 13

663		Horiz. strip of 4	8.50 8.50
a.	A310	100b multi	.70 .70
b.	A310	200b multi	1.40 1.40
c.	A310	400b multi	2.80 2.80
d.	A310	500b multi	3.50 3.50
e.		Souvenir sheet of 4, #663a-663d	8.50 8.50

Sultan Qaboos (1940-2020) A311

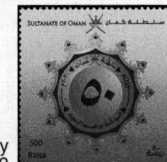

50th National Day Emblem — A312

Sultan Haitham — A313

2020, Nov. 18   Litho.   Perf. 13

664		Horiz. strip of 3	10.50 10.50
a.	A311	500b multi	3.50 3.50
b.	A312	500b multi	3.50 3.50
c.	A313	500b multi	3.50 3.50
d.		Souvenir sheet of 3, #664a-644c	10.50 10.50

50th National Day.

Whales and Dolphins A314

No. 665: a, Blue whale. b, Arabian Sea humpback whale. c, Indian Ocean humpback dolphin. d, Spinner dolphin. e, Indo-Pacific bottlenose dolphin.

2020, Dec. 24   Litho.   Perf. 13¼

665		Horiz. strip of 5	8.50 8.50
a.-b.	A314	100b Either single	.70 .70
c.	A314	200b gold & multi	1.40 1.40
d.	A314	300b gold & multi	2.10 2.10
e.	A314	500b gold & multi	3.50 3.50
f.		Souvenir sheet of 5, #665a-665e	8.50 8.50

Dar Al Hanan Children's Cancer Home, 10th Anniv. — A315

2021, Jan. 28   Litho.   Perf. 13¼x13

666	A315	1r multi	7.00 7.00

Computer Security — A316

2021, Feb.   Litho.   Perf. 13

667	A316	500b multi	3.50 3.50
a.		Souvenir sheet of 1	3.50 3.50

Al Saida School, Muscat, 80th Anniv. (in 2020) — A317

No. 668: a, School building. b, Students and teachers in classroom. c, Photograph of students and faculty. e, Students with flags.

2021, Mar. 9   Litho.   Perf. 13

668		Horiz. strip of 4	7.00 7.00
a.-b.	A317	100b Either single	.70 .70
c.	A317	300b multi	2.10 2.10
d.	A317	500b multi	3.50 3.50
e.		Souvenir sheet of 4, #668a-668d	7.00 7.00

Lizards — A318

No. 669: a, Thomas' mastigur. b, Dhofar agama. c, Carter's semaphore gecko. d, Chamaeleo arabicus.

Litho. & Embossed

2021, May 22   Perf. 13x13¼

669		Horiz. strip of 4	7.00 7.00
a.-d.	A318	250b Any single	1.75 1.75
e.		Souvenir sheet of 4, #669a-669d	7.00 7.00

Nursing and Midwifery — A319

No. 670: a, 200b, Nurse. b, 300b, Midwife and infant.

1r, Nurse, diff.

2021, May 29   Litho.   Perf. 13
670 A319 Horiz. pair, #a-b   3.50   3.50
		Size: 100x100mm
		Imperf
671 A319 1r multi   7.00   7.00

Omani
Wheat
Harvest
A320

Inscriptions: Nos. 672a, 673b, Ripe Wheat
Spikes. Nos. 672b, 673a, Harvesting Wheat
Crops. Nos. 672c, 673d, Omani Wheat Grains.
Nos. 672d, 673c, Filtering the Wheat Crop.

**No Wheat Spikes in Top and
Bottom Panels on Nos. 672a-672b,
672d, Top and Bottom Panels in
Orange Brown on No. 672c**

2021, Aug.   Litho.   Perf. 13x13¼
672 A320 250b Block of 4, #a-d   7.00   7.00
		Miniature Sheet
**Wheat Spikes in Top and Bottom
Panels on Nos. 673a-673c, Top and
Bottom Panels in Light Brown on
No. 673d**
673 A320 250b Sheet of 4, #a-d 7.00 7.00

Sand
Dunes — A321

No. 674 — Man and: a, Sugar Dunes,
Mahut. b, Empty Quarter, Ibri.

2021, Oct.   Litho.   Perf. 13
674 A321 500b Vert. pair, #a-b   7.00   7.00
	c. Souvenir sheet of 2, #674a-674b 7.00 7.00

A322

A323

A324

Corals — A325

2021, Oct. 12   Litho.   Perf. 13
675		Block of 4 7.00 7.00
	a. A322 100b multi .70 .70
	b. A323 200b multi 1.40 1.40
	c. A324 200b multi 1.40 1.40
	d. A325 500b multi 3.50 3.50
	e. Souvenir sheet of 4, #675a-675d 7.00 7.00

A326

A327

A328

Women's
Costumes — A329

Litho. With Foil Application
2021, Oct. 21   Perf. 13¼x13
676		Block of 4 7.00 7.00
	a. A326 100b gold & multi .70 .70
	b. A327 200b gold & multi 1.40 1.40
	c. A328 200b gold & multi 1.40 1.40
	d. A329 500b gold & multi 3.50 3.50
	e. Souvenir sheet of 4, #676a-676d 7.00 7.00

ICC Men's T20
Cricket World
Cup Tournament,
Oman and United
Arab
Emirates — A330

2021, Oct. 28   Litho.   Perf. 14
677 A330 250b multi   1.75   1.75
		Souvenir Sheet
677A A330 1r multi   7.00   7.00

The ICC Men's T20 Cricket World Cup Tournament was originally to be held in Australia in
2020, but was postponed until 2021 and
moved to Oman and the United Arab Emirates
because of the COVID-19 pandemic.

Admisssion of
Oman to United
Nations, 50th
Anniv. — A331

2021, Nov. 14   Litho.   Perf. 13
678 A331 500b multi   3.50   3.50
		Souvenir Sheet
679 A331 5r multi   35.00 35.00

Sultan
Haitham — A332

Litho. With Foil Application
2021, Nov. 27   Perf. 14¼
680 A332 500b gold & multi   3.50   3.50
		Souvenir Sheet
		Perf. 14½
681 A332 2r gold & multi   14.00 14.00
51st National Day. No. 681 contains one
44x59mm stamp.

Ahmad Bin
Majid al Saadi
(1421-1500),
Navigator
A333

Al Muhallab
Bin Abi Sufra
Al Azdi (632-
702), General
and Governor
A334

Abdullah Bin
Suleiman Al
Harthy (1886-
1940),
Newspaper
Publisher in
Zanzibar
A335

Nasser Bin
Salim Al
Bahlani (1273-
1339), Poet
A336

Al Khalil Bin Ahmad
Al Farahidi (718-86),
Lexicographer and
Grammarian — A337

2021, Dec. 7   Litho.   Perf. 13
682		Horiz. strip of 5 9.75 9.75
	a. A333 100b multi .70 .70
	b. A334 200b multi 1.40 1.40
	c. A335 200b multi 1.40 1.40
	d. A336 400b multi 2.75 2.75
	e. A337 500b multi 3.50 3.50
	f. Souvenir sheet of 5, #682a-682e 9.75 9.75

Sultan
Haitham — A338

2021, Dec.   Litho.   Perf. 13
683 A338 500b cop & multi   3.50   3.50
		Souvenir Sheet
**Litho. With Foil Application, Sheet
Margin Embossed with Foil
Application**
		Imperf
684 A338 1r cop, gold & multi 7.00   7.00
No. 684 contains one 40x60mm stamp.

Omani
Kummah
(Man's Cap)
Design
A339

Omani
Kummah
Being Created
A340

2021, Dec.   Litho.   Perf. 13¼x13
685 A339 1r multi   7.00   7.00
686 A340 3r multi   21.00 21.00

Opening
of
National
Museum,
5th
Anniv.
A341

No. 687: a, 100b, Will of Sultan Qaboos. b,
100b, Saidi-style dagger. c, 100b, Oldest
incense burner in Oman. d, 500b, Throne of
Sultan Qaboos.

2022, Jan. 2   Litho.   Perf. 14¼
687 A341 Block of 4, #a-d   5.75   5.75
	e. Souvenir sheet of 4, #687a-687d 5.75 5.75

Expo
2020,
Dubai
A342

No. 688 — Inscription: a, 100b, Use. b,
200b, Trade. c, 300b, Harvest. d, 400b,
Growth.

2022, Jan. 18   Litho.   Perf. 14
688 A342 Block of 4, #a-d   7.00   7.00
	e. Souvenir sheet of 4, #688a-688d 7.00 7.00

Expo 2020 was postponed until 2021
because of the COVID-19 pandemic.

Royal Opera
House,
Muscat, 10th
Anniv.
A343

Opera House: 200b, Interior. 300b, Exterior.

		Perf. 12¾x13¼
2022, Mar. 28   Litho.
689-690 A343 Set of 2   3.50   3.50
690a	Souvenir sheet of 2, #689-690,
		+ 2 labels 3.50 3.50

Petroleum
Development
Oman, 85th
Anniv. — A344

Designs: 50b, Boats in harbor, 1937. 150b,
Oil tanker carrying first shipment of Omani oil,
1967. 200b, Oil worker at plant, 2002. 250b,
85th anniversary emblem, 2022.

2022, May 12   Litho.   Perf. 14
691 A344 50b multi   .35   .35
692 A344 150b multi   1.10   1.10
693 A344 200b multi   1.40   1.40
694 A344 250b multi   1.75   1.75
	a. Block of 4, #691-694 4.75 .75
	b. Souvenir sheet of 4, #691-694 4.75 4.75
	Nos. 691-694 (4) 4.60 4.60

Issued in panes of 16, with each pane containing blocks of 4 of Nos. 691-694. A se-tenant block of 4 is in the center of the pane.

Date
Varieties
A345

No. 695: a, 100b, Khalas Al Dahirah dates.
b, 200b, Fardh dates. c, 300b, Naghal dates.
d, 300b, Zabad dates.

OMAN (continued)

2022, July 21 Litho. Perf. 14
695 A345 Block of 4, #a-d 6.50 6.50
e. Souvenir sheet of 4, #695a-695d 6.50 6.50

Freshwater Fish — A346

No. 696: a, Awaous jayakari. b, Aphaniops kruppi. c, Cyprinion muscatense. d, Glossogobius tenuiformis.

2022, Sept. 18 Litho. Perf. 14x13¾
696 Horiz. strip of 4 7.00 7.00
a. A346 100b multi .70 .70
b. A346 200b multi 1.40 1.40
c. A346 300b multi 2.10 2.10
d. A346 400b multi 2.75 2.75
e. Souvenir sheet of 4, #696a-696d 7.00 7.00

House of Wonders, Stonetown, Zanzibar, Tanzania — A347

2022, Oct. 9 Litho. Perf. 14¼
697 A347 500b multi 3.50 3.50

See Tanzania No.

A349

2022 World Cup Soccer Championships, Qatar — A350

2022 Litho. Perf. 13¼x13
700 A349 500b multi 3.50 3.50

Souvenir Sheets
701 A349 1r multi 7.00 7.00

Perf. 13¼
702 A350 1r multi 7.00 7.00

·Issued: Nos. 700-701, 10/27; No. 702, 12/18.

2022 Aga Khan Awards for Architecture and Music Ceremony, Muscat — A351

No. 703: a, Royal Opera House, Muscat, as seen through archway. b, Building and four lamp posts.

2022, Oct. 31 Litho. Perf. 13¾
703 A351 500b Vert. pair, #a-b 7.00 7.00
c. Souvenir sheet of 2, #703a-703b 7.00 7.00

Muscat, 2022 Arab Digital Capital — A352

2022, Nov. 3 Litho. Perf. 13¼x13½
704 A352 500b multi 3.50 3.50

Souvenir Sheet
705 A352 1r multi 7.00 7.00

Miniature Sheet

52nd National Day A353

No. 706 — Inscriptions: a, 100b, Oman Convention and Exhibition Center (30x40mm). b, 100b, Sultan Qaboos Mosque, Sohar, (30x40mm). c, 100b, Oman Across Ages Museum (30x40mm). d, 100b, Oman Botanic Garden (30x40mm). e, 100b, Muttrah Fort (30x40mm). f, 100b, Forseeing the Future (30x40mm). g, 100b, Wakan Village (30x40mm). h, 100b, Ayn Athum (30x40mm). i, 100b, Khor Najd (30x40mm). j, 100b, Pink Lakes (30x40mm). k, 100b, Duqm Refinery, Zinat al Bihaar Ship (30x40mm). l, 100b, Barr al Hikman (30x40mm). m, 100b, Ras al Ruwais (30x40mm). n, 100b, Sohat Port and Freezone (30x40mm). o, 500b, Maidan Muttrah (and Sultan Haitham) (60x40mm).

Perf. 13¼x13 on 2, 3 or 4 Sides
2022, Nov. 18 Litho.
706 A353 Sheet of 15, #a-o 13.50 13.50

Omani Armed Forces — A355

No. 708 — Inscriptions: a, Office of Chief of Staff of Sultan's Armed Forces. b, Royal Army of Oman. c, Royal Air Force of Oman. d, Royal Navy of Oman.

2022, Dec. 11 Litho. Perf. 14
708 Horiz. strip of 4 7.00 7.00
a. A355 200b multi 1.40 1.40
b. A355 250b multi 1.75 1.75
c. A355 250b multi 1.75 1.75
d. A355 300b multi 2.10 2.10
e. Souvenir sheet of 4, #708a-708d 7.00 7.00

Oman Daily Newspaper, 50th Anniv. — A358

Perf. 13¾x13¼
2022, Dec. 14 Litho.
711 A358 500b multi 3.50 3.50

Souvenir Sheet
712 A358 1r multi 7.00 7.00

SEMI-POSTAL STAMP

UNICEF Emblem, Girl with Book — SP1

Wmk. 314
1971, Dec. 25 Litho. Perf. 14
B1 SP1 50b + 25b multicolored 42.50 6.50
25th anniv. of UNICEF.

OFFICIAL STAMPS

Official Stamps of India 1938-43 Overprinted in Black

Perf. 13½x14
1944, Nov. 20 Wmk. 196
O1 O8 3p slate .80 15.00
O2 O8 ½a dk rose violet .80 15.00
O3 O8 9p green .80 15.00
O4 O8 1a carmine rose .80 15.00
O5 O8 1½a dull purple .80 15.00
O6 O8 2a scarlet .80 15.00
O7 O8 2½a purple 5.50 15.00
O8 O8 4a dark brown 2.00 15.00
O9 O8 8a blue violet 3.50 17.50
O10 A82 1r brown & slate 6.00 27.50
Nos. O1-O10 (10) 21.80 165.00

Al Busaid Dynasty, 200th anniv. On Nos. O1-O9 the overprint is smaller — 13x6mm. Used values for Nos. O1-O10 are for stamps canceled with contemporaneous postmarks of the Indian postal administration. Examples with the later British post office cancellations are worth much less.

ORANGE RIVER COLONY

ˈär-inj ˈri-vər ˈkä-lə-nē

(Orange Free State)

LOCATION — South Africa, north of the Cape of Good Hope between the Orange and Vaal Rivers
GOVT. — A former British Crown Colony
AREA — 49,647 sq. mi.
POP. — 528,174 (1911)
CAPITAL — Bloemfontein

Orange Free State was an independent republic, 1854-1900. Orange River Colony existed from May, 1900, to June, 1910, when it united with Cape of Good Hope, Natal and the Transvaal to form the Union of South Africa.

12 Pence = 1 Shilling

Values for unused stamps are for examples with original gum as defined in the catalogue introduction. Very fine examples of Nos. 1-60c will have perforations touching the design on one or more sides due to the narrow spacing of the stamps on the plates. Stamps with perfs clear of the design on all four sides are scarce and will command higher prices.

Een = 1
Twee = 2
Drie = 3
Vier = 4

Issues of the Republic

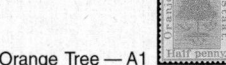

Orange Tree — A1

1868-1900 Unwmk. Typo. Perf. 14
1 A1 ½p red brown ('83) 8.25 .75
2 A1 ½p orange ('97) 3.00 .60
a. 1p yellow ('97) 3.00 .40
3 A1 1p red brown 22.50 .50
a. 1p pale brown 35.00 2.50
b. 1p deep brown 32.50 .60
4 A1 1p violet ('94) 5.00 .35
5 A1 2p violet ('83) 20.00 1.75
a. 2p pale mauve ('83-'84) 23.00 .30
6 A1 3p ultra ('83) 8.25 2.25
7 A1 4p ultra ('78) 6.50 4.50
a. 4p pale blue ('78) 26.00 5.25
8 A1 6p car rose ('90) 30.00 13.00
a. 6p rose ('71) 37.50 8.00
b. 6p pale rose ('68) 72.50 8.75
c. 6p bright carmine ('94) 18.50 2.25
9 A1 6p ultramarine ('00) 80.00
10 A1 1sh orange 65.00 1.75
a. 1sh orange buff 110.00 7.25

---

11 A1 1sh brown ('97) 32.50 1.75
12 A1 5sh green ('78) 14.00 24.00
Nos. 1-8,10-12 (11) 215.00 51.20

No. 8b was not placed in use without surcharge.
For surcharges see #13-53, 44j-53c, 57-60.

No. 13

No. 8a Surcharged in Four Different Types

1877
13 (a) 4p on 6p rose 450.00 65.00
a. Inverted surcharge 600.00
b. Double surcharge, one inverted ("a" + "c" inverted) 4,250.
c. Double surcharge, one inverted ("a" inverted + "c") 6,000.
14 (b) 4p on 6p rose 1,450. 225.00
a. Inverted surcharge 1,250.
b. Double surcharge, one inverted ("b" and "d") 220.00 42.50
15 (c) 4p on 6p rose 220.00 42.50
a. Inverted surcharge 400.00
16 (d) 4p on 6p rose 325.00 50.00
a. Inverted surcharge 1,500. 500.00
b. Double surcharge, one inverted ("d" and "c" inverted) 4,250.
c. Double surcharge, one inverted ("d" inverted and "c") 6,500.

No. 17

No. 12 Surcharged with Bar and

f g h
i k l

1881
First Printing
17 (f) 1p on 5sh green 120.00 32.50
Second Printing
18 (g) 1p on 5sh green 65.00 32.50
a. Inverted surcharge 1,250.
b. Double surcharge 1,450.
19 (h) 1p on 5sh green 300.00 95.00
a. Inverted surcharge 1,450.
b. Double surcharge 1,650.
20 (i) 1p on 5sh green 100.00 32.50
a. Inverted surcharge 1,325.
b. Inverted surcharge 2,000. 1,000.
21 (k) 1p on 5sh green 600.00 275.00
a. Inverted surcharge 2,500.
b. Double surcharge 2,500.
Third Printing
21C (l) 1p on 5sh green 95.00 32.50
d. Inverted surcharge 875.00
e. Double surcharge 900.00
Nos. 17-21C (6) 1,280. 500.00

No. 12 Surcharged

1882
22 A1 ½p on 5sh green 27.50 7.50
a. Double surcharge 575.00 400.00
b. Inverted surcharge 1,500. 1,000.

No. 7 Surcharged with Thin Line and

m n

o   **p**

q

1882

23	(m) 3p on 4p ultra		100.00	40.00
a.	Double surcharge			1,400.
24	(n) 3p on 4p ultra		100.00	20.00
a.	Double surcharge			1,400.
25	(o) 3p on 4p ultra		55.00	30.00
a.	Double surcharge			1,400.
26	(p) 3p on 4p ultra		275.00	80.00
a.	Double surcharge			3,500.
27	(q) 3p on 4p ultra		100.00	25.00
a.	Double surcharge			1,400.
	Nos. 23-27 (5)		630.00	195.00

No. 6 Surcharged

1888

28	A1 2p on 3p ultra		60.00	2.25
a.	Wide "2" at top		77.50	10.00
b.	As No. 28, invtd. surch.		350.00	
c.	As No. 28a, invtd. surch.		825.00	
d.	Curved base on "2"		1,450.	650.00

Nos. 6 and 7 Surcharged

r   **s**

t

1890-91

29	(r) 1p on 3p ultra ('91)		9.50	1.00
a.	Double surcharge		100.00	77.50
b.	"1" and "d" wide apart		170.00	135.00
30	(r) 1p on 4p ultra		45.00	12.50
a.	Double surcharge		170.00	135.00
b.	Triple surcharge			3,250.
31	(s) 1p on 3p ultra ('91)		27.50	3.00
a.	Double surcharge		325.00	300.00
32	(s) 1p on 4p ultra		95.00	60.00
a.	Double surcharge		475.00	375.00
33	(t) 1p on 4p ultra		2,500.	675.00

No. 6 Surcharged

1892

34	A1 2½p on 3p ultra		21.00	.80
a.	Without period		92.50	55.00

No. 6 Surcharged

v   **w**

x   **y**

z

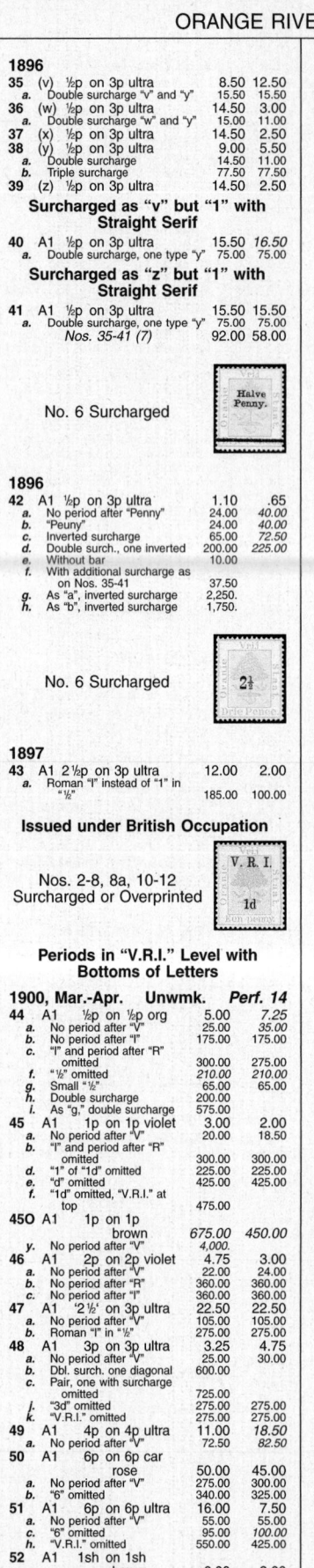

1896

35	(v) ½p on 3p ultra		8.50	12.50
a.	Double surcharge "v" and "y"		15.50	15.50
36	(w) ½p on 3p ultra		14.50	3.00
a.	Double surcharge "w" and "y"		15.00	11.00
37	(x) ½p on 3p ultra		14.50	2.50
38	(y) ½p on 3p ultra		9.00	5.50
a.	Double surcharge		14.50	11.00
b.	Triple surcharge		77.50	77.50
39	(z) ½p on 3p ultra		14.50	2.50

Surcharged as "v" but "1" with Straight Serif

40	A1 ½p on 3p ultra		15.50	16.50
a.	Double surcharge, one type "y"		75.00	75.00

Surcharged as "z" but "1" with Straight Serif

41	A1 ½p on 3p ultra		15.50	15.50
a.	Double surcharge, one type "y"		75.00	75.00
	Nos. 35-41 (7)		92.00	58.00

No. 6 Surcharged

1896

42	A1 ½p on 3p ultra		1.10	.65
a.	No period after "Penny"		24.00	40.00
b.	"Peuny"		24.00	40.00
c.	Inverted surcharge		65.00	72.50
d.	Double surch., one inverted		200.00	225.00
e.	Without bar		10.00	
f.	With additional surcharge as on Nos. 35-41		37.50	
g.	As "a", inverted surcharge		2,250.	
h.	As "b", inverted surcharge		1,750.	

No. 6 Surcharged

1897

43	A1 2½p on 3p ultra		12.00	2.00
a.	Roman "I" instead of "1" in "½"		185.00	100.00

Issued under British Occupation

Nos. 2-8, 8a, 10-12 Surcharged or Overprinted

Periods in "V.R.I." Level with Bottoms of Letters

1900, Mar.-Apr.   Unwmk.   Perf. 14

44	A1 ½p on ½p org		5.00	7.25
a.	No period after "V"		25.00	35.00
b.	No period after "I"		175.00	175.00
c.	"I" and period after "R" omitted		300.00	275.00
f.	"½" omitted		210.00	210.00
g.	Small "½"		65.00	65.00
h.	Double surcharge		200.00	
i.	As "g," double surcharge		575.00	
45	A1 1p on 1p violet		3.00	2.00
a.	No period after "V"		20.00	18.50
b.	"I" and period after "R" omitted		300.00	300.00
d.	"1" of "1d" omitted		225.00	225.00
e.	"d" omitted		425.00	425.00
f.	"1d" omitted, "V.R.I." at top		475.00	
45O	A1 1p on 1p brown		675.00	450.00
y.	No period after "V"		4,000.	
46	A1 2p on 2p violet		4.75	3.00
a.	No period after "V"		22.00	24.00
b.	No period after "R"		360.00	360.00
c.	No period after "I"		360.00	360.00
47	A1 "2½" on 3p ultra		22.50	22.50
a.	No period after "V"		105.00	105.00
b.	Roman "I" in "½"		275.00	275.00
48	A1 3p on 3p ultra		3.25	4.75
a.	No period after "V"		25.00	30.00
b.	Dbl. surch. one diagonal		600.00	
c.	Pair, one with surcharge omitted		725.00	
j.	"3d" omitted		275.00	275.00
k.	"V.R.I." omitted		275.00	275.00
49	A1 4p on 4p ultra		11.00	18.50
a.	No period after "V"		72.50	82.50
50	A1 6p on 6p car rose		50.00	45.00
a.	No period after "V"		275.00	300.00
b.	"6" omitted		340.00	325.00
51	A1 6p on 6p ultra		16.00	7.50
a.	No period after "V"		55.00	55.00
c.	"6" omitted		95.00	100.00
h.	"V.R.I." omitted		550.00	425.00
52	A1 1sh on 1sh brown		8.00	3.00
a.	No period after "V"		55.00	35.00
c.	"1" of "1s" omitted		165.00	155.00
j.	"1s" omitted		225.00	220.00
k.	"V.R.I." omitted		225.00	220.00
52G	A1 1sh on 1sh org		4,100.	2,750.
53	A1 5sh on 5sh green		32.50	60.00
a.	No period after "V"		300.00	360.00
b.	"5" omitted		1,100.	1,100.

#47, 47c overprinted "V.R.I." on #43.

No. 45f ("1d" omitted) with "V.R.I." at bottom is a shift which sells for a fifth of the value of the listed item. Varieties such as "V.R.I." omitted, denomination omitted and pair, one without surcharge are also the result of shifts. For surcharges see Nos. 57, 60.

Nos. 2, 4-12 Surcharged or Overprinted

Periods in "V.R.I." Raised Above Bottoms of Letters

1900-01

44j	A1 ½p on ½p orange		.35	.25
k.	Mixed periods		3.25	2.25
l.	Pair, one with level periods		17.50	21.00
m.	No period after "V"		4.50	5.00
n.	No period after "I"		45.00	45.00
o.	"V" omitted		675.00	
p.	Small "½"		22.50	25.00
q.	"1" for "I" in "V.R.I."		10.00	
r.	Thick "V"		6.00	4.00
45i	A1 1p on 1p violet		.35	.25
j.	Mixed periods		2.75	3.25
k.	Pair, one with level periods		27.50	29.00
l.	No period after "V"		4.50	9.00
m.	No period after "R"		19.00	19.00
n.	No period after "I"		19.00	19.00
p.	Double surcharge		130.00	120.00
q.	Inverted surcharge		425.00	
s.	Small "1" in "1d"		120.00	120.00
t.	"1" for "I" in "V.R.I."		13.00	
u.	Thick "V"		9.00	.40
v.	As "u," invtd. "1" for "I" in "V.R.I."		30.00	30.00
w.	As "u," double surcharge		400.00	400.00
z.	As "u," no period after "R"		70.00	75.00
za.	Pair, one without surcharge		325.00	
zb.	Stamp double impression, one inverted		2,750.	
46e	A1 2p on 2p violet		3.75	.35
f.	Mixed periods		9.00	5.50
g.	Pair, one with level periods		16.00	17.00
h.	Inverted surcharge		375.00	375.00
i.	Thick "V"		16.50	15.50
j.	As "i," invtd. "1" for "I" in "V.R.I."		32.50	35.00
47c	A1 "2½" on 3p ultra		250.00	250.00
d.	Thick "V"		4,250.	
f.	As "d," Roman "I" on "½"			
48d	A1 3p on 3p ultra		2.75	.35
e.	Mixed periods		12.00	12.00
f.	Pair, one with level periods		26.00	27.50
g.	Double surcharge		440.00	
h.	Thick "V"		12.50	22.50
i.	As "h," invtd. "1" for "I" in "V.R.I."		72.50	85.00
l.	Double surcharge, one diagonal		600.00	
m.	As "l", thick "V"		600.00	
n.	As "l", mixed periods		7,500.	
o.	As "n", thick "V"			
49b	A1 4p on 4p ultra		3.25	5.00
c.	Mixed periods		11.00	16.00
d.	Pair, one with level periods		24.00	37.50
50c	A1 6p on 6p car rose		45.00	55.00
d.	Mixed periods		160.00	175.00
e.	Pair, one with level periods		300.00	350.00
f.	Thick "V"		500.00	525.00
51d	A1 6p on 6p ultra		1.10	.45
e.	Mixed periods		12.00	13.00
f.	Pair, one with level periods		27.50	32.50
g.	Thick "V"		25.00	37.50
i.	"6d" omitted		500.00	
52e	A1 1sh on 1sh brown		12.00	.50
f.	Mixed periods		29.00	25.00
h.	Pair, one with level periods		55.00	55.00
i.	Thick "V"		45.00	14.00
52j	A1 1sh on 1sh orange		1,500.	1,500.
53c	A1 5sh on 5sh green		11.00	22.50
d.	Mixed periods		400.00	400.00
e.	Pair, one with level periods		1,100.	
f.	"5" with short flag		65.00	77.50
g.	Thick "V"		72.50	60.00

Stamps with mixed periods have one or two periods level with the bottoms of letters. One stamp in each pane had all periods level. Later settings had several stamps with thick "V." Forgeries of the scarcer varieties exist.

"V.R.I." stands for Victoria Regina Imperatrix. On No. 59, "E.R.I." stands for Edward Rex Imperator.

Cape of Good Hope Stamps of 1893-98 Overprinted

1900   Wmk. 16

54	A15 ½p green		.70	.25
a.	No period after "COLONY"		14.00	27.50
b.	Double overprint		750.00	800.00
55	A13 2½p ultramarine		9.00	2.00
a.	No period after "COLONY"		82.50	82.50

Overprinted as in 1900

1902, May

56	A15 1p carmine rose		2.75	.25
a.	No period after "COLONY"		27.00	37.50

Nos. 51d, 53c, Surcharged and No. 8b Surcharged like No. 51 but Reading "E.R.I."

Carmine or Vermilion and Black Surcharges

1902   Unwmk.

57	A1 4p on 6p on 6p ultra		2.25	4.50
a.	Thick "V"		3.00	11.00
b.	As "a," invtd. "1" instead of "I"		9.00	32.50
c.	No period after "R"		42.50	57.50

Black Surcharge

59	A1 6p on 6p ultra		9.00	23.00
a.	Double surcharge, one invtd.			

Orange Surcharge

60	A1 1sh on 5sh on 5sh grn		13.00	27.50
a.	Thick "V"		19.00	55.00
b.	"5" with short flag		80.00	95.00
c.	Double surcharge		1,100.	
	Nos. 57-60 (3)		24.25	55.00

"E.R.I." stands for Edward Rex Imperator.

King Edward VII — A8

"IOSTAGE" Variety

The "IOSTAGE" variety on the 4p is the result of filled in type.

1903-04   Wmk. 2   Typo.

61	A8 ½p yellow green		10.00	2.50
62	A8 1p carmine		14.00	.25
63	A8 2p chocolate		12.00	2.25
64	A8 2½p ultra		9.00	2.75
65	A8 3p violet		11.50	1.50
66	A8 4p olive grn & car		42.50	9.00
67	A8 6p violet & car		9.25	2.50
68	A8 1sh bister & car		55.00	4.50
69	A8 5sh red brn & bl ('04)		175.00	35.00
	Nos. 61-69 (9)		338.25	60.25

Some of the above stamps are found with the overprint "C.S.A.R." for use by the Central South African Railway.

Issue dates: 1p, Feb. 3. ½p, 2p, 2½p, 3p, 4p, 6p, 1sh, July 6. 5sh, Oct. 31.

1907-08   Wmk. 3

70	A8 ½p yellow green		19.00	1.60
71	A8 1p carmine		12.00	.35
72	A8 4p olive grn & car		5.00	8.25
73	A8 1sh bister & car		85.00	30.00
	Nos. 70-73 (4)		121.00	40.20

The "IOSTAGE" variety on the 4p is the result of filled-in type.

Stamps of Orange River Colony were replaced by those of Union of South Africa.

MILITARY STAMP

M1

1899, Oct. 15   Unwmk.   Perf. 12

M1	M1 black, *bister yellow*		50.00	85.00

No. M1 was provided to members of the Orange Free State army on active service during the Second Boer War. Soldiers' mail carried free was required to bear either No. M1 or be signed by the sender's unit commander. The stamps were used extensively from Oct. 1899 until the fall of Kroonstad in May 1900.

No. M1 was typeset and printed by Curling & Co., Bloemfontein, in sheets of 20 (5x4), with each row of five containing slightly different types.

Forgeries exist. The most common counterfeits either have 17 pearls, rather than 16, in the top and bottom frames, or omit the periods after "BRIEF" and "FRANKO."

PAKISTAN
'pa-ki-ˌstan

LOCATION — In southern, central Asia
GOVT. — Republic
AREA — 307,293 sq. mi.
POP. — 130,579,571 (1998)
CAPITAL — Islamabad

Pakistan was formed August 14, 1947, when India was divided into the Dominions of the Union of India and Pakistan, with some princely states remaining independent. Pakistan became a republic on March 23, 1956.

Pakistan had two areas made up of all or part of several predominantly Moslem provinces in the northwest and northeast corners of pre-1947 India. West Pakistan consists of the entire provinces of Baluchistan, Sind (Scinde) and "Northwest Frontier" (now Khyber Pukhtunkhwa), and 15 districts of the Punjab. East Pakistan, consisting of the Sylhet district in Assam and 14 districts in Bengal Province, became independent as Bangladesh in December 1971.

The state of Las Bela was incorporated into Pakistan.

12 Pies = 1 Anna
16 Annas = 1 Rupee
100 Paisa = 1 Rupee (1961)

> **Catalogue values for all unused stamps in this country are for Never Hinged items.**

Watermarks

Wmk. 274

Wmk. 351 — Crescent and Star Multiple

Stamps of India, 1937-43, Overprinted in Black

Nos. 1-12   Nos. 13-19

Perf. 13½x14

			Wmk. 196	
1947, Oct. 1				
1	A83	3p slate	.25	.25
2	A83	½a rose violet	.25	.25
3	A83	9p lt green	.25	.25
4	A83	1a car rose	.25	.25
4A	A84	1a3p bister ('49)	4.75	4.00
5	A84	1½a dk purple	2.00	.25
6	A84	2a scarlet	.25	.25
7	A84	3a violet	.25	.25
8	A84	3½a ultra	1.25	1.75
9	A85	4a chocolate	.55	.25
10	A85	6a peacock blue	1.50	1.25
11	A85	8a blue violet	.65	.65
12	A85	12a carmine lake	2.00	.25
13	A81	14a rose violet	3.00	4.25
14	A82	1r brn & slate	8.00	1.50
a.		Inverted overprint	250.00	
b.		Pair, one without ovpt.	950.00	
15	A82	2r dk brn & dk vio	4.00	6.00
16	A82	5r dp ultra & dk grn	9.00	10.00
17	A82	10r rose car & dk vio	11.00	10.50
18	A82	15r dk grn & dk brn	90.00	100.00

19	A82	25r dk vio & bl vio	100.00	120.00
		Nos. 1-19 (20)	239.20	262.15
		Set, hinged	135.00	

Provisional use of stamps of India with handstamped or printed "PAKISTAN" was authorized in 1947-49. Nos. 4A, 14a 14b exist only as provisional issues.

Used values are for postal cancels. Telegraph cancels (concentric circles) sell for much less.

Constituent Assembly Building, Karachi
A1

Crescent and Urdu Inscription
A2

Designs: 2½a, Karachi Airport entrance. 3a, Lahore Fort gateway.

Unwmk.

				Perf. 14
1948, July 9			**Engr.**	
20	A1	1½a bright ultra	1.25	2.00
21	A1	2½a green	1.25	.25
22	A1	3a chocolate	1.25	.30
				Perf. 12
23	A2	1r red	1.25	.85
a.		Perf. 14	6.00	25.00
		Nos. 20-23 (4)	5.00	3.40

Pakistan's independence, Aug. 15, 1947.
Examples of No. 23a used on cover are unknown. Used examples of No. 23a are cto.

Scales, Star and Crescent
A3

Star and Crescent
A4

Karachi Airport Building
A5

Karachi Port Authority Building
A6

Khyber Pass — A7

2½a, 3½a, 4a, Sukkur Barrage. 1r, 2r, 5r, Salimullah Hostel.

Perf. 12½, 14 (3a, 10a), 14x13½ (2½a, 3½a, 6a, 12a)

				Unwmk.
1948-57				
24	A3	3p org red, perf. 12½	.25	.25
a.		Perf. 13½ ('54)	3.75	1.00
25	A3	6p pur, perf. 12½	1.25	.25
a.		Perf. 13½ ('54)	8.00	5.00
26	A3	9p dk grn, perf. 12½	.55	.25
a.		Perf. 13½ ('54)	11.50	1.75
27	A4	1a dark blue	.25	.50
28	A4	1½a gray green	.25	.25
29	A4	2a orange red	7.00	.70
30	A6	2½a green	9.00	12.50
31	A5	3a olive green	8.00	1.00
32	A6	3½a violet blue	8.50	5.00
33	A6	4a chocolate	1.25	.25
34	A6	6a deep blue	2.00	.55
35	A6	8a black	1.40	1.40
36	A6	10a red	8.00	10.50
37	A6	12a red	11.00	1.00
				Perf. 14
38	A5	1r ultra	25.00	.25
a.		Perf. 13½ ('54)	24.00	12.00

39	A5	2r dark brown	17.50	.80
a.		Perf. 13½ ('54)	23.00	11.00
				Perf. 13½
40	A5	5r car ('54)	23.00	2.50
a.		Perf. 13½x14	17.00	.25
				Perf. 13
41	A7	10r rose lilac ('51)	19.00	3.00
a.		Perf. 14	22.50	45.00
b.		Perf. 12	130.00	11.50
42	A7	15r blue green ('57)	27.50	37.50
a.		Perf. 14	22.50	110.00
b.		Perf. 12	18.00	30.00
				Perf. 14
43	A7	25r purple	55.00	150.00
a.		Perf. 13 ('54)	45.00	42.50
b.		Perf. 12	42.50	40.00
		Nos. 24-43 (20)	225.70	228.45
		Set, hinged	100.00	

Many compound perforations exist.

See No. 259, types A9-A11. For surcharges and overprints see Nos. 124, O14-O26, O35-O37, O41-O43A, O52, O63, O68.

Imperfs of Nos. 24-43 are from proof sheets improperly removed from the printer's archives.

"Quaid-i-Azam" (Great Leader), "Mohammed Ali Jinnah" — A8

1949, Sept. 11		**Engr.**	*Perf. 13½x14*	
44	A8	1½a brown	2.00	1.75
45	A8	3a dark green	2.00	1.00
46	A8	10a blk (English inscriptions)	7.50	7.50
		Nos. 44-46 (3)	11.50	10.25

1st anniv. of the death of Mohammed Ali Jinnah (1876-1948), Moslem lawyer, president of All-India Moslem League and first Governor General of Pakistan.

Re-engraved (Crescents Reversed)

A9   A10

A11

Perf. 12½, 13½x14 (3a, 10a), 14x13½ (6a, 12a)

1949-53				
47	A10	1a dk blue ('50)	3.50	.75
a.		Perf. 13 ('52)	11.00	.25
48	A10	1½a gray green	3.50	.75
a.		Perf. 13 ('53)	3.00	.25
49	A10	2a orange red	4.00	.25
a.		Perf. 13 ('53)	6.00	.25
50	A9	3a olive green	15.00	1.00
51	A11	6a deep blue ('50)	24.00	2.00
52	A11	8a black ('50)	24.00	2.00
53	A9	10a red	27.50	3.50
54	A11	12a red ('50)	30.00	.50
		Nos. 47-54 (8)	131.50	10.75

For overprints see #O27-O31, O38-O40.

Vase and Plate — A12

Star and Crescent, Plane and Hour Glass — A13

Moslem Leaf Pattern
A14

Arch and Lamp of Learning
A15

1951, Aug. 14		**Engr.**	*Perf. 13*	
55	A12	2½a dark red	1.90	1.25
56	A13	3a dk rose lake	1.00	.25
57	A12	3½a dp ultra (Urdu "⅓")		1.25	8.00
57A	A12	3½a dp ultra (Urdu "3½") ('56)	5.00	6.00
58	A14	4a deep green	1.75	.25
59	A14	6a red orange	1.75	.25
60	A15	8a brown	4.50	.35
61	A15	10a purple	2.00	2.00
62	A13	12a dk slate blue	2.75	.25
		Nos. 55-62 (9)	21.90	18.60

Fourth anniversary of independence. On No. 57, the characters of the Urdu denomination at right appears as "⅓." On the reengraved No. 57A, they read "3½."
Issue date: Dec. 1956.
See Nos. 88, O32-O34.
For surcharges see Nos. 255, 257.

Scinde District Stamp and Camel Train — A16

1952, Aug. 14				
63	A16	3a olive green, *citron*	1.00	.85
64	A16	12a dark brown, *salmon*	1.75	.25

5th anniv. of Pakistan's Independence and the cent. of the 1st postage stamps in the Indo-Pakistan sub-continent.

Peak K-2, Karakoram Mountains — A17

1954, Dec. 25				
65	A17	2a violet	.50	.30

Conquest of K-2, world's 2nd highest mountain peak, in July 1954.

Kaghan Valley
A18

Gilgit Mountains
A19

Tea Garden, East Pakistan — A20

Designs: 1a, Badshahi Mosque, Lahore. 1½a, Emperor Jahangir's Mausoleum, Lahore. 1r, Cotton field. 2r, River craft and jute field.

1954, Aug. 14			**Engr.**	
66	A18	6p rose violet	.25	.25
67	A19	9p blue	5.00	3.00
68	A19	1a carmine rose	.25	.25
69	A18	1½a red	.25	.25
70	A20	14a dark green	5.00	.25
71	A20	1r yellow green	12.00	.25
72	A20	2r orange	3.00	.25
		Nos. 66-72 (7)	25.75	4.50

Seventh anniversary of independence.
Nos. 66, 69 exist in booklet panes of 4 torn from sheets. Value of booklet, $9.
For overprints & surcharges see #77, 101, 123, 126, O44-O50, O53-O56, O60-O62, O67, O69-O71.

Karnaphuli Paper Mill, East Pakistan (Urdu "½2") — A21

6a, Textile mill. 8a, Jute mill. 12a, Sui gas plant.

1955, Aug. 14		**Unwmk.**	*Perf. 13*	
73	A21	2½a dk car (Urdu "½2")	1.00	1.50
73A	A21	2½a dk car (Urdu "2½") ('56)	3.50	1.50
74	A21	6a dark blue	1.75	.25

75	A21	8a violet	4.00	.25
76	A21	12a car lake & org	4.00	.25
		Nos. 73-76 (5)	14.25	3.75

Eighth anniversary of independence.
On No. 73, the characters of the Urdu denomination at right appear as "½2." On the reengraved No. 73A, they read "2½."
Issue date: Dec. 1956.
See No. 87. For overprints and surcharges see Nos. 78, 102-103, 256, O51, O58-O59.

Nos. 69 and 76
Overprinted in
Ultramarine

1955, Oct. 24

77	A18	1½a red	1.75	4.50
78	A21	12a car lake & org	1.75	3.50

UN, 10th anniv.
Beware of forgeries. Two settings exists, "United Nations," 1mm to left of normal "N" over "NI". Value set, $32.50.

Map of West
Pakistan — A22

1955, Dec. 7   Unwmk.   Perf. 13½x13

79	A22	1½a dark green	1.30	2.00
80	A22	2a dark brown	1.25	.40
81	A22	12a deep carmine	2.00	.50
		Nos. 79-81 (3)	4.55	2.90

West Pakistan unification, Nov. 14, 1955.
Nos. 79-81 from the bottom (eighth) row of the sheet are 41.5mm tall instead of 40.5mm. Value, $4 each.

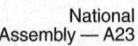

National
Assembly — A23

1956, Mar. 23   Litho.   Perf. 13x12½

82	A23	2a green	.75	.25

Proclamation of the Republic of Pakistan, Mar. 23, 1956.

Crescent and Star — A24

1956, Aug. 14   Engr.   Perf. 13

83	A24	2a red	.60	.25

Ninth anniversary of independence.
For surcharges and overprints see Nos. 127, O57, O72-O73.

Map of East
Pakistan — A25

1956, Oct. 15   Perf. 13½x13

84	A25	1½a dark green	.60	1.50
85	A25	2a dark brown	.60	.25
86	A25	12a deep red	.60	1.25
		Nos. 84-86 (3)	1.80	3.00

1st Session at Dacca (East Pakistan) of the National Assembly of Pakistan.
Nos. 84-86 from the bottom (eighth) row of the sheet are 1mm taller. Value, $4 each.

Redrawn Types of 1951, 1955 and

Orange Tree — A26

Perf. 13x13½, 13½x13

1957, Mar. 23   Engr.

87	A21	2½a dark carmine	.25	.25
88	A12	3½a bright blue	.35	.25
89	A26	10r dk green & orange	.90	.25
		Nos. 87-89 (3)	1.50	.75

Nos. 87-89 inscribed "Pakistan" in English, Urdu and Bengali. Denomination in English only.
Islamic Republic of Pakistan, 1st anniv.
See Nos. 95, 258, 475A. For surcharge and overprint see Nos. 159, O64.

Flag and Broken
Chain — A27

1957, May 10   Litho.   Perf. 13

90	A27	1½a green	.50	.60
91	A27	12a blue	1.25	.25

Cent. of the struggle for Independence (Indian Mutiny).
Examples of Nos. 90-91 exist that are 1mm taller than other stamps from the sheet. Value, $4 each.

Industrial Plants
and Roses as
Symbols of
Progress — A28

1957, Aug. 14   Unwmk.   Perf. 13½

92	A28	1½a light ultra	.25	.40
93	A28	4a orange vermilion	.50	1.50
94	A28	12a red lilac	.40	.50
		Nos. 92-94 (3)	1.15	2.40

Tenth anniversary of independence.

Type of 1957

Design: 15r, Coconut Tree.

1958, Mar. 23   Engr.   Perf. 13½x13

95	A26	15r rose lilac & red	2.50	1.50

Issued to commemorate the second anniversary of the Islamic Republic of Pakistan.

Verse of Iqbal
Poem — A29

1958, Apr. 21   Photo.   Perf. 14½x14
Black Inscriptions

96	A29	1½a citron	.50	1.00
97	A29	2a orange brown	.50	.25
98	A29	14a aqua	2.50	.25
		Nos. 96-98 (3)	3.50	1.50

20th anniv. of the death of Mohammad Iqbal (1877-1938), Moslem poet and philosopher.

Globe and Book — A30

1958, Dec. 10   Litho.   Perf. 13

99	A30	1½a Prus blue	.25	.25
100	A30	14a dark brown	.50	.25

10th anniv. of the signing of the Universal Declaration of Human Rights.

Nos. 66 and 75
Overprinted

1958, Dec. 28   Engr.   Perf. 13

101	A18	6p rose violet	.40	.25
102	A21	8a violet	.75	.25

2nd National Boy Scout Jamboree held at Chittagong, Dec. 28-Jan. 4.
Numerous plate flaws exist for Nos. 101-102. Value: $2 each.

No. 74 Overprinted
in Red

1959, Oct. 27

103	A21	6a dark blue	1.00	.25

First anniversary of the 1958 Revolution.

Red Cross — A31

Engr.; Cross Typo.
1959, Nov. 19   Unwmk.   Perf. 13

104	A31	2a green & red	.30	.25
105	A31	10a dk blue & red	.60	.25

Armed Forces
Emblem — A32

1960, Jan. 10   Litho.   Perf. 13

106	A32	2a blue grn, red & ultra	.50	.25
107	A32	14a ultra & red	1.00	.25

Issued for Armed Forces Day.

Map Showing
Disputed
Areas — A33

1960, Mar. 23   Engr.   Unwmk.

108	A33	6p purple	.40	.25
109	A33	2a copper red	.60	.25
110	A33	8a green	1.20	.25
111	A33	1r blue	1.90	.25
		Nos. 108-111 (4)	4.10	1.00

Publicizing the border dispute with India over Jammu and Kashmir, Junagarh and Manavadar.
For overprints and surcharges see Nos. 122, 125, 128, 178, O65-O66, O74-O75.

Uprooted Oak
Emblem — A34

1960, Apr. 7

112	A34	2a carmine rose	.30	.25
113	A34	10a green	.30	.25

Issued to publicize World Refugee Year, July 1, 1959-June 30, 1960.

House, Field and
Column (Allegory of
Democratic
Development) — A35

1960, Oct. 27   Photo.   Perf. 13

114	A35	2a brown, pink & grn	.25	.25
a.		Green & pink omitted	27.50	
115	A35	14a multicolored	.50	.25

Revolution Day, Oct. 27, 1960.
No. 114a is easily counterfeited.

Punjab
Agricultural
College,
Lyallpur — A36

Design: 8a, College shield.

1960, Oct.   Engr.   Perf. 12½x14

116	A36	2a rose red & gray blue	.25	.25
117	A36	8a lilac & green	.35	.25

50th anniv. of the Punjab Agricultural College, Lyallpur.

Caduceus, College
Emblem — A37

1960, Nov. 16   Photo.   Perf. 13½x13

118	A37	2a blue, yel & blk	.65	.25
119	A37	14a car rose, blk & emerald	1.75	1.00

King Edward Medical College, Lahore, cent.

Map of South-East
Asia and Commission
Emblem — A38

1960, Dec. 5   Engr.   Perf. 13

120	A38	14a red orange	1.00	.25

Conf. of the Commission on Asian and Far Eastern Affairs of the Intl. Chamber of Commerce, Karachi, Dec. 5-9.

"Kim's Gun" and
Scout
Badge — A39

Perf. 12½x14

1960, Dec. 24   Unwmk.

121	A39	2a dk green, car & yel	.85	.25

3rd Natl. Boy Scout Jamboree, Lahore, Dec. 24-31.

No. 110 Ovptd. in
Red

1961, Feb. 12

122	A33	8a green	.95	1.75

10th Lahore Stamp Exhibition, Feb. 12.

New Currency
Nos. 24, 68-69, 83, 108-109
Surcharged with New Value in Paisa

1961   Perf. 13

123	A18	1p on 1½a red	.40	.25
124	A3	2p on 3p orange red	.25	.25
125	A33	3p on 6p purple	.25	.25
126	A19	7p on 1a car rose	.40	.25
127	A24	13p on 2a red	.40	.25
128	A33	13p on 2a copper red	.30	.25
		Nos. 123-128 (6)	2.00	1.50

Various violet handstamped surcharges were applied to a variety of regular-issue stamps. Most of these repeat the denomination of the basic stamp and add the new value. Example: "8 Annas (50 Paisa)" on No. 75. Many errors exist from printer's waste.
For overprints see Nos. O74-O75.

Many errors exist from No. 123 onwards on stamps printed within Pakistan. These are generally printer's waste.

Khyber Pass — A40

Chota Sona Masjid Gate — A41

Design: 10p, 13p, 25p, 40p, 50p, 75p, 90p, Shalimar Gardens, Lahore.

Type I

Type II

Two types of 1p, 2p and 5p:
I — First Bengali character beside "N" lacks appendage at left side of loop.
II — This character has a downward-pointing appendage at left side of loop, correcting "sh" to read "p".

On Nos. 129, 130, 132 the corrections were made individually on the plates, and each stamp may differ slightly. On No. 131a, the corrected letter is more clearly corrected, and the added appendage comes close to, almost touching, the leg of the first Bengali character.

1961-63   Engr.   Perf. 13½x14
129	A40	1p violet (II)	.50	.25
a.		Type I	1.50	
130	A40	2p rose red (II)	.50	.25
a.		Type I	1.50	
131	A40	3p magenta	.75	.25
a.		Retouched plate	8.00	5.00
132	A40	5p ultra (II)	4.50	1.00
a.		Type I	2.50	.25
133	A40	7p emerald	.90	.25
134	A40	10p brown	.25	.25
135	A40	13p blue vio	.25	.25
136	A40	25p dark blue ('62)	2.75	.25
137	A40	40p dull purple ('62)	.75	.25
138	A40	50p dull green ('62)	.40	.25
139	A40	75p dk carmine ('62)	.80	.70
140	A40	90p lt olive grn ('62)	1.00	.70

Perf. 13½x13
141	A41	1r vermilion ('63)	7.00	.25
142	A41	1.25r purple	1.00	1.75
143	A41	2r orange ('63)	5.00	.25
144	A41	5r green ('63)	6.00	3.00
		Nos. 129-144 (16)	32.35	9.90

See #200-203. For surcharge and overprints see Nos. 184, O76-O82, O85-O93A.

Designs Redrawn

1961-62 Bengali Inscription

Redrawn Bengali Inscription

Bengali inscription redrawn with straight connecting line across top of characters. Shading of scenery differs, especially in Shalimar Gardens design where reflection is strengthened and trees at right are composed of horizontal lines instead of vertical lines and dots.
Designs as before; 15p, 20p, Shalimar Gardens.

1963-70   Perf. 13½x14
129b	A40	1p violet	.25	.25
130b	A40	2p rose red ('64)	3.00	.25
131b	A40	3p magenta ('70)	15.00	7.00
132b	A40	5p ultra	.25	.25
133a	A40	7p emerald ('64)	7.00	3.00
134a	A40	10p brown	.25	.25
135a	A40	13p blue violet	.25	.25
135B	A40	15p rose lilac ('64)	.25	.25
135C	A40	20p dull green ('70)	.35	.25
136a	A40	25p dark blue	10.00	.25
137a	A40	40p dull purple ('64)	.35	.25
138a	A40	50p dull green ('64)	.35	.25
139a	A40	75p dark carmine ('64)	.90	.70
140a	A40	90p lt olive green ('64)	1.00	1.00
		Nos. 129b-140a (14)	39.20	14.20

Many exists imperf.
For overprints see #174, O76b, O77b, O78a, O79b, O80a, O81a, O82, O83-O84A, O85a, O86a.

Warsak Dam, Kabul River — A42

1961, July 1   Engr.   Perf. 12½x13½
150 A42 40p black & lt ultra   .70 .25
Dedication of hydroelectric Warsak Project.

Symbolic Flower A43

1961, Oct. 2   Unwmk.   Perf. 14
151 A43 13p greenish blue   .50 .25
152 A43 90p red lilac   1.20 .25
Issued for Children's Day.

Roses — A44

1961, Nov. 4   Perf. 13½x13
153 A44 13p deep green & ver   .40 .25
154 A44 90p blue & vermilion   .90 .90
Cooperative Day.

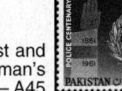
Police Crest and Traffic Policeman's Hand — A45

1961, Nov. 30   Photo.   Perf. 13x12½
155 A45 13p dk blue, sil & blk   .60 .25
156 A45 40p red, silver & blk   1.10 .25
Centenary of the police force.

"Eagle Locomotive, 1861" — A46

Design: 50pa, Diesel Engine, 1961.

1961, Dec. 31   Perf. 13½x14
157 A46 13p yellow, green & blk   .75 .80
158 A46 50p green, blk & yellow   1.00 1.50
Centenary of Pakistan railroads.

No. 87 Surcharged in Red with New Value, Boeing 720-B Jetliner and: "FIRST JET FLIGHT KARACHI-DACCA"
1962, Feb. 6   Engr.   Perf. 13
159 A21 13p on 2½a dk carmine   1.75 1.25
1st jet flight from Karachi to Dacca, Feb. 6, 1962.

Mosquito and Malaria Eradication Emblem — A47

13p, Dagger pointing at mosquito, and emblem.

1962, Apr. 7   Photo.   Perf. 13½x14
160 A47 10p multicolored   .45 .25
161 A47 13p multicolored   .45 .25
WHO drive to eradicate malaria.

Map of Pakistan and Jasmine A48

1962, June 8   Unwmk.   Perf. 12
162 A48 40p grn, yel grn & gray   1.15 .25
Introduction of new Pakistan Constitution.

Soccer — A49

13p, Hockey & Olympic gold medal. 25p, Squash rackets & British squash rackets championship cup. 40p, Cricket & Ayub challenge cup.

1962, Aug. 14   Engr.   Perf. 12½x13½
163 A49 7p blue & black   .25 .25
164 A49 13p green & black   .60 1.50
165 A49 25p lilac & black   .25 .25
166 A49 40p brown org & blk   3.00 2.25
| | Nos. 163-166 (4) | 4.10 | 4.25 |

Marble Fruit Dish and Clay Flask — A50

13p, Sporting goods. 25p, Camel skin lamp, brass jug. 40p, Wooden powder bowl, cane basket. 50p, Inlaid box, brassware.

1962, Nov. 10   Perf. 13½x13
167 A50 7p dark red   .25 .25
168 A50 13p dark green   1.50 1.50
169 A50 25p bright purple   .25 .25
170 A50 40p yellow green   .25 .25
171 A50 50p dull red   .25 .25
| | Nos. 167-171 (5) | 2.50 | 2.50 |
Pakistan Intl. Industries Fair, Oct. 12-Nov. 20, publicizing Pakistan's small industries.

Children's Needs — A51

1962, Dec. 11   Photo.   Perf. 13½x14
172 A51 13p blue, plum & blk   .40 .25
173 A51 40p multicolored   .40 .25
16th anniv. of UNICEF.

No. 135a Overprinted in Red: "U.N. FORCE W. IRIAN"
1963, Feb. 15   Engr.   Unwmk.
174 A40 13p blue violet   .25 2.00
Issued to commemorate the dispatch of Pakistani troops to West New Guinea.

Camel, Bull, Dancing Horse and Drummer — A52

1963, Mar. 13   Photo.   Perf. 12
175 A52 13p multicolored   .25 .25
National Horse and Cattle Show, 1963.

Wheat and Tractor — A53

Design: 50p, Hands and heap of rice.

1963, Mar. 21   Engr.   Perf. 12½x13½
176 A53 13p brown orange   3.75 .25
177 A53 50p brown   5.00 .65
FAO "Freedom from Hunger" campaign.

No. 109 Surcharged with New Value and: "INTERNATIONAL/DACCA STAMP/EXHIBITION/1963"
1963, Mar. 23   Perf. 13
178 A33 13p on 2a copper red   .60 .50
International Stamp Exhibition at Dacca.

Centenary Emblem — A54

Engr. and Typo.
1963, June 25   Perf. 13½x12½
179 A54 40p dark gray & red   2.50 .25
International Red Cross, cent.

Paharpur Stupa — A55

Designs: 13p, Cistern, Mohenjo-Daro, vert. 40p, Stupas, Taxila. 50pa, Stupas, Mainamati.

Perf. 12½x13½, 13½x12½
1963, Sept. 16   Engr.   Unwmk.
180 A55 7p ultra   .60 .25
181 A55 13p brown   .60 .25
182 A55 40p carmine rose   1.10 .25
183 A55 50p dark violet   1.10 .25
| | Nos. 180-183 (4) | 3.40 | 1.00 |

No. 131 Surcharged and Overprinted: "100 YEARS OF P.W.D. OCTOBER, 1963"
1963, Oct. 7   Perf. 13½x14
184 A40 13p on 3pa magenta   .25 .25
Centenary of Public Works Department.

Atatürk Mausoleum, Ankara — A56

1963, Nov. 10   Perf. 13x13½
185 A56 50p red   .50 .25
25th anniv. of the death of Kemal Atatürk, pres. of Turkey.

Globe and UNESCO Emblem — A57

1963, Dec. 10   Photo.   Perf. 13½x14
186 A57 50p dk brn, vio blue & red   .45 .25
15th anniv. of the Universal Declaration of Human Rights.

Multan Thermal Power Station — A58

1963, Dec. 25   Engr.   Perf. 12½x13½
187 A58 13p ultra   .25 .25
Issued to mark the opening of the Multan Thermal Power Station.

Type of 1961-63
Perf. 13½x13
1963-65   Engr.   Wmk. 351
200 A41 1r vermilion   1.50 .25
201 A41 1.25r purple ('64)   3.00 2.00
202 A41 2r orange   1.25 .25
203 A41 5r green ('65)   7.50 .90
| | Nos. 200-203 (4) | 13.25 | 3.40 |
For overprints see Nos. O92-O93A.

A59

13p, Temple of Thot, Dakka, and Queen Nefertari with Goddesses Hathor and Isis. 50p, Ramses II, Abu Simbel, and View of Nile.

Perf. 13x13½
1964, Mar. 30   Unwmk.
204 A59 13p brick red & turq
          blue   .60 .25
205 A59 50p black & rose lilac 1.20 .25
UNESCO world campaign to save historic monuments in Nubia.

Pakistan Pavilion and Unisphere — A60

1.25r, Pakistan pavilion, Unisphere, vert.

Perf. 12½x14, 14x12½
1964, Apr. 22   Engr.   Unwmk.
206 A60 13p ultramarine   .25 .25
207 A60 1.25r dp orange & ultra .45 .25
New York World's Fair, 1964-65.

Mausoleum of Shah Abdul Latif — A61

1964, June 25   Perf. 13½x13
208 A61 50p magenta & ultra   1.00 .25
Bicentenary (?) of the death of Shah Abdul Latif of Bhit (1689-1752).
Examples of No. 208 exist that are 1mm taller than other stamps from the sheet. Value, $4.

Mausoleum of Jinnah — A62

Design: 15p, Mausoleum, horiz.

1964, Sept. 11   Unwmk.   Perf. 13
209 A62 15p green   1.00 .25
210 A62 50p greenish gray   2.00 .25
16th anniv. of the death of Mohammed Ali Jinnah (1876-1948), the Quaid-i-Azam (Great Leader), founder and president of Pakistan.

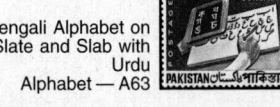

Bengali Alphabet on Slate and Slab with Urdu Alphabet — A63

1964, Oct. 5   Engr.
211 A63 15p brown   .25 .25
Issued for Universal Children's Day.

West Pakistan University of Engineering and Technology A64

1964, Dec. 21   Perf. 12½x14
212 A64 15p henna brown   .25 .25
1st convocation of the West Pakistan University of Engineering & Technology, Lahore, Dec. 1964.

Eyeglasses and Book — A65

Perf. 13x13½
1965, Feb. 28   Litho.   Unwmk.
213 A65 15p yellow & ultra   .25 .25
Issued to publicize aid for the blind.

ITU Emblem, Telegraph Pole and Transmission Tower — A66

1965, May 17   Engr.   Perf. 12½x14
214 A66 15p deep claret   1.90 .30
Cent. of the ITU.

ICY Emblem — A67

1965, June 26   Litho.   Perf. 13½
215 A67 15p blue & black   1.25 .25
216 A67 50p yellow & green   1.75 .40
International Cooperation Year, 1965.

Hands Holding Book — A68

50p, Map & flags of Turkey, Iran & Pakistan.

Perf. 13½x13, 13x12½
1965, July 21   Litho.   Unwmk.
Size: 46x35mm
217 A68 15p org brn, dk brn &
          buff   .25 .25
Size: 54x30½mm
218 A68 50p multicolored   1.10 .25
1st anniv. of the signing of the Regional Cooperation for Development Pact by Turkey, Iran and Pakistan.
See Iran 1327-1328, Turkey 1648-1649.

Tanks, Army Emblem and Soldier — A69

Designs: 15p, Navy emblem, corvette No. O204 and officer. 50p, Air Force emblem, two F-104 Starfighters and pilot.

1965, Dec. 25   Litho.   Perf. 13½x13
219 A69 7p multicolored   .70 .25
220 A69 15p multicolored   1.50 .25
221 A69 50p multicolored   2.50 .30
  Nos. 219-221 (3)   4.70 .80
Issued to honor the Pakistani armed forces.

Emblems of Pakistan Armed Forces — A70

1966, Feb. 13   Litho.   Perf. 13½x13
222 A70 15p buff, grn & dk bl 1.00 .25
Issued for Armed Forces Day.

Atomic Reactor, Islamabad — A71

Unwmk.
1966, Apr. 30   Engr.   Perf. 13
223 A71 15p black   .25 .25
Pakistan's first atomic reactor.

Habib Bank Emblem — A72

Perf. 12½x13½
1966, Aug. 25   Litho.   Unwmk.
224 A72 15p brown, org & dk grn .25 .25
25th anniversary of the Habib Bank.

Boy and Girl — A73

1966, Oct. 3   Litho.   Perf. 13x13½
225 A73 15p multicolored   .25 .25
Issued for Children's Day.

UNESCO Emblem — A74

1966, Nov. 24   Unwmk.   Perf. 14
226 A74 15p multicolored   4.00 .30
20th anniv. of UNESCO.

Secretariat Buildings, Islamabad, Flag and Pres. Mohammed Ayub Khan — A75

1966, Nov. 29   Litho.   Perf. 13
227 A75 15p multicolored   .30 .25
228 A75 50p multicolored   .60 .25
Publicizing the new capital, Islamabad.

Avicenna — A76

1966, Dec. 3   Perf. 13½
229 A76 15p sal pink & slate grn .30 .25
Issued to publicize the Health Institute.

Mohammed Ali Jinnah — A77

Design: 50p, Different frame.

Lithographed and Engraved
1966, Dec. 25   Unwmk.   Perf. 13
230 A77 15p orange, blk & bl   .25 .25
231 A77 50p lilac, blk & vio bl .35 .25
90th anniv. of the birth of Mohammed Ali Jinnah (1876-1948), 1st Governor General of Pakistan.

ITY Emblem A78

1967, Jan. 1   Litho.
232 A78 15p bis brn, blue & blk .25 .25
International Tourist Year, 1967.

Red Crescent Emblem — A79

1967, Jan. 10   Litho.   Perf. 13½
233 A79 15p brn, brn org & red .25 .25
Tuberculosis eradication campaign.

Scout Sign and Emblem — A80

Perf. 12½x13½
1967, Jan. 29   Photo.
234 A80 15p dp plum & brn org .25 .25
4th National Pakistan Jamboree.
"Faisa" is a plate flaw, not an error. Value, unused or used, $5.

Justice Holding Scales — A81

Unwmk.
1967, Feb. 17   Litho.   Perf. 13
235 A81 15p multicolored   .25 .25
Centenary of High Court of West Pakistan.

Mohammad Iqbal — A82

1967, Apr. 21   Litho.   Perf. 13
236 A82 15p red & brown   .25 .25
237 A82 1r dk green & brn   .40 .25
90th anniv. of the birth of Mohammad Iqbal (1877-1938), poet and philosopher.

Flag of Valor A83

1967, May 15   Litho.   Perf. 13
238 A83 15p multicolored   .25   .25
  Flag of Valor awarded to the cities of Lahore, Sialkot and Sargodha.

Star and "20" — A84

1967, Aug. 14   Photo.   Unwmk.
239 A84 15p red & slate green   .25   .25
  20th anniversary of independence.

Rice Plant and Globe — A85

Cotton Plant, Bale and Cloth — A86

Design: 50p, Raw jute, bale and cloth.

1967, Sept. 26   Photo.   Perf. 13x13½
240 A85 10p dk blue & yellow   .25   .25
          Perf. 13
241 A86 15p orange, bl grn & yel   .25   .25
242 A86 50p blue grn, brn & tan   .25   .25
    Nos. 240-242 (3)   .75   .75
  Issued to publicize major export products.

Toys — A87

1967, Oct. 2   Litho.   Perf. 13
243 A87 15p multicolored   .25   .25
  Issued for International Children's Day.

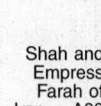

Shah and Empress Farah of Iran — A88

Lithographed and Engraved
1967, Oct. 26   Perf. 13
244 A88 50p yellow, blue & lilac 1.50   .40
  Coronation of Shah Mohammed Riza Pahlavi and Empress Farah of Iran.

"Each for all, . . ." — A89

1967, Nov. 4   Litho.   Perf. 13
245 A89 15p multicolored   .25   .25
  Cooperative Day, 1967.

Mangla Dam — A90

1967, Nov. 23   Litho.   Perf. 13
246 A90 15p multicolored   .25   .25
  Indus Basin Project, harnessing the Indus River for flood control and irrigation.

"Fight Against Cancer" — A91

1967, Dec. 26
247 A91 15p red & dk brown   .70   .25
  Issued to publicize the fight against cancer.

Human Rights Flame — A92

1968, Jan. 31   Photo.   Perf. 14x12½
248 A92 15p Prus green & red   .25   .25
249 A92 50p yellow, silver & red   .25   .25
  International Human Rights Year 1968.

Agricultural University and Produce — A93

1968, Mar. 28   Litho.   Perf. 13½
250 A93 15p multicolored   .25   .25
  Issued to publicize the first convocation of the East Pakistan Agricultural University.

WHO Emblem — A94

1968, Apr. 7   Photo.   Perf. 13½x12½
251 A94 15p emerald & orange   .25   .25
252 A94 50p orange & dk blue   .25   .25
  20th anniv. of WHO. "Pais" is a plate flaw, not an error. Value $2.

Kazi Nazrul Islam — A95

Lithographed and Engraved
1968, June 25   Unwmk.   Perf. 13
253 A95 15p dull yellow & brown   .40   .25
254 A95 50p rose & brown   .90   .25
  Kazi Nazrul Islam, poet and composer.

Nos. 56, 61 and 74 Surcharged with New Value and Bars in Black or Red
1968, Sept.   Engr.   Perf. 13
255 A13 4p on 3a dk rose lake   1.00 1.75
256 A21 4p on 6a dk blue (R)   1.25 1.75
257 A15 60p on 10a purple (R)   1.00   .35
  a.   Black surcharge   .35 2.00
     Nos. 255-257 (3)   3.25 3.85

Types of 1948-57
1968   Wmk. 351   Engr.   Perf. 13
258 A26 10r dk grn & org   5.00 5.50
259 A7 25r purple   8.00 13.00

Children with Hoops — A96

Unwmk.
1968, Oct. 7   Litho.   Perf. 13
260 A96 15p buff & multi   .25   .25
  Issued for International Children's Day.

Symbolic of Political Reforms A97

Designs: 15p, Agricultural and industrial development. 50p, Defense. 60p, Scientific and cultural advancement.

1968, Oct. 27   Litho.   Perf. 13
261 A97 10p multicolored   .25   .40
262 A97 15p multicolored   .25   .25
263 A97 50p multicolored   2.00   .35
264 A97 60p multicolored   .50 1.40
    Nos. 261-264 (4)   3.00 2.40
  Development Decade, 1958-1968.

Chittagong Steel Mill — A98

1969, Jan. 7   Unwmk.   Perf. 13
265 A98 15p lt gray grn, lt blue & blk   .25   .25
  Opening of Pakistan's first steel mill.

Family of Four — A99

1969, Jan. 14   Litho.   Perf. 13½
266 A99 15p lt blue & plum   .25   .25
  Issued to publicize family planning.

Hockey Player and Medal — A100

1969, Jan. 30   Photo.   Perf. 13½
267 A100 15p green, lt bl, blk & gold   1.00   .40
268 A100 1r grn, sal pink, blk & gold   2.50   .90
  Pakistan's hockey victory at the 19th Olympic Games in Mexico.

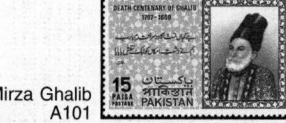

Mirza Ghalib A101

1969, Feb. 15   Litho.   Perf. 13
269 A101 15p blue & multi   .25   .25
270 A101 50p multicolored   .60   .25
  Mirza Ghalib (Asad Ullab Beg Khan, 1797-1869), poet who modernized the Urdu language.

Dacca Railroad Station — A102

1969, Apr. 27   Litho.   Perf. 13
271 A102 15p yel, grn, blk & dl bl .90   .30
  Opening of the new railroad station in Kamalpur area of Dacca.

ILO Emblem and Ornamental Border — A103

1969, May 15   Litho.   Perf. 13½
272 A103 15p brt grn & ocher   .25   .25
273 A103 50p car rose & ocher   .50   .25
  50th anniv. of the ILO.

Lady on Balcony, Mogul Miniature, Pakistan — A104

50p, Lady Serving Wine, Safavi miniature, Iran. 1r, Sultan Suleiman Receiving Sheik Abdul Latif, 16th cent. miniature, Turkey.

1969, July 21   Litho.   Perf. 13
274 A104 20p multicolored   .25   .25
275 A104 50p multicolored   .25   .25
276 A104 1r multicolored   .75   .75
    Nos. 274-276 (3)   1.25 1.25
  5th anniv. of the signing of the Regional Cooperation for Development Pact by Turkey, Iran and Pakistan.
  See Iran 1513-1515, Turkey 1813-1815.

Eastern Refinery, Chittagong — A105

1969, Sept. 14   Photo.   Perf. 13½
277 A105 20p yel, blk & vio bl   .25   .25
  Opening of the 1st oil refinery in East Pakistan.

Children Playing A106

1969, Oct. 6   Perf. 13
278 A106 20p blue & multi   .30   .25
  Issued for Universal Children's Day.

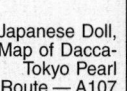

Japanese Doll, Map of Dacca-Tokyo Pearl Route — A107

1969, Nov. 1   Litho.   Perf. 13½x13
279 A107 20p multicolored   .65   .25
280 A107 50p ultra & multi   .90   .30
  Inauguration of the Pakistan International Airways' Dacca-Tokyo "Pearl Route."

Reflection of Light Diagram A108

1969, Nov. 4   *Perf. 13*
281 A108 20p multicolored   .25   .25

Alhazen (abu-Ali al Hasan ibn-al-Haytham, 965-1039), astronomer and optician.

Vickers Vimy and London-Darwin Route over Karachi — A109

1969, Dec. 2   **Photo.**   *Perf. 13½x13*
282 A109 50p multicolored   2.00   .40

50th anniv. of the 1st England to Australia flight.

View of EXPO '70, Sun Tower, Flags of Pakistan, Iran and Turkey — A110

1970, Feb. 15   **Litho.**   *Perf. 13*
283 A110 50p multicolored   .25   .25

Issued to publicize EXPO '70 International Exhibition, Osaka, Japan, Mar. 15-Sept. 13.

UPU Headquarters, Bern — A111

1970, May 20   **Litho.**   *Perf. 13½x13*
284 A111 20p multicolored   .25   .25
285 A111 50p multicolored   .25   .25

Opening of new UPU headquarters in Bern. A souvenir sheet of 2 exists, inscribed "U.P.U. Day 9th Oct. 1971." It contains stamps similar to Nos. 284-285, imperf. Value, $25.

UN Headquarters, New York — A112

Design: 50p, UN emblem.

1970, June 26
286 A112 20p green & multi   .25   .25
287 A112 50p violet & multi   .25   .25

25th anniversary of the United Nations.

Education Year Emblem and Open Book — A113

1970, July 6   **Litho.**   *Perf. 13*
288 A113 20p blue & multi   .25   .25
289 A113 50p orange & multi   .25   .25

International Education Year, 1970.

Saiful Malook Lake, Pakistan — A114

Designs: 50p, Seeyo-Se-Pol Bridge, Esfahan, Iran. 1r, View, Fethiye, Turkey.

1970, July 21
290 A114 20p yellow & multi   .25   .25
291 A114 50p yellow & multi   .35   .25
292 A114 1r yellow & multi   .40   .25
   Nos. 290-292 (3)   1.00   .75

6th anniv. of the signing of the Regional Cooperation for Development Pact by Pakistan, Iran and Turkey.
See Iran 1558-1560, Turkey 1857-1859.

Asian Productivity Year Emblem — A115

1970, Aug. 18   **Photo.**   *Perf. 12½x14*
293 A115 50p black, yel & grn   .25   .25

Asian Productivity Year, 1970.

Dr. Maria Montessori — A116

1970, Aug. 31   **Litho.**   *Perf. 13*
294 A116 20p red & multi   .25   .25
295 A116 50p multicolored   .25   .25

Maria Montessori (1870-1952) Italian educator and physician.

Tractor and Fertilizer Factory A117

1970, Sept. 12
296 A117 20p yel grn & brn org   .25   .40

10th Regional Food and Agricultural Organization Conf. for the Near East in Islamabad.

Boy, Girl, Open Book — A118

1970, Oct. 5   **Photo.**   *Perf. 13*
297 A118 20p multicolored   .25   .25

Issued for Children's Day.

Flag and Inscription — A119

1970, Dec. 7   **Litho.**   *Perf. 13½x13*
298 A119 20p violet & green   .25   .25
299 A119 20p brt pink & green   .25   .25

No. 298 inscribed "Elections for National Assembly 7th Dec. 1970," No. 299 inscribed "Elections for Provincial Assemblies 17th Dec. 1970."

Emblem and Burning of Al Aqsa Mosque A120

1970, Dec. 26   *Perf. 13½x12½*
300 A120 20p multicolored   1.25   .25

Islamic Conference of Foreign Ministers, Karachi, Dec. 26-28.

Coastal Embankment A121

1971, Feb. 25   **Litho.**   *Perf. 13*
301 A121 20p multicolored   .25   .25

Development of coastal embankments in East Pakistan.

Men of Different Races — A122

1971, Mar. 21   **Litho.**   *Perf. 13*
302 A122 20p multicolored   .25   .25
303 A122 50p lilac & multi   .25   .25

Intl. Year against Racial Discrimination.

Cement Factory, Daudkhel A123

1971, July 1   **Litho.**   *Perf. 13*
304 A123 20p purple, blk & brn   .25   .25

20th anniversary of Colombo Plan.

Badshahi Mosque, Lahore A124

Designs: 10pa, Mosque of Selim, Edirne, Turkey. 50pa, Religious School, of Chaharbagh, Isfahan, Iran, vert.

1971, July 21   **Litho.**   *Perf. 13*
305 A124 10p red & multi   .25   .25
306 A124 20p green & multi   .25   .25
307 A124 50p blue & multi   .50   .30
   Nos. 305-307 (3)   1.00   .80

7th anniversary of Regional Cooperation among Pakistan, Iran and Turkey.
See Iran 1599-1601, Turkey 1886-1888.

Electric Train and Boy with Toy Locomotive — A125

1971, Oct. 4   **Litho.**   *Perf. 13*
308 A125 20p slate & multi   1.50   .50

Children's Day.

Messenger and Statue of Cyrus the Great — A126

1971, Oct. 15
309 A126 10p green & multi   .30   .25
310 A126 20p blue & multi   .50   .30
311 A126 50p red & multi   .90   .50
   Nos. 309-311 (3)   1.70   1.05

2500th anniversary of the founding of the Persian Empire by Cyrus the Great.
A souvenir sheet of 3 contains stamps similar to Nos. 309-311, imperf. Value, $52.50.

Hockey Player and Cup — A127

1971, Oct. 24
312 A127 20p red & multi   2.00   .50

First World Hockey Cup, Barcelona, Spain, Oct. 15-24.

Great Bath at Mohenjo-Daro — A128

1971, Nov. 4
313 A128 20p dp org, dk brn & blk   .25   .25

25th anniv. of UNESCO.

UNICEF Emblem — A129

1971, Dec. 11   **Litho.**   *Perf. 13*
314 A129 50p dull bl, org & grn   .25   .25

25th anniv. of UNICEF.

King Hussein and Jordan Flag — A130

1971, Dec. 25
315 A130 20p blue & multi   .25   .25

50th anniversary of the Hashemite Kingdom of Jordan.

Pakistan Hockey Federation Emblem, and Cup — A131

1971, Dec. 31
316 A131 20p yellow & multi   2.75   .75

Pakistan, world hockey champions, Barcelona, Oct. 1971.

Arab
Scholars — A132

1972, Jan. 15   Litho.   Perf. 13½
317 A132 20p brown, blk & blue   .25   .30
International Book Year 1972.

Angels and
Grand
Canal,
Venice
A133

1972, Feb. 5   Perf. 13
318 A133 20p blue & multi   .35   .35
UNESCO campaign to save Venice.

ECAFE
Emblem
A134

1972, Mar. 28   Litho.   Perf. 13
319 A134 20p blue & multi   .25   .30
Economic Commission for Asia and the Far
East (ECAFE), 25th anniversary.

"Your Heart is your
Health" — A135

1972, Apr. 7   Perf. 13x13½
320 A135 20p vio blue & multi   .25   .30
World Health Day 1972.

"Only One
Earth" — A136

1972, June 5   Litho.   Perf. 12½x14
321 A136 20p ultra & multi   .25   .30
UN Conference on Human Environment,
Stockholm, June 5-16.

Young Man, by
Abdur Rehman
Chughtai — A137

Paintings: 10p, Fisherman, by Cevat Dereli
(Turkey). 20p, Persian Woman, by Behzad.

1972, July 21   Litho.   Perf. 13
322 A137 10p multicolored   .30   .25
323 A137 20p multicolored   .50   .30
324 A137 50p multicolored   1.20   .60
Nos. 322-324 (3)   2.00   1.15
Regional Cooperation for Development Pact
among Pakistan, Turkey and Iran, 8th
anniversary.
See Iran 1647-1649, Turkey 1912-1914.

Jinnah and
Independence
Memorial — A138

"Land
Reforms"
A139

Designs: Nos. 326-329, Principal reforms.
60pa, State Bank, Islamabad, meeting-place
of National Assembly, horiz.

Perf. 13 (A138), 13½x12½ (A139)
1972, Aug. 14
325 A138 10p shown   .25   .25
326 A139 20p shown   .25   .25
327 A139 20p Labor reforms   .25   .25
328 A139 20p Education   .25   .25
329 A139 20p Health care   .25   .25
a.   Vert. strip of 4, As #326-329
    plus "labels"   1.00   1.00
330 A138 60p rose lilac & car   .35   .30
Nos. 325-330 (6)   1.60   1.55
25th anniversary of independence. No.
329a contains designs of Nos. 326-329, each
with a decorative label, separated by simulated perfs.

Blood Donor, Society
Emblem — A140

1972, Sept. 6   Litho.   Perf. 14x12½
331 A140 20p multicolored   .25   .35
Pakistan National Blood Transfusion Service.

Census
Chart — A141

1972, Sept. 16   Litho.   Perf. 13½
332 A141 20p multicolored   .25   .25
Centenary of population census.

Children
Leaving Slum
for Modern
City — A142

1972, Oct. 2   Litho.   Perf. 13
333 A142 20p multicolored   .25   .30
Children's Day.

Giant Book and
Children
A143

1972, Oct. 23
334 A143 20p purple & multi   .25   .30
Education Week.

Nuclear Power
Plant,
Karachi — A144

1972, Nov. 28   Litho.   Perf. 13
335 A144 20p multicolored   .25   .40
Pakistan's first nuclear power plant.

Copernicus in
Observatory, by
Jan
Matejko — A145

1973, Feb. 19   Litho.   Perf. 13
336 A145 20p multicolored   .60   .30

Dancing Girl,
Public Baths,
Mohenjo-Daro
A146

1973, Feb. 23   Perf. 13½x13
337 A146 20p multicolored   .35   .30
Mohenjo-Daro excavations, 50th anniv.

Radar, Lightning,
WMO
Emblem — A147

1973, Mar. 23   Litho.   Perf. 13
338 A147 20p multicolored   .25   .40
Cent. of intl. meteorological cooperation.

Prisoners of
War — A148

1973, Apr. 18
339 A148 1.25r black & multi   1.50   2.50
A plea for Pakistani prisoners of war in India.

National
Assembly,
Islamabad
A149

1973, Apr. 21   Perf. 12½x13½
340 A149 20p green & multi   .55   .55
Constitution Week.

State Bank
and Emblem
A150

1973, July 1   Litho.   Perf. 13
341 A150 20p multicolored   .25   .25
342 A150 1r multicolored   .30   .35
State Bank of Pakistan, 25th anniversary.

Street, Mohenjo-
Daro,
Pakistan — A151

Designs: 20p, Statue of man, Shahdad, Ker-
man, Persia, 4000 B.C. 1.25r, Head from mausoleum of King Antiochus I (69-34 B.C.),
Turkey.

1973, July 21   Perf. 13x13½
343 A151 20p blue & multi   .25   .25
344 A151 60p emerald & multi   .65   .35
345 A151 1.25r red & multi   1.00   .75
Nos. 343-345 (3)   1.90   1.35
Regional Cooperation for Development Pact
among Pakistan, Turkey and Iran, 9th
anniversary.
See Iran 1714-1716, Turkey 1941-1943.

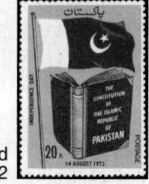

Pakistani Flag and
Constitution — A152

1973, Aug. 14   Litho.   Perf. 13
346 A152 20p blue & multi   .25   .25
Independence Day.

Mohammed Ali
Jinnah — A153

1973, Sept. 11   Litho.   Perf. 13
347 A153 20p emerald, yel & blk   .25   .25
Mohammed Ali Jinnah (1876-1948), president of All-India Moslem League.

Wallago
Attu — A154

Fish: 20p, Labeo rohita. 60p, Tilapia mos-
sambica. 1r, Catla catla.

1973, Sept. 24   Litho.   Perf. 13½
348 A154 10p multicolored   1.10   1.10
349 A154 20p multicolored   1.25   1.25
350 A154 60p multicolored   1.40   1.40
351 A154 1r ultra & multi   1.40   1.40
a.   Strip of 4, #348-351   6.00   6.00

Book, Torch,
Child and
School
A155

1973, Oct. 1
352 A155 20p multicolored   .25   .25
Universal Children's Day.

Sindhi Farmer
and FAO
Emblem
A156

1973, Oct. 15   Litho.   Perf. 13
353 A156 20p multicolored   .75   .35
World Food Organization, 10th anniv.

Kemal Ataturk and Ankara
A157

1973, Oct. 29
354 A157 50p multicolored .75 .40
50th anniversary of Turkish Republic.

Scout Pointing to Planet and Stars — A158

Perf. 13½x12½
1973, Nov. 11 Litho.
355 A158 20p dull blue & multi 2.00 .50
25th anniversary of Pakistani Boy Scouts and Silver Jubilee Jamboree.

Human Rights Flame, Sheltered Home — A159

1973, Nov. 16
356 A159 20p multicolored .45 .40
25th anniversary of the Universal Declaration of Human Rights.

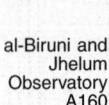

al-Biruni and Jhelum Observatory A160

1973, Nov. 26 Litho. *Perf. 13*
357 A160 20p multicolored .50 .25
358 A160 1.25r multicolored 1.25 .50
International Congress on Millenary of abu-al-Rayhan al-Biruni, Nov. 26-Dec. 12.

Dr. A. G. Hansen — A161

1973, Dec. 29
359 A161 20p ultra & multi 1.20 .50
Centenary of the discovery by Dr. Armauer Gerhard Hansen of the Hansen bacillus, the cause of leprosy.

Family and WPY Emblem A162

1974, Jan. 1 Litho. *Perf. 13*
360 A162 20p yellow & multi .30 .25
361 A162 1.25r salmon & multi .30 .40
World Population Year 1974.

Summit Emblem and Ornament A163

Emblem, Crescent and Rays A164

1974, Feb. 22 *Perf. 14x12½, 13*
362 A163 20p multicolored .25 .25
363 A164 65p multicolored .30 .40
a. Souvenir sheet of 2 2.50 3.25
Islamic Summit Meeting. No. 363a contains two stamps similar to Nos. 362-363 with simulated perforations.

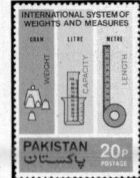

Metric Measures — A165

1974, July 1 Litho. *Perf. 13*
364 A165 20p multicolored .25 .30
Introduction of metric system.

Kashan Rug, Lahore — A166

Designs: 60p, Persian rug, late 16th century. 1.25r, Anatolian rug, 15th century.

1974, July 21
365 A166 20p multicolored .25 .25
366 A166 60p multicolored .40 .50
367 A166 1.25r multicolored .75 1.00
Nos. 365-367 (3) 1.40 1.75
10th anniversary of the Regional Cooperation for Development Pact among Pakistan, Iran and Turkey.
See Iran 1806-1808, Turkey 1979-1981.

Hands Protecting Sapling — A167

1974, Aug. 9 Litho. *Perf. 13*
368 A167 20p multicolored .60 .60
Arbor Day.

Torch over Map of Africa with Namibia — A168

1974, Aug. 26
369 A168 60p green & multi .55 .60
Namibia (South-West Africa) Day. See note after United Nations No. 241.

Map of Pakistan with Highways and Disputed Area — A169

1974, Sept. 23
370 A169 20p multicolored 1.25 1.00
Highway system under construction.

Child and Students — A170

1974, Oct. 7 Litho. *Perf. 13*
371 A170 20p multicolored .40 .50
Universal Children's Day.

UPU Emblem — A171

2.25r, Jet, UPU emblem, mail coach.

1974, Oct. 9 Size: 24x36mm
372 A171 20p multicolored .25 .25
Size: 29x41mm
373 A171 2.25r multicolored .55 .70
a. Souv. sheet of 2, #372-373, imperf. 2.00 2.00
Centenary of Universal Postal Union.

Liaqat Ali Khan — A172

1974, Oct. 16 Litho. *Perf. 13x13½*
374 A172 20p black & red .45 .35
Liaqat Ali Khan, Prime Minister 1947-1951.

Mohammad Allama Iqbal — A173

1974, Nov. 9 Litho. *Perf. 13*
375 A173 20p multicolored .45 .35
Mohammad Allama Iqbal (1877-1938), poet and philosopher.

Dr. Schweitzer on Ogowe River, 1915 — A174

1975, Jan. 14 Litho. *Perf. 13*
376 A174 2.25r multicolored 4.50 *4.50*
Dr. Albert Schweitzer (1875-1965), medical missionary, birth centenary.

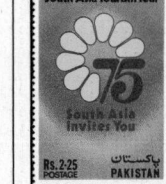

Tourism Year 75 Emblem — A175

1975, Jan. 15
377 A175 2.25r multicolored .60 .80
South Asia Tourism Year, 1975.

Flags of Participants, Memorial and Prime Minister Bhutto A176

1975, Feb. 22 Litho. *Perf. 13*
378 A176 20p lt blue & multi .25 .25
379 A176 1r brt pink & multi 1.25 1.00
2nd Lahore Islamic Summit, Feb. 22, 1st anniv.

IWY Emblem and Woman Scientist A177

Design: 2.25r, Old woman and girl learning to read and write.

1975, June 15 Litho. *Perf. 13*
380 A177 20p multicolored .25 .25
381 A177 2.25r multicolored 1.40 1.75
International Women's Year 1975.

Globe with Dates, Arabic "X" — A178

1975, July 14 Litho. *Perf. 13*
382 A178 20p multicolored .75 .60
International Congress of Mathematical Sciences, Karachi, July 14-20.

Camel Leather Vase, Pakistan — A179

60p, Ceramic plate and RCD emblem, Iran, horiz. 1.25r, Porcelain vase, Turkey.

1975, July 21
383 A179 20p lilac & multi .30 .25
384 A179 60p violet blk & multi .60 .75
385 A179 1.25r blue & multi 1.00 1.10
Nos. 383-385 (3) 1.90 2.10
Regional Cooperation for Development Pact among Turkey, Iran and Pakistan.
See Iran 1871-1873, Turkey 2006-2008.

Sapling, Trees and Ant — A180

1975, Aug. 9   Litho.   Perf. 13x13½
386 A180 20p multicolored   .45 .45
Tree Planting Day.

Black Partridge — A181

1975, Sept. 30   Litho.   Perf. 13
387 A181 20p blue & multi   1.50 .25
388 A181 2.25r yellow & multi   4.50 3.50
Wildlife Protection.

Universal Children's Day — A182

1975, Oct. 6
389 A182 20p multicolored   .45 .50

Hazrat Amir Khusrau, Sitar and Tabla A183

1975, Oct. 24   Litho.   Perf. 14x12½
390 A183 20p lt blue & multi   .25 .50
391 A183 2.25r pink & multi   1.00 2.00
700th anniversary of Hazrat Amir Khusrau (1253-1325), musician who invented the sitar and tabla instruments.

Mohammad Iqbal — A184

1975, Nov. 9   Perf. 13
392 A184 20p multicolored   .50 .50
Mohammad Allama Iqbal (1877-1938), poet and philosopher, birth centenary.

Wild Sheep of the Punjab — A185

1975, Dec. 31   Litho.   Perf. 13
393 A185 20p multicolored   .45 .25
394 A185 3r multicolored   2.20 1.75
Wildlife Protection. See Nos. 410-411.

Mohenjo-Daro and UNESCO Emblem — A186

View of Mohenjo-Daro excavations.

1976, Feb. 29   Litho.   Perf. 13
395 A186 10p multicolored   .70 .80
396 A186 20p multicolored   .80 .90
397 A186 65p multicolored   .80 .90
398 A186 3r multicolored   .80 .90
399 A186 4r multicolored   .90 1.00
  a. Strip of 5, #395-399   4.25 4.25
UNESCO campaign to save Mohenjo-Daro excavations.

Dome and Minaret of Rauza-e-Mubarak Mausoleum — A187

1976, Mar. 3   Photo.   Perf. 13½x14
400 A187 20p blue & multi   .25 .25
401 A187 3r gray & multi   .75 .70
International Congress on Seerat, the teachings of Mohammed, Mar. 3-15.

Alexander Graham Bell, 1876 Telephone and Dial — A188

1976, Mar. 10   Perf. 13
402 A188 3r blue & multi   1.50 2.00
Centenary of first telephone call by Alexander Graham Bell, Mar. 10, 1876.

College Emblem A189

1976, Mar. 15   Litho.   Perf. 13
403 A189 20p multicolored   .45 .45
Cent. of Natl. College of Arts, Lahore.

Peacock A190

1976, Mar. 31   Litho.   Perf. 13
404 A190 20p lt blue & multi   1.00 .40
405 A190 3r pink & multi   4.00 3.75
Wildlife protection.

Eye and WHO Emblem A191

1976, Apr. 7
406 A191 20p multicolored   1.10 .75
World Health Day: "Foresight prevents blindness."

Mohenjo-Daro, UNESCO Emblem, Bull (from Seal) — A192

1976, May 31   Litho.   Perf. 13
407 A192 20p multicolored   .45 .40
UNESCO campaign to save Mohenjo-Daro excavations.

Jefferson Memorial, US Bicentennial Emblem A193

Declaration of Independence, by John Trumbull — A194

1976, July 4   Perf. 13
408 A193 90p multicolored   .90 .50

Perf. 13½x13
409 A194 4r multicolored   3.25 3.50
American Bicentennial.

Wildlife Type of 1975

Wildlife protection: 20p, 3r, Ibex.

1976, July 12
410 A185 20p multicolored   .50 .35
411 A185 3r multicolored   1.75 2.00

Mohammed Ali Jinnah A195

65p, Riza Shah Pahlavi. 90p, Kemal Ataturk.

1976, July 21   Litho.   Perf. 14
412 A195 20p multicolored   .70 .50
413 A195 65p multicolored   .70 .50
414 A195 90p multicolored   .70 .50
  a. Strip of 3, #412-414   2.50 3.25
Regional Cooperation for Development Pact among Pakistan, Turkey and Iran, 12th anniversary.
See Iran 1903-1905, Turkey 2041-2043.

Ornament A196

Jinnah and Wazir Mansion A197

Designs (Jinnah and): 40p, Sind Madressah (building). 50p, Minar Qarardad (minaret). 3r, Mausoleum.

1976, Aug. 14   Litho.   Perf. 13½
415 A196 5p multicolored   .25 .25
416 A196 10p multicolored   .25 .25
417 A196 15p multicolored   .25 .25
418 A197 20p multicolored   .25 .25
419 A197 40p multicolored   .25 .25
420 A197 50p multicolored   .25 .25
421 A196 1r multicolored   .35 .40
422 A197 3r multicolored   .50 .50
  a. Block of 8, #415-422   3.50 3.50
Mohammed Ali Jinnah (1876-1948), first Governor General of Pakistan, birth centenary. Horizontal rows of types A196 and A197 alternate in sheet.

Mohenjo-Daro and UNESCO Emblem — A198

1976, Aug. 31   Perf. 14
423 A198 65p multicolored   .45 .50
UNESCO campaign to save Mohenjo-Daro excavations.

Racial Discrimination Emblem — A199

Perf. 12½x13½
1976, Sept. 15   Litho.
424 A199 65p multicolored   .50 .50
Fight against racial discrimination.

Child's Head, Symbols of Health, Education and Food — A200

1976, Oct. 4   Perf. 13
425 A200 20p blue & multi   .65 .45
Universal Children's Day.

Verse by Allama Iqbal — A201

1976, Nov. 9   Litho.   Perf. 13
426 A201 20p multicolored   .30 .30
Mohammed Allama Iqbal (1877-1938), poet and philosopher, birth centenary.

Scout Emblem, Jinnah Giving Salute — A202

1976, Nov. 20
427 A202 20p multicolored   1.10 .45
Quaid-I-Azam Centenary Jamboree, Nov. 1976.

Children Reading — A203

1976, Dec. 15   Litho.   Perf. 13
428 A203 20p multicolored   .60 .30
Books for children.

Mohammed Ali Jinnah — A204

Lithographed and Embossed
1976, Dec. 25   *Perf. 12½*
429 A204 10r gold & green   3.00 3.00

Mohammed Ali Jinnah (1876-1948), 1st Governor General of Pakistan.
An imperf presentation sheet of 1 exists. Value $100.

Farm Family and Village, Tractor, Ambulance — A205

1977, Apr. 14   *Perf. 13*
430 A205 20p multicolored   .45 .25

Social Welfare and Rural Development Year, 1976-77.

Terracotta Bullock Cart, Pakistan A206

Designs: 20p, Terra-cotta jug, Turkey. 90p, Decorated jug, Iran.

1977, July 21   *Perf. 13*
431 A206 20p ultra & multi   .50 .25
432 A206 65p blue green & multi   .70 .35
433 A206 90p lilac & multi   1.10 1.40
      Nos. 431-433 (3)   2.30 2.00

Regional Cooperation for Development Pact among Pakistan, Turkey and Iran, 13th anniversary.
See Iran 1946-1948, Turkey 2053-2055.

Trees — A207

1977, Aug. 9   *Perf. 13*
434 A207 20p multicolored   .25 .30

Tree planting program.

Desert — A208

1977, Sept. 5   *Perf. 13*
435 A208 65p multicolored   .45 .30

UN Conference on Desertification, Nairobi, Kenya, Aug. 29-Sept. 9.

"Water for the Children" — A209

1977, Oct. 3   *Litho.*   *Perf. 14x12½*
436 A209 50p multicolored   .45 .40

Universal Children's Day.

Aga Khan III — A210

1977, Nov. 2   *Litho.*   *Perf. 13*
437 A210 2r multicolored   .75 .75

Aga Khan III (1877-1957), spiritual ruler of Ismaeli sect, statesman, birth centenary.

Mohammad Iqbal — A211

20p, Spirit appearing to Iqbal, painting by Behzad. 65p, Iqbal looking at Jamaluddin Afghani & Saeed Halim offering prayers, by Behzad. 1.25r, Verse in Urdu. 2.25r, Verse in Persian.

1977, Nov. 9
438 A211   20p multicolored   .60 .60
439 A211   65p multicolored   .60 .60
440 A211   1.25r multicolored   .70 .70
441 A211   2.25r multicolored   .75 .75
442 A211   3r multicolored   .85 .85
   a.   Strip of 5, #438-442   4.50 4.50

Mohammad Allama Iqbal (1877-1938), poet and philosopher, birth centenary.

Holy Kaaba, Mecca — A212

1977, Nov. 21   *Perf. 14*
443 A212 65p green & multi   .45 .30

1977 pilgrimage to Mecca.

Healthy and Sick Bodies — A213

1977, Dec. 19   *Litho.*   *Perf. 13*
444 A213 65p blue green & multi   .50 .30

World Rheumatism Year.

Woman from Rawalpindi-Islamabad A214

1978, Feb. 5   *Litho.*   *Perf. 12½x13½*
445 A214 75p multicolored   .45 .25

Indonesia-Pakistan Economic and Cultural Cooperation Organization.

Blood Circulation and Pressure Gauge — A215

1978, Apr. 20   *Litho.*   *Perf. 13*
446 A215 20p blue & multi   .30 .25
447 A215   2r yellow & multi   .90 .75

Campaign against hypertension.

Henri Dunant, Red Cross, Red Crescent — A216

1978, May 8   *Perf. 14*
448 A216 1r multicolored   1.00 .30

Henri Dunant (1828-1910), founder of Red Cross, 150th birth anniversary.

Red Roses, Pakistan — A217

90p, Pink roses, Iran. 2r, Yellow rose, Turkey.

1978, July 21   *Litho.*   *Perf. 13½*
449 A217 20p multicolored   .35 .25
450 A217 90p multicolored   .50 .25
451 A217   2r multicolored   .75 .35
   a.   Strip of 3, #449-451   2.00 2.00

Regional Cooperation for Development Pact among Turkey, Iran and Pakistan.
See Iran 1984-1986, Turkey 2094-2096.

Hockey Stick and Ball, Championship Cup — A218

Fair Building, Fountain, Piazza Tourismo — A219

1978, Aug. 26   *Litho.*   *Perf. 13*
452 A218 1r multicolored   1.40 .25
453 A219 2r multicolored   .60 .30

Riccione '78, 30th International Stamp Fair, Riccione, Italy, Aug. 26-28. No. 452 also commemorates Pakistan as World Hockey Cup Champion.

Globe and Cogwheels A220

1978, Sept. 3
454 A220 75p multicolored   .45 .25

UN Conference on Technical Cooperation among Developing Countries, Buenos Aires, Argentina, Sept. 1978.

St. Patrick's Cathedral, Karachi — A221

Design: 2r, Stained-glass window.

1978, Sept. 29   *Litho.*   *Perf. 13*
455 A221 1r multicolored   .25 .25
456 A221 2r multicolored   .65 .25

St. Patrick's Cathedral, Karachi, centenary.

"Four Races" — A222

1978, Nov. 20   *Litho.*   *Perf. 13*
457 A222 1r multicolored   .45 .25

Anti-Apartheid Year.

Maulana Jauhar — A223

1978, Dec. 10   *Litho.*   *Perf. 13*
458 A223 50p multicolored   .55 .25

Maulana Muhammad Ali Jauhar, writer, journalist and patriot, birth centenary.

Type of 1957 and

Qarardad Monument — A224

Tractor — A225

Tomb of Ibrahim Khan Makli — A225a

Engr.; Litho. (10p, 25p, 40p, 50p, 90p)
1978-81   *Perf. 14*
459 A224 2p dark green   .25 .25
460 A224 3p black   .25 .25
461 A224 5p violet blue   .25 .25
462 A225 10p lt blue & blue ('79)   .25 .25
463 A225 20p yel green ('79)   .40 .25
464 A225 25p rose car & grn ('79)   .75 .25

465	A225	40p carmine & blue	.25	.25
466	A225	50p bl grn & vio ('79)	.25	.25
467	A225	60p black	.25	.25
468	A225	75p dull red	.50	.25
469	A225	90p blue & carmine	.25	.25

Perf. 13½x13

Engr.   **Wmk. 351**

470	A225a	1r olive ('80)	.25	.25
471	A225a	1.50r dp org ('79)	.25	.25
472	A225a	2r car rose ('79)	.25	.25
473	A225a	3r indigo ('80)	.25	.25
474	A225a	4r black ('81)	.25	.25
475	A225a	5r dk brn ('81)	.25	.25
475A	A26	15r rose lil & red ('79)	1.50	1.50

Nos. 459-475A (18)   6.65   5.75

Lithographed stamps, type A225, have bottom panel in solid color with colorless lettering and numerals 2mm high instead of 3mm.
For overprints see Nos. O94-O110.

Tornado Jet Fighter, de Havilland Rapide and Flyer A — A226

Wright Flyer A and: 1r, Phantom F4F jet fighter & Tristar airliner. 2r, Bell X15 fighter & TU-104 airliner. 2.25r, MiG fighter & Concorde.

Unwmk.

1978, Dec. 24   Litho.   Perf. 13

476	A226	65p multicolored	1.10	1.60
477	A226	1r multicolored	1.20	1.90
478	A226	2r multicolored	1.25	2.00
479	A226	2.25r multicolored	1.25	2.00
a.		Block of 4, #476-479	6.50	6.50

75th anniv. of 1st powered flight.

Koran Lighting the World and Mohammed's Tomb — A227

1979, Feb. 10   Litho.   Perf. 13

480 A227 20p multicolored   .45   .25

Mohammed's birth anniversary.

Mother and Children A228

1979, Feb. 25

481 A228 50p multicolored   .75   .25

APWA Services, 30th anniversary.

Lophophorus Impejanus A229

Pheasants: 25p, Lophura leucomelana. 40p, Puccrasia macrolopha. 1r, Catreus walichii.

1979, June 17   Litho.   Perf. 13

482	A229	20p multicolored	1.35	.60
483	A229	25p multicolored	1.35	.75
484	A229	40p multicolored	1.60	1.75
485	A229	1r multicolored	3.25	2.00

Nos. 482-485 (4)   7.55   5.10

For overprint see No. 525.

At the Well, by Allah Baksh A230

Paintings: 75p, Potters, by Kamalel Molk, Iran. 1.60r, Plowing, by Namik Ismail, Turkey.

1979, July 21   Litho.   Perf. 14x13

486	A230	40p multicolored	.25	.25
487	A230	75p multicolored	.25	.25
488	A230	1.60r multicolored	.25	.25
a.		Strip of 3, #486-488	.90	.90

Regional Cooperation for Development Pact among Pakistan, Iran and Turkey, 15th anniversary.
See Iran 2020-2022, Turkey 2112-2114.

Guj Embroidery A231

Handicrafts: 1r, Enamel inlay brass plate. 1.50r, Baskets. 2r, Peacock, embroidered rug.

1979, Aug. 23   Litho.   Perf. 14x13

489	A231	40p multicolored	.25	.25
490	A231	1r multicolored	.25	.25
491	A231	1.50r multicolored	.30	.30
492	A231	2r multicolored	.40	.35
a.		Block of 4, #489-492	1.50	1.50

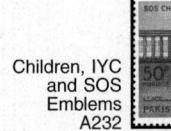

Children, IYC and SOS Emblems A232

1979, Sept. 10   Litho.   Perf. 13

493 A232 50p multicolored   .50   .30

SOS Children's Village, Lahore, opening.

Playground, IYC Emblem A233

IYC Emblem and: Children's drawings.

1979, Oct. 22   Perf. 14x12½

494	A233	40p multicolored	.25	.25
495	A233	75p multicolored	.25	.25
496	A233	1r multicolored	.25	.30
497	A233	1.50r multicolored	.30	.30
a.		Block of 4, #494-497	1.25	1.25

Souvenir Sheet
Imperf

498 A233 2r multi, vert.   1.50   *2.10*

IYC. For overprints see #520-523.

Fight Against Cancer — A234

Unwmk.

1979, Nov. 12   Litho.   Perf. 14

499 A234 40p multicolored   .75   .70

Pakistan Customs Service Centenary — A235

1979, Dec. 10   Perf. 13x13½

500 A235 1r multicolored   .35   .25

"1378" is a plate flaw, not an error.

Tippu Sultan Shaheed A236

15r, Syed Ahmad Khan. 25r, Altaf Hussain Hali.

1979, Mar. 23   Wmk. 351   Perf. 14

501	A236	10r shown	.75	1.00
502	A236	15r multicolored	1.00	1.50
503	A236	25r multicolored	1.50	2.25
a.		Strip of 3, #501-503	4.00	4.00

See No. 699.

A237   A238

   Ornament — A239

Perf. 12x11½, 11½x12

1980   Unwmk.

506	A237	10p dk grn & yel org	.25	.25
507	A237	15p dk grn & apple grn	.25	.25
508	A237	25p multicolored	.25	.25
509	A237	35p multicolored	.25	.25
510	A238	40p red & lt brown	.25	.25
511	A239	50p olive & vio bl	.25	.25
512	A239	80p black & yel grn	.25	.30

Nos. 506-512 (7)   1.75   1.80

Issued: 25, 35, 50, 80p, 3/10; others, 1/15.
See Nos. O111-O117.

Pakistan International Airline, 25th Anniversary A240

1980, Jan. 10   Litho.   Perf. 13

516 A240 1r multicolored   2.00   1.00

Infant, Rose — A241

1980, Feb. 16   Perf. 13

517 A241 50p multicolored   1.00   1.25

5th Asian Congress of Pediatric Surgery, Karachi, Feb. 16-19.

Conference Emblem — A242

1980, May 17   Litho.   Perf. 13

518 A242 1r multicolored   .80   .50

11th Islamic Conference of Foreign Ministers, Islamabad, May 17-21.

Lighthouse, Oil Terminal, Map Showing Karachi Harbor — A243

1980, July 15   Perf. 13½

519 A243 1r multicolored   2.00   1.50

Karachi Port, cent, of independent management.

Nos. 494-497 Overprinted in Red: RICCIONE 80

1980, Aug. 30   Perf. 14x12½

520	A233	40p multicolored	.30	*.50*
521	A233	75p multicolored	.40	*.60*
522	A233	1r multicolored	.45	*.65*
523	A233	1.50r multicolored	.60	*.75*
a.		Block of 4, #520-523	2.00	*3.00*

RICCIONE 80 International Stamp Exhibition, Riccione, Italy, Aug. 30-Sept. 2.

Quetta Command and Staff College, 75th Anniversary — A244

1980, Sept. 18   Litho.   Perf. 13

524 A244 1r multicolored   .25   .40

No. 485 Overprinted: "World Tourism Conference/Manila 80"

1980, Sept. 27

525 A229 1r multicolored   1.00   .50

World Tourism Conf., Manila, Sept. 27.

Birth Centenary of Mohammed Shairani — A245

1980, Oct. 5   Litho.   Perf. 13

526 A245 40p multicolored   .45   .45

Aga Khan Architecture Award A246

1980, Oct. 23   Litho.   Perf. 13½

527 A246 2r multicolored   .60   .55

Rising Sun — A247

1981, Mar. 7   Litho.   Perf. 13
Size: 30x41mm
528 A247 40p Hegira emblem   .25   .40

1980, Nov. 6   Litho.   Perf. 13
529 A247 40p shown   .25   .25
Perf. 14
Size: 33x33mm
530 A247 2r Moslem symbols   .25   .35
Perf. 13x13½
Size: 31x54mm
531 A247 3r Globe, hands hold-
ing Koran   .25   .50
Nos. 528-531 (4)   1.00 1.50
Souvenir Sheet
Imperf
532 A247 4r Candles   1.00 1.00
Hegira (Pilgrimage Year).

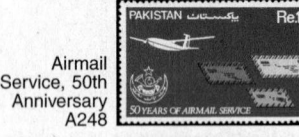

Airmail
Service, 50th
Anniversary
A248

Postal History: No. 533, Postal card cent.
No. 534, Money order service cent.

1980-81   Perf. 13
533 A248 40p multi, vert.   .25   .35
534 A248 40p multi, vert.   .25   .35
535 A248 1r multi   .75   .25
Nos. 533-535 (3)   1.25   .95
Issued: #533, 12/27; #534, 12/20; #535,
2/15/81.

Heinrich von
Stephan, UPU
Emblem — A249

1981, Jan. 7   Perf. 13½
536 A249 1r multicolored   .45   .25
Von Stephan (1831-97), founder of UPU.

Conference
Emblem, Afghan
Refugee — A250

Conference
Emblem, Flags
of Participants,
Men — A251

Conference
Emblem,
Map of
Afghanistan
A252

1981, Mar. 29   Litho.   Perf. 13
537 A250 40p multicolored   .25   .25
538 A251 40p multicolored   .25   .25
539 A250 1r multicolored   .50   .25
540 A251 1r multicolored   .50   .25
541 A252 2r multicolored   .65   .35
Nos. 537-541 (5)   2.15 1.35

Conference
Emblem in
Ornament
A253

Conference
Emblem, Flags
of Participants
A254

1981, Mar. 29   Perf. 13½
542 A253 40p multicolored   .25   .25
543 A254 40p multicolored   .25   .25
544 A253 85p multicolored   .25   .25
545 A254 85p multicolored   .25   .25
Nos. 542-545 (4)   1.00 1.00
3rd Islamic Summit Conference, Makkah al-
Mukarramah, Jan. 25-28.

Kemal Ataturk (1881-
1938), First
President of
Turkey — A255

1981, May 19   Litho.   Perf. 13x13½
546 A255 1r multicolored   .60   .25

Green
Turtle — A256

1981, June 20   Litho.   Perf. 12x11½
547 A256 40p multicolored   1.50   .75

Palestinian
Cooperation — A257

1981, July 25   Litho.   Perf. 13
548 A257 2r multicolored   .55   .25

Mountain
Ranges
and
Peaks
A258

Designs: No. 549, Malubiting West, range.
No. 550, Peak. No. 551, Mt. Maramosh, range.
No. 552, Mt. Maramosh, peak. No. 553, K6,
range. No. 554, Peak. No. 555, K2, range. No.
556, Peak.

1981, Aug. 20   Perf. 14x13½
549   40p multicolored   .45   .30
550   40p multicolored   .45   .30
a.   A258 Pair, #549-550   1.00 1.00
551   1r multicolored   .65   .50
552   1r multicolored   .65   .50
a.   A258 Pair, #551-552   1.50 1.50
553   1.50r multicolored   .80   .60
554   1.50r multicolored   .80   .60
a.   A258 Pair, #553-554   1.75 1.75
555   2r multicolored   .80   .80
556   2r multicolored   .80   .80
a.   A258 Pair, #555-556   1.75 1.75
Nos. 549-556 (8)   5.40 4.40

Inauguration of
Pakistan Steel
Furnace No. 1,
Karachi — A260

1981, Aug. 31   Perf. 13
557 A260 40p multicolored   .25   .25
558 A260 2r multicolored   .60   .75

Western
Tragopan in
Summer — A261

1981, Sept. 15   Litho.   Perf. 14
559 A261 40p shown   2.50   .75
560 A261 2r Winter   4.75 4.00

Intl. Year of the
Disabled
A262

1981, Dec. 12   Litho.   Perf. 13
561 A262 40p multicolored   .25   .30
562 A262 2r multicolored   1.25 1.00

World Cup
Championship
A263

1982, Jan. 31   Litho.   Perf. 13½x13
563 A263 1r Cup, flags in arc   2.00 1.00
564 A263 1r shown   2.00 1.00
a.   Pair, #563-564   4.50 4.50
Nos. 563-564 were printed with a vertical
strip of labels, picturing different scenes, in the
middle of each sheet, allowing for pairs with
label between. Value, pair with label $4.

Camel Skin
Lampshade
A264

1982, Feb. 20   Litho.   Perf. 14
565 A264 1r shown   .80   .60
566 A264 1r Hala pottery   .80   .60
See Nos. 582-583.

TB Bacillus
Centenary — A265

1982, Mar. 24
567 A265 1r multicolored   1.50 1.25

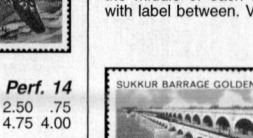

Blind Indus
Dolphin — A266

1982, Apr. 24   Litho.   Perf. 12x11½
568 A266 40p Dolphin   1.50   .75
569 A266 1r Dolphin, diff.   3.50 1.50

Peaceful
Uses of
Outer Space
A267

1982, June 7   Litho.   Perf. 13
570 A267 1r multicolored   2.00 1.10
No. 570 was printed with a vertical strip of
labels, picturing different space satellites, in
the middle of each sheet, allowing for pairs
with label between. Value, pair with label $4.

50th Anniv.
of Sukkur
Barrage
A268

1982, July 17   Litho.   Perf. 13
571 A268 1r multicolored   .35   .25
For overprint see No. 574.

Independence
Day — A269

1982, Aug. 14
572 A269 40p Flag   .25   .25
573 A269 85p Map   .50   .50

No. 571 Overprinted "RICCIONE-
82/1932-1982"

1982, Aug. 28
574 A268 1r multicolored   .25   .25
RICCIONE '82 Intl. Stamp Exhibition, Riccione, Italy, Aug. 28-30.

University of the Punjab
Centenary — A270

1982, Oct. 14   Litho.   Perf. 13½
575 A270 40p multicolored   1.20   .40
No. 575 was printed with a vertical strip of
labels, picturing different university buildings,
in the middle of each sheet, allowing for pairs
with label between. Value, pair with label: $4.

Scouting Year — A271

1982, Dec. 23   Litho.   Perf. 13
576 A271 2r Emblem   .50   .35

Quetta Natural Gas Pipeline Project — A272

1983, Jan. 6   Litho.   Perf. 13
577 A272 1r multicolored   .35   .25

Common Peacock — A273

Designs: 50p, Common rose. 60p, Plain tiger. 1.50r, Lemon butterfly.

1983, Feb. 15   Litho.   Perf. 14
578 A273 40p shown   1.25   .25
579 A273 50p multi   1.50   .25
580 A273 60p multi   1.75   .55
581 A273 1.50r multi   2.50 2.25
    Nos. 578-581 (4)   7.00 3.30

Handicraft Type of 1982
Designs: No. 582, Straw mats. No. 583, Five-flower cloth design.

1983, Mar. 9
582 A264 1r multi   .30   .25
583 A264 1r multi   .30   .25

Opening of Aga Khan University — A274

1983, Mar. 16   Perf. 13½
584 A274 2r multicolored   1.25 1.00

No. 584 was printed with a vertical strip of labels, picturing different university views, in the middle of each sheet, allowing for pairs with label between. Value, pair with label $4.

Yak Caravan, Zindiharam-Darkot Pass, Hindu Kush Mountains — A275

1983, Apr. 28   Litho.   Perf. 13
585 A275 1r multicolored   1.60   .50

Marsh Crocodile — A276

1983, May 19   Perf. 13½x14
586 A276 3r multicolored   4.00 1.60

1983, June 20   Litho.   Perf. 14
Size: 50x40mm
587 A276 1r Gazelle   3.25 1.60

36th Anniv. of Independence A277

1983, Aug. 14   Perf. 13
588 A277 60p Star   .25   .25
589 A277 4r Torch   .40   .40

25th Anniv. of Indonesia-Pakistan Economic and Cultural Cooperation Org. — A278

Weavings — No. 590, Pakistani (geometric). No. 591, Indonesian (figures).

1983, Aug. 19   Litho.   Perf. 13
590 A278 2r multicolored   .30   .25
591 A278 2r multicolored   .30   .25

Siberian Cranes A279

1983, Sept. 8   Perf. 13½
592 A279 3r multicolored   4.00 3.00

World Communications Year — A280

1983, Oct. 9   Litho.   Perf. 13
593 A280 2r multicolored   .35   .25
Size: 33x33mm
594 A280 3r Symbol, diff.   .30   .25

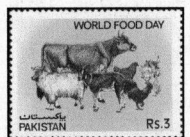

World Food Day — A281

1983, Oct. 24   Litho.   Perf. 13
595 A281 3r Livestock   1.50 1.50
596 A281 3r Fruit   1.50 1.50
597 A281 3r Grain   1.50 1.50
598 A281 3r Seafood   1.50 1.50
  a. Strip of 4, #595-598   6.50 6.50

National Fertilizer Corp. — A282

1983, Oct. 24   Litho.   Perf. 13½
599 A282 60p multicolored   .25   .25

View of Lahore City, 1852 — A283

1983, Nov. 13   Litho.   Perf. 13
600   Strip of 6   3.50 3.50
  a.-f. A283 60p any single   .50   .50
PAKPHILEX '83 Natl. Stamp Exhibition.

Yachting Victory in 9th Asian Games, 1982 — A284

1983, Dec. 31   Litho.   Perf. 13
601 A284 60p OK Dinghy   1.75 1.75
602 A284 60p Enterprise   1.75 1.75

Snow Leopard A285

1984, Jan. 21   Perf. 14
603 A285 40p lt green & multi   2.00 1.00
604 A285 1.60r blue & multi   5.00 5.00

Jehangir Khan (b. 1963), World Squash Champion — A286

1984, Mar. 17   Litho.   Perf. 13
605 A286 3r multicolored   2.75 1.40

Pakistan Intl. Airway China Service, 20th Anniv. — A287

1984, Apr. 29   Litho.   Perf. 13
606 A287 3r Jet   5.75 4.50

Glass Work, Lahore Fort — A288

Various glass panels.

1984, May 31   Litho.   Perf. 13
607 A288 1r green & multi   .25   .25
608 A288 1r purple & multi   .25   .25
609 A288 1r vermilion & multi   .25   .25
610 A288 1r brt blue & multi   .25   .25
    Nos. 607-610 (4)   1.00 1.00

Forts — A289

1984-88   Litho.   Perf. 11
613 A289 5p Kot Diji   .40   .25
614 A289 10p Rohtas   .40   .25
615 A289 15p Bala Hissar ('86)   .75   .25
616 A289 20p Attock   1.50   .25
617 A289 50p Hyderabad ('86)   1.50   .25
618 A289 60p Lahore   1.25   .25
619 A289 70p Sibi ('88)   1.50   .25
620 A289 80p Ranikot ('86)   1.50   .25
    Nos. 613-620 (8)   8.80 2.00

Issued: 5p, 11/1; 10p, 9/25; 80p, 7/1.
For overprints see Nos. O118-O124.

Shah Rukn-i-Alam Tomb, Multan A290

1984, June 26   Litho.   Perf. 13
624 A290 60p multicolored   2.50 1.40

Aga Khan Award for Architecture.

Asia-Pacific Broadcasting Union, 20th Anniv. — A290a

1984, July 1   Litho.   Perf. 13
625 A290a 3r multicolored   .90   .50

1984 Summer Olympics, Los Angeles — A291

1984, July 31
626 A291 3r Athletics   1.35 1.00
627 A291 3r Boxing   1.35 1.00
628 A291 3r Hockey   1.35 1.00
629 A291 3r Yachting   1.35 1.00
630 A291 3r Wrestling   1.35 1.00
    Nos. 626-630 (5)   6.75 5.00

Issued in sheets of 10.
A press sheet containing sheets of 10 each of Nos. 626-630 was produced for limited sales overseas. Value, $100.

Independence, 37th Anniv. — A292

1984, Aug. 14
631 A292 60p Jasmine   .25   .25
632 A292 4r Lighted torch   .50   .45

Intl. Trade Fair, Sept. 1-21, Karachi — A293

1984, Sept. 1
633 A293 60p multicolored   .60   .30

1984 Natl. Tourism Convention, Karachi, Nov. 5-8 — A293a

Shah Jahan Mosque: a, Main dome interior. b, Tile work. c, Entrance. d, Archways. e, Dome interior, diff.

1984, Nov. 5   Litho.   Perf. 13½
634   Strip of 5   3.00 3.00
  a.-e. A293a 1r any single   .50   .40

United Bank Limited, 25th Anniv. — A294

1984, Nov. 7
635 A294 60p multicolored   .75   .60

UNCTAD, UN Conference on Trade
and Development, 20th
Anniv. — A294a

1984, Dec. 24   Perf. 14½x14
636 A294a 60p multicolored   .85 .35

Postal Life Insurance,
Cent. — A295

1984, Dec. 29   Perf. 13½x14
637 A295 60p multicolored   .50 .25
638 A295 1r multicolored   .75 .25

UNESCO World Heritage
Campaign — A296

No. 639, Unicorn, rock painting. No. 640,
Unicorn seal, round.

1984, Dec. 31
639   2r multicolored   1.50 .80
640   2r multicolored   1.50 .80
  a.   A296 Pair, #639-640   3.50 3.50
Restoration of Mohenjo-Daro.

IYY, Girl Guides
75th
Anniv. — A297

1985, Jan. 5   Perf. 13½
641 A297 60p Emblems   3.75 1.25

Smelting — A298   Pouring
                      Steel — A299

1985, Jan. 15   Perf. 13
642 A298 60p multicolored   .75 .30
643 A299 1r multicolored   1.25 .40

Referendum
Reinstating Pres.
Zia — A300

1985, Mar. 20 Litho. Perf. 13
644 A300 60p Map, sunburst   1.25 .40

Minar-e-Qarardad-e-Pakistan
Tower — A301

Ballot
Box — A302

1985 Elections.

1985, Mar. 23
645 A301 1r multicolored   .70 .25
646 A302 1r multicolored   .70 .25

Mountaineering — A303

40p, Mt. Rakaposhi, Karakoram. 2r, Mt.
Nangaparbat, Western Himalayas.

1985, May 27   Litho.   Perf. 14
647 A303 40p multicolored   2.00 .75
648 A303 2r multicolored   4.25 5.50

Championship Pakistani Men's Field
Hockey Team — A304

Design: 1984 Olympic gold medal, 1985
Dhaka Asia Cup, 1982 Bombay World Cup.

1985, June 5   Litho.   Perf. 13
649 A304 1r multicolored   2.50 1.25

King Edward Medical College, Lahore,
125th Anniv.
A305

1985, July 28   Litho.   Perf. 13
650 A305 3r multicolored   2.25 .80

Natl. Independence Day — A306

Designs: No. 651a, 37th Independence Day
written in English. No. 651b, In Urdu.

1985, Aug. 14
651   A306 Pair + 2 labels   .75 .75
  a.-b.   60p any single   .35 .30
Printed in sheets of 4 stamps + 4 labels.

Sind Madressah-Tul-Islam, Karachi,
Education Cent. — A307

1985, Sept. 1
652 A307 2r multicolored   2.10 .80

Mosque,
Jinnah
Avenue,
Karachi
A308

1985, Sept. 14
653 A308 1r Mosque by day   1.00 .35
654 A308 1r At night   1.00 .35
35th anniv. of the Jamia Masjid Pakistan
Security Printing Corporation's miniature rep-
lica of the Badshahi Mosque, Lahore.

Lawrence College, Murree, 125th
Anniv. — A309

1985, Sept. 21
655 A309 3r multicolored   2.50 .75

UN, 40th
Anniv.
A310

1985, Oct. 24   Litho.   Perf. 14x14½
656 A310 1r UN building, sun   .40 .25
657 A310 2r Building emblem   .60 .30

10th Natl. Scouting Jamboree, Lahore,
Nov. 8-15 — A311

1985, Nov. 8   Perf. 13
658 A311 60p multicolored   3.00 1.90

Islamabad and
Capital Development
Authority
Emblem — A312

1985, Nov. 30   Perf. 14½
659 A312 3r multicolored   2.10 .50
Islamabad, capital of Pakistan, 25th anniv.

Flags and Map of
SAARC
Nations — A313

Flags as Flower
Petals — A314

1985, Dec. 8   Perf. 13½, 13
660 A313 1r multicolored   2.75 3.50
661 A314 2r multicolored   1.25 1.75
SAARC, South Asian Assoc. for Regional
Cooperation.

Dove and World
Map — A315

1985, Dec. 14   Perf. 13
662 A315 60p multicolored   1.00 .60
UN Declaration on the Granting of Independence to Colonial Countries and Peoples, 25th
Anniv.

Shaheen
Falcon — A316

1986, Jan. 20   Perf. 13½x14
663 A316 1.50r multicolored   5.00 4.00

Agricultural
Development
Bank, 25th
Anniv. — A317

1986, Feb. 18   Litho.   Perf. 13
664 A317 60p multicolored   1.00 .40

Sadiq Egerton
College,
Bahawalpur,
Cent. — A318

1986, Apr. 25
665 A318 1r multicolored   3.50 1.00

A319

1986, May 11   Perf. 13½
666 A319 1r multicolored   3.25 .85
Asian Productivity Organization, 25th anniv.

A320

1986, Aug. 14   Litho. Perf. 14½x14
667 A320 80p "1947-1986"   1.25 .60
668 A320 1r Urdu text, fire-
                works   1.25 .60
Independence Day, 39th anniv.

Intl. Literacy
Day — A321

1986, Sept. 8   Perf. 13
669 A321 1r Teacher, students   1.50 .60

A322

1986, Oct. 28   Litho.   Perf. 13½x13
670 A322 80p multicolored   2.50 .40
UN Child Survival Campaign.

Aitchison
College,
Lahore, Cent.
A323

1986, Nov. 3   Perf. 13½
671 A323 2.50r multicolored   1.25 .60

Intl. Peace
Year — A324

1986, Nov. 20   Perf. 13
672 A324 4r multicolored   .65 .55

4th Asian Cup
Table Tennis
Tournament,
Karachi — A325

1986, Nov. 25   Perf. 14½
673 A325 2r multicolored   2.50 .50

Marcopolo
Sheep
A326

1986, Dec. 4   Litho.   Perf. 14
674 A326 2r multicolored   3.25 2.50
See No. 698.

Eco Philex
'86 — A327

Mosques: No. 675a, Selimiye, Turkey. No. 675b, Gawhar Shad, Iran. No. 675c, Grand Mosque, Pakistan.

1986, Dec. 20   Perf. 13
675   Strip of 3   4.00 4.00
a.-c. A327 3r any single   1.25 1.25

St. Patrick's School, Karachi, 125th
Anniv.
A328

1987, Jan. 29   Litho.   Perf. 13
676 A328 5r multicolored   3.00 1.10

Savings Bank
Week — A329

Birds, berries and: a, National defense. b, Education. c, Agriculture. d, Industry.

1987, Feb. 21   Litho.   Perf. 13
677   Block of 4 + 2 labels   5.00 5.00
a.-d. A329 5r any single   1.00 .75

Parliament House Opening,
Islamabad — A330

1987, Mar. 23
678 A330 3r multicolored   .60 .25

Fight Against Drug
Abuse — A331

1987, June 30   Litho.   Perf. 13
679 A331 1r multicolored   .60 .25

Natl. Independence, 40th
Anniv. — A332

Natl. flag and: 80p, Natl. anthem, written in Urdu. 3r, Jinnah's first natl. address, the Minar-e-Qarardad-e-Pakistan and natl. coat of arms.

1987, Aug. 14   Litho.   Perf. 13
680 A332 80p multicolored   .60 .25
681 A332 3r multicolored   1.75 .75

Miniature Sheet

Air
Force,
40th
Anniv.
A333

Aircraft: a, Tempest II. b, Hawker Fury. c, Super Marine Attacker. d, F86 Sabre. e, F104 Star Fighter. f, C130 Hercules. g, F6. h, Mirage III. i, A5. j, F16 Fighting Falcon.

1987, Sept. 7   Litho.   Perf. 13½
682   Sheet of 10   16.00 16.00
a.-j. A333 3r any single   1.25 1.00

Tourism
Convention
1987 — A334

Views along Karakoram Highway: a, Pasu Glacier. b, Apricot trees. c, Highway winding through hills. d, Khunjerab peak.

1987, Oct. 1   Perf. 13
683   Block of 4   2.50 2.50
a.-d. A334 1.50r any single   .50 .25

Shah Abdul Latif Bhitai
Mausoleum — A335

1987, Oct. 8   Perf. 13
684 A335 80p multicolored   .25 .25

D.J. Sind
Government
Science
College,
Karachi,
Cent. — A336

1987, Nov. 7
685 A336 80p multicolored   .25 .25

College of
Physicians
and
Surgeons,
25th Anniv.
A337

1987, Dec. 9   Litho.   Perf. 13
686 A337 1r multicolored   1.75 .60

Intl. Year of Shelter for
the Homeless — A338

1987, Dec. 15
687 A338 3r multicolored   .50 .35

Cathedral
Church of the
Resurrection,
Lahore,
Cent. — A339

1987, Dec. 20
688 A339 3r multicolored   .50 .25

Natl. Postal
Service, 40th
Anniv. — A340

1987, Dec. 28
689 A340 3r multicolored   .50 .25

Radio Pakistan
A341

1987, Dec. 31
690 A341 80p multicolored   .25 .25

A342

Design: Jamshed Nusserwanjee Mehta (1886-1952), Mayor of Karachi, member of the Sind Legislative assembly.

1988, Jan. 7
691 A342 3r multicolored   .50 .35

World Leprosy
Day — A343

1988, Jan. 31
692 A343 3r multicolored   .75 .25

World Health
Organization,
40th Anniv.
A344

1988, Apr. 7   Litho.   Perf. 13
693 A344 4r multicolored   .75 .30

Intl. Red Cross and
Red Crescent
Organizations, 125th
Annivs. — A345

1988, May 8
694 A345 3r multicolored   .70 .45

Independence
Day, 41st
Anniv. — A346

1988, Aug. 14   Litho.   Perf. 13½
695 A346 80p multicolored   .35 .25
696 A346 4r multicolored   .35 .35

Miniature Sheet

1988 Summer Olympics,
Seoul — A347

Events: a, Discus, shot put, hammer throw, javelin. b, Relay, hurdles, running, walking. c, High jump, long jump, triple jump, pole vault. d, Gymnastic floor exercises, rings, parallel bars. e, Table tennis, tennis, field hockey, baseball. f, Volleyball, soccer, basketball, team handball. g, Wrestling, judo, boxing, weight lifting. h, Sport pistol, fencing, rifle shooting, archery. i, Swimming, diving, yachting, quadruple-sculling, kayaking. j, Equestrian jumping, cycling, steeplechase.

1988, Sept. 17   Litho.   Perf. 13½x13
697   A347 Sheet of 10 + 32
       labels   13.00 13.00
a.-j. 10r any single   1.00 1.00
Labels contained in No. 697 picture the Seoul Games character trademark or emblem. Size of No. 697: 251x214mm.

Fauna Type of 1986

2r, Suleman markhor, vert.

1988, Oct. 29   Litho.   Perf. 14
698 A326 2r multi   .85 .40

Pioneers of Freedom Type of 1979

3r, Maulana Hasrat Mohani.

1989, Jan. 23   Litho.   Wmk. 351
699 A236 3r multi   .45 .25

Islamia College, Peshawar, 75th Anniv. A348

1988, Dec. 22   Unwmk.   Perf. 13½
700 A348 3r multicolored   .60   .25

SAARC Summit Conference, Islamabad A349

Designs: 25r, Flags, symbols of commerce. 50r, Globe, communication and transportation. 75r, Bangladesh #69, Maldive Islands #1030, Bhutan #132, Pakistan #403, Ceylon #451, India #580, Nepal #437.

1988, Dec. 29   Perf. 13
701 A349 25r shown   1.75 1.50

No. 701 exists with attached label. Values: $10 mint, $20 used.

Size: 33x33mm
Perf. 14
702 A349 50r multicolored   4.75 3.25

Size: 52x28mm
Perf. 13½x13
703 A349 75r multicolored   3.75 3.50
Nos. 701-703 (3)   10.25 8.25

No. 703 exists with attached label. Value, strip of three with label $20.

Adasia '89, 16th Asian Advertising Congress, Lahore, Feb. 18-22 — A350

1989, Feb. 18   Litho.   Perf. 13
704   Strip of 3   3.50 3.25
a. A350 1r deep rose lilac & multi   .95   .65
b. A350 1r green & multi   .95   .65
c. A350 1r bright vermilion & multi   .95   .65
Printed in sheets of 9.

Pres. Zulfikar Ali Bhutto (1928-1979), Ousted by Military Coup and Executed — A351

Portraits.

1989, Apr. 4   Litho.   Perf. 13
705 A351 1r shown   .25   .25
706 A351 2r multi, diff.   .40   .25

Submarine Operations, 25th Anniv. — A352

Submarines: a, Agosta. b, Daphne. c, Fleet Snorkel.

1989, June 1   Litho.   Perf. 13½
707   Strip of 3   4.25 4.25
a.-c. A352 1r any single   1.25 1.25

Oath of the Tennis Court, by David A353

1989, June 24   Litho.   Perf. 13½
708 A353 7r multicolored   2.25   .80
French revolution, bicent.

Archaeological Heritage — A354

Terra cotta vessels excavated in Baluchistan: a, Pirak, c. 2200 B.C. b, Nindo Damb, c. 2300 B.C. c, Mehrgarh, c. 3600 B.C. d, Nausharo, c. 2600 B.C.

1989, June 28   Perf. 14½x14
709   Block of 4   1.50 1.25
a.-d. A354 1r any single   .25   .25

Asia-Pacific Telecommunity, 10th Anniv. — A355

1989, July 1   Perf. 13½x14
710 A355 3r multicolored   .50   .25

Laying the Foundation Stone for the 1st Integrated Container Terminal, Port Qasim — A356

1989, Aug. 5   Litho.   Perf. 14
711 A356 6r Ship in berth   3.25 3.25

Abdul Latif Bhitai Memorial — A358

1989, Sept. 16   Litho.   Unwmk.
718 A358 2r multicolored   .60   .25
245th death and 300th birth annivs. of Shah Abdul Latif Bhitai.

Mohammad Ali Jinnah — A357

Litho. & Engr.
1989, Aug. 14   Wmk. 351   Perf. 13
712 A357   1r multicolored   .65   .25
713 A357 1.50r multicolored   .80   .25
714 A357   2r multicolored   .90   .25
715 A357   3r multicolored   1.00   .30
716 A357   4r multicolored   1.50   .35
717 A357   5r multicolored   1.75   .40
Nos. 712-717 (6)   6.60 1.80

Independence Day.
Nos. 712-717 exist overprinted "NATIONAL SEMINAR ON PHILATELY MULTAN 1992." These were available only at the seminar and were not sold in post offices. Value $125. Beware of forgeries.

World Wildlife Fund A359

Himalayan black bears and WWF emblem: a, Bear on slope, emblem UR. b, Bear on slope, emblem UL. c, Bear on top of rock, emblem UR. d, Seated bear, emblem UL.

Perf. 14x13½
1989, Oct. 7   Litho.   Unwmk.
719 A359 Block of 4   4.00 4.00
a.-d.   4r, any single   .75   .75

World Food Day — A360

1989, Oct. 16   Perf. 14x12½
720 A360 1r multicolored   .45   .30

Quilt and Bahishiti Darwaza (Heavenly Gate) A361

1989, Oct. 20   Perf. 13
721 A361 3r multicolored   .50   .25
800th Birth anniv. of Baba Farid.

4th SAF Games, Islamabad — A362

1989, Oct. 20
722 A362 1r multicolored   .45   .40

Pakistan Television, 25th Anniv. — A363

1989, Nov. 26   Litho.   Perf. 13½
723 A363 3r multicolored   .50   .25

SAARC Year Against Drug Abuse and Drug Trafficking — A364

1989, Dec. 8   Perf. 13
724 A364 7r multicolored   2.75   .85

Murray College, Sialkot, Cent. — A365

1989, Dec. 18   Perf. 14
725 A365 6r multicolored   .60   .40

Government College, Lahore, 125th Anniv. — A366

1989, Dec. 21   Perf. 13
726 A366 6r multicolored   .60   .50

Center on Integrated Rural Development for Asia and the Pacific (CIRDAP), 10th Anniv. — A367

1989, Dec. 31
727 A367 3r multicolored   .60   .40

Organization of the Islamic Conference (OIC), 20th Anniv. A368

1990, Feb. 9   Litho.   Perf. 13
728 A368 1r multicolored   1.40   .50

7th World Field Hockey Cup, Lahore, Feb. 12-23 A369

1990, Feb. 12   Perf. 14x13½
729 A369 2r multicolored   5.25 4.00

A370

Pakistan Resolution, 50th Anniv. — A371

Designs: a, Allama Mohammad Iqbal addressing the Allahabad Session of the All-India Muslim League and swearing-in of Liat Ali Khan as league secretary-general. b, Freedom fighter Maulana Mohammad Ali Jauhar at Muslim rally and Mohammed Ali Jinnah at microphone. c, Muslim woman holding flag and swearing-in of Mohammed Ali Jinnah as governor-general of Pakistan, Aug. 14, 1947. 7r, English and Urdu translations of the resolution, natl. flag and Minar-e-Qarardade Pakistan.

1990, Mar. 23   Litho.   Perf. 13
730   Strip of 3   3.00 3.00
a.-c. A370 1r any single   1.00   .75

Size: 90x45mm
Perf. 13½
731 A371 7r multicolored   2.00 2.00

Safe Motherhood South Asia Conference, Lahore A372

1990, Mar. 24   *Perf. 13½*
732 A372 5r multicolored   .75 .50

Calligraphic Painting of a Ghalib Verse, by Shakir Ali (1916-1975) — A373

1990, Apr. 19   **Litho.**   *Perf. 13½x13*
733 A373 1r multicolored   2.00 .65
See Nos. 757-758.

Badr-1 Satellite A374

1990, July 26   **Litho.**   *Perf. 13*
734 A374 3r multicolored   3.75 2.50

Pioneers of Freedom — A375

No. 735: a, Allama Mohammad Iqbal (1877-1938). b, Mohammad Ali Jinnah (1876-1948). c, Sir Syed Ahmad Khan (1817-98). d, Nawab Salimullah (1884-1915). e, Mohtarma Fatima Jinnah (1893-1967). f, Aga Khan III (1877-1957). g, Nawab Mohammad Ismail Khan (1884-1958). h, Hussain Shaheed Suhrawardy (1893-1963). i, Syed Ameer Ali (1849-1928).

No. 736: a, Nawab Bahadur Yar Jung (1905-44). b, Khawaja Nazimuddin (1894-1964). c, Maulana Obaidullah Sindhi (1872-1944). d, Sahibzada Abdul Qaiyum Khan (c. 1863-1937). e, Begum Jahanara Shah Nawaz (1896-1979). f, Sir Ghulam Hussain Hidayatullah (1879-1948). g, Qazi Mohammad Isa (1913-76). h, Sir M. Shahnawaz Khan Mamdot (1883-1942). i, Pir Shaib of Manki Sharif (1923-60).

No. 737: a, Liaquat Ali Khan (1895-1951). b, Maulvi A.K. Fazl-Ul-Haq (1873-1962). c, Allama Shabbir Ahmad Usmani (1885-1949). d, Sardar Abdur Rab Nishtar (1899-1958). e, Bi Amma (c. 1850-1924). f, Sir Abdullah Haroon (1872-1942). g, Chaudhry Rahmat Ali (1897-1951). h, Raja Sahib of Mahmudabad (1914-73). i, Hassanally Effendi (1830-1895).

No. 737J: k, Maulana Zafar Ali Khan (1873-1956). l, Maulana Mohamed Ali Jauhar (1878-1931). m, Chaudhry Khaliquzzaman (1889-1973). n, Hameed Nizami (1915-62). o, Begum Ra'ana Liaquat Ali Khan (1905-90). p, Mirza Abol Hassan Ispahani (1902-81). q, Raja Ghazanfar Ali Khan (1895-1963). r, Malik Barkat Ali (1886-1946). s, Mir Jaffer Khan Jamali (c. 1911-67).

1990-91   **Litho.**   *Perf. 13*
Miniature Sheets
735   Sheet of 9   4.00 3.50
  a.-i. A375 1r any single   .40 .25
736   Sheet of 9   4.00 3.50
  a.-i. A375 1r any single   .40 .25
737   Sheet of 9   4.00 3.50
  a.-i. A375 1r any single   .40 .25
737J   Sheet of 9 ('91)   6.75 6.00
  k.-s. A375 1r any single   .40 .25
   Nos. 735-737J (4)   18.75 16.50

Issued: #735-737, Aug. 19; #737J, 1991.
See Nos. 773, 792, 804, 859-860, 865, 875-876, 922-924.

Indonesia Pakistan Economic and Cultural Cooperation Organization, 1968-1990 A376

1990, Aug. 19
738 A376 7r multicolored   1.75 1.10

Intl. Literacy Year — A377

1990, Sept. 8
739 A377 3r multicolored   1.25 .75

A378

1990, Sept. 22
740 A378 2r multicolored   1.10 .40

Joint meeting of Royal College of Physicians, Edinburgh and College of Physicians and Surgeons, Pakistan.

World Summit for Children — A379

1990, Sept. 19
741 A379 7r multicolored   .85 .50

Year of the Girl Child — A380

1990, Nov. 21   **Litho.**   *Perf. 13½*
742 A380 2r multicolored   .75 .50

Security Papers Ltd., 25th Anniv. — A381

1990, Dec. 8   *Perf. 13*
743 A381 3r multicolored   2.50 1.50

Intl. Civil Defense Day — A382

1991, Mar. 1   **Litho.**   *Perf. 13*
744 A382 7r multicolored   2.75 2.00

South & West Asia Postal Union A383

1991, Mar. 21
745 A383 5r multicolored   2.10 1.50

World Population Day — A384

1991, July 11
746 A384 10r multicolored   2.50 1.50

Intl. Special Olympics — A385

1991, July 19
747 A385 7r multicolored   2.10 1.50

Habib Bank Limited, 50th Anniv. — A386

1991, Aug. 25   **Litho.**   *Perf. 13*
748 A386 1r brt red & multi   1.25 .45
749 A386 4r brt green & multi   4.50 3.25

St. Joseph's Convent School, Karachi A387

1991, Sept. 8
750 A387 5r multicolored   4.25 3.00

Emperor Sher Shah Suri (c. 1472-1545) — A388

1991, Oct. 5
751 A388 5r multicolored   1.75 1.75

Souvenir Sheet
Size: 90x81mm
Imperf
752 A388 7r multicolored   2.00 2.00

Pakistani Scientific Expedition to Antarctica A389

1991, Oct. 28
753 A389 7r multicolored   3.50 2.50

Houbara Bustard — A390

1991, Nov. 4
754 A390 7r multicolored   3.00 2.00

Asian Development Bank, 25th Anniv. — A391

1991, Dec. 19   **Litho.**   *Perf. 13*
755 A391 7r multicolored   2.75 1.50

Hazrat Sultan Bahoo, 300th Death Anniv. — A392

1991, Dec. 22
756 A392 7r multicolored   2.10 1.10

Painting Type of 1990

Paintings and artists: No. 757, Village Life, by Allah Ustad Bux (1892-1978). No. 758, Miniature of Royal Procession, by Muhammad Haji Sharif (1889-1978).

1991, Dec. 24
757 A373 1r multicolored   2.25 1.25
758 A373 1r multicolored   2.25 1.25

American Express Travelers Cheques, 100th Anniv. — A393

1991, Dec. 26   *Perf. 13½*
759 A393 7r multicolored   2.50 1.50

Muslim Commercial Bank, First Year of Private Operation A394

7r, City skyline, worker, cogwheels, computer operators.

1992, Apr. 8   **Litho.**   *Perf. 13*
760 A394 1r multicolored   .25 .25
761 A394 7r multicolored   1.00 .65

Pakistan, 1992 World Cricket Champions A395

World Cricket Cup and: 2r, Pakistani player, vert. 7r, Pakistan flag, fireworks, vert.

1992, Apr. 27
762 A395 2r multicolored	.75	.50
763 A395 5r multicolored	1.75	1.10
764 A395 7r multicolored	2.00	1.40
Nos. 762-764 (3)	4.50	3.00

Intl. Space
Year — A396

Design: 2r, Globe, satellite.

1992, June 7   Litho.   Perf. 13
771 A396 1r multicolored	.35	.25
772 A396 5r multicolored	.55	.35

30th anniv. of first Pakistani rocket (#771).

Pioneers of Freedom Type of 1990
Designs: a, Syed Suleman Nadvi (1884-1953). b, Nawab Iftikhar Hussain Khan Mamdot (1906-1969). c, Maulana Muhammad Shibli Naumani (1857-1914).

1992, Aug. 14   Litho.   Perf. 13
773 A375 1r Strip of 3, #a.-c.	4.50	3.75

World
Population
Day — A397

1992, July 25
774 A397 6r multicolored	1.10	1.10

Medicinal
Plants — A398

1992, Nov. 22   Litho.   Perf. 13
775 A398 6r multicolored	3.75	3.50
See No. 791.		

Extraordinary Session of Economic
Cooperation Organization Council of
Ministers, Islamabad
A399

1992, Nov. 28
776 A399 7r multicolored	1.40	1.00

Intl. Conference on
Nutrition,
Rome — A400

1992, Dec. 5   Perf. 14
777 A400 7r multicolored	.85	.85

Islamic Cultural
Heritage — A401

1992, Dec. 14   Perf. 13
778 A401 7r Alhambra, Spain	.75	.60

Islamic Scouts,
Islamabad — A402

1992, Aug. 23   Perf. 14x12½
779 A402 6r 6th Jamboree	.70	.60
780 A402 6r 4th Conference	.70	.60

Government Islamia College, Lahore,
Cent.
A403

1992, Nov. 1   Perf. 13
781 A403 3r multicolored	.60	.60

Industries — A404

Designs: a, 10r, Surgical instruments. b, 15r, Leather goods. c, 25r, Sports equipment.

1992, July 5   Litho.   Perf. 13½x13
782 A404 Strip of 3, #a.-c.	5.50	5.50

World
Telecommunications
Day — A405

1993, May 17   Litho.   Perf. 13
783 A405 1r multicolored	1.50	.55

21st Islamic Foreign
Ministers
Conference — A406

1993, Apr. 25
784 A406 1r buff & multi	.50	.50
785 A406 6r green & multi	2.25	1.40

A407

Traditional costumes of provinces.

1993, Mar. 10
786 A407 6r Sindh	1.50	1.00
787 A407 6r North West Frontier	1.50	1.00
788 A407 6r Baluchistan	1.50	1.00
789 A407 6r Punjab	1.50	1.00
Nos. 786-789 (4)	6.00	4.00

A408

Birds: a, Gadwall. b, Common shelduck. c, Mallard. d, Greylag goose.

The order of the birds is different on each row. Therefore the arc of the rainbow is different on each of the 4 Gadwalls, etc.

1992, Dec. 31   Perf. 14x13
790 A408 5r Sheet of 16	10.00	15.00
a.-d. Any single	.60	.60
e. Horiz. strip of 4, #a-d	2.00	3.00

Medicinal Plants Type
1993, June 20   Litho.   Perf. 13
791 A398 6r Fennel, chemistry equipment	3.25	1.25

Pioneers of Freedom Type of 1990
Designs: a, Rais Ghulam Mohammad Bhurgri (1878-1924). b, Mir Ahmed Yar Khan, Khan of Kalat (1902-1977). c, Mohammad Abdul Latif Pir Sahib Zakori Sharif (1914-1978).

1993, Aug. 14   Litho.   Perf. 13
792 A375 1r Strip of 3, #a.-c.	3.50	2.50

Gordon College, Rawalpindi,
Cent. — A410

1993, Sept. 1
793 A410 2r multicolored	1.50	1.00

Juniper Forests,
Ziarat — A411

1993, Sept. 30
794 A411 7r multicolored	7.00	3.00
See No. 827.		

World Food
Day — A412

1993, Oct. 16   Perf. 14
795 A412 6r multicolored	1.00	1.00

A413

Wmk. 351
1993, Dec. 25   Litho.   Perf. 13½
796 A413 1r multicolored	1.50	.55

Wazir Mansion, birthplace of Muhammad Ali Jinnah.

A414

Perf. 13x13½
1993, Oct. 28   Unwmk.
797 A414 7r multicolored	2.50	1.00

Burn Hall Institutions, 50th anniv.

South & West Asia
Postal Union — A415

1993, Nov. 18   Perf. 13
798 A415 7r multicolored	2.00	1.00

Pakistani College of
Physicians &
Surgeons, Intl.
Medical
Congress — A416

1993, Dec. 10
799 A416 1r multicolored	1.75	.65

ILO, 75th
Anniv.
A417

1994, Apr. 11   Litho.   Perf. 13
800 A417 7r multicolored	1.75	1.00

Bio-diversity — A418

a, Ratan jot, medicinal plant. b, Wetlands. c, Mahseer fish. d, Himalayan brown bear.

1994, Apr. 20   Litho.   Perf. 13½
801 A418 6r Strip or block of 4, #a.-d.	3.50	2.00

Intl. Year of the
Family — A419

1994, May 15   Perf. 13
802 A419 7r multicolored	.75	.75

World
Population
Day — A420

1994, July 11   Litho.   Perf. 13
803 A420 7r multicolored	.75	.75

Pioneers of Freedom Type of 1990
Miniature Sheet of 8
Designs: a, Nawab Mohsin-Ul-Mulk (1837-1907). b, Sir Shahnawaz Bhutto (1888-1957). c, Nawab Viqar-Ul-Mulk (1841-1917). d, Pir Ilahi Bux (1890-1975). e, Sheikh Sir Abdul Qadir (1874-1950). f, Dr. Sir Ziauddin Ahmed (1878-1947). g, Jam Mir Ghulam Qadir Khan (1920-88). h, Sardar Aurangzeb Khan (1899-1953).

1994, Aug. 14   Litho.   Perf. 13
804 A375 1r #a.-h. + label	3.25	3.25

A421

1994, Oct. 2   *Perf. 13x13½*
805 A421 2r multicolored   1.35 .45
First Intl. Festival of Islamic Artisans.

Intl. Literacy
Day — A422

1994, Sept. 8
806 A422 7r multicolored   .75 .75

Hyoscyamus
Niger — A423

1994   *Perf. 13*
807 A423 6r multicolored   1.00 .75

Mohammad Ali
Jinnah — A424

    Litho. & Engr.
1994, Sept. 11   **Wmk. 351**   *Perf. 13*
808 A424 1r slate & multi   .25 .25
809 A424 2r claret & multi   .35 .25
810 A424 3r brt bl & multi   .45 .25
811 A424 4r emer & multi   .50 .25
812 A424 5r lake & multi   .55 .25
813 A424 7r blue & multi   .70 .25
814 A424 10r green & multi   .55 .30
815 A424 12r orange & multi   .65 .60
816 A424 15r violet & multi   .70 .80
817 A424 20r rose & multi   .75 1.00
818 A424 25r brown & multi   .90 1.25
818A A424 28r blk & multi
819 A424 30r olive brn &
       multi   1.25 1.25
   Nos. 808-819 (12)   7.60 6.70
    Issued: 28r, 9/30/2011.

2nd SAARC & 12th
Natl. Scout
Jamboree,
Quetta — A425

1994, Sept. 22   **Litho.**
820 A425 7r multicolored   1.25 .60

Publication of
Ferdowsi's Book of
Kings, 1000th
Anniv. — A426

1994, Oct. 27
821 A426 1r multicolored   .50 .50

Indonesia-Pakistan
Economic & Cultural
Cooperation
Organization — A427

1994, Aug. 19
822 A427 10r Hala pottery   1.25 .60
823 A427 10r Lombok pottery   1.25 .60
  a.   Pair, #822-823   4.25 4.25
   See Indonesia Nos. 1585-1586.

Lahore Museum,
Cent. — A428

    Wmk. 351
1994, Dec. 27   **Litho.**   *Perf. 13*
824 A428 4r multicolored   .60 .60

Pakistan, 1994
World Cup Field
Hockey
Champions
A429

1994, Dec. 31
825 A429 5r multicolored   .65 .40

World Tourism Organization, 20th
Anniv. — A430

1995, Jan. 2
826 A430 4r multicolored   .65 .30

   Juniper Forests Type of 1993
1995, Feb. 14   **Litho.**   *Perf. 13*
827 A411 1r like #794   .75 .25

Third Economic
Cooperation
Organization
Summit,
Islamabad — A431

1995, Mar. 14   **Litho.**   *Perf. 14*
828 A431 6r multicolored   .95 1.10

Khushall Khan
Khatak (1613-
89) — A432

1995, Feb. 28   *Perf. 13*
829 A432 7r multicolored   2.25 2.25

Earth
Day — A433

    Wmk. 351
1995, Apr. 20   **Litho.**   *Perf. 13*
830 A433 6r multicolored   1.25 .75

Snakes — A434

  a, Krait. b, Cobra. c, Python. d, Viper.

1995, Apr. 15   **Unwmk.**   *Perf. 13½*
831 A434 6r Block of 4, #a.-d.   4.00 4.00

Traditional
Means of
Transportation
A435

  5r, Horse-drawn carriage.

    Wmk. 351
1995, May 22   **Litho.**   *Perf. 13*
832 A435 5r multicolored   .85 .85

Louis Pasteur (1822-
95) — A436

    Wmk. 351
1995, Sept. 28   **Litho.**   *Perf. 13*
833 A436 5r multicolored   .85 .80

UN, FAO,
50th Anniv.
A437

1995, Oct. 16
834 A437 1.25r multicolored   .25 .25

Kinnaird College for
Women, Lahore — A438

1995, Nov. 3   *Perf. 14x13*
835 A438 1.25r multicolored   .25 .25

4th World Conference on Women,
Beijing — A439

  Women in various activities: a, Playing golf,
in armed forces, repairing technical device. b,
Graduates, student, chemist, computer operator, reading gauge. c, At sewing machine,
working with textiles. d, Making rugs, police
woman, laborers.

1995, Sept. 15   *Perf. 13*
836 A439 1.25r Strip of 4, #a.-d.   2.00 1.40

Presentation
Convent School,
Rawalpindi,
Cent. — A440

    Wmk. 351
1995, Sept. 8   **Litho.**   *Perf. 13½*
837 A440 1.25r multicolored   .80 .45

A440a

  Panel colors: 5p, Orange. 15p, Violet. 25p,
Red. 75p, Red brown.

1995-96 Litho. Unwmk.   *Perf. 13½*
837A-837D   A440a Set of 4   2.50 .60
   Issued: 5p, 15p, 10/10/95; 25p, 9/28/95;
75p, 5/15/96.

Liaquat Ali
Khan (1895-
1951)
A441

1995, Oct. 1   *Perf. 13*
838 A441 1.25r multicolored   .40 .40

1st Conference of Women
Parliamentarians from Muslim
Countries — A442

  Designs: No. 839, Dr. Tansu Ciller, Prime
Minister of Turkey. No. 840, Mohtarma Benazir
Bhutto, Prime Minister of Pakistan.

1995, Aug. 1   **Unwmk.**
839 A442 5r multicolored   .90 .90
840 A442 5r multicolored   .90 .90
  a.   Pair, #839-840   2.00 7.50

Intl. Conference of
Writers and
Intellectuals
A443

    Wmk. 351
1995, Nov. 30   **Litho.**   *Perf. 14*
841 A443 1.25r multicolored   .40 .40

Allama Iqbal
Open
University,
20th Anniv.
A444

1995, Dec. 16   *Perf. 13*
842 A444 1.25r multicolored   .45 .30

Butterflies — A445

  Designs: a, Érasmie. b, Catogramme. c,
Ixias. d, Héliconie.

    Wmk. 351
1995, Sept. 1   **Litho.**   *Perf. 13½*
843 A445 6r Strip of 4, #a.-d.   3.00 2.50

Fish — A446

  Designs: a, Sardinella long. b, Tilapia mos-
sambica. c, Salmo fario. d, Labeo rohita.

1995, Sept. 1
844 A446 6r Strip of 4, #a.-d.   3.50 3.50

SAARC, 10th
Anniv. — A447

1995, Dec. 8 *Perf. 13*
845 A447 1.25r multicolored .75 .40

UN, 50th
Anniv. —
A448

Wmk. 351
1995, Oct. 24 Litho. *Perf. 13½*
846 A448 7r multicolored 1.25 1.25

Karachi '95, Natl. Water Sports
Gala — A449

Designs: a, Man on jet ski. b, Gondola race.
c, Sailboard race. d, Man water skiing.

1995, Dec. 14 *Perf. 14x13*
847 A449 1.25r Block of 4, #a.-d. 1.50 1.50

University of
Baluchistan,
Quetta, 25th
Anniv. — A452

Wmk. 351
1995, Dec. 31 Litho. *Perf. 13*
850 A452 1.25r multicolored .25 .25

Zulfikar Ali Bhutto (1928-79), Politician,
President — A455

Designs: 1.25r, Bhutto, flag, crowd of people, vert. 8r, like No. 855.

Wmk. 351
1996, Apr. 4 Litho. *Perf. 13*
855 A455 1.25r multicolored .75 .35
856 A455 4r shown 2.25 1.10
Size: 114x69mm
Imperf
857 A455 8r multicolored 2.50 2.50

Raja Aziz Bhatti
Shaheed (1928-
65)
A456

Wmk. 351
1995, Sept. 5 Litho. *Perf. 13*
858 A456 1.25r multicolored 1.25 .40
See Nos. 953, 983, 997, 1016.

Pioneers of Freedom Type of 1990

#859, Maulana Shaukat Ali (1873-1938).
#860, Chaudhry Ghulam Abbas (1904-67).

1995, Aug. 14 Unwmk. *Perf. 13*
859 A375 1r green & brown .65 .50
860 A375 1r green & brown .65 .50
a.   Pair, #859-860 1.50 1.50

1996
Summer
Olympic
Games,
Atlanta
A457

Design: 25r, #861-864 without denominations, simulated perfs, Olympic rings, "100,"
Atlanta '96 emblem.

Wmk. 351
1996, Aug. 3 Litho. *Perf. 13*
861 A457 5r Wrestling .60 .60
862 A457 5r Boxing .60 .60
863 A457 5r Pierre de
            Coubertin .60 .60
864 A457 5r Field hockey .60 .60
      Nos. 861-864 (4) 2.40 2.40
Imperf
Size: 111x101mm
864A A457 25r multicolored 3.00 3.00

Pioneers of Freedom Type of 1990

Allama Abdullah Yousuf Ali (1872-1953).

Unwmk.
1996, Aug. 14 Litho. *Perf. 13*
865 A375 1r green & brown .45 .40

Restoration of
General Post
Office,
Lahore — A458

1996, Aug. 21 Wmk. 351 *Perf. 14*
866 A458 5r multicolored .45 .45

Intl. Literacy
Day — A459

1996, Sept. 8 Wmk. 351 *Perf. 13*
867 A459 2r multicolored .45 .40

Yarrow — A459a

Wmk. 351
1996, Nov. 25 Litho. *Perf. 13*
867A A459a 3r multicolored 1.75 .65

Faiz Ahmed Faiz,
Poet, 86th
Birthday — A460

Unwmk.
1997, Feb. 13 Litho. *Perf. 13*
868 A460 3r multicolored .25 .25

Tamerlane (1336-
1405) — A461

Unwmk.
1997, Apr. 8 Litho. *Perf. 13*
869 A461 3r multicolored .45 .40

Famous Men — A462

Designs: No. 870, Allama Mohammad Iqbal.
No. 871, Jalal-Al-Din Moulana Rumi.

1997, Apr. 21 *Perf. 13½*
870 A462 3r multicolored .25 .25
871 A462 3r multicolored .25 .25
Compare with Iran 2726-2727.

Pakistani
Independence, 50th
Anniv. — A463

1997, Mar. 23 *Perf. 13*
872 A463 2r multicolored .45 .45
Special Summit of Organization of Islamic
Countries, Islamabad.

World Population
Day — A464

Unwmk.
1997, July 11 Litho. *Perf. 13*
873 A464 2r multicolored .45 .40

Intl. Atomic Energy
Agency-Pakistan
Atomic Energy
Commission
Cooperation, 40th
Anniv. — A465

1997, July 29 *Perf. 14*
874 A465 2r multicolored .45 .40

Pioneers of Freedom Type of 1990

No. 875, Begum Salma Tassaduq Hussain
(1908-95). No. 876, Mohammad Ayub Khuhro
(1901-80).

1997, Aug. 14 Litho. *Perf. 13*
875 A375 1r green & brown .55 .55
876 A375 1r green & brown .55 .55

Fruits of
Pakistan — A466

1997, May 8
877 A466 2r Apples .45 .45

Independence, 50th Anniv. — A467

Designs: a, Allama Mohammad Iqbal. b,
Mohammad Ali Jinnah. c, Liaquat Ali Khan. d,
Mohtarma Fatima Jinnah.

Block of 4 + 2 Labels
1997, Aug. 14
878 A467 3r gold & multi 2.00 .75
No. 878 exists with No. 878d unretouched.
Value, $5 mint or used.

Lophophorus
Impejanus — A468

Wmk. 351
1997, Oct. 29 Litho. *Perf. 13*
879 A468 2r multicolored 2.50 .90

Lahore College for
Women, 75th
Anniv. — A469

1997, Sept. 23
880 A469 3r multicolored .40 .40

Intl. Day of the
Disabled
A470

Unwmk.
1997, Dec. 3 Litho. *Perf. 13*
881 A470 4r multicolored .45 .45

Protection of the
Ozone Layer — A471

1997, Nov. 15
882 A471 3r multicolored 1.25 1.00

Pakistan
Motorway, 50th
Anniv. — A472

1997, Nov. 26 *Perf. 13½*
883 A472 10r multicolored 2.25 2.25
a.   Souvenir sheet of 1 2.50 2.50
No. 883a sold for 15r.

Karachi Grammar School, 150th Anniv. — A473

1997, Dec. 30 Litho. Perf. 13½
884 A473 2r multicolored .50 .50

Garlic — A474

1997, Oct. 22 Perf. 13
885 A474 2r multicolored .70 .25

Mirza Asad Ullah Khan Ghalib (1797-1869), Poet — A475

1998, Feb. 15
886 A475 2r multicolored .40 .40

Pakistan Armed Forces, 50th Anniv. — A476

Wmk. 351
1997, Mar. 23 Litho. Perf. 13½
887 A476 7r multicolored .75 .75

Sir Syed Ahmad Khan (1817-98), Educator, Jurist, Author A477

1998, Mar. 27 Perf. 14
888 A477 7r multicolored .65 .65

27th Natl. Games, Peshawar — A478

Wmk. 351
1998, Apr. 22 Litho. Perf. 13
889 A478 7r multicolored .65 .65

Jimsonweed — A479

1998, Apr. 27
890 A479 2r multicolored .25 .25

Faisalabad Government College, Cent. (in 1997) — A480

1998, Aug. 14 Litho. Perf. 13
891 A480 5r multicolored .30 .30

Pakistan Senate, 25th Anniv. — A481

1998, Aug. 6 Perf. 13½
892 A481 2r green & multi .25 .25
893 A481 5r blue & multi .30 .30

Mohammed Ali Jinnah — A482

Litho. & Engr.
1998-2001 Wmk. 351 Perf. 14
893A A482 1r red & black 3.00 3.00
894 A482 2r dk bl & red .25 .25
895 A482 3r slate grn & brn .25 .25
896 A482 4r dp vio blk & org .25 .25
897 A482 5r dp brn & grn .65 .65
898 A482 6r dp grn & bl grn .75 .65
899 A482 7r dp brn red & dp vio .90 .90
Nos. 894-899 (6) 3.05 2.95

Nos. 894 issued 8/14/98. No. 893A, 2001(?).

21st Intl. Congress of Ophthalmology, Islamabad — A483

Wmk. 351
1998, Sept. 11 Litho. Perf. 13
900 A483 7r multicolored 1.60 1.60

Syed Ahmed Shah Patrus Bukhari, Birth Cent. — A484

1998, Oct. 1
901 A484 5r multicolored .25 .25

Philately in Pakistan, 50th Anniv. — A485

Various portions of stamps inside "50," #20-23.

1998, Oct. 4
902 A485 6r multicolored .25 .25

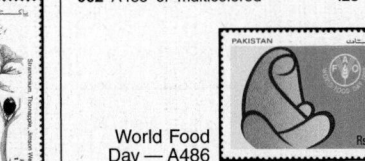

World Food Day — A486

Wmk. 351
1998, Oct. 16 Photo. Perf. 13
903 A486 6r multicolored .25 .25

Mohammad Ali Jinnah (1876-1948) — A487

Wmk. 351
1998, Sept. 11 Photo. Perf. 13½
904 A487 15r multicolored .90 .90
a. Souvenir sheet of 1, unwmk. 1.75 1.75
No. 904a sold for 20r.

Universal Declaration of Human Rights, 50th Anniv. — A488

Perf. 13x14
1998, Dec. 10 Wmk. 351
905 A488 6r multicolored .35 .35

Better Pakistan, 2010 — A489

No. 906, Harvesting grain. No. 907, Health care. No. 908, Satellite dishes. No. 909, Airplane.

1998, Nov. 27 Unwmk.
906 A489 2r multicolored .45 .35
907 A489 2r multicolored .45 .35
908 A489 2r multicolored .45 .35
909 A489 2r multicolored .45 .35
Nos. 906-909 (4) 1.80 1.40

Dr. Abdus Salam, Scientist — A490

Unwmk.
1998, Nov. 21 Litho. Perf. 13
910 A490 2r multicolored .30 .30
See No. 916.

National Flag March — A491

1998, Dec. 16 Wmk. 351
911 A491 2r multicolored .25 .25

Intl. Year of the Ocean — A492

1998, Dec. 15 Perf. 14
912 A492 5r multicolored 1.50 1.00

UNICEF in Pakistan, 50th Anniv. — A493

a, Distributing water. b, Child holding book. c, Girl. d, Child receiving oral vaccine.

1998, Dec. 15
913 A493 2r Block of 4, #a.-d. 1.50 1.50

Kingdom of Saudi Arabia, Cent. — A494

Perf. 13½
1999, Jan. 27 Litho. Unwmk.
914 A494 2r Emblem on sand .40 .40
915 A494 15r Emblem on carpet 1.25 1.25
a. Souvenir sheet of 1 2.25 2.25
No. 915a sold for 20r.

Scientists of Pakistan Type
Dr. Salimuz Zaman Siddiqui (1897-1994).

1999, Apr. 14 Perf. 13
916 A490 5r multicolored .40 .40

Pakistani Nuclear Test, 1st Anniv. A495

1999, May 28 Litho. Perf. 13
917 A495 5r multicolored .30 .30

Completion of Data Darbar Mosque Complex — A496

1999, May 31 Litho. Perf. 13
918 A496 7r multicolored .25 .25

Fasting Buddha, c. 3-4 A.D. — A497

1999, July 21 Litho. Perf. 13½x13¾
919 A497 7r shown .80 .80
920 A497 7r Facing forward .80 .80
a. Souv. sheet of 2, #919-920 2.50 2.50

No. 920a sold for 25r. China 1999 World Philatelic Exhibition (No. 920a).

Geneva Conventions, 50th Anniv. — A498

Perf. 12¾x13¾
1999, Aug. 12 Litho.
921 A498 5r pink, black & red .60 .60

Pioneers of Freedom Type of 1990

Designs: No. 922, Chaudhry Muhammad Ali (1905-80), 1st Secretary General. No. 923, Sir Adamjee Haji Dawood (1880-1948), banker. No. 924, Maulana Abdul Hamid Badayuni (1898-1970), religious scholar.

1999, Aug. 14　Litho.　Perf. 13
922 A375 2r green & brown　.45 .45
923 A375 2r green & brown　.45 .45
924 A375 2r green & brown　.45 .45
　　Nos. 922-924 (3)　1.35 1.35

Ustad Nusrat Fateh Ali Khan (1948-97), Singer — A499

1999, Aug. 16
925 A499 2r multicolored　.60 .60

Islamic Development Bank, 25th Anniv. (in 2000) — A500

1999, Sept. 18
926 A500 5r multicolored　.30 .30

People's Republic of China, 50th Anniv. — A501

2r, Gate of Heavenly Peace. 15r, Arms, Mao Zedong, horiz.

1999, Sept. 21
927 A501 2r multicolored　.25 .25
928 A501 15r multicolored　1.00 1.00

Ninth Asian Sailing Championship — A502

No. 929: a, Enterprise class. b, 470 class. c, Optimist class. d, Laser class. e, Mistral class.

1999, Sept. 28　Perf. 13½x13¼
929 A502 2r Strip of 5, #a.-e.　1.25 1.25

10th Asian Optimist Sailing Championships — A502a

1999, Oct. 7　Litho.　Perf. 13¾x13½
929F A502a 2r multi + label　.60 .60

UPU, 125th Anniv. — A503

1999, Oct. 9　Perf. 14¼
930 A503 10r multicolored　1.00 1.00

Hakim Mohammed Said (1920-98), Physician — A504

1999, Oct. 17　Litho.　Perf. 13
931 A504 5r multicolored　.65 .65

National Bank of Pakistan, 50th Anniv. — A505

Perf. 13¼x13¾
1999, Nov. 8　Litho.　Wmk. 351
932 A505 5r multi　.80 .80

Shell Oil in Pakistan, Cent. — A506

Perf. 13¼x13
1999, Nov. 15　Wmk. 351
933 A506 4r multi　.80 .80

Rights of the Child, 10th Anniv. — A507

Perf. 13x13¼
1999, Nov. 20　Unwmk.
934 A507 2r multi　.25 .25

Allam Iqbal Open University, Islamabad A508

Designs: 2r, University crest, flasks, microphone, mortarboard, book, computer. 3r, Similar to 2r, crest in center. 5r, Crest, map, mortarboard, book.

Unwmk.
1999, Nov. 20　Litho.　Perf. 13
935 A508 2r bl grn & multi　.35 .35
936 A508 3r multi　.45 .45
937 A508 5r multi　1.75 1.00
　　Nos. 935-937 (3)　2.55 1.80

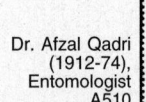

Shabbir Hassan Khan Josh Malihabadi (1898-1982), Poet — A509

1999, Dec. 5
938 A509 5r multi　.25 .25

Dr. Afzal Qadri (1912-74), Entomologist A510

1999, Dec. 6
939 A510 3r multi　.25 .25

Ghulam Bari Aleeg (1907-49), Journalist — A511

1999, Dec. 10　Litho.　Perf. 13
940 A511 5r multi　.25 .25
　　See No. 982.

Plantain — A512

1999, Dec. 20
941 A512 5r multi　.50 .50

Eid-Ul-Fitr — A513

Perf. 13¾x13½
1999, Dec. 24　Litho.
942 A513 2r green & multi　.75 .75
943 A513 15r blue & multi　2.25 2.25

SOS Children's Villages of Pakistan, 25th Anniv. — A514

2000, Mar. 12　Perf. 13
944 A514 2r multi　.50 .50

International Cycling Union, Cent. — A515

2000, Apr. 14　Litho.　Perf. 13¼
945 A515 2r multi　1.00 1.00

Convention on Human Rights and Dignity — A516

Perf. 13¼
2000, Apr. 21　Litho.　Unwmk.
946 A516 2r multi　.50 .50

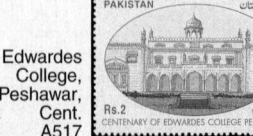

Edwardes College, Peshawar, Cent. A517

2000, Apr. 24　Perf. 13½
947 A517 2r multi　.50 .50

Mahomed Ali Habib (1904-59), Banker, Philantropist A518

2000, May 15　Litho.　Perf. 13
948 A518 2r multi　.50 .50

Institute of Cost and Management Accountants, 50th Anniv. — A519

Design: 2r, Arrow. 15r, Globe.

2000, June 23　Litho.　Perf. 13
949 A519 2r multi　.30 .30
950 A519 15r multi　2.00 2.00

Ahmed E. H. Jaffer (1909-90), Politician — A520

2000, Aug. 9　Litho.　Perf. 13
951 A520 10r multi　.75 .75

Creation of Pakistan, 53rd Anniv. A521

a, No tree. b, Tree in foreground. c, Tree behind people, cart. d, Tree in distance.

2000, Aug. 14　Litho.　Perf. 13
952 A521 5r Strip of 4, #a-d　2.50 2.50

Nishan-e-Haider Medal Type of 1995

Nishan-e-haider gallantry award winners: a, Capt. Muhammad Sarwar Shaheed (1910-48). b, Maj. Tufail Muhammad (1914-58).

2000, Sept. 6　Litho.　Perf. 13
953 A456 5r Pair, #a-b　1.75 1.75

2000 Summer Olympics, Sydney — A523

No. 954: a, Runners. b, Field hockey. c, Weight lifting. d, Cycling.

2000, Sept. 20　Perf. 14¼
954 A523 4r Block of 4, #a-d　2.25 2.25

Natl. College of Arts, 125th Anniv. — A524

2000, Oct. 28
955 A524 5r multi　.45 .45

Creating the
Future — A525

2000, Nov. 4
956 A525 5r multi   1.25 1.25

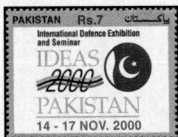

Intl. Defense
Exhibition and
Seminar
A526

2000, Nov. 14   **Litho.**   **Perf. 13**
957 A526 7r multi   .60 .60

Licorice — A527

2000, Nov. 28   **Litho.**   **Perf. 13**
958 A527 2r multi   .65 .65

Rotary Intl. Campaign
Against Polio — A528

2000, Dec. 13
959 A528 2r multi   .75 .75

UN High
Commissioner
for Refugees,
50th
Anniv. — A529

2000, Dec. 14
960 A529 2r multi   .45 .45

Poets — A530

Design: 2r, Hafeez Jalandhri (1900-82). 5r,
Khawaja Ghulam Farid.

2001   **Litho.**   **Perf. 13**
961 A530 2r multi   .50 .50
962 A530 5r multi   1.25 1.25

Issued: 2r, 1/14. 5r, 9/25.
See No. 986.

Habib
Bank AG
Zurich
A531

2001, Mar. 20   **Litho.**   **Perf. 13**
963 A531 5r multi   1.25 1.25

Chashma
Nuclear Power
Plant — A532

2001, Mar. 29
964 A532 4r multi   1.40 1.25

9th SAF Games,
Islamabad
A533

Background colors: No. 965, 4r, Light blue.
No. 966, 4r, Lilac.

2001, Apr. 9   **Perf. 13½x13¼**
965-966 A533   Set of 2   1.40 1.40

Pakistan-People's
Rep. of China
Diplomatic Relations,
50th Anniv. — A534

Designs: No. 967, Yugur and Hunza women,
flags.
No. 968 — Paintings by Yao Youdou: a, Ma
Gu's Birthday Offering. b, Two Pakistani
Women Drawing Water.

2001, May 12   **Perf. 13**
967 A534 4r multi   .25 .25
968 A534 4r Horiz. pair, #a-b   2.00 2.00

Mohammed Ali Jinnah
(1876-1948) — A535

2001, Aug. 14
969 A535 4r multi   .90 .90

Sindh
Festival — A536

Unwmk.
2001, Sept. 22   **Litho.**   **Perf. 13**
970 A536 4r multi   .75 .75

Year of Dialogue Among
Civilizations — A537

2001, Oct. 9   **Perf. 13½**
971 A537 4r multi   1.25 1.25

Turkmenistan, 10th
Anniv. of
Independence — A538

2001, Oct. 27   **Perf. 13**
972 A538 5r multi   .90 .90

Convent of Jesus and Mary, Lahore,
125th Anniv.
A539

2001, Nov. 15   **Wmk. 351**
973 A539 4r multi   1.00 1.00

Men of Letters Type of 1999

Design: 4r, Dr. Ishtiaq Husain Qureshi
(1903-81), historian.

2001, Nov. 20   **Unwmk.**
974 A511 4r multi   .75 .75

Birds
A540

No. 975: a, Blue throat. b, Hoopoe. c, Pin-
tailed sandgrouse. d, Magpie robin.

2001, Nov. 26   **Perf. 13¼x13**
975 A540 4r Block of 4, #a-d   3.00 3.00

Pakistan —
United Arab
Emirates
Friendship,
30th Anniv. —
A541

Designs: 5r, Flags, handshake, vert. 30r,
Sheik Zaid bin Sultan al Nahayan, Mohammed
Ali Jinnah.

2001, Dec. 2   **Perf. 13**
976-977 A541   Set of 2   3.75 3.75

Nishtar Medical
College, Multan, 50th
Anniv. — A542

2001, Dec. 20
978 A542 5r multi   .75 .75

Quaid
Year
A543

No. 979: a, Mohammed Ali Jinnah reviewing
troops, 1948. b, Jinnah, soldiers, artillery gun,
1948.
No. 980, vert.: a, Jinnah taking oath as Governor General, 1947. b, Jinnah at opening ceremony of State Bank of Pakistan, 1948. c, Jinnah saluting at presentation of colors, 1948.

2001, Dec. 25   **Perf. 13**
979   Horiz. pair   .80 .80
a.-b. A543 4r Any single   .25 .25

Size: 33x56mm
Perf. 13x13¼
980   Horiz. strip of 3   1.00 1.00
a.-c. A543 4r Any single   .25 .25

Pakistan Ordnance
Factories, 50th
Anniv. — A544

2001, Dec. 28   **Perf. 13¼x13½**
981 A544 4r multi   .75 .75

Men of Letters Type of 1999

Design: 5r, Syed Imtiaz Ali Taj (1900-70),
playwright.

2001, Oct. 13   **Perf. 13**
982 A511 5r multi   .60 .60

Nishan-e-Haider Type of 1995

No. 983: a, Maj. Mohammad Akram
Shaheed (1938-71). b, Maj. Shabbir Sharif
Shaheeb (1943-71).

2001, Sept. 6   **Perf. 13**
983   Horiz. pair   .75 .75
a.-b. A456 4r Any single   .30 .30

Peppermint — A545

Design: 5r, Hyssop.

2001-02   **Litho.**   **Wmk. 351**   **Perf. 13**
984 A545 4r multi   1.00 1.00
985 A545 5r multi   .80 .80

Issued: 4r, 11/12/01. 5r, 2/15/02.

Poets Type of 2001

Design: Samandar Khan Samandar (1901-
90).

2002, Jan. 17   **Litho.**   **Perf. 13**
986 A530 5r multi   .60 .60

Pakistan — Japan
Diplomatic
Relations, 50th
Anniv. — A546

2002, Apr. 28   **Litho.**   **Perf. 14**
987 A546 5r multi   .85 .85

Pakistan - Kyrgyzstan
Diplomatic Relations,
10th Anniv. — A547

2002, May 27   **Perf. 13¾x12¾**
988 A547 5r multi   .75 .75

Mangoes
A548

No. 989: a, Anwar Ratol. b, Dusheri. c,
Chaunsa. d, Sindhri.

2002, June 18
989 A548 4r Block of 4, #a-d   2.40 2.40

Independence, 55th
Anniv. — A549

Famous people: No. 990, 4r, Noor-us-Sabah Begum (1908-78), Muslim leader and writer. No. 991, 4r, Prime Minister Ismail I. Chundrigar (1897-1960). No. 992, 4r, Habib Ibrahim Rahimtoola (1912-91), governmental minister. No. 993, 4r, Qazi Mureed Ahmed (1913-89), politician.

2002, Aug. 14   **Litho.**   *Perf. 13¼x13*
990-993   A549   Set of 4   2.40   2.40

World Summit on
Sustainable
Development,
Johannesburg — A550

Designs: No. 994, 4r, Children, Pakistani flag, dolphin, goat. No. 995, 4r, Water droplet, mountain (33x33mm).

2002, Aug. 26   *Perf. 13¼, 14¼ (#995)*
994-995   A550   Set of 2   1.50   1.50

Mohammad Aly
Rangoonwala (1924-98),
Philanthropist — A551

2002, Aug. 31   *Perf. 13*
996   A551   4r multi   .60   .60

Nishan-e-Haidar type of 1995

No. 997: a, Lance Naik Muhammad Mahfuz Shaheed (1944-71). b, Sawar Muhammad Hussain Shaheed (1949-71).

2002, Sept. 6   *Perf. 13*
997   Horiz. pair   1.00   1.00
   a.-b.   A456   4r Either single   .25   .25

Muhammad Iqbal Year — A552

No. 998: a, Iqbal wearing hat. b, Iqbal without hat.

Unwmk.
2002, Nov. 9   **Litho.**   *Perf. 13*
998   A552   4r Horiz. pair, #a-b   1.25   1.25

Eid ul-Fitr — A553

Perf. 13¾x14
2002, Nov. 14   **Wmk. 351**
999   A553   4r multi   .75   .75

Shifa-ul-Mulk
Hakim Muhammad
Hassan Qarshi
(1896-1974),
Physician — A554

2002, Dec. 20   **Unwmk.**   *Perf. 13½*
1000   A554   4r multi   1.00   1.00

Pakistan 2003 Natl. Philatelic
Exhibition, Karachi — A555

Wmk. 351
2003, Jan. 31   **Litho.**   *Perf. 13*
1001   A555   4r multi + label   1.25   1.25

Pakistan Academy
of Sciences, 50th
Anniv. — A556

2003, Feb. 15   **Unwmk.**   *Perf. 14¼*
1002   A556   4r multi   .60   .60

North West Frontier
Province, Cent. — A557

Perf. 13½x13¼
2003, Mar. 23   **Litho.**   **Wmk. 351**
1003   A557   4r multi   .60   .60

Pakistan Council of
Scientific and Industrial
Research, 50th
Anniv. — A558

2003, Mar. 31   *Perf. 14x13¾*
1004   A558   4r multi   .75   .75

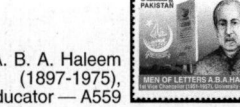

A. B. A. Haleem
(1897-1975),
Educator — A559

2003, Apr. 20   *Perf. 13½x13¼*
1005   A559   2r multi   .60   .60

Campaign
Against Illegal
Drugs — A560

2003, Apr. 21   *Perf. 13*
1006   A560   2r multi   1.25   1.25

Sir Syed Memorial,
Islamabad — A561

2003, Apr. 30   *Perf. 13¼x13½*
1007   A561   2r multi   .60   .60

Rosa
Damascena — A562

Perf. 13¼x12¾
2003, July 14   **Unwmk.**
1008   A562   4r multi   1.00   1.00

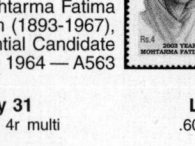

Mohtarma Fatima
Jinnah (1893-1967),
Presidential Candidate
in 1964 — A563

2003, July 31   **Litho.**
1009   A563   4r multi   .60   .60

Famous
Men — A564

Designs: No. 1010, 2r, M. A. Rahim (1919-2003), labor leader. No. 1011, 2r, Abdul Rahman (1959-2002), slain postal worker.

2003, Aug. 3   *Perf. 12¾x13¼*
1010-1011   A564   Set of 2   1.00   1.00

Famous Men — A565

Designs: No. 1012, 2r, Moulana Abdul Sattar Khan Niazi (1915-2001), politician. No. 1013, 2r, Muhammad Yousaf Khattak (1917-91), politician. No. 1014, 2r, Moulana Muhammad Ismail Zabeeh (1913-2001), political leader and journalist.

2003, Apr. 14   *Perf. 13¼x12¾*
1012-1014   A565   Set of 3   1.75   1.75

UN Literacy Decade,
2003-12 — A566

2003, Sept. 6
1015   A566   1r multi   .60   .60

Nishan-e-Haider Type of 1995

2003, Sept. 7   *Perf. 14*
1016   A456   2r Pilot Officer Rashid
         Minhas Shaheed   .75   .75

Pakistan Academy of
Letters, 25th
Anniv. — A567

2003, Sept. 24   *Perf. 13¼x12¾*
1017   A567   2r multi   .60   .60

Karakoram Highway,
25th Anniv. — A568

Perf. 12¾x13
2003, Oct. 1   **Litho.**   **Unwmk.**
1018   A568   2r multi   .60   .60

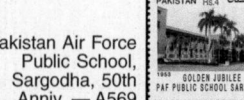

Pakistan Air Force
Public School,
Sargodha, 50th
Anniv. — A569

Perf. 13x13¼
2003, Oct. 10   **Litho.**   **Wmk. 351**
1019   A569   4r multi   1.00   1.00

First Ascent of
Nanga Parbat, 50th
Anniv. — A570

Perf. 12¾x13
2003, Oct. 6   **Litho.**   **Unwmk.**
1020   A570   2r multi   1.75   1.75

Exports — A571

No. 1021: a, Leather garments. b, Towels. c, Ready-made garments. d, Karachi Port Trust and Port Qasim. e, Fisheries. f, Yarn. g, Sporting goods. h, Fabrics. i, Furniture. j, Surgical instruments. k, Gems and jewelry. l, Leather goods. m, Information technology. n, Rice. o, Auto parts. p, Carpets. q, Marble and granite. r, Fruits. s, Cutlery. t, Engineering goods.

2003, Oct. 20   *Perf. 13x12¾*
1021   Sheet of 20   7.50   7.50
   a.-t.   A571   1r Any single   .35   .35

Intl. Day of the
Disabled — A572

2003, Dec. 3   *Perf. 12¾x13*
1022   A572   2r multi   1.00   1.00

World Summit on the
Information Society,
Geneva,
Switzerland — A573

2003, Dec. 10   *Perf. 13x12¾*
1023   A573   2r multi   1.25   1.25

Submarines — A574

Khalid Class (Agosta 90B) submarine and flag of: 1r, Pakistan Navy, vert. 2r, Pakistan.

2003, Dec. 12   *Perf. 13x12¾, 12¾x13*
1024-1025   A574   Set of 2   3.00   3.00

Powered Flight,
Cent. — A575

Designs: No. 1026, 2r, Pakistan Air Force's transition into jet age, 1956. No. 1027, 2r, Air Force in action at Siachen, 1988-90.

2003, Dec. 17   *Perf. 12¾x13*
1026-1027   A575   Set of 2   1.75   1.75

12th South Asian
Association for
Regional
Cooperation
Summit,
Islamabad — A576

2004, Jan. 4
1028   A576   4r multi   .60   .60

Sadiq Public School, Bahawalpur, 50th Anniv. — A577

2004, Jan. 28   Litho.   **Perf. 14**
1029 A577 4r multi   .60 .60

Ninth SAF Games, Islamabad — A578

No. 1030: a, Gold medal. b, Running. c, Squash (yellow and blue uniform). d, Boxing. e, Wrestling. f, Judo. g, Javelin. h, Soccer. i, Rowing. j, Shooting. k, Shot put. l, Badminton (white uniform). m, Weight lifting. n, Volleyball. o, Table tennis. p, Swimming.

2004, Mar. 29   Litho.   **Perf. 13x12¾**
1030 A578 2r Sheet of 16, #a-p   6.00 6.00

Pir Muhammad Karam Shah Al-Azhari (1918-98), Jurist — A579

2004, Apr. 7
1031 A579 2r multi   .60 .60

Cadet College, Hasan Abdal — A580

2004, Apr. 8   **Perf. 12¾x13**
1032 A580 4r multi   .60 .60

Central Library, Bahawalpur — A581

2004, Apr. 26   Litho.   **Perf. 13x12¾**
1033 A581 2r multi   .60 .60

Mosque, Bhong — A582

2004, May 12   **Perf. 12¾x13**
1034 A582 4r multi   .60 .60

FIFA (Fédération Internationale de Football Association), Cent. — A583

No. 1035 — FIFA centenary emblem and: a, Player. b, Blue panel at bottom. c, Player, green panel at bottom.

2004, May 21   **Perf. 14**
1035 A583   Horiz. strip of 3   2.40 2.40
a.-c.   5r Any single   .70 .70

Silk Road — A584

Designs: No. 1036, 4r, Indus River near Chilas. No. 1037, 4r, Haramosh Peak near Gilgit, vert.

2004, June 7   **Perf. 12¾x13, 13x12¾**
1036-1037 A584   Set of 2   .75 .75

Sui Southern Gas Company, 50th Anniv. — A585

2004, July 24   Litho.   **Perf. 12¾x13**
1038 A585 4r multi   .60 .60

First Ascent of K2, 50th Anniv. — A586

2004, July 31   **Perf. 13x12¾**
1039 A586   5r shown   .60 .60
Imperf
Size: 95x64mm
1040 A586   30r Tent, K2   2.75 2.75

2004 Summer Olympics, Athens — A587

No. 1041: a, Track. b, Boxing. c, Field hockey. d, Wrestling.

2004, Aug. 13   **Perf. 13x12¾**
1041 A587   Horiz. strip of 4   2.40 2.40
a.-d.   5r Any single   .60 .60

7 Lines of Text — A588   6½ Lines of Text — A589

6 Lines of Text — A590   6¾ Lines of Text — A591

2004, Aug. 14
1042   Horiz. strip of 4   1.50 1.50
a.   A588 5r multi   .30 .30
b.   A589 5r multi   .30 .30
c.   A590 5r multi   .30 .30
d.   A591 5r multi   .30 .30

Independence, 57th anniv.

Maulvi Abdul Haq (1870-1961), Lexicographer — A592

2004, Aug. 16
1043 A592 4r multi   .60 .60

Fourth Intl. Calligraphy and Calligraphic Art Exhibitiion and Competition, Lahore — A593

2004, Oct. 1
1044 A593 5r multi   .50 .50

Tropical Fish — A594

No. 1045: a, Neon tetra. b, Striped gourami. c, Black widow. d, Yellow dwarf cichlid. e, Tiger barb.

2004, Oct. 9   **Perf. 12½**
1045   Horiz. strip of 5   2.00 2.00
a.-e.   A594 2r Any single   .35 .35

Japanese Economic Assistance, 50th Anniv. — A595

Designs: No. 1046, 5r, Training for handicapped. No. 1047, 5r, Polio eradication. No. 1048, 5r, Ghazi Barotha hydroelectric power project. No. 1049, 5r, Kohat Friendship Tunnel. 30r, Vignettes of Nos. 1046-1049, Friendship Tunnel.

2004, Nov. 8   Litho.   **Perf. 12¾x13**
1046-1049 A595   Set of 4   .75 .75
Imperf
1050 A595   multi   3.00 3.00

Year of Child Welfare and Rights — A596

2004, Nov. 20   **Perf. 12½**
1051 A596 4r multi   .45 .45

Allama Iqbal Open University, Islamabad, 30th Anniv. — A597

2004, Dec. 6   **Perf. 12¾x13**
1052 A597 20r multi   .65 .65

Khyber Medical College, Peshawar, 50th Anniv. — A598

2004, Dec. 30
1053 A598 5r multi   .60 .60

Prof. Ahmed Ali (1910-94), Writer — A599

2005, Jan. 14   Litho.   **Perf. 13x12¾**
1054 A599 5r multi   .50 .50

Pakistan — Romania Friendship — A600

Poets Mihai Eminescu and Allama Iqbal and: No. 1055, 5r, Flags of Romania and Pakistan. No. 1056, 5r, Flags, monument to Eminescu and Iqbal by Emil Ghitulescu, Islamabad.

2005, Jan. 14
1055-1056 A600   Set of 2   1.40 1.40

Saadat Hasan Manto (1912-55), Writer — A601

2005, Jan. 18   **Perf. 13x12¾**
1057 A601 5r multi   .50 .50

A602   A603

A604

Pakistan Air Force, 50th Anniv. — A605

2005, Mar. 23   Litho.   **Perf. 12¾x13**
1058 A602 5r multi   .40 .40
1059 A603 5r multi   .40 .40
1060 A604 5r multi   .40 .40
   Perf. 13x12¾
1061 A605 5r multi   .40 .40
   Nos. 1058-1061 (4)   1.60 1.60

Command and Staff College, Quetta, Cent. — A606

2005, Apr. 2   **Perf. 12¾x13**
1062 A606 5r multi   .50 .50

Turkish Grand National Assembly, 85th Anniv. — A607

No. 1063 — Assembly building and: a, Kemal Ataturk, Turkish flag. b, Ataturk, Mohammed Ali Jinnah, Turkish and Pakistani flags.

2005, Apr. 23   **Perf. 14**
1063 A607 10r Horiz. pair, #a-b   2.00 2.00

Institute of Business Administration, Karachi, 50th Anniv. — A608

Various views of campus with country name at: No. 1064, 3r, Right. No. 1065, 3r, Bottom.

2005, Apr. 30   **Perf. 12¾x13**
1064-1065 A608   Set of 2   .50 .50

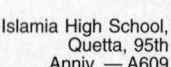

Islamia High School, Quetta, 95th Anniv. — A609

2005, May 25 *Perf. 13x12¾*
1066 A609 5r multi .40 .40

Akhtar Shairani (1905-48), Poet — A610

2005, June 30
1067 A610 5r multi .50 .50

World Summit on Information Technology, Tunis, Tunisia — A611

2005, July 15
1068 A611 5r multi 1.00 1.00

Abdul Rehman Baba (1632-1707), Poet — A612

2005, Aug. 4
1069 A612 5r multi .50 .50

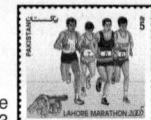

Lahore Marathon — A613

2005, Sept. 10 *Perf. 12¾x13*
1070 A613 5r multi .50 .50

Mushrooms — A614

No. 1071: a, Lepiota procera. b, Tricholoma gambosum. c, Amanita caesarea. d, Cantharellus cibarius. e, Boletus luridus. f, Morchella vulgaris. g, Amanita vaginata. h, Agaricus arvensis. i, Coprinus comatus. j, Clitocybe geotropa.

2005, Oct. 1 Litho. Perf. 13¼x12¾
1071 A614 Block of 10 4.50 4.50
a.-j. 5r Any single .40 .40

Intl. Year of Sports and Physical Education A615

2005, Nov. 5 *Perf. 14*
1072 A615 5r multi .75 .75

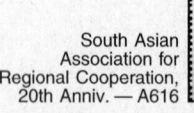

South Asian Association for Regional Cooperation, 20th Anniv. — A616

2005, Nov. 12 *Perf. 13¼x12¾*
1073 A616 5r multi 1.25 1.25

Khwaja Sarwar Hasan (1902-73), Diplomat — A617

2005, Nov. 18 *Perf. 14*
1074 A617 5r multi .40 .40

SOS Children's Villages in Pakistan, 30th Anniv. — A618

2005, Nov. 20 *Perf. 12¾x13¼*
1075 A618 5r multi .50 .50

20th World Men's Team Squash Championships, Islamabad A619

2005, Dec. 8 Litho. Perf. 14
1076 A619 5r multi .50 .50

Supreme Court, 50th Anniv. — A620

Supreme Court Building: 4r, In daylight. 15r, At night.

2006, Mar. 23
1077-1078 A620 Set of 2 1.60 1.60

Mohammed Ali Jinnah's 1948 Visit to Armored Corps Center — A621

Jinnah, soldiers and: No. 1079, 5r, Tanks. No. 1080, 5r, Flags, vert.

2006, Apr. 14
1079-1080 A621 Set of 2 .80 .80

Begum Ra'na Liaquat Ali Khan (1905-90), Diplomat — A622

2006, June 13 *Perf. 13½*
1081 A622 4r multi .40 .40

Sri Arjun Dev Jee (1563-1606), Sikh Guru — A623

2006, June 16
1082 A623 5r multi .50 .50

Polo at Shandur Pass — A624

2006, July 1 *Perf. 14*
1083 A624 5r multi .60 .60

Tourism A625

No. 1084: a, Hanna Lake. b, Lake Payee. c, Lake Saiful Maluk. d, Lake Dudi Pat Sar.

2006, July 20
1084 A625 5r Block of 4, #a-d 2.50 2.50

Miniature Sheet

Painters A626

No. 1085: a, Shakir Ali (1916-75). b, Anna Molka Ahmed (1917-94). c, Sadequain (1930-87). d, Ali Imam (1924-2002). e, Zubeida Agha (1922-97). f, Laila Shahzada (1926-94). g, Ahmed Parvez (1926-79). h, Bashir Mirza (1941-2000). i, Zahoorul Akhlaque (1941-99). j, Askari Mian Irani (1940-2004).

2006, Aug. 14 *Perf. 13x12¾*
1085 A626 4r Sheet of 10, #a-j 2.50 2.50

Hamdard Services, Cent. — A627

2006, Aug. 25 *Perf. 13¼x13*
1086 A627 5r multi .40 .35

Oct. 8, 2005 Earthquake, 1st Anniv. — A628

2006, Oct. 8 *Perf. 13½x13¾*
1087 A628 5r multi .60 .50

Medicinal Plants — A629

Designs: No. 1088, 5r, Aloe vera. No. 1089, 5r, Chamomile, vert.

Perf. 13½x13¼, 13¼x13½
2006, Oct. 28
1088-1089 A629 Set of 2 .80 .80

Intl. Anti-Corruption Day — A630

2006, Dec. 9 *Perf. 13*
1090 A630 5r multi .60 .60

Baltit Fort Heritage Trust, 10th Anniv. — A631

2006, Dec. 20 *Perf. 13¼*
1091 A631 15r multi 1.25 1.25

Miniature Sheet

Muslim League, Cent. A632

No. 1092: a, Mohammed Ali Jinnah's letter requesting membership in Muslim League. b, Jinnah in sherwani and cap. c, Jinnah addressing Lucknow session. d, Jinnah and wife with youth and women's wing. e, Jinnah hoisting Muslim League flag. f, Jinnah addressing Lahore session. g, Crowd, flags and ballot box. h, Jinnah addressing first Constituent Assembly.

Wmk. 351
2006, Dec. 28 Litho. Perf. 13
1092 A632 4r Sheet of 8, #a-h 2.50 2.50

Karachi Municipal Corporation Building, 75th Anniv. — A633

2007, Jan. 16 *Perf. 14¼*
1093 A633 10r multi .75 .75

Cadet College Petaro, 50th Anniv. — A634

Wmk. 351
2007, Feb. 28 Litho. Perf. 14¼
1094 A634 10r multi .60 .60

Intl. Women's Day — A635

2007, Mar. 8 *Perf. 13*
1095 A635 10r multi .60 .60

Hugh Catchpole (1907-97), Educator — A636

2007, May 26
1096 A636 10r multi .60 .60

Pakistan Post
Emblem — A637

2007, June 7   *Perf. 14¼*
1097 A637 4r multi   .50 .50

First Public
Appearance
of JF-17
Thunder
Airplane
A638

2007, Sept. 6   *Perf. 13*
1098 A638 5r multi   .80 .80

Completion
of Term of
National
Assembly
A639

2007, Nov. 15
1099 A639 15r multi   .75 .75

Catholic Cathedral, Lahore,
Cent. — A640

2007, Nov. 19
1100 A640 5r multi   .50 .50

Third Meeting of Economic
Cooperation Organization Postal
Authorities, Tehran (in 2006)
A641

     Wmk. 351
2007, Sept. 22   Litho.   *Perf. 13*
1101 A641 10r multi   10.00 12.50

No. 1101 was withdrawn from sale a few
weeks after issuance as it is inscribed "I. R.
Iran" and lacks the "Pakistan" country name. It
is additionally inscribed with a denomination in
Iranian currency, and dated "2006" though
issued in 2007. This stamp was not valid in
Iran, as Iran issued a similar stamp, No. 2917,
in 2006.

Pres. Zulfikar Ali Bhutto (1928-79) and
Prime Minister Benazir Bhutto (1953-
2007) — A642

     Wmk. 351
2008, Apr. 4   Litho.   *Perf. 13*
1102 A642 4r multi   .40 .40
     Imperf
     Size: 106x71mm
1103 A642 20r multi   2.00 2.00

No. 1103 contains No. 1102 with simulated
perforations.

Benazir Bhutto (1953-
2007), Prime
Minister — A643

Designs: 4r, Head. 5r, 20r, Bhutto waving.

     Wmk. 351
2008, June 21   Litho.   *Perf. 13*
1104 A643 4r multi   .40 .40
     Size: 34x57mm
     Perf. 13x13¼
1105 A643 5r multi   .40 .40
     Size: 67x99mm
     Imperf
1106 A643 20r multi   1.40 1.40

No. 1106 has simulated perforations.

Oct. 8, 2005
Earthquake,
3rd Anniv.
A644

2008, Oct. 8   *Perf. 13*
1107 A644 4r multi   .60 .60

Selection of Benazir
Bhutto for 2008
United Nations
Human Rights
Award — A645

     Wmk. 351
2008, Dec. 10   Litho.   *Perf. 13*
1108 A645 4r multi   .40 .40

Assassination of Benazir Bhutto, 1st
Anniv. — A646

2008, Dec. 27   **Wmk. 351**   *Perf. 13*
1109 A646 4r multi   .60 .60
     Size: 98x67mm
     Imperf
     Unwmk.
1110 A646 20r multi   1.50 1.50

10th Economic
Cooperation
Organization
Summit,
Tehran — A647

     Perf. 13¼x13½
2009, Mar. 11   **Wmk. 351**
1111 A647 5r multi   1.25 1.25

Compare with Azerbaijan 895, Iran 2981.

Natl. Environment Year — A648

Designs: No. 1112, 5r, Deodar tree. No.
1113, 5r, Jasmine flower. No. 1114, 5r,
Markhor. No. 1115, 5r, Chukar.

2009, Mar. 23   *Perf. 13*
1112-1115 A648   Set of 4   1.50 1.50

Habib Public
School, 50th
Anniv. — A649

2009, Mar. 29
1116 A649 5r multi   .35 .35

Bai Virbaiji Soparivala Parsi High
School, Karachi, 150th Anniv. — A650

2009, May 23   *Perf. 13¼x13½*
1117 A650 5r multi   .40 .40

Karachi
Chamber of
Commerce
and Industry
Building,
75th Anniv.
A651

     Wmk. 351
2009, May 30   Litho.   *Perf. 13*
1118 A651 4r multi   .40 .40

Ahmad Nadeem
Qasmi (1916-2006),
Writer — A652

2009, July 10
1119 A652 5r multi   .40 .40

Minorities Week — A653

     Wmk. 351
2009, Aug. 11   Litho.   *Perf. 13*
1120 A653 5r multi   .50 .50

Independence
Day — A654

     Wmk. 351
2009, Aug. 14   Litho.   *Perf. 13*
1121 A654 5r multi   .40 .40

Festival of Hazrat
Musa Pak
Shaheed — A655

2009, Aug. 15
1122 A655 5r multi   .60 .60

"United For
Peace" — A656

2009, Aug. 16   *Perf. 13½*
1123 A656 5r multi   .60 .60

Diplomatic Relations Between Pakistan
and the Philippines, 60th Anniv.
A657

     Wmk. 351
2009, Sept. 9   Litho.   *Perf. 13*
1124 A657 5r multi   1.25 1.25

People's Republic of
China, 60th
Anniv. — A658

2009, Oct. 1
1125 A658 5r multi   .90 .90

A659

Polio-free
Pakistan
A660

2009, Oct. 10
1126 A659 5r multi   .40 .40
1127 A660 5r multi   .40 .40

Seventh Natl. Finance Commission
Award — A661

     Wmk. 351
2010, Jan. 11   Litho.   *Perf. 13*
1128 A661 8r multi   .60 .60

Port of
Gwardar
A662

2010, Jan. 11
1129 A662 8r multi   .60 .60

Navy Rifle
Association
50th Anniv.
Meet — A663

Wmk. 351
2010, Feb. 13 Litho. Perf. 13½
1130 A663 10r multi   .60 .60

Awarding of
Hilal-i-Eissar
(Selflessness)
Awards to
Cities — A664

No. 1131 — Flag and: a, War Memorial,
Nowshera. b, Islamia College, Peshawar. c,
Judicial Complex, Swabi. d, Takht-e-Bahi,
Mardan. e, Sugar mills, Charsadda.

2010, Feb. 22   Perf. 13
1131   Vert. strip of 5   1.50 1.50
a.-e. A664 5r Any single   .30   .30

Overseas Investors Chamber of
Commerce and Industry, 150th
Anniv. — A665

2010, Apr. 7   Perf. 13x13¼
1132 A665 8r multi   .60 .60

2010 Youth Olympics,
Singapore — A666

Wmk. 351
2010, Aug. 14 Litho. Perf. 13¼
1133 A666 8r multi   1.25 1.25

Lawrence College, Murree Hills, 150th
Anniv. — A667

No. 1134 — Crest of college and: a, Building and flagpoles. b, Building in brown. c,
Aerial view of building. d, Building and plaza.

2010, Oct. 7   Litho.   Perf. 13
1134 A667   Block of 4 + 2 cen-
              tral labels   1.75 1.75
a.-d.   8r Any single   .30   .30

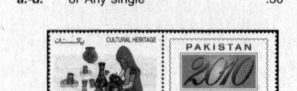

Children's Art Competition — A668

2010, Nov. 5
1135 A668 8r multi + label   .60 .60

International Islamic University,
Islamabad, 25th Anniv. — A669

Perf. 13x13¼
2010, Dec. 15   Wmk. 351
1136 A669 8r multi   .60 .60

Islamabad,
50th Anniv.
A670

2010, Dec. 31   Perf. 13½
1137 A670 5r multi   1.25 1.25

100 Million Cell Phone Subscribers of
Pakistan Telecommunications
Authority — A671

2011, Jan. 19   Perf. 13x13¼
1138 A671 8r multi   1.75 1.75

Sixth Population and Housing
Census — A672

2011, Feb. 10   Wmk. 351
1139 A672 10r multi   1.75 1.75

Railways in
Pakistan,
150th Anniv.
A673

2011, May 13   Litho.
1140 A673 8r multi   .60 .60

Diplomatic Relations Between Pakistan
and People's Republic of China, 60th
Anniv. — A674

No. 1141 — Flags of Pakistan and People's
Republic of China and: a, Pakistan President
Asif Ali Zardari and Chinese President Hu
Jintao (handshake above baseline). b, Pakistan Prime Minister and Yousuf Raza Gilani
and Chinese Premier Wen Jiabao (handshake
touching baseline).

2011, May 21   Perf. 13x13¼
1141 A674 4r Horiz. pair, #a-b   2.00 2.00

Campaign Against Human
Immunodeficiency Virus — A675

Perf. 13½x13¾
2011, June 8   Wmk. 351
1142 A675 8r multi   1.25 1.25

Friendship Between Pakistan and
Russia — A676

Perf. 13x13¼
2011, June 10 Litho.   Wmk. 351
1143 A676 8r multi   .60 .60

A677

A678

A679

A680

A681

A682

A683

Works From
Children's Art
Competition at
National Stamp
Exhibition,
Kurrachee
A684

2011, June 24   Unwmk.   Perf. 13
1144   Sheet of 8 + 2 labels   4.50 4.50
a. A677 8r multi   .40   .40
b. A678 8r multi   .40   .40
c. A679 8r multi   .40   .40
d. A680 8r multi   .40   .40
e. A681 8r multi   .40   .40
f. A682 8r multi   .40   .40
g. A683 8r multi   .40   .40
h. A684 8r multi   .40   .40

Institute of Chartered Accountants of
Pakistan, 50th Anniv. — A685

Perf. 13x13¼
2011, July 1   Wmk. 351
1145 A685 8r multi   .60 .60

Dr. Syedna Mohammed Burhannudin
Saheb, Religious Leader, 100th
Birthday — A686

2011, July 17
1146 A686 8r multi   .60 .60
Dr. Burhanuddin Saheb was born in 1915.
The centenary of his birth is based on the
Islamic calendar.

Zarai Taraqiati
Bank, Ltd., 50th
Anniv. — A687

2011, Aug. 14   Perf. 13
1147 A687 8r multi   .60 .60

Frequency Allocation Board, 60th
Anniv. — A688

2011, Aug. 18   Perf. 13x13¼
1148 A688 8r multi   .60 .60

Towers
in
Pakistan
and Iran
A689

No. 1149: a, Milad Tower, Tehran. b, Minar-
e-Pakistan, Lahore.

2011, Aug. 29   Perf. 13
1149 A689 8r Horiz. pair, #a-b, +
              flanking label   2.00 2.00
See Iran No. 3023.

Pakistan Space and Upper
Atmosphere Research Commission,
50th Anniv. — A690

2011, Sept. 16   Wmk. 351
1150 A690 8r multi   .60 .60

Karachi Gymkhana, 125th
Anniv. — A691

No. 1151: a, Building with archways, tree at
right. b, Building, white pole at right. c, Building, two white poles and trees in front. d, Building, shelter with awning at left.

2011, Sept. 23   *Perf. 13x13¼*
1151 A691 8r Block of 4, #a-d   2.00 2.00

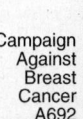

Campaign
Against
Breast
Cancer
A692

2011, Nov. 30   *Perf. 13*
1152 A692 8r multi   .60   .60

Diplomatic
Relations Between
Pakistan and
Thailand, 60th
Anniv. — A693

2011, Dec. 13   *Perf. 13¼x13*
1153 A693 8r multi   .60   .60

St. Patrick's High
School, Karachi,
150th
Anniv. — A694

2011, Dec. 31
1154 A694 8r multi   .60   .60

100th
Meeting of
Federal
Cabinet
A695

2012, Jan. 18   *Perf. 13x13¼*
1155 A695 8r multi   .60   .60

Arfa Karim
(1995-2012),
World's
Youngest
Microsoft
Certified
Professional
A696

2012, Feb. 2
1156 A696 8r multi   .60   .60

Nur Khan
(1923-2011),
Air Marshal
A697

2012, Feb. 22   *Perf. 13¾x13½*
1157 A697 8r multi   .60   .60

Gemstones — A698

No. 1158: a, Emerald. b, Ruby. c, Sapphire.
d, Peridot.

2012, Feb. 24   *Perf. 13*
1158 A698 8r Block of 4, #a-d   2.00 2.00

Aitchison College,
Lahore, 125th
Anniv. — A699

2012, Mar. 3
1159 A699 8r multi   .60   .60

St. Joseph's
Convent
School,
Karachi,
150th Anniv.
A700

2012, Mar. 19   *Perf. 13¾x13½*
1160 A700 8r multi   .60   .60

Asian-Pacific Postal Union, 50th
Anniv. — A701

2012, Apr. 1   Wmk. 351   *Perf. 13*
1161 A701 8r multi   .60   .60

Government High School No. 1,
Thana, Cent. — A702

2012, Apr. 15   *Perf. 13½*
1162 A702 8r multi   .60   .60

Martyr's
Day — A703

2012, Apr. 30   *Perf. 13x13¼*
1163 A703 8r multi   .60   .60

State Visit of Thailand's King Bhumibol
Adulyadej and Queen Sirikit to
Pakistan, 50th Anniv.
A704

2012, May 5   *Litho.*
1164 A704 8r multi   .60   .60

Campaign
Against
Thalassemia
A705

2012, May 8   Wmk. 351
1165 A705 8r multi   .60   .60

World Environment Day — A706

No. 1166: a, Mountains and lake. b, Horses
and riders. c, Arches at Shalimar Gardens,
Lahore. d, Khyber Pass Gateway and flag.

2012, June 5   *Perf. 13x13¼*
1166 A706 8r Block of 4, #a-d   1.50 1.50

United Nations Environment Program, 40th
anniv.

Ayub
Bridge,
50th
Anniv.
A707

2012, June 15
1167 A707 8r multi   .60   .60

A708

A709

A710

A711

A712

A713

A714

Works From Children's Art
Competition at 2012 National Stamp
Exhibition, Kurrachee
A715

2012, June 22   *Perf. 13*
1168   Sheet of 8 + 2 labels   3.50 3.50
 a. A708 8r multi   .40   .40
 b. A709 8r multi   .40   .40
 c. A710 8r multi   .40   .40
 d. A711 8r multi   .40   .40
 e. A712 8r multi   .40   .40
 f. A713 8r multi   .40   .40
 g. A714 8r multi   .40   .40
 h. A715 8r multi   .40   .40

Eid Greetings — A716

No. 1169: a, Yellow roses, pale orange
frame. b, Rink roses, yellow frame. c, White
roses, light blue frame. d, Yellow roses, light
green frame.

2012, Aug. 13
1169 A716 8r Block of 4, #a-d   1.50 1.50

King Edward Medical University,
Lahore, 150th Anniv. — A717

2012, Aug. 28   *Perf. 13x13¼*
1170 A717 8r multi   .60   .60

Pakistan No. 23,
Abdur Rahman
Chughtai (1897-
1975),
Painter — A718

2012, Aug. 30   *Perf. 13¼x13½*
1171 A718 10r multi   .60   .60

Independence, 65th anniv.

Sialkot Chamber of Commerce and
Industry, 30th Anniv. — A719

2012, Sept. 26   *Perf. 13x13¼*
1172 A719 8r multi   .60   .60

Birds in
Flight
A720

No. 1173: a, White storks. b, Shoveler
ducks. c, Snow geese. d, Siberian cranes.

2012, Sept. 27   *Wmk. 351*
1173 A720 8r Block of 4, #a-d   1.50 1.50

A721

A722

A723

Arabian Sea
Coral Reefs
A724

2012, Oct. 4   **Litho.**
1174   Block of 4   2.00 2.00
   a.   A721 8r multi   .50 .50
   b.   A722 8r multi   .50 .50
   c.   A723 8r multi   .50 .50
   d.   A724 8r multi   .50 .50

Hameed Naseem
(1920-98),
Writer — A725

2012, Oct. 19   **Perf. 13**
1175   A725 8r multi   .60 .60

Men of Letters. See Nos. 1181-1183, 1185-
1189, 1196, 1202, 1206, 1248.

University of Karachi Geography
Department, 60th Anniv. — A726

2012, Nov. 19   **Perf. 13x13¼**
1176   A726 15r multi   .90 .90

National Investment Trust Limited, 50th
Anniv. — A727

2012, Nov. 21   **Wmk. 351**
1177   A727 15r multi   .90 .90

Muhammad
Luthfullah Khan
(1916-2012), Writer
and Recordings
Collector — A728

2012, Nov. 25   **Perf. 13**
1178   A728 15r multi   .90 .90

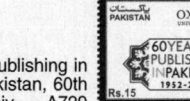

Publishing in
Pakistan, 60th
Anniv. — A729

2012, Dec. 15   **Perf. 13½x13¼**
1179   A729 15r multi   .30 .30

Commercial Operation of First Wind
Farm Power Project in
Pakistan — A730

2012, Dec. 24   **Perf. 13x13¼**
1180   A730 15r multi   .90 .90

Men of Letters Type of 2012

Designs: No. 1181, Syed Nasir Raza Kazmi
(1925-72), poet. No. 1182, Allama Muhammad
Asad (1900-92), writer. No. 1183, Qudrat
Ullah Shahab (1917-86), writer.

2013
1181   A725 15r multi   .60 .60
1182   A725 15r multi   .60 .60
1183   A725 15r multi   .60 .60
     Nos. 1181-1183 (3)   1.80 1.80

Issued: No. 1181, 3/2; Nos. 1182, 1183,
3/23.

Kinnaird
College,
Lahore,
Cent. — A732

2013, Apr. 11
1184   A732 15r multi   .90 .90

Men of Letters Type of 2012

Design: No. 1185, Sufi Barkat Ali (1911-97),
Muslim Sufi saint. No. 1186, Syed Zamir Jafri
(1916-99), poet. No. 1187, Shafiq-ur-Rehman
(1920-2000), writer. No. 1188, Mumtaz Mufti
(1905-95), writer. No. 1189, Ishfaq Ahmed
(1925-2004), writer.

2013
1185   A725 8r multi   .60 .60
1186   A725 8r multi   .60 .60
1187   A725 8r multi   .60 .60
1188   A725 8r multi   .60 .60
1189   A725 8r multi   .60 .60
     Nos. 1185-1189 (5)   3.00 3.00

Issued: No. 1185, 4/27; No. 1186, 5/29; No.
1187, 6/6; Nos. 1188-1189, 6/12.

Sir Muhammad
Iqbal (1877-
1938),
Poet — A733

2013, Apr. 21   **Wmk. 351**
     Litho.   **Perf. 13½**
1190   A733 15r multi   .90 .90

Reopening of Pakistan Army Museum,
Rawalpindi — A734

2013, Apr. 30   **Perf. 13x13¼**
1191   A734 15r multi   .90 .90

2013
General
Elections
A735

2013, May 11
1192   A735 8r multi   .60 .60

Recipients of Pakistan's Highest
Military Medals — A736

No. 1193: a, Capt. Karnal Sher Khan
Shaheed (1970-99), Nishan-e-Haider medal.
b, Havildar Lalak Jan Shaheed (1967-99),
Nishan-e-Haider medal. c, Naik Saif Ali Janjua
Shaheed (1922-48), Hilal-i-Kashmir medal.

Perf. 13½x13¼
2013, Apr. 30   **Litho.**   **Wmk. 351**
1193   A736   Horiz. strip of 3   1.50 1.50
   a.-c.   8r Any single   .50 .50

Sadiq Muhammad
Khan Abbasi V
(1904-66), Nawab of
Bahawalpur — A737

Wmk. 351
2013, May 24   **Litho.**   **Perf. 13**
1194   A737 8r multi   .60 .60

Islamia
College,
Peshawar,
Cent.
A738

2013, May 30
1195   A738 8r multi   .60 .60

Men of Letters Type of 2012

Design: Ibn-e-Insha (1927-78), poet.

2013, June 15
1196   A725 8r multi   .50 .50

All-Pakistan
Newspaper Society,
60th Anniv. — A739

2013, June 20
1197   A739 8r multi   .60 .60

Red-vented
Bulbul — A740

Perf. 13½x13¼
2013, July 1   **Litho.**   **Wmk. 351**
1198   A740 8r multi   .60 .60

Pir Meher Ali Shah
(1859-1937), Sufi
Scholar — A741

Wmk. 351
2013, July 30   **Litho.**   **Perf. 13**
1199   A741 8r multi   — —

Frigate PNS
Aslat — A742

Wmk. 351
2013, Sept. 3   **Litho.**   **Perf. 13¼**
1200   A742 10r multi   .60 .60

Noor Jahan
(1926-2000),
Singer
A743

Wmk. 351
2013, Sept. 21   **Litho.**   **Perf. 13¼**
1201   A743 8r multi   .60 .60

Men of Letters Type of 2012

Design: Jon Elia (1931-2002), writer.

Wmk. 351
2013, Nov. 8   **Litho.**   **Perf. 13**
1202   A725 8r multi   .50 .50

Two Decades of
Extended
Cooperation with
Economic
Cooperation
Organization
A744

Perf. 13¼x13
2013, Nov. 28   **Litho.**   **Wmk. 351**
1203   A744 25r multi   .60 .60

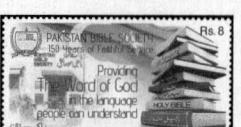

Perveen Shakir (1952-
94), Poet — A745

Wmk. 351
2013, Dec. 26   **Litho.**   **Perf. 13**
1204   A745 10r multi   .60 .60

Pakistan
Bible
Society,
150th
Anniv.
A746

Wmk. 351
2013, Dec. 28   **Litho.**   **Perf. 13**
1205   A746 8r multi   .60 .60

Men of Letters Type of 2012

Design: Habib Jalib (1928-93), poet.

Wmk. 351
2014, Mar. 12   **Litho.**   **Perf. 13**
1206   A725 15r multi   .50 .50

Air
Commodore
Muhammad
Mahmood
Alam (1935-
2013)
A747

Perf. 13¾x13½

2014, Mar. 20   Litho.   Wmk. 351
1207 A747 8r multi   .60   .60

Hyder M. Habib (1931-2011), Banker A748

Wmk. 351

2014, Apr. 6   Litho.   Perf. 13
1208 A748 8r multi   .60   .60

Forman Christian College, 150th Anniv. A749

Wmk. 351

2014, May 14   Litho.   Perf. 13
1209 A749 8r multi   .25   .25

Pakistan Navy Submarine Force, 50th Anniv. — A750

Wmk. 351

2014, June 1   Litho.   Perf. 13
1210 A750 10r multi   .25   .25

Frontier Constabulary, Cent. A751

Wmk. 351

2014, July 11   Litho.   Perf. 13½
1211 A751 8r multi   .25   .25

Sahiwal Cattle Conservation, Cent. — A752

Perf. 13x13¼

2014, Aug. 5   Litho.   Wmk. 351
1212 A752 8r multi   .25   .25

A753

Pakistan 2025 Planning Program A754

Perf. 13½x13¼

2014, Aug. 11   Litho.   Wmk. 351
1213 A753 8r multi   .25   .25

Perf. 13

1214 A754 10r multi   .25   .25

Norman Borlaug (1914-2009), 1970 Nobel Peace Laureate A755

Perf. 13x13¼

2014, Dec. 4   Litho.   Wmk. 351
1215 A755 8r multi   .25   .25

Intl. Anti-Corruption Day — A756

Perf. 13x13¼

2014, Dec. 9   Litho.   Wmk. 351
1216 A756 8r multi   .25   .25

Gems and Minerals A757

No. 1217: a, Apatite. b, Aquamarine. c, Black tourmaline. d, Garnet. e, Epidot. f, Vesuvianite. g, Topaz. h, Sphene.

Perf. 13x13¼

2014, Dec. 11   Litho.   Wmk. 351
1217   Block of 8   1.60 1.60
  a.-h. A757 10r Any single   .25   .25

14th National Scout Jamboree, Khairpur A758

Perf. 13x13¼

2014, Dec. 23   Litho.   Wmk. 351
1218 A758 8r multi   .25   .25

Artifacts of Ancient Civilizations — A759

No. 1219: a, Artifacts from Trypillia, Ukraine archaeological site, flag of Ukraine. b, Artifacts from Mohenjo-daro, Pakistan archaeological site, flag of Pakistan.

Perf. 13¼x13

2014, Dec. 25   Litho.   Wmk. 351
1219 A759 20r Horiz. pair, #a-b   1.00 1.00
  c.   Souvenir sheet of 2, #1219a-
         1219b, imperf.   1.00 1.00

No. 1219c has simulated perforations and sold for 50r.
See Ukraine No. 997.

Moulana Altaf Hussain Hali (1837-1914), Poet — A760

Perf. 13x13¼

2014, Dec. 31   Litho.   Wmk. 351
1220 A760 8r multi   .25   .25

First 100 Megawatt Solar Plant in Pakistan — A762

Wmk. 351

2015, May 4   Litho.   Perf. 13½
1222 A762 8r multi   .25   .25

Year of Pakistan-China Friendly Exchanges A763

No. 1223: a, Flag of People's Republic of China and Pres. Xi Jinping. b, Great Wall of China. c, Karakoram Highway. d, Shalimar Garden, Pakistan. e, Flag of Pakistan and Prime Minister Nawaz Sharif.

Wmk. 351

2015, Aug. 14   Litho.   Perf. 13
1223   Horiz. strip of 5   1.25 1.25
  a.-f. A763 10r Any single   .25   .25

A764

A765

A766

A767

A768

India-Pakistan War, 50th Anniv. — A769

Perf. 13x13¼

2015, Sept. 7   Litho.   Wmk. 351
1224   Block of 6   1.50 1.50
  a.   A764 10r multi   .25   .25
  b.   A765 10r multi   .25   .25
  c.   A766 10r multi   .25   .25
  d.   A767 10r multi   .25   .25
  e.   A768 10r multi   .25   .25
  f.   A769 10r multi   .25   .25

Cadet College, Kohat, 50th Anniv. A770

Wmk. 351

2015, Oct. 10   Litho.   Perf.
1225 A770 8r multi   .25   .25

Urdu Language in Turkey, Cent. A771

Wmk. 351

2015, Oct. 12   Litho.   Perf. 13
1226 A771 10r multi   .25   .25

Restoration of Murree General Post Office A772

Wmk. 351

2015, Nov. 4   Litho.   Perf. 13
1227 A772 8r multi   .25   .25

Army Public School Massacre, 1st Anniv. — A773

Wmk. 351

2015, Dec. 16   Litho.   Perf. 13
1228 A773 16r multi   .30   .30

Reopening of Murree General Post Office — A774

Wmk. 351

2015, Dec. 29   Litho.   Perf. 13
1229 A774 10r multi   .25   .25

Safe Operation of First Pinstech Nuclear Reactor, 50th Anniv. — A775

Perf. 14 Syncopated

2016, Feb. 10   Litho.   Wmk. 351
1230 A775 50r multi   1.00 1.00

Water Conservation — A776

Wmk. 351
2016, Mar. 22   Litho.   *Perf. 13*
1231 A776 8r multi   .25   .25

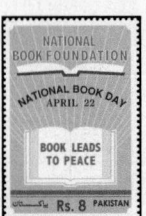

National Book Day — A777

Wmk. 351
2016, Apr. 22   Litho.   *Perf. 13*
1232 A777 8r multi   .25   .25

S. P Singha (1893-1948), Politician — A778

Perf. 14 Syncopated
2016, Apr. 26   Litho.   **Wmk. 351**
1233 A778 10r multi   .25   .25

Diplomatic Relations Between Pakistan and People's Republic of China, 65th Anniv. — A779

Wmk. 351
2016, May 21   Litho.   *Perf. 13*
1234 A779 8r multi   .25   .25

Abdul Sattar Edhi (1928-2016), Philanthropist A780

Perf. 13¼x13½
2016, Aug. 14   Litho.   **Wmk. 351**
1235 A780 20r multi   .40   .40

Souvenir Sheet

Directorate General of Training and Research Building (Old Custom House), Karachi, Cent. — A781

No. 1236 — Various views of building with: a, Country name in white at left, "100" in red at bottom. b, Country name in black at right, "100" in blue at bottom. c, Country name in black at right, "100" in magenta at bottom.

Wmk. 351
2016, Sept. 6   Litho.   *Perf.*
1236 A781 8r Sheet of 3, #a-c   .50   .50

Habib Bank Limited, 75th Anniv. A782

Wmk. 351
2016, Sept. 23   Litho.   *Perf. 13*
1237 A782 8r multi   .25   .25

National Parks of Pakistan and Belarus A783

No. 1238: a, Saiful Muluk National Park, flag and arms of Pakistan. b, Narachanski National Park, flag and arms of Belarus.

Perf. 13¼x13½
2016, Oct. 5   Litho.   **Wmk. 351**
1238   Horiz. pair   .80   .80
a.-b. A783 20r Either single   .40   .40
   See Belarus No. 1014.

Diplomatic Relations Between Pakistan and Singapore, 50th Anniv. — A784

No. 1239: a, Vanda Miss Joaquim orchid, Merlion's head. b, Jasmine flower, flag of Pakistan.

Wmk. 351
2016, Oct. 18   Litho.   *Perf. 13*
1239 A784 8r Horiz. pair, #a-b   .30   .30
   See Singapore Nos. 1800-1801.

Rotary Foundation, Cent. — A785

Wmk. 351
2016, Nov. 20   Litho.   *Perf. 13*
1240 A785 8r multi   .25   .25

Lahore High Court, 150th Anniv. A786

Wmk. 351
2016, Nov. 26   Litho.   *Perf. 13*
1241 A786 8r multi   .25   .25

National Voter's Day — A787

Perf. 14 Syncopated
2016, Dec. 7   Litho.   **Wmk. 351**
1242 A787 8r multi   .25   .25

Dinshaw B. Avari (1902-88), Philanthropist A788

Wmk. 351
2016, Dec. 18   Litho.   *Perf. 13*
1243 A788 8r multi   .25   .25

A789

A790

A791

A792

A793

A794

A795

Works From Children's Art Competition at 2016 National Stamp Exhibition, Karachi — A796

Wmk. 351
2016, Dec. 30   Litho.   *Perf. 13*
1244   Sheet of 8 + 2 labels   2.00   2.00
a. A789 8r multi   .25   .25
b. A790 8r multi   .25   .25
c. A791 8r multi   .25   .25
d. A792 8r multi   .25   .25
e. A793 8r multi   .25   .25
f. A794 8r multi   .25   .25
g. A795 8r multi   .25   .25
h. A796 8r multi   .25   .25

International Year of Sustainable Tourism for Development

No. 1245 — United Nations World Tourism Organization emblem and mountains: a, Broad Peak. b, Gasherbrum I. c, Nangaparbat. d, K2.

Perf. 13¼x13½
2017, Jan. 1   Litho.   **Wmk. 351**
1245   Horiz. strip of 4, #a-d   1.00   1.00
a.-d. A797 10r Any single   .25   .25

A798

13th Econonic Cooperation Organization Summit, Islamabad — A799

Perf. 14 Syncopated
2017, Mar. 6   Litho.   **Wmk. 351**
1246 A798 8r multi   .25   .25
Perf. 13
1247 A799 8r multi   .25   .25

Men of Letters Type of 2012

Design: Majeed Amjad (1914-74), poet.

Wmk. 351
2017, June 29   Litho.   *Perf. 13*
1248 A725 8r multi   .25   .25

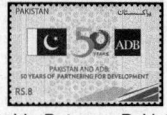

Partnership Between Pakistan and Asian Development Bank, 50th Anniv. — A800

Perf. 13¼x13½
2017, July 6   Litho.   **Wmk. 351**
1249 A800 8r multi   .25   .25

Maulana Mufti Mahmood (1919-80), Governmental Minister — A801

Wmk. 351
2017, Oct. 14   Litho.   *Perf. 13*
1250 A801 8r multi   .25   .25

Sir Syed Ahmed Khan (1817-98), Educator, Jurist, Philosopher A802

Wmk. 351
2017, Oct. 17   Litho.   *Perf. 13½*
1251 A802 10r multi   .25   .25
a.   Souvenir sheet of 1, imperf.   .40   .40

No. 1251a has simulated perforations, smaller-sized reproductions of Nos. 502, 735c, 888, and sold for 20r.

Government Islamia College, Lahore, 125th Anniv. — A803

Wmk. 351
2017, Nov. 1   Litho.   *Perf. 14*
1252 A803 8r multi   .25   .25

Pakistan Cricket Team, Winners of 2017 ICC Champions Trophy A804

No. 1253: a, Team standing behind orange letters spelling "Champions." b, Trophy and stadium. c, Team on victory platform.

Wmk. 351
2017, Nov. 2 Litho. *Perf. 13*
1253 Horiz. strip of 3 .75 .75
a.-c. A804 10r Any single .25 .25
d. Souvenir sheet of 3, #1253a-1253c, imperf. .95 .95

No. 1253d sold for 50r and stamps have simulated perforations.

Souvenir Sheet

Diplomatic Relations Between Pakistan and Turkey, 70th Anniv. — A805

No. 1254: a, Mehmet Akif Ersoy (1873-1936), poet. b, Allama Muhammad Iqbal (1877-1938), poet.

Perf. 13¼x13½
2017, Nov. 9 Litho. **Wmk. 351**
1254 A805 10r Sheet of 2, #a-b .40 .40
See Turkey No. 3577.

Pakistan Air Force's No. 6 Air Transport Support Squadron, 75th Anniv. A806

Wmk. 351
2017, Dec. 1 Litho. *Perf. 13*
1255 A806 10r multi .25 .25

Souvenir Sheet

Dr. Ruth Katharina Martha Pfau (1929-2017), Nun and Physician to Lepers — A807

Wmk. 351
2017, Dec. 3 Litho. *Perf.*
1256 A807 8r brt pur, dp vio & multi .25 .25

Aga Khan IV, 60th Anniv. as Imam A808

No. 1257 — Inscriptions: a, Providing clean drinking water. b, Early childhood development. c, Aga Khan University. d, Restoration of Shahi Hammam. e, Skills development. f, Aga Khan Medical Center.

Wmk. 351
2017, Dec. 8 Litho. *Perf. 13*
1257 A808 10r Block of 6, #a-f 1.10 1.10

Green Pakistan Program A809

A810

Design: No. 1260, Foliage in background, denomination in white.

Wmk. 351
2018, Feb. 9 Litho. *Perf. 13*
1258 A809 8r multi .25 .25
1259 A810 8r multi .25 .25
1260 A809 8r multi .25 .25
Nos. 1258-1260 (3) .75 .75

Army Burn Hall College, Abbottabad, 75th Anniv. — A811

Wmk. 351
2018, Mar. 5 Litho. *Perf. 13*
1261 A811 8r multi .25 .25

Mosques A812

No. 1262: a, Heydar Mosque, Baku, Azerbaijan, flag of Azerbaijan. b, Wazir Khan Mosque, Lahore, Pakistan, flag of Pakistan.

Wmk. 351
2018, June 9 Litho. *Perf. 13*
1262 A812 8r Pair, #a-b .30 .30

A souvenir sheet containing Nos. 1262a-1262b sold for 50r.
Joint Issue between Pakistan and Azerbaijan. See Azerbaijan No. 1215.

2018 Summit of Shanghai Cooperation Organization, Qingdao, People's Republic of China — A813

Perf. 13¼x13½
2018, June 9 Litho. **Wmk. 351**
1263 A813 10r multi .25 .25

Urdu Dictionary Board, 60th Anniv. A814

Wmk. 351
2018, June 14 Litho. *Perf. 13*
1264 A814 8r multi .25 .25

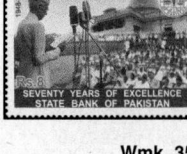

State Bank of Pakistan, 70th Anniv. A815

Wmk. 351
2018, July 1 Litho. *Perf. 13*
1265 A815 8r multi .25 .25

Atrocities in Indian-Occupied Kashmir — A816

No. 1266 — Inscriptions at LL: a, Use of chemical weapons. b, Half widows (sign behind woman). c, Children abuse. d, Fake encounters. e, Freedom prayer. f, Use of pellet guns. g, Half widows (woman and child). h, Human shield. i, Women harassment. j, Missing persons. k, Mass graves. l, Over 100,000 Kashmiris martyred. m, Burhan Wani (1994-2016), freedom icon. n, Bleeding Kashmir. o, Protest against killers. p, Braid chopping. q, Homeless children. r, Freedom struggle. s, Brutality. t, Tortured women.

Perf. 13x13¼
2018, July 13 Litho. **Wmk. 351**
1266 Sheet of 20 2.60 2.60
a.-t. A816 8r Any single .25 .25

Mama Parsi Girls Secondary School, Cent. — A817

Wmk. 351
2018, July 24 Litho. *Perf. 13*
1267 A817 8r multi .25 .25

Jamsheed Marker (1922-2018), Diplomat — A818

Wmk. 351
2018, Nov. 24 Litho. *Perf. 13*
1268 A818 8r multi .25 .25

10th International Defense Exhibition and Seminar, Karachi A819

Wmk. 351
2018, Nov. 27 Litho. *Perf. 13*
1269 A819 10r multi .25 .25

Anti-Corruption Day — A820

Wmk. 351
2018, Dec. 9 Litho. *Perf.*
1270 A820 8r multi .25 .25

Gulam Ishaq Khan Institute of Engineering Sciences and Technology, Topi, 25th Anniv. — A821

Wmk. 351
2018, Dec. 24 Litho. *Perf. 13*
1271 A821 8r multi .25 .25

Crescent Model Higher Secondary School, Lahore, 50th Anniv. A822

Wmk. 351
2018, Dec. 26 Litho. *Perf. 13*
1272 A822 8r multi .25 .25

Mirza Asadullah Khan Ghalib (1797-1869), Poet — A823

Perf. 14 Syncopated
2019, Feb. 15 Litho. **Wmk. 351**
1273 A823 8r multi .25 .25

Launch of PRSS-1 and PakTES-1A Satellites, 1st Anniv. A824

Wmk. 351
2019, July 9 Litho. *Perf. 13¼*
1274 A824 20r multi .25 .25

Commonwealth of Nations, 70th Anniv. — A825

Perf. 13¼x13¾
2019, Aug. 14 Litho. **Wmk. 351**
1275 A825 20r multi .25 .25

Commission on Science and Technology for Sustainable Development in the South, 25th Anniv. A826

Wmk. 351
2019, Oct. 4 Litho. *Perf. 13¼*
1276 A826 20r multi .25 .25

Co-operation Between Pakistan and Japan — A827

No. 1277 — Inscriptions: a, Capacity building in construction technology. b, Irrigation management system. c, Skills development &

market diversification. d, Kohat Friendship Tunnel.

Wmk. 351

2019, Oct. 22   Litho.   *Perf. 13*
1277 A827 20r Block of 4, #a-d,
      + 2 central la-
      bels   1.10 1.10

Convention on the Rights of the Child, 30th Anniv. — A828

Wmk. 351

2019, Nov. 4   Litho.   *Perf. 13*
1278 A828 20r multi   .25   .25

Gurdwara Janam Asthan, Nankana Sahib — A829

No. 1279: a, Orange panel at left, denomination at UL. b, Dark blue panel at right, denomination at UR.

Wmk. 351

2019, Nov. 12   Litho.   *Perf. 13*
1279   Horiz. pair + central la-
          bel   .50   .50
a.-b.   A829 20r Either single .25   .25

Sri Guru Nanak Dev Ji (1469-1539), founder of Sikhism. A souvenir sheet containing perf. 11¼x13 examples of Nos. 1279a-1279b sold for 550r.

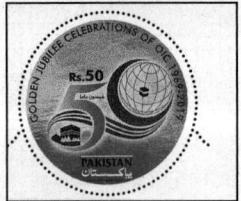

Organization of Islamic Cooperation, 50th Anniv. — A830

Wmk. 351

2019, Dec. 30   Litho.   *Perf.*
1280 A830 50r multi   .65   .65

A souvenir sheet of 1 sold for 250r.

Hakim Mohammed Said (1920-98), Medical Researcher and Governor of Sindh Province
A831

Wmk. 351

2020, Jan. 10   Litho.   *Perf. 13*
1281 A831 20r multi   .25   .25

Kashmir Solidarity Day — A832

Perf. 13¼x13

2020, Feb. 5   Litho.   **Wmk. 351**
1282 A832 20r multi   .30   .30

Presence of Afghan Refugees in Pakistan, 40th Anniv. — A833

No. 1283: a, Afghan refugees in front of building. b, Trucks and refugees. c, Refugees praying. d, Doctor examining child.

Wmk. 351

2020, Feb. 17   Litho.   *Perf. 13*
1283 A833 20r Block or vert. strip
      of 4, #a-d   1.10 1.10

No. 1283 was printed in sheets of 16 + 4 central labels.

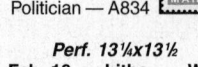

Mahmud Ali (1919-2006), Politician — A834

Perf. 13¼x13½

2020, Feb. 18   Litho.   **Wmk. 351**
1284 A834 20r multi   .30   .30

International Day Against Drug Abuse and Illicit Trafficking
A835

Perf. 13x13¼

2020, June 26   Litho.   **Wmk. 351**
1285 A835 20r multi   .25   .25

World Population Day — A836

Perf. 13¼x13

2020, July 11   Litho.   **Wmk. 351**
1286 A836 20r multi   .25   .25

Indian Reorganization Act for Jammu and Kashmir, 1st Anniv. — A837

Perf. 13x13¼

2020, Aug. 5   Litho.   **Wmk. 351**
1287 A837 58r multi   .70   .70

Shaukat Khanum Memorial Cancer Hospital and Research Center, Lahore, 25th Anniv. — A838

Perf. 13¼x13

2020, Aug. 6   Litho.   **Wmk. 351**
1288 A838 20r multi   .25   .25

Miangul Abdul Haq Jahan Zeb (1908-87), Wali of Swat State — A839

Perf. 13¼x13

2020, Sept. 14   Litho.   Wmk. 351
1289 A839 20r multi   .25   .25

United Nations, 75th Anniv. A840

Perf. 13¼ Syncopated

2020, Oct. 24   Litho.   Wmk. 351
1290 A840 20r multi   .25   .25

Breast Cancer Awareness Campaign — A841

Wmk. 351

2020, Nov. 11   Litho.   *Perf. 13*
1291 A841 20r multi   .30   .30

Political Maps of Pakistan in 2020
A842

No. 1292 — Map of Pakistan with: a, Two inset maps. b, Three inset maps, including inset map of Jammu and Kashmir disputed territory.

Wmk. 351

2020, Dec. 25   Litho.   *Perf. 13¼*
1292 A842 20r Horiz. pair, #a-b .50 .50

Karnal Sher Khan Cadet College, Swabi, 10th Anniv.
A843

Perf. 13¼ Syncopated

2021, Apr. 4   Litho.   **Wmk. 351**
1293 A843 20r multi   .30   .30

Gwadar Port, Pakistan
A844

Zhuhai Port, People's Republic of China
A845

Wmk. 351

2021, May 21   Litho.   *Perf. 14*
1294   Horiz. pair   .60   .60
a.   A844 20r multi   .30   .30
b.   A845 20r multi   .30   .30

Diplomatic relations between Pakistan and People's Republic of China, 70th anniv.

World Environment Day — A846

Perf. 13¼ Syncopated

2021, June 5   Litho.   Wmk. 351
1295 A846 20r multi   .30   .30

Discovery of Insulin, Cent.
A847

Perf. 13¼ Syncopated

2021, June 24   Litho.   Wmk. 351
1296 A847 20r multi   .30   .30

State Bank Museum, Karachi, 10th Anniv.
A848

Wmk. 351

2021, July 1   Litho.   *Perf. 13*
1297 A848 20r multi   .30   .30

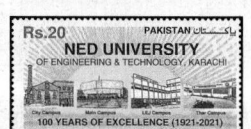

NED University of Engineering and Technology, Karachi, Cent. — A849

Wmk. 351

2021, Aug. 1   Litho.   *Perf. 13*
1298 A849 20r multi   .30   .30

National Newspaper Readership Day — A850

Perf. 13¼ Syncopated

2021, Sept. 25   Litho.   Wmk. 351
1299 A850 20r multi   .30   .30

Pakistan Telecommunication Authority, 25th Anniv. — A851

Wmk. 351

2021, Sept. 30   Litho.   *Perf. 13*
1300 A851 20r multi   .30   .30

Inauguration of 1100-Megawatt Karachi Nuclear Power Plant Unit 2 — A852

Wmk. 351

2021, Sept. 30   Litho.   Perf. 13
1301 A852 20r multi   .30   .30

University of Engineering and Technology, Lahore, Cent. — A853

Wmk. 351

2021, Nov. 1   Litho.   Perf. 13
1302 A853 20r multi   .30   .30

Johann Wolfgang von Goethe (1749-1832) and Allama Muhammad Iqbal (1877-1938), Writers — A854

Wmk. 351

2021, Nov. 9   Litho.   Perf. 13
1303 A854 20r multi   .30   .30

Diplomatic relations between Pakistan and Germany, 70th anniv.

Sinking of Indian Navy Frigate Khukri by Pakistani Submarine Hangor, 50th Anniv. — A855

Wmk. 351

2021, Dec. 9   Litho.   Perf. 13
1304 A855 20r multi   .30   .30

Diplomatic Relations Between Pakistan and Thailand, 70th Anniv. — A856

No. 1305: a, Religious statues in Pakistan. b, Temple and religious statue in Thailand.

Wmk. 351

2021, Dec. 31   Litho.   Perf. 13
1305 A856 20r Horiz. pair, #a-b   .45   .45

Parliament House, Islamabad, and Diet Building, Tokyo — A857

Perf. 13¼x13½

2022, Jan. 1   Litho.   Wmk. 351
1306 A857 20r multi   .30   .30

Diplomatic relations between Pakistan and Japan, 70th anniv. (in 2021).

Diplomatic Relations Between Pakistan and Spain, 70th Anniv. (in 2021) — A858

No. 1307: a, Plaza de Cibeles, Madrid. b, Islamia College, Peshawar.

Wmk. 351

2022, Jan. 14   Litho.   Perf. 13
1307 A858 20r Horiz. pair, #a-b   .45   .45

48th Organization of Islamic Cooperation Council of Foreign Ministers Conference, Islamabad — A859

Wmk. 351

2022, Mar. 23   Litho.   Perf. 13
1308 A859 20r multi   .30   .30

Lahore College for Women, Cent. — A860

Wmk. 351

2022, May 25   Litho.   Perf. 13
1309 A860 20r multi   .30   .30

Attock Refinery Limited, Cent. A861

Wmk. 351

2022, July 25   Litho.   Perf. 13
1310 A861 20r multi   .30   .30

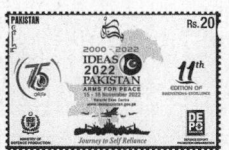

11th International Defense Exhibition and Seminar, Karachi — A862

Wmk. 351

2022, Aug. 14   Litho.   Perf. 13
1311 A862 20r multi   .30   .30

A863

A864

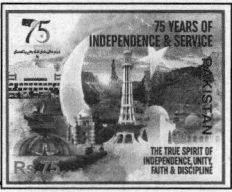

Independence, 75th Anniv. — A865

Perf. 13¼ Syncopated

2022, Aug. 14   Litho.   Wmk. 351
1312 A863 20r multi   .30   .30
1313 A864 20r multi   .30   .30

Imperf
1314 A865 75r multi   .70   .70

Pakistan Institute of International Affairs, 75th Anniv. — A866

Perf. 13¼ Syncopated

2022, Nov. 15   Litho.   Wmk. 351
1315 A866 20r multi   .30   .30

Parliament House, Islamabad, and Parliament House, Canberra — A867

Perf. 13¼x13½

2022, Nov. 15   Litho.   Wmk. 351
1316 A867 20r multi   .30   .30

Diplomatic relations between Pakistan and Australia, 75th anniv.

Ida Rieu School for the Blind and Deaf, Karachi, Cent. A868

Wmk. 351

2022, Nov. 23   Litho.   Perf. 13
1317 A868 20r multi   .30   .30

Statue of Liberty, New York and Minar-e-Pakistan, Lahore — A869

Perf. 13¼ Syncopated

2022, Dec. 27   Litho.   Wmk. 351
1318 A869 20r multi   .30   .30

Diplomatic relations between Pakistan and the United States, 75th anniv.

Asian-Pacific Postal Union, 60th Anniv. — A870

Wmk. 351

2022, Dec. 28   Litho.   Perf. 13½
1319 A870 20r multi   .30   .30

Allama Muhammad Iqbal (1877-1938), Writer — A871

Perf. 13¼x13¾

2022   Litho. & Engr.   Wmk. 351
1320 A871 68r multi   .65   .65

No. 1320 lacks 'Pakistan' inscription.

Campaign Against Violence Against Women A873

Wmk. 351

2023, Mar. 8   Litho.   Perf. 13
1322 A873 20r multi   .30   .30

International Women's Day.

SEMI-POSTAL STAMPS

Earthquake Relief — SP1

2005, Oct. 27   Litho.   Perf. 13¾x14
B1 SP1 4r +(8.50r) multi   1.25 1.25

Printed in sheets of 8 stamps +17 labels.

Child and Man at Refugee Camp — SP2

Perf. 13x13½

2009, Aug. 1   Litho.   Unwmk.
B2 SP2 5r +(7.50r) multi   2.00 2.00

Printed in sheets of eight stamps + 17 labels. Surtax for Prime Minister's Relief Fund for Swat Refugees.

OFFICIAL STAMPS

Official Stamps of India, 1939-43, Overprinted in Black

1947-49   Wmk. 196   Perf. 13½x14
O1   O8   3p slate   3.25   3.25
O2   O8   ½a dk rose vio   .60   .25
O3   O8   9p green   5.00   4.00
O4   O8   1a carmine rose   .60   .25
O4A O8   1a3p bister ('49)   15.00 42.50
O5   O8   1½a dull purple   .60   .25

O6	O8	2a scarlet	.60	.90
O7	O8	2½a purple	6.25	15.00
O8	O8	4a dk brown	1.40	1.50
O9	O8	8a blue violet	2.00	3.00

India Nos. O100-O103 Overprinted in Black

O10	A82	1r brown & slate	1.00	4.00
O11	A82	2r dk brn & dk vio	17.50	14.00
O12	A82	5r dp ultra & dk grn	40.00	67.50
		Telegraph cancel		7.50
O13	A82	10r rose car & dk vio	85.00	170.00
		Telegraph cancel		5.00
		Nos. O1-O13 (14)	178.80	326.40
		Set, hinged	90.00	

Regular Issue of 1948 Overprinted in Black or Carmine — a

"C" in "SERVICE" is nearly round.

Perf. 12½, 13, 13½x14, 14x13½

1948, Aug. 14   Unwmk.

O14	A3	3p orange red	.25	.25
O15	A3	6p purple (C)	.25	.25
O16	A3	9p dk green (C)	.40	.25
O17	A4	1a dk blue (C)	3.50	.25
O18	A4	1½a gray grn (C)	3.50	.25
O19	A4	2a orange red	2.00	.25
O20	A5	3a olive green	27.50	22.50
O21	A6	4a chocolate	3.00	.25
O22	A6	8a black (C)	3.00	10.00
O23	A5	1r ultra	1.25	.25
O24	A5	2r dark brown	12.75	10.00
O25	A5	5r carmine	60.00	27.50
O26	A7	10r rose lil, perf. 14x13½	25.00	75.00
a.		Perf. 12	35.00	80.00
b.		Perf. 13	24.00	85.00
		Nos. O14-O26 (13)	142.40	147.00
		Set, hinged	72.50	

Issued: No. O26a, 10/10/51; No. O26b, 1954(?).

Nos. 47-50 and 52 Overprinted Type "a" in Black or Carmine

1949-50   Perf. 12½, 13½x14

O27	A10	1a dark blue (C)	7.50	.25
O28	A10	1½a gray green (C)	5.00	.25
a.		Inverted ovpt.	350.00	55.00
O29	A10	2a orange red	12.50	.25
O30	A9	3a olive grn ('49)	40.00	8.00
O31	A11	8a black (C)	60.00	25.00
		Nos. O27-O31 (5)	125.00	33.75

No. O32   No. O33

No. O34

Inscribed "SERVICE"

Unwmk.

1951, Aug. 14   Engr.   Perf. 13

O32	A13	3a dark rose lake	9.25	10.00
O33	A14	4a deep green	2.40	.25
O34	A15	8a brown	13.00	12.00
		Nos. O32-O34 (3)	24.65	22.25

See Nos. 56, 58, 60.

Nos. 24-26, 47-49, 38-41 Overprinted in Black or Carmine — b

"C" in "SERVICE" is oval.

1954

O35	A3	3p orange red	.25	.25
O36	A3	6p purple (C)	.25	.25
O37	A3	9p dk green (C)	.25	.25
O38	A10	1a dk blue (C)	.25	.25

O39	A10	1½a gray grn (C)	.25	.25
O40	A10	2a orange red	.40	.25
O41	A5	1r ultra	9.00	7.50
O42	A5	2r dark brown	8.00	1.00
O43	A5	5r carmine	90.00	35.00
O43A	A7	10r rose lilac	30.00	90.00
		Nos. O35-O43A (10)	138.65	135.00

Nos. 66-72 Overprinted Type "b" in Carmine or Black

1954, Aug. 14

O44	A18	6p rose violet (C)	.25	3.50
O45	A19	9p blue (C)	4.50	13.50
O46	A19	1a carmine rose	.25	2.50
O47	A18	1½a red	.25	2.50
O48	A20	14a dk green (C)	2.75	14.00
O49	A20	1r yellow grn (C)	.90	.25
O50	A20	2r orange	8.00	.25
		Nos. O44-O50 (7)	16.90	36.50

No. 75 Overprinted in Carmine Type "b" Overprint: 13x2½mm

1955, Aug. 14   Unwmk.   Perf. 13

O51	A21	8a violet	1.75	.25

Nos. 24, 40, 66-72, 74-75, 83, 89 Overprinted in Black or Carmine — c

1957-61

O52	A3	3p org red ('58)	.25	.25
O53	A18	6p rose vio (C)	.25	.25
O54	A19	9p blue (C) ('58)	.25	.25
O55	A19	1a carmine rose	.25	.25
O56	A18	1½a red	.25	.25
O57	A24	2a red ('58)	.25	.25
O58	A21	6a dk bl (C) ('60)	.25	.25
O59	A21	8a vio (C) ('58)	.25	.25
O60	A20	14a dk grn (C) ('58)	.90	6.50
O61	A20	1r yel grn ('58)	.90	.25
O62	A20	2r orange ('58)	7.50	.25
O63	A5	5r carmine ('58)	9.00	.25
O64	A26	10r dk grn & org (C) ('61)	6.75	11.00
		Nos. O52-O64 (13)	27.05	20.25

For surcharges see Nos. O67-O73.

Nos. 110-111 Overprinted Type "c"

1961, Apr.

O65	A33	8a green	.90	.25
O66	A33	1r blue	.90	.25
a.		Inverted overprint	11.00	

New Currency

Nos. O52, O55-O57 Surcharged with New Value in Paisa

1961

O67	A18	1p on 1½a red	.25	.25
a.		Overprinted type "b"	9.00	2.00
O68	A3	2p on 3p orange red	.25	.25
a.		Overprinted type "b"	27.50	6.00
O69	A19	6p on 1a car rose		
O70	A19	7p on 1a car rose	.25	.25
a.		Overprinted type "b"	27.50	22.00
O71	A18	9p on 1½a red		
O72	A24	13p on 2a red ("PAISA")	.25	.25
O73	A24	13p on 2a red ("Paisa")		

Nos. O69, O71, O73 were locally overprinted at Mastung. On these stamps "paisa" is in lower case.
Forgeries of No. O69, O71 and O73 abound.

Nos. 125, 128 Overprinted Type "c"

1961

O74	A33	3p on 6p purple	.25	.25
O75	A33	13p on 2a copper red	.25	.25

Various violet handstamped surcharges were applied to several official stamps. Most of these repeat the denomination of the basic stamp and add the new value. Example: "4 ANNAS (25 Paisa)" on No. O33.

Nos. 129-135, 135B, 135C, 136a, 137-140a Overprinted in Carmine — d

1961-78   Perf. 13½x14

O76	A40	1p violet (II)	11.00	.25
a.		Type I	.25	.25
O77	A40	2p rose red (II)	1.25	.25
a.		Type I	.25	.25
O78	A40	3p magenta	.25	.25
O79	A40	5p ultra (II)	9.00	.25
a.		Type I	.25	.25
O80	A40	7p emerald	.25	.25
O81	A40	10p brown	.25	.25
O82	A40	13p blue violet	.25	.25
O83	A40	40p dull pur ('62)	.25	.25

O86	A40	50p dull grn ('62)	.25	.25
O87	A40	75p dk car ('62)	.30	.25
		Nos. O76-O87 (10)	23.05	2.50

1961-78   Designs Redrawn

O76b	A40	1p violet (#129b) ('63)	.25	.25
O77b	A40	2p rose red (#130b) ('64)	.25	.25
O78a	A40	3p mag (#131a) ('66)	4.00	1.25
O78b	A40	3p mag (#131b)	3.00	1.00
O79b	A40	5p ultra (#132b) ('63)	.25	.25
O80a	A40	7p emerald (#133a)	45.00	16.00
O81a	A40	10p brown (#134a) ('64)	.25	.25
O82a	A40	13p blue vio (#135a) ('63)	.25	.25
O83	A40	15p rose lil (#135B; '64)	.25	2.00
O84	A40	20p dl grn (#135C; '70)	.25	.35
O84A	A40	25p dk blue (#136a; '77)	20.00	5.00
O85a	A40	40p dull purple (#137a)	27.50	12.50
O86a	A40	50p dull grn (#138a) ('64)	.25	.25
O87a	A40	75p dark carmine (#139a)	40.00	32.50
O88	A40	90p lt ol grn (#140a) ('78)	17.50	12.50
		Nos. O76b-O88 (14)	156.00	83.60

Nos. 141, 143-144 Overprinted Type "c" in Black or Carmine

1963, Jan. 7   Unwmk.   Perf. 13½x13

O89	A41	1r vermilion	.40	.25
O90	A41	2r orange	1.50	.25
O91	A41	5r green (C)	4.00	9.00
		Nos. O89-O91 (3)	5.90	9.50

Nos. 200, 202-203 Overprinted Type "c"

1968-?   Wmk. 351   Perf. 13½x13

O92	A41	1r vermilion	4.50	1.00
O93	A41	2r orange	22.00	.25
O93A	A41	5r green (C)	47.50	13.00
		Nos. O92-O93A (3)	74.00	16.00

Nos. 459-468, 470-475 Overprinted Type "d" in Carmine or Black

1979-84

O94	A224	2p dark green	.25	.30
O95	A224	3p black	.25	.30
O96	A224	5p violet blue	.25	.30
O97	A225	10p grnsh blue	.25	.30
O98	A225	20p yel grn ('81)	.25	.25
O99	A225	25p rose car & grn ('81)	.25	.25
O100	A225	40p car & bl	.45	.25
O101	A225	50p bl grn & vio	.25	.25
O102	A225	60p black	1.75	.25
O103	A225	75p dp orange	1.75	.25
O105	A225a	1r olive ('81)	4.00	.25
O106	A225a	1.50r dp orange	.25	.30
O107	A225a	2r car rose	.25	.25
O108	A225a	3r indigo ('81)	.30	.25
O109	A225a	4r black ('84)	3.50	.50
O110	A225a	5r dk brn ('84)	3.50	.50
		Nos. O94-O110 (16)	17.50	4.80

Types A237-A239 Inscribed "SERVICE POSTAGE"

No. O111   No. O115

No. O117

1980   Litho.   Perf. 12x11½, 11½x12

O111	A237	10p dk grn & yel org	1.40	.25
O112	A237	15p dk grn & apr grn	1.40	.25
O113	A237	25p dp vio & rose car	.25	1.00
O114	A237	35p rose pink & brt yel grn	.25	7.50
O115	A238	40p red & lt brn	1.40	.25
O116	A239	50p olive & vio bl	.25	.60
O117	A239	80p blk & yel grn	.40	1.50
		Nos. O111-O117 (7)	5.35	11.35

Issued: 10p, 15p, 40p, 1/15; others, 3/10.

Nos. 613-614, 616-620 Ovptd. "SERVICE" in Red

1984-87   Litho.   Perf. 11

O118	A289	5p Kot Diji	.25	.60
O119	A289	10p Rohtas	.25	.25
O120	A289	20p Attock Fort	.30	.40
O121	A289	50p Hyderabad	.40	.40
O122	A289	60p Lahore ('86)	.45	.50

O123	A289	70p Sibi	.50	.70
O124	A289	80p Ranikot	.55	.70
		Nos. O118-O124 (7)	2.70	3.55

Issued: 10p, 9/25; 80p, 8/3/87.

No. 712 Ovptd. "SERVICE" Litho. & Engr.

1989, Dec. 24   Perf. 13

O124A	A357	1r multicolored	5.00	5.00

National Assembly, Islamabad — O1

Wmk. 351

1991-99   Litho.   Perf. 13½

O125	O1	1r green & red	.25	.25
O126	O1	2r rose car & red	.25	.25
O127	O1	3r ultra & red	.35	.25
O128	O1	4r red brown & red	.45	.25
O129	O1	5r rose lilac & red	.50	.25
O130	O1	10r brown & red	1.25	.40
		Nos. O125-O130 (6)	3.05	1.65

Issued: 10r, 2/6/99; others, 4/12/91.

1999   Unwmk.

O131	O1	2r rose car & red	.40	.25

National Assembly Type of 1991-99 Perf. 13¼x13½

2012 ?   Litho.   Wmk. 351

O132	O1	8r claret & red	.25	.25

BAHAWALPUR

LOCATION — A State of Pakistan.
AREA — 17,494 sq. mi.
POP. — 1,341,209 (1941)
CAPITAL — Bahawalpur

Bahawalpur was an Indian princely state located in the Punjab region of India. In anticipation of receipt of approval from the Imperial Government to operate its own postal system for ordinary mail, Bahawalpur ordered stamps from security printer Thomas De La Rue & Co. in London in 1933. After several years of persistence, records show that an agreement was finally reached with the Imperial Government to allow Bahawalpur to use its own "SERVICE" overprinted stamps on Official mail carried within the state boundaries beginning Jan.1, 1945.

Bahawalpur was autonomous from Aug. 15, 1947, until it acceded to Pakistan Oct. 3, 1947. These stamps had franking power solely within Bahawalpur.

Catalogue values for unused stamps in this country are for Never Hinged items.

On cover values are for a single example used on cover.

STAMPS OF INDIA USED IN BAHAWALPUR

Nos. A1 - A110 were produced locally using a rubber die. Stamps of India were overprinted as provisional stamps, immediately after Bahawalpur became an independent kingdom Aug. 15, 1947, pending receipt of machine-overprinted stamps from Nasik, India (Nos. 111 - 127). In most cases, fewer than 10 examples exist; in some as few as only one or two have been recorded. These stamps are found in somewhat toned condition.

Handstamped in Black on Regular Issues of India

No. A3

Perf. 13½x14, 14x13½

		1947, Aug. Typo.	Wmk. 196
A1	A80	9p green	—
A2	A80	1a carmine	
A3	A81	12a car lake	2,000.
A4	A82	1r brn & slate	2,500.
A5	A82	2r dk brn & dk vio	5,000.
A6	A82	10r rose car & dk vio	10,000.
A7	A83	3p slate	1,000.
A8	A83	½a rose vio	1,000.
A9	A83	9p green	1,000.
A10	A83	1a car rose	1,000.
A11	A84	1a3p yel brn	1,500.
A12	A84	2a scarlet	1,000.
A13	A84	13½a ultra	1,250.
A14	A85	4ar chocolate	1,250.
A15	A85	6a peacock bl	1,500.
A16	A85	8a blue vio	1,500.
A17	A85	12a car lake	1,500.
A18	A85	14a rose vio	2,000.
A19	A86	9p green	1,500.
A20	A86	1½a dull purple	1,500.
A21	A86	3½a ultra	2,000.
A22	A86	12a brown lake	2,500.
A23	A85	3p on 1a3p bis	1,000.

India Official Stamps Handstamped "SERVICE" Type "a" in Black

1947, Aug.

A24	A80	9p green	1,250.

"SERVICE" Type "b" Overprint

A25	A82	1r brown & slate	2,500.
A26	A82	2r dk brn & dk vio	5,000.
A27	A82	5r dp ultra & dk grn	7,500.
A28	A82	10r rose car & dk vio	10,000.
A29	O8	½a brown	1,000.
A30	O8	½a dk rose vio	1,000.
A31	O8	9p green	1,000.
A32	O8	1a car rose	1,000.
A33	O8	4a dk brown	1,000.
A34	O8	8a dk brown	1,000.

Regular Issues of India Handstamped in Purple

No. A41

No. A51

1947, Aug.

A35	A81	2a6p purple	2,000.
A36	A81	3a6p ultra	2,000.
A37	A81	4a dk brown	2,000.
A38	A82	1r brown & slate	2,500.
A39	A82	2r dk brn & dk vio	5,000.
A40	A82	5r dk brn & dk vio	
A41	A82	10r rose car & dk vio	10,000.
A42	A83	3p slate	1,000.
A43	A83	½a rose vio	1,000.
A44	A83	9p green	1,000.
A45	A83	1a car rose	1,000.
A46	A84	1a3p yel brown	1,500.
A47	A84	1½a dk purple	1,500.
A48	A84	2a scarlet	1,000.
A49	A84	3½a ultra	1,250.
A50	A85	4a chocolate	1,250.
A51	A85	6a peacock bl	1,500.
A52	A85	8a blue vio	1,500.
A53	A85	12a car lake	1,500.
A54	A81	14a rose vio	2,000.
A55	A86	3½a ultra	2,000.
A56	A86	12a brn lake	2,500.
A57	A84	3p on 1a3p bis	1,000.

Official Stamps of India Handstamped "SERVICE" Type "a" in Purple

1947, Aug.

A58	A80	½a brown	1,250.
A59	A82	1r brown & slate	2,500.
A60	A82	5r dp ultra & dk grn	7,500.
A61	A82	10r rose car & dk vio	10,000.
A62	A69	1a on 1a3p vio	2,000.
A63	O8	9p green	1,000.
A64	O9	1a car rose	1,000.
A65	O8	1a3p bister	1,000.
A66	O8	1½a dl purple	1,000.
A67	O8	2a scarlet	1,000.
A68	O8	4a dk brown	1,000.
A69	O8	8a dk brown	1,000.

Regular Issues of India Handstamped in Green

1947, Aug.

A70	A80	½a brown	—
A71	A81	2a scarlet	2,000.
A71	A81	2a scarlet	2,000.
A72	A82	10a rose car & dk vio	10,000.
A73	A83	½a rose vio	1,000.
A74	A83	9p green	1,000.
A75	A83	1a car rose	1,000.
A76	A84	1a3p yel brn	1,500.
A77	A84	2a scarlet	1,000.
A78	A84	3½a ultra	1,250.
A79	A85	4a chocolate	1,250.
A80	A85	6a peacock bl	1,500.
A81	A85	8a blue vio	1,500.
A82	A85	12a car lake	1,500.
A83	A81	14a rose vio	2,000.
A84	A86	12a brn lake	2,500.

Regular Issues of India Handstamped "SERVICE" Type "b" in Green

1947, Aug.

A85	A82	1r brown & slate	2,500.
A86	A69	1a on 1a3p vio	2,000.
A87	O8	½a dk rose vio	1,000.
A88	O9	1a car rose	1,000.

Regular Issues of India Handstamped "SERVICE" Type "b" in Red

1947, Aug.

A89	A81	3a yel green	2,000.
A90	A82	1r brown & slate	2,500.
A91	A82	2r dk brn & dk vio	5,000.
A92	A82	10r rose car & dk vio	—
A93	A83	3p slate	1,000.
A94	A83	½a rose vio	1,000.
A95	A83	9p green	1,000.
A96	A83	1a car rose	1,000.
A97	A84	1a3p yel brown	1,500.
A98	A84	2a scarlet	1,000.
A99	A84	3a violet	1,250.
A100	A85	4a chocolate	1,250.
A101	A85	8a bl vio	1,500.
A102	A85	12a car lake	1,500.
A103	A81	14a rose vio	2,000.
A104	A86	9p green	1,500.
A105	A86	1½a dl purple	1,500.
A106	A86	3½a ultra	2,000.
A107	A84	3p on 1a3p bis	1,000.

Official Stamps of India Handstamped "SERVICE" Type "b" in Red

1947, Aug.

A108	A82	2r dk brn & dk vio	5,000.
A109	A82	5r dp ultra & dk grn	7,000.
A110	A86	9p green	1,500.

Nos. A111-A127 were overprinted in Bombay using a metal die supplied by Thomas De La Rue & Co.

Stamps of India Machine Overprinted in Black or Red

1947, Aug. 15

A111	A83	3p slate (R)	150.00
A112	A83	½a rose vio	150.00
A113	A83	9p green (R)	150.00
		Hinged	100.00
A114	A83	1a car rose	150.00
A115	A84	1½a dk purple (R)	150.00
A116	A84	2a scarlet	150.00
		Hinged	100.00
a.		Double overprint	22,500.
A117	A84	3a violet (R)	150.00
		Hinged	100.00
A118	A84	3½a ultramarine	150.00
		Hinged	100.00
A119	A85	4a chocolate	150.00
		Hinged	100.00

A120	A85	6a peacock bl (R)	150.00
		Hinged	100.00
a.		Double overprint	22,500.
A121	A85	8a blue vio (R)	150.00
		Hinged	100.00
A122	A85	12a car lake	150.00
		Hinged	100.00
A123	A81	14a rose vio	375.00
A124	A82	1r brown & slate	300.00
A125	A82	2r dk brn & dk vio (R)	13,000.
A126	A82	5r dp ultra & dk grn (R)	13,000.
A127	A82	10r rose car & dk vio	13,000.

Catalogue values for unused stamps in this section, from this point to the end of the section are for Never Hinged items.

Nos. 1-29 were issued after Bahawalpur acceded to Pakistan.

Amir Muhammad Bahawal Khan I Abbasi — A1

Perf. 12½x12

		1947, Dec. 1 Wmk. 274 Engr.	
1	A1	½a brt car rose & blk	7.50 25.00

Bicentenary of the ruling family.

Nawab Sadiq Muhammad Khan V Abbasi Bahadur A2

Tombs of the Amirs A3

Mosque, Sadiq Garh — A4

Fort Dirawar — A5

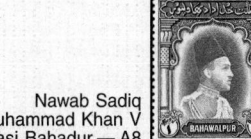

Nur-Mahal Palace — A6

Palace, Sadiq Garh — A7

Nawab Sadiq Muhammad Khan V Abbasi Bahadur — A8

A9

Perf. 12½ (A2), 12x12½ (A3, A5, A6, A7), 12½x12 (A4, A8), 13x13½ (A9)

		1948, Apr. 1 Engr.	Wmk. 274
2	A2	3p dp blue & blk	4.00 40.00
3	A2	½a lake & blk	4.00 40.00
4	A2	9p dk green & blk	4.00 40.00
5	A2	1a dp car & blk	4.00 40.00
6	A2	1½a violet & blk	6.00 40.00
7	A3	2a car & dp grn	6.00 40.00
8	A4	4a brn & org red	6.00 40.00
9	A5	6a dp bl & vio brn	6.00 40.00
10	A6	8a brt pur & car	7.00 40.00
11	A7	12a dp car & dk bl grn	10.00 70.00
12	A8	1r chocolate & vio	10.00 110.00
13	A8	2r dp mag & dk grn	4.50 200.00
14	A8	5r purple & black	4.50 240.00
15	A9	10r black & car	50.00 300.00
		Nos. 2-15 (14)	126.00 1,280.

See Nos. 18-21. For overprints see Nos. O17-O24.

Soldiers of 1848 and 1948 — A10

		1948, Oct. 15 Engr.	Perf. 11½
16	A10	1½a dp car & blk	3.00 20.00

Centenary of the Multan Campaign.

Amir Khan V and Mohammed Ali Jinnah — A11

		1948, Oct. 3	Perf. 13x12½
17	A11	1½a grn & car rose	3.00 20.00

1st anniv. of the union of Bahawalpur with Pakistan.

Types of 1948

		1948	Perf. 12x11½
18	A8	1r orange & dp grn	1.50 40.00
19	A8	2r carmine & blk	1.50 50.00
20	A8	5r ultra & red brn	1.50 85.00
			Perf. 13½
21	A9	10r green & red brn	1.50 110.00
		Nos. 18-21 (4)	6.00 285.00

Panjnad Weir — A12

		1949, Mar. 3	Perf. 14
22	A12	3p shown	1.00 20.00
23	A12	½a Wheat	1.00 20.00
24	A12	9p Cotton	1.00 20.00
25	A12	1a Sahiwal Bull	1.00 20.00
		Nos. 22-25 (4)	4.00 80.00

25th anniv. of the acquisition of full ruling powers by Amir Khan V.

UPU Monument, Bern — A13

		1949, Oct. 10 Center in Black	Perf. 13
26	A13	9p green	.30 5.00
a.		Perf. 17x17½	5.00 35.00
27	A13	1a red violet	.30 5.00
a.		Perf. 17x17½	5.00 35.00
28	A13	1½a brown orange	.30 5.00
a.		Perf. 17x17½	5.00 35.00
29	A13	2½a blue	.30 5.00
a.		Perf. 17x17½	5.00 35.00
		Nos. 26-29, O25-O28 (8)	2.40 44.00

UPU, 75th anniv. Exist perf 17½x17; value, each $3. Exist imperf.
For overprints see Nos. O25-O28.

LOCAL STAMPS

In 1924 Crown Prince Sadiq Moham-mad Khan Abbasi V became ruler of Bahawalpur.The amir ordered from security printer Thomas De La Rue & Co., London, a set of seven stamps to be used on mail within Bahawalpur in an attempt to revive the State Dawk postal service. A small number of these stamps were used on mail between special post offices at Sadiqgarh Palace and other government departments. The Imperial Government refused to authorize the use of the stamps until an agreement was reached in 1945.

Crest with State Shield — L1

1933, Feb. 3   Unwmk.   Perf. 14
1L1   L1   1a black, *grn*   25.00

Centenary of trade alliance between Bahawalpur and the British East India Company.

OFFICIAL STAMPS

> Catalogue values for unused stamps in this section, from this point to the end of the section are for Never Hinged items.

Two printings of Nos. O1-O10 exist. The first printing has brownish, streaky gum, and the second printing has clear, even gum.

Panjnad Weir — O1

Camel and Calf — O2

Antelopes — O3

Pelicans — O4

Juma Masjid Palace, Fort Derawar — O5

Temple at Pattan Munara — O6

SARKARI

SARKARK

Red Overprint
Wmk. 274

1945, Jan. 1   Engr.   Perf. 14

O1	O1	½a brt grn & blk	40.00 25.00
		Hinged	25.00
O2	O2	1a carmine & blk	7.50 25.00
		Hinged	5.00
O3	O3	2a violet & blk	7.50 25.00
		Hinged	5.00
O4	O4	4a olive & blk	45.00 65.00
		Hinged	30.00
O5	O5	8a brown & blk	100.00 35.00
		Hinged	65.00
O6	O6	1r orange & blk	115.00 35.00
		Hinged	75.00
		Nos. O1-O6 (6)	315.00 210.00

For types overprinted, see Nos. O7-O9, O11-O13.

Two stamps exist overprinted in black on unwatermarked revenue stamps. The 1a black on green shows crest with state shield. Value, $750 never hinged, $500 hinged, $25,000 on cover. The 1a brown & black shows type O2. Value, $750 never hinged, $500 hinged, $5,000 on cover.

Camels — O7

Unwmk.
1945, Mar. 10   Engr.   Perf. 14
Red Overprint
O7	O7	1a brown & black	300.00 150.00
		Hinged	200.00

Black Overprint & Surcharge

1945, Mar.-May   Unwmk.
O8	O5	½a on 8a lake & blk	30.00 10.00
		Hinged	20.00
O9	O6	1½a on 1r org & blk	110.00 16.00
		Hinged	75.00
O10	O1	1½a on 2r ultra & blk	400.00 15.00
		Hinged	250.00
		Nos. O8-O10 (3)	540.00 41.00

Black Overprint

Wmk. 274
1945, June   Engr.   Perf. 14
O11	O1	1½a carmine & black	5.00 15.00
		Hinged	3.00
O12	O2	1a carmine & black	8.00 17.00
		Hinged	5.00
O13	O3	2a orange & black	12.00 75.00
		Hinged	8.00
		Nos. O11-O13 (3)	25.00 107.00

Nawab Sadiq Muhammad Khan V Abbasi Bahadur — O8

Unwmk.
1945, Sept.   Engr.   Perf. 14
O14	O8	3p dp blue & blk	18.00 30.00
		Hinged	12.00
O15	O8	1½a dp violet & blk	50.00 12.00
		Hinged	35.00

Flags of Allied Nations — O9

Unwmk.
1946, May 1   & Litho.   Perf. 14
O16	O9	1½a emerald & gray	15.00 10.00
		Hinged	10.00

Victory of Allied Nations in World War II.

Nos. O17-O28 were issued after Bahawalpur acceded to Pakistan.

Stamps of 1948 Overprinted in Carmine or Black

Perf. 12½, 12½x12, 12x11½, 13½
1948   Wmk. 274
O17	A2	3p dp bl & blk (C)	1.50 25.00
O18	A2	1a dp carmine & blk	1.50 25.00
O19	A3	2a car & dp grn	1.50 25.00
O20	A4	4a brown & org red	1.50 25.00
O21	A8	1r org & dp grn (C)	1.50 30.00
O22	A8	2r car & blk (C)	1.50 35.00
O23	A8	5r ultra & red brn (C)	1.50 75.00
O24	A9	10rgrn & red brn (C)	1.50 75.00
		Nos. O17-O24 (8)	12.00 315.00

Same Ovpt. in Carmine on #26-29

1949   Center in Black   Perf. 13, 18
O25	A13	9p green	.30 6.00
a.		Perf. 17x17½	4.00 40.00
O26	A13	1a red violet	.30 6.00
a.		Perf. 17x17½	4.00 40.00
O27	A13	1½a brown orange	.30 6.00
a.		Perf. 17x17½	4.00 40.00
O28	A13	2½a blue	.30 6.00
a.		Perf. 17x17½	4.00 40.00
		Nos. O25-O28 (4)	1.20 24.00

75th anniv. of the UPU.
Exist imperf.

PALAU
pə-'lau

LOCATION — Group of 100 islands in the West Pacific Ocean about 1,000 miles southeast of Manila
AREA — 179 sq. mi.
POP. — 18,467 (1999 est.)
CAPITAL — Melekeok

Palau, the western section of the Caroline Islands (Micronesia), was part of the US Trust Territory of the Pacific, established in 1947. By agreement with the USPS, the republic began issuing its own stamps in 1984, with the USPS continuing to carry the mail to and from the islands.

On Jan. 10, 1986 Palau became a Federation as a Sovereign State in Compact of Free Association with the US.

100 Cents = 1 Dollar

> Catalogue values for all unused stamps in this country are for Never Hinged items.

Inauguration of Postal Service — A1

1983, Mar. 10   Litho.   Perf. 14
1	A1	20c Constitution preamble	.55 .55
2	A1	20c Hunters	.55 .55
3	A1	20c Fish	.55 .55
4	A1	20c Preamble, diff.	.55 .55
a.		Block of 4, #1-4	2.75 2.75

Palau Fruit Dove — A2

1983, May 16   Perf. 15
5	A2	20c shown	.45 .45
6	A2	20c Palau morningbird	.45 .45
7	A2	20c Giant white-eye	.45 .45
8	A2	20c Palau fantail	.45 .45
a.		Block of 4, #5-8	2.50 2.50

Sea Fan — A3

3c, Map cowrie. 5c, Jellyfish. 10c, Hawksbill turtle. 13c, Giant Clam. 20c, Parrotfish. 28c, Chambered Nautilus. 30c, Dappled sea cucumber. 37c, Sea Urchin. 50c, Starfish. $1, Squid. $2, Dugong. $5, Pink sponge.

1983-84   Litho.   Perf. 13½x14
9	A3	1c shown	.25 .25
10	A3	3c multicolored	.25 .25
11	A3	5c multicolored	.25 .25
12	A3	10c multicolored	.25 .25
13	A3	13c multicolored	.25 .25
a.		Booklet pane of 10	10.00
b.		Bkt. pane of 10 (5 #13, 5 #14)	12.00 —
14	A3	20c multicolored	.35 .35
b.		Booklet pane of 10	11.00
15	A3	28c multicolored	.45 .45
16	A3	30c multicolored	.50 .50
17	A3	37c multicolored	.55 .55
18	A3	50c multicolored	.80 .80
19	A3	$1 multicolored	1.60 1.60

Perf. 15x14
20	A3	$2 multicolored	4.25 4.25
21	A3	$5 multicolored	10.50 10.50
		Nos. 9-21 (13)	20.25 20.25

See Nos. 75-85.

Humpback Whale, World Wildlife Emblem — A4

1983, Sept. 21   Perf. 14
24	A4	20c shown	1.25 1.25
25	A4	20c Blue whale	1.25 1.25
26	A4	20c Fin whale	1.25 1.25
27	A4	20c Great sperm whale	1.25 1.25
a.		Block of 4, #24-27	6.50 6.50

Christmas 1983 — A5

Paintings by Charlie Gibbons, 1971 — No. 28, First Child ceremony. No. 29, Spearfishing from Red Canoe. No. 30, Traditional feast at the Bai. No. 31, Taro gardening. No. 32, Spearfishing at New Moon.

1983, Oct.   Litho.   Perf. 14½
28	A5	20c multicolored	.50 .50
29	A5	20c multicolored	.50 .50
30	A5	20c multicolored	.50 .50
31	A5	20c multicolored	.50 .50
32	A5	20c multicolored	.50 .50
a.		Strip of 5, #28-32	2.75 2.75

A6   Capt. Wilson's Voyage, Bicentennial — A7

No. 33, Capt. Henry Wilson. No. 34, Approaching Pelew. No. 35, Englishman's Camp on Ulong. No. 36, Prince Lee Boo. No. 37, King Abba Thulle. No. 38, Mooring in Koror. No. 39, Village scene of Pelew Islands. No. 40, Ludee.

1983, Dec. 14   Perf. 14x15
33 A6 20c multicolored   .45   .45
34 A7 20c multicolored   .45   .45
35 A7 20c multicolored   .45   .45
36 A6 20c multicolored   .45   .45
37 A7 20c multicolored   .45   .45
38 A7 20c multicolored   .45   .45
39 A7 20c multicolored   .45   .45
40 A6 20c multicolored   .45   .45
 a. Block or strip of 8, #33-40   5.00 5.00

Local Seashells — A8

Shell paintings (dorsal and ventral) by Deborah Dudley Max.

1984, Mar. 15   Litho.   Perf. 14
41 A8 20c Triton trumpet, d.   .45   .45
42 A8 20c Horned helmet, d.   .45   .45
43 A8 20c Giant clam, d.   .45   .45
44 A8 20c Laciniate conch, d.   .45   .45
45 A8 20c Royal cloak scallop, d.   .45   .45
46 A8 20c Triton trumpet, v.   .45   .45
47 A8 20c Horned helmet, v.   .45   .45
48 A8 20c Giant clam, v.   .45   .45
49 A8 20c Laciniate conch, v.   .45   .45
50 A8 20c Royal cloak scallop, v.   .45   .45
 a. Block of 10, #41-50   5.50 5.50

Explorer Ships — A9

1984, June 19   Litho.   Perf. 14
51 A9 40c Oroolong, 1783   .85   .85
52 A9 40c Duff, 1797   .85   .85
53 A9 40c Peiho, 1908   .85   .85
54 A9 40c Albatross, 1885   .85   .85
 a. Block of 4, #51-54   4.25 4.25

UPU Congress.

Ausipex '84 A10

Fishing Methods: No. 55, Throw spear fishing. No. 56, Kite fishing. No. 57, Underwater spear fishing. No. 58, Net fishing.

1984, Sept. 6   Litho.   Perf. 14
55 A10 20c multicolored   .40   .40
56 A10 20c multicolored   .40   .40
57 A10 20c multicolored   .40   .40
58 A10 20c multicolored   .40   .40
 a. Block of 4, #55-58   2.25 2.25

Christmas Flowers — A11

No. 59, Mountain Apple. No. 60, Beach Morning Glory. No. 61, Turmeric. No. 62, Plumeria.

1984, Nov. 28   Litho.   Perf. 14
59 A11 20c multicolored   .40   .40
60 A11 20c multicolored   .40   .40
61 A11 20c multicolored   .40   .40
62 A11 20c multicolored   .40   .40
 a. Block of 4, #59-62   2.00 2.00

Audubon Bicentenary A12

1985, Feb. 6   Litho.   Perf. 14
63 A12 22c Shearwater chick   .85   .85
64 A12 22c Shearwater's head   .85   .85
65 A12 22c Shearwater in flight .85   .85
66 A12 22c Swimming   .85   .85
 a. Block of 4, #63-66   4.50 4.50
  Nos. 63-66,C5 (5)   4.50 4.50

Canoes and Rafts A13

1985, Mar. 27   Litho.
67 22c Cargo canoe   .55   .55
68 22c War canoe   .55   .55
69 22c Bamboo raft   .55   .55
70 22c Racing/sailing canoe .55   .55
 a. A13 Block of 4, #67-70 2.25 2.25

Marine Life Type of 1983
14c, Trumpet triton. 22c, Bumphead parrotfish. 25c, Soft coral, damsel fish. 33c, Sea anemone, clownfish. 39c, Green sea turtle. 44c, Pacific sailfish. $10, Spinner dolphins.

1985, June 11   Litho.   Perf. 14½x14
75 A3 14c multicolored   .30   .30
 a.   Booklet pane of 10   8.50   —
76 A3 22c multicolored   .55   .55
 a.   Booklet pane of 10   10.50   —
 b.   Booklet pane, 5 14c, 5 22c 12.00 —
77 A3 25c multicolored   .60   .60
79 A3 33c multicolored   .80   .80
80 A3 39c multicolored   .95   .95
81 A3 44c multicolored   1.10 1.10

**   Perf. 15x14**
85 A3 $10 multicolored   19.00 19.00
  Nos. 75-85 (7)   23.30 23.30

A14

IYY emblem and children of all nationalities joined in a circle.

1985, July 15   Litho.   Perf. 14
86 A14 44c multicolored   .85   .85
87 A14 44c multicolored   .85   .85
88 A14 44c multicolored   .85   .85
89 A14 44c multicolored   .85   .85
 a. Block of 4, #86-89   3.75 3.75

No. 89a has a continuous design.

A15

Christmas: Island mothers and children.

1985, Oct. 21   Litho.   Perf. 14
90 A15 14c multicolored   .35   .35
91 A15 22c multicolored   .50   .50
92 A15 33c multicolored   .80   .80
93 A15 44c multicolored   1.10 1.10
  Nos. 90-93 (4)   2.75 2.75

Souvenir Sheet

Pan American Airways Martin M-130 China Clipper — A16

1985, Nov. 21   Litho.   Perf. 14
94 A16 $1 multicolored   2.50 2.50
1st Trans-Pacific Mail Flight, Nov. 22, 1935. See Nos. C10-C13.

Return of Halley's Comet — A17

Fictitious local sightings — No. 95, Kaeb canoe, 1758. No. 96, U.S.S. Vincennes, 1835. No. 97, S.M.S. Scharnhorst, 1910. No. 98, Yacht, 1986.

1985, Dec. 21   Litho.   Perf. 14
95 A17 44c multicolored   .80   .80
96 A17 44c multicolored   .80   .80
97 A17 44c multicolored   .80   .80
98 A17 44c multicolored   .80   .80
 a. Block of 4, #95-98   4.00 4.00

Songbirds — A18

No. 99, Mangrove flycatcher. No. 100, Cardinal honeyeater. No. 101, Blue-faced parrotfinch. No. 102, Dusky and bridled white-eyes.

1986, Feb. 24   Litho.   Perf. 14
99   A18 44c multicolored   .85   .85
100 A18 44c multicolored   .85   .85
101 A18 44c multicolored   .85   .85
102 A18 44c multicolored   .85   .85
 a. Block of 4, #99-102   4.00 4.00

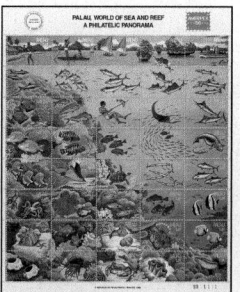

World of Sea and Reef A19

Designs: a, Spear fisherman. b, Native raft. c, Sailing canoes. d, Rock islands, sailfish. e, Inter-island boat, flying fish. f, Bonefish. g, Common jack. h, Mackerel. i, Sailfish. j, Barracuda. k, Triggerfish. l, Dolphinfish. m, Spear fisherman, grouper. n, Manta ray. o, Marlin. p, Parrotfish. q, Wrasse. r, Red snapper. s, Herring. t, Dugong. u, Surgeonfish. v, Leopard ray. w, Hawksbill turtle. x, Needlefish. y, Tuna. z, Octopus. aa, Clownfish. ab, Squid. ac, Grouper. ad, Moorish idol. ae, Queen conch, starfish. af, Squirrelfish. ag, Starfish, sting ray. ah, Lion fish. ai, Angel fish. aj, Butterfly fish. ak, Spiny lobster. al, Mangrove crab. am, Tridacna. an, Moray eel.

1986, May 22   Litho.   Perf. 15x14
103   Sheet of 40   37.50
 a.-an.   A19 14c any single   .75   .50
AMERIPEX '86, Chicago, May 22-June 1 See Nos. 854, 1326.

Seashells — A20

1986, Aug. 1   Litho.   Perf. 14
104 A20 22c Commercial trochus .55   .55
105 A20 22c Marble cone   .55   .55
106 A20 22c Fluted giant clam   .55   .55
107 A20 22c Bullmouth helmet   .55   .55
108 A20 22c Golden cowrie   .55   .55
 a. Strip of 5, #104-108   3.25 3.25

See Nos. 150-154, 191-195, 212-216.

Intl. Peace Year A21

1986, Sept. 19   Litho.
109 22c Soldier's helmet   .75   .75
110 22c Plane wreckage   .75   .75
111 22c Woman playing guitar   .75   .75
112 22c Airai vista   .75   .75
 a. A21 Block of 4, #109-112   3.50 3.50
  Nos. 109-112,C17 (5)   4.00 4.00

Reptiles — A22

1986, Oct. 28   Litho.   Perf. 14
113 A22 22c Gecko   .65   .65
114 A22 22c Emerald tree skink   .65   .65
115 A22 22c Estuarine crocodile   .65   .65
116 A22 22c Leatherback turtle   .65   .65
 a. Block of 4, #113-116   2.75 2.75

Christmas — A23

Joy to the World, carol by Isaac Watts and Handel: No. 117, Girl playing guitar, boys, goat. No. 118, Girl carrying bouquet, boys singing. No. 119, Palauan mother and child. No. 120, Children, baskets of fruit. No. 121, Girl, fairy tern. Nos. 117-121 printed in a continuous design.

1986, Nov. 26   Litho.
117 A23 22c multicolored   .40   .40
118 A23 22c multicolored   .40   .40
119 A23 22c multicolored   .40   .40
120 A23 22c multicolored   .40   .40
121 A23 22c multicolored   .40   .40
 a. Strip of 5, #117-121   2.50 2.50

Butterflies — A23a

No. 121B, Tangadik, soursop. No. 121C, Dira amartal, sweet orange. No. 121D, Ilhuochel, swamp cabbage. No. 121E, Bauosech, fig.

1987, Jan. 5   Litho.   Perf. 14
121B A23a 44c multicolored   1.00   .90
121C A23a 44c multicolored   1.00   .90
121D A23a 44c multicolored   1.00   .90
121E A23a 44c multicolored   1.00   .90
 f. Block of 4, #121B-121E 4.50 4.50

See Nos. 183-186.

Fruit Bats A24

1987, Feb. 23   **Litho.**
122	44c	In flight	.85	.85
123	44c	Hanging	.85	.85
124	44c	Eating	.85	.85
125	44c	Head	.85	.85
a.		A24 Block of 4, #122-125	4.00	4.00

Indigenous Flowers — A25

1c, Ixora casei. 3c, Lumnitzera littorea. 5c, Sonneratia alba. 10c, Tristellateia australasiae. 14c, Bikkia palauensis. 15c, Limnophila aromatica. 22c, Bruguiera gymnorhiza. 25c, Fagraea ksid. 36c, Ophiorrhiza palauensis. 39c, Cerbera manghas. 44c, Sandera indica. 45c, Maesa canfieldiae. 50c, Dolichandrone spathacea. $1, Barringtonia racemosa. $2, Nepenthes mirabilis. $5, Dendrobium palawense. $10, Bouquet.

1987-88   **Litho.**   **Perf. 14**
126	A25	1c multicolored	.25	.25
127	A25	3c multicolored	.25	.25
128	A25	5c multicolored	.25	.25
129	A25	10c multicolored	.25	.25
130	A25	14c multicolored	.25	.25
a.		Booklet pane of 10	4.00	
131	A25	15c multi ('88)	.25	.25
a.		Booklet pane of 10 ('88)	3.25	
132	A25	22c multicolored	.40	.40
a.		Booklet pane of 10	6.50	—
b.		Booklet pane, 5 each 14c, 22c	6.50	—
133	A25	25c multi ('88)	.50	.50
a.		Booklet pane of 10 ('88)	5.00	—
b.		Booklet pane, 5 each 15c, 25c ('88)	5.00	
134	A25	36c multi ('88)	.65	.65
135	A25	39c multi ('88)	.70	.70
136	A25	44c multicolored	.85	.85
137	A25	45c multi ('88)	.90	.90
138	A25	50c multicolored	1.00	1.00
139	A25	$1 multicolored	2.00	2.00
140	A25	$2 multicolored	4.25	4.00
141	A25	$5 multicolored	10.00	9.50

Size: 49x28mm
142	A25	$10 multi ('88)	17.00	16.00
		Nos. 126-142 (17)	39.75	38.00

Issued: 3/12; $10, 3/17; 15c, 25c, 36c, 45c, 7/1; #131a, 133a-133b, 7/5.

CAPEX '87 — A26

1987, June 15   **Litho.**   **Perf. 14**
146	22c	Babeldaob Is.	.50	.50
147	22c	Floating Garden Isls.	.50	.50
148	22c	Rock Is.	.50	.50
149	22c	Koror	.50	.50
a.		A26 Block of 4, #146-149	2.25	2.25

Seashells Type of 1986

1987, Aug. 25   **Litho.**   **Perf. 14**
150	A20	22c Black-striped triton	.55	.55
151	A20	22c Tapestry turban	.55	.55
152	A20	22c Adusta murex	.55	.55
153	A20	22c Little fox miter	.55	.55
154	A20	22c Cardinal miter	.55	.55
a.		Strip of 5, #150-154	3.00	3.00

US Constitution Bicentennial — A27

Excerpts from Articles of the Palau and US Constitutions and Seals: No. 155, Art. VIII, Sec. 1, Palau. No. 156, Presidential seals. No. 157, Art. II, Sec. 1, US. No. 158, Art. IX, Sec. 1, Palau. No. 159, Legislative seals. No. 160,

Art. I, Sec. 1, US. No. 161, Art X, Sec. 1, Palau. No. 162, Supreme Court seals. No. 163, Art. III, Sec. 1, US.

1987, Sept. 17   **Litho.**   **Perf. 14**
155	A27	14c multicolored	.25	.25
156	A27	14c multicolored	.25	.25
157	A27	14c multicolored	.25	.25
a.		Triptych + label, #155-157	.80	.80
158	A27	22c multicolored	.40	.40
159	A27	22c multicolored	.40	.40
160	A27	22c multicolored	.40	.40
a.		Triptych + label, #158-160	1.50	1.50
161	A27	44c multicolored	.75	.75
162	A27	44c multicolored	.75	.75
163	A27	44c multicolored	.75	.75
a.		Triptych + label, #161-163	3.00	3.00
		Nos. 155-163 (9)	4.20	4.20

Nos. 156, 159 and 162 are each 28x42mm. Labels picture national flags.

Japanese Links to Palau — A28

Japanese stamps, period cancellations and installations: 14c, No. 257 and 1937 Datsun sedan used as mobile post office, near Ngerchelechuus Mountain. 22c, No. 347 and phosphate mine at Angaur. 33c, No. B1 and Japan Airways DC-2 over stone monuments at Badrulchau. 44c, No. 201 and Japanese post office, Koror. $1, Aviator's Grave, Japanese Cemetary, Peleliu, vert.

1987, Oct. 16   **Litho.**   **Perf. 14x13½**
164	A28	14c multicolored	.30	.30
165	A28	22c multicolored	.45	.45
166	A28	33c multicolored	.65	.65
167	A28	44c multicolored	.85	.85
		Nos. 164-167 (4)	2.25	2.25

Souvenir Sheet
Perf. 13½x14
168	A28	$1 multicolored	2.25	2.25

Christmas — A30

Verses from carol "I Saw Three Ships," Biblical characters, landscape and Palauans in outrigger canoes.

1987, Nov. 24   **Litho.**   **Perf. 14**
173	A30	22c I saw...	.50	.50
174	A30	22c And what was...	.50	.50
175	A30	22c 'Twas Joseph...	.50	.50
176	A30	22c Saint Michael...	.50	.50
177	A30	22c And all the bells...	.50	.50
a.		Strip of 5, #173-177	3.00	3.00

Symbiotic Marine Species — A31

#178, Snapping shrimp, goby. #179, Mauve vase sponge, sponge crab. #180, Pope's damselfish, cleaner wrasse. #181, Clown anemone fish, sea anemone. #182, Four-color nudibranch, banded coral shrimp.

1987, Dec. 11   **Litho.**   **Perf. 14**
178	A31	22c multicolored	.55	.55
179	A31	22c multicolored	.55	.55
180	A31	22c multicolored	.55	.55
181	A31	22c multicolored	.55	.55
182	A31	22c multicolored	.55	.55
a.		Strip of 5, #178-182	3.25	3.25

Butterflies and Flowers Type of 1987

Designs: No. 183, Dannaus plexippus, Tournefotia argentia. No. 184, Papilio machaon, Citrus reticulata. No. 185, Captopsilia, Crataeva speciosa. No. 186, Colias philodice, Crataeva speciosa.

1988, Jan. 25
183	A23a	44c multicolored	.75	.75
184	A23a	44c multicolored	.75	.75
185	A23a	44c multicolored	.75	.75
186	A23a	44c multicolored	.75	.75
a.		Block of 4, #183-186	3.50	3.50

Ground-dwelling Birds — A32

1988, Feb. 29   **Litho.**   **Perf. 14**
187	A32	44c Whimbrel	.75	.75
188	A32	44c Yellow bittern	.75	.75
189	A32	44c Rufous night-heron	.75	.75
190	A32	44c Banded rail	.75	.75
a.		Block of 4, #187-190	3.50	3.50

Seashells Type of 1986

1988, May 11   **Litho.**   **Perf. 14**
191	A20	25c Striped engina	.55	.55
192	A20	25c Ivory cone	.55	.55
193	A20	25c Plaited miter	.55	.55
194	A20	25c Episcopal miter	.55	.55
195	A20	25c Isabelle cowrie	.55	.55
a.		Strip of 5, #191-195	4.00	4.00

Souvenir Sheet

Postal Independence, 5th Anniv. — A33

FINLANDIA '88: a, Kaep (pre-European outrigger sailboat). b, Spanish colonial cruiser. c, German colonial cruiser SMS Cormoran, c. 1885. d, Japanese mailbox, WWII machine gun, Koror Museum. e, US Trust Territory ship, Malakal Harbor. f, Koror post office.

1988, June 8   **Litho.**   **Perf. 14**
196	A33	Sheet of 6	3.00	3.00
a.-f.		25c multicolored	.45	.45

Souvenir Sheet

US Possessions Phil. Soc., 10th Anniv. — A34

PRAGA '88: a, "Collect Palau Stamps," original artwork for No. 196f and head of a man. b, Soc. emblem. c, Nos. 1-4. d, China Clipper original artwork and covers. e, Man and boy studying covers. f, Girl at show cancel booth.

1988, Aug. 26   **Litho.**   **Perf. 14**
197	A34	Sheet of 6	5.00	5.00
a.-f.		45c any single	.80	.80

Christmas — A35

Hark! The Herald Angels Sing: No. 198, Angels playing the violin, singing and sitting. No. 199, 3 angels and 3 children. No. 200, Nativity. No. 201, 2 angels, birds. No. 202, 3 children and 2 angels playing horns. Se-tenant in a continuous design.

1988, Nov. 7   **Litho.**   **Perf. 14**
198	A35	25c multicolored	.50	.50
199	A35	25c multicolored	.50	.50
200	A35	25c multicolored	.50	.50
201	A35	25c multicolored	.50	.50
202	A35	25c multicolored	.50	.50
a.		Strip of 5, #199-202 + 5 labels	2.75	2.75

Printed in sheets containing 3 strips + 5 labels.

Miniature Sheet

Chambered Nautilus — A36

Designs: a, Fossil and cross section. b, Palauan *bai* symbols for the nautilus. c, Specimens trapped for scientific study. d, *Nautilus belauensis, pompilius, macromphalus, stenomphalus* and *scrobiculatus*. e, Release of a tagged nautilus.

1988, Dec. 23   **Litho.**   **Perf. 14**
203	A36	Sheet of 5	3.00	3.00
a.-e.		25c multicolored	.60	.60

Endangered Birds of Palau — A37

No. 204, Nicobar pigeon. No. 205, Ground dove. No. 206, Micronesian megapode. No. 207, Owl.

1989, Feb. 9   **Litho.**   **Perf. 14**
204	A37	45c multicolored	.85	.85
205	A37	45c multicolored	.85	.85
206	A37	45c multicolored	.85	.85
207	A37	45c multicolored	.85	.85
a.		Block of 4, #204-207	4.00	4.00

Exotic Mushrooms A38

1989, Mar. 16   **Litho.**   **Perf. 14**
208	A38	45c Gilled auricularia	.90	.80
209	A38	45c Rock mushroom	.90	.80
210	A38	45c Polyporous	.90	.80
211	A38	45c Veiled stinkhorn	.90	.80
a.		Block of 4, #208-211	4.00	4.00

Seashells Type of 1986

No. 212, Robin redbreast triton. No. 213, Hebrew cone. No. 214, Tadpole triton. No. 215, Lettered cone. No. 216, Rugose miter.

1989, Apr. 12   **Litho.**   **Perf. 14x14½**
212	A20	25c multicolored	.55	.55
213	A20	25c multicolored	.55	.55
214	A20	25c multicolored	.55	.55
215	A20	25c multicolored	.55	.55
216	A20	25c multicolored	.55	.55
a.		Strip of 5, #212-216	3.25	3.25

Souvenir Sheet

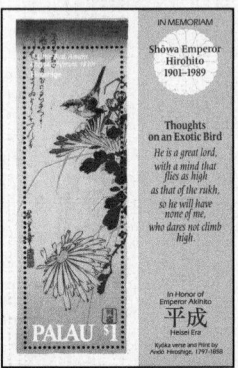

A Little Bird, Amidst Chrysanthemums, 1830s, by Hiroshige (1797-1858) — A39

1989, May 17   **Litho.**   **Perf. 14**
217	A39	$1 multicolored	2.25	2.25

Hirohito (1901-1989) and enthronement of Akihito as emperor of Japan.

Miniature Sheet

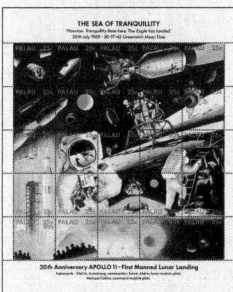

THE SEA OF TRANQUILITY

First
Moon
Landing,
20th
Anniv.
A40

Apollo 11 mission: a, Third stage jettison. b, Lunar spacecraft. c, Module transposition (*Eagle*). d, *Columbia* module transposition (command module). e, *Columbia* module transposition (service module). f, Third stage burn. g, Vehicle entering orbit, Moon. h, *Columbia* and *Eagle*. i, *Eagle* on the Moon. j, *Eagle* in space. k, Three birds, Saturn V third stage, lunar spacecraft and escape tower. l, Astronaut's protective visor, pure oxygen system. m, Astronaut, American flag. n, Footsteps on lunar plain Sea of Tranquillity, pure oxygen system. o, Armstrong descending from *Eagle*. p, Mobile launch tower, Saturn V second stage. q, Space suit remote control unit and oxygen hoses. r, *Eagle* lift-off from Moon. s, Armstrong's first step on the Moon. t, Armstrong descending ladder, module transposition (*Eagle* and *Columbia*). u, Launch tower, spectators and Saturn V engines achieving thrust. v, Spectators, clouds of backwash. w, Parachute splashdown, U.S. Navy recovery ship and helicopter. x, Command module reentry. y, Jettison of service module prior to reentry.

1989, July 20   Litho.   Perf. 14
218 A40 Sheet of 25   12.00 12.00
a.-y. 25c any single   .45   .45

Buzz Aldrin
Photographed on
the Moon by Neil
Armstrong — A41

1989, July 20   Perf. 13½x14
219 A41 $2.40 multicolored   4.75 4.75
First Moon landing 20th anniv.

Literacy
A42

Imaginary characters and children reading: a, Youth astronaut. b, Boy riding dolphin. c, Cheshire cat in palm tree. d, Mother Goose. e, New York Yankee at bat. f, Girl reading. g, Boy reading. h, Mother reading to child. i, Girl holding flower and listening to story. j, Boy dressed in baseball uniform. Printed se-tenant in a continuous design.

1989, Oct. 13   Litho.   Perf. 14
220 A42 Block of 10   4.75 4.75
a.-j. 25c any single   .40   .40

No. 220 printed in sheets containing two blocks of ten with strip of 5 labels between. Inscribed labels contain book, butterflies and "Give Them / Books / Give Them / Wings." Value, sheet $15.

Miniature Sheet

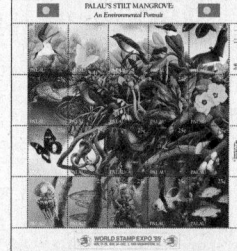

PALAU'S STILT MANGROVE
An Environmental Portrait

Stilt Mangrove Fauna — A43

World Stamp Expo '89: a, Bridled tern. b, Sulphur butterfly. c, Mangrove flycatcher. d, Collared kingfisher. e, Fruit bat. f, Estuarine crocodile. g, Rufous night-heron. h, Stilt mangrove. i, Bird's nest fern. j, Beach hibiscus tree. k, Common eggfly. l, Dog-faced watersnake. m, Jingle shell. n, Palau bark cricket. o, Periwinkle, mangrove oyster. p, Jellyfish. q, Striped mullet. r, Mussels, sea anemones, algae. s, Cardinalfish. t, Snapper.

1989, Nov. 20   Litho.   Perf. 14½
221 A43 Block of 20   12.00 12.00
a.-t. 25c any single   .55   .55

Christmas — A44

Whence Comes this Rush of Wings? a carol: No. 222, Dusky tern, Audubon's shearwater, angels, island. No. 223, Fruit pigeon, angel. No. 224, Madonna and Child, ground pigeons, fairy terns, rails, sandpipers. No. 225, Angel, blue-headed green finch, red flycatcher, honeyeater. No. 226, Angel, black-headed gulls. Printed se-tenant in a continuous design.

1989, Dec. 18   Litho.   Perf. 14
222 A44 25c multicolored   .55 .55
223 A44 25c multicolored   .55 .55
224 A44 25c multicolored   .55 .55
225 A44 25c multicolored   .55 .55
226 A44 25c multicolored   .55 .55
a. Strip of 5, #222-226   3.25 3.25

PALAU 25

Soft Coral — A45

1990, Jan. 3
227 A45 25c Pink coral   .50 .50
228 A45 25c Pink & violet coral .50 .50
229 A45 25c Yellow coral   .50 .50
230 A45 25c Red coral   .50 .50
a. Block of 4, #227-230   3.00 3.00

Birds of the
Forest — A46

1990, Mar. 16
231 A46 45c Siberian rubythroat   .85 .85
232 A46 45c Palau bush-warbler   .85 .85
233 A46 45c Micronesian starling .85 .85
234 A46 45c Cicadabird   .85 .85
a. Block of 4, #231-234   4.00 4.00

Miniature Sheet

PALAU'S PRINCE LEE BOO
IN ENGLAND

ULONG (OROOLONG)

State Visit of Prince Lee Boo of Palau
to England, 1784 — A47

Prince Lee Boo, Capt. Henry Wilson and: a, HMS *Victory* docked at Portsmouth. b, St. James's Palace, London. c, Rotherhithe Docks, London. d, Capt. Wilson's residence, Devon. e, Lunardi's Grand English Air Balloon. f, St. Paul's and the Thames. g, Lee Boo's tomb, St. Mary's Churchyard, Rotherhithe. h, St. Mary's Church. i, Memorial tablet, St. Mary's Church.

1990, May 6   Litho.   Perf. 14
235 A47 Sheet of 9   4.50 4.50
a.-i. 25c any single   .45   .45

Stamp World London '90.

Souvenir Sheet

PALAU

Penny
Black,
150th
Anniv.
A48

1990, May 6
236 A48 $1 Great Britain #1   2.00 2.00

Orchids — A49

No. 237, Corymborkis veratrifolia. No. 238, Malaxis setipes. No. 239, Dipodium freycinetianum. No. 240, Bulbophyllum micronesiacum. No. 241, Vanda teres and hookeriana.

1990, June 7   Perf. 14
237 A49 45c multicolored   .90 .90
238 A49 45c multicolored   .90 .90
239 A49 45c multicolored   .90 .90
240 A49 45c multicolored   .90 .90
241 A49 45c multicolored   .90 .90
a. Strip of 5, #237-241   5.00 5.00

Butterflies and
Flowers — A50

No. 242, Wedelia strigulosa. No. 243, Erthrina variegata. No. 244, Clerodendrum inerme. No. 245, Vigna marina.

1990, July 6   Litho.   Perf. 14
242 A50 45c multicolored   .85 .85
243 A50 45c multicolored   .85 .85
244 A50 45c multicolored   .85 .85
245 A50 45c multicolored   .85 .85
a. Block of 4, #242-245   3.75 3.75

Miniature Sheet

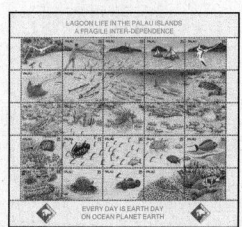

LAGOON LIFE IN THE PALAU ISLANDS
A FRAGILE INTER-DEPENDENCE

EVERY DAY IS EARTH DAY   ON OCEAN PLANET EARTH

Fairy Tern, Lesser Golden Plover,
Sanderling — A51

Lagoon life: b, Bidekill fisherman. c, Sailing yacht, insular halfbeaks. d, Palauan kaeps. e, White-tailed tropicbird. f, Spotted eagle ray. g, Great barracuda. h, Reef needlefish. i, Reef blacktip shark. j, Hawksbill turtle. k, Octopus. l, Batfish. m, Lionfish. n, Snowflake moray. o, Porcupine fish, sixfeeler threadfins. p, Blue sea star, regal angelfish, cleaner wrasse. q, Clown triggerfish. r, Spotted garden eel and orange fish. s, Blue-lined sea bream, blue-green chromis, sapphire damselfish. t, Orangespine unicornfish, white-tipped soldierfish. u, Slatepencil sea urchin, leopard sea cucumber. v, Partridge tun shell. w, Mandarinfish. x, Tiger cowrie. y, Feather starfish, orange-fin anemonefish.

1990, Aug. 10   Litho.   Perf. 15x14½
246 A51 25c Sheet of 25, #a.-
y.   12.50 12.50
Nos. 246a-246y inscribed on reverse.

Pacifica
A52

1990, Aug. 24   Litho.   Perf. 14
247 45c Mailship, 1890   1.50 1.50
248 45c US #803 on cover, fork-
lift, plane   1.50 1.50
a. A52 Pair, #247-248   3.25 3.25

Christmas — A53

Here We Come A-Caroling: No. 250, Girl with music, poinsettias, doves. No. 251, Boys playing guitar, flute. No. 252, Family. No. 253, Three girls singing.

1990, Nov. 28
249 A53 25c multicolored   .50 .40
250 A53 25c multicolored   .50 .40
251 A53 25c multicolored   .50 .40
252 A53 25c multicolored   .50 .40
253 A53 25c multicolored   .50 .40
a. Strip of 5, #249-253   3.00 3.00

U.S. FORCES IN PALAU — WORLD WAR II

US Forces in
Palau,
1944 — A54

Designs: No. 254, B-24s over Peleliu. No. 255, LCI launching rockets. No. 256, First Marine Division launching offensive. No. 257, Soldier, children. No. 258, USS *Peleliu*.

1990, Dec. 7
254 A54 45c multicolored   1.00 .85
255 A54 45c multicolored   1.00 .85
256 A54 45c multicolored   1.00 .85
257 A54 45c multicolored   1.00 .85
a. Block of 4, #254-257   4.25 4.25

Souvenir Sheet
Perf. 14x13½
258 A54 $1 multicolored   2.50 2.50

No. 258 contains one 51x38mm stamp. See No. 339 for No. 258 with added inscription.

PALAU 30 hard corals

Coral
A55

1991, Mar. 4   Litho.   Perf. 14

259	30c	Staghorn	.65 .65
260	30c	Velvet Leather	.65 .65
261	30c	Van Gogh's Cypress	.65 .65
262	30c	Violet Lace	.65 .65
a.	A55	Block of 4, #259-262	3.25 3.25

Miniature Sheet

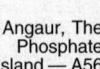

Angaur, The Phosphate Island — A56

Designs: a, Virgin Mary Statue, Nkulangelul Point. b, Angaur kaep, German colonial postmark. c, Swordfish, Caroline Islands No. 13. d, Phosphate mine locomotive. e, Copra ship off Lighthouse Hill. f, Dolphins. g, Estuarine crocodile. h, Workers cycling to phosphate plant. i, Ship loading phosphate. j, Hammerhead shark, German overseer. k, Marshall Islands No. 15. l, SMS Scharnhorst. m, SMS Emden. n, Crab-eating macaque monkey. o, Great sperm whale. p, HMAS Sydney.

1991, Mar. 14

263	A56	30c Sheet of 16, #a.-	10.00 10.00

Nos. 263b-263c, 263f-263g, 263j-263k, 263n-263o printed in continuous design showing map of island.

 Birds — A57

1c, Palau bush-warbler. 4c, Common moorhen. 6c, Banded rail. 19c, Palau fantail. 20c, Mangrove flycatcher. 23c, Purple swamphen. 29c, Palau fruit dove. 35c, Great crested tern. 40c, Pacific reef heron. 45c, Micronesian pigeon. 50c, Great frigatebird. 52c, Little pied cormorant. 75c, Jungle night jar. 95c, Cattle egret. $1.34, Great sulphur-crested cockatoo. $2, Blue-faced parrotfinch. $5, Eclectus parrot. $10, Palau bush warbler.

Perf. 14½x15, 13x13½

1991-92   Litho.

266	A57	1c	multicolored	.25 .25
267	A57	4c	multicolored	.25 .25
268	A57	6c	multicolored	.25 .25
269	A57	19c	multicolored	.35 .30
b.		Booklet pane, 10 #269		3.50 —
		Complete booklet, #269b		3.75
270	A57	20c	multicolored	.40 .30
271	A57	23c	multicolored	.45 .35
272	A57	29c	multicolored	.55 .45
a.		Booklet pane, 5 each #269, #272		5.00 —
		Complete booklet, #272a		5.25
b.		Booklet pane, 10 #272		4.50 —
		Complete booklet, #272b		4.50
273	A57	35c	multicolored	.70 .55
274	A57	40c	multicolored	.80 .60
275	A57	45c	multicolored	.90 .70
276	A57	50c	multicolored	1.00 .80
277	A57	52c	multicolored	1.00 .90
278	A57	75c	multicolored	1.50 1.25
279	A57	95c	multicolored	2.00 1.50
280	A57	$1.34	multicolored	2.25 2.00
281	A57	$2	multicolored	3.25 3.00
282	A57	$5	multicolored	8.00 7.75

Size: 52x30mm

283	A57	$10	multicolored	16.00 15.00
		Nos. 266-283 (18)		39.90 36.20

The 1, 6, 20, 52, 75c, $10 are perf. 14½x15.
Issued: 1, 6, 20, 52, 75c, $5, 4/6/92; $10, 9/10/92; #269b, 272a, 272b, 8/23/91; others, 4/18/91.

Miniature Sheet

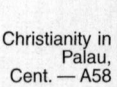

Christianity in Palau, Cent. — A58

Designs: a, Pope Leo XIII, 1891. b, Ibedul Ilengelekei, High Chief of Koror, 1871-1911. c, Fr. Marino de la Hoz, Br. Emilio Villar, Fr. Elias Fernandez. d, Fr. Edwin G. McManus (1908-1969), compiler of Palauan-English dictionary. e, Sacred Heart Church, Koror. f, Pope John Paul II.

1991, Apr. 28   Perf. 14½

288	A58	29c Sheet of 6, #a.-f.	3.50 3.50

Miniature Sheet

Marine Life A59

Designs: a, Pacific white-sided dolphin. b, Common dolphin. c, Rough-toothed dolphin. d, Bottlenose dolphin. e, Harbor porpoise. f, Killer whale. g, Spinner dolphin, yellowfin tuna. h, Dall's porpoise. i, Finless porpoise. j, Map of Palau, dolphin. k, Dusky dolphin. l, Southern right-whale dolphin. m, Striped dolphin. n, Fraser's dolphin. o, Peale's dolphin. p, Spectacled porpoise. q, Spotted dolphin. r, Hourglass dolphin. s, Risso's dolphin. t, Hector's dolphin.

1991, May 24   Litho.   Perf. 14

289	A59	29c Sheet of 20, #a.-
t.			13.50 13.50

Miniature Sheet

Operations Desert Shield / Desert Storm — A60

Designs: a, F-4G Wild Weasel fighter. b, F-117A Stealth fighter. c, AH-64A Apache helicopter. d, TOW missile launcher on M998 HMMWV. e, Pres. Bush. f, M2 Bradley fighting vehicle. g, Aircraft carrier USS Ranger. h, Corvette fast patrol boat. i, Battleship Wisconsin. No. 291, Fairy tern, yellow ribbon.

1991, July 2   Litho.   Perf. 14

290	A60	20c Sheet of 9, #a.-i.	3.75 3.75

Size: 38x51mm

291	A60	$2.90 multicolored	5.25 5.25

Souvenir Sheet

292	A60	$2.90 like #291	5.75 5.75

No. 291 has a white border around design. No. 292 printed in continuous design.

Republic of Palau, 10th Anniv. — A61

Designs: a, Palauan bai. b, Palauan bai interior, denomination UL. c, Same, denomination UR. d, Demi-god Chedechuul. e, Spider, denomination at UL. f, Money bird facing right. g, Money bird facing left. h, Spider, denomination at UR.

1991, July 9   Perf. 14½

293	A61	29c Sheet of 8, #a.-h.	5.00 5.00

See No. C21.

Miniature Sheet

Giant Clams — A62

Designs: a, Tridacna squamosa, Hippopus hippopus, Hippopus porcellanus, and Tridacna derasa. b, Tridacna gigas. c, Hatchery and tank culture. d, Diver, bottom-based clam

nursery. e, Micronesian Mariculture Demonstration Center.

1991, Sept. 17   Litho.   Perf. 14

294	A62	50c Sheet of 5, #a.-e.	5.00 5.00

No. 294e is 109x17mm and imperf on 3 sides, perf 14 at top.

Miniature Sheet

Japanese Heritage in Palau — A63

Designs: No. 295: a, Marine research. b, Traditional arts, carving story boards. c, Agricultural training. d, Archaeological research. e, Training in architecture and building. f, Air transportation. $1, Map, cancel from Japanese post office at Parao.

1991, Nov. 19

295	A63	29c Sheet of 6, #a.-f.	3.50 3.50

Souvenir Sheet

296	A63	$1 multicolored	3.00 3.00

Phila Nippon '91.

Miniature Sheet

Peace Corps in Palau, 25th Anniv. — A64

Children's drawings: No. 297a, Flag, doves, children, and islands. b, Airplane, people being greeted. c, Red Cross instruction. d, Fishing industry. e, Agricultural training. f, Classroom instruction.

1991, Dec. 6   Litho.   Perf. 13½

297	A64	29c Sheet of 6, #a.-f.	3.75 3.75

Christmas — A65

Silent Night: No. 298: a, Silent night, holy night. b, All is calm, all is bright. c, Round yon virgin, mother and Child. d, Holy Infant, so tender and mild. e, Sleep in heavenly peace.

1991, Nov. 14   Perf. 14

298	A65	29c Strip of 5, #a.-e.	2.75 2.75

Miniature Sheet

World War II in the Pacific — A66

Designs: No. 299a, Pearl Harbor attack begins. b, Battleship Nevada gets under way. c, USS Shaw explodes. d, Japanese aircraft carrier Akagi sunk. e, USS Wasp sunk off Guadalcanal. f, Battle of the Philippine Sea. g, US landing craft approach Saipan. h, US 1st Cavalry on Leyte. i, Battle of Bloody Nose Ridge, Peleliu. j, US troops land on Iwo Jima.

1991, Dec. 6   Perf. 14½x15

299	A66	29c Sheet of 10, #a.-j.	8.50 8.50

See No. C22.

A67

Butterflies: a, Troides criton. b, Alcides zodiaca. c, Papillio poboroi. d, Vindula arsinoe.

1992, Jan. 20   Litho.   Perf. 14

300	A67	50c Block of 4, #a.-d.	4.00 4.00

A68

Shells: a, Common hairy triton. b, Eglantine cowrie. c, Sulcate swamp cerith. d, Black-spined murex. e, Black-mouth moon.

1992, Mar. 11

301	A68	29c Strip of 5, #a.-e.	3.00 3.00

Miniature Sheet

Age of Discovery — A69

Designs: a, Columbus. b, Magellan. c, Drake. d, Wind as shown on old maps.
Maps and: e, Compass rose. f, Dolphin, Drake's ship Golden Hinde. g, Corn, Santa Maria. h, Fish. i, Betel palm, cloves and black pepper. j, Victoria, shearwater and great crested tern. k, White-tailed tropicbird, bicolor parrotfish, pineapple and potatoes. l, Compass. m, Sea monster. n, Paddles and astrolabe. o, Parallel ruler, dividers and Inca gold treasures. p, Back staff.
Portraits: q, Wind, diff. r, Vespucci. s, Pizarro. t, Balboa.

1992, May 25   Litho.   Perf. 14

302	A69	29c Sheet of 20, #a.-
t.			12.00 12.00

Miniature Sheet

Biblical Creation of the World — A70

Designs: a, "And darkness was..." b, Sun's rays. c, Water, sun's rays. d, "...and it was good." e, "Let there be a..." f, Land forming. g, Water and land. h, "...and it was so." i, "Let the waters..." j, Tree branches. k, Shoreline. l, Shoreline, flowers, tree. m, "Let there be lights..." n, Comet, moon. o, Mountains. p, Sun, hillside. q, "Let the waters..." r, Birds. s, Fish, killer whale. t, Fish. u, "Let the earth..." v, Woman, man. w, Animals. x, "...and it was very good."

1992, June 5   Perf. 14½

303	A70	29c Sheet of 24, #a.-
x.			14.00 14.00

Nos. 303a-303d, 303e-303h, 303i-303l, 303m-303p, 303q-303t, 303u-303x are blocks of 4.

Souvenir Sheets

1992 Summer Olympics,
Barcelona — A71

1992, July 10   **Perf. 14**
304 A71 50c Dawn Fraser   1.00   1.00
305 A71 50c Olga Korbut   1.00   1.00
306 A71 50c Bob Beamon   1.00   1.00
307 A71 50c Carl Lewis   1.00   1.00
308 A71 50c Dick Fosbury   1.00   1.00
309 A71 50c Greg Louganis   1.00   1.00
     Nos. 304-309 (6)   6.00   6.00

Miniature Sheet

Elvis
Presley — A72

Various portraits.

1992, Aug. 17   **Perf. 13½x14**
310 A72 29c Sheet of 9, #a.-i.   7.00   7.00
     See No. 350.

Christmas — A73

The Friendly Beasts carol depicting animals in Nativity Scene: No. 312a, "Thus Every Beast." b, "By Some Good Spell." c, "In The Stable Dark Was Glad to Tell." d, "Of The Gift He Gave Emanuel." e, "The Gift He Gave Emanuel."

1992, Oct. 1   **Litho.**   **Perf. 14**
312 A73 29c Strip of 5, #a.-e.   3.00   3.00

Fauna — A74

Designs: a, Dugong. b, Masked booby. c, Macaque. d, New Guinean crocodile.

1993, July 9   **Litho.**   **Perf. 14**
313 A74 50c Block of 4, #a.-d.   4.00   4.00

Seafood — A75

Designs: a, Giant crab. b, Scarlet shrimp. c, Smooth nylon shrimp. d, Armed nylon shrimp.

1993, July 22
314 A75 29c Block of 4, #a.-d.   2.25   2.25

Sharks
A76

Designs: a, Oceanic whitetip. b, Great hammerhead. c, Leopard. d, Reef black-tip.

1993, Aug. 11   **Litho.**   **Perf. 14½**
315 A76 50c Block of 4, #a.-d.   4.00   4.00

Miniature Sheet

World War II in
the Pacific — A77

Actions in 1943: a, US takes Guadalcanal, Feb. b, Hospital ship Tranquility supports action. c, New Guineans join Allies in battle. d, US landings in New Georgia, June. e, USS California participates in every naval landing. f, Dauntless dive bombers over Wake Island, Oct. 6. g, US flamethrowers on Tarawa, Nov. h, US landings on Makin, Nov. i, B-25s bomb Simpson Harbor, Rabaul, Oct. 23. j, B-24s over Kwajalein, Dec. 8.

1993, Sept. 23   **Litho.**   **Perf. 14½x15**
316 A77 29c Sheet of 10, #a.-j. +
     label   8.00   8.00
     See Nos. 325-326.

Christmas — A78

Christmas carol, "We Wish You a Merry Christmas," with Palauan customs: a, Girl, goat. b, Goats, children holding leis, prow of canoe. c, Santa Claus. d, Children singing. e, Family with fruit, fish.

1993, Oct. 22   **Litho.**   **Perf. 14**
317 A78 29c Strip of 5, #a.-e.   3.00   3.00

Miniature Sheet

Prehistoric and Legendary Sea
Creatures — A79

1993, Nov. 26   **Litho.**   **Perf. 14**
318 A79 29c Sheet of 25, #a.-
     y.   14.00   14.00

Miniature Sheet

Intl. Year of Indigenous People — A80

Paintings, by Charlie Gibbons: No. 319: a, After Child-birth Ceremony. b, Village in Early Palau.
Storyboard carving, by Ngiraibuuch: $2.90, Quarrying of Stone Money, vert.

1993, Dec. 8   **Perf. 14x13½**
319 A80   29c Sheet, 2 ea
     #a.-b.   2.25   2.25

Souvenir Sheet
Perf. 13½x14
320 A80 $2.90 multicolored   6.00   6.00

Miniature Sheet

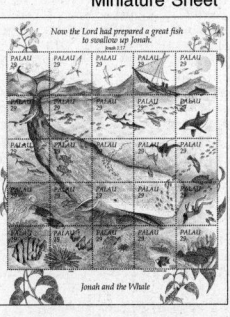

Jonah
and the
Whale
A81

1993, Dec. 28   **Litho.**   **Perf. 14**
321 A81 29c Sheet of 25, #a.-
     y.   14.50   14.50

Hong Kong
'94 — A82

Rays: a, Manta (b). b, Spotted eagle (a). c, Coachwhip (d). d, Black spotted.

1994, Feb. 18   **Litho.**   **Perf. 14**
322 A82 40c Block of 4, #a.-d.   3.00   3.00

Estuarine
Crocodile — A83

Designs: a, With mouth open. b, Hatchling. c, Crawling on river bottom. d, Swimming.

1994, Mar. 14
323 A83 20c Block of 4, #a.-d.   3.50   3.50
     World Wildlife Fund.

Large Seabirds — A84

a, Red-footed booby. b, Great frigatebird. c, Brown booby. d, Little pied cormorant.

1994, Apr. 22   **Litho.**   **Perf. 14**
324 A84 50c Block of 4, #a.-d.   4.00   4.00

World War II Type of 1993
Miniature Sheets

Action in the Pacific, 1944: No. 325: a, US Marines capture Kwajalien, Feb. 1-7. b, Japanese enemy base at Truk destroyed, Feb. 17-18. c, SS-284 Tullibee participates in Operation Desecrate, March. d, US troops take Saipan, June 15-July 9. e, Great Marianas Turkey Shoot, June 19-20. f, Guam liberated, July-Aug. g, US troops take Peleliu, Sept. 15-Oct. 14. h, Angaur secured in fighting, Sept. 17-22. i, Gen. Douglas MacArthur returns to Philippines, Oct. 20. j, US Army Memorial, Palau, Nov. 27.
D-Day, Allied Invasion of Normandy, June 6, 1944: No. 326: a, C-47 transport aircraft dropping Allied paratroopers. b, Allied warships attack beach fortifications. c, Commandos attack from landing craft. d, Tanks land. e, Sherman flail tank beats path through minefields. f, Allied aircraft attack enemy reinforcements. g, Gliders deliver troops behind enemy lines. h, Pegasus Bridge, first French house liberated. i, Allied forces move inland to form bridgehead. j, View of beach at end of D-Day.

1994, May   **Sheets of 10**   **Perf. 14½**
325 A77 29c #a.-j. + label   8.50   8.50
326 A77 50c #a.-j. + label   12.00   12.00

Pierre de
Coubertin (1863-
1937)
A85

Winter Olympic medalists: No. 328, Anne-Marie Moser, vert. No. 329, James Craig. No. 330, Katarina Witt. No. 331, Eric Heiden, vert. No. 332, Nancy Kerrigan. $2, Dan Jansen.

1994, July 20   **Litho.**   **Perf. 14**
327 A85 29c multicolored   .70   .70

Souvenir Sheets
328 A85 50c multicolored   1.00   1.00
329 A85 50c multicolored   1.00   1.00
330 A85 $1 multicolored   2.00   2.00
331 A85 $1 multicolored   2.00   2.00
332 A85 $1 multicolored   2.00   2.00
333 A85 $2 multicolored   4.00   4.00
     Intl. Olympic Committee, cent.

Miniature Sheets

PHILAKOREA '94 — A86

Wildlife carrying letters: No. 334: a, Sailfin goby. b, Sharpnose puffer. c, Lightning butterflyfish. d, Clown anemonefish. e, Parrotfish. f, Batfish. g, Clown triggerfish. h, twinspot wrasse.
No. 335a, Palau fruit bat. b, Crocodile. c, Dugong. d, Banded sea snake. e, Bottle-nosed dophin. f, Hawksbill turtle. g, Octopus. h, Manta ray.
No. 336: a, Palau fantail. b, Banded crake. c, Island swiftlet. d, Micronesian kingfisher. e, Red-footed booby. f, Great frigatebird. g, Palau owl. h, Palau fruit dove.

1994, Aug. 16   **Litho.**   **Perf. 14**
334 A86 29c Sheet of 8, #a.-h.   6.00   6.00
335 A86 40c Sheet of 8, #a.-h.   8.00   8.00
336 A86 50c Sheet of 8, #a.-h.   10.00   10.00
     No. 336 is airmail.

Miniature Sheet

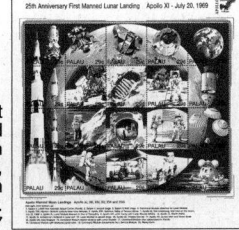

First
Manned
Moon
Landing,
25th
Anniv.
A87

Various scenes from Apollo moon missions.

1994, July 20
337 A87 29c Sheet of 20, #a.-
     t.   12.00   12.00

Independence
Day — A88

#338: b, Natl. seal. c, Pres. Kuniwo Nakamura, Palau, US Pres. Clinton. d, Palau, US flags. e, Musical notes of natl. anthem.

1994, Oct. 1   **Perf. 14**
338 A88 29c Strip of 5, #a.-e.   2.75   2.75
     No. 338c is 57x42mm.

No. 258 with added text "50th ANNIVERSARY / INVASION OF PELELIU / SEPTEMBER 15, 1944"

1994	Litho.	Perf. 14X13½
339 A54 $1 multicolored		2.50 2.50

Miniature Sheet

Disney Characters Visit Palau — A89

No. 340: a, Mickey, Minnie arriving. b, Goofy finding way to hotel. c, Donald enjoying beach. d, Minnie, Daisy learning the Ngloik. e, Minnie, Mickey sailing to Natural Bridge. f, Scrooge finding money in Babeldaob jungle. g, Goofy, Napoleon Wrasse. h, Minnie, Clam Garden. i, Grandma Duck weaving basket.

No. 341, Mickey exploring underwater shipwreck. No. 342, Donald visiting Airai Bai on Babeldaob. No. 343, Pluto, Mickey in boat, vert.

1994, Oct. 14	Perf. 13½x14
340 A89 29c Sheet of 9, #a.-i.	6.00 6.00

Souvenir Sheets

341-342 A89 $1 each	3.00 3.00
Perf. 14x13½	
343 A89 $2.90 multicolored	7.75 7.75

Miniature Sheet

Intl. Year of the Family — A90

Story of Tebruchel: a, With mother as infant. b, Father. c, As young man. d, Wife-to-be. e, Bringing home fish. f, Pregnant wife. g, Elderly mother. h, Elderly father. i, With first born. j, Wife seated. k, Caring for mother. l, Father, wife and baby.

1994, Nov. 1	Litho.	Perf. 14
344 A90 20c Sheet of 12, #a.-l.		4.75 4.75

Christmas — A91

O Little Town of Bethlehem: a, Magi, cherubs. b, Angel, shepherds, sheep. c, Angels, nativity. d, Angels hovering over town, shepherd, sheep. e, Cherubs, doves.

1994, Nov. 23	Litho.	Perf. 14
345 A91 29c Strip of 5, #a-e		3.00 3.00

No. 345 is a continuous design and is printed in sheets containing three strips. The bottom strip is printed with se-tenant labels.

Miniature Sheets

1994 World Cup Soccer Championships, US — A92

US coach, players: No. 346: a, Bora Milutinovic. b, Cle Kooiman. c, Ernie Stewart. d,

---

Claudio Reyna. e, Thomas Dooley. f, Alexi Lalas. g, Dominic Kinnear. h, Frank Klopas. i, Paul Caligiuri. j, Marcelo Balboa. k, Cobi Jones. l, US flag, World Cup trohpy.

US players: No. 347a, Tony Meola. b, John Doyle. c, Eric Wynalda. d, Roy Wegerle. e, Fernando Clavijo. f, Hugo Perez. g, John Harkes. h, Mike Lapper. i, Mike Sorber. j, Brad Friedel. k, Tab Ramos. l, Joe-Max Moore.

No. 348: a, Babeto, Brazil. b, Romario, Brazil. c, Franco Baresi, Italy. d, Roberto Baggio, Italy. e, Andoni Zubizarreta, Spain. f, Oleg Salenko, Russia. g, Gheorghe Hagi, Romania. h, Dennis Bergkamp, Netherlands. i, Hristo Stoichkov, Bulgaria. j, Tomas Brolin, Sweden. k, Lothar Matthaus, Germany. l, Arrigo Sacchi, Italy, Carlos Alberto Parreira, Brazil, flags of Italy & Brazil, World Cup trophy.

1994, Dec. 23	
346 A92 29c Sheet of 12, #a.-l.	6.25 6.25
347 A92 29c Sheet of 12, #a.-l.	6.25 6.25
348 A92 50c Sheet of 12, #a.-l.	10.50 10.50

Elvis Presley Type of 1992
Miniature Sheet

Various portraits.

1995, Feb. 28	Litho.	Perf. 14
350 A72 32c Sheet of 9, #a.-i.		6.25 6.25

Fish — A93

1c, Cube trunkfish. 2c, Lionfish. 3c, Longjawed squirrelfish. 4c, Longnose filefish. 5c, Ornate butterflyfish. 10c, Yellow seahorse. 20c, Magenta dottyback. 32c, Reef lizardfish. 50c, Multibarred goatfish. 55c, Barred blenny. $1, Fingerprint sharpnose puffer. $2, Longnose hawkfish. $3, Mandarinfish. $5, Blue surgeonfish. $10, Coral grouper.

1995, Apr. 3	Litho.	Perf. 14½
351 A93 1c multicolored		.25 .25
352 A93 2c multicolored		.25 .25
353 A93 3c multicolored		.25 .25
354 A93 4c multicolored		.25 .25
355 A93 5c multicolored		.25 .25
356 A93 10c multicolored		.25 .25
357 A93 20c multicolored		.35 .30
358 A93 32c multicolored		.50 .45
359 A93 50c multicolored		.85 .70
360 A93 55c multicolored		1.00 .75
361 A93 $1 multicolored		1.75 1.50
362 A93 $2 multicolored		3.50 3.00
363 A93 $3 multicolored		5.00 4.50
364 A93 $5 multicolored		8.50 7.75
Size: 48x30mm		
365 A93 $10 multicolored		17.50 16.00
Nos. 351-365 (15)		40.45 36.45

Booklet Stamps
Size: 18x21mm
Perf. 14x14½ Syncopated

366 A93 20c multicolored	.40	.40
a. Booklet pane of 10	3.75	
Complete booklet, #366a	4.00	
367 A93 32c multicolored	.60	.60
a. Booklet pane of 10	6.00	
Complete booklet, #367a	6.25	
b. Booklet pane, 5 ea #366, 367	5.25	
Complete booklet, #367b	5.50	

Miniature Sheet

Lost Fleet of the Rock Islands — A94

Underwater scenes, silhouettes of Japanese ships sunk during Operation Desecrate, 1944: a, Unyu Maru 2. b, Wakatake. c, Teshio Maru. d, Raizan Maru. e, Chuyo Maru. f, Shinsei Maru. g, Urakami Maru. h, Ose Maru. i, Iro. j, Shosei Maru. k, Patrol boat 31. l, Kibi Maru. m, Amatsu Maru. n, Gozan Maru. o, Matuei Maru. p, Nagisan Maru. q, Akashi. r, Kamikazi Maru.

1995, Mar. 30	Litho.	Perf. 14
368 A94 32c Sheet of 18, #a.-r.		12.00 12.00

Miniature Sheet

Flying Dinosaurs — A95

Designs: a, Pteranodon sternbergi. b, Pteranodon ingens (a, c). c, Pterodoctyls (b). d, Dorygnathus (e). e, Dimorphodon (f). f, Nyctosaurus (e, c). g, Pterodactylus kochi. h, Ornithodesmus (g, i). i, Diatryma (l). j, Archaeopteryx. k, Campylognathoides (l). l, Gallodactylus. m, Batrachognathus (j). n, Scaphognathus (j, k, m, o). o, Peteinosaurus (l). p, Ichthyorinis. q, Ctenochasma (m, p, r). r, Rhamphorhynchus (n, o, q).

1995	Litho.	Perf. 14
369 A95 32c Sheet of 18, #a.-r.		12.00 12.00

Earth Day, 25th anniv.

Miniature Sheet

Research & Experimental Jet Aircraft — A96

Designs: a, Fairey Delta 2. b, B-70 "Valkyrie." c, Douglas X-3 "Stilletto." d, Northrop/NASA HL-10. e, Bell XS-1. f, Tupolev Tu-144. g, Bell X-1. h, Boulton Paul P.111. i, EWR VJ 101C. j, Handley Page HP-115. k, Rolls Royce TMR "Flying Bedstead." l, North American X-15.

$2, BAC/Aerospatiale Concorde SST.

1995	Litho.	Perf. 14
370 A96 50c Sheet of 12, #a.-l.		12.00 12.00

Souvenir Sheet

371 A96 $2 multicolored	3.75 3.75

No. 370 is airmail. No. 371 contains one 85x29mm stamp.

Miniature Sheet

Submersibles A97

Designs: a, Scuba gear. b, Cousteau diving saucer. c, Jim suit. d, Beaver IV. e, Ben Franklin. f, USS Nautilus. g, Deep Rover. h, Beebe Bathysphere. i, Deep Star IV. j, DSRV. k, Aluminaut. l. Nautile. m, Cyana. n, FNRS Bathyscaphe. o, Alvin. p, Mir 1. q, Archimede. r, Trieste.

1995, July 21	Litho.	Perf. 14
372 A97 32c Sheet of 18, #a.-r.		12.00 12.00

Singapore '95 — A98

Designs: a, Dolphins, diver snorkeling, marine life. b, Turtle, diver, seabirds above. c, Fish, coral, crab. d, Coral, fish, diff.

1995, Aug. 15	Litho.	Perf. 13½
373 A98 32c Block of 4, #a.-d.		2.50 2.50

No. 373 is a continuous design and was issued in sheets of 24 stamps.

UN, FAO, 50th Anniv. — A99

Designs: No. 374a, Outline of soldier's helmet, dove, peace. b, Outline of flame, Hedul Gibbons, human rights. c, Books, education. d, Outline of tractor, bananas, agriculture. No. 375, Palau flag, bird, UN emblem. No. 376, Water being put on plants, UN emblem, vert.

1995, Sept. 15	Litho.	Perf. 14
374 A99 60c Block of 4, #a.-d.		4.75 4.75

Souvenir Sheets

375 A99 $2 multicolored	4.00 4.00
376 A99 $2 multicolored	4.00 4.00

Independence, 1st Anniv. — A100

Palau flag and: a, Fruit doves. b, Rock Islands. c, Map of islands. d, Orchid, hibiscus. 32c, Marine life.

1995, Sept. 15	Perf. 14½
377 A100 20c Block of 4, #a.-d.	1.50 1.50
378 A100 32c multicolored	.65 .65

No. 377 was issued in sheets of 16 stamps. See US No. 2999.

Miniature Sheets

A101

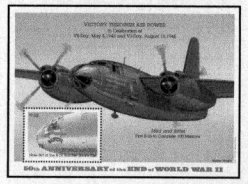

End of World War II, 50th Anniv. A102

Paintings by Wm. F. Draper: No. 379a, Preparing Tin-Fish. b, Hellcats Take-off into Palau's Rising Sun. c, Dauntless Dive Bombers over Malakai Harbor. d, Planes Return from Palau. e, Communion Before Battle. f, The Landing. g, First Task Ashore. h, Fire Fighters Save Flak-torn Pilot.

Paintings by Tom Lea: No. 379i, Young Marine Headed for Peleliu. j, Peleliu. k, Last Rites. l, The Thousand-Yard Stare.

Portraits by Albert Murray, vert.: No. 380a, Adm. Chester W. Nimitz. b, Adm. William F. Halsey. c, Adm. Raymond A. Spruance. d, Vice Adm. Marc A. Mitscher. e, Gen. Holland M. Smith, USMC.

$3, Nose art of B-29 Bock's Car.

1995, Oct. 18	Perf. 14x13½
379 A101 32c Sheet of 12, #a.-l.	7.75 7.75
Perf. 13½x14	
380 A101 60c Sheet of 5, #a.-e.	7.50 7.50
Souvenir Sheet	
Perf. 14	
381 A102 $3 multicolored	6.00 6.00

Christmas — A103

Native version of "We Three Kings of Orient Are:" a, Angel, animals. b, Two wise men. c,

Joseph, Mary, Jesus in manger. d, Wise man, shepherd, animals. e, Girl with fruit, goat, shepherd.

1995, Oct. 31   Litho.   Perf. 14
382   A103   32c Strip of 5, #a.-e.   3.00   3.00

No. 382 is a continuous design and was issued in sheets of 15 stamps + 5 labels se-tenant with bottom row of sheet.

Miniature Sheet

Life Cycle of the Sea Turtle A104

Small turtles, arrows representing routes during life cycle and: a, Large turtle. b, Upper half of turtle shell platter, Palau map. c, Rooster in tree, island scene. d, Native woman. e, Lower half of turtle shell platter, Palau map, island couple. f, Fossil, palm trees, native house

1995, Nov. 15   Litho.   Perf. 14
383   A104   32c Sheet of 12, 2 each, #a.-f.   9.50   9.50

John Lennon (1940-80) — A105

1995, Dec. 8   Litho.   Perf. 14
384   A105   32c multicolored   1.10   1.10

No. 384 was issued in sheets of 16.

Miniature Sheet

New Year 1996 (Year of the Rat) — A106

Stylized rats in parade: No. 385: a, One carrying flag, one playing horn. b, Three playing musical instruments. c, Two playing instruments. d, Family in front of house.
Mirror images, diff. colors: No. 386: a, Like #385c-385d. b, Like #385a-385b.

1996, Feb. 2   Litho.   Perf. 14
385   A106   10c Strip of 4, #a.-d.   1.75   1.75

Miniature Sheet
386   A106   60c Sheet of 2, #a.-b.   2.25   2.25

No. 385 was issued in sheets of 2 + 4 labels like No. 386. Nos. 386a-386b are airmail and are each 56x43mm.

UNICEF, 50th Anniv. — A107

Three different children from Palau in traditional costumes, child in middle wearing: a, Red flowerd dress. b, Pink dress. c, Blue shorts. d, Red headpiece and shorts.

1996, Mar. 12   Litho.   Perf. 14
387   A107   32c Block of 4, #a.-d.   2.50   2.50

No. 387 was issued in sheets of 4.

Marine Life A108

Letter spelling "Palau," and: a, "P," fairy basslet, vermiculate parrotfish. b, "A," yellow cardinalfish. c, "L," Marten's butterflyfish. d, "A," starry moray, slate pencil sea urchin. e, "U," cleaner wrasse, coral grouper.

1996, Mar. 29   Litho.   Perf. 14
388   A108   32c Strip of 5, #a.-e.   3.00   3.00

No. 388 was issued in miniature sheets of 3. China '96, Intl. Stamp Exhibition, Beijing.

Capex '96 — A109

Circumnavigators of the earth: No. 389: a, Ferdinand Magellan, ship Victoria. b, Charles Wilkes, ship Vincennes. c, Joshua Slocum, oyster boat Spray. d, Ben Carlin, amphibious vehicle Half-Safe. e, Edward L. Beach, submarine USS Triton. f, Naomi James, yacht Express Crusader. g, Sir Ranulf Fiennes, polar vehicle. h, Rick Hansen, wheel chair. i, Robin Knox-Johnson, catamaran Enza New Zealand.
No. 390: a, Lowell Smith, Douglas World Cruisers. b, Ernst Lehmann, Graf Zeppelin. c, Wiley Post, Lockheed Vega Winnie Mae. d, Yuri Gagarin, spacecraft Vostok I. e, Jerrie Mock, Cessna 180 Spirit of Columbus. f, Ross Perot, Jr., Bell Longranger III, Spirit of Texas. g, Brooke Knapp, Gulfstream III, The American Dream. h, Jeana Yeager, Dick Rutan, airplane Voyager. i, Fred Lasby, piper Commanche.
Each $3: No. 391, Bob Martin, Mark Sullivan, Troy Bradley, Odyssey Gondola. No. 392, Sir Francis Chichester, yacht Gipsy Moth IV.

1996, May 3   Litho.   Perf. 14
389   A109   32c Sheet of 9, #a.-i.   5.50   5.50
390   A109   60c Sheet of 9, #a.-i.   11.00 11.00

Souvenir Sheets
391-392   A109   Set of 2   12.00   12.00

No. 390 is airmail.

Miniature Sheet

Disney Sweethearts A110

1c, like #393a. 2c, #393c. 3c, #393d. 4c, like #393e. 5c, #393f. 6c, #393h.

#393: a, Simba, Nala, Timon. b, Bernard, Bianca, Mr. Chairman. c, Georgette, Tito, Oliver. d, Duchess, O'Malley, Marie. e, Bianca, Jake, Polly. f, Tod, Vixey, Copper. g, Robin Hood, Maiden Marian, Alan-a-Dale. h, Thumper, Flower, their sweethearts. i, Pongo, Perdita, puppies.
Each $2: #394, Lady, vert. #395, Bambi, Faline.

1996, May 30   Litho.   Perf. 14x13½
392A-392F   A110   Set of 6   1.00   1.00

Sheet of 9
393   A110   60c #a.-i.   13.50   13.50

Souvenir Sheets
Perf. 13½x14, 14x13½
394-395   A110   Set of 2   9.50   9.50

Jerusalem, 3000th Anniv. — A111

Biblical illustrations of the Old Testament appearing in "In Our Image," by Guy Rowe (1894-1969): a, Creation. b, Adam and Eve. c, Noah and his Wife. d, Abraham. e, Jacob's Blessing. f, Jacob Becomes Israel. g, Joseph and his Brethren. h, Moses and the Burning

Bush. i, Moses and the Tablets. j, Balaam. k, Joshua. l, Gideon. m, Jephthah. n, Samson. o, Ruth and Naomi. p, Saul Anointed. q, Saul Denounced. r, David and Jonathan. s, David and Nathan. t, David Mourns. u, Solomon Praying. v, Solomon Judging. w, Elijah. x, Elisha. y, Job. z, Isaiah. aa, Jeremiah. ab, Ezekiel. ac, Nebuchadnezzar's Dream. ad, Amos.

1996, June 15   Litho.   Perf. 14
396   A111   20c Sheet of 30, #a.-ad.   12.00   12.00

For overprint see No. 461.

1996 Summer Olympics, Atlanta — A112

No. 397, Fanny Blankers Koen, gold medalist, 1948, vert. No. 398, Bob Mathias, gold medalist, 1948, 1952, vert. No. 399, Torchbearer entering Wembley Stadium, 1948. No. 400, Olympic flag, flags of Palau and U.K. before entrance to Stadium, Olympia, Greece.
Athletes: No. 401: a, Hakeem Olajuwan, US. b, Pat McCormick, US. c, Jim Thorpe, US. d, Jesse Owens, US. e, Tatyana Gutsu, Unified Team. f, Michael Jordan, US. g, Fu Mingxia, China. h, Robert Zmelik, Czechoslovakia. i, Ivan Pedroso, Cuba. j, Nadia Comaneci, Romania. k, Jackie Joyner-Kersee, US. l, Michael Johnson, US. m, Kristin Otto, E. Germany. n, Vitali Scherbo, Unified Team. o, Johnny Weissmuller, US. p, Babe Didrikson, US. q, Eddie Tolan, US. r, Krisztina Egerszegi, Hungary. s, Sawao Kato, Japan. t, Alexander Popov, Unified Team.

1996, June 17   Litho.   Perf. 14
397   A112   40c multicolored   .90   .90
398   A112   40c multicolored   .90   .90
   a.   Pair, #397-398   2.00   2.00
399   A112   60c multicolored   1.40   1.40
400   A112   60c multicolored   1.40   1.40
   a.   Pair, #399-400   3.00   3.00
401   A112   32c Sheet of 20, #a.-t.   13.00   13.00

Nos. 398a, 400a were each issued in sheets of 20 stamps. No. 401 is a continuous design.

Birds Over Palau Lagoon A113

Designs: a, Lakkotsiang, female. b, Maladaob. c, Belochel (g). d, Lakkotsiang, male. e, Sechosech. f, Mechadelbedaoch (j). g, Laib. h, Cheloteachel. i, Deroech. j, Kerkirs. k, Dudek. l, Lakkotsiang. m, Bedaoch. n, Bedebedchaki. o, Sechou (gray Pacific reef-heron) (p). p, Kekereiderariik. q, Sechou (white Pacific reef-heron). r, Ochaieu. s, Oltirakladial. t, Omechederiibabad.

1996, July 10
402   A113   50c Sheet of 20, #a.-t.   20.00   20.00

Aircraft A114

Stealth, surveillance, and electronic warfare: No. 403: a, Lockheed U-2. b, General Dynamics EF-111A. c, Lockheed YF-12A. d, Lockheed SR-71. e, Teledyne-Ryan-Tiere II Plus. f, Lockheed XST. g, Lockheed ER-2. h, Lockheed F-117A Nighthawk. i, Lockheed EC-130E. j, Ryan Firebee. k, Lockheed Martin/Boeing "Darkstar." l, Boeing E-3A Sentry.

No. 404: a, Northrop XB-35. b, Leduc O.21. c, Convair Model 118. d, Blohm Und Voss BV 141. e, Vought V-173. f, McDonnell XF-85 Goblin. g, North American F-82B Twin Mustang. h, Lockheed XFV-1. i, Northrop XP-79B. j, Saunders Roe SR/A1. k, Caspian Sea Monster. l, Grumman X-29.
No. 405, Northrop B-2A Stealth Bomber. No. 406, Martin Marietta X-24B.

1996, Sept. 9   Litho.   Perf. 14
403   A114   40c Sheet of 12, #a.-l.   10.00   10.00
404   A114   60c Sheet of 12, #a.-l.   15.00   15.00

Souvenir Sheets
405   A114 $3 multicolored   6.50   6.50
406   A114 $3 multicolored   6.50   6.50

No. 404 is airmail. No. 406 contains one 85x28mm stamp.

Independence, 2nd Anniv. — A115

Paintings, by Koh Sekiguchi: No. 407, "In the Blue Shade of Trees-Palau (Kirie). No. 408 "The Birth of a New Nation (Kirie).

1996, Oct. 1   Litho.   Perf. 14½
407   20c multicolored   .40   .40
408   20c multicolored   .40   .40
   a.   A115   Pair, #407-408   .80   .80

#408a issued in sheets of 16 stamps.

Christmas — A116

Christmas trees: a, Pandanus. b, Mangrove. c, Norfolk Island pine. d, Papaya. e, Casuarina.

1996, Oct. 8   Perf. 14
409   A116   32c Strip of 5, #a.-e.   3.25   3.25

No. 409 was issued in sheets of 3.

Voyage to Mars A117

No. 410: a, Viking 1 (US) in Mars orbit. b, Mars Lander fires de-orbit engines. c, Viking 1 symbol (top). d, Viking 1 symbol (bottom). e, Martian moon phobos. f, Mariner 9 in Mars orbit. g, Viking lander enters Martian atmosphere. h, Parachute deploys for Mars landing, heat shield jettisons. i, Proposed manned mission to Mars, 21st cent., US-Russian spacecraft (top). j, US-Russian spacecraft (bottom). k, Lander descent engines fire for Mars landing. l, Viking 1 lands on Mars, July 20, 1976.
Each $3: No. 411, NASA Mars rover. No. 412, NASA water probe on Mars. Illustration reduced.

1996, Nov. 8   Litho.   Perf. 14x14½
410   A117   32c Sheet of 12, #a.-l.   7.75   7.75

Souvenir Sheets
411-412   A117   Set of 2   12.00   12.00

No. 411 contains one 38x30mm stamp.

Souvenir Sheet

New Year 1997 (Year of the Ox) A117a

1997, Jan. 2   Litho.   Perf. 14
412A   A117a $2 multicolored   4.25 4.25

Souvenir Sheet

South Pacific Commission, 50th Anniv. — A118

1997, Feb. 6   Litho.   Perf. 14
413   A118 $1 multicolored   2.00 2.00

Hong Kong '97 — A119

Flowers: 1c, Pemphis acidula. 2c, Sea lettuce. 3c, Tropical almond. 4c, Guettarda. 5c, Pacific coral bean. $3, Sea hibiscus.
No. 420: a, Black mangrove. b, Cordia. c, Lantern tree. d, Palau rock-island flower.
No. 421: a, Fish-poison tree. b, Indian mulberry. c, Pacific poison-apple. d, Ailanthus.

1997, Feb. 12   Perf. 14½, 13½ (#419)
414-419   A119   Set of 6   7.00 7.00
420   A119   32c Block of 4, #a.-d.   2.50 2.50
421   A119   50c Block of 4, #a.-d.   4.00 4.00

Size of No. 419 is 73x48mm.
Nos. 420-421 were each issued in sheets of 16 stamps.

Bicent. of the Parachute A120

Uses of parachute: No. 422: a, Apollo 15 Command Module landing safely. b, "Caterpillar Club" flyer ejecting safely over land. c, Skydiving team formation. d, Parasailing. e, Military parachute demonstration teams. f, Parachute behind dragster. g, Dropping cargo from C-130 aircraft. h, "Goldfish Club" flyer ejecting safely at sea.
No. 423: a, Demonstrating parachute control. b, A.J. Gernerin, first successful parachute descent, 1797. c, Slowing down world land-speed record breaking cars. d, Dropping spies behind enemy lines. e, C-130E demonstrating "LAPES." f, Parachutes used to slow down high performance aircraft. g, ARD parachutes. h, US Army parachutist flying Parafoil.
Each $2: No. 424 Training tower at Ft. Benning, Georgia. No. 425, "Funny Car" safety chute.

Perf. 14½x14, 14x14½
1997, Mar. 13   Litho.
422   A120   32c Sheet of 8, #a.-h.   5.25 5.25
423   A120   60c Sheet of 8, #a.-h.   9.75 9.75
Souvenir Sheets
Perf. 14
424-425   A120   Set of 2   10.00 10.00

Nos. 422a-423a, 422b-423b, 422g-423g, 422h-423h are 20x48mm. No. 424 contains one 28x85mm, No. 425 one 57x42mm stamps.
No. 423 is airmail.

Postage Stamp Mega-Event, NYC, Mar. 1997 (#422-423).

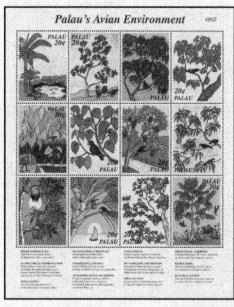

Native Birds A121

a, Gray duck, banana tree. b, Red junglefowl, calamondin. c, Nicobar pigeon, fruited parinari tree. d, Cardinal honeyeater, wax apple tree. e, Yellow bittern, purple swamphen, giant taro, taro. f, Eclectus parrot, pangi football fruit tree. g, Micronesian pigeon, Rambutan. h, Micronesian starling, mango tree. i, Fruit bat, breadfruit tree. j, Collared kingfisher, coconut palm. k, Palau fruit dove, sweet orange tree. l, Chestnut mannikin, soursop tree.

1997, Mar. 27   Litho.   Perf. 13½x14
426   A121   20c Sheet of 12, #a.-l.   5.00 5.00

UNESCO, 50th Anniv. A122

Sites in Japan, vert: Nos. 427: a, c-h, Himeji-jo. b, Kyoto.
Sites in Germany: Nos. 428: a-b, Augustusburg Castle. c, Falkenlust Castle. d, Roman ruins, Trier. e, Historic house, Trier.
Each $2: No. 429, Forest, Shirakami-Sanchi, Japan. No. 430, Yakushima, Japan.

Perf. 13½x14, 14x13½
1997, Apr. 7   Litho.
Sheets of 8 or 5 + Label
427   A122   32c #a.-h.   5.50 5.50
428   A122   60c #a.-e.   6.25 6.25
Souvenir Sheets
429-430   A122   Set of 2   8.75 8.75

A123

Paintings by Hiroshige (1797-1858): No. 431: a, Swallows and Peach Blossoms under a Full Moon. b, A Parrot on a Flowering Branch. c, Crane and Rising Sun. d, Cock, Umbrella, and Morning Glories. e, A Titmouse Hanging Head Downward on a Camellia Branch.
Each $2: No. 432, Falcon on a Pine Tree with the Rising Sun. No. 433, Kingfisher and Iris.

1997, June 2   Litho.   Perf. 14
431   A123   32c Sheet of 5, #a.-e.   4.00 4.00
Souvenir Sheets
432-433   A123   Set of 2   8.25 8.25

A124

Volcano Goddesses of the Pacific: a, Darago, Philippines. b, Fuji, Japan. c, Pele, Hawaii. d, Pare, Maori. e, Dzalarhons, Haida. f, Chuginadak, Aleuts.

1997   Litho.   Perf. 14
434   A124   32c Sheet of 6, #a.-f.   4.50 4.50
PACIFIC 97.

Independence, 3rd Anniv. — A125

1997, Oct. 1   Litho.   Perf. 14
435   A125   32c multicolored   .65   .65

No. 435 was issued in sheets of 12.

Oceanographic Research — A126

Ships: No. 436: a, Albatross. b, Mabahiss. c, Atlantis II. d, Xarifa. e, Meteor. f, Egabras III. g, Discoverer. h, Kaiyo. i, Ocean Defender.
Each $2: No. 437, Jacques-Yves Cousteau (1910-97). No. 438, Cousteau, diff., vert. No. 439, Pete Seeger, vert.

1997, Oct. 1   Perf. 14x14½, 14½x14
436   A126   32c Sheet of 9, #a.-i.   6.00 6.00
Souvenir Sheets
437-439   A126   Set of 3   13.00 13.00

Diana, Princess of Wales (1961-97) — A127

1997, Nov. 26   Litho.   Perf. 14
440   A127   60c multicolored   1.25 1.25

No. 440 was issued in sheets of 6.

Disney's "Let's Read" A128

Various Disney characters: 1c, like #447i. 2c, like #447d. 3c, like #447c. 4c, like #447f. 5c, #447b. 10c, like #447h.
No. 447: a, "Exercise your right to read." b, "Reading is the ultimate luxury." c, "Share your knowledge." d, "Start them Young." e, "Reading is fundamental." f, "The insatiable reader." g, "Reading time is anytime." h, "Real men read." i, "I can read by myself."
No. 448, Daisy, "The library is for everyone," vert. No. 449, Mickey, "Books are magical."

1997, Oct. 21   Perf. 14x13½, 13½x14
441-446   A128   Set of 6   1.00 1.00
Sheet of 9
447   A128   32c #a.-i.   5.75 5.75
Souvenir Sheets
448   A128 $2 multicolored   4.50 4.50
449   A128 $3 multicolored   6.50 6.50

Christmas — A129

Children singing Christmas carol, "Some Children See Him:" No. 450: a, Girl, boy in striped shirt. b, Boy, girl in pigtails. c, Girl, boy, Madonna and Child. d, Girl, two children. e, Boy, girl with long black hair.

1997, Oct. 28   Perf. 14
450   A129   32c Strip of 5, #a.-e.   3.25 3.25

No. 450 was issued in sheets of 3 strips, bottom strip printed se-tenant with 5 labels containing lyrics.

Souvenir Sheets

New Year 1998 (Year of the Tiger) A130

Chinese toys in shape of tiger: No. 451, White background. No. 452, Green background.

1998, Jan. 2   Litho.   Perf. 14
451   A130   50c multicolored   1.25 1.25
452   A130   50c multicolored   1.25 1.25

Repair of Hubble Space Telescope — A131

No. 453: a, Photograph of nucleus of galaxy M100. b, Top of Hubble telescope with solar arrays folded. c, Astronaut riding robot arm. d, Astronaut anchored to robot arm. e, Astronaut in cargo space with Hubble mounted to shuttle Endeavor. f, Hubble released after repair.
Each $2: No. 454, Hubble cutaway, based on NASA schematic drawing. No. 455, Edwin Hubble (1889-1953), astronomer who proved existence of star systems beyond Milky Way. No. 456, Hubble Mission STS-82/Discovery.

1998, Mar. 9   Litho.   Perf. 14
453   A131   32c Sheet of 6, #a.-
        f.   4.00 4.00
Souvenir Sheets
454-456   A131   Set of 3   12.50 12.50

Mother Teresa (1910-97) — A132

Various portraits.

1998, Mar. 12   Litho.   Perf. 14
457 A132 60c Sheet of 4, #a.-d.   5.00 5.00

Deep Sea Robots — A133

No. 458: a, Ladybird ROV. b, Slocum Glider. c, Hornet. d, Scorpio. e, Odyssey AUV. f, Jamstec Survey System Launcher. g, Scarab. h, USN Torpedo Finder/Salvager. i, Jamstec Survey System Vehicle. j, Cetus Tether. k, Deep Sea ROV. l, ABE. m, OBSS. n, RCV 225G Swimming Eyeball. o, Japanese UROV. p, Benthos RPV. q, CURV. r, Smartie.
Each $2: No. 459, Jason Jr. inspecting Titanic. No. 460, Dolphin 3K.

1998, Apr. 21
458 A133 32c Sheet of 18, #a.-r.   12.00 12.00

Souvenir Sheets
459-460 A133 Set of 2   8.50 8.50
UNESCO Intl. Year of the Ocean.

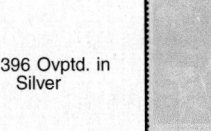

No. 396 Ovptd. in Silver

1998, May 13   Litho.   Perf. 14
461 A111 20c Sheet of 30, #a.-ad.   12.00 12.00
No. 461 is overprinted in sheet margin, "ISRAEL 98 — WORLD STAMP EXHIBITION / TEL AVIV 13-21 MAY 1998." Location of overprint varies.

Legend of Orachel — A134

#462: a, Bai (hut), people. b, Bai, lake. c, Bai, lake, person in canoe. d, Bird on branch over lake. e, Men rowing in canoe. f, Canoe, head of snake. g, Alligator under water. h, Fish, shark. i, Turtle, body of snake. j, Underwater bai, "gods". k, Snails, fish, Orachel swimming. l, Orachel's feet, coral, fish.

1998, May 29   Litho.   Perf. 14
462 A134 40c Sheet of 12, #a.-l.   9.50 9.50

1998 World Cup Soccer Championships, France — A135

Players, color of shirt — #463: a, Yellow, black & red. b, Blue, white & red. c, Green & white. d, White, red & blue. e, Green & white (black shorts). f, White, red & black. g, Blue & yellow. h, Red & white.
$3, Pele.

1998, June 5
463 A135 50c Sheet of 8, #a.-h.   8.00 8.00

Souvenir Sheet
464 A135 $3 multicolored   6.00 6.00

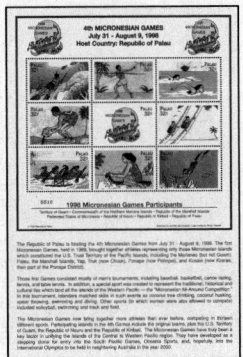

4th Micronesian Games, Palau — A136

Designs: a, Spear fishing. b, Spear throwing. c, Swimming. d, Pouring milk from coconut. e, Logo of games. f, Climbing coconut trees. g, Canoeing. h, Husking coconut. i, Deep sea diving.

1998, July 31   Litho.   Perf. 14
465 A136 32c Sheet of 9, #a.-i.   5.75 5.75

Rudolph The Red-Nosed Reindeer — A137

Christmas: a, Rudolph, two reindeer, girl. b, Two reindeer, girl holding flowers. c, Girl, two reindeer, boy. d, Two reindeer, girl smiling. e, Santa, children, Christmas gifts.

1998, Sept. 15   Litho.   Perf. 14
466 A137 32c Strip of 5, #a.-e.   3.25 3.25
No. 466 is a continuous design and was issued in sheets of 15 stamps.

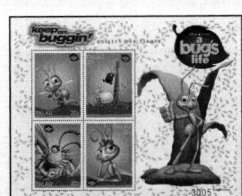

Disney/Pixar's "A Bug's Life" — A138

No. 467: a, Dot. b, Heimlich, Francis, Slim. c, Hopper. d, Princess Atta.
No. 468: Various scenes with Flik, Princess Atta.
No. 469, horiz.: a, Circus bugs. b, Slim, Francis, Heimlich. c, Manny. d, Francis.
No. 470: a, Slim, Flik. b, Heimlich, Slim, Francis performing. c, Manny, Flik. d, Gypsy, Manny, Rosie.
Each $2: No. 471, Gypsy. No. 472, Princess Atta, Flik, horiz. No. 473, Slim, Francis, Heimlich, horiz. No. 474, Francis, Slim, Flik, Heimlich, horiz.

Perf. 13½x14, 14x13½
1998, Dec. 1   Litho.   Sheets of 4
467 A138 20c #a.-d.   1.75 1.75
468 A138 32c #a.-d.   2.75 2.75
469 A138 50c #a.-d.   4.25 4.25
470 A138 60c #a.-d.   5.25 5.25

Souvenir Sheets
471-474 A138 Set of 4   18.00 18.00
Nos. 473-474 each contain one 76x51mm stamp.

John Glenn's Return to Space — A139

No. 475, Various photos of Project Mercury, Friendship 7 mission, 1962, each 60c.
No. 476, Various photos of Discovery Space Shuttle mission, 1998, each 60c.
Each $2: No. 477, Portrait, 1962. No. 478, Portrait, 1998.

1999, Jan. 7   Litho.   Perf. 14
Sheets of 8, #a-h
475-476 A139 Set of 2   19.00 19.00

Souvenir Sheets
477-478 A139 Set of 2   8.50 8.50
Nos. 477-478 each contain one 28x42mm stamp.

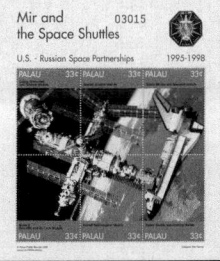

Environmentalists — A140

a, Rachel Carson. b, J.N. "Ding" Darling, US Duck stamp #RW1. c, David Brower. d, Jacques Cousteau. e, Roger Tory Peterson. f, Prince Philip. g, Joseph Wood Krutch. h, Aldo Leopold. i, Dian Fossey. j, US Vice-President Al Gore. k, David Attenborough. l, Paul McCready. m, Sting (Gordon Sumner). n, Paul Winter. o, Ian MacHarg. p, Denis Hayes.

1999, Feb. 1   Litho.   Perf. 14½
479 A140 33c Sheet of 16, #a.-p.   10.50 10.50
No. 479i shows Dian Fossey's name misspelled "Diane."

MIR Space Station A141

No. 480: a, Soyuz Spacecraft; Science Module. b, Specktr Science Module. c, Space Shuttle, Spacelab Module. d, Kvant 2, Scientific and Air Lock Module. e, Kristall Technological Module. f, Space Shuttle, Docking Module.
Each $2: No. 481, Astronaut Charles Precout, Cosmonaut Talgat Musabayev. No. 482, Cosmonaut Valeri Poliakov. No. 483, US Mission Specialist Shannon W. Lucid, Cosmonaut Yuri Y. Usachov. No. 484, Cosmonaut Anatoly Solovyov.

1999, Feb. 18   Litho.   Perf. 14
480 A141 33c Sheet of 6, #a.-f.   3.75 3.75

Souvenir Sheets
481-484 A141 Set of 4   16.00 16.00

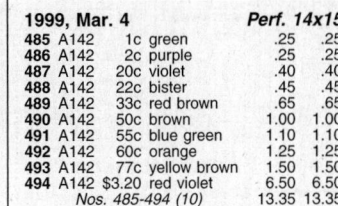

Personalities — A142

1c, Haruo Remiliik. 2c, Lazarus Salil. 20c, Charlie W. Gibbons. 22c, Adm. Raymond A. Spruance. 33c, Kuniwo Nakamura. 50c, Adm. William F. Halsey. 55c, Col. Lewis "Chesty" Puller. 60c, Franklin D. Roosevelt. 77c, Harry S Truman. $3.20, Jimmy Carter.

1999, Mar. 4   Perf. 14x15
485 A142 1c green   .25 .25
486 A142 2c purple   .25 .25
487 A142 20c violet   .40 .40
488 A142 22c bister   .45 .45
489 A142 33c red brown   .65 .65
490 A142 50c brown   1.00 1.00
491 A142 55c blue green   1.10 1.10
492 A142 60c orange   1.25 1.25
493 A142 77c yellow brown   1.50 1.50
494 A142 $3.20 red violet   6.50 6.50
Nos. 485-494 (10)   13.35 13.35
Nos. 485, 492 exist dated 2001.

Australia '99 World Stamp Expo A143

Endangered species — #495: a, Leatherback turtle. b, Kemp's ridley turtle. c, Green turtle. d, Marine iguana. e, Table mountain ghost frog. f, Spiny turtle. g, Hewitt's ghost frog. h, Geometric tortoise. i, Limestone salmander. j, Desert rain frog. k, Cape plantanna. l, Long-toed tree frog.
Each $2: No. 496, Marine crocodile. No. 497, Hawksbill turtle.

1999, Mar. 19   Litho.   Perf. 13
495 A143 33c Sheet of 12, #a.-l.   8.00 8.00

Souvenir Sheets
496-497 A143 Set of 2   8.00 8.00

IBRA '99, Nuremburg — A144

No. 498, Leipzig-Dresden Railway, Caroline Islands Type A4. No. 499, Gölsdorf 4-8-0, Caroline Islands #8, 10.
$2, Caroline Islands #1.

1999, Apr. 27   Litho.   Perf. 14
498-499 A144 55c Set of 2   2.25 2.25

Souvenir Sheet
500 A144 $2 multicolored   4.00 4.00

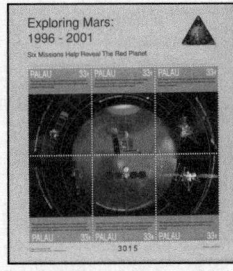

Exploration of Mars — A145

No. 501: a, Mars Global Surveyor. b, Mars Climate Orbiter. c, Mars Polar Lander. d, Deep Space 2. e, Mars Surveyor 2001 Orbiter. f, Mars Surveyor 2001 Lander.
Each $2: No. 502, Mars Global Surveyor. No. 503, Mars Climate Orbiter. No. 504, Mars Polar Lander. No. 505, Mars Surveyor 2001 Lander.

1999, May 10   Litho.   Perf. 14
501 A145 33c Sheet of 6, #a.-f.   4.00 4.00

Souvenir Sheets
502-505 A145 Set of 4   16.00 16.00
Nos. 502-505 each contain one 38x50mm stamp.
See Nos. 507-511.

Earth Day A146

Pacific insects: a, Banza Natida. b, Drosophila heteroneura. c, Nesomicromus vagus. d, Megalagrian leptodemus. e, Pseudopsectra cookearum. f, Ampheida neacaledonia. g, Pseudopsectra swezeyi. h, Deinacrida heteracantha. i, Beech forest butterfly. j, Hercules moth. k, Striped sphinx moth. l, Tussock butterfly. m. Elytrocheilus. n, Bush cricket. o, Longhorn beetle. p, Abathrus bicolor. q, Stylagymnusa subantartica. r, Moth butterfly. s, Paraconosoma naviculare. t, Ornithoptera priamus.

1999, May 24
506 A146 33c Sheet of 20,
   #a.-t.   13.50 13.50

Space Type

International Space Station — #507: a, Launch 1R. b, Launch 14A. c, Launch 8A. d, Launch 1J. e, Launch 1E. f, Launch 16A.
Each $2: No. 508, Intl. Space Station. No. 509, Cmdr. Bob Cabana, Cosmonaut Sergei Krikalev. No. 510, Crew of Flight 2R, horiz. No. 511, X-38 Crew Return Vehicle, horiz.

1999, June 12   **Litho.**   **Perf. 14**
507 A145 33c Sheet of 6, #a.-
   f.   4.00 4.00
Souvenir Sheets
508-511 A145 Set of 4   16.00 16.00

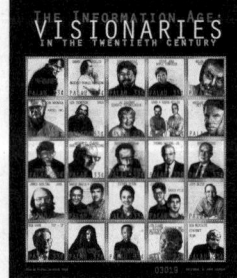

20th Century Visionaries — A147

Designs: a, William Gibson, "Cyberspace." b, Danny Hillis, Massively Parallel Processing. c, Steve Wozniak, Apple Computer. d, Steve Jobs, Apple Computer. e, Nolan Bushnell, Atari, Inc. f, John Warnock, Adobe, Inc. g, Ken Thompson, Unix. h, Al Shugart, Seagate Technologies. i, Rand & Robyn Miller, "MYST." j, Nicolas Negroponte, MIT Media Lab. k, Bill Gates, Microsoft, Inc. l, Arthur C. Clarke, Orbiting Communications Satellite. m, Marshall Mcluhan, "The Medium is the Message." n, Thomas Watson, Jr., IBM. o, Gordon Moore, Intel Corporation, "Moore's Law." p, James Gosling, Java. q, Sabeer Bhatia & Jack Smith, Hotmail.com. r, Esther Dyson, "Release 2.0." s, Jerry Yang, David Filo, Yahoo! t, Jeff Bezos, Amazon.com. u, Bob Kahn, TCP-IP. v, Jaron Lanter, "Virtual Reality." w, Andy Grove, Intel Corporation. x, Jim Clark, Silicon Graphics, Inc., Netscape Communications Corp. y, Bob Metcalfe, Ethernet, 3com.

1999, June 30   **Litho.**   **Perf. 14**
512 A147 33c Sheet of 25,
   #a.-y.   17.00 17.00

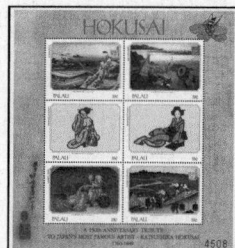

Paintings by Hokusai (1760-1849) — A148

No. 513, each 33c: a, Women Divers. b, Bull and Parasol. c, Drawings of Women (partially nude). d, Drawings of Women (seated, facing forward). e, Japanese spaniel. f, Porters in Landscape.
No. 514, each 33c: a, Bacchanalian Revelry. b, Bacchanalian Revelry (two seated back to back). c, Drawings of Women (crawling). d, Drawings of Women (facing backward). e, Ox-Herd. f, Ox-Herd (man on bridge).
Each $2: No. 515, Mount Fuji in a Thunderstorm, vert. No. 516, At Swan Lake in Shinano.

1999, July 20   **Perf. 14x13¾**
Sheets of 6, #a-f
513-514 A148 Set of 2   8.00 8.00
Souvenir Sheets
515-516 A148 Set of 2   8.00 8.00

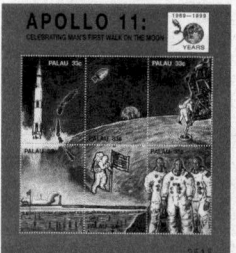

Apollo 11, 30th Anniv. A149

No. 517: a, Lift-off, jettison of stages. b, Earth, moon, capsule. c, Astronaut on lunar module ladder. d, Lift-off. e, Planting flag on moon. f, Astronauts Collins, Armstrong and Aldrin.
Each $2: No. 518, Rocket on launch pad. No. 519, Astronaut on ladder, earth. No. 520, Lunar module above moon. No. 521, Capsule in ocean.

1999, July 20 **Litho.** **Perf. 13½x14**
517 A149 33c Sheet of 6, #a.-
   f.   4.00 4.00
Souvenir Sheets
518-521 A149 Set of 4   16.00 16.00

Queen Mother (b. 1900) — A150

No. 522: a, In Australia, 1958. b, In 1960. c, In 1970. d, In 1987.
$2, Holding book, 1947.

Gold Frames

1999, Aug. 4   **Perf. 14**
522 A150 60c Sheet of 4, #a.-d.,
   + label   4.75 4.75
Souvenir Sheet
Perf. 13¾
523 A150 $2 black   4.00 4.00
No. 523 contains one 38x51mm stamp.
See Nos. 636-637.

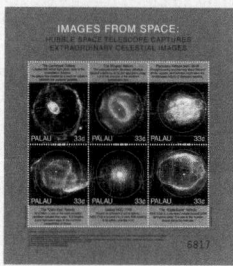

Hubble Space Telescope Images — A151

No. 524: a, Cartwheel Galaxy. b, Stingray Nebula. c, NGC 3918. d, Cat's Eye Nebula (NGC 6543). e, NGC 7742. f, Eight-burst Nebula (NGC 3132).
Each $2: No. 525, Eta Carinae. No. 526, Planetary nebula M2-9. No. 527, Supernova 1987-A. No. 528, Infrared aurora of Saturn.

1999, Oct. 15 **Litho.** **Perf. 13¾**
524 A151 33c Sheet of 6, #a.-
   f.   4.00 4.00
Souvenir Sheets
525-528 A151 Set of 4   16.00 16.00

Christmas — A152

Birds and: a, Cows, chickens. b, Donkey, geese, rabbit. c, Infant, cat, lambs. d, Goats, geese. e, Donkey, rooster.

1999, Nov. 15   **Perf. 14**
529 A152 20c Strip of 5, #a.-e.   2.00 2.00

Love for Dogs — A153

No. 530: a, Keep safe. b, Show affection. c, A place of one's own. d, Communicate. e, Good food. f, Annual checkup. g, Teach rules. h, Exercise & play. i, Let him help. j, Unconditional love.
Each $2: No. 531, Pleasure of your company. No. 532, Love is a gentle thing.

1999, Nov. 23 **Litho.** **Perf. 14**
530 A153 33c Sheet of 10, #a.-j. 6.75 6.75
Souvenir Sheets
531-532 A153 Set of 2   8.00 8.00

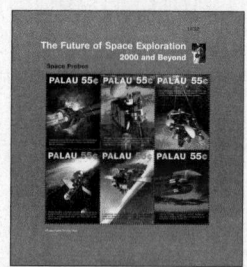

Futuristic Space Probes — A154

Text starting with — No. 533: a, Deep space probes like. . . b, This piggy-back. . . c, Deep space telescope. . . d, Mission planning. . . e, In accordance. . . f, Utilizing onboard. . .
Each $2: No. 534, This secondary. . . No. 535, Deep space probes are an integral. . . No. 536, Deep space probes are our. . ., horiz. No. 537, With the. . . , horiz.

2000, Jan. 18 **Litho.** **Perf. 13¾**
533 A154 55c Sheet of 6, #a.-
   f.   6.00 6.00
Souvenir Sheets
534-537 A154 Set of 4   16.00 16.00

Millennium — A155

Highlights of 1800-50 — No. 538, each 20c: a, Brazilian Indians. b, Haiti slave revolt. c, Napoleon becomes Emperor of France. d, Shaka Zulu. e, "Frankenstein" written. f, Simon Bolivar. g, Photography invented. h, First water purification works built. i, First all-steam railway. j, Michael Faraday discovers electromagnetism. k, First use of anesthesia. l, Samuel Morse completes first telegraph line. m, Women's rights convention in Seneca Falls, NY. n, Birth of Karl Marx. o, Revolution in German Confederation. p, Charles Darwin's voyages on the "Beagle" (60x40mm). q, Beijing, China.
Highlights of 1980-89 — No. 539, each 20c: a, Lech Walesa organizes Polish shipyard workers. b, Voyager I photographs Saturn. c, Ronald Reagan elected US president. d, Identification of AIDS virus. e, Wedding of Prince Charles and Lady Diana Spencer. f, Compact discs go into production. g, Bhopal, India gas disaster. h, I. M. Pei's Pyramid entrance to the Louvre opens. i, Mikhail Gorbachev becomes leader of Soviet Union. j, Chernobyl nuclear disaster. k, Explosion of Space Shuttle "Challenger." l, Klaus Barbie convicted of crimes against humanity. m, Life of author Salman Rushdie threatened by Moslems. n, Benazir Bhutto becomes first woman prime minister of a Moslem state. o, Tiananmen Square revolt. p, Berlin Wall falls (60x40mm). q, World Wide Web.

2000, Feb. 2 **Litho.** **Perf. 12¾x12½**
Sheets of 17, #a.-q.
538-539 A155 Set of 2   14.00 14.00
Misspellings and historical inaccuracies abound on Nos. 538-539.
See No. 584.

New Year 2000 (Year of the Dragon) A156

2000, Feb. 5   **Perf. 13¾**
540 A156 $2 multi   4.00 4.00

US Presidents — A157

2000, Mar. 1 **Litho.** **Perf. 13½x13¼**
541 A157 $1 Bill Clinton   2.00 2.00
542 A157 $2 Ronald Reagan   4.00 4.00
543 A157 $3 Gerald Ford   6.00 6.00
544 A157 $5 George Bush   10.00 10.00
Size: 40x24mm
Perf. 14¾x14
545 A157 $11.75 Kennedy   22.50 22.50
   Nos. 541-545 (5)   44.50 44.50

20th Century Discoveries About Prehistoric Life — A158

Designs: a, Australopithecines. b, Australopithecine skull. c, Homo habilis. d, Hand axe. e, Homo habilis skull. f, Lucy, Australopithecine skeleton. g, Archaic Homo sapiens skull. h, Diapithicine skull. i, Homo erectus. j, Wood hut. k, Australopithecine ethopsis skull. l, Dawn of mankind. m, Homo sapiens skull. n, Taung baby's skull. o, Homo erectus skull. p, Louis Leakey (1903-72), paleontologist. q, Neanderthal skull. r, Neandertahal. s, Evolution of the foot. t, Raymond Dart (1893-1988), paleontologist.

2000, Mar. 15   *Perf. 14¼*
546 A158 20c Sheet of 20, #a.-t.   8.00 8.00

Misspellings and historical inaccuracies are found on Nos. 546g, 546m, 546p, 546t and perhaps others.

2000 Summer Olympics,
Sydney — A159

Designs: a, Charlotte Cooper, tennis player at 1924 Olympics. b, Women's shot put. c, Helsinki Stadium, site of 1952 Olympics. d, Ancient Greek athletes.

2000, Mar. 31   *Perf. 14*
547 A159 33c Sheet of 4, #a.-d.   2.75 2.75

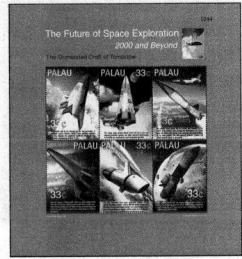

Future of Space Exploration — A160

Text starting with — No. 548: a, This vehicle will be. . . b, This single stage. . . c, This robotic rocket. . . d, Dynamic. . . e, This fully. . . f, This launch vehicle. . .
Each $2: No. 549, Increasingly, space travel. . . No. 550, Designed with projects. . ., horiz. No. 551, Design is currently. . ., horiz. No. 552, Inevitably, the future. . ., horiz.

2000, Apr. 10   *Perf. 13¾*
548 A160 33c Sheet of 6, #a.-f.   4.00 4.00
Souvenir Sheets
549-552 A160 Set of 4   16.00 16.00

Birds — A161

No. 553: a, Slatey-legged crake. b, Micronesian kingfisher. c, Little pied cormorant. d, Pacific reed egret. e, Nicobar pigeon. f, Rufous night heron.
No. 554: a, Palau ground dove. b, Palau scops owl. c, Mangrove flycatcher. d, Palau bush warbler. e, Palau fantail. f, Morningbird.
Each $2: No. 555, Palau fruit dove, horiz. No. 556, Palau white-eye, horiz.

2000, Apr. 14   *Litho.*   *Perf. 14¼*
553 A161 20c Sheet of 6, #a.-f.   2.40 2.40
554 A161 33c Sheet of 6, #a.-f.   4.00 4.00
Souvenir Sheets
555-556 A161 Set of 2   8.00 8.00

Visionaries of the 20th
Century — A162

a, Booker T. Washington. b, Buckminster Fuller. c, Marie Curie. d, Walt Disney. e, F. D. Roosevelt. f, Henry Ford. g, Betty Friedan. h, Sigmund Freud. i, Mohandas Gandhi. j, Mikhail Gorbachev. k, Stephen Hawking. l, Martin Luther King, Jr. m, Toni Morrison. n, Georgia O'Keeffe. o, Rosa Parks. p, Carl Sagan. q, Jonas Salk. r, Sally Ride. s, Nikola Tesla. t, Wilbur and Orville Wright.

2000, Apr. 28   *Litho.*   *Perf. 14¼x14½*
557 A162 33c Sheet of 20,
     #a.-t.   13.50 13.50

20th Century Science and Medicine
Advances — A163

No. 558, each 33c: a, James D. Watson, 1962 Nobel laureate. b, Har Gobind Khorana and Robert Holley, 1968 Nobel laureates. c, Hamilton O. Smith and Werner Arber, 1978 Nobel laureates. d, Extraction fo DNA from cells. e, Richard J. Roberts, 1993 Nobel laureate.
No. 559, each 33c: a, Francis Crick, 1962 Nobel laureate. b, Marshall W. Nirenberg, 1968 Nobel laureate. c, Daniel Nathans, 1978 Nobel laureate. d, Harold E. Varmus and J. Michael Bishop, 1989 Nobel laureates. e, Phillip A. Sharp, 1993 Nobel laureate.
No. 560, each 33c: a, Maurice H. F. Wilkins, 1962 Nobel laureate. b, DNA strand. c, Frederick Sanger and Walter Gilbert, 1980 Nobel laureates. d, Kary B. Mullis, 1993 Nobel laureate. e, Two DNA strands.
No. 561, each 33c: a, Four sheep, test tube. b, Two DNA strands, diagram of DNA fragments. c, Paul Berg, 1980 Nobel laureate. d, Michael Smith, 1993 Nobel laureate. e, Deer, DNA strands.
Each $2: #562, Deer. #563, Dolly, 1st cloned sheep.
Illustration reduced.

2000, May 10   *Perf. 13¾*
Sheets of 5, #a.-e.
558-561 A163 Set of 4   14.00 14.00
Souvenir Sheets
562-563 A163 Set of 2   8.00 8.00

Nos. 562-563 each contain one 38x50mm stamp.

Marine
Life
A164

No. 564, each 33c: a, Prawn. b, Deep sea angler. c, Rooster fish. d, Grenadier. e, Platyberix opalescens. f, Lantern fish.
No. 565, each 33c: a, Emperor angelfish. b, Nautilus. c, Moorish idol. d, Sea horse. e, Clown triggerfish. f, Clown fish.
Each $2: No. 566, Giant squid. No. 567, Manta ray.

2000, May 10   *Litho.*   *Perf. 14*
Sheets of 6, #a-f
564-565 A164 Set of 2   8.00 8.00
Souvenir Sheets
566-567 A164 Set of 2   8.00 8.00

A165

Millennium — A165a

No. 568, horiz. — "2000," hourglass, and map of: a, North Pacific area. b, U.S. and Canada. c, Europe. d, South Pacific. e, South America. f, Southern Africa.
No. 569 — Clock face and: a, Sky. b, Building. c, Cove and lighthouse. d, Barn. e, Forest. f, Desert.

2000, May 25   *Perf. 13¾*
568 A165 20c Sheet of 6, #a-f   2.40 2.40
569 A165a 55c Sheet of 6, #a-f   6.75 6.75

The Stamp Show 2000, London.

New and Recovering Species — A166

No. 570, each 33c: a, Aleutian Canada goose. b, Western gray kangaroo. c, Palau scops owl. d, Jocotoco antpitta. e, Orchid. f, Red lechwe.
No. 571, each 33c: a, Bald eagle. b, Smallwhorled pogonia. c, Arctic peregrine falcon. d, Golden lion tamarin. e, American alligator. f, Brown pelican.
Each $2: No. 572, Leopard. No. 573, Lahontan cutthroat trout, horiz.

2000, June 20   *Perf. 14*
Sheets of 6, #a-f
570-571 A166 Set of 2   8.00 8.00
Souvenir Sheets
572-573 A166 Set of 2   8.00 8.00

Dinosaurs — A167

No. 574: a, Rhamphorhynchus. b, Ceratosaurus. c, Apatosaurus. d, Stegosaurus. e, Archaeopteryx. f, Allosaurus.
No. 575: a, Parasaurolophus. b, Pteranodon. c, Tyrannosaurus. d, Triceratops. e, Ankylosaurus. f, Velociraptor.
Each $2: No. 576, Jurassic era view. No. 577, Cretaceous era view.

2000, June 20
574 A167 20c Sheet of 6, #a-f   2.40 2.40
575 A167 33c Sheet of 6, #a-f   4.00 4.00
Souvenir Sheets
576-577 A167 Set of 2   8.00 8.00

Queen
Mother,
100th
Birthday
A168

No. 578, 55c: a, With King George VI. b, Wearing brown hat.
No. 579, 55c: a, Wearing green hat. b, Wearing white hat.

2000, Sept. 1   *Litho.*   *Perf. 14*
Sheets of 4, 2 each #a-b
578-579 A168 Set of 2   9.00 9.00
Souvenir Sheet
580 A168 $2 Wearing yellow hat 4.00 4.00

First
Zeppelin
Flight,
Cent.
A169

No. 581: a, Le Jaune. b, Forlanini's Leonardo da Vinci. c, Baldwin's airship. d, Astra-Torres I. e, Parseval PL VII. f, Lebaudy's Liberte.
No. 582, $2, Santos-Dumont No. VI. No. 583, $2, Santos-Dumont Baladeuse No. 9.

2000, Sept. 1
581 A169 55c Sheet of 6, #a-f   6.75 6.75
Souvenir Sheets
582-583 A169 Set of 2   8.00 8.00

Millennium Type of 2000
Sheet of 17

Undersea History and Exploration: a, Viking diver. b, Arab diver Issa. c, Salvage diver. d, Diver. e, Diving bell. f, Turtle. g, Siebe helmet. h, C.S.S. Hunley. i, Argonaut. j, Photosphere. k, Helmet diver. l, Bathysphere. m, Coelacanth. n, WWII charioteers. o, Trieste. p, Alvin visits geothermal vents (60x40mm). q, Jim suit.

2000, Oct. 16   *Perf. 12¾x12½*
584 A155 33c #a-q + label   13.00 13.00

POPE JOHN PAUL II
Celebrates his 80th Birthday

Photomosaic of Pope John Paul II — A170

Various photos with religious themes.

2000, Dec. 1   **Perf. 13¾**
585 A170 50c Sheet of 8, #a-h   8.00 8.00

Souvenir Sheets

New Year 2001 (Year of the Snake) A171

Snake color: #586, Black. #587, Red.

2000, Dec. 1   **Perf. 14¼**
586-587 A171 60c Set of 2   2.40 2.40

Pacific Ocean Marine Life A172

No. 588: a, Scalloped hammerhead shark. b, Whitetip reef shark. c, Moon jellyfish. d, Lionfish. e, Seahorse. f, Spotted eagle ray.

2000   **Perf. 14½x14¼**
588 A172 55c Sheet of 6, #a-f   6.75 6.75

Atlantic Ocean Fish A173

No. 589, horiz.: a, Reef bass. b, White shark. c, Sharptail eel. d, Sailfish. e, Southern stingray. f, Ocean triggerfish.
#590, Short bigeye. #591, Gafftopsail catfish.

2000   **Perf. 13¾**
589 A173 20c Sheet of 6, #a-f   2.40 2.40
Souvenir Sheets
590-591 A173 $2 Set of 2   8.00 8.00

Pacific Arts Festival A174

No. 592: a, Dancers, by S. Adelbai. b, Story Board Art, by D. Inabo. c, Traditional Money, by M. Takeshi. d, Clay Lamp and Bowl, by W. Watanabe. e, Meeting House, by Pasqual Tiakl. f, Outrigger Canoe, by S. Adelbai. g, Weaver, by M. Vitarelli. h, Rock Island Scene, by W. Marcil. i, Contemporary Music, by J. Imetuker.

2000, Nov. 1   Litho.   Perf. 14¼
592 A174 33c Sheet of 9, #a-i   6.00 6.00

National Museum, 45th Anniv. A175

No. 593: a, Klilt, turtle shell bracelet. b, Sculpture by H. Hijikata. c, Turtle shell women's money. d, Cherecheroi, by T. Suzuki. e, Money jar, by B. Sylvester. f, Prince Lebu by Ichikawa. g, Beach at Lild, by H. Hijikata. h, Traditional mask. i, Taro platter, by T. Rebluud. j, Meresebang, by Ichikawa. k, Wood sculpture, by B. Sylvester. l, Birth Ceremony, by I. Kishigawa.

2000, Nov. 1   Perf. 14x14¾
593 A175 33c Sheet of 12, #a-l   8.00 8.00

Butterflies A176

Designs: No. 594, 33c, Indian red admiral. No. 595, 33c, Fiery jewel. No. 596, 33c, Checkered swallowtail. No. 597, 33c, Yamfly.
No. 598, 33c: a, Large green-banded blue. b, Union Jack. c, Broad-bordered grass yellow. d, Striped blue crow. e, Red lacewing. f, Palmfly.
No. 599, 33c: a, Cairn's birdwing. b, Meadow argus. c, Orange albatross. d, Glasswing. e, Beak. f, Great eggfly.
No. 600, $2, Clipper. No. 601, $2, Blue triangle.

2000, Dec. 15   Perf. 14
594-597 A176 Set of 4   2.75 2.75
Sheets of 6, #a-f
598-599 A176 Set of 2   8.00 8.00
Souvenir Sheets
600-601 A176 Set of 2   8.00 8.00

Flora and Fauna A177

No. 602, 33c: a, Giant spiral ginger. b, Good luck plant. c, Ti tree, coconuts. d, Butterfly. e, Saltwater crocodile. f, Orchid.
No. 603, 33c: a, Little kingfisher. b, Mangrove snake. c, Bats, breadfruit. d, Giant tree frog. e, Giant centipede. f, Crab-eating macaque.
No. 604, $2, Soft coral, surgeonfish. No. 605, $2, Land crab, vert.

2000, Dec. 29 Perf. 14x14¼, 14¼x14
Sheets of 6, #a-f
602-603 A177 Set of 2   8.00 8.00
Souvenir Sheets
604-605 A177 Set of 2   8.00 8.00

Personalities Type of 1999

Designs: 11c, Lazarus Salil. 70c, Gen. Douglas MacArthur. 80c, Adm. Chester W. Nimitz. $12.25, John F. Kennedy.

2001   Litho.   Perf. 14x14¾
606 A142   11c purple   .25 .25
607 A142   70c lilac   1.40 1.40
608 A142   80c green   1.60 1.60
609 A142 $12.25 red   25.00 25.00
  Nos. 606-609 (4)   28.25 28.25
Issued: Nos. 607-609, 6/10.

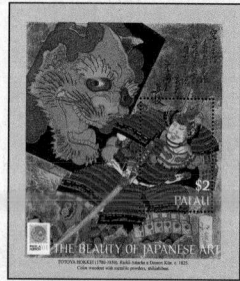

Phila Nippon '01, Japan A178

No. 610, 60c: a, Ono no Komachi Washing the Copybook, by Kiyomitsu Torii. b, Woman Playing Samisen and Woman Reading al Letter, by School of Matabei Iwasa. c, The Actor Danjura Ichikawa V as a Samurai in a Wrestling Arena Striking a Pose on a Go Board, by Shunsho Katsukawa. d, Gentleman Entertained by Courtesans, by Kiyonaga Torii. e, Geisha at a Teahouse in Shinagawa, by Kiyonaga Torii.
No. 611, 60c: a, Preparing Sashimi, by Utamaro. b, Ichimatsu Sanogawa I as Sogo no Goro and Kikugoro Onoe as Kyo no Jiro in Umewakana Futaba Soga, by Toyonobu Ishikawa. c, Courtesan Adjusting Her Comb, by Dohan Kaigetsudo. d, The Actor Tomijuro Nakamura I in a Female Role Dancing, by Shunsho Katsukawa. e, Woman with Poem Card and Writing Brush, by Gakutei Yashima.
No. 612, Six panels of screen, Kitano Shrine in Kyoto, by unknown artist.
No. 613, $2, Raiko Attacks a Demon Kite, by Hokkei Totoya. No. 614, $2, Beauty Writing a Letter, by Doshin Kaigetsudo. No. 615, $2, Fireworks at Ikenohata, by Kiyochika Kobayashi.

2001, Aug. 13   Litho.   Perf. 14
Sheets of 5, #a-e
610-611 A178   Set of 2   12.00 12.00
612 A178 60c Sheet of 6, #a-f   7.25 7.25
Souvenir Sheets
613-615 A178   Set of 3   12.00 12.00

Moths — A179

Designs: 20c, Veined tiger moth. 21c, Basker moth. 80c, White-lined sphinx moth. $1, Isabella tiger moth.
No. 620, 34c: a, Cinnabar moth. b, Beautiful tiger moth. c, Great tiger moth. d, Provence burnet moth. e, Jersey tiger moth. f, Ornate moth.
No. 621, 70c: a, Hoop pine moth. b, King's bee hawk moth. c, Banded bagnest moth. d, Io moth. e, Tau emperor moth. f, Lime hawkmoth.
No. 622, $2, Spanish moon moth. No. 623, $2, Owl moth.

2001, Oct. 15   Litho.   Perf. 14
616-619 A179   Set of 4   4.50 4.50
Sheets of 6, #a-f
620-621 A179   Set of 2   12.50 12.50
Souvenir Sheets
622-623 A179   Set of 2   8.00 8.00

Nobel Prizes, Cent. A180

Literature laureates — No. 624, 34c: a, Ivo Andric, 1961. b, Eyvind Johnson, 1974. c, Salvatore Quasimodo, 1959. d, Mikhail Sholokhov, 1965. e, Pablo Neruda, 1971. f, Saul Bellow, 1976.
No. 625, 70c: a, Boris Pasternak, 1958. b, Francois Mauriac, 1952. c, Frans Eemil Sillanpää, 1939. d, Roger Martin du Gard, 1937. e, Pearl Buck, 1938. f, André Gide, 1947.
No. 626, 80c: a, Karl Gjellerup, 1917. b, Anatole France, 1921. c, Sinclair Lewis, 1930. d, Jacinto Benavente, 1922. e, John Galsworthy, 1932. f, Erik A. Karlfeldt, 1931.
No. 627, $2, Luigi Pirandello, 1934. No. 628, $2, Bertrand Russell, 1950. No. 629, Harry Martinson, 1974.

2001, Oct. 30   Sheets of 6, #a-f
624-626 A180   Set of 3   22.50 22.50
Souvenir Sheets
627-629 A180   Set of 3   12.00 12.00

2002 World Cup Soccer Championships, Japan and Korea — A181

No. 630, 34c — World Cup posters from: a, 1950. b, 1954. c, 1958. d, 1962. e, 1966. f, 1970.
No. 631, 80c — World Cup posters from: a, 1978. b, 1982. c, 1986. d, 1990. e, 1994. f, 1998.
No. 632, $2, World Cup poster, 1930. No. 633, $2, Head and globe from World Cup trophy.

2001, Nov. 29   Perf. 13¾x14¼
Sheets of 6, #a-f
630-631 A181   Set of 2   14.00 14.00
Souvenir Sheets
Perf. 14½x14¼
632-633 A181   Set of 2   8.00 8.00

Christmas — A182

Denominations: 20c, 34c.

2001, Nov. 29   Perf. 14
634-635 A182   Set of 2   1.10 1.10

Queen Mother Type of 1999
Redrawn

No. 636: a, In Australia, 1958. b, In 1960. c, In 1970. d, In 1987.
$2, Holding book, 1947.

2001, Dec. 13   Perf. 14
Yellow Orange Frames
636 A150 60c Sheet of 4, #a-d, +
         label   4.75 4.75
Souvenir Sheet
Perf. 13¾
637 A150 $2 black   4.00 4.00

Queen Mother's 101st birthday. No. 637 contains one 38x51mm stamp that is slightly darker than that found on No. 523. Sheet margins of Nos. 636-637 lack embossing and gold arms and frames found on Nos. 522-523.

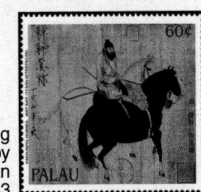

Pasturing Horses, by Han Kan — A183

2001, Dec. 17 **Perf. 14x14¾**
638 A183 60c multi   1.25 1.25
New Year 2002 (Year of the Horse). Printed in sheets of 4.

Birds A184

No. 639, 55c: a, Yellow-faced myna. b, Red-bellied pitta. c, Red-bearded bee-eater. d, Superb fruit dove. e, Coppersmith barbet. f, Diard's trogon.
No. 640, 60c: a, Spectacled monarch. b, Banded pitta. c, Rufous-backed kingfisher. d, Scarlet robin. e, Golden whistler. f, Jewel babbler.
No. 641, $2, Paradise flycatcher. No. 642, $2, Common kingfisher.

2001, Dec. 26 **Perf. 14**
Sheets of 6, #a-f
639-640 A184 Set of 2   14.00 14.00
Souvenir Sheets
Perf. 14¾
641-642 A184 Set of 2   8.00 8.00

Opening of Palau-Japan Frendship Bridge — A185

No. 643, 20c; No. 644, 34c: a, Bird on orange rock. b, Island, one palm tree. c, Island, three palm trees. d, Rocks, boat prow. e, Boat, bat. f, Cove, foliage. g, Red boat with two people. h, Buoy, birds. i, Birds, dolphin's tail. j, Dolphins. k, Person on raft. l, Two people standing in water. m, Person with fishing pole in water. n, Bridge tower. o, Bicyclist, taxi. p, Front of taxi. q, People walking on bridge, bridge tower. r, Truck, boat. s, School bus. t, Base of bridge tower. u, Birds under bridge, oar. v, Birds under bridge. w, Base of bridge tower, tip of sail. x, Motorcyclist. y, Birds on black rock. z, Kayakers. aa, Kayak, boat. ab, Boat, sailboat. ac, Sailboat, jetty. ad, Jetski.

2002, Jan. 11 **Perf. 13**
Sheets of 30, #a-ad
643-644 A185 Set of 2   32.50 32.50

United We Stand — A186

2002, Jan. 24 **Perf. 14**
645 A186 $1 multi   2.00 2.00

Reign of Queen Elizabeth II, 50th Anniv. A187

No. 646: a, In uniform. b, Wearing flowered hat. c, Prince Philip. d, Wearing tiara. $2, Wearing white dress.

2002, Feb. 6 **Perf. 14¼**
646 A187 80c Sheet of 4, #a-d   6.50 6.50
Souvenir Sheet
647 A187 $2 multi   4.00 4.00

Birds — A188

Designs: 1c, Gray-backed white-eye. 2c, Great frigatebird. 3c, Eclectus parrot. 4c, Red-footed booby. 5c Cattle egret. 10c, Cardinal honeyeater. 11c, Blue-faced parrot-finch. 15c, Rufous fantail. 20c, White-faced storm petrel. 21c, Willie wagtail. 23c, Black-headed gull. 50c, Sanderling. 57c, White-tailed tropicbird. 70c, Rainbow lorikeet. 80c, Moorhen. $1, Buff-banded rail. $2, Beach thick-knee. $3, Common tern. $3.50, Ruddy turnstone. $3.95, White-collared kingfisher. $5, Sulphur-crested cockatoo. $10, Barn swallow.

2002, Feb. 20 **Perf. 14¼**
648 A188 1c multi   .25 .25
649 A188 2c multi   .25 .25
650 A188 3c multi   .25 .25
651 A188 4c multi   .25 .25
652 A188 5c multi   .25 .25
653 A188 10c multi   .25 .25
654 A188 11c multi   .25 .25
655 A188 15c multi   .30 .30
656 A188 20c multi   .40 .40
657 A188 21c multi   .40 .40
658 A188 23c multi   .45 .45
659 A188 50c multi   1.00 1.00
660 A188 57c multi   1.10 1.10
661 A188 70c multi   1.40 1.40
662 A188 80c multi   1.60 1.60
663 A188 $1 multi   2.00 2.00
664 A188 $2 multi   4.00 4.00
665 A188 $3 multi   6.00 6.00
666 A188 $3.50 multi   7.00 7.00
667 A188 $3.95 multi   8.00 8.00
668 A188 $5 multi   10.00 10.00
669 A188 $10 multi   20.00 20.00
Nos. 648-669 (22)   65.40 65.40

Flowers — A189

Designs: 20c, Euanthe sanderiana. 34c, Ophiorrhiza palauensis. No. 672, 60c, Cerbera manghas. 80c, Mendinilla pterocaula.
No. 674, 60c: a, Bruguiera gymnorhiza. b, Samadera indiccal. c, Maesa canfieldiae. d, Lumnitzera litorea. e, Dolichandrone palawense. f, Limnophila aromatica (red and white orchids).
No. 675, 60c: a, Sonneratia alba. b, Barringtonia racemosa. c, Ixora casei. d, Tristellateia australasiae. e, Nepenthes mirabilis. f, Limnophila aromatica (pink flowers).
No. 676, $2, Fagraea ksid. No. 677, $2, Cerbera manghas, horiz.

2002, Mar. 4 **Perf. 14**
670-673 A189 Set of 4   4.00 4.00
Sheets of 6, #a-f
674-675 A189 Set of 2   14.50 14.50
Souvenir Sheets
676-677 A189 Set of 2   8.00 8.00

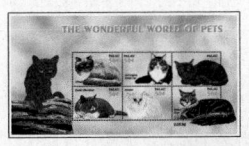

2002 Winter Olympics, Salt Lake City — A190

Skier with: No. 678, $1, Blue pants. No. 679, $1, Yellow pants.

2002, Mar. 18 **Perf. 14¼**
678-679 A190 Set of 2   4.00 4.00
679a Souvenir sheet, #678-679   4.00 4.00

A191

Cats and Dogs — A191a

No. 680, 50c, horiz.: a, Himalayan. b, Norwegian forest cat. c, Havana. d, Exotic shorthair. e, Persian. f, Maine coon cat.
No. 681, 50c, horiz.: a, Great Dane. b, Whippet. c, Bedlington terrier. d, Golden retriever. e, Papillon. f, Doberman pinscher.
No. 682, $2, British shorthair. No. 683, $2, Shetland sheepdog.

2002, Mar. 18 **Litho.** **Perf. 14**
Sheets of 6, #a-f
680-681 A191 Set of 2   12.00 12.00
Souvenir Sheets
682-683 A191a Set of 2   8.00 8.00

Intl. Year of Mountains — A192

No. 684: a, Mt. Fuji, Japan. b, Mt. Everest, Nepal and China. c, Mt. Owen, US. d, Mt. Huascarán, Peru.
$2, Mt. Eiger, Switzerland.

2002, June 17 **Litho.** **Perf. 14**
684 A192 80c Sheet of 4, #a-d   6.50 6.50
Souvenir Sheet
685 A192 $2 multi   4.00 4.00

Flags of Palau and its States A193

No. 686: a, Palau (no inscription). b, Kayangel. c, Ngarchelong. d, Ngaraard. e, Ngardmau. f, Ngaremlengui. g, Ngiwal. h, Ngatpang. i, Melekeor. j, Ngchesar. k, Aimeliik. l, Airai. m, Koror. n, Peleliu. o, Angaur. p, Sonsorol. q, Hatohobei.

2002, July 9
686 A193 37c Sheet of 17, #a-q   13.00 13.00
All stamps on No. 686 lack country name.

Winter Olympics Type of 2002
Redrawn with White Olympic Rings

Skier with: No. 687, $1, Blue pants. No. 688, $1, Yellow pants.

2002, July 29 **Perf. 13½**
687-688 A190 Set of 2   4.00 4.00
688a Souvenir sheet, #687-688   4.00 4.00

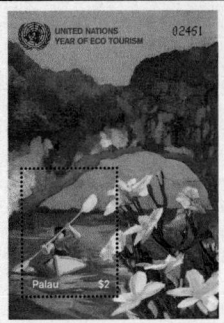

Intl. Year of Ecotourism — A194

No. 689: a, Divers, angelfish facing right. b, Ray. c, Sea cucumber. d, Emperor angelfish facing left. e, Sea turtle. f, Nautilus.
$2, Person in canoe.

2002, Apr. 26 **Perf. 14½x14¼**
689 A194 60c Sheet of 6, #a-f   7.25 7.25
Souvenir Sheet
690 A194 $2 multi   4.00 4.00

Japanese Art — A195

No. 691, vert. (38x50mm): a, The Actor Shuka Bando as Courtesan Shiraito, by Kunisada Utagawa. b, The Actor Danjuro Ichikawa VII as Sugawara no Michizane, by Kunisada Utagawa. c, The Actor Sojuro Sawamura III as Yuranosuke Oboshi, by Toyokuni Utagawa. d, The Actor Nizaemon Kataoka VII as Shihei Fujiwara, by Toyokuni Utagawa. e, Bust Portrait of the Actor Noshio Nakamura II, by Kunimasa Utagawa. f, The Actor Gon-Nosuke Kawarazaki as Daroku, by Kunichika Toyohara.
No. 692, 80c, vert. (27x88mm): a, Bush Clover Branch and Sweetfish, by Kuniyoshi Utagawa. b, Catfish, by Kuniyoshi Utagawa. c, Scene at Takanawa, by Eisen Keisai. d, Ochanomizu, by Keisai.
No. 693, 80c (50x38mm): a, Gaslight Hall, by Kiyochika Kobayashi. b, Cherry Blossoms at Night at Shin Yoshiwara, by Yasuji Inoue. c, Night Rain at Oyama, by Toyokuni Utagawa II. d, Kintai Bridge, by Keisai.
No. 694, $2, Okane, a Strong Woman of Omi, by Kuniyoshi Utagawa. No. 695, $2, Scene on the Banks of the Oumaya River, by Kuniyoshi Utagawa.

Perf. 14¼, 13½ (#692)
2002, Sept. 23
691 A195 60c Sheet of 6, #a-f   7.25 7.25
Sheets of 4, #a-d
692-693 A195   13.00 13.00
Size: 105x85mm
Imperf
694-695 A195 Set of 2   8.00 8.00

Popeye A196

No. 696, vert.: a, Wimpy. b, Swee'Pea. c, Popeye. d, Fish. e, Jeep. f, Brutus. $2, Popeye golfing.

2002, Oct. 7 **Perf. 14**
696 A196 60c Sheet of 6, #a-f   7.25 7.25
Souvenir Sheet
697 A196 $2 multi   4.00 4.00

Elvis Presley (1935-77) — A197

No. 698: a, On horse. b, Holding guitar, wearing white jacket, no hat. c, Wearing black hat. d, With guitar with two necks. e, Holding guitar, wearing colored jacket, no hat. f, Wearing shirt.

2002, Oct. 23
698 A197 37c Sheet of 6, #a-f   4.75 4.75

Christmas
A198

Designs: 23c, Presentation of Jesus in the Temple, by Perugino, vert. 37c, Madonna and Child Enthroned Between Angels and Saints, by Domenico Ghirlandaio, vert. 60c, Maesta, by Simone Martini, vert. 80c, Sacred Conversation, by Giovanni Bellini. $1, Nativity, by Ghirlandaio.
$2, Sacred Conversation (detail), by Bellini.

2002, Nov. 5
699-703 A198   Set of 5   6.00 6.00
Souvenir Sheet
704 A198 $2 multi   4.00 4.00

The painting shown on No. 704 does not appear to be a detail of the painting shown on No. 702.

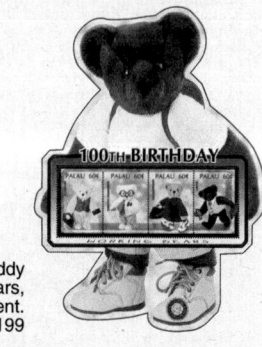

Teddy Bears, Cent.
A199

No. 705: a, Accountant bear. b, Computer programmer bear. c, Businesswoman bear. d, Lawyer bear.

2002, Nov. 19
705 A199 60c Sheet of 4, #a-d   5.00 5.00

Queen Mother Elizabeth (1900-2002) — A200

No. 706: a, Holding bouquet. b, Wearing blue blouse and pearls. c, Wearing purple hat. d, Wearing tiara.
$2, Wearing flowered hat.

2002, Dec. 30
706 A200 80c Sheet of 4, #a-d   6.50 6.50
Souvenir Sheet
707 A200 $2 multi   4.00 4.00

20th World Scout Jamboree, Thailand (in 2002) — A201

No. 708, horiz.: a, Scout climbing rocks. b, Scout emblem, knife. c, Branches lashed together with rope. d, Cub scout (wearing cap). e, Knot. f, Boy scout (without cap).
$2 Lord Robert Baden-Powell.

2003, Jan. 13   *Perf. 14*
708 A201 60c Sheet of 6, #a-f   7.25 7.25
Souvenir Sheet
709 A201 $2 multi   4.00 4.00

Shells
A202

No. 710: a, Leafy murex. b, Trumpet triton. c, Giant tun. d, Queen conch. e, Spotted tun. f, Emperor helmet.
$2, Angular triton.

2003, Jan. 13
710 A202 60c Sheet of 6, #a-f   7.25 7.25
Souvenir Sheet
711 A202 $2 multi   4.00 4.00

New Year 2003 (Year of the Ram) — A203

No. 712: a, Ram facing right. b, Ram facing forward. c, Ram facing left.

2003, Jan. 27   *Perf. 14¼x13¾*
712 A203 37c Vert. strip of 3,
    #a-c   2.25 2.25
    Sheet of 2 strips
No. 712 printed in sheets of 2 strips with slightly different backgrounds.

Pres. John F. Kennedy (1917-63) — A204

No. 713: a, Wearing cap. b, Facing left. c, Facing right. d, Holding ship's wheel.

2003, Feb. 10   *Perf. 14*
713 A204 80c Sheet of 4, #a-d   6.50 6.50

Bird Type of 2002 With Unserifed Numerals

Designs: 26c, Golden whistler. 37c, Pale white-eye.

2003, Mar. 1   *Perf. 14¼x13¾*
714 A188 26c multi   .55 .55
715 A188 37c multi   .75 .75

Astronauts Killed in Space Shuttle Columbia Accident — A205

No. 716: a, Mission Specialist 1 David M. Brown. b, Commander Rick D. Husband. c, Mission Specialist 4 Laurel Blair Salton Clark. d, Mission Specialist 4 Kalpana Chawla. e, Payload Commander Michael P. Anderson. f, Pilot William C. McCool. g, Payload Specialist 4 Ilan Ramon.

2003, Apr. 7   *Perf. 13¼*
716 A205 37c Sheet of 7, #a-g   5.25 5.25

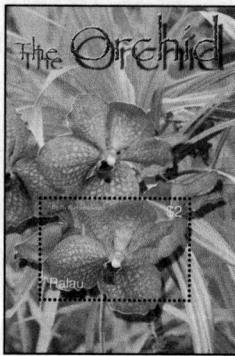

Orchids
A206

No. 717: a, Phalaenopsis grex. b, Cattleya loddigesii. c, Phalaenopsis joline. d, Dendrobium. e, Laelia anceps. f, Cymbidium Stanley Fouracre.
$2, Vanda rothschildiana.

2003, Jan. 13   *Litho.*   *Perf. 14*
717 A206 60c Sheet of 6, #a-f   7.25 7.25
Souvenir Sheet
718 A206 $2 multi   4.00 4.00

Insects
A207

No. 719: a, Giant water bug. b, Weevil. c, Blister beetle. d, Bess beetle. e, Metallic stag beetle. f, Violin beetle.
$2, Aheteropteran shield.

2003, Jan. 13
719 A207 60c Sheet of 6, #a-f   7.25 7.25
Souvenir Sheet
720 A207 $2 multi   4.00 4.00

First Non-stop Solo Transatlantic Flight, 75th Anniv. — A208

No. 721: a, Charles Lindbergh, Donald Hall and Spirit of St. Louis, Apr. 28, 1927. c, Spirit of St. Louis towed from Curtiss Field, May 20, 1927. d, Spirit of St. Louis takes off, May 20, 1927. e, Arrival in Paris, May 21, 1927. f, New York ticker tape parade.

2003, Feb. 10
721 A208 60c Sheet of 6, #a-f   7.25 7.25

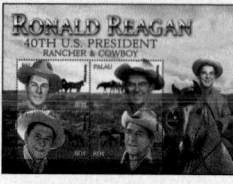

Pres. Ronald Reagan
A209

Reagan with: a, Orange bandana. b, Red shirt. c, Blue shirt, head at left. d, Blue shirt, head at right.

2003, Feb. 10
722 A209 80c Sheet of 4, #a-d   6.50 6.50

Princess Diana (1961-97) — A210

Diana and clothing worn in: a, India. b, Canada. c, Egypt. d, Italy.

2003, Feb. 10
723 A210 80c Sheet of 4, #a-d   6.50 6.50

Coronation of Queen Elizabeth II, 50th Anniv. — A211

No. 724 — Queen with: a, Tiara. b, Pink dress. c, Hat.
$2, Tiara, diff.

2003, May 13
724 A211 $1 Sheet of 3, #a-c   6.00 6.00
Souvenir Sheet
725 A211 $2 multi   4.00 4.00

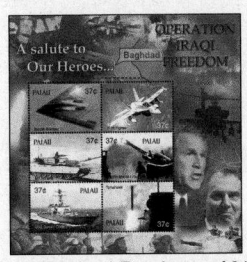

Operation Iraqi Freedom — A212

No. 726: a, Stealth bomber. b, F-18 fighter. c, MT Abrams tank. d, 203mm M-110s. e, USS Donald Cook. f, Tomahawk missile.

2003, May 14
726 A212 37c Sheet of 6, #a-f   4.50 4.50

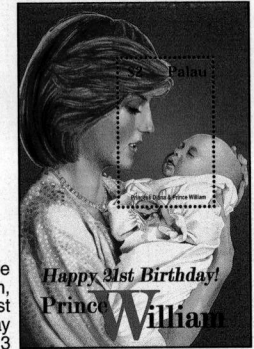

Prince William, 21st Birthday A213

No. 727 — William: a, In yellow green shirt. b, As infant. c, In black sweater.
$2, As infant with Princess Diana.

2003, June 21
727 A213 $1 Sheet of 3, #a-c   6.00 6.00
Souvenir Sheet
728 A213 $2 multi   4.00 4.00

Tour de France Bicycle Race, Cent. A214

No. 729: a, Henri Pelissier, 1923. b, Ottavio Bottecchia, 1924. c, Bottecchia, 1925. d, Lucien Buysse, 1926.
$2, Philippe Thys, 1920.

2003, Aug. 23   *Perf. 13¼*
729 A214 60c Sheet of 4, #a-d   5.00 5.00
Souvenir Sheet
730 A214 $2 multi   4.00 4.00

Powered Flight, Cent. A215

No. 731: a, Fokker 70. b, Boeing 747-217B. c, Curtiss T-32 Condor. d, Vickers Viscount Type 761. e, Wright Flyer III. f, Avro Ten Achilles.
$2, Wright Flyer III, diff.

2003, Aug. 25   *Perf. 14*
731 A215 55c Sheet of 6, #a-f   6.75 6.75
Souvenir Sheet
732 A215 $2 multi   4.00 4.00

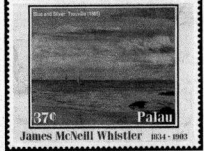

Paintings by James McNeill Whistler A216

Designs: 37c, Blue and Silver: Trouville. 55c, The Last of Old Westminster. 60c, Wapping. $1, Cremorne Gardens, No. 2.
No. 737, vert.: a, Arrangement in Flesh Color and Black, Portrait of Theodore Duret. b, Arrangement in White and Black. c, Harmony in Pink and Gray, Portrait of Lady Meux. d, Arrangement in Black and Gold, Comte Robert de Montesquiou-Fezensac.
$2, Arrangement in Gray and Black No. 1, Portrait of Painter's Mother, vert.

Perf. 14¼, 13¼ (#737)
2003, Sept. 22
733-736 A216 Set of 4   5.25 5.25
737 A216 80c Sheet of 4, #a-d   6.50 6.50
Souvenir Sheet
738 A216 $2 multi   4.00 4.00
No. 737 contains four 35x71mm stamps.

Circus Performers — A217

No. 739, 80c — Clowns: a, Apes. b, Mo Life. c, Gigi. d, "Buttons" McBride.
No. 740, 80c: a, Dogs. b, Olena Yaknenko. c, Mountain High. d, Chinese Circus.

2003, Sept. 29   *Perf. 14*
Sheets of 4, #a-d
739-740 A217 Set of 2   13.00 13.00

Christmas — A218

Designs: 37c, Madonna della Melagrana, by Botticelli. 60c, Madonna del Magnificat, by Botticelli. 80c, Madonna and Child with the Saints and the Angels, by Andrea del Sarto. $1, La Madonna del Roseto, by Botticelli.
$2, Madonna and Child with the Angels and Saints, by Domenico Ghirlandaio.

2003, Dec. 1   *Perf. 14¼*
741-744 A218 Set of 4   5.75 5.75
Souvenir Sheet
745 A218 $2 multi   4.00 4.00

Sea Turtles A219

No. 746: a, Mating. b, Laying eggs at night. c, Hatching. d, Turtles going to sea. e, Growing up at sea. f, Returning to lay eggs.
$2, Head of sea turtle.

2004, Feb. 6   *Perf. 14*
746 A219 60c Sheet of 6, #a-f   7.25 7.25
Souvenir Sheet
747 A219 $2 multi   4.00 4.00

Paintings by Norman Rockwell A220

No. 748, vert.: a, The Connoisseur. b, Artist Facing a Blank Canvas (Deadline). c, Art Critic. d, Stained Glass Artistry.
$2, Painting Tavern Sign.

2004, Feb. 6   Litho.   *Perf. 14¼*
748 A220 80c Sheet of 4, #a-d   6.50 6.50
Souvenir Sheet
749 A220 $2 multi   4.00 4.00

Paintings by Pablo Picasso A221

No. 750: a, Dora Maar. b, The Yellow Sweater (Dora). c, Woman in Green (Dora). d, Woman in an Armchair (Dora).
$2, Woman Dressing Her Hair (Dora).

2004, Feb. 16   Litho.   *Perf. 14¼*
750 A221 80c Sheet of 4, #a-d   6.50 6.50
Imperf
751 A221 $2 multi   4.00 4.00
No. 750 contains four 37x50mm stamps.

Paintings in the Hermitage, St. Petersburg, Russia — A222

Designs: 37c, Antonia Zarate, by Francisco de Goya. 55c, Portrait of a Lady, by Antonio Correggio. 80c, Portrait of Count Olivarez, by Diego Velázquez. $1, Portrait of a Young Man With a Lace Collar, by Rembrandt.
$2, Family Portrait, by Anthony Van Dyck.

2004, Feb. 16   Litho.   *Perf. 14¼*
752-755 A222 Set of 4   5.50 5.50
Size: 62x81mm
Imperf
756 A222 $2 multi   4.00 4.00

Marine Life A223

No. 757: a, Coral hind. b, Sea octopus. c, Manta ray. d, Dugong. e, Marine crab. f, Grouper.
$2, Gray reef shark.

2004, Feb. 16   *Perf. 14¼*
757 A223 55c Sheet of 6, #a-f   6.75 6.75
Souvenir Sheet
758 A223 $2 multi   4.00 4.00

Minerals A224

No. 759: a, Phosphate. b, Antimony. c, Limonite. d, Calcopyrite. e, Bauxite. f, Manganite.
$2, Gold.

2004, Feb. 16
759 A224 55c Sheet of 6, #a-f   6.75 6.75
Souvenir Sheet
760 A224 $2 multi   4.00 4.00

New Year 2004 (Year of the Monkey) — A225

Green Bamboo and a White Ape, by Ren Yu: 50c, Detail. $1, Entire painting.

2004, Mar. 9   *Perf. 13¼*
761 A225 50c multi   1.00 1.00
Souvenir Sheet
Perf. 13½x13¼
762 A225 $1 multi   2.00 2.00
No. 761 printed in sheets of 4. No. 762 contains one 27x83mm stamp.

Ninth Festival of Pacific Arts A226

No. 763, 26c: a, Oraschel, by M. Takeshi. b, Flute, by Sim Adelbai. c, Rur, by W. Watanabe. d, Bamboo Raft, by P. Tiakl. e, Story Telling, by K. Murret. f, Yek, by A. Imetuker. g, Canoe House, by W. Marsil. h, Carving Axe, by Watanabe. i, Weaving, by Marsil. j, Dancing Props, by Adelbai.
No. 764, 37c: a, Ongall, by Tiakl. b, Bai, by S. Weers. c, Taro Plant, by S. Smaserui. d, Toluk, by Watanabe. e, Medicinal Plants, by Smaserui. f, War Canoe, by Takeshi. g, Painting, by Adelbai. h, Pounding Taro, by Imetuker. i, Llengel, by Takeshi. i, Spear Technique, by Imetuker.

2004, Apr. 13   *Perf. 13*
Sheets of 10, #a-j
763-764 A226 Set of 2   13.00 13.00

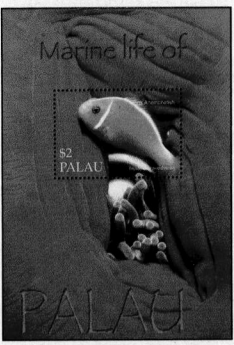

Marine Life A227

No. 765, 26c: a, Cuttlefish. b, Long fin bannerfish. c, Red sponge, Medusa worm. d, Risbecia tryoni. e, Emperor angelfish. f, Chromodoris coi.
No. 766, 37c: a, Spotted eagle ray. b, Jellyfish. c, Nautilus. d, Gray reef shark. e, Tunicates. f, Manta ray.
No. 767, $2, Pink anemonefish. No. 768, $2, Dusky anemonefish.

2004, May 20   *Perf. 14*
Sheets of 6, #a-f
765-766 A227 Set of 2   7.75 7.75
Souvenir Sheets
767-768 A227 Set of 2   8.00 8.00
No. 765 contains six labels.

Intl. Year
of Peace
A228

No. 769, vert.: a, Mahatma Gandhi. b, Nelson Mandela. c, Dr. Martin Luther King, Jr. $2, Dove.

2004, May 24   *Perf. 13½x13¼*
769 A228 $3 Sheet of 3, #a-c   18.00 18.00
Souvenir Sheet
Perf. 13¼x13½
770 A228 $2 multi   4.00 4.00

2004
Summer
Olympics,
Athens
A229

Designs: 37c, Athletes. 55c, Gold medals, Atlanta, 1996. 80c, Johannes Edström, Intl. Olympic Committee President, 1942-52, vert. $1, Women's soccer, Atlanta, 1996.

2004, June 18   *Perf. 14¼*
771-774 A229 Set of 4   5.50 5.50

Election
of Pope
John
Paul,
25th
Anniv.
(in 2003)
A230

Pope John Paul II: a, With Mehmet Agca, 1983. b, Visiting Poland, 2002. c, At concert in Ischia, Italy, 2002. d, With Patriarch Zakka, 2003.

2004, June 18
775 A230 80c Sheet of 4, #a-d   6.50 6.50
Souvenir Sheet

Deng Xiaoping (1904-97) Chinese
Leader — A231

2004, June 18
776 A231 $2 multi   4.00 4.00

D-Day,
60th
Anniv.
A232

No. 777: a, LCA 1377. b, Landing Craft, Infantry. c, LCVP. d, U-309. e, HMS Begonia. f, HMS Roberts. $2, LSTs.

2004, June 18
777 A232 50c Sheet of 6, #a-f   6.00 6.00
Souvenir Sheet
778 A232 $2 multi   4.00 4.00

European Soccer Championships,
Portugal — A233

No. 779, vert.: a, Rinus Michels. b, Rinat Dasaev. c, Marco Van Basten. d, Olympiastadion. $2, 1988 Netherlands team.

2004, June 18
779 A233 80c Sheet of 4, #a-d   6.50 6.50
Souvenir Sheet
780 A233 $2 multi   4.00 4.00
No. 779 contains four 28x42mm stamps.

Babe Ruth (1895-
1948), Baseball
Player — A234

Ruth and: No. 781, 37c, Signed baseball. No. 782, 37c, World Series 100th anniversary emblem.

2004, Sept. 3   *Perf. 13½x13¼*
781-782 A234 Set of 2   1.50 1.50
Nos. 781-782 each printed in sheets of 8.

Trains,
Bicent.
A235

No. 783: a, ATSF 315. b, Amtrak 464. c, Railway N52. d, SD 70 MAC Diesel-electric locomotive. No. 784, 50c: a, CS SO2002. b, P 36 N0032. c, SW-600. d, Gambier LNV 9703 4-4-0 NG.
No. 785, $2, CN5700 locomotive. No. 786, $2, Eurostar.

2004, Sept. 27   *Perf. 13¼x13½*
783 A235 26c Sheet of 4, #a-d   2.10 2.10
784 A235 50c Sheet of 4, #a-d   4.00 4.00
Souvenir Sheet
785 A235 $2 multi   4.00 4.00
786 A235 $2 multi   4.00 4.00

Butterflies, Reptiles, Amphibians and
Birds — A236

No. 787, 80c — Butterflies: a, Cethosia hypsea. b, Cethosia myrina. c, Charaxes durnfordi. d, Charaxes nitebis.
No. 788, 80c — Reptiles: a, Bull snake. b, Garter snake. c, Yellow-lipped sea snake. d, Yellow-bellied sea snake.
No. 789, 80c, vert. — Birds: a, Blue-faced parrot finch. b, Mangrove flycatcher. c, Palau swiftlet. d, Bridled white-eye.
No. 790, $2, Charaxes nitebis, diff. No. 791, $2, Glass frog. No. 792, $2, Dusky white-eye, vert.

2004, Oct. 13   *Litho.*   *Perf. 14*
Sheets of 4, #a-d
787-789 A236 Set of 3   19.50 19.50
Souvenir Sheets
790-792 A236 Set of 3   12.00 12.00

Dinosaurs — A237

No. 793, 26c, vert.: a, Kritosaurus. b, Triceratops. c, Hypselosaurus. d, Yingshanosaurus.
No. 794, 80c: a, Hadrosaurus. b, Pterodaustro. c, Agilisaurus. d, Amargasaurus.
No. 795, 80c, vert.: a, Corythosaurus. b, Dryosaurus. c, Euoplocephalus. d, Compsognathus.
No. 796, $2, Ornithomimus. No. 797, $2, Archaeopteryx. No. 798, $2, Deinonychus, vert.

2004, Oct. 13   **Sheets of 4, #a-d**
793-795 A237 Set of 3   15.00 15.00
Souvenir Sheets
796-798 A237 Set of 3   12.00 12.00

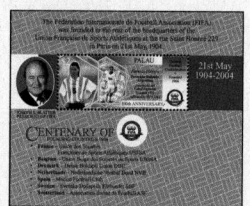

FIFA (Fédération Internationale de
Football Association), Cent. — A238

No. 799: a, Diego Maradona. b, David Seaman. c, Andreas Brehme. d, Paul Ince. $2, Fernando Redondo.

2004, Oct. 27   *Perf. 12¾x12½*
799 A238 80c Sheet of 4, #a-d   6.50 6.50
Souvenir Sheet
800 A238 $2 multi   4.00 4.00

National Basketball
Association
Players — A239

Designs: No. 801, 26c, Chris Bosh, Toronto Raptors. No. 802, 26c, Tim Duncan, San Antonio Spurs. No. 803, 26c, Kevin Garnett, Minnesota Timberwolves.

2004, Nov. 3   *Perf. 14*
801-803 A239 Set of 3   1.60 1.60
Each stamp printed in sheets of 12.

Christmas
A240

Paintings of Madonna and Child by: 37c, Quentin Metsys. 60c, Adolphe William Bouguereau. 80c, William Dyce. $1, Carlo Crivelli. $2, Peter Paul Rubens, vert.

2004, Dec. 23   *Perf. 14¼*
804-807 A240 Set of 4   5.75 5.75
Souvenir Sheet
808 A240 $2 multi   4.00 4.00

Miniature Sheet

Palau — Republic of China Diplomatic
Relations, 5th Anniv. — A241

No. 809: a, Agricultural products. b, Republic of China Navy ship. c, Ngarachamayong Cultural Center. d, Palau National Museum.

2004, Dec. 29   *Perf. 14*
809 A241 80c Sheet of 4, #a-d   6.50 6.50

Souvenir Sheet

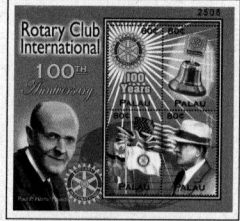

New
Year
2005
(Year of
the
Rooster)
A242

No. 810: a, Rooster facing right, tail feathers at LL. b, Rooster facing left, tail feathers at LR. c, Rooster facing right, no tail feathers at LL. d, Rooster facing left, no tail feathers at LR.

2005, Jan. 26   *Litho.*   *Perf. 12½*
810 A242 50c Sheet of 4, #a-d   4.00 4.00

Souvenir Sheet

Rotary International, Cent. — A243

No. 811: a, Rotary International emblem. b, Rotary Centennial bell. c, Flags of Rotary International, US, Great Britain, Canada, Germany, China and Italy. d, James Wheeler Davidson.

2005, Apr. 4   *Perf. 14*
811 A243 80c Sheet of 4, #a-d   6.50 6.50

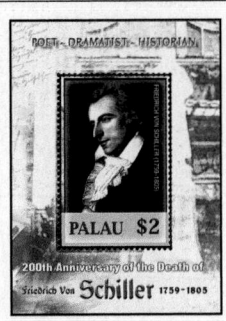

Friedrich von Schiller (1759-1805),
Writer — A244

No. 812 — Schiller facing: a, Right (sepia tone). b, Right (color). c, Left (sepia tone).
$2, Facing left, diff.

2005, Apr. 4
812 A244 $1 Sheet of 3, #a-c 6.00 6.00
Souvenir Sheet
813 A244 $2 multi 4.00 4.00

Hans Christian Andersen (1805-75),
Author — A245

No. 814, vert. — Book covers: a, Hans Christian Andersen Fairy Tales. b, Hans Christian Andersen's The Ugly Duckling. c, Tales of Hans Christian Andersen.
$2, The Little Match Girl.

2005, Apr. 4
814 A245 $1 Sheet of 3, #a-c 6.00 6.00
Souvenir Sheet
815 A245 $2 multi 4.00 4.00

Battle of Trafalgar, Bicent. A246

Various ships in battle: 37c, 55c, 80c, $1.
$2, Admiral Horatio Nelson Wounded During Battle of Trafalgar.

2005, Apr. 4 Perf. 14¼
816-819 A246 Set of 4 5.50 5.50
Souvenir Sheet
820 A246 $2 multi 4.00 4.00

End of World War II, 60th Anniv. A247

No. 821, 80c — Dambuster Raid: a, Pilots review routes prior to mission. b, Dambuster crew. c, Ground crews prepare Lancaster bomber. d, Bomber over Möhne Dam.
No. 822, 80c — Battle of Kursk: a, Russian tanks move forward. b, Tank commanders review maps. c, Russian and German armor clash. d, Destroyed German tank.
No. 823, $2, Squadron 617 leader Guy Gibson and "Highball Bouncing Bomb." No. 824,

$2, Russian troops converge on destroyed German tank.

2005, May 9 Perf. 13½
Sheets of 4, #a-d
821-822 A247 Set of 2 13.00 13.00
Souvenir Sheets
823-824 A247 Set of 2 8.00 8.00

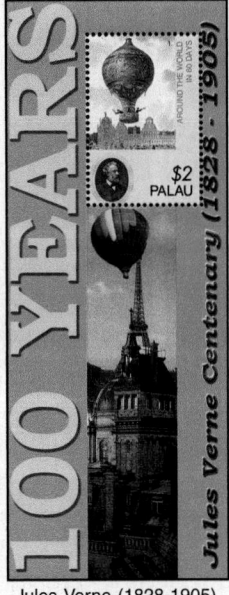

Jules Verne (1828-1905),
Writer — A248

No. 825, horiz.: a, 20,000 Leagues Under the Sea. b, Mysterious Island. c, Journey to the Center of the Earth.
$2, Around the World in 80 Days.

2005, June 7 Perf. 12¾
825 A248 $1 Sheet of 3, #a-c 6.00 6.00
Souvenir Sheet
826 A248 $2 multi 4.00 4.00

Pope John Paul II (1920-2005) — A249

2005, June 27 Perf. 13½x13¼
827 A249 $1 multi 2.00 2.00

A250

Elvis Presley (1935-77) — A251

No. 829 — Color of Presley: a, Blue. b, Green. c, Yellow. d, Orange.

2005, July 2 Perf. 14
828 A250 80c multi 1.60 1.60
829 A251 80c Sheet of 4, #a-d 6.50 6.50
No. 828 printed in sheets of 4.

Trains Type of 2004
No. 830: a, Birney N62 Interurban. b, C62-2-103103. c, WR MO 2007. d, Atchison, Topeka & Santa Fe locomotive 314.
$2, Royal Hudson #2860, vert.

2005 Perf. 13¼x13½
830 A235 80c Sheet of 4, #a-d 6.50 6.50
Souvenir Sheet
Perf. 13½x13¼
831 A235 $2 multi 4.00 4.00

V-J Day, 60th Anniv. A252

No. 832, vert.: a, Audie Murphy. b, John F. Kennedy. c, Fleet Admiral Chester W. Nimitz. d, Marines recapture Guam from the Japanese.
$2, Sailors going home.

2005, June 7 Litho. Perf. 12¾
832 A252 80c Sheet of 4, #a-d 6.50 6.50
Souvenir Sheet
833 A252 $2 multi 4.00 4.00

Miniature Sheet

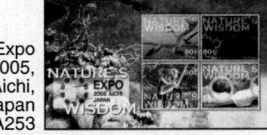

Expo 2005, Aichi, Japan A253

No. 834: a, Seagulls. b, The cosmos. c, Koala. d, Childbirth.
2005, June 27 Perf. 12
834 A253 80c Sheet of 4, #a-d 6.50 6.50

Sailing A254

No. 835: a, Tepukei. b, Tainui. c, Palauan canoe. d, Yap outrigger.
$2, Kon-Tiki.

2005, June 27 Perf. 12¾
835 A254 80c Sheet of 4, #a-d 6.50 6.50
Souvenir Sheet
836 A254 $2 multi 4.00 4.00

World Cup Soccer Championships, 75th Anniv. — A255

No. 837, $1 — Scene from final match of: a, 1954. b, 1966. c, 1974.
No. 838, $1: a, Scene from 2002 final match. b, Lothar Matthias. c, Gerd Muller.
No. 839, $2, Sepp Herberger. No. 840, $2, Franz Beckenbauer.

2005, July 19 Perf. 12
Sheets of 3, #a-c
837-838 A255 Set of 2 12.00 12.00
Souvenir Sheets
839 A255 $2 multi 4.00 4.00
Perf. 12¾
840 A255 $2 multi 4.00 4.00
No. 840 contains one 42x28mm stamp.

Vatican City No. 61 — A256

2005, Aug. 9 Perf. 13x13¼
841 A256 37c multi .75 .75
Printed in sheets of 12.

Miniature Sheet

Taipei 2005 Intl. Stamp Exhibition — A257

No. 842: a, Wildeve rose. b, Graham Thomas rose. c, Crocus rose. d, Tes of the d'Urbervilles rose.

2005, Aug. 19 Perf. 14
842 A257 80c Sheet of 4, #a-d 6.50 6.50

Miniature Sheet

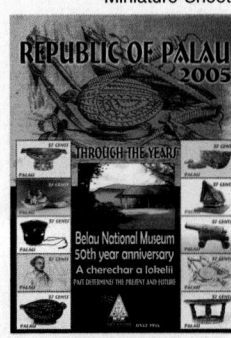

Items from National Museum A258

No. 843: a, Decorated bowl, light yellow background. b, Potsherds, dull rose background. c, Sculpture with three people, blue background. d, Model of native house, light yellow background. e, Lidded container with strings. f, Cannon. g, Drawing of man on ship. h, Drawing of native craftwork. i, Bird-shaped figurine. j, Decorated bowl, pink background.

2005, Sept. 30
843 A258 37c Sheet of 10, #a-j 7.50 7.50

Pope Benedict XVI — A259

2005, Nov. 21 Perf. 13¾x13½
844 A259 80c multi 1.60 1.60
Printed in sheets of 4.

Christmas — A260

Paintings: 37c, Madonna and Child, by Daniel Seghers. 60c, Madonna and Child, by Raphael. 80c, The Rest on the Flight to Egypt, by Gerard David. $1, Granducci Madonna, by Raphael.

$2, Madonna and Child, by Bartolome Esteban Murillo.

2005, Dec. 21   **Perf. 14**
845-848 A260 Set of 4   5.75 5.75
Souvenir Sheet
849 A260 $2 multi   4.00 4.00

New Year 2006
(Year of the
Dog) — A261

2006, Jan. 3   **Perf. 13¼**
850 A261 50c multi   1.00 1.00
Printed in sheets of 4.

Birds — A262

Designs: 24c, Black oystercatcher. 39c, Great blue heron, vert.

2006, Feb. 21   **Litho.**   **Perf. 12**
851 A262 24c multi   .50 .50
852 A262 39c multi   .80 .80

Worldwide
Fund for
Nature
(WWF)
A263

No. 853 — Chambered nautilus: a, Two facing right. b, Two facing left. c, One, near coral. d, One, no coral.

2006, Feb. 21   **Perf. 12¾**
853 A263 63c Block of 4, #a-d   5.25 5.25
   e.   Sheet, 2 each #853a-853d   10.50 10.50

World of Sea and Reef Type of 1986
Redrawn
Miniature Sheet

No. 854: a, Spear fisherman. b, Native raft. c, Sailing canoes. d, Rock islands, sailfish. e, Inter-island boat, flying fish. f, Bonefish. g, Common jack. h, Mackerel. i, Sailfish. j, Barracuda. k, Triggerfish. l, Dolphinfish. m, Spear fisherman, grouper. n, Manta ray. o, Marlin. p, Parrotfish. q, Wrasse. r, Red snapper. s, Herring. t, Dugong. u, Surgeonfish. v, Leopard ray. w, Hawksbill turtle. x, Needlefish. y, Tuna. z, Octopus. aa, Clownfish. ab, Squid. ac, Grouper. ad, Moorish idol. ae, Queen conch. af, Squirrelfish. ag, Starfish, sting ray. ah, Lionfish. ai, Angelfish. aj, Butterflyfish. ak, Spiny lobster. al, Mangrove crab, am, Tridacna. an, Moray eel.

2006, May 29   **Litho.**   **Perf. 13**
854   Sheet of 40   14.50 14.50
  a.-an.   A19 18c Any single   .35 .35
Washington 2006 World Philatelic Exhibition.

Souvenir Sheet

Wolfgang Amadeus Mozart (1756-91),
Composer — A264

2006, June 23   **Perf. 12¾**
855 A264 $2 multi   4.00 4.00

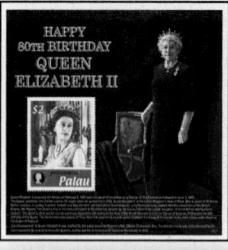

Queen
Elizabeth
II, 80th
Birthday
A265

No. 856 — Queen wearing crown or tiara with background color of: a, Tan. b, Red. c, Blue. d, Lilac.
$2, Sepia photograph.

2006, June 23   **Perf. 14¼**
856 A265 84c Sheet of 4, #a-d   6.75 6.75
Souvenir Sheet
857 A265 $2 multi   4.00 4.00

Rembrandt (1606-69), Painter — A266

No. 858: a, Old Man in a Fur Hat. b, Head of a Man. c, An Old Man in a Cap. d, Portrait of an Old Man.
$2, Saskia With a Veil.

2006, June 23   **Perf. 13¼**
858 A266 $1 Sheet of 4, #a-d   8.00 8.00
Size: 70x100mm
Imperf
859 A266 $2 multi   4.00 4.00
No. 858 contains four 38x50mm stamps.

A267

Space Achievements — A268

No. 860 — Inscription, "International Space Station": a, At left. b, At UR, in white. c, At LL. d, AT UR, in black.
No. 861, 75c — Viking 1: a, Viking orbiting Mars. b, Simulation of Viking on Mars. c, Viking probe. d, Solar panels. e, Picture from Viking on Mars, parts of spacecraft at right. f, Picture from Viking on Mars, large rock at right.
No. 862, 75c, vert. — First flight of Space Shuttle Columbia: a, Shuttle on launch pad. b, Half of shuttle, denomination at UL. c, Half of shuttle, denomination at UR. d, Mission emblem. e, Astronaut Robert Crippen. f, Commander John Young.
No. 863, $2, Sputnik 1. No. 864, $2, Apollo 11. No. 865, $2, Space Shuttle Columbia lifting off.

2006, July 10   **Perf. 14¼**
860 A267 $1 Sheet of 4, #a-d   8.00 8.00
Sheets of 6, #a-f
861-862 A267   Set of 2   18.00 18.00
Souvenir Sheets
863-865 A268   Set of 3   12.00 12.00

Souvenir Sheet

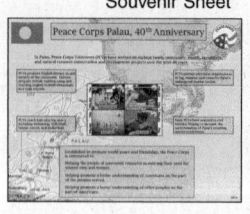

Peace
Corps,
40th
Anniv.
A269

No. 867: a, English literacy. b, Sea turtle conservation. c, Swim camp. d, Reef survey.

2006, Nov. 6   **Litho.**   **Perf. 14x14¾**
867 A269 75c Sheet of 4, #a-d   6.00 6.00

Concorde — A270

No. 868, 75c: a, Concorde over New York City. b, Concorde over London
No. 869, 75c: a, Wheel. b, Nose.

2006, Dec. 20   **Perf. 13¼x13½**
Pairs, #a-b
868-869 A270   Set of 2   6.00 6.00

Souvenir Sheet

Christmas — A271

No. 870 — Tree ornaments: a, Soldier. b, Santa Claus. c, Elf holding gift. d, Mice in sleigh.

2006   **Perf. 13¼**
870 A271 84c Sheet of 4, #a-d   6.75 6.75

New Year 2007 (Year
of the Pig) — A272

2007, Jan. 3   **Litho.**   **Perf. 13¼**
871 A272 75c multi   1.50 1.50
Printed in sheets of 4.

Souvenir Sheet

Marilyn Monroe (1926-62),
Actress — A273

Various drawings.

2007, Feb. 15
872 A273 84c Sheet of 4, #a-d   6.75 6.75

A274

Elvis Presley (1935-77) — A275

No. 873 — Presley with: a, Microphone. b, Shirt with design on pocket. c, Dark shirt. d, White shirt. e, Hat. f, Sweater. g, Dog. h, Jacket and microphone. i, Guitar.
No. 874 — Presley with or without guitar and background color of: a, Yellow. b, Red violet. c, Pale green. d, Red. e, Pale blue. f, Orange.

2007, Feb. 15   **Perf. 13¼**
873 A274 39c Sheet of 9, #a-i   7.25 7.25
Perf. 14¼
874 A275 75c Sheet of 6, #a-f   9.00 9.00

Scouting,
Cent.
A276

No. 875, horiz. — Dove, Scouting flag, globe featuring Europe and frame color of: a, Purple. b, Bright pink. c, Green and blue.
$2, Lord Robert Baden-Powell.

2007, Feb. 15   **Perf. 13¼**
875 A276 $1 Sheet of 3, #a-c   6.00 6.00
Souvenir Sheet
876 A276 $2 multi   4.00 4.00

Mushrooms — A277

No. 877, vert.: a, Entoloma hochstetteri. b, Aseroe rubra. c, Omphalotus nidiformis. d, Amanita sp.
$2, Aseroe rubra, diff.

2007, Feb. 15   *Perf. 14¼x14*
877 A277 $1 Sheet of 4, #a-d   8.00 8.00
     Souvenir Sheet
     Perf. 14x14¼
878 A277 $2 multi   4.00 4.00

Helicopters, Cent. — A278

Designs: 10c, Bell 206B JetRanger III. 19c, McDonnell Douglas MD500D. 20c, McDonnell Douglas AH-64A Apache. 22c, Aérospatiale AS 332 Super Puma. 75c, Aérospatiale AS 355F-1 Twin Squirrel. 84c, MBB Eurocopter BO 105DBS/4. $1, Sikorsky MH-53J Pave Low III.
$2, Boeing Helicopters 234LR Chinook.

2007, Feb. 26   *Perf. 14x14¼*
879-885 A278 Set of 7   6.75 6.75
     Souvenir Sheet
886 A278 $2 multi   4.00 4.00

Souvenir Sheet

Triton Horn Shell A279

2007, Mar. 1   *Perf. 13¼*
887 A279 $2 multi   4.00 4.00

Miniature Sheets

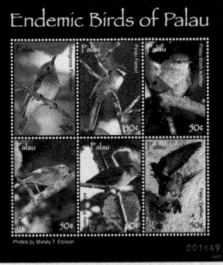

Endemic Birds of Palau

Birds A280

No. 888, 50c: a, Mangrove flycatcher. b, Palau fantail. c, Palau bush warbler. d, Giant white-eye. e, Dusky white-eye. f, Palau swiftlet.
No. 889, 50c: a, Palau owl. b, Palau fruit dove. c, Palau ground dove. d, Morning bird. e, Palau megapode. f, Rusty-capped kingfisher.

2007, Mar. 1   *Litho.*
     Sheets of 6, #a-f
888-889 A280 Set of 2   12.00 12.00

Wedding of Queen Elizabeth II and Prince Philip, 60th Anniv. — A281

No. 890 — Photograph from: a, July 1947. b, November 1947.

2007, May 1
890 A281 60c Pair, #a-b   2.40 2.40
     Printed in sheets containing three of each stamp.

Souvenir Sheet

Crabs A282

No. 891: a, Fiddler crab. b, Ghost crab. c, Coconut crab. d, Land crab.

2007, May 16
891 A282 $1 Sheet of 4, #a-d   8.00 8.00

Flowers A283

No. 892: a, Plumeria. b, Streptosolen jamesonii. c, Heliconia pseudoaemygdiana. d, Mananita.
$2, Spider lily.

2007, May 16   *Perf. 13¼*
892 A283 $1 Sheet of 4, #a-d   8.00 8.00
     Souvenir Sheet
893 A283 $2 multi   4.00 4.00

Pope Benedict XVI — A284

2007, June 20
894 A284 41c multi   .85 .85
     Printed in sheets of 8.

Princess Diana (1961-97) — A285

No. 895 — Diana with: a, Earring at right, white dress. b, Choker. c, Earring at right. d, Earring at left, country name in white.
$2, Wearing veiled hat.

2007, June 20
895 A285 90c Sheet of 4, #a-d   7.25 7.25
     Souvenir Sheet
896 A285 $2 multi   4.00 4.00

Butterflies — A286

Designs: 2c, Troides amphrysus. 3c, Paraeronia boebera. 4c, Delias catisa. 5c, Chilasa clytia. 11c, Ornithoptera goliath. 15c, Graphium delesserii. 20c, Euploea sp. 23c, Papilio euchenor. 26c, Ornithoptera tithonus. 41c, Hypolimnas misippus. 45c, Delias meeki. 50c, Papilio ulysses autolycus. 75c, Ornithoptera croesus. 90c, Trogonoptera brookiana. $1, Idea lynceus. $2, Parantica weiskei. $3, Graphium weiskei. $4, Ornithoptera goliath titan. $5, Attacus lorquini. $10, Delias henningia voconia.

2007, July 5		*Perf. 12½x13½*	
897	A286	2c multi	.25	.25

2007, July 5   *Perf. 12½x13½*
897 A286 2c multi   .25 .25
898 A286 3c multi   .25 .25
899 A286 4c multi   .25 .25
900 A286 5c multi   .25 .25
901 A286 11c multi   .25 .25
902 A286 15c multi   .30 .30
903 A286 20c multi   .40 .40
904 A286 23c multi   .50 .50
905 A286 26c multi   .55 .55
906 A286 41c multi   .85 .85
907 A286 45c multi   .90 .90
908 A286 50c multi   1.00 1.00
909 A286 75c multi   1.50 1.50
910 A286 90c multi   1.90 1.90
911 A286 $1 multi   2.00 2.00
912 A286 $2 multi   4.00 4.00
913 A286 $3 multi   6.00 6.00
914 A286 $4 multi   8.00 8.00
915 A286 $5 multi   10.00 10.00
916 A286 $10 multi   20.00 20.00
   Nos. 897-916 (20)   59.15 59.15

Miniature Sheet

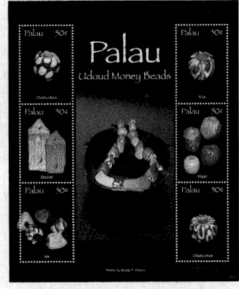

Udoud Money Beads A287

No. 917: a, Black and white Chelbucheb. b, Kluk. c, Bachel. d, Kldait. e, Iek. f, Green and white Chelbucheb.

2007, Mar. 1   *Litho.*   *Perf. 13¼*
917 A287 50c Sheet of 6, #a-f   6.00 6.00

Miniature Sheet

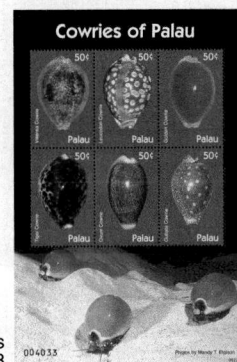

Cowries A288

No. 918: a, Valentia cowrie. b, Leucodon cowrie. c, Golden cowrie. d, Tiger cowrie. e, Ovum cowrie. f, Guttata cowrie.

2007, Mar. 1
918 A288 50c Sheet of 6, #a-f   6.00 6.00

Miniature Sheet

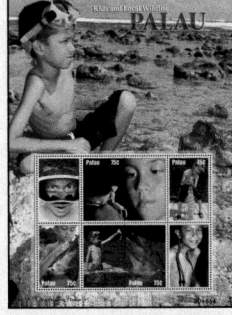

Children and Wildlife A289

No. 919: a, Praying mantis. b, Boy holding lobster. c, Boy holding bat. d, Dolphins.

2007, Mar. 1
919 A289 75c Sheet of 4, #a-d, +
     4 labels   6.00 6.00

Birds of Southeast Asia — A290

No. 920: a, Red-billed leiothrix. b, Unidentified bird. c, Wahne's parotia. d, White-bellied yuhina.
$2, Wilson's bird-of-paradise.

2007, May 16
920 A290 80c Sheet of 4, #a-d   6.50 6.50
     Souvenir Sheet
921 A290 $2 multi   4.00 4.00

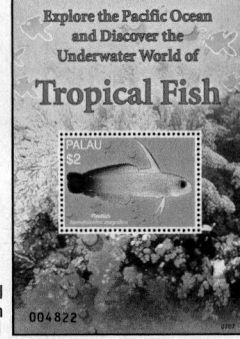

Tropical Fish A291

No. 922: a, Boxfish. b, Copperband butterflyfish. c, Long-nosed hawkfish. d, Emperor angelfish.
$2, Firefish.

2007, May 16
922 A291 80c Sheet of 4, #a-d   6.50 6.50
     Souvenir Sheet
923 A291 $2 multi   4.00 4.00

Miniature Sheet

Intl. Holocaust Remembrance Day — A292

No. 924 — United Nations diplomats and delegates: a, Eduardo J. Sevilla Somoza, Nicaragua. b, Aminu Bashir Wali, Nigeria. c, Stuart Beck, Palau. d, Ricardo Alberto Arias, Panama. e, Robert G. Aisi, Papua New Guinea. f, Eladio Loizaga, Paraguay. g, Jorge Voto-Bernales, Peru. h, Ban-Ki Moon, United Nations Secretary General.

2007, Nov. 20
924 A292 50c Sheet of 8, #a-h   8.00 8.00

Christmas — A293

Color of ornament: 22c, Red. 26c, Green. 41c, Blue. 90c, Yellow brown.

2007, Nov. 20   *Litho.*   *Perf. 12*
925-928 A293 Set of 4   3.75 3.75

32nd America's Cup Yacht Races — A294

Various yachts.

2007, Dec. 13 — *Perf. 13¼*
929 Strip of 4 .... 8.50 8.50
 a. A294 26c multi .... .50 .50
 b. A294 80c multi 1.60 1.60
 c. A294 $1.14 multi 2.40 2.40
 d. A294 $2 multi 4.00 4.00

New Year 2008 (Year of the Rat) — A295

2008, Jan. 2 — *Perf. 12*
930 A295 50c multi 1.00 1.00
 Printed in sheets of 4.

Miniature Sheet

Pres. John F. Kennedy (1917-63) — A296

No. 931: a, Crowd, Kennedy campaign poster. b, Kennedy shaking hands with crowd. c, Kennedy at lectern. d, Kennedy behind microphones, with hands showing.

2008, Jan. 2 — *Perf. 14¼*
931 A296 90c Sheet of 4, #a-d 7.25 7.25

2008 Summer Olympics, Beijing — A297

No. 932 — Items and athletes from 1908 London Olympics: a, Fencing poster. b, Program cover. c, Wyndham Halswelle, track gold medalist. d, Dorando Pietri, marathon runner.

2008, Jan. 8
932 A297 50c Sheet of 4, #a-d 4.00 4.00

Taiwan Tourist Attractions — A298

No. 933: a, National Taiwan Democracy Memorial Hall. b, Chinese ornamental garden, Taipei. c, Taipei skyline. d, Eastern coast of Taiwan.
$2, Illuminated temple, Southern Taiwan.

2008, Apr. 11 — *Perf. 11½*
933 A298 50c Sheet of 4, #a-d 4.00 4.00
 Souvenir Sheet
 Perf. 13¼
934 A298 $2 multi 4.00 4.00
 2008 Taipei Intl. Stamp Exhibition. No. 933 contains four 40x30mm stamps.

2008 World Stamp Championships, Israel — A299

2008, May 14 — *Imperf.*
935 A299 $3 multi 6.00 6.00

Miniature Sheet

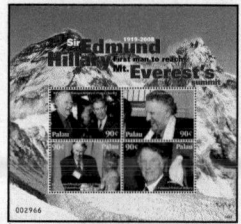

Sir Edmund Hillary (1919-2008), Mountaineer — A300

No. 936: a, Hillary and Prince Charles. b, Hillary. c, Hillary and Nepal Prime Minister Lokendra Bahadur Chand. d, Hillary with bird on shoulder.

2008, May 28 — *Perf. 13¼*
936 A300 90c Sheet of 4, #a-d 7.25 7.25

Miniature Sheet

Elvis Presley (1935-77) — A301

No. 301 — Presley wearing: a, Gray shirt. b, Green shirt. c, Red shirt. d, Gold suit. e, White shirt, no jacket. f, White shirt, black suit.

2008, June 12
937 A301 75c Sheet of 6, #a-f 9.00 9.00

Miniature Sheet

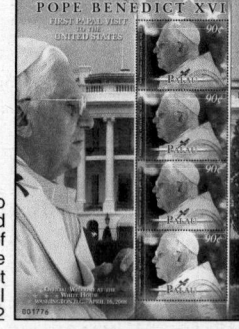

Visit to United States of Pope Benedict XVI — A302

No. 938 — Pope Benedict XVI and US flag faintly in background: a, Part of flag star on Pope's head (no frame line above denomination). b, Red stripe under "au" of "Palau." c, Red stripe under "P" of Palau. d, Red stripe under entire country name.

2008, July 28
938 A302 90c Sheet of 4, #a-d 7.25 7.25

Miniature Sheets

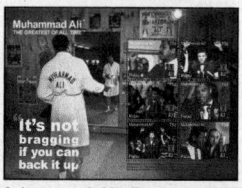

Muhammad Ali, Boxer — A303

No. 939 — Ali: a, In suit, clenching fist. b, Behind microphones, with both arms raised, with hands around his right forearm. c, Behind microphones, with towel around neck. d, Behind microphones, scratching head. e, Behind microphones, raising arms, with crowd. f, With hand of Howard Cosell on shoulder.
No. 940 — Ali: a, Pointing up, wearing short-sleeved shirt. b, Pointing to left, wearing suit. c, Making fist, in robe. d, Pointing to right, wearing suit.

2008, Sept. 22 — *Perf. 11½x12*
939 A303 75c Sheet of 6, #a-f 9.00 9.00
 Perf. 13¼
940 A303 94c Sheet of 4, #a-d 7.50 7.50
 No. 940 contains four 50x37mm stamps.

Miniature Sheets

Space Exploration, 50th Anniv. (in 2007) — A304

No. 941, 75c — Mir Space Station: a, With black background. b, With Earth at bottom. c, Technical drawing. d, Above clouds. e, With Space Shuttle Atlantis. f, Against starry background.
No. 942, 75c: a, Pres. John F. Kennedy. b, Apollo 11 Command Module. c, Apollo 11 Lunar Module, Earth and Moon. d, Lunar Module and Moon. e, Kennedy, Astronaut John Glenn and Friendship 7 capsule. f, Edwin "Buzz" Aldrin on Moon.
No. 943, 94c: a, Technical drawing of R-7 launch vehicle. b, Sputnik 1, antennae at right. c, Technical drawing of Sputnik 1. d, Sputnik 1, antennae at left.
No. 944, 94c: a, Yuri Gagarin, first man in space, wearing medals. b, Technical drawing of Vostok rocket. c, Technical drawing of Vostok 1. d, Gagarin in space helmet.

2008, Sept. 22 — *Perf. 13¼*
 Sheets of 6, #a-f
941-942 A304 Set of 2 .... 18.00 18.00
 Sheets of 4, #a-d
943-944 A304 Set of 2 .... 15.00 15.00

Miniature Sheets

Star Trek The Next Generation — A305

No. 945: a, Capt. Jean-Luc Picard. b, Lt. Commander Data. c, Commander William T. Riker. d, Counselor Deanna Troi. e, Lt. Commander Geordi La Forge. f, Lieutenant Worf.
No. 946: a, Wesley Crusher. b, Worf. c, Picard. d, Dr. Beverly Crusher.

2008, Dec. 4 — *Perf. 11½*
945 A305 75c Sheet of 6, #a-f 9.00 9.00
 Perf. 13¼
946 A305 94c Sheet of 4, #a-d 7.50 7.50
 No. 946 contains four 37x50mm stamps.

Christmas — A306

Designs: 22c, Angel holding candle. 26c, Angel with violin. 42c, Angel and conifer wreath. 94c, Angel in light display.

2008, Dec. 11 — *Litho.* *Perf. 14x14¾*
947-950 A306 Set of 4 .... 3.75 3.75

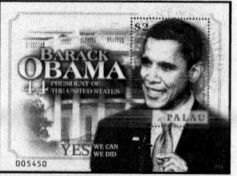

Inauguration of US Pres. Barack Obama — A307

No. 951, horiz. — Pres. Obama: a, Holding microphone. b, Smiling, denomination at LL. c, Smiling, denomination at UL. d, With index finger raised.
$2, Head of Pres. Obama.

2009, Jan. 20 — *Perf. 11½x11¼*
951 A307 94c Sheet of 4, #a-d 7.75 7.75
 Souvenir Sheet
952 A307 $2 multi 4.00 4.00
 No. 951 contains four 40x30mm stamps.

New Year 2009 (Year of the Ox) A308

No. 953 — Ox and Chinese characters in diamond in: a, Black. b, White.

2009, Jan. 26 — *Perf. 12*
953 A308 94c Horiz. pair, #a-b 4.00 4.00
 Printed in sheets containing two pairs.

Miniature Sheet

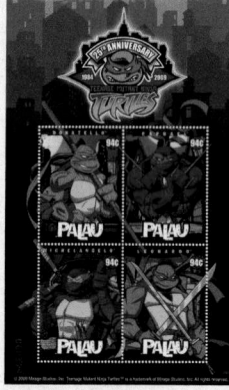

Teenage Mutant Ninja Turtles, 25th Anniv. A309

No. 954: a, Donatello. b, Raphael. c, Michelangelo. d, Leonardo.

2009, Feb. 25 — *Perf. 13¼*
954 A309 94c Sheet of 4, #a-d 7.75 7.75

Miniature Sheets

A310

Michael Jackson (1958-2009),
Singer — A311

No. 955 — Background color: a, Red (Jackson with mouth open). b, Green. c, Blue. d, Red (Jackson with mouth closed).
No. 956 — Jackson dancing with denomination at: a, 28c, Right. b, 28c, Left. c, 75c, Right. d, 75c, Left.

2009, Sept. 3   **Perf. 12x11½**
955 A310 44c Sheet of 4, #a-d 3.75 3.75
956 A311 Sheet of 4, #a-d 4.25 4.25

Miniature Sheet

Palau Pacific Resort, 25th Anniv. A312

No. 957: a, Four beach umbrellas, shadow of palm trees. b, Palm trees near beach under cloudy skies. c, Resort at night. d, Lounge chairs on beach. e, Swimming pool. f, Palm tree, two beach umbrellas.

2009, Oct. 5   **Perf. 11½**
957 A312 26c Sheet of 6, #a-f 3.25 3.25

Dolphins — A313

Designs: 28c, Spinner dolphin. 44c, Hourglass dolphin. 98c, Costero. $1.05, Risso's dolphin.
No. 962: a, Heaviside's dolphin. b, Chilean dolphin. c, Dusky dolphin. d, Commerson's dolphin. e, Fraser's dolphin. f, Striped dolphin.

2009, Oct. 13   **Perf. 14¾x14**
958-961 A313 Set of 4 5.50 5.50
962 A313 75c Sheet of 6, #a-f 9.00 9.00

Shells — A314

Designs: 28c, Morula musiva. 44c, Littoraria articulata. 98c, Architectonica perdix. $1.05, Scalptia crossei.
No. 967: a, Pugilina cochlidium. b, Epitonium scalare. c, Ellobium tornatelliforme. d, Polinices sebae. e, Cyclophorus siamensis. f, Acrosterigma maculosum.

2009, Oct. 13
963-966 A314 Set of 4 5.50 5.50
967 A314 75c Sheet of 6, #a-f 9.00 9.00

A315

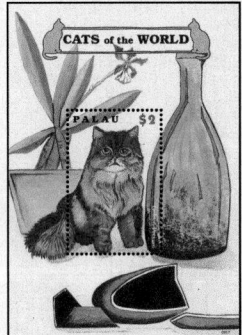

Cats
A316

No. 968: a, Devon Rex cream lynx point sirex. b, Ocicat chocolate. c, Asian chocolate smoke. d, Burmilla lilac shaded. e, Egyptian Mau bronze. f, Himalayan blue tortie point.
No. 969: a, Turkish Van and fireplace. b, Tiffany. c, Turkish Van, diff. d, Birman seal lynx point.
No. 970, $2, Golden Persian. No. 971, $2, Red silver tabby.

2009, Oct. 13   **Perf. 14**
968 A315 75c Sheet of 6, #a-f 9.00 9.00
969 A315 94c Sheet of 4, #a-d 7.75 7.75
Souvenir Sheets
970-971 A316 Set of 2 8.00 8.00

Miniature Sheet

Fish
A317

No. 972: a, Two-spot snappers. b, Goggleeye. c, Bluestreak cardinalfish. d, Bluefin trevally. e, Rainbow runners. f, Fire goby.

2009, Oct. 13   **Perf. 11½x11¼**
972 A317 75c Sheet of 6, #a-f 9.00 9.00

Miniature Sheet

Pres. Abraham Lincoln (1809-65) — A318

No. 973 — Photographs of Lincoln: a, Hands showing, denomination in white. b, Hands not showing, denomination in white. c, Hands not showing, denomination in black. d, Hand showing, denomination in black.

2009, Oct. 13   **Perf. 11¼x11½**
973 A318 44c Sheet of 4, #a-d 3.75 3.75

Souvenir Sheet

Visit of Pope Benedict XVI to Yad Vashem Holocaust Memorial, Israel — A319

No. 974 — Pope Benedict XVI: a, 98c, Looking at flame (30x40mm). b, $2, Praying in front of flowers (60x40mm).

2009, Oct. 13
974 A319 Sheet of 3, #974b, 2 #974a 8.00 8.00

Souvenir Sheets

A320

A321

A322

Elvis Presley (1935-77) — A323

2009, Oct. 13   **Perf. 13¼**
975 A320 $2.50 multi 5.00 5.00
976 A321 $2.50 multi 5.00 5.00
977 A322 $2.50 multi 5.00 5.00
978 A323 $2.50 multi 5.00 5.00
    Nos. 975-978 (4) 20.00 20.00

A324

Fish — A325

Designs: 1c, Giant trevally. 2c, Pink anemonefish. 3c, Gray reef shark. 4c, Leaf fish. 5c, Scissor-tailed fusiliers. 26c, Helfrich's dartfish. 44c, Bigscale soldierfish. $1, Peach anthias. $2, Spotted eagle ray. $3, African

pompano. $4, Harlequin grouper. $5, Pyramid butterflyfish. $10, Longnose hawkfish.

2009, Oct. 13 Litho. Perf. 11¾x12¼
979 A324 1c multi .25 .25
980 A324 2c multi .25 .25
981 A324 3c multi .25 .25
982 A324 4c multi .25 .25
983 A324 5c multi .25 .25
984 A325 26c multi .55 .55
985 A324 44c multi .90 .90
986 A324 $1 multi 2.00 2.00
987 A324 $2 multi 4.00 4.00
988 A324 $3 multi 6.00 6.00
989 A324 $4 multi 8.00 8.00
990 A324 $5 multi 10.00 10.00
991 A324 $10 multi 20.00 20.00
    Nos. 979-991 (13) 52.70 52.70

Worldwide Fund for Nature (WWF) — A326

No. 992 — Red lionfish: a, Two fish. b, One fish facing forward, brown background. c, One fish facing right. d, One fish facing forward, blue background.

2009, Nov. 9 Litho. Perf. 13¼
992 A326 53c Block of 4, #a-d 4.25 4.25
a. Sheet of 8, 2 each #992a-992d 8.50 8.50

Miniature Sheet

First Man on the Moon, 40th Anniv. A327

No. 993: a, Lunar Module before landing. b, Lunar Module ascent stage. c, Command module. d, Mission patch and plaque left on Moon.

2009, Dec. 10   **Perf. 12x11½**
993 A327 98c Sheet of 4, #a-d 8.00 8.00

    Intl. Year of Astronomy.

Christmas — A328

Designs: 26c, Christmas ornaments and stocking on coral. 44c, Wreath and "Merry Christmas". 98c, Gingerbread house with flag of Palau. $2, Wreath and bell.

2009, Dec. 10   **Perf. 14¼x14¾**
994-997 A328 Set of 4 7.50 7.50

Miniature Sheet

Charles Darwin (1809-82), Naturalist — A329

No. 998: a, HMS Beagle. b, Captain Robert Fitzroy. c, Sextant of HMS Beagle. d, Diagram of HMS Beagle. e, Darwin. f, Darwin's report on the zoology of the voyage of the HMS Beagle.

2010, Mar. 2   **Perf. 13¼**
998 A329 75c Sheet of 6, #a-f 9.00 9.00

Reptiles and Amphibians A330

Designs: 26c, Bufo marinus. 44c, Chelonia mydas. 98c, Lepidodactylus lugubris. $1.05, Varanus olivaceus.
No. 1003: a, Northern forest dragon. b, Common house gecko. c, Hawksbill turtle. d, Indopacific tree gecko. e, Amboina box turtle. f, Flying dragon.

2010, Mar. 2 — Perf. 12
999-1002 A330 Set of 4 — 5.50 5.50
1003 A330 75c Sheet of 6, #a-f — 9.00 9.00

Pope John Paul II (1920-2005) — A331

2010, Apr. 22 — Perf. 12x11½
1004 A331 75c multi — 1.50 1.50
Printed in sheets of 4. Compare with type A451.

Miniature Sheet

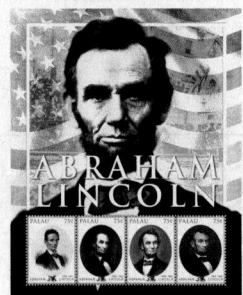

Pres. Abraham Lincoln (1809-65) — A332

No. 1005 — Lincoln: a, Without beard. b, With beard, no cowlick on forehead. c, With beard, cowlick on forehead, point of shirt above "M." d, With beard, cowlick on forehead, point of shirt above "LIN."

2010, Apr. 22 — Perf. 11½
1005 A332 75c Sheet of 4, #a-d — 6.00 6.00

Miniature Sheet

Elvis Presley (1935-77) — A333

No. 1005 — Presley: a, Facing backwards. b, Wearing sequined suit. c, With hand and microphone cord at left. d, Wearing suit with bordered lapels.

2010, Apr. 22 — Perf. 11½
1006 A333 75c Sheet of 4, #a-d — 6.00 6.00

Girl Guides, Cent. A334

No. 1007, horiz.: a, Two Girl Guides in blue uniforms. b, Two Girl Guides, one wearing cap. c, Girl Guide playing bongo drum. d, Four Girl Guides.
$2.50, Girl Guide in green uniform.

2010, June 9 — Perf. 11½x12
1007 A334 94c Sheet of 4, #a-d — 7.75 7.75
Souvenir Sheet
Perf. 11½
1008 A334 $2.50 multi — 5.00 5.00

Souvenir Sheet

Governmental Buildings — A335

No. 1009: a, Executive Building. b, OEK Congress. c, Judiciary Building.

2010, July 1 — Perf. 13½
1009 A335 $1 Sheet of 3, #a-c — 6.00 6.00

Princess Diana (1961-97) — A336

No. 1010 — Princess Diana wearing: a, Tiara. b, Blue violet gown.

2010, Sept. 8 — Perf. 12x11½
1010 A336 75c Pair, #a-b — 3.00 3.00
Printed in sheets containing two pairs.

Miniature Sheet

Mother Teresa (1910-97), Humanitarian — A337

No. 1011 — Mother Teresa and: a, Blue sky behind name and country name. b, Blue sky behind country name, cloud behind name. c, Cloud behind country name, blue sky partly behind name. d, Blue sky partly behind country name, cloud behind name.

2010, Sept. 8 — Perf. 11½
1011 A337 94c Sheet of 4, #a-d — 7.75 7.75

Henri Dunant (1828-1910), Founder of Red Cross — A338

No. 1012 Dunant and: a, Frédèric Passy. b, Czar Nicholas II, c, Henri Dufour. d, Bertha von Suttner.
$2.50, Obverse and reverse of Nobel medal.

2010, Sept. 8 — Perf. 11½x12
1012 A338 94c Sheet of 4, #a-d — 7.75 7.75
Souvenir Sheet
Perf. 11½
1013 A338 $2.50 multi — 5.00 5.00

Souvenir Sheet

Paintings by Sandro Botticelli (1445-1510) — A339

No. 1014, vert.: a, Madonna and Child. b, Nastagio Degli Onesti. c, Calumny of Apelles. d, Primavera.
$2.50, Orazione Nell'Orto.

2010, Sept. 8 — Perf. 12x11½
1014 A339 94c Sheet of 4, #a-d — 7.75 7.75
Souvenir Sheet
Perf. 11½
1015 A339 $2.50 multi — 5.00 5.00

Souvenir Sheet

Issuance of the Penny Black, 170th Anniv. A340

No. 1016: a, Penny Black (Great Britain #1). b, Palau #2.

2010, Sept. 8 — Perf. 13¼
1016 A340 $2 Sheet of 2, #a-b — 8.00 8.00

Christmas — A341

Paintings: 26c, Adoration of the Magi, by Leonardo da Vinci. 44c, Adoration of the Shepherds, by Carlo Crivelli. 98c, Adoration of the Magi, by Hieronymus Bosch. $2, Adoration of the Magi, by Albrecht Altdorfer.

2010, Sept. 8 — Perf. 11½
1017-1020 A341 Set of 4 — 7.50 7.50

Miniature Sheets

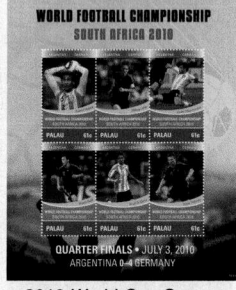

2010 World Cup Soccer Championships, South Africa — A342

No. 1021, 61c: a, Gabriel Heinze. b, Philipp Lahm. c, Javier Mascherano. d, Mesut Dezil. e, Angel Di Maria. f, Lukas Podolski.
No. 1022, 61c: a, Antolin Alcaraz. b, Cesc Fabregas. c, Dario Veron. d, Carlos Puyol. e, Victor Caceres. f, Xabi Alonso.

2010, Dec. 16 — Perf. 12
Sheets of 6, #a-f
1021-1022 A342 Set of 2 — 15.00 15.00

Paintings by Michelangelo Merisi da Caravaggio (1571-1610) — A343

No. 1023: a, Supper at Emmaus. b, Ecce Homo. c, Omnia Vincit Amor. d, Flagellazione di Cristo.
$2.50, The Incredulity of Saint Thomas.

2010, Dec. 16 — Perf. 12
1023 A343 94c Sheet of 4, #a-d — 7.75 7.75
Souvenir Sheet
Perf. 12½
1024 A343 $2.50 multi — 5.00 5.00
No. 1023 contains four 40x30mm stamps.

Pope Benedict XVI — A344

2010, Dec. 16 — Perf. 12
1025 A344 75c multi — 1.50 1.50
Printed in sheets of 4 with slight color differences in the background.

Miniature Sheets

Sharks A346

Sea Turtles A347

Dugongs
A348

No. 1027 — Shark with dorsal fin: a, Touching "R" in "Shark." b, Between "A" and "R" in "Shark." c, Touching "A" in "Shark."
No. 1028 — Sea turtle: a, Swimming left. b, At ocean floor. c, Swimming right.
No. 1029: a, Dugong at water's surface. b, Two dugongs. c, Dugong and fish.

Perf. 13 Syncopated
2010, Dec. 21 Litho.
1027 A346 98c Sheet of 3,
#a-c 6.00 6.00
1028 A347 98c Sheet of 3,
#a-c 6.00 6.00
1029 A348 98c Sheet of 3,
#a-c 6.00 6.00
Nos. 1027-1029 (3) 18.00 18.00

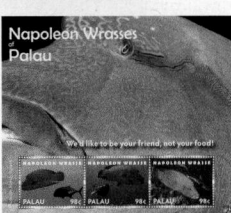

The top sheet, containing poorly cropped stamp images, was received by Palau postal officials but was never put on sale in Palau. The bottom sheet was sold by dealers, but was never received by Palau postal officials.

Miniature Sheet

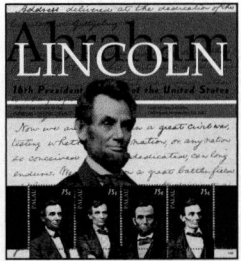

Pres. Abraham Lincoln (1809-65) — A349

Various photographs of Lincoln.

2011, Mar. 11 **Perf. 12**
1030 A349 75c Sheet of 4, #a-d 6.00 6.00

Miniature Sheet

Inauguration of Pres. John F. Kennedy, 50th Anniv. — A350

No. 1031 — Kennedy: a, Behind microphone. b, At inauguration. c, In rocking chair. d, Shaking person's hand.

2011, Mar. 11
1031 A350 75c Sheet of 4, #a-d 6.00 6.00

Miniature Sheet

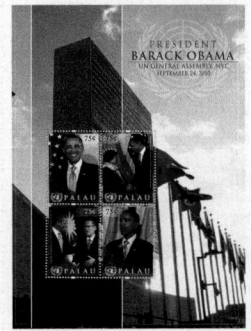

Pres. Barack Obama's Visit to the United Nations A351

No. 1032 — Pres. Obama and: a, US flag. b, Kyrgyzstan Pres. Rosa Otunbaeva. c, Philippines Pres. Benigno Aquino III. d, United Nations flags.

2011, Mar. 11 **Perf. 13 Syncopated**
1032 A351 75c Sheet of 4, #a-d 6.00 6.00

Indipex 2011 Intl. Philatelic Exhibition, New Delhi — A352

No. 1033: a, Bhagat Singh (1907-31), nationalist. b, Lal Bahadur Shastri (1904-66), Prime Minister. c, Subhas Chandra Bose (1897-1945), politician. d, Dr. Rajendra Prasad (1884-1963), politician. e, Jawaharlal Nehru (1889-1964), Prime Minister. f, Sardar Patel (1875-1950), Deputy Prime Minister.
$2.50, Mohandas K. Gandhi (1869-1948), independence leader.

2011, Mar. 11 **Perf. 12**
1033 A352 50c Sheet of 6, #a-f 6.00 6.00
Souvenir Sheet
Perf. 13 Syncopated
1034 A352 $2.50 multi 5.00 5.00

Whales A353

No. 1035: a, Blainville's beaked whale. b, Shepherd's beaked whale. c, Cuvier's beaked whale. d, Baird's beaked whale. e, Stejneger's beaked whale. f, Ginkgo-toothed beaked whale.
$2.50, Pygmy sperm whale.

2011, Mar. 11 **Perf. 13 Syncopated**
1035 A353 75c Sheet of 6, #a-f 9.00 9.00
Souvenir Sheet
1036 A353 $2.50 multi 5.00 5.00

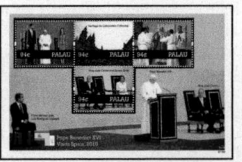

Visit to Spain of Pope Benedict XVI A354

No. 1037: a, Pope Benedict XVI, Prince Felipe and Princess Letizia of Spain. b, Santiago de Compostela Cathedral. c, Pope Benedict XVI celebrating mass. d, King Juan Carlos and Queen Sofia of Spain.
$2.50, Pope Benedict XVI and Sagrada Familia Basilica, Barcelona, vert.

2011, Mar. 11 Litho.
1037 A354 94c Sheet of 4, #a-d 7.75 7.75
Souvenir Sheet
1038 A354 $2.50 multi 5.00 5.00

Miniature Sheet

Pres. Ronald Reagan (1911-2004) — A355

No. 1039: a, Pres. Reagan at podium. b, Pres. Reagan with wife, Nancy. c, Pres. Reagan. d, Pres. Reagan with Soviet Union General Secretary Mikhail Gorbachev.

2011, Apr. 5 **Perf. 13 Syncopated**
1039 A355 98c Sheet of 4, #a-d 8.00 8.00

A356

A357

A358

A359

A360

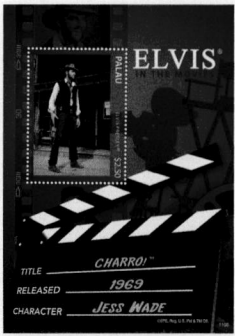

Elvis Presley (1935-77) — A361

No. 1040: a, Presley with guitar, two microphones. b, Presley facing right. c, Presley with closed mouth, microphone at left. d, Presley singing, microphone at left.
No. 1041 — Presley: a, With hand on ear. b, Microphone at left. c, Microphone at right, denomination in white. d, Microphone at right, denomination in black.

2011 **Perf. 13 Syncopated**
1040 A356 75c Sheet of 4,
#a-d 6.00 6.00
1041 A357 75c Sheet of 4,
#a-d 6.00 6.00
Souvenir Sheets
Perf. 12¾
1042 A358 $2.50 multi 5.00 5.00
1043 A359 $2.50 multi 5.00 5.00
1044 A360 $2.50 multi 5.00 5.00
1045 A361 $2.50 multi 5.00 5.00
Nos. 1042-1045 (4) 20.00 20.00

Issued: Nos. 1040-1041, 7/14; Nos. 1042-1045, 4/5.

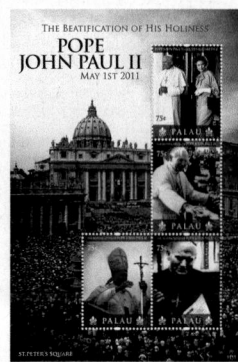

Beatification of Pope John Paul II — A362

No. 1046 — Pope John Paul II: a, With Queen Elizabeth II. b, Greeting crowd. c, Wearing miter. d, Holding paper.
$2.50, Wearing miter, priests in background.

2011, May 25 **Perf. 13 Syncopated**
1046 A362 75c Sheet of 4,
#a-d 6.00 6.00
Souvenir Sheet
Perf. 12¾
1047 A362 $2.50 multi 5.00 5.00
No. 1047 contains one 38x51mm stamp.

Wedding of Prince William and Catherine Middleton — A363

Designs: 98c, Couple.
No. 1049, $2, Prince William. No. 1050, $2, Catherine Middleton.

2011, June 17 **Perf. 12x12½**
1048 A363 98c multi 2.00 2.00
Souvenir Sheets
Perf. 13½
1049-1050 A363 Set of 2 8.00 8.00
Nos. 1049-1050 each contain one 51x32mm triangular stamp.

Miniature Sheets

A364

Princess Diana (1961-97) — A365

No. 1051 — Princess Diana wearing: a, Black lace dress and choker on black ribbon. b, White dress. c, Pink hat. d, Black dress, no choker.
No. 1052 — Princess Diana wearing: a, Earring. b, Plaid jacket. c, Red Cross uniform. d, Black hat with veil.

2011, July 6   **Perf. 13 Syncopated**
1051 A364 75c Sheet of 4, #a-d   6.00 6.00
1052 A365 75c Sheet of 4, #a-d   6.00 6.00

Taro Festival — A366

No. 1053 — Taro plant and inscription: a, Dung er a terrekaki. b, Renged. c, Meuarch. d, Okelang. e, Metengal e ngas. f, Kirang. g, Rriu. h, Ngerbachel. i, Saikerei. j, Oiremech. k, Terebkul. l, Esuuch. m, Dungersuul. n, Ngesuas. o, Kerdeu. p, Terrekaki. q, Ngiroi-lang. r, Dilisior. s, Brak. t, Ulechem. u, Homusted. v, Besechel. w, Ungildil. x, Urungel. y, Ngatmadei. z, Dois. aa, Bsachel. ab, Ochab. ac, Kirang (redil). ad, Ngeruuch.

2011, July 8   **Perf. 12¾x13**
1053   Sheet of 30   18.00 18.00
a.-ad. A366 29c Any single   .60 .60

Souvenir Sheet

Haruo I. Remeliik (1933-85), First President of Palau — A367

2011, July 8   **Perf. 13¼**
1054 A367 $2 multi   4.00 4.00

Birds A368

No. 1055, 98c: a, Black-headed gull. b, Red-tailed tropicbird. c, Intermediate egret. d, Yellow bittern.
No., 1056, vert.: a, Cattle egret. b, Red-footed booby. c, Australian pelican. d, Little pied cormorant.
No. 1057, $2, Greater crested tern. No. 1058, $2, Brown noddy, vert.

2011, July 14   **Perf. 13 Syncopated**
Sheets of 4, #a-d
1055-1056 A368 Set of 2   16.00 16.00
Souvenir Sheets
1057-1058 A368 Set of 2   8.00 8.00

Pres. Abraham Lincoln (1809-65) — A369

No. 1059 — Details from First Reading of the Emancipation Proclamation of President Lincoln, by Francis Bicknell Carpenter: a, Treasury Secretary Salmon P. Chase, Secretary of War Edwin M. Stanton. b, Lincoln. c, Secretary of the Navy Gideon Welles. d, Postmaster General Montgomery Blair, Interior Secretary, Caleb B. Smith, Secretary of State William H. Seward. e, Attorney General Edward Bates. $2.50, Photograph of Lincoln.

2011, July 27   **Perf. 11½x11¾**
1059 A369 60c Sheet of 5, #a-d   6.00 6.00
Souvenir Sheet
Perf. 12x12½
1060 A369 $2.50 multi   5.00 5.00
No. 1060 contains one 30x80mm stamp.

Miniature Sheet

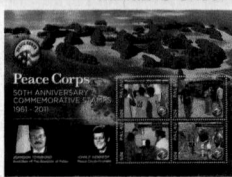

Peace Corps, 50th Anniv. A370

No. 1061 — Peace Corps emblem and: a, Students and volunteer painting. b, Palauan host family and volunteers walking. c, Volunteer and teachers work on Internet project. d, Volunteers working in community garden.

2011, Aug. 2   **Perf. 13x13¼**
1061 A370 50c Sheet of 4, #a-d   4.00 4.00

Sept. 11, 2001 Terrorist Attacks, 10th Anniv. A371

No. 1062 — Firefighters, soldiers, U.S. flag and: a, Firefighter on rubble pile. b, Flags and flowers. c, Person looking at candlelight tribute. d, Tribute in light.
$2.50, World Trade Center and U.S flag.

2011, Sept. 11   **Perf. 12**
1062 A371 75c Sheet of 4, #a-d   6.00 6.00
Souvenir Sheet
Perf. 12¾
1063 A371 $2.50 multi   5.00 5.00
No. 1063 contains one 38x51mm stamp.

Miniature Sheets

A372

Women's World Cup Soccer Championships, Germany — A373

No. 1064: a, Nahomi Kawasumi. b, Japanese team members lifting trophy, "Team Japan" in black. c, Members of Japanese team. d, Yuki Nagasato.
No. 1065: a, Japan coach Norio Sasaki. b, Japanese team members lifting trophy, "Team Japan" in white. c, U.S. team. d, U.S. coach Pia Sundhage.

2011, Sept. 21   **Perf. 12x12½**
1064 A372 98c Sheet of 4, #a-d   8.00 8.00
1065 A373 98c Sheet of 4, #a-d   8.00 8.00

Pres. Barack Obama, 50th Birthday A374

No. 1066 — Pres. Obama, White House, and one-quarter of Presidential Seal at: a, LR. b, LL. c, UR. d, UL.
$2.50, Pres. Obama.

2011, Oct. 26   **Perf. 13 Syncopated**
1066 A374 98c Sheet of 4, #a-d   8.00 8.00
Souvenir Sheet
1067 A374 $2.50 multi   5.00 5.00

Crustaceans — A375

No. 1068, $1.25, vert.: a, Calcinus elegans. b, Dardanus pedunculatus. c, Odontodactylus scyllarus. d, Dardanus megistos.
No. 1069, $1.25, vert.: a, Birgus latro. b, Goneplax rhomboides. c, Bellia picta. d, Etisus dentatus.
No. 1070, $3, Grapsus grapsus. No. 1071, $3, Zebra mantis shrimp, vert.

2011, Oct. 26   **Perf. 12**
Sheets of 4, #a-d
1068-1069 A375 Set of 2   20.00 20.00
Souvenir Sheets
1070-1071 A375 Set of 2   12.00 12.00
No. 1071 contains one 30x50mm stamp.

Marine Life A376

No. 1072: a, Gray reef shark. b, Blue-spotted ray. c, Red lionfish. d, Feather duster worm. e, Regal tang. Yellow tang.
No. 1073: a, Pfeffer's flamboyant cuttlefish. b, Striped surgeonfish. c, Spiny sea urchin.
No. 1074, Box jellyfish, vert. No. 1075, Sawtooth barracuda.

2011, Nov. 29   **Perf. 11½x12**
1072 A376 75c Sheet of 5, #a-e   7.50 7.50
Perf. 12½x12
1073 A376 $1 Sheet of 3, #a-c   6.00 6.00
Souvenir Sheets
Perf. 13½
1074 A376 $2.50 multi   5.00 5.00
Perf.
1075 A376 $2.50 multi   5.00 5.00
No. 1074 contains one 38x51mm stamp.
No. 1075 contains one 35mm diameter stamp.

Christmas — A377

Paintings: 22c, Landscape with the Flight into Egypt, by Annibale Carracci. 44c, Madonna and Saints, by Giovanni Bellini. 98c, Merode Altarpiece, by Robert Campin. $4.25, The Annunciation, by Matthias Grünewald.

2012, Jan. 2   **Perf. 14**
1076-1079 A377 Set of 4   12.00 12.00

Lizards A378

No. 1080, 98c: a, Snake-eyed skink. b, Solomon Islands skink. c, Vanuatu gecko. d, White-bellied skink.
No. 1081, 98c: a, Emerald tree skink. b, Common dwarf gecko. c, Mourning gecko. d, Moth skink.
No. 1082, $2.50, White-line gecko. No. 1083, $2.50, Mangrove monitor.

2012, Jan. 2   **Perf. 13 Syncopated**
Sheets of 4, #a-d
1080-1081 A378 Set of 2   16.00 16.00
Souvenir Sheets
1082-1083 A378 Set of 2   10.00 10.00

Miniature Sheet

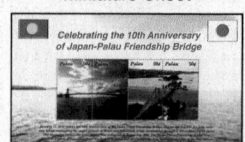

Japan-Palau Friendship Bridge, 10th Anniv. — A379

No. 1084: a, Side view of bridge, tower at left. b, Side view of bridge, tower at right. c, Aerial view of bridge, approach at bottom. d, Aerial view of bridge with road connecting other islands in distance.

2012, Jan. 11   **Perf. 12**
1084 A379 50c Sheet of 4, #a-d   4.00 4.00

Painting of the Sistine Chapel Ceiling by Michelangelo, 500th Anniv. — A380

No. 1085, horiz.: a, Downfall of Adam and Eve. b, The Ignudi. c, The Prophet Jonah. $3.50, The Persian Sibyl.

2012, Jan. 24   *Perf. 12*
1085 A380 $1.25 Sheet of 3, #a-
   c   7.50 7.50
Souvenir Sheet
1086 A380 $3.50 multi   7.00 7.00

Nos. 1085 and 1086 are erroneously inscribed "700th Anniversary."

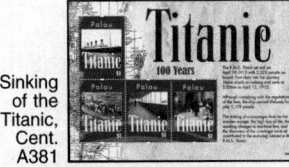

Sinking of the Titanic, Cent. A381

No. 1087: a, Titanic at sea. b, Lifeboat. c, Man walking on deck. d, People reading newspapers reporting on the sinking.
$3, Titanic, diff.

2012, Jan. 25   *Perf. 13 Syncopated*
1087 A381 $1 Sheet of 4, #a-d
             8.00 8.00
Souvenir Sheet
1088 A381 $3 multi   6.00 6.00

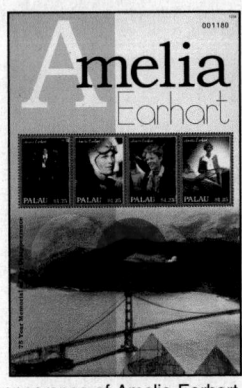

Disappearance of Amelia Earhart, 75th Anniv. — A382

No. 1089 — Earhart: a, Standing in front of airplane without helmet, hands visible. b, Wearing helmet and goggles. c, Standing in front of airplane without helmet, hands not visible. d, Standing in airplane cockpit without helmet.
No. 1090 — Earhart in helmet and goggles, airplane diagram, and text, "Amelia Earhart" in: a, White. b, Black.

2012, Feb. 6   *Perf. 13½*
1089 A382 $1.25 Sheet of 4,
   #a-d   10.00 10.00
Souvenir Sheet
Perf. 12x12½
1090 A382 $1.25 Sheet of 2,
   #a-b   5.00 5.00

Miniature Sheet

2012 Summer Olympics, London — A383

No. 1091: a, Tennis. b, Swimming. c, Weight lifting. d, Basketball.

2012, Mar. 26   *Perf. 13¼x13*
1091 A383 80c Sheet of 4, #a-d   6.50 6.50

Cherry Trees in Bloom and Washington Monument — A384

No. 1092, horiz. — Blossoms of flowering trees: a, Washington hawthorn. b, Flowering dogwood. c, Callery pear. d, Crabapple. e, Magnolia. f, Eastern redbud.

2012, Mar. 26   *Perf. 12*
1092 A384 $1 Sheet of 6,
   #a-f   12.00 12.00
Souvenir Sheet
1093 A384 $3.50 shown   7.00 7.00

Miniature Sheets

A385

Elvis Presley (1935-77) — A386

No. 1094 — Color of "35" and silhouette: a, Red violet. b, Green. c, Yellow. d, Violet.
No. 1095 — Presley wearing: a, Red jacket, white shirt. b, Tan shirt. c, Red jacket, black shirt. d, Gray jacket, white shirt.

2012, Apr. 11   *Perf. 12½*
1094 A385 98c Sheet of 4, #a-d   8.00 8.00
1095 A386 98c Sheet of 4, #a-d   8.00 8.00

Stingrays A387

No. 1096: a, Spotted eagle ray. b, Pacific electric ray. c, Blue-spotted stingray. d, Blotched fantail ray.
$3.50, Southern stingray.

2012, May 7   *Perf. 12*
1096 A387 $1.25 Sheet of 4,
   #a-d   10.00 10.00
Souvenir Sheet
1097 A387 $3.50 multi   7.00 7.00

Souvenir Sheets

Elvis Presley (1935-77) — A388

Designs: No. 1098, $3.50, Presley on *Love Me Tender* record cover. No. 1099, $3.50, Presley on *Jailhouse Rock* album cover. No. 1100, $3.50, Presley on *Blue Hawaii* album cover. No. 1101, $3.50, Presley on *Just Tell Her Jim Said Hello/She's Not You* record cover. No. 1102, $3.50, Presley on *G.I. Blues* record cover.

2012, May 14   *Perf. 12½*
1098-1102 A388   Set of 5   35.00 35.00

Miniature Sheet

Characters From *Peter Pan*, by Sir James M. Barrie (1860-1937) — A389

No. 1103: a, Peter Pan. b, Tiger Lily. c, Captain Hook. d, Wendy Darling.

2012, June 7   *Perf. 12*
1103 A389 $1.25 Sheet of 4,
   #a-d   10.00 10.00

Miniature Sheet

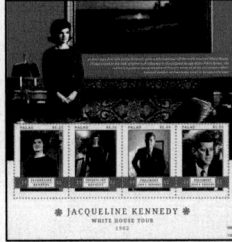

Televised Tour of the White House, 50th Anniv. A390

No. 1104: a, Jacqueline Kennedy, chandelier. b, Jacqueline Kennedy, table and chairs. c, Pres. John F. Kennedy, picture frame. d, Pres. Kennedy, White House.

2012, Aug. 28   *Litho.*
1104 A390 $1.25 Sheet of 4,
   #a-d   10.00 10.00

Pope Benedict XVI, 85th Birthday A391

No. 1105 — Pope Benedict wearing: a, Miter. b, Zucchetto.

2012, Aug. 28   *Perf. 14*
1105 A391 $1.25 Horiz. pair,
   #a-b   5.00 5.00
Printed in sheets containing two pairs.

Miniature Sheets

End of Apollo Moon Missions, 40th Anniv. A392

No. 1106, $1.25: a, Apollo 9. b, Apollo 7. c, Apollo 15. d, Apollo 12.
No. 1107, $1.25: a, Apollo 14. b, Apollo 17. c, Apollo 8. d, Apollo 11.

2012, Aug. 28   *Perf. 13 Syncopated*
       Sheets of 4, #a-d
1106-1107 A392   Set of 2   20.00 20.00

Paintings by Raphael A393

No. 1108: a, Giuliano de' Medici. b, Saint Sebastian. c, Portrait of Julius II. d, Bindo Altoviti.
$3, St. Catherine of Alexandria.

2012, Sept. 5   *Perf. 12½*
1108 A393 $1 Sheet of 4, #a-d   8.00 8.00
Souvenir Sheet
1109 A393 $3 multi   6.00 6.00

Dog Breeds A394

No. 1110: a, Akita. b, Cane Corso. c, Collie. d, Rottweiler.
$3.50, Golden retriever.

2012, Sept. 5   *Perf. 13¾*
1110 A394 $1.25 Sheet of 4,
   #a-d   10.00 10.00
Souvenir Sheet
1111 A394 $3.50 multi   7.00 7.00

Souvenir Sheets

Famous Speeches — A395

Orators of famous speeches: No. 1112, $3.50, Pres. Theodore Roosevelt. No. 1113, $3.50, Mahatma Gandhi. No. 1114, $3.50, Pres. John F. Kennedy. No. 1115, $3.50, Dr. Martin Luther King, Jr.

2012, Sept. 5   *Perf. 12½*
1112-1115 A395   Set of 4   28.00 28.00

Carnivorous Plants — A396

No. 1116: a, Pale butterwort. b, Corkscrew plant. c, Alice sundew. d, Zigzag bladderwort.
$3.50, King sundew, vert.

2012, Nov. 28   *Perf. 13¾*
1116 A396 $1.20 Sheet of 4, #a-
   d   9.75 9.75
Souvenir Sheet
Perf. 12½
1117 A396 $3.50 multi   7.00 7.00
No. 1117 contains one 38x51mm stamp.

Christmas — A397

Paintings by Albrecht Dürer: No. 1118, 29c, Madonna and Child. No. 1119, 29c, The Flight to Egypt. No. 1120, 45c, The Virgin and Child with St. Anne. No. 1121, 45c, Virgin and Child Holding a Half-eaten Pear. No. 1122, $1.05, Mother of Sorrows. No. 1123, $1.05, The Virgin Mary in Prayer.
$3.50, Jesus Boy with a Globe.

2012, Dec. 24   Perf. 12½
1118-1123 A397   Set of 6   7.25 7.25
Souvenir Sheet
1124 A397 $3.50 multi   7.00 7.00

The Hindenburg — A398

Designs: $1.20, Hindenburg. $3.50, Hindenburg, Chrysler Building, Eiffel Tower, Empire State Building, 40 Wall Street Building, vert.

2012, Dec. 31   Perf. 12
1125 A398 $1.20 multi   2.40 2.40
Souvenir Sheet
Perf. 12½
1126 A398 $3.50 multi   7.00 7.00

No. 1125 was printed in sheets of 4. No. 1126 contains one 38x51mm stamp.

World Radio Day A399

No. 1127: a, Microphone. b, Antenna and waves. c, Table radio. d, Radio waves, diagram of ear canals.
$3.50, Solar system, radio wave, horiz.

2013, Jan. 2   Litho.   Perf. 13¾
1127 A399 $1.20 Sheet of 4, #a-d   9.75 9.75
Souvenir Sheet
Perf. 12½
1128 A399 $3.50 multi   7.00 7.00

No. 1128 contains one 51x38mm stamp.

Paintings by Paul Signac (1863-1935) — A400

No. 1129: a, L'Orage (The Storm). b, The Pine, Saint Tropez. c, Portrait of Félix Fénéon. $3.50, Femmes au Puits (Women at the Well).

2013, Jan. 8   Litho.   Perf. 12½
1129 A400 $1.50 Sheet of 3, #a-c   9.00 9.00
Souvenir Sheet
1130 A400 $3.50 multi   7.00 7.00

Reign of Queen Elizabeth II, 60th Anniv. (in 2012) A401

No. 1131 — Queen Elizabeth II: a, With Prince Philip. b, With dog. c, Waving. d, With Prince Charles.
$3.50, Queen Elizabeth II, vert.

2013, Jan. 8   Litho.   Perf. 13¾
1131 A401 $1.20 Sheet of 4, #a-d   9.75 9.75
Souvenir Sheet
Perf. 12½
1132 A401 $3.50 multi   7.00 7.00

No. 1132 contains one 38x51mm stamp.

Shells A402

No. 1133: a, Conus gloriamaris. b, Hydatina albocincta. c, Marginella strigata. d, Conus betulinus.
$3.50, Tellina pharaonis, horiz.

2013, Mar. 20   Litho.   Perf. 12
1133 A402 $1.20 Sheet of 4, #a-d   9.75 9.75
Souvenir Sheet
1134 A402 $3.50 multi   7.00 7.00

Cat Breeds A403

Cat Depictions From Other Cultures — A404

No. 1135, $1.20: a, Russian Blue. b, Turkish Angora. c, Norwegian forest cat. d, Siamese.
No. 1136, $1.20: a, Siberian. b, Oriental shorthair. c, Japanese bobtail. d, Chartreux.
No. 1137, $3.50, Egyptian goddess Bastet.
No. 1138, $3.50, Japanese Maneki-neko figurine.

2013, Mar. 20   Litho.   Perf. 12
Sheets of 4, #a-d
1135-1136 A403   Set of 2   19.50 19.50
Souvenir Sheets
Perf. 13¾
1137-1138 A404   Set of 2   14.00 14.00

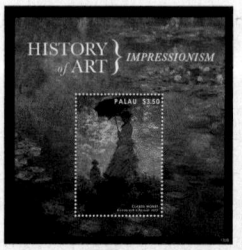

History of Art A405

No. 1139, $1.50: a, Sunset at Ivry, by Armand Guillaumin. b, Landscape with Big Trees, by Camille Pissarro. c, A Box at the Theater, by Pierre-Auguste Renoir.
No. 1140, $1.50: a, Sunshine in the Blue Room, by Anna Ancher. b, Woman Washing Her Feet in a Brook, by Pissarro. c, Woman in the Bath, by Edgar Degas.
No. 1141, $3.50, Woman with a Parasol, by Claude Monet. No. 1142, $3.50, The Star, by Edgar Degas.

2013, Apr. 4   Litho.   Perf. 12½
Sheets of 3, #a-c
1139-1140 A405   Set of 2   18.00 18.00
Souvenir Sheets
1141-1142 A405   Set of 2   14.00 14.00

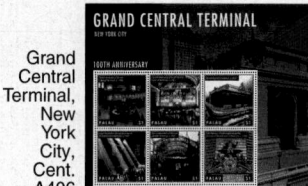

Grand Central Terminal, New York City, Cent. A406

No. 1143: a, Ticket window, c. 1945. b, Commuters in station, c. 1941. c, Terminal exterior, c. 1920. d, Light shining through windows, c. 1930. e, Terminal under construction, c. 1907. f, Mercury Clock, c. 1988.
$3.50, Terminal exterior, horiz.

2013, Apr. 29   Litho.   Perf. 13¾
1143 A406 $1 Sheet of 6, #a-f   12.00 12.00
Souvenir Sheet
Perf. 12½
1144 A406 $3.50 multi   7.00 7.00

No. 1144 contains one 51x38mm stamp.

A407

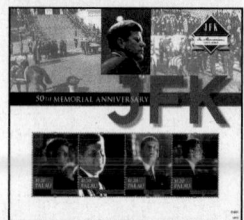

Pres. John F. Kennedy (1917-63) — A408

No. 1145 — Black-and-white images of Pres. Kennedy: a, Facing right, flag in background. b, Facing left, flag in background. c, With people in background. d, With door in background.
No. 1146 — Color images of Pres. Kennedy: a, Facing right, with woman's head in background. b, With black background. c, With tie pattern visible. d, Facing right, with indistinguishable light reflections in background.
No. 1147, $3.50, Pres. Kennedy, country name at LL in blue panel. No. 1148, $3.50, Pres. Kennedy pointing, country name at UL in blue panel.

Perf. 13 Syncopated
2013, Apr. 29   Litho.
1145 A407 $1.20 Sheet of 4, #a-d   9.75 9.75
1146 A408 $1.20 Sheet of 4, #a-d   9.75 9.75
Souvenir Sheets
1147-1148 A408   Set of 2   14.00 14.00

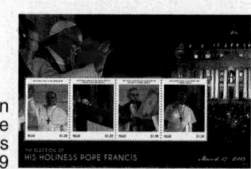

Election of Pope Francis A409

No. 1150 — Pope Francis: a, Waving to crowd below (orange background). b, Addressing crowd from balcony of St. Peter's Basilica (with cardinals). c, Behind microphone, addressing crowd, with assistant holding Bible. d, Waving to crowd (shadow and wall in background).
$3.50, Pope Francis, diff.

2013, June 3   Litho.   Perf. 12
1149 A409 $1.20 Sheet of 4, #a-d   9.75 9.75
Souvenir Sheet
Perf. 12½
1150 A409 $3.50 multi   7.00 7.00

No. 1150 contains one 38x51mm stamp.

Lady Margaret Thatcher (1925-2013), British Prime Minister — A410

No. 1151 — Thatcher: a, Wearing black dress. b, With Pres. George H. W. Bush. c, Wearing gray striped dress. d, Wearing black dress with whtie dots.

$3.50, Thatcher in doorway of bus.

2013, June 3   Litho.   Perf. 12
1151 A410 $1.25 Sheet of 4, #a-d   10.00 10.00
Souvenir Sheet
Perf. 12½
1152 A410 $3.50 multi   7.00 7.00

No. 1152 conatins one 38x51mm stamp.

Henry Ford (1863-1947), Automobile Manufacturer — A411

No. 1153: a, Ford and first car. b, Assembly line. c, Parked Model T autombiles. d, Ford and Model T.
$3.50, Ford, vert.

2013, June 25   Litho.   Perf. 12
1153 A411 $1.20 Sheet of 4, #a-d   9.75 9.75
Souvenir Sheet
1154 A411 $3.50 multi   7.00 7.00

Tropical Fish A412

No. 1155, $1.20: a, Australasian snapper. b, Tomato clownfish. c, Pennant coralfish. d, Yellow watchman goby.
No. 1156, $1.20: a, Pink-spotted shirmp goby. b, Ocellated dragonet. c, Common warehou. d, Gray moray.
No. 1157, $3.50, Blue-eyed triplefin. No. 1158, $3.50, Barred mudskipper.

2013, June 25   Litho.   Perf. 12
Sheets of 4, #a-d
1155-1156 A412   Set of 2   19.50 19.50
Souvenir Sheets
1157-1158 A412   Set of 2   14.00 14.00

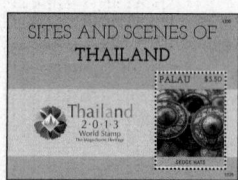

Thailand 2013 World Stamp Exhibition, Bangkok — A413

No. 1159: a, Mondop Staircases. b, Floating market. c, Asian elephants. d, Buddhist temple.
$3.50, Sedge hats.

2013, July 7   Litho.   Perf. 12
1159 A413 $1.20 Sheet of 4, #a-d   9.75 9.75
Souvenir Sheet
1160 A413 $3.50 multi   7.00 7.00

Butterflies — A414

No. 1161, horiz.: a, Tailed jay swallowtail. b, Old world swallowtail. c, Common albatross. d, Australian lurcher.
$3.50, Macleay's swallowtail.

2013, Sept. 17 Litho. *Perf. 12*

1161 A414 $1.20 Sheet of 4, #a-d 9.75 9.75

Souvenir Sheet

1162 A414 $3.50 multi 7.00 7.00

Cultured Pearls A415

No. 1163: a, Large brown pearl in oyster shell, upper shell. b, Large white pearl. c, Three pearls. d, Small pearl in oyster shell.
$4, Pearl, tan background.

2013, Sept. 17 Litho. *Perf. 13¾*

1163 A415 $2 Sheet of 4, #a-d 16.00 16.00

Souvenir Sheet

1164 A415 $4 multi 8.00 8.00

Birth of Prince George of Cambridge — A416

No. 1165: a, Duchess of Cambridge holding Prince George. b, Prince George, close-up. c, Prince Charles, Princess Diana, Prince William. d, Duke and Duchess of Cambridge with Prince George.
$3.50, Duke and Duchess of Cambridge with Prince George, diff.

2013, Sept. 17 Litho. *Perf. 14*

1165 A416 $1.20 Sheet of 4, #a-d 9.75 9.75

Souvenir Sheet

Perf. 12

1166 A416 $3.50 multi 7.00 7.00

No. 1166 contains one 30x50mm stamp.

Miniature Sheets

Photographs by Kevin Davidson — A417

No. 1167: a, Oxypora coral, country name at UL, reading across. b, Coral dweller cobie, country name at UL, reading across. c, Bannerfish. d, Mushroom Rock Island, country name at UL, reading across. e, Medusa worm on red sponge. f, Eagle ray, decimal point of denomination to right of ray, wing of ray just touching vertical line of first "1" in denomination.

No. 1168: a, Baby green turtles. b, Mandarin fish, country name at UL, reading across. c, Eagle ray, decimal point of denomination on ray. d, Pink anemone fish, country name at UL, reading across. e, Head of fish (incorrectly inscribed "Medusa worm on red sponge"). f, Masked angelfish.

No. 1169: a, Harlequin sweetlips. b, Nautilus. c, Eagle Ray, decimal point of denomination to right of ray, wing of ran not touching vertical line of first "1" in denomination. d, Red sea fan. e, Soft coral crab.

No. 1170: a, Oxypora coral, country name at left, reading up. b, Coral dweller cobie, country name at left, reading up. c, Pink anemone fish, country name at left, reading up. d, Mushroom Rock Island, country name at left, reading up. e, Mandarin fish, country name at left, reading up. f, Longnose hawkfish.

No. 1171, vert.: a, Three jellyfish. b, Starfish on red coral fan, country name at UL, reading across. c, Jellyfish and diver. d, Oxypora coral, country name at UL, reading across. e, Seahorse. f, Lionfish.

No. 1172, vert.: a, Coconut climber. b, Pink anemone fish, country name at UL, reading across. c, Cup coral, country name at UL, reading across. d, Humphead wrasse, e, Shark.

No. 1173, vert.: a, Cup coral, country name at UL, reading up. b, Manta ray. c, Rock Island. d, Red seahorse. e, Pink anemone fish, country name at UL, reading up. f, Starfish on red coral fan, country name at UL, reading up.

2013, Oct. 1 Litho. *Perf. 12*

1167 A417 $1.10 Sheet of 6, #a-f 13.50 13.50
1168 A417 $1.10 Sheet of 6, #a-f 13.50 13.50
1169 A417 $1.10 Sheet of 6, #a-e, 1168f 13.50 13.50
1170 A417 $1.10 Sheet of 6, #a-f 13.50 13.50
1171 A417 $1.10 Sheet of 6, #a-f 13.50 13.50
1172 A417 $1.10 Sheet of 6, #a-e, 1171d 13.50 13.50
1173 A417 $1.10 Sheet of 6, #a-f 13.50 13.50
Nos. 1167-1173 (7) 94.50 94.50

Souvenir Sheet

Elvis Presley (1935-77) — A418

Litho., Margin Embossed With Foil Application

2013, Oct. 1 *Imperf.*

1174 A418 $10 multi 20.00 20.00

Coronation of Queen Elizabeth II, 60th Anniv. — A419

No. 1175 — Queen Elizabeth II: a, With Prince Philip. b, Wearing pink hat. c, Wearing white hat. d, Alone, wearing sash and tiara.
$3.50, Queen Elizabeth II in coach, vert.

2013, Oct. 7 Litho. *Perf. 14*

1175 A419 $1.20 Sheet of 4, #a-d 9.75 9.75

Souvenir Sheet

1176 A419 $3.50 multi 7.00 7.00

World Water Day — A420

Designs: $1.20, Water droplets. $3.50, Water droplet, vert.

2013, Nov. 18 Litho. *Perf. 13¾*

1177 A420 $1.20 multi 2.40 2.40

Souvenir Sheet

Perf. 12½

1178 A420 $3.50 multi 7.00 7.00

No. 1177 was printed in sheets of 4. No. 1178 contains one 38x51mm stamp.

Christmas — A421

Paintings: 29c, Madonna Worshipping the Child and an Angel, by Biagio D'Antonio Tucci. 44c, Nativity, by unknown artist. $1.05, The Annunciation, by Simone Martini. $3.50, Virgin and Child, by Gentile da Fabriano.

2013, Dec. 2 Litho. *Perf. 12½*

1179-1182 A421 Set of 4 11.00 11.00

A422

Nelson Mandela (1918-2013), President of South Africa — A423

No. 1183: a, Mandela and wife, Winnie, waving. b, Mandela as young man wearing traditional collar. c, Mandela in crowd, laughing.

No. 1184 — Mandela: a, wearing black and gray shirt. b, Wearing suit and tie, building in background. c, Holding microphone stand. d, Seated. e, Behind microphone, pointing. f, With raised fist.

No. 1185, $3.50, Mandela holding ballot, wearing shirt with pens in pocket, vert. No. 1186, $3.50, Mandela with arm raised, wearing patterned shirt, vert.

2013, Dec. 15 Litho. *Perf. 13¾*

1183 A422 $1.20 Vert. strip of 3, #a-c 7.25 7.25
1184 A423 $1.20 Sheet of 6, #a-f 14.50 14.50

Souvenir Sheets

Perf. 12½

1185-1186 A423 Set of 2 14.00 14.00

No. 1183 was printed in sheet of 6 stamps containing two each of Nos. 1183a-1183c. Nos. 1185-1186 each contain on 38x51mm stamp.

Orchids A424

No. 1187: Various Phalaenopsis orchids, as shown.
$3.50, Lady's slipper, horiz.

2013, Dec. 18 Litho. *Perf. 13¾*

1187 A424 $1 Sheet of 6, #a-f 12.00 12.00

Souvenir Sheet

Perf. 12½

1188 A424 $3.50 multi 7.00 7.00

No. 1188 contains one 51x38mm stamp.

Chess in Art A425

No. 1189: a, Etude of the Life of the Russian Tsars, by Vyacheslav Schwarz (players, table with green tablecloth). b, Scene from the Court of King Christian VII, by Kristian Zahrtmann (woman and man playing). c, The Chess Players, by Giulio Rosati (players on bench). d, The Chess Game, by Charles Bargue (woman and cardinal playing).
$3.50, Proposal, by Knut Ekwall, vert.

2013, Dec. 23 Litho. *Perf. 12½*

1189 A425 $1.20 Sheet of 4, #a-d 9.75 9.75

Souvenir Sheet

1190 A425 $3.50 multi 7.00 7.00

Modern Art A426

No. 1191, $1.50 — Paintings: a, Ajax, by John Steuart Curry. b, Landscape, by Diego Rivera. c, Red Tree, by Marsden Hartley.

No. 1192, $1.50 — Photographs: a, Power Farming Displaces Tenants, by Dorothea Lange. b, Toward Los Angeles, California, by Lange. c, Power House Mechanic Working on Steam Pump, by Lewis Hine.

No. 1193, $3.50, Red Cavalry, by Kazimir Malevich. No. 1194, $3.50, The Alarm Clock, by Rivera.

2014, Jan. 2 Litho. *Perf. 12½*

Sheets of 3, #a-c

1191-1192 A426 Set of 2 18.00 18.00

Souvenir Sheets

1193-1194 A426 Set of 2 14.00 14.00

Shells
A427

No. 1195, $1.75: a, Chicoreus palma-rosae. b, Phalium glaucum. c, Conus generalis (blue background at top). d, Conus episcopus.

No. 1196, $1.75: a, Conus generalis (purple background at top). b, Harpa articularis. c, Strombus minimus. d, Strombus gibberulus.

No. 1197, $3.50: a, Chicoreus ramosus. b, Murex troscheli.

No. 1198, $3.50: a, Charonia tritonis. b, Syrinx aruanus.

2014, Feb. 26   Litho.   Perf. 12
Sheets of 4, #a-d
1195-1196 A427   Set of 2   28.00 28.00
Souvenir Sheets of 2, #a-b
Perf. 12½
1197-1198 A427   Set of 2   28.00 28.00
No Nos. 1197-1198 each contain two 38x51mm stamps.

Caroline Kennedy, United States
Ambassador to Japan — A428

No. 1199 — Caroline Kennedy: a, Greeting Japanese students. b, With parents and brother. c, As young woman at graduation ceremony. d, As child, with father.
$4, Caroline Kennedy, vert.

2014, Mar. 5   Litho.   Perf. 13¾
1199 A428 $1.50 Sheet of 4,
        #a-d   12.00 12.00
Souvenir Sheet
Perf. 12½
1200 A428 $4 multi   8.00 8.00
No. 1200 contains one 38x51mm stamp.

Miniature Sheets

Winter
Sports
A429

No. 1201: a, Ice hockey. b, Speed skating. c, Bobsled. d, Figure skating.
No. 1202, horiz.: a, Freestyle skiing. b, Nordic combined skiing. c, Curling. d, Luge. f, Skeleton. g, Bobsled, diff.

2014, Mar. 5   Litho.   Perf. 12½
1201 A429 $1.20 Sheet of 4,
        #a-d   9.75 9.75
Perf. 14
1202 A429 $1.20 Sheet of 6,
        #a-f   14.50 14.50
No. 1202 contains six 40x30mm stamps.

Pope
Francis
A430

No. 1203, $1.20: a, Pres. Horacio Cartes of Paraguay. b, Pope Francis (painting in backgound). c, Pres. Cartes and Pope Francis (painting in background). d, Pres. Cartes and Pope Francis (painting and table in background).

No. 1204, $1.20: a, Pres. Denis Sassou Nguesso of Congo Republic. b, Pope Francis (book shelves in background). c, Pres. Sassou Nguesso and Pope Francis (painting and chairs in background). d, Pres. Sassou Nguesso and Pope Francis (corner of room in background).

No. 1205, $2: a, Pope Francis hugging person. b, Pope Francis patting child's head.

No. 1206, $2: a, Pope Francis looking upwards. b, Pope Francis with hands together.

2014, Mar. 10   Litho.   Perf. 12½
Sheets of 4, #a-d
1203-1204 A430   Set of 2   19.50 19.50
Souvenir Sheets of 2, #a-b
Perf. 12
1205-1206 A430   Set of 2   16.00 16.00
Nos. 1205-1206 each contain two 30x40mm stamps.

World
War I,
Cent.
A431

No. 1207, $2.50: a, London Scottish Regiment drill. b, British Army recruits in training. c, New recruits with officers, London. d, British Army volunteers, Aldershot.

No. 1208, $2.50: a, Bergmann MP18 machine gun, Germany. b, Carl Gustav Mauser M96, Sweden. c, Browning 1917 A1 machine gun, Belgium. d, Fedorov Avtomat rifle, Russia.

No. 1209, $2: a, Herbert Henry Asquith, British Prime Minister. b, Winston Churchill, First Lord of the Admiralty.

No. 1210, $2: a, Luger P08, Germany. b, Model 1892 revolver, France.

2014, Apr. 23   Litho.   Perf. 14
Sheets of 4, #a-d
1207-1208 A431   Set of 2   40.00 40.00
Souvenir Sheets of 2, #a-b
Perf. 12½
1209-1210 A431   Set of 2   16.00 16.00
Nos. 1209-1210 each contain two 51x38mm stamps.

Miniature Sheet

South
Korean
Stamps
A432

No. 1211: a, South Korea #936 (1975 stamp). b, South Korea #1398 (1985 stamp). c, South Korea #1635 (1991 stamp). d, South Korea #704 (1970 stamp). e, South Korea #948 (1975 stamp). f, Never-used stamp of 1884. g, South Korea #861 (1973 stamp). h, South Korea #300 (1959 stamp).

2014, May 12   Litho.   Perf. 12
1211 A432 $1 Sheet of 8, #a-h 16.00 16.00
Philakorea 2014 World Stamp Exhibition, Seoul.

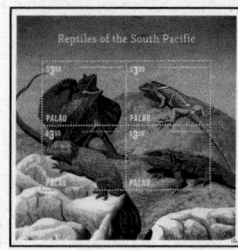

Reptiles
A433

No. 1212, $3.50: a, Frilled lizard. b, Fiji crested iguana. c, Knob-tailed gecko. d, Tuatara.

No. 1213, $3.50: a, Eastern brown snake (35x35mm). b, Children's python (35x35mm). c, Copperhead (35x70mm). d, Red-bellied black snake (35x35mm).

No. 1214, $3.50, Green sea turtle. No. 1215, $3.50, Saltwater crocodile.

Perf. 12½, 13¾ (#1213)
2014, July 1   Litho.
Sheets of 4, #a-d
1212-1213 A433   Set of 2   56.00 56.00
Souvenir Sheets
1214-1215 A433   Set of 2   14.00 14.00

Miniature Sheets

A434

Seagulls
A435

Various depictions of seagulls, as shown.

Perf. 13 Syncopated
2014, July 21   Litho.
1216 A434 $1 Sheet of 6, #a-f 12.00 12.00
1217 A435 $1 Sheet of 6, #a-f 12.00 12.00

Prince George of Cambridge — A436

No. 1218: a, Duke and Duchess of Cambridge, Prince George. b, Prince George. c, Duchess of Cambridge and Prince George.

No. 1219: a, Duke of Cambridge and Prince George. b, Prince George, diff.

No. 1220, $4, Prince George facing left, horiz. No. 1221, $4, Prince George facing right, horiz.

2014, July 21   Litho.   Perf. 14
1218 A436 75c Horiz. strip of
        3, #a-c   4.50 4.50
1219 A436 $1 Pair, #a-b   4.00 4.00
Souvenir Sheets
1220-1221 A436   Set of 2   16.00 16.00
No. 1218 was printed in sheets of 8 stamps containing 4 #1218b and 2 each #1218a and 1218c. No. 1219 was printed in sheets containing 3 pairs.

Miniature Sheet

Fish
A437

No. 1222: a, Brown surgeonfish. b, Striped surgeonfish. c, Convict surgeonfish. d, Eyestripe surgeonfish. e, Roundspot surgeonfish. f, Yellowfin surgeonfish.

2014, July 30   Litho.   Perf. 12½x13¼
1222 A437 45c Sheet of 6, #a-f   5.50 5.50
45th Pacific Islands Forum, Palau.

Illustrations for *Alice's Adventures in
Wonderland*, by Sir John Tenniel
(1820-1914) — A438

No. 1223, $1.75: a, Alice, Flamingo and Duchess (club in panel). b, Playing Cards painting rose bush (diamond in panel). c, Fish delivers letter to frog (heart in panel). d, Alice and the Queen of Hearts (spade in panel).

No. 1224, $1.75: a, Alice at tea party (club in panel). b, Alice and flowers (diamond in panel). c; Alice holding bottle (heart in panel). d, Alice and playing cards (spade in panel).

No. 1225, $2.50: a, King of Hearts (club in panel). b, Queen of Hearts (heart in panel).

No. 1226, $2.50: a, Knave of Hearts (spade in panel). b, Birds in powdered wigs (diamond in panel).

2014, July 31   Litho.   Perf. 12½
Sheets of 4, #a-d
1223-1224 A438   Set of 2   28.00 28.00
Souvenir Sheets of 2, #a-b
1225-1226 A438   Set of 2   20.00 20.00

Tourist Attractions in Russia — A439

No. 1227: a, Uzon Caldera. b, Mt. Elbrus. c, Trans-Siberian Railway.

No. 1228, vert.: a, Peter and Paul Cathedral, St. Petersburg. b, St. Sophia Cathedral, Vologda.

2014, Aug. 14   Litho.   Perf. 12
1227 A439 $1.50 Sheet of 3, #a-
        c   9.00 9.00
Souvenir Sheet
1228 A439 $2 Sheet of 2, #a-
        b   8.00 8.00

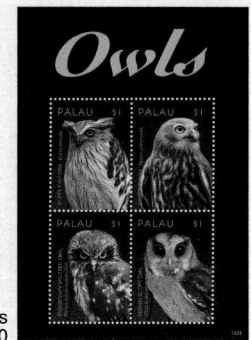

Owls
A440

No. 1229: a, Buffy fish owl. b, Barking owl.
c, Tasmanian spotted owl. d, Indian scops owl.
$3, Ural owl. $4, Short-eared owl.

2014, Aug. 14   Litho.   *Perf. 12*
1229 A440 $1 Sheet of 4, #a-d   8.00 8.00
Souvenir Sheets
1230 A440 $3 multi   6.00 6.00
1231 A440 $4 multi   8.00 8.00

Marine Life — A441

Designs: 2c, Damselfish. 3c, Green sea turtle. 5c, Mailed butterflyfish. 10c, Ornate butterflyfish. 15c, Queen triggerfish. 20c, Reef manta ray. 75c, Yellow boxfish. $1, Palau nautilus.

2014, Aug. 27   Litho.   *Perf. 13¾*
1232 A441   2c multi   .25   .25
1233 A441   3c multi   .25   .25
1234 A441   5c multi   .25   .25
1235 A441 10c multi   .25   .25
1236 A441 15c multi   .30   .30
1237 A441 20c multi   .40   .40
1238 A441 75c multi   1.50 1.50
1239 A441 $1 multi   2.00 2.00
     Nos. 1232-1239 (8)   5.20 5.20

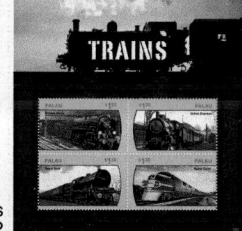

Trains
A442

No. 1240: a, Golden Arrow. b, Orient Express. c, Royal Scot. d, Super Chief. $3.50, 20th Century Limited.

2014, Sept. 3   Litho.   *Perf. 12*
1240 A442 $1.20 Sheet of 4, #a-
      d   9.75 9.75
Souvenir Sheet
1241 A442 $3.50 multi   7.00 7.00

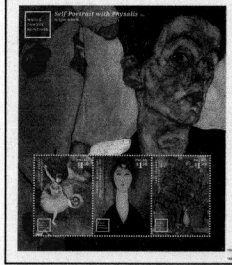

Paintings
A443

No. 1242, $1.50: a, Dancer Taking a Bow, by Edgar Degas. b, Portrait of a Young Woman, by Amedeo Modigliani. c, Terracotta Pots and Flowers, by Paul Cézanne.
No. 1243, $1.50: a, The Ballet Class, by Degas. b, Anxiety, by Edvard Munch. c, The Child's Bath, by Mary Cassatt.
No. 1244, $4, In the Kitchen, by Carl Larsson. No. 1245, $4, Farewell, by August Macke.

2014, Sept. 3   Litho.   *Perf. 12½*
Sheets of 3, #a-c
1242-1243 A443 Set of 2   18.00 18.00
Size: 100x100mm
Imperf
1244-1245 A443 Set of 2   16.00 16.00

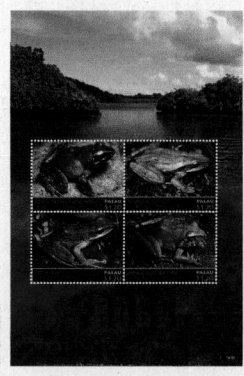

Frogs
and
Toads
A444

No. 1246, $1.20: a, Rough-backed forest frog. b, Common tree frog. c, Luzon frog. d, Wrinkled ground frog.
No. 1247, $1.20: a, Taylor's wrinkled ground frog. b, Woodworth's wart frog. c, Pygmy forest frog. d, Kalinga narrowmouth toad.
No. 1248, $4, Luzon fanged frog. No. 1249, $4, Harlequin tree frog.

Perf. 14, 12 (#1249)
2014, Sept. 15   Litho.
Sheets of 4, #a-d
1246-1247 A444 Set of 2   19.50 19.50
Souvenir Sheets
1248-1249 A444 Set of 2   16.00 16.00

Miniature Sheets

Characters From *Downton Abbey*
Television Series — A445

No. 1250, $1.20: a, Dowager Countess of Grantham. b, Earl of Grantham. c, Countess of Grantham. d, Lady Mary Crawley. e, Lady Edith Crawley.
No. 1251, $1.20: a, Thomas Barrow. b, Mr. Carson. c, Mrs. Hughes. d, Mrs. Patmore. e, Daisy Mason.

2014, Nov. 11   Litho.   *Perf. 14*
Sheets of 5, #a-e
1250-1251 A445 Set of 2   24.00 24.00

Christmas — A446

Paintings and details of paintings by Raphael: 34c, The Adoration of the Magi. 49c, The Adoration of the Magi, diff. $1.50, Ansidei Madonna. $3.50, Colonna Madonna.

2014, Nov. 24   Litho.   *Perf. 12½*
1252-1255 A446 Set of 4   12.00 12.00

Worldwide Fund for Nature
(WWF) — A447

Nos. 1256 and 1257 — Lagoon jellyfish: a, Near water's surface. b, Two jellyfish. c, Above seafloor. d, In sea cave.

2014, Dec. 1   Litho.   *Perf. 14*
1256 A447 40c Block or horiz.
            strip of 4, #a-d   3.25 3.25
1257 A447 90c Block or horiz.
            strip of 4, #a-d   7.25 7.25

Pope
Benedict
XVI
A448

No. 1258 — Pope Benedict XVI: a, Wearing red vestments. b, Swinging censer. c, Close-up. d, Standing in front of bushes.
$4, Pope Benedict XVI in green vestments.

2014, Dec. 16   Litho.   *Perf. 14*
1258 A448 $1.20 Sheet of 4, #a-
            e   9.75 9.75
Souvenir Sheet
1259 A448 $4 multi   8.00 8.00

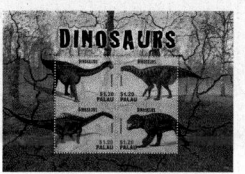

Dinosaurs — A449

No. 1260, $1.20: a, Nigersaurus. b, Iguanodon. c, Agustinia. d, Doliosauriscus.
No. 1261, $1.20: a, Ankylosaurus. b, Giganotosaurus. c, Diplodocus. d, Tyrannosaurus.
No. 1262, $4, Stegosaurus. No. 1263, $4, Gigantspinosaurus.

2014, Dec. 22   Litho.   *Perf. 12*
Sheets of 4, #a-d
1260-1261 A449 Set of 2   19.50 19.50
Souvenir Sheets
1262-1263 A449 Set of 2   16.00 16.00
No. 1261 contains four 50x30mm stamps.

Bubble
Tea
A450

No. 1264 — Cup of tea with straw and inscription of: a, Pineapple. b, Taro. c, Strawberry. d, Mango. e, Avocado. f, Blueberry.

$4, Cup of tea with lid and straw.

2015, Jan. 5   Litho.   *Perf. 13¾*
1264 A450 $1.20 Sheet of 6,
            #a-f   14.50 14.50
Souvenir Sheet
Perf. 12
1265 A450 $4 multi   8.00 8.00
No. 1265 contains one 30x40mm stamp.
Asian International Stamp Exhibition, 30th Anniv.

Pope John Paul II
(1920-2005) — A451

2015, Feb. 2   Litho.   *Perf. 12*
1266 A451 75c multi   1.50 1.50
Printed in sheets of 4. Compare with type A331.

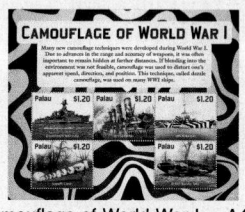

Camouflage of World War I — A452

No. 1267: a, Dreadnought Battleship. b, USS Leviathan. c, HMS Kildangan. d, Sopwith Camel airplane. e, British dummy tank.
$4, Soldier in tree-climbing camouflage.

2015, Feb. 2   Litho.   *Perf. 14*
1267 A452 $1.20 Sheet of 5,
            #a-e   12.00 12.00
Souvenir Sheet
Perf. 13¾
1268 A452 $4 multi   8.00 8.00
No. 1268 contains one 35x35mm stamp.

UNESCO World Heritage
Sites — A453

No. 1269: a, Great Barrier Reef, Australia. b, Prambanan Temple Compounds, Indonesia. c, Rice Terraces of the Philippine Cordilleras, Philippines. d, Kinabalu Park, Malaysia. e, Komodo National Park, Indonesia.
$4, Rock Islands Southern Lagoon, Palau.

2015, Mar. 9   Litho.   *Perf. 14*
1269 A453 $1.20 Sheet of 5,
            #a-e   12.00 12.00
Souvenir Sheet
Perf. 13¾
1270 A453 $4 multi   8.00 8.00
No. 1270 contains one 70x35mm stamp.

Ships Involved in the 1940 Evacuation
of Dunkirk — A454

No. 1271, 45c: a, Minnehaha. b, Cygnet. c, Rapid. d, Skylark. e, Wanda. f, Marchioness. g, Jovial. h, Fedalma II. i, Jane Hannah MacDonald. j, Massey Shaw. k, Mimosa. l, Aberdonia. m, Reda. n, Blue Bird. o, Dorian. p, White Heathe.

No. 1272, 45c: a, Cachalot. b, Fervant. c, Omega. d, Greater London. e, Jane Holland. f, Lucy Lavers. g, Tom Tit. h, Cyril and Lillian Bishop. i, Latona. j, Endeavour. k, Polly. l, Tigris. m, Eothen. n, Lazy Days. o, Wairakei II. p, Matoya.

2015, May 25   Litho.   *Perf. 14*
Sheets of 16, #a-p, + Label
1271-1272 A454 Set of 2   29.00 29.00

Queen Elizabeth II, Longest-Reigning British Monarch — A455

No. 1273 — Queen Elizabeth II wearing: a, Dark green dress, light green hat and gloves. b, Pink dress and hat, black gloves. c, Green coat. b, Dark blue dress. c, White gown and tiara. d, Lilac dress.
$4, Queen Elizabeth II in white and blue dress with blue buttons and matching hat.

2015, May 25   Litho.   *Perf. 14*
1273 A455 $1.20 Sheet of 6,
     #a-f   14.50 14.50
Souvenir Sheet
Perf. 12
1274 A455 $4 multi   8.00   8.00

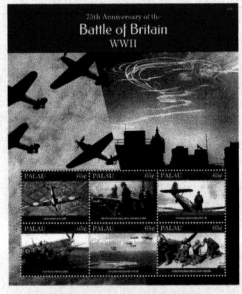

Battle of Britain, 75th Anniv. A456

No. 1275: a, Hawker Hurricane. b, Prime Minister Winston Churchill inspects bomb damage in London. c, British soldier guards a German fighter plane. d, Pilots push a Spitfire onto a runway. e, Spitfires patrol a coastline. f, Ground crew replenishes Hurricane aircraft ammunition.
$4, Churchill and Queen Elizabeth inspect damage to Buckingham Palace.

2015, June 1   Litho.   *Perf. 12*
1275 A456 65c Sheet of 6, #a-f   8.00 8.00
Souvenir Sheet
1276 A456 $4 multi   8.00   8.00

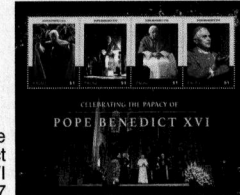

Pope Benedict XVI A457

No. 1277 — Pope Benedict XVI: a, With arms raised. b, Seated next to bishop. c, Seated alone. d, With hand outstretched.
$3.50, Pope Benedict XVI wearing large crucifix.

2015, June 8   Litho.   *Perf. 12½*
1277 A457 $1 Sheet of 4, #a-
     d   8.00 8.00
Souvenir Sheet
1278 A457 $3.50 multi   7.00 7.00

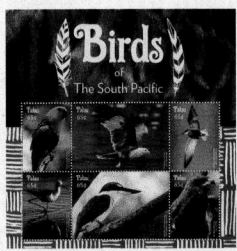

Birds A458

No. 1279: a, Eclectus parrot (30x40mm). b, Brahminy kite (60x40mm). c, Whiskered tern (30x40mm). d, Black-winged stilt (30x40mm). e, Collared kingfisher (60x40mm). f, Black kite (30x40mm).
$4, Sulphur-crested cockatoo, horiz.

2015, June 15   Litho.   *Perf. 12*
1279 A458 65c Sheet of 6, #a-f   8.00 8.00
Souvenir Sheet
1280 A458 $4 multi   8.00 8.00
No. 1280 contains one 40x30mm stamp.

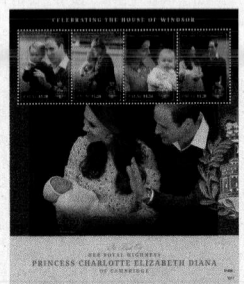

Birth of Princess Charlotte of Cambridge — A459

No. 1281: a, Duke of Cambridge and Prince George. b, Princess Diana and Prince William. c, Duchess of Cambridge and Prince George. d, Duke and Duchess of Cambridge, Princess Charlotte.
$4, Duchess of Cambridge holding Princess Charlotte.

2015, July 13   Litho.   *Perf. 12*
1281 A459 $1.20 Sheet of 4, #a-
     d   9.75 9.75
Souvenir Sheet
1282 A459 $4 multi   8.00 8.00

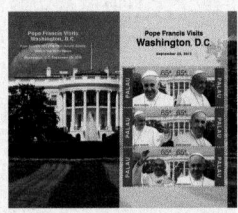

Visit of Pope Francis to Washington, D.C. — A460

No. 1283 — Pope Francis: a, Smiling, denomination at UR. b, Facing right, denomination at UL. c, Waving, hand at right, denomination at UR. d, Smiling, denomination at UL. e, Waving, hand at left, denomination at UR. f, Waving, hand at left, denomination at UL.
$4, Pope Francis with Pres. Barack Obama and wife, Michelle.

2015, Nov. 25   Litho.   *Perf. 14*
1283 A460 65c Sheet of 6, #a-f   8.00 8.00
Souvenir Sheet
1284 A460 $4 multi   8.00 8.00
No. 1284 contains one 80x30mm stamp.

Pres. Dwight D. Eisenhower (1890-1969) — A461

No. 1285 — Pres. Eisenhower: a, Wearing golf cap. b, With three men on golf course. c, Giving "V" for victory sign. d, Holding baseball. e, Waving to crowd from train. f, Wearing military uniform, standing in car.
$4, Pres. Eisenhower with wife, Mamie, horiz.

2015, Dec. 7   Litho.   *Perf. 14*
1285 A461 65c Sheet of 6, #a-f   8.00 8.00
Souvenir Sheet
Perf. 12½
1286 A461 $4 multi   8.00 8.00
No. 1286 contains one 51x38mm stamp.

Sir Winston Churchill (1874-1965), British Prime Minister — A462

No. 1287 — Churchill: a, Smoking cigar. b, Aiming submachine gun. c, With Pres. Franklin D. Roosevelt. d, Giving "V" for Victory sign.
$4, Churchill speaking in front of picture of Abraham Lincoln, horiz.

2015, Dec. 7   Litho.   *Perf. 12½*
1287 A462 $1.20 Sheet of 4, #a-
     d   9.75 9.75
Souvenir Sheet
1288 A462 $4 multi   8.00 8.00

William Shakespeare (1564-1616), Writer — A463

No. 1289: a, Portrait of Shakespeare. b, Statue of Shakespeare. c, Shakespeare's burial place, Stratford-upon-Avon. d, Shakespeare Memorial Theater, Stratford-upon-Avon. e, Shakespeare's birthplace, Stratford-upon-Avon. f, Globe Theater, London.
$4, Shakespeare's first folio, 1623, vert.

2015, Dec. 7   Litho.   *Perf. 14*
1289 A463 65c Sheet of 6, #a-f   8.00 8.00
Souvenir Sheet
Perf. 12
1290 A463 $4 multi   8.00 8.00
No. 1290 contains one 30x50mm stamp.

Christmas — A464

Paintings by Bartolomé Esteban Murillo: 34c, The Annunciation. 49c, Virgin and Child in Glory. $1, Madonna and Child. $2, Virgin with Child.

2015, Dec. 7   Litho.   *Perf. 12½*
1291-1294 A464   Set of 4   7.75 7.75

German Reunification, 25th Anniv. — A465

No. 1295 — Reichstag Building, Berlin: a, Side towers in red light. b, Side towers in yellow light. c, Side towers in purple light, statues near dome not visible. d, Side towers in purple light, statues near dome in blue light.
$4, Reichstag Building with columns in red and white light, vert.

2015, Dec. 17   Litho.   *Perf. 12*
1295 A465 $1.20 Sheet of 4, #a-
     d   9.75 9.75
Souvenir Sheet
Perf. 12½
1296 A465 $4 multi   8.00 8.00
No. 1296 contains one 38x51mm stamp.

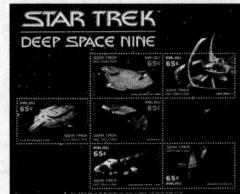

Spacecraft from *Star Trek Deep Space Nine* — A466

No. 1297: a, U.S.S. Defiant, denomination at UR. b, Deep Space 9. c, U.S.S. Defiant, denomination at UL. d, Runabout. e, Cardassian Galor Class. f, Bajoran Solar Sail.
$4, U.S.S. Defiant, diff.

2015, Dec. 31   Litho.   *Perf. 12*
1297 A466 65c Sheet of 6, #a-f   8.00 8.00
Souvenir Sheet
Perf. 14
1298 A466 $4 multi   8.00 8.00
No. 1298 contains one 80x30mm stamp.

Mollusks A467

No. 1299: a, Palau nautilus, tentacles at left. b, Chambered nautilus, tentacles at left. c, Palau nautilus, tentacles at right. d, Chambered nautilus, tentacles at right.
$4, Palau nautilus, vert.

2015, Dec. 31   Litho.   *Perf. 14*
1299 A467 $1.20 Sheet of 4, #a-
     d   9.75 9.75
Souvenir Sheet
Perf. 12
1300 A467 $4 multi   8.00 8.00

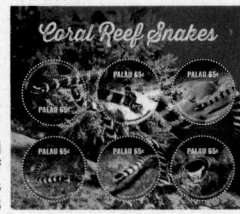

Coral Reef Snakes A468

No. 1301: a, Turtle-headed sea snake, name in white at top. b, Turtle-headed sea snake, name in black at bottom. c, Yellow-lipped sea krait, snake's body extending to right. d, Yellow-lipped sea krait, snake's body extending to left. e, Yellow-lipped sea krait and orange rock. f, Yellow-lipped sea krait, snake's body going through coral.
$4, Head of Yellow-lipped sea krait, horiz.

2015, Dec. 31	**Litho.**		**Perf.**
1301 A468	65c Sheet of 6, #a-f		8.00 8.00
	Souvenir Sheet		
1302 A468	$4 multi		8.00 8.00

No. 1302 contains one 44x33mm oval stamp.

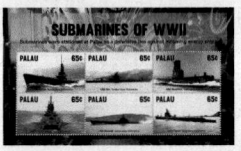

World War II Submarines — A469

No. 1303: a, USS Archerfish. b, USS Gar. c, USS Blackfish. d, USS Tullibee, e, USS Seawolf. f, USS Darter.
$4, USS Seal.

2015, Dec. 31	**Litho.**		**Perf. 12**
1303 A469	65c Sheet of 6, #a-f		8.00 8.00
	Souvenir Sheet		
	Perf. 14		
1304 A469	$4 multi		8.00 8.00

No. 1304 contains one 80x30mm stamp.

Flora A470

No. 1305: a, Screw pine. b, Coral tree flowers. c, Bayhops. d, Breadfruit. e, Coconut palm. f, Beach naupaka.
$4, Mangrove flowers.

2016, Feb. 2	**Litho.**		**Perf.**
1305 A470	65c Sheet of 6, #a-f		8.00 8.00
	Souvenir Sheet		
1306 A470	$4 multi		8.00 8.00

2016 Summer Olympics, Rio de Janeiro — A471

No. 1307 — Gold medalists: a, Mikio Oda, 1928 triple jump, Japan. b, Robert Garrett, 1896 discus and shot put, United States. c, James Connolly, 1896 triple jump, United States. d, Ellery Clark, 1896 high jump and long jump, United States.

$4, Yoshiyuki Tsuruta, 1928 200-meter breaststroke, Japan.

2016, Mar. 8	**Litho.**		**Perf. 14**
1307 A471	$1.20 Sheet of 4, #a-d		9.75 9.75
	Souvenir Sheet		
	Perf. 12½		
1308 A471	$4 multi		8.00 8.00

No. 1308 contains one 38x51mm stamp.

1888 Paintings of the Roulin Family by Vincent van Gogh (1853-90) — A472

No. 1309: a, Portrait of the Postman Joseph Roulin (Nov.-Dec.). b, Portrait of Madame Augustine Roulin. c, Portrait of Madame Augustine Roulin and Baby Marcelle. d, Young Man with a Cap (Armand Roulin). e, The Schoolboy with Uniform Cap (Camille Roulin). f, Portait of Marcelle Roulin.
$4, Portrait of the Postman Joseph Roulin (April).

2016, Mar. 8	**Litho.**		**Perf. 14**
1309 A472	65c Sheet of 6, #a-f		8.00 8.00
	Souvenir Sheet		
	Perf. 12½		
1310 A472	$4 multi		8.00 8.00

No. 1310 contains one 38x51mm stamp.

A473

No. 1311 — Various photographs of Hendrix with frame color of: a, Magenta. b, Purple. c, Green. d, Greenish blue. e, Red orange. f, Yellow.
No. 1312 — Various photographs of Hendrix with frame color of: a, Red orange. b, Greenish blue. c, Yellow. d, Green. e, Magenta. f, Purple.
$4, Hendrix, greenish blue frame, vert.

Jimi Hendrix (1942-70), Rock Guitarist — A474

2016, Mar. 8	**Litho.**		**Perf.**
1311 A473	65c Sheet of 6, #a-f		8.00 8.00
1312 A474	65c Sheet of 6, #a-f		8.00 8.00
	Souvenir Sheet		
	Perf. 12½		
1313 A474	$4 multi		8.00 8.00

No. 1313 contains one 38x51mm stamp.

Souvenir Sheets

Elvis Presley (1935-77) — A475

Presley: No. 1314, $4, Donating blood to the Red Cross. No. 1315, $4, At recording session, vert. No. 1316, $4, At 1975 Tornado Victim Benefit Concert, vert. No. 1317, $4, Enjoying a moment of Army downtime, vert.

2016, Mar. 8	**Litho.**		**Perf. 14**
1314-1317 A475	Set of 4		32.00 32.00

Queen Elizabeth II, 90th Birthday A476

No. 1318 — Queen Elizabeth II: a, Waving. b, Wearing deep violet hat. c, Wearing pale yellow hat.
$5, Queen Elizabeth II wearing blue dress.

2016, Apr. 1	**Litho.**		**Perf. 12½**
1318 A476	$1.50 Sheet of 3, #a-c		9.00 9.00
	Souvenir Sheet		
1319 A476	$5 multi		10.00 10.00

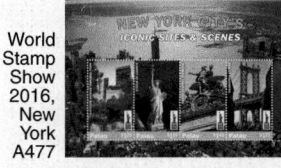

World Stamp Show 2016, New York A477

No. 1320: a, Gapstow Bridge, Central Park. b, Statue of Liberty. c, Grand Central Terminal. d, Manhattan Bridge.
$3, New York City skyline, horiz.

2016, Apr. 19	**Litho.**		**Perf. 12**
1320 A477	$1.25 Sheet of 4, #a-d		10.00 10.00
	Souvenir Sheet		
	Perf. 14		
1321 A477	$3 multi		6.00 6.00

No. 1321 contains one 160x60mm stamp.

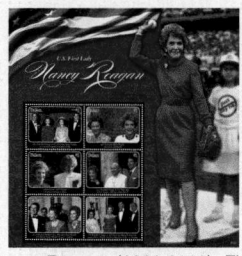

Nancy Reagan (1921-2016), First Lady — A478

No. 1322 — Mrs. Reagan with: a, Pres. Ronald Reagan, Queen Elizabeth II and Prince Philip. b, Queen Elizabeth II. c, Princess Diana. d, Pres. Reagan, Pope John Paul II. e, British Prime Minister Margaret Thatcher. f, Pres. Reagan, Japanese Prime Minister Yasuhiro Nakasone and his wife, Tsutako.
No. 1323 — Mrs. Reagan with: a, Pres. Reagan, Vice-President George H.W. Bush and his wife, Barbara. b, Pres. George W. Bush and his wife, Laura. c, First ladies Rosalynn Carter, Barbara Bush, Betty Ford and Hillary Clinton. d, Pres. Barack Obama.
No. 1324, Mrs. Reagan as actress with picture having: a, White background. b, Black background.
$5, Mrs. Reagan seated, vert.

2016, Apr. 19	**Litho.**		**Perf. 14**
1322 A478	$1 Sheet of 6, #a-f		12.00 12.00
1323 A478	$1.20 Sheet of 4, #a-d		9.75 9.75
	Souvenir Sheets		
	Perf. 13¾		
1324 A478	$2.50 Sheet of 2, #a-b		10.00 10.00
	Perf. 12		
1325 A478	$5 multi		10.00 10.00

No. 1324 contains two 50x50mm diamond-shaped stamps.

World of Sea and Reef Type of 1986 Redrawn
Miniature Sheet

No. 1326: a, Spear fisherman. b, Native raft. c, Sailing canoes. d, Rock islands, sailfish. e, Inter-island boat, flying fish. f, Bonefish. g, Common jack. h, Mackerel. i, Sailfish. j, Barracuda. k, Triggerfish. l, Dolphinfish. m, Spear fisherman, grouper. n, Manta ray. o, Marlin. p, Parrotfish. q, Wrasse. r, Red snapper. s, Herring. t, Dugong. u, Surgeonfish. v, Leopard ray. w, Hawksbill turtle. x, Needlefish. y, Tuna. z, Octopus. aa, Clownfish. ab, Squid. ac, Grouper. ad, Moorish idol. ae, Queen conch, starfish. af, Squirrelfish. ag, Starfish, sting ray. ah, Lionfish. ai, Angelfish. aj, Butterflyfish. ak, Spiny lobster. al, Mangrove crab. am, Tridacna. an, Moray eel.

2016, May 18	**Litho.**		**Perf. 13¼**
1326	Sheet of 40		38.00 38.00
a.-an.	A19 47c Any single		.95 .95

World Stamp Show 2016, New York. No. 1326 contains forty 26x21mm stamps.

Characters From *Star Trek* Television Series — A479

No. 1327: a, Capt. James T. Kirk. b, Mr. Spock. c, Scotty. d, Sulu. e, Dr. McCoy. f, Uhura.
$3, Kirk, Spock, McCoy, Uhura and Sulu.

2016, Aug. 15	**Litho.**		**Perf. 14**
1327 A479	$1 Sheet of 6, #a-f		12.00 12.00
	Souvenir Sheet		
	Perf. 12		
1328 A479	$3 multi		6.00 6.00

No. 1328 contains one 40x60mm stamp.

Birds A480

No. 1329: a, Dusky white-eye. b, Palau flycatcher. c, Palau fantail. d, Giant white-eye.
$5, Palau fruit dove, vert.

2016, Sept. 22	**Litho.**		**Perf. 12½**
1329 A480	$1.50 Sheet of 4, #a-d		12.00 12.00
	Souvenir Sheet		
1330 A480	$5 multi		10.00 10.00

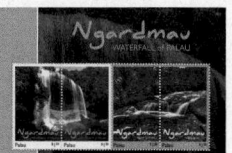

Ngardmau Waterfall — A481

No. 1331 — Waterfall with: a, White frame at left, top and bottom. b, White frame at right,

top and bottom. c, Orange frame at left, top and bottom. d, Orange frame at right, top and bottom.
$5, Waterfall, diff.

2016, Sept. 22   Litho.   Perf. 12
1331 A481 $1.50 Sheet of 4,
#a-d   12.00 12.00
Souvenir Sheet
1332 A481 $5 multi   10.00 10.00

Visit of Pres. Barack Obama to the United Kingdom A482

No. 1333: a, Pres. Obama, flags in background. b, British Prime Minister David Cameron, flags in background. c, Pres. Obama waving, open airplane door in background. d, Pres. Obama waving. e, Pres. Obama shaking hands with Cameron. f, Pres. Obama and Cameron, fence in background.
No. 1334: a, Pres. Obama shaking hands with Queen Elizabeth II (40x30mm). b, Queen Elizabeth II, Pres. Obama and his wife, Michelle (40x30mm). c, The Obamas with Prince Harry, Duke and Duchess of Cambridge (80x30mm).
No. 1335: a, Pres. Obama seated. b, Cameron seated.

2016, Sept. 22   Litho.   Perf. 14
1333 A482 $1 Sheet of 6,
#a-f   12.00 12.00
1334 A482 $2 Sheet of 3,
#a-c   12.00 12.00
Souvenir Sheet
Perf. 12
1335 A482 $2.50 Sheet of 2,
#a-b   10.00 10.00

William Shakespeare (1564-1616), Writer — A483

No. 1336: a, 1873 engraving depicting scene from *As You Like It*. b, Line from *As You Like It*. c, Line from *Twelfth Night*. d, 1873 engraving depicting scene from *Twelfth Night*. e, 1873 engraving depicting scene from *King Richard II*. f, Line from *King Richard II*.
No. 1337 — 1870 engravings depicting scenes from: a, *Hamlet*. b, *The Winter's Tale*. c, *A Midsummer Night's Dream*. d, *Twelfth Night*.
$5, Shakespeare, vert.

2016, Sept. 30   Litho.   Perf. 14
1336 A483 $1 Sheet of 6,
#a-f   12.00 12.00
Perf. 12½
1337 A483 $1.50 Sheet of 4,
#a-d   12.00 12.00
Souvenir Sheet
Perf.
1338 A483 $5 multi   10.00 10.00
No. 1337 contains four 51x38mm stamps.
No. 1338 contains one 33x43mm oval stamp.

A484

A485

A486

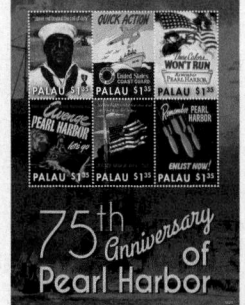

Tourism A487

No. 1339, $1.20: Various photographs of golden jellyfish in Jellyfish lake, as shown.
No. 1340, $1.20 — Giant clams: a, True giant clam. b, Bear claw giant clam. c, China giant clam. d, Smooth giant clam. e, Elongated giant clam. f, Fluted giant clam.
No. 1341, $1.25 — Abais: a, Koror Abai. b, Melekeok Abai. c, Aimeliik Abai. d, Airai Abai.
No. 1342, $1.50 — Rock Islands landscapes: a, Tutkalrenguis. b, Milky Way. c, Akasi Island. d, Arc Island.
No. 1343, $1.75 — Rays: a, Manta ray. b, Manta ray and diver. c, Devil ray. d, Two Manta rays.
No. 1344, $1.75 — Underwater World War II airplane wreckage: a, Jake float plane wing and engine. b, Jake float plane fuselage. c, Jake float plane propeller. d, Zero plane.
No. 1345, $1.50 — Protected species: a, Gray reef shark. b, Hawksbill turtle. c, Napoleon wrasse.
No. 1346, $1.75 — Crabs: a, Hermit crab. b, Land crab. c, Coconut crab.

2016, Oct. 1   Litho.   Perf. 12½
Sheets of 6, #a-f
1339-1340 A484 Set of 2   29.00 29.00
Sheets of 4, #a-d
Perf. 14
1341-1342 A485 Set of 2   22.00 22.00
1343-1344 A486 Set of 2   28.00 28.00
Sheets of 3, #a-c
1345-1346 A487 Set of 3   19.50 19.50

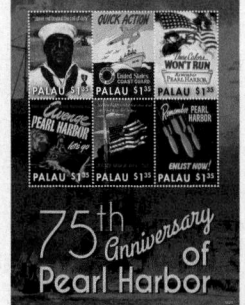

Attack on Pearl Harbor, 75th Anniv. A488

No. 1347: a, Sailor. b, U. S. Coast Guard poster. c, These Colors Won't Run poster. d, Avenge Pearl Harbor poster. e, American flag

at half-staff. f, Remember Pearl Harbor recruitment poster.
No. 1348, horiz.: a, USS West Virginia. b, USS Arizona.

2016, Dec. 30   Litho.   Perf. 14
1347 A488 $1.35 Sheet of 6,
#a-f   16.50 16.50
Souvenir Sheet
Perf. 12
1348 A488 $3 Sheet of 2,
#a-b   12.00 12.00
No. 1348 contains two 64x32mm triangular stamps.

Fish A489

No. 1349: a, Orange-striped wrasse. b, Palauan deepwater cardinalfish. c, Aurora anthias. d, Dabra goby. e, Bullseye pygmy goby. f, Needlespine coral goby.
No. 1350: a, Giant pygmy goby. b, Deep blue chromis.

2016, Dec. 30   Litho.   Perf. 12
1349 A489 $1 Sheet of 6,
#a-f   12.00 12.00
Souvenir Sheet
1350 A489 $2.50 Sheet of 2,
#a-b   10.00 10.00

Miniature Sheet

2016 Summer Olympics, Rio de Janeiro — A490

No. 1351 — Photographs of Palauan Olympic Team: a, 50c, Shawn Dingilius Wallace (30x40mm). b, 50c, Dirngulbau Ub Misech (30x40mm). c, 50c, Florian Temengil (30x40mm). d, 50c, Rodman Teltull (30x40mm). e, 50c, Marina Toribiong (30x40mm). f, $1, Olympic team following Palauan flagbearer (90x40mm). g, $1, Palauan athletes and Olympic rings (60x40mm).

2016, Dec. 20   Litho.   Perf. 14
1351 A490 Sheet of 7, #a-g   9.00   9.00

Miniature Sheet

2016 Festival of the Pacific Arts A491

No. 1352: a, 50c, Man and woman (30x40mm). b, 50c, Man and woman, large pole in background (30x40mm). c, 50c, Man dancing with spears (30x40mm). d, 50c, Man standing (30x40mm). e, 50c, Man kneeling, holding shell (30x40mm). f, 50c, Woman facing right (30x40mm). g, 50c, Women dancing (30x40mm). h, 50c, Two women, one with greenish blue skirt (30x40mm). i, $1, Festival participants in front of building (120x40mm). j, $1, Four women (60x40mm). k, $1, Male dancers holding spears (60x40mm).

2016, Dec. 30   Litho.   Perf. 14
1352 A491 Sheet of 11, #a-k 14.00 14.00

Legends of the Wild West A492

No. 1353: a, Bat Masterson. b, Annie Oakley. c, Kit Carson. d, Wild Bill Hickok. e, John Frémont. f, Wyatt Earp.
$5, Buffalo Bill Cody.

Perf. 13¼x12½
2017, Feb. 28   Litho.
1353 A492 $1 Sheet of 6, #a-f 12.00 12.00
Souvenir Sheet
Perf. 13¼
1354 A492 $5 multi   10.00 10.00
No. 1354 contains one 38x51mm stamp.

Miniature Sheets

A493

Princess Diana (1961-97) — A494

No. 1355 — Photograph of Princess Diana and flag of: a, $1, Saudi Arabia (30x40mm). b, $1, Hong Kong (30x40mm). c, $1, Italy (30x40mm). d, $1, Pakistan (30x40mm). e, $1, Egypt (30x40mm). f, $1, Nepal (30x40mm). g, $1.50, India (60x40mm).
No. 1356 — Princess Diana wearing: a, Black dress and pearl necklace. b, Purple dress. c, Black dress, no necklace. d, Yellow jacket.

2017, Apr. 14   Litho.   Perf. 14
1355 A493 Sheet of 7, #a-g   15.00 15.00
Perf.
1356 A494 $1.80 Sheet of 4,
#a-d   14.50 14.50

Miniature Sheets

A495

Pres. John F. Kennedy (1917-63) — A496

No. 1357 — Pres. John F. Kennedy: a, As baby. b, As young boy, holding dog. c, In Navy uniform. d, On sailboat with wife, Jacqueline. e, With wife and children. f, Seated at desk.
No. 1358 — Pres. Kennedy with: a, His father, mother and siblings. b, Mother, Rose and sister, Eunice. c, Brother Joe, Jr., sisters Kathleen and Rosemary. d, Brothers Robert and Edward.

2017, Apr. 14   Litho.   Perf. 14
1357 A495 $1.35 Sheet of 6,
#a-f   16.50 16.50
Perf. 12
1358 A496 $1.60 Sheet of 4,
#a-d   13.00 13.00

Seals
A497

No. 1359: a, Baby harp seal. b, Australian sea lion. c, Harbor seal. d, Antarctic fur seal. e, Galapagos sea lion. f, Grey seal. $4.50, New Zealand fur seal.

2017, May 5   **Litho.**   *Perf.*
1359 A497 $1.25 Sheet of 6,
     #a-f   15.00 15.00

Souvenir Sheet
1360 A497 $4.50 multi   9.00 9.00

Animals
A498

No. 1361: a, Waxy monkey frog. b, Persian leopard. c, Alexandrine parakeet. d, Yellow-bellied slider. $4, Golden lion tamarin, vert.

2017, May 15   **Litho.**   *Perf. 12½x12¾*
1361 A498 $2 Sheet of 4, #a-d 16.00 16.00

Souvenir Sheet
1362 A498 $4 multi   8.00 8.00

Paintings by Gustav Klimt (1862-1918) — A499

No. 1363: a, Portrait of Hermine Gallia. b, Portrait of Helene Klimt. c, Portrait of Serena Lederer. d, Margaret Stonborough-Wittgenstein. $4, Adele Bloch-Bauer I (not named on stamp).

2017, Oct. 19   **Litho.**   *Perf. 12*
1363 A499 $1.60 Sheet of 4,
     #a-d   13.00 13.00

Souvenir Sheet
Perf. 12½
1364 A499 $4 multi   8.00 8.00
No. 1364 contains one 38x51mm stamp.

Souvenir Sheets

Elvis Presley (1935-77) — A500

Inscriptions: No. 1365, $4, Inducted into the Gospel Hall of Fame. No. 1366, $4, Joins Country Music Hall of Fame. No. 1367, $4,

---

Receives W. C. Handy Award. No. 1368, $4, Inducted into the Rock 'n' Roll Hall of Fame.

2017, Oct. 26   **Litho.**   *Perf. 12½*
1365-1368 A500   Set of 4   32.00 32.00

Miniature Sheet

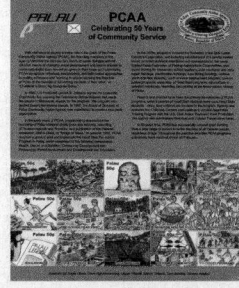

Palau Community Action Agency, 50th Anniv. — A501

No. 1369 — Inscriptions: a, Agriculture. b, Apprentice Program. c, History. d, Small Business. e, Care for Environment. f, Fishing Industry. g, Pre-school Head Start. h, Health Screening. i, Nutrition Healthy Food. j, Play to Learn. k, Education. l, Local Produce Market. m, Local Medicine. n, Tourism & Community. o, Youth Programs.

2017, Nov. 10   **Litho.**   *Perf. 11*
1369 A501 50c Sheet of 15,
     #a-o   15.00 15.00

Birds
A502

No. 1370: a, 50c, Red bird-of-paradise. b, 50c, Northern cardinal. c, $1.50, European robin. d, $1.50, Bali myna. e, $2, Sulphur-crested cockatoo. f, $2.50, Bluethroat.
No. 1371: a, $1.25, Atlantic puffin. b, $2.25, Lilac-breasted roller. c, $3.25, Nicobar pigeon.

2018, Jan. 24   **Litho.**   *Perf. 14*
1370 A502   Sheet of 6, #a-f   17.00 17.00

Souvenir Sheet
Perf. 12
1371 A502   Sheet of 3, #a-c   13.50 13.50

Jellyfish
A503

No. 1372: a, 50c, Mediterranean jelly. b, $1.25, Barrel jellyfish. c, $2.25, Portuguese man o' war. d, $3.25, White-spotted jellyfish.
No. 1373, vert.: a, Lion's mane jellyfish. b, Mediterranean jelly, turquoise blue background.

2018, Jan. 24   **Litho.**   *Perf. 13¾*
1372 A503   Sheet of 4, #a-d   14.50 14.50

Souvenir Sheet
Perf. 12¾x12½
1373 A503 $3 Sheet of 2, #a-b 12.00 12.00
No. 1373 contains two 38x51mm stamps.

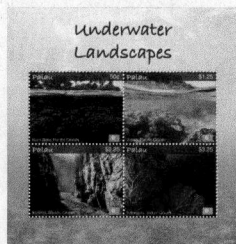

Underwater Landscapes — A504

No. 1374: a, 50c, Bora Bora, Pacific Ocean. b, $1.25, Japan, Pacific Ocean. c, $2.25, Iceland, Atlantic Ocean. d, $3.25, Indonesia, Indian Ocean.
No. 1375: a, Palau, Pacific Ocean. b, Maldives, Indian Ocean.

2018, Jan. 24   **Litho.**   *Perf. 14*
1374 A504   Sheet of 4, #a-d 14.50 14.50

Souvenir Sheet
Perf. 12½
1375 A504 $3 Sheet of 2, #a-b 12.00 12.00
No. 1375 contains two 51x38mm stamps.

Visit of Pres. Donald Trump to Japan
A505

No. 1376: a, First Lady Melania Trump. b, Pres. Donald Trump. c, Japanese Prime Minister Shinzo Abe. d, Akie Abe. $4, Abe and Pres. Trump, horiz.

2018, Jan. 24   **Litho.**   *Perf. 12*
1376 A505 $1.60 Sheet of 4,
     #a-d   13.00 13.00

Souvenir Sheet
Perf. 12¾
1377 A505 $4 multi   8.00 8.00
No. 1376 contains one 51x38mm stamp.

Souvenir Sheet

Engagement of Prince Harry and Meghan Markle — A506

No. 1378 — Couple and background of: a, Grass. b, Brick wall.

2018, Jan. 31   **Litho.**   *Perf. 12*
1378 A506 $3 Sheet of 2, #a-b 12.00 12.00

Miniature Sheet

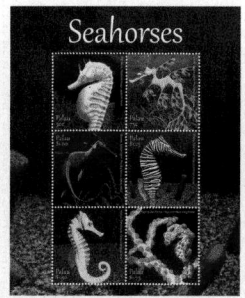

Seahorses — A507

No. 1379: a, 50c, Big belly seahorse. b, 75c, Leafy seadragon. c, $1, Weedy seadragon. d, $1.25, Zebra seahorse. e, $1.50, Yellow seahorse. f, $1.75, Pygmy seahorse.

2018, Feb. 1   **Litho.**   *Perf. 13¾*
1379 A507   Sheet of 6, #a-f   13.50 13.50

Miniature Sheet

Elvis Presley (1935-77) — A508

No. 1380 — Presley: a, Holding microphone, both hands visible. b, Wearing

---

vest and red shirt. c, Playing guitar. d, Holding microphone, one hand visible.

2018, June 5   **Litho.**   *Perf. 14*
1380 A508 $2 Sheet of 4, #a-d 16.00 16.00

Souvenir Sheet

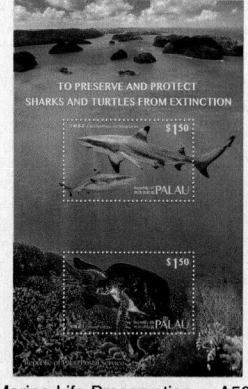

Marine Life Preservation — A509

No. 1381: a, Carcharhinus melanopterus. b, Chelonia mydas.

2018, June 26   **Litho.**   *Perf. 12*
1381 A509 $1.50 Sheet of 2, #a-
     b   6.00 6.00

Palau Fruit Dove — A510

2018, July 5   **Litho.**   *Perf. 14*
1382 A510 $2 multi   4.00 4.00
Printed in sheets of 4.

Palau Nautilus
A511

No. 1383: a, Two nautiluses, one facing right, other facing left. b, Nautilus facing left. c, Two nautiluses facing left. d, Nautilus facing right.
No. 1384: a, Nautilus facing right. b, Nautilus facing left.

2018, July 5   **Litho.**   *Perf. 12*
1383 A511 $2 Sheet of 4, #a-d 16.00 16.00

Souvenir Sheet
1384 A511 $3 Sheet of 2, #a-b 12.00 12.00

Miniature Sheet

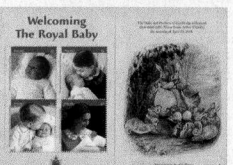

Birth of Prince Louis of Cambridge — A512

No. 1385: a, Prince Louis. b, Princess Charlotte and Prince Louis. c, Princes George and Louis. d, Duchess of Cambridge and Prince Louis.

2018, July 13   **Litho.**   *Perf. 13¾*
1385 A512 $2 Sheet of 4, #a-d 16.00 16.00

Wedding of Prince Harry and Meghan Markle A513

No. 1386: a, $1, Bride (30x40mm). b, $1, Groom (30x40mm). c, $2, Couple (30x40mm). d, $4, Couple riding in carriage (90x40mm).
No. 1387, $4, Couple standing.

2018, July 13   Litho.   Perf. 14
1386 A513   Sheet of 4, #a-d   16.00 16.00
Souvenir Sheet
Perf. 12
1387 A513 $4 multi   8.00   8.00
No. 1387 contains one 30x50mm stamp.

Miniature Sheet

Summit Meeting of U. S. Pres. Donald Trump and North Korean Supreme Leader Kim Jong Un A514

No. 1388: a, Pres. Trump holding signed document. b, Trump and Kim shaking hands. c, Kim. d, Trump and Kim standing apart. e, Signed document. f, Trump touching Kim's shoulder.

2018, July 30   Litho.   Perf. 14
1388 A514 $1 Sheet of 6, #a-f   12.00 12.00

First Man on the Moon, 50th Anniv. (in 2019) A515

No. 1389: a, 50c, Crew of Apollo 11. b, 75c, Footprint on moon. c, $1, Lunar Module on moon. d, $1.25, Astronaut Edwin E. Aldrin, Jr. saluting flag. e, $1.50, Aldrin on Moon. f, $1.75, Earthrise.
$4, Launch of Apollo 11, vert.

2018, Aug. 30   Litho.   Perf. 12
1389 A515   Sheet of 6, #a-f   13.50 13.50
Souvenir Sheet
Perf. 14
1390 A515 $4 multi   8.00   8.00
No. 1390 contains one 30x80mm stamp.

Miniature Sheet

Visit of Pres. Donald Trump to Helsinki, Finland A516

No. 1391: a, $1, Pres. Trump and Russian Pres. Vladimir Putin shaking hands. b, $2,

Trump and Putin standing. c, $3, Trump and Finland Pres. Sauli Niinistö. d, $4, Trump, Niinistö and their wives.

2018, Nov. 9   Litho.   Perf. 12
1391 A516   Sheet of 4, #a-d   20.00 20.00

Miniature Sheet

Sea Turtles A517

No. 1392: a, 50c, Green sea turtle. b, 75c, Green sea turtle, diff. c, $1, Hawksbill sea turtle. d, $1.25, Hawksbill sea turtle, diff. e, $1.50, Loggerhead sea turtle. f, $1.75, Loggerhead sea turtle, diff.

2018, Nov. 9   Litho.   Perf. 14
1392 A517   Sheet of 6, #a-f   13.50 13.50

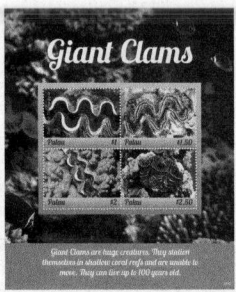

Giant Clams A518

No. 1393 — Various photographs of clams: a, $1. b, $1.50. c, $2. d, $2.50.
$4, Giant clam, vert.

2018, Nov. 9   Litho.   Perf. 14
1393 A518   Sheet of 4, #a-d   14.00 14.00
Souvenir Sheet
Perf. 12½
1394 A518 $4 multi   8.00   8.00
No. 1394 contains one 38x51mm stamp.

Miniature Sheet

Frangipani Flowers — A519

No. 1395: a, Bunch of flowers with white petals. b, Bunch of flowers with pink petals. c, Single flower with pink petals. d, Two flowers with white petals.

2018, Nov. 30   Litho.   Perf.
1395 A519 $2 Sheet of 4, #a-d   16.00 16.00

Whales A520

No. 1396: a, 75c, Beluga whale. b, $1, Blue whale. c, $1.25, Humpback whale. d, $1.50, Minke whale. e, $1.75, Killer whale. f, $2, Sperm whale.

No. 1397, vert. — Killer whale and: a, Cubes. b, Sphere.

2018, Nov. 30   Litho.   Perf. 14
1396 A520   Sheet of 6, #a-f   16.50 16.50
Souvenir Sheet
Perf. 12½
1397 A520 $3 Sheet of 2, #a-b 12.00 12.00
No. 1397 contains two 38x51mm stamps.

Sea Birds A521

No. 1398: a, 25c, Sooty tern. b, 50c, Black-billed plover. c, $1, Bulwer's petrel. d, $1.50, Whiskered tern. e, $2, Pacific golden plover. f, $2.50, Common tern.
No. 1399: a, $1, Brown noddy. b, $2, Dunlin. c, $3, Ruddy turnstone.

2018, Dec. 10   Litho.   Perf. 14
1398 A521   Sheet of 6, #a-f   15.50 15.50
Souvenir Sheet
1399 A521   Sheet of 3, #a-c   12.00 12.00

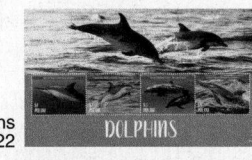

Dolphins A522

No. 1400: a, $1, Spinner dolphin. b, $2, Pantropical spotted dolphin. c, $3, Atlantic spotted dolphins. d, $4, Striped dolphin.
No. 1401, Common bottlenose dolphin.

2018, Dec. 10   Litho.   Perf. 14
1400 A522   Sheet of 4, #a-d   20.00 20.00
Souvenir Sheet
Perf. 12½
1401 A522 $4 multi   8.00   8.00
No. 1401 contains one 51x38mm stamp.

Nicobar Pigeons A523

No. 1402 — Various photographs of Nicobar pigeons: a, $1. b, $1.50. c, $2. d, $2.50.
No. 1403, horiz. — Various photographs of Nicobar pigeons: a, $3. b, $3.50.

2018, Dec. 19   Litho.   Perf. 14
1402 A523   Sheet of 4, #a-d   14.00 14.00
Souvenir Sheet
1403 A523   Sheet of 2, #a-b   13.00 13.00

A524

Birds A525

No. 1404: a, 25c, Nutmeg mannikin. b, 50c, Slaty-legged crake. c, 75c, Red-legged crake. d, $1, Western yellow wagtail. e, $1.50, Nocobar pigeon. f, $2, Palau flycatcher.
No. 1405: a, 50c, Buff-banded rail. b, $1, Micronesian myzomela. c, $2, Micronesian myzomela, diff. d, $3, Buff-banded rail, diff.
$4, Citrine white-eye.

2018, Dec. 19   Litho.   Perf. 14
1404 A524   Sheet of 6, #a-f   12.00 12.00
1405 A525   Sheet of 4, #a-d   13.00 13.00
Souvenir Sheet
Perf. 12½
1406 A525 $4 multi   8.00   8.00
No. 1406 contains one 51x38mm stamp.

Miniature Sheet

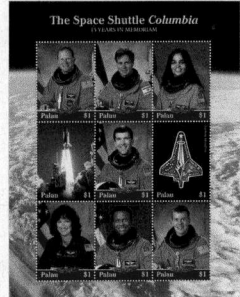

Space Shuttle Columbia Disaster, 15th Anniv. — A527

No. 1409: a, Mission specialist David M. Brown (1956-2003). b, Mission specialist Ilan Ramon (1954-2003). c, Mission specialist Kalpana Chawla (1962-2003). d, Lift-off of Space Shuttle Columbia. e, Commander Rick D. Husband (1957-2003). f, Insignia of Shuttle mission STS-107. g, Mission specialist Laurel Clark (1961-2003). h, Payload commander Michael B. Anderson (1959-2003). i, Pilot William C. McCool (1961-2003).

2018, Dec. 25   Litho.   Perf. 14
1409 A527 $1 Sheet of 9, #a-i 18.00 18.00

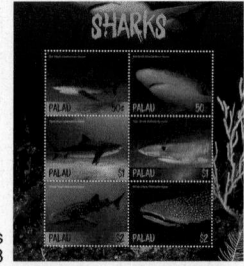

Sharks A528

No. 1410: a, 50c, Bull shark, country name in purple. b, 50c, Bull shark, country name in orange. c, $1, Tiger shark, country name in purple. d, $1, Tiger shark, country name in orange. e, $2, Whale shark, country name in purple. f, $2, Whale shark, country name in orange.
$4, Great white shark.

2018, Dec. 25   Litho.   Perf. 14
1410 A528   Sheet of 6, #a-f   14.00 14.00
Souvenir Sheet
Perf. 12½
1411 A528 $4 multi   8.00   8.00
No. 1411 contains one 51x38mm stamp.

Miniature Sheets

Waterfowl — A529

No. 1412: a, 50c, Two Eurasian teal. b, 75c, One Eurasian teal. c, $1, Eurasian wigeons. d, $1.25, Eurasian wigeons, diff. e, $1.50, Mallard in flight. f, $1.75, Mallard on water.
No. 1413: a, 50c, Northern pintail facing right. b, 75c, Northern pintail facing left. c, $1, Northern shoveler in flight. d, $1.25, Northern shoveler standing. e, $1.50, Tufted duck facing left. f, $1.75, Tufted duck facing right.

2018, Dec. 27   Litho.   Perf. 14
Sheets of 6, #a-f
1412-1413 A529   Set of 2   27.00 27.00

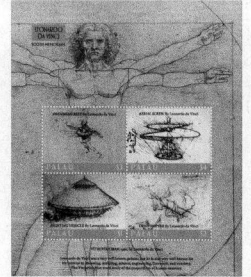

Drawings by Leonardo da Vinci (1452-1519), Sculptor and Painter — A530

No. 1414 — Drawing of: a, $1, Fighting vehicle. b, $2, Ornithopter. c, $3, Aerial screw. d, $4, Swimming belt.
$5, Self-portrait, Vitruvian Man, and Town Plan of Imola.

2018, Dec. 27   Litho.   Perf. 14
1414 A530   Sheet of 4, #a-d   20.00 20.00
Size: 130x80mm
Imperf
1415 A530 $5 multi   10.00 10.00

Souvenir Sheets

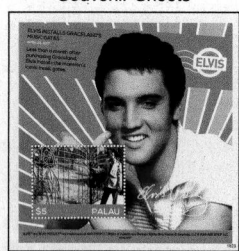

Elvis Presley (1935-77) — A531

Inscriptions: No. 1416, $5, Elvis installs Graceland's music gates. No. 1417, $5, What have you got? No. 1418, $5, Elvis rides "Bear" at Graceland, vert. No. 1419, $5, A hard day of basic training, vert.

2018, Dec. 27   Litho.   Perf. 14
1416-1419 A531   Set of 4   40.00 40.00

Protanguila
Palau — A532

Groupers
A533

Pufferfish
A534

Sharks
A535

Sharks
A536

Manta
Ray
A537

Golden
Jellyfish
A538

No. 1420 — Background color: a, Black. b, Blue violet.
No. 1421: a, Brown marbled grouper. b, Honey comb grouper. c, Red mouth grouper. d, Square tail coral grouper. e, Camouflage grouper. f, Barramundi grouper.
No. 1422: a, Papuan toby. b, Black-saddled toby. c, Blue-spotted puffer. d, Map puffer. e, Star pufferfish.
No. 1423: a, Tiger shark. b, Black-tip reef shark. c, Gray reef shark. d, Great hammerhead shark.
No. 1424: a, Black-tip reef sharks. b, Gray reef shark, facing left, and other marine life. c, Gray reef shark, facing left, dark background. d, Gray reef shark, facing right, and fish.

2019, Jan. 1   Litho.   Perf. 14
1420 A532 $1.95 Pair, #a-b   8.00 8.00
Miniature Sheets
1421 A533 $1.50 Sheet of 6, #a-f   18.00 18.00
1422 A534 $1.20 Sheet of 5, #a-e   12.00 12.00
1423 A535 $1.20 Sheet of 4, #a-d   9.75 9.75
1424 A536 $1.20 Sheet of 4, #a-d   9.75 9.75
Nos. 1421-1424 (4)   49.50 49.50
Souvenir Sheets
Perf. 12½
1425 A537 $4 multi   8.00 8.00
1426 A538 $4 multi   8.00 8.00
No. 1420 was printed in sheets containing two each Nos. 1420a-1420b.

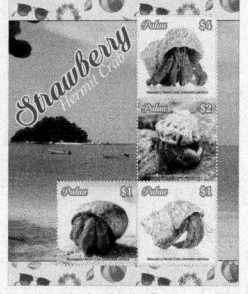

Strawberry Hermit Crab — A539

No. 1427: a, $1, Crab facing forward. b, $1, Crab facing right. c, $2, Crab, diff. d, $4, Crab, diff.
$5, Crab, diff.

2019, Apr. 21   Litho.   Perf. 13¾
1427 A539   Sheet of 4, #a-d   16.00 16.00
Souvenir Sheet
1428 A539 $5 multi   10.00 10.00

A540

Mimic
Octopus
A541

Nos. 1429 and 1430 — Various depictions of Mimic octopus: a, $1. b, $2. c, $3.
$5, Mimic octopus, horiz.

2019, May 1   Litho.   Perf. 12
1429 A540   Sheet of 3, #a-c   12.00 12.00
1430 A541   Sheet of 3, #a-c   12.00 12.00
Souvenir Sheet
Perf. 14
1431 A541 $5 multi   10.00 10.00
No. 1431 contains one 80x30mm stamp.

Clearfin
Lionfish
A542

No. 1432: Various depictions of Clearfin lionfish, as shown.
$5, Clearfin lionfish, vert.

2019, May 6   Litho.   Perf. 13¾
1432 A542 $2 Sheet of 4, #a-d   16.00 16.00
Souvenir Sheet
Perf. 12½
1433 A542 $5 multi   10.00 10.00
No. 1433 contains one 38x51mm stamp.

Miniature Sheet

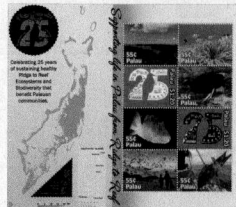

Palau Conservation Society, 25th Anniv. — A543

No. 1434: a, 55c, Aerial view of lagoon. b, 55c, Fish and coral. c, 55c, Bird. d, 55c, Grouper. e, 55c, Children on beach, flock of birds. f, 55c, Fishing boat and caught fish. g, $1.20, Bird, "25" in white. h, $1.20, Bird, "25" in black.

2019, June 14   Litho.   Perf. 12
1434 A543   Sheet of 8, #a-h   11.50 11.50

Miniature Sheet

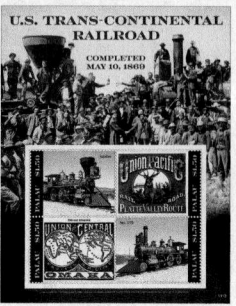

U.S. Transcontinental Railroad, 150th Anniv. — A544

No. 1435: a, Jupiter locomotive. b, Union Pacific Railroad emblem. c, Union and Central Pacific Railroad emblem. d, Locomotive No. 119.

2019, July 2   Litho.   Perf. 14
1435 A544 $1.50 Sheet of 4, #a-d   12.00 12.00

Miniature Sheet

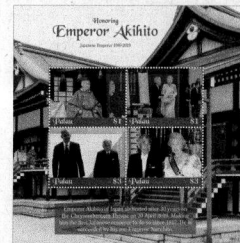

Abdication of Japanese Emperor Akihito — A545

No. 1436: a, $1, Emperor Akihito. b, $1, Emperor Akihito and Empress Michiko. c, $3, U.S. President Barack Obama and Emperor Akihito. d, $3, Emperor Akihito and Queen Elizabeth II.

2019, July 2   Litho.   Perf. 14
1436 A545   Sheet of 4, #a-d   16.00 16.00

Miniature Sheet

Birth of Archie Mountbatten-Windsor — A546

No. 1437: a, Duke and Duchess of Sussex, with son, Archie. b, As "a," Duchess waving hand. c, Princess Diana holding infant Prince

Harry. d, Queen Mother holding infant Princess Elizabeth.

2019, July 11   Litho.   Perf. 14
1437 A546 $2 Sheet of 4, #a-d 16.00 16.00

Long-tailed Macaque — A547

Emblem of 2019 Singpex International Stamp Exhibition and: a, $1, Macaque eating. b, $1, Macaque's head. c, $2, Adult macaque and juvenile. d, $2, Macaque looking left.
$5, Emblem and macaque, diff.

2019, July 31   Litho.   Perf. 14
1438 A547 Sheet of 4, #a-d 12.00 12.00
Souvenir Sheet
Perf. 12½
1439 A547 $5 multi 10.00 10.00
No. 1439 contains one 38x51mm stamp.

Miniature Sheet

Mohandas K. Gandhi (1869-1948), Indian Nationalist Leader — A548

No. 1440: a, 50c, Drawing of Gandhi. b, $1.50, Photograph of Gandhi. c, $2.50, Drawing of Gandhi, diff. d, $3.50, Photograph of Gandhi, diff.

2019, Oct. 11   Litho.   Perf. 14
1440 A548 Sheet of 4, #a-d 16.00 16.00

Dorje Chang Buddha III, Religious Leader — A549

2019, Dec. 8   Litho.   Perf. 13x13½
1441 A549 $1 multi 2.00 2.00

Maroon Clownfish — A550

No. 1442 — Various photographs of clownfish and sea anemones: a, $1. b, $2. c, $3.
No. 1443, vert. — Various photographs of clownfish and sea anemones: a, $3. b, $4.

2019, Dec. 27   Litho.   Perf. 12
1442 A550 Sheet of 3, #a-c 12.00 12.00
Souvenir Sheet
Perf. 14
1443 A550 Sheet of 2, #a-b 14.00 14.00
No. 1443 contains two 30x40mm stamps.

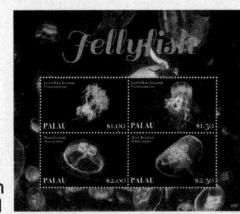

Jellyfish
A551

No. 1444: a, $1, Lion's mane jellyfish. b, $1.50, Lion's mane jellyfish, diff. c, $2, Moon jellyfish. d, $2.50, Moon jellyfish, diff.
$5, White spotted jellyfish.

2019, Dec. 27   Litho.   Perf. 12
1444 A551 Sheet of 4, #a-d 14.00 14.00
Souvenir Sheet
Perf. 13¾
1445 A551 $5 multi 10.00 10.00
No. 1445 contains one 35x35mm stamp.

Miniature Sheet

Diplomatic Relations Between Palau and Japan, 25th Anniv. — A552

No. 1446: a, Itabori. b, Japan-Palau Frienship Bridge. c, Palau International Coral Reef Center. d, Judo. e, Belau Eco Glass. f, Future Palauan Olympians in training.

2019, Dec. 28   Litho.   Perf. 14
1446 A552 $1 Sheet of 6, #a-f 12.00 12.00

Miniature Sheets

A553

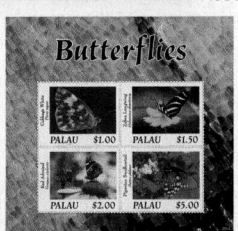

Butterflies — A554

No. 1447: a, $1, Cabbage white butterfly, purple flowers. b, $1.50, Zebra longwing butterfly, pink flowers. c, $2, Red admiral butterfly, yellow flower. d, $2.50, Pipevine swallowtail butterfly, red flowers.
No. 1448: a, $1, Cabbage white butterfly, green background. b, $1.50, Zebra longwing butterfly, yellow flower. c, $2, Red admiral butterfly, pink flowers. d, $5, Pipevine swallowtail butterfly, light purple flowers.

2020, June 15   Litho.   Perf. 14
1447 A553 Sheet of 4, #a-d 14.00 14.00
1448 A554 Sheet of 4, #a-d 19.00 19.00

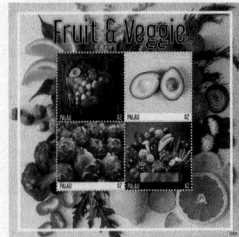

Fruits and Vegetables — A555

No. 1449: a, Heart-shaped tray of various fruits and vegetables. b, Avocado. c, Dragonfruit. d, Vegetables and shopping bag.
No. 1450: a, Pineapple, orange background (40x30mm). b, Pineapple, yellow background (30x40mm).

2020, June 15   Litho.   Perf. 13¾
1449 A555 $2 Sheet of 4, #a-d 16.00 16.00
Souvenir Sheet
Perf. 14
1450 A555 $3 Sheet of 2, #a-b 12.00 12.00

Miniature Sheet

Medical Workers During the COVID-19 Pandemic — A556

No. 1451: a, Military corpsman wearing cap and protective face mask. b, Technician wearing two proetective face masks, yellow gown and gloves. c, Globe and group of medical workers wearing protective clothing and masks. d, Two medical workers wearing protective face masks, hands with thumbs up.

2020, Aug. 7   Litho.   Perf. 12
1451 A556 $2 Sheet of 4, #a-d 16.00 16.00

Paintings by Raphael (1483-1520) — A557

No. 1452: a, Portrait of Agnolo Doni, 1506. b, Portrait of Pietro Bembo, 1506. c, La Donna Gravida, 1506. d, Portrait of a Cardinal, 1510.
$4, La Donna Velata, 1515.

2020, Aug. 7   Litho.   Perf. 14
1452 A557 $1.60 Sheet of 4, #a-d 13.00 13.00
Souvenir Sheet
Perf. 12½
1453 A557 $4 multi 8.00 8.00
No. 1453 contains one 38x51mm stamp.

Souvenir Sheets

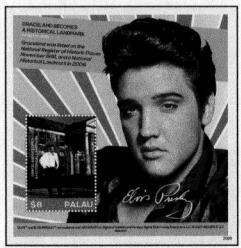

Elvis Presley (1935-77) — A558

Inscriptions: No. 1454, $8, Graceland becomes a historic landmark. No. 1455, $8, "I wish." No. 1456, $8, "Rhythm is something you either have or don't." No. 1457, $8, "I've been so lucky," horiz.

2020, Aug. 7   Litho.   Perf. 14
1454-1457 A558 Set of 4 64.00 64.00

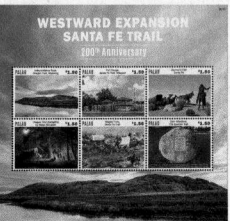

Westward Expansion of Settlers in the United States — A559

No. 1458: a, Independence Rock, Oregon Trail, Wyoming. b, Fort Osage, Santa Fe Trail, Missouri. c, Journey's End Monument, Santa Fe National Historic Trail. d, Oregon Trail (Campfire), painting by Albert Bierstadt (1830-1902). e, Wagon train, Santa Fe Trail. f, Zero Milestone, Old Spanish Trail.
$8, Fort Union, Santa Fe Trail, New Mexico.

2020, Sept. 4   Litho.   Perf. 14
1458 A559 $1.50 Sheet of 6, #a-f 18.00 18.00
Souvenir Sheet
Perf. 12½
1459 A559 $8 multi 16.00 16.00
No. 1459 contains one 51x38mm stamp.

Mohandas K. Gandhi (1869-1948), Indian Nationalist Leader — A560

2020, Nov. 30   Litho.   Perf. 14
1460 A560 25c multi .50 .50

Miniature Sheet

World War II Victory in Europe (V-E Day), 75th Anniv. A561

No. 1461: a, Gen. Charles de Gaulle (1890-1970), and flag of France. b, Gen. Dwight D. Eisenhower (1890-1969), and flag of the United States. c, Winston Churchill (1874-1965), Prime Minister of Great Britain, flag of Great Britain. d, Harry S. Truman (1884-1972), 33rd President, flag of the United States. e, Churchill and the British royal family. f, Field Marshal Bernard Montgomery (1887-1976), flag of Great Britain.

2020, Nov. 30   Litho.   Perf. 14¼x14
1461 A561 $1.60 Sheet of 6, #a-f 19.50 19.50

A562

Rabbits A563

No. 1462: a, Brown rabbit, no grass. b, Brown rabbit on grass. c, White rabbit with ears up. d, White rabbit with ears down.
No. 1463: a, Two rabbits. b, One rabbit.

Perf. 13¼x13¾
2020, Nov. 30   Litho.
1462 A562 $2 Sheet of 4, #a-d   16.00 16.00

Souvenir Sheet
Perf. 13¾x13¼
1463 A563 $3 Sheet of 2, #a-b   12.00 12.00

A564

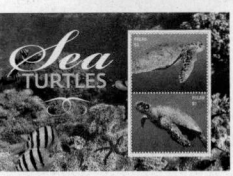

Sea
Turtles
A565

No. 1464: a, Turtle swimming forward. b,
Turtle swimming to right. c, Turtle swimming to
left. d, Turtle's head.
No. 1465: a, Turtle swiming to right, diff. b,
Turtle swimming to left, diff.

Perf. 13¾x13¼
2020, Nov. 30   Litho.
1464 A564 $2 Sheet of 4, #a-d   16.00 16.00

Souvenir Sheet
1465 A565 $3 Sheet of 2, #a-b   12.00 12.00

A566

Meeting of U.S. Pres. Donald Trump
and North Korean Supreme Leader
Kim Jong-un
A567

No. 1466: a, Kim and Trump shaking hands
at Demilitarized Zone border. b, Kim, Trump
and North Koreans. c, Kim watching Trump
cross border at Demilitarized Zone. d, Kim and
Trump seated.
No. 1467: a, Trump and South Korean Pres.
Moon Jae-in. b, Trump and Kim standing in
front of Demilitarized Zone building. c, Presidents Trump and Moon shaking hands with
soldiers. d, Trump writing on brick wall.

Perf. 14¼x13¾
2020, Nov. 30   Litho.
1466 A566 $2 Sheet of 4, #a-d   16.00 16.00
1467 A567 $2 Sheet of 4, #a-d   16.00 16.00

SEMI-POSTAL STAMPS

Olympic
Sports — SP1

No. B1, Baseball glove, player. No. B2, Running shoe, athlete. No. B3, Goggles, swimmer.
No. B4, Gold medal, diver.

1988, Aug. 8   Litho.   *Perf. 14*
B1 SP1 25c +5c multi   .50 .50
B2 SP1 25c +5c multi   .50 .50
   a.   Pair, #B1-B2   1.25 1.25
B3 SP1 45c +5c multi   1.25 1.25
B4 SP1 45c +5c multi   1.25 1.25
   a.   Pair, #B3-B4   2.75 2.75

AIR POST STAMPS

White-tailed
Tropicbird
AP1

1984, June 12   Litho.   *Perf. 14*
C1 AP1 40c shown   .75 .75
C2 AP1 40c Fairy tern   .75 .75
C3 AP1 40c Black noddy   .75 .75
C4 AP1 40c Black-naped tern   .75 .75
   a.   Block of 4, #C1-C4   3.50 3.50

Audubon Type of 1985
1985, Feb. 6   Litho.   *Perf. 14*
C5 A12 44c Audubon's Shear-
       water   1.10 1.10

Palau-Germany Political, Economic &
Cultural Exchange Cent. — AP2

Germany Nos. 40, 65, Caroline Islands Nos.
19, 13 and: No. C6, German flag-raising at
Palau, 1885. No. C7, Early German trading
post in Angaur. No. C8, Abai architecture
recorded by Prof. & Frau Kramer, 1908-1910.
No. C9, S.M.S. Cormoran.

1985, Sept. 19   Litho.   *Perf. 14x13½*
C6 AP2 44c multicolored   .95 .95
C7 AP2 44c multicolored   .95 .95
C8 AP2 44c multicolored   .95 .95
C9 AP2 44c multicolored   .95 .95
   a.   Block of 4, #C6-C9   4.50 4.50

Trans-Pacific Airmail Anniv. Type of
1985

Aircraft: No. C10, 1951 Trans-Ocean Air-
ways PBY-5A Catalina Amphibian. No. C11,
1968 Air Micronesia DC-6B Super
Cloudmaster. No. C12, 1960 Trust Territory
Airline SA-16 Albatross. No. C13, 1967 Pan
American Douglas DC-4.

1985, Nov. 21   Litho.   *Perf. 14*
C10 A16 44c multicolored   .85 .85
C11 A16 44c multicolored   .85 .85
C12 A16 44c multicolored   .85 .85
C13 A16 44c multicolored   .85 .85
   a.   Block of 4, #C10-C13   3.75 3.75

Haruo I. Remeliik (1933-1985), 1st
President — AP3

Designs: No. C14, Presidential seal, excerpt
from 1st inaugural address. No. C15, War
canoe, address excerpt. No. C16, Remeliik, US Pres. Reagan, excerpt from Reagan's
speech, Pacific Basin Conference, Guam,
1984.

1986, June 30   Litho.   *Perf. 14*
C14 AP3 44c multicolored   1.10 1.10
C15 AP3 44c multicolored   1.10 1.10
C16 AP3 44c multicolored   1.10 1.10
   a.   Strip of 3, #C14-C16   3.75 3.75

Intl. Peace Year, Statue
of Liberty Cent. — AP4

1986, Sept. 19   Litho.
C17 AP4 44c multicolored   1.00 1.00

Aircraft — AP5

36c, Cessna 207 Skywagon. 39c, Embraer
EMB-110 Bandeirante. 45c, Boeing 727.

1989, May 17   Litho.   *Perf. 14x14½*
C18 AP5 36c multicolored   .65 .65
   a.   Booklet pane of 10   7.00 —
C19 AP5 39c multicolored   .85 .85
   a.   Booklet pane of 10   7.50 —
C20 AP5 45c multicolored   1.00 1.00
   a.   Booklet pane of 10   8.25 —
   b.   Booklet pane, 5 each 36c, 45c   8.50 —
   Nos. C18-C20 (3)   2.50 2.50

Palauan Bai Type
1991, July 9   Litho.   *Die Cut*
Self-Adhesive
C21 A61 50c like #293a   1.50 1.50

World War II in the Pacific Type
Miniature Sheet

Aircraft: No. C22: a, Grumman TBF
Avenger, US Navy. b, Curtiss P-40C, Chinese
Air Force "Flying Tigers." c, Mitsubishi A6M
Zero-Sen, Japan. d, Hawker Hurricane, Royal
Air Force. e, Consolidated PBY Catalina,
Royal Netherlands Indies Air Force. f, Curtiss
Hawk 75, Netherlands Indies. g, Boeing B-
17E, US Army Air Force. h, Brewster Buffalo,
Royal Australian Air Force. i, Supermarine
Walrus, Royal Navy. j, Curtiss P-40E, Royal
New Zealand Air Force.

1992, Sept. 10   Litho.   *Perf. 14½x15*
C22 A66 50c Sheet of 10, #a.-
     j.   11.00 11.00

Birds
AP6

a, Palau swiftlet. b, Barn swallow. c, Jungle
nightjar. d, White-breasted woodswallow.

1994, Mar. 24   Litho.   *Perf. 14*
C23 AP6 50c Block of 4, #a.-d.   4.00 4.00

No. C23 is printed in sheets of 16 stamps.

PALESTINE

ˈpa-lə-ˌstin

LOCATION — Western Asia bordering
on the Mediterranean Sea
GOVT. — Former British Mandate
AREA — 10,429 sq. mi.
POP. — 1,605,816 (estimated)
CAPITAL — Jerusalem

Formerly a part of Turkey, Palestine
was occupied by the Egyptian Expedi-
tionary Forces of the British Army in
World War I and was mandated to
Great Britain in 1923. Mandate ended
May 14, 1948.

10 Milliemes = 1 Piaster
1000 Milliemes = 1 Egyptian Pound
1000 Mils = 1 Palestine Pound (1928)

Jordan stamps overprinted with "Palestine" in English and Arabic are listed
under Jordan.

Watermark

Wmk. 33

Issued under British Military Occupation

For use in Palestine, Transjordan,
Lebanon, Syria and in parts of Cilicia
and northeastern Egypt

A1

Wmk. Crown and "GvR" (33)
1918, Feb. 10   Litho.   *Rouletted 20*
1 A1 1pi deep blue   190.00 105.00
2 A1 1pi ultra   2.50 2.50

Nos. 2 & 1 Surcharged in
Black

1918, Feb. 16
3 A1 5m on 1pi ultra   8.50 4.25
   a.   5m on 1pi gray blue   110.00 600.00

Nos. 1 and 3a were issued without gum. No.
3a is on paper with a surface sheen.

1918	Typo.		*Perf. 15x14*	
4	A1	1m dark brown	.35	.45
5	A1	2m blue green	.35	.50
6	A1	3m light brown	.50	.40
7	A1	4m scarlet	.40	.45
8	A1	5m orange	.75	.35
9	A1	1pi indigo	.50	.30
10	A1	2pi olive green	3.50	1.00
11	A1	5pi plum	3.75	2.50
12	A1	9pi bister	12.50	7.50
13	A1	10pi ultramarine	12.50	4.50
14	A1	20pi gray	18.50	20.00
	Nos. 4-14 (11)		53.60	37.95

Many shades exist.
Nos. 4-11 exist with rough perforation.
Issued: 1m, 2m, 4m, 2pi, 5pi, 7/16; 5m,
9/25; 1pi, 11/9; 3m, 9pi, 10pi, 12/17; 20pi,
12/27.
Nos. 4-11 with overprint "O. P. D. A." (Otto-
man Public Debt Administration) or "H.J.Z."
(Hejaz-Jemen Railway) are revenue stamps;
they exist postally used.
For overprints on stamps and types see
#15-62 & Jordan #1-63, 73-90, 92-102, 130-
144, J12-J23.

Issued under British Administration
Overprinted at Jerusalem

Stamps and Type of 1918
Overprinted in Black or
Silver

1920, Sept. 1   Wmk. 33   *Perf. 15x14*
Arabic Overprint 8mm long
15 A1 1m dark brown   10.00 2.25
16 A1 2m bl grn, perf 14   4.50 1.75
   d.   Perf 15x14   14.00 6.00
17 A1 3m lt brown   18.50 8.50
   d.   Perf. 14   140.00 70.00
   e.   Inverted overprint   550.00 700.00
18 A1 4m scarlet   5.25 1.75
19 A1 5m org, perf 14   8.00 .75
   e.   Perf 15x14   27.50 10.00
20 A1 1pi indigo (S)   5.75 1.25
21 A1 2pi olive green   7.00 2.50
22 A1 5pi plum   27.50 30.00
23 A1 9pi bister   15.00 23.00
24 A1 10pi ultra   13.00 19.50
25 A1 20pi gray   35.00 50.00
   Nos. 15-25 (11)   149.50 141.25

Forgeries exist of No. 17e.

Similar Ovpt., with Arabic
Line 10mm Long, Arabic
"S" and "T" Joined, ".." at
Left Extends Above Other
Letters

1920-21   *Perf. 15x14*
15a A1 1m dark brown   2.75 1.20
   e.   Perf. 14   875.00 975.00
   g.   As "a," invtd. ovpt.   450.00

16a	A1	2m blue green	12.00	4.50
e.		"PALESTINE" omitted	2,500.	1,500.
f.		Perf. 14	6.00	6.00
17a	A1	3m light brown	4.25	1.20
18a	A1	4m scarlet	6.25	1.60
b.		Perf. 14	95.00	125.00
19a	A1	5m orange	4.50	.90
f.		Perf. 14	12.00	1.25
20a	A1	1pi indigo, perf. 14 (S) ('21)	67.50	2.00
d.		Perf. 15x14	575.00	40.00
21a	A1	2pi olive green ('21)	90.00	42.50
22a	A1	5pi plum ('21)	52.50	11.00
d.		Perf. 14	225.00	525.00
		Nos. 15a-22a (8)	239.75	64.90

This overprint often looks grayish to grayish black. In the English line the letters are frequently uneven and damaged.

Similar Ovpt., with Arabic Line 10mm Long, Arabic "S" and "T" Separated and 6mm Between English and Hebrew Lines

1920, Dec. 6

15b	A1	1m dk brn, perf 14	62.50	37.50
17b	A1	3m lt brn, perf 14	60.00	37.50
19b	A1	5m orange, perf 14	475.00	37.50
d.		Perf. 15x14	16,000.	13,750.
		Nos. 15b-19b (3)	597.50	112.50

Overprinted as Before, 7½mm Between English and Hebrew Lines, ".." at Left Even With Other Letters

1921   Perf. 15x14

15c	A1	1m dark brown	21.00	4.00
f.		1m dull brown, perf 14		2,300.
16c	A1	2m blue green	32.50	6.25
17c	A1	3m light brown	47.50	3.50
18c	A1	4m scarlet	50.00	4.00
19c	A1	5m orange	82.50	1.10
20c	A1	1pi indigo (S)	32.50	1.60
21c	A1	2pi olive green	26.50	7.00
22c	A1	5pi plum	29.00	9.25
23c	A1	9pi bister	75.00	125.00
24c	A1	10pi ultra	90.00	16.00
25c	A1	20pi pale gray	135.00	75.00
d.		Perf. 14	13,750.	2,900.
		Nos. 15c-25c (11)	621.50	252.70

Overprinted at London

Stamps of 1918 Overprinted

1921   Perf. 15x14

37	A1	1m dark brown	2.25	.35
38	A1	2m blue green	3.25	.35
39	A1	3m light brown	3.50	.35
40	A1	4m scarlet	4.00	.70
41	A1	5m orange	3.75	.35
42	A1	1pi bright blue	3.00	.40
43	A1	2pi olive green	5.00	.45
44	A1	5pi plum	12.50	5.75
45	A1	9pi bister	26.00	16.00
46	A1	10pi ultra	29.00	675.00
47	A1	20pi gray	85.00	1,600.
		Nos. 37-47 (11)	140.00	
		Nos. 37-45 (9)		24.70

The 2nd character from left on bottom line that looks like quotation marks consists of long thin lines.
Deformed or damaged letters exist in all three lines of the overprint.

Similar Overprint on Type of 1921

1922   Wmk. 4   Perf. 14

48	A1	1m dark brown	2.50	.35
a.		Inverted overprint	—	13,750.
b.		Double overprint	260.00	500.00
49	A1	2m yellow	3.25	.35
50	A1	3m Prus blue	3.50	.25
51	A1	4m rose	3.50	.35
52	A1	5m orange	2.75	.35
53	A1	6m blue green	3.00	.35
54	A1	7m yellow brown	3.00	.35
55	A1	8m red	3.00	.35
56	A1	1pi gray	3.50	.35
57	A1	13m ultra	4.00	.25
58	A1	2pi olive green	4.00	.40
a.		Inverted overprint	350.00	575.00
b.		2pi yellow bister	140.00	7.50
59	A1	5pi plum	6.25	1.40
a.		Perf. 15x14	67.50	7.50

Perf. 15x14

60	A1	9pi bister	10.00	10.00
a.		Perf. 14	1,150.	275.00
61	A1	10pi light blue	8.50	4.25
a.		Perf. 14	95.00	17.50
62	A1	20pi violet	12.50	6.25
a.		Perf. 14	225.00	125.00
		Nos. 48-62 (15)	73.25	25.50

The 2nd character from left on bottom line that looks like quotation marks consists of short thick lines.
The "E. F. F." for "E. E. F." on No. 61 is caused by damaged type.

Rachel's Tomb
A3

Mosque of Omar (Dome of the Rock)
A4

Citadel at Jerusalem
A5

Tiberias and Sea of Galilee
A6

1927-42   Typo.   Perf. 13½x14½

63	A3	2m Prus blue	2.75	.25
64	A3	3m yellow green	1.75	.25
65	A4	4m rose red	9.00	1.60
66	A4	4m violet brn ('32)	3.25	.25
67	A5	5m brown org	4.25	.25
c.		Perf. 14½x14 (coil stamp) ('36)	16.00	21.00
68	A4	6m deep green	1.50	.25
69	A5	7m deep red	12.00	.70
70	A5	7m dk violet ('32)	1.00	.25
71	A4	8m yellow brown	18.50	7.00
72	A4	8m scarlet ('32)	1.50	.25
73	A3	10m deep gray	2.25	.25
a.		Perf. 14½x14 (coil stamp) ('38)	23.50	27.50
74	A4	13m ultra	17.50	.40
75	A4	13m olive bister ('32)	3.75	.25
76	A4	15m ultra ('32)	5.75	.25
77	A5	20m olive green	2.50	.25

Perf. 14

78	A6	50m brown purple	3.50	.40
79	A6	90m bister	87.50	60.00
80	A6	100m bright blue	2.60	.80
81	A6	200m dk violet	9.25	5.75
82	A6	250m dp brown ('42)	7.50	3.50
83	A6	500m red ('42)	9.00	3.50
84	A6	£1 gray black ('42)	13.00	4.00
		Nos. 63-84 (22)	219.60	90.40

Issued: 3m, #74, 6/1; 2m, 5m, 6m, 10m, #65, 69, 71, 77-81, 8/14; #70, 72, 6/1/32; #75, 15m, 8/1/32; #66, 11/1/32; #82-84, 1/15/42.

POSTAGE DUE STAMPS

D1

1923   Unwmk.   Typo.   Perf. 11

J1	D1	1m bister brown	27.50	40.00
b.		Horiz. pair, imperf. btwn.	1,300.	750.00
J2	D1	2m green	22.50	11.50
J3	D1	4m red	12.00	13.50
J4	D1	8m violet	8.50	8.50
b.		Horiz. pair, imperf. btwn.		2,300.
J5	D1	13m dark blue	7.50	8.50
a.		Horiz. pair, imperf. btwn.	1,200.	
		Nos. J1-J5 (5)	78.00	82.00

Imperfs. of 1m, 2m, 8m, are from proof sheets.
Values for Nos. J1-J5 are for fine centered copies.

D2

1924, Dec. 1   Wmk. 4

J6	D2	1m brown	1.10	2.00
J7	D2	2m yellow	4.00	1.75
J8	D2	4m green	2.00	1.50
J9	D2	8m red	3.00	1.00
J10	D2	13m ultramarine	3.50	2.50
J11	D2	5pi violet	15.00	1.75
		Nos. J6-J11 (6)	28.60	10.50

D3

1928-45   Perf. 14

J12	D3	1m lt brown	2.75	1.00
a.		Perf. 15x14 ('45)	42.50	80.00
J13	D3	2m yellow	3.75	.70
J14	D3	4m green	4.25	1.60
a.		4m bluish grn, perf. 15x14 ('43)	75.00	120.00
J15	D3	6m brown org ('33)	19.00	5.00
J16	D3	8m red	2.75	2.00
J17	D3	10m light gray	2.00	.70
J18	D3	13m ultra	4.50	3.00
J19	D3	20m olive green	4.50	1.25
J20	D3	50m violet	5.00	2.50
		Nos. J12-J20 (9)	48.50	17.75

The Hebrew word for "mil" appears below the numeral on all values but the 1m.
Issued: 6m, Oct. 1933; others, Feb. 1, 1928.

PALESTINIAN AUTHORITY

ˈpa-lə-ˌs-ti-nē-ən ˈo-thōr-itē

LOCATION — Areas of the West Bank and the Gaza Strip.
AREA — 2,410 sq. mi.
POP. — 2,825,000 (2000 est.)

1000 Fils (Mils) = 5 Israeli Shekels
1000 Fils = 1 Jordanian Dinar (Jan. 1, 1998)

> **Catalogue values for all unused stamps in this country are for Never Hinged items.**

Hisham Palace, Jericho — A1

5m, 10m, 20m, Hisham Palace. 30m, 40m, 50m, 75m, Mosque, Jerusalem. 125, 150m, 250m, 300m, 500m, Flag. 1000m, Dome of the Rock.

1994   Litho.   Perf. 14

1	A1	5m multicolored	.25	.25
2	A1	10m multicolored	.25	.25
3	A1	20m multicolored	.25	.25
4	A1	30m multicolored	.25	.25
5	A1	40m multicolored	.25	.25
6	A1	50m multicolored	.30	.30
7	A1	75m multicolored	.35	.35
8	A1	125m multicolored	.60	.60
9	A1	150m multicolored	.90	.90
10	A1	250m multicolored	1.25	1.25
11	A1	300m multicolored	1.75	1.75

Size: 51x29mm

12	A1	500m multicolored	2.50	2.50
13	A1	1000m multicolored	4.00	4.00
		Nos. 1-13 (13)	12.90	12.90

Issued: 125m-500m, 8/15; others, 9/1.

Nos. 1-13 Surcharged "FILS" in English and Arabic in Black or Silver and with Black Bars Obliterating "Mils"

1995, Apr. 10   Litho.   Perf. 14

14	A1	5f multicolored	.25	.25
15	A1	10f multicolored	.25	.25
16	A1	20f multicolored	.25	.25
17	A1	30f multicolored (S)	.25	.25
18	A1	40f multicolored (S)	.25	.25
19	A1	50f multicolored (S)	.30	.30
20	A1	75f multicolored (S)	.35	.35
21	A1	125f multicolored	.50	.50
22	A1	150f multicolored	.65	.65
23	A1	250f multicolored	1.10	1.10
24	A1	300f multicolored	1.40	1.40

Size: 51x29mm

25	A1	500f multicolored	2.25	2.25
26	A1	1000f multicolored	4.00	4.00
		Nos. 14-26 (13)	11.80	11.80

Palestine No. 63 — A2

350f, Palestine #67. 500f, Palestine #72.

1995, May 17   Litho.   Perf. 14

27	A2	150f multicolored	1.00	1.00
28	A2	350f multicolored	1.60	1.60
29	A2	500f multicolored	2.00	2.00
		Nos. 27-29 (3)	4.60	4.60

Traditional Costumes — A3

Women wearing various costumes.

1995, May 31

30	A3	250f multicolored	.90	.90
31	A3	300f multicolored	1.00	1.00
32	A3	550f multicolored	2.00	2.00
33	A3	900f multicolored	3.00	3.00
		Nos. 30-33 (4)	6.90	6.90

Christmas — A4

Designs: 10f, Ancient view of Bethlehem. 20f, Modern view of Bethlehem. 50f, Entrance to grotto, Church of the Nativity. 100f, Yasser Arafat, Pope John Paul II. 1000f, Star of the Nativity, Church of the Nativity, Bethlehem. 10f, 20f, 100f, 1000f are horiz.

1995, Dec. 18

34	A4	10f multicolored	.25	.25
35	A4	20f multicolored	.25	.25
36	A4	50f multicolored	.25	.25
37	A4	100f multicolored	.60	.60
38	A4	1000f multicolored	5.00	5.00
		Nos. 34-38 (5)	6.35	6.35

Pres. Yasser Arafat — A5

1996, Mar. 20

39	A5	10f red vio & bluish blk	.25	.25
40	A5	20f yellow & bluish black	.25	.25
41	A5	50f blue & bluish black	.25	.25
42	A5	100f apple grn & bluish blk	.50	.50
43	A5	1000f org & bluish blk	4.25	4.25
		Nos. 39-43 (5)	5.50	5.50

1996 Intl. Philatelic Exhibitions
A6

Exhibition, site: 20f, CHINA '96, Summer Palace, Beijing. 50f, ISTANBUL '96, Hagia Sofia. 100f, ESSEN '96, Villa Hugel. 1000f, CAPEX '96, Toronto skyline.

1996, May 18

44	A6	20f multicolored	.25	.25
45	A6	50f multicolored	.30	.30
46	A6	100f multicolored	.45	.45
47	A6	1000f multicolored	4.50	4.50
a.		Sheet, 2 each #44-47 + 2 labels	13.00	
		Nos. 44-47 (4)	5.50	5.50

Souvenir Sheet

1st Palestinian Parliamentary & Presidential Elections — A7

1996, May 20

48	A7	1250f multicolored	5.50	5.50

1996 Summer
Olympic Games,
Atlanta — A8

Designs: 30f, Boxing. 40f, Medal, 1896. 50f,
Runners. 150f, Olympic flame. 1000f, Palestinian Olympic Committee emblem.

1996, July 19   **Perf. 13½**
49 A8   30f multicolored   .25 .25
50 A8   40f multicolored   .25 .25
51 A8   50f multicolored   .35 .35
52 A8   150f multicolored   .70 .70
  a.   Sheet of 3, #49, 51-52   5.50 5.50
53 A8   1000f multicolored   4.25 4.25
  Nos. 49-53 (5)   5.80 5.80

Flowers — A9

1996, Nov. 22
54 A9   10f Poppy   .25 .25
55 A9   25f Hibiscus   .25 .25
56 A9   100f Thyme   .50 .50
57 A9   150f Lemon   .70 .70
58 A9   750f Orange   3.00 3.00
  Nos. 54-58 (5)   4.70 4.70

Souvenir Sheet
59 A9   1000f Olive   4.50 4.50

Souvenir Sheet

Christmas — A10

a, 150f, Magi. b, 350f, View of Bethlehem. c,
500f, Shepherds, sheep. d, 750f, Nativity
scene.

1996, Dec. 14   **Perf. 14**
60 A10   Sheet of 4, #a.-d.   6.50 6.50

Birds — A11

1997, May 29
61 A11   25f Great tit   .30 .30
62 A11   75f Blue rock thrush   .40 .40
63 A11   150f Golden oriole   .85 .85
64 A11   350f Hoopoe   2.00 2.00
65 A11   600f Peregrine falcon   2.75 2.75
  Nos. 61-65 (5)   6.30 6.30

Historic
Views
A12

1997, June 19
66 A12   350f Gaza, 1839   1.50 1.50
67 A12   600f Hebron, 1839   2.50 2.50

Souvenir Sheet

Return of
Hong
Kong to
China
A13

1997, July 1
68 A13   225f multicolored   2.40 2.40

Friends of
Palestine
A14

#69, Portraits of Yasser Arafat, Hans-Jürgen
Wischnewski. #70, Wischnewski shaking
hands with Arafat. #71, Mother Teresa. #72,
Mother Teresa with Arafat.

1997   **Litho.**   **Perf. 14**
69 A14   600f multicolored   1.75 1.75
70 A14   600f multicolored   1.75 1.75
  a.   Pair, #69-70   4.50 4.50
71 A14   600f multicolored   2.00 2.00
72 A14   600f multicolored   2.00 2.00
  a.   Pair, #71-72   4.75 4.75
  Nos. 69-72 (4)   7.50 7.50

#70a, 72a were issued in sheets of 4
stamps.
Issued: #69-70, 7/24; #71-72, 12/17.

Christmas — A15

1997, Nov. 28
73 A15   350f multicolored   1.25 1.25
74 A15   700f multicolored   2.25 2.25
  a.   Pair, #73-74   3.75 3.75

Mosaics from Floor
of Byzantine
Church, Jabalia-
Gaza — A16

50f, Rabbit, palm tree. 125f, Goat, rabbit,
dog. 200f, Basket, fruit tree, jar. 400f, Lion.

1998, June 22   **Litho.**   **Perf. 13½**
75 A16   50f multicolored   .30 .30
76 A16   125f multicolored   .90 .60
77 A16   200f multicolored   1.25 1.00
78 A16   400f multicolored   2.75 1.75
  Nos. 75-78 (4)   5.20 3.65

Souvenir Sheet

Baal
A17

1998, June 15   **Perf. 14**
79 A17   600f multicolored   2.75 2.75

Medicinal Plants — A18

1998, Sept. 30   **Litho.**   **Perf. 14**
80 A18   40f Urginea maritima   .25 .25
81 A18   80f Silybum marianum   .30 .30
82 A18   500f Foeniculum vulgare   1.50 1.50
83 A18   800f Inula viscosa   3.00 3.00
  Nos. 80-83 (4)   5.05 5.05

Raptors — A19

1998, Nov. 12   **Litho.**   **Perf. 14**
84 A19   20f Bonelli's eagle   .25 .25
85 A19   60f Hobby   .30 .30
86 A19   340f Verreaux's eagle   1.75 1.75
87 A19   600f Bateleur   2.75 2.75
88 A19   900f Buzzard   3.75 3.75
  Nos. 84-88 (5)   8.80 8.80

Souvenir Sheet

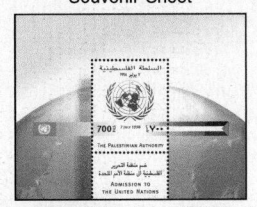

Granting of Additional Rights to
Palestinian Authority's Observer to
UN — A20

1998, Nov. 12
89 A20   700f multicolored   3.00 3.00

Butterflies — A21

Designs: a, 100f, Papilio alexanor. b, 200f,
Danaus chrysippus. c, 300f, Gonepteryx cle-
opatra. d, 400f, Melanargia titea.

1998, Dec. 3
90 A21   Sheet of 4, #a.-d.   4.50 4.50

Souvenir Sheet

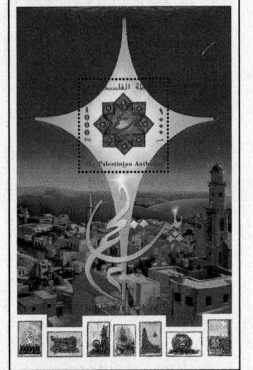

Christmas, Bethlehem 2000 — A22

1998, Dec. 3
91 A22   1000f multicolored   4.25 4.25

Souvenir Sheet

Signing of Middle East Peace
Agreement, Wye River Conference,
Oct. 23, 1998 — A23

Palestinian Pres. Yasser Arafat and US
Pres. Bill Clinton.

1999   **Litho.**   **Perf. 14**
92 A23   900f multicolored   3.75 3.75

New Airport,
Gaza — A24

Designs: 80f, Control tower, vert. 300f, Airplane. 700f, Terminal building.

1999
93 A24   80f multicolored   .25 .25
94 A24   300f multicolored   .90 .90
95 A24   700f multicolored   2.50 2.50
  Nos. 93-95 (3)   3.65 3.65

Intl. Philatelic Exhibitions & UPU,
125th Anniv. — A25

a, 20f, Buildings, China 1999. b, 260f, Buildings, Germany, IBRA '99. c, 80f, High-rise
buildings, Australia '99. d, 340f, Eiffel Tower,
Philex France '99. e, 400f, Aerial view of countryside, denomination LR, UPU, 125th anniv. f,
400f, like #96e, denomination LL.

1999
96   A25   Block of 6, #a.-f.   6.75 6.75

Hebron — A26

a, 400f, Lettering in gold. b, 500f, Lettering
in white.

1999, Aug. 20   **Litho.**   **Perf. 14**
97 A26   Pair, #a.-b.   4.00 4.00

Arabian Horses — A27

a, 25f. b, 75f. c, 150f. d, 350f. e, 800f.

1999, Apr. 27
98 A27   Strip of 5, #a.-e.   5.50 5.50

Souvenir Sheet

Palestinian Sunbird — A28

1999		Litho.	Perf. 13¾
99	A28	750f multi	3.50 3.50

A29

Christmas, Bethlehem 2000 — A30

Giotto Paintings (Type A30): 200f, 280f, 2000f, The Nativity. 380f, 460f, The Adoration of the Magi. 560f, The Flight into Egypt. Inscription colors: Nos. 108a, 110a, Black. Nos. 109a, 111a, White. No. 112a, Yellow. Nos. 108b-112b have silver inscriptions and frames. No. 113, country name at lower left. No. 113A, country name at upper right, denomination at lower left.

1999, Dec. 8   Litho.   Perf. 13¼x13
Background Color

100	A29	60f black	.35	.35
101	A29	80f light blue	.35	.35
102	A29	100f dark gray	.45	.45
103	A29	280f lilac rose	1.15	1.15
104	A29	300f green	1.20	1.20
105	A29	400f red violet	1.75	1.75
106	A29	500f dark red	2.00	2.00
107	A29	560f light gray	2.40	2.40
		Perf. 13¼		
108	A30	200f Pair, #a-b.	3.25	3.25
109	A30	280f Pair, #a-b.	3.50	3.50
110	A30	380f Pair, #a-b.	4.25	4.25
111	A30	460f Pair, #a-b.	5.50	5.50
112	A30	560f Pair, #a-b.	8.75	8.75

Litho. & Embossed Foil Application
113	A30	2000f multi	6.50	6.50
113A	A30	2000f multi, booklet pane of 1	9.00	9.00
		Nos. 100-113 (14)	41.40	41.40

Nos. 108-112 each printed in sheets of 10 containing 9 "a" +1 "b." No. 113 printed in sheets of 4. Nos. 108a-112a also exist in sheets of 10.
Issued: No. 113A, 2000.

Easter A31

Designs: 150f, Last Supper, by Giotto, white inscriptions. 200f, Last Supper, yellow inscriptions. 300f, Lamentation, by Giotto, white inscriptions. 350f, Lamentation, yellow inscriptions. 650f, Crucifix, by Giotto, orange frame.
No. 119, 2000f, Crucifix, gold frame, denomination and country name in orange. No. 119A, 2000f, denomination and country name in white.

2000		Litho.	Perf. 13¼
114-118	A31	Set of 5	5.50 5.50

Souvenir Sheet
Litho. & Embossed Foil Application
119	A31	2000f multi	7.00	7.00
119A	A31	2000f multi, booklet pane of 1	11.00	

See Nos. 140-144.

Christmas A32

Madonna of the Star by Fra Angelico.

Litho. & Embossed Foil Application
2000			Perf. 13¼
120	A32	2000f Miniature sheet of 1	8.50 8.50
a.		Booklet pane of 1	10.50 10.50
		Complete booklet, #113A, 119A, 120a	31.00

See Nos. 134-139.

Holy Land Visit of Pope John Paul II — A33

Designs: 500f, Pope, Yasser Arafat holding hands. 600f, Pope with miter. 750f, Pope touching Arafat's shoulder. 800f, Pope, creche. 1000f, Pope, back of Arafat's head.

2000		Litho.	Perf. 13¾
121-125	A33	Set of 5	12.00 12.00

Intl. Children's Year — A34

Designs: 50f, Landscape. 100f, Children. 350f, Domed buildings. 400f, Family.

2000			
126-129	A34	Set of 4	3.25 3.25

Pres. Arafat's Visit to Germany — A35

Arafat and: 200f, German Chancellor Gerhard Schröder. 300f, German President Johannes Rau.

2000			Perf. 14x14¼
130-131	A35	Set of 2	2.75 2.75

Marine Life A36

No. 132: a, Parrotfish. b, Mauve stinger. c, Ornate wrasse. d, Rainbow wrasse. e, Red starfish. f, Common octopus. g, Purple sea urchin. h, Striated hermit crab.

2000		Litho.	Perf. 13¾
132	A36	700f Sheet of 8, #a-h	16.50 16.50

Souvenir Sheet

Blue Madonna A37

2000			Perf. 14x13¾
133	A37	950f multi	3.25 3.25

Christmas Type of 2000

Designs: No. 134, 100f, No. 138, 500f, Nativity, by Gentile da Fabriano, horiz. No. 135, 150f, Adoration of the Magi, by Fabriano, horiz. No. 136, 250f, Immaculate Conception, by Fabriano, horiz. No. 137, 350f, No. 139, 1000f, Like #120.

2000		Litho.	Perf. 13¼
134-139	A32	Set of 6	7.75 7.75

Easter Type of 2000

Designs: 150f, Christ Carrying Cross, by Fra Angelico, blue inscriptions. 200f, Christ Carrying Cross, white inscriptions. 300f, Removal of Christ from Cross, by Fra Angelico, yellow inscriptions. 350f, Removal of Christ from the Cross, white inscriptions.
2000f, Crucifix, by Giotto, vert.

2001		Litho.	Perf. 13¼
140-143	A31	Set of 4	6.50 6.50

Souvenir Sheet
Litho. & Embossed
144	A31	2000f gold & multi	16.50 16.50

A38

Palestinian Authority flag and flag of various organizations: 50f, 100f, 200f, 500f.

2001		Litho.	Perf. 13¾
145-148	A38	Set of 4	3.25 3.25

Souvenir Sheet

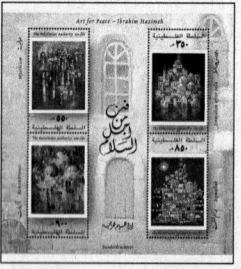

Art by Ibrahim Hazimeh A39

No. 149: a, 350f, Jerusalem After Rain. b, 550f, Mysticism. c, 850f, Ramallah. d, 900f, Remembrance.

2001			Perf. 14x13¾
149	A39	Sheet of 4, #a-d	12.00 12.00

Worldwide Fund for Nature (WWF) — A40

No. 150 — Houbara bustard, WWF emblem at: a, 350f, UR. b, 350f, LR. c, 750f, UL. d, 750f, LL.

2001		Litho.	Perf. 13¾x14
150	A40	Block of 4, #a-d	11.50 11.50

Graf Zeppelin Over Holy Land — A41

Zeppelin and: 200f, Map of voyage. 600f, Hills.

2001			Perf. 13¾
151-152	A41	Set of 2	3.25 3.25

Legends — A42

Designs: 300f, Man with magic lamp, buildings. 450f, Eagle, snake, gemstones, man. 650f, Man and woman on flying horse. 800f, Man hiding behind tree.

2001			Perf. 13¾x14
153-156	A42	Set of 4	9.00 9.00

Souvenir Sheet

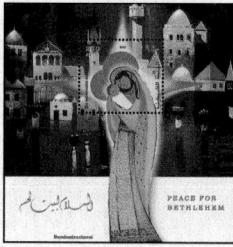

Peace for Bethlehem — A43

2001			Perf. 14x13¾
157	A43	950f multi	6.50 6.50

City Views — A44

Designs: 450f, Jerusalem. 650f, El-Eizariya. 850f, Nablus.

2002		Litho.	Perf. 13¾
158-160	A44	Set of 3	7.25 7.25

Women's Traditional Clothing — A44a

Various costumes: 50f, 100f, 500f.

2002, June		Litho.	Perf. 14
160A-160C	A44a	Set of 3	17.50 17.50

Souvenir Sheet

Christmas — A45

2002, Dec. 20			Perf. 14¼x14
161	A45	1000f multi	16.50 16.50

Succulent
Plants — A46

Designs: 550f, Prickly pear. 600f, Big-horned euphorbia. 750f, Century plant.

2003, May 10   Litho.   Perf. 13¾x14
162-164 A46   Set of 3   8.00 8.00
164a   Souvenir sheet, #162-164   8.00 8.00

Trees — A47

Designs: 300f, Olive tree. 700f, Blessing tree.

2003, July 12
165-166 A47   Set of 2   8.50 8.50

Universities
A48

Designs: 250f, Al-Azhar University, Gaza. 650f, Hebron University, Hebron. 800f, Arab American University, Jenin.

2003, July 19
167-169 A48   Set of 3   7.75 7.75

Handicrafts — A49

Designs: 150f, Glass necklaces. 200f, Headdress. 450f, Embroidery. 500f, Costume embroidery. 950f, Head veil.

2003, Oct. 11   Litho.   Perf. 13¾
170-174 A49   Set of 5   11.00 11.00

French President
Jacques
Chirac — A50

No. 175 — Chirac and: a, 200f, Yasser Arafat, French flag. b, 450f, Palestinian flag.

2004   Litho.   Perf. 14
175 A50   Pair, #a-b   5.25 5.25
Printed in sheets containing two each of Nos. 175a-175b.

Souvenir Sheet

Worship
of the
Virgin
Mary
A51

2004
176 A51   1000f multi   5.25 5.25

Souvenir Sheet

Arab
League,
60th
Anniv.
A52

2005   Litho.   Perf. 13¾
177 A52   750f multi   30.00 30.00

Mahmoud Darwish
(1941-2008),
Poet — A53

Denominations: 150f, 250f, 350f, 400f.

2008, July 29   Litho.   Perf. 13
178-181 A53   Set of 4   9.00 9.00

A54

Jericho,
10,000th
Anniv. — A55

2010, Dec. 26   Perf. 13¼x13
Background Color
182 A54   50f white   .40 .40
183 A55   150f pink   1.25 1.25
184 A54   350f gray   2.75 2.75
185 A55   1000f light green   7.75 7.75
    Nos. 182-185 (4)   12.15 12.15

Christmas — A56

Color of panel above denomination: 100f, Red. 150f, Purple. 250f, Green. 500f, Blue.

2010, Dec. 26
186-189 A56   Set of 4   7.50 7.50

Souvenir Sheet

Arab
Postal
Day
A57

No. 190 — Emblem and: a, 350f, Camel caravan. b, 500f, Pigeon and map.

Litho. With Foil Application
2011, Mar. 17   Perf. 13¾x13¼
190 A57   Sheet of 2, #a-b   9.50 9.50

Ramadan — A58

Designs: 50f, Dome of the Rock, crescent, arches, flag. 100f, Lantern, arabesque, flag. 250f, Lantern, crescent, arabesque, arch, flag. 500f, Dome of the Rock, crescent, flag.
No. 195, 1000f, Dome of the Rock, lantern, crescent. No. 196, 1000f, Flag, crescent, Arabic text.

2011, Aug. 1   Litho.   Perf. 13x13¼
191-194 A58   Set of 4   8.25 8.25

Souvenir Sheets
Perf. 13¼x14¼
195-196 A58   Set of 2   16.00 16.00
Nos. 195 and 196 each contain one 45x35mm stamp.

Yasser Arafat (1929-2004), President of the Palestinian Authority — A59

Various photographs of Arafat: 50f, 100f, 150f, 5000f.

2012, June 6   Litho.   Perf. 14¼
197-200 A59   Set of 4   21.00 21.00
A booklet containing five 250f, three 500f, three 750f, and four 1000f stamps, each depicting Arafat, sold for 20,000f.

Souvenir Sheet

Soccer Ball and Flag of Palestinian Authority — A60

2012, June 6   Litho.   Perf. 13
201 A60   1000f multi   4.25 4.25
Recognition by FIFA of first home soccer match of Palestinian Authority team, 4th anniv. Compare with type A68.

Miniature Sheet

Governmental Ministries — A61

No. 202 — Ministry of: a, Transport. b, Public Works and Housing. c, Telecommunication and Information Technology. d, Finance. e, Interior.

2012, June 6   Litho.   Perf. 13¼
202 A61   300f Sheet of 5, #a-e   7.25 7.25

Miniature Sheet

Fruit
A62

No. 203: a, 150f, Grapes. b, 300f, Oranges. c, 350f, Bananas. d, 450f, Dates.

2012, June 6   Litho.   Perf. 14
203 A62   Sheet of 8, 2 each
    #a-d   12.00 12.00
The two examples of Nos. 203a-203d on the sheet have different frames, being placed in different areas on the marginal illustration depicting trees.

Arab Postal
Day — A63

Denominations: 150f, 250f, 350f, 1000f, 5000f.

2012, Aug. 3   Litho.   Perf. 13¼
204-208 A63   Set of 5   25.00 25.00

Christmas — A64

Various depictions of Christmas trees: 20f, 250f, 600f.
1000f, Man praying.

2012, Dec. 24   Litho.   Perf. 14
209-211 A64   Set of 3   7.25 7.25
Souvenir Sheet
212 A64   1000f multi   9.00 9.00

Intl. Day of Civil
Defense — A65

Designs: 200f, Firemen in smoke. 250f, Firemen and fire truck. 500f, Firemen spraying water on building, ladder truck.
1000f, Firemen and fire truck, diff.

2013   Litho.   Perf. 14
213-215 A65   Set of 3   4.50 4.50
Souvenir Sheet
216 A65   1000f multi   5.00 5.00

Flora and
Fauna — A66

Designs: 20f, White flower. 100f, Caracal. 200f, Bird. 480f, Poppies. 720f, Turtle. 1080f, Nubian ibex.
No. 223, 1000f, Daisies, horiz. No. 224, 1000f, Eagle, horiz.

2013, June 3   Litho.   Perf. 14
217-222 A66   Set of 6   13.50 13.50
Souvenir Sheets
223-224 A66   Set of 2   13.50 13.50

Police — A67

Designs: 100f, Policeman directing traffic. 200f, Policemen inspecting plants. 250f, Policemen with pick and hoe.
500f, Policeman assisting elderly woman, vert.

2013   Litho.   Perf. 14
225-227 A67   Set of 3   3.25 3.25
Souvenir Sheet
228 A67   500f multi   3.00 3.00

Souvenir Sheet

Soccer Ball and Flag of Palestinian Authority — A68

2013   Litho.   Perf. 13
229 A68 1000f multi   9.00 9.00

Recognition by FIFA of first home soccer match of Palestinian Authority team, 5th anniv. Compare with type A60.

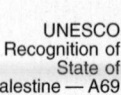

UNESCO Recognition of State of Palestine — A69

Dove, text, UNESCO emblem and panel color of: 100f, Green. 200f, Red brown. 420f, Black.
1000f, Dove, text and UNESCO emblem on Palestinian Authority flag, vert.

2013, Oct. 31   Litho.   Perf. 14
230-232 A69   Set of 3   4.25 4.25
Souvenir Sheet
233 A69 1000f multi   5.75 5.75

Abdel Rahim Mahmoud (1913-48), Poet — A70

Background color: 80f, Apple green. 200f, Yellow orange. 500f, Gray.
1800f, Turquoise green background.

2013, July 13   Litho.   Perf. 14
234-236 A70   Set of 3   4.50 4.50
Souvenir Sheet
237 A70 1800f multi   10.00 10.00

Declaration of State of Palestine, 1st Anniv. — A71

No. 238: a, Folk dancers. b, Musical score. c, Woman and olive tree. d, Dove, Al-Aqsa Mosqu, Church of the Holy Sepulchre. e, Sunbird and anemone flowers.
1000f, Dove, Pres. Mahmoud Abbas speaking at United Nations.

2013, Nov. 29   Litho.   Perf. 13¼
238 A71 200f Sheet of 5, #a-e   5.75 5.75
Souvenir Sheet
239 A71 1000f multi   5.75 5.75

International Anti-Corruption Day — A72

Designs: 200f, Stop sign. 360f, Man refusing bribe. 420f, Money and gavel on balance. 720f, Hand.
1000f, "No" symbol over hand accepting bribe, horiz.

2013, Dec. 9   Litho.   Perf. 14
240-243 A72   Set of 4   7.75 7.75
Souvenir Sheet
244 A72 1000f multi   5.75 5.75

Souvenir Sheet

Mosques A73

No. 245: a, Al-Aqsa Mosque, Jerusalem (one minaret). b, Sultan Ahmed Mosque, Istanbul (six minarets).

2014, Apr.   Litho.   Perf. 13½x13¾
245 A73 1000f Sheet of 2, #a-   b   11.00 11.00

Joint issue between Palestine Authority and Turkey.
See Turkey No. 3371.

Palestinian Prisoners' Day — A74

Designs: 200f, Dove, chained hands, barbed wire. 360f, Prisoner holding prison bars. 600f, Blindfolded prisoner, barbed wire. 1200f, Maysara Abu Hamdiya (1948-2013), jailed Palestinian Liberation Organization fighter.

2014, Apr. 17   Litho.   Perf. 14
246-248 A74   Set of 3   6.50 6.50
Souvenir Sheet
249 A74 1200f multi   6.75 6.75

Palestinian Scouts, Cent. (in 2012) — A75

Emblem with panel color of: 120f, Red. 480f, Yellow. 720f, Green.
1500f, Scouting trefoil.

2014, May 7   Litho.   Perf. 14
250-252 A75   Set of 3   7.00 7.00
Souvenir Sheet
253 A75 1500f multi   8.00 8.00

Popular Resistence — A76

Designs: 60f, Bab Al-Shams. 920f, Tents, flag of Palestinian Authority.
1500f, Tent, flag of Palestinian Authority, horiz.

2014, May 15   Litho.   Perf. 14
254-255 A76   Set of 2   5.25 5.25
Souvenir Sheet
256 A76 1500f multi   8.00 8.00

Visit of Pope Francis — A77

Pope Francis, Pres. Mahmoud Abbas, and Ecumenical Patriarch of Constantinople Bartholomew I and: 250f, People near doorway of Church of the Nativity, Jerusalem. 480f, Stylized key.
1500f, Pope Francis, Abbas, Patriarch Bartholomew I and Church of the Nativity, Jerusalem.

2014, May 25   Litho.   Perf. 14
257-258 A77   Set of 2   4.00 4.00
Souvenir Sheet
259 A77 1500f multi   8.00 8.00

Euromed Postal Emblem and Mediterranean Sea — A78

2014, July 9   Litho.   Perf. 12¾x13¼
260 A78 500f multi   3.00 3.00

Souvenir Sheet

Arab Lawyers Union, 70th Anniv. A79

2014, Aug. 12   Litho.   Perf. 14
261 A79 1200f multi   6.25 6.25

A80   A81

National Reading Campaign — A82

2014, Oct. 22   Litho.   Perf. 14
262 A80 200f multi   1.00 1.00
263 A81 250f multi   1.25 1.25
Souvenir Sheet
264 A82 1000f multi   5.00 5.00

International Year of Solidarity With the Palestinian People — A83

Palestinians and flag with background color of: 200f, Buff. 420f, Rose lilac.
1800f, Palestinians, flag and houses of worship.

2014, Nov. 29   Litho.   Perf. 14
265-266 A83   Set of 2   3.00 3.00
Souvenir Sheet
267 A83 1800f multi   8.75 8.75

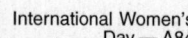

International Women's Day — A84

Images of various women: 250f, 600f. 1500f, Woman holding tree.

2015, Mar. 8   Litho.   Perf. 14
268-269 A84   Set of 2   4.50 4.50
Souvenir Sheet
270 A84 1500f multi   7.75 7.75

Miniature Sheet

Canonization of Saints — A85

No. 271: a, 500f, St. Marie Alphonsine Gattas (1843-1927). b, 500f, St. Mariam Baouardy (1846-78). c, 750f, Both saints. d, 750f, Pope Francis and Pres. Mahmoud Abbas.

2015, May 17   Litho.   Perf. 14
271 A85   Sheet of 4, #a-d   33.00 33.00

Euromed Postal Emblem and Fishing Boat — A86

2015, July 9   Litho.   Perf. 14
272 A86 500f multi   2.60 2.60

Jerusalem, Permanent Capital of Arab Culture — A87

Emblem and panel color of: 100f, Olive green. 200f, Red orange. 500f, Lilac.
1000f, Emblem and Jerusalem buildings.

2015, Oct. 2   Litho.   Perf. 14
273-275 A87   Set of 3   4.25 4.25
Souvenir Sheet
276 A87 1000f multi   5.25 5.25

Figs and Olives — A88

Designs: 480f, Figs, green and black olives. 920f, Fig leaf and olive branch. 1200f, Olives on tree and figs.

2015, Oct. 10   Litho.   Perf. 14
277-278 A88   Set of 2   7.25 7.25
Souvenir Sheet
279 A88 1200f multi   6.25 6.25

Islamic New Year — A89

Designs: 200f, Camel caravan in desert. 420f, Camels, mosque, Holy Ka'aba. 1500f, Camel, spider web, bird, palm tree.

2015, Nov. 15   Litho.   Perf. 14
280-281 A89   Set of 2   3.25 3.25
Souvenir Sheet
282 A89 1500f multi   7.75 7.75

Speeches by Palestinian Leaders at United Nations — A90

No. 283: a, 2012 speech by Pres. Mahmoud Abbas. b, 1974 speech by Yasser Arafat. 1500f, Like No. 283b.

2015, Nov. 29   Litho.   Perf. 14
283 A90   750f Sheet of 2, #a-b   7.75 7.75
Souvenir Sheet
284 A90   1500f multi   7.75 7.75

Grotto of the Nativity — A91

Serpentine Die Cut 14x15
2016, Mar. 27   Litho.
Self-Adhesive
285 A91   250f multi   1.40 1.40

International Workers' Day — A92

Designs: 250f, Man holding large claw hammer. 920f, Man, pliers, mallet, wrench. 1500f, Man, crane, mortared bricks.

2016, May 1   Litho.   Perf. 14
286-287 A92   Set of 2   6.00 6.00
Souvenir Sheet
288 A92   1500f multi   7.75 7.75

Fish — A93

No. 289: a, Gray mullet. b, Red mullet. c, Grouper. d, Malabar grouper. e, Sea bass. f, Meagre. g, Sardine. h, Mackerel. i, Blue runner. j, Albacore tuna.

2016, July 3   Litho.   Perf. 12¾x13¼
289   Sheet of 10   26.00 26.00
a.-j.   A93 500f Any single   2.60   2.60

Solomon's Pools — A94

Various photographs of pools: 250f, 420f. 1500f, Pool at night, vert.

2016, Aug. 8   Litho.   Perf. 14
290-291 A94   Set of 2   3.50 3.50
Souvenir Sheet
292 A94   1500f multi   7.75 7.75

Water Rights A95

No. 293: a, "No water no life." b, "Water is a human right."
No. 294, vert.: a, "Our water is our right." b, "Water for development."
1200f, "Water is life," vert.

2016, Aug. 8   Litho.   Perf. 14
293 A95   420f Horiz. pair, #a-b   4.50 4.50

---

294 A95   800f Vert. pair, #a-b   8.25 8.25
Souvenir Sheet
295 A95   1200f multi   6.25 6.25

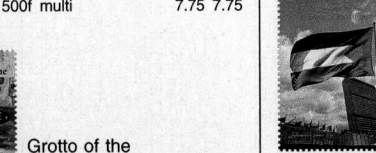

Arab Postal Day A96

No. 296: a, 10f, Green background, denomination at LL. b, 480f, Blue background, denomination at LR.

2016, Oct. 17   Litho.   Perf. 14
296 A96   Horiz. pair, #a-b   2.60 2.60

Flag Day — A97

Designs: 250f, Palestinian Authority flag at United Nations Headquarters. 420f, Woman, flag and tree.
1800f, Dove carrying flag over Jerusalem.

Litho. With Foil Application
2016, Sept. 30   Perf. 14
297-298 A97   Set of 2   3.50 3.50
Souvenir Sheet
299 A97   1800f multi   9.25 9.25

Olive Tree — A98

2016, Nov. 15   Litho.   Perf. 14
Background Color
300 A98   200f pale orange   1.00 1.00
301 A98   1400f pale green   7.00 7.00
302 A98   4500f white   22.00 22.00
Nos. 300-302 (3)   30.00 30.00

A99

Arabic Calligraphy Day — A100

Calligraphic designs with background color of: 250f, Dark brown. 420f, Grayish green.
No. 305: a, Calligraphic design with four dots at bottom, floral embellishment at UL and LL. b, Calligraphic design, diff. c, As "a," floral embellishment at UR and LR.

2016, Dec. 18   Litho.   Perf. 13x13¼
303-304 A99   Set of 2   3.25 3.25
Souvenir Sheet
Perf. 14
305 A100 600f Sheet of 3, #a-c   9.00 9.00

Fadwa Touqan (1917-2003), Poet — A101

Denominations: 150f, 500f.
1800f, Touqan, diff.

2017, Mar. 1   Litho.   Perf. 14
306-307 A101 Set of 2   3.50 3.50
Souvenir Sheet
308 A101 1800f multi   9.75 9.75

Faqqu'a Iris — A102

2017, Apr. 5   Litho.   Perf. 14
309 A102 500f shown   2.75 2.75
Souvenir Sheet
310 A102 1500f Irises   8.50 8.50

Miniature Sheet

Stones A103

No. 311: a, 100f, Jerusalem stone. b, 200f, Nablus stone. c, 300f, Jenin stone. d, 400f, Ramallah stone. e, 500f, Hebron stone. f, 600f, Tulkarm stone. g, 700f, Bethlehem stone. h, 800f, Qalqilya stone.

2017, June 1   Litho.   Perf. 14
311 A103 Sheet of 8, #a-h   20.00 20.00

Miniature Sheet

Dead Sea A104

No. 312: a, 150f, No shoreline. b, 280f, Shoreline at UL and LL. c, 420f, Shoreline at top. d, 950f, Shoreline at top and left.

2017, July 17   Litho.   Perf. 14
312 A104 Sheet of 4, #a-d   10.00 10.00

Dates — A105

Designs: 150f, Medjool dates. 200f, Berhi dates. 500f, Hayani dates.
1500f, Date palms.

2017, Aug. 25   Litho.   Perf. 14
313-315 A105 Set of 3   4.75 4.75
Souvenir Sheet
316 A105 1500f multi   8.50 8.50

World Post Day — A106

2017, Oct. 9   Litho.   Perf. 14
317 A106 500f multi   2.75 2.75

Teachers' Day — A107

Teacher pointing to map, with background color of: 200f, Light blue. 400f, Red brown. 1500f, Buff.

2017, Dec. 14   Litho.   Perf. 14
318-319 A107 Set of 2   3.50 3.50
Souvenir Sheet
320 A107 1500f multi   8.50 8.50

Silver Star of Grotto of the Nativity — A108

Serpentine Die Cut 14x14¾
2019, Jan. 15   Litho.
Self-Adhesive
321 A108 250f multi   1.40 1.40

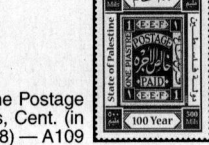

Palestine Postage Stamps, Cent. (in 2018) — A109

Designs: 500f, Palestine #1. 1000f, Part of sheet of Palestine #1.

2019, Jan. 15   Litho.   Perf. 14
322 A109 500f dark blue   2.75 2.75
Souvenir Sheet
323 A109 1000f dark blue   10.00 10.00

Archbishop Hilarion Capucci (1922-2017) — A110

Background color: 400f, Blue. 480f, Brown. 1500f, Capucci, diff.

2019, Jan. 15   Litho.   Perf. 14
324-325 A110 Set of 2   5.00 5.00
Souvenir Sheet
326 A110 1500f multi   8.50 8.50

Miniature Sheet

1937 Palestine Banknotes — A111

No. 327: a, 150f, 500-mils note. b, 250f, 1-pound note. c, 350f, 5-pound note. d, 450f, 10-pound note. e, 550f, 50-pound note. f, 650f, 100-pound note.

2019, Jan. 15   Litho.   Perf. 14
327 A111 Sheet of 6, #a-f   13.50 13.50

Miniature Sheet

1927 Coins of Palestine A112

No. 328: a, 100f, 1-mil coin. b, 200f, 2-mil coin. c, 300f, 5-mil coin. d, 400f, 10-mil coin. e, 500f, 20-mil coin. f, 600f, 50-mil coin. g, 700f, 100-mil coin.

2019, Jan. 15   Litho.   Perf. 14
328 A112 Sheet of 7, #a-g, +
           label   15.50 15.50

A113

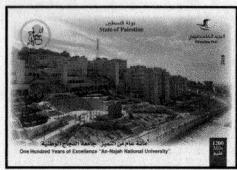

An-Najah National University, Nablus,
Cent. — A114

Emblem with: 200f, One circle. 420f, Two
circles.

2019, Jan. 15   Litho.   Perf. 14
329-330 A113 Set of 2   3.50 3.50
                Imperf
331 A114 1200f multi   6.75 6.75

Shqaif (Beaufort)
Castle.
Lebanon — A115

Yassir Arafat and
Others at Shqaif
(Beaufort) Castle.
Lebanon — A116

Design: 2000f, Shqaif (Beaufort) Castle, diff.

2019, Jan. 15   Litho.   Perf. 14
332 A115 200f multi   1.10 1.10
333 A116 400f multi   2.25 2.25
                Size: 106x71mm
                Imperf
334 A115 2000f multi   11.00 11.00

Souvenir Sheet

Al Khan
Al Ahmar
A117

No. 335: a, Palestinian Authority flag on
rock. b, Backhoe destroying house.

2019, Jan. 15   Litho.   Perf. 14
335 A117 1000f Sheet of 2,
                #a-b   11.00 11.00

Souvenir Sheet

Pres. Mahmoud Abbas at Opening
Ceremony for Palestinian Authority
Embassy in Vatican City — A118

2019, Jan. 15   Litho.   Perf. 14
336 A118 2000f Sheet of 2,
                #a-b   11.00 11.00

World Telecommunications
Day — A119

Designs: 250f, Globe, musical notes, telephone handset, cameras, envelope, information and wi-fi symbols. 350f, Globe in envelope, world map.
1500f, Various symbols.

2019, Jan. 15   Litho.   Perf. 14
337-338 A119 Set of 2   3.25 3.25
                Souvenir Sheet
339 A119 1500f multi   8.25 8.25
                Dated 2018.

Diplomatic Relations Between the
Palestinian Authority and People's
Republic of China, 20th Anniv. (in
2018) — A120

No. 340: a, Palestinian Authority President
Mahmoud Abbas and People's Republic of
China President Xi Jinping, flags of Palestinian
Authority and People's Republic of China. b,
Flags of Palestinian Authority and People's
Republic of China.
2000f, Abbas, Xi and flags, vert.

2019, Aug. 8   Litho.   Perf. 12
340 A120 1000f Horiz. pair,
                #a-b   11.50 11.50
  c.   Souvenir sheet of 2, #340a-
                340b   11.50 11.50
                **Souvenir Sheet
                On Plastic
                Without Gum**
341 A120 2000f gold & multi   13.50 13.50
No. 341 contains one 50x76mm stamp.

A121

A122

Palestinian Authority's 2019
Chairmanship of Group of 77 — A123

No. 342 — Group of 77 emblem, Palestinian
Authority flag and: a, Anemone flower. b,
Dove. c, Palestinian sunbird. d, Olive tree. e,
Palestinian gazelle.

Litho. With Foil Application
2019, Aug. 8   Perf. 14¼
342 A121 300f Sheet of 5, #a-e   8.50 8.50
                **Souvenir Sheets
                Perf. 14x13**
343 A122 1500f gold & multi   8.50 8.50
344 A123 1500f gold & multi   8.50 8.50

SEMI-POSTAL STAMPS

Souvenir Sheet

Gaza-Jericho Peace
Agreement — SP1

1994, Oct. 7   Litho.   Perf. 14
B1 SP1 750m +250m multi   6.50 6.50
        For surcharge see No. B3.

Souvenir Sheet

Arab
League,
50th
Anniv.
SP2

Painting: View of Palestine, by Ibrahim
Hazimeh.

1995, Mar. 22   Perf. 13½
B2 SP2 750f +250f multi   3.50 3.50

**No. B1 Surcharged "FILS" in
English & Arabic and with Added
Text at Left and Right**
1995, Apr. 10   Litho.   Perf. 14
B3 SP1 750f +250f multi   6.50 6.50
        Honoring 1994 Nobel Peace Prize winners
Arafat, Rabin and Peres.

International Day of
Persons With
Disabilities — SP3

2015, Dec. 3   Litho.   Perf. 14
B4 SP3 100f +100f multi   1.10 1.10

OFFICIAL STAMPS

Natl. Arms — O1

1994, Aug. 15   Litho.   Perf. 14
O1 O1   50m yellow   .25 .25
O2 O1 100m green blue   .45 .45
O3 O1 125m blue   .65 .65
O4 O1 200m orange   .90 .90
O5 O1 250m olive   1.25 1.25
O6 O1 400m maroon   1.75 1.75
        Nos. O1-O6 (6)   5.25 5.25
        Nos. O1-O6 could also be used by the gen-
eral public, and non-official-use covers are
known.

PANAMA

ˈpa-nə-ˌmä

LOCATION — Central America between Costa Rica and Colombia
GOVT. — Republic
AREA — 30,134 sq. mi.
POP. — 2,778,526 (1999 est.)
CAPITAL — Panama

Formerly a department of the Republic of Colombia, Panama gained its independence in 1903. Dividing the country at its center is the Panama Canal.

100 Centavos = 1 Peso
100 Centesimos = 1 Balboa (1904)

Catalogue values for unused stamps in this country are for Never Hinged items, beginning with Scott 350 in the regular postage section, Scott C82 in the airpost section, Scott CB1 in the airpost semi-postal section, and Scott RA21 in the postal tax section.

Watermarks

Wmk. 229 — Wavy Lines

Wmk. 233 — "Harrison & Sons, London." in Script

Wmk. 311 — Star and RP Multiple

Wmk. 334 — Rectangles

Wmk. 365 — Argentine Arms, Casa de Moneda de la Nacion & RA Multiple

Wmk. 377 — Interlocking Circles

Wmk. 382 — Stars

Wmk. 382 may be a sheet watermark. It includes stars, wings with sun in middle and "Panama R de P."

Issues of the Sovereign State of Panama Under Colombian Dominion
Valid only for domestic mail.

Coat of Arms
A1   A2

1878   Unwmk.   Litho.   Imperf.
Thin Wove Paper
1	A1	5c gray green	25.00	30.00
a.		5c yellow green	25.00	30.00
2	A1	10c blue	60.00	60.00
3	A1	20c rose red	40.00	32.50
		Nos. 1-3 (3)	125.00	122.50

Very Thin Wove Paper
4	A2	50c buff	1,500.	

All values of this issue are known rouletted unofficially.

Medium Thick Paper
5	A1	5c blue green	25.00	30.00
6	A1	10c blue	65.00	70.00
7	A2	50c orange	13.00	
		Nos. 5-7 (3)	103.00	100.00

Nos. 5-7 were printed before Nos. 1-4, according to Panamanian archives.
Values for used Nos. 1-5 are for hand-stamped postal cancellations.
These stamps have been reprinted in a number of shades, on thin to moderately thick, white or yellowish paper. They are without gum or with white, crackly gum. All values have been reprinted from new stones made from retouched dies. The marks of retouching are plainly to be seen in the sea and clouds. On the original 10c the shield in the upper left corner has two blank sections; on the reprints the design of this shield is completed. The impression of these reprints is frequently blurred.
Reprints of the 50c are rare. Beware of remainders of the 50c offered as reprints.

Issues of Colombia for use in the Department of Panama
Issued because of the use of different currency.

Map of Panama — A3

1887-88   Perf. 13½
8	A3	1c black, *green*	.90	.80
9	A3	2c black, *pink* ('88)	1.60	1.25
a.		2c black, *salmon*	1.60	
10	A3	5c black, *blue*	.90	.35
11	A3	10c black, *yellow*	.90	.40
a.		Imperf., pair		
12	A3	20c black, *lilac*	1.00	.50
13	A3	50c brown ('88)	2.00	1.00
a.		Imperf.		
		Nos. 8-13 (6)	7.30	4.30

See No. 14. For surcharges and overprints see Nos. 24-30, 107-108, 115-116, 137-138.

1892   Pelure Paper
14	A3	50c brown	2.50	1.10

The stamps of this issue have been reprinted on papers of slightly different colors from those of the originals.
These are: 1c yellow green, 2c deep rose, 5c bright blue, 10c straw, 20c violet.
The 50c is printed from a very worn stone, in a lighter brown than the originals. The series includes a 10c on lilac paper.
All these stamps are to be found perforated, imperforate, imperforate horizontally or imperforate vertically. At the same time that they were made, impressions were struck upon a variety of glazed and surface-colored papers.

Map of Panama — A4

Wove Paper
1892-96   Engr.   Perf. 12
15	A4	1c green	.25	.25
16	A4	2c rose	.40	.25
17	A4	5c blue	1.50	.50
18	A4	10c orange	.35	.25
19	A4	20c violet ('95)	.50	.35
20	A4	50c bister brn ('96)	.50	.40
21	A4	1p lake ('96)	6.50	4.00
		Nos. 15-21 (7)	10.00	6.00

In 1903 Nos. 15-21 were used in Cauca and three other southern Colombia towns. Stamps canceled in these towns are worth much more.
For surcharges and overprints see Nos. 22-23, 51-106, 109-114, 129-136, 139, 151-161, 181-184, F12-F15, H4-H5.

Nos. 16, 12-14 Surcharged

a   b

c   d

e   f

g

1894   Black Surcharge
22	(a)	1c on 2c rose	.50	.40
a.		Inverted surcharge	2.50	2.50
b.		Double surcharge		
23	(b)	1c on 2c rose	.40	.50
a.		"CCNTAVO"	2.50	2.50
b.		Inverted surcharge	2.50	2.50
c.		Double surcharge		

Red Surcharge
24	(c)	5c on 20c black, *lil*	2.50	1.50
a.		Inverted surcharge	12.50	12.50
b.		Double surcharge		
c.		Without "HABILITADO"		
25	(d)	5c on 20c black, *lil*	3.50	3.00
a.		"CCNTAVOS"	7.50	7.50
b.		Inverted surcharge	12.50	12.50
c.		Double surcharge		
d.		Without "HABILITADO"		
26	(e)	5c on 20c black, *lil*	6.00	5.00
a.		Inverted surcharge	12.50	12.50
b.		Double surcharge		
27	(f)	10c on 50c brown	3.00	3.00
a.		"1894" omitted		
b.		Inverted surcharge		
c.		"CCNTAVOS"	15.00	
28	(g)	10c on 50c brown	12.50	12.50
a.		"CCNTAVOS"	32.50	

Pelure Paper
29	(f)	10c on 50c brown	4.00	3.00
a.		"1894" omitted	7.50	
b.		Inverted surcharge	12.50	12.50
c.		Double surcharge		

30	(g)	10c on 50c brown	10.00	10.00
a.		"CCNTAVOS"		
b.		Without "HABILITADO"		
c.		Inverted surcharge	25.00	25.00
d.		Double surcharge		
		Nos. 22-30 (9)	42.40	38.90

There are several settings of these surcharges. Usually the surcharge is about 15½mm high, but in one setting, it is only 13mm. All the types are to be found with a comma after "CENTAVOS." Nos. 24, 25, 26, 29 and 30 exist with the surcharge printed sideways. Nos. 23, 24 and 29 may be found with an inverted "A" instead of "V" in "CENTAVOS." There are also varieties caused by dropped or broken letters.

Issues of the Republic
Issued in the City of Panama

Stamps of 1892-96 Overprinted

1903, Nov. 16   Rose Handstamp
51	A4	1c green	2.00	1.50
52	A4	2c rose	5.00	3.00
53	A4	5c blue	2.00	1.25
54	A4	10c yellow	2.00	2.00
55	A4	20c violet	4.00	3.50
56	A4	50c bister brn	10.00	7.00
57	A4	1p lake	50.00	40.00
		Nos. 51-57 (7)	75.00	58.25

Blue Black Handstamp
58	A4	1c green	2.00	1.25
59	A4	2c rose	1.00	1.00
60	A4	5c blue	7.00	6.00
61	A4	10c yellow	5.00	3.50
62	A4	20c violet	10.00	7.50
63	A4	50c bister brn	10.00	7.50
64	A4	1p lake	50.00	42.50
		Nos. 58-64 (7)	85.00	69.25

The stamps of this issue are to be found with the handstamp placed horizontally, vertically or diagonally; inverted; double; double, one inverted; double, both inverted; in pairs, one without handstamp; etc.
This handstamp is known in brown rose on the 1, 5, 20 and 50c, in purple on the 1, 2, 50c and 1p, and in magenta on the 5, 10, 20 and 50c.
Reprints were made in rose, black and other colors when the handstamp was nearly worn out, so that the "R" of "REPUBLICA" appears to be shorter than usual, and the bottom part of "LI" has been broken off. The "P" of "PANAMA" leans to the left and the tops of "NA" are broken. Many of these varieties are found inverted, double, etc.

Overprinted

Bar in Similar Color to Stamp
1903, Dec. 3   Black Overprint
65	A4	2c rose	2.50	2.50
a.		"PANAMA" 15mm long	3.50	
b.		Violet bar	5.00	
66	A4	5c blue	100.00	
a.		"PANAMA" 15mm long	100.00	
67	A4	10c orange	2.50	2.50
a.		"PANAMA" 15mm long	6.00	
b.		Horizontal overprint	17.50	

Gray Black Overprint
68	A4	2c rose	2.00	2.00
a.		"PANAMA" 15mm long	2.50	

Carmine Overprint
69	A4	5c blue	2.50	2.50
a.		"PANAMA" 15mm long	3.50	
b.		Bar only	75.00	75.00
c.		Double overprint		
70	A4	20c violet	7.50	6.50
a.		"PANAMA" 15mm long	10.00	
b.		Double overprint, one in black	150.00	
		Nos. 65,67-70 (5)	17.00	16.00

This overprint was set up to cover fifty stamps. "PANAMA" is normally 13mm long and 1¾mm high but, in two rows in each sheet, it measures 15 to 16mm.
This word may be found with one or more of the letters taller than usual; with one, two or three inverted "V's" instead of "A's"; with an inverted "Y" instead of "A"; an inverted "N"; an "A" with accent; and a fancy "P."
Owing to misplaced impressions, stamps exist with "PANAMA" once only, twice on one side, or three times.

Overprinted in Red

1903, Dec.

71 A4 1c green .75 .60
- a. "PANAMA" 15mm long 1.25
- b. "PANAMA" reading down 3.00 .75
- c. "PANAMA" reading up and down 3.00
- d. Double overprint 8.00

72 A4 2c rose .50 .40
- a. "PANAMA" 15mm long 1.00
- b. "PANAMA" reading down .75 .50
- c. "PANAMA" reading up and down 4.00
- d. Double overprint 8.00

73 A4 20c violet 1.50 1.00
- a. "PANAMA" 15mm long 2.25
- b. "PANAMA" reading down
- c. "PANAMA" reading up and down 8.00 8.00
- d. Double overprint 18.00 18.00

74 A4 50c bister brn 3.00 2.50
- a. "PANAMA" 15mm long 5.00
- b. "PANAMA" reading up and down 12.00 12.00
- c. Double overprint 6.00 6.00

75 A4 1p lake 6.00 4.50
- a. "PANAMA" 15mm long 6.25
- b. "PANAMA" reading up and down 15.00 15.00
- c. Double overprint 15.00
- d. Inverted overprint 25.00

Nos. 71-75 (5) 11.75 9.00

This setting appears to be a re-arrangement (or two very similar re-arrangements) of the previous overprint. The overprint covers fifty stamps. "PANAMA" usually reads upward but sheets of the 1, 2 and 20c exist with the word reading upward on one half the sheet and downward on the other half.

In one re-arrangement one stamp in fifty has the word reading in both directions. Nearly all the varieties of the previous overprint are repeated in this setting excepting the inverted "Y" and fancy "P." There are also additional varieties of large letters and "PANAMA" occasionally has an "A" missing or inverted. There are misplaced impressions, as the previous setting.

Overprinted in Red

1904-05

76 A4 1c green .25 .25
- a. Both words reading up 1.50
- b. Both words reading down 2.75
- c. Double overprint
- d. Pair, one without overprint 15.00
- e. "PANAAM" 20.00
- f. Inverted "M" in "PANAMA" 5.00

77 A4 2c rose .25 .25
- a. Both words reading up 2.50
- b. Both words reading down 2.50
- c. Double overprint 10.00
- d. Double overprint, one inverted 14.00
- e. Inverted "M" in "PANAMA" 5.00

78 A4 5c blue .30 .25
- a. Both words reading up 3.00
- b. Both words reading down 4.25
- c. Inverted overprint 12.50
- d. "PANAAM" 25.00
- e. "PANANA" 8.00
- f. "PAMAMA" 5.00
- g. Inverted "M" in "PANAMA" 5.00
- h. Double overprint 20.00

79 A4 10c orange .30 .25
- a. Both words reading up 5.00
- b. Both words reading down 5.00
- c. Double overprint 15.00
- d. Inverted overprint 6.75
- e. "PANANA" 8.00
- f. Inverted "M" in "PANAMA" 15.00
- g. Red brown overprint 7.50 3.50

80 A4 20c violet 2.00 1.00
- a. Both words reading up 5.00
- b. Both words reading down 10.00

81 A4 50c bister brn 2.00 1.60
- a. Both words reading up 10.50
- b. Both words reading down 10.00
- c. Double overprint

82 A4 1p lake 5.00 5.00
- a. Both words reading up 12.50
- b. Both words reading down 12.50
- c. Double overprint
- d. Double overprint, one inverted 20.00
- e. Inverted "M" in "PANAMA" 45.00

Nos. 76-82 (7) 10.10 8.60

This overprint is also set up to cover fifty stamps. One stamp in each fifty has "PANAMA" reading upward at both sides. Another has the word reading downward at both sides, a third has an inverted "V" in place of the last "A" and a fourth has a small thick "N." In a resetting all these varieties are corrected except the inverted "V." There are misplaced overprints as before.

Later printings show other varieties and have the bar 2½mm instead of 2mm wide. The colors of the various printings of Nos. 76-82 range from carmine to almost pink.

Experts consider the black overprint on the 50c to be speculative.

The 20c violet and 50c bister brown exist with bar 2½mm wide, including the error "PAMANA," but are not known to have been issued. Some examples have been canceled "to oblige."

Issued in Colon

Handstamped in Magenta or Violet

1903-04 On Stamps of 1892-96

101 A4 1c green .75 .75
102 A4 2c rose .75 .75
103 A4 5c blue 1.00 1.00
104 A4 10c yellow 3.50 3.00
105 A4 20c violet 8.00 6.50
106 A4 1p lake 80.00 70.00

On Stamps of 1887-92
Ordinary Wove Paper

107 A3 50c brown 25.00 20.00
Nos. 101-107 (7) 119.00 102.00

Pelure Paper

108 A3 50c brown 70.00

Handstamped in Magenta, Violet or Red

On Stamps of 1892-96

109 A4 1c green 5.50 5.00
110 A4 2c rose 5.50 5.00
111 A4 5c blue 5.50 5.00
112 A4 10c orange 8.25 7.00
113 A4 20c violet 12.00 9.00
114 A4 1p lake 70.00 60.00

On Stamps of 1887-92
Ordinary Wove Paper

115 A3 50c brown 35.00 25.00
Nos. 109-115 (7) 141.75 116.00

Pelure Paper

116 A3 50c brown 50.00 37.50

The first note after No. 64 applies also to Nos. 101-116.
The handstamps on Nos. 109-116 have been counterfeited.

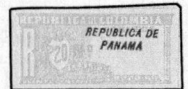

Stamps with this overprint were a private speculation. They exist on cover. The overprint was to be used on postal cards.

Overprinted On Stamps Of 1892-96

On Stamps of 1892-96
Carmine Overprint

129 A4 1c green .40 .40
- a. Inverted overprint 6.00
- b. Double overprint 2.25
- c. Double overprint, one inverted 6.00
130 A4 5c blue .50 .50

Brown Overprint

131 A4 1c green 12.00
- a. Double overprint, one inverted

Black Overprint

132 A4 1c green 60.00 30.00
- a. Vertical overprint 42.50
- b. Inverted overprint 42.50
- c. Double overprint 42.50
133 A4 2c rose .50 .50
- a. Inverted overprint
134 A4 10c orange .50 .50
- a. Inverted overprint 4.00
- b. Double overprint 16.00
- c. Double overprint, one inverted 6.00
135 A4 20c violet .50 .50
- a. Inverted overprint 4.00
- b. Double overprint 5.50
136 A4 1p lake 16.00 14.00

On Stamps of 1887-88
Blue Overprint
Ordinary Wove Paper

137 A3 50c brown 3.00 3.00

Pelure Paper

138 A3 50c brown 3.00 3.00

This overprint is set up to cover fifty stamps. In each fifty there are four stamps without accent on the last "a" of "Panama," one with accent on the "a" of "Republica" and one with a thick, upright "i."

Overprinted in Carmine

On Stamp of 1892-96

139 A4 20c violet 200.00
- a. Double overprint 14.00

Unknown with genuine cancels.

Issued in Bocas del Toro

Stamps of 1892-96 Overprinted Handstamped in Violet

1903-04

151 A4 1c green 20.00 14.00
152 A4 2c rose 20.00 14.00
153 A4 5c blue 25.00 16.00
154 A4 10c yellow 15.00 8.25
155 A4 20c violet 50.00 30.00
156 A4 50c bister brn 100.00 55.00
157 A4 1p lake 140.00 110.00
Nos. 151-157 (7) 370.00 247.25

The handstamp is known double and inverted. Counterfeits exist.

Handstamped in Violet

158 A4 1c green 100.00
159 A4 2c rose 70.00
160 A4 5c blue 80.00
161 A4 10c yellow 100.00
Nos. 158-161 (4) 350.00

This handstamp was applied to these 4 stamps only by favor, experts state. Counterfeits are numerous. The 1p exists only as a counterfeit.

General Issues

A5

1905, Feb. 4 Engr. Perf. 12
179 A5 1c green .60 .40
180 A5 2c rose .80 .50

Panama's Declaration of Independence from the Colombian Republic, Nov. 3, 1903.

Surcharged in Vermilion on Stamps of 1892-96 Issue

1906

181 A4 1c on 20c violet .25 .25
- a. "Panrma" 2.25 2.25
- b. "Pnnama" 2.25 2.25
- c. "Pauama" 2.25 2.25
- d. Inverted surcharge 4.00 4.00
- e. Double surcharge 3.50 3.50
- f. Double surcharge, one inverted

Stamps of 1892-96 Surcharged in Vermilion

182 A4 2c on 50c bister brn .25 .25
- a. 3rd "A" of "PANAMA" inverted 2.25 2.25
- b. Both "PANAMA" reading down 4.00 4.00
- c. Double surcharge
- d. Inverted surcharge 2.50

The 2c on 20c violet was never issued to the public. All examples are inverted. Value, 75c.

Carmine Surcharge

183 A4 5c on 1p lake .60 .40
- a. Both "PANAMA" reading down 6.00 6.00
- b. "5" omitted
- c. Double surcharge
- d. Inverted surcharge
- e. 3rd "A" of "PANAMA" inverted 5.50 5.50

On Stamp of 1903-04, No. 75

184 A4 5c on 1p lake .60 .40
- a. "PANAMA" 15mm long
- b. "PANAMA" reading up and down
- c. Both "PANAMA" reading down
- d. Inverted surcharge
- e. Double surcharge
- f. 3rd "A" of "PANAMA" inverted
Nos. 181-184 (4) 1.70 1.30

National Flag A6 — Vasco Núñez de Balboa A7

Fernández de Córdoba A8 — Coat of Arms A9

 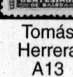

Justo Arosemena A10 — Manuel J. Hurtado A11

José de Obaldía A12 — Tomás Herrera A13

José de Fábrega — A14

1906-07 Engr. Perf. 11½
185 A6 ½c orange & multi .70 .35
186 A7 1c dk green & blk ('07) .70 .35
187 A8 2c scarlet & blk 1.00 .35
188 A9 2½c red orange 1.00 .35
189 A10 5c blue & black 1.75 .35
- a. 5c ultramarine & black 2.00 .50
190 A11 8c purple & blk 1.50 .65
191 A12 10c violet & blk 1.50 .50
192 A13 25c brown & blk 3.50 1.10
193 A14 50c black 9.00 3.50
Nos. 185-193 (9) 20.65 7.50

Inverted centers exist of Nos. 185-187, 189, 189a, 190-193, Value, each $25. Nos. 185-193 exist imperf.
For surcharge see No. F29.
Issued: Nos. 185, 188-193, 11/20; No. 187, 9/1.

Map
A17

Córdoba
A19

Arosemena
A21

Balboa
A18

Arms
A20

Obaldía
A23

1909-16 **Perf. 12**
195 A17 ½c org ('11) 1.00 .30
196 A17 ½c rose ('15) .70 .60
197 A18 1c dk grn & blk 1.00 .50
  a. Inverted center 7,500. 7,500.
  b. Booklet pane of 6 ('16) 160.00
    Complete booklet, 4 —
    #197b
198 A19 2c ver & blk 1.00 .30
  a. Booklet pane of 6 160.00
199 A20 2½c red orange 1.50 .30
200 A21 5c blue & blk 2.00 .30
  a. Booklet pane of 6 ('16) 350.00
201 A23 10c violet & blk 3.75 1.10
  Complete booklet,
  panes of 6 (3x2) of
  #195 (3), 197 (3),
  199 (2), 200, 201
  ('11) —
  Nos. 195-201 (7) 10.95 3.40

Value for No. 197a used is for an off-center example with faults.
The panes contained in the booklet listed following No. 201 are marginal blocks of 6 (3x2), without gum, stapled within the booklet cover, with advertising paper interleaving. The complete booklet was sold for B1.50.
Nos. 197b and 198a are gummed panes of 6 (2x3), imperf on outside edges.
For overprints and surcharges see #H23, I4-I7.

Balboa Sighting Pacific Ocean, His Dog "Leoncico" at His Feet — A24

1913, Sept. 1
202 A24 2½c dk grn & yel grn 1.75 .65
400th anniv. of Balboa's discovery of the Pacific Ocean.

Panama-Pacific Exposition Issue

Chorrera
Falls — A25

Map of Panama
Canal — A26

Balboa Taking
Possession of the
Pacific — A27

Ruins of
Cathedral of Old
Panama — A28

Palace of
Arts — A29

Gatun
Locks — A30

Culebra
Cut — A31

Santo Domingo
Monastery's Flat
Arch — A32

1915, Mar. 1 **Perf. 12**
204 A25 ½c ol grn & blk .40 .30
205 A26 1c dk grn & blk .95 .30
206 A27 2c car & blk .75 .30
  a. 2c ver & blk ('16) .75 .30
208 A28 2½c scarlet & blk .95 .35
209 A29 3c violet & blk 1.60 .55
210 A30 5c blue & blk 2.10 .35
  a. Center inverted 1,500. 650.00
211 A31 10c orange & blk 2.10 .70
212 A32 20c brown & blk 10.50 3.25
  a. Center inverted 300.00
  Nos. 204-212 (8) 19.35 6.10

For surcharges and overprints see Nos. 217, 233, E1-E2.

Manuel J.
Hurtado — A33

1916
213 A33 8c violet & blk 9.00 4.25
For surcharge see No. F30.

S. S. Panama in
Culebra Cut Aug.
11, 1914 — A34

S. S. Panama in
Culebra Cut Aug.
11, 1914 — A35

S. S. Cristobal in
Gatun Lock — A36

1918, Aug. 23
214 A34 12c purple & blk 15.00 5.75
215 A35 15c brt blue & blk 15.00 3.50
216 A36 24c yellow brn & blk 15.00 3.50
  Nos. 214-216 (3) 40.00 12.75

No. 208
Surcharged in Dark
Blue

1919, Aug. 15
217 A28 2c on 2½c scar & blk .35 .35
  a. Inverted surcharge 11.00 5.00
  b. Double surcharge 15.00 6.00
City of Panama, 400th anniversary.

Dry Dock at
Balboa — A38

Ship in Pedro
Miguel
Lock — A39

1920, Sept. 1 **Engr.**
218 A38 50c orange & blk 30.00 22.50
219 A39 1b dk violet & blk 40.00 27.50
For overprint and surcharge see Nos. C6, C37.

Arms of
Panama
City
A40

José
Vallarino
A41

"Land Gate"
A42

Statue of
Cervantes
A44

Carlos de
Ycaza
A46

Statue of
Balboa
A48

Herrera
A50

Simón
Bolívar
A43

Bolívar's Tribute
A45

Municipal
Building in
1821 and
1921
A47

Villa de Los
Santos
Church
A49

Fábrega
A51

1921, Nov.
220 A40 ½c orange .80 .25
221 A41 1c green 1.00 .25
222 A42 2c carmine 1.25 .25
223 A43 2½c red 2.75 1.10
224 A44 3c dull violet 2.75 1.10
225 A45 5c blue 2.75 .35
226 A46 8c olive green 10.00 3.50
227 A47 10c violet 6.75 1.50
228 A48 15c lt blue 8.00 2.00
229 A49 20c olive brown 14.50 3.50
230 A50 24c black brown 14.50 4.25
231 A51 50c black 25.00 8.00
  Nos. 220-231 (12) 90.05 26.05
Centenary of independence.
For overprints and surcharges see Nos. 264, 275-276, 299, 304, 308-310, C35.

Hurtado — A52

1921, Nov. 28
232 A52 2c dark green .65 .65
Manuel José Hurtado (1821-1887), president and folklore writer.
For overprints see Nos. 258, 301.

No. 208
Surcharged in
Black

1923
233 A28 2c on 2½c scar & blk .45 .45
  a. "1923" omitted 4.00
  b. Bar over "CENTESIMOS" 4.00
  c. Inverted surcharge 4.00
  d. Double surcharge 4.00
  e. Pair, one without surcharge 4.00
Two stamps in each sheet have a bar above "CENTESIMOS" (No. 233b).

Arms — A53

1924, May **Engr.**
234 A53 ½c orange .25 .25
235 A53 1c dark green .25 .25
236 A53 2c carmine .25 .25
237 A53 5c dark blue .45 .25
238 A53 10c dark violet .60 .25
239 A53 12c olive green .75 .40
240 A53 15c ultra .95 .40
241 A53 24c yellow brown 1.90 .60
242 A53 50c orange 4.50 1.10
243 A53 1b black 6.75 2.50
  Nos. 234-243 (10) 16.65 6.25

For overprints & surcharges see Nos. 277, 321A, 331-338, 352, C19-C20, C68, RA5, RA10-RA22.

Bolívar
A54

Statue of
Bolívar
A55

Bolívar Hall — A56

1926, June 10 **Perf. 12½**
244 A54 ½c orange .55 .25
245 A54 1c dark green .55 .25
246 A54 2c scarlet .70 .30
247 A54 4c gray .90 .35
248 A54 5c dark blue 1.40 .50
249 A55 8c lilac 2.25 .80
250 A55 10c dull violet 1.60 .80
251 A55 12c olive green 2.50 1.00
252 A55 15c ultra 3.25 1.25
253 A55 20c brown 6.75 1.60
254 A56 24c black violet 8.00 2.00
255 A56 50c black 13.50 5.00
  Nos. 244-255 (12) 41.95 14.10

Bolivar Congress centennial.
For surcharges and overprints see Nos. 259-263, 266-267, 274, 298, 300, 302-303, 305-307, C33-C34, C36, C38-C39.

Lindbergh's
Airplane,
"The Spirit of
St.
Louis" — A57

Lindbergh's Airplane
and Map of
Panama — A58

1928, Jan. 9 **Typo.** **Rouletted 7**
256 A57 2c dk red & blk, salmon .40 .25
257 A58 5c dk blue, grn .60 .40
Visit of Colonel Charles A. Lindbergh to Central America by airplane.
No. 256 has black overprint.

No. 232 Overprinted in
Red

1928, Nov. 1 **Perf. 12**
258 A52 2c dark green .25 .25
25th anniversary of the Republic.

No. 247 Surcharged in Black

1930, Dec. 17   *Perf. 12½, 13*
259 A54 1c on 4c gray   .25 .25
    Centenary of the death of Simón Bolívar, the Liberator.

Nos. 244-246 Overprinted in Red or Blue

1932   *Perf. 12½*
260 A54 ½c orange (R)   .25 .25
261 A54 1c dark green (R)   .35 .25
  a.   Double overprint   18.00
262 A54 2c scarlet (Bl)   .35 .25

No. 252 Surcharged in Red

263 A55 10c on 15c ultra   1.00 .50
  a.   Double surcharge   55.00
    Nos. 260-263 (4)   1.95 1.25

No. 220 Overprinted as in 1932 in Black

1933, May 25   *Perf. 12*
   Overprint 19mm Long
264 A40 ½c orange   .35 .25
  a.   Overprint 17mm long   —

Dr. Manuel Amador Guerrero — A60

1933, June 30   Engr.   *Perf. 12½*
265 A60 2c dark red   .50 .25
    Centenary of the birth of Dr. Manuel Amador Guerrero, founder of the Republic of Panama and its first President.

No. 251 Surcharged in Red

1933
266 A55 10c on 12c olive grn   1.25 .65

No. 253 Overprinted in Red

267 A55 20c brown   2.25 1.75

José Domingo de Obaldía A61

Quotation from Emerson A63

National Institute — A64

Designs: 2c, Eusebio A. Morales. 12c, Justo A. Facio. 15c, Pablo Arosemena.

1934, July 24   Engr.   *Perf. 14*
268 A61 1c dark green   1.00 .50
269 A61 2c scarlet   1.00 .45
270 A63 5c dark blue   1.25 .80
271 A64 10c brown   3.25 1.50
272 A61 12c yellow green   6.50 2.00
273 A61 15c Prus blue   8.50 2.50
    Nos. 268-273 (6)   21.50 7.75
    Set, never hinged   32.50

    25th anniv. of the Natl. Institute.

Nos. 248, 227 Overprinted in Black or Red

1935-36   *Perf. 12½, 12*
274 A54 5c dark blue   .90 .30
275 A47 10c violet (R) ('36)   1.25 .60

No. 225 Surcharged in Red

1936. Sept. 19   *Perf. 11½*
276 A45 1c on 5c blue   .40 .40
  a.   Lines of surcharge 1½mm btwn.   6.50

No. 241 Surcharged in Blue

1936, Sept. 24   *Perf. 12*
277 A53 2c on 24c yellow brn   .60 .50
  a.   Double surcharge   20.00
    Centenary of the birth of Pablo Arosemena, president of Panama in 1910-12. See Nos. C19-C20.

Panama Cathedral — A67

Designs: ½c, Ruins of Custom House, Portobelo. 1c, Panama Tree. 2c, "La Pollera." 5c, Simon Bolivar. 10c, Cathedral Tower Ruins. Old Panama. 15c, Francisco Garcia y Santos. 20c, Madden Dam, Panama Canal. 25c, Columbus. 50c, Gaillard Cut. 1b, Panama Cathedral.

1936, Dec. 1   Engr.   *Perf. 11½*
278 A67 ½c yellow org   .55 .25
279 A67 1c blue green   .55 .25
280 A67 2c carmine rose   .55 .25
281 A67 5c blue   .80 .50
282 A67 10c dk violet   1.75 .75
283 A67 15c turq blue   1.75 .75
284 A67 20c red   2.00 1.50
285 A67 25c black brn   3.50 2.00
286 A67 50c orange   7.75 5.00
287 A67 1b black   18.00 12.00
    Nos. 278-287,C21-C26 (16)   62.70 40.00
    Set, never hinged   95.00

    4th Postal Congress of the Americas and Spain.

Stamps of 1936 Overprinted in Red or Blue

1937, Mar. 9
288 A67 ½c yellow org (R)   .35 .30
  a.   Inverted overprint   25.00
289 A67 1c blue green (R)   .45 .25
290 A67 2c car rose (Bl)   .45 .25
291 A67 5c blue (R)   .70 .25
292 A67 10c dk vio (R)   1.10 .35
293 A67 15c turq bl (R)   5.25 3.25
294 A67 20c red (Bl)   2.00 1.25
295 A67 25c black brn (R)   2.75 1.25

---

296 A67 50c orange (Bl)   9.00 6.00
297 A67 1b black (R)   14.50 10.00
    Nos. 288-297,C27-C32 (16)   84.60 54.15
    Set, never hinged   135.00

Stamps of 1921-26 Overprinted in Red or Blue

1937, July   *Perf. 12, 12½*
298 A54 ½c orange (R)   1.10 .80
  a.   Inverted overprint   30.00
299 A41 1c green (R)   .35 .25
  a.   Inverted overprint   30.00
300 A54 1c dk green (R)   .35 .25
301 A52 1c dk green (R)   .45 .35
302 A54 2c scarlet (Bl)   .55 .35

Stamps of 1921-26 Surcharged in Red

303 A54 2c on 4c gray   .70 .45
304 A46 2c on 8c ol grn   .70 .60
305 A55 2c on 8c lilac   .70 .45
306 A55 2c on 10c dl vio   .70 .50
307 A55 2c on 12c ol grn   .70 .45
308 A48 2c on 15c lt blue   .70 .60
309 A50 2c on 24c blk brn   .70 .75
310 A51 2c on 50c black   .70 .35
    Nos. 298-310 (13)   8.40 6.15
    Set, never hinged   12.50

Ricardo Arango A77

Juan A. Guizado A78

La Concordia Fire — A79

Modern Fire Fighting Equipment A80

Firemen's Monument A81

David H. Brandon — A82

   Perf. 14x14½, 14½x14
1937, Nov. 25   Photo.   Wmk. 233
311 A77 ½c orange red   2.10 .35
312 A78 1c green   2.10 .35
313 A79 2c red   2.10 .25
314 A80 5c brt blue   4.00 .50
315 A81 10c purple   7.25 1.25
316 A82 12c yellow grn   11.50 2.00
    Nos. 311-316,C40-C42 (9)   49.30 7.05
    Set, never hinged   66.00

    50th anniversary of the Fire Department.

Old Panama Cathedral Tower and Statue of Liberty Enlightening the World, Flags of Panama and US — A83

   Engr. & Litho.
1938, Dec. 7   Unwmk.   *Perf. 12½*
Center in Black; Flags in Red and Ultramarine
317 A83 1c deep green   .35 .25
318 A83 2c carmine   .55 .25
319 A83 5c blue   .80 .30
320 A83 12c olive   1.40 .75
321 A83 15c brt ultra   1.75 1.25
    Nos. 317-321,C49-C53 (10)   22.45 15.35
    Set, never hinged   33.75

    150th anniv. of the US Constitution.

No. 236 Overprinted in Black

1938, June 5   *Perf. 12*
321A A53 2c carmine   .45 .25
    ever hinged   .70
  b.   Inverted overprint   22.50
    Nos. 321A,C53A-C53B (3)   1.25 1.05

    Opening of the Normal School at Santiago, Veraguas Province, June 5, 1938.

Gatun Lake — A84

Designs: 1c, Pedro Miguel Locks. 2c, Allegory. 5c, Culebra Cut. 10c, Ferryboat. 12c, Aerial View of Canal. 15c, Gen. William C. Gorgas. 50c, Dr. Manuel A. Guerrero. 1b, Woodrow Wilson.

1939, Aug. 15   Engr.   *Perf. 12½*
322 A84 ½c yellow   .35 .25
323 A84 1c dp blue grn   .55 .25
324 A84 2c dull rose   .65 .25
325 A84 5c dull blue   1.00 .25
326 A84 10c dk violet   1.10 .35
327 A84 12c olive green   1.10 .50
328 A84 15c ultra   1.10 .80
329 A84 50c orange   2.75 1.60
330 A84 1b dk brown   5.75 3.00
    Nos. 322-330,C54-C61 (17)   34.35 14.45
    Set, never hinged   51.50

    25th anniversary of the opening of the Panama Canal. For surcharges see Nos. C64, G2.

Stamps of 1924 Overprinted in Black or Red

1941, Jan. 2   *Perf. 12*
331 A53 ½c orange   .35 .25
332 A53 1c dk grn (R)   .35 .25
333 A53 2c carmine   .35 .25
334 A53 5c dk bl (R)   .55 .30
335 A53 10c dk vio (R)   .80 .50
336 A53 15c ultra (R)   1.75 .65
337 A53 50c dp org   6.25 3.50
338 A53 1b blk (R)   14.50 6.00
    Nos. 331-338,C67-C71 (13)   49.90 31.25

    New Panama constitution, effective 1/241.

Black Overprint

1942, Feb. 19   Engr.
339 A93 10c purple   1.40 1.00

   Surcharged with New Value
340 A93 2c on 5c dk bl   1.75 .50
    Nos. 339-340,C72 (3)   7.15 4.00

Flags of Panama and Costa Rica — A94

Engraved and Lithographed
1942, April 25

341 A94 2c rose red, dk bl & dp
rose   .30 .40

1st anniv. of the settlement of the Costa Rica-Panama border dispute. See No. C73.

National Emblems A95

Farm Girl in Work Dress A96

Cart Laden with Sugar Cane (Inscribed "ACARRERO DE CAÑA") — A97

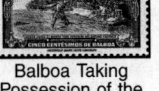

Balboa Taking Possession of the Pacific — A98

Golden Altar of San José — A99

San Blas Indian Woman and Child A101

Santo Tomas Hospital A100

Modern Highway — A102

Engr.; Flag on ½c Litho.
1942, May 11

342	A95	½c dl vio, bl & car	.25 .25
343	A96	1c dk green	.25 .25
344	A97	2c vermilion	.25 .25
345	A98	5c dp bl & blk	.25 .25
346	A99	10c car rose & org	.65 .25
347	A100	15c lt bl & blk	1.00 .50
348	A101	50c org red & ol blk	2.50 1.00
349	A102	1b black	3.50 1.00
		Nos. 342-349 (8)	8.65 3.75

See Nos. 357, 365, 376-377, 380, 395, 409.
For surcharges and overprints see Nos. 366-370, 373-375, 378-379, 381, 387-388, 396, C129-C130, RA23.

> Catalogue values for unused stamps in this section, from this point to the end of the section, are for Never Hinged items.

Flag of Panama A103

Arms of Panama A104

Engraved; Flag on 2c Lithographed
1947, Apr. 7   Unwmk.   Perf. 12½

350 A103 2c car, bl & red   .80 .40
351 A104 5c deep blue   .80 .40

Natl. Constitutional Assembly of 1945, 2nd anniv.

No. 241 Surcharged in Black

1947, Oct. 29   Perf. 12

352 A53 50c on 24c yel brn   3.75 1.50
   a. "Habilitada"   2.25 2.25

Nos. C6C, C75, C74 and C87 Surcharged in Black or Carmine

1948, June 10 type box

353 AP5   ½c on 8c gray blk   .45 .25
   a. "B/.0.00 ½ CORREOS" (transposed)   3.00 3.00
354 AP34 ½c on 8c dk ol brn & blk (C)   .45 .25
355 AP34 1c on 7c rose car   .45 .25
356 AP42 2c on 8c vio   .45 .25
   Nos. 352-356 (5)   5.55 2.50

Flag Type of 1942
1948   Engr. and Litho.

357 A95 ½c car, org, bl & dp car   .80 .40

Monument to Firemen of Colon — A105

American-La France Fire Engine — A106

20c, Firemen & hose cart. 25c, New Central Fire Station, Colon. 50c, Maximino Walker. 1b, J. J. A. Ducruet.

1948, June 10   Engr.
Center in Black

358	A105	5c dp car	.80 .35
359	A106	10c orange	1.10 .35
360	A106	20c gray bl	2.10 .50
361	A106	25c chocolate	2.10 .90
362	A105	50c purple	4.00 .90
363	A105	1b dp grn	6.00 2.00
		Nos. 358-363 (6)	16.10 5.00

50th anniversary of the founding of the Colon Fire Department.
For overprint see No. C125.

Cervantes — A107

1948, Nov. 15   Unwmk.   Perf. 12½

364 A107 2c car & blk   1.25 .40
   Nos. 364,C105-C106 (3)   3.75 1.20

Miguel de Cervantes Saavedra, novelist, playwright and poet, 400th birth anniv.

Oxcart Type of 1942 Redrawn

Inscribed: "ACARREO DE CANA"

1948   Perf. 12

365 A97 2c vermilion   1.10 .40

No. 365 Surcharged or Overprinted in Black

1949, May 26

366 A97 1c on 2c ver   .45 .25
367 A97 2c vermilion   .45 .25
   a. Inverted overprint   1.00 1.00
   Nos. 366-367,C108-C111 (6)   6.90 3.90

Incorporation of Chiriqui Province, cent.

Stamps and Types of 1942-48 Issues Overprinted in Black or Red

1949, Sept. 9   Engr.

368 A96 1c dk green   .35 .25
369 A97 2c ver (#365)   .90 .25
370 A98 5c blue (R)   1.30 .25
   Nos. 368-370,C114-C118 (8)   12.45 4.55

75th anniv. of the UPU.
Overprint on No. 368 is slightly different and smaller, 15½x12mm.

Francisco Javier de Luna — A108

1949, Dec. 7   Perf. 12½

371 A108 2c car & blk   .65 .40

200th anniversary of the founding of the University of San Javier. See No. C119.

Dr. Carlos J. Finlay — A109

1950, Jan. 12   Unwmk.   Perf. 12

372 A109 2c car & gray blk   .75 .25

Issued to honor Dr. Carlos J. Finlay (1833-1915), Cuban physician and biologist who found that a mosquito transmitted yellow fever. See No. C120.

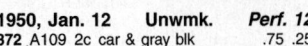

Nos. 343, 357 and 345, Overprinted or Surcharged in Carmine or Black

1950, Aug. 17

373 A96 1c dk green   .45 .25
374 A95 2c on ½c car, org, bl & dp car (Bk)   .45 .25
375 A98 5c dp bl & blk   .50 .25
   Nos. 373-375,C121-C125 (8)   10.75 3.75

Gen. José de San Martin, death cent.
The overprint is in four lines on No. 375.

Types of 1942
1950, Oct. 13   Engr.

376 A97 2c ver & blk   .80 .40
377 A98 5c blue   .80 .40

No. 376 is inscribed "ACARREO DE CANA."

Nos. 376 and 377 Overprinted in Green or Carmine

1951, Sept. 26

378 A97 2c ver & blk (G)   .50 .40
   a. Inverted overprint   20.00 20.00
   b. First line omitted, second line repeated   20.00 20.00
379 A98 5c blue (C)   1.20 .40
   a. Inverted overprint   20.00 20.00

St. Jean-Baptiste de la Salle, 500th birth anniv.

Altar Type of 1942
1952   Engr.   Perf. 12

380 A99 10c pur & org   1.25 .40

No. 357 Surcharged in Black

1952, Oct. 29

381 A95 1c on ½c multi   .80 .40

Queen Isabella I and Arms — A110

1952, Oct. 20   Engr.   Perf. 12½
Center in Black

382	A110	1c green	.65 .40
383	A110	2c carmine	.65 .40
384	A110	5c dk bl	.65 .40
385	A110	10c purple	.90 .40
		Nos. 382-385,C131-C136 (10)	20.50 7.55

Queen Isabella I of Spain. 500th birth anniv.

No. 380 and Type of 1942 Srchd. "B/ .0.01 1953" in Black or Carmine
1953   Perf. 12

387 A99 1c on 10c pur & org   .80 .40
388 A100 1c on 15c black (C)   .80 .40

Issued: No. 387, 4/22; No. 388, 9/4.
A similar surcharge on No. 346 was privately applied.

A111   A112

2c, Baptism of the Flag. 5c, Manuel Amador Guerrero & Senora de Amador. 12c, Santos Jorge A. & Jeronimo de la Ossa. 20c, Revolutionary Junta. 50c, Old city hall. 1b, Natl. coinage.

1953, Nov. 2   Engr.   Perf. 12

389	A111	2c purple	.55 .25
390	A112	5c red orange	.65 .25
391	A112	12c dp red vio	1.50 .25
392	A112	20c slate gray	2.75 .25
393	A111	50c org yel	4.00 .60
394	A112	1b blue	7.25 1.25
		Nos. 389-394 (6)	16.70 2.85

Founding of the Republic of Panama, 50th anniv.
See #C140-C145. For surcharge see #413.

Farm Girl Type of 1942
1954   Unwmk.   Perf. 12

395 A96 1c dp car rose   .80 .40

Surcharged in Black

396 A96 3c on 1c dp car rose   .80 .40
   Issued: No. 395, 4/21; No. 396, 6/21.

Monument to Gen. Tomas Herrera — A113

1954, Dec. 4   Litho.   Perf. 12½

397 A113 3c purple   .35 .25
   Nos. 397,C148-C149 (3)   5.85 2.75

Gen. Tomas Herrera, death cent.

Tocumen International Airport — A114

1955, Apr. 16
398 A114 ½c org brn   .95 .40
For surcharges see Nos. 411-412.

General Remon Cantera, 1908-1955 — A115

1955, June 1
399 A115 3c lilac rose & blk   .80 .40
See No. C153.

Victor de la Guardia y Ayala and Miguel Chiari — A116

1955, Sept. 12
400 A116 5c violet   .85 .40
Centenary of province of Coclé.

Ferdinand de Lesseps A117

First Excavation of Panama Canal A118

Design: 50c, Theodore Roosevelt.

1955, Nov. 22
401 A117 3c rose brn, *rose*   .65 .25
402 A118 25c vio bl, *lt bl*   2.75 1.40
403 A117 50c vio, *lt vio*   3.50 1.50
  Nos. 401-403,C155-C156 (5)   13.85 5.90

Ferdinand de Lesseps, 150th birth anniv., French promoter connected with building of Panama Canal. 75th anniv. of the 1st French excavations.
Imperfs exist, but were not sold at any post office.

St. Pius I — A118a

Pope Pius XII — A118b

Designs: Heads of Pope Pius's. 2c, St. Pius I (140-155). 3c, Pius II (1458-1464). 4c, Pius III (1503). 5c, Pius IV (1559-1565). 6c, Pius V (1566-1572). 10c, Pius VI (1775-1799). 20c, Pius VII (1800-1823). 25c, Pius VIII (1829-1830). 50c, Pius IX (1846-1878). 75c, Pius X (1903-1914). 1b, Pius XI (1922-1939). 2b, Pius XII (1939-1958).

Unwmk.
1956, July 2   Litho.   Perf. 12
403A A118a 2c bright gr   3.50 3.50
403B A118a 3c red   4.00 4.00
403C A118a 4c brnsh red   6.25 6.25
403D A118a 5c lil pur   8.00 8.00
403E A118a 6c gray bl   5.75 5.75
403F A118a 10c blue   6.75 6.75
403G A118a 20c green   8.00 8.00
403H A118a 25c org red   9.25 9.25
403I A118a 50c brown   12.50 12.50
403J A118a 75c org   13.00 13.00
403K A118a 1b yellow   13.00 13.00
403L A118b 2b purple   13.00 13.00
  Nos. 403A-403L (12)   103.00 103.00

Because of the speculative creation of the Popes issue, Nos. 403A-403L were sold in

Panama and valid for postage for a period limited to six months from the issue date. The remainder were then removed from sale and destroyed.

Arms of Panama City — A119

Perf. 12½
1956, Aug. 17   Litho.   Unwmk.
404 A119 3c green   .40 .40
Sixth Inter-American Congress of Municipalities, Panama City, Aug. 14-19, 1956.
For souvenir sheet see C182a.

Carlos A. Mendoza — A120

1956, Oct. 31   Wmk. 311
405 A120 10c rose red & dp grn   .65 .40
Pres. Carlos A. Mendoza, birth cent.

National Archives — A121

1956, Nov. 27
406 A121 15c shown   1.00 .35
407 A121 25c Pres. Belisario
           Porras   1.40 .40
  Nos. 406-407,C183-C184 (4)   3.45 1.55
Centenary of the birth of Pres. Belisario Porras. For surcharge see No. 446.

Pan-American Highway, Panama — A122

1957, Aug. 1
408 A122 3c gray green   .35 .25
  Nos. 408,C185-C187 (4)   4.80 3.30
7th Pan-American Highway Congress.

Hospital Type of 1942
Unwmk.
1957, Aug. 17   Engr.   Perf. 12
409 A100 15c black   .75 .40

Manuel Espinosa Batista — A123

Wmk. 311
1957, Sept. 12   Litho.   Perf. 12½
410 A123 5c grn & ultra   .65 .40
Centenary of the birth of Manuel Espinosa B., independence leader.

No. 398 Surcharged "1957" and New Value in Violet or Black

1957, Dec. 21   Unwmk.
411 A114 1c on ½c org brn (V)   .65 .40
412 A114 3c on ½c org brn   .65 .40

No. 391 Surcharged "1958," New Value and Dots

1958, June 6   Engr.   Perf. 12
413 A112 3c on 12c dp red vio   .65 .40

Flags of 21 American Nations — A124

Center yellow & black; flags in national colors

Perf. 12½
1958, Aug. 12   Litho.   Unwmk.
414 A124 1c lt gray   .40 .25
415 A124 2c brt yel grn   .40 .25
416 A124 3c red org   .40 .25
417 A124 7c vio bl   .40 .25
  Nos. 414-417,C203-C206 (8)   6.65 3.70
Organization of American States, 10th anniv.

Brazilian Pavilion, Brussels Fair — A125

3c, Argentina. 5c, Venezuela. 10c, Great Britain.

1958, Sept. 8   Wmk. 311
418 A125 1c org yel & emer   .40 .25
419 A125 3c lt bl & olive   .40 .25
420 A125 5c lt brn & slate   .40 .25
421 A125 10c aqua & redsh brn   .40 .25
  Nos. 418-421,C207-C209 (7)   5.70 3.30
World's Fair, Brussels, Apr. 17-Oct. 19.

Pope Pius XII as Young Man — A126

Wmk. 311
1959, Jan. 21   Litho.   Perf. 12½
422 A126 3c orange brown   .40 .25
  Nos. 422,C210-C212 (4)   3.30 1.55
Pope Pius XII, 1876-1958. See #C212a.

UN Headquarters Building — A127

Design: 15c, Humanity looking into sun.

1959, Apr. 14   Wmk. 311
423 A127 3c maroon & olive   .35 .25
424 A127 15c orange & emer   .35 .25
  Nos. 423-424,C213-C217 (7)   5.10 3.30
10th anniv. (in 1958) of the signing of the Universal Declaration of Human Rights.
For overprints see Nos. 425-426, C219-C221.

Nos. 423-424 Overprinted in Dark Blue

1959, May 16
425 A127 3c maroon & olive   .40 .25
426 A127 15c orange & emer   .55 .25
  Nos. 425-426,C218-C221 (6)   5.65 3.15
Issued to commemorate the 8th Reunion of the Economic Commission for Latin America.

Eusebio A. Morales A128

National Institute A129

Wmk. 311
1959, Aug. 5   Litho.   Perf. 12½
427 A128 3c shown   .50 .40
428 A128 13c Abel Bravo   .80 .40
429 A129 21c shown   1.20 .40
  Nos. 427-429,C222-C223 (5)   3.40 2.00
50th anniversary, National Institute.

Soccer — A130

1959, Oct. 26
430 A130 1c shown   .30 .25
431 A130 3c Swimming   .45 .25
432 A130 20c Hurdling   2.10 .80
  Nos. 430-432,C224-C226 (6)   7.65 3.05
3rd Pan American Games, Chicago, 8/27-9/7/59.
For overprint and surcharge see #C289, C349.

Fencing — A131

Wmk. 343
1960, Sept. 23   Litho.   Perf. 12½
433 A131 3c shown   .35 .25
434 A131 5c Soccer   .60 .25
  Nos. 433-434,C234-C237 (6)   6.30 2.55
17th Olympic Games, Rome, 8/25-9/11.
For surcharges & overprints see #C249-C250, C254, C266-C270, C290, C298, C350, RA40.

Agricultural Products and Cattle — A132

1961, Mar. 3   Wmk. 311   Perf. 12½
435 A132 3c blue green   .65 .40
Issued to publicize the second agricultural and livestock census, Apr. 16, 1961.

Children's Hospital — A133

1961, May 2
436 A133 3c greenish blue   .55 .40
  Nos. 436,C245-C247 (4)   2.60 1.60
25th anniv. of the Lions Club of Panama. See #C245-C247.

Flags of Panama and Costa Rica — A134

1961, Oct. 2   Wmk. 343   Perf. 12½
437 A134 3c car & bl   .65 .40
Meeting of Presidents Mario Echandi of Costa Rica and Roberto F. Chiari of Panama at Paso Canoa, Apr. 21, 1961. See No. C251.

Arms of Colon — A135

1962, Feb. 28   Litho.   Wmk. 311
438 A135 3c car, yel & vio bl   .40 .40
3rd Central American Municipal Assembly, Colon, May 13-17. See No. C255.

Mercury and Cogwheel — A136

1962, Mar. 16   Wmk. 343
439 A136 3c red orange   .70 .40
First industrial and commercial census.

Social Security Hospital — A137

1962, June 1   Perf. 12½
440 A137 3c vermilion & gray   .65 .40
Opening of the Social Security Hospital. For surcharge see No. 445.

San Francisco de la Montana Church, Veraguas A138

Ruins of Old Panama Cathedral (1519-1671) A139

Designs: 3c, David Cathedral. 5c, Natá Church. 10c, Don Bosco Church. 15c, Church of the Virgin of Carmen. 20c, Colon Cathedral. 25c, Greek Orthodox Temple. 50c, Cathedral of Panama. 1b, Protestant Church of Colon.

1960-64   Litho.   Wmk. 343
Buildings in Black
441   A138 1c red & bl   .35 .25
441A A139 2c red & yel   .35 .25
441B A138 3c vio & yel   .35 .25
441C A139 5c rose & lt grn   .35 .25
441D A139 10c grn & yel   .35 .25
441E A139 10c red & bl ('64)   .35 .25
441F A139 15c ultra & lt grn   .50 .25
441G A139 20c red & pink   .75 .25
441H A138 25c grn & pink   .90 .45
441I A139 50c ultra & pink   1.50 .60
441J A138 1b lilac & yel   3.75 1.60
Nos. 441-441J (11)   9.50 4.65

Freedom of religion in Panama.
Issued: #441E, 6/4/64; others, 7/29/60.
See #C256-C265; souvenir sheet #C264a.
For surcharges and overprints see Nos. 445A, 451, 467, C288, C296-C297, C299.

Bridge of the Americas during Construction A140

1962, Oct. 12   Perf. 12½
442 A140 3c carmine & gray   .65 .40
Opening of the Bridge of the Americas (Thatcher Ferry Bridge), Oct. 12, 1962. See No. C273. For surcharge see No. 445B.

Fire Brigade Exercises, Inauguration of Aqueduct, 1906 A141

Portraits of Fire Brigade Officials: 3c, Lt. Col. Luis Carlos Endara P., Col. Raul Arango N. and Major Ernesto Arosemena A. 5c, Guillermo Patterson Jr., David F. de Castro, Pres. T. Gabriel Duque, Telmo Rugliancich and Tomas Leblanc.

1963, Jan. 22   Wmk. 311   Perf. 12½
443   A141 1c emer & blk   .65 .40
443A A141 3c vio bl & blk   .65 .40
444   A141 5c mag & blk   1.25 .40
Nos. 443-444, C279-C281 (6)   6.50 2.40
75th anniversary (in 1962) of the Panamanian Fire Brigade.
For surcharge see No. 445C.

Nos. 440, 441A, 442, 443A and 407 Surcharged in Black or Red

1963   Wmk. 343   Perf. 12½
445   A137 4c on 3c ver & gray   .75 .40
445A A138 4c on 3c vio & yel   .75 .40
445B A140 4c on 3c car & gray   .75 .40
Wmk. 311
445C A141 4c on 3c vio bl & blk   .75 .40
446   A121 10c on 25c dk car rose & bluish blk (R)   1.00 .40
Nos. 445-446 (5)   4.00 2.00
Issued: Nos. 445-445C, 8/30; No. 446, 10/9.

1964 Winter Olympics, Innsbruck — 141a

Perf. 14x13½, 13½x14 (#447A, 447C)
1963, Dec. 20   Litho.
447   A141a ½c Mountains   .35 .25
447A A141a 1c Speed skating   .35 .25
447B A141a 3c like No. 447   .75 .25
447C A141a 4c like No. 447A   .85 .25
447D A141a 5c Slalom skiing   1.10 .25
447E A141a 15c like No. 447D   2.00 .60
447F A141a 21c like No. 447D   3.75 1.00
447G A141a 31c like No. 447D   5.50 1.50
h. Souv. sheet of 2, #447F-447G, perf. 13½x14   19.00 10.00
Nos. 447-447G (8)   14.65 4.35
#447D-447G are airmail. #447Gh exists imperf., with background colors switched. Value, $17.50.

Pres. Francisco J. Orlich, Costa Rica — A142

Flags and Presidents: 2c, Luis A. Somoza, Nicaragua. 3c, Dr. Ramon Villeda M., Honduras. 4c, Roberto F. Chiari, Panama.

Perf. 12½x12
1963, Dec. 18   Litho.   Unwmk.
Portrait in Slate Green
448   A142 1c lt grn, red & ultra   .50 .25
448A A142 2c lt bl, red & ultra   .50 .25
448B A142 3c pale pink, red & ultra   .50 .25
448C A142 4c rose, red & ultra   .50 .25
Nos. 448-448C, C292-C294 (7)   6.45 2.70
Meeting of Central American Presidents with Pres. John F. Kennedy, San José, Mar. 18-20, 1963.

Vasco Nuñez de Balboa — A143

1964, Jan. 22   Photo.   Perf. 13
449 A143 4c green, pale rose   .80 .40
450th anniv. of Balboa's discovery of the Pacific Ocean. See No. C295.

No. C231 Surcharged "Correos B/.0.10" in Red
Wmk. 311
1964, Feb. 25   Litho.   Perf. 12½
450 AP74 10c on 21c lt bl   .80 .40

Type of 1962 Overprinted in Red

1964, Oct. 20   Wmk. 343
451 A138 1b red, bl & blk   3.00 2.50

1964 Summer Olympics, Tokyo A144

1964, Mar. 4   Perf. 13½x14
452   A144 ½c shown   .35 .25
452A A144 1c Torch bearer   .35 .25
Perf. 14x13½
452B A144 5c Olympic stadium   .65 .25
452C A144 10c like No. 452B   1.00 .30
452D A144 21c like No. 452B   2.40 .60
452E A144 50c like No. 452B   4.75 1.25
f. Souv. sheet of 1, perf. 13½x14   18.00 16.00
Nos. 452-452E (6)   9.50 2.90
Nos. 452B-452E are airmail. No. 452Ef exists imperf. with different colors. Value, $18.

Space Conquest A145

½c, Projected Apollo spacecraft. 1c, Gemini, Agena spacecraft. 5c, Astronaut Walter M. Schirra. 10c, Astronaut L. Gordon Cooper. 21c, Schirra's Mercury capsule. 50c, Cooper's Mercury capsule.

1964, Apr. 24   Perf. 14x14x13½
453   A145 ½c bl grn & multi   .35 .25
453A A145 1c dk blue & multi   .35 .25
453B A145 5c yel bis & multi   .45 .35
453C A145 10c lil rose & multi   .75 .45
453D A145 21c blue & multi   1.75 1.00

453E A145 50c violet & multi   7.75 5.00
f. Souvenir sheet of 1   23.50 20.00
Nos. 453-453E (6)   11.40 7.30
Nos. 453B-453E are airmail. No. 453Ef exists imperf. with different colors. Value, $23.50.

Aquatic Sports — A146

Perf. 14x13½, 13½x14
1964, Jun3. 17
454   A146 ½c Water skiing   .35 .25
454A A146 1c Skin diving   .35 .25
454B A146 5c Fishing   .45 .25
454C A146 10c Sailing, vert.   2.25 .50
454D A146 21c Hydroplane racing   4.25 1.00
454E A146 31c Water polo   5.25 1.25
f. Souvenir sheet of 1   21.00 20.00
Nos. 454-454E (6)   12.90 3.50
Nos. 454B-454E are airmail.
Nos. 454-454Ef exist imperf in different colors. Value imperf, Nos. 454-454E $22. Value imperf, No. 454Ef $21.

Eleanor Roosevelt — A147

Perf. 12x12½
1964, Oct. 9   Litho.   Unwmk.
455 A147 4c car & blk, grnsh   .70 .25
Issued to honor Eleanor Roosevelt (1884-1962). See Nos. C330-C330a.

Canceled to Order
Canceled sets of new issues have been sold by the government. Postally used examples are worth more.

1964 Winter Olympics, Innsbruck A147a

Olympic medals and winners: ½c, Women's slalom. 1c, Men's 500-meter speed skating. 2c, Four-man bobsled. 3c, Women's figure skating. 4c, Ski jumping. 5c, 15km cross country skiing. 6c, 50km cross country skiing. 7c, Women's 3000-meter speed skating. 10c, Men's figure skating. 21c, Two-man bobsled. 31c, Men's downhill skiing.

Litho. & Embossed
Perf. 13½x14
1964, Oct. 14   Unwmk.
456   A147a ½c bl grn & multi   .35 .25
456A A147a 1c dk bl & multi   .35 .25
456B A147a 2c brn vio & multi   .35 .25
456C A147a 3c lil rose & multi   .65 .25
456D A147a 4c brn lake & multi   1.00 .25
456E A147a 5c brt vio & multi   .75 .30
456F A147a 6c grn bl & multi   1.00 .40
456G A147a 7c dp vio & multi   1.60 .65
456H A147a 10c emer grn & multi   2.50 1.00
456I A147a 21c ver & multi   3.00 1.10
456J A147a 31c ultra & multi   5.25 2.00
k. Souv. sheet of 3, #456H-456J   19.00 16.00
Nos. 456-456J (11)   16.80 6.70
Nos. 456E-456J are airmail.
No. 456Jk exists imperf. Value $19.
See Nos. 458-458J.

Satellites
A147b

Designs: ½c, Telstar 1. 1c, Transit 2A. 5c, OSO 1 Solar Observatory. 10c, Tiros 2 weather satellite. 21c, Weather station. 50c, Syncom 3.

1964, Dec. 21   *Perf. 14x14x13½*

457	A147b	½c ver & multi	.75	.25
457A	A147b	1c vio & multi	.75	.25
457B	A147b	5c lil rose & multi	.75	.40
457C	A147b	10c blue & multi	1.00	.25
457D	A147b	21c bl grn & multi	2.80	.25
457E	A147b	50c green & multi	4.40	1.75
f.		Souvenir sheet of 1	22.00	16.00
		Nos. 457-457E (6)	10.45	4.15

Nos. 457B-457E are airmail. No. 457Ef exists imperf in different colors. Value, $22.
For overprints see Nos. 489-489b.

1964 Olympic Medals Type

Summer Olympic Medals and Winners: ½c, Parallel bars. 1c, Dragon-class sailing. 2c, Individual show jumping. 3c, Two-man kayak. 4c, Team road race cycling. 5c, Individual dressage. 6c, Women's 800-meter run. 7c, 3000-meter steeplechase. 10c, Men's floor exercises. 21c, Decathlon. 31c, Men's 100-meter freestyle swimming.

Litho. & Embossed

1964, Dec. 28   *Perf. 13½x14*

458	A147a	½c org & multi	.45	.25
458A	A147a	1c plum & multi	.45	.25
458B	A147a	2c bl grn & multi	.45	.25
458C	A147a	3c red brn & multi	.45	.25
458D	A147a	4c lilac rose & multi	.55	.25
458E	A147a	5c dull grn & multi	1.00	.25
458F	A147a	6c blue & multi	1.20	.25
458G	A147a	7c dk vio & multi	1.40	.30
458H	A147a	10c ver & multi	2.10	.40
458I	A147a	21c dl vio & multi	3.25	.65
458J	A147a	31c dk bl grn & multi	6.00	1.00
k.		Souv. sheet of 3, #458H-458J	25.00	17.50
		Nos. 458-458J (11)	17.30	4.10

#458E-458J are airmail. #458Jk exists imperf. Value, $25.

John F. Kennedy & Cape Kennedy
A147c

Designs: 1c, Launching of Titan II rocket, Gemini capsule. 2c, Apollo lunar module. 3c, Proposed Apollo command and service modules. 5c, Gemini capsule atop Titan II rocket. 6c, Soviet cosmonauts Komarov, Yegorov, Feoktistov. 11c, Ranger VII. 31c, Lunar surface.

1965, Feb. 25   Litho.   *Perf. 14*

459	A147c	½c vio bl & multi	.75	.25
459A	A147c	1c blue & multi	.75	.25
459B	A147c	2c plum & multi	.75	.25
459C	A147c	3c ol grn & multi	1.00	.30
459D	A147c	5c lilac rose & multi	1.00	.40
459E	A147c	10c dull grn & multi	1.75	.70
459F	A147c	11c brt vio & multi	2.90	1.10
459G	A147c	31c grn & multi	5.25	2.00
h.		Souvenir sheet of 1	22.00	20.00
		Nos. 459-459G (8)	14.15	5.25

Nos. 459D-459G are airmail. Nos. 459-459Gh exist imperf. in different colors. Values: set, $24; souvenir sheet, $22. For overprints see Nos. 491-491b.

Atomic Power for Peace
A147d

Designs: ½c, Nuclear powered submarine *Nautilus*. 1c, Nuclear powered ship *Savannah*. 4c, First nuclear reactor, Calderhall, England. 6c, Nuclear powered icebreaker *Lenin*. 10c, Nuclear powered observatory. 21c, Nuclear powered space vehicle.

1965, May 12

460	A147d	½c blue & multi		
460A	A147d	1c grn & multi		
460B	A147d	4c red & multi		
460C	A147d	6c dl bl grn & multi		
460D	A147d	10c blue grn & multi		
460E	A147d	21c dk vio & multi		
f.		Souv. sheet of 2, #460D-460E	13.00	12.50
		Set, #460-460E	9.75	3.50

Nos. 460C-460E are airmail.
Nos. 460-460Ef exists imperf in different colors. Value imperf, Nos. 460-460E $15. Value imperf, No. 460Ef $13.

John F. Kennedy Memorial — A147e

Kennedy and: ½c, PT109. 1c, Space capsule. 10c, UN emblem. 21c, Winston Churchill. 31c, Rocket launch at Cape Kennedy.

1965, Aug. 23   *Perf. 13½x13*

461	A147e	½c multicolored		
461A	A147e	1c multicolored		
461B	A147e	10c + 5c, multi		
461C	A147e	21c + 10c, multi		
461D	A147e	31c + 15c, multi		
e.		Souv. sheet of 2, #461A, 461D, perf. 12½x12	21.00	20.00
		Set, #461-461D	9.50	1.50

Nos. 461B-461D are airmail semipostal. Nos. 461-461De exist imperf in different colors. Value $21.
For overprints see Nos. C367A-C367B.

Keel-billed Toucan — A148

Song Birds: 2c, Scarlet macaw. 3c, Red-crowned woodpecker. 4c, Blue-gray tanager, horiz.

1965, Oct. 27   Unwmk.   *Perf. 14*

462	A148	1c brt pink & multi	.40	.40
462A	A148	2c multicolored	.40	.40
462B	A148	3c brt vio & multi	1.40	.40
462C	A148	4c org yel & multi	1.40	.40
		Nos. 462-462C,C337-C338 (6)	9.10	2.40

Snapper A149

1965, Dec. 7   Litho.

463	A149	1c shown	.65	.40
463A	A149	2c Dorado	.65	.40
		Nos. 463-463A,C339-C342 (6)	7.60	2.40

Pope Paul VI, Visit to UN — A149a

Designs: ½c, Pope on Balcony of St. Peter's, Vatican City. 1c, Pope Addressing UN General Assembly. 5c, Arms of Vatican City, Panama, UN emblem. 10c, Lyndon Johnson, Pope Paul VI, Francis Cardinal Spellman. 21c, Ecumenical Council, Vatican II. 31c, Earlybird satellite.

1966 Apr. 4   *Perf. 12x12½*

464	A149a	½c multicolored		
464A	A149a	1c multicolored		
464B	A149a	5c multicolored		
464C	A149a	10c multicolored		
464D	A149a	21c multicolored		
464E	A149a	31c multicolored		
f.		Souv. sheet of 2, #464B, 464E, perf. 13x13½	22.00	20.00
		Set, #464-464E	11.00	3.00

Nos. 464B-464E are airmail. No. 464Ef exists imperf. with different margin color. Value $22.
For overprints see Nos. 490-490B.

Famous Men — A149b

Designs: ½c, William Shakespeare. 10c, Dante Alighieri. 31c, Richard Wagner.

1966, May 26   *Perf. 14*

465	A149b	½c multicolored		
465A	A149b	10c multicolored		
465B	A149b	31c multicolored		
c.		Souv. sheet of 2, #465A-465B, perf. 13½x14	19.00	15.00
		Set, #465-465B	8.25	3.25

Nos. 465A-465B are airmail. No. 465Bc exists imperf. with different margin color. Value $19.

Works by Famous Artists — A149c

Paintings: ½c, Elizabeth Tucher by Durer. 10c, Madonna of the Rocky Grotto by Da Vinci. 31c, La Belle Jardiniere by Raphael.

1966, May 26

466	A149c	½c multicolored		
466A	A149c	10c multicolored		
466B	A149c	31c multicolored		
c.		Souv. sheet of 2, #466-466B	15.00	15.00
		Set, #466-466B	8.50	2.25

Nos. 466A-466B are airmail. No. 466Bc exists imperf. with different margin color. Value $30.

No. 441H Surcharged

1966, June 27   Wmk. 343   *Perf. 12½*

467	A138	13c on 25c grn & pink	.90	.40

The "25c" has not been obliterated.

A149d

No. 468A, Uruguay, 1930, 1950. No. 468B, Italy, 1934, 1938. No. 468C, Brazil, 1958, 1962. No. 468D, Germany, 1954. No. 468E, Great Britain.

1966, July 11   *Perf. 14*

468	A149d	½c multi	
468A	A149d	.005b multi	
468B	A149d	10c multi	
468C	A149d	10c multi	
468D	A149d	21c multi	
468E	A149d	21c multi	
f.		Souv. sheet of 2, #468B, 468D	16.00	15.00

---

g.		Souv. sheet of 2, #468, 468E, imperf.	13.00	11.00
		Set, #468-465E	9.00	2.25

World Cup Soccer Championships, Great Britain. Nos. 468B-468E are airmail.
Nos. 468-468E exist imperf in different colors. Value, $27.50.

A149e

Italian Contributions to Space Research: ½c, Launch of Scout rocket, San Marco satellite. 1c, San Marco in orbit, horiz. 5c, Italian scientists, rocket. 10c, Arms of Panama, Italy, horiz. 21c, San Marco boosted into orbit, horiz.

     Perf. 12x12½, 12½x12

1966, Aug. 12

469	A149e	½c multicolored	
469A	A149e	1c multicolored	
469B	A149e	5c multicolored	
469C	A149e	10c multicolored	
469D	A149e	21c multicolored	
e.		Souv. sheet of 2, #469C-469D, imperf.	17.00	15.00
		Set, #469-469D	9.75	4.00

Nos. 469B-469D are airmail.
Nos. 469-469D exist imperf in different colors. Value: set, $27.

Nos. 468-468g Ovptd.

1966, Nov. 21   *Perf. 14*

470	A149d	½c on #468		
470A	A149d	.005b on #468A		
470B	A149d	10c on #468B		
470C	A149d	10c on #468C		
470D	A149d	21c on #468D		
470E	A149d	21c on #468E		
f.		on #468Ef	30.00	30.00
g.		on #468Eg, imperf.	30.00	30.00
		Set, #470-470E	16.50	3.75

Nos. 470B-470E are airmail.
Nos. 470-470E exist imperf in different colors. Value: set, $27.50.

A149f

Religious Paintings — A149g

Paintings: ½c, Coronation of Mary. 1c, Holy Family with Angel. 2c, Adoration of the Magi. 3c, Madonna and Child. No. 471D, The Annunciation. No. 471E, The Nativity. No. 471Fh, Madonna and Child.

1966, Oct. 24   *Perf. 11*

Size of No. 471D: 32x34mm

471	A149f	½c Velazquez	
471A	A149f	1c Saraceni	
471B	A149f	2c Durer	
471C	A149f	3c Orazio	
471D	A149g	21c Rubens	
471E	A149f	21c Boticelli	

Souvenir Sheet
Perf. 14

471F Sheet of 2
  g. A149f 21c like No. 471E, black inscriptions ... 12.50 11.00
  h. A149f 31c Mignard ... 18.00 18.00
  Set, #471-471E ... 12.00 1.25

Nos. 471D-471F are airmail.
Nos. 471-471F exist imperf in different colors. Value imperf, Nos. 471-471E $12. Value imperf, No. 471F $17.50.

Sir Winston Churchill, British Satellites A149h

Churchill and: 10c, Blue Streak, NATO emblem. 31c, Europa 1, rocket engine.

1966, Nov. 25   Perf. 12x12½
472 A149h ½c shown
472A A149h 10c org & multi
472B A149h 31c dk bl & multi
  c. Souv. sheet of 2, #472A-472B, perf. 13½x14 ... 13.00 11.50
  Set, #472-472B ... 7.25 2.00

Nos. 472A-472B are airmail.
No. 472Bc exists imperf in different colors. Value $15.
For overprints see Nos. 492-492B.

John F. Kennedy, 3rd Death Anniv. A149i

10c, Kennedy, UN building. 31c, Kennedy, satellites & map.

1966, Nov. 25   Perf. 14
473 A149i ½c shown
473A A149i 10c multi
473B A149i 31c multi
  c. Souv. sheet of 2, #473A-473B ... 19.00 18.00
  Set, #473-473B ... 7.25 2.00

Nos. 473A-473B are airmail.
No. 473Bc exists imperf in different colors. Value $19.

Jules Verne (1828-1905), French Space Explorations A149j

Designs: ½c, Earth, A-1 satellite. 1c, Verne, submarine. 5c, Earth, FR-1 satellite. 10c, Verne, telescope. 21c, Verne, capsule heading toward Moon. 31c, D-1 satellite over Earth.

1966, Dec. 28   Perf. 13½x14
474 A149j ½c bl & multi
474A A149j 1c bl grn & multi
474B A149j 5c ultra & multi
474C A149j 10c lil, blk & red
474D A149j 21c vio & multi
  f. Souv. sheet of 2, #474C, 474D, imperf. ... 14.00 12.50
474E A149j 31c dl bl & multi
  g. Souvenir sheet of 1 ... 17.50 15.00
  Set, #474-474E ... 11.50 2.00

Nos. 474B-474E are airmail.
Nos. 474-474Eg exist imperf in different colors. Value imperf. Nos. 474-474E $22.50. Value imperf, No. 474Eg $17.50.

Hen and Chicks — A150

Domestic Animals: 3c, Rooster. 5c, Pig, horiz. 8c, Cow, horiz.

1967, Feb. 3   Unwmk.   Perf. 14
475 A150 1c multi ... .40 .40
475A A150 3c multi ... .40 .40
475B A150 5c multi ... .40 .40
475C A150 8c multi ... .40 .40
Nos. 475-475C,C353-C356 (8) ... 13.60 3.20

Easter — A150a

Paintings: ½c, Christ at Calvary, by Giambattista Tiepolo. 1c, The Crucifixion, by Rubens. 5c, Pieta, by Sarto, horiz. 10c, Body of Christ, by Raphael Santi. 21c, The Arisen Christ, by Multscher. No. 476E, Christ Ascending into Heaven, by Grunewald. No. 476F, Christ on the Cross, by Van der Weyden. No. 476G, Madonna and Child, by Rubens.

1967, Mar. 13   Perf. 14x13½, 13½x14
476 A150a ½c multi
476A A150a 1c multi
476B A150a 5c multi
476C A150a 10c multi
476D A150a 21c multi
476E A150a 31c multi
  Set, #476-476E ... 10.50 3.00

Souvenir Sheets
Perf. 12½x12x12½x13½

476F A150a 31c multi ... 22.00 20.00

Imperf

476G A150a 31c multi ... 22.00 20.00

Nos. 476B-476G are airmail.

1968 Summer Olympics, Mexico City A150b

Indian Ruins at: ½c, Teotihuacan. 1c, Tajin. 5c, Xochicalco. 10c, Monte Alban. 21c, Palenque. 31c, Chichen Itza.

1967, Apr. 18   Perf. 12x12½
477 A150b ½c plum & multi
477A A150b 1c red lil & multi
477B A150b 5c blue & multi
477C A150b 10c ver & multi
477D A150b 21c grn bl & multi
477E A150b 31c grn & multi
  Set, #477-477E ... 11.00 3.00

Souvenir Sheet
Perf. 12x12½x14x12½

477F A150a 31c multi ... 20.00 18.00

Nos. 477B-477E are airmail.

New World Anhinga — A151

Birds: 1c, Quetzals. 3c, Turquoise-browed motmot. 4c, Double-collared aracari, horiz. 5c, Macaw. 13c, Belted kingfisher. 50c, Hummingbird.

1967, July 20   Perf. 14
478 A151 ½c lt bl & multi ... 1.20 .60
478A A151 1c lt gray & multi ... 1.20 .60
478B A151 3c pink & multi ... 1.40 .60
478C A151 4c lt grn & multi ... 1.75 .60
478D A151 5c buff & multi ... 2.10 .60
478E A151 13c yel & multi ... 8.25 2.00
Nos. 478-478E (6) ... 15.90 5.00

Souvenir Sheet
Perf. 14½

478F A151 50c Sheet of 1 ... 23.00 17.50
No. 478A exists imperf. with blue background. Value $32.

Works of Famous Artists — A151a

Paintings: No. 479, Maiden in the Doorway, by Rembrandt. No. 479A, Blueboy, by Gainsborough. No. 479B, The Promise of Louis XIII, by Ingres. No. 479C, St. George and the Dragon, by Raphael. No. 479D, The Blacksmith's Shop, by Velazquez, horiz. No. 479E, St. Hieronymus, by Durer. Nos. 479F-479K, Self-portraits.

Perf. 14x13½, 13½x14
1967, Aug. 23
479 A151a 5c multi
479A A151a 5c multi
479B A151a 5c multi
479C A151a 21c multi
479D A151a 21c multi
479E A151a 21c multi
  Set, #479-479E ... 8.75 2.00

Souvenir Sheets
Various Compound Perfs.

479F A151a 21c Gainsborough ... 17.00 8.00
479G A151a 21c Rembrandt ... 17.00 8.00
479H A151a 21c Ingres ... 17.00 8.00
479I A151a 21c Raphael ... 17.00 8.00
479J A151a 21c Velazquez ... 17.00 8.00
479K A151a 21c Durer ... 17.00 8.00
Nos. 479F-479K (6) ... 102.00 48.00
Nos. 479C-479K are airmail.

Red Deer, by Franz Marc — A152

Animal Paintings by Franz Marc: 3c, Tiger, vert. 5c, Monkeys. 8c, Blue Fox.

1967, Sept. 1   Perf. 14
480 A152 1c multicolored ... .65 .40
480A A152 3c multicolored ... .65 .40
480B A152 5c multicolored ... .65 .40
480C A152 8c multicolored ... .65 .40
Nos. 480-480C,C357-C360 (8) ... 14.00 3.20

Paintings by Goya — A152a

Designs: 2c, The Water Carrier. 3c, Count Floridablanca. 4c, Senora Francisca Sebasa y Garcia. 5c, St. Bernard and St. Robert. 8c, Self-portrait. 10c, Dona Isabel Cobos de Porcel. 13c, Clothed Maja, horiz. 21c, Don Manuel Osoria de Zuniga as a child. 50c, Cardinal Luis of Bourbon and Villabriga.

1967, Oct. 17   Perf. 14x13½, 13½x14
481 A152a 2c multicolored
481A A152a 3c multicolored
481B A152a 4c multicolored
481C A152a 5c multicolored
481D A152a 8c multicolored
481E A152a 10c multicolored
481F A152a 13c multi, horiz.
481G A152a 21c multicolored
  Set, #481-481G ... 13.00 3.20

Souvenir Sheet

481H A152a 50c multicolored ... 22.00 20.00
Nos. 481C-481H are airmail.

Life of Christ — A152b

Paintings: No. 482, The Holy Family, by Michaelangelo. No. 482A, Christ Washing Feet, by Brown. 3c, Christ's Charge to Peter, by Rubens. 4c, Christ and the Money Changers in the Temple, by El Greco, horiz. No. 482D, Christ's Entry into Jerusalem, by Van Dyck, horiz. No. 482E, The Last Supper, by de Juanes.

No. 482FI, Pastoral Adoration. No. 482Fm, The Holy Family. No. 482Gn, Christ with Mary and Martha. No. 482Go, Flight from Egypt. No. 482Hp, St. Thomas. No. 482Hq, The Tempest. No. 482Ir, The Transfiguration. No. 482Is, The Crucifixion.

No. 482J, The Baptism of Christ, by Guido Reni. No. 482K, Christ at the Sea of Galilee, by Tintoretto, horiz.

1968, Jan. 10   Perf. 14x13½x13½x14
482 A152b 1c multi
482A A152b 1c multi
482B A152b 3c multi
482C A152b 4c multi
482D A152b 21c multi
482E A152b 21c multi
  Set, #482-482E ... 10.00 3.00

Souvenir Sheets
Various Perfs.

482F Sheet of 2 ... 19.00 16.00
  l. A152b 1c Schongauer
  m. A152b 21c Raphael
482G Sheet of 2 ... 19.00 16.00
  n. A152b 3c Tintoretto
  o. A152b 21c Caravaggio
482H Sheet of 2 ... 19.00 16.00
  p. A152b 21c Anonymous, 12th cent.
  q. A152b 31c multicolored
482I Sheet of 2 ... 19.00 16.00
  r. A152b 21c Raphael
  s. A152b 31c Montanez
482J A152b 22c Sheet of 1 ... 19.00 16.00
482K A152b 24c Sheet of 1 ... 19.00 16.00
Nos. 482C-482K are airmail.
Nos. 482J-482K also exist imperf.

Butterflies A152c

½c, Apodemia albinus. 1c, Caligo ilioneus, vert. 3c, Meso semia tenera. 4c, Pamphila epictetus. 5c, Entheus peleus. 13c, Tmetoglene drymo. 50c, Thymele chalco, vert.

1968, Feb. 23   Perf. 14
483 A152c ½c multi
483A A152c 1c multi
483B A152c 3c multi
483C A152c 4c multi
483D A152c 5c multi
483E A152c 13c multi
  Set, #483-483E ... 24.50 5.00

Souvenir Sheet
Perf. 14½

483F A152c 50c multi ... 50.00 15.00
Nos. 483D-483F are airmail.
No. 483F exists imperf with pink margin. Value $50.

10th Winter Olympics, Grenoble A152d

½c, Emblem, vert. 1c, Ski jumper. 5c, Skier. 10c, Mountain climber. 21c, Speed skater. 31c, Two-man bobsled.

1968, Feb. 2   Perf. 14x13½, 13½x14
484 A152d ½c multi
484A A152d 1c multi
484B A152d 5c multi
484C A152d 10c multi

484D A152d 21c multi
484E A152d 31c multi
Set, #484-484E   10.00   1.50

Souvenir Sheets
Perf. 14

484F   Sheet of 2   18.00 15.00
   h.   A152d 10c Emblem, snowflake
   i.   A152d 31c Figure skater
484G   Sheet of 2   18.00 15.00
   j.   A152d 31c Biathlon
   k.   A152d 10c Skier on ski lift
Nos. 484B-484G are airmail.

Sailing Ships
A152e

Paintings by: ½c, Gamiero, vert. 1c, Lebreton. 3c, Anonymous Japanese. 4c, Le Roi. 5c, Van de Velde. 13c, Duncan. 50c, Anonymous Portuguese, vert.

1968, May 7   *Perf. 14*
485 A152e ½c multicolored
485A A152e 1c multicolored
485B A152e 3c multicolored
485C A152e 4c multicolored
485D A152e 5c multicolored
485E A152e 13c multicolored
Set, #485-485E   11.00   5.00

Souvenir Sheet
Perf. 14½

485F A152e 50c multicolored 10.00 9.00

Nos. 485D-485E are airmail. No. 485F exists imperf. with light blue margin. Value $10.

Tropical
Fish — A152f

½c, Balistipus undulatus. 1c, Holacanthus ciliaris. 3c, Chaetodon ephippium. 4c, Epinephelus elongatus. 5c, Anisotremus virginicus. 13c, Balistoides conspicillum. 50c, Raja texana, vert.

1968, June 26   *Perf. 14*
486 A152f ½c multi
486A A152f 1c multi
486B A152f 3c multi
486C A152f 4c multi
486D A152f 5c multi
486E A152f 13c multi
Set, #486-486E   9.75   2.00

Souvenir Sheet
Perf. 14½

486F A152f 50c multi   25.00   9.00

Nos. 486D-486F are airmail. No. 486F exists imperf. with pink margin. Value $25 .

Olympic
Medals and
Winners,
Grenoble
A152g

Olympic Medals and Winners: 1c, Men's giant slalom. 2c, Women's downhill. 3c, Women's figure skating. 4c, 5000-meter speed skating. 5c, 10,000-meter speed skating. 6c, Women's slalom. 8c, Women's 1000-meter speed skating. 13c, Women's 1500-meter speed skating. 30c, Two-man bobsled. 70c, Nordic combined.

Litho. & Embossed
1968, July 30   *Perf. 13½x14*
487 A152g 1c pink & multi
487A A152g 2c vio & multi
487B A152g 3c grn & multi
487C A152g 4c plum & multi
487D A152g 5c red brn & multi
487E A152g 6c brt vio & multi

487F A152g 8c Prus bl & multi
487G A152g 13c bl & multi
487H A152g 30c rose lil & multi
Set, #487-487H   11.25   3.60

Souvenir Sheet

487I A152g 70c red & multi 19.00 18.00
Nos. 487G-487H are airmail.

Miniature Sheet

Music — A152h

Paintings of Musicians, Instruments: 5c, Mandolin, by de la Hyre. 10c, Lute, by Caravaggio. 15c, Flute, by ter Brugghen. 20c, Chamber ensemble, by Tourmer. 25c, Violin, by Caravaggio. 30c, Piano, by Vermeer. 40c, Harp, by Memling.

1968, Sept. 11 Litho.   *Perf. 13½x14*
488 A152h Sheet of 6   13.00 2.40
   a.   5c multicolored
   b.   10c multicolored
   c.   15c multicolored
   d.   20c multicolored
   e.   25c multicolored
   f.   30c multicolored

Souvenir Sheet
Perf. 14

488A A152h 40c multicolored 19.00 18.00

Nos. 457, 457E Ovptd. in Black

1968, Oct. 17
489 A147b ½c on No. 457   11.50   .75
489A A147b 50c on No. 457E 11.50   .75
   b.   Souv. sheet of 1, on No. 457Ef   22.50 22.50

Nos. 489-489A exist with gold overprint. Value: set, $100. Overprint differs on No. 489Ab.

Nos. 464, 464D & 464Ef Ovptd. in Black or Gold

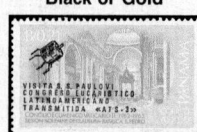

1968, Oct. 18   *Perf. 12x12½*
490 A149a ½c on No. 464   7.25
490A A149a 21c on No. 464D   7.25

Souvenir Sheet
Perf. 13½x13½

490B   on No. 464Ef (G) 27.50 27.50

Nos. 490A-490B are airmail. No. 490B exists imperf. with different colored border. Value same as No. 490B. Overprint differs on No. 490B.

Nos. 459, 459G-459Gh Ovptd. in Black

1968, Oct. 21   *Perf. 14*
491 A147c ½c on No. 459   7.50
491A A147c 31c on No. 459G   7.50
   b.   on souv. sheet, No. 459Gh 22.00 19.00

Nos. 491A-491Ab are airmail.
Nos. 491-491A exist overprinted in gold, and imperf., overprinted in gold. No. 491Ab exists imperf in different colors and black or gold overprints. Values, black $9, gold $105.

Nos. 472-472A, 472Bc Overprinted in Black or Gold

1968, Oct. 22   *Perf. 12x12½*
492 A149h ½c (#472)   11.00
492A A149h 10c (#472A)   11.00

Souvenir Sheet
Perf. 13½x14

492B   on No. 472Bc   13.50 13.50

Nos. 492A-492B are airmail.
Nos. 492-492A with gold overprint, value $105. No. 492B exists imperf in different colors.

Hunting on
Horseback
A152i

Paintings and Tapestries: 1c, Koller. 3c, Courbet. 5c, Tischbein, the Elder. 10c, Gobelin, vert. 13c, Oudry. 30c, Rubens.

1968, Oct. 29   *Perf. 14*
493 A152i 1c multicolored
493A A152i 3c multicolored
493B A152i 5c multicolored
493C A152i 10c multicolored
493D A152i 13c multicolored
493E A152i 30c multicolored
Set, #493-493E   8.75 4.00

Nos. 493D-493E are airmail.

Miniature Sheet

Famous
Race
Horses
— A152j

Horse Paintings: a, 5c, Lexington, by Edward Troye. b, 10c, American Eclipse, by Alvan Fisher. c, 15c, Plenipotentiary, by Abraham Cooper. d, 20c, Gimcrack, by George Stubbs. e, 25c, Flying Childers, by James Seymour. f, 30c, Eclipse, by Stubbs.

1968, Dec. 18   *Perf. 13½x14*
494 A152j Sheet of 6, #a.-f. 17.50 12.50

1968
Summer
Olympics,
Mexico
City — A152k

Mexican art: 1c, Watermelons, by Diego Rivera. 2c, Women, by Jose Clemente Orozco. 3c, Flower Seller, by Miguel Covarrubias, vert. 4c, Nutall Codex, vert. 5c, Mayan statue, vert. 6c, Face sculpture, vert. 8c, Seated figure, vert. 13c, Ceramic angel, vert.

30c, Christ, by David Alfaro Siqueiros. 70c, Symbols of Summer Olympic events.

1968, Dec. 23   *Perf. 13½x14, 14x13½*
495 A152k 1c multicolored
495A A152k 2c multicolored
495B A152k 3c multicolored
495C A152k 4c multicolored
495D A152k 5c multicolored
495E A152k 6c multicolored
495F A152k 8c multicolored
495G A152k 13c multicolored
495H A152k 30c multicolored
Set, #495-495H   15.00 3.60

Souvenir Sheet
Perf. 14

495I A152k 70c multicolored 16.00 16.00
Nos. 495G-495H are airmail.

First Visit of Pope
Paul VI to Latin
America — A152l

Paintings: 1c, Madonna and Child, by Raphael. 2c, Madonna and Child, by Ferruzzi. 3c, Madonna and Child, by Bellini. 4c, The Annunciation, 17th cent. 5c, Madonna and Child, by Van Dyck. 6c, Madonna and Child, by Albani. 7c, Adoration of the Magi, by Master of the Viennese Schottenaltar. 8c, Adoration of the Magi, by Van Dyck. 10c, Holy Family, 16th cent.
50c, Madonna and Child, angel, by Del Sarto.

1969, Aug. 5   *Perf. 14*
496 A152l 1c multi
496A A152l 2c multi
496B A152l 3c multi
496C A152l 4c multi
496D A152l 5c multi
496E A152l 6c multi
496F A152l 7c multi
496G A152l 8c multi
496H A152l 13c multi
Set, #496-496H   14.00 3.60

Souvenir Sheet
Perf. 14½

496I A152l 50c multi   15.00 7.50
Nos. 496E-496I are airmail.

Map of Americas and
People — A153

5c, Map of Panama, People and Houses, horiz.

1969, Aug. 14 Photo.   Wmk. 350
500 A153 5c violet blue   .70   .40
501 A153 10c bright rose lilac   .90   .40
Issued to publicize the 1970 census.

Cogwheel
A154

1969, Aug. 14
502 A154 13c yel & dk bl gray   .65   .40
50th anniv. of Rotary Intl. of Panama.

Cornucopia and
Map of
Panama — A155

Perf. 14½x15
1969, Oct. 10 Litho.   Unwmk.
503 A155 10c lt bl & multi   .65   .40
1st anniv. of the October 11 Revolution.

Map of Panama and Ruins A156

Natá Church A157

Designs: 5c, Farmer, wife and mule. 13c, Hotel Continental. 20c, Church of the Virgin of Carmen. 21c, Gold altar, San José Church. 25c, Del Rey bridge. 30c, Dr. Justo Arosemena monument. 34c, Cathedral of Panama. 38c, Municipal Palace. 40c, French Plaza. 50c, Thatcher Ferry Bridge (Bridge of the Americas). 59c, National Theater.

Perf. 14½x15, 15x14½
1969-70 Litho. Unwmk.
504	A156	3c org & blk	.40	.25
505	A156	5c lt bl grn ('70)	.40	.25
506	A157	8c dl brn ('70)	.40	.25
507	A156	13c emer & blk	.55	.25
508	A157	20c vio brn ('70)	.80	.25
509	A157	21c yellow ('70)	.80	.40
510	A156	25c lt bl grn ('70)	1.00	.25
511	A157	30c black ('70)	1.25	.40
512	A156	34c org brn ('70)	1.50	.50
513	A157	38c brt bl ('70)	1.50	.40
514	A156	40c org yel ('70)	2.00	.60
515	A156	50c brt rose lil & blk	2.10	.70
516	A156	59c brt rose lil ('70)	3.00	.90
		Nos. 504-516 (13)	15.70	5.40

Issued: Nos. 504, 507, 515, 10/10/69. Others, 1/28/70.
For surcharges see Nos. 541, 543, 545-547, RA78-RA80.

Stadium and Discus Thrower A158

Flor del Espiritu Santo — A159

Wmk. 365
1970, Jan. 6 Litho. Perf. 13½
517	A158	1c ultra & multi	.45	.25
518	A158	2c ultra & multi	.45	.25
519	A158	3c ultra & multi	.45	.25
520	A158	5c ultra & multi	.45	.25
521	A158	10c ultra & multi	.60	.25
522	A158	13c ultra & multi	.65	.25
523	A159	13c pink ultra	.80	.25
524	A158	25c ultra & multi	1.60	.50
525	A158	30c ultra & multi	2.00	.75
		Nos. 517-525,C368-C369 (11)	11.95	4.05

11th Central American and Caribbean Games, Feb. 28-Mar. 14.

Office of Comptroller General, 1970 — A160

Designs: 5c, Alejandro Tapia and Martin Sosa, first Comptrollers, 1931-34, horiz. 8c, Comptroller's emblem. 13c, Office of Comptroller General, 1955-70, horiz.

1971, Feb. 25 Litho. Wmk. 365
526	A160	3c yel & multi	.80	.40
527	A160	5c brn, buff & gold	.80	.40
528	A160	8c gold & multi	.80	.40
529	A160	13c blk & multi	.80	.40
		Nos. 526-529 (4)	3.20	1.60

Comptroller General's Office, 40th anniv.

Indian Alligator Design — A161

1971, Aug. 18 Wmk. 343 Perf. 13½
530	A161	8c multicolored	1.25	.40

SENAPI (Servicio Nacional de Artesania y Pequeñas Industrias), 5th anniv.

Education Year Emblem, Map of Panama — A162

1971, Aug. 19 Litho.
531	A162	1b multicolored	4.00	2.50

International Education Year, 1970.
For surcharge see No. 542.

Congress Emblem A163

1972, Aug. 25
532	A163	25c multicolored	1.50	.60

9th Inter-American Conference of Saving and Loan Associations, Panama City, Jan. 23-29, 1971.

UPU Headquarters, Bern — A164

Design: 30c, UPU Monument, Bern, vert.

1971, Dec. 14 Wmk. 343
533	A164	8c multicolored	.85	.40
534	A164	30c multicolored	2.60	.60

Inauguration of Universal Postal Union Headquarters, Bern, Switzerland.
For surcharge see No. RA77.

Cow, Pig and Produce A165

1971, Dec. 15
535	A165	3c yel, brn & blk	.80	.40

3rd agricultural census.

Map of Panama and "4-S" Emblem A166

1971, Dec. 16
536	A166	2c multicolored	.80	.40

Rural youth 4-S program.

UNICEF Emblem, Children A167

Wmk. 365
1972, Sept. 12 Litho. Perf. 13½
537	A167	1c yel & multi	.45	.25
		Nos. 537,C390-C392 (4)	4.05	1.30

25th anniv. (in 1971) of UNICEF. See No. C392a.

Tropical Fruits — A168

1972, Sept. 13
538	A168	1c shown	.50	.25
539	A168	2c Isla de Noche	.50	.25
540	A168	3c Carnival float, vert.	.50	.25
		Nos. 538-540,C393-C395 (6)	7.00	1.70

Tourist publicity.
For surcharges see Nos. RA75-RA76.

Nos. 516, 531 and 511 Surcharged in Red

Perf. 14½x15, 15x14½, 13½
Wmk. 343, Unwmkd.
1973, Mar. 15
541	A156	8c on 59c brt rose lil	.85	.25
542	A162	10c on 1b multi	.85	.25
543	A157	13c on 30c blk	.85	.25
		Nos. 541-543,C402 (4)	3.55	1.05

UN Security Council Meeting, Panama City, Mar. 15-21. Surcharges differ in size and are adjusted to fit shape of stamp.

José Daniel Crespo, Educator — A169

Wmk. 365
1973, June 20 Litho. Perf. 13½
544	A169	3c lt bl & multi	.55	.25
		Nos. 544,C403-C413 (12)	18.90	4.35

For overprints and surcharges see Nos. C414-C416, C418-C421, RA81-RA82, RA84.

Nos. 511-512 and 509 Surcharged in Red

Perf. 15x14½, 14½x15
1974, Nov. 11 Unwmk.
545	A157	5c on 30c blk	.80	.25
546	A156	10c on 34c org brn	.80	.25
547	A157	13c on 21c yel	.80	.25
		Nos. 545-547,C417-C421 (8)	6.40	2.00

Surcharge vertical on No. 546.

Bolivar, Bridge of the Americas, Men with Flag — A170

Perf. 12½
1976, Mar. 30 Litho. Unwmk.
548	A170	6c multicolored	.45	.25
		Nos. 548,C426-C428 (4)	4.95	1.40

150th anniversary of Congress of Panama.

Evibacus Princeps — A171

Marine life: 3c, Ptitosarcus sinuosus, vert. 4c, Acanthaster planci. 7c, Starfish. 1b, Mithrax spinosissmus.

Perf. 12½x13, 13x12½
1976, May 6 Litho. Wmk. 377
549	A171	2c multi	.95	.25
550	A171	3c multi	.95	.25
551	A171	4c multi	.95	.25
552	A171	7c multi	.95	.25
		Nos. 549-552,C429-C430 (6)	9.45	2.15

Souvenir Sheet
Imperf
553	A171	1b multi	7.25

Bolivar from Bolivar Monument A172

Bolivar and Argentine Flag — A173

Stamps of design A172 show details of Bolivar Monument, Panama City; design A173 shows head of Bolivar and flags of Latin American countries.

Perf. 13½
1976, June 22 Unwmk. Litho.
554	A172	20c shown	1.40	1.00
555	A173	20c shown	1.40	1.00
556	A173	20c Bolivia	1.40	1.00
557	A173	20c Brazil	1.40	1.00
558	A173	20c Chile	1.40	1.00
559	A172	20c Battle scene	1.40	1.00
560	A173	20c Colombia	1.40	1.00
561	A173	20c Costa Rica	1.40	1.00
562	A173	20c Cuba	1.40	1.00
563	A173	20c Ecuador	1.40	1.00
564	A173	20c El Salvador	1.40	1.00
565	A173	20c Guatemala	1.40	1.00
566	A173	20c Guyana	1.40	1.00
567	A173	20c Haiti	1.40	1.00
568	A172	20c Assembly	1.40	1.00
569	A172	20c Liberated people	1.40	1.00
570	A173	20c Honduras	1.40	1.00
571	A173	20c Jamaica	1.40	1.00
572	A173	20c Mexico	1.40	1.00
573	A173	20c Nicaragua	1.40	1.00
574	A173	20c Panama	1.40	1.00
575	A173	20c Paraguay	1.40	1.00
576	A173	20c Peru	1.40	1.00
577	A173	20c Dominican Rep.	1.40	1.00
578	A172	20c Bolivar and flag bearer	1.40	1.00
579	A173	20c Surinam	1.40	1.00
580	A173	20c Trinidad-Tobago	1.40	1.00
581	A173	20c Uruguay	1.40	1.00
582	A173	20c Venezuela	1.40	1.00
583	A172	20c Indian delegation	1.40	1.00
a.		Sheet of 30, #554-583	42.00	36.00
		Nos. 554-583 (30)	42.00	30.00

Souvenir Sheet
584		Sheet of 3	8.25	8.25
a.		A172 30c Bolivar and flag bearer	1.40	1.40
b.		A172 30c Monument, top	1.40	1.40
c.		A172 40c Inscription tablet	1.75	1.75

Amphictyonic Congress of Panama, sesquicentennial. No. 584 comes perf. and imperf. Values the same.

Nos. 554-583 and 584 were overprinted to honor the 1980 Olympics. The overprinted sets were issued Nov. 27, 1980.

Nicanor Villalaz, Designer of Coat of Arms — A174

National Lottery Building, Panama City — A175

1976, Nov. 12	Litho.	Perf. 12½		
585	A174	5c dk blue	1.00	.40
586	A175	6c multicolored	1.00	.40

Contadora Island — A176

1976, Dec. 29			Perf. 12½	
587	A176	3c multicolored	.75	.40

Pres. Carter and Gen. Omar Torrijos Signing Panama Canal Treaties A177

Design: 23c, like No. 588. Design includes Alejandro Orfila, Secretary General of OAS.

1978, Jan. 3	Litho.	Perf. 12		
Size: 90x40mm				
588	A177	50c Strip of 3	9.75	9.75
a.		3c multicolored	.25	.25
b.		40c multicolored	1.00	1.00
c.		50c multicolored	1.25	1.25
Perf. 14				
Size: 36x26mm				
589	A177	23c multicolored	.75	.40

Signing of Panama Canal Treaties, Washington, DC, Sept. 7, 1977.

Pres. Carter and Gen. Torrijos Signing Treaties A178

1978, Nov. 13	Litho.	Perf. 12		
590	A178	Strip of 3	9.00	8.00
a.		5c multi (30x40mm)	.40	.40
b.		35c multi (30x40mm)	1.10	.45
c.		41c multi (45x40mm)	1.10	.50
Size: 36x26mm				
591	A178	3c Treaty signing	.40	.40

Signing of Panama Canal Treaties ratification documents, Panama City, Panama, June 6, 1978.

World Commerce Zone, Colon — A179

1978, Nov. 13	Litho.	Perf. 12		
592	A179	6c multicolored	.80	.40

Free Zone of Colon, 30th anniversary.

Melvin Jones, Lions Emblem — A180

1978, Nov. 13				
593	A180	50c multicolored	1.75	1.25

Birth centenary of Melvin Jones, founder of Lions International.

Torrijos with Children, Ship, Flag — A181

"75," Coat of Arms — A182

Rotary Emblem, "75" — A183

Gen. Torrijos and Pres. Carter, Flags, Ship — A184

UPU Emblem, Globe — A185

Boy and Girl Inside Heart — A186

1979, Oct. 1	Litho.	Perf. 14		
594	A181	3c multicolored	1.10	.25
595	A182	6c multicolored	1.10	.25
596	A183	17c multicolored	1.10	.30
597	A184	23c multicolored	1.75	.25
598	A185	35c multicolored	2.25	.60
599	A186	50c multicolored	3.75	.50
Nos. 594-599 (6)			11.05	2.15

Return of Canal Zone to Panama, Oct. 1 (3c, 23c); Natl. Bank, 75th anniv.; Rotary Intl., 75th anniv.; 18th UPU Cong., Rio, Sept.-Oct., 1979; Intl. Year of the Child.

Colon Station, St. Charles Hotel, Engraving A187

Postal Headquarters, Balboa, Inauguration A188

Return of Canal Zone to Panama, Oct. 1, 1979 — A189

Census of the Americas — A190

Panamanian Tourist and Convention Center Opening — A191

Inter-American Development Bank, 25th Anniversary A192

Canal Centenary A193

Olympic Stadium, Moscow '80 Emblem — A194

1980, May 21	Litho.	Perf. 12		
600	A187	1c rose violet	.75	.40
601	A188	3c multicolored	.75	.40
602	A189	6c multicolored	.75	.40
603	A190	17c multicolored	.75	.40
604	A191	23c multicolored	.90	.40
605	A192	35c multicolored	1.50	.50
606	A193	41c pale rose & blk	1.80	.75
607	A194	50c multicolored	1.90	1.25
Nos. 600-607 (8)			9.10	4.50

Transpanamanian Railroad, 130th anniv. (1c); 22nd Summer Olympic Games, Moscow, July 19-Aug. 3 (50c).

La Salle Congregation, 75th Anniv. (1979) — A195

1981, May 15	Litho.	Perf. 12		
608	A195	17c multicolored	1.10	.40

Louis Braille — A196

1981, May 15				
609	A196	23c multicolored	1.40	.40

Intl. Year of the Disabled.

Bull's Blood A197

6c, Lory, vert. 41c, Hummingbird, vert. 50c, Toucan.

1981, June 26	Litho.	Perf. 12		
610	A197	3c shown	1.20	.45
611	A197	6c multicolored	1.20	.45
612	A197	41c multicolored	5.00	.90
613	A197	50c multicolored	6.25	.75
Nos. 610-613 (4)			13.65	2.55

Apparition of the Virgin to St. Catherine Laboure, 150th Anniv. — A198

1981, June 26	Litho.	Perf. 12		
614	A198	35c multicolored	1.50	.40

Gen. Torrijos and Bayano Dam — A199

Wmk. 311

1982, Mar. 22	Litho.	Perf. 10½		
615	A199	17c multicolored	.85	.40

78th Anniv. of Independence Soldiers Institute — A200

1981, Mar. 17	Litho.	Perf. 10½		
616	A200	3c multicolored	.85	.40

First Death Anniv. of Gen. Omar Torrijos Herrera — A201

5c, Aerial view. 6c, Army camp. 50c, Felipillo Engineering Works.

1982, May 14	Litho.	Perf. 10½		
617	A201	5c multicolored	.40	.25
618	A201	6c multicolored	.40	.25
619	A201	50c multicolored	1.60	.40
Nos. 617-619,C433-C434 (5)			6.25	1.70

Ricardo J. Alfaro (1882-1977), Statesman — A202

1982, Aug. 18			Wmk. 382	
620	A202	3c multicolored	.50	.25

See Nos. C436-C437.

1982 World Cup — A203

1982, Dec. 27	Litho.	Perf. 10½		
621	A203	50c Italian team	2.25	.50

See Nos. C438-C440.

Expo Comer '83, Panama Intl. Commerce Exposition, Jan. 12-16 — A204

Wmk. 382

1983, Jan. 12	Litho.	Perf. 10½		
622	A204	17c multicolored	1.20	.40

Visit of Pope John
Paul II — A205

Various portraits of the Pope. 35c airmail.

Perf. 12x11

1983, Mar. 1		**Litho.**	**Wmk. 382**	
623	A205	6c multicolored	1.20	.65
624	A205	17c multicolored	1.20	.65
625	A205	35c multicolored	2.75	.65
	Nos. 623-625 (3)		5.15	1.95

Bank Emblem — A206

1983, Mar. 18
626 A206 50c multicolored 1.75 .40
24th Council Meeting of Inter-American Development Bank, Mar. 21-23.

Simon Bolivar (1783-1830) — A207

1983, July 25		**Litho.**	**Perf. 12**	
627	A207	50c multicolored	2.50	.50

Souvenir Sheet
Imperf
628 A207 1b like 50c 4.25 1.25

World
Communications
Year — A208

1983, Oct. 9		**Litho.**	**Perf. 14**	
629	A208	30c UPAE emblem	1.10	.25
630	A208	40c WCY emblem	1.40	.35
631	A208	50c UPU emblem	1.75	.45
632	A208	60c Dove in flight	2.40	.55
	Nos. 629-632 (4)		6.65	1.60

Souvenir Sheet
Imperf
633 A208 1b multicolored 5.50 2.75
No. 633 contains designs of Nos. 629-632 without denominations.

Freedom of
Worship — A209

3c, Panama Mosque. 5c, Bahai Temple. 6c, St. Francis Church. 17c, Kol Shearit Israel Synagogue.

1983, Oct. 21		**Litho.**	**Perf. 11½**	
634	A209	3c multicolored	1.60	.25
635	A209	5c multicolored	1.60	.25
636	A209	6c multicolored	1.60	.25
637	A209	17c multicolored	4.50	.25
	Nos. 634-637 (4)		9.30	1.00

No. 637 incorrectly inscribed.

Ricardo Miro (1883-1940), Poet — A210

Famous Men: 3c, Richard Newman (1883-1946), educator. 5c, Cristobal Rodriguez (1883-1943), politician. 6c, Alcibiades Arosemena (1883-1958), industrialist and financier. 35c, Cirilo Martinez (1883-1924), linguist.

1983, Nov. 8		**Litho.**	**Perf. 14**	
638	A210	1c multicolored	.50	.25
639	A210	3c multicolored	.50	.25
640	A210	5c multicolored	.50	.25
641	A210	6c multicolored	.50	.25
642	A210	35c multicolored	2.50	.35
	Nos. 638-642 (5)		4.50	1.35

The Prophet, by
Alfredo
Sinclair — A211

#643, Village House, by Juan Manuel Cedeno. #644, Large Nude, by Manuel Chong Neto. 3c, On Another Occasion, by Spiros Vamvas. 6c, Punta Chame Landscape, by Guillermo Trujillo. 28c, Neon Light, by Alfredo Sinclair. 41c, Highland Girls, by Al Sprague. 1b, Bright Morning, by Ignacio Mallol Pibernat. Nos. 643-647, 650 horiz.

1983, Dec. 12			**Perf. 12**	
643	A211	1c multicolored	.45	.35
644	A211	1c multicolored	.45	.35
645	A211	3c multicolored	.45	.35
646	A211	6c multicolored	.45	.35
647	A211	28c multicolored	1.40	.85
648	A211	35c multicolored	1.75	1.10
649	A211	41c multicolored	2.00	1.30
650	A211	1b multicolored	5.50	4.00
	Nos. 643-650 (8)		12.45	8.65

Double Cup,
Indian
Period — A212

Pottery: 40c, Raised dish, Tonosi period. 50c, Jug with face, Canazas period, vert. 60c, Bowl, Conte, vert.

1984, Jan. 16		**Litho.**	**Perf. 12**	
651	A212	30c multicolored	1.40	1.10
652	A212	40c multicolored	1.60	1.40
653	A212	50c multicolored	2.10	1.90
654	A212	60c multicolored	2.50	2.25
	Nos. 651-654 (4)		7.60	6.65

Souvenir Sheet
Imperf
655 A212 1b like 30c 7.00 7.00

Pre-Olympics
A213

1984, Mar. 15		**Litho.**	**Perf. 14**	
656	A213	19c Baseball	2.35	.40
657	A213	19c Basketball, vert.	2.35	.40
658	A213	19c Boxing	2.35	.40
659	A213	19c Swimming, vert.	2.35	.40
	Nos. 656-659 (4)		9.40	1.60

Roberto
Duran — A214

1984, June 14		**Litho.**	**Perf. 14**	
660	A214	26c multicolored	2.50	.40

1st Panamanian to hold 3 boxing championships.

1984
Olympic
Games
A214a

1984, July, 12		**Litho.**	**Perf. 14**	
660A	A214a	6c Shooting	.55	.40
660B	A214a	30c Weight lifting	1.60	.40
660C	A214a	37c Wrestling	1.75	.40
660D	A214a	1b Long jump	5.50	1.50
	Nos. 660A-660D (4)		9.40	2.70

Souvenir Sheet
660E A214a 1b Running 5.25 5.00
Nos. 660B-660D are airmail. No. 660E contains one 45x45x64mm stamp.

Paintings — A215

Paintings by Panamanian artists: 1c, Woman Thinking, by Manuel Chong Neto. 3c, The Child, by Alfredo Sinclair. 6c, A Day in the Life of Rumalda, by Brooke Alfaro. 30c, Highlands People, by Al Sprague. 37c, Intermission during the Dance, by Roberto Sprague. 44c, Punta Chame Forest, by Guillermo Trujillo. 50c, The Blue Plaza, by Juan Manuel Cedeno. 1b, Ira, by Spiros Vamvas.

1984, Sept. 17		**Litho.**	**Perf. 14**	
661	A215	1c multi	.40	.40
662	A215	3c multi, horiz.	.40	.40
663	A215	6c multi, horiz.	.40	.40
664	A215	30c multi	1.30	.40
665	A215	37c multi, horiz.	1.50	.40
666	A215	44c multi, horiz.	1.78	.50
667	A215	50c multi, horiz.	2.25	.55
668	A215	1b multi, horiz.	4.50	1.50
	Nos. 661-668 (8)		12.53	4.55

Postal
Sovereignty
A216

19c, Gen. Torrijos, canal.

1984, Oct. 1		**Litho.**	**Perf. 12**	
669	A216	19c multicolored	1.40	.30

Fauna — A217

3c, Manatee. 30c, Gato negro. 44c, Tigrillo congo. 50c, Puerco de monte.
1b, Perezoso de tres dedos, vert.

1984, Dec. 5		**Engr.**	**Perf. 14**	
670	A217	3c black	.40	.40
671	A217	30c black	2.25	.50
672	A217	44c black	3.25	.75
673	A217	50c black	3.50	.90
	Nos. 670-673 (4)		9.40	2.55

Souvenir Sheet
674 A217 1b black 8.00 5.00
Nos. 671-673 are airmail.

Coins — A218

Perf. 11x12

1985, Jan. 17		**Litho.**	**Wmk. 353**	
675	A218	3c 1935 1c	.40	.40
676	A218	3c 1904 10c	.40	.40
677	A218	6c 1916 5c	.40	.40
678	A218	30c 1904 50c	1.90	.50
679	A218	37c 1962 half-balboa	2.40	.60
680	A218	44c 1953 balboa	3.00	.70
	Nos. 675-680 (6)		8.50	3.00

Nos. 678-680 are airmail.

Contadora Type of 1985
Souvenir Sheet
Perf. 13½x13

1985, Oct. 1		**Litho.**	**Unwmk.**	
680A	AP108	1b Dove, flags, map	8.75	8.00

Cargo Ship in
Lock — A219

1985, Oct. 16			**Perf. 14**	
681	A219	19c multicolored	1.60	.40

Panama Canal, 70th anniv. (1984).

UN 40th
Anniv. — A220

1986, Jan. 17		**Litho.**	**Perf. 14**	
682	A220	23c multicolored	1.25	.40

Intl. Youth
Year — A221

1986, Jan. 17
683 A221 30c multicolored 1.50 .40

Waiting Her Turn, by
Al Sprague
(b.1938) — A222

Oil paintings: 5c, Aerobics, by Guillermo Trujillo (b. 1927). 19c, Cardboard House, by Eduardo Augustine (b. 1954). 30c, Door to the Homeland, by Juan Manuel Cedeno (b. 1914). 36c, Supper for Three, by Brooke Alfaro (b. 1949). 42c, Tenderness, by Alfredo Sinclair (b. 1915). 50c, Woman and Character, by Manuel Chong Neto (b. 1927). 60c, Calla lillies, by Maigualida de Diaz (b. 1950).

1986, Jan. 21				
684	A222	3c multicolored	.35	.35
685	A222	5c multicolored	.35	.35
686	A222	19c multicolored	1.10	.40
687	A222	30c multicolored	1.75	.50
688	A222	36c multicolored	2.00	.55
689	A222	42c multicolored	2.40	.65
690	A222	50c multicolored	3.00	.80
691	A222	60c multicolored	3.75	1.00
	Nos. 684-691 (8)		14.70	4.60

Miss Universe
Pageant — A223

1986, July 7		**Litho.**	**Perf. 12**	
692	A223	23c Atlapa Center	1.00	.40
693	A223	60c Emblem, vert.	2.90	.80

Halley's
Comet — A224

30c, Old Panama Cathedral tower, vert.

1986, Oct. 30		**Litho.**	**Perf. 13½**	
694	A224	23c multicolored	1.50	.40
695	A224	30c multicolored	2.10	.40

Size: 75x86mm
Imperf
695A A224 1b multicolored 8.50

A225

1986 World Cup Soccer Championships, Mexico — Illustrations from Soccer History, by Sandoval and Meron: 23c, Argentina, winner. 30c, Fed. Rep. of Germany, 2nd. 37c, Argentina, Germany.

1b, Argentina, two players one with black shorts, one with blue shorts.

1986, Oct. 30
696	A225	23c multicolored	1.30	.40
697	A225	30c multicolored	1.50	.40
698	A225	37c multicolored	1.90	.60
	Nos. 696-698 (3)		4.70	1.40

Souvenir Sheet
698A	A225	1b multicolored	4.50	

A226

1986, Nov. 21
699	A226	20c shown	1.40	.40
700	A226	23c Montage of events	1.50	.35

15th Central American and Caribbean Games, Dominican Republic.

Christmas — A227

1986, Dec. 18 **Litho.**
701	A227	23c shown	1.25	.40
702	A227	36c Green tree	2.00	.50
703	A227	42c Silver tree	2.25	.55
	Nos. 701-703 (3)		5.50	1.45

Intl. Peace Year — A228

1986, Dec. 30 **Perf. 13½**
704	A228	8c multicolored	.50	.40
705	A228	19c multicolored	1.40	.40

Tropical Carnival, Feb.-Mar. — A229

20c, Diablito Sucio mask. 35c, Sun.

1987, Jan. 27 **Litho.** **Perf. 13½**
706	A229	20c multi	.90	.40
707	A229	35c multi	2.00	.50

Size: 74x84mm
Imperf
708	A229	1b like 35c	4.50	1.50
	Nos. 706-708 (3)		7.40	2.40

1st Panamanian Eye Bank — A230

1987, Feb. 17 **Litho.** **Perf. 14**
709	A230	37c multicolored	2.75	.75

Panama Lions Club, 50th Anniv. (in 1985). Dated 1986.

Flowering Plants — A231

Birds — A232

3c, Brownea macrophylla. 5c, Thraupis episcopus. 8c, Solandra grandiflora. 15c, Tyrannus melancholicus. 19c, Barleria micans. 23c, Pelecanus occidentalis. 30c, Cordia dentata. 36c, Columba cayennensis.

1987, Mar. 5
710	A231	3c multicolored	.50	.40
711	A232	5c multicolored	.50	.40
712	A231	8c multicolored	.50	.40
713	A232	15c multicolored	1.10	.40
714	A231	19c multicolored	1.50	.40
715	A232	23c multicolored	1.60	.40
716	A231	30c multicolored	2.25	.45
717	A232	36c multicolored	3.00	.55
	Nos. 710-717 (8)		10.95	3.40

Dated 1986.

Monument and Octavio Mendez Pereira, Founder — A233

1987, Mar. 26 **Litho.** **Perf. 14**
718	A233	19c multicolored	1.10	.40

University of Panama, 50th anniv. (in 1985). Stamp dated "1986."

UNFAO, 40th Anniv. (in 1985) — A234

1987, Apr. 9 **Perf. 13½**
719	A234	10c blk, pale ol & yel org	.40	.40
720	A234	45c blk, dk grn & yel grn	2.40	.70

Natl. Theater, 75th Anniv. — A235

Baroque composers: 19c, Schutz (1585-1672). 37c, Bach. 60c, Handel. Nos. 721, 723-724 vert.

1987, Apr. 28 **Perf. 14**
721	A235	19c multicolored	.90	.40
722	A235	30c shown	1.30	.50
723	A235	37c multicolored	1.50	.60
724	A235	60c multicolored	2.50	1.00
	Nos. 721-724 (4)		6.20	2.50

A236

1987, May 13 **Litho.** **Perf. 14**
725	A236	23c multicolored	1.25	.45

Inter-American Development Bank, 25th anniv.

Panama Fire Brigade, Cent. — A237

25c, Fire wagon, 1887, and modern ladder truck. 35c, Fireman carrying victim.

1987, Nov. 28 **Litho.** **Perf. 14**
726	A237	25c multicolored	2.50	.40
727	A237	35c multicolored	3.50	.60

A238

1987, Dec. 11
728	A238	15c Wrestling, horiz.	1.10	.40
729	A238	23c Tennis	1.60	.40
730	A238	30c Swimming, horiz.	2.10	.50
731	A238	41c Basketball	2.90	.70
732	A238	60c Cycling	4.50	1.00
	Nos. 728-732 (5)		12.20	3.00

Souvenir Sheet
733	A238	1b Weight lifting	4.25	4.00

10th Pan American Games, Indianapolis. For surcharges see Nos. 813, 817.

A239

Christmas (Religious paintings): 22c, Adoration of the Magi, by Albrecht Nentz (d. 1479). 35c, Virgin Adored by Angels, by Matthias Grunewald (d. 1528). 37c, The Virgin and Child, by Konrad Witz (c. 1400-1445).

1987, Dec. 17
734	A239	22c multicolored	1.00	.35
735	A239	35c multicolored	1.60	.60
736	A239	37c multicolored	1.90	.60
	Nos. 734-736 (3)		4.50	1.55

Intl. Year of Shelter for the Homeless A240

45c, by A. Sinclair. 50c, Woman, boy, girl, shack, housing in perspective by A. Pulido.

1987, Dec. 29 **Perf. 14**
737	A240	45c multicolored	1.75	.75
738	A240	50c multicolored	2.25	.80

For surcharge see No. 814.

Reforestation Campaign — A241

1988, Jan. 14 **Litho.** **Perf. 14½x14**
739	A241	35c dull grn & yel grn	2.00	.55
740	A241	40c red & pink	2.25	.70
741	A241	45c brn & lemon	2.50	.75
	Nos. 739-741 (3)		6.75	2.00

Dated 1987. For surcharge see No. 816.

Say No to Drugs — A242

1988, Jan. 14
742	A242	10c org lil rose	.55	.40
743	A242	17c yel grn & lil rose	1.30	.40
744	A242	25c pink & sky blue	2.10	1.20
	Nos. 742-744 (3)		3.95	1.20

Child Survival Campaign A243

20c, Breast-feeding. 31c, Universal immunization. 45c, Growth and development, vert.

1988, Feb. 29 **Litho.** **Perf. 14**
745	A243	20c multicolored	.90	.40
746	A243	31c multicolored	1.60	.60
747	A243	45c multicolored	2.50	.90
	Nos. 745-747 (3)		5.00	1.90

For surcharge see No. 816A.

Fish — A244

7c, Myripristis jacobus. 35c, Pomacanthus paru. 60c, Holocanthus tricolor. 1b, Equetus punctatus.

1988, Mar. 14
748	A244	7c multicolored	.40	.40
749	A244	35c multicolored	1.40	.40
750	A244	60c multicolored	2.50	1.00
751	A244	1b multicolored	4.50	1.60
	Nos. 748-751 (4)		8.80	3.60

The 7c actually shows the Holocanthus tricolor, the 60c the Myripristis jacobus. For surcharge see No. 819.

Girl Guides, 75th Anniv. — A245

1988, Apr. 14
752	A245	35c multicolored	1.60	.60

Christmas — A246

Paintings: 17c, Virgin and Gift-givers. 45c, Virgin of the Rosary and St. Dominic.

1988, Dec. 29 **Litho.** **Perf. 12**
753	A246	17c multicolored	1.00	.40
754	A246	45c multicolored	2.10	.75

See No. C446.

St. John Bosco (1815-1888) — A247

1989, Jan. 31
755 A247 10c Portrait .50 .40
756 A247 20c Minor Basilica 1.50 .40

1988 Summer
Olympics,
Seoul — A248

Athletes and medals.

1989, Mar. 17   Litho.   Perf. 12
757 A248 17c Running .70 .40
758 A248 25c Wrestling 1.10 .40
759 A248 60c Weight lifting 2.75 1.00
  Nos. 757-759 (3) 4.55 1.80
Souvenir Sheet
760 A248 1b Swimming, vert. 4.75 3.75
  See No. C447.

A249

1b, Emergency and rescue services.

1989, Apr. 12   Litho.   Perf. 12
761 A249 40c red, blk & blue 1.50 .75
762 A249 1b multicolored 4.00 1.75

Intl. Red Cross and Red Crescent organizations, 125th anniv.

America Issue: Pre-
Columbian
Artifacts — A250

20c, Monolith of Barriles. 35c, Vessel.

1989, Oct. 12   Litho.   Perf. 12
767 A250 20c multi 1.75 .50
768 A250 35c multi 3.25 1.30

French
Revolution,
Bicent. — A251

1989, Nov. 14   Perf. 13½
769 A251 25c multicolored 1.40 .50
  Nos. 769,C450-C451 (3) 6.40 2.00

Christmas
A252

17c, Holy family in Panamanian costume.
35c, Creche. 45c, Holy family, gift givers.

1989, Dec. 1
770 A252 17c multicolored 1.00 .40
771 A252 35c multicolored 2.25 .65
772 A252 45c multicolored 2.50 .85
  Nos. 770-772 (3) 5.75 1.90

Rogelio Sinán (b.
1902), Writer — A253

1990, July 3
773 A253 23c brown & blue 1.40 .45

A254

1990, Nov. 20   Litho.   Perf. 13½
774 A254 25c blue & black 1.40 .45
775 A254 35c Experiment 1.75 .60
776 A254 45c Beakers, test
      tubes, books 2.25 .75
  Nos. 774-776 (3) 5.40 1.80

Dr. Guillermo Patterson, Jr., chemist.

Fruits — A255

20c, Byrsonima crassifolia. 35c, Bactris
gasipaes. 40c, Anacardium occidentale.

1990, May 18   Perf. 13½
777 A255 20c multicolored .90 .40
778 A255 35c multicolored 1.60 .60
779 A255 40c multicolored 2.10 .70
  Nos. 777-779 (3) 4.60 1.70

Tortoises — A256

35c, Pseudemys scripta. 45c, Lepidochelys
olivacea. 60c, Geochelone carbonaria.

1990, Sept. 11
780 A256 35c multicolored 1.60 .60
781 A256 45c multicolored 2.10 .75
782 A256 60c multicolored 3.50 1.00
  Nos. 780-782 (3) 7.20 2.35

For surcharges see Nos. 815, 818.

Native
American — A257

1990, Oct. 12
783 A257 20c shown 1.80 .40
784 A257 35c Native, vert. 2.75 .85

Discovery of
Isthmus of
Panama,
490th Anniv.
A258

1991, Nov. 19   Litho.   Perf. 12
785 A258 35c multicolored 2.25 1.25

St. Ignatius of Loyola,
500th Birth
Anniv. — A259

No. 786, St. Ignatius of Loyola.
No. 786B: c, St. Ignatius' seal over map of
Panama (horiz.); d, 5c stamp, Panama Scott
No. C119 in black (horiz.).

1991, Nov. 29
786 A259 20c multicolored 1.40 .40
  a. Tete beche pair 2.25 1.25
Souvenir Sheet
786B   Sheet of 2, #a.-b. — —
  c. A259 25c multi — —
  d. A259 25c multi — —

Society of Jesus, 450th anniv.

Christmas
A260

1991, Dec. 2
787 A260 35c Luke 2:14 1.40 .65
788 A260 35c Nativity scene 1.40 .65
  a. Pair, #787-788 3.25 2.50

Social Security
Administration,
50th
Anniv. — A261

Design: No. 790, Dr. Arnulfo Arias Madrid
(1901-1988), Constitution of Panama, 1941.

1991, Feb. 20   Litho.   Perf. 12
789 A261 10c multicolored .85 .40
790 A261 10c multicolored .85 .40

Women's citizenship rights, 50th anniv. (No.
790).

Epiphany
A262

1992, Feb. 5   Litho.   Perf. 12
791 A262 10c multicolored 1.00 .40
  a. Tete beche pair 2.00 .80

New Life
Housing
Project
A263

1992, Feb. 17
792 A263 5c multicolored 1.00 .40
  a. Tete beche pair 2.00 .80

Border Treaty
Between
Panama and
Costa Rica,
50th Anniv.
A264

a, 20c, Hands clasped. b, 40c, Map. c, 50c,
Pres. Rafael A. Calderon, Costa Rica, Pres.
Arnulfo Arias Madrid, Panama.

1992, Feb. 20
793 A264 Strip of 3, #a.-c. 5.00 3.25

Causes of Hole in
Ozone Layer — A265

1992, Feb. 24
794 A265 40c multicolored 2.25 .70
  a. Tete beche pair 5.00 4.00

Expocomer
'92, Intl.
Commercial
Exposition
A266

1992, Mar. 11
795 A266 10c multicolored .80 .40

A267

Margot Fonteyn (1919-91), ballerina: a, 35c,
Wearing dress. b, 45c, In costume.

1992, Mar. 13
796 A267 Pair, #a.-b. 8.50 4.50

A268

1992, June 22   Litho.   Perf. 12
797 A268 10c multicolored 1.00 .40
  a. Tete beche pair 2.00 .75

Maria Olimpia de Obaldia (1891-1985), poet.

1992
Summer
Olympics,
Barcelona
A269

1992, June 22   Litho.   Perf. 12
798 A269 10c multicolored 1.00 .40
  a. Tete-beche pair 2.00 .75

Zion Baptist
Church,
Bocas del
Toro, 1892
A270

1992, Oct. 1   Litho.   Perf. 12
799 A270 20c multicolored 1.10 .40
  a. Tete beche pair 2.25 1.50

Baptist Church in Panama, Cent.

Discovery of America, 500th
Anniv. — A271

a, 20c, Columbus' fleet. b, 35c, Coming
ashore.

1992, Oct. 12
800 A271 Pair, #a.-b. 4.00 3.00

Endangered Wildlife — A272

a, 5c, Agouti paca. b, 10c, Harpia harpyja. c,
15c, Felis onca. d, 20c, Iguana iguana.

1992, Sept. 23
801 A272 Strip of 4, #a.-d. 8.25 6.25

Expo '92,
Seville — A273

1992, Dec. 21   Litho.   Perf. 12
802 A273 10c multicolored 1.00 .40
  a. Tete beche pair 2.00 .75

Worker's Health
Year — A274

1992, Dec. 21
803 A274 15c multicolored   1.00   .40
a.   Tete beche pair   2.25 1.50

Unification of
Europe — A275

1992, Dec. 21   Litho.   Perf. 12
804 A275 10c multi + label   1.25   .40

Christmas — A276

a, 20c, Angel announcing birth of Christ. b,
35c, Mary and Joseph approaching city gate.

1992, Dec. 21
805 A276 Pair, #a.-b.   2.75 1.75

Evangelism
in America,
500th Anniv.
(in 1992)
A277

1993, Apr. 13   Litho.   Perf. 12
806 A277 10c multicolored   1.00   .40
a.   Tete beche pair   2.25 1.50

Natl. Day for the
Disabled — A278

1993, May 10
807 A278 5c multicolored   1.00   .40
a.   Tete beche pair   2.25 1.80

Dr. Jose de la Cruz
Herrera (1876-1961),
Humanitarian — A279

1993, May 26
808 A279 5c multicolored   1.00   .40
a.   Tete beche pair   2.25 1.80

1992 Intl.
Conference
on Nutrition,
Rome
A280

1993, June 22   Litho.   Perf. 12
809 A280 10c multicolored   1.00   .40
a.   Tete beche pair   2.25   .75

Columbus' Exploration of the Isthmus
of Panama, 490th Anniv.
A281

1994, June 2   Litho.   Perf. 12
810 A281 50c multicolored   2.40   .95
a.   Tete beche pair + 2 labels   5.50 3.50
            Dated 1993.

Greek Community
in Panama, 50th
Anniv. — A282

Designs: 20c, Greek influences in Panama,
Panamanian flag, vert. No. 812a, Parthenon.
No. 812b, Greek Orthodox Church.

1995, Feb. 16   Litho.   Perf. 12
811 A282 20c multicolored   1.10   .40
Souvenir Sheet
812 A282 75c Sheet of 2, #a.-b.   5.00 2.50

Nos. 729, 731, 737,
741, 747, 750, 781-
782 Surcharged

1995   Perfs., Etc. as Before
813   A238 20c on 23c #729   .95   .40
814   A240 25c on 45c #737   1.30   .50
815   A256 30c on 45c #781   1.60   .65
816   A241 35c on 45c #741   1.75   .75
816A A243 35c on 45c No.
           747   2.00   .85
817   A238 40c on 41c #731   2.25   .90
818   A256 50c on 60c #782   3.75 1.25
819   A244 1b on 60c No.
           750   6.25 2.50
      Nos. 813-819 (8)   19.85 7.80
Issued: #816A, 819, 5/3; Others, 4/6.

First Settlement
of Panama,
475th Anniv. (in
1994) — A283

Designs: 15c, Horse and wagon crossing
bridge. 20c, Arms of first Panama City, vert.
25c, Model of an original cathedral. 35c, Ruins
of cathedral, vert.

1996, Oct. 11   Litho.   Perf. 14
820 A283 15c beige, blk & brn   .75   .40
821 A283 20c multicolored   1.00   .40
822 A283 25c beige, blk & brn   1.25   .45
823 A283 35c beige, blk & brn   2.00   .70
      Nos. 820-823 (4)   5.00 1.95

Endangered
Species — A284

1996, Oct. 18   Litho.   Perf. 14
824 A284 20c Tinamus major   1.75   .60

Mammals
A285

a, Nasua narica. b, Tamandua mexicana. c,
Cyclopes didactylus. d, Felis concolor.

1996, Oct. 18
825 A285 25c Block of 4, #a.-d.   6.75 4.75

A286

1996, Oct. 22   Litho.   Perf. 14
826 A286 40c multicolored   1.50   .75
Kiwanis Clubs of Panama, 25th anniv. (in
1993.)

A287

1996, Oct. 15
827 A287 5b multicolored   17.50 9.50
Rotary Clubs of Panama, 75th anniv. (in
1994).

UN, 50th anniv. (in
1995) — A288

1996, Oct. 21
828 A288 45c multicolored   2.00   .85

A289

Design: Ferdinand de Lesseps (1805-94),
builder of Suez Canal.

1996, Oct. 21
829 A289 35c multicolored   1.75   .70

Andrés Bello Covenant,
25th Anniv. (in
1995) — A290

1996, Oct. 23
830 A290 35c multicolored   1.75   .70

Chinese Presence
in Panama — A291

1996, June 10   Perf. 14½
831 A291 60c multicolored   2.75 1.10
Litho.
Imperf
Size: 80x68mm

Patterns depicting four seasons: 1.50b,
Invierno, Primavera, Verano, Otono.

832 A291 1.50b multicolored   22.00 22.00

Radiology, Cent.
(in
1995) — A292

1996, Oct. 24   Litho.   Perf. 14
833 A292 1b multicolored   3.75 1.90

University of
Panama, 60th
Anniv. — A293

1996, Oct. 14
834 A293 40c multicolored   1.90   .75

Christmas — A295

1996, Oct. 24   Litho.   Perf. 14
836 A295 35c multicolored   1.75   .70

Mail
Train — A296

1996, Dec. 10   Litho.   Perf. 14
837 A296 30c multicolored   2.50   .60
            America issue.

Universal Congress of the Panama
Canal — A297

No. 838: a, Pedro Miguel Locks. b,
Miraflores Double Locks.
1.50b, Gatún Locks.

1997, Sept. 9   Litho.   Perf. 14½x14
838 A297 45c Pair, #a.-b.   4.00 2.75
Imperf
839 A297 1.50b multicolored   5.50 5.00
Perforated portion of No. 839 is 76x31mm.

Torrijos-Carter Panama Canal Treaties,
20th Anniv. — A298

Designs: 20c, Painting, "Panama, More
Than a Canal," by C. Gonzalez P. 30c, "Cur-
tain of Our Flag," by A. Siever M., vert. 45c,
"Huellas Perpetuas," by R. Marinez R. 50c,
1.50b, #588.

1997, Sept. 9   Perf. 14
840 A298 20c multicolored   1.10   .50
841 A298 30c multicolored   1.50   .75
842 A298 45c multicolored   2.00 1.10
843 A298 50c multicolored   2.40 1.25
      Nos. 840-843 (4)   7.00 3.60
Imperf
844 A298 1.50b multicolored   5.50 5.00
Perforated portion of No. 844 is 114x50mm.

India's Independence,
50th Anniv. — A299

1997, Oct. 2   *Perf. 14x14½*
845 A299 50c Mahatma Gandhi   4.25 1.25

Crocodylus Acutus — A300

World Wildlife Fund: a, Heading right. b,
Looking left. c, One in distance, one up close.
d, With mouth wide open.

1997, Nov. 18   *Perf. 14½x14*
846 A300 25c Block of 4, #a.-d.   7.50 5.00

Christmas — A301

1997, Nov. 18 Litho.   *Perf. 14x14½*
847 A301 35c multicolored   2.25 .70

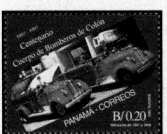

Colon Fire
Brigade,
Cent. — A302

1997, Nov. 21 Litho.   *Perf. 14½x14*
848 A302 20c multicolored   1.20 .50

Frogs — A303

Designs: a, Eleutherodactylus biporcatus. b,
Hyla colymba. c, Hyla rufitela. d, Nelson-
phryne aterrima.

1997, Nov. 21
849 A303 25c Block of 4, #a.-d.   5.25 3.25

National
Costumes
A304

1997, Nov. 25
850 A304 20c multicolored   1.50 .75
        America issue.

Colon Chamber of
Commerce, Agriculture
and Industry, 85th
Anniv. — A305

1997, Nov. 27   *Perf. 14x14½*
851 A305 1b multicolored   3.75 2.50

Justo Arosemena,
Lawyer, Politician,
Death Cent. (in
1996) — A306

1997, Nov. 27
852 A306 40c multicolored   1.90 1.00

Panamanian Aviation Co., 50th
Anniv. — A307

Designs: a, Douglas DC-3. b, Martin-404. c,
Avro HS-748. d, Electra L-168. e, Boeing
B727-100. f, Boeing B737-200 Advanced.

1997, Dec. 3   *Perf. 14½x14*
853 A307 35c Block of 6, #a.-f.   10.00 7.00

Jerusalem, 3000th
Anniv. — A308

20c, Jewish people at the Wailing Wall. 25c,
Christians being led in worship at Church of
the Holy Sepulchre. 60c, Muslims at the Dome
of the Rock.

1997, Dec. 29   *Perf. 14x14½*
854 A308 20c multicolored   1.95 .50
855 A308 25c multicolored   1.30 .65
856 A308 60c multicolored   2.75 1.50
        Nos. 854-856 (3)   6.00 2.65
                Imperf
857 A308 1.50b like #854-856   5.50 4.75
Perforated portion of No. 857 is 90x40mm.

Tourism — A309

10c, Old center of town, Panama City. 20c,
Soberania Park. 25c, Panama Canal. 35c,
Panama Bay. 40c, Fort St. Jerónimo. 45c,
Rafting on Chagres River. 60c, Beach, Kuna
Yala Region.

        Perf. 14x14½, 14½x14
1998, July 7   Litho.
858 A309 10c multi, vert   .40 .40
859 A309 20c multi, vert   .95 .40
860 A309 25c multi   1.20 .50
861 A309 35c multi   1.60 .70
862 A309 40c multi   1.80 .80
863 A309 45c multi   2.25 .90
864 A309 60c multi   2.90 1.25
        Nos. 858-864 (7)   11.10 4.95

Organization of
American States
(OAS), 50th
Anniv. — A310

1998, Apr. 30   *Perf. 14½x14*
865 A310 40c multicolored   1.75 .80

Colón Free Trade
Zone, 50th
Anniv. — A311

        Perf. 14x14½
1998, Feb. 2 Litho.   Unwmk.
866 A311 15c multi   1.20 .40

Protection of the Harpy Eagle — A312

Contest-winning art by students: a, Luis
Mellilo. b, Jorvisis Jiménez. c, Samuel Castro.
d, Jorge Ramos.

1998, Jan. 20
867 A312 20c Block of 4, #a.-d.   6.50 4.50

Universal Declaration
of Human Rights, 50th
Anniv. — A313

1998, Feb. 10
868 A313 15c multi   1.20 .40

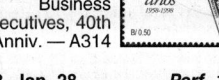

Panamanian
Assoc. of
Business
Executives, 40th
Anniv. — A314

1998, Jan. 28   *Perf. 14½x14*
869 A314 50c multi   2.75 1.00

Beetles — A315

Designs: a, Platyphora haroldi. b, Stilodes
leoparda. c, Stilodes fuscolineata. d,
Platyphora boucardi.

1998, Feb. 10
870 A315 30c Block of 4, #a.-d.   8.75 6.75

Christmas — A316

1998, Jan. 14 Litho.   *Perf. 14x14½*
871 A316 40c multi   1.90 .80

Panama Pavilion,
Expo '98,
Lisbon — A317

1998, Jan. 14 Litho.   *Perf. 14½x14*
872 A317 45c multi   2.10 .90

Panama Canal, 85th Anniv. (in 1999)
A318

No. 873: a, Canal builders and crane on
train trestle. b, Partially built structures, construction equipment.

2000, Sept. 7 Litho.   *Perf. 14½x14*
873 A318 40c Pair, #a-b   5.00 4.00
        Souvenir Sheet
874 A318 1.50b Valley   8.00 7.25
        No. 874 contains one label.

Reversion of
Panama Canal to
Panama (in
1999) — A319

Various ships. Denominations: 20c, 35c,
40c, 45c.

2000, Sept. 7   *Perf. 14½x14*
875-878 A319 Set of 4   8.25 3.50

Pres. Arnulfo Arias Madrid (1901-
88) — A320

No. 879: a, 20c, Arias as medical doctor,
with people. b, 20c, Arias giving speech, holding glasses.
No. 880, a, 30c, Arias in 1941, 1951 and
1969, Panamanian flag. b, 30c, Arias giving
speech, crowd.

2001, Aug. 14 Litho.   *Perf. 13x13½*
        Horiz. pairs, #a-b
879-880 A320 Set of 2   6.00 4.50

Christmas — A321

2001, Dec. 4 Litho.   *Perf. 14x14½*
881 A321 35c multi   1.25 .70
        Dated 1999.

Holy Year (in
2000) — A322

2001, Dec. 4   *Perf. 14½x14*
882 A322 20c multi   1.40 .50
        Dated 2000.

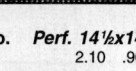

18th UPAEP
Congress (in
2000) — A323

2001, Dec. 4
883 A323 5b multi   23.00 17.50
        Dated 2000.

Dreaming of the Future — A324

Children's art by: No. 884, 20c, I. Guerra. No. 885, 20c, D. Órtega. No. 886, horiz.: a, J. Aguilar P. b, S. Sittón.

2001, Dec. 4   **Perf. 14x14½**
884-885 A324 Set of 2   3.75 2.75

Souvenir Sheet
Perf. 14½x14
886 A324 75c Sheet of 2, #a-b   7.75 6.75
Dated 2000.

Architecture of the 1990s — A325

Designs: No. 887, 35c, Los Delfines Condominium, by Edwin Brown. No. 888, 35c, Banco General Tower, by Carlos Medina.
No. 889, horiz.: a, Building with round sides, by Ricardo Moreno. b, Building with three peaked roofs, by Moreno.

2001, Dec. 4   **Perf. 14x14½**
887-888 A325 Set of 2   4.25 3.50

Souvenir Sheet
Perf. 14½x14
889 A325 75c Sheet of 2, #a-b   7.75 7.00
Dated 2000.

Orchids — A326

Designs: No. 890, 35c, Cattleya dowiana. No. 891, 35c, Psychopsis krameriana. No. 892: a, Peristeria clata. b, Miltoniopsis roezlii.

2001, Dec. 4   **Perf. 14½x14**
890-891 A326 Set of 2   8.50 5.00

Souvenir Sheet
892 A326 75c Sheet of 2, #a-b 10.50 10.00
Dated 2000.

San Fernando Hospital, 50th Anniv. (in 1999) — A327

2001, Dec. 21 Litho. Perf. 14½x14
893 A327 20c multi   1.30 .80
Dated 2000.

Pres. Mireya Moscoso — A328

2002, Mar. 25
894 A328 35c multi   2.10 1.00
Dated 2000.

Independence From Spain, 180th Anniv. — A329

Details from mural by Roberto Lewis: No. 895, 15c, "180" at L. No. 896, 15c, "180" at R.

2002, Apr. 30   **Perf. 13¼x13**
895-896 A329 Set of 2   2.25 .85
Dated 2001.

Discovery of the Isthmus, 500th Anniv. — A330

Designs: 50c, Natives, ship. 5b, Native, European, crucifix, ships.

2002, Apr. 30   **Perf. 13x13¼**
897-898 A330 Set of 2   21.00 15.00
Dated 2001. No. 898 is airmail.

America Issue — UNESCO World Heritage — A331

No. 899, 15c: a, Castle of San Lorenzo. b, Salón Bolivar, Panama City.
No. 900, 1.50b, horiz.: a, Cathedral, Panama City. b, Portobelo Fortifications.

2002, May 30 Perf. 13¼x13, 13x13¼
Horiz. Pairs, #a-b
899-900 A331 Set of 2   16.00 10.00
Dated 2001. No. 900 is airmail.

Murals by Roberto Lewis in Palacio de las Garzas — A332

No. 901: a, Heron, flagbearer and natives. b, Battle with natives. c, Woman, horse, men. d, Heron, woman in dress, woman picking fruit.

2002, June 19   **Perf. 13x13¼**
901   Horiz. strip of 4   3.50 2.00
a.-d. A332 5c Any single   .75 .25
Dated 2001.

Corals — A333

No. 902: a, Montastraea annularis. b, Pavona chiriquiensis.
1b, Siderastrea glynni. 2b, Pociliopora.

2002, June 28
902 A333 10c Horiz. pair, #a-b   .80 .50
903 A333 1b multi   4.50 3.00
904 A333 2b multi   9.00 6.00
Nos. 902-904 (3)   14.30 9.50
Dated 2001. Nos. 903-904 are airmail.

Butterflies and Caterpillars A334

Designs: No. 905, 10c, Ophioderes materna. No. 906, 10c, Rhuda focula. 1b, Morpho peleides. 2b, Tarchon felderi.

2002, June 28 Litho. Perf. 13x13¼
905-908 A334 Set of 4   25.00 10.00
Dated 2001. Nos. 907-908 are airmail.

Christmas 2002 — A335

2003, June 16 Litho. Perf. 14
909 A335 15c multi   5.50 2.50
Dated 2002.

America Issue — Youth, Education and Literacy — A336

2003, June 23
910 A336 45c multi   1.90 1.00
Dated 2002.

Clara González de Behringer, First Female Lawyer in Panama — A337

2003, July 10   **Perf. 13½x13**
911 A337 30c multi   1.50 .80
Dated 2002.

Colón, 150th Anniv. (in 2002) — A338

2003, July 17
912 A338 15c multi   1.00 .50
Dated 2002.

Luis C. Russell (b. 1902), Jazz Musician — A339

2003, Aug. 6   **Perf. 14**
913 A339 10c multi   2.50 1.50
Dated 2002.

Artwork in the National Theater — A340

Designs: No. 914, 5c, Statue of Erato (holding lyre). No. 915, 5c, Statue of Melpomene (holding mask). 50c, Decoration on front of theater box, horiz. 60c, Theater facade and painting, horiz.

Perf. 13½x13, 14 (50c), 13x13½ (60c)
2003, Aug. 12
914-917 A340 Set of 4   7.00 3.50
Dated 2002. Nos. 916-917 are airmail.

St. Josemaría Escrivá de Balaguer (1902-75) — A341

2003, Aug. 13   **Perf. 14**
918 A341 10c multi   1.10 .40
Dated 2002.

Republic of Panama, Cent. — A342

Designs: 5c, National arms. 10c, First national flag. No. 921a, Manuel Amador Guerrero, first president. No. 921b, Pres. Mireya Moscoso. 25c, Declaration of Independence. No. 923a, Sterculia apetala. No. 923b, Peristeria elata. 35c, Revolutionary junta. 45c, Flag, Constitution of 1904, Constituent Delegates.

2003, Nov. 26   **Perf. 12**
919 A342 5c multi   .60 .40
920 A342 10c multi   .70 .40
921 A342 15c Horiz. pair, #a-b   1.75 .95
922 A342 25c multi   1.75 .80
923 A342 30c Horiz. pair, #a-b   3.75 2.10
924 A342 35c multi   2.25 1.10
925 A342 45c multi   2.90 1.40
Nos. 919-925 (7)   13.70 7.15
Nos. 924-925 are airmail.

Republic of Panama, Cent. Type of 2003 Redrawn
2003, Nov. 26 Litho. Perf. 12
925A   Souvenir booklet   16.00
b.   Booklet pane, #f-g   .85 —
c.   Booklet pane, #h-i   1.75 —
d.   Booklet pane, #j, m   3.75 —
e.   Booklet pane, #k-l   3.75 —
f.   A342 5c Similar to #919   .40 .25
g.   A342 10c Similar to #920   .40 .25
h.   A342 15c Similar to #921a   .85 .30
i.   A342 15c Similar to #921b   .85 .30
j.   A342 25c Similar to #922   1.75 .50
k.   A342 30c Similar to #923a   1.75 .60
l.   A342 30c Similar to #923b   1.75 .60
m.   A342 35c Similar to #924   1.75 .70

The text "1903 — Centenario de lar República de Panamá - 2003" is inscribed across the se-tenant pair stamps in each booklet pane. Other differences in text are also on each of Nos. 925Af-925Am.

Christmas A343

2003, Nov. 28
926 A343 10c multi   5.50 2.75

Panama, 2003 Iberoamerican Cultural Capital — A344

2003, Dec. 4
927 A344 5c multi   1.00 .25
For surcharges, see Nos. 945-948.

Pres. Mireya Moscoso — A345

2004, Aug. 10 Litho. Perf. 14½x14
928 A345 35c multi   2.10 1.60
Compare with Type A328. Dated 2000.

A346

Publication of Don Quixote, by Miguel de Cervantes, 400th Anniv. (in 2005).

2007, Apr. 23 Litho. Perf. 12
929 A346 45c multi   1.80 1.40

St. Augustine
High School,
Panama, 50th
Anniv. — A347

2007, May 7
930 A347 35c multi   5.50 4.50

A348

A349

A350

Worldwide Fund
for Nature
(WWF) — A351

2007, June 27
931   Horiz. strip of 4   5.25 5.25
a. A348 20c multi   .90 .90
b. A349 20c multi   .90 .90
c. A350 20c multi   .90 .90
d. A351 20c multi   .90 .90

Popes
A352

No. 932: a, Pope John Paul II (1920-2005).
b, Pope Benedict XVI.

Imperf. x Perf. 12 on 1 Side
2007, June 29
932 A352 50c Horiz. pair, #a-b   4.25 3.50

Tourism
A353

2007, July 10   *Perf. 12*
933 A353 5c multi   1.00 .40
See Nos. 936-941.

Panama Canal
Railway
Company, 150th
Anniv. (in
2005) — A354

Designs: 20c, Emblem, Diesel and steam
trains. 30c, Emblem, Diesel and steam trains,
Diesel train in foreground.

2007, Nov. 27   Litho.   *Perf. 12*
934-935 A354   Set of 2   2.25 1.50

Tourism Type of 2007
Designs: 15c, Devil's mask. 20c, Chorrera
Waterfalls, vert. 25c, Sarigua National Park.
35c, Pottery from Barilles archaeological site.

45c, San Fernando Fort, Portobelo. 60c, Colonial era buildings, vert.

2008, Feb. 27   Litho.   *Perf. 12*
936-941 A353   Set of 6   9.00 4.00
Dated 2007.

Carter-Torrijos
Panama Canal
Treaty, 30th
Anniv. — A355

2008, Nov. 11   Litho.   *Perf. 14*
942 A355 35c multi   1.75 1.10

Souvenir Sheet

Various
Airplanes
of Copa
Airlines
A356

2010, July 30   *Perf. 14 on 3 Sides*
943 A356 1b multi   4.00 3.00
Copa Airlines, 60th anniv.

Miniature Sheet

United Nations Millennium
Objectives — A357

No. 944: a, Objective #1, Eradication of
extreme poverty and hunger. b, Objective #2,
Universal primary education. c, Objective #3,
Promotion of equality of the sexes and
women's rights. d, Objective #4, Reduction of
infant mortality.

2010, Aug. 18   *Perf. 14*
944 A357 20c Sheet of 4, #a-d   4.50 3.00
Dated 2008.

No. 927 Surcharged in Black or Blue

No. 945

No. 946

No. 947

No. 948

Methods and Perfs. As Before
2014
945 A344 10c on 5c #927 (Bl)   1.00 .40
946 A344 20c on 5c #927 (Bl)   1.60 .40
947 A344 25c on 5c #927 (Bl)   2.00 .50
948 A344 35c on 5c #927   2.75 .70
   Nos. 945-948 (4)   7.35 2.00
Issued: No. 945, 7/7; No. 946, 6/18; No.
947, 8/24; No. 948, 6/2.

Nos. 873, 902, 923 Surcharged in Black or Silver

No. 949a

No. 949b

No. 950a

No. 950b

No. 951a

No. 951b

No. 952a

No. 952b

No. 953a

No. 953b

Methods and Perfs As Before
2015, Dec. 1
949   Horiz. pair (S)   8.00 8.00
a. A342 1b on 30c #923a (S)   4.00 4.00
b. A342 1b on 30c #923b (S)   4.00 4.00

950   Horiz. pair   12.00 12.00
a. A318 1b on 40c #873a   6.00 6.00
b. A318 1b on 40c #873b   6.00 6.00
951   Horiz. pair   16.00 16.00
a. A318 2b on 40c #873a   8.00 8.00
b. A318 2b on 40c #873b   8.00 8.00
952   Horiz. pair (S)   32.00 40.00
a. A342 4b on 30c #923a (S)   16.00 16.00
b. A342 4b on 30c #923b (S)   16.00 16.00
953   Horiz. pair (S)   40.00 40.00
a. A333 5b on 10c #902a (S)   20.00 20.00
b. A333 5b on 10c #902b (S)   20.00 20.00
   Nos. 949-953 (5)   108.00 116.00

Tourism — A358

Designs: 20c, San Francisco de la Montaña
Church, Veraguas Province. 25c, Centennial
Bridge over Panama Canal. 35c, Presidential
Palace, Panama City. 60c, Building, Mi Pueb-
lito Afroantilliano Complex, Cerro Ancón. 1b,
Beach, Guna Yala Province. 4b, Cinta Costera
1, Panama City. 10b, Royal Customs House,
San Felipe Portobelo.

2016, Nov. 29   Litho.   *Perf. 13x13¼*
954-960 A358   Set of 7   44.00 40.00

National
Library, 75th
Anniv.
A359

2018, July 11   Litho.   *Perf. 11½*
961 A359 35c multi   1.30 .70

Winning Items by
Estefania Zevallos
L. in 2010
National Pollera
Contest — A360

Designs: 30c, Pollera. 40c, Earrings & necklace, horiz. 50c, Hairpins, butterfly broch. 60c,
Jewelry, diff., horiz.

2018, July 22   Litho.   *Perf. 11½*
962-965 A360   Set of 4   6.50 3.75

A361

Justo Arosemena Quesada (1817-96),
Pro-Independence Politician — A361a

Paintings of Arosemena with his name and
"1817-2017": No. 966, Above and below painting. No. 967, Above painting.
1.50b, Arosemena, diff.

2018, Aug. 1   Litho.   *Perf. 11½*
966 A361 35c multicolored   1.30 .70
967 A361a 35c multicolored   1.30 .70
Size: 120x59mm
Imperf
968 A361 1.50b multi   4.50 3.00

Panamanian Red Cross, Cent. (in 2017) — A362

2018, Aug. 8   Litho.   Perf. 11½
969 A362 35c multi   1.30   .70

Lions Clubs International, Cent. (in 2017) — A363

2018, Aug. 16   Litho.   Perf. 11½
970 A363 5b multi   13.00 12.50

Widening of the Panama Canal A364

Designs: 1b, Canal at night. 2b, Cocolí Locks. 3b, Agua Clara Locks. 4b, Container ship in canal.
No. 975: a, Ship and tugboat in Cocolí Locks. b, Ship in Agua Clara Locks.

2018, Aug. 20   Litho.   Perf. 11½
971-974 A364 Set of 4   27.00 20.00
Souvenir Sheet
975 A364 75c Sheet of 2, #a-b   4.75   3.00
No. 975 contains two 40x30mm stamps.

Demetrio H. Brid Municipal Palace A365

Designs: 20c, Shown. 25c, Brid and other members of the 1903 Municipal Council of the District of Panama. 35c, Brid and Gallery of Rulers.
$1.50, Brid (1859-1917), leader of Municipal Council, independence movement leader, and first de facto President of Panama, vert.

2018, Sept. 19   Litho.   Perf. 11½
976-978 A365 Set of 3   3.50   1.60
Size: 88x124mm
Imperf
979 A365 1.50b multi   4.75   3.00

Firefighters of Panama, 130th Anniv. (in 2017) A366

2018, Sept. 27   Litho.   Perf. 11½
980 A366 5c multi   .85   .25

Republican Band, 150th Anniv. (in 2017) A367

2018, Oct. 16   Litho.   Perf. 11½
981 A367 35c multi   1.30   .70

Artifacts From Gran Coclé Archaeological Site — A368

Designs: 20c, Seahorse-shaped pendant. 35c, Warrior and birds pendant. 45c, Two-headed idol, horiz.
No. 985, 75c: a, Like 20c, with frame line. b, Like 35c, with frame line.

2018, Oct.23   Litho.   Perf. 11½
982-984 A368 Set of 3   4.00   2.00
Souvenir Sheet
985 A368 75c Sheet of 2, #a-b   4.50   3.00
No. 985 contains two 32x40mm stamps.

National Symbols and People Connected With Them A369

Designs: 10c, National flag. 20c, Manuel E. Amador (1869-1952), designer of flag, vert. 25c, María Ossa de Amador (1855-1948), creator of first flag, vert. 30c, National coat of arms, vert. 35c, Nicanor Villalaz (1855-1932), creator of coat of arms, vert. 45c Max Lemm (1868-1939), artist for coat of arms, vert. 50c, National anthem, vert. 60c, Santos Jorge (1870-1941), composer of national anthem, vert. 75c, Jerónimo Ossa (1847-1907), lyricist of national anthem, vert.

2018, Nov. 14   Litho.   Perf. 11½
986-994 A369 Set of 9   12.50   7.00
Nos. 986-992 has text in black, Nos. 993-994 has text in red.

Flag of Panama and Ernestina Sucre Tapia (1892-1982), Writer of Flag Pledge — A370

2019, June 7   Litho.   Perf. 14¼
995 A370 5c multi   .85   .25
Flag and pledge of Panama, 60th anniv.

Postal Service of the Republic of Panama, 115th Anniv. — A371

Designs: 5b, Modern forms of telecommunication. 10b, Old and modern post offices.

Perf. 13¼ Syncopated
2019, June 7   Litho.
996-997 A371 Set of 2   30.00 30.00

Popes and Their Coats of Arms — A372

Designs: No. 998, 25c, Pope John Paul II (1920-2005). No. 999, 25c, Pope Benedict XVI. No. 1000, 25c, Pope Francis.

2019, June 7   Litho.   Perf. 14¼
998-1000 A372 Set of 3   3.50   1.50

Basilicas A373

Designs: No. 1001, 25c, Minor Basilica of Jesús Nazareno de Atalaya. No. 1002, 25c, Santiago Apóstol Minor Basilica, Natá fr los Caballeros. 35c, Don Bosco Minor Basilica, Panama. 45c, Santa María Cathedral Basilica, Panama.

2019, June 7   Litho.   Perf. 14¼
1001-1004 A373 Set of 4   5.25   2.60

World Youth Day, Panama — A374

Designs: 20c, Cross, crowd and icon. 25c, Youth carrying cross. 35c, Stylized city skyline and crowd. 45c, Santa María la Antigua, patron saint of Panama.

2019, June 7   Litho.   Perf. 14¼
1005 A374 20c multi   .80   .40
  a. Booklet pane of 6   5.00
1006 A374 25c multi   1.00   .50
  a. Booklet pane of 6   6.00
1007 A374 35c multi   1.50   .70
  a. Booklet pane of 6   9.00
1008 A374 45c multi   1.80   .90
  a. Booklet pane of 6   11.00
      Complete booklet, #1005a,
      1006a, 1007a, 1008a   31.00
  b. Souvenir sheet of 4, #1005-
      1008   6.00   6.00
      Nos. 1005-1008 (4)   5.10   2.50
Complete booklet sold for 10b. No. 1008b sold for 1.50b.

Fruit and Nuts — A375

Designs: Nos. 1009, 1016, Annona muricata. Nos. 1010, 1017, Hylocereus triangularis and Hylocereus ocamposis. Nos. 1011, 1018, Anacardium occidentale. Nos. 1012, 1019, Inga feuillei. Nos. 1013, 1020, Acronomia aculeata. Nos. 1014, 1021, Mammea americana. Nos. 1015, 1022, Carica papaya.

2019, June 7   Litho.   Perf. 13¼
1009 A375 25c multi   .75   .50
  a. Booklet pane of 6   6.25   —
1010 A375 25c multi   .75   .50
  a. Booklet pane of 6   6.25   —
1011 A375 25c multi   .75   .50
  a. Booklet pane of 6   6.25   —
1012 A375 25c multi   .75   .50
  a. Booklet pane of 6   6.25   —
1013 A375 25c multi   .75   .50
  a. Booklet pane of 6   6.25   —
1014 A375 25c multi   .75   .50
  a. Booklet pane of 6   6.25   —
1015 A375 25c multi   .75   .50
  a. Booklet pane of 6   6.25   —
      Complete booklet, #1009a,
      1010a, 1011a, 1012a,
      1013a, 1014a, 1015a   42.00
1016 A375 1b multi   3.00   2.00
1017 A375 2b multi   6.00   4.00
1018 A375 3b multi   9.00   6.00
1019 A375 4b multi   12.00   8.00
1020 A375 5b multi   14.00 10.00
1021 A375 10b multi   30.00 20.00
1022 A375 15b multi   45.00 30.00
      Nos. 1009-1022 (14) 124.25 83.50
Complete booklet sold for 15b.

Old Quarter, Panama, 500th Anniv. — A376

Designs: No. 1023, 20c, Santo Domingo Convent. No. 1024, 20c, Concepción Convent. No. 1025, 20c, Cathedral Tower. No. 1026, 20c, Ruins of Jesuit Church. No. 1027, 20c, King's Bridge (Puente del Rey).

Litho. & Thermography With Grit Embedded
2019, June 18   Perf. 14¼
1023-1027 A376 Set of 5   5.00   2.00

University of Panama School of Law and Political Science, Cent. — A377

2019, June 20   Litho.   Perf. 14¼
1028 A377 20c multi   1.00   .40

Panama City, 2019 Iberoamerican Capital of Culture — A378

2019, June 24   Litho.   Perf. 14¼
1029 A378 25c multi   1.10   .50

Panama Soccer Team at 2018 World Cup Soccer Championships, Russia — A379

Photograph of team members at: 20c, Nizhny Novgorod. 35c, Nizhny Novgorod, diff. 45c, Sochi. 60c, Saransk.
No. 1034, 75c: a, Like 45c. b, Like 60c.

2019, June 27   Litho.   Perf. 14¼
1030-1033 A379 Set of 4   6.00   3.25
Souvenir Sheet
1034 A379 75c Sheet of 2, #a-b   4.75   3.00

Pres. Belisario Porras (1856-1942), Leading People — A380

Maria "Pantalones" Carter (1929-2013), Community Activist — A381

Cultural Diversity A382

People in Parque Norte — A383

Litho. & Thermography With Grit Embedded
2019, June 27   Perf. 14¼
1035 A380 25c multi   .80   .50
  a. Booklet pane of 6   8.00   5.50
1036 A381 25c multi   .80   .50
  a. Booklet pane of 6   8.00   5.50
1037 A382 25c multi   .80   .50
  a. Booklet pane of 6   8.00   5.50

1038 A383 25c multi .80 .50
  a. Booklet pane of 6 8.00 5.50
    Complete booklet, #1035a,
    1036a, 1037a, 1038a 27.50
1039 A380 1b multi 3.25 2.00
1040 A381 2b multi 5.25 4.00
1041 A382 3b multi 9.25 6.00
1042 A383 4b multi 11.50 8.00
  Nos. 1035-1042 (8) 32.45 22.00

Panama City, 500th anniv. Complete booklet sold for 10b.

AIR POST STAMPS

Special Delivery Stamp No. E3 Srchd. in Dark Blue

1929, Feb. 8   **Unwmk.**   *Perf. 12½*
C1 SD1 25c on 10c org 1.00 .80
  a. Inverted surcharge 22.50 22.50

Nos. E3-E4 Overprinted in Blue

1929, May 22
C2 SD1 10c orange .50 .50
  a. Inverted overprint 20.00 17.50
  b. Double overprint 20.00 17.50

Some specialists claim the red overprint is a proof impression.

With Additional Surcharge of New Value
C3 SD1 15c on 10c org .50 .50
C4 SD1 25c on 20c dk brn 1.10 1.00
  a. Double surcharge 20.00 20.00
  Nos. C2-C4 (3) 2.10 2.00

No. E3 Surcharged in Blue

1930, Jan. 25
C5 SD1 5c on 10c org .50 .50

No. 219 Overprinted in Red

1930, Feb. 28   *Perf. 12*
C6 A39 1b dk vio & blk 16.00 12.50

AP5

1930-41   **Engr.**   *Perf. 12*
C6A AP5 5c blue ('41) .25 .25
C6B AP5 7c rose car ('41) .25 .25
C6C AP5 8c gray blk ('41) .25 .25
C7 AP5 15c dp grn .30 .25
C8 AP5 20c rose .35 .25
C9 AP5 25c deep blue .65 .65
  Nos. C6A-C9 (6) 2.05 1.90

Issued: Nos. C7-C9, 1/20; Nos. C6A-C6C, 7/1/41. See No. C112.
For surcharges and overprints see Nos. 353, C16-C16A, C53B, C69, C82-C83, C109, C122, C124.

Airplane over Map of Panama — AP6

1930, Aug. 4   *Perf. 12½*
C10 AP6 5c ultra .25 .25
C11 AP6 10c orange .30 .25
C12 AP6 30c dp vio 5.50 4.00
C13 AP6 50c dp red 1.50 .50
C14 AP6 1b black 5.50 4.00
  Nos. C10-C14 (5) 13.05 9.00

For surcharge and overprints see Nos. C53A, C70-C71, C115.

Amphibian — AP7

1931, Nov. 28   **Typo.**
Without Gum
C15 AP7 5c deep blue .80 1.00
  a. 5c gray blue .80 1.00
  b. Horiz. pair, imperf. btwn. 50.00

For the start of regular airmail service between Panama City and the western provinces, but valid only on Nov. 28-29 on mail carried by hydroplane "3 Noviembre."
Many sheets have a papermaker's watermark "DOLPHIN BOND" in double-lined capitals.

No. C9 Surcharged in Red 19mm long

1932, Dec. 14   *Perf. 12*
C16 AP5 20c on 25c dp bl 6.25 .70

Surcharge 17mm long
C16A AP5 20c on 25c dp bl 200.00 2.50

Special Delivery Stamp No. E4 Overprinted in Red or Black

1934   *Perf. 12½*
C17 SD1 20c dk brn 1.00 .50
C17A SD1 20c dk brn (Bk) 100.00 55.00
  Issued: No. C17, 7/31.

Surcharged In Black

1935, June
C18 SD1 10c on 20c dk brn .80 .50
Same Surcharge with Small "10"
C18A SD1 10c on 20c dk brn 40.00 5.00
  b. Horiz. pair, imperf. vert. 100.00

Nos. 234 and 242 Surcharged in Blue

1936, Sept. 24
C19 A53 5c on ½c org 400.00 250.00
C20 A53 5c on 50c org 1.00 .80
  a. Double surcharge 60.00 60.00

Centenary of the birth of President Pablo Arosemena.
It is claimed that No. C19 was not regularly issued. Counterfeits of No. C19 exist.

Urracá Monument AP8   Palace of Justice AP9

10c, Human Genius Uniting the Oceans. 20c, Panama City. 30c, Balboa Monument. 50c, Pedro Miguel Locks.

1936, Dec. 1   **Engr.**   *Perf. 12*
C21 AP8 5c blue .65 .40
C22 AP9 10c yel org .85 .60
C23 AP9 20c red 3.00 1.50
C24 AP8 30c dk vio 3.50 2.50
C25 AP9 50c car rose 8.00 5.75
C26 AP9 1b black 9.50 6.00
  Nos. C21-C26 (6) 25.50 16.75

4th Postal Congress of the Americas and Spain.

Nos. C21-C26 Overprinted in Red or Blue

1937, Mar. 9
C27 AP8 5c blue (R) .55 .30
  a. Inverted overprint 50.00
C28 AP9 10c yel org (Bl) .75 .45
C29 AP9 20c red (Bl) 1.75 1.00
  a. Double overprint 50.00
C30 AP8 30c dk vio (R) 4.50 3.25
C31 AP8 50c car rose (Bl) 18.00 13.00
  a. Double overprint 175.00
C32 AP9 1b black (R) 22.50 13.00
  Nos. C27-C32 (6) 48.05 31.00

Regular Stamps of 1921-26 Surcharged in Red

1937, June 30   *Perf. 12, 12½*
C33 A55 5c on 15c ultra .75 .75
C34 A55 5c on 20c brn .75 .75
C35 A47 10c on 10c vio 1.75 1.50

Regular Stamps of 1920-26 Surcharged in Red

C36 A56 5c on 24c blk vio .75 .75
C37 A39 5c on 1b dk vio & blk .75 .50
C38 A56 10c on 50c blk 2.25 2.00
  a. Inverted surcharge 30.00

No. 248 Overprinted in Red

C39 A54 5c dark blue .75 .75
  a. Double overprint 18.00
  Nos. C33-C39 (7) 7.75 7.00

Fire Dept. Badge AP14   Florencio Arosemena AP15

José Gabriel Duque — AP16

Perf. 14x14½
1937, Nov. 25   **Photo.**   **Wmk. 233**
C40 AP14 5c blue 4.50 .60
C41 AP15 10c orange 6.75 1.00
C42 AP16 20c crimson 9.00 .75
  Nos. C40-C42 (3) 20.25 2.35

50th anniversary of the Fire Department.

Basketball AP17   Baseball AP18

1938, Feb. 12   *Perf. 14x14½, 14½x14*
C43 AP17 1c shown 2.25 .25
C44 AP18 2c shown 2.25 .25
C45 AP18 7c Swimming 3.00 .25
C46 AP18 8c Boxing 3.00 .25
C47 AP17 15c Soccer 5.00 1.25
  a. Souv. sheet of 5, #C43-C47 18.00 18.00
  b. As "a," No. C43 omitted 3,500.
  Nos. C43-C47 (5) 15.50 2.25
  Set, never hinged 23.25

4th Central American Caribbean Games.

US Constitution Type
Engr. & Litho.
1938, Dec. 7   **Unwmk.**   *Perf. 12½*
Center in Black, Flags in Red and Ultramarine
C49 A83 7c gray .35 .25
C50 A83 8c brt ultra .55 .35
C51 A83 15c red brn .70 .45
C52 A83 50c orange 8.00 5.75
C53 A83 1b black 8.00 5.75
  Nos. C49-C53 (5) 17.60 12.55

Nos. C12 and C7 Surcharged in Red

1938, June 5   *Perf. 12½, 12*
C53A AP6 7c on 30c dp vio .40 .40
  c. Double surcharge 27.50
  d. Inverted surcharge 27.50
C53B AP5 8c on 15c dp grn .40 .40
  e. Inverted surcharge 22.50

Opening of the Normal School at Santiago, Veraguas Province, June 5, 1938. The 8c surcharge has no bars.

Belisario Porras — AP23

Designs: 2c, William Howard Taft. 5c, Pedro J. Sosa. 10c, Lucien Bonaparte Wise. 15c, Armando Reclus. 20c, Gen. George W. Goethals. 50c, Ferdinand de Lesseps. 1b, Theodore Roosevelt.

1939, Aug. 15   **Engr.**
C54 AP23 1c dl rose .40 .25
C55 AP23 2c dp bl grn .40 .25
C56 AP23 5c indigo .65 .25
C57 AP23 10c dk vio .70 .25
C58 AP23 15c ultra 1.60 .35
C59 AP23 20c rose pink 4.00 1.40
C60 AP23 50c dk brn 5.00 .70
C61 AP23 1b black 7.25 3.75
  Nos. C54-C61 (8) 20.00 7.00

Opening of Panama Canal, 25th anniv.
For surcharges see Nos. C63, C65, G1, G3.

Flags of the 21 American Republics — AP31

1940, Apr. 15   **Unwmk.**
C62 AP31 15c blue .40 .35

Pan American Union, 50th anniversary.
For surcharge see No. C66.

Stamps of 1939-40 Surcharged in Black

a   b

c   d

1940, Aug. 12
C63 AP23 (a) 5c on 15c lt ultra .25 .25
  a. "7 AEREO 7" on 15c 60.00 60.00

C64 A84 (b) 7c on 15c ultra .40 .25
C65 A23 (c) 7c on 20c rose
pink .40 .25
C66 A31 (d) 8c on 15c blue .40 .25
Nos. C63-C66 (4) 1.45 1.00

Stamps of 1924-30 Overprinted in Black or Red

e

f

g

1941, Jan. 2   Perf. 12½, 12
C67 SD1 (e) 7c on 10c org 1.00 1.00
C68 A53 (f) 15c on 24c yel
brn (R) 2.50 2.50
C69 AP5 (g) 20c rose 2.00 2.00
C70 AP6 (g) 50c deep red 6.00 4.00
C71 AP6 (g) 1b black (R) 13.50 10.00
Nos. C67-C71 (5) 25.00 19.50

New constitution of Panama which became
effective Jan. 2, 1941.

Liberty — AP32

Black Overprint
1942, Feb. 19   Engr.   Perf. 12
C72 AP32 20c chestnut brn 4.00 2.50

Costa Rica - Panama Type
Engr. & Litho.
1942, Apr. 25   Unwmk.
C73 A94 15c dp grn, dk bl & dp
rose .70 .40

Swordfish   J. D.
AP34   Arosemena
Normal
School
AP35

Designs: 8c, Gate of Glory, Portobello. 15c,
Taboga Island, Balboa Harbor. 50c, Fire-
house. 1b, Gold animal figure.

1942, May 11   Engr.   Perf. 12
C74 AP34 7c rose carmine .90 .25
C75 AP34 8c dk ol brn & blk .25 .25
C76 AP34 15c dark violet .45 .25
C77 AP35 20c red brown .65 .25
C78 AP34 50c olive green 1.10 .40
C79 AP34 1b blk & org yel 2.75 .80
Nos. C74-C79 (6) 6.10 2.20

See Nos. C96-C99, C113, C126. For
surcharges and overprints see Nos. 354-355,
C84-C86, C108, C110-C111, C114, C116,
C118, C121, C123, C127-C128, C137.

Alejandro Meléndez
G. — AP40

Design: 5b, Ernesto T. Lefevre.

1943, Dec. 15
C80 AP40 3b dk olive gray 6.00 4.75
C81 AP40 5b dark blue 9.00 7.50

For overprint & surcharge see #C117,
C128A.

> Catalogue values for unused
> stamps in this section, from this
> point to the end of the section, are
> for Never Hinged items.

Nos. C6C and C7
Surcharged in Carmine

1947, Mar. 8   Perf. 12
C82 AP5 5c on 8c gray blk .65 .40
a. Double overprint 25.00 22.50
C83 AP5 10c on 15c dp grn 1.40 .40

Nos. C74 to C76
Surcharged in
Black or Carmine

C84 AP34 5c on 7c rose
car (Bk) .65 .40
a. Double surcharge 500.00
b. Pair, one without
surcharge 75.00
C85 AP34 5c on 8c dk ol
brn & blk .65 .40
C86 AP34 10c on 15c dk vio .65 .40
a. Double surcharge 30.00 30.00
Nos. C82-C86 (5) 4.00 2.00

National
Theater — AP42

1947, Apr. 7   Engr.   Unwmk.
C87 AP42 8c violet .90 .40
Natl. Constitutional Assembly of 1945, 2nd
anniv.
For surcharge see No. 356.

Manuel Amador   Manuel
Guerrero — AP43   Espinosa
B. — AP44

5c, José Agustin Arango. 10c, Federico
Boyd. 15c, Ricardo Arias. 50c, Carlos Constantino Arosemena. 1b, Nicanor de Obarrio.
2b, Tomas Arias.

1948, Feb. 20   Perf. 12½
Center in Black
C88 AP43 3c blue .55 .25
C89 AP43 5c brown .55 .25
C90 AP43 10c orange .55 .25
C91 AP43 15c deep claret .55 .25
C92 AP44 20c deep carmine .95 .55
C93 AP44 50c dark gray 1.75 .80
C94 AP44 1b green 5.50 2.50
C95 AP44 2b yellow 12.00 6.00
Nos. C88-C95 (8) 22.40 10.85
Members of the Revolutionary Junta of 1903.

Types of 1942
1948, June 14   Perf. 12
C96 AP34 2c carmine 1.10 .25
C97 AP34 15c olive gray .55 .25
C98 AP35 20c green .55 .25
C99 AP34 50c rose carmine 8.75 3.00
Nos. C96-C99 (4) 10.95 3.75

Franklin D.   Four Freedoms
Roosevelt and   AP46
Juan D.
Arosemena
AP45

Monument   Map showing
to F. D.   Boyd-Roosevelt
Roosevelt   Trans-Isthmian
AP47   Highway
AP48

Franklin D.
Roosevelt — AP49

1948, Sept. 15   Perf. 12½
C100 AP45 5c dp car & blk .45 .25
C101 AP46 10c yellow org .60 .30
C102 AP47 20c dull green .75 .35
C103 AP48 50c dp ultra & blk 1.20 .60
C104 AP49 1b gray black 3.00 1.25
Nos. C100-C104 (5) 6.00 2.75

Franklin Delano Roosevelt (1882-1945).
For surcharges see Nos. RA28-RA29.

Monument to
Cervantes
AP50

10c, Don Quixote attacking windmill.

1948, Nov. 15
C105 AP50 5c dk blue & blk .90 .40
C106 AP50 10c purple & blk 1.60 .40

400th anniv. of the birth of Miguel de
Cervantes Saavedra, novelist, playwright and
poet.

No. C106 Ovptd.
in Carmine

1949, Jan. 18
C107 AP50 10c purple & blk 1.10 .40
a. Inverted overprint 52.50

José Gabriel Duque (1849-1918), newspaper publisher and philanthropist.

Nos. C96, C6A, C97 and C99 Overprinted in Black or Red

h   i

1949, May 26
C108 AP34(h) 2c carmine .45 .25
a. Double overprint 7.50 7.00
b. Inverted surcharge 20.00 20.00
c. On No. C74 (error) 70.00
C109 AP5(i) 5c blue (R) .45 .25
C110 AP34(h) 15c ol gray (R) 1.10 .65
C111 AP34(h) 50c rose car 4.00 2.25
Nos. C108-C111 (4) 6.00 3.40

Centenary of the incorporation of Chiriqui
Province.

Types of 1930-42
Design: 10c, Gate of Glory, Portobelo.

1949, Aug. 3   Perf. 12
C112 AP5 5c orange .80 .40
C113 AP34 10c dk blue & blk .80 .40
For surcharge see No. C137.

Stamps of 1943-49 Overprinted or Surcharged in Black, Green or Red

1949, Sept. 9
C114 AP34 2c carmine .35 .25
a. Inverted overprint 24.00
b. Double overprint 32.50
c. Double overprint, one inverted 37.50 35.00
C115 AP5 5c orange (G) 1.60 .35
a. Inverted overprint 12.50
b. Double overprint 30.00 30.00
c. Double ovpt., one inverted 30.00 30.00
C116 AP34 10c dk bl & blk (R) 1.60 .40
C117 AP40 25c on 3b dk ol
gray (R) 2.10 .70
C118 AP34 50c rose carmine 4.25 2.10
Nos. C114-C118 (5) 9.90 3.80

75th anniv. of the UPU.
No. C115 has small overprint, 15½x12mm,
like No. 368. Overprint on Nos. C114, C116
and C118 as illustrated. Surcharge on No.
C117 is arranged vertically, 29x18mm.

University of San
Javier — AP51

1949, Dec. 7   Engr.   Perf. 12½
C119 AP51 5c dk blue & blk .90 .40
See note after No. 371.

Mosquito — AP52

1950, Jan. 12   Perf. 12
C120 AP52 5c dp ultra & gray blk 2.25 .65
See note after No. 372.

Nos. C96, C112, C113
and C9 Overprinted in
Black or Carmine (5 or
4 lines)

1950, Aug. 17   Unwmk.
C121 AP34 2c carmine .90 .25
C122 AP5 5c orange 1.10 .35
C123 AP34 10c dk bl & blk (C) 1.10 .40
C124 AP5 25c deep blue (C) 1.25 .75
Same on No. 362, Overprinted "AEREO"
C125 A105 50c pur & blk (C) 5.00 1.25
Nos. C121-C125 (5) 9.35 3.00

Gen. José de San Martin, death cent.

Firehouse Type of 1942
1950, Oct. 30   Engr.
C126 AP34 50c deep blue 4.00 1.00

Nos. C113 and C81 Surcharged in Carmine or Orange

1952, Feb. 20
C127 AP34 2c on 10c .50 .25
a. Pair, one without surch. 375.00
C128 AP34 5c on 10c (O) .50 .25
b. Pair, one without surch. 375.00
C128A AP40 1b on 5b 29.00 20.00

The surcharge on No. C128A is arranged to
fit stamp, with four bars covering value panel
at bottom, instead of crosses.

Nos. 376 and 380 Srchd. "AEREO 1952" and New Value in Carmine or Black

1952, Aug. 1
C129	A97	5c on 2c ver & blk (C)	.50	.25
a.		Inverted surcharge	32.50	
C130	A99	25c on 10c pur & org	1.75	1.00

Isabella Type of Regular Issue
Perf. 12½

1952, Oct. 20   Unwmk.   Engr.
Center in Black
C131	A110	4c red orange	.65	.40
C132	A110	5c olive green	.65	.40
C133	A110	10c orange	.85	.40
C134	A110	25c gray blue	2.25	.40
C135	A110	50c chocolate	3.25	.85
C136	A110	1b black	10.00	3.50
		Nos. C131-C136 (6)	17.65	5.95

Queen Isabella I of Spain, 500th birth anniv.

No. C113 Surcharged "5 1953" in Carmine

1953, Apr. 22   Perf. 12
C137	AP34	5c on 10c dk bl & blk	.85	.40

Masthead of La Estrella — AP54

1953, July 15
C138	AP54	5c rose carmine	.50	.40
C139	AP54	10c blue	1.10	.40

Panama's 1st newspaper, La Estrella de Panama, cent.
For surcharges see Nos. C146-C147.

Act of Independence AP55

Senora de Remon and Pres. José A. Remon Cantera AP56

Designs: 7c, Pollera. 25c, National flower. 50c, Marcos A. Salazar, Esteban Huertas and Domingo Diaz A. 1b, Dancers.

1953, Nov. 2
C140	AP55	2c deep ultra	.55	.25
C141	AP56	5c deep green	.55	.25
C142	AP56	7c gray	.65	.25
C143	AP56	25c black	4.00	.65
C144	AP56	50c dark brown	2.75	.75
C145	AP56	1b red orange	7.25	1.50
		Nos. C140-C145 (6)	15.75	3.65

Founding of republic, 50th anniversary.
For overprints see Nos. C227-C229.

Nos. C138-C139 Surcharged with New Value in Black or Red

1953-54
C146	AP54	1c on 5c rose car ('54)	.80	.40
C147	AP54	1c on 10c blue (R)	.80	.40

Gen. Herrera at Conference Table — AP57

Design: 1b, Gen. Herrera leading troops.

1954, Dec. 4   Litho.   Perf. 12½
C148	AP57	6c deep green	.50	.25
C149	AP57	1b scarlet & blk	5.00	2.25

Death of Gen. Tomas Herrera, cent.
For surcharge see No. C198.

Rotary Emblem and Map — AP58

1955, Feb. 23
C150	AP58	6c rose violet	.35	.25
C151	AP58	21c red	.90	.35
C152	AP58	1b black	6.50	2.50
a.		1b violet black	7.00	3.75
		Nos. C150-C152 (3)	7.75	3.10

Rotary International, 50th anniv.
For surcharge see No. C154.

Cantera Type

1955, June 1
C153	A115	6c rose vio & blk	.80	.40

Issued in tribute to Pres. José Antonio Remon Cantera, 1908-1955.
For surcharge see No. C188.

No. C151 Surcharged

1955, Dec. 7
C154	AP58	15c on 21c red	.90	.40

Pedro J. Sosa AP60

First Barge Going through Canal and de Lesseps AP61

Perf. 12½

1955, Nov. 22   Unwmk.   Litho.
C155	AP60	5c grn, lt grn	.45	.25
C156	AP61	1b red lilac & blk	6.50	2.50

150th anniversary of the birth of Ferdinand de Lesseps. Imperforates exist.

Pres. Dwight D. Eisenhower AP62

Statue of Bolivar AP63

Bolivar Hall — AP64

Portraits-Presidents: C158, Pedro Aramburu, Argentina. C159, Dr. Victor Paz Estenssoro, Bolivia. C160, Dr. Juscelino Kubitschek O., Brazil. C161, Gen. Carlos Ibanez del Campo, Chile. C162, Gen. Gustavo Rojas Pinilla, Colombia. C163, Jose Figueres, Costa Rica. C164, Gen. Fulgencio Batista y Zaldivar, Cuba. C165, Gen. Hector B. Trujillo Molina, Dominican Rep. C166, Jose Maria Velasco Ibarra, Ecuador. C167, Col. Carlos Castillo Armas, Guatemala. C168, Gen. Paul E. Magloire, Haiti. C169, Julio Lozano Diaz, Honduras. C170, Adolfo Ruiz Cortines, Mexico. C171, Gen. Anastasio Somoza, Nicaragua. C172, Ricardo Arias Espinosa, Panama. C173, Gen. Alfredo Stroessner, Paraguay. C174, Gen. Manuel Odria, Peru. C175, Col. Oscar Osorio, El Salvador. C176, Dr. Alberto F. Zubiria, Uruguay. C177, Gen. Marcos Perez Jimenez, Venezuela. 1b, Simon Bolivar.

1956, July 18
C157	AP62	6c rose car & vio bl	.75	.30
C158	AP62	6c brt grnsh bl & blk	.75	.30
C159	AP62	6c bister & blk	.75	.30
C160	AP62	6c emerald & blk	.75	.30
C161	AP62	6c lt grn & brn	.75	.30
C162	AP62	6c yellow & grn	.75	.30
C163	AP62	6c brt vio & grn	.75	.30
C164	AP62	6c dl pur & vio bl	.75	.30
C165	AP62	6c red lil & sl grn	.75	.30
C166	AP62	6c citron & vio bl	.75	.30

C167	AP62	6c ap grn & brn	.75	.30
C168	AP62	6c brn & vio bl	.75	.30
C169	AP62	6c brt car & grn	.75	.30
C170	AP62	6c red & brn	.75	.30
C171	AP62	6c lt bl & grn	.75	.30
C172	AP62	6c vio bl & grn	.75	.30
C173	AP62	6c orange & blk	.75	.30
C174	AP62	6c bluish gray & brn	.75	.30
C175	AP62	6c sal rose & blk	.75	.30
C176	AP62	6c dk grn & vio bl	.75	.30
C177	AP62	6c dk org brn & dk grn	.75	.30
C178	AP63	20c dk bluish gray	1.90	.65
C179	AP63	50c green	3.00	1.10
C180	AP63	1b brown	8.50	2.00
		Nos. C157-C180 (24)	29.15	10.05

Pan-American Conf., Panama City, July 21-22, 1956, and 130th anniv. of the 1st Pan-American Conf. Imperforates exist.

Ruins of First Town Council Building — AP65

Design: 50c, City Hall, Panama City.

1956, Aug. 17
C181	AP65	25c red	1.00	.40
C182	AP65	50c black	2.00	.90
a.		Souv. sheet of 3, #404, C181-C182, imperf.	2.75	2.40

6th Inter-American Congress of Municipalities, Panama City, Aug. 14-19, 1956.
No. C182a sold for 85c.
For overprint see No. C187a.

Monument AP66

St. Thomas Hospital AP67

1956, Nov. 27   Wmk. 311
C183	AP66	5c green	.40	.40
C184	AP67	15c dk carmine	.65	.40

Centenary of the birth of Pres. Belisario Porras.

Highway Construction — AP68

20c, Road through jungle, Darien project.
1b, Map of Americas showing Pan-American Highway.

Wmk. 311

1957, Aug. 1   Litho.   Perf. 12½
C185	AP68	10c black	.35	.25
C186	AP68	20c lt blue & blk	.85	.55
C187	AP68	1b green	3.25	2.25
a.		AP65 Souvenir sheet of 3, unwmkd.	16.00	16.00
		Nos. C185-C187 (3)	4.45	3.05

7th Pan-American Highway Congress.
No. C187a is No. C182a overprinted in black: "VII degree CONGRESSO INTER-AMERICANO DE CARRETERAS 1957."

No. C153 Surcharged "1957" and New Value

1957, Aug. 13   Unwmk.
C188	A115	10c on 6c rose vio & blk	.80	.40

Remon Polyclinic AP69

Customs House, Portobelo AP70

Buildings: #C191, Portobelo Castle. #C192, San Jeronimo Castle. #C193, Remon Hippodrome. #C194, Legislature. #C195, Interior & Treasury Department. #C196, El Panama Hotel. #C197, San Lorenzo Castle.

Wmk. 311

1957, Nov. 1   Litho.   Perf. 12½
Design in Black
C189	AP69	10c lt blue	.45	.25
C190	AP70	10c lilac	.45	.25
C191	AP70	10c gray	.45	.25
C192	AP70	10c lilac rose	.45	.25
C193	AP70	10c ultra	.45	.25
C194	AP70	10c brown ol	.45	.25
C195	AP70	10c orange yel	.45	.25
C196	AP70	10c yellow grn	.45	.25
C197	AP70	1b red	4.75	1.60
		Nos. C189-C197 (9)	8.35	3.60

No. C148 Surcharged in Red

1958, Feb. 11   Unwmk.
C198	AP57	5c on 6c dp grn	.80	.40

United Nations Emblem AP71

Flags of Panama and UN AP72

1958, Mar. 5   Litho.   Wmk. 311
C199	AP71	10c brt green	.40	.25
C200	AP71	21c lt ultra	.65	.25
C201	AP71	50c orange	1.60	.85
C202	AP72	1b gray, ultra & car	3.25	1.60
a.		Souv. sheet of 4, #C199-C202, imperf.	7.00	5.25
		Nos. C199-C202 (4)	5.90	2.95

10th anniv. of the UN (in 1955).
The sheet also exists with the 10c and 50c omitted.

OAS Type of Regular Issue, 1958

Designs: 10c, 1b, Flags of 21 American Nations. 50c, Headquarters in Washington.

1958, Aug. 12   Unwmk.   Perf. 12½
Center yellow and black; flags in national colors
C203	A124	5c lt blue	.40	.25
C204	A124	10c carmine rose	.40	.25
C205	A124	50c gray	1.00	.60
C206	A124	1b black	3.25	1.60
		Nos. C203-C206 (4)	5.05	2.70

Type of Regular Issue

Pavilions: 15c, Vatican City. 50c, United States. 1b, Belgium.

1958, Sept. 8   Wmk. 311   Perf. 12½
C207	A125	15c gray & lt vio	.40	.25
C208	A125	50c dk gray & org brn	1.10	.65
C209	A125	1b brt vio & bluish grn	2.60	1.40
a.		Souv. sheet of 7, #418-421, C207-C209	8.75	5.25
		Nos. C207-C209 (3)	4.10	2.30

No. C209a sold for 2b.

Pope Type of Regular Issue

Portraits of Pius XII: 5c, As cardinal. 30c, Wearing papal tiara. 50c, Enthroned.

1959, Jan. 21   Litho.   Wmk. 311

C210	A126	5c violet	.40	.25
C211	A126	30c lilac rose	1.00	.40
C212	A126	50c bluish gray	1.50	.65
a.		Souv. sheet of 4, #422, C210-C212, imperf.	4.25	2.25
		Nos. C210-C212 (3)	2.90	1.30

#C212a is watermarked sideways and sold for 1b. The sheet also exists with 30c omitted. #C212a with C.E.P.A.L. overprint is listed as #C221a.

Human Rights Issue Type

Designs: 5c, Humanity looking into sun. 10c, 20c, Torch and UN emblem. 50c, UN Flag. 1b, UN Headquarters building.

1959, Apr. 14   Perf. 12½

C213	A127	5c emerald & bl	.35	.25
C214	A127	10c gray & org brn	.35	.25
C215	A127	20c brown & gray	.35	.25
C216	A127	50c green & ultra	1.10	.65
C217	A127	1b red & blue	2.25	1.40
		Nos. C213-C217 (5)	4.40	2.80

Nos. C213-C215, C212a Overprinted and C216 Surcharged in Red or Dark Blue

1959, May 16

C218	A127	5c emer & bl (R)	.40	.25
C219	A127	10c gray & org brn (Bl)	.40	.25
C220	A127	20c brown & gray (R)	.65	.25
C221	A127	1b on 50c grn & ultra (R)	3.25	1.90
a.		Souvenir sheet of 4	9.00	7.00
		Nos. C218-C221 (4)	4.70	2.65

8th Reunion of the Economic Commission for Latin America.

This overprint also exists on Nos. C216-C217. These were disavowed by Panama's postmaster general.

No. C221a is No. C212a with two-line black overprint at top of sheet: "8a. REUNION DE LA C.E.P.A.L. MAYO 1959."

Type of Regular Issue, 1959

Portraits: 5c, Justo A. Facio, Rector. 10c, Ernesto de la Guardia, Jr., Pres. of Panama.

1959, Aug. 5   Litho.   Wmk. 311   Perf. 12½

C222	A128	5c black	.50	.40
C223	A128	10c black	.40	.40

Type of Regular Issue, 1959

1959, Oct. 26   Wmk. 311   Perf. 12½

C224	A130	5c Boxing	.45	.25
C225	A130	10c Baseball	.85	.25
C226	A130	50c Basketball	3.50	1.25
		Nos. C224-C226 (3)	4.80	1.75

For surcharge see No. C349.

Nos. C143-C145 Overprinted in Vermilion, Red or Black

Unwmk.

1960, Feb. 6   Engr.   Perf. 12

C227	AP56	25c black (V)	1.20	.25
C228	AP56	50c dk brown (R)	1.75	.40
C229	AP56	1b red orange	2.75	1.25
		Nos. C227-C229 (3)	5.70	1.90

World Refugee Year, July 1, 1959-June 30, 1960.

The revenues from the sale of Nos. C227-C229 went to the United Nations Refugee Fund.

Administration Building, National University — AP74

Designs: 21c, Humanities building. 25c, Medical school. 30c, Dr. Octavio Mendez Pereria first rector of University.

Wmk. 311

1960, Mar. 23   Perf. 12½

C230	AP74	10c brt green	.45	.40
C231	AP74	21c lt blue	1.00	.40
C232	AP74	25c ultra	1.40	.40
C233	AP74	30c black	1.75	.40
		Nos. C230-C233 (4)	4.60	1.60

National University, 25th anniv.

For surcharges see Nos. 450, C248, C253, C287, C291.

Olympic Games Type

5c, Basketball. 10c, Bicycling, horiz. 25c, Javelin thrower. 50c, Athlete with Olympic torch.

1960, Sept. 22   Wmk. 343   Perf. 12½

C234	A131	5c orange & red	.35	.25
C235	A131	10c ocher & blk	.75	.25
C236	A131	25c lt bl & dk bl	1.50	.55
C237	A131	50c brown & blk	2.75	1.00
a.		Souv. sheet of 2, #C236-C237	5.50	4.50
		Nos. C234-C237 (4)	5.35	2.05

For surcharges see Nos. C249-C250, C254, C266-C270, C290, C350, RA40.

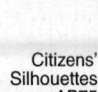

Citizens' Silhouettes AP75

10c, Heads and map of Central America.

1960, Oct. 4   Litho.   Wmk. 229

C238	AP75	5c black	.80	.40
C239	AP75	10c brown	.80	.40

6th census of population and the 2nd census of dwellings (No. C238), Dec. 11, 1960, and the All America Census, 1960 (No. C239).

Boeing 707 Jet Liner — AP76

1960, Dec. 1   Wmk. 343   Perf. 12½

C240	AP76	5c lt grnsh blue	.65	.40
C241	AP76	10c emerald	.65	.40
C242	AP76	20c red brown	1.25	.40
		Nos. C240-C242 (3)	2.55	1.20

1st jet service to Panama. For surcharge see No. RA41.

Souvenir Sheet

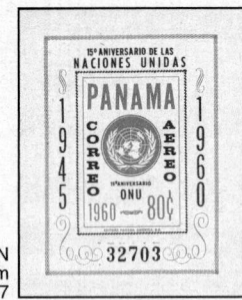

UN Emblem AP77

Wmk. 311

1961, Mar. 7   Litho.   Imperf.

C243	AP77	80c blk & car rose	2.75	2.50

15th anniv. (in 1960) of the UN. Counterfeits without control number exist.

No. C243 Overprinted in Blue with Large Uprooted Oak Emblem and "Ano de los Refugiados"

1961, June 2

C244	AP77	80c blk & car rose	3.25	3.00

World Refugee Year, July 1, 1959-June 30, 1960.

Lions International Type

Designs: 5c, Helen Keller School for the Blind. 10c, Children's summer camp. 21c, Arms of Panama and Lions emblem.

1961, May 2   Wmk. 311   Perf. 12½

C245	A133	5c black	.55	.40
C246	A133	10c emerald	.55	.40
C247	A133	21c ultra, yel & red	.95	.40
		Nos. C245-C247 (3)	2.05	1.20

For overprints see Nos. C284-C286.

Nos. C230 and C236 Surcharged in Black or Red

1961   Wmk. 311 (1c); Wmk. 343

C248	AP74	1c on 10c	.35	.25
C249	A131	1b on 25c (Bk)	2.75	2.00
C250	A131	1b on 25c (R)	2.90	2.00
		Nos. C248-C250 (3)	6.00	4.25

Issued: Nos. C248-C249, 7/6; No. C250, 9/5.

Pres. Roberto F. Chiari and Pres. Mario Echandi — AP78

1961, Oct. 2   Litho.   Perf. 12½

C251	AP78	1b black & gold	3.25	1.60

Meeting of the Presidents of Panama and Costa Rica at Paso Canoa, Apr. 21, 1961.

Dag Hammarskjold — AP79

1961, Dec. 27   Perf. 12½

C252	AP79	10c black	.80	.40

Dag Hammarskjold, UN Secretary General, 1953-61.

No. C230 Surcharged

1962, Feb. 21   Wmk. 311

C253	AP74	15c on 10c brt grn	.80	.40

No. C236 Surcharged

Wmk. 343

C254	A131	1b on 25c	3.25	1.25

City Hall, Colon — AP80

1962, Feb. 28   Litho.   Wmk. 311

C255	AP80	5c vio bl & blk	.90	.40

Issued to publicize the third Central American Municipal Assembly, Colon, May 13-17.

Church Type of Regular Issue, 1962

Designs: 5c, Church of Christ the King. 7c, Church of San Miguel. 8c, Church of the Sanctuary. 10c, Saints Church. 15c, Church of St. Ann. 21c, Canal Zone Synagogue (Now used as USO Center). 25c, Panama Synagogue. 30c, Church of St. Francis. 50c, Protestant Church, Canal Zone. 1b, Catholic Church, Canal Zone.

Wmk. 343

1962-64   Litho.   Perf. 12½

Buildings in Black

C256	A138	5c purple & buff	.45	.25
C257	A138	7c lil rose & brt pink	.45	.25
C258	A139	8c purple & bl	.45	.25
C259	A139	10c lilac & sal	.45	.25
C259A	A139	10c grn & dl red brn ('64)	.45	.25
C260	A139	15c red & buff	.65	.25
C261	A138	21c brown & blue	.95	.40
C262	A138	25c blue & pink	1.20	.35
C263	A139	30c lil rose & bl	1.30	.40
C264	A138	50c lilac & lt grn	1.90	.65
a.		Souv. sheet of 4, #441H-441I, C262, C264, imperf.	7.75	5.75
C265	A139	1b bl & sal	4.00	1.40
		Nos. C256-C265 (11)	12.25	4.70

Freedom of religion in Panama. Issue dates: #C259A, 6/4/64; others, 7/20/62.

For overprints and surcharges see Nos. C288, C296-C297, C299.

Nos. C234, C236 Overprinted & Surcharged in Black, Green, Orange or Red

1962, July 27   Wmk. 343   Perf. 12½

C266	A131	5c org & red	.45	.25
C267	A131	10c on 25c (G)	1.10	.35
C268	A131	15c on 25c (O)	1.40	.45
C269	A131	20c on 25c (R)	1.50	.50
C270	A131	25c lt bl & dk bl	1.75	.55
		Nos. C266-C270 (5)	6.20	2.10

Ninth Central American and Caribbean Games, Kingston, Jamaica, Aug. 11-25.

Nos. CB1-CB2 Surcharged

1962, May 3   Wmk. 311

C271	SPAP1	10c on 5c + 5c	1.75	.75
C272	SPAP1	20c on 10c + 10c	2.75	1.50

Type of Regular Issue, 1962

Design: 10c, Canal bridge completed.

1962, Oct. 12   Wmk. 343

C273	A140	10c blue & blk	.65	.40

John H. Glenn, "Friendship 7" Capsule — AP81

Designs: 10c, "Friendship 7" capsule and globe, horiz. 31c, Capsule in space, horiz. 50c, Glenn with space helmet.

1962, Oct. 19   Wmk. 311   Perf. 12½

C274	AP81	5c rose red	.40	.25
C275	AP81	10c yellow	.55	.25
C276	AP81	31c blue	2.25	.80
C277	AP81	50c emerald	2.75	1.00
a.		Souv. sheet of 4, #C274-C277, imperf.	6.50	6.50
		Nos. C274-C277 (4)	5.95	2.30

1st orbital flight of US astronaut Lt. Col. John H. Glenn, Jr., Feb. 20, 1962. No. C277a sold for 1b.

For surcharges see Nos. C290A-C290D, C367, CB4-CB7.

UPAE Emblem — AP82

1963, Jan. 8   Litho.   Wmk. 343
C278 AP82 10c multi   .85 .40

50th anniversary of the founding of the Postal Union of the Americas and Spain, UPAE.

Type of Regular Issue

10c, Fire Engine "China", Plaza de Santa Ana. 15c, 14th Street team. 21c, Fire Brigade emblem.

1963, Jan. 22   Wmk. 311   Perf. 12½
C279 A141 10c orange & blk   .85 .40
C280 A141 15c lilac & blk   1.00 .40
C281 A141 21c gold, red & ultra   2.10 .40
Nos. C279-C281 (3)   3.95 1.20

"FAO" and Wheat Emblem — AP83

1963, Mar. 21   Litho.
C282 AP83 10c green & red   .80 .40
C283 AP83 15c ultra & red   1.00 .40

FAO "Freedom from Hunger" campaign.

No. C245 Ovptd. in Yellow, Orange or Green

1963, Apr. 18   Wmk. 311   Perf. 12½
C284 A133 5c black (Y)   1.15 .25
C285 A133 5c black (O)   1.15 .25
C286 A133 5c black (G)   1.15 .25
Nos. C284-C286 (3)   3.45 .75

22nd Central American Lions Congress, Panama, Apr. 18-21.

No. C230 Surcharged

1963, June 11
C287 AP74 4c on 10c brt grn   .80 .40

Nos. 445 and 432 Overprinted Vertically

1963   Wmk. 343   Perf. 12½
C288 A139 10c green, yel & blk   .80 .40
Wmk. 311
C289 A130 20c emerald & red brn   1.15 .40

No. C234 Overprinted

1963, Aug. 20   Wmk. 343
C290 A131 5c orange & red   .80 .40

Freedom of Press Day, Aug. 20, 1963.

Nos. C274, C277a Overprinted or Surcharged — a

No. C274 Surcharged in Black — b

Wmk. 311
1963, Aug. 22   Litho.   Perf. 12½
C290A AP81(a) 5c on #C274   3.50
C290B AP81(a) 10c on 5c #C274   7.50
C290C AP81(b) 10c on 5c #C274   9.25

Souvenir Sheet
Imperf.
C290D AP81(a) Sheet of 4, #C277a   54.00

Overprint on No. C290D has names in capital letters and covers all four stamps.

No. C232 Surcharged in Red

1963, Oct. 9   Wmk. 311   Perf. 12½
C291 AP74 10c on 25c ultra   .80 .40

Type of Regular Issue, 1963

Flags and Presidents: 5c, Julio A. Rivera, El Salvador. 10c, Miguel Ydigoras F., Guatemala. 21c, John F. Kennedy, US.

Perf. 12½x12
1963, Dec. 18   Litho.   Unwmk.
Portrait in Slate Green
C292 A142 5c yel, red & ultra   .70 .25
C293 A142 10c bl, red & ultra   1.00 .35
C294 A142 21c org yel, red & ultra   2.75 1.10
Nos. C292-C294 (3)   4.45 1.70

Balboa Type of Regular Issue, 1964
1964, Jan. 22   Photo.   Perf. 13
C295 A143 10c dk vio, pale pink   .80 .40

No. C261 Srchd. in Red

1964   Wmk. 343   Litho.   Perf. 12½
C296 A138 50c on 21c brn, bl & blk   1.50 .70

Type of 1962 Overprinted

C297 A139 1b emer, yel & blk   2.50 2.25
Issued. No. C296, 2/25; No. C297, 2/20.

Nos. 434 and 444 Surcharged

1964   Wmk. 343   Perf. 12½
C298 A131 10c on 5c bl grn & emer   .80 .40
C299 A139 10c on 5c rose, lt grn & blk   .80 .40

Issued: No. C298, 4/6; No. C299, 3/30.

St. Patrick's Cathedral, New York — AP84

Cathedrals: #C301, St. Stephen's, Vienna. #C302, St. Sofia's, Sofia. #C303, Notre Dame, Paris. #C304, Cologne. #C305, St. Paul's, London. #C306, Metropolitan, Athens. #C307, St. Elizabeth's, Kosice, Czechoslovakia (inscr. Kassa, Hungary). #C308, New Delhi. #C309, Milan. #C310, Guadalupe Basilica. #C311, New Church, Delft, Netherlands. #C312, Lima. #C313, St. John's Poland. #C314, Lisbon. #C315, St. Basil's, Moscow. #C316, Toledo. #C317, Stockholm. #C318, Basel. #C319, St. George's Patriarchal Church, Istanbul. 1b, Panama City. 2b, St. Peter's Basilica, Rome.

Unwmk.
1964, Feb. 17   Engr.   Perf. 12
Center in Black
C300 AP84 21c olive   1.75 .90
C301 AP84 21c chocolate   1.75 .90
C302 AP84 21c aqua   1.75 .90
C303 AP84 21c red brown   1.75 .90
C304 AP84 21c magenta   1.75 .90
C305 AP84 21c red   1.75 .90
C306 AP84 21c orange red   1.75 .90
C307 AP84 21c blue   1.75 .90
C308 AP84 21c brown   1.75 .90
C309 AP84 21c green   1.75 .90
C310 AP84 21c violet bl   1.75 .90
C311 AP84 21c dk slate grn   1.75 .90
C312 AP84 21c violet   1.75 .90
C313 AP84 21c black   1.75 .90
C314 AP84 21c emerald   1.75 .90
C315 AP84 21c dp violet   1.75 .90
C316 AP84 21c olive grn   1.75 .90
C317 AP84 21c carmine rose   1.75 .90
C318 AP84 21c Prus green   1.75 .90
C319 AP84 21c dark brown   1.75 .90
C320 AP84 1b dark blue   9.00 5.00
C321 AP84 2b yellow green   17.50 9.00
a.   Souv. sheet of 6   18.00 15.00
Nos. C300-C321 (22)   61.50 32.00

Vatican II, the 21st Ecumenical Council of the Roman Catholic Church.
No. C321a contains 6 imperf. stamps similar to Nos. C300, C303, C305, C315, C320 and C321. Size: 198x138mm. Sold for 3.85b.
For overprints, see Nos. C329C-C329i.

World's Fair, New York — AP84a

5c, 10c, 15c, Various pavilions. 21c, Unisphere.

1964, Sept. 14   Wmk. 311   Perf. 12½
C322 AP84a 5c yellow & blk
C323 AP84a 10c red & blk
C324 AP84a 15c green & blk
C325 AP84a 21c ultra & blk
Set, #C322-C325   9.25 3.00

Souvenir Sheet
Perf. 12
C326 AP84a 21c ultra & blk   12.50 6.00

No. C326 contains one 49x35mm stamp. Exists imperf. Value, same as No. C326.

AP84b

Hammarskjold Memorial, UN Day: No. C327, C329a, Dag Hammarskjold. No. C328, C329b, UN emblem.

Perf. 13½x14
1964, Sept. 1   Unwmk.
C327 AP84b 21c black & blue   1.50 .60
C328 AP84b 21c black & blue   1.50 .60

Souvenir Sheet
Imperf
C329   Sheet of 2   7.75 6.75
a.-b.   AP84b 21c blk & grn, any single   1.25 1.25

Nos. C327-C328 exist imperf in black and green. Value $5.

Nos. C300//C321a Overprinted "1964"

1964, Sept. 28
C329C AP84 21c olive (#C300)   1.30 .75
C329D AP84 21c red (#C305)   1.30 .75
C329E AP84 21c grn (#C309)   1.30 .75
C329F AP84 21c dk brn (#C319)   1.30 .75
C329G AP84 1b dk blue (#C320)   5.00 3.25
C329H AP84 2b yel grn (#C321)   11.00 7.50
i.   Souv. sheet of 6 (#C321a)   80.00 80.00
Nos. C329C-C329H (6)   21.20 13.75

Vatican II, the 21st Ecumenical Council of the Roman Catholic Church, Third Period.
On No. C329i, the original dates are obliterated by a bar, with "1964" and papal arms overprinted below.
The overprint is olive bister on the stamps, yellow on the souvenir sheet. The overprint also exists in yellow gold on the same six stamps and in olive bister on the souvenir sheet. Values: set, $400; souvenir sheet $325.

Roosevelt Type of Regular Issue
Perf. 12x12½
1964, Oct. 9   Litho.   Unwmk.
C330 A147 20c grn & blk, buff   .95 .40
a.   Souv. sheet of 2, #455, C330, imperf.   1.50 1.00

AP84c

1964, Sept. 1   Perf. 13½x14
C331 AP84c 21c shown   2.50 2.00
C332 AP84c 21c Papal coat of arms   2.50 2.00
a.   Souv. sheet of 2, #C331-C332   9.75 5.00

Pope John XXIII (1881-1963). Nos. C331-C332 exist imperf in different colors. Value $20.

Galileo, 400th Birth Anniv. AP84d

21c, Galileo, studies of gravity.

1965, May 12   Perf. 14
C333 AP84d 10c blue & multi   5.75 .75
C334 AP84d 21c green & multi   5.75 .75
a.   Souv. sheet of 2, #C333-C334   30.00 30.00

Nos. C333-C334a exist imperf in different colors. Value, $11.

Alfred Nobel (1833-1896), Founder of Nobel Prize — AP84e

10c, Peace Medal, rev. 21c, Peace Medal, obv.

1965, May 12   Litho. & Embossed
C335 AP84e 10c multi   2.75 .75
C336 AP84e 21c multi   2.75 .75
a.   Souv. sheet of 2, #C335-C336   23.50 23.50

Nos. C335-C336a exist imperf in different colors. Value $5, set; $23.50, souvenir sheet.

Bird Type of Regular Issue, 1965

Song Birds: 5c, Common troupial, horiz. 10c, Crimson-backed tanager, horiz.

1965, Oct. 27   Unwmk.   Perf. 14
C337	A148	5c dp org & multi	2.00	.40
C338	A148	10c brt blue & multi	3.50	.40
a.		Souv. sheet of 6, #462-462C, C337-C338	24.00	24.00

No. C338a exists imperf. Value, $24.

Fish Type of Regular Issue

Designs: 8c, Shrimp. 12c, Hammerhead. 13c, Atlantic sailfish. 25c, Seahorse, vert.

1965, Dec. 7   Litho.
C339	A149	8c multi	.90	.40
C340	A149	12c multi	1.30	.40
C341	A149	13c multi	1.10	.40
C342	A149	25c multi	3.00	.40
a.		Souv. sheet of 3, #C340-C342	16.00	16.00
		Nos. C339-C342 (4)	6.30	1.60

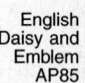

English Daisy and Emblem AP85

Junior Chamber of Commerce Emblem and: #C344, Hibiscus. #C345, Orchid. #C346, Water lily. #C347, Gladiolus. #C348, Flor del Espiritu Santo.

1966, Mar. 16
C343	AP85	30c brt pink & multi	1.30	.35
C344	AP85	30c salmon & multi	1.30	.35
C345	AP85	30c pale yel & multi	1.30	.35
C346	AP85	40c lt grn & multi	1.80	.35
C347	AP85	40c blue & multi	1.80	.35
C348	AP85	40c pink & multi	1.80	.35
a.		Souv. sheet of 2, #C345, C347	30.00	15.00
b.		Souv. sheet of 2, #C347, C348	30.00	15.00
		Nos. C343-C348 (6)	9.30	2.10

50th anniv. of the Junior Chamber of Commerce. A souvenir sheet containing Nos. C344 and C348, and one containing Nos. C345 and C347, exist.

Nos. C224 and C236 Surcharged

1966, June 27   Wmk. 311   Perf. 12½
C349	A130	3c on 5c blk & red brn	.80	.40

Wmk. 343
C350	A131	13c on 25c lt & dk bl	.80	.40

The old denominations are not obliterated on Nos. C349-C350.

ITU Cent. — AP85a

1966, Aug. 12   Perf. 13½x14
C351	AP85a	31c multicolored	5.00	4.75

Souvenir Sheet
Perf. 14
C352	AP85a	31c multicolored	18.00	18.00

No. C352 exists imperf. with blue green background. Value $15.

Animal Type of Regular Issue, 1967

Domestic Animals: 10c, Pekingese dog. 13c, Zebu, horiz. 30c, Cat. 40c, Horse, horiz.

1967, Feb. 3   Unwmk.   Perf. 14
C353	A150	10c multi	1.60	.40
C354	A150	13c multi	2.40	.40
C355	A150	30c multi	3.50	.40
C356	A150	40c multi	4.50	.40
		Nos. C353-C356 (4)	12.00	1.60

Nos. C353 and C355 exist with changed colors in imperforate souvenir sheets of 1.

Young Hare, by Durer — AP86

10c, St. Jerome and the Lion, by Albrecht Durer. 20c, Lady with the Ermine, by Leonardo Da Vinci. 30c, The Hunt, by Delacroix, horiz.

1967, Sept. 1
C357	AP86	10c black, buff & car	1.40	.40
C358	AP86	13c lt yellow & multi	2.25	.40
C359	AP86	20c multicolored	3.00	.40
C360	AP86	30c multicolored	4.75	.40
		Nos. C357-C360 (4)	11.40	1.60

Panama-Mexico Friendship AP86a

Designs: 1b, Pres. Gustavo Diaz Ordaz of Mexico and Pres. Marco A. Robles of Panama, horiz.

1968, Jan. 20   Perf. 14
C361	AP86a	50c shown	2.25	.60
C361A	AP86a	1b multi	4.75	1.10
b.		Souv. sheet of 2, #C361-C361A, imperf.	8.25	8.25

For overprints see Nos. C364-C364B.

Souvenir Sheet

Olympic Equestrian Events — AP86b

1968, Oct. 29   Imperf.
C362	AP86b	Sheet of 2	50.00	40.00
a.		8c Dressage	1.50	1.00
b.		30c Show jumping	5.00	3.50

Intl. Human Rights Year AP86c

1968, Dec. 18   Perf. 14
C363	AP86c	40c multicolored	11.50	7.50
a.		Miniature sheet of 1	42.00	42.00

Nos. C361-C361b Ovptd. in Red or Black

1969, Jan. 31
C364	AP86a	50c on #C361 (R)	6.75	1.50
C364A	AP86a	1b on #C361A (B)	6.75	1.50

Souvenir Sheet
C364B		on #C361b (R)	11.75	11.75

Intl. Philatelic and Numismatic Expo. Overprint larger on No. C364A, larger and in different arrangement on No. C364B.

Intl. Space Exploration AP86d

Designs: a, France, Diadem I. b, Italy, San Marco II. c, Great Britain, UK 3. d, US, Saturn V/Apollo 7. e, US, Surveyor 7. f, Europe/US, Esro 2.

1969, Mar. 14
C365		Sheet of 6	22.50	18.00
a.		AP86d 5c multicolored	.50	.25
b.		AP86d 10c multicolored	1.00	.40
c.		AP86d 15c multicolored	1.50	.50
d.		AP86d 20c multicolored	2.00	.75
e.		AP86d 25c multicolored	3.00	1.00
f.		AP86d multicolored	4.00	1.25

Satellite Transmission of Summer Olympics, Mexico, 1968 AP86e

1969, Mar. 14   Perf. 14½
C366	AP86e	1b multi	11.00	1.00
a.		Miniature sheet of 1	27.00	2.00

Nos. CB4, 461B & 461C Surcharged

1969, Apr. 5   Perf. 13½x13
C367	AP81	5c on 5c+5c	4.00	.50
C367A	A147e	5c on 10c+5c	4.00	.50
C367B	A147e	10c on 21c+10c	4.00	.50

Games Type of Regular Issue and

San Blas Indian Girl — AP87

Design: 13c, Bridge of the Americas.

1970, Jan. 6   Litho.   Perf. 13½
C368	A158	13c multi	2.00	.30
C369	AP87	30c multi	2.50	.75
a.		"AEREO" omitted	50.00	50.00

See notes after No. 525.

Juan D. Arosemena and Arosemena Stadium AP88

Designs: 2c, 3c, 5c, like 1c. No. C374, Basketball. No. C375, New Panama Gymnasium. No. C376, Revolution Stadium. No. C377, Panamanian man and woman in Stadium. 30c, Stadium, eternal flame, arms of Mexico, Puerto Rico and Cuba.

1970, Oct. 7   Wmk. 365   Perf. 13½
C370	AP88	1c pink & multi	.45	.25
C371	AP88	2c pink & multi	.60	.25
C372	AP88	3c pink & multi	.60	.25
C373	AP88	5c pink & multi	.60	.25
C374	AP88	13c lt blue & multi	1.00	.25
C375	AP88	13c lilac & multi	1.00	.25
C376	AP88	13c yellow & multi	1.00	.25
C377	AP88	13c pink & multi	1.00	.25
C378	AP88	30c yellow & multi	3.00	.50
a.		Souv. sheet of 1, imperf.	3.50	3.50
		Nos. C370-C378 (9)	9.25	2.50

11th Central American and Caribbean Games, Feb. 28-Mar. 14.

US astronauts Charles Conrad, Jr., Richard F. Gordon, Jr. and Alan L. Bean. — AP89

No. C379, Astronaut on Moon.

1971, Aug. 20   Wmk. 343   Perf. 13½
C379	AP89	13c gold & multi	1.00	.50
C380	AP89	13c lt green & multi	1.00	.50

Man's first landing on the moon, Apollo 11, July 20, 1969 (No. C379) and Apollo 12 moon mission, Nov. 14-24, 1969.

EXPO '70 Emblem and Pavilion — AP90

1971, Aug. 24   Litho.
C381	AP90	10c pink & multi	1.00	.40

EXPO '70 International Exposition, Osaka, Japan, Mar. 15-Sept. 13.

Flag of Panama AP91

Design: 13c, Map of Panama superimposed on Western Hemisphere, and tourist year emblem.

1971, Dec. 11   Wmk. 343
C382	AP91	5c multi	.95	.45
C383	AP91	13c multi	.95	.45

Proclamation of 1972 as Tourist Year of the Americas.

Mahatma Gandhi — AP92

1971, Dec. 17
C384	AP92	10c black & multi	60.00	25.00

Centenary of the birth of Mohandas K. Gandhi (1869-1948), leader in India's fight for independence.

Central American Independence Issue

Flags of Central American States — AP92a

1971, Dec. 20
C385	AP92a	13c multi	.85	.40

160th anniv. of Central America independence.

AP93

1971, Dec. 21
C386	AP93	8c Panama #4	.80	.40

2nd National Philatelic and Numismatic Exposition, 1970.

AP94

1972, Sept. 7   **Wmk. 365**
C387 AP94 40c Natá Church   1.25   .80
450th anniversary of the founding of Natá.
For surcharges see Nos. C402, RA85.

Telecommunications Emblem — AP95

1972, Sept. 8
C388 AP95 13c lt bl, dp bl & blk   1.00   .40
3rd World Telecommunications Day (in 1971).

Apollo 14 — AP96

1972, Sept. 11
C389 AP96 13c tan & multi   1.30   .50
Apollo 14 US moon mission, 1/1-2/9/71.

Shoeshine Boy Counting Coins — AP97

1972, Sept. 12
C390 AP97 5c shown   .55   .25
C391 AP97 8c Mother & Child   .55   .25
C392 AP97 50c UNICEF emblem   2.50   .55
  a.   Souv. sheet of 1, imperf.   4.75   2.50
       Nos. C390-C392 (3)   3.60   1.05
25th anniv. (in 1971) of the UNICEF.

San Blas Cloth, Cuna Indians — AP98

8c, Beaded necklace, Guaymi Indians. 25c, View of Portobelo.

1972, Sept. 13
C393 AP98 5c multicolored   .50   .25
C394 AP98 8c multicolored   .50   .25
C395 AP98 25c multicolored   4.50   .45
  a.   Souv. sheet of 2, #C393,
       C395, imperf.   5.00   3.50
       Nos. C393-C395 (3)   5.50   .95
Tourist publicity.
For surcharges see Nos. C417, RA83.

Baseball and Games' Emblem AP99

Games' Emblem and: 10c, Basketball, vert. 13c, Torch, vert. 25c, Boxing. 50c, Map and flag of Panama, Bolivar. 1b, Medals.

                         Perf. 12½
1973, Feb. 10   **Litho.**   **Unwmk.**
C396 AP99 8c rose red & yel   .40   .30
C397 AP99 10c black & ultra   .40   .30
C398 AP99 13c blue & multi   .70   .70
C399 AP99 25c blk, yel grn &
            red   1.20   .75
C400 AP99 50c green & multi   2.60   1.75
C401 AP99 1b multicolored   5.50   2.75
      Nos. C396-C401 (6)   10.80   6.55
7th Bolivar Games, Panama City, 2/17-3/3.

**No. C387 Surcharged in Red Similar
to No. 542**
1973, Mar. 15 Wmk. 365   Perf. 13½
C402 AP94 13c on 40c multi   1.00   .30
UN Security Council Meeting, Panama City, Mar. 15-21.

Portrait Type of Regular Issue 1973
Designs: 5c, Isabel Herrera Obaldia, educator. 8c, Nicolas Victoria Jaén, educator. 10c, Forest Scene, by Roberto Lewis. No. C406, Portrait of a Lady, by Manuel E. Amador. No. C407, Ricardo Miró, poet. 20c, Portrait, by Isaac Benitez. 21c, Manuel Amador Guerrero, statesman. 25c, Belisario Porras, statesman. 30c, Juan Demostenes Arosemena, statesman. 34c, Octavio Mendez Pereira, writer. 38c, Ricardo J. Alfaro, writer.

1973, June 20 Litho.   Perf. 13½
C403 A169 5c pink & multi   .55   .25
C404 A169 8c pink & multi   .55   .25
C405 A169 10c gray & multi   .80   .25
C406 A169 13c pink & multi   1.40   .25
C407 A169 13c pink & multi   1.40   .25
C408 A169 20c blue & multi   1.50   .40
C409 A169 21c yellow & multi   1.60   .25
C410 A169 25c pink & multi   1.90   .40
C411 A169 30c gray & multi   2.25   .45
C412 A169 34c lt blue & multi   2.40   .60
C413 A169 38c lt blue & multi   4.00   .60
      Nos. C403-C413 (11)   18.35   4.10
Famous Panamanians.
For overprints and surcharges see Nos. C414-C416, C418-C421.

Nos. C403, C410, and C412 Overprinted in Black or Red

1973, Sept. 14 Litho.   Perf. 13½
C414 A169 5c pink & multi   .45   .25
C415 A169 25c pink & multi   1.50   .45
C416 A169 34c bl & multi (R)   1.75   .75
      Nos. C414-C416 (3)   3.70   1.45
50th anniversary of the Isabel Herrera Obaldia Professional School.

**Nos. C395, C408, C413, C412 and
C409 Surcharged in Red**

1974, Nov. 11   Litho.   Perf. 13½
C417 AP98 1c on 25c multi   .80   .25
C418 A169 3c on 20c multi   .80   .25
C419 A169 8c on 38c multi   .80   .25
C420 A169 10c on 34c multi   .80   .25
C421 A169 13c on 21c multi   .80   .25
      Nos. C417-C421 (5)   4.00   1.25

Women's Hands, Panama Map, UN and IWY Emblems — AP100

                         Perf. 12½
1975, May 6   **Litho.**   **Unwmk.**
C422 AP100 17c blue & multi   1.10   .40
  a.   Souv. sheet, typo., imperf., no
       gum   2.50   2.00
International Women's Year 1975.

Victoria Sugar Plant, Sugar Cane, Map of Veraguas Province — AP101

Designs: 17c, Bayano electrification project and map of Panama, horiz. 33c, Tocumen International Airport and map, horiz.

1975, Oct. 9   Litho.   Perf. 12½
C423 AP101 17c bl, buff & blk   .85   .35
C424 AP101 27c ultra & yel grn   1.20   .45
C425 AP101 33c bl & multi   1.30   .45
      Nos. C423-C425 (3)   3.35   1.25
Oct. 11, 1968, Revolution, 7th anniv.

Bolivar Statue and Flags — AP102

Bolivar Hall, Panama City — AP103

Design: 41c, Bolivar with flag of Panama, ruins of Old Panama City.

1976, Mar.
C426 AP102 23c multi   1.00   .25
C427 AP103 35c multi   1.75   .30
C428 AP102 41c multi   1.75   .60
      Nos. C426-C428 (3)   4.50   1.15
150th anniversary of Congress of Panama. Issued: 23c, Mar. 5; others Mar. 30.

Marine Life Type of 1976
Marine life: 17c, Diodon hystrix, vert. 27c, Pocillopora damicornis.

            Perf. 13x12½, 12½x13
1976, May 6   Litho.   Wmk. 377
C429 A171 17c multi   2.40   .50
C430 A171 27c multi   3.25   .65

Cerro Colorado AP104

1976, Nov. 12   Litho.   Perf. 12½
C431 AP104 23c multi   1.00   .40
Cerro Colorado copper mines, Chiriqui Province.

Gen. Omar Torrijos Herrera (1929-1981) — AP105

1982, Feb. 13   Litho.   Perf. 10½
C432 AP105 23c multi   1.30   .40

Torrijos Type of 1982
35c, Security Council reunion, 1973. 41c, Torrijos Airport.

            Wmk. 311
1982, May 14   Litho.   Perf. 10½
C433 A201 35c multicolored   1.60   .30
C434 A201 41c multicolored   2.25   .50

                    Souvenir Sheet
                       Imperf
C435 A201 23c like #C432   4.50   3.00
No. C435 sold for 1b.

Alfaro Type of 1982
Photos by Luiz Gutierrez Cruz.

1982, Aug. 18   **Wmk. 382**
C436 A202 17c multi   1.30   .25
C437 A202 23c multi   1.50   .25

World Cup Type of 1982
1982, Dec. 27   Litho.   Perf. 10½
C438 A203 23c Map   1.10   .25
C439 A203 35c Pele, vert.   1.60   .30
C440 A203 41c Cup, vert.   2.00   .40
      Nos. C438-C440 (3)   4.70   .95
1b imperf. souvenir sheet exists in design of 23c; black control number. Size; 85x75mm. Value $13.50.

Nicolas A. Solano (1882-1943), Tuberculosis Researcher — AP106

            Wmk. 382 (Stars)
1983, Feb. 8   Litho.   Perf. 10½
C441 AP106 23c brown   1.20   .40

World Food Day — AP107

1984, Oct. 16   Litho.   Perf. 12
C442 AP107 30c Hand grasping
             fork   1.75   .50

Contadora Group for Peace — AP108

1985, Oct. 1   Litho.   Perf. 14
C443 AP108 10c multi   1.75   .30
C444 AP108 20c multi   2.10   .35
C445 AP108 30c multi   3.00   .50
      Nos. C443-C445 (3)   6.85   1.15
See No. 680A.

Christmas Type of 1988
1988, Dec. 29   Litho.   Perf. 12
C446 A246 35c St. Joseph and
            the Infant   1.60   .40

Olympics Type of 1989
1989, Mar. 17   Litho.   Perf. 12
C447 A248 35c Boxing   1.60   .40

Opening of the Panama Canal, 75th Anniv. — AP109

35c, Ancon in lock, 1914. 60c, Ship in lock, 1989.

1989, Sept. 29   Litho.   Perf. 13½
C448 AP109 35c multicolored   1.60   .65
C449 AP109 60c multicolored   2.50   1.10

Revolution Type of 1989
1989, Nov. 14   **Litho.**
C450 A251 35c Storming of the
            Bastille   2.25   .65
C451 A251 45c Anniv. emblem   2.75   .85
French revolution, bicent.

Christmas
2001 — AP110

Designs: 60c, Man, woman, drums. 1b, Guitar, drum, candle. 2b, Pots, potted plant.

2002, Apr. 30   Litho.   Perf. 13x13¼
C452-C454 AP110   Set of 3   16.00 15.00
Dated 2001.

La Salle Schools
in Panama, Cent.
(in
2002) — AP111

2003, May 15   Litho.   Perf. 13x13½
C455 AP111 5b multi   16.00 10.00
Dated 2002.

Natá, 480th Anniv.
(in
2002) — AP112

2003, May 20
C456 AP112 1b multi   3.75 2.00
Dated 2002.

Trains — AP113

Designs: 40c, Colón locomotive. 50c, Panama Railroad, vert.

Perf. 13x13½, 14 (50c)
2003, July 17
C457-C458 AP113   Set of 2   5.00 2.50
Dated 2002.

Santa María de
Belén, 500th
Anniv. — AP114

2003, July 31   Perf. 14
C459 AP114 1.50b multi   5.50 3.00
Dated 2002.

Fourth Voyage of
Christopher
Columbus, 500th
Anniv. (in
2002) — AP115

2003, July 31   Perf. 13x13½
C460 AP115 2b multi   7.25 4.00
Dated 2002.

Kuna
Indians — AP116

Designs: No. C461, 50c, Village, people in canoe, woman. No. C462, 50c, Man and woman, vert. No. C463, 60c, Woman sewing. No. C464, 60c, Dancers. 1.50b, Fish.

Perf. 14 (#C461), 13½x13 (#C462), 13x13½
2003, Aug. 13
C461-C464 AP116   Set of 4   9.00 5.00
Souvenir Sheet
Perf. 13½x14
C465 AP116 1.50b multi   8.00 5.75
Dated 2002. No. C465 contains one 50x45mm stamp.

Medicine in
Panama
AP117

Designs: No. C466, 50c, Santo Tomás de Villanueva Hospital, 300th anniv. No. C467, 50c, Gorgas Memorial Institute of Tropical and Preventative Medicine, 75th anniv.

2003   Perf. 12
C466-C467 AP117   Set of 2   4.25 3.25
Issued: No. C466, 12/17; No. C467, 11/17.

Jewelry — AP118

Designs: 45c, Necklaces. 60c, Brooches.

2003, Nov. 24
C468-C469 AP118   Set of 2   4.25 3.25
For surcharges, see Nos. C474-C475.

America Issue -
Endangered
Species — AP119

2003, Nov. 26
C470 AP119 2b multi   7.00 6.50

La Estrella de
Panama
Newspaper,
150th
Anniv. — AP120

2003, Dec. 3
C471 AP120 40c multi   1.75 1.40

Scouting,
Cent. — AP121

2010, Sept. 3   Litho.   Perf. 14
C472 AP121 20c multi   1.10 .60
Printed in sheets of 4.

Salesian Order in
Panama,
Cent. — AP122

2010, Aug. 27
C473 AP122 20c multi   1.10 .80

No. C468 Surcharged

No. C474

No. C475

Methods and Perfs. As Before
2014
C474 AP118 15c on 45c #C468   1.10 .30
C475 AP118 30c on 45c #C468   2.40 .60
Issued: No. C474, 6/25; No. C475, 6/11.

Ships
AP123

No. C476: a, MSC Oscar. b, Carnival Horizon. c, Drive Green. d, Ship of COSCO fleet. e, Ship of EMAS fleet. f, Navios Coral.

2019, June 19   Litho.   Perf. 14¼
C476 AP123 35c Block of 6, #a-f   7.00 4.25
Panamanian ship registry, 102nd anniv.

AIR POST SEMI-POSTAL STAMPS

Catalogue values for unused stamps in this section are for Never Hinged items.

"The World Against
Malaria" — SPAP1

Wmk. 311
1961, Dec. 20   Litho.   Perf. 12½
CB1 SPAP1 5c + 5c car rose   1.00 .50
CB2 SPAP1 10c + 10c vio bl   1.00 .50
CB3 SPAP1 15c + 15c dk grn   1.00 .50
 Nos. CB1-CB3 (3)   3.00 1.50
WHO drive to eradicate malaria.
For surcharges see Nos. C271-C272.

Nos. C274-C276
Surcharged in Red

Wmk. 311
1963, Mar. 4   Litho.   Perf. 12½
CB4 AP81   5c +5c on #C274   1.50 .75
CB5 AP81 10c +10c on #C275   3.00 1.50
CB6 AP81 15c +31c on #C276   3.00 1.50
Surcharge on No. CB4 differs to fit stamp. See No. CB7.

No. CB4 Surcharged in
Black

1963, Aug. 22
CB7 AP81 10c on 5c+5c   7.00 5.00
Intl. Red. Cross cent.

SPECIAL DELIVERY STAMPS

Nos. 211-212
Overprinted in
Red

1926   Unwmk.   Perf. 12
E1 A31 10c org & blk   7.50 3.25
 a. "EXRPESO"   40.00
E2 A32 20c brn & blk   10.00 3.25
 a. "EXRPESO"   40.00
 b. Double overprint   35.00 35.00

Bicycle
Messenger — SD1

1929, Feb. 8   Engr.   Perf. 12½
E3 SD1 10c orange   1.25 1.00
E4 SD1 20c dk brn   4.75 2.50
For surcharges and overprints see Nos. C1-C5, C17-C18A, C67.

REGISTRATION STAMPS

Issued under Colombian Dominion

R1

1888   Unwmk.   Engr.   Perf. 13½
F1 R1 10c black, gray   8.00 5.25
Imperforate and part-perforate examples without gum and those on surface-colored paper are reprints.

Magenta, Violet or Blue
Black Handstamped
Overprint

1898   Perf. 12
F2 A4 10c orange   7.00 6.50
The handstamp on No. F2 was also used as a postmark.

R3

1900   Litho.   Perf. 11
F3 R3 10c blk, lt bl   4.00 3.50

1901
F4 R3 10c brown red   30.00 20.00

R4

1902   Blue Black Surcharge
F5 R4 20c on 10c brn red   20.00 16.00

Issues of the Republic
Issued in the City of Panama
Registration Stamps of Colombia
Handstamped in Violet, Blue Black or
Rose

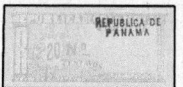

1903-04   Imperf.
F6 R9 20c red brn, bl   45.00 42.50
F7 R9 20c blue, blue (R)   45.00 42.50
For surcharges and overprints see Nos. F8-F11, F16-F26.
Reprints exist of Nos. F6 and F7; see note after No. 64.

With Additional Surcharge in Rose

F8	R9 10c on 20c red brn, *bl*	60.00	55.00
b.	"10" in blue black	60.00	60.00
F9	R9 10c on 20c bl, *bl*	60.00	45.00

Handstamped in Rose

F10	R9 10c on 20c red brn, *bl*	60.00	55.00
F11	R9 10c on 20c blue, *blue*	45.00	42.50

Issued in Colon
Regular Issues Handstamped
"R/COLON" in Circle (as on F2)
Together with Other Overprints and
Surcharges

Handstamped

1903-04		**Perf. 12**
F12	A4 10c orange	3.00 2.50

Handstamped

F13	A4 10c orange	22.50

Overprinted in Red

F14	A4 10c orange	3.00 2.50

Overprinted in Black

F15	A4 10c orange	7.50 5.00

The handstamps on Nos. F12 to F15 are in magenta, violet or red; various combinations of these colors are to be found. They are struck in various positions, including double, inverted, one handstamp omitted, etc.

Colombia No. F13 Handstamped Like No. F12 in Violet
Imperf

F16	R9 20c red brn, *bl*	60.00	55.00

Overprinted Like No. F15 in Black

F17	R9 20c red brn, *bl*	6.00	5.75

No. F17 Surcharged in Manuscript

F18	R9 10c on 20c red brn, *bl*	60.00	55.00

No. F17 Surcharged in Purple **10**

F19	R9 10c on 20c	82.50 80.00

No. F17 Surcharged in Violet

F20	R9 10c on 20c	82.50 80.00

The varieties of the overprint which are described after No. 138 are also to be found

---

on the Registration and Acknowledgment of Receipt stamps. It is probable that Nos. F17 to F20 inclusive owe their existence more to speculation than to postal necessity.

Issued in Bocas del Toro
Colombia Nos. F17 and F13
Handstamped in Violet

1903-04			
F21	R9 20c blue, *blue*	125.00	125.00
F22	R9 20c red brn, *bl*	125.00	125.00

No. F21 Surcharged in Manuscript in Violet or Red

F23	R9 10c on 20c bl, *bl*	150.00	140.00

Colombia Nos. F13, F17 Handstamped in Violet

Surcharged in Manuscript "10", "10c", "10cs" in Red

F25	R9 10c on 20c red brn, *bl*	70.00	65.00
F26	R9 10c on 20c bl, *bl*	55.00	50.00
	Nos. F21-F26 (5)	525.00	505.00

No. F25 without surcharge is bogus, according to leading experts.

General Issue

 R5

1904, Aug. 1	**Engr.**	**Perf. 12**
F27	R5 10c green	1.00 .50

Nos. 190 and 213 Surcharged in Red

#F29   #F29b

#F30

1916-17			
F29	A11 5c on 8c pur & blk	3.00	2.25
a.	"5" inverted	75.00	
b.	Large, round "5"	50.00	
c.	Inverted surcharge	12.50	11.00
d.	Tête bêche surcharge		
e.	Pair, one without surcharge	10.00	
F30	A33 5c on 8c vio & blk	3.50	.80
a.	Inverted surcharge	13.00	8.25
b.	Tête bêche surcharge		
c.	Double surcharge		60.00

Issued: No. F29, 1/1/16; No. F30, 1/28/17. Stamps similar to No. F30, overprinted in green were unauthorized.

INSURED LETTER STAMPS

Stamps of 1939
Surcharged in Black

1942, Nov. 14	**Unwmk.**	**Perf. 12½**
G1	AP23 5c on 1b blk	.75 .50
G2	A84 10c on 1b dk brn	1.25 .80
G3	AP23 25c on 50c dk brn	3.00 2.00
	Nos. G1-G3 (3)	5.00 3.30

ACKNOWLEDGMENT OF RECEIPT STAMPS

Issued under Colombian Dominion

Experts consider this handstamp—"A.R. / COLON / COLOMBIA"-to be a cancellation or a marking intended for a letter to receive special handling. It was applied at Colon to various stamps in 1897-1904 in different colored inks for philatelic sale. It exists on cover, usually with the bottom line removed by masking the handstamp.

Nos. 17-18
Handstamped in Rose

1902		
H4	A4 5c blue	5.00 5.00
H5	A4 10c yellow	10.00 10.00

This handstamp was also used as a postmark.

Issues of the Republic Issued in the City of Panama

Colombia No. H3
Handstamped in Rose

1903-04	**Unwmk.**	**Imperf.**
H9	AR2 10c blue, *blue*	10.00 8.00

Reprints exist of No. H9, see note after No. 64.

No. H9 Surcharged

H10	AR2 5c on 10c bl, *bl*	5.00 5.00

Colombia No. H3
Handstamped in Rose

H11	AR2 10c blue, *blue*	17.50 14.00

Issued in Colon

Handstamped in
Magenta or Violet

Imperf

H17	AR2 10c blue, *blue*	15.00 15.00

Handstamped

H18	AR2 10c blue, *blue*	82.50 70.00

Overprinted in Black

H19	AR2 10c blue, *blue*	11.00 8.00

No. H19 Surcharged in Manuscript

H20	AR2 10c on 5c on 10c	100.00 82.50

Issued in Bocas del Toro
Colombia No. H3 Handstamped in Violet and Surcharged in Manuscript in Red Like Nos. F25-F26

1904		
H21	AR2 5c on 10c blue, *blue*	

No. H21, unused, without surcharge is bogus.

General Issue

AR3

1904, Aug. 1	**Engr.**	**Perf. 12**
H22	AR3 5c blue	1.00 .80

No. 199 Overprinted in
Violet

1916, Jan. 1			
H23	A20 2½c red orange	1.00	.80
a.	"R.A." for "A.R."	50.00	
b.	Double overprint	8.00	
c.	Inverted overprint	8.00	

LATE FEE STAMPS

Issues of the Republic Issued in the City of Panama
Colombia No. I4 Handstamped in Rose or Blue Black

LF3

REPUBLICA DE PANAMA

1903-04	**Unwmk.**	**Imperf.**
I1	LF3 5c pur, *rose*	12.50 9.00
I2	LF3 5c pur, *rose* (Bl Blk)	17.50 12.50

Reprints exist of #I1-I2; see note after #64.

General Issue

LF4

1904   Engr.   Perf. 12
I3   LF4 2½c lake   1.00   .65

No. 199 Overprinted with Typewriter

1910, Aug. 12
I4   A20 2½c red orange   125.00 100.00
Used only on Aug. 12-13.
Counterfeits abound.

Handstamped

1910
I5   A20 2½c red orange   60.00 50.00
Counterfeits abound.

No. 195 Surcharged in Green

1917, Jan. 1
I6   A17 1c on ½c orange   .80   .80
a.   "UN CENTESIMO" inverted   50.00
b.   Double surcharge   10.00
c.   Inverted surcharge   6.50   6.50

No. 196 Surcharged in Green

1921
I7   A17 1c on ½c rose   25.00 20.00

POSTAGE DUE STAMPS

San Lorenzo
Castle Gate,
Mouth of
Chagres River
D1

Statue of
Columbus
D2

Pedro J. Sosa — D4

Design: 4c, Capitol, Panama City.

Unwmk.
1915, Mar. 25   Engr.   Perf. 12
J1   D1 1c olive brown   3.50   .75
J2   D2 2c olive brown   5.25   .65
J3   D1 4c olive brown   7.25 1.25
J4   D4 10c olive brown   5.25 1.75
      Nos. J1-J4 (4)   21.25 4.40

Type D1 was intended to show a gate of San Lorenzo Castle, Chagres, and is so inscribed.

D5

1930, Dec. 30   Perf. 12½
J5   D5 1c emerald   1.00   .60
J6   D5 2c dark red   1.00   .60
J7   D5 4c dark blue   1.60   .80
J8   D5 10c violet   1.60   .80
      Nos. J5-J8 (4)   5.20 2.80

POSTAL TAX STAMPS

Pierre and Marie
Curie — PT1

Unwmk.
1939, June 15   Engr.   Perf. 12
RA1 PT1 1c rose carmine   .60   .25
RA2 PT1 1c green   .60   .25
RA3 PT1 1c orange   .60   .25
RA4 PT1 1c blue   .60   .25
      Nos. RA1-RA4 (4)   2.40 1.00
      Set, never hinged   3.90

See Nos. RA6-RA18, RA24-RA27, RA30.

Stamp of 1924 Overprinted in Black

1940, Dec. 20
RA5 A53 1c dark green   1.40   .75
      Never hinged   2.40

1941, Jan. 30   Inscribed 1940
RA6 PT1 1c rose carmine   .65   .40
RA7 PT1 1c green   .65   .40
RA8 PT1 1c orange   .65   .40
RA9 PT1 1c blue   .65   .40
      Nos. RA6-RA9 (4)   2.60 1.60
      Set, never hinged   3.90

1942   Inscribed 1942
RA10 PT1 1c violet   .40   .40
      Never hinged   .65

1943   Inscribed 1943
RA11 PT1 1c rose carmine   .40   .40
RA12 PT1 1c green   .40   .40
RA13 PT1 1c orange   .40   .40
RA14 PT1 1c blue   .40   .40
      Nos. RA11-RA14 (4)   1.60 1.60
      Set, never hinged   2.60

1945   Inscribed 1945
RA15 PT1 1c rose carmine   .90   .40
RA16 PT1 1c green   .90   .40
RA17 PT1 1c orange   .90   .40
RA18 PT1 1c blue   .90   .40
      Nos. RA15-RA18 (4)   3.60 1.60
      Set, never hinged   5.40

Nos. 234 and 235 Surcharged in Black or Red

1946   Unwmk.   Perf. 12
RA19 A53 1c on ½c orange   .60   .40
RA20 A53 1c on 1c dk grn (R)   .60   .40
      Set, never hinged   2.00

Catalogue values for unused stamps in this section, from this point to the end of the section, are for Never Hinged items.

Nos. 239 and 241 Surcharged in Black

1947, Apr. 7
RA21 A53 1c on 12c ol grn   1.50   .40
RA22 A53 1c on 24c yel brn   1.50   .40

Surcharged in Red on No. 342

RA23 A95 1c on ½c dl vio, bl &
               car   1.50   .40

Type of 1939 Inscribed 1947

1947, July 21
RA24 PT1 1c rose carmine   1.75   .40
RA25 PT1 1c green   1.75   .40
RA26 PT1 1c orange   1.75   .40
RA27 PT1 1c blue   1.75   .40
      Nos. RA24-RA27 (4)   7.00 1.60

Nos. C100 and C101 Surcharged in Black

        a   b

1949, Feb. 16   Unwmk.   Perf. 12½
RA28 AP45 (a) 1c on 5c   1.10   .40
a.   Inverted surcharge   15.00
RA29 AP46 (b) 1c on 10c yel
               org   1.10   .40
a.   Inverted surcharge

Type of 1939

1949   Inscribed 1949   Perf. 12
RA30 PT1 1c brown   2.50   .40

The tax from the sale of Nos. RA1-RA30 was used for the control of cancer.

Juan D.   Torch
Arosemena   Emblem
Stadium   PT3
PT2

No. RA33, Adan Gordon Olympic Swimming Pool.

1951   Unwmk.   Engr.   Perf. 12½
RA31 PT2 1c carmine & blk   2.10   .40
RA32 PT3 1c dk bl & blk   2.10   .40
RA33 PT2 1c grn & blk   2.10   .40
      Nos. RA31-RA33 (3)   6.30 1.20

Issued: No. RA31, 2/21; No. RA32, 7/12; No. RA33, 12/13.

Discobolus — PT4

No. RA34, Turners' emblem.

1952
RA34 PT3 1c org & blk   2.10   .40
RA35 PT4 1c pur & blk   2.10   .40

Issued: No. RA34, 4/18; No. RA35, 9/10.
The tax from the sale of Nos. RA31-RA35 was used to promote physical education.

Boys Doing Farm
Work — PT5

Wmk. 311
1958, Jan. 24   Litho.   Perf. 12½
Size: 35x24mm
RA36 PT5 1c rose red & gray   .80   .40

Type of 1958 Inscribed 1959

1959   Size: 35x24mm
RA37 PT5 1c gray & emerald   .80   .40
RA38 PT5 1c vio bl & gray   .80   .40

Issued: No. RA37, 4/8; No. RA38, 9/28.

Type of 1958 Inscribed 1960
Wmk. 334
1960, July 20   Litho.   Perf. 13½
Size: 32x23mm
RA39 PT5 1c carmine & gray   .80   .40

Nos. C235 and C241 Surcharged in Black or Red

1961, May 24 Wmk. 343 Perf. 12½
RA40 A131 1c on 10c ocher &
               blk   .80   .40
RA41 AP76 1c on 10c emer (R)   .80   .40

Girl at Sewing
Machine — PT6

Wmk. 343
1961, Nov. 24   Litho.   Perf. 12½
RA42 PT6 1c brt vio   .80   .40
RA43 PT6 1c rose lilac   .80   .40
RA44 PT6 1c yellow   .80   .40
RA45 PT6 1c blue   .80   .40
RA46 PT6 1c emerald   .80   .40
      Nos. RA42-RA46 (5)   4.00 2.00

1961, Dec. 1

Design: Boy with hand saw.

RA47 PT6 1c red lilac   .80   .40
RA48 PT6 1c rose   .80   .40
RA49 PT6 1c orange   .80   .40
RA50 PT6 1c blue   .80   .40
RA51 PT6 1c gray   .80   .40
      Nos. RA47-RA51 (5)   4.00 2.00

Boy Scout — PT7

Designs: Nos. RA57-RA61, Girl Scout.

1964, Feb. 7   Wmk. 343
RA52 PT7 1c olive   .80   .40
RA53 PT7 1c gray   .80   .40
RA54 PT7 1c lilac   .80   .40
RA55 PT7 1c carmine rose   .80   .40
RA56 PT7 1c blue   .80   .40
RA57 PT7 1c bluish green   .80   .40
RA58 PT7 1c violet   .80   .40
RA59 PT7 1c orange   .80   .40
RA60 PT7 1c yellow   .80   .40
RA61 PT7 1c brn org   .80   .40
      Nos. RA52-RA61 (10)   8.00 4.00

The tax from Nos. RA36-RA61 was for youth rehabilitation.

Map of Panama,
Flags — PT8

1973, Jan. 22   Unwmk.
RA62 PT8 1c black   .80   .40

7th Bolivar Sports Games, Feb. 17-Mar. 3, 1973. The tax was for a new post office in Panama City.

Post Office — PT9

Designs: No. RA63, Farm Cooperative. No. RA64, 5b silver coin. No. RA65, Victoriano Lorenzo. No. RA66, RA69, Cacique Urraca. No. RA67, RA70, Post Office.

1973-75
RA63	PT9	1c brt yel grn & ver	.95	.40
RA64	PT9	1c gray & red	.95	.40
RA65	PT9	1c ocher & red	.95	.40
RA66	PT9	1c org & red	.95	.40
RA67	PT9	1c bl & red	.95	.40
RA68	PT9	1c blue ('74)	.95	.40
RA69	PT9	1c orange ('74)	.95	.40
RA70	PT9	1c vermilion ('75)	.95	.40
	Nos. RA63-RA70 (8)		7.60	3.20

Issued: No. RA63, 3/19; No. RA64, 6/4; No. RA65, 6/6; No. RA66, 8/16; No. RA67, 8/17; Nos. RA68-RA69, 4/9/74; No. RA70, 11/24/75.
The tax was for a new post office in Panama City.

Stamps of 1969-1973 Surcharged in Violet Blue, Yellow, Black or Carmine

1975, Sept. 3
RA75	A168	1c on 1c (#538; VB)	.95	.40
RA76	A168	1c on 2c (#539; Y)	.95	.40
RA77	A164	1c on 30c (#534; B)	.95	.40
RA78	A157	1c on 30c (#511; B)	.95	.40
RA79	A156	1c on 40c (#514; B)	.95	.40
RA80	A156	1c on 50c (#515; B)	.95	.40
RA81	A169	1c on 20c (#C408; C)	.95	.40
RA82	A169	1c on 25c (#C410; B)	.95	.40
RA83	AP98	1c on 25c (#C395; B)	.95	.40
RA84	A169	1c on 30c (#C411; B)	.95	.40
RA85	AP94	1c on 40c (#C387; C)	.95	.40
	Nos. RA75-RA85 (11)		10.45	4.40

The tax was for a new post office in Panama City. Surcharge vertical, reading down on No. RA75 and up on Nos. RA76, RA78 and RA83. Nos. RA75-RA85 were obligatory on all mail.

PT10

No. RA86, Boys. No. RA87, Boy and chicks. RA88, Working in fields. RA89, Boys feeding piglet.

1980, Dec. 3   Litho.   Perf. 12
RA86	PT10	2c multi	.80	.40
RA87	PT10	2c multi	.80	.40
RA88	PT10	2c multi	.80	.40
RA89	PT10	2c multi	.80	.40
a.	Souv. sheet of 4, #RA86-RA89		13.00	
b.	Block of 4, #RA86-RA89		3.20	

Tax was for Children's Village (Christmas 1980). #RA89a sold for 1b.

PT11

1981, Nov. 1   Litho.   Perf. 12
RA90	PT11	2c Boy, pony	.80	.40
RA91	PT11	2c Nativity	.80	.40
RA92	PT11	2c Tree	.80	.40
RA93	PT11	2c Church	.80	.40
a.	Block of 4, #RA90-RA93		3.20	

Souvenir Sheet
RA94		Sheet of 4	14.00	
a.-d.	PT11 2c, Children's drawings			

Tax was for Children's Village. No. RA94 sold for 5b.

PT12

1982, Nov. 1   Litho.   Perf. 13½x12½
RA95	PT12	2c Carpentry	.80	.40
RA96	PT12	2c Beekeeping	.80	.40
a.	Pair, #RA95-RA96		1.60	

RA97	PT12	2c Pig farming, vert.	.80	.40
RA98	PT12	2c Gardening, vert.	.80	.40
a.	Pair, #RA97-RA98		1.60	

Tax was for Children's Village (Christmas 1982).
Two imperf souvenir sheets solf for 2B each. Value, each $17.

Children's Drawings — PT13

No. RA99, Annunciation. No. RA100, Bethlehem and Star. No. RA101, Church and Houses. No. RA102, Flight into Egypt.

1983, Nov. 1   Litho.   Perf. 14½
RA99	PT13	2c multicolored	.80	.40
RA100	PT13	2c multicolored	.80	.40
RA101	PT13	2c multicolored	.80	.40
RA102	PT13	2c multicolored	.80	.40
	Nos. RA99-RA102 (4)		3.20	1.60

Nos. RA100-RA102 are vert.
Souvenir sheets exist showing undenominated designs of Nos. RA99, RA101 and Nos. RA100, RA102 respectively. They sold for 2b each. Value $10.50 each.

Boy — PT14

1984, Nov. 1   Litho.   Perf. 12x12½
RA103	PT14	2c White-collared shirt	.80	.40
RA104	PT14	2c T-shirt	.80	.40
RA105	PT14	2c Checked shirt	.80	.40
RA106	PT14	2c Scout uniform	.80	.40

a. Tax was for Children's Village. An imperf. souvenir sheet sold for 2b, with designs similar to Nos. RA103-RA106, exists. Value $11.

Christmas 1985 — PT15

Inscriptions: No. RA107, "Ciudad del Nino es . . . mi vida." No. RA108, "Feliz Navidad." No. RA109, "Feliz Ano Nuevo." No. RA110, "Gracias."

1985, Dec. 10   Litho.   Perf. 13½x13
RA107	PT15	2c multi	.80	.40
RA108	PT15	2c multi	.80	.40
RA109	PT15	2c multi	.80	.40
RA110	PT15	2c multi	.80	.40
a.	Block of 4, #RA107-RA110		3.20	

Tax for Children's Village. A souvenir sheet, perf. and imperf., sold for 2b, with designs of Nos. RA107-RA110. Value, each $14.

Children's Village, 20th Anniv. — PT16

Inscriptions and Embera, Cuna, Embera and Guaymies tribal folk figures: No. RA111, "1966-1986." No. RA112, "Ciudad del Nino es . . . mi vida." No. RA113, "20 anos de fundacion." No. RA114, "Gracias."

1986, Nov. 1   Litho.   Perf. 13½
RA111	PT16	2c multi	.90	.40
RA112	PT16	2c multi	.90	.40
RA113	PT16	2c multi	.90	.40
RA114	PT16	2c multi	.90	.40
	Nos. RA111-RA114 (4)		3.60	1.60

Nos. RA111-RA114 obligatory on all mail through Nov., Dec. and Jan.; tax for Children's Village. Printed se-tenant. Sheets of 4 exist perf. and imperf. Sold for 2b. Sheet exists, perf and imperf, with one 58x68mm 2b stamp showing similar characters. Value $8.50 each.

PAPUA NEW GUINEA
'pa-pyə-wə 'nü 'gi-nē

LOCATION — Eastern half of island of New Guinea, north of Australia
GOVT. — Independent state in British Commonwealth.
AREA — 185,136 sq. mi.
POP. — 4,705,126 (1999 est.)
CAPITAL — Port Moresby

In 1884 a British Protectorate was proclaimed over this part of the island, called "British New Guinea." In 1905 the administration was transferred to Australia and in 1906 the name was changed to Territory of Papua.

In 1949 the administration of Papua and New Guinea was unified, as the 1952 issue indicates. In 1972 the name was changed to Papua New Guinea. In 1973 came self-government, followed by independence on September 16, 1975.

Issues of 1925-39 for the mandated Territory of New Guinea are listed under New Guinea.

12 Pence = 1 Shilling
20 Shillings = 1 Pound
100 Cents = 1 Dollar (1966)
100 Toea = 1 Kina (1975)

> **Catalogue values for unused stamps in this country are for Never Hinged items, beginning with Scott 122 in the regular postage section and Scott J1 in the postage due section.**

Watermarks

Wmk. 13 — Crown and Double-Lined A

Wmk. 47 — Multiple Rosette

Wmk. 74 — Crown and Single-Lined A Sideways

Wmk. 228 — Small Crown and C of A Multiple

Wmk. 387

British New Guinea

Lakatoi — A1

Wmk. 47
1901, July 1   Engr.   Perf. 14
Center in Black
1	A1	½p yellow green	24.00	6.00
2	A1	1p carmine	13.50	5.50
3	A1	2p violet	13.50	7.50
4	A1	2½p ultra	40.00	12.00
5	A1	4p black brown	45.00	40.00
6	A1	6p dark green	65.00	40.00
7	A1	1sh orange	65.00	75.00
8	A1	2sh6p brown ('05)	700.00	700.00
	Nos. 1-8 (8)		966.00	886.00

The paper varies in thickness and the watermark is found in two positions, with the greater width of the rosette either horizontal or vertical.
For stamps inscribed "Papua New Guinea" see Nos. 1024-1029.
For overprints see Nos. 11-26.

Papua

Stamps of British New Guinea, Overprinted

Large Overprint
1906, Nov. 8   Wmk. 47   Perf. 14
Center in Black
11	A1	½p yellow green	12.00	25.00
12	A1	1p carmine	20.00	22.50
13	A1	2p violet	19.00	5.00
14	A1	2½p ultra	12.00	18.00
15	A1	4p black brown	250.00	160.00
16	A1	6p dark green	50.00	50.00
17	A1	1sh orange	30.00	50.00
18	A1	2sh6p brown	200.00	225.00
	Nos. 11-18 (8)		593.00	555.50

Small Overprint

1907
Center in Black
19	A1	½p yel grn	24.00	29.00
a.	Double overprint		3,500.	
20	A1	1p carmine	12.00	7.50
a.	Vertical overprint, up		8,250.	4,500.
21	A1	2p violet	8.00	4.00
a.	Double overprint		4,250.	
22	A1	2½p ultra	21.00	24.00
a.	Double overprint			
23	A1	4p blk brn	50.00	70.00
24	A1	6p dk grn	50.00	50.00
a.	Double overprint		7,000.	13,000.
25	A1	1sh orange	55.00	60.00
a.	Double overprint		21,000.	14,000.
26	A1	2sh6p brown	60.00	75.00
b.	Vert. ovpt., down		8,500.	
d.	Double horiz. ovpt.			4,500.
	Nos. 19-26 (8)		280.00	324.50

A2   Small "PAPUA"

Perf. 11, 12½
1907-08   Litho.   Wmk. 13
Center in Black
28	A2	1p carmine ('08)	7.50	5.75
29	A2	2p violet ('08)	27.50	8.00
30	A2	2½p ultra ('08)	17.50	9.00
31	A2	4p black brown	9.00	9.00
32	A2	6p dk green ('08)	17.50	18.50
33	A2	1sh orange ('08)	57.50	25.00
	Nos. 28-33 (6)		136.50	75.25

Perf. 12½
30a	A2	2½p	180.00	190.00
31a	A2	4p	13.00	13.00
33a	A2	1sh	77.50	100.00
	Nos. 30a-33a (3)		270.50	303.00

1909-10   Wmk. Sideways
Center in Black
34	A2	½p yellow green	5.50	6.50
a.	Perf. 11x12½		5,500.	5,500.
b.	Perf. 11		3.00	3.50
35	A2	1p carmine	10.00	14.00
b.	Perf. 11		11.00	9.25
36	A2	2p violet ('10)	10.00	15.00
a.	Perf. 11x12½		1,700.	
b.	Perf. 11		27.50	10.50
37	A2	2½p ultra ('10)	10.00	26.00
a.	Perf. 12½		13.00	45.00
38	A2	4p black brn ('10)	6.50	12.00
a.	Perf. 11x12½		16,000.	
39	A2	6p dark green	12.50	22.50
a.	Perf. 12½		5,500.	14,000.

40	A2	1sh orange ('10)	25.00	65.00
a.		Perf. 11	65.00	85.00
		Nos. 34-40 (7)	76.50	161.00

One stamp in each sheet has a white line across the upper part of the picture which is termed the "rift in the clouds."

Large "PAPUA"

2sh6p:
Type I — The numerals are thin and irregular. The body of the "6" encloses a large spot of color. The dividing stroke is thick and uneven.
Type II — The numerals are thick and well formed. The "6" encloses a narrow oval of color. The dividing stroke is thin and sharp.

1910   Wmk. 13
Center in Black

41	A2	½p yellow green	6.00	14.00
42	A2	1p carmine	15.00	16.00
43	A2	2p violet	7.50	.00
44	A2	2½p blue violet	13.00	22.50
45	A2	4p black brown	13.50	14.00
46	A2	6p dark green	11.00	13.00
47	A2	1sh orange	14.00	22.50
48	A2	2sh6p brown, type II	77.50	75.00
a.		Type I	60.00	60.00
		Nos. 41-48 (8)	157.50	185.00

Wmk. Sideways

49	A2	2sh6p choc, type I	85.00	100.00

1911   Typo.   Wmk. 74   Perf. 12½

50	A2	½p yellow green	1.25	4.00
51	A2	1p lt red	2.25	1.25
52	A2	2p lt violet	4.00	1.25
53	A2	2½p ultra	6.75	11.00
54	A2	4p olive green	3.50	14.00
55	A2	6p orange brown	5.00	6.50
56	A2	1sh yellow	14.00	20.00
57	A2	2sh6p rose	46.00	50.00
		Nos. 50-57 (8)	82.75	108.00

For surcharges see Nos. 74-79.

1915, June   Perf. 14

59	A2	1p light red	22.50	3.00

A3

1916-31

60	A3	½p pale yel grn & myr grn ('19)	1.00	1.50
61	A3	1p rose red & blk	2.50	1.50
62	A3	1½p yel brn & gray bl ('25)	2.50	1.00
63	A3	2p red vio & vio brn ('19)	2.75	1.25
64	A3	2p red brn & vio brn ('31)	3.25	1.25
a.		2p cop red & vio brn ('31)	29.00	2.25
65	A3	2½p ultra & dk grn ('19)	5.75	15.00
66	A3	3p emerald & blk	4.75	3.00
a.		3p dp bl grn & blk	5.75	9.25
67	A3	4p org & lt brn ('19)	4.00	7.00
68	A3	5p ol brn & sl ('31)	5.50	18.00
69	A3	6p vio & dl vio ('23)	5.50	11.00
70	A3	1sh ol grn & dk brn ('19)	7.00	9.00
71	A3	2sh6p rose & red brn ('19)	27.50	47.50
72	A3	5sh dp grn & blk	55.00	60.00
73	A3	10sh gray bl & grn ('25)	175.00	200.00
		Nos. 60-73 (14)	302.00	377.00

Type A3 is a redrawing of type A2. The lines of the picture have been strengthened, making it much darker, especially the sky and water.
See Nos. 92-93. For surcharges & overprints see Nos. 88-91, O1-O10.

Stamps of 1911
Surcharged

ONE PENNY

1917   Perf. 12½

74	A2	1p on ½p yellow grn	1.75	1.90
75	A2	1p on 2p lt violet	14.50	17.50
76	A2	1p on 2½p ultra	1.50	4.50
77	A2	1p on 4p olive green	2.10	5.25

78	A2	1p on 6p org brn	10.00	24.50
79	A2	1p on 2sh6p rose	4.00	7.00
		Nos. 74-79 (6)	33.85	60.65

No. 62 Surcharged

TWO PENCE

1931, Jan. 1   Perf. 14

88	A3	2p on 1½p yellow brn & gray blue	1.50	2.25

Nos. 70, 71 and 72
Surcharged in Black

1931

89	A3	5p on 1sh #70	1.75	3.00
90	A3	9p on 2sh6p #71	7.50	12.00
91	A3	1sh3p on 5sh #72	7.50	14.00
		Nos. 89-91 (3)	16.75	29.00

Type of 1916 Issue
1932   Wmk. 228   Perf. 11

92	A3	9p dp violet & gray	9.50	37.50
93	A3	1sh3p pale bluish grn & grayish vio	14.50	37.50

For overprints see Nos. O11-O12.

Motuan
Girl — A5

Bird of
Paradise and
Boar's
Tusk — A6

Mother and
Child
A7

Papuan
Motherhood
A8

Dubu
(Ceremonial
Platform)
A9

Fire Maker
A10

Designs: 1p, Steve, son of Oala. 1½p, Tree houses. 3p, Papuan dandy. 5p, Masked dancer. 9p, Shooting fish. 1sh3p, Lakatoi. 2sh, Delta art. 2sh6p, Pottery making. 5sh, Sgt.-Major Simoi. £1, Delta house.

Unwmk.
1932, Nov. 14   Engr.   Perf. 11

94	A5	½p orange & blk	4.50	4.00
95	A5	1p yel grn & blk	4.00	.70
96	A5	1½p red brn & blk	4.50	9.25
97	A6	2p light red	12.50	.35
98	A5	3p blue & blk	4.25	7.50
99	A7	4p olive green	12.00	11.00
100	A5	5p grnsh sl & blk	7.00	3.50
101	A8	6p bister brown	8.50	6.25
102	A5	9p lilac & blk	11.50	24.00
103	A9	1sh bluish gray	10.00	10.00
104	A5	1sh3p brown & blk	19.00	29.00
105	A5	2sh bluish slate	18.00	26.00
106	A5	2sh6p rose lilac & blk	29.00	42.50
107	A5	5sh olive & blk	70.00	60.00
108	A10	10sh gray lilac	150.00	120.00
109	A5	£1 lt gray & black	275.00	180.00
		Nos. 94-109 (16)	639.75	534.05

For overprints see Nos. 114-117.

Hoisting Union
Jack at Port
Moresby — A21

H. M. S.
"Nelson" at Port
Moresby — A22

1934, Nov. 6

110	A21	1p dull green	3.00	3.50
111	A22	2p red brown	2.75	3.00
112	A21	3p blue	3.00	3.00
113	A22	5p violet brown	12.00	22.50
		Nos. 110-113 (4)	20.75	32.00
		Set, never hinged	27.50	

Declaration of British Protection, 50th anniv.

Silver Jubilee Issue
Stamps of 1932 Issue Overprinted in Black

a   b

1935, July 9   Glazed Paper

114	A5(a)	1p yellow grn & blk	1.20	4.00
115	A6(b)	2p light red	3.50	5.50
116	A5(a)	3p lt blue & blk	2.25	4.00
117	A5(a)	5p grnsh slate & blk	2.25	4.00
		Nos. 114-117 (4)	9.20	17.50
		Set, never hinged	16.50	

25th anniv. of the reign of George V.

Coronation Issue

King George VI — A22a

Unwmk.
1937, May 14   Engr.   Perf. 11

118	A22a	1p green	.40	.25
119	A22a	2p salmon rose	.40	1.50
120	A22a	3p blue	.40	1.50
121	A22a	5p brown violet	.40	2.00
		Nos. 118-121 (4)	1.60	5.25
		Set, never hinged	2.50	

> Catalogue values for unused stamps in this section, from this point to the end of the section, are for Never Hinged items.

Papua and New Guinea

Tree-
climbing
Kangaroo
A23

Kiriwina
Chief's
House
A24

Copra
Making — A25

Designs: 1p, Buka head-dress. 2p, Youth. 2½p, Bird of paradise. 3p, Policeman. 3½p, Chimbu headdress. 7½p, Kiriwina yam house. 1sh, Trading canoe. 1sh6p, Rubber tapping. 2sh, Shields and spears. 2sh6p, Plumed shepherd. 10sh, Map. £1, Spearing fish.

Unwmk.
1952, Oct. 30   Engr.   Perf. 14

122	A23	½p green	.30	.25
123	A23	1p chocolate	.25	.25
124	A23	2p deep ultra	.75	.25
125	A23	2½p orange	3.50	.60
126	A23	3p dark green	.85	.25
127	A23	3½p dk carmine	.85	.25

128	A24	6½p vio brown	2.25	.25
129	A24	7½p dp ultra	5.00	2.50
130	A25	9p chocolate	4.75	.75
131	A24	1sh yellow green	3.50	.25
132	A24	1sh6p dark green	8.50	1.50
133	A24	2sh deep blue	7.50	.25
134	A25	2sh6p dk red brown	7.00	.75
135	A25	10sh gray black	50.00	16.00
136	A24	£1 chocolate	65.00	20.00
		Nos. 122-136 (15)	160.00	44.10
		Set, hinged		

See #139-141. For surcharges & overprints see #137-138, 147, J1-J3, J5-J6.

Nos. 125 Surcharged

Nos. 131
Surcharged

1957, Jan. 29   Perf. 14

137	A23	4p on 2½p orange	.85	.30
138	A25	7p on 1sh yellow green	1.75	.40

Type of 1952 and

Klinki
Plymill — A26

Designs: 3½p, Chimbu headdress. 4p, 5p, Cacao. 8p, Klinki Plymill. 1sh7p, Cattle. 2sh5p, Cattle. 5sh, Coffee, vert.

1958-60   Engr.   Perf. 14

139	A23	3½p black	7.00	2.00
140	A23	4p vermilion	1.25	.25
141	A23	5p green ('60)	1.50	.25
142	A26	7p gray green	11.00	.25
143	A26	8p dk ultra ('60)	2.50	2.00
144	A26	1sh7p red brown	30.00	16.00
145	A26	2sh5p vermilion ('60)	6.00	2.50
146	A26	5sh gray olive & brn red	11.00	2.10
		Nos. 139-146 (8)	70.25	25.35

Issued: June 2, 1958, Nov. 10, 1960.
For surcharge see No. J4.

No. 122 Surcharged

1959, Dec. 1

147	A23	5p on ½p green	1.00	.25

Council Chamber
and Frangipani
Flowers — A27

1961, Apr. 10   Photo.   Perf. 14½x14

148	A27	5p green & yellow	.90	.35
149	A27	2sh3p grn & salmon	9.00	4.00

Reconstitution of the Legislative Council.

Woman's
Head
A28

Red-
plumed Bird
of Paradise
A29

Port Moresby
Harbor — A30

Constable Ragas
Amis Matia, Port
Moresby — A32

View of Rabaul,
by Samuel
Terarup Cham
A33

Woman
Dancer
A31

Elizabeth II — A34

Designs: 3p, Man's head. 6p, Golden opossum. 2sh, Male dancer with drum. 2sh3p, Piaggio transport plane landing at Tapini.

Perf. 14 (A28, A31, A32), 11½ (A29, A33), 14x13½ (A30), 14½ (A34)

			Unwmk.	
1961-63		**Engr.**		
153	A28	1p dk carmine	.70	.25
154	A28	3p bluish black	.45	.25
		Photo.		
155	A29	5p lt brn, red brn, blk & yel	.50	.25
156	A29	6p gray, ocher & slate	.75	1.25
		Engr.		
157	A30	8p green	.30	.25
158	A31	1sh gray green	4.75	.90
159	A31	2sh rose lake	1.50	.45
160	A30	2sh3p dark blue	.90	.40
161	A32	3sh green	2.25	2.00
		Photo.		
162	A33	10sh multicolored	16.50	13.00
163	A34	£1 brt grn, blk & gold	9.00	8.50
		Nos. 153-163 (11)	37.60	27.50

The 5p and 6p are on granite paper.
Issued: 3sh, 9/5/62; 10sh, 2/13/63: 5p, 6p, 3/27/63; 8p, 2sh3p, 5/8/63; £1, 7/3/63; others, 7/26/61.

Malaria Eradication
Emblem — A35

1962, Apr. 7		**Litho.**	**Perf. 14**	
164	A35	5p lt blue & maroon	1.15	.50
165	A35	1sh lt brown & red	2.10	.75
166	A35	2sh yellow green & blk	2.50	3.25
		Nos. 164-166 (3)	5.75	4.50

WHO drive to eradicate malaria.

Map of Australia
and South
Pacific — A36

			Unwmk.	
1962, July 9		**Engr.**		
167	A36	5p dk red & lt grn	1.75	.30
168	A36	1sh6p dk violet & yel	2.75	1.00
169	A36	2sh6p green & lt blue	2.75	2.25
		Nos. 167-169 (3)	7.25	3.55

5th So. Pacific Conf., Pago Pago, July 1962.

High Jump — A37

1962, Oct. 24   Photo.   Perf. 11½
Size: 26x21mm
Granite Paper

171	A37	5p shown	.50	.30
172	A37	5p Javelin	.50	.30

Size: 32½x22½mm

173	A37	2sh3p runners	2.50	2.00
		Nos. 171-173 (3)	3.50	2.60

British Empire and Commonwealth Games, Perth, Australia, Nov. 22-Dec. 1.
Nos. 171 and 172 printed in alternating horizontal rows in sheet.

Red Cross Centenary
Emblem — A38

1963, May 1   Perf. 13½
174	A38	5p blue grn, gray & red	.55	.25

Games Emblem —
A38a

1963, Aug. 14   Engr.   Perf. 13½x14
176	A38a	5p olive bister	.25	.25
177	A38a	1sh green	.75	.50

So. Pacific Games, Suva, Aug. 29-Sept. 7.

Top of Wooden
Shield — A39

Various Carved Heads.

Perf. 11½
1964, Feb. 5   Unwmk.   Photo.
Granite Paper

178	A39	11p multicolored	.60	.25
179	A39	2sh5p multicolored	.65	1.75
180	A39	2sh6p multicolored	.75	.25
181	A39	5sh multicolored	.90	.25
		Nos. 178-181 (4)	2.90	2.50

Casting Ballot — A40

1964, Mar. 4   Unwmk.   Perf. 11½
Granite Paper

182	A40	5p dk brn & pale brn	.25	.25
183	A40	2sh3p dk brn & lt bl	.80	.50

First Common Roll elections.

Territorial Health
Services — A41

Designs: 5p, Patients at health center clinic. 8p, Dentist and school child patient. 1sh, Nurse holding infant. 1sh2p, Medical student using microscope.

1964, Aug. 5   Engr.   Perf. 14
184	A41	5p violet	.25	.25
185	A41	8p green	.25	.25
186	A41	1sh deep ultra	.25	.25
187	A41	1sh2p rose brown	.40	.40
		Nos. 184-187 (4)	1.15	1.15

A42

Designs: 1p, Striped gardener bower birds. 3p, New Guinea regent bower birds. 5p, Blue birds of paradise. 6p, Lawes six-wired birds of

paradise. 8p, Sickle-billed birds of paradise. 1sh, Emperor birds of paradise. 2sh, Brown sickle-billed bird of paradise. 2sh3p, Lesser bird of paradise. 3sh, Magnificent bird of paradise. 5sh, Twelve-wired bird of paradise. 10sh, Magnificent rifle birds.

Birds in Natural Colors
Size: 21x26mm

1964-65	**Unwmk.**	**Photo.**	**Perf. 11½**	
188	A42	1p brt cit & dk brn	.55	.25
189	A42	3p gray & dk brn	.65	.25
190	A42	5p sal pink & blk	.70	.25
191	A42	6p pale grn & sep	1.05	.25
192	A42	8p pale lil & dk brn	1.50	.35

Size: 25x36mm

193	A42	1sh salmon & blk	1.50	.25
194	A42	2sh blue & dk brn	1.05	.40
195	A42	2sh3p lt grn & dk brn	1.05	1.10
196	A42	3sh yel & dk brn	1.05	1.50
197	A42	5sh lt ultra & dk brn	11.00	2.25
198	A42	10sh gray & dk blue	4.75	11.00
		Nos. 188-198 (11)	24.85	17.85

Issued: 6p, 8p, 1sh, 10sh, 10/28/64; others, 1/20/65.

Carved
Crocodile's
Head — A43

Designs: Wood carvings from Sepik River Region used as ship's prows and as objects of religious veneration.

1965, Mar. 24   Photo.   Perf. 11½
199	A43	4p multicolored	.60	.25
200	A43	1sh2p gray brn, bister & dk brn	1.75	1.75
201	A43	1sh6p lil, dk brn & buff	.60	.25
202	A43	4sh bl, dk vio & mar	.90	.55
		Nos. 199-202 (4)	3.85	2.80

"Simpson and His
Donkey" by Wallace
Anderson — A43a

1965, Apr. 14   Perf. 13½x13
203	A43a	2sh3p brt grn, sep & blk	.80	.50

ANZAC issue. See note after Australia No. 387.

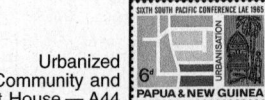

Urbanized
Community and
Stilt House — A44

Design: 1sh, Stilt house at left.

1965, July 7   Photo.   Perf. 11½
204	A44	6p multicolored	.25	.25
205	A44	1sh multicolored	.25	.25

6th South Pacific Conf., Lae, July, 1965.

UN Emblem,
Mother and
Child — A45

UN Emblem and: 1sh, Globe and orbit, vert. 2sh, Four globes in orbit, vert.

1965, Oct. 13   Unwmk.   Perf. 11½
206	A45	6p brown, grnsh bl & dp bl	.25	.25
207	A45	1sh dull pur, blue & org	.25	.25
208	A45	2sh dp blue, pale grn & grn	.25	.25
		Nos. 206-208 (3)	.75	.75

20th anniversary of the United Nations.

New Guinea
Birdwing — A46

Butterflies: 1c, Blue emperor, vert. 3c, White-banded map butterfly, vert. 4c, Mountain swallowtail, vert. 5c, Port Moresby terinos, vert. 12c, Blue crow. 15c, Euchenor butterfly. 20c, White-spotted parthenos. 25c, Orange Jezebel. 50c, New Guinea emperor. $1, Blue-spotted leaf-wing. $2, Paradise birdwing.

1966   Photo.   Perf. 11½
Granite Paper

209	A46	1c sal, blk & aqua	.40	1.00
210	A46	3c gray grn, brn & org	.40	1.00
211	A46	4c multicolored	.40	1.00
212	A46	5c multicolored	.45	.25
213	A46	10c multicolored	.55	.30
214	A46	12c salmon & multi	3.75	2.25
215	A46	15c pale vio, dk brn & buff	1.75	.80
216	A46	20c yel bister, dk brn & yel org	.65	.25
217	A46	25c gray, blk & yel	1.40	1.25
218	A46	50c multicolored	11.00	2.00
219	A46	$1 pale blue, dk brn & dp org	3.50	2.75
220	A46	$2 multicolored	6.25	10.00
		Nos. 209-220 (12)	30.50	22.85

In 1967 Courvoisier made new plates for the $1 and $2. Stamps from these plates show many minor differences and slight variations in shade.
Issued: 12c, 10/10; others, 2/14.

Molala Harai and Paiva
Streamer — A47

Myths of Elema People: 7c, Marai, the fisherman. 30c, Meavea Kivovia and the Black Cockatoo. 60c, Toivita Tapaivita (symbolic face decorations).

1966, June 8   Photo.   Perf. 11½
Granite Paper

221	A47	2c black & carmine	.35	.25
222	A47	7c blue, blk & yel	.35	.35
223	A47	30c blk, yel grn & car	.40	.25
224	A47	60c blk, org & car	.90	.60
		Nos. 221-224 (4)	2.00	1.45

Discus — A48

1966, Aug. 31   Perf. 11½
Granite Paper

225	A48	5c shown	.25	.25
226	A48	10c Soccer	.30	.25
227	A48	20c Tennis	.40	.35
		Nos. 225-227 (3)	.95	.85

Second South Pacific Games, Noumea, New Caledonia, Dec. 8-18.

d'Albertis'
Creeper — A49

Flowers: 10c, Tecomanthe dendrophila. 20c, Rhododendron macgregoriae. 60c, Rhododendron konori.

1966, Dec. 7   Photo.   Perf. 11½
228	A49	5c multicolored	.30	.25
229	A49	10c multicolored	.30	.25
230	A49	20c multicolored	.65	.25
231	A49	60c multicolored	1.75	1.50
		Nos. 228-231 (4)	3.00	2.25

Book and Pen ("Fine
Arts") — A50

3c, "Surveying," transit, view finder, pencil. 4c, "Civil Engineering," buildings, compass. 5c, "Science," test tubes, chemical formula. 20c, "Justice," Justitia, scales.

1967, Feb. 8　Photo.　Perf. 12½x12

232	A50	1c orange & multi	.25	.25
233	A50	3c blue & multi	.25	.25
234	A50	4c brown & multi	.25	.25
235	A50	5c green & multi	.25	.25
236	A50	20c pink & multi	.25	.25
	Nos. 232-236 (5)		1.25	1.25

Issued to publicize the development of the University of Papua and New Guinea and the Institute of Higher Technical Education.

Leaf Beetle — A51

Beetles: 10c, Eupholus schoenherri. 20c, Sphignotus albertisi. 25c, Cyphogastra albertisi.

1967, Apr. 12　Unwmk.　Perf. 11½

237	A51	5c blue & multi	.40	.25
238	A51	10c lt green & multi	.55	.25
239	A51	20c rose & multi	.85	.35
240	A51	25c yellow & multi	1.20	.45
	Nos. 237-240 (4)		3.00	1.30

Hydroelectric Power — A52

Designs: 10c, Pyrethrum (Chrysanthemum cinerariaefolium). 20c, Tea. 25c, like 5c.

1967, June 28　Photo.　Perf. 12x12½

241	A52	5c multicolored	.25	.25
242	A52	10c multicolored	.25	.25
243	A52	20c multicolored	.35	.25
244	A52	25c multicolored	.35	.25
	Nos. 241-244 (4)		1.20	1.00

Completion of part of the Laloki River Hydroelectric Works near Port Moresby, and the Hydrological Decade (UNESCO), 1965-74.

Battle of Milne Bay — A53

Designs: 5c, Soldiers on Kokoda Trail, vert. 20c, The coast watchers. 50c, Battle of the Coral Sea.

1967, Aug. 30　Unwmk.　Perf. 11½

245	A53	2c multicolored	.25	.45
246	A53	5c multicolored	.25	.25
247	A53	20c multicolored	.35	.25
248	A53	50c multicolored	.90	.75
	Nos. 245-248 (4)		1.75	1.70

25th anniv. of the battles in the Pacific, which stopped the Japanese from occupying Papua and New Guinea.

Pesquet's Parrot — A54

Parrots: 5c, Fairy lory. 20c, Dusk-orange lory. 25c, Edward's fig parrot.

1967, Nov. 29　Photo.　Perf. 12

249	A54	5c multicolored	.60	.25
250	A54	7c multicolored	.75	.90
251	A54	20c multicolored	1.15	.25
252	A54	25c multicolored	1.40	.25
	Nos. 249-252 (4)		3.90	1.65

Chimbu District Headdress — A55

Headdress from: 10c, Southern Highlands District, horiz. 20c, Western Highlands District, horiz. 60c, Chimbu District (different from 5c).

Perf. 12x12½, 12½x12

1968, Feb. 21　Photo.　Unwmk.

253	A55	5c multi	.25	.25
254	A55	10c multi	.35	.25
255	A55	20c multi	.35	.25
256	A55	60c multi	1.10	.80
	Nos. 253-256 (4)		2.05	1.55

Frogs — A56

1968, Apr. 24　Photo.　Perf. 11½

257	A56	5c Tree	.60	.45
258	A56	10c Tree, diff.	.60	.25
259	A56	15c Swamp	.60	.25
260	A56	20c Tree, diff.	.80	.55
	Nos. 257-260 (4)		2.60	1.50

Human Rights Flame and Headdress — A57

Symbolic Designs: 10c, Human Rights Flame surrounded by the world. 20c, 25c, "Universal Suffrage" in 2 abstract designs.

1968, June 26　Litho.　Perf. 14x13

261	A57	5c black & multi	.30	.25
262	A57	10c black & multi	.30	.25
263	A57	20c black & multi	.35	.30
264	A57	25c black & multi	.35	.30
	Nos. 261-264 (4)		1.30	1.10

Issued for Human Rights Year, 1968, and to publicize free elections.

Sea Shells — A58

Designs: 1c, Ovula ovum. 3c, Strombus sinuatus. 4c, Conus litoglyphus. 5c, Conus marmoreus. 7c, Mitra mitra. 10c, Cymbiola rutila ruckeri. 12c, Phalium areola. 15c, Lambis scorpius. 20c, Tridacna squamosa. 25c, Lioconcha castrensis. 30c, Murex ramosus. 40c, Nautilus pompilius. 60c, Charonia tritonis. $1, Papustyla pulcherrima. $2, Conus gloriamaris, vert.

1968-69　Photo.　Perf. 12½x12
Granite Paper
Size: 30x22½mm

265	A58	1c multicolored	.25	.25
266	A58	3c multicolored	.40	1.40
267	A58	4c multicolored	.25	1.40
268	A58	5c multicolored	.35	.25
269	A58	7c multicolored	.45	.25
270	A58	10c multicolored	.60	.25
271	A58	12c multicolored	1.75	2.25
272	A58	15c multicolored	1.80	1.25
273	A58	20c multicolored	1.00	.25

Size: 30x25mm
Perf. 11

274	A58	25c multicolored	1.00	1.75
275	A58	30c multicolored	1.00	1.10
276	A58	40c multicolored	1.10	1.40
277	A58	60c multicolored	1.00	.60
278	A58	$1 multicolored	1.60	1.00

Size: 25x30mm
Perf. 12x12½

279	A58	$2 multicolored	12.00	4.50
	Nos. 265-279 (15)		24.55	17.90

Issued: 5c, 20c, 25c, 30c, 60c, 8/28/68; 3c, 10c, 15c, 40c, $1, 10/30/68; others, 1/29/69.

Legend of Tito-Iko — A59

Myths of Elema People: No. 281, 5c inscribed "Iko." No. 282, 10c inscribed "Luvuapo." No. 283, 10c inscribed "Miro."

Nos. 280, 282: Perf. 12½x13½xRoul. 9xPerf. 13½
Nos. 281, 283: Roul. 9 x Perf. 13½x12½x13½

1969, Apr. 9　Litho.　Unwmk.

280		5c black, yellow & red	.25	.25
281		5c black, yellow & red	.25	.25
a.	A59	Vert. pair, #280-281	.55	.90
282		10c black, gray & red	.25	.25
283		10c black, gray & red	.25	.25
a.		Vert. pair, #282-283	.60	.90
	Nos. 280-283 (4)		1.00	1.00

Nos. 281a, 283a have continuous designs, rouletted between.

Fireball Class Sailboat, Port Moresby Harbor — A60

Designs: 10c, Games' swimming pool, Boroko, horiz. 20c, Main Games area, Konedobu, horiz.

Perf. 14x14½, 14½x14

1969, June 25　　　　Engr.

284	A60	5c black	.25	.25
285	A60	10c bright violet	.25	.25
286	A60	20c green	.40	.30
	Nos. 284-286 (3)		.90	.80

3rd S. Pacific Games, Port Moresby, Aug. 13-23.

Dendrobium Ostrinoglossum — A61

Orchids: 10c, Dendrobium lawesii. 20c, Dendrobium pseudofrigidum. 30c, Dendrobium conanthum.

1969, Aug. 27　Photo.　Perf. 11½
Granite Paper

287	A61	5c multicolored	.70	.25
288	A61	10c multicolored	.80	.50
289	A61	20c multicolored	1.00	.80
290	A61	30c multicolored	1.10	.85
	Nos. 287-290 (4)		3.60	2.40

Issued to publicize the 6th World Orchid Conference, Sydney, Australia, Sept. 1969.

Potter — A62

1969, Sept. 24　Photo.　Perf. 11½
Granite Paper

291	A62	5c multicolored	.35	.25

50th anniv. of the ILO.

Bird of Paradise — A63

Coil Stamps

1969-71　　　　Perf. 14½ Horiz.

291A	A63	2c red, dp blue & blk	.35	.50
292	A63	5c orange & emerald	.35	.25

Issue dates: 5c, Sept. 24, 2c, Apr. 1, 1971.

Seed Pod Rattle (Tareko) — A64

Musical Instruments: 10c, Hand drum (garamut). 25c, Pan pipes (iviliko). 30c, Hour-glass drum (kundu).

1969, Oct. 29　Photo.　Perf. 12½

293	A64	5c multicolored	.25	.25
294	A64	10c multicolored	.25	.25
295	A64	25c multicolored	.40	.35
296	A64	30c multicolored	.80	.40
	Nos. 293-296 (4)		1.70	1.25

Prehistoric Ambum Stone and Skull — A65

Designs: 10c, Masawa canoe of the Kula Circuit. 25c, Map of Papua and New Guinea made by Luis Valez de Torres, 1606. 30c, H.M.S. Basilisk, 1873.

1970, Feb. 11　Photo.　Perf. 12½

297	A65	5c violet brown & multi	.25	.25
298	A65	10c ocher & multi	.25	.25
299	A65	25c org brn & multi	.50	.25
300	A65	30c olive green & multi	1.10	.40
	Nos. 297-300 (4)		2.10	1.25

King of Saxony Bird of Paradise — A66

Birds of Paradise: 10c, King. 15c, Augusta Victoria. 25c, Multi-crested.

1970, May 13　Photo.　Perf. 11½

301	A66	5c tan & multi	.90	.25
302	A66	10c multicolored	1.10	.60
303	A66	15c lt blue & multi	1.50	1.00
304	A66	25c multicolored	2.25	.75
	Nos. 301-304 (4)		5.75	2.60

Canceled to Order

Starting in 1970 or earlier, the Philatelic Bureau at Port Moresby began to sell new issues canceled to order at face value.

Douglas DC-3 and Matupi Volcano — A67

Aircraft: No. 305, DC-6B and Mt. Wilhelm. No. 306, Lockheed Mark II Electra and Mt. Yule. No. 307, Boeing 727 and Mt. Giluwe. No. 308, Fokker F27 Friendship and Manam Island Volcano. 30c, Boeing 707 and Hombom's Bluff.

1970, July 8　Photo.　Perf. 14½x14

305	A67	5c "TAA" on tail	.30	.25
306	A67	5c Striped tail	.30	.25
307	A67	5c "T" on tail	.30	.25
308	A67	5c Red tail	.30	.25
a.		Block of 4, #305-308	1.60	2.00
309	A67	25c multicolored	.75	.40
310	A67	30c multicolored	.75	.55
	Nos. 305-310 (6)		2.70	1.95

Development of air service during the last 25 years between Australia and New Guinea.

Nicolaus N. de Miklouho-Maclay, Explorer, and Mask — A68

Designs: 10c, Bronislaw Kaspar Malinowski, anthropologist, and hut. 15c, Count Tommaso Salvadori, ornithologist, and cassowary. 20c, Friedrich R. Schlechter, botanist, and orchid.

1970, Aug. 19   Photo.   *Perf. 11½*
311	A68	5c brown, blk & lilac	.25	.25
312	A68	10c multicolored	.25	.25
313	A68	15c dull lilac & multi	.80	.35
314	A68	20c slate & multi	.80	.35
		Nos. 311-314 (4)	2.10	1.20

42nd Cong. of the Australian and New Zealand Assoc. for the Advancement of Science, Port Moresby, Aug. 17-21.

Wogeo Island Food Bowl — A69

National Handicraft: 10c, Lime pot. 15c, Aibom sago storage pot. 30c, Manus Island bowl, horiz.

1970, Oct. 28   Photo.   *Perf. 12½*
315	A69	5c multicolored	.30	.25
316	A69	10c multicolored	.40	.25
317	A69	15c multicolored	.40	.25
318	A69	30c multicolored	.60	.50
		Nos. 315-318 (4)	1.70	1.25

Eastern Highlands Round House — A70

Local Architecture: 7c, Milne Bay house. 10c, Purari Delta house. 40c, Sepik or Men's Spirit House.

1971, Jan. 27   Photo.   *Perf. 11½*
319	A70	5c dark olive & multi	.30	.25
320	A70	7c Prus blue & multi	.35	.60
321	A70	10c deep org & multi	.35	.25
322	A70	40c brown & multi	.80	.75
		Nos. 319-322 (4)	1.80	1.85

Spotted Cuscus — A71

Animals: 10c, Brown and white striped possum. 15c, Feather-tailed possum. 25c, Spiny anteater, horiz. 30c, Good-fellow's tree-climbing kangaroo, horiz.

1971, Mar. 31   Photo.   *Perf. 11½*
323	A71	5c blue green & multi	.50	.25
324	A71	10c multicolored	.55	.25
325	A71	15c multicolored	.85	.90
326	A71	25c dull yellow & multi	1.20	.90
327	A71	30c olive & multi	1.20	.60
		Nos. 323-327 (5)	4.30	2.90

Basketball — A72

1971, June 9   Litho.   *Perf. 14*
328	A72	7c shown	.35	.25
329	A72	14c Yachting	.50	.25
330	A72	21c Boxing	.50	.30
331	A72	28c Field events	.50	.45
		Nos. 328-331 (4)	1.85	1.25

Fourth South Pacific Games, Papeete, French Polynesia, Sept. 8-19.

Bartering Fish for Coconuts and Taro — A73

Primary industries: 9c, Man stacking yams and taro. 14c, Market scene. 30c, Farm couple tending yams.

1971, Aug. 18   Photo.   *Perf. 11½*
332	A73	7c multicolored	.30	.25
333	A73	9c multicolored	.40	.25
334	A73	14c multicolored	.55	.25
335	A73	30c multicolored	.75	.50
		Nos. 332-335 (4)	2.00	1.25

Siaa Dancer — A74

Designs: 9c, Urasena masked dancer. 20c, Two Siassi masked dancers, horiz. 28c, Three Siaa dancers, horiz.

1971, Oct. 27   Photo.   *Perf. 11½*
336	A74	7c orange & multi	.30	.25
337	A74	9c yel green & multi	.30	.25
338	A74	20c bister & multi	.80	.80
339	A74	28c multicolored	1.00	.95
		Nos. 336-339 (4)	2.40	2.25

Papua New Guinea and Australia Arms — A75

#341, Papua New Guinea & Australia flags.

1972, Jan. 26   *Perf. 12½x12*
340	A75	7c gray blue, org & blk	.30	.30
341	A75	7c gray blue, blk, red & yel	.30	.30
a.		Pair, #340-341	.75	.75

Constitutional development for the 1972 House of Assembly elections.

Papua New Guinea Map, South Pacific Commission Emblem — A76

#343, Man's head, So. Pacific Commission flag.

1972, Jan. 26
342	A76	15c brt green & multi	.55	.40
343	A76	15c brt green & multi	.55	.40
a.		Pair, #342-343	1.50	1.50

South Pacific Commission, 25th anniv.

Pitted-shelled Turtle — A77

Designs: 14c, Angle-headed agamid. 21c, Green python. 30c, Water monitor.

1972, Mar. 15   Photo.   *Perf. 11½*
344	A77	7c multicolored	.40	.25
345	A77	14c car rose & multi	1.10	1.10
346	A77	21c yellow & multi	1.10	1.10
347	A77	30c yel green & multi	1.40	1.10
		Nos. 344-347 (4)	4.00	3.70

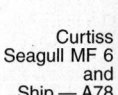

Curtiss Seagull MF 6 and Ship — A78

14c, De Havilland 37 & porters from gold fields. 20c, Junkers G 31 & heavy machinery. 25c, Junkers F 13 & Lutheran mission church.

1972, June 7   Granite Paper
348	A78	7c dp yellow & multi	.25	.25
349	A78	14c dp orange & multi	.65	1.10
350	A78	20c olive & multi	1.10	1.10
351	A78	25c multicolored	1.25	1.10
		Nos. 348-351 (4)	3.25	3.55

50th anniv. of aviation in Papua New Guinea.

National Day Unity Emblem — A79

Designs: 10c, Unity emblem and kundu (drum). 30c, Unity emblem and conch.

1972, Aug. 16   *Perf. 12x12½*
352	A79	7c violet blue & multi	.30	.25
353	A79	10c orange & multi	.40	.30
354	A79	30c vermilion & multi	.60	.55
		Nos. 352-354 (3)	1.30	1.10

National Day, Sept. 15, 1972.

Rev. Copland King — A80

Pioneering Missionaries: No. 356, Pastor Ruatoka. No. 357, Bishop Stanislaus Henry Verjus. No. 358, Rev. Dr. Johannes Flierl.

1972, Oct. 25   Photo.   *Perf. 11½*
355	A80	7c dark blue & multi	.40	.40
356	A80	7c dark red & multi	.40	.40
357	A80	7c dark green & multi	.40	.40
358	A80	7c dark olive bister & multi	.40	.40
		Nos. 355-358 (4)	1.60	1.60

Christmas 1972.

Relay Station on Mt. Tomavatur — A81

1973, Jan. 24   Photo.   *Perf. 12½*
359		7c shown	.35	.25
360		7c Mt. Kerigomna	.35	.25
361		7c Sattelburg	.35	.25
362		7c Wideru	.35	.25
a.		A81 Block of 4, #359-362	1.50	1.50
		Complete booklet, 3 each #359, 361, 2 each #360, 362	13.00	
363	A81	9c Teleprinter	.40	.25
364	A81	30c Map of network	1.40	.85
		Nos. 359-364 (6)	3.20	2.10

Telecommunications development 1968-1972. No. 362a has a unifying frame.

Queen Carol's Bird of Paradise — A82

Birds of Paradise: 14c, Goldie's. 21c, Ribbon-tailed astrapia. 28c, Princess Stephanie's.

1973, Mar. 30   Photo.   *Perf. 11½*
   Size: 22½x38mm
365	A82	7c citron & multi	.90	.45
366	A82	14c dull green & multi	2.25	1.25

   Size: 17x48mm
367	A82	21c lemon & multi	2.75	1.75
368	A82	28c lt blue & multi	3.50	2.50
		Nos. 365-368 (4)	9.40	5.95

Wood Carver, Milne Bay — A83

Designs: 3c, Wig makers, Southern Highlands. 5c, Bagana Volcano, Bougainville. 6c, Pig Exchange, Western Highlands. 7c, Coastal village, Central District. 8c, Arawe mother, West New Britain. 9c, Fire dancers, East New Britain. 10c, Tifalmin hunter, West Sepik District. 14c, Crocodile hunters, Western District. 15c, Mt. Elimbari, Chimbu. 20c, Canoe racing, Manus District. 21c, Making sago, Gulf District. 25c, Council House, East

Sepik. 28c, Menyamya bowmen, Morobe. 30c, Shark snaring, New Ireland. 40c, Fishing canoes, Madang. 60c, Women making tapa cloth, Northern District. $1, Asaro mudmen, Eastern Highlands. $2, Sing festival, Enga District.

1973-74   Photo.   *Perf. 11½*
   Granite Paper
369	A83	1c multicolored	.25	.25
370	A83	3c multi ('74)	.35	.25
371	A83	5c multicolored	.65	.25
372	A83	6c multi ('74)	.90	2.00
373	A83	7c multicolored	.30	.25
374	A83	8c multi ('74)	.35	.30
375	A83	9c multicolored	.40	.25
376	A83	10c multi ('74)	.60	.25
377	A83	14c multicolored	.45	.90
378	A83	15c multicolored	.95	.35
379	A83	20c multi ('74)	.90	.45
380	A83	21c multicolored	.50	1.25
381	A83	25c multicolored	.50	.60
382	A83	28c multicolored	.50	1.25
383	A83	30c multicolored	.60	.60
385	A83	40c multicolored	.50	.50
386	A83	60c multi ('74)	.60	.75
387	A83	$1 multi	.75	1.00
388	A83	$2 multi ('74)	3.00	6.50
		Nos. 369-383,385-388 (19)	12.75	18.45

Issued: 1c, 7c, 9c, 15c, 25c, 40c, 6/13; 5c, 14c, 21c, 28c, 30c, Aug.; 3c, 8c, 10c, 20c, 60c, $1, 1/23/74.

Papua New Guinea No. 7 — A84

1c, Ger. New Guinea #1-2. 6c, Ger, New Guinea #17. 7c, New Britain #43. 25c, New Guinea #1. 30c, Papua New Guinea #108.

   Litho. (1c, 7c); Litho. & Engr. (others)

1973, Oct. 24   *Perf. 13½x14*
   Size: 54x31mm
389	A84	1c gold, brn, grn & blk	.30	.25
390	A84	6c silver, blue & indigo	.35	.25
391	A84	7c gold, red, blk & buff	.35	.25

   Perf. 14x14½
   Size: 45x38mm
392	A84	9c gold, org, blk & brn	.45	.35
393	A84	25c gold & orange	.75	.90
394	A84	30c silver & dp lilac	.80	1.00
		Nos. 389-394 (6)	3.00	3.00

75th anniv. of stamps in Papua New Guinea.

Masks — A85

1973, Dec. 5   Photo.   *Perf. 12½*
   Granite Paper
395	A85	7c multicolored	.35	.25
396	A85	10c violet blue & multi	.65	.65

Self-government.

Queen Elizabeth II — A86

1974, Feb. 22   Photo.   *Perf. 14x14½*
397	A86	7c dp carmine & multi	.35	.25
398	A86	30c vio blue & multi	.90	.90

Visit of Queen Elizabeth II and the Royal Family, Feb. 22-27.

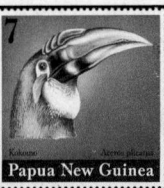

Wreathed Hornbill — A87

Size of No. 400, 32½x48mm.

Perf. 12, 11½ (10c)
1974, June 12   **Photo.**
Granite Paper
399	A87	7c shown	1.50	.75
400	A87	10c Great cassowary	2.50	3.25
401	A87	30c Kapul eagle	5.50	7.50
		Nos. 399-401 (3)	9.50	11.50

Dendrobium Bracteosum — A88

Orchids: 10c, Dendrobium anosmum. 20c, Dendrobium smillieae. 30c, Dendrobium insigne.

1974, Nov. 20   **Photo.**   **Perf. 11½**
Granite Paper
402	A88	7c dark green & multi	.95	.25
403	A88	10c dark blue & multi	.75	.60
404	A88	20c bister & multi	1.25	1.25
405	A88	30c green & multi	1.60	1.60
		Nos. 402-405 (4)	4.55	3.70

Motu Lakatoi — A89

Traditional Canoes: 10c, Tami two-master morobe. 25c, Aramia racing canoe. 30c, Buka Island canoe.

1975, Feb. 26   **Photo.**   **Perf. 11½**
Granite Paper
406	A89	7c multicolored	.30	.25
407	A89	10c orange & multi	.50	.50
408	A89	25c apple green & multi	.90	2.50
409	A89	30c citron & multi	1.00	1.25
		Nos. 406-409 (4)	2.70	4.50

Paradise Birdwing Butterfly, 1t Coin — A90

Ornate Butterfly Cod on 2t and Plateless Turtle on 5t — A91

New coinage: 10t, Cuscus on 10t. 20t, Cassowary on 20t. 1k, River crocodiles on 1k coin with center hole; obverse and reverse of 1k.

Perf. 11, 11½ (A91)
1975, Apr. 21   **Photo.**
Granite Paper
410	A90	1t green & multi	.25	.25
411	A91	7t brown & multi	.35	.35
412	A90	10t violet blue & multi	.35	.35
413	A90	20t carmine & multi	.70	.70
414	A91	1k dull blue & multi	2.00	2.75
		Nos. 410-414 (5)	3.65	4.40

Ornithoptera Alexandrae — A92

Birdwing Butterflies: 10t, O. victoriae regis. 30t, O. allottei. 40t, O. chimaera.

1975, June 11   **Photo.**   **Perf. 11½**
Granite Paper
415	A92	7t multicolored	.40	.25
416	A92	10t multicolored	.45	.45
417	A92	30t multicolored	1.40	1.40
418	A92	40t multicolored	1.75	3.25
		Nos. 415-418 (4)	4.00	5.35

Boxing and Games' Emblem — A93

1975, Aug. 2   **Photo.**   **Perf. 11½**
Granite Paper
419	A93	7t shown	.35	.25
420	A93	20t Track and field	.60	.45
421	A93	25t Basketball	.65	.60
422	A93	30t Swimming	.70	.75
		Nos. 419-422 (4)	2.30	2.05

5th South Pacific Games, Guam, Aug. 1-10.

Map of South East Asia and Flag of PNG — A94

Design: 30t, Map of South East Asia and Papua New Guinea coat of arms.

1975, Sept. 10   **Photo.**   **Perf. 11½**
Granite Paper
423	A94	7t red & multi	.25	.25
424	A94	30t blue & multi	.60	.60
a.		Souvenir sheet of 2, #423-424	1.40	1.40

Papua New Guinea independence, Sept. 16, 1975.

M. V. Bulolo — A95

Ships of the 1930's: 15t, M.V. Macdhui. 25t, M.V. Malaita. 60t, S.S. Montoro.

1976, Jan. 21   **Photo.**   **Perf. 11½**
Granite Paper
425	A95	7t multicolored	.25	.25
426	A95	15t multicolored	.30	.30
427	A95	25t multicolored	.60	.50
428	A95	60t multicolored	1.40	2.25
		Nos. 425-428 (4)	2.55	3.30

Rorovana Carvings — A96

Bougainville Art: 20t, Upe hats. 25t, Kapkaps (tortoise shell ornaments). 30t, Carved canoe paddles.

1976, Mar. 17   **Photo.**   **Perf. 11½**
Granite Paper
429	A96	7t multicolored	.30	.25
430	A96	20t blue & multi	.50	.45
431	A96	25t dp orange & multi	.60	1.10
432	A96	30t multicolored	.75	.75
		Nos. 429-432 (4)	2.15	2.55

Houses — A97

1976, June 9   **Photo.**   **Perf. 11½**
Granite Paper
433	A97	7t Rabaul	.25	.25
434	A97	15t Aramia	.30	.25
435	A97	30t Telefomin	.60	.60
436	A97	40t Tapini	.60	1.25
		Nos. 433-436 (4)	1.75	2.35

Boy Scouts and Scout Emblem — A98

De Havilland Sea Plane, Map of Pacific — A99

Designs: 15t, Sea Scouts on outrigger canoe, Scout emblem. 60t, Plane on water.

1976, Aug. 18   **Photo.**   **Perf. 11½**
Granite Paper
437	A98	7t multicolored	.30	.25
438	A99	10t lilac & multi	.30	.25
439	A98	15t multicolored	.40	.40
440	A99	60t multicolored	1.00	2.00
		Nos. 437-440 (4)	2.00	2.90

50th anniversaries: Papua New Guinea Boy Scouts; 1st flight from Australia.

Father Ross and Mt. Hagen — A100

1976, Oct. 28   **Photo.**   **Perf. 11½**
Granite Paper
441	A100	7t multicolored	.50	.25

Rev. Father William Ross (1896-1973), American missionary in New Guinea.

Clouded Rainbow Fish — A101

Tropical Fish: 15t, Imperial angelfish. 30t, Freckled rock cod. 40t, Threadfin butterflyfish.

1976, Oct. 28   **Granite Paper**
442	A101	5t multicolored	.25	.25
443	A101	15t multicolored	.70	.50
444	A101	30t multicolored	1.40	.80
445	A101	40t multicolored	1.90	1.90
		Nos. 442-445 (4)	4.25	3.45

Kundiawa Man A102

Mekeo Headdress A103

Headdresses: 5t, Masked dancer, East Sepik Province. 10t, Dancer, Koiari area. 15t, Hanuabada woman. 20t, Young woman, Orokaiva. 25t, Haus Tambaran dancer, East Sepik Province. 30t, Asaro Valley man. 35t, Garaina man, Morobe. 40t, Waghi Valley man. 50t, Trobriand dancer, Milne Bay. 1k, Wasara.

Sizes: 25x30mm (1, 5, 20t), 26x26mm (10, 15, 25, 30, 50t), 23x38mm (35, 40t)

Perf. 12 (15, 25, 30t), 11½ (others)
1977-78   **Photo.**
446	A102	1t multicolored	.25	.25
447	A102	5t multicolored	.25	.25
448	A102	10t multicolored	.30	.25
449	A102	15t multicolored	.30	.25
450	A102	20t multicolored	.55	.25
451	A102	25t multicolored	.35	.30
452	A102	30t multicolored	.40	.40
453	A102	35t multicolored	.65	.50
454	A102	40t multicolored	.60	.30
455	A102	50t multicolored	.85	.90

Litho.
Perf. 14½x14
Size: 28x35½mm
456	A102	1k multicolored	1.25	1.75

Perf. 14½x15
Size: 33x23mm
457	A103	2k multicolored	1.75	3.25
		Nos. 446-457 (12)	7.50	8.65

Issued: #456-457, 1/12/77; #448, 450, 453, 455, 6/7/78; others, 3/29/78.

Elizabeth II and P.N.G. Arms — A104

Designs: 7t, Queen and P.N.G. flag. 35t, Queen and map of P.N.G.

1977, Mar. 16   **Photo.**   **Perf. 15x14**
462	A104	7t multicolored	.35	.25
a.		Silver omitted	500.00	

463	A104	15t multicolored	.40	.40
464	A104	35t multicolored	.70	.90
		Nos. 462-464 (3)	1.45	1.55

25th anniv. of the reign of Elizabeth II.

Whitebreasted Ground Dove — A105

Protected Birds: 7t, Victoria crowned pigeon. 15t, Pheasant pigeon. 30t, Orange-fronted fruit dove. 50t, Banded imperial pigeon.

1977, June 8   **Photo.**   **Perf. 11½**
Granite Paper
465	A105	5t multicolored	.55	.25
466	A105	7t multicolored	.55	.25
467	A105	15t multicolored	.90	.85
468	A105	30t multicolored	1.00	1.25
469	A105	50t multicolored	1.50	3.00
		Nos. 465-469 (5)	4.50	5.60

Girl Guides and Gold Badge — A106

Designs (Girl Guides): 15t, Mapping and blue badge. 30t, Doing laundry in brook and red badge. 35t, Wearing grass skirts, cooking and green badge.

1977, Aug. 10   **Litho.**   **Perf. 14½**
470	A106	7t multicolored	.25	.25
471	A106	15t multicolored	.30	.25
472	A106	30t multicolored	.60	.60
473	A106	35t multicolored	.60	.60
		Nos. 470-473 (4)	1.75	1.70

Papua New Guinea Girl Guides, 50th anniv.

Legend of Kari Marupi — A107

Myths of Elema People: 20t, Savoripi Clan. 30t, Oa-Laea. 35t, Oa-Iriarapo.

1977, Oct. 19   **Litho.**   **Perf. 13½**
474	A107	7t black & multi	.25	.25
475	A107	20t black & multi	.50	.35
476	A107	30t black & multi	.65	.65
477	A107	35t black & multi	.65	.65
		Nos. 474-477 (4)	2.05	1.90

Blue-tailed Skink — A108

Lizards: 15t, Green tree skink. 35t, Crocodile skink. 40t, New Guinea blue-tongued skink.

1978, Jan. 25   **Photo.**   **Perf. 11½**
Granite Paper
478	A108	10t blue & multi	.30	.25
479	A108	15t lilac & multi	.40	.25
480	A108	35t olive & multi	.60	.75
481	A108	40t orange & multi	.85	.85
		Nos. 478-481 (4)	2.15	2.10

Roboastra Arika — A109

Sea Slugs: 15t, Chromodoris fidelis. 35t, Flabellina macassarana. 40t, Chromodoris trimarginata.

1978, Aug. 29   **Photo.**   **Perf. 11½**
482	A109	10t multicolored	.30	.25
483	A109	15t multicolored	.40	.40
484	A109	35t multicolored	.65	.65
485	A109	40t multicolored	.90	1.15
		Nos. 482-485 (4)	2.25	2.45

Mandated New
Guinea Constabulary
A110

Constabulary and Badge: 10t, Royal Papua
New Guinea. 20t, Armed British New Guinea.
25t, German New Guinea police. 30t, Royal
Papua and New Guinea.

1978, Oct. 26   Photo.   Perf. 14½x14
486	A110	10t multicolored	.25 .25
487	A110	15t multicolored	.35 .35
488	A110	20t multicolored	.40 .40
489	A110	25t multicolored	.45 .45
490	A110	30t multicolored	.55 .55
	Nos. 486-490 (5)		2.00 2.00

Ocarina, Chimbu
Province — A111

Musical Instruments: 20t, Musical bow, New
Britain, horiz. 28t, Launut, New Ireland. 35t,
Nose flute, New Hanover, horiz.

Perf. 14½x14, 14x14½
1979, Jan. 24   Litho.
491	A111	7t multicolored	.30 .25
492	A111	20t multicolored	.40 .30
493	A111	28t multicolored	.60 .60
494	A111	35t multicolored	.70 .70
	Nos. 491-494 (4)		2.00 1.85

Prow and Paddle, East
New Britain — A112

Canoe Prows and Paddles: 21t, Sepik war
canoe. 25t, Trobriand Islands. 40t, Milne Bay.

1979, Mar. 28   Litho.   Perf. 14½
495	A112	14t multicolored	.30 .25
496	A112	21t multicolored	.40 .25
497	A112	25t multicolored	.55 .55
498	A112	40t multicolored	.70 .70
	Nos. 495-498 (4)		1.95 1.75

Belt of Shell
Disks — A113

Traditional Currency: 15t, Tusk chest ornament. 25t, Shell armband. 35t, Shell necklace.

1979, June 6   Litho.   Perf. 12½x12
499	A113	7t multicolored	.25 .25
500	A113	15t multicolored	.35 .30
501	A113	25t multicolored	.55 .55
502	A113	35t multicolored	.65 .65
	Nos. 499-502 (4)		1.80 1.75

Oenetus — A114

Moths: 15t, Celerina vulgaris. 20t, Alcidis
aurora, vert. 25t, Phyllodes conspicillator. 30t,
Nyctalemon patroclus, vert.

1979, Aug. 29   Photo.   Perf. 11½
503	A114	7t multicolored	.25 .25
504	A114	15t multicolored	.40 .35
505	A114	20t multicolored	.45 .45
506	A114	25t multicolored	.50 .75
507	A114	30t multicolored	.65 .90
	Nos. 503-507 (5)		2.25 2.70

Baby in String Bag
Scale — A115

IYC (Emblem and): 7t, Mother nursing baby.
30t, Boy playing with dog and ball. 60t, Girl in
classroom.

1979, Oct. 24   Litho.   Perf. 14x13½
508	A115	7t multicolored	.30 .25
509	A115	15t multicolored	.35 .25
510	A115	30t multicolored	.45 .45
511	A115	60t multicolored	.80 .80
	Nos. 508-511 (4)		1.90 1.75

Mail Sorting,
Mail
Truck — A116

UPU Membership: 25t, Wartime mail delivery. 35t, UPU monument, airport and city. 40t,
Hand canceling, letter carrier.

1980, Jan. 23   Litho.   Perf. 13½x14
512	A116	7t multicolored	.30 .25
513	A116	25t multicolored	.40 .30
514	A116	35t multicolored	.50 .50
515	A116	40t multicolored	.65 .65
	Nos. 512-515 (4)		1.85 1.70

Male Dancer, Betrothal
Ceremony — A117

Third South Pacific Arts Festival, Port
Moresby (Minj Betrothal Ceremony Mural): a,
One dancer, orange and yellow. b, Two dancers, red, yellow & blk. c, Two dancers side by
side, orange, black. d, Two dancers, one in
front of the other one. e, One dancer, yellow
and red.
No. 516 has continuous design.

1980, Mar. 26   Photo.   Perf. 11½
Granite Paper
516	A117	Strip of 5	1.75 2.00
a.-e.		20t any single	.30 .30

National
Census
A118

1980, June 4   Litho.   Perf. 14
517	A118	7t shown	.25 .25
518	A118	15t Population symbol	.25 .25
519	A118	40t P. N. G. map	.55 .55
520	A118	50t Faces	.75 .75
	Nos. 517-520 (4)		1.80 1.80

Blood Transfusion,
Donor's
Badge — A119

15t, Donating blood. 30t, Map of donation
centers. 60t, Blood components and types.

1980, Aug. 27   Litho.   Perf. 14½
521	A119	7t shown	.25 .25
522	A119	15t multicolored	.25 .25
523	A119	30t multicolored	.50 .50
524	A119	60t multicolored	.85 .85
	Nos. 521-524 (4)		1.85 1.85

Dugong — A120

30t, Native spotted cat, vert. 35t, Tube-
nosed bat, vert. 45t, Raffray's bandicoot.

1980, Oct. 29   Photo.   Perf. 11½
525	A120	7t shown	.25 .25
526	A120	30t multicolored	.60 .60
527	A120	35t multicolored	.70 .70
528	A120	45t multicolored	.95 .95
	Nos. 525-528 (4)		2.50 2.50

Beach
Kingfisher — A121

7t, Forest kingfisher. 20t, Sacred kingfisher.
25t, White-tailed paradise kingfisher. 60t,
Blue-winged kookaburra.

1981, Jan. 21   Photo.   Perf. 12
Granite Paper
529	A121	3t shown	.30 .60
530	A121	7t multicolored	.30 .25
531	A121	20t multicolored	.45 .45
	Size: 26x45½mm		
532	A121	25t multicolored	.55 .55
	Size: 26x36mm		
533	A121	60t multicolored	1.40 2.75
	Nos. 529-533 (5)		3.00 4.60

Mask — A122

Coil Stamps
Perf. 14½ Horiz.
1981, Jan. 21   Photo.
534	A122	2t shown	.25 .25
535	A122	5t Hibiscus	.25 .25

Defense
Force Soldiers
Firing Mortar
A123

15t, DC-3 military plane. 40t, Patrol boat
Eitape. 50t, Medics treating civilians.

1981, Mar. 25   Photo.   Perf. 13½x14
536	A123	7t shown	.25 .25
537	A123	15t multicolored	.30 .25
538	A123	40t multicolored	.65 .65
539	A123	50t multicolored	.80 .80
	Nos. 536-539 (4)		2.00 1.95

For surcharge see No. 615.

Missionary Aviation
Fellowship
Plane — A124

Planes of Missionary Organizations: 15t,
Holy Ghost Society. 20t, Summer Institute of
Linguistics. 30t, Lutheran Mission. 35t, Sev-
enth Day Adventist.

1981, June 17   Litho.   Perf. 14
540	A124	10t multicolored	.25 .25
541	A124	15t multicolored	.30 .25
542	A124	20t multicolored	.40 .30
543	A124	30t multicolored	.50 .50
544	A124	35t multicolored	.60 .60
	Nos. 540-544 (5)		2.05 1.90

Scoop Net
Fishing — A125

1981, Aug. 26
545	A125	10t shown	.25 .25
546	A125	15t Kite fishing	.30 .30
547	A125	30t Rod fishing	.55 .55
548	A125	60t Scissor net fishing	1.00 1.00
	Nos. 545-548 (4)		2.10 2.10

Forcartia
Buhleri — A126

15t, Naninia citrina. 20t, Papuina adonis,
papuina hermione. 30t, Papustyla hindei,
papustyla novaepommeraniae. 40t, Rhynchotrochus strabo.

1981, Oct. 28   Photo.   Perf. 12
Granite Paper
549	A126	5t multicolored	.25 .25
550	A126	15t multicolored	.30 .30
551	A126	20t multicolored	.40 .40
552	A126	30t multicolored	.55 .55
553	A126	40t multicolored	.70 .70
	Nos. 549-553 (5)		2.20 2.20

75th Anniv. of Boy
Scouts — A127

15t, Lord Baden-Powell, flag raising. 25t,
Leader, campfire. 35t, Scout, hut building. 50t,
Percy Chatterton, first aid.

1982, Jan. 20   Photo.   Perf. 11½
Granite Paper
554	A127	15t multicolored	.25 .25
555	A127	25t multicolored	.40 .40
556	A127	35t multicolored	.55 .55
557	A127	50t multicolored	.80 .80
	Nos. 554-557 (4)		2.00 2.00

Wanigela
Pottery — A128

10t, Boiken, East Sepik. 20t, Gumalu,
Madang. 50t, Ramu Valley, Madang.

1982, Mar. 24   Litho.   Perf. 14
Size: 29x29mm
558	A128	10t multicolored	.25 .25
559	A128	20t multicolored	.40 .40
	Perf. 14½		
	Size: 36x23mm		
560	A128	40t shown	.65 .65
561	A128	50t multicolored	.80 .80
	Nos. 558-561 (4)		2.10 2.10

Nutrition — A129

1982, May 5   Litho.   Perf. 14½x14
562	A129	10t Mother, child	.25 .25
563	A129	15t Protein	.35 .35
564	A129	30t Fruits, vegetables	.65 .65
565	A129	40t Carbohydrates	.85 .85
	Nos. 562-565 (4)		2.10 2.10

Coral — A130

1t, Stony Coral (Stylophora). 5t, Finger
Coral (Acropora humilis). 15t, Lace Coral (Distichopora). 1k, Pulse Coral (Xenia).

1982, July 21   Photo.   Perf. 11½
Granite Paper
566	A130	1t Stylophora sp.	.35 .25
567	A130	5t Acropora humilis	.35 .25
568	A130	15t Distichopora sp.	.75 .40
569	A130	1k Xenia sp.	3.75 2.75
	Nos. 566-569 (4)		5.20 3.65

See Nos. 575-579, 588-591, 614.

Centenary of Catholic Church in
Papua New Guinea — A131

a, Ship and Men, one dog. b, Men and three
dogs. c, Men and tree.

1982, Sept. 15   Photo.   Perf. 11½
570 A131 Strip of 3   1.00 1.00
a.-c.   10t any single   .30 .30

12th Commonwealth
Games, Brisbane,
Australia, Sept. 30-
Oct. 9 — A132

1982, Oct. 6   Litho.   Perf. 14½
571 A132 10t Running   .25 .25
572 A132 15t Boxing   .25 .25
573 A132 45t Shooting   .80 .80
574 A132 50t Lawn bowling   .90 .90
     Nos. 571-574 (4)   2.20 2.20

Coral Type of 1982

3t, Cup Coral (Dendrophyllia). 10t, Carnation Tree Coral (Dendronephthya), orange
coral, gray background. 30t, Carnation Tree
Coral (Dendronephthya), red coral, blue green
background. 40t, Black Coral (Antipathes). 3k,
Lace Coral (Distichopora).

1983, Jan. 12   Photo.   Perf. 11½
Granite Paper
575 A130 3t multi   .70 1.25
576 A130 10t multi   .90 .90
577 A130 30t multi   1.40 .90
578 A130 40t multi   1.50 1.50
579 A130 3k multi   6.50 6.50
     Nos. 575-579 (5)   11.00 11.05
     Nos. 575-579 vert.

Commonwealth
Day — A133

10t, Flag, arms. 15t, Youth, recreation. 20t,
Technical assistance. 50t, Export assistance.

1983, Mar. 9   Litho.   Perf. 14
580 A133 10t multi   .25 .25
581 A133 15t multi   .25 .25
582 A133 20t multi   .40 .40
583 A133 50t multi   .90 .90
     Nos. 580-583 (4)   1.80 1.80

World
Communications
Year — A134

10t, Mail transport. 25t, Writing & receiving
letter. 30t, Telephone calls. 60t, Family
reunion.

1983, Sept. 7   Litho.   Perf. 14
584 A134 10t multi   .30 .70
585 A134 25t multi   .50 .40
586 A134 30t multi   .55 .45
587 A134 60t multi   1.00 1.00
     Nos. 584-587 (4)   2.35 2.10

Coral Type of 1982

20t, Bamboo Coral (Isis). 25t, Small Polyp
Stony Coral (Acropora). 35t, Elegant
Hydrocoral (Stylaster elegans). 45t, Cup Coral
(Turbinaria).

1983, Nov. 9   Photo.   Perf. 11½
588 A130 20t multi   1.10 .90
589 A130 25t multi   .90 .90
590 A130 35t multi   1.60 1.40
591 A130 45t multi   2.50 1.75
     Nos. 588-591 (4)   6.10 4.75

     Nos. 588-591 vert.

Turtles — A135

5t, Chelonia depressa. 10t, Chelonia
mydas. 15t, Eretkmochelys imbricata. 20t,
Lepidochelys olivacea. 25t, Caretta caretta.
40t, Dermochelys coriacea.

1984, Feb. 8   Photo.
Granite Paper
592 A135 5t multicolored   .25 .25
593 A135 10t multicolored   .30 .30
594 A135 15t multicolored   .50 .50
595 A135 20t multicolored   .65 .60
596 A135 25t multicolored   1.00 1.00
597 A135 40t multicolored   1.10 1.10
     Nos. 592-597 (6)   3.80 3.75

Papua-Australia
Airmail Service,
50th
Anniv. — A136

Mail planes — 20t, Avro X VH-UXX. 25t,
DH86B VH-UYU Carmania. 40t, Westland
Widgeon. 60t, Consolidated Catalina NC777.

1984, May 9   Litho.   Perf. 14½x14
598 A136 20t multicolored   .45 .45
599 A136 25t multicolored   .55 .55
600 A136 40t multicolored   .90 .90
601 A136 60t multicolored   1.25 1.25
     Nos. 598-601 (4)   3.15 3.15

Parliament
House
Opening
A137

1984, Aug. 7   Litho.   Perf. 13½x14
602 A137 10t multicolored   .40 .40

Bird of
Paradise — A138

1984, Aug. 7   Photo.   Perf. 11½
Granite Paper
603 A138 5k multicolored   10.00 10.00

Ceremonial
Shield — A139

1984, Sept. 21
604 A139 10t Central Province   .25 .25
605 A139 20t West New Britain   .55 .55
606 A139 30t Madang   .85 .85
607 A139 50t East Sepik   .90 2.50
     Nos. 604-607 (4)   2.55 4.15

     See Nos. 677-680.

British New Guinea Proclamation
Centenary — A140

1984, Nov. 6   Litho.   Perf. 14½x14
608 A140   Pair   .50 .90
a.   10t Nelson, Port Moresby, 1884 .25 .45
b.   10t Port Moresby, 1984   .25 .45
609 A140   Pair   2.50 3.25
a.   45t Rabaul, 1984   1.10 1.60
b.   45t Elizabeth, Rabaul, 1884 1.10 1.60

Chimbu
Gorge — A142

10t, Fergusson Island, vert. 25t, Sepik
River, vert. 60t, Dali Beach, Vanimo.

1985, Feb. 6   Photo.   Perf. 11½
610 A142 10t multicolored   .25 .25
611 A142 25t multicolored   .65 .65
612 A142 40t shown   1.05 1.05
613 A142 60t multicolored   1.75 1.75
     Nos. 610-613 (4)   3.70 3.70

Coral Type of 1982

12t, Carnation Tree Coral (Dendronephthya), orange coral, blue green background, vert.

1985, May 29   Photo.   Perf. 11½
614 A130 12t multicolored   4.50 4.50

     For surcharge see No. 686.

No. 536 Surcharged
1985, Apr. 1   Litho.   Perf. 13½x14
615 A123 12t on 7t multi   .70 1.00
a.   Inverted surcharge   —

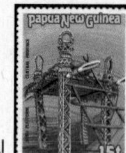

Ritual
Structures — A143

Designs: 15t, Dubu platform, Central Province. 20t, Tamuniai house, West New Britain.
30t, Yam tower, Trobriand Island. 60t, Huli
grave, Tari.

1985, May 1   Perf. 13x13½
616 A143 15t multicolored   .45 .45
617 A143 20t multicolored   .65 .65
618 A143 30t multicolored   .90 .90
619 A143 60t multicolored   1.40 1.40
     Nos. 616-619 (4)   3.40 3.40

A set of four with designs similar to Nos.
616-619 and without the "t" in the denomination was prepared but not officially issued. A
small number of sets found their way into the
marketplace. Value, set $200.

Indigenous Birds of Prey — A144

1985, Aug. 26   Perf. 14x14½
620 12t Accipiter brachyurus   .75 .75
621 12t In flight   .75 .75
a.   A144 Pair, #629-621   1.75 1.75
622 30t Megatriorchis doriae   1.25 1.25
623 30t In Flight   1.25 1.25
a.   A144 Pair, #622-623   3.00 3.00
624 60t Henicopernis longicauda 2.50 2.50
625 60t In flight   2.50 2.50
a.   A144 Pair, #624-625   6.00 6.00
     Nos. 620-625 (6)   9.00 9.00

Flag and Gable of
Parliament House, Port
Moresby — A145

1985, Sept. 11   Perf. 14½x15
626 A145 12t multicolored   .60 .60

Post Office
Centenary — A146

Designs: 12t, No. 631a, 1901 Postal card,
aerogramme, spectacles and inkwell. 30t, No.
631b, Queensland Type A15, No. 628. 40t,
No. 631c, Plane and news clipping, 1885. 60t,
No. 631d, 1892 German canceler, 1985 first
day cancel.

1985, Oct. 9   Perf. 14½x14
627 A146 12t multicolored   .60 .60
628 A146 30t multicolored   1.60 1.60
629 A146 40t multicolored   2.25 2.25
630 A146 60t multicolored   2.75 2.75
     Nos. 627-630 (4)   7.20 7.20

Souvenir Sheet
631   Sheet of 4   8.00 8.00
a.   A146 12t multicolored   .80 .80
b.   A146 30t multicolored 1.40 1.40
c.   A146 40t multicolored 1.75 1.75
d.   A146 60t multicolored 3.00 3.00

Nombowai Cave Carved
Funerary
Totems — A147

12t, Bird Rulowlaw, headman. 30t, Barn owl
Raus, headman. 60t, Melerawuk. 80t, Cock-
erel, woman.

1985, Nov. 13   Perf. 11½
632 A147 12t multicolored   .60 .30
633 A147 30t multicolored   1.25 .70
634 A147 60t multicolored   2.00 2.25
635 A147 80t multicolored   2.50 3.75
     Nos. 632-635 (4)   6.35 7.00

Conch
Shells — A148

15t, Cypraea valentia. 35t, Oliva buelowi.
45t, Oliva parkinsoni. 70t, Cypraea aurantium.

1986, Feb. 12   Perf. 11½
636 A148 15t multicolored   .70 .45
637 A148 35t multicolored   1.75 1.50
638 A148 45t multicolored   2.00 2.00
639 A148 70t multicolored   2.75 4.25
     Nos. 636-639 (4)   7.20 8.20

Common Design Types
pictured following the introduction.

Queen Elizabeth II 60th Birthday
Common Design Type

Designs: 15t, In ATS officer's uniform, 1945.
35t, Silver wedding anniv. portrait by Patrick
Lichfield, Balmoral, 1972. 50t, Inspecting
troops, Port Moresby, 1982. 60t, Banquet
aboard Britannia, state tour, 1982. 70t, Visiting
Crown Agents' offices, 1983.

**   Perf. 14½**
1986, Apr. 21   Litho.   Unwmk.
640 CD337 15t scar, blk & sil   .30 .30
641 CD337 35t ultra & multi   .65 .65
642 CD337 50t green & multi   .90 .90
643 CD337 60t violet & multi   1.00 1.00
644 CD337 70t rose vio & multi 1.25 1.25
     Nos. 640-644 (5)   4.10 4.10

AMERIPEX '86
A149

Small birds — 15t, Pitta erythrogaster. 35t,
Melanocharis striativentris. 45t, Rhipidura
rufifrons. 70t, Poecilodryas placens, vert.

1986, May 22   Photo.   Perf. 12½
Granite Paper
645 A149 15t multicolored   1.10 .70
646 A149 35t multicolored   2.25 1.60
647 A149 45t multicolored   2.50 2.10
648 A149 70t multicolored   3.75 4.50
     Nos. 645-648 (4)   9.60 8.90

Lutheran Church,
Cent. — A150

15t, Monk, minister. 70t, Churches from
1886, 1986.

1986, July 7   Litho.   Perf. 14x15
649 A150 15t multicolored   .60 .55
650 A150 70t multicolored   2.75 2.75

Indigenous Orchids — A151

15t, Dendrobium vexillarius. 35t, Dendrobium lineale. 45t, Dendrobium johnsoniae. 70t, Dendrobium cuthbertsonii.

1986, Aug. 4   Litho.   Perf. 14

651	A151	15t multicolored	1.10	.75
652	A151	35t multicolored	2.25	1.60
653	A151	45t multicolored	2.50	2.10
654	A151	70t multicolored	3.25	5.00
		Nos. 651-654 (4)	9.10	9.45

Folk Dancers — A152

1986, Nov. 12   Litho.   Perf. 14

655	A152	15t Maprik	.95	.65
656	A152	35t Kiriwina	1.75	1.50
657	A152	45t Kundiawa	2.00	1.90
658	A152	70t Fasu	3.50	4.50
		Nos. 655-658 (4)	8.20	8.55

Fish — A153

17t, White-cap anemonefish. 30t, Black anemonefish. 35t, Tomato clownfish. 70t, Spine-cheek anemonefish.

Unwmk.
1987, Apr. 15   Litho.   Perf. 15

659	A153	17t multicolored	1.00	.35
660	A153	30t multicolored	1.50	1.75
661	A153	35t multicolored	2.00	1.40
662	A153	70t multicolored	3.00	4.50
		Nos. 659-662 (4)	7.50	8.00

For surcharges see Nos. 720, 823, 868.

Ships — A154

1t, La Boudeuse, 1768. 5t, Roebuck, 1700. 10t, Swallow, 1767. 15t, Fly, 1845. 17t, like No. 666. 20t, Rattlesnake, 1849. 30t, Vitiaz, 1871. 35t, San Pedrico, Zabre, 1606. 40t, L'Astrolabe, 1827. 45t, Neva, 1876. 60t, Caravel of Jorge De Meneses, 1526. 70t, Eendracht, 1616. 1k, Blanche, 1872. 2k, Merrie England, 1889. 3k, Samoa, 1884.

1987-88   Photo.   Unwmk.   Perf. 11½
Granite Paper

663	A154	1t multicolored	.55	1.25
664	A154	5t multicolored	1.10	1.50
665	A154	10t multicolored	1.40	1.40
666	A154	15t multicolored	2.00	1.25
667	A154	17t multicolored	2.00	.75
668	A154	20t multicolored	2.00	1.00
669	A154	30t multicolored	2.00	2.00
670	A154	35t multicolored	.75	.90
671	A154	40t multicolored	2.25	2.25
672	A154	45t multicolored	.90	.90
673	A154	60t multicolored	2.75	3.25
674	A154	70t multicolored	2.25	2.25
675	A154	1k multicolored	2.75	2.75
676	A154	2k multicolored	4.25	4.25
676A	A154	3k multicolored	5.25	7.00
		Nos. 663-676A (15)	32.20	32.70

Issued: 5, 35, 45, 70t, 2k, 6/15/87; 15, 20, 40, 60t, 2/17/88; 17t, 1k, 3/1/88; 1, 10, 30t, 3k, 11/16/88.
See Nos. 960-963. For surcharge see No. 824.

Shield Type of 1984

War shields — 15t, Elema shield, Gulf Province, c. 1880. 35t, East Sepik Province. 45t, Simbai region, Madang Province. 70t, Telefomin region, West Sepik.

Perf. 11½x12
1987, Aug. 19   Photo.   Unwmk.

677	A139	15t multicolored	.30	.30
678	A139	35t multicolored	.65	.65
679	A139	45t multicolored	.80	.80
680	A139	70t multicolored	1.25	1.25
		Nos. 677-680 (4)	3.00	3.00

Starfish — A156

17t, Protoreaster nodosus. 35t, Gomophia egeriae. 45t, Choriaster granulatus. 70t, Neoferdina ocellata.

1987, Sept. 30   Litho.   Perf. 14

682	A156	17t multicolored	.75	.40
683	A156	35t multicolored	1.50	.90
684	A156	45t multicolored	1.75	1.10
685	A156	70t multicolored	2.25	3.50
		Nos. 682-685 (4)	6.25	5.90

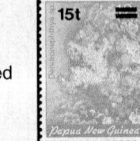

No. 614 Surcharged

1987, Sept. 23   Photo.   Perf. 11½
Granite Paper

686	A130	15t on 12t multi	1.60	1.25

Aircraft — A157

Designs: 15t, Cessna Stationair 6, Rabaraba Airstrip. 35t, Britten-Norman Islander over Hombrum Bluff. 45t, DHC Twin Otter over the Highlands. 70t, Fokker F28 over Madang.

Unwmk.
1987, Nov. 11   Litho.   Perf. 14

687	A157	15t multicolored	1.25	.45
688	A157	35t multicolored	1.75	1.00
689	A157	45t multicolored	2.00	1.25
690	A157	70t multicolored	3.00	5.25
		Nos. 687-690 (4)	8.00	7.95

Royal Papua New Guinea Police Force, Cent. — A158

Historic and modern aspects of the force: 17t, Motorcycle constable and pre-independence officer wearing a lap-lap. 35t, Sir William McGregor, Armed Native Constabulary founder, 1890, and recruit. 45t, Badges. 70t, Albert Hahl, German official credited with founding the island's police movement in 1888, and badge, early officer.

Perf. 14x15
1988, June 15   Litho.   Unwmk.

691	A158	17t multicolored	.60	.45
692	A158	35t multicolored	1.10	.85
693	A158	45t multicolored	1.40	1.10
694	A158	70t multicolored	2.00	2.00
		Nos. 691-694 (4)	5.10	4.40

Sydney Opera House and a Lakatoi (ship)
A159

Fireworks and Globes — A160

1988, July 30   Litho.   Perf. 13½

695	A159	35t multicolored	.85	.85
696	A160	Pair	1.90	1.90
a.-b.		35t any single	.85	.85
c.		Souvenir sheet of 2, #a.-b.	2.60	2.60

SYDPEX '88, Australia (No. 695); Australia bicentennial (No. 696).

World Wildlife Fund — A161

Metamorphosis of a Queen Alexandra's birdwing butterfly — 5t, Courtship. 17t, Ovipositioning and larvae, vert. 25t, Emergence from pupa, vert. 35t, Adult male on leaf.

1988, Sept. 19   Perf. 14½

697	A161	5t multicolored	2.50	2.00
698	A161	17t multicolored	3.75	1.25
699	A161	25t multicolored	4.25	3.50
700	A161	35t multicolored	5.50	4.50
		Nos. 697-700 (4)	16.00	11.25

1988 Summer Olympics, Seoul — A162

1988, Sept. 19   Litho.   Perf. 13½

701	A162	17t Running	.75	.75
702	A162	45t Weight lifting	1.50	1.50

Rhododendrons A163

Wmk. 387
1989, Jan. 25   Litho.   Perf. 14

703	A163	3t R. zoelleri	.25	.25
704	A163	20t R. cruttwellii	.65	.65
705	A163	60t R. superbum	1.60	1.60
706	A163	70t R. christianae	2.00	2.00
		Nos. 703-706 (4)	4.50	4.50

Intl. Letter Writing Week — A164

1989, Mar. 22   Perf. 14½

707	A164	20t Writing letter	.40	.40
708	A164	35t Mailing letter	.70	.60
709	A164	60t Stamping letter	1.15	1.15
710	A164	70t Reading letter	1.35	1.35
		Nos. 707-710 (4)	3.60	3.50

Thatched Dwellings A165

20t, Buka Is., 1880s. 35t, Koiari tree houses. 60t, Lauan, New Ireland, 1890s. 70t, Basilaki, Milne Bay Province, 1930s.

1989, May 17   Wmk. 387   Perf. 15

711	A165	20t multicolored	.45	.40
712	A165	35t multicolored	.95	.75
713	A165	60t multicolored	1.50	1.50
714	A165	70t multicolored	1.75	1.75
		Nos. 711-714 (4)	4.65	4.40

Small Birds — A166

No. 715, Oreocharis arfaki female, shown. No. 716, Male. No. 717, Ifrita kowaldi. No. 718, Poecilodryas albonotata. No. 719, Sericornis nouhuysi.

1989, July 12   Unwmk.   Perf. 14½

715	A166	20t multicolored	1.40	1.40
716	A166	20t multicolored	1.40	1.40
a.		Pair, #715-716	3.25	3.25
717	A166	35t multicolored	1.90	1.40
718	A166	45t multicolored	1.90	1.60
719	A166	70t multicolored	2.50	2.50
		Nos. 715-719 (5)	9.10	8.30

No. 659 Surcharged

1989, July 12   Unwmk.   Perf. 15

720	A153	20t on 17t multi	.90	.90
a.		Double surcharge		180.00

Traditional Dance — A167

Designs: 20t, Motumotu, Gulf Province. 35t, Baining, East New Britain Province. 60t, Vailala River, Gulf Province. 70t, Timbunke, East Sepik Province.

Perf. 14x14½
1989, Sept. 6   Wmk. 387

721	A167	20t multicolored	.70	.65
722	A167	35t multicolored	1.25	1.10
723	A167	60t multicolored	2.40	2.40
724	A167	70t multicolored	2.75	2.75
		Nos. 721-724 (4)	7.10	6.90

For surcharge see No. 860.

Christmas A168

Designs: 20t, Hibiscus, church and symbol from a gulf gope board, Kavaumai. 35t, Rhododendron, madonna and child, and mask, Murik Lakes region. 60t, D'Albertis creeper, candle, and shield from Oksapmin, West Sepik highlands. 70t, Pacific frangipani, peace dove and flute mask from Chungrebu, a Rao village in Ramu.

Perf. 14x14½
1989, Nov. 8   Litho.   Unwmk.

725	A168	20t multicolored	.55	.50
726	A168	35t multicolored	.85	.85
727	A168	60t multicolored	1.60	1.60
728	A168	70t multicolored	1.75	1.75
		Nos. 725-728 (4)	4.75	4.70

Waterfalls — A169

Unwmk.
1990, Feb. 1   Litho.   Perf. 14

729	A169	20t Guni Falls	.75	.55
730	A169	35t Rouna Falls	1.10	.90
731	A169	60t Ambua Falls	2.10	2.10
732	A169	70t Wawoi Falls	2.40	2.40
		Nos. 729-732 (4)	6.35	5.95

For surcharges see Nos. 866, 870.

Natl.
Census — A170

20t, Three youths, form. 70t, Man, woman, child, form.

1990, May 2   **Perf. 14½x15**
733 A170 20t multicolored   .60 .60
734 A170 70t multicolored   2.50 2.50

For surcharge see No. 869.

Gogodala Dance
Masks — A171

1990, July 11   **Litho.**   **Perf. 13½**
735 A171 20t shown   1.25 .50
736 A171 35t multi, diff.   1.75 .90
737 A171 60t multi, diff.   2.75 3.75
738 A171 70t multi, diff.   3.00 3.75
    Nos. 735-738 (4)   8.75 8.90

For surcharges see Nos. 867, 871.

Waitangi Treaty,
150th
Anniv. — A172

Designs: 20t, Dwarf Cassowary, Great Spotted Kiwi. No. 740, Double Wattled Cassowary, Brown Kiwi. No. 741, Sepik mask and Maori carving.

1990, Aug. 24   **Litho.**   **Perf. 14½**
739 A172 20t multicolored   1.25 .90
740 A172 35t multicolored   1.75 .90
741 A172 35t multicolored   2.25 1.40
    Nos. 739-741 (3)   5.25 3.20

No. 741 for World Stamp Exhibition, New Zealand 1990.
For surcharges see Nos. 862-863.

Birds — A173

20t, Whimbrel. 35t, Sharp-tailed sandpiper. 60t, Ruddy turnstone. 70t, Terek sandpiper.

1990, Sept. 26   **Litho.**   **Perf. 14**
742 A173 20t multi   1.25 .70
743 A173 35t multi   1.90 1.10
744 A173 60t multi   3.00 3.75
745 A173 70t multi   3.75 3.75
    Nos. 742-745 (4)   9.90 9.30

Musical
Instruments — A174

1990, Oct. 31   **Litho.**   **Perf. 13**
746 A174 20t Jew's harp   .90 .75
747 A174 35t Musical bow   1.40 1.25
748 A174 60t Wantoat drum   2.75 2.75
749 A174 70t Gogodala rattle   3.00 3.00
    Nos. 746-749 (4)   8.05 7.75

For surcharge see No. 861.

Snail
Shells — A174a

Designs: 21t, Rhynchotrochus weigmani. 40t, Forcartia globula, Canefriula azonata. 50t,

---

Planispira deaniana. 80t, Papuina chancel, Papuina xanthocheila.

1991, Mar. 6   **Litho.**   **Perf. 14x14½**
750 A174a 21t multicolored   1.00 .65
751 A174a 40t multicolored   1.60 1.10
752 A174a 50t multicolored   2.25 2.25
753 A174a 80t multicolored   3.25 3.25
    Nos. 750-753 (4)   8.10 7.25

For surcharge see No. 864.

A175   A176

1t, Ptiloris magnificus. 5t, Loria loriae. 10t, Cnemophilus macgregorii. 20t, Parotia wahnesi. 21t, Manucodia chalybata. 30t, Paradisaea decora. 40t, Loboparadisea sericea. 45t, Cicinnurus regius. 50t, Paradigalla brevicauda. 60t, Parotia carolae. 90t, Paradisaea guilielmi. 1k, Diphyllodes magnificus. 2k, Lophorina superba. 5k, Phonygammus keraudrenii. 10k, Paradisaea minor.

1991-94   **Litho.**   **Perf. 14½**
755 A175 1t multicolored   .25 .25
756 A175 5t multicolored   .25 .25
757 A175 10t multicolored   .25 .25
758 A175 20t multicolored   .45 .45
759 A175 21t multicolored   .50 .50
760 A175 30t multicolored   .70 .70
761 A175 40t multicolored   .90 .90
762 A175 45t multicolored   2.25 1.10
763 A175 50t multicolored   1.25 1.25
764 A175 60t multicolored   3.75 1.40
765 A175 90t multicolored   3.75 2.10
766 A175 1k multicolored   2.25 2.25
767 A175 2k multicolored   4.10 4.50
    a. Strip of 4, #761, 763, 766-767 + label   9.00 9.00
768 A175 5k multicolored   10.00 10.00

Perf. 13
769 A176 10k multicolored   20.00 20.00
    Nos. 755-769 (15)   50.65 45.90

No. 767a for Hong Kong '94 and sold for 4k. Stamps in No. 767a do not have "1992 BIRD OF PARADISE" at bottom of design. Issued: 21t, 45t, 60t, 90t, 3/25/92; 5t, 40t, 50t, 1k, 2k, 9/2/92; 1t, 10t, 20t, 30t, 5k, 1993; 10k, 5/1/91; No. 767a, 2/18/94.
For surcharges see #878A, 878C.

Large T — A176a

1993   **Litho.**   **Perf. 14½**
770A A176a 21T like #759   1.50 .75
770B A176a 45T like #762   3.00 1.60
770C A176a 60T like #764   3.50 3.50
770D A176a 90T like #765   4.25 4.25
    Nos. 770A-770D (4)   12.25 10.10

Originally scheduled for release on Feb. 19, 1992, #770A-770D were withdrawn when the denomination was found to have an upper case "T." Corrected versions with a lower case "T" are #759, 762, 764-765. A quantity of the original stamps appeared in the market and to prevent speculation in these items, the Postal Administration of Papua New Guinea released the stamps with the upper case "T."
For surcharges see #878B, 878D.

1991 South
Pacific
Games — A177

1991, June 26   **Litho.**   **Perf. 13**
771 A177 21t Cricket   2.50 .80
772 A177 40t Running   2.10 1.60
773 A177 50t Baseball   2.50 2.50
774 A177 80t Rugby   4.75 4.75
    Nos. 771-774 (4)   11.85 9.65

Anglican Church
in Papua New
Guinea,
Cent. — A178

Churches: 21t, Cathedral of St. Peter & St. Paul, Dogura. 40t, Kaieta Shrine, Anglican landing site. 80t, First thatched chapel, modawa tree.

1991, Aug. 7   **Litho.**   **Perf. 14½**
775 A178 21t multicolored   1.00 .70
776 A178 40t multicolored   2.00 2.00
777 A178 80t multicolored   3.00 3.50
    Nos. 775-777 (3)   6.00 6.20

Traditional
Headdresses — A179

Designs: 21t, Rambutso, Manus Province. 40t, Marawaka, Eastern Highlands. 50t, Tufi, Oro Province. 80t, Sina Sina, Simbu Province.

1991, Oct. 16   **Litho.**   **Perf. 13**
778 A179 21t multicolored   .95 .60
779 A179 40t multicolored   1.75 1.75
780 A179 50t multicolored   2.00 2.00
781 A179 80t multicolored   2.75 4.25
    Nos. 778-781 (4)   7.45 8.60

Discovery of
America, 500th
Anniv. — A180

1992, Apr. 15   **Litho.**   **Perf. 14**
782 A180 21t Nina   .70 .50
783 A180 45t Pinta   1.75 1.10
784 A180 60t Santa Maria   2.10 2.10
785 A180 90t Columbus, ships   3.00 3.50
    a. Souvenir sheet of 2, #784-785   7.00 7.00
    Nos. 782-785 (4)   7.55 7.20

World Columbian Stamp Expo '92, Chicago. Issue date: No. 785a, June 3.

A181

Papuan Gulf Artifacts: 21t, Canoe prow shield, Bamu. 45t. Skull rack, Kerewa. 60t, Ancestral figure, Era River. 90t, Gope (spirit) board, Urama.

1992, June 3   **Litho.**   **Perf. 14**
786 A181 21t multicolored   .75 .55
787 A181 45t multicolored   1.50 1.25
788 A181 60t multicolored   1.75 1.60
789 A181 90t multicolored   2.75 2.75
    Nos. 786-789 (4)   6.75 6.15

A182

Soldiers from: 21t, Papuan Infantry Battalion. 45t, Australian Militia. 60t, Japanese Nankai Force. 90t, US Army.

1992, July 22   **Litho.**   **Perf. 14**
790 A182 21t multicolored   .95 .60
791 A182 45t multicolored   1.75 1.25
792 A182 60t multicolored   2.50 2.10
793 A182 90t multicolored   3.25 3.25
    Nos. 790-793 (4)   8.45 7.20

World War II, 50th anniv.

Flowering
Trees — A183

21t, Hibiscus tiliaceus. 45t, Castanospermum australe. 60t, Cordia subcordata. 90t, Acacia auriculiformis.

1992, Oct. 28   **Litho.**   **Perf. 14**
794 A183 21t multicolored   1.00 .60
795 A183 45t multicolored   1.90 1.25
796 A183 60t multicolored   3.25 2.40
797 A183 90t multicolored   4.00 4.00
    Nos. 794-797 (4)   10.15 8.25

Mammals — A184

21t, Myoictis melas. 45t, Microperoryctes longicauda. 60t, Mallomys rothschildi. 90t, Pseudocheirus forbesi.

1993, Apr. 7   **Litho.**   **Perf. 14**
798 A184 21t multicolored   .70 .50
799 A184 45t multicolored   1.30 1.20
800 A184 60t multicolored   1.90 1.90
801 A184 90t multicolored   2.60 2.60
    Nos. 798-801 (4)   6.50 6.20

Small Birds — A185

21t, Clytomyias insignis. 45t, Pitta superba. 60t, Rhagologus leucostigma. 90t, Toxorhamphus poliopterus.

1993, June 9   **Litho.**   **Perf. 14**
802 A185 21t multicolored   .85 .50
803 A185 45t multicolored   1.40 1.10
804 A185 60t multicolored   2.00 2.00
805 A185 90t multicolored   2.75 2.75
    Nos. 802-805 (4)   7.00 6.35

Nos. 802-805 Redrawn with Taipei '93 emblem in Blue and Yellow

1993, Aug. 13   **Litho.**   **Perf. 14**
806 A185 21t multicolored   1.10 .45
807 A185 45t multicolored   2.10 1.15
808 A185 60t multicolored   2.40 2.40
809 A185 90t multicolored   2.75 4.50
    Nos. 806-809 (4)   8.35 8.50

Freshwater
Fish — A186

Designs: 21t, Iriatherina werneri. 45t, Tateurndina ocellicauda. 60t, Melanotaenia affinis. 90t, Pseudomugil connieae.

1993, Sept. 29   **Litho.**   **Perf. 14x14½**
810 A186 21t multicolored   1.10 .70
811 A186 45t multicolored   2.10 1.40
812 A186 60t multicolored   2.50 2.50
813 A186 90t multicolored   3.50 3.50
    Nos. 810-813 (4)   9.20 8.10

For surcharges see Nos. 876-878.

Air Niugini, 20th
Anniv. — A187

1993, Oct. 27   **Perf. 14**
814 A187 21t DC3   1.10 .65
815 A187 45t F27   2.50 1.25
816 A187 60t Dash 7   3.00 3.00
817 A187 90t Airbus A310-300   3.25 4.50
    Nos. 814-817 (4)   9.85 9.40

Souvenir Sheet

Paradisaea Rudolphi — A188

1993, Sept. 29   Litho.   Perf. 14
818 A188 2k multicolored   11.00 11.00
Bangkok '93.

Huon Tree
Kangaroo — A189

21t, Domesticated joey. 45t, Adult male. 60t, Female, joey in pouch. 90t, Adolescent.

1994, Jan. 19   Litho.   Perf. 14½
819 A189 21t multicolored   .75   .65
820 A189 45t multicolored   1.60 1.25
821 A189 60t multicolored   2.25 2.25
822 A189 90t multicolored   3.25 3.75
      Nos. 819-822 (4)   7.85 7.90

No. 661 Surcharged

No. 671 Surcharged

Perfs. and Printing Methods as Before

1994, Mar. 23
823 A153 21t on 35t multi   15.00   .80
824 A154 1.20k on 40t multi   4.50 1.75

No. 824 exists with double surcharge. Other varieties may exist.

Artifacts — A190

Designs: 1t, Hagen ceremonial axe, Western Highlands. 2t, Telefomin war shield, West Sepik. 20t, Head mask, Gulf of Papua. 21t, Kanganaman stool, East Sepik. 45t, Trobriand lime gourd, Milne Bay. 60t, Yuat River flute stopper, East Sepik. 90t, Tami island dish, Morobe. 1k, Kundu drum, Ramu River estuary. 5k, Gogodala dance mask, Western Province. 10k, Malanggan mask, New Ireland.

1994-95   Litho.   Perf. 14½
825 A190   1t multicolored   .25   .25
826 A190   2t multicolored   .25   .25
828 A190 20t multicolored   .35   .35
829 A190 21t multicolored   .35   .35
833 A190 45t multicolored   .80   .80
835 A190 60t multicolored   1.10 1.10
836 A190 90t multicolored   1.65 1.65
837 A190   1k multicolored   5.00 3.00
839 A190   5k multicolored   9.00 9.00
840 A190 10k multicolored   15.00 15.00
      Nos. 825-840 (10)   33.75 31.75

Issued: 21, 45, 60, 90t, 3/23; 1, 2, 20t, 5k, 6/29/94; 1k, 10k, 4/12/95.

Classic
Cars — A191

1994, May 11   Litho.   Perf. 14
841 A191 21t Model T Ford   .80   .65
842 A191 45t Chevrolet 490   1.50 1.15
843 A191 60t Baby Austin   2.25 2.25
844 A191 90t Willys Jeep   3.00 3.00
      Nos. 841-844 (4)   7.55 7.05

PHILAKOREA '94 — A192

Tree kangaroos: 90t, Dendrolagus inustus. 1.20k, Dendrolagus dorianus.

1994, Aug. 10   Litho.   Perf. 14
845 A192 Sheet of 2, #a.-b.   8.50 8.50

Moths — A193

Designs: 21t, Daphnis hypothous pallescens. 45t, Tanaorhinus unipuncta. 60t, Neodiphthera sciron. 90t, Parotis maginata.

1994, Oct. 26   Litho.   Perf. 14
846 A193 21t multicolored   .60   .50
847 A193 45t multicolored   1.50 1.00
848 A193 60t multicolored   1.75 1.75
849 A193 90t multicolored   3.00 3.00
      Nos. 846-849 (4)   6.85 6.25

Beatification of Peter
To Rot — A194

No. 850, Peter To Rot. No. 851, Pope John Paul II.

1995, Jan. 11   Litho.   Perf. 14
850 A194 21t multi   .80   .80
851 A194 1k on 90t multi   4.50 4.50
  a.   Pair, #850-851 + label   6.50 6.50

No. 851 was not issued without surcharge. For surcharge see No. 1008.

Tourism — A195

#852, Cruising. #853, Handicrafts. #854, Jet. #855, Resorts. #856, Trekking adventure. #857, White-water rafting. #858, Boat, diver. #859, Divers, sunken plane.

1995, Jan. 11
852 A195 21t multicolored   .80   .80
853 A195 21t multicolored   .80   .80
  a.   Pair, #852-853   2.25 2.25
854 A195 50t on 45t multi   2.00 2.00
855 A195 50t on 45t multi   2.00 2.00
  a.   Pair, #854-855   5.00 5.00
856 A195 65t on 60t multi   2.60 2.60
  a.   "65t" omitted   35.00
857 A195 65t on 60t multi   2.60 2.60
  a.   Pair, #856-857   6.00 6.00
858 A195 1k on 90t multi   4.00 4.00
859 A195 1k on 90t multi   4.00 4.00
  a.   Pair, #858-859   9.25 9.25
      Nos. 852-859 (8)   18.80 18.80

Nos. 854-859 were not issued without surcharge.

Nos. 662, 722, 730, 732, 734, 736, 738, 740-741, 747, 753, 762, 765, 770B, 770D Surcharged

Thick "t" in Surcharge

1994   Perfs., Etc. as Before
860 A167   5t on 35t #722   5.75 1.00
861 A174   5t on 35t #747   27.50 17.50
862 A172 10t on 35t #740   24.00 16.00
863 A172 10t on 35t #741   17.50 6.50
864 A174a 21t on 80t #753   75.00 3.50
866 A169 50t on 35t #730   35.00 17.50
867 A171 50t on 35t #736   80.00 50.00
  a.   Inverted surcharge   625.00
868 A153 65t on 70t #662   4.00 1.75
869 A170 65t on 70t #734   4.00 1.75
870 A169   1k on 70t #732   20.00 6.50
871 A171   1k on 70t #738   27.50 2.50
      Nos. 860-871 (11)   320.25 124.50

Size, style and location of surcharge varies. No. 861 exists in pair, one without surcharge. Other varieties exist.

Issued: #862, 8/23/94; #864, 8/28/94; #861, 863, 864, 10/3/94; #860, 871, 10/6/94; #866-868, 869-870, 11/28/94.

Mushrooms — A196

25t, Lentinus umbrinus. 50t, Amanita hemibapha. 65t, Boletellus emodensis. 1k, Ramaria zippellii.

1995, June 21   Litho.   Perf. 14
872 A196 25t multicolored   .80   .60
        Complete booklet, 10 #872   15.00
873 A196 50t multicolored   1.50 1.50
        Complete booklet, 10 #873   22.50
874 A196 65t multicolored   1.90 1.90
875 A196   1k multicolored   3.00 3.00
      Nos. 872-875 (4)   7.20 7.00

1996   Litho.   Perf. 12
875A A196 25t like #872   2.25 2.25

No. 875A has a taller vignette, a smaller typeface for the description, denomination, and country name and does not have a date inscription like #872.

Nos. 876-878 Surcharged Thick "t"
Nos. 878A-878D Surcharged Thin "t"

Thin "t" in Srch.

See illustration above #860.

1995   Litho.   Perf. 14x14½
876   A186 21t on 45t #811   1.25   .35
877   A186 21t on 60t #812   3.50 1.75
878   A186 21t on 90t #813   1.25   .70
878A A175 21t on 45t #762   12.00 .70
878B A176a 21t on 45T
            #770B   35.00 1.75
878C A175 21t on 90t #765   12.00 .70
878D A176a 21t on 90T
            #770D   35.00 1.75
      Nos. 876-878D (7)   100.00 7.70

Nos. 878A-878D exist with thick surcharge. This printing of 3200 each does not seem to have seen much, if any, public sale. Value, $10 to $150 each.

Nos. 878A, 878C dated 1993. Nos. 878B, 878D dated 1992. Nos. 878A, 878C exist dated 1992.

Issued: Nos. 876-878, 6/20; Nos. 878A-878B, 5/16; No. 878C, 3/27; No. 878D, 4/25.

Independence, 20th
Anniv. — A197

Designs: 50t, 1k, "20" emblem.

1995, Aug. 30   Perf. 14
879 A197 21t multi   .65   .65
880 A197 50t multi   1.40 1.40
881 A197   1k multi   2.75 2.75
      Nos. 879-881 (3)   4.80 4.80

Souvenir Sheet

Singapore '95 — A198

Orchids: a, 21t, Dendrobium rigidifolium. b, 45t, Dendrobium convolutum. c, 60t, Dendrobium spectabile. d, 90t, Dendrobium tapiniense.

1995, Aug. 30   Litho.   Perf. 14
882 A198 Sheet of 4, #a.-d.   6.00 6.00

No. 882 sold for 3k.

Souvenir Sheet

New Year 1995 (Year of the Boar) — A199

1995, Sept. 14
883 A199 3k multicolored   7.25 7.25
Beijing '95.

Eruption of Rabaul Volcano, 1st Anniv. — A200

1995, Sept. 19
884 A200 2k multicolored   4.75 4.75

Crabs — A201

1995, Oct. 25   Litho.   Perf. 14
885 A201 21t Zosimus aeneus   .70   .55
886 A201 50t Cardisoma carnifex 1.25 1.25
887 A201 65t Uca tetragonon   1.75 1.75
888 A201   1k Eriphia sebana   2.40 2.40
      Nos. 885-888 (4)   6.10 5.95

For surcharge see #939B.

Parrots — A202

Designs: 25t, Psittrichas fulgidas. 50t, Trichoglossus haematodus. 65t, Alisterus chloropterus. 1k, Aprosmictus erythropterus.

1996, Jan. 17   Litho.   Perf. 12
889 A202 25t multicolored   1.75   .60
890 A202 50t multicolored   2.50 1.05
891 A202 65t multicolored   3.00 2.25
892 A202   1k multicolored   3.75 3.75
      Nos. 889-892 (4)   11.00 7.65

Beetles — A203

Designs: 25t, Lagriomorpha indigacea. 50t, Eupholus geoffroyi. 65t, Promechus pulcher. 1k, Callistola pulchra.

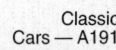

1996, Mar. 20   **Litho.**   *Perf. 12*
893	A203	25t multicolored	.65	.65
894	A203	50t multicolored	1.30	1.30
895	A203	65t multicolored	1.70	1.70
896	A203	1k multicolored	2.60	2.60
	Nos. 893-896 (4)		6.25	6.25

Souvenir Sheet

Zhongshan Memorial Hall,
Guangzhou, China — A204

1996, Apr. 22   **Litho.**   *Perf. 14*
897	A204	70t multicolored	2.50	2.50

CHINA '96, 9th Asian Intl. Philatelic
Exhibition.

1996 Summer
Olympics,
Atlanta — A205

1996, July 24   **Litho.**   *Perf. 12*
898	A205	25t Shooting	.45	.45
899	A205	50t Track	.85	.85
900	A205	65t Weight lifting	1.60	1.60
901	A205	1k Boxing	2.25	2.25
	Nos. 898-901 (4)		5.15	5.15

Olymphilex '96.

Radio,
Cent. — A206

25t, Air traffic control. 50t, Commercial
broadcasting. 65t, Gerehu earth station. 1k,
1st transmission in Papua New Guinea.

1996, Sept. 11   **Litho.**   *Perf. 12*
902	A206	25t multicolored	.40	.40
903	A206	50t multicolored	.85	.85
904	A206	65t multicolored	1.10	1.10
905	A206	1k multicolored	1.60	1.60
	Nos. 902-905 (4)		3.95	3.95

Souvenir Sheet

Taipei '96, 10th Asian Intl. Philatelic
Exhibition — A207

a, Dr. Sun Yat-sen (1866-1925). b, Dr. John
Guise (1914-91).

1996, Oct. 16   **Litho.**   *Perf. 14*
906	A207	65t Sheet of 2, #a.-b.	4.50	4.50

Flowers — A208

Designs: 1t, Hibiscus rosa-sinensis. 5t, Bougainvillea spectabilis. 65t, Plumeria rubra. 1k,
Mucuna novo-guineensis.

1996, Nov. 27   **Litho.**   *Perf. 14*
907	A208	1t multicolored	.40	.25
908	A208	5t multicolored	.40	.25
909	A208	65t multicolored	1.25	1.25
910	A208	1k multicolored	1.90	1.90
	Nos. 907-910 (4)		3.95	3.65

Souvenir Sheet

Oxen
and Natl.
Flag
A209

1997, Feb. 3   **Litho.**   *Perf. 14*
911	A209	1.50k multicolored	3.75	3.75

Hong Kong '97.

Boat
Prows — A210

1997, Mar. 19   **Litho.**   *Perf. 14½x14*
912	A210	25t Gogodala	.35	.35
913	A210	50t East New Britain	.75	.75
914	A210	65t Trobriand Island	1.10	1.10
915	A210	1k Walomo	1.60	1.60
	Nos. 912-915 (4)		3.80	3.80

Queen Elizabeth II
and Prince Philip, 50th
Wedding
Anniv. — A211

#916, Princess Anne, polo players. #917,
Queen up close. #918, Prince in riding attire.
#919, Queen, another person riding horses.
#920, Grandsons riding horses, Prince wav-
ing. #921, Queen waving, riding pony.
2k, Queen, Prince riding in open carriage.

1997, June 25   **Litho.**   *Perf. 13½*
916	A211	25t multicolored	.45	.45
917	A211	25t multicolored	.45	.45
a.		Pair, #916-917	1.10	1.10
918	A211	50t multicolored	.90	.90
919	A211	50t multicolored	.90	.90
a.		Pair, #918-919	2.25	2.25
920	A211	1k multicolored	1.60	1.60
921	A211	1k multicolored	1.60	1.60
a.		Pair, #920-921	3.75	3.75
	Nos. 916-921 (6)		5.90	5.90

Souvenir Sheet
922	A211	2k multicolored	3.75	3.75

Souvenir Sheet

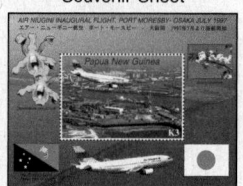

Air Niugini, First Flight, Port Moresby-
Osaka — A212

1997, July 19   **Litho.**   *Perf. 12*
923	A212	3k multicolored	5.75	5.75

1997 Pacific Year
of Coral
Reef — A213

Designs: 25t, Pocillopora woodjonesi. 50t,
Subergorgia mollis. 65t, Oxypora glabra. 1k,
Turbinaria reinformis.

1997, Aug. 27   **Litho.**   *Perf. 12*
924	A213	25t multicolored	.45	.45
925	A213	50t multicolored	.90	.90
926	A213	65t multicolored	1.40	1.40
927	A213	1k multicolored	1.75	1.75
	Nos. 924-927 (4)		4.50	4.50

Flowers — A214

Designs: 10t, Thunbergia fragrans. 20t,
Caesalpinia pulcherrima. 25t, Hoya. 30t,
Heliconia. 50t, Amomum goliathensis.

1997, Nov. 26   **Litho.**   *Perf. 12*
928	A214	10t multicolored	.60	.40
929	A214	20t multicolored	.80	.70
930	A214	25t multicolored	1.00	.90
931	A214	30t multicolored	1.25	1.25
932	A214	50t multicolored	1.75	1.40
	Nos. 928-932 (5)		5.40	4.65

Birds — A215

Designs: 25t, Tyto tenebricosa. 50t, Aepy-
podius arfakianus. 65t, Accipiter poliocephalus. 1k, Zonerodius heliosylus.

1998, Jan. 28   **Litho.**   *Perf. 12*
933	A215	25t multicolored	1.40	.75
934	A215	50t multicolored	1.75	1.40
935	A215	65t multicolored	2.75	2.75
936	A215	1k multicolored	3.75	3.75
	Nos. 933-936 (4)		9.65	8.65

Diana, Princess of Wales (1961-97)
Common Design Type

Designs: a, In beige colored dress. b, In
violet dress with lace collar. c, Wearing plaid
jacket. d, Holding flowers.

1998, Apr. 29   **Litho.**   *Perf. 14½x14*
937	CD355	1k Sheet of 4, #a.-d.	6.25	6.25

No. 937 sold for 4k + 50t with surtax from
international sales being donated to the Princess Diana Memorial fund and surtax from
national sales being donated to designated
local charity.

Mother Teresa
(1910-97) — A216

1998, Apr. 29   *Perf. 14½*
938	A216	65t With child	1.25	1.25
939	A216	1k shown	1.90	1.90
a.		Pair, #938-939	4.00	4.00

No. 887
Surcharged

1998, May 28   **Litho.**   *Perf. 14*
939B	A201	25t on 65t multi	1.10	1.10

Moths — A217

25t, Daphnis hypothous pallescens. 50t,
Theretra polistratus. 65t, Psilogramma
casurina. 1k, Meganoton hyloicoides.

1998, June 17   **Litho.**   *Perf. 14*
940	A217	25t multicolored	.55	.55
941	A217	50t multicolored	.90	.90
942	A217	65t multicolored	1.25	1.25
943	A217	1k multicolored	1.75	1.75
	Nos. 940-943 (4)		4.45	4.45

A218

First Orchid Spectacular '98: 25t, Coelogyne
fragrans. 50t, Den. cuthbertsonii. 65t, Den.
vexillarius. 1k, Den. finisterrae.

1998, Sept. 15   **Litho.**   *Perf. 14*
944	A218	25t multicolored	.60	.60
945	A218	50t multicolored	1.00	1.00
946	A218	65t multicolored	1.40	1.40
947	A218	1k multicolored	2.00	2.00
	Nos. 944-947 (4)		5.00	5.00

A219

Sea Kayaking World Cup, Manus Island:
25t, Couple in kayak. 50t, Competitor running
through Loniu Caves. 65t, Man standing in
boat with sail, man seated in kayak. 1k, Competitor in kayak, bird of paradise silhouette.

1998, Oct. 5   **Litho.**   *Perf. 14*
948	A219	25t multicolored	.60	.60
949	A219	50t multicolored	1.00	1.00
950	A219	65t multicolored	1.40	1.40
951	A219	1k multicolored	2.00	2.00
	Nos. 948-951 (4)		5.00	5.00

1998 Commonwealth
Games, Kuala
Lumpur — A220

1998, Sept. 30   **Litho.**   *Perf. 14*
952	A220	25t Weight lifting	.40	.40
953	A220	50t Lawn bowls	.70	.70
954	A220	65t Rugby	.95	.95
955	A220	1k Squash	1.25	1.25
	Nos. 952-955 (4)		3.30	3.30

Christmas
A221

Designs: 25t, Infant in manger. 50t, Mother
breastfeeding infant. 65t, "Wise men" in traditional masks, headdresses looking at infant.
1k, Map of Papua New Guinea.

1998, Nov. 18   **Litho.**   *Perf. 14*
956	A221	25t multicolored	.35	.35
957	A221	50t multicolored	.70	.70
958	A221	65t multicolored	.95	.95
959	A221	1k multicolored	1.40	1.40
	Nos. 956-959 (4)		3.40	3.40

Australia '99, World
Stamp
Expo — A222

Ships: 25t, "Boudeuse," 1768. 50t, "Neva,"
1876. 65t, "Merrir England," 1889. 1k,
"Samoa," 1884.
#964: a, 5t, Rattlesnake, 1849. b, 10t, Swal-
low, 1767. c, 15t, Roebeck, 1700. d, 20t,
Blanche, 1872. e, 30t, Vitiaz, 1871. f, 40t, San
Pedrico and Eabre, 1606. g, 60t, Jorge de
Menesis, 1526. h, 1.20k, L'Astrolabe, 1827.

1999, Mar. 17
960	A222	25t multicolored	.30	.30
961	A222	50t multicolored	.65	.65
962	A222	65t multicolored	1.05	1.05
963	A222	1k multicolored	1.25	1.25
		Nos. 960-963 (4)	3.25	3.25

Sheet of 8
964	A222	#a.-h.	5.75	5.75

No. 964a is incorrectly inscribed "Simpson Blanche '1872."

IBRA '99, World Philatelic Exhibition, Nuremberg — A223

Exhibition emblem and: a, German New Guinea #17. b, German New Guinea #1, #2.

1999   Litho.   Perf. 14
965	A223	1k Pair, #a.-b.	3.00	3.00

Millennium A224

Map and: 25t, Stopwatch, computer keyboard. 50t, Concentric circles. 65t, Internet page, computer user. 1k, Computers, satellite dish.

1999   Litho.   Perf. 12¾
966	A224	25t multicolored	.50	.25
967	A224	50t multicolored	.70	.40
968	A224	65t multicolored	1.25	.90
969	A224	1k multicolored	1.75	1.75
		Nos. 966-969 (4)	4.20	3.30

For surcharge see No. 1010.

PhilexFrance '99 — A225

Frenchmen with historical ties to Papua New Guinea: 25t, Father Jules Chevalier. 50t, Bishop Alain-Marie. 65t, Chevalier D'Entrecasteaux. 1k, Count de Bougainville.

1999, Mar. 2   Litho.   Perf. 12¾
970	A225	25t multicolored	.30	.25
971	A225	50t multicolored	.55	.55
972	A225	65t multicolored	.85	.85
973	A225	1k multicolored	1.25	1.40
		Nos. 970-973 (4)	2.95	3.05

For surcharge see No. 1011.

Hiri Moale Festival — A226

Designs: 25t, Clay pots, native. 50t, Hanenamo, native. 65t, Lakatoi, native. #977, 1k, Sorcerer, native.
No. 978: a, Sorcerer. b, Clay pots. c, Lakatoi.

1999, Sept. 8   Perf. 12¾
974	A226	25t multicolored	.35	.30
975	A226	50t multicolored	.55	.55
976	A226	65t multicolored	.85	.85
977	A226	1k multicolored	1.25	1.25
		Nos. 974-977 (4)	3.00	2.95

Souvenir Sheet
978	A226	1k Sheet of 3, #a.-c.	3.75	3.75

For surcharge see No. 1012.

Souvenir Sheet

Year of the Rabbit (in 1999) A227

Color of rabbit: a, Gray. b, Tan. c, White. d, Pink.

2000, Apr. 21   Litho.   Perf. 12¾
979	A227	65t Sheet of 4, #a-d	3.75	3.75

Queen Mother, 100th Birthday — A228

Various photos. Color of frame: 25t, Yellow. 50t, Lilac. 65t, Green. 1k, Dull orange.

2000, Aug. 4   Perf. 14
980-983	A228	Set of 4	3.50	3.50

Shells — A229

Designs: 25t, Turbo petholatus. 50t, Charonia tritonis. 65t, Cassis cornuta. 1k, Ovula ovum.

2000, Feb. 23   Litho.   Perf. 14
984-987	A229	Set of 4	3.75	3.75

Independence, 25th Anniv. — A230

Designs: 25t, Shell. 50t, Bird of Paradise. 65t, Ring. 1k, Coat of arms.

2000, June 21   Perf. 14
Stamps with se-tenant label
988-991	A230	Set of 4	3.75	3.75
991a		Souvenir sheet, #988-991, no labels	3.75	3.75

Strips with two stamps alternating with two different labels exist for Nos. 989 and 990.

2000 Summer Olympics, Sydney — A231

Designs: 25t, Running. 50t, Swimming. 65t, Boxing. 1k, Weight lifting.

2000, July 12
992-995	A231	Set of 4	3.75	3.75

For surcharge see No. 1009.

Souvenir Sheet

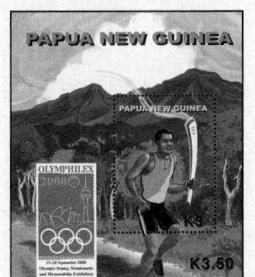

Olymphilex 2000, Sydney — A232

2000, July 12   Perf. 14¼
996	A232	3k multi	4.00	4.00

Sold for 3.50k.

Birds — A233

Designs: 35t, Comb-crested jacana. 70t, Masked lapwing. 90t, White ibis. 1.40k, Black-tailed godwit.

2001, Mar. 21   Litho.   Perf. 14
997-1000	A233	Set of 4	5.00	5.00

Mission Aviation Fellowship, 50th Anniv. in Papua New Guinea A234

Designs: 35t, Cessna 170, pig, bird, Bibles. 70t, Harry Hartwig (1916-51), Auster Autocar. 90t, Pilot and Cessna 260. 1.40k, Twin Otter and plane mechanics.

2001, Oct. 17   Perf. 13¼x13¾
1001-1004	A234	Set of 4	4.50	4.50

A235

Designs: 10t, Flags, world map. 50t, Dragon, bird of paradise. 2k, Tien An Men Square, Papua New Guinea Parliament Building.

2001, Oct. 12   Litho.   Perf. 12
1005-1007	A235	Set of 3	5.25	5.25

Papua New Guinea and People's Republic of China Diplomatic Relations, 25th Anniv.

Nos. 850, 968, 972, 976 and 992 Srchd.

Methods and Perfs As Before
2001, Dec. 1
1008	A194	50t on 21t #850	2.50	1.25
a.		Horiz. pair, 1008, 851 + central label	6.00	4.00
1009	A231	50t on 25t #992	1.00	.50
a.		Obliterator present, missing new denomination	—	
1010	A224	50t on 65t #968	1.00	.50
1011	A225	2.65k on 65t #972	4.00	4.00
1012	A226	2.65k on 65t #976	4.00	4.00
		Nos. 1008-1012 (5)	12.50	10.25

Provincial Flags — A236

2001, Dec. 12   Litho.   Perf. 14
1013	A236	10t Enga	.45	.25
1014	A236	15t Simbu	.45	.25
1015	A236	20t Manus	.45	.25
1016	A236	50t Central	1.10	.40
1017	A236	2k New Ireland	3.50	2.25
1018	A236	5k Sandaun	4.75	4.75
		Nos. 1013-1018 (6)	10.70	8.15

For surcharge see No. 1113.

Reign Of Queen Elizabeth II, 50th Anniv. Issue
Common Design Type

Designs: Nos. 1019, 1023a, 1.25k, Princess Elizabeth with Queen Mother and Princess Margaret, 1941. Nos. 1020, 1023b, 1.45k, Wearing tiara, 1975. Nos. 1021, 1023c, 2k, With Princes Philip and Charles, 1951. Nos. 1022, 1023d, 2.65k, Wearing red hat. No. 1023e, 5k, 1955 portrait by Annigoni (38x50mm).

Perf. 14¼x14½, 13¾ (#1023e)
2002, Feb. 6   Litho.   Wmk. 373
With Gold Frames
1019	CD360	1.25k multicolored	1.20	1.20
1020	CD360	1.45k multicolored	1.40	1.40
1021	CD360	2k multicolored	1.90	1.90
1022	CD360	2.65k multicolored	2.50	2.50
		Nos. 1019-1022 (4)	7.00	7.00

Souvenir Sheet
Without Gold Frames
1023	CD360	Sheet of 5, #a-e	7.50	7.50

Lakatoi Type of 1901 Inscribed "Papua New Guinea"

Frame colors: 5t, Red. 15t, Brown violet. 20t, Light blue. 1.25k, Brown. 1.45k, Green. 10k, Orange.

Perf. 14½x14
2002, June 5   Litho.   Unwmk.
Center in Brown Black
1024-1029	A1	Set of 6	14.00	14.00
1029a		Souvenir sheet, #1024-1029	16.00	16.00

British New Guinea stamps, cent. (in 2001).

Orchids — A237

Designs: 5t, Cadetia taylori. 30t, Dendrobium anosmum. 45t, Dendrobium bigibbum. 1.25k, Dendrobium cuthbertsonii. 1.45k, Spriranthes sinensis. 2.65k, Thelymitra carnea.
No. 1036, horiz.: a, Dendrobium bracteosum. b, Calochilus campestris. c, Anastomus oscitans. d, Thelymitra carnea, diff. e, Dendrobium macrophyllum. f, Dendrobium johnsoniae.
7k, Bulbophyllum graveolens, horiz.

2002, Aug. 28   Perf. 14
1030-1035	A237	Set of 6	8.00	8.00
1036	A237	2k Sheet of 6, #a-f	11.50	11.50

Souvenir Sheet
1037	A237	7k multi	9.00	9.00

Protected Butterflies A238

Designs: No. 1038, 50t, Ornithoptera chimaera. No. 1039, 50t, Ornithoptera goliath. 1.25k, Ornithoptera meridionalis. 1.45k, Ornithoptera paradisea. 2.65k, Ornithoptera victoriae. 5k, Ornithoptera alexandrae.

2002, Oct. 16
1038-1043	A238	Set of 6	15.00	15.00

Queen Mother Elizabeth (1900-2002) — A239

No. 1044, horiz.: a, With Queen Elizabeth II (28x23mm). b, With Elizabeth and two other women (28x23mm). c, With pearl necklace visible at left (26x29mm). d, Color photograph (40x29mm). e, With pearl necklace visible at right (26x29mm). f, With man in top hat at right (28x23mm). g, With King George VI (28x23mm).
No. 1045, blue shading in UR of stamps : a, 3k, As child. b, 3k, Wearing black hat.
No. 1046, blue shading in UL of stamps: a, 3k, Wearing white hat. b, 3k, Wearing hat and brooch.

Perf. 13¼x14¼ (#1044d), Compound x 14¼ (#1044c, 1044e) 13¼x10¾
2002
1044	A239	2k Sheet of 7, #a-g	14.00	14.00

Souvenir Sheets
Perf. 14¾
1045-1046	A239	Set of 2	14.00	14.00

A240 United We Stand

United We Stand — A241

2002, Nov. 20   Litho.   Perf. 14
1047 A240 50t multi   1.25 1.25
1048 A241 50t multi   1.25 1.25
No. 1048 was printed in sheets of 4.

Intl. Year of Mountains A242

Designs: 50t, Mt. Wilhelm, Papua New Guinea. 1.25k, Matterhorn, Switzerland. 1.45k, Mt. Fuji, Japan. 2.65k, Massif des Aravis, France.

2002, Nov. 20
1049-1052 A242   Set of 4   6.25 6.25

Clay Pots — A243

Designs: 65t, Sago storage pot. 1k, Smoking pot. 1.50k, Water jar. 2.50k, Water jar, diff. 4k, Ridge pot.

2003, Jan. 22
1053-1057 A243   Set of 5   9.00 9.00

20th World Scout Jamboree, Thailand — A244

Designs: 50t, Group of scouts. 1.25k, Two scouts seated. 1.45k, Scouts on tower. 2.65k, Two scouts standing.

2003, Feb. 12
1058-1061 A244   Set of 4   8.00 8.00

A245

Various portraits of Queen Elizabeth II with background colors of: No. 1062, 65t, Purple. No. 1063, 65t, Olive green. 1.50k, Dark blue. No. 1065, 2k, Red. 2.50k, Dull green. 4k, Orange.
No. 1068, 2k — Yellow orange background with Queen: a, Without hat. b, Wearing crown and sash. c, Wearing hat with blue flowers. d, Wearing tiara. e, Wearing red dress. f, Wearing black hat.
8k, Wearing black robe, gray green background.

2003, Apr. 30   Litho.   Perf. 14
1062-1067 A245   Set of 6   9.50 9.50
1068 A245 2k Sheet of 6, #a-f   10.00 10.00

Souvenir Sheet
1069 A245 8k multi   7.00 7.00
Coronation of Queen Elizabeth, 50th anniv.

A246

Prince William: No. 1070, 65t, Wearing colored sports shirt. No. 1071, 65t, Wearing white shirt. 1.50k, As child. No. 1073, 2k, Wearing suit and tie, gray green background. 2.50k, Wearing plaid shirt. 4k, On polo pony.
No. 1076, 2k — Lilac background: a, As toddler. b, Wearing sunglasses. c, Wearing suit and tie (full face). d, Wearing suit and tie (profile). e, Wearing deep blue shirt. f, Wearing yellow shirt with black collar.
8k, Wearing suit and tie, gray green background, diff.

2003, June 18
1070-1075 A246   Set of 6   8.25 8.25
1076 A246 2k Sheet of 6, #a-f   9.25 9.25

Souvenir Sheet
1077 A246 8k multi   6.75 6.75
Prince William, 21st birthday.

Coastal Villages — A247

Designs: No. 1078, 65t, Gabagaba. No. 1079, 65t, Wanigela (Koki). 1.50k, Tubuserea. 2k, Hanuabada. 2.50k, Barakau. 4k, Porebada.

2003, July 24
1078-1083 A247   Set of 6   9.25 9.25
For surcharges see Nos. 1114-1115.

Powered Flight, Cent. — A248

Designs: 65t, Orville Wright circles plane over Fort Myer, Va., 1908. 1.50k, Orville Wright pilots "Baby Grand" Belmont, 1910. No. 1086, 2.50k, Wilbur Wright holding anemometer, Pau, France, 1909. 4k, Wilbur Wright pilots Model A, Pau, France, 1909.
No. 1088, 2.50k — 1903 photos from Kitty Hawk: a, Untried airplane outside hangar. b, Rollout of airplane from hangar. c, Preparing airplane for takeoff. d, Airplane takes off.
10k, Airplane takes off, diff.

2003, Aug. 27
1084-1087 A248   Set of 4   8.00 8.00
1088 A248 Sheet of 4, #a-d   9.00 9.00

Souvenir Sheet
1089 A248 10k multi   9.00 9.00

Worldwide Fund for Nature (WWF) — A249

Tree kangaroos: Nos. 1090a, 1091a, Dendrolagus inustus. Nos. 1090b, 1091b, Dendrolagus matschiei. Nos. 1090c, 1091c, Dendrolagus dorianus. Nos. 1090d, 1091d, Dendrolagus goodfellowi.

2003, Oct. 15   Perf. 14½x14¾
With White Frames
1090   Horiz. strip of 4   8.00 8.00
a. A249 65t multi   .75   .75
b. A249 1.50k multi   1.40 1.40
c. A249 2.50k multi   2.25 2.25
d. A249 4k multi   3.25 3.25

Without White Frames
1091   Sheet, 2 each #a-d   14.00 14.00
a. A249 65t multi   .65   .65
b. A249 1.50k multi   1.25 1.25
c. A249 2.50k multi   2.00 2.00
d. A249 4k multi   2.75 2.75

Endangered Dolphins — A250

Designs: No. 1092, 65t, Humpback dolphin. No. 1093, 65t, Bottlenose dolphins. No. 1094, 1.50k, Bottlenose dolphin, with frame line. 2k, Irrawaddy dolphin. 2.50k, Humpback dolphin and fishermen. 4k, Irrawaddy dolphin and diver.
No. 1098, 1.50k: a, Humpback dolphin and sailboat. b, Bottlenose dolphin, without frame line. c, Bottlenose dolphins, diff. d, Irrawaddy dolphin and diver, diff. e, Irrawady dolphin, diff. f, Humpback dolphin underwater.

2003, Nov. 19   Perf. 13½
1092-1097 A250   Set of 6   10.00 10.00
1098 A250 1.50k Sheet of 6,
                     #a-f   8.00 8.00
For surcharges see Nos. 1116-1117.

Freshwater Fish — A251

Designs: No. 1099, 70t, Lake Wanam rainbowfish. No. 1100, 70t, Kokoda mogurnda. 1k, Sepik grunter. 2.70k, Papuan black bass. 4.60k, Lake Tebera rainbowfish. 20k, Wichmann's mouth almighty.

2004, Jan. 30   Perf. 14¼
1099-1104 A251   Set of 6   25.00 25.00
  Complete booklet, 10 #1099   6.00
  Complete booklet, 10 #1100   6.00
For surcharges see Nos. 1154-1155.

Dinosaurs A252

Designs: 70t, Ankylosaurus. 1k, Oviraptor. 2k, Tyrannosaurus. 2.65k, Gigantosaurus. 2.70k, Centrosaurus. 4.60k, Carcharodontosaurus.
No. 1111: a, Edmontonia. b, Struthiomimus. c, Psittacosaurus. d, Gastonia. e, Shunosaurus. f, Iguanodon.
7k, Afrovenator.

2004, Feb. 25   Perf. 14
1105-1110 A252   Set of 6   11.50 11.50
1111 A252 1.50k Sheet of 6,
                     #a-f   8.75 8.75

Souvenir Sheet
1112 A252   7k multi   6.25 6.25

Nos. 1015, 1078, 1079, 1092 and 1093 Surcharged

a

b

Methods and Perfs As Before
2004
1113 A236(a) 5t on 20t #1015   .75   .75
1114 A247(b) 70t on 65t #1078   1.50 1.50
1115 A247(b) 70t on 65t #1079   1.75 1.75
1116 A250(a) 70t on 65t #1092   1.75 1.75
1117 A250(a) 70t on 65t #1093   1.75 1.75
      Nos. 1113-1117 (5)   7.25 7.25
Issued: Nos. 1114-1115, 1/20; others, 6/2.

Orchids — A253

Designs: 70t, Phalaenopsis amabilis. 1k, Phaius tankervilleae. No. 1120, 2k, Bulbophyllum macranthum. 2.65k, Dendrobium rhodostictum. 2.70k, Diplocaulobium ridleyanum. 4.60k, Spathoglottis papuana.
No. 1124, 2k: a, Dendrobium cruttwellii. b, Dendrobium coeloglossum. c, Dendrobium alaticaulinum. d, Dendrobium obtusisepalum.

e, Dendrobium johnsoniae. f, Dendrobium insigne.
7k, Dendrobium biggibum.

2004, May 19   Litho.   Perf. 14
1118-1123 A253   Set of 6   13.50 13.50
1124 A253 2k Sheet of 6, #a-f   12.50 12.50

Souvenir Sheet
1125 A253 7k multi   7.75 7.75

Headdresses A254

Province of headdress: No. 1126, 70t, Simbu. No. 1127, 70t, East Sepik. 2.65k, Southern Highlands. 2.70k, Western Highlands. 4.60k, Eastern Highlands. 5k, Central.

2004, June 2
1126-1131 A254   Set of 6   14.00 14.00
  Complete booklet, 10 #1126   7.50
  Complete booklet, 10 #1127   7.50
For surcharges see Nos. 1156-1157.

2004 Summer Olympics, Athens A255

Designs: 70t, Swimming. 2.65k, Weight lifting, vert. 2.70k, Torch race, vert. 4.60k, Poster for 1952 Helsinki Olympics, vert.

2004, Aug. 11   Perf. 13¼
1132-1135 A255   Set of 4   10.50 10.50

National Soccer Team A256

Various players in action: 70t, 2.65k, 2.70k, 4.60k.

2004, Sept. 8   Perf. 14¼
1136-1139 A256   Set of 4   13.00 13.00

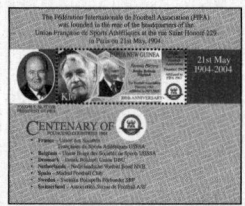

FIFA (Fédération Internationale de Football Association), Cent. — A257

No. 1140: a, Bruno Conti. b, Oliver Kahn. c, Mario Kempes. d, Bobby Moore. 10k, Bobby Robson.

2004, Sept. 8   Perf. 13¼x13½
1140 A257 2.50k Sheet of 4,
                     #a-d   11.50 11.50

Souvenir Sheet
1141 A257 10k multi   10.00 10.00

Provincial Flags — A258

Province: No. 1142, 70t, East New Britain. No. 1143, 70t, Madang. 2.65k, Eastern Highlands. 2.70k, Morobe. 4.60k, Milne Bay. 10k, East Sepik.

2004, Oct. 20   Perf. 14
1142-1147 A258   Set of 6   20.00 20.00

Shells — A259

Designs: No. 1148, 70t, Phalium areola. No. 1149, 70t, Conus auratus. 2.65k, Oliva miniacea. 2.70k, Lambis chiragra. 4.60k, Conus suratensis. 10k, Architectonica perspectiva.

2004, Nov. 17
1148-1153	A259	Set of 6	17.50	17.50

For surcharges see Nos. 1223-1224.

Nos. 1099, 1100, 1126, 1127
Surcharged

Methods and Perfs as Before
2005, Jan. 3
1154	A251	75t on 70t #1099	1.10	1.10
1155	A251	75t on 70t #1100	1.10	1.10
1156	A254	75t on 70t #1126	1.10	1.10
1157	A254	75t on 70t #1127	1.10	1.10
	Nos. 1154-1157 (4)		4.40	4.40

Birds — A260

Designs: 5t, Little egret. No. 1159, 75t, White-faced heron. No. 1160, 75t, Nankeen night heron. 3k, Crested tern. 3.10k, Bar-tailed godwit. 5.20k, Little pied heron.

2005, Jan. 26   Litho.   Perf. 14
1158-1163	A260	Set of 6	10.00	10.00

Rotary International, Cent. — A261

Designs: 75t, Mobilizing communities in the fight against HIV and AIDS. 3k, Barefoot child, PolioPlus and Rotary centennial emblems. 3.10k, Co-founders of first Rotary Club. 5.20k, Chicago skyline.
No. 1168, vert.: a, Silvester Schiele (1870-1945), first Rotary President. b, Paul Harris, founder. c, Children.
10k, Emblem and globe, vert.

2005, Feb. 23   Litho.   Perf. 14
1164-1167	A261	Set of 4	9.00	9.00
1168	A261	4k Sheet of 3, #a-c	9.00	9.00

Souvenir Sheet
1169	A261	10k multi	7.25	7.25

Frangipani Varieties A262

Designs: No. 1170, 75t, Evergreen. No. 1171, 75t, Lady in Pink. 1k, Carmine Flush. 3k, Cultivar acutifolia. 3.10k, American Beauty. 5.20k, Golden Kiss.

2005, Apr. 6   Perf. 12¾
1170-1175	A262	Set of 6	10.50	10.50

Mushrooms — A263

Designs: No. 1176, 75t, Gymnopilus spectabilis. No. 1177, 75t, Melanogaster ambiguus. 3.10k, Microporus xanthopus. 5.20k, Psilocybe subcubensis.
No. 1180: a, Amanita muscaria. b, Amanita rubescens. c, Suillus luteus. d, Stropharia cubensis. e, Aseroes rubra. f, Psilocybe aucklandii.
10k, Mycena pura.

2005, May 18
1176-1179	A263	Set of 4	7.50	7.50
1180	A263	2k Sheet of 6, #a-f	9.25	9.25

Souvenir Sheet
1181	A263	10k multi	7.25	7.25

Beetles — A264

Designs: No. 1182, 75t, Promechus pulcher. No. 1183, 75t, Callistola pulchra. 1k, Lagriomorpha indigacea. 3k, Hellerhinus papuanus. 3.10k, Aphorina australis. 5.20k, Bothricara pulchella.

2005, June 29   Perf. 14
1182-1187	A264	Set of 6	9.50	9.50

Souvenir Sheet

Pope John Paul II (1920-2005) — A265

No. 1188 — Denomination and country name in: a, Blue. b, Green. c, Orange. d, Red violet.

2005, Aug. 10   Litho.   Perf. 12¾
1188	A265	2k Sheet of 4, #a-d	6.25	6.25

Provincial Flags — A266

Province: No. 1189, 75t, Gulf. No. 1190, 75t, Southern Highlands. 1k, North Solomons. 3k, Oro. 3.10k, Western Highlands. 5.20k, Western.

2005, Sept. 21   Perf. 14
1189-1194	A266	Set of 6	10.00	10.00

Cats and Dogs — A267

Designs: No. 1195, 75t, Somali Rudy cat. No. 1196, 75t, Balinese Seal Lynx Point cat. 3k, Sphynx Brown Mackerel Tabby and White cat. 3.10k, Korat Blue cat. 5.20k, Bengal Brown Spotted Tabby cat.
No. 1200: a, Yorkshire terrier. b, Basenji. c, Neapolitan mastiff. d, Poodle.
10k, Boston terrier, horiz.

2005, Nov. 2   Perf. 12¾
1195-1199	A267	Set of 5	10.00	10.00
1200	A267	2.50k Sheet of 4, #a-d	8.00	8.00

Souvenir Sheet
1201	A267	10k multi	8.00	8.00

Summer Institute of Languages in Papua New Guinea, 50th Anniv. — A268

Designs: No. 1202, 80t, Postal services. No. 1203, 80t, Literacy. 1k, Jim Dean, first director. 3.20k, Tokples preschools. 3.25k, Aviation. 5.35k, Community development.

2006, Jan. 4   Litho.   Perf. 13¼
1202-1207	A268	Set of 6	16.00	16.00

Miniature Sheets

Queen Elizabeth II, 80th Birthday A269

No. 1208, 2.50k: a, Wearing polka dot dress. b, Engraving in brown from Canadian bank note. c, Engraving in blue from banknote. d, With Queen Mother.
No. 1209: a, 80t, With Pres. Bill Clinton. b, 3.20k, Dancing with Pres. Gerald Ford. c, 3.25k, With Pres. Ronald Reagan. d, 5.35k, With Pres. George W. Bush.

2006, Feb. 22   Litho.   Perf. 13½
Sheets of 4, #a-d
1208-1209	A269	Set of 2	17.00	17.00

Contemporary Art — A270

Designs: 5t, Shown. No. 1211, 80t, One head. No. 1212, 80t, Two heads. 3.20k, Man wearing headdress. 3.25k, Man and woman. 5.35k, Man with beads and man with painted face.

2006, Apr. 12   Perf. 13¼x13½
1210-1215	A270	Set of 6	10.50	10.50

Miniature Sheet

2006 World Cup Soccer Championships, Germany — A271

No. 1216 — Player and uniform from: a, 80t, England. b, 3.20k, Germany. c, 3.25k, Argentina. d, 5.35k, Australia.

2006, May 17   Perf. 12
1216	A271	Sheet of 4, #a-d	9.50	9.50

Salvation Army in Papua New Guinea, 50th Anniv. — A272

Designs: 5t, Salvation Army emblem. 80t, Emblem, flags of Papua New Guinea and Salvation Army Papua New Guinea Territory. 1k, Lt. Ian Cutmore and Senior Major Keith Baker. 3.20k, Colonels, Andrew and Julie Kalai. 3.25k, Kei Geno. 5.35k, Lt. Dorothy Elphick holding baby.

2006, June 14   Perf. 13¼
1217-1222	A272	Set of 6	10.00	10.00

Nos. 1148-1149 Surcharged

2006, July 5   Litho.   Perf. 14
1223	A259	80t on 70t #1148	.80	.80
1224	A259	80t on 70t #1149	.80	.80

Butterflies A273

Designs: 80t, Delias iltis. 3.20k, Ornithoptera paradisea. 3.25k, Taenaris catops. 5.35k, Papilio ulysses autolycus.

2006, Aug. 30   Perf. 13¼
1225-1228	A273	Set of 4	10.50	10.50

Snakes — A274

Designs: 5t, Black whip snake. 80t, Papuan taipan. 2k, Smooth-scaled death adder. 3.20k, Papuan black snake. 3.25k, New Guinea small-eyed snake. 5.35k, Eastern brown snake.

2006, Sept. 13   Perf. 14¼x14
1229-1234	A274	Set of 6	11.50	11.50

A275

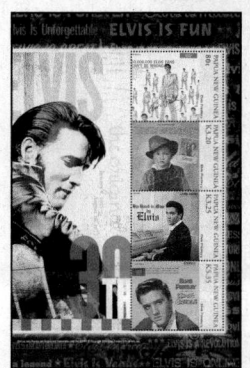

Elvis Presley (1935-77) — A276

Designs: 80t, Wearing white jacket and pants. 3.20k, Wearing red shirt. 3.25k, Wearing white jacket and black bow tie. 5.35k, With guitar.
No. 1239 — Record covers: a, 80t, 50,000 Elvis Fans Can't Be Wrong. b, 3.20k, Elvis Country. c, 3.25k, His Hand in Mine. d, 5.35k, King Creole.
10k, Holding teddy bears.

Perf. 13½, 13¼ (#1239)
2006, Nov. 15   Litho.
1235-1238	A275	Set of 4	9.50	9.50
1239	A276	Sheet of 4, #a-d	9.00	9.00

Souvenir Sheet
1240	A275	10k multi	8.25	8.25

Tropical Fruits — A277

Designs: 5t, Mangos. No. 1242, 85t, Watermelons. No. 1243, 85t, Pineapples. No. 1244, 3.35k, Guavas. No. 1245, 3.35k, Pawpaws (papaya). 5.35k, Lemons.

2007, Jan. 2   Perf. 14x14¼
1241-1246	A277	Set of 6	9.50	9.50

Endangered
Turtles — A278

Designs: 10t, Hawksbill turtle. 35t, Flatback
turtle. No. 1249, 85t, Loggerhead turtle. No.
1250, 3k, Leatherback turtle (blue violet
panel). No. 1251, 3.35k, Green turtle (emerald
panel). No. 1252, 5.35k, Olive Ridley turtle
(tan panel).
   No. 1253: a, 85t, Flatback turtle, diff. b, 3k,
Leatherback turtle, diff. (olive green panel). c,
3.35k, Green turtle, diff. (olive green panel). d,
5.35k, Olive Ridley turtle, diff. (emerald panel).

2007, Mar. 23   Litho.   Perf. 13¼
1247-1252 A278   Set of 6   13.00 13.00
Souvenir Sheet
1253 A278   Sheet of 4, #a-d   13.00 13.00

Scouting,
Cent. — A279

Designs: 10t, Scouts standing at attention.
85t, Scouts carrying flag. 3.35k, Scouts and
leaders at campsite. 5.35k, Scouts and leader.
10k, Lord Robert Baden-Powell, vert.

2007, May 23   Litho.   Perf. 14x14¼
1254-1257 A279   Set of 4   8.00 8.00
1257a   Souvenir sheet, #1254-1257   6.25 6.25
Souvenir Sheet
1257B A279 10k multi   6.50 6.50

Law, Justice,
Health and
Education
A280

Inscriptions: 5t, "A Just, Safe & Secure Society for All." 30t, "Prosperity Through self-reli-
ance." 85t, "HIV/AIDS." 3k, "Crime Reduction."
3.35k, "Infant Care & Child Immunization."
5.35k, "Minimizing Illiteracy."

2007, July 25   Perf. 13¼
1258-1263 A280   Set of 6   8.25 8.25

A281

A282

A283

A284

A285

A286

A287

A288

A289

A290

A291

Orchids
A292

2007, Aug. 3   Litho.   Perf. 14
1264   Sheet of 12 +12 la-
        bels   13.50 13.50
  a. A281 1k multi + label   1.10 1.10
  b. A282 1k multi + label   1.10 1.10
  c. A283 1k multi + label   1.10 1.10
  d. A284 1k multi + label   1.10 1.10
  e. A285 1k multi + label   1.10 1.10
  f. A286 1k multi + label   1.10 1.10
  g. A287 1k multi + label   1.10 1.10
  h. A288 1k multi + label   1.10 1.10
  i. A289 1k multi + label   1.10 1.10
  j. A290 1k multi + label   1.10 1.10
  k. A291 1k multi + label   1.10 1.10
  l. A292 1k multi + label   1.10 1.10

   Labels could not be personalized.

Dendrobium Conanthum, Dendrobium
Lasianthera — A293

Dendrobium Conanthum — A294

Dendrobium Lasianthera "May River
Red" — A295

Dendrobium Wulaiense — A296

2007, Aug. 21   Litho.   Perf. 14
1265 A293   85t multi + label   .60   .60
1266 A294   3k multi + label   2.10 2.10
1267 A295 3.35k multi + label   2.40 2.40
1268 A296 5.35k multi + label   3.75 3.75
      Nos. 1265-1268 (4)   8.85 8.85

   Nos. 1265-1268 were each issued in sheets
of 20 + 20 labels. The labels illustrated are
generic labels. Labels could be personalized
for an additional fee.

Rotary
International in
Papua New
Guinea, 50th
Anniv. — A297

Inscriptions: 85t, Rotary's humanitarian service. 3.35k, Rotary against malaria. 5k, Rotary
clubs in Papua New Guinea. 5.35k, Donations
in kind.

2007, Sept. 5   Litho.   Perf. 13¼
1269-1272 A297   Set of 4   9.50 9.50
1272a   Souvenir sheet, #1269-
         1272   9.50 9.50

A298

Wedding of Queen Elizabeth II and
Prince Philip, 60th Anniv. — A299

   No. 1273: a, Couple, pink background. b,
Queen, pink background. c, Queen, lilac background. d, Couple, lilac background. e,
Couple, pale yellow background. f, Queen,
pale yellow background.

2007, Oct. 31   Litho.   Perf. 14
1273 A298   2k Sheet of 6, #a-f   8.00 8.00
Souvenir Sheet
1274 A299 10k multi   7.00 7.00

A300

Princess Diana (1961-97) — A301

No. 1275 — Photographs of Diana from: a,
85t, 1965. b, 2.45k, 1971. c, 3.35k, 1981. d,
5.35k, 1983.

2007, Oct. 31
1275 A300   Sheet of 4, #a-d   8.00 8.00
Souvenir Sheet
1276 A301 10k multi   6.75 6.75

St. John
Ambulance in
Papua New
Guinea, 50th
Anniv. — A302

Inscriptions: 5t, St. John Health Service.
20t, St. John Blood Service. 85t, St. John
Blind Service. 1k, St. John Ambulance Service. 3.35k, St. John Volunteer Service. 5.35k,
Order of St. John.

2007, Nov. 30   Perf. 14¼
1277-1282 A302   Set of 6   7.75 7.75
1282a   Miniature sheet, #1277-1282 7.75 7.75

Contemporary
Art — A303

Designs: 5t, Oro Gagara. 30t, Western
Province tribesman. 85t, Sorcerer. 3k, Hewa
wigman. 3.35k, Pigs Into Python Legend.
5.35k, Tolai masks.

2007, Dec. 12
1283-1288 A303   Set of 6   9.25 9.25
1288a   Miniature sheet, #1283-
         1288   9.25 9.25

Protected
Birds — A304

Designs: 10t, Papuan hornbill. 50t, Osprey.
85t, New Guinea harpy eagle. 3k, Victoria
crowned pigeon.
   No. 1293: a, 1k, Palm cockatoo. b, 5.35k,
Great white egret.
   10k, Like #1293a.

2008, Jan. 25   Litho.   Perf. 14x14¼
1289-1292 A304   Set of 4   4.00 4.00
1293 A304   Sheet of 6, #1289-
             1292, 1293a, 1293b 9.00 9.00
Souvenir Sheet
1294 A304 10k multi   8.50 8.50

Asaro Mudmen
Legend — A305

Designs: 85t, Two Mudmen, large skull. 3k,
Three Mudmen scouting for enemies in forest.
3.35k, Mudmen attacking enemies.
   Retreat of enemies.
   10k, Similar to 85t.

2008, Feb. 27   *Perf. 13¼*
1295-1298 A305   Set of 4   9.25 9.25
1298a   Miniature sheet, #1295-1298   9.25 9.25
Souvenir Sheet
1299 A305 10k multi   8.00 8.00

Marine Life — A306

Designs: No. 1300, 85t, Leather coral. No. 1301, 3k, Kunei's chromodoris. No. 1302, 3.35k, Scorpion spider snail. No. 1303, 5.35k, Veined sponge.
No. 1304: a, 85t, Radiant sea urchin. b, 3k, Varicose. c, 3.35k, Sea squirt. d, 5.35k, Heffernan's sea star.
10k, White grape coral.

2008, Mar. 21   *Perf. 14x14¼*
1300-1303 A306   Set of 4   13.00 13.00
1304 A306   Sheet of 4, #a-d   16.00 16.00
Souvenir Sheet
1305 A306 10k multi   11.00 11.00

Miniature Sheet

2008 Summer Olympics, Beijing — A307

No. 1306: a, Weight lifting. b, Diving. c, Hurdles. d, Boxing.

2008, Apr. 16   *Perf. 12¾*
1306 A307 1.40k Sheet of 4, #a-d   4.50 4.50

Papua New Guinea Partnership With European Union, 30th Anniv. — A308

Flags of Papua New Guinea and European Union, bird of paradise, circle of stars and background color of: Nos. 1307, 1311a, 85t, Gray. Nos. 1308, 1311b, 3k, Yellow. Nos. 1309, 1311c, 3.35k, Rose pink. Nos. 1310, 1311d, 5.35k, Light blue.
10k, Gray, without blue panel at bottom.

2008, May 9   *Perf. 13x13¼*
Stamps With Blue Panel With Bold White Drawings
1307-1310 A308   Set of 4   9.50 9.50
Stamps With Blue Panel With Faint White Drawings
1311 A308   Sheet of 4, #a-d   9.50 9.50
Souvenir Sheet
1312 A308 10k multi   8.00 8.00

Art by Timothy Akis (1944-84) — A309

Designs: No. 1313, 85t, Long Hair. No. 1314, 3k, Alone. No. 1315, 3.35k, Woman with Cassowary and Child. No. 1316, 5.35k, Man Shooting Cassowary.

No. 1317: a, 85t, Five Men in Their Gardens (top half). b, 3k, The Crocodile Woman and Two Headed Man (top half). c, 3.35k, As "a," bottom half. d, 5.35k, As "b," bottom half.
10k, Flying Fox.

2008, June 25   Litho.   *Perf. 14¼x14*
1313-1316 A309   Set of 4   9.25 9.25
1317 A309   Sheet of 4, #a-d   9.25 9.25
Souvenir Sheet
1318 A309 10k multi   7.25 7.25

Headdresses — A310

Headdresses of: No. 1319, 85t, Central Province (person showing shoulder). No. 1320, 3k, Western Highlands Province. No. 1321, 3.35k, Oro Province. No. 1322, 5.35k, Western Highlands Province, diff.
No. 1323: a, 85t, Central Province (headdress with yellow side tassels). b, 3k, Central Province, diff. c, 3.35k, Southern Highlands Province, diff. d, 5.35k, Oro Province, diff.
10k, Central Province, diff.

2008, July 31
1319-1322 A310   Set of 4   9.75 9.75
1323 A310   Sheet of 4, #a-d   9.75 9.75
Souvenir Sheet
1324 A310 10k multi   7.75 7.75

Marilyn Monroe (1926-62), Actress — A311

No. 1325, horiz. — Various photographs of Monroe: a, 85t. b, 3k. c, 3.35k. d, 5.35k.
10k, Monroe in automobile.

2008, Aug. 6   Litho.   *Perf. 13¼*
1325 A311   Sheet of 4, #a-d   9.00 9.00
Souvenir Sheet
1326 A311 10k multi   7.00 7.00

Birds of Paradise — A312

Designs: No. 1327, 85t, Paradisaea guilielmi. No. 1328, 3k, Parotia lawesi. No. 1329, 3.35k, Epimachus meyeri. No. 1330, 5.35k, Diphyllodes magnificus.
No. 1331: a, 85t, Astrapia stephaniae. b, 3k, Cnemophilus macgregorii. c, 3.35k, Pteridophora alberti. d, 5.35k, Astrapia meyeri.
10k, Cicinnurus regius.

2008, Sept. 3   Litho.   *Perf. 14¼x14*
1327-1330 A312   Set of 4   10.00 10.00
1331 A312   Sheet of 4, #a-d   11.00 11.00
Souvenir Sheet
1332 A312 10k multi   8.00 8.00

For surcharge, see No. 1734C.

Gold Mining — A313

Designs: No. 1333, 85t, Tunnel drilling. No. 1334, 3k, Logistics. No. 1335, 3.35k, Refinery. No. 1336, 5.35k, Gold bars.
No. 1337: a, 85t, Open pit mining. b, 3k, Conveyor belt. c, 3.35k, Plant site. d, 5.35k, Refinery.
10k, Gold bar.

2008, Oct. 31   *Perf. 14¼*
1333-1336 A313   Set of 4   9.50 9.50
1337 A313   Sheet of 4, #a-d   9.50 9.50
Souvenir Sheet
1338 A313 10k multi   7.75 7.75

World AIDS Day — A314

Red ribbon and inscription: 5t, HIV and the workplace. 10t, Voluntary counseling and testing. 50t, Role of men and women. Nos. 1342, 1348a, 85t, Education. 1k, 10k, Eradicating stigma and discrimination. 2k, Living with the virus. Nos. 1345, 1348b, 3k, Care, support and the role of family. Nos. 1346, 1348c, 3.70k, Building leadership. Nos. 1347, 1348d, 6k, Health and nutrition.

2008, Dec. 1   Litho.   *Perf. 14¼*
1339-1347 A314   Set of 9   14.00 14.00
1348 A314   Sheet of 4, #a-d   13.00 13.00
Souvenir Sheet
1349 A314 10k multi   8.75 8.75

No. 1348 contains four 42x28 stamps; No. 1349 contains one 42x28mm stamp.

Christmas A315

Designs: No. 1350, 85t, Holy Family. No. 1351, 3k, Santa Claus on reindeer. No. 1352, 3.35k, Book and candle. No. 1353, 5.35k, Bell and book.
No. 1354: a, 85t, Journey to Bethlehem. b, 3k, Silent night. c, 3.35k, Behold that star. d, 5.35k, Three wise men.
10k, Gift and map of Papua New Guinea.

2008, Dec. 3   *Perf. 14¼*
1350-1353 A315   Set of 4   9.50 9.50
1354 A315   Sheet of 4, #a-d   9.50 9.50
Souvenir Sheet
1355 A315 10k multi   7.75 7.75

Plants — A316

Designs: No. 1356, 85t, Bixa. No. 1357, 3k, Perfume tree. No. 1358, 3.70k, Beach kalofilum. No. 1359, 6k, Macaranga.
No. 1360: a, 85t, Native frangipani. b, 3k, Ten cent flower. c, 3.70k, Beach terminali. d, 6k, Red beech.
10k, Beach convolvulus (morning glory).

2009, Jan. 14   *Perf. 14¼*
1356-1359 A316   Set of 4   9.75 9.75
1360 A316   Sheet of 4, #a-d   9.75 9.75
Souvenir Sheet
1361 A316 10k multi   7.50 7.50

For surcharges, see Nos. 1732K, 1732V, 1732W.

Worldwide Fund for Nature (WWF) — A317

Designs: No. 1362, 85t, Albericus siegfriedi. No. 1363, 3k, Cophixalus nubicola. No. 1364, 3.70k, Nyctimystes pulcher. No. 1365, 6k, Sphenophryne cornuta.
No. 1366: a, 85t, Litoria sauroni. b, 3k, Litoria prora. c, 3.70k, Litoria multiplica. d, 6k, Litoria pronimia.
10k, Oreophryne sp.

2009, Feb. 18   Litho.   *Perf. 13¼*
1362-1365 A317   Set of 4   10.00 10.00
1366 A317   Sheet of 4, #a-d   10.00 10.00
Souvenir Sheet
1367 A317 10k multi   7.50 7.50

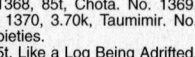

Art by David Lasisi A318

Designs: No. 1368, 85t, Chota. No. 1369, 3k, Stability. No. 1370, 3.70k, Taumimir. No. 1371, 6k, The Moieties.
No. 1372: a, 85t, Like a Log Being Adrifted. b, 3k, Lasisi. c, 3.70k, Lupa. d, 6k, In Memory of Marker Craftsman.
10k, Trapped by Cobweb of Stinging Pain.

2008, Mar. 11   *Perf. 13½*
1368-1371 A318   Set of 4   9.25 9.25
1372 A318   Sheet of 4, #a-d   9.25 9.25
Souvenir Sheet
1373 A318 10k multi   7.00 7.00

A319

China 2009 World Stamp Exhibition, Luoyang — A320

2009, Apr. 10   *Perf. 12¾x12½*
1374 A319 1k multi   .90 .90
Souvenir Sheet
1375 A320 6k multi   4.75 4.75

Chinese Antiquities — A321

Designs: Nos. 1376, 1382a, 5t, Vessel with design of deities, animals and masks. Nos. 1377, 1382b, 10t, Evening in the Peach and Plum Garden, by Li Bai. Nos. 1378, 1382c, 85t, Reliquary with Buddhist figures. Nos. 1379, 1382d, 3k, Brick relief figure. Nos. 1380, 1382e, 3.70k, Round tray with scroll designs. Nos. 1381, 1382f, 6k, Plate in the shape of two peach halves with design of two foxes.

2009, Apr. 10   *Perf. 14¼x14¾*
With Inscription "World Stamp Exhibition / China 2009" At Left
1376-1381 A321   Set of 6   9.25 9.25

Stamps Without Inscription "World Stamp Exhibition / China 2009" At Left
1382 A321   Sheet of 6, #a-f   9.25 9.25

Assets of Coral Triangle — A322

Designs: No. 1383, 85t, Fish. No. 1384, 3k, Marine turtle (blue green frame). No. 1385, 3.70k, Mangroves. No. 1386, 6k, Coral reefs.

No. 1387: a, 85t, Dolphins. b, 3k, Marine turtle (no frame). c, 3.70k, Reef fish. d, 6k, Killer whale.
10k, Grouper.

2009, May 22 Litho. Perf. 14½x14¼
1383-1386 A322　Set of 4　10.00 10.00
1387 A322　Sheet of 4, #a-d　10.00 10.00
Souvenir Sheet
1388 A322　10k multi　7.50 7.50

Kokoda Trail — A323

Designs: No. 1389, 85t, Guides assisting a trekker. No. 1390, 3k, Crossing Vabuyavi River. No. 1391, 3.70k, Waterfall near Abuari. No. 1392, 6k, Crossing Lake Myola 1.
No. 1393: a, 85t, Crossing Emune River. b, 3k, Entering Imita Ridge. c, 3.70k, Crossing Alo Creek. d, 6k, Templeton's Crossing No. 2.
10k, Golden Staircase, Imita Ridge.

2009, June 23 Perf. 14¼
1389-1392 A323　Set of 4　10.50 10.50
1393 A323　Sheet of 4, #a-d　10.50 10.50
Souvenir Sheet
1394 A323　10k multi　7.50 7.50

Bats — A324

Designs: No. 1395, 85t, Black-bellied bat. No. 1396, 3k, Least blossom bat. No. 1397, 3.70k, Sanborn's broad-nosed bat. No. 1398, 6k, Mantled mastiff bat.
No. 1399: a, 85t, Trident leaf-nosed bat. b, 3k, Flower-faced bat. c, 3.70k, Eastern horseshoe bat. d, 6k, Greater tube-nosed bat.
10k, Bougainville's fruit bat.

2009, July 15
1395-1398 A324　Set of 4　10.50 10.50
1399 A324　Sheet of 4, #a-d　10.50 10.50
Souvenir Sheet
1400 A324　10k multi　7.75 7.75

For surcharge, see No. 1732I.

Intl. Day of Non-violence — A325

Doves and: No. 1401, 85t, Abraham Lincoln. No. 1402, 3k, Princess Diana. No. 1403, 3.70k, Nelson Mandela. No. 1404, 6k, Barack Obama.
No. 1405: a, 85t, Obama. b, 3k, Dr. Martin Luther King, Jr. c, 3.70k, Mohandas K. Gandhi. d, 6k, Princess Diana.
10k, Obama, diff.

2009, Aug. 6 Perf. 13¼
1401-1404 A325　Set of 4　10.50 10.50
1405 A325　Sheet of 4, #a-d　10.50 10.50
Souvenir Sheet
1406 A325　10k multi　7.50 7.50

No. 1406 contains one 38x51mm stamp.

Volcanoes A326

Designs: No. 1407, 85t, Mount Vulcan. No. 1408, 3k, Mount Tavurvur. No. 1409, 3.70k, Mount Bagana. No. 1410, 6k, Manam Island.
No. 1411: a, 85t, Mount Tavurvur, diff. b, 3k, Manam Island, diff. c, 3.70k, Mount Tavurvur, diff. d, 6k, Mount Ulawun.
10k, Mount Tavurvur, diff.

2009, Sept. 9 Perf. 14¼
1407-1410 A326　Set of 4　10.00 10.00

1411 A326　Sheet of 4, #a-d　10.00 10.00
Souvenir Sheet
1412 A326　10k multi　7.50 7.50

Palm Oil Production A327

Designs: No. 1413, 85t, Oil palm fruitlets. No. 1414, 3k, Oil palm nursery. No. 1415, 3.70k, Oil palm bunches. No. 1416, 6k, Fruit collection.
No. 1417: a, 85t, Irrigation. b, 3k, Oil palm bunches. c, 3.70k, Loose fruits. d, 6k, Mill.
10k, Oil palm fruitlets in hand.

2009, Oct. 7 Litho. Perf. 14¼
1413-1416 A327　Set of 4　10.00 10.00
1417 A327　Sheet of 4, #a-d　10.00 10.00
Souvenir Sheet
1418 A327　10k multi　7.50 7.50

For surcharge, see No. 1732P.

Canoes A328

Canoe from: No. 1419, 85t, Mortlock Island. No. 1420, 3k, Manus Province. No. 1421, 3.70k, Bilbil. No. 1422, 6k, Central Province.
No. 1423: a, 85t, Kimbe. b, 3k, Vuvulu Island. c, 3.70k, Suau Island. d, 6k, Mailu.
10k, Gogodala.

2009, Nov. 4 Litho. Perf. 12¾
1419-1422 A328　Set of 4　10.00 10.00
1423 A328　Sheet of 4, #a-d　10.00 10.00
Souvenir Sheet
1424 A328　10k multi　7.25 7.25

Traditional Dances A329

Designs: No. 1425, 1k, Engagement dance, Western Highlands Province. No. 1426, 3k, Bride price dance, Central Province. No. 1427, 4.65k, Engagement dance, Manus Province. No. 1428, 6.30k, Trobriand love dance, Milne Bay Province.
No. 1429: a, 1k, Courtship dance, Chimbu Province. b, 3k, Engagement dance, Enga Province. c, 4.65k, Engagement Dance, Central Province. d, 6.30k, Womanhood dance, Central Province.
10k, Trobriand love dance, Milne Bay Province, diff.

2009, Dec. 2 Perf. 14¼
1425-1428 A329　Set of 4　11.00 11.00
1429 A329　Sheet of 4, #a-d　11.00 11.00
Souvenir Sheet
1430 A329　10k multi　7.25 7.25

Pioneer Art — A330

Paintings by Jakupa Ako: No. 1431, 1k, Fish Man. No. 1432, 3k, Story Board. No. 1433, 4.65k, Hunting Trip. No. 1434, 6.30k, Warrior.
No. 1435: a, 1k, Bird Art. b, 3k, Bird Eating. c, 4.65k, Bird Nest. d, 6.30k, Marsupial.
10k, Spirit Mask.

2010, Jan. 1 Perf. 14¼
1431-1434 A330　Set of 4　10.50 10.50

1435 A330　Sheet of 4, #a-d　10.50 10.50
Souvenir Sheet
1436 A330　10k multi　7.25 7.25

Beche-de-Mer Industry — A331

Edible sea cucumbers: No. 1437, 1k, Chalkfish. No. 1438, 3k, Elephant trunk fish. No. 1439, 4.65k, Curryfish. No. 1440, 6.30k, Tigerfish.
No. 1441: a, 1k, Surf redfish. b, 3k, Lollyfish. c, 4.65k, Brown sandfish. d, 6.30k, Sandfish. 10k, Pinkfish.

2010, Feb. 8 Litho. Perf. 14x14¼
1437-1440 A331　Set of 4　11.00 11.00
1441 A331　Sheet of 4, #a-d　11.00 11.00
Souvenir Sheet
1442 A331　10k multi　7.50 7.50

For surcharge, see No. 1732M.

Carteret Atoll — A332

Designs: No. 1443, 1k, Huene Island divided. No. 1444, 3k, Upsurge of water through man-made barriers. No. 1445, 4.65k, Salt water intrusion No. 1446, 6.30k, Tree killed by salt water.
No. 1447: a, 1k, Dwindling island. b, 3k, Tree killed by salt water, diff. c, 4.65k, Storm surge and erosion. d, 6.30k, Man-made barriers.
10k, Divided atolls.

2010, Mar. 18
1443-1446 A332　Set of 4　11.00 11.00
1447 A332　Sheet of 4, #a-d　11.00 11.00
Souvenir Sheet
1448 A332　10k multi　7.50 7.50

Girl Guides, Cent. — A333

Designs: No. 1449, 1k, Guides learning cooking for badge work, 1970. No. 1450, 3k, Guide creating a wash bowl for badge work. No. 1451, 4.65k, Trainer teaching knot tying. No. 1452, 6.30k, Brownies displaying badge work.
No. 1453: a, 1k, Lady Kala Olewale, Second Papua New Guinea Chief Commissioner. b, 3k, Lady Christian Chartterton, founder of Papua New Guinea Girl Guides. c, 4.65k, Princess Anne visiting Papua New Guinea Girl Guides. d, 6.30k, Enny Moaitz, First Papua New Guinea Chief Commissioner.
10k, Lady Olave Baden-Powell.

2010, Apr. 10 Litho. Perf. 14x14¼
1449-1452 A333　Set of 4　11.00 11.00
1453 A333　Sheet of 4, #a-d　11.00 11.00
Souvenir Sheet
1454 A333　10k multi　7.50 7.50

For surcharges, see Nos. 1732O, 1732R.

Kokoda Campaigns, 68th Anniv. — A334

No. 1455: a, Soldiers in battle. b, Injured Australian soldier, Papuan natives. c, Tourists at Kokoda.
No. 1456: a, Veterans at Kokoda Campaign Memorial, Isurava. b, Veterans of Kokoda Campaign, Papuan houses.

2010, Apr. 20 Litho. Perf. 14¾x14
1455 A334　Horiz. strip of 3　2.40 2.40
　a.-c.　1k Any single　.80 .80
1456 A334　Horiz. pair　7.50 7.50
　a.-b.　4.65k Either single　3.75 3.75
　c.　Souvenir sheet, #1455a-1455c, 1456a-1456b　10.00 10.00

See Australia Nos. 3244-3252.

National Population and Housing Census — A335

Inscriptions: No. 1457, 1k, Young and old. No. 1458, 1k, Youths. No. 1459, 3k, Infants. No. 1460, 3k, Villagers.
No. 1461: a, 1k, School kids. b, 1k, Elderly men. c, 3k, Elderly women. d, 3k, All walks of life.

2010, May 3 Perf. 14x14¼
1457-1460 A335　Set of 4　6.00 6.00
1461 A335　Sheet of 4, #a-d　6.00 6.00

For surcharge, see No. 1732Q.

Expo 2010, Shanghai — A336

Designs: 1k, Summer Palace, Wenchang Tower. No. 1463, 3k, Dancer, Shanghai Intl. Culture and Art Festival. 4.65k, Oriental Pearl Tower, Pudong, Shanghai. 6.30k, Male Chinese acrobatic performers.
No. 1466: a, 5t, Like 1k. b, 10t, Like #1463. c, 85t, Like 4.65k. d, 3k, Female Chinese acrobatic performers. e, 3.70k, Like 6.30k. f, 6k, Ancient Chinese building.
10k, Tower, Suzhou.

2010, May 21 Perf. 11¼x11½
1462-1465 A336　Set of 4　11.00 11.00
1466 A336　Sheet of 6, #a-f　10.00 10.00
Souvenir Sheet
1467 A336　10k multi　9.00 9.00

Sport Fishing A337

Inscriptions: No. 1468, 1k, Female angler. No. 1469, 3k, Team effort. No. 1470, 4.65k, 25kg Sailfish. No. 1471, 6.30k, 10kg Barramundi.
No. 1472: a, 1k, Game fishing boat. b, 3k, Male angler. c, 4.65k, 14kg Wahoo. d, 6.30k, 11kg Barramundi.
10k, Irene Robinson's world record catch blue fin trevally (92.6kg) on a 4kg line.

2010, June 11 Perf. 13½
1468-1471 A337　Set of 4　11.00 11.00
1472 A337　Sheet of 4, #a-d　11.00 11.00
Souvenir Sheet
1473 A337　10k multi　7.25 7.25

Coffee — A338

Designs: 15t, Coffee tree with cherries. No. 1475, 1k, Budding beans. No. 1476, 4.65k, Green coffee cherries. No. 1477, 6.30k, Red coffee cherries.
No. 1478: a, 1k, Man harvesting cherries. b, 3k, Fermentation. c, 4.65k, Drying parchment. d, 6.30k, Man holding green coffee beans.
10k, Green and red coffee cherries.

2010, July 7 Litho. Perf. 14¼
1474-1477 A338　Set of 4　9.00 9.00
1478 A338　Sheet of 4, #a-d　11.00 11.00
Souvenir Sheet
1479 A338　10k multi　7.25 7.25

Bowerbirds — A339

Designs: 5t, Macgregor's gardener bowerbird. No. 1481, 1k, Flame bowerbird. No. 1482, 4.65k, Archbold's bowerbird. No. 1483, 6.30k, Adelbert regent bowerbird.
No. 1484: a, 1k, Pair of Flame bowerbirds. b, 3k, Yellow-fronted gardener bowerbird. c, 4.65k, Vogelkop gardener bowerbird. d, 6.30k, Lauterbach's bowerbird.
10k, Head of Flame bowerbird.

2010, Aug. 4
1480-1483 A339 Set of 4   8.75   8.75
1484 A339 Sheet of 4, #a-d   11.00   11.00
Souvenir Sheet
1485 A339 10k multi   7.25   7.25

2010 Commonwealth Games, Delhi — A340

Designs: No. 1486, 1k, Rugby sevens. No. 1487, 3k, Boxing. No. 1488, 4.65k, Netball. No. 1489, 6.30k, Hurdles.
No. 1490: a, 1k, Weight lifting. b, 3k, Swimming. c, 4.65k, Lawn bowling. d, 6.30k, Sprinting.
10k, Tennis.

2010, Sept. 3   *Perf. 13½*
1486-1489 A340 Set of 4   11.00   11.00
1490 A340 Sheet of 4, #a-d   11.00   11.00
Souvenir Sheet
1491 A340 10k multi   7.25   7.25

Orchids — A341

Designs: No. 1492, 1k, Dendrobium lasianthera May River Red. No. 1493, 3k, Dendrobium violaceoflavens J.J. Smith. No. 1494, 4.65k, Dendrobium mirbelianum var. Vanimo. No. 1495, 6.30k, Dendrobium helix.
No. 1496: a, 1k, Dendrobium nindii W. Hill. b, 3k, Dendrobium sp. off. D. gouldii Reichb. f. c, 4.65k, Dendrobium gouldii Reichb. f. var. Bougainville White. d, 6.30k, Dendrobium discolor var. pink Bensbach.
10k, Dendrobium lasianthera var. Sepik Blue.

2010, Sept. 28   *Perf. 14¼*
1492-1495 A341 Set of 4   11.00   11.00
1496 A341 Sheet of 4, #a-d   11.00   11.00
Souvenir Sheet
1497 A341 10k multi   7.25   7.25

For surcharge, see No. 1732L.

Mother Teresa (1910-97) — A342

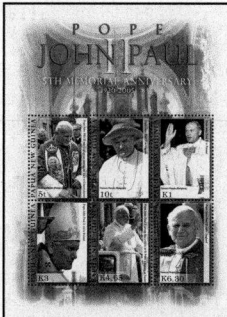

Pope John Paul II (1920-2005) — A343

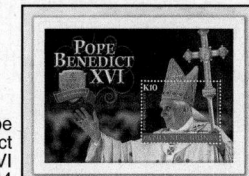

Pope Benedict XVI A344

Photographs of Mother Teresa from: 1k, 1997. 3k, 1971. 4.65k, 1988. 6.30k, 1984.
No. 1502 — Photographs of Pope John Paul II: a, 5t, Meeting with pilgrims at Czestochowa. b, 10t, In Nigeria. c, 1k, In Poland, as young man (without miter). d, 3k, In Poland (wearing miter). e, 4.65k, Greeting crowds in St. Peter's Square. f, 6.30k, In England.

2010, Oct. 13   *Perf. 12*
1498-1501 A342 Set of 4   11.00   11.00
1502 A343 Sheet of 6, #a-f   11.00   11.00
Souvenir Sheet
1503 A344 10k multi   7.25   7.25

Spiders — A345

Designs: No. 1504, 1k, Nephila pilipes. No. 1505, 3k, Argiope aemula. No. 1506, 4.65k, Gasterocantha (blue violet color at UL). No. 1507, 6.30k, Cyrtophora moluccensis.
No. 1508: a, 1k, Leucauge celebesiana. b, 3k, Holconia. c, 4.65k, Gasterocantha (red background color at UL). d, 6.30k, Ocrisiona.
10k, Nephila pilipes, diff.

2010, Nov. 3   Litho.   *Perf. 14½*
1504-1507 A345 Set of 4   11.00   11.00
1508 A345 Sheet of 4, #a-d   11.00   11.00
Souvenir Sheet
1509 A345 10k multi   7.25   7.25

War Dances — A346

Designs: 50t, Warrior with bow and arrow, Western Highlands Province. 1.05k, Simbu warrior with spear, Chimbu Province. 5k, Warrior with spear and shield, Western Highlands Province. 7k, Mudman with bow and arrow, Eastern Highlands Province.
10k, Tasman Island knife dancer, North Solomons Province.

2010, Dec. 1   Litho.   *Perf. 14¼x14*
1510-1513 A346 Set of 4   10.00   10.00
Souvenir Sheet
1514 A346 10k multi   7.25   7.25

Monitor Lizards — A347

Designs: No. 1515, 1.05k, Emerald tree monitor. No. 1516, 5k, Papuan argus monitor. No. 1517, 5k, Papuan monitor. 7k, Blue-tailed monitor.
No. 1519: a, 1.05k, Blue-tailed monitor, diff. b, 2k, Spotted tree monitor. c, 5k, Mangrove monitor. d, 5k, Peach-throat monitor.
No. 1520, Papuan argus monitor with tongue extended.

2011, Jan. 5   Litho.   *Perf. 14x14¼*
1515-1518 A347 Set of 4   13.00   13.00
1519 A347 Sheet of 4, #a-d   10.00   10.00
Souvenir Sheet
1520 A347 5k multi   3.75   3.75

Chinese Zodiac Animals — A348

Designs: No. 1521, 5t, Dragon. No. 1522, 50t, Tiger. No. 1523, 1.05k, Horse. 2k, Monkey. No. 1525, 5k, Snake. No. 1526, 5k, Dog. No. 1527: a, 5t, Ox. b, 50t, Rooster. c, 55t, Sheep. d, 1.05k, Rat. e, 5k, Boar. f, 7k, Rabbit.

2011, Feb. 8   *Perf. 13 Syncopated*
1521-1526 A348 Set of 6   10.50   10.50
1527 A348 Sheet of 6 #a-f   10.50   10.50

Paintings by Mathias Kauage (1944-2003) A349

Designs: No. 1528, 1.05k, Pailet Draivim Balus (Pilot Flying an Airplane). No. 1529, 5k, Fes Misineri (First Missionary). No. 1530, 5k, Pailet i Trein Long Draivim Balus (Trainee Pilot at Training). No. 1531, 7k, Eia Bas (Airbus).
No. 1532 — Details from Eia Bas Bilong Eiu Gini (Air New Guinea's Airbus): a, 1.05k, Wing at top. b, 5k, Bird at top. c, 5k, Wing at bottom. 7k, Rear wheel.
10k, Barasut Man (Parachute Man).

2011, Mar. 18   Litho.   *Perf. 13¼*
1528-1531 A349 Set of 4   14.50   14.50
1532 A349 Sheet of 4, #a-d   14.50   14.50
Souvenir Sheet
1533 A349 10k multi   8.00   8.00

Fish — A350

Designs: No. 1534, 1.05k, Cephalopholis miniata. No. 1535, 1.05k, Cromileptes altivelis. 5k, Plectropomus areolatus. 7k, Epinephelus lanceolatus.
10k, Epinephelus polyphekadion.

2011, Apr. 6   *Perf. 14¼*
1534-1537 A350 Set of 4   11.50   11.50
Souvenir Sheet
1538 A350 10k multi   8.00   8.00

American Civil War, 150th Anniv. — A351

Designs: 1k, Pres. Abraham Lincoln, text "With malice toward none, with charity for all." No. 1540, 1.05k, Lincoln, text "Of the people, by the people, for the people." No. 1541, 5k, Slave and banner. No. 1542, 7k, Lincoln, Confederate States Pres. Jefferson Davis, US and Confederate flags, eagle, banner.
No. 1543: a, 5t, The Peacemakers, painting by George P. A. Healy. b, 50t, Battle of Fort Sumter. c, 55t, Lincoln and his Cabinet. d, 1.05k, Lincoln, Generals Ulysses S. Grant and Robert E. Lee. e, 5k, Lincoln, slave, text "If slavery is not wrong, nothing is wrong." f, 7k, Battle of Gettysburg.
10k, Lincoln, text "A house divided cannot stand."

2011, Apr. 20   *Perf. 12*
1539-1542 A351 Set of 4   11.50   11.50
13 Syncopated
1543 A351 Sheet of 6, #a-f   11.50   11.50
Souvenir Sheet
1544 A351 10k multi   7.50   7.50

Butterflies A352

Designs: No. 1545, 1.05k, Orange birdwing. No. 1546, 1.05k, Green birdwing. 5k, Blue birdwing. 7k, Goliath birdwing.
10k, Pair of Queen Alexandra's birdwings.

2011, May 3   Litho.   *Perf. 14x14¼*
1545-1548 A352 Set of 4   12.00   12.00
Souvenir Sheet
1549 A352 10k multi   8.50   8.50

Pineapples A353

Pineapple slices and: No. 1550, 1.05k, African Queen pineapples sliced. No. 1551, 1.05k, African Queen and Hawaiian pineapples sliced. No. 1552, 5k, One Hawaiian and Two African Queen pineapples, one basket. No. 1553, 7k, One Hawaiian and two African Queen pineapples, two baskets.
No. 1554 — Popular pineapple varieties found in Papua New Guinea: a, 10t. b, 2k. c, 5k. d, 7k.
10k, African pineapple species cut.

2011, May 25   *Perf. 14x14¼*
1550-1553 A353 Set of 4   12.00   12.00
1554 A353 Sheet of 4, #a-d   12.00   12.00
Souvenir Sheet
1555 A353 10k multi   8.25   8.25

Nos. 1550-1555 are impregnated with a pineapple scent.

Urban Safety and Crime Prevention — A354

Designs: 5t, National Capital District Commission emblem. No. 1557, 1.05k, No guns emblem. No. 1558, 5k, Meri SEIF Ples emblem. No. 1559, 7k, UN-Habitat certificate of recognition.
No. 1560: a, 1.05k, Shelter for women and children. b, 1.05k, Krismas SEIF Kempan members. c, 5k, Meri SEIF Ples members. d, 7k, Port Moresby Chamber of Commerce and Industry emblem.
10k, National Capital District Commission emblem, diff.

2011, June 15   *Perf. 14¼x14*
1556-1559 A354 Set of 4   11.50   11.50
1560 A354 Sheet of 4, #a-d   12.00   12.00
Souvenir Sheet
1561 A354 10k multi   8.75   8.75

For surcharge, see No. 1732J.

Cacao Production A355

Designs: 5t, Harvesting cocoa pods. No. 1563, 1.05k, Breaking cocoa pod. No. 1564, 5k, Drying cocoa. No. 1565, 7k, Exporting cocoa bags.
No. 1566: a, 1.05k, Cocoa seedling. b, 1.05k, Cocoa flower. c, 5k, Pruning cocoa treas. d, 7k, Cocoa pods.
10k, Exporting cocoa bags, diff.

2011, July 7   *Perf. 14x14¼*
1562-1565 A355 Set of 4   11.50   11.50
1566 A355 Sheet of 4, #a-d   12.00   12.00
Souvenir Sheet
1567 A355 10k multi   8.75   8.75

Tattoos — A356

Designs: No. 1568, 1.05k, Face tattoo from Tufi. No. 1569, 1.05k, Face tattoo from Nondugl-Banz. No. 1570, 5k, Face tattoo from Asaro. No. 1571, 7k, Face tattoo from Kudjip.
No. 1572: a, 1.05k, Arm tattoo from Kairuku. b, 1.05k, Chest tattoo from Gumine. c, 5k, Leg tattoo from South Whagi. d, 7k, Minei tribe arm tattoo, Manus.

10k, Face tattoo from Tufi, diff.

2011, Aug. 4   *Perf. 14¼x14*
1568-1571 A356   Set of 4   13.00 13.00
1572 A356   Sheet of 4, #a-d   13.00 13.00
Souvenir Sheet
1573 A356 10k multi   9.00 9.00

Southern Cassowaries — A357

Designs: No. 1574, 1.05k, Two newly-weaned chicks feeding. No. 1575, 1.05k, One weaned chick feeding. No. 1576, 5k, Adult feeding. No. 1577, 7k, Heads of two adults.
No. 1578: a, 1.05k, Head and shoulder of adult. b, 1.05k, Back rump of adult. c, 5k, Full view of chick. d, 7k, Legs of adult.
10k, Cassowary in natural habitat.

2011, Aug. 25
1574-1577 A357   Set of 4   13.00 13.00
1578 A357   Sheet of 4, #a-d   13.00 13.00
Souvenir Sheet
1579 A357 10k multi   9.25 9.25

Waterfalls A358

Designs: No. 1580, 1.05k, Kesesoru Falls. No. 1581, 1.05k, Mageni Falls aerial view. No. 1582, 5k, Mageni Falls outlet. No. 1583, 7k, Waghi Falls.
No. 1584: a, 1.05k, Sogeri Falls. b, 1.05k, Beaver Falls. c, 5k, Wawoi Falls. d, 7k, Remote Island Falls.
10k, Ambua Falls.

2011, Sept. 22   *Perf. 14x14¼*
1580-1583 A358   Set of 4   13.00 13.00
1584 A358   Sheet of 4, #a-d   13.00 13.00
Souvenir Sheet
1585 A358 10k multi   9.25 9.25

Wedding of Prince William and Catherine Middleton A359

Badge of the House of Windsor and: No. 1586, 1.05k, Catherine Middleton (at right). No. 1587, 1.05k, Middleton and sister, Pippa. No. 1588, 5k, Prince William. No. 1589, 7k, Couple.
No. 1590 — Badge of the House of Windsor and: a, 1.05k, Middleton (at left). b, 1.05k, Couple waving. c, 5k, Couple holding hands. d, 7k, Prince William, diff.
10k, Couple and badge of the House of Windsor.

2011, Oct. 19   *Perf. 12, 14 (#1590)*
1586-1589 A359   Set of 4   13.50 13.50
1590 A359   Sheet of 4, #a-d   13.50 13.50
Souvenir Sheet
1591 A359 10k multi   9.50 9.50

World War II Relics — A360

Designs: No. 1592, 1.05k, American B-17E 41-2446. No. 1593, 1.05k, Japanese Ki-21 Sally. No. 1594, 5k, American P-38F 12647-S. No. 1595, 7k, American B17E 41-9234.
No. 1596: a, 1.05k, Japanese 95 Ha Go tank. b, 1.05k, Australian Hudson A16-91. c, 5k, New Zealand PV-1 Ventura NZ4613 Tail 13. d, 7k, Japanese 120mm dual purpose gun.
10k, American B-17F "Black Jack."

2011, Nov. 16   *Perf. 13¼*
1592-1595 A360   Set of 4   13.50 13.50
1596 A360   Sheet of 4, #a-d   13.50 13.50
Souvenir Sheet
1597 A360 10k multi   9.50 9.50

Victory Dancers — A361

Designs: No. 1598, 1.05k, Kiriwina woman. No. 1599, 1.05k, Oro man. No. 1600, 5k, Kandep woman. No. 1601, 7k, Siasi man.
No. 1602: a, 1.05k, Kerowagi man. b, 1.05k, Tolai man. c, 5k, Rigo man. d, 7k, Huli man.
10k, Baining fire dancer.

2011, Dec. 1   *Perf. 14¼x14*
1598-1601 A361   Set of 4   13.50 13.50
1602 A361   Sheet of 4, #a-d   13.50 13.50
Souvenir Sheet
1603 A361 10k multi   9.50 9.50
For surcharge, see No. 1732S.

Fish — A362

Designs: No. 1604, 1.20k, Emperor angelfish. No. 1605, 1.20k, Yellow-mask angelfish. No. 1606, 6k, Meyer's butterflyfish. No. 1607, 8k, Barrier Reef anemonefish.
No. 1608: a, 1.20k, Clown anemonefish. b, 1.20k, Clown triggerfish. c, 6k, Clark's anemonefish. d, 8k, Spotfin lionfish.
10k, Bearded scorpionfish.

2012, Jan. 5   *Perf. 14x14¼*
1604-1607 A362   Set of 4   15.50 15.50
1608 A362   Sheet of 4, #a-d   15.50 15.50
Souvenir Sheet
1609 A362 10k multi   9.25 9.25

A363   A364

A365   A366

Paintings by Philip Yobale (1968-2009) — A367

Designs: No. 1610, Fish Berserk. No. 1611, Facing Faces. No. 1612, Regiana Bird of Paradise and Its Four Captors. No. 1613, Face Without Eye.
No. 1614 — Untitled works with: a, 1.20k, Faces. b, 1.20k, Head with headband. c, 6k, Eye at UL. d, 8k, Mask at UR.
10k, On-looking Eyes.

2012, Feb. 22   *Perf. 14¼x14*
1610 A363 1.20k multi   1.10 1.10
1611 A364 1.20k multi   1.10 1.10
1612 A365 6k multi   5.75 5.75
1613 A366 8k multi   7.50 7.50
   Nos. 1610-1613 (4)   15.45 15.45
1614 A367   Sheet of 4, #a-d   15.50 15.50
Souvenir Sheet
1615 A367 10k multi   9.50 9.50

Blessed Peter To Rot (1912-45), Christian Martyr — A368

Designs: No. 1616, 1.20k, Beatification ceremony, 1995. No. 1617, 1.20k, To Rot baptizing child. No. 1618, 6k, Beatification ceremony, diff. No. 1619, 8k, To Rot giving holy communion.
No. 1620: a, 1.20k, To Rot in Taliligap Catechist School. b, 1.20k, To Rot officiating a marriage. c, 6k, To Rot leading worship and devotion. d, 8k, Murder of To Rot in cell in Japanese concentration camp.
10k, Statue of To Rot.

2012, Mar. 14   *Perf. 14x14¼*
1616-1619 A368   Set of 4   16.50 16.50
          Perf. 14
1620 A368   Sheet of 4, #a-d   16.50 16.50
Souvenir Sheet
1621 A368 10k multi   10.00 10.00

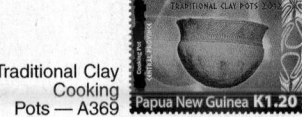

Traditional Clay Cooking Pots — A369

Cooking pots from: No. 1622, 1.20k, Central Province. No. 1623, 1.20k, Madang Province. No. 1624, 6k, Autonomous Region of Bougainville. No. 1625, 8k, East Sepik Province.
No. 1626: a, 1.20k, Milne Bay Province (brown pot). b, 1.20k, Milne Bay Province (black pot). c, 6k, East Sepik Province, diff. d, 8k, Manus Province.
10k, West Sepik Province.

2012, Apr. 11   *Perf. 14x14¼*
1622-1625 A369   Set of 4   15.50 15.50
          Perf. 14
1626 A369   Sheet of 4, #a-d   15.50 15.50
Souvenir Sheet
1627 A369 10k multi   9.50 9.50
For surcharges, see Nos. 1732A, 1732B, 1734D, 1734E.

Marsupials A370

Designs: No. 1628, 1.20k, Common gray cuscus. No. 1629, 1.20k, Common spotted cuscus. No. 1630, 6k, Black spotted cuscus. No. 1631, 8k, Woodlark cuscus.
No. 1632: a, 1.20k, Sugar glider. b, 1.20k, Feather-tail possum. c, 6k, Striped possum. d, 8k, Northern glider.
10k, Common spotted cuscus, diff.

2012, May 7   *Perf. 13¼*
1628-1631 A370   Set of 4   15.50 15.50
1632 A370   Sheet of 4, #a-d   15.50 15.50
Souvenir Sheet
1633 A370 10k multi   9.50 9.50
For surcharges, see Nos. 1732C, 1732D, 1734A, 1734B.

Sports Legends A371

Designs: No. 1634, 1.20k, Iamo Launa, track and field. No. 1635, 1.20k, Martin Beni, boxer. No. 1636, 6k, Stanley Nandex, kick boxer. No. 1637, 8k, Will Genia, rugby player.
No. 1638: a, 1.20k, Tau John, track. b, 1.20k, Iwila Jacobs, weight lifter. c, 6k, Takale Tuna, track. d, 8k, John Aba, boxer.
10k, Genia, diff.

2012, June 18
1634-1637 A371   Set of 4   15.50 15.50
1638 A371   Sheet of 4, #a-d   15.50 15.50
Souvenir Sheet
1639 A371 10k multi   9.50 9.50
For surcharge, see No. 1732E.

Orchids — A372

Designs: No. 1640, 1.20k, Dendrobium macrophyllum. No. 1641, 1.20k, Dendrobium williamsianum. No. 1642, 6k, Pink Dendrobium bracteosum. No. 1643, 8k, Phalaenopsis amabilis.
No. 1644: a, 1.20k, White Dendrobium bracteosum. b, 1.20k, Dendrobium bifalce. c, 6k, Dendrobium strepsiceros. d, 8k, Vanda hindsii.
10k, Dendrobium spectabile.

2012, July 2   *Perf. 14x14¼*
1640-1643 A372   Set of 4   15.50 15.50
          Perf. 14
1644 A372   Sheet of 4, #a-d   15.50 15.50
Souvenir Sheet
1645 A372 10k multi   9.50 9.50
For surcharges, see Nos. 1732F, 1732G, 1734F, 1734G.

2012 Summer Olympics, London — A373

No. 1646: a, 50t, Weight lifting. b, 55t, Swimming. c, 1k, Relay race.
5k, Boxing.

2012, July 27   *Perf. 12*
1646 A373   Sheet of 3, #a-c   2.00 2.00
Souvenir Sheet
1647 A373 5k multi   4.75 4.75

New Year 2012 (Year of the Snake) — A374

Flags of Papua New Guinea and People's Republic of China and snake with background color of: No. 1648, 1.20k, Pink. No. 1649, 1.20k, Blue. No. 1650, 6k, Yellow orange. No. 1651, 8k, Green.
No. 1652: a, 1.20k, Green. b, 1.20k, Yellow orange. c, 6k, Pink. d, 8k, Blue.
10k, Yellow.

2012, Aug. 1   *Perf. 14, 12 (#1652)*
1648-1651 A374   Set of 4   15.50 15.50
1652 A374   Sheet of 4, #a-d   15.50 15.50
Souvenir Sheet
1653 A374 10k multi   9.50 9.50

Traditional Costumes — A375

Designs: No. 1654, 1.20k, Man from Telefomin, Sandaun Province. No. 1655, 1.20k, Woman from Pomio, East New Britain Province. No. 1656, 6k, Women from Hanuabada, National Capital District. No. 1657, 8k, Woman and child from Duna, Southern Highlands Province.
No. 1658: a, 1.20k, Bride from Mendi, Southern Highlands Province. b, 1.20k, Woman from Tari, Southern Highlands Province. c, 6k, Family from Trobriand Islands, Milne Bay Province. d, 8k, Women from Mukawa, Milne Bay Province.
10k, Woman from Popondetta, Oro Province.

2012, Sept. 5   *Perf. 14¼*
1654-1657 A375   Set of 4   15.50 15.50
1658 A375   Sheet of 4, #a-d   15.50 15.50
Souvenir Sheet
1659 A375 10k multi   9.50 9.50
For surcharges, see Nos. 1732H, 1734H, 1734I.

Reign of Queen Elizabeth II, 60th Anniv. — A376

Profile of Queen Elizabeth II, Diamond Jubilee emblem, and: 25t, Duchess of Cornwall and Prince of Wales. 50t, Prince of Wales. 1k, Prince of Wales, Duchess of Cornwall, Queen Elizabeth II and Prince Philip. 1.25k, Prince of Wales with sword. 6k, Queen Elizabeth II and Prince of Wales. 8k, Queen Elizabeth II and Prince Philip.
10k, Queen Elizabeth II, vert.

2012, Nov. 4   *Perf. 14¼*
1660-1665 A376   Set of 6   16.50 16.50
Souvenir Sheet
1666 A376 10k multi   9.75 9.75

Public Transportation A377

Designs: No. 1667, 1.30k, Passenger truck. No. 1668, 1.30k, Banana boat. No. 1669, 6k, Remote service airplane. No. 1670, 8.70k, Trading canoe.
No. 1671: a, 1.30k, Taxi. b, 1.30k, Passenger bus. c, 6k, Domestic and international airplane. d, 8k, Ship.
10k, Dugout canoe.

2013, Jan. 2   *Perf. 13¾x13¼*
1667-1670 A377   Set of 4   17.00 17.00
1671 A377   Sheet of 4, #a-d   17.00 17.00
Souvenir Sheet
1672 A377 10k multi   9.75 9.75

Sculptures by Gigmai Kundun — A378

Designs: No. 1673, 1.30k, Hiri Trade Canoe (Lakatoi). No. 1674, 1.30k, Kundu Slit Gong. No. 1675, 6k, Hiri Moale Queen. No. 1676, 8.70k, Bird of Paradise.
No. 1677: a, 1.30k, Follow the Leader. b, 1.30k, Walking Together. c, 6k, Relieving Education Burden. d, 8k, Inherited Believe System.
10k, Indo-Pacific Lionfish (Pterois).

2013, Feb. 20   *Perf. 12*
1673-1676 A378   Set of 4   16.50 16.50
1677 A378   Sheet of 4, #a-d   16.50 16.50
Souvenir Sheet
1678 A378 10k multi   9.50 9.50

In 2012, Papua New Guinea postal officials permitted customers who wished to purchase personalized stamps to work with them in designing the stamps and labels, instead of only providing the image for the attached label, as had been done with previous personalized stamp issues. Some of the items produced by customers are known to lack the country name on the stamp and label. These stamps are known to have a number of different denominations. Beyond Nos. 1264-1268, Papua New Guinea postal officials have not provided any information on other personalizable stamps that are available to any customer.

Pres. John F. Kennedy (1917-63) — A379

Designs: No. 1679, 1.30k, Pres. Kennedy seated. No. 1680, 1.30k, Pres. Kennedy, wife, Jacqueline, and Vice-president Lyndon B. Johnson. No. 1681, 6k, Pres. Kennedy in limousine. No. 1682, 8.70k, Honor guard holding flag over Pres. Kennedy's casket.
No. 1683: a, 1.30k, Pres. Kennedy and flag. b, 1.30k, Pres. Kennedy and wife at Love Field, Dallas, Texas. c, 6k, Flag-draped coffin of Pres. Kennedy. d, 8.70k, Johnson being sworn in as President.
10k, Pres. Kennedy, vert.

2013, Mar. 13   Litho.   *Perf. 14*
1679-1682 A379   Set of 4   16.00 16.00
1683 A379   Sheet of 4, #a-d   16.00 16.00
Souvenir Sheet
    Perf. 12
1684 A379 10k multi   9.25 9.25

Root Crops — A380

Designs: No. 1685, 1.30k, Cassava. No. 1686, 1.30k, Chinese taro. No. 1687, 6k, Sweet potatoes. No. 1688, 8.70k, Taro.
No. 1689: a, 1.30k, Five-leaflet yam. b, 1.30k, Lesser yam. c, 6k, Greater yam. d, 8.70k, Nummularia yam.
10k, Queensland arrowroot.

2013, Apr. 10   Litho.   *Perf. 12*
1685-1688 A380   Set of 4   16.00 16.00
1689 A380   Sheet of 4, #a-d   16.00 16.00
Souvenir Sheet
1690 A380 10k multi   9.25 9.25

Orchids — A381

Designs: No. 1691, 1.30k, Dendrobium gouldii. No. 1692, 1.30k, Dendrobium lineale. No. 1693, 6k, Dendrobium mirbelianum. No. 1694, 8.70k, Dendrobium sp. aff. D. cochiliodes.
No. 1695: a, 1.30k, Dendrobium sp. aff. D. gouldii. b, 1.30k, Dendrobium sp. aff. D. conanthum. c, 6k, Dendrobium lineale, diff. d, 8.70k, Dendrobium carronii.
10k, Dendrobium mussauense.

2013, May 24   Litho.   *Perf. 12*
1691-1694 A381   Set of 4   15.50 15.50
1695 A381   Sheet of 4, #a-d   15.50 15.50
Souvenir Sheet
1696 A381 10k multi   9.00 9.00

Spacecraft and Space Stations — A382

Designs: No. 1697, 1.30k, Skylab. No. 1698, 1.30k, Salyut 6 Space Station. No. 1699, 6k, Spacehab. No. 1700, 8.70k, Mir Space Station.
No. 1701: a, 1.30k, Skylab, diff. b, 1.30k, Salyut 6 Space Station, diff. c, 6k, Space shuttle re-entering atmosphere. d, 8.70k, Mir Space Station, diff.
10k, Space shuttle as seen from International Space Station window.

2013, July 15   Litho.   *Perf. 14*
1697-1700 A382   Set of 4   15.50 15.50
    Perf. 12
1701 A382   Sheet of 4, #a-d   15.50 15.50
Souvenir Sheet
1702 A382 10k multi   9.00 9.00
Launch of the International Space Station, 15th anniv.

Woven Baskets — A383

Designs: No. 1703, 1.30k, Common "Tolai" carry basket, East New Britain Province. No. 1704, 1.30k, Pepeni (yam basket), Kitava Island, Milne Bay Province. No. 1705, 6k, Carry basket, Milne Bay Province. No. 1706, 8.70k, Carry baskets, Ialibu, Southern Highlands Province.
No. 1707: a, 1.30k, Common Sepik basket, East Sepik Province. b, 1.30k, Carry basket, Milne Bay Province, diff. c, 6k, Carry basket, Gulf Province. d, 8.70k, Manus carry basket, Manus Province.
10k, Temporary palm leaf basket, Coastal and Island Provinces.

2013, Aug. 9   Litho.   *Perf. 12*
1703-1706 A383   Set of 4   15.00 15.00
1707 A383   Sheet of 4, #a-d   15.00 15.00
Souvenir Sheet
1708 A383 10k multi   8.75 8.75

Coconuts — A384

Designs: 4k, Green coconuts. No. 1710, 6k, Coconut husking. No. 1711, 8.70k, Coconut juice. 12k, Coconut meat.
No. 1713: a, 1k, Dry coconut. b, 1.30k, Inner shell. c, 6k, Meat. d, 8.70k, Apple.
10k, Inner shell.

2013, Aug. 21   Litho.   *Perf. 12*
1709-1712 A384   Set of 4   25.00 25.00
1713 A384   Sheet of 4, #a-d   14.00 14.00
Souvenir Sheet
1714 A384 10k multi   8.25 8.25

Birth of Prince George of Cambridge — A385

Designs (inscribed "22nd of July 2013" at top: No. 1715, 1.30k, Duke and Duchess of Cambridge, Prince George. No. 1716, 1.30k, Duke of Cambridge, Prince George. No. 1717, 6k, Duchess of Cambridge, Prince George. No. 1718, 8.70k, Duke and Duchess of Cambridge, Prince George, diff.
No. 1719 (stamps without "22nd of July 2013" inscription at top): a, 1.30k, Like #1715. b, 1.30k, Like #1716. c, 6k, Like #1717. d, 8.70k, Like #1718.
10k, Prince George in arms of Duchess of Cambridge.

    Perf. 13¼x12½
2013, Sept. 11   Litho.
1715-1718 A385   Set of 4   14.00 14.00
    Perf. 12x12½
1719 A385   Sheet of 4, #a-d   14.00 14.00
Souvenir Sheet
1720 A385 10k multi   8.25 8.25

Cooking Methods — A386

Designs: No. 1721, 1.30k, Boiling. No. 1722, 1.30k, Drying. No. 1723, 6k, Drying, diff. No. 1724, 8.70k, Roasting.
No. 1725: a, 1.30k, Dug out mumu pit. b, 1.30k, Stones being heated in mumu pit. c, 6k, Food placed in mumu pit. d, 8.70k, Covered mumu pit.
10k, Hot stones steaming in pot.

2013, Nov. 6   Litho.   *Perf. 12*
1721-1724 A386   Set of 4   13.50 13.50
1725 A386   Sheet of 4, #a-d   13.50 13.50
Souvenir Sheet
1726 A386 10k multi   7.75 7.75

New Year 2014 (Year of the Horse) — A387

Various horses with background colors of: No. 1727, 1.70k, Grayish lilac. No. 1728, 1.70k, Tan. No. 1729, 6k, Red. No. 1730, 8.70k, Blue violet.
No. 1731 — Various horses with background colors of: a, 1.30k, Violet. b, 1.30k, Olive bister. c, 6k, Grayish lilac. d, 8.70k, Blue green.
10k, Horse with greenish gray background.

2014, Jan. 2   Litho.   *Perf. 12*
1727-1730 A387   Set of 4   14.50 14.50
1731 A387   Sheet of 4, #a-d   14.00 14.00
Souvenir Sheet
1732 A387 10k multi   8.00 8.00
For surcharges, see Nos. 1733-1734.

Nos. 1358, 1395, 1416, 1440, 1451, 1452, 1460, 1494, 1495, 1512, 1557, 1601, 1622, 1623, 1628, 1629, 1634, 1640, 1641, 1654, 1655 Surcharged in Black or Black and Red

Serifed "K"   Sans-serif "K"

Methods and Perfs. As Before
2014, Jan.
Serifed "K" Surcharges
1732A A369 1.30k on 1.20k #1622 — —
1732B A369 1.30k on 1.20k #1623 — —
1732C A370 1.30k on 1.20k #1628 — —
1732D A370 1.30k on 1.20k #1629 — —
1732E A371 1.30k on 1.20k #1634 — —
1732F A372 1.30k on 1.20k #1640 (Bk&R) — —
1732G A372 1.30k on 1.20k #1641 — —
Sans-serif "K" Surcharges
1732H A375 1.30k on 1.20k #1654· — —
1732I A324 15k on 85t #1395 — —
1732J A354 15k on 1.05k #1557 — —
1732K A316 15k on 3.70k #1358 — —
1732L A341 25k on 4.65k #1494 — —
1732M A331 25k on 6.30k #1440 — —
1732N A341 25k on 6.30k #1495 — —
1732O A333 40k on 4.65k #1451 — —
1732P A327 40k on 6k #1416 — —
1732Q A335 90k on 3k #1460 — —
1732R A333 90k on 6.30k #1452 — —
1732S A361 90k on 7k #1601 — —

Obliterators and sizes of surcharges vary. Nos. 1732A, 1732B, 1732C, 1732G have horizontal single straight-line obliterators and Nos. 1732D, 1732F, 1732H has a rectangular obliterator. Compare these stamps with Nos. 1734A, 1734B, 1734D-1734G, which have slanted single straight-line obliterators.

Nos. 1512, 1601 With Sans-Serif Surcharge Like No. 1732H
Methods and Perfs As Before
2014
1732T A346 25k on 5k #1512 — —
1732U A361 90k on 7k #1601 — —

Nos. 1356, 1358 With Sans-Serif Surcharge Like No. 1732H
Methods and Perfs As Before
2014
1732V A316 40k on 3.70k #1358 — —
1732W A316 45k on 85t #1356 — —

No. 1641 With Serifed Surcharge in Black and Red

2014   Method and Perf. As Before
1732X A372 1.30k on 1.20k   —
         #1641
         (Bk&R)

No. 1655 With Sans-Serif Surcharge

2014   Method and Perf. As Before Rectangular Obliterator
1732Y A375 1.30k on 1.20k   —
         #1655

Compare with No. 1734H, which has a slanted, single-line obliterator.

Nos. 1727-1728 Surcharged in Black and Red

2014, Feb. 12   Litho.   Perf. 12
1733 A387 5k on 1.70k #1727   4.50 4.50
1734 A387 5k on 1.70k #1728   4.50 4.50

Nos. 1327, 1622-1623, 1628-1629, 1640-1641, 1654-1655 Surcharged With Slanted Single-Line Obliterator

Methods and Perfs. As Before
2014
Serifed "K" Surcharges
1734A A370 1.30k on 1.20k   —
         #1628
1734B A370 1.30k on 1.20k   —
         #1629
Sans-serif "K" Surcharges
1734C A312 1.30k on 85t #1327   —
1734D A369 1.30k on 1.20k   —
         #1622
1734E A369 1.30k on 1.20k   —
         #1623
1734F A372 1.30k on 1.20k   —
         #1640
1734G A372 1.30k on 1.20k   —
         #1641
1734H A375 1.30k on 1.20k   —
         #1654
1734I A375 1.30k on 1.20k   —
         #1655

Nelson Mandela (1918-2013), President of South Africa — A388

Various photographs of Mandela (stamps with white frames): No. 1735, 1.30k. No. 1736, 3k. No. 1737, 6k. No. 1738, 8k.
No. 1739 — Various photographs of Mandela (stamps with green frames): a, 1.30k. b, 3k. c, 6k. d, 8k.
10k, Mandela, diff. (stamp without frame).

2014, Mar. 31   Litho.   Perf. 12
1735-1738 A388 Set of 4   13.50 13.50
1739 A388 Sheet of 4, #a-d 13.50 13.50
Souvenir Sheet
1740 A388 10k multi   7.25 7.25

Spirit of Hela Liquified Natural Gas Tanker — A389

Various photographs of Spirit of Hela with side panel color of: 1.30k, Pale green, 3k, Beige. 6k, Light blue green. 8k, Lilac.
10k, Spirit of Hela, light blue panel.

2014, Apr. 7   Litho.   Perf. 13½
1741-1744 A389 Set of 4   13.00 13.00
1744a Souvenir sheet of 4,
         #1741-1744   13.00 13.00
Souvenir Sheet
1745 A389 10k multi   7.25 7.25

World War I, Cent. — A390

Designs: No. 1746, 1.30k, Russian soldier. No. 1747, 5k, American bugler. No. 1748, 6k, French airplanes. No. 1749, 8k, German observation balloon.
No. 1750: a, 1.30k, French lancers. b, 5k, British Army. c, 6k, American National Guard. 8k, French battleship.
10k, British soldier.

2014, Apr. 24 Litho. Perf. 13¼x12½
1746-1749 A390 Set of 4   14.50 14.50
Perf. 12x12½
1750 A390 Sheet of 4, #a-d 14.50 14.50
Souvenir Sheet
1751 A390 10k multi   7.25 7.25

Pope Francis — A391

Coat of arms of Pope Francis and various photographs with frame color of: No. 1752, 1.30k, Red violet. No. 1753, 5k, Green. No. 1754, 6k, Blue. No. 1755, 8k, Vermilion.
No. 1756 — Coat of arms of Pope Francis and photographs with bister frame: a, 1.30k, Photo like #1753. b, 5k, Photo like #1754. c, 6k, Photo like #1755. d, 8k, Photo like #1752
10k, Pope Francis, coat of arms.

2014, July 28 Litho. Perf. 13¼x12½
1752-1755 A391 Set of 4   16.00 16.00
Perf. 12x12½
1756 A391 Sheet of 4, #a-d 16.00 16.00
Souvenir Sheet
1757 A391 10k multi   8.00 8.00

Artifacts — A392

Designs: No. 1758, 1.30k, Trobriand Islands lime pot. No. 1759, 5k, Manus Island bowl. No. 1760, 6k, Wogeo Island food bowl. No. 1761, 8k, Sepik Region pan pipes.
No. 1762, horiz. — Various Sepik River canoe prows: a, 1.30k. b, 5k. c, 6k. d, 8k.
10k, Kiriwina lime pot.

Perf. 13¼x13¾, 13¾x13¼ (#1762)
2014, Aug. 28   Litho.
1758-1761 A392 Set of 4   16.50 16.50
1762 A392 Sheet of 4, #a-d 16.50 16.50
Souvenir Sheet
1763 A392 10k multi   8.25 8.25

Bank of Papua New Guinea, 40th Anniv. — A393

Bank building, 40th anniv. emblem and bank governors: No. 1764, 1.30k, Loi M. Bakani. No. 1765, 4k, Sir Mekere Morauta. No. 1766, 6k, Sir Henry ToRobert. No. 1767, 8k, Sir Wilson Kamit.
No. 1768 — 40th anniv. emblem and: a, 1.30k, Bank building, bank governor John Vulupindi. b, 4k, Bank building, bank governor Koiari Tarata. c, 6k, Bank building. d, 8k, Bank building, bank governor Morea Vele.
10k, 40th anniv. emblem, native costume, vert.

Litho. With Foil Application
2014, Sept. 15   Perf. 13¾x13¼
1764-1767 A393 Set of 4   15.50 15.50
1768 A393 Sheet of 4, #a-d 15.50 15.50
Souvenir Sheet
Perf. 13¼x13¾
1769 A393 10k multi   8.00 8.00

A394   A395

A396   New Year 2015 (Year of the Ram) — A397

No. 1774: a, 1.35k, Ram in circle. b, 1.35k, Ram in rectangle. c, 6.20k, Ram on pot. d, 8.95, Ram in circle, flowers at top.
10k, Ram and Chinese characters.

2015, Jan. 5 Litho. Perf. 13¼x12½
1770 A394 1.35k multi   1.00 1.00
1771 A395 1.35k multi   1.00 1.00
1772 A396 6.20k multi   4.75 4.75
1773 A397 8.95k multi   6.75 6.75
  Nos. 1770-1773 (4)   13.50 13.50
Miniature Sheet
1774 A397 Sheet of 4, #a-d 13.50 13.50
Souvenir Sheet
1775 A397 10k multi   7.75 7.75

Traditional Paintings A398

Designs: No. 1776, 1.35k, Arawe Mother and Child. No. 1777, 1.35k, Motuan Village Totem Pole. No. 1778, 6.20k, Baining Fire Dancers. No. 1779, 8.95k, Crocodile Hunters.
No. 1780: a, 1.35k, Mount Elimbari. b, 1.35k, Wig Makers. c, 6.20k, Tifalmin Hunter. d, 8.95k, Wood Carver.
10k, Like No. 1777.

2015, Mar. 9   Litho.   Perf. 14½x14
1776-1779 A398 Set of 4   13.50 13.50
1780 A398 Sheet of 4, #a-d 13.50 13.50
Souvenir Sheet
1781 A398 10k multi   7.50 7.50

Christian Leaders' Training College, 50th Anniv. — A399

Designs: No. 1782, 1.35k, College founder Dr. Gilbert J. McArthur and student leader, Jezreel Flora. No. 1783, 1.35k, Students of 1967. No. 1784, 6.20k, Graduates. No. 1785, 8.95k, Aerial view of Banz Campus.
No. 1786: a, 1.35k, Banz Campus, 1965. b, 1.35k, Banz Campus, 2015. c, 6.20k, Port Moresby Campus. d, 8.95k, Lae Campus.
10k, Graduation ceremony.

Litho. With Foil Application
2015, Mar. 30   Perf. 14½x14
1782-1785 A399 Set of 4   13.50 13.50
1786 A399 Sheet of 4, #a-d 13.50 13.50
Souvenir Sheet
1787 A399 10k multi   7.50 7.50

Traditional Headdresses A400

Headdress from: No. 1788, 1.35k, Central Province. No. 1789, 1.35k, Eastern Highlands Province. 6.20k, Central Province, diff. 8.95k, East Sepik Province.
10k, Headdress from Simbu Province.

2015, June 22 Litho. Perf. 14¼x14
1788-1791 A400 Set of 4   13.00 13.00
1791a Souvenir sheet of 4,
         #1788-1791   13.00 13.00
Souvenir Sheet
1792 A400 10k multi   7.25 7.25

2015 Pacific Games, Port Moresby A401

Emblem, mascot and: No. 1793, 1.35k, Dika Toua, weight lifting. No. 1794, 1.35k, Toea Wisil, running. No. 1795, 6.20k, Ryan Pini, swimming. No. 1796, 8.95k, Jack Biyufa, body building.
No. 1797: a, 1.35k, Abigail Tere Apisah, tennis. b, 1.35k, Betty Burua, running. c, 6.20k, Linda Pulsan, powerlifting. d, 8.95k, Steven Kari, weight lifting.
10k, Emblem and mascot.

2015, June 22 Litho. Perf. 14¼x14
1793-1796 A401 Set of 4   13.00 13.00
1797 A401 Sheet of 4, #a-d 13.00 13.00
Souvenir Sheet
1798 A401 10k multi   7.25 7.25

Queen Elizabeth II, Longest Reigning British Monarch — A402

Designs: No. 1799, 1.35k, Princesses Elizabeth and Margaret as children. No. 1800, 1.35k, Color photograph of Queen Elizabeth II. 6.20k, Queen Elizabeth II wearing crown. 8.95k, Queen Elizabeth II and Prince Philip.
10k, Queen Elizabeth II wearing crown, diff.

2015, July 6   Litho.   Perf. 14
1799-1802 A402 Set of 4   13.00 13.00
1802a Souvenir sheet of 4,
         #1799-1802, perf. 12 13.00 13.00
Souvenir Sheet
Perf. 12
1803 A402 10k multi   7.25 7.25

Birth of Princess Charlotte of Cambridge — A403

Designs: No. 1804, 1.35k, Princess Charlotte in arms of Duchess of Cambridge. No. 1805, 1.35k, Duke and Duchess of Cambridge, Princess Charlotte. 6.20k, Duke and

Duchess of Cambridge, Princess Charlotte, diff. 8.95k, Duke and Duchess of Cambridge, Princess Charlotte, diff.
10k, Duchess of Cambridge holding Princess Charlotte.

2015, Aug. 3	Litho.	Perf. 14	
1804-1807	A403	Set of 4	13.00 13.00
1807a		Souvenir sheet of 4, #1804-1807	13.00 13.00
Souvenir Sheet			
1808	A403	10k multi	7.25 7.25

Singapore 2015 Intl. Stamp Exhibition — A404

Designs: No. 1809, 3.75k, Bird of paradise. No. 1810, 3.75k, Merlion.
No. 1811: a, Bird of paradise. b, Merlion.

2015, Aug. 14	Litho.	Perf. 12	
1809-1810	A404	Set of 2	5.25 5.25
Embossed With Foil Application, Litho. Sheet Margin			
Souvenir Sheet			
1811	A404	20k Sheet of 2, #a-b	28.00 28.00

Nos. 1809-1810 were each printed in sheets of 4.

University of Papua New Guinea, 50th Anniv. — A405

Designs: No. 1812, 1.35k, Cockatoo sculpture. No. 1813, 1.35k, University Chapel. 6.20k, Michael Somare Library. 8.95k, Graduation day.
10k, Sir John Gunther (1910-84), first university vice-chancellor.

2015, Oct. 19	Litho.	Perf. 14x14¼	
1812-1815	A405	Set of 4	12.50 12.50
1815a		Souvenir sheet of 4, #1812-1815	12.50 12.50
Souvenir Sheet			
1816	A405	10k multi	6.75 6.75

Papuan Hornbills — A406

Designs: No. 1817, 1.45k, Two hornbills in flight, orange pink background. No. 1818, 6.60k, Hornbill, lilac background. No. 1819, 15k, Two hornbills on perches, light green background. No. 1820, 25k, Two hornbills in flight, gray background.
No. 1821 — Stamps with pink background: a, 1.45k, Like #1817. b, 6.60k, Like #1818. c, 15k, Like #1819. d, 25k, Like #1820.
10k, Two hornbills on perches, light green background.

2016, Jan. 4	Litho.	Perf. 12	
1817-1820	A406	Set of 4	32.00 32.00
1821	A406	Sheet of 4, #a-d	32.00 32.00
Souvenir Sheet			
1822	A406	10k multi	6.75 6.75

New Year 2016 (Year of the Monkey) — A407

Monkey: No. 1823, 1.45k, Walking to left, green and orange background. No. 1824, 1.45k, Leaping with one arm raised, yellow and purple background. No. 1825, 3.30k, Sitting, purple and red background. No. 1826, 6.60k, Leaping with both arms raised, blue and green background.
No. 1827 — Orange and purple background, monkey: a, 1.45k, Running to right. b, 1.45k, Holding peach. c, 3.30k, Sitting. d, 6.60k, Walking to left.
10k, Monkey leaping with one arm raised.

2016, Mar. 30	Litho.	Perf. 13½	
1823-1826	A407	Set of 4	8.50 8.50
1827	A407	Sheet of 4, #a-d	8.50 8.50
Souvenir Sheet			
1828	A407	10k multi	6.50 6.50

No. 1827 contains four 30x40mm stamps.

Coins and Banknotes A408

Bank of Papua New Guinea Governor Loi M. Bakani, standard and colored 2015 Pacific Games coins, and: No. 1829, 1.45k, Detail of 10-kina Pacific Games banknote at UR, denomination in bright purple. No. 1830, 1.45k, Detail of 20-kina Pacific Games banknote at UR, denomination in violet. No. 1831, 3.30k, Detail of standard 2015 Pacific Games coin at UR, denomination in brown purple. No. 1832, 6.60k, Detail of colored 2015 Pacific Games coin at UR, denomination in deep green.
No. 1833 — Bakani, standard and colored 2015 Pacific Games coin, detail of 2015 Independence Anniversary banknote, red denomination, and at upper right: a, 1.45k, Butterfly. b, 1.45k, Opossum. c, 3.30k, Cassowary. d, 6.60k, Turtle.
No. 1834, 5k — Bakani, standard and colored 2015 Pacific Games coin, detail of 2015 Independence Anniversary banknote, red denomination, and at upper right: a, Turtle. b, Cassowary.

2016, May 19	Litho.	Perf. 13¾x13¼	
1829-1832	A408	Set of 4	8.25 8.25
1833	A408	Sheet of 4, #a-d	8.25 8.25
Souvenir Sheet			
1834	A408	5k Sheet of 2, #a-b	6.50 6.50

A409

A410

A411

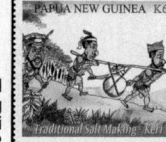

Traditional Salt Making of Keri Tribe — A412

No. 1839 — Two men with: a, 1.45k, One holding hatchet, one pouring water. b, 2k, One holding sticks, one pointing at salt block. c, 4k, One holding water containers, one pouring water on salt block. d, 6.60k, One pointing at other, salt block and flowers on fabric.
10k, Man holding salt block.

2016, Oct. 28	Litho.	Perf. 14½x14	
1835	A409	1.45k multi	.95 .95
1836	A410	2k multi	1.25 1.25
1837	A411	4k multi	2.50 2.50
1838	A412	6.60k multi	4.25 4.25
		Nos. 1835-1838 (4)	8.95 8.95
Miniature Sheet			
1839	A412	Sheet of 4, #a-d	9.00 9.00
Souvenir Sheet			
1840	A412	10k multi	6.50 6.50

Tunas — A413

Designs: No. 1841, 1.45k, Yellowfin tuna. No. 1842, 2k, Bluefin tuna. No. 1843, 5k, Skipjack tuna. No. 1844, 6.60k, Albacore tuna.
No. 1845: a, 1.45k, Like #1842. b, 2k, Like #1844. c, 5k, Like #1841. d, 6.60k, Like #1843.
10k, Bluefin tuna, diff.

2016, Oct. 29	Litho.	Perf. 14x14¼	
1841-1844	A413	Set of 4	9.50 9.50
1845	A413	Sheet of 4, #a-d	9.50 9.50
Souvenir Sheet			
1846	A413	10k multi	6.50 6.50

For surcharges, see Nos. 1994-1996.

Worldwide Fund for Nature (WWF) — A414

No. 1847 — Various photographs of pig-nosed turtle with denomination in: a, 1.45k, Green. b, 3.80k, Yellow. c, 3.80k, Green. d, 6.60k, Green.

2016, Nov. 4	Litho.	Perf. 14	
1847	A414	Block or horiz.	
		strip of 4, #a-d	10.00 10.00
e.		Miniature sheet of 8, 2 each #1847a-1847d	20.00 20.00

Women's Under-20 World Cup Soccer Championships, Papua New Guinea — A415

Emblem, mascot and: 75t, Woman kicking ball. 1.50k, Goaltender reaching for ball. 3.40k, Flags and woman kicking ball. 5k, Athletic shoes and ball.
10k, Two women chasing ball.

2016, Dec. 23	Litho.	Perf. 12	
1848-1851	A415	Set of 4	6.75 6.75
1851a		Souvenir sheet of 4, #1848-1851	6.75 6.75
Souvenir Sheet			
1852	A415	10k multi	6.50 6.50

New Year 2017 (Year of the Rooster) — A416

Rooster facing: No. 1853, 1.50k, Right, both feet on ground. No. 1854, 2k, Left, one leg raised. No. 1855, 3.40k, Right, one leg raised. No. 1856, 6.80k, Left, both feet on ground.
No. 1857 — Two roosters: a, 1.50k. b, 2k. c, 3.40k. d, 6.80k.
13k, Two roosters, diff.

2017, June 23	Litho.	Perf. 12	
1853-1856	A416	Set of 4	8.75 8.75
1857	A416	Sheet of 4, #a-d	8.75 8.75
Souvenir Sheet			
1858	A416	13k multi	8.25 8.25

No. 1857 contains four 30x40mm stamps.
No. 1858 contains one 30x60mm stamp.

Faces of People From Southern Region — A417

Designs: No. 1859, 1.50k, Michael Hota, Motuan. No. 1860, 3.40k, Ruthie Masihada, Trobriand Islander. No. 1861, 5k, Madlyn Hera, Kairukuan. No. 1862, 6.80k, Rosemary Patrick, Motuan.
No. 1863: a, 1.50k, Hota, diff. b, 3.40k, Masihada, diff. c, 5k, Hera, diff. d, 6.80k, Patrick, diff.
13k, Pamela Lougaha, Tufian.

2017, June 26	Litho.	Perf. 12	
1859-1862	A417	Set of 4	10.50 10.50
1863	A417	Sheet of 4, #a-d	10.50 10.50
Souvenir Sheet			
1864	A417	13k multi	8.25 8.25

No. 1863 contains four 30x40mm stamps.

A418

Princess Diana (1961-97) — A419

No. 1865 — Princess Diana wearing: a, Tiara. b, White hat.
No. 1866 — Princess Diana wearing a, Dark green hat. b, White hat, diff.

2017, June 28	Litho.	Perf. 14	
1865	A418	5k Pair, #a-b	6.25 6.25
1866	A419	8k Horiz. pair, #a-b	10.00 10.00

No. 1865 was printed in sheets containing three each of Nos. 1865a-1865b. No. 1866 was printed in sheets containing two pairs.

Shells — A420

Designs: No. 1867, 75t, Tulip shells used for necklace. No. 1868, 1.50k, Conch shell used for communication. No. 1869, 3.40k, Cypraeidae shells used for traditional attire. No. 1870, 6.80k, Nassarius shells used for currency.

No. 1871: a, 75t, Man blowing into conch shell. b, 1.50k, Traditional costume made of Cypraeidae shells. c, 3.40k, Nassarius shell ring. d, 6.80k, Necklace made of shells.

13k, Papustyla pulcherrima used in Manus Province emblem.

2017, Aug. 17		Litho.	Perf. 14	
1867-1870	A420	Set of 4	7.75	7.75
1871	A420	Sheet of 4, #a-d	7.75	7.75
Souvenir Sheet				
1872	A420	13k multi	8.25	8.25

New Year 2018 (Year of the Dog) — A421

No. 1873: a, Chinese character for "dog." b, Dog.

18k, Dog, horiz.

2017, Aug. 18		Litho.	Perf. 14	
1873	A421	5k Pair, #a-b	6.25	6.25
Souvenir Sheet				
1874	A421	18k multi	11.50	11.50

Birds — A422

Designs: No. 1875, 75t, Slaty-mantled goshawk. No. 1876, 1.50k, New Britain goshawk. No. 1877, 3.40k, Brown-collared brush turkey. No. 1878, 6.80k, Black honey buzzard.

No. 1879: a, 75t, Little eagle. b, 1.50k, Black-billed brush turkey. c, 3.40k, Magnificent ground pigeon. d, 6.80k, Collared sparrowhawk.

13k, Raggiana bird of paradise.

2017, Aug. 24		Litho.	Perf. 14	
1875-1878	A422	Set of 4	7.75	7.75
1879	A422	Sheet of 4, #a-d	7.75	7.75
Souvenir Sheet				
1880	A422	13k multi	8.25	8.25

Bananas — A423

Designs: No. 1881, 75t, Buka. No. 1882, 1.50k, Goum. No. 1883, 3.40k, Itonia. No. 1884, 6.80k, Arawa.

No. 1885: a, 75t, Baby banana. b, 1.50k, Duma. c, 3.40k, Bubun. d, 6.80k, Abaus.

13k, Kalapua.

Perf. 13¼x13½				
2017, Aug. 28		Litho.		
1881-1884	A423	Set of 4	7.75	7.75
1885	A423	Sheet of 4, #a-d	7.75	7.75
Souvenir Sheet				
1886	A423	13k multi	8.25	8.25

Protestant Reformation, 500th Anniv. — A424

Martin Luther (1483-1546), Reformation 500th anniv. emblem, and emblem of Evangelical Lutheran Church of Papua New Guinea, and: No. 1887, 1.50k, Stained-glass window. No. 1888, 2k, Painting. No. 1889, 5k, Luther nailing 95 Theses on church door. No. 1890, 6.80k, Luther.

No. 1891, vert. — Head of Luther in: a, 1.50k, Bister. b, 2k, Dull ultramarine. c, 5k, Olive gray. d, 6.80k, Dull blue.

13k, Luther and Papua New Guinea church.

2017, Oct. 25		Litho.	Perf. 13¼x13½	
1887-1890	A424	Set of 4	9.50	9.50
1891	A424	Sheet of 4, #a-d	9.50	9.50
Souvenir Sheet				
1892	A424	13k multi	8.25	8.25

No. 1891 contains four 30x40mm stamps.

Christmas — A425

Inscriptions: No. 1893, 75t, Hailareva soa (natives and hut). No. 1894, 1.50k, Bolmahogu wai (woman and infant). No. 1895, 3.40k, Abona lukara na kinakava (candles). No. 1896, 6.80k, Tamwasawasi towatanawa (natives carrying baskets).

No. 1897: a, 75t, Awogu amozin orande (Nativity scene). b, 1.50k, Lang nahpwen (natives carrying baskets). c, 3.40k, Abona lukara na kinakava (infant Jesus). d, 6.80k, Numan enem (three men wearing headdresses).

13k, Shondha gavo andha (Santa Claus).

Perf. 13¼x13½				
2017, Nov. 11		Litho.		
1893-1896	A425	Set of 4	7.75	7.75
Perf. 13½x13¼				
1897	A425	Sheet of 4, #a-d	7.75	7.75
Souvenir Sheet				
1898	A425	13k multi	8.25	8.25

No. 1897 contains four 40x30mm stamps. No. 1898 contains one 40x30mm stamp.

Battle of Kokoda, 75th Anniv. — A426

Designs: No. 1899, 75t, Soldier assisting wounded soldier. No. 1900, 1.50k, Four Papuan natives carrying wounded soldier. No. 1901, 3.40k, Papuan soldiers. No. 1902, 6.80k, Papuan native assisting wounded soldier.

No. 1903, horiz.: a, 75t, Soldier assisting wounded soldier. Papuan natives carrying medical supplies. b, 1.50k, Soldiers on hike. c, 3.40k, Eleven Papuan natives carrying wounded soldier. d, 6.80k, Papuan natives carrying medical supplies.

13k, Veterans embracing.

Perf. 13¼x13½, 13½x13¼ (#1903)				
2017, Nov. 18		Litho.		
1899-1902	A426	Set of 4	7.75	7.75
1903	A426	Sheet of 4, #a-d	7.75	7.75
Souvenir Sheet				
1904	A426	13k multi	8.25	8.25

Papua New Guinea's Chairmanship of Asia-Pacific Economic Cooperation Area — A427

Inscription at left: 75t, People. 1.50k, Planet. No. 1907, 3.40k, Peace. No. 1908, 3.40k, Prosperity. No. 1909, 6.80k, Partnership. No. 1910, 6.80k, APEC.

No. 1911: a, 75t, Woman and child. b, 1.50k, Building and flags. c, 3.40k, Airplane, ship and dump truck. d, 6.80k, People and workers.

No. 1912, 20k, Map with lines leading to Papua New Guinea. No. 1913, 20k, Emblem of Papua New Guinea.

Perf. 13¼x13½, 13½x13¼ (#1911)				
2017, Dec. 4		Litho.		
1905-1910	A427	Set of 6	14.00	14.00
1911	A427	Sheet of 4, #a-d	7.75	7.75
Souvenir Sheets				
1912-1913	A427	Set of 2	25.00	25.00

No. 1911 contains four 40x30mm stamps. For surcharges, see Nos. 1997-2000.

Birds — A428

Designs: No. 1914, 1.50k, Peacock. No. 1914A, 6.80k, 1915a, 10k, Bird of paradise.

Perf. 14 Syncopated				
2017, Dec. 30		Litho.		
1914-1914A	A428	Set of 2	5.25	5.25
Souvenir Sheet				
1915	A428	Sheet of 2, #1914, 1915a	7.25	7.25
a.		10k multi	6.25	6.25

See India Nos. 2984-2985.

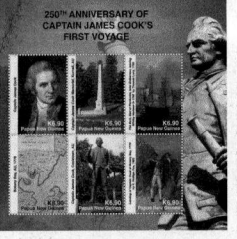

First Voyage of Capt. James Cook, 250th Anniv. A429

No. 1916: a, Capt. James Cook (1728-79). b, Captain Cook Memorial, Kurnell, New South Wales, Australia. c, The Bark, Earl of Pembroke, Later Endeavour, Leaving Whitby Harbor in 1768, by Thomas Luny. d, Map of Botany Bay, 1770. e, Statue of Captain Cook, Cooktown, Queensland, Australia. f, Landing of Captain Cook at Botany Bay, 1770, by E. Phillips Fox.

20k, Map of first voyage, horiz.

2018, Feb. 15		Litho.	Perf. 14	
1916	A429	6.90k Sheet of 6, #a-f	26.00	26.00
Souvenir Sheet				
1917	A429	20k multi	12.50	12.50

Drawings by Joseph Bayagau — A430

Designs: No. 1918, 20t, Kundu Drummer, Momase. No. 1919, 1.60k, Bamboo Harp, Highlands. No. 1920, 5k, Bougainville Panpiper, New Guinea Islands. No. 1921, 6.90k, Mekea Dancer, Southern.

No. 1922: a, 20t, Ging Hunting, Highlands. b, 1.60k, Oxokaiven Dancer, Southern. c, 5k, Headdress, New Guinea Islands. d, 6.90k, Morobe Meri, Momase.

13k, Baby Bilas, Momase.

Perf. 13¼x13½				
2018, Mar. 24		Litho.		
1918-1921	A430	Set of 4	8.50	8.50
1922	A430	Sheet of 4, #a-d	8.50	8.50
Souvenir Sheet				
1923	A430	13k multi	8.00	8.00

Birdpex 8 Philatelic Exhibition, Mondorf-les-Bains, Luxembourg — A431

Designs: No. 1924, 1.60k, Red-billed brush turkey. 2.50k, Meyer's goshawk. 3.45k, Gurney's eagle. No. 1927, 10k, Dusky scrubfowl.

No. 1928: a, 1.60k, Head of Dusky scrubfowl. b, 8k, Leg of Dusky scrubfowl. c, 10k, Eggs of Dusky scrubfowl.

No. 1929: a, 8k, Chestnut-shouldered goshawk facing left. b, 8k, Chestnut-shouldered goshawk facing right.

2018, Apr. 16		Litho.	Perf. 13¼x13½	
1924-1927	A431	Set of 4	11.00	11.00
1928	A431	Sheet of 3, #a-c	12.00	12.00
Souvenir Sheet				
1929	A431	8k Sheet of 2, #a-b	9.75	9.75

Activities of the European Union in Papua New Guinea, 40th Anniv. — A432

Inscriptions: No. 1930, 80t, Supporting access to clean water for rural communities. No. 1931, 1.60k, Support to promoting sustainable fisheries. No. 1932, 3.45k, Supporting the National WaSH Policy: Water tanks to remote islands. No. 1933, 6.90k, Supporting the National WaSH Policy: Water tanks to remote highlands.

No. 1934: a, 80t, Support to promoting children's rights. b, 1.60k, Support to teachers' training college infrastructure development. c, 3.45k, Support to producing Braille materials for children. d, 6.90k, Support to rural teacher training.

13k, Signing of the Lomé Convention.

2018, May 14		Litho.	Perf. 13¼x13½	
1930-1933	A432	Set of 4	8.00	8.00
1934	A432	Sheet of 4, #a-d	8.00	8.00
Souvenir Sheet				
1935	A432	13k multi	8.00	8.00

Coffee Processing A433

Designs: No. 1936, 1.60k, Hand sorting. 3.45k, Roasting. 5k, Grinding. No. 1939, 6.90k, Packaging.

No. 1940: a, 1.60k, Picking coffee berries. b, 3.40k, Drying beans. c, 5k, Packing coffee beans. d, 6.90k, Export.

16k, Cup of coffee and coffee beans.

Perf. 13½x13¼, 14¼ (#1940)				
2018, May 21		Litho.		
1936-1939	A433	Set of 4	10.50	10.50
1940	A433	Sheet of 4, #a-d	10.50	10.50
Souvenir Sheet				
1941	A433	16k multi	10.00	10.00

No. 1940 contains four 45x30mm triangular stamps. Nos. 1936-1941 are impregnated with a coffee scent.

Faces of Papua New Guineans — A434

Designs: Nos. 1942, 1946a, 1.60k, Esther Kelege, Autonomous Region of Bougainville. Nos. 1943, 1946b, 3k, Lydia Gitaria, East New Britain. Nos. 1944, 1946c, 5k, Margaret Talereng, New Ireland. Nos. 1945, 1946d, 6.90k, Sophie Mengai, Manus.
No. 1947: a, Jonathan Telek, West New Britain. b, Michelangelo Telek, West New Britain.

2018, May 21   Litho.   Perf. 12
1942-1945 A434   Set of 4   10.50 10.50
1946 A434   Sheet of 4, #a-d   10.50 10.50
Souvenir Sheet
1947 A434   6.50k Sheet of 2, #a-b   8.00 8.00
No. 1946 contains four 30x40mm stamps.
No. 1947 contains two 30x40mm stamps.

Miniature Sheet

Birth of Prince Louis of Cambridge — A435

No. 1948: a, Prince Louis with parents, Duke and Duchess of Cambridge. b, Prince Louis. c, Princess Charlotte of Cambridge. d, Prince George of Cambridge.

2018, June 11   Litho.   Perf. 13¾
1948 A435   8k Sheet of 4, #a-d   20.00 20.00

Coronation of Queen Elizabeth II, 65th Anniv. — A436

No. 1949 — Black-and-white images of Queen Elizabeth II: a, Seated in coach. b, Receiving scepter. c, Seated on throne holding scepters. d, Waving.
20k, Color photograph.

2018, June 11   Litho.   Perf. 14
1949 A436   8k Sheet of 4, #a-d   20.00 20.00
Souvenir Sheet
Perf. 12
1950 A436   20k multi   12.50 12.50
No. 1950 contains one 30x50mm stamp.

Wedding of Prince Harry and Meghan Markle A437

No. 1951 — Couple: a, Facing left. b, Facing forward. c, Kissing. d, In car, waving.
20k, Couple holding hands, Princess Diana with infant Prince Harry, horiz..

2018, June 11   Litho.   Perf. 13¾
1951 A437   8k Sheet of 4, #a-d   20.00 20.00
Souvenir Sheet
Perf. 12½
1952 A437   20k multi   12.50 12.50
No. 1952 contains one 102x38mm stamp.

United Church in Papua New Guinea, 50th Anniv. A438

Designs: No. 1953, 1.60k, Arua Daera, first Papuan Christian, facing right. 2k, Rev. Jack Sharp. 5k, Rev. Leslie Boseto. No. 1956, 6.90k, Rev. George Brown.
No. 1957: a, 80t, Macfarlane Samuel, missionary. b, 1.60k, Daera, facing forward. c, 3.45k, The Act of Union. d, 6.90k, James Chalmers, missionary.
20k, First church in Port Moresby.

Perf. 13¼x13½
2018, June 18   Litho.
1953-1956 A438   Set of 4   9.50 9.50
1957 A438   Sheet of 4, #a-d   8.00 8.00
Souvenir Sheet
1958 A438   20k multi   12.50 12.50

New Year 2019 (Year of the Pig) A439

No. 1959: a, Black pig in foreground. b, Red pig in foreground.
No. 1960: a, Rat. b, Ox. c, Tiger. d, Rabbit. e, Dragon. f, Snake. g, Horse. h, Goat. i, Monkey. j, Rooster. k, Dog. l, Pig.

2019, Feb. 18   Litho.   Perf. 12
1959 A439   8k Pair, #a-b   9.50 9.50
Perf. 14
1960 A440   1k Sheet of 12, #a-l   7.25 7.25
No. 1959 was printed in sheets containing two each of Nos. 1959a-1959b.

Chinese Zodiac Animals A440

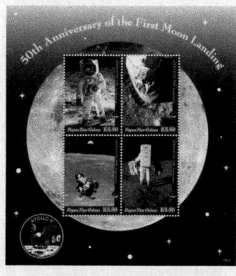

Team Sports — A441

Designs: 1.60k, Women's rugby. 3k, Women's basketball. 5k, Men's cricket. 6.90k, Men's rugby.
No. 1965: a, Men's soccer. b, Men's basketball. c, Women's soccer. d, Men's field hockey.
20k, Men's rugby, diff.

Perf. 14x14½, 13¼x13¾ (No. 1965)
2019, Mar. 15   Litho.
1961-1964 A441   Set of 4   9.75 9.75
1965 A441   2k Sheet of 4, #a-d   4.75 4.75
Souvenir Sheet
1966 A441   20k multi   12.00 12.00
No. 1965 contains four 30x40mm stamps.

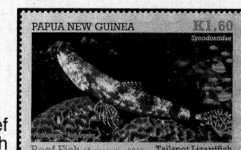

First Man on the Moon, 50th Anniv. A442

No. 1967: a, Astronaut on Moon. b, Astronaut's foot and footprint on Moon. c, Lunar Module above Moon. d, Astronaut carrying equipment on Moon.
20k, Rocket on launch pad.

2019, July 31   Litho.   Perf. 14
1967 A442   5.50k Sheet of 4, #a-d   13.00 13.00
Souvenir Sheet
1968 A442   20k multi   12.00 12.00
No. 1968 contains one 30x80mm stamp.

Reef Fish A443

Designs: 1.60k, Tailspot lizardfish. 2k, Scorpionfish. 5k, Juvenile Sweetlips. 6.90k, Pink anemonefish.
No. 1973: a, Lionfish. b, Parrotfish. c, Coral trout. d, Black saddled puffer.
20k, Anemonefish.

Perf. 13½, 14½ (No. 1973)
2019, Sept. 25   Litho.
1969-1972 A443   Set of 4   9.25 9.25
1973 A443   4k Sheet of 4, #a-d   9.50 9.50
Souvenir Sheet
1974 A443   20k multi   12.00 12.00
No. 1973 contains four 40x28mm stamps.
No. 1974 contains one 40x30mm stamp.

Fruits and Vegetables — A444

Designs: No. 1975, 1.60k, Yams. No. 1976, 3.45k, Potatoes. No. 1977, 5k, Taro. No. 1978, 6.90k, Sweet potatoes.
No. 1979: a, 1.60k, Bananas. b, 3.45k, Avocados. c, 5k, Cucumbers. d, 6.90k, Tomatoes.
20k, Broccoli.

Perf. 13½, 14x14½ (No. 1979)
2019, Sept. 26   Litho.
1975-1978 A444   Set of 4   10.00 10.00
1979 A444   Sheet of 4, #a-d   10.00 10.00
Souvenir Sheet
1980 A444   20k multi   12.00 12.00
No. 1979 contains four 40x28mm stamps.

Paintings by Laben Sakale John — A445

Various unnamed paintings depicting people: 1.60k, 3k, 5k, 6.90k.
No. 1985: a, Mother and child. b, Child. c, Native facing right. d, Mask.
20k, Face.

2019, Sept. 30   Litho.   Perf. 13½
1981-1984 A445   Set of 4   9.75 9.75
1985 A445   8k Sheet of 4, #a-d   19.00 19.00
Souvenir Sheet
1986 A445   20k multi   12.00 12.00

A446

Galip Nuts A447

Designs: 1.60k, Cross-section of nut in shell. 2k, Immature nuts on tree. 5k, Matured nuts ready to be collected. No. 1990, 6.90k, Kernels of nuts at market.
No. 1991 — Various drawings of fresh nut kernels, as shown.
20k, Man cracking nut kernels.

2019, Oct. 1   Litho.   Perf. 13½
1987-1990 A446   Set of 4   9.25 9.25
1991 A447   6.90k Sheet of 4, #a-d   16.50 16.50
Souvenir Sheet
1992 A446   20k multi   12.00 12.00

Dorje Chang Buddha III, Religious Leader — A448

2019, Dec. 21   Litho.   Perf. 13x13½
1993 A448   5k multi   3.00 3.00

Nos. 1841-1842 Surcharged in Red and Black

Methods and Perfs. As Before
2020, Mar. 6
1994 A413   1.60k on 2k #1842   .95 .95
  a.   Red obliterator bar omitted   — —
  b.   New denomination omitted, red obliterator bar doubled, one inverted   — —
  c.   Inverted surcharge   — —
1995 A413   5k on 1.45k #1841   3.00 3.00
1996 A413   6.90k on 1.45k #1841   4.00 4.00
  a.   Red obliterator bar omitted   — —
  b.   New denomination omitted   — —
    Nos. 1994-1996 (3)   7.95 7.95

Nos. 1907-1910 Surcharged in Red and Black

Methods and Perfs. As Before
2020, Mar. 7
1997 A427   1.60k on 6.80k #1909   .95 .95
  a.   New denomination omitted   — —
1998 A427   1.60k on 6.80k #1910   .95 .95
1999 A427   5k on 3.40k #1907   3.00 3.00
2000 A427   6.90k on 3.40k #1908   4.00 4.00
    Nos. 1997-2000 (4)   8.90 8.90

Breadfruit — A449

Designs: 1.60k, Male and female flowers. 2.50k, Female flower. 3.45k, Fruit starting. 10k, Matured fruit.
No. 2005: a, Flower. b, Sprouting fruit. c, Leaf. d, Fruit.
20k, Matured fruit, diff.

2020, May 27   Litho.   Perf. 12
2001-2004 A449   Set of 4   10.50 10.50
2005 A449   5k Sheet of 4, #a-d   11.50 11.50

Souvenir Sheet
2006 A449   20k multi   11.50 11.50

Post-Courier Daily Newspaper, 50th Anniv. — A450

Designs: 1.60k, Front page of newspaper. 3.45k, Luke Sela, founding editor. 5k, Printing press. 6.90k, Front page of Papua New Guinea Independence Day newspaper.
No. 2011, horiz.: a, Man reading newspaper. b, Delivery of newspaper bundles. c, Newsroom. d, Newspapers coming out of press.
20k, Newspaper being printed on press.

Perf. 13½x13¼, 13¼x13½ (#2011)
2020, June 30   Litho.
2007-2010 A450   Set of 4   9.75 9.75
2011 A450   5k Sheet of 4, #a-d   11.50 11.50

Souvenir Sheet
2012 A450   20k multi   11.50 11.50

String Bags — A451

Various string bags with denomination color of: No. 2013, 1.60k, Dark green. No. 2014, 1.60k, Lilac. No. 2015, 6.90k, Blue. No. 2016, 6.90k, Brown.
20k, Brown.

2021   Litho.   Perf. 12
2013-2016 A451   Set of 4   11.50 11.50
2016a   Souvenir sheet of 4, #2013-2016   11.50 11.50

Souvenir Sheet
2017 A451   20k multi   11.50 11.50

Nos. 2013-2017 and 2016a were scheduled to be issued July 25, 2020, but because of the COVID-19 pandemic, the stamps were not delivered to Papua New Guinea until early 2021.

Saltwater Crocodiles A452

Various depictions of saltwater crocodiles with denomination having Roman lettering and numbers: 1.60k, 5k, 6.90k, 20k.
No. 2022, 20k, Like No. 2021, with denomination having italic lettering and numbers.

2021   Litho.   Perf. 12
2018-2021 A452   Set of 4   19.00 19.00
2021a   Souvenir sheet of 4, #2018-2021   19.00 19.00

Souvenir Sheet
2022 A452   20k multi   11.50 11.50

Nos. 2018-2022 and 2021a were scheduled to be issued July 28, 2020, but because of the COVID-19 pandemic, the stamps were not

delivered to Papua New Guinea until early 2021.

Mission Aviation Fellowship, 70th Anniv. — A453

Inscriptions: No. 2023, 1.60k, Investing in education for remote schools. No. 2024, 1.60k, Life saving medevac flights. No. 2025, 6.90k, Taking the Gospel to the communities. No. 2026, 6.90k, Facilitating community development.
No. 2027: a, 1.60k, Training the next generation. b, 1.60k, Encouraging the local church. c, 6.90k, Delivering life-saving medical supplies. d, 6.90k, Responding to disaster.
20k, Fellowship members standing around airplane.

2021, June 30   Litho.   Perf. 13¼
2023-2026 A453   Set of 4   9.75 9.75
2027 A453   Sheet of 4, #a-d   9.75 9.75

Souvenir Sheet
2028 A453   20k multi   11.50 11.50

AIR POST STAMPS

Regular Issue of 1916 Overprinted

1929   Wmk. 74   Perf. 14
C1 A3 3p blue grn & dk gray   3.50 20.00
   b. Vert. pair, one without ovpt.   6,000.
   c. Horiz. pair, one without ovpt.   6,500.
   d. 3p blue grn & sepia blk   57.50 75.00
   e. Overprint on back, vert.   5,000.

No. C1 exists on white and on yellowish paper, No. C1d on yellowish paper only.

Regular Issues of 1916-23 Overprinted in Red

1930, Sept. 15   Wmk. 74
C2 A3 3p blue grn & blk   2.00 11.00
   a. Yellowish paper   3,800. 5,600.
   b. Double overprint   1,500.
C3 A3 6p violet & dull vio   8.00 12.00
   a. Yellowish paper   5.00 15.00
C4 A3 1sh ol grn & ol brn   6.00 17.50
   a. Inverted overprint   15,500.
   b. Yellowish paper   10.00 26.00
   Nos. C2-C4 (3)   16.00 40.50

Port Moresby — AP1

1938, Sept. 6   Unwmk.   Engr.   Perf. 11
C5 AP1 2p carmine   2.75 3.50
C6 AP1 3p ultra   2.75 2.50
C7 AP1 5p dark green   2.75 3.75
C8 AP1 8p red brown   6.50 24.00
C9 AP1 1sh violet   17.50 27.50
   Nos. C5-C9 (5)   32.25 61.25
   Set, never hinged   65.00

Papua as a British possession, 50th anniv.

Papuans Poling Rafts — AP2

1939-41
C10 AP2 2p carmine   3.00 8.50
C11 AP2 3p ultra   3.00 14.00
C12 AP2 5p dark green   3.00 2.50

C13 AP2 8p red brown   7.50 6.00
C14 AP2 1sh violet   9.00 10.00
C15 AP2 1sh6p lt olive ('41)   27.50 42.50
   Nos. C10-C15 (6)   53.00 83.50
   Set, never hinged   90.00

POSTAGE DUE STAMPS

Catalogue values for unused stamps in this section are for Never Hinged items.

Nos. 128, 122, 129, 139 and 125 Surcharged in Black, Blue, Red or Orange

1960   Unwmk.   Engr.   Perf. 14
J1 A24 1p on 6½p (Bl)   7.00 7.00
J2 A23 3p on ½p (Bl)   8.25 5.00
   a. Double surcharge   700.00
J3 A24 6p on 7½p (R)   25.00 12.00
   a. Double surcharge   700.00
J4 A23 1sh3p on 3½p (O)   9.50 7.50
J5 A23 3sh on 2½p   25.00 15.00
   Nos. J1-J5 (5)   74.75 46.50

No. 129 Surcharged in Red

J6 A24 6p on 7½p   1,100. 775.
   a. Double surcharge   4,000. 2,200.

Surcharge forgeries exist.

D1

Perf. 13½x14
1960, June 2   Litho.   Wmk. 228
J7 D1 1p orange   .50 .75
J8 D1 3p ocher   .55 .55
J9 D1 6p light ultra   .55 .35
J10 D1 9p vermilion   .55 1.25
J11 D1 1sh emerald   .55 .30
J12 D1 1sh3p bright violet   .80 1.40
J13 D1 1sh6p light blue   4.00 4.50
J14 D1 3sh yellow   3.50 .70
   Nos. J7-J14 (8)   11.00 9.80

OFFICIAL STAMPS

Nos. 60-63, 66-71, 92-93 Overprinted

1931   Wmk. 74   Perf. 14½
O1 A3 ½p #60   3.00 5.50
O2 A3 1p #61   7.00 15.00
O3 A3 1½p #62   2.00 14.00
O4 A3 2p #63   7.00 16.00
O5 A3 3p #66   3.00 25.00
O6 A3 4p #67   3.25 21.00
O7 A3 5p #68   7.00 42.50
O8 A3 6p #69   5.00 9.75
O9 A3 1sh #70   10.00 35.00
O10 A3 2sh6p #71   47.50 97.50
1932   Wmk. 228   Perf. 11½
O11 A3 9p #92   37.50 55.00
O12 A3 1sh3p #93   37.50 55.00
   Nos. O1-O12 (12)   169.75 391.25

PARAGUAY

ˈpar-ə-ˌgwī

LOCATION — South America, bounded by Bolivia, Brazil and Argentina
GOVT. — Republic
AREA — 157,042 sq. mi.
POP. — 5,434,095 (1999 est.)
CAPITAL — Asuncion

10 Reales = 100 Centavos = 1 Peso
100 Centimos = 1 Guarani (1944)

Catalogue values for unused stamps in this country are for Never Hinged items, beginning with Scott 430 in the regular postage section, Scott B11 in the semipostal section, and Scott C154 in the airpost section.

Watermarks

Wmk. 319 — Stars and R P Multiple

Wmk. 320 — Interlacing Lines

Wmk. 347 — RP Multiple

Vigilant Lion Supporting Liberty Cap
A1   A2

A3

1870, Aug.   Unwmk.   Litho.   Imperf.
1 A1 1r rose   6.50 10.00
2 A2 2r blue   120.00 150.00
3 A3 3r black   230.00 250.00
   Nos. 1-3 (3)   356.50 410.00

Counterfeits of 2r in blue and other colors are on thicker paper than originals. They show a colored dot in upper part of "S" of "DOS" in upper right corner.
For surcharges see Nos. 4-9, 19.

Handstamp Surcharged

1878   Black Surcharge
4 A1 5c on 1r rose   100. 120.
5 A2 5c on 2r blue   450. 400.
5E A3 5c on 3r black   550. 550.
   Nos. 4-5E (3)   1,100. 1,070.

Blue Surcharge
5F A1 5c on 1r rose   100. 120.
5H A2 5c on 2r blue   1,200. 1,200.
6 A3 5c on 3r black   675. 650.
   Nos. 5F-6 (3)   1,975. 1,970.

The surcharge may be found inverted, double, sideways and others.
Remainders of Nos. 4 and 5F were placed on sale at Post Offices during 1892. Covers dated 1892 are worth about $7,500.

The originals are surcharged in dull black or dull blue. The reprints are in intense black and bright blue. The reprint surcharges are over-inked and show numerous breaks in the handstamp.

Handstamp Surcharged

Black Surcharge
7	A2	5c on 2r blue	450.00	375.00
8	A3	5c on 3r black	575.00	550.00

Blue Surcharge
9	A3	5c on 3r black	550.00	550.00
a.		Dbl. surch., large & small "5"	—	
		Nos. 7-9 (3)	1,575.	1,475.

The surcharge on Nos. 7, 8 and 9 is usually placed sideways. It may be found double or inverted on Nos. 8 and 9.

Nos. 4 to 9 have been extensively counterfeited.

Two examples recorded of No. 9a, one without gum, the other with full but disturbed original gum.

A4

1879	**Litho.**		**Perf. 12½**
		Thin Paper	
10	A4	5r orange	.80
11	A4	10r red brown	.90
a.		Imperf.	
b.		Horiz. pair, imperf. vert.	60.00

Nos. 10 and 11 were never placed in use.
For surcharges see Nos. 17-18.

A4a

1879-81			**Thin Paper**	
12	A4a	5c orange brown	2.50	2.50
13	A4a	10c blue grn ('81)	3.50	3.50
a.		Imperf., pair	50.00	60.00

Reprints of Nos. 10-13 are imperf., perf. 11½, 12, 12½ or 14. They have yellowish gum and the 10c is deep green.

A5   A6

A7

1881, Aug.	**Litho.**		**Perf. 11½-13½**	
14	A5	1c blue	.80	.80
a.		Imperf., pair	—	
b.		Horiz. pair, imperf. btwn.	—	
15	A6	2c rose red	.80	.80
a.		2c dull orange red	1.00	.90
b.		Imperf., pair	—	
c.		Horiz. pair, imperf. vert.	25.00	25.00
d.		Vert. pair, imperf. horiz.	25.00	25.00
16	A7	4c brown	.80	1.20
a.		Imperf., pair	—	
b.		Horiz. pair, imperf. vert.	25.00	25.00
c.		Vert. pair, imperf. horiz.	25.00	25.00

No. 11 Handstamped Surcharge in Black or Gray

1881, July			**Perf. 12½**	
17	A4	1c on 10c blue grn	16.00	15.00
18	A4	2c on 10c blue grn	16.00	15.00

Gray handstamps sell for 10 times more than black as many specialists consider the black to be reprints.

No. 1 Handstamped Surcharge in Black

1884, May 8			**Imperf.**	
19	A1	1c on 1r rose	10.00	8.00

The surcharges on Nos. 17-19 exist double, inverted and in pairs with one omitted. Counterfeits exist.

Seal of the Treasury — A11

1884, Aug. 3	**Litho.**		**Perf. 12½**	
20	A11	1c green	1.00	.80
21	A11	2c rose pink, thin paper	1.00	.80
		Perf. 11½		
22	A11	5c pale blue, yellowish paper	1.00	.80
		Nos. 20-22 (3)	3.00	2.40

There are two types of each value differing mostly in the shape of the numerals. In addition, there are numerous small flaws in the lithographic transfers.
For overprints see Nos. O1, O8, O15.

Imperf., Pairs
20a	A11	1c green	12.50
21a	A11	2c rose red	16.00
22a	A11	5c blue	16.00
		Nos. 20a-22a (3)	44.50

Seal of the Treasury — A12

Perf. 11½, 11½x12, 12½x11½				
1887			**Typo.**	
23	A12	1c green	.30	.25
24	A12	2c rose	.30	.25
25	A12	5c blue	.50	.35
26	A12	7c brown	.90	.50
27	A12	10c lilac	.60	.35
28	A12	15c orange	.60	.35
29	A12	20c pink	.60	.35
		Nos. 23-29 (7)	3.80	2.40

See #42-45. For surcharges & overprints see #46, 49-50, 71-72, 167-170A, O20-O41, O49.

Symbols of Liberty from Coat of Arms — A13

1889, Feb.	**Litho.**		**Perf. 11½**	
30	A13	15c red violet	2.50	2.00
a.		Imperf., pair	10.00	8.00

For overprints see Nos. O16-O19.

Overprint Handstamped in Violet

1892, Oct. 12			**Perf. 12x12½**	
31	A15	10c violet blue	10.00	5.00

Discovery of America by Columbus, 400th anniversary. Overprint reads: "1492 / 12 DE OCTUBRE / 1892." Sold only on day of issue.

Cirilo A. Rivarola — A15

Designs: 2c, Salvador Jovellanos. 4c, Juan B. Gil. 5c, Higinio Uriarte. 10c, Cándido Bareiro. 14c, Gen. Bernardino Caballero. 20c, Gen. Patricio Escobar. 30c, Juan G. González.

1892-96	**Litho.**		**Perf. 12x12½**	
32	A15	1c gray (centavos)	.25	.25
33	A15	1c gray (centavo) ('96)	.25	.25
34	A15	2c green	.25	.25
a.		Chalky paper ('96)	.25	.25
35	A15	4c carmine	.25	.25
a.		Chalky paper ('96)	.25	.25
36	A15	5c violet ('93)	.25	.25
a.		Chalky paper ('96)	.25	.25
37	A15	10c vio bl (punched) ('93)	.25	.25
		Unpunched ('96)	5.00	
38	A15	10c dull blue ('96)	.25	.25
39	A15	14c yellow brown	.75	.50
40	A15	20c red ('93)	1.25	.50
41	A15	30c light green	2.00	.80
		Nos. 32-41 (10)	5.75	3.55

The 10c violet blue (No. 37) was, until 1896, issued punched with a circular hole in order to prevent it being fraudulently overprinted as No. 31.
Nos. 33 and 38 are on chalky paper.
For surcharge see No. 70.

Seal Type of 1887

1892			**Typo.**	
42	A12	40c slate blue	3.00	1.25
43	A12	60c yellow	1.50	.50
44	A12	80c light blue	1.40	.50
45	A12	1p olive green	1.40	.50
		Nos. 42-45 (4)	7.30	2.75

For surcharges see Nos. 71-72.

No. 26 Surcharged in Black

1895, Aug. 1			**Perf. 11½x12**	
46	A12	5c on 7c brown	.75	.75

Telegraph Stamps Surcharged

1896, Apr.	**Engr.**		**Perf. 11½**	
		Denomination in Black		
47		5c on 2c brown & gray	.90	.60
a.		Inverted surcharge	10.00	10.00
48		5c on 4c yellow & gray	.90	.60
a.		Inverted surcharge	7.50	7.50

Nos. 28, 42 Surcharged

1898-99			**Typo.**	
49	A12	10c on 15c org ('99)	.75	.45
a.		Inverted surcharge	17.50	17.50
b.		Double surcharge	11.00	11.00
50	A12	10c on 40c slate bl	.35	.25

Surcharge on No. 49 has small "c."

Telegraph Stamps Surcharged

1900, May 14	**Engr.**		**Perf. 11½**	
50A		5c on 30c grn, gray & blk	2.75	1.50
50B		10c on 50c dl vio, gray & blk	6.00	3.75

The basic telegraph stamps are like those used for Nos. 47-48, but the surcharges on Nos. 50A-50B consist of "5 5" and "10 10" above a blackout rectangle covering the engraved denominations.

A 40c red, bluish gray and black telegraph stamp (basic type of A24) was used provisionally in August, 1900, for postage. Value, postally used, $5.

Seal of the Treasury — A25

1900, Sept.	**Engr.**		**Perf. 11½, 12**	
51	A25	2c gray	.40	.30
52	A25	3c orange brown	.40	.30
53	A25	5c dark green	.40	.30
54	A25	8c dark brown	.40	.30
55	A25	10c carmine rose	1.00	.30
56	A25	24c deep blue	1.20	.30
		Nos. 51-56 (6)	3.80	1.80

See Nos. 57-67. For surcharges see Nos. 69, 74, 76, 156-157.

Small Figures

1901, Apr.	**Litho.**		**Perf. 11½**	
57	A25	2c rose	.25	.25
58	A25	5c violet brown	.25	.25
59	A25	40c blue	.85	.40
		Nos. 57-59 (3)	1.35	.90

1901-02			**Larger Figures**	
60	A25	1c gray green ('02)	.30	.30
61	A25	2c gray	.30	.30
a.		Half used as 1c on cover		10.00
62	A25	4c pale blue	.30	.30
63	A25	5c violet	.30	.30
64	A25	8c gray brown ('02)	.30	.30
65	A25	10c rose red ('02)	.75	.30
66	A25	28c orange ('02)	1.50	.30
67	A25	40c blue	.75	.30
		Nos. 60-67 (8)	4.50	2.40

For surcharges see Nos. 74, 76.

J. B. Egusquiza — A26

Chalky Paper

1901, Sept. 24	**Typo.**		**Perf. 12x12½**	
68	A26	1p slate	.30	.30

For surcharge see No. 73.

No. 56 Surcharged in Red

1902, Aug.				
69	A25	20c on 24c dp blue	.50	.40
a.		Inverted surcharge	6.25	

Counterfeit surcharges exist.

Nos. 39, 43-44 Surcharged

1902, Dec. 22			**Perf. 12x12½**	
70	A15	1c on 14c yellow brn	.30	.30
a.		No period after "cent"	.90	.75
b.		Comma after "cent"	.65	.50
c.		Accent over "Un"	.65	.50

1903			**Perf. 11½**	
71	A12	5c on 60c yellow	.35	.30
72	A12	5c on 80c lt blue	.30	.30

Nos. 68, 64, 66 Surcharged

No. 73   No. 74

No. 76

1902-03			**Perf. 12**	
73	A26	1c on 1p slate ('03)	.40	.40
a.		No period after "cent"	4.00	3.00
		Perf. 11½		
74	A25	5c on 8c gray brown	.50	.40
a.		No period after "cent"	1.75	1.50
b.		Double surcharge	7.00	6.00
76	A25	5c on 28c orange	.50	.40
a.		No period after "cent"	1.75	1.50
b.		Comma after "cent"	.80	.60
		Nos. 73-76 (3)	1.40	1.20

The surcharge on Nos. 73 and 74 is found reading both upward and downward.

Sentinel Lion with Right
Paw Ready to Strike for
"Peace and
Justice" — A32

Perf. 11½

			Unwmk.	
1903, Feb. 28		**Litho.**		
77	A32	1c gray	.30	.30
78	A32	2c blue green	.45	.30
79	A32	5c blue	.60	.30
80	A32	10c orange brown	.75	.30
81	A32	20c carmine	.75	.30
82	A32	30c deep blue	.90	.30
83	A32	60c purple	2.10	1.00
		Nos. 77-83 (7)	5.85	2.80

For surcharges and overprints see Nos.
139-140, 166, O50-O56.

Sentinel Lion with Right
Paw Ready to Strike for
"Peace and
Justice" — A33

1903, Sept.				
84	A33	1c yellow green	.30	.30
85	A33	2c red orange	.30	.30
86	A33	5c dark blue	.45	.30
87	A33	10c purple	.45	.30
88	A33	30c dark green	5.00	.45
89	A33	30c ultramarine	1.50	.30
90	A33	60c ocher	1.75	.75
		Nos. 84-90 (7)	9.75	2.70

Nos. 84-90 exist imperf. Value for pairs, $3
each for 1c-20c, $4 for 30c, $5 for 60c.
The three-line overprint "Gobierno
provisorio Ago. 1904" is fraudulent.

Sentinel Lion at
Rest — A35

Perf. 11½, 12, 11½x12

1905-10				**Engr.**
		Dated "1904"		
91	A35	1c orange	.30	.25
92	A35	1c vermilion ('07)	.30	.25
93	A35	1c grnsh bl ('07)	.30	.25
94	A35	2c vermilion ('06)	.30	.25
95	A35	2c olive grn ('07)	60.00	
96	A35	2c car rose ('08)	.45	.25
97	A35	5c dark blue	.30	.25
98	A35	5c slate blue ('06)	.30	.25
99	A35	5c yellow ('06)	.30	.25
100	A35	10c bister ('06)	.30	.25
101	A35	10c emerald ('07)	.30	.25
102	A35	10c dp ultra ('08)	.30	.25
103	A35	20c violet ('06)	.45	.25
104	A35	20c bister ('07)	.45	.25
105	A35	20c apple grn ('07)	.45	.25
106	A35	30c turq bl ('06)	.65	.25
107	A35	30c blue gray ('07)	.65	.25
108	A35	30c dull lilac ('08)	.90	.25
109	A35	60c chocolate ('07)	.60	.25
110	A35	60c org brn ('07)	5.25	1.60
111	A35	60c salmon pink ('10)	5.25	1.60
		Nos. 91-111 (21)	78.10	
		Nos. 91-94,96-111 (20)	18.10	7.70

All but Nos. 92 and 104 exist imperf. Value
for pair, $10 each, except No. 95 at $35.00
and Nos. 109-111 at $15.00 each pair.
For surcharges and overprints see Nos.
129-130, 146-155, 174-190, 266.

Sentinel Lion at
Rest — A36

1904, Aug.		**Litho.**	**Perf. 11½**	
112	A36	10c light blue	.50	.40
a.		*Imperf., pair*	6.00	

No. 112 Surcharged in
Black

1904, Dec.

113	A36	30c on 10c light blue	.80	.50

Peace between a successful revolutionary
party and the government previously in power.

Governmental Palace,
Asunción — A37

Dated "1904"
Center in Black

1906-10		**Engr.**	**Perf. 11½, 12**	
114	A37	1p bright rose	2.50	1.50
115	A37	1p brown org ('07)	1.00	.50
116	A37	1p ol gray ('07)	1.00	.50
117	A37	2p turquoise ('07)	.50	.40
118	A37	2p lake ('09)	.50	.40
119	A37	2p brn org ('10)	.60	.40
120	A37	5p red ('07)	1.50	1.00
121	A37	5p ol grn ('10)	1.50	1.00
122	A37	5p dull bl ('10)	1.50	1.00
123	A37	10p brown org ('07)	1.40	1.00
124	A37	10p dp blue ('10)	1.40	1.00
125	A37	10p choc ('10)	1.50	1.00
126	A37	20p olive grn ('07)	3.50	3.25
127	A37	20p violet ('10)	3.50	3.25
128	A37	20p yellow ('10)	3.50	3.25
		Nos. 114-128 (15)	25.40	19.45

Nos. 94 and 95
Surcharged

1907				
129	A35	5c on 2c vermilion	.45	.30
a.		*"5" omitted*	1.50	1.50
b.		*Inverted surcharge*	5.25	5.25
c.		*Double surcharge*		
d.		*Double surcharge, one invert-ed*	1.50	1.50
e.		*Double surcharge, both invtd.*	9.00	9.00
130	A35	5c on 2c olive grn	.60	.30
a.		*"5" omitted*	1.50	1.50
b.		*Inverted surcharge*	3.25	3.25
c.		*Double surcharge*	3.00	3.00
d.		*Bar omitted*	3.00	3.00

Official Stamps of 1906-
08 Surcharged

1908				
131	O17	5c on 10c bister	.45	.30
a.		*Double surcharge*	4.50	4.50
132	O17	5c on 10c violet	.45	.30
a.		*Inverted surcharge*	3.50	3.50
133	O17	5c on 20c emerald	.45	.30
134	O17	5c on 20c violet	.45	.30
a.		*Inverted surcharge*	4.75	4.75
135	O17	5c on 30c slate bl	1.50	1.00
136	O17	5c on 30c turq bl	1.50	1.00
a.		*Inverted surcharge*		
b.		*Double surcharge*	9.00	9.00
137	O17	5c on 60c choc	.45	.30
a.		*Double surcharge*	9.00	9.00
138	O17	5c on 60c red brown	.90	.30
a.		*Inverted surcharge*	1.60	1.60
		Nos. 131-138 (8)	6.15	3.80

Same Surcharge on Official Stamps
of 1903

139	A32	5c on 30c dp blue	3.75	3.25
140	A32	5c on 60c purple	1.50	.90
a.		*Double surcharge*	7.50	7.50

Official Stamps of 1906-
08 Overprinted

141	O17	5c deep blue	.40	.40
a.		*Inverted overprint*	3.00	3.00
b.		*Bar omitted*	9.00	9.00
c.		*Double overprint*	4.00	4.00
142	O17	5c slate blue	.50	.40
a.		*Inverted overprint*	4.00	4.00
b.		*Double overprint*	3.50	3.50
c.		*Bar omitted*	9.00	

143	O17	5c greenish blue	.40	.40
a.		*Inverted overprint*	2.50	2.50
b.		*Bar omitted*	7.50	7.50
144	O18	1p brown org & blk	.50	.50
a.		*Double overprint*	2.00	2.00
b.		*Double overprint, one inverted*	11.00	11.00
c.		*Triple overprint, two inverted*	4.50	4.50
145	O18	1p brt rose & blk	.90	.70
a.		*Bar omitted*		
		Nos. 141-145 (5)	2.70	2.40

Regular Issues of 1906-
08 Surcharged

1908				
146	A35	5c on 1c grnsh bl	.30	.30
a.		*Inverted surcharge*	1.50	1.50
b.		*Double surcharge*	2.25	2.25
c.		*"5" omitted*	2.25	2.25
147	A35	5c on 2c car rose	.30	.30
a.		*Inverted surcharge*	2.50	2.50
b.		*"5" omitted*	3.00	3.00
c.		*Double surcharge*	5.25	5.25
d.		*Double surcharge, one invtd.*		
148	A35	5c on 60c org brn	.30	.30
a.		*Inverted surcharge*	3.75	3.75
b.		*"5" omitted*	1.50	1.50
149	A35	5c on 60c sal pink	.30	.30
a.		*Double surcharge*	2.50	2.50
b.		*Double surcharge, one invtd.*	5.25	5.25
150	A35	5c on 60c choc	.30	.30
a.		*Inverted surcharge*	7.50	7.50
151	A35	20c on 1c grnsh bl	.30	.30
a.		*Inverted surcharge*	5.00	5.00
152	A35	20c on 2c ver	9.00	7.50
153	A35	20c on 2c car rose	5.25	4.50
a.		*Inverted surcharge*	19.00	
154	A35	20c on 30c dl lil	.30	.30
a.		*Inverted surcharge*	2.25	2.25
b.		*Double surcharge*		
155	A35	20c on 30c turq bl	2.25	2.25
		Nos. 146-155 (10)	18.60	16.35

Same Surcharge on Regular Issue
of 1901-02

156	A25	5c on 28c org	2.25	2.25
157	A25	5c on 40c dk bl	.75	.45
a.		*Inverted surcharge*	6.00	6.00

Same Surcharge on Official Stamps
of 1908

158	O17	5c on 10c emer	.40	.40
a.		*Double surcharge*	14.00	
159	O17	5c on 10c red lil	.40	.40
a.		*Double surcharge*	4.00	4.00
b.		*"5" omitted*	3.00	3.00
160	O17	5c on 20c bis	.80	.60
a.		*Double surcharge*	2.50	2.50
161	O17	5c on 20c sal pink	.80	.60
a.		*"5" omitted*	3.50	3.50
162	O17	5c on 30c bl gray	.40	.40
a.		*"5" omitted*	3.00	3.00
163	O17	5c on 30c yel	.40	.40
a.		*"5" omitted*	2.50	2.50
b.		*Inverted surcharge*		
164	O17	5c on 60c org brn	.40	.40
a.		*Double surcharge*	12.00	12.00
165	O17	5c on 60c dp ultra	.40	.40
a.		*Inverted surcharge*	5.00	5.00
b.		*"5" omitted*		
		Nos. 158-165 (8)	4.00	3.60

Same Surcharge on No. O52

166	A32	20c on 5c blue	2.50	2.00
a.		*Inverted surcharge*	9.50	9.50

Stamp of 1887 Surcharged

1908		**On Stamp of 1887**		
167	A12	20c on 2c car	6.50	3.00
a.		*Inverted surcharge*	22.50	

On Official Stamps of 1892

168	A12	5c on 15c org	10.00	5.25
169	A12	5c on 20c pink	120.00	95.00
170	A12	5c on 50c gray	52.50	37.50
170A	A12	20c on 5c blue	4.50	3.75
b.		*Inverted surcharge*	25.00	25.00
		Nos. 167-170A (5)	193.50	144.50

Nos. 151, 152, 153, 155, 167, 170A, while
duly authorized, all appear to have been sold
to a single individual, and although they paid
postage, it is doubtful whether they can be
considered as ever having been placed on
sale to the public.

Nos. O82-O84
Surcharged (Date in
Red)

1908-09				
171	O18	1c on 1p brt rose & blk	.50	.50
172	O18	1c on 1p lake & blk	.50	.50
173	O18	1c on 1p brn org & blk		
		('09)	5.00	5.00
		Nos. 171-173 (3)	6.00	6.00

Varieties of surcharge on Nos. 171-173
include: "CETTAVO"; date omitted, double or
inverted; third line double or omitted.

Types of 1905-1910
Overprinted

1908, Mar. 5			**Perf. 11½**	
174	A35	1c emerald	.30	.30
175	A35	5c yellow	.30	.30
176	A35	10c lilac brown	.30	.30
177	A35	20c yellow orange	.30	.30
178	A35	30c red	.40	.30
179	A35	60c magenta	.30	.30
180	A37	1p light blue	.30	.30
		Nos. 174-180 (7)	2.20	2.10

Overprinted

1909, Sept.				
181	A35	1c blue gray	.40	.40
182	A35	1c scarlet	.40	.40
183	A35	5c dark green	.40	.40
184	A35	5c deep orange	.40	.40
185	A35	10c rose	.40	.40
186	A35	10c bister brown	.40	.40
187	A35	20c yellow	.40	.40
188	A35	20c violet	.40	.40
189	A35	30c orange brown	.60	.40
190	A35	30c dull blue	.60	.40
		Nos. 181-190 (10)	4.40	4.00

Counterfeits exist.

Coat of Arms above
Numeral of Value — A38

1910-21		**Litho.**	**Perf. 11½**	
191	A38	1c brown	.50	.30
192	A38	5c bright violet	.50	.30
a.		*Pair, imperf. between*	2.00	2.00
193	A38	5c blue grn ('19)	.50	.30
194	A38	5c lt blue ('21)	.50	.30
195	A38	10c yellow green	.50	.30
196	A38	10c dp vio ('19)	.50	.30
197	A38	10c red ('21)	.50	.30
198	A38	20c red	.50	.30
199	A38	50c car rose	.50	.30
200	A38	75c deep blue	.50	.30
a.		*Diag. half perforated ('11)*	.40	.25
		Nos. 191-200 (10)	5.00	3.00

Nos. 191-200 exist imperforate.
No. 200a was authorized for use as 20c.
For surcharges see Nos. 208, 241, 261,
265.

"The Republic" — A39

1911			**Engr.**	
201	A39	1c olive grn & blk	.30	.30
202	A39	2c dk blue & blk	.45	.30
203	A39	5c carmine & indigo	.45	.30
204	A39	10c dp blue & brn	.45	.30
205	A39	20c olive grn & ind	.60	.30
206	A39	50c lilac & indigo	.75	.30
207	A39	75c ol grn & red lil	.75	.30
		Nos. 201-207 (7)	3.75	2.10

Centenary of National Independence.
The 1c, 2c, 10c and 50c exist imperf. Value
for pairs, $2.25 each.

No. 199 Surcharged

1912
208	A38	20c on 50c car rose	.30	.30
a.		Inverted surcharge	2.00	2.00
b.		Double surcharge	2.00	2.00
c.		Bar omitted	2.50	2.50

National Coat of Arms — A40

1913   **Engr.**   **Perf. 11½**
209	A40	1c gray	.30	.30
210	A40	2c orange	.30	.30
211	A40	5c lilac	.30	.30
212	A40	10c green	.30	.30
213	A40	20c dull red	.30	.30
214	A40	40c rose	.30	.30
215	A40	75c deep blue	.30	.30
216	A40	80c yellow	.30	.30
217	A40	1p light blue	.45	.30
218	A40	1.25p pale blue	.45	.30
219	A40	3p greenish blue	.45	.30
		Nos. 209-219 (11)	3.75	3.30

For surcharges see Nos. 225, 230-231, 237, 242, 253, 262-263, L3-L4.

Nos. J7-J10 Overprinted

1918
220	D2	5c yellow brown	.30	.30
221	D2	10c yellow brown	.30	.30
222	D2	20c yellow brown	.30	.30
223	D2	40c yellow brown	.30	.30

Nos. J10 and 214 Surcharged

224	D2	5c on 40c yellow brn	.30	.30
225	A40	30c on 40c rose	.30	.30
		Nos. 220-225 (6)	1.80	1.80

Nos. 220-225 exist with surcharge inverted, double and double with one inverted.

The surcharge "Habilitado-1918-5 cents 5" on the 1c gray official stamps of 1914, is bogus.

No. J11 Overprinted

1920
229	D2	1p yellow brown	.30	.30
a.		Inverted overprint	.65	.65
e.		As "g," "AABILITADO"	.75	.75
f.		As "g," "1929" for "1920"	.75	.75
g.		Overprint lines 8mm apart	.25	.25

Nos. 216 and 219 Surcharged

230	A40	50c on 80c yellow	.30	.30
231	A40	1.75p on 3p grnsh bl	.75	.65

Same Surcharge on No. J12
232	D2	1p on 1.50p yel brn	.30	.30
		Nos. 229-232 (4)	1.65	1.55

Nos. 229-232 exist with various surcharge errors, including inverted, double, double inverted and double with one inverted. Those that were issued are listed.

Parliament Building — A41

1920   **Litho.**   **Perf. 11½**
233	A41	50c red & black	.35	.30
a.		"CORRLOS"	5.00	5.00
234	A41	1p lt blue & blk	1.00	.45
235	A41	1.75p dk blue & blk	.30	.30
236	A41	3p orange & blk	1.50	.30
		Nos. 233-236 (4)	3.15	1.35

50th anniv. of the Constitution.

All values exist imperforate and Nos. 233, 235 and 236 with center inverted. It is doubtful that any of these varieties were regularly issued.

No. 215 Surcharged

1920
237	A40	50c on 75c deep blue	.60	.40

Nos. 200, 215 Surcharged

1921
241	A38	50c on 75c deep blue	.40	.40
242	A40	50c on 75c deep blue	.40	.40

A42

1922, Feb. 8   **Litho.**   **Perf. 11½**
243	A42	50c car & dk blue	.40	.40
a.		Imperf. pair	5.00	
b.		Center inverted	25.00	25.00
244	A42	1p dk blue & brn	.40	.40
a.		Imperf. pair	5.00	
b.		Center inverted	30.00	30.00
c.		As "b," imperf. pair	110.00	

For overprints see Nos. L1-L2.

Rendezvous of Conspirators A43

1922-23
245	A43	1p deep blue	.40	.40
246	A43	1p scar & dk bl ('23)	.40	.40
247	A43	1p red vio & gray ('23)	.40	.40
248	A43	1p org & gray ('23)	.40	.40
249	A43	5p dark violet	1.20	.40
250	A43	5p dk bl & org brn ('23)	1.20	.40
251	A43	5p dl red & lt bl ('23)	1.20	.40
252	A43	5p emer & blk ('23)	1.20	.40
		Nos. 245-252 (8)	6.40	3.20

National Independence.

No. 218 Surcharged "Habilitado en $1:-1924" in Red

1924
253	A40	1p on 1.25p pale blue	.40	.40

This stamp was for use in Asunción. Nos. L3 to L5 were for use in the interior, as is indicated by the "C" in the surcharge.

Map of Paraguay — A44

1924   **Litho.**   **Perf. 11½**
254	A44	1p dark blue	.40	.40
255	A44	2p carmine rose	.40	.40
256	A44	4p light blue	.40	.40
a.		Perf. 12	.80	.40
		Nos. 254-256 (3)	1.20	1.20

#254-256 exist imperf. Value $3 each pair.
For surcharges and overprint see Nos. 267, C5, C15-C16, C54-C55, L7.

Gen. José E. Díaz — A45

1925-26   **Perf. 11½, 12**
257	A45	50c red	.30	.30
258	A45	1p dark blue	.30	.30
259	A45	1p emerald ('26)	.30	.30
		Nos. 257-259 (3)	.90	.90

#257-258 exist imperf. Value $1 each pair.
For overprints see Nos. L6, L8, L10.

Columbus — A46

1925   **Perf. 11½**
260	A46	1p blue	.50	.40
a.		Imperf., pair	10.00	

For overprint see No. L9.

Nos. 194, 214-215, J12 Surcharged in Black or Red

1926
261	A38	1c on 5c lt blue	.30	.30
262	A40	7c on 40c rose	.30	.30
263	A40	15c on 75c dp bl (R)	.30	.30
264	D2	1.50p on 1.50p yel brn	.30	.30
		Nos. 261-264 (4)	1.20	1.20

Nos. 194, 179 and 256 Surcharged "Habilitado" and New Values

1927
265	A38	2c on 5c lt blue	.30	.30
266	A35	50c on 60c magenta	.30	.30
a.		Inverted surcharge	2.00	
267	A44	1.50p on 4p lt blue	.30	.30

Official Stamp of 1914 Surcharged "Habilitado" and New Value
268	O19	50c on 75c dp bl	.30	.30
		Nos. 265-268 (4)	1.20	1.20

National Emblem A47   Pedro Juan Caballero A48

Map of Paraguay A49   Fulgencio Yegros A50

Ignacio Iturbe A51   Oratory of the Virgin, Asunción A52

Perf. 12, 11, 11½, 11x12

1927-38   **Typo.**
269	A47	1c lt red ('31)	.25	.25
270	A47	2c org red ('30)	.25	.25
271	A47	7c lilac	.25	.25
272	A47	7c emerald ('29)	.25	.25
273	A47	10c gray grn ('28)	.25	.25
a.		10c light green ('31)	.25	.25
274	A47	10c lil rose ('30)	.25	.25
275	A47	10c light bl ('35)	.25	.25
276	A47	20c dull bl ('28)	.25	.25
277	A47	20c lil brn ('30)	.25	.25
278	A47	20c lt vio ('31)	.25	.25
279	A47	20c rose ('35)	.25	.25
280	A47	50c ultramarine	.25	.25
281	A47	50c dl red ('28)	.25	.25
282	A47	50c orange ('30)	.25	.25
283	A47	50c gray ('31)	.25	.25
284	A47	50c brn vio ('34)	.25	.25
285	A47	50c rose ('36)	.25	.25
286	A47	70c ultra ('28)	.25	.25
287	A48	1p emerald	.25	.25
288	A48	1p org red ('30)	.25	.25
289	A48	1p brn org ('34)	.25	.25
290	A49	1.50p brown	.25	.25
291	A49	1.50p lilac ('28)	.25	.25
292	A49	1.50p rose red ('32)	.25	.25
293	A50	2.50p bister	.25	.25
294	A51	3p gray	.25	.25
295	A51	3p rose red ('36)	.25	.25
296	A51	3p brt vio ('36)	.25	.25

297	A52	5p chocolate	.25	.25
298	A52	5p violet ('36)	.25	.25
299	A52	5p pale org ('38)	.25	.25
300	A49	20p red ('29)	7.00	5.50
301	A49	20p emerald ('29)	7.00	5.50
302	A49	20p vio brn ('29)	7.00	5.50
		Nos. 269-302 (34)	28.75	24.25

No. 281 is also known perf. 10½x11½.
Papermaker's watermarks are sometimes found on No. 271 ("GLORIA BOND" in double-lined circle) and No. 280 ("Extra Vencedor Bond" or "ADBANCE/M M C").

For surcharges and overprints see Nos. 312, C4, C6, C13-C14, C17-C18, C25-C32, C34-C35, L11-L30, O94-O96, O98.

Arms of Juan de Salazar de Espinosa — A53

1928, Aug. 15   **Perf. 12**
303	A53	10p violet brown	3.00	2.00

Juan de Salazar de Espinosa, founder of Asunción.

A papermaker's watermark ("INDIAN BOND EXTRA STRONG S.&C") is sometimes found on Nos 303, 305-307.

Columbus — A54

1928   **Litho.**
304	A54	10p ultra	2.40	1.50
305	A54	10p vermilion	2.40	1.50
306	A54	10p deep red	2.40	1.50
		Nos. 304-306 (3)	7.20	4.50

For surcharge and overprint see Nos. C33, L37.

President Rutherford B. Hayes of US and Villa Occidental A55

1928, Nov. 20   **Perf. 12**
307	A55	10p gray brown	10.00	3.50
308	A55	10p red brown	10.00	3.50

50th anniv. of the Hayes' Chaco decision.

Portraits of Archbishop Bogarin — A56

1930, Aug. 15
309	A56	1.50p lake	2.00	1.50
310	A56	1.50p turq blue	2.00	1.50
311	A56	1.50p dull vio	2.00	1.50
		Nos. 309-311 (3)	6.00	4.50

Archbishop Juan Sinforiano Bogarin, first archbishop of Paraguay.
For overprints see Nos. 321-322.

No. 272 Surcharged

1930
312	A47	5c on 7c emer	.25	.25

A57

1930-39   Typo.   Perf. 11½, 12
313	A57	10p brown	5.00	2.00
314	A57	10p brn red, bl ('31)	5.00	2.00
315	A57	10p dk bl, pink ('32)	5.00	2.00
316	A57	10p gray brn ('36)	4.00	2.00
317	A57	10p gray ('37)	4.00	1.75
318	A57	10p blue ('39)	2.00	1.25
		Nos. 313-318 (6)	25.00	11.00

1st Paraguayan postage stamp, 60th anniv.
For overprint see No. L31.

Gunboat "Humaitá" A58

1931   Perf. 12
319	A58	1.50p purple	.80	.50
		Nos. 319,C39-C53 (16)	50.60	18.05

Constitution, 60th anniv.
For overprint see No. L33.

View of San Bernardino A59

1931, Aug.
320	A59	1p light green	.50	.40

Founding of San Bernardino, 50th anniv.
For overprint see No. L32.

Nos. 309-310 Overprinted in Blue or Red

FELIZ AÑO NUEVO 1932

1931, Dec. 31
321	A56	1.50p lake (Bl)	3.00	3.00
322	A56	1.50p turq blue (R)	3.00	3.00

Map of the Gran Chaco — A60

1932-35   Typo.   Perf. 12
323	A60	1.50p deep violet	5.00	.40
324	A60	1.50p rose ('35)	5.00	.40

For overprints see Nos. L34-L36, O97.

Nos. C74-C78 Surcharged

CORREOS 1 PESO FELIZ AÑO NUEVO 1933

1933   Litho.
325	AP18	50c on 4p ultra	1.75	.40
326	AP18	1p on 8p red	3.25	.80
327	AP18	1.50p on 12p bl grn	3.25	.80
328	AP18	2p on 16p dk vio	3.25	.80
329	AP18	5p on 20p org brn	8.00	1.75
		Nos. 325-329 (5)	19.50	4.55

Flag of the Race Issue

Flag with Three Crosses: Caravels of Columbus — A61

1933, Oct. 10   Litho.   Perf. 11
330	A61	10c multicolored	.50	.50
331	A61	20c multicolored	.75	.75
332	A61	50c multicolored	.75	.75
333	A61	1p multicolored	.75	.75
334	A61	1.50p multicolored	.75	.75
335	A61	2p multicolored	.90	.90
336	A61	5p multicolored	1.40	1.40
337	A61	10p multicolored	1.75	.75
		Nos. 330-337 (8)	7.55	6.55

441st anniv. of the sailing of Christopher Columbus from the port of Palos, Aug. 3, 1492, on his first voyage to the New World.
Nos. 332, 334 and 335 exist with Maltese crosses omitted.

Monstrance — A62

1937, Aug.   Unwmk.   Perf. 11½
338	A62	1p dk blue, yel & red	.40	.40
339	A62	3p dk blue, yel & red	.40	.40
340	A62	10p dk blue, yel & red	.40	.40
		Nos. 338-340 (3)	1.20	1.20

1st Natl. Eucharistic Congress, Asuncion.

Arms of Asunción — A63

1937, Aug.
341	A63	50c violet & buff	.60	.40
342	A63	1p bis & lt grn	.60	.40
343	A63	3p red & lt bl	.60	.40
344	A63	10p car rose & buff	.60	.40
345	A63	20p blue & drab	.60	.40
		Nos. 341-345 (5)	3.00	2.00

Founding of Asuncion, 400th anniv.

Oratory of the Virgin, Asunción — A64

1938-39   Typo.   Perf. 11, 12
346	A64	5p olive green	1.50	.40
347	A64	5p pale rose ('39)	1.50	.40
348	A64	11p violet brown	2.00	.50
		Nos. 346-348 (3)	5.00	1.30

Founding of Asuncion, 400th anniv.

Carlos Antonio Lopez — A65   José Eduvigis Diaz — A66

1939   Perf. 12
349	A65	2p lt ultra & pale brn	.90	.60
350	A66	2p lt ultra & brn	.90	.60

Reburial of ashes of Pres. Carlos Antonio Lopez (1790-1862) and Gen. José Eduvigis Diaz in the National Pantheon, Asuncion.

Pres. Patricio Escobar and Ramon Zubizarreta — A67

Design: 5p, Pres. Bernardino Caballero and Senator José S. Decoud.

1939-40   Litho.   Perf. 11½
Heads in Black
351	A67	50c dull org ('40)	.60	.60
352	A67	1p lt violet ('40)	.60	.60
353	A67	2p red brown ('40)	.60	.60
354	A67	5p lt ultra	.75	.60
		Nos. 351-354,C122-C123,O99-O104 (12)	34.45	26.20

Founding of the University of Asuncion, 50th anniv.
Varieties of this issue include inverted heads (50c, 1p, 2p); doubled heads; Caballero and Decoud heads in 50c frame: imperforates and part-perforates. Examples with inverted heads were not officially issued.

Coats of Arms — A69   Flags of Paraguay, United States — A70

Designs: 1p, Pres. Baldomir, flags of Paraguay, Uruguay. 2p, Pres. Benavides, flags of Paraguay, Peru. 5p, Pres. Alessandri, flags of Paraguay, Chile. 6p, Pres. Vargas, flags of Paraguay, Brazil. 10p, Pres. Ortiz, flags of Paraguay, Argentina.

1939   Engr.; Flags Litho.   Perf. 12
Flags in National Colors
355	A69	50c violet blue	.30	.30
356	A70	1p olive	.30	.30
357	A70	2p blue green	.30	.30
358	A70	3p sepia	.35	.35
359	A70	5p orange	.30	.30
360	A70	6p dull violet	.75	.60
361	A70	10p bister brn	.60	.35
		Nos. 355-361,C113-C121 (16)	42.45	28.25

First Buenos Aires Peace Conference.
For overprint and surcharge, see Nos.387-390, B10 in the Scott Standard Postage Stamp Catalogue.

Coats of Arms of New York and Asunción — A76

1939, Nov. 30
362	A76	5p scarlet	.55	.55
363	A76	10p deep blue	.85	.80
364	A76	11p dk blue grn	.85	1.20
365	A76	22p olive blk	1.40	1.60
		Nos. 362-365,C124-C126 (7)	33.65	31.15

New York World's Fair.

Paraguayan Soldier A77   Paraguayan Woman A78

Cowboys A79   Plowing A80

View of Paraguay River — A81   Oxcart — A82

Pasture — A83

Pirareta Falls — A84

1940, Jan. 1   Photo.   Perf. 12½
366	A77	50c deep orange	.40	.25
367	A78	1p brt red violet	.40	.25
368	A79	3p bright green	.40	.25
369	A80	5p chestnut	.40	.25
370	A81	10p magenta	.40	.25
371	A82	20p violet	1.00	.30
372	A83	50p cobalt blue	2.00	.45
373	A84	100p black	4.00	1.40
		Nos. 366-373 (8)	9.00	3.40

Second Buenos Aires Peace Conference.
For surcharge see No. 386.

Map of the Americas — A85

1940, May   Engr.   Perf. 12
374	A85	50c red orange	.30	.25
375	A85	1p green	.30	.25
376	A85	5p dark blue	.50	.25
377	A85	10p brown	1.00	.50
		Nos. 374-377,C127-C130 (8)	12.20	9.20

Pan American Union, 50th anniversary.

Reproduction of Type A1 — A86

Sir Rowland Hill — A87

Designs: 6p, Type A2. 10p, Type A3.

1940, Aug. 15   Photo.   Perf. 13½
378	A86	1p aqua & brt red vio	.50	.25
379	A87	5p dp yel grn & red brn	.65	.30
380	A86	6p org brn & ultra	1.50	.65
381	A86	10p ver & black	1.50	1.00
		Nos. 378-381 (4)	4.15	2.20

Postage stamp centenary.

Dr. José Francia A90   A91

1940, Sept. 20   Engr.   Perf. 12
382	A90	50c carmine rose	.30	.30
383	A91	50c plum	.30	.30
384	A90	1p bright green	.30	.30
385	A91	5p deep blue	.30	.30
		Nos. 382-385 (4)	1.20	1.20

Centenary of the death of Dr. Jose Francia (1766-1840), dictator of Paraguay, 1814-1840.

No. 366 Surcharged in Black

1940, Sept. 7   Perf. 12½
386	A77	5p on 50c dp org	.40	.25

In honor of Pres. Jose F. Estigarribia who died in a plane crash Sept. 7, 1940.

No. 360
Overprinted in
Black

1941, Aug.   **Perf. 12**
387 A70 6p multi   .40 .40
  Never hinged   .65

Visit to Paraguay of Pres. Vargas of Brazil.

Nos. C113-C115
Overprinted in Blue
or Red

1942, Jan. 17   **Perf. 12½**
388 A69 1p multi (Bl)   .30 .25
389 A69 3p multi (R)   .30 .25
390 A70 5p multi (R)   .30 .25
  Nos. 388-390 (3)   .90 .75
Set, never hinged   1.65

Coat of Arms — A92

1942-43 Litho. Perf. 11, 12, 11x12
391 A92 1p light green   .50 .25
392 A92 1p orange ('43)   .50 .25
393 A92 7p light blue   .50 .25
394 A92 7p yel brn ('43)   .50 .25
  Nos. 391-394 (4)   2.00 1.00
Set, never hinged   3.00

Values are for examples perforated 11.
Stamps perforated 12 and 11x12 are worth
more. Nos. 391-394 exist imperf.

The Indian
Francisco
A93

Domingo Martinez
de Irala and His
Vision
A94

Arms of Irala — A95

1942, Aug. 15   **Engr.**   **Perf. 12**
395 A93 2p green   1.10 .50
396 A94 5p rose   1.10 .50
397 A95 7p sapphire   1.10 .50
  Nos. 395-397,C131-C133 (6)   13.80 8.60
Set, never hinged   16.00

400th anniversary of Asuncion.

Pres. Higinio Morinigo,
Scenes of Industry &
Agriculture — A96

1943, Aug. 15   **Unwmk.**
398 A96 7p blue   .25 .25

For surcharges see Nos. 404, 428.

Christopher
Columbus — A97

1943, Aug. 15
399 A97 50c violet   .25 .25
400 A97 1p gray brn   .25 .25
401 A97 5p dark grn   .50 .25
402 A97 7p brt ultra   .25 .25
  Nos. 399-402 (4)   1.25 1.00
Set, never hinged   2.75

Discovery of America, 450th anniv.
For surcharges see Nos. 405, 429.

No. 296 Surcharged in
Black

1944   **Perf. 12, 11, 11½, 11x12**
403 A51 1c on 3p brt vio   .50 .25

Nos. 398 and 402
Surcharged in Red

1944   **Perf. 12**
404 A96 5c on 7p blue   .50 .25
405 A97 5c on 7p brt ultra   .50 .25
  Nos. 404-405 (2)   1.00 .50
Set, never hinged   1.50

Imperforates
Starting with No. 406, many
Paraguayan stamps exist imperf.

Primitive Postal
Service among
Indians — A98

Ruins of
Humaitá
Church — A99

Locomotive of
early
Paraguayan
Railroad
A100

Marshal
Francisco S.
Lopez
A101

Early
Merchant Ship
A102

Port of
Asunción
A103

Birthplace of
Paraguay's
Liberation
A104

Monument to
Heroes of
Itororó
A105

1944-45 Unwmk. Engr. Perf. 12½
406 A98 1c black   .25 .25
407 A99 2c copper brn ('45)   .25 .25
408 A100 5c light olive   1.00 .25
409 A101 7c light blue ('45)   .40 .25
410 A102 10c green ('45)   .50 .25
411 A103 15c dark blue ('45)   .50 .30

412 A104 50c black brown   .65 .40
413 A105 1g dk rose car ('45)   1.90 1.00
  Nos. 406-413 (8)   5.45 2.95
  Nos. 406-413,C134-C146 (21)   37.25 14.50
Set, never hinged   40.00

See #435, 437, 439, 441, C158-C162.
For surcharges see #414, 427.

No. 409 Surcharged
in Red

1945
414 A101 5c on 7c light blue   .50 .25

Handshake, Map and
Flags of Paraguay
and Panama — A106

Designs: 3c, Venezuela Flag. 5c, Colombia
Flag. 2g, Peru Flag.

Engr.; Flags Litho. in Natl. Colors
1945, Aug. 15 Unwmk. Perf. 12½
415 A106 1c dark green   .25 .25
416 A106 3c lake   .25 .25
417 A106 5c blue blk   .25 .25
418 A106 2g brown   1.10 .75
  Nos. 415-418,C147-C153 (11)   21.40 21.05
Set, never hinged   32.00

Goodwill visits of Pres. Higinio Morinigo during 1943.

Nos. B6 to B9
Surcharged in Black

1945   **Engr.**   **Perf. 12**
419 SP4 2c on 7p + 3p red brn   .40 .40
420 SP4 2c on 7p + 3p purple   .40 .40
421 SP4 2c on 7p + 3p car
    rose   .40 .40
422 SP4 2c on 7p + 3p saph   .40 .40
423 SP4 5c on 7p + 3p red brn   .40 .40
424 SP4 5c on 7p + 3p purple   .40 .40
425 SP4 5c on 7p + 3p car
    rose   .40 .40
426 SP4 5c on 7p + 3p saph   .40 .40
  Nos. 419-426 (8)   3.20 3.20
Set, never hinged   15.00

Similar Surcharge in Red on Nos.
409, 398 and 402
    Perf. 12½, 12
427 A101 5c on 7c lt blue   .40 .40
428 A96 5c on 7p blue   .40 .40
429 A97 5c on 7p brt ultra   .40 .40
  Nos. 427-429 (3)   1.20 1.20
Set, never hinged   1.95

Nos. 427-429 exist with black surcharge.

**Catalogue values for unused
stamps in this section, from this
point to the end of the section, are
for Never Hinged items.**

Coat of Arms ("U.P.U." at
bottom) — A110

1946   **Litho.**   **Perf. 11, 12**
430 A110 5c gray   .65 .25

See Nos. 459-463, 478-480, 498-506, 525-
536, 646-658.
For overprints see Nos. 464-466.

**Nos. B6 to B9 Surcharged "1946"
and New Value in Black**
1946   **Perf. 12**
431 SP4 5c on 7p + 3p red brn   6.25 1.50
432 SP4 5c on 7p + 3p purple   6.25 1.50
433 SP4 5c on 7p + 3p car rose   6.25 1.50
434 SP4 5c on 7p + 3p saph   6.25 1.50
  Nos. 431-434 (4)   25.00 6.00

Types of 1944-45 and

First Telegraph
in South
America
A111

Monument to
Antequera
A112

Colonial Jesuit
Altar — A113

1946, Sept. 21 Engr. Perf. 12½
435 A102 1c rose car   .60 .40
436 A111 2c purple   .60 .40
437 A98 5c ultra   .60 .40
438 A112 10c org yel   .60 .40
439 A105 15c brn olive   .60 .40
440 A113 50c deep grn   1.00 .40
441 A104 1g brt ultra   1.90 .80
  Nos. 435-441 (7)   5.90 3.20

See Nos. C135-C138, C143, C172.

Marshal Francisco
Solano Lopez — A114

1947, May 15   **Perf. 12**
442 A114 1c purple   .30 .25
443 A114 2c org red   .30 .25
444 A114 5c green   .30 .25
445 A114 15c ultra   .30 .25
446 A114 50c dark grn   1.00 .65
  Nos. 442-446,C163-C167 (10)   11.25 10.70

Juan
Sinforiano
Bogarin,
Archbishop of
Asunción
A115

Archbishopric
Coat of Arms
A116

Projected
Monument of
the Sacred
Heart of
Jesus
A117

Vision of
Projected
Monument
A118

1948, Jan. 6 Engr. Perf. 12½
447 A115 2c dark blue   .40 .25
448 A116 5c deep car   .40 .25
449 A117 10c gray blk   .40 .25
450 A118 15c green   .70 .25
  Nos. 447-450,C168-C175 (12)   19.10 10.00

Archbishopric of Asunción, 50th anniv.
See Nos. C168-C171, C173-C175.

"Political
Enlightenment" — A119

1948, Sept. 11   Engr. & Litho.

451	A119	5c car red	.30	.30
452	A119	15c red org	.30	.30
		Nos. 451-452,C176-C177 (4)	9.50	9.50

Issued to honor the Barefeet, a political group.
See Nos. C176-C177.

C. A. Lopez, J. N. Gonzalez and Freighter Paraguari — A120

Centers in Carmine, Black, Ultramarine and Blue

1949   Litho.

453	A120	2c orange	.50	.25
454	A120	5c blue vio	.50	.25
455	A120	10c black	.50	.25
456	A120	15c violet	.50	.25
457	A120	50c blue grn	.50	.25
458	A120	1g dull vio brn	.60	.25
		Nos. 453-458 (6)	3.10	1.50

Paraguay's merchant fleet centenary.

Arms Type of 1946

1950   Unwmk.   Perf. 10

459	A110	5c red	.50	.25
460	A110	10c blue	.50	.25
461	A110	50c rose lilac	.75	.25
462	A110	1g pale violet	.75	.25

1951   Coarse Impression

463	A110	30c green	.75	.25
		Nos. 459-463 (5)	3.25	1.25

Nos. 459, 460 and 463 Overprinted in Various Colors

1951, Apr. 18

464	A110	5c red (Bk), block	1.50	1.00
465	A110	10c blue (R), block	3.00	2.00
466	A110	30c green (V), block	4.50	3.00
		Nos. 464-466 (3)	9.00	6.00

1st Economic Cong. of Paraguay, 4/18/51.

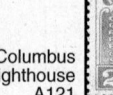

Columbus Lighthouse A121

1952, Feb. 11   Perf. 10

467	A121	2c org brn	.95	.25
468	A121	5c light ultra	.95	.25
469	A121	10c rose	.95	.25
470	A121	15c light blue	.95	.25
471	A121	20c lilac	.95	.25
472	A121	50c orange	.95	.25
473	A121	1g bluish grn	.95	.25
		Nos. 467-473 (7)	6.65	1.75

Silvio Pettirossi, Aviator — A122

1954, Mar.   Litho.   Perf. 10

474	A122	5c blue	.55	.25
475	A122	20c rose pink	.55	.25
476	A122	50c vio brn	.55	.25
477	A122	60c lt vio	.55	.25
		Nos. 474-477,C201-C204 (8)	4.40	2.00

Arms Type of 1946

1954   Perf. 11

478	A110	10c vermilion	2.00	.25

Perf. 10

478A	A110	10c ver, redrawn	.75	.25
479	A110	10g orange	5.00	2.00
480	A110	50g vio brn	9.00	7.00
		Nos. 478-480 (4)	16.75	9.50

No. 478A measures 20½x24mm, has 5 frame lines at left and 6 at right. No. 478 measures 20x24½mm, has 6 frame lines at left and 5 at right.

Three National Heroes A123

1954, Aug. 15   Litho.   Perf. 10

481	A123	5c light vio	.25	.25
482	A123	20c light blue	.25	.25
483	A123	50c rose pink	.25	.25
484	A123	1g org brn	.25	.25
485	A123	2g blue grn	.35	.25
		Nos. 481-485,C216-C220 (10)	17.35	10.10

Marshal Francisco S. Lopez, Pres. Carlos A. Lopez and Gen. Bernardino Caballero.

Pres. Alfredo Stroessner and Pres. Juan D. Peron — A124

Photo. & Litho.

1955, Apr.   Wmk. 90   Perf. 13x13½

486	A124	5c multicolored	.40	.25
487	A124	10c multicolored	.40	.25
488	A124	50c multicolored	.40	.25
489	A124	1.30g multicolored	.40	.25
490	A124	2.20g multicolored	.55	.25
		Nos. 486-490,C221-C224 (9)	5.95	4.45

Visit of Pres. Juan D. Peron of Argentina.

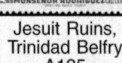

Jesuit Ruins, Trinidad Belfry A125

Santa Maria Cornice A126

Jesuit Ruins: 20c, Corridor at Trinidad. 2.50g, Tower of Santa Rosa. 5g, San Cosme gate. 15g, Church of Jesus. 25g, Niche at Trinidad.

Perf. 12½x12, 12x12½

1955, June 19   Engr.   Unwmk.

491	A125	5c org yel	.60	.25
492	A125	20c olive bister	.60	.25
493	A126	50c lt red brn	.60	.25
494	A126	2.50g olive	.60	.25
495	A125	5g yel brn	.60	.25
496	A125	15g blue grn	.60	.25
497	A126	25g deep grn	1.40	.25
		Nos. 491-497,C225-C232 (15)	10.85	3.80

25th anniv. of the priesthood of Monsignor Rodriguez.
For surcharges see Nos. 545-551.

Arms Type of 1946
Perf. 10, 11 (No. 500)

1956-58   Litho.   Unwmk.

498	A110	5c brown ('57)	1.00	.50
499	A110	30c red brn ('57)	2.00	.25
500	A110	45c gray olive	3.00	.50
500A	A110	90c lt vio bl	5.00	.75
501	A110	2g ocher	5.00	.25
502	A110	2.20g lil rose	2.00	.25
503	A110	3g ol bis ('58)	3.00	.25
503A	A110	4.20g emer ('57)	6.00	.25
504	A110	5g ver ('57)	10.00	5.00
505	A110	10g lt grn ('57)	10.00	5.00
506	A110	20g blue ('57)	10.00	5.00
		Nos. 498-506 (11)	57.00	18.25

No. 500A exists with four-line, carmine overprint: "DIA N. UNIDAS 24 Octubre 1945-1956". It was not regularly issued and no decree authorizing it is known.

Soldiers, Angel and Asuncion Cathedral — A127

Nos. 513-519, Soldier & nurse in medallion & flags.

Perf. 13½

1957, June 12   Photo.   Unwmk.
Granite Paper
Flags in Red and Blue

508	A127	5c bl grn	.55	.25
509	A127	10c carmine	.55	.25
510	A127	15c ultra	.55	.25
511	A127	20c dp claret	.55	.25
512	A127	25c gray blk	.55	.25
513	A127	30c lt blue	.55	.25
514	A127	40c gray blk	.55	.25
515	A127	50c dark car	.55	.25
516	A127	1c bluish grn	.55	.25
517	A127	1.30g ultra	.55	.25
518	A127	1.50g dp claret	.55	.25
519	A127	2g brt green	.55	.25
		Nos. 508-519 (12)	6.60	3.00

Heroes of the Chaco war. See #C233-C245.

Statue of St. Ignatius (Guarani Carving) A128

Blessed Roque Gonzales and St. Ignatius A129

A129a

1.50g, St. Ignatius and San Ignacio Monastery.

Wmk. 319

1958, Mar. 15   Perf. 11

520	A128	50c dk red brn	1.00	1.25
521	A129	50c lt bl grn	1.00	1.25
522	A129a	1.50g brt vio	1.00	1.25
523	A128	3g light bl	1.00	.50
524	A129	6.25g rose car	1.00	.25
		Nos. 520-524 (5)	5.00	4.50

St. Ignatius of Loyola (1491-1556).
See Nos. 935-942.
On designs A129a text under Paraguay is different from those of design A185b (Nos. 939-942).

Arms Type of 1946

1958-64   Litho.   Perf. 10, 11

525	A110	45c gray olive	2.40	1.00
526	A110	50c rose vio	1.50	1.00
527	A110	70c lt brn ('59)	2.40	1.00
527A	A110	90c vio blue	2.40	1.00
528	A110	1g violet	1.50	.50
529	A110	1.50g lilac ('59)	1.75	1.00
529A	A110	2g bister ('64)	6.00	3.00
530	A110	3g ol bis ('59)	6.00	3.00
531	A110	4.50g lt ultra ('59)	2.40	2.00
531A	A110	5g rose red ('59)	1.25	1.00
531B	A110	10g bl grn ('59)	2.40	1.00
532	A110	12.45g yel green	3.50	3.00
533	A110	15g dl orange	12.00	2.00
534	A110	30g citron	3.50	2.00
535	A110	50g brown red	2.40	1.00
536	A110	100g gray vio	3.50	2.00
		Nos. 525-536 (16)	54.90	25.50

Pres. Alfredo Stroessner — A130

Wmk. 320

1958, Aug. 15   Litho.   Perf. 13½
Center in Slate

537	A130	10c sal pink	.25	.30
538	A130	15c violet	.25	.30
539	A130	25c yel grn	.25	.30
540	A130	30c light fawn	.25	.30

541	A130	50c rose car	.35	.30
542	A130	75c light ultra	.35	.30
543	A130	5g lt bl grn	.55	.50
544	A130	10g brown	1.10	.50
		Nos. 537-544,C246-C251 (14)	26.50	17.80

Re-election of President General Alfredo Stroessner.

Nos. 491-497 Srchd. in Red

Perf. 12½x12, 12x12½

1959, May 14   Engr.   Unwmk.

545	A125	1.50g on 5c org yel	.30	.50
546	A125	1.50g on 20c ol bis	.30	.50
547	A126	1.50g on 50c lt red brn	.30	.50
548	A126	3g on 2.50g ol	.30	.50
549	A125	6.25g on 5g yel brn	.30	.50
550	A125	20g on 15g bl grn	.85	.80
551	A126	30g on 25g dp grn	1.25	1.00
		Nos. 545-551,C252-C259 (15)	19.15	12.30

The surcharge is made to fit the stamps. Counterfeits of surcharge exist.

Goalkeeper Catching Soccer Ball — A131

1960, Mar. 18   Photo.   Perf. 12½

556	A131	30c brt red & bl grn	.45	.30
557	A131	50c plum & dk bl	.45	.30
558	A131	75c lt brn & org	.45	.30
559	A131	1.50g dk vio & bl grn	.45	.30
		Nos. 556-559,C262-C264 (7)	3.45	2.25

Olympic Games of 1960.

WRY Emblem — A132

1960, Apr. 7   Litho.   Perf. 11

560	A132	25c sal & yel grn	.75	.25
561	A132	50c lt yel grn & red org	.75	.25
562	A132	70c lt brn & lil rose	.90	.25
563	A132	1.50g lt bl & ultra	.90	.25
564	A132	3g gray & bis brn	1.75	.45
		Nos. 560-564,C265-C268 (9)	12.00	4.75

World Refugee Year, July 1, 1959-June 30, 1960 (1st issue).

UN Emblem and Dove — A133

UN Declaration of Human Rights: 3g, Hand holding scales. 6g, Hands breaking chains. 20g, Flame.

1960, Apr. 21   Perf. 12½x13

565	A133	1g dk car & bl	.50	.25
566	A133	3g lt blue & org	.50	.25
567	A133	6g gray grn & sal	.65	.25
568	A133	20g ver & yel	.90	.25
		Nos. 565-568,C269-C271 (7)	4.75	2.20

Miniature sheets exist, perf. and imperf., containing one each of Nos. 565-568, all printed in purple and orange. Values: perf. $4; imperf. $15.

Flags of UN and Paraguay and UN Emblem — A134

Perf. 13x13½

1960, Oct. 24   **Photo.**   **Unwmk.**
569	A134	30c lt bl, red & bl	.50	.30
570	A134	75c yel, red & bl	.50	.30
571	A134	90c pale lil, red & bl	.50	.30

Nos. 569-571,C272-C273 (5)   2.90   1.50

15th anniversary of the United Nations.

International Bridge,
Arms of Brazil,
Paraguay — A135

1961, Jan. 26   **Litho.**   **Perf. 14**
572	A135	15c green	.65	.50
573	A135	30c dull blue	.65	.50
574	A135	50c orange	.65	.50
575	A135	75c vio blue	.65	.50
576	A135	1g violet	.65	.50

Nos. 572-576,C274-C277 (9)   8.75   6.75

Inauguration of the International Bridge between Paraguay and Brazil.

Truck Carrying
Logs — A136

90c, 2g, Logs on river barge. 1g, 5g, Radio tower.

Unwmk.
1961, Apr. 10   **Photo.**   **Perf. 13**
577	A136	25c yel grn & rose car	.30	.25
578	A136	90c dbl bu & yel	.30	.25
579	A136	1g car rose & org	.30	.25
580	A136	2g ol grn & sal	.30	.25
581	A136	5g lilac & emer	.30	.25

Nos. 577-581,C278-C281 (9)   5.80   3.70

Paraguay's progress, "Paraguay en Marcha."

P. J. Caballero,
José G. R.
Francia, F.
Yegros,
Revolutionary
Leaders — A137

1961, May 16   **Litho.**   **Perf. 14½**
582	A137	30c green	.55	.25
583	A137	50c lil rose	.55	.25
584	A137	90c violet	.55	.25
585	A137	1.50g Prus bl	.55	.25
586	A137	3g olive bis	.55	.25
587	A137	4g ultra	.55	.25
588	A137	5g brown	.55	.25

Nos. 582-588,C282-C287 (13)   13.25   7.90

150th anniv. of Independence (1st issue).

"Chaco Peace" — A138

1961, June 12   **Perf. 14x14½**
589	A138	25c vermilion	.50	.40
590	A138	30c green	.50	.40
591	A138	50c red brn	.50	.40
592	A138	1g bright vio	.50	.40
593	A138	2g dk bl gray	.50	.40

Nos. 589-593,C288-C290 (8)   9.90   7.10

Chaco Peace; 150th anniv. of Independence (2nd issue).

Puma — A139

1961, Aug. 16   **Unwmk.**   **Perf. 14**
594	A139	75c dull vio	1.10	1.00
595	A139	1.50g brown	1.10	1.00
596	A139	4.50g green	1.10	1.00
597	A139	10g Prus blue	1.10	1.00

Nos. 594-597,C291-C293 (7)   16.90   13.00

150th anniv. of Independence (3rd issue).

University Seal — A140

1961, Sept. 18   **Perf. 14x14½**
598	A140	15c ultra	.50	.30
599	A140	25c dk red	.50	.30
600	A140	75c bl grn	.50	.30
601	A140	1g orange	.50	.30

Nos. 598-601,C294-C296 (7)   5.20   2.80

Founding of the Catholic University in Asuncion; 150th anniv. of Independence (4th issue).

Hotel
Guarani — A141

1961, Oct. 14   **Litho.**   **Perf. 15**
602	A141	50c slate bl	.55	1.00
603	A141	1g green	.55	1.00
604	A141	4.50g lilac	.55	1.00

Nos. 602-604,C297-C300 (7)   12.65   10.25

Opening of the Hotel Guarani; 150th anniv. of Independence (5th issue).

Tennis Racket and
Balls in Flag
Colors — A142

1961, Oct. 16   **Litho.**   **Perf. 11**
605	A142	35c multi	.80	.25
606	A142	75c multi	.80	.25
607	A142	1.50g multi	.80	.25
608	A142	2.25g multi	.80	.25
609	A142	4g multi	.80	.25

Nos. 605-609 (5)   4.00   1.25

28th South American Tennis Championships, Asuncion, Oct. 15-23 (1st issue). Some specialists question the status of this issue. See Nos. C301-C303.
Imperforates exist in changed colors as well as two imperf. souvenir sheets with stamps in changed colors. Values: stamps, set $27; souvenir sheets, pair $40.

Alan B. Shepard,
First US
Astronaut — A143

18.15g, 36g, 50g, Shepard, Saturn, horiz.

1961, Dec. 22   **Litho.**   **Perf. 11**
610	A143	10c blue & brown	.30	.25
611	A143	25c blue & car rose	.30	.25
612	A143	50c blue & yel org	.30	.25
613	A143	75c blue & green	.30	.25
614	A143	18.15g green & blue	11.00	6.50
615	A143	36g org & blue	11.00	6.50
616	A143	50g car rose & blue	14.50	9.75
a.		Souvenir sheet of 1	40.00	

Nos. 610-616 (7)   37.70   23.75

Nos. 614-616a are airmail.
Also exist imperf in different colors. Value, set $36, souvenir sheet $210.

Uprooted Oak
Emblem — A145

1961, Dec. 30   **Unwmk.**   **Perf. 11**
619	A145	10c ultra & lt bl	.30	.25
620	A145	25c maroon & org	.30	.25
621	A145	50c car rose & pink	.30	.25
622	A145	75c dk bl & yel grn	.30	.25

Nos. 619-622 (4)   1.20   1.00

World Refugee Year, 1959-60 (2nd issue). Imperforates in changed colors and souvenir sheets exist. Values: imperf. set of 7, $5; souvenir sheet, perf. or imperf., each $15. Some specialists question the status of this issue. See Nos. C307-C309.

Europa — A146

Design: 20g, 50g, Dove.

1961, Dec. 31
623	A146	50c multicolored	.35	.35
624	A146	75c multicolored	.35	.35
625	A146	1g multicolored	.35	.35
626	A146	1.50g multicolored	.35	.35
627	A146	4.50g multicolored	.80	.75
a.		Souvenir sheet of 5, #623-627	21.00	
628	A146	20g multicolored	21.00	
629	A146	50g multicolored	25.00	
a.		Souvenir sheet of 1	90.00	

Nos. 623-629 (7)   48.20   2.15

Nos. 628-629 are airmail.
Imperforates in changed colors exist. Values: set, $67.50; souvenir sheets, pair $100.

Tennis Player — A147

1962, Jan. 5   **Perf. 15x14½**
630	A147	35c Prussian bl	.70	.25
631	A147	75c dark vio	.70	.25
632	A147	1.50g red brn	.70	.25
633	A147	2.25g emerald	.70	.25
634	A147	4g carmine	2.40	.25
635	A147	12.45g red lil	2.40	.25
636	A147	20g lil grn	2.40	.40
637	A147	50g org brn	2.40	.65

Nos. 630-637 (8)   12.40   2.55

28th South American Tennis Championships, 1961 (2nd issue) and the 150th anniv. of Independence (6th issue).
Nos. 634-637 are airmail.

Scout Bugler — A148

Lord Baden-
Powell — A148a

1962, Feb. 6   **Perf. 11**
Olive Green Center
638	A148	10c dp magenta	.30	.25
639	A148	20c red orange	.30	.25
640	A148	25c dk brown	.30	.25
641	A148	30c emerald	.30	.25
642	A148	50c indigo	.30	.25
643	A148a	12.45g car rose & bl	1.90	.85
644	A148a	36g car rose & emer	5.25	2.40

645	A148a	50g car rose & org yel	7.25	3.25

Nos. 638-645 (8)   15.90   7.75

Issued to honor the Boy Scouts. Imperfs in changed colors exist and imperf souvenir sheets exist. Value, set $24, souvenir sheet $95. Some specialists question the status of this issue.
Nos. 643-645 are airmail.

Arms Type of 1946
1962-68   **Litho.**   **Wmk. 347**
646	A110	50c steel bl ('63)	3.00	2.00
647	A110	70c dull lil ('63)	3.00	2.00
648	A110	1.50g violet ('63)	3.00	1.00
649	A110	3g dp bl ('68)	5.00	2.00
650	A110	4.50g redsh brn ('67)	5.00	1.00
651	A110	5g lilac ('64)	5.00	1.00
652	A110	10g car rose ('63)	10.00	3.00
653	A110	12.45g ultra	7.00	3.00
654	A110	15.45g org ver	10.00	2.00
655	A110	18.15g lilac	10.00	2.00
656	A110	20g lt brn ('63)	10.00	2.00
657	A110	50g dl red brn ('67)	10.00	3.00
658	A110	100g bl gray ('63)	3.00	2.00

Nos. 646-658 (13)   84.00   27.00

Map and Laurel
Branch — A149

Design: 20g, 50g, Hands holding globe.

Perf. 14x14½
1962, Apr. 14   **Unwmk.**
659	A149	50c ocher	.50	.30
660	A149	75c vio blue	.50	.30
661	A149	1g purple	.50	.30
662	A149	1.50g brt grn	.50	.30
663	A149	4.50g vermilion	.50	.30
664	A149	20g lil rose	.50	.30
665	A149	50g orange	1.50	.90

Nos. 659-665 (7)   4.50   2.70

Day of the Americas; 150th anniv. of Independence (7th issue).
Nos. 664-665 are airmail.

UN
Emblem — A150

Design: #670-673, UN Headquarters, NYC.

1962, Apr. 23   **Perf. 15**
666	A150	50c bister brn	.45	.25
667	A150	75c dp claret	.45	.25
668	A150	1g Prussian bl	.45	.25
669	A150	2g orange brn	2.40	.25
670	A150	12.45g dl vio	2.40	.35
671	A150	18.15g ol grn	2.40	.65
672	A150	23.40g brn red	2.40	.95
673	A150	30g carmine	2.40	1.10

Nos. 666-673 (8)   13.35   4.05

UN; Independence, 150th anniv. (8th issue).
Nos. 670-673 are airmail.

Malaria
Eradication
Emblem and
Mosquito — A151

Design: 75c, 1g, 1.50g, Microscope, anopheles mosquito and eggs. 3g, 4g, Malaria eradication emblem. 12.45g, 18.15g, 36g, Mosquito, UN emblem and microscope.

Perf. 14x13½
1962, May 23   **Wmk. 346**
674	A151	30c pink, ultra & blk	.45	.30
675	A151	50c bis, grn & blk	.45	.30
676	A151	75c rose red, blk & bis	.45	.30
677	A151	1g brt grn, blk & bis	.45	.30
678	A151	1.50g dl red brn, blk & bis	.45	.30
679	A151	3g bl, red & blk	.45	.30
680	A151	4g grn, red & blk	.45	.30
681	A151	12.45g ol bis, grn & blk	.45	.30

682 A151	18.15g rose lil, red & blk	.90	.45
683 A151	36g rose red, vio bl & blk	2.25	1.10
Nos. 674-683 (10)		6.75	3.95

WHO drive to eradicate malaria.
Imperforates exist in changed colors. Value,
$12.50. Also, two souvenir sheets exist, one
containing one copy of No. 683, the other an
imperf 36g in blue, red & black. Value, each
$21.
Some specialists question the status of this
issue.
Nos. 679-683 are airmail.

Stadium
A152

Soccer Players and
Globe
A152a

Perf. 13½x14
1962, July 28   Litho.   Wmk. 346

684 A152	15c yel & dk brn	.30	.25
685 A152	25c brt grn & dk brn	.30	.25
686 A152	30c lt vio & dk brn	.30	.25
687 A152	40c dl org & dk brn	.30	.25
688 A152	50c brt yel grn & dk brn	.30	.25
689 A152a	12.45g brt rose, blk & vio	1.00	.35
690 A152a	18.15g lt red brn, blk & vio	1.40	.45
691 A152a	36g gray grn, blk & brn	3.25	.80
Nos. 684-691 (8)		7.15	2.85

World Soccer Championships, Chile, May
30-June 17.
Imperfs exist. Value $11. A souvenir sheet
containing one No. 691 exists, both perforated
and imperf. Value, $25 and $60, respectively.
Some specialists question the status of this
issue.
Nos. 689-691 are airmail.

Freighter
A153

Ship's Wheel
A153a

Designs: Various merchantmen. 44g, Like
12.45g with diagonal colorless band in
background.

Perf. 14½x15
1962, July 31   Unwmk.

692 A153	30c bister brn	.30	.25
693 A153	90c slate bl	.30	.25
694 A153	1.50g brown red	.30	.25
695 A153	2g green	.30	.25
696 A153	4.20g vio blue	.35	.25

Perf. 15x14½

697 A153a	12.45g dk red	5.75	.25
698 A153a	44g blue	5.75	.35
Nos. 692-698 (7)		13.05	1.85

Issued to honor the merchant marine.
Nos. 697-698 are airmail.

Friendship 7
over South
America
A154

Lt. Col. John
H. Glenn, Jr.,
Lt. Cmdr.
Scott
Carpenter
A154a

Perf. 13½x14
1962, Sept. 4   Litho.   Wmk. 346

699 A154	15c dk bl & bis	1.25	.45
700 A154	25c dk vio brn & bis	1.25	.45
701 A154	30c dk sl grn & bis	1.25	.45
702 A154	40c dk gray & bis	1.25	.45
703 A154	50c dk vio & bis	1.25	.45
704 A154a	12.45g car lake & gray	1.25	.45
705 A154a	18.15g red lil & gray	1.25	.45
706 A154a	36g dl cl & gray	1.25	.80
Nos. 699-706 (8)		10.00	3.95

U.S. manned space flights. A souvenir sheet
containing one No. 706 exists. Value $20.
Imperfs in changed colors exist. Values:
set, $18; souvenir sheet $60. Some specialists
question the status of this issue.
Nos. 704-706 are airmail.

Discus
Thrower — A155

Olympic flame &: 12.45g, Melbourne, 1956.
18.15g, Rome, 1960. 36g, Tokyo, 1964.

1962, Oct. 1   Litho.

707 A155	15c blk & yel	1.50	.25
708 A155	25c blk & lt grn	1.50	.25
709 A155	30c blk & pink	1.50	.25
710 A155	40c blk & pale vio	1.50	.25
711 A155	50c blk & lt bl	1.50	.25
712 A155	12.45g brt grn, lt grn & choc	1.75	.75
713 A155	18.15g ol brn, yel & choc	1.75	.75
714 A155	36g rose red, pink & choc	3.00	1.00
Nos. 707-714 (8)		14.00	3.75

Olympic Games from Amsterdam 1928 to
Tokyo 1964. Each stamp is inscribed with date
and place of various Olympic Games. A sou-
venir sheet containing one No. 714 exists.
Value $12.
Imperfs in changed colors exist. Values:
set, $27.50; souvenir sheet $125.
Some specialists question the status of this
issue.
Nos. 712-714 are airmail.

Peace Dove and
Cross — A156

Dove
Symbolizing
Holy
Ghost — A156a

Perf. 14½
1962, Oct. 11   Litho.   Unwmk.

715 A156	50c olive	.30	.25
716 A156	70c dark blue	.30	.25
717 A156	1.50g bister	.30	.25
718 A156	2g violet	.30	.25
719 A156	3g brick red	.30	.25
720 A156a	5g vio bl	1.40	.25
721 A156a	10g brt grn	1.40	.25
722 A156a	12.45g lake	1.40	.25
723 A156a	18.15g orange	1.40	.30
724 A156a	23.40g violet	1.40	.40
725 A156a	36g rose red	1.40	.50
Nos. 715-725 (11)		9.90	3.20

Vatican II, the 21st Ecumenical Council of
the Roman Catholic Church, which opened
Oct. 11, 1962.
Nos. 720-725 are airmail.

Europa — A157

Perf. 11
1962, Dec. 17

726 A157	4g yel, red & brn	.65	.50
727 A157	36g multi, diff.	12.50	3.00
a.	Souvenir sheet of 2, #726-727	25.00	
Nos. 726-727 (2)		13.15	3.50

No. 727 is airmail.
Exist imperf. in changed colors. Values: set,
$45; souvenir sheet $70.

Solar
System — A158

12.45g, 36g, 50g, Inner planets, Jupiter &
rocket.

Perf. 14x13½
1962, Dec. 17   Wmk. 346

728 A158	10c org & purple	.50	.35
729 A158	20c org & brn vio	.50	.35
730 A158	25c org & dk vio	.50	.35
731 A158	30c org & ultra	.50	.35
732 A158	50c org & dull green	.50	.35
733 A158	12.45g org & brown	3.25	1.25
734 A158	36g org & blue	6.25	2.00
735 A158	50g org & green	12.50	4.25
a.	Souvenir sheet of 1	17.50	
Nos. 728-735 (8)		24.50	9.25

Nos. 733-735 are airmail.
Exist imperf. in changed colors. Values: set,
$25; souvenir sheet, $80.

The following stamps exist imperf. in
different colors: Nos. 736-743a, 744-
751a, 752-759a, 760-766a, 775-782a,
783-790a, 791-798a, 799-805a, 806-
813a, 814-821a, 828-835a, 836-843,
841a, 850-857a, 858-865a, 871-878,
876a, 887-894a, 895-902, 900a, 903-
910a, 911-918a, 919-926a, 927-934a,
943-950a, 951-958a, 959-966a, 978-
985a, 986-993a, 994-1001a, 1002-
1003, 1003d, 1004-1007a, 1051-1059,
B12-B19.

Pierre de
Coubertin (1836-
1937), Founder of
Modern Olympic
Games — A159

Summer Olympic Games sites and: 15c,
Athens, 1896. 25c, Paris, 1900. 30c, St. Louis,
1904. 40c, London, 1908. 50c, Stockholm,
1912. 12.45g, No games, 1916. 18.15g, Antwerp, 1920. 36g, Paris, 1924.
12.45g, 18.15g, 36g, Torch bearer &
stadium.

Perf. 14x13½
1963, Feb. 16   Wmk. 346

736 A159	15c multicolored	.30	.25
737 A159	25c multicolored	.30	.25
738 A159	30c multicolored	.30	.25
739 A159	40c multicolored	.30	.25
740 A159	50c multicolored	.30	.25
741 A159	12.45g multicolored	3.75	3.50
742 A159	18.15g multicolored	3.75	3.50
743 A159	36g multicolored	5.00	4.50
a.	Souvenir sheet of 1	35.00	
Nos. 736-743 (8)		14.00	12.75

Nos. 741-743a are airmail.
Exist imperf. in changed colors. Values: set,
$32; souvenir sheet $120.

Walter M. Schirra, US
Astronaut — A160

Design: 12.45g, 36g, 50g, Schirra.

Perf. 13½x14
1963, Mar. 16

744 A160	10c brn org & blk	.30	.25
745 A160	20c car & blk	.30	.25
746 A160	25c lake & blk	.30	.25
747 A160	30c ver & blk	.30	.25
748 A160	50c mag & blk	.30	.25
749 A160	12.45g bl blk & lake	4.50	4.25
750 A160	36g dl gray vio & lake	4.50	4.25

751 A160	50g dk grn bl & lake	5.75	5.25
a.	Souvenir sheet of 1	15.00	
Nos. 744-751 (8)		16.25	15.00

Nos. 749-751a are airmail.
Exist imperf. in changed colors. Values: set,
$27; souvenir sheet, $125.

Winter
Olympics — A161

Games sites and: 10c, Chamonix, 1924.
20c, St. Moritz, 1928. 25c, Lake Placid, 1932.
30c, Garmisch-Partenkirchen, 1936. 50c, St.
Moritz, 1948. 12.45g, Oslo, 1952. 36g, Cortina
d'Ampezzo, 1956. 50g, Squaw Valley, 1960.
12.45g, 36g, 50g, Snowflake.

1963, May 16   Perf. 14x13½

752 A161	10c multicolored	.30	.25
753 A161	20c multicolored	.30	.25
754 A161	25c multicolored	.30	.25
755 A161	30c multicolored	.30	.25
756 A161	50c multicolored	.30	.25
757 A161	12.45g multicolored	4.75	3.75
758 A161	36g multicolored	4.75	3.75
759 A161	50g multicolored	5.75	4.50
a.	Souvenir sheet of 1	25.00	25.00
Nos. 752-759 (8)		16.75	13.25

Nos. 757-759a are airmail.
Exist imperf. in changed colors. Values: set,
$29.50; souvenir sheet $175.

Freedom from
Hunger — A162

1963, May 31   Perf. 13½x14, 14x13½

760 A162	10c yel grn & brn	.30	.25
761 A162	25c lt bl & brn	.30	.25
762 A162	50c lt grn bl & brn	.30	.25
763 A162	75c lt lil & brn	.30	.25
764 A162	18.15g yel org & brn	5.25	1.75
765 A162	36g lt bl grn & brn	5.25	1.75
766 A162	50g bis & brn	5.25	1.75
a.	Souvenir sheet of 1	18.00	
Nos. 760-766 (7)		16.95	6.25

Nos. 760-763 are vert. Nos. 764-766a are
airmail.
Exist imperf. in changed colors. Values: set,
$19; souvenir sheet $24.

Pres. Alfredo
Stroessner — A163

1963, Aug. 6   Wmk. 347   Perf. 11

767 A163	50c ol gray & sep	1.10	2.50
768 A163	75c buff & sepia	1.10	2.50
769 A163	1.50g lt lil & sep	1.10	2.50
770 A163	3g emer & sepia	1.10	1.00
771 A163	12.45g pink & claret	5.50	1.00
772 A163	18.15g pink & grn	5.50	1.00
773 A163	36g pink & vio	5.50	1.00
Nos. 767-773 (7)		20.90	11.50

Third presidential term of Alfredo Stroess-
ner. A 36g imperf. souvenir sheet exists.
Value, $20.
Nos. 771-773 are airmail.

Souvenir Sheet

Dag Hammarskjold, UN Secretary
General — A164

1963, Aug. 21   Unwmk.   Imperf.

| 774 A164 2g Sheet of 2 | 25.00 | 25.00 |

Project Mercury
Flight of L.
Gordon
Cooper — A165

12.45g, 18.15g, 50g, L. Gordon Cooper,
vert.

Perf. 14x13½, 13½x14

			Wmk. 346	
1963, Aug. 23			**Litho.**	
775	A165	15c brn & orange	.30	.25
776	A165	25c brn & blue	.30	.25
777	A165	30c brn & violet	.30	.25
778	A165	40c brn & green	.30	.25
779	A165	50c brn & red vio	.30	.25
780	A165	12.45g brn & bl grn	4.00	2.50
781	A165	18.15g brn & blue	4.00	2.50
782	A165	50c brn & pink	4.00	2.50
a.		Souvenir sheet of 1	25.00	
		Nos. 775-782 (8)	13.50	8.75

Nos. 780-782 are airmail.
Exist imperf. in changed colors. Values: set,
$24; souvenir sheet, $30.

1964 Winter
Olympics,
Innsbruck — A166

Design: 12.45g, 18.15g, 50g, Innsbruck
Games emblem, vert.

Perf. 14x13½, 13½x14

			Unwmk.	
1963, Oct. 28				
783	A166	15c choc & red	.30	.25
784	A166	25c gray grn & red	.30	.25
785	A166	30c plum & red	.30	.25
786	A166	40c sl grn & red	.30	.25
787	A166	50c dp bl & red	.30	.25
788	A166	12.45g sep & red	4.00	1.75
789	A166	18.15g grn bl & red	4.00	1.75
790	A166	50g tan & red	4.00	1.75
a.		Souvenir sheet of 1	20.00	
		Nos. 783-790 (8)	13.50	6.50

Nos. 788-790 are airmail.
Exist imperf. in changed colors. Values: set,
$26; souvenir sheet, $26.

1964 Summer
Olympics,
Tokyo — A167

12.45g, 18.15g, 50g, Tokyo games emblem.

1964, Jan. 8			**Perf. 13½x14**	
791	A167	15c blue & red	.30	.25
792	A167	25c org & red	.30	.25
793	A167	30c tan & red	.30	.25
794	A167	40c vio brn & red	.30	.25
795	A167	50c grn bl & red	.30	.25
796	A167	12.45g vio & red	2.50	1.60
797	A167	18.15g brn & red	2.50	1.60
798	A167	50g grn bl & red	2.50	1.60
a.		Souvenir sheet of 1	30.00	
		Nos. 791-798 (8)	9.00	6.05

Nos. 796-798 are airmail.
Exist imperf. in changed colors. Values: set,
$22; souvenir sheet, $42.50.

Intl. Red Cross,
Cent. — A168

Designs: 10c, Helicopter. 25c, Space ambulance. 30c, Red Cross symbol, vert. 50c, Clara
Barton, founder of American Red Cross, vert.
18.15g, Jean Henri Dunant, founder of Intl.
Red Cross, vert. 36g, Red Cross space hospital, space ambulance. 50g, Plane, ship, ambulance, vert.

1964, Feb. 4			**Perf. 14x13½, 13½x14**	
799	A168	10c vio brn & red	.30	.25
800	A168	25c bl grn & red	.30	.25
801	A168	30c dk bl & red	.30	.25
802	A168	50c ol blk & red	.30	.25
803	A168	18.15g choc, red, & pink	1.90	.80
804	A168	36g grn bl & red	2.75	1.10
805	A168	50g vio & red	4.25	2.00
a.		Souvenir sheet of 1	15.00	11.00
		Nos. 799-805 (7)	10.10	4.90

Nos. 803-805 are airmail.
Exist imperf. in changed colors. Values: set,
$52; souvenir sheet, $21.

Space
Research — A169

15c, 25c, 30c, Gemini spacecraft rendezvous with Agena rocket. 40c, 50c, Future
Apollo and Lunar Modules, vert. 12.45g,
18.15g, 50g, Telstar communications satellite,
Olympic rings, vert.

1964, Mar. 11				
806	A169	15c vio & tan	.30	.25
807	A169	25c grn & tan	.30	.25
808	A169	30c bl & tan	.30	.25
809	A169	40c brt bl & red	.30	.25
810	A169	50c sl grn & red	.30	.25
811	A169	12.45g dk bl & tan	3.50	2.00
812	A169	18.15g dk grn bl & tan	3.50	2.00
813	A169	50g dp vio & tan	3.50	2.00
a.		Souvenir sheet of 1	15.00	13.00
		Nos. 806-813 (8)	12.00	7.25

1964 Summer Olympic Games, Tokyo (Nos.
811-813a). Nos. 811-813a are airmail.
Exist imperf. in changed colors. Values: set,
$27; souvenir sheet, $17.

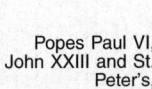

Rockets and
Satellites — A170

15c, 25c, Apollo command module mock-
up. 30c, Tiros 7 weather satellite, vert. 40c,
50c, Ranger 6. 12.45g, 18.15g, 50g, Saturn I
lift-off, vert.

1964, Apr. 25				
814	A170	15c brn & tan	.30	.25
815	A170	25c vio & tan	.30	.25
816	A170	30c Prus bl & lake	.30	.25
817	A170	40c ver & tan	.30	.25
818	A170	50c ultra & tan	.30	.25
819	A170	12.45g grn bl & choc	1.90	.85
820	A170	18.15g bl & choc	3.00	1.60
821	A170	50g lil rose & choc	4.75	2.50
a.		Souvenir sheet of 1	25.00	
		Nos. 814-821 (8)	11.15	6.20

Nos. 819-821a are airmail.
Exist imperf. in changed colors. Values: set,
$29; souvenir sheet, $18.

Popes Paul VI,
John XXIII and St.
Peter's,
Rome — A171

Design: 12.45g, 18.15g, 36g, Asuncion
Cathedral, Popes Paul VI and John XXIII.

1964, May 23			**Wmk. 347**	
822	A171	1.50g claret & org	.30	.25
823	A171	3g claret & dk grn	.30	.25
824	A171	4g claret & bister	.30	.25
825	A171	12.45g sl grn & lem	1.25	1.00
826	A171	18.15g pur & lem	1.25	1.00
827	A171	36g vio bl & lem	2.50	2.00
		Nos. 822-827 (6)	5.90	4.75

National holiday of St. Maria Auxiliadora
(Our Lady of Perpetual Help).
Nos. 825-827 are airmail.

United
Nations — A172

Designs: 15c, John F. Kennedy. 25c,
12.45g, Pope Paul VI and Patriarch
Atenagoras. 30c, Eleanor Roosevelt, Chairman of UN Commission on Human Rights.
40c, Relay, Syncom and Telstar satellites. 50c,
Echo 2 satellite. 18.15g, U Thant, UN Sec.
Gen. 50g, Rocket, flags of Europe, vert.

Perf. 14x13½, 14 (15c, 25c, 12.45g)

1964, July 30			**Unwmk.**	
Size: 35x35mm (#830, 834),				
40x29mm (#831-832, 835)				
828	A172	15c blk & brn	.30	.25
829	A172	25c blk, bl & red	.30	.25
830	A172	30c blk & ver	.30	.25
831	A172	40c dk bl & sep	.30	.25
832	A172	50c vio & car	.30	.25
833	A172	12.45g blk, grn & red	1.10	.75
834	A172	18.15g blk & grn	1.10	.75

Perf. 13½x14

835	A172	50g multicolored	2.50	1.75
a.		Souvenir sheet of 1	32.50	
		Nos. 828-835 (8)	6.20	4.50

Nos. 833-835a are airmail.
Exist imperf. in changed colors. Values: set,
$17.50; souvenir sheet, $35.

Space Achievements — A173

Designs: 10c, 30c, Ranger 7, Moon, vert.
15c, 12.45+6g, Wernher von Braun looking
through periscope, vert. 20c, 20+10g, John F.
Kennedy, rockets, vert. 40c, 18.15+9g, Rockets, von Braun.

1964, Sept. 12			**Perf. 12½x12**	
836	A173	10c bl & blk	.30	.25
837	A173	15c yel grn & brt pink	.30	.25
838	A173	20c yel org & bl	.30	.25
839	A173	30c mag & blk	.30	.25
840	A173	40c yel org, bl & blk	.30	.25
841	A173	12.45g +6g red & bl	2.90	1.60
a.		Souvenir sheet of 2, #840-841	24.00	
842	A173	18.15g +9g grn bl, brn & blk	2.90	1.60
843	A173	20g +10g red & bl	4.00	2.40
		Nos. 836-843 (8)	11.30	6.85

Nos. 841-843 are airmail.
Exist imperf. in changed colors. Values: set,
$24.50; souvenir sheet, $40.

Coats of Arms of
Paraguay and
France — A174

Designs: 3g, 12.45g, 36g, Presidents
Stroessner and de Gaulle. 18.15g, Coats of
Arms of Paraguay and France.

1964, Oct. 6			**Wmk. 347**	
844	A174	1.50g brown	.45	.30
845	A174	3g ultramarine	.45	.30
846	A174	4g gray	.45	.30
847	A174	12.45g lilac	.65	.40
848	A174	18.15g bl grn	1.00	.60
849	A174	36g magenta	4.00	1.75
		Nos. 844-849 (6)	7.00	3.65

Visit of Pres. Charles de Gaulle of France.
Nos. 847-849 are airmail.

Boy Scout
Jamborees
A175

Boy Scout Emblem —
A175a

Designs: 10c, Argentina, 1961. 15c, Peru,
canceled. 20c, Chile, 1959. 30c, Brazil, 1954.
50c, Uruguay, 1957. 12.45g, Brazil, 1960.
18.15g, Venezuela, 1964. 36g, Brazil, 1963.
15c, 18.15g, Lord Robert Baden-Powell
(1857-1941), Boy Scouts founder.

1965, Jan. 15			**Unwmk.**	**Perf. 14**
850	A175	10c multicolored	.30	.25
851	A175	15c multicolored	.30	.25
852	A175a	20c multicolored	.30	.25
853	A175a	30c multicolored	.30	.25
854	A175	50c multicolored	.30	.25
855	A175a	12.45g multicolored	1.90	1.50
856	A175	18.15g multicolored	2.00	1.40
857	A175	36g multicolored	3.75	2.50
a.		Souvenir sheet of 1, perf. 12x12½	25.00	
		Nos. 850-857 (8)	9.15	6.65

Nos. 855-857a are airmail.
Exist imperf. in changed colors. Values: set,
$27; souvenir sheet, $85.

A176

Olympic and Paraguayan Medals: 25c, John
F. Kennedy. 30c, Medal of Peace and Justice,
reverse. 40c, Gens. Stroessner and DeGaulle,
profiles. 50c, 18.15g, DeGaulle and Stroessner, in uniform. 12.45g, Medal of Peace and
Justice, obverse.

Litho. & Embossed

1965, Mar. 30			**Perf. 13½x13**	
Background Color				
858	A176	15c dull turq grn	.30	.25
859	A176	25c pink	.30	.30
860	A176	30c dull pale grn	.30	.30

Perf. 12½x12

861	A176	40c dull pale org	.30	.30
862	A176	50c grnsh gray	.30	.30
863	A176	12.45g multicolored	2.75	1.50
864	A176	18.15g multicolored	3.50	1.75
865	A176	50g multicolored	5.25	1.75
a.		Souv. sheet of 1, perf. 13½x13	35.00	
		Nos. 858-865 (8)	13.00	6.45

Nos. 863-865a are airmail. Medal on Nos.
858-862 is gold foil.
Exist imperf. in changed colors. Values: set,
$22; souvenir sheet, $60.

Overprinted in
Black — A177

Design: Map of Americas.

1965, Apr. 26			**Wmk. 347**	**Perf. 11**
866	A177	1.50g dull grn	.60	.40
867	A177	3g car red	.60	.40
868	A177	4g dark blue	.60	.40
869	A177	12.45g brn & blk	.60	.40
870	A177	36g brt lil & blk	1.50	.70
		Nos. 866-870 (5)	3.90	2.30

Centenary of National Epic. Not issued without overprint.
Nos. 869-870 are airmail.

Scientists — A178

1965, June 5			**Litho.**	**Perf. 14**
			Unwmk.	
871	A178	10c Newton	.30	.25
872	A178	15c Copernicus	.30	.25
873	A178	20c Galileo	.30	.25
874	A178	30c like #871	.30	.25
875	A178	40c Einstein	.30	.25
876	A178	12.45g +6g like #873	1.40	.50
a.		Souvenir sheet of 2, #875-876	21.00	
877	A178	18.15g +9g like #875	2.10	1.00
878	A178	20g +10g like #872	2.50	1.50
		Nos. 871-878 (8)	7.50	4.25

Nos. 876-878 are airmail.
Exist imperf. in changed colors. Values: set,
$22; souvenir sheet, $21.

Cattleya
Warscewiczii
A179

Ceibo Tree
A179a

1965, June 28   Unwmk.   Perf. 14½

879	A179	20c purple	.30	.25
880	A179	30c blue	.30	.25
881	A179	90c bright mag	.30	.25
882	A179	1.50g green	.30	.25
883	A179a	3g brn red	1.60	.90
884	A179a	4g green	2.10	.90
885	A179	4.50g orange	2.10	.90
886	A179a	66g brn org	4.25 1.40
		Nos. 879-886 (8)	11.25 5.10

150th anniv. of Independence (1811-1961).
Nos. 883-884, 886 are airmail.

John F.
Kennedy and
Winston
Churchill
A180

Designs: 15c, Kennedy, PT 109. 25c, Kennedy family. 30c, 12.45g, Churchill, Parliament building. 40c, Kennedy, Alliance for Progress emblem. 50c, 18.15g, Kennedy, rocket launch at Cape Canaveral. 50g, John Glenn, Kennedy, Lyndon Johnson examining Friendship 7.

1965, Sept. 4   Perf. 12x12½

887	A180	15c bl & brn	.30	.25
888	A180	25c red & brn	.30	.25
889	A180	30c vio & blk	.30	.25
890	A180	40c org & sep	.30	.25
891	A180	50c bl grn & sep	.30	.25
892	A180	12.45g yel & blk	1.75	.75
893	A180	18.15g car & blk	2.50 1.20
894	A180	50g grn & blk	4.25 1.75
a.		Souvenir sheet of 1	21.00
		Nos. 887-894 (8)	10.00 4.95

Nos. 892-894a are airmail.
Exist imperf. in changed colors. Values: set, $17; souvenir sheet, $21.

ITU, Cent.
A181

Satellites: 10c, 40c, Ranger 7 transmitting to Earth. 15c, 20g+10g, Syncom, Olympic rings. 20c, 18.15g+9g, Early Bird. 30c, 12.45g+6g, Relay, Syncom, Telstar, Echo 2.

1965, Sept. 30

895	A181	10c dull bl & sep	.30	.25
896	A181	15c lilac & sepia	.30	.25
897	A181	20c ol grn & sep	.30	.25
898	A181	30c blue & sepia	.30	.25
899	A181	40c grn & sep	.30	.25
900	A181	12.45g +6g ver & sep	1.50	.50
a.		Souvenir sheet of 2, #899-900	22.50
901	A181	18.15g +9g org & sep	2.25	.75
902	A181	20g +10g vio & sep	3.75 1.25
		Nos. 895-902 (8)	9.00 3.75

Nos. 900-902 are airmail.
Exist imperf. in changed colors. Values: set, $19.50; souvenir sheet, $27.50.

Pope Paul
VI, Visit to
UN — A182

Designs: 10c, 50c, Pope Paul VI, U Thant, A. Fanfani. 15c, 12.45g, Pope Paul VI, Lyndon B. Johnson. 20c, 36g, Early Bird satellite, globe, papal arms. 30c, 18.15g, Pope Paul VI, Unisphere.

1965, Nov. 19

903	A182	10c multicolored	.30	.25
904	A182	15c multicolored	.30	.25
905	A182	20c multicolored	.30	.25
906	A182	30c multicolored	.30	.25
907	A182	50c multicolored	.30	.25
908	A182	12.45g multicolored	1.00	.50
909	A182	18.15g multicolored	1.60 1.25
910	A182	36g multicolored	3.25 1.75
a.		Souvenir sheet of 1	22.50
		Nos. 903-910 (8)	7.35 4.75

Nos. 908-910a are airmail.
Exist imperf. in changed colors. Values: set, $27; souvenir sheet, $32.50.

Astronauts
and Space
Exploration
A183

15c, 50g, Edward White walking in space, 6/3/65. 25c, 18.15g, Gemini 7 & 8 docking, 12/16-18/65. 30c, Virgil I. Grissom, John W. Young, 3/23/65. 40c, 50c, Edward White, James McDivitt, 6/3/65. 12.45g, Photographs of lunar surface.

1966, Feb. 19   Perf. 14

911	A183	15c multicolored	.30	.25
912	A183	25c multicolored	.30	.25
913	A183	30c multicolored	.30	.25
914	A183	40c multicolored	.30	.25
915	A183	50c multicolored	.30	.25
916	A183	12.45g multicolored	1.40 1.10
917	A183	18.15g multicolored	2.40 1.90
918	A183	50g multicolored	4.25 3.25
a.		Souvenir sheet of 1	30.00
		Nos. 911-918 (8)	9.55 7.50

Nos. 916-918a are airmail.
Exist imperf. in changed colors. Values: set, $14; souvenir sheet, $25.

Events of
1965
A184

10c, Meeting of Pope Paul VI & Cardinal Spellman, 10/4/65. 15c, Intl. Phil. Exposition, Vienna. 20c, OAS, 75th anniv. 30c, 36g, Intl. Quiet Sun Year, 1964-65. 50c, 18.15g, Saturn rockets at NY World's Fair. 12.45g, UN Intl. Cooperation Year.

1966, Mar. 9

919	A184	10c multicolored	.30	.25
920	A184	15c multicolored	.30	.25
921	A184	20c multicolored	.30	.25
922	A184	30c multicolored	.30	.25
923	A184	50c multicolored	.30	.25
924	A184	12.45g multicolored	1.40	.75
925	A184	18.15g multicolored	2.40 1.50
926	A184	36g multicolored	4.75 1.25
a.		Souvenir sheet of 1	25.00
		Nos. 919-926 (8)	10.05 4.75

Nos. 924-926a are airmail.
Exist imperf. in changed colors. Values: set, $27; souvenir sheet, $32.50.

1968 Summer
Olympics, Mexico
City — A185

15c, God of Death. 20c, Aztec calendar stone. 50c, Zapotec deity.

Perf. 12½x12 (Nos. 927, 929, 931, 933), 13½x13

1966, Apr. 1

927	A185	10c shown	.30	.25
928	A185	15c multi	.30	.25
929	A185	20c multi	.30	.25
930	A185	30c like No. 928	.30	.25
931	A185	50c multi	.30	.25
932	A185	12.45g like No. 931	1.60	.75
933	A185	18.15g like No. 927	2.50 1.25

934	A185	36g like No. 929	6.00 3.00
a.		Souvenir sheet of 1	17.50
		Nos. 927-934 (8)	11.60 6.25

Nos. 932-934a are airmail.
Exist imperf. in changed colors. Values: set, $17; souvenir sheet, $37.50.

A185a

St. Ignatius and
San Ignacio
Monastery
A185b

1966, Apr. 20   Wmk. 347   Perf. 11

935	A185a	15c ultramarine	1.40	.50
936	A185a	25c ultramarine	1.40	.50
937	A185a	75c ultramarine	1.40	.50
938	A185a	90c ultramarine	1.40	.50
939	A185b	3g brown	1.40	.50
940	A185b	12.45g sepia	1.40	.50
941	A185b	18.15g sepia	1.40	.50
942	A185b	23.40g sepia	1.40	.50
		Nos. 935-942 (8)	11.20 4.00

350th anniv. of the founding of San Ignacio Guazu Monastery.
Nos. 939-942 are airmail.
On designs A185b text under Paraguay is different from that of design A129a (No. 522).

A186

A186a

German Contributors
in Space Research —
A186b

Designs: 10c, 36g, Paraguay #835, C97, Germany #C40. 15c, 50c, 18.15g, 3rd stage of Europa 1 rocket. 20c, 12.45g, Hermann Oberth, jet propulsion engineer. 30c, Reinhold K. Tiling, builder of 1st German rocket, 1931, vert.

Perf. 12x12½ (Nos. 943, 950), 12½x12 (Nos. 945, 947, 949), 13½x13

1966, May 16   Unwmk.

943	A186	10c multicolored	.30	.25
944	A186a	15c multicolored	.30	.25
945	A186b	20c multicolored	.30	.25
946	A186b	30c multicolored	.30	.25
947	A186a	50c multicolored	.30	.25
948	A186b	12.45g multicolored	1.90	.50
949	A186a	18.15g multicolored	2.40 1.00
950	A186	36g multicolored	4.50 2.25
a.		Souvenir sheet of 1, perf. 12x13½x13x13½	30.00
		Nos. 943-950 (8)	10.30 5.00

Nos. 948-950a are airmail.
Exist imperf. in changed colors. Values: set, $27; souvenir sheet, $45.

Writers
A187

1966, June 11   Perf. 12x12½

951	A187	10c Dante	.30	.25
952	A187	15c Moliere	.30	.25
953	A187	20c Goethe	.30	.25
954	A187	30c Shakespeare	.30	.25
955	A187	50c like #952	.30	.25
956	A187	12.45g like #953	2.25 1.50
957	A187	18.15g like #954	2.75 1.50
958	A187	36g like #951	4.50 1.50
a.		Souvenir sheet of 1, perf. 13½x14	15.00
		Nos. 951-958 (8)	11.00 5.75

Nos. 956-958a are airmail.
Exist imperf. in changed colors. Values: set, $14; souvenir sheet, $22.

Italian
Contributors
in Space
Research
A188

10c, 36g, Italian satellite, San Marco 1. 15c, 18.15g, Drafting machine, Leonardo Da Vinci. 20c, 12.45g, Map, Italo Balbo (1896-1940), aviator. 30c, 50c, Floating launch & control facility, satellite.

1966, July 11

959	A188	10c multicolored	.30	.25
960	A188	15c multicolored	.30	.25
961	A188	20c multicolored	.30	.25
962	A188	30c multicolored	.30	.25
963	A188	50c multicolored	.30	.25
964	A188	12.45g multicolored	1.75	.50
965	A188	18.15g multicolored	3.00	.50
966	A188	36g multicolored	5.50 3.00
a.		Souvenir sheet of 1, perf. 13½x13	15.00
		Nos. 959-966 (8)	11.75 5.25

Nos. 964-966a are airmail.
Exist imperf. in changed colors. Values: set, $14; souvenir sheet, $22.

Rubén Dario
A189

"Paraguay
de Fuego" by
Dario
A189a

1966, July 16   Wmk. 347

967	A189	50c ultramarine	.65	.40
968	A189	70c bister brn	.65	.40
969	A189	1.50g rose car	.65	.40
970	A189	3g violet	.65	.40
971	A189	4g greenish bl	.65	.40
972	A189	5g black	.65	.40
973	A189a	12.45g blue	1.90	.40
974	A189a	18.15g red lil	1.90	.40
975	A189a	23.40g org brn	1.90	.40
976	A189a	36g brt grn	1.90	.90
977	A189a	50g rose car	1.90 1.20
		Nos. 967-977 (11)	13.40 5.70

50th death anniv. of Ruben Dario (pen name of Felix Rubén Garcia Sarmiento, 1867-1916), Nicaraguan poet, newspaper correspondent and diplomat.
Nos. 973-977 are airmail.

Space
Missions
A190

10c, Gemini 8. 15c, Gemini 9. 20c, Surveyor 1 on moon. 30c, Gemini 10.

1966, Aug. 25   Unwmk.

978	A190	10c multi	.30	.25
979	A190	15c multi	.30	.25
980	A190	20c multi	.30	.25
981	A190	30c multi	.30	.25
982	A190	50c like #981	.30	.25
983	A190	12.45g like #980	3.25 1.25
984	A190	18.15g like #979	3.25 1.25
985	A190	36g like #978	18.00 6.00
a.		Souvenir sheet of 1, perf. 13x13½	22.00
		Nos. 978-985 (8)	26.00 9.75

Nos. 983-985a are airmail.
Exist imperf. in changed colors. Values: set, $37; souvenir sheet, $30.

1968
Winter
Olympics,
Grenoble
A191

1966, Sept. 30 *Perf. 14*
986	A191	10c Figure skating	.30	.25
987	A191	15c Downhill skiing	.30	.25
988	A191	20c Speed skating	.30	.25
989	A191	30c 2-man luge	.30	.25
990	A191	50c like #989	.30	.25
991	A191	12.45g like #988	1.25	.50
992	A191	18.15g like #987	1.60	.50
993	A191	36g like #986	3.25	2.50
a.		Souvenir sheet of 1	15.00	
		Nos. 986-993 (8)	7.60	4.75

Nos. 987, 992, World Skiing Championships, Portillo, Chile, 1966. Nos. 991-993a are airmail.

Exist imperf. in changed colors. Values: set, $15; souvenir sheet, $27.50.

Pres. John F.
Kennedy, 3rd
Death Anniv.
A192

10c, Echo 1 & 2. 15c, Telstar 1 & 2. 20c, Relay 1 & 2. 30c, Syncom 1, 2 & 3, Early Bird.

Perf. 12x12½, 13½x14 (#997-998, 1001)

1966, Nov. 7
994	A192	10c multi	.30	.25
995	A192	15c multi	.30	.25
996	A192	20c multi	.30	.25
997	A192	30c multi	.30	.25
998	A192	50c like #997	.30	.25
999	A192	12.45g like #996	1.50	.50
1000	A192	18.15g like #995	1.75	.50
1001	A192	36g like #994	6.00	3.50
a.		Souvenir sheet of 1, perf. 13x14x13½x14	21.00	
		Nos. 994-1001 (8)	10.75	5.75

Nos. 999-1001a are airmail.
Exist imperf. in changed colors. Values: set, $22; souvenir sheet, $25.

Paintings — A193

Portraits of women by: No. 1002a, 10c, De Largilliere. b, 15c, Rubens. c, 20c, Titian. d, 30c, Hans Holbein. e, 50c, Sanchez Coello.

Paintings: No. 1003a, 12.45g, Mars and Venus with United by Love by Veronese. b, 18.15g, Allegory of Prudence, Peace and Abundance by Vouet. c, 36g, Madonna and Child by Andres Montegna.

1966, Dec. 10 *Perf. 14x13½*
1002	A193	Strip of 5, #a.-e.	1.75	1.25
1003	A193	Strip of 3, #a.-c.	6.00	4.50
d.		Souvenir sheet of 1, #1003c	23.00	
		Nos. 1002-1003 (2)	7.75	5.75

Nos. 1003a-1003d are airmail. No. 1003d has green pattern in border and is perf. 12½x12.

Exist imperf. in changed colors. Values: set, $17; souvenir sheet, $23.

Holy Week
Paintings — A194

Life of Christ by: No. 1004a, 10c, Raphael. b, 15c, Rubens. c, 20c, Da Ponte. d, 30c, El Greco. e, 50c, Murillo, horiz.
12.45g, G. Reni. 18.15g, Tintoretto. 36g, Da Vinci, horiz.

1967, Feb. 28 *Perf. 14x13½, 13½x14*
1004	A194	Strip of 5, #a.-e.	2.50	1.25
1005	A194	12.45g multicolored	1.10	.50
1006	A194	18.15g multicolored	1.10	.50
1007	A194	36g multicolored	13.50	5.00
a.		Souvenir sheet of 1	16.00	
		Nos. 1004-1007 (4)	18.20	7.25

Nos. 1005-1007a are airmail. No. 1007a has salmon pattern in border and contains one 60x40mm, perf. 14 stamp.

Exist imperf. in changed colors. Values: set, $17; souvenir sheet, $16.

Birth of Christ by
Barocci — A195

16th Cent. Paintings: 12.45g, Madonna and Child by Caravaggio. 18.15g, Mary of the Holy Family (detail) by El Greco. 36g, Assumption of the Virgin by Vasco Fernandes.

1967, Mar. 10 *Perf. 14½*
1008	A195	10c lt bl & multi	.30	.25
1009	A195	15c lt grn & multi	.30	.25
1010	A195	20c lt brn & multi	.30	.25
1011	A195	30c lil & multi	.30	.25
1012	A195	50c pink & multi	.30	.25
1013	A195	12.45g lt bl grn & multi	.60	.50
1014	A195	18.15g brt pink & multi	.60	.50
1015	A195	36g lt vio & multi	7.50	4.00
a.		Souv. sheet of 1, sep & multi	23.00	
		Nos. 1008-1015 (8)	10.20	6.25

Nos. 1013-1015a are airmail.
Exist imperf. with changed borders. Values: set, $17; souvenir sheet, $23.

Globe and
Lions
Emblem
A196

Medical
Laboratory
"Health"
A196a

Designs: 1.50g, 3g, Melvin Jones. 4g, 5g, Lions' Headquarters, Chicago. 12.45g, 18.15g, Library "Education."

1967, May 9 *Litho.* *Wmk. 347*
1016	A196	50c light vio	1.10	.50
1017	A196	70c blue	1.10	.50
1018	A196	1.50g ultra	1.10	.50
1019	A196	3g brown	1.10	.50
1020	A196	4g Prus grn	1.10	.50
1021	A196	5g ol gray	2.25	.50
1022	A196a	12.45g dk brn	2.25	.50
1023	A196a	18.15g violet	2.25	.50
1024	A196a	23.40g rose cl	2.25	.50
1025	A196a	36g Prus blue	2.25	.50
1026	A196a	50g rose car	2.25	.50
		Nos. 1016-1026 (11)	19.00	5.50

50th anniversary of Lions International. Nos. 1022-1026 airmail.

Vase of Flowers
by
Chardin — A197

Still Life Paintings by: No. 1027b, 15c, Fontanesi, horiz. c, 20c, Cezanne. d, 30c, Van Gogh. e, 50c, Renoir.
Paintings: 12.45g, Cha-U-Kao at the Moulin Rouge by Toulouse-Lautrec. 18.15g, Gabrielle with Jean Renoir by Renoir. 36g, Patience Escalier, Shepherd of Provence by Van Gogh.

1967, May 16 *Perf. 12½x12*
1027	A197	Strip of 5, #a.-e.	1.60	1.25
1028	A197	12.45g multicolored	.65	.50
1029	A197	18.15g multicolored	.65	.50
1030	A197	36g multicolored	5.25	4.00
a.		Souvenir sheet of 1, perf. 14x12x14x13½	22.00	
		Nos. 1027-1030 (4)	8.15	6.25

Nos. 1028-1030a are airmail. No. 1030a has a green pattern in border.
Exist imperf. with changed borders. Values: set, $17; souvenir sheet, $25.

Famous
Paintings
A198

10c, Jan Steen. 15c, Frans Hals, vert. 20c, Jordaens. 25c, Rembrandt. 30c, de Marees, vert. 50c, Quentin, vert. 12.45g, Nicolaes Maes, vert. 18.15g, Vigee-Lebrun, vert. 36g, Rubens, vert.
50g, G. B. Tiepolo.

1967, July 16 *Perf. 12x12½*
1031	A198	10c multicolored	.30	.25

Perf. 14x13½, 13½x14
1032	A198	15c multicolored	.30	.25
1033	A198	20c multicolored	.30	.25
1034	A198	25c multicolored	.30	.25
1035	A198	30c multicolored	.30	.25
1036	A198	50c multicolored	.30	.25
1037	A198	12.45g multicolored	.75	.50
1038	A198	18.15g multicolored	.75	.50
1039	A198	36g multicolored	7.50	4.00
		Nos. 1031-1039 (9)	10.80	6.50

Souvenir Sheet
Perf. 12x12½
1040	A198	50g multicolored	11.00

Nos. 1037-1039 are airmail. An imperf. souvenir sheet of 3, Nos. 1037-1039 exists with dark green pattern in border. Value $16.

John F. Kennedy,
50th Birth
Anniv. — A199

Kennedy and: 10c, Recovery of Alan Shepard's capsule, Lyndon Johnson, Mrs. Kennedy. 15c, John Glenn. 20c, Mr. and Mrs. M. Scott Carpenter. 25c, Rocket 2nd stage, Wernher Von Braun. 30c, Cape Canaveral, Walter Schirra. 50c, Syncom 2 satellite, horiz. 12.45g, Launch of Atlas rocket. 18.15g, Theorized lunar landing, horiz. 36g, Portrait of Kennedy by Torres. 50g, Apollo lift-off, horiz.

1967, Aug. 19 *Perf. 14x13½, 13½x14*
1041	A199	10c multicolored	.30	.25
1042	A199	15c multicolored	.30	.25
1043	A199	20c multicolored	.30	.25
1044	A199	25c multicolored	.30	.25
1045	A199	30c multicolored	.30	.25
1046	A199	50c multicolored	.30	.25
1047	A199	12.45g multicolored	1.75	.75
1048	A199	18.15g multicolored	2.50	1.00
1049	A199	36g multicolored	9.00	4.00
		Nos. 1041-1049 (9)	15.05	7.25

Souvenir Sheet
1050	A199	50g multicolored	22.50

Nos. 1047-1050 are airmail. An imperf. souvenir sheet of 3 containing Nos. 1047-1049 exists with violet border. Value $32.50.

Sculptures
A200

10c, Head of athlete. 15c, Myron's Discobolus. 20c, Apollo of Belvedere. 25c, Artemis. 30c, Venus De Milo. 50c, Winged Victory of

Samothrace. 12.45g, Laocoon Group. 18.15g, Moses. 50g, Pieta.

1967, Oct. 16 *Perf. 14x13½*
1051	A200	10c multicolored	.30	.25
1052	A200	15c multicolored	.30	.25
1053	A200	20c multicolored	.30	.25
1054	A200	25c multicolored	.30	.25
1055	A200	30c multicolored	.30	.25
1056	A200	50c multicolored	.30	.25
1057	A200	12.45g multicolored	1.25	.40
1058	A200	18.15g multicolored	1.90	.40
1059	A200	36g multicolored	8.50	3.00
		Nos. 1051-1059 (9)	13.45	5.30

Nos. 1057-1059 are airmail.
Exist imperf. in changed colors. Value, set $19.

Mexican
Art — A201

Designs: 10c, Bowl, Veracruz. 15c, Knobbed vessel, Colima. 20c, Mixtec jaguar pitcher. 25c, Head, Veracruz. 30c, Statue of seated woman, Teotihuacan. 50c, Vessel depicting a woman, Aztec. 12.45g, Mixtec bowl, horiz. 18.15g, Three-legged vessel, Teotihuacan, horiz. 36g, Golden mask, Teotihuacan, horiz. 50g, The Culture of the Totonac by Diego Rivera, 1950, horiz.

1967, Nov. 29 *Perf. 14x13½*
1060	A201	10c multicolored	.30	.25
1061	A201	15c multicolored	.30	.25
1062	A201	20c multicolored	.30	.25
1063	A201	25c multicolored	.30	.25
1064	A201	30c multicolored	.30	.25
1065	A201	50c multicolored	.30	.25

Perf. 13½x14
1066	A201	12.45g multicolored	2.40	.60
1067	A201	18.15g multicolored	2.90	.60
1068	A201	36g multicolored	14.00	6.00
		Nos. 1060-1068 (9)	21.10	8.70

Souvenir Sheet
Perf. 14
1069	A201	50g multicolored	21.00

1968 Summer Olympics, Mexico City (#1065-1069).
Nos. 1066-1069 are airmail. An imperf. souvenir sheet of 3 containing #1066-1068 exists with green pattern in border. Value $34.

Paintings of the
Madonna and
Child — A202

1968, Jan. 27 *Perf. 14x13½, 13½x14*
1070	A202	10c Bellini	.30	.25
1071	A202	15c Raphael	.30	.25
1072	A202	20c Correggio	.30	.25
1073	A202	25c Luini	.30	.25
1074	A202	30c Bronzino	.30	.25
1075	A202	50c Van Dyck	.30	.25
1076	A202	12.45g Vignon, horiz.	.75	.40
1077	A202	18.15g de Ribera	.75	.40
1078	A202	36g Botticelli	10.00	3.00
		Nos. 1070-1078 (9)	13.30	5.30

Nos. 1076-1078 are airmail and also exist as imperf. souvenir sheet of 3 with olive brown pattern in border. Value $37.50.

Paintings of
Winter
Scenes
A203

1968 Winter
Olympics
Emblem — A204

10c, Pissarro. 15c, Utrillo, vert. 20c, Monet. 25c, Breitner, vert. 30c, Sisley. 50c, Brueghel, vert. 12.45g, Avercampe, vert. 18.15g, Brueghel, diff. 36g, P. Limbourg & brothers, vert.

1968, Apr. 23   Perf. 13½x14, 14x13½
1079	A203	10c multi	.30	.25
1080	A203	15c multi	.30	.25
1081	A203	20c multi	.30	.25
1082	A203	25c multi	.30	.25
1083	A203	30c multi	.30	.25
1084	A203	50c multi	.30	.25
1085	A203	12.45g multi	1.00	.40
1086	A203	18.15g multi	1.50	.40
1087	A203	36g multi	5.00	2.00
		Nos. 1079-1087 (9)	9.30	4.30

Souvenir Sheet
1088		Sheet of 2	30.00	
a.		A204 50g multicolored		

Nos. 1087-1088, 1088a are airmail. No. 1088 contains #1088a and #1087 with red pattern.

Paraguayan
Stamps,
Cent. (in
1970)
A205

Perf. 13½x14, 14x13½
1968, June 3   Litho.
1089	A205	10c #1, 4	.30	.25
1090	A205	15c #C21, 310, vert.	.30	.25
1091	A205	20c #203, C140	.30	.25
1092	A205	25c #C72, C61, vert.	.30	.25
1093	A205	30c #638, 711	.30	.25
1094	A205	50c #406, C38, vert.	.30	.25
1095	A205	12.45g #B2, B7	1.20	.45
1096	A205	18.15g #C10, C11, vert.	1.20	.45
1097	A205	36g #828, C76, 616	12.00	4.50
		Nos. 1089-1097 (9)	16.20	6.90

Souvenir Sheet
Perf. 14
1098		Sheet of 2	42.00	25.00
a.		A205 50g #929 & #379		

Nos. 1095-1098a are airmail. No. 1098 contains No. 1098a and No. 1097 with light brown pattern in border.

Paintings — A206

#1099-1106, paintings of children. #1107-1108, paintings of sailboats at sea.

1968, July 9   Perf. 14x13½, 13½x14
1099	A206	10c Russell	.30	.25
1100	A206	15c Velazquez	.30	.25
1101	A206	20c Romney	.30	.25
1102	A206	25c Lawrence	.30	.25
1103	A206	30c Caravaggio	.30	.25
1104	A206	50c Gentileschi	.30	.25
1105	A206	12.45g Renoir	.80	.45
1106	A206	18.15g Copley	.80	.45
1107	A206	36g Sessions, horiz.	8.25	3.00
		Nos. 1099-1107 (9)	11.65	5.40

Souvenir Sheet
Perf. 14
1108		Sheet of 2	50.00	50.00
a.		A206 50g Currier & Ives, horiz.		

1968 Summer Olympics, Mexico City (Nos. 1107-1108).

Nos. 1106-1108a are airmail. No. 1108 contains No. 1108a and No. 1107 with a red pattern in border.

A207

WHO Emblem — A207a

1968, Aug. 12   Wmk. 347   Perf. 11
1109	A207	3g bluish grn	.65	.40
1110	A207	4g brt pink	.65	.40
1111	A207	5g bister brn	.65	.40
1112	A207	10g violet	.65	.40
1113	A207a	36g blk brn	2.50	
1114	A207a	50g rose claret	2.50	.50
1115	A207a	100g brt bl	2.50	1.20
		Nos. 1109-1115 (7)	10.10	3.70

WHO, 20th anniv.; cent. of the natl. epic. Nos. 1113-1115 are airmail.

39th Intl.
Eucharistic
Congress — A208

Paintings of life of Christ by various artists (except No. 1125a).

Perf. 14x13½
1968, Sept. 25   Litho.   Unwmk.
1116	A208	10c Caravaggio	.30	.25
1117	A208	15c El Greco	.30	.25
1118	A208	20c Del Sarto	.30	.25
1119	A208	25c Van der Weyden	.30	.25
1120	A208	30c De Patinier	.30	.25
1121	A208	50c Plockhorst	.30	.25
1122	A208	12.45g Bronzino	.90	.40
1123	A208	18.15g Raphael	.90	.40
1124	A208	36g Correggio	9.50	3.00
		Nos. 1116-1124 (9)	13.10	5.30

Souvenir Sheet
Perf. 14
1125		Sheet of 2	23.00	
a.		A208 36g Pope Paul VI		
b.		A208 50g Tiepolo		

Pope Paul VI's visit to South America (No. 1125). Nos. 1122-1125b are airmail.

Events of
1968 — A209

Designs: 10c, Mexican 25p Olympic coin. 15c, Rentry of Echo 1 satellite. 20c, Visit of Pope Paul VI to Fatima, Portugal. 25c, Dr. Christian Barnard, 1st heart transplant. 30c, Martin Luther King, assasination. 50c, Pres. Alfredo Stroessner laying wreath at grave of Pres. Kennedy, vert. 12.45g, Pres. Stroessner, Pres. Lyndon B. Johnson. 18.15g, John F. Kennedy, Abraham Lincoln, Robert Kennedy. 50g, Summer Olympics, Mexico City, satellite transmissions, vert.

1968, Dec. 21   Perf. 13½x14, 14x13½
1126	A209	10c multicolored	.30	.25
1127	A209	15c multicolored	.30	.25
1128	A209	20c multicolored	.30	.25
1129	A209	25c multicolored	.30	.25
1130	A209	30c multicolored	.30	.25
1131	A209	50c multicolored	.30	.25
1132	A209	12.45g multicolored	1.25	.40
1133	A209	18.15g multicolored	1.75	.40
1134	A209	36g multicolored	9.00	3.00
		Nos. 1126-1134 (9)	13.80	5.30

Nos. 1132-1134 are airmail. Set exists imperf. in sheets of 3 in changed colors. Value, set of 3 sheets $63.

1968 Summer
Olympics, Mexico
City — A210

Olympic
Stadium — A210a

Gold Medal Winners: 10c, Felipe Munoz, Mexico, 200-meter breast stroke. 15c, Daniel Rebillard, France, 4000-meter cycling. 20c, David Hemery, England, 400-meter hurdles. 25c, Bob Seagren, US, pole vault. 30c, Francisco Rodriguez, Venezuela, light flyweight boxing. 50c, Bjorn Ferm, Sweden, modern pentathlon. 12.45g, Klaus Dibiasi, Italy, platform diving. 50g, Ingrid Becker, West Germany, fencing, women's pentathlon.

1969, Feb. 13   Perf. 14x13½
1135	A210	10c multicolored	.30	.25
1136	A210	15c multicolored	.30	.25
1137	A210	20c multicolored	.30	.25
1138	A210	25c multicolored	.30	.25
1139	A210	30c multicolored	.30	.25
1140	A210	50c multicolored	.30	.25
1141	A210	12.45g multicolored	.90	.30
1142	A210a	18.15g multicolored	1.25	.40
1143	A210	50g multicolored	7.00	3.00
		Nos. 1135-1143 (9)	10.95	5.20

Nos. 1141-1143 are airmail. Set exists imperf. in sheets of 3 in changed colors. Value, set of 3 sheets $35.

Space
Missions
A211

Designs: 10c, Apollo 7, John F. Kennedy. 15c, Apollo 8, Kennedy. 20c, Apollo 8, Kennedy, diff. 25c, Study of solar flares, ITU emblem. 30c, ESRO satellite. 50c, Canary Bird satellite. 12.45g, Wernher von Braun, rocket launch. 18.15g, Global satellite coverage, ITU emblem. 50g, Otto Lilienthal, Graf Zeppelin, Hermann Oberth, evolution of flight.

1969, Mar. 10   Perf. 13½x14
1144	A211	10c multicolored	.30	.25
1145	A211	15c multicolored	.30	.25
1146	A211	20c multicolored	.30	.25
1147	A211	25c multicolored	.30	.25
1148	A211	30c multicolored	.30	.25
1149	A211	50c multicolored	.30	.25
1150	A211	12.45g multicolored	1.00	.40
1151	A211	18.15g multicolored	1.60	.40
1152	A211	50g multicolored	5.50	2.00
		Nos. 1144-1152 (9)	9.90	4.30

Nos. 1150-1152 are airmail. Set exists imperf. in sheets of 3 in changed colors. Value, set of 3 sheets $100.

"World United in
Peace" — A212

1969, June 28   Wmk. 347   Perf. 11
1153	A212	50c rose	.70	.50
1154	A212	70c ultra	.70	.50
1155	A212	1.50g light brn	.70	.50
1156	A212	3g lil rose	.70	.50

1157	A212	4g emerald	1.00	.50
1158	A212	5g violet	1.25	.50
1159	A212	10g brt lilac	3.50	.50
		Nos. 1153-1159 (7)	8.55	3.50

Peace Week.

Birds
A213

Designs: 10c, Pteroglossus viridis. 15c, Phytotoma rutila. 20c, Porphyrula martinica. 25c, Oxyrunchus cristatus. 30c, Spizaetus ornatus. 50c, Phoenicopterus ruber. 75c, Amazona ochrocephala. 12.45g, Ara ararauna, Ara macao. 18.15g, Colibri coruscans.

Perf. 13½x14, 14x13½
1969, July 9   Unwmk.
1160	A213	10c multicolored	1.20	.25
1161	A213	15c multicolored	1.20	.25
1162	A213	20c multicolored	1.20	.25
1163	A213	25c multicolored	1.20	.25
1164	A213	30c multicolored	1.20	.25
1165	A213	50c multicolored	1.20	.25
1166	A213	75c multicolored	1.20	.25
1167	A213	12.45g multicolored	3.50	.50
1168	A213	18.15g multicolored	8.50	1.00
		Nos. 1160-1168 (9)	20.40	3.25

Nos. 1167-1168 are airmail. Nos. 1161, 1164-1168 are vert.

Fauna
A214

1969, July 9
1169	A214	10c Porcupine	.30	.25
1170	A214	15c Lemur, vert.	.30	.25
1171	A214	20c 3-toed sloth, vert.	.30	.25
1172	A214	25c Puma	.30	.25
1173	A214	30c Alligator	.30	.25
1174	A214	50c Jaguar	.30	.25
1175	A214	75c Anteater	.30	.25
1176	A214	12.45g Tapir	1.00	.25
1177	A214	18.15g Capybara	2.90	1.00
		Nos. 1169-1177 (9)	6.00	3.00

Nos. 1176-1177 are airmail.

Olympic Soccer
Champions,
1900-1968
A215

Designs: 10c, Great Britain, Paris, 1900. 15c, Canada, St. Louis, 1904. 20c, Great Britain, London, 1908 and Stockholm, 1912. 25c, Belgium, Antwerp, 1920. 30c, Uruguay, Paris, 1924 and Amsterdam, 1928. 50c, Italy, Berlin, 1936. 75c, Sweden, London, 1948; USSR, Melbourne, 1956. 12.45g, Yugoslavia, Rome, 1960. 18.15g, Hungary, Helsinki, 1952, Tokyo, 1964 and Mexico, 1968.

No. 1187, Soccer ball, Mexico 1968 emblem. No. 1188, Soccer player and ball.

1969, Nov. 26   Perf. 14
1178	A215	10c multicolored	.30	.25
1179	A215	15c multicolored	.30	.25
1180	A215	20c multicolored	.30	.25
1181	A215	25c multicolored	.30	.25
1182	A215	30c multicolored	.30	.25
1183	A215	50c multicolored	.30	.25
1184	A215	75c multicolored	.30	.25
1185	A215	12.45g multicolored	.85	.40
1186	A215	18.15g multicolored	8.25	2.50
		Nos. 1178-1186 (9)	11.20	4.65

Souvenir Sheet
1187	A215	23.40g multicolored	12.00	12.00
1188	A215	23.40g multi	20.00	20.00

Nos. 1185-1188 are airmail. No. 1187 contains one 49x60mm stamp. No. 1188 contains one 50x61mm stamp.

A216

World Cup or South American Soccer Champions: 10c, Paraguay, 1953. 15c, Uruguay, 1930. 20c, Italy, 1934. 25c, Italy, 1938. 30c, Uruguay, 1950. 50c, Germany, 1954, horiz. 75c, Brazil, 1958. 12.45g, Brazil, 1962. 18.15g, England, 1966. No. 1198, Trophy. No. 1199, Soccer player, satellite.

1969, Nov. 26   *Perf. 14*
1189	A216	10c multicolored	.30	.25
1190	A216	15c multicolored	.30	.25
1191	A216	20c multicolored	.30	.25
1192	A216	25c multicolored	.30	.25
1193	A216	30c multicolored	.30	.25
1194	A216	50c multicolored	.35	.25
1195	A216	75c multicolored	.55	.25
1196	A216	12.45g multicolored	2.50	.25
1197	A216	18.15g multicolored	5.75	1.50
	Nos. 1189-1197 (9)		10.65	3.50

Souvenir Sheets
Perf. 13½, Imperf(#1199)
1198	A216	23.40g multicolored	50.00	50.00
1199	A216	23.40g multicolored	25.00	25.00

Nos. 1196-1199 are airmail. No. 1198 contains one 50x60mm stamp. No. 1199 contains one 45x57mm stamp.

Paintings by Francisco de Goya (1746-1828) A217

Designs: 10c, Miguel de Lardibazal. 15c, Francisca Sabasa y Gracia. 20c, Don Manuel Osorio. 25c, Young Women with a Letter. 30c, The Water Carrier. 50c, Truth, Time and History. 75c, The Forge. 12.45g, The Spell. 18.15g, Duke of Wellington on Horseback. 23.40g, "La Maja Desnuda."

1969, Nov. 29   *Litho.*   *Perf. 14x13½*
1200	A217	10c multicolored	.30	.25
1201	A217	15c multicolored	.30	.25
1202	A217	20c multicolored	.30	.25
1203	A217	25c multicolored	.30	.25
1204	A217	30c multicolored	.30	.25
1205	A217	50c multicolored	.30	.25
1206	A217	75c multicolored	.45	.25
1207	A217	12.45g multicolored	3.00	.60
1208	A217	18.15g multicolored	6.50	1.25
	Nos. 1200-1208 (9)		11.75	3.60

Souvenir Sheet
Perf. 14
1209	A217	23.40g multicolored	27.50	27.50

Nos. 1207-1209 are airmail.

Christmas A218

Various paintings of The Nativity or Madonna and Child: 10c, Master Bertram. 15c, Procaccini. 20c, Di Crediti. 25c, De Flemalle. 30c, Correggio. 50c, Borgianni. 75c, Botticelli. 12.45g, El Greco. 18.15g, De Morales.

23.40g, Isenheimer Altar.

1969, Nov. 29   *Perf. 14x13½*
1210	A218	10c multi	.30	.25
1211	A218	15c multi	.30	.25
1212	A218	20c multi	.30	.25
1213	A218	25c multi	.30	.25
1214	A218	30c multi	.30	.25
1215	A218	50c multi	.30	.25
1216	A218	75c multi	.30	.25

1217	A218	12.45g multi	3.50	.60
1218	A218	18.15g multi	6.00	1.50
	Nos. 1210-1218 (9)		11.60	3.85

Souvenir Sheet
Perf. 13½
1219	A218	23.40g multi	22.50	22.50

Nos. 1217-1219 are airmail.

Souvenir Sheet

European Space Program — A219

No. 1220, ESRO 1B. No. 1221, Ernst Stuhlinger.

1969, Nov. 29   *Litho.*   *Perf. 14*
1220	A219	23.40g multi	21.00	21.00

Imperf
1221	A219	23.40g multi	25.00	25.00

Francisco Solano — A220

1970, Mar. 1   *Wmk. 347*   *Perf. 11*
1222	A220	1g bis brn	1.25	1.00
1223	A220	2g violet	1.25	1.00
1224	A220	3g brt pink	1.25	.50
1225	A220	4g rose claret	1.25	1.00
1226	A220	5g blue	1.25	1.00
1227	A220	10g bright grn	1.25	.75
1228	A220	15g lt Prus bl	1.25	2.00
1229	A220	20g org brn	1.25	2.00
1230	A220	30g gray grn	1.25	1.00
1231	A220	40g gray brn	1.25	3.00
	Nos. 1222-1231 (10)		12.50	13.25

Marshal Francisco Solano Lopez (1827-1870), President of Paraguay. Nos. 1228-1231 are airmail.

1st Moon Landing, Apollo 11 — A221

Designs: 10c, Wernher von Braun, lift-off. 15c, Eagle and Columbia in lunar orbit. 20c, Deployment of lunar module. 25c, Landing on Moon. 30c, First steps on lunar surface. 50c, Gathering lunar soil. 75c, Lift-off from Moon. 12.45g, Rendevouz of Eagle and Columbia. 18.15g, Pres. Kennedy, von Braun, splashdown. No. 1241, Gold medal of Armstrong, Aldrin and Collins. No. 1242, Moon landing medal, Kennedy, von Braun. No. 1243, Apollo 12 astronauts Charles Conrad and Alan Bean on moon, and Dr. Kurt Debus.

1970, Mar. 11   *Unwmk.*   *Perf. 14*
1232	A221	10c multicolored	.30	.25
1233	A221	15c multicolored	.30	.25
1234	A221	20c multicolored	.30	.25
1235	A221	25c multicolored	.30	.25
1236	A221	30c multicolored	.30	.25
1237	A221	50c multicolored	.30	.25
1238	A221	75c multicolored	.30	.25
1239	A221	12.45g multicolored	3.50	.60
1240	A221	18.15g multicolored	7.00	1.25
	Nos. 1232-1240 (9)		12.60	3.60

Souvenir Sheets
1241	A221	23.40g multicolored	16.00	12.00

Imperf
1242	A221	23.40g multicolored	35.00	30.00
1243	A221	23.40g multicolored	21.00	16.00

Nos. 1239-1243 are airmail. Nos. 1241-1242 contain one 50x60mm stamp, No. 1243 one 60x50mm stamp.

Easter A222

Designs: 10c, 15c, 20c, 25c, 30c, 50c, 75c, Stations of the Cross. 12.45g, Christ appears to soldiers, vert. 18.15g, Christ appears to disciples, vert. 23.40g, The sad Madonna, vert.

1970, Mar. 11
1244	A222	10c multicolored	.30	.25
1245	A222	15c multicolored	.30	.25
1246	A222	20c multicolored	.30	.25
1247	A222	25c multicolored	.30	.25
1248	A222	30c multicolored	.30	.25
1249	A222	50c multicolored	.30	.25
1250	A222	75c multicolored	.55	.25
1251	A222	12.45g multicolored	2.25	.60
1252	A222	18.15g multicolored	6.00	1.50
	Nos. 1244-1252 (9)		10.60	3.75

Souvenir Sheet
Perf. 13½
1253	A222	23.40g multicolored	10.00	

Nos. 1251-1253 are airmail. No. 1253 contains one 50x60mm stamp.

Paraguay No. 2 — A223

Designs (First Issue of Paraguay): 2g, 10g, #1. 3g, #3. 5g, #2. 15g, #3. 30g, #2. 36g, #1.

1970, Aug. 15   *Litho.*   *Wmk. 347*
1254	A223	1g car rose	1.20	1.00
1255	A223	2g ultra	1.20	1.00
1256	A223	3g org brn	1.20	1.00
1257	A223	5g violet	1.20	1.00
1258	A223	10g lilac	1.20	1.00
1259	A223	15g vio brn	2.40	2.00
1260	A223	30g dp grn	2.40	2.00
1261	A223	36g brt pink	2.40	2.00
	Nos. 1254-1261 (8)		13.20	11.00

Centenary of stamps of Paraguay. #1259-1261 are airmail.

1972 Summer Olympics, Munich — A224

No. 1262: a, 10c, Discus. b, 15c, Cycling. c, 20c, Men's hurdles. d, 25c, Fencing. e, 30c, Swimming, horiz.
50c, Shotput. 75c, Sailing. 12.45, Women's hurdles, horiz. 18.15g, Equestrian, horiz. No. 1267, Flags, Olympic coins. No. 1268, Frauenkirche Church, Munich. No. 1269, Olympic Village, Munich, horiz.

1970, Sept. 28   *Unwmk.*   *Perf. 14*
1262	A224	Strip of 5, #a.-e.	1.75	1.25
1263	A224	50c multicolored	.30	.25
1264	A224	75c multicolored	.45	.25
1265	A224	12.45g multicolored	2.00	.45
1266	A224	18.15g multicolored	5.00	1.25
	Nos. 1262-1266 (5)		9.50	3.45

Souvenir Sheets
Perf. 13½
1267	A224	23.40g multicolored	27.00	

Imperf
1268	A224	23.40g multicolored	62.00	
1269	A224	23.40g multicolored	24.00	24.00

Nos. 1265-1269 are airmail. Nos. 1267-1269 each contain one 50x60mm stamp.

Paintings, Pinakothek, Munich, 1972 — A225

Nudes by: No. 1270a, 10c, Cranach. b, 15c, Baldung. c, 20c, Tintoretto. d, 25c, Rubens. e, 30c, Boucher, horiz. 50c, Baldung, diff. 75c, Cranach, diff.
12.45g, Self-portrait, Durer. 18.15g, Alterpiece, Altdorfer. 23.40g, Madonna and Child.

1970, Sept. 28   *Perf. 14*
1270	A225	Strip of 5, #a.-e.	1.50	1.25
1271	A225	50c multicolored	.65	.25
1272	A225	75c multicolored	.65	.25
1273	A225	12.45g multicolored	3.25	.50
1274	A225	18.15g multicolored	4.50	1.50
	Nos. 1270-1274 (5)		10.55	3.75

Souvenir Sheet
Perf. 13½
1275	A225	23.40g multicolored	27.50	27.50

Nos. 1273-1275 are airmail. No. 1275 contains one 50x60mm stamp.

Apollo Space Program A226

No. 1276: a, 10c, Ignition, Saturn 5. b, 15c, Apollo 1 mission emblem, vert. c, 20c, Apollo 7, Oct. 1968. d, 25c, Apollo 8, Dec. 1968. e, 30c, Apollo 9, Mar. 1969.
50c, Apollo 10, May 1969. 75c, Apollo 11, July 1969. 12.45g, Apollo 12, Nov. 1969. 18.15g, Apollo 13, Apr. 1970. No. 1281, Lunar landing sites. No. 1282, Wernher von Braun, rockets. No. 1283, James A. Lovell, John L. Swigert, Fred W. Haise.

1970, Oct. 19   *Perf. 14*
1276	A226	Strip of 5, #a.-e.	1.50	1.25
1277	A226	50c multicolored	.40	.25
1278	A226	75c multicolored	.40	.25
1279	A226	12.45g multicolored	2.00	.50
1280	A226	18.15g multicolored	7.00	1.50
	Nos. 1276-1280 (5)		11.30	3.75

Souvenir Sheets
Perf. 13½
1281	A226	23.40g multicolored	10.00	

Imperf
1282	A226	23.40g multicolored	65.00	
1283	A226	23.40g multicolored	30.00	

Nos. 1279-1283 are airmail. Nos. 1281-1283 each contain one 60x50mm stamp.

1970, Oct. 19   *Perf. 14*
Future Space Projects: No. 1284a, 10c, Space station, 2000. b, 15c, Lunar station, vert. c, 20c, Space transport. d, 25c, Lunar rover. e, 30c, Skylab.
50c, Space station, 1971. 75c, Lunar vehicle. 12.45g, Lunar vehicle, diff., vert. 18.15g, Vehicle rising above lunar surface. 23.40g, Moon stations, transport.

1284	A226	Strip of 5, #a.-e.	1.50	1.25
1285	A226	50c multicolored	.40	.25
1286	A226	75c multicolored	.40	.25
1287	A226	12.45g multicolored	2.25	.50
1288	A226	18.15g multicolored	3.75	1.00
	Nos. 1284-1288 (5)		8.30	3.25

Souvenir Sheet
Perf. 13½
1289	A226	23.40g multicolored	16.00	16.00

Nos. 1287-1289 are airmail. No. 1289 contains one 50x60mm stamp. For overprints see Nos. 2288-2290, C653.

EXPO '70,
Osaka,
Japan — A228

Paintings from National Museum, Tokyo:
No. 1288a, 10c, Buddha. b, 15c, Fire, people.
c, 20c, Demon, Ogata Korin. d, 25c, Japanese
play, Hishikawa Moronobu. e, 30c, Birds.
50c, Woman, Utamaro. 75c, Samurai,
Wantabe Kazan. 12.45c, Women Beneath
Tree, Kano Hideroi. 18.15g, Courtesans, Torrii
Kiyonaga. 50g, View of Mt. Fuji, Hokusai,
horiz. No. 1296, Courtesan, Kaigetsudo Ando.
No. 1297, Emblem of Expo '70. No. 1298,
Emblem of 1972 Winter Olympics, Sapporo.

1970, Nov. 26		Litho.	Perf. 14	
1290	A228	Strip of 5, #a.-e.	1.50	1.25
1291	A228	50c multicolored	.50	.25
1292	A228	75c multicolored	.50	.25
1293	A228	12.45g multicolored	1.00	.50
1294	A228	18.15g multicolored	1.75	.60
1295	A228	50g multicolored	7.50	1.50
		Nos. 1290-1295 (6)	12.75	4.35

Souvenir Sheets

Perf. 13½

1296	A228	20g multicolored	12.00	
1297	A228	20g multicolored	18.00	
1298	A228	20g multicolored	42.50	

Nos. 1293-1298 are airmail. Nos. 1296-
1298 each contain one 50x60mm stamp.

Flower
Paintings — A229

Artists: No. 1299a, 10c, Von Jawlensky. b,
15c, Purrmann. c, 20c, De Vlaminck. d, 25c,
Monet. e, 30c, Renoir.
50c, Van Gogh. 75c, Cezanne. 12.45g, Van
Huysum. 18.15g, Ruysch. 50g, Walscappelle.
20g, Bosschaert.

1970, Nov. 26			Perf. 14	
1299	A229	Strip of 5, #a.-e.	1.50	1.25
1300	A229	50c multicolored	.50	.25
1301	A229	75c multicolored	.50	.25
1302	A229	12.45g multicolored	2.00	.40
1303	A229	18.15g multicolored	2.75	.40
1304	A229	50g multicolored	5.50	1.00
		Nos. 1299-1304 (6)	12.75	3.55

Souvenir Sheet

Perf. 13½

| 1305 | A229 | 20g multicolored | 17.50 | 17.50 |

Nos. 1302-1305 are airmail. No. 1305 contains one 50x60mm stamp.

Paintings
from The
Prado,
Madrid
A230

Nudes by: No. 1306a, 10c, Titian. b, 15c,
Velazquez. c, 20c, Van Dyck. d, 25c, Tintoretto. e, 30c, Rubens.
50c, Venus and Sleeping Adonis, Veronese.
75c, Adam and Eve, Titian. 12.45g, The Holy
Family, Goya. 18.15g, Shepherd Boy, Murillo.
50g, The Holy Family, El Greco.

1970, Dec. 16			Perf. 14	
1306	A230	Strip of 5, #a.-e.	1.50	1.25
1307	A230	50c multicolored	.60	.25
1308	A230	75c multicolored	.60	.25
1309	A230	12.45g multicolored	1.40	.25
1310	A230	18.15g multicolored	1.40	.25
1311	A230	50g multicolored	6.50	1.50
		Nos. 1306-1311 (6)	12.00	3.75

Nos. 1309-1311 are airmail. Nos. 1307-
1311 are vert.

1970, Dec. 16

Paintings by Albrecht Durer (1471-1528):
No. 1312a, 10c, Adam and Eve. b, 15c, St.
Jerome in the Wilderness. c, 20c, St. Eusta-
chius and George. d, 25c, Piper and drummer.
e, 30c, Lucretia's Suicide.
50c, Oswald Krel. 75c, Stag Beetle. 12.45g,
Paul and Mark. 18.15g, Lot's Flight. 50g,
Nativity.

1312	A230	Strip of 5, #a.-e.	1.50	1.25
1313	A230	50c multicolored	.45	.25
1314	A230	75c multicolored	.45	.25
1315	A230	12.45g multicolored	1.00	.40
1316	A230	18.15g multicolored	2.25	.40
1317	A230	50g multicolored	6.50	1.25
		Nos. 1312-1317 (6)	12.15	3.80

Nos. 1315-1317 are airmail. See No. 1273.

Christmas
A232

Paintings: No. 1318a, 10c, The Annunciation, Van der Weyden. b, 15c, The Madonna,
Zeitblom. c, 20c, The Nativity, Von Soest. d,
25c, Adoration of the Magi, Mayno. e, 30c,
Adoration of the Magi, Da Fabriano.
50c, Flight From Egypt, Masters of Martyrdom. 75c, Presentation of Christ, Memling.
12.45g, The Holy Family, Poussin, horiz.
18.15g, The Holy Family, Rubens. 20g, Adoration of the Magi, Giorgione, horiz. 50g,
Madonna and Child, Batoni.

1971, Mar. 23				
1318	A232	Strip of 5, #a.-e.	1.50	1.25
1319	A232	50c multicolored	.35	.25
1320	A232	75c multicolored	.35	.25
1321	A232	12.45g multicolored	.90	.40
1322	A232	18.15g multicolored	2.25	.40
1323	A232	50g multicolored	5.25	1.25
		Nos. 1318-1323 (6)	10.60	3.80

Souvenir Sheet

Perf. 13½

| 1324 | A232 | 20g multicolored | 26.00 | 25.00 |

Nos. 1321-1324 are airmail. No. 1324 contains one 60x50mm stamp.

1972 Summer
Olympics,
Munich — A233

Olympic decathlon gold medalists: No.
1325a, 10c, Hugo Wieslander, Stockholm
1912. b, 15c, Helge Lovland, Antwerp 1920. c,
20c, Harold M. Osborn, Paris 1924. d, 25c,
Paavo Yrjola, Amsterdam 1928. e, 30c, James
Bausch, Los Angeles 1932.
50c, Glenn Morris, Berlin 1936. 75c, Bob
Mathias, London 1948, Helsinki 1952. 12.45g,
Milton Campbell, Melbourne 1956. 18.15g,
Rafer Johnson, Rome 1960. 50g, Willi Holdorf,
Tokyo 1964. No. 1331, Bill Toomey, Mexico
City 1968.
No. 1332, Pole vaulter, Munich, 1972.

1971, Mar. 23			Perf. 14	
1325	A233	Strip of 5, #a.-e.	1.50	1.25
1326	A233	50c multicolored	.45	.25
1327	A233	75c multicolored	.45	.25
1328	A233	12.45g multicolored	1.00	.40
1329	A233	18.15g multicolored	2.50	.40
1330	A233	50g multicolored	6.25	1.25
		Nos. 1325-1330 (6)	12.15	3.80

Souvenir Sheets

Perf. 13½

| 1331 | A233 | 20g multicolored | 20.00 | 15.00 |
| 1332 | A233 | 20g multicolored | 20.00 | 15.00 |

Nos. 1328-1332 are airmail. Nos. 1331-
1332 each contain one 50x60mm stamp.

Art — A234

Paintings by: No. 1333a, 10c, Van Dyck. b,
15c, Titian. c, 20c, Van Dyck, diff. d, 25c, Walter. e, 30c, Orsi.
50c, 17th cent. Japanese artist, horiz. 75c,
David. 12.45g, Huguet. 18.15g, Perugino. 20g,
Van Eyck. 50g, Witz.

1971, Mar. 26			Perf. 14	
1333	A234	Strip of 5, #a.-e.	1.50	1.25
1334	A234	50c multicolored	.45	.25
1335	A234	75c multicolored	.45	.25
1336	A234	12.45g multicolored	1.40	.40
1337	A234	18.15g multicolored	2.50	.40
1338	A234	50g multicolored	6.00	1.25
		Nos. 1333-1338 (6)	12.30	3.80

Souvenir Sheet

Perf. 13½

| 1339 | A234 | 20g multicolored | 26.00 | 25.00 |

Nos. 1336-1339 are airmail. No. 1339 contains one 50x60mm stamp.

Paintings from the Louvre, Paris

Portraits of women by: No. 1340a, 10c, De
la Tour. b, 15c, Boucher. c, 20c, Delacroix. d,
25c, 16th cent. French artist. e, 30c, Ingres.
50c, Ingres, horiz. 75c, Watteau, horiz.
12.45g, 2nd cent. artist. 18.15g, Renoir. 20g,
Mona Lisa, Da Vinci. 50g, Liberty Guiding the
People, Delacroix.

1971, Mar. 26			Perf. 14	
1340	A234	Strip of 5, #a.-e.	1.50	1.25
1341	A234	50c multicolored	.60	.25
1342	A234	75c multicolored	.60	.25
1343	A234	12.45g multicolored	1.75	.40
1344	A234	18.15g multicolored	2.25	.40
1345	A234	50g multicolored	5.50	1.00
		Nos. 1340-1345 (6)	12.20	3.55

Souvenir Sheet

Perf. 13½

| 1346 | A234 | 20g multicolored | 21.00 | 20.00 |

Nos. 1343-1346 are airmail. No. 1346 contains one 50x60mm stamp.

Paintings — A236

Artist: No. 1347a, 10c, Botticelli. b, 15c,
Titian. c, 20c, Raphael. d, 25c, Pellegrini. e,
30c, Caracci.
50c, Titian, horiz. 75c, Ricci, horiz. 12.45g,
Courtines. 18.15g, Rodas. 50g, Murillo.

1971, Mar. 29			Perf. 14	
1347	A236	Strip of 5, #a.-e.	1.50	1.25
1348	A236	50c multicolored	.50	.25
1349	A236	75c multicolored	.50	.25
1350	A236	12.45g multicolored	1.75	.40
1351	A236	18.15g multicolored	2.75	.40
1352	A236	50g multicolored	6.50	1.00
		Nos. 1347-1352 (6)	13.50	3.55

Nos. 1350-1352 are airmail.

Hunting
Scenes
A237

Different Paintings by: No. 1353a, 10c, Goz-
zoli, vert. b, 15c, Velazquez, vert. c, 20c, Brun.
d, 25c, Fontainebleau School, 1550, vert. e,
30c, Uccello, vert.
50c, P. De Vos. 75c, Vernet. 12.45g,
18.15g, 50g, Alken & Sutherland. No. 1359,
Paul & Derveaux. No. 1360, Degas.

1971, Mar. 29				
1353	A237	Strip of 5, #a.-e.	1.50	1.25
1354	A237	50c multicolored	.50	.25
1355	A237	75c multicolored	.50	.25
1356	A237	12.45g multicolored	1.50	.40
1357	A237	18.15g multicolored	1.90	.40
1358	A237	50g multicolored	6.75	1.00
		Nos. 1353-1358 (6)	12.65	3.55

Souvenir Sheets

Perf. 13½

| 1359 | A237 | 20g multicolored | 18.00 | 17.00 |
| 1360 | A237 | 20g multicolored | 18.00 | 17.00 |

Nos. 1356-1360 are airmail. Nos. 1359-
1360 each contain one 60x50mm stamp.

Philatokyo
'71 — A238

Designs: Nos. 1361a-1361e, 10c, 15c, 20c,
25c, 30c, Different flowers, Gukei. 50c, Birds,
Lu Chi. 75c, Flowers, Sakai Hoitsu. 12.45g,
Man and Woman, Utamaro. 18.15g, Tea Cere-
mony, from Tea museum. 50g, Bathers,
Utamaro. No. 1367, Woman, Kamakura
Period. No. 1368, Japan #1, #821, #904,
#1023.

1971, Apr. 7			Perf. 14	
1361	A238	Strip of 5, #a.-e.	2.50	1.25
1362	A238	50c multicolored	.55	.25
1363	A238	75c multicolored	.55	.25
1364	A238	12.45g multicolored	1.75	.40
1365	A238	18.15g multicolored	1.75	.40
1366	A238	50g multicolored	8.00	1.00
		Nos. 1361-1366 (6)	15.10	3.55

Souvenir Sheets

Perf. 13½

| 1367 | A238 | 20g multicolored | 15.00 | 15.00 |
| 1368 | A238 | 20g multicolored | 17.00 | 17.00 |

Nos. 1364-1368 are airmail. Nos. 1367-
1368 each contain one 50x60mm stamp.
See Nos. 1375-1376.

1972 Winter
Olympics,
Sapporo — A239

Paintings of women by: No. 1369a, 10c,
Harunobu. b, 15c, Hosoda. c, 20c, Harunobu,
diff. d, 25c, Uemura Shoen. e, 30c, Ketao.
50c, Three Women, Torii. 75c, Old Man,
Kakizahi. 12.45g, 2-man bobsled. 18.15g, Ice
sculptures, horiz. 50g, Mt. Fuji, Hokusai, horiz.
No. 1375, Skier, horiz. No. 1376, Sapporo
Olympic emblems.

1971, Apr.			Perf. 14	
1369	A239	Strip of 5, #a.-e.	1.50	1.25
1370	A239	50c multicolored	.50	.25
1371	A239	75c multicolored	.50	.25
1372	A239	12.45g multicolored	1.40	.40
1373	A239	18.15g multicolored	2.75	.40
1374	A239	50g multicolored	7.25	1.00
		Nos. 1369-1374 (6)	13.90	3.55

Souvenir Sheets

Perf. 14½

| 1375 | A239 | 20g multicolored | 37.50 | 37.50 |

Perf. 13½

| 1376 | A239 | 20g multicolored | 22.50 | 22.50 |

Nos. 1372-1376 are airmail. No. 1375 contains one 35x25mm stamp with PhilaTokyo 71
emblem. No. 1376 contains one 50x60mm
stamp.
For Japanese painting stamps with white
border and Winter Olympics emblem see
#1409-1410.

UNESCO and
Paraguay
Emblems, Globe,
Teacher and
Pupil — A240

Wmk. 347

1971, May 18   **Litho.**   **Perf. 11**

1377	A240	3g ultra	1.10 1.00
1378	A240	5g lilac	1.10 1.00
1379	A240	10g emerald	1.10 1.00
1380	A240	20g claret	2.25 2.00
1381	A240	25g brt pink	2.25 2.00
1382	A240	30g brown	2.25 2.00
1383	A240	50g gray olive	2.25 2.00
		Nos. 1377-1383 (7)	12.30 11.00

International Education Year.
Nos. 1380-1383 are airmail.

Paintings, Berlin-Dahlem Museum — A241

Artists: 10c, Caravaggio. No. 1385: a, 15c, b, 20c, Di Cosimo. 25c, Cranach. 30c, Veneziano. 50g, Holbein. 75c, Baldung. 12.45g, Cranach, diff. 18.15g, Durer. 50g, Schongauer.

1971, Dec. 24   **Unwmk.**   **Perf. 14**

1384	A241	10c multicolored	.30 .25
1385	A241	Pair, #a.-b.	.30 .25
1386	A241	25c multicolored	.30 .25
1387	A241	30c multicolored	.30 .25
1388	A241	50c multicolored	.30 .25
1389	A241	75c multicolored	.30 .25
1390	A241	12.45g multicolored	1.90 .40
1391	A241	18.15g multicolored	1.90 .40
1392	A241	50g multicolored	7.25 1.00
		Nos. 1384-1392 (9)	12.85 3.30

Nos. 1390-1392 are airmail. No. 1385 has continuous design.

Napoleon I, 150th Death Anniv. — A242

Paintings: No. 1393a, 10c, Desiree Clary, Gerin. b, 15c, Josephine de Beauharnais, Gros. c, 20c, Maria Luisa, Gerard. d, 25c, Juliette Recamier, Gerard. e, 30c, Maria Walewska, Gerard.
50c, Victoria Kraus, unknown artist, horiz. 75c, Napoleon on Horseback, Chabord. 12.45g, Trafalgar, A. Mayer, horiz. 18.15g, Napoleon Leading Army, Gautherot, horiz. 50g, Napoleon's tomb.

1971, Dec. 24

1393	A242	Strip of 5, #a.-e.	1.50 1.25
1394	A242	50c multicolored	.30 .25
1395	A242	75c multicolored	.30 .25
1396	A242	12.45g multicolored	1.75 .40
1397	A242	18.15g multicolored	2.00 .40
1398	A242	50g multicolored	7.50 1.00
		Nos. 1393-1398 (6)	13.35 3.55

Nos. 1396-1398 are airmail.

Locomotives A243

Designs: No. 1399a, 10c, Trevithick, Great Britain, 1804. b, 15c, Blenkinsops, 1812. c, 20c, G. Stephenson #1, 1825. d, 25c, Marc Seguin, France, 1829. e, 30c, "Adler," Germany, 1835.
50c, Sampierdarena #1, Italy, 1854. 75c, Paraguay #1, 1861. 12.45g, "Munich," Germany, 1841. 18.15g, US, 1875. 20g, Japanese locomotives, 1872-1972. 50g, Mikado D-50, Japan, 1923.

1972, Jan. 6

1399	A243	Strip of 5, #a.-e.	1.50 1.25
1400	A243	50c multicolored	.30 .25
1401	A243	75c multicolored	.30 .25
1402	A243	12.45g multicolored	2.00 .40
1403	A243	18.15g multicolored	2.00 .40
1404	A243	50g multicolored	7.50 .90
		Nos. 1399-1404 (6)	13.60 3.45

Souvenir Sheet
Perf. 13½

1405	A243	20g multicolored	62.50 60.00

Nos. 1402-1405 are airmail. No. 1405 contains one 60x50mm stamp.
See Nos. 1476-1480.

1972 Winter Olympics, Sapporo A244

Designs: Nos. 1406a, 10c, Hockey player. b, 15c, Jean-Claude Killy. c, 20c, Gaby Seyfert. d, 25c, 4-Man bobsled. e, 30c, Luge.
50c, Ski jumping, horiz. 75c, Slalom skiing, horiz. 12.45g, Painting, Kuniyoshi. 18.15g, Winter Scene, Hiroshige, horiz. 50g, Ski lift, man in traditional dress.

1972, Jan. 6   **Perf. 14**

1406	A244	Strip of 5, #a.-e.	1.60 1.25
1407	A244	50c multicolored	.30 .25
1408	A244	75c multicolored	.30 .25
1409	A244	12.45g multicolored	1.60 .40
1410	A244	18.15g multicolored	1.60 .40
1411	A244	50g multicolored	6.00 1.25
		Nos. 1406-1411 (6)	11.40 3.80

Souvenir Sheet
Perf. 13½

1412	A244	20g Skier	17.50 17.50
1413	A244	20g Flags	25.00 25.00

Nos. 1409-1413 are airmail. Nos. 1412-1413 each contain one 50x60mm stamp. For overprint see Nos. 2295-2297. For Winter Olympic stamps with gold border, see Nos. 1372-1373.

UNICEF, 25th Anniv. (in 1971) — A245

1972, Jan. 24   **Granite Paper**

1414	A245	1g red brn	1.20 1.00
1415	A245	2g ultra	1.20 1.00
1416	A245	3g lil rose	1.20 1.00
1417	A245	4g violet	1.20 1.00
1418	A245	5g emerald	1.20 1.00
1419	A245	10g claret	2.40 3.00
1420	A245	20g brt bl	2.40 3.00
1421	A245	25g lt ol	2.40 3.00
1422	A245	30g dk brn	2.40 3.00
		Nos. 1414-1422 (9)	15.60 17.00

Nos. 1420-1422 are airmail.

Race Cars — A246

No. 1423: a, 10c, Ferrari. b, 15c, B.R.M. c, 20c, Brabham. d, 25c, March. e, 30c, Honda.
50c, Matra-Simca MS 650. 75c, Porsche. 12.45g, Maserati-8 CTF, 1938. 18.15g, Bugatti 35B, 1929. 20g, Lotus 72 Ford. 50g, Mercedes, 1924.

1972, Mar. 20   **Unwmk.**   **Perf. 14**

1423	A246	Strip of 5, #a.-e.	1.50 1.25
1424	A246	50c multicolored	.50 .25
1425	A246	75c multicolored	.50 .25
1426	A246	12.45g multicolored	2.00 .45
1427	A246	18.15g multicolored	2.00 .45
1428	A246	50g multicolored	7.50 5.25
		Nos. 1423-1428 (6)	14.00 7.90

Souvenir Sheet
Perf. 13½

1429	A246	20g multicolored	28.00

Nos. 1426-1429 are airmail. No. 1429 contains one 60x50mm stamp.

Sailing Ships A247

Paintings: No. 1430a, 10c, Holbein. b, 15c, Nagasaki print. c, 20c, Intrepid, Roux. d, 25c, Portuguese ship, unknown artist. e, 30c, Mount Vernon, US, 1798, Corne.
50c, Van Eertvelt. 75c, Santa Maria, Van Eertvelt. vert. 12.45g, Royal Prince, 1679, Van Beecq. 18.15g, Van Bree. 50g, Book of Arms, 1497, vert.

1972, Mar. 29   **Perf. 14**

1430	A247	Strip of 5, #a.-e.	1.50 1.25
1431	A247	50c multicolored	.50 .25
1432	A247	75c multicolored	.65 .25
1433	A247	12.45g multicolored	1.75 .35
1434	A247	18.15g multicolored	2.50 .40
1435	A247	50g multicolored	5.50 .75
		Nos. 1430-1435 (6)	12.40 3.25

Nos. 1433-1435 are airmail.

Paintings in Vienna Museum — A248

Nudes by: No. 1436a, 10c, Rubens. b, 15c, Bellini. c, 20c, Carracci. d, 25c, Cagnacci. e, 30c, Spranger.
50c, Mandolin Player, Strozzi. 75c, Woman in Red Hat, Cranach the elder. 12.45g, Adam and Eve, Coxcie. 18.15g, Legionary on Horseback, Poussin. 50g, Madonna and Child, Bronzino.

1972, May 22

1436	A248	Strip of 5, #a.-e.	1.50 1.25
1437	A248	50c multicolored	.50 .25
1438	A248	75c multicolored	.50 .25
1439	A248	12.45g multicolored	1.50 .40
1440	A248	18.15g multicolored	1.50 .40
1441	A248	50g multicolored	6.25 1.25
		Nos. 1436-1441 (6)	11.75 3.80

Nos. 1439-1441 are airmail.

Paintings in Asuncion Museum — A249

No. 1442: a, 10c, Man in Straw Hat, Holden Jara. b, 15c, Portrait, Tintoretto. c, 20c, Indians, Holden Jara. d, 25c, Nude, Bouchard. e, 30c, Italian School.
50c, Reclining Nude, Berisso, horiz. 75c, Carracci, horiz. 12.45g, Reclining Nude, Schiaffino, horiz. 18.15g, Reclining Nude, Lostow, horiz. 50g, Madonna and Child, 17th cent. Italian School.

1972, May 22

1442	A249	Strip of 5, #a.-e.	1.50 1.25
1443	A249	50c multicolored	.45 .25
1444	A249	75c multicolored	.45 .25
1445	A249	12.45g multicolored	1.50 .40
1446	A249	18.15g multicolored	1.50 .40
1447	A249	50g multicolored	5.25 1.25
		Nos. 1442-1447 (6)	10.65 3.80

Nos. 1445-1447 are airmail.

Presidential Summit — A250

No. 1448: a, 10c, Map of South America. b, 15c, Brazil natl. arms. c, 20c, Argentina natl. arms. d, 25c, Bolivia natl. arms. e, 30c, Paraguay natl. arms.
50c, Pres. Emilio Garrastazu, Brazil. 75c, Pres. Alejandro Lanusse, Argentina. 12.45g, Pres. Hugo Banzer Suarez, Bolivia. 18.15g, Pres. Stroessner, Paraguay, horiz. 23.40g, Flags.

1972, Nov. 18

1448	A250	Strip of 5, #a.-e.	1.50 1.25
1449	A250	50c multicolored	.35 .25
1450	A250	75c multicolored	.35 .25
1451	A250	12.45g multicolored	2.00 .25
1452	A250	18.15g multicolored	2.75 .30
		Nos. 1448-1452 (5)	6.95 2.30

Souvenir Sheet
Perf. 13½

1453	A250	23.40g multicolored	10.50

Nos. 1451-1453 are airmail. No. 1453 contains one 50x60mm stamp. For overprint see No. 2144.

Pres. Stroessner's Visit to Japan — A251

No. 1454: a, 10c, Departure of first Japanese mission to US & Europe, 1871. b, 15c, First railroad, Tokyo-Yokahama, 1872. c, 20c, Samurai. d, 25c, Geishas. e, 30c, Cranes, Hiroshige.
50c, Honda race car. 75c, Pres. Stroessner, Emperor Hirohito, Mt. Fuji, bullet train, horiz. 12.45g, Rocket. 18.15g, Stroessner, Hirohito, horiz. No. 1459, Mounted samurai, Masanobu, 1740. No. 1460, Hirohito's speech, state dinner, horiz. No. 1461, Delegations at Tokyo airport, horiz.

1972, Nov. 18   **Perf. 14**

1454	A251	Strip of 5, #a.-e.	1.50 1.25
1455	A251	50c multicolored	.50 .25
1456	A251	75c multicolored	.50 .25
1457	A251	12.45g multicolored	4.50 2.00
1458	A251	18.15g multicolored	5.50 2.50
		Nos. 1454-1458 (5)	12.50 6.25

Souvenir Sheets
Perf. 13½

1459	A251	23.40g multicolored	18.00 18.00
1460	A251	23.40g multicolored	18.00 18.00

Imperf

1461	A251	23.40g multicolored	18.00 18.00

Nos. 1457-1461 are airmail. Nos. 1459-1460 each contain one 50x60mm stamp. No. 1461 contains one 85x42mm stamp with simulated perforations. For overprints see Nos. 2192-2194, 2267.

Wildlife — A252

Paintings — #1462: a, 10c, Cranes, Botke. b, 15c, Tiger, Utamaro. c, 20c, Horses, Arenys. d, 25c, Pheasant, Dietzsch. e, 30c, Monkey, Brueghel, the Elder. All vert.
50c, Deer, Marc. 75c, Crab, Durer. 12.45g, Rooster, Jakuchu, vert. 18.15g, Swan, Asselyn.

1972, Nov. 18   **Perf. 14**

1462	A252	Strip of 5, #a.-e.	1.50 1.25
1463	A252	50c multicolored	.30 .25
1464	A252	75c multicolored	.30 .25
1465	A252	12.45g multicolored	4.50 .75
1466	A252	18.15g multicolored	5.25 1.00
		Nos. 1462-1466 (5)	11.85 3.50

Nos. 1465-1466 are airmail.

Acaray Dam — A253

Designs: 2g, Francisco Solano Lopez monument. 3g, Friendship Bridge. 5g, Tebicuary River Bridge. 10g, Hotel Guarani. 20g, Bus and car on highway. 25g, Hospital of Institute for Social Service. 50g, "Presidente Stroessner" of state merchant marine. 100g, "Electra C" of Paraguayan airlines.

Perf. 13½x13
1972, Nov. 16　　　　　**Wmk. 347**
Granite Paper

1467	A253	1g sepia	2.25 1.00
1468	A253	2g brown	2.25 1.00
1469	A253	3g brt ultra	2.25 1.00
1470	A253	5g brt pink	2.25 1.00
1471	A253	10g dl grn	3.25 2.00
1472	A253	20g rose car	3.25 2.00
1473	A253	25g gray	3.25 2.00
1474	A253	50g violet	3.25 2.00
1475	A253	100g brt lil	3.25 2.00
	Nos. 1467-1475 (9)		25.25 14.00

Tourism Year of the Americas.
Nos. 1472-1475 are airmail.

Locomotives Type

No. 1476: a, 10c, Stephenson's Rocket, 1829. b, 15c, First Swiss railroad, 1847. c, 20c, 1st Spanish locomotive, 1848. d, 25c, Norris, US, 1850. e, 30c, Ansaldo, Italy, 1859. 50c, Badenia, Germany, 1863. 75c, 1st Japanese locomotive, 1895. 12.45g, P.L.M., France, 1924. 18.15g, Stephenson's Northumbrian.

1972, Nov. 25　**Unwmk.**　**Perf. 14**

1476	A243	Strip of 5, #a.-e.	1.50 1.25
1477	A243	50c multicolored	.30 .25
1478	A243	75c multicolored	.30 .25
1479	A243	12.45g multicolored	4.25 .40
1480	A243	18.15g multicolored	6.00 1.00
	Nos. 1476-1480 (5)		12.35 3.15

Nos. 1479-1480 are airmail.

South American Wildlife A254

No. 1481: a, 10c, Tetradactyla. b, 15c, Nasua socialis. c, 20c, Priodontes giganteus. d, 25c, Blastocerus dichotomus. e, 30c, Felis pardalis. 50c, Aotes, vert. 75c, Rhea americana. 12.45g, Desmodus rotundus. 18.15g, Urocyon cinereo-argenteus.

1972, Nov. 25

1481	A254	Strip of 5, #a.-e.	1.50 1.25
1482	A254	50c multicolored	.40 .25
1483	A254	75c multicolored	.40 .25
1484	A254	12.45g multicolored	4.50 .75
1485	A254	18.15g multicolored	6.00 1.25
	Nos. 1481-1485 (5)		12.80 3.75

Nos. 1484-1485 are airmail.

OAS Emblem — A255

Perf. 13x13½
1973　**Litho.**　**Wmk. 347**
Granite Paper

1486	A255	1g multi	1.10 1.00
1487	A255	2g multi	1.10 1.00
1488	A255	3g multi	1.10 1.00
1489	A255	4g multi	1.10 1.00
1490	A255	5g multi	1.10 1.00
1491	A255	10g multi	1.10 1.00
1492	A255	20g multi	2.25 1.00
1493	A255	25g multi	2.25 1.00
1494	A255	50g multi	3.25 1.00
1495	A255	100g multi	5.50 1.00
	Nos. 1486-1495 (10)		19.85 10.00

Org. of American States, 25th anniv.
Nos. 1492-1495 are airmail.

Paintings in Florence Museum — A256

Artists: No. 1496: a, 10c, Cranach, the Elder. b, 15c, Caravaggio. c, 20c, Fiorentino. d, 25c, Di Credi. e, 30c, Liss. f, 50c, Da Vinci. g, 75c, Botticelli.
No. 1497: a, 5g, Titian, horiz. b, 10g, Del Piombo, horiz. c, 20g, Di Michelino, horiz.

1973, Mar. 13　**Unwmk.**　**Perf. 14**

1496	A256	Strip of 7, #a.-g.	3.50 1.00
1497	A256	Strip of 3, #a.-c.	8.00 2.50
	Nos. 1496-1497 (2)		11.50 3.50

No. 1497 is airmail.

Butterflies A257

#1498: a, 10c, Catagramma patazza. b, 15c, Agrias narcissus. c, 20c, Papilio zagreus. d, 25c, Heliconius chestertoni. e, 30c, Metamorphadido. f, 50c, Catagramma astarte. g, 75c, Papilio brasiliensis.
No. 1499a, 5g, Agrias sardanapalus. b, 10g, Callithea saphhira. c, 20g, Jemadia hospita.

1973, Mar. 13

1498	A257	Strip of 7, #a.-g.	4.00 1.00
1499	A257	Strip of 3, #a.-c.	13.50 3.50
	Nos. 1498-1499 (2)		17.50 4.50

No. 1499 is airmail.

Cats — A258

Faces of Cats: No. 1500: a, 10c, b, 15c. c, 20c, d, 25c, e, 30c. f, 50c, g, 75c.
No. 1501a, 5g, Cat under rose bush, by Desportes. b, 10g, Two cats, by Marc, horiz. c, 20g, Man with cat, by Rousseau.

1973, June 29

1500	A258	Strip of 7, #a.-g.	3.50 1.00
1501	A258	Strip of 3, #a.-c.	14.00 3.50
	Nos. 1500-1501 (2)		17.50 4.50

No. 1500 is airmail. For other cat designs, see type A287.

Flemish Paintings — A259

Nudes by: No. 1502: a, 10c, Spranger. b, 15c, Jordaens. c, 20c, de Clerck. d, 25c, Spranger, diff. e, 30c, Goltzius. f, 50c, Rubens. g, 75c, Vase of flowers, J. Brueghel.
No. 1503a, 5g, Nude, de Clerck, horiz. b, 10g, Woman with mandolin, de Vos. c, 20g, Men, horses, Rubens, horiz.

1973, June 29　**Litho.**　**Perf. 14**

1502	A259	Strip of 7, #a.-g.	3.50 1.00
1503	A259	Strip of 3, #a.-c.	9.00 3.00
	Nos. 1502-1503 (2)		12.50 4.00

No. 1503 is airmail.

Hand Holding Letter — A260

Wmk. 347
1973, July 10　**Litho.**　**Perf. 11**
1504　A260　2g lil rose & blk　5.00 1.50

No. 1504 was issued originally as a nonobligatory stamp to benefit mailmen, but its status was changed to regular postage.

EXPOPAR 73, Paraguayan Industrial Exhib. — A261

1973, Aug. 11　　　**Perf. 13x13½**
Granite Paper

1505	A261	1g org brn	2.25 2.00
1506	A261	2g vermilion	2.25 2.00
1507	A261	3g blue	2.25 2.00
1508	A261	4g emerald	2.25 2.00
1509	A261	5g lilac	2.25 2.00
1510	A261	20g lilac rose	8.00 3.00
1511	A261	25g rose claret	8.00 3.00
	Nos. 1505-1511 (7)		27.25 16.00

Nos. 1510-1511 are airmail.

1974 World Cup Soccer Championships, Munich — A262

No. 1512: a, 10c, Uruguay vs. Paraguay. b, 15c, Crerand, England and Eusebio, Portugal. c, 20c, Bobby Charlton, England. d, 25c, Franz Beckenbauer, Germany. e, 30c, Erler, Germany and McNab, England. f, 50c, Pele, Brazil and Willi Schulz, Germany. g, 75c, Arsenio Erico, Paraguay.
5g, Brian Labone, Gerd Mueller, Bobby Moore. No. 1514a, 10g, Luigi Riva, Italy. No. 1514b, 20g, World Cup medals. No. 1515, World Cup trophy. 25g, Player scoring goal.

1973　**Litho.**　**Unwmk.**　**Perf. 14**

1512	A262	Strip of 7, #a.-g.	2.00 1.00
1513	A262	5g multicolored	9.50 1.50
1514	A262	Pair, #a.-b.	4.25 1.00
	Nos. 1512-1514 (3)		15.75 3.50

Souvenir Sheets
Perf. 13½

1515	A262	25g multicolored	62.00 62.00
1516	A262	25g multicolored	22.50 22.50

Nos. 1513-1516 are airmail. Issue dates: Nos. 1512-1514, 1516, Oct. 8. No. 1515, June 29. For overprint see No. 2131.

Paintings — A263

Details from paintings, artist: No. 1517a, 10c, Lion of St. Mark, Carpaccio. b, 15c, Venus and Mars, Pittoni. c, 20c, Rape of Europa, Veronese. d, 25c, Susannah and the Elders, Tintoretto. e, 30c, Euphrosyne, Amigoni. f, 50c, Allegory of Moderation, Veronese. g, 75c, Ariadne, Tintoretto.
5g, Pallas and Mars, Tintoretto. No. 1519a, 10g, Portrait of Woman in Fur Hat, G.D. Tiepolo. b, 20g, Dialectic of Industry, Veronese.

1973, Oct. 8　　　　**Perf. 14**

1517	A263	Strip of 7, #a.-g.	2.00 1.00
1518	A263	5g multicolored	4.00 .75
1519	A263	Pair, #a.-b.	4.75 1.25
	Nos. 1517-1519 (3)		10.75 3.00

Nos. 1518-1519 are airmail.

Birds — A264

No. 1520: a, 10c, Tersina viridis. b, 15c, Pipile cumanensis. c, 20c, Pyrocephalus rubinus. d, 25c, Andigena laminirostris. e, 30c, Xipholena punicea. f, 50c, Tangara chilensis. g, 75, Polytmus guainumbi.
5g, Onychorhynchus mexicanus, vert. No. 1522a, 10g, Rhinocrypta lanceolata, vert. b, 20g, Trogon collaris, vert. 25g, Colibri florisuga mellivora, vert.

1973, Nov. 14

1520	A264	Strip of 7, #a.-g.	2.00 1.10
1521	A264	5g multicolored	6.00 1.50
1522	A264	Pair, #a.-b.	4.00 .50
	Nos. 1520-1522 (3)		12.00 3.10

Souvenir Sheet
Perf. 13½
1523　A264　25g multicolored　30.00 30.00

Nos. 1521-1523 are airmail. No. 1523 contains one 50x60mm stamp.

Space Exploration A265

No. 1524a, 10c, Apollo 11. b, 15c, Apollo 12. c, 20c, Apollo 13. d, 25c, Apollo 14. e, 30c, Apollo 15. f, 50c, Apollo 16. g, 75c, Apollo 17.
5g, Skylab. No. 1526a, 10g, Space shuttle. b, 20g, Apollo-Soyuz mission. No. 1527, Pioneer 11, Jupiter. No. 1528, Pioneer 10, Jupiter, vert.

1973, Nov. 14　　　　**Perf. 14**

1524	A265	Strip of 7, #a.-g.	2.00 1.10
1525	A265	5g multicolored	4.50 1.50
1526	A265	Pair, #a.-b.	2.00 1.00
	Nos. 1524-1526 (3)		8.50 3.60

Souvenir Sheet
Perf. 14½
1527　A265　25g multicolored　30.00 20.00
Perf. 13½
1528　A265　25g multicolored　26.00 15.00

Nos. 1525-1528 are airmail. No. 1527 contains on 35x25mm stamp, No. 1528 one 50x60mm stamp.

Souvenir Sheet

Women of Avignon, Pablo Picasso A266

1973, Nov. 14　　　　**Perf. 13½**
1529　A266　25g multicolored　25.00 25.00

Traditional Costumes A267

No. 1530: a, 25c, Indian girl. b, 50c, Bottle dance costume. c, 75c, Dancer balancing vase on head. d, 1g, Dancer with flowers. e, 1.50g, Weavers. f, 1.75g, Man, woman in dance costumes. g, 2.25g, Musicians in folk dress, horiz.

1973, Dec. 30 **Perf. 14**
1530 A267 Strip of 7, #a.-g.   7.75 5.00

Flowers — A268

Designs: No. 1531a, 10c Passion flower. b, 20c, Dahlia. c, 25c, Bird of paradise. d, 30c, Freesia. e, 40c, Anthurium. f, 50c, Water lily. g, 75c, Orchid.

1973, Dec. 31
1531 A268 Strip of 7, #a.-g.   9.75 5.00

Roses — A269

Designs: No. 1532a, 10c, Hybrid perpetual. b, 15c, Tea scented. c, 20c, Japanese rose. d, 25c, Bouquet of roses and flowers. e, 30c, Rose of Provence. f, 50c, Hundred petals rose. g, 75c, Bouquet of roses, dragonfly.

1974, Feb. 2
1532 A269 Strip of 7, #a.-g.   10.00 3.00

Paintings in Gulbenkian Museum — A270

Designs and artists: No. 1533a, 10c, Cupid and Three Graces, Boucher. b, 15c, Bath of Venus, Burne-Jones. c, 20c, Mirror of Venus, Burne-Jones. d, 25c, Two Women, Natoire. e, 30c, Fighting Cockerels, de Vos. f, 50c, Portrait of a Young Girl, Bugiardini. g, 75c, Madonna and Child, J. Gossaert.

5g, Outing on Beach at Enoshima, Utamaro. No. 1535: a, 10g, Woman with Harp, Lowrence. b, 20g, Centaurs Embracing, Rubens.

1974, Feb. 4
1533 A270 Strip of 7, #a.-g.   2.00 1.10
1534 A270 5g multicolored   3.50 1.75
1535 A270 Pair, #a.-b.   5.25 3.50
   Nos. 1533-1535 (3)   10.75 6.35
   Nos. 1534-1535 are airmail.

UPU Cent. A271

Horse-drawn mail coaches: No. 1536a, 10c, London. b, 15c, France. c, 20c, England. d, 25c, Bavaria. e, 30c, Painting by C.C. Henderson. f, 50c, Austria, vert. g, 75c, Zurich, vert.

5g, Hot air balloon, Apollo spacecraft, airplane, Graf Zeppelin. No. 1538a, 10g, Steam locomotive. b, 20g, Ocean liner, sailing ship. No. 1539, Airship, balloon. No. 1540, Mail coach crossing river.

1974, Mar. 20 **Perf. 14**
1536 A271 Strip of 7, #a.-g.   2.00 1.25
1537 A271 5g multicolored   1.75 .65
1538 A271 Pair, #a.-b.   7.00 3.50
   Nos. 1536-1538 (3)   10.75 5.40
Souvenir Sheets
Perf. 14½
1539 A271 15g multicolored   26.00 26.00
Perf. 13½
1540 A271 15g multicolored   26.00 26.00

Nos. 1537-1540 are airmail. No. 1539 contains one 50x35mm stamp, No. 1540 one 60x50mm stamp. Nos. 1539-1540 each include a 5g surtax for a monument to Francisco Solano Lopez. For overprint see No. 2127.

Paintings — A272

Details from works, artist: No. 1541a, 10c, Adam and Eve, Mabuse. b, 15c, Portrait, Piero di Cosimo. c, 20c, Bathsheba in her Bath, Cornelisz. d, 25c, Toilet of Venus, Boucher. e, 30c, The Bathers, Renoir. f, 50c, Lot and his Daughters, Dix. g, 75c, Bouquet of Flowers, van Kessel.

5g, King's Pet Horse, Seele. No. 1543a, 10g, Woman with Paintbrushes, Batoni. b, 20g, Three Musicians, Flemish master.

1974, Mar. 20
1541 A272 Strip of 7, #a.-g.   2.00 1.25
1542 A272 5g multicolored   2.50 .40
1543 A272 Pair, #a.-b.   15.00 3.00
   Nos. 1541-1543 (3)   19.50 4.65
   Nos. 1542-1543 are airmail.

Sailing Ships A272a

Designs: No. 1544a, 5c, Ship, map. b, 10c, English ship. c, 15c, Dutch ship. d, 20c, Whaling ships. e, 25c, Spanish ship. f, 35c, USS Constitution. g, 40c, English frigate. h, 50c, "Fanny," 1832.

1974, Sept. 13 **Perf. 14½**
1544 A272a Strip of 8, #a.-h.   7.00 1.00

Strip price includes a 50c surtax.

Paintings in Borghese Gallery, Rome — A273

Details from works and artists: No. 1545a, 5c, Portrait, Romano. b, 10c, Boy Carrying Fruit, Caravaggio. c, 15c, A Sybil, Domenichino. d, 20c, Nude, Titian. e, 25c, The Danae, Correggio. f, 35c, Nude, Savoldo. g, 40c, Nude, da Vinci. h, 50c, Nude, Rubens. 15g, Christ Child, Piero di Cosimo.

1975, Jan. 15 **Perf. 14**
1545 A273 Strip of 8, #a.-h.   5.50 1.50
Souvenir Sheet
Perf. 14½
1546 A273 15g multicolored   17.50 10.00

No. 1546 is airmail and price includes a 5g surtax used for a monument to Franciso Solano Lopez.

Christmas A274

Paintings, artists: No. 1547a, 5c, The Annunciation, della Robbia. b, 10c, The Nativity, G. David. c, 15c, Madonna and Child, Memling. d, 20c, Adoration of the Shepherds, Giorgione. e, 25c, Adoration of the Magi, French school, 1400. f, Madonna and Child with Saints, 35c, Pulzone. g, 40c, Madonna and Child, van Orley. h, 50c, Flight From Egypt, Pacher.

15g, Adoration of the Magi, Raphael.

1975, Jan. 17 **Perf. 14**
1547 A274 Strip of 8, #a.-h.   7.00 1.50
Souvenir Sheet
Perf. 14½
1548 A274 15g multicolored   10.00 5.00

No. 1548 is airmail and price includes a 5g surtax for a monument to Franciso Solano Lopez.

"U.P.U.," Pantheon, Carrier Pigeon, Globe — A275

1975, Feb. Wmk. 347 Perf. 13½x13
1549 A275 1g blk & lilac   .30 .25
1550 A275 2g blk & rose red   .30 .25
1551 A275 3g blk & ultra   .30 .25
1552 A275 5g blk & blue   .30 .25
1553 A275 10g blk & lil rose   .70 .25
1554 A275 20g blk & brn   2.10 .25
1555 A275 25g blk & emer   2.10 .25
   Nos. 1549-1555 (7)   6.10 1.75

Centenary of Universal Postal Union. Nos. 1554-1555 are airmail.

Paintings in National Gallery, London — A276

Details from paintings, artist: 5c, The Rokeby Venus, Velazquez, horiz. 10c, The Range of Love, Watteau. 15c, Venus (The School of Love), Correggio. 20c, Mrs. Sarah Siddons, Gainsborough. 25c, Cupid Complaining to Venus, L. Cranach the Elder. 35c, Portrait, Lotto. 40c, Nude, Rembrandt. 50c, Origin of the Milky Way, Tintoretto. 15g, Rider and Hounds, Pisanello.

1975, Apr. 25 Unwmk. Perf. 14
1556 A276 5c multicolored   .70 .25
1557 A276 10c multicolored   .85 .25
1558 A276 15c multicolored   1.10 .25
1559 A276 20c multicolored   1.25 .25
1560 A276 25c multicolored   1.40 .25
1561 A276 35c multicolored   1.75 .25
1562 A276 40c multicolored   2.00 .25
1563 A276 50c multicolored   2.25 .25
   Nos. 1556-1563 (8)   11.30 2.00
Souvenir Sheet
Perf. 13½
1564 A276 15g multicolored   15.00 15.00

No. 1564 is airmail, contains one 50x60mm stamp and price includes a 5g surtax for a monument to Francisco Solano Lopez.

Dogs — A277

1975, June 7 **Perf. 14**
1565 A277 5c Boxer   .75 .25
1566 A277 10c Poodle   .75 .25
1567 A277 15c Basset hound   .75 .25
1568 A277 20c Collie   .75 .25
1569 A277 25c Chihuahua   1.00 .25
1570 A277 35c German shepherd   1.50 .25
1571 A277 40c Pekinese   1.60 .25
1572 A277 50c Chow   2.10 .25
   Nos. 1565-1572 (8)   9.20 2.00
Souvenir Sheet
Perf. 13½
1573 A277 15g Fox hound, horse   21.00 12.00

No. 1573 is airmail, contains one 39x57mm stamp and price includes a 5g surtax for a monument to Francisco Solano Lopez.

South American Fauna A278

Designs: No. 1574a, 5c, Piranha (Pirana). b, 10c, Anaconda. c, 15c, Turtle (Tortuga). d, 20c, Iguana. e, 25c, Mono, vert. f, 35c, Mara. g, 40c, Marmota, vert. h, 50c, Peccary.

1975, Aug. 20 Litho. Perf. 14
1574 A278 Strip of 8, #a.-h.   7.00 1.50
Souvenir Sheet
Perf. 13½
1575 A278 15g Aguara guazu   10.00 7.50

No. 1575 is airmail, contains and one 60x50mm stamp, and price includes a 5g surtax for a monument to Francisco Solano Lopez.

For overprints see Nos. 2197.

Michelangelo (1475-1564), Italian Sculptor and Painter — A279

No. 1583: Statues, a, 5c, David. b, 10c, Aurora.

Paintings, c, 15c, Original Sin. d, 20c, The Banishment. e, 25c, The Deluge. f, 35c, Eve. g, 40c, Mary with Jesus and John. h, 50c, Judgement Day.

4g, Adam Receiving Life from God, horiz. No. 1585a, 5g, Libyan Sibyl. b, 10g, Delphic Sibyl. No. 1586, God Creating the Heaven and the Earth, horiz. No. 1587, The Holy Family.

1975, Aug. 23 Litho. Perf. 14
1583 A279 Strip of 8, #a.-h.   2.00 1.50
1584 A279 4g multicolored   7.50 2.75
1585 A279 Pair, #a.-b.   1.90 .75
Souvenir Sheets
Perf. 12
1586 A279 15g multicolored   29.00 15.00
Perf. 13½
1587 A279 15g multicolored   18.00 15.00

Nos. 1586-1587 sold for 20g with surtax for a monument to Francisco Solano Lopez. Nos. 1584-1587 are airmail.

Winter Olympics, Innsbruck, 1976 — A280

No. 1596, Luge. No. 1599, 4-Man bobsled. No. 1597a, 2g, Slalom skier. b, 3g, Cross country skier. c, 4g, Pair figure skating. d, 5g, Hockey.

No. 1598a, 10g, Speed skater. b, 15g, Downhill skier.

No. 1600, Ski jumper. No. 1601, Woman figure skater.

1975, Aug. 27   Litho.   Perf. 14
1596	A280	1g multi	.30	.25
1597	A280	Strip of 4, #a.-d.	3.25	1.00
1598	A280	Pair, #a.-b.	4.00	.80
1599	A280	20g multi	5.00	1.50
		Nos. 1596-1599 (4)	12.55	3.55

Souvenir Sheet
Perf. 13½
1600	A280	25g multi	35.00	35.00
1601	A280	25g multi	22.50	22.50

Nos. 1596, 1598-1601 are horiz. Nos. 1598-1601 are airmail. Nos. 1600-1601 each contain one 60x50mm stamp.

Summer Olympics, Montreal, 1976 — A281

No. 1606: a, 1g, Weightlifting. b, 2g, Kayak. c, 3g, Hildegard Flack, 800 meter run. d, 4g, Lasse Viren, 5,000 meter run.
No. 1607: a, 5g, Dieter Kottysch, boxing. b, 10g, Lynne Evans, archery. c, 15g, Akinori Nakayama, balance rings. d, 20g, Heide Rosendahl, broad jump. No. 1609, Decathlon. No. 1610, Liselott Linsenhoff, dressage, horiz.

1975, Aug. 28   Perf. 14
1606	A281	Strip of 4, #a.-d.	1.00	.80
1607	A281	Strip of 3, #a.-c.	4.25	1.00
1608	A281	20g multicolored	5.25	1.50
		Nos. 1606-1608 (3)	10.50	3.30

Souvenir Sheets
Perf. 14½
1609	A281	25g multicolored	36.00	30.00
1610	A281	25g multicolored	36.00	30.00

Nos. 1607b-1610 are airmail.

US, Bicent.
A282

Ships: 5c, Sachem, vert. 10c, Reprisal, Lexington. 15c, Wasp. 20c, Mosquito, Spy. 25c, Providence, vert. 35c, Yankee Hero, Milford. 40c, Cabot, vert. 50c, Hornet, vert.
15g, Montgomery.

Unwmk.
1975, Oct. 20   Litho.   Perf. 14
1616	A282	5c multicolored	.55	.25
1617	A282	10c multicolored	.80	.25
1618	A282	15c multicolored	.80	.25
1619	A282	20c multicolored	1.25	.25
1620	A282	25c multicolored	1.25	.25
1621	A282	35c multicolored	1.10	.25
1622	A282	40c multicolored	1.25	.25
1623	A282	50c multicolored	1.75	.30
		Nos. 1616-1623 (8)	8.75	2.05

Souvenir Sheet
1624	A282	15g multicolored	23.50	22.50

No. 1624 is airmail and contains one 50x70mm stamp.

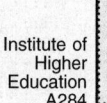

US, Bicent.
A283

Details from paintings, artists: No. 1625a, 5c, The Collector, Kahill. b, 10c, Morning Interlude, Brackman, vert. c, 15c, White Cloud, Catlin, vert. d, 20c, Man From Kentucky, Benton, vert. e, 25c, The Emigrants, Remington. f, 35c, Spirit of '76, Willard, vert. g, John Paul Jones capturing Serapis, unknown artist. h, 50c, Declaration of Independence, Trumbull. 15g, George Washington, Stuart and Thomas Jefferson, Peale.

1975, Nov. 20   Perf. 14
1625	A283	Strip of 8, #a.-h.	8.00	1.50

Souvenir Sheet
Perf. 13½
1625A	A283	15g multicolored	30.00	30.00

No. 1625A is airmail, contains one 60x50mm stamp and price includes a 5g surtax for a monument to Francisco Solano Lopez.

Institute of Higher Education
A284

Perf. 13½x13
1976, Mar. 16   Litho.   Wmk. 347
1626	A284	5g vio, blk & red	1.25	.50
1627	A284	10g ultra, blk & red	2.25	1.50
1628	A284	30g brn, blk & red	2.25	1.50
		Nos. 1626-1628 (3)	5.75	3.50

Inauguration of Institute of Higher Education, Sept. 23, 1974.
No. 1628 is airmail.

Rotary Intl., 70th Anniv. — A285

1976, Mar. 16   Perf. 13x13½
1629	A285	3g blk, bl & citron	1.10	.75
1630	A285	4g car, bl & citron	1.10	.75
1631	A285	25g emer, bl & lemon	3.50	2.00
		Nos. 1629-1631 (3)	5.70	3.50

No. 1631 is airmail.

IWY Emblem, Woman's Head — A286

1976, Mar. 16
1632	A286	1g ultra & brn	1.10	.75
1633	A286	2g car & brn	1.10	.75
1634	A286	20g grn & brn	3.50	2.00
		Nos. 1632-1634 (3)	5.70	3.50

Intl Women's Year (1975).
No. 1634 is airmail.

Cats — A287

Various cats: No. 1635a, 5c. b, 10c. c, 15c. d, 20c. e, 25c. f, 35c. g, 40c. h, 50c. 15g.

1976, Apr. 2   Unwmk.   Perf. 14
1635	A287	Strip of 8, #a.-h.		
			12.00	1.00

Souvenir Sheet
Perf. 13½
1636	A287	15g multicolored	42.00	12.00

No. 1636 is airmail, contains one 50x60mm stamp and price includes a 5g surtax for a monument to Francisco Solano Lopez.
See Nos. 2132-2133, 2201-2202, 2274-2275. For overprint see No. 2212.

Railroads, 150th Anniv. (in 1975)
A288

Locomotives: 1g, Planet, England, 1830. 2g, Koloss, Austria, 1844. 3g, Tarasque, France, 1846. 4g, Lawrence, Canada, 1853. 5g, Carlsruhe, Germany, 1854. 10g, Great Sagua, US, 1856. 15g, Berga, Spain. 20g, Encarnacion, Paraguay. 25g, English locomotive, 1825.

1976, Apr. 2   Perf. 13x13½
1637	A288	1g multicolored	.30	.25
1638	A288	2g multicolored	.30	.25
1639	A288	3g multicolored	.30	.25
1640	A288	4g multicolored	.30	.25
1641	A288	5g multicolored	.30	.25
1642	A288	10g multicolored	4.00	.40
1643	A288	15g multicolored	6.50	.60
1644	A288	20g multicolored	8.00	1.00
		Nos. 1637-1644 (8)	20.00	3.25

Souvenir Sheet
1645	A288	25g multicolored	52.50	52.50

Nos. 1642-1645 are airmail. No. 1645 contains one 40x27mm stamp.

Painting by Spanish Artists
A289

Paintings: 1g, The Naked Maja by Goya. 2g, Nude by J. de Torres. 3g, Nude holding oranges by de Torres, vert. 4g, Woman playing piano by Z. Velazquez, vert. 5g, Knight on white horse by Esquivel, vert. 10g, The Shepherd by Murillo, vert. 15g, The Immaculate Conception by Antolinez, vert. 20g, Nude by Zuloaga. 25g, Prince Baltasar Carlos on Horseback by D. Velasquez.

1976, Apr. 2   Perf. 13x13½, 13½x13
1646	A289	1g multicolored	.30	.25
1647	A289	2g multicolored	.30	.25
1648	A289	3g multicolored	.30	.25
1649	A289	4g multicolored	.30	.25
1650	A289	5g multicolored	.90	.25
1651	A289	10g multicolored	2.25	.40
1652	A289	15g multicolored	3.25	.50
1653	A289	20g multicolored	4.50	.60
		Nos. 1646-1653 (8)	12.10	2.75

Souvenir Sheet
1654	A289	25g multicolored	9.50	5.00

Nos. 1651-1654 are airmail. No. 1654 contains one 58x82mm stamp.

Butterflies
A290

No. 1655: a, 5c, Prepona praeneste. b, 10c, Prepona proschion. c, 15c, Pereute leucodrosime. d, 20c, Agrias amydon. e, 25c, Morpho aegea gynandromorphe. f, 35c, Pseudatteria leopardina. g, 40c, Morpho helena. h, 50c, Morpho hecuba.

1976, May 12   Unwmk.   Perf. 14
1655	A290	Strip of 8, #a.-h.	9.50	1.50

Farm Animals
A291

1976, June 15
1656	A291	1g Rooster, vert.	.75	.25
1657	A291	2g Hen, vert.	1.10	.25
1658	A291	3g Turkey, vert.	1.10	.25
1659	A291	4g Sow	1.25	.25
1660	A291	5g Donkeys	1.50	.25
1661	A291	10g Brahma cattle	1.75	.35

1662	A291	15g Holstein cow	2.00	.35
1663	A291	20g Horse	2.50	.50
		Nos. 1656-1663 (8)	11.95	2.45

Nos. 1661-1663 are airmail.

US and US Post Office, Bicent.
A292

Designs: 1g, Pony Express rider. 2g, Stagecoach. 3g, Steam locomotive, vert. 4g, American steamship, vert. 5g, Curtiss Jenny biplane. 10g, Mail bus. 15g, Mail car, rocket train. 20g, First official missile mail, vert. No. 1672, First flight cover, official missile mail. No. 1673, US #C76 tied to cover by moon landing cancel.

1976, June 18
1664	A292	1g multicolored	.50	.25
1665	A292	2g multicolored	.70	.25
1666	A292	3g multicolored	.80	.25
1667	A292	4g multicolored	1.00	.25
1668	A292	5g multicolored	1.25	.25
1669	A292	10g multicolored	1.75	.50
1670	A292	15g multicolored	3.25	.70
1671	A292	20g multicolored	5.00	1.00
		Nos. 1664-1671 (8)	14.25	3.45

Souvenir Sheets
Perf. 14½
1672	A292	25g multicolored	24.00	24.00
1673	A292	25g multicolored	24.00	24.00

Nos. 1669-1673 are airmail and each contain one 50x40mm stamp.

Mythological Characters
A293

Details from paintings, artists: No. 1674a, 1g, Jupiter, Ingres. b, 2g, Saturn, Rubens. c, 3g, Neptune, Tiepolo. d, 4g, Uranus and Aphrodite, Medina, horiz. e, 5g, Pluto and Proserpine, Giordano, horiz. f, 10g, Venus, Ingres. g, 15g, Mercury, de la Hyre. No. 1675, Mars and Venus, Veronese.
25g, Viking Orbiter descending to Mars, horiz.

1976, July 18   Perf. 14
1674	A293	Strip of 7, #a.-g.	7.25	3.25
1675	A293	20g multicolored	4.00	1.60
		Nos. 1674-1675 (2)	11.25	4.85

Souvenir Sheet
Perf. 14½
1676	A293	25g multicolored	52.00	52.00

Nos. 1674f-1674g, 1675-1676 are airmail.

Sailing Ships
A294

Paintings: No. 1677a, 1g, Venice frigate of the Spanish Armada, vert. b, 2g, Swedish war ship, Vasa, 1628, vert. c, 3g, Spanish galleon being attacked by pirates by Puget. d, 4g, Combat by Dawson. e, 5g, European boat in Japan, vert. f, 10g, Elizabeth Grange in Liverpool by Walters. g, 15g, Prussen, 1903, by Holst. 20g, Grand Duchess Elizabeth, 1902, by Bohrdt.

1976, July 15   Perf. 14
1677	A294	Strip of 7, #a.-g.	9.00	2.50
1678	A294	20g multicolored	5.00	.50
		Nos. 1677-1678 (2)	14.00	3.00

Nos. 1677f-1678 are airmail.

German
Sailing Ships
A295

Ship, artist: 1g, Bunte Kuh, 1402, Zeeden. 2g, Arms of Hamburg, 1667, Wichman, vert. 3g, Kaiser Leopold, 1667, Wichman, vert. 4g, Deutschland, 1848, Pollack, vert. 5g, Humboldt, 1851, Fedeler. 10g, Borussia, 1855, Seitz. 15g, Gorch Fock, 1958, Stroh, vert. 20g, Grand Duchess Elizabeth, 1902, Bohrdt. 25g, SS Pamir, Zeytline, vert.

Unwmk.
				Perf. 14	
1976, Aug. 20		Litho.			
1685	A295	1g multicolored		.55	.25
1686	A295	2g multicolored		.80	.25
1687	A295	3g multicolored		1.00	.25
1688	A295	4g multicolored		1.25	.25
1689	A295	5g multicolored		1.40	.30
1690	A295	10g multicolored		1.60	.45
1691	A295	15g multicolored		2.90	.80
1692	A295	20g multicolored		3.50	1.00
	Nos. 1685-1692 (8)			13.00	3.55

Souvenir Sheet
Perf. 14½
1693	A295	25g multicolored	21.00	21.00

Intl. German Naval Exposition, Hamburg; NORDPOSTA '76 (No. 1693). Nos. 1690-1693 are airmail.

US Bicentennial
A296

Western Paintings by: No. 1694a, 1g, E. C. Ward. b, 2g, William Robinson Leigh. c, 3g, A. J. Miller. d, 4g, Charles Russell. e, 5g, Frederic Remington. f, 10g, Remington, horiz. g, 15g, Carl Bodmer.
No. 1695, A. J. Miller. No. 1696, US #1, 2, 245, C76.

Unwmk.
				Perf. 14	
1976, Sept. 9		Litho.			
1694	A296	Strip of 7, #a.-g.		11.00	2.00
1695	A296	20g multicolored		6.00	1.00
	Nos. 1694-1695 (2)			17.00	3.00

Souvenir Sheet
Perf. 13x13½
1696	A296	25g multicolored	47.50	47.50

Nos. 1694f-1694g, 1695-1696 are airmail. No. 1696 contains one 65x55mm stamp.

1976 Summer
Olympics,
Montreal — A297

Gold Medal Winners: No. 1703a, 1g, Nadia Comaneci, Romania, gymnastics, vert. b, 2g, Kornelia Ender, East Germany, swimming. c, 3g, Luann Ryan, US, archery, vert. d, 4g, Jennifer Chandler, US, diving. e, 5g, Shirley Babashoff, US, swimming. f, 10g, Christine Stuckelberger, Switzerland, equestrian. g, 15g, Japan, volleyball, vert.
20g, Annegret Richter, W. Germany, running, vert. No. 1705, Bruce Jenner, US, decathlon. No. 1706, Alwin Schockemohle, equestrian. No. 1707, Medals list, vert.

Unwmk.
				Perf. 14	
1976, Dec. 18		Litho.			
1703	A297	Strip of 7, #a.-g.		7.00	2.00
1704	A297	20g multicolored		3.00	.75
	Nos. 1703-1704 (2)			10.00	2.75

Souvenir Sheets
Perf. 14½
1705	A297	25g multicolored	37.50	37.50
1706	A297	25g multicolored	37.50	37.50
1707	A297	25g multicolored	37.50	37.50

Nos. 1703f-1703g, 1705-1707 are airmail. Nos. 1705-1706 each contain one 50x40mm stamp. No. 1707 contains one 50x70mm stamp.

Titian, 500th Birth
Anniv. — A298

Details from paintings: No. 1708a, 1g, Venus and Adonis. b, 2g, Diana and Callisto. c, 3g, Perseus and Andromeda. d, 4g, Venus of the Mirror. e, 5g, Venus Sleeping, horiz. f, 10g, Bacchanal, horiz. g, 15g, Venus, Cupid and the Lute Player, horiz. 20g, Venus and the Organist, horiz.

1976, Dec. 18				Perf. 14	
1708	A298	Strip of 7, #a.-g.		12.00	2.50
1709	A298	20g multicolored		4.00	1.00
	Nos. 1708-1709 (2)			16.00	3.50

No. 1708f-1708g, 1709 are airmail.

Peter Paul
Rubens, 400th
Birth
Anniv. — A299

Paintings: No. 1710a, 1g, Adam and Eve. b, 2g, Tiger and Lion Hunt. c, 3g, Bathsheba Receiving David's Letter. d, 4g, Susanna in the Bath. e, 5g, Perseus and Andromeda. f, 10g, Andromeda Chained to the Rock. g, 15g, Shivering Venus. 20g, St. George Slaying the Dragon. 25g, Birth of the Milky Way, horiz.

1977, Feb. 18					
1710	A299	Strip of 7, #a.-g.		8.00	2.00
1711	A299	20g multicolored		4.00	1.00
	Nos. 1710-1711 (2)			12.00	3.00

Souvenir Sheet
Perf. 14½
1712	A299	25g multicolored	57.50	35.00

Nos. 1710f-1710g, 1711-1712 are airmail.

US, Bicent.
A300

Space exploration: No. 1713a, 1g, John Glenn, Mercury 7. b, 2g, Pres. Kennedy, Apollo 11. c, 3g, Wernher von Braun, Apollo 17. d, 4g, Mercury, Venus, Mariner 10. e, 5g, Jupiter, Saturn, Pioneer 10/11. f, 10g, Viking, Mars. g, 15g, Viking A on Mars. 20g, Viking B on Mars. No. 1715, Future space projects on Mars, vert. No. 1716, Future land rover on Mars.

1976, Mar. 3				Perf. 14	
1713	A300	Strip of 7, #a.-g.		6.50	2.50
1714	A300	20g multicolored		3.50	1.50
	Nos. 1713-1714 (2)			10.00	4.00

Souvenir Sheets
Perf. 13½
1715	A300	25g multicolored	35.00	35.00
1716	A300	25g multicolored	35.00	35.00

Nos. 1713f-1713g, 1714-1716 are airmail. No. 1715 contains one 50x60mm stamp, No. 1716 one 60x50mm stamp.

Olympic
History — A301

Designs: 1g, Spiridon Louis, marathon 1896, Athens, Pierre de Coubertin. 2g, Giuseppe Delfino, fencing 1960, Rome, Pope John XXIII. 3g, Jean Claude Killy, skiing 1968, Grenoble, Charles de Gaulle. 4g, Ricardo Delgado, boxing 1968, Mexico City, G. Diaz Ordaz. 5g, Hayata, gymnastics 1964, Tokyo, Emperor Hirohito. 10g, Klaus Wolfermann, javelin 1972, Munich, Avery Brundage. 15g, Michel Vaillancourt, equestrian 1976, Montreal, Queen Elizabeth II. 20g, Franz Klammer, skiing 1976, Innsbruck, Austrian national arms.
25g, Emblems of 1896 Athens games and 1976 Montreal games.

1977, June 7				Perf. 14	
1717	A301	1g multicolored		.30	.25
1718	A301	2g multicolored		.30	.25
1719	A301	3g multicolored		.50	.25
1720	A301	4g multicolored		.80	.25
1721	A301	5g multicolored		1.00	.40
1722	A301	10g multicolored		1.25	.50
1723	A301	15g multicolored		1.60	.50
1724	A301	20g multicolored		2.60	1.00
	Nos. 1717-1724 (8)			8.35	3.40

Souvenir Sheet
Perf. 13½
1725	A301	25g multicolored	32.00	22.50

Nos. 1722-1725 are airmail. No. 1725 contains one 49x60mm stamp.

LUPOSTA '77,
Intl. Stamp
Exhibition,
Berlin — A302

Graf Zeppelin 1st South America flight and: 1g, German girls in traditional costumes. 2g, Bull fighter, Seville. 3g, Dancer, Rio de Janeiro. 4g, Gaucho breaking bronco, Uruguay. 5g, Like #1530b. 10g, Argentinian gaucho. 15g, Ceremonial indian costume, Bolivia. 20g, Indian on horse, US.
No. 1734, Zeppelin over sailing ship. No. 1735, Ferdinand Von Zeppelin, zeppelin over Berlin, horiz.

1977, June 9				Perf. 14	
1726	A302	1g multicolored		.60	.25
1727	A302	2g multicolored		.60	.25
1728	A302	3g multicolored		.70	.25
1729	A302	4g multicolored		1.20	.25
1730	A302	5g multicolored		1.50	.30
1731	A302	10g multicolored		1.90	.40
1732	A302	15g multicolored		2.40	.45
1733	A302	20g multicolored		4.00	.75
	Nos. 1726-1733 (8)			12.90	2.90

Souvenir Sheets
Perf. 13½
1734	A302	25g multicolored	62.50	62.50
1735	A302	25g multicolored	22.50	22.50

#1731-1735 are airmail. #1734 contains one 49x60mm stamp, #1735 one 60x49mm stamp.

Mburucuya
Flowers — A303

Weaver with
Spider Web
Lace — A304

Designs: 1g, Ostrich feather panel. 2g, Black palms. 20g, Rose tabebuia. 25g, Woman holding ceramic pot.

		Perf. 13x13½		
1977		Litho.	Wmk. 347	
1736	A304	1g multicolored	2.25	1.50
1737	A303	2g multicolored	2.25	1.50
1738	A303	3g multicolored	2.25	1.50
1739	A304	5g multicolored	2.25	1.50
1740	A303	20g multicolored	3.25	2.00
1741	A304	25g multicolored	3.25	2.50
	Nos. 1736-1741 (6)		15.50	10.50

Issued: 2g, 3g, 20g, 4/25; 1g, 5g, 25g, 6/27. Nos. 1740-1741 are airmail.

Aviation
History
A305

Designs: No. 1742a, 1g, Orville and Wilbur Wright, Wright Flyer, 1903. b, 2g, Alberto Santos-Dumont, Canard, 1906. c, 3g, Louis Bleriot, Bleriot 11, 1909. d, 4g, Otto Lilienthal, Glider, 1891. e, 5g, Igor Sikorsky, Avion le Grande, 1913. f, 10g, Juan de la Cierva, Autogiro. g, 15g, Silvio Pettirossi, Deperdussin acrobatic plane. No. 1743, Concorde jet. No. 1744, Lindbergh, Spirit of St. Louis, Statue of Liberty, Eiffel Tower. No. 1745, Design of flying machine by da Vinci.

1977, July 18		Unwmk.		Perf. 14	
1742	A305	Strip of 7, #a.-g.		7.50	2.50
1743	A305	20g multicolored		4.00	1.50
	Nos. 1742-1743 (2)			11.50	4.00

Souvenir Sheet
Perf. 14½
1744	A305	25g multicolored	35.00	35.00
1745	A305	25g multicolored	37.50	37.50

Nos. 1742f-1745 are airmail. No. 1745 contains one label.

Francisco Solano
Lopez — A306

	Perf. 13x13½			
1977, July 24		Litho.	Wmk. 347	
1752	A306	10g brown	1.50	2.00
1753	A306	50g dk vio	3.25	1.50
1754	A306	100g green	5.50	3.00
	Nos. 1752-1754 (3)		10.25	6.50

Marshal Francisco Solano Lopez (1827-1870), President of Paraguay.
Nos. 1753-1754 are airmail.

Paintings
A307

Paintings by: No. 1755a, 1g, Gabrielle Rainer Istvanffy. b, 2g, L. C. Hoffmeister. c, 3g, Frans Floris. d, 4g, Gerard de Lairesse. e, 5g, David Teniers I. f, 10g, Jacopo Zucchi. g, 15g, Pierre Paul Prudhon. 20g, Francois Boucher. 25g, Ingres. 5g-25g vert.

1977, July 25				Perf. 14	
1755	A307	Strip of 7, #a.-g.		9.25	3.50
1756	A307	20g multicolored		3.25	1.50
	Nos. 1755-1756 (2)			12.50	5.00

Souvenir Sheet
Perf. 14½
1757	A307	25g multicolored	27.50	27.50

Nos. 1755f-1757 are airmail.

German
Sailing Ships
A308

Designs: No. 1764a, 1g, De Beurs van Amsterdam. b, 2g, Katharina von Blankenese. c, 3g, Cuxhaven. d, 4g, Rhein. e, 5g, Churprinz and Marian. f, 10g, Bark of Bremen, vert. g, 15g, Elbe II, vert. 20g, Karacke. 25g, Admiral Karpeanger.

Unwmk.

1977, Aug. 27		Litho.	Perf. 14	
1764	A308	Strip of 7, #a.-g.	2.25	3.00
1765	A308	20g multicolored	3.75	2.00
		Nos. 1764-1765 (2)	6.00	5.00

Souvenir Sheet
Perf. 13½

1766	A308	25g multicolored	15.50	15.50

Nos. 1764f-1766 are airmail. No. 1766 contains one 40x30mm stamp.

Nobel Laureates for Literature
A309

Authors and scenes from books: No. 1773a, 1g, John Steinbeck, Grapes of Wrath, vert. b, 2g, Ernest Hemingway, Death in the Afternoon. c, 3g, Pearl S. Buck, The Good Earth, vert. d, 4g, George Bernard Shaw, Pygmalion, vert. e, 5g, Maurice Maeterlinck, Joan of Arc, vert. f, 10g, Rudyard Kipling, The Jungle Book. g, 15g, Henryk Sienkiewicz, Quo Vadis. 20g, C. Theodor Mommsen, History of Rome. 25g, Nobel prize medal.

1977, Sept. 5			Perf. 14	
1773	A309	Strip of 7, #a.-g.	6.50	2.50
1774	A309	20g multicolored	3.50	1.50
		Nos. 1773-1774 (2)	10.00	4.00

Souvenir Sheet
Perf. 14½

1775	A309	25g multicolored	48.50	48.50

Nos. 1773f-1775 are airmail.

1978 World Cup Soccer Championships, Argentina — A310

Posters and World Cup Champions: No. 1782a, 1g, Uruguay, 1930. b, 2g, Italy, 1934. c, 3g, Italy, 1938. d, 4g, Uruguay, 1950. e, 5g, Germany, 1954. f, 10g, Soccer player by Fritz Genkinger. g, 15g, Soccer player, orange shirt by Genkinger.
No. 1783a, 1g, Brazil, 1958. b, 2g, Brazil, 1962. c, 3g, England, 1966. d, 4g, Brazil, 1970. e, 5g, Germany, 1974. f, 10g, Player #4 by Genkinger. g, 15g, Player #1 by Genkinger, horiz.
No. 1784, World Cup Trophy. No. 1785, German players, Argentina '78. No. 1786, The Loser, by Genkinger. No. 1787, The Defender, (player #11) by Genkinger.

1977, Oct. 28		Unwmk.	Perf. 14	
1782	A310	Strip of 7, #a.-g.	7.75	2.25
1783	A310	Strip of 7, #a.-g.	7.50	2.25
1784	A310	20g multicolored	2.25	.65
1785	A310	20g multicolored	2.50	.65
		Nos. 1782-1785 (4)	20.00	5.80

Souvenir Sheets
Perf. 14½

1786	A310	25g red & multi	40.00	40.00
1787	A310	25g black & multi	40.00	40.00

Nos. 1782f-1782g, 1783f-1783g, 1784-1787 are airmail.

Peter Paul Rubens, 400th Birth Anniv. — A312

Details from paintings: No. 1788a, 1g, Rubens and Isabella Brant under Honeysuckle

Bower. b, 2g, Judgment of Paris. c, 3g, Union of Earth and Water. d, 4g, Daughters of Kekrops Discovering Erichthonius. e, 5g, Holy Family with the Lamb. f, 10c, Adoration of the Magi. g, 15c, Philip II on Horseback.
20g, Education of Marie de Medici, horiz. 25g, Triumph of Eucharist Over False Gods.

1978, Jan. 19		Unwmk.	Perf. 14	
1788	A312	Strip of 7, #a.-g.	9.00	2.50
1789	A312	20g multicolored	5.00	1.40
		Nos. 1788-1789 (2)	14.00	3.90

Souvenir Sheet
Perf. 14½

1790	A312	25g multi, gold	25.00	25.00
1790A	A312	25g multi, silver	37.00	37.00

Nos. 1788f-1788g, 1789-1790 are airmail. No. 1790 contains one 50x70mm stamp and exists inscribed in gold or silver.

1978 World Chess Championships, Argentina — A313

Paintings of chess players: No. 1791a, 1g, De Cremone. b, 2g, L. van Leyden. c, 3g, H. Muehlich. d, 4g, Arabian artist. e, 5g, Benjamin Franklin playing chess, E. H. May. f, 10g, G. Cruikshank. g, 15g, 17th cent. tapestry. 20g, Napoleon playing chess on St. Helena. 25g, Illustration from chess book, Shah Name.

1978, Jan. 23			Perf. 14	
1791	A313	Strip of 7, #a.-g.	28.00	9.50
1792	A313	20g multicolored	14.00	4.50
		Nos. 1791-1792 (2)	42.00	14.00

Souvenir Sheet
Perf. 14½

1793	A313	25g multicolored	47.00	47.00

Nos. 1791f-1791g, 1792-1793 are airmail. No. 1793 contains one 50x40mm stamp.

Jacob Jordaens, 300th Death Anniv. — A314

Paintings: No. 1794a, 3g, Satyr and the Nymphs. b, 4g, Satyr with Peasant. c, 5g, Allegory of Fertility. d, 6g, Upbringing of Jupiter. e, 7g, Holy Family. f, 8g, Adoration of the Shepherds. g, 20g, Jordaens with his family. 10g, Meleagro with Atalanta, horiz. No. 1796, Feast for a King, horiz. No. 1797, Holy Family with Shepherds.

1978, Jan. 25			Perf. 14	
1794	A314	Strip of 7, #a.-g.	12.00	2.75
1795	A314	10g multicolored	2.75	.75
1796	A314	25g multicolored	5.50	1.40
		Nos. 1794-1796 (3)	20.25	4.90

Souvenir Sheet
Perf. 14½

1797	A314	25g multicolored	15.00	15.00

Nos. 1795-1797 are airmail. No. 1797 contains one 50x70mm stamp.

Albrecht Durer, 450th Death Anniv. — A315

Monograms and details from paintings: No. 1804a, 3g, Temptation of the Idler. b, 4g, Adam and Eve. c, 5g, Satyr Family. d, 6g, Eve. e, 7g, Adam. f, 8g, Portrait of a Young Man. g, 20g, Squirrels and Acorn. 10g, Madonna and Child. No. 1806, Brotherhood of the Rosary (Lute-playing Angel) No. 1807, Soldier on Horseback with a Lance.

1978, Mar. 10			Perf. 14	
1804	A315	Strip of 7, #a.-g.	7.25	2.25
1805	A315	10g multicolored	2.25	.50
1806	A315	25g multicolored	4.25	1.20
		Nos. 1804-1806 (3)	13.75	3.95

Souvenir Sheet
Perf. 13½

1807	A315	25g blk, buff & sil	47.50	47.50

Nos. 1805-1807 are airmail. No. 1807 contains one 30x40mm stamp.

Francisco de Goya, 150th Death Anniv. — A316

Paintings: No. 1814a, 3g, Allegory of the Town of Madrid. b, 4g, The Clothed Maja. c, 5g, The Parasol. d, 6g, Dona Isabel Cobos de Porcel. e, 7g, The Drinker. f, 8g, The 2nd of May 1908. g, 20g, General Jose Palafox on Horseback. 10g, Savages Murdering a Woman. 25g, The Naked Maja, horiz.

1978, May 11			Perf. 14	
1814	A316	Strip of 7, #a.-g.	7.50	.90
1815	A316	10g multicolored	1.90	.55
1816	A316	25g multicolored	3.00	1.10
		Nos. 1814-1816 (3)	12.40	2.55

Nos. 1815-1816 are airmail.

Future Space Projects A317

Various futuristic space vehicles and imaginary creatures: No. 1817a, 3g. b, 4g. c, 5g. d, 6g. e, 7g. f, 8g. g, 20g.

1978, May 16				
1817	A317	Strip of 7, #a.-g.	7.50	2.25
1818	A317	10g multicolored	1.50	.50
1819	A317	25g multi, diff.	4.50	1.40
		Nos. 1817-1819 (3)	13.50	3.75

Nos. 1818-1819 are airmail.

Racing Cars — A318

No. 1820: a, 3g, Tyrell Formula I. b, 4g, Lotus Formula 1, 1978. c, 5g, McLaren Formula 1. d, 6g, Brabham Alfa Romeo Formula 1. e, 7g, Renault Turbo Formula 1. f, 8g, Wolf Formula 1. g, 20g, Porsche 935. 10g, Bugatti. 25g, Mercedes Benz W196, Stirling Moss, driver. No. 1823, Ferrari 312T.

1978, June 28			Perf. 14	
1820	A318	Strip of 7, #a.-g.	7.50	1.90
1821	A318	10g multicolored	1.20	.25
1822	A318	25g multicolored	2.90	.80
		Nos. 1820-1822 (3)	11.60	2.95

Souvenir Sheet
Perf. 14½

1823	A318	25g multicolored	26.00	26.00

Nos. 1821-1823 are airmail. No. 1823 contains one 50x35mm stamp.

Paintings by Peter Paul Rubens — A319

3g, Holy Family with a Basket. 4g, Amor Cutting a Bow. 5g, Adam & Eve in Paradise. 6g, Crown of Fruit, horiz. 7g, Kidnapping of Ganymede. 8g, The Hunting of Crocodile & Hippopotamus. 10g, The Reception of Marie de Medici at Marseilles. 20g, Two Satyrs. 25g, Felicity of the Regency.

1978, June 30			Perf. 14	
1824	A319	3g multicolored	.40	.25
1825	A319	4g multicolored	.70	.25
1826	A319	5g multicolored	.90	.25
1827	A319	6g multicolored	.95	.25
1828	A319	7g multicolored	1.20	.30
1829	A319	8g multicolored	1.40	.40
1830	A319	10g multicolored	3.25	.80
1831	A319	20g multicolored	4.75	1.10
1832	A319	25g multicolored	6.50	1.60
		Nos. 1824-1832 (9)	20.05	5.20

Nos. 1830, 1832 are airmail.

National College A320

Perf. 13½x13

1978		Litho.	Wmk. 347	
1833	A320	3g claret	2.25	2.00
1834	A320	4g violet blue	2.25	2.00
1835	A320	5g lilac	2.25	2.00
1836	A320	20g brown	2.25	2.00
1837	A320	25g violet black	3.25	2.00
1838	A320	30g bright green	3.25	2.00
		Nos. 1833-1838 (6)	15.50	12.00

Centenary of National College in Asuncion. Nos. 1836-1838 are airmail.

José Estigarribia, Bugler, Flag of Paraguay — A321

1978		Litho.	Perf. 13x13½	
1839	A321	3g multi	3.25	2.00
1840	A321	4g multi	3.25	2.00
1841	A321	10g multi	3.25	2.00
1842	A321	20g multi	5.25	3.00
1843	A321	25g multi	5.25	3.00
1844	A321	30g multi	5.25	3.00
		Nos. 1839-1844 (6)	25.50	15.00

Induction of Jose Felix Estigarribia (1888-1940), general and president of Paraguay, into Salon de Bronce (National Heroes' Hall of Fame).
Nos. 1842-1844 are airmail.

Queen Elizabeth II Coronation, 25th Anniv. — A322

Flowers and: 3g, Barbados #234. 4g, Tristan da Cunha #13. 5g, Bahamas #157. 6g, Seychelles #172. 7g, Solomon Islands #88. 8g, Cayman Islands #150. 10g, New Hebrides #77. 20g, St. Lucia #156. 25g, St. Helena #139.
No. 1854, Solomon Islands #368a-368c, Gilbert Islands #312a-312c. No. 1855, Great Britain #313-316.

1978, July 25		Unwmk.	Perf. 14	
1845	A322	3g multicolored	.40	.25
1846	A322	4g multicolored	.80	.25
1847	A322	5g multicolored	.90	.25
1848	A322	6g multicolored	.95	.25
1849	A322	7g multicolored	1.20	.30
1850	A322	8g multicolored	1.40	.40
1851	A322	10g multicolored	3.25	.80
1852	A322	20g multicolored	4.75	1.20
1853	A322	25g multicolored	6.50	1.60
		Nos. 1845-1853 (9)	20.15	5.30

Souvenir Sheets
Perf. 13½

1854	A322	25g multicolored	62.50	62.50
1855	A322	25g multicolored	62.50	62.50

Nos. 1851, 1853-1855 are airmail. Nos. 1854-1855 each contain one 60x40mm stamp.

Intl. Philatelic
Exhibitions
A323

Various paintings, ship, nudes, etc. for: No. 1856a, 3g, Nordposta '78. b, 4g, Riccione '78. c, 5g, Uruguay '79. d, 6g, ESSEN '78. e, 7g, ESPAMER '79. f, 8g, London '80. g, 20g, PRAGA '78. 10g, EUROPA '78. No. 1858, Eurphila '78.

No. 1859, Francisco de Pinedo, map of his flight.

1978, July 19   **Perf. 14**

1856	A323	Strip of 7, #a.-g.	9.00	1.25
1857	A323	10g multicolored	2.10	.40
1858	A323	25g multicolored	3.25	.70
	Nos. 1856-1858 (3)		*14.35*	*2.35*

Souvenir Sheet
Perf. 13½x13

1859	A323	25g multicolored	30.00	30.00

No. 1859 for Riccione '78 and Eurphila '78 and contains one 54x34mm stamp. Nos. 1857-1859 are airmail. Nos. 1856b-1858 are vert.

Intl. Year of the
Child — A324

Grimm's Snow White and the Seven Dwarfs: No. 1866a, 3g, Queen pricking her finger. b, 4g, Queen and mirror. c, 5g, Man with dagger, Snow White. d, 6g, Snow White in forest. e, 7g, Snow White asleep, seven dwarfs. f, 8g, Snow White dancing with dwarfs. g, 20g, Snow White being offered apple. 10g, Snow White in repose. 25g, Snow White, Prince Charming on horseback.

1978, Oct. 26

1866	A324	Strip of 7, #a.-g.	7.50	2.25
1867	A324	10g multicolored	1.75	.50
1868	A324	25g multicolored	4.25	1.00
	Nos. 1866-1868 (3)		*13.50*	*3.75*

Nos. 1867-1868 are airmail.
See Nos. 1893-1896, 1916-1919.

Mounted South
American
Soldiers — A325

No. 1869a, 3g, Gen. Jose Felix Bogado (1771-1829). b, 4g, Colonel, First Volunteer Regiment, 1806. c, 5g, Colonel wearing dress uniform, 1860. d, 6g, Soldier, 1864-1870. e, 7g, Dragoon, 1865. f, 8g, Lancer. g, 20g, Soldier, 1865. 10g, Gen. Bernardo O'Higgins, 200th birth anniv. 25g, Jose de San Martin, 200th birth anniv.

1978, Oct. 31

1869	A325	Strip of 7, #a.-g.	8.75	1.75
1870	A325	10g multicolored	1.50	.25
1871	A325	25g multicolored	4.25	.45
	Nos. 1869-1871 (3)		*14.50*	*2.45*

Nos. 1870-1871 are airmail.

1978 World Cup Soccer
Championships, Argentina — A326

Soccer Players: No. 1872a, 3g, Paraguay, vert. b, 4g, Austria, Sweden. c, 5g, Argentina, Poland. d, 6g, Italy, Brazil. e, 7g, Netherlands, Austria. f, 8g, Scotland, Peru. g, 20g, Germany, Italy. 10g, Argentina, Holland. 25g, Germany, Tunisia.

No. 1875, Stadium.

1979, Jan. 9   **Perf. 14**

1872	A326	Strip of 7, #a.-g.	9.25	2.00
1873	A326	10g multicolored	1.25	.25
1874	A326	25g multicolored	3.75	.50
	Nos. 1872-1874 (3)		*14.25*	*2.75*

Souvenir Sheet
Perf. 13½

1875	A326	25g multicolored	52.50	52.50

Nos. 1873-1875 are airmail. No. 1875 contains one 60x40mm stamp.
For overprint see No. C610.

Christmas
A327

Paintings of the Nativity and Madonna and Child by: No. 1876a, 3g, Giorgione, horiz. b, 4g, Titian. c, 5g, Titian, diff. d, 6g, Raphael. e, 7g, Schongauer. f, 8g, Muratti. g, 20g, Van Oost. 10g, Memling. No. 1878, Rubens.

No. 1879, Madonna and Child Surrounded by a Garland and Boy Angels, Rubens.

1979, Jan. 10   **Litho.**   **Perf. 14**

1876	A327	Strip of 7, #a.-g.	7.75	1.40
1877	A327	10g multicolored	1.50	.25
1878	A327	25g multicolored	3.25	.50
	Nos. 1876-1878 (3)		*12.50*	*2.15*

Souvenir Sheet
Photo. & Engr.
Perf. 12

1879	A327	25g multicolored	87.50	87.50

Nos. 1877-1879 are airmail.

First
Powered
Flight, 75th
Anniv. (in
1978)
A328

Airplanes: No. 1880a, 3g, Eole, C. Ader, 1890. b, 4g, Flyer III, Wright Brothers. c, 5g, Voisin, Henri Farman, 1908. d, 6g, Curtiss, Eugene Ely, 1910. e, 7g, Etrich-Taube A11. f, 8g, Fokker EIII. g, 20g, Albatros C, 1915. 10g, Boeing 747 carrying space shuttle. No. 1882, Boeing 707. No. 1883, Zeppelin flight commemorative cancels.

1979, Apr. 24   **Litho.**   **Perf. 14**

1880	A328	Strip of 7, #a.-g.	7.00	1.40
1881	A328	10g multicolored	1.00	.25
1882	A328	25g multicolored	2.50	.50
	Nos. 1880-1882 (3)		*10.50*	*2.15*

Souvenir Sheet
Perf. 14½

1883	A328	25g blue & black	72.50	72.50

Nos. 1881-1883 are airmail. Nos. 1880-1883 incorrectly commemorate 75th anniv. of ICAO. No. 1883 contains one 50x40mm stamp.

Albrecht Durer,
450th Death
Anniv. (in
1978) — A329

Paintings: No. 1884a, 3g, Virgin with the Dove. b, 4g, Virgin Praying. c, 5g, Mater Dolorosa. d, 6g, Virgin with a Carnation. e, 7g, Madonna and Sleeping Child. f, 8g, Virgin Before the Archway. g, 20g, Flight Into Egypt. No. 1885, Madonna of the Haller family. No. 1886, Virgin with a Pear.

No. 1887, Lamentation Over the Dead Christ for Albrecht Glimm. No. 1888, Space station, horiz., with Northern Hemisphere of Celestial Globe in margin.

1979, Apr. 28   **Perf. 14**

1884	A329	Strip of 7, #a.-g.	6.75	2.00
1885	A329	10g multicolored	1.50	.50
1886	A329	25g multicolored	4.50	1.00
	Nos. 1884-1886 (3)		*12.75*	*3.50*

Souvenir Sheets
Perf. 13½

1887	A329	25g multicolored	17.00	17.00
1888	A329	25g multicolored	25.00	25.00

Intl. Year of the Child (#1885-1886).
Nos. 1885-1886, 1888 are airmail. No. 1887 contains one 30x40mm stamp, No. 1888 one 40x30mm stamp.

Sir Rowland
Hill, Death
Cent.
A330

Hill and: No. 1889a, 3g, Newfoundland #C1, vert. b, 4g, France #C14. c, 5g, Spain #B106. d, 6g, Similar to Ecuador #C2, vert. e, 7g, US #C3a. f, 8g, Gelber Hund inverted overprint, vert. g, 20g, Switzerland #C20a.

10g, Privately issued Zeppelin stamp. No. 1891, Paraguay #C82, #C96, vert. No. 1892, Italy #C49. No. 1892A, France #C3-C4.

1979, June 11   **Perf. 14**

1889	A330	Strip of 7, #a.-g.	7.50	1.50
1890	A330	10g multicolored	2.00	.50
1891	A330	25g multicolored	5.75	1.20
	Nos. 1889-1891 (3)		*15.25*	*3.20*

Souvenir Sheet
Perf. 13½x13

1892	A330	25g multicolored	32.00	32.00

Perf. 14½

1892A	A330	25g multicolored	21.00	21.00

Issue dates: No. 1892A, Aug. 28. Others, June 11. Nos. 1890-1892A are airmail.

Grimm's Fairy Tales Type of 1978

Cinderella: No. 1893a, 3g, Two stepsisters watch Cinderella cleaning. b, 4g, Cinderella, father, stepsisters. c, 5g, Cinderella with birds while working. d, 6g, Finding dress. e, 7g, Going to ball. f, 8g, Dancing with prince. g, 20g, Losing slipper leaving ball.

10g, Prince Charming trying slipper on Cinderella's foot. No. 1895, Couple riding to castle. No. 1896, Couple entering ballroom.

1979, June 24   **Perf. 14**

1893	A324	Strip of 7, #a.-g.	7.50	2.25
1894	A324	10g multicolored	1.75	.55
1895	A324	25g multicolored	5.00	1.20
	Nos. 1893-1895 (3)		*14.25*	*4.00*

Souvenir Sheet
Perf. 13½

1896	A324	25g multicolored	25.00	25.00

Intl. Year of the Child.

Congress
Emblem — A331

1979, Aug.   **Litho.**   **Perf. 13x13½**

1897	A331	10g red, blue & black	5.00	2.00
1898	A331	50g red, blue & black	5.00	2.00

22nd Latin-American Tourism Congress, Asuncion. No. 1898 is airmail.

1980 Winter
Olympics,
Lake Placid
A332

#1899: a, 3g, Monica Scheftschik, luge. b, 4g, E. Deufl, Austria, downhill skiing. c, 5g, G. Thoeni, Italy, slalom skiing. d, 6g, Canada Two-man bobsled. e, 7g, Germany vs. Finland, ice hockey. f, 8g, Hoenl, Russia, ski jump. g, 20g, Dianne De Leeuw, Netherlands, figure skating, vert.

10g, Hanni Wenzel, Liechtenstein, slalom skiing. No. 1901, Frommelt, Liechtenstein, slalom skiing, vert. No. 1902, Kulakova, Russia, cross country skier. No. 1903, Dorothy Hamill, US, figure skating, vert. No. 1904, Brigitte Totschnig, skier.

1979   **Unwmk.**   **Perf. 14**

1899	A332	Strip of 7, #a.-g.	6.50	2.75
1900	A332	10g multicolored	1.50	.75
1901	A332	25g multicolored	4.25	1.50
	Nos. 1899-1901 (3)		*12.25*	*5.00*

Souvenir Sheets
Perf. 13½

1902	A332	25g multicolored	21.00	21.00
1903	A332	25g multicolored	22.50	22.50
1904	A332	25g multicolored	62.50	62.50

#1900-1904 are airmail. #1902-1903 each contain one 40x30mm stamp, #1904, one 25x36mm stamp.

Issued: #1899-1902, 8/22; #1903, 6/11; #1904, 4/24.

Sailing Ships
A333

No. 1905: a, 3g, Caravel, vert. b, 4g, Warship. c, 5g, Warship, by Jan van Beeck. d, 6g, H.M.S. Britannia, vert. e, 7g, Salamis, vert. f, 8g, Ariel, vert. g, 20g, Warship, by Robert Salmon.

1979, Aug. 28   **Perf. 14**

1905	A333	Strip of 7, #a.-g.	8.00	2.50
1906	A333	10g Lisette	1.25	.30
1907	A333	25g Holstein, vert.	3.50	.70
	Nos. 1905-1907 (3)		*12.75*	*3.50*

Nos. 1906-1907 are airmail.

Intl. Year of the
Child — A334

Various kittens: No. 1908a, 3g. b, 4g. c, 5g. d, 6g. e, 7g. f, 8g. g, 20g.

1979, Nov. 29   **Perf. 14**

1908	A334	Strip of 7, #a.-g.	6.50	2.00
1909	A334	10g multicolored	2.50	.30
1910	A334	25g multicolored	2.25	2.75
	Nos. 1908-1910 (3)		*11.25*	*5.05*

Nos. 1909-1910 are airmail.

Grimm's Fairy Tales Type of 1978

Little Red Riding Hood: No. 1916a, 3g, Leaving with basket. b, 4g, Meets wolf. c, 5g, Picks flowers. d, 6g, Wolf puts on Granny's gown. e, 7g, Wolf in bed. f, 8g, Hunter arrives. g, 20g, Saved by the hunter.

10g, Hunter enters house. No. 1918, Hunter leaves. No. 1919, Overall scene.

1979, Dec. 4   *Perf. 14*
1916	A324	Strip of 7, #a.-g.	6.25	4.25
1917	A324	10g multicolored	1.50	1.00
1918	A324	25g multicolored	4.25	2.25
		Nos. 1916-1918 (3)	12.00	7.50

Souvenir Sheet
Perf. 14½
1919	A324	25g multicolored	25.00	25.00

Intl. Year of the Child. No. 1919 contains one 50x70mm stamp.

Greek Athletes — A335

Paintings on Greek vases: No. 1926a, 3g, 3 runners. b, 4g, 2 runners. c, 5g, Throwing contest. d, 6g, Discus. e, 7g, Wrestlers. f, 8g, Wrestlers, diff. g, 20g, 2 runners, diff.

10g, Horse and rider, horiz. 25g, 4 warriors with shields, horiz.

1979, Dec. 20   *Perf. 14*
1926	A335	Strip of 7, #a.-g.	7.25	5.00
1927	A335	10g multicolored	1.25	.75
1928	A335	25g multicolored	2.75	1.75
		Nos. 1926-1928 (3)	11.25	7.50

Nos. 1927-1928 are airmail.

Electric Trains A336

No. 1929: a, 3g, First electric locomotive, Siemens, 1879, vert. b, 4g, Switzerland, 1897. c, 5g, Model E71 28, Germany. d, 6g, Mountain train, Switzerland. e, 7g, Electric locomotive used in Benelux countries. f, 8g, Locomotive "Rheinpfeil," Germany. g, 20g, Model BB-9004, France.

10g, 200-Km/hour train, Germany. 25g, Japanese bullet train.

1979, Dec. 24   *Litho.*   *Perf. 14*
1929	A336	Strip of 7, #a.-g.	8.00	2.40
1930	A336	10g multicolored	4.75	1.30
1931	A336	25g multicolored	5.25	1.30
		Nos. 1929-1931 (3)	18.00	5.00

Nos. 1930-1931 are airmail.

Sir Rowland Hill, Death Cent. A337

Hill and: No. 1938a, 3g, Spad S XIII, 1917-18. b, 4g, P-51 D Mustang, 1944-45. c, 5g, Mitsubishi A6M6c Zero-Sen, 1944. d, 6g, Depperdussin float plane, 1913. e, 7g, Savoia Marchetti SM 7911, 1936. f, 8g, Messerschmitt Me 262B, 1942-45. g, 20g, Nieuport 24bis, 1917-18.

10g, Zeppelin LZ 104-/l59, 1917. No. 1940, Fokker Dr-1 Caza, 1917. No. 1941, Vickers Supermarine "Spitfire" Mk.IX, 1942-45.

1980, Apr. 8   *Perf. 14*
1938	A337	Strip of 7, #a.-g.	6.75	2.00
1939	A337	10g multicolored	1.25	.55
1940	A337	25g multicolored	4.25	1.10
		Nos. 1938-1940 (3)	12.25	3.65

Souvenir Sheet
Perf. 13½
1941	A337	25g multicolored	35.00	30.00

Incorrectly commemorates 75th anniv. of ICAO. Nos. 1939-1941 are airmail. No. 1941 contains one 37x27mm stamp.

Sir Rowland Hill, Paraguayan Stamps — A338

Hill and: No. 1948a, 3g, #1. b, 4g, #5. c, 5g, #6. d, 6g, #379. e, 7g, #381. f, 8g, #C384. g, 20g, #C389.

10g, #C83, horiz. No. 1950, #C92, horiz. No. 1951, #C54, horiz. No. 1952, #C1, horiz.

1980, Apr. 14   *Litho.*   *Perf. 14*
1948	A338	Strip of 7, #a.-g.	8.50	2.75
1949	A338	10g multicolored	1.75	.65
1950	A338	25g multicolored	4.00	1.60
		Nos. 1948-1950 (3)	14.25	5.00

Souvenir Sheets
Perf. 14½
1951	A338	25g multicolored	35.00	32.50
1952	A338	25g multicolored	35.00	32.50

#1949-1952 are airmail. #1951 contains one 50x40mm stamp. #1952 one 50x35mm stamp.

1980 Winter Olympics, Lake Placid — A339

No. 1953: a, 3g, Thomas Wassberg, Sweden, cross country skiing. b, 4g, Scharer & Benz, Switzerland, 2-man bobsled. c, 5g, Annemarie Moser-Proll, Austria, women's downhill skiing. d, 6g, Hockey team, US. e, 7g, Leonhard Stock, Austria, men's downhill skiing. f, 8g, Anton (Toni) Innauer, Austria, ski jump. g, 20g, Christa Kinshofer, Germany, slalom skiing.

10g, Ingemar Stenmark, slalom, Sweden. No. 1955, Robin Cousins, figure skating, Great Britain. No. 1956, Eric Heiden, speed skating, US, horiz.

1980, June 4   *Perf. 14*
1953	A339	Strip of 7, #a.-g.	7.75	3.50
1954	A339	10g multi, horiz.	1.60	.70
1955	A339	25g multi, horiz.	5.50	2.75
		Nos. 1953-1955 (3)	14.85	6.95

Souvenir Sheet
Perf. 13½
1956	A339	25g multicolored	26.00	25.00

Nos. 1954-1956 are airmail. No. 1956 contains one 60x49mm stamp.

Composers and Paintings of Young Ballerinas A340

Paintings of ballerinas by Cydney or Degas and: No. 1957a, 3g, Gioacchino Rossini. b, 4g, Johann Strauss, the younger. c, 5g, Debussy. d, 6g, Beethoven. e, 7g, Chopin. f, 8g, Richard Wagner. g, 20g, Johann Sebastian Bach, horiz. 10g, Robert Stoltz. 25g, Verdi.

1980, July 1   *Perf. 14*
1957	A340	Strip of 7, #a.-g.	7.75	2.50
1958	A340	10g multicolored	1.75	.60
1959	A340	25g multicolored	5.25	1.40
		Nos. 1957-1959 (3)	14.75	4.50

Birth and death dates are incorrectly inscribed on 4g, 8g, 10g. No. 1957f is incorrectly inscribed "Adolph" Wagner. Nos. 1958-1959 are airmail. For overprints see Nos. 1998-1999.

Pilar City Bicentennial A341

Perf. 13½x13
1980, July 17   *Litho.*   *Wmk. 347*
1966	A341	5g multi	5.25	2.00
1967	A341	25g multi	5.25	2.00

No. 1967 is airmail.

Christmas, Intl. Year of the Child — A342

No. 1968: a, 3g, Christmas tree. b, 4g, Santa filling stockings. c, 5g, Nativity scene. d, 6g, Adoration of the Magi. e, 7g, Three children, presents. f, 8g, Children, dove, fruit. g, 20g, Children playing with toys. 10g, Madonna and Child, horiz. No. 1970, Children blowing bubbles, horiz. No. 1971, Five children, horiz.

1980, Aug. 4   *Unwmk.*   *Perf. 14*
1968	A342	Strip of 7, #a.-g.	9.00	5.00
1969	A342	10g multicolored	1.40	.90
1970	A342	25g multicolored	2.50	1.40
		Nos. 1968-1970 (3)	12.90	7.30

Souvenir Sheet
1971	A342	25g multicolored	26.00	25.00

Nos. 1969-1970 are airmail.

Ships A343

Emblems and ships: No. 1972a, 3g, ESPAMER '80, Spanish Armada. b, 4g, NORWEX '80, Viking longboat. c, 5g, RICCIONE '80, Battle of Lepanto. d, 6g, ESSEN '80, Great Harry of Cruickshank. e, 7g, US Bicentennial, Mount Vernon. f, 8g, LONDON '80, H.M.S. Victory. g, 20g, ESSEN '80, Hamburg 11, vert. 10g, ESSEN '80, Gorch Fock. 25g, vert. PHILATOKYO '81, Nippon Maru, horiz.

1980, Sept. 15   *Perf. 14*
1972	A343	Strip of 7, #a.-g.	6.25	2.25
1973	A343	10g multicolored	1.50	.55
1974	A343	25g multicolored	4.50	1.40
		Nos. 1972-1974 (3)	12.25	4.20

Nos. 1973-1974 are airmail. For overprint see No. 2278.

Souvenir Sheet

King Juan Carlos A344

1980, Sept. 19   *Perf. 14½*
1975	A344	25g multicolored	22.00	21.00

Paraguay Airlines Boeing 707 Service Inauguration A345

A346

Perf. 13½x13
1980, Sept. 17   *Litho.*   *Wmk. 347*
1976	A345	20g multi	2.75	1.50
1977	A345	100g multi	2.75	1.50

No. 1977 is airmail.

World Cup Soccer Championships, Spain — A346a

Various soccer players, winning country: No. 1978a, 3g, Uruguay 1930, 1950. b, 4g, Italy 1934, 1938. c, 5g, Germany 1954, 1974. d, 6g, Brazil 1958, 1962, 1970. e, 7g, England, 1966. f, 8g, Argentina, 1978. g, 20g, Espana '82 emblem.

10g, World Cup trophy, flags. 25g, Soccer player from Uruguay.

1980, Dec. 10   *Unwmk.*   *Perf. 14*
1978	A346	Strip of 7, #a.-g.	7.00	1.75
1979	A346	10g multicolored	2.10	.50
1980	A346	25g multicolored	7.25	1.75
		Nos. 1978-1980 (3)	16.35	4.00

Souvenir Sheet
Perf. 14½
1981	A346a	25g Sheet of 1 + 2 labels	26.00	25.00

Nos. 1979-1981 are airmail.

1980 World Chess Championships, Mexico — A347

Illustrations from The Book of Chess: No. 1982a, 3g, Two men, chess board. b, 4g, Circular chess board, players. c, 5g, Four-person chess match. d, 6g, King Alfonso X of Castile and Leon. e, 7g, Two players, chess board, horiz. f, 8g, Two veiled women, chess board, horiz. g, 20g, Two women in robes, chess board, horiz.

10g, Crusader knights, chess board, horiz. 25g, Three players, chess board, horiz.

1980, Dec. 15   *Litho.*   *Perf. 14*
1982	A347	Strip of 7, #a.-g.	11.00	2.50
1983	A347	10g multicolored	2.00	.35
1984	A347	25g multicolored	2.25	.70
		Nos. 1982-1984 (3)	15.25	3.55

Nos. 1983-1984 are airmail.
See Nos. C506-C510. Compare with illustration AP199.

1980 Winter Olympics, Lake Placid — A348

Olympic scenes, gold medalists: No. 1985a, 25c, Lighting Olympic flame. b, 50c, Hockey team, US. c, 1g, Eric Heiden, US, speed skating. d, 2g, Robin Cousins, Great Britain, figure skating. e, 3g, Thomas Wassberg, Sweden, cross country skiing. f, 4g, Annie Borckinck,

Netherlands, speed skating. g, 5g, Gold, silver, and bronze medals.
No. 1986, Irene Epple, silver medal, slalom, Germany. 10g, Ingemar Stenmark, slalom, giant slalom, Sweden. 30g, Annemarie Moser-Proll, downhill, Austria. 25g, Baron Pierre de Coubertin.

1981, Feb. 4 — Litho. — Perf. 14

1985	A348	Strip of 7, #a.-g.	4.50	1.90
1986	A348	5g multicolored	1.20	.35
1987	A348	5g multicolored	1.60	.50
1988	A348	30g multicolored	4.50	1.00
		Nos. 1985-1988 (4)	11.80	3.75

Souvenir Sheet
Perf. 13½

1988A	A348	25g multicolored	21.00	20.00

No. 1985 exists in strips of 4 and 3. Nos. 1986-1988A are airmail. No. 1988A contains one 30x40mm stamp.

Locomotives
A349

No. 1989, 25c, Electric model 242, Germany. b, 50c, Electric, London-Midlands-Lancashire, England. c, 1g, Electric, Switzerland. d, 2g, Diesel-electric, Montreal-Vancouver, Canada. e, 3g, Electric, Austria. f, 4g, Electric inter-urban, Lyons-St. Etienne, France, vert. g, 5g, First steam locomotive in Paraguay.
No. 1990, 5g, Steam locomotive, Japan. No. 1991, 10g, Stephenson's steam engine, 1830 England. No. 1992, 30g, Stephenson's Rocket, 1829, England, vert.
No. 1993, 25g, Crocodile locomotive, Switzerland.

1981, Feb. 9 — Litho. — Perf. 14

1989	A349	Strip of 7, #a.-g.	4.25	1.10
1990	A349	5g multicolored	2.00	.35
1991	A349	10g multicolored	3.50	.65
1992	A349	30g multicolored	11.00	2.00
		Nos. 1989-1992 (4)	20.75	4.10

Souvenir Sheet
Perf. 13½x13

1993	A349	25g multicolored	37.50	35.00

Electric railroads, cent. (#1989a-1989f), steam-powered railway service, 150th anniv. (#1989c, 1990-1991), Liverpool-Manchester Railway, 150th anniv. (#1992). Swiss Railways, 75th anniv. (#1993).
Nos. 1990-1993 are airmail. No. 1993 contains one 54x34mm stamp.

Intl. Year of the
Child — A350

Portraits of children with assorted flowers: No. 1994a, 10g. b, 25g. c, 50g. d, 100g. e, 200g. f, 300g. g, 400g.

1981, Apr. 13 — Litho. — Perf. 14

1994	A350	Strip of 7, #a.-g.	20.00	8.25
1995	A350	75g multicolored	2.00	.70
1996	A350	500g multicolored	10.50	4.00
1997	A350	1000g multicolored	19.00	8.00
		Nos. 1994-1997 (4)	51.50	20.95

Nos. 1995-1997 are airmail.

Nos. 1957b and 1958 Overprinted in Red

1981, May 22

1998	A340	4g on #1957b	1.25	.60
1999	A340	10g on #1958	2.25	1.00

No. 1999 is airmail.

The following stamps were issued in sheets of 8 with 1 label: Nos. 2001, 2013, 2037, 2044, 2047, 2055, 2140.
The following stamp was issued in sheets of 10 with 2 labels: No. 1994a.
The following stamps were issued in sheets of 6 with 3 labels: Nos. 2017, 2029, 2035, 2104, 2145.
The following stamps were issued in sheets of 3 with 6 labels: 2079, 2143.
The following stamps were issued in sheets of 5 with 4 labels: Nos. 2050-2051, 2057, 2059, 2061, 2067, 2069, 2077, 2082, 2089, 2092, 2107, 2117, 2120, 2121, 2123, 2125, 2129, 2135, 2138, 2142, 2146, 2148, 2151, 2160, 2163, 2165, 2169, 2172, 2176, 2179, 2182, 2190, 2196, 2202, 2204, 2214, 2222, 2224, 2232, 2244, 2246, 2248, 2261, 2263, 2265, 2269, 2271, 2273, 2275, 2277.
The following stamps were issued in sheets of 4 with 5 labels: Nos. 2307, 2310, 2313, 2316, 2324, 2329.

Royal
Wedding of
Prince
Charles and
Lady Diana
Spencer
A351

Prince Charles, sailing ships: No. 2000a, 25c, Royal George. b, 50c, Great Britain. c, 1g, Taeping. d, 2g, Star of India. e, 3g, Torrens. f, 4g, Loch Etive. No. 2001, Medway.
No. 2002, Charles, flags, and Concorde. 10g, Flags, flowers, Diana, Charles. 25g, Charles, Diana, flowers, vert. 30g, Coats of arms, flags.

1981, June 27

2000	A351	Strip of 6, #a.-f.	5.00	1.40
2001	A351	5g multicolored	1.60	.35
2002	A351	5g multicolored	1.00	.45
2003	A351	10g multicolored	3.25	.75
2004	A351	30g multicolored	5.50	2.25
		Nos. 2000-2004 (5)	16.35	5.20

Souvenir Sheet
Perf. 13½

2005	A351	25g multicolored	26.00	25.00

Nos. 2002-2005 are airmail. No. 2005 contains one 50x60mm stamp. For overprint see No. 2253.
No. 2005 has an orange margin. It also exists with gray margin. Same value.

Traditional
Costumes and
Itaipu
Dam — A352

Women in various traditional costumes: a, 10g. b, 25g. c, 50g. d, 100g. e, 200g. f, 300g. g, 400g, President Stroessner, Itaipu Dam.

1981, June 30 — Perf. 14

2006	A352	Strip of 7, #a.-g.	27.00	8.00

For overprints see No. 2281.

UPU
Membership
Centenary
A353

1981, Aug. 18 — Litho. — Perf. 13½x13

2007	A353	5g rose lake & blk	2.25	1.00
2008	A353	10g lil & blk	2.25	1.00
2009	A353	20g grn & blk	2.25	1.00
2010	A353	25g lt red brn & blk	2.25	1.00
2011	A353	50g bl & blk	3.25	2.00
		Nos. 2007-2011 (5)	12.25	6.00

Peter Paul
Rubens,
Paintings — A354

Details from paintings: No. 2012: a, 25c, Madonna Surrounded by Saints. b, 50c, Judgment of Paris. c, 1g, Duke of Buckingham Conducted to the Temple of Virtus. d, 2g, Minerva Protecting Peace from Mars. e, 3g, Henry IV Receiving the Portrait of Marie de Medici. f, 4g, Triumph of Juliers. 5g, Madonna and Child Reigning Among Saints (Cherubs).

1981, July 9 — Litho. — Perf. 14

2012	A354	Strip of 6, #a.-f.	5.25	.75
2013	A354	5g multicolored	1.50	.25
		Nos. 2012-2013 (2)	6.75	1.00

Jean Auguste-Dominique Ingres
(1780-1867), Painter — A355

Details from paintings: No. 2014: a, 25c, c, 1g, d, 2g, f, 4g, The Turkish Bath. b, 50c, The Source. e, 3g, Oediphus and the Sphinx. g, 5g, Half-figure of a Bather.

1981, Oct. 13

2014	A355	Strip of 7, #a.-g.	6.75	1.50

A horiz. strip of 5 containing Nos. 2014a-2014e exists.
No. 2014f and 2014g exist in sheet of 8 (four each) plus label.
For overprints see No. 2045.

Pablo
Picasso,
Birth Cent.
A356

Designs: No. 2015: a, 25c, Women Running on the Beach. b, 50c, Family on the Beach.
No. 2016: a, 1g, Still-life. b, 2g, Bullfighter. c, 3g, Children Drawing. d, 4g, Seated Woman. 5g, Paul as Clown.

1981, Oct. 19

2015	A356	Pair, #a.-b.	.90	.50
2016	A356	Strip of 4, #a.-d.	8.75	1.50
2017	A356	5g multicolored	2.10	.40
		Nos. 2015-2017 (3)	11.75	2.40

Nos. 2015-2016 Ovptd. in Silver

1981, Oct. 22

2018	A356	on #2015a-2015b	1.00	.50
2019	A356	on #2016a-2016d	4.50	1.00
		Nos. 2018-2019 (2)	5.50	1.50

Philatelia '81, Frankfurt.

Nos. 2015-2016 Ovptd. in Gold

1981, Oct. 25

2020	A356	on #2015a-2015b	1.00	.50
2021	A356	on #2016a-2016d	4.50	1.00
		Nos. 2020-2021 (2)	5.50	1.50

Espamer '81 Philatelic Exhibition.

Royal Wedding of
Prince Charles
and Lady
Diana — A357

Designs: No. 2022a-2022c, 25c, 50c, 1g, Diana, Charles, flowers. d, 2g, Couple. e, 3g, Couple leaving church. f, 4g, Couple, Queen Elizabeth II waving from balcony. 2022G, 5g, Diana. No. 2023, Wedding party, horiz. 10g, Riding in royal coach, horiz. 30g, Yeomen of the guard, horiz.

1981, Dec. 4 — Litho. — Perf. 14

2022	A357	Strip of 6, #a.-f.	2.40	1.50
2022G	A357	5g multicolored	.40	.25
2023	A357	5g multicolored	3.50	.70
2024	A357	10g multicolored	6.75	1.40
2025	A357	30g multicolored	24.00	4.50
		Nos. 2022-2025 (5)	37.05	8.35

Souvenir Sheets
Perf. 14½

2026	A357	25g like #2022d	40.00	37.50
2027	A357	25g Wedding portrait	40.00	37.50

No. 2022g exists in sheets of 8 plus label. Nos. 2023-2027 are airmail. Nos. 2026-2027 contain one each 50x70mm stamp.

Christmas
A358

Designs: No. 2028a, 25c, Jack-in-the-box. b, 50c, Jesus and angel. c, 1g, Santa, angels. d, 2g, Angels lighting candle. e, 3g, Christmas plant. f, 4g, Nativity scene. 5g, Children singing by Christmas tree.

1981, Dec. 17 — Perf. 14

2028	A358	Strip of 6, #a.-f.	5.00	1.00

Size: 28x45mm
Perf. 13½

2029	A358	5g multicolored	2.75	.55

Intl. Year of the Child (Nos. 2028-2029). For overprints see No. 2042.

Intl. Year of the
Child — A359

Story of Puss 'n Boots: No. 2030a, 25c, Boy, Puss. b, 50c, Puss, rabbits.
1g, Puss, king. 2g, Prince, princess, king. 3g, Giant ogre, Puss. 4g, Puss chasing mouse. 5g, Princess, prince, Puss.

1982, Apr. 16   Litho.   Perf. 14

2030	A359	Pair, #a.-b.	.70	.50
2031	A359	1g multicolored	.35	.25
2032	A359	2g multicolored	.70	.25
2033	A359	3g multicolored	1.00	.25
2034	A359	4g multicolored	1.60	.25
2035	A359	6.50g multicolored	6.50	1.50
		Nos. 2030-2035 (6)	10.85	3.00

Nos. 2031-2034 printed se-tenant with label.

Scouting, 75th Anniv. and Lord Baden-Powell, 125th Birth Anniv. — A360

No. 2036: a, 25c, Tetradactyla, Scout hand salute. b, 50c, Nandu (rhea), Cub Scout and trefoil. c, 1g, Peccary, Wolf's head totem. d, 2g, Coatimundi, emblem on buckle. e, 3g, Mara, Scouting's Intl. Communications emblem. f, 4g, Deer, boy scout.
No. 2037, Aotes, Den mother, Cub Scout. No. 2038, Ocelot, scouts cooking. 10g, Collie, boy scout. 30g, Armadillo, two scouts planting tree. 25g, Lord Robert Baden-Powell, founder of Boy Scouts.

1982, Apr. 21

2036	A360	Strip of 6, #a.-f.	2.75	1.00
2037	A360	5g multicolored	2.25	.40
2038	A360	5g multicolored	2.25	.40
2039	A360	10g multicolored	3.25	.45
2040	A360	30g multicolored	4.00	.40
		Nos. 2036-2040 (5)	14.50	2.65

Souvenir Sheet
Perf. 14½

2041	A360	25g multicolored	33.00	32.00

Nos. 2038-2041 are airmail. For overprint see No. 2140.

No. 2028 Overprinted with ESSEN 82 Emblem

1982, Apr. 28   Perf. 14

2042	A358	on #2028a-2028f	4.00	2.50

Essen '82 Intl. Philatelic Exhibition.

Cats and Kittens A361

Various cats or kittens: No. 2043a, 25c. b, 50c. c, 1g. d, 2g. e, 3g. f, 4g.

1982, June 7   Perf. 14

2043	A361	Strip of 6, #a.-f.	5.00	1.00
2044	A361	5g multi, vert.	1.75	.35
		Nos. 2043-2044 (2)	6.75	1.35

For overprints see Nos. 2054-2055.

Nos. 2014a-2014e Ovptd. PHILEXFRANCE 82 Emblem ans "PARIS 11-21.6.82" in Blue

1982, June 11

2045	A355	Strip of 5, #a.-e.	4.75	1.00

Philexfrance '82 Intl. Philatelic Exhibition. Size of overprint varies.

World Cup Soccer Championships, Spain — A362

Designs: 2046a, 25c, Brazilian team. b, 50c, Chilean team. c, 1g, Honduran team. d, 2g, Peruvian team. e, 3g, Salvadoran team. f, 4g, Globe as soccer ball, flags of Latin American finalists. No. 2047, Ball of flags. No. 2048, Austrian team. No. 2049, Players from Brazil, Austria. No. 2050, Spanish team. No. 2051, Two players from Argentina, Brazil, vert. No. 2052, W. German team. No. 2053, Players

from Argentina, Brazil. No. 2053A, World Cup trophy, world map on soccer balls. No. 2053B, Players from W. Germany, Mexico, vert.

1982   Litho.   Perf. 14

2046	A362	Strip of 6, #a.-f.	3.75	1.25
2047	A362	5g multicolored	.35	.25
2048	A362	5g multicolored	1.95	1.40
2049	A362	5g multicolored	3.25	1.00
2050	A362	10g multicolored	.90	.25
2051	A362	5g multicolored	.50	.50
2052	A362	30g multicolored	2.25	.25
2053	A362	30g multicolored	.25	.25
		Nos. 2046-2053 (8)	13.20	5.15

Souvenir Sheets
Perf. 14½

2053A	A362	25g multicolored	18.00	17.00
2053B	A362	25g multicolored	18.00	17.00

Issued: #2049, 2051, 2053, 2053A, 4/19; others, 6/13.
Nos. 2047 exists in sheets of 8 plus label.
Nos. 2048-2053B are airmail.
For overprints see Nos. 2086, 2286, C593.

Nos. 2043-2044 Overprinted in Silver With PHILATECIA 82 and Intl. Year of the Child Emblems

1982, Sept. 12   Perf. 14

2054	A361	Strip of 5, #a.-e.	5.50	1.25
2055	A361	5g on #2044	2.25	.40
		Nos. 2054-2055 (2)	7.75	1.65

Philatelia '82, Hanover, Germany and Intl. Year of the Child.

Raphael, 500th Birth Anniv. — A363

Details from paintings: No. 2056a, 25c, Adam and Eve (The Fall). b, 50c, Creation of Eve. c, 1g, Portrait of a Young Woman (La Fornarina). d, 2g, The Three Graces. e, 3g, f, 4g, Cupid and the Three Graces. 5g. Leda and the Swan.

1982, Sept. 27

2056	A363	Strip of 6, #a.-f.	6.75	1.50
2057	A363	5g multicolored	5.00	1.00
		Nos. 2056-2057 (2)	11.75	2.50

Nos. 2056e-2056f have continuous design.

Christmas A364

Entire works or details from paintings by Raphael: No. 2058a, 25c, The Belvedere Madonna. b, 50c, The Ansidei Madonna. c, 1g, La Belle Jardiniere. d, 2g, The Aldobrandini (Garvagh) Madonna. e, 3g, Madonna of the Goldfinch. f, 4g, The Alba Madonna. No. 2059, Madonna of the Grand Duke. No. 2060, Madonna of the Linen Window. 10g, The Alba Madonna, diff. 25g, The Holy Family with St. Elizabeth and the Infant St. John and Two Angels. 30g, The Canigiani Holy Family.

1982   Perf. 14, 13x13½ (#2061)

2058	A364	Strip of 6, #a.-f.	6.00	2.50
2059	A364	5g multicolored	2.40	.90
2060	A364	5g multicolored	5.50	1.75
2061	A364	10g multicolored	2.50	.90
2062	A364	30g multicolored	1.25	.40
		Nos. 2058-2062 (5)	17.65	6.45

Souvenir Sheet
Perf. 14½

2063	A364	25g multicolored	19.00	17.50

Issued: #2058-2059, 9/30; others, 12/17.
Nos. 2058a-2058f and 2059 exist perf. 13.
Nos. 2060-2063 are airmail and have silver lettering. For overprint see No. 2087.

Life of Christ, by Albrecht Durer — A365

Details from paintings: No. 2064a, 25c, The Flight into Egypt. b, 50c, Christ Among the Doctors. c, 1g, Christ Carrying the Cross. d, 2g, Nailing of Christ to the Cross. e, 3g, Christ on the Cross. f, 4g, Lamentation Over the Dead Christ. 5g, The Circumcision of Christ.

1982, Dec. 14   Perf. 14

2064	A365	Strip of 6, #a.-f.	7.75	2.75

Perf. 13x13½

2065	A365	5g multicolored	4.00	.75
		Nos. 2064-2065 (2)	11.75	3.50

For overprint see No. 2094.

South American Locomotives A366

Locomotives from: No. 2066a, 25c, Argentina. b, 50c, Uruguay. c, 1g, Ecuador. d, 2g, Bolivia. e, 3g, Peru. f, 4g, Brazil. 5g, Paraguay.

1983, Jan. 17   Litho.   Perf. 14

2066	A366	Strip of 6, #a.-f.	3.75	1.00
2067	A366	5g multicolored	3.00	.75
		Nos. 2066-2067 (2)	6.75	1.75

For overprint see No. 2093.

Race Cars — A367

No. 2068: a, 25c, ATS-Ford D 06. b, 50c, Ferrari 126 C 2. c, 1g, Brabham-BMW BT 50. d, 2g, Renault RE 30 B. e, 3g, Porsche 956. f, 4g, Talbot-Ligier-Matra JS 19. 5g, Mercedes Benz C-111.

1983, Jan. 19   Perf. 14

2068	A367	Strip of 6, #a.-f.	5.25	1.60

Perf. 13½x13

2069	A367	5g multicolored	2.50	.90
		Nos. 2068-2069 (2)	7.75	2.50

For overprint see No. 2118.

Itaipua Dam, Pres. Stroessner A368

1983, Jan. 22   Litho.   Wmk. 347

2070	A368	3g multi	2.25	1.00
2071	A368	5g multi	2.25	1.00
2072	A368	10g multi	2.25	1.00
2073	A368	20g multi	2.25	1.00
2074	A368	25g multi	2.25	1.00
2075	A368	50g multi	2.25	1.00
		Nos. 2070-2075 (6)	13.50	6.00

25th anniv. of Stroessner City.
Nos. 2073-2075 airmail.

1984 Winter Olympics, Sarajevo A369

Ice skaters: No. 2076a, 25c, Marika Kilius, Hans-Jurgens Baumler, Germany, 1964. b, 50c, Tai Babilonia, Randy Gardner, US, 1976. c, 1g, Anett Poetzsch, E. Germany, 1980, vert. d, 2g, Tina Riegel, Andreas Nischwitz, Germany, 1980, vert. e, Dagmar Lurz, Germany, 1980, vert. f, 4g, Trixi Schuba, Austria, 1972, vert. 5g, Peggy Fleming, US, 1968, vert.

Perf. 13½x13, 13x13½

1983, Feb. 23   Unwmk.

2076	A369	Strip of 6, #a.-f.	3.25	1.00
2077	A369	5g multicolored	5.00	.75
		Nos. 2076-2077 (2)	8.25	1.75

For overprints see Nos. 2177, 2266.

Pope John Paul II — A370

#2078: a, 25c, Virgin of Caacupe. b, 50c, Cathedral of Caacupe. c, 1g, Cathedral of Asuncion. d, 2g, Pope holding crucifix. e, 3g, Our Lady of the Assumption. f, 4g, Pope giving blessing. 5g, Pope with hands clasped. 25g, Madonna & child.

1983, June 11   Litho.   Perf. 14

2078	A370	Strip of 6, #a.-f.	6.75	2.00
2079	A370	5g multicolored	3.25	.80
		Nos. 2078-2079 (2)	10.00	2.80

Souvenir Sheet
Perf. 14½

2080	A370	25g multicolored	18.50	14.00

No. 2080 is airmail. For overprint see No. 2143.

Antique Automobiles A371

No. 2081: a, 25c, Bordino Steamcoach, 1854. b, 50c, Panhard & Levassor, 1892. c, 1g, Benz Velo, 1894. d, 2g, Peugeot-Daimler, 1894. e, 3g, 1st car with patented Lutzmann system, 1898. f, 4g, Benz Victory, 1891-92. No. 2082, Ceirano 5CV. No. 2083, Mercedes Simplex PS 32 Turismo, 1902. 10g, Stae Electric, 1909. 25g, Benz Velocipede, 1885. 30g, Rolls Royce Silver Ghost, 1913.

1983, July 18   Perf. 14

2081	A371	Strip of 6, #a.-f.	3.00	1.25
2082	A371	5g multicolored	1.90	.40
2083	A371	5g multicolored	7.00	1.10
2084	A371	10g multicolored	1.25	.25
2085	A371	30g multicolored	2.75	.25
		Nos. 2081-2085 (5)	15.90	3.25

Souvenir Sheet
Perf. 14½

2085A	A371	25g Sheet of 1 + label	21.00	20.00

Nos. 2083-2085A are airmail.

No. 2046 Ovptd. in Red, No. 2058 Ovptd. in Black with "52o CONGRESO F.I.P." and Brasiliana 83 Emblem

1983, July 27   Perf. 14

2086	A362	Strip of 6, #a.-f.	6.50	5.00
2087	A364	Strip of 6, #a.-f.	6.50	5.00

Brasiliana '83, Rio de Janeiro and 52nd FIP Congress. No. 2087 exists perf. 13.

Aircraft Carriers A372

Carriers and airplanes: No. 2088a, 25c, 25 de Mayo, A-4Q Sky Hawk, Argentina. b, 50c, Minas Gerais, Brazil. c, 1g, Akagi, A6M3 Zero,

Japan. d, 2g, Guiseppe Miraglia, Italy. e, 3g, Enterprise, S-3A Viking, US. f, 4g, Dedalo, AV-8A Matador, Spain. No. 2089, 5g, Schwabenland, Dornier DO-18, Germany.

No aircraft on Nos. 2088b, 2088d.

25g, US astronauts Donn Eisele, Walter Schirra & Walt Cunningham, Earth & Apollo 7.

1983, Aug. 29   *Perf. 14*
2088	A372	Strip of 6, #a.-f.	5.50 1.50
2089	A372	5g multicolored	2.50 .75
		Nos. 2088-2089 (2)	8.00 2.25

Souvenir Sheet
Perf. 13½
2090	A372	25g multicolored	22.00 21.00

No. 2090 is airmail and contains one 55x45mm stamp.

Birds — A373

#2091: a, 25c, Pulsatrix perspicillata. b, 50c, Ortalis ruficauda. c, 1g, Chloroceryle amazona. d, 2g, Trogon violaceus. e, 3g, Pezites militaris. f, 4g, Bucco capensis. 5g, Cyanerpes cyaneus.

1983, Oct. 22   *Perf. 14*
2091	A373	Strip of 6, #a.-f.	5.50 1.00

Perf. 13
2092	A373	5g multicolored	2.25 .40
		Nos. 2091-2092 (2)	7.75 1.40

No. 2066 Ovptd. for PHILATELICA 83 in Silver
1983, Oct. 28
2093	A366	Strip of 6, #a.-f.	6.75 2.00

Philatelia '83, Dusseldorf, Germany.

No. 2064 Overprinted in Silver for EXFIVIA - 83
1983, Nov. 5
2094	A365	Strip of 6, #a.-f.	7.50 2.00

Exfivia '83 Philatelic Exhibition, La Paz, Bolivia.

Re-election of President Stroessner
A374

10g, Passion flower, vert. 25g, Miltonia phalaenopsis, vert. 50g, Natl. arms, Chaco soldier. 75g, Acaray hydroelectric dam. 100g, Itaipu hydroelectric dam. 200g, Pres. Alfredo Stroessner, vert.

1983, Nov. 24   *Perf. 14*
2095	A374	10g multicolored	.50 .30
2096	A374	25g multicolored	.80 .30
2097	A374	50g multicolored	1.60 .30
2098	A374	75g multicolored	1.25 .30

Perf. 13
2099	A374	100g multicolored	1.60 .30
2100	A374	200g multicolored	3.25 1.00
		Nos. 2095-2100 (6)	9.00 2.50

Nos. 2099-2100 are airmail. No. 2096 exists perf. 13. For overprint see No. C577.

Montgolfier Brothers' 1st Flight, Bicent.
A375

No. 2101: a, 25c, Santos-Dumont's Biplane, 1906. b, 50c, Airship. c, 1g, Paulhan's biplane over Juvisy. d, 2g, Zeppelin LZ-3, 1907. e, 3g, Biplane of Henri Farman. f, 4g, Graf Zeppelin over Friedrichshafen. 5g, Lebaudy's dirigible. 25g, Detail of painting, Great Week of Aviation at Betheny, 1910.

1984, Jan. 7   *Perf. 13*
2101	A375	Strip of 6, #a.-f.	3.00 1.25

Perf. 14
2104	A375	5g multicolored	5.25 .75
		Nos. 2101-2104 (2)	8.25 2.00

Souvenir Sheet
Perf. 13½
2105	A375	25g multicolored	22.00 21.00

No. 2105 is airmail and contains one 75x55mm stamp. For overprint see No. 2145.

Dogs — A376

#2106: a, 25c, German Shepherd. b, 50c, Great Dane, vert. c, 1g, Poodle, vert. d, 2g, Saint Bernard. e, 3g, Greyhound. f, 4g, Dachshund. 5g, Boxer.

1984, Jan. 11   Litho.   *Perf. 14*
2106	A376	Strip of 6, #a.-f.	4.50 2.10
2107	A376	5g multicolored	2.25 .90
		Nos. 2106-2107 (2)	6.75 3.00

See nos. 2181-2182.

Animals, Anniversaries
A377

1984, Jan. 24   *Perf. 13*
2108	A377	10g Puma	.45 .30
2109	A377	25g Alligator	1.20 .30
2110	A377	50g Jaguar	2.25 .45
2111	A377	75g Peccary	3.50 .70
2112	A377	100g Simon Bolivar, vert.	5.25 1.10
2113	A377	200g Girl scout, vert.	10.00 3.25
		Nos. 2108-2113 (6)	22.65 6.10

Simon Bolivar, birth bicent. and Girl Scouts of Paraguay, 76th anniv.
Nos. 2112-2113 are airmail.

Christmas — A378

Designs: No. 2114a, 25c, Pope John Paul II. b, 50c, Christmas tree. c, 1g, Children. d, 2g, Nativity Scene. e, 3g, Three Kings. f, 4g, Madonna and Child. No. 2115, Madonna and Child by Raphael.

1984, Mar. 23   *Perf. 13x13½*
2114	A378	Strip of 6, #a.-f.	8.75 1.50
2115	A378	5g multicolored	4.00 1.00
		Nos. 2114-2115 (2)	12.75 2.50

Illustrations of medieval miniatures: No. 2116a, 25c, Ulrich von Liechtenstein. b, 50c, Ulrich von Gutenberg. c, 1g, Der Putter. d, 2g, Walther von Metz. e, 3g, Hartman von Aue. f, 4g, Lutok von Seuen. 5g, Werner von Teufen.

1984, Mar. 27   *Perf. 14*
2116	A379	Strip of 6, #a.-f.	5.50 1.25

Perf. 13
2117	A379	5g multicolored	3.25 .75
		Nos. 2116-2117 (2)	8.75 2.00

For overprint see No. 2121.

No. 2068 Ovptd. in Silver with ESSEN 84 Emblem
1984, May 10
2118	A367	Strip of 6, #a.-f.	5.50 1.25

Essen '84 Intl. Philatelic Exhibition.

Endangered Animals
A380

#2119: a, 25c, Priodontes giganteus. b, 50c, Catagonus wagneri. c, 1g, Felis pardalis. d, 2g, Chrysocyon brachyurus. e, 3g, Burmeisteria retusa. f, 4g, Myrmecophaga tridactyla. 5g, Caiman crocodilus.

1984, June 16   *Perf. 14*
2119	A380	Strip of 6, #a.-f.	6.25 3.25

Perf. 13
2120	A380	5g multicolored	3.00 .75
		Nos. 2119-2120 (2)	9.25 4.00

A canceled-to-order perf. 13 strip of seven stamps containing Nos. 2119a-2119g and 2120 exists. For overprint see No. 2129.

No. 2117 Ovptd. in Silver with Emblems, etc., for U.P.U. 19th World Congress, Hamburg
1984, June 19   *Perf. 13*
2121	A379	5g on #2117	2.75 2.00

UPU Congress, Hamburg '84 — A381

Sailing ships: No. 2122a, 25c, Admiral of Hamburg. b, 50c, Neptune. c, 1g, Archimedes. d, 2g, Passat. e, 3g, Finkenwerder cutter off Heligoland. f, 4g, Four-masted ship. 5g, Deutschland.

1984, June 19   *Perf. 13*
2122	A381	Strip of 6, #a.-f.	5.75 1.50
2123	A381	5g multicolored	2.25 .50
		Nos. 2122-2123 (2)	8.00 2.00

For overprints see Nos. 2146, 2279-2280.

British Locomotives
A382

No. 2124: a, 25c, Pegasus 097, 1868. b, 50c, Pegasus 097, diff. c, 1g, Cornwall, 1847. d, 2g, Cornwall, 1847, diff. e, 3g, Patrick Stirling #1, 1870. f, 4g, Patrick Stirling #1, 1870, diff. 5g, Stepney Brighton Terrier, 1872.

1984, June 20   *Perf. 14*
2124	A382	Strip of 6, #a.-f.	7.50 1.50

Perf. 13
2125	A382	5g multicolored	3.25 .50
		Nos. 2124-2125 (2)	10.75 2.00

No. C486 Overprinted in Blue on Silver with UN emblem and "40o Aniversario de la / Fundacion de las / Naciones Unidas 26.6.1944"
1984, Aug. 1   Litho.   *Perf. 14½*
2126	AP161	25g on No. C486	21.00 20.00

No. 1536 Ovptd. in Orange (#a.-d.) or Silver (#e.-g.)

and

A383

1984, Aug. 21   *Perf. 14*
2127	A271	Strip of 7, #a.-g.	9.25 1.75

Souvenir Sheet
Perf. 14½
2128	A383	25g multicolored	14.50 14.00

Ausipex '84 Intl. Philatelic Exhibition, Melbourne, Australia. No. 2128 is airmail.

Nos. 2120 and C551 Ovptd. in Black and Red

1984   *Perf. 13*
2129	A380	5g on #2120	2.90 2.00

Perf. 14
2130	AP178	30g on #C551	4.25 4.00

Issued: #2129, Sept. 20; #2130, Aug. 30. No. 2130 is airmail.

No. 1512 Ovptd. "VFB STUTTGART CAMPEON NACIONAL DE FUTBOL DE ALEMANIA 1984" and Emblem
1984, Sept. 5   *Perf. 14*
2131	A262	Strip of 7, #a.-g.	4.75 3.00

VFB Stuttgart, 1984 German Soccer Champions.

Cat Type of 1976

Various cats: No. 2132: a, 25c. b, 50c. c, 1g. d, 2g. e, 3g. f, 4g.

1984, Sept. 10   *Perf. 13x13½*
2132	A287	Strip of 6, #a.-f.	4.25 3.25
2133	A287	5g multicolored	3.50 1.75
		Nos. 2132-2133 (2)	7.75 5.00

1984 Summer Olympics, Los Angeles
A384

Gold medalists: No. 2134a, 25c, Michael Gross, W. Germany, swimming. b, 50c, Peter Vidmar, US, gymnastics. c, 1g, Fredy Schmidtke, W. Germany, cycling. d, 2g, Philippe Boisse, France, fencing. e, 3g, Ulrike Meyfarth, W. Germany, women's high jump. f, 4g, Games emblem. 5g, Mary Lou Retton, US, women's all-around gymnastics, vert. 30g, Rolf Milser, W. Germany, weight lifting, vert.

1985, Jan. 16   Litho.   *Perf. 13*
2134 A384   Strip of 6, #a.-f.   3.50 1.90
2135 A384   5g multicolored   5.25 1.10
    Nos. 2134-2135 (2)   8.75 3.00

Souvenir Sheet
Perf. 13½

2136 A384   30g multicolored   17.50 15.00
    No. 2136 is airmail and contains one
50x60mm stamp. For overprints see Nos.
2174, 2199, 2200. Compare with type A399.

Mushrooms
A385

    #2137: a, 25c, Boletus luteus. b, 50c,
Agaricus campester. c, 1g, Pholiota
spectabilis. d, 2g, Tricholoma terreum. e, 3g,
Laccaria laccata. f, 4g, Amanita phalloides.
5g, Scleroderma verrucosum.

1985, Jan. 19   *Perf. 14*
2137 A385   Strip of 6, #a.-f.   10.00 3.00
2138 A385   5g multicolored   9.00 3.00
    Nos. 2137-2138 (2)   19.00 6.00

    See Nos. 2166-2167.

World Wildlife
Fund — A386

    Endangered or extinct species: No. 2139a,
25c, Capybara. b, 50c, Mono titi, vert. c, 1g,
Rana cornuda adornada. d, 2g, Priodontes
giganteus, digging. e, 3g, Priodontes
giganteus, by water. f, 4g, Myrmecophaga
tridactyla. g, 5g, Myrmecophaga tridactyla,
with young.

1985, Mar. 13   *Perf. 14*
2139 A386   Strip of 7, #a.-g.   50.00 5.00
    See No. 2252.

**No. 2037 Ovptd. in Red with
ISRAPHIL Emblem**
1985, Apr. 10
2140 A360   5g on No. 2037   2.50 2.00
    Israel '85 Intl. Philatelic Exhibition.

John James
Audubon, Birth
Bicent. — A387

    Birds: No. 2141a, 25c, Piranga flava. b, 50c,
Polyborus plancus. c, 1g, Chiroxiphia caudata.
d, 2g, Xolmis irupero. e, 3g, Phloeoceastes
leucopogon. f, 4g, Thraupis bonariensis. 5g,
Parula pitiayumi, horiz.

1985, Apr. 18   *Perf. 13*
2141 A387   Strip of 6, #a.-f.   6.50 1.25
2142 A387   5g multicolored   3.00   .50
    Nos. 2141-2142 (2)   9.50 1.75

**No. 2079 Ovptd. in Silver with Italia
'85 Emblem**
1985, May 20   *Perf. 14*
2143 A370   5g on #2079   6.50 2.00
    Italia '85 Intl. Philatelic Exhibition.

No. 1448e Ovptd.
in Red on Silver

1985, June 12
2144 A250   30c on #1448e   2.40 1.25

**No. 2104 Ovptd. in Silver and Blue
with LUPO 85 Congress Emblem**
1985, July 5
2145 A375   5g on No. 2104   1.25   .50
    LUPO '85, Lucerne, Switzerland.

**No. 2123 Ovptd. in Silver and Blue
with MOPHILA 85 Emblem and
"HAMBURGO 11-12. 9. 85"**
1985, July 5   *Perf. 13*
2146 A381   5g on #2123   1.25   .50
    Mophila '85 Intl. Philatelic Exhibition,
Hamburg.

Intl. Youth
Year — A388

    Scenes from Tom Sawyer and Huckleberry
Finn: No. 2147a, 25c, Mississippi riverboat. b,
50c, Finn. c, 1g, Finn and friends by campfire.
d, 2g, Finn and Joe, sinking riverboat. e, 3g,
Finn, friends, riverboat. f, 4g, Cemetery. 5g,
Finn, Sawyer. 25g, Raft, riverboat.

1985, Aug. 5   *Perf. 13½x13*
2147 A388   Strip of 6, #a.-f.   4.50 1.50
2148 A388   5g multicolored   3.75   .75
    Nos. 2147-2148 (2)   8.25 2.25

Souvenir Sheet
Perf. 14½

2149 A388   25g multicolored   18.00 17.00
    No. 2149 is airmail. For overprint see No.
C612.

German
Railroads,
150th Anniv.
A389

    Locomotives: No. 2150a, 25c, T3, 1883. b,
50c, T18, 1912. c, 1g, T16, 1914. d, 2g, #01
118, Historic Trains Society, Frankfurt. e, 3g,
#05 001 Express, Nuremberg Transit
Museum. f, 4g, #10 002 Express, 1957. 5g,
Der Adler, 1835.
    25g, Painting of 1st German Train, Dec. 7,
1835.

1985, Aug. 8   *Perf. 14*
2150 A389   Strip of 6, #a.-f.   5.75 1.90
                                   Perf. 13
2151 A389   5g multicolored   2.25   .60
    Nos. 2150-2151 (2)   8.00 2.50

Souvenir Sheet
Perf. 13½

2152 A389   25g multicolored   32.00 30.00
    No. 2152 is airmail and contains one
75x53mm stamp. For overprint see No. 2165.

Development
Projects
A390

    Pres. Stroessner and: 10g, Soldier, map,
vert. 25g, Model of Yaci Reta Hydroelectric
Project. 50g, Itaipu Dam. 75g, Merchantman

Lago Ipoa. 100g, 1975 Coin, vert. 200g, Asuncion Intl. Airport.

1985, Sept. 17   Litho.   *Perf. 13*
2153 A390   10g multicolored   .50   .35
2154 A390   25g multicolored   .50   .35
2155 A390   50g multicolored   1.00   .35
2156 A390   75g multicolored   1.50   .35
2157 A390   100g multicolored   2.00   .35
2158 A390   200g multicolored   4.00   .70
    Nos. 2153-2158 (6)   9.50 2.45
    Chaco Peace Agreement, 50th Anniv.
(#2153, 2157). Nos. 2157-2158 are airmail.
For overprints see Nos. 2254-2259.

Nudes by Peter
Paul
Rubens — A391

    Details from paintings: No. 2159a, 25c, b,
50c, Venus in the Forge of Vulcan. c, 1g,
Cimon and Iphigenia, horiz. d, 2g, The Horrors
of War. e, 3g, Apotheosis of Henry IV and the
Proclamation of the Regency. f, 4g, The
Reception of Marie de Medici at Marseilles.
5g, Union of Earth and Water.
    25g, Nature Attended by the Three Graces.

1985, Oct. 18   *Perf. 14*
2159 A391   Strip of 6, #a.-f.   9.50 1.50
                                 Perf. 13x13½
2160 A391   5g multicolored   4.25   .50
    Nos. 2159-2160 (2)   13.75 2.00

Souvenir Sheet
Perf. 14

2161 A391   25g multicolored   26.00 25.00
    No. 2161 is airmail.

1986, Jan. 16   *Perf. 14*
    Nudes by Titian: details from paintings. No.
2162a, 25c, Venus, an Organist, Cupid and a
Little Dog. b, 50c, Diana and Acteon. c, 1g,
Diana and Actaeon. d, 2g, Danae. e, 3g,
Nymph and a Shepherd. f, 4g, Venus of
Urbino. 5g, Cupid Blindfolded by Venus, vert.
    25g, Diana and Callisto, vert.
2162 A391   Strip of 6, #a.-f.   8.25 2.00
                                    Perf. 13
2163 A391   5g multicolored   3.50 1.00
    Nos. 2162-2163 (2)   11.75 3.00

Souvenir Sheet
Perf. 13½

2164 A391   25g multicolored   26.00 25.00
    No. 2164 is airmail and contains one
50x60mm stamp.

Nos. 2150 Ovptd. in Red

1986, Feb. 25   *Perf. 14*
2165 A389   Strip of 6, #a.-f.   6.75 2.00
    Essen '86 Intl. Philatelic Exhibition.

Mushrooms Type of 1985
    Designs: No. 2166a, 25g, Lepiota procera.
b, 50c, Tricholoma albo-brunneum. c, 1g,
Clavaria. d, 2g, Volvaria. e, 3g, Licoperdon
perlatum. f, 4g, Dictyophora duplicata. 5g,
Polyporus rubrum.

1986, Mar. 17   *Perf. 14*
2166 A385   Strip of 6, #a.-f.   7.25 1.50
                                    Perf. 13
2167 A385   5g multicolored   3.00   .50
    Nos. 2166-2167 (2)   10.25 2.00

Automobile,
Cent.
A393

    No. 2168: a, 25c, Wolseley, 1904. b, 50c,
Peugeot, 1892. c, 1g, Panhard, 1895. d, 2g,
Cadillac, 1903. e, 3g, Fiat, 1902. f, 4g, Stanley
Steamer, 1898. 5g, Carl Benz Velocipede,
1885. 25g, Carl Benz (1844-1929), automotive
engineer.

1986, Apr. 28   Litho.   *Perf. 13½x13*
2168 A393   Strip of 6, #a.-f.   4.00 1.50
2169 A393   5g multicolored   4.75 1.25
    Nos. 2168-2169 (2)   8.75 2.75

Souvenir Sheet
Perf. 13½

2170 A393   25g multicolored   17.50 17.00
    No. 2170 is airmail and contains one
30x40mm stamp.

World Cup Soccer Championships,
Mexico City — A394

    Various match scenes, Paraguay vs.: No.
2171a, 25c, b, 50c, US, 1930. c, 1g, d, 2g,
Belgium, 1930. e, 3g, Bolivia, 1985. f, 4g, Brazil, 1985.
    5g, Natl. Team, 1986. 25g, Player, vert.

1986, Mar. 12   *Perf. 13½x13*
2171 A394   Strip of 6, #a.-f.   4.00 1.50
2172 A394   5g multicolored   4.75 1.00
    Nos. 2171-2172 (2)   8.75 2.50

Souvenir Sheet
Perf. 14½

2173 A394   25g multicolored   20.00 19.00
    No. 2173 is airmail. For overprints see Nos.
2283, 2287.

**No. 2135 Ovptd. in Silver "JUEGOS
/ PANAMERICANOS /
INDIANAPOLIS / 1987"**
1986, June 9   *Perf. 13*
2174 A384   5g on No. 2135   3.75 2.00
    1987 Pan American Games, Indianapolis.

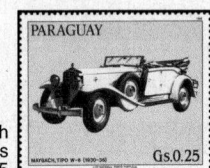

Maybach
Automobiles
A395

    #2175: a, 25c, W-6, 1930-36. b, 50c, SW-38
convertible. c, 1g, SW-38 hardtop, 1938. d, 2g,
W-6/DSG, 1933. e, 3g, Zeppelin DS-8, 1931. f,
4g, Zeppelin DS-8, 1936. 5g, Zeppelin DS-8
aerodynamic cabriolet, 1936.

1986, June 19   *Perf. 13½x13*
2175 A395   Strip of 6, #a.-f.   3.50 1.25
2176 A395   5g multicolored   6.25 1.25
    Nos. 2175-2176 (2)   9.75 2.50

**No. 2077 Overprinted in Bright Blue
with Olympic Rings and "CALGARY
1988"**
1986, July 9   *Perf. 13*
2177 A369   5g on #2077   2.75 1.25
    1988 Winter Olympics, Calgary.

Statue of
Liberty, Cent.
A396

Passenger liners: No. 2178a, 25c, City of Paris, England, 1867. b, 50c, Mauretania, England. c, 1g, Normandie, France, 1932. d, 2g, Queen Mary, England, 1938. e, 3g, Kaiser Wilhelm the Great II, Germany, 1897. f, 4g, United States, US, 1952. 5g, Bremen, Germany, 1928. 25g, Sailing ship Gorch Fock, Germany, 1976, vert.

			Perf. 13
1986, July 25			
2178	A396	Strip of 6, #a.-f.	7.00 1.50
2179	A396	5g multicolored	7.00 .60
		Nos. 2178-2179 (2)	14.00 2.10

Souvenir Sheet
Perf. 14½

2180	A396	25g multicolored	16.00 15.00

No. 2180 is airmail and contains one 50x70mm stamp.

Dog Type of 1984

#2181: a, 25c, German shepherd. b, 50c, Icelandic shepherd. c, 1g, Collie. d, 2g, Boxer. e, 3g, Scottish terrier. f, 4g, Welsh springer spaniel. 5g, Painting of Labrador retriever by Ellen Krebs, vert.

			Perf. 13x13½
1986, Aug. 28			
2181	A376	Strip of 6, #a.-f.	5.75 2.00

Perf. 13½x13

2182	A376	5g multicolored	3.50 1.00
		Nos. 2181-2182 (2)	9.25 3.00

Paraguay Official
Stamps,
Cent. — A397

#2183-2185, #O1. #2186-2188, #O4.

			Litho.	Perf. 13x13½
1986, Aug. 28				
2183	A397	5g multi		1.75 1.50
2184	A397	15g multi		1.75 1.50
2185	A397	40g multi		1.75 1.50
2186	A397	65g multi		1.75 1.50
2187	A397	100g multi		1.75 1.50
2188	A397	150g multi		1.75 1.50
		Nos. 2183-2188 (6)		10.50 9.00

Nos. 2186-2188 are airmail.

Tennis
Players — A398

Designs: No. 2189a, Victor Pecci, Paraguay. b, 50c, Jimmy Connors, US. c, 1g, Gabriela Sabatini, Argentina. d, 2g, Boris Becker, W. Germany. e, 3g, Claudia Kohde, E. Germany. f, 4g, Sweden, 1985 Davis Cup team champions, horiz. 5g, Steffi Graf, W. Germany. 25g, 1986 Wimbledon champions Martina Navratilova and Boris Becker, horiz.

Perf. 13x13½, 13½x13

			Unwmk.
1986, Sept. 17			
2189	A398	Strip of 6, #a.-f.	4.50 1.25
2190	A398	5g multicolored	2.25 .50
		Nos. 2189-2190 (2)	6.75 1.75

Souvenir Sheet
Perf. 13½

2191	A398	25g multicolored	15.00 15.00

No. 2191 is airmail and contains one 75x55mm stamp. For overprints see No. 2229.

Nos. 1454-1456 Ovptd. in Red or Silver (#2192c, 2192d): "Homenage a la visita de Sus Altezas Imperiales los Principees Hitachi --28.9-3.10.86"

			Perf. 14
1986, Sept. 28			
2192	A251	Strip of 5, #a.-e.	
2193	A251	50c on #1455	1.40 .75
2194	A251	75c on #1456	1.50 1.00
		Nos. 2192-2194 (3)	6.40 3.25

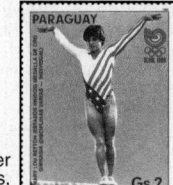

1988 Summer
Olympics,
Seoul — A399

Athletes, 1984 Olympic medalists: No. 2195a, 25c, Runner. b, 50c, Boxer. c, 1g, Joaquim Cruz, Brazil, 800-meter run. d, 2g, Mary Lou Retton, US, individual all-around gymnastics. e, 3g, Carlos Lopes, Portugal, marathon. f, 4g, Fredy Schmidtke, W. Germany, 1000-meter cycling, horiz. 5g, Joe Fargis, US, equestrian, horiz.

1986, Oct. 29	**Perf. 13x13½, 13½x13**		
2195	A399	Strip of 6, #a.-f.	7.50 1.25
2196	A399	5g multicolored	10.75 1.75
		Nos. 2195-2196 (2)	18.25 3.00

For overprints see Nos. 2227-2228, 2230.

**Nos. 1574c-1574g Ovptd. in Silver,
Ship Type of 1983 Ovptd. in Red**

			Perf. 14
1987, Mar. 20	**Litho.**		
2197	A278	Strip of 5, #a.-e.	5.50 3.00
2198	AP176	10g multicolored	2.50 1.50
		Nos. 2197-2198 (2)	8.00 4.50

500th Anniv. of the discovery of America and the 12th Spanish-American Stamp & Coin Show, Madrid.

Olympics Type of 1985 Overprinted in Silver with Olympic Rings and 500th Anniv. of the Discovery of America Emblems and "BARCELONA 92 / Sede de las Olimpiadas en el ano del 500o Aniversario del Descubrimiento de America"

Designs like Nos. 2134a-2134f.

			Perf. 14
1987, Apr. 24			
2199	A384	Strip of 6, #a.-f.	9.50 8.00

1992 Summer Olympics, Barcelona and discovery of America, 500th anniv. in 1992.

No. 2135 Overprinted in Silver "ROMA / OLYMPHILEX" / Olympic Rings / "SEOUL / CALGARY / 1988"

			Perf. 13
1987, Apr. 30			
2200	A384	5g on No. 2135	3.50 2.50

Olymphilex '87 Intl. Philatelic Exhibition, Rome.

Cat Type of 1976

Various cats and kittens: No. 2201: a, 1g. b, 2g. c, 3g. d, 5g. 60g, Black cat.

			Perf. 13x13½
1987, May 22			
2201	A287	Strip of 4, #a.-d.	3.75 .75
2202	A287	60g multicolored	2.50 .95
		Nos. 2201-2202 (2)	6.25 1.70

No. 2202 also exists perf. 14. For overprint see No. 2212.

Paintings by
Rubens — A400

No. 2203: a, 1g, The Four Corners of the World, horiz. b, 2g, Jupiter and Calisto. c, 3g, Susanna and the Elders. d, 5g, Marriage of Henry IV and Marie de Medici in Lyon.

60g, The Last Judgment. 100g, The Holy Family with St. Elizabeth and John the Baptist. No. 2205A, War and Peace.

1987	**Litho.**	**Perf. 13x13½, 13½x13**	
2203	A400	Strip of 4, #a.-d.	4.00 1.00
2204	A400	60g multicolored	5.75 1.50
		Nos. 2203-2204 (2)	9.75 2.50

Souvenir Sheets

2205	A400	100g multicolored	18.00 17.00
2205A	A400	100g multicolored	18.00 17.00

Christmas 1986 (#2205).
Issued: #2204, May 25; #2205, May 26.
Nos. 2205-2205A are airmail and contain one 54x68mm stamp.

MUESTRA

Some illustrated stamps show the word "MUESTRA" ("SPECIMEN"). This overprint is not on the actual stamps. The editors would like to borrow examples without the overprint so that replacement illustrations can be made.

Places and
Events
A401

10g, ACEPAR Industrial Plant. 25g, Franciscan monk, native, vert. 50g, Yaguaron Church altar, vert. 75g, Founding of Asuncion, 450th anniv. 100g, Paraguay Airlines passenger jet. 200g, Pres. Stoessner, vert.

			Perf. 13
1987, June 2	**Litho.**		
2206	A401	10g multicolored	1.75 .25
2207	A401	25g multicolored	1.75 .25
2208	A401	50g multicolored	1.75 .25
2209	A401	75g multicolored	3.75 .25
2210	A401	100g multicolored	5.75 .30
2211	A401	200g multicolored	7.50 .50
		Nos. 2206-2211 (6)	22.25 1.80

Nos. 2210-2211 are airmail. For overprints see Nos. 2225-2226, C685, C722.

No. 2201 Ovptd.
in Blue

			Perf. 13x13½
1987, June 12			
2212	A287	Strip of 4, #a.-d.	3.25 3.25

Discovery of
America,
500th Anniv.
(in 1992)
A402

Discovery of America anniv. emblem and ships: No. 2213a, 1g, Spanish galleon, 17th cent. b, 2g, Victoria, 1st to circumnavigate the globe, 1519-22. c, 3g, San Hermenegildo. d, 5g, San Martin, c.1582. 60g, Santa Maria, c.1492, vert.

			Perf. 14
1987, Sept. 9			
2213	A402	Strip of 4, #a.-d.	8.25 1.50

Perf. 13x13½

2214	A402	60g multicolored	3.00 1.60
		Nos. 2213-2214 (2)	11.25 3.10

Colorado Party,
Cent. — A403

Bernardino Caballero (founder), President Stroessner and: 5g, 10g, 25g, Three-lane highway. 150g, 170g, 200g, Power lines.

Perf. 13½x13			
1987, Sept. 11			**Wmk. 347**
2215	A403	5g multi	3.25 2.00
2216	A403	10g multi	3.25 2.00
2217	A403	25g multi	3.25 2.00
2218	A403	150g multi	3.25 2.00
2219	A403	170g multi	3.25 2.00
2220	A403	200g multi	3.25 2.00
		Nos. 2215-2220 (6)	19.50 12.00

Nos. 2218-2220 are airmail.

Berlin, 750th
Anniv.
A404

Berlin Stamps and Coins: No. 2221: a, 1g, #9NB145. b, 2g, #9NB154. c, 3g, #9N57, vert. d, 5g, #9N170, vert. 60g, 1987 Commemorative coin, vert.

Perf. 13½x13, 13½x13			
1987, Sept. 12			**Unwmk.**
2221	A404	Strip of 4, #a.-d.	7.25 2.00
2222	A404	60g multicolored	4.00 3.00
		Nos. 2221-2222 (2)	11.25 5.00

For overprints see Nos. 2239, 2294.

Race
Cars — A405

No. 2223: a, 1g, Audi Sport Quattro. b, 2g, Lancia Delta S 4. c, 3g, Fiat 131. d, 5g, Porsche 911 4x4. 60g, Lancia Rally.

			Perf. 13
1987, Sept. 27			
2223	A405	Strip of 4, #a.-d.	2.60 1.00

Perf. 14

2224	A405	60g multicolored	2.60 1.00
		Nos. 2223-2224 (2)	5.20 2.00

Nos. 2209-2210 Ovptd. in Blue

			Perf. 13
1987, Sept. 30			
2225	A401	75g on #2209	.90 .70
2226	A401	100g on #2210	1.10 .80
		Nos. 2225-2226 (2)	2.00 1.50

EXFIVIA '87 Intl. Philatelic Exhibition, LaPaz, Bolivia. No. 2226 is airmail. No. 2225 surcharge is in dark blue; and No. 2226 is bright blue.

Nos. 2195d-2195f, 2196 Overprinted in Black or Silver

			Perf. 13½x13
1987, Oct. 1			
2227	A399	Strip of 3, #a.-c.	6.50 3.00
2228	A399	5g on No. 2196 (S)	3.50 3.00
		Nos. 2227-2228 (2)	10.00 6.00

Olymphilex '87 Intl. Phil. Exhib., Seoul.

No. 2189 Ovptd. with Emblem and "PHILATELIA '87," etc.

1987, Oct. 15   Perf. 13x13½, 13½x13
2229 A398   Strip of 6, #a.-f.   5.75   4.25

PHILATELIA '87 Intl. Phil. Exhib., Cologne. Size and configuration of overprint varies.

Nos. 2195a-2195b Ovptd. in Bright Blue for EXFILNA '87 and BARCELONA 92

1987, Oct. 24   Perf. 13x13½
2230 A399   Pair, #a.-b.   4.75   4.00

Exfilna '87 Intl. Philatelic Exhibition.

Ship Paintings — A406

No. 2231: a, 1g, San Juan Nepomuceno. b, 2g, San Eugenio. c, 3g, San Telmo. d, 5g, San Carlos. 60g, Spanish galleon, 16th cent. 100g, One of Columbus's ships.

1987   Litho.   Perf. 14
2231 A406   Strip of 4, #a.-d.   8.00   2.50

Perf. 13x13½
2232 A406   60g multicolored   3.25   1.50
    Nos. 2231-2232 (2)   11.25   4.00

Souvenir Sheet
Perf. 13½
2233 A406   100g multicolored   18.00   17.00

Discovery of America, 500th anniv. in 1992 (#2233). Issue dates: Nos. 2231-2232, Dec. 10. No. 2233, Dec. 12.
No. 2233 is airmail and contains one 54x75mm stamp.

1988 Winter Olympics, Calgary A407

#2237: a, 5g, Joel Gaspoz. b, 60g, Peter Mueller.

1987, Dec. 31   Perf. 14
2234 A407   1g Maria Walliser   3.75   1.25
2235 A407   2g Erika Hess   3.75   1.25
2236 A407   3g Pirmin Zurbriggen   3.75   1.25
    Nos. 2234-2236 (3)   11.25   3.75

Miniature Sheet
Perf. 13½x13
2237 A407   Sheet of 4 each #2237a, 2237b+label   40.00   40.00

Souvenir Sheet
Perf. 14½
2238 A407   100g Walliser, Zurbriggen   17.50   16.50

No. 2238 is airmail. For overprints see Nos. 2240-2242.

No. 2221 Ovptd. in Silver "AEROPEX 88 / ADELAIDE"

1988, Jan. 29   Perf. 13
2239 A404   Strip of 4, #a.-d.   9.00   5.00

Aeropex '88, Adelaide, Australia.

Nos. 2234-2236 Ovptd. in Gold with Olympic Rings and "OLYMPEX / CALGARY 1988"

1988, Feb. 13   Perf. 14
2240 A407   1g on #2234   1.20   .75
2241 A407   2g on #2235   2.40   1.50
2242 A407   3g on #2236   3.25   2.00
    Nos. 2240-2242 (3)   6.85   4.25

Olympex '88, Calgary. Size and configuration of overprint varies.

1988 Summer Olympics, Seoul A408

Equestrians: No. 2243a, 1g, Josef Neckermann, W. Germany, on Venetia. b, 2g, Henri Chammartin, Switzerland. c, 3g, Christine Stueckelberger, Switzerland, on Granat. d, 5g, Liselott Linsenhoff, W. Germany, on Piaff. 60g, Hans-Guenter Winkler, W. Germany.

1988, Mar. 7   Perf. 13
2243 A408   Strip of 4, #a.-d.   6.25   2.00

Perf. 13½x13
2244 A408   60g multicolored   3.00   2.00
    Nos. 2243-2244 (2)   9.25   4.00

For overprint see No. 2291.

Berlin, 750th Anniv. — A409

Paintings: No. 2245a, 1g, Virgin and Child, by Jan Gossaert. b, 2g, Virgin and Child, by Rubens. c, 3g, Virgin and Child, by Hans Memling. d, 5g, Madonna, by Albrecht Durer. 60g, Adoration of the Shepherds, by Martin Schongauer.

1988, Apr. 8   Perf. 13
2245 A409   Strip of 4, #a.-d.   7.25   2.00
2246 A409   60g multicolored   4.00   3.00
    Nos. 2245-2246 (2)   11.25   5.00

Christmas 1987. See Nos. C727-C731.

Visit of Pope John Paul II — A410

Religious art: No. 2247a, 1g, Pope John Paul II, hands clasped. b, 2g, Statue of the Virgin. c, 3g, Czestochowa Madonna. d, 5g, Our Lady of Caacupe. Nos. 2247a-2247d are vert.

1988, Apr. 11   Perf. 13
2247 A410   Strip of 4, #a.-d.   6.00   1.00
2248 A410   60g multicolored   3.50   1.00
    Nos. 2247-2248 (2)   9.50   2.00

Visit of Pope John Paul II — A411

Rosette window and crucifix.

1988, May 5   Litho.   Perf. 13x13½
2249 A411   10g blue & blk   2.25   .75
2250 A411   20g blue & blk   2.25   .75
2251 A411   50g blue & blk   2.25   .75
    Nos. 2249-2251 (3)   6.75   2.25

World Wildlife Fund Type of 1985

Endangered Animals: No. 2252a, 1g, like #2139g. b, 2g, like #2139f. c, 3g, like #2139d. d, 5g, like #2139e.

1988, June 14   Unwmk.   Perf. 14
2252 A386   Strip of 4, #a.-d.   37.50   6.00

Nos. 2252a-2252d have denomination and border in blue.

Nos. 2000a-2000d Ovptd. in Gold with Emblem and "Bicentenario de / AUSTRALIA / 1788-1988"

1988, June 17
2253 A351   Strip of 4, #a.-d.   6.00   6.00

Australia, bicent.

Types of 1985 Overprinted in 2 or 4 Lines in Gold "NUEVO PERIODO PRESIDENCIAL CONSTITUCIONAL 1988-1993"

1988, Aug. 12   Perf. 14
2254 A390   10g like #2153   .55   .55
2255 A390   25g like #2154   .55   .55
2256 A390   50g like #2155   .90   .90
2257 A390   75g like #2156   1.75   1.75
2258 A390   100g like #2157   2.10   2.10
2259 A390   200g like #2158   3.50   3.50
    Nos. 2254-2259 (6)   9.35   9.35

Pres. Stroessner's new term in office. Nos. 2258-2259 are airmail.

Olympic Tennis, Seoul — A412

Designs: No. 2260a, 1g, Steffi Graf, W. Germany. b, 2g, Olympic gold medal, horiz. c, 3g, Boris Becker, W. Germany. d, 5g, Emilio Sanchez, Spain. 60g, Steffi Graf, diff.

1988, Aug. 16   Perf. 13
2260 A412   Strip of 4, #a.-d.   13.00   3.25
2261 A412   60g multicolored   3.25   2.50
    Nos. 2260-2261 (2)   16.25   5.75

1992 Summer Olympics, Barcelona A413

Olympic medalists from Spain: No. 2262a, 1g, Ricardo Zamora, soccer, Antwerp, 1920, vert. b, 2g, Equestrian team, Amsterdam, 1928. c, 3g, Angel Leon, shooting, Helsinki, 1952. d, 5g, Kayak team, Montreal, 1976. 60g, Francisco Fernandez Ochoa, slalom, Sapporo, 1972, vert. 100g, Olympic Stadium, Barcelona, vert.

1989, Jan. 5   Perf. 14
2262 A413   Strip of 4, #a.-d.   8.00   3.25

Perf. 13
2263 A413   60g multicolored   2.25   1.25
    Nos. 2262-2263 (2)   10.25   4.50

Souvenir Sheet
Perf. 13½
2264 A413   100g multicolored   17.50   17.00

Discovery of America 500th anniv. (in 1992). No. 2264 is airmail and contains one 50x60mm stamp. For overprint see No. 2293.

Columbus Space Station — A414

1989, Jan. 7   Litho.   Perf. 13x13½
2265 A414   60g multicolored   4.25   2.00

Discovery of America 500th anniv. (in 1992). Printed in sheets of 4 + 5 labels.

No. 2076 Overprinted in Silver, Red and Blue with Olympic Rings, "1992" and Emblem

1989, Jan. 10   Perf. 13½x13, 13x13½
2266 A369   Strip of 6, #a.-f.   8.75   8.75

1992 Winter Olympics, Albertville. Location and configuration of overprint varies.

No. 1454 Ovptd. in Silver "HOMENAJE AL EMPERADOR HIROITO DE JAPON 29.IV,1901-6.1.1989"

1989, Feb. 8   Perf. 14
2267 A251   Strip of 5, #a.-e.   4.75   4.75

Death of Emperor Hirohito of Japan.

Formula 1 Drivers, Race Cars — A415

No. 2268: a, 1g, Stirling Moss, Mercedes W196. b, 2g, Emerson Fittipaldi, Lotus. c, 3g,

---

Nelson Piquet, Lotus. d, 5g, Niki Lauda, Ferrari 312 B. 60g, Juan Manuel Fangio, Maserati 250F.

1989, Mar. 6   Perf. 13
2268 A415   Strip of 4, #a.-d.   8.75   2.50
2269 A415   60g multicolored   3.50   3.00
    Nos. 2268-2269 (2)   12.25   5.50

No. 2269 was printed in sheets of 5 + 4 labels.

Paintings by Titian — A416

No. 2270: a, 1g, Bacchus and Ariadne (Bacchus). b, 2g, Bacchus and Ariadne (tutelary spirit). c, 3g, Death of Actaeon. d, 5g, Portrait of a Young Woman with a Fur Cape. 60g, Concert in a Field. 100g, Holy Family with Donor.

1989, Apr. 17   Perf. 13x13½
2270 A416   Strip of 4, #a.-d.   9.00   1.75
2271 A416   60g multicolored   4.25   .75
    Nos. 2270-2271 (2)   13.25   2.50

Souvenir Sheet
Perf. 13½
2271A A416   100g multicolored   19.00   18.00

No. 2271A is airmail and contains one 60x49mm stamp. Issue date: May 27.

1994 Winter Olympics, Lillehammer A417

Athletes: No. 2272a, 1g, Torbjorn Lokken, 1987 Nordic combined world champion. b, 2g, Atle Skardal, skier, Norway. c, 3g, Geir Karlstad, Norway, world 10,000-meter speed skating champion, 1987. d, 5g, Franck Piccard, France, 1988 Olympic medalist, skiing. 60g, Roger Ruud, ski jumper, Norway.

1989, May 23   Perf. 13½x13
2272 A417   Strip of 4, #a.-d.   13.00   4.25
2273 A417   60g multicolored   5.75   3.75
    Nos. 2272-2273 (2)   18.75   8.00

Cat Type of 1976

Various cats: #2274a, 1g. b, 2g. c, 3g. d, 5g.

1989, May 25   Perf. 13
2274 A287   Strip of 4, #a.-d.   10.00   2.00
2275 A287   60g Siamese   3.75   2.00
    Nos. 2274-2275 (2)   13.75   4.00

Federal Republic of Germany, 40th Anniv. A418

Famous men and automobiles: No. 2276a, 1g, Konrad Adenauer, chancellor, 1949-1963, Mercedes. b, 2g, Ludwig Erhard, chancellor, 1963-1966, Volkswagen Beetle. c, 3g, Felix Wankel, engine designer, 1963 NSU Spider. d, 5g, Franz Josef Strauss, President of Bavarian Cabinet, BMW 502. 60g, Pres. Richard von Weizsacker and Dr. Josef Neckermann.

1989, May 27   Perf. 13½x13
2276 A418   Strip of 4, #a.-d.   9.50   2.50
2277 A418   60g multicolored   3.75   3.00
    Nos. 2276-2277 (2)   13.25   5.50

For overprints see No. 2369.

Ship Type of 1980 Overprinted with Discovery of America, 500th Anniv. Emblem in Red on Silver

1989, May 29   *Perf. 14½*
Miniature Sheet
2278 A343   Sheet of 7+label, like #1972   40.00 37.50

Discovery of America 500th anniv. (in 1992).

No. 2122a Overprinted with Hamburg Emblem and Nos. 2122b-2122f, 2123 Ovptd. with Diff. Emblem in Red on Silver

1989, May 30   Litho.   *Perf. 13½x13*
2279 A381   Strip of 6, #a.-f.   20.00 20.00
2280 A381   5g on #2123   5.25   5.25
    Nos. 2279-2280 (2)   25.25 25.25

City of Hamburg, 800th anniv.

Nos. 2006a-2006b Ovptd. "BRASILIANA / 89"

1989, July 5   *Perf. 14*
2281 A352   Pair, #a.-b.   4.50 2.00

No. 2171 Overprinted in Metallic Red and Silver with FIFA and Italia 90 Emblems and "PARAGUAY PARTICIPO EN 13 CAMPEONATOS MUNDIALES"

1989, Sept. 14   Litho.   *Perf. 13½x13*
2283 A394   Strip of 6, #a.-f.   5.50 5.50

Size and configuration of overprint varies.

Nos. C738, C753 Ovptd. in metallic red with Italia '90 emblem & "SUDAMERICA-GRUPO 2 / PARAGUAY-COLOMBIA / PARAGUAY-ECUADOR / COLOMBIA-PARAGUAY / ECUADOR-PARAGUAY" and in metallic red on silver with FIFA emblem

1989, Sept. 14   Litho.   *Perf. 13*
2284 AP228 25g on #C738   9.00 4.00
2285 AP232 25g on #C753   9.00 4.00
    Nos. 2284-2285 (2)   18.00 8.00

Nos. 2046, 2172 Overprinted in Metallic Red on Silver at top: "PARAGUAY CLASIFICADO EN 1930, 1950, 1958 Y 1986" and Emblems or "ITALIA '90". Overprinted Silver on stamps and Blue on Silver on side margins

1989, Sept. 15   Litho.   *Perf. 14*
2286 A362   Strip of 6, #a.-f.   17.00 5.00

    Perf. 13½x13
2287 A394   5g multicolored   5.75 3.25
    Nos. 2286-2287 (2)   22.75 8.25

1990 World Cup Soccer Championships, Italy. Location and size of overprint varies.

Nos. 1284-1286 Ovptd. in Gold "...BIEN ESTUVIMOS EN LA LUNA AHORA NECESITAMOS LOS MEDIOS PARA LLEGAR A LOS PLANETAS" Wernher von Braun's Signature and UN and Space Emblems

1989, Sept. 16   *Perf. 14*
2288 A226   Strip of 5, #a.-e.   6.25 6.25
2289 A226 50c multicolored   3.00 3.00
2290 A226 75c multicolored   4.50 4.50
    Nos. 2288-2290 (3)   13.75 13.75

Location, size and configuration of overprint varies.

Nos. 2243, C764 Overprinted in Silver or Gold with Emblem and "ATENAS 100 ANOS DE LOS JUEGOS OLIMPICOS 1896-1996"

1989, Sept. 18   *Perf. 13*
2291 A408   Strip of 4, #a.-d.   5.75 5.75
2292 AP233 25g on #C764 (G)   11.00 11.00
    Nos. 2291-2292 (2)   16.75 16.75

1992 Summer Olympics Barcelona, Spain. Size and location of overprint varies.

Nos. 2262a-2262d Ovptd. in Silver with Heads of Steffi Graf or Boris Becker and: "WIMBLEDON 1988 / SEUL 1988 / WIMBLEDON 1989 / EL TENIS NUEVAMENTE EN / LAS OLIMPIADAS 1988-1992" or Similar

1989, Sept. 19   *Perf. 14*
2293 A413   Strip of 4, #a.-d.   19.00 8.00

Addition of tennis as an Olympic sport in 1992. Size and configuration of overprint varies.

No. 2221 Ovptd. in Gold and Blue "PRIMER AEROPUERTO PARA / /COHETES, BERLIN 1930 OBERTH, / NEBEL, RITTER, VON BRAUN" space emblem and "PROF. DR. HERMANN / OBERTH 95o ANIV. / NACIMIENTO 25.6.1989"

    Perf. 13½x13, 13x13½
1989, Sept. 20
2294 A404   Strip of 4, #a.-d.   19.00 6.00

Dr. Hermann Oberth, rocket scientist, 95th birth anniv. Overprint size, etc, varies.

Nos. 1406-1408 Ovptd. in Metallic Red and Silver with Emblems and "OLIMPIADAS / DE INVIERNO / ALBERTVILLE 1992" in 2 or 3 Lines

1989, Sept. 21   *Perf. 14*
2295 A244   Strip of 5, #a.-e.   10.00 3.00
2296 A244 50c multicolored   4.75 2.50
2297 A244 75c multicolored   7.00 4.00
    Nos. 2295-2297 (3)   21.75 9.50

1992 Winter Olympics, Albertville. Size and configuration of overprint varies.

Nos. 2251, C724
Overprinted

    Perf. 13½, 13½x13
1989, Oct. 9   Litho.   Wmk. 347
2298 A411   50g on #2251   10.00 7.50
2299 AP226 120g on #C724   10.00 8.00

Parafil '89, Paraguay-Argentina philatelic exhibition.

Birds Facing Extinction A419

50g, Ara chloroptera. 100g, Mergus octosetaceus. 300g, Rhea americana. 500g, Ramphastos toco. 1000g, Crax fasciolata. 2000g, Ara ararauna.

    Perf. 13½x13
1989, Dec. 19   Litho.   Wmk. 347
2300 A419   50g multicolored   .60 .30
2301 A419   100g multicolored   .60 .30
2302 A419   300g multicolored   1.50 .75
2303 A419   500g multicolored   2.40 1.20
2304 A419 1000g multicolored   4.50 2.25
2305 A419 2000g multicolored   8.50 4.25
    Nos. 2300-2305 (6)   18.10 9.05

Nos. 2302-2305 airmail. Nos. 2300 & 2305 vert. Frames and typestyles vary greatly. Watermark on 50g, 100g, 300g is 8mm high.

1992 Summer Olympics, Barcelona — A420

Athletes: No. 2306a, 1g, A. Fichtel and S. Bau, W. Germany, foils, 1988. b, 2g, Spanish basketball team, 1984. c, 3g, Jackie Joyner-Kersee, heptathalon and long jump, 1988, horiz. d, 5g, L. Beerbaum, W. Germany, show jumping, team, 1988. 60g, W. Brinkmann, W. Germany, show jumping, team, 1988. 100g, Emilio Sanchez, tennis.

    Unwmk.
1989, Dec. 26   Litho.   *Perf. 14*
2306 A420   Strip of 4, #a.-d.   7.00 2.00
    Perf. 13
2307 A420   60g multicolored   7.50 3.50
    Nos. 2306-2307 (2)   14.50 5.50
    Souvenir Sheet
    Perf. 13½
2308 A420 100g multicolored   20.00 15.00

No. 2308 is airmail and contains one 47x57mm stamp.

World Cup Soccer Championships, Italy — A421

1986 World Cup soccer players in various positions: No. 2309a, 1g, England vs. Paraguay. b, 2g, Spain vs. Denmark. c, 3g, France vs. Italy. d, 5g, Germany vs. Morocco. 60g, Mexico vs. Paraguay. 100g, Germany vs. Argentina.

1989, Dec. 29   *Perf. 14*
2309 A421   Strip of 4, #a.-d.   9.25 2.50
    Perf. 13½
2310 A421   60g multicolored   6.00 2.50
    Nos. 2309-2310 (2)   15.25 5.00
    Souvenir Sheet
    Perf. 14½
2311 A421 100g multicolored   43.00 25.00

No. 2311 is airmail and contains one 40x50mm stamp.
For overprints see Nos. 2355-2356.

1992 Summer Olympics, Barcelona — A422

Barcelona '92, proposed Athens '96 emblems and: No. 2312a, 1g, Greece #128. b, 2g, Greece #126, vert. c, 3g, Greece #127, vert. d, 5g, Greece #123, vert. 60g, Paraguay #736. 100g, Horse and rider, vert.

1990, Jan. 4   *Perf. 13½x13, 13x13½*
2312 A422   Strip of 4, #a.-d.   6.25 2.00
2313 A422   60g multicolored   12.00 4.00
    Nos. 2312-2313 (2)   18.25 6.00
    Souvenir Sheet
    Perf. 13½
2314 A422 100g multicolored   21.00 17.50

No. 2314 is airmail and contains one 50x60mm stamp and exists with either white or yellow border, same value. Stamps inscribed 1989.
For overprints see No. 2357.

Swiss Confederation, 700th Anniv. — A423

No. 2315: a, 3g, Monument to William Tell. b, 5g, Manship Globe, UN Headquarters, Geneva.
60g, 15th cent. messenger, Bern.
No. 2317, 1st Swiss steam locomotive, horiz. No. 2318, Jean Henri Dunant, founder of the Red Cross, horiz.

1990, Jan. 25   *Perf. 14*
2315 A423   Pair, #a.-b.   8.50 2.00
    Perf. 13
2316 A423   60g multicolored   7.50 3.50
    Nos. 2315-2316 (2)   16.00 5.50
    Souvenir Sheets
    Perf. 14½
2317 A423 100g multicolored   26.00 25.00
2318 A423 100g multicolored   26.00 25.00

Nos. 2317-2318 are airmail. For overprints see Nos. 2352-2354.

Wood Carving — A424

Discovery of America, 500th anniv. emblem &: #2319: a, 1g, 1st cathechism in Guarani. b, 2g, shown. #2319 has continuous design.

1990, Jan. 26   *Perf. 14*
2319 A424   Pair, #a.-b. + label   6.25 1.40

Organization of American States, Cent. — A425

Designs: 50g, Letter showing "100 OEA" design on green background, horiz. 200g, Map of Paraguay.

    Perf. 13½x13
1990, Feb. 9   Litho.   Wmk. 347
2320 A425   50g multicolored   .60 .30
2321 A425   100g multicolored   .90 .35
2322 A425   200g multicolored   1.80 .65
    Nos. 2320-2322 (3)   3.30 1.30

1992 Winter Olympics, Albertville A426

Calgary 1988 skiers: No. 2323a, 1g, Alberto Tomba, Italy, slalom and giant slalom. b, 2g, Vreni Schneider, Switzerland, women's slalom and giant slalom, vert. c, 3g, Luc Alphand, France, skier, vert. d, 5g, Matti Nykaenen, Finland, ski-jumping.
60g, Marina Kiehl, W. Germany, women's downhill. 100g, Frank Piccard, France, super giant slalom.

1990, Mar. 7   Unwmk.   *Perf. 14*
2323 A426   Strip of 4, #a.-d.   6.50 2.25
    Perf. 13
2324 A426   60g multicolored   2.75 2.25
    Nos. 2323-2324 (2)   9.25 4.50
    Souvenir Sheet
    Perf. 14½
2325 A426 100g multicolored   15.00 15.00

No. 2325 is airmail, contains one 40x50mm stamp and exists with either white or yellow border.

Pre-Columbian Art, Customs — A427

UPAE Emblem and: 150g, Pre-Columbian basket. 500g, Aboriginal ceremony.

1990, Mar. 8   Wmk. 347   *Perf. 13*
2326 A427 150g multicolored   1.75 1.10
2327 A427 500g multicolored   4.00 2.25

No. 2327 is airmail.
For overprints see Nos. 2345-2346.

First Postage Stamp, 150th
Anniv. — A428

Penny Black, Mail Transportation 500th
anniv. emblem and: No. 2328a, 1g, Penny
Black on cover. b, 2g, Mauritius #1-2 on cover.
c, 3g, Baden #4b on cover. d, 5g, Roman
States #4 on cover. 60g, Paraguay #C38 and
four #C54 on cover.

1990, Mar. 12		Unwmk.		Perf. 14	
2328	A428	Strip of 4, #a.-d.		7.00	5.00

Perf. 13½x13

2329	A428	60g multicolored	3.00	2.00

Postal Union of the
Americas and Spain
(UPAE) — A429

1990, July 2			Perf. 13x13½	
2330	A429	200g Map, flags	1.00	.45
2331	A429	250g Paraguay #1	1.25	.50
2332	A429	350g FDC of #2326-2327, horiz.	2.90	.65
		Nos. 2330-2332 (3)	5.15	1.60

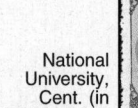

National
University,
Cent. (in
1989) — A430

1990, Sept. 8				
2333	A430	300g Future site	1.50	1.00
2334	A430	400g Present site	2.00	1.25
2335	A430	600g Old site	3.00	2.00
		Nos. 2333-2335 (3)	6.50	4.25

Franciscan
Churches
A431

Perf. 13½x13

1990, Sept. 25		Litho.	Wmk. 347	
2336	A431	50g Guarambare	.40	.30
2337	A431	100g Yaguaron	.65	.35
2338	A431	200g Ita	1.25	.65
		Nos. 2336-2338 (3)	2.30	1.30

For overprints see Nos. 2366-2368.

Democracy in
Paraguay
A432

Designs: 100g, State and Catholic Church,
vert. 200g, Human rights, vert. 300g, Freedom
of the Press, vert. 500g, Return of the exiles.
3000g, People and democracy.

Perf. 13½x13, 13x13½

1990, Oct. 5		Litho.	Wmk. 347	
2339	A432	50g multicolored	.45	.30
2340	A432	100g multicolored	.45	.30
2341	A432	200g multicolored	.95	.50
2342	A432	300g multicolored	1.40	.80
2343	A432	500g multicolored	17.50	1.90
2344	A432	3000g multicolored	12.50	7.50
		Nos. 2339-2344 (6)	33.25	10.80

Nos. 2343-2344 are airmail.

Nos. 2326-2327
Overprinted in
Magenta

1990		Litho.	Wmk. 347	Perf. 13	
2345	A427	150g multicolored		5.00	.60
2346	A427	500g multicolored		15.00	1.90

No. 2346 is airmail.

UN Development
Program, 40th
Anniv. — A433

Designs: 50m, Human Rights, sculpture by
Hugo Pistilli. 100m, United Nations, sculpture
by Hermann Guggiari. 150m, Miguel de
Cervantes Literature Award, won by Augusto
Roa Bastos.

1990, Oct. 26				
2347	A433	50g lilac & multi	.60	.30
2348	A433	100g gray & multi	.90	.35
2349	A433	150g green & multi	1.40	.60
		Nos. 2347-2349 (3)	2.90	1.25

America
A434

50g, Paraguay River banks. 250g, Chaco
land.

Perf. 13½x13

1990, Oct. 31			Wmk. 347	
2350	A434	50g multicolored	20.00	5.00
2351	A434	250g multicolored	40.00	10.00

No. 2351 is airmail.

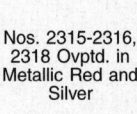

Nos. 2315-2316,
2318 Ovptd. in
Metallic Red and
Silver

Unwmk.

1991, Apr. 2		Litho.	Perf. 14	
2352	A423	Pair, #a.-b.	5.75	4.00

Perf. 13

2353	A423	60g on #2316	5.00	3.50
		Nos. 2352-2353 (2)	10.75	7.50

Souvenir Sheet

Perf. 14½

2354	A423	100g on #2318	25.00	25.00

Swiss Confederation, 700th anniv. and Red
Cross, 125th anniv. No. 2354 is airmail. No.
2352 exists perf. 13. Location of overprint
varies.

Nos. 2309-2310
Ovptd. in Silver

1991, Apr. 4			Perf. 14	
2355	A421	Strip of 4, #a.-d.	8.25	6.25

Perf. 13x13½

2356	A421	60g on #2310	5.00	3.75
		Nos. 2355-2356 (2)	13.25	10.00

1994 World Cup Soccer Championships.
Location of overprint varies.

Nos. 2312, C822,
C766 Ovptd. in
Silver

1991, Apr. 4			Perf. 13	
2357	A422	Strip of 4, #a.-d.	7.50	5.00
2358	AP246	25g on #C822	5.00	3.00

Perf. 13x13½

2359	AP233	30g on #C766	6.50	4.00

Participation of reunified Germany in 1992
Summer Olympics. Nos. 2358-2359 are airmail. Location of overprint varies.

Professors — A435

Designs: 50g, Julio Manuel Morales, gyne-
cologist. 100g, Carlos Gatti, clinician. 200g,
Gustavo Gonzalez, geologist. 300g, Juan Max
Boettner, physician and musician. 350g, Juan
Boggino, pathologist. 500g, Andres Barbero,
physician, founder of Paraguayan Red Cross.

Perf. 13x13½

1991, Apr. 5			Wmk. 347	
2360	A435	50g multicolored	.60	.30
2361	A435	100g multicolored	.60	.30
2362	A435	200g multicolored	1.25	.50
2363	A435	300g multicolored	1.90	.80
2364	A435	350g multicolored	2.00	.90
2365	A435	500g multicolored	3.00	1.40
		Nos. 2360-2365 (6)	9.35	4.20

Nos. 2364-2365 are airmail.

**Nos. 2336-2338 Ovptd. in Black and
Red**

1991			Wmk. 347	Perf. 13½x13	
2366	A431	50g on #2336		.65	.50
2367	A431	100g on #2337		.85	.60
2368	A431	200g on #2338		1.25	.90
		Nos. 2366-2368 (3)		2.75	2.00

Espamer '91 Philatelic Exhibition.

Nos. 2276a-2276b Ovptd. in Silver

Nos. 2276c-2276d Ovptd. in Silver

1991		Unwmk.	Perf. 13	
2369	A418	Strip of 4, #a.-d.	11.25	5.00

Writers and
Muscians
A436

Designs: 50g, Ruy Diaz de Guzman, historian. 100g, Maria Talavera, war correspondent,
vert. 150g, Augusto Roa Bastos, writer, vert.
200g, Jose Asuncion Flores, composer, vert.
250g, Felix Perez Cardozo, harpist. 300g,
Juan Carlos Moreno Gonzalez, composer.

Perf. 13½x13, 13x13½

1991, Aug. 27		Litho.	Wmk. 347	
2373	A436	50g multicolored	.40	.30
2374	A436	100g multicolored	.45	.35
2375	A436	150g multicolored	.80	.50
2376	A436	200g multicolored	1.00	.65
2377	A436	250g multicolored	1.25	.80
2378	A436	300g multicolored	1.50	1.00
		Nos. 2373-2378 (6)	5.40	3.60

Nos. 2376-2378 are airmail.

America — A437

100g, War of Tavare. 300g, Arrival of Spanish explorer Domingo Martinez de Irala in
Paraguay.

Perf. 13x13½

1991, Oct. 9		Litho.	Wmk. 347	
2379	A437	100g multicolored	1.75	.35
2380	A437	300g multicolored	2.00	.90

No. 2380 is airmail.

Paintings — A438

Designs: 50g, Compass of Life, by Alfredo
Moraes. 100g, The Lighted Alley, by Michael
Burt. 150g, Earring, by Lucy Yegros. 200g,
Migrant Workers, by Hugo Bogado Barrios.
250g, Passengers Without a Ship, by Ber-
nardo Ismachoviez. 300g, Native Guarani, by
Lotte Schulz.

Perf. 13x13½

1991, Nov. 12		Litho.	Wmk. 347	
2381	A438	50g multicolored	.55	.30
2382	A438	100g multicolored	.65	.35
2383	A438	150g multicolored	1.10	.50
2384	A438	200g multicolored	1.40	.65

2385	A438	250g multicolored	1.60	.80
2386	A438	300g multicolored	2.00	1.00
		Nos. 2381-2386 (6)	7.30	3.60

Nos. 2384-2386 are airmail.

Endangered Species A439

Perf. 13x13½, 13½x13

		1992, Jan. 28	**Litho.**	**Wmk. 347**
2387	A439	50g Catagonus wagneri, vert.	1.20	.30
2388	A439	100g Felis pardalis	1.40	.35
2389	A439	150g Tapirus terrestri	2.40	.50
2390	A439	200g Chrysocyon brachyurus	3.00	.65
		Nos. 2387-2390 (4)	8.00	1.80

Tile Designs of Christianized Indians — A440

Perf. 13x13½

		1992, Mar. 2	**Litho.**	**Wmk. 347**
2391	A440	50g Geometric	.50	.30
2392	A440	100g Church	.50	.30
2393	A440	150g Missionary ship	.75	.35
2394	A440	200g Plant	1.10	.50
		Nos. 2391-2394 (4)	2.85	1.45

Discovery of America, 500th anniv.

Leprosy Society of Paraguay, 60th Anniv. — A441

Designs: 50g, Society emblem, Malcolm L. Norment, founder. 250g, Gerhard Henrik Armauer Hansen (1841-1912), discoverer of leprosy bacillus.

Perf. 13x13½

		1992, Apr. 28	**Litho.**	**Wmk. 347**
2395	A441	50g multicolored	.75	.30
2396	A441	250g multicolored	2.25	.80

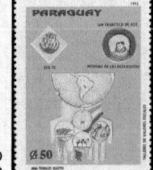

Earth Summit, Rio de Janeiro — A442

Earth Summit emblem, St. Francis of Assisi, and: 50g, Hands holding symbols of clean environment. 100g, Butterfly, industrial pollution. 250g, Globe, calls for environmental protection.

1992, June 9

2397	A442	50g multicolored	.65	.30
2398	A442	100g multicolored	.75	.30
2399	A442	250g multicolored	1.75	.80
		Nos. 2397-2399 (3)	3.15	1.45

For overprints see Nos. 2422-2424.

Natl. Census A443

1992, July 30   Perf. 13½x13, 13x13½

2400	A443	50g Economic activity	.40	.30
2401	A443	200g Houses, vert.	.85	.65
2402	A443	250g Population, vert.	1.20	.80
2403	A443	300g Education	1.50	1.00
		Nos. 2400-2403 (4)	3.95	2.75

1992 Summer Olympics, Barcelona A444

1992, Sept. 1   Perf. 13½x13, 13x13½

2404	A444	50g Soccer, vert.	.45	.30
2405	A444	100g Tennis, vert.	.50	.35
2406	A444	150g Running, vert.	.85	.50
2407	A444	200g Swimming	1.10	.60
2408	A444	250g Judo, vert.	1.25	.80
2409	A444	350g Fencing	1.75	1.10
		Nos. 2404-2409 (6)	5.90	3.65

Evangelism in Paraguay, 500th Anniv. — A445

Designs: 50g, Friar Luis Bolanos. 100g, Friar Juan de San Bernardo. 150g, San Roque Gonzalez de Santa Cruz. 200g, Father Amancio Gonzalez. 250g, Monsignor Juan Sinforiano Bogarin, vert.

Rough Perf. 13½x13, 13x13½

		1992, Oct. 9		**Unwmk.**
2410	A445	50g multicolored	.70	.30
2411	A445	100g multicolored	.70	.35
2412	A445	150g multicolored	1.40	.50
2413	A445	200g multicolored	1.75	.65
2414	A445	250g multicolored	2.10	.80
		Nos. 2410-2414 (5)	6.65	2.60

For overprints see Nos. 2419-2421.

America A446

Designs: 150g, Columbus, fleet arriving in New World. 350g, Columbus, vert.

Rough Perf. 13½x13, 13x13½

1992, Oct. 12

2415	A446	150g multicolored	1.00	.50
2416	A446	350g multicolored	1.50	1.10

No. 2416 is airmail.

Ovptd. "PARAFIL 92" in Blue

1992, Nov. 9

2417	A446	150g multicolored	4.25	4.25
2418	A446	350g multicolored	6.25	6.25

No. 2418 is airmail.

Nos. 2410-2412 Ovptd. in Green

1992, Nov. 6   Rough Perf. 13½x13

2419	A445	50g multicolored	5.00	5.00
2420	A445	100g multicolored	6.00	6.00
2421	A445	150g multicolored	10.00	10.00
		Nos. 2419-2421 (3)	21.00	21.00

Nos. 2397-2399 Ovptd. in Blue

Perf. 13x13½

		1992, Oct. 24		**Wmk. 347**
2422	A442	50g multicolored	2.00	2.00
2423	A442	100g multicolored	2.50	2.50
2424	A442	250g multicolored	6.25	6.25
		Nos. 2422-2424 (3)	10.75	10.75

Inter-American Institute for Cooperation in Agriculture, 50th Anniv. — A447

Designs: 50g, Field workers. 100g, Test tubes, cattle in pasture. 200g, Hands holding flower. 250g, Cows, corn, city.

Perf. 13x13½

		1992, Nov. 27		**Unwmk.**
2425	A447	50g multicolored	.65	.30
2426	A447	100g multicolored	.75	.35
2427	A447	200g multicolored	1.20	.75
2428	A447	250g multicolored	1.50	.90
		Nos. 2425-2428 (4)	4.10	2.30

For overprints see Nos. 2461-2462.

Notary College of Paraguay, Cent. — A448

Designs: 50g, Yolanda Bado de Artecona. 100g, Jose Ramon Silva. 150g, Abelardo Brugada Valpy. 200g, Tomas Varela. 250g, Jose Livio Lezcano. 300g, Francisco I. Fernandez.

1992, Nov. 29   Rough Perf. 13½x13

2429	A448	50g multicolored	.40	.30
2430	A448	100g multicolored	.50	.35
2431	A448	150g multicolored	.80	.60
2432	A448	200g multicolored	1.00	.75
2433	A448	250g multicolored	1.25	.90
2434	A448	300g multicolored	1.50	1.00
		Nos. 2429-2434 (6)	5.45	3.90

Opening of Lopez Palace, Cent. — A449

Paintings of palace by: 50g, Michael Burt. 100g, Esperanza Gill. 200g, Emili Aparici. 250g, Hugo Bogado Barrios, vert.

1993, Mar. 9   Perf. 13½x13, 13x13½

2435	A449	50g multicolored	.55	.30
2436	A449	100g multicolored	.65	.35
2437	A449	200g multicolored	1.40	.75
2438	A449	250g multicolored	1.60	.90
		Nos. 2435-2438 (4)	4.20	2.30

For overprints see Nos. 2453-2456.

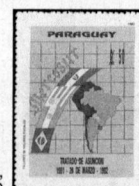

Treaty of Asuncion, 1st Anniv. — A450

Rough Perf. 13x13½

		1993, Mar. 10		**Wmk. 347**
2439	A450	50g Flags, map	.75	.30
2440	A450	350g Flags, globe	1.75	1.25

Santa Isabel Leprosy Assoc., 50th Anniv. — A451

Various flowers.

Perf. 13x13½

		1993, May 24		**Unwmk.**
2441	A451	50g multicolored	.40	.30
2442	A451	200g multicolored	1.00	.75
2443	A451	250g multicolored	1.20	.90
2444	A451	350g multicolored	1.60	1.25
		Nos. 2441-2444 (4)	4.20	3.20

Goethe College, Cent. — A452

Designs: 50g, Goethe, by Johann Heinrich Lips, inscription. 100g, Goethe (close-up), by Johann Heinrich Wilhelm Tischbein.

1993, June 18

2445	A452	50g multicolored	.45	.30
2446	A452	200g multicolored	1.10	.75

For overprints see Nos. 2451-2452.

World Friendship Crusade, 35th Anniv. — A453

Designs: 50g, Stylized globe. 100g, Map, Dr. Ramon Artemio Bracho. 200g, Children. 250g, Two people embracing.

1993, July 1

2447	A453	50g multicolored	.55	.30
2448	A453	100g multicolored	.55	.35
2449	A453	200g multicolored	1.10	.75
2450	A453	350g multicolored	1.40	.90
		Nos. 2447-2450 (4)	3.60	2.30

For overprint see No. 2486.

Nos. 2445-2446 Ovptd. "BRASILIANA 93"

1993, July 12

2451	A452	50g multicolored	2.75	2.75
2452	A452	200g multicolored	7.75	7.75

Nos. 2435-2438 Ovptd.

Perf. 13½x13, 13x13½

1993, Aug. 13

2453	A449	50g multicolored	1.25	1.25
2454	A449	100g multicolored	1.75	1.75
2455	A449	200g multicolored	3.50	3.50
2456	A449	250g multicolored	4.50	4.50
		Nos. 2453-2456 (4)	11.00	11.00

Size of overprint varies.

Church of the Incarnation, Cent. — A454

Design: 50g, Side view of church, vert.

1993, Oct. 8 — Unwmk. Litho. Perf. 13
2457 A454 50g multicolored .40 .30
2458 A454 350g multicolored 1.60 .60

Endangered Animals A455

America: 50g, Myrmecophaga tridactyla. 250g, Speothos venaticus.

1993, Oct. 27
2459 A455 50g multicolored 2.75 .60
2460 A455 250g multicolored 1.75 .75

No. 2459 is airmail.

Nos. 2426-2427 Ovptd.

1993, Nov. 16 — Perf. 13x13½
2461 A447 100g multicolored 3.50 3.50
2462 A447 200g multicolored 7.00 7.00

Christmas — A456

1993, Nov. 24
2463 A456 50g shown .40 .30
2464 A456 250g Stars, wise men 1.10 .30

Scouting in Paraguay, 80th Anniv. — A457

50g, Girl scouts watching scout instuctor. 100g, Boy scouts learning crafts. 200g, Lord Robert Baden-Powell. 250g, Girl scout with flag.

1993, Dec. 30
2465 A457 50g multicolored .45 .30
2466 A457 100g multicolored .45 .30
2467 A457 200g multicolored .90 .30
2468 A457 250g multicolored 1.20 .50
Nos. 2465-2468 (4) 3.00 1.40

First Lawyers to Graduate from Natl. University of Ascuncion, Cent. — A458

50g, Cecilio Baez. 100g, Benigno Riquelme, vert. 250g, Emeterio Gonzalez. 500g, J. Gaspar Villamayor.

1994, Apr. 8 — Perf. 13
2469 A458 50g multicolored .55 .30
2470 A458 100g multicolored .70 .30
2471 A458 250g multicolored .85 .45
2472 A458 500g multicolored 1.40 .75
Nos. 2469-2472 (4) 3.50 1.80

Phoenix Sports Corporation, 50th Anniv. — A459

Designs: 50g, Basketball player, vert. 200g, Soccer players, vert. 250g, Pedro Andrias Garcia Arias, founder, tennis player.

1994, May 20 — Litho. Perf. 13
2473 A459 50g multicolored .50 .30
2474 A459 200g multicolored .55 .35
2475 A459 250g multicolored .85 .45
Nos. 2473-2475 (3) 1.90 1.10

1994 World Cup Soccer Championships, U.S. — A460

Various soccer plays.

1994, June 2
2476 A460 250g multicolored .60 .45
2477 A460 500g multicolored 1.25 .75
2478 A460 1000g multicolored 2.10 1.50
Nos. 2476-2478 (3) 3.95 2.70

For overprints see Nos. 2483-2485.

Intl. Olympic Committee, Cent. — A461

350g, Runner. 400g, Lighting Olympic flame.

1994, June 23 — Unwmk. Litho. Perf. 13
2479 A461 350g multicolored .85 .60
2480 A461 400g multicolored .90 .65

World Congress on Physical Education, Asuncion A462

Designs: 1000g, Stylized family running to break finish line, vert.

Perf. 13½x13, 13x13½
1994, July 19 — Litho.
2481 A462 200g multicolored .70 .45
2482 A462 1000g multicolored 3.25 2.25

Nos. 2476-2478 Ovptd.

1994, Aug. 2 — Perf. 13
2483 A460 250g multicolored 1.50 1.50
2484 A460 500g multicolored 3.00 3.00
2485 A460 1000g multicolored 6.25 6.25
Nos. 2483-2485 (3) 10.75 10.75

No. 2448 Ovptd.

1994, Aug. 3 — Perf. 13x13½
2486 A453 100g multicolored 16.25 16.25

Agustin Pio Barrios Mangore (1885-1944), Musician — A463

250g, In tuxedo. 500g, In traditional costume.

1994, Aug. 5 — Perf. 13x13½
2487 A463 250g multi .75 .50
2488 A463 500g multi 1.60 1.00

Paraguayan Police, 151st Anniv. — A464

50g, 1913 Guardsman on horseback. 250g, Pedro Nolasco Fernandez, 1st capital police chief; Carlos Bernadino Cacabelos, 1st commissioner.

1994, Aug. 26 — Perf. 13x13½
2489 A464 50g multicolored .45 .30
2490 A464 250g multicolored 1.00 .60

For overprint see Nos. 2569-2570.

Parafil '94 — A465

Birds: 100g, Ciconia maquari. 150g, Paroaria capitata. 400g, Chloroceryle americana, vert. 500g, Jabiru mycteria, vert.

1994, Sept. 9 — Perf. 13
2491 A465 100g multicolored .60 .30
2492 A465 150g multicolored .85 .40
2493 A465 400g multicolored 2.25 .90
2494 A465 500g multicolored 3.25 1.10
Nos. 2491-2494 (4) 6.95 2.70

Solar Eclipse — A466

Designs: 50g, Eclipse, Copernicus. 200g, Sundial, Johannes Kepler.

1994, Sept. 23 — Unwmk. Litho. Perf. 13
2495 A466 50g multicolored .45 .30
2496 A466 200g multicolored .95 .45

America Issue — A467

100g, Derelict locomotive. 1000g, Motorcycle.

1994, Oct. 11 — Perf. 13½
2497 A467 100g multicolored .60 .45
2498 A467 1000g multicolored 5.00 3.00

Intl. Year of the Family — A468

1994, Oct. 25 — Perf. 13x13½
2499 A468 50g Mother, child .60 .30
2500 A468 250g Family faces 1.10 .60

Christmas A469

Ceramic figures: 150g, Nativity. 700g, Joseph, infant Jesus, Mary, vert.

1994, Nov. 4 — Perf. 13½
2501 A469 150g multicolored .55 .35
2502 A469 700g multicolored 2.50 1.60

Paraguayan Red Cross, 75th Anniv. — A470

Black Red Cross — A470a

Designs: 150g, Boy Scouts, Jean-Henri Dunant. 700g, Soldiers, paramedics, Dr. Andres Barbero.

1994, Nov. 25 — Perf. 13½x13
2503 A470 150g multi .70 .45
2503A A470a 500g multi 200.00
2504 A470 700g multi 3.40 2.40

When it was discovered that No. 2503A contained a black cross instead of a red cross it was withdrawn.

San Jose College, 90th Anniv. — A471

Pope John Paul II and: 200g, Eternal flame. 250g, College entrance.

1994, Dec. 4
2505 A471 200g multicolored .85 .45
2506 A471 250g multicolored 1.00 .60

Louis Pasteur (1822-95) — A472

1995, Mar. 24 — Litho. Perf. 13½
2507 A472 1000g multicolored 3.25 2.10

Fight Against
AIDS — A473

1995, May 4
2508 A473 500g Faces   1.75 .75
2509 A473 1000g shown   3.25 1.50

FAO, 50th
Anniv. — A474

1995, June 23
2510 A474 950g Bread, pitcher   2.40 1.50
2511 A474 2000g Watermelon   5.25 3.00

Fifth
Neotropical
Ornithological
Congress
A475

100g, Parula pitiayumi. 200g, Chirroxiphia
caudata. 600g, Icterus icterus. 1000g,
Carduelis magellanica.

1995, July 6
2512 A475 100g multicolored   .70 .45
2513 A475 200g multicolored   .90 .45
2514 A475 600g multicolored   3.00 1.20
2515 A475 1000g multicolored 3.50 2.10
   Nos. 2512-2515 (4)   8.10 4.20

Fifth Intl.
Symposium on
Municipalities,
Ecology &
Tourism — A476

Designs: 1150g, Rio Monday rapids. 1300g,
Areguá Railroad Station.

1995, Aug. 4   Litho.   Perf. 13½
2516 A476 1150g multicolored 2.10 1.25
2517 A476 1300g multicolored 2.40 1.40

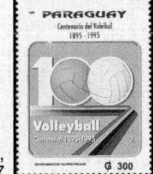

Volleyball,
Cent. — A477

600g, Ball, net. 1000g, Hands, ball, net.

1995, Sept. 28
2518 A477 300g shown   .65 .30
2519 A477 600g multi   1.40 .60
2520 A477 1000g multi   1.95 1.00
   Nos. 2518-2520 (3)   4.00 1.90

America
Issue — A478

Preserve the environment: 950g, Macizo
Monument, Achay. 2000g, Tinfunique
Reserve, Chaco, vert.

1995, Oct. 12
2521 A478 950g multicolored   3.25 1.00
2522 A478 2000g multicolored 5.25 2.10

UN, 50th
Anniv. — A479

Designs: 200g, Flags above olive branch.
3000g, UN emblem, stick figures.

1995, Oct. 20
2523 A479 200g multicolored   .35 .30
2524 A479 3000g multicolored 5.00 3.00

Christmas — A480

1995, Nov. 7
2525 A480 200g shown   .60 .30
2526 A480 1000g Nativity   2.40 1.00

Jose Marti
(1853-95)
A481

Designs: 200g, Hedychium coronarium,
Marti, vert. 1000g, Hedychium coronarium,
map & flag of Cuba, Marti.

1995, Dec. 19   Litho.   Perf. 13½
2527 A481 200g multicolored   .75 .30
2528 A481 1000g multicolored 2.75 1.10

Lion's Clubs of
South America
& the
Caribbean, 25th
Anniv. — A482

1996, Jan. 11
2529 A482 200g Railway station .50 .30
2530 A482 1000g Viola House   2.10 1.10

Orchids
A483

Designs: 100g, Cattleya nobilior. 200g,
Oncidium varicosum. 1000g, Oncidium jone-
sianum, vert. 1150g, Sophronitis cernua.

Perf. 13½x13, 13x13½
1996, Apr. 22   Litho.
2531 A483 100g multicolored   .60 .45
2532 A483 200g multicolored   .60 .45
2533 A483 1000g multicolored 2.60 1.20
2534 A483 1150g multicolored 2.90 1.40
   Nos. 2531-2534 (4)   6.70 3.50

1996 Summer
Olympic
Games,
Atlanta — A484

1996, June 6   Perf. 13½x13
2535 A484 500g Diving   1.25 .45
2536 A484 1000g Running   2.25 .90

Founding of
Society of
Salesian
Fathers in
Paraguay,
Cent. — A485

Pope John Paul II, St. John Bosco (1815-
88), and: 200g, Men, boys from Salesian
Order, natl. flag. 300g, Madonna and Child,
vert. 1000g, Map of Paraguay, man following
light.

1996, July 22   Perf. 13½x13, 13x13½
2537 A485 200g multicolored   .50 .30
2538 A485 300g multicolored   .65 .30
2539 A485 1000g multicolored 2.10 .90
   Nos. 2537-2539 (3)   3.25 1.50

UNICEF, 50th
Anniv. — A486

Children's paintings: 1000g, Outdoor scene,
by S. Báez, 1300g, Four groups of children, by
C. Pérez.

1996, Sept. 27   Perf. 13½x13
2540 A486 1000g multicolored 2.50 .90
2541 A486 1300g multicolored 2.75 1.25

Visit of Pope
John Paul II to
Caacupe, Site
of Apparition of
the
Virgin — A487

Design: 200g, Pope John Paul II, church,
Virgin of Caacupe, vert.

1996, Oct. 4   Perf. 13x13½, 13½x13
2542 A487 200g multicolored   .50 .35
2543 A487 1300g multicolored 3.00 1.50

Traditional
Costumes — A488

America issue: 500g, Woman in costume.
1000g, Woman, man, in costumes.

1996, Oct. 11   Perf. 13½x13½
2544 A488 500g multicolored   1.40 .45
2545 A488 1000g multicolored 3.25 .90

UN Year for
Eradication of
Poverty — A489

1996, Oct. 17 Perf. 13½x13, 13x13½
2546 A489 1000g Food products 1.75 .90
2547 A489 1150g Boy, fruit, vert. 2.10 1.10

Christmas — A490

Madonna and Child, by: 200g, Koki Ruíz.
1000g, Hernán Miranda.

1996, Nov. 7   Perf. 13x13½
2548 A490 200g multicolored   .90 .30
2549 A490 1000g multicolored 2.10 .90

Butterflies — A491

Designs: 200g, Eryphanis automedon.
500g, Dryadula phaetusa. 1000g, Vanessa
myrinna. 1150g, Heliconius ethilla.

1997, Mar. 5   Litho.   Perf. 13x13½
2550 A491 200g multicolored   .65 .30
2551 A491 500g multicolored   1.90 .45
2552 A491 1000g multicolored 3.25 .80
2553 A491 1150g multicolored 4.00 .95
   Nos. 2550-2553 (4)   9.80 2.50

Official
Buildings
A492

200g, 1st Legistlature. 1000g, Postal
Headquarters.

1997, May 5   Perf. 13½x13
2554 A492 200g multicolored   .90 .30
2555 A492 1000g multicolored 2.10 .90

1997, Year of Jesus
Christ — A493

1000g, Crucifix, Pope John Paul II.

1997, June 10   Perf. 13x13½
2556 A493 1000g multi   2.25 .75

11th Summit of
the Rio Group
Chiefs of State,
Asunción
A494

1997, Aug. 23   Perf. 13½x13
2557 A494 1000g multicolored 2.25 1.00

Environmental
and Climate
Change
A495

Flowers: 300g, Opunita elata. 500g, Brome-
lia balansae, 1000g, Monvillea kroenlaini.

Perf. 13½x13, 13x13½
1997, Aug. 25
2558 A495 300g multi   .75 .30
2559 A495 500g multi, vert. 1.00 .50
2560 A495 1000g multi   2.10 1.00
   Nos. 2558-2560 (3)   3.85 1.80

1st Philatelic
Exposition of
MERCOSUR
Countries, Chile
and
Bolivia — A496

Fauna: 200g, Felis tigrina. 1000g, Alouatta
caraya, vert. 1150g, Agouti paca.

Perf. 13½x13, 13x13½
1997, Aug. 29
2561 A496 200g multicolored   .60 .25
2562 A496 1000g multicolored 2.25 1.00
2563 A496 1150g multicolored 2.75 1.10
   Nos. 2561-2563 (3)   5.60 2.35

MERCOSUR
(Common Market of
Latin
America) — A497

1997, Sept. 26   *Perf. 13x13½*
2564 A497 1000g multicolored   2.25 .90
  See Argentina #1975, Bolivia #1019, Brazil #2646, Urugray #1681.

America
Issue — A498

Life of a postman: 1000g, Postman, letters going around the world, vert. 1150g, Window with six panes showing weather conditions, different roads, postman.

1997, Oct. 10 *Perf. 13x13½, 13½x13*
2565 A498 1000g multicolored   2.75 1.00
2566 A498 1150g multicolored   2.75 1.25

Natl. Council on
Sports, 50th
Anniv. — A499

200g, Neri Kennedy throwing javelin. 1000g, Ramón Milciades Giménez Gaona throwing discus.

1997, Oct. 16   *Perf. 13x13½*
2567 A499 200g multicolored   .60 .30
2568 A499 1000g multicolored   2.40 1.10

Nos. 2489-2490
Ovptd. in Red

1997, Nov. 14
2569 A464 50g multicolored   2.50 .45
2570 A464 250g multicolored   7.50 2.00

Christmas — A500

Paintings of Madonna and Child: 200g, By Olga Blinder. 1000g, By Hermán Miranda.

1997, Nov. 17
2571 A500 200g multicolored   .60 .30
2572 A500 1000g multicolored 2.40 1.00

UN Fund for
Children of the
World with
AIDS — A501

Children's paintings: 500g, Boy. 1000g, Girl.

1997, Dec. 5
2573 A501 500g multicolored   1.10 .45
2574 A501 1000g multicolored 1.90 .90

Rotary Club of
Asunción, 70th
Anniv. — A502

1997, Dec. 11
2575 A502 1150g multicolored 2.25 1.00

1998 World Cup Soccer
Championships, France — A503

200g, Julio César Romero, vert. 500g, Carlos Gamarra, vert. 1000g, 1998 Paraguayan team.

1998, Jan. 22   Litho.   *Perf. 13*
2576 A503 200g multicolored   .35 .25
2577 A503 500g multicolored   1.10 .45
2578 A503 1000g multicolored 2.25 .90
  Nos. 2576-2578 (3)   3.70 1.60

Fish — A504

Designs: 200g, Tetrogonopterus argenteus. 300g, Pseudoplatystoma coruscans. 500g, Salminus brasiliensis. 1000g, Acestrorhynchus altus.

1998, Apr. 17   Litho.   *Perf. 13½*
2579 A504 200g multicolored   .80 .30
2580 A504 300g multicolored   1.00 .30
2581 A504 500g multicolored   1.50 .45
2582 A504 1000g multicolored 3.25 .90
  Nos. 2579-2582 (4)   6.55 1.95

Contemporary
Paintings
A505

200g, Hands, geometric shape, by Carlos Colombino. 300g, Mother nursing infant, by Félix Toranzos. 400g, Flowers, by Edith Giménez. 1000g, Woman lifting tray of food, by Ricardo Migliorisi.

1998, June 5
2583 A505 200g multi, vert.   .40 .25
2584 A505 300g multi, vert.   .80 .30
2585 A505 400g multi, vert.   .90 .30
2586 A505 1000g multi   2.10 .75
  Nos. 2583-2586 (4)   4.20 1.60

Mushrooms — A506

400g, Boletus edulis. 600g, Macrolepiota procera. 1000g, Geastrum triplex.

1998, June 26
2587 A506 400g multicolored   .90 .30
2588 A506 600g multicolored   1.20 .50
2589 A506 1000g multicolored 2.10 .90
  Nos. 2587-2589 (3)   4.20 1.70

Organization of
American
States (OAS),
50th
Anniv. — A507

Designs: 500g, Home of Carlos A. López, botantical and zooligical gardens, Asunción. 1000g, Palmerola Villa, Areguá.

1998, July 16
2590 A507 500g multicolored   1.10 .40
2591 A507 1000g multicolored 2.40 .90

Episcopacy of
Hernando de
Trejo y
Sanabria,
400th
Anniv. — A508

Pope John Paul II and: 400g, Sacrarium doors, Caazapá Church, vert. 1700g, Statue of St. Francis of Assisi, Atyrá Church.

Perf. 13x13½, 13½x13
1998, Sept. 5   Litho.
2592 A508 400g multi   1.25 .40
2593 A508 1700g multi   3.25 1.75

Ruins of Jesuit
Mission
Church — A509

1998, Sept. 16 Litho. *Perf. 13½x13*
2594 A509 5000g multicolored 8.25 5.00

Flowers — A510

Designs: 100g, Acacia caven. 600g, Cordia trichotoma. 1900g, Glandularia sp.

1998, Sept. 16 Litho. *Perf. 13x13½*
2595 A510 100g multi   .35 .25
2596 A510 600g multi   1.40 .50
2597 A510 1900g multi   3.25 1.75
  Nos. 2595-2597 (3)   5.00 2.50

America
Issue — A511

Famous women and buildings: 1600g, Serafina Davalos (1883-1957), first woman lawyer, National College building. 1700g, Adela Speratti (1865-1902), director of Normal School.

1998, Oct. 12 Litho. *Perf. 13½x13*
2598 A511 1600g multi   3.25 1.50
2599 A511 1700g multi   4.25 1.75

Universal
Declaration of
Human Rights, 50th
Anniv. — A512

Artwork by: 500g, Carlos Colombino. 1000g, Jose Filártiga.

1998, Oct. 23   *Perf. 13x13½*
2600 A512 500g multi   1.10 .50
2601 A512 1000g multi   2.25 1.00

Christmas
Creche
Figures — A513

Perf. 13½x13, 13x13½
1998, Sept. 16   Litho.
2602 A513 300g shown   2.00 .25
2603 A513 1600g Stable, vert. 6.50 1.75

Reptiles
A514

Designs: 100g, Micrurus frontalis. 300g, Ameiva ameiva. 1600g, Geochelone carbonaria. 1700g, Caiman yacare.

1999, May 13 Litho. *Perf. 13½x13*
2604-2607 A514 Set of 4   10.00 4.00

Paintings
A515

Paintings by: 500g, Ignacio Nuñez Soler. 1600g, Modesto Delgado Rodas. 1700g, Jaime Bestard.

1999, June 23 Litho. *Perf. 13½x13*
2608 A515 500g multi   .75 .40
2609 A515 1600g multi   2.25 1.40
2610 A515 1700g multi   2.75 1.40
  Nos. 2608-2610 (3)   5.75 3.20

America Soccer
Cup — A516

Designs: 300g, Carlos Humberto Paredes, vert. 500g, South American Soccer Confederation Building, Luque. 1900g, Feliciano Cáceres Stadium, Luque.

Perf. 13x13½, 13½x13
1999, June 24
2611 A516 300g multi   .50 .25
2612 A516 500g multi   .85 .35
2613 A516 1900g multi   3.25 1.50
  Nos. 2611-2613 (3)   4.60 2.10

SOS Children's
Villages, 50th
Anniv. — A517

1999, July 16 *Perf. 13½x13, 13x13½*
2614 A517 1700g Toucan   2.75 1.10
2615 A517 1900g Toucan, vert. 3.75 1.40

Protests of
Assassination
of Vice-
President Luis
Maria
Argaña — A518

Designs: 100g, Protest at Governmental Palace. 500g, Argaña, vert. 1500g, Protest at National Congress.

1999, Aug. 26
2616 A518 100g multi   .30 .25
2617 A518 500g multi   .90 .40
2618 A518 1500g multi   2.40 1.25
  Nos. 2616-2618 (3)   3.60 1.90

Medicinal
Plants — A519

Designs: 600g, Cochlospermum regium.
700g, Borago officinalis. 1700g, Passiflora
cincinnata.

1999, Sept. 8   *Perf. 13x13½*
2619 A519 600g multi   .90 .35
2620 A519 700g multi   .90 .45
2621 A519 1700g multi   2.50 1.00
   Nos. 2619-2621 (3)   4.30 1.80

America Issue,
A New
Millennium
Without
Arms — A520

Various artworks by Ricardo Migliorisi.

Perf. 13½x13, 13x13½
1999, Oct. 12   **Litho.**
2622 A520 1500g multi   2.25 1.10
2623 A520 3000g multi, vert.   3.75 2.25

Intl. Year of the
Elderly — A521

Artwork by: 1000g, Olga Blinder. 1900g,
Maria de los Reyes Omella Herrero, vert.

Perf. 13½x13, 13x13½
1999, Oct. 20   **Litho.**
2624-2625 A521 Set of 2   4.00 2.00

Christmas — A522

Artwork by: 300g, Manuel Viedma. 1600g,
Federico Ordiñana.

1999, Nov. 11 Litho.   *Perf. 13x13½*
2626 A522 300g multi   1.00 .25
2627 A522 1600g multi   2.50 1.00

City of Pedro
Juan Caballero,
Cent. — A523

Flowers: 1000g, Tabebuia impetiginosa.
1600g, Tabebuia pulcherrima, vert.

Perf. 13½x13, 13x13½
1999, Dec. 1   **Litho.**
2628 A523 1000g multi   1.50 .70
2629 A523 1600g multi   2.00 1.00

Inter-American
Development
Bank, 40th
Anniv. — A524

Designs: 600g, Oratory of Our Lady of
Asuncion and Pantheon of Heroes, Asuncion.
700g, Governmental Palace.

1999, Dec. 6   *Perf. 13½x13*
2630 A524 600g multi   1.25 .35
2631 A524 700g multi   1.50 .45

Intl. Women's
Day — A525

Carmen Casco de Lara Castro and sculpture: 400g, Conjunction, by Domingo Rivarola.
2000g, Violation, by Gustavo Beckelmann.

2000, Apr. 7 Litho.   *Perf. 13x13½*
2632-2633 A525 Set of 2   3.50 3.00

Expo 2000,
Hanover
A526

Designs: 500g, Yacyreta Dam and deer.
2500g, Itaipú Dam, tapir.

2000, May 5   *Perf. 13½x13*
2634-2635 A526 Set of 2   4.00 3.50

Salesians in
Paraguay,
Cent. — A527

Madonna and Child, Pope John Paul II and:
600g, Salesians, vert. 2000g, College building.

Perf. 13x13½, 13½x13
2000, May 19   **Litho.**
2636-2637 A527 Set of 2   3.00 3.00

2000 Summer
Olympics,
Sydney — A528

Designs: 2500g, Soccer, vert. 3000g, Runner Francisco Rojas Soto.

2000, July 28   *Perf. 13½x13½, 13½x13*
2638-2639 A528 Set of 2   7.50 7.50

Rights of the
Child — A529

Designs: 1500g, Child between hands, vert.
1700g, Handprints.

Perf. 13x13½, 13½x13
2000, Aug. 16
2640-2641 A529 Set of 2   4.50 4.50

Fire Fighters
A530

Designs: 100g, Fire fighters, white truck,
vert. 200g, Fire fighter in old uniform, emblem,
vert. 1500g, Fire fighters at fire. 1600g, Fire
fighters, yellow truck.

Perf. 13x13½, 13½x13
2000, Sept. 28
2642-2645 A530 Set of 4   5.00 4.50

Roads and
Flowers
A531

Designs: 500g, Paved road between San
Bernardino and Altos, Rosa banksiae. 3000g,
Gaspar Rodriguez de Francia Highway, Cal-
liandra brevicaulis.

2000, Oct. 5 Litho.   *Perf. 13½x13¼*
2646-2647 A531 Set of 2   5.00 5.00

America Issue,
Fight Against
AIDS — A532

Designs: 1500g, Signs with arrows. 2500g,
Tic-tac-toe game.

2000, Oct. 19   *Perf. 13x13½*
2648-2649 A532 Set of 2   5.50 5.50

Intl. Year of Culture
and Peace — A533

Sculptures by: 500g, Hugo Pistilli. 2000g,
Herman Guggiari.

2000, Oct. 27 Litho.   *Perf. 13¼x13½*
2650-2651 A533 Set of 2   3.25 3.25

Christmas — A534

Designs: 100g, Holy Family, sculpture by
Hugo Pistilli. 500g, Poem by José Luis
Appleyard. 2000g, Creche figures, horiz.

Perf. 13x13½, 13½x13
2000, Nov. 17   **Litho.**
2652-2654 A534 Set of 3   3.50 3.50

Artisan's
Crafts — A535

Designs: 200g, Campesina Woman, by
Behage. 1500g, Cattle horns, by Quintin
Velazquez, horiz. 2000g, Silver filigree orchid,
by Quirino Torres.

Perf. 13¼x13½, 13½x13¼
2000, Nov. 28   **Litho.**
2655-2657 A535 Set of 3   5.25 5.25

Guarania Music,
75th Anniv. — A536

Designs: 100g, José Asunción Flores
(1904-72), composer. 1500g, Violin. 2500g,
Trombone.

2000, Dec. 20   *Perf. 13¼x13½*
2658-2660 A536 Set of 3   5.00 5.00

Signing of
Asunción
Treaty, 10th
Anniv. — A537

Designs: 500g, Delegates signing treaty.
2500g, Map of South America with signatory
nations colored, vert.

Perf. 13½x13¼, 13¼x13½
2001, June 20
2661-2662 A537 Set of 2   3.50 3.50

Cacti — A538

Designs: 2000g, Opuntia sp. 2500g, Cereus
stenogonus.

2001, June 29   *Perf. 13¼x13½*
2663-2664 A538 Set of 2   6.00 6.00

Second Paz del Chaco Philatelic Exhibition.

Under 20
Soccer
Championships,
Argentina
A539

Designs: 2000g, Players. 2500g, Players,
diff., vert.

Perf. 13½x13¼, 13¼x13½
2001, June 29
2665-2666 A539 Set of 2   6.00 6.00

Cattle — A540

Designs: 200g, Holando-Argentino. 500g,
Nelore. 1500g, Pampa Chaqueño.

2001, July 20   *Perf. 13½x13¼*
2667-2669 A540 Set of 3   3.50 3.50

Engravings
A541

Woodcuts by: No. 2670, 500g, Josefina Plá.
No. 2671, 500g, Leonor Cecotto, vert. 1500g,
Jacinto Rivero. 2000g, Livio Abramo.

Perf. 13½x13¼, 13¼x13½
2001, Aug. 28
2670-2673 A541 Set of 4   6.00 6.00

Mythological
Heavens of the
Guarani
A542

Designs: 100g, Eichu (Pleiades). 600g, Mborevi Rape (Milky Way). 1600g, Jagua Ho'u Jasy (lunar eclipse).

2001, Sept. 24   **Perf. 13½x13¼**
2674-2676 A542   Set of 3   3.25 3.25

America Issue — UNESCO World Heritage Sites — A543

No. 2677: a, 500g, St. Ignatius of Loyola, Jesuit Mission Ruins, Trinidad. b, 2000g, Jesuit Mission Ruins.

2001, Oct. 9   **Perf. 13¼x13½**
2677 A543   Horiz. pair, #a-b, +   2 flanking labels   3.50 3.50

World Teachers' Day — A544

Designs: 200g, Children studying, school blackboard, J. Inocencio Lezcano (1889-1935), educator. 1600g, Symbols of education, Ramón I. Cardozo (1876-1943), educator.

2001, Oct. 9   **Perf. 13½x13¼**
2678-2679 A544   Set of 2   2.50 2.50

Year of Dialogue Among Civilizations — A545

2001, Oct. 23   **Perf. 13¼x13½**
2680 A545 3000g multi + 2 flanking labels   4.25 4.25

Christmas A546

Nativity scenes by: 700g, Gladys and Maria de Feliciangeli. 4000g, Mercedes Servin.

2001, Nov. 29   **Perf. 13½x13¼**
2681-2682 A546   Set of 2   5.00 5.00

No to Terrorism A547

Designs: 700g, Statue of Liberty, World Trade Center, vert. 5000g, Flags of Paraguay and U.S., chain becoming doves.

Perf. 13¼x13½, 13½x13¼
2001, Dec. 19   **Litho.**
2683-2684 A547   Set of 2   8.50 8.50

Passiflora Caerulea — A548

2001, Dec. 21   **Perf. 13¼x13½**
2685 A548 4000g multi   4.50 4.00

Paraguayan, Bolivian, and Argentinian Scout Jamboree, Boquerón Province — A549

2002, Jan. 24
2686 A549 6000g multi   9.50 9.50

El Mbiguá Social Club, Asunción, Cent. — A550

2002, May 3   **Perf. 13½x13¼**
2687 A550 700g multi   1.10 1.10

Juan de Salazar Spanish Cultural Center, 25th Anniv. — A551

Jesuit wood carvings, 18th cent.: 2500g, Pieta. 5000g, St. Michael Archangel.

2002, May 7   **Perf. 13¼x13½**
2688-2689 A551   Set of 2   11.00 11.00

2002 World Cup Soccer Championships, Japan and Korea — A552

Designs: 3000g, Paraguay team. 5000g, Players in action, vert.

Perf. 13½x13¼, 13¼x13½
2002, May 18
2690-2691 A552   Set of 2   12.00 12.00

For overprint see No. 2705.

Arrival of Mennonites in Paraguay, 75th Anniv. — A553

Cross, plow, Menno Simons (1496-1561), Religious Leader, and: 2000g, Mennonite Church, Filadelfia. 4000g, Mennonite Church, Loma Plata.

2002, June 25   **Perf. 13½x13¼**
2692-2693 A553   Set of 2   7.50 7.50

Horses — A554

Designs: 700g, Criollo. 1000g, Cuarto de Milla (quarterhorse). 6000g, Arabian.

2002, July 12
2694-2696 A554   Set of 3   9.50 9.50

Olimpia Soccer Team, Cent. A555

2002, July 24
2697 A555 700g multi + 2 flanking labels   2.00 2.00

Pan-American Health Organization, Cent. — A556

Medicinal plants: 4000g, Stevia rebaudiana bertoni. 5000g, Ilex paraguayensis.

2002, Sept. 16   **Perf. 13¼x13½**
2698-2699 A556   Set of 2   13.00 13.00

International Forum on Postal Service Modernization and Reform — A557

Forum emblem and statues by Serafin Marsal: 1000g, Campesina. 4000g, Quygua-vera.

2002, Sept. 30   **Perf. 13½x13¼**
2700-2701 A557   Set of 2   7.00 7.00

Paraguay — Republic of China Diplomatic Relations, 45th Anniv. — A558

2002, Oct. 10   **Perf. 13¼x13½**
2702 A558 4000g multi + 2 flanking labels   6.00 6.00

America Issue — Youth, Education and Literacy — A559

Designs: 3000g, Classroom. 6000g, Children playing.

2002, Oct. 12   **Perf. 13½x13¼**
2703-2704 A559   Set of 2   12.00 12.00

No. 2690 Overprinted

2002
2705 A552 3000g on #2690   4.00 4.00

Christmas — A560

Various creche figures: a, 1000g. b, 4000g. c, 700g.

2002, Dec. 2   **Litho.**   **Perf. 13¼**
2706 A560   Horiz. strip of 3, #a-c   7.00 7.00

Church, Areguá — A561

2002, Dec. 18
2707 A561 4000g multi   4.50 4.50

District of San Antonio, Cent. — A562

2003, Apr. 21   **Litho.**   **Perf. 13¼**
2708 A562 700g multi   .50 .50

Josefina Plá (1903-99), Artist — A563

Designs: 700g, Plate. 6000g, Carving.

2003, May 30   **Litho.**   **Perf. 13¼**
2709-2710 A563   Set of 2   5.00 5.00

Parrots — A564

Designs: 1000g, Amazona aestiva. 2000g, Myiopsitta monachus. 4000g, Aratinga leucophtalmus.

2003, June 9
2711-2713 A564   Set of 3   6.50 6.50

Paraguay Philatelic Center, 90th anniv. (#2711), Paz del Chaco Bi-national Philatelic Exhibition (#2712), PARAFIL Bi-national Philatelic Exhibition (#2713).

Legislative Palace — A565

2003, June 24   **Perf. 13½x13¼**
2714 A565 4000g multi + label   3.50 3.50

Printed in sheets of 12 stamps and 18 labels.

Pontificate of Pope John Paul II, 25th Anniv. — A566

2003, June 27   **Perf. 13¼**
2715 A566 6000g multi + label   3.50 3.50

Farm Animals A567

Designs: 1000g, Pig. 3000g, Sheep. 8000g, Goat.

2003, July 18
2716-2718 A567   Set of 3   8.50 8.50

Foods — A568

Designs: 700g, Peanuts, honey and nougat. 2000g, Sopa Paraguaya. 3000g, Chipá.

2003, July 25
2719-2721 A568 Set of 3   4.00 4.00

Folk Artists — A569

Designs: 700g, Julio Correa (1890-1953), playwright. 1000g, Emiliano Rivarola Fernández (1894-1949), singer. 2000g, Manuel Ortiz Guerrero (1894-1933), poet.

2003, Sept. 12
2722-2724 A569 Set of 3   2.75 2.75

Dances — A570

Designs: 700g, Golondriana. 3000g, Polka. 4000g, Galopera.

2003, Sept. 23
2725-2727 A570 Set of 3   5.50 5.50

Guaraní Soccer Team, Cent. A571

2003, Oct. 9
2728 A571 700g multi + label   .50 .50

Native Clothing — A572

Designs: 4000g, Sixty-strip poncho, Para'i. 5000g, Shirt, Ao Poí.

2003, Oct. 22
2729-2730 A572 Set of 2   6.00 6.00

Christmas — A573

Designs: 700g, Journey to Egypt. 1000g, Adoration of the Shepherds. 4000g, Nativity.

2003, Nov. 12
2731-2733 A573 Set of 3   4.00 4.00

Indoor Soccer World Cup Championships, Paraguay — A574

No. 2734 — Various players: a, 4000g. b, 5000g.

2003, Nov. 14
2734 A574 Horiz. pair, #a-b   5.50 5.50
Printed in sheets with two columns of five pairs separated by a column of labels.

No. 2734 Overprinted "PARAGUAY / CAMPEON MUNDIAL" in Silver
No. 2734C: d, On #2734a. e, On #2734b.

2003   Litho.   Perf. 13¼
2734C A574 Horiz. pair, #d-e   5.50 5.50

America Issue - Flowers — A575

Designs: 1000g, Cordia bordasii. No. 2736, 5000g, Bulnesia sarmientoi. No. 2737, 5000g, Chorisia insignis.

2003, Nov. 26
2735-2737 A575 Set of 3   7.50 7.50
For overprints see Nos. 2797-2798.

Comics by Robin Wood — A576

Designs: 1000g, Anahí. 3000g, Nippur de Lagash. 5000g, Dago.

2004, May 24   Litho.   Perf. 13¼
2738-2740 A576 Set of 3   7.00 7.00

National Soccer Team, Cent. A577

2004, June 25
2741 A577 700g multi + label   .50 .50

San José College, Cent. — A578

2004, July 2   Litho.   Perf. 13¼
2742 A578 700g multi   .65 .65

Pablo Neruda (1904-73), Poet — A579

2004, July 6   Litho.   Perf. 13¼
2743 A579 5000g multi   3.50 3.50

World of the Guaranís A580

Designs: 700g, Monday Waterfalls. 6000g, Entrance to Ciudad de Tobati.

2004, July 7
2744-2745 A580 Set of 2   4.00 4.00
Nos. 2744 and 2745 were issued in sheets of 15 stamps and 10 labels.

Independence House — A581

Dr. Carlos Pussineri and: 700g, Mural by José Laterza Parodi. 5000g, Independence House.

2004, Aug. 13   Litho.   Perf. 13¼
2746-2747 A581 Set of 2   4.00 4.00

José Asunción Flores (1904-72), Composer — A582

2004, Aug. 24   Litho.   Perf. 13¼
2748 A582 5000g multi   3.50 3.50

Museo del Barro, 25th Anniv. — A583

Designs: 2000g, Painting by Enrique Careaga. 3000g, Anthropomorphic jug, vert. 4000g, Christ of the Column, vert.

2004, Aug. 26
2749-2751 A583 Set of 3   6.00 6.00
For overprint see No. 2799.

Paraguayan Railroads, 150th Anniv. — A584

Designs: 2000g, Locomotive No. 151, Camello. 3000g, Locomotive No. 104, El Coqueto, horiz. 6000g, Locomotiove No. 10, Sapucai, horiz.

2004, Sept. 22   Perf. 13¼
2752-2753 A584 Set of 2   3.00 3.00
Souvenir Sheet
Rouletted 5¼
2754 A584 6000g multi   5.00 5.00
No. 2754 contains one 50x40mm stamp.

America Issue — Environmental Protection A585

Designs: No. 2755, Procnias nudicollis. No. 2756, Ceratophrys cranwelli.

2004, Oct. 11   Litho.   Perf. 13¼
2755 A585 6000g multi   3.50 3.50
Souvenir Sheet
Rouletted 5¼
2756 A585 6000g multi   5.00 5.00

Water Conservation A586

Designs: 3000g, Felis pardalis, storks, telephone poles. 4000g, Myrmecophaga

tridactyla, Hydrochoerus hydrochaeris, Chauna torquata.

2004, Oct. 22
2757-2758 A586 Set of 2   7.00 7.00

Crops — A587

Designs: 2000g, Corn. 4000g, Cotton. 6000g, Soybeans.

2004, Oct. 22   Litho.   Perf. 13¼
2759-2761 A587 Set of 3   6.50 6.50

Christmas A588

Paintings by Ricardo Migliorisi: 3000g, Madonna and Child. 5000g, Angel, vert.

2004, Nov. 12
2762-2763 A588 Set of 2   5.50 5.50

Latin American Parliament, 40th Anniv. — A589

2004, Nov. 16
2764 A589 4000g multi + label   2.50 2.50
For overprint, see No. 3006.

Itaipú Dam, 30th Anniv. — A590

Designs: 4000g, Dam and spillway. 5000g, Aerial view of dam, vert.

2004, Dec. 10   Litho.   Perf. 13¼
2765-2766 A590 Set of 2   5.00 5.00

Rotary International, Cent. — A591

Jesuit Mission ruins, Trinidad: 3000g, Building ruins. 4000g, Religious statue, vert.

2005, Feb. 23   Litho.   Perf. 13¼
2767-2768 A591 Set of 2   4.50 4.50

Castelvi House, Asunción, 200th Anniv. — A592

2005, Mar. 14
2769 A592 5000g multi   3.00 3.00

Herminio Giménez (1905-91), Conductor A593

2005, Apr. 22
2770 A593 700g multi   .50   .50

Cabildo Cultural Center, Asunción, 1st Anniv. — A594

2005, May 19
2771 A594 1000g multi   .70   .70

Fernheim Colony, 75th Anniv. — A595

Designs: 5000g, Pioneer's Monument. 6000g, Cross, cactus, oxcart.

2005, June 15   *Perf. 13¼*
2772 A595 5000g multi   3.50 3.50
     Souvenir Sheet
     Rouletted 5¼
2773 A595 6000g multi   3.50 3.50

Libertad Soccer Team, Cent. A596

Illustration reduced.

2005, July 20   *Perf. 13¼*
2774 A596 700g multi + label   .50   .50

Publication of Don Quixote, 400th Anniv. — A597

2005, July 26
2775 A597 8000g multi   5.00 5.00

Writers — A598

Designs: 3000g, Herib Campos Cervera (1905-53), poet. 5000g, Gabriel Casaccia (1907-80), novelist.

2005, July 27
2776-2777 A598   Set of 2   5.00 5.00

Pope John Paul II (1920-2005) A599

2005, Aug. 18
2778 A599 2000g multi   2.00 2.00

Truth and Justice — A600

2005, Aug. 23
2779 A600 8000g multi   4.50 4.50

America Issue, Fight Against Poverty — A601

Designs: 5000g, Women selling vegetables. 6000g, Cobbler.

2005, Aug. 31
2780-2781 A601   Set of 2   6.50 6.50

Dogs and Cats — A602

Designs: No. 2782, 2000g, Samoyed. No. 2783, 2000g, Three European cats. No. 2784, 3000g, Doberman pinscher. No. 2785, 3000g, White European cat.

2005, Oct. 7
2782-2785 A602   Set of 4   6.00 6.00

Anthropologists A603

Designs: 1000g, Branislava Susnik, bracelet. 2000g, Miguel Chase-Sardi, poncho. 8000g, León Cadogan, basket.

2005, Oct. 26
2786-2788 A603   Set of 3   6.50 6.50

Intl. Year of Sports and Physical Education A604

Designs: 5000g, Lucy Aguero throwing hammer and javelin. 6000g, Golfer Carlos Franco.

2005, Nov. 9   *Perf. 13¼*
2789 A604 5000g multi   3.00 3.00
     Souvenir Sheet
     Rouletted 5¼
2790 A604 6000g multi   5.00 5.00

Christmas — A605

Designs: 700g, Angels, people celebrating Christmas, rooftops. 5000g, Nativity scene.

2005, Nov. 22   *Perf. 13¼*
2791-2792 A605   Set of 2   3.50 3.50

Yacyreta Dam — A606

Various views of dam: 3000g, 5000g.

2005, Nov. 28
2793-2794 A606   Set of 2   4.75 4.75

Ministry of Defense, 150th Anniv. — A607

Designs: 700g, Monument to the Residents, by Javier Báez Rolón. 1000g, Defense Ministry Building, Marshal Francisco Solano López.

2005, Dec. 21
2795-2796 A607   Set of 2   1.25 1.25

Nos. 2736-2737 Overprinted

2005, Dec. 28   *Perf. 13¼*
2797 A575 5000g On #2736   3.00 3.00
2798 A575 5000g On #2737   3.00 3.00

No. 2751 Overprinted

2005, Dec. 28   *Perf. 13¼*
2799 A583 4000g On #2751   2.40 2.40

Paraguay — Germany Chamber of Commerce and Industry, 50th Anniv. — A608

2006, Mar. 14
2800 A608 8000g multi   5.00 5.00

2006 World Cup Soccer Championships, Germany — A609

Emblem and: 3000g, Paraguayan team. 5000g, World Cup.

2006, May 17   **Litho.**   *Perf. 13¼*
2801-2802 A609   Set of 2   5.00 5.00

French Alliance of Asuncion, 50th Anniv. — A610

2006, June 20
2803 A610 8000g multi + label   5.00 5.00

Cervantes Club, 50th Anniv. — A611

2006, June 27
2804 A611 700g multi   .60   .60

Paraguayan Soccer Association, Cent. — A612

2006, Aug. 1
2805 A612 1000g multi   .75   .75

National Commerce School, Cent. — A613

2006, Sept. 7
2806 A613 700g multi   .65   .65

Japanese Emigration to Paraguay, 70th Anniv. — A614

Flags of Paraguay and Japan and butterflies: 1000g, Junonia evarete. 2000g, Anartia jatrophae. 3000g, Agraulis vanillae. 6000g, Danaus plexippus.

2006, Sept. 8   *Perf. 13¼*
2807-2809 A614   Set of 3   4.00 4.00
     Souvenir Sheet
     Rouletted 5¼
2810 A614 6000g multi   5.00 5.00
No. 2810 contains one 50x40mm stamp.

OPEC Intl. Development Fund, 30th Anniv. — A615

2006, Sept. 18   *Perf. 13¼*
2811 A615 8000g multi   5.00 5.00

Tuparenda Shrine, 25th Anniv. — A616

2006, Oct. 9
2812 A616 700g multi   .50 .50

America Issue, Energy Conservation A617

Designs: 5000g, Windmills. 6000g, Solar collector.

2006, Oct. 11
2813-2814 A617   Set of 2   6.50 6.50

Agronomy and Veterinary Medicine Faculties of Asuncion National University, 50th Anniv. — A618

Designs: No. 2815, 4000g, Symbols of agronomy. No. 2816, 4000g, Livestock.

2006, Oct. 20
2815-2816 A618   Set of 2   5.00 5.00

South American Soccer Confederation, 90th Anniv. — A619

2006, Nov. 6
2817 A619 8000g multi   5.00 5.00

Musical Instruments A620

Designs: 5000g, Harp. 6000g, Guitar.

2006, Nov. 10
2818-2819 A620   Set of 2   6.50 6.50

Christmas — A621

Designs: 4000g, Our Lady of Asuncion Cathedral. 6000g, Holy Trinity Church, horiz.

2006, Nov. 17
2820-2821 A621   Set of 2   6.00 6.00

First Lieutenant Adolfo Rojas Silva (1906-27), Military Hero — A622

Designs: 4000g, Rojas Silva and hut. 6000g, Rojas Silva, vert.

2007, Feb. 27   Litho.
2822-2823 A622   Set of 2   6.50 6.50

B'nai B'rith of Paraguay, 50th Anniv. — A623

2007, Mar. 29   *Perf. 13¼*
2824 A623 8000g multi   5.00 5.00

Junior Chamber International Conference, Asuncion A624

2007, Apr. 18
2825 A624 8000g multi   5.00 5.00

World Tobacco-Free Day — A625

Emblem and: 5000g, Person wearing gas mask. 6000g, Map of Paraguay with umbrella, vert.

2007, May 30
2826-2827 A625   Set of 2   6.50 6.50

Arlequin Theater, Asuncion, 25th Anniv. — A626

2007, June 11
2828 A626 700g multi   .60 .60

Paz del Chaco 07 Philatelic Exhibition, Asuncion A627

Exhibition emblem and: 700g, Felis pardalis. 8000g, Chaco War postman riding cow.

2007, June 11
2829-2830 A627   Set of 2   5.00 5.00

Diplomatic Relations Between Paraguay and South Korea, 45th Anniv. — A628

Flags of Paraguay and South Korea and: 1000g, Open horse-drawn wagon. 2000g, Covered horse-drawn carriage. 3000g, Ox cart, vert. 6000g, Mugungfa flower.

2007, June 15   *Perf. 13¼*
2831-2833 A628   Set of 3   3.50 3.50
Souvenir Sheet
Rouletted 7¼
2834 A628 6000g multi   5.00 5.00
No. 2834 contains one 50x40mm stamp.

Friendship Between Paraguay and Republic of China, 50th Anniv. — A628a

2007, July 8   *Perf. 13¼*
2834A A628a 7000g multi + 2 flanking labels   4.25 4.25

Diplomatic Relations Between Paraguay and Indonesia, 25th Anniv. — A629

2007, July 9
2835 A629 11,000g multi   6.50 6.50

Official Veterinary Service, 40th Anniv. — A630

Designs: 5000g, Prize-winning cow. 7000g, Veterinarian inspecting cow, cattle herd, prize-winning cow, horiz.

2007, June 11
2836-2837 A630   Set of 2   7.00 7.00

Peace Corps in Paraguay, 40th Anniv. — A631

2007, Sept. 19
2838 A631 7000g multi   4.50 4.50

Scouting, Cent. — A632

Designs: 700g, Scouts near campfire. 6000g, Lord Robert Baden-Powell, female Scouts.

2007, Oct. 11
2839-2840 A632   Set of 2   4.00 4.00

Institute of Fine Arts, 50th Anniv. — A633

Designs: 4000g, Pendants, by Engelberto Giménez Legal. 8000g, Sculpture by Hugo Pistilli, vert.

2007, Nov. 20
2841-2842 A633   Set of 2   7.00 7.00

Gabriel Casaccia Bibolini (1907-80), Writer — A634

2007, Nov. 23
2843 A634 8000g multi   5.00 5.00

Marco Aguayo Foundation, 15th Anniv. — A635

Designs: 1000g, Dr. Marco Aguayo (1956-92), red ribbon. 8000g, Red ribbon and geometrical design.

2007, Dec. 11
2844-2845 A635   Set of 2   5.50 5.50

Dr. Nicolas Leoz Stadium A636

2007, Oct. 22
2846 A636 700g multi   1.00 1.00

Gen. Martin T. McMahon (1838-1906), US Minister to Paraguay — A637

2007, Sept. 19
2847 A637 700g multi   .50 .50

Intl. Day of Deserts and Desertification (in 2006) — A638

2007, Nov. 28
2848 A638 7000g multi   4.00 4.00

Parks and Reserves A639

Designs: 3000g, Nú Guazú Park, Luque. 6000g, Monkey.

2007, Nov. 27   *Perf. 13¼*
2849 A639 3000g multi   1.90 1.90
Souvenir Sheet
Rouletted 7¼
2850 A639 6000g multi   4.00 4.00
No. 2850 contains one 50x40mm stamp.

America Issue, Education for All — A640

Teachers and school children in class: 5000g, 6000g.

2007, Sept. 3   *Perf. 13¼*
2851-2852 A640   Set of 2   6.50 6.50

Architecture — A641

Designs: 6000g, Nautilus Building, by Genaro Pindú. 7000g, Museo del Barro, by Carlos Colombino.

2007, Sept. 3
2853-2854 A641 Set of 2 8.00 8.00

Christmas A642

Designs: 700g, Coconut flower. 8000g, Creche figures.

2007, Nov. 29 Litho. Perf. 13¼
2855-2856 A642 Set of 2 5.00 5.00

Paraguayan Atheneum, 125th Anniv. — A643

2008, July 28
2857 A643 700g multi .60 .60

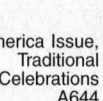

America Issue, Traditional Celebrations A644

2008, July 30
2858 A644 11,000g multi 7.50 7.50

Nasta Publicity Agency, 40th Anniv. — A645

Designs: 700g, Flower. 5000g, Flower, vert.

2008, Apr. 1
2859-2860 A645 Set of 2 3.50 3.50

Scouting in Paraguay, 70th Anniv. — A646

Designs: 3000g, Three scouts, tent. 4000g, Scout troop.

2008, Oct. 11
2861-2862 A646 Set of 2 4.75 4.75

Asuncion Rotary Club, 80th Anniv. — A647

Rotary International emblem and: 2000g, Stylized gearwheels. 8000g, Forest path, horiz.

2008, Apr. 4
2863-2864 A647 Set of 2 6.50 6.50

Birds — A648

Designs: 5000g, Coryphospingus cucullatus. 6000g, Pitangus sulphuratus.

2008, July 28
2865-2866 A648 Set of 2 7.50 7.50

Christmas — A649

Paintings: 700g, Madonna and Child, by unknown artist. 5000g, Madonna and Child, by José Laterza Parodi.

2008, Oct. 9
2867-2868 A649 Set of 2 4.00 4.00

Carter-Torrijos Treaty, 30th Anniv. (in 2007) — A650

Designs: 700g, Signing ceremony. 7000g, Panamanian General Omar Torrijos, U.S. President Jimmy Carter, ship in Panama Canal.

2008, Aug. 5
2869-2870 A650 Set of 2 5.00 5.00

City of Coronel Oviedo, 250th Anniv. — A651

Cotton boll and: 3000g, Cathedral. 7000g, Road.

2008, Oct. 28
2871-2872 A651 Set of 2 7.00 7.00

Arbitration Decision of Pres. Rutherford B. Hayes in Chaco Land Dispute in Favor of Paraguay, 130th Anniv. — A652

2008, Nov. 10 Litho. Perf. 13¼
2873 A652 1000g multi .75 .75

SOS Children's Village, Asuncion, 25th Anniv. — A653

SOS Children's Village emblem and: 2000g, Children and flower. 7000g, Red, white and blue ribbon.

2008, Nov. 18 Litho. Perf. 13¼
2874-2875 A653 Set of 2 6.50 6.50

Year of the Harp — A654

2008, Oct. 20 Perf. 13¼x13½
2876 A654 5000g multi 3.50 3.50

Schoenstatt Movement in Paraguay, 50th Anniv. — A655

2009, Oct. 18 Perf. 13¼
2877 A655 3000g multi 1.90 1.90

Christmas — A656

Designs: 800g, Our Lady of Caacupé. 5000g, Our Lady of Asunción.

2009, Dec. 1
2878-2879 A656 Set of 2 3.75 3.75

Dr. José Segundo Decoud (1848-1909), Politician and Journalist A657

2009, Dec. 3
2880 A657 7000g multi 5.00 5.00

Exports A658

Designs: 2000g, Nelore cow. 5000g, Stevia rebaudiana.

2009, Dec. 18
2881-2882 A658 Set of 2 4.50 4.50

Arsenio Erico (1915-77), Soccer Player — A659

Erico: 700g, Kicking soccer ball. 1000g, Holding four soccer balls, vert.

2009, Dec. 22
2883-2884 A659 Set of 2 1.20 1.20

Ceryle Torquata A660

2009
2885 A660 7000g multi 3.00 3.00
Charles Darwin (1809-82), naturalist. Printed in sheets of 15 + 10 labels.

Diplomatic Relations Between Paraguay and Russia, Cent. — A661

2009
2886 A661 7000g multi 3.00 3.00
Printed in sheets of 15 + 10 labels.

America Issue, Children's Games — A662

Children: 4000g, Spinning top. 7000g, Playing marbles, horiz.

2010, Jan. 2
2887-2888 A662 Set of 2 7.50 7.50

Independence, Bicent. — A663

Designs: 700g, Governor's House. 2000g, Painting by Jaime Bestard.

2010, Feb. 23
2889-2890 A663 Set of 2 2.10 2.10

Astronomy Aided By Telescopes, 400th Anniv. — A664

2010, Mar. 3
2891 A664 2500g multi 1.90 1.90
Printed in sheets of 15 + 10 labels.

2010 World Cup Soccer Championships, South Africa — A665

Designs: 700g, Paraguayan players. 6000g, Team, crowd holding Paraguayan flags.

2010, July 2 Litho. Perf. 13¼
2892 A665 700g multi + label — —
2893 A665 6000g multi — —

America Issue — A666

National symbols: 5000g, National anthem. 6000g, Flag and emblems, horiz.

2010, Oct. 9 **Litho.** ***Perf. 13¼***
2894-2895 A666 Set of 2 7.00 7.00

Christmas A667

Designs: 700g, Magi following Star of Bethlehem. 6000g, Nativity, vert. 11,000g, Journey to Bethlehem.

2010, Nov. 19
2896-2898 A667 Set of 3 11.50 11.50

Road Safety Day — A668

2010
2899 A668 700g multi .60 .60

Famous Paraguayan Buildings A669

Designs: 700g, Venancio López Palace. 2000g, Residencia Patri.

2010, Dec. 17
2900-2901 A669 Set of 2 1.75 1.75

2010 Youth Olymmpics, Singapore A670

Emblem and: 2000g, Diego Galeano Harrison, tennis player. 5000g, Paraguayan athletes.

2010, Dec. 31
2902-2903 A670 Set of 2 5.00 5.00

Decade for Culture of Peace — A671

Designs: 2000g, Hand below rose. 6000g, Hand holding rose.

2010, Dec. 31
2904-2905 A671 Set of 2 5.25 5.25

Postal Union of the Americas, Spain and Portugal (UPAEP), Cent. — A672

Designs: 6000g, Map of South and Central America, Spain and Portugal with flags. 11,000g, Building and flags, horiz.

2011, Mar. 18
2906-2907 A672 Set of 2 11.00 11.00

Dated 2010.

National Development Bank, 50th Anniv. — A673

2011, Apr. 12 ***Perf. 13¼***
2908 A673 700g multi + label .60 .60

Republic of China, Cent. A674

No. 2909: a, National Pantheon of Heroes, Paraguay. b, Pantheon of the Martyrs of the National Revolution, Taiwan.

2011, Apr. 24 **Litho.**
2909 A674 6000g Horiz. pair, #a-b, + central label 8.50 8.50

Asunción Buildings — A675

No. 2910: a, Asunción, Cathedral. b, Train station. c, Governmental Palace. d, Municipal Theater. e, Town Hall (Cabildo).
11,000g, Independence House, horiz.

2011, May 6 ***Perf. 13¼***
2910 Horiz. strip of 5 + flanking label 3.50 3.50
a.-e. A675 1000g Any single .65 .65

Souvenir Sheet

Rouletted

2911 A675 11,000g multi 7.75 7.75

Marie Curie (1867-1934), Chemist and Physicist — A676

2011, May 9 ***Perf. 13¼***
2912 A676 2000g multi + label 1.75 1.75

Intl. Year of Chemistry.

Campaign Against Violence Towards Women — A677

2011, Apr. 29 **Litho.** ***Perf. 13¼***
2913 A677 700g multi + label .60 .60

Souvenir Sheet

Beatification of Pope John Paul II — A678

2011, May 9 **Litho.** ***Rouletted 1¼***
2914 A678 10,000g multi 7.25 7.25

Masons in Paraguay, 140th Anniv. — A679

2011, May 25 **Litho.** ***Perf. 13¼***
2915 A679 11,000g multi + label 8.00 8.00

Intl. Friendship Day — A680

2011, Nov. 8 **Litho.** ***Perf. 13¼***
2916 A680 700g multi + label .60 .60

Radio Cáritas, 75th Anniv. A681

2011, Nov. 21 **Litho.** ***Perf. 13¼***
2917 A681 700g multi + label .55 .55

San José Academy, Cent. — A682

2011, Nov. 29 **Litho.** ***Perf. 13¼***
2918 A682 700g multi + label .55 .55

America Issue A683

No. 2919: a, 5000g, Red mailbox. b, 6000g, Green mailbox.

2011, Dec. 13 **Litho.** ***Perf. 13¼***
2919 A683 Horiz. pair, #a-b 8.25 8.25

Campaign Against AIDS, 30th Anniv. — A684

2011, Dec. 13 **Litho.** ***Perf. 13¼***
2920 A684 1000g multi + label .85 .85

Intl. Year of Forests — A685

Designs: 5000g, Animals and forest. 6000g, Trees and map of North and South America.

2011, Dec. 13 **Litho.** ***Perf. 13¼***
2921 A685 5000g multi 4.00 4.00

Souvenir Sheet

Rouletted 4

2922 A685 6000g multi 4.75 4.75

Actors and Actresses — A686

Designs: 2000g, Map of Paraguay, Perlita Fernández (1951-2002), César Alvarez Blanco (1927-2003), Máxima Lugo (1925-91), José Olitte (1937-2000). 6000g, Edda de los Rios (1942-2007).

2011, Dec. 13 **Litho.** ***Perf. 13¼***
2923 A686 2000g multi + label 1.60 1.60

Souvenir Sheet

Rouletted 5

2924 A686 6000g multi 4.75 4.75

A687

Christmas — A688

Designs: 700g, Star of Bethlehem and Magi. 5000g, Star of Bethlehem and manger. 11,000g, Holy Family and lambs.

2011, Dec. 13 **Litho.** ***Perf. 13¼***

2925	A687	700g multi	.50	.50
2926	A687	5000g multi	3.25	3.25
2927	A688	11,000g multi	6.50	6.50
		Nos. 2925-2927 (3)	10.25	10.25

Campaign Against Terrorism — A689

No. 2928 — Handprint in: a, 2000g, Black. b, 5000g, White.

2011, Dec. 30　Litho.　Perf. 13¼
2928 A689　Horiz. pair, #a-b　5.50 5.50

A690

2011 Copa America Soccer Tournament, Argentina A691

2011, Dec. 30　Litho.　Perf. 13¼
2929 A690　700g multi + label　.55 .55
2930 A691　6000g multi　4.75 4.75

José Luis Chilavert, Soccer Player, Estaban Casarino, Squash Player, Olegario Farrés, Shooter, Juan Carlos Giménez, Boxer — A692

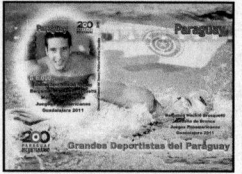

Benjamin Hockin Brusquetti, Swimmer — A693

2011, Dec. 30　Litho.　Perf. 13¼
2931 A692　700g multi + label　.55 .55
Souvenir Sheet
Rouletted 5x6
2932 A693　6000g multi　4.75 4.75

Miniature Sheet

Expo 2012, Yeosu, South Korea A694

No. 2933, 2000g — Expo 2012 emblem and: a, Small waterfall in Ybycuí National Park. b, Karapa Waterfall. c, Large waterfall in Ybycuí National Park. d, Monday Waterfall. e, Cristal Waterfall,

2012, May 28　Litho.　Perf. 13¼
2933 A694　2000g Sheet of 5, #a-e, + 25 labels　7.75 7.75

Souvenir Sheet

National Police Band, Cent. A695

2012, June 1　Litho.　Rouletted 5
2934 A695　7000g multi　5.50 5.50

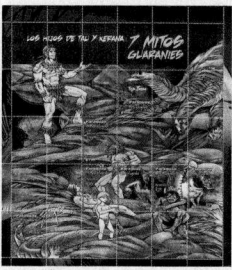

Myths and Legends A696

No. 2935 — Guarani monsters: a, Teju Jagua. b, Moñai. c, Jasy Jatere. d, Luisón. e, Kurupi. f, Ao Ao. g, Mbói Tui. 7000p, Kerana, horiz.

2012, June 7　Litho.　Perf. 13¼
2935 A696　1000g Sheet of 7, #a-g, + 23 labels　5.50 5.50

Souvenir Sheet
Rouletted 5
2936 A696　7000g multi　5.50 5.50

America Issue.

Souvenir Sheets

Korean and Paraguayan Dancers — A697

Paraguayan Dancers — A698

Korean Dancers A699

2012, June 26　Litho.　Rouletted 5
2937 A697　2000g multi　1.75 1.75
2938 A698　2000g multi　1.75 1.75
2939 A699　2000g multi　1.75 1.75
　Nos. 2937-2939 (3)　5.25 5.25

Diplomatic relations between Paraguay and South Korea, 50th anniv.

Authentic Radical Liberal Party, 125th Anniv. A700

Party flag and: 2000g, Anodorhynchus hyacinthinus. 16,000g, Morpho peleides.

2012, July 14　Litho.　Perf. 13¼
Stamp + Label
2940-2941 A700　Set of 2　14.00 14.00

2012 Summer Olympics, London — A701

No. 2942 — Paraguayan flag, emblem of Paraguayan Olympic Committee and: a, Judo.

---

b, Javelin. c, Running. d, Tennis. e, Table tennis. f, Rowing and swimming.
No. 2943, 4000g, Paraguayan flag, emblem of Paraguayan Olympic Committee, Marcelo Aguirre, table tennis player, and Benjamin Hockin Busquetti, swimmer. No. 2944, 4000g, Paraguayan flag, emblem of Paraguayan Olympic Committee and various athletes.

2012, Aug. 9　Litho.　Perf. 13¼
2942　Horiz. strip of 6　5.50 5.50
　a.-f.　A701 1000g Any single　.90 .90
Souvenir Sheets
Rouletted 5
2943-2944 A701　Set of 2　7.50 7.50

Paraguayan Academy of History, 75th Anniv. — A702

No. 2945 — Academy emblem, building and: a, Ruy Díaz de Guzmán (c. 1558-1692), conquistador and historian. b, Dr. Manuel Domínguez (1868-1935), Vice-President of Paraguay and writer. c, Dr. Fulgencio R. Moreno (1872-1933), historian. d, Dr. Efraím Cardozo (1906-73), historian. e, Dr. Rafael E. Velázquez (1926-94), historian.

2012, Aug. 10　Litho.　Perf. 13¼
2945　Horiz. strip of 5　5.50 5.50
　a.-e.　A702 1400g Any single　1.10 1.10

Souvenir Sheet

Asunción, 475th Anniv. — A703

2012, Aug. 14　Litho.　Rouletted 5
2946 A703　10,000g multi　7.00 7.00

Souvenir Sheet

Locomotive — A704

2012, Aug. 14　Litho.　Rouletted 5
2947 A704　8000g multi　6.00 6.00

Carlos Antonio López (1792-1862), first President of Paraguay.

National University of Asunción Economic Sciences Faculty, 75th Anniv. — A705

2012, Aug. 22　Litho.　Perf. 13¼
2948 A705　1400g multi　1.10 1.10

Technical Planning Ministry, 50th Anniv. A706

2012, Sept. 17　Litho.　Perf. 13¼
2949 A706　8000g multi + label　6.00 6.00

Cerro Porteño Basketball Team — A707

Cerro Porteño Soccer Team A708

2012, Oct. 1　Litho.　Perf. 13¼
2950 A707　1000g multi　.80 .80
2951 A708　6000g multi + label　4.25 4.25

Cerro Porteño Sports Club, cent.

Independence of Slovakia, 20th Anniv. — A709

2012, Nov. 13　Litho.　Perf. 13¼
2952 A709　11,000g multi + label　8.25 8.25

No. 2952 was printed in sheets of 10 stamps + 15 labels.

First National Eucharistic Congress, 75th Anniv. — A710

2012, Nov. 19　Litho.　Perf. 13¼
2953 A710　3000g multi + label　2.25 2.25

Ardea Alba A711

2012, Nov. 20　Litho.　Perf. 13¼
2954 A711　1400g multi + label　1.10 1.10

Completion of new dam near Encarnacion. No. 2954 was printed in sheets containing 10 stamps + 15 labels.

Radio Nanduti, 50th Anniv. A712

2012, Nov. 29　Litho.　Perf. 13¼
2955 A712　1400g multi + label　1.10 1.10

United Nations Environmental Program, 40th Anniv. — A713

Designs: 3000g, Butorides striatus. 16,000g, Platalea ajaja.

2012, Dec. 18　Litho.　Perf. 13¼
2956 A713　3000g multi　2.25 2.25
Souvenir Sheet
Rouletted 5
2957 A713　16,000g multi　12.00 12.00

Christmas
A714

No. 2958 — Various creche figures: a,
1000g. b, 5000g. c, 11,000g.

2012, Dec. 18   Litho.   Perf. 13¼
2958 A714   Vert. strip of 3,
#a-c   13.00 13.00

National
Library, 125th
Anniv. — A715

2012, Dec. 27   Litho.   Perf. 13¼
2959 A715 1400g multi   1.10 1.10

Alternative Energy
Sources — A716

No. 2960: a, Wind energy (wind turbines). b,
Solar energy (solar collector). c, Biodiesel (jatropha tree). d, Biomass (hay roll). e, Biodiesel
(corn).
3000g, Biodiesel (sunflower), horiz.

2012, Dec. 27   Litho.   Perf. 13¼
2960   Horiz. strip of 5   6.00 6.00
a.-e. A716 1500g Any single   1.20 1.20
Souvenir Sheet
Rouletted 5
2961 A716 3000g multi   2.25 2.25

First Tramway in
Paraguay,
Cent. — A717

No. 2962: a, Van following tram. b, Motorcyclist and tram.
7000p, Line 5 tram, vert.

2013, Aug. 19   Litho.   Perf. 13¼
2962   Horiz. pair + central label   1.90 1.90
a.-b. A717 2000g Either single   .95 .95
Souvenir Sheet
Rouletted 5
2963 A717 7000g multi   3.25 3.25

Paraguayan-Japanese Center,
Asuncion — A718

No. 2964: a, Building exterior and flags. b,
Cherry blossoms.

2013, Aug. 19   Litho.   Perf. 13¼
2964   Horiz. pair + central label   8.75 8.75
a. A718 1400g multi   1.00 1.00
b. A718 11,000g multi   7.75 7.75

Birds — A719

No. 2965: a, Dendrocygna viduata. b,
Amazona aestiva. c, Chlorostilbon aureoven-
tris. d, Jabiru mycteria. e, Zenaida auriculata.
f, Athene cunicularia. g, Aramides ypecaha. h,
Dendrocygna autumnalis. i, Caracara plancus.
j, Vanellus chilensis.

2013, Aug. 19   Litho.   Perf. 13¼
2965   Block of 10   15.00 15.00
a.-j. A719 2000g Any single   1.50 1.50

Mammals
A720

No. 2966: a, Lycalopex gymnocercus. b,
Myrmecophaga tridactyla. c, Cebus apella
paraguayanus. d, Tayassu pecari. e, Nasua
nasua.
6000g, Panthera onca, vert.

2013, Aug. 19   Litho.   Perf. 13¼
2966   Horiz. strip of 5   10.00 10.00
a.-e. A720 3000g Any single   2.00 2.00
Souvenir Sheet
Rouletted 5
2967 A720 6000g multi   4.50 4.50

Scouting in
Paraguay,
Cent. — A721

No. 2968: a, Group of Scouts. b, Scouts
running.

2013, Aug. 23   Litho.   Perf. 13¼
2968   Horiz. pair + central label   9.50 9.50
a. A721 5000g multi   3.75 3.75
b. A721 8000g multi   5.75 5.75

Rubio Nú
Soccer Team,
Cent. — A722

Designs: 1400g, Six palyers celebrating.
6000g, Team photograph.

2013, Aug. 24   Litho.   Perf. 13¼
2969-2970 A722   Set of 2   5.50 5.50

Flowers — A723

No. 2971 — Inscriptions at LL: a, Azahar. b,
Aguape. c, Agosto Poty. d, Chivato Poty. e,
Santa Lucia. f, Ceibo.
No. 2972, 10,000g, Samu'u (yellow flower),
horiz. No. 2973, 10,000g, Mburucuja (blue
flower), horiz.

2013, Sept. 17   Litho.   Perf. 13¼
2971   Horiz. strip of 6   21.00 21.00
a.-f. A723 5000g Any single   3.50 3.50
Souvenir Sheets
Rouletted 5
2972-2973 A723   Set of 2   16.00 16.00

Agustín Barboza
(1913-98),
Musician — A724

Barboza: 1400g, Holding neck of guitar.
4000g, Playing guitar.

2013, Oct. 9   Litho.   Perf. 13¼
2974-2975 A724   Set of 2   4.00 4.00

Campaign Against
Discrimination
A725

Paintings by Juan de Dios Valdez depicting:
5000g, Old man. 10,000g, Old woman.

2013, Oct. 9   Litho.   Perf. 13¼
2976 A725 5000g multi   3.50 3.50
Souvenir Sheet
Rouletted 5
2977 A725 10,000g multi   7.00 7.00
America Issue.

Republic of Paraguay, 200th
Anniv. — A726

200th Anniv. emblem and: 1000g, Map of
Asuncion, 1809. 8000g, Consuls Fulgencio
Yegros (1780-1821) and Dr. José Gaspar de
Francia (1766-1840), vert.

2013, Oct. 12   Litho.   Perf. 13¼
2978 A726 1000g multi + label   .75 .75
Souvenir Sheet
Rouletted 5
2979 A726 8000g multi   5.75 5.75

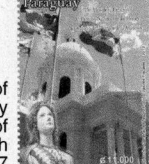

National Pantheon of
Heroes and Oratory
of Our Lady of
Asuncion, 150th
Anniv. — A727

Design: 6000g Building's dome and flags,
horiz.

2013, Nov. 1   Litho.   Perf. 13¼
2980 A727 11,000g multi   8.00 8.00
Souvenir Sheet
Rouletted 5
2981 A727 6000p multi   2.75 2.75

Paraguayan
Atheneum,
130th
Anniv. — A728

2013, Dec. 5   Litho.   Perf. 13¼
2982 A728 1400g multi   1.00 1.00

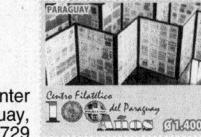

Philatelic Center
of Paraguay,
Cent. — A729

2013, Dec. 6   Litho.   Perf. 13¼
2983 A729 1400g multi   1.00 1.00

Christmas — A730

Designs: 3000g, Virgin Mary and St.
Joseph. 8000g, Holy Family creche figurines.
16,000g, Creche figurines, horiz.

2013, Dec. 6   Litho.   Perf. 13¼
2984-2986 A730   Set of 3   19.00 19.00

Paraguayan postal officials declared
as "illegal" two blocks of nine stamps
and two souvenir sheets of four dated
2013 and inscribed "Winter War."

Encarnación,
400th Anniv. (in
2015) — A731

Designs: 3000g, Mirador San José, Virgin of
Itacuá. 11,000g, Woman in Carnaval costume,
vert.

2014, Feb. 6   Litho.   Perf. 13¼
2987 A731 3000g multi   2.10 2.10
Souvenir Sheet
Rouletted 5
2988 A731 11,000g multi   8.00 8.00

Asuncion
Tennis Club,
Cent. — A732

2014, Mar. 4   Litho.   Perf. 13¼
2989 A732 1400g multi   1.00 1.00

Villeta,
300th
Anniv.
A733

2014, Mar. 5   Litho.   Perf. 13¼
2990 A733 1400g multi + label   1.00 1.00

Campaign Against
Violence Towards
Women — A734

2014, Mar. 7   Litho.   Perf. 13¼
2991 A734 700g multi   .50 .50

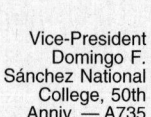

Vice-President Domingo F. Sánchez National College, 50th Anniv. — A735

2014, Mar. 28   Litho.   Perf. 13¼
2992 A735 1400g multi   1.00 1.00

Jorge Castro, Singer — A736

Castro: 1400g, On horse. 5000g, With orchestra.

2014, Apr. 25   Litho.   Perf. 13¼
2993 A736 1400g multi   1.00 1.00

Souvenir Sheet
Rouletted 5
2994 A736 5000g multi   3.50 3.50

Cabildo Cultural Center, Asuncion, 10th Anniv. — A737

2014, May 13   Litho.   Perf. 13¼
2995 A737 1400g multi   1.00 1.00

Itaipu Dam and Speothos Venaticus A738

2014, May 20   Litho.   Perf. 13¼
2996 A738 16,000g multi   11.00 11.00
Itaipu Binacional, 40th anniv.

44th General Assembly of the Organization of American States, Asuncion — A739

2014, June 5   Litho.   Perf. 13¼
2997 A739 5000g multi + label   3.50 3.50

Pope Francis and Map of South America A740

2014, June 27   Litho.   Perf. 13¼
2998 A740 9000g multi   6.00 6.00

Gen. José Gervasio Artigas (1764-1850), National Hero of Uruguay — A741

2014, July 18   Litho.   Perf. 13¼
2999 A741 4000g multi + label   2.75 2.75

Salvador Cabañas and Emblem of 12 de Octubre Soccer Team A742

2014, Aug. 8   Litho.   Perf. 13¼
3000 A742 1400g multi + label   1.00 1.00
12 de Octubre Soccer Team, cent.

Apostolic Movement of Schoenstatt, Cent. — A743

2014, Oct. 6   Litho.   Perf. 13¼
3001 A743 3000g multi + label   2.00 2.00

Paraguayan Presidents — A744

Designs: 1400g, José Félix Estigarribia (1888-1940). 4000g, Bernardino Caballero (1839-1912)

2014, Oct. 9   Litho.   Perf. 13¼
3002-3003 A744 Set of 2   3.75 3.75
America issue.

Telecommunications in Paraguay, 150th Anniv. — A745

2014, Oct. 9   Litho.   Perf. 13¼
3004 A745 9000g multi + label   6.00 6.00

Asuncion Zoo and Botanical Gardens, Cent. — A746

No. 3005: a, Ara ararauna. b, Rhea americana.

2014, Oct. 15   Litho.   Perf. 13¼
3005 Horiz. pair + central label   9.00 9.00
  a. A746 3000g multi   2.00 2.00
  b. A746 10,000g multi   7.00 7.00

No. 2764 Overprinted

Method and Perf. As Before
2014, Oct. 16
3006 A589 4000g multi + label   2.75 2.75
Latin American Parliament, 50th anniv.

Asuncion, Green Capital — A747

2014, Nov. 6   Litho.   Perf. 13¼
3007 A747 1400g multi + label   1.00 1.00

Carlos Miguel Jiménez (1914-70), Musician — A748

2014, Nov. 10   Litho.   Perf. 13¼
3008 A748 2000g black + label   1.75 1.75

Silvio Pettirossi (1887-1916), Aviator — A749

No. 3009: a, Pettirossi, airplane inverted in flight, note written by Pettirossi. b, Pettirossi in airplace cockpit.

2014, Nov. 17   Litho.   Perf. 13¼
3009 Horiz. pair + central label   8.00 8.00
  a. A749 2500g multi   1.75 1.75
  b. A749 9000g multi   6.25 6.25

Spanish Academy, 300th Anniv. — A750

Designs: No. 3010, Flowers. No. 3011, Emblem of Paraguayan Spanish Language Academy.

2014, Nov. 21   Litho.   Perf. 13¼
3010 A750 11,000g multi   8.00 8.00

Souvenir Sheet
Rouletted 5
3011 A750 11,000g multi   8.00 8.00

Christmas — A751

Designs: 1400g, Star, pottery, angel. 5000g, Star, pottery, melons, grapes.

2014, Dec. 5   Litho.   Perf. 13¼
3012-3013 A751 Set of 2   4.50 4.50

Campaign Against Discrimination A752

Designs: 1000g, Three empty chairs of different heights. 10,000g, Handicapped child with other children.

2015, Jan. 7   Litho.   Perf. 13¼
3014-3015 A752 Set of 2   7.50 7.50
Dated 2014.

Visit of United Nations Secretary General Ban Ki-moon — A753

2015, Feb. 25   Litho.   Perf. 13¼
3016 A753 10,000g multi + label 7.00 7.00

Encarnación, 400th Anniv. — A754

No. 3017: a, Municipal Building, horse-drawn carriage. b, San Roque González de Santa Cruz Basilica, St. Roque González de Santa Cruz (1576-1628).

2015, Mar. 25   Litho.   Perf. 13¼
3017 Horiz. pair + central label   6.00 6.00
  a. A754 1000g multi   .50   .50
  b. A754 10,000g multi   5.50 5.50

Lorenzo Prieto, Record-Setting Bicyclist — A755

2015, Apr. 24   Litho.   Perf. 13¼
3018 A755 2000g multi + label   1.40 1.40

Efrén Echeverría, Guitarist — A756

2015, Apr. 24   Litho.   Perf. 13¼
3019 A756 5000g multi + label   3.25 3.25

Secretary of Social Action, 20th Anniv. — A757

2015, May 7   Litho.   Perf. 13¼
3020 A757 10,000g multi + label 5.50 5.50

Instruments of the Recycled Orchestra of Catuera A758

2015, May 25   Litho.   Perf. 13¼
3021 A758 5000g Trumpet   2.75 2.75

Souvenir Sheet
Rouletted 5
3022 A758 2000g Saxophone, vert.   .80   .80

Santa Teresa de Jesus College, Cent.
A759

2015, May 25   Litho.   Perf. 13¼
3023 A759 13,000g multi + label   7.25 7.25

Animals
A760

No. 3024: a, 1000g, Azara's night monkey (ka'i pyhare). b, 1400g, Geoffroy's cat (gato montés). c, 3000g, Capybara (carpincho).
No. 3025, 3000g, Blue-fronted Amazons (loro hablador).

2015, June 12   Litho.   Perf. 13¼
3024 A760   Block of 3, #a-c, +
    label   3.00 3.00
Souvenir Sheet
Rouletted 5
3025 A760 3000g multi   2.40 2.40
Junior Chamber International in Paraguay, cent.

Francisco Lopez Military Academy,
Cent. — A761

2015, June 18   Litho.   Perf. 13¼
3026 A761 10,000g multi + label 4.00 4.00

Visit of Pope Francis to Paraguay
A762

Designs: 5000g, Pope Francis, map and flag of Paraguay.
6000g, Pope Francis, church.

2015, July 6   Litho.   Perf. 13¼
3027 A762 5000g multi + label   2.75 2.75
Souvenir Sheet
Rouletted 8
3028 A762 6000g multi   3.50 3.50
See Nos. 3032-3033.

St. John Bosco (1815-88) — A763

2015, Aug. 12   Litho.   Perf. 13¼
3029 A763 2000g multi + label   1.40 1.40

Postal Headquarters — A764

No. 3030 — Postal Headquarters in: a, 5000g, Guatemala (denomination at left). b, 10,000g, Paraguay (denomination at right).

2015, Aug. 13   Litho.   Perf. 13¼
3030 A764   Horiz. pair, #a-b   6.50 6.50
See Guatemala No. 708.

Luis Alberto del Paraná (1926-74) and Los Paraguayos, Musical Group — A765

No. 3031: a, 2000g, Three band members. b, 5000g, Del Paraná.

2015, Sept. 15   Litho.   Perf. 13¼
3031 A765   Horiz. pair, #a-b, +
    flanking label   1.40 1.40

Visit of Pope Francis Type of 2015
2015, Oct. 27   Litho.   Perf. 13¼
Stamp + Label
3032 A762 6000g Like #3027   2.25 2.25
Souvenir Sheet
Rouletted 8
3033 A762 5000g Like #3028   1.90 1.90

Paraguay, Land of Water — A766

2015, Nov. 4   Litho.   Perf. 13¼
3034 A766 4000g multi + label   1.75 1.75

Campaign Against Human
Trafficking — A767

No. 3035: a, 5000g, Woman bound in ropes. b, 11,000g, Silhouettes of two people.

2015, Nov. 9   Litho.   Perf. 13¼
3035 A767   Horiz. pair, #a-b   7.25 7.25
America Issue.

Children's Drawing of Farm — A768

2015, Nov. 20   Litho.   Perf. 13¼
3036 A768 2500g multi + label   1.10 1.10

Miniature Sheet

Tourism Ambassadors of
Paraguay — A769

No. 3037: a, Roque Santa Cruz, soccer player. b, Ismael Ledesma playing harp. c, Daiana Ferreira, guitarist. d, Luis Szarán, orchestra conductor. e, Arnaldo André, actor.

2015, Dec. 3   Litho.   Perf. 13¼
3037 A769 2000g Sheet of 5, #a-
    e, + 7 labels   4.50 4.50

Souvenir Sheet

Christmas — A770

No. 3038 — Altar of Corn, by Koki Ruiz, and: a, 2000g, Pope Francis at pulpit. b, 12,000g, Statue of Madonna and Child.

2015, Dec. 3   Litho.   Perf. 13¼
3038 A770   Sheet of 2, #a-b, +
    2 labels   6.25 6.25

Canonization of St. Emilie de
Villeneuve (1811-54) — A771

2016, May 26   Litho.   Perf. 13¼
3039 A771 2500g multi + label   .90 .90

Campaign Against Child Abuse and
Sexual Violence — A772

2016, May 31   Litho.   Perf. 13¼
3040 A772 9000g multi + label   3.25 3.25

Souvenir Sheet

Japanese Immigration to Paraguay,
80th Anniv. — A773

2016, May 31   Litho.   Perf. 13¼
3041 A773 9000g multi + 3 labels 3.25 3.25

College of Accounting, Cent. — A774

2016, June 10   Litho.   Perf. 13¼
3042 A774 1400g multi + label   .50 .50

International Day of
Responsible
Gambling — A775

2016, June 15   Litho.   Perf. 13¼
3043 A775 2500g multi   .90 .90

Diplomatic Relations Between
Paraguay and Israel — A776

No. 3044 — Flags of Paraguay and Israel and: a, 6000g, Bare-throated bellbird. b, 10,000g, Hoopoes.

2016, June 20   Litho.   Perf. 13¼
3044 A776   Horiz. pair, #a-b   5.75 5.75

Hotel Guarani,
Asuncion — A777

2016, June 27   Litho.   Perf. 13¼
3045 A777 10,000g multi   3.75 3.75

Employment of
Prisoners
A778

2016, June 27   Litho.   Perf. 13¼
3046   Horiz. pair + central la-
    bel   4.75 4.75
    a. A778 3000g Embroiderer   1.00 1.00
    b. A778 10,000g Polisher   3.75 3.75

Miniature Sheet

Tourism Ambassadors — A779

No. 3047: a, Nelson Sanabria, racer in Dakar Rally. b, Chiara D'Odorico, pianist. c, Koki Ruiz, artist. d, José Mongelos, opera singer.

2016, June 27   Litho.   Perf. 13¼
3047 A779 2000g Sheet of 4, #a-
    d, + 6 labels   3.00 3.00

Demetrio Ortiz (1916-75),
Musician — A780

2016, June 30   Litho.   Perf. 13¼
3048 A780 10,000g multi + label 3.75 3.75

Social
Security
Week
A781

2016, July 20   Litho.   Perf. 13¼
3049 A781 2000g multi + label   .75 .75

Paraguayan Customs Broker Center,
90th Anniv. — A782

2016, July 28   Litho.   Perf. 13¼
3050 A782 1400g multi + label   .50 .50

Souvenir Sheet

Paraguayan Olympic Committee
Emblem — A783

2016, July 29   Litho.   *Rouletted 8*
3051 A783 4000g multi   1.50 1.50

Famous
People — A784

No. 3052: a, Doña Máxima Lugo (1925-91),
actress. b, Pedro Sosa Melgarejo (Carlos
Sosa) (1926-89), composer.

2016, Aug. 22   Litho.   *Perf. 13¼*
3052   Horiz. pair + central la-
          bel   1.60 1.60
a.   A784 1400g multi   .50 .50
b.   A784 3000g multi   1.10 1.10

Itaipú Technological Park — A785

2016, Nov. 28   Litho.   *Perf. 13¼*
3053 A785 2500g multi + label   .85 .85

Christmas — A786

No. 3054: a, 3000g, Flight into Egypt. b,
10,000g, Nativity.

2016, Dec. 1   Litho.   *Perf. 13¼*
3054   Horiz. pair, #a-b, +
          central label   4.50 4.50

Paraguayan
Industrial Union,
Cent. — A787

2016, Dec. 6   Litho.   *Perf. 13¼*
3055 A787 9000g multi   3.25 3.25

Miniature Sheet

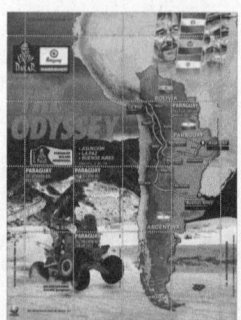

39th
Dakar
Rally
A788

No. 3056: a, 1400g, Wheels of rally vehicle.
b, 2000g, Vehicle number and visor of driver.
c, 2500g, Nelson Sanabria on vehicle. d,
3000g, Map of Paraguayan portion of rally,
flag of Paraguay.

2016, Dec. 13   Litho.   *Perf. 13¼*
3056 A788   Sheet of 4, #a-d, +
             12 labels   3.25 3.25

Souvenir Sheet

Annual Meeting of Governors of the
Interamerican Development Bank,
Paraguay — A789

No. 3057: a, 1400g, Palacio Alegre, Asunción. b, 2000g, Grain field. c, 3000g,
Paraguayan coins and banknotes.

2017, Mar. 13   Litho.   *Perf. 13¼*
3057 A789   Sheet of 3, #a-c, +
             label   2.25 2.25

Miniature Sheet

Flowers and Butterflies — A790

No. 3058: a, 700g, Cereus forbesii. b, 700g,
Harrisia bonplandii. c, 1000g, Agraulis vanillae. d, 1400g, Male Euryades duponcheli. e,
2000g, Female Euryades duponcheli. f,
2500g, Echinopsis rhodotricha.

2017, Mar. 28   Litho.   *Perf. 13¼*
3058 A790   Sheet of 6, #a-f, + 2
             labels   3.00 3.00

Mother's
Day — A791

No. 3059: a, 1400g, Family in archway. b,
2000g, Family making meal.

2017, May 15   Litho.   *Perf. 13¼*
3059 A791   Pair, #a-b   1.25 1.25

Miniature Sheet

Russian Immigrants to
Paraguay — A792

No. 3060: a, 1000g, First Russian immigrants. b, 1400g, Sergio Bobrovsky and
Sergio Conradi. c, 2000g, Tala Ern de Retivoff
and Agripina Voitenko. d, 2500g, Nicolás Ern
and Stephan Vysokolan. e, 3000g, Oreliev de
Serebriakoff and Boris Kassianoff. f, 5000g,
Dr. Arturo Weiss and Dr. Constantino
Gramatchicoff. g, 6000g, Gen. Juan Belaieff
and Paraguayans.

2017, June 5   Litho.   *Perf. 13¼*
3060 A792   Sheet of 7, #a-g, +
             9 labels   7.50 7.50

Pres. Horacio
Cartes and
Patriarch Kirill
of Moscow
A793

Chamaemelum
Nobile — A794

2017, June 8   Litho.   *Perf. 13¼*
3061   Horiz. pair + central la-
          bel   5.50 5.50
a.   A793 6000g multi   2.25 2.25
b.   A794 9000g multi   3.25 3.25

Visit of Patriarch Kirill to Paraguay.

Souvenir Sheet

Augusto Roa Bastos (1917-2005),
Writer — A795

2017, June 13   Litho.   *Perf. 13¼*
3062 A795 13,000g multi + 3 la-
          bels   4.75 4.75

Peace Corps in Paraguay, 50th
Anniv. — A796

2017, June 19   Litho.   *Perf. 13¼*
3063 A796 10,000g multi + label 3.75 3.75

Institute
of Fine
Arts,
60th
Anniv.
A797

2017, July 5   Litho.   *Perf. 13¼*
3064 A797 5000g multi + label   1.90 1.90

Diplomatic
Relations
Between
Paraguay and
Republic of
China, 60th
Anniv. — A798

No. 3065: a, 1000g, Presidential Palace,
Taipei, Republic of China. b, 3000g, López
Presidential Palace, Asunción.

2017, July 12   Litho.   *Perf. 13¼*
3065   Horiz. pair + central la-
          bel   1.50 1.50
a.   A798 1000g multi   .35 .35
b.   A798 3000g multi   1.10 1.10

Souvenir Sheet

Asunción, 480th Anniv. — A799

2017, Aug. 11   Litho.   *Perf. 13¼*
3066 A799 1400g multi + 3 labels .50 .50

Souvenir Sheet

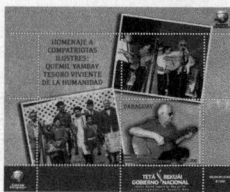

Quemil
Yambay,
Guitarist
A800

2017, Aug. 22   Litho.   *Perf. 13¼*
3067 A800 5000g multi + 3 labels 1.75 1.75

Souvenir Sheet

National Radio of Paraguay, 75th
Anniv. — A801

2017, Aug. 30   Litho.   *Perf. 13¼*
3068 A801 1400g multi + 3 labels .50 .50

Flower and
Cactus — A802

Hummingbird
and Cactus
Flower — A803

2017, Sept. 29   Litho.   *Perf. 13¼*
3069   Horiz. pair + central la-
          bel   1.50 1.50
a.   A802 1000g multi   .35 .35
b.   A803 3000g multi   1.10 1.10

National Secretary of Youth.

International Year of Sustainable
Tourism for Development — A804

Designs: 2500g, Jesuit Mission of Santísima
Trinidad UNESCO World Heritage Site.
3000p, Ypacaraí Lake.

2017, Oct. 9   Litho.   *Perf. 13¼*
3070 A804 2500g multi + label   .90 .90
          Souvenir Sheet
          Rouletted 5
3071 A804 3000g multi   1.10 1.10

Souvenir Sheet

Laguna
Salada
A805

2017, Oct. 9   Litho.   *Perf. 13¼*
3072 A805 4000g multi + 3 labels 1.40 1.40

America issue.

Souvenir Sheet

Paraguay Central Railway, 160th Anniv. (in 2021) A806

No. 3073: a, 5000g, Locomotive and Central Station, Asunción. b, 8000g, Locomotive and line of people.

2017, Oct. 26   Litho.   Perf. 13¼
3073 A806   Sheet of 2, #a-b, + 2 labels   4.75 4.75

Souvenir Sheet

Flowers A807

2017, Nov. 6   Litho.   Perf. 13¼
3074 A807   5000g multi + 3 labels 1.75 1.75
Atyra, model of sustainable city.

Alberto de Luque (1938-2020), Musician — A808

2017, Nov. 20   Litho.   Perf. 13¼
3075 A808   1400g multi + label   .50 .50

Souvenir Sheet

Municipal Theater, Asunción, 128th Anniv. — A809

2017, Nov. 28   Litho.   Perf. 13¼
3076 A809   5000g multi + 3 labels 1.75 1.75

Souvenir Sheet

Christmas — A810

2017, Dec. 11   Litho.   Perf. 13¼
3077 A810   9000g multi + 3 labels 3.25 3.25

Consumer and User Protection Secretariat, 20th Anniv. — A811

2018, Mar. 16   Litho.   Perf. 13¼
3078 A811   2000g multi   .75 .75

Italo-Latin American Institute, 50th Anniv. — A812

No. 3079: a, 5000g, Distorted globe. b, 10,000g, Oranges, olives, flags of Paraguay and Italy.

2018, Mar. 26   Litho.   Perf. 13¼
3079 A812   Horiz. pair, #a-b   5.50 5.50

Marie Curie (1867-1934), Chemist and Physicist, and Emblem of National University of Asunción — A813

2018, May 8   Litho.   Perf. 13¼
3080 A813   10,000g multi + label 3.50 3.50
Chemistry faculty of National University, 80th Anniv. Printed in sheets of 2 + 2 labels.

Passage of Law 5777 to end Violence Against Women A814

2018, May 11   Litho.   Perf. 13¼
3081 A814   8000g multi   3.00 3.00

Souvenir Sheet

Hats A815

2018, May 29   Litho.   Rouletted 5
3082 A815   3000g multi   1.10 1.10
ZP12 Radio Station, Pilar, 55th anniv.

Souvenir Sheet

Locomotives — A816

No. 3083: a, 4000g, Model of Sapucai locomotive. b, 10,000g, Baldwin steam locomotive.

2018, June 13   Litho.   Perf. 13¼
3083 A816   Sheet of 2, #a-b, + 2 labels   5.00 5.00
Joint Issue between Paraguay & Ecuador. See Ecuador No. 2207.

Souvenir Sheet

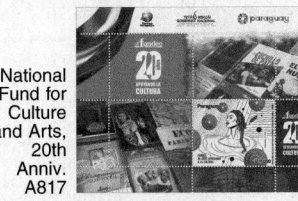

National Fund for Culture and Arts, 20th Anniv. A817

2018, July 6   Litho.   Perf. 13¼
3084 A817   9000g multi + 3 labels 3.25 3.25

Souvenir Sheet

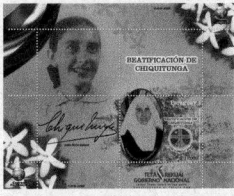

Beatification of María Guggiari Echeverría (1925-59) — A818

2018, July 9   Litho.   Perf. 13¼
3085 A818   11,000g multi + 3 labels   4.00 4.00

National Youth Tourism Program — A819

Designs: 1400g, Youths wearing helmets. 2000g, Youth Tourism emblem, horiz.

2018, Aug. 6   Litho.   Perf. 13¼
3086 A819   1400g multi   .50 .50
Souvenir Sheet
Rouletted 7x8
3087 A819   2000g multi   .70 .70

Nasta Advertising Agency, 50th Anniv. — A820

50th anniversary emblem and: 2000g, Buildings. 5000g, Woman, motorcycle and buildings.

2018, Aug. 14   Litho.   Perf. 13¼
3088 A820   2000g multi   .70 .70
Souvenir Sheet
Rouletted 5
3089 A820   5000g multi   1.75 1.75

Souvenir Sheet

Rafael Rojas Doria (1931-2018) and César Alvarez Blanco (1927-2003), Comedians — A821

2018, Sept. 14   Litho.   Perf. 13¼
3090 A821   13,000g multi + 3 labels   4.50 4.50

Miniature Sheet

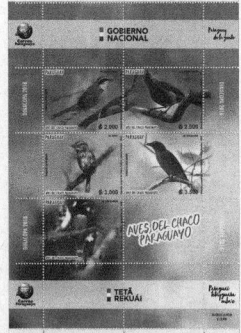

Birds of the Chaco A822

No. 3091: a, 2000g, Gallito de collar (olive-crowned crescentchest). b, 2500g, Hornerito copetón (crested hornero). c, 3000g, Durmili (Caatinga puffbird). d, 3500g, Fueguero rojo (hepatic tanager). e, 4000g, Surucuá aurora (blue-crowned trogon).

2018, Sept. 21   Litho.   Perf. 13¼
3091 A822   Sheet of 5, #a-e, + label   5.25 5.25

America Issue A823

No. 3092: a, 1400g, Mestizo dog. b, 2500g, Dalmatian. 9000g, Shih tzu.

2018, Oct. 9   Litho.   Perf. 13¼
3092 A823   Horiz. pair, #a-b   1.40 1.40
Souvenir Sheet
Rouletted 7x8
3093 A823   9000g multi   3.25 3.25

Meeting of the Postal Union of the Americas, Spain and Portugal Advisory and Executive Council — A824

No. 3094 — Flags of member nations and: a, 5000g, Patri Palace (Post Office), Asunción, and map of Paraguay. b, 10,000g, Patri Palace.

2018, Nov. 19   Litho.   Perf. 13¼
3094 A824   Horiz. pair, #a-b   5.25 5.25
America issue.

Diplomatic Relations Between Paraguay and Peru, 160th Anniv. — A825

No. 3095: a, 6000g, Benigno López Palace (Paraguayan Ministry of Foreign Affairs), Asunción. b, 10,000g, Torre Tagle Palace (Peruvian Ministry of Foreign Affairs), Lima, Peru.

2018, Nov. 30   Litho.   Perf. 13¼
3095 A825   Horiz. pair, #a-b   5.50 5.50

Organization of American States, 70th Anniv. — A826

2018, Dec. 7   Litho.   Perf. 13¼
3096 A826   10,000g multi   3.50 3.50

Christmas — A827

No. 3097: a, 2000g, Paper cutting, poinsettia, candle in lantern. b, 2500g, Nativitiy scene in lantern, Christmas ornaments.

2018, Dec. 7   Litho.   Perf. 13¼
3097 A827   Horiz. pair, #a-b   1.60 1.60

Map of Airline Flights Leaving
Paraguay and Emblems of
International and Paraguayan Civil
Aviation Organizations — A828

2018, Dec. 10   Litho.   Perf. 13¼
3098 A828 4000g multi + label   1.40 1.40

Souvenir Sheet

International Day of Disabled
Persons — A829

No. 3099: a, 6000g, Brain in head. b, 7000g,
Stylized person in wheelchair.

2018, Dec. 10   Litho.   Perf. 13¼
3099 A829   Sheet of 2, #a-b, + 2
labels   4.50 4.50

First Paraguay
Postage Stamp,
150th Anniv. — A830

2018, Dec. 27   Litho.   Perf. 13¼
3100 A830 200g multi   .25 .25

Souvenir Sheet

Volunteer Firefighter Corps of
Paraguay, 40th Anniv. — A831

No. 3101: a, 1500g, Yellow fire truck. b,
2500g, Orange fire trucks.

2019, Feb. 22   Litho.   Perf. 13¼
3101 A831   Sheet of 2, #a-b, +
2 labels   1.40 1.40

Souvenir Sheet

International Labor Organization,
Cent. — A832

No. 3102: a, 5000g, Woman working in factory. b, 10,000g, Construction workers.

2019, May 22   Litho.   Perf. 13¼
3102 A832   Sheet of 2, #a-b, +
2 labels   4.75 4.75

Souvenir Sheet

Isla Po'i Social Welfare Institute Clinic,
Asuncion, 75th Anniv. — A833

2019, May 31   Litho.   Perf. 13¼
3103 A833 2200g multi + 3 labels   .70 .70

Souvenir Sheet

Mohandas K. Gandhi (1869-1948),
Indian Nationalist Leader — A834

2019, July 10   Litho.   Rouletted 5
3104 A834 10,000g multi   3.50 3.50

Horses — A835

Various horses: 1000g, 2500g, 9000g.

2019, July 15   Litho.   Perf. 13¼
3105-3107 A835   Set of 3   4.25 4.25

Cultural Center of the Republic,
Asuncion
A836

2019, Aug. 14   Litho.   Perf. 13¼
3108 A836 5000g multi + label   1.60 1.60

Souvenir Sheet

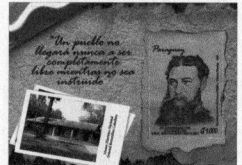

General Bernardino Caballero (1839-
1912), Ninth President of
Paraguay — A837

2019, Sept. 11   Litho.   Rouletted 5
3109 A837 1000g multi   .35 .35

Express Mail
Service, 20th
Anniv. — A838

2019, Sept. 20   Litho.   Perf. 13¼
3110 A838 16,000g multi   5.00 5.00

Tree
Flowers — A839

Designs: 800g, Ceiba chodatii. 4000g,
Flamboyant. 8000g, Cocos nucifera.

2019, Sept. 20   Litho.   Perf. 13¼
3111-3113 A839   Set of 3   4.00 4.00

Miniature Sheet

America
Issue
A840

No. 3114 — Traditional Paraguayan dishes:
a, 1000g, Vorí vorí (soup with dumplings). b,
3000g, Sopa Paraguaya (corn bread). c,
6000g, Empanadas de mandioca (meat and
cassava empanadas). d, 10,000g, Chipa
almidón (cassava bread).

2019, Oct. 9   Litho.   Perf. 13¼
3114 A840   Sheet of 4, #a-d   6.25 6.25

Miniature Sheet

Reconstruction of Paraguay After
Paraguayan War — A841

No. 3115: a, 1000g, Handwritten document.
b, 1400g, Picture postcard depicting Port of
Asunción. c, 2200g, Picture postcard depicting
Palacio de López and flag. d, 5000g, Picture
postcard depicting Palacio de López.

2019, Oct. 21   Litho.   Perf. 13¼
3115 A841   Sheet of 4, #a-d   3.00 3.00

World Hemophilia
Day — A842

2019, Nov. 28   Litho.   Perf. 13¼
3116 A842 1400g multi   .45 .45

Cayo Sila Godoy
(1919-2014),
Guitarist — A843

2019, Dec. 2   Litho.   Perf. 13¼
3117 A843 2200g dark gray   .70 .70

Art by Edith
Jiménez (1918-
2004)
A844

2019, Dec. 2   Litho.   Perf. 13¼
3118 A844 4000g multi   1.25 1.25

Christmas — A845

No. 3119: a, 1000g, Holy Family. b,
10,000g, Child looking at bird.

2019, Dec. 11   Litho.   Perf. 13¼
3119 A845   Horiz. pair, #a-b   3.50 3.50

Souvenir Sheet

First Paraguay-Argentina Airmail
Flight, Cent. — A846

2019, Dec. 16   Litho.   Perf. 13¼
3120 A846 2500g multi + 3 labels   .80 .80

Executive
Branch Human
Rights Network,
10th
Anniv. — A847

No. 3121 — Peace dove with inscription in:
a, Guarani. b, Spanish.

2019, Dec. 18   Litho.   Perf. 13¼
3121 A847 1400g Vert. pair, #a-b   .90 .90

Souvenir Sheet

Diplomatic Relations Between
Paraguay and Japan, Cent. — A848

No. 3122 — Flags of Paraguay and Japan
and: a, Cherry tree in bloom. b, Cherry
blossom.

2019, Dec. 18   Litho.   Perf. 13¼
3122 A848 10,000g Sheet of 2,
#a-b, + 2 la-
bels   6.25 6.25

Souvenir Sheet

International Year of Indigenous
Languages — A849

2019, Dec. 23   Litho.   Perf. 13¼
3123 A849 1400g multi + 3 labels   .45 .45

Souvenir Sheet

Paraguayan Red Cross, Cent. — A850

No. 3124: a, 2200g, Air ambulance. b,
2500g, Red Cross ambulances and drivers.

2019, Dec. 27   Litho.   Perf. 13¼
3124 A850   Sheet of 2, #a-b, +
2 labels   1.50 1.50

Promotion of Breastfeeding by Itapúa
Department — A851

2020, Feb. 27   Litho.   Perf. 13¼
3125 A851   2400g multi + label   .75 .75

Souvenir Sheet

Secretary of National Emergencies,
15th Anniv. — A852

2020, June 10   Litho.   Perf. 13¼
3126 A852   1500g multi + 3 labels   .45 .45

Souvenir Sheet

First Paraguayan Stamps, 150th
Anniv. — A853

No. 3127: a, 2200g, Paraguay #1. b, 4000g,
Paraguay #2. c, 10,000g, Paraguay #3.

2020, Oct. 9   Litho.   Perf. 13¼
3127 A853   Sheet of 3, #a-c, +
label   4.75 4.75

Souvenir Sheet

Asunción Architecture — A854

No. 3128: a, 4000g, Villa Arcallana. b,
6000g, Central Bank of Paraguay.

2020, Oct. 9   Litho.   Perf. 13¼
3128 A854   Sheet of 2, #a-b, +
2 labels   3.00 3.00
America issue.

Souvenir Sheet

Superior Tribunal of Electoral Justice, 25th Anniv. A855

2020, Oct. 13   Litho.   Perf. 13¼
3129 A855   5000g multi + 3 labels   1.50 1.50

Souvenir Sheet

Sustainable Paraguay — A856

No. 3130: a, 2500g, Sun, cow, and flowers.
b, 3000g, Bird.

2020, Oct. 23   Litho.   Perf. 13¼
3130 A856   Sheet of 2, #a-b, +
2 labels   1.60 1.60

Paraguayan Sustainable Development
Goals Commission, 5th anniv. and United
Nations, 75th anniv.

Souvenir Sheet

Paraguayan Olympic Committee, 50th
Anniv. — A857

2020, Oct. 30   Litho.   Rouletted 7x8
3131 A857   3000g multi   .90 .90

Latin American Integration Association,
40th Anniv. — A858

2020, Dec. 2   Litho.   Perf. 13¼
3132 A858   2500g multi + label   .75 .75

Christmas — A859

2020, Dec. 2   Litho.   Perf. 13¼
3133 A859   5500g multi + label   1.60 1.60

Battle of Acosta Nu, 150th Anniv. (in 2019) A860

2020, Dec. 17   Litho.   Perf. 13¼
3134 A860   3000g multi + label   .90 .90

Founding of Scientific Society of Paraguay by Andrés Barbero (1877-1951), Cent. — A861

2021, Jan. 9   Litho.   Perf. 13¼
3135 A861   2400g multi   .75 .75

María Elena Sachero, Actress A862

2021, June 30   Litho.   Perf. 13¼
3136 A862   2500g multi + label   .75 .75

Independence of Peru, 200th
Anniv. — A863

2021, July 15   Litho.   Perf. 13¼
3137 A863   1500g multi + label   .50 .50

Souvenir Sheet

Monsignor Lasagna Salesian School,
125th Anniv. — A864

2021, July 23   Litho.   Perf. 13¼
3138 A864   1900g multi + 3 labels   .60 .60

Souvenir Sheet

National Development Bank, 60th
Anniv. — A865

2021, Sept. 13   Litho.   Perf. 13¼
3139 A865   2000g multi + 3 labels   *.60 .60*

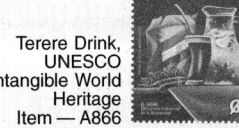

Terere Drink, UNESCO Intangible World Heritage Item — A866

2021, Sept. 15   Litho.   Perf. 13¼
3140 A866   10,000g multi   3.00 3.00

Souvenir Sheet

Tourism A867

No. 3141: a, 2200g, Boats on Cerrito Beach.
b, 2400g, Victoria cruziana a Piquete Cué.

2021, Oct. 12   Litho.   Perf. 13¼
3141 A867   Sheet of 3, #a-b, +
2 labels   1.40 1.40
America issue.

Souvenir Sheet

Luqueño Sports Club, Cent. A868

2021, Oct. 13   Litho.   Perf. 13¼
3142 A868   3000g multi + 3 labels   .90 .90

Asunción Classical and Modern
Municipal Ballet Company, 50th
Anniv. — A869

2021, Nov. 17   Litho.   Perf. 13¼
3143 A869   2000g multi + label   .60 .60

Souvenir Sheet

Jaguars A870

No. 3144 — Various depictions of jaguars
with denomination of: a, 1400g. b, 1500g. c,
2200g.

2021, Nov. 22   Litho.   Perf. 13¼
3144 A870   Sheet of 3, #a-c, +
5 labels   1.50 1.50

Maneco Galeano (1945-80), Musician and Journalist — A871

2021, Nov. 26   Litho.   Perf. 13¼
3145 A871   1000g multi   .30 .30

Painting by Modesto Delgado Rodas (1886-1963) — A872

2021, Dec. 14   Litho.   Perf. 13¼
3146 A872   2200g multi   .65 .65

Christmas — A873

2021, Dec. 17   Litho.   Perf. 13¼
3147 A873   16,000g multi + label   4.75 4.75

Souvenir Sheet

Bluecrown Passionflower, National Flower of Paraguay — A874

2021, Dec. 20   Litho.   Perf. 13¼
3148 A874 2500g multi + 3 labels .75 .75
Mercosur (Southern Common Market), 30th anniv.

Supreme Council of the Ancient and Accepted Scottish Rite Masons in Paraguay, 150th Anniv. — A875

2021, Dec. 21   Litho.   Perf. 13¼
3149 A875 4000g multi 1.25 1.25

Radio Caritas, 85th Anniv. — A876

2021, Dec. 28   Litho.   Perf. 13¼
3150 A876 2200g multi .65 .65

Carmen de Lara Castro (1918-93), Politician and Human Rights Advocate — A877

2022, Mar. 4   Litho.   Perf. 13¼
3151 A877 2000g multi .60 .60
Dated 2021.

Souvenir Sheet

2020 Summer Olympics, Tokyo — A878

No. 3152 — Paraguayan athletes: a, 10,000g, Alejandra Alonso. b, 11,000g, Aguamarina Espinola, Verónica Cepede.

2022, Mar. 30   Litho.   Perf. 13¼
3152 A878 Sheet of 2, #a-b, +
2 labels 6.00 6.00
The 2020 Summer Olympics was postponed until 2021 because of the COVID-19 pandemic. Dated 2021.

Melissa Nair Tillner Galeano, Paraguayan Paralympian A879

Rodrigo Fabian Hermosa Ayala, Paraguayan Paralympian A880

2022, Mar. 30   Litho.   Perf. 13¼
3153 Horiz. pair + central label 1.25 1.25
 a. A879 1500g multi .45 .45
 b. A880 2500g multi .75 .75
2020 Summer Paralympics, Tokyo. The 2020 Summer Paralympics was postponed until 2021 because of the COVID-19 pandemic. Dated 2021.

Souvenir Sheet

Club Centro de Balderrama, Luque, 112th Anniv. — A881

2022, Apr. 22   Litho.   Perf. 13¼
3154 A881 3000g multi + 3 labels .90 .90

Souvenir Sheet

Campaign Against COVID-19 — A882

2022, June 21   Litho.   Rouletted 5
3155 A882 4000g multi + 3 labels 1.25 1.25

Diplomatic Relations Between Paraguay and South Korea, 60th Anniv. — A883

2022, June 28   Litho.   Perf. 13¼
3156 A883 3000g multi + label .90 .90

20th World Conference of Supreme Councils, Asuncion — A884

2022, July 27   Litho.   Perf. 13¼
3157 A884 5500g multi 1.60 1.60

Jacinto Herrera (1919-69), Actor — A885

2022, Aug. 25   Litho.   Perf. 13¼
3158 A885 10,000g black 3.00 3.00

SEMI-POSTAL STAMPS

Red Cross Nurse — SP1

Unwmk.
1930, July 22   Typo.   Perf. 12
B1 SP1 1.50p + 50c gray violet 2.00 1.20
B2 SP1 1.50p + 50c deep rose 2.00 1.20
B3 SP1 1.50p + 50c dark blue 2.00 1.20
  Nos. B1-B3 (3) 6.00 3.60
The surtax was for the benefit of the Red Cross Society of Paraguay.

College of Agriculture SP2

1930
B4 SP2 1.50p + 50c blue, *pale pink* .60 .50
Surtax for the Agricultural Institute. The sheet of No. B4 has a papermaker's watermark: "Vencedor Bond."
A 1.50p+50c red on pale yellow was prepared but not regularly issued. Value, 40 cents.

Red Cross Headquarters — SP3

1932
B5 SP3 50c + 50c rose .60 .60

Our Lady of Asunción — SP4

1941   **Engr.**
B6 SP4 7p + 3p red brown .65 .35
B7 SP4 7p + 3p purple .65 .35
B8 SP4 7p + 3p carmine rose .65 .35
B9 SP4 7p + 3p sapphire .65 .35
  Nos. B6-B9 (4) 2.60 1.40
For surcharges see Nos. 419-426, 431-434.

No. 361 Surcharged in Black

1944
B10 A70 10c on 10p multicolored .70 .50
The surtax was for the victims of the San Juan earthquake in Argentina.

Catalogue values for unused stamps in this section, from this point to the end of the section, are for Never Hinged items.

No. C169 Surcharged in Carmine "AYUDA AL ECUADOR 5 + 5"
1949   Unwmk.   Perf. 12½
B11 A117 5c + 5c on 30c dk blue .30 .30
Surtax for the victims of the Ecuador earthquake.

38th Intl. Eucharistic Congress, Bombay SP5

Various coins and coat of arms.

Litho. & Engr.
1964, Dec. 11   Perf. 12x12½
B12 SP5 20g +10g multi 6.50 6.50
B13 SP5 30g +15g multi 6.50 6.50
B14 SP5 50g +25g multi 6.50 6.50
B15 SP5 100g +50g multi 6.50 6.50
 a. Souvenir sheet of 4, #B12-B15 26.00 26.00
  Nos. B12-B15 (4) 26.00 26.00

Buildings and Coats of Arms of Popes John XXIII & Paul VI — SP6

#B16, Dome of St. Peters. #B17, Site of Saint Peter's tomb. #B18, Saint Peter's Plaza. #B19, Taj Mahal.

1964, Dec. 12
B16 SP6 20g +10g multi 6.50 6.50
B17 SP6 30g +15g multi 6.50 6.50
B18 SP6 50g +25g multi 6.50 6.50
B19 SP6 100g +50g multi 6.50 6.50
 a. Souvenir sheet of 4, #B16-B19 140.00 140.00
  Nos. B16-B19 (4) 26.00 26.00

AIR POST STAMPS

Official Stamps of 1913 Surcharged

1929, Jan. 1   Unwmk.   Perf. 11½
C1 O19 2.85p on 5c lilac 2.25 1.50
C2 O19 5.65p on 10c grn 1.25 1.50
C3 O19 11.30p on 50c rose 2.00 1.25
  Nos. C1-C3 (3) 5.50 4.25
Counterfeits of surcharge exist.

Regular Issues of 1924-27 Surcharged

1929, Feb. 26   Perf. 12
C4 A51 3.40p on 3p gray 4.50 4.00
 a. Surch. "Correo / en $3.40 / Habilitado / Aereo" 60.00
 b. Double surcharge 8.75
 c. "Aéro" instead of "Aéreo"
C5 A44 6.80p on 4p lt bl 4.50 3.25
 a. Surch. "Correo / Aereo / en $6.80 / Habilitado" 4.50
C6 A52 17p on 5p choc 4.50 3.25
 a. Surch. "Correo / Habilitado / Habilitado / en 17p" 4.50
 b. Double surcharge 25.00 25.00
  Nos. C4-C6 (3) 13.50 10.50

Wings — AP1

Pigeon with Letter — AP2

Airplanes
AP3

1929-31   Typo.   Perf. 12
C7 AP1 2.85p gray green   1.75 1.25
a.   Imperf., pair   37.50
C8 AP1 2.85p turq grn ('31)   .50   .50
C9 AP2 5.65p brown   2.00 1.25
C10 AP2 5.65p scar ('31)   1.00   .50
C11 AP3 11.30p chocolate   1.75 1.25
a.   Imperf., pair   37.50
C12 AP3 11.30p dp blue ('31)   .50   .50
   Nos. C7-C12 (6)   7.50 5.25

Sheets of these stamps sometimes show portions of a papermaker's watermark "Indian Bond C. Extra Strong."
Excellent counterfeits are plentiful.

Regular Issues of 1924-28 Surcharged in Black or Red

1929   Perf. 11½, 12
C13 A47 95c on 7c lilac   .35   .30
C14 A47 1.90p on 20c dull bl   .35   .30
C15 A44 3.40p on 4p lt bl (R)   .40   .30
a.   Double surcharge   3.00
C16 A44 4.75p on 4p lt bl (R)   .95   .75
a.   Double surcharge   3.00
C17 A51 6.80p on 3p gray   1.00   .90
a.   Double surcharge   4.50
C18 A52 17p on 5p choc   3.00 3.00
a.   Horiz. pair, imperf. between   37.50
   Nos. C13-C18 (6)   6.05 5.55

Six stamps in the sheet of No. C17 have the "$" and numerals thinner and narrower than the normal type.

Airplane and Arms AP4   Cathedral of Asunción AP5

Airplane and Globe — AP6

1930   Perf. 12
C19 AP4 95c dp red, pink   1.50   .90
C20 AP4 95c dk bl, blue   1.50   .90
C21 AP5 1.90p lt red, pink   1.50   .90
C22 AP5 1.90p violet, blue   1.50   .90
C23 AP6 6.80p blk, lt bl   1.50   .90
C24 AP6 6.80p green, pink   1.50   .90
   Nos. C19-C24 (6)   9.00 5.40

Sheets of Nos. C19-C24 have a papermaker's watermark: "Extra Vencedor Bond."
Counterfeits exist.

Stamps and Types of 1927-28 Overprinted in Red

1930
C25 A47 10c olive green   .60   .40
a.   Double overprint   6.00
C26 A47 20c dull blue   .60   .40
a.   "CORREO CORREO" instead of "CORREO AEREO"   5.00
b.   "AEREO AEREO" instead of "CORREO AEREO"   5.00
C27 A48 1p emerald   1.40 1.40
C28 A51 3p gray   1.40 1.40
   Nos. C25-C28 (4)   4.00 3.60

Counterfeits of Nos. C26a and C26b exist.

Nos. 273, 282, 286, 288, 300, 302, 305 Surcharged in Red or Black

#C29-C30, C32   #C31

#C33   #C34-C35

1930   Red or Black Surcharge
C29 A47 5c on 10c gray grn (R)   .50   .50
a.   "AEREO" omitted   30.00
C30 A47 5c on 70c ultra (R)   .50   .50
a.   Vert. pair, imperf. between   40.00
C31 A48 20c on 1p org red   .60   .50
a.   "CORREO" double   6.00 6.00
b.   "CORREO" double   6.00 6.00
C32 A47 40c on 50c org (R)   .60   .50
a.   "AEREO" omitted   9.00 9.00
b.   "CORREO" double   6.00 6.00
c.   "CORREO" double   6.00 6.00
C33 A54 6p on 10p red   2.50 2.00
C34 A49 10p on 20p red   10.00 10.00
C35 A49 10p on 20p vio brn   10.00 10.00
   Nos. C29-C35 (7)   24.70 24.00

Declaration of Independence AP11

1930, May 14   Typo.
C36 AP11 2.85p dark blue   .70   .50
C37 AP11 3.40p dark green   .70   .40
C38 AP11 4.75p deep lake   .70   .40
   Nos. C36-C38 (3)   2.10 1.30

Natl. Independence Day, May 14, 1811.

Gunboat Type
Gunboat "Paraguay."

1931-39   Perf. 11½, 12
C39 A58 1p claret   1.20   .60
C40 A58 1p dk blue ('36)   1.20   .60
C41 A58 2p orange   1.20   .60
C42 A58 2p dk brn ('36)   1.20   .60
C43 A58 3p turq green   1.50   .75
C44 A58 3p lt ultra ('36)   1.75   .75
C45 A58 3p brt rose ('39)   1.20   .60
C46 A58 6p dk green   2.40   .90
C47 A58 6p violet ('36)   2.75   .90
C48 A58 6p dull bl ('39)   2.40   .75
C49 A58 10p vermilion   6.00 1.75
C50 A58 10p bluish grn ('35)   9.00 3.00
C51 A58 10p yel brn ('36)   6.50 2.25
C52 A58 10p dk blue ('36)   5.50 1.50
C53 A58 10p lt pink ('39)   6.00 2.00
   Nos. C39-C53 (15)   49.80 17.55

1st constitution of Paraguay as a Republic and the arrival of the "Paraguay" and "Humaita."
Counterfeits of #C39-C53 are plentiful.

Regular Issue of 1924 Surcharged

1931, Aug. 22
C54 A44 3p on 4p lt bl   16.00 16.00

Overprinted

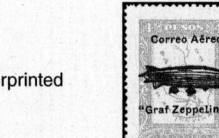

C55 A44 4p lt blue   16.00 16.00
On Nos. C54-C55 the Zeppelin is hand-stamped. The rest of the surcharge or overprint is typographed.

War Memorial AP13   Orange Tree and Yerba Mate AP14

Yerba Mate — AP15   Palms — AP16

Eagle — AP17

1931-36   Litho.
C56 AP13 5c lt blue   .25   .40
a.   Horiz. pair, imperf. btwn.   6.25
C57 AP13 5c dp grn ('33)   .25   .40
C58 AP13 5c lt red ('33)   .30   .40
C59 AP13 5c violet ('35)   .25   .40
C60 AP14 10c dp violet   .25   .40
C61 AP14 10c brn lake ('33)   .25   .40
C62 AP14 10c yel brn ('33)   .25   .40
C63 AP14 10c ultra ('35)   .25   .40
a.   Imperf., pair   5.50
C64 AP15 20c red   .25   .40
C65 AP15 20c dl blue ('33)   .30   .40
C66 AP15 20c emer ('33)   .25   .40
C67 AP15 20c yel brn ('35)   .25   .40
a.   Imperf., pair   4.00
C68 AP16 40c dp green   .25   .40
C69 AP16 40c slate bl ('35)   .25   .40
C70 AP16 40c red ('36)   .30   .40
C71 AP17 80c dull blue   .25   .40
C72 AP17 80c dl grn ('33)   .55   .40
C73 AP17 80c scar ('33)   .30   .40
   Nos. C56-C73 (18)   5.00 7.20

Airship "Graf Zeppelin" AP18

1932, Apr.   Litho.
C74 AP18 4p ultra   3.75 3.75
a.   Imperf., pair   35.00
C75 AP18 8p red   6.25 5.00
C76 AP18 12p blue grn   5.00 5.00
C77 AP18 16p redsh pur   8.75 6.25
C78 AP18 20p orange brn   8.75 6.25
   Nos. C74-C78 (5)   32.50 26.25

For surcharges see Nos. 325-329.

"Graf Zeppelin" over Brazilian Terrain — AP19

"Graf Zeppelin" over Atlantic AP20

1933, May 5
C79 AP19 4.50p dp blue   4.00 3.00
C80 AP19 9p dp rose   7.00 5.00
a.   Horiz. pair, imperf. between   150.00
C81 AP19 13.50p blue grn   8.00 6.00
C82 AP20 22.50p bis brn   18.00 14.00
C83 AP20 45p dull vio   24.00 24.00
   Nos. C79-C83 (5)   61.00 52.00

Excellent counterfeits are plentiful.
For overprints see Nos. C88-C97.

Posts and Telegraph Building, Asunción AP21

1934-37   Perf. 11½
C84 AP21 33.75p ultra   6.00 5.25
C85 AP21 33.75p car ('35)   6.00 5.25
a.   33.75p rose ('37)   5.25 4.50
C86 AP21 33.75p emerald ('36)   7.50 6.00
C87 AP21 33.75p bis brn ('36)   2.25 2.25
   Nos. C84-C87 (4)   21.75 18.75

Excellent counterfeits exist.
For surcharge see No. C107.

Nos. C79-C83 Overprinted in Black

1934, May 26
C88 AP19 4.50p deep bl   3.75 2.25
C89 AP19 9p dp rose   4.75 3.00
C90 AP19 13.50p blue grn   13.00 7.50
C91 AP20 22.50p bis brn   11.00 6.00
C92 AP20 45p dull vio   17.00 10.50
   Nos. C88-C92 (5)   49.50 29.25

Types of 1933 Issue Overprinted in Black

1935
C93 AP19 4.50p rose red   6.50 6.50
C94 AP19 9p lt green   8.25 8.25
C95 AP19 13.50p brown   17.50 17.50
C96 AP20 22.50p violet   14.00 14.00
C97 AP20 45p blue   40.00 40.00
   Nos. C93-C97 (5)   86.25 86.25

Tobacco Plant AP22

1935-39   Typo.
C98 AP22 17p lt brown   12.50 12.50
C99 AP22 17p carmine   21.00 21.00
C100 AP22 17p dark blue   15.00 15.00
C101 AP22 17p pale yel grn ('39)   8.00 8.00
   Nos. C98-C101 (4)   56.50 56.50

Excellent counterfeits are plentiful.

Church of Incarnation — AP23

1935-38
C102 AP23 102p carmine   7.50 5.00
C103 AP23 102p blue   7.50 5.00
C103A AP23 102p indigo ('36)   4.50 4.50
C104 AP23 102p yellow brn   5.50 4.75
a.   Imperf., pair   30.00
C105 AP23 102p violet ('37)   2.50 2.50
C106 AP23 102p brn org ('38)   2.25 2.25
   Nos. C102-C106 (6)   29.75 24.00

Excellent counterfeits are plentiful.
For surcharges see Nos. C108-C109.

Types of 1934-35 Surcharged in Red

1937, Aug. 1
C107 AP21 24p on 33.75p sl bl   1.00   .70
C108 AP23 65p on 102p ol bis   2.50 1.75
C109 AP23 84p on 102p bl grn   2.50 1.50
   Nos. C107-C109 (3)   6.00 3.95

Plane over Asunción — AP24

1939, Aug. 3 Typo. Perf. 10½, 11½
C110	AP24	3.40p yel green	1.00	.65
C111	AP24	3.40p orange brn	.60	.50
C112	AP24	3.40p indigo	.60	.50
		Nos. C110-C112 (3)	2.20	1.65

Buenos Aires Peace Conference Type and

Map of Paraguay with New Chaco Boundary — AP28

Designs: 1p, Flags of Paraguay and Bolivia. 3p, Coats of Arms. 5p, Pres. Ortiz of Argentina, flags of Paraguay, Argentina. 10p, Pres. Vargas, Brazil. 30p, Pres. Alessandri, Chile. 50p, US Eagle and Shield. 100p, Pres. Benavides, Peru. 200p, Pres. Baldomir, Uruguay.

Engr.; Flags Litho.
1939, Nov. Perf. 12½
Flags in National Colors
C113	A69	1p red brown	.65	.60
C114	A69	3p dark blue	.65	.60
C115	A70	5p olive blk	.65	.60
C116	A70	10p violet	.65	.60
C117	A70	30p orange	.65	.60
C118	A70	50p black brn	1.00	.60
C119	A70	100p brt green	1.30	.90
C120	A70	200p green	6.00	3.75
C121	AP28	500p black	28.00	17.50
		Nos. C113-C121 (9)	39.55	25.75

For overprints see Nos. 388-390.

University of Asuncion Type
Pres. Bernardino Caballero and Senator José S. Decoud.

1939, Sept. Litho. Perf. 12
C122	A67	28p rose & blk	10.00	10.00
C123	A67	90p yel grn & blk	12.00	12.00

Map with Asunción to New York Air Route — AP35

1939, Nov. 30 Engr.
C124	AP35	30p brown	8.00	6.00
C125	AP35	80p orange	9.50	9.00
C126	AP35	90p purple	12.50	12.00
		Nos. C124-C126 (3)	30.00	27.00

New York World's Fair.

Pan American Union Type
1940, May Perf. 12
C127	A85	20p rose car	.60	.60
C128	A85	70p violet bl	1.25	.60
C129	A85	100p Prus grn	1.50	1.50
C130	A85	500p dk violet	6.75	5.25
		Nos. C127-C130 (4)	10.10	7.95

Asuncion 400th Anniv. Type
1942, Aug. 15
C131	A93	20p deep plum	.90	.50
C132	A94	70p fawn	2.60	1.60
C133	A95	500p olive gray	7.00	5.00
		Nos. C131-C133 (3)	10.50	7.10

Imperforates
Starting with No. C134, many Paraguayan air mail stamps exist imperforate.

Port of Asunción — AP40

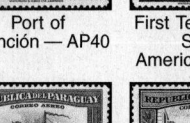
First Telegraph in South America — AP41

Early Merchant Ship AP42

Birthplace of Paraguay's Liberation AP43

Monument to Antequera AP44

Locomotive of First Paraguayan Railroad AP45

Monument to Heroes of Itororó AP46

Primitive Postal Service among Indians AP48

Government House — AP47

Colonial Jesuit Altar — AP49

Ruins of Humaitá Church AP50

Oratory of the Virgin AP51

Marshal Francisco S. Lopez — AP52

1944-45 Unwmk. Perf. 12½
C134	AP40	1c blue	.60	.25
C135	AP41	2c green	.60	.25
C136	AP42	3c brown vio	.60	.25
C137	AP43	5c brt bl grn	.60	.25
C138	AP44	10c dk violet	.60	.25
C139	AP45	20c dk brown	.60	.25
C140	AP46	30c lt blue	.60	.25
C141	AP47	40c olive	.60	.25
C142	AP48	70c brown red	.75	.30
C143	AP49	1g orange yel	2.25	.60
C144	AP50	2g copper brn	3.00	.90
C145	AP51	5g black brn	6.00	2.75
C146	AP52	10g indigo	15.00	5.00
		Nos. C134-C146 (13)	31.80	11.55

See Nos. C158-C162. For surcharges see Nos. C154-C157.

Flags Type
20c, Ecuador. 40c, Bolivia. 70c, Mexico. 1g, Chile. 2g, Brazil. 5g, Argentina. 10g, US.

Engr.; Flags Litho. in Natl. Colors
1945, Aug. 15
C147	A106	20c orange	.60	.60
C148	A106	40c olive	.60	.60
C149	A106	70c lake	.60	.60
C150	A106	1g slate bl	1.00	1.00
C151	A106	2g blue vio	1.50	1.50
C152	A106	5g green	4.25	4.25
C153	A106	10g brown	11.00	11.00
		Nos. C147-C153 (7)	19.55	19.55

Sizes: Nos. C147-C151, 30x26mm; 5g, 32x28mm; 10g, 33x30mm.

Catalogue values for unused stamps in this section, from this point to the end of the section, are for Never Hinged items.

Nos. C139-C142 Srchd. in Black

1946 Engr. Perf. 12½
C154	AP45	5c on 20c dk brn	.80	.80
C155	AP46	5c on 30c lt blue	.80	.80
C156	AP47	5c on 40c olive	.80	.80
C157	AP48	5c on 70c brn red	.80	.80
		Nos. C154-C157 (4)	3.20	3.20

Types of 1944-45
1946, Sept. 21 Engr.
C158	AP50	10c dp car	.40	.40
C159	AP40	20c emerald	.40	.40
C160	AP47	1g brown org	.70	.70
C161	AP52	5g purple	2.00	2.00
C162	AP51	10g rose car	10.00	10.00
		Nos. C158-C162 (5)	13.50	13.50

Marshal Francisco Solano Lopez Type
1947, May. 15 Perf. 12
C163	A114	32c car lake	.30	.30
C164	A114	64c orange brn	.45	.45
C165	A114	1g Prus green	.90	.90
C166	A114	5g Prus grn & brn vio	2.40	2.40
C167	A114	10g dk car rose & dk yel grn	5.00	5.00
		Nos. C163-C167 (5)	9.05	9.05

Archbishopric of Asunción Types
1948, Jan. 6 Unwmk. Perf. 12½
Size: 25½x31mm
C168	A116	20c gray blk	.40	.25
C169	A117	30c dark blue	.40	.25
C170	A118	40c lilac	.70	.35
C171	A115	70c orange red	.90	.45
C172	A112	1g brown red	.90	.45
C173	A118	2g red	1.90	1.25

Size: 25½x34mm
C174	A115	5g brt car & dk bl	4.50	2.25
C175	A115	10g dk grn & brn	7.50	3.75
		Nos. C168-C175 (8)	17.20	8.90

For surcharges see Nos. B11, C178.

Type of Regular Issue of 1948 Inscribed "AEREO"
1948, Sept. 11 Engr. & Litho.
C176	A119	69c dk grn	1.40 1.40
C177	A119	5g dk blue	7.50 7.50

The Barefeet, a political group.

No. C171 Surcharged in Black

1949, June 29
C178	A115	5c on 70c org red	.30 .25

Archbishop Juan Sinforiano Bogarin (1863-1949).

Symbols of UPU — AP65

1950, Sept. 4 Engr. Perf. 13½x13
C179	AP65	20c green & violet	.60	.25
C180	AP65	30c rose vio & brn	.90	.40
C181	AP65	50c gray & green	1.20	.50
C182	AP65	1g blue & brown	1.50	.65
C183	AP65	5g rose & black	3.50	1.00
		Nos. C179-C183 (5)	7.70	2.80

UPU, 75th anniv. (in 1949).

Franklin D. Roosevelt — AP66

Engr.; Flags Litho.
1950, Oct. 2 Perf. 12½
Flags in Carmine & Violet Blue
C184	AP66	20c red	.30	.25
C185	AP66	30c black	.30	.25
C186	AP66	50c claret	.30	.25
C187	AP66	1g dk gray grn	.40	.25
C188	AP66	5g deep blue	.50	.40
		Nos. C184-C188 (5)	1.80	1.40

Franklin D. Roosevelt (1882-1945).

Urn Containing Remains of Columbus AP67

1952, Feb. 11 Litho. Perf. 10
C189	AP67	10c ultra	.40	.25
C190	AP67	20c green	.40	.25
C191	AP67	30c lilac	.40	.25
C192	AP67	40c rose	.40	.25
C193	AP67	50c bister brn	.40	.25
C194	AP67	1g blue	.40	.25
C195	AP67	2g orange	.40	.25
C196	AP67	5g red brown	.60	.30
		Nos. C189-C196 (8)	3.40	2.05

Queen Isabella I — AP68

1952, Oct. 12
C197	AP68	1g vio blue	.30	.25
C198	AP68	2g chocolate	.40	.30
C199	AP68	5g dull green	.80	.50
C200	AP68	10g lilac rose	1.60	1.00
		Nos. C197-C200 (4)	3.10	2.05

500th birth anniv. of Queen Isabella I of Spain (in 1951).

Pettirossi Type
1954, Mar.
C201	A122	40c brown	.55	.25
C202	A122	55c green	.55	.25
C203	A122	80c ultra	.55	.25
C204	A122	1.30g gray blue	.55	.25
		Nos. C201-C204 (4)	2.20	1.00

Church of San Roque — AP70

1954, June 20 Engr. Perf. 12x13
C205	AP70	20c carmine	.30	.25
C206	AP70	30c brown vio	.30	.25
C207	AP70	50c ultra	.30	.25
C208	AP70	1g red brn & bl grn	.35	.25
C209	AP70	1g red brn & lil rose	.35	.25
C210	AP70	1g red brn & blk	.35	.25
C211	AP70	1g red brn & org	.35	.25
a.		Min. sheet of 4, #C208-C211, perf. 12x12½	14.00	7.00
C212	AP70	5g dk red brn & vio	.70	.30
C213	AP70	5g dk red brn & ol grn	.70	.30
C214	AP70	5g dk red brn & org yel	.70	.30
C215	AP70	5g dk red brn & yel org	.70	.30
a.		Min. sheet of 4, #C212-C215, perf. 12x12½	14.00	7.00
		Nos. C205-C215 (11)	5.10	2.95

Centenary (in 1953) of the establishment of the Church of San Roque, Asuncion.

Nos. C211a and C215a issued without gum.

Heroes Type
Unwmk.
1954, Aug. 15   Litho.   *Perf. 10*

C216	A123	5g violet	.50	.25
C217	A123	10g olive green	1.00	.40
C218	A123	20g gray brown	1.75	.70
C219	A123	50g vermilion	2.75	1.75
C220	A123	100g blue	10.00	5.75
	Nos. C216-C220 (5)		16.00	8.85

Peron Visit Type
Photo. & Litho.
1955, Apr.   Wmk. 90   *Perf. 13x13½*
Frames & Flags in Blue & Carmine

C221	A124	60c ol grn & cream	.95	.80
C222	A124	2g bl grn & cream	.95	.80
C223	A124	3g brn org & cream	.95	.80
C224	A124	4.10g brt rose pink & cr	.95	.80
	Nos. C221-C224 (4)		3.80	3.20

Monsignor Rodriguez Type

Jesuit Ruins: 3g, Corridor at Trinidad. 6g, Tower of Santa Rosa. 10g, San Cosme gate. 20g, Church of Jesus. 30g, Niche at Trinidad. 50g, Sacristy at Trinidad.

Perf. 12½x12, 12x12½
1955, June 19   Engr.   Unwmk.

C225	A125	2g aqua	.60	.25
C226	A125	3g olive grn	.60	.25
C227	A124	4g lt blue grn	.60	.25
C228	A126	6g brown	.60	.25
C229	A125	10g rose	.60	.25
C230	A125	20g brown ol	.60	.25
C231	A126	30g dk green	1.00	.25
C232	A126	50g dp aqua	1.25	.30
	Nos. C225-C232 (8)		5.85	2.05

For surcharges see Nos. C252-C259.

Soldier and Flags AP75

"Republic" and Soldier AP76

1957, June 12   Photo.   *Perf. 13½*
Granite Paper
Flags in Red and Blue

C233	AP75	10c ultra	.45	.25
C234	AP75	15c dp claret	.45	.25
C235	AP75	20c red	.45	.25
C236	AP75	25c light blue	.45	.25
C237	AP75	50c bluish grn	.45	.25
C238	AP75	1g rose car	.55	.25
C239	AP76	1.30g dp claret	.55	.25
C240	AP76	1.50p light blue	.55	.25
C241	AP76	2g emerald	.55	.25
C242	AP76	4.10g red	.55	.25
C243	AP76	5g gray black	.55	.25
C244	AP76	10g bluish grn	.65	.25
C245	AP76	25g ultra	.55	.25
	Nos. C233-C245 (13)		6.75	3.25

Heroes of the Chaco war.

Stroessner Type of Regular Issue
1958, Aug. 16   Litho.   Wmk. 320
Center in Slate

C246	A130	12g rose lilac	1.10	1.00
C247	A130	18g orange	1.40	1.00
C248	A130	23g orange brn	1.40	1.00
C249	A130	36g emerald	2.75	2.00
C250	A130	50g citron	5.50	4.00
C251	A130	65g gray	11.00	6.00
	Nos. C246-C251 (6)		23.15	15.00

Re-election of Pres. General Alfredo Stroessner.

Nos. C225-C232 Surcharged like #545-551 in Red
Perf. 12½x12, 12x12½
1959, May 26   Engr.   Unwmk.

C252	A125	4g on 2g aqua	.60	1.00
C253	A125	12.45g on 3g ol grn	.60	.50
C254	A126	18.15g on 6g brown	.85	.50
C255	A125	23.40g on 10g rose	1.00	.50
C256	A125	34.80g on 20g brn ol	1.25	1.00
C257	A126	36g on 4g lt bl grn	2.50	1.00
C258	A126	43.95g on 30g dk grn	2.50	1.00

C259	A126	100g on 50g deep aqua	6.25	2.50
	Nos. C252-C259 (8)		15.55	8.00

The surcharge is made to fit the stamps. Counterfeits of surcharge exist.

UN Emblem — AP77

Unwmk.
1959, Aug. 27   Typo.   *Perf. 11*

C260	AP77	5g ocher & ultra	1.00	.80

Visit of Dag Hammarskjold, Secretary General of the UN, Aug. 27-29.

Map and UN Emblem — AP78

1959, Oct. 24   Litho.   *Perf. 10*

C261	AP78	12.45g blue & salmon	.50	.25

United Nations Day, Oct. 24, 1959.

Olympic Games Type of Regular Issue

Design: Basketball.

1960, Mar. 18   Photo.   *Perf. 12½*

C262	A131	12.45g red & dk bl	.45	.30
C263	A131	18.15g lilac & gray ol	.45	.30
C264	A131	36g bl grn & rose car	.75	.45
	Nos. C262-C264 (3)		1.65	1.05

The Paraguayan Philatelic Agency reported as spurious the imperf. souvenir sheet reproducing one of No. C264. Value, $10.

Uprooted Oak Emblem — AP79

1960, Apr. 7   Litho.   *Perf. 11*

C265	AP79	4g green & pink	.85	.40
C266	AP79	12.45g bl & yel grn	1.50	.65
C267	AP79	18.15g car & ocher	2.10	.75
C268	AP79	23.40g red org & bl	2.50	1.50
	Nos. C265-C268 (4)		6.95	3.30

World Refugee Year, July 1, 1959-June 30, 1960 (1st issue).

Human Rights Type of Regular Issue, 1960

Designs: 40g, UN Emblem. 60g, Hands holding scales. 100g, Flame.

1960, Apr. 21   *Perf. 12½x13*

C269	A133	40g dk ultra & red	.30	.25
C270	A133	60g grnsh bl & org	.50	.30
C271	A133	100g dk ultra & red	1.40	.65
	Nos. C269-C271 (3)		2.20	1.20

An imperf. miniature sheet exists, containing one each of Nos. C269-C271, all printed in green and vermilion. Value, $15.

UN Type of Regular Issue
Perf. 13x13½
1960, Oct. 24   Photo.   Unwmk.

C272	A134	3g orange, red & bl	.70	.30
C273	A134	4g pale grn, red & bl	.70	.30

International Bridge, Paraguay-Brazil AP80

1961, Jan. 26   Litho.   *Perf. 14*

C274	AP80	3g carmine	.65	.50
C275	AP80	12.45g brown lake	1.00	.75
C276	AP80	18.15g Prus grn	1.25	1.00

C277	AP80	36g dk blue	2.60	2.00
a.	Souv. sheet of 4, #C274-C277, imperf.		15.00	15.00
	Nos. C274-C277 (4)		5.50	4.25

Inauguration of the International Bridge between Paraguay and Brazil.

"Paraguay en Marcha" Type of 1961

12.45g, Truck carrying logs. 18.15g, Logs on river barge. 22g, Radio tower. 36g, Jet plane.

1961, Apr. 10   Photo.   *Perf. 13*

C278	A136	12.45g yel & vio bl	.65	.35
C279	A136	18.15g pur & ocher	.90	.50
C280	A136	22g ultra & ocher	1.00	.60
C281	A136	36g brt grn & yel	1.75	1.00
	Nos. C278-C281 (4)		4.30	2.45

Declaration of Independence AP81

1961, May 16   Litho.   *Perf. 14½*

C282	AP81	12.45g dl red brn	.80	.40
C283	AP81	18.15g dk blue	.90	.60
C284	AP81	23.40g green	1.25	.90
C285	AP81	30g lilac	1.60	1.00
C286	AP81	36g rose	2.10	1.50
C287	AP81	44g olive	2.75	1.75
	Nos. C282-C287 (6)		9.40	6.15

150th anniv. of Independence (1st issue).

"Paraguay" and Clasped Hands — AP82

1961, June 12   *Perf. 14x14½*

C288	AP82	3g vio blue	.75	.50
C289	AP82	4g rose claret	.90	.60
C290	AP82	100g gray green	5.75	4.00
	Nos. C288-C290 (3)		7.40	5.10

Chaco Peace; 150th anniv. of Independence (2nd issue).

South American Tapir — AP83

1961, Aug. 16   Unwmk.   *Perf. 14*

C291	AP83	12.45g claret	3.25	2.00
C292	AP83	18.15g ultra	3.25	2.50
C293	AP83	34.80g red brown	6.00	4.50
	Nos. C291-C293 (3)		12.50	9.00

150th anniv. of Independence (3rd issue).

Catholic University Type of 1961
1961, Sept. 18   *Perf. 14x14½*

C294	A140	3g bister brn	.80	.40
C295	A140	12.45g lilac rose	.80	.40
C296	A140	36g blue	1.60	.80
	Nos. C294-C296 (3)		3.20	1.60

Hotel Guarani Type of 1961

Design: Hotel Guarani, different view.

1961, Oct. 14   Litho.   *Perf. 15*

C297	A141	3g dull red brn	2.00	1.75
C298	A141	4g ultra	2.00	1.75
C299	A141	18.15g orange	2.25	1.75
C300	A141	36g rose car	4.75	2.00
	Nos. C297-C300 (4)		11.00	7.25

Tennis Type
1961, Oct. 16   Unwmk.   *Perf. 11*

C301	A142	12.45g multi	2.10	.65
C302	A142	20g multi	4.00	1.25
C303	A142	50g multi	10.00	3.00
	Nos. C301-C303 (3)		16.10	4.90

Some specialists question the status of this issue.

Two imperf. souvenir sheets exist containing four 12.45g stamps each in a different color with simulated perforations and black marginal inscription.

WRY Type

Design: Oak emblem rooted in ground, wavy-lined frame.

1961, Dec. 30

C307	A145	18.15g brn & red	.60	.50
C308	A145	36g car & emer	2.90	1.25
C309	A145	50g emer & org	3.50	1.60
	Nos. C307-C309 (3)		7.00	3.35

Imperforates in changed colors and souvenir sheets exist. Some specialists question the status of this issue.

Pres. Alfredo Stroessner and Prince Philip — AP84

1962, Mar. 9   Litho.
Portraits in Ultramarine

C310	AP84	12.45g grn & buff	3.00	2.00
C311	AP84	18.15g red & pink	3.00	2.00
C312	AP84	36g brn & yel	3.00	2.00
	Nos. C310-C312 (3)		9.00	6.00

Visit of Prince Philip, Duke of Edinburgh, perf. and imperf. souvenir sheets exist. Values: each $5.

Illustrations AP85-AP89, AP92-AP94, AP96-AP97, AP99-AP105, AP107-AP110, AP113-AP115, AP117, AP123, AP127a, AP132-AP133, AP136, AP138, AP140, AP142, AP144-AP145, AP149-AP150, AP152-AP153, AP156, AP158-AP159, AP165, AP167, AP171, AP180, AP183-AP184, AP187, AP196, AP202, AP205, AP208, AP211, AP221-AP222, AP224-AP225, AP229, AP234-AP235, AP237 and AP240 are reduced.

Souvenir Sheet

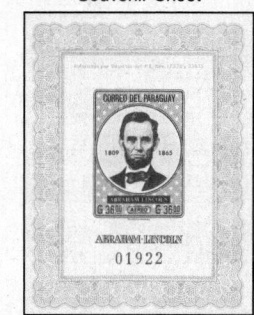

Abraham Lincoln (1809-1865), 16th President of U.S. — AP85

1963, Aug. 21   Litho.   *Imperf.*

C313	AP85	36g gray & vio brn	10.00	10.00

Souvenir Sheet

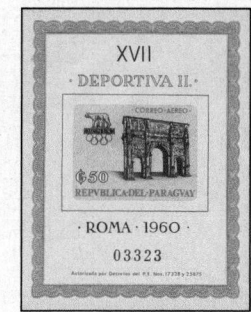

1960 Summer Olympics, Rome — AP86

1963, Aug. 21   Litho. & Engr.

C314	AP86	50g lt bl, vio brn & sep	77.50	75.00

Souvenir Sheet

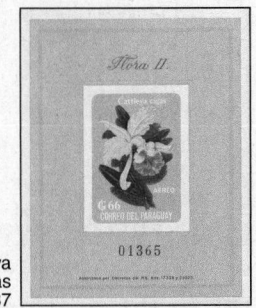

Cattleya
Cigas
AP87

1963, Aug. 21 **Litho.**
C315 AP87 66g multicolored 60.00 60.00

Souvenir Sheet

Pres. Alfredo Stroessner — AP88

1964, Nov. 3
C316 AP88 36g multicolored 8.00 7.00

Souvenir Sheet

Saturn V
Rocket,
Pres.
John F.
Kennedy
AP89

1968, Jan. 27 **Perf. 14**
C317 AP89 50g multicolored 20.00 20.00
Pres. Kennedy, 4th death anniv. (in 1967).

Torch, Book,
Houses — AP90

1969, June 28 **Wmk. 347** **Perf. 11**
C318 AP90 36g blue 2.00 1.00
C319 AP90 50g bister brn 4.00 2.00
C320 AP90 100g rose car 6.00 3.00
Nos. C318-C320 (3) 12.00 6.00
National drive for teachers' homes.

Souvenir Sheets

U.S.
Space
Program
AP91

John F. Kennedy, Wernher von Braun,
moon and: No. C321, Apollo 11 en route to

moon. No. C322, Saturn V lift-off. No. C323,
Apollo 9. No. C324, Apollo 10.

1969, July 9 **Perf. 14**
C321 AP91 23.40g multi 15.00 15.00
C322 AP91 23.40g multi 22.50 22.50
Imperf
C323 AP91 23.40g multi 22.50 22.50
C324 AP91 23.40g multi 27.50 27.50
Nos. C323-C324 each contain one
56x46mm stamp.

Souvenir Sheets

Events and Anniversaries — AP92

#C325, Apollo 14. #C326, Dwight D. Eisen-
hower, 1st death anniv. #C327, Napoleon
Bonaparte, birth bicent. #C328, Brazil, winners of Jules Rimet World Cup Soccer Trophy.

1970, Dec. 16 **Perf. 13½**
C325 AP92 20g multicolored 22.50 22.50
C326 AP92 20g multicolored 12.00 12.00
C327 AP92 20g multicolored 15.00 15.00
C328 AP92 20g multicolored 15.00 15.00
Nos. C325-C328 (4) 64.50 64.50

Souvenir Sheets

Paraguayan Postage Stamps,
Cent. — AP93

No. C329, Marshal Francisco Solano Lopez,
Pres. Alfredo Stroessner, Paraguay #1. No.
C330, #3, 1014, 1242. No. C331, #1243, C8,
C74.

1971, Mar. 23
C329 AP93 20g multicolored 7.50 7.50
C330 AP93 20g multicolored 14.00 14.00
C331 AP93 20g multicolored 14.00 14.00
Nos. C329-C331 (3) 35.50 35.50
Issued: #C329, 3/23; #C330-C331, 3/29.

Souvenir Sheets

Emblems
of Apollo
Space
Missions
AP94

Designs: No. C332, Apollo 7, 8, 9, & 10. No.
C333, Apollo 11, 12, 13, & 14.

1971, Mar. 26
C332 AP94 20g multicolored 13.00 13.00
C333 AP94 20g multicolored 13.00 13.00

Souvenir Sheet

Charles
de
Gaulle
AP95

1971, Dec. 24 **Perf. 14**
C334 AP95 20g multicolored 17.50 17.50

Souvenir Sheet

Taras Shevchenko (1814-1861),
Ukrainian Poet — AP96

1971, Dec. 24 **Perf. 13½**
C335 AP96 20g multicolored 7.50 7.50

Souvenir Sheets

Johannes Kepler (1571-1630),
German Astronomer — AP97

Kepler and: No. C336, Apollo lunar module
over moon. No. C337, Astronaut walking in
space.

1971, Dec. 24
C336 AP97 20g multicolored 17.00 17.00
C337 AP97 20g multicolored 17.00 17.00

Souvenir Sheet

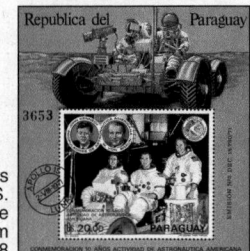

10 years
of U.S.
Space
Program
AP98

1972, Jan. 6 **Perf. 13½**
C338 AP98 20g multicolored 17.00 17.00

Souvenir Sheet

Apollo
16 Moon
Mission
AP99

1972, Mar. 29 **Litho.** **Perf. 13½**
C339 AP99 20g multicolored 17.00 17.00

Souvenir Sheets

History
of the
Olympics
AP100

Designs: No. C340, Pierre de Coubertin
(1863-1937), founder of modern Olympics.
No. C341, Skier, Garmisch-Partenkirchen,
1936. No. C342, Olympic flame, Sapporo,
1972. No. C343, French, Olympic flags. No.
C344, Javelin thrower, Paris, 1924. No. C345,
Equestrian event.

1972, Mar. 29 **Perf. 14½**
C340 AP100 20g multicolored 15.00 12.00
C341 AP100 20g multicolored 15.00 12.00
C342 AP100 20g multicolored 15.00 15.00
C343 AP100 20g multicolored 15.00 15.00
C344 AP100 20g multicolored 15.00 15.00
C345 AP100 20g multicolored 15.00 15.00
Nos. C340-C345 (6) 90.00 84.00

Souvenir Sheet

Medal Totals, 1972 Winter Olympics,
Sapporo — AP101

1972, Nov. 18 **Perf. 13½**
C346 AP101 23.40g multi 15.00 15.00

Souvenir Sheets

French Contributions to Aviation and
Space Exploration — AP102

Georges Pompidou, Charles de Gaulle and:
No. C347, Concorde. No. C348, Satellite D2A,
Mirage G 8 jets.

1972, Nov. 25
C347 AP102 23.40g multi 50.00 50.00
C348 AP102 23.40g multi 45.00 45.00

Souvenir Sheets

Summer Olympic Gold Medals, 1896-
1972 — AP103

No. C349, 9 medals, 1896-1932, vert. No.
C350, 8 medals, 1936-1972.

1972, Nov. 25
C349 AP103 23.40g multi 15.00 15.00
C350 AP103 23.40g multi 15.00 15.00

Souvenir Sheet

Adoration of the Shepherds by Murillo — AP104

1972, Nov. 25
C351 AP104 23.40g multi   15.00 15.00
Christmas.

Souvenir Sheet

Apollo 17 Moon Mission AP105

1973, Mar. 13
C352 AP105 25g multicolored   20.00 20.00

Souvenir Sheet

Medal Totals, 1972 Summer Olympics, Munich — AP106

1973, Mar. 15   *Perf. 13½*
C353 AP106 25g multicolored   25.00 25.00

Souvenir Sheets

The Holy Family by Peter Paul Rubens AP107

Design: No. C355, In the Forest at Pierrefonds by Alfred de Dreux.

1973, Mar. 15
C354 AP107 25g multicolored   20.00 20.00
C355 AP107 25g multicolored   15.00 15.00

Souvenir Sheet

German Championship Soccer Team F.C. Bayern, Bavaria #2 — AP108

1973, June 29   *Imperf.*
C356 AP108 25g multicolored   15.00 15.00
IBRA '73 Intl. Philatelic Exhibition, Munich,

Souvenir Sheet

Copernicus, 500th Birth Anniv. and Space Exploration — AP109

#C357, Lunar surface, Apollo 11. #C358, Copernicus, position of Earth at soltices and equinoxes, vert. #C359, Skylab space laboratory.

1973, June 29   *Perf. 13½*
C357 AP109 25g multicolored   30.00 30.00
C358 AP109 25g multicolored   30.00 30.00
C359 AP109 25g multicolored   20.00 20.00
  Nos. C357-C359 (3)   80.00 80.00

Souvenir Sheets

Exploration of Mars — AP110

1973, Oct. 8
C360 AP110 25g Mariner 9   20.00 20.00
C361 AP110 25g Viking probe,
          horiz.   30.00 30.00

Pres. Stroessner's Visit to Europe and Morocco AP111

Designs: No. C362a, 5g, Arms of Paraguay, Spain, Canary Islands. b, 10g, Gen. Franco, Stroessner, vert. c, 25g, Arms of Paraguay, Germany. d, 50g, Stroessner, Giovanni Leone, Italy, vert. No. C363, Itaipu Dam between Paraguay and Brazil.

1973, Dec. 30   *Perf. 14*
C362 AP111   Strip of 4,
                  #a.-d.   2.00 1.25
C363 AP111 150g multicolored 2.50 1.75
  Nos. C362-C363 (2)   4.50 3.00

Souvenir Sheet
Imperf
C364 AP111 100g Country
            flags   15.00 15.00
No. C364 contains one 60x50mm stamp.
See Nos. C375-C376.

1974 World Cup Soccer Championships, Munich — AP112

Abstract paintings of soccer players: No. C366a, 10g, Player seated on globe. b, 20g, Player as viewed from under foot. No. C367, Player kicking ball. No. C368, Goalie catching ball, horiz.

1974, Jan. 31   *Perf. 14*
C365 AP112 5g shown   10.00 3.50
C366 AP112   Pair, #a.-b.   2.00 1.00
  Nos. C365-C366 (2)   12.00 4.50

Souvenir Sheets
Perf. 13½
C367 AP112 25g multicolored   15.00 15.00
C368 AP112 25g multicolored   15.00 15.00
Nos. C367-C368 each contain one 50x60mm stamp.

Souvenir Sheets

Tourism Year AP113

Design: No. C370, Painting, Birth of Christ by Louis le Nain (1593-1648), horiz.

1974, Feb. 4   *Perf. 13½*
C369 AP113 25g multicolored   12.00 12.00
C370 AP113 25g multicolored   7.00 7.00
          Christmas (No. C370).

Souvenir Sheets

Events and Anniversaries — AP114

No. C371, Rocket lift-off. No. C372, Solar system, horiz. No. C373, Skylab 2 astronauts, horiz. No. C374, Olympic Flame.

1974, Mar. 20
C371 AP114 25g multicolored   20.00 20.00
C372 AP114 25g multicolored   20.00 20.00
C373 AP114 25g multicolored   12.00 12.00
C374 AP114 25g multicolored   12.00 12.00
  Nos. C371-C374 (4)   64.00 64.00
UPU centennial (#C371-C372). 1976 Olympic Games (#C374).

President Stroessner Type of 1973
100g, Stroessner, Georges Pompidou. 200g, Stroessner and Pope Paul VI.

1974, Apr. 25   *Perf. 14*
C375 AP111 100g multicolored   2.00 1.00
Souvenir Sheet
Perf. 13½
C376 AP111 200g multicolored   5.00 5.00
No. C376 contains one 60x50mm stamp.

Souvenir Sheet

Lufthansa Airlines Intercontinental Routes, 40th Anniv. — AP115

1974, July 13   *Perf. 13½*
C377 AP115 15g multicolored   15.00 15.00
No. C377 face value was 15g plus 5g extra for a monument to Francisco Solano Lopez.

Souvenir Sheet

Hermann Oberth, 80th Anniv. of Birth AP115a

1974, July 13 Litho.   *Perf. 13½*
C378 AP115a 15g multi   25.00 25.00
No. C378 face value was 15g plus 5g extra for a monument to Francisco Solano Lopez.

1974 World Cup Soccer Championships, West Germany — AP116

1974, July 13   *Perf. 14*
C379 AP116 4g Goalie   10.00 5.00
C380 AP116 5g Soccer ball   2.50 1.10
C381 AP116 10g shown   3.50 1.50
  Nos. C379-C381 (3)   16.00 7.60
Souvenir Sheet
Perf. 13½
C382 AP116 15g Soccer ball,
              diff.   22.50 22.50
No. C382 contains one 53x46mm stamp. No. C382 face value was 15g plus 5g extra for a monument for Francisco Solano Lopez.

Souvenir Sheet

First Balloon Flight over English Channel AP117

1974, Sept. 13   *Imperf.*
C383 AP117 15g multicolored 24.00 24.00
No. C383 face value was 15g plus 5g extra for a monument for Francisco Solano Lopez.

Anniversaries and Events — AP118

Designs: 4g, US #C76 on covers that went to Moon. No. C385a, 5g, Pres. Pinochet of Chile. No. C385b, 10g, Pres. Stroessner's visit to South Africa. No. C386, Mariner 10 over Mercury, horiz.

1974, Dec. 2   *Perf. 14*
C384 AP118 4g multicolored   5.00 5.00
C385 AP118   Pair #a.-b.   1.25 1.00
  Nos. C384-C385 (2)   6.25 6.00
Souvenir Sheets
Perf. 13½
C386 AP118 15g multicolored 15.00 15.00
Nos. C386 contains one 60x50mm stamp. Face value was 15g plus 5g extra for a monument to Francisco Solano Lopez. Compare No. C386 with No. C392.

Anniversaries and
Events — AP119

Designs: 4g, UPU, cent. 5g, 17th Congress,
UPU, Lausanne. 10g, Intl. Philatelic Exposition, Montevideo, Uruguay. No. C392, Mariner
10 orbiting Mercury, horiz. No. C393, Figure
skater, horiz. No. C394, Innsbruck Olympic
emblem.

1974, Dec. 7   **Perf. 14**
C389 AP119 4g multicolored   3.00   2.00
C390 AP119 5g multicolored   1.10   .75
C391 AP119 10g multicolored   1.10   .75
      Nos. C389-C391 (3)   5.20   3.50
           Souvenir Sheets
               Perf. 13½
C392 AP119 15g bl & multi   15.00   15.00
C393 AP119 15g multicolored   15.00   15.00
C394 AP119 15g multicolored   15.00   15.00

UPU centennial (#C389). Nos. C392-C394
each contain one 60x50mm stamp and face
value was 15g plus 5g extra for a monument to
Francisco Solano Lopez.

German
World Cup
Soccer
Champions
AP120

4g, Holding World Cup trophy, vert. 5g,
Team on field. 10g, Argentina '78 emblem,
vert.
No. C398, Players holding trophy, vert. No.
C399, Hemispheres, emblems of 1974 and
1978 World Cup championships.

1974, Dec. 20   **Perf. 14**
C395 AP120 4g multicolored   5.00   3.25
C396 AP120 5g multicolored   .75   .35
C397 AP120 10g multicolored   1.50   .35
      Nos. C395-C397 (3)   7.25   3.95
           Souvenir Sheets
               Perf. 13½
C398 AP120 15g multicolored   20.00   20.00
C399 AP120 15g multicolored   20.00   20.00

No. C398 contains one 50x60mm stamp,
and No. C399 contains one 60x50mm stamp.
Face value of each sheet was 15g plus 5g
extra for a monument to Francisco Solano
Lopez.

Souvenir Sheet

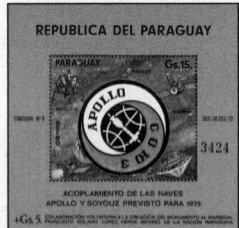

Apollo-Soyuz — AP121

1974, Dec. 20   **Perf. 13½**
C400 AP121 15g multicolored   17.50   17.50

Expo
'75 — AP122

4g, Ryukyumurasaki. 5g, Hibiscus, horiz.
10g, Ancient sailing ship, horiz.
15g, Expo emblem, vert.

1975, Feb. 24   **Perf. 14**
C401 AP122 4g multicolored   3.00   1.10
C402 AP122 5g multicolored   .75   .25
C403 AP122 10g multicolored   1.50   .25
      Nos. C401-C403 (3)   5.25   1.60
           Souvenir Sheet
               Perf. 14½
C404 AP122 15g multicolored   10.00   10.00

No. C404 face value was 15g plus 5g extra
for a monument to Francisco Solano Lopez.

Souvenir Sheets

Anniversaries and Events — AP123

Designs: No. C405, Dr. Kurt Debus, space
scientist, 65th birth anniv. No. C406, 1976
Summer Olympics, Montreal, horiz.

1975, Feb. 24   **Perf. 13½**
C405 AP123 15g multicolored   17.00   17.00
C406 AP123 15g multicolored   17.00   17.00

Nos. C405-C406 face value was 15g plus
5g extra for a monument to Francisco Solano
Lopez.

GEOS
Satellite — AP124

No. C408a, 5g, ESPANA 75. b, 10g, Mother
and Child, Murillo.
No. C409, Spain #1139, 1838, C167, charity
stamp. No. C410, Zeppelin, plane, satellites.
No. C411, Jupiter.

1975, Aug. 21   **Perf. 14**
C407 AP124 4g shown   3.00   1.90
C408 AP124 Pair, #1.-b.   2.25   .50
      Nos. C407-C408 (2)   5.25   2.40
           Souvenir Sheet
               Perf. 13½
C409 AP124 15g multicolored   30.00   30.00
C410 AP124 15g multicolored   40.00   40.00
               Perf. 14½
C411 AP124 15g multicolored   15.00   15.00

Nos. C409-C411 face value was 15g plus
5g extra for a monument to Francisco Solano
Lopez.
Size of stamps: No. C409, 45x55mm; C410,
55x45mm; C411, 32x22mm.

Souvenir Sheets

Anniversaries and Events — AP125

#C413, UN emblem, Intl. Women's Year,
vert. #C414, Helios space satellite.

1975, Aug. 26   **Perf. 13½**
C413 AP125 15g multicolored   15.00   15.00
C414 AP125 15g multicolored   15.00   15.00

Nos. C413-C414 face value was 15g plus
5g extra for a monument to Francisco Solano
Lopez.

Anniversaries
and Events
AP125a

Designs: 4g, First Zeppelin flight, 75th
anniv. 5g, Emblem of 1978 World Cup Soccer
Championships, Argentina, vert. 10g, Emblem
of Nordposta 75, statue.

1975, Oct. 13   Litho.   Perf. 14
C415-C417 AP125a Set of 3   6.00   3.00
           Souvenir Sheets

Anniversaries and Events — AP126

No. C418, Zeppelin, boats. No. C419, Soccer, Intelsat IV, vert. No. C420, Viking Mars
landing.

1975, Oct. 13   **Perf. 13½**
C418 AP126 15g multicolored   17.50   17.50
C419 AP126 15g multicolored   17.50   17.50
C420 AP126 15g multicolored   17.50   17.50
      Nos. C418-C420 (3)   52.50   52.50

Nos. C418-C420 face value was 15g plus
5g extra for a monument to Francisco Solano
Lopez.

United
States,
Bicent.
AP127

#C421: a, 4g, Lunar rover. b, 5g, Ford Elite,
1975. c, 10g, Ford, 1896. No. C422, Airplanes
and spacecraft. No. C423, Arms of Paraguay
& US.

1975, Nov. 28   Litho.   Perf. 14
C421 AP127 Strip of 3, #a.-c.   6.00   3.00
           Souvenir Sheets
               Perf. 13½
C422 AP127 15g multicolored   22.50   22.50
C423 AP127 15g multicolored   22.50   22.50

Nos. C422-C423 each contain one
60x50mm stamp and face value was 15g plus
5g surtax for a monument to Francisco Solano
Lopez.

Souvenir Sheet

La
Musique
by
Francois
Boucher
AP127a

1975, Nov. 28   **Perf. 13½**
C424 AP127a 15g multicolored   7.50   7.50

No. C424 face value was 15g plus 5g extra
for a monument to Francisco Solano Lopez.

Anniversaries
and Events
AP128

Designs: 4g, Flight of Concorde jet. 5g, JU
52/3M, Lufthansa Airlines, 50th anniv. 10g,
EXFILMO '75 and ESPAMER '75. No. C428,
Concorde, diff. No. C429, Dr. Albert Schweitzer, missionary and Konrad Adenauer, German statesman. No. C430, Ferdinand
Porsche, auto designer, birth cent., vert.

1975, Dec. 20   **Perf. 14**
C425 AP128 4g multicolored   4.00   2.50
C426 AP128 5g multicolored   .40   .40
C427 AP128 10g multicolored   .40   .40
      Nos. C425-C427 (3)   4.80   3.30
           Souvenir Sheets
               Perf. 13½
C428 AP128 15g multicolored   27.50   25.00
C429 AP128 15g multicolored   15.00   12.00
C430 AP128 15g multicolored   40.00   40.00

Nos. C428-C430 face value was 15g plus
5g extra for a monument to Francisco Solano
Lopez. No. C428 contains one 54x34mm
stamp, No. C429 one 60x50mm stamp, No.
C430 one 30x40mm stamp.

Anniversaries
and Events
AP129

Details: 4g, The Transfiguration by Raphael,
vert. 5g, Nativity by Del Mayno. 10g, Nativity
by Vignon. No. C434, Detail from Adoration of
the Shepherds by Ghirlandaio. No. C435, Austria, 1000th anniv., Leopold I, natl. arms, vert.
No. C436, Sepp Herberger and Helmut Schon,
coaches for German soccer team.

1976, Feb. 2   Litho.   Perf. 14
C431 AP129 4g multicolored   4.00   2.00
C432 AP129 5g multicolored   .80   .40
C433 AP129 10g multicolored   .80   .40
      Nos. C431-C433 (3)   5.60   2.80
           Souvenir Sheets
               Perf. 13½
C434 AP129 15g multicolored   10.00   10.00
C435 AP129 15g multicolored   40.00   40.00
               Perf. 13½x13
C436 AP129 15g multicolored   75.00   75.00

Nos. C434-C436 face value was 15g plus
5g extra for a monument to Francisco Solano
Lopez. No. C434 contains one 40x30mm
stamp, No. C435 one 30x40mm stamp, No.
C436 one 54x34mm stamp.

Souvenir Sheet

Apollo-Soyuz — AP130

1976, Apr. 2   **Perf. 13½x13**
C437 AP130 25g multicolored   17.00   17.00

Souvenir Sheet

Lufthansa, 50th Anniv. — AP131

1976, Apr. 7   **Perf. 13½x13**
C438 AP131 25g multicolored   14.00   14.00

PARAGUAY

663

Souvenir Sheet

Interphil
'76
AP132

1976, May 12   *Perf. 13½*
C439 AP132 15g multicolored   9.00 9.00

No. C439 face value was 15g plus 5g extra for a monument to Francisco Solano Lopez.

Souvenir Sheets

Anniversaries and Events — AP133

Designs: No. C440, Alexander Graham Bell, telephone cent. No. C441, Gold, silver, and bronze medals, 1976 Winter Olympics, Innsbruck. No. C442, Gold medalist Rosi Mittermaier, downhill and slalom, vert. No. C443, Viking probe on Mars. No. C444, UN Postal Administration, 25th anniv. and UPU, cent., vert. No. C445, Prof. Hermann Oberth, Wernher von Braun. No. C446, Madonna and Child by Durer, vert.

1976   *Perf. 13½*
C440 AP133 25g multi   30.00 30.00
C441 AP133 25g multi   17.50 17.50
C442 AP133 25g multi 125.00 125.00

            Perf. 14½
C443 AP133 25g multi   15.00 15.00
C444 AP133 25g multi   30.00 30.00
C445 AP133 25g multi   60.00 60.00
C446 AP133 25g multi   60.00 60.00
   Nos. C440-C446 (7) 337.50 337.50

No. C442 contains one 35x54mm stamp, No. C443 one 46x36mm stamp, No. C444 one 25x35mm stamp.
  Issued: #C440-C441, 6/15; #C443, 7/8; #C442, C444, 7/15; #C445, 8/20; #C446, 9/9.

Souvenir Sheet

UN Offices in Geneva #22, UN #42 AP136

1976, Dec. 18   *Perf. 13½*
C447 AP136 25g multicolored 14.00 14.00

UN Postal Administration, 25th anniv. and telephone, cent.

Souvenir Sheet

Ludwig van Beethoven (1770-1827) — AP137

1977, Feb. 28 Litho. *Perf. 14¼*
C448 AP137 25g multi   6.00 6.00

Souvenir Sheet

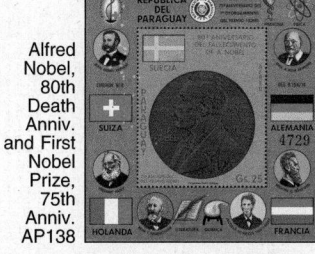

Alfred Nobel, 80th Death Anniv. and First Nobel Prize, 75th Anniv. AP138

1977, June 7   *Perf. 13½*
C449 AP138 25g multicolored 22.50 22.50

Souvenir Sheet

Coronation of Queen Elizabeth II, 25th Anniv. — AP139

1977, July 25   *Perf. 14½*
C450 AP139 25g multicolored 20.00 20.00

Souvenir Sheet

Uruguay '77 Intl. Philatelic Exhibition — AP140

1977, Aug. 27 Litho. *Perf. 13½*
C451 AP140 25g multicolored 14.00 14.00

Souvenir Sheets

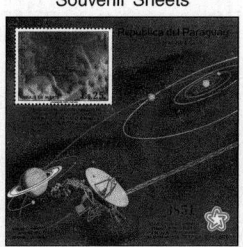

Exploration of Mars — AP141

No. C452, Martian craters. No. C453, Wernher von Braun. No. C454, Projected Martian lander.

1977, Sept. 5   *Perf. 13½*
C452 AP141 25g multicolored 35.00 35.00
       Perf. 14¼x14½
1977, Nov. 28   Litho.
C453 AP141 25g multicolored 40.00 40.00
1977, Oct. 28 Litho. *Perf. 13½*
C454 AP141 25g multicolored 60.00 60.00

Souvenir Sheet

Sepp Herberger, German Soccer Team Coach — AP142

1978, Jan. 23 Litho. *Perf. 13½*
C455 AP142 25g multicolored 35.00 35.00

Souvenir Sheet

Austria #B331, Canada #681, US #716, Russia #B66 AP143

1978, Mar. 10 Litho. *Perf. 14½*
C456 AP143 25g multicolored 25.00 25.00

Inner perforations are simulated.

Souvenir Sheet

Alfred Nobel AP144

1978, Mar. 15 Litho. *Perf. 13½*
C457 AP144 25g multicolored 35.00 35.00

Souvenir Sheets

Anniversaries and Events — AP145

Designs: No. C458, Queen Elizabeth II wearing St. Edward's Crown, holding orb and scepter. No. C459, Queen Elizabeth II presenting World Cup Trophy to English team captain. No. C460, Flags of nations participating in 1978 World Cup Soccer Championships. No. C461, Soccer action. No. C462, Argentina, 1978 World Cup Champions.

1978   *Perf. 14½, 13½ (#C461)*
C458 AP145 25g multi   15.00 15.00
C459 AP145 25g multi   25.00 25.00
C460 AP145 25g multi   30.00 30.00
C461 AP145 25g multi   25.00 25.00
C462 AP145 25g multi   25.00 25.00
   Nos. C458-C462 (5) 120.00 120.00

Coronation of Queen Elizabeth II, 25th Anniv. (#C458-C459). 1978 World Cup Soccer Championships, Argentina (#C460-C462). No. C460 contains one 70x50mm stamp, No. C461 one 39x57mm stamp.
  Issued: #C458, 5/11; #C459-C460, 5/16; #C461, 6/30; #C462, 10/26.

Souvenir Sheet

Jean-Henri Dunant, 150th Birth Anniv. — AP146

1978, June 28   *Perf. 14½*
C463 AP146 25g multicolored 20.00 20.00

Souvenir Sheet

Capt. James Cook, 250th Birth Anniv. AP147

1978, July 19   *Perf. 13½*
C464 AP147 25g multicolored 15.00 15.00

Discovery of Hawaii, Death of Capt. Cook, bicentennial; Hawaii Statehood, 20th anniv.

Aregua Satellite Communication Station — AP148

Coat of Arms AP148a

Pres. Alfredo Stroessner — AP148b

1978, Aug. 15 Litho. *Perf. 14*
C465 AP148 75g multi   1.60   .30
C466 AP148a 500g multi 6.50 2.00
C467 AP148b 1000g multi 12.00 4.00
   Nos. C465-C467 (3) 20.10 6.30

Souvenir Sheet

Adoration of the Magi by Albrecht Durer — AP149

1978, Oct. 31   *Perf. 13½*
C468 AP149 25g multicolored 15.00 15.00

Souvenir Sheet

Prof. Hermann Oberth, 85th Birth Anniv. AP150

1979, Aug. 28   *Perf. 14½*
C469 AP150 25g multicolored   20.00 20.00

Souvenir Sheet

World Cup Soccer Championships — AP151

1979, Nov. 29
C470 AP151 25g multicolored   25.00 25.00

Souvenir Sheet

Helicopters — AP152

1979, Nov. 29   **Litho.**   *Perf. 13½*
C471 AP152 25g multicolored   20.00 20.00

Souvenir Sheet

1980 Summer Olympics, Moscow — AP153

1979, Dec. 20   *Perf. 14½*
C472 AP153 25g Two-man ca-
    noe   30.00 30.00

Souvenir Sheet

1982 World Cup Soccer Championships, Spain — AP154

1979, Dec. 24   **Litho.**   *Perf. 13x13½*
C473 AP154 25g Sheet of 1 +
    label   25.00 25.00

Souvenir Sheet

Maybach DS-8 "Zeppelin" — AP155

1980, Apr. 8   *Perf. 14½*
C474 AP155 25g multicolored   30.00 30.00

Wilhelm Maybach, 50th death anniv. Karl Maybach, 100th birth anniv.

Souvenir Sheet

Rotary Intl., 75th Anniv. AP156

1980, July 1   **Litho.**   *Perf. 14½*
C475 AP156 25g multicolored   20.00 20.00

Apollo 11 Type of 1970
Souvenir Sheet

Design: 1st steps on lunar surface.

1980, July 30   *Perf. 13½*
Size: 36x26mm
C476 A221 25g multicolored   17.50 17.50

Souvenir Sheet

Virgin Surrounded by Animals by Albrecht Durer — AP158

Photo. & Engr.
1980, Sept. 24   *Perf. 12*
C477 AP158 25g multi   125.00 125.00

Souvenir Sheet

1980 Olympic Games AP159

1980, Dec. 15   **Litho.**   *Perf. 14*
C478 AP159 25g multi   20.00 20.00

Metropolitan Seminary Centenary AP160

1981, Mar. 26   **Litho.**   **Wmk. 347**
C479 AP160 5g ultra   1.50 1.00
C480 AP160 10g red brn   1.50 1.00
C481 AP160 25g green   1.50 1.00
C482 AP160 50g gray   3.00 1.00
    Nos. C479-C482 (4)   7.50 4.00

Anniversaries and Events — AP161

5g, George Washington, 250th birth anniv. (in 1982). 10g, Queen Mother Elizabeth, 80th birthday (in 1980). 30g, Phila Tokyo '81.
No. C486, Emperor Hirohito, 80th birthday. No. C487, Washington Crossing the Delaware.

1981, July 10   **Unwmk.**   *Perf. 14*
C483 AP161 5g multicolored   6.50 2.25
C484 AP161 10g multicolored   1.25 .45
C485 AP161 30g multicolored   1.50 .55
    Nos. C483-C485 (3)   9.25 3.25
    Souvenir Sheets
    Perf. 14½
C486 AP161 25g multicolored   17.50 17.50
C487 AP161 25g multicolored   17.50 17.50

No. C484 issued in sheets of 8 plus label. For overprints see Nos. 2126, C590-C591, C611.

First Space Shuttle Mission AP162

Pres. Ronald Reagan and: 5g, Columbia in Earth orbit. 10g, Astronauts John Young and Robert Crippen. 30g, Columbia landing.
George Washington and: No. C491, Columbia re-entering atmosphere. No. C492, Columbia inverted above Earth.

1981, Oct. 9   *Perf. 14*
C488 AP162 5g multicolored   6.50 3.25
C489 AP162 10g multicolored   1.25 .80
C490 AP162 30g multicolored   2.00 1.00
    Nos. C488-C490 (3)   9.75 5.05
    Souvenir Sheets
    Perf. 13½
C491 AP162 25g multicolored   17.50 17.50
C492 AP162 25g multicolored   17.50 17.50

Nos. C491-C492 each contain one 60x50mm stamp. Inauguration of Pres. Reagan, George Washington, 250th birth anniv. (in 1982) (#C491-C492).

World Cup Soccer, Spain, 1982 — AP163

1981, Oct. 15   *Perf. 14*
Color of Shirts
C493 AP163 5g yellow, green   4.00 2.00
C494 AP163 10g blue, white   1.10 .50
C495 AP163 30g white & blk,
    org   .60 .30
    Nos. C493-C495 (3)   5.70 2.80
    Souvenir Sheet
    Perf. 14½
C496 AP163 25g Goalie   17.50 17.50

No. C494 exists in sheets of 5 plus 4 labels.

Christmas AP164

Paintings: 5g, Virgin with the Child by Stefan Lochner. 10g, Our Lady of Caacupe. 25g, Altar of the Virgin by Albrecht Durer. 30g, Virgin and Child by Matthias Grunewald.

1981, Dec. 21   *Perf. 14*
C497 AP164 5g multicolored   1.25 .40
C498 AP164 10g multicolored   2.50 .85
C499 AP164 30g multicolored   6.75 2.10
    Nos. C497-C499 (3)   10.50 3.35
    Souvenir Sheet
    Perf. 13½
C500 AP164 25g multicolored   20.00

No. C500 contains one 54x75mm stamp.

Souvenir Sheet

Graf Zeppelin's First Flight to South America, 50th Anniv. — AP165

1981, Dec. 28   *Perf. 14½*
C501 AP165 25g multicolored   24.00 24.00

Mother Maria Mazzarello (1837-1881), Co-Founder of Daughters of Mary — AP166

Perf. 13x13½
1981, Dec. 30   **Litho.**   **Wmk. 347**
C502 AP166 20g blk & grn   1.00 1.00
C503 AP166 25g blk & red brn   1.00 1.00
C504 AP166 50g blk & gray vio   1.00 1.00
    Nos. C502-C504 (3)   3.00 3.00

Souvenir Sheet

The Magus (Dr. Faust) by Rembrandt — AP167

Litho. & Typo.
1982, Apr. 23   **Unwmk.**   *Perf. 14½*
C505 AP167 25g blk, buff &
    gold   20.00 20.00

Johann Wolfgang von Goethe, 150th death anniv.

The following stamps were issued 4 each in sheets of 8 with 1 label: Nos. C590-C591, C669-C670, C677-C678, C682-C683, C690-C691, C699-C700, C718-C719, C747-C748.
The following stamps were issued in sheets of 4 with 5 labels: Nos. C765-C766, C774, C779-C780, C785, C803, C813, C818, C823.
The following stamps were issued in sheets of 3 with 6 labels: Nos. C739, C754.
The following stamps were issued in sheets of 5 with 4 labels: Nos. C507, C512, C515, C519, C524, C529, C535, C539, C542, C548, C550, C559, C569, C572, C579, C582, C585, C588, C596, C598, C615, C622, C626, C634, C642, C647, C650, C656, C705, C711, C731, C791, C798, C808.
The following stamp was issued in sheets of 7 with 2 labels: No. C660.

World Chess Championships Type of 1980

Illustrations from The Book of Chess: 5g, The Game of the Virgins. 10g, Two gothic ladies. 30g, Chess game at apothecary shop.
No. C509, Christians and Jews preparing to play in garden. No. C510, Indian prince introducing chess to Persia.

1982, June 10   **Litho.**   *Perf. 14*
C506 A347 5g multicolored   3.50 1.10
C507 A347 10g multicolored   1.60 .55
C508 A347 30g multicolored   .80 .25
    Nos. C506-C508 (3)   5.90 1.90

PARAGUAY

665

Souvenir Sheets
Perf. 13½
C509 A347 25g multicolored 15.00 15.00
Perf. 14½
C510 A347 25g multicolored 20.00 20.00

No. C509 contains one 50x60mm stamp, No. C510 one 50x70mm stamp. For overprint see No. C665.

Italy, Winners of 1982 World Cup Soccer Championships AP168

Players: 5g, Klaus Fischer, Germany. 10g, Altobelli holding World Cup Trophy. 25g, Forster, Altobelli, horiz. 30g, Fischer, Gordillo.

1982, Oct. 20 **Perf. 14**
C511 AP168 5g multicolored 5.50 1.20
C512 AP168 10g multicolored 1.60 .55
C513 AP168 30g multicolored .80 .25
Nos. C511-C513 (3) 7.90 2.00

Souvenir Sheet
C513A AP168 25g multicolored 14.00 14.00

Christmas AP169

Paintings by Peter Paul Rubens: 5g, The Massacre of the Innocents. 10g, The Nativity, vert. 25g, The Madonna Adored by Four Penitents and Saints. 30g, The Flight to Egypt.

1982, Oct. 23
C514 AP169 5g multicolored 3.50 1.20
C515 AP169 10g multicolored 1.60 .55
C516 AP169 30g multicolored .80 .25
Nos. C514-C516 (3) 5.90 2.00

Souvenir Sheet
Perf. 14½
C517 AP169 25g multicolored 14.00 14.00

No. C517 contains one 50x70mm stamp.

The Sampling Officials of the Draper's Guild by Rembrandt AP170

Details from Rembrandt Paintings: 10g, Self portrait, vert. 25g, Night Watch, vert. 30g, Self portrait, diff., vert.

1983, Jan. 21 **Perf. 14, 13 (10g)**
C518 AP170 5g multicolored 3.50 1.20
C519 AP170 10g multicolored 1.60 .55
C520 AP170 30g multicolored .80 .25
Nos. C518-C520 (3) 5.90 2.00

Souvenir Sheet
Perf. 13½
C521 AP170 25g multicolored 15.00 15.00

No. C521 contains one 50x60mm stamp.

Souvenir Sheet

1982 World Cup Soccer Championships, Spain — AP171

1983, Jan. 21 **Perf. 13½**
C522 AP171 25g Fuji blimp 16.00 16.00

German Rocket Scientists AP172

Designs: 5g, Dr. Walter R. Dornberger, V2 rocket ascending. 10g, Nebel, Ritter, Öberth, Riedel, and Von Braun examining rocket mock-up. 30g, Dr. A. F. Staats, Cyrus B research rocket.

No. C526, Dr. Eugen Sanger, rocket design. No. C527, Fritz Von Opel, Opel-Sander rocket plane. No. C528, Friedrich Schmiedl, first rocket used for mail delivery.

1983 **Perf. 14**
C523 AP172 5g multicolored 4.00 1.25
C524 AP172 10g multicolored 1.75 .60
C525 AP172 30g multicolored .80 .25
Nos. C523-C525 (3) 6.55 2.10

Souvenir Sheets
Perf. 14½
C526 AP172 25g multicolored 35.00 35.00
C527 AP172 25g multicolored 35.00 35.00
C528 AP172 25g multicolored 35.00 35.00

Issued: No. C528, Apr. 13; others, Jan. 24.

First Manned Flight, 200th Anniv. — AP173

Balloons: 5g, Montgolfier brothers, 1783. 10g, Baron von Lutgendorf's, 1786. 30g, Adorne's, 1784.

No. C532, Montgolfier brothers, diff. No. C533, Profiles of Montgolfier Brothers. No. C534, Bicentennial emblem, nova.

1983 **Perf. 14, 13 (10g)**
C529 AP173 5g multicolored 4.00 1.25
C530 AP173 10g multicolored 2.50 .65
C531 AP173 30g multicolored 1.60 .25
Nos. C529-C531 (3) 8.10 2.15

Souvenir Sheets
Perf. 13½
C532 AP173 25g multicolored 17.00 17.00
C533 AP173 25g multicolored 17.00 17.00
C534 AP173 25g multicolored 17.00 17.00

Nos. C532-C533 each contain one 50x60mm stamp, No. C534 one 30x40mm stamp.
Issued: #C529-C533, 2/25; #C534, 10/19.

1984 Summer Olympics, Los Angeles — AP174

1932 Gold medalists: 5g, Wilson Charles, US, 100-meter dash. 10g, Ellen Preis, Austria, fencing. 25g, Rudolf Ismayr, Germany, weight lifting. 30g, John Anderson, US, discus.

1983, June 13 **Perf. 14**
C535 AP174 5g multicolored .80 .30
C536 AP174 10g multicolored 1.25 .40
C537 AP174 30g multicolored 3.25 .55
Nos. C535-C537 (3) 5.30 1.25

Souvenir Sheet
Perf. 14½
C538 AP174 25g Sheet of 1 + label 20.00 20.00

No. C535 incorrectly credits Charles with gold medal.

Flowers — AP175

1983, Aug. 31 **Perf. 14**
C539 AP175 5g Episcia reptans 1.60 .40
C540 AP175 10g Lilium .80 .25
C541 AP175 30g Heliconia 1.60 .25
Nos. C539-C541 (3) 4.00 .90

Intl. Maritime Organization, 25th Anniv. — AP176

5g, Brigantine Undine. 10g, Training ship Sofia, 1881, horiz. 30g, Training ship Stein, 1879.

No. C545, Santa Maria. No. C546, Santa Maria and Telstar communications satellite.

Perf. 14, 13½x13 (10g)
1983, Oct. 24 **Litho.**
C542 AP176 5g multicolored 2.50 .55
C543 AP176 10g multicolored 1.25 .40
C544 AP176 30g multicolored 1.50 .25
Nos. C542-C544 (3) 5.25 1.20

Souvenir Sheets
Perf. 14½
C545 AP176 25g multicolored 20.00 15.00
Perf. 13½
C546 AP176 25g multicolored 20.00 15.00

No. C546 contains one 90x57mm stamp. Discovery of America, 490th Anniv. (in 1982) (#C545-C546). For overprint see No. 2198.

Space Achievements — AP177

Designs: 5g, Space shuttle Challenger. 10g, Pioneer 10, vert. 30g, Herschel's telescope, Cerro Tololo Obervatory, Chile, vert.

1984, Jan. 9 **Perf. 14**
C547 AP177 5g multicolored 2.75 .90
C548 AP177 10g multicolored 2.75 .90
C549 AP177 30g multicolored .95 .35
Nos. C547-C549 (3) 6.45 2.15

Summer Olympics, Los Angeles — AP178

5g, 400-meter hurdles. 10g, Small bore rifle, horiz. 25g, Equestrian, Christine Stuckleberger. 30g, 100-meter dash.

1984, Jan. **Perf. 14**
C550 AP178 5g multicolored 2.75 .80
C551 AP178 10g multicolored 2.75 .55
C552 AP178 30g multicolored 1.20 .25
Nos. C550-C552 (3) 6.70 1.60

Souvenir Sheet
Perf. 14½
C553 AP178 25g multicolored 25.00 25.00

For overprint see No. 2130.

1984 Winter Olympics, Sarajevo AP179

No. C554, Steve Podborski, downhill. No. C555, Olympic Flag. No. C556, Gaetan Boucher, speed skating.

Perf. 14, 13x13½ (10g)
1984, Mar. 24
C554 AP179 5g multicolored 2.40 .55
C555 AP179 10g multicolored 1.60 .40
C556 AP179 30g multicolored 1.60 .25
Nos. C554-C556 (3) 5.60 1.20

No. C555 printed se-tenant with label.

Souvenir Sheets

Cupid and Psyche by Peter Paul Rubens AP180

Design: No. C558, Satyr and Maenad (copy of Rubens' Bacchanal) by Jean-Antoine Watteau (1684-1721).

1984, Mar. 26 **Perf. 13½**
C557 AP180 25g multicolored 15.00 15.00
C558 AP180 25g multicolored 17.00 17.00

No. C558 contains one 78x57mm stamp.

1982, 1986 World Cup Soccer Championships, Spain, Mexico City — AP181

Soccer players: 5g, Tardelli, Breitner. 10g, Zamora, Stielke. 30g, Walter Schachner, player on ground.
No. C562, Player from Paraguay. No. C563, World Cup Trophy, Spanish, Mexican characters, horiz.

1984, Mar. 29 **Perf. 14, 13 (10g)**
C559 AP181 5g multicolored 2.40 .55
C560 AP181 10g multicolored 1.50 .55
C561 AP181 30g multicolored 1.50 .25
Nos. C559-C561 (3) 5.40 1.35

Souvenir Sheets
Perf. 14½
C562 AP181 25g multicolored 15.00 15.00
C563 AP181 25g multicolored 15.00 15.00

Souvenir Sheet

ESPANA
'84
AP182

1984, Mar. 31
C564 AP182 25g multicolored   20.00 20.00
No. C564 has one stamp and a label.

Souvenir Sheets

ESPANA
'84
AP183

No. C565, Holy Family of the Lamb by Raphael. No. C566, Adoration of the Magi by Rubens.

1984, Apr. 16   *Perf. 13½*
C565 AP183 25g multicolored   15.00 12.00
C566 AP183 25g multicolored   15.00 12.00

Souvenir Sheet

19th UPU Congress — AP184

1984, June 9
C567 AP184 25g multicolored   15.00 12.00

Intl. Chess
Federation, 60th
Anniv. — AP185

10g, Woman holding chess piece. 30g, Bishop, knight.

Perf. 14, 13x13½ (10g)
1984, June 18
C568 AP185 5g shown   3.75 1.20
C569 AP185 10g multicolored 3.00   .80
C570 AP185 30g multicolored 2.25   .25
   Nos. C568-C570 (3)   9.00 2.25

First Europe
to South
America
Airmail Flight
by Lufthansa,
50th Anniv.
AP186

Designs: 5g, Lockheed Superconstellation. 10g, Dornier Wal. 30g, Boeing 707.

Perf. 14, 13½x13 (10g)
1984, June 22
C571 AP186 5g multicolored 2.75   .75
C572 AP186 10g multicolored 1.50   .30
C573 AP186 30g multicolored 1.10   .25
   Nos. C571-C573 (3)   5.35 1.30
For overprint see No. C592.

Souvenir Sheets

First
Moon
Landing,
15th
Anniv.
AP187

No. C574, Apollo 11 lunar module. No. C575, Prof. Hermann Oberth.

1984, June 23   *Perf. 14½*
C574 AP187 25g multicolored 35.00 35.00
C575 AP187 25g multicolored 35.00 35.00

Hermann Oberth, 90th Birthday (#C575).

Souvenir Sheet

The Holy
Family
with
John the
Baptist
AP188

Photo. & Engr.
1984, Aug. 3   *Perf. 14*
C576 AP188 20g multicolored 45.00 45.00
Raphael, 500th birth anniv. (in 1983).

No. 2099 Overprinted ANIVERSARIO GOBIERNO CONSTRUCTIVO Y DE LA PAZ DEL PRESIDENTE CONSTITUCIONAL GRAL. DE EJERCITO ALFREDO STROESSNER 15 / 8 / 1964 in Red

1984, Aug. 15   Litho.   Perf. 13
C577 A374 100g on No. 2099   1.50 1.50

1984 Winter
Olympics,
Sarajevo
AP189

Gold medalists: 5g, Max Julen, giant slalom, Switzerland. 10g, Hans Stanggassinger, Franz Wembacher, luge, West Germany. 30g, Peter Angerer, biathlon, Germany.

Perf. 14, 13½x13 (10g)
1984, Sept. 12   **Litho.**
C578 AP189 5g multicolored 2.75   .80
C579 AP189 10g multicolored 3.50 1.20
C580 AP189 30g multicolored 1.25   .25
   Nos. C578-C580 (3)   7.50 2.25
For overprint see No. C596.

Motorcycles,
Cent.
AP190

5g, Reitwagen, Daimler-Maybach, 1885. 10g, BMW, 1980. 30g, Opel, 1930.

1984, Nov. 9   Perf. 14, 13½x13 (10g)
C581 AP190 5g multicolored 2.50   .50
C582 AP190 10g multicolored 1.90   .60
C583 AP190 30g multicolored 1.10   .25
   Nos. C581-C583 (3)   5.50 1.35

Christmas
AP191

10g, Girl playing guitar. 30g, Girl, candle, basket.

1985, Jan. 18   *Perf. 13*
C584 AP191 5g shown   1.90   .45
C585 AP191 10g multicolored 1.10   .30
C586 AP191 30g multicolored   .80   .25
   Nos. C584-C586 (3)   3.80 1.00

1986 World Cup
Soccer
Championships,
Mexico — AP192

Various soccer players.

1985, Jan. 21   Perf. 13x13½, 13½x13
Color of Shirt
C587 AP192 5g red & white   2.25   .80
C588 AP192 10g white &
                black, horiz. 1.50   .40
C589 AP192 30g blue   1.50   .25
   Nos. C587-C589 (3)   5.25 1.45

No. C484 Ovptd. in Silver
No. C590, INTERPEX / 1985. No. C591, STAMPEX / 1985.

1985, Feb. 6   *Perf. 14*
C590 AP161 10g multicolored 1.50   .75
C591 AP161 10g multicolored 1.50   .75

No. C572 Ovptd. in Vermilion

1985, Feb. 16   *Perf. 13½x13*
C592 AP186 10g on No. C572   4.00 1.50

No. 2053A Ovptd. "FINAL / ALEMANIA 1 : 3 ITALIA"
1985, Mar. 7   *Perf. 14½*
C593 A362 25g multicolored 14.00 14.00

Souvenir Sheets

Rotary
Intl., 80th
Anniv.
AP193

Designs: No. C594, Paul Harris, founder of Rotary Intl. No. C595, Rotary Intl. Headquarters, Evanston, IL, horiz.

1985, Mar. 11
C594 AP193 25g multicolored 30.00 30.00
C595 AP193 25g multicolored 30.00 30.00

No. C579 Ovptd. "OLYMPHILEX 85" in Black and Olympic Rings in Silver
1985, Mar. 18   *Perf. 13½x13*
C596 AP189 10g on No. C579   3.00 1.50

Music
Year — AP194

Designs: 5g, Agustin Barrios (1885-1944), musician, vert. 10g, Johann Sebastian Bach, composer, score. 30g, Folk musicians.

Perf. 14, 13½x13 (10g)
1985, Apr. 16
C597 AP194 5g multicolored 1.75   .75
C598 AP194 10g multicolored 1.00   .70
C599 AP194 30g multicolored 1.25   .55
   Nos. C597-C599 (3)   4.00 2.00

1st
Paraguayan
Locomotive,
1861
AP195

Transrapid
06, Germany
— AP195a

30g, TGV, France.

1985, Apr. 20   *Perf. 14*
C600 AP195   5g shown   10.00 3.50
   a.   Horiz. Pair   40.00 40.00
C601 AP195a 10g multi   2.50   .75
C602 AP195a 30g multi   2.50   .75
   Nos. C600-C602 (3)   15.00 5.00

Souvenir Sheet

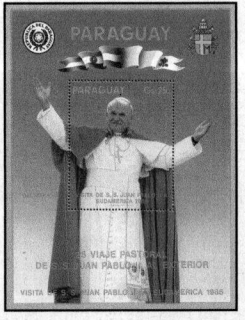

Visit of
Pope
John
Paul II to
South
America
AP196

1985, Apr. 22   Litho.   Perf. 13½
C603 AP196 25g silver & multi 17.00 17.00
No. C603 also exists with gold inscriptions.

Inter-American
Development Bank,
25th
Anniv. — AP197

1985, Apr. 25   Litho.   Wmk. 347
C604 AP197 3g dl red brn, org
                  & yel   1.25 1.00
C605 AP197 5g vio, org & yel 1.25 1.00
C606 AP197 10g rose vio, org &
                  yel   1.25 1.00
C607 AP197 50g sep, org & yel 1.25 1.00
C608 AP197 65g bl, org & yel   1.25 1.00
C609 AP197 95g pale bl grn, org
                  & yel   1.25 1.00
   Nos. C604-C609 (6)   7.50 6.00

No. 1875 Ovptd. in Black

1985, May 24   Unwmk.   Perf. 13½
C610 A326 25g on No. 1875   12.00 12.00

No. C485 Ovptd. in Dark Blue with Emblem and: "Expo '85/TSUKUBA"

1985, July 5   Perf. 14
C611 AP161 30g on No. C485   3.00 1.50

No. 2149 Overprinted in Dark Blue

1985, Aug. 5   Perf. 14½
C612 A388 25g on No. 2149   12.00 12.00

Jean-Henri Dunant, Founder of Red Cross, 75th Death Anniv. AP198

Dunant and: 5g, Enclosed ambulance. 10g, Nobel Peace Prize, Red Cross emblem. 30g, Open ambulance with passengers.

1985, Aug. 6   Perf. 13
C614 AP198 5g multicolored   5.25 1.60
C615 AP198 10g multicolored   4.75 1.60
C616 AP198 30g multicolored   2.00 .60
  Nos. C614-C616 (3)   12.00 3.80

World Chess Congress, Austria AP199

5g, The Turk, copper engraving, Book of Chess by Racknitz, 1789. 10g, King seated, playing chess, Book of Chess, 14th cent. 25g, Margrave Otto von Brandenburg playing chess with his wife, Great Manuscript of Heidelberg Songs, 13th cent. 30g, Three men playing chess, Book of Chess, 14th cent.

1985, Aug. 9   Litho.   Perf. 13
C617 AP199 5g multicolored   6.25 2.10
C618 AP199 10g multicolored   1.50 .50
C619 AP199 30g multicolored   1.50 .50
  Nos. C617-C619 (3)   9.25 3.10

Souvenir Sheet
Perf. 13½
C620 AP199 25g multicolored   25.00 25.00
No. C620 contains one 60x50mm stamp.

Discovery of America 500th Anniv. — AP200

Explorers, ships: 5g, Marco Polo and ship. 10g, Vicente Yanez Pinzon, Nina, horiz. 25g,

Christopher Columbus, Santa Maria. 30g, James Cook, Endeavor.

Perf. 14, 13½x13 (10g)
1985, Oct. 19   Litho.
C621 AP200 5g multicolored   2.50 .60
C622 AP200 10g multicolored   .85 .40
C623 AP200 30g multicolored   1.25 .45
  Nos. C621-C623 (3)   4.60 1.45

Souvenir Sheet
Perf. 14½
C624 AP200 25g multicolored   22.00 22.00
Year of Cook's death is incorrect on No. C623. For overprint see No. C756.

ITALIA '85 — AP201

Nudes (details): 5g, La Fortuna, by Guido Reni, vert. 10g, The Triumph of Galatea, by Raphael. 30g, Sleeping Venus, by Il Giorgione.
25g, The Birth of Venus, by Botticelli, vert.

1985, Dec. 3   Perf. 14
C625 AP201 5g multicolored   4.50 1.50
C626 AP201 10g multicolored   2.00 .60
C627 AP201 30g multicolored   1.75 .40
  Nos. C625-C627 (3)   8.25 2.50

Souvenir Sheet
Perf. 13½
C628 AP201 25g multicolored   35.00 35.00
No. C628 contains one 49x60mm stamp.

Souvenir Sheet

Maimonides, Philosopher, 850th Birth Anniv. — AP202

1985, Dec. 31   Perf. 13½
C629 AP202 25g multicolored   22.50 22.50

UN, 40th Anniv. — AP203

1986, Feb. 27   Wmk. 392
C630 AP203 5g bl & sepia   1.00 1.00
C631 AP203 10g bl & gray   1.00 1.00
C632 AP203 50g bl & grysh brn   1.00 1.00
  Nos. C630-C632 (3)   3.00 3.00

For overprint see No. C726.

AMERIPEX '86 — AP204

Discovery of America 500th anniv. emblem and: 5g, Spain #424. 10g, US #233. 25g, Spain #426, horiz. 30g, Spain #421.

Perf. 14, 13½x13 (10g)
1986, Mar. 19   Unwmk.
C633 AP204 5g multicolored   5.00 1.75
C634 AP204 10g multicolored   2.00 .70
C635 AP204 30g multicolored   1.75 .60
  Nos. C633-C635 (3)   8.75 3.05

Souvenir Sheet
Perf. 13½
C636 AP204 25g multicolored   12.00 12.00
No. C636 contains one 60x40mm stamp. For overprint see No. C755.

Souvenir Sheet

1984 Olympic Gold Medalist, Dr. Reiner Klimke on Ahlerich AP205

1986, Mar. 20   Perf. 14½
C637 AP205 25g multicolored   20.00 20.00

Tennis Players — AP206

Designs: 5g, Martina Navratilova, US. 10g, Boris Becker, W. Germany. 30g, Victor Pecci, Paraguay.

1986, Mar. 26   Perf. 14, 13 (10g)
C638 AP206 5g multicolored   4.25 1.25
C639 AP206 10g multicolored   2.25 .55
C640 AP206 30g multicolored   .50 .25
  Nos. C638-C640 (3)   7.00 2.05

Nos. C638-C640 exist with red inscriptions, perf. 13. For overprints see Nos. C672-C673.

Halley's Comet AP207

5g, Bayeux Tapestry, c. 1066, showing comet. 10g, Edmond Halley, comet. 25g, Comet, Giotto probe. 30g, Rocket lifting off, Giotto probe, vert.

Perf. 14, 13½x13 (10g)
1986, Apr. 30
C641 AP207 5g multicolored   5.50 2.00
C642 AP207 10g multicolored   3.50 1.10
C643 AP207 30g multicolored   2.50 .65
  Nos. C641-C643 (3)   11.50 3.75

Souvenir Sheet
Perf. 14½
C644 AP207 25g multicolored   20.00 20.00

Souvenir Sheet

Madonna by Albrecht Durer AP208

1986, June 4   Typo.   Rough Perf. 11
Self-Adhesive
C645 AP208 25g black & red   20.00 20.00
No. C645 was printed on cedar.

Locomotives AP209

5g, #3038. 10g, Canadian Pacific A1E, 1887. 30g, 1D1 #483, 1925.

1986, June 23   Litho.   Perf. 13
C646 AP209 5g multi   2.25 .50
C647 AP209 10g multi   1.50 .50
C648 AP209 30g multi   2.25 .50
  Nos. C646-C648 (3)   6.00 1.50

1986 World Cup Soccer Championships — AP210

Paraguay vs.: 5g, Colombia. 10g, Chile. 30g, Chile, diff.
25g, Paraguay Natl. team.

Perf. 13, 13½x13 (10g)
1986, June 24
C649 AP210 5g multicolored   2.25 .50
C650 AP210 10g multicolored   1.50 .50
C651 AP210 30g multicolored   2.50 .45
  Nos. C649-C651 (3)   6.25 1.45

Souvenir Sheet
Perf. 14½
C652 AP210 25g multicolored   13.00 13.00
No. C652 contains one 81x75mm stamp. For overprints see Nos. C693-C695.

No. 1289 Ovptd. in Silver on Dark Blue with Mercury Capsule and "MERCURY / 5-V-1961 / 25 Anos Primer / Astronauta / Americano / Alan B. Shepard / 1986"

1986, July 11   Perf. 13½
C653 A226 23.40g on No. 1289   13.00 13.00

Souvenir Sheet

Trajectory Diagram of Halley's Comet, Giotto Probe — AP211

1986, July 28
C654 AP211 25g multicolored   15.00 15.00

German Railroads, 150th Anniv. AP212

5g, VT 10 501DB, 1954. 10g, 1st Electric, 1879. 30g, Hydraulic diesel, class 218.
25g, Christening of the 1st German Train, 1835, by E. Schilling & B. Goldschmitt.

1986, Sept. 1   Perf. 13½x13
C655 AP212 5g multicolored   4.50 1.50
C656 AP212 10g multicolored   1.75 .50
C657 AP212 30g multicolored   2.00 2.00
  Nos. C655-C657 (3)   8.25 4.00

Souvenir Sheet
Perf. 13½
C658 AP212 25g multicolored   18.00 18.00
No. C658 contains one 54x75mm stamp.

Intl. Peace Year — AP213

Details from The Consequences of War by Rubens: 5g, Two women. 10g, Woman nursing child. 30g, Two men.

1986, Oct. 27   **Perf. 13**
C659	AP213	5g multicolored	5.00 1.75
C660	AP213	10g multicolored	2.60 2.60
C661	AP213	30g multicolored	1.75 .40
	Nos. C659-C661 (3)		9.35 4.75

Japanese Emigrants in Paraguay, 50th Anniv. AP214

5g, La Colemna Vineyard. 10g, Cherry, lapacho flowers. 20g, Integration monument, vert.

1986, Nov. 6   **Perf. 13½x13, 13x13½**
C662	AP214	5g multicolored	2.00 2.00
C663	AP214	10g multicolored	2.00 2.00
C664	AP214	20g multicolored	2.00 2.00
	Nos. C662-C664 (3)		6.00 6.00

No. C507 Ovptd. in Silver "XXVII-DUBAI / Olimpiada de / Ajedrez - 1986"

1986, Dec. 30   **Unwmk.**   **Perf. 14**
C665	A347	10g on No. C507	6.00 2.00

1986 World Cup Soccer Championships, Mexico — AP214a

Match scenes — 5g, England vs. Paraguay. 10g, Larios catching ball. 20g, Trejo, Ferreira. 25g, Torales, Flores, Romero. 30g, Mendoza. 100g, Romero.

1987, Feb. 19   **Perf. 14**
C666	AP214a	5g multicolored	.60 .25
C667	AP214a	10g multicolored	4.50 1.50
C668	AP214a	20g multicolored	1.25 .40

Perf. 13½x13
C669	AP214a	25g multicolored	1.20 1.20
C670	AP214a	30g multicolored	1.50 1.50
	Nos. C666-C670 (5)		9.05 4.85

Souvenir Sheet
Perf. 14½
C671	AP214a	100g multi	15.00 13.00

Nos. C669-C670 are horiz. No. C671 contains one 40x50mm stamp.

Nos. C639-C640 Ovptd. in Silver including Olympic Rings and "NUEVAMENTE EL / TENIS EN LAS / OLYMPIADAS 1988 / SEOUL COREA"

1987, Apr. 15   **Perf. 13**
C672	AP206	10g on No. C639	4.50 3.00
C673	AP206	30g on No. C640	4.50 3.00

Automobiles AP215

5g, Mercedes 300 SEL 6.3. 10g, Jaguar Mk II 3.8. 20g, BMW 635 CSI. 25g, Alfa Romeo GTA. 30g, BMW 1800 Tisa.

1987, May 29   **Litho.**   **Perf. 13½**
C674	AP215	5g multicolored	.60 .25
C675	AP215	10g multicolored	4.50 1.50
C676	AP215	20g multicolored	1.25 .40
C677	AP215	25g multicolored	1.50 1.50
C678	AP215	30g multicolored	1.50 1.50
	Nos. C674-C678 (5)		9.35 5.15

1988 Winter Olympics, Calgary AP216

Gold medalists or Olympic competitors: 5g, Michela Figini, Switzerland, downhill, 1984, vert. 10g, Hanni Wenzel, Liechtenstein, slalom and giant slalom, 1980. 20g, 4-Man bobsled, Switzerland, 1956, 1972. 25g, Markus Wasmeier, downhill. 30g, Ingemar Stenmark, Sweden, slalom and giant slalom, 1980. 100g, Pirmin Zurbriggen, Switzerland, vert. (downhill, 1988).

1987, Sept. 10   **Perf. 14**
C679	AP216	5g multicolored	.75 .25
C680	AP216	10g multicolored	4.50 1.40
C681	AP216	20g multicolored	1.50 .40

Perf. 13½x13
C682	AP216	25g multicolored	1.40 1.10
C683	AP216	30g multicolored	1.60 1.40
	Nos. C679-C683 (5)		9.75 4.55

Souvenir Sheet
Perf. 13½
C684	AP216	100g multicolored	14.00 14.00

No. C684 contains one 45x57mm stamp.

Nos. 2211 and C467 Ovptd. in Red on Silver "11.IX.1887 - 1987 / Centenario de la fundacion de / la A.N.R. (Partido Colorado) / Bernardino Caballero Fundador / General de Ejercito / D. Alfredo Stroessner Continuador"

1987, Sept. 11   **Perf. 13, 14**
C685	A401	200g on No. 2211	.50 .50
C686	AP148	1000g on No. C467	2.75 2.75
	Nos. C685-C686 (2)		3.25 3.25

1988 Summer Olympics, Seoul AP217

Medalists and competitors: 5g, Sabine Everts, West Germany, javelin. 10g, Carl Lewis, US, 100 and 200-meter run, 1984. 20g, Darrell Pace, US, archery, 1976, 1984. 25g, Juergen Hingsen, West Germany, decathlon, 1984. 30g, Claudia Losch, West Germany, shot put, 1984. 100g, Fredy Schmidtke, West Germany, cycling, 1984.

1987, Sept. 22   **Perf. 14**
C687	AP217	5g multi	.50 .25
C688	AP217	10g multi, vert.	2.00 .55
C689	AP217	20g multi	1.20 .40

Perf. 13½x13
C690	AP217	25g multi, vert.	1.10 1.10
C691	AP217	30g multi, vert.	1.40 1.40
	Nos. C687-C691 (5)		6.20 3.70

Souvenir Sheet
Perf. 14½
C692	AP217	100g multi, vert.	13.00 13.00

Nos. C650-C652 Ovptd. in Violet or Blue (#C694) with Soccer Ball and "ZURICH 10.VI.87 / Lanzamiento ITALIA '90 / Italia 3 - Argentina 1"
Perf. 13½x13, 13

1987, Oct. 19   **Litho.**
C693	AP210	10g on No. C650	2.00 2.00
C694	AP210	30g on No. C651	3.00 3.00
	Nos. C693-C694 (2)		5.00 5.00

Souvenir Sheet
Perf. 14½
C695	AP210	25g on No. C652	12.00 12.00

Paintings by Rubens — AP218

Details from: 5g, The Virtuous Hero Crowned. 10g, The Brazen Serpent, 1635. 20g, Judith with the Head of Holofernes, 1617. 25g, Assembly of the Gods of Olympus. 30g, Venus, Cupid, Bacchus and Ceres.

1987, Dec. 14   **Perf. 13**
C696	AP218	5g multicolored	.80 .25
C697	AP218	10g multicolored	4.50 1.60
C698	AP218	20g multicolored	1.40 .40

Perf. 13x13½
C699	AP218	25g multicolored	1.10 1.10
C700	AP218	30g multicolored	1.25 1.25
	Nos. C696-C700 (5)		9.05 4.60

Christmas AP219

Details from paintings: 5g, Virgin and Child with St. Joseph and St. John the Baptist, anonymous. 10g, Madonna and Child under the Veil with St. Joseph and St. John, by Marco da Siena. 20g, Sacred Conversation with the Donors, by Titian. 25g, The Brotherhood of the Rosary, by Durer. 30g, Madonna with Standing Child, by Rubens. 100g, Madonna and Child, engraving by Albrecht Durer.

1987   **Litho.**   **Perf. 14**
C701	AP219	5g multicolored	.40 .25
C702	AP219	10g multicolored	1.40 .55
C703	AP219	20g multicolored	.80 .25
C704	AP219	25g multicolored	1.20 .40

Perf. 13x13½
C705	AP219	30g multicolored	2.00 2.00
	Nos. C701-C705 (5)		5.80 3.45

Souvenir Sheet
Perf. 14½
C706	AP219	100g multi	20.00 20.00

Issued: #C701-C705, 12/16; #C706, 12/17.

Austrian Railways, Sesquicentennial — AP220

Locomotives: 5g, Steam #3669, 1899. 10g, Steam #GZ 44074. 20g, Steam, diff. 25g, Diesel-electric. 30g, Austria No. 1067. 100g, Steam, vert.

1988, Jan. 2   **Perf. 14**
C707	AP220	5g multicolored	.75 .25
C708	AP220	10g multicolored	3.25 1.00
C709	AP220	20g multicolored	1.00 .30
C710	AP220	25g multicolored	1.75 .45

Perf. 13½x13
C711	AP220	30g multicolored	2.75 2.75
	Nos. C707-C711 (5)		9.50 4.75

Souvenir Sheet
Perf. 13½
C712	AP220	100g multicolored	25.00 25.00

No. C712 contains one 50x60mm stamp.

Christmas — AP221

1988, Jan. 4   **Perf. 13½**
C713	AP221	100g Madonna, by Rubens	20.00 20.00

Souvenir Sheet

1988 Summer Olympics, Seoul — AP222

1988, Jan. 18   **Perf. 14½**
C714	AP222	100g gold & multi	12.00 12.00

Exists with silver lettering and frame. Same value.

Colonization of Space AP223

5g, NASA-ESA space station. 10g, Eurospace module Columbus docked at space station. 20g, NASA space sation. 25g, Ring section of space station, vert. 30g, Space station living quarters in central core, vert.

1988, Mar. 9   **Litho.**   **Perf. 13½x13**
C715	AP223	5g multicolored	.55 .25
C716	AP223	10g multicolored	2.60 .90
C717	AP223	20g multicolored	1.00 .35

Perf. 13x13½
C718	AP223	25g multicolored	1.40 .50
C719	AP223	30g multicolored	2.25 2.25
	Nos. C715-C719 (5)		7.80 4.25

Souvenir Sheet

Berlin, 750th Anniv. AP224

1988, Mar. 10   **Litho.**   **Perf. 14½**
C720	AP224	100g multicolored	25.00 25.00

LUPOSTA '87.

Souvenir Sheet

Apollo 15 Launch, 1971 AP225

1988, Apr. 12
C721 AP225 100g multicolored 20.00 20.00

No. 2210 Ovptd. in Metallic Red

1988, Apr. 28   *Perf. 13*
C722 A401 100g on No. 2210 2.00 2.00

Caacupe Basilica and Pope John Paul II — AP226

Perf. 13½x13
1988, May 5   Litho.   Wmk. 347
C723 AP226 100g multi 2.00 2.00
C724 AP226 120g multi 2.00 2.00
C725 AP226 150g multi 2.00 2.00
   Nos. C723-C725 (3) 6.00 6.00
Visit of Pope John Paul II.

No. C631 Overprinted

Perf. 13x13½
1988, June 15   Wmk. 392
C726 AP203 10g blue & gray .40 .25
Paraguay Philatelic Center, 75th Anniv.

Berlin, 750th Anniv. Paintings Type of 1988

5g, Venus and Cupid, 1742, by Francois Boucher. 10g, Perseus Liberates Andromeda, 1662, by Rubens. 20g, Venus and the Organist by Titian. 25g, Leda and the Swan by Correggio. 30g, St. Cecilia by Rubens.

1988, June 15   Unwmk.   *Perf. 13*
C727 A409 5g multi, horiz. .35 .25
C728 A409 10g multi, horiz. .75 .35
C729 A409 20g multi, horiz. 1.10 .50
C730 A409 25g multi, horiz. 1.60 .80
   Perf. 13x13½
C731 A409 30g multicolored 2.50 2.50
   Nos. C727-C731 (5) 6.30 4.40

Founding of "New Germany" and 1st Cultivation of Herbal Tea, Cent. — AP227

90g, Cauldron, vert. 105g, Farm workers carrying crop.

Perf. 13x13½, 13½x13
1988, June 18   Litho.   Wmk. 347
C732 AP227 90g multi 3.00 2.50
C733 AP227 105g multi 3.00 2.50
C734 AP227 120g like 105g 3.00 2.50
   Nos. C732-C734 (3) 9.00 7.50

1990 World Cup Soccer Championships, Italy — AP228

5g, Machine slogan cancel from Montevideo, May 21, 1930. 10g, Italy #324, vert. 20g, France #349. 25g, Brazil #696, vert. 30g, Paraguayan commemorative cancel for ITALIA 1990.

1988, Aug. 1   Unwmk.   *Perf. 13*
C735 AP228 5g multicolored .85 .25
C736 AP228 10g multicolored 2.60 .90
C737 AP228 20g multicolored 1.60 .50
C738 AP228 25g multicolored 1.40 .95
   Perf. 13½x13
C739 AP228 30g multicolored 1.60 1.20
   Nos. C735-C739 (5) 8.05 3.80
For overprint see No. 2284.

Souvenir Sheet

Count Ferdinand von Zeppelin, Airship Designer, Birth Sesquicentennial — AP229

1988, Aug. 3   *Perf. 14½*
C740 AP229 100g multicolored 20.00 20.00

Government Palace and Pres. Stroessner AP230

   Wmk. 347
1988, Aug. 5   Litho.   *Perf. 13½*
C741 AP230 200g multi .60 .50
C742 AP230 500g multi 1.40 1.40
C743 AP230 1000g multi 2.50 2.50
   Nos. C741-C743 (3) 4.50 4.40
Pres. Stroessner's new term in office, 1988-1993. Size of letters in watermark on 200g, 1000g: 5mm. On 500g, 10mm.

1988 Winter Olympics, Calgary AP231

Gold medalists: 5g, Hubert Strolz, Austria, Alpine combined. 10g, Alberto Tomba, Italy, giant slalom and slalom. 20g, Franck Piccard, France, super giant slalom. 25g, Thomas Muller, Hans-Peter Pohl and Hubert Schwarz, Federal Republic of Germany, Nordic combined team, vert. 30g, Vreni Schneider, Switzerland, giant slalom and slalom, vert. 100g, Marina Kiehl, Federal Republic of Germany, downhill, vert.

Perf. 13½x13
1988, Sept. 2   Unwmk.
C744 AP231 5g multicolored .85 .25
C745 AP231 10g multicolored 2.60 .90
C746 AP231 10g multicolored 1.60 .50

Perf. 13x13½
C747 AP231 25g multicolored 1.40 .95
C748 AP231 30g multicolored 1.60 1.20
   Nos. C744-C748 (5) 8.05 3.80
Souvenir Sheet
   Perf. 14½
C749 AP231 100g multicolored 13.00 13.00

1990 World Cup Soccer Championships, Italy — AP232

Designs: 5g, Mexico #C350. 10g, Germany #1146. 20g, Argentina #1147, vert. 25g, Spain #2211. 30g, Italy #1742.

1988, Oct. 4   *Perf. 13*
C750 AP232 5g multicolored .55 .25
C751 AP232 10g multicolored 2.50 .85
C752 AP232 20g multicolored .95 .30
C753 AP232 25g multicolored 1.40 .50
   Perf. 14
C754 AP232 30g multicolored 1.60 1.20
   Nos. C750-C754 (5) 7.00 3.10
For overprint see No. 2285.

No. C635 Ovptd. in Metallic Red

1988, Nov. 25   *Perf. 14*
C755 AP204 30g on No. C635 4.00 4.00

No. C623 Ovptd. in Gold

1988, Nov. 25   *Perf. 14*
C756 AP200 30g on No. C623 2.00 2.00

1988 Summer Olympics, Seoul AP233

Gold medalists: No. C757, Nicole Uphoff, individual dressage. No. C758, Anja Fichtel, Sabine Bau, Zita Funkenhauser, Anette Kluge and Christine Weber, team foil. No. C759, Silvia Sperber, smallbore standard rifle. No. C760, Mathias Baumann, Claus Erhorn, Thies Kaspareit and Ralph Ehrenbrink, equestrian team 3-day event. No. C761, Anja Fichtel, individual foil, vert. No. C762, Franke Sloothaak, Ludger Beerbaum, Wolfgang Brinkmann and Dirk Hafemeister, equestrian team jumping. No. C763, Arnd Schmitt, individual epee, vert. No. C764, Jose Luis Doreste, Finn class yachting. No. C765, Steffi Graf, tennis. No. C766, Michael Gross, 200-meter butterfly, vert. No. C767, West Germany, coxed eights. No. C768, Nicole Uphoff, Monica Theodorescu, Ann Kathrin Linsenhoff and Reiner Klimke, team dressage.

1989   *Perf. 13*
C757 AP233 5g multicolored .55 .25
C758 AP233 5g multicolored .55 .25
C759 AP233 10g multicolored 2.60 .25
C760 AP233 10g multicolored 2.60 .25
C761 AP233 20g multicolored .95 .40
C762 AP233 20g multicolored .95 .40
C763 AP233 25g multicolored 1.40 .60
C764 AP233 25g multicolored 1.40 .60

Perf. 13½x13
C765 AP233 30g multicolored 2.60 2.60
C766 AP233 30g multicolored 2.60 2.60
   Nos. C757-C766 (10) 16.20 8.20
Souvenir Sheets
   Perf. 14½
C767 AP233 100g multicolored 10.00 10.00
C768 AP233 100g multicolored 10.00 10.00
Nos. C767-C768 each contain one 80x50mm stamp.
Issue dates: Nos. C757, C759, C761, C763, C765, and C767, Mar. 3. Others, Mar. 20.
For overprints see Nos. 2292, 2359.

Souvenir Sheet

Intl. Red Cross, 125th Anniv. (in 1988) AP234

1989, Apr. 17   Litho.   *Perf. 13½*
C769 AP234 100g #803 in changed colors 10.00 10.00
No. C769 has perforated label picturing Nobel medal.

Olympics Type of 1989

1988 Winter Olympic medalists or competitors: 5g, Pirmin Zurbriggen, Peter Mueller, Switzerland, and Franck Piccard, France, Alpine skiing. 10g, Sigrid Wolf, Austria, super giant slalom, vert. 20g, Czechoslovakia vs. West Germany, hockey, vert. 25g, Piccard, skiing, vert. 30g, Piccard, wearing medal, vert.

1989, Apr. 17   *Perf. 13½x13*
C770 AP233 5g multicolored .80 .25
   Perf. 13x13½
C771 AP233 10g multicolored 1.60 .55
C772 AP233 20g multicolored 1.20 .40
C773 AP233 25g multicolored 1.40 .50
C774 AP233 30g multicolored 2.60 2.60
   Nos. C770-C774 (5) 7.60 4.30

Souvenir Sheet

1990 World Cup Soccer Championships, Italy — AP235

1989, Apr. 21   *Perf. 14½*
C775 AP235 100g Sheet of 1 + label 10.00 10.00

1st Moon Landing, 20th Anniv. AP236

Designs: 5g, Wernher von Braun, Apollo 11 launch, vert. 10g, Michael Collins, lunar module on moon. 20g, Neil Armstrong, astronaut on lunar module ladder, vert. 25g, Buzz Aldrin, solar wind experiment, vert. 30g, Kurt Debus, splashdown of Columbia command module, vert.

1989, May 24   *Perf. 13*
C776 AP236 5g multicolored .55 .25
C777 AP236 10g multicolored 4.00 1.40
C778 AP236 20g multicolored 2.40 .80
C779 AP236 25g multicolored 1.40 1.40
C780 AP236 30g multicolored 1.60 1.60
   Nos. C776-C780 (5) 9.95 5.45

Souvenir Sheet

Luis Alberto del Parana and the
Paraguayans — AP237

1989, May 25   *Perf. 14½*
C780A AP237 100g multi   30.00 30.00

A clear plastic phonograph record is affixed
to the souvenir sheet.

Hamburg,
800th Anniv.
AP238

Hamburg anniv. emblem, SAIL '89 emblem,
and: 5g, Galleon and Icarus, woodcut by Pieter Brueghel. 10g, Windjammer, vert. 20g,
Bark in full sail. 25g, Old Hamburg by A.E.
Schliecker, vert. 30g, Commemorative coin
issued by Federal Republic of Germany. 100g,
Hamburg, 13th cent. illuminated manuscript,
vert.

1989, May 26 *Perf. 13½x13, 13x13½*
C781 AP238 5g multicolored   .80   .25
C782 AP238 10g multicolored   3.50   1.10
C783 AP238 20g multicolored   1.20   .40
C784 AP238 25g multicolored   1.60   .50
C785 AP238 30g multicolored   3.00   3.00
     Nos. C781-C785 (5)   10.10   5.25

Souvenir Sheet
Perf. 14½

C786 AP238 100g multicolored 20.00 20.00

No. C786 contains one 40x50mm stamp.

French
Revolution,
Bicent.
AP239

Details from paintings: 5g, Esther Adorns
Herself for her Presentation to King Ahasue-
rus, by Theodore Chasseriau, vert. 10g, Olympia, by Manet, vert. 20g, The Drunker Erigone
with a Panther, by Louis A. Reisener. 25g,
Anniv. emblem and natl. coats of arms. 30g,
Liberty Leading the People, by Delacroix, vert.
100g, The Education of Maria de Medici, by
Rubens, vert.

1989, May 27 *Perf. 13x13½, 13½x13*
C787 AP239 5g multicolored   .80   .25
C788 AP239 10g multicolored   3.50   1.20
C789 AP239 20g multicolored   1.20   .40
C790 AP239 25g multicolored   1.60   .60
C791 AP239 30g multicolored   2.40   2.40
     Nos. C787-C791 (5)   9.50   4.75

Souvenir Sheet
Perf. 14½

C792 AP239 100g multicolored 14.00 14.00

Souvenir Sheet

Railway
Zeppelin,
1931
AP240

1989, May 27   *Litho.*   *Perf. 13½*
C793 AP240 100g multicolored 18.00 18.00

Jupiter and
Calisto by
Rubens — AP241

Details from paintings by Rubens: 10g,
Boreas Abducting Oreithyia (1619-20). 20g,
Fortuna (1625). 25g, Mars with Venus and
Cupid (1625). 30g, Virgin with Child (1620).

1989, Dec. 27   *Litho.*   *Perf. 14*
C794 AP241 5g multicolored   .50   .25
C795 AP241 10g multicolored   .80   .25
C796 AP241 20g multicolored   1.75   .55
C797 AP241 25g multicolored   2.25   .75
Perf. 13
C798 AP241 30g multicolored   2.10   2.10
     Nos. C794-C798 (5)   7.40   3.90

Death of Rubens, 350th anniversary.

Penny Black,
150th
Anniv. — AP242

Penny Black, 500 years of postal services
emblem, Stamp World '90 emblem and: 5g,
Brazil #1. 10g, British Guiana #2. 20g, Chile
#1. 25g, Uruguay #1. 30g, Paraguay #1.

1989, Dec. 30   *Perf. 14*
C799 AP242 5g multicolored   .40   .25
C800 AP242 10g multicolored   .80   .25
C801 AP242 20g multicolored   1.60   .50
C802 AP242 25g multicolored   2.00   .65
Perf. 13
C803 AP242 30g multicolored   2.75   2.75
     Nos. C799-C803 (5)   7.55   4.40

Animals — AP243

Designs: 5g, Martucha. 10g, Mara. 20g,
Lobo de crin. 25g, Rana cornuda tintorera,
horiz. 30g, Jaguar, horiz. Inscribed 1989.

1990, Jan. 8   *Perf. 13x13½, 13½x13*
C804 AP243 5g multicolored   .75   .25
C805 AP243 10g multicolored   1.60   .50
C806 AP243 20g multicolored   2.00   .65
C807 AP243 25g multicolored   2.60   .90
C808 AP243 30g multicolored   2.75   1.75
     Nos. C804-C808 (5)   9.70   4.05

Columbus'
Fleet — AP244

Discovery of America 500th anniversary
emblem and: 10g, Olympic rings, stylized basketball player, horiz. 20g, Medieval nave, Expo
'92 emblem. 25g, Four-masted barkentine,
Expo '92 emblem, horiz. 30g, Similar to Spain
Scott 2571, Expo '92 emblem.

1990, Jan. 27   *Perf. 14*
C809 AP244 5g multicolored   .55   .25
C810 AP244 10g multicolored   1.10   .35
C811 AP244 20g multicolored   1.20   .40
C812 AP244 25g multicolored   1.40   .55
Perf. 13½x13
C813 AP244 30g multicolored   1.75   1.75
     Nos. C809-C813 (5)   6.00   3.30

Postal Transportation, 500th
Anniv. — AP245

500th Anniv. Emblem and: 5g, 10g, 20g,
25g, Penny Black and various post coaches.
10g, vert. 30g, Post coach.

1990, Mar. 9 *Perf. 13½x13, 13x13½*
C814 AP245 5g multicolored   .50   .25
C815 AP245 10g multicolored   .90   .35
C816 AP245 20g multicolored   2.00   .65
C817 AP245 25g multicolored   2.60   .85
C818 AP245 30g multicolored   3.50   3.50
     Nos. C814-C818 (5)   9.50   5.60

Fort and City
of Arco by
Durer
AP246

Paintings by Albrecht Durer, postal transportation 500th anniversary emblem and: 10g,
Trent Castle. 20g, North Innsbruck. 25g, Fort
yard of Innsbruck, vert. 30g, Virgin of the Animals. No. C824, Madonna and Child, vert. No.
C825, Postrider, vert.

1990, Mar. 14   *Perf. 14*
C819 AP246 5g multicolored   .50   .25
C820 AP246 10g multicolored   .95   .35
C821 AP246 20g multicolored   2.00   .65
C822 AP246 25g multicolored   2.75   1.00
Perf. 13
C823 AP246 30g multicolored   3.75   3.75
     Nos. C819-C823 (5)   9.95   6.00

Souvenir Sheets
Perf. 14½

C824 AP246 100g multicolored 17.00 17.00
C825 AP246 100g multicolored 17.00 17.00

Nos. C824-C825 each contain one
40x50mm stamp.
For overprint see No. 2358.

AP247

Wmk. 347
1986-88?   *Photo.*   *Perf. 11*
C826 AP247 40g red lilac   1.00   .85
C827 AP247 60g brt grn ('88) 1.50   1.25

POSTAGE DUE STAMPS

D1

1904   *Unwmk.*   *Litho.*   *Perf. 11½*
J1 D1 2c green   1.00   2.00
J2 D1 4c green   1.00   2.00
J3 D1 10c green   1.00   2.00
J4 D1 20c green   1.00   2.00
     Nos. J1-J4 (4)   4.00   8.00

D2

1913   *Engr.*
J5 D2 1c yellow brown   1.00   1.00
J6 D2 2c yellow brown   1.00   1.00
J7 D2 5c yellow brown   1.00   1.00
J8 D2 10c yellow brown   1.00   1.00
J9 D2 20c yellow brown   1.00   1.00

J10 D2 40c yellow brown   1.00   1.00
J11 D2   1p yellow brown   1.00   1.00
J12 D2 1.50p yellow brown   1.00   1.00
     Nos. J5-J12 (8)   8.00   8.00

For overprints and surcharges see Nos.
220-224, 229, 232, 264, L5.

INTERIOR OFFICE ISSUES

The "C" signifies "Campana" (rural).
These stamps were sold by Postal
Agents in country districts, who
received a commission on their sales.
These stamps were available for postage in the interior but not in Asunción or
abroad.

Nos. 243-244
Overprinted in Red

1922
L1 A42 50c car & dk bl   .50   .50
L2 A42 1p dk bl & brn   .50   .50

The overprint on Nos. L2 exists double or
inverted. Counterfeits exist. Double or inverted
overprints on No. L1 and all overprints in black
are counterfeit.

Nos. 215, 218, J12
Surcharged

1924
L3 A40 50c on 75c deep bl   .60   .60
L4 A40 1p on 1.25p pale bl .60   .60
L5 D2   1p on 1.50p yel brn .60   .60
     Nos. L3-L5 (3)   1.80   1.80

Nos. L3-L4 exist imperf.

Nos. 254, 257-260
Overprinted in Black or
Red

1924-26
L6 A45 50c red ('25)   1.00   1.00
L7 A44 1p dk blue (R)   1.00   1.00
L8 A45 1p dk bl (R) ('25) 1.00   1.00
L9 A46 1p blue (R) ('25)   1.00   1.00
L10 A45 1p emerald ('26)   2.00   .75
     Nos. L6-L10 (5)   6.00   4.75

Nos. L6, L8-L9 exist imperf. Value $2.50
each pair.

Same Overprint on Stamps and
Type of 1927-36 in Red or Black
1927-39
L11 A47 50c ultra (R)   .50   .50
L12 A47 50c dl red ('28)   .50   .50
L13 A47 50c orange ('29)   .50   .50
L14 A47 50c lt bl ('30)   .50   .50
L15 A47 50c gray (R) ('31)   .50   .50
L16 A47 50c bluish grn (R)
                   ('33)   .50   .50
L17 A47 50c vio (R) ('34)   .50   .50
L18 A48 1p emerald   .50   .50
L19 A48 1p org red ('29)   .50   .50
L20 A48 1p lil brn ('31)   .50   .50
L21 A48 1p dk bl (R) ('33)   .50   .50
L22 A48 1p brt vio (R) ('35) .50   .50
L23 A49 1.50p brown   .50   .50
 a.   Double overprint   3.00
L24 A49 1.50p lilac ('28)   .50   .50
L25 A49 1.50p dull bl (R)   .50   .50
L26 A50 2.50p bister ('28)   .50   .50
L27 A50 2.50p vio (R) ('36)   .50   .50
L28 A51 3p gray (R)   .50   .50
L29 A51 3p rose red ('39)   .50   .50
L30 A52 5p vio (R) ('36)   .50   .50
L31 A57 10p gray brn (R)
                   ('36)   5.00   3.00
     Nos. L11-L31 (21)   15.00 13.00

Types of 1931-35 and No. 305 Overprinted in Black or Red

1931-36

L32	A59	1p light red		2.00	1.00
L33	A58	1.50p dp bl (R)		1.00	.75
L34	A60	1.50p bis brn ('32)		2.00	1.00
L35	A60	1.50p grn (R) ('34)		2.00	1.00
L36	A60	1.50p bl (R) ('36)		2.00	1.00
L37	A54	10p vermilion		8.00	2.50
		Nos. L32-L37 (6)		17.00	7.25

OFFICIAL STAMPS

O1   O2

O3   O4

O5   O6

O7

Unwmk.

1886, Aug. 20		Litho.		Imperf.	
O1	O1	1c orange		7.00	7.00
O2	O2	2c violet		7.00	7.00
O3	O3	5c red		7.00	7.00
O4	O4	7c green		7.00	7.00
O5	O5	10c brown		7.00	7.00
O6	O6	15c slate blue		7.00	7.00
	a.	Wavy lines on face of stamp			
	b.	"OFICIAL" omitted		1.25	
O7	O7	20c claret		7.00	7.00
		Nos. O1-O7 (7)		49.00	49.00

Nos. O1 to O7 have the date and various control marks and letters printed on the back of each stamp in blue and black.

The overprints exist inverted on all values.

Nos. O1 to O7 have been reprinted from new stones made from slightly retouched dies.

Types of 1886 With Overprint

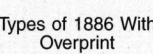

1886   **Perf. 11½**

O8	O1	1c dark green		1.50	1.50
O9	O2	2c scarlet		1.50	1.50
O10	O3	5c dull blue		1.50	1.50
O11	O4	7c orange		1.50	1.50
O12	O5	10c lake		1.50	1.50
O13	O6	15c brown		1.50	1.50
O14	O7	20c blue		1.50	1.50
		Nos. O8-O14 (7)		10.50	10.50

The overprint exists inverted on all values. Value, each $1.50.

No. 20 Overprinted

1886, Sept. 1

O15	A11	1c dark green	6.00	6.00

Types of 1889 Regular Issue Surcharged

Handstamped Surcharge in Black

1889				Imperf.	
O16	A13	3c on 15c violet		3.75	2.75
O17	A13	5c on 15c red brn		3.75	2.25

Perf. 11½

O18	A13	1c on 15c maroon		4.00	2.25
O19	A13	2c on 15c maroon		4.00	2.25
		Nos. O16-O19 (4)		15.50	9.50

Counterfeits of Nos. O16-O19 abound.

Regular Issue of 1887 Handstamp Overprinted in Violet

Perf. 11½-12½ & Compounds					
1890				Typo.	
O20	A12	1c green		.75	.30
O21	A12	2c rose red		.75	.30
O22	A12	5c blue		.75	.30
O23	A12	7c brown		10.00	8.00
O24	A12	10c lilac		.75	.35
O25	A12	15c orange		1.75	.45
O26	A12	20c pink		1.90	.45
		Nos. O20-O26 (7)		16.65	10.15

Nos. O20-O26 exist with double overprint and all but the 20c with inverted overprint.

Nos. O20-O22, O24-O26 exist with blue overprint. The status is questioned. Value, set $15.

Stamps and Type of 1887 Regular Issue Overprinted in Black

1892					
O33	A12	1c green		.30	.30
O34	A12	2c rose red		.30	.30
O35	A12	5c blue		.30	.30
O36	A12	7c brown		4.00	1.75
O37	A12	10c lilac		1.25	.55
O38	A12	15c orange		.35	.35
O39	A12	20c pink		.65	.35
O40	A12	50c gray		.75	.35
		Nos. O33-O40 (8)		7.90	4.20

No. 26 Overprinted

1893				
O41	A12	7c brown	20.00	20.00

Counterfeits of No. O41 exist.

O16

1901, Feb.		Engr.	Perf. 11½, 12½		
O42	O16	1c dull blue		.75	.50
O43	O16	2c rose red		.75	.50
O44	O16	4c dark brown		.75	.50
O45	O16	5c dark green		.75	.50
O46	O16	8c orange brn		.75	.50
O47	O16	10c car rose		2.50	1.00
O48	O16	20c deep blue		2.50	1.00
		Nos. O42-O48 (7)		8.75	4.50

A 12c deep green, type O16, was prepared but not issued.

No. 45 Overprinted

1902			Perf. 12x12½		
O49	A12	1p olive grn		2.00	2.00
	a.	Inverted overprint		10.00	

Counterfeits of No. O49a exist.

Regular Issue of 1903 Overprinted

1903			Perf. 11½		
O50	A32	1c gray		.90	.60
O51	A32	2c blue green		.90	.60
O52	A32	5c blue		.90	.60
O53	A32	10c orange brn		.90	.60
O54	A32	20c carmine		.90	.60
O55	A32	30c deep blue		.90	.60
O56	A32	60c purple		.90	.60
		Nos. O50-O56 (7)		6.30	4.20

O17

1905-08		Engr.	Perf. 11½, 12		
O57	O17	1c gray grn		.50	.30
O58	O17	1c ol grn ('05)		.90	.30
O59	O17	1c brn org ('06)		.80	.30
O60	O17	1c ver ('08)		.50	.30
O61	O17	2c brown org		.35	.30
O62	O17	2c gray grn ('05)		.35	.30
O63	O17	2c red ('06)		2.00	.75
O64	O17	2c gray ('08)		1.00	.50
O65	O17	5c deep bl ('06)		.50	.35
O66	O17	5c gray bl ('08)		4.00	2.00
O67	O17	5c grnsh bl ('08)		2.00	1.50
O68	O17	10c violet ('06)		.35	.50
O69	O17	20c violet ('08)		2.00	1.25
		Nos. O57-O69 (13)		15.25	8.65

O18

1908				
O70	O17	10c bister	10.50	
O71	O17	10c emerald	10.50	
O72	O17	10c red lilac	13.50	
O73	O17	20c bister	9.00	
O74	O17	20c salmon pink	10.50	
O75	O17	20c green	10.50	
O76	O17	30c turquoise bl	10.50	
O77	O17	30c blue gray	10.50	
O78	O17	30c yellow	4.50	
O79	O17	60c chocolate	12.00	
O80	O17	60c orange brn	15.00	
O81	O17	60c deep ultra	12.00	
O82	O18	1p brt rose & blk	72.50	
O83	O18	1p lake & blk	72.50	
O84	O18	1p brn org & blk	75.00	
		Nos. O70-O84 (15)	349.00	

Nos. O70-O84 were not issued, but were surcharged or overprinted for use as regular postage stamps. See Nos. 131-138, 141-145, 158-165, 171-173.

O19

1913			Perf. 11½		
O85	O19	1c gray		.30	.35
O86	O19	2c orange		.30	.35
O87	O19	5c lilac		.30	.35
O88	O19	10c green		.30	.35
O89	O19	20c dull red		.30	.35
O90	O19	50c rose		.30	.35
O91	O19	75c deep blue		.30	.35
O92	O19	1p dull blue		1.00	.50
O93	O19	2p yellow		1.00	.50
		Nos. O85-O93 (9)		4.10	3.45

For surcharges see Nos. 268, C1-C3.

Type of Regular Issue of 1927-38 Overprinted in Red

1935				
O94	A47	10c light ultra	.40	.30
O95	A47	50c violet	.40	.30
O96	A48	1p orange	.40	.30

O97	A60	1.50p green	.40	.30
O98	A50	2.50p violet	.40	.30
		Nos. O94-O98 (5)	2.00	1.50

Overprint is diagonal on 1.50p.

University of Asunción Type

1940		Litho.	Perf. 12		
O99	A67	50c red brn & blk		1.65	.30
O100	A67	1p rose pink & blk		1.65	.30
O101	A67	2p lt bl grn & blk		1.65	.30
O102	A67	5p ultra & blk		1.65	.30
O103	A67	10p lt vio & blk		1.65	.30
O104	A67	50p dp org & blk		1.65	.30
		Nos. O99-O104 (6)		9.90	1.80

PENRHYN ISLAND

pen-ˈrin ˈi-lənd

(Tongareva)

AREA — 3 sq. mi.
POP. — 395 (1926)

Stamps of Cook Islands were used in Penrhyn from 1932 until 1973.

12 Pence = 1 Shilling

> Catalogue values for unused stamps in this country are for Never Hinged items, beginning with Scott 35 in the regular postage section, Scott B1 in the semipostal section and Scott O1 in the officials section.

Watermarks

Wmk. 61 — N Z and Star Close Together	Wmk. 63 — Double-lined N Z and Star

On watermark 61 the margins of the sheets are watermarked "NEW ZEALAND POSTAGE" and parts of the double-lined letters of these words are frequently found on the stamps. It occasionally happens that a stamp shows no watermark whatever.

Stamps of New Zealand Surcharged in Carmine, Vermilion, Brown or Blue

½ pence	1 pence

2½ pence

1902		Wmk. 63	Perf. 14	
1	A18	½p green (C)	1.00	14.00
a.		No period after "ISLAND"	175.00	325.00
2	A35	1p carmine (Br)	3.00	27.50
a.		Perf. 11	1,000.	1,200.
b.		Perf. 11x14	1,200.	1,400.
		Wmk. 61		
5	A18	½p green (V)	4.75	12.50
a.		No period after "ISLAND"	180.00	375.00
6	A35	1p carmine (Bl)	1.25	9.50
a.		No period after "ISLAND"	60.00	170.00
b.		Perf. 11x14	15,000.	8,500.
		Unwmk.	**Perf. 11**	
8	A22	2½p blue (C)	17.50	17.50
a.		"½" and "PENI" 2mm apart	30.00	30.00
9	A22	2½p blue (V)	14.50	10.00
a.		"½" and "PENI" 2mm apart	42.00	91.00
		Nos. 1-9 (6)	42.00	91.00

Stamps with compound perfs. also exist perf. 11 or 14 on one or more sides.

d	e

f

1903		Wmk. 61	
10	A23(d)	3p yel brn (Bl)	11.00	42.50
11	A26(e)	6p rose (Bl)	16.00	50.00
12	A29(f)	1sh org red (Bl)	62.50	67.50
a.		1sh bright red (Bl)	47.50	47.50
b.		1sh brown red (Bl)	65.00	65.00
		Nos. 10-12 (3)	89.50	160.00

1914-15		Perf. 14, 14x14½	
13	A41(a)	½p yel grn (C)	.90	12.00
a.		No period after "ISLAND"	25.00	110.00
b.		No period after "PENI"	110.00	350.00
14	A41(a)	½p yel grn (V) ('15)	.90	9.25
a.		No period after "ISLAND"	11.50	70.00
b.		No period after "PENI"	55.00	190.00
15	A41(e)	6p car rose (Bl)	25.00	82.50
16	A41(f)	1sh ver (Bl)	50.00	110.00
		Nos. 13-16 (4)	76.80	213.75

New Zealand Stamps of 1915-19 Overprinted in Red or Dark Blue

		Perf. 14x13½, 14x14½	
1917-20			**Typo.**
17	A43	½p yel grn (R) ('20)	1.00	2.25
18	A47	1½p gray black (R)	7.00	27.50
19	A47	1½p brn org (R) ('19)	1.00	27.50
20	A43	3p choc (Bl) ('19)	4.75	47.50
		Engr.		
21	A44	2½p dull bl (R) ('20)	2.00	11.00
22	A45	3p vio brn (Bl) ('18)	9.00	70.00
23	A45	6p car rose (Bl)		
		('18)	5.00	21.00
24	A45	1sh vermilion (Bl)	14.00	40.00
		Nos. 17-24 (8)	43.75	246.75

Landing of Capt. Cook A10	Avarua Waterfront A11

Capt. James Cook A12	Coconut Palm A13

Arorangi Village, Rarotonga A14	Avarua Harbor A15

1920		Unwmk.	Perf. 14	
25	A10	½p emerald & blk	1.25	22.50
a.		Center inverted	1,000.	
26	A11	1p red & black	1.50	17.00
a.		Center inverted	1,000.	
27	A12	1½p violet & blk	6.00	18.00
28	A13	3p red org & blk	2.25	17.50
29	A14	6p dk brn & red brn	3.00	20.00
30	A15	1sh dull bl & blk	12.00	30.00
		Nos. 25-30 (6)	26.00	125.00

Rarotongan Chief (Te Po) — A16

1927		Engr.	Wmk. 61	
31	A16	2½p blue & red brn	19.00	50.00

Types of 1920 Issue

1928-29				
33	A10	½p yellow grn & blk	6.50	25.00
34	A11	1p carmine rose & blk	6.50	25.00

PENRHYN

Northern Cook Islands

POP. — 606 (1996).

The Northern Cook Islands include six besides Penrhyn that are inhabited: Nassau, Palmerston (Avarua), Manihiki (Humphrey), Rakahanga (Reirson), Pukapuka (Danger) and Suwarrow (Anchorage).

100 Cents = 1 Dollar

> Catalogue values for unused stamps in this section are for Never Hinged items.

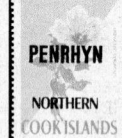

Cook Islands Nos. 200-201, 203, 205-208, 211-212, 215-217 Overprinted

1973		Photo. Unwmk.	Perf. 14x13½	
35	A34	1c gold & multi	.25	.25
36	A34	2c gold & multi	.25	.25
37	A34	3c gold & multi	.25	.25
38	A34	4c gold & multi	.25	.25
a.		Overprinted on #204	38.00	38.00
39	A34	5c gold & multi	.25	.25
40	A34	6c gold & multi	.25	.35
41	A34	8c gold & multi	.25	.45
42	A34	15c gold & multi	.35	.60
43	A34	20c gold & multi	1.25	1.00
44	A34	50c gold & multi	.90	2.00
45	A35	$1 gold & multi	.90	2.25
46	A35	$2 gold & multi	.90	4.50
		Nos. 35-46 (12)	6.05	12.40

Nos. 45-46 are overprinted "Penrhyn" only. Overprint exists with broken "E" or "O."

Issued with and without fluorescent security underprinting.

Issued: #35-45, Oct. 24; #46, Nov. 14.

Cook Islands Nos. 369-371 Overprinted in Silver: "PENRHYN / NORTHERN"

1973, Nov. 14		Photo.	Perf. 14	
47	A60	25c Princess Anne	.35	.25
48	A60	30c Mark Phillips	.35	.25
49	A60	50c Princess and Mark Phillips	.35	.25
		Nos. 47-49 (3)	1.05	.75

Wedding of Princess Anne and Capt. Mark Phillips.

Fluorescence

Starting with No. 50, stamps carry a "fluorescent security underprinting" in a multiple pattern combining a sailing ship, "Penrhyn Northern Cook Islands" and stars.

Ostracion — A17

Aerial View of Penrhyn Atoll A18

Designs: ½c-$1, Various fish of Penrhyn. $5, Map showing Penrhyn's location.

1974-75		Photo.	Perf. 13½x14	
50	A17	½c multicolored	.25	.25
51	A17	1c multicolored	.25	.25
52	A17	2c multicolored	.25	.25
53	A17	3c multicolored	.25	.25
54	A17	4c multicolored	.25	.25
55	A17	5c multicolored	.25	.25
56	A17	8c multicolored	.25	.25
57	A17	10c multicolored	.25	.25
58	A17	20c multicolored	.75	.40
59	A17	25c multicolored	.80	.45
60	A17	60c multicolored	2.00	1.10
61	A17	$1 multicolored	3.25	1.75

62	A18	$2 multicolored	6.50	10.00
63	A18	$5 multicolored	8.50	3.50
		Nos. 50-63 (14)	23.80	19.20

Issued: $2, 2/12/75; $5, 3/12/75; others 8/15/74.

For surcharges and overprints see Nos. 72, 352-353, O1-O12.

Map of Penrhyn and Nos. 1-2 — A19

UPU, cent.: 50c, UPU emblem, map of Penrhyn and Nos. 27-28.

1974, Sept. 27			Perf. 13	
64	A19	25c violet & multi	.30	.30
65	A19	50c slate grn & multi	.60	.60

Adoration of the Kings, by Memling A20

Christmas: 10c, Adoration of the Shepherds, by Hugo van der Goes. 25c, Adoration of the Kings, by Rubens. 30c, Holy Family, by Orazio Borgianni.

1974, Oct. 30				
66	A20	5c multicolored	.25	.25
67	A20	10c multicolored	.25	.25
68	A20	25c multicolored	.30	.30
69	A20	30c multicolored	.40	.40
		Nos. 66-69 (4)	1.20	1.20

Churchill Giving "V" Sign — A21

1974, Nov. 30			Photo.	
70	A21	30c shown	.35	.80
71	A21	50c Portrait	.45	.90

Winston Churchill (1874-1965).

No. 63 Overprinted

1975, July 24			Perf. 13½x13	
72	A18	$5 multicolored	2.25	2.75

Safe splashdown of Apollo space capsule.

Madonna, by Dirk Bouts — A22

Madonna Paintings: 15c, by Leonardo da Vinci. 35c, by Raphael.

1975, Nov. 21		Photo.	Perf. 14½x13	
73	A22	7c gold & multi	.45	.25
74	A22	15c gold & multi	.75	.30
75	A22	35c gold & multi	1.10	.45
		Nos. 73-75 (3)	2.30	1.00

Christmas 1975.

Pietà, by
Michelangelo — A23

1976, Mar. 19 Photo. Perf. 14x13
76	A23	15c gold & dark brown	.25	.25
77	A23	20c gold & deep purple	.40	.30
78	A23	35c gold & dark green	.55	.35
a.		Souvenir sheet of 3, #76-78	1.60	1.60
		Nos. 76-78 (3)	1.20	.90

Easter and for the 500th birth anniv. of
Michelangelo Buonarroti (1475-1564), Italian
sculptor, painter and architect.

The Spirit of '76, by Archibald M.
Willard
A24

No. 79, Washington Crossing the Delaware,
by Emmanuel Leutze.

1976, May 20 Photo. Perf. 13½
79	A24	Strip of 3	1.00	1.00
a.		30c Boatsman	.30	.30
b.		30c Washington	.30	.30
c.		30c Men in boat	.30	.30
80	A24	Strip of 3	2.00	2.00
a.		50c Drummer boy	.50	.50
b.		50c Old drummer	.50	.50
c.		50c Fifer	.50	.50
d.		Souvenir sheet, #79-80	3.25	3.25

American Bicentennial. Nos. 79-80 printed
in sheets of 15, 5 strips of 3 and 3-part corner
labels.
For overprint see No. O13.

Running — A25

Montreal Olympic Games Emblem and: 30c,
Long jump. 75c, Javelin.

1976, July 9 Photo. Perf. 13½
81	A25	25c multicolored	.30	.25
82	A25	30c multicolored	.35	.30
83	A25	75c multicolored	.75	.50
a.		Souvenir sheet of 3, #81-83,		
		perf. 14½x13½	1.40	1.40
		Nos. 81-83 (3)	1.40	1.05

21st Olympic Games, Montreal, Canada,
July 17-Aug. 1. Nos. 81-83 printed in sheets of
6 (2x3).

Flight into Egypt,
by Dürer — A26

Etchings by Albrecht Dürer: 15c, Adoration
of the Shepherds. 35c, Adoration of the Kings.

1976, Oct. 20 Photo. Perf. 13x13½
84	A26	7c silver & dk brown	.25	.25
85	A26	15c silver & slate grn	.25	.25
86	A26	35c silver & purple	.45	.35
		Nos. 84-86 (3)	.95	.85

Christmas. Nos. 84-86 printed in sheets of 8
(2x4) with decorative border.

Elizabeth II and
Westminster
Abbey — A27

$1, Elizabeth II & Prince Philip. $2, Elizabeth II.

1977, Mar. 24 Photo. Perf. 13½x13
87	A27	50c silver & multi	.25	.25
88	A27	$1 silver & multi	.30	.30
89	A27	$2 silver & multi	.45	.45
a.		Souvenir sheet of 3, #87-89	1.25	1.25
		Nos. 87-89 (3)	1.00	1.00

25th anniversary of reign of Queen Elizabeth II. Nos. 87-89 issued in sheets of 4.
For overprints see Nos. O14-O15.

Annunciation — A28

Designs: 15c, Announcement to Shepherds.
35c, Nativity. Designs from "The Bible in
Images," by Julius Schnorr von Carolsfeld
(1794-1872).

1977, Sept. 23 Photo. Perf. 13½
90	A28	7c multicolored	.25	.25
91	A28	15c multicolored	.65	.65
92	A28	35c multicolored	1.10	1.10
		Nos. 90-92 (3)	2.00	2.00

Christmas. Issued in sheets of 6.

A29

No. 93a, Red Sickle-bill (I'wii). No. 93b,
Chief's Feather Cloak. No. 94a, Crimson
creeper (apapane). No. 94b, Feathered head
of Hawaiian god. No. 95a, Hawaiian gallinule
(alae). No. 95b, Chief's regalia: feather cape,
staff (kahili) and helmet. No. 96a, Yellow-tufted
bee-eater (o'o). No. 96b, Scarlet feathered
image (head).
Birds are extinct; their feathers were used
for artifacts shown.

1978, Jan. 19 Photo. Perf. 12½x13
93	A29	20c Pair, #a.-b.	1.40	.70
94	A29	30c Pair, #a.-b.	1.75	.90
95	A29	35c Pair, #a.-b.	1.90	1.00
96	A29	75c Pair, #a.-b.	3.00	1.60
c.		Souv. sheet, #93a, 94a, 95a,		
		96a	4.25	4.25
d.		Souv. sheet, #93b, 94b, 95b,		
		96b	4.25	4.25
		Nos. 93-96 (4)	8.05	4.20

Bicentenary of Capt. Cook's arrival in
Hawaii. Printed in sheets of 8 (4x2).

A31

Rubens' Paintings: 10c, St. Veronica by
Rubens. 15c, Crucifixion. 35c, Descent from
the Cross.

1978, Mar. 10 Photo. Perf. 13½x13
Size: 25x36mm
101	A31	10c multicolored	.25	.25
102	A31	15c multicolored	.25	.25
103	A31	35c multicolored	.50	.50
a.		Souvenir sheet of 3	1.10	1.10
		Nos. 101-103 (3)	1.00	1.00

Easter and 400th birth anniv. of Peter Paul
Rubens (1577-1640). Nos. 101-103 issued in
sheets of 6. No. 103a contains one each of
Nos. 101-103 (27x36mm).

Miniature Sheet

A32

1978, May 24 Photo. Perf. 13
104	A32	Sheet of 6	1.75	1.75
a.		90c Arms of United Kingdom	.35	.25
b.		90c shown	.35	.25
c.		90c Arms of New Zealand	.35	.25
d.		Souvenir sheet of 3, #104a- 104c	1.40	1.40

25th anniv. of coronation of Elizabeth II.
No. 104 contains 2 horizontal se-tenant
strips of Nos. 104a-104c, separated by horizontal gutter showing coronation.

A33

Paintings by Dürer: 30c, Virgin and Child.
35c, Virgin and Child with St. Anne.

1978, Nov. 29 Photo. Perf. 14x13½
105	A33	30c multicolored	.70	.60
106	A33	35c multicolored	.75	.65
a.		Souvenir sheet of 2, #105-106	1.45	1.25

Christmas and 450th death anniv. of
Albrecht Dürer (1471-1528), German painter.
Nos. 105-106 issued in sheets of 6.

A34

#107a, Penrhyn #64-65. #107b, Rowland
Hill, Penny Black. #108a, Penrhyn #104b.
#108b, Hill portrait.

1979, Sept. 26 Photo. Perf. 14
107	A34	75c Pair, #a.-b.	1.00	1.00
108	A34	90c Pair, #a.-b.	1.25	1.25
c.		Souvenir sheet of 4, #107-108	2.25	2.25

Sir Rowland Hill (1795-1879), originator of
penny postage. Issued in sheets of 8.

Max and Moritz, IYC
Emblem — A35

IYC: Scenes from Max and Moritz, by Wilhelm Busch (1832-1908).

1979, Nov. 20 Photo. Perf. 13x12½
111		Sheet of 4	1.00	
a.	A35	12c shown	.25	
b.	A35	12c Looking down chimney	.25	
c.	A35	12c With stolen chickens	.25	
d.	A35	12c Woman and dog, empty pan	.25	
112		Sheet of 4	1.00	
a.	A35	15c Sawing bridge	.25	
b.	A35	15c Man falling into water	.25	
c.	A35	15c Broken bridge	.25	
d.	A35	15c Running away	.25	
113		Sheet of 4	1.00	
a.	A35	20c Baker	.25	
b.	A35	20c Sneaking into bakery	.25	
c.	A35	20c Falling into dough	.25	
d.	A35	20c Baked into breads	.25	
		Nos. 111-113 (3)	3.00	

Sheets come with full labels at top and bottom showing text from stories or trimmed with
text removed. Values of 3 sheets with full
labels $11.

A36

Easter (15th Century Prayerbook Illustrations): 12c, Jesus Carrying the Cross. 20c,
Crucifixion, by William Vreland. 35c, Descent
from the Cross.

1980, Mar. 28 Photo. Perf. 13x13½
114	A36	12c multicolored	.25	.25
115	A36	20c multicolored	.25	.25
116	A36	35c multicolored	.40	.40
a.		Souvenir sheet of 3, #114-116	.75	.75
		Nos. 114-116 (3)	.90	.90

See Nos. B4-B6.

A37

1980, Sept. 17 Photo. Perf. 13
117	A37	$1 multicolored	1.20	1.20

Souvenir Sheet
118	A37	$2.50 multicolored	2.00	2.00

Queen Mother Elizabeth, 80th birthday.

A38

Platform diving: #119a, Falk Hoffman, DDR.
#119b, Martina Jaschke.
Archery: #120a, Tomi Polkolainen. #120b,
Kete Losaberidse.
Soccer: #121a, Czechoslovakia, gold.
#121b, DDR, silver.
Running: #122a, Barbel Wockel. #122b,
Pietro Mennea.

1980, Nov. 14 Photo. Perf. 13½
119	A38	10c Pair, #a.-b.	.25	.25
120	A38	20c Pair, #a.-b.	.45	.45
121	A38	30c Pair, #a.-b.	.70	.70
122	A38	50c Pair, #a.-b.	1.10	1.10
		Nos. 119-122 (4)	2.50	2.50

Souvenir Sheet
123	A38	Sheet of 8	2.50	2.50

22nd Summer Olympic Games, Moscow,
July 19-Aug. 3.
No. 123 contains #119-122 with gold bor-
ders and white lettering at top and bottom.

A39

Christmas (15th Century Virgin and Child
Paintings by): 20c, Virgin and Child, by Luis
Dalmau. 35c, Serra brothers. 50c, Master of
the Porciuncula.

1980, Dec. 5 Photo. Perf. 13
127	A39	20c multicolored	.25	.25
128	A39	35c multicolored	.30	.30
129	A39	50c multicolored	.45	.45
a.		Souvenir sheet of 3, #127-129	2.25	2.25
		Nos. 127-129 (3)	1.00	1.00

See Nos. B7-B9.

A40

A41

Cutty Sark, 1869 — A42

#160a, 165a, Amatasi. #160b, 165b, Ndrua. #160c, 165c, Waka. #160d, 165d, Tongiaki. #161a, 166a, Va'a teu'ua. #161b, 166b, Victoria, 1500. #161c, 166c, Golden Hinde, 1560. #161d, 166d, Boudeuse, 1760. #162a, 167a, Bounty, 1787. #162b, 167b, Astrolabe, 1811. #162c, 167c, Star of India, 1861. #162d, 167d, Great Rep., 1853. #163a, 168a, Balcutha, 1886. #163b, 168b, Coonatto, 1863. #163c, 168c, Antiope, 1866. #163d, 168d, Teaping, 1863. #164a, 169a, Preussen, 1902. #164b, 169b, Pamir, 1921. #164c, 169c, Cap Hornier, 1910. #164d, 169d, Patriarch, 1869.

1981		Photo.	Perf. 14	
160	A40	1c Block of 4, #a.-d.	.30	.30
161	A40	3c Block of 4, #a.-d.	.50	.50
162	A40	4c Block of 4, #a.-d.	.65	.65
163	A40	6c Block of 4, #a.-d.	1.00	1.00
164	A40	10c Block of 4, #a.-d.	1.25	1.25
		Perf. 13½x14½		
165	A41	15c Block of 4, #a.-d.	1.40	1.40
166	A41	20c Block of 4, #a.-d.	1.60	1.60
167	A41	30c Block of 4, #a.-d.	2.75	2.75
168	A41	50c Block of 4, #a.-d.	4.50	4.50
169	A41	$1 Block of 4, #a.-d.	11.00	11.00
		Perf. 13½		
170	A42	$2 shown	5.00	5.00
171	A42	$4 Mermerus, 1872	10.00	10.00
172	A42	$6 Resolution, Discovery, 1776	17.00	17.00
		Nos. 160-172 (13)	56.95	56.95

Issued: 1c-10c, Feb. 16; 15c-50c, Mar. 16; $1, May 15; $2, $4, June 26; $6, Sept. 21.
For surcharges and overprints see Nos. 241-243, 251, 254, 395, O35, O37, O39.

Christ with Crown of Thorns, by Titian — A44

Easter: 30c, Jesus at the Grove, by Paolo Veronese. 50c, Pieta, by Van Dyck.

1981, Apr. 5			Perf. 14	
173	A44	30c multicolored	.40	.30
174	A44	40c multicolored	.60	.45
175	A44	50c multicolored	.75	.60
a.		Souv. sheet, #173-175, perf 13½	3.00	3.00
		Nos. 173-175 (3)	1.75	1.35

See Nos. B10-B12.

A45

Designs: Portraits of Prince Charles.

1981, July 10		Photo.	Perf. 14	
176	A45	40c multicolored	.25	.25
177	A45	50c multicolored	.25	.25
178	A45	60c multicolored	.25	.25
179	A45	70c multicolored	.30	.30

180	A45	80c multicolored	.35	.35
a.		Souv. sheet of 5, #176-180+label	2.00	2.00
		Nos. 176-180 (5)	1.40	1.40

Royal wedding. Nos. 176-180 each issued in sheets of 5 plus label showing couple.
For overprints and surcharges see Nos. 195-199, 244-245, 248, 299-300, B13-B18.

1982 World Cup Soccer — A46

Shirts: No. 181: a, Red. b, Striped. c, Blue. No. 182: a, Blue. b, Red. c, Striped. No. 183: a, Orange. b, Purple. c, Black.

1981, Dec. 7		Photo.	Perf. 13	
181	A46	15c Strip of 3, #a.-c.	1.00	1.00
182	A46	35c Strip of 3, #a.-c.	1.75	1.75
183	A46	60c Strip of 3, #a.-c.	2.75	2.75
		Nos. 181-183 (3)	5.50	5.50

See No. B19.

Christmas — A47

Dürer Engravings: 30c, Virgin on a Crescent, 1508. 40c, Virgin at the Fence, 1503. 50c, Holy Virgin and Child, 1505.

1981, Dec. 15		Photo.	Perf. 13x13½	
184	A47	30c multicolored	.75	.75
185	A47	40c multicolored	1.25	1.25
186	A47	50c multicolored	1.50	1.50
a.		Souvenir sheet of 3	3.25	3.25
		Nos. 184-186 (3)	3.50	3.50
		Souvenir Sheets		
		Perf. 14x13½		
187	A47	70c + 5c like #184	1.10	1.10
188	A47	70c + 5c like #185	1.10	1.10
189	A47	70c + 5c like #186	1.10	1.10

No. 186a contains Nos. 184-186 each with 2c surcharge. Nos. 187-189 each contain one 25x40mm stamp. Surtaxes were for childrens' charities.

21st Birthday of Princess Diana — A48

Designs: Portraits of Diana.

1982, July 1		Photo.	Perf. 14	
190	A48	30c multicolored	.65	.65
191	A48	50c multicolored	.85	.85
192	A48	70c multicolored	1.05	1.05
193	A48	80c multicolored	1.25	1.25
194	A48	$1.40 multicolored	2.75	2.75
a.		Souv. sheet, #190-194 + label	6.50	6.50
		Nos. 190-194 (5)	6.55	6.55

For new inscriptions, overprints and surcharges, see Nos. 200-204, 246-247, 249-250, 301-302.

Nos. 176-180a Overprinted

1982, July 30

195	A45	40c multicolored	.40	.40
196	A45	50c multicolored	.55	.55
197	A45	60c multicolored	.60	.60
198	A45	70c multicolored	.70	.70

199	A45	80c multicolored	.75	.75
a.		Souv. sheet, #195-199 + label	5.50	5.50
		Nos. 195-199 (5)	3.00	3.00

Nos. 190-194a Inscribed in Silver

1982		Photo.	Perf. 14	
200	A48	30c Pair, #a.-b.	.70	.70
201	A48	50c Pair, #a.-b.	.90	.90
202	A48	70c Pair, #a.-b.	1.60	1.60
203	A48	80c Pair, #a.-b.	1.75	1.75
204	A48	$1.40 Pair, #a.-b.	3.00	3.00
c.		Souv. sheet #200a, 201a, 202a, 203a, 204a + label	6.00	6.00
		Nos. 200-204 (5)	7.95	7.95

Miniature sheets of each denomination were issued containing 2 "21 JUNE 1982...," 3 "COMMEMORATING....," and a label. Value, set of 5 sheets, $21.
Se-tenant pairs come with or without label.
For surcharges see Nos. 247, 250, 253.

A49

Christmas — Virgin and Child Paintings: 35c, Joos Van Cleve (1485-1540). 48c, Filippino Lippi (1457-1504). 60c, Cima Da Conegliano (1459-1517).

1982, Dec. 10		Photo.	Perf. 14	
205	A49	35c multicolored	.50	.50
206	A49	48c multicolored	.70	.70
207	A49	60c multicolored	.80	.80
a.		Souvenir sheet of 3	3.00	3.00
		Nos. 205-207 (3)	2.00	2.00
		Souvenir Sheets		
208	A49	70c + 5c like 35c	1.60	1.60
209	A49	70c + 5c like 48c	1.60	1.60
210	A49	70c + 5c like 60c	1.60	1.60

Nos. 205-207 were printed in sheets of five plus label. No. 207a contains Nos. 205-207 each with 2c surcharge. Nos. 208-210 each contain one stamp, perf. 13½. Surtaxes were for childrens' charities.

A50

#a, Red coral. #b, Aerial view. #c, Eleanor Roosevelt, grass skirt. #d, Map.

1983, Mar. 14			Perf. 13½x13	
211	A50	60c Block of 4, #a.-d.	2.25	2.25

Commonwealth day.
For surcharges see No. O27-O30.

Scouting Year — A51

Emblem and various tropical flowers.

1983, Apr. 5			Perf. 13½x14½	
215	A51	36c multicolored	1.75	.75
216	A51	48c multicolored	2.25	1.00
217	A51	60c multicolored	2.50	1.25
		Nos. 215-217 (3)	6.50	3.00
		Souvenir Sheet		
218	A51	$2 multicolored	3.50	3.50

Nos. 215-218 Overprinted: "XV / WORLD JAMBOREE / CANADA / 1983"

1983, July 8		Photo.	Perf. 13½x14½	
219	A51	36c multicolored	1.60	.65
220	A51	48c multicolored	2.10	1.25
221	A51	60c multicolored	2.50	1.25
		Nos. 219-221 (3)	6.20	3.15
		Souvenir Sheet		
222	A51	$2 multicolored	3.50	3.50

15th World Boy Scout Jamboree.

Save the Whales Campaign — A52

Various whale hunting scenes.

1983, July 29		Photo.	Perf. 13	
223	A52	8c multicolored	.80	.70
224	A52	15c multicolored	1.20	1.00
225	A52	35c multicolored	2.40	1.40
226	A52	60c multicolored	3.75	2.00
227	A52	$1 multicolored	5.75	2.75
		Nos. 223-227 (5)	13.90	7.85

World Communications Year — A53

Designs: Cable laying Vessels.

1983, Sept.		Photo.	Perf. 13	
228	A53	36c multicolored	1.00	.50
229	A53	48c multicolored	1.25	.70
230	A53	60c multicolored	1.50	.90
		Nos. 228-230 (3)	3.75	2.10
		Souvenir Sheet		
231		Sheet of 3	2.75	2.75
a.	A53	36c + 3c like No. 228	.65	.65
b.	A53	48c + 3c like No. 229	.85	.85
c.	A53	60c + 3c like No. 230	1.00	1.00

Surtax was for local charities.

Nos. 164, 166-167, 170, 172, 178-180, 192-194, 202-204 Surcharged

Blocks of 4, #a.-d. (#241-243)
Pairs, #a.-b. (#247, 250, 253)

Perf. 14, 13½x14½, 13½

1983				Photo.	
241	A40	18c on 10c #164		3.50	3.25
242	A41	36c on 20c #166		4.25	4.00
243	A41	36c on 30c #167		4.25	4.00
244	A45	48c on 60c multi		1.05	1.00
245	A45	72c on 70c multi		1.50	1.40
246	A48	72c on 70c #192		1.50	1.40
247	A48	72c on 70c #202		3.50	3.00
248	A45	96c on 80c multi		3.00	1.75
249	A48	96c on 80c #193		3.25	1.75
250	A48	96c on 80c #203		4.00	3.25
251	A42	$1.20 on $2 multi		4.25	2.50
252	A48	$1.20 on $1.40 #194		3.50	2.50
253	A48	$1.20 on $1.40 #204		6.00	4.00
254	A42	$5.60 on $6 multi		18.00	12.25
		Nos. 241-254 (14)		61.55	46.05

Issued: #241-243, 245, 251, Sept. 26; #244, 246, 249, 252, 254, Oct. 28; others Dec. 1.

First Manned
Balloon Flight,
200th
Anniv. — A54

Designs: 36c, Airship, Sir George Cayley (1773-1857). 48c, Man-powered airship, Dupuy de Lome (1818-1885). 60c, Brazilian Aviation Pioneer, Alberto Santos Dumont (1873-1932). 96c, Practical Airship, Paul Lebaudy (1858-1937). $1.32, L-Z 127 Graf Zeppelin.

1983, Oct. 31   Litho.   Perf. 13
255 A54 36c multicolored .75 .75
256 A54 48c multicolored 1.10 1.10
257 A54 60c multicolored 1.30 1.30
258 A54 96c multicolored 1.70 1.70
259 A54 $1.32 multicolored 2.60 2.60
  a. Souvenir sheet of 5, #255-259 7.50 7.50
    Nos. 255-259 (5) 7.45 7.45

Nos. 255-259 se-tenant with labels. Sheets of 5 for each value exist.
Nos. 255-259 are misspelled "ISLANS." For correcting overprints see Nos. 287-291.

Christmas — A55

Raphael Paintings: 36c, Madonna in the Meadow. 42c, Tempi Madonna. 48c, Small Cowper Madonna. 60c, Madonna Della Tenda.

1983, Nov. 30   Photo.   Perf. 13x13½
260 A55 36c multicolored .75 .45
261 A55 42c multicolored 1.00 .55
262 A55 48c multicolored 1.25 .60
263 A55 60c multicolored 1.50 .80
  a. Souvenir sheet of 4 4.50 4.50
    Nos. 260-263 (4) 4.50 2.40

Souvenir Sheets
Perf. 13½
264 A55 75c + 5c like #260 1.20 1.20
265 A55 75c + 5c like #261 1.20 1.20
266 A55 75c + 5c like #262 1.20 1.20
267 A55 75c + 5c like #263 1.20 1.20

No. 263a contains Nos. 260-263 each with 3c surcharge. Nos. 264-267 each contain one 29x41mm stamp. Issued Dec. 28. Surtaxes were for children's charities.

Waka Canoe — A56

4c, Amatasi fishing boat. 5c, Ndrua canoe. 8c, Tongiaki canoe. 10c, Victoria, 1500. 18c, Golden Hind, 1560. 20c, Boudeuse, 1760. 30c, Bounty, 1787. 36c, Astrolabe, 1811. 48c, Great Republic, 1853. 50c, Star of India, 1861. 60c, Coonatto, 1863. 72c, Antiope, 1866. 80c, Balcutha, 1886. 96c, Cap Hornier, 1910. $1.20, Pamir, 1921. $3, Mermerus, 1872. $5, Cutty Sark, 1869. $9.60, Resolution, Discovery.

1984   Photo.   Perf. 14½
268 A56 2c multicolored .25 .25
269 A56 4c multicolored .25 .25
270 A56 5c multicolored .25 .25
271 A56 8c multicolored .25 .25
272 A56 10c multicolored .25 .25
273 A56 18c multicolored .75 .45
274 A56 20c multicolored .50 .50
275 A56 30c multicolored 1.00 .70
276 A56 36c multicolored .40 .90
277 A56 48c multicolored 1.20 1.20
278 A56 50c multicolored 1.30 1.30
279 A56 60c multicolored 1.40 1.40
280 A56 72c multicolored 1.80 1.80
281 A56 80c multicolored 2.00 2.00
282 A56 96c multicolored 2.60 2.60
283 A56 $1.20 multicolored 1.30 1.30
Perf. 13
Size: 42x34mm
284 A56 $3 multicolored 5.00 5.00
285 A56 $5 multicolored 8.00 8.00
286 A56 $9.60 multicolored 16.00 16.00
    Nos. 268-286 (19) 44.50 44.40

Issue dates: Nos. 268-277, Feb. 8. Nos. 278-283, Mar. 23. Nos. 284-286 June 15.
For overprints and surcharges see Nos. O16-O26, O31-O34, O36, O38, O40.

Nos. 255-259a Overprinted

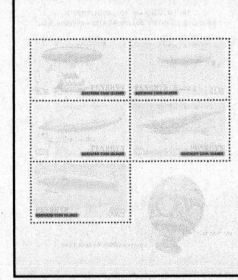

1984   Litho.   Perf. 13
287 A54 36c multicolored .80 .80
288 A54 48c multicolored 1.00 1.00
289 A54 60c multicolored 1.30 1.30
290 A54 96c multicolored 2.10 2.10
291 A54 $1.32 multicolored 2.75 2.75
  a. Souvenir sheet of 5, #287-291 7.50 8.75
    Nos. 287-291 (5) 7.95 7.95

1984 Los
Angeles
Summer
Olympic
Games — A57

35c, Olympic flag. 60c, Torch, flags. $1.80, Classic runners, Memorial Coliseum.

1984, July 20   Photo.   Perf. 13½x13
292 A57 35c multicolored .45 .45
293 A57 60c multicolored .80 .80
294 A57 $1.80 multicolored 2.00 2.00
    Nos. 292-294 (3) 3.25 3.25

Souvenir Sheet
295   Sheet of 3 + label 3.00 3.00
  a. A57 35c + 5c like #292 .35 .35
  b. A57 60c + 5c like #293 .50 .50
  c. A57 $1.80 + 5c like #294 1.75 1.75

Surtax for amateur sports.

AUSIPEX
'84 — A57a

60c, Nos. 161c, 107b, 180, 104b. $1.20, Map of South Pacific.

1984, Sept. 20
296 A57a 60c multicolored .85 .85
297 A57a $1.20 multicolored 1.75 1.75

Souvenir Sheet
298   Sheet of 2 3.00 3.00
  a. A57a 96c like #296 1.50 1.50
  b. A57a 96c like #297 1.50 1.50

For surcharge see No. 345.

Nos. 176-177, 190-191 Ovptd. "Birth of/Prince Henry/15 Sept. 1984" and Surcharged in Black or Gold

1984, Oct. 18   Perf. 14
299 A45 $2 on 40c 1.60 1.60
300 A45 $2 on 50c 1.60 1.60
301 A48 $2 on 30c 1.60 1.60
302 A48 $2 on 50c 1.60 1.60
    Nos. 299-302 (4) 6.40 6.40

Nos. 209-302 printed in sheets of 5 plus one label each picturing a portrait of the royal couple or an heraldic griffin.

Christmas
1984 — A58

Paintings: 36c, Virgin and Child, by Giovanni Bellini. 48c, Virgin and Child, by Lorenzo di Credi. 60c, Virgin and Child, by Palma, the Older. 96c, Virgin and Child, by Raphael.

1984, Nov. 15   Photo.   Perf. 13x13½
303 A58 36c multicolored .55 .55
304 A58 48c multicolored .90 .90
305 A58 60c multicolored 1.00 1.00

306 A58 96c multicolored 1.75 1.75
  a. Souvenir sheet of 4 4.25 4.25
    Nos. 303-306 (4) 4.20 4.20
Souvenir Sheets
307 A58 96c + 10c like #303 1.60 1.60
308 A58 96c + 10c like #304 1.60 1.60
309 A58 96c + 10c like #305 1.60 1.60
310 A58 96c + 10c like #306 1.60 1.60

No. 306a contains Nos. 303-306, each with 5c surcharge. Nos. 307-310 issued Dec. 10. Surtax for children's charities.

Audubon
Bicentenary
A59

20c, Harlequin duck. 55c, Sage grouse. 65c, Solitary sandpiper. 75c, Red-backed sandpiper.

1985, Apr. 9   Photo.   Perf. 13
311 A59 20c multi 1.50 1.50
312 A59 55c multi 4.00 4.00
313 A59 65c multi 4.75 4.75
314 A59 75c multi 5.25 5.25
    Nos. 311-314 (4) 15.50 15.50

Souvenir Sheets
Perf. 13½x13
315 A59 95c Like #311 3.00 2.00
316 A59 95c Like #312 3.00 2.00
317 A59 95c Like #313 3.00 2.00
318 A59 95c Like #314 3.00 2.00

For surcharges see Nos. 391-394.

Queen Mother, 85th
Birthday — A60

75c, Photograph, 1921. 95c, New mother, 1926. $1.20, Coronation day, 1937. $2.80, 70th birthday.
$5, Portrait, c. 1980.

1985, June 24   Photo.   Perf. 13x13½
319 A60 75c multicolored .55 .65
320 A60 95c multicolored .70 .80
321 A60 $1.20 multicolored 1.00 1.00
322 A60 $2.80 multicolored 2.25 2.50
  a. Souvenir sheet of 4, #319-322 15.00 15.00
    Nos. 319-322 (4) 4.50 4.95

Souvenir Sheet
323 A60 $5 multicolored 3.75 3.75

No. 322a issued on 8/4/86, for 86th birthday.

Intl. Youth
Year — A61

Grimm Brothers' fairy tales: 75c, House in the Wood. 95c, Snow White and Rose Red. $1.15, Goose Girl.

1985, Sept. 10   Perf. 13x13½
324 A61 75c multicolored 2.25 2.25
325 A61 95c multicolored 3.25 3.25
326 A61 $1.15 multicolored 4.50 4.50
    Nos. 324-326 (3) 10.00 10.00

Christmas
1985 — A62

Paintings (details) by Murillo: 75c, No. 330a, The Annunciation. $1.15, No. 330b, Adoration of the Shepherds. $1.80, No. 330c, The Holy Family.

1985, Nov. 25   Photo.   Perf. 14
327 A62 75c multicolored 1.50 1.50
328 A62 $1.15 multicolored 2.25 2.25
329 A62 $1.80 multicolored 3.75 3.75
    Nos. 327-329 (3) 7.50 7.50

Souvenir Sheets
Perf. 13½
330   Sheet of 3 4.25 4.25
  a.-c. A62 95c any single 1.30 1.30
331 A62 $1.20 like #327 1.75 1.75
332 A62 $1.45 like #328 2.00 2.00
333 A62 $2.75 like #329 3.25 3.25

Halley's
Comet — A63

Fire and Ice, by Camille Rendal. Nos. 334-335 se-tenant in continuous design.

1986, Feb. 4   Perf. 13½x13
334 A63 $1.50 Comet head 3.50 3.50
335 A63 $1.50 Comet tail 3.50 3.50
  a. Pair, #334-335 7.00 7.00
Size: 109x43mm
Imperf
336 A63 $3 multicolored 6.00 6.00
    Nos. 334-336 (3) 13.00 13.00

Elizabeth II, 60th
Birthday — A64

1986, Apr. 21   Perf. 14
337 A64 95c Age 3 1.25 1.25
338 A64 $1.45 Wearing crown 1.60 1.60
Size: 60x34mm
Perf. 13½x13
339 A64 $2.50 Both portraits 2.75 2.75
    Nos. 337-339 (3) 5.60 5.60

A65

Statue of Liberty, Cent.: 95c, Statue, scaffolding. $1.75 Removing copper facade. $3, Restored statue on Liberty Island.

1986, June 27   Photo.   Perf. 13½
340 A65 95c multicolored .85 .85
341 A65 $1.75 multicolored 1.75 1.75
342 A65 $3 multicolored 3.00 3.00
    Nos. 340-342 (3) 5.60 5.60

A66

1986, July 23   Perf. 13x13½
343 A66 $2.50 Portraits 3.00 3.00
344 A66 $3.50 Profiles 3.75 3.75

Wedding of Prince Andrew and Sarah Ferguson. Nos. 343-344 each printed in sheets of 4 plus 2 center decorative labels.

No. 298 Surcharged with Gold Circle, Bar, New Value in Black and Exhibition Emblem in Gold and Black

1986, Aug. 4
345   Sheet of 2 8.75 8.75
  a. A57a $2 on 96c #298a 4.25 4.25
  b. A57a $2 on 96c #298b 4.25 4.25

STAMPEX '86, Adelaide, Aug. 4-10.

Christmas — A67

Engravings by Rembrandt: 65c, No. 349a, Adoration of the Shepherds. $1.75, No. 349b, Virgin and Child. $2.50, No. 349c, The Holy Family.

1986, Nov. 20   Litho.   Perf. 13x13½
346	A67	65c multicolored	2.50 2.50
347	A67	$1.75 multicolored	3.50 3.50
348	A67	$2.50 multicolored	5.00 5.00
		Nos. 346-348 (3)	11.00 11.00

Souvenir Sheet
Perf. 13½x13
349		Sheet of 3	13.00 13.00
a.-c.		A67 $1.50 any single	4.00 4.00

Corrected inscription is black on silver. For surcharges see Nos. B20-B23.

Souvenir Sheets

Statue of Liberty, Cent. — A68

Photographs: No. 350a, Workmen, crown. No. 350b, Ellis Is., aerial view. No. 350c, Immigration building, Ellis Is. No. 350d, Buildings, opposite side of Ellis Is. No. 350e, Workmen inside torch structure. No. 351a, Liberty's head and torch. No. 351b, Torch. No. 351c, Workmen on scaffold. No. 351d, Statue, full figure. No. 351e, Workmen beside statue. Nos. 351a-351e vert.

1987, Apr. 15   Litho.   Perf. 14
350	A68	Sheet of 5 + label	5.75 5.75
a.-e.		65c any single	1.05 1.05
351	A68	Sheet of 5 + label	5.75 5.75
a.-e.		65c any single	1.05 1.05

Nos. 62-63 Ovptd. "Fortieth Royal Wedding / Anniversary 1947-87" in Lilac Rose

1987, Nov. 20   Photo.   Perf. 13½x14
352	A18	$2 multicolored	2.00 2.00
353	A18	$5 multicolored	5.50 5.50

Christmas — A69

Paintings (details) by Raphael: 95c, No. 357a, The Garvagh Madonna, the National Gallery, London. $1.60, No. 357b, The Alba Madonna, the National Gallery of Art, Washington. $2.25, No. 357c, $4.80, The Madonna of the Fish, Prado Museum, Madrid.

1987, Dec. 11   Photo.   Perf. 13½
354	A69	95c multicolored	2.40 2.40
355	A69	$1.60 multicolored	3.00 3.00
356	A69	$2.25 multicolored	4.75 4.75
		Nos. 354-356 (3)	10.15 10.15

Souvenir Sheets
357		Sheet of 3 + label	16.00 16.00
a.-c.		A69 $1.15 any single	4.75 4.75
358	A69	$4.80 multicolored	16.00 16.00

No. 358 contains one 31x39mm stamp.

1988 Summer Olympics, Seoul — A70

Events and: 55c, $1.25, Seoul Games emblem. 95c, Obverse of a $50 silver coin issued in 1987 to commemorate the participation of Cook Islands athletes in the Olympics for the 1st time. $1.50, Coin reverse.

Perf. 13½x13, 13x13½
1988, July 29   Photo.
359	A70	55c Running	1.10 1.10
360	A70	95c High jump, vert.	2.20 2.20
361	A70	$1.25 Shot put	2.50 2.50
362	A70	$1.50 Tennis, vert.	4.00 4.00
		Nos. 359-362 (4)	9.80 9.80

Souvenir Sheet
363		Sheet of 2	9.00 9.00
a.		A70 $2.50 like 95c	4.25 4.25
b.		A70 $2.50 like $1.50	4.25 4.25

Nos. 359-363 Ovptd. for Olympic Gold Medalists
a. "CARL LEWIS / UNITED STATES / 100 METERS"
b. "LOUISE RITTER / UNITED STATES / HIGH JUMP"
c. "ULF TIMMERMANN / EAST GERMANY / SHOT-PUT"
d. "STEFFI GRAF / WEST GERMANY / WOMEN'S TENNIS"
e. "JACKIE / JOYNER-KERSEE / United States / Heptathlon"
f. "STEFFI GRAF / West Germany / Women's Tennis / MILOSLAV MECIR / Czechoslovakia / Men's Tennis"

Perf. 13½x13, 13x13½
1988, Oct. 14   Photo.
364	A70(a)	55c on No. 359	1.20 1.20
365	A70(b)	95c on No. 360	2.40 2.40
366	A70(c)	$1.25 on No. 361	2.75 2.75
367	A70(d)	$1.50 on No. 362	4.50 4.50
		Nos. 364-367 (4)	10.85 10.85

Souvenir Sheet
368		Sheet of 2	9.00 9.00
a.		A70(e) $2.50 on No. 363a	4.25 4.25
b.		A70(f) $2.50 on No. 363b	4.25 4.25

Christmas — A71

Virgin and Child paintings by Titian.

1988, Nov. 9   Perf. 13x13½
369	A71	70c multicolored	1.40 1.40
370	A71	85c multi, diff.	1.75 1.75
371	A71	95c multi, diff.	2.25 2.25
372	A71	$1.25 multi, diff.	2.50 2.50
		Nos. 369-372 (4)	7.90 7.90

Souvenir Sheet
Perf. 13
373	A71	$6.40 multi, diff.	9.00 9.00

No. 373 contains one diamond-shaped stamp, size: 55x55mm.

1st Moon Landing, 20th Anniv. — A72

Apollo 11 mission emblem, US flag and: 55c, First step on the Moon. 75c, Astronaut carrying equipment. 95c, Conducting experiment. $1.25, Crew members Armstrong, Collins and Aldrin. $1.75, Armstrong and Aldrin aboard lunar module.

1989, July 24   Photo.   Perf. 14
374-378	A72	Set of 5	12.00 12.00

Christmas — A73

Details from *The Nativity*, by Albrecht Durer, 1498, center panel of the Paumgartner altarpiece: 55c, Madonna. 70c, Christ child, cherubs. 85c, Joseph. $1.25, Attendants. $6.40, Entire painting.

1989, Nov. 17   Photo.   Perf. 13x13½
379-382	A73	Set of 4	6.00 6.00

Souvenir Sheet
383	A73	$6.40 multicolored	9.50 9.50

No. 383 contains one 31x50mm stamp.

Queen Mother, 90th Birthday A74

1990, July 24   Photo.   Perf. 13½
384	A74	$2.25 multicolored	3.25 3.25

Souvenir Sheet
385	A74	$7.50 multicolored	16.00 16.00

Christmas — A75

Paintings: 55c, Adoration of the Magi by Veronese. 70c, Virgin and Child by Quentin Metsys. 85c, Virgin and Child Jesus by Van Der Goes. $1.50, Adoration of the Kings by Jan Gossaert. $6.40, Virgin and Child with Saints Francis, John the Baptist, Zenobius and Lucy by Domenico Veneziano.

1990, Nov. 26   Litho.   Perf. 14
386-389	A75	Set of 4	9.00 9.00

Souvenir Sheet
390	A75	$6.40 multicolored	10.50 10.50

Nos. 311-314 Surcharged in Red or Black

1990, Dec. 5   Photo.   Perf. 13
391	A59	$1.50 on 20c (R)	2.75 2.75
392	A59	$1.50 on 55c	2.75 2.75
393	A59	$1.50 on 65c	2.75 2.75
394	A59	$1.50 on 75c (R)	2.75 2.75
		Nos. 391-394 (4)	11.00 11.00

Birdpex '90, 20th Intl. Ornithological Cong., New Zealand. Surcharge appears in various locations.

No. 172 Overprinted "COMMEMORATING 65th BIRTHDAY OF H.M. QUEEN ELIZABETH II"

1991, Apr. 22   Photo.   Perf. 13½
395	A42	$6 multicolored	13.00 13.00

Christmas — A76

Paintings: 55c, Virgin and Child with Saints, by Gerard David. 85c, The Nativity, by Tintoretto. $1.15, Mystic Nativity, by Botticelli. $1.85, Adoration of the Shepherds, by Murillo. $6.40, Madonna of the Chair, by Raphael.

1991, Nov. 11   Litho.   Perf. 14
396-399	A76	Set of 4	9.00 9.00

Souvenir Sheet
400	A76	$6.40 multicolored	15.00 15.00

1992 Summer Olympics, Barcelona A77

1992, July 27   Litho.   Perf. 14
401	A77	75c Runners	2.25 2.25
402	A77	95c Boxing	2.60 2.60
403	A77	$1.15 Swimming	3.00 3.00
404	A77	$1.50 Wrestling	3.25 3.25
		Nos. 401-404 (4)	11.10 11.10

6th Festival of Pacific Arts, Rarotonga A78

Festival poster and: $1.15, Marquesan canoe. $1.75, Statue of Tangaroa. $1.95, Manihiki canoe.

1992, Oct. 16   Litho.   Perf. 14x15
405	A78	$1.15 multicolored	2.50 2.50
406	A78	$1.75 multicolored	3.00 3.00
407	A78	$1.95 multicolored	3.50 3.50
		Nos. 405-407 (3)	9.00 9.00

For overprints see Nos. 455-457.

Overprinted "ROYAL VISIT"
1992, Oct. 16
408	A78	$1.15 on #405	3.00 3.00
409	A78	$1.75 on #406	3.75 3.75
410	A78	$1.95 on #407	4.25 4.25
		Nos. 408-410 (3)	11.00 11.00

Christmas — A79

Paintings by Ambrogio Bergognone: 55c, $6.40, Virgin with Child and Saints. 85c, Virgin on Throne. $1.05, Virgin on Carpet. $1.85, Virgin of the Milk.

1992, Nov. 18   Litho.   Perf. 13½
411-414	A79	Set of 4	8.25 8.25

Souvenir Sheet
415	A79	$6.40 multicolored	11.00 11.00

No. 415 contains one 38x48mm stamp.

Discovery of America, 500th Anniv. — A80

Designs: $1.15, Vicente Yanez Pinzon, Nina. $1.35, Martin Alonso Pinzon, Pinta. $1.75, Columbus, Santa Maria.

1992, Dec. 4   Perf. 15x14
416	A80	$1.15 multicolored	2.75 2.75
417	A80	$1.35 multicolored	3.00 3.00
418	A80	$1.75 multicolored	4.25 4.25
		Nos. 416-418 (3)	10.00 10.00

Coronation of Queen Elizabeth II, 40th Anniv. — A81

1993, June 4   Litho.   Perf. 14x14½
419	A81	$6 multicolored	9.50 9.50

Marine Life — A82

Marine Life — A82a

5c, Helmet shell. 10c, Daisy coral. 15c, Hydroid coral. 20c, Feather star. 25c, Sea star. 30c, Nudibranch. 50c, Smooth sea star. 70c, Black pearl oyster. 80c, Pyjama nudibranch. 85c, Prickly sea cucumber. 90c, Organ pipe coral. $1, Aeolid nudibranch. $2, Textile cone shell.

1993-98		Litho.		Perf. 14	
420	A82	5c multi		.25	.25
421	A82	10c multi		.25	.25
422	A82	15c multi		.25	.25
423	A82	20c multi		.25	.25
424	A82	25c multi		.30	.30
425	A82	30c multi		.35	.35
426	A82	50c multi		.55	.55
427	A82	70c multi		.85	.80
428	A82	80c multi		.95	.90
429	A82	85c multi		1.05	.95
430	A82	90c multi		1.05	1.00
431	A82	$1 multi		1.25	1.10
432	A82	$2 multi		3.50	2.25
433	A82a	$3 pink & multi		5.00	3.25
434	A82a	$5 lilac & multi		8.50	5.50
		Perf. 14x13½			
435	A82a	$8 blue & multi		12.00	11.00
435A	A82a	$10 grn & multi		13.00	12.00
	Nos. 420-435A (17)			49.35	40.95

For overprints see #O41-O53.
Issued: 80c, 85c, 90c, $1, $2, 12/3/93; $3, $5, 11/21/94; $8, 11/17/97; $10, 10/1/98; others, 10/18/93.

Christmas — A83

Details from Virgin on Throne with Child, by Cosimo Tura: 55c, Madonna and Child. 85c, Musicians. $1.05, Musicians, diff. $1.95, Woman. $4.50, Entire painting.

1993, Nov. 2		Litho.	Perf. 14	
436	A83	55c multicolored	1.40	1.40
437	A83	85c multicolored	2.10	2.10
438	A83	$1.05 multicolored	2.50	2.50
439	A83	$1.95 multicolored	3.75	3.75
		Size: 32x47mm		
		Perf. 13½		
440	A83	$4.50 multicolored	6.25	6.25
	Nos. 436-440 (5)		16.00	16.00

First Manned Moon Landing, 25th Anniv. — A84

1994, July 20		Litho.	Perf. 14	
441	A84	$3.25 multicolored	10.00	10.00

Christmas — A85

Details or entire paintings: No. 442a, Virgin and Child with Saints Paul & Jerome, by Vivarini. b, The Virgin and Child with St. John, by B. Luini. c, The Virgin and Child with Saints Jerome & Dominic, by F. Lippi. d, Adoration of Shepherds, by Murillo.
No. 443a, Adoration of the Kings, by Reni. b, Madonna & Child with the Infant Baptist, by Raphael. c, Adoration of the Kings, by Reni, diff. d, Virgin and Child, by Bergognone.

1994, Nov. 30		Litho.	Perf. 14	
442	A85	90c Block of 4, #a-d.	5.75	5.75
443	A85	$1 Block of 4, #a-d.	6.25	6.25

End of World War II, 50th Anniv. A86

Designs: a, Battleships on fire, Pearl Harbor, Dec. 7, 1941. b, B-29 bomber Enola Gay, A-bomb cloud, Aug. 1945.

1995, Sept. 4		Litho.	Perf. 13	
444	A86	$3.75 Pair, #a-b.	22.00	22.00

Queen Mother, 95th Birthday — A87

1995, Sept. 14		Litho.	Perf. 13½	
445	A87	$4.50 multicolored	12.00	12.00

No. 445 was issued in sheets of 4.

UN, 50th Anniv. A88

1995, Oct. 20		Litho.	Perf. 13½	
446	A88	$4 multicolored	5.75	5.75

No. 446 was issued in sheets of 4.

1995, Year of the Sea Turtle — A89

No. 447: a, Loggerhead. b, Hawksbill.
No. 448: a, Olive ridley. b, Green.

1995, Dec. 7		Litho.	Perf. 13½	
447	A89	$1.15 Pair, #a-b.	4.75	4.75
448	A89	$1.65 Pair, #a-b.	7.25	7.25

Queen Elizabeth II, 70th Birthday — A90

1996, June 20		Litho.	Perf. 14	
449	A90	$4.25 multicolored	7.50	7.50

No. 449 was issued in sheets of 4.

1996 Summer Olympic Games, Atlanta — A91

1996, July 12		Litho.	Perf. 14	
450	A91	$5 multicolored	9.50	9.50

Queen Elizabeth II and Prince Philip, 50th Wedding Anniv. — A92

1997, Nov. 20		Litho.	Perf. 14	
451	A92	$3 multicolored	4.50	4.50
		Souvenir Sheet		
452	A92	$4 multicolored	5.50	5.50

No. 452 is a continuous design.

Diana, Princess of Wales (1961-97) — A93

1998, May 7		Litho.	Perf. 14	
453	A93	$1.50 multicolored	3.00	3.00
		Souvenir Sheet		
454	A93	$3.75 like #453	6.00	6.00

No. 453 was issued in sheets of 5 + label.
For surcharge see #B24.

Nos. 405-407 Ovptd. "KIA ORANA / THIRD MILLENNIUM"

Methods and Perfs as before

1999, Dec. 31				
455	A78	$1.15 multi	1.30	1.30
456	A78	$1.75 multi	2.10	2.10
457	A78	$1.95 multi	2.60	2.60
	Nos. 455-457 (3)		6.00	6.00

Queen Mother, 100th Birthday A94

No. 458: a, With King George VI. b, With Princess Elizabeth. c, With King George VI, Princesses Elizabeth and Margaret. d, With Princesses.

2000, Oct. 20		Litho.	Perf. 14	
458	A94	$2.50 Sheet of 4, #a-d	12.00	12.00
		Souvenir Sheet		
459	A94	$10 Portrait	12.00	12.00

2000 Summer Olympics, Sydney — A95

No. 460, horiz.: a, Ancient javelin. b, Javelin. c, Ancient discus. d, Discus.

2000, Dec. 14		Litho.	Perf. 14	
460	A95	$2.75 Sheet of 4, #a-d	12.00	12.00
		Souvenir Sheet		
461	A95	$3.50 Torch relay	5.00	5.00

Worldwide Fund for Nature (WWF) — A96

Various photos of ocean sunfish: 80c, 90c, $1.15, $1.95.

2003, Feb. 24				
462-465	A96	Set of 4	7.00	7.00

Each printed in sheets of 4.

United We Stand — A97

2003, Sept. 30				
466	A97	$1.50 multicolored	1.75	1.75

Printed in sheets of 4.

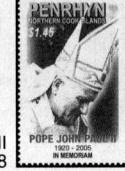

Pope John Paul II (1920-2005) — A98

2005, Nov. 11				
467	A98	$1.45 multicolored	2.75	2.75

Printed in sheets of 5 + label.

Worldwide Fund for Nature (WWF) — A99

Pacific reef egret: 80c, Male and female. 90c, Bird at water's edge. $1.15, Bird in flight. $1.95, Adult and chicks.

2008, Oct. 16				Perf. 13½	
468-471	A99	Set of 4		5.75	5.75

Nos. 468-471 each were printed in sheets of 4.

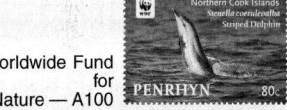

Worldwide Fund for Nature — A100

Striped dolphin: 80c, Breaching. 90c Pair underwater. $1.10, Breaching, diff. $1.20, Pod breaching.

2010, Dec. 9				Perf. 14	
472-475	A100	Set of 4		6.00	6.00

Nos. 472-475 each were printed in sheets of 4.

A101

Engagement of Prince William and Catherine Middleton — A102

Designs: Nos. 476, 479a, 481, Prince. Nos. 477, 479b, 482, Middleton.
No. 478: a, Prince in military uniform. b, Prince playing polo. c, Middleton, fence. d, Prince, man and woman in background. e, Middleton, woman in background. f, Couple, Prince at left. g, Middleton with black hat. h, Prince. i, Couple, Middleton at left. j, Hands of couple, engagement ring.
$8.10, Couple, Prince in uniform at left.

2011, Jan. 14			Perf. 14	
476	A101	$2 multi	3.25	3.25
477	A101	$2 multi	3.25	3.25

Miniature Sheets

478	A102	50c Sheet of 10, #a-j	7.75	7.75
		Perf. 13¾x13½		
479	A101	$2 Sheet of 2, #a-b	6.25	6.25

Souvenir Sheets
Perf. 14¼

480	A101	$8.10 multi	12.50	12.50
481	A101	$11 multi	17.00	17.00
482	A101	$11 multi	17.00	17.00
		Nos. 480-482 (3)	46.50	46.50

No. 479 contains two 28x44mm stamps. Nos. 480-482 each contain one 38x50mm stamp.

A103

Peonies A104

2011, Apr. 8	Litho.		Perf. 13¼	
483	A103	$1.10 multi	1.75	1.75

Souvenir Sheet
Perf. 14¾x14

484	A104	$7.20 multi	11.50	11.50

Miniature Sheets

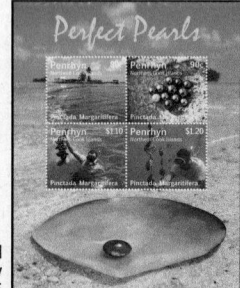

Pearl Industry A105

No. 485 — Inscription "Pinctada Margaritifera" and: a, 80c, Buildings near shore. b, 90c, Pearls. c, $1.10, Diver at surface holding

string of oysters. d, $1.20, Diver tending string of oysters underwater.
No. 486 — Inscription "Pearl Industry" and: a, 20c, Shark. b, 30c, Diver at surface. c, 50c, Pearls, diff. d, $1, Pearl in tongs. e, $2, Pearl oysters.

2011, May 5			Perf. 13¾	
485	A105	Sheet of 4, #a-d	6.50	6.50
486	A105	Sheet of 5, #a-e	6.50	6.50

Tourism — A106

Designs: 10c, Birds flying over ocean. 20c, Ray. 30c, Buildings on shore. 40c, Rocky coastline. 50c, Road in forest. 60c, Sharks. 70c, Aerial view of island. 80c, Clouds over ocean. 90c, Palm trees near shore. $1, Sharks, diff. $1.10, Saab 340 airplane, aerial view of island. $1.20, Pearls. $1.50, Sea turtle. $2, Aerial view of island, diff. $3, Sun and clouds above island.

2011, May 6			Perf. 14	
487	A106	10c multi	.25	.25
488	A106	20c multi	.35	.35
489	A106	30c multi	.50	.50
490	A106	40c multi	.65	.65
491	A106	50c multi	.80	.80
492	A106	60c multi	.95	.95
493	A106	70c multi	1.10	1.10
494	A106	80c multi	1.25	1.25
495	A106	90c multi	1.50	1.50
496	A106	$1 multi	1.60	1.60
497	A106	$1.10 multi	1.75	1.75
498	A106	$1.20 multi	1.90	1.90
499	A106	$1.50 multi	2.40	2.40
500	A106	$2 multi	3.25	3.25
501	A106	$3 multi	4.75	4.75
a.		Miniature sheet of 15, #487-501	23.00	23.00
		Nos. 487-501 (15)	23.00	23.00

Souvenir Sheet

Wedding of Prince William and Catherine Middleton — A107

No. 502 — Couple in wedding procession: a, $1. b, $1.20.

2011, July 15		Perf. 15x14¼	
502	A107	Sheet of 2, #a-b	3.75	3.75

Christmas — A108

No. 503: a, Partridge in a pear tree. b, Two turtle doves. c, Three French hens. d, Four calling birds.

2011, Dec. 24			Perf. 13¼	
503		Horiz. strip of 4	6.00	6.00
a.	A108	30c multi	.50	.50
b.	A108	50c multi	.80	.80
c.	A108	90c multi	1.40	1.40
d.	A108	$2 multi	3.25	3.25
e.		Souvenir sheet of 4, #503a-503d	6.00	6.00

Beatification of Pope John Paul II — A109

No. 504: a, $1.20, Pope Benedict XVI. b, $5, Pope John Paul II.

2012, Jan. 10		Perf. 13¾	
504	A109	Horiz. pair, #a-b	10.50	10.50

Christ Taking Leave of His Mother, by Correggio A110

Deposition, by Correggio A111

The Martyrdom of Four Saints, by Correggio A112

Mystic Marriage of St. Catherine and St. Sebastian, by Correggio A113

Nativity, by Correggio, c. 1510 — A114

The Nativity of Christ, by Correggio, c. 1529-30 — A115

Perf. 14¾x14¼

2012, Nov. 16		Litho.	

Stamps With White Frames

505		Horiz. pair	2.80	2.80
a.	A110	80c multi	1.40	1.40
b.	A111	80c multi	1.40	1.40
506		Horiz. pair	3.00	3.00
a.	A112	90c multi	1.50	1.50
b.	A113	90c multi	1.50	1.50
507		Horiz. pair	10.00	10.00
a.	A114	$3 multi	5.00	5.00
b.	A115	$3 multi	5.00	5.00
		Nos. 505-507 (3)	15.80	15.80

Miniature Sheet
Stamps With Colored Frames

508		Sheet of 6	16.00	16.00
a.	A110	80c multi	1.40	1.40
b.	A111	80c multi	1.40	1.40
c.	A112	90c multi	1.50	1.50
d.	A113	90c multi	1.50	1.50
e.	A114	$3 multi	5.00	5.00
f.	A115	$3 multi	5.00	5.00

Fish A116

Nos. 509 and 512: a, 80c, Myripristis hexagonia. b, 90c, Scarus psittacus. c, $1.10, Zanclus cornutus. d, $1.20, Acanthurus guttatus.
Nos. 510 and 513: a, $2, Pygoplites diacanthus. b, $2.25, Chaetodon flavirostris. c, $4, Pseudanthias pleurotaenia. d, $5, Chaetodon ornatissimus.
Nos. 511 and 514: a, $6, Chaetodon melanotus. b, $8, Gymnothorax rueppellii. c, $10, Synchiropus ocellatus. d, $20, Kyphosus sandwichensis.

2012, Nov. 27		Litho.	Perf. 14	

Stamps With White Frames

509	A116	Block of 4, #a-d	6.75	6.75
510	A116	Block of 4, #a-d	22.00	22.00
511	A116	Block of 4, #a-d	72.50	72.50
		Nos. 509-511 (3)	101.25	101.25

Stamps Without White Frames

512	A116	Sheet of 4, #a-d	6.75	6.75
513	A116	Sheet of 4, #a-d	22.00	22.00
514	A116	Sheet of 4, #a-d	72.50	72.50
e.		Sheet of 12, #512a-512d, 513a-513d, 514a-514d	102.00	102.00
		Nos. 512-514 (3)	101.25	101.25

Personalizable Stamp — A117

A117a   A117b

2012, Dec. 21		Litho.	Perf. 14x14¾	
515	A117	$4 multi	6.75	6.75
a.		A117a 50c multi	.70	.70
b.		A117b $1 multi	1.40	1.40

Christmas (#515a, 515b). Issued: Nos. 515a, 515b, 12/16/19. Nos. 515a-515b have the same frame as the personalizable stamp No. 515, but have different denominations. The editors do not know if 50c and $1 stamps having these frames were made available to the public that may have different personalized images other than the images shown above placed in the vignette area. The editors also do not know if there are stamps of type A117 that are available in denominations other than 50c, $1, or $4.

Miniature Sheet

New Year 2013 (Year of the Snake) A118

No. 516 — Various snakes with background color of: a, Blue. b, Bright rose. c, Green. d, Yellow.

Perf. 14¾x14¼

2013, Feb. 21		Litho.	
516	A118	$1.20 Sheet of 4, #a-d	8.00	8.00

Souvenir Sheet

Duchess of Cambridge — A119

No. 517 — Various photographs of pregnant Duchess of Cambridge: a, $1.30. b, $1.50. c, $1.70.

2013, Aug. 1	Litho.	Perf. 13¾x13½	
517	A119	Sheet of 3, #a-c	7.25	7.25

Birth of Prince George of Cambridge.

Souvenir Sheet

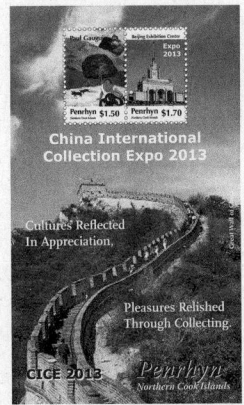

China International Collection Expo 2013, Beijing — A120

No. 518: a, $1.50, Painting by Paul Gauguin. b, $1.70, Beijing Exhibition Center.

2013, Sept. 26   Litho.   Perf. 12
518 A120   Sheet of 2, #a-b   5.50 5.50

Pres. John F. Kennedy (1917-63) — A121

Designs: $2, Photograph of Kennedy. $3, Photograph of Kennedy and crowd, quote from Kennedy.

2013, Nov. 8   Litho.   Perf. 14x14¼
519-520 A121   Set of 2   8.25 8.25

Fish — A122

Designs: 30c, Chaetodon ornatissimus. 50c, Kyphosus pacificus. $1, Acanthurus guttatus. $1.30, Chaetodon flavirostris. $1.50, Myripristis murdjan. $1.70, Pygoplites diacanthus. $2.40, Zanclus cornutus. $2.50, Scarus psittacus. $3, Rhinomuraena quaesita. $4.50, Synchiropus ocellatus. $7.50, Gymnothorax rueppelliae. $12.90, Hoplolatilus starcki.

2013, Nov. 11   Litho.   Perf. 14
Stamps With White Frames
521 A122	30c multi	.50	.50
522 A122	50c multi	.85	.85
523 A122	$1 multi	1.75	1.75
524 A122	$1.30 multi	2.25	2.25
525 A122	$1.50 multi	2.50	2.50
526 A122	$1.70 multi	2.75	2.75
527 A122	$2.40 multi	4.00	4.00
528 A122	$2.50 multi	4.25	4.25
529 A122	$3 multi	5.00	5.00
530 A122	$4.50 multi	7.50	7.50
531 A122	$7.50 multi	12.50	12.50
532 A122	$12.90 multi	21.50	21.50
	Nos. 521-532 (12)	65.35	65.35

Stamps Without White Frames
533	Sheet of 12	66.00	66.00
a.	A122 30c multi	.50	.50
b.	A122 50c multi	.85	.85
c.	A122 $1 multi	1.75	1.75
d.	A122 $1.30 multi	2.25	2.25
e.	A122 $1.50 multi	2.50	2.50
f.	A122 $1.70 multi	2.75	2.75
g.	A122 $2.40 multi	4.00	4.00
h.	A122 $2.50 multi	4.25	4.25
i.	A122 $3 multi	5.00	5.00
j.	A122 $4.50 multi	7.50	7.50
k.	A122 $7.50 multi	12.50	12.50
l.	A122 $12.90 multi	21.50	21.50

Christmas — A123

Paintings by: $1, Peter Paul Rubens. $1.30, Albrecht Dürer.

No. 536 — Paintings by: a, $2, Sandro Botticelli. b, $2.40, William Brassey Hole. c, $2.60, Gerard van Honthorst.

2013, Nov. 18   Litho.   Perf. 13¼
534-535 A123   Set of 2   3.75 3.75
Souvenir Sheet
536 A123   Sheet of 3, #a-c   11.50 11.50

Miniature Sheet

New Year 2014 (Year of the Horse) A124

No. 537 — Background color: a, $1, Yellow. b, $1.30, Red. c, $1.50, Blue. d, $1.70, Green.

2014, Jan. 10   Litho.   Perf. 13¾
537 A124   Sheet of 4, #a-d   9.00 9.00

Easter A125

No. 538 — Religious paintings by: a, 50c, Peter Paul Rubens. b, $1, Lambert Lombard. c, $1.30, Titian. d, $1.50, Paolo Veronese. e, $1.70, Raphael.
$9.50, Painting by Dirck Bouts.

2014, Apr. 9   Litho.   Perf. 13¼
538 A125   Sheet of 5, #a-e, + label   10.50 10.50
Souvenir Sheet
539 A125 $9.50 multi   16.50 16.50

Worldwide Fund for Nature (WWF) — A126

Pacific green turtle: Nos. 540, 544a, $1, On beach. Nos. 541, 544b, $1.70, Swimming. Nos. 542, 544c, $2, Swimming, diff. Nos. 543, 544d, $2.40, Pair on seafloor.
$7.50, Turtle swimming, diff.

Perf. 14¾x14¼
2014, Nov. 28   Litho.
Stamps With White Frames
540-543 A126   Set of 4   11.50 11.50
Stamps Without White Frames
544 A126   Strip of 4, #a-d   11.50 11.50
Souvenir Sheet
545 A126 $7.50 multi   12.00 12.00

Souvenir Sheet

Christmas — A127

No. 546 — Religious paintings by: a, Antonio da Correggio. b, Piero della Francesca. c, Sandro Botticelli.

Perf. 14¾x14¼
2014, Dec. 14   Litho.
546 A127 $1.50 Sheet of 3, #a-c   7.00 7.00

Souvenir Sheet

New Year 2015 (Year of the Sheep) A128

No. 547: a, $3.80, Red sheep. b, $4.10, Green sheep.

2015, Jan. 5   Litho.   Perf. 13½
547 A128   Sheet of 2, #a-b   12.50 12.50

Miniature Sheet

Easter A129

No. 548 — Details from religious paintings by: a, Peter Paul Rubens. b, Edouard Manet. c, Carl Heinrich Bloch. d, Jacopo Tintoretto.

2015, Mar. 31   Litho.   Perf. 14
548 A129 $2 Sheet of 4, #a-d   12.50 12.50

Souvenir Sheet

Birth of Princess Charlotte of Cambridge — A130

No. 549: a, Duke and Duchess of Cambridge, Princess Charlotte. b, Duke of Cambridge holding Prince George.

Perf. 14¾x14¼
2015, June 23   Litho.
549 A130 $4.50 Sheet of 2, #a-b   12.00 12.00

New Year 2016 (Year of the Monkey) — A131

Monkey with: $2.60, Both arms raised. $3, One arm raised.
No. 552 — Monkey with: a, $3.80, Both arms raised. b, $4.10, One arm raised.

2015, Sept. 25   Litho.   Perf. 13¼
550-551 A131   Set of 2   7.50 7.50
Souvenir Sheet
552 A131   Sheet of 2, #a-b   10.50 10.50

No. 552 contains two 50x50mm diamond-shaped stamps.

Miniature Sheet

Queen Elizabeth II, Longest-Reigning British Monarch — A132

No. 553 — Various photographs of Queen Elizabeth II: a, $1.30. b, $1.50. c, $1.70. d, $2.

2015, Nov. 20   Litho.   Perf. 14
553 A132   Sheet of 4, #a-d   8.75 8.75

Souvenir Sheet

Christmas — A133

No. 554 — Nativity, by Gerard David (details): a, Virgin Mary. b, Infant Jesus and animals. c, St. Joseph.

2015, Dec. 9   Litho.   Perf. 13¼
554 A133 $1 Sheet of 3, #a-c   4.25 4.25

Souvenir Sheet

Queen Elizabeth II, 90th Birthday A134

No. 555 — Queen Elizabeth II wearing: a, Gown. b, Hat and coat.

2016, May 10   Litho.   Perf. 13¼
555 A134 $3 Sheet of 2, #a-b   8.25 8.25

Marae Moana Marine Park — A135

Designs: 30c, Blue whale. 50c, Brown booby. 80c, Gray reef shark. $1, Emblem of Marae Moana Marine Park. $1.10, Humphead wrasse. $1.30, Scalloped hammerhead shark. $1.50, Hawksbill turtle. $1.70 False killer whale. $2, Brown noddy. $2.40, Blue shark. $2.50, Shortfin mako shark.

2016, May 27   Litho.   Perf. 14x14¾
556 A135	30c multi	.45	.45
557 A135	50c multi	.80	.80
558 A135	80c multi	1.20	1.20
559 A135	$1 multi	1.55	1.55
560 A135	$1.10 multi	1.65	1.65
561 A135	$1.30 multi	1.90	1.90
562 A135	$1.50 multi	2.30	2.30
563 A135	$1.70 multi	2.65	2.65
564 A135	$2 multi	3.00	3.00
565 A135	$2.40 multi	3.50	3.50
566 A135	$2.50 multi	3.75	3.75
	Nos. 556-566 (11)	22.75	22.75

New Year 2017 (Year of the Rooster) — A136

Rooster facing: $2.30, Right. $4.50, Left.

2016, Aug. 10   **Litho.**   ***Perf. 13¼***
567-568	A136	Set of 2	11.00	11.00
568a		Souvenir sheet of 2, #567-568	11.00	11.00

Christmas — A137

No. 569 — Stained-glass windows depicting: a, 50c, Madonna and Child, farm animals. b, 50c, Madonna and Child. c, $1, Madonna and Child. d, $1, Nativity with farm animals.

2016, Dec. 19   **Litho.**   ***Perf. 13¼***
569	A137	Block of 4, #a-d	4.25	4.25

Miniature Sheet

First Contact of Explorers with Penrhyn Islanders, 200th Anniv. — A138

No. 570: a, $1, Aerial view of Penrhyn Island (36x36mm). b, $2, Otto von Kotzebue (1787-1846), explorer (36x36mm). c, $3, Map of Kotzebue's route (36x29mm). d, $4, Kotzebue's ship, Rurick (36x29mm).

2016, Dec. 28   **Litho.**   ***Perf. 13¼***
570	A138	Sheet of 4, #a-d	14.00	14.00

Miniature Sheet

Easter A139

No. 571 — Paintings of the Resurrection of Jesus by: a, Caravaggio. b, Mikhail Vasilyevich Nesterov. c, Rembrandt. d, Tintoretto.

2017, Apr. 12   **Litho.**   ***Perf. 13***
571	A139	$1 Sheet of 4, #a-d	5.75	5.75

Miniature Sheet

Pres. John F. Kennedy (1917-63) — A140

No. 572: a, $1, Pres. Kennedy and wife, Jacqueline at ceremony awarding medal to Alan B. Shepard, Jr. b, $1, Pres. Kennedy giving address at Rice University. c, $2.50, Nuclear weapon test on Bikini Atoll and radioactivity symbol. d, $2.50, Pres. Kennedy

speaking after signing Nuclear Test Ban Treaty.

2017, July 3   **Litho.**   ***Perf. 13***
572	A140	Sheet of 4, #a-d	10.50	10.50

Miniature Sheet

Reign of Queen Elizabeth II, 65th Anniv. A141

No. 573 — Queen Elizabeth II: a, Wearing coat with fur collar. b, Wearing tiara. c, Wearing maroon hat. d, Standing with military officer.

2017, July 17   **Litho.**   ***Perf. 13***
573	A141	$2.50 Sheet of 4, #a-d	15.00	15.00

New Year 2018 (Year of the Dog) — A142

Dog facing: $3, Right. $3.80, Left.

2017, Nov. 1   **Litho.**   ***Perf. 13¼***
574-575	A142	Set of 2	10.00	10.00
575a		Souvenir sheet of 2, #574-575	10.00	10.00

Worldwide Fund for Nature (WWF) — A143

Photographs of Bennett's butterflyfish: Nos. 576, 580a, $1, With three other fish. Nos. 577, 580b, $1.70, Nose facing UL corner. Nos. 578, 580c, $2, Nose facing LR corner. Nos. 579, 580d, $2.40, facing left.

2017, Nov. 6   **Litho.**   ***Perf. 13x13¼***
Stamps With White Frames
576-579	A143	Set of 4	10.75	10.75

Stamps Without White Frames
580	A143	Block or horiz. strip of 4, #a-d	10.75	10.75

No. 580 was printed in sheets containing two each of Nos. 580a-580d.

Christmas — A144

No. 581: a, $1, Seahorse. b, $1, Sailboat. c, $2.40, Bird. d, $2.40, Shell.

2017, Dec. 5   **Litho.**   ***Perf. 12½***
581	A144	Block of 4, #a-d	9.75	9.75

Miniature Sheet

Easter A145

No. 582: a, $1, Church and palm tree. b, $1, Flowers. c, $2.40, Palm trees and Easter eggs. d, $2.40, Crosses, butterflies, shell, starfish.

2018, Mar. 19   **Litho.**   ***Perf. 12½***
582	A145	Sheet of 4, #a-d	10.00	10.00

Birdpex 2018 Philatelic Exhibition, Mondorf-les-Bains, Luxembourg — A146

No. 583: a, Marbled godwit. b, Temminck's stint. c, Wilson's phalarope. d, Common sandpiper.

2018, May 4   **Litho.**   ***Perf. 13¼x13***
583	A146	$1.50 Block of 4, #a-d	8.50	8.50

Wedding of Prince Harry and Meghan Markle A147

No. 584: a, Bride walking down aisle. b, Princes Harry and William. $8, Bride and groom in coach.

2018, Aug. 2   **Litho.**   ***Perf. 13***
584	A147	$4.80 Sheet of 2, #a-b	12.50	12.50

Souvenir Sheet
585	A147	$8 multi	10.50	10.50

New Year 2019 (Year of the Pig) — A148

Designs: $3, Pig. $3.80, Pig, diff.

2018, Dec. 10   **Litho.**   ***Perf. 13¼***
586-587	A148	Set of 2	9.25	9.25

Birds — A149

Designs: Nos. 588, 600a, Secretarybirds. Nos. 589, 600b, White-tailed eagle. Nos. 590, 600c, European honey buzzard. Nos. 591, 600d, Black-shouldered kite. Nos. 592, 600e, Swallow-tailed kite. Nos. 593, 600f, Osprey. Nos. 594, 600g, Snail kite. Nos. 595, 600h, Pallas's sea eagle. Nos. 596, 600i, Steller's sea eagles. Nos. 597, 600j, Bald eagle. Nos.

598, 600k, Yellow-billed kite. Nos. 599, 600l, Bearded vulture.

2018, Dec. 20   **Litho.**   ***Perf. 12¾***
Stamps With White Frames
588	A149	20c multi	.25	.25
589	A149	30c multi	.40	.40
590	A149	40c multi	.55	.55
591	A149	50c multi	.65	.65
592	A149	$1 multi	1.40	1.40
593	A149	$2 multi	2.75	2.75
a.		Souvenir sheet of 6, #588-593	7.00	7.00
594	A149	$2.40 multi	3.25	3.25
595	A149	$2.60 multi	3.50	3.50
596	A149	$4.50 multi	6.00	6.00
597	A149	$5 multi	6.75	6.75
598	A149	$7.50 multi	10.00	10.00
599	A149	$10 multi	13.50	13.50
a.		Souvenir sheet of 6, #594-599	45.00	45.00
		Nos. 588-599 (12)	49.00	49.00

Stamps Without White Frame
600		Sheet of 12	50.00	50.00
a.	A149	20c multi	.25	.25
b.	A149	30c multi	.40	.40
c.	A149	40c multi	.55	.55
d.	A149	50c multi	.65	.65
e.	A149	$1 multi	1.40	1.40
f.	A149	$2 multi	2.75	2.75
g.	A149	$2.40 multi	3.25	3.25
h.	A149	$2.60 multi	3.50	3.50
i.	A149	$4.50 multi	6.00	6.00
j.	A149	$5 multi	6.75	6.75
k.	A149	$7.50 multi	10.00	10.00
l.	A149	$7.50 multi	13.50	13.50

Stamps from Nos. 593a and 599a have white frames on 1 or 2 sides. See Nos. 603-607, 608-612, 623-627, 628-632.

New Year 2020 (Year of the Rat) — A150

Designs: $3, Rat. $3.80, Rat, diff.

2019, Oct. 11   **Litho.**   ***Perf. 13¼***
601-602	A150	Set of 2	8.75	8.75

Birds Type of 2018

Designs: Nos. 603, 607a, Military macaw. Nos. 604, 607b, Blue-throated macaw. Nos. 605, 607c, Scarlet macaws. Nos. 606, 607d, Chestnut-fronted macaw.

2019, Oct. 11   **Litho.**   ***Perf. 12¾***
Stamps With White Frames
603	A149	$5.50 multi	7.25	7.25
604	A149	$6.70 multi	8.75	8.75
605	A149	$22.40 multi	29.00	29.00
606	A149	$29.90 multi	38.50	38.50
		Nos. 603-606 (4)	83.50	83.50

Stamps Without White Frames
Size:48x40mm
Perf. 13½x13
607		Block or vert. strip of 4	83.50	83.50
a.	A149	$5.50 multi	7.25	7.25
b.	A149	$6.70 multi	8.75	8.75
c.	A149	$22.40 multi	29.00	29.00
d.	A149	$29.90 multi	38.50	38.50
e.		Souvenir sheet of 4, #607a-607d	83.50	83.50

Stamps on No. 607e have white frames on two sides.

Birds Type of 2018

Designs: Nos. 608, 612a, Mississippi kite. Nos. 609, 612b, Snowy owl. Nos. 610, 612c, Black kite. Nos. 611, 612d, African goshawk.

2019, Nov. 15   **Litho.**   ***Perf. 12¾***
Stamps With White Frames
608	A149	$2.50 multi	3.25	3.25
609	A149	$3 multi	3.75	3.75
610	A149	$4 multi	5.25	5.25
611	A149	$6 multi	7.75	7.75
		Nos. 608-611 (4)	20.00	20.00

Stamps Without White Frames
Size:48x40mm
Perf. 13½x13
612		Block or vert. strip of 4	20.00	20.00
a.	A149	$2.50 multi	3.25	3.25
b.	A149	$3 multi	3.75	3.75
c.	A149	$4 multi	5.25	5.25
d.	A149	$6 multi	7.75	7.75
e.		Souvenir sheet of 4, #612a-612d	20.00	20.00

Stamps on No. 612e have white frames on two sides.

Butterflies
A151

Designs: Nos. 613, 621a, 50c, Large marble butterfly. Nos. 614, 621b, $1, Luzon peacock swallowtail butterfly. Nos. 615, 621c, $5, Blue morpho butterfly. Nos. 616, 621d, $7, Banded Orange butterfly. Nos. 617, 622a, $10, Question mark butterfly. Nos. 618, 622b, $20, Glasswinged butterfly. Nos 619, 622c, $30, Common buckeye butterfly. Nos. 620, 622d, $34.70, Ceylon rose butterfly.

2020, Jan. 15   Litho.   *Perf. 13*
Stamps With White Frames

613	A151	50c multi	.65	.65
614	A151	$1 multi	1.30	1.30
615	A151	$5 multi	6.50	6.50
616	A151	$7 multi	9.00	9.00
617	A151	$10 multi	13.00	13.00
618	A151	$20 multi	26.00	26.00
619	A151	$30 multi	39.00	39.00
620	A151	$34.70 multi	45.00	45.00
		Nos. 613-620 (8)	140.45	140.45

Stamps Without White Frames
Stamp Size: 48x40mm
Perf. 13¼x13

621	A151	Block or vert.		
		strip of 4, #a-d	17.50	17.50
e.		Souvenir sheet of 4, #621a-621d		
			17.50	17.50
622	A151	Block or vert.		
		strip of 4, #a-d	125.00	125.00
e.		Souvenir sheet of 4, #622a-622d		
			125.00	125.00

Nos. 621a-621d and 622a-622d were printed in sheets of 8 containing two of each stamp. Stamps on Nos. 621e and 622e have white frames on two adjacent sides.
Nos. 621d-621e have wrong inscription of "Ceylon Rose Butterfly."

Birds Type of 2018

Designs: Nos. 623, 627a, $2.50, Brown sicklebill. Nos. 624, 627b, $3, Twelve-wired bird-of-paradise. Nos. 625, 627c, $4, Lesser bird-of-paradise. Nos. 626, 627d, $6, Magnificent bird-of-paradise.

2020, May 8   Litho.   *Perf. 13*
Stamps With White Frames

623	A149	$2.50 multi	3.25	3.25
624	A149	$3 multi	3.75	3.75
625	A149	$4 multi	5.00	5.00
626	A149	$6 multi	7.50	7.50
		Nos. 623-626 (4)	19.50	19.50

Stamps Without White Frames
Stamp Size: 48x40mm
Perf. 13¼x13

627	A149	Block or vert. strip of 4, #a-d	19.50	19.50
e.		Souvenir sheet of 4, #627a-627d	19.50	19.50

Nos. 627a-627d were printed in sheets of 8 containing two of each stamp. Stamps on No. 627e have white frames on two adjacent sides.

Birds Type of 2018

Designs: Nos. 628, 632a, $5.50, American flamingos. Nos. 629, 632b, $6.70, Chilean flamingo. Nos. 630, 632c, $22.40, Greater flamingo. Nos. 631, 632d, $29.90, Andean flamingo.

2020, May 20   Litho.   *Perf. 13*
Stamps With White Frames

628	A149	$5.50 multi	7.00	7.00
629	A149	$6.70 multi	8.50	8.50
630	A149	$22.40 multi	28.00	28.00
631	A149	$29.90 multi	37.50	37.50
		Nos. 628-631 (4)	81.00	81.00

Stamps Without White Frames
Stamp Size: 48x40mm
Perf. 13¼x13

632	A149	Block or vert. strip of 4, #a-d	81.00	81.00
e.		Souvenir sheet of 4, #632a-632d	81.00	81.00

Nos. 632a-632d were printed in sheets of 8 containing two of each stamp. Stamps on No. 632e have white frames on two adjacent sides.

Whales and Dolphins — A152

Designs: Nos. 633, 641a, 50c, Blue whale. Nos. 634, 641b, $1, Long-beaked common dolphin. Nos. 635, 641c, $5, Spinner dolphins. Nos. 636, 641d, $7, Sperm whale. Nos. 637, 642a, $10, Striped dolphin. Nos. 638, 642b, $20, Killer whale. Nos. 639, 642c, $30, Atlantic spotted dolphin. Nos. 640, 642d, $34.70, Humpback whale.

2020, June 15   Litho.   *Perf. 13*
Stamps With White Frames

633	A152	50c multi	.65	.65
634	A152	$1 multi	1.30	1.30
635	A152	$5 multi	6.50	6.50
636	A152	$7 multi	9.00	9.00
637	A152	$10 multi	13.00	13.00
638	A152	$20 multi	26.00	26.00
639	A152	$30 multi	39.00	39.00
640	A152	$34.70 multi	45.00	45.00
		Nos. 633-640 (8)	140.45	140.45

Stamps Without White Frames
Stamp Size: 48x40mm
Perf. 13¼x13

641	A152	Block or vert.		
		strip of 4, #a-d	17.50	17.50
e.		Souvenir sheet of 4, #641a-641d	17.50	17.50
642	A152	Block or vert.		
		strip of 4, #a-d	125.00	125.00
e.		Souvenir sheet of 4, #642a-642d	125.00	125.00

Nos. 641a-641d and 642a-642d were printed in sheets of 8 containing two of each stamp. Stamps on Nos. 641e and 642e have white frames on two adjacent sides.

Souvenir Sheet

New Year 2021 (Year of the Ox)
A153

2021, Apr. 7   Litho.   *Perf. 13¼x13*

643	A153	$5 multi	7.25	7.25

Spaceflight of Freedom 7, 60th Anniv. — A154

No. 644: a, Diagram showing trajectory and descent of Freedom 7. b, Launch of Freedom 7.
$3, Helicopter over Freedom 7 capsule in ocean, horiz. $4, Helicopter recovering Freedom 7 pilot Alan B. Shepard, Jr., horiz.

2021, May 5   Litho.   *Perf. 13*

644	A154	$1.30 Pair, #a-b	3.75	3.75

Souvenir Sheets
Perf. 13¼x13

645	A154	$3 multi	4.50	4.50
646	A154	$4 multi	5.75	5.75

Nos. 645 and 646 each contain one 48x40mm stamp.

Miniature Sheets

Smithsonian Institution Programs and Museums — A155

No. 647: a, African mask. b, Airplane cockpit. c, Illustration of Parisian fashions of 1914. d, Advertisement illustration for John A. Salzer Seed Company. e, Tractor and barn. f, Compass rose.
No. 648, horiz.: a, Animal skull. b, Photograph taken by Chandra X-ray Observatory. c, Heads of two flamingos. d, Butterfly on flower. e, Volcano. f, Flower.

2021, May 5   Litho.   *Perf. 13*

647	A155	20c Sheet of 6, #a-f	1.75	1.75
648	A155	40c Sheet of 6, #a-f	3.50	3.50

SEMI-POSTAL STAMPS

> Catalogue values for unused stamps in this section are for Never Hinged items.

Easter Type of 1978
Souvenir Sheets

Rubens Paintings: No. B1, like #101. No. B2, like #102. No. B3, like #103.

1978, Apr. 17   Photo.   *Perf. 13½x13*

B1	A31	60c + 5c multi	.50	.50
B2	A31	60c + 5c multi	.50	.50
B3	A31	60c + 5c multi	.50	.50
		Nos. B1-B3 (3)	1.50	1.50

Surtax was for school children.

Easter Type of 1980
Souvenir Sheets

1980, Mar. 28   Photo.   *Perf. 13x13½*

B4	A36	70c + 5c like #114	.45	.45
B5	A36	70c + 5c like #115	.45	.45
B6	A36	70c + 5c like #116	.45	.45
		Nos. B4-B6 (3)	1.35	1.35

Surtax was for local charities.

Christmas Type of 1980
Souvenir Sheets

1980, Dec. 5   Photo.   *Perf. 13*

B7	A39	70c + 5c like #127	1.00	1.00
B8	A39	70c + 5c like #128	1.00	1.00
B9	A39	70c + 5c like #129	1.00	1.00
		Nos. B7-B9 (3)	3.00	3.00

Surtax was for local charities.

Easter Type of 1981
Souvenir Sheets

1981, Apr. 5   Photo.   *Perf. 13½*

B10	A44	70c + 5c like #173	1.00	1.00
B11	A44	70c + 5c like #174	1.00	1.00
B12	A44	70c + 5c like #175	1.00	1.00
		Nos. B10-B12 (3)	3.00	3.00

Surtax was for local charities.

Nos. 176-180a Surcharged

1981, Nov. 30   Photo.   *Perf. 14*

B13	A45	40c + 5c like #176	.25	.25
B14	A45	50c + 5c like #177	.25	.25
B15	A45	60c + 5c like #178	.25	.25
B16	A45	70c + 5c like #179	.30	.30
B17	A45	80c + 5c like #180	.30	.30
		Nos. B13-B17 (5)	1.35	1.35

Souvenir Sheet

B18		Sheet of 5	1.50	1.50
a.	A45	40c + 10c like #176	.25	.25
b.	A45	50c + 10c like #177	.25	.25
c.	A45	60c + 10c like #178	.25	.25
d.	A45	70c + 10c like #179	.25	.25
e.	A45	80c + 10c like #180	.25	.25

Intl. Year of the Disabled. Surtax was for the disabled.

Soccer Type of 1981

1981, Dec. 7   *Perf. 13*

B19	A46	Sheet of 9	5.75	4.75

No. B19 contains Nos. 181-183. Surtax was for local sports.

Nos. 346-349 Surcharged ".SOUTH PACIFIC PAPAL VISIT . 21 TO 24 NOVEMBER 1986" in Metallic Blue

1986, Nov. 24   Litho.   *Perf. 13x13½*

B20	A67	65c + 10c multi	4.50	4.50
B21	A67	$1.75 + 10c multi	6.50	6.50
B22	A67	$2.50 + 10c multi	8.00	8.00
		Nos. B20-B22 (3)	19.00	19.00

Souvenir Sheet
Perf. 13½x13

B23		Sheet of 3	23.00	23.00
a.-c.	A67	$1.50 + 10c on #349a-349c	7.00	7.00

No. B23 inscribed "COMMEMORATING FIRST PAPAL VISIT TO SOUTH PACIFIC / VISIT OF POPE JOHN PAUL II . NOVEMBER 1986."

No. 454 Surcharged "CHILDREN'S CHARITIES" in Silver
Souvenir Sheet

1998, Nov. 19   Litho.   *Perf. 14*

B24	A93	$3.75 +$1 multi	6.00	6.00

OFFICIAL STAMPS

> Catalogue values for unused stamps in this section are for Never Hinged items.

Nos. 51-60, 80, 88-89 Overprinted or Surcharged in Black, Silver or Gold

Perf. 13½x14, 13½, 13½x13

1978, Nov. 14   Photo.

O1	A17	1c multi	.25	.25
O2	A17	2c multi	.25	.25
O3	A17	3c multi	.30	.25
O4	A17	4c multi	.30	.25
O5	A17	5c multi	.40	.25
O6	A17	8c multi	.45	.25
O7	A17	10c multi	.50	.25
O8	A17	15c on 60c multi	.55	.35
O9	A17	18c on 60c multi	.60	.35
O10	A17	20c multi	.60	.35
O11	A17	25c multi (S)	.65	.40
O12	A17	30c on 60c multi	.70	.60
O13	A24	Strip of 3, multi	4.25	2.75
a.		50c, No. 80a (G)	1.25	.80
b.		50c, No. 80b (G)	1.25	.80
c.		50c, No. 80c (G)	1.25	.80
O14	A27	$1 multi (S)	2.75	.65
O15	A27	$2 multi (G)	5.25	.70
		Nos. O1-O15 (15)	17.80	7.90

Overprint on No. O14 diagonal.

Nos. 268-276, 278, 277, 211-214, 280, 282, 281, 283, 170, 284, 171, 285, 172, 286 Surcharged with Bar and New Value or Ovptd. "O.H.M.S." in Silver or Metallic Red

1985-87	Photo.		Perfs. as before	
O16	A56	2c multi	.25	.25
O17	A56	4c multi	.25	.25
O18	A56	5c multi	.25	.25
O19	A56	8c multi	.25	.25
O20	A56	10c multi	.25	.25
O21	A56	18c multi	.25	.25
O22	A56	20c multi	.25	.25
O23	A56	30c multi	.25	.25
O24	A56	40c on 36c	.35	.35
O25	A56	50c multi	.40	.40
O26	A56	55c on 48c	.45	.45
O27	A50	65c on 60c #211a	.55	.55
O28	A50	65c on 60c #211b	.55	.55
O29	A50	65c on 60c #211c	.55	.55
O30	A50	65c on 60c #211d	.55	.55
O31	A56	75c on 72c	1.05	.65
O32	A56	75c on 96c	1.05	.65
O33	A56	80c multi	1.05	.65
O34	A56	$1.20 multi	1.25	.85
O35	A42	$2 multi (R)	1.75	1.25
O36	A56	$3 multi	3.50	2.10
O37	A42	$4 multi (R)	4.00	3.50
O38	A56	$5 multi	6.50	4.00
O39	A42	$6 multi (R)	9.25	6.50
O40	A56	$9.60 multi	12.00	10.00
		Nos. O16-O40 (25)	46.80	35.55

Issued: Nos. O16-O30, 8/15; Nos. O31-O37, 4/29/86; Nos. O38-O40, 11/2/87.

Nos. 420-432 Ovptd. in Silver

1998		Litho.	Perf. 14	
O41	A82	5c multicolored	.30	.30
O42	A82	10c multicolored	.30	.30
O43	A82	15c multicolored	.30	.30
O44	A82	20c multicolored	.30	.30
O45	A82	25c multicolored	.30	.30
O46	A82	30c multicolored	.40	.40
O47	A82	50c multicolored	.55	.55
O48	A82	70c multicolored	.70	.70
O49	A82	80c multicolored	.95	.95
O50	A82	85c multicolored	1.10	1.10
O51	A82	90c multicolored	1.20	1.20

O52	A82	$1 multicolored	1.30	1.30
O53	A82	$2 multicolored	4.00	4.00
		Nos. O41-O53 (13)	11.70	11.70

Nos. O41-O52 were not sold unused to local customers.
Issued: $2, 9/30; others, 7/20.

PERU

pə-'rü

LOCATION — West coast of South America
GOVT. — Republic
AREA — 496,093 sq. mi.
POP. — 24,800,768 (1998 est.)
CAPITAL — Lima

8 Reales = 1 Peso (1857)
100 Centimos = 8 Dineros =
4 Pesetas = 1 Peso (1858)
100 Centavos = 1 Sol (1874)
100 Centimos = 1 Inti (1985)
100 Centimos = 1 Sol (1991)

Catalogue values for unused stamps in this country are for Never Hinged items, beginning with Scott 426 in the regular postage section, Scott B1 in the semipostal section, Scott C78 in the airpost section, Scott CB1 in the airpost semi-postal section, and Scott RA31 in the postal tax section.

Watermark

Wmk. 346 — Parallel Curved Lines

ISSUES OF THE REPUBLIC

Sail and Steamship — A1

Design: 2r, Ship sails eastward.

1857, Dec. 1   Engr.   Imperf.
1	A1	1r blue, *blue*	1,700.	2,250.
2	A1	2r brn red, *blue*	1,900.	3,000.

The Pacific Steam Navigation Co. gave a quantity of these stamps to the Peruvian government so that a trial of prepayment of postage by stamps might be made.
Stamps of 1 and 2 reales, printed in various colors on white paper, laid and wove, were prepared for the Pacific Steam Navigation Co. but never put in use. Value $50 each on wove paper, $400 each on laid paper.

Coat of Arms A2 A3

A4

Wavy Lines in Spandrels
1858, Mar. 1   Litho.
3	A2	1d deep blue	275.00	47.50
4	A3	1p rose red	1,100.	160.00
5	A4	½ peso rose red	6,500.	4,750.
6	A4	½ peso buff	2,750.	375.00
a.	½ peso orange yellow	2,750.	375.00

A5   A6

Large Letters
1858, Dec.   Double-lined Frame
7	A5	1d slate blue	450.00	45.00
8	A6	1p red	450.00	65.00

A7   A8

1860-61
Zigzag Lines in Spandrels
9	A7	1d blue	175.00	10.50
a.	1d Prussian blue	175.00	20.00
b.	Cornucopia on white ground	375.00	80.00
c.	Zigzag lines broken at angles	225.00	22.50
10	A8	1p rose	450.00	42.50
a.	1p brick red	450.00	42.50
b.	Cornucopia on white ground	450.00	42.50

Retouched, 10 lines instead of 9 in left label
11	A8	1p rose	250.00	27.50
a.	Pelure paper	425.00	32.50
		Nos. 9-11 (3)	875.00	80.50

A9   A10

1862-63   Embossed
12	A9	1d red	14.50	4.50
a.	Arms embossed sideways	550.00	150.00
b.	Thick paper	120.00	37.50
c.	Diag. half used on cover		350.00
13	A10	1p brown ('63)	120.00	37.50
a.	Diag. half used on cover		1,000.

Counterfeits of Nos. 13 and 15 exist.

A11

1868-72
14	A11	1d green	19.00	3.75
a.	Arms embossed inverted	2,250.	1,200.
b.	Diag. half used on cover		2,000.
15	A10	1p orange ('72)	150.00	55.00
a.	Diag. half used on cover		1,100.

Nos. 12-15, 19 and 20 were printed in horizontal strips. Stamps may be found printed on two strips of paper where the strips were joined by overlapping.

Llamas — A12

A13   A14

1866-67   Engr.   Perf. 12
16	A12	5c green	10.50	.95
17	A13	10c vermilion	15.00	2.25
18	A14	20c brown	35.00	7.00
a.	Diagonal half used on cover		675.00
		Nos. 16-18 (3)	60.50	10.20

See Nos. 109, 111, 113.

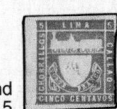
Locomotive and Arms — A15

1871, Apr.   Embossed   Imperf.
19	A15	5c scarlet	125.00	42.50
a.	5c pale red	125.00	42.50

20th anniv. of the first railway in South America, linking Lima and Callao.
The so-called varieties "ALLAO" and "CALLA" are due to over-inking.

Llama — A16

1873, Mar.   Rouletted Horiz.
20	A16	2c dk ultra	50.00	325.00

Counterfeits are plentiful.

Sun God of the Incas — A17

Coat of Arms A18   A19

A20   A21

A22   A23

Embossed with Grill
1874-84   Engr.   Perf. 12
21	A17	1c orange ('79)	.90	.65
22	A18	2c dk violet	1.25	.95
23	A19	5c blue ('77)	1.40	.45
24	A19	5c ultra ('79)	13.00	3.25
25	A20	10c green ('76)	.45	.30
a.	Imperf., pair	35.00	
26	A20	10c slate ('84)	2.00	.45
a.	Diag. half used as 5c on cover		
27	A21	20c brown red	3.50	1.10
28	A22	50c green	15.00	4.25
29	A23	1s rose	2.40	2.40
		Nos. 21-29 (9)	39.90	13.80

No. 25a lacks the grill.
No. 26 with overprint "DE OFICIO" is said to have been used to frank mail of Gen. A. A. Caceres during the civil war against Gen. Miguel Iglesias, provisional president. Experts question its status.

1880
30	A17	1c green		2.50
31	A18	2c rose		2.50

Nos. 30 and 31 were prepared for use but not issued without overprint.
See Nos. 104-108, 110, 112, 114-115.

For overprints see Nos. 32-103, 116-128, J32-J33, O2-O22, N11-N23, 1N1-1N9, 3N11-3N20, 5N1, 6N1-6N2, 7N1-7N2, 8N7, 8N10-8N11, 9N1-9N3, 10N3-10N8, 10N10-10N11, 11N1-11N5, 12N1-12N3, 13N1, 14N1-14N16, 15N5-15N8, 15N13-15N18, 16N1-16N22.

Stamps of 1874-80 Overprinted in Red, Blue or Black

1880, Jan. 5
32	A17	1c green (R)	.90	.65
a.	Inverted overprint	10.00	10.00
b.	Double overprint	13.50	13.50
33	A18	2c rose (Bl)	1.75	1.10
a.	Inverted overprint	10.00	10.00
b.	Double overprint	14.00	12.00
34	A18	2c rose (Bk)	75.00	60.00
a.	Inverted overprint		
b.	Double overprint		
35	A19	5c ultra (R)	3.50	1.75
a.	Inverted overprint	10.00	10.00
b.	Double overprint	14.00	14.00
36	A22	50c green (R)	45.00	27.50
a.	Inverted overprint	45.00	45.00
b.	Double overprint	55.00	55.00
37	A23	1s rose (Bl)	70.00	50.00
a.	Inverted overprint	110.00	110.00
b.	Double overprint	110.00	110.00
		Nos. 32-37 (6)	196.15	141.00

Stamps of 1874-80 Overprinted in Red or Blue

1881, Jan. 28
38	A17	1c green (R)	1.25	.95
a.	Inverted overprint	8.25	8.25
b.	Double overprint	14.00	14.00
39	A18	2c rose (Bl)	24.00	15.00
a.	Inverted overprint	17.50	15.00
b.	Double overprint	25.00	20.00
40	A19	5c ultra (R)	2.75	1.25
a.	Inverted overprint	14.00	14.00
b.	Double overprint	20.00	20.00
41	A22	50c green (R)	750.00	425.00
a.	Inverted overprint	850.00	
42	A23	1s rose (Bl)	140.00	90.00
a.	Inverted overprint	175.00	

Reprints of Nos. 38 to 42 were made in 1884. In the overprint the word "PLATA" is 3mm high instead of 2½mm. The cross bars of the letters "A" of that word are set higher than on the original stamps. The 5c is printed in blue instead of ultramarine.
For stamps of 1874-80 overprinted with Chilean arms or small UPU "horseshoe," see Nos. N11-N23.

Stamps of 1874-79 Handstamped in Black or Blue

1883

65	A17	1c orange (Bk)		1.25	1.10
66	A17	1c orange (Bl)		50.00	50.00
68	A19	5c ultra (Bk)		25.00	12.00
69	A20	10c green (Bk)		1.25	1.10
70	A20	10c green (Bl)		10.00	10.00
71	A22	50c green (Bk)		10.00	4.25
73	A23	1s rose (Bk)		10.00	8.00
		Nos. 65-73 (7)		107.50	86.45
		Nos. 65,68-73 (6)		57.50	36.45

This overprint is found in 11 types.
The 1c green, 2c dark violet and 20c brown red, overprinted with triangle, are fancy varieties made for sale to collectors and never placed in regular use.

Overprinted Triangle and "Union Postal Universal Peru" in Oval

1883

77	A22	50c grn (R & Bk)		210.00	110.00
78	A23	1s rose (Bl & Bk)		250.00	160.00

The 1c green, 2c rose and 5c ultramarine, over printed with triangle and "U. P. U. Peru" oval, were never placed in regular use.

Overprinted Triangle and "Union Postal Universal Lima" in Oval

1883

79	A17	1c grn (R & Bl)		70.00	70.00
80	A17	1c grn (R & Bk)		7.00	7.00
a.		Oval overprint inverted		7.00	7.00
b.		Double overprint of oval			
81	A18	2c rose (Bl & Bk)		7.00	7.00
82	A19	5c ultra (R & Bk)		15.00	10.00
83	A19	5c ultra (R & Bl)		25.00	10.00
84	A22	50c grn (R & Bk)		250.00	150.00
85	A23	1s rose (Bl & Bk)		275.00	275.00
		Nos. 79-85 (7)		649.00	529.00

Some authorities question the status of No. 79.

Nos. 80, 81, 84, and 85 were reprinted in 1884. They have the second type of oval overprint with "PLATA" 3mm high.

Overprinted Triangle and

86	A17	1c grn (Bk & Bk)		1.75	1.25
a.		Horseshoe inverted		10.00	
87	A17	1c grn (Bl & Bk)		5.00	3.50
88	A18	2c ver (Bk & Bk)		1.75	1.25
89	A19	5c bl (Bk & Bk)		5.00	1.60
90	A19	5c bl (Bl & Bk)		12.00	10.50
91	A19	5c bl (R & Bk)		1,500.	1,100.

Overprinted Horseshoe Alone

1883, Oct. 23

95	A17	1c green		2.25	2.25
96	A18	2c vermilion		6.50	6.50
a.		Double overprint			
97	A19	5c blue		3.50	3.50
98	A19	5c ultra		20.00	15.00
99	A22	50c rose		57.50	57.50
100	A23	1s ultra		75.00	75.00
		Nos. 95-100 (6)		164.75	107.25

The 2c dark violet (A18) overprinted with the above design in red and triangle in black also the 1c green (A17) overprinted with the same combination plus the horseshoe in black, are fancy varieties made for sale to collectors.

No. 23 Overprinted in Black

1884, Apr. 28

103	A19	5c blue		.65	.40
a.		Double overprint		5.00	5.00

Stamps of 1c and 2c with the above overprint, also with the above and "U. P. U. LIMA" oval in blue or "CORREOS LIMA" in a double-lined circle in red, were made for sale to collectors and were never placed in use.

Without Overprint or Grill

1886-95

104	A17	1c dull violet		.90	.30
105	A17	1c vermilion ('95)		.65	.30
106	A18	2c green		1.25	.30
107	A18	2c dp ultra ('95)		.55	.30
108	A19	5c orange		1.00	.45
109	A12	5c claret ('95)		2.25	.85
110	A20	10c slate		.65	.30
111	A13	10c orange ('95)		1.00	.55
112	A21	20c blue		8.75	1.10
113	A14	20c dp ultra ('95)		10.50	2.25
114	A22	50c red		2.75	1.10
115	A23	1s brown		2.25	.85
		Nos. 104-115 (12)		32.50	8.65

Overprinted Horseshoe in Black and Triangle in Rose Red

1889

116	A17	1c green		.75	.75
a.		Horseshoe inverted		7.50	

Nos. 30 and 25 Overprinted "Union Postal Universal Lima" in Oval in Red

1889, Sept. 1

117	A17	1c green		5.00	1.60
117A	A20	10c green		5.00	2.00

The overprint on Nos. 117 and 117A is of the second type with "PLATA" 3mm high.

Stamps of 1874-80 Overprinted in Black

Pres. Remigio Morales Bermúdez

1894, Oct. 23

118	A17	1c orange		1.00	.65
a.		Inverted overprint		7.00	7.00
b.		Double overprint		7.00	7.00
119	A17	1c green		.65	.55
a.		Inverted overprint		3.50	3.50
b.		Dbl. inverted ovpt.		5.00	5.00
120	A18	2c violet		.65	.55
a.		Diagonal half used as 1c			
b.		Inverted overprint		7.00	7.00
c.		Double overprint		7.00	7.00
121	A18	2c rose		.65	.55
a.		Double overprint		7.00	7.00
b.		Inverted overprint		9.75	7.00
122	A19	5c blue		4.50	2.75
122A	A19	5c ultra		7.25	3.50
a.		Inverted overprint		10.00	10.00
123	A20	10c green		.65	.55
a.		Inverted overprint		7.00	7.00
124	A22	50c green		2.40	2.00
a.		Inverted overprint		10.00	10.00
		Nos. 118-124 (8)		17.75	11.10

Same, with Additional Ovpt. of Horseshoe

125	A18	2c vermilion		.55	.45
a.		Head inverted		2.50	2.50
b.		Head double		5.00	5.00
126	A19	5c blue		1.75	.85
a.		Head inverted		7.00	7.00
127	A22	50c rose		70.00	42.50
a.		Head double		55.00	45.00
b.		Head inverted		75.00	60.00
128	A23	1s ultra		175.00	150.00
a.		Both overprints inverted		200.00	110.00
b.		Head double		200.00	110.00
		Nos. 125-128 (4)		247.30	193.80

A23a

Vermilion Surcharge

1895   Perf. 11½

129	A23a	5c on 5c grn		18.00	13.00
130	A23a	10c on 10c ver		13.00	10.00
131	A23a	20c on 20c brn		14.00	10.00

132	A23a	50c on 50c ultra		18.00	13.00
133	A23a	1s on 1s red brn		18.00	13.00
		Nos. 129-133 (5)		81.00	59.00

Nos 129-133 were used only in Tumbes. The basic stamps were prepared by revolutionaries in northern Peru.

A23b   "Liberty" — A23c

1895, Sept. 8   Engr.

134	A23b	1c gray violet		1.90	1.10
135	A23b	2c green		1.90	1.10
136	A23b	5c yellow		1.90	1.10
137	A23b	10c ultra		1.90	1.10
138	A23c	20c orange		1.90	1.25
139	A23c	50c dark blue		10.00	7.00
140	A23c	1s car lake		55.00	35.00
		Nos. 134-140 (7)		74.50	47.65

Success of the revolution against the government of General Caceres and of the election of President Pierola.

Manco Capac, Founder of Inca Dynasty A24   Francisco Pizarro Conqueror of the Inca Empire A25

General José de La Mar — A26

1896-1900

141	A24	1c ultra		.90	.30
a.		1c blue (error)		70.00	60.00
142	A24	1c yel grn ('98)		.90	.30
143	A24	2c blue		.90	.30
144	A24	2c scar ('99)		.90	.30
145	A25	5c indigo		1.25	.30
146	A25	5c green ('97)		1.25	.30
147	A25	5c grnsh bl ('99)		.90	.55
148	A25	10c yellow		1.75	.45
149	A25	10c gray blk ('00)		1.75	.30
150	A25	20c orange		3.50	.45
151	A26	50c car rose		8.75	1.60
152	A26	1s orange red		13.00	1.60
153	A26	2s claret		3.50	1.25
		Nos. 141-153 (13)		39.25	8.00

The 5c in black is a chemical changeling.

For surcharges and overprints see Nos. 187-188, E1, O23-O26.

Paucartambo Bridge — A27   Post and Telegraph Building, Lima — A28

Pres. Nicolás de Piérola — A29

1897, Dec. 31

154	A27	1c dp ultra		1.25	.60
155	A28	2c brown		1.25	.40
156	A29	5c bright rose		1.75	.60
		Nos. 154-156 (3)		4.25	1.60

Opening of new P.O. in Lima.

No. J1 Overprinted in Black

1897, Nov. 8

157	D1	1c bister		.90	.75
a.		Inverted overprint		4.50	4.50
b.		Double overprint		17.50	17.50

A31

1899

158	A31	5s orange red		2.75	2.75
159	A31	10s blue green		850.00	600.00

For surcharge see No. J36.

Pres. Eduardo de Romaña — A32

1900   Frame Litho., Center Engr.

160	A32	22c yel grn & blk		13.00	1.40

Admiral Miguel L. Grau — A33

2c, Col. Francisco Bolognesi. 5c, Pres. Romaña.

1901, Jan.

161	A33	1c green & blk		3.25	.75
162	A33	2c red & black		3.25	.75
163	A33	5c dull vio & blk		3.25	.75
		Nos. 161-163 (3)		9.75	2.25

Advent of 20th century.

A34

1902   Engr.

164	A34	22c green		.55	.30

Municipal Hygiene Institute Lima — A35

1905

165	A35	12c dp blue & blk		5.00	.50

For surcharges see Nos. 166-167, 186, 189.

Same Surcharged in Red or Violet

1907

166	A35	1c on 12c (R)		.35	.30
a.		Inverted surcharge		8.00	8.00
b.		Double surcharge		8.00	8.00
167	A35	2c on 12c (V)		.65	.45
a.		Double surcharge		8.00	8.00
b.		Inverted surcharge		8.00	8.00

Monument of
Bolognesi
A36

Admiral
Grau
A37

Llama
A38

Statue of
Bolivar
A39

City Hall,
Lima, formerly
an Exhibition
Building — A40

School of
Medicine,
Lima — A41

Post and Telegraph
Building,
Lima — A42

Grandstand at
Santa Beatrix
Race
Track — A43

Columbus
Monument — A44

1907

168	A36	1c yel grn & blk	.55	.30
169	A37	2c red & violet	.55	.30
170	A38	4c olive green	9.25	1.25
171	A39	5c blue & blk	1.00	.30
172	A40	10c red brn & blk	1.75	.45
173	A41	20c dk grn & blk	40.00	.75
174	A42	50c black	40.00	1.60
175	A43	1s purple & grn	200.00	3.75
176	A44	2s dp bl & blk	200.00	160.00
		Nos. 168-176 (9)	493.10	168.70

For surcharges and overprint see #190-195, E2.

Manco
Capac
A45

Columbus
A46

Pizarro
A47

San Martin
A48

Bolívar
A49

La Mar
A50

Ramón
Castilla
A51

Grau
A52

Bolognesi — A53

1909

177	A45	1c gray	.35	.25
178	A46	2c green	.35	.25
179	A47	4c vermilion	.45	.30
180	A48	5c violet	.35	.25
181	A49	10c deep blue	.75	.30
182	A50	12c pale blue	1.75	.30
183	A51	20c brown red	1.90	.45
184	A52	50c yellow	8.25	.55
185	A53	1s brn red & blk	17.00	.65
		Nos. 177-185 (9)	31.15	3.30

See types A54, A78-A80, A81-A89.
For surcharges and overprint see Nos. 196-200, 208, E3.

No. 165 Surcharged in
Red

1913, Jan.

186	A35	8c on 12c dp bl & blk	.90	.35

Stamps of 1899-1908 Surcharged in Red

a   b

c

1915   On Nos. 142, 149

187	A24(a)	1c on 1c	27.50	22.50
a.		Inverted surcharge	32.50	37.50
188	A25(a)	1c on 10c	1.75	1.25
a.		Inverted surcharge	4.50	4.50

On No. 165

189	A35(c)	2c on 12c	.45	.30
a.		Inverted surcharge	7.75	7.75

On Nos. 168-170, 172-174

190	A36(a)	1c on 1c	1.10	1.10
a.		Inverted surcharge	3.50	3.50
191	A37(a)	1c on 2c	1.75	1.60
a.		Inverted surcharge	4.50	4.50
192	A38(b)	1c on 4c	3.25	2.75
a.		Inverted surcharge	10.50	10.50
193	A40(b)	1c on 10c	1.75	1.25
a.		Inverted surcharge	3.75	3.75
193C	A40(c)	2c on 10c	175.00	125.00
b.		Inverted surcharge	175.00	
194	A41(c)	2c on 20c	22.50	21.00
a.		Inverted surcharge	45.00	45.00
195	A42(c)	2c on 50c	3.25	3.25
a.		Inverted surcharge	13.00	13.00
		Nos. 187-195 (10)	238.30	180.00

Nos. 182-184, 179, 185 Surcharged in Red, Green or Violet

d   e

f

1916

196	A50(d)	1c on 12c (R)	.35	.25
a.		Double surcharge	5.00	5.00
b.		Green surcharge	7.50	7.50

197	A51(d)	1c on 20c (G)	.35	.25
198	A52(d)	1c on 50c (G)	.35	.25
a.		Inverted surcharge	5.00	5.00
199	A47(e)	2c on 4c (V)	.35	.25
a.		Green surcharge	1.60	1.25
200	A53(f)	10c on 1s (G)	1.10	.75
a.		"VALF"	10.50	10.50
		Nos. 196-200 (5)	2.50	1.75

Official Stamps of 1909-14 Ovptd. or Srchd. in Green or Red

g

h

1916

201	O1(g)	1c red (G)	.25	.25
202	O1(h)	2c on 50c ol grn (R)	.35	.25
203	O1(g)	10c bis red (G)	.35	.25

Postage Due Stamps of 1909 Surcharged in Violet-Black

204	D7	2c on 1c brown	.75	.75
205	D7	2c on 5c brown	.25	.25
206	D7	2c on 10c brown	.25	.25
207	D7	2c on 50c brown	.25	.25
		Nos. 201-207 (7)	2.45	2.25

Many examples of Nos. 187 to 207 have a number of pin holes. It is stated that these holes were made at the time the surcharges were printed.

The varieties listed of the 1915 and 1916 issues were sold to the public at post offices. Many other varieties which were previously listed are now known to have been delivered to one speculator or to have been privately printed by him from the surcharging plates which he had acquired.

No. 179 Surcharged in
Black

1917

208	A47	1c on 4c ver	.55	.55
a.		Double surcharge	8.25	8.25
b.		Inverted surcharge	8.25	8.25

San
Martin
A54

Columbus at
Salamanca
A62

Funeral of Atahualpa
— A63

Battle of Arica,
"Arica, the Last
Cartridge" — A64

Designs: 2c, Bolívar. 4c, José Gálvez. 5c, Manuel Pardo. 8c, Grau. 10c, Bolognesi. 12c, Castilla. 20c, General Cáceres.

1918   Centers in Black   Engr.

209	A54	1c orange	.35	.25
210	A54	2c green	.35	.25
211	A54	4c lake	.45	.30
212	A54	5c dp ultra	.45	.30
213	A54	8c red brn	1.25	.45
214	A54	10c grnsh bl	.55	.30
215	A54	12c dl vio	1.75	.30
216	A54	20c ol grn	2.10	.30
217	A62	50c vio brn	8.25	.55
218	A63	1s greenish bl	21.00	.75
219	A64	2s deep ultra	35.00	1.10
		Nos. 209-219 (11)	71.50	4.85

For surcharges see Nos. 232-233, 255-256.

Augusto B.
Leguía — A65

1919, Dec.   Litho.

220	A65	5c bl & blk	.35	.30
a.		Imperf.	.35	.35
b.		Center inverted	15.00	15.00
221	A65	5c brn & blk	.35	.30
a.		Imperf.	.35	.35
b.		Center inverted	15.00	15.00

Constitution of 1919.

San Martín
A66

Thomas
Cochrane
A70

Oath of
Independence
A69

Designs: 2c, Field Marshal Arenales. 4c, Field Marshal Las Heras. 10c, Martin Jorge Guisse. 12c, Vidal. 20c, Leguia. 50c, San Martin monument. 1s, San Martin and Leguia.

1921, July 28   Engr.; 7c Litho.

222	A66	1c ol brn & red brn	.45	.25
a.		Center inverted	600.00	600.00
223	A66	2c green	.55	.30
224	A66	4c car rose	1.90	.90
225	A69	5c ol brn	.60	.25
226	A70	7c violet	1.90	.65
227	A66	10c ultra	1.90	.65
228	A66	12c blk & slate	4.50	.90
229	A66	20c car & gray blk	4.50	1.10
230	A66	50c vio brn & dl vio	13.00	3.75
231	A69	1s car rose & yel grn	19.00	8.00
		Nos. 222-231 (10)	48.30	16.75

Centenary of Independence.

Nos. 213, 212 Surcharged in Black or Red Brown

1923-24

232	A54	5c on 8c No. 213	.75	.55
233	A54	4c on 5c (RB) ('24)	.55	.25
a.		Inverted surcharge	5.00	5.00
b.		Double surcharge, one inverted	6.00	6.00

A78

A79

Simón Bolívar — A80

Perf. 14, 14x14½, 14½, 13½

1924   Engr.; Photo. (4c, 5c)

234	A78	2c olive grn	.40	.25
235	A79	4c yellow grn	.65	.25
236	A79	5c black	2.25	.25
237	A80	10c carmine	.80	.25
238	A78	20c ultra	2.25	.30
239	A78	50c dull violet	5.50	1.10
240	A78	1s yellow brn	13.00	4.25
241	A78	2s dull blue	35.00	18.00
		Nos. 234-241 (8)	59.85	24.65

Centenary of the Battle of Ayacucho which ended Spanish power in South America. No. 237 exists imperf.

José
Tejada
Rivadeneyra
A81

Mariano
Melgar
A82

Iturregui
A83

Leguía
A84

José de
La Mar
A85

Monument
of José
Olaya
A86

Statue of
María
Bellido
A87

De Saco
A88

José Leguía — A89

1924-29   Engr.   Perf. 12
Size: 18½x23mm

242	A81	2c olive gray	.35	.25
243	A82	4c dk grn	.35	.25
244	A83	8c black	3.25	3.25
245	A84	10c org red	.35	.25
245A	A85	15c dp bl ('28)	1.00	.30
246	A86	20c blue	1.75	.30
247	A86	20c yel ('29)	2.75	.30
248	A87	50c violet	8.25	.45
249	A88	1s bis brn	15.00	1.60
250	A89	2s ultra	40.00	8.00
		Nos. 242-250 (10)	73.05	14.95

See Nos. 258, 260, 276-282.
For surcharges and overprint see Nos. 251-253, 257-260, 262, 268-271, C1.

No. 246 Surcharged in Red

a

b

1925
251	A86(a)	2c on 20c blue	*550.00*	*550.00*
252	A86(b)	2c on 20c blue	1.75	1.10
a.		Inverted surcharge	50.00	50.00
b.		Double surch., one inverted	50.00	50.00

No. 245 Overprinted

1925
253	A84	10c org red	1.75	1.75
a.		Inverted overprint	21.00	21.00

This stamp was for exclusive use on letters from the plebiscite provinces of Tacna and Arica, and posted on the Peruvian transport "Ucayali" anchored in the port of Arica.

No. 213 Surcharged

a

b

1929
255	A54(a)	2c on 8c	1.25	1.25
256	A54(b)	2c on 8c	1.25	1.25

No. 247 Surcharged

257	A86	15c on 20c yellow	1.25	1.25
a.		Inverted surcharge	13.00	13.00
		Nos. 255-257 (3)	3.75	3.75

Types of 1924
Coil Stamps

1929   Perf. 14 Horizontally
258	A81	2c olive gray	65.00	40.00
260	A84	10c orange red	70.00	37.50

Postal Tax Stamp of 1928 Overprinted

1930   Perf. 12
261	PT6	2c dark violet	.55	.55
a.		Inverted overprint	3.25	3.25

No. 247 Surcharged

262	A86	2c on 20c yellow	.55	.55

Air Post Stamp of 1928 Surcharged

263	AP1	2c on 50c dk grn	.55	.55
a.		"Habitada"	2.10	2.10

Coat of
Arms — A91

Lima
Cathedral — A92

10c, Children's Hospital. 50c, Madonna & Child.

Perf. 12x11½, 11½x12
1930, July 5   Litho.
264	A91	2c green	1.75	.95
265	A92	5c scarlet	3.75	2.10
266	A92	10c dark blue	2.25	1.60
267	A91	50c bister brown	30.00	19.00
		Nos. 264-267 (4)	37.75	23.65

6th Pan American Congress for Child Welfare. By error the stamps are inscribed "Seventh Congress."

Type of 1924 Overprinted in Black, Green or Blue

1930, Dec. 22   Photo.   Perf. 15x14
Size: 18¼x22mm

268	A84	10c orange red (Bk)	1.00	.80
a.		Inverted overprint	14.00	14.00
b.		Without overprint	8.50	8.50
c.		Double surcharge	7.00	7.00

Same with Additional Surcharge of Numerals in Each Corner
269	A84	2c on 10c org red (G)	.35	.25
a.		Inverted surcharge	17.00	
270	A84	4c on 10c org red (G)	.35	.25
a.		Double surcharge	12.50	12.50

Engr.
Perf. 12
Size: 19x23½mm
271	A84	15c on 10c org red (Bl)	.35	.25
a.		Inverted surcharge	14.00	14.00
b.		Double surcharge	14.00	14.00
		Nos. 268-271 (4)	2.05	1.55

Bolívar — A95

1930, Dec. 16   Litho.
272	A95	2c buff	.55	.55
273	A95	4c red	.90	.75
274	A95	10c blue green	.45	.30
275	A95	15c slate gray	.90	.90
		Nos. 272-275 (4)	2.80	2.50

Death cent. of General Simón Bolivar.
For surcharges see Nos. RA14-RA16.

Types of 1924-29 Issues
Size: 18x22mm
1931   Photo.   Perf. 15x14
276	A81	2c olive green	.45	.30
277	A82	4c dark green	.45	.30
279	A85	15c deep blue	1.25	.30
280	A86	20c yellow	2.10	.30
281	A87	50c violet	2.10	.45
282	A88	1s olive brown	3.25	1.95
		Nos. 276-282 (6)	9.60	2.20

Pizarro — A96

Old
Stone
Bridge,
Lima
A97

1931, July 28   Litho.   Perf. 11
283	A96	2c slate blue	2.10	1.75
284	A96	4c deep brown	2.10	1.75
285	A96	15c dark green	2.10	1.75
286	A97	10c rose red	2.10	1.75
287	A97	10c mag & lt grn	2.10	1.75
288	A97	15c yel & bl gray	2.10	1.75
289	A97	15c dk slate & red	2.10	1.75
		Nos. 283-289 (7)	14.70	12.25

1st Peruvian Phil. Exhib., Lima, July, 1931.

Manco
Capac
A99

Oil Refinery
A100

Sugar
Cane
Field
A102

Picking
Cotton
A103

Guano
Deposits
A104

Mining
A105

Llamas — A106

1931-32   Perf. 11, 11x11½
292	A99	2c olive black	.35	.25
293	A100	4c dark green	.65	.30
295	A102	10c red orange	1.75	.25
a.		Vertical pair, imperf. between	30.00	
296	A103	15c turq blue	2.00	.30
297	A104	20c yellow	8.25	.30
298	A105	50c gray lilac	8.25	.30
299	A106	1s brown olive	20.00	1.40
		Nos. 292-299 (7)	41.25	3.10

Arms of Piura — A107

1932, July 28   Perf. 11½x12
300	A107	10c dark blue	8.25	8.00
301	A107	15c deep violet	8.25	8.00
		Nos. 300-301,C3 (3)	42.50	38.50

400th anniv. of the founding of the city of Piura. On sale one day. Counterfeits exist.
See No. C7.

Parakas
A108

Chimu
A109

Inca — A110

1932, Oct. 15   Perf. 11½, 12, 11½x12
302	A108	10c dk vio	.35	.25
303	A109	15c brn red	.65	.30
304	A110	50c dk brn	1.50	.30
		Nos. 302-304 (3)	2.50	.85

4th cent. of the Spanish conquest of Peru.

Arequipa and
El Misti
A111

President
Luis M.
Sánchez
Cerro
A112

Monument to Simón
Bolívar at Lima — A115

1932-34   Photo.   Perf. 13½
305	A111	2c black	.25	.25
306	A111	2c blue blk	.25	.25
307	A111	2c grn ('34)	.25	.25
308	A111	4c dk brn	.25	.25
309	A111	4c org ('34)	.25	.25
310	A112	10c vermilion	27.50	16.00
311	A115	15c ultra	.60	.25
312	A115	15c mag ('34)	.60	.25
313	A115	20c red brn	1.25	.25
314	A115	20c vio ('34)	1.25	.25
315	A115	50c dk grn ('33)	1.25	.25
316	A115	1s dp org	11.00	1.60
317	A115	1s org brn	12.00	1.10
		Nos. 305-317 (13)	56.70	21.20

For overprint see No. RA24.

Statue of Liberty — A116

1934
318 A116 10c rose   .75   .30

Pizarro
A117

The Inca
A119

Coronation of
Huascar — A118

1934-35			**Perf. 13**	
319	A117	10c crimson	.40	.25
320	A117	15c ultra	1.10	.25
321	A118	20c deep bl ('35)	2.00	.25
322	A118	50c dp red brn	1.60	.25
323	A119	1s dark vio	11.00	1.10
		Nos. 319-323 (5)	16.10	2.10

For surcharges and overprint see Nos. 354-
355, J54, O32.

Pizarro and the
Thirteen — A120

Belle of
Lima — A122

Francisco
Pizarro — A123

4c, Lima Cathedral. 1s, Veiled woman of
Lima.

1935, Jan. 18			**Perf. 13½**	
324	A120	2c brown	.55	.30
325	A120	4c violet	.60	.45
326	A122	10c rose red	.60	.30
327	A123	15c ultra	1.10	.75
328	A120	20c slate gray	2.25	.95
329	A122	50c olive grn	3.25	1.90
330	A122	1s Prus bl	6.00	3.75
331	A123	2s org brn	14.50	10.00
		Nos. 324-331,C6-C12 (15)	91.05	60.50

Founding of Lima, 4th cent.

View of
Ica — A125

Lake Huacachina,
Health Resort
A126

Grapes
A127

Cotton
Boll — A128

Zuniga y Velazco
and Philip
IV — A129

Supreme God of the
Nazcas — A130

Engr.; Photo. (10c)

1935, Jan. 17			**Perf. 12½**	
332	A125	4c gray blue	.45	1.25
333	A126	5c dark car	.45	1.25
334	A127	10c magenta	6.50	3.25
335	A126	20c green	2.25	2.25
336	A128	35c dark car	11.00	8.00
337	A129	50c org & brn	7.75	7.00
338	A130	1s pur & red	22.50	17.00
		Nos. 332-338 (7)	50.90	40.00

Founding of the City of Ica, 300th anniv.

Pizarro and the
Thirteen — A131

1935-36			**Photo.**	**Perf. 13½**	
339	A131	2c dp claret		.35	.35
340	A131	4c bl grn ('36)		.35	.35

For surcharge and overprints see Nos. 353,
J53, RA25-RA26.

"San
Cristóbal,"
First Peruvian
Warship
A132

Naval College at
Punta
A133

Independence
Square,
Callao — A134

Aerial View of
Callao — A135

Plan of Walls of
Callao in
1746 — A137

Grand
Marshal José
de La
Mar — A138

Packetboat
"Sacramento"
A139

Viceroy José
Antonio
Manso de
Velasco
A140

Fort
Maipú — A141

Plan of Fort Real
Felipe — A142

Design: 15c, Docks and Custom House.

1936, Aug. 27			**Photo.**	**Perf. 12½**	
341	A132	2c black		.75	.30
342	A133	4c bl grn		.75	.30
343	A134	5c yel brn		.75	.30
344	A135	10c bl gray		.75	.30
345	A135	15c green		.75	.30
346	A137	20c dk brn		1.00	.30
347	A138	50c purple		1.90	.55
348	A139	1s olive grn		12.00	1.75

Engr.

349	A140	2s violet	20.00	9.00
350	A141	5s carmine	27.50	19.00
351	A142	10s red org & brn	65.00	55.00
		Nos. 341-351,C13 (12)	134.40	88.85

Province of Callao founding, cent.

Nos. 340, 321 and
323 Surcharged in
Black

1936			**Perf. 13½, 13**	
353	A131	2c on 4c bl grn	.35	.30
a.		"0.20" for "0.02"	4.25	4.25
354	A118	10c on 20c dp bl	.35	.30
a.		Double surcharge	4.25	4.25
b.		Inverted surcharge	4.25	4.25
355	A119	10c on 1s dk vio	.55	.55
		Nos. 353-355 (3)	1.25	1.15

Many varieties of the surcharge are found
on these stamps: no period after "S," no
period after "Cts," period after "2," "S" omitted,
various broken letters, etc.

The surcharge on No. 355 is horizontal.

Peruvian
Cormorants
(Guano
Deposits)
A143

Oil Well at
Talara
A144

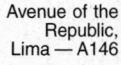

Avenue of the
Republic,
Lima — A146

San Marcos
University at
Lima — A148

Post Office,
Lima — A149

Viceroy Manuel de
Amat y
Junyent — A150

Designs: 10c, "El Chasqui" (Inca Courier).
20c, Municipal Palace and Museum of Natural
History. 5s, Joseph A. de Pando y Riva. 10s,
Dr. José Dávila Condemarin.

1936-37			**Photo.**	**Perf. 12½**	
356	A143	2c lt brn		.75	.30
357	A143	2c grn ('37)		1.00	.30
358	A144	4c blk brn		.75	.30
359	A144	4c int blk ('37)		.45	.30
360	A143	10c crimson		.45	.30
361	A143	10c ver ('37)		.35	.30
362	A146	15c ultra		.90	.30
363	A146	15c brt bl ('37)		.45	.30
364	A146	20c black		.90	.30
365	A146	20c blk brn ('37)		.35	.30
366	A148	50c org yel		3.25	.85
367	A148	50c dk gray vio ('37)		1.00	.30
368	A149	1s brn vio		6.50	1.10
369	A149	1s ultra ('37)		1.90	.30

Engr.

370	A150	2s ultra	13.00	2.75
371	A150	2s dk vio ('37)	4.50	.85
372	A150	5s slate bl	13.00	2.75
373	A150	10s dk vio & brn	75.00	37.50
		Nos. 356-373 (18)	124.50	49.40

No. 370 Surcharged in
Black

1937
374 A150 1s on 2s ultra   3.25 3.25

Children's
Holiday
Center, Ancón
A153

Chavin
Pottery
A154

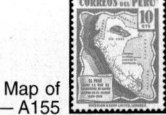

Highway Map of
Peru — A155

Archaeological
Museum, Lima — A156

Industrial
Bank of
Peru
A157

Worker's
Houses, Lima
A158

Toribio de
Luzuriaga
A159

Historic Fig
Tree
A160

Idol from
Temple of
Chavin
A161

Mt. Huascarán
A162

Imprint: "Waterlow & Sons Limited, Londres"

1938, July 1   Photo.   Perf. 12½, 13
375 A153 2c emerald   .25   .25
376 A154 4c org brn   .25   .25
377 A155 10c scarlet   .35   .25
378 A156 15c ultra   .40   .25
379 A157 20c magenta   .25   .25
380 A158 50c greenish blue   .50   .25
381 A159 1s dp claret   1.60   .25
382 A160 2s green   6.50   .25
Engr.
383 A161 5s dl vio & brn   13.00   .75
384 A162 10s blk & ultra   27.50   1.25
       Nos. 375-384 (10)   50.60   4.00

See Nos. 410-418, 426-433, 438-441.
For surcharges see Nos. 388, 406, 419,
445-446A, 456, 758.

Palace
Square — A163

Lima Coat of
Arms — A164

Government
Palace — A165

1938, Dec. 9   Photo.   Perf. 12½
385 A163 10c slate green   .65   .45
Engraved and Lithographed
386 A164 15c blk, gold, red & bl 1.10 .55
Photo.
387 A165 1s olive   2.75   1.60
       Nos. 385-387,C62-C64 (6) 9.30 5.90

8th Pan-American Conf., Lima, Dec. 1938.

No. 377 Surcharged in
Black

1940   Perf. 13
388 A155 5c on 10c scarlet   .35   .35
a.   Inverted surcharge

National Radio
Station — A166

Black Overprint
1941   Litho.   Perf. 12
389 A166 50c dull yel   3.25   .25
390 A166 1s violet   3.25   .30
391 A166 2s dl gray grn   5.25   .85
392 A166 5s fawn   30.00   8.50
393 A166 10s rose vio   45.00   7.00
       Nos. 389-393 (5)   86.75 16.90

Gonzalo
Pizarro
and
Orellana
A167

Francisco
Pizarro
A169

Map of South
America with
Amazon as
Spaniards Knew
It in 1542
A170

Gonzalo
Pizarro
A171

Discovery of the
Amazon River
A172

1943, Feb.   Perf. 12½
394 A167 2c crimson   .35   .25
395 A168 4c slate   .35   .25
396 A169 10c org brn   .35   .25
397 A170 15c vio blue   .65   .30
398 A171 20c yel olive   .35   .30
399 A172 25c dull org   3.00   .55
400 A168 30c dp magenta   .45   .30
401 A170 50c blue grn   .55   .45
402 A167 70c violet   2.75   1.50
403 A171 80c lt bl   2.75   1.50
404 A172 1s cocoa brn   5.50   .90
405 A169 5s intense blk   11.00   5.50
       Nos. 394-405 (12)   28.05 12.05

400th anniv. of the discovery of the Amazon
River by Francisco de Orellana in 1542.

No. 377 Surcharged in
Black

1943   Perf. 13
406 A155 10c on 10c scar   .30   .30

Samuel Finley Breese
Morse — A173

1944   Perf. 12½
407 A173 15c light blue   .35   .30
408 A173 30c olive gray   1.00   .30

Centenary of invention of the telegraph.

Types of 1938
Imprint: "Columbian Bank Note Co."
1945-47   Litho.   Perf. 12½
410 A153 2c green   .25   .25
411 A154 4c org brn ('46)   .25   .25
412 A156 15c ultra   .25   .25
413 A157 20c magenta   2.40   .25
414 A158 50c grnsh bl   .25   .25
415 A159 1s vio brn   .25   .25
416 A160 2s dl grn   1.00   .25
417 A161 5s dl vio & brn   6.00   .50
418 A162 10s blk & ultra ('47) 7.50 .75
       Nos. 410-418 (9)   18.15   3.00

No. 415 Surcharged in
Black

1946
419 A159 20c on 1s vio brn .50   .30
a.   Surcharge reading down 8.25 8.25

A174

A175

A176   A177

A178

Black Overprint
Perf. 12½
1947, Apr. 15   Litho.   Unwmk.
420 A174 15c blk & car   .30   .25
421 A175 1s olive brn   .60   .35
422 A176 1.35s yel grn   .60   .45
423 A177 3s Prus blue   1.10   .75
424 A178 5s dull grn   2.25   1.60
       Nos. 420-424 (5)   4.85   3.40

1st National Tourism Congress, Lima. The
basic stamps were prepared, but not issued,
for the 5th Pan American Highway Congress
of 1944.

> **Catalogue values for unused
> stamps in this section, from this
> point to the end of the section, are
> for Never Hinged items.**

Types of 1938
**Imprint: "Waterlow & Sons Limited,
Londres."**
Perf. 13x13½, 13½x13
1949-51   Photo.
426 A154 4c chocolate   .35   .25
427 A156 15c aquamarine   .35   .25
428 A157 20c blue vio   .35   .25
429 A158 50c red brn   .45   .25
430 A159 1s blk brn   1.00   .30
431 A160 2s ultra   2.00   .30
Engr.
Perf. 12½
432 A161 5s ultra & red brn
             ('50)   2.25   .65
433 A162 10s dk bl grn & blk
             ('51)   6.00   1.25
       Nos. 426-433 (8)   12.75   3.50

Nos. 375 and 438
Surcharged in Black

1951-52   Perf. 12½, 12½x12
445 A153 1c on 2c   .60   .30
446 A156 10c on 15c   .60   .30
446A A156 10c on 15c ('52) .60   .30
       Nos. 445-446A (3)   1.80   .90

On No. 446A "Sl. 0.10" is in smaller type
measuring 11½mm. See No. 456.
Nos. 445-446A exist with surcharge double.

Water
Promenade
A180

Post Boy
A181

Designs: 4c, 50c, 1s, 2s, Various buildings,
Lima. 20c, Post Office Street, Lima. 5s, Lake
Llangamuco, Ancachs. 10s, Ruins of Machu-
Picchu.

**Black Overprint: "V Congreso
Panamericano de Carreteras 1951"**

1951, Oct. 13   Unwmk.   Perf. 12
447 A180 2c dk grn   .35   .25
448 A180 4c brt red   .35   .25
449 A181 15c gray   .35   .25
450 A181 20c ol brn   .35   .25
451 A180 50c dp plum   .50   .25
452 A180 1s blue   .65   .30
453 A180 2s deep blue   1.10   .30
454 A181 5s brn lake   2.50   2.10
455 A181 10s chocolate   4.50   2.10
       Nos. 447-455 (9)   10.65   6.05

5th Pan-American Congress of Highways,
1951.

No. 438 Surcharged in
Black

1952   Unwmk.   Perf. 12½x12
456 A156 5c on 15c pck grn .60   .30

Engineering
School
A182

Vicuña
A183

Contour Farming,
Cuzco — A184

Designs: 2c, Tourist Hotel, Tacna. 5c, Fish-
ing boat and principal fish. 10c, Matarani. 15c,
Locomotive No. 80 and coaches. 30c, Ministry
of Public Health and Social Assistance. 1s,
Paramonga fortress. 2s, Monument to Native
Farmer.

**Imprint: "Thomas De La Rue & Co.
Ltd."**
Perf. 13, 12 (A184)
1952-53   Litho.   Unwmk.
457 A182 2c red lil ('53)   .30   .25
458 A182 5c green   .30   .25
459 A182 10c yel grn ('53) .30   .25
460 A182 15c gray ('53)   .30   .25
461 A183 20c red brn ('53) .90   .25
462 A182 25c rose red   .30   .25
463 A182 30c indigo ('53)   .30   .25
464 A184 50c green ('53)   1.10   .25
465 A184 1s brown   .80   .25
466 A184 2s Prus grn ('53) 1.60   .25
       Nos. 457-466 (10)   6.20   2.50

See Nos. 468-478, 483-488, 497-501,
C184-C185, C209.
For surcharges see Nos. C434, C437,
C440-C441, C454, C494.

Gen. Marcos Perez
Jimenez — A185

1956, July 25   Engr.   Perf. 13½x13
467 A185 25c brown   .60 .25
Visit of Gen. Marcos Perez Jimenez, Pres.
of Venezuela, June 1955.

Types of 1952-53
Imprint: "Thomas De La Rue & Co.
Ltd."
Designs as before.

1957-59   Litho.   Perf. 13, 12
468 A182 15c brown ('59)   .75 .25
469 A182 25c green ('59)   .75 .25
470 A182 30c brown red   .40 .25
471 A184 50c dull pur   .65 .25
472 A184 1s lt vio bl   .70 .25
473 A184 2s gray ('58)   1.25 .25
   Nos. 468-473 (6)   4.50 1.50

Types of 1952-53
Imprint: "Joh. Enschedé en Zonen-
Holland"
Designs as before.

Perf. 12½x13½, 13½x12½, 14x13
1960   Litho.   Unwmk.
474 A183 20c lt red brn   .30 .25
475 A182 30c lilac rose   .30 .25
476 A184 50c rose vio   .55 .25
477 A184 1s lt vio bl   1.00 .25
478 A184 2s gray   1.40 .30
   Nos. 474-478 (5)   3.55 1.30

#475 measures 33x22mm, #470 32x22½mm.

Symbols of the
Eucharist — A186

1960, Aug. 10   Photo.   Perf. 11½
479 A186 50c Cross and "JHS"   .30 .25
480 A186 1s shown   1.00 .50

Nos. 479-480 were intended for voluntary
use to help finance the 6th National Euchares-
tic Congress at Piura, Aug. 25-28, 1960.
Authorized for payment of postage on day of
issue only, Aug. 10, but through misunder-
standing within the Peruvian postal service
they were accepted for payment of postage by
some post offices until late in December. Re-
authorized for postal use, they were again sold
and used, starting in July, 1962. See Nos.
RA37-RA38.

Trumpeting
Angels — A187

1961, Dec. 20   Litho.   Perf. 10½
481 A187 20c bright blue   .80 .30

Christmas. Valid for postage for one day,
Dec. 20. Used thereafter as a voluntary seal to
benefit a fund for postal employees.

Centenary Cedar,
Main Square,
Pomabamba
A188

Unwmk.
1962, Sept. 7   Engr.   Perf. 13
482 A188 1s red & green   .80 .30

Cent. (in 1961) of Pomabamba province.

Types of 1952-53

Designs: 20c, Vicuña. 30c, Port of
Matarani. 40c, Gunboat. 50c, Contour farm-
ing. 60c, Tourist hotel, Tacna. 1s, Paramonga,
Inca fortress.

Imprint: "Thomas De La Rue & Co.
Ltd."
Perf. 13x13½, 13½x13, 12 (A184)
1962, Nov. 19   Litho.   Wmk. 346
483 A183 20c rose claret   .35 .25
484 A182 30c dark blue   .35 .25
485 AP49 40c orange   .35 .25
486 A184 50c lt bluish grn   .35 .25
487 A182 60c grnsh blk   .90 .25
488 A184 1s rose   1.40 .25
   Nos. 483-488 (6)   3.70 1.50

Wheat Emblem and
Symbol of
Agriculture,
Industry — A189

1963, July 23   Unwmk.   Perf. 12½
489 A189 1s red org & ocher   .30 .25
FAO "Freedom from Hunger" campaign. See
No. C190.

Alliance for Progress
Emblem — A190

1964, June 22   Litho.   Perf. 12x12½
490 A190 40c multi   .30 .25
   Nos. 490,C192-C193 (3)   1.75 1.10
Alliance for Progress. See note after US No.
1234.

Pacific Fair
Emblem — A191

1965, Oct. 30   Litho.   Perf. 12x12½
491 A191 1.50s multi   .50 .25
492 A191 2.50s multi   .50 .25
493 A191 3.50s multi   1.00 .30
   Nos. 491-493 (3)   2.00 .80
4th Intl. Pacific Fair, Lima, Oct. 30-Nov. 14.

Santa Claus and
Letter — A192

1965, Nov. 2   Perf. 11
494 A192 20c red & blk   .35 .25
495 A192 50c grn & blk   .65 .30
496 A192 1s bl & blk   1.25 .55
   Nos. 494-496 (3)   2.25 1.10

Christmas. Valid for postage for one day,
Nov. 2. Used Nov. 3, 1965-Jan. 31, 1966, as
voluntary seals for the benefit of a fund for
postal employees. See #522-524. For
surcharges see #641-643.

Types of 1952-62
20c, Vicuña. 30c, Port of Matarani. 40c,
Gunboat. 50c, Contour farming. 1s,
Paramonga, Inca fortress.
Imprint: "I.N.A."
Perf. 12, 13½x14 (A184)
1966, Aug. 8   Litho.   Unwmk.
497 A183 20c brn red   .60 .30
498 A182 30c dk bl   .60 .30
499 AP49 40c orange   .60 .30
500 A184 50c gray grn   .60 .30
501 A184 1s rose   .60 .30
   Nos. 497-501 (5)   3.00 1.50

**Postal Tax Stamps Nos. RA40, RA43
Surcharged**

a   b

Perf. 14x14½, 12½x12
1966, May 9   Litho.
501A PT11 (a) 10c on 2c lt brn   .60 .25
501B PT14 (b) 10c on 3c lt car   .60 .25

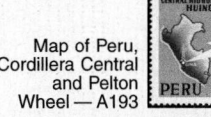

Map of Peru,
Cordillera Central
and Pelton
Wheel — A193

1966, Nov. 24   Photo.   Perf. 13½x14
502 A193 70c bl, blk & vio bl   .50 .25
Opening of the Huinco Hydroelectric Center.
See No. C205.

Inca Window and
Sun — A194

Perf. 13½x14
1967, Apr. 18   Photo.   Unwmk.
503 A194 90c dp lil rose, blk &
            gold   .50 .25
6-year building program. See No. C212.

Pacific Fair
Emblem — A195

1967, Oct. 9   Photo.   Perf. 12
504 A195 1s gold, dk grn & blk   .50 .25
5th Intl. Pacific Fair, Lima, Oct. 27-Nov. 12.
See No. C216.

Gold Alligator,
Mochica
Culture — A196

Designs (gold sculptures of the pre-Inca
Yunca tribes): 2.60s, Bird, vert. 3.60s, Lizard.
4.60s, Bird, vert. 5.60s, Jaguar.

**Sculptures in Gold Yellow and
Brown**
1968, Aug. 16   Photo.   Perf. 12
505 A196 1.90s dp magenta   1.60 .45
506 A196 2.60s black   2.25 .55
507 A196 3.60s dp magenta   2.75 .65
508 A196 4.60s black   3.25 .65
509 A196 5.60s dp magenta   5.00 .95
   Nos. 505-509 (5)   14.85 3.25
See Nos. B1-B5. For surcharge see No. 685.

Indian and
Wheat — A197

Designs: 3s, 4s, Farmer digging in field.
Black Surcharge
1969, Mar. 3   Litho.   Perf. 11
510 A197 2.50s on 90c brn & yel   .35 .25
511 A197 3s on 90c lil & brn   .60 .25
512 A197 4s on 90c rose &
            grn   .80 .30
   Nos. 510-512,C232-C233 (5)   3.55 1.50
Agrarian Reform Law.
#510-512 were not issued without
surcharge.

Flag, Worker
Holding Oil Rig
and Map — A198

1969, Apr. 9   Litho.   Perf. 12
513 A198 2.50s multi   .50 .25
514 A198 3s gray & multi   .50 .25
515 A198 4s lil & multi   .90 .30
516 A198 5.50s lt bl & multi   1.40 .30
   Nos. 513-516 (4)   3.30 1.10
Nationalization of the Brea Parinas oilfields,
Oct. 9, 1968.

Kon Tiki Raft. Globe
and Jet — A199

1969, June 17   Litho.   Perf. 11
517 A199 2.50s dp bl & multi   .90 .30
   Nos. 517,C238-C241 (5)   4.75 2.10
1st Peruvian Airlines (APSA) flight to Europe.

Capt. José A.
Quiñones
Gonzales
(1914-41),
Military
Aviator
A200

1969, July 23   Litho.   Perf. 11
518 A200 20s red & multi   3.00 1.25
See No. C243.

Freed Andean
Farmer — A201

1969, Aug. 28   Litho.   Perf. 11
519 A201 2.50s dk bl, lt bl & red .40 .25
   Nos. 519,C246-C247 (3)   1.80 .95
Enactment of the Agrarian Reform Law of
June 24, 1969.

Adm. Miguel
Grau — A202

1969, Oct. 8   Litho.   Perf. 11
520 A202 50s dk bl & multi   5.75 3.25
Issued for Navy Day.

Flags and
"6" — A203

1969, Nov. 14
521 A203 2.50s gray & multi   .80 .30
   Nos. 521,C251-C252 (3)   2.40 .80
6th Intl. Pacific Trade Fair, Lima, Nov. 14-30.

Santa Claus Type of 1965
Design: Santa Claus and letter inscribed
"FELIZ NAVIDAD Y PROSPERO AÑO
NUEVO."

1969, Dec. 1   Litho.   Perf. 11
522 A192 20c red & blk   .60 .25
523 A192 20c org & blk   .60 .25
524 A192 20c brn & blk   .60 .25
   Nos. 522-524 (3)   1.80 .75

Christmas. Valid for postage for one day,
Dec. 1, 1969. Used after that date as postal
tax stamps.

Gen. Francisco Bolognesi and Soldier — A204

1969, Dec. 9
525 A204 1.20s lt ultra, blk & gold .65 .25
Army Day, Dec. 9. See No. C253.

Puma-shaped Jug, Vicus Culture — A205

1970, Feb. 23   Litho.   Perf. 11
526 A205 2.50s buff, blk & brn .90 .25
Nos. 526,C281-C284 (5) 9.30 2.80

Ministry of Transport and Communications A206

1970, Apr. 1   Litho.   Perf. 11
527 A206 40c org & gray .60 .60
528 A206 40c gray & lt gray .60 .60
529 A206 40c brick red & gray .60 .60
530 A206 40c brt pink & gray .60 .60
531 A206 40c org brn & gray .60 .60
Nos. 527-531 (5) 3.00 1.25

Ministry of Transport and Communications, 1st anniv.

Anchovy — A207

Fish: No. 533, Pacific hake.

1970, Apr. 30   Litho.   Perf. 11
532 A207 2.50s vio bl & multi 2.00 .30
533 A207 2.50s vio bl & multi 2.00 .30
a. Strip of 5, #532-533, C285-C287 11.00 11.00

Composite Head; Soldier and Farmer — A208

1970, June 24   Litho.   Perf. 11
534 A208 2.50s gold & multi .75 .45
Nos. 534,C290-C291 (3) 3.00 .95

"United people and army building a new Peru."

Cadets, Chorrillos College, and Arms — A209

Coat of Arms and: No. 536, Cadets of La Punta Naval College. No. 537, Cadets of Las Palmas Air Force College.

1970, July 27   Litho.   Perf. 11
535 A209 2.50s blk & multi 1.00 .30
536 A209 2.50s blk & multi 1.00 .30
537 A209 2.50s blk & multi 1.00 .30
a. Strip of 3, #535-537 5.75 5.00
Peru's military colleges.

Courtyard, Puruchuco Fortress, Lima — A210

1970, Aug. 6
538 A210 2.50s multi 1.20 .25
Nos. 538,C294-C297 (5) 9.15 1.85
Issued for tourist publicity.

Nativity, Cuzco School — A211

Christmas paintings: 1.50s, Adoration of the Kings, Cuzco School. 1.80s, Adoration of the Shepherds, Peruvian School.

1970, Dec. 23   Litho.   Perf. 11
539 A211 1.20s multi .60 .25
540 A211 1.50s multi .60 .25
541 A211 1.80s multi .65 .25
Nos. 539-541 (3) 1.85 .75

St. Rosa of Lima — A212

1971, Apr. 12   Litho.   Perf. 11
542 A212 2.50s multi .60 .30

300th anniv. of the canonization of St. Rosa of Lima (1586-1617), first saint born in the Americas.

Tiahuanacoide Cloth — A213

Design: 2.50s, Chancay cloth.

1971, Apr. 19
543 A213 1.20s bl & multi .40 .25
544 A213 2.50s yel & multi .75 .25
Nos. 543-544,C306-C308 (5) 6.25 2.05

Nazca Sculpture, 5th Century, and Seriolella — A214

1971, June 7   Litho.   Perf. 11
545 A214 1.50s multi .65 .25
Nos. 545,C309-C312 (5) 6.15 2.40

Publicity for 200-mile zone of sovereignty of the high seas.

Mateo Garcia Pumacahua A215

#547, Mariano Melgar. #548, Micaela Bastidas. #549, Jose Faustino Sanchez Carrion. #550, Francisco Antonio de Zela. #551, Jose Baquijano y Carrillo. #552, Martin Jorge Guise.

1971
546 A215 1.20s ver & blk .50 .25
547 A215 1.20s gray & multi .50 .25
548 A215 1.50s dk bl & multi .50 .25
549 A215 2s dk bl & multi .50 .25
550 A215 2.50s ultra & multi .70 .25
551 A215 2.50s gray & multi .70 .25
552 A215 2.50s dk bl & multi .70 .25
Nos. 546-552,C313-C325 (20) 16.35 5.80

150th anniv. of independence, and to honor the heroes of the struggle for independence. Issue dates: Nos. 546, 550, May 10; Nos. 547, 551, July 5; Nos. 548-549, 552, July 27.

Gongora Portentosa — A216

Designs: Various Peruvian orchids.

1971, Sept. 27   Perf. 13½x13
553 A216 1.50s pink & multi 1.75 .25
554 A216 2s pink & multi 2.25 .25
555 A216 2.50s pink & multi 2.25 .25
556 A216 3s pink & multi 2.50 .25
557 A216 3.50s pink & multi 2.50 .25
Nos. 553-557 (5) 11.25 1.25

"Progress of Liberation," by Teodoro Nuñez Ureta — A217

3.50s, Detail from painting by Nuñez Ureta.

1971, Nov. 4   Perf. 13x13½
558 A217 1.20s multi .30 .25
559 A217 3.50s multi .60 .25
Nos. 558-559,C331 (3) 7.90 2.75

2nd Ministerial meeting of the "Group of 77."

Plaza de Armas, Lima, 1843 — A218

3.50s, Plaza de Armas, Lima, 1971.

1971, Nov. 6
560 A218 3s pale grn & blk .90 .30
561 A218 3.50s lt brick red & blk .90 .30

3rd Annual Intl. Stamp Exhibition, EXFILIMA '71, Lima, Nov. 6-14.

Army Coat of Arms — A219

1971, Dec. 9   Litho.   Perf. 13½x13
562 A219 8.50s multi 1.50 .55

Sesquicentennial of Peruvian Army.

Flight into Egypt — A220

Old Stone Sculptures of Huamanga: 2.50s, Three Kings. 3s, Nativity.

1971, Dec. 18   Perf. 13x13½
563 A220 1.80s multi .50 .30
564 A220 2.50s multi .80 .30
565 A220 3s gray & multi 1.25 .30
Nos. 563-565 (3) 2.55 .90

Christmas. See Nos. 597-599.

Fisherman, by J. M. Ugarte Elespuru — A221

Paintings by Peruvian Workers: 4s, Threshing Grain in Cajamarca, by Camilo Blas. 6s, Huanca Highlanders, by José Sabogal.

1971, Dec. 30   Perf. 13½x13
566 A221 3.50s blk & multi 1.25 .25
567 A221 4s blk & multi 1.25 .25
568 A221 6s blk & multi 2.00 .25
Nos. 566-568 (3) 4.50 .75

To publicize the revolution and change of order.

Gold Statuette, Chimu, c. 1500 — A222

Ancient Jewelry: 4s, Gold drummer, Chimu. 4.50s, Quartz figurine, Lambayeque culture, 5th century. 5.40s, Gold necklace and pendant, Mochiqua, 4th century. 6s, Gold insect, Lambayeque culture, 14th century.

1972, Jan. 31   Litho.   Perf. 13½x13
569 A222 3.90s red, blk & ocher .65 .25
570 A222 4s red, blk & ocher .65 .25
571 A222 4.50s brt bl, blk & ocher 1.40 .25
572 A222 5.40s red, blk & ocher 1.40 .25
573 A222 6s red, blk & ocher 2.25 .25
Nos. 569-573 (5) 6.35 1.25

Popeye Catalufa — A223

Fish: 1.50s, Guadara. 2.50s, Jack mackerel.

1972, Mar. 20   Perf. 13x13½
574 A223 1.20s lt bl & multi .80 .25
575 A223 1.50s lt bl & multi .80 .25
576 A223 2.50s lt bl & multi 1.75 .25
Nos. 574-576,C333-C334 (5) 8.10 2.25

Seated Warrior, Mochica — A224

Painted pottery jugs of Mochica culture, 5th cent.: 1.50s, Helmeted head. 2s, Kneeling deer. 2.50s, Helmeted head. 3s, Kneeling warrior.

1972, May 8   Perf. 13½x13
Emerald Background

577 A224 1.20s multi .70 .25
578 A224 1.50s multi .90 .25
579 A224 2s multi 1.50 .25
580 A224 2.50s multi 1.50 .25
581 A224 3s multi 2.25 .25
Nos. 577-581 (5) 6.85 1.25

"Bringing in the Harvest" (July) — A225

Monthly woodcuts from Calendario Incaico.

1972-73   Litho.   Perf. 13½x13
Black Vignette & Inscriptions

582	A225	2.50s red brn (July)	2.10	.30
583	A225	3s grn (Aug.)	2.10	.30
584	A225	2.50s rose (Sept.)	2.10	.30
585	A225	3s lt bl (Oct.)	2.10	.30
586	A225	2.50s org (Nov.)	2.10	.30
587	A225	3s lil (Dec.)	2.10	.30
588	A225	2.50s brn (Jan.) ('73)	2.10	.30
589	A225	3s pale grn (Feb.) ('73)	2.10	.30
590	A225	2.50s bl (Mar.) ('73)	2.10	.30
591	A225	3s org (Apr.) ('73)	2.10	.30
592	A225	2.50s lil rose (May) ('73)	2.10	.30
593	A225	3s yel & blk (June) ('73)	2.10	.30
		Nos. 582-593 (12)	25.20	3.60

400th anniv. of publication of the Calendario Incaico by Felipe Guaman Poma de Ayala.

Family Tilling Field — A226

Sovereignty of the Sea (Inca Frieze) — A227

Oil Derricks — A228

Perf. 13½x13, 13x13½
1972, Oct. 31   Litho.

594	A226	2s multi	.65	.30
595	A227	2.50s multi	.65	.30
596	A228	3s gray & multi	.65	.30
		Nos. 594-596 (3)	1.95	.90

4th anniversaries of land reforms and the nationalization of the oil industry and 15th anniv. of the claim to a 200-mile zone of sovereignty of the sea.

Christmas Type of 1971

Sculptures from Huamanga, 17-18th cent.: 1.50s, Holy Family, wood, vert. 2s, Holy Family with lambs, stone. 2.50s, Holy Family in stable, stone, vert.

1972, Nov. 30

597	A220	1.50s buff & multi	.60	.25
598	A220	2s buff & multi	.60	.25
599	A220	2.50s buff & multi	.60	.25
		Nos. 597-599 (3)	1.80	.75

Morning Glory — A228a

2.50s, Amaryllis. 3s, Liabum excelsum. 3.50s, Bletia (orchid). 5s, Cantua buxifolia.

1972, Dec. 29   Litho.   Perf. 13

600	A228a	1.50s shown	1.00	.25
601	A228a	2.50s multi	1.10	.25
602	A228a	3s multi	1.50	.25
603	A228a	3.50s multi	1.90	.25
604	A228a	5s multi	3.00	.55
		Nos. 600-604 (5)	8.50	1.55

Mayor on Horseback, by Fierro — A229

Paintings by Francisco Pancho Fierro (1803-1879): 2s, Man and Woman, 1830. 2.50s, Padre Abregu Riding Mule. 3.50s, Dancing Couple. 4.50s, Bullfighter Estevan Arredondo on Horseback.

1973, Aug. 13   Litho.   Perf. 13

605	A229	1.50s salmon & multi	.40	.25
606	A229	2s salmon & multi	.65	.25
607	A229	2.50s salmon & multi	.90	.25
608	A229	3.50s salmon & multi	1.40	.25
609	A229	4.50s salmon & multi	1.60	.60
		Nos. 605-609 (5)	4.95	1.60

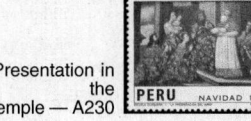

Presentation in the Temple — A230

Christmas Paintings of the Cuzqueña School: 2s, Holy Family, vert. 2.50s, Adoration of the Kings.

Perf. 13x13½, 13½x13
1973, Nov. 30   Litho.

610	A230	1.50s multi	.45	.25
611	A230	2s multi	.65	.25
612	A230	2.50s multi	.70	.30
		Nos. 610-612 (3)	1.80	.80

Peru No. 20 — A231

1974, Mar. 1   Litho.   Perf. 13

613	A231	6s brnsh gray & dk bl	1.10	.40

Peruvian Philatelic Assoc., 25th anniv.

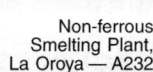

Non-ferrous Smelting Plant, La Oroya — A232

Colombia Bridge, San Martin — A233

Designs: 8s, 10s, Different views, Santiago Antunez Dam, Tayacaja.

1974   Litho.   Perf. 13x13½

614	A232	1.50s blue	.35	.25
615	A232	2s multi	.35	.25
616	A232	3s rose claret	.75	.25
617	A232	4.50s green	1.25	.45
618	A233	8s multi	1.50	.55
619	A233	10s multi	1.50	.55
		Nos. 614-619 (6)	5.70	2.30

"Peru Determines its Destiny."
Issued: 2s, 8s, 10s, 7/1; 1.50s, 3s, 4.50s, 12/6.

Battle of Junin, by Felix Yañez — A234

2s, 3s, Battle of Ayacucho, by Felix Yañez.

1974   Litho.   Perf. 13x13½

620	A234	1.50s multi	.35	.25
621	A234	2s multi	.35	.25
622	A234	2.50s multi	.45	.30
623	A234	3s multi	.45	.30
		Nos. 620-623,C400-C404 (9)	8.10	2.85

Sesquicentennial of the Battles of Junin and Ayacucho.
Issued: 1.50s, 2.50s, Aug. 6; 2s, 3s, Oct. 9.

Indian Madonna — A235

1974, Dec. 20   Litho.   Perf. 13½x13

624	A235	1.50s multi	.40	.25

Christmas. See No. C417.

Maria Parado de Bellido A236

International Women's Year Emblem A237

IWY Emblem, Peruvian Colors and: 2s, Micaela Bastidas. 2.50s, Juana Alarco de Dammert.

Perf. 13x13½, 13½x13
1975, Sept. 8   Litho.

625	A236	1.50s bl grn, red & blk	.40	.25
626	A237	2s blk & red	.55	.25
627	A236	2.50s pink, blk & red	.55	.25
628	A237	3s red, blk & ultra	1.00	.25
		Nos. 625-628 (4)	2.50	1.00

International Women's Year.

St. Juan Macias — A238

1975, Nov. 14   Perf. 13½x13

629	A238	5s blk & multi	.80	.25

Canonization of Juan Macias in 1975.

Louis Braille — A239

1976, Mar. 2   Litho.   Perf. 13x13½

630	A239	4.50s gray, red & blk	.80	.45

Sesquicentennial of the invention of Braille system of writing for the blind by Louis Braille (1809-1852).

Peruvian Flag — A240

1976, Aug. 29   Litho.   Perf. 13x13½

631	A240	5s gray, blk & red	.60	.25

Revolutionary Government, phase II, 1st anniv.

St. Francis, by El Greco — A241

1976, Dec. 9   Litho.   Perf. 13½x13

632	A241	5s gold, buff & brn	1.00	.25

St. Francis of Assisi, 750th death anniv.

Indian Mother — A242

1976, Dec. 23

633	A242	4s multi	.90	.25

Christmas.

Chasqui Messenger — A243

1977   Litho.   Perf. 13½x13

634	A243	6s grnsh bl & blk	.65	.25
635	A243	8s red & blk	.65	.25
636	A243	10s ultra & blk	.80	.50
637	A243	12s lt grn & blk	.80	.50
		Nos. 634-637,C465-C467 (7)	10.35	4.10

For surcharge see No. C502.

"X" over Flags — A244

1977, Nov. 25   Litho.   Perf. 13½x13

638	A244	10s multi	.60	.25

10th Intl. Pacific Fair, Lima, Nov. 16-27.

Republican Guard Badge — A245

1977, Dec. 1

639	A245	12s multi	.80	.30

58th anniversary of Republican Guard.

Indian Nativity — A246

1977, Dec. 23

640	A246	8s multi	.65	.35

Christmas. See No. C484.

Nos. 495, 494, 496 Surcharged with New Value and Bar in Red, Dark Blue or Black: "FRANQUEO / 10.00 / RD-0161-77"

1977, Dec. **Perf. 11**
641	A192	10s on 50c (R)	.55	.30
642	A192	20s on 20c (DB)	1.10	.55
643	A192	30s on 1s (B)	1.60	.75
		Nos. 641-643 (3)	3.25	1.60

Inca Head — A247

1978 **Litho.** **Perf. 13½x13**
644	A247	6s bright green	.30	.25
645	A247	10s red	.30	.25
646	A247	16s red brown	.55	.30
		Nos. 644-646,C486-C489 (7)	8.40	4.30

For surcharges see Nos. C498-C499, C501.

Flags of Germany, Argentina, Austria, Brazil — A248

Argentina '78 Emblem and Flags of Participants: No. 648, 652, Hungary, Iran, Italy, Mexico. No. 649, 653, Scotland, Spain, France, Netherlands. No. 650, 654, Peru, Poland, Sweden and Tunisia. No. 651, like No. 647.

1978 **Litho.** **Perf. 13x13½**
647	A248	10s blue & multi	1.00	.30
648	A248	10s blue & multi	1.00	.30
649	A248	10s blue & multi	1.00	.30
650	A248	10s blue & multi	1.00	.30
a.		Block of 4, #647-650	5.00	4.00
651	A248	16s blue & multi	1.00	.40
652	A248	16s blue & multi	1.00	.40
653	A248	16s blue & multi	1.00	.40
654	A248	16s blue & multi	1.00	.40
a.		Block of 4, #651-654	7.00	5.00
		Nos. 647-654 (8)	8.00	2.80

11th World Soccer Cup Championship, Argentina, June 1-25.
Issued: #647-650, 6/28; #651-654, 12/4.

Thomas Faucett, Planes of 1928, 1978 — A249

1978, Oct. 19 **Litho.** **Perf. 13**
655	A249	40s multicolored	1.25	.50

Faucett Aviation, 50th anniversary.

Nazca Bowl, Huaco — A250

1978-79 **Litho.** **Perf. 13x13½**
656	A250	16s violet bl ('79)	.60	.25
657	A250	20s green ('79)	.60	.25
658	A250	25s lt green ('79)	.75	.55
659	A250	35s rose red ('79)	1.25	.30
660	A250	45s dk brown	1.50	.55
661	A250	50s black	1.75	.65
662	A250	55s car rose ('79)	1.75	.65
663	A250	70s lilac rose ('79)	2.00	1.10
664	A250	75s blue	2.40	1.00
665	A250	80s salmon ('79)	2.40	1.00
667	A250	200s brt vio ('79)	6.00	3.25
		Nos. 656-667 (11)	21.00	9.55

For surcharges see Nos. 715, 731.

Peruvian Nativity — A252

1978, Dec. 28 **Litho.** **Perf. 13½x13**
672	A252	16s multicolored	.90	.50

Ministry of Education, Lima — A253

1979, Jan. 4
673	A253	16s multicolored	.70	.35

National Education Program.

Nos. RA40, B1-B5 and 509 Surcharged in Various Colors

a   b

c

1978, July-Aug.
674	PT11(a)	2s on 2c (O)	.25	.25
675	PT11(b)	3s on 2c (Bk)	.25	.25
676	PT11(a)	4s on 2c (G)	.25	.25
677	PT11(a)	5s on 2c (V)	.25	.25
678	PT11(b)	6s on 2c (DBl)	.25	.25
679	SP1	20s on 1.90s + 90c (G)	1.25	1.25
680	SP1	30s on 2.60s + 1.30s (Bl)	1.25	1.25
681	PT11(c)	35s on 2c (C)	1.60	1.60
682	PT11(c)	50s on 2c (LtBl)	5.50	5.50
683	SP1	55s on 3.60s + 1.80s (VBl)	1.75	1.75
684	SP1	65s on 4.60s + 2.30s (Go)	1.75	1.75
685	A196	80s on 5.60s (VBl)	1.40	1.40
686	SP1	85s on 20s + 10s (Bk)	2.75	2.75
		Nos. 674-686 (13)	18.50	18.50

Surcharge on Nos. 679-680, 683-684, 686 includes heavy bar over old denomination.

Battle of Iquique — A254   Heroes' Crypt — A255

Col. Francisco Bolognesi — A256

War of the Pacific: No. 688, Col. Jose J. Inclan. No. 689, Corvette Union running Arica blockade. No. 690, Battle of Angamos, Aguirre, Miguel Grau (1838-1879), Perre. No. 690A, Lt. Col. Pedro Ruiz Gallo. 85s, Marshal Andres A. Caceres. No. 692, Naval Battle of Angamos. No. 693, Battle of Tarapaca. 115s, Adm. Miguel Grau. No. 697, Col. Bolognesi's Reply, by Angeles de la Cruz. No. 698, Col. Alfonso Ugarte on horseback.

Perf. 13½x13, 13x13½
1979-80 **Litho.**
687	A254	14s multicolored	.45	.35
688	A256	25s multicolored	.75	.25
689	A254	25s multicolored	1.20	.35
690	A254	25s multicolored	1.20	.35
690A	A256	25s multi ('80)	.60	.25
691	A256	85s multicolored	1.20	.65
692	A254	100s multicolored	1.25	.65
693	A254	100s multicolored	1.40	.65
694	A256	115s multicolored	2.60	1.10
695	A256	200s multicolored	14.50	7.00
696	A256	200s multicolored	2.60	1.60
697	A254	200s multicolored	2.60	1.60
698	A254	200s multicolored	3.50	1.60
		Nos. 687-698 (13)	33.85	16.40

For surcharges see Nos. 713, 732.

Peruvian Red Cross, Cent. — A257

1979, May 4 **Perf. 13x13½**
699	A257	16s multicolored	.70	.40

Billiard Balls — A258

1979, June 4 **Perf. 13½x13**
700	A258	34s multicolored	.75	.25

For surcharge see No. 714.

Arms of Cuzco — A259

1979, June 24
701	A259	50s multicolored	1.40	.35

Inca Sun Festival, Cuzco.

Peru Colors, Tacna Monument — A260

1979, Aug. 28 **Litho.** **Perf. 13½x13**
702	A260	16s multicolored	.80	.35

Return of Tacna Province to Peru, 50th anniv.
For surcharge see No. 712.

Telecom 79 — A261

1979, Sept. 20
703	A261	15s multicolored	.60	.35

3rd World Telecommunications Exhibition, Geneva, Sept. 20-26.

Caduceus — A262

1979, Nov. 13
704	A262	25s multicolored	.80	.35

Stomatology Academy of Peru, 50th anniv.; 4th Intl. Congress.

World Map, "11," Fair Emblem — A263

1979, Nov. 24
705	A263	55s multicolored	.90	.45

11th Pacific Intl. Trade Fair, Lima, 11/14-25.

Gold Jewelry — A264

1979, Dec. 19 **Perf. 13½x13**
706	A264	85s multicolored	3.00	1.25

Larco Herrera Archaeological Museum.

Christmas A265

1979, Dec. 27 **Litho.** **Perf. 13½x13**
707	A265	25s multicolored	.80	.35

Queen Sofia and King Juan Carlos I, Visit to Peru — A266

1979, Feb. 7 **Litho.** **Perf. 13½x13**
708	A266	75s multicolored	1.10	.25

No. RA40 Surcharged in Black, Green or Blue

No. 709   No. 710

No. 711

1979, Oct. 8
709	PT11	7s on 2c brown	.65	.40
710	PT11	9s on 2c brown (G)	.65	.40
711	PT11	15s on 2c brown (B)	.65	.40
		Nos. 709-711 (3)	1.95	1.20

Nos. 702, 687, 700, 663 Surcharged
Perf. 13½x13, 13x13½
1980, Apr. 14 **Litho.**
712	A260	20s on 16s multi	.55	.40
713	A254	25s on 14s multi	.55	.40
714	A258	65s on 34s multi	1.20	.70
715	A250	80s on 70s lilac rose	1.75	.50
		Nos. 712-715,C501-C502 (6)	5.70	2.95

Liberty Holding Arms
of Peru — A267

Civic duties: 15s, Respect the Constitution.
20s, Honor country. 25s, Vote. 30s, Military
service. 35s, Pay taxes. 45s, Contribute to
national progress. 50s, Respect rights.

1980   **Litho.**

716	A267	15s greenish blue	.45	.30
717	A267	20s salmon pink	.45	.30
718	A267	25s ultra	.45	.30
719	A267	30s lilac rose	.45	.30
720	A267	35s black	.75	.35
721	A267	45s light blue green	.85	.50
722	A267	50s brown	1.50	.50
	Nos. 716-722 (7)		4.90	2.55

Chimu Cult
Cup — A268

1980, July 9   **Litho.**

723	A268	35s multicolored	1.75	.80

Map of Peru   Return to Civilian
and Liberty   Government
A269   A270

Perf. 13½x13, 13x13½

1980, Sept. 9   **Litho.**

724	A269	25s multicolored	.70	.40
725	A270	35s multicolored	1.00	.40

For surcharge see No. 730.

Machu
Picchu — A271

1980, Nov. 10   **Litho.**   *Perf. 13x13½*

726	A271	25s multicolored	2.25	2.00

World Tourism Conf., Manila, Sept. 27.

Tupac Amaru
Rebellion
Bicent. — A272

1980, Dec. 22   **Litho.**   *Perf. 13½x13*

727	A272	25s multicolored	.70	.35

Christmas
A273

1980, Dec. 31   **Litho.**   *Perf. 13*

728	A273	15s multicolored	.90	.55

150th Death Anniv. of
Simon Bolivar (in
1980) — A274

1981, Jan. 28   **Litho.**   *Perf. 13½x13*

729	A274	40s multicolored	.75	.25

Nos. 725, 667, 694 Surcharged

1981   **Litho.**   *Perf. 13x13½*

730	A270	25s on 35s multi	.40	.25
731	A250	85s on 200s brt violet	1.40	.80
732	A256	100s on 115s multi	2.00	.95
	Nos. 730-732 (3)		3.80	2.00

Return to
Constitutional
Government, July 28,
1980 — A275

1981, Mar. 26   **Litho.**   *Perf. 13½x13*

733	A275	25s multicolored	.85	.40

For surcharges see Nos. 736-737, 737C.

Tupac Amaru and Micaela Bastidas,
Bronze Sculptures, by Miguel Baca-
Rossi
A276

1981, May 18   **Litho.**   *Perf. 13x13½*

734	A276	60s multicolored	.95	.60

Rebellion of Tupac Amaru and Micaela Bastidas, bicentenary.

**Nos. 733, RA41 and Voluntary
Postal Tax Stamps of 1965
Surcharged in Black, Dull Brown or
Lake and**

 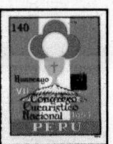

Cross,   Chalice,
Unleavened   Host
Bread,   A276b
Wheat
A276a

*Perf. 13½x13, Rouletted 11 (#735,
737B), 11½ (#737A)*

1981   **Litho., Photo. (#737A-737B)**

735	PT17	40s on 10c #RA41	.40	.25
736	A275	40s on 25s #733	1.25	.55
737	A275	130s on 25s #733 (DB)	1.25	.55
737A	A276a	140s on 50c brn, yel & red	.75	.40
737B	A276b	140s on 1s multi	.75	.40
737C	A275	140s on 25s #733 (L)	1.25	.55
	Nos. 735-737C (6)		5.65	2.70

Issued: #735, Apr. 12; #736, 737, 737C,
Apr. 6; #737A, Apr. 15; #737B, Apr. 28.

Carved Stone
Head, Pallasca
Tribe — A277

#739, 742, 749 Pottery vase, Inca, vert.
#740, Head, diff., vert. #743, 749A-749B,
Huaco idol (fish), Nazca. 100s, Pallasca, vert.
140s, Puma.

Perf. 13½x13, 13x13½

1981-82   **Litho.**

738	A277	30s dp rose lilac	.65	.60
739	A277	40s orange ('82)	.75	.25
740	A277	40s ultra	.75	.25
742	A277	80s brown ('82)	2.25	1.50
743	A277	80s red ('82)	2.25	1.40
745	A277	100s lilac rose	1.90	1.50
748	A277	140s lt blue grn	2.75	2.10
749	A277	180s green ('82)	5.00	3.75
749A	A277	240s grnsh blue ('82)	3.00	2.10
749B	A277	280s violet ('82)	4.00	2.75
	Nos. 738-749B (10)		23.30	16.20

For surcharges see #789, 798-799, 1026.

A278

1981, May 31   *Perf. 13½x13*

750	A278	130s multicolored	1.10	.90

Postal and Philatelic Museum, 50th anniv.

A279

1981, Oct. 7   **Litho.**   *Perf. 13½x13*

751	A279	30s purple & gray	.65	.40

1979 Constitution Assembly President
Victor Raul Haya de la Torre.

Inca Messenger, by
Guaman Poma (1526-
1613) — A280

1981   **Litho.**   *Perf. 12*

752	A280	30s lilac & blk	1.40	1.00
753	A280	40s vermilion & blk	1.10	2.00
754	A280	130s brt yel grn & blk	2.75	2.00
755	A280	140s brt blue & blk	2.75	2.50
756	A280	200s yel brn & blk	5.00	4.50
	Nos. 752-756 (5)		13.00	12.00

Christmas. Issue dates: 30s, 40s, 200s,
Dec. 21; others, Dec. 31.

Intl. Year of the
Disabled — A280a

1981   **Litho.**   *Perf. 13½x13*

756A	A280a	100s multicolored	1.50	.85

**Nos. 377, C130, C143, J56, O33,
RA36, RA39, RA40, RA42, RA43
Surcharged in Brown, Black,
Orange, Red, Green or Blue**

1982

757	PT11	10s on 2c (#RA40, Br)	1.00	.40
758	A155	10s on 10c (#377)	.75	.30
758A	AP60	40s on 1.25s (#C143)	.75	.30
758B	PT15	70s on 5c (#RA36, R)	1.00	.40
759	D7	80s on 10c (#J56)	.75	.30
760	O1	80s on 10c (#O33)	.75	.30
761	PT14	80s on 3c (#RA43, O)	.75	.30
762	PT17	100s on 10c (#RA42, R)	1.00	.40
763	AP57	100s on 2.20s (#C130, R)	1.25	.50
764	PT14	150s on 3c (#RA39, G)	1.50	.60
765	PT14	180s on 3c (#RA43, R)	1.50	.60
766	PT14	200s on 3c (#RA43, Bl)	1.75	.70
767	AP60	240s on 1.25s (#C143, R)	3.00	1.25
768	PT15	280s on 5c (#RA36)	2.75	1.10
	Nos. 757-768 (14)		18.50	7.45

Nos. 758A, 763, 767 airmail. Nos. 759 and
760 surcharged "Habilitado / Franq. Postal / 80
Soles".

Jorge Basadre   Julio C. Tello
(1903-1980),   (1882-1947),
Historian   Archaeologist
A281   A282

Perf. 13½x13, 13x13½

1982, Oct. 13   **Litho.**

769	A281	100s pale green & blk	.50	.30
770	A282	200s lt green & dk bl	1.20	.55

9th Women's World
Volleyball
Championship, Sept.
12-26 — A283

1982, Oct. 18   *Perf. 12*

771	A283	80s black & red	.60	.25

For surcharge see No. 791.

Rights of the
Disabled — A284

1982, Oct. 22

772	A284	200s blue & red	1.10	.30

Brena Campaign
Centenary
A285

70s, Andres Caceres medallion.

1982, Oct. 26   *Perf. 13x13½*

773	A285	70s multi	.60	.25

For surcharge see No. 790.

1982 World
Cup — A286

1982, Nov. 2   *Perf. 12*

774	A286	80s multicolored	1.00	.30

For surcharge see No. 800.

694 PERU

16th Intl. Congress of
Latin Notaries, Lima,
June — A287

1982, Nov. 6
775 A287 500s Emblem   1.50 .85

Handicrafts
Year — A288

1982, Nov. 24   *Perf. 13x13½*
776 A288 200s Clay bull figurine .85 .40

Christmas — A289

1982   *Perf. 13½x13*
777 A289 280s Holy Family   .95 .70
For surcharge see No. 797.

Pedro
Vilcapaza — A290

1982, Dec. 2   *Perf. 13½x13*
778 A290 240s black & lt brn   .90 .50
Death centenary of Indian leader against
Spanish during Andes Rebellion.
For surcharges see Nos. 792.

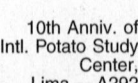

Jose Davila
Condemarin
(1799-1882),
Minister of Posts
(1849-76) — A291

1982, Dec. 10   *Perf. 13x13½*
779 A291 150s blue & blk   .65 .40

10th Anniv. of
Intl. Potato Study
Center,
Lima — A292

1982, Dec. 27   *Perf. 13x13½*
780 A292 240s multicolored   .90 .45
For surcharge see No. 793.

450th Anniv. of
City of San
Miguel de
Piura — A293

1982, Dec. 31   *Perf. 13x13½*
781 A293 280s Arms   1.10 .65
For surcharge see No. 795.

TB Bacillus
Centenary
A294

1983, Jan. 18   *Perf. 12*
782 A294 240s Microscope, slide .95 .70
For surcharge see No. 794.

St. Teresa of Jesus of
Avila (1515-1582), by
Jose Espinoza de los
Monteros,
1682 — A295

1983, Mar. 1
783 A295 100s multicolored   .60 .30

10th Anniv. of
State Security
Service — A296

1983, Mar. 8
784 A296 100s blue & orange   .60 .30

Horseman's
Ornamental Silver
Shoe, 19th
Cent. — A297

1983, Mar. 18
785 A297 250s multicolored   .90 .55

30th Anniv. of
Santiago
Declaration — A298

1983, Mar. 25
786 A298 280s Map   1.25 .60
For surcharge see No. 796.

25th Anniv. of
Lima-Bogota
Airmail
Service — A299

1983, Apr. 8
787 A299 150s Jet   .85 .50

75th Anniv. of Lima
and Callao State
Lotteries — A300

1983, Apr. 26
788 A300 100s multicolored   .60 .30

Nos. 739, 773, 771, 778, 780, 782,
781, 786, 777, 749, 774 Srchd. in
Black or Green

1983   Litho.
789 A277 100s on 40s orange 1.60 .35
790 A285 100s on 70s multi 1.60 .35
791 A283 100s on 80s blk &
        red   1.60 .35
792 A290 100s on 240s multi 1.60 .35
793 A292 100s on 240s multi 1.60 .35
794 A294 100s on 240s ol grn 1.60 .35
795 A293 150s on 280s multi
        (G)   1.90 .65
796 A298 150s on 280s multi 1.90 .65
797 A289 200s on 280s multi 2.90 .75

798 A277 300s on 180s green 4.50 1.25
799 A277 400s on 180s green 5.75 1.60
800 A286 500s on 80s multi 1.60 1.60
    Nos. 789-800 (12)   28.15 8.60

Military
Ships — A301

150s, Cruiser Almirante Grau, 1907. 350s,
Submarine Ferre, 1913.

1983, May 2   *Perf. 12*
801 A301 150s multicolored   1.00 .75
802 A301 350s multicolored   2.25 2.25

Simon Bolivar Birth
Bicentenary — A302

1983, Dec. 13 Litho. *Perf. 14*
803 A302 100s black & lt bl   1.00 .80

Christmas — A303

1983, Dec. 16
804 A303 100s Virgin and Child 1.40 1.10

25th Anniv. of Intl.
Pacific Fair — A304

1983
805 A304 350s multicolored   1.10 .75

World
Communications
Year (in
1983) — A305

1984, Jan. 27 Litho. *Perf. 14*
806 A305 700s multicolored   3.00 1.75

Col. Leoncio Prado
(1853-83) — A306

1984, Feb. 3 Litho. *Perf. 14*
807 A306 150s ol & ol brn   1.00 .60

Postal Building
A307

Pottery
A308

Shipbuilding and
Repair — A309

Arms of City of
Callao — A310

Peruvian
Flora — A311

Peruvian
Fauna — A312

50s, Ministry of Posts, Lima. 100s, Water
jar. 150s, Llama. 200s, Painted vase. 300s,
Mixed cargo ship. 400s, Arms of Cajamarca.
500s, Arms of Ayacucho. 700s, Canna edulis
ker. 1000s, Lagothrix flavicauda.

1984   Litho.   *Perf. 14*
808 A307 50s multi   .35 .35
809 A308 100s multi   .95 .35
810 A308 150s multi   .95 .35
811 A308 200s multi   .95 .35
812 A309 250s shown   .95 .35
813 A309 300s multi   1.40 .50
814 A310 350s shown   .75 .40
815 A310 400s multi   1.75 .50
816 A310 500s multi   2.25 .50
817 A311 700s multi   1.40 .60
818 A312 1000s multi   2.75 1.50
    Nos. 808-818 (11)   14.45 5.75
Issued: 50s, 8/29; 100s-200s, 5/9; 250s-
300s, 2/22; 350s, 4/23; 400s, 6/21; 500s, 6/22;
700s, 9/12; 1000s, 7/3.
See Nos. 844-853, 880-885.

A313

Designs: 50s, Hipolito Unanue (1758-1833).
200s, Ricardo Palma (1833-1919), Writer.

1984   *Perf. 14*
819 A313 50s dull green   .90 .50
820 A313 200s purple   .90 .50
Issue dates: 50s, Nov. 14; 200s, Mar. 20.
See No. 828.

1984 Summer
Olympics — A315

1984, Mar. 30
821 A315 500s Shooting   1.20 .50
822 A315 750s Hurdles   1.75 .85

Independence Declaration Act — A316

1984, July 18   Litho.   Perf. 14
823 A316 350s Signing document   1.00 .40

Admiral Grau — A317

Naval Battle A318

1984, Oct. 8   Litho.   Perf. 12½
824   Block of 4   6.00 6.00
  a. A317 600s Knight of the Seas, by Pablo Muniz   1.40 1.25
  b. A318 600s Battle of Angamos   1.40 1.25
  c. A317 600s Congressional seat   1.40 1.25
  d. A318 600s Battle of Iquique   1.40 1.25

Admiral Miguel Grau, 150th birth anniv.

Peruvian Naval Vessels — A319

250s, Destroyer Almirante Guise, 1934. 400s, Gunboat America, 1905.

1984, Dec.   Litho.   Perf. 14
825 A319 250s multicolored   1.50 .80
826 A319 400s multicolored   1.50 .80

Christmas A320

1984, Dec. 11   Litho.   Perf. 13x13½
827 A320 1000s multi   1.75 .75

Famous Peruvians Type of 1984

1984, Dec. 14   Litho.   Perf. 14
828 A313 100s brown lake   .75 .50

Victor Andres Belaunde (1883-1967), Pres. of UN General Assembly, 1959-60.

450th Anniv., Founding of Cuzco — A322

1984, Dec. 20   Litho.   Perf. 13½x13
829 A322 1000s Street scene   1.25 .75

15th Pacific Intl. Fair, Lima — A323

1984, Dec. 28   Litho.   Perf. 13½x13
830 A323 1000s Llama   1.25 .75

450th Anniv., Lima — A324

The Foundation of Lima, by Francisco Gamarra

1985, Jan. 17   Litho.   Perf. 13½x13
831 A324 1500s multicolored   3.25 2.10

Visit of Pope John Paul II — A325

1985, Jan. 31   Litho.   Perf. 13½x13
832 A325 2000s Portrait   2.75 2.25

Microwave Tower — A326

1985, Feb. 28   Litho.   Perf. 13½x13
833 A326 1100s multi   1.50 .45

ENTEL Peru, Natl. Telecommunications Org., 15th anniv.

Jose Carlos Mariategui (1894-1924), Author — A327

Designs: 500s, Francisco Garcia Calderon (1832-1905), president. No. 838, Oscar Miro Quesada (1884-1981), jurist. No. 839, Cesar Vallejo (1892-1938), author. No. 840, Jose Santos Chocano (1875-1934), poet.

1985-86   Photo.   Perf. 13½x13
836 A327 500s lt olive grn   .85 .50
837 A327 800s dull red   .85 .50
838 A327 800s dk olive grn   .85 .50
839 A327 800s Prus blue ('86)   .85 .50
840 A327 800s dk red brn ('86)   .85 .50
      Nos. 836-840 (5)   4.25 2.50

See Nos. 901-905.

American Air Forces Cooperation System, 25th Anniv. — A328

1985, Apr. 16
842 A328 400s Member flags, emblem   .85 .50

Jose A. Quinones Gonzales (1914-1941), Air Force Captain — A329

1985, Apr. 22   Perf. 13x13½
843 A329 1000s Portrait, bomber   1.40 .45

Types of 1984

Design: 200s, Entrance arch and arcade, Central PO admin. building, vert. No. 845, Spotted Robles Moqo bisque vase, Pacheco, Ica. No. 846, Huaura bisque cat. No. 847, Robles Moqo bisque llama head. No. 848, Huancavelica city arms. No. 849, Huanuco city arms. No. 850, Puno city arms. No. 851, Llama wool industry. No. 852, Hymenocallis amancaes. No. 853, Penguins, Antarctic landscape.

1985-86   Litho.   Perf. 13½x13
844 A307 200s slate blue   .60 .60
845 A308 500s bister brn   .35 .30
846 A308 500s dull yellow brn   .35 .30
847 A308 500s black brn   .35 .30
848 A310 700s brt org yel   .80 .70
849 A310 700s brt bl ('86)   .80 .70
850 A310 900s brown ('86)   1.10 .70
851 A309 1100s multicolored   .80 .50
852 A311 1100s multicolored   .80 .50
853 A312 1500s multicolored   1.10 .60
      Nos. 844-853 (10)   7.05 5.20

Natl. Aerospace Institute Emblem, Globe — A330

1985, May 24   Perf. 13x13½
858 A330 900s ultra   .95 .60

14th Inter-American Air Defense Day.

Founding of Constitution City — A333

1985, July   Litho.   Perf. 13½x13
859 A333 300s Map, flag, crucifix   .95 .60

Natl. Radio Society, 55th Anniv. — A334

1985, July 24   Perf. 13x13½
860 A334 1300s bl & brt org   1.40 .60

San Francisco Convent Church — A335

1985, Oct. 12   Perf. 13½x13
861 A335 1300s multicolored   1.40 .60

Doctrina Christiana Frontispiece, 1585, Lima — A336

1985, Oct. 23
862 A336 300s pale buff & blk   1.50 .70

1st printed book in South America, 400th anniv.

Intl. Civil Aviation Org., 40th Anniv. — A337

1100s, 1920 Curtis Jenny.

1985, Oct. 31   Perf. 13x13½
863 A337 1100s multicolored   1.40 .80

Christmas — A338

2.50i, Virgin and child, 17th cent.

1985, Dec. 30   Litho.   Perf. 13½x13
864 A338 2.50i multi   1.50 .50

Postman, Child — A338a

1985, Dec. 30   Litho.   Perf. 13½x13
864A A338a 2.50i multi   1.00 .40

Christmas charity for children's and postal workers' funds.

Founding of Trujillo, 450th Anniv. — A339

1986, Mar. 5   Litho.   Perf. 13½x13
865 A339 3i City arms   1.25 .85

Restoration of Chan Chan Ruins, Trujillo Province — A340

1986, Apr. 5   Litho.   Perf. 13x13½
866 A340 50c Bas-relief   1.40 .50

Saint Rose of Lima, Birth Quadricent. — A341

1986, Apr. 30   Litho.   Perf. 13½x13
867 A341 7i multicolored   2.90 1.25

16th Intl. Pacific Fair — A342

1i, Natl. products symbols.

1986, May 20
868 A342 1i multicolored   .95 .50

Intl. Youth Year — A343

1986, May 23   Perf. 13½x13
869 A343 3.50i multicolored   1.10 .50

A344

1986, June 27 Litho. Perf. 13½x13
870 A344 50c brown   .75   .45
Pedro Vilcapaza (1740-81), independence hero.

UN, 40th
Anniv. — A345

1986, Aug. 8 Litho. Perf. 13x13½
871 A345 3.50i multi   1.40   .75

A346

1986, Aug. 11   Perf. 13½x13
872 A346 50c grysh brown   .75   .40
Fernando and Justo Albujar Fayaque, Manuel Guarniz Lopez, natl. heroes.

Peruvian
Navy — A347

1986, Aug. 19   Perf. 13x13½
873 A347 1.50i R-1, 1926   .90   .65
874 A347 2.50i Abtao, 1954   1.75 1.00

Flora and Fauna Type of 1984
No. 880, Tropaeolum majus. No. 881, Datura candida. No. 884, Canis ludus. No. 885, Penelope albipennis.

1986   Litho.   Perf. 13½x13
880 A311 80c multicolored   .60   .45
881 A311 80c multicolored   .60   .45
884 A312 2i multicolored   1.40 1.00
885 A312 2i multicolored   1.60 1.10
    Nos. 880-885 (4)   4.20 3.00

Canchis Province Folk
Costumes — A348

1986, Aug. 26 Litho. Perf. 13½x13
890 A348 3i multicolored   1.50   .75

Tourism
Day — A349

1986, Aug. 29   Perf. 13x13½
891 A349 4i Sacsayhuaman   1.90 1.00

1986, Oct. 12 Litho. Perf. 13½x13
891A A349 4i Intihuatana, Cuzco   2.25 1.75

Interamerican
Development
Bank, 25th
Anniv. — A350

1986, Sept. 4
892 A350 1i multicolored   .70   .45

Beatification of
Sr. Ana de Los
Angeles — A351

6i, Sr. Ana, Pope John Paul II.

1986, Sept. 15
893 A351 6i multicolored   3.25 2.00

Jorge Chavez (1887-
1910), Aviator, and
Bleriot XI 1M — A352

1986, Sept. 23   Perf. 13½x13
894 A352 5i multicolored   1.75 1.00
Chavez's flight over the Alps, 75th anniv.

VAN '86 — A353

1986, Sept. 26
895 A353 50c light blue   .70   .45
Ministry of Health vaccination campaign, Sept. 27-28, Oct. 25-26, Nov. 22-23.

Natl. Journalism
Day — A354

1986, Oct. 1
896 A354 1.50i multi   .75   .50

Peruvian
Navy — A355

No. 897, Brigantine Gamarra, 1848. No. 898, Monitor Manco Capac, 1880.

1986, Oct. 7 Litho. Perf. 13x13½
897 A355 1i multicolored   1.00   .70
898 A355 1i multicolored   1.00   .70

Institute of Higher
Military Studies,
35th
Anniv. — A356

1986, Oct. 31 Litho. Perf. 13x13½
899 A356 1i multicolored   .80   .35

Boy, Girl — A357

1986, Nov. 3   Perf. 13½x13
900 A357 2.50i red, brn & blk   1.00   .50
Christmas charity for children and postal workers' funds.

Famous Peruvians Type of 1985
No. 901, Daniel A .Carrión. No. 902, José Gálvez Barrenechea. No. 904, José de la Riva Agüero. No. 905, Raúl Porras Barrenechea.

1986-87
901 A327 50c blackish brown   .65   .35
902 A327 50c red brown   .65   .35
904 A327 80c brown   .85   .45
905 A327 80c orange brown   .65   .35
    Nos. 901-905 (4)   2.80 1.50
Issued: No. 901, 5/16/86; No. 902, 11/19/86; No. 904, 10/22/87; No. 905, 11/9/87.

Christmas — A358

1986, Dec. 3
908 A358 5i St. Joseph and Child 2.25 1.40

SENATI, 25th
Anniv. — A359

1986, Dec. 19   Perf. 13½x13
909 A359 4i multicolored   1.40   .75

Shipibo Tribal
Costumes — A360

1987, Apr. 24 Litho. Perf. 13½x13
910 A360 3i multicolored   1.25   .75

World Food
Day — A361

1987, May 26
911 A361 50c multicolored   1.00   .35

Preservation of
the Nazca
Lines — A362

Design: Nazca Lines and Dr. Maria Reiche (b. 1903), archaeologist.

1987, June 13 Litho. Perf. 13½x13
912 A362 8i multicolored   3.25 2.00

A363

1987, July 15 Litho. Perf. 13½x13
913 A363 50c violet   .80   .35
Mariano Santos (1850-1900), "The Hero of Tarapaca," 1879, Chilean war. Dated 1986.

A364

1987, July 19   Perf. 13x13½
914 A364 3i multicolored   1.40   .60
Natl. Horse Club, 50th anniv. Dated 1986.

A365

1987, Aug 13   Perf. 13½x13
915 A365 2i multicolored   1.00   .65
Gen. Felipe Santiago Salaverry (1806-1836), revolution leader. Dated 1986.

Colca's
Canyon — A366

1987, Sept. 8 Litho. Perf. 13½x13
916 A366 6i multicolored   1.25   .70
10th Natl. Philatelic Exposition, Arequipa. Dated 1986.

AMIFIL '87 — A367

1987, Sept. 10
917 A367 1i Nos. 1-2   .70   .45
Dated 1986.

Jose Maria Arguedas
(b. 1911),
Anthropologist,
Author — A368

1987, Sept. 19
918 A368 50c brown   .70   .45

Arequipa
Chamber of
Commerce &
Industry — A369

1987, Sept. 23   Perf. 13x13½
919 A369 2i multicolored   1.00   .30

Vaccinate Every Child Campaign A370

1987, Sept. 30 Litho. Perf. 13x13½
920 A370 50c brown purple   .70 .45

Argentina, Winner of the 1986 World Cup Soccer Championships A371

1987, Nov. 18
921 A371 4i multicolored   1.10 .90

Restoration of Chan Chan Ruins, Trujillo Province — A372

Chimu culture (11th-15th cent.) bas-relief.

1987, Nov. 27
922 A372 50c multicolored   1.40 1.10
See No. 936.

Halley's Comet — A373

4i, Comet, Giotto satellite.

1987, Dec. 7
923 A373 4i multicolored   1.75 1.10

Jorge Chavez Dartnell (1887-1910), Aviator — A374

1987, Dec. 15   Perf. 13½x13
924 A374 2i yel bis, claret brn & gold   .85 .50

Founding of Lima, 450th Anniv. (in 1985) — A375

1987, Dec. 18 Litho. Perf. 13½x13
925 A375 2.50i Osambela Palace .85 .50
Dated 1985.

Discovery of the Ruins at Machu Picchu, 75th Anniv. (in 1986) — A376

1987, Dec.   Perf. 13x13½
926 A376 9i multicolored   3.50 2.00
Dated 1986.

St. Francis's Church, Cajamarca A377

1988, Jan. 23 Litho. Perf. 13x13½
927 A377 2i multicolored   .80 .25
Cultural Heritage. Dated 1986.

Participation of Peruvian Athletes in the Olympics, 50th Anniv. — A378

Design: Athletes on parade, poster publicizing the 1936 Berlin Games.

1988, Mar. 1 Litho. Perf. 13½x13
928 A378 1.50i multicolored   1.00 .35
Dated 1986.

Ministry of Education, 150th Anniv. — A379

1988, Mar. 10   Perf. 13x13½
929 A379 1i multicolored   .95 .70

Coronation of the Virgin of the Evangelization by Pope John Paul II — A380

1988, Mar. 14 Litho. Perf. 13x13½
930 A380 10i multicolored   1.50 .60
Dated 1986.

Rotary Intl. Involvement in Anti-Polio Campaign A381

1988, Mar. 16
931 A381 2i org, gold & dark blue   .80 .55

Postman, Cathedral — A382

1988, Apr. 29 Litho. Perf. 13½x13
932 A382 9i brt blue   1.25 .75
Christmas charity for children and postal workers' funds.

Meeting of 8 Latin-American Presidents, Acapulco, 1st Anniv. — A383

1988, May 4   Perf. 13x13½
933 A383 9i multicolored   1.50 .75

St. John Bosco (1815-1888), Educator — A384

1988, June 1   Perf. 13½x13
934 A384 5i multicolored   .70 .45

1st Peruvian Scientific Expedition to the Antarctic — A385

7i, Ship Humboldt, globe.

1988, June 2   Perf. 13x13½
935 A385 7i multicolored   .95 .70

Restoration of Chan-Chan Ruins, Trujillo Province — A386

1988, June 7
936 A386 4i Bas-relief   .80 .50

Cesar Vallejo (1892-1938), Poet — A387

1988, June 15   Perf. 13½x13
937 A387 25i buff, blk & brn   1.50 1.25

Journalists' Fund — A388

1988, July 12 Litho. Perf. 13½x13
938 A388 4i buff & deep ultra   .70 .45

Type A44 — A389

1988, Sept. 1 Litho. Perf. 13½x13
939 A389 20i blk, lt pink & ultra .75 .50
EXFILIMA '88, discovery of America 500th anniv.

17th Intl. Pacific Fair — A390

1988, Sept. 6   Perf. 13½x13
940 A390 4i multicolored   1.25 1.00

Painting by Jose Sabogal (1888-1956) A391

1988, Sept. 7
941 A391 12i multicolored   .70 .45

Peru Kennel Club Emblem, Dogs — A392

1988, Sept. 9   Perf. 13½x13
942 A392 20i multicolored   1.90 1.25
CANINE '88 Intl. Dog Show, Lima.

Alfonso de Silva (1902-1934), Composer, and Score to Esplendido de Flores — A393

1988, Sept. 27 Litho. Perf. 13x13½
943 A393 20i multicolored   .95 .45

2nd State Visit of Pope John Paul II — A394

1988, Oct. 10   Perf. 13½x13
944 A394 50i multicolored   1.00 .75

1988 Summer Olympics, Seoul — A395

1988, Nov. 10 Litho. Perf. 13½x13
945 A395 25i Women's volleyball 1.25 .45

Women's Volleyball Championships (1982) — A396

Surcharged in Red

1988, Nov. 16   Perf. 12
946 A396 95i on 300s multi   1.60 1.40
No. 946 not issued without overprint. Christmas charity for children's and postal workers' funds.

Chavin Culture Ceramic Vase — A397

Surcharged in Henna or Black

1988   Litho.   Perf. 12
947 A397 40i on 100s red brn   1.75 1.40
948 A397 80i on 10s blk   3.50 2.25
Nos. 947-948 not issued without surcharge. Issue dates: 40i, Dec. 15. 80i, Dec. 22.

Rain Forest Border Highway — A398

Surcharged in Black

1989, Jan. 27   Litho.   *Perf. 12*
949 A398 70i on 80s multi   .85 .60

Not issued without surcharge.

Codex of the Indian
Kings, 1681 — A399

Surcharged in Olive Brown

1989, Feb. 10
950 A399 230i on 300s multi   1.50 1.25

Not issued without surcharge.

Credit Bank of
Peru,
Cent. — A400

500i, Huari Culture weaving.

1989, Apr. 9   Litho.   *Perf. 13x13½*
951 A400 500i multicolored   1.75 1.50

Postal Services
A401

1989, Apr. 20   *Perf. 13*
952 A401 50i SESPO, vert.   .65 .35
953 A401 100i CAN   .85 .40

El Comercio, 150th
Anniv. — A402

1989, May 15
954 A402 600i multicolored   1.25 .50

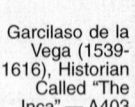

Garcilaso de la
Vega (1539-
1616), Historian
Called "The
Inca" — A403

1989, July 11   Litho.   *Perf. 12½*
955 A403 300i multicolored   .85 .35

Express Mail
Service — A404

1989, July 12
956 A404 100i dark red, org &
dark blue   .85 .35

Federation
Emblem and
Roca — A405

1989, Aug. 29   Litho.   *Perf. 13*
957 A405 100i multicolored   .70 .45

Luis Loli Roca (1925-1988), founder of the
Federation of Peruvian Newspaper Publishers.

Restoration of
Chan Chan
Ruins, Trujillo
Province — A406

Chimu culture (11th-15th cent.) bas-relief.

1989, Sept. 17   *Perf. 12½*
958 A406 400i multicolored   2.75 2.50

Geographical Society
of Lima,
Cent. — A407

1989, Sept. 18   *Perf. 13*
959 A407 600i Early map of So.
America   2.75 2.50

Founders of
Independence
Soc. — A408

1989, Sept. 28   Litho.   *Perf. 12½*
960 A408 300i multicolored   .85 .60

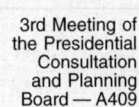

3rd Meeting of
the Presidential
Consultation
and Planning
Board — A409

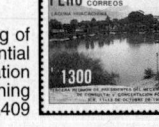

1989, Oct. 12   *Perf. 13*
961 A409 1300i Huacachina Lake 2.75 2.50

For surcharge see No. 1027.

Children Mailing
Letters — A410

1989, Nov. 29   Litho.   *Perf. 12½*
962 A410 1200i multicolored   .90 .65

Christmas charity for children's and postal
workers' funds.

Cacti — A411

No. 963, Loxanthocereus acanthurus. No.
964, Corryocactus huincoensis. No. 965,
Haageocereus clavispinus. No. 966,
Trichocereus pervianus. No. 967, Matucana
cereoides.

1989, Dec. 21   Litho.   *Perf. 13*
963 A411 500i multicolored   1.25 .45
964 A411 500i multicolored   1.25 .45
965 A411 500i multicolored   1.25 .45
966 A411 500i multicolored   1.25 .45
967 A411 500i multicolored   1.25 .45
Nos. 963-967 (5)   6.25 2.25

Nos. 965-967 vert. For surcharges see Nos.
1028-1031

America
Issue — A412

UPAE emblem and pre-Columbian medicine
jars.

1989, Dec. 28   *Perf. 12½*
968 A412 5000i shown   8.25 5.00
969 A412 5000i multi, diff.   8.25 5.00

Belen Church,
Cajamarca
A413

1990, Feb. 1   Litho.   *Perf. 12½*
970 A413 600i multicolored   1.85 .35

Historic patrimony of Cajamarca and culture
of the Americas.

Huascaran
Natl.
Park — A414

No. 971, Llanganuco Lagoons. No. 972,
Mountain climber, Andes, vert. No. 973,
Alpamayo mountain. No. 974, Puya raimondi,
vert. No. 975, Condor and Quenual. No. 976,
El Huascaran.

1990, Feb. 4   *Perf. 13*
971 A414 900i multicolored   .80 .70
972 A414 900i multicolored   .80 .70
973 A414 1000i multicolored   .90 .70
974 A414 1000i multicolored   .90 .70
975 A414 1100i multicolored   1.10 .70
976 A414 1100i multicolored   1.10 .70
Nos. 971-976 (6)   5.60 4.20

Pope and Icon of the
Virgin — A415

1990, Feb. 6   *Perf. 12½*
977 A415 1250i multicolored   1.50 1.25

Visit of Pope John Paul II. For surcharge see
No. 1039.

Butterflies
A416

No. 978, Amydon. No. 979, Agrias beata,
female. No. 980, Sardanapalus, male. No.
981, Sardanapalus, female. No. 982, Agrias
beata, male.

1990, Feb. 11   *Perf. 13*
978 A416 1000i multi   3.00 .75
979 A416 1000i multi   3.00 .75
980 A416 1000i multi   3.00 .75
981 A416 1000i multi   3.00 .75
982 A416 1000i multi   3.00 .75
Nos. 978-982 (5)   15.00 3.75

For surcharges see Nos. 1033-1037.

A417

Victor Raul Haya de La Torre and Seat of
Government.

1990, Feb. 24   *Perf. 12½*
983 A417 2100i multicolored   1.10 .90

Return to constitutional government, 10th
anniv.

A418

1990, May 24   Litho.   *Perf. 12½*
984 A418 300i multicolored   .85 .60

Peruvian Philatelic Assoc., 40th anniv.
Dated 1989. For surcharge see No. 1038.

Prenfil
'88 — A419

1990, May 29
985 A419 300i multicolored   .60 .40

World Exposition of Stamp & Literature
Printers, Buenos Aires. Dated 1989. For
surcharge see No. 1032.

French Revolution,
Bicentennial — A420

#986, Liberty. #987, Storming the Bastille.
#988, Lafayette celebrating the Republic.
#989, Rousseau & symbols of the Revolution.

1990, June 5
986 A420 2000i multicolored   1.60 .75
987 A420 2000i multicolored   1.60 .75
988 A420 2000i multicolored   1.60 .75
989 A420 2000i shown   1.60 .75
   a.   Strip of 4, #986-989 + label   5.50 5.50

Dated 1989.

Arequipa, 450th
Anniv. — A421

1990, Aug. 15   Litho.   *Perf. 13*
990 A421 50,000i multi   1.10 .90

Lighthouse
A422

Design: 230,000i, Hospital ship Morona.

Surcharged in Black

1990, Sept. 19   *Perf. 12½*
991 A422 110,000i on 200i blue   1.60 1.50
992 A422 230,000i on 400i blue   3.50 3.00

Not issued without surcharge. No. 991
exists with albino surcharge.

A423

110,000i, Torch bearer. 280,000i, Shooting.
290,000i, Running, horiz. 300,000i, Soccer.
560,000i, Swimming, horiz. 580,000i, Equestrian. 600,000i, Sailing. 620,000i, Tennis.

1990-91 Litho. Perf. 13
993 A423 110,000i multi 1.25 .50
994 A423 280,000i multi 2.50 1.10
995 A423 290,000i multi 2.50 1.10
996 A423 300,000i multi 2.75 1.25
997 A423 560,000i multi 3.75 1.75
998 A423 580,000i multi 4.25 2.00
999 A423 600,000i multi 4.50 2.00
1000 A423 620,000i multi 4.50 2.00
Nos. 993-1000 (8) 26.00 11.70

4th South American Games, Lima. Issue dates: #993-996, Oct. 19. #997-1000, Feb. 5, 1991.

A424

1990, Nov. 22 Litho. Die Cut
Self-Adhesive
1001 A424 250,000i No. 1 2.75 1.25
1002 A424 350,000i No. 2 3.75 1.75

Pacific Steam Navigation Co., 150th anniv.

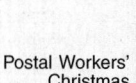

Postal Workers' Christmas Fund — A425

1990, Dec. 7 Litho. Perf. 12½
1003 A425 310,000i multi 3.25 3.00

A426

Design: Maria Jesus Castaneda de Pardo, First Woman President of Peruvian Red Cross.

1991, May 15 Litho. Perf. 12½
1004 A426 .15im on 2500i red & blk 1.60 1.40

Dated 1990. Not issued without surcharge.

2nd Peruvian Scientific Expedition to Antarctica A427

.40im, Penguins, man. .45im, Peruvian research station, skua. .50im, Whale, map, research station.

1991, June 20
1005 A427 .40im on 50,000i 3.50 1.60
1006 A427 .45im on 80,000i 3.75 1.75
1007 A427 .50im on 100,000i 4.75 2.10
Nos. 1005-1007 (3) 12.00 5.45

Not issued without surcharge.

A428

St. Anthony Natl. Univ., Cuzco, 300th Anniv.: 10c, Siphoonandra ellipitica. 20c, Don Manuel de Mollinedo y Angulo, founder. 1s, University coat of arms.

1991, Sept. 26 Litho. Perf. 13½x13
1008 A428 10c multicolored .45 .35
1009 A428 20c multicolored .90 .75
1010 A428 1s multicolored 4.25 4.00
Nos. 1008-1010 (3) 5.60 5.10

A429

Paintings: No. 1011, Madonna and child. No. 1012, Madonna with lambs and angels.

1991, Dec. 3 Litho. Perf. 13½x13
1011 A429 70c multicolored 3.75 3.50
1012 A429 70c multicolored 3.75 3.50

Postal Workers' Christmas fund.

America Issue — A430

No. 1013, Mangrove swamp. No. 1014, Gera waterfall, vert.

1991, Dec. 23 Perf. 13
1013 A430 .50im multi 3.25 3.00
1014 A430 .50im multi 3.25 3.00

Dated 1990.

Sir Rowland Hill and Penny Black — A431

1992, Jan. 15 Litho. Perf. 13
1015 A431 .40im gray, blk & bl 2.00 1.40

Penny Black, 150th anniv. (in 1990).

A432

1992, Jan. 28
1016 A432 .30im multicolored 1.35 .85

Our Lady of Guadalupe College, 150th anniv. (in 1990)

Entre Nous Society, 80th Anniv. — A433

1992, Jan. 30 Perf. 13½x13
1017 A433 10c multicolored .60 .35

Peru-Bolivia Port Access Agreement A434

1992, Feb. 25 Litho. Perf. 12½
1018 A434 20c multicolored 1.05 .75

Restoration of Chan-Chan Ruins — A435

1992, Mar. 17
1019 A435 .15im multicolored 1.50 1.25

Dated 1990.

Antonio Raimondi, Naturalist and Publisher, Death Cent. — A436

1992, Mar. 31
1020 A436 .30im multicolored 1.60 1.40

Dated 1990.

Newspaper "Diario de Lima", Bicent. (in 1990) — A437

1992, May 22 Litho. Perf. 13
1021 A437 .35im pale yel & black 1.40 1.10

Dated 1990.

Mariano Melgar (1790-1815), Poet — A438

1992, Aug. 5 Litho. Perf. 12½x13
1022 A438 60c multicolored 2.50 2.25

8 Reales, 1568, First Peruvian Coinage — A439

1992, Aug. 7 Perf. 13x12½
1023 A439 70c multicolored 2.25 2.00

Catholic Univeristy of Peru, 75th Anniv. A440

1992, Aug. 18 Perf. 12½
1024 A440 90c black & tan 3.00 2.75

Pan-American Health Organization, 90th Anniv. — A441

1992, Dec. 2 Litho. Die Cut
Self-Adhesive
1025 A441 3s multicolored 7.25 7.00

Nos. 749, 961 Surcharged

Perf. 13½x13, 13
1992, Nov. 18 Litho.
1026 A277 50c on 180s #749 1.50 1.00
1027 A409 1s on 1300i #961 3.00 2.25

Nos. 963, 965-967, 977-982, & 984-985 Surcharged

Perfs. as Before
1992, Dec. 24 Litho.
1028 A411 40c on 500i #963 10.00 10.00
1029 A411 40c on 500i #965 10.00 10.00
1030 A411 40c on 500i #966 10.00 10.00
1031 A411 40c on 500i #967 10.00 10.00
1032 A419 50c on 300i #985 10.00 10.00
1033 A416 50c on 1000i #978 10.00 10.00
1034 A416 50c on 1000i #979 10.00 10.00
1035 A416 50c on 1000i #980 10.00 10.00
1036 A416 50c on 1000i #981 13.50 10.00
1037 A416 50c on 1000i #982 13.50 10.00
1038 A418 1s on 300i #984 20.00 10.00
1039 A415 1s on 1250i #977 20.00 10.00
Nos. 1028-1039 (12) 147.00 120.00

Virgin with a Spindle, by Urbina — A442

1993, Feb. 10 Litho. Die Cut
Self-Adhesive
1040 A442 80c multicolored 2.75 2.50

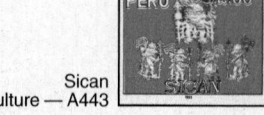

Sican Culture — A443

Various artifacts.

1993, Feb. 10 Self-Adhesive
1041 A443 2s multicolored 4.75 4.50
1042 A443 5s multi, vert. 10.75 10.50

Evangelization in Peru, 500th Anniv. — A444

1993, Feb. 12 Self-Adhesive
1043 A444 1s multicolored 3.25 2.75

Fruit Sellers, by Angel Chavez A445

Dancers, by Monica Rojas A446

1993, Feb. 12   **Self-Adhesive**
1044 A445 1.50s multicolored   4.25 2.00
1045 A446 1.50s multicolored   4.25 2.00

Statue of Madonna and Child — A447

1993, Feb. 24   **Litho.**   **Die Cut**
          Self-Adhesive
1046 A447 70c multicolored   2.10 1.90
Salesian Brothers in Peru, cent. (in 1991).

America Issue A448

UPAEP: No. 1047a, 90c, Francisco Pizarro, sailing ship. b, 1s, Sailing ship, map of northwest coast of South America.

1993, Mar. 19   **Perf. 12½**
1047 A448   Pair, #a.-b.   5.50 4.50

Sipan Gold Head A449

1993, Apr. 1
1048 A449 50c multicolored   10.50 10.00

Beatification of Josemaria Escriva, 1st Anniv. — A450

1993, July 7   **Litho.**   **Die Cut**
          Self-Adhesive
1049 A450 30c multicolored   1.25 1.00

Peru-Japan Treaty of Peace and Trade, 120th Anniv. — A451

Designs: 1.50s, Flowers. 1.70s, Peruvian, Japanese children, mountains.

1993, Aug. 21   **Litho.**   **Perf. 11**
1050 A451 1.50s multicolored   3.50 2.00
1051 A451 1.70s multicolored   3.75 3.25

Sea Lions — A452

1993, Sept. 20   **Litho.**   **Perf. 11**
1052 A452 90c shown   2.25 1.50
1053 A452 1s Parrot, vert.   2.75 2.00

Amifil '93 (#1052). Brasiliana '93 (#1053).

A453

1993, Nov. 9   **Litho.**   **Die Cut**
          Self-Adhesive
1054 A453 50c olive brown   2.25 2.00
Honorio Delgado, Physician and Author, Birth Cent. (in 1992).

A454

1993, Nov. 12   **Self-Adhesive**
1055 A454 80c orange brown   3.00 2.50
Rosalia De LaValle De Morales Macedo, Social Reformer, Birth Cent.

A455

Sculptures depicting Peruvian ethnic groups.

1993, Nov. 22   **Self-Adhesive**
1056 A455   2s Quechua   10.00 10.00
1057 A455 3.50s Orejon   12.50 10.00

Intl. Pacific Fair, Lima — A456

1993, Nov. 25   **Litho.**   **Perf. 11**
1058 A456 1.50s multicolored   5.75 5.50

Christmas — A457

Design: 1s, Madonna of Loreto.

1993, Nov. 30   **Perf. 11**
1059 A457 1s multicolored   3.25 3.00

Cultural Artifacts — A458

2.50s, Sican artifacts. 4s, Sican mask. 10s, Chancay ceramic statue, vert. 20s, Chancay textile.

          Self-Adhesive
1993, Nov. 30   **Die Cut**
1060 A458 2.50s mul-
          ticolored   12.50 9.00
1061 A458   4s mul-
          ticolored   15.00 12.50
1062 A458   10s mul-
          ticolored   35.00 20.00
1063 A458   20s mul-
          ticolored   75.00 72.50
    Nos. 1060-1063 (4)   137.50 114.00
See Nos. 1079-1082.

Prevention of AIDS — A459

1993, Dec. 1   **Litho.**   **Perf. 11**
1064 A459 1.50s multicolored   4.50 4.25

A460

1994, Mar. 4   **Litho.**   **Die Cut**
          Self-Adhesive
1065 A460 1s multicolored   2.75 2.50
Natl. Council on Science and Technology (Concytec), 25th Anniv. Dated 1993.

A461

20c, 30c, 40c, 50c, Bridge of Huaman Poma de Ayala.

1994   **Self-Adhesive**
1066 A461 20c blue   .85 .75
1067 A461 40c orange   1.90 1.50
1068 A461 50c purple   2.50 2.00
    Nos. 1066-1068 (3)   5.25 4.25
          Litho.
        Perf. 12x11
1073 A461 30c brown   1.25 1.10
1074 A461 40c black   2.00 1.75
1075 A461 50c vermilion   2.25 2.00
    Nos. 1073-1075 (3)   5.50 4.85
Issued: Nos. 1066-1068, 3/11/94; Nos. 1073-1075, 5/13/94.

Cultural Artifacts Type of 1993

No. 1079, Engraved silver container, vert. No. 1080, Engraved medallion. No. 1081, Carved bull, Pucara. No. 1082, Plate with fish designs.

1994, Mar. 25   **Self-Adhesive**
1079 A458 1.50s multicolored   4.00 4.00
1080 A458 1.50s multicolored   4.00 4.00
1081 A458   3s multicolored   7.50 7.00
1082 A458   3s multicolored   7.50 7.00
    Nos. 1079-1082 (4)   23.00 22.00
Dated 1993.

Sipan Artifacts — A464

3s, Peanut-shaped beads. 5s, Mask, vert.

1994, May 19   **Litho.**   **Perf. 11**
1083 A464 3s multi   9.00 7.50
1084 A464 5s multi   15.00 10.00

El Brujo Archaelogical Site, Trujillo — A465

1994, Nov. 3   **Litho.**   **Perf. 14**
1085 A465 70c multicolored   2.00 1.75

Christmas A466

Ceramic figures: 1.80s, Christ child. 2s, Nativity scene. Dated 1994.

1995, Mar. 17   **Litho.**   **Perf. 13x13½**
1086 A466 1.80s multicolored   4.25 3.50
1087 A466   2s multicolored   4.50 4.00

1994 World Cup Soccer Championships, U.S. — A467

1995, Mar. 20   **Perf. 13½x13**
1088 A467 60c shown   1.50 1.00
1089 A467 4.80s Mascot, flags   10.00 6.50
Dated 1994.

Ministry of Transportation, 25th Anniv. — A468

1995, Mar. 22   **Perf. 13x13½**
1090 A468 20c multicolored   .75 .35
Dated 1994.

Cultural Artifacts — A469

Mochican art: 40c, Pitcher with figures beneath blanket. 80c, Jeweled medallion. 90c, Figure holding severed head.

1995, Mar. 27   **Perf. 14**
1091 A469 40c multicolored   1.25 1.10
1092 A469 80c multicolored   2.25 1.75
1093 A469 90c multicolored   2.50 2.25
    Nos. 1091-1093 (3)   6.00 5.10
Dated 1994.

Juan Parra del Riego, Birth Cent. — A470

No. 1095, Jose Carlos Mariategui, birth cent.

1995, Mar. 28   **Perf. 14**
1094 A470 90c multicolored   3.25 2.50
          Perf. 13½x13
1095 A470 90c multicolored   3.25 2.50
Dated 1994.

Las Carmelitas Monastery, 350th Anniv. — A471

1995, Mar. 31   **Litho.**   **Perf. 13**
1096 A471 70c multicolored   2.25 1.50
Dated 1994.

Peru's Volunteer Fireman's Assoc. — A472

Fire trucks: 50c, Early steam ladder. 90c, Modern aerial ladder.

1995, Apr. 12 *Perf. 14*
1097 A472 50c multicolored 1.75 1.25
1098 A472 90c multicolored 2.75 2.00
Dated 1994.

Musical
Instruments — A473

1995, Apr. 10 Litho. *Perf. 13½x13*
1099 A473 20c Cello .75 .50
1100 A473 40c Drum 1.50 1.00

Union Club,
Fountain, Plaza of
Arms — A474

Design: 1s, Santo Domingo Convent, Lima.

1995, Apr. 19 Litho. *Perf. 14*
1101 A474 90c multicolored 4.50 4.25
1102 A474 1s multicolored 4.50 4.25

Cultural history of Lima.

Ethnic Groups — A475

1995, Apr. 26 *Perf. 13½x13*
1103 A475 1s Bora girl 3.00 2.75
1104 A475 1.80s Aguaruna man 5.00 4.50

World Food
Program, 30th
Anniv. — A476

1995, May 3 *Perf. 13x13½*
1105 A476 1.80s multicolored 5.00 3.00

Solanum
Ambosinum — A477

Design: 2s, Mochica ceramic representation
of papa flower.

1995, May 8 *Perf. 13½x13*
1106 A477 1.80s multicolored 5.00 3.00
1107 A477 2s multicolored 5.50 3.00

Reed Boat, Lake
Titicaca — A478

1995, May 12
1108 A478 2s multicolored 5.75 5.50

Fauna — A479

1s, American owl, vert. 1.80s, Jaguar.

1995, May 18 Perf. 13½x13, 13x13½
1109 A479 1s multi 3.25 2.75
1110 A479 1.80s multi 4.75 4.50

Andes Development
Corporation, 25th
Anniv. — A480

1995, Aug. 29 Litho. *Perf. 14*
1111 A480 5s multicolored 12.75 10.00

World Tourism
Day — A481

1995, Sept. 27 *Perf. 13x13½*
1112 A481 5.40s multicolored 17.50 17.00
Dated 1994.

World Post
Day — A482

1.80s, Antique mail box.

1995, Oct. 9 *Perf. 14*
1113 A482 1.80s multi 4.75 4.50
Dated 1994.

America
Issue — A483

1.50s, Landing of Columbus. 1.70s, Guanaco, vert. 1.80s, Early mail cart. 2s, Postal
trucks.

Perf. 13½x14, 14x13½ (#1115)
1995, Oct. 12
1114 A483 1.50s multi 3.75 3.50
1115 A483 1.70s multi 4.25 4.00
1116 A483 1.80s multi 4.25 4.00
1117 A483 2s multi 4.75 4.50
Nos. 1114-1117 (4) 17.00 16.00

No. 1116-1117 are dated 1994.

UN, 50th
Anniv. — A484

Design: 90c, Peruvian delegates, 1945.

1995, Oct. 28 *Perf. 14*
1118 A484 90c multicolored 2.50 2.25

Entries, Lima
Cathedrals — A485

Designs: 30c, St. Apolonia. 70c, St. Louis,
side entry to St. Francis.

1995, Oct. 20
1119 A485 30c multicolored 1.00 .80
1120 A485 70c multicolored 2.00 1.75
Dated 1994.

Artifacts from Art
Museums — A486

Carvings and sculptures: No. 1121, St.
James on horseback, 19th cent. No. 1122,
Church. 40c, Woman on pedestal. 50c,
Archangel.

1995, Oct. 31 *Perf. 14½x14*
1121 A486 20c multicolored .85 .75
1122 A486 20c multicolored .85 .75
1123 A486 40c multicolored 1.50 1.00
1124 A486 50c multicolored 2.10 1.75
Nos. 1121-1124 (4) 5.30 4.25
Dated 1994.

Scouting
A487

Designs: a, 80c, Lady Olave Baden-Powell.
b, 1s, Lord Robert Baden-Powell.

1995, Nov. 9 Litho. *Perf. 13½x13*
1125 A487 Pair, #a.-b. 4.50 4.00
Dated 1994.

Folk Dances — A488

1,80s, Festejo. 2s, Marinera limeña, horiz.

1995, Nov. 16 *Perf. 14*
1126 A488 1.80s multicolored 4.00 3.50
1127 A488 2s multicolored 4.75 4.00
Dated 1994.

Biodiversity — A489

50c, Manu Natl. Park. 90c, Anolis punctatus,
horiz.

1995, Nov. 23
1128 A489 50c multicolored 4.00 4.00
1129 A489 90c multicolored 7.50 7.00
Dated 1994.

Electricity for
Development — A490

20c, Toma de Huinco. 40c, Antacoto Lake.

1995, Nov. 27
1130 A490 20c multicolored .60 .40
1131 A490 40c multicolored 1.25 1.00
Dated 1994.

Peruvian
Saints — A491

90c, St. Toribio de Mogrovejo. 1s, St.
Franciso Solano.

1995, Dec. 4
1132 A491 90c multicolored 2.00 1.75
1133 A491 1s multicolored 2.50 2.25
Dated 1994.

FAO, 50th
Anniv. — A492

1996, Apr. 24 Litho. *Perf. 14*
1134 A492 60c multicolored 1.50 1.00

Christmas
1995 — A493

Local crafts: 30c, Nativity scene with folding
panels, vert. 70c, Carved statues of three
Magi.

1996, May 2
1135 A493 30c multicolored .75 .50
1136 A493 70c multicolored 2.00 1.50

America
Issue — A494

Designs: 30c, Rock formations of Lachay.
70c, Coastal black crocodile.

1996, May 9
1137 A494 30c multicolored 1.75 1.50
1138 A494 70c multicolored 2.50 2.25

Intl. Pacific
Fair — A495

1996, May 16
1139 A495 60c multicolored 1.50 1.25

1992 Summer
Olympic Games,
Barcelona — A496

a, 40c Shooting. b, 40c Tennis. c, 60c Swimming. d, 60c Weight lifting.

1996, June 10 Litho. *Perf. 12½*
1140 A496 Block of 4, #a.-d. 6.00 5.00
Dated 1992.
For surcharges see #1220-1223.

Expo '92,
Seville — A497

1996, June 17
1141 A497 1.50s multicolored   6.00 5.75
       Dated 1992.

Cesar Vallejo (1892-
1938),
Writer — A498

1996, June 25
1142 A498 50c black & gray   1.90 1.60
       Dated 1992.

Lima, City of
Culture
A499

1996, July 1
1143 A499 30c brown & tan   1.00 .80
       Dated 1992.
       For surcharge see No. 1219.

Kon-Tiki Expedition,
50th Anniv. — A500

1997, Apr. 28   Litho.   Perf. 12½
1144 A500 3.30s multicolored   6.00 5.50

Beginning with No. 1145, most
stamps have colored lines printed on
the back creating a granite paper effect.

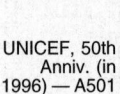

UNICEF, 50th
Anniv. (in
1996) — A501

1997, Aug. 7   Litho.   Perf. 13½x14
1145 A501 1.80s multicolored   3.75 3.25

Mochica Pottery — A502

    Designs: 20c, Owl. 30c, Ornamental
container. 50c, Goose jar. 1s, Two monkeys
on jar. 1.30s, Duck pitcher. 1.50s, Cat pitcher.

1997, Aug. 18   Litho.   Perf. 14½
1146 A502   20c green   .65   .45
1147 A502   30c lilac   1.10   .65
1148 A502   50c black   1.60 1.10
1149 A502   1s red brown   3.25 3.00
1150 A502 1.30s red   4.50 4.25
1151 A502 1.50s brown   5.25 5.00
    Nos. 1146-1151 (6)   16.35 14.45
    See Nos. 1179-1183, 1211-1214.

1996 Summer
Olympics,
Atlanta — A503

    a, Shooting. b, Gymnastics. c, Boxing. d,
Soccer.

1997, Aug. 25   Perf. 14x13½
1152 A503 2.70s Strip of 4,
      #a.-d.   20.00 17.50

College of Biology,
25th Anniv. — A504

1997, Aug. 26
1153 A504 5s multicolored   9.00 7.50

Scouting, 90th
Anniv. — A505

1997, Aug. 29
1154 A505 6.80s multicolored   12.00 10.00

8th Intl.
Conference
Against
Corruption,
Lima — A506

1997, Sept. 7   Perf. 13½x14
1155 A506 2.70s multicolored   3.75 3.25

Montreal Protocol on
Substances that
Deplete Ozone Layer,
10th Anniv. — A507

1997, Sept. 16   Perf. 14x13½
1156 A507 6.80s multicolored   13.50 10.00

Lord of Sipan
Artifacts — A508

    Designs: 2.70s, Animal figure with large
hands, feet. 3.30s, Medallion with warrior figure, vert.
    10s, Tomb of Lord of Sipan, vert.

1997, Sept. 22   Litho.   Perf. 13½x14
1157 A508 2.70s multicolored   5.25 4.00
1158 A508 3.30s multicolored   6.75 4.75
        Souvenir Sheet
1159 A508   10s multicolored   18.00 13.50

Peruvian
Indians — A509

1997, Oct. 12   Litho.   Perf. 14x13½
1160 A509 2.70s Man   5.75 5.00
1161 A509 2.70s Woman   5.75 5.00
    America Issue. Nos. 1160-1161 are dated
1996.

Heinrich von Stephan
(1831-97) — A510

1997, Oct. 9
1162 A510 10s multicolored   19.00 19.00

America Issue — A511

    No. 1163, Early post carrier. No. 1164, Mod-
ern letter carrier.

1997, Oct. 12
1163 A511 2.70s multicolored   6.50 5.00
1164 A511 2.70s multicolored   6.50 5.00

13th Bolivar
Games — A512

    a, Tennis. b, Soccer. c, Basketball. d, Shot
put.

1997, Oct. 17   Litho.   Perf. 14x13½
1165 A512 2.70s Block of 4,
      #a.-d.   23.50 20.00

Marshal Ramon
Castilla (1797-
1867) — A513

1997, Oct. 17
1166 A513 1.80s multicolored   4.25 3.50

Treaty of Tlatelolco
Banning Nuclear
Weapons in Latin
America, 30th
Anniv. — A514

1997, Nov. 3
1167 A514 20s multicolored   37.50 37.00

Manu Natl.
Park — A515

    Birds: a, Kingfisher. b, Woodpecker. c,
Crossbill. d, Eagle. e, Jabiru. f, Owl.

1997, Oct. 24   Sheet of 6
1168 A515 3.30s #a.-f. + label 40.00 35.00

8th Peruvian Antarctic
Scientific
Expedition — A516

1997, Nov. 10
1169 A516 6s multicolored   12.50 10.00

Christmas — A517

1997, Nov. 26
1170 A517 2.70s multicolored   5.25 5.00

Hipolito Unanue
Agreement, 25th
Anniv. — A518

1997, Dec. 18   Litho.   Perf. 14x13½
1171 A518 1s multicolored   2.25 2.00

      Souvenir Sheet

Peruvian
Gold
Libra,
Cent.
A519

1997, Dec. 18
1172 A519 10s multicolored 26.00 25.00

Dept. of Post and
Telegraph,
Cent. — A520

1997, Dec. 31
1173 A520 1s multicolored   2.00 1.75

Organization of
American States
(OAS), 50th
Anniv. — A521

1998, Apr. 30   Litho.   Perf. 14x13½
1174 A521 2.70s multicolored   5.50 5.00

Chorrillos Military
School,
Cent. — A522

1998, Apr. 29   Perf. 13½x14
1175 A522 2.70s multicolored   5.50 5.25

Tourism — A523

1998, June 22   Litho.   Perf. 14x13½
1176 A523 5s multicolored   9.25 9.00

Peruvian Horse — A524

1998, June 5
1177 A524 2.70s pale vio & vio   6.00 5.75

1998 World Cup Soccer Championships, France — A525

a, 2.70s, Goalie. b, 3.30s, Two players. 10s, Player kicking ball.

1998, June 26
1178 A525   Pair, #a.-b.   10.50 10.00

Souvenir Sheet
Perf. 13½x14
1178C A525 10s multicolored   18.50 18.00

Mochica Pottery Type of 1997

1s, like #1149. 1.30s, like #1146. 1.50s, like #1151. 2.70s, like #1148. 3.30s, like #1150.

1998, June 19   Litho.   Perf. 14½
1179 A502   1s slate   3.00 3.00
1180 A502   1.30s violet   3.75 3.75
1181 A502   1.50s pale blue 5.00 4.50
1182 A502   2.70s bister   9.00 8.25
1183 A502   3.30s black brown 9.50 9.50
      Nos. 1179-1183 (5)   30.25 29.00

Aero Peru, 25th Anniv. — A526

1.50s, Cuzco Cathedral. 2.70s, Airplane.

1998, May 22   Perf. 13½x14
1184 A526 1.50s multicolored   3.00 2.75
1185 A526 2.70s multicolored   5.50 5.25

Restoration of the Cathedral of Lima, Cent. — A527

1998, June 15   Perf. 14x13½
1186 A527 2.70s multicolored   5.25 5.00

Inca Rulers — A528

No. 1187, Lloque Yupanqui. No. 1188, Sinchi Roca. No. 1189, Manco Capac.

1998, July 17   Litho.   Perf. 14x13½
1187 A528 2.70s multicolored   7.50 7.00
1188 A528 2.70s multicolored   7.50 7.00
1189 A528 9.70s multicolored   23.00 22.50
      Nos. 1187-1189 (3)   38.00 36.50
      See Nos. 1225-1228.

Intl. Year of the Ocean — A529

1998, Aug. 8   Perf. 13½x14
1190 A529 6.80s multicolored   13.25 13.00

Natl. Symphony Orchestra, 60th Anniv. — A530

1998, Aug. 11   Perf. 14x13½
1191 A530 2.70s multicolored   5.25 5.00

Mother Teresa (1910-97) — A531

1998, Sept. 5
1192 A531 2.70s multicolored   6.25 6.00

Peruvian Children's Foundation — A532

1998, Sept. 17
1193 A532 8.80s multicolored   16.00 16.00

Souvenir Sheet

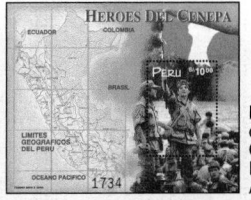

Heroes of the Cenepa River A533

1998, June 5
1194 A533 10s multicolored   18.50 18.00

Souvenir Sheet

Princess De Ampato A534

1998, Sept. 8
1195 A534 10s multicolored   18.50 18.00

Fauna of Manu Natl. Park — A535

1998, Sept. 27   Litho.   Perf. 14x13½
1196 A535 1.50s multicolored   3.75 3.50

America Issue — A536

1998, Oct. 12
1197 A536 2.70s Chabuca   5.25 5.00

Stamp Day — A537

1998, Oct. 9
1198 A537 6.80s No. 3   11.25 11.00

Frogs — A538

No. 1199: a, Agalychnis craspedopus. b, Ceratophrys cornuta. c, Epipedobates macero. d, Phyllomedusa vaillanti. e, Dendrobates biolat. f, Hemiphractus proboscideus.

1998, Oct. 23   Litho.   Perf. 14x13½
1199 A538 3.30s Block of 6, #a.-f. + label   34.00 32.50

Christmas A539

1998, Nov. 16   Perf. 13½x14
1200 A539 3.30s multicolored   4.00 3.75

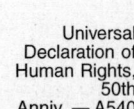

Universal Declaration of Human Rights, 50th Anniv. — A540

1998, Dec. 10   Litho.   Perf. 13½x14
1201 A540 5s multicolored   5.25 5.00

Peru-Ecuador Peace Treaty — A541

1998, Nov. 26   Litho.   Perf. 13½x14
1202 A541 2.70s multicolored   4.00 3.75
      Brasilia '98.

19th World Scout Jamboree, Chile — A542

Designs: a, Scouting emblem, stylized tents. b, Emblem, tents, "SIEMPRE LISTO."

1999, Jan. 5   Litho.   Perf. 14x13½
1203 A542 5s Pair, #a.-b.   11.50 10.00

Peruvian Philatelic Assoc., 50th Anniv. — A543

1999, Jan. 10
1204 A543 2.70s No. 19   3.00 2.75

Paintings by Pancho Fierro (1809-79) — A544

Designs: 2.70s, Once Upon Time in a Shaded Grove. 3.30s, Sound of the Devil.

1999, Jan. 16
1205 A544 2.70s multicolored   4.00 3.50
1206 A544 3.30s multicolored   4.50 4.00

Regional Dance — A545

1999, Feb. 10   Litho.   Perf. 14x13½
1207 A545 3.30s multicolored   3.50 3.25

CENDAF, 25th Anniv. — A546

1999, Mar. 1   Perf. 13½x14
1208 A546 1.80s multicolored   2.10 1.90

Ernest Malinowski (1818-99), Central Railroad — A547

1999, Mar. 3
1209 A547 5s multicolored   5.25 5.00

Peruvian Foundation for Children's Heart Disease — A548

1999, Mar. 6
1210 A548 2.70s multicolored   3.00 2.75

Mochica Pottery Type of 1997

Designs: 1s, like #1151. 1.50s, like #1148. 1.80s, like #1146. 2s, like #1150.

1999, Feb. 16   Litho.   Perf. 14½
1211	A502	1s lake	.95	.95
1212	A502	1.50s dark blue blk	2.00	1.75
1213	A502	1.80s brown	2.25	1.90
1214	A502	2s orange	2.50	2.10
		Nos. 1211-1214 (4)	7.70	6.70

Fauna of the Peruvian
Rain Forest — A549

1999, Apr. 23   Perf. 14x13½
1215	A549	5s multicolored	5.75	5.50

Souvenir Sheet

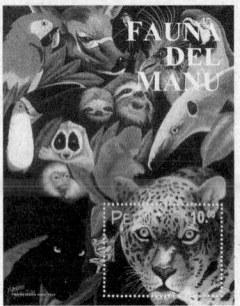

Fauna of
Manu
Natl.
Park
A550

1999, Apr. 23   Perf. 13½x14
1216	A550	10s multicolored	13.25	13.00

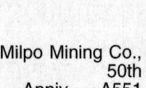

Milpo Mining Co.,
50th
Anniv. — A551

1999, Apr. 6   Perf. 13½x14
1217	A551	1.50s multicolored	1.90	1.60

See note after No. 1145.

Japanese Immigration
to Peru, Cent. — A552

1999, Apr. 3   Perf. 14x13½
1218	A552	6.80s multicolored	7.25	7.00

Nos. 1140, 1143 Surcharged in Black, Brown, Dark Blue, Red or Green

1999   Litho.   Perf. 12½
1219	A499	2.40s on 30c (Br) multi	2.50	2.50

Blocks of 4
1220	A496	1s on each value, #a.-d.	4.25	4.25
1221	A496	1.50s on each value, #a.-d.	6.00	6.00
1222	A496	2.70s on each value, #a.-d.	12.00	11.50
1223	A496	3.30s on each value, #a.-d.	14.00	13.00

Size and location of surcharge varies.

Antarctic Treaty,
40th
Anniv. — A553

1999, May 24   Perf. 13½x14
1224	A553	6.80s multicolored	8.75	8.50

Inca Rulers Type of 1998
No. 1225, Capac Yupanqui. No. 1226, Yahuar Huaca. No. 1227, Inca Roca. No. 1228, Maita Capac.

1999, June 24   Litho.   Perf. 14x13½
1225	A528	3.30s multi	3.50	3.25
1226	A528	3.30s multi	3.50	3.25
1227	A528	3.30s multi	3.50	3.25
1228	A528	3.30s multi	3.50	3.25
		Nos. 1225-1228 (4)	14.00	13.00

Souvenir Sheet

Nazca
Lines
A554

1999, June 8
1229	A554	10s multicolored	10.50	10.00

Margin shows Maria Reiche (1903-98), expert in Nazca Lines.

Minerals — A555

Designs: 2.70s, Galena. 3.30s, Scheelite. 5s, Virgotrigonia peterseni.

1999, July 3   Perf. 13½x14
1230	A555	2.70s multicolored	2.75	2.50
1231	A555	3.30s multicolored	3.50	3.25
1232	A555	5s multicolored	5.50	5.25
		Nos. 1230-1232 (3)	11.75	11.00

See Nos. 1339-1341.

Virgin of
Carmen — A556

1999, July 16   Perf. 14x13½
1233	A556	3.30s multicolored	4.75	4.50

Santa Catalina
Monastery,
Arequipa — A557

1999, Aug. 15   Litho.   Perf. 14x13½
1234	A557	2.70s multicolored	3.00	2.75

Chinese
Immigration to
Peru, 150th
Anniv. — A558

1999   Litho.   Perf. 13½x14
1235	A558	1.50s red & black	3.00	2.75

Peruvian Medical
Society, 25th
Anniv. — A559

1999   Litho.   Perf. 14x13½
1236	A559	1.50s multicolored	1.90	1.60

UPU, 125th
Anniv. — A560

1999, Oct. 9   Litho.   Perf. 13½x14
1237	A560	3.30s multicolored	3.50	3.25

America Issue

A New Millennium
Without
Arms — A561

2.70s, Earth, sunflower, vert.

1999, Oct. 12   Perf. 14x13½, 13½x14
1238	A561	2.70s multi	2.75	2.50
1239	A561	3.30s shown	3.50	3.25

Señor de los Milagros
Religious
Procession — A562

1999, Oct. 18   Perf. 14x13½
1240	A562	1s Incense burner	1.25	1.10
1241	A562	1.50s Procession	1.75	1.50

Inter-American
Development
Bank, 40th
Anniv. — A563

1999, Oct. 22   Perf. 13½x14
1242	A563	1.50s multicolored	1.75	1.50

Butterflies — A564

Designs: a, Pterourus zagreus chrysome-lus. b, Asterope buckleyi. c, Parides chabrias. d, Mimoides pausanias. e, Nessaea obrina. f, Pterourus zagreus zagreus.

Block of 6 + Label
1999, Oct. 23   Perf. 14x13½
1243	A564	3.30s #a.-f.	23.50	22.00

Border Disputes
Settled by Brasilia
Peace
Accords — A565

Maps of regions from: No. 1244, Cusumasa Bumbuiza to Yaupi Santiago. No. 1245, Lagatococha to Güeppi, vert. No. 1246, Cunhime Sur to 20 de Noviembre, vert.

1999, Oct. 26   Perf. 13½x14, 14x13½
1244	A565	1s multicolored	1.25	1.00
1245	A565	1s multicolored	1.25	1.00
1246	A565	1s multicolored	1.25	1.00
		Nos. 1244-1246 (3)	3.75	3.00

See Nos. 1282-1286.

Peruvian Postal
Services, 5th
Anniv. — A566

1999, Nov. 22   Perf. 14x13½
1247	A566	2.70s multicolored	3.00	2.75

Christmas — A567

1999, Dec. 1   Litho.   Perf. 14x13½
1248	A567	2.70s multicolored	4.00	3.75

Ricardo Bentín
Mujica (1899-
1979),
Businessman
A568

1999, Dec. 29   Litho.   Perf. 13½x14
1249	A568	2.70s multicolored	3.00	2.75

Souvenir Sheet

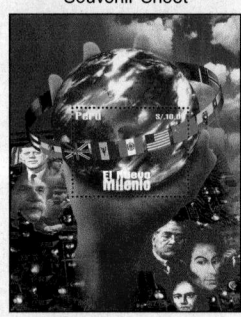

Millennium — A569

2000, Jan. 1
1250	A569	10s multicolored	11.50	11.00

Ricardo Cillóniz
Oberti,
Businessman — A570

2000, Jan. 17   Perf. 14x13½
1251	A570	1.50s multicolored	1.75	1.50

Printed se-tenant with label.

Alpaca
Wool
Industry
A571

a, Alpacas at right. b, Alpacas at left.

2000, Jan. 27   Litho.   Perf. 14x13½
1252	A571	1.50s Pair, #a.-b.	3.75	3.25

Nuclear Energy Institute — A572

2000, Feb. 4
1253 A572 4s multicolored 4.25 4.00

Retamas S.A. Gold Mine A573

Miner, mine and buildings: a, Text in white. b, Text in blue violet.

2000, Feb. 7
1254 A573 1s Pair, #a.-b. 2.50 2.00

Comptroller General, 70th Anniv. — A574

2000, Feb. 28 *Perf. 13½x14*
1255 A574 3.30s multicolored 3.50 3.25

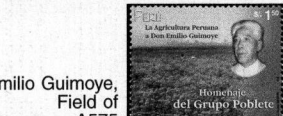

Emilio Guimoye, Field of Flowers A575

2000, Mar. 19 Litho. *Perf. 13½x14*
Granite Paper
1256 A575 1.50s multicolored 2.00 1.75

1999 Natl. Scholastic Games — A576

2000, May 3 *Perf. 14x13½*
Granite Paper
1257 A576 1.80s multi + label 2.50 2.25

Machu Picchu — A577

2000, July 20 *Perf. 13½x14*
Granite Paper
1258 A577 1.30s multicolored 2.25 2.00

Campaign Against Domestic Violence — A578

2000, Aug. 22 Litho. *Perf. 13½x14*
Granite Paper
1259 A578 3.80s multicolored 4.75 4.50

Holy Year 2000 — A579

2000, Aug. 23 Granite Paper
1260 A579 3.20s multicolored 3.75 3.50

Children's Drawing Contest Winners — A580

Designs: No. 1261, 3.20s, Lake Yarinacocha, by Mari Trini Ramos Vargas. No. 1262, 3.20s, Ahuashiyacu Falls, by Susan Hidalgo Bacalla, vert. 3.80s, Arequipa Countryside, by Anibal Lajo Yañez.

Perf. 13½x14, 14x13½
2000, Aug. 25 Granite Paper
1261-1263 A580 Set of 3 12.75 12.00

"Millennium Assembly" of UN General Assembly — A581

2000, Aug. 28 *Perf. 13½x14*
Granite Paper
1264 A581 3.20s multi 3.75 3.50

Gen. José de San Martín (1777-1850) A582

2000, Sept. 1 Granite Paper
1265 A582 3.80s multi 4.25 4.00

Ormeño Bus Co., 30th Anniv. A583

No. 1266: a, 1s, Bus and map of South America. b, 2.70s, Bus and map of North America.

2000, Sept. 3 *Perf. 14x13½*
Granite Paper
1266 A583 Pair, #a-b 5.50 5.00

Intl. Cycling Union, Cent. — A584

2000, Sept. 11 *Perf. 13½x14*
Granite Paper
1267 A584 3.20s multi 4.25 4.00

World Meteorological Organization, 50th Anniv. — A585

2000, Sept. 13 Granite Paper
1268 A585 1.50s multi 2.00 1.75

Lizards of Manu Natl. Park A586

No. 1269: a, Tropidurus plica. b, Ameiva ameiva. c, Mabouya bistriata. d, Neusticurus ecpleopus. e, Anolis fuscoauratus. f, Enyalioides palpebralis.

2000, Sept. 15 *Perf. 14x13½*
Granite Paper
1269 A586 3.80s Block of 6, #a-f 28.00 26.50

Matucana Madisoniorum A587

2000, Sept. 18 *Perf. 13½x14*
Granite Paper
1270 A587 3.80s multi 4.75 4.50

Carlos Noriega, First Peruvian Astronaut — A588

2000, Sept. 20 Granite Paper
1271 A588 3.80s multi 4.75 4.50

Toribio Rodríguez de Mendoza (1750-1825), Theologian — A589

2000, Sept. 21 *Perf. 14x13½*
Granite Paper
1272 A589 3.20s multi 4.25 4.00

Ucayali Province, Cent. — A590

2000, Sept. 25 *Perf. 13½x14*
Granite Paper
1273 A590 3.20s multi 4.25 4.00

Pisco Wine — A591

2000, Sept. 27 Granite Paper
1274 A591 3.80s multi 4.75 4.50

Latin American Integration Association, 20th Anniv. — A592

2000, Sept. 29 *Perf. 14x13½*
Granite Paper
1275 A592 10.20s multi 13.00 12.50

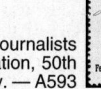

Peruvian Journalists Federation, 50th Anniv. — A593

2000, Sept. 30 Granite Paper
1276 A593 1.50s multi 2.40 2.10

Sexi Petrified Forest — A594

2000, Oct. 3 *Perf. 13½x14*
Granite Paper
1277 A594 1.50s multi 2.50 2.25

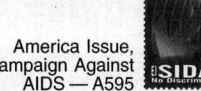

America Issue, Campaign Against AIDS — A595

2000, Oct. 12 Granite Paper
1278 A595 3.80s multi 5.25 5.00

Supreme Court — A596

2000, Oct. 16 Granite Paper
1279 A596 1.50s multi 2.00 1.75

Salvation Army in Peru, 90th Anniv. — A597

2000, Nov. 3 *Perf. 14x13½*
Granite Paper
1280 A597 1.50s multi 2.40 2.10

Peruvian Cancer League's Fight Against Cancer, 50th Anniv. — A598

2000, Nov. 9 *Perf. 13½x14*
Granite Paper
1281 A598 1.50s multi 2.25 2.00

Border Map Type of 1999

Flags and maps of border separating Peru and: 1.10s, Chile, vert. 1.50s, Brazil, vert. 2.10s, Colombia. 3.20s, Ecuador. 3.80s, Bolivia, vert.

Perf. 14x13½, 13½x14
2000, Nov. 27 Granite Paper
1282-1286 A565 Set of 5 15.50 14.50

Railroads in Peru, 150th Anniv. — A599

2000, Nov. 27 *Perf. 13½x14*
Granite Paper
1287 A599 1.50s multi 2.00 1.75

Luis Alberto Sanchez (1900-94), Politician — A600

2000, Nov. 27 *Perf. 14x13½*
Granite Paper
1288 A600 3.20s multi 4.25 4.00

National Congress — A601

2000, Dec. 7 *Perf. 13½x14*
Granite Paper
1289 A601 3.80s multi 4.75 4.50

Caretas Magazine, 50th Anniv. — A602

2000, Dec. 15 **Granite Paper**
1290 A602 3.20s multi 4.25 4.00

Cacti — A603

Designs: 1.10s, Haageocereus acranthus, vert. 1.50s, Cleistocactus xylorhizus, vert. No. 1293, 2.10s, Mila caespitosa, vert. No. 1294, 2.10s, Haageocereus setosus, vert. 3.20s, Opuntia pachypus. 3.80s, Haageocereus tenuis.

Perf. 13½x13¾, 13¾x13½
2001, Aug. 24 **Litho.**
1291-1296 A603 Set of 6 25.00 24.00

San Marcos University, 450th Anniv. — A604

2001, Sept. 4 *Perf. 13½x13¾*
1297 A604 1.50s multi 2.90 1.75

Alianza Lima Soccer Team, Cent. A605

No. 1298: a, Players. b, Players, ball.

2001, Sept. 6
1298 A605 3.20s Horiz. pair,
#a-b 11.50 7.50

Anti-Drug Campaign A606

2001, Sept. 7 *Perf. 13¾x13½*
1299 A606 1.10s multi 1.75 1.50

Gen. Roque Sáenz Peña (1851-1914), Pres. of Argentina A607

2001, Sept. 7
1300 A607 3.80s multi 7.00 4.50

Lurín River Valley — A608

2001, Sept. 10
1301 A608 1.10s multi 2.10 1.25

Amphipoda Hyalella — A609

2001, Sept. 10
1302 A609 1.80s multi 4.00 2.50

Postal and Philatelic Museum, 70th Anniv. — A610

2001, Oct. 9 *Perf. 13½x13¾*
1303 A610 3.20s multi 4.00 3.75

9th Iberoamerican Summit of Heads of State — A611

Country names and: a, 1.10s, Rectangle. b, 2.70s, Angled line.

2002, Mar. 6 **Litho.** *Perf. 14x13½*
1304 A611 Horiz. pair, #a-b 7.25 4.50
Dated 2001.

Peru — Costa Rica Diplomatic Relations, 150th Anniv. — A612

Flags, handshake and: a, 1.10s, Ruins. b, 2.70s, Grassland.

2002, Mar. 12
1305 A612 Horiz. pair, #a-b 7.25 4.50
Dated 2001.

World Conference Against Racism, Durban, South Africa — A613

2002, Mar. 13 *Perf. 13½x14*
1306 A613 3.80s multi 7.00 4.50
Dated 2001.

Intl. Day of Indigenous People — A614

2002, Mar. 13 *Perf. 14x13½*
1307 A614 5.80s multi 7.00 6.75
Dated 2001.

Intl. Organization for Migration, 50th Anniv. — A615

2002, Apr. 2
1308 A615 3.80s multi 7.00 4.50
Dated 2001.

Pan-American Health Organization, Cent. — A616

2002, Apr. 8 *Perf. 13½x14*
1309 A616 3.20s multi 6.00 3.75
Dated 2001.

La Molina Agricultural University, Cent. — A617

Arms and: a, 1.10s, Sepia photograph of building. b, 2.70s, Color photograph of building.

2002, Apr. 16 *Perf. 14x13½*
1310 A617 Horiz. pair, #a-b 8.00 5.00
Dated 2001.

Pisco Distilling — A618

Designs: 3.20s, Alembics. 3.80s, Jugs. 10s, La Fiesta de la Chicha y el Pisco, by José Sabogal.

2002, Apr. 18 *Perf. 13½x14*
1311-1312 A618 Set of 2 15.00 8.00
Souvenir Sheet
1313 A618 10s multi 15.00 12.00
Dated 2001.

Orchids — A619

Designs: 1.50s, Stanhopea sp. 3.20s, Chloraea pavoni. 3.80s, Psychopsis sp.

2002, Apr. 30 *Perf. 14x13½*
1314-1316 A619 Set of 3 16.00 10.00
Dated 2001.

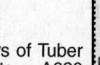

Flowers of Tuber Plants — A620

Designs: 1.10s, Solanum stenotomum. 1.50s, Ipomoea batatas. 2.10s, Ipomoea purpurea.

2002, May 7 *Perf. 13½x14*
1317-1319 A620 Set of 3 9.00 5.25

America Issue — UNESCO World Heritage Sites — A621

Balconies of Lima buildings: 2.70s, Palacio de Osambela. 5.80s, Palacio de Torre Tagle.

2002, May 14 Litho. *Perf. 14x13½*
1320-1321 A621 Set of 2 10.50 10.00
Dated 2001.

Year of Dialogue Among Civilizations — A622

Designs: 1.50s, Flower. 1.80s, shown.

2002, May 16
1322-1323 A622 Set of 2 5.50 4.25
Dated 2001.

Paracas National Reserve — A623

Designs: 1.10s, Sula dactilatra, vert. 1.50s, Sula variegata. 3.20s, Haematopus palliatus. 3.80s, Grapsus grapsus.

2002, May 21 *Perf. 14x13½, 13½x14*
1324-1327 A623 Set of 4 12.00 11.00
Dated 2001.

Souvenir Sheet

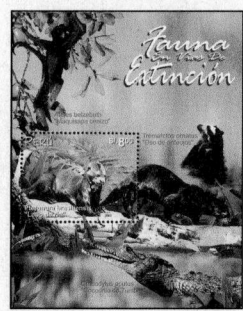

Endangered Animals — A624

2002, May 22 *Perf. 13½x14*
1328 A624 8s multi 12.50 10.00
Dated 2001.

Scouting in Peru, 90th Anniv. A625

No. 1329: a, Lord Robert Baden-Powell. b, Juan Luis Rospigliosi.
10.20s, First Peruvian Scouts.

2002, June 4   *Perf. 14x13½*
1329 A625 3.20s Horiz. pair,
#a-b   8.00 7.50
Souvenir Sheet
1330 A625 10.20s multi   12.00 12.00
Dated 2001.

Folk Dances — A626

Designs: 2.10s, Zamacueca. 2.70s, Alcatraz.

2002, June 4
1331-1332 A626 Set of 2   8.75 5.50
Dated 2001.

International Express Service — A627

2002, June 10   *Perf. 13½x14*
1333 A627 20s multi   23.00 22.50
Dated 2001.

Inca Rulers — A628

Designs: 1.50s, Viracocha. 2.70s, Pachacutec. 3.20s, Inca Yupanqui. 3.80s, Tupac Inca Yupanqui.

2002, June 24   *Litho.*   *Perf. 14x13½*
1334-1337 A628 Set of 4   14.50 13.50
Dated 2001.

Primates A629

No. 1338: a, Aotus nancymaea. b, Pithecia irrorata. c, Pithecia aequatorialis. d, Cebus albifrons. e, Saimiri boliviensis. f, Aotus vociferans.

2002, June 25
1338 A629 3.80s Block of 6,
#a-f   31.00 26.50
Dated 2001.

Minerals Type of 1999
Designs: 1.80s, Chalcopyrite. No. 1340, 3.20s, Sphalerite. No. 1341, 3.20s, Pyrargyrite.

2002, July 3   *Perf. 13½x14*
1339-1341 A555 Set of 3   14.00 9.00
Dated 2001.

Pre-Columbian Artifacts — A630

Designs: 1.50s, Crab-like man, Sipán. 3.20s, Warrior, Sicán. 3.80s, Gold breastplate, Kuntur Wasi, horiz.

10.20s, Pinchudo, Gran Pajatén, horiz.

2002, July 3   *Perf. 14x13½, 13½x14*
1342-1344 A630 Set of 3   14.00 10.00
Souvenir Sheet
1345 A630 10.20s multi   16.50 12.00
Dated 2001.

Admiral Miguel Grau — A631

2002, July 23   *Perf. 13½x14*
1346 A631 3.80s multi   7.00 4.50
Dated 2001.

Peruvian — Spanish Business Meeting — A632

2002, Aug. 7
1347 A632 3.80s multi   4.75 4.50
Dated 2001.

National Fisheries Society, 50th Anniv. — A633

    Perf. 13½x13¾
2002, Nov. 12   *Litho.*
1348 A633 3.20s multi   4.00 3.75
    a.   Tete beche pair   8.00 7.50

Alexander von Humboldt's Visit to Peru, Bicent. — A634

2002, Nov. 20   *Perf. 13¾x13½*
1349 A634 3.20s multi + label   4.00 3.75
    a.   Tete beche strip, 2 #1349 +2
      central labels   8.00 8.00

Peru - Bolivia Integration for Development A635

2002, Nov. 29   *Perf. 13½x14*
1350 A635 3.20s multi   4.00 3.75

Natl. Commission on Andean and Amazonian Peoples — A636

2002, Dec. 12
1351 A636 1.50s multi   2.00 1.75

Hydrography and Navigation Dept., Cent. — A637

2003, June 13   *Litho.*   *Perf. 14x13½*
1352 A637 1.10s multi   1.75 1.50

Manuela Ramos Movement, 25th Anniv. — A638

2003, July 1
1353 A638 3.80s multi   4.25 4.00

Radioprogramas del Peru Network, 40th Anniv. — A639

2003, Oct. 1   *Litho.*   *Perf. 13½x14*
1354 A639 4s multi   4.50 4.00

Pres. Fernando Belaunde Terry (1912-2002) — A640

2003, Oct. 7   *Perf. 14x13½*
1355 A640 1.60s multi   2.00 1.60

Canonization of St. Josemaría Escrivá de Balaguer — A641

2003, Oct. 11   *Perf. 13½x14*
1356 A641 1.20s multi   1.90 1.60

Sister Teresa de la Cruz Candamo (1875-1953), Founder of Canonesas de la Cruz — A642

2003, Nov. 3
1357 A642 4s multi   4.75 4.50

Treaty of Friendship, Commerce and Navigation Between Peru and Italy, 150th Anniv. — A643

No. 1358: a, Maps of Peru and Western Hemisphere. b, Map of Italy and Eastern Hemisphere.

2003, Nov. 13   *Perf. 14x13½*
1358 A643 2s Horiz. pair, #a-b   4.75 4.25

Water Snake Bilingual Education Project — A644

No. 1359: a, Head of snake, project emblem. b, Tail of snake, children's drawing.

2003, Nov. 28
1359 A644 2s Horiz. pair, #a-b   7.00 4.25

UNESCO Associated Schools Project Network, 50th Anniv. — A645

2003, Nov.   *Perf. 13½x14*
1360 A645 1.20s multi   1.75 1.50

America Issue - Fauna A646

No. 1361: a, Four Rupicola peruviana and butterfly. b, One Rupicola peruviana.

2003, Dec. 1   *Perf. 14x13½*
1361 A646 2s Horiz. pair, #a-b   5.00 4.50

Peru — Panama Diplomatic Relations, Cent. — A647

2003, Dec. 12
1362 A647 4r multi   7.00 4.50

Powered Flight, Cent. A648

2003, Dec. 17   *Perf. 13½x14*
1363 A648 4.80s multi + label   5.50 4.50

Cajón — A649

2003, Dec. 18
1364 A649 4.80s multi   5.25 4.50

Chess — A650

2004, Jan. 5
1365 A650 1.20s multi   1.75 1.50
Dated 2003.

National Rehabilitation Institute — A651

2004, Jan. 5
1366 A651 1.20s multi   2.40 2.10
Dated 2003.
School and Labor Integration "Year of the Rights of Persons with Disabilities."

Swimming — A652

2004, Jan. 5   *Perf. 14x13½*
1367 A652 1.20s multi   1.25 1.00
Dated 2003.

National Civil Defense System, 30th Anniv. (in 2002) — A653

2004, Jan. 14
1368 A653 4.80s multi   5.00 4.75
Dated 2002.

Christmas 2003 — A654

2004, Jan. 14   **Perf. 13½x14**
1369 A654 4.80s multi   4.00 3.75
Dated 2002.

Cebiche — A655

2004, Jan. 14
1370 A655 4.80s multi   7.50 4.75
Dated 2003.

Viceroys A656

No. 1371: a, 1.20s, Antonio de Mendoza (1495-1552). b, 1.20s, Andres Hurtado de Mendoza (1500-61). c, 1.20s, Diego Lopez de Zúñiga y Velasco (d. 1564). d, 4.80s, Blasco Nuñez de Vela (d. 1546).

2004, Jan. 14   **Perf. 14x13½**
1371 A656 Block of 4, #a-d   9.00 8.00
Dated 2003.

Minerals — A657

Designs: 1.20s, Orpiment. 4.80s, Rhodochrosite.

2004, Jan. 21   **Perf. 13½x14**
1372-1373 A657 Set of 2   5.25 4.75
Dated 2002.

Peruvian Saints — A658

Designs: No. 1374, 4.80s, St. Rose of Lima (1586-1617). No. 1375, 4.80s, St. Martin de Porres (1579-1639), vert.

2004, Jan. 21 Perf. 13½x14, 14x13½
1374-1375 A658 Set of 2   7.50 7.00
Dated 2002.

Orchids — A659

Designs: 1.20s, Chaubardia heteroclita, vert. 2.20s, Cochleanther amazonica, vert. 4.80s, Sobralia sp.

2004, Jan. 21 Perf. 14x13½, 13½x14
1376-1378 A659 Set of 3   9.50 6.50
Dated 2002.

Jorge Basadre (1903-80), Historian — A660

2004, Jan. 30 Engr. Perf. 14x13½
1379 A660 4.80s blue   4.25 4.00
Dated 2003.

Trains — A661

Designs: 1.20s, Locomotive and train station. 4.80s, Train on Galeras Bridge.

2004, Jan. 30 Litho. Perf. 13½x14
1380-1381 A661 Set of 2   8.00 5.00
Dated 2002.

Endangered Species — A662

Designs: No. 1382, 1.80s, Londra felina. No. 1383, 1.80s, Ara couloni, vert.

2004, Jan. 30 Perf. 13½x14, 14x13½
1382-1383 A662 Set of 2   4.25 3.75
Dated 2002.

Fire Fighting — A663

Designs: No. 1384, 2.20s, Firefighters with hose. No. 1385, 2.20s, Fire truck.

2004, Jan. 30   **Perf. 13½x14**
1384-1385 A663 Set of 2   8.50 6.00
Dated 2002.

Incan Emperors — A664

Designs: No. 1386, 1.20s, Huáscar (d. 1533). No. 1387, 1.20s, Atahualpa (d. 1533). 4.80s, Huayna Cápac (d. 1525).

2004, Jan. 30   **Perf. 14x13½**
1386-1388 A664 Set of 3   6.75 6.00
Dated 2002.

Rubén Vargas Ugarte, Historian — A665

2004, Feb. 4   **Perf. 13½x14**
1389 A665 4.80s multi   4.25 4.00
Dated 2002.

2002 World Cup Soccer Championships, Japan and Korea — A666

2004, Feb. 4
1390 A666 4.80s multi   4.25 4.00
Dated 2002.

National Stadium, 50th Anniv. (in 2002) — A667

2004, Feb. 4
1391 A667 4.80s multi   4.25 4.00
Dated 2002.

National Day of Biological Diversity, May 22, 2002 — A668

2004, Feb. 4
1392 A668 4.80s multi   4.25 4.00
Dated 2002.

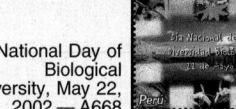

World Population Day — A669

2004, Feb. 4
1393 A669 4.80s multi   4.25 4.00
Dated 2002.

José Jiménez Borja (1901-82), Writer — A670

2004, Feb. 4   **Perf. 14x13½**
1394 A670 4.80s multi   4.25 4.00
Dated 2002.

Cacti — A671

Designs: No. 1395, 1.20s, Eriosyce islayensis. No. 1395, 1.20s, Matucana haynei. 4.80s, Pigmaeocereus bylesianus.

2004, Feb. 4
1395-1397 A671 Set of 3   12.00 9.00
Dated 2002.

Antarctic Fauna — A672

Designs: No. 1398, 1.80s, Leucocarbo atriceps. No. 1399, 1.80s, Pygosceles papua, vert. No. 1400, 1.80s, Asteroidea sp., vert.

2004, Feb. 4 Perf. 13½x14, 14x13½
1398-1400 A672 Set of 3   6.75 6.00
Dated 2002.

Pisco Sour — A673

2004, Feb. 10   **Perf. 13½x14**
1401 A673 4.80s multi   4.50 4.25

Daniel Alcides Carrión (1857-1885), Medical Martyr — A674

2004, Feb. 19 Litho. Perf. 14x13½
1402 A674 4.80s multi   4.50 4.25
Dated 2002.

Souvenir Sheet

Foundation of Jauja, by Wenceslao Hinostroza — A675

2004, Feb. 20   **Perf. 13½x14**
1403 A675 7s multi   6.25 6.00
Dated 2002.

Animals — A676

2004, Feb. 23   **Perf. 14x14½**
1404 A676 20c Alpaca   .70 .25
1405 A676 30c Vicuna   .70 .25
1406 A676 40c Guanaco   .90 .25
1407 A676 50c Llama   1.10 .30
Nos. 1404-1407 (4)   3.40 1.05
Dated 2002.

Vipers A677

No. 1408: a, Bothrops roedingeri. b, Micrurus lemniscatus. c, Bothrops atrox. d, Bothrops microphtalmus. e, Micrurus surinamensis. f, Bothrops barnetti.

2004, Feb. 23   **Perf. 14x13½**
1408 A677 1.80s Block of 6, #a-f, + label 11.50 10.00
Dated 2003.

Souvenir Sheet

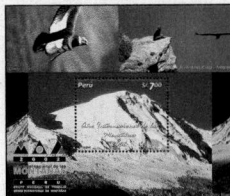

Intl. Year of Mountains (in 2002) — A678

2004, Feb. 23   **Perf. 13½x14**
1409 A678 7s multi   6.25 6.00
    Dated 2002.

Royal Tombs of Sipán Museum — A679

2004, Feb. 24
1410 A679 4.80s multi   6.00 3.75
    Dated 2003.

Lighthouses — A680

No. 1411: a, Punta Capones Lighthouse. b, Chincha Islands Lighthouse.

2004, Feb. 26   **Perf. 14x13½**
1411 A680 2s Horiz. pair, #a-b   11.00 7.00
    Dated 2003.

Volunteer Firefighters of Peru, 130th Anniv. — A681

2004, Mar. 2
1412 A681 4.80s multi   9.25 6.00

Miniature Sheet

Fish A682

No. 1413: a, Trachurus murphyi. b, Mugil cephalus. c, Engraulis ringens. d, Odontesthes regia regia. e, Merluccius gayi peruanus.

2004, Mar. 3   **Perf. 13½x14**
1413 A682 1.60s Sheet of 5, #a-e   12.50 7.50
    Dated 2002.

Souvenir Sheet

Arequipa Department — A683

No. 1414: a, Cathedral tower. b, Misti Volcano, horiz.

Perf. 14x13½, 13½x14 (#1414b)
2004, Mar. 18
1414 A683 4s Sheet of 2, #a-b   7.00 6.50
    Dated 2002.

Machu Picchu A684

No. 1415: a, 1.20s, Sundial. b, 1.20s, Temple of the Three Windows. c, 1.20s, Waterfall, Huayna Picchu. d, 4.80s, Aerial view of Machu Picchu.

2004, Mar. 20   **Perf. 14x13½**
1415 A684   Block of 4, #a-d   9.50 7.50
    Dated 2003.

Medicinal Plants — A685

Designs: No. 1416, 4.80s, Uncaria tomentosa. No. 1417, 4.80s, Myrciaria dubia. No. 1418, 4.80s, Lepidium meyenii.

2004, Mar. 26   **Perf. 13½x14**
1416-1418 A685   Set of 3   11.00 10.00

Annual Assembly of Governors of the Inter-American Development Bank — A686

2004, Mar. 29
1419 A686 4.80s multi   4.50 4.00

Dogs A687

No. 1420: a, Italian Volpino. b, Peruvian hairless dog. c, Beauceron. d, Italian Spinone.

2004, Apr. 2   **Perf. 14x13½**
1420 A687 4.80s Block of 4, #a-d   16.00 15.00
    Dated 2003.

Dances — A688

Designs: No. 1421, 1.20s, Huaylash. No. 1422, 1.20s, Huayno.

2004
1421-1422 A688   Set of 2   2.75 2.25
    Issued: No. 1421, 4/16; No. 1422, 5/28.
    Dated 2003.

Preparation for "El Niño" — A689

2004, Apr. 21   **Perf. 13½x14**
1423 A689 4.80s multi   4.75 4.00
    Dated 2002.

Tourism — A690

Designs: No. 1424, 4.80s, Lake Paca, Jauja. No. 1425, 4.80s, Ballestas Islands, Ica, vert. No. 1426, 4.80s, Inca Baths, Cajamarca, vert. No. 1427, 4.80s, Huanchaco, Trujillo, vert.

2004   **Perf. 13½x14, 14x13½**
1424-1427 A690   Set of 4   27.00 17.00

    Issued: No. 1424, 4/22; No. 1425, 4/29; No. 1426, 5/6; No. 1427, 6/10. Dated 2002 (#1425-1427) or 2003 (#1424).

Santiago Apostol Temple, Puno — A691

2004, July 2   **Perf. 13½x14**
1428 A691 1.80s multi   2.00 1.75
    Dated 2003.

America Issue — Youth, Education and Literacy — A692

Designs: 1.20s, Children, stylized flower. 4.80s, Computer operator, horiz.

2004, July 5   **Perf. 14x13½, 13½x14**
1429-1430 A692   Set of 2   5.50 4.00
    Dated 2002 (#1429) or 2003 (#1430).

Souvenir Sheet

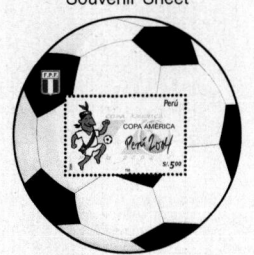

2004 Copa America Soccer Tournament, Peru — A693

2004, July 9   **Perf. 14x14½**
1431 A693 5s multi   7.25 5.00

Horses A694

No. 1432: a, 1.20s, White horse. b, 1.20s, Black horse, rider with raised hand. c, 1.20s, Black horse, rider with white poncho. d, 4.80s, Horse's head.

2004, Aug. 6   **Perf. 14x13½**
1432 A694   Block of 4, #a-d, + label   7.50 6.50
    Dated 2002.

Miniature Sheet

Worldwide Fund for Nature (WWF) — A695

No. 1433 — Pteronura brasiliensis: a, 30c. Looking. b, 50c, With mouth open. c, 1.50s, Eating. d, 1.50s, Sleeping.

2004, Oct. 15   **Litho.**
1433 A695   Sheet of 4, #a-d   7.00 4.00

America Issue — Environmental Protection A696

2004, Oct. 25   **Perf. 13½x14**
1434 A696 4.50s multi   4.75 3.25

Railroads — A697

Designs: 5s, Modern train on bridge, 1870 train on bridge. 10s, Train on Infiernillo Bridge, horiz.

2004, Oct. 29   **Perf. 14x13½**
1435 A697 5s multi   4.75 4.00

Souvenir Sheet
Perf. 13½x14
1436 A697 10s multi   9.25 7.50

Peruvian Song Day, 60th Anniv. — A698

2004, Oct. 31   **Perf. 13½x14**
1437 A698 5s multi   4.75 4.00

FIFA (Fédération Internationale de Football Association), Cent. — A699

2004, Nov. 2
1438 A699 5s multi   4.75 4.00

Election of Pope John Paul II, 25th Anniv. (in 2003) — A700

2004, Nov. 2
1439 A700 5s multi   4.75 4.00

Canonization of Mother Teresa — A701

2004, Nov. 2   *Perf. 14x13½*
1440 A701 5s multi   4.75 4.00

Miniature Sheet

Musicians — A702

No. 1441: a, Juan Diego Flórez. b, Susana Baca. c, Gianmarco. d, Eva Ayllón, horiz. e, Libido, horiz.

Perf. 14x13½, 14x14x13½x14 (#1441d, 1441e)
2004, Nov. 12
1441 A702 2s Sheet of 5, #a-e   9.75 7.50

Flora Tristan Women's Center, 25th Anniv. — A703

2004, Nov. 9   *Litho.*   *Perf. 14*
1442 A703 5s multi   4.75 4.00

Exporter's Day — A704

2004, Nov. 9
1443 A704 5s multi   4.75 4.00

Latin American Parliament, 40th Anniv. — A705

No. 1444: a, Parliament emblem. b, Andrés Townsend Escurra, first President of Latin American Parliament, and flags.

2004, Nov. 16   *Perf. 13½x14*
1444 A705 2.50s Horiz. pair, #a-b   5.00 4.00

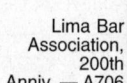

Lima Bar Association, 200th Anniv. — A706

2004, Nov. 17
1445 A706 5s multi   4.75 4.00

Serpost, 10th Anniv. — A707

2004, Nov. 22
1446 A707 5s multi   4.75 4.00

Jungle River Fauna — A708

Designs: 2s, Serrasalmus. 4.50s, Pontoporia blainvillei. 5s, Arapaima gigas, vert.

Perf. 13½x14, 14x13½
2004, Nov. 30
1447-1449 A708 Set of 3   10.50 9.00

Christmas — A709

2004, Dec. 2   *Perf. 14x13½*
1450 A709 5s multi   5.50 4.00

Antarctica — A710

Designs: 1.50s, Machu Picchu Scientific Base, King George Island. 2s, Megaptera novaeangliae, horiz. 4.50s, Orcinus orca, horiz.

2004, Dec. 3   *Perf. 14x13½, 13½x14*
1451-1453 A710 Set of 3   9.00 6.00

Prehistoric Animals — A711

No. 1454: a, 1.80s, Drawings of Smilodon neogaeus and Toxodon platensis Owen. 3.20s, Fossils, depiction of body of Toxodon platensis.

2004, Dec. 6   *Perf. 14x13½*
1454 A711 Horiz. pair, #a-b   4.75 4.00

Mochica Ceramics — A712

Various ceramic pieces with background colors of: No. 1455, 4.50s, Dark blue. No. 1456, 4.50s, Red violet. 5s, Blue, horiz.

2004, Dec. 6   *Perf. 14x14½, 14½x14*
1455-1457 A712 Set of 3   14.00 10.00

Third Meeting of South American Presidents — A713

2004, Dec. 8   *Perf. 14x13½*
1458 A713 5s multi   4.75 4.00

Lima Museum of Art, 50th Anniv. — A714

2004, Dec. 9   *Litho.*
1459 A714 5s multi   4.75 4.00

Battles, 180th Anniv. A715

No. 1460: a, 1.80s, Map and scene of Battle of Ayacucho. b, 3.20s, Map and scene of Battle of Junín.

2004, Dec. 9
1460 A715   Horiz. pair, #a-b   5.00 4.00

Lighthouses — A716

No. 1461: a, Pijuayal Lighthouse, Amazon River. b, Suana Lighhouse, Lake Titicaca.

2004, Dec. 10
1461 A716 4.50s Horiz. pair, #a-b   8.50 7.00

Souvenir Sheet

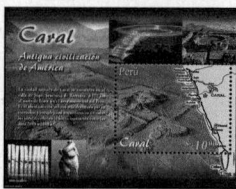

Sacred City of Caral A717

2004, Dec. 15   *Perf. 13½x14*
1462 A717 10s multi   10.00 7.50

Parque de las Leyendas, 40th Anniv. — A718

No. 1463: a, Cantua buxifolia. b, Puma concolor.

2005, Jan. 14   *Perf. 14x13½*
1463 A718 5s Horiz. pair, #a-b   9.00 7.50

Dated 2004.

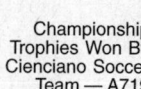

Championship Trophies Won By Cienciano Soccer Team — A719

2005, Jan. 22
1464 A719 5s multi   4.50 4.00

Dated 2004.

Stomatology Academy of Peru, 75th Anniv. — A720

2005, Jan. 24
1465 A720 5s multi   4.50 4.00

Dated 2004.

National Health Crusade A721

2005, Feb. 2   *Perf. 14*
1466 A721 2s multi + label   2.00 1.50

Dated 2004.

Houses of Worship — A722

Designs: 4.50s, San Cristóbal Church, Huamanga. 5s, Huancayo Cathedral.

2005, Feb. 7   *Litho.*   *Perf. 13½x14*
1467-1468 A722 Set of 2   10.50 7.00

Abolition of Slavery, 150th Anniv. — A723

2005, Feb. 25   *Engr.*
1469 A723 5s claret   4.50 4.00

Armed Forces A724

No. 1470: a, 1.80s, Army tank. b, 1.80s, Navy submarine. c, 1.80s, Air Force Mirage jets. d, 3.20s, Air Force Sukhoi jet. e, 3.20s, Army soldiers. f, 3.20s, Navy frigate.

2005, Feb. 28   *Litho.*
1470 A724   Block of 6, #a-f, + label   14.00 10.00

Fruit — A725

Designs: No. 1471, 4.50s, Eugenia stipitata. No. 1472, 4.50s, Mauritia flexuosa. 5s, Solanum sessiflorum dunal, vert.

2005, Mar. 4   *Perf. 13½x14, 14x13½*
1471-1473 A725 Set of 3   12.50 10.00

Opera Singer
Luis Alva Talledo,
Founder of
Prolirica — A726

2005, Mar. 10   **Perf. 13½x14**
1474 A726 1.50s multi   1.50 1.10

Allpahuayo Reserve Wildlife — A727

No. 1475: a, Hormiguero norteño de cola
castaña. b, Tiranuelo de Mishana. c, Rana
arboricola. d, Sacha runa.

2005, Mar. 21   **Perf. 14x13½**
1475 A727 4.50s Block of 4,
     #a-d, + la-
     bel   16.00 13.00

Paintings
A728

No. 1476 — Unidentified paintings by: a,
Pancho Fierro. b, Ignacio Moreno. c, Daniel
Hernández. d, Camilo Blas. e, Ricardo Grau. f,
Fernando de Szyszlo.

2005, Apr. 4
1476 A728 2s Block of 6, #a-f, +
     label   12.50 9.00

Science of Antonio Raimondo — A729

No. 1477: a, 1.80s, Sculptures, Chavín de
Huántar. b, 3.20s, Bird and bat. c, 4.50s, Sta-
nophea. d, 5s, Fossil of N. C. Roemoceras
Subplanum Hyatt.

2005, Apr. 18
1477 A729   Block of 4, #a-d,
     + label   13.00 11.00

Souvenir Sheet

Penelope Albipennis — A730

2005, May 2
1478 A730 10s multi   8.75 8.00

Architecture — A731

Designs: a, 4.50s, Government Palace. b,
4.50s, Italian Art Museum. c, 5s, Larco Mar. d,
5s, Mega Plaza.

2005, May 18   **Perf. 13½x14**
1479 A731   Block of 4, #a-d,
     + label   18.00 14.00

Postal Money
Orders — A732

2005, May 30
1480 A732 5s multi   5.50 4.00

Pope John Paul
II (1920-2005)
A733

2005, Nov. 24   **Litho.**   **Perf. 13½**
1481 A733 1.80s multi   2.40 1.75

Souvenir Sheet

Europa
Stamps,
50th
Anniv.
(in 2006)
A734

No. 1482: a, Mochica headdress and Spain
#1526. b, Chimú ceremonial jewelry and
Spain #941. c, Mochica earrings and Spain
#1567. d, Mochica headdress and Spain
#1607.

2005, Nov. 24   **Litho.**   **Perf. 14**
1482 A734 2s Sheet of 4, #a-d   9.00 6.00

Miniature Sheet

Naval
Victories
A735

No. 1483: a, Battle of Punta Malpelo. b, Battle of Callao. c, Sinking of the Covadonga. d,

---

Battle of Abtao. e, Battle of Iquique. f, Battle of
Pedrera.

2005, Dec. 21   **Litho.**   **Perf. 13½x14**
1483 A735 2s Sheet of 6, #a-f   10.00 8.50

Medical College
of Peru, 35th
Anniv. — A736

2005, Dec. 29
1484 A736 5.50s multi   5.25 4.00

Christmas
2005 — A737

2006, Jan. 9
1485 A737 5.50s multi   4.25 4.00

Dated 2005.

Eighth Cultural
Patrimony Colloquium,
Cuzco — A738

2006, Jan. 9   **Perf. 14x13½**
1486 A738 5.50s multi   4.25 4.00

Dated 2005.

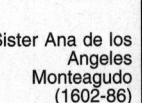

Sister Ana de los
Angeles
Monteagudo
(1602-86)
A739

2006, Jan. 10   **Perf. 13½x14**
1487 A739 5.50s multi   5.00 4.00

Dated 2005.

Publication of
Don Quixote,
400th Anniv. (in
2005) — A740

2006, Jan. 11
1488 A740 5s multi   4.50 4.00

Dated 2005.

Pope
Benedict
XVI
A741

No. 1489: a, Profile. b, With arms raised.

2006, Jan. 11   **Perf. 14x13½**
1489 A741 2.50s Horiz. pair, #a-b 5.25 4.00

Dated 2005.

Rotary
International,
Cent. (in
2005) — A742

2006, Jan. 13   **Perf. 13½x14**
1490 A742 5.50s multi   5.25 4.00

Dated 2005.

America Issue, Fight
Against
Poverty — A743

2006, Jan. 16   **Perf. 14x13½**
1491 A743 5.50s multi   5.00 4.00

Dated 2005.

Natl. Academy of
History, Cent. (in
2005) — A744

2006, Jan. 20   **Perf. 13½x14**
1492 A744 5.50s multi   5.25 4.00

Dated 2005.

St.
Peter's
Church,
Lima
A745

No. 1493: a, Exterior. b, Interior.

2006, Jan. 20   **Perf. 14x13½**
1493 A745 2.50s Horiz. pair, #a-b 5.00 3.50

Dated 2005.

Volcanoes — A746

No. 1494: a, Pichupichu. b, Chachani. c,
Misti.

2006, Jan. 20
1494 A746   Horiz. strip of 3   7.25 5.00
   a.-c.   2.50s Any single   2.00 1.60

Dated 2005.

YMCA in Peru, 85th
Anniv. (in
2005) — A747

2006, Jan. 23   **Litho.**
1495 A747 5.50s multi   5.25 4.00

Dated 2005.

Dr. Julio C. Tello
(1880-1947),
Anthropologist
and Archaeologist
A748

2006, Jan. 26   **Perf. 13½x14**
1496 A748 5s multi   5.00 3.50

Dated 2005.

Cáritas, 50th
Anniv. (in
2005) — A749

2006, Jan. 28
1497 A749 5.50s multi   5.00 4.00

Dated 2005.

Comptroller General, 75th Anniv. (in 2005) — A750

2006, Feb. 6　　　**Perf. 14x13½**
1498 A750 5.50s multi　　　　5.25 4.00
Dated 2005.

Creation of Cajamarca Department, 150th Anniv. (in 2005) — A751

2006, Feb. 11　　　**Perf. 13½x14**
1499 A751 6s multi　　　　5.25 4.25
Dated 2005.

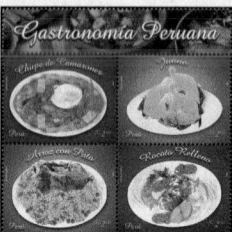

Traditional Foods — A752

No. 1500: a, Chupe de camarones. b, Juane. c, Arroz con pato (duck and rice). d, Rocoto relleno.

2006, Feb. 16
1500 A752 2s Block of 4, #a-d, +
　　　label　　　　　8.25 5.50
Dated 2005.

Butterflies — A753

No. 1501: a, Heliconius sara. b, Morpho achilles. c, Dryas iulia. d, Caligo eurilochus.

2006, Feb. 17
1501 A753 2s Block of 4, #a-d, +
　　　label　　　　　9.00 4.00
Dated 2005.

12th Panamerican Scout Jamboree, Argentina — A754

No. 1502: a, Scout in foreground. b, Flag in foreground.

2006, Feb. 20　　　**Perf. 14x13½**
1502 A754 2s Horiz. pair, #a-b　4.00 2.75
Dated 2005.

Pre-Columbian Cultures — A755

Artifacts of: No. 1503, 6s, Paracas culture, c. 500. No. 1504, 6s, Chavin culture, c. 1200.

2006, Feb. 22　　　**Perf. 13½x14**
1503-1504 A755　Set of 2　　11.00 7.50
Dated 2005.
See also Nos. 1602-1603, 1648-1649, 1700-1701, 1740-1741, 1774-1775.

Legend of the Ayar Brothers, Incan Creation Myth — A756

2006, Feb. 24
1505 A756 6s multi　　　　5.00 4.00
Dated 2005.

National Symbols — A757

No. 1506: a, Flag. b, Coat of arms. c, National anthem.

2006, Feb. 27　　　**Perf. 14x13½**
1506 A757　Horiz. strip of 3　　5.75 4.00
a.-c.　2s Any single　　　1.50 1.25
Dated 2005.

Fruit — A758

Designs: No. 1507, 6s, Pouteria lucuma. No. 1508, 6s, Annona cherimola.

2006, Mar. 1　　　**Perf. 13½x14**
1507-1508 A758　Set of 2　　11.50 8.00
Dated 2005.

Peru to Brazil Interoceanic Highway — A759

2006, Mar. 3
1509 A759 6s multi　　　　5.00 4.00
Dated 2005.

Writers — A760

Designs: No. 1510, 6s, Mario Vargas Llosa. No. 1511, 6s, Alfredo Bryce Echenique.

2006, Mar. 28　Engr.　Perf. 14x13½
1510-1511 A760　Set of 2　　10.50 8.00
Dated 2005.

Health Ministry, 70th Anniv. (in 2005) — A761

2006, Apr. 7　Litho.　Perf. 13½x14
1512 A761 6s multi　　　　5.25 4.00
Dated 2005.

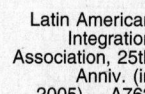

Latin American Integration Association, 25th Anniv. (in 2005) — A762

2006, Apr. 7
1513 A762 6s multi　　　　6.00 4.00
Dated 2005.

Hubnerite — A763

2006, Apr. 28
1514 A763 6s multi　　　　6.25 4.00
Compare with type A657.

Purple Corn Chicha Beverage — A764

2006, Apr. 28
1515 A764 6s multi　　　　5.25 4.00

Fauna of Lake Titicaca A765

No. 1516: a, Orestias spp. b, Plegadis ridgwayi. c, Phoenicoparrus andinus. d, Telmatobius culeus.

2006, May 2　　　**Perf. 14x13½**
1516 A765 5.50s Block of 4,
　　　#a-d, + la-
　　　bel　　　　　19.00 14.50

Parrots A766

No. 1517: a, Pionopsitta barrabandi. b, Tovit huetii. c, Pionites melanocephala. d, Ara severa. e, Amazona festiva. f, Ara ararauna.

2006, May 5
1517 A766 5.50s Block of 6,
　　　#a-f, + label 32.50 22.50

Viceroys of Peru A767

No. 1518: a, Francisco de Toledo (1515-82). b, Martín Enríquez de Almansa (c. 1525-83). c, Fernando Torres y Portugal. d, García Hurtado de Mendoza (1535-1609).

2006, May 8
1518 A767 5.50s Block of 4,
　　　#a-d, + la-
　　　bel　　　　　19.00 14.50
See Nos. 1569, 1575, 1622, 1681, 1737, 1776, 1858. Compare with type A1063.

Souvenir Sheet

Lighthouses — A768

No. 1519: a, Isla Lobos de Tierra Lighthouse. b, Isla Blanca Lighthouse.

2006, May 10
1519 A768 6s Sheet of 2, #a-b　10.00 8.00

Birds — A769

Designs: No. 1520, 6s, Perlita de Iquitos. No. 1521, 6s, Tortolita moteada (turtledove). No. 1522, 6s, Ganse Andino (Andean geese), vert.

2006, May 15　Perf. 13½x14, 14x13½
1520-1522 A769　Set of 3　　17.50 12.00

El Peruano Newspaper, 180th Anniv. — A770

2006, May 16　　　**Perf. 13½x14**
1523 A770 6s multi　　　　6.00 4.00

Surfing A771

No. 1524: a, Surfers on waves. b, Sofía Mulanovich, 2004 Surfing World Champion.

2006, May 16　　　**Perf. 14x13½**
1524 A771 5.50s Horiz. pair, #a-b 9.50 7.50

PERU 713

Souvenir Sheet

Lima-Callao Railway, 150th
Anniv. — A772

2006, May 16   *Perf. 13½x14*
1525 A772 6s multi   5.25 4.00

Miniature Sheet

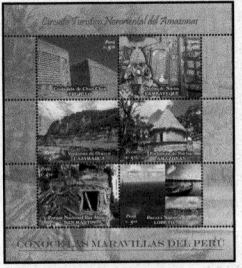

Tourism
A773

No. 1526: a, Chan Chan. b, Sipán man. c,
Ventanas de Otuzco. d, Kuelap Fort. e, Río
Abiseo Natl. Park. f, Pacaya Samiria.

2006, May 17
1526 A773 5.50s Sheet of 6,
      #a-f   30.00 22.50

Miniature Sheet

Visit of
Pope
John
Paul II to
Peru,
20th
Anniv.
A774

No. 1527 — Pope in: a, Lima. b, Arequipa.
c, Ayacucho. d, Cuzco. e, Piura. f, Trujillo. g,
Iquitos. h, Callao.

2006, May 19
1527 A774 2s Sheet of 8, #a-h 15.00 10.50

Peruvian
Air Force
A775

No. 1528: a, Air Force emblem. b, Airplanes
and pilot.

2006, May 22
1528 A775 6s Horiz. pair, #a-b   10.50 8.00

Carnival
Participants — A776

Participants in carnivals from: No. 1529, 6s,
Cajamarca. No. 1530, 6s, Arequipa. No. 1531,
6s, Puno.

2006, May 22   *Perf. 14x13½*
1529-1531 A776 Set of 3   12.50 12.00

Precursors of Independence — A777

No. 1532: a, Micaela Bastidas. b, Plaza
Mayor, Cuzco.

2006, May 31
1532 A777 2s Horiz. pair, #a-b   4.00 2.75

Intl. Year of
Deserts and
Desertification
A778

2006, Dec. 22 Litho. Perf. 13½x14
1533 A778 2s multi   2.00 1.50

Christmas
A779

2006, Dec. 22
1534 A779 2s multi   2.00 1.50

Wolfgang
Amadeus Mozart
(1756-91),
Composer
A780

2006, Dec. 22
1535 A780 5.50s multi   5.00 3.75

2006 World Cup
Soccer
Championships,
Germany — A781

2006, Dec. 22   *Perf. 14x13½*
1536 A781 8.50s multi   9.00 5.75

Christopher
Columbus (1451-
1506),
Explorer — A782

2006, Dec. 27   *Perf. 13½x14*
1537 A782 6s multi   5.25 4.00

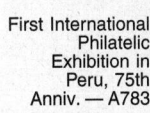

First International
Philatelic
Exhibition in
Peru, 75th
Anniv. — A783

Litho. With Foil Application
2006, Dec. 29   *Perf. 13½x14*
1538 A783 8.50s #286   7.50 5.75

America Issue, Energy
Conservation — A784

No. 1539: a, 3s, Solar panels. b, 5.50s, Natural gas.

2006, Dec. 29 Litho. Perf. 14x13½
1539 A784 Horiz. pair, #a-b   8.00 5.75

Diplomatic Relations Between Peru
and People's Republic of China, 35th
Anniv. — A785

No. 1540: a, Giant panda. b, Guanaco. c,
Machu Picchu. d, Great Wall of China.

2006, Dec. 29
1540 A785 2s Block of 4, #a-d, +
      label   7.75 5.25

"The Pirates of
Callao," First
Peruvian 3-D
Animated
Film — A786

Parrot and: No. 1541, 2s, Boy with sword.
No. 1542, 2s, Captain with sword.

Litho. With Foil Application
2007, Jan. 5   *Perf. 13½x14*
1541-1542 A786 Set of 2   4.00 2.75
      Dated 2006.

Peruvian
Art — A787

Designs: No. 1543, 2.20s, Sculpture of
horse by Victor Delfin. No. 1544, 2.20s, Painting by Fernando de Szyszlo.

2007, Jan. 9   Litho.
1543-1544 A787 Set of 2   4.25 3.00
      Dated 2006.

Souvenir Sheet

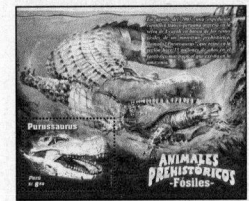

Purussaurus Fossil — A788

**Litho. (Foil Application on Sheet
Margin)**
2007, Jan. 16
1545 A788 8.50s multi   7.50 5.75
      Dated 2006.

Flutes — A789

Designs: No. 1546, 5.50s, Antara. No. 1547,
5.50s, Quena. No. 1548, 5.50s, Zampoña.

2007, Jan. 23   Litho.
1546-1548 A789 Set of 3   14.50 11.00
      Dated 2006.

St. Toribio de
Mogrovejo (1538-
1606), Founder of
First Seminary in
Americas — A790

2007, Jan. 27 Engr. Perf. 14x13½
1549 A790 2s chocolate   2.00 1.40
      Dated 2006.

Miniature Sheet

Religious
Festivals
A791

No. 1550: a, Señor de los Milagros. b,
Virgen de las Mercedes. c, Virgen de la
Candelaria. d, Señor de Muruhuay.

2007, Jan. 30   Litho.
1550 A791 5.50s Sheet of 4,
      #a-d   20.00 14.50
      Dated 2006.

Peruvian Film,
"Dragones Destino de
Fuego" — A792

Designs: No. 1551, 2s, Flying dragons. No.
1552, 2s, Head of dragon.

Litho. With Foil Application
2007, Feb. 5
1551-1552 A792 Set of 2   4.00 2.75
      Dated 2006.

National Board of
Elections, 75th Anniv.
(in 2006) — A793

2007, Feb. 13   Engr.
1553 A793 2.20s brown   2.00 1.50
      Dated 2006.

Desserts — A794

No. 1554: a, Suspiro de limeña. b,
Picarones. c, Mazamorra morada.

2007, Mar. 12 Litho. Perf. 13½x14
1554 A794 Horiz. strip of 3   7.00 5.00
a.-c.   2.50s Any single   1.75 1.60
      Dated 2006.

Dogs
A795

No. 1555: a, Perro sin pelo (hairless dog). b, Dachshund. c, Samoyed. d, Siberian husky.

2007, Mar. 26   Litho.   Perf. 13½x14
1555 A795 6s Block of 4, #a-d,
+ label   21.00 16.00
        Dated 2006.

Miniature Sheet

Architecture of the Viceregal Era in
Lima — A796

No. 1556: a, St. Augustine Church. b, Sacristy of St. Francis. c, St. Apollonia Gate. d, Metropolitan Cathedral.

2007, Apr. 2   Litho.   Perf. 14x13½
1556 A796 5.50s Sheet of 4,
#a-d   20.00 14.50
        Dated 2006.

Incan
Temples — A797

Designs: No. 1557, 6s, Tambo Colorado, Ica. No. 1558, 6s, Pachacamac, Lima. No. 1559, 6s, Tambo Machay, Cusco.

2007, Apr. 23   Litho.   Perf. 13½x14
1557-1559 A797 Set of 3   16.00 12.00
        Dated 2006.

Felipe Pinglo Alva (1899-1936),
Composer — A798

No. 1560: a, Photographs of Pinglo Alva and buildings. b, Guitar, photograph of Pinglo Alva.

2007, May 7   Perf. 14x13½
1560 A798 3s Horiz. pair, #a-b   5.25 4.00
        Dated 2006.

Pre-Columbian
Cultures — A799

Artifacts and maps of: No. 1561, 6s, Vicús culture, 500 B.C. No. 1562, 6s, Salinar culture, 200 B.C.

2007, May 21   Perf. 13½x14
1561-1562 A799 Set of 2   10.50 8.00
        Dated 2006.

Dances and Costumes — A800

No. 1563: a, Danza de los Negritos. b, Danza de las Tijeras. c, Danza Cápac Colla. d, Danza La Diablada.

2007, June 4   Perf. 14x13½
1563 A800 2.50s Block of 4, #a-
d, + label   9.50 6.75
        Dated 2006.

Exports — A801

Designs: No. 1564, 6s, Alpaca yarn. No. 1565, 6s, Mangos. No. 1566, 6s, Asparagus.

2007, June 18   Perf. 13½x14
1564-1566 A801 Set of 3   16.00 12.00
        Dated 2006.

Adventure Sports — A802

No. 1567: a, Rafting. b, Cycling. c, Rock climbing.

2007, July 2
1567 A802   Horiz. strip of 3   16.00 12.00
a.-c.   6s Any single   4.00 4.00
        Dated 2006.

Miniature Sheet

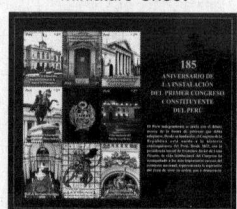

First Peruvian Congress, 185th
Anniv. — A803

No. 1568: a, Exposition Palace. b, Painting of Francisco González Gamarra. c, Tribunal of the Inquisition Building. d, Statue of Simón Bolívar. e, Legislative Palace at night. f, Pasos Perdidos Hall. g, Stained-glass window. h, Legislative Palace sculpture.

**Litho., Foil Application on Margin
and Label**
2007, July 12   Perf. 14x13½
1568 A803 2.50s Sheet of 8,
#a-h, + central label   19.00 13.50

Viceroys Type of 2006
No. 1569: a, Luis de Velasco (c. 1534-1617). b, Gaspar de Zuniga y Acevedo (1560-

1606). c, Juan de Mendoza y Luna (1571-1628). d, Francisco de Borja y Aragon (1581-1658).

2007, July 16   Litho.
1569 A767 6s Block of 4, #a-d,
+ label   16.00 16.00

Giuseppe
Garibaldi (1807-
82), Italian
Leader — A804

2007, July 26   Perf. 13½x14
1570 A804 6s multi   5.25 4.00

Scouting,
Cent.
A805

No. 1571: a, Scouting emblem, pictures of Scouts. b, Lord Robert Baden-Powell blowing kudu horn, flags.

2007, July 30   Perf. 14x13½
1571 A805 3s Horiz. pair, #a-b 5.50 4.00

Endangered Animals — A806

No. 1572: a, 3s, Oncifelis colocolo. b, 3s, Lontra felina. c, 6s, Harpia harpyja. d, 6s, Odocoileus virginianus.

2007, July 30   Perf. 13½x14
1572 A806   Block of 4, #a-d,
+ label   16.00 12.00

Medicinal Plants — A807

No. 1573: a, Bixa orellana. b, Cestrum auriculatum. c, Brugmansia suaveolens. d, Anacardium occidentale. e, Caesalpinia spinosa. f, Croton lechleri.

2007, Aug. 6   Litho.
1573 A807 2.50s Block of 6,
#a-f, + label   14.00 10.00

Raul Maria
Pereira, Architect,
and Postal
Headquarters,
Lima — A808

2007, Aug. 10
1574 A808 2s multi   2.00 1.50
        See Portugal No. 2940.

Viceroys Type of 2006
No. 1575: a, Diego Fernández de Cordoba (1578-1630). b, Luis Jerónimo de Cabrera (1589-1647). c, Pedro de Toledo y Leiva (c. 1585-1654). d, Garcia Sarmiento de Sotomayor (c. 1595-1659).

2007, Aug. 20   Perf. 14x13½
1575 A767 6s Block of 4, #a-d,
+ label   21.00 16.00

Souvenir Sheet

Riva-Agüero Institute, 60th
Anniv. — A809

2007, Sept. 10
1576 A809 10.50s multi   9.00 7.00

Peruvian National
Police Band,
Cent. (in
2006) — A810

Band: 2s, On steps of building. 8.50s, In parade.

2007, Sept. 15   Perf. 13½x14
1577-1578 A810 Set of 2   9.25 7.00

Birds — A811

Designs: No. 1579, 5.50s, Coeraba flaveola. No. 1580, 5.50s, Mimus longicaudatus. No. 1581, 5.50s, Pyrocephalus rubinus. No. 1582, 5.50s, Sarcoramphus papa.

Litho. With Foil Application
2007, Sept. 15
1579-1582 A811 Set of 4   20.00 15.00

Grand Masonic Lodge
of Peru, 125th
Anniv. — A812

2007, Sept. 17   Litho.   Perf. 14x13½
1583 A812 6.50s multi   5.75 4.50

Souvenir Sheet

Joint Command of the Armed Forces,
50th Anniv. — A813

2007, Sept. 24   Perf. 13½x14
1584 A813 14s multi   12.00 9.50

Children's
Art — A814

Winning pictures in children's art contest: No. 1585, 2s, River Scene, by Juana Chuquipiondo Mesía. No. 1586, 2s, Crane on Stump, by Rubén Saavedra Cobeñas, vert.

Perf. 13½x14, 14x13½
2007, Sept. 28
1585-1586 A814 Set of 2   4.50 2.75

Miniature Sheet

Automobiles — A815

No. 1587: a, 1935 Auburn Speedster 851 SC. b, 1903 Clément Brass Phaeton 9 CV. c, 1926 Dodge Special Pickup truck. d, 1928 Stutz BB Sedan Convertible Victoria. e, 1936 Pierce Arrow 1603 Touring D 700.

2007, Sept. 28   *Perf. 13½x14*
1587 A815 3s Sheet of 5, #a-e   14.00 10.00

Santa Clara Monastery, Cusco, 450th Anniv. — A816

2007, Oct. 1   *Perf. 14x13½*
1588 A816 5.50s multi   5.00 3.75

Cats A817

No. 1589: a, Angora. b, Persian. c, Bengal. d, Siamese.

2007, Oct. 1   **Litho.**
1589 A817 6s Block of 4, #a-d, + label   21.00 16.00

Miniature Sheet

Insects A818

No. 1590: a, Macrodontia cervicornis. b, Dynastes hercules. c, Titanus giganteus. d, Megasoma sp.

2007, Oct. 1   *Perf. 13½x14*
1590 A818 5.50s Sheet of 4, #a-d   15.00 15.00

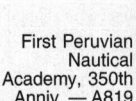

First Peruvian Nautical Academy, 350th Anniv. — A819

2007, Oct. 8
1591 A819 5.50s multi   5.00 3.75

America Issue, Education for All — A820

Designs: No. 1592, 5.50s, Two boys reading. No. 1593, 5.50s, Two girls reading.

2007, Oct. 9   *Perf. 14x13½*
1592-1593 A820   Set of 2   9.75 7.50

Daniel Alcides Carrión (1857-85), Describer of Carrion's Disease — A821

2007, Oct. 13   **Engr.**   *Perf. 13½x14*
1594 A821 3s brown   2.75 2.00

Miniature Sheet

Mushrooms — A822

No. 1595: a, Dyctiophora indusiata. b, Sepultaria arenicola. c, Marasmius haematocephalus. d, Marasmiellus volvatus.

Litho., Foil Application in Margin
2007, Oct. 15   *Perf. 14x13½*
1595 A822 2.50s Sheet of 4, #a-d   9.50 6.75

Peru No. 18 Volunteer Fire Brigade, Cent. A823

No. 1596 — Fire trucks: a, 1908 Merry Weather. b, 1969 Mack.

2007, Nov. 4   **Litho.**   *Perf. 13½x14*
1596 A823 3s Horiz. pair, #a-b   5.50 4.50

Víctor Raúl Haya de la Torre (1895-1979), Politician — A824

2007, Aug. 16   **Engr.**   *Perf. 14x13½*
1597 A824 3s claret   2.75 2.10

Souvenir Sheet

Megatherium Fossils — A825

2007, Sept. 28   **Litho.**
1598 A825 10s multi   8.75 7.25

Miniature Sheet

Bush Dog A826

No. 1599: a, 2s, Two dogs. b, 2s, One dog. c, 5.50s, One dog, facing right. d, 5.50s, One dog, facing left.

2007, Oct. 19   *Perf. 13½x14*
1599 A826   Sheet of 4, #a-d   13.50 11.00

Souvenir Sheet

Real Felipe Fort, Callao A827

2007, Oct. 29
1600 A827 6s multi   5.25 4.50

Familia Serrana, by Camilo Blas (1910-85) — A828

2007, Nov. 5   *Perf. 14x13½*
1601 A828 6s multi   5.25 4.50

Pre-Columbian Cultures Type of 2006

Artifacts of: 6s, Nasca culture, A.D. 600. 7s, Mochica culture, 700 B.C.-A.D. 200.

2007, Nov. 12   *Perf. 13½x14*
1602-1603 A755   Set of 2   11.50 9.50

Souvenir Sheet

Cahuachi Archaeological Site — A829

2007, Nov. 12
1604 A829 14.50s multi   12.50 10.50

Founders of Independence Society, 150th Anniv. — A830

2007, Dec. 1
1605 A830 6s multi   5.25 4.50

Christmas — A831

2007, Dec. 1   *Perf. 14x13½*
1606 A831 6.50s multi   5.75 5.00

First Peruvian Postage Stamps, 150th Anniv. A832

No. 1607: a, Peru #1. b, Peru #2.

2007, Dec. 1
1607 A832 2.50s Horiz. pair, #a-b 4.75 3.75

Altars in Lima Churches — A833

Altar from: 6s, Carmelite Church. 8.50s, Lima Cathedral.

2007, Dec. 1
1608-1609 A833   Set of 2   12.50 10.50

Asia-Pacific Economic Cooperation Forum — A834

2007, Dec. 3
1610 A834 6s multi   5.25 4.50

Roots — A835

Designs: No. 1611, 6s, Smallanthus sonchifolius. No. 1612, 6s, Manihot esculenta.

2007, Dec. 17
1611-1612 A835   Set of 2   10.50 8.50

Launch of First Peruvian Rocket, 1st Anniv. A836

No. 1613 — Emblem of National Space Commission and: a, Pedro Paulet Mostajo (1874-1945), aeronautical pioneer and Paulet I rocket in flight. b, Paulet I rocket on launch pad and civil ensign.

Litho., Litho. With Foil Application (#1613b)
2007, Dec. 27   *Perf. 13½x14*
1613 A836 3s Horiz. pair, #a-b   5.50 4.50

Souvenir Sheet

First Peruvian Scientific Expedition to the Antarctic, 20th Anniv. — A837

No. 1614: a, Ship "Humboldt." b, Expedition members, horiz.

Perf. 13½x14, 14x13½ (#1614b)
Litho. With Foil Application
2008, Feb. 22
1614 A837 10s Sheet of 2, #a-b 17.50 14.00

Arms Stamps of 1858, 150th Anniv. — A838

Designs: No. 1615, 5.50s, Peru #3. No. 1616, 5.50s, Peru #4. No. 1617, 5.50s, Peru #6.

2008, Mar. 10   Litho.   Perf. 14x13½
1615-1617 A838   Set of 3   15.00 12.50

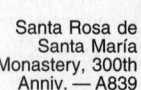

Santa Rosa de Santa María Monastery, 300th Anniv. — A839

2008, June 3   Perf. 13½x14
1618 A839 5.50s multi   5.00 4.00

Lima Philharmonic Society, Cent. — A840

No. 1619 — Emblem and: a, Violin. b, Musicians.

2008, June 8   Perf. 14x13½
1619 A840 3s Horiz. pair, #a-b   5.50 4.25

Lima General Cemetery, Bicent. — A841

Designs: No. 1620, 6.50s, Statue of angel and cross. No. 1621, 6.50s, Statue of praying woman, vert.

Perf. 13½x14, 14x13½
2008, June 17
1620-1621 A841   Set of 2   11.50 8.75

Viceroys Type of 2006

No. 1622: a, Luis Enríquez de Guzmán (c. 1605-61). b, Diego de Benavides y de la Cueva (1607-66). c, Pedro Antonio Fernandez de Castro (1634-72). d, Baltasar de la Cueva Enríquez (1626-86).

2008, June 24   Perf. 14x13½
1622 A767 6s Block of 4, #a-d, + label   21.00 16.50

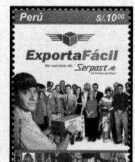

ExportaFacil Package Service — A842

2008, June 24
1623 A842 10s multi   8.75 6.75

America Issue A843

No. 1624: a, Inti Raymi (Festival of the Sun), Cuzco. b, Grape Harvest Festival, Ica.

2008, June 24   Perf. 13½x14
1624 A843 6.50s Horiz. pair, #a-b   11.50 8.75

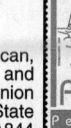

Latin American, Caribbean and European Union Heads of State Summit, Lima — A844

2008, July 1   Perf. 14x13½
1625 A844 6.50s red & black   5.75 4.50

2008 Summer Olympics, Beijing — A845

No. 1626 — Olympic mascots and places in Peru: a, Beibei, Máncora. b, Jingjing, Lima Cathedral. c, Yingying, Machu Picchu. d, Nini, Tambopata.

2008, July 1   Perf. 13½x14
1626 A845 1.40s Block of 4, #a-d, + label   5.75 4.00

Latin American and European Parliamentary Summit, Lima — A846

2008, July 2
1627 A846 6.50s multi   5.75 4.50

Aurelio Miró Quesada Sosa (1907-98), Lawyer and Writer — A847

2008, July 3
1628 A847 2.50s multi   2.40 1.75

National Literacy Program — A848

2008, July 4
1629 A848 2.50s multi   2.40 1.75

Exports Type of 2007

Designs: No. 1630, 5.50s, Olives (aceituna). No. 1631, 5.50s, Cotton (algodón). No. 1632, 5.50s, Avocados (palta).

2008, July 8
1630-1632 A801   Set of 3   14.50 12.00

Miniature Sheet

River Fish A849

No. 1633: a, Phractocephalus hemioliopterus. b, Mylossoma duriventre. c, Piaractus braphyomus. d, Ageneiosus ucayalensis. e, Brycon melanopterus.

2008, July 18
1633 A849 3s Sheet of 5, #a-e   14.00 11.00

A850

A851

A852

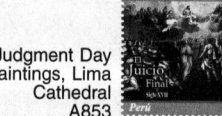

Judgment Day Paintings, Lima Cathedral A853

2008, Aug. 5
1634 A850 6.50s multi   5.75 4.50
1635 A851 6.50s multi   5.75 4.50
1636 A852 6.50s multi   5.75 4.50
1637 A853 6.50s multi   5.75 4.50
Nos. 1634-1637 (4)   23.00 18.00

A854

Design: Edwin Vásquez Cam (1922-93), First Peruvian Olympic Gold medalist.

2008, Aug. 6
1638 A854 6s multi   5.00 4.25

Cacti — A855

Designs: No. 1639, 7.50s, Melocactus onychacanthus. No. 1640, 7.50s, Matucana oreodoxa. No. 1641, 7.50s, Espostoa mirabilis.

2008, Aug. 13
1639-1641 A855   Set of 3   20.00 15.50

Dr. Javier Arias Stella, Pathologist — A856

2008, Aug. 22   Perf. 14x13½
1642 A856 2s multi   2.00 1.40

Miniature Sheet

Seven Wonders of the Modern World A857

No. 1643: a, 2.50s, Petra, Jordan. b, 2.50s, Machu Picchu, Peru. c, 2.50s, Great Wall of China. d, 2.50s, Statue of Christ the Redeemer, Brazil. e, 7.50s, Chichén Itzá, Mexico. f, 10s, Roman Colosseum, Italy. g, 10.50s, Taj Mahal, India.

2008, July 7   Litho.   Perf. 13½x14
1643 A857   Sheet of 7, #a-g   34.00 27.00

Intl. Year of the Potato — A858

Litho. With Foil Application
2008, Sept. 3
1644 A858 5.50s multi   5.00 3.75

Orchids — A859

Designs: No. 1645, 7s, Cattleya rex. No. 1646, 7s, Cattleya máxima.

2008, Sept. 3   Litho.   Perf. 14x13½
1645-1646 A859   Set of 2   12.50 9.50

Souvenir Sheet

Crypt of the Heroes, Cent. A860

2008, Sept. 8
1647 A860 10.50s multi   9.00 7.00

Pre-Columbian Cultures Type of 2006

Artifacts of: 2s, Tiahuanaco culture, 100 B.C.-A.D. 1200. 6s, Recuay culture, A.D. 1-600.

2008, Sept. 10   Perf. 13½x14
1648-1649 A755   Set of 2   7.25 5.50

Performing Arts Productions — A861

Designs: No. 1650, 6.50s, Play Na Catita. No. 1651, 6.50s, Ballet Huatyacuri.

Litho. with Foil Application
2008, Sept. 21   **Perf. 14x13½**
1650-1651 A861   Set of 2   11.50 8.75
Nos. 1650-1651 exist imperf.

National University of Trujillo Medical School, 50th Anniv. — A862

2008, Oct. 3   **Litho.**
1652 A862 6s multi   5.25 4.00

Miniature Sheet

Spiders A863

No. 1653: a, Micrathena sp. b, Lycosinae sp. c, Salticidae. d, Aglaoctenus castaneus.

2008, Oct. 3   **Perf. 13½x14**
1653 A863 2s Sheet of 4, #a-d   7.75 5.50

Souvenir Sheet

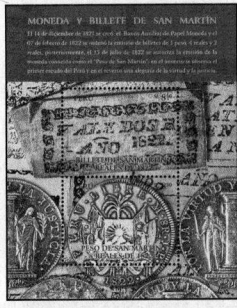

1822 José de San Martín Currency A864

No. 1654: a, 2-real note. b, 1-peso coin.

Litho. & Engr. (Foil Application in Margin)
2008, Oct. 13
1654 A864 8.50s Sheet of 2, #a-b   15.00 11.00

Souvenir Sheet

Choquequirao Ruins — A865

2008, Oct. 21   **Litho.**   **Perf. 14x13½**
1655 A865 10.50s multi   9.00 7.00

Museum of the Inquisition and Congress, Lima, 40th Anniv. — A866

No. 1656: a, Museum building (old National Senate Building). b, Inquisitors.

2008, Oct. 28
1656 A866 6s Horiz. pair, #a-b   10.50 8.00

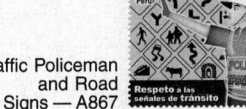

Traffic Policeman and Road Signs — A867

2008, Oct. 29   **Perf. 13½x14**
1657 A867 6.50s multi   5.75 4.25
Campaign for obeying traffic signs. No. 1657 exists imperf.

Edgardo Rebagliati National Hospital, 50th Anniv. — A868

2008, Nov. 3
1658 A868 2s multi   2.00 1.40

Paracas Mantles A869

No. 1659: a, Unbordered mantle with white and illustrated squares. b, Fringed mantle with hexagons in design. c, Fringed mantle with black squares. d, Mantle with illustrated border.

2008, Nov. 5   **Perf. 14x13½**
1659 A869 6s Block of 4 #a-d, + label   21.00 15.50

Xenoglaux Loweryi — A870

2008, Nov. 19   **Perf. 13½x14**
1660 A870 7.50s multi   6.50 5.00

Campaign Against Drug Abuse — A871

Winning art in children's stamp design contest depicting: No. 1661, 2s, Boys and Hand, by Diego Gutierrez. No. 1662, 2s, Crossed bones and marijuana leaves, by Carolina Luna Polo, vert.

Perf. 13½x14, 14x13½
2008, Nov. 21
1661-1662 A871   Set of 2   4.00 2.60

Christmas A872

2008, Dec. 1   **Perf. 13½x14**
1663 A872 8.50s multi   7.50 5.50

Free Trade Agreement Between Peru and United States, 1st Anniv. — A873

2008, Dec. 4
1664 A873 6s multi   5.50 4.00

Jerónimo de Loayza Gonzáles (1498-1575), First Archbishop of Lima — A874

2008, Dec. 10
1665 A874 2s multi   2.00 1.40

Souvenir Sheet

Inca God Wiracocha — A875

No. 1666 — Wiracocha: a, Breathing. b, With arm extended. c, Walking.

2008, Dec. 10
1666 A875 2.50s Sheet of 3, #a-c 7.00 5.00

Miniature Sheet

Intl. Polar Year A876

No. 1667: a, Iceberg. b, Raising of Peruvian flag. c, Map of Antarctica, International Polar Year emblem. d, Quelccaya Glacier, Peru.

2009, Jan. 15
1667 A876 2.20s Sheet of 4, #a-d   8.50 5.50

College of Administrators, 30th Anniv. — A877

2009, Feb. 11   **Litho.**   **Perf. 13½x14**
1668 A877 6.50s multi   5.75 4.00

Intl. Heliophysical Year — A878

Litho. With Foil Application
2009, Mar. 9   **Perf. 14x13½**
1669 A878 5.50s multi   5.25 3.50
Intl. Heliophysical Year was in 2007-08. The Intl. Year of Astronomy was in 2009.

Lighthouses — A879

Designs: No. 1670, 6.50s, La Marina Lighthouse. No. 1671, 6.50s, Muelle Dársena Lighthouse and boat.

2009, Mar. 9   **Litho.**
1670-1671 A879   Set of 2   11.50 8.50

A880

Sunflowers A881

2009, Mar. 13   **Perf. 13½x14**
1672 A880 2.50s multi   2.40 1.60
1673 A881 2.50s multi   2.40 1.60

Honesty A882

Punctuality A883

2009, Mar. 16   **Perf. 13½x14**
1674 A882 6.50s multi   5.75 4.25
        Perf. 14x13½
1675 A883 6.50s multi   5.75 4.25

Intl. Meteorology Day — A884

2009, Mar. 23   **Perf. 14x13½**
1676 A884 2s multi   2.00 1.40

Canyons A885

No. 1677: a, Colca Canyon. b, Cotahuasi Canyon. c, Pato Canyon.

2009, Mar. 23
1677 A885 2s Horiz. strip of 3, #a-c, + label   5.75 4.00

Parachuting — A886

No. 1678 — Skydivers with denomination in: a, UL. b, LR.

2009, Mar. 31   **Perf. 13½x14**
1678 A886 7s Horiz. pair, #a-b   12.50 9.00

New Year 2009 (Year of the Ox) A887

No. 1679 — Ring of Zodiac animals and: a, Rider on ox. b, Head of ox.

2009, Apr. 8   **Litho.**
1679 A887 2.50s Horiz. pair, #a-b 4.75 3.25

Earth
Day — A888

2009, Apr. 22
1680 A888 5.50s multi   5.00 3.75

Viceroys Type of 2006

No. 1681: a, Melchor de Liñán y Cisneros (1629-1708). b, Melchor de Navarra y Rocafull (1626-91). c, Melchor Portocarrero Lasso de la Vega (1636-1705). d, Manuel de Oms y de Santa Pau (1651-1710).

2009, Apr. 23   Perf. 14x13½
1681 A767 6s Block of 4 #a-d,
        + label   21.00 16.00

National University of
Central Peru,
Huancayo, 50th
Anniv. — A889

2009, Apr. 30
1682 A889 2s multi   2.00 1.40

Royal Commentaries
of the Incas, 400th
Anniv. — A890

Designs: No. 1683, 2s, Royal Commentaries of the Incas, book, by Garcellaso de la Vega. No. 1684, 2s, De la Vega (1539-1616), historian.

2009, Apr. 30
1683-1684 A890 Set of 2   4.00 2.75

America Issue,
Children's
Games — A891

Designs: No. 1685, 10.50s, Boy flying kite. No. 1686, 10.50s, Children playing ronda.

2009, Apr. 30   Litho.
1685-1686 A891 Set of 2   18.00 14.00

Endangered Animals — A892

No. 1687: a, Blastocerus dichotomus. b, Pelecanoides garnotii. c, Podocnemis expansa. d, Crax unicornis.

2009, May 4   Perf. 13½x14
1687 A892 7.50s Block of 4,
        #a-d, + la-
        bel   26.00 20.00

Souvenir Sheet

"Libertad
Parada"
Coin
A893

No. 1688: a, Obverse (arms). b, Reverse (Liberty), vert.

**Perf. 13½x14 (#1688a), 14x13½
(#1688b)**
2009, May 8
1688 A893 3s Sheet of 2, #a-b   5.25 4.00

Folk Art — A894

Designs: No. 1689, 6.50s, Retable, Ayacucho (Retablo Ayacuchano). No. 1690, 6.50s, Native clothing, Cusco (Muñequería Cusqueña). No. 1691, 6.50s, Decorated bull, Pucará (Torito de Pucará).

2009, May 11   Perf. 14x13½
1689-1691 A894 Set of 3   17.00 13.50

Crustaceans — A895

No. 1692: a, Farfantepenaeus californiensis. b, Sicyonia aliaffnis. c, Ucides occidentalis. d, Palinurus elephas.

2009, May 15   Perf. 13½x14
1692 A895 10s Block of 4, #a-
        d, + label   35.00 27.00

Souvenir Sheet

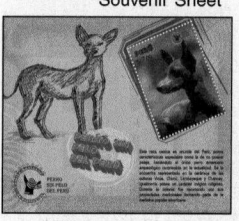

Peruvian
Hairless
Dog
A896

2009, May 15   Perf. 14x13½
1693 A896 7s multi   6.25 4.75

Santiago de Surco
Municipality, 80th
Anniv. — A897

2009, May 21   Litho.
1694 A897 5.50s multi   5.00 3.75

Submarines
A898

No. 1695: a, BAP Pisagua. b, BAP Arica.

2009, May 22   Perf. 13½x14
1695 A898 2.50s Vert. pair, #a-b   4.75 3.50

Cuzco as
UNESCO World
Heritage Site,
25th Anniv. (in
2008) — A899

Litho. With Foil Application
2009, May 24
1696 A899 2.50s multi   2.40 1.75

Odontological
College of Peru,
45th
Anniv. — A900

2009, May 29   Litho.
1697 A900 2s multi   2.00 1.40

Campaign
Against
Rabies — A901

2009, June 25 Litho. Perf. 13½x14
1698 A901 5.50s multi   5.00 3.75

Louis Braille (1809-52), Educator of
the Blind — A902

No. 1699: a, Braille. b, Braille text.

Litho. & Engr.
2009, June 30   Perf. 14x13½
1699 A902 2.20s Horiz. pair, #a-b 4.25 3.00

**Pre-Columbian Cultures Type of
2006**

Designs: No. 1700, 2s, Huari culture, 550-900. No. 1701, 2s, Chimú culture, 1000-1400.

2009, July 3 Litho. Perf. 13½x14
1700-1701 A755 Set of 2   4.00 2.75

Ciro Alegría (1909-67),
Journalist and
Politician — A903

2009, July 8   Perf. 14x13½
1702 A903 2.50s multi   2.40 1.75

Peruvian Tourist
Attractions
A904

Designs: No. 1703, 2.50s, Amazon River, Loretio Region. No. 1704, 2.50s, Boat on Lake Titicaca, Puno Region. No. 1705, 7.50s, Cumbemayo Archaeological Site, Cajamarca Region.

2009   Perf. 13½x14
1703-1705 A904 Set of 3   11.00 8.50
    Issued: Nos. 1703-1704, 7/17; No. 1705, 7/10.

Peruvian Philatelic
Association, 60th
Anniv. — A905

2009, July 21   Perf. 14x13½
1706 A905 2s multi   2.00 1.40

Víctor Raúl Haya
de la Torre
(1895-1975),
Politician — A906

2009, Aug. 2 Litho. Perf. 13½x14
1707 A906 2s multi   2.00 1.40

Miniature Sheet

Peruvian
Cuisine
A907

No. 1708: a, Tacacho con cecina. b, Ocopa. c, Cebiche de conchas negras. d, Picante de papa con cuy frito. e, Frejoles con cabrito.

2009, Aug. 3
1708 A907 3s Sheet of 5, #a-e 14.00 10.50

Miniature Sheet

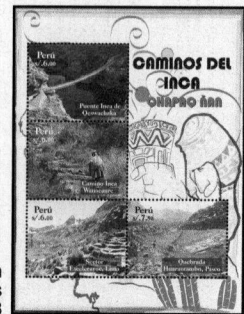

Incan
Roads
A908

No. 1709: a, 6s, Inca Bridge, Qeswachaka. b, 6s, Inca Road, Wanacaure. c, 6s, Escalerayoc Sector, Lima. d, 7.50s, Quebrada Huarautambo, Pasco.

2009, Aug. 6
1709 A908 Sheet of 4, #a-d 22.50 17.50

Exports Type of 2007

Designs: No. 1710, 2.50s, Guinea pig. No. 1711, 2.50s, Coffee.

2009, Aug. 19
1710-1711 A801 Set of 2   4.75 3.50

Souvenir Sheet

Baguatherium Jaureguii Fossil — A909

2009, Aug. 26   *Perf. 14x13½*
1712 A909 7s multi   6.25 4.75

Miniature Sheet

Mollusks
A910

No. 1713: a, Megalobulimus popelairianus. b, Megalobulimus capillaccus. c, Scutalus versicolor. d, Scutalus proteus.

2009, Aug. 31   *Perf. 13½x14*
1713 A910 6.50s Sheet of 4,
    #a-d   23.00 18.00

Free Trade Treaty Between Peru and People's Republic of China — A911

2009, Sept. 10   *Litho.*   *Perf. 13½x14*
1714 A911 7.50s multi   6.50 5.25

Chinese Immigration to Peru, 160th Anniv. — A912

2009, Oct. 12
1715 A912 8.50s multi   7.50 6.00

Natl. Museum of Archaeology, Anthropology and History of Peru — A913

2009, Oct. 13   *Perf. 14x13½*
1716 A913 5.50s multi   5.00 4.00

Miniature Sheet

Birds
A914

No. 1717: a, Actitis macularia. b, Glaucidium brasilianum. c, Numenius phaeopus. d, Egretta caerulea.

2009, Nov. 9   *Perf. 13½x14*
1717 A914 6s Sheet of 4, #a-d 21.00 17.00

Luciano Pavarotti (1935-2007), Singer — A915

2009, Nov. 12
1718 A915 10.50s multi   9.00 7.50

Children's Art — A916

Winning art in children's environmental protection stamp design contest: No. 1719, 2s, Orchid, parrot and hand, by Ahmed Lonia Heredia Pérez. No. 1720, 2s, Children, flora and fauna, by Scarie Estefany Rojas Reátegui.

2009, Nov. 22   *Perf. 14x13½*
1719-1720 A916   Set of 2   4.00 3.00

Christmas
A917

2009, Nov. 30   *Perf. 13½x14*
1721 A917 2.20s multi   2.10 1.60

Souvenir Sheet

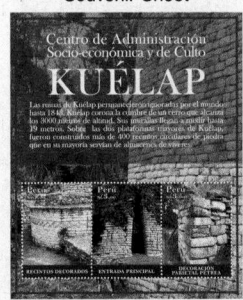

Kuélap Archaeological Site — A918

No. 1722: a, Decorated enclosures (Recintos decorados). b, Principal entrance (Entrada principal). c, Decorated stone walls (Decoración parietal petrea).

2010, June 7   *Litho.*   *Perf. 14x13½*
1722 A918 3s Sheet of 3, #a-c   8.75 6.50

Central Station for Lima Metropolitan Bus Line — A919

No. 1723: a, Road over tunnel. b, Bus.

2010, June 22   *Perf. 13½x14*
1723 A919 2.20s Horiz. pair, #a-b 4.50 3.25

Javier Pérez de Cuéllar, Fifth Secretary-General of the United Nations, 90th Birthday — A920

2010, Aug. 9
1724 A920 50c multi   .75 .35

St. Francis Solano (1549-1610) — A921

2010, Aug. 12   *Perf. 14x13½*
1725 A921 40c multi   .65 .30

Gustavo Pons Muzzo (1916-2008), Historian — A922

2010, Aug. 12
1726 A922 50c multi   .75 .35

Archdiocese of Arequipa, 400th Anniv. — A923

2010, Aug. 12   *Perf. 13½x14*
1727 A923 2s multi   2.00 1.50

Dogs
A924

No. 1728: a, Samoyed. b, Siberian husky.

2010, Aug. 12   *Perf. 14x13½*
1728 A924 30c Horiz. pair, #a-b 1.10 .45

Rebeca Carrión Cachot, Archaeologist, 50th Anniv. of Death — A925

2010, Aug. 13   *Litho.*
1729 A925 40c multi   .75 .30

Afro-Peruvian Culture Day — A926

No. 1730: a, Musical instruments. b, National Afro-Peruvian Museum, Lima.

2010, Aug. 13   *Perf. 13½x14*
1730 A926 10c Horiz. pair, #a-b 1.20 .25

Miniature Sheet

2010 World Cup Soccer Championships, South Africa — A927

No. 1731: a, Mascot. b, Emblem. c, World Cup trophy. d, Soccer player and ball.

2010, Aug. 13   *Perf. 14x13½*
1731 A927 10s Sheet of 4, #a-
    d   36.00 29.00

Tourist Sites in Lima — A928

Designs: No. 1732, 3s, Magic Fountains. No. 1733, 3s, Lake, Huascar Park.

2010, Aug. 21
1732-1733 A928   Set of 2   6.00 4.50

Souvenir Sheet

"Seated Liberty" Coin
A929

2010, Aug. 21   *Perf. 14x13½*
1734 A929 3s multi   3.00 2.25

Mushrooms — A930

No. 1735: a, Suillus luteus. b, Pleurotus cornucopiae.

2010, Aug. 24   *Litho.*
1735 A930 6s Horiz. pair, #a-b   11.00 8.75

New Year 2010 (Year of the Tiger) — A931

No. 1736: a, Tiger at left. b, Tiger at right.

2010, Aug. 26   *Perf. 13½x14*
1736 A931 20c Vert. pair, #a-b   1.20 .30

Viceroys Type of 2006

No. 1737: a, Diego Ladrón de Guevara Orozco y Calderon (1641-1718). b, Carmine Nicolao Caracciolo (1671-1726). c, Diego Morcillo Rubio de Auñón (1642-1730). d, José de Armendariz (1670-1740).

2010, Sept. 1   *Perf. 14x13½*
1737 A767 3s Block of 4, #a-d,
    + label   12.00 8.75

Jorge Chavez (1887-1910), Pilot — A932

Litho. & Engr.
2010, Sept. 3   *Perf. 13½x14*
1738 A932 2s multi   2.00 1.50

Centenary of Chavez's flight over Alps, after which he crash-landed and later died.

Souvenir Sheet

Stone
Heads of
the
Chavin
Culture
A933

2010, Sept. 3   Litho.   *Perf. 14x13½*
1739 A933 10s multi   9.25 7.25

Pre-Columbian Cultures Type of 2006

Artifacts of: No. 1740, 50c, Chincha culture, c. 1000. No. 1741, 50c, Chancay culture, c. 1000.

2010, Sept. 7   *Perf. 13½x14*
1740-1741 A755   Set of 2   1.40 .75

Volunteer Fire Brigades in Peru, 150th
Anniv.
A934

No. 1742: a, 1860 Merryweather fire carriage. b, Pierce Contender fire truck.

2010, Sept. 9
1742 A934 6s Horiz. pair, #a-b   11.00 8.75

Club Alianza
Lima Soccer
Team — A935

2010, Sept. 10
1743 A935 3s multi   3.00 2.25

Miniature Sheet

Orchids
A936

No. 1744: a, Anguloa virginalis. b, Masdevallia pernix. c, Stanhopea marizaiana. d, Telipogon campoverdei.

2010, Sept. 16   Litho.
1744 A936 3s Sheet of 4, #a-d   12.00 8.75

Colegio Nacional
Iquitos Soccer
Team — A937

2010, Sept. 17
1745 A937 3s multi   3.00 2.25

Frédéric Chopin
(1810-49),
Composer
A938

2010, Sept. 21   Litho. & Engr.
1746 A938 3s multi   3.00 2.25

Windsurfing
A939

Litho. With Foil Application
2010, Sept. 21
1747 A939 3s multi   3.00 2.25

Souvenir Sheet

Thalassocnus Littoralis — A940

2010, Sept. 21   Litho.
1748 A940 10s multi   9.25 7.25

Melgar Soccer
Team — A941

2010, Sept. 24
1749 A941 3s multi   3.00 2.25

America Issue,
National
Symbols — A942

Peruvian: No. 1750, 5s, Arms. No. 1751, 5s, Flag.

2010, Oct. 5   *Perf. 14x13½*
1750-1751 A942   Set of 2   9.50 7.25

Ollantaytambo
Archaeological
Site — A943

2010, Oct. 29   *Perf. 13½x14*
1752 A943 5s multi   4.75 3.75

Christmas
A944

2010, Nov. 2
1753 A944 10s multi   9.25 7.25

Children's Art — A945

Winning art in children's art contest by: No. 1754, 2s, Jimena P. Vega Gonzáles, 1st place. No. 1755, 2s, Bettina Paz Pinto, 2nd place.

2010, Nov. 22   *Perf. 14x13½*
1754-1755 A945   Set of 2   4.00 3.00

Folk Art — A946

Designs: No. 1756, 2s, Virgin of Pino, statue by Antonio Olave Palomino. No. 1757, 2s, San Marcos, retable by Jesús Urbano Rojas. No. 1758, 2s, Procession of St. Peter, carving by Fidel Barrientos Bustos.

2010, Nov. 25   Litho.
1756-1758 A946   Set of 3   6.25 4.25

Ninth Lions
International Forum of
Latin America and the
Caribbean,
Lima — A947

2011, Jan. 15
1759 A947 7.80s multi   7.50 5.75

José María
Arguedas (1911-
69),
Writer — A948

2011, Jan. 31   *Perf. 13½x14*
1760 A948 6.60s multi   6.25 4.75

Postal Union of
the Americas,
Spain and
Portugal
(UPAEP),
Cent. — A949

2011, Mar. 23
1761 A949 2s multi   2.10 1.50

Transportation
Infrastructure
A950

Designs: 5s, Southern Pier, Port of Callao. 5.20s, Southern Interoceanic Highway.

2011, May 16   Litho.
1762-1763 A950   Set of 2   10.00 7.50

Scouting in Peru,
Cent. — A951

Peruvian and Scouting flags and: No. 1764, 6.40s, Boy Scout. No. 1765, 6.40s, Girl Scout.

2011, May 25   *Perf. 14x13½*
1764-1765 A951   Set of 2   12.50 9.25

Jicamarca Radio
Observatory, 50th
Anniv. — A952

2011, June 7   *Perf. 13½x14*
1766 A952 6.60s multi   6.25 4.75

Awarding of 2010
Nobel Prize for
Literature to Mario
Vargas Llosa — A953

2011, June 8   *Perf. 14x13½*
1767 A953 7.80s multi   7.50 5.75

Peruvian Submarine Force,
Cent. — A954

No. 1768 — Emblem of Submarine Force, various submarines with denomination at: a, UR. b, UL.

2011, June 9   *Perf. 13½x14*
1768 A954 7.20s Horiz. pair,
        #a-b   14.00 10.50

Javier Pulgar Vidal
(1911-2003),
Geographer — A955

2011, June 13   *Perf. 14x13½*
1769 A955 2.40s multi   2.50 1.75

Campaign Against HIV and
AIDS — A956

No. 1770 — Text, AIDS ribbon and: a, Man. b, Woman.

2011, June 13   *Perf. 13½x14*
1770 A956 5.50s Horiz. pair, #a-
        b   11.00 8.00

First Call for Peruvian Independence by Francisco Antonio de Zela y Arizaga, Bicent. — A957

No. 1771: a, Painting of Zela. b, Statue of Zela.

2011, June 20   Litho.
1771 A957 7.20s Horiz. pair,
        #a-b   14.00 10.50

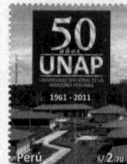

Amazonia National
University of Peru,
50th Anniv. — A958

2011, June 23   *Perf. 14x13½*
1772 A958 2.70s multi   8.75 2.00

National Theater,
Lima — A959

2011, June 23   *Perf. 13½x14*
1773 A959 5s multi   5.00 3.75

Pre-Columbian Cultures Type of 2006

Artifacts of: No. 1774, 6.40s, Chachapoya culture, 700-1500. No. 1775, 6.40s, Inca culture, 1400-1572.

2011, June 24		**Perf. 13½x14**
1774-1775 A755	Set of 2	12.50 9.50

Viceroys Type of 2006

No. 1776: a, José Antonio de Mendoza Caamano y Sotomayor (1667-1746). b, José Antonio Manso de Velasco (1688-1767). c, Manuel de Amat y Junyent (1707-82). d, Manuel Guirior (1708-88).

2011, July 1		**Perf. 14x13½**
1776 A767	7.80s Block of 4, #a-d, + label	30.00 23.00

Motocross Racing — A960

2011, July 5		**Litho.**
1777 A960	7.80s multi	7.50 5.75

Dances — A961

Designs: No. 1778, 9s, Tijeras (scissors) dance. No. 1779, 9s, Huaconada.

2011, July 5		**Perf. 13½x14**
1778-1779 A961	Set of 2	17.00 13.50

Year of the Rabbit — A962

No. 1780: a, Rabbit. b, Chinese character for "rabbit."

2011, July 5		**Perf. 14x13½**
1780 A962	5.50s Horiz. pair, #a-b	11.00 8.00

Souvenir Sheet

Discovery of Machu Picchu, Cent. — A963

2011, July 5		
1781 A963	7.80s multi	7.50 5.75

Electric Trains A964

No. 1782: a, One train. b, Two trains.

2011, July 16		**Litho.**
1782 A964	5.50s Horiz. pair, #a-b	11.00 8.00

Maxillaria Pyhalae — A965

2011, July 19		
1783 A965	10.50s multi	10.00 7.75

Governmental Palace and Presidents of Peru — A966

No. 1784: a, Government Palace, 18th cent. b, Marshal José de La Mar (1778-1830). c, Gen. Agustín Gamarra (1785-1841). d, Gen. Luis José de Orbegoso (1795-1847). e, Gen. Felipe Santiago Salaverry (1805-36). f, Marshal Andrés de Santa Cruz (1792-1865). g, Manuel Menéndez (1793-1847). h, Gen. Juan Crisóstomo Torrico (1808-75). i, Justo Figuerola (1771-1854). j, Government Palace, 20th cent. k, Gen. Manuel Ignacio de Vivanco (1806-73). l, Gen. Ramón Castilla (1797-1867). m, Gen. José Rufino Echenique (1808-87). n, Gen. Miguel de San Roman (1802-63). o, Gen. Juan Antonio Pezet (1809-79). p, Gen. Mariano Ignacio Prado (1826-1901). q, Col. José Balta (1814-72). r, Manuel Pardo y Lavalle (1834-78). s, Gen. Luis La Puerta (1811-96). t, Nicolás de Piérola (1839-1913). u, Francisco García Calderón (1834-1905). v, Admiral Lizardo Montero (1832-1905). w, Gen. Miguel Iglesias (1830-1909). x, Gold Room, Government Palace. y, Grand Hall, Government Palace. z, Flag and arms of Peru, Government Palace. aa, Túpac Amaru Room, Government Palace. ab, Gen. Andrés A. Cáceres (1836-1923). ac, Col. Remigio Morales Bermúdez (1836-94). ad, Eduardo López de Romaña (1847-1912). ae, Manuel Candamo (1841-1904). af, José Pardo Barreda (1864-1947). ag, Augusto B. Leguía (1863-1932). ah, Guillermo Billinghurst (1851-1915). ai, Gen. Oscar R. Benavides (1876-1945). aj, Lieutenant Colonel Luis M. Sánchez Cerro (1889-1933). ak, Manuel Prado y Ugarteche (1889-1967). al, José Luis Bustamante y Rivero (1894-1989). am, Gen. Manuel A. Odría (1897-1974). an, Gen. Ricardo Pérez Godoy (1905-82). ao, Honor Guard, Government Palace. ap, Gen. Nicolás Lindley (1908-95). aq, Fernando Belaunde Terry (1912-2002). ar, Gen. Juan Velasco Alvarado (1910-77). as, Gen. Francisco Morales Bermúdez. at, Alan García Pérez. au, Alberto Fujimori. av, Valentín Paniagua (1936-2006). aw, Alejandro Toledo Manrique. ax, Government Palace, 21st cent.

2011, July 25		**Perf. 14x13½**
1784 A966	Sheet of 50	120.00 87.50
a.-ax.	2.40s Any single	2.25 1.75

Intl. Year of Chemistry — A967

2011, Aug. 1		**Litho.**
1785 A967	7.20s multi	7.00 5.25

Children's Art — A968

Winning art in children's prevention of natural disasters stamp design contest: 20c, Overturned boat, hand, tornado, dead fish and flooded house, by Carlos Renato Huaynasi Calcina. 2.40s, Children at school, by Sherley Breshley Suclupe Calderon.

2011, Aug. 18		**Perf. 13½x14**
1786-1787 A968	Set of 2	3.00 1.90

National Archives, 150th Anniv. — A969

2011, Aug. 19		
1788 A969	5.80s multi	5.50 4.25

Miniature Sheet

Peruvian Cuisine A970

No. 1789: a, Lomo Saltado (beef with onions, tomatoes, rice and fried potatoes). b, Ají de Gallina (creamed chicken with chili peppers). c, Tiradito de Pescado (raw fish in spicy sauce). d, Chicharrón (fried pork rinds).

2011, Aug. 25		
1789 A970	7.80s Sheet of 4, #a-d	30.00 23.00

Statue of St. Sebastian, Patron Saint of Chepén — A971

2011, Aug. 30		**Perf. 14x13½**
1790 A971	2s multi	2.10 1.50

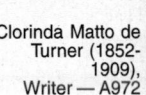

Clorinda Matto de Turner (1852-1909), Writer — A972

2011, Sept. 9		**Perf. 13½x14**
1791 A972	3.60s multi	3.50 2.75

1838 South Peru Gold 8-Escudo Coin — A973

No. 1792: a, Reverse. b, Obverse.

2011, Sept. 12		**Perf. 14x13½**
1792 A973	5.80s Horiz. pair, #a-b	11.00 8.50

Cayetano Heredia University, 50th Anniv. — A974

2011, Sept. 22		**Perf. 13½x14**
1793 A974	3.60s multi	3.50 2.75

First Airplane Flight in Peru by Juan Bielovucic Cavalie, Cent. — A975

2011, Sept. 23		**Litho. & Engr.**
1794 A975	7.20p multi	7.00 5.25

Miniature Sheet

Primates A976

No. 1795: a, Lagothrix flavicauda. b, Callicebus oenanthe. c, Aotus miconax. d, Cacajao calvus.

2011, Oct. 10	**Litho.**	**Perf. 14x13½**
1795 A976	7.80s Sheet of 4, #a-d	30.00 23.00

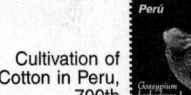

Cultivation of Cotton in Peru, 700th Anniv. — A977

Gossypium barbadense with panel at bottom in: No. 1796, 8.50s, Blue. No. 1797, 8.50s, Red brown.

2011, Oc. 11		**Perf. 13½x14**
1796-1797 A977	Set of 2	16.00 12.50

Souvenir Sheet

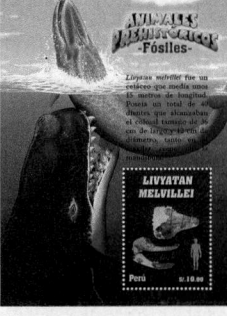

Fossils of Livyatan Melvillei A978

Litho. (With Foil Application in Sheet Margin)	
2011, Oct. 17	**Perf. 14x13½**
1798 A978 10s multi	9.50 7.50

Franz Liszt (1811-86), Composer — A979

Litho. & Engr.	
2011, Oct. 22	**Perf. 14x13½**
1799 A979 5.80s multi	5.50 4.25

Endangered Birds — A980

Designs: No. 1800, 10s, Loddigesia mirabilis. No. 1801, 10s, Cinclodes palliatus.

2011, Oct. 28   Litho.   Perf. 13½x14
1800-1801 A980   Set of 2   19.00 15.00

Christmas
A981

2011, Nov. 1
1802 A981 5.50s multi   5.25 4.25

America
Issue — A982

Designs: No. 1803, 10s, Lion's head mailbox. No. 1804, 10s, Red rectangular mailbox.

2011, Nov. 2   Perf. 14x13½
1803-1804 A982   Set of 2   19.00 15.00

Martín Chambi (1891-1973),
Photographer — A983

2011, Nov. 4
1805 A983 5.20s multi   5.00 4.00

Peruvian
Coffee — A984

2011, Nov. 10   Perf. 13½x14
1806 A984 6.60s multi   6.25 5.00

Summit of South American and Arab Countries — A985

2011, Dec. 2   Perf. 14x13½
1807 A985 8.40s multi   8.00 6.25

Diplomatic Relations Between Peru and Australia, 50th Anniv. — A986

No. 1808: a, Sloth (oso perezoso). b, Koala.

2013, Mar. 1
1808 A986 3.30s Horiz. pair, #a-b 6.75 5.25

Diplomatic Relations Between Peru and India, 50th Anniv. — A987

No. 1809: a, Machu Picchu, Peru. b, Taj Mahal, India.

2013, Mar. 19
1809 A987 3.60s Horiz. pair, #a-b 7.25 5.75

Diplomatic Relations Between Peru and South Korea, 50th Anniv. — A988

No. 1810: a, 2.50s, Machu Picchu, Peru. b, 3s, Seongsan Ilchulbong, South Korea.

2013, Apr. 1   Perf. 13½x14
1810 A988   Horiz. pair, #a-b   5.75 4.25
See South Korea No. 2399.

Service and Maintenance for Peru Air Force, 80th Anniv. — A989

2013, June 13   Litho.   Perf. 14x13½
1811 A989 5.50s multi   5.00 4.00

World Record Black Marlin Catch, 60th Anniv. — A990

Designs: No. 1812, 2.50s, Alfred C. Glassell, Jr. and 1,560-pound black marlin. No. 1813, 2.50s, Fishing boat "Miss Texas," horiz.

Perf. 14x13½, 13½x14
2013, Aug. 2   Litho.
Stamps + Label
1812-1813 A990   Set of 2   4.75 3.75

New Year 2013 (Year of the Dragon) A991

No. 1814: a, Chinese Zodiac wheel and Chinese character for "dragon." b, Dragon figurine.

2013, Aug. 15   Litho.   Perf. 14x13½
1814 A991 6s Horiz. pair, #a-b   12.00 8.75

Diplomatic Relations Between Peru and Japan, 140th Anniv. — A992

No. 1815: a, Machu Picchu, Peru. b, Kinkaku-ji, Japan.

2013, Aug. 21   Litho.   Perf. 14x13½
1815 A992 6s Horiz. pair, #a-b   12.00 8.75

Santa Teresa Convent, Arequipa — A993

2013, Aug. 23   Litho.   Perf. 14x13½
1816 A993 6s multi   5.75 4.50

Anthropomorphic Monoliths, Ancash Archaeological Park and Museum — A994

2013, Aug. 28   Litho.   Perf. 13½
1817 A994 6s multi   5.75 4.50

Benavidesite
A995

2013, Aug. 29   Litho.   Perf. 13½x14
1818 A995 8s multi   7.50 5.75

Federico Villarreal National University, 50th Anniv. — A996

2013, Sept. 5   Perf. 13½x14
1819 A996 4s multi   4.00 3.00

Souvenir Sheet

Inkayacu Paracasensis and Its Fossilized Remains — A997

Litho. (With Foil Application in Sheet Margin)
2013, Sept. 12   Perf. 14x13½
1820 A997 10s multi   9.25 7.25

Diocese of Cuzco, 475th Anniv. — A998

2013, Sept. 13   Litho.   Perf. 14x13½
1821 A998 4s multi   4.00 3.00

Intl. Year of Quinoa — A999

2013, Sept. 27   Litho.   Perf. 13½x14
1822 A999 5.50s multi   5.25 4.00

Souvenir Sheet

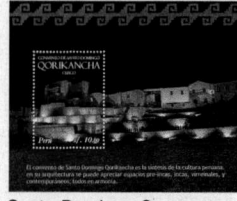

Santo Domingo Convent and Qorikancha Incan Temple, Cuzco — A1000

2013, Sept. 27   Litho.   Perf. 14x13½
1823 A1000 10s multi   9.25 7.25

Souvenir Sheet

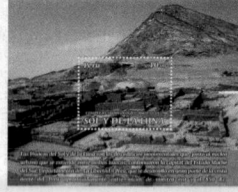

Temples of the Sun and Moon Archaeological Sites — A1001

2013, Sept. 27   Litho.   Perf. 13½x14
1824 A1001 10s multi   9.25 7.25

Souvenir Sheet

Five-Peseta Coin of Peru From 1880 — A1002

No. 1825: a, Reverse (head of Ceres). b, Obverse (coat of arms).

2013, Oct. 1   Litho.   Perf. 14x13½
1825 A1002 5s Sheet of 2, #a-b 11.00 7.25

Souvenir Sheet

1863 Centavo Coins A1003

No. 1826 — Reverse of: a, One-centavo coin. b, Two-centavo coin.

2013, Oct. 1   Litho.   Perf. 14x13½
1826 A1003 6s Sheet of 2, #a-b 11.00 8.75

Museum of Natural History, Lima, 95th Anniv. — A1004

2013, Oct. 4   Litho.   Perf. 14x13½
1827 A1004 4s multi   4.00 3.00

Souvenir Sheet

Chahuaytiri Rock Paintings — A1005

2013, Oct. 11 Litho. Perf. 14x13½
1828 A1005 10s multi   9.25 7.25

Souvenir Sheet

Canaanimys Maquiensis and Its Fossilized Remains — A1006

Litho. (With Foil Application in Sheet Margin)
2013, Oct. 12   Perf. 14x13½
1829 A1006 10s multi   9.50 7.25

Miniature Sheet

Eagles
A1007

No. 1830: a, Harpia harpyja. b, Morphus guianensis. c, Spizaetus ornatus. d, Spizaetus isidori.

Litho. (With Foil Application in Sheet Margin)
2013, Oct. 14   Perf. 14x13½
1830 A1007 3s Sheet of 4, #a-d 12.00 8.75

Miniature Sheet

Butterflies — A1008

No. 1831: a, Hypanartia splendida. b, Isanthrene flavizonata. c, Protesilaus glaucolaus. d, Histioea peruana.

2013, Oct. 24 Litho. Perf. 13½x14
1831 A1008 4s Sheet of 4, #a-d   15.50 11.50

Miniature Sheet

Hummingbirds — A1009

No. 1832: a, Heliangelus regalis. b, Myrtis fanny. c, Taphrolesbia griseiventris. d, Rhodopis vesper.

2013, Oct. 31 Litho. Perf. 13½x14
1832 A1009 5s Sheet of 4, #a-d   19.00 14.50

Canonization of St. Martin de Porres, 50th Anniv. (in 2012) — A1010

2013, Nov. 4 Litho. Perf. 13½x14
1833 A1010 4s multi   4.00 3.00

Diplomatic Relations Between Peru and Russia, 45th Anniv. — A1011

No. 1834: a, Machu Picchu, Peru. b, Kizhi Pogost, Russia.

2013, Nov. 4 Litho. Perf. 13½x14
1834 A1011 6s Horiz. pair, #a-b 12.00 8.75

America Issue A1012

No. 1835: a, Animals and corn stalk from Myth of the Garden of Gold. b, Sun God from Myth of the Garden of Gold. c, Eyes of 14 people, face paint above 5th eye on top row. d, Eyes of 14 people, face paint below 3rd and 4th eyes on bottom row.

2013, Nov. 4 Litho. Perf. 13½x14
1835 A1012 4s Block of 4, #a-d, + label 16.00 11.50

Souvenir Sheet

Boat Dock on Amazon River A1013

2013, Nov. 11 Litho. Perf. 13½x14
1836 A1013 8s multi   7.50 5.75

Miniature Sheet

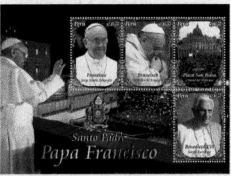

Election of Pope Francis A1014

No. 1837: a, Pope Francis, hands not visible. b, Pope Francis, hand visible. c, St. Peter's Square. d, Pope Benedict XVI.

2013, Nov. 13 Litho. Perf. 14x13½
1837 A1014 6s Sheet of 4, #a-d   22.50 17.50

Souvenir Sheet

Walls Built by the Incas, Cuzco A1015

2013, Nov. 13 Litho. Perf. 14x13½
1838 A1015 10s multi   9.25 7.25

A1016

Winning Designs in 6th Children's Art Contest — A1017

2013, Dec. 2 Litho. Perf. 13½x14
1839 A1016 4s multi   3.75 3.00
                Perf. 14x13½
1840 A1017 4s multi   3.75 3.00

A1018

Winning Designs in 7th Children's Art Contest — A1019

2013, Dec. 6 Litho. Perf. 13½x14
1841 A1018 4s multi   3.75 3.00
1842 A1019 4s multi   3.75 3.00

Resolution of Ecuador-Peru Border Dispute, 15th Anniv. — A1020

2014, Jan. 30 Litho. Perf. 14x13½
1843 A1020 8s multi   7.75 5.75

Commercial Accords Between Peru, Colombia and the European Union — A1021

2014, Feb. 28 Litho. Perf. 14x13½
1844 A1021 9.50s multi   9.25 6.75

A1022

Design: Captain José Abelardo Quiñones Gonzales (1914-41), military hero.

2014, Apr. 8 Litho. Perf. 13½x14
1845 A1022 3.80s multi   4.00 2.75

Miguel Grau Seminario (1834-79), Admiral — A1023

2014, July 23 Litho. Perf. 14x13½
1846 A1023 6s multi   5.25 4.25

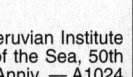

Peruvian Institute of the Sea, 50th Anniv. — A1024

2014, Sept. 5 Litho. Perf. 13½x14
1847 A1024 3.80s multi   3.50 2.60

Caballito de Totoro (Traditional Reed Watercraft) — A1025

2014, Sept. 17 Litho. Perf. 14x13½
1848 A1025 7s multi   6.25 5.00

Tambomachay Temple Archaeological Site — A1026

2014, Sept. 19 Litho. Perf. 14x13½
1849 A1026 6s multi   5.25 4.25

Manuel González Prada (1844-1918), Literary Critic — A1027

2014, Sept. 22 Litho. Perf. 13½x14
1850 A1027 7s multi   6.25 5.00

Kotosh Temple Archaeological Site — A1028

2014, Sept. 24 Litho. Perf. 14x13½
1851 A1028 6s multi   5.25 4.25

2014 Canonization of Popes — A1029

Designs: No. 1852, 7s, Pope John XXIII. No. 1853, 7s, Pope John Paul II.

2014, Sept. 26 Litho. Perf. 14x13½
1852-1853 A1029 Set of 2   15.00 9.75

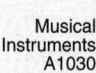

Musical Instruments A1030

Designs: No. 1854, 6s, Botella silbadora. No. 1855, 6s, Antara (pan flute).

2014, Sept. 30 Litho. Perf. 13½x14
1854-1855 A1030 Set of 2   10.50 8.25

Souvenir Sheet

Leymebamba Mummy — A1031

2014, Sept. 30 Litho. Perf. 14x13½
1856 A1031 8s multi   7.00 5.50

William Shakespeare (1564-1616), Writer — A1032

2014, Oct. 3 Litho. Perf. 14x13½
1857 A1032 6s multi   5.25 4.25

Viceroys Type of 2006

No. 1858: a, Agustín de Jáuregui y Aldecoa (1711-84). b, Teodoro de Croix (1730-92). c, Francisco Gil de Taboada y Lemus (1736-1809). d, Ambrosio O'Higgins (1720-1801).

2014, Oct. 7 Litho. Perf. 14x13½
1858 A767 6.50s Block of 4,
               #a-d, + label   23.00 18.00

Souvenir Sheet

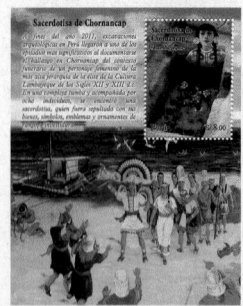

Forensic Facial Reconstruction of the Priestess of Chornancap — A1033

2014, Oct. 13 Litho. Perf. 14x13½
1859 A1033 8s multi   7.00 5.50

Dances — A1034

Designs: No. 1860, 8s, La Wuallata. No. 1861, 8s, Carnaval Cusqueño.

2014, Oct. 17 Litho. Perf. 13½x14
1860-1861 A1034 Set of 2   17.00 11.00

Miniature Sheet

Birds A1035

No. 1862: a, Crotophaga sulcirostris. b, Xenospingus concolor. c, Burhinus superciliaris. d, Glaucidium peruanum.

2014, Oct. 17 Litho. Perf. 13½x14
1862 A1035 9s Sheet of 4, #a-
               d   32.50 24.50

Miniature Sheet

Trees A1036

No. 1863: a, Swietenia macrophylla. b, Cedrela fissilis. c, Ceiba pentandra. d, Prosopis pallida.

2014, Oct. 20 Litho. Perf. 14x13½
1863 A1036 9.50s Sheet of 4,
               #a-d   32.50 26.00

Iquitos, 150th Anniv. — A1037

2014, Oct. 23 Litho. Perf. 13½x14
1864 A1037 6s multi   5.25 4.25

Barranco District, 140th Anniv. — A1038

2014, Oct. 26 Litho. Perf. 14x13½
1865 A1038 7s multi   5.25 4.75

Miniature Sheet

Mammals — A1039

No. 1866: a, Panthera onca. b, Dinomys branickii. c, Tapirus pinchaque. d, Leopardus jacobitus.

2014, Nov. 3 Litho. Perf. 14x13½
1866 A1039 11s Sheet of 4,
               #a-d   34.00 30.00
The inscription on No. 1866d is incorrect. The stamp shows Leopardus colocolo.

Souvenir Sheet

Sycorax Peruensis Preserved in Amber — A1040

Litho. (With Foil Application in Sheet Margin)
2014, Nov. 5 Perf. 14x13½
1867 A1040 8s multi   8.00 5.50

Minerals — A1041

Designs: 6s, Quartz (Cuarzo). 8s, Jasper (Jaspe).

2014, Nov. 10 Litho. Perf. 13½x14
1868-1869 A1041 Set of 2   12.50 9.50

Christmas — A1042

2014, Nov. 14 Litho. Perf. 14x13½
1870 A1042 6s multi   5.25 4.25

Parque de las Leyendas Zoo, 50th Anniv. — A1043

No. 1871: a, Cebuella pygmaea. b, Ateles belzebuth.

2014, Nov. 17 Litho. Perf. 14x13½
1871 A1043 9.50s Horiz. pair,
               #a-b   16.50 13.00

Serpost (Peruvian Postal Service), 20th Anniv. — A1044

2014, Nov. 22 Litho. Perf. 13½x14
1872 A1044 6s multi   5.25 4.25

Miniature Sheet

2014 World Cup Soccer Championships, Brazil — A1045

No. 1873: a, Mascot Fuleco. b, Emblem. c, Soccer player and ball. d, World Cup Trophy.

2014, Nov. 28 Litho. Perf. 13½x14
1873 A1045 3.80s Sheet of 4,
               #a-d   14.00 10.50

Pancho Fierro (1807-79), Painter — A1046

No. 1874 — Paintings: a, El Soldado y la Rabona. b, Fraile de la Buena Muerte. c, El Notario Público. d, La Hermana de la Caridad.

2014, Dec. 1 Litho. Perf. 14x13½
1874 A1046 10s Sheet of 4,
               #a-d   35.00 27.50

Famous Men — A1047

Designs: No. 1875, 9s, Mariano Melgar (1790-1815), poet. No. 1876, 9s, José Olaya Balandra (1782-1823), hero in War of Independence.

2014, Dec. 3 Litho. Perf. 14x13½
1875-1876 A1047 Set of 2   16.00 12.00

America Issue.

Chinese Zodiac Animals A1048

No. 1877: a, Snake. b, Horse.

2014, Dec. 5 Litho. Perf. 14x13½
1877 A1048 6.50s Horiz. pair,
               #a-b   11.50 8.75

Souvenir Sheet

1898 Gold Libra Coin A1049

No. 1878: a, Obverse (Anverso). b, Reverse (Reverso).

2014, Dec. 9   Litho.   Perf. 14x13½
1878 A1049 10s multi   17.50 13.50

Battle of Ayacucho, 190th Anniv. — A1050

2014, Dec. 9   Litho.   Perf. 13½x14
1879 A1050 7s multi   6.25 4.75

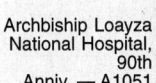

Archbiship Loayza National Hospital, 90th Anniv. — A1051

2014, Dec. 10   Litho.   Perf. 13½x14
1880 A1051 3.80s multi   3.50 2.60

Miniature Sheet

Carriages — A1052

No. 1881: a, Front view of covered carriage. b, Open-air carriage with red seats. c, Side view of covered carriage. d, Open-air carriage with white seats.

2014, Dec. 15   Litho.   Perf. 13½x14
1881 A1052 11s Sheet of 4, #a-d   34.00 30.00

2016 Asia-Pacific Economic Cooperation Meetings, Peru — A1053

2016, Nov. 17   Litho.   Perf. 14x13½
1882 A1053 10s multi   11.00 6.00

Diplomatic Relations Between Peru and People's Republic of China, 45th Anniv. — A1054

No. 1883 — Flags of Peru and People's Republic of China and: a, Machu Picchu. b, Temple of Heaven, Beijing.

2016, Nov. 17   Litho.   Perf. 14x13½
1883 A1054 4s Horiz. pair, #a-b   7.25 4.75

Diplomatic Relations Between Peru and Malaysia, 30th Anniv. — A1055

No. 1884 — Flags of Peru and Malaysia, handshake and: a, Mt. Kinabalu, Malaysia. b, Machu Picchu.

2016, Nov. 17   Litho.   Perf. 14x13½
1884 A1055 9s Horiz. pair, #a-b   14.50 10.50

Christmas — A1056

2016, Nov. 17   Litho.   Perf. 14x13½
1885 A1056 6.50s multi   5.25 4.00

Colonel Francisco Bolognesi Cervantes (1816-80), Hero in War of the Pacific — A1057

2016, Dec. 19   Litho.   Perf. 14x13½
1886 A1057 8s multi   3.50 3.25

Cajamarca, 30th Anniv. on Organization of American States Cultural and Historical Heritage List — A1058

No. 1887: a, Cerro Santa Apolonia. b, Santa Catalina Cathedral.

2016, Dec. 21   Litho.   Perf. 13½x14
1887 A1058 3s Horiz. pair, #a-b   5.50 3.50

Banco de la Nación, 50th Anniv. — A1059

2016, Dec. 22   Litho.   Perf. 13½x14
1888 A1059 10s multi   8.25 6.00

Dr. Carlos Monge Medrano (1884-1970), Founder of National Institute of Andean Biology — A1060

2016, Dec. 23   Litho.   Perf. 13½x14
1889 A1060 10s multi   8.00 6.00
National Institute of Andean Biology, 85th anniv.

Office of the National Prosecutor, 35th Anniv. — A1061

2016, Dec. 26   Litho.   Perf. 14x13½
1890 A1061 10s multi   8.25 6.00

World Autism Awareness Day — A1062

2016, Dec. 28   Litho.   Perf. 13½x14
1891 A1062 10s multi   11.00 6.00

Viceroys of Peru — A1063

Designs: No. 1892, 5s, Gabriel de Avilés y del Fierro (c. 1735-1810). No. 1893, 5s, José Fernando de Abascal y Sousa (1743-1821). No. 1894, 5s, Joaquín de la Pezuela (1761-1830). No. 1895, 5s, José de la Serna e Hinojosa (1770-1832).

2017, Jan. 2   Litho.   Perf. 14x13½
1892-1895 A1063   Set of 4   17.50 12.00
Dated 2016. Compare with type A767.

Pre-Hispanic Musical Instruments A1064

Designs: No. 1896, 6.50s, Huayllaquepa de Punkuri. No. 1897, 6.50s, Antara de Caña de Caral.

2017, Jan. 4   Litho.   Perf. 13½x14
1896-1897 A1064   Set of 2   11.00 8.00
Dated 2016.

Dominican Order, 800th Anniv. (in 2016) — A1065

2017, Jan. 6   Litho.   Perf. 14x13½
1898 A1065 10s multi   8.25 6.25
Dated 2016.

Flora — A1066

Designs: No. 1899, 4s, Rhizophora mangle. No. 1900, 4s, Azorella compacta. No. 1901, 4s, Cinchona pubescens. No. 1902, 4s, Puya raimondii.

2017, Jan. 6   Litho.   Perf. 13½x14
1899-1902 A1066   Set of 4   13.50 9.75
Dated 2016.

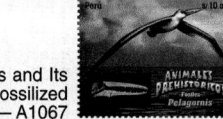

Pelagornis and Its Fossilized Remains — A1067

2017, Jan. 10   Litho.   Perf. 13½x14
1903 A1067 10s multi   8.25 6.25
Dated 2016.

Cuzco School Paintings A1068

Designs: No. 1904, 6.50s, San Cristobal. No. 1905, 6.50s, Patrón Santiago. No. 1906, 6.50s, Paso de las Ordenes Religiosas. No. 1907, 6.50s, El Obispo Mollinedo Llevando la Custodia.

2017, Jan. 12   Litho.   Perf. 13½x14
1904-1907 A1068   Set of 4   22.00 16.00
Dated 2016.

1879 20-Centavo Coin — A1069

Designs: No. 1908, 10s, Obverse (anverso). No. 1909, 10s, Reverse (reverso).

2017, Jan. 16   Litho.   Perf. 14x13½
1908-1909 A1069   Set of 2   17.00 12.50

National Institute of Health, 120th Anniv. (in 2016) — A1070

2017, Jan. 17   Litho.   Perf. 13½x14
1910 A1070 10s multi   8.25 6.25
Dated 2016.

Chess A1071

No. 1911: a, Black bishop (alfil). b, White pawn (peón).

2017, Jan. 19   Litho.   Perf. 14x13½
1911 A1071 4s Horiz. pair, #a-b   7.25 5.00
Dated 2016.

Campaign Against Human Trafficking A1072

Designs: No. 1912, 9s, Photographs of people in blue heart. No. 1913, 9s, Raised hands and map, vert.

Perf. 13½x14, 14x13½
2017, Jan. 23   Litho.
1912-1913 A1072   Set of 2   15.00 11.00
America Issue. Dated 2016.

Pisco Sour Drink, Cent. (in 2016) A1073

No. 1914: a, Pisco Sour in glass, Pisco Sour bottle. b, Grapes and glass of Pisco Sour.

2017, Jan. 26   Litho.   Perf. 14x13½
1914 A1073 9s Horiz. pair, #a-b   15.00 11.00
Dated 2016.

New Year 2015 (Year of the Goat) A1074

No. 1915: a, Ring of Chinese Zodiac animals, Chinese character for "goat." b, Goat.

2017, Jan. 27   Litho.   Perf. 14x13½
1915 A1074 6.50s Horiz. pair, #a-b   10.50 8.00
Dated 2016.

New Year 2016 (Year of the Monkey) A1075

No. 1916: a, Monkeys. b, Ring of Chinese Zodiac animals, Chinese character for "monkey."

2017, Jan. 27 Litho. *Perf. 14x13½*
1916 A1075 6.50s Horiz. pair,
#a-b   11.50 8.00
Dated 2016.

Fish — A1076

Designs: No. 1917, 6.50s, Piaractus brachypomus. No. 1918, 6.50s, Anisotremus interruptus. No. 1919, 6.50s, Lebiasina bimaculata. No. 1920, 6.50s, Panaque schaeferi.

2017, Feb. 1 Litho. *Perf. 13½x14*
1917-1920 A1076   Set of 4   22.00 16.00
Dated 2016.

Poisonous Frogs — A1077

Designs: No. 1921, 8s, Excidobates mysteriosus. No. 1922, 8s, Ameerega parvula. No. 1923, 8s, Ranitomeya fantastica. No. 1924, 8s, Ameerega pongoensis.

2017, Feb. 6 Litho. *Perf. 13½x14*
1921-1924 A1077   Set of 4   27.00 19.50
Dated 2016.

Peruvian-Chinese Food — A1078

Flags of People's Republic of China and Peru and: No. 1925, 3s, Sopa wantan (wonton soup). No. 1926, 3s, Arroz chaufa (rice). No. 1927, 3s, Chi Jau Cuy (guinea pig). No. 1928, 3s, Tallarín Saltado Taipa (noodles and vegetables).

2017, Feb. 8 Litho. *Perf. 13½x14*
1925-1928 A1078   Set of 4   11.00 7.50
Dated 2016.

Independence of Peru, 200th Anniv. (in 2021) — A1079

No. 1929 — Heroes: a, Juan José Crespo (1747-1812), leader of Huánuco Rebellion. b, Francisco de Zela (1768-1819), leader of Tacna Revolution. c, Mateo Pumacahua (1740-1815), leader of Cuzco Rebellion.

2017, Feb. 10 Litho. *Perf. 14x13½*
1929 A1079 3s Horiz. strip of 3,
#a-c   7.75 5.50
Dated 2016.

Awajún Man — A1080

2017, Feb. 13 Litho. *Perf. 14x13½*
1930 A1080 5s multi   4.25 3.25
Dated 2016.

Vultur Gryphus
A1081

Podocnemis Unifilis
A1082

2017, June Litho. *Perf. 14x13½*
1931 A1081 5s multi   4.25 3.25
Perf. 13½x14
1932 A1082 5s multi   4.25 3.25
Dated 2016.

National Institute for the Defense of Competition and Protection of Intellectual Property (INDECOPI), 25th Anniv. — A1083

2017, Nov. 21 Litho. *Perf. 13x13¼*
1933 A1083 6.50s multi   5.50 4.00

Miniature Sheet

Visit to Peru of Pope Francis in 2018 A1084

No. 1934 — Pope Francis: a, In map of Peru. b, Waving, bright green panel, arms of Puerto Maldonado. c, Waving, blue panel, arms of Trujillo. d, Touching child, orange panel, arms of Lima.

2017, Nov. 29 Litho. *Perf. 13¼x13*
1934 A1084 4s Sheet of 4, #a-
d   14.00 10.00

Apparition of the Virgin Mary at Fatima, Portugal, Cent. (in 2017) — A1085

2018, Jan. 5 Litho. *Perf. 13x13¼*
1935 A1085 3s multi   2.75 1.90
Dated 2017.

Holy Cross of Motupe — A1086

2018, Jan. 8 Litho. *Perf. 13¼x13*
1936 A1086 6.50s multi   5.50 4.00
Christmas. Dated 2017.

St. Rose of Lima (1586-1617) — A1087

No. 1937: a, Religious statue, roses. b, St. Rose of Lima, drawing of Lima.

2018, Jan. 10 Litho. *Perf. 13x13¼*
1937 A1087 6.50s Horiz. pair,
#a-b   11.00 8.25
Dated 2017.

Pontifical Catholic University of Peru, Cent. (in 2017) — A1088

No. 1938: a, Star. b, Ship.

2018, Jan. 10 Litho. *Perf. 13¼x13*
1938 A1088 4s Horiz. pair, #a-b   7.00 5.00
Dated 2017.

Lima Central Post Office, 120th Anniv. — A1089

2018, Jan. 11 Litho. *Perf. 13x13¼*
1939 A1089 2s multi   2.00 1.25
Dated 2017.

International Decade for People of African Descent — A1090

2018, Jan. 12 Litho. *Perf. 13¼x13*
1940 A1090 2s multi   2.00 1.25
Dated 2017.

Pampa Galeras-Bárbara D'Achille National Reserve, 50th Anniv. — A1091

2018, Jan. 13 Litho. *Perf. 13x13¼*
1941 A1091 2s multi   2.00 1.25
Dated 2017.

Winning Art in "Healthy Sentiments and Values" Stamp Design Contest — A1092

2018, Jan. 13 Litho. *Perf. 13x13¼*
1942 A1092 2s multi   2.00 1.25
America issue. Dated 2017.

Inti Raymi Festival, 50th Anniv. (in 2017) — A1093

2018, Jan. 15 Litho. *Perf. 13¼x13*
1943 A1093 3s multi   2.75 1.90
Dated 2017.

Souvenir Sheet

International Year of Sustainable Tourism for Development — A1094

No. 1944: a, Amazilia viridicauda. b, Pipreola pulchra.

2018, Jan. 15 Litho. *Perf. 13¼x13*
1944 A1094 8s Sheet of 2, #a-
b   13.50 10.00
Dated 2017.

A1095

Sipán Royal Jewelry — A1096

2018, Jan. 16 Litho. *Perf. 13x13¼*
1945 A1095 6.50s multi   5.50 4.00
Perf. 13¼x13
1946 A1096 6.50s multi   5.50 4.00
Dated 2017.

Miniature Sheet

Ancash Tourism A1097

No. 1947: a, Sechin Archaeological Site, Casma. b, Jancapampa, Pomabamba. c, Hatun Machay, Recuay. d, Yayno Archaeological Site, Pomabamba.

2018, Jan. 18 Litho. *Perf. 13x13¼*
1947 A1097 3s Sheet of 4, #a-d 11.00 7.50
Dated 2017.

Steatornis Caripensis
A1098

Hippocamelus Antisensis
A1099

2018, Jan. 19 Litho. *Perf. 13x13¼*
1948 A1098 9s multi   7.50 5.75
Perf. 13¼x13
1949 A1099 9s multi   7.50 5.75
Dated 2017.

Souvenir Sheet

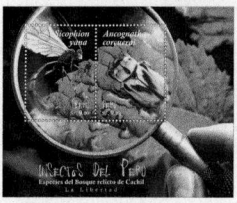

Insects
A1100

No. 1950: a, Sicophion yana. b, Ancognatha corcuerai.

2018, Jan. 22 Litho. *Perf. 13¼x13*
1950 A1100 9s Sheet of 2, #a-
  b   15.00 11.50
  Dated 2017.

Miniature Sheet

Cuzco
School
Paintings
A1101

No. 1951: a, Virgen de Belén. b, La Ultima Cena. c, San Sebastián. d, Procesión de San Pedro.

2018, Jan. 26 Litho. *Perf. 13x13¼*
1951 A1101 6.50s Sheet of 4,
  #a-d   22.50 16.00
  Dated 2017.

Souvenir Sheet

Minerals
A1102

No. 1952: a, Plata (silver). b, Oro (gold).

2018, Jan. 29 Litho. *Perf. 13x13¼*
1952 A1102 10s Sheet of 2,
  #a-b   17.00 12.50
  Dated 2017.

Outdoor Activities in Apurímac
Region — A1103

No. 1953: a, Cyclist on Cerro Quisapata. b, Kayaker on Rio Pachachaca.

2018, Jan. 31 Litho. *Perf. 13x13¼*
1953 A1103 10s Horiz. pair,
  #a-b   17.00 12.50
  Dated 2017.

Great Cave, Huayna Picchu
A1104

No. 1954: a, Corner of wall. b, Three doorways.

2018, Feb. 2 Litho. *Perf. 13x13¼*
1954 A1104 10s Horiz. pair,
  #a-b   17.00 12.50
  Dated 2017.

America
Issue — A1105

Holy Week decorations in: No. 1955, 10s, Ayacucho. No. 1956, 10s, Tarma.

2018, Feb. 5 Litho. *Perf. 13x13¼*
1955-1956 A1105   Set of 2   17.00 12.50
  Dated 2017.

Souvenir Sheet

Friendship Between Peru and
Dominican Republic — A1106

No. 1957: a, Ramón Castilla y Marquesado (1797-1867), 20th President of Peru, and flag of Peru. b, Gregorio Luperón (1839-97), 20th President of Dominican Republic, flag of Dominican Republic.

2018, Feb. 7 Litho. *Perf. 13x13¼*
1957 A1106 10s Sheet of 2,
  #a-b   17.00 12.50
  Dated 2017. See Dominican Republic No. 1626.

New
Year
2017
(Year of
the
Rooster)
A1107

No. 1958: a, Rooster and ring of Chinese zodiac animals. b, Two roosters.

2018, Feb. 9 Litho. *Perf. 13¼x13*
1958 A1107 10s Horiz. pair,
  #a-b   17.00 12.50
  Dated 2017.

Independence of
Peru, 200th Anniv.
(in 2021) — A1108

No. 1959: a, Crossing of the Andes, 1817. b, First Peruvian coat of arms. c, Battle of Ayacucho, 1824.

2018, Feb. 12 Litho. *Perf. 13x13¼*
1959   Horiz. strip of 3   25.00 18.50
  a.-c. A1108 10s Any single   8.00   6.25
  Dated 2017.

Miniature Sheet

Fish
A1109

No. 1960: a, Manta birostris. b, Sphyrna zygaena. c, Hippocampus ingens. d, Strongylura exilis.

2018, Feb. 12 Litho. *Perf. 13x13¼*
1960 A1109 3s Sheet of 4, #a-d 11.00 7.50
  Dated 2017.

Souvenir Sheet

Peruvian Gastronomy — A1110

No. 1961: a, Puca picante. b, Sopa menestrón. c, Cebiche de paiche con camu camu.

2018, Feb. 14 Litho. *Perf. 13x13¼*
1961 A1110 10s Sheet of 3,
  #a-c   25.00 18.50
  Dated 2017.

Epidendrum
Nocturnum
A1111

2018, Feb. 16 Litho. *Perf. 13x13¼*
1962 A1111 5s multi   4.50 3.25
  Dated 2017.

Traditional
Dances — A1112

Designs: No. 1963, 10s, Shacshas dancers. No. 1964, 10s, Pallas dancers, vert.

Perf. 13x13¼, 13¼x13
2018, Feb. 19   Litho.
1963-1964 A1112   Set of 2   17.00 12.50
  Dated 2017.

Pedro Pablo Kuczynski
Godard, 66th President
of Peru — A1113

2018, Feb. 20 Litho. *Perf. 13¼x13*
1965 A1113 6s multi   5.25 3.75
  Dated 2017.

Leonardo da Vinci (1452-1519),
Painter — A1114

No. 1966 — Half of Vitruvian Man and: a, Mona Lisa, and Lady with an Ermine. b, The Last Supper, and The Baptism of Christ.

2018, Feb. 20 Litho. *Perf. 13x13¼*
1966 A1114 10s Horiz. pair,
  #a-b   17.00 12.50
  Dated 2017.

Cacao Pods   Cochineal
A1115   A1116

2018, Feb. 20 Litho. *Perf. 13x13¼*
1967 A1115 10s multi   8.50 6.25
       Perf. 13¼x13
1968 A1116 10s multi   8.50 6.25
  Peruvian exports. Dated 2017.

2018 World Cup Soccer
Championships, Russia — A1117

Peruvian
National
Soccer
Team
A1118

No. 1969: a, 3s, Zabivaka, 2018 World Cup mascot. b, 3s, World Cup. c, 3.50s, Emblem of 2018 World Cup. d, 3.50s, Soccer player kicking ball.

No. 1970: a, Emblem of national soccer team. b, Team members, goaltender in yellow shirt at right. c, Team members, goaltender in blue and black shirt at right. d, Players in huddle.

2018, May 22 Litho. *Perf. 13¼x13*
1969 A1117   Sheet of 4, #a-d 17.50 10.50
       Perf. 13x13¼
1970 A1118 6.50s Sheet of 4,
  #a-d   30.00 20.50
  Nos. 1969-1970 were sold together for 50s, or individually for 20s and 35s, respectively.

10th World Potato Congress,
Cusco — A1119

No. 1971: a, Hands holding potato and potato plant, Machu Picchu. b, Machu Picchu.

2018, May 23 Litho. *Perf. 13x13¼*
1971 A1119 4s Horiz. pair, #a-b 7.00 5.00

Pres. Ollanta Moisés
Humala
Tasso — A1120

2018, June 21 Litho. *Perf. 13¼x13*
1972 A1120 10s multi   8.25 6.25
  Dated 2017.

Ernest Malinowski (1818-99), Builder
of Ferrocarril Central Andino — A1121

No. 1973: a, Malinowski. b, Train and bridge of Ferrocarril Central Andino.

2019, Jan. 28   Litho.   *Perf. 13¼x13*
1973 A1121 6.50s Horiz. pair,
#a-b   11.00 7.75
Dated 2018.

National School of Fine Arts, Lima, Cent. (in 2018) A1122

No. 1974 — Half of building, with "1918-2018" at: a, LL. b, LR.

2019, Jan. 31   Litho.   *Perf. 13¼x13*
1974 A1122 5s Horiz. pair, #a-b   8.50 6.00
Dated 2018.

Television Broadcasting in Peru, 60th Anniv. (in 2018) — A1123

2019, Feb. 4   Litho.   *Perf. 13¼x13*
1975 A1123 5s multi   4.25 3.00
Dated 2018.

Lima Regional Office of the International Civil Aviation Organization, 70th Anniv. — A1124

2019, Feb. 8   Litho.   *Perf. 13x13¼*
1976 A1124 7s multi   4.25 4.25
Dated 2018.

Natural History Museum, Lima, Cent. (in 2018) — A1125

2019, Feb. 11   Litho.   *Perf. 13x13¼*
1977 A1125 6s multi   5.00 3.75
Dated 2018.

Yoshitaro Amano (1898-1982), Founder of Amano Textile Museum — A1126

2019, Feb. 15   Litho.   *Perf. 13x13¼*
1978 A1126 6.50s multi   5.50 4.00
Dated 2018.

Domesticated Animals — A1127

Designs: No. 1979, 6.50s, Dog. No. 1980, 6.50s, Cat.

2019, Feb. 18   Litho.   *Perf. 13x13¼*
1979-1980 A1127   Set of 2   11.00 8.00
America issue. Dated 2018.

New Year 2018 (Year of the Dog) A1128

No. 1981: a, Dog and ring of Chinese zodiac animals. b, Two dogs.

2019, Feb. 22   Litho.   *Perf. 13¼x13*
1981 A1128 6s Horiz. pair, #a-b 10.00 7.25
Dated 2018.

2018 Visit of Pope Francis to Peru — A1129

2019, Feb. 25   Litho.   *Perf. 13x13¼*
1982 A1129 5s multi   4.25 3.00
Dated 2018.

2019 Pan American Games, Lima — A1130

No. 1983: a, Runners on track. b, Mascot.

2019, Feb. 28   Litho.   *Perf. 13¼x13*
1983 A1130 6.50s Horiz. pair,
#a-b   11.00 8.00
Dated 2018.

Independence of Peru, 200th Anniv. (in 2021) — A1131

No. 1984 — Paintings depicting: a, José, Vicente, and Mariano Angulo, leaders of 1814 Cuzco Rebellion. b, Manco Inca (1516-44), leader of 1536 rebellion against Spaniards.

2019, Mar. 1   Litho.   *Perf. 13¼x13*
1984 A1131 6.50s Horiz. pair,
#a-b   11.00 8.00
Dated 2018.

Christmas 2018 — A1132

2019, Mar. 4   Litho.   *Perf. 13¼x13*
1985 A1132 6.50s multi   5.50 4.00

Souvenir Sheet

Ministry of Transport and Communications, 50th Anniv. — A1133

2020, Jan. 2   Litho.   *Perf. 13x13¼*
1986 A1133 1.20s multi   .70   .70

Souvenir Sheet

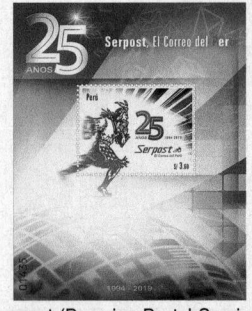

Serpost (Peruvian Postal Service), 25th Anniv. (in 2019) — A1134

2020, Jan. 2   Litho.   *Perf. 13x13¼*
1987 A1134 3.60s multi   2.25 2.25
Dated 2019.

Christmas 2019 — A1135

2020, Jan. 3   Litho.   *Perf. 13¼x13*
1988 A1135 3.60s multi   2.25 2.25
Dated 2019.

Rupicola Peruvianus A1136

Vultur Gryphus A1137

Cantua Buxifolia A1138

Phragmipedium Kovachii A1139

Chavín Culture Stone Head A1140

Machu Picchu A1141

Perf. 14x13½, 13½x14 (#1992, 1994)
2020, Jan. 13   Litho.
1989 A1136 1.20s multi   .70   .70
1990 A1137 2.60s multi   1.60 1.60
1991 A1138 3.60s multi   2.25 2.25
1992 A1139   4s multi   2.40 2.40
1993 A1140 10s multi   6.00 6.00
1994 A1141 20s multi   12.00 12.00
Nos. 1989-1994 (6)   24.95 24.95
Dated 2019.

Souvenir Sheet

National University of San Marcos Museum of Archaeology and Anthropology, Cent. (in 2019) — A1142

2020, Jan. 27   Litho.   *Perf. 13x13¼*
1995 A1142 10s multi   6.00 6.00
Dated 2019.

Souvenir Sheet

Japanese Emigration to Peru, 120th Anniv. (in 2019) — A1143

2020, Jan. 29   Litho.   *Perf. 13x13¼*
1996 A1143 7.60s multi   4.50 4.50
Dated 2019.

Souvenir Sheet

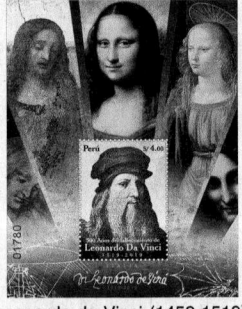

Leonardo da Vinci (1452-1519), Painter and Sculptor — A1144

2020, Jan. 30   Litho.   *Perf. 13¼x13*
1997 A1144 4s multi   2.40 2.40
Dated 2019.

Express Mail Service, 20th Anniv. (in 2019) — A1145

2020, Feb. 3   Litho.   *Perf. 13*
1998 A1145 2.60s multi   1.60 1.60
Dated 2019.

International Year of Indigenous Languages — A1146

2020, Feb. 6   Litho.   *Perf. 13¼x13*
1999 A1146 2.60s multi   1.50 1.50
Dated 2019.

Souvenir Sheet

Mohandas K. Gandhi (1869-1948), Indian Nationalist Leader — A1147

2020, Feb. 7 Litho. Perf. 13¼x13
2000 A1147 10s multi 6.00 2.40

Dated 2019.

Day of Latin American Integration — A1148

2020, Feb. 17 Litho. Perf. 13¼x13
2001 A1148 1.20s multi .70 .70

Dated 2019.

Souvenir Sheet

Traditional Foods — A1149

No. 2002: a, 1.20s, People preparing Pachamanca. b, 7.60s, Plate of Pachamanca.

2020, Feb. 26 Litho. Perf. 13x13¼
2002 A1149 Sheet of 2, #a-b 5.25 5.25

America issue.

Souvenir Sheet

New Year 2019 (Year of the Pig) A1150

2020, Feb. 24 Litho. Perf. 13¼x13
2003 A1150 10s multi 6.00 6.00

Dated 2019.

Peruvian Patriots A1151

No. 2004: a, José Manuel Valdés (1767-1843), physician. b, Matiaza Rimachi, heroine of 1821 Battle of Higos Urco. c, Ventura Ccalamaqui, Huamanga woman who exhorted troops to fight Spanish forces in 1814. d, Francisco Antonio de Zela y Arizaga (1768-1819), leader of 1810 Rebellion of Tacna.

2020, Feb. 28 Litho. Perf. 13½
2004 A1151 3.60s Block of 4, #a-d, + label 8.50 8.50

Souvenir Sheet

Historic Center of Moquegua — A1152

No. 2005: a, House of Ten Windows. b, Ornamental fountain.

2020, Mar. 6 Litho. Perf. 13x13¼
2005 A1152 3.60s Sheet of 2, #a-b 4.25 4.25

Souvenir Sheet

Machu Picchu Antarctic Scientific Station, 30th Anniv. (in 2019) A1153

2020, Apr. 17 Litho. Perf. 13x13¼
2006 A1153 1.20s multi .75 .75

Dated 2019.

Javier Pérez de Cuéllar (1920-2020), Peruvian Prime Minister and United Nations Secretary-General A1154

2021, July 2 Litho. Perf. 14¼x13½
2007 A1154 3.60s multi 1.75 1.75

Ministry of Foreign Relations, 200th Anniv. — A1155

2021, July 2 Litho. Perf. 13½x14¼
2008 A1155 4s multi 2.00 2.00

Peruvian Navy, 200th Anniv. — A1156

2021, July 6 Litho. Perf. 14¼x13½
2009 A1156 4s multi 2.00 2.00

Brüning National Archaeological Museum, Lambayeque, Cent. — A1157

2021, July 9 Litho. Perf. 13½x14¼
2010 A1157 3.60s multi 1.75 1.75

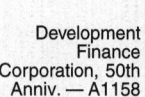

Development Finance Corporation, 50th Anniv. — A1158

2021, July 12 Litho. Perf. 13½x14¼
2011 A1158 2.60s multi 1.30 1.30

Masonic Participation in Peruvian Independence Movement A1159

2021, July 15 Litho. Perf. 13½x14¼
2012 A1159 2.60s multi 1.30 1.30

National Library, 200th Anniv. — A1160

2021, July 16 Litho. Perf. 14¼x13½
2013 A1160 4s multi 2.00 2.00

A1161

Famous Peruvians — A1162

No. 2014: a, 1.20s, Túpac Amaru II (1738-81), leader of Inca rebellion against Spanish rulers. b, 1.20s, Micaela Bastidas (1744-81), wife of Túpac Amaru II and rebellion leader. c, 3.60s, Juan Santos Atahualpa (c. 1710-c. 1756), leader of Asháninka rebellion against Spanish rulers. d, 3.60s, Tomasa Tito Condemayta (1729-81), leader in Túpac Amaru II rebellion.

No. 2105: a, 1.20s, Mariano Melgar Valdivieso (1790-1815), poet and soldier in Peruvian War of Independence. b, 1.20s, María Andrea Parado de Bellido (1777-1822), executed spy for Peruvian forces. c, 3.60s, José Faustino Sánchez Carrión (1787-1825), pro-independence politician. d, José Olaya Balandra (1789-1823), executed emissary.

2021, July 21 Litho. Perf. 14¼x13½
2014 A1161 Block of 4, #a-d, + label 4.75 4.75
2015 A1162 Block of 4, #a-d, + label 4.75 4.75

History of the Peruvian Coat of Arms — A1163

No. 2016: a, Third coat of arms, 1950. b, First coat of arms, 1821. c, Second coat of arms, 1825.

2021, July 23 Litho. Perf. 14¼x13½
2016 Horiz. strip of 3 5.25 5.25
  a. A1163 2.60s multi 1.30 1.30
  b. A1163 3.60s multi 1.75 1.75
  c. A1163 4s multi 2.00 2.00

Miniature Sheet

History of the Flag of Peru A1164

No. 2017: a, 1.20s, Third flag, 1822. b, 2.60s, Fourth flag, 1825. c, 3.60s, Second flag, 1822. d, 3.60s, Current flag, 1950, vert. e, 4s, First flag, 1820.

Perf. 13½x14¼, 14¼x13½
2021, July 23 Litho.
2017 A1164 Sheet of 5, #a-e 7.50 7.50

Landing of Troops of José de San Martín at Paracas, 1820 — A1165

2021, July 30 Litho. Perf. 13½x14¼
2018 A1165 7.60s multi 3.75 3.75

Souvenir Sheet

Casa Rosell-Ríos, Lima — A1166

No. 2019: a, 4s, Building wing. b, 7.60s, Central dome and pillars.

2021, Aug. 2 Litho. Perf. 14¼x13½
2019 A1166 Sheet of 2, #a-b 5.75 5.75

America issue.

Souvenir Sheet

Stevedore Sculpture, Lima, by Constantin Meunier (1831-1905) — A1167

2021, Aug. 5 Litho. *Perf. 14¼x13½*
2020 A1167 3.60s multi 1.75 1.75

Souvenir Sheet

University Park Clock Tower, Lima — A1168

2021, Aug. 9 Litho. *Perf. 14¼x13½*
2021 A1168 4s multi 2.00 2.00

Battle of Pasco, 1820 — A1169

Perf. 13½x14¼
2021, Aug. 13 Litho.
2022 A1169 7.60s multi 3.75 3.75

Peruvian Army, 200th Anniv. — A1170

Perf. 14¼x13½
2021, Aug. 16 Litho.
2023 A1170 4s multi 2.00 2.00

Machu Picchu — A1171

Vinicunca A1172

2021 Litho. *Perf. 13½x14¼*
2024 A1171 4s multi 2.00 2.00
2025 A1172 7.60s multi 3.75 3.75
America issue. Issued: 4s, 8/19; 7.60s, 8/26.

Souvenir Sheet

Manco Cápac Monument, Lima — A1173

2021, Aug. 30 Litho. *Perf. 14x13½*
2026 A1173 3.60s multi 1.75 1.75

Chabuca Granda (1920-83), Singer — A1174

2021, Sept. 2 Litho. *Perf. 14¼x13½*
2027 A1174 7.60s multi 3.75 3.75

Souvenir Sheet

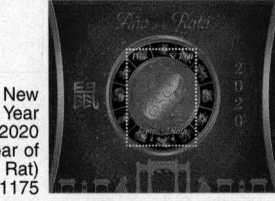

New Year 2020 (Year of the Rat) A1175

2021, Sept. 6 Litho. *Perf. 14¼x13½*
2028 A1175 7.60s multi 3.75 3.75
Dated 2020.

Campaign Against COVID-19 Pandemic — A1176

2021, Sept. 9 Litho. *Perf. 14¼x13½*
2029 A1176 4s multi 2.00 2.00

Souvenir Sheet

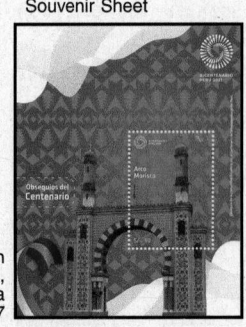

Moorish Arch, Lima A1177

Perf. 14¼x13½
2021, Sept. 13 Litho.
2030 A1177 3.60s multi 1.75 1.75

Souvenir Sheet

Museum of Italian Art, Lima A1178

Perf. 14¼x13½
2021, Sept. 15 Litho.
2031 A1178 4s multi 2.00 2.00

Souvenir Sheet

Ornamental Fountain, Exhibition Park, Lima — A1179

Perf. 14¼x13½
2021, Sept. 17 Litho.
2032 A1179 4s multi 2.00 2.00

1820 Declaration in Huaura by Gen. José de San Martín of Peruvian Independence A1180

2021, Sept. 20 Litho. *Perf. 13½x14*
2033 A1180 7.60s multi 3.75 3.75

Souvenir Sheet

Fountain of the Three Figures, Lima A1181

2021, Sept. 23 Litho. *Perf. 14x13½*
2034 A1181 3.60s multi 1.75 1.75

Souvenir Sheet

Statue of Marshal Antonio José de Sucre, Lima A1182

2021, Sept. 27 Litho. *Perf. 14x13½*
2035 A1182 4s multi 2.00 2.00

Souvenir Sheet

Statue of Liberty, Plazuela de la Recoleta, Lima — A1183

2021, Sept. 30 Litho. *Perf. 14x13½*
2036 A1183 3.60s multi 1.75 1.75

Souvenir Sheet

Old National Stadium, Lima A1184

2021, Oct. 4 Litho. *Perf. 14x13½*
2037 A1184 4s multi 2.00 2.00

SEMI-POSTAL STAMPS

Catalogue values for unused stamps in this section are for Never Hinged items.

Gold Funerary Mask — SP1

Designs: 2.60s+1.30s, Ceremonial knife, vert. 3.60s+1.80s, Ceremonial vessel. 4.60s+2.30s, Goblet with precious stones, vert. 20s+10s, Earplug.

Perf. 12x12½, 12½x12
1966, Aug. 16 Photo. Unwmk.
B1 SP1 1.90s + 90c multi 1.10 .90
B2 SP1 2.60s + 1.30s multi 1.25 1.10
B3 SP1 3.60s + 1.80s multi 2.00 1.75
B4 SP1 4.60s + 2.30s multi 2.75 2.25
B5 SP1 20s + 10s multi 10.00 9.00
Nos. B1-B5 (5) 17.10 15.00

The designs show gold objects of the 12th-13th centuries Chimu culture. The surtax was for tourist publicity.
For surcharges see Nos. 679-680, 683-684, 686.

AIR POST STAMPS

No. 248 Overprinted in Black

1927, Dec. 10   Unwmk.   Perf. 12
C1   A87 50c violet   50.00 26.00
  a.   Inverted overprint   500.00 —

Two types of overprint: first printing, dull black ink; second printing, shiny black ink. Values are the same. No. C1a occurs in the first printing.
Counterfeits exist.

President Augusto
Bernardino
Leguía — AP1

1928, Jan. 12   Engr.
C2   AP1 50c dark green   1.10   .55
  For surcharge see No. 263.

Coat of Arms of Piura Type
1932, July 28   Litho.
C3   A107 50c scarlet   26.00 22.50
  Counterfeits exist.

Airplane in
Flight — AP3

1934, Feb.   Engr.   Perf. 12½
C4   AP3 2s blue   6.50   .60
C5   AP3 5s brown   15.00   1.25
  For surcharges see Nos. C14-C15.

Funeral of   Palace of
Atahualpa   Torre-Tagle
AP4   AP7

Designs: 35c, Mt. San Cristobal. 50c, Avenue of Barefoot Friars. 10s, Pizarro and the Thirteen.

1935, Jan. 18   Photo.   Perf. 13½
C6   AP4 5c emerald   .35   .25
C7   AP4 35c brown   .45   .45
C8   AP4 50c orange yel   .90   .75
C9   AP4 1s plum   1.75   1.25
C10   AP7 2s red orange   2.75   2.40
C11   AP4 5s dp claret   11.00   7.00
C12   AP4 10s dk blue   45.00   30.00
      Nos. C6-C12 (7)   62.20   42.10

4th centenary of founding of Lima.
Nos. C6-C12 overprinted "Radio Nacional" are revenue stamps.

"La Callao," First
Locomotive in
South
America — AP9

1936, Aug. 27   Perf. 12½
C13   AP9 35c gray black   3.25   1.75
  Founding of the Province of Callao, cent.

Nos. C4-C5 Surcharged "Habilitado" and New Value, like Nos. 353-355
1936, Nov. 4
C14   AP3 5c on 2s blue   .55   .30
C15   AP3 25c on 5s brown   1.10   .55
  a.   Double surcharge   14.00   14.00
  b.   No period btwn. "0" & "25
         Cts"   1.60   1.60
  c.   Inverted surcharge   21.00

There are many broken letters in this setting.

Mines of
Peru — AP10

Jorge
Chávez — AP14

Aerial View of   View of the
Peruvian Coast   "Sierra"
AP16   AP17

St. Rosa of
Lima — AP22

Designs: 5c, La Mar Park, Lima. 15c, Mail Steamer "Inca" on Lake Titicaca. 20c, Native Queña (flute) Player and Llama. 30c, Ram at Model Farm, Puno. 1s, Train in Mountains. 1.50s, Jorge Chavez Aviation School. 2s, Transport Plane. 5s, Aerial View of Virgin Forests.

1936-37   Photo.   Perf. 12½
C16   AP10 5c brt green   .35   .25
C17   AP10 5c emer ('37)   .35   .25
C18   AP10 15c lt ultra   .55   .25
C19   AP10 15c blue ('37)   .35   .25
C20   AP10 20c gray blk   1.50   .25
C21   AP10 20c pale ol grn
              ('37)   1.00   .30
C22   AP14 25c mag ('37)   .45   .25
C23   AP10 30c henna brn   4.75   1.10
C24   AP10 30c dk ol brn ('37)   1.50   .25
C25   AP14 35c brown   2.75   2.25
C26   AP10 50c yellow   .45   .30
C27   AP10 50c brn vio ('37)   .65   .25
C28   AP16 70c Prus grn   5.50   5.00
C29   AP10 70c pck grn ('37)   1.00   .85
C30   AP17 80c brn blk   6.50   5.00
C31   AP17 80c ol blk ('37)   1.25   .55
C32   AP10 1s ultra   4.75   .45
C33   AP10 1s red brn ('37)   2.40   .30
C34   AP14 1.50s red brn   7.75   6.00
C35   AP14 1.50s org yel ('37)   4.75   .45

Engr.
C36   AP10 2s deep blue   13.00   7.75
C37   AP10 2s yel grn
              ('37)   9.25   .80
C38   AP16 5s green   17.00   3.75
C39   AP22 10s car & brn   125.00 110.00
      Nos. C16-C39 (24)   212.80 146.85

Nos. C23, C25,
C28, C30, C36
Surcharged in
Black or Red

1936, June 26
C40   AP10 15c on 30c hn brn   .65   .45
C41   AP14 15c on 35c brown   .65   .45
C42   AP16 15c on 70c Prus
              grn   4.50   3.50

C43   AP17 25c on 80c brn blk
              (R)   4.50   3.50
C44   AP10 1s on 2s dp bl   7.75   6.50
      Nos. C40-C44 (5)   18.05   14.40

Surcharge on No. C43 is vertical, reading down.

First Flight in   Jorge
Peru, 1911   Chávez
AP23   AP24

Airport of   Map of Aviation
Limatambo at   Lines from
Lima — AP25   Peru — AP26

Designs: 10c, Juan Bielovucic (1889-?) flying over Lima race course, Jan. 14, 1911. 15c, Jorge Chavez-Dartnell (1887-1910), French-born Peruvian aviator who flew from Brixen to Domodossola in the Alps and died of plane-crash injuries.

1937, Sept. 15   Engr.   Perf. 12
C45   AP23 10c violet   .65   .25
C46   AP24 15c dk green   .90   .25
C47   AP25 25c gray brn   .65   .25
C48   AP26 1s black   3.00   2.10
      Nos. C45-C48 (4)   5.20   2.85

Inter-American Technical Conference of Aviation, Sept. 1937.

Government   Monument
Restaurant at   on the
Callao   Plains of
AP27   Junin
                       AP28

Rear   View of Tarma
Admiral   AP30
Manuel
Villar
AP29

Dam, Ica   View of
River   Iquitos
AP31   AP32

Highway   Mountain
and   Road
Railroad   AP34
Passing
AP33

Plaza San   National Radio
Martín,   of
Lima — AP35   Peru — AP36

Stele from   Ministry of
Chavin   Public Works,
Temple   Lima
AP37   AP38

Crypt of the Heroes,
Lima — AP39

Imprint: "Waterlow & Sons Limited, Londres."
1938, July 1   Photo.   Perf. 12½, 13
C49   AP27 5c violet brn   .25   .25
C50   AP28 15c dk brown   .25   .25
C51   AP29 20c dp magenta   .55   .30
C52   AP30 25c dp green   .25   .25
C53   AP31 30c orange   .25   .25
C54   AP32 50c green   .45   .30
C55   AP33 70c slate bl   .65   .30
C56   AP34 80c olive   1.25   .30
C57   AP35 1s slate grn   10.00   4.25
C58   AP36 1.50s purple   2.25   .30

Engr.
C59   AP37 2s ind & org
              brn   3.75   .95
C60   AP38 5s brown   18.00   1.75
C61   AP39 10s ol grn & ind   70.00 37.50
      Nos. C49-C61 (13)   107.90 46.95

See Nos. C73-C75, C89-C93, C103.
For surcharges see Nos. C65, C76-C77, C82-C88, C108.

Torre-Tagle   National Congress
Palace   Building
AP40   AP41

Manuel
Ferreyros, José
Gregorio Paz
Soldán and
Antonio
Arenas — AP42

1938, Dec. 9   Photo.   Perf. 12½
C62   AP40 25c brt ultra   .90   .65
C63   AP41 1.50s brown vio   2.40   1.90
C64   AP42 2s black   1.50   .75
      Nos. C62-C64 (3)   4.80   3.30

8th Pan-American Conference at Lima.

No. C52 Surcharged in
Black

1942   Perf. 13
C65   AP30 15c on 25c dp grn   1.75   .25

Types of 1938
Imprint: "Columbian Bank Note Co."
1945-46   Unwmk.   Litho.   Perf. 12½
C73   AP27 5c violet brown   .25   .25
C74   AP31 30c orange   .25   .25
C75   AP36 1.50s purple ('46)   .35   .30
      Nos. C73-C75 (3)   .85   .80

Nos. C73 and C54
Overprinted in Black

1947, Sept. 25   *Perf. 12½, 13*
C76 AP27 5c violet brown   .30 .30
C77 AP32 50c green   .30 .30

1st Peru Intl. Airways flight from Lima to New York City, Sept. 27-28, 1947.

> Catalogue values for unused stamps in this section, from this point to the end of the section, are for Never Hinged items.

Peru-Great Britain Air Route — AP43

Designs: 5s, Discus thrower. 10s, Rifleman.

1948, July 29   **Photo.**   *Perf. 12½*
C78 AP43 1s blue   4.00 2.75

Basketball Players — AP44

Carmine Overprint, "AEREO"

C79 AP44 2s red brown   5.50 3.50
C80 AP44 5s yellow green   9.75 5.75
C81 AP44 10s yellow   11.50 7.00
   a. Souv. sheet, #C78-C81, perf 13   52.50 50.00
   Nos. C78-C81 (4)   30.75 19.00

Peru's participation in the 1948 Olympic Games held at Wembley, England, during July and August. Postally valid for four days, July 29-Aug. 1, 1948. Proceeds went to the Olympic Committee.

A surtax of 2 soles on No. C81a was for the Children's Hospital.

Remainders of Nos. C78-C81 and C81a were overprinted "Melbourne 1956" and placed on sale Nov. 19, 1956, at all post offices as "voluntary stamps" with no postal validity. Clerks were permitted to postmark them to please collectors, and proceeds were to help pay the cost of sending Peruvian athletes to Australia. On April 14, 1957, postal authorities declared these stamps valid for one day, April 15, 1957. The overprint was applied to 10,000 sets and 21,000 souvenir sheets. Value, set, $23.50; sheet, $18.

No. C55 Surcharged in Red

1948, Dec.   *Perf. 13*
C82 AP33 10c on 70c slate blue   .60 .25
C83 AP33 20c on 70c slate blue   .60 .25
C84 AP33 55c on 70c slate blue   .60 .25
   Nos. C82-C84 (3)   1.80 .75

Nos. C52, C55 and C56 Surcharged in Black

1949, Mar. 25
C85 AP30 5c on 25c dp grn   .35 .25
C86 AP30 10c on 25c dp grn   .35 .25
C87 AP33 15c on 70c slate bl   .50 .25
C88 AP34 30c on 80c olive   1.75 .65
   Nos. C85-C88 (4)   2.95 1.40

The surcharge reads up, on No. C87.

Types of 1938
Imprint: "Waterlow & Sons Limited, Londres."

Perf. 13x13½, 13½x13
1949-50   **Photo.**
C89 AP27 5c olive bister   .35 .25
C90 AP31 30c red   .35 .25
C91 AP33 70c blue   .60 .25
C92 AP34 80c cerise   1.75 .45
C93 AP36 1.50s vio brn ('50)   1.25 .55
   Nos. C89-C93 (5)   4.30 1.75

Overprinted "U. P. U. 1874-1949" in Red or Black

Air View, Reserva Park, Lima — AP45   Flags of the Americas and Spain — AP46

Designs: 30c, National flag. 55c, Huancayo Hotel. 95c, Blanca-Ancash Cordillera. 1.50s, Arequipa Hotel. 2s, Coal chute and dock, Chimbote. 5s, Town hall, Miraflores. 10s, Hall of National Congress, Lima.

1951, Apr. 2   **Engr.**   *Perf. 12*
C94 AP45 5c blue grn   .30 .25
C95 AP45 30c black & car   .30 .25
   a. Inverted overprint
C96 AP45 55c yel grn (Bk)   .30 .25
C97 AP45 95c dk green   .30 .25
C98 AP45 1.50s dp car (Bk)   .40 .30
C99 AP45 2s deep blue   .40 .30
C100 AP45 5s rose car (Bk)   4.50 3.25
C101 AP45 10s purple   5.75 4.50
C102 AP46 20s dk brn & ultra   9.50 7.00
   Nos. C94-C102 (9)   21.75 16.35

UPU, 75th anniv. (in 1949).
Nos. C94-C102 exist without overprint, but were not regularly issued. Value, set, $225.

Type of 1938
Imprint: "Inst. de Grav. Paris."

1951, May   **Engr.**   *Perf. 12½x12*
C103 AP27 5c olive bister   .55 .25

Type of 1938 Surcharged in Black

1951
C108 AP31 25c on 30c rose red   .55 .25

Thomas de San Martin y Contreras and Jerónimo de Aliaga y Ramirez AP47

San Marcos University AP48

Designs: 50c, Church and convent of Santo Domingo. 1.20s, P. de Peralta Barnuevo, T. de San Martin y Contreras and J. Baquijano y Carrillo de Cordova. 2s, T. Rodriguez de Mendoza, J. Hipolito Unanue y Pavon and J. Cayetano Heredia y Garcia. 5s, Arms of the University, 1571 and 1735.

Perf. 11½x12½
1951, Dec. 10   **Litho.**
C109 AP48 30c gray   .55 .45
C110 AP48 40c ultra   .55 .45
C111 AP48 50c car rose   .55 .45
C112 AP47 1.20s emerald   .55 .45
C113 AP47 2s slate   1.75 .45
C114 AP47 5s multicolored   3.75 .45
   Nos. C109-C114 (6)   7.70 2.70

400th anniv. of the founding of San Marcos University.

River Gunboat Marañon AP49   Peruvian Cormorants AP50

National Airport, Lima — AP51   Tobacco Plant — AP52

Manco Capac Monument AP54   Garcilaso de la Vega AP53

Designs: 1.50s, Housing Unit No. 3. 2.20s, Inca Solar Observatory.

Imprint: "Thomas De La Rue & Co. Ltd."

1953-60   **Unwmk.**   *Perf. 13, 12*
C115 AP49 40c yellow grn   .30 .25
   a. 40c blue green ('57)   .30 .25
C116 AP50 75c dk brown   1.75 .30
C116A AP50 80c pale brn red ('60)   .80 .25
C117 AP51 1.25s blue   .40 .25
C118 AP49 1.50s cerise   .55 .30
C119 AP51 2.20s dk blue   2.60 .45
C120 AP52 3s brown   2.25 .65
C121 AP53 5s bister   1.75 .30
C122 AP54 10s dull vio brn   4.50 .85
   Nos. C115-C122 (9)   14.90 3.60

See #C158-C162, C182-C183, C186-C189, C210-C211.
For surcharges see #C420-C422, C429-C433, C435-C436, C438, C442-C443, C445-C450, C455, C471-C474, C476, C478-C479, C495.

Queen Isabella I — AP55

Fleet of Columbus AP56

Perf. 12½x11½, 11½x12½
1953, June 18   **Engr.**   **Unwmk.**
C123 AP55 40c dp carmine   .30 .25
C124 AP56 1.25s emerald   .85 .25
C125 AP56 2.15s dp plum   1.40 .60
C126 AP56 2.20s black   1.90 .65
   Nos. C123-C126 (4)   4.45 1.75

500th birth anniv. (in 1951) of Queen Isabella I of Spain.
For surcharge see No. C475.

Arms of Lima and Bordeaux AP57

Designs: 50c, Eiffel Tower and Cathedral of Lima. 1.25s, Admiral Dupetit-Thouars and frigate "La Victorieuse." 2.20s, Presidents Coty and Prado and exposition hall.

1957, Sept. 16   *Perf. 13*
C127 AP57 40c claret, grn & ultra   .35 .25
C128 AP57 50c grn, blk & hn brn   .35 .25
C129 AP57 1.25s bl, ind & dk grn   .80 .45
C130 AP57 2.20s bluish blk, bl & red brn   1.40 .90
   Nos. C127-C130 (4)   2.90 1.85

French Exposition, Lima, Sept. 15-Oct. 1.
For surcharges see Nos. 763, C503-C505.

Pre-Stamp Postal Markings — AP58

10c, 1r Stamp of 1857. 15c, 2r Stamp of 1857. 25c, 1d Stamp of 1860. 30c, 1p Stamp of 1858. 40c, ½p Stamp of 1858. 1.25s, José Davila Condemarin. 2.20s, Ramon Castilla. 5s, Pres. Manuel Prado. 10s, Shield of Lima containing stamps.

Perf. 12½x13
1957, Dec. 1   **Engr.**   **Unwmk.**
C131 AP58 5c silver & blk   .30 .25
C132 AP58 10c lil rose & bl   .30 .25
C133 AP58 15c grn & red brn   .30 .25
C134 AP58 25c org yel & bl   .30 .25
C135 AP58 30c vio brn & org brn   .30 .25
C136 AP58 40c black & bis   .30 .25
C137 AP58 1.25s dk bl & dk brn   .90 .55
C138 AP58 2.20s red & sl bl   1.40 .75
C139 AP58 5s lil rose & mar   3.00 1.50
C140 AP58 10s ol grn & lil   5.50 2.50
   Nos. C131-C140 (10)   12.60 6.80

Centenary of Peruvian postage stamps. No. C140 issued to publicize the Peruvian Centenary Phil. Exhib. (PEREX).

Carlos Paz Soldan AP59   Port of Callao and Pres. Manuel Prado AP60

Design: 1s, Ramon Castilla.

Perf. 14x13½, 13½x14
1958, Apr. 7   **Litho.**   **Wmk. 116**
C141 AP59 40c brn & pale rose   .35 .30
C142 AP59 1s grn & lt grn   .50 .30
C143 AP60 1.25s dull pur & ind   1.10 .30
   Nos. C141-C143 (3)   1.95 .90

Centenary of the telegraph connection between Lima and Callao and the centenary of the political province of Callao.
For surcharges see Nos. 758A, 767.

Flags of France and Peru — AP61   Cathedral of Lima and Lady — AP62

1.50s, Horseback rider & mail in Lima. 2.50s, Map of Peru showing national products.

Perf. 12½x13, 13x12½
1958, May 20   **Engr.**   **Unwmk.**
C144 AP61 50c dl vio, bl & car   .35 .25
C145 AP62 65c multi   .35 .25
C146 AP62 1.50s bl, brn vio & ol   .75 .25
C147 AP61 2.50s sl grn, grnsh bl & claret   1.10 .30
   Nos. C144-C147 (4)   2.55 1.05

Peruvian Exhib. in Paris, May 20-July 10.

Bro. Martin de Porres Velasquez — AP63

First Royal School of Medicine (Now Ministry of Government and Police) — AP64

Designs: 1.20s, Daniel Alcides Carrion Garcia. 1.50s, Jose Hipolito Unanue Pavon.

Perf. 13x13½, 13½x13

		1958, July 24	**Litho.**	**Unwmk.**
C148	AP63	60c multi	.40	.25
C149	AP63	1.20s multi	.40	.25
C150	AP63	1.50s multi	.40	.25
C151	AP64	2.20s black	1.20	.65
		Nos. C148-C151 (4)	2.40	1.40

Daniel A. Carrion (1857-85), medical martyr.

Gen. Ignacio Alvarez Thomas — AP65

1958, Nov. 13   **Perf. 13x12½**
C152	AP65	1.10s brn lake, bis & ver	.40	.30
C153	AP65	1.20s blk, bis & ver	.95	.55

General Thomas (1787-1857), fighter for South American independence.

"Justice" and Emblem — AP66

1958, Nov. 13
Star in Blue and Olive Bister
C154	AP66	80c emerald	.55	.25
C155	AP66	1.10s red orange	.55	.25
C156	AP66	1.20s ultra	.55	.25
C157	AP66	1.50s lilac rose	.55	.25
		Nos. C154-C157 (4)	2.20	1.00

Lima Bar Assoc., 150th anniv.

Types of 1953-57
Designs: 80c, Peruvian cormorants. 3.80s, Inca Solar Observatory.

Imprint: "Joh. Enschedé en Zonen-Holland"

Perf. 12½x14, 14x13, 13x14

		1959, Dec. 9		**Unwmk.**
C158	AP50	80c brown red	.40	.25
C159	AP52	3s lt green	1.25	.45
C160	AP51	3.80s orange	2.60	.55
C161	AP53	5s brown	1.25	.55
C162	AP54	10s orange ver	2.60	.65
		Nos. C158-C162 (5)	8.10	2.45

WRY Emblem, Dove, Rainbow and Farmer — AP67

1960, Apr. 7   **Litho.**   **Perf. 14x13**
C163	AP67	80c multi	.80	.55
C164	AP67	4.30s multi	1.25	1.00
a.		Souv. sheet of 2, #C163-C164, imperf.	15.00	15.00

World Refugee Year, 7/1/59-6/30/60.
No. C164a sold for 15s.

Peruvian Cormorant Over Ocean — AP68

1960, May 30
C165	AP68	1s multi	4.00	1.75

Intl. Pacific Fair, Lima, 1959.

Lima Coin of 1659 — AP69

1961, Jan. 19 Unwmk. Perf. 13x14
C166	AP69	1s org brn & gray	.80	.45
C167	AP69	2s Prus bl & gray	.80	.45

1st National Numismatic Exposition, Lima, 1959; 300th anniv. of the first dated coin (1659) minted at Lima.

The Earth — AP70

1961, Mar. 8 Litho. Perf. 13½x14
C168	AP70	1s multicolored	1.60	.65

International Geophysical Year.

Frigate Amazonas — AP71

1961, Mar. 8 Engr. Perf. 13½
C169	AP71	50c brown & grn	.45	.30
C170	AP71	80c dl vio & red org	.55	.30
C171	AP71	1s green & sepia	.95	.30
		Nos. C169-C171 (3)	1.95	.90

Centenary (in 1958) of the trip around the world by the Peruvian frigate Amazonas.

Machu Picchu Sheet
A souvenir sheet was issued Sept. 11, 1961, to commemorate the 50th anniversary of the discovery of the ruins of Machu Picchu, ancient Inca city in the Andes, by Hiram Bingham. It contains two bi-colored imperf. airmail stamps, 5s and 10s, lithographed in a single design picturing the mountaintop ruins. The sheet was valid for one day and was sold in a restricted manner. Value $21.

Olympic Torch, Laurel and Globe — AP72

1961, Dec. 13 Unwmk. Perf. 13
C172	AP72	5s gray & ultra	1.00	.60
C173	AP72	10s gray & car	2.40	1.25
a.		Souv. sheet of 2, #C172-C173, imperf.	4.50	4.25

17th Olympic Games, Rome, 8/25-9/11/60.

Fair Emblem and Llama — AP73

1962, Jan. Litho. Perf. 10½x11
C174	AP73	1s multi	.60	.25

2nd International Pacific Fair, Lima, 1961.

Map Showing Disputed Border, Peru-Ecuador AP74

1962, May 25   Perf. 10½
Gray Background
C175	AP74	1.30s blk, red & car rose	.50	.25
C176	AP74	1.50s blk, red & emer	.50	.25
C177	AP74	2.50s blk, red & dk bl	1.10	.70
		Nos. C175-C177 (3)	2.10	1.20

Settlement of the border dispute with Ecuador by the Protocol of Rio de Janeiro, 20th anniv.

Cahuide and Cuauhtémoc AP75

2s, Tupac Amaru (Jose G. Condorcanqui) & Miguel Hidalgo. 3s, Pres. Manuel Prado & Pres. Adolfo Lopez Mateos of Mexico.

1962, May 25   Engr.   Perf. 13
C178	AP75	1s dk car rose, red & brt grn	.35	.25
C179	AP75	2s grn, red & brt grn	.70	.30
C180	AP75	3s brn, red & brt grn	1.10	.50
		Nos. C178-C180 (3)	2.15	1.05

Exhibition of Peruvian art treasures in Mexico.

Agriculture, Industry and Archaeology AP76

1962, Sept. 7 Litho. Perf. 14x13½
C181	AP76	1s black & gray	.60	.25

Cent. (in 1961) of Pallasca Ancash province.

Types of 1953-60
1.30s, Guanayes. 1.50s, Housing Unit No. 3. 1.80s, Locomotive No. 80 (like #460). 2s, Monument to Native Farmer. 3s, Tobacco plant. 4.30s, Inca Solar Observatory. 5s, Garcilaso de la Vega. 10s, Inca Monument.

Imprint: "Thomas De La Rue & Co. Ltd."

		1962-63 Wmk. 346 Litho.	**Perf. 13**	
C182	AP50	1.30s pale yellow	.95	.25
C183	AP49	1.50s claret	.65	.25
C184	A182	1.80s dark blue	.65	.25
		Perf. 12		
C185	A184	2s emerald ('63)	.65	.25
C186	AP52	3s lilac rose	.75	.25
C187	AP51	4.30s orange	1.60	.45
C188	AP53	5s citron	1.60	.75
		Perf. 13½x14		
C189	AP54	10s vio bl ('63)	3.50	.90
		Nos. C182-C189 (8)	10.35	3.35

For surcharges see Nos. C429, C432, C446, C449, C473.

Freedom from Hunger Type
1963, July 23 Unwmk. Perf. 12½
C190	A189	4.30s lt grn & ocher	1.75	1.10

Jorge Chávez and Wing — AP77

1964, Feb. 20 Engr. Perf. 13
C191	AP77	5s org brn, dk brn & bl	1.10	.45

1st crossing of the Alps by air (Sept. 23, 1910) by the Peruvian aviator Jorge Chávez, 50th anniv.

Alliance for Progress Type
Design: 1.30s, Same, horizontal.

Perf. 12½x12, 12x12½

		1964, June 22		**Litho.**
C192	A190	1.30s multi	.35	.25
C193	A190	3s multi	1.10	.60

Fair Poster — AP78

1965, Jan. 15 Unwmk. Perf. 14½
C194	AP78	1s multi	.55	.25

3rd International Pacific Fair, Lima 1963.

Basket, Globe, Pennant — AP79

1965, Apr. 19   Perf. 12x12½
C195	AP79	1.30s violet & red	.90	.60
C196	AP79	4.30s bis brn & red	2.10	1.40

4th Women's Intl. Basketball Championship.
For surcharge see No. C493.

St. Martin de Porres — AP80

Designs: 1.80s, St. Martin's miracle: dog, cat and mouse feeding from same dish. 4.30s, St. Martin with cherubim in Heaven.

1965, Oct. 29 Litho. Perf. 11
C197	AP80	1.30s gray & multi	.55	.25
C198	AP80	1.80s gray & multi	.70	.25
C199	AP80	4.30s gray & multi	1.50	.95
		Nos. C197-C199 (3)	2.75	1.45

Canonization of St. Martin de Porres Velasquez (1579-1639), on May 6, 1962.
For surcharges see Nos. C439, C496 and footnote below No. RA57.

Victory Monument, Lima, and Battle Scene — AP81

Designs: 3.60s, Monument and Callao Fortress. 4.60s, Monument and José Galvez.

1966, May 2 Photo. Perf. 14x13½
C200	AP81	1.90s multicolored	.85	.50
C201	AP81	3.60s brn, yel & bis	.95	.75
C202	AP81	4.60s multicolored	1.60	1.00
		Nos. C200-C202 (3)	3.40	2.25

Centenary of Peru's naval victory over the Spanish Armada at Callao, May, 1866.

Civil Guard
Emblem — AP82

1.90s, Various activities of Civil Guard.

1966, Aug. 30 Photo. Perf. 13½x14
C203 AP82 90c multicolored .40 .25
C204 AP82 1.90s dp lil rose, gold
& blk .90 .25
Centenary of the Civil Guard.

Hydroelectric Center Type
1966, Nov. 24 Photo. Perf. 13½x14
C205 A193 1.90s lil, blk & vio bl .70 .25

Sun Symbol, Ancient
Carving — AP83

Designs: 3.60s, Map of Peru and spiral,
horiz. 4.60s, Globe with map of Peru.

Perf. 14x13½, 13½x14
1967, Feb. 16 Litho.
C206 AP83 2.60s red org & blk .70 .25
C207 AP83 3.60s dp blue & blk .90 .45
C208 AP83 4.60s tan & multi 1.10 .55
Nos. C206-C208 (3) 2.70 1.25

Photography exhibition "Peru Before the
World" which opened simultaneously in Lima,
Madrid, Santiago de Chile and Washington,
Sept. 27, 1966.
For surcharges see #C444, C470, C492.

Types of 1953-60
2.60s, Monument to Native Farmer. 3.60s,
Tobacco plant. 4.60s, Inca Solar Observatory.
Imprint: "I.N.A."
1967, Jan. Perf. 13½x14, 14x13½
C209 A184 2.60s brt green 1.20 .30
C210 AP52 3.60s lilac rose 1.60 .45
C211 AP51 4.60s orange 1.75 .90
Nos. C209-C211 (3) 4.55 1.65

For surcharges see Nos. C433, C436-C438,
C440-C442, C445, C447-C450, C454-C455,
C471-C472, C474, C476, C478.

**Window and Sun Type of Regular
Issue**
1967, Apr. 18 Photo. Perf. 13½x14
C212 A194 1.90s yel brn, blk &
gold .80 .30

St. Rosa of Lima by
Angelino
Medoro — AP84

St. Rosa Painted by: 2.60s, Carlo Maratta.
3.60s, Cuzquena School, 17th century.

**1967, Aug. 30 Photo. Perf. 13½
Black, Gold & Multi**
C213 AP84 1.90s .80 .25
C214 AP84 2.60s 1.40 .30
C215 AP84 3.60s 1.50 .55
Nos. C213-C215 (3) 3.70 1.10
350th death anniv. of St. Rosa of Lima.
For surcharge see No. C477.

Fair Type of Regular Issue
1967, Oct. 27 Photo. Perf. 12
C216 A195 1s gold, brt red lil &
blk .60 .25

Lions Emblem — AP85

1967, Dec. 29 Litho. Perf. 14x13½
C217 AP85 1.60s brt bl & vio bl,
grysh .70 .30
50th anniversary of Lions International.

Decorated Jug, Nazca
Culture — AP86

Painted pottery jugs of pre-Inca Nazca culture: 2.60s, Falcon. 3.60s, Round jug decorated with grain-eating bird. 4.60s, Two-
headed snake. 5.60s, Marine bird.

1968, June 4 Photo. Perf. 12
C218 AP86 1.90s multi .80 .30
C219 AP86 2.60s multi .90 .35
C220 AP86 3.60s black & multi .90 .35
C221 AP86 4.60s brown & multi 1.40 .55
C222 AP86 5.60s gray & multi 2.75 1.10
Nos. C218-C222 (5) 6.75 2.65

For surcharges see #C451-C453, C497,
C500.

Antarqui, Inca
Messenger — AP87

Design: 5.60s, Alpaca and jet liner.

1968, Sept. 2 Litho. Perf. 12
C223 AP87 3.60s multi .75 .45
C224 AP87 5.60s red, blk & brn 1.00 .65
12th anniv. of Peruvian Airlines (APSA).
For surcharges see Nos. C480-C482.

Human Rights
Flame — AP88

1968, Sept. 5 Photo. Perf. 14x13½
C225 AP88 6.50s brn, red & grn .80 .30
International Human Rights Year.

Discobolus and
Mexico Olympics
Emblem — AP89

1968, Oct. 19 Photo. Perf. 13½
C226 AP89 2.30s yel, brn & dk bl .50 .25
C227 AP89 3.50s yel grn, sl bl &
red .50 .25
C228 AP89 5s brt pink, blk &
ultra .50 .30
C229 AP89 6.50s lt blu, mag &
brn .85 .40
C230 AP89 8s lil, ultra & car .85 .40
C231 AP89 9s org, vio & grn .85 .40
Nos. C226-C231 (6) 4.05 2.00
19th Olympic Games, Mexico City, 10/12-27.

Hand, Corn and
Field — AP90

1969, Mar. 3 Litho. Perf. 11
C232 AP90 5.50s on 1.90s grn &
yel .80 .30
C233 AP90 6.50s on 1.90s bl,
grn & yel 1.00 .40
Agrarian Reform Law. Not issued without
surcharge.

Peruvian Silver 8-
reales Coin,
1568 — AP91

1969, Mar. 17 Litho. Perf. 12
C234 AP91 5s yellow, gray & blk .80 .45
C235 AP91 5s bl grn, gray & blk .80 .45
400th anniv. of the first Peruvian coinage.

Ramon Castilla
Monument — AP92

Design: 10s, Pres. Ramon Castilla.

**1969, May 30 Photo. Perf. 13½
Size: 27x40mm**
C236 AP92 5s emerald & indigo .75 .30
**Perf. 12
Size: 21x37mm**
C237 AP92 10s plum & brn 1.60 .65
Ramon Castilla (1797-1867), president of
Peru (1845-1851 and 1855-1862), on the
occasion of the unveiling of the monument in
Lima.

Airline Type of Regular Issue
1969, June 17 Litho. Perf. 11
C238 A199 3s org & multi .75 .45
C239 A199 4s multi .90 .45
C240 A199 5.50s ver & multi 1.10 .45
C241 A199 6.50s vio & multi 1.10 .45
Nos. C238-C241 (4) 3.85 1.80
First Peruvian Airlines (APSA) flight to
Europe.

Radar
Antenna,
Satellite and
Earth
AP93

1969, July 14 Litho. Perf. 11
C242 AP93 20s multi 2.50 1.10
a. Souv. sheet 3.75 3.50
Opening of the Lurin satellite earth station
near Lima.
No. C242a contains one imperf. stamp with
simulated perforations similar to No. C242.

**Gonzales Type of Regular Issue
inscribed "AEREO"**
1969, July 23 Litho. Perf. 11
C243 A200 20s red & multi 3.00 1.25

WHO
Emblem — AP94

1969, Aug. 14 Photo. Perf. 12
C244 AP94 5s gray, red brn,
gold & blk .55 .30
C245 AP94 6.50s dl org, gray bl,
gold & blk .75 .30
WHO, 20th anniv.

**Agrarian Reform Type of Regular
Issue**
1969, Aug. 28 Litho. Perf. 11
C246 A201 3s lil & blk .50 .35
C247 A201 4s brn & buff .90 .35

Garcilaso de la
Vega — AP95

Designs: 2.40s, De la Vega's coat of arms.
3.50s, Title page of "Commemtarios Reales
que tratan del origen de los Yncas," Lisbon,
1609.

1969, Sept. 18 Litho. Perf. 12x12½
C248 AP95 2.40s emer, sil & blk .50 .30
C249 AP95 3.50s ultra, buff & blk .55 .30
C250 AP95 5s sil, yel, blk &
brn .85 .30
a. Souv. sheet of 3, #C248-
C250, imperf. 2.50 2.25
Nos. C248-C250 (3) 1.90 .90
Garcilaso de la Vega, called "Inca" (1539-
1616), historian of Peru.

Fair Type of Regular Issue, 1969
1969, Nov. 14 Litho. Perf. 11
C251 A203 3s bis & multi .40 .25
C252 A203 4s multi 1.20 .25

Bolognesi Type of Regular Issue
1969, Dec. 9 Litho. Perf. 11
C253 A204 50s lt brn, blk & gold 4.25 1.90
Nos. C248-C250 (3)

Arms of
Amazonas
AP96

1970, Jan. 6 Litho. Perf. 11
C254 AP96 10s multi 1.50 1.00

ILO
Emblem — AP97

1970, Jan. 16
C278 AP97 3s dk vio bl & lt ultra .85 .25
ILO, 50th anniv.

Motherhood and
UNICEF
Emblem — AP98

1970, Jan. 16 Photo. Perf. 13½x14
C279 AP98 5s yel, gray & blk .65 .30
C280 AP98 6.50s brt pink, gray &
blk .95 .40

Vicus Culture Type of Regular Issue
Ceramics of Vicus Culture, 6th-8th Centu-
ries: 3s, Squatting warrior. 4s, Jug. 5.50s,
Twin jugs. 6.50s, Woman and jug.

1970, Feb. 23 Litho. Perf. 11
C281 A205 3s buff, blk &
brn 1.20 .30
C282 A205 4s buff, blk &
brn 1.20 .30
C283 A205 5.50s buff, blk &
brn 2.50 .85
C284 A205 6.50s buff, blk &
brn 3.50 1.10
a. Vert. strip, #526, C281-
C284 11.00 11.00
Nos. C281-C284 (4) 8.40 2.55

Fish Type of Regular Issue
1970, Apr. 30 Litho. Perf. 11
C285 A207 3s Swordfish 3.00 1.40
C286 A207 3s Yellowfin tuna 3.00 1.40
C287 A207 5.50s Wolf fish 3.00 2.10
Nos. C285-C287 (3) 9.00 4.90

Telephone — AP99

1970, June 12   Litho.   *Perf. 11*

C288	AP99	5s multi	.70	.25
C289	AP99	10s multi	1.40	.55

Nationalization of the Peruvian telephone system, Mar. 25, 1970.

Soldier-Farmer Type of Regular Issue

1970, June 24   Litho.   *Perf. 11*

C290	A208	3s gold & multi	.75	.25
C291	A208	5.50s gold & multi	1.50	.25

UN Headquarters, NY — AP100

1970 June 26

C292	AP100	3s vio bl & lt bl	.60	.25

25th anniversary of United Nations.

Rotary Club Emblem AP101

1970, July 18

C293	AP101	10s blk, red & gold	1.50	.80

Rotary Club of Lima, 50th anniversary.

Tourist Type of Regular Issue

3s, Ruins of Sun Fortress, Trujillo. 4s, Sacsayhuaman Arch, Cuzco. 5.50s, Arch & Lake Titicaca, Puno. 10s, Machu Picchu, Cuzco.

1970, Aug. 6   Litho.   *Perf. 11*

C294	A210	3s multi	1.20	.25
C295	A210	4s multi, vert.	1.50	.25
C296	A210	5.50s multi, vert.	2.25	.35
C297	A210	10s multi, vert.	3.00	.75
a.		Souvenir sheet of 5	7.50	6.00
		Nos. C294-C297 (4)	7.95	1.60

No. C297a contains 5 imperf. stamps similar to Nos. 538, C294-C297 with simulated perforations.

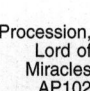

Procession, Lord of Miracles AP102

4s, Cockfight, by T. Nuñez Ureta. 5.50s, Altar of Church of the Nazarene, vert. 6.50s, Procession, by J. Vinatea Reinoso. 8s, Procession, by José Sabogal, vert.

1970, Nov. 30   Litho.   *Perf. 11*

C298	AP102	3s blk & multi	.45	.35
C299	AP102	4s blk & multi	.45	.35
C300	AP102	5.50s blk & multi	.90	.40
C301	AP102	6.50s blk & multi	1.00	.50
C302	AP102	8s blk & multi	1.50	.60
		Nos. C298-C302 (5)	4.30	2.20

October Festival in Lima.

"Tight Embrace" (from ancient monolith) AP103

1971, Feb. 8   Litho.   *Perf. 11*

C303	AP103	4s ol gray, yel & red	.80	.30
C304	AP103	5.50s dk bl, pink & red	.80	.30
C305	AP103	6.50s sl, buff & red	.80	.30
		Nos. C303-C305 (3)	2.40	.90

Issued to express Peru's gratitude to the world for aid after the Ancash earthquake, May 31, 1970.

Textile Type of Regular Issue

Designs: 3s, Chancay tapestry, vert. 4s, Chancay lace. 5.50s, Paracas cloth, vert.

1971, Apr. 19   Litho.   *Perf. 11*

C306	A213	3s multi	1.50	.50
C307	A213	4s grn & multi	1.50	.50
C308	A213	5.50s multi	2.10	.55
		Nos. C306-C308 (3)	5.10	1.55

Fish Type of Regular Issue

Fish Sculptures and Fish: 3.50s, Chimu Inca culture, 14th century and Chilean sardine. 4s, Mochica culture, 5th century, and engraulis ringens. 5.50s, Chimu culture, 13th century, and merluccios peruanos. 8.50s, Nazca culture, 3rd century, and brevoortis maculatachilcae.

1971, June 7   Litho.   *Perf. 11*

C309	A214	3.50s multi	.85	.25
C310	A214	4s multi	1.00	.25
C311	A214	5.50s multi	1.40	.55
C312	A214	8.50s multi	2.25	1.10
		Nos. C309-C312 (4)	5.50	2.15

Independence Type of 1971

Paintings: No. C313, Toribio Rodriguez de Mendoza. No. C314, José de la Riva Aguero. No. C315, Francisco Vidal. 3.50s, José de San Martin. No. C317, Juan P. Viscardo y Guzman. No. C318, Hipolito Unanue. 4.50s, Liberation Monument, Paracas. No. C320, José G. Condorcanqui-Tupac Amaru. No. C321, Francisco J. de Luna Pizarro. 6s, March of the Numancia Battalion, horiz. 7.50s, Peace Tower, monument for Alvarez de Arenales, horiz. 9s, Liberators' Monument, Lima, horiz. 10s, Independence Proclamation in Lima, horiz.

1971   Litho.   *Perf. 11*

C313	A215	3s brt mag & blk	.50	.25
C314	A215	3s gray & multi	.50	.25
C315	A215	3s dk bl & multi	.50	.25
C316	A215	3.50s dk bl & multi	.70	.25
C317	A215	4s emer & blk	.70	.25
C318	A215	4s gray & multi	.70	.25
C319	A215	4.50s dk bl & multi	.70	.25
C320	A215	5.50s brn & blk	1.10	.25
C321	A215	5.50s gray & multi	1.10	.25
C322	A215	6s dk bl & multi	1.25	.30
C323	A215	7.50s dk bl & multi	1.50	.50
C324	A215	9s dk bl & multi	1.50	.50
C325	A215	10s dk bl & multi	1.50	.50
		Nos. C313-C325 (13)	12.25	4.05

150th anniversary of independence, and to honor the heroes of the struggle for independence. Sizes: 6s, 10s, 45x35mm, 7.50s, 9s, 41x39mm. Others 31x49mm.

Issued: #C313, C317, C320, 5/10; #C314, C318, C321, 7/5; others 7/27.

Ricardo Palma — AP104

1971, Aug. 27   *Perf. 13*

C326	AP104	7.50s ol bis & blk	1.40	.55

Sesquicentennial of National Library. Ricardo Palma (1884-1912) was a writer and director of the library.

Weight Lifter — AP105

1971, Sept. 15

C327	AP105	7.50s brt bl & blk	1.40	.55

25th World Weight Lifting Championships, Lima.

Flag, Family, Soldier's Head — AP106

1971, Oct. 4

C328	AP106	7.50s blk, lt bl & red	1.10	.30
a.		Souv. sheet of 1, imperf.	2.75	2.50

3rd anniv. of the revolution of the armed forces.

"Sacramento" AP107

1971, Oct. 8

C329	AP107	7.50s lt bl & dk bl	1.40	.55

Sesquicentennial of Peruvian Navy.

Peruvian Order of the Sun — AP108

1971, Oct. 8

C330	AP108	7.50s multi	1.00	.80

Sesquicentennial of the Peruvian Order of the Sun.

Liberation Type of Regular Issue

Design: 50s, Detail from painting "Progress and Liberation," by Teodoro Nuñez Ureta.

1971, Nov. 4   Litho.   *Perf. 13x13½*

C331	A217	50s multi	7.00	2.25

2nd Ministerial meeting of the "Group of 77."

Fair Emblem — AP109

1971, Nov. 12   *Perf. 13*

C332	AP109	4.50s multi	.80	.30

7th Pacific International Trade Fair.

Fish Type of Regular Issue

3s, Pontinus furcirhinus dubius. 5.50s, Hogfish.

1972, Mar. 20   Litho.   *Perf. 13x13½*

C333	A223	3s lt bl & multi	1.75	.75
C334	A223	5.50s lt bl & multi	3.00	.75

Teacher and Children, by Teodoro Nuñez Ureta — AP110

1972, Apr. 10   Litho.   *Perf. 13x13½*

C335	AP110	6.50s multi	.85	.30

Enactment of Education Reform Law.

White-tailed Trogon — AP111

2.50s, Amazonian umbrella bird. 3s, Peruvian cock-of-the-rock. 6.50s, Cuvier's toucan. 8.50s, Blue-crowned motmot.

1972, June 19   Litho.   *Perf. 13½x13*

C336	AP111	2s multi	2.50	1.75
C337	AP111	2.50s multi	2.50	1.75
C338	AP111	3s multi	2.90	1.75
C339	AP111	6.50s multi	5.25	1.75
C340	AP111	8.50s multi	7.75	1.75
		Nos. C336-C340 (5)	20.90	8.75

Quipu and Map of Americas — AP112

1972, Aug. 21

C341	AP112	5s blk & multi	1.25	.50

4th Interamerican Philatelic Exhibition, EXFILBRA, Rio de Janeiro, Aug. 26-Sept. 2.

Inca Runner, Olympic Rings — AP113

1972, Aug. 28

C342	AP113	8s buff & multi	1.40	.55

20th Olympic Games, Munich, 8/26-9/11.

Woman of Catacaos, Piura — AP114

Regional Costumes: 2s, Tupe (Yauyos) woman of Lima. 4s, Indian with bow and arrow, from Conibo, Loreto. 4.50s, Man with calabash, Cajamarca. 5s, Moche woman, Trujillo. 6.50s, Man and woman of Ocongate, Cuzco. 8s, Chucupana woman, Ayacucho. 8.50s, Cotuncha woman, Junin. 10s, Woman of Puno dancing "Pandilla."

1972-73   Design AP114

C343		2s blk & multi	.50	.45
C344		3.50s blk & multi	1.50	.70
C345		4s blk & multi	1.75	.80
C346		4.50s blk & multi	1.00	.90
C346A		5s blk & multi	1.00	.90
C347		6.50s blk & multi	2.60	1.10
C347A		8s blk & multi	2.00	1.40
C347B		8.50s blk & multi	2.00	1.50
C348		10s blk & multi	2.00	1.75
		Nos. C343-C348 (9)	14.35	9.50

Issued: 3.50s, 4s, 6.50s, 9/29/72; 2s, 4.50s, 10s, 4/30/73; 5s, 8s, 8.50s, 10/15/73.
See Nos. C414-C415.

Funerary Tower, Sillustani, Puno — AP115

Archaeological Monuments: 1.50s, Stone of the 12 angles, Cuzco. 3.50s, Ruins of Chavin, Ancash. 5s, Wall and gate, Chavin, Ancash. 8s, Ruins of Machu Picchu.

Perf. 13½x13, 13x13½

1972, Oct. 16   Litho.

C349	AP115	1.50s multi	.60	.25
C350	AP115	3.50s multi, horiz.	.95	.25
C351	AP115	4s multi	.95	.25
C352	AP115	5s multi, horiz.	1.40	.40
C353	AP115	8s multi, horiz.	2.25	.55
		Nos. C349-C353 (5)	6.15	1.70

AP116

Inca ponchos, various textile designs.

1973, Jan. 29   Litho.   *Perf. 13½x13*

C354	AP116	2s multi	.75	.50
C355	AP116	3.50s multi	1.00	.50
C356	AP116	4s multi	1.00	.50

C357	AP116	5s multi	1.00	.55
C358	AP116	8s multi	2.50	.55
Nos. C354-C358 (5)			6.25	2.60

AP117

Antique Jewelry: 1.50s, Goblets and Ring, Mochica, 10th cent. 2.50s, Golden hands and arms, Lambayeque, 12th cent. 4s, Gold male statuette, Mochica, 8th ceny. 5s, Two gold brooches, Nazca, 8th cent. 8s, Flayed puma, Mochica, 8th cent.

1973, Mar. 19 Litho. Perf. 13½x13

C359	AP117	1.50s multi	1.25	.80
C360	AP117	2.50s multi	1.25	.80
C361	AP117	4s multi	1.25	.80
C362	AP117	5s multi	1.60	1.25
C363	AP117	8s multi	3.25	.80
Nos. C359-C363 (5)			8.60	4.45

Andean Condor — AP118

Protected Animals: 5s, Vicuña. 8s, Spectacled bear.

1973, Apr. 16 Litho. Perf. 13½x13

C364	AP118	4s blk & multi	.70	.25
C365	AP118	5s blk & multi	.95	.40
C366	AP118	8s blk & multi	2.00	.70
Nos. C364-C366 (3)			3.65	1.35

See Nos. C372-C376, C411-C412.

Indian Guide, by José Sabogal — AP119

Peruvian Paintings: 8.50s, Portrait of a Lady, by Daniel Hernandez. 20s, Man Holding Figurine, by Francisco Laso.

1973, May 7 Litho. Perf. 13½x13

C367	AP119	1.50s multi	.50	.40
C368	AP119	8.50s multi	.95	.60
C369	AP119	20s multi	3.00	1.10
Nos. C367-C369 (3)			4.45	2.10

Basket and World Map — AP120

1973, May 26 Perf. 13x13½

| C370 | AP120 | 5s green | .75 | .30 |
| C371 | AP120 | 20s lil rose | 2.90 | 1.00 |

1st International Basketball Festival.

Darwin's Rhea — AP121

3.50s, Giant otter. 6s, Greater flamingo. 8.50s, Bush dog, horiz. 10s, Chinchilla, horiz.

1973, Sept. 3 Litho. Perf. 13½x13

C372	AP121	2.50s shown	1.90	1.00
C373	AP121	3.50s multi	3.00	1.25
C374	AP121	6s multi	3.75	1.25
C375	AP121	8.50s multi	3.75	1.75
C376	AP121	10s multi	4.75	2.50
Nos. C372-C376 (5)			17.15	7.75

Protected animals.

Orchid — AP122

Designs: Various orchids.

1973, Sept. 27

C377	AP122	1.50s blk & multi	1.40	.75
C378	AP122	2.50s blk & multi	2.40	.75
C379	AP122	3s blk & multi	2.75	.75
C380	AP122	3.50s blk & multi	3.00	.75
C381	AP122	8s blk & multi	6.75	.75
Nos. C377-C381 (5)			16.30	3.75

Pacific Fair Emblem — AP123

1973, Nov. 14 Litho. Perf. 13½x13

| C382 | AP123 | 8s blk, red & gray | 1.40 | .45 |

8th International Pacific Fair, Lima.

Cargo Ship ILO — AP124

Designs: 2.50s, Boats of Pescaperu fishing organization. 8s, Jet and seagull.

1973, Dec. 14 Litho. Perf. 13

C383	AP124	1.50s multi	.35	.25
C384	AP124	2.50s multi	.55	.30
C385	AP124	8s multi	1.75	.30
Nos. C383-C385 (3)			2.65	.85

Issued to promote government enterprises.

Lima Monument AP125

1973, Nov. 27 Perf. 13

| C386 | AP125 | 8.50s red & multi | 1.40 | .35 |

50th anniversary of Air Force Academy. Monument honors Jorge Chavez, Peruvian aviator.

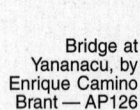

Bridge at Yananacu, by Enrique Camino Brant — AP126

Paintings: 10s, Peruvian Birds, by Teodoro Nuñez Ureta, vert. 50s, Boats of Totora, by Jorge Vinatea Reinoso.

1973, Dec. 28 Perf. 13x13½, 13½x13½

C387	AP126	8s multi	1.20	.30
C388	AP126	10s multi	1.90	.65
C389	AP126	50s multi	7.50	3.25
Nos. C387-C389 (3)			10.60	4.20

Moral House, Arequipa AP127

2.50s, El Misti Mountain, Arequipa. 5s, Puya Raymondi (cacti), vert. 6s, Huascaran Mountain. 8s, Lake Querococha. Views on 5s, 6s, 8s are views in White Cordilleras Range, Ancash Province.

1974, Feb. 11

C390	AP127	1.50s multi	.30	.25
C391	AP127	2.50s multi	.65	.25
C392	AP127	5s multi	.95	.25

C393	AP127	6s multi	1.40	.25
C394	AP127	6s multi	2.25	.65
Nos. C390-C394 (5)			5.55	1.65

San Jeronimo's, Cuzco — AP128

Churches of Peru: 3.50s, Cajamarca Cathedral. 5s, San Pedro's, Zepita-Puno, horiz. 6s, Cuzco Cathedral. 8.50s, Santo Domingo, Cuzco.

1974, May 6

C395	AP128	1.50s multi	.90	.30
C396	AP128	3.50s multi	.90	.30
C397	AP128	5s multi	1.50	.30
C398	AP128	6s multi	1.50	.40
C399	AP128	8.50s multi	2.50	.50
Nos. C395-C399 (5)			7.30	1.80

Surrender at Ayacucho, by Daniel Hernandez AP129

Designs: 6s, Battle of Junin, by Felix Yañez. 7.50s, Battle of Ayachucho, by Felix Yañez.

1974 Litho. Perf. 13x13½

C400	AP129	3.50s multi	.75	.25
C401	AP129	6s multi	1.25	.30
C402	AP129	7.50s multi	1.25	.30
C403	AP129	8.50s multi	1.50	.30
C404	AP129	10s multi	1.75	.60
Nos. C400-C404 (5)			6.50	1.75

Sesquicentennial of the Battles of Junin and Ayacucho and of the surrender at Ayacucho. Issued: 7.50s, 8/6; 6s, 10/9; others, 12/9.

Chavin Stone, Ancash — AP130

Machu Picchu, Cuzco — AP131

#C407, C409, Different bas-reliefs from Chavin Stone. #C408, Baths of Tampumacchay, Cuzco. #C410, Ruins of Kencco, Cuzco.

1974, Mar. 25 Perf. 13½x13, 13x13½

C405	AP130	3s multi	1.25	.25
C406	AP131	3s multi	.90	.25
C407	AP130	5s multi	2.40	.65
C408	AP131	5s multi	1.00	.25
C409	AP130	10s multi	2.40	.65
C410	AP131	10s multi	2.00	.25
Nos. C405-C410 (6)			9.95	2.30

Cacajao Rubicundus — AP132

1974, Oct. 21 Perf. 13½x13

| C411 | AP132 | 8s multi | 1.25 | .45 |
| C412 | AP132 | 20s multi | 3.00 | 1.10 |

Protected animals.

Inca Gold Mask — AP133

1974, Nov. 8 Perf. 13x13½

| C413 | AP133 | 8s yel & multi | 2.10 | .60 |

8th World Mining Congress, Lima.

Chalan, Horseman's Cloak — AP134

1974, Nov. 11 Litho. Perf. 13½x13

| C414 | AP134 | 5s multi | .75 | .25 |
| C415 | AP134 | 8.50s multi | 1.40 | .55 |

See Nos. C343-C348.

Pedro Paulet and Aerial Torpedo — AP135

1974, Nov. 28 Litho. Perf. 13x13½

| C416 | AP135 | 8s bl & vio | 1.00 | .35 |

UPU, cent. Pedro Paulet, inventor of the mail-carrying aerial torpedo.

Christmas Type of 1974

Design: 6.50s, Indian Nativity scene.

1974, Dec. 20 Perf. 13½x13

| C417 | A235 | 6.50s multi | .90 | .30 |

Andean Village, Map of South American West Coast — AP136

1974, Dec. 30

| C418 | AP136 | 6.50s multi | .90 | .40 |

Meeting of Communications Ministers of Andean Pact countries.

Map of Peru, Modern Buildings, UN Emblem — AP137

1975, Mar. 12 Litho. Perf. 13½x13

| C419 | AP137 | 6s blk, gray & red | .80 | .45 |

2nd United Nations Industrial Development Organization Conference, Lima.

Nos. C187, C211 and C160 Surcharged with New Value and Heavy Bar in Dark Blue Wmk. 346

1975, April Litho. Perf. 12

| C420 | AP51 | 2s on 4.30s org | .65 | .25 |

Perf. 13½x14, 13x14 Unwmk.

C421	AP51	2.50s on 4.60s org	.80	.25
C422	AP51	5s on 3.80s org	.90	.40
Nos. C420-C422 (3)			2.35	.90

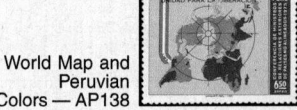

World Map and Peruvian Colors — AP138

1975, Aug. 25 Litho. *Perf. 13x13½*
C423 AP138 6.50s lt bl, vio bl &
           red   1.40   .30

Conference of Foreign Ministers of Nonaligned Countries.

Map of Peru and
Flight
Route — AP139

1975, Oct. 23 Litho. *Perf. 13x13½*
C424 AP139 8s red, pink & blk   1.25   .30

AeroPeru's first flights: Lima-Rio de Janeiro, Lima-Los Angeles.

Fair Poster — AP140

1975, Nov. 21 Litho. *Perf. 13½x13*
C425 AP140 6s blk, bis & red   1.00   .30

9th International Pacific Fair, Lima, 1975.

Col. Francisco
Bolognesi — AP141

1975, Dec. 23 Litho. *Perf. 13½x13*
C426 AP141 20s multi   3.00 1.10

160th birth anniv. of Col. Bolognesi.

Indian Mother and
Child — AP142

1976, Feb. 23 Litho. *Perf. 13½x13*
C427 AP142 6s gray & multi   1.00   .30

Christmas 1975.

Inca Messenger, UPAE
Emblem — AP143

1976, Mar. 19 Litho. *Perf. 13½x13*
C428 AP143 5s red, blk & tan   1.00   .30

11th Congress of the Postal Union of the Americas and Spain, UPAE.

**Nos. C187, C211, C160, C209, C210
Surcharged in Dark Blue or Violet
Blue (No Bar)**

1976			As Before
C429	AP51	2s on 4.30s org	.30 .25
C430	AP51	3.50s on 4.60s org	.30 .25
C431	AP51	4.50s on 3.80s org	.30 .25
C432	AP51	5s on 4.30s org	.45 .25
C433	AP51	6s on 4.60s org	.70 .25
C434	A184	10s on 2.60s brt grn	.85 .40
C435	AP52	50s on 3.60s lil rose (VB)	4.75 3.00
		Nos. C429-C435 (7)	7.65 4.65

**Stamps of 1962-67 Surcharged with
New Value and Heavy Bar in Black,
Red, Green, Dark Blue or Orange**

1976-77			As Before
C436	AP52	1.50s on 3.60s (Bk) #C210	.40 .25
C437	A184	2s on 2.60s (R) #C209 ('77)	.40 .25
C438	AP52	2s on 3.60s (G) #C210	.40 .25
C439	AP80	2s on 4.30s (Bk) #C199	.40 .25
C440	A184	3s on 2.60s (Bk) #C209 ('77)	.40 .25
C441	A184	4s on 2.60s (DBl) #C209	.55 .30
C442	AP52	4s on 3.60s (DBl) #C210 ('77)	.55 .30
C443	AP51	5s on 4.30s (R) #C187	.80 .30
C444	AP83	6s on 4.60s (Bk) #C208 ('77)	.80 .30
C445	AP51	6s on 4.60s (DBl) #C211 ('77)	.80 .30
C446	AP51	7s on 4.30s (Bk) #C187 ('77)	.55 .30
C447	AP52	7.50s on 3.60s (DBl) #C210	.90 .40
C448	AP52	8s on 3.60s (O) #C210	1.20 .30
C449	AP51	10s on 4.30s (Bk) #C187 ('77)	.65 .30
C450	AP51	10s on 4.60s (DBl) #C211	1.25 .30
C451	AP86	24s on 3.60s (Bk) #C220 ('77)	3.25 .95
C452	AP86	28s on 4.60s (Bk) #C221 ('77)	2.75 1.10
C453	AP86	32s on 5.60s (Bk) #C222 ('77)	2.75 1.10
C454	A184	50s on 2.60s (O) #C209 ('77)	6.00 1.75
C455	AP52	50s on 3.60s (G) #C210	4.75 2.25
		Nos. C436-C455 (20)	29.55 11.50

AP144

Map of Tacna and Tarata Provinces.

1976, Aug. 28 Litho. *Perf. 13½x13*
C456 AP144 10s multi   1.00   .30

Re-incorporation of Tacna Province into Peru, 47th anniversary.

AP145

Investigative Police badge.

1976, Sept. 15 Litho. *Perf. 13½x13*
C457 AP145 20s multi   1.50   .70

Investigative Police of Peru, 54th anniv.

Declaration of
Bogota — AP146

1976, Sept. 22
C458 AP146 10s multi   1.00   .30

Declaration of Bogota for cooperation and world peace, 10th anniversary.

AP147

Pal Losonczi and map of Hungary.

1976, Nov. 2 Litho. *Perf. 13½x13*
C459 AP147 7s ultra & blk   1.00   .30

Visit of Pres. Pal Losonczi of Hungary, Oct. 1976.

Map of Amazon
Basin, Colors of
Peru and
Brazil — AP148

1976, Dec. 16 Litho. *Perf. 13*
C460 AP148 10s bl & multi   1.00   .30

Visit of Gen. Ernesto Geisel, president of Brazil, Nov. 5, 1976.

Liberation
Monument,
Lima — AP149

1977, Mar. 9 Litho. *Perf. 13x13½*
C461 AP149 20s red buff & blk   1.90   .65

Army Day.

Map of Peru and
Venezuela, South
America — AP150

1977, Mar. 14
C462 AP150 12s buff & multi   1.40   .55

Meeting of Pres. Francisco Morales Bermudez Cerrutti of Peru and Pres. Carlos Andres Perez of Venezuela, Dec. 1976.

Electronic
Tree — AP151

1977, May 30 Litho. *Perf. 13½x13*
C463 AP151 20s gray, red & blk   2.40   .75

World Telecommunications Day.

Map of Peru, Refinery,
Tanker — AP152

1977, July 13 Litho. *Perf. 13½x13*
C464 AP152 14s multi   1.00   .45

Development of Bayovar oil complex.

Messenger Type of 1977

1977		Litho.	*Perf. 13½x13*
C465	A243	24s mag & blk	2.10 .75
C466	A243	28s bl & blk	3.25 .75
C467	A243	32s rose brn & blk	2.10 1.10
		Nos. C465-C467 (3)	7.45 2.60

For surcharge see No. C502.

Arms of
Arequipa — AP153

1977, Sept. 3 Litho. *Perf. 13½x13*
C468 AP153 10s multi   .60   .25

Gold of Peru Exhibition, Arequipa 1977.

Gen. Jorge Rafael
Videla — AP154

1977, Oct. 8 Litho. *Perf. 13½x13*
C469 AP154 36s multi   1.40   .40

Visit of Jorge Rafael Videla, president of Argentina.

**Stamps of 1953-67 Surcharged with
New Value and Heavy Bar in Black,
Dark Blue or Green**

1977			As Before
C470	AP83	2s on 3.60s #C207	.40 .25
C471	AP51	2s on 4.60s (DB) #C211	.40 .25
C472	AP51	4s on 4.60s (DB) #C211	.55 .25
C473	AP51	5s on 4.30s #C187	.65 .40
C474	AP52	5s on 3.60s #C210	.40 .25
C475	AP55	10s on 2.15s #C125	.90 .30
C476	AP52	10s on 3.60s (DB) #C210	1.50 .45
C477	AP84	10s on 3.60s #C215	1.40 .45
C478	AP52	20s on 3.60s (DB) #C210	1.40 .55
C479	AP51	100s on 3.80s (G) #C160	6.00 3.00
		Nos. C470-C479 (10)	13.60 6.15

**Nos. C223-C224 Surcharged with
New Value, Heavy Bars and:
"FRANQUEO"**

1977		Litho.	*Perf. 12*
C480	AP87	6s on 3.60s multi	1.25 .65
C481	AP87	8s on 3.60s multi	1.60 .90
C482	AP87	10s on 5.60s multi	1.60 1.00
		Nos. C480-C482 (3)	4.45 2.55

Adm. Miguel
Grau — AP155

1977, Dec. 15 Litho. *Perf. 13½x13*
C483 AP155 28s multi   1.00   .45

Navy Day. Miguel Grau (1838-1879), Peruvian naval commander.

Christmas Type of 1977

1977, Dec. 23
C484 A246 20s Indian Nativity   1.00   .35

Andrés Bello,
Flag and Map of
Participants
AP156

1978, Jan. 12 Litho. *Perf. 13*
C485 AP156 30s multi   .85   .35

8th Meeting of Education Ministers honoring Andrés Bello, Lima.

Inca Type of 1978

1978		**Litho.**	**Perf. 13½x13**
C486	A247	24s dp rose lil	.80 .45
C487	A247	30s salmon	.95 .45
C488	A247	65s brt bl	2.25 1.00
C489	A247	95s dk bl	3.25 1.60
	Nos. C486-C489 (4)		7.25 3.50

For surcharge see No. C501.

Antenna, ITU Emblem — AP157

1978, July 3		**Litho.**	**Perf. 13x13½**
C490	AP157	50s gray & multi	1.50 1.25

10th World Telecommunications Day.

San Martin, Flag Colors of Peru and Argentina — AP158

1978, Sept. 4		**Litho.**	**Perf. 13½x13**
C491	AP158	30s multi	1.00 .75

Gen. José de San Martin (1778-1850), soldier and statesman, protector of Peru.

Stamps of 1965-67 Surcharged "Habilitado / R.D. No. O118" and New Value in Red, Green, Violet Blue or Black

1978			**Litho.**
C492	AP83	34s on 4.60s multi (R) #C208	.55 .40
C493	AP79	40s on 4.30s multi (G) #C196	.65 .50
C494	A184	70s on 2.60s brt grn (VB) #C209	1.10 .85
C495	AP52	110s on 3.60s lil rose (Bk) #C210	2.25 1.10
C496	AP80	265s on 4.30s gray & multi (Bk) #C199	4.00 3.25
	Nos. C492-C496 (5)		8.55 6.10

Stamps and Type of 1968-78 Surcharged in Violet Blue, Black or Red

1978			**Litho.**
C497	AP86	25s on 4.60s (VB) #C221	.55 .50
C498	A247	45s on 28s dk grn (Bk)	1.10 .55
C499	A247	75s on 28s dk grn (R)	1.75 1.10
C500	AP86	105s on 5.60s (R) #C222	2.50 1.75
	Nos. C497-C500 (4)		5.90 3.90

Nos. C498-C499 not issued without surcharge.

Nos. C486, C467 Surcharged

1980, Apr. 14		**Litho.**	**Perf. 13½x13**
C501	A247	35s on 24s dp rose lil	.75 .45
C502	A243	45s on 32s rose brn & blk	.80 .50

No. C130 Surcharged in Black

1981, Nov.		**Engr.**	**Perf. 13**
C503	AP57	30s on 2.20s multi	.75 .45
C504	AP57	40s on 2.20s multi	.75 .40

No. C130 Surcharged and Overprinted in Green: "12 Feria / Internacional / del / Pacifico 1981"

1981, Nov. 30			
C505	AP57	140s on 2.20s multi	2.25 1.25

12th Intl. Pacific Fair.

AIR POST SEMI-POSTAL STAMPS

> Catalogue values for unused stamps in this section are for Never Hinged items.

Chavin Griffin — SPAP1

1.50s+1s, Bird. 3s+2.50s, Cat. 4.30s+3s, Mythological figure, vert. 6s+ 4s, Chavin god, vert.

Perf. 12½x12, 12x12½

1963, Apr. 18 Litho. Wmk. 346
Design in Gray and Brown

CB1	SPAP1	1s + 50c sal pink	.40 .35
CB2	SPAP1	1.50s + 1s blue	.65 .55
CB3	SPAP1	3s + 2.50s lt grn	1.00 .85
CB4	SPAP1	4.30s + 3s green	2.00 1.60
CB5	SPAP1	6s + 4s citron	2.50 2.00
	Nos. CB1-CB5 (5)		6.55 5.35

The designs are from ceramics found by archaeological excavations of the 14th century Chavin culture. The surtax was for the excavations fund.

Henri Dunant and Centenary Emblem — SPAP2

Perf. 12½x12

1964, Jan. 29 Unwmk.

CB6	SPAP2	1.30s + 70c multi	.75 .55
CB7	SPAP2	4.30s + 1.70s multi	1.40 1.10

Centenary of International Red Cross.

SPECIAL DELIVERY STAMPS

No. 149 Overprinted in Black

1908		**Unwmk.**	**Perf. 12**
E1	A25	10c gray black	25.00 19.00

No. 172 Overprinted in Violet

1909			
E2	A40	10c red brn & blk	40.00 22.50

No. 181 Handstamped in Violet

1910			
E3	A49	10c deep blue	24.00 20.00

Two handstamps were used to make No. E2. Impressions from them measure 22½x6½mm and 24x6½mm.
Counterfeits exist of Nos. E1-3.

POSTAGE DUE STAMPS

Coat of Arms — D1

Steamship and Llama
D2　　D3

D4　　D5

With Grill

1874-79		**Unwmk. Engr.**	**Perf. 12**
J1	D1	1c bister ('79)	.45 .30
J2	D2	5c vermilion	.55 .30
J3	D3	10c orange	.65 .30
J4	D4	20c blue	1.10 .55
J5	D5	50c brown	17.00 6.50
	Nos. J1-J5 (5)		19.75 7.95

A 2c green exists, but was not regularly issued.
For overprints and surcharges see Nos. 157, J6-J31, J37-J38, 8N14-8N15, 14N18.

1902-07 Without Grill

J1a	D1	1c bister	.35
J2a	D2	5c vermilion	.55
J3a	D3	10c orange	.55
J4a	D4	20c blue	.65
	Nos. J1a-J4a (4)		2.10

Nos. J1-J5 Overprinted in Blue or Red

1881		**"PLATA" 2½mm High**	
J6	D1	1c bis (Bl)	6.00 5.00
J7	D2	5c ver (Bl)	12.00 11.00
a.		Double overprint	
b.		Inverted overprint	24.00 24.00
J8	D3	10c org (Bl)	12.00 11.00
a.		Inverted overprint	24.00 24.00
J9	D4	20c bl (R)	45.00 32.50
J10	D5	50c brn (Bl)	100.00 90.00
	Nos. J6-J10 (5)		175.00 149.50

In the reprints of this overprint "PLATA" is 3mm high instead of 2½mm. Besides being struck in the regular colors it was also applied to the 1, 5, 10 and 50c in red and the 20c in blue.

Overprinted in Red

1881			
J11	D1	1c bister	9.00 9.00
J12	D2	5c vermilion	11.00 10.00
J13	D3	10c orange	13.00 13.00
J14	D4	20c blue	55.00 37.50
J15	D5	50c brown	125.00 125.00
	Nos. J11-J15 (5)		213.00 194.50

Originals of Nos. J11 to J15 are overprinted in brick-red, oily ink; reprints in thicker, bright red ink. The 5c exists with reprinted overprint in blue.

Overprinted "Union Postal Universal Lima Plata" in Oval in first named color and Triangle in second named color

1883			
J16	D1	1c bis (Bl & Bk)	9.00 6.50
J17	D1	1c bis (Bk & Bl)	13.00 13.00
J18	D2	5c ver (Bl & Bk)	13.00 13.00
J19	D3	10c org (Bl & Bk)	13.00 13.00
J20	D4	20c bl (R & Bk)	850.00 850.00
J21	D5	50c brn (Bl & Bk)	60.00 60.00

Reprints of Nos. J16 to J21 have the oval overprint with "PLATA" 3mm. high. The 1c also exists with the oval overprint in red.

Overprinted in Black

1884			
J22	D1	1c bister	.90 .90
J23	D2	5c vermilion	.90 .90
J24	D3	10c orange	.90 .90

J25	D4	20c blue	1.90 .90
J26	D5	50c brown	5.50 1.75
	Nos. J22-J26 (5)		10.10 5.35

The triangular overprint is found in 11 types.

Overprinted "Lima Correos" in Circle in Red and Triangle in Black

1884			
J27	D1	1c bister	42.50 42.50

Reprints of No. J27 have the overprint in bright red. At the time they were made the overprint was also printed on the 5, 10, 20 and 50c Postage Due stamps.
Postage Due stamps overprinted with Sun and "CORREOS LIMA" (as shown above No. 103), alone or in combination with the "U. P. U. LIMA" oval or "LIMA CORREOS" in double-lined circle, are fancy varieties made to sell to collectors and never placed in use.

Overprinted

1896-97			
J28	D1	1c bister	.65 .55
a.		Double overprint	
J29	D2	5c vermilion	.75 .45
a.		Double overprint	
b.		Inverted overprint	
J30	D3	10c orange	1.00 .65
a.		Inverted overprint	
J31	D4	20c blue	1.25 .85
a.		Double overprint	
J32	A22	50c red ('97)	1.25 .85
J33	A23	1s brown ('97)	1.90 1.25
a.		Double overprint	
b.		Inverted overprint	
	Nos. J28-J33 (6)		6.80 4.60

Liberty — D6

1899			**Engr.**
J34	D6	5s yel grn	1.90 10.50
J35	D6	10s dl vio	1,700. 1,700.

For surcharge see No. J39.

No. J36　　No. J37

1902			**On No. 159**
J36	A31	5c on 10s bl grn	1.90 1.50
a.		Double surcharge	20.00 20.00
			On No. J4
J37	D4	1c on 20c blue	1.10 .75
a.		"DEFICIT" omitted	15.00 3.50
b.		"DEFICIT" double	15.00 3.50
c.		"UN CENTAVO" double	15.00 3.50
d.		"UN CENTAVO" omitted	18.00 10.00

Surcharged Vertically

J38	D4	5c on 20c blue	2.75 1.75

No. J35 Surcharged Diagonally

1899			
J39	D6	1c on 10s dull vio	.75 .75
	Nos. J36-J39 (4)		6.50 4.75

D7

1909 Engr. Perf. 12

J40	D7	1c red brown	.90	.30
J41	D7	5c red brown	.90	.30
J42	D7	10c red brown	1.10	.45
J43	D7	50c red brown	1.75	.45
		Nos. J40-J43 (4)	4.65	1.50

1921 Size: 18¼x22mm

J44	D7	1c violet brown	.45	.30
J45	D7	2c violet brown	.45	.30
J46	D7	5c violet brown	.65	.30
J47	D7	10c violet brown	.90	.45
J48	D7	50c violet brown	2.75	1.25
J49	D7	1s violet brown	13.00	6.50
J50	D7	2s violet brown	22.50	6.50
		Nos. J44-J50 (7)	40.70	14.35

Nos. J49 and J50 have the circle at the center replaced by a shield containing "S/.", in addition to the numeral.

In 1929 during a shortage of regular postage stamps, some of the Postage Due stamps of 1921 were used instead.

See Nos. J50A-J52, J55-J56. For surcharges see Nos. 204-207, 757.

Type of 1909-22
Size: 18¾x23mm

J50A	D7	1c violet brown	1.25	.30
J50B	D7	10c violet brown	1.75	.45

Type of 1909-22 Issues

1932 Photo. Perf. 14½x14

J51	D7	2c violet brown	1.25	.45
J52	D7	10c violet brown	1.25	.45

Regular Stamps of 1934-35 Overprinted in Black

"Deficit"

1935 Perf. 13

J53	A131	2c deep claret	1.25	.50
J54	A117	10c crimson	1.25	.50

Type of 1909-32
Size: 19x23mm
Imprint: "Waterlow & Sons, Limited, Londres."

1936 Engr. Perf. 12½

J55	D7	2c light brown	.45	.45
J56	D7	10c gray green	.90	.90

OFFICIAL STAMPS

Regular Issue of 1886 Overprinted in Red

GOBIERNO

1890, Feb. 2

O2	A17	1c dl vio	2.40	2.40
a.		Double overprint	14.00	14.00
O3	A18	2c green	2.40	2.40
a.		Double overprint	14.00	14.00
b.		Inverted overprint	14.00	14.00
O4	A19	5c orange	3.50	2.75
a.		Inverted overprint	14.00	14.00
b.		Double overprint	14.00	14.00
O5	A20	10c slate	2.00	1.25
a.		Double overprint	14.00	14.00
b.		Inverted overprint	14.00	14.00
O6	A21	20c blue	5.50	3.50
a.		Double overprint	14.00	14.00
b.		Inverted overprint	14.00	14.00
O7	A22	50c red	7.25	3.25
a.		Inverted overprint	20.00	
b.		Double overprint		
O8	A23	1s brown	9.00	8.00
a.		Double overprint	27.50	27.50
b.		Inverted overprint	27.50	27.50
		Nos. O2-O8 (7)	32.05	23.55

Nos. 118-124 (Bermudez Ovpt.) Overprinted Type "a" in Red

1894, Oct.

O9	A17	1c green	2.40	2.40
a.		"Gobierno" and head invtd.	11.00	9.25
b.		Dbl. ovpt. of "Gobierno"		
O10	A17	1c orange	40.00	32.50
O11	A18	2c rose	2.40	2.40
a.		Overprinted head inverted	17.00	17.00
b.		Both overprints inverted		
O12	A18	2c violet	2.40	2.40
a.		"Gobierno" double		
O13	A19	5c ultra	40.00	32.50
a.		Both overprints inverted		

O14	A19	5c blue	19.00	16.00
O15	A20	10c green	6.00	6.00
O16	A22	50c green	9.00	9.00
		Nos. O9-O16 (8)	121.20	103.20

Nos. 125-126 ("Horseshoe" Ovpt.) Overprinted Type "a" in Red

O17	A18	2c vermilion	3.50	3.50
O18	A19	5c blue	3.50	3.50

Nos. 105, 107, 109, 113 Overprinted Type "a" in Red

1895, May

O19	A17	1c vermilion	13.00	13.00
O20	A18	2c dp ultra	13.00	13.00
O21	A12	5c claret	11.00	11.00
O22	A14	20c dp ultra	11.00	11.00
		Nos. O19-O22 (4)	48.00	48.00

Nos. O2-O22 have been extensively counterfeited.

Nos. 141, 148, 149, 151 Overprinted in Black

GOBIERNO

1896-1901

O23	A24	1c ultra	.35	.30
O24	A25	10c yellow	1.00	.50
a.		Double overprint	22.50	
O25	A25	10c gray blk ('01)	.35	.30
O26	A26	50c brt rose	5.00	5.00
		Nos. O23-O26 (4)	6.70	6.10

O1

1909-14 Engr. Perf. 12
Size: 18½x22mm

O27	O1	1c red	.55	.30
a.		1c brown red	.55	.30
O28	O1	1c orange ('14)	.90	.65
O29	O1	10c bis brn ('14)	.35	.30
a.		10c violet brown	.90	.45
O30	O1	50c ol grn ('14)	1.25	.65
a.		50c blue green	2.00	.65

Size: 18¾x23½mm

O30B	O1	10c viol brown	.90	.30
		Nos. O27-O30B (5)	3.95	2.20

See Nos. O31, O33-O34. For overprints and surcharge see Nos. 201-203, 760.

1933 Photo. Perf. 15x14

O31	O1	10c violet brown	1.25	.45

No. 319 Overprinted in Black

"Servicio Oficial"

1935 Unwmk. Perf. 13

O32	A117	10c crimson	.35	.25

Type of 1909-33
Imprint: "Waterlow & Sons, Limited, Londres."

1936 Engr. Perf. 12½
Size: 19x23mm

O33	O1	10c light brown	.25	.25
O34	O1	50c gray green	.65	.65

PARCEL POST STAMPS

Porte de Conduccion
1
CENTAVO

PP1

Porte de Conduccion
2
CENTAVOS

PP2

Porte de Conduccion
5
CENTAVOS

PP3

1897 Typeset Unwmk. Perf. 12

Q1	PP1	1c dull lilac	4.00	3.50
Q2	PP2	2c bister	5.50	3.75
a.		2c olive	5.50	3.75
b.		2c yellow	5.50	3.75
Q3	PP3	5c dk bl	19.00	10.50
a.		Laid paper	65.00	65.00
		Tête bêche pair	375.00	
Q4	PP3	10c vio brn	24.00	18.00
Q5	PP3	20c rose red	29.00	22.50
Q6	PP3	50c bl grn	85.00	75.00
		Nos. Q1-Q6 (6)	166.50	133.25

Surcharged in Black

UN CENTAVO

1903-04

Q7	PP3	1c on 20c rose red	12.00	10.00
Q8	PP3	1c on 50c bl grn	12.00	10.00
Q9	PP3	5c on 10c vio brn	80.00	65.00
a.		Inverted surcharge	125.00	110.00
b.		Double surcharge		
		Nos. Q7-Q9 (3)	104.00	85.00

POSTAL TAX STAMPS

Plebiscite Issues

These stamps were not used in Tacna and Arica (which were under Chilean occupation) but were used in Peru to pay a supplementary tax on letters, etc.

It was intended that the money derived from the sale of these stamps should be used to help defray the expenses of the plebiscite.

Morro Arica — PT1

Adm. Grau and Col. Bolognesi Reviewing Troops
PT2

Bolognesi Monument
PT3

1925-26 Unwmk. Litho. Perf. 12

RA1	PT1	5c dp bl	2.75	.75
RA2	PT1	5c rose red	1.40	.55
RA3	PT1	5c yel grn	1.25	.55
RA4	PT2	10c brown	5.50	22.50
RA5	PT3	50c bl grn	35.00	17.00
		Nos. RA1-RA5 (5)	45.90	41.35

PT4

1926

RA6	PT4	2c orange	1.10	.30

PT5

1927-28

RA7	PT5	2c dp org	1.10	.30
RA8	PT5	2c red brn	1.10	.30
RA9	PT5	2c dk bl	1.10	.30
RA10	PT5	2c gray vio	1.10	.30
RA11	PT5	2c bl grn ('28)	1.10	.30
RA12	PT5	20c red	5.50	1.75
		Nos. RA7-RA12 (6)	11.00	3.25

PT6

1928 Engr.

RA13	PT6	2c dk vio	.55	.25

The use of the Plebiscite stamps was discontinued July 26, 1929, after the settlement of the Tacna-Arica controversy with Chile. For overprint see No. 261.

Unemployment Fund Issues

These stamps were required in addition to the ordinary postage, on every letter or piece of postal matter. The money obtained by their sale was to assist the unemployed.

Nos. 273-275 Surcharged

Habilitada Pro Desocupados 2 Cts.

1931

RA14	A95	2c on 4c red	1.75	.75
a.		Inverted surcharge	4.25	4.25
RA15	A95	2c on 10c bl grn	.75	.75
a.		Inverted surcharge	4.25	4.25
RA16	A95	2c on 15c sl gray	.75	.75
a.		Inverted surcharge	4.25	4.25
		Nos. RA14-RA16 (3)	3.25	2.25

"Labor" — PT7

Two types of Nos. RA17-RA18:
I — Imprint 15mm.
II — Imprint 13¾mm.

Perf. 12x11½, 11½x12

1931-32 Litho.

RA17	PT7	2c emer (I)	.30	.25
a.		Type II	.30	
RA18	PT7	2c rose car (I) ('32)	.30	.25
a.		Type II	.30	

Blacksmith — PT8

1932-34

RA19	PT8	2c dp gray	.25	.25
RA20	PT8	2c pur ('34)	.35	.25

Monument of 2nd of May — PT9

Perf. 13, 13½, 13x13½

1933-35 Photo.

RA21	PT9	2c bl vio	.30	.25
RA22	PT9	2c org ('34)	.30	.25
RA23	PT9	2c brn vio ('35)	.30	.25
		Nos. RA21-RA23 (3)	.90	.75

For overprint see No. RA27.

No. 307 Overprinted in Black

1934			Perf. 13½
RA24	A111	2c green	.30 .25
a.	Inverted overprint		2.25 2.00

No. 339 Overprinted in Black

1935			
RA25	A131	2c deep claret	.30 .25

No. 339 Overprinted Type "a" in Black

1936	Unwmk.		Perf. 13½
RA26	A131	2c deep claret	.30 .25

No. RA23 Overprinted in Black

1936			Perf. 13x13½
RA27	PT9	2c brn vio	.30 .25
a.	Double overprint		3.50
b.	Overprint reading down		3.50
c.	Overprint double, reading down		3.50

St. Rosa of Lima — PT10

1937	Engr.		Perf. 12
RA28	PT10	2c car rose	.30 .25

Nos. RA27 and RA28 represented a tax to help erect a church.

"Protection" by John Q. A. Ward — PT11

Imprint: "American Bank Note Company"

1938		Litho.
RA29	PT11	2c red brown	.35 .25

The tax was to help the unemployed.
See Nos. RA30, RA34, RA40.

Type of 1938 Redrawn
Imprint: "Columbian Bank Note Company."

1943			Perf. 12½
RA30	PT11	2c dl claret brn	.35 .25

See note above #RA14. See #RA29, #RA34, RA40.

> Catalogue values for unused stamps in this section, from this point to the end of the section, are for Never Hinged items.

PT12   PT13

Black Surcharge

1949			Perf. 12½, 12
RA31	PT12	3c on 4c vio bl	1.25 .25
RA32	PT13	3c on 10c blue	1.25 .25

The tax was for an education fund.

Symbolical of Education — PT14

1950	Typo.		Perf. 14
	Size: 16½x21mm		
RA33	PT14	3c dp car	.30 .25

See Nos. RA35, RA39, RA43
For surcharges see Nos. 501B, 761, 764-766, RA45-RA48, RA58.

Type of 1938
Imprint: "Thomas De La Rue & Co. Ltd."

1951		Litho.
RA34	PT11	2c lt redsh brn	.30 .25

See Nos. RA29, RA30, RA40.

Type of 1950
Imprint: "Thomas De La Rue & Company, Limited."

1952	Unwmk.		Perf. 14, 13
	Size: 16½x21½mm		
RA35	PT14	3c brn car	.30 .25

Emblem of Congress — PT15

1954			Rouletted 13
RA36	PT15	5c bl & red	.35 .25

The tax was to help finance the National Marian Eucharistic Congress.
For surcharges see Nos. 758B, 768.

Piura Arms and Congress Emblem — PT16

1960		Litho.		Perf. 10½
RA37	PT16	10c ultra, red, grn & yel		.30 .25
a.	Green ribbon inverted			
RA38	PT16	10c ultra & red		.35 .25

Nos. RA37-RA38 were used to help finance the 6th National Eucharistic Congress, Piura, Aug. 25-28. Obligatory on all domestic mail until Dec. 31, 1960. Both stamps exist imperf.

Type of 1950
Imprint: "Bundesdruckerei Berlin"

1961	Size: 17½x22½mm		Perf. 14
RA39	PT14	3c dp car	.30 .25

Type of 1938
Imprint: "Harrison and Sons Ltd"

1962, Apr.		Litho.	Perf. 14x14½
RA40	PT11	2c lt brn	.30 .25

See Nos. RA29, RA30, RA34. For surcharges see Nos. 501A, 674-678, 681-682, 709-711, 757.

Symbol of Eucharist — PT17

1962, May 8			Rouletted 11
RA41	PT17	10c bl & org	.30 .25

Issued to raise funds for the Seventh National Eucharistic Congress, Huancayo, 1964. Obligatory on all domestic mail.
See No. RA42. For surcharges and overprint see Nos. 735, 762, RA44.

1962		Imprint: "Iberia"
RA42	PT17	10c bl & org	.30 .25

Type of 1950
Imprint: "Thomas de la Rue"
Size: 18x22mm

1965, Apr.		Litho.	Perf. 12½x12
RA43	PT14	3c light carmine	.30 .25

Type of 1962 Overprinted in Red

Imprint: "Iberia"

1966, July 2		Litho.	Pin Perf.
RA44	PT17	10c vio & org	.30 .25

No. RA43 Surcharged in Green or Black

b   c

d

1966-67			Perf. 12½x12
RA45	PT14 (b)	10c on 3c (G)	1.25 .25
RA46	PT14 (c)	10c on 3c (Bk)	1.25 .25
RA47	PT14 (c)	10c on 3c (G)	.35 .25
RA48	PT14 (d)	10c on 3c (G)	.35 .25
	Nos. RA45-RA48 (4)		3.20 1.00

The surtax of Nos. RA44-RA48 was for the Peruvian Journalists' Fund.

Pen Made of Newspaper — PT18

1967, Dec.		Litho.	Perf. 11
RA49	PT18	10c dk red & blk	.30 .25

The surtax was for the Peruvian Journalists' fund.
For surcharges see Nos. RA56-RA57.

Temple at Chan-Chan — PT19

Designs: No. RA51, Side view of temple. Nos. RA52-RA55, Various stone bas-reliefs from Chan-Chan.

1967, Dec. 27			
RA50	PT19	20c bl & multi	.30 .25
RA51	PT19	20c lil rose & multi	.30 .25
RA52	PT19	20c brt bl & blk	.30 .25
RA53	PT19	20c emer & blk	.30 .25
RA54	PT19	20c sep & blk	.30 .25
RA55	PT19	20c lil rose & blk	.30 .25
	Nos. RA50-RA55 (6)		1.80 1.50

The surtax was for the excavations at Chan-Chan, northern coast of Peru (Mochica-Chimu pre-Inca period).

Type of 1967 Surcharged in Red: "VEINTE / CENTAVOS / R.S. 16-8-68"

Designs: No. RA56, Handshake. No. RA57, Globe and pen.

1968, Oct.		Litho.	Perf. 11
RA56	PT18	20c on 50c multi	.90 .90
RA57	PT18	20c on 1s multi	.90 .90

Nos. RA56-RA57 without surcharge were not obligatory tax stamps.
No. C199 surcharged "PRO NAVIDAD/ Veinte Centavos/R.S. 5-11-68" was not a compulsory postal tax stamp.

No. RA43 Srchd. Similar to Type "c"

1968, Oct.			Perf. 12½x12
RA58	PT14	20c on 3c lt car	.30 .25

Surcharge lacks quotation marks and 4th line reads: Ley 17050.

OCCUPATION STAMPS

Issued under Chilean Occupation

Stamps formerly listed as Nos. N1-N10 are regular issues of Chile canceled in Peru.

Stamps of Peru, 1874-80, Overprinted in Red, Blue or Black

1881-82			Perf. 12
N11	A17	1c org (Bl)	.50 1.00
a.	Inverted overprint		
N12	A18	2c dk vio (Bk)	.50 4.00
a.	Inverted overprint		16.50
b.	Double overprint		22.50
N13	A18	2c rose (Bk)	1.60 18.00
a.	Inverted overprint		
N14	A19	5c bl (R)	55.00 62.50
a.	Inverted overprint		
N15	A19	5c ultra (R)	90.00 100.00
N16	A20	10c grn (R)	.50 1.60
a.	Inverted overprint		6.50 6.50
b.	Double overprint		12.00 12.00
N17	A21	20c brn red (Bl)	80.00 125.00
	Nos. N11-N17 (7)		228.10 312.10

Reprints of No. N17 have the overprint in bright blue; on the originals it is in dull ultramarine. Nos. N11 and N12 exist with reprinted overprint in red or yellow. There are numerous counterfeits with the overprint in both correct and fancy colors.

Same, with Additional Overprint in Black

1882			
N19	A17	1c grn (R)	.50 .80
a.	Arms inverted		8.25 10.00
b.	Arms double		5.50 6.50
c.	Horseshoe inverted		12.00 13.50
N20	A19	5c bl (R)	.80 .80
a.	Arms inverted		13.50 15.00
b.	Arms double		13.50 15.00
N21	A22	50c rose (Bk)	1.60 2.00
a.	Arms inverted		10.00
N22	A22	50c rose (Bl)	1.60 2.75
N23	A23	1s ultra (R)	3.25 4.50
a.	Arms inverted		13.50
b.	Horseshoe inverted		16.50
c.	Arms and horseshoe inverted		20.00
d.	Arms double		13.50
	Nos. N19-N23 (5)		7.75 10.85

PROVISIONAL ISSUES

Stamps Issued in Various Cities of Peru during the Chilean Occupation of Lima and Callao

During the Chilean-Peruvian War which took place in 1879 to 1882, the Chilean forces occupied the two largest cities in Peru, Lima & Callao. As these cities were the source of supply of postage stamps, Peruvians in other sections of the country were left without stamps and were forced to the expedient of making provisional issues from whatever material was at hand. Many of these were former canceling devices made over for this purpose. Counterfeits exist of many of the overprinted stamps.

ANCACHS

(See Note under "Provisional Issues")

Regular Issue of Peru, Overprinted in Manuscript in Black

1884	Unwmk.		Perf. 12
1N1	A19	5c blue	57.50 55.00

Regular Issues of Peru, Overprinted in Black

| 1N2 | A19 | 5c blue | 18.00 16.50 |

Regular Issues of Peru,
Overprinted in Black

1N3	A19	5c blue	90.00 82.50
1N4	A20	10c green	55.00 40.00
1N5	A20	10c slate	55.00 35.00

**Same, with Additional Overprint
"FRANCA"**

1N6	A20	10c green	82.50 42.50

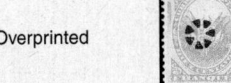

Overprinted

1N7	A19	5c blue	30.00 30.00
1N8	A20	10c green	30.00 30.00

**Same, with Additional Overprint
"FRANCA"**

1N9	A20	10c green	

A1

**Revenue Stamp of Peru, 1878-79,
Ovptd. in Black "CORREO FISCAL"
and/or "FRANCA"**

1N10	A1	10c yellow	37.50 37.50

APURIMAC

(See Note under "Provisional Issues")
**Provisional Issue of Arequipa
Overprinted in Black**

ADMON. PRAL. DE
CORREOS DEL DEPTO. DE
APURIMAC
═ABANCAY═

Overprint Covers Two Stamps

1885		Unwmk.	Imperf.
2N1	A6	10c gray	100.00 90.00

Some experts question the status of No. 2N1.

AREQUIPA

(See Note under "Provisional Issues")

Coat of Arms
A1   A2
**Overprint ("PROVISIONAL 1881-
1882") in Black**

1881, Jan.		Unwmk.	Imperf.
3N1	A1	10c blue	3.50 4.50
a.	10c ultramarine		12.00 13.50
b.	Double overprint		12.00 13.50
c.	Overprinted on back of stamp		8.25 10.00
3N2	A2	25c rose	3.50 6.00
a.	"2" in upper left corner invtd.		8.25
b.	"Cevtavos"		8.25 10.00
c.	Double overprint		8.25 13.50

The overprint also exists on 5s yellow. Value, $100.
The overprints "1883" in large figures or "Habilitado 1883" are fraudulent.
For overprints see Nos. 3N3, 4N1, 8N1, 10N1, 15N1-15N3.

With Additional Overprint
Handstamped in Red

1881, Feb.			
3N3	A1	10c blue	3.50 3.50
a.	10c ultramarine		13.50 11.50

A4

1883			Litho.
3N7	A4	10c dull rose	3.50 3.50
a.	10c vermilion		3.50 5.00

Overprinted in Blue like No. 3N3

3N9	A4	10c vermilion	5.00 4.00
a.	10c dull rose		5.00 4.00

See No. 3N10. For overprints see Nos. 8N2, 8N9, 10N2, 15N4.
Reprints of No. 3N9 are in different colors from the originals, orange, bright red, etc. They are printed in sheets of 20 instead of 25.

		Redrawn	
3N10	A4	10c brick red (Bl)	160.00

The redrawn stamp has small triangles without arabesques in the lower spandrels. The palm branch at left of the shield and other parts of the design have been redrawn.

**Same Overprint in Black, Violet or
Magenta On Regular Issues of Peru**

1884	**Embossed with Grill**		**Perf. 12**
3N11	A17	1c org (Bk, V or M)	6.50 6.50
3N12	A18	2c dk vio (Bk)	6.50 6.50
3N13	A19	5c bl (Bk, V or M)	2.00 1.40
a.	5c ultramarine (Bk or M)		8.25 6.50
3N15	A20	10c sl (Bk)	3.50 2.50
3N16	A21	20c brn red (Bk, V or M)	25.00 25.00
3N18	A22	50c grn (Bk or V)	25.00 25.00
3N20	A23	1s rose (Bk or V)	35.00 35.00
	Nos. 3N11-3N20 (7)		103.50 101.90

A5   A6

Rear
Admiral M.
L. Grau
A7

Col.
Francisco
Bolognesi
A8

**Same Overprint as on Previous
Issues**

1885			Imperf.
3N22	A5	5c olive (Bk)	5.25 5.25
3N23	A6	10c gray (Bk)	5.25 4.75
3N25	A7	5c blue (Bk)	5.25 4.75
3N26	A8	10c olive (Bk)	5.25 3.25
	Nos. 3N22-3N26 (4)		21.00 18.00

For overprints see Nos. 2N1, 8N5-8N6, 8N12-8N13, 10N9, 10N12, 15N10-15N12.
These stamps have been reprinted without overprint; they exist however with forged overprint. Originals are on thicker paper with distinct mesh, reprints on paper without mesh.

Without Overprint

3N22a	A5	5c olive	5.25 5.25
3N23a	A6	10c gray	4.00 3.25
3N25a	A7	5c blue	4.00 3.25
3N26a	A8	10c olive	4.00 3.25
	Nos. 3N22a-3N26a (4)		17.25 15.00

AYACUCHO

(See Note under "Provisional Issues")

**Provisional Issue of
Arequipa Overprinted
in Black**

1881		Unwmk.	Imperf.
4N1	A1	10c blue	150.00 125.00
a.	10c ultramarine		150.00 125.00

CHACHAPOYAS

(See Note under "Provisional Issues")

**Regular Issue of Peru
Overprinted in Black**

1884		Unwmk.	Perf. 12
5N1	A19	5c ultra	190.00 160.00

CHALA

(See Note under "Provisional Issues")

**Regular Issues of Peru
Overprinted in Black**

1884		Unwmk.	Perf. 12
6N1	A19	5c blue	25.00 13.00
6N2	A20	10c slate	35.00 16.00

CHICLAYO

(See Note under "Provisional Issues")

**Regular Issue of Peru
Overprinted in Black**

1884		Unwmk.	Perf. 12
7N1	A19	5c blue	29.00 18.00

Same, Overprinted   **FRANCA**

7N2	A19	5c blue	65.00 37.50

CUZCO

(See Note under "Provisional Issues")

**Provisional Issues of
Arequipa Overprinted in
Black**

1881-85		Unwmk.	Imperf.
8N1	A1	10c blue	125.00 110.00
8N2	A4	10c red	125.00 110.00

**Overprinted "CUZCO" in an oval of
dots**

8N5	A5	5c olive	200.00 175.00
8N6	A6	10c gray	200.00 175.00

**Regular Issue of Peru Overprinted
in Black "CUZCO" in a Circle
Perf. 12**

8N7	A19	5c blue	50.00 50.00

**Provisional Issues of
Arequipa Overprinted in
Black**

1883			Imperf.
8N9	A4	10c red	18.00 18.00

**Same Overprint in Black on Regular
Issues of Peru**

1884			Perf. 12
8N10	A19	5c blue	27.50 18.00
8N11	A20	10c slate	29.00 18.00

**Same Overprint in Black on
Provisional Issues of Arequipa
Imperf**

8N12	A5	5c olive	27.50 27.50
8N13	A6	10c gray	8.00 8.00

**Postage Due Stamps of
Peru Surcharged in Black**

		Perf. 12	
8N14	D1	10c on 1c bis	200.00 175.00
8N15	D3	10c on 10c org	200.00 175.00

HUACHO

(See Note under "Provisional Issues")

**Regular Issues of Peru
Overprinted in Black**

1884		Unwmk.	Perf. 12
9N1	A19	5c blue	16.00 16.00
9N2	A20	10c green	13.00 13.00
9N3	A20	10c slate	27.50 27.50
	Nos. 9N1-9N3 (3)		56.50 56.50

MOQUEGUA

(See Note under "Provisional Issues")

**Provisional Issues of
Arequipa Overprinted in
Violet**

Overprint 27mm wide.

1881-83		Unwmk.	Imperf.
10N1	A1	10c blue	75.00 70.00
10N2	A4	10c red ('83)	75.00 70.00

**Same Overprint on Regular Issues
of Peru in Violet**

1884			Perf. 12
10N3	A17	1c orange	75.00 70.00
10N4	A19	5c blue	55.00 35.00

Red Overprint

10N5	A19	5c blue	65.00 55.00

**Same Overprint in Violet on
Provisional Issues of Peru of 1880
Perf. 12**

10N6	A17	1c grn (R)	12.00 9.75
10N7	A18	2c rose (Bl)	15.00 15.00
10N8	A19	5c bl (R)	30.00 30.00

**Same Overprint in Violet on
Provisional Issue of Arequipa**

1885			Imperf.
10N9	A6	10c gray	85.00 42.50

**Regular Issues of Peru
Overprinted in Violet**

			Perf. 12
10N10	A19	5c blue	200.00 125.00
10N11	A20	10c slate	85.00 42.50

Same Overprint in Violet
on Provisional Issue of
Arequipa

Imperf

10N12 A6 10c gray　　　125.00 110.00

PAITA

(See Note under "Provisional Issues")

Regular Issues of Peru
Overprinted

Black Overprint

1884	**Unwmk.**	**Perf. 12**	
11N1	A19	5c blue	40.00 40.00
a.		5c ultramarine	40.00 40.00
11N2	A20	10c green	27.50 27.50
11N3	A20	10c slate	40.00 40.00

Red Overprint

11N4	A19	5c blue	40.00 40.00

Overprint lacks ornaments on #11N4-11N5.

Violet Overprint Letters 5½mm High

11N5	A19	5c ultra	40.00 40.00
a.		5c blue	40.00

PASCO

(See Note under "Provisional Issues")

Regular Issues of Peru
Overprinted in Magenta or
Black

1884	**Unwmk.**	**Perf. 12**	
12N1	A19	5c blue (M)	27.50 12.50
a.		5c ultramarine (M)	45.00 22.50
12N2	A20	10c green (Bk)	65.00 55.00
12N3	A20	10c slate (Bk)	125.00 90.00
Nos. 12N1-12N3 (3)			217.50 157.50

PISCO

(See Note under "Provisional Issues")

Regular Issue of Peru
Overprinted in Black

1884	**Unwmk.**	**Perf. 12**	
13N1	A19	5c blue	350.00 275.00

PIURA

(See Note under "Provisional Issues")

Regular Issues of Peru
Overprinted in Black

1884	**Unwmk.**	**Perf. 12**	
14N1	A19	5c blue	21.00 21.00
a.		5c ultramarine	45.00 30.00
14N2	A21	20c brn red	150.00 150.00
14N3	A22	50c green	350.00 350.00

Same Overprint in Black on Provisional Issues of Peru of 1881

14N4	A17	1c grn (R)	35.00 35.00
14N5	A18	2c rose (Bl)	55.00 55.00
14N6	A19	5c ultra (R)	70.00 70.00

Regular Issues of Peru
Overprinted in Violet, Black or
Blue **PIURA**

14N7	A19	5c bl (V)	27.50 25.00
a.		5c ultramarine (V)	27.50 25.00
b.		5c ultramarine (Bk)	27.50 25.00
14N8	A21	20c brn red (Bk)	150.00 150.00
14N9	A21	20c brn red (Bl)	150.00 150.00

Same Overprint in Black on Provisional Issues of Peru of 1881

14N10	A17	1c grn (R)	35.00 35.00
14N11	A19	5c bl (R)	42.50 42.50
a.		5c ultramarine (R)	70.00 70.00

Regular Issues of Peru
Overprinted in Black

14N13	A19	5c blue	10.00 6.50
14N14	A21	20c brn red	150.00 150.00

Regular Issues of Peru
Overprinted in Black

14N15	A19	5c ultra	110.00 100.00
14N16	A21	20c brn red	250.00 225.00

Same Overprint on Postage Due Stamp of Peru

14N18	D3	10c orange	125.00 125.00

PUNO

(See Note under "Provisional Issues")

Provisional Issue of
Arequipa Overprinted in
Violet or Blue

Diameter of outer circle 20½mm, PUNO 11½mm wide, M 3½mm wide. Other types of this overprint are fraudulent.

1882-83	**Unwmk.**	**Imperf.**	
15N1	A1	10c blue (V)	30.00 30.00
a.		10c ultramarine (V)	35.00 35.00
15N3	A2	25c red (V)	45.00 35.00
15N4	A4	10c dl rose (Bl)	29.00 29.00
a.		10c vermilion (Bl)	29.00 29.00

The overprint also exists on 5s yellow of Arequipa.

Same Overprint in
Magenta on Regular
Issues of Peru

1884		**Perf. 12**	
15N5	A17	1c orange	19.00 15.00
15N6	A18	2c violet	65.00 65.00
15N7	A19	5c blue	10.00 10.00

Violet Overprint

15N8	A19	5c blue	10.00 10.00
a.		5c ultramarine	20.00 20.00

Same Overprint in Black on Provisional Issues of Arequipa

1885		**Imperf.**	
15N10	A5	5c olive	16.00 13.50
15N11	A6	10c gray	10.00 10.00
15N12	A8	10c olive	19.00 19.00

Regular Issues of Peru
Overprinted in Magenta

1884		**Perf. 12**	
15N13	A17	1c orange	21.00 21.00
15N14	A18	2c violet	24.00 21.00
15N15	A19	5c blue	10.00 10.00
a.		5c ultramarine	20.00 20.00
15N16	A20	10c green	29.00 22.50
15N17	A21	20c brn red	150.00 150.00
15N18	A22	50c green	

YCA

(See Note under "Provisional Issues")

Regular Issues of Peru
Overprinted in Violet

1884	**Unwmk.**	**Perf. 12**	
16N1	A17	1c orange	70.00 70.00
16N3	A19	5c blue	22.50 18.00

Black Overprint

16N5	A19	5c blue	19.00 9.00

Magenta Overprint

16N6	A19	5c blue	19.00 9.00
16N7	A20	10c slate	55.00 55.00

Regular Issues of Peru
Overprinted in Black

16N12	A19	5c blue	275.00 225.00
16N13	A21	20c brown	350.00 275.00

Regular Issues of Peru
Overprinted in Carmine

16N14	A19	5c blue	275.00 225.00
16N15	A20	10c slate	350.00 275.00

Same, with Additional
Overprint

16N21	A19	5c blue	275.00 275.00
16N22	A21	20c brn red	475.00 450.00

Various other stamps exist with the overprints "YCA" and "YCA VAPOR" but they are not known to have been issued. Some of them were made to fill a dealer's order and others are reprints or merely cancellations.

PHILIPPINES

ˌfi-lə-ˈpēnz

LOCATION — Group of about 7,100 islands and islets in the Malay Archipelago, north of Borneo, in the North Pacific Ocean
GOVT. — Republic
AREA — 115,830 sq. mi.
POP. — 68,614,536 (1995)
CAPITAL — Manila

The islands were ceded to the United States by Spain in 1898. On November 15, 1935, they were given their independence, subject to a transition period. The Japanese occupation from 1942 to early 1945 delayed independence until July 4, 1946. On that date the Commonwealth became the Republic of the Philippines.

20 Cuartos = 1 Real
100 Centavos de Peso = 1 Peso (1864)
100 Centimos de Escudo = 1 Escudo (1871)
100 Centimos de Peseta = 1 Peseta (1872)
1000 Milesimas de Peso = 100 Centimos or Centavos = 1 Peso (1878)
100 Cents = 1 Dollar (1899)
100 Centavos = 1 Peso (1906)
100 Centavos (Sentimos) = 1 Peso (Piso) (1946)

Catalogue values for unused stamps in this country are for Never Hinged items, beginning with Scott 500 in the regular postage section, Scott B1 in the semipostal section, Scott C64 in the air post section, Scott E11 in the special delivery section, Scott J23 in the postage due section, and Scott O50 in the officials section.

Watermarks

Wmk. 104 — Loops

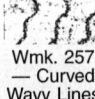
Wmk. 257 — Curved Wavy Lines

Watermark 104: loops from different watermark rows may or may not be directly opposite each other.

Wmk. 190PI — Single-lined PIPS

Wmk. 191PI — Double-lined PIPS

Watermark 191 has double-lined USPS.

Wmk. 233 — "Harrison & Sons, London." in Script

Wmk. 372 — "RPKK" Multiple

Watermark 372 comes in two types: Type I - 24mm high Type II - 19mm high
Type II was printed by the Japanese on white paper with white gum.

Wmk. 385

Wmk. 389

Wmk. 391 — Natl. Crest, Rising Sun and Eagle, with inscr. "REPUBLIKA / NG / PILIPINAS," "KAWANIHAN / NG / KOREO"

Issued under Spanish Dominion

The stamps of Philippine Islands punched with a round hole were used on telegraph receipts or had been withdrawn from use and punched to indicate that they were no longer available for postage. In this condition they sell for less, as compared to postally used copies.
Many color varieties exist of Nos. 1-88. Only major varieties are listed.

Queen Isabella II
A1   A2

1854	Unwmk.	Engr.	Imperf.
1	A1 5c orange	4,000.	350.
2	A1 10c carmine	700.	250.
a.	10c pale rose	800.	350.
4	A2 1r blue	1,000.	300.
a.	1r slate blue	800.	300.
5	A2 2r slate green	1,000.	250.

Forty plate varieties of each value. Many color varieties exist.
A 10c black exists. This is a proof or an unissued trial color. Value about $8,000.
For overprints see Nos. 24A-25A.

A3

1855		Litho.
6	A3 5c pale red	1,800. 500.

Four varieties.

A3a

Redrawn

7	A3a 5c vermilion	8,000. 1,000.

In the redrawn stamp the inner circle is smaller and is not broken by the labels at top and bottom. Only one variety.

Queen Isabella II — A4

Blue Paper

1856	Typo.	Wmk. 104
8	A4 1r green	75.00 75.00
9	A4 2r carmine	375.00 200.00

Nos. 8 and 9 used can be distinguished from Cuba Nos. 2 and 3 only by the cancellations.
For overprints, see Nos. 26-27.

Queen Isabella II — A5

Dot After "CORREOS"

1859, Jan. 1	Litho.	Unwmk.
10	A5 5c vermilion	15.00 8.00
a.	5c scarlet	24.00 12.00
b.	5c orange	32.50 17.50
11	A5 10c lilac rose	17.00 35.00

Four varieties of each value, repeated in the sheet.
For overprint see No. 28.

Dot after CORREOS
A6   A7

1861-62		
12	A6 5c vermilion	40.00 40.00
13	A7 5c dull red ('62)	190.00 95.00

No. 12, one variety only, repeated in the sheet.
For overprint see No. 29.

Colon after CORREOS — A8

A8a   A9

1863		
14	A8 5c vermilion	13.50 8.25
15	A8 10c carmine	37.50 —
16	A8 1r violet	750.00 —
17	A8 2r blue	600.00 —
18	A8a 1r gray grn	600.00 140.00
20	A9 1r green	200.00 60.00
	Nos. 14-20 (6)	2,201. 208.25

No. 18 has "CORREOS" 10½mm long, the point of the bust is rounded and is about 1mm from the circle which contains 94 pearls.
No. 20 has "CORREOS" 11mm long, and the bust ends in a sharp point which nearly touches the circle of 76 pearls. Authorized use of Nos. 15-17 is questionable.
For overprints see Nos. 30-34.

A10

1864		Typo.
21	A10 3⅛c blk, *yellow*	4.75 2.00
22	A10 6⅜c grn, *rose*	6.75 2.00
23	A10 12½c blue, *sal*	9.00 1.75
24	A10 25c red, *buff*	10.00 3.75
	Nos. 21-24 (4)	32.50 9.50

For overprints see Nos. 35-38.

Preceding Issues Handstamped

1868-74		
24A A1	5c orange ('74)	8,000. 9,000.
25 A2	1r sl bl ('74)	2,000. 1,050.
25A A2	2r grn ('74)	7,000. 7,000.
26 A4	1r grn, *bl* ('72)	180.00 80.00
27 A4	2r car, *bl* ('72)	290.00 225.00
27A A5	5c vermilion ('72)	8,000. 10,000.
28 A5	10c rose ('74)	80.00 35.00
29 A7	5c dull red ('73)	250.00 175.00
30 A8	5c ver ('72)	115.00 35.00
30A A8	10c car ('70)	6,000. —
31 A8	1r vio ('70)	900.00 600.00
32 A8	2r bl ('72)	500.00 425.00
33 A8a	1r gray grn ('70)	175.00 85.00
34 A9	1r grn ('70)	50.00 30.00
35 A10	3⅛c blk, *yellow*	9.50 4.75
36 A10	6⅜c grn, *rose*	9.50 4.75
37 A10	12½c bl, *salmon*	27.50 12.00
38 A10	25c red, *buff*	29.00 15.00

Reprints exist of #24A-38. These have crisp, sharp letters and usually have a broken first "A" of "HABILITADO."

Imperforates
Imperforates of designs A11-A16 probably are from proof or trial sheets.

"Spain" — A11

1871	Typo.	Perf. 14
39	A11 5c blue	95.00 9.25
40	A11 10c deep green	15.00 6.00
41	A11 20c brown	110.00 50.00
42	A11 40c rose	190.00 60.00
	Nos. 39-42 (4)	410.00 125.25

King Amadeo — A12

1872		
43	A12 12c rose	20.00 5.50
44	A12 16c blue	90.00 37.50
45	A12 25c gray lilac	13.50 5.50
46	A12 62c violet	40.00 9.75
47	A12 1p25c yellow brn	85.00 42.50
	Nos. 43-47 (5)	348.50 100.75

A 12c in deep blue and a 62c in rose exist but were not issued. Value $30 each.

"Peace" — A13

1874		
48	A13 12c gray lilac	22.50 5.50
49	A13 25c ultra	8.25 4.00
50	A13* 62c rose	65.00 5.50
51	A13 1p25c brown	300.00 82.50
	Nos. 48-51 (4)	395.75 97.50

King Alfonso XII — A14

1875-77		
52	A14 2c rose	3.50 .95
53	A14 2c dk blue ('77)	260.00 100.00
54	A14 6c orange ('77)	14.00 *16.00*
55	A14 10c blue ('77)	4.50 1.50
56	A14 12c lilac ('76)	4.50 1.50
57	A14 20c vio brn ('76)	20.00 5.00
58	A14 25c dp green ('76)	25.00 5.00
	Nos. 52-58 (7)	331.50 129.95

Imperforates of type A14 are from proof or trial sheets.

Nos. 52, 63 Handstamp Surcharged in Black or Blue

1877-79

59	A14	12c on 2c rose (Bk)	85.00	22.50
a.		Surcharge inverted	400.00	375.00
b.		Surcharge double	400.00	350.00
60	A16	12c on 25m blk (Bk) ('79)	105.00	47.50
a.		Surcharge inverted	875.00	600.00
61	A16	12c on 25m blk (Bl) ('79)	300.00	150.00
		Nos. 59-61 (3)	490.00	220.00

Forgeries of Nos. 59-61 exist.

A16

1878-79

				Typo.
62	A16	25m black	3.50	.45
63	A16	25m green ('79)	67.50	50.00
64	A16	50m dull lilac	34.00	10.00
65	A16	0.0625 (62½m) gray	65.00	10.00
66	A16	100m car ('79)	110.00	37.50
67	A16	100m yel grn ('79)	10.00	2.75
68	A16	125m blue	6.00	.50
69	A16	200m rose ('79)	37.50	5.75
70	A16	200m vio rose ('79)	350.00	—
71	A16	250m bister ('79)	13.00	2.75
		Nos. 62-71 (10)	696.50	119.70

Imperforates of type A16 are from proof or trial sheets.
For surcharges see Nos. 60-61, 72-75.

Stamps of 1878-79 Surcharged

a   b

1879

72	A16 (a)	2c on 25m grn	55.00	11.00
b.		Inverted surcharge	425.00	325.00
73	A16 (a)	8c on 100m car	52.50	6.50
a.		"COREROS"	150.00	80.00
b.		Surcharge double	400.00	—
74	A16 (b)	2c on 25m grn	400.00	57.50
75	A16 (b)	8c on 100m car	400.00	57.50
		Nos. 72-75 (4)	907.50	132.50

A19

Original state: The medallion is surrounded by a heavy line of color of nearly even thickness, touching the line below "Filipinas"; the opening in the hair above the temple is narrow and pointed.

1st retouch: The line around the medallion is thin, except at the upper right, and does not touch the horizontal line above it; the opening in the hair is slightly wider and rounded; the lock of hair above the forehead is shaped like a broad "V" and ends in a point; there is a faint white line below it, which is not found on the original. The shape of the hair and the width of the white line vary.

2nd retouch: The lock of hair is less pointed; the white line is much broader.

1880-86

				Typo.
76	A19	2c carmine	.90	.80
77	A19	2½c brown	8.00	1.90
78	A19	2⅝c ultra ('82)	1.25	2.25
79	A19	2⅝c ultra, 1st retouch ('83)	.90	1.90
80	A19	2⅝c ultra, 2nd retouch ('86)	10.50	4.25
81	A19	5c gray blue ('82)	.90	1.90
82	A19	6⅛c dp grn ('82)	7.00	18.00
83	A19	8c yellow brn	15.00	6.25
84	A19	10c green	350.00	500.00
85	A19	10c brn lil ('82)	3.75	4.25
86	A19	12⅜c brt rose ('82)	1.90	1.90
87	A19	20c bis brn ('82)	3.50	1.75
88	A19	25c dk brn ('82)	4.75	1.90
		Nos. 76-88 (13)	408.35	547.05

See #137-139. For surcharges see #89-108, 110-111.

Surcharges exist double or inverted on many of the Nos. 89-136. Several different surcharge types exist.

Many bogus surcharges exist on the 1881-97 issues, prepared using the original surcharge handstamps in various colors on the same or different stamps after the end of the Spanish period. These bogus stamps include the previously listed Nos. 184 and 186, and the previously footnoted reprints. Many more bogus surcharged issues exist.

Stamps and Type of 1880-86
Handstamp Surcharged in Black, Green or Red

c   d

e   f

Design A19

1881-88   **Black Surcharge**

89	(c)	2c on 2½c	4.25	2.25
91	(f)	10c on 2⅝c (#80) ('87)	6.25	2.10
92	(d)	20c on 8c brn ('83)	10.00	3.25
93	(d)	1r on 2c ('83)	140.00	140.00
94	(d)	2r on 2⅝c (#78; '83)	6.25	2.10
a.		On No. 79	60.00	60.00
b.		On No. 80	75.00	75.00

Most used examples of No. 93 are hole punched. Postally used examples are rare.

Green Surcharge

95	(e)	8c on 2c ('83)	11.00	2.25
95A	(d+e)	8c on 1r on 2c ('83)	250.00	150.00
96	(d)	10c on 2c ('83)	5.50	2.25
97	(d)	1r on 2c ('83)	140.00	140.00
98	(d)	1r on 5c gray bl ('83)	8.00	3.25
99	(d)	1r on 8c brn ('83)	10.00	3.25

Red Surcharge

100	(f)	1c on 2⅝c (#79; '87)	1.25	2.00
101	(f)	1c on 2⅝c (#80; '87)	3.50	3.00
102	(d)	16c on 2⅝c (#78; '83)	10.00	4.00
103	(d)	1r on 2c ('83)	6.25	3.25
		On cover		550.00
104	(d)	1r on 5c bl gray ('83)	12.00	6.00

Handstamp Surcharged in Magenta

g   h

1887

105	A19 (g)	8c on 2⅝c (#79)	1.25	.90
106	A19 (g)	8c on 2⅝c (#80)	2.75	2.00

1888

107	A19 (h)	2⅝c on 1c gray grn	1.75	1.00
108	A19 (h)	2⅝c on 5c bl gray	1.90	1.50
109	N1 (h)	2⅝c on ⅛c grn	1.90	1.40
110	A19 (h)	2⅝c on 50m bis	1.90	.80
111	A19 (h)	2⅝c on 10c grn	1.75	.65
		Nos. 107-111 (5)	9.20	5.35

No. 109 is surcharged on a newspaper stamp of 1886-89 and has the inscriptions shown on cut N1.

On Revenue Stamps

R1   R2

R3(d)

Handstamp Surcharged in Black, Yellow, Green, Red, Blue or Magenta

j   k

m

1881-88   **Black Surcharge**

112	R1(c)	2c on 10c bis	50.00	40.00
113	R1(j)	2⅝c on 10c bis	12.00	1.75
114	R1(j)	2⅝c on 2r bl	200.00	140.00
115	R1(j)	8c on 10c bis	550.00	5,000.
116	R1(j)	8c on 2r bl	8.50	2.10
118	R1(d)	1r on 12⅜c gray bl ('83)	7.75	3.75
119	R1(d)	1r on 10c bis ('82)	11.50	4.00

Yellow Surcharge

120	R2(e)	2c on 200m grn ('82)	6.25	8.00
121	R1(d)	16c on 2r bl ('83)	6.00	7.00

Green Surcharge

122	R1(d)	1r on 10c bis ('83)	11.50	4.00

Red Surcharge

123	R1(d+e)	2r on 8c on 2r blue	65.00	45.00
a.		On 8c on 2r blue (d+d)	100.00	80.00
124	R1(d)	1r on 12⅜c gray bl ('83)	16.50	13.00
125	R1(k)	6⅜c on 12⅜c gray bl ('85)	5.00	24.00
126	R3(d)	1r on 10p bis ('83)	95.00	45.00
127	R1(m)	1r green	350.00	700.00
127A	R1(m)	2r blue	900.00	1,150.
127B	R1(d)	1r on 1r grn ('83)	700.00	800.00
128	R2(d)	1r on 1p grn ('83)	150.00	65.00
129	R2(d)	1r on 200m grn ('83)	600.00	800.00
129A	R1(d)	1r on 2r blue	900.00	900.00

The surcharge on No. 129A is pale red.

Blue Surcharge

129B	R1(m)	10c bister ('81)	900.00	

Magenta Surcharge

130	R2(h)	2⅝c on 200m grn ('88)	4.25	3.75
131	R2(h)	2⅝c on 20c brn ('88)	20.00	10.00

On Telegraph Stamps

T1   T2

Surcharged in Red, or Black

1883-88

132	T1(d)	2r on 250m ultra (R)	7.75	3.00
133	T1(d)	20c on 250m ultra	750.00	375.00
134	T1(d)	2r on 250m ultra	10.00	4.75
135	T1(d)	1r on 20c on 250m ultra (R & Bk)	15.00	8.00

Magenta Surcharge

136	T2(h)	2⅝c on 1c bis ('88)	.95	3.00

Most, if not all, used stamps of No. 133 are hole-punched. Used value is for examples with hole punches.

Type of 1880-86 Redrawn

1887-89

137	A19	50m bister	.50	6.00
138	A19	1c gray grn ('88)	.50	5.00
a.		1c yellow green ('89)	.70	10.00
139	A19	6c yel brn ('88)	8.00	47.50
		Nos. 137-139 (3)	9.00	58.50

King Alfonso XIII — A36

1890-97   **Typo.**

140	A36	1c violet ('92)	1.00	.75
141	A36	1c rose ('94)	17.50	40.00
142	A36	1c bl grn ('96)	2.25	1.00
143	A36	1c claret ('97)	16.00	16.00
144	A36	2c claret ('94)	.25	.25
145	A36	2c violet ('92)	.25	.25
146	A36	2c dk brn ('94)	.25	3.50
147	A36	2c ultra ('96)	.35	.35
148	A36	2c gray brn ('96)	.85	2.25
149	A36	2⅜c dull blue	.55	.30
150	A36	2⅝c ol gray ('92)	.30	1.40
151	A36	5c dark blue	.50	1.40
152	A36	5c slate green	.85	1.40
153	A36	5c green ('92)	.80	.55
155	A36	5c vio brn ('96)	7.50	3.25
156	A36	5c blue grn ('96)	6.00	3.00
157	A36	6c brown vio ('92)	.30	1.40
158	A36	6c red orange ('94)	.95	4.00
159	A36	6c car rose ('96)	4.75	7.00
160	A36	8c yellow grn	.30	.30
161	A36	8c ultra ('92)	.75	.30
162	A36	8c red brn ('94)	.85	.30
163	A36	10c blue grn	1.75	1.25
164	A36	10c pale cl ('91)	1.60	.40
165	A36	10c claret ('94)	.75	.40
166	A36	10c yel brn ('96)	.85	.30
167	A36	12⅜c yellow grn	.30	.25
168	A36	12⅜c org ('92)	.85	1.25
169	A36	15c red brn ('92)	.85	.30
170	A36	15c rose ('94)	2.10	.75
171	A36	15c bl grn ('96)	2.60	2.10
172	A36	20c pale vermilion	30.00	40.00
174	A36	20c gray brn ('92)	2.75	.45
175	A36	20c dk vio ('94)	15.00	8.00
176	A36	20c org ('96)	4.50	2.25
177	A36	25c brown	9.50	2.00
178	A36	25c dull bl ('91)	2.50	1.50
179	A36	40c dk vio ('97)	13.50	35.00
180	A36	80c claret ('97)	30.00	60.00
		Nos. 140-180 (39)	182.50	245.15

Many of Nos. 140-180 exist imperf and in different colors. These are considered to be proofs. Only major varieties are listed. Color varieties of most issues exist.

Stamps of Previous Issues Handstamp Surcharged in Blue, Red, Black or Violet

1897   **Blue Surcharge**

181	A36	5c on 5c green	2.00	5.00
182	A36	15c on 15c red brn	5.50	3.00
183	A36	20c on 20c gray brn	12.00	12.00

Red Surcharge

185	A36	5c on 5c green	4.50	4.75

Black Surcharge

187	A36	5c on 5c green	100.00	300.00
188	A36	15c on 15c rose	5.50	3.00
189	A36	20c on 20c dk vio	35.00	35.00
190	A36	20c on 25c brown	25.00	40.00

Violet Surcharge

191	A36	15c on 15c rose	15.00	30.00
		Nos. 181-191 (9)	204.50	432.75

Inverted, double and other variations of this surcharge exist.

The 5c on 5c blue gray (#81a) was released during US Administration. The surcharge is a mixture of red and black inks.

Impressions in violet black are believed to be reprints. The following varieties are known: 5c on 2⅝c olive gray, 5c on 5c blue green, 5c on 25c brown, 15c on 15c rose, 15c on 15c red brown, 25c on 25c brown, 20c on 20c gray brown, 20c on 20c dark violet, 20c on 25c brown. Value: each $40. These surcharges are to be found double, inverted, etc.

King Alfonso XIII — A39

1898   **Typo.**

192	A39	1m orange brown	.25	1.25
193	A39	2m orange brown	.25	1.75
194	A39	3m orange brown	.25	1.75

195 A39 4m orange brown — 10.00 / 40.00
196 A39 5m orange brown — .25 / 2.75
197 A39 1c black violet — .25 / .60
198 A39 2c dk bl grn — .25 / .60
199 A39 3c dk brown — .25 / .60
200 A39 4c orange — 20.00 / 40.00
201 A39 5c car rose — .25 / .60
202 A39 6c dk blue — 1.15 / 1.75
203 A39 8c gray brown — .60 / .35
204 A39 10c vermilion — 2.75 / 1.25
205 A39 15c dull ol grn — 2.25 / 1.10
206 A39 20c maroon — 2.50 / 1.60
207 A39 40c violet — 1.25 / 1.75
208 A39 60c black — 6.00 / 4.00
209 A39 80c red brown — 8.00 / 7.00
210 A39 1p yellow green — 20.00 / 10.00
211 A39 2p slate blue — 40.00 / 12.00
Nos. 192-211 (20) — 116.50 / 130.70

Nos. 192-211 exist imperf. Value, set $2,000.

Wmk. 191PI — Double-lined PIPS   Wmk. 190PI — Single-lined PIPS

Wmk. 257 — Curved Wavy Lines

Issued under U.S. Administration

Regular Issues of the United States Overprinted in Black

1899-1901 Unwmk. Perf. 12
On U.S. Stamp No. 260
212 A96 50c orange — 300. / 225.
 Never hinged 775.

On U.S. Stamps Nos. 279, 279B, 279Bd, 279Bj, 279Bf, 279Bc, 268, 281, 282C, 283, 284, 275, 275a

Regular Issues of the United States Overprinted in Black

Wmk. Double-lined USPS (191)
213 A87 1c yellow green — 3.50 / .60
 Never hinged 10.00
 a. Inverted overprint — 77,500.
214 A88 2c red, type IV — 1.75 / .60
 Never hinged 4.25
 a. 2c orange red, type IV, ('01) — 1.75 / .60
 Never hinged 4.25
 b. Bklt. pane of 6, red, type IV ('00) — 200.00 / 300.00
 Never hinged 450.00
 c. 2c reddish carmine, type IV — 2.50 / 1.00
 Never hinged 6.00
 d. 2c rose carmine, type IV — 3.00 / 1.10
 Never hinged 7.25
215 A89 3c purple — 9.00 / 1.25
 Never hinged 21.50
216 A91 5c blue — 9.00 / 1.00
 Never hinged 21.50
 a. Inverted overprint — 6,500.

No. 216a is valued in the grade of fine.

217 A94 10c brown, type I — 35.00 / 4.00
 Never hinged 80.00
217A A94 10c org brn, type II — 110.00 / 27.50
 Never hinged 275.00

No. 217A was overprinted on U.S. No. 283a, vertical watermark. The watermark on No. 217 is horizontal.

218 A95 15c olive green — 40.00 / 8.00
 Never hinged 95.00
219 A96 50c orange — 125.00 / 37.50
 Never hinged 300.00
 a. 50c red orange — 250.00 / 55.00
 Never hinged 600.00
Nos. 213-219 (8) — 333.25 / 80.45

Regular Issue

U.S. Stamps Nos. 280b, 282 and 272 Overprinted in Black

1901, Aug. 30
220 A90 4c orange brown — 35.00 / 5.00
 Never hinged 80.00
221 A92 6c lake — 40.00 / 7.00
 Never hinged 95.00
222 A93 8c purple brown — 40.00 / 7.50
 Never hinged 95.00
Nos. 220-222 (3) — 115.00 / 19.50

Same Overprint in Red On U.S. Stamps Nos. 276, 276A, 277a and 278
223 A97 $1 black, type I — 300.00 / 200.00
 Never hinged 1,000.
223A A97 $1 black, type II — 1,500. / 750.00
 Never hinged 5,000.
224 A98 $2 dark blue — 350.00 / 325.00
 Never hinged 1,150.
225 A99 $5 dark green — 500.00 / 900.00
 Never hinged 1,600.

U.S. Stamps Nos. 300-310 and Shades Overprinted in Black

Regular Issue
1903-04
226 A115 1c blue green — 7.00 / .40
 Never hinged 15.50
227 A116 2c carmine — 9.00 / 1.10
 Never hinged 20.00
228 A117 3c bright violet — 67.50 / 12.50
 Never hinged 150.00
229 A118 4c brown — 80.00 / 22.50
 Never hinged 175.00
 a. 4c orange brown — 80.00 / 20.00
 Never hinged 175.00
230 A119 5c blue — 17.50 / 1.00
 Never hinged 40.00
231 A120 6c brnsh lake — 85.00 / 22.50
 Never hinged 190.00
232 A121 8c violet black — 50.00 / 15.00
 Never hinged 125.00
233 A122 10c pale red brn — 35.00 / 2.25
 Never hinged 80.00
 a. 10c red brown — 35.00 / 3.00
 Never hinged 80.00
 b. Pair, one without overprint — 1,500.
234 A123 13c purple black — 35.00 / 17.50
 Never hinged 80.00
 a. 13c brown violet — 35.00 / 17.50
 Never hinged 80.00
235 A124 15c olive green — 60.00 / 15.00
 Never hinged 135.00
236 A125 50c orange — 125.00 / 35.00
 Never hinged 275.00
Nos. 226-236 (11) — 571.00 / 144.75
Set, never hinged 1,285.

Same Overprint in Red On U.S. Stamps Nos. 311, 312 and 313
237 A126 $1 black — 300.00 / 200.00
 Never hinged 800.00
238 A127 $2 dark blue — 550.00 / 800.00
 Never hinged 1,500.
239 A128 $5 dark green — 800.00 / 2,750.
 Never hinged 2,000.

Same Overprint in Black On U.S. Stamp Nos. 319 and 319c
240 A129 2c carmine — 8.00 / 2.25
 Never hinged 17.50
 a. Booklet pane of 6 — 1,500.
 b. 2c scarlet — 8.00 / 2.75
 Never hinged 19.00
 c. As "b," booklet pane of 6 — —

José Rizal A40   Arms of City of Manila A41

Designs: 4c, McKinley. 6c, Ferdinand Magellan. 8c, Miguel Lopez de Legaspi. 10c, Gen. Henry W. Lawton. 12c, Lincoln. 16c, Adm. William T. Sampson. 20c, Washington. 26c, Francisco Carriedo. 30c, Franklin. 2p-10p, Arms of City of Manila.

Wmk. Double-lined PIPS (191PI)
1906, Sept. 8 — Perf. 12
241 A40 2c deep green — .40 / .25
 Never hinged 1.00
 a. 2c yellow green ('10) — .60 / .25
 Never hinged 1.50
 b. Booklet pane of 6 — 750.00 / 800.00
 Never hinged 1,500.
242 A40 4c carmine — .50 / .25
 Never hinged 1.25
 a. 4c carmine lake ('10) — 1.00 / .25
 Never hinged 2.50
 b. Booklet pane of 6 — 650.00 / 700.00
 Never hinged 1,250.
243 A40 6c violet — 2.50 / .25
 Never hinged 6.25
244 A40 8c brown — 4.50 / .90
 Never hinged 11.00

245 A40 10c blue — 3.50 / .30
 Never hinged 8.75
 a. 10c dark blue — 3.50 / .30
 Never hinged 8.75
246 A40 12c brown lake — 9.00 / 2.50
 Never hinged 22.50
247 A40 16c violet black — 6.00 / .35
 Never hinged 15.00
248 A40 20c org brn — 7.00 / .35
 Never hinged 17.50
249 A40 26c vio brn — 11.00 / 3.00
 Never hinged 27.50
250 A40 30c olive green — 6.50 / 1.75
 Never hinged 16.00
251 A41 1p orange — 55.00 / 17.50
 Never hinged 130.00
252 A41 2p black — 50.00 / 1.75
 Never hinged 130.00
253 A41 4p dark blue — 160.00 / 20.00
 Never hinged 375.00
254 A41 10p dark green — 225.00 / 80.00
 Never hinged 575.00
Nos. 241-254 (14) — 540.90 / 129.15
Set, never hinged 1,316.

1909-13 — Change of Colors
255 A40 12c red orange — 11.00 / 3.00
 Never hinged 27.50
256 A40 16c olive green — 6.00 / .75
 Never hinged 15.00
257 A40 20c yellow — 9.00 / 1.25
 Never hinged 22.50
258 A40 26c blue green — 3.50 / 1.25
 Never hinged 8.75
259 A40 30c ultramarine — 13.00 / 3.50
 Never hinged 32.50
260 A41 1p pale violet — 45.00 / 5.00
 Never hinged 110.00
260A A41 2p vio brn ('13) — 100.00 / 12.00
 Never hinged 250.00
Nos. 255-260A (7) — 187.50 / 26.75
Set, never hinged 466.25

Wmk. Single-lined PIPS (190PI)
1911
261 A40 2c green — .75 / .25
 Never hinged 1.80
 a. Booklet pane of 6 — 800.00 / 900.00
 Never hinged 1,400.
262 A40 4c carmine lake — 3.00 / .25
 Never hinged 6.75
 a. 4c carmine — —
 b. Booklet pane of 6 — 600.00 / 700.00
 Never hinged 1,100.
263 A40 6c deep violet — 3.00 / .25
 Never hinged 6.75
264 A40 8c brown — 9.50 / .50
 Never hinged 21.50
265 A40 10c blue — 4.00 / .25
 Never hinged 9.00
266 A40 12c orange — 4.00 / .45
 Never hinged 9.00
267 A40 16c olive green — 4.50 / .40
 Never hinged 10.00
 a. 16c pale olive green — 4.50 / .50
 Never hinged 10.00
268 A40 20c yellow — 3.50 / .25
 Never hinged 7.75
 a. 20c orange — 4.00 / .30
 Never hinged 9.00
269 A40 26c blue green — 6.00 / .30
 Never hinged 13.50
270 A40 30c ultramarine — 6.00 / .50
 Never hinged 13.50
271 A41 1p pale violet — 27.50 / .60
 Never hinged 62.50
272 A41 2p violet brown — 45.00 / 1.00
 Never hinged 100.00
273 A41 4p deep blue — 550.00 / 110.00
 Never hinged 1,100.
274 A41 10p deep green — 200.00 / 30.00
 Never hinged 400.00
Nos. 261-274 (14) — 866.75 / 145.00
Set, never hinged 1,862.

1914
275 A40 30c gray — 12.00 / .50
 Never hinged 27.50

1914 — Perf. 10
276 A40 2c green — 3.00 / .25
 Never hinged 7.00
 a. Booklet pane of 6 — 600.00 / 800.00
 Never hinged 1,250.
277 A40 4c carmine — 4.00 / .30
 Never hinged 9.00
 a. Booklet pane of 6 — 600.00
 Never hinged 1,300.
278 A40 6c light violet — 45.00 / 9.50
 Never hinged 100.00
 a. 6c deep violet — 50.00 / 6.25
 Never hinged 110.00
279 A40 8c brown — 55.00 / 10.50
 Never hinged 125.00
280 A40 10c dark blue — 30.00 / .25
 Never hinged 67.50
281 A40 16c olive green — 100.00 / 5.00
 Never hinged 225.00
282 A40 20c orange — 40.00 / 1.00
 Never hinged 85.00
283 A40 30c gray — 60.00 / 4.50
 Never hinged 130.00
284 A41 1p pale violet — 150.00 / 3.75
 Never hinged 350.00
Nos. 276-284 (9) — 487.00 / 35.05
Set, never hinged 1,020.

Wmk. Single-lined PIPS (190PI)
1918 — Perf. 11
285 A40 2c green — 21.00 / 4.25
 Never hinged 40.00
 a. Booklet pane of 6 — 600.00 / 800.00
 Never hinged 1,100.

286 A40 4c carmine — 26.00 / 6.00
 Never hinged 55.00
 a. Booklet pane of 6 — 1,350. / 2,000.
287 A40 6c deep violet — 40.00 / 6.00
 Never hinged 90.00
287A A40 8c light brown — 220.00 / 25.00
 Never hinged 400.00
288 A40 10c dark blue — 60.00 / 3.00
 Never hinged 140.00
289 A40 16c olive green — 110.00 / 10.00
 Never hinged 250.00
289A A40 20c orange — 175.00 / 12.00
 Never hinged 400.00
289C A40 30c gray — 95.00 / 18.00
 Never hinged 215.00
289D A41 1p pale violet — 100.00 / 25.00
 Never hinged 225.00
Nos. 285-289D (9) — 847.00 / 109.25
Set, never hinged 1,815.

1917 — Unwmk. — Perf. 11
290 A40 2c yellow green — .25 / .25
 Never hinged .55
 Never hinged 140.00
 a. 2c dark green — .30 / .25
 Never hinged .65
 b. Vert. pair, imperf. horiz. — 2,750.
 c. Horiz. pair, imperf. between — 1,500.
 d. Vertical pair, imperf. btwn. — 1,750. / 1,000.
 e. Booklet pane of 6 — 27.50 / 30.00
 Never hinged 60.00
291 A40 4c carmine — .30 / .25
 Never hinged .65
 a. 4c light rose — .30 / .25
 Never hinged .65
 b. Booklet pane of 6 — 20.00 / 22.50
 Never hinged 35.00
292 A40 6c deep violet — .35 / .25
 Never hinged .70
 a. 6c lilac — .40 / .25
 Never hinged .80
 b. 6c red violet — .40 / .25
 Never hinged .70
 c. Booklet pane of 6 — 550.00 / 800.00
 Never hinged 900.00
293 A40 8c yellow brown — .30 / .25
 Never hinged .50
 a. 8c orange brown — .30 / .25
 Never hinged .50
294 A40 10c deep blue — .30 / .25
 Never hinged .65
295 A40 12c red orange — .35 / .25
 Never hinged .75
296 A40 16c light olive green — 65.00 / .25
 Never hinged 130.00
 a. 16c olive bister — 65.00 / .50
 Never hinged 130.00
297 A40 20c orange yellow — .35 / .25
 Never hinged .75
298 A40 26c green — .50 / .45
 Never hinged 1.10
 a. 26c blue green — .60 / .25
 Never hinged 1.35
299 A40 30c gray — .55 / .25
 Never hinged 1.35
300 A41 1p pale violet — 40.00 / 2.00
 Never hinged 90.00
 a. 1p red lilac — 40.00 / 2.50
 Never hinged 90.00
 b. 1p pale rose lilac — 40.00 / 1.10
 Never hinged 90.00
301 A41 2p violet brown — 35.00 / 1.00
 Never hinged 77.50
302 A41 4p blue — 32.50 / .50
 Never hinged 72.50
 a. 4p dark blue — 35.00 / .55
 Never hinged 77.50
Nos. 290-302 (13) — 175.75 / 6.20
Set, never hinged 377.00

1923-26
Design: 16c, Adm. George Dewey.
303 A40 16c olive bister — 1.00 / .25
 Never hinged 2.25
 a. 16c olive green — 1.25 / .25
 Never hinged 2.75
304 A41 10p dp grn ('26) — 50.00 / 20.00
 Never hinged 110.00

Legislative Palace — A42

1926, Dec. 20 — Perf. 12
319 A42 2c green & black — .50 / .25
 Never hinged 1.25
 a. Horiz. pair, imperf. between — 275.00 / —
 b. Vert. pair, imperf. between — 375.00
320 A42 4c car & blk — .55 / .40
 Never hinged 1.20
 a. Horiz. pair, imperf. between — 350.00 / —
 b. Vert. pair, imperf. between — 400.00
321 A42 16c ol grn & blk — 1.00 / .65
 Never hinged 2.25
 a. Horiz. pair, imperf. between — 250.00 / —
 b. Vert. pair, imperf. between — 425.00
 c. Double impression of center — 675.00
322 A42 18c lt brn & blk — 1.10 / .50
 Never hinged 2.50
 a. Double impression of center — 850.00
 b. Vertical pair, imperf. between — 475.00
323 A42 20c orange & black — 2.00 / 1.00
 Never hinged 4.50
 a. 20c orange & brown — 600.00
 b. As No. 323, imperf., pair — 575.00 / 575.00
 c. As "a," imperf., pair — 1,750.
 d. Vert. pair, imperf. between — 500.00
324 A42 24c gray & black — 1.00 / .55
 Never hinged 2.25
 a. Vert. pair, imperf. between — 500.00

325	A42	1p rose lil & blk	47.50	50.00
		Never hinged	70.00	
a.		Vert. pair, imperf. between	500.00	
		Nos. 319-325 (7)	53.65	53.35
		Set, never hinged	83.95	

Opening of the Legislative Palace.
No. 322a is valued in the grade of fine.
For overprints, see Nos. O1-O4.

Rizal Type of 1906
Coil Stamp

1928　　　　　　　**Perf. 11 Vertically**

326	A40	2c green	7.50	12.50
		Never hinged	19.00	

Types of 1906-1923

1925-31　　　　　　　　　　**Imperf.**

340	A40	2c yel green		
		('31)	.50	.50
		Never hinged	.90	
a.		2c green ('25)	.80	.75
		Never hinged	1.80	
341	A40	4c car rose		
		('31)	.50	1.00
		Never hinged	1.00	
a.		4c carmine ('25)	1.20	1.00
		Never hinged	2.75	
342	A40	6c violet ('31)	3.00	3.75
		Never hinged	5.00	
a.		6c deep violet ('25)	12.00	8.00
		Never hinged	26.00	
343	A40	8c brown ('31)	2.00	5.00
		Never hinged	4.00	
a.		8c yellow brown ('25)	13.00	8.00
		Never hinged	26.00	
344	A40	10c blue ('31)	5.00	7.50
		Never hinged	12.00	
a.		10c deep blue ('25)	45.00	20.00
		Never hinged	100.00	
345	A40	12c dp orange		
		('31)	8.00	10.00
		Never hinged	15.00	
a.		12c red orange ('25)	60.00	35.00
		Never hinged	135.00	
346	A40	16c olive green	6.00	7.50
		Never hinged	11.00	
a.		16c bister green ('25)	42.50	18.00
		Never hinged	100.00	
347	A40	20c dp yel org		
		('31)	5.00	7.50
		Never hinged	11.00	
a.		20c yellow orange ('25)	45.00	20.00
		Never hinged	100.00	
348	A40	26c green ('31)	6.00	9.00
		Never hinged	11.00	
a.		26c blue green ('25)	45.00	25.00
		Never hinged	110.00	
349	A40	30c light gray		
		('31)	8.00	10.00
		Never hinged	16.00	
a.		30c gray ('25)	45.00	25.00
		Never hinged	110.00	
350	A41	1p light violet		
		('31)	10.00	15.00
		Never hinged	20.00	
a.		1p violet ('25)	200.00	100.00
		Never hinged	425.00	
351	A41	2p brn vio ('31)	30.00	45.00
		Never hinged	80.00	
a.		2p violet brown ('25)	400.00	400.00
		Never hinged	675.00	
352	A41	4p blue ('31)	80.00	90.00
		Never hinged	150.00	
a.		4p deep blue ('25)	2,200.	1,100.
		Never hinged	3,500.	
353	A41	10p green ('31)	175.00	225.00
		Never hinged	300.00	
a.		10p deep green ('25)	2,750.	2,950.
		Never hinged	4,250.	
		Nos. 340-353 (14)	339.00	436.75
		Set, never hinged	636.90	
		Nos. 340a-353a (14)	5,860.	4,711.

Nos. 340a-353a were the original post office
issue. These were reprinted twice in 1931 for
sale to collectors (Nos. 340-353).

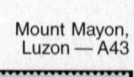

Mount Mayon,
Luzon — A43

Post Office,
Manila — A44

Pier No. 7, Manila
Bay
A45

(See
footnote)
A46

Rice
Planting — A47

Rice
Terraces — A48

Baguio
Zigzag — A49

1932, May 3　　　　　　　**Perf. 11**

354	A43	2c yellow green	.75	.30
		Never hinged	1.25	
355	A44	4c rose carmine	.75	.30
		Never hinged	1.25	
356	A45	12c orange	.90	.75
		Never hinged	1.30	
357	A46	18c red orange	45.00	15.00
		Never hinged	72.50	
358	A47	20c yellow	1.00	.75
		Never hinged	1.60	
359	A48	24c deep violet	1.60	1.00
		Never hinged	2.75	
360	A49	32c olive brown	1.60	1.00
		Never hinged	2.75	
		Nos. 354-360 (7)	51.60	19.10
		Set, never hinged	83.40	

The 18c vignette was intended to show Pag-
sanjan Falls in Laguna, central Luzon, and is
so labeled. Through error the stamp pictures
Vernal Falls in Yosemite National Park,
California.
For overprints see #C29-C35, C47-C51,
C63.

Nos. 302, 302a
Surcharged in Orange or
Red

1932

368	A41	1p on 4p blue (O)	6.00	1.00
		Never hinged	9.75	
a.		1p on 4p dark blue (O)	6.00	1.00
		Never hinged	9.25	
		P# block of 10, Impt.	140.00	
		Never hinged	175.00	
369	A41	2p on 4p dark blue		
		(R)	9.00	1.50
		Never hinged	15.00	
		P# block of 10, Impt.	160.00	
		Never hinged	200.00	
a.		2p on 4p blue (R)	9.00	1.00
		Never hinged	15.00	

Far Eastern Championship

Issued in commemoration of the Tenth
Far Eastern Championship Games.

Baseball
Players — A50

Tennis
Player — A51

Basketball
Players — A52

1934, Apr. 14　　　　　　　**Perf. 11½**

380	A50	2c yellow brown	1.50	.80
		Never hinged	2.25	
381	A51	6c ultramarine	.25	.25
		Never hinged	.30	
a.		Vertical pair, imperf. between	700.00	
		Never hinged	1,100.	
382	A52	16c violet brown	.50	.50
		Never hinged	.75	
a.		Vert. pair, imperf. horiz.	950.00	
		Never hinged	1,500.	
		Nos. 380-382 (3)	2.25	1.55
		Set, never hinged	3.30	

For overprints & surcharges see Nos. 411-
424, 433-446, 449, 463-466, 468, 472-474,
478-484, 485-494, C52-C53, O15-O36, O38,
O40-O43, N2-N9, N28, NO2-NO6.

José Rizal
A53

Woman and
Carabao
A54

La Filipina
A55

Pearl Fishing
A56

Fort
Santiago — A57

Salt
Spring — A58

Magellan's
Landing, 1521
A59

"Juan de
la Cruz"
A60

Rice
Terraces — A61

"Blood Compact,"
1565 — A62

Barasoain
Church,
Malolos — A63

Battle of Manila
Bay, 1898 — A64

Montalban Gorge
A65

George
Washington
A66

1935, Feb. 15　　　　　　**Perf. 11**

383	A53	2c rose	.25	.25
		Never hinged	.25	
384	A54	4c yellow green	.25	.25
		Never hinged	.25	
385	A55	6c dark brown	.25	.25
		Never hinged	.35	
386	A56	8c violet	.25	.25
		Never hinged	.35	
387	A57	10c rose carmine	.30	.25
		Never hinged	.45	
388	A58	12c black	.35	.25
		Never hinged	.50	
389	A59	16c dark blue	.35	.25
		Never hinged	.55	
390	A60	20c light olive green	.35	.25
		Never hinged	.45	
391	A61	26c indigo	.40	.40
		Never hinged	.60	
392	A62	30c orange red	.40	.40
		Never hinged	.60	
393	A63	1p red org & blk	2.00	1.25
		Never hinged	3.00	
394	A64	2p bis brn & blk	12.00	2.00
		Never hinged	16.00	
395	A65	4p blue & black	12.00	4.00
		Never hinged	16.00	
396	A66	5p green & black	25.00	5.00
		Never hinged	50.00	
		Nos. 383-396 (14)	54.15	15.05
		Set, never hinged	74.45	

Issues of the Commonwealth
Issued to commemorate the
inauguration of the Philippine
Commonwealth, Nov. 15, 1935.

The Temples
of Human
Progress
A67

1935, Nov. 15

397	A67	2c carmine rose	.25	.25
		Never hinged	.35	
398	A67	6c deep violet	.25	.25
		Never hinged	.35	
399	A67	16c blue	.25	.25
		Never hinged	.40	
400	A67	36c yellow green	.40	.30
		Never hinged	.65	
401	A67	50c brown	.70	.55
		Never hinged	1.00	
		Nos. 397-401 (5)	1.85	1.60
		Set, never hinged	2.75	

Jose Rizal Issue

75th anniversary of the birth of Jose
Rizal (1861-1896), national hero of the
Filipinos.

Jose Rizal — A68

1936, June 19　　　　　　**Perf. 12**

402	A68	2c yellow brown	.25	.25
		Never hinged	.25	
403	A68	6c slate blue	.25	.25
		Never hinged	.25	
a.		Imperf. vertically, pair	1,000.	
		Never hinged	1,500.	
404	A68	36c red brown	.50	.70
		Never hinged	.75	
		Nos. 402-404 (3)	1.00	1.20
		Set, never hinged	1.25	

Commonwealth Anniversary Issue

Issued in commemoration of the first
anniversary of the Commonwealth.

President Manuel L.
Quezon — A69

1936, Nov. 15　　　　　　**Perf. 11**

408	A69	2c orange brown	.25	.25
		Never hinged	.30	
409	A69	6c yellow green	.25	.25
		Never hinged	.30	
410	A69	12c ultramarine	.25	.25
		Never hinged	.30	
		Nos. 408-410 (3)	.75	.75
		Set, never hinged	.90	

Stamps of 1935 Overprinted in Black

a　　　　　　　b

1936-37

411	A53(a)	2c rose	.25	.25
		Never hinged	.25	
a.		Bklt. pane of 6 ('37)	2.50	2.00
		Never hinged	4.00	
b.		Hyphen omitted	125.00	100.00
412	A54(b)	4c yel grn ('37)	.45	4.00
		Never hinged	.70	
		P# block of 6	35.00	
		Never hinged	45.00	
413	A55(a)	6c dark brown	.25	.25
		Never hinged	.25	
414	A56(b)	8c violet ('37)	.25	.25
		Never hinged	.35	
415	A57(b)	10c rose carmine	.25	.25
		Never hinged	.25	
a.		"COMMONWEALT"	20.00	—
		Never hinged	30.00	
416	A58(b)	12c black ('37)	.25	.25
		Never hinged	.30	
417	A59(b)	16c dark blue	.25	.25
		Never hinged	.40	
418	A60(a)	20c lt ol grn ('37)	.90	.40
		Never hinged	1.50	
419	A61(b)	26c indigo ('37)	.80	.35
		Never hinged	1.40	
420	A62(b)	30c orange red	.45	.25
		Never hinged	.75	
421	A63(b)	1p red org & blk	.90	.25
			1.50	

422 A64(b) 2p bis brn & blk
　　　　　('37)　　　12.50　4.00
　　Never hinged　　21.00
423 A65(b) 4p bl & blk ('37)　45.00　8.00
　　Never hinged　　72.50
424 A66(b) 5p grn & blk
　　　　　('37)　　　12.50　25.00
　　Never hinged　　21.00
　　Nos. 411-424 (14)　75.00　43.75
　　Set, never hinged　122.15

Eucharistic Congress Issue
Issued to commemorate the 33rd International Eucharistic Congress held at Manila, Feb. 3-7, 1937.

Map of Philippines — A70

1937, Feb. 3
425 A70 2c yellow green　　.25　.25
　　Never hinged　　　　　.25
426 A70 6c light brown　　.25　.25
　　Never hinged　　　　　.25
427 A70 12c sapphire　　　.25　.25
　　Never hinged　　　　　.25
428 A70 20c deep orange　.30　.25
　　Never hinged　　　　　.50
429 A70 36c deep violet　.55　.40
　　Never hinged　　　　　.80
430 A70 50c carmine　　　.70　.35
　　Never hinged　　　　1.10
　　Nos. 425-430 (6)　　2.30　1.75
　　Set, never hinged　　3.15

Arms of Manila — A71

1937, Aug. 27
431 A71 10p gray　　　　5.00　2.00
　　Never hinged　　　　7.25
　　P# block of 6　　　67.50
　　Never hinged　　　85.00
432 A71 20p henna brown　4.00　1.40
　　Never hinged　　　　6.50

Stamps of 1935 Overprinted in Black

a　　　　　　b

1938-40
433 A53(a) 2c rose ('39)　.25　.25
　　Never hinged　　　　　.25
　　P# block of 6　　　8.00
　　Never hinged　　　10.00
a.　Booklet pane of 6　3.50　3.50
　　Never hinged　　　5.50
b.　As "a," lower left-hand
　　stamp overprinted
　　"WEALTH COMMON-"　2,000.
　　Never hinged　　3,250.
c.　Hyphen omitted　100.00　50.00
　　Never hinged　　　140.00
434 A54(b) 4c yel grn ('40)　3.00　30.00
　　Never hinged　　　　4.75
　　P# block of 6　　　35.00
　　Never hinged　　　45.00
435 A55(a) 6c dk brn ('39)　.25　.25
　　Never hinged　　　　　.40
a.　6c golden brown　　.25　.25
　　Never hinged　　　　.40
　　P# block of 6　　　5.50
　　Never hinged　　　7.00
436 A56(b) 8c violet ('39)　.25　1.75
　　Never hinged　　　　　.25
　　P# block of 6　　　8.00
　　Never hinged　　　10.00
a.　"COMMONWEALT" (LR
　　31)　　　　　　90.00
　　Never hinged　　140.00
437 A57(b) 10c rose car
　　　　　('39)　　　.25　.25
　　Never hinged　　　　　.25
　　P# block of 6　　　8.00
　　Never hinged　　　10.00
a.　"COMMONWEALT" (LR
　　31)　　　　　　65.00　—
　　Never hinged　　100.00
438 A58(b) 12c black ('40)　.25　1.00
　　Never hinged　　　　　.25
　　P# block of 6　　　8.00
　　Never hinged　　　10.00
439 A59(b) 16c dark blue　.25　.25
　　Never hinged　　　　　.25
　　P# block of 6　　　16.00
　　Never hinged　　　20.00
440 A60(a) 20c lt ol grn
　　　　　('39)　　　.25　.25
　　Never hinged　　　　　.25
　　P# block of 6　　　12.00
　　Never hinged　　　15.00
441 A61(b) 26c indigo ('40)　1.00　2.50
　　Never hinged　　　　1.50
　　P# block of 6　　　16.00
　　Never hinged　　　20.00

442 A62(b) 30c org red ('39)　3.00　.70
　　Never hinged　　　　5.00
　　P# block of 6　　　22.50
　　Never hinged　　　35.00
443 A63(b) 1p red org &
　　　　　blk　　　　.60　.25
　　Never hinged　　　1.00
444 A64(b) 2p bis brn & blk
　　　　　('39)　　　10.00　1.00
　　Never hinged　　　15.00
　　P# block of 4　　87.50
　　Never hinged　　110.00
445 A65(b) 4p bl & blk ('40)　150.00　250.00
　　Never hinged　　325.00
446 A66(b) 5p grn & blk
　　　　　('40)　　　20.00　8.00
　　Never hinged　　　35.00
　　P# block of 4　　200.00
　　Never hinged　　250.00
　　Nos. 433-446 (14)　189.35　296.45
　　Set, never hinged　414.15

Overprint "b" measures 18½x1¾mm.
No. 433b occurs in booklet pane, No. 433a, position 5; all examples are straight-edged, left and bottom.

First Foreign Trade Week Issue
Nos. 384, 298a and 432 Surcharged in Red, Violet or Black

a　　　　　　b

c

1939, July 5
449 A54(a) 2c on 4c yel grn
　　　　　(R)　　　　.25　.25
　　Never hinged　　　　　.35
450 A40(b) 6c on 26c blue grn
　　　　　(V)　　　　.25　.50
　　Never hinged　　　　　.35
a.　6c on 26c green　　3.00　1.00
　　Never hinged　　　5.00
451 A71(c) 50c on 20p henna
　　　　　brn (Bk)　　1.25　1.00
　　Never hinged　　　2.00　5.00
　　Nos. 449-451 (3)　1.75　1.75
　　Set, never hinged　2.70

Commonwealth 4th Anniversary Issue (#452-460)

Triumphal Arch — A72

1939, Nov. 15
452 A72 2c yellow green　.25　.25
　　Never hinged　　　　　.25
453 A72 6c carmine　　　.25　.25
　　Never hinged　　　　　.25
454 A72 12c bright blue　.25　.25
　　Never hinged　　　　　.25
　　Nos. 452-454 (3)　　.75　.75
　　Set, never hinged　　.75

For overprints see Nos. 469, 476.

Malacañan Palace — A73

1939, Nov. 15
455 A73 2c green　　　　.25　.25
　　Never hinged　　　　　.25
456 A73 6c orange　　　.25　.25
　　Never hinged　　　　　.25
457 A73 12c carmine　　.25　.25
　　Never hinged　　　　　.25
　　Nos. 455-457 (3)　　.75　.75
　　Set, never hinged　　.75

For overprint, see No. 470.

Pres. Quezon Taking Oath of Office — A74

1940, Feb. 8
458 A74 2c dark orange　.25　.25
　　Never hinged　　　　　.25
459 A74 6c dark green　.25　.25
　　Never hinged　　　　　.25

460 A74 12c purple　　　.25　.25
　　Never hinged　　　　　.30
　　Nos. 458-460 (3)　　.75　.75
　　Set, never hinged　　.80

For overprints, see Nos. 471, 477.

José Rizal — A75

ROTARY PRESS PRINTING
1941, Apr. 14　　　Perf. 11x10½
Size: 19x22½mm
461 A75 2c apple green　　.25　.50
　　Never hinged　　　　　.25

FLAT PLATE PRINTING
1941, Nov. 14　　　Perf. 11
Size: 18¾x22¼mm
462 A75 2c pale apple green　1.00　—
　　　　　　　　　　　1.25
a.　Booklet pane of 6　6.00
　　Never hinged　　　7.50

No. 461 was issued only in sheets. No. 462 was issued only in booklet panes on Nov. 14, 1941, just before the war, and only a few used stamps and covers exist. All examples have one or two straight edges. Mint booklets reappeared after the war. In August 1942, the booklet pane was reprinted in a darker shade (apple green). However, the apple green panes were available only to U.S. collectors during the war years, so no war-period used stamps from the Philippines exist. Value of apple green booklet pane, never hinged, $6.
For type A75 overprinted, see Nos. 464, O37, O39, N1 and NO1.

Philippine Stamps of 1935-41, Handstamped in Violet

1944　　　　　Perf. 11, 11x10½
463 A53 2c rose (On 411)　1,250.　650.00
a.　Booklet pane of 6　12,500.
463B A53 2c rose (On 433)　2,000.　1,750.
464 A75 2c apple grn (On
　　　　　461)　　　12.50　10.00
　　　　　　　　　　　22.50
a.　Pair, one without ovpt.
465 A54 4c yel grn (On
　　　　　384)　　　47.50　50.00
　　　　　　　　　　　80.00
466 A55 6c dk brn (On
　　　　　385)　　　3,250.　2,000.
467 A69 6c yel grn (On
　　　　　409)　　　300.00　150.00
　　　　　　　　　　525.00
468 A55 6c dk brn (On
　　　　　413)　　　4,000.　825.00
469 A72 6c car (On 453)　350.00　125.00
470 A73 6c org (On 456)　1,750.　725.00
471 A74 6c dk grn (On
　　　　　459)　　　500.00　225.00
472 A56 8c vio (On 436)　17.50　30.00
　　　　　　　　　　　30.00
473 A57 10c car rose (On
　　　　　415)　　　350.00　150.00
474 A57 10c car rose (On
　　　　　437)　　　275.00　200.00
475 A69 12c ultra (On 410)　1,100.　400.00
476 A72 12c brt bl (On
　　　　　454)　　　7,000.　2,500.
477 A74 12c pur (On 460)　500.00　275.00
478 A59 16c dk bl (On
　　　　　389)　　　3,000.
479 A59 16c dk bl (On
　　　　　417)　　　1,500.　1,000.
480 A59 16c dk bl (On
　　　　　439)　　　500.00　200.00
481 A60 20c lt ol grn (On
　　　　　440)　　　140.00　35.00
　　　　　　　　　　230.00
482 A62 30c org red (On
　　　　　420)　　　450.00　1,500.
483 A62 30c org red (On
　　　　　442)　　　800.00　375.00
484 A63 1p red org & blk
　　　　　(On 443)　6,250.　4,500.

Nos. 463-484 are valued in the grade of fine to very fine.
No. 463 comes only from the booklet pane. All examples have one or two straight edges.

Types of 1935-37 Overprinted

a　　　　　　b

Nos. 431-432 Overprinted in Black — c

1945　　　　　　　Perf. 11
485 A53(a) 2c rose　　　.25　.25
486 A54(b) 4c yellow green　.25　.25
　　　　　　　　　　　.25
487 A55(a) 6c golden brown　.25　.25
　　　　　　　　　　　.25
488 A56(b) 8c violet　　　.25　.25
　　　　　　　　　　　.25
489 A57(b) 10c rose carmine　.25　.25
　　　　　　　　　　　.25
490 A58(b) 12c black　　.25　.25
　　　　　　　　　　　.25
491 A59(b) 16c dark blue　.25　.25
　　　　　　　　　　　.30
492 A60(a) 20c lt olive green　.30　.25
　　　　　　　　　　　.40
493 A62(b) 30c orange red　.50　.35
　　　　　　　　　　　.60
494 A63(b) 1p red org & blk　1.10　.25
　　　　　　　　　　　1.60
495 A71(c) 10p gray　　55.00　13.50
　　Never hinged　　　90.00
496 A71(c) 20p henna brown　50.00　15.00
　　Never hinged　　　75.00
　　Nos. 485-496 (12)　108.65　31.10
　　Set, never hinged　169.55

José Rizal — A76

1946, May 28　　　Perf. 11x10½
497 A76 2c sepia　　　　.25　.25
　　Never hinged　　　　　.25

For overprints see Nos. 503, O44.

> **Catalogue values for unused stamps in this section, from this point to the end of the section, are for Never Hinged items.**

Later issues, released by the Philippine Republic on July 4, 1946, and thereafter, are listed in Scott's Standard Postage Stamp Catalogue, Vol. 5A.

Republic

Philippine Girl Holding Flag of the Republic — A77

Unwmk.
1946, July 4　Engr.　Perf. 11
500 A77 2c carmine　　　.50　.25
501 A77 6c green　　　　.50　.25
502 A77 12c blue　　　1.25　.40
　　Nos. 500-502 (3)　2.25　.90

Philippine independence, July 4, 1946.

No. 497 Overprinted in Brown

1946, Dec. 30　　Perf. 11x10½
503 A76 2c sepia　　　　.40　.25

50th anniv. of the execution of José Rizal.

Rizal Monument A78　　Bonifacio Monument A79

Jones Bridge
A80

Santa Lucia
Gate
A81

Mayon
Volcano
A82

Avenue of
Palms
A83

1947   **Engr.**   **Perf. 12**
504 A78 4c black brown   .50   .25
505 A79 10c red orange   .50   .25
506 A80 12c deep blue   .50   .25
507 A81 16c slate gray   3.50   .60
508 A82 20c red brown   3.50   .25
509 A83 50c dull green   3.50   .50
510 A83 1p violet   3.50   .50
    Nos. 504-510 (7)   15.50   2.60

   Issued: Nos. 505 & 508, 3/23; Nos. 506-07, 509, 6/19; Nos. 504 & 510, 8/1.
   For surcharges see Nos. 613-614, 809. For overprints see Nos. 609, O50-O52, O54-O55.

Manuel L. Quezon — A84

1947, May 1   **Typo.**
511 A84 1c green   .50   .25
   a.   Vert. pair, imperf. between   50.00
        See No. 515.

Pres. Manuel A.
Roxas Taking
Oath of
Office — A85

1947, July 4   **Unwmk.**   **Perf. 12½**
512 A85 4c carmine rose   .60   .25
513 A85 6c dk green   .90   .45
514 A85 16c purple   1.50   .85
    Nos. 512-514 (3)   3.00   1.55
     First anniversary of republic.

Quezon Type
Souvenir Sheet

1947, Nov. 28   **Imperf.**
515   Sheet of 4   1.75   1.25
   a.   A84 1c bright green   .25   .25

United Nations
Emblem — A87

1947, Nov. 24   **Perf. 12½**
516 A87 4c dk car & pink   2.40   1.40
   a.   Imperf.   5.50   3.75
517 A87 6c pur & pale vio   2.60   1.40
   a.   Imperf.   5.00   3.75
518 A87 12c dp bl & pale bl   3.50   2.10
   a.   Imperf.   5.50   3.75
    Nos. 516-518 (3)   8.50   4.90
    Nos. 516a-518a (3)   17.50   11.25

   Conference of the Economic Commission in Asia and the Far East, held at Baguio.

Gen. Douglas
MacArthur — A88

1948, Feb. 3   **Engr.**   **Perf. 12**
519 A88 4c purple   1.20   .50
520 A88 6c rose car   1.60   .50
521 A88 16c brt ultra   2.00   .75
    Nos. 519-521 (3)   4.80   1.75

Threshing
Rice — A89

1948, Feb. 23   **Typo.**   **Perf. 12½**
522 A89 2c grn & pale yel grn   1.50   .60
523 A89 6c brown & cream   2.50   .60
524 A89 18c dp bl & pale bl   4.00   1.80
    Nos. 522-524 (3)   8.00   3.00

   Conf. of the FAO held at Baguio. Nos. 522 and 524 exist imperf. Value, set $125.
     See No. C67.

Manuel A. Roxas — A90

1948, July 15   **Engr.**   **Perf. 12**
525 A90 2c black   .30   .25
526 A90 4c black   .45   .25

   Issued in tribute to President Manuel A. Roxas who died April 15, 1948.

José Rizal — A91

1948, June 19   **Unwmk.**
527 A91 2c bright green   .40   .25
   a.   Booklet pane of 6 ('44)   6.00   4.00

   For surcharges see Nos. 550, O56. For overprint see No. O53.

Scout Saluting — A92

1948, Oct. 31   **Typo.**   **Imperf.**
528 A92 2c chocolate & green   1.25   .55
   a.   Perf. 11½   1.75   1.40
529 A92 4c chocolate & pink   1.50   .70
   a.   Perf. 11½   2.50   2.00

   Boy Scouts of the Philippines, 25th anniv. Nos. 528 and 529 exist part perforate.

Sampaguita, National
Flower — A93

1948, Dec. 8   **Perf. 12½**
530 A93 3c blk, pale grn & grn   .60   .30

UPU Monument,
Bern — A94

         Unwmk.
1949, Oct. 9   **Engr.**   **Perf. 12**
531 A94 4c green   .90   .25
532 A94 6c dull violet   .60   .25
533 A94 18c blue gray   .60   .25
    Nos. 531-533 (3)   2.10   .75

Souvenir Sheet
Imperf
534   Sheet of 3   3.00   2.00
   a.   A94 4c green   .70   .35
   b.   A94 6c dull violet   .70   .35
   c.   A94 18c blue   .70   .60

     75th anniv. of the UPU.
   In 1960 an unofficial, 3-line overprint ("President D. D. Eisenhower /Visit to the Philippines/June 14-16, 1960") was privately applied to No. 534.
   For surcharge & overprint see #806, 901.

Gen. Gregorio del
Pilar at Tirad
Pass — A95

1949, Dec. 2   **Perf. 12**
535 A95 2c red brown   .40   .25
536 A95 4c green   .60   .25

   50th anniversary of the death of Gen. Gregorio P. del Pilar and fifty-two of his men at Tirad Pass.

Globe — A96

1950, Mar. 1
537 A96 2c purple   .40   .25
538 A96 6c dk green   .50   .25
539 A96 18c dp blue   .60   .25
    Nos. 537-539,C68-C69 (5)   5.50   1.85

   5th World Cong. of the Junior Chamber of Commerce, Manila, Mar. 1-8, 1950.
   For surcharge see No. 825.

Red Lauan Tree — A97

1950, Apr. 14
540 A97 2c green   .60   .25
541 A97 4c purple   .75   .25
   50th anniversary of the Bureau of Forestry.

F. D. Roosevelt with
his Stamps — A98

1950, May 22
542 A98 4c dark brown   1.50   .25
543 A98 6c carmine rose   .75   .45
544 A98 18c blue   .75   .60
    Nos. 542-544 (3)   3.00   1.30

   Honoring Franklin D. Roosevelt and for the 25th anniv. of the Philatelic Association of the Philippines. See No. C70.

Lions Club
Emblem — A99

1950, June 4   **Engr.**
545 A99 2c orange   1.20   .30
546 A99 4c violet   1.20   .35
    Nos. 545-546,C71-C72 (4)   6.90   1.70

   Convention of the Lions Club, Manila, June 1950.

Pres. Elpidio
Quirino Taking
Oath — A100

1950, July 4   **Unwmk.**   **Perf. 12**
547 A100 2c car rose   .30   .25
548 A100 4c magenta   .30   .25
549 A100 6c blue green   .50   .25
    Nos. 547-549 (3)   1.10   .75
   Republic of the Philippines, 4th anniv.

No. 527 Surcharged in Black
1950, Sept. 20
550 A91 1c on 2c bright green   .60   .25

Dove over
Globe — A101

1950, Oct. 23
551 A101 5c green   .80   .25
552 A101 6c rose carmine   .60   .25
553 A101 18c ultra   .60   .35
    Nos. 551-553 (3)   2.00   .85

     Baguio Conference of 1950.
   For surcharge see No. 828.

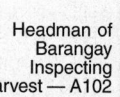
Headman of
Barangay
Inspecting
Harvest — A102

1951, Mar. 31   **Litho.**   **Perf. 12½**
554 A102 5c dull green   1.00   .25
555 A102 6c red brown   .50   .25
556 A102 18c violet blue   .50   .30
    Nos. 554-556 (3)   2.00   .80

   The government's Peace Fund campaign.

Imperf., Pairs
554a A102 5c dull green   4.00   2.00
555a A102 6c red brown   2.00   .90
556a A102 18c violet blue   1.50   .75
    Nos. 554a-556a (3)   7.50   3.65

Arms of
Manila
A103

Arms of
Cebu
A104

Arms of
Zamboanga
A105

Arms of
Iloilo
A106

Various Frames
1951   **Engr.**   **Perf. 12**
557 A103 5c purple   1.50   .25
558 A103 6c gray   1.00   .25
559 A103 18c bright ultra   .70   .40

Various Frames
560 A104 5c crimson rose   1.50   .25
561 A104 6c bister brown   .50   .25
562 A104 18c violet   1.20   .40

Various Frames
563 A105 5c blue green   1.60   .25
564 A105 6c red brown   1.20   .25
565 A105 18c light blue   1.20   .40

Various Frames
566 A106 5c bright green   1.60   .25
567 A106 6c violet   1.20   .25
568 A106 18c deep blue   1.20   .40
    Nos. 557-568 (12)   14.40   3.60

   Issued: A103, 2/3; A104, 4/27; A105, 6/19; A106, 8/26.
   For surcharges see Nos. 634-636.

UN Emblem and Girl
Holding Flag — A107

1951, Oct. 24   **Unwmk.**   **Perf. 11½**
569 A107 5c red   1.75   .30
570 A107 6c blue green   1.00   .30
571 A107 18c violet blue   1.00   .40
    Nos. 569-571 (3)   3.75   1.00

   United Nations Day, Oct. 24, 1951.

Liberty Holding Declaration of Human Rights — A108

1951, Dec. 10   **Perf. 12**
572 A108 5c green   1.75 .25
573 A108 6c red orange   1.00 .25
574 A108 18c ultra   1.00 .35
     Nos. 572-574 (3)   3.75 .85

Universal Declaration of Human Rights.

Students and Department Seal — A109

1952, Jan. 31
575 A109 5c orange red   .75 .35

50th anniversary (in 1951) of the Philippine Educational System.

Milkfish and Map — A111

1952, Oct. 23   **Perf. 12½**
578 A111 5c orange brown   1.60 .45
  a. Vert. pair, imperf. between 65.00
  b. Horiz. pair, imperf. between 65.00
579 A111 6c deep blue   .80 .30
  a. Vert. pair, imperf. horiz. 80.00

4th Indo-Pacific Fisheries Council Meeting, Quezon City, Oct. 23-Nov. 7, 1952.
Nos. 578-579 exist imperf. Value, set $60.

Maria Clara — A112

1952, Nov. 16
580 A112 5c deep blue   1.20 .30
581 A112 6c brown   .80 .30
     Nos. 580-581,C73 (3)   4.00 1.35

1st Pan-Asian Philatelic Exhibition, PANAPEX, Manila, Nov. 16-22.
Nos. 580-81 exist imperf. Value, set $75.

Wright Park, Baguio City — A113

1952, Dec. 15   **Perf. 12**
582 A113 5c red orange   1.60 .45
583 A113 6c dp blue green   1.10 .45

3rd Lions District Convention, Baguio City.

Francisco Baltazar, Poet — A114

1953, Mar. 27
584 A114 5c citron   1.00 .30

National Language Week.

"Gateway to the East" — A115

1953, Apr. 30
585 A115 5c turq green   .60 .25
586 A115 6c vermilion   .50 .25

Philippines International Fair.

Presidents Quirino and Sukarno — A116

1953, Oct. 5   **Engr. & Litho.**
587 A116 5c multicolored   .65 .35
588 A116 6c multicolored   .35 .30

2nd anniversary of the visit of Indonesia's President Sukarno.

Marcelo H. del Pilar — A117

1c, Manuel L. Quezon. 2c, José Abad Santos (diff. frame). 3c, Apolinario Mabini (diff. frame). 10c, Father José Burgos. 20c, Lapu-Lapu. 25c, Gen. Antonio Luna. 50c, Cayetano Arellano. 60c, Andres Bonifacio. 2p, Graciano L. Jaena.

Perf. 12, 12½, 13, 14x13½
1952-60   **Engr.**
589 A117 1c red brn ('53)   .30 .25
590 A117 2c gray ('60)   .30 .25
591 A117 3c brick red ('59)   .30 .25
592 A117 5c crim rose   .30 .25
595 A117 10c ultra ('55)   .60 .25
597 A117 20c car lake ('55)   1.00 .25
598 A117 25c yel grn ('58)   1.25 .25
599 A117 50c org ver ('59)   1.50 .25
600 A117 60c car rose ('58)   2.00 .50
601 A117 2p violet   6.00 1.00
     Nos. 589-601 (10)   13.55 3.50

For overprints & surcharges see #608, 626, 641-642, 647, 830, 871, 875-877, O57-O61.

Doctor Examining Boy — A118

1953, Dec. 16
603 A118 5c lilac rose   .80 .25
604 A118 6c ultra   .60 .25

50th anniversary of the founding of the Philippine Medical Association.

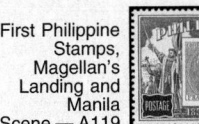

First Philippine Stamps, Magellan's Landing and Manila Scene — A119

Stamp of 1854 in Orange

1954, Apr. 25   **Perf. 13**
605 A119 5c purple   .80 .35
606 A119 18c deep blue   1.90 .90
607 A119 30c green   4.80 2.40
     Nos. 605-607,C74-C76 (6)   25.50 9.60

Centenary of Philippine postage stamps.
For surcharge see No. 829.

Nos. 592 and 509 Overprinted or Surcharged in Black

1954, Apr. 23   **Perf. 12**
608 A117 5c crimson rose   2.00 .90
609 A83 18c on 50c dull grn   2.50 1.40

1st National Boy Scout Jamboree, Quezon City, April 23-30, 1954.
The surcharge on No. 609 is reduced to fit the size of the stamp.

Discus Thrower and Games Emblem — A120

1954, May 31   **Perf. 13**
610 A120 5c shown   3.50 .80
611 A120 18c Swimmer   1.50 .40
612 A120 30c Boxers   3.00 1.50
     Nos. 610-612 (3)   8.00 2.70

2nd Asian Games, Manila, May 1-9.

Nos. 505 and 508 Surcharged in Blue

1954, Sept. 6   **Perf. 12**
613 A79 5c on 10c red org   .75 .45
614 A82 18c on 20c red brn   .75 .45

Manila Conference, 1954.
The surcharge is arranged to obliterate the original denomination.

Allegory of Independence — A121

1954, Nov. 30   **Perf. 13**
615 A121 5c dark carmine   1.00 .25
616 A121 18c deep blue   .80 .30

56th anniversary of the declaration of the first Philippine Independence.
For surcharge see No. 826.

"Immaculate Conception," by Murillo — A122

1954, Dec. 30   **Perf. 12**
617 A122 5c blue   .70 .25

Issued to mark the end of the Marian Year.

Mayon Volcano, Moro Vinta and Rotary Emblem — A123

1955, Feb. 23   **Engr.**   **Perf. 13**
618 A123 5c dull blue   .60 .25
619 A123 18c dk car rose   1.40 .85
     Nos. 618-619,C77 (3)   4.50 2.10

Rotary Intl., 50th anniv. For surcharge see #827.

Allegory of Labor — A124

1955, May 26   **Perf. 13x12½**
620 A124 5c brown   1.75 .70

Issued in connection with the Labor-Management Congress, Manila, May 26-28, 1955.

Pres. Ramon Magsaysay — A125

1955, July 4   **Perf. 12½**
621 A125 5c blue   .50 .25
622 A125 20c red   1.50 .50
623 A125 30c green   1.75 .50
     Nos. 621-623 (3)   3.75 1.25

9th anniversary of the Republic.

Village Well — A126

1956, Mar. 16   **Perf. 12½x13½**
624 A126 5c violet   .75 .25
625 A126 20c dull green   1.25 .40

Issued to publicize the drive for improved health conditions in rural areas.

No. 592 Overprinted

1956, Aug. 1   **Unwmk.**   **Perf. 12**
626 A117 5c crimson rose   .65 .35

5th Annual Conf. of the World Confederation of Organizations of the Teaching Profession, Manila, Aug. 1-8, 1956.

Nurse and Disaster Victims — A127

Engraved; Cross Lithographed in Red

1956, Aug. 30
627 A127 5c violet   .40 .30
628 A127 20c gray brown   1.25 .60

50 years of Red Cross Service in the Philippines.

Monument to US Landing, Leyte — A128

1956, Oct. 20   **Litho.**   **Perf. 12½**
629 A128 5c carmine rose   .70 .25
  a. Imperf, pair ('57)   5.00 3.00

Landing of US forces under Gen. Douglas MacArthur on Leyte, Oct. 20, 1944.
Issue date: No. 629a, Feb. 16.

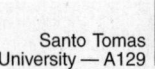

Santo Tomas
University — A129

1956, Nov. 13   Photo.   Perf. 11½
630 A129 5c brown car & choc   .60   .35
631 A129 60c lilac & red brn   4.00 1.60

Statue of Christ by
Rizal — A130

1956, Nov. 28   Engr.   Perf. 12
632 A130 5c gray olive   .50   .25
633 A130 20c rose carmine   1.25   .60

2nd Natl. Eucharistic Cong., Manila, Nov. 28-Dec. 2, and for the centenary of the Feast of the Sacred Heart.

Nos. 561, 564 and 567 Surcharged with New Value in Blue or Black
1956, Dec. 7   Unwmk.   Perf. 12
634 A104 5c on 6c bis brn (Bl)   .60   .25
635 A105 5c on 6c red brn (Bl)   .60   .25
636 A106 5c on 6c vio (Bk)   .60   .25
     Nos. 634-636 (3)   1.80   .75

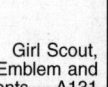

Girl Scout,
Emblem and
Tents — A131

1957, Jan. 19   Litho.   Perf. 12½
637 A131 5c dark blue   .80   .40
  a.   Imperf, pair   7.00   6.00

Centenary of the Scout movement and for the Girl Scout World Jamboree, Quezon City, Jan. 19-Feb. 2, 1957.
Exmaples of Nos. 637 and 637a (No. 48 in sheet) exist with heavy black rectangular handstamps obliterating erroneous date at left, denomination and cloverleaf emblem.

Pres. Ramon
Magsaysay (1907-
57) — A132

1957, Aug. 31   Engr.   Perf. 12
638 A132 5c black   .40   .25

"Spoliarium"
by Juan
Luna — A133

1957, Oct. 23   Perf. 14x14½
639 A133 5c rose carmine   .50   .30

Centenary of the birth of Juan Luna, painter.

Sergio
Osmena and
First National
Assembly
A134

1957, Oct. 16   Perf. 12½x13½
640 A134 5c blue green   .40   .25

1st Philippine Assembly and honoring Sergio Osmeña, Speaker of the Assembly.

Nos. 595 and 597
Surcharged in Carmine
or Black

1957, Dec. 30   Perf. 14x13½
641 A117 5c on 10c ultra (C)   .70   .25
642 A117 10c on 20c car lake   .70   .30

Inauguration of Carlos P. Garcia as president and Diosdado Macapagal as vice-president, Dec. 30.

University of
the
Philippines
A135

1958, June 18   Engr.   Perf. 13½x13
643 A135 5c dk carmine rose   .50   .25

50th anniversary of the founding of the University of the Philippines.

Pres. Carlos P.
Garcia — A136

1958, July 4   Photo.   Perf. 11½
Granite Paper
644 A136 5c multicolored   .30   .25
645 A136 20c multicolored   .60   .30

12th anniversary of Philippine Republic.

Manila
Cathedral
A137

1958, Dec. 8   Engr.   Perf. 13x13½
646 A137 5c multicolored   .35   .25
  a.   Perf 12   3.00   2.00

Issued to commemorate the inauguration of the rebuilt Manila Cathedral, Dec. 8, 1958.

No. 592 Surcharged

1959, Jan. 11   Perf. 12
647 A117 1c on 5c crim rose   .35   .25

Nos. B4-B5 Surcharged with New Values and Bars
1959, Feb. 3   Perf. 13
648 SP4 1c on 2c + 2c red   .30   .25
649 SP5 6c on 4c + 4c vio   .30   .25

14th anniversary of the liberation of Manila from the Japanese forces.

Philippine
Flag — A138

1959, Feb. 8   Unwmk.   Perf. 13
650 A138 6c dp ultra, yel & dp
            car   .30   .25
651 A138 20c dp car, yel & dp
            ultra   .55   .25

Seal of Bulacan
Province — A139

1959, Jan. 21   Engr.   Perf. 13
652 A139 6c lt yellow grn   .30   .25
653 A139 20c rose red   .50   .25

60th anniversary of the Malolos constitution.

1959, Apr. 15
Design: 6c, 25c, Seal of Capiz Province and portrait of Pres. Roxas.
654 A139 6c lt brown   .30   .25
655 A139 25c purple   .50   .25

Pres. Manuel A. Roxas, 11th death anniv.
For surcharge see No. 848.

Seal of Bacolod
City — A140

1959, Oct. 1
656 A140 6c blue green   .30   .25
657 A140 10c rose lilac   .50   .25

Nos. 658-803 were reserved for the rest of a projected series showing seals and coats of arms of provinces and cities.

Camp John
Hay
Amphitheater,
Baguio — A141

1959, Sept. 1   Perf. 13½
804 A141 6c bright green   .30   .25
  a.   Perf 12   2.00   1.50
805 A141 25c rose red   .50   .25

50th anniversary of the city of Baguio.

No. 533 Surcharged in Red

1959, Oct. 24   Perf. 12
806 A94 6c on 18c blue   .50   .25

Issued for United Nations Day, Oct. 24.

Maria Cristina
Falls — A142

1959, Nov. 18   Photo.   Perf. 13½
807 A142 6c vio & dp yel grn   .30   .25
  a.   Perf 12   2.00   1.10
808 A142 30c green & brown   .75   .30
  a.   Perf 12   6.25   4.75

No. 504 Surcharged with New Value and Bars
1959, Dec. 1   Engr.   Perf. 12
809 A78 1c on 4c blk brn   .35   .25

Manila
Atheneum
Emblem
A143

1959, Dec. 10   Perf. 13½
810 A143 6c ultra   .30   .25
  a.   Perf 12   1.50   1.25
811 A143 30c rose red   .70   .30
  a.   Perf 12   20.00   8.00

Centenary of the Manila Atheneum (Ateneo de Manila), a school, and to mark a century of progress in education.

Manuel
Quezon
A144

José Rizal
A145

1959-60   Engr.   Perf. 13
812 A144 1c olive gray ('60)   .30   .25
           Perf. 14x12
813 A145 6c gray blue   .40   .25

Issued: No. 812, 11/15/60; No. 813, 12/30/59. For overprint see No. O62.

A146

Perf. 12½x13½
1960, Feb. 8   Unwmk.   Photo.
814 A146 6c brown & gold   .55   .25

25th anniversary of the Philippine Constitution. See No. C82.

Site of Manila
Pact — A147

1960, Mar. 26   Engr.   Perf. 12½
815 A147 6c emerald   .30   .25
816 A147 25c orange   .45   .25

5th anniversary (in 1959) of the Congress of the Philippines establishing the South-East Asia Treaty Organization (SEATO).
First Day Covers Issued 9/8/59.
For overprints see Nos. 841-842.

Sunset at
Manila Bay and
Uprooted Oak
Emblem
A148

1960, Apr. 7   Photo.   Perf. 13½
817 A148 6c multicolored   .30   .25
818 A148 25c multicolored   .70   .25

World Refugee Year, 7/1/59-6/30/60.

A149

1960, July 29   Perf. 13½
819 A149 5c lt grn, red & gold .40   .25
820 A149 6c bl, red & gold   .40   .25

Philippine Tuberculosis Society, 50th anniv.

Basketball
A150

1960, Nov. 30   Perf. 13x13½
821 A150 6c shown   .40   .25
822 A150 10c Runner   .60   .25
     Nos. 821-822,C85-C86 (4)   3.00   1.55

17th Olympic Games, Rome, 8/25-9/11.

Presidents Eisenhower
and Garcia and
Presidential
Seals — A151

1960, Dec. 30   *Perf. 13½*
823 A151 6c multi   .35   .25
824 A151 20c ultra, red & yel   .60   .25

Visit of Pres. Dwight D. Eisenhower to the
Philippines, June 14, 1960.

**Nos. 539, 616, 619, 553, 606 and 598
Surcharged with New Values and
Bars in Red or Black**

1960-61   *Perf. 12, 13, 12½*
825 A96 1c on 18c dp bl (R)   .30   .25
826 A121 5c on 18c dp bl (R)   .65   .25
827 A123 5c on 18c dp car rose   .65   .25
828 A101 10c on 18c ultra (R)   .65   .25
829 A119 10c on 18c dp bl & org
       (R)   .65   .25
830 A117 20c on 25c yel grn
       ('61)   .65   .25
    Nos. 825-830 (6)   3.55 1.50

On No. 830, no bars are overprinted, the
surcharge "20 20" serving to cancel the old
denomination.
Issued: Nos. 825, 827, 829, 7/4/60; Nos.
826, 828, 9/15/60; No. 830, 2/16/61.

Mercury and
Globe
A152

1961, Jan. 23   Photo.   *Perf. 13½*
831 A152 6c red brn, bl, blk &
       gold   .70   .25

Manila Postal Conf., Jan. 10-23. See #C87.

**Nos. B10, B11 and B11a Surcharged
"2nd National Boy Scout Jamboree
Pasonanca Park" and New Value in
Black or Red**

1961, May 2   Engr.   *Perf. 13*
Yellow Paper
832 SP8 10c on 6c + 4c car   .40   .25
833 SP8 30c on 25c + 5c bl (R)   .70   .50
   a. Tete beche, wht (10c on 6c + 4c
       & 30c on 25c + 5c) (Bk)   1.50 2.00

Second National Boy Scout Jamboree,
Pasonanca Park, Zamboanga City.

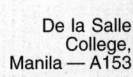

De la Salle
College,
Manila — A153

1961, June 16   Photo.   *Perf. 11½*
834 A153 6c multi   .35   .25
835 A153 10c multi   .35   .25

De la Salle College, Manila, 50th anniv.

José Rizal as
Student
A154

6c, Rizal & birthplace at Calamba, Laguna.
10c, Rizal & parents. 20c, Rizal with Juan
Luna & F. R. Hidalgo in Madrid. 30c, Rizal's
execution.

1961   Unwmk.   *Perf. 13½*
836 A154 5c multi   .40   .25
837 A154 6c multi   .40   .25
838 A154 10c grn & red brn   .50   .25
839 A154 20c brn red & grnsh bl   .60   .25
840 A154 30c vio, lil & org brn   .90   .30
    Nos. 836-840 (5)   2.80 1.30

Centenary of the birth of José Rizal.
Issued: Nos. 836-839, 1/19; No. 840 12/30.

Nos. 815-816 Overprinted

1961, July 4   Engr.   *Perf. 12½*
841 A147 6c emerald   .30   .25
842 A147 25c orange   .40   .25

15th anniversary of the Republic.

Colombo Plan Emblem
and Globe Showing
Member
Countries — A155

1961, Oct. 8   Photo.   *Perf. 13x11½*
843 A155 5c multi   .30   .25
844 A155 6c multi   .30   .25

7th anniversary of the admission of the Philippines to the Colombo Plan.

Government
Clerk — A156

1961, Dec. 9   Unwmk.   *Perf. 12½*
845 A156 6c vio, bl & red   .30   .25
846 A156 10c gray bl & red   .50   .25

Honoring Philippine government employees.

No. C83 Surcharged

1961, Nov. 30   Engr.   *Perf. 14x14½*
847 AP11 6c on 10c car   .45   .25

Philippine Amateur Athletic Fed., 50th anniv.

**No. 655 Surcharged with New Value
and: "MACAPAGAL-PELAEZ
INAUGURATION DEC. 30, 1961"**

1961, Dec. 30   *Perf. 12½*
848 A139 6c on 25c pur   .40   .25

Inauguration of Pres. Diosdado Macapagal
and Vice-Pres. Emanuel Pelaez.

No. B8 Surcharged

1962, Jan. 23   Photo.   *Perf. 13½x13*
849 SP7 6c on 5c grn & red   .50   .25
   a. Perf. 12   15.00 5.00

Vanda
Orchids
A157

Orchids: 6c, White mariposa. 10c, Sander's
dendrobe. 20c, Sanggumay.

1962, Mar. 9   Photo.   *Perf. 13½x14*
Dark Blue Background
850 5c rose, grn & yel   .60   .25
851 6c grn & yel   .60   .25
852 10c grn, car & brn   .60   .25
853 20c lil, brn & grn   .60   .25
   a. A157 Block of 4, #850-853   2.50 2.25
   b. As "a," imperf.   4.50 3.00

Apolinario Mabini — A158

Portraits: 1s, Manuel L. Quezon. 5s,
Marcelo H. del Pilar. No. 857, José Rizal. No.
857A, Rizal (wearing shirt). 10s, Father José
Burgos. 20s, Lapu-Lapu. 30s, Rajah Soliman.
50s, Cayetano Arellano. 70s, Sergio Osmena.
No. 863, Emilio Jacinto. No. 864, José M.
Panganiban.

Perf. 13½; 14 (1s); 13x12 (#857, 10s)
1962-69   Engr.   Unwmk.
854 A158 1s org brn ('63)   .30   .25
855 A158 3s rose red   .30   .25
856 A158 5s car rose ('63)   .30   .25
857 A158 6s dk red brn   .30   .25
857A A158 6s pck bl ('64)   .30   .25
858 A158 10s brt pur ('63)   .35   .25
859 A158 20s Prus bl ('63)   .40   .25
860 A158 30s vermilion   1.00   .25
861 A158 50s vio ('63)   1.25   .30
862 A158 70s brt bl ('63)   1.75   .25
863 A158 1p grn ('63)   4.00   .40
864 A158 1p dp org ('69)   3.00   .40
    Nos. 854-864 (12)   13.25 3.35

Issued: Nos. 854, 856, 9/23/63; No. 855,
5/13/62; No. 857, 6/19/62; No. 857A, 6/19/64;
No. 858, 3/24/63; No. 859, 10/20/63; No. 860,
11/30/62; No. 861, 5/1/63; No. 862, 12/10/63;
No. 863, 1/23/63; No. 864, 2/1/69.
For surcharges & overprints see #873-874,
946, 969, 1054, 1119, 1209, O63-O69.

Pres.
Macapagal
Taking Oath of
Office — A159

1962, June 12   Photo.   *Perf. 13½*
Vignette Multicolored
865 A159 6s blue   .30   .25
866 A159 10s green   .30   .25
867 A159 30s violet   .45   .25
    Nos. 865-867 (3)   1.05   .75

Swearing in of President Diosdado Macapagal, Dec. 30, 1961.

Volcano in Lake
Taal and Malaria
Eradication
Emblem — A160

1962, Oct. 24   Unwmk.   *Perf. 11½*
Granite Paper
868 A160 6s multi   .30   .25
869 A160 10s multi   .30   .25
870 A160 70s multi   1.60 1.60
    Nos. 868-870 (3)   2.20 2.10

Issued on UN Day for the WHO drive to
eradicate malaria.

No. 598 Surcharged in
Red

1962, Nov. 15   Engr.   *Perf. 12*
871 A117 20s on 25c yel grn   .50   .25

Issued to commemorate the bicentennial of
the Diego Silang revolt in Ilocos Province.

**No. B6 Overprinted with Sideways
Chevron Obliterating Surtax**
1962, Dec. 23   *Perf. 12*
872 SP6 5c on 5c + 1c dp bl   .50   .25

**Nos. 855, 857 Surcharged with New
Value and Old Value Obliterated**
1963   *Perf. 13½*
873 A158 1s on 3s rose red   .30   .25
          Perf. 13x12
874 A158 5s on 6s dk red brn   .30   .25
   a. Inverted overprint   20.00
   b. Double overprint   15.00

Issued: No. 873, 3/12/63; No. 874, 2/19/63.

No. 601 Surcharged

1963, June 12   *Perf. 12*
875 A117 6s on 2p vio   .30   .25
876 A117 20s on 2p vio   .50   .25
877 A117 70s on 2p vio   .80   .30
    Nos. 875-877 (3)   1.60   .80

Diego Silang Bicentennial Art and Philatelic
Exhibition, ARPHEX, Manila, May 28-June 30.

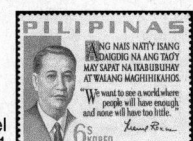

Pres. Manuel
Roxas — A161

1963-73   Engr.   *Perf. 13½*
878 A161 6s brt bl & blk,
       bluish   .45   .25
879 A161 30s brn & blk,
       brownish   .90   .25
Pres. Ramon Magsaysay
880 A161 6s lil & blk   .45   .25
881 A161 30s yel grn & blk   .90   .25
Pres. Elpidio Quirino
882 A161 6s grn & blk ('65)   .45   .25
883 A161 30s rose lil & blk
       ('65)   .90   .25
Gen. (Pres.) Emilio Aguinaldo
883A A161 6s dp cl & blk
       ('66)   .45   .25
883B A161 30s bl & blk ('66)   .90   .25
Pres. José P. Laurel
883C A161 6s red brn & blk
       ('66)   .45   .25
883D A161 30s bl & blk ('66)   .90   .25
Pres. Manuel L. Quezon
883E A161 10s bl gray & blk
       ('67)   .45   .25
883F A161 30s vio & blk ('67)   .90   .25
Pres. Sergio Osmeña
883G A161 10s rose lil & blk
       ('70)   .45   .25
883H A161 40s grn & blk ('70)   .90   .25
Pres. Carlos P. Garcia
883I A161 10s buff & blk ('73)   .50   .25
883J A161 30s pink & blk ('73)   1.00   .25
    Nos. 878-883J (16)   10.95 4.00

Nos. 878-883J honor former presidents.
Issued: Nos. 878-879, 7/4/63; Nos. 880-
881, 12/30/63; Nos. 882-883, 2/28/65; Nos.
883A-883B, 2/6/66; Nos. 883C-883D, 11/6/66;
Nos. 883E-883F, 11/16/67; Nos. 883G-883H,
6/12/70; Nos. 883I-883J, 2/22/73.
For surcharges see Nos. 984-985, 1120,
1146, 1160-1161.

Globe, Flags of Thailand, Korea, China, Philippines — A162

1963, Aug. 26   Photo.   Perf. 13½x13
884 A162 6s dk grn & multi   .30   .25
885 A162 20s dk grn & multi   .45   .25

Asian-Oceanic Postal Union, 1st anniv.
For surcharge see No. 1078.

Red Cross Centenary Emblem — A163

1963, Sept. 1   Perf. 11½
886 A163 5s lt vio, gray & red   .30   .25
887 A163 6s ultra, gray & red   .30   .25
888 A163 20s grn, gray & red   .40   .25
         Nos. 886-888 (3)   1.00   .75

Centenary of the International Red Cross.

Bamboo Dance A164

Folk Dances: 6s, Dance with oil lamps. 10s, Duck dance. 20s, Princess Gandingan's rock dance.

1963, Sept. 15   Unwmk.   Perf. 14
889 A164 5s multi   .40   .25
890   6s multi   .40   .25
891   10s multi   .40   .25
892   20s multi   .40   .25
  a. A164 Block of 4, #889-892   2.50 1.50

For surcharges and overprints see #1043-1046.

Pres. Macapagal and Filipino Family A165

1963, Sept. 28   Perf. 14
893 A165 5s bl & multi   .30   .25
894 A165 6s yel & multi   .30   .25
895 A165 20s lil & multi   .45   .25
         Nos. 893-895 (3)   1.05   .75

Issued to publicize Pres. Macapagal's 5-year Socioeconomic Program.
For surcharge see No. 1181.

Presidents Lopez Mateos and Macapagal A166

1963, Sept. 28   Photo.   Perf. 13½
896 A166 6s multi   .30   .25
897 A166 30s multi   .50   .25

Visit of Pres. Adolfo Lopez Mateos of Mexico to the Philippines.
For surcharge see No. 1166.

Andres Bonifacio — A167

1963, Nov. 30   Unwmk.   Perf. 12
898 A167 5s gold, brn, gray & red   .30   .25
899 A167 6s sil, brn, gray & red   .45   .25
900 A167 25s brnz, brn, gray & red   .60   .25
         Nos. 898-900 (3)   1.35   .75

Centenary of the birth of Andres Bonifacio, national hero and poet.
For surcharges see Nos. 1147, 1162.

No. 534 Overprinted: "UN ADOPTION/DECLARATION OF HUMAN RIGHTS/15TH ANNIVERSARY DEC. 10, 1963"

1963, Dec. 10   Engr.   Imperf.
Souvenir Sheet
901 A94 Sheet of 3   3.25 2.50

15th anniv. of the Universal Declaration of Human Rights.

Woman holding Sheaf of Rice — A168

1963, Dec. 20   Photo.   Perf. 13½x13
902 A168 6s brn & multi   .35   .25
         Nos. 902,C88-C89 (3)   1.50   .80

FAO "Freedom from Hunger" campaign.

Bamboo Organ — A169

1964, May 4   Perf. 13½
903 A169 5s multi   .30   .25
904 A169 6s multi   .30   .25
905 A169 20s multi   .45   .25
         Nos. 903-905 (3)   1.05   .75

The bamboo organ in the Church of Las Pinas, Rizal, was built by Father Diego Cera, 1816-1822.
For surcharge see No. 1055.

Apolinario Mabini — A170

Wmk. 233
1964, July 23   Photo.   Perf. 14½
906 A170 6s pur & gold   .35   .25
907 A170 10s red brn & gold   .35   .25
908 A170 30s brt grn & gold   .50   .25
         Nos. 906-908 (3)   1.20   .75

Apolinario Mabini (1864-1903), national hero and a leader of the 1898 revolution.
For surcharge see No. 1056.

Flags Surrounding SEATO Emblem — A171

Unwmk.
1964, Sept. 8   Photo.   Perf. 13
Flags and Emblem Multicolored
909 A171 6s dk bl & yel   .30   .25
910 A171 10s dp grn & yel   .40   .25
911 A171 25s dk brn & yel   .45   .25
         Nos. 909-911 (3)   1.20   .75

10th anniversary of the South-East Asia Treaty Organization (SEATO).
For surcharge see No. 1121.

Pres. Macapagal Signing Code — A172

1964, Dec. 21   Wmk. 233   Perf. 14½
912 A172 3s multi   .35   .25
913 A172 6s multi   .40   .25
         Nos. 912-913,C90 (3)   1.35   .75

Signing of the Agricultural Land Reform Code. For surcharges see Nos. 970, 1234.

Basketball — A173

Sport: 10s, Women's relay race. 20s, Hurdling. 30s, Soccer.

1964, Dec. 28   Perf. 14½x14
915 A173 6s lt bl, dk brn & gold   .30 1.25
916 A173 10s gold, pink & dk brn   .30 1.25
  b.   Gold omitted
917 A173 20s gold, dk brn & yel   .60   .25
918 A173 30s emer, dk brn & gold   .80   .25
         Nos. 915-918 (4)   2.00 3.00

18th Olympic Games, Tokyo, Oct. 10-25.
For overprints and surcharge see Nos. 962-965, 1079.

1965, Mar. 22   Imperf., Pairs
915a A173 6s   1.25 1.25
916a A173 10s   1.25 1.25
917a A173 20s   2.75 1.75
918a A173 30s   2.75 1.75
         Nos. 915a-918a (4)   8.00 6.00

Presidents Lubke and Macapagal and Coats of Arms — A174

1965, Apr. 19   Unwmk.   Perf. 13½
919 A174 6s ol grn & multi   .30   .25
920 A174 10s multi   .35   .25
921 A174 25s dp bl & multi   .40   .25
         Nos. 919-921 (3)   1.05   .75

Visit of Pres. Heinrich Lubke of Germany, Nov. 18-23, 1964.
For surcharge see No. 1167.

Emblems of Manila Observatory and Weather Bureau — A175

1965, May 22   Photo.   Perf. 13½
922 A175 6s lt ultra & multi   .30   .25
923 A175 20s lt vio & multi   .30   .25
924 A175 50s bl grn & multi   .55   .25
         Nos. 922-924 (3)   1.15   .75

Issued to commemorate the centenary of the Meteorological Service in the Philippines.
For surcharge see No. 1069.

Pres. John F. Kennedy (1917-63) — A176

Perf. 14½x14
1965, May 29   Wmk. 233
Center Multicolored
925 A176 6s gray   .30   .25
926 A176 10s brt vio   .35   .25
927 A176 30s ultra   .50   .25
         Nos. 925-927 (3)   1.15   .75

Nos. 925-927 exist with ultramarine of tie omitted. No. 926 exist with red on face omitted. Value, $100. No. 927 exist with yellow on face omitted. Value, $100.

Nos. 925 and 927 exist imperf. Value, set $100.
For surcharges see Nos. 1148, 1210.

King and Queen of Thailand, Pres. and Mrs. Macapagal A177

Perf. 12½x13
1965, June 12   Unwmk.
928 A177 2s brt bl & multi   .40   .25
929 A177 6s bis & multi   .50   .25
930 A177 30s red & multi   .80   .25
         Nos. 928-930 (3)   1.70   .75

Visit of King Bhumibol Adulyadej and Queen Sirikit of Thailand, July 1963.
For surcharge see No. 1122.

Princess Beatrix and Evangelina Macapagal A178

Perf. 13x12½
1965, July 4   Photo.   Unwmk.
931 A178 2s bl & multi   .30   .25
932 A178 6s blk & multi   .30   .25
933 A178 10s multi   .40   .25
         Nos. 931-933 (3)   1.00   .75

Visit of Princess Beatrix of the Netherlands, Nov. 21-23, 1962.
For surcharge see No. 1188.

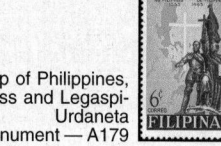

Map of Philippines, Cross and Legaspi-Urdaneta Monument — A179

Design: 3s, Cross and Rosary held before map of Philippines.

1965, Oct. 4   Unwmk.   Perf. 13
934 A179 3s multi   .30   .25
935 A179 6s multi   .35   .25
         Nos. 934-935,C91-C92 (4) 2.85 1.25

400th anniv. of the Christianization of the Philippines. See souvenir sheet No. C92a. For overprint see No. C108.

Presidents Sukarno and Macapagal and Prime Minister Tunku Abdul Rahman — A180

1965, Nov. 25   Perf. 13
936 A180 6s multi   .30   .25
937 A180 10s multi   .40   .25
938 A180 25s multi   .60   .25
         Nos. 936-938 (3)   1.30   .75

Signing of the Manila Accord (Mapilindo) by Malaya, Philippines and Indonesia.
For surcharge see No. 1182.

Bicyclists and Globe — A181

1965, Dec. 5   Perf. 13½
939 A181 6s multi   .30   .25
940 A181 10s multi   .30   .25
941 A181 25s multi   .55   .25
         Nos. 939-941 (3)   1.15   .75

Second Asian Cycling Championship, Philippines, Nov. 28-Dec. 5.

Nos. B21-B22 Surcharged

1965, Dec. 30   Engr.   Perf. 13
942 SP12 10s on 6s + 4s   .40   .25
943 SP12 30s on 30s + 5s   .60   .25

Inauguration of President Ferdinand Marcos and Vice-President Fernando Lopez.

Antonio Regidor — A182

1966, Jan. 21   Perf. 12x11
944 A182 6s blue   .35   .25
945 A182 30s brown   .45   .25

Dr. Antonio Regidor, Sec. of the High Court of Manila and Pres. of Public Instruction.
For surcharges see Nos. 1110-1111.

No. 857A Overprinted in Red

1966, May 1   Engr.   Perf. 13½
946 A158 6s peacock blue   .35   .25

Anti-smuggling drive.
Exists with black overprint. Value, $35.
Exists with overprint inverted, double, double inverted and double with one inverted.
For surcharge see No. 1209.

Girl Scout Giving Scout Sign — A183

1966, May 26   Litho.   Perf. 13x12½
947 A183 3s ultra & multi   .30   .25
948 A183 6s emer & multi   .30   .25
949 A183 20s brn & multi   .40   .25
     Nos. 947-949 (3)   1.00   .75

Philippine Girl Scouts, 25th anniversary.
For surcharge see No. 1019.

Pres. Marcos Taking Oath of Office A184

1966, June 12   Perf. 12½
950 A184 6s bl & multi   .30   .25
951 A184 20s emer & multi   .40   .25
952 A184 30s yel & multi   .50   .25
     Nos. 950-952 (3)   1.20   .75

Inauguration of Pres. Ferdinand E. Marcos, 12/30/65.
For overprints & surcharge see #960-961, 1050.

Seal of Manila and Historical Scenes A185

1966, June 24
953 A185 6s multi   .35   .25
954 A185 30s multi   .45   .25

Adoption of the new seal of Manila.
For surcharges see Nos. 1070, 1118, 1235.

Old and New Philippine National Bank Buildings A186

Designs: 6s, Entrance to old bank building and 1p silver coin.

1966, July 22   Photo.   Perf. 14x13½
955 A186 6s gold, ultra, sil & blk   .30   .25
956 A186 10s multi   .40   .25

50th anniv. of the Philippine Natl. Bank. See #C93. For surcharges see #1071, 1100, 1236.

Post Office, Annex Three — A187

1966, Oct. 1   Wmk. 233   Perf. 14½
957 A187 6s lt vio, yel & grn   .30   .25
958 A187 10s rose cl, yel & grn .30   .25
959 A187 20s ultra, yel & grn   .40   .25
     Nos. 957-959 (3)   1.00   .75

60th anniversary of Postal Savings Bank.
For surcharges see Nos. 1104, 1112, 1189.

Nos. 950 and 952 Overprinted in Emerald or Black

Perf. 12½
1966, Oct. 24   Litho.   Unwmk.
960 A184 6s multi (E)   .30   .25
961 A184 30s multi   .50   .25

Manila Summit Conference, Oct. 23-27.
No. 960 eixsts with overprint in black and double impression of blue on base stamp. Value, $35. No. 961 exists with overprint inverted. Value, $40. No. 961 exists imperf. with emerald overprint. Value, $60.

Nos. 915a-918a Overprinted

Wmk. 233
1967, Jan. 14   Photo.   Imperf.
962 A173 6s lt bl, dk brn & gold   .50   .25
963 A173 10s gold, dk brn & pink   .50   .25
964 A173 20s gold, dk brn & yel   .60   .35
965 A173 30s emer, dk brn & gold   .80   .55
     Nos. 962-965 (4)   2.40 1.40

Lions Intl., 50th anniv. The Lions emblem is in the lower left corner on the 6s, in the upper left corner on the 10s and in the upper right corner on the 30s.
No. 962 exist both perf and imperf with overprint (for No. 963) inverted. Values: $75 perf, $50 imperf.

"Succor" by Fernando Amorsolo A188

Unwmk.
1967, Apr. 9   Litho.   Perf. 14
966 A188 5s sepia & multi   .40   .25
967 A188 20s blue & multi   .85   .25
968 A188 2p green & multi   1.75   .60
     Nos. 966-968 (3)   3.00 1.10

25th anniversary of the Battle of Bataan.

Nos. 857A and 913 Surcharged
1967, Aug.   Engr.   Perf. 13½
969 A158 4s on 6s pck bl   .40   .25

Wmk. 233
Photo.   Perf. 14½
970 A172 5s on 6s multi   .45   .25

Issue dates: 4s, Aug. 10; 5s, Aug. 7.

Gen. Douglas MacArthur and Paratroopers Landing on Corregidor A189

Unwmk.
1967, Aug. 31   Litho.   Perf. 14
971 A189 6s multi   1.00   .25
972 A189 5p multi   9.00 3.00

25th anniversary, Battle of Corregidor.

Bureau of Posts, Manila, Jones Bridge over Pasig River A190

1967, Sept. 15   Litho.   Perf. 14x13½
973 A190 4s multi & blk   .40   .25
974 A190 20s multi & red   .40   .25
975 A190 50s multi & vio   .55   .30
     Nos. 973-975 (3)   1.35   .80

65th anniversary of the Bureau of Posts.
For overprint see No. 1015.

Philippine Nativity Scene — A191

1967, Dec. 1   Photo.   Perf. 13½
976 A191 10s multi   .50   .25
977 A191 40s multi   .70   .30

Christmas 1967.

Chinese Garden, Rizal Park, Presidents Marcos and Chiang Kai-shek A192

Presidents' heads & scenes in Chinese Garden, Rizal Park, Manila: 10s, Gate. 20s, Landing pier.

1967-68   Photo.   Perf. 13½
978 A192 5s multi   .30   .25
979 A192 10s multi ('68)   .60   .25
980 A192 20s multi   1.00   .25
     Nos. 978-980 (3)   1.90   .75

Sino-Philippine Friendship Year 1966-67.
Issued: Nos. 978, 980, 12/30/67; No. 979, 3/12/68.

Makati Center Post Office, Mrs. Marcos and Rotary Emblem A193

1968, Jan. 9   Litho.   Perf. 14
981 A193 10s bl & multi   .40   .25
982 A193 20s grn & multi   .50   .25
983 A193 40s multi   .80   .35
     Nos. 981-983 (3)   1.70   .85

1st anniv. of the Makati Center Post Office.

Nos. 882, 883C and B27 Surcharged

1968, Mar. 8
984 A161 5s on 6s grn & blk   .55   .25
a.   Double overprint   15.00
985 A161 5s on 6s lt red brn & blk   .55   .25
986 SP14 10s on 6s + 5s ultra & red   .70   .25
a.   Double overprint   18.00
     Nos. 984-986 (3)   1.80   .75

The "1" in the surcharged value on No. 986 is serifed. For surcharge without serif on "1," see No. 1586.

Felipe G. Calderon, Barasoain Church and Malolos Constitution A194

1968, Apr. 4   Litho.   Perf. 14
987 A194 10s lt ultra & multi   .40   .25
988 A194 40s grn & multi   .70   .25
989 A194 75s multi   1.30   .60
     Nos. 987-989 (3)   2.40 1.10

Calderon (1868-1909), lawyer and author of the Malolos Constitution.

Earth and Transmission from Philippine Station to Satellite — A195

1968, Oct. 21   Photo.   Perf. 13½
990 A195 10s blk & multi   .40   .25
991 A195 40s multi   .70   .25
992 A195 75s multi   1.60   .50
     Nos. 990-992 (3)   2.70 1.00

Issued to commemorate the inauguration of the Philcomsat Station in Tany, Luzon, May 2, 1968.

Tobacco Industry and Tobacco Board's Emblem A196

1968, Nov. 15   Photo.   Perf. 13½
993 A196 10s blk & multi   .30   .25
994 A196 40s bl & multi   .70   .50
995 A196 70s crim & multi   1.10   .90
     Nos. 993-995 (3)   2.10 1.65

Philippine tobacco industry.

Kudyapi A197

Philippine Musical Instruments: 20s, Ludag (drum). 30s, Kulintangan. 50s, Subing (bamboo flute).

1968, Nov. 22   Photo.   Perf. 13½
996 A197 10s multi   .40   .25
997 A197 20s multi   .50   .25
998 A197 30s multi   .80   .25
999 A197 50s multi   1.20   .45
     Nos. 996-999 (4)   2.90 1.20

Concordia College — A198

1968, Dec. 8   *Perf. 13x13½*
1000 A198 10s multi   .30 .25
1001 A198 20s multi   .40 .25
1002 A198 70s multi   .70 .30
    Nos. 1000-1002 (3)   1.40 .80
Centenary of the Colegio de la Concordia, Manila, a Catholic women's school. Issued Dec. 8 (Sunday), but entered the mail Dec. 9.

Singing Children — A199

1968, Dec. 16   *Perf. 13½*
1003 A199 10s multi   .60 .25
1004 A199 40s multi   .70 .45
1005 A199 75s multi   1.20 .80
    Nos. 1003-1005 (3)   2.50 1.50
Christmas 1968.

Animals — A200

1969, Jan. 8   Photo.   *Perf. 13½*
1006 A200 2s Tarsier   .40 .25
1007 A200 10s Tamarau   .60 .25
1008 A200 20s Carabao   .80 .25
1009 A200 75s Mouse deer   2.50 .75
    Nos. 1006-1009 (4)   4.30 1.50
Opening of the hunting season.

Emilio Aguinaldo and Historical Building, Cavite A201

1969, Jan. 23   Litho.   *Perf. 14*
1010 A201 10s yel & multi   .40 .25
1011 A201 40s bl & multi   .80 .30
1012 A201 70s multi   1.20 .70
    Nos. 1010-1012 (3)   2.40 1.25
Emilio Aguinaldo (1869-1964), commander of Filipino forces in rebellion against Spain.

Guard Turret, San Andres Bastion, Manila, and Rotary Emblem A202

1969, Jan. 29   Photo.   *Perf. 12½*
1013 A202 10s ultra & multi   .50 .25
    Nos. 1013,C96-C97 (3)   2.20 1.00
50th anniv. of the Manila Rotary Club.

Senator Claro M. Recto (1890-1960), Lawyer and Supreme Court Judge — A203

1969, Feb. 8   Engr.   *Perf. 13*
1014 A203 10s bright rose lilac   .50 .25

No. 973 Overprinted

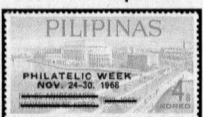

1969, Feb. 14   Litho.   *Perf. 14x13½*
1015 A190 4s multi & blk   .50 .25
Philatelic Week, Nov. 24-30, 1968.

José Rizal College, Mandaluyong A204

1969, Feb. 19   Photo.   *Perf. 13*
1016 A204 10s multicolored   .30 .25
1017 A204 40s multicolored   .45 .25
1018 A204 50s multicolored   .90 .30
    Nos. 1016-1018 (3)   1.65 .80
Founding of Rizal College, 50th anniv.

No. 948 Surcharged in Red

1969, May 10   Litho.   *Perf. 13x12½*
1019 A183 5s on 6s multi   .50 .25

A205

Map of Philippines, Red Crescent, Cross, Lion and Sun emblems.

1969, May 26   Photo.   *Perf. 12½*
1020 A205 10s gray, ultra & red   .30 .25
1021 A205 40s lt ultra, dk bl & red   .45 .30
1022 A205 75s bister, brn & red   .85 .35
    Nos. 1020-1022 (3)   1.60 .90
League of Red Cross Societies, 50th anniv.

A206

Pres. and Mrs. Marcos harvesting miracle rice.

1969, June 12   Photo.   *Perf. 14*
1023 A206 10s multicolored   .40 .25
1024 A206 40s multicolored   .50 .30
1025 A206 75s multicolored   1.10 .35
    Nos. 1023-1025 (3)   2.00 .90
Introduction of IR8 (miracle) rice, produced by the International Rice Research Institute.

Holy Child of Leyte and Map of Leyte A207

1969, June 30   *Perf. 13½*
1026 A207 5s emerald & multi   .40 .25
1027 A207 10s crimson & multi   .40 .25
80th anniv. of the return of the image of the Holy Child of Leyte to Tacloban. See No. C98.

Philippine Development Bank — A208

1969, Sept. 12   Photo.   *Perf. 13½*
1028 A208 10s dk bl, blk & grn   .30 .25
1029 A208 40s rose car, blk & grn   .85 .45
1030 A208 75s brown, blk & grn   1.35 .55
    Nos. 1028-1030 (3)   2.50 1.25
Inauguration of the new building of the Philippine Development Bank in Makati, Rizal.

Common Birdwing — A209

Butterflies: 20s, Tailed jay. 30s, Red Helen. 40s, Birdwing.

1969, Sept. 15   Photo.   *Perf. 13½*
1031 A209 10s multicolored   .60 .25
1032 A209 20s multicolored   1.40 .25
1033 A209 30s multicolored   1.40 .35
1034 A209 40s multicolored   1.40 .45
    Nos. 1031-1034 (4)   4.80 1.30

World's Children and UNICEF Emblem A210

1969, Oct. 6
1035 A210 10s blue & multi   .30 .25
1036 A210 20s multicolored   .35 .25
1037 A210 30s multicolored   .40 .25
    Nos. 1035-1037 (3)   1.05 .75
15th anniversary of Universal Children's Day.

Monument and Leyte Landing — A211

1969, Oct. 20   *Perf. 13½x14*
1038 A211 5s lt grn & multi   .30 .25
1039 A211 10s yellow & multi   .40 .25
1040 A211 40s pink & multi   .60 .25
    Nos. 1038-1040 (3)   1.30 .75
25th anniv. of the landing of the US forces under Gen. Douglas MacArthur on Leyte, Oct. 20, 1944.

Philippine Cultural Center, Manila — A212

1969, Nov. 4   Photo.   *Perf. 13½*
1041 A212 10s ultra   .30 .25
1042 A212 30s brt rose lilac   .60 .25
Cultural Center of the Philippines, containing theaters, a museum and libraries.

Nos. 889-892 Surcharged or Overprinted: "1969 PHILATELIC WEEK"

1969, Nov. 24   Photo.   *Perf. 14*
1043 A164 5s multicolored   .45 .25
1044 A164 5s on 6s multi   .45 .25
1045 A164 10s multicolored   .45 .25
1046 A164 10s on 20s multi   .45 .25
    a.   Block of 4, #1043-1046   2.75 1.75
Philatelic Week, Nov. 23-29.

Melchora Aquino — A213

1969, Nov. 30   *Perf. 12½*
1047 A213 10s multicolored   .30 .25
1048 A213 20s multicolored   .30 .25
1049 A213 30s dk bl & multi   .50 .25
    Nos. 1047-1049 (3)   1.10 .75
Melchora Aquino (Tandang Sora; 1812-1919), the Grand Old Woman of the Revolution.

No. 950 Surcharged with New Value, 2 Bars and: "PASINAYA, IKA -2 PANUNUNGKULAN / PANGULONG FERDINAND E. MARCOS / DISYEMBRE 30, 1969"
Type I dash> Text has serifs. Type II dash> Text has no serifs.

1969, Dec. 30   Litho.   *Perf. 12½*
1050 A184 5s on 6s multi   .55 .25
    a.   Type II   1.25 .50
    b.   Double overprint   40.00
    c.   Double impression of blue   25.00
Inauguration of Pres. Marcos and Vice Pres. Fernando Lopez for 2nd term, 12/30.

Pouring Ladle and Iligan Steel Mills A214

1970, Jan. 20   Photo.   *Perf. 13½*
1051 A214 10s ver & multi   .50 .25
1052 A214 20s multicolored   .80 .25
1053 A214 30s ultra & multi   .80 .25
    Nos. 1051-1053 (3)   2.10 .75
Iligan Integrated Steel Mills, Northern Mindanao, the first Philippine steel mills.

Nos. 857A, 904 and 906 Surcharged with New Value and Two Bars

1970, Apr. 30   As Before
1054 A158 4s on 6s peacock bl   .50 .25
1055 A169 5s on 6s multi   .85 .25
1056 A170 5s on 6s pur & gold   .85 .25
    a.   Double overprint   25.00
    Nos. 1054-1056 (3)   2.20 .75

New UPU Headquarters and Monument, Bern — A215

    Perf. 13½
1970, May 20   Unwmk.   Photo.
1057 A215 10s bl, dk bl & yel   .30 .25
1058 A215 30s lt grn, dk bl & yel   .50 .25
Opening of the new UPU Headquarters in Bern.

Emblem, Mayon Volcano and Filipina A216

1970, Sept. 6   Photo.   *Perf. 13½x14*
1059 A216 10s brt blue & multi   .30 .25
1060 A216 20s multicolored   .35 .25
1061 A216 30s multicolored   .50 .25
    Nos. 1059-1061 (3)   1.15 .75
15th International Conference on Social Welfare, Manila, Sept. 6-12.

Crab, by Alexander Calder, and Map of Philippines A217

1970, Oct. 5   *Perf. 13x13½*
1062 A217 10s emerald & multi   .30 .25
1063 A217 40s multicolored   .45 .25
1064 A217 50s ultra & multi   .65 .45
    Nos. 1062-1064 (3)   1.40 .95
Campaign against cancer.

Scaled Tridacna — A218

Sea Shells: 10s, Royal spiny oyster. 20s, Venus comb. 40s, Glory of the sea.

1970, Oct. 19   Photo.   Perf. 13½
1065 A218 5s black & multi   .50   .25
1066 A218 10s dk grn & multi   1.00   .25
1067 A218 20s multicolored   1.00   .30
1068 A218 40s dk blue & multi   1.75   .50
      Nos. 1065-1068 (4)   4.25 1.30

Nos. 922, 953 and 955 Surcharged

Photogravure; Lithographed
1970, Oct. 26   Perf. 13½, 12½
1069 A175 4s on 6s multi   .85   .25
1070 A185 4s on 6s multi   1.20   .25
1071 A186 4s on 6s multi   1.25   .25
      Nos. 1069-1071 (3)   3.30   .75

On No. 1070, old denomination is obliterated by two bars.
One line surcharge on No. 1071.

Map of Philippines and
FAPA Emblem — A219

1970, Nov. 16   Photo.   Perf. 13½
1072 A219 10s dp org & multi   .30   .25
1073 A219 50s lt violet & multi   .75   .25

Opening of the 4th General Assembly of the Federation of Asian Pharmaceutical Assoc. (FAPA) & the 3rd Asian Cong. of Pharmaceutical Sciences.

Hundred Islands of Pangasinan, Peddler's Cart — A220

20s, Tree house in Pasonanca Park, Zamboanga City. 30s, Sugar industry, Negros Island, Mt. Kanlaon, Woman & Carabao statue, symbolizing agriculture. 2p, Miagao Church, Iloilo, & horse-drawn calesa.

1970, Nov. 12   Perf. 12½x13½
1074 A220 10s multicolored   .30   .25
1075 A220 20s multicolored   .50   .25
1076 A220 30s multicolored   1.00   .30
1077 A220 2p multicolored   3.00 1.00
      Nos. 1074-1077 (4)   4.80 1.80

Tourist publicity. See Nos. 1086-1097.

No. 884 Surcharged: "UPU-AOPU / Regional Seminar / Nov. 23-Dec. 5, 1970 / TEN 10s"
1970, Nov. 22   Photo.   Perf. 13½x13
1078 A162 10s on 6s multi   .60   .50

Universal Postal Union and Asian-Oceanic Postal Union Regional Seminar, 11/23-12/5.

No. 915 Surcharged Vertically: "1970 PHILATELIC WEEK"
Perf. 14½x14
1970, Nov. 22   Wmk. 233
1079 A173 10s on 6s multi   .50   .25

Philatelic Week, Nov. 22-28.
Exists imperf. Value, $60.

Pope Paul VI, Map of Far East and Australia A221

Perf. 13½x14
1970, Nov. 27   Photo.   Unwmk.
1080 A221 10s ultra & multi   .40   .25
1081 A221 30s multicolored   .70   .25
      Nos. 1080-1081,C99 (3)   2.10   .80

Visit of Pope Paul VI, Nov. 27-29, 1970.

Mariano Ponce — A222

1970, Dec. 30   Engr.   Perf. 14½
1082 A222 10s rose carmine   .45   .25

Mariano Ponce (1863-1918), editor and legislator. See #1136-1137. For surcharges & overprint see #1190, 1231, O70.

PATA Emblem A223

1971, Jan. 21   Photo.   Perf. 14½
1083 A223 5s brt green & multi   .35   .25
1084 A223 10s blue & multi   .35   .25
1085 A223 70s brown & multi   1.00   .35
      Nos. 1083-1085 (3)   1.85

Pacific Travel Association (PATA), 20th annual conference, Manila, Jan. 21-29.

Tourist Type of 1970

Designs: 10s, Filipina and Ang Nayong (7 village replicas around man-made lagoon). 20s, Woman and fisherman, Estancia. 30s, Pagsanjan Falls. 5p, Watch Tower, Punta Cruz, Boho.

Perf. 12½x13½
1971, Feb. 15   Photo.
1086 A220 10s multicolored   .40   .25
1087 A220 20s multicolored   .50   .30
1088 A220 30s multicolored   1.20   .35
1089 A220 5p multicolored   3.50 1.75
      Nos. 1086-1089 (4)   5.60 2.65

1971, Apr. 19
Designs: 10s, Cultured pearl farm, Davao. 20s, Coral divers, Davao, Mindanao. 40s, Moslem Mosque, Zamboanga. 1p, Rice terraces, Banaue.
1090 A220 10s multicolored   .30   .25
1091 A220 20s multicolored   .50   .30
1092 A220 40s multicolored   1.20   .35
1093 A220 1p multicolored   2.50   .80
      Nos. 1090-1093 (4)   4.50 1.70

1971, May 3
10s, Spanish cannon, Zamboanga. 30s, Magellan's cross, Cebu City. 50s, Big Jar monument in Calamba, Laguna. 70s, Mayon Volcano, Legazpi city.
1094 A220 10s multicolored   .30   .25
1095 A220 30s multicolored   .50   .25
1096 A220 50s multicolored   1.20   .25
1097 A220 70s multicolored   1.40   .35
      Nos. 1094-1097 (4)   3.40 1.10

 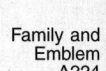

Family and Emblem A224

1971, Mar. 21   Photo.   Perf. 13½
1098 A224 20s lt grn & multi   .30   .25
1099 A224 40s pink & multi   .40   .25

Regional Conf. of the Intl. Planned Parenthood Federation for SE Asia & Oceania, Baguio City, Mar. 21-27.

No. 955 Surcharged

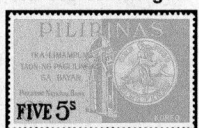

1971, June 10   Photo.   Perf. 14x13½
1100 A186 5s on 6s multi   .80   .25

Allegory of Law — A225

1971, June 15   Photo.   Perf. 13
1101 A225 15s orange & multi   .50   .30

60th anniversary of the University of the Philippines Law College. See No. C100.

Manila Anniversary Emblem — A226

1971, June 24
1102 A226 10s multicolored   .50   .35
Founding of Manila, 400th anniv. See #C101.

Santo Tomas University, Arms of Schools of Medicine and Pharmacology A227

1971, July 8   Photo.   Perf. 13½
1103 A227 5s yellow & multi   .50   .35

Centenary of the founding of the Schools of Medicine and Surgery, and Pharmacology at the University of Santo Tomas, Manila. See No. C102.

No. 957 Surcharged

1971, July 11   Wmk. 233   Perf. 14½
1104 A187 5s on 6s multi   .50   .25
  a.   Inverted overprint   12.00
  b.   Double overprint   20.00

World Congress of University Presidents, Manila.

Our Lady of Guia Appearing to Filipinos and Spanish Soldiers A228

1971, July 8   Photo.   Perf. 13½
1105 A228 10s multi   .30   .25
1106 A228 75s multi   1.20   .35

4th centenary of appearance of the statue of Our Lady of Guia, Ermita, Manila.

Bank Building, Plane, Car and Workers A229

1971, Sept. 14   Perf. 12½
1107 A229 10s blue & multi   .30   .25
1108 A229 30s lt grn & multi   .30   .25
1109 A229 1p multicolored   .90   .35
      Nos. 1107-1109 (3)   1.50   .85

1st Natl. City Bank in the Philippines, 70th anniv.

No. 944 Surcharged

Perf. 12x11
1971, Nov. 24   Engr.   Unwmk.
1110 A182 4s on 6s blue   .35   .25
1111 A182 5s on 6s blue   .40   .25

No. 957 Surcharged

Wmk. 233
1971, Nov. 24   Photo.   Perf. 14½
1112 A187 5s on 6s multi   .55   .25

Philatelic Week, 1971.

Radar with Map of Far East and Oceania A230

1972, Feb. 29   Photo.   Perf. 14x14½
1113 A230 5s org yel & multi   .30   .25
1114 A230 40s red org & multi   .55   .25

Electronics Conferences, Manila, 12/1-7/71.

Fathers Gomez, Burgos and Zamora — A231

1972, Apr. 3   Perf. 13x12½
1115 A231 5s gold & multi   .40   .25
1116 A231 60s gold & multi   1.00   .25

Centenary of the deaths of Fathers Mariano Gomez, José Burgos and Jacinto Zamora, martyrs for Philippine independence from Spain.

Digestive Tract — A232

1972, Apr. 11   Photo.   Perf. 12½x13
1117 A232 20s ultra & multi   .60   .25

4th Asian Pacific Congress of Gastroenterology, Manila, Feb. 5-12. See No. C103.

No. 953 Surcharged

1972, Apr. 20   Perf. 12½
1118 A185 5s on 6s multi   1.20   .25

No. O69 with Two Bars over "G." and "O."
1972, May 16   Engr.   Perf. 13½
1119 A158 50s violet   1.20   .25

Nos. 883A, 909 and 929 Surcharged with New Value and 2 Bars

1972, May 29
1120	A161	10s on 6s dp cl & blk	1.20	.25
1121	A171	10s on 6s multi	1.20	.25
a.		Inverted surcharge	20.00	
1122	A177	10s on 6s multi	1.00	.25
		Nos. 1120-1122 (3)	3.40	.75

During the production of No. 1121 some sheets of No. 911 were mixed with those of No. 909 and surcharged. Value for No. 911 surcharged 10s, $30 unused.

Independence Monument, Manila — A233

1972, May 31 Photo. Perf. 13x12½
1123	A233	5s brt blue & multi	.30	.25
1124	A233	50s red & multi	.80	.25
1125	A233	60s emerald & multi	1.10	.25
		Nos. 1123-1125 (3)	2.20	.75

Visit ASEAN countries (Association of South East Asian Nations).

"K," Skull and Crossbones A234

Development of Philippine Flag: No. 1126, 3 "K's" in a row ("K" stands for Katipunan). No. 1127, 3 "K's" as triangle. No. 1128, One "K." No. 1130, 3 "K's," sun over mountain on white triangle. No. 1131, Sun over 3 "K's." No. 1132, Tagalog "K" in sun. No. 1133, Sun with human face. No. 1134, Tricolor flag, forerunner of present flag. No. 1135, Present flag. Nos. 1126, 1128, 1130-1131, 1133, 1135 inscribed in Tagalog.

1972, June 12 Photo. Perf. 13
1126	A234	30s ultra & red	2.00	.30
1127	A234	30s ultra & red	2.00	.30
1128	A234	30s ultra & red	2.00	.30
1129	A234	30s ultra & blk	2.00	.30
1130	A234	30s ultra & red	2.00	.30
1131	A234	30s ultra & red	2.00	.30
1132	A234	30s ultra & red	2.00	.30
1133	A234	30s ultra & red	2.00	.30
1134	A234	30s ultra, red & blk	2.00	.30
1135	A234	30s ultra, yel & red	2.00	.30
a.		Block of 10	25.00	10.00

Portrait Type of 1970

40s, Gen. Miguel Malvar. 1p, Julian Felipe.

1972 Engr. Perf. 14
1136	A222	40s rose red	.55	.25
1137	A222	1p deep blue	1.20	.25

Honoring Gen. Miguel Malvar (1865-1911), revolutionary leader, and Julian Felipe (1861-1944), composer of Philippine national anthem.

Issue dates: 40s, July 10; 1p, June 26.

Parrotfish — A235

1972, Aug. 14 Photo. Perf. 13
1138	A235	5s shown	.40	.25
1139	A235	10s Sunburst butterflyfish	1.25	.25
1140	A235	20s Moorish idol	1.40	.30
		Nos. 1138-1140,C104 (4)	4.80	1.40

Tropical fish.

Development Bank of the Philippines — A236

1972, Sept. 12
1141	A236	10s gray blue & multi	.30	.25
1142	A236	20s lilac & multi	.35	.25
1143	A236	60s tan & multi	.45	.25
		Nos. 1141-1143 (3)	1.10	.75

Development Bank of the Philippines, 25th anniv.

Pope Paul VI — A237

1972, Sept. 26 Unwmk. Perf. 14
1144	A237	10s lt green & multi	.50	.25
1145	A237	50s lt violet & multi	1.00	.30
		Nos. 1144-1145,C105 (3)	2.50	.95

First anniversary (in 1971) of the visit of Pope Paul VI to the Philippines, and for his 75th birthday.

Nos. 880, 899 and 925 Surcharged with New Value and 2 Bars

1972, Sept. 29 As Before
1146	A161	10s on 6s lil & blk	1.10	.25
a.		Inverted overprint	20.00	
1147	A167	10s on 6s multi	1.10	.25
a.		Inverted overprint	20.00	
1148	A176	10s on 6s multi	.90	.25
a.		Inverted overprint	15.00	
		Nos. 1146-1148 (3)	3.10	.75

Charon's Bark, by Resurrección Hidalgo — A238

Paintings: 10s, Rice Workers' Meal, by F. Amorsolo. 30s, "Spain and the Philippines," by Juan Luna, vert. 70s, Song of Maria Clara, by F. Amorsolo.

Perf. 14x13

1972, Oct. 16 Unwmk. Photo.

Size: 38x40mm
1149	A238	5s silver & multi	.50	.25
1150	A238	5s silver & multi	.50	.30

Size: 24x56mm
1151	A238	30s silver & multi	1.00	.35

Size: 38x40mm
1152	A238	70s silver & multi	1.00	.40
		Nos. 1149-1152 (4)	3.00	1.30

25th anniversary of the organization of the Stamp and Philatelic Division.

Lamp, Nurse, Emblem A239

1972, Oct. 22 Perf. 12½x13½
1153	A239	5s violet & multi	.30	.25
1154	A239	10s blue & multi	.35	.25
1155	A239	70s orange & multi	.60	.25
		Nos. 1153-1155 (3)	1.25	.75

Philippine Nursing Association, 50th anniv.

Heart, Map of Philippines — A240

1972, Oct. 24 Perf. 13
1156	A240	5s pur, emer & red	.30	.25
1157	A240	10s blue, emer & red	.35	.25
1158	A240	30s emerald, bl & red	.45	.25
		Nos. 1156-1158 (3)	1.10	.75

"Your heart is your health," World Health Month.

First Mass on Limasawa, by Carlos V. Francisco A241

1972, Oct. 31 Perf. 14
1159	A241	10s brown & multi	.50	.25

450th anniversary of the first mass in the Philippines, celebrated by Father Valderama on Limasawa, Mar. 31, 1521. See No. C106.

Nos. 878, 882, 899 Surcharged: "ASIA PACIFIC SCOUT CONFERENCE NOV. 1972"

1972, Nov. 13 As Before
1160	A161	10s on 6s bl & blk	.90	.25
1161	A161	10s on 6s grn & blk	1.25	.30
1162	A167	10s on 6s multi	1.25	.50
		Nos. 1160-1162 (3)	3.40	1.10

Asia Pacific Scout Conference, Nov. 1972.

Torch, Olympic Emblems A242

Perf. 12½x13½

1972, Nov. 15 Photo.
1163	A242	5s blue & multi	.35	.25
1164	A242	10s multicolored	.50	.25
1165	A242	70s orange & multi	1.15	.40
		Nos. 1163-1165 (3)	2.00	.90

20th Olympic Games, Munich, 8/26-9/11. For surcharges see Nos. 1297, 1758-1760.

Nos. 896 and 919 Surcharged with New Value, Two Bars and: "1972 PHILATELIC WEEK"

1972, Nov. 23 Photo. Perf. 13½
1166	A166	10s on 6s multi	.65	1.50
1167	A174	10s on 6s multi	.65	1.50

Philatelic Week 1972.

Manunggul Burial Jar, 890-710 B.C. — A243

#1169, Ngipet Duldug Cave ritual earthenware vessel, 155 B.C. #1170, Metal age chalice, 200-600 A.D. #1171, Earthenware vessel, 15th cent.

1972, Nov. 29
1168	A243	10s green & multi	.50	.25
1169	A243	10s lilac & multi	.50	.25
1170	A243	10s blue & multi	.50	.25
1171	A243	10s yellow & multi	.50	.25
		Nos. 1168-1171 (4)	2.00	1.00

College of Pharmacy and Univ. of the Philippines Emblems A244

1972, Dec. 11 Perf. 12½x13½
1172	A244	5s lt vio & multi	.35	.25
1173	A244	10s yel grn & multi	.35	.25
1174	A244	30s ultra & multi	.50	.25
		Nos. 1172-1174 (3)	1.20	.75

60th anniversary of the College of Pharmacy of the University of the Philippines.

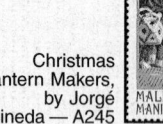

Christmas Lantern Makers, by Jorgé Pineda — A245

1972, Dec. 14 Photo. Perf. 12½
1175	A245	10s dk bl & multi	.40	.25
1176	A245	30s brown & multi	.80	.30
1177	A245	50s green & multi	1.75	.35
		Nos. 1175-1177 (3)	2.95	.90

Christmas 1972.

Red Cross Flags, Pres. Roxas and Mrs. Aurora Quezon — A246

1972, Dec. 21
1178	A246	5s ultra & multi	.30	.25
1179	A246	20s multicolored	.40	.25
1180	A246	30s brown & multi	.50	.25
		Nos. 1178-1180 (3)	1.20	.75

25th anniv. of the Philippine Red Cross.

Nos. 894 and 936 Surcharged with New Value and 2 Bars

1973, Jan. 22 Photo. Perf. 14, 13
1181	A165	10s on 6s multi	.65	.25
a.		Double overprint	20.00	
1182	A180	10s on 6s multi	.65	.25
a.		Double overprint	20.00	

San Luis University, Luzon A247

1973, Mar. 1 Photo. Perf. 13½x14
1183	A247	5s multicolored	.35	.25
1184	A247	10s yellow & multi	.40	.25
1185	A247	75s multicolored	.60	.25
		Nos. 1183-1185 (3)	1.35	.75

60th anniversary of San Luis University, Baguio City, Luzon. For surcharge see No. 1305.

Jesus Villamor and Fighter Planes A248

1973, Apr. 9 Photo. Perf. 13½x14
1186	A248	10s multicolored	.40	.25
1187	A248	2p multicolored	1.60	.70

Col. Jesus Villamor (1914-1971), World War II aviator who fought for liberation of the Philippines. For surcharge see No. 1230.

Nos. 932, 957, O70 Surcharged with New Values and 2 Bars

1973, Apr. 23   *As Before*
1188 A178 5s on 6s multi   1.10 1.10
1189 A187 5s on 6s multi   1.10 .40
  a. Inverted overprint   20.00
1190 A222 15s on 10s rose car   .80 .25
  Nos. 1188-1190 (3)   3.00 1.75

Two additional bars through "G.O." on No. 1190.

ITI Emblem, Performance and Actor Vic Silayan A249

1973, May 15   **Photo.**   *Perf. 13x12½*
1191 A249 5s blue & multi   .30 .25
1192 A249 10s yel grn & multi   .30 .25
1193 A249 50s orange & multi   .60 .30
1194 A249 70s rose & multi   .80 .35
  Nos. 1191-1194 (4)   2.00 1.15

1st Third World Theater Festival, sponsored by the UNESCO affiliated International Theater Institute, Manila, Nov. 19-30, 1971.
For surcharge see No. 1229.

Josefa Llanes Escoda — A250

#1196, Gabriela Silang. No. 1197, Rafael Palma. 30s, Jose Rizal. 60s, Marcela Agoncillo. 90s, Teodoro R. Yangco. 1.10p, Dr. Pio Valenzuela. 1.20p, Gregoria de Jesus. #1204, Pedro A. Paterno. #1205, Teodora Alonso. 1.80p, Edilberto Evangelista. 5p, Fernando M. Guerrero.

1973-78   **Engr.**   *Perf. 14½*
1195 A250 15s sepia   .30 .25
  Litho.   *Perf. 12½*
1196 A250 15s violet ('74)   .50 .25
  b. Wmk. 372   5.00 2.00
1197 A273 15s emerald ('74)   .40 .25
  b. Wmk. 372   7.00 2.00
1198 A250 30s vio bl ('78)   .40 .25
1199 A250 60s dl red brn   1.00 .40
1200 A273 90s brt bl ('74)   1.00 .40
1202 A273 1.10p brt bl ('74)   1.50 .45
  b. Wmk. 372   5.00 3.00
1203 A250 1.20p dl red ('78)   1.20 .45
1204 A250 1.50p lil rose   2.50 1.50
1205 A273 1.50p brown ('74)   2.00 .40
  b. Wmk. 372   10.00 3.50
1206 A250 1.80p green   3.50 2.00
1208 A250 5p blue   7.00 4.00
  Nos. 1195-1208 (12)   21.30 10.60

1973-74   *Imperf.*
1196a A250 15s violet ('74)   1.25 1.00
1197a A273 15s emerald ('74)   1.25 1.00
1198a A250 60s dull red brown   3.50 2.00
1200a A273 90s bright blue ('74)   3.00 2.00
1202a A273 1.10p bright blue ('74)   4.00 3.00
1204a A250 1.50p lilac rose   5.00 3.50
1205a A273 1.50p brown ('74)   4.00 3.50
1206a A250 1.80p green   6.00 4.00
1208a A250 5p blue   13.00 4.00
  Nos. 1196a-1208a (9)   41.00 24.00

Honoring: Escoda (1898-194?), leader of Girl Scouts and Federation of Women's Clubs. Silang (1731-63), "the Ilocana Joan of Arc". Palma (1874-1939), journalist, statesman, educator. Rizal (1861-96), natl. hero. Agoncillo (1859-1946), designer of 1st Philippine flag, 1898. Yangco (1861-1939), patriot and philanthropist. Valenzuela (1869-1956), physician and newspaperman.
Gregoria de Jesus, independence leader. Paterno (1857-1911), lawyer, writer, patriot. Alonso (1827-1911), mother of Rizal. Evangelista (1862-97), army engineer, patriot. Guerrero (1873-1929), journalist, political leader.
For overprint & surcharges see #1277, 1310, 1311, 1470, 1518, 1562..

No. 946 surcharged with New Value

1973, June 4   **Engr.**   *Perf. 13½*
1209 A158 5s on 6s pck blue   .75 .25

Anti-smuggling campaign.

No. 925 Surcharged

1973, June 4   **Wmk. 233**
1210 A176 5s on 6s multi   .75 .25
  a. Inverted overprint   20.00
  b. Double overprint   20.00

10th anniv. of death of John F. Kennedy.

Pres. Marcos, Farm Family, Unfurling of Philippine Flag — A251

1973, Sept. 24   **Photo.**   **Unwmk.**
  Perf. 12½x13½
1211 A251 15s ultra & multi   .40 .30
1212 A251 45s red & multi   .70 .40
1213 A251 90s multi   1.20 .50
  Nos. 1211-1213 (3)   2.30 1.20

75th anniversary of Philippine independence and 1st anniversary of proclamation of martial law.
First day covers exist dated Sept. 21, 1973.

Imelda Romualdez Marcos, First Lady of the Philippines — A252

1973, Oct. 31   **Photo.**   *Perf. 13*
1214 A252 15s dl bl & multi   .40 .30
1215 A252 50s multicolored   .70 .40
1216 A252 60s lil & multi   .90 .40
  Nos. 1214-1216 (3)   2.00 1.10

Presidential Palace, Manila, Pres. and Mrs. Marcos A253

1973, Nov. 15   **Litho.**   *Perf. 14*
1217 A253 15s rose & multi   .40 .30
1218 A253 50s ultra & multi   .80 .40
  Nos. 1217-1218,C107 (3)   2.40 1.05

INTERPOL Emblem — A254

1973, Dec. 18   **Photo.**   *Perf. 13*
1219 A254 15s ultra & multi   .40 .25
1220 A254 65s lt grn & multi   .60 .25

Intl. Criminal Police Organization, 50th anniv.

Cub and Boy Scouts — A255

15s, Various Scout activities; inscribed in Tagalog.

1973, Dec. 28   **Litho.**   *Perf. 12½*
1221 A255 15s bister & emer   .70 .50
  a. Imperf, pair ('74)   4.00 3.00
1222 A255 65s bister & brt bl   1.30 .50
  a. Imperf, pair ('74)   6.00 5.00

50th anniv. of Philippine Boy Scouts. Nos. 1221a-1222a issued Feb. 4, although first day covers are dated Dec. 28, 1973.

Manila, Bank Emblem and Farmers A256

Designs: 60s, Old bank building. 1.50p, Modern bank building.

1974, Jan. 3   **Photo.**   *Perf. 12½x13½*
1223 A256 15s silver & multi   .30 .25
1224 A256 60s silver & multi   .50 .25
1225 A256 1.50p silver & multi   1.20 .40
  Nos. 1223-1225 (3)   2.00 .90

Central Bank of the Philippines, 25th anniv.

UPU Emblem, Maria Clara Costume — A257

Filipino Costumes: 60s, Balintawak and UPU emblem. 80s, Malong costume and UPU emblem.

1974, Jan. 15   *Perf. 12½*
1226 A257 15s multicolored   .30 .25
1227 A257 60s multicolored   .70 .30
1228 A257 80s multicolored   1.00 .40
  Nos. 1226-1228 (3)   2.00 .95

Centenary of Universal Postal Union.

No. 1192 Surcharged in Red with New Value, 2 Bars and: "1973 / PHILATELIC WEEK"

1974, Feb. 4   **Photo.**   *Perf. 13x12½*
1229 A249 15s on 10s multi   .80 .25

Philatelic Week, 1973. First day covers exist dated Nov. 26, 1973.

Nos. 1186 and 1136 Overprinted and Surcharged

1974, Mar. 25   **Photo.**   *Perf. 13½x14*
1230 A248 15s on 10s multi   .75 .25

  Engr.   *Perf. 14*
1231 A222 45s on 40s rose red   .75 .25

Lions Intl. of the Philippines, 25th anniv. The overprint on #1230 arranged to fit shape of stamp.

Pediatrics Congress Emblem and Map of Participating Countries — A258

1974, Apr. 30   **Litho.**   *Perf. 12½*
1232 A258 30s brt bl & red   .50 .25
  a. Imperf, pair   3.00 2.50
1233 A258 1p dl grn & red   1.20 .40
  a. Imperf, pair   5.50 4.50

Asian Congress of Pediatrics, Manila, Apr. 30-May 4.

Nos. 912, 954-955 Surcharged with New Value and Two Bars

1974, Aug. 1   *As Before*
1234 A172 5s on 3s multi   .80 .30
1235 A185 5s on 6s multi   1.00 .30
1236 A186 5s on 6s multi   1.20 .30
  Nos. 1234-1236 (3)   3.00 .90

WPY Emblem — A259

1974, Aug. 15   **Litho.**   *Perf. 12½*
1237 A259 5s org & bl blk   .40 .25
  a. Imperf, pair   2.00 1.50
1238 A259 2p lt grn & dk bl   2.00 .75
  a. Imperf, pair   11.00 8.50

World Population Year, 1974.

Red Feather Community Chest Emblem — A260

Wmk. 372
1974, Sept. 5   **Litho.**   *Perf. 12½*
1239 A260 15s brt bl & red   .35 .25
1240 A260 40s emer & red   .65 .25
1241 A260 45s red brn & red   .70 .25
  Nos. 1239-1241 (3)   1.70 .75

Philippine Community Chest, 25th anniv.

  Imperf. Pairs
1239a A260 15s   4.50 4.50
1240a A260 40s   3.00 2.00
1241a A260 45s   3.00 2.00
  Nos. 1239a-1241a (3)   10.50 8.50

Sultan Kudarat, Flag, Order and Map of Philippines A261

  Perf. 13½x14
1975, Jan. 13   **Photo.**   **Unwmk.**
1242 A261 15s multicolored   .50 .25

Sultan Mohammad Dipatuan Kudarat, 16th-17th century ruler.

Mental Health Association Emblem — A262

Wmk. 372
1975, Jan. 20   **Litho.**   *Perf. 12½*
1243 A262 45s emer & org   .45 .25
  a. Imperf, pair   2.00 1.50
1244 A262 1p emer & pur   .85 .30
  a. Imperf, pair   4.00 3.00

Philippine Mental Health Assoc., 25th anniv.

4-Leaf Clover — A263

1975, Feb. 14
1245 A263 15s vio bl & red   .45 .25
  a. Imperf, pair   2.50 2.00
1246 A263 50s emer & red   .85 .35
  a. Imperf, pair   5.00 4.00

Philippine Heart Center for Asia, inauguration.

Military Academy, Cadet and Emblem A264

  Perf. 13½x14
1975, Feb. 17   **Unwmk.**
1247 A264 15s grn & multi   .35 .25
1248 A264 45s plum & multi   .65 .25

Philippine Military Academy, 70th anniv.

Helping the Disabled A265

Perf. 12½, Imperf.

1975, Mar. 17   Wmk. 372
1249 A265 Block of 10   7.50   9.00
a.-j.   45s grn, any single   .55   .35

25th anniversary (in 1974) of Philippine Orthopedic Association.
For surcharge see No. 1635.
No. 1249 exists imperf. Value unused, $12.

Nos. B43, B50-B51 Surcharged with New Value and Two Bars

1975, Apr. 15   Unwmk.
1250 SP18   5s on 15s + 5s   .60   .25
1251 SP16   60s on 70s + 5s   1.00   .30
1252 SP18   1p on 1.10p + 5s   1.40   .60
a.   Double overprint   18.00
       Nos. 1250-1252 (3)   3.00   1.15

"Grow and Conserve Forests" A266

1975, May 19   Litho.   Perf. 14½
1253 45s "Grow"   .45   .25
1254 45s "Conserve"   .45   .25
a.   A267 Pair, #1253-1254   1.00   .75

Forest conservation.

Jade Vine — A268

1975, June 9   Photo.   Perf. 14½
1255 A268 15s multicolored   .40   .25

Imelda R. Marcos, IWY Emblem — A269

Wmk. 372
1975, July 2   Litho.   Perf. 12½
1256 A269 15s bl & blk   .50   .25
a.   Imperf, pair   3.00   2.50
1257 A269 80s pink, bl & grn   .70   .30
a.   Imperf, pair   7.00   5.00

International Women's Year 1975.
For surcharges see Nos. 1500, 1505.

Civil Service Emblem — A270

1975, Sept. 19   Litho.   Perf. 12½
1258 A270 15s multicolored   .50   .25
a.   Imperf, pair   3.00   2.25
1259 A270 50s multicolored   .70   .25
a.   Imperf, pair   4.50   3.75

Dam and Emblem — A271

1975, Sept. 30
1260 A271 40s org & vio bl   .60   .25
a.   Imperf, pair   2.50   2.00
1261 A271 1.50p brt rose & vio bl   1.20   .35
a.   Imperf, pair   6.00   5.00

For surcharges see Nos. 1517, 1520.

Manila Harbor, 1875 — A272

1975, Nov. 4   Unwmk.   Perf. 13x13½
1262 A272 1.50p red & multi   1.50   .50

Hong Kong and Shanghai Banking Corporation, centenary of Philippines service.

Norberto Romualdez (1875-1941), Scholar and Legislator A273

Jose Rizal Monument, Luneta Park — A273a

Noted Filipinos: No. 1264, Rafael Palma (1874-1939), journalist, statesman, educator. No. 1265, Rajah Kalantiaw, chief of Panay, author of ethical-penal code (1443). 65s, Emilio Jacinto (1875-1899), patriot. No. 1269, Gen. Gregorio del Pilar (1875-1899), military hero. No. 1270, Lope K. Santos (1879-1963), grammarian, writer. 1.60p, Felipe Agoncillo (1859-1941), lawyer, cabinet member.

Wmk. 372
1975-81   Litho.   Perf. 12½
1264 A273   30s brn ('77)   .60   .25
1265 A273   30s dp rose ('78)   .60   .25
1266 A273a   40s yel & blk
                      ('81)   .70   .30
1267 A273   60s violet   1.75   .35
a.   Imperf, pair   6.00   4.00
1268 A273   65s lilac rose   1.50   .50
a.   Imperf, pair   5.00   4.00
1269 A273   90s lilac rose   2.50   .75
a.   Imperf, pair   6.00   4.50
1270 A273   90s grn ('78)   1.50   .40
1272 A273   1.60p blk ('76)   3.25   .60
       Nos. 1264-1272 (8)   12.40   3.40

See #1195-1208. For overprint & surcharges see #1278, 1310, 1367, 1440, 1469, 1514, 1562, 1574, 1758-1760.

A274

1975, Nov. 22   Litho.   Perf. 12½
1275 A274 60s multicolored   .80   .50
1276 A274 1.50p multicolored   2.00   .60

1st landing of the Pan American World Airways China Clipper in the Philippines, 40th anniv.

Nos. 1199 and 1205 Overprinted

1975, Nov. 22   Unwmk.
1277 A250 60s dl red brn   .60   .30
1278 A273 1.50p brown   1.60   .40

Airmail Exhibition, Nov. 22-Dec. 9.

APO Emblem — A275

1975, Nov. 24   Wmk. 372
1279 A275 5s ultra & multi   .30   .25
a.   Imperf, pair   2.00   1.50
1280 A275 1p bl & multi   .90   .35
a.   Imperf, pair   6.00   5.00

Amateur Philatelists' Org., 25th anniv.

For surcharge see No. 1338.

A276

Philippine Churches: 20s, San Agustin Church. 30s, Morong Church, horiz. 45s, Basilica of Taal, horiz. 60s, San Sebastian Church.

1975, Dec. 23   Litho.   Perf. 12½
1281 A276 20s bluish grn   .50   .25
1282 A276 30s yel org & blk   .50   .25
a.   Horiz. pair, imperf. vert.   35.00
1283 A276 45s rose, brn &
                      blk   .75   .25
1284 A276 60s yel, bis & blk   1.25   .30
       Nos. 1281-1284 (4)   3.00   1.05

Holy Year 1975.

Imperf. Pairs
1281a A276   20s   2.50   2.00
1282a A276   30s   2.50   2.00
1283a A276   45s   4.00   3.50
1284a A276   60s   5.00   5.00
       Nos. 1281a-1284a (4)   16.00 12.50

Conductor's Hands — A277

1976, Jan. 27
1285 A277 5s org & multi   .40   .25
1286 A277 50s brt yel grn &
                      multi   .80   .30

Manila Symphony Orchestra, 50th anniv.

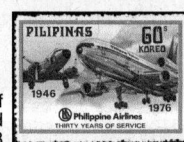
PAL Planes of 1946 and 1976 — A278

1976, Feb. 14
1287 A278 60s bl & multi   .80   .50
1288 A278 1.50p red & multi   2.20   .60

Philippine Airlines, 30th anniversary.

National University — A279

1976, Mar. 30
1289 A279 45s bl, vio bl & yel   .50   .25
1290 A279 60s lt bl, vio bl & pink .90   .25

National University, 75th anniversary.

Eye Exam — A280

1976, Apr. 7   Litho.   Perf. 12½
1291 A280 15s multicolored   .80   .35

World Health Day: "Foresight prevents blindness."

Book and Emblem — A281

1976, May 24   Unwmk.
1292 A281 1.50p grn & multi   1.50   .40

National Archives, 75th anniversary.

Santo Tomas University, Emblems A282

1976, June 7   Wmk. 372
1293 A282 15s yel & multi   .40   .25
1294 A282 50s multicolored   .90   .30

Colleges of Education and Science, Santo Tomas University, 50th anniversary.

Maryknoll College A283

Wmk. 372
1976, July 26   Perf. 12½
1295 A283 15s lt bl & multi   .50   .25
1296 A283 1.50p bis & multi   1.20   .40

Maryknoll College, Quezon City, 50th anniv.

No. 1164 Surcharged in Dark Violet

Perf. 12½x13½
1976, July 30   Photo.
1297 A242 15s on 10s multi   1.00   .50

21st Olympic Games, Montreal, Canada, July 17-Aug. 1.

Police College, Manila A284

1976, Aug. 8   Litho.   Perf. 12½
1298 A284 15s multicolored   .50   .25
a.   Imperf, pair   1.75   1.50
1299 A284 60s multicolored   1.00   .25
a.   Imperf, pair   5.75   5.00

Philippine Constabulary, 75th anniversary. Imperfs. issued on Oct. 14 1976.

Surveyors A285

1976, Sept. 2   Wmk. 372
1300 A285 80s multicolored   1.70   .40

Bureau of Lands, 75th anniversary.
No. 1300 exists imperf. Value for pair, $40.

Monetary Fund and World Bank Emblems — A286

1976, Oct. 4   **Litho.**   *Perf. 12½*
1301   A286   60s multicolored   .50   .40
   a.   Imperf. pair   50.00
1302   A286   1.50p multicolored   1.20   .60

Joint Annual Meeting of the Board of Governors of the International Monetary Fund and the World Bank, Manila, Oct. 4-8.
For surcharge see No. 1575.

Virgin of
Antipollo — A287

1976, Nov. 26   *Perf. 12½*
1303   A287   30s multicolored   .40   .25
1304   A287   90s multicolored   1.10   .30

Virgin of Antipolo, Our Lady of Peace and Good Voyage, 350th anniv. of arrival of statue in the Philippines and 50th anniv. of the canonical coronation.

**No. 1184 Surcharged with New
Value and 2 Bars and Overprinted:
"1976 PHILATELIC WEEK"**
Perf. 13½x14
1976, Nov. 26   **Photo.**   **Unwmk.**
1305   A247   30s on 10s multi   .75   .25

Philatelic Week 1976.

People Going
to
Church — A288

Wmk. 372
1976, Dec. 1   **Litho.**   *Perf. 12½*
1306   A288   15s bl & multi   .60   .35
1307   A288   30s bl & multi   1.20   .45

Christmas 1976.

Symbolic Diamond and
Book — A289

1976, Dec. 13
1308   A289   30s grn & multi   .50   .25
1309   A289   75s grn & multi   .85   .30

Philippine Educational System, 75th anniv.
Nos. 1308-1309 exist imperf. Value for pair, $40.

**No. 1202 and 1208 Surcharged with
New Value and 2 Bars**
1977, Jan. 17   **Unwmk.**
1310   A273   1.20p on 1.10p brt bl   1.20   .50
1311   A250   3p on 5p bl   3.00   .70

Galicano
Apacible — A290

Design: 30s, José Rizal.

1977   **Litho.**   **Wmk. 372**   *Perf. 12½*
1313   A290   30s multicolored   .35   .30
   a.   Horiz. pair, imperf. between   50.00
   b.   Horiz. pair, imperf. vertically   30.00
1318   A290   2.30p multicolored   1.75   .50

Dr. José Rizal (1861-1896) physician, poet and national hero (30s). Dr. Galicano Apacible (1864-1949), physician, statesman (2.30p).
Issue dates: 30s, Feb. 16; 2.30p, Jan. 24.

Emblem, Flags,
Map of
AOPU — A291

1977, Apr. 1   **Wmk. 372**
1322   A291   50s multicolored   .50   .40
1323   A291   1.50p multicolored   1.50   .60

Asian-Oceanic Postal Union (AOPU), 15th anniv.

Cogwheels and
Worker — A292

1977, Apr. 21   *Perf. 12½*
1324   A292   90s blk & multi   .70   .30
1325   A292   2.30p blk & multi   1.70   .60

Asian Development Bank, 10th anniversary.

Farmer at Work and
Receiving
Money — A293

1977, May 14   **Litho.**   **Wmk. 372**
1326   A293   30s org red & multi   .45   .30

National Commission on Countryside Credit and Collection, campaign to strengthen the rural credit system.

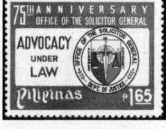

Solicitor
General's
Emblem — A294

1977, June 30   **Litho.**   *Perf. 12½*
1327   A294   1.65p multicolored   1.40   .35

Office of the Solicitor General, 75th anniv.
For surcharges see Nos. 1483, 1519.

Conference
Emblem — A295

1977, July 29   **Litho.**   *Perf. 12½*
1328   A295   2.20p bl & multi   1.50   .40

8th World Conference of the World Peace through Law Center, Manila, Aug. 21-26.
For surcharge see No. 1576.

ASEAN
Emblem — A296

1977, Aug. 8
1329   A296   1.50p grn & multi   1.75   .50
   a.   Horiz. pair, imperf. vertically   125.00

Association of South East Asian Nations (ASEAN), 10th anniversary.
For surcharge see No. 1559.

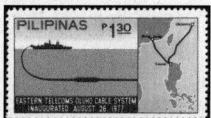

Cable-laying
Ship, Map
Showing
Cable Route
A297

1977, Aug. 26   **Litho.**   *Perf. 12½*
1330   A297   1.30p multicolored   1.20   .35

Inauguration of underwater telephone cable linking Okinawa, Luzon and Hong Kong.

President
Marcos
A298

1977, Sept. 11   **Wmk. 372**
1331   A298   30s multicolored   .60   .40
1332   A298   2.30p multicolored   1.75   .60

Ferdinand E. Marcos, president of the Philippines, 60th birthday.

People Raising
Flag — A299

1977, Sept. 21   **Litho.**   *Perf. 12½*
1333   A299   30s multicolored   .35   .25
1334   A299   2.30p multicolored   1.50   .45

5th anniversary of "New Society."

Bishop Gregorio
Aglipay — A300

1977, Oct. 1   **Litho.**   *Perf. 12½*
1335   A300   30s multicolored   .40   .25
1336   A300   90s multicolored   1.35   .30

Philippine Independent Aglipayan Church, 75th anniversary.

Fokker F VIIa
over World
Map — A301

1977, Oct. 28   **Wmk. 372**
1337   A301   2.30p multicolored   2.20   .50

First scheduled Pan American airmail service, Havana to Key West, 50th anniversary.

**No. 1280 Surcharged with New
Value, 2 Bars and Overprinted in
Red: "1977 / PHILATELIC / WEEK"**
1977, Nov. 22   **Litho.**   *Perf. 12½*
1338   A275   90s on 1p multi   1.20   *.50*

Philatelic Week.

Children Celebrating
and Star from
Lantern — A302

1977, Dec. 1   **Unwmk.**
1339   A302   30s multicolored   .50   .30
1340   A302   45s multicolored   .70   .40

Christmas 1977.

Scouts and Map
showing
Jamboree
Locations
A303

1977, Dec. 27
1341   A303   30s multicolored   .50   .25

National Boy Scout Jamboree, Tumauini, Isabela; Capitol Hills, Cebu City; Mariano Marcos, Davao, Dec. 27, 1977-Jan. 5, 1978.

Far Eastern
University
Arms — A304

1978, Jan. 26   **Litho.**   **Wmk. 372**
1342   A304   30s gold & multi   .50   .25

Far Eastern University, 50th anniversary.

Sipa — A305

Various positions of Sipa ball-game.

1978, Feb. 28   *Perf. 12½*
1343   A305   5s bl & multi   .30   .25
1344   A305   10s bl & multi   .30   .25
1345   A305   40s bl & multi   .40   .25
1346   A305   75s bl & multi   .75   .25
   a.   Block, #1343-1346   2.20   1.50

No. 1346a has continuous design.

Arms of
Meycauayan — A306

1978, Apr. 21   **Litho.**   *Perf. 12½*
1347   A306   1.05p multicolored   1.00   .30

Meycauayan, founded 1578-1579.
For surcharge see No. 1560.

Moro
Vinta
and UPU
Emblem
A307

2.50p, No. 1350b, Horse-drawn mail cart. No. 1350a, like 5p. No. 1350c, Steam locomotive. No. 1350d, Three-master.

1978, June 9   **Litho.**   *Perf. 13½*
1348   A307   2.50p multi   2.50   1.50
1349   A307   5p multi   3.50   2.00
   a.   Pair, #1348-1349   6.00   6.00
Souvenir Sheet
Perf. 12½x13
1350   Sheet of 4   20.00   20.00
   a.-d.   A307 7.50p, any single   4.25   4.00
   e.   Sheet, imperf   20.00   18.00

CAPEX International Philatelic Exhibition, Toronto, Ont., June 9-18. No. 1350 contains 36½x25mm stamps.
No. 1350 exists imperf. in changed colors.

Andres Bonifacio Monument, by Guillermo Tolentino A308

Wmk. 372
1978, July 10 **Litho.** *Perf. 12½*
1351 A308 30s multicolored .60 .30
   a. Imperf. pair 25.00

Rook, Knight and Globe — A309

1978, July 17
1352 A309 30s vio bl & red .50 .25
1353 A309 2p vio bl & red 1.50 .40

World Chess Championship, Anatoly Karpov and Viktor Korchnoi, Baguio City, 1978.

Miners — A310

1978, Aug. 12 **Litho.** *Perf. 12½*
1354 A310 2.30p multicolored 2.00 .40

Benguet gold mining industry, 75th anniv.

Manuel Quezon and Quezon Memorial — A311

1978, Aug. 19
1355 A311 30s multicolored .40 .30
1356 A311 1p multicolored 1.40 .50

Manuel Quezon (1878-1944), first president of Commonwealth of the Philippines.

Law Association Emblem, Philippine Flag — A312

1978, Aug. 27 **Litho.** *Perf. 12½*
1357 A312 2.30p multicolored 1.70 .40

58th Intl. Law Conf., Manila, 8/27-9/2.

Pres. Sergio Osmeña (1878-1961) — A313

1978, Sept. 8
1358 A313 30s multicolored .50 .30
1359 A313 1p multicolored 1.50 .50

For surcharge see No. 1501.

 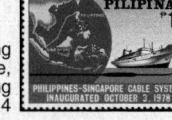

Map Showing Cable Route, Cablelaying Ship — A314

1978, Sept. 30
1360 A314 1.40p multicolored 1.40 .50

ASEAN Submarine Cable Network, Philippines-Singapore cable system, inauguration.

Basketball, Games' Emblem — A315

1978, Oct. 1
1361 A315 30s multicolored .50 .30
1362 A315 2.30p multicolored 2.00 .50

8th Men's World Basketball Championship, Manila, Oct. 1-15.

San Lazaro Hospital and Dr. Catalino Gavino — A316

1978, Oct. 13 **Litho.** *Perf. 12½*
1363 A316 50s multicolored .65 .25
   a. Vert. pair, imperf. horiz. 200.00
1364 A316 90s multicolored 1.20 .35

San Lazaro Hospital, 400th anniversary. For surcharge see No. 1512.

Nurse Vaccinating Child — A317

1978, Oct. 24
1365 A317 30s multicolored .50 .25
1366 A317 1.50p multicolored 1.70 .75

Eradication of smallpox.

No. 1268 Surcharged

1978, Nov. 23
1367 A273 60s on 65s lil rose .85 .25

Philatelic Week.

"The Telephone Across Country and World" — A318

Wmk. 372
1978, Nov. 28 **Litho.** *Perf. 12½*
1368 30s multicolored .40 .30
1369 2p multicolored 1.50 .40
   a. A318 Pair, #1368-1369 2.40 1.50

Philippine Long Distance Telephone Company, 50th anniversary.

Traveling Family — A320

1978, Nov. 28
1370 A320 30s multicolored .50 .25
1371 A320 1.35p multicolored 1.20 .30

Decade of Philippine children. For surcharges see Nos. 1504, 1561.

Church and Arms of Agoo — A321

1978, Dec. 7 **Litho.** *Perf. 12½*
1372 A321 30s multicolored .45 .25
1373 A321 45s multicolored .45 .25

400th anniversary of the founding of Agoo.

Church and Arms of Balayan — A322

1978, Dec. 8
1374 A322 30s multicolored .45 .25
1375 A322 90s multicolored .75 .30

400th anniv. of the founding of Balayan.

Dr. Honoria Acosta Sison (1888-1970), 1st Philippine Woman Physician — A323

1978, Dec. 15
1376 A323 30s multicolored .60 .30

Family, Houses, UN Emblem — A324

1978, Dec. 10 **Litho.** *Perf. 12½*
1377 A324 30s multicolored .50 .25
1378 A324 3p multicolored 2.00 .60

30th anniversary of Universal Declaration of Human Rights.

Chaetodon Trifasciatus A325

Fish: 1.20p, Balistoides niger. 2.20p, Rhinecanthus aculeatus. 2.30p, Chelmon rostratus. No. 1383, Chaetodon mertensi. No. 1384, Euxiphipops xanthometapon.

1978, Dec. 29 **Perf. 14**
1379 A325 30s multi .35 .30
1380 A325 1.20p multi 1.00 .40
1381 A325 2.20p multi 1.65 .50
1382 A325 2.30p multi 1.80 .50
1383 A325 5p multi 3.50 1.00
1384 A325 5p multi 3.50 1.00
   Nos. 1379-1384 (6) 11.80 3.70

A total of 500,000 sets of Nos. 1379-1384 were CTO Dec. 29, 1978. Value for CTO set, $2.50.

Carlos P. Romulo, UN Emblem — A326

1979, Jan. 14 **Litho.** *Perf. 12½*
1385 A326 30s multi .60 .30
1386 A326 2p multi 1.75 .70

Carlos P. Romulo (1899-1985), pres. of UN General Assembly and Security Council.

Rotary Emblem and "60" — A327

1979, Jan. 26 **Wmk. 372**
1387 A327 30s multi .50 .25
1388 A327 2.30p multi 1.50 .50

Rotary Club of Manila, 60th anniversary.

Rosa Sevilla de Alvero — A328

1979, Mar. 4 **Litho.** *Perf. 12½*
1389 A328 30 rose .60 .30

Rosa Sevilla de Alvero, educator and writer, birth centenary. For surcharges see Nos. 1479-1482.

Oil Well and Map of Palawan — A329

Wmk. 372
1979, Mar. 21 **Litho.** *Perf. 12½*
1390 A329 30s multi .50 .25
1391 A329 45s multi .65 .25

First Philippine oil production, Nido Oil Reef Complex, Palawan.

Merrill's Fruit Doves — A330

Birds: 1.20p, Brown tit babbler. 2.20p, Mindoro imperial pigeons. 2.30p, Steere's pittas. No. 1396, Koch's and red-breasted pittas. No. 1397, Philippine eared nightjar.

Perf. 14x13½
1979, Apr. 16 **Unwmk.**
1392 A330 30s multi .40 .30
1393 A330 1.20p multi *1.40* .50
1394 A330 2.20p multi 3.00 .75
1395 A330 2.30p multi 3.00 .75
1396 A330 5p multi 11.00 4.00
1397 A330 5p multi 11.00 4.00
   Nos. 1392-1397 (6) 29.80 10.30

A total of 500,000 sets of Nos. 1392-1397 were CTO April 16, 1979. Value for CTO set, $4.

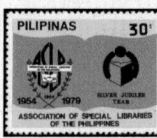

Association Emblem and Reader — A331

Wmk. 372
1979, Apr. 30 **Litho.** *Perf. 12½*
1398 A331 30s multi .35 .25
1399 A331 75s multi .85 .30
1400 A331 1p multi 1.10 .35
   Nos. 1398-1400 (3) 2.30 .90

Association of Special Libraries of the Philippines, 25th anniversary.

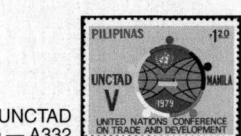

UNCTAD Emblem — A332

Wmk. 372
1979, May 3 **Litho.** *Perf. 12½*
1401 A332 1.20p multi .85 .30
1402 A332 2.30p multi 1.80 .50

5th Session of UN Conference on Trade and Development, Manila, May 3-June 1.

Civet Cat — A333

Philippine Animals: 1.20p, Macaque. 2.20p, Wild boar. 2.30p, Dwarf leopard. No. 1407, Asiatic dwarf otter. No. 1408, Anteater.

1979, May 14   **Perf. 14**
1403	A333	30s multi	.35	.30
1404	A333	1.20p multi	1.00	.40
1405	A333	2.20p multi	1.75	.50
1406	A333	2.30p multi	2.25	.50
1407	A333	5p multi	3.50	1.50
1408	A333	5p multi	3.50	1.50
	Nos. 1403-1408 (6)		12.35	4.70

A total of 500,000 sets of Nos. 1403-1408 were CTO May 20, 1979. Value for CTO set, $2.50.

Dish Antenna — A334

1979, May 17   **Perf. 12½**
1409	A334	90s shown	1.50	.30
1410	A334	1.30p World map	1.10	.40

11th World Telecommunications Day, 5/17.

Mussaenda Donna Evangelina A335

Philippine Mussaendas: 1.20p, Dona Esperanza. 2.20p, Dona Hilaria. 2.30p, Dona Aurora. No. 1415, Gining Imelda. No. 1416, Dona Trining.

1979, June 11   **Litho.**   **Perf. 14**
1411	A335	30s multi	.40	.30
1412	A335	1.20p multi	1.20	.40
1413	A335	2.20p multi	1.75	.50
1414	A335	2.30p multi	2.25	.50
1415	A335	5p multi	3.50	1.75
1416	A335	5p multi	3.50	1.75
	Nos. 1411-1416 (6)		12.60	5.20

A total of 500,000 sets of Nos. 1411-1416 were CTO June 15, 1979. Value for CTO set, $2.50.

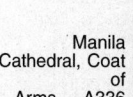

Manila Cathedral, Coat of Arms — A336

1979, June 25   **Perf. 12½**
1417	A336	30s multi	.40	.25
1418	A336	75s multi	.80	.30
1419	A336	90s multi	1.10	.35
	Nos. 1417-1419 (3)		2.30	.90

Archdiocese of Manila, 400th anniversary.

Patrol Boat, Naval Arms — A337

1979, June 23
1420	A337	30s multi	.60	.30
1421	A337	45s multi	.85	.40

Philippine Navy Day.

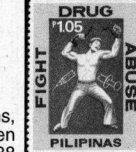

Man Breaking Chains, Broken Syringe — A338

1979, July 23   **Litho.**   **Perf. 12½**
1422	A338	30s multi	.35	.25
1423	A338	90s multi	.85	.30
1424	A338	1.05p multi	1.20	.35
	Nos. 1422-1424 (3)		2.40	.90

Fight drug abuse.
For surcharge see Nos. 1480, 1513.

Afghan Hound — A339

Designs: 90s, Striped tabbies. 1.20p, Dobermann pinscher. 2.20p, Siamese cats. 2.30p, German shepherd. 5p, Chinchilla cats.

1979, July 6   **Perf. 14**
1425	A339	30s multi	.50	.30
1426	A339	90s multi	1.20	.35
1427	A339	1.20p multi	1.30	.40
1428	A339	2.20p multi	2.00	.45
1429	A339	2.30p multi	2.00	.45
1430	A339	5p multi	4.25	1.50
	Nos. 1425-1430 (6)		11.25	3.45

A total of 500,000 sets of Nos. 1425-1430 were CTO July 30, 1979. Value for CTO set, $2.

Children Playing IYC Emblem — A340

Children playing and IYC emblem, diff.

1979, Aug. 31   **Litho.**   **Perf. 12½**
1431	A340	15s multi	.35	.25
1432	A340	20s multi	.40	.25
1433	A340	25s multi	.40	.40
1434	A340	1.20p multi	1.00	.50
	Nos. 1431-1434 (4)		2.15	1.40

International Year of the Child.

Hands Holding Emblem — A341

1979, Sept. 27   **Litho.**   **Perf. 12½**
1435	A341	30s multi	.35	.25
1436	A341	1.35p multi	1.00	.35

Methodism in the Philippines, 80th anniv.

Emblem and Coins — A342

Wmk. 372
1979, Nov. 15   **Litho.**   **Perf. 12½**
1437	A342	30s multi	.50	.50

Philippine Numismatic and Antiquarian Society, 50th anniversary.

Concorde over Manila and Paris — A343

Design: 2.20p, Concorde over Manila.

1979, Nov. 22
1438	A343	1.05p multi	1.50	.45
1439	A343	2.20p multi	3.00	.75

Air France service to Manila, 25th anniversary.

No. 1272 Surcharged in Red
1979, Nov. 23
1440	A273	90s on 1.60 blk	1.00	.25

Philatelic Week. Surcharge similar to No. 1367.

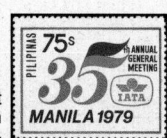

Transport Association Emblem — A344

1979, Nov. 27
1441	A344	75s multi	.85	.30
1442	A344	2.30p multi	2.00	.50

International Air Transport Association, 35th annual general meeting, Manila.

Local Government Year — A345

1979, Dec. 14   **Litho.**   **Perf. 12½**
1443	A345	30s multi	.30	.25
a.		A318 Horiz. pair, imperf. vert.	25.00	
1444	A345	45s multi	.45	.25

For surcharge, see No. 1481.

Mother and Children, Ornament — A346

1979, Dec. 17
1445	A346	30s shown	.50	.30
1446	A346	90s Stars	1.50	.40

Christmas. For surcharges see Nos. 1482, 1515.

Rheumatic Pain Spots and Congress Emblem — A347

Wmk. 372
1980, Jan. 20   **Litho.**   **Perf. 12½**
1447	A347	30s multi	1.00	.75
1448	A347	90s multi	2.50	2.00

Southeast Asia and Pacific Area League Against Rheumatism, 4th Congress, Manila, Jan. 19-24.

Gen. Douglas MacArthur — A348

30s, MacArthur's birthplace (Little Rock, AR) & burial place (Norfolk, VA). 75s, MacArthur's cap, Sunglasses & pipe. 2.30p, MacArthur & troops wading ashore at Leyte, Oct. 20, 1944.

1980, Jan. 26   **Wmk. 372**   **Perf. 12½**
1449	A348	30s multi	.50	.30
1450	A348	75s multi	.80	.50
1451	A348	2.30p multi	2.75	1.00
	Nos. 1449-1451 (3)		4.05	1.80

Souvenir Sheet
Imperf
1452	A348	5p multi	4.50	3.00

Gen. Douglas MacArthur (1880-1964). No. 1449 exists imperf. Value for pair, $40. For overprint see No. 2198.

Knights of Columbus of Philippines, 75th Anniversary — A349

1980, Feb. 14
1453	A349	30s multi	.35	.25
1454	A349	1.35p multi	1.00	.50

Philippine Military Academy, 75th Anniversary A350

Wmk. 372
1980, Feb. 17   **Litho.**   **Perf. 12½**
1455	A350	30s multi	1.00	.60
1456	A350	1.20p multi	3.00	1.40

No. 1455-1456 exist imperf. Value for pair, $40.

Philippines Women's University, 75th Anniversary — A351

1980, Feb. 21
1457	A351	30s multi	.35	.25
1458	A351	1.05p multi	1.00	.30

A352

Disaster Relief — A352a

Rotary International, 75th Anniversary (Paintings by Carlos Botong Francisco): Nos. 1459 and 1460 each in continuous design.

1980, Feb. 23   **Perf. 12½**
1459	A352	Strip of 5	5.00	10.00
a.-e.		30s any single	.70	.50
1460	A352a	Strip of 5	13.00	11.00
a.-e.		2.30p any single	1.75	1.50

A353

Wmk. 372
1980, Mar. 28   **Litho.**   **Perf. 12½**
1461	A353	30s multi	.80	.50
1462	A353	1.30p multi	2.00	.30

6th centenary of Islam in Philippines.

A354

Hand crushing cigarette, WHO emblem.

1980, Apr. 7
1463	A354	30s multi	1.00	1.00
1464	A354	75s multi	3.00	2.00

World Health Day (Apr. 7); anti-smoking campaign.

Philippine Girl Scouts, 40th Anniversary A355

Wmk. 372
1980, May 26   **Litho.**   **Perf. 12½**
1465	A355	30s multi	.50	.25
1466	A355	2p multi	1.90	.60

Jeepney (Public Jeep) — A356

1980, June 24   Litho.   Perf. 12½
1467 A356 30s Jeepney, diff. .65 .25
1468 A356 1.20p shown 1.65 .45

For surcharge see No. 1503.

Nos. 1272, 1206 Surcharged in Red

Wmk. 372 (1.35p)
1980, Aug. 1   Litho.   Perf. 12½
1469 A273 1.35p on 1.60p blk 1.50 .35
1470 A250 1.50p on 1.80p grn 2.20 .60
  a. Inverted overprint 25.00
  b. Imperf. pair, overprint inverted 25.00

Independence, 82nd Anniversary.

Association Emblem — A357

1980, Aug. 1   Wmk. 372
1471 A357 30s multi .35 .25
1472 A357 2.30p multi 2.00 .45

International Association of Universities, 7th General Conference, Manila, Aug. 25-30.

Congress Emblem, Map of Philippines — A358

Wmk. 372
1980, Aug. 18   Litho.   Perf. 12½
1473 A358 30s lt grn & blk .35 .35
1474 A358 75s lt bl & blk .55 .45
1475 A358 2.30p sal & blk 1.60 .60
  Nos. 1473-1475 (3) 2.50 1.40

Intl. Federation of Library Associations and Institutions, 46th Congress, Manila, 8/18-23.

Kabataang Barangay (New Society), 5th Anniversary — A359

1980, Sept. 19   Litho.   Perf. 12½
1476 A359 30s multi .35 .25
1477 A359 40s multi .50 .25
1478 A359 1p multi 1.00 .35
  Nos. 1476-1478 (3) 1.85 .85

Nos. 1389, 1422, 1443, 1445, 1327 Surcharged in Blue, Black or Red
1980 Litho. Wmk. 372 Perf. 12½
1479 A328 40s on 30s rose (Bl) 1.00 .40
1480 A338 40s on 30s multi 1.00 .25
1481 A345 40s on 30s multi 1.00 .30
1482 A346 40s on 30s multi (R) 2.00 .25
1483 A294 2p on 1.65p multi (R) 4.00 .60
  Nos. 1479-1483 (5) 9.00 1.80

Issue dates for Nos. 1479-1483: Nos. 1479, 1481, Sept. 26, 1980. No. 1480, Oct. 13, 1980. Nos. 1482, 1483, Oct. 14, 1980.
Nos. 1479-1483 exist with overprints inverted. Value, from $35 each.

Catamaran, Conference Emblem — A360

1980, Sept. 27
1484 A360 30s multi .40 .30
1485 A360 2.30p multi 1.80 .50

World Tourism Conf., Manila, Sept. 27.

Stamp Day — A361

1980, Oct. 9
1486 A361 40s multi .50 .25
1487 A361 1p multi 1.20 .50
1488 A361 2p multi 2.50 1.25
  Nos. 1486-1488 (3) 4.20 2.00

UN, 35th Anniv. — A362

Designs: 40s, UN Headquarters and Emblem, Flag of Philippines. 3.20p, UN and Philippine flags, UN headquarters.

1980, Oct. 20
1489 A362 40s multi .50 .25
1490 A362 3.20p multi 2.70 .65

Murex Alabaster — A363

Designs: 60s, Bursa bubo. 1.20p, Homalocantha zamboi. 2p, Xenophora pallidula.

1980, Nov. 2
1491 A363 40s shown 1.10 .35
1492 A363 60s multi .80 .35
1493 A363 1.20p multi 1.10 .65
1494 A363 2p multi 2.00 1.00
  Nos. 1491-1494 (4) 5.00 2.35

INTERPOL Emblem on Globe — A364

1980, Nov. 5   Litho.   Wmk. 372
1495 A364 40s multi .40 .25
1496 A364 1p multi .85 .30
1497 A364 3.20p multi 2.25 .75
  Nos. 1495-1497 (3) 3.50 1.30

49th General Assembly Session of INTERPOL (Intl. Police Organization), Manila, Nov. 13-21.

Central Philippine University, 75th Anniversary — A365

1980, Nov. 17   Unwmk.
1498 A365 40s multi .85 .30
1499 A365 3.20p multi 3.00 1.00

No. 1257 Surcharged
Wmk. 372
1980, Nov. 21   Litho.   Perf. 12½
1500 A269 1.20p on 80s multi 1.70 .35

Philatelic Week. Surcharge similar to No. 1367.

No. 1358 Surcharged

1980, Nov. 30
1501 A313 40s on 30s multi 1.70 .50

APO Philatelic Society, 30th anniversary.

Christmas Tree, Present and Candy Cane — A366

Perf. 12½
1980, Dec. 15   Litho.   Unwmk.
1502 A366 40s multi .75 .35

Christmas 1980.

No. 1467 Surcharged

1981, Jan. 2
1503 A356 40c on 30s multi 1.00 .50

Nos. 1370, 1257 Surcharged in Red or Black
1981
1504 A320 10s on 30s (R) multi 1.00 .50
1505 A269 85s on 80s multi 3.00 1.50

Issue dates: 10s, Jan. 12; 85s, Jan. 2.

Heinrich Von Stephan, UPU Emblem — A367

1981, Jan. 30
1506 A367 3.20p multi 3.00 .75

Heinrich von Stephan (1831-1897), founder of UPU, birth sesquicentennial.

Pope John Paul II Greeting Crowd A368

Designs: 90s, Pope, signature, vert. 1.20p, Pope, cardinals, vert. 3p, Pope giving blessing, Vatican arms, Manila Cathedral. 7.50p, Pope, light on map of Philippines, vert.

Perf. 13½x14
1981, Feb. 17   Unwmk.
1507 A368 90s multi 1.00 .40
1508 A368 1.20p multi 1.50 .60
1509 A368 2.30p multi 2.50 1.20
1510 A368 3p multi 3.00 1.75
  Nos. 1507-1510 (4) 8.00 3.95

Souvenir Sheet
Perf. 13¾x13¼
1511 A368 7.50p multi 8.00 6.00

Visit of Pope John Paul, Feb. 17-22.
Nos. 1507-1511 with year date "1980" were created but not issued. Value, $15 each, souvenir sheet $50,
For surcharge, see No. 3046.

No. 1358 Surcharged

Nos. 1364, 1423, 1268, 1446, 1261, 1206, 1327 Surcharged
1981   Litho.   Perf. 12½
1512 A316 40s on 90s multi 1.35 .25
1513 A338 40s on 90s multi 1.35 .25
1514 A273 40s on 65s lil
           rose 1.20 .25
1515 A346 40s on 90s multi 1.70 .75
1517 A271 1p on 1.50p brt
           rose & vio bl 2.00 .40
1518 A250 1.20p on 1.80p grn 2.10 .60
1519 A294 1.20p on 1.65p
           multi 2.75 1.00
1520 A271 2p on 1.50p brt
           rose & vio bl 3.50 1.00
  Nos. 1512-1520 (8) 15.95 4.50

A369

1981, Apr. 20   Wmk. 372
1521 A369 2p multi 1.70 .50
1522 A369 3.20p multi 2.50 .75

68th Spring Meeting of the Inter-Parliamentary Union, Manila, Apr. 20-25.

Unless otherwise stated, Nos. 1523-1580 are on granite paper.

A370

Wmk. 372
1981, May 22   Litho.   Perf. 12½
1523 40s Bubble coral .90 .40
1524 40s Branching coral .90 .40
1525 40s Brain coral .90 .40
1526 40s Table coral .90 .40
  a. A370 Block of 4, #1523-1526 5.00 3.50

Philippine Motor Assoc., 50th Anniv. — A371

Vintage cars.

1981, May 25
1527 40s Presidents car .80 .25
1528 40s 1930 .80 .25
1529 40s 1937 .80 .25
1530 40s shown .80 .25
  a. A371 Block of 4, #1527-1530 4.00 3.00

Re-inauguration of Pres. Ferdinand E. Marcos — A372

Granite Paper
1531 A372 40s multi .75 .30
  a. Wmk. 372 (II) ('83) 2.50 1.20

Souvenir Sheet
Imperf
1532 A372 5p multi 5.00 4.00
  a. Wmk. 372 (II) ('84) 20.00 20.00
  b. On glossy, fiberless paper 50.00 50.00

No. 1531 exists imperf. Value $1.
For overprint see No. 1753.
Nos. 1531-1532 exist with a surface varnish applied for use in presentation folders. Values, 7-8 times values for regular stamps.

St. Ignatius
Loyola, Founder
of Jesuit
Order — A373

400th Anniv. of Jesuits in Philippines: No.
1534, Jose Rizal, Ateneo University. No. 1535,
Father Federico Faura, Manila Observatory.
No. 1536, Father Saturnino Urios, map of
Philippines.

1981, July 31
1533	A373	40s multi	.60	.30
1534	A373	40s multi	.60	.30
1535	A373	40s multi	.60	.30
1536	A373	40s multi	.60	.30
a.	Block of 4, #1533-1536		3.00	2.50

Souvenir Sheet
Imperf
1537	A373	2p multi	4.00	3.50

#1537 contains vignettes of #1533-1536.
For surcharge see No. 1737.

A374

Design: 40s, Isabelo de los Reyes (1867-
1938), labor union founder. 1p, Gen. Gregorio
del Pilar (1875-1899). No. 1540, Magsaysay.
No. 1541, Francisco Dagohoy. No. 1543,
Ambrosia R. Bautista, signer of Declaration of
Independence, 1898, No. 1544, Juan
Sumulong (1875-1942), statesman. 2.30p,
Nicanor Abelardo (1893-1934), composer.
3.20p, Gen. Vicente Lim (1888-1945), first
Philippine graduate of West Point.

Wmk. 372
1981-82		**Litho.**	**Perf. 12½**	
1538	A374	40s grnsh bl ('82)	.45	.25
1539	A374	1p blk & red brn	1.00	.25
1540	A374	1.20p blk & lt red brn	1.40	.40
1541	A374	1.20p brown ('82)	1.75	.50
1543	A374	2p blk & red brn	1.75	.50
1544	A374	2p rose lil ('82)	2.00	.50
a.	Wmk. 372 (II)		4.00	.70
1545	A374	2.30p lt red brn ('82)	2.50	.60
1546	A374	3.20p gray bl ('82)	3.00	.70
a.	Wmk. 372 (II)		5.50	.90
	Nos. 1538-1546 (8)		13.85	3.70

See Nos. 1672-1680, 1682-1683, 1685. For
surcharges see Nos. 1668-1669.

A375

1981, Sept. 2   Granite Paper
1551	A375	40s multi	.60	.30

Chief Justice Fred Ruiz Castro, 67th birth
anniv.
No. 1551 exists on dull ordinary paper.
Value, $10 unused, $5 used.

Intl. Year of the
Disabled — A376

Wmk. 372
1981, Oct. 24		**Litho.**	**Perf. 12½**	
1552	A376	40s multi	.50	.25
1553	A376	3.20p multi	2.90	.65

A376a

1981, Nov. 7   Granite Paper
1554	A376a	40s multi	.50	.25
1555	A376a	2p multi	1.80	.50
1556	A376a	3.20p multi	2.50	.70
	Nos. 1554-1556 (3)		4.80	1.45

24th Intl. Red Cross Conf., Manila, 11/7-14.
No. 1556 exists on glossy ordinary paper,
issued Feb. 17, 1983. Value, $10 mint, $5
used.

Intramuros Gate,
Manila — A377

1981, Nov. 13
1557	A377	40s black	.60	.25

No. 1557 exists on dull ordinary paper,
issued April 2, 1982. Value, $2 mint, 50¢ used.

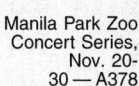

Manila Park Zoo
Concert Series,
Nov. 20-
30 — A378

1981, Nov. 20
1558	A378	40s multi	.65	.30

No. 1558 exists on dull ordinary paper,
issued April 26, 1982. Value, $10 mint, $6
used.

**No. 1329 Overprinted "1981
Philatelic Week" and Surcharged
Wmk. 372**
1981, Nov. 23		**Litho.**	**Perf. 12½**	
1559	A296	1.20p on 1.50p multi	2.40	1.00

Nos. 1205, 1347, 1371 Surcharged
1981, Nov. 25		**Litho.**	**Perf. 12½**	
1560	A306	40s on 1.05p multi	1.25	.50
1561	A320	40s on 1.35p multi	1.25	.50
1562	A273	1.20p on 1.50p brn	3.50	1.00
	Nos. 1560-1562 (3)		6.00	2.00

11th Southeast
Asian Games,
Manila, Dec. 6-
15 — A379

40s, Running. 1p, Bicycling. 2p, Pres.
Marcos, Intl. Olympic Pres. Samaranch.
2.30p, Soccer. 2.80p, Shooting. 3.20p,
Bowling.

1981, Dec. 3
1563	A379	40s multi	.70	.30
1564	A379	1p multi	1.20	.35
1565	A379	2p multi	2.25	.40
1566	A379	2.30p multi	2.75	.50
1567	A379	2.80p multi	3.50	1.00
1568	A379	3.20p multi	3.75	1.00
	Nos. 1563-1568 (6)		14.15	3.55

Manila Intl. Film
Festival, Jan. 18-
29 — A380

40s, Film Center. 2p, Golden trophy, vert.
3.20p, Trophy, diff., vert.

Wmk. 372
1982, Jan. 18		**Litho.**	**Perf. 12½**	
1569	A380	40s multicolored	.50	.30
1570	A380	2p multicolored	2.00	.45
1571	A380	3.20p multicolored	3.00	.80

No. 1570-1571 exist on dull ordinary paper.
Value, $10 each mint, $5 each used.

Dull paper examples issued Aug. 3, 1982
(No. 1570), July 9, 1982 (No. 1571),
	Nos. 1569-1571 (3)	5.50	1.55

Manila Metropolitan Waterworks and
Sewerage System Centenary
A381

1982, Jan. 22
1572	A381	40s blue	.40	.30
1573	A381	1.20p brown	1.60	.40

**Nos. 1268, 1302, 1328 Surcharged
1981**
1574	A273	1p on 65s lil rose	2.00	.60
1575	A286	1p on 1.50p multi	1.25	.40
1576	A295	3.20p on 2.20p multi	4.00	1.00
	Nos. 1574-1576 (3)		7.25	2.00

Issue dates: No. 1574, Feb. 24; No. 1575,
Feb. 10; No. 1576, March 19.

Scouting Year — A382

40s, Portrait. 2p, Scout giving salute.

1982, Feb. 22
1577	A382	40s multi	.50	.30
a.	Wmk. 372 (II)		25.00	20.00
1578	A382	2p multi	2.50	.55

Nos. 1577-1578 exist on dull ordinary
paper. Issue dates: No. 1577, Jun. 8, 1982.
Value, $1.25 mint, 75¢ used; No. 1578, Sept.
21, 1983. Value, $4.25 mint, $2.75 used.

25th Anniv. of
Children's
Museum and
Library
Foundation
A383

1982, Feb. 25
1579	A383	40s Mural	.50	.25
a.	Wmk. 372 (II)		1.50	.50
1580	A383	1.20p Children playing	1.35	.35
a.	Wmk. 372 (II)		3.50	1.00

77th Anniv. of
Philippine Military
Academy — A384

Wmk. 372
1982, Mar. 25		**Litho.**	**Perf. 12½**	
1581	A384	40s multi	.50	.30
1582	A384	1p multi	1.20	.40

Nos. 1581 and 1582 exist on orinary
paper. Value No. 1581, $1.50 mint, 50¢ used;
No. 1582, $2.50 mint, 75¢ used.

40th Bataan
Day — A385

40s, Soldier. 2p, "Reunion for Peace."
3.20p, Cannon, flag.

1982, Apr. 9
1583	A385	40s multi	.50	.25
a.	Wmk. 372 (II)		3.50	1.50
1584	A385	2p multi	1.90	.45

Souvenir Sheet
Imperf
1585	A385	3.20p multi	4.00	3.00

No. 1585 contains one 38x28mm stamp.
No. 1585 comes on two different papers, the
second being thicker with cream gum.
For surcharge see No. 2114.

No. B27 Surcharged

1982, Mar. 15   Photo.   Perf. 13½
1586	SP14	10s on 6 + 5s multi	1.50	.40

The "1" in the surcharged value of No. 1586
is unserifed. For similar surcharge with serifed
"1," see No. 986.

A386

1982, Apr. 28   Litho.   Perf. 12½
1587	A386	1p rose pink	1.75	.35
a.	Wmk. 372 (II)		5.50	.70

Aurora Aragon Quezon (1888-1949), former
First Lady.
There are three types of No. 1587.
See Nos. 1684-1684A.

Man Holding
Award — A387

1982, May 1
1588	A387	40s multi	.50	.30
a.	Wmk. 372 (II)		125.00	125.00
1589	A387	1.20p Award	1.50	.40
a.	Wmk. 372 (II)		10.00	9.00

7th Towers Awards.
No. 1588a bottom inscription in brown
instead of green.
See Nos. 1611B-1611C.

UN Conf. on
Human
Environment,
10th
Anniv. — A388

1982, June 5
1590	A388	40s Turtle	1.00	.40
a.	Wmk. 372 (II)		2.00	.50
1591	A388	3.20p Philippine eagle	5.00	1.00
a.	Wmk. 372 (II)		8.00	2.50

75th Anniv. of
Univ. of
Philippines
College of
Medicine — A389

1982, June 10
1592	A389	40s multi	.50	.25
a.	Wmk. 372 (II)		1.25	.40
1593	A389	3.20p multi	2.50	.75
a.	Wmk. 372 (II)		4.75	1.60

Natl. Livelihood
Movement — A390

1982, June 12
1594	A390	40s multi	.50	.25
a.	Wmk. 372 (II)		1.50	.40

See #1681-1681A. For overprint see #1634.

Adamson Univ., 50th Anniv. — A391

1982, June 21
1595 A391 40s bl & multi .50 .25
a. Wmk. 372 (II) ('83) 25.00 25.00
1596 A391 1.20p lt vio & multi 1.50 .25

Social Security, 25th Anniv. — A392

1982, Sept. 1 Perf. 13½x13
1597 A392 40s multi .50 .25
1598 A392 1.20p multi 1.20 .30

Pres. Marcos, 65th Birthday — A393

1982, Sept. 11 Perf. 13¼x13
1599 A393 40s sil & multi .50 .25
a. Wmk. 372 (II) 1.50 .40
b. Perf. 12½ .50 .25
c. As "b," Wmk. 372 (II) 1.00 .25
1600 A393 3.20p sil & multi 2.25 .75
a. Souv. sheet of 2, #1599-1600, imperf. 5.00 4.00
b. Perf. 12½ 2.25 .75
c. Wmk. 372 (II) 4.00 1.00
d. As "a," Wmk. 372 (II) 25.00 25.00
e. As "b," Wmk. 372 (II) 15.00 12.00

For surcharge see No. 1666.
Perf. 13¼x13 was comb perforated; perf. 12½ was line perforated.

15th Anniv. of Assoc. of Southeast Asian Nations (ASEAN) — A394

1982, Sept. 22 Litho. Perf. 12½
1601 A394 40s Flags .75 .30
c. Wmk. 372 (II) 2.00 .50

St. Teresa of Avila (1515-1582) A395

1982, Oct. 15 Perf. 13x13½
1602 A395 40s Text .50 .25
1603 A395 1.20p Map 1.00 .30
a. 3.50 .50
b. As "a," Wmk. 372 (II) 4.50 1.75
1604 A395 2p like #1603 1.75 .40
a. Perf. 12½ 5.00 3.50
Nos. 1602-1604 (3) 3.25 .95

A396

A396a

On Type I the shading on President Marcos is much darker as if he is under the shade of a tree. This was changed in Type II so that he

appears under the sun. The new design plates are ½mm shorter than that of the original cutting off the bottom of the design. There are also numerous other slight differences.

Perf. 13x13½
1982, Oct. 21 Litho. Wmk. 372
1605 A396 40s Type I 3.25 1.00
1605A A396a 40s Type II 1.75 .40

10th Anniv. of Tenant Farmers' Emancipation Decree.
See No. 1654.

350th Anniv. of St. Isabel College — A397

1982, Oct. 22
1606 A397 40s multi .40 .25
1607 A397 1p multi 1.60 .40

Reading Campaign A398

1982, Nov. 4
1608 A398 40s yel & multi .50 .25
a. Wmk. 372 (II) 2.50 .50
1609 A398 2.30p grn & multi 2.00 1.00
a. Wmk. 372 (II) 5.00 2.00

For surcharge see No. 1713.

42nd Skal Club World Congress, Manila, Nov. 7-12 — A399

1982, Nov. 7
1610 A399 40s Heads .50 .35
a. Perf. 12½, Wmk. 372 (II) 1.75 .75
1611 A399 2p Chief 3.00 .60
a. Perf. 12½, Wmk. 372 (II) 5.00 1.75

Man Holding Award — A399a

1982, Nov. Perf. 12½
1611B A399a 40s multi 3.00 .75
1611C A399a 1.20p Award 6.00 2.75

Issue dates: No. 1611A, 11/24; No. 1611B, 11/8.
Nos. 1611B-1611C are actually the first printing of Nos. 1588-1589 containing the misspelling "Mangagawa" instead of "Manggagawa".
See Nos. 1588-1589.

25th Anniv. of Bayanihan Folk Arts Center — A400

Designs: Various folk dances.

1982, Nov. 10 Litho. Perf. 13x13½
1612 A400 40s multi .50 .25
a. Perf. 12½, Wmk. 372 (II) 1.25 .35
1613 A400 2.80p multi 3.00 .65

TB Bacillus Centenary A401

1982, Dec. 7 Wmk. 372
1614 A401 40s multi .50 .25
1615 A401 2.80p multi 3.00 .75

Christmas 1982 — A402

1982, Dec. 10
1616 A402 40s multi 1.20 .40
1617 A402 1p multi 3.75 .60

Philatelic Week, Nov. 22-28 — A403

Perf. 13x13½
1983, Jan. 21 Litho. Wmk. 372
1618 A403 40s yel & multi .50 .25
a. Perf. 12½, Wmk. 372 (II) 1.00 .35
1619 A403 1p sil & multi 1.10 .30
a. Perf. 12½ 2.50 .50
b. As "a," Wmk. 372 (II) 3.00 1.00

For surcharge see No. 1667.
First-day covers dated 1982, Nov. 28.

Visit of Pres. Marcos to the US, Sept. — A404

1982, Dec. 18
1620 A404 40s multi .50 .40
1621 A404 3.20p multi 3.25 1.00
a. Souv. sheet of 2, #1620-1621 5.00 4.00

UN World Assembly on Aging, July 26-Aug. 6 — A405

1982, Dec. 24
1622 A405 1.20p Woman 1.10 .35
a. Wmk. 372 (II) 15.00 7.00
1623 A405 2p Man 2.20 .50

Senate Pres. Eulogio Rodriguez, Sr. (1883-1964) — A406

1983, Jan. 21
1624 A406 40s grn & multi .75 .25
a. Wmk. 372 (II) 1.00 .35
1625 A406 1.20p org & multi 1.25 .35
a. Perf. 12½ 4.75 1.75
b. As "a," Wmk. 372 (II) 1.75 .50

1983 Manila Intl. Film Festival, Jan. 24-Feb. 4 — A407

1983, Jan. 24
1626 A407 40s blk & multi .50 .30
a. Wmk. 372 (II) 1.00 .50
b. As "a," perf 12½ 4.75 2.75
1627 A407 3.20p pink & multi 3.50 .70
a. Wmk. 372 (II) 6.00 1.75
b. As "a," perf 12½ 14.00 8.75

Beatification of Lorenzo Ruiz (1981) — A408

Perf. 13x13½
1983, Feb. 18 Litho. Wmk. 372
1628 A408 40s multi .65 .35
a. Wmk. 372 (II) 1.50 .40
b. Perf 12½ 5.00 2.00

1629 A408 1.20p multi 1.75 .60
a. Wmk. 372 (II) 2.50 .60
b. Perf 12½ 8.50 5.00

400th Anniv. of Local Printing Press — A409

1983, Mar. 14
1630 A409 40s blk & grn .60 .30
a. Wmk. 372 (II) 1.50 .40

Safety at Sea — A410

1983, Mar. 17 Perf. 13½x13
1631 A410 40s multi .60 .30
a. Wmk. 372 (II) 1.75 .40

25th anniv. of Inter-Governmental Maritime Consultation Org. Convention.

Intl. Org. of Supreme Audit Institutions, 11th Congress, Manila, Apr. 19-27 — A411

Perf. 13x13½
1983, Apr. 8 Litho. Wmk. 372
1632 A411 40s Symbols .50 .30
a. Wmk. 372 (II) 1.75 .75
1633 A411 2.80p Emblem 2.00 1.00
a. Souv. sheet of 2, 1632-1633, imperf. 4.50 4.00
b. Wmk. 372 (II) 5.00 1.75
c. As "a," Wmk. 372 (II) 15.00 12.00

No. 1633a comes on two papers: cream gum, normal watermark; white gum, watermark made up of smaller letters.

Type of 1982 Overprinted in Red: "7th BSP NATIONAL JAMBOREE 1983"

1983, Apr. 13 Perf. 12½
1634 A390 40s multi 1.00 .35

Boy Scouts of Philippines jamboree.

No. 1249 Surcharged
1983, Apr. 15
1635 Block of 10 12.00 12.00
a.-j. A265 40s on 45s, any single .70 .35

A412

Perf. 13½x13
1983, May 9 Litho. Wmk. 372
1636 A412 40s multi .60 .30
b. Wmk. 372 (II) 1.75 .75

75th anniv. of Dental Assoc.

A413

Perf. 13½x13
1983, June 17 Litho. Wmk. 372
1637 A413 40s Statue .50 .30
a. Perf. 12½, Wmk. 372 (II) 3.50 1.50
1638 A413 1.20p Statue, diff., diamond 1.25 .50
a. Perf. 12½, Wmk. 372 (II) 4.50 2.00

75th anniv. of University of the Philippines.

Visit of Japanese Prime Minister Yasuhiro Nakasone, May 6-8 — A414

Perf. 13x13½

1983, June 20   Litho.   Wmk. 372
1639 A414 40s multi .... .60 .30
    a.   Wmk. 372 (II) 6.00 5.00

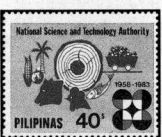

25th Anniv. of Natl. Science and Technology Authority — A415

No. 1640, Animals, produce. No. 1641, Heart, food, pill. No. 1642, Factories, windmill, car. No. 1643, Chemicals, house, book.

1983, July 11
1640 A415 40s multicolored .... .50 .40
    a.   Perf. 12½, Wmk. 372 (II) 1.25 1.00
1641 A415 40s multicolored .... .50 .40
    a.   Perf. 12½, Wmk. 372 (II) 1.25 1.00
1642 A415 40s multicolored .... .50 .40
    a.   Perf. 12½, Wmk. 372 (II) 1.25 1.00
1643 A415 40s multicolored .... .50 .40
    a.   Perf. 12½, Wmk. 372 (II) 1.25 1.00
    b.   Block of 4, #1640-1643 .... 3.00 2.50
    b.   Block of 4, #1640a-1643a 7.50 5.00

Science Week.

World Communications Year — A416

Wmk. 372 (II)

1983, Oct. 24   Litho.   Perf. 12½
1644 A416 3.20p multi 3.00 1.00

Philippine Postal System Bicentennial A417

1983, Oct. 31
1645 A417 40s multi .... .50 .25

Christmas — A418

Star of the East and Festival Scene in continuous design.

Wmk. 372 (I)

1983, Nov. 15   Litho.   Perf. 12½
1646 Strip of 5 .... 5.00 4.00
    a.-e.   A418 40s single stamp .... .80 .40
    f.   Souvenir sheet 4.50 4.00
    g.   Strip of 5, Wmk. 372 (II) 10.00 7.00
    h.-i.   As "g," any single 1.25 1.00

Xavier University, 50th Anniv. — A419

Wmk. 372 (II)

1983, Dec. 1   Litho.   Perf. 14
1647 A419 40s multi .... .50 .30
    a.   Wmk. 372 (I) .... 1.50 .50
1648 A419 60s multi .... 1.25 .35
    a.   Wmk. 372 (I) 3.00 1.00

A420

1983, Dec. 8   Litho.   Perf. 12½
1649 A420 40s brt ultra & multi .... .50 .30
    a.   Wmk. 372 (I) 5.00 2.75
1650 A420 60s gold & multi .... 1.25 .35
    a.   Wmk. 372 (I) 4.25 2.50

Ministry of Labor and Employment, golden jubilee.

A421

1983, Dec. 7
1651 A421 40s multi .... .50 .40
1652 A421 60s multi .... 1.25 .40

50th anniv. of Women's Suffrage Movement.

Philatelic Week — A422

Stamp Collecting: a, Cutting. b, Sorting. c, Soaking. d, Affixing hinges. e, Mounting stamp.

1983, Dec. 20
1653 Strip of 5 .... 4.00 3.50
    a.-e.   A422 50s any single .... .75 .50
    f.   Strip of 5, Wmk. 372 (I) 30.00 30.00
    g.-k.   As "f," any single 5.00 4.00

Emancipation Type of 1982

1983   Litho.   Perf. 13
Size: 32x22mm
1654 A396 40s multi .... 2.50 .30
    a.   Perf. 12½ 15.00 1.00

Philippine Cockatoo — A423

40s, Philippine Cockatoo, 2.30p, Guaiabero. 2.80p, Crimson-spotted racket-tailed parrots. 3.20p, Large-billed parrot. 3.60p, Tanygnathus sumatranus. 5p, Hanging parakeets.

1984, Jan. 9   Unwmk.   Perf. 14
1655 A423 40s multi .... .55 .30
1656 A423 2.30p multi .... 1.60 .60
1657 A423 2.80p multi .... 2.10 .80
1658 A423 3.20p multi 2.50 1.00
1659 A423 3.60p multi 2.75 1.00
1660 A423 5p multi 3.50 1.50
    Nos. 1655-1660 (6) 13.00 5.20

There were 500,000 of each value created cto with Jan 9 1984, cancel in the center of each block of 4. These were sold at 15 percent of face value. Value for CTO set, $3.

Princess Tarhata Kiram — A424

Wmk. 372 (II)

1984, Jan. 16   Perf. 13
1661 A424 3p grn & red .... 2.25 .50
    a.   Perf. 12½ 7.00 2.00
    b.   As "a," Wmk. 372 (I) 5.00 1.25

Order of Virgin Mary, 300th Anniv. — A425

Perf. 13½x13

1984, Jan. 23   Wmk. 372 (I)
1662 A425 40s blk & multi .... .60 .25
    a.   Perf. 12½ .... 1.75 .70
1663 A425 60s red & multi .... 1.25 .50
    a.   Perf. 12½ 4.00 1.30

Dona Concha Felix de Calderon — A426

1984, Feb. 9   Wmk. 372 (II)   Perf. 13
1664 A426 60s blk & bl grn .... .60 .30
    a.   Perf. 12½ .... 2.00 .50
    b.   Wmk. 372 (I) 25.00 18.00
1665 A426 3.60p red & bl grn .... 2.00 .70
    a.   Perf. 12½ 4.00 1.00
    b.   As "a," Wmk. 372 (I) 5.00 1.75
    c.   Wmk. 372 (I) 25.00 18.00

Nos. 1546, 1599, 1618 Surcharged

1984, Feb. 20
1666 A393 60s on 40s (R) .... .50 .25
    a.   Perf. 12½ .... .50 .25
    b.   As "a," Wmk. 372 (I) 8.00 5.00
1667 A403 60s on 40s, Wmk. 372 (I) .... .65 .25
1668 A374 3.60p on 3.20p, perf. 12½ (R) 3.55 1.00
    Nos. 1666-1668 (3) 4.70 1.50

No. 1685 Surcharged

1985, Oct. 21   Litho.   Perf. 12½
1669 A374 3.60p on 4.20p rose lil 5.50 3.00
    a.   Perf. 13 .... 35.00 25.00

Portrait Type of 1981

Designs: No. 1672, Gen. Artemio Ricarte. No. 1673, Teodoro M. Kalaw. No. 1674, Pres. Carlos P. Garcia. No. 1675, Senator Quintin Paredes. No. 1676, Dr. Deogracias V. Villadolid (1896-1976), 1st director, Bureau of Fisheries. No. 1677, Santiago Fonacier (1885-1940), archbishop. No. 1678, 2p, Vicente Orestes Romualdez (1885-1970), lawyer. 3p, Francisco Dagohoy.

Types of 3p:
Type I — Medium size "PILIPINAS," large, heavy denomination.

Type II — Large "PILIPINAS," medium denomination.

Perf. 13, 12¾ (#1678, 2p), 12½x13 (3p)

			Litho.
1984-85			
1672	A374	60s blk & lt brn	1.40 .30
1673	A374	60s blk & pur	1.75 .30
1674	A374	60s black	1.75 .30
1675	A374	60s dull blue	.70 .25
a.		Perf. 12½	1.75 .30
b.		Wmk. 391	1.00 .25
c.		As "a." Wmk. 391	3.50 .30
1676	A374	60s brn blk ('85)	.85 .25
a.		Perf. 12½	1.75 .30
1677	A374	60s dk red ('85)	.60 .25
a.		Horiz. miniature sheet of 20	45.00 45.00
b.		Vert. miniature sheet of 20	37.50 37.50
c.		Wmk. 391	.75 .25
1678	A374	60s cobalt blue ('85)	.85 .40
1679	A374	2p brt rose ('85)	3.00 .40
1680	A374	3p pale brn, type I	5.25 .40
a.		Perf. 12½	10.00 .65
1680A	A374	3p pale brn, type II	8.50 .50
		Nos. 1672-1680A (10)	24.65 3.35

Issued: #1672, 3/22; #1673, 3/31; #1674, 6/14; #1675, 9/12; #1676, 3/22; #1677, 5/21; #1678, 2p, 7/3; 3p, 9/7.

No. 1677 was normally issued in panes of 100.

Types of 1982

Types of 3.60p:
Type I — Thick Frame line, large "P," "360" with line under "60."

Type II — Medium Frame line, small "p," "3.60."

Perf. 12½ (#1684), 12¾x13, 13x12¾ (#1681, 1681A)
Wmk. 372 (II), 391 (#1684A)

1984-86				
1681	A390	60s green & multi	.35	.25
a.		Perf. 12½		
b.		Wmk. 372 (I)	25.00	18.00
1681A	A390	60s red & multi	.75	.30
a.		Perf. 12½	4.00	.60
c.		As "b," Wmk. 372 (I)	15.00	9.00
1682	A374	1.80p #1546	1.50	.35
a.		Perf. 12½	2.50	.35
1683	A374	2.40p #1545	1.60	.40
a.		As "a," Wmk. 372 (I)	20.00	10.00
1684	A386	3.60p Quezon, type I	2.00	.40
b.		Wmk. 372 (I)	35.00	22.50
1684A	A386	3.60p As #1684, type II	3.50	.50
1685	A374	4.20p #1544	2.75	.75
		Nos. 1681-1685 (7)	12.45	2.95

Issued: #1681A, 10/19; #1684A, 2/14/86; others 3/26.
Postal forgeries of No. 1684 exist perf. 11.

Ayala Corp. Sesquicentenary A427

Night Views of Manila.

1984, Apr. 25   Litho.   Perf. 13x13½
1686 A427 70s multi .... .65 .30
    a.   Perf. 12½ .... 1.75 .50
1687 A427 3.60p multi .... 2.75 .70

ESPANA '84 — A428

Designs: 2.50p, No. 1690d, Our Lady of the Most Holy Rosary with St. Dominic, by C. Francisco. 5p, No. 1690a, Spoliarium, by Juan Luna. No. 1690b, Blessed Virgin of Manila as Patroness of Voyages, Galleon showing map of Panama-Manila. No. 1690c. Illustrations from The Monkey and the Turtle, by Rizal (first children's book published in Philippines, 1885.)

1984, Apr. 27   Unwmk.   Perf. 14
1688 A428 2.50p multi 3.00 3.00
1689 A428 5p multi 8.00 6.00
    a.   Pair, #1688-1689 .... 13.00 10.00

Souvenir Sheet
Perf. 14½x15, Imperf.
1690 Sheet of 4, #a.-d. 25.00 20.00
    a.-d.   A428 7.50p, any single 5.00 3.00
    e.   Sheet of 4, one value ovpt. "O.L. Lady" instead of "O.L. Holy" 300.00 300.00
    f.   Error single from No 1690e sheet 50.00 50.00

Surcharged in Black
Perf. 14½x15
1690A Sheet of 4, #a.-d. 200.00 200.00
    a.-d.   A428 7.20p on 7.50p, any single 22.00 20.00

Surcharged in Red
Imperf
1690B Sheet of 4, #a.-d. 200.00 200.00
    a.-d.   A428 7.20p on 7.50p, any single 22.00 20.00

Surcharged in Black
Imperf
1690C Sheet of 4, #a.-d. 250.00 250.00
    a.-d.   A428 7.20p on 7.50p, any single 60.00 60.00

Nos. 1690Aa-1690Ad and 1690Ba-1690Bd are each surcharged 7.20p and bear the following overprints: #1690Aa and #1690Ba, "10-5-84 NATIONAL MUSEUM WEEK" on #1690a; #1690Ab and #1690Bb, "8-3-84 PHILIPPINE-MEXICAN FRIENDSHIP 420th ANNIVERSARY" on #1690b; #1690Ac and #1690Bc, "7-17-84 NATIONAL CHILDREN'S BOOK DAY" on #1690c; #1690Ad and #1690Bd, "9-1-84 O.L. OF HOLY ROSARY PARISH 300TH YEAR" on #1690d. Nos. 1690Aa-1690Bd were released as single stamps on the dates shown in their respective overprints. A few intact sheets were sold after the release of the last of these stamps.

Maria Paz Mendoza Guazon — A429

1984, May 26	Wmk. 372	Perf. 13	
1691 A429 60s brt blue & red		1.20	.30
1692 A429 65s brt blue, red & blk		1.50	.40

Butterflies A430

60s, Adolias amlana. 2.40p, Papilio daedalus. 3p, Prothoe frankii semperi. 3.60p, Troides magellanus. 4.20p, Yoma sabina vasuki. 5p, Chilasa idaeoides.

Unwmk.			
1984, Aug. 2	Litho.	Perf. 14	
1693 A430	60s multi	.60	.40
1694 A430	2.40p multi	1.25	.80
1695 A430	3p multi	1.50	1.00
1696 A430	3.60p multi	1.50	1.00
1697 A430	4.20p multi	2.00	1.25
1698 A430	5p multi	3.00	1.50
Nos. 1693-1698 (6)		9.85	5.95

There were 500,000 of each value created cto with Jul 5 1984 cancel in the center of each block of 4. These were sold at 15 percent face value. Value for CTO set, $3.50.

Summer Olympics, Los Angeles, 1984 — A431

Designs: 60s, Running (man). 2.40p, Boxing. 6p, Swimming. 7.20p, Windsurfing. 8.40p, Cycling. 20p, Running (woman).

Unwmk.			
1984, Aug. 9	Litho.	Perf. 14	
1699 A431	60s multi	.50	.40
1700 A431	2.40p multi	1.00	.50
1701 A431	6p multi	2.50	1.50
1702 A431	7.20p multi	3.00	2.00
1703 A431	8.40p multi	3.25	2.50
1704 A431	20p multi	8.00	5.00
Nos. 1699-1704 (6)		18.25	11.40

Souvenir Sheet			
1705	Sheet of 4	15.00	15.00
a.-d.	A431 6p, any single	2.50	2.50

There were 500,000 of each value created cto with Aug 8 1984 cancel in the center of each block of 4. These were sold at 15 percent face value. Used value, set of 6 cto, $3.75.
Nos. 1699-1705 were also issued imperf, with blue, instead of red, stars at sides. Value, set of 6 stamps $100, souvenir sheet $40.

Baguio City, 75th Anniv. — A432

	Wmk. 372		
1984, Aug. 24	Litho.	Perf. 12½	
1706 A432 1.20p The Mansion		1.75	.60

Light Rail Transit — A433

1984, Sept. 10		Perf. 13x13½	
1707 A433 1.20p multi		1.75	.40

No. 1, Australia No. 59 and Koalas — A434

Perf. 14½x15			
1984, Sept. 21		Unwmk.	
1708 A434	3p multi	3.00	1.50
1709 A434	3.60p multi	4.00	2.00

Souvenir Sheet			
1710	Sheet of 3	20.00	18.00
a.	A434 20p multi	6.00	5.00

AUSIPEX '84. No. 1710 exists imperf. Value, $25.

No. 1609 Surcharged with 2 Black Bars and Ovptd. "14-17 NOV. 84 / R.I. ASIA REGIONAL CONFERENCE"

Perf. 13x13½			
1984, Nov. 11	Wmk. 372	Litho.	
1713 A398 1.20p on 2.30p multi		2.00	.80
a.	Wmk. 372 (II)	2.00	.80

Philatelic Week — A435

1.20p, Gold medal. 3p, Winning stamp exhibit.

Wmk. 372 (II)			
1984, Nov. 22		Perf. 13½x13	
1714 A435 1.20p multi		.70	.40
1715 A435 3p multi		2.00	1.00
a.	Pair, #1714-1715	3.50	2.50

AUSIPEX '84 and Mario Que, 1st Philippine exhibitor to win FIP Gold Award.
For overprints see Nos. 1737A and 1737B.

Ships — A436

60s, Caracao canoes. 1.20p, Chinese junk. 6p, Spanish galleon. 7.20p, Casco. 8.40p, Steamboat. 20p, Cruise liner.

Unwmk.			
1984, Nov. 26	Litho.	Perf. 14	
1718 A436	60s multi	.50	.30
1719 A436	1.20p multi	.60	.40
1720 A436	6p multi	1.90	.60
1721 A436	7.20p multi	2.25	1.00
1722 A436	8.40p multi	2.50	1.25
1723 A436	20p multi	5.25	2.00
Nos. 1718-1723 (6)		13.00	5.55

There were 500,000 of each value created cto with Oct 5 1984 cancel in the center of each block of 4. These were sold at 15 percentf face value. Value, set of 6 cto, $3.50.
For surcharge, see No. 3051.

Ateneo de Manila University, 125th Anniv. — A438

Wmk. 372 (II)			
1984, Dec. 7	Litho.	Perf. 13x13½	
1730 A438	60s ultra & gold	.65	.30
1731 A438	1.20p dk ultra & sil	1.35	.40

A438a

60s, Manila-Dagupan, 1892. 1.20p, Light rail transit, 1984. 6p, Bicol Express, 1955. 7.20p, Tranvis (1905, electric street car). 8.40, Commuter train, 1984. 20p, Early street car pulled by horses, 1898.

Perf. 14x13¾			
1984, Dec. 18		Unwmk.	
1731A A438a	60s multi	.50	.35
1731B A438a	1.20p multi	1.00	.40
1731C A438a	6p multi	3.00	.65
1731D A438a	7.20p multi	4.00	1.60
1731E A438a	8.40p multi	3.50	1.25
1731F A438a	20p multi	7.50	2.25
Nos. 1731A-1731F (6)		19.50	6.50

There were 500,000 of each value created cto with Dec 5 1984 cancel in the center of each block of 4. These were sold at 15 percentf face value. Value, set of 6 cto, $3.50.
For surcharges see #1772-1773.

Christmas — A439

60s, Madonna and Child. 1.20p, Holy family.

Wmk. 372 (II)			
1984, Dec. 8		Perf. 13½x13	
1732 A439	60s multi	.80	.30
1733 A439	1.20p multi	2.00	.80
a.	Pair, #1732-1733	3.25	2.25

Natl. Jaycees Awards, 25th anniv. — A440

Philippines Jaycees Commitment to Youth Development.
Abstract painting by Raoul G. Isidro.

1984, Dec. 19			
1734	Strip of 10	24.00	24.00
a.-e.	A440 60s any single	1.00	.75
f.-j.	A440 3p any single	3.00	2.00
k.	Strip of 10, Wmk. 372 (I)	125.00	125.00
l.-p.	A440 60s any single	5.00	4.00
q.-u.	A440 3p any single	15.00	12.50

Dried Tobacco Leaf and Plant — A441

1985, Jan. 14		Perf. 13x13½	
1735 A441	60s multicolored	.80	.30
1736 A441	3p multicolored	2.25	.80

Philippine-Virginia Tobacco Admin., 25th anniv.

No. 1537 Surcharged

1984, Nov. 28	Litho.	Imperf.	
1737 A373 3p on 2p multi		4.00	3.00

First printing had missing period ("p300"). Value $10.
First-day cancels are for Nov. 20.

Nos. 1714-1715 Overprinted "Philatelic Week 1984"

1.20p, Gold medal. 3p, Winning stamp exhibit.

1985, Jan. 25		Perf. 13½x13	
1737A A435	1.20p multi	.70	.40
1737B A435	3p multi	2.00	1.00
c.	Pair, #1737A-1737B	3.50	2.50

Natl. Research Council Emblem — A442

1985, Feb. 3	Litho.	Perf. 13x13½	
1738 A442	60s bl, dk bl & blk	.35	.25
1739 A442	1.20p org, dk bl & blk	1.00	.30

Pacific Science Assoc., 5th intl. congress, Manila, Feb. 3-7.

Medicinal Plants — A443

60s, Carmona retusa. 1.20p, Orthosiphon aristatus. 2.40p, Vitex negundo. 3p, Aloe barbadensis. 3.60p, Quisqualis indica. 4.20p, Blumea balsamifera.

Wmk. 372 (II)			
1985, Mar. 15		Perf. 13x13½	
1740 A443	60s multi	1.00	.30
a.	Perf. 12½	1.75	.80
1741 A443	1.20p multi	2.25	.80
a.	Perf. 12½	2.00	.50
1742 A443	2.40p multi	3.50	1.75
a.	Perf. 12½	3.50	.80
1743 A443	3p multi	5.00	1.75
a.	Perf. 12½	3.50	1.00
1744 A443	3.60p multi	4.00	1.75
a.	Perf. 12½	5.50	2.50
b.	Wmk. 372 (I)	80.00	80.00
c.	As "a," Wmk. 372 (I)	40.00	40.00
1745 A443	4.20p multi	6.00	3.00
a.	Perf. 12½	6.00	2.75
Nos. 1740-1745 (6)		21.75	9.35

INTELSAT, 20th Anniv. — A444

1985, Apr. 6		Perf. 13x13½	
1746 A444	60s multicolored	.50	.30
1747 A444	3p multicolored	2.50	.70

A444a

Philippine Horses: 60s, Pintos. 1.20p, Palomino. 6p, Bay. 7.20p, Brown. 8.40p, Gray. 20p, Chestnut.
#1747G: h, as 1.20p. i, as 7.20p. j, as 6p. k, as 20p.

Perf. 14x13¾			
1984, Dec. 18		Unwmk.	
1747A A444a	60s multi	.50	.40
1747B A444a	1.20p multi	1.00	.50
1747C A444a	6p multi	2.00	.80
1747D A444a	7.20p multi	3.00	1.20
1747E A444a	8.40p multi	3.25	1.60
1747F A444a	20p multi	6.75	2.00
Nos. 1747A-1747F (6)		16.50	6.50

Souvenir Sheet of 4			
1747G A444a 8.40p h.-k.		15.00	15.00

There were 500,000 each of #1747A-1747F created cto with Apr 12 1985 cancel in the center of each block of 4. These were sold at 15 percentf face value. Value, set of 6 cto, $3.50.

Tax Research Institute, 25th Anniv. — A445

Perf. 13½x13			
1985, Apr. 22		Wmk. 372	
1748 A445 60s multicolored		.70	.30

Intl. Rice Research Institute, 25th Anniv. — A446

1985, May 27		Perf. 13x13½	
1749 A446	60s Planting	.50	.40
a.	Perf. 12½	6.50	3.00
1750 A446	3p Paddies	2.50	.80

1st Spain-Philippines Peace Treaty, 420th Anniv. — A447

Designs: 1.20p, Blessed Infant of Cebu, statue, shrine and basilica. 3.60p, King Tupas of Cebu and Miguel Lopez de Legaspi signing treaty, 1565.

1985, June 4			Perf. 12½	
1751	A447	1.20p multi	.70	.30
1752	A447	3.60p multi	1.70	.70
a.	Pair, #1751-1752 + label		4.50	3.50

No. 1532 Ovptd. "10th Anniversary Philippines and People's Republic of China Diplomatic Relations 1975-1985"

1985, June 8			Imperf.	
1753	A372	5p multi	6.00	5.00

In the first printing, the apostrophe in *People's* was omitted and then added by hand. Value: $12 unused, $10 used. The apostrophe is included in later printings.

Arbor Week, June 9-15 — A448

1985, June 9			Perf. 13½x13	
1754	A448	1.20p multi	1.25	.40
a.	Perf. 12½		75.00	75.00

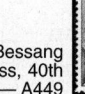

Battle of Bessang Pass, 40th Anniv. — A449

1985, June 14			Perf. 13x13½	
1755	A449	1.20p multi	1.50	.50

Natl. Tuberculosis Soc., 75th Anniv. — A450

60s, Immunization, research. 1.20p, Charity seal.

1985, July 29				
1756	A450	60s multi	.70	.40
1757	A450	1.20p multi	1.00	.60
a.	Pair, #1756-1757		2.50	2.00

No. 1297 Surcharged with Bars, New Value and Scout Emblem in Gold, Ovptd. "GSP" and "45th Anniversary Girl Scout Charter" in Black

Perf. 12½x13½				
1985, Aug. 19	**Unwmk.**		**Photo.**	
1758	A242	2.40p on 15s on 10s	1.50	1.00
1759	A242	4.20p on 15s on 10s	2.50	1.50
1760	A242	7.20p on 15s on 10s	4.00	2.50
	Nos. 1758-1760 (3)		8.00	5.00

Virgin Mary Birth Bimillennium — A451

Statues and paintings.

Perf. 13½x13				
1985, Sept. 8	**Wmk. 372**		**Litho.**	
1761	A451	1.20p multi	1.00	.40
1762	A451	2.40p Beaterio	1.60	.60
1763	A451	3p Penafrancia	2.40	1.00
1764	A451	3.60p Guadalupe	3.00	1.50
	Nos. 1761-1764 (4)		8.00	3.50

A small quantity of No. 1762 was issued with a large 2 in the denomination. The top of

the *2* touches the frameline. Value, $10 mint, $4 used.

Intl. Youth Year — A452

Prize-winning children's drawings.

1985, Sept. 23			Perf. 13x13½	
1765	A452	2.40p Agriculture	1.50	.35
1766	A452	3.60p Education	2.50	.85

Girl and Rice Terraces — A453

1985, Sept. 26				
1767	A453	2.40p multi	2.50	.65
a.	Perf. 12½		8.50	8.50

World Tourism Organization, 6th general assembly, Sofia, Bulgaria, Sept. 17-26.

Export Year — A454

1985, Oct. 8			Perf. 13½x13	
1768	A454	1.20p multi	1.50	.35

UN, 40th Anniv. — A455

1985, Oct. 24				
1769	A455	3.60p multi	3.00	.70

1st Transpacific Airmail Service, 50th Anniv. — A456

3p, China Clipper on water. 3.60p, China Clipper, map.

1985, Nov. 22			Perf. 13x13½	
1770	A456	3p multi	2.50	1.00
1771	A456	3.60p multi	3.00	1.00

Nos. 1731C-1731D Surcharged in Black

Perf. 14x13¾				
1985, Nov. 24			**Unwmk.**	
1772	A438a	60s on 6p	.80	.50
1773	A438a	3p on 7.20p	4.20	1.50

No. 1773 is airmail.

Natl. Bible Week — A457

1985, Dec. 3		Wmk. 372	Perf. 12½	
1774	A457	60s multicolored	.50	.40
1775	A457	3p multicolored	2.50	1.00

Christmas 1985 — A458

1985, Dec. 8			Perf. 13x13½	
1776	A458	60s Panuluyan	.70	.40
a.	Perf. 12½		5.00	3.50
1777	A458	3p Pagdalaw	3.30	1.00
a.	Perf. 12½		13.00	10.00

Scales of Justice — A459

1986, Jan. 12				
1778	A459	60s lilac rose & blk	.50	.30
1779	A459	3p brt grn, lil rose & blk	2.10	.80

University of the Philippines, College of Law, 75th anniv. See No. 1838.

Flores de Heidelberg, by Jose Rizal — A460

Design: 60s, Noli Me Tangere.

1986	Wmk. 391	Litho.	Perf. 13	
1780	A460	60s violet	.40	.25
a.	Wmk. 372 (II)		20.00	20.00
1781	A460	1.20p bluish grn	1.50	.30
a.	Wmk. 372 (II)		15.00	15.00
1782	A460	3.60p redsh brn	2.40	.35
	Nos. 1780-1782 (3)		4.30	.90

Issued: 60s, 1.20p, Feb. 21; 3.60p, July 10. For surcharges see Nos. 1834, 1913.
Nos. 1780a-1781a were printed for presentation purposes. Remainders were sold over post office counters.

Philippine Airlines, 45th Anniv. — A461

Aircraft: No. 1783a, Douglas DC3, 1946. b, Douglas DC4 Skymaster, 1946. c, Douglas DC6, 1948. d, Vickers Viscount 784, 1957.
No. 1784a, Fokker Friendship F27 Mark 100, 1960. b, Douglas DC8 Series 50, 1962. c, Bac One Eleven Series 500, 1964. d, McDonnell Douglas DC10 Series 30, 1974.
No. 1785a, Beech Model 18, 1941. b, Boeing 747, 1980.

1986, Mar. 15				
1783	A461	Block of 4	4.00	4.00
a.-d.	60s, any single		.50	.30
e.	Block of 4, Wmk. 372 (II)		80.00	80.00
f.-i.	As "e," 60s, any single		16.00	16.00
1784	A461	Block of 4	8.00	8.00
a.-d.	2.40p, any single		1.00	1.00
e.	Block of 4, Wmk. 372 (II)		100.00	100.00
f.-i.	As "e," 2.40p, any single		20.00	20.00
1785	A461	Pair	5.50	5.50
a.-b.	3.60p, any single		2.25	1.50
c.	Pair, Wmk. 372 (II)		50.00	50.00
d.-e.	As "c," 3.60p, any single		10.00	10.00
	Nos. 1783-1785 (3)		17.50	17.50

See No. 1842.

Bataan Oil Refining Corp., 25th Anniv. — A462

Perf. 13½x13, 13x13½				
1986, Apr. 12			**Wmk. 372**	
1786	A462	60s Refinery, vert.	.50	.35
a.	Wmk. 391		1.00	.50
1787	A462	3p shown	2.50	.85
a.	Wmk. 391		4.00	2.00

EXPO '86, Vancouver — A463

Perf. 13x13½				
1986, May 2			**Wmk. 391**	
1788	A463	60s multicolored	.50	.35
a.	Wmk. 372 (II)		30.00	30.00
1789	A463	3p multicolored	2.50	1.00
a.	Wmk. 372 (II)		30.00	30.00

Asian Productivity Organization, 25th Anniv. — A464

1986, May 15				
1790	A464	60s multicolored	.50	.40
a.	Wmk. 372 (II)		15.00	15.00
1791	A464	3p multicolored	2.50	2.00
a.	Wmk. 372 (II)		15.00	15.00
	Size: 30x22mm			
1792	A464	3p pale brown	1.25	.30
	Nos. 1790-1792 (3)		4.25	2.70

Issued: #1790-1791, 5/15; #1792, 7/10.

AMERIPEX '86 — A465

1986, May 22			Perf. 13½x13	
1793	A465	60s No. 241	.60	.35
a.	Wmk. 372 (II)		7.00	5.00
1794	A465	3p No. 390	2.75	1.00
a.	Wmk. 372 (II)		7.00	5.00

See No. 1835.

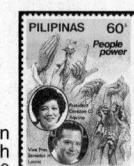

Election of Corazon Aquino, 7th Pres. — A466

Portrait of Aquino and: 60s, Salvador Laurel, vice-president, and hands in symbolic gestures of peace and freedom. 1.20p, Symbols of communication and transportation. 2.40p, Parade. 3p, Military. 7.20p, Vice-president, parade, horiz.

1986, May 25			Wmk. 372	
1795	A466	60s multi	.50	.30
a.	Wmk. 389		.50	.60
1796	A466	1.20p multi	.70	.35
a.	Wmk. 389		.90	.70
1797	A466	2.40p multi	1.25	.40
a.	Wmk. 389		1.60	.80
1798	A466	3p multi	1.50	.50
a.	Wmk. 389		2.00	.90
	Nos. 1795-1798 (4)		3.95	1.55

Souvenir Sheet				
Imperf				
1799	A466	7.20p multi	4.25	4.25
a.	Wmk. 389		4.50	4.00

For surcharge see No. 1939.

De La Salle University, 75th Anniv. — A467

60s, Statue of St. John the Baptist de la Salle, Paco buildings, 1911, & university, 1986. 2.40p, St. Miguel Febres Cordero, buildings, 1911. 3p, St. Benilde, buildings, 1986. 7.20p, Founding fathers.

Perf. 13x13½				
1986, June 16			**Wmk. 391**	
1800	A467	60s grn, blk & pink	.50	.30
1801	A467	2.40p grn, blk & bl	1.50	.50
1802	A467	3p grn, blk & yel	2.50	.75
	Nos. 1800-1802 (3)		4.50	1.55

Souvenir Sheet
Imperf
1803 A467 7.20p grn & blk   6.00 *5.00*

For surcharge see No. 1940.

A468

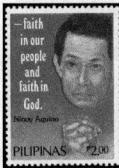

Memorial to Benigno
S. Aquino, Jr. (1932-
83) — A469

3.60p, The Filipino is worth dying for, horiz.
10p, Hindi ka nag-iisa, horiz.

Perf. 13½x13, 13x13½
1986, Aug. 21   **Wmk. 389**
1804 A468   60s dl bluish grn   .60   .30
1805 A469   2p shown   1.25   .40
1806 A469   3.60p multicolored   2.40 1.00
     Nos. 1804-1806 (3)   4.25 1.70

Souvenir Sheet
Imperf
1807 A469   10p multicolored   5.00 4.00

See No. 1836. For surcharges see No. 1914
and 2706A.

Indigenous
Orchids — A470

60s, Vanda sanderiana. 1.20p, Epigeneium
lyonii. 2.40p, Paphiopedilum philippinense. 3p,
Amesiella philippinensis.

1986, Aug. 28   Perf. 13½x13
1808 A470   60s multi   .50   .30
1809 A470   1.20p multi   2.00   .40
1810 A470   2.40p multi   3.50   .80
1811 A470   3p multi   3.50 1.50
     Nos. 1808-1811 (4)   9.50 3.00

For surcharge see No. 1941.

Quiapo District, 400th
Anniv. — A471

60s, Our Lord Jesus the Nazarene, statue,
Quiapo church. 3.60p, Quiapo church, 1930,
horiz.

Perf. 13½x13, 13x13½
1986, Aug. 29   **Wmk. 391**
1812 A471   60s pink, blk & lake   .50   .30
1813 A471   3.60p pale grn, blk &
     dk ultra   3.10   .90

For surcharge see No. 1915.

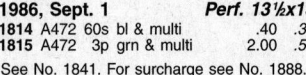

General Hospital,
75th Anniv. — A472

1986, Sept. 1   Perf. 13½x13
1814 A472   60s bl & multi   .40   *.30*
1815 A472   3p grn & multi   2.00   *.50*

See No. 1841. For surcharge see No. 1888.

Halley's
Comet — A473

60s, Comet, Earth. 2.40p, Comet, Earth,
Moon.

Perf. 13x13½
1986, Sept. 25   **Wmk. 389**
1816 A473   60s multi   .80   .30
1817 A473   2.40p multi   2.75   .50

For surcharge see No. 1942.

74th FDI World
Dental Congress,
Manila — A474

1986, Nov. 10   Litho.   Perf. 13x13½
1818 A474   60s Handshake   .80   .30
1819 A474   3p Jeepney bus   5.00 2.00

See Nos. 1837, 1840.

Insects — A475   Intl. Peace
              Year — A476

Perf. 13x13½, 13½x13
1986, Nov. 21
1820 A475   60s Butterfly, beetles   *1.00*   *.40*
1821 A476   1p blue & blk   *2.00*   *.60*
1822 A475   3p Dragonflies   *3.50* 2.00
     Nos. 1820-1822 (3)   *6.50* 3.00

Philately Week.

Manila YMCA, 75th
Anniv. — A477

Perf. 13x13½
1986, Nov. 28   **Wmk. 391**
1823 A477   2p blue   *1.25*   .40
1824 A477   3.60p red   *3.25*   .60

See No. 1839. For surcharge see No. 1916.

Philippine Normal
College, 85th
Anniv. — A478

Various arrangements of college crest and
buildings, 1901-1986.

1986, Dec. 12   Wmk. 389
1825 A478   60s multi   *1.00*   .80
1826 A478   3.60p buff, ultra &
     gldn brn   3.25 1.00

For surcharge see No. 1917.

Christmas
A479

No. 1827, Holy family. No. 1828, Mother
and child, doves. No. 1829, Child touching
mother's face. No. 1830, Adoration of the
shepherds. No. 1831, Mother, child signaling
peace. No. 1832, Holy family, lamb. No. 1833,
Mother, child blessing food.

1986, Dec. 15   Perf. 13½x13, 13x13½
1827 A479   60s multicolored   .50   .30
1828 A479   60s multicolored   .80   .30
1829 A479   60s multicolored   .80   .30
1830 A479   1p multicolored   1.00   .40
1831 A479   1p multicolored   1.00   .40
1832 A479   1p multicolored   1.00   .40
1833 A479   1p multicolored   1.00   .40
     Nos. 1827-1833 (7)   6.10 2.50

Nos. 1827-1829, vert.

No. 1780 Surcharged
Wmk. 391
1987, Jan. 6   *Perf. 13*
1834 A460   1p on 60s vio   1.00   .25

Types of 1986
Designs: 75s, No. 390, AMERIPEX '86. 1p,
Benigno S. Aquino, Jr. 3.25p, Handshake,
74th World Dental Congress. 3.50p, Scales of
Justice. 4p, Manila YMCA emblem. 4.75p,
Jeepney bus. 5p, General Hospital. 5.50p,
Boeing 747, 1980.

Types of 4p
Type I — "4" is taller than "0's."
Type II — "4" is same height as "0's."

1987   Litho.   Perf. 13
Size: 22x31mm, 31x22mm
1835 A465   75s brt yel grn   .75   .25
1836 A468   1p blue   .75   .25
1837 A474   3.25p dull grn   1.50   .75
1838 A459   3.50p dark car   2.00   .40
1839 A477   4p blue, type I   3.00   .40
1839A A477   4p blue, type II   6.00 3.00
1840 A474   4.75p dl yel grn   3.00   .50
1841 A472   5p olive bister   3.00   .50
1842 A461   5.50p dk bl gray   3.00   .80
     Nos. 1835-1842 (9)   23.00 6.85

All No. 1839 dated "1-1-87."
Issued: #1839A, 12/17; others, 1/16.

Manila Hotel, 75th
Anniv. — A480

Perf. 13x13½
1987, Jan. 30   **Wmk. 389**
1843 A480   1p Hotel, c. 1912   .60   .40
1844 A480   4p Hotel, 1987   2.30   .85
1845 A480   4.75p Lobby   3.00 1.25
1846 A480   5.50p Foyer   4.60 1.50
     Nos. 1843-1846 (4)   10.50 4.00

Intl. Eucharistic
Congress, Manila,
50th
Anniv. — A481

1987, Feb. 7   Perf. 13½x13, 13x13½
1847 A481   75s Emblem, vert.   .50   .25
1848 A481   1p shown   .80   .40

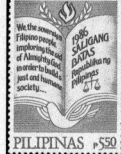

Pres. Aquino   Text — A483
Taking
Oath — A482

1987, Mar. 4   Perf. 13½x13, 13x13½
1849 A482   1p multi   .50   .40
1850 A483   5.50p bl & deep bis   3.00   .80

Ratification of the new constitution.
See No. 1905. For surcharge see No. 2005.

Lyceum College
and Founder,
Jose P.
Laurel — A484

1987, May 7   Litho.   Perf. 13x13½
1851 A484   1p multi   .70   .40
1852 A484   2p multi   1.70 1.00

Lyceum of the Philippines, 35th anniv.

Government Service
Insurance
System — A485

1p, Salary and policy loans. 1.25p, Disabil-
ity, medicare. 2p, Retirement benefits. 3.50p,
Life insurance.

1987, June 1   Perf. 13½x13
1853 A485   1p multi   .50   .40
1854 A485   1.25p multi   .40   .50
1855 A485   2p multi   1.70   .80
1856 A485   3.50p multi   2.00 1.00
     Nos. 1853-1856 (4)   4.60 2.70

Davao City, 50th
Anniv. — A486

1p, Falconer, woman planting, city seal.

1987, Mar. 16   Litho.   Perf. 13x13½
1857 A486   1p multicolored   .85   .40

Salvation Army in the
Philippines, 50th
Anniv. — A487

1987, June 5   Photo.   Perf. 13½x13
1858 A487   1p multi   1.40   .40

Natl. League of
Women Voters, 50th
Anniv. — A488

1987, July 15
1859 A488   1p pink & blue   1.00   .40

A489

#1861, Gen. Vicente Lukban (1860-1916).
#1862, Wenceslao Q. Vinzons (1910-1942).
#1863, Brig.-gen. Mateo M. Capinpin (1887-
1958). #1864, Jesus Balmori (1882-1948).

Perf. 13x13½, 12½ (#1862)
1987   **Litho.**   **Wmk. 391**
1861 A489   1p olive grn   .60   .25
1862 A489   1p dull greenish blue   .70   .25
1863 A489   1p dull red brn   .70   .25
1864 A489   1p rose red &
     claret   .70   .25
     Nos. 1861-1864 (4)   2.70 1.00

Issued: #1861, 7/31; #1862, 9/9; #1863, 10/
15; #1864, 12/17.

A490

Nuns (1862-1987), children, Crucifix,
Sacred Heart.

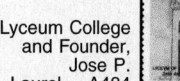

Perf. 13½x13

1987, July 22   Litho.   Wmk. 389
1881 A490 1p multi   1.00   .40

Daughters of Charity of St. Vincent de Paul in the Philippines, 125th anniv.

Map of Southeast Asia, Flags of ASEAN Members — A491

1987, Aug. 7   Perf. 13x13½
1882 A491 1p multi   1.40   .50

ASEAN, 20th anniv.

Exports Campaign — A492

1987, Aug. 11   Wmk. 391   Perf. 13
1883 A492 1p shown   .50   .25
1884 A492 2p Worker, gearwheel   1.00   .30

See No. 1904.

Canonization of Lorenzo Ruiz by Pope John Paul II, Oct. 18 — A493

First Filipino saint: 1p, Ruiz, stained glass window showing Crucifixion. 5.50p, Ruiz at prayer, execution in 1637.

Perf. 13½x13

1987, Oct. 10   Litho.   Wmk. 389
1885 A493 1p multi   1.00   .40
1886 A493 5.50p multi   4.25   1.00

Size: 57x57mm
Imperf
1887 A493 8p like 5.50p   6.00   4.50
Nos. 1885-1887 (3)   11.25   5.90

No. 1887 has denomination at LL.

No. 1841 Surcharged

1987, Oct. 12   Wmk. 391   Perf. 13
1888 A472 4.75p on 5p olive bis   2.30   .70

Order of the Good Shepherd Sisters in Philippines, 65th Anniv. — A494

Perf. 13x13½

1987, Oct. 27   Wmk. 389
1889 A494 1p multi   1.50   .75

Natl. Boy Scout Movement, 50th Anniv. — A495

Founders: J. Vargas, M. Camus, J.E.H. Stevenot, A.N. Luz, V. Lim, C. Romulo and G.A. Daza.

1987, Oct. 28   Litho.   Perf. 13x13½
1890 A495 1p multi   1.40   1.00

Philippine Philatelic Club, 50th Anniv. — A496

1987, Nov. 7   Perf. 13x13½
1891 A496 1p multi   1.25   .75

Order of the Dominicans in the Philippines, 400th Anniv. — A497

Designs: 1p, First missionaries shipwrecked, church and image of the Virgin, vert. 4.75p, J.A. Jeronimo Guerrero, Br., Diego de St. Maria and Letran Dominican College. 5.50p, Pope with Dominican representatives.

Perf. 13½x13, 13x13½

1987, Nov. 11
1892 A497 1p multi   .50   .40
1893 A497 4.75p multi   2.00   .60
1894 A497 5.50p multi   3.00   1.25
Nos. 1892-1894 (3)   5.50   2.25

3rd ASEAN Summit Meeting, Dec. 14-15 — A498

1987, Dec. 5   Perf. 13x13½
1895 A498 4p multicolored   2.75   1.25

Christmas 1987 — A499

No. 1896, Postal service. No. 1897, 5-Pointed stars. No. 1898, Procession, church. No. 1899, Gift exchange. No. 1900, Bamboo cannons. No. 1901, Pig, holiday foods. No. 1902, Traditional foods. No. 1903, Serving meal.

1987, Dec. 8   Perf. 13½x13
1896 A499 1p multicolored   .75   .45
1897 A499 1p multicolored   .75   .45
1898 A499 4p multicolored   2.50   .80
1899 A499 4.75p multicolored   2.50   .80
1900 A499 5.50p multicolored   3.50   1.00
1901 A499 8p multicolored   4.50   1.50
1902 A499 9.50p multicolored   5.00   2.00
1903 A499 11p multicolored   6.00   2.50
Nos. 1896-1903 (8)   25.50   9.50

Exports Type of 1987

Design: Worker, gearwheel.

Wmk. 391
1987, Dec. 16   Litho.   Perf. 13
1904 A492 4.75p lt blue & blk   1.70   .40

Constitution Ratification Type of 1987

1987, Dec. 16   Perf. 13
Size: 22x31½mm
1905 A483 5.50p brt yel grn & fawn   2.00   .50

Grand Masonic Lodge of the Philippines, 75th Anniv. — A500

Perf. 13x13½

1987, Dec. 19   Wmk. 389
1906 A500 1p multi   2.00   .60
a. Wmk. 372 (II)   17.50   8.50

United Nations Projects — A501

Designs: a, Intl. Fund for Agricultural Development (IFAD). b, Transport and Communications Decade for Asia and the Pacific. c, Intl. Year of Shelter for the Homeless (IYSH). d, World Health Day, 1987.

1987, Dec. 22   Litho.   Perf. 13x13½
1907 Strip of 4 + label   7.50   6.00
a.-d. A501 1p, any single   1.50   1.25

Label pictures UN emblem. Exists imperf. Value $25.

7th Opening of Congress — A502

Designs: 1p, Official seals of the Senate and Quezon City House of Representatives, gavel, vert. 5.50p, Congress in session.

Perf. 13½x13, 13x13½

1988, Jan. 25   Wmk. 389
1908 A502 1p multi   .85   .40
1909 A502 5.50p multi   3.85   1.00

St. John Bosco (1815-1888), Educator — A503

1988, Jan. 31   Perf. 13x13½
1910 A503 1p multi   .50   .40
a. Wmk. 372 (II)   1.75   .75
1911 A503 5.50p multi   3.00   .80
a. Wmk. 372 (II)   10.00   2.75

Buy Philippine Goods — A504

1988, Feb. 1   Litho.   Perf. 13½x13
1912 A504 1p buff, ultra, blk & scar   .75   .35
a. Wmk. 372 (II)   1.25   .45

Nos. 1782, 1806, 1813, 1824, 1826 Surcharged
Wmk. 389 (#1914, 1917), 391 (#1913, 1915, 1916)
Perf. 13 (#1782), 13x13½
1988, Feb. 14
1913 A460 3p on 3.60p redsh brn   2.50   .65
1914 A469 3p on 3.60p multi   3.00   .90
1915 A471 3p on 3.60p pale grn, blk & dark ultra   3.50   1.00
1916 A477 3p on 3.60p red   3.00   .65
1917 A478 3p on 3.60p buff, ultra & golden brn   4.00   1.25
Nos. 1913-1917 (5)   16.00   4.45

Use Zip Codes — A505

1988, Feb. 25   Wmk. 391   Perf. 13
1918 A505 60s multi   .35   .25
1919 A505 1p multi   .55   .25

Insects That Prey on Other Insects — A506

1p, Vesbius purpureus. 5.50p, Campsomeris aurulenta.

1988, Mar. 11   Perf. 13
1920 A506 1p multi   .50   .25
1921 A506 5.50p multi   3.00   .65

Solar Eclipse 1988 — A507

Perf. 13x13½

1988, Mar. 18   Wmk. 389
1922 A507 1p multi   .80   .30
a. Wmk. 372 (II)   1.40   .45
1923 A507 5.50p multi   3.75   1.00
a. Wmk. 372 (II)   5.00   1.50

Toribio M. Teodoro (1887-1965), Shoe Manufacturer A508

Wmk. 391
1988, Apr. 27   Litho.   Perf. 13
1924 A508 1p multicolored   .50   .25
1925 A508 1.20p multicolored   1.00   .25

A509   A509a

College of the Holy Spirit, 75th anniv.: 1p, Emblem and motto "Truth in Love." 4p, Arnold Janssen, founder, and Sr. Edelwina, director 1920-1947.

Wmk. 372 (II)
1988, May 22   Perf. 13½x13
1926 A509 1p blk, mar & gold   .50   .35
a. Miniature sheet of 15   17.50
1927 A509a 4p blk, ol grn & mar   2.25   1.00
a. Miniature sheet of 15   70.00

Nos. 1926-1927 were issued in sheets of 50.

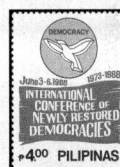

A510

Wmk. 372 (II)
1988, June 4   Litho.   Perf. 13½x13
1928 A510 4p dark ultra, brt blue & blk   3.00   .75
a. Miniature sheet of 15   100.00

Intl. Conf. of Newly Restored Democracies. No. 1928 was issued in sheets of 50. They were also issued in a miniature sheet of 15.

A511

Juan Luna and Felix Hidalgo.

1988, June 15   Wmk. 391   Perf. 13
1929 A511 1p multi   .40   .25
1930 A511 5.50p multi   2.20   .55

First Natl. Juan Luna and Felix Resurrecion Hidalgo Commemorative Exhibition, June 15-Aug. 15. Artists Luna and Hidalgo won medals at the 1884 Madrid Fine Arts Exhibition.

A512

Wmk. 372 (II)
1988, June 22 Litho. Perf. 13½x13

1931	A512	1p multi	.50	.25
a.		Miniature sheet of 15	17.50	
1932	A512	5.50p multi	3.00	.75
a.		Miniature sheet of 15	100.00	

Natl. Irrigation Administration, 25th anniv. Nos. 1931-1932 were issued in sheets of 50. They were also issued in miniature sheets of 15.

Natl. Olympic Committee Emblem and Sporting Events — A513

Designs: 1p, Scuba diving, Siquijor Is. 1.20p, Big game fishing, Aparri, Cagayan Province. 4p, Yachting, Manila Central. 5.50p, Climbing Mt. Apo. 8p, Golf, Cebu, Cebu Is. 11p, Cycling through Marawi, Mindanao Is.

1988, July 11 Perf. 13x13½

1933	A513	1p multi	.50	.35
1934	A513	1.20p multi	.60	.45
1935	A513	4p multi	2.00	.70
1936	A513	5.50p multi	2.40	1.20
1937	A513	8p multi	3.50	1.75
1938	A513	11p multi	4.00	2.00
		Nos. 1933-1938 (6)	13.00	6.45

Exist imperf. 4p, 8p, 1p and 5.50p also exist in strips of 4 plus center label, perf and imperf, picturing torch and inscribed "Philippine Olympic Week, May 1-7, 1988."

Nos. 1797, 1801, 1810 and 1817 Surcharged with 2 Bars and New Value in Black or Gold (#1942)
1988, Aug. 1 As Before

1939	A466	1.90p on 2.40p #1797	1.50	.60
1940	A467	1.90p on 2.40p #1801	2.00	1.25
1941	A470	1.90p on 2.40p #1810	1.50	.60
1942	A473	1.90p on 2.40p #1817	2.00	.60
		Nos. 1939-1942 (4)	7.00	3.05

Land Bank of the Philippines, 25th Anniv. — A514

Philippine Intl. Commercial Bank, 50th Anniv. — A515

Wmk. 372 (II)
1988, Aug. 8 Litho. Perf. 13x13½

1943	A514	1p shown	.50	.40
a.		Miniature sheet of 6	10.00	
1944	A515	1p shown	.50	.40
a.		Miniature sheet of 6	35.00	
1945	A514	5.50p like No. 1943	3.00	.80
a.		Miniature sheet of 6	10.00	
1946	A515	5.50p like No. 1944	3.00	.80
a.		Miniature sheet of 6	35.00	
		Nos. 1943-1946 (4)	7.00	2.40

Nos. 1943-1944 and 1945-1946 exist in se-tenant pairs from center rows of the sheet. Value, $25 and $85, respectively.
Joint uncut sheets of 12 with gutter in between the two miniature sheets of the same denomination exist. Nos. 1944a and 1945a, value, $25. Nos. 1946a and 1947a, value, $85.

Profile of Francisco Balagtas Baltasar (b. 1788), Tagalog Language Poet, Author — A516

Wmk. 391
1988, Aug. 8 Litho. Perf. 13

1947	A516	1p Facing right	.35	.25
1948	A516	1p Facing left	.35	.25
a.		Pair, #1947-1948	1.25	1.25

Quezon Institute, 50th Anniv. — A517

Wmk. 372 (II)
1988, Aug. 18 Litho. Perf. 13x13½

1949	A517	1p multi	.50	.25
a.		Miniature sheet of 15	17.50	
1950	A517	5.50p multi	3.50	.65
a.		Miniature sheet of 15	175.00	

Philippine Tuberculosis Soc. Nos. 1949-1950 were printed in sheets of 50 and were also issued in minature sheets of 15.

Mushrooms — A518

1988, Sept. 13 Wmk. 391 Perf. 13

1951	A518	60s Brown	.35	.25
1952	A518	1p Rat's ear fungus	.50	.25
1953	A518	2p Abalone	1.35	.50
1954	A518	4p Straw	1.80	.75
		Nos. 1951-1954 (4)	4.00	1.75

1988 Summer Olympics, Seoul — A519

1p, Women's archery. 1.20p, Women's tennis. 4p, Boxing. 5.50p, Women's running. 8p, Swimming. 11p, Cycling.

Wmk. 372 (II)
1988, Sept. 19 Perf. 13½x13

1955	A519	1p multi	.50	.45
1956	A519	1.20p multi	.65	.50
1957	A519	4p multi	.65	.85
1958	A519	5.50p multi	2.15	1.20
1959	A519	8p multi	3.00	2.00
1960	A519	11p multi	3.85	2.50
		Nos. 1955-1960 (6)	10.80	7.50

Souvenir Sheet
Imperf

1961		Sheet of 4	15.00	15.00
a.	A519	5.50p Weight lifting	3.25	2.75
b.	A519	5.50p Basketball, horiz.	3.25	2.75
c.	A519	5.50p Judo	3.25	2.75
d.	A519	5.50p Shooting, horiz.	3.25	2.75

Nos. 1955-1960 exist imperf. Value $25.

Department of Justice, Cent. — A520

1988, Sept. 26 Perf. 13x13½

1962	A520	1p multi	.70	.30
a.		Miniature sheet of 6	10.00	

No. 1962 was normally issued in sheets of 50 stamps.

Intl. Red Cross and Red Crescent Organizations, 125th Annivs. — A521

1988, Sept. 30 Perf. 13½x13

1963	A521	1p multi	.50	.25
a.		Miniature sheet of 6	10.00	
1964	A521	5.50p multi	3.00	.75
a.		Miniature sheet of 6	50.00	

No. 1963-1964 were normally issued in sheets of 50.

Christian Children's Fund, 50th Anniv. — A522

1988, Oct. 6

1965	A522	1p multi	.75	.30
a.		Miniature sheet of 6	12.00	

No. 1965 normally issued in sheets of 50.

UN Campaigns — A523

Designs: a, Breast-feeding. b, Growth monitoring. c, Immunization. d, Oral rehydration. e, Oral rehydration therapy. f, Youth on crutches.

1988, Oct. 24 Litho. Perf. 13½x13

1966		Strip of 5	4.00	4.00
a.-e.	A523	1p any single	.60	.40
f.		Miniature sheet of 15	25.00	

Child Survival Campaign (Nos. 1966a-1966d); Decade for Disabled Persons (No. 1966e).
No. 1966 normally issued in sheets of 50.

Bacolod City Charter, 50th Anniv. — A524

1988, Oct. 19 Litho. Perf. 13x13½

1967	A524	1p multi	.80	.35
a.		Miniature sheet of 6	12.00	

No. 1967 normally issued in sheets of 50.

UST Graduate School, 50th Anniv. — A525

1988, Dec. 20 Litho. Perf. 13½x13

1968	A525	1p multi	.75	.30
a.		Miniature sheet of 6	12.00	

No. 1968 was normally issued in sheets of 50.

Dona Aurora Aragon Quezon (b. 1888) — A526

1988, Nov. 7 Wmk. 391 Perf. 13

1969	A526	1p multi	.40	.25
1970	A526	5.50p multi	2.30	.40

Malate Church, 400th Anniv. A527

a, Church, 1776. b, Statue & anniv. emblem. c, Church, 1880. d, Church, 1988. Continuous design.

1988, Dec. 16 Wmk. 391

1971	A527	Block of 4	2.00	2.00
a.-d.		1p any single	.40	.30

UN Declaration of Human Rights, 40th Anniv. — A528

No. 1973, Commission on human rights.

Wmk. 372 (II)
1988, Dec. 9 Perf. 13½x13

1972	A528	1p shown	.65	.35
1973	A528	1p multicolored	.65	.35
a.		Miniature sheet of 12, 6 #1972 and 6 #1973 with gutter between	22.00	
b.		Pair, Nos. 1972-1973 from #1973a	3.00	3.00

Long Distance Telephone Company — A529

1p, Communications tower.

1988, Nov. 28

1974	A529	1p multi	.70	.30
a.		Miniature sheet of 6	9.00	

No. 1974 normally issued in sheets of 50.

Philatelic Week, Nov. 24-30 A530

Emblem and: a, Post Office. b, Stamp counter. c, Framed stamp exhibits, four people. d, Exhibits, 8 people. Has a continuous design.

1988, Nov. 24 Wmk. 391 Perf. 13

1975	A530	Block of 4	3.50	2.50
a.-d.		1p any single	.55	.40
e.		As "a," dated "1938" (error)	8.00	6.50

Christmas — A531

Designs: 75s, Handshake, peave dove, vert. 1p, Children making ornaments, vert. 2p, Boy carrying decoration. 3.50p, Tree, vert. 4.75p, Candle, vert. 5.50p, Man, star, heart.

1988, Dec. 2

1976	A531	75s multi	.50	.30
1977	A531	1p multi	.50	.25
1978	A531	2p multi	1.00	.30
1979	A531	3.50p multi	1.50	.35
1980	A531	4.75p multi	2.00	.40
1981	A531	5.50p multi	2.50	.50
		Nos. 1976-1981 (6)	8.00	2.10

Gen. Santos City, 50th Anniv. — A532

Wmk. 372 (II)
1989, Feb. 27 Litho. Perf. 13x13½

1982	A532	1p multi	.80	.30
a.		Miniature sheet of 6	10.00	

No. 1982 normally issued in sheets of 50.

Guerrilla Fighters A533

Emblem and: No. 1983, Miguel Z. Ver (1918-42). No. 1984, Eleuterio L. Adevoso (1922-75). Printed in continuous design.

1989, Feb. 18   **Wmk. 391**
1983	1p multi	.50	.25
1984	1p multi	.50	.25
a.	A533 Pair, #1983-1984	1.50	.75

Oblates of Mary Immaculate, 50th Anniv. — A534

Wmk. 372 (II)
1989, Feb. 17   *Perf. 13½x13*
1985	A534 1p multicolored	.60	.30
a.	Miniature sheet of 6	14.00	

No. 1985 normally issued in sheets of 50.

Fiesta Islands '89 — A535

No. 1986, Turumba. No. 1987, Pahiyas. No. 1988, Pagoda Sa Wawa. No. 1989, Masskara. No. 1990, Independence Day. No. 1990A, like #1995. No. 1991, Sinulog. No. 1992, Cagayan de Oro. No. 1993, Grand Canao. No. 1994, Lenten festival. No. 1995, Penafrancia. No. 1996, Fireworks. No. 1997, Iloilo Paraw regatta.

Perf. 13 (Nos. 1991, 1994, 1997), 13½x14
1989-90   **Litho.**   **Wmk. 391**
1986	A535	60s multicolored	.35	.25
1987	A535	75s multicolored	.35	.25
1988	A535	1p multicolored	.35	.25
1989	A535	1p multicolored	.50	.25
1990	A535	3.50p multicolored	1.20	.35
1990A	A535	4p multicolored	2.50	.40
1991	A535	4.75p multicolored	1.30	.35
1992	A535	4.75p multicolored	1.30	.35
1993	A535	4.75p multicolored	1.30	.35
1994	A535	5.50p multicolored	1.30	.50
1995	A535	5.50p multicolored	1.65	.55
1996	A535	5.50p multicolored	1.85	.60
1997	A535	6.25p multicolored	2.30	.90
	Nos. 1986-1997 (13)		16.25	5.35

Issued: No. 1991, 1994, 6.25p, 3/1/89; 60s, 75s, 3.50p, 6/28/89; No. 1988, 1992, 1995, 9/1/89; No. 1989, 1993, 1996, 12/4/89; 4p, 8/6/90.

Great Filipinos — A536

Men and women: a, Don Tomas B. Mapua (1888-), educator. b, Camilo O. Osias (1889-), educator. c, Dr. Olivia D. Salamanca (1889-), physician. d, Dr. Francisco S. Santiago (1889-), composer. e, Leandro H. Fernandez (1889-), educator.

Wmk. 372 (II)
1989, May 18   **Litho.**   *Perf. 14x13½*
1998	Strip of 5	4.00	3.00
a.-e.	A536 1p any single	.50	.30

See Nos. 2022, 2089, 2151, 2240, 2307, 2360, 2414, 2486, 2536.

26th World Congress of the Intl. Federation of Landscape Architects — A537

Designs: a, Adventure Pool. b, Paco Park. c, Beautification of Malacanang area streets. d, Erosion control at an upland farm.

1989, May 31   **Wmk. 391**
1999	A537 Block of 4	2.00	2.00
a.-d.	1p any single	.40	.30

Printed in continuous design.

French Revolution, Bicent. — A538

1989, July 1   **Wmk. 372 (II)**   *Perf. 14*
2000	A538 1p multicolored	.50	.30
a.	Miniature sheet of 6	10.00	
2001	A538 5.50p multicolored	2.50	.60
a.	Miniature sheet of 6	40.00	

Nos. 2000-2001 normally issued in sheets of 50.

Supreme Court — A539

1989, June 11   **Wmk. 372 (II)**
2002	A539 1p multicolored	.65	.30
a.	Miniature sheet of 6	10.00	

No. 2002 normally issued in sheets of 50.

Natl. Science and Technology Week — A540

No. 2003, GNP chart. No. 2004, Science High School emblem.

1989, July 14
2003	1p multicolored	.40	.30
2004	1p multicolored	.40	.30
a.	A540 Pair, #2003-2004	1.00	.70
b.	Miniature sheet of 6, #2003-2004	7.50	

No. 2003-2004 normally issued in sheets of 50.

No. 1905 Surcharged
Wmk. 391
1989, Aug. 21   **Litho.**   *Perf. 13*
2005	A483 4.75p on 5.50p	1.50	.40

Philippine Environment Month A542

No. 2006, Palawan peacock pheasant. No. 2007, Palawan bear cat.

Wmk. 391
1989, June 5   **Litho.**   *Perf. 14*
2006	1p multicolored	.60	.30
2007	1p multicolored	.60	.30
a.	A542 Pair, #2006-2007	2.00	2.00

Asia-Pacific Telecommunity, 10th Anniv. — A544

Wmk. 372 (II)
1989, Oct. 30   **Litho.**   *Perf. 14*
2008	A544 1p multicolored	.75	.30
a.	Miniature sheet of 6	10.00	

No. 2008 normally issued in sheets of 50.

Dept. of Natl. Defense, 50th Anniv. — A545

1989, Oct. 23
2009	A545 1p multicolored	.75	.30
a.	Miniature sheet of 6	10.00	

No. 2009 normally issued in sheets of 50.

Intl. Maritime Organization A546

1989, Nov. 13   *Perf. 14*
2010	A546 1p multicolored	.80	.30
a.	Miniature sheet of 6	12.00	

No. 2010 normally issued in sheets of 50.

World Stamp Expo '89 — A546a

1989, Nov. 17   **Litho.**   *Perf. 14*
2010A	A546a 1p #1, Y1	.70	.40
d.	Miniature sheet of 6	12.00	12.00
2010B	A546a 4p #219, 398	2.50	.80
e.	Miniature sheet of 6	35.00	35.00
2010C	A546a 5.50p #N1, 500	3.70	1.00
f.	Miniature sheet of 6	65.00	65.00
	Nos. 2010A-2010C (3)	6.90	2.20

Nos. 2010A-2010C withdrawn from sale week of release, but placed on sale again a few weeks later.

Nos. 2010A-2010C normally issued in sheets of 50.

Teaching Philately in the Classroom, Close-up of Youth Collectors — A547

1989, Nov. 20   *Perf. 14x13½*
2011	A547 1p shown	.60	.30
2012	A547 1p Class, diff.	.60	.30

Christmas — A548

60s, Annunciation. 75s, Visitation. 1p, Journey to Bethlehem. 2p, Search for the inn. 4p, Appearance of the star. 4.75p, Birth of Jesus Christ.

1989, Nov. 10   *Perf. 13½x14*
2013	A548 60s multi	.40	.25
2014	A548 75s multi	.50	.25
2015	A548 1p multi	.50	.25
2016	A548 2p multi	1.00	.40
2017	A548 4p multi	1.50	.60
2018	A548 4.75p multi	2.00	1.00
	Nos. 2013-2018 (6)	5.90	2.75

First-day covers are canceled Nov. 8.

11th World Cardiology Congress — A549

Wmk. 391
1990, Feb. 12   **Photo.**   *Perf. 14*
2019	A549 5.50p black, dark red & deep blue	1.50	.40

Beer Production, Cent. — A550

1990, Apr. 16
2020	A550 1p multicolored	.40	.30
2021	A550 5.50p multicolored	1.60	.50

Great Filipinos Type of 1989

Designs: a, Claro M. Recto (1890-1960), politician. b, Manuel H. Bernabe. c, Guillermo E. Tolentino. d, Elpidio R. Quirino (1890-1956), politician. e, Bienvenido Ma. Gonzalez.

Wmk. 372 (II)
1990, June 1   **Litho.**   *Perf. 14x13½*
2022	Strip of 5, #a.-e.	4.00	3.00

1990 Census A551

Wmk. 391
1990, Apr. 30   **Photo.**   *Perf. 14*
Color of Buildings
2023	1p light blue	.50	.30
2024	1p peach	.50	.30
a.	A551 Pair, #2023-2024	1.25	1.25

Legion of Mary, 50th Anniv. — A552

1990, July 21   **Photo.**   *Perf. 14*
2025	A552 1p multicolored	.75	.30

Girl Scouts of the Philippines, 50th Anniv. — A553

1990, May 21
2026	A553 1p yellow & multi	.50	.30
2027	A553 1.20p lt lilac & multi	.60	.35

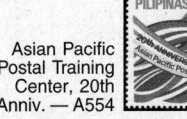

Asian Pacific Postal Training Center, 20th Anniv. — A554

Wmk. 391
1990, Sept. 10   **Photo.**   *Perf. 14*
2028	A554 1p red & multi	.50	.30
2029	A554 4p blue & multi	1.50	.50

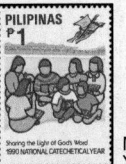

Natl. Catechetical Year — A555

1990, Sept. 28
2030	A555	1p blk & multi	.50	.30
2031	A555	3.50p grn & multi	1.30	.40

Intl. Literacy Year — A556

1990, Oct. 24   Photo.   Perf. 14
2032	A556	1p blk, org & grn	.50	.30
2033	A556	5.50p blk, yel & grn	2.00	.50

UN Development Program, 40th Anniv. — A557

1990, Oct. 24
2034	A557	1p yel & multi	.50	.30
2035	A557	5.50p orange & multi	2.00	.50

Flowers — A558

1990   Photo.   Wmk. 391   Perf. 14
2036	A558	1p Waling waling	1.00	.35
2037	A558	4p Sampaguita	2.25	.70

29th Orient and Southeast Asian Lions forum.
Issued: 1p, Oct. 3; 4p, Oct. 18.

A559

Christmas — A560

Drawings of the Christmas star: a, Yellow star, pink beading. b, Yellow star, white beading. c, Green, blue, yellow and orange star. d, Red star, white outlines.

1990, Dec. 3
2038	A559	Strip of 4	3.00	2.50
a.-d.		1p any single	.60	.40
2039	A560	5.50p multicolored	4.00	1.50

Blind Safety Day — A561

1990, Dec. 7   Photo.   Perf. 14
2040	A561	1p bl, blk & yel	.75	.40

Publication of Rizal's "Philippines After 100 Years," Cent. — A562

1990, Dec.17
2041	A562	1p multicolored	.75	.40

Philatelic Week — A563

Paintings: 1p, Family by F. Amorsolo. 4.75p, The Builders by V. Edades. 5.50p, Laughter by A. Magsaysay-Ho.

1990, Nov. 16
2042	A563	1p multicolored	.50	.30
2043	A563	4.75p multi, vert.	1.50	.40
2044	A563	5.50p multi, vert.	1.75	.60
		Nos. 2042-2044 (3)	3.75	1.20

A564

1991, Jan. 30
2045	A564	1p multicolored	.60	.30

2nd Plenary Council of the Philippines.

A565

1991, Mar. 15   Litho.   Perf. 14
2046	A565	1p multicolored	.50	.30
2047	A565	5.50p multicolored	1.00	.50

Philippine Airlines, 50th anniv. No. 2047 is airmail.

Flowers — A566

Flowers: 1p, 2p, Plumeria. 4p, 6p, Ixora. 4.75p, 7p, Bougainvillea. 5.50p, 8p, Hibiscus.

1991   Photo.   Perf. 14x13½
"1991" Below Design
2048	A566	60s Gardenia	.35	.25
2049	A566	75s Allamanda	.35	.25
2050	A566	1p yellow	.40	.25
2051	A566	1p red	.40	.25
2052	A566	1p salmon	.40	.25
2053	A566	1p white	.40	.25
a.		Block of 4, #2050-2053	2.00	2.00
2054	A566	1.20p Nerium	.70	.25
2055	A566	1.50p like #2048	.85	.30
2056	A566	2p yellow	.90	.30
2057	A566	2p red	.90	.30
2058	A566	2p rose & yel	.90	.30
2059	A566	2p white	.90	.30
a.		Block of 4, #2056-2059	4.25	4.25
2060	A566	3p like #2054	1.40	.35
2061	A566	3.25p Cananga	1.50	.45
2062	A566	4p dull rose	1.50	.50
2063	A566	4p pale yellow	1.50	.50
2064	A566	4p orange yel	1.50	.50
2065	A566	4p scarlet	1.50	.50
a.		Block of 4, #2062-2065	9.00	9.00
2066	A566	4.75p vermilion	2.00	.70
2067	A566	4.75p brt rose lil	2.00	.70
2068	A566	4.75p white	2.00	.70
2069	A566	4.75p lilac rose	2.00	.70
a.		Block of 4, #2066-2069	10.00	10.00
2070	A566	5p Canna	2.50	.80
2071	A566	5p like #2061	2.50	.80
2072	A566	5.50p red	2.00	.85
2073	A566	5.50p yellow	2.00	.85
2074	A566	5.50p white	2.00	.85
2075	A566	5.50p pink	2.00	.85
a.		Block of 4, #2072-2075	12.50	12.50
2076	A566	6p dull rose	2.75	1.00
2077	A566	6p pale yellow	2.75	1.00
2078	A566	6p orange yel	2.75	1.00
2079	A566	6p scarlet	2.75	1.00
a.		Block of 4, #2076-2079	13.00	13.00
2080	A566	7p vermilion	3.00	1.10
2081	A566	7p brt rose lil	3.00	1.10
2082	A566	7p white	3.00	1.10
2083	A566	7p dp lil rose	3.00	1.10
a.		Block of 4, #2080-2083	15.00	15.00
2084	A566	8p red	3.50	1.25
2085	A566	8p yellow	3.50	1.25
2086	A566	8p white	3.50	1.25
2087	A566	8p deep pink	3.50	1.25
a.		Block of 4, #2084-2087	16.50	16.50
2088	A566	10p like #2070	5.00	2.00
		Nos. 2048-2088 (41)	79.35	29.25

Issued: Nos. 2053a, 2075a, 4/1/91. Nos. 2048, 2049, 2061, 4/11. Nos. 2054, 2065a, 2069a, 2070, 6/7. Nos. 2059a, 2079a, 2083a, 2087a, 12/1. Nos. 2055, 2060, 2071, 2088, 12/13.

1992-93   "1992" Below Design
2048a	A566	60s Gardenia	1.50	.50
2050a	A566	1p yellow	1.50	.50
2051a	A566	1p red	1.50	.50
2052a	A566	1p salmon	1.50	.50
2053c	A566	1p white	1.50	.50
d.		Block of 4, #2050a- 2052a, 2053c	8.50	8.50
2053B	A566	1p like		
		#2049	.75	.35
2055a	A566	1.50p like #2048	4.00	.60
2056a	A566	2p yellow	2.00	.45
2057a	A566	2p red	2.00	.45
2058a	A566	2p rose & yel	2.00	.45
2059b	A566	2p white	2.00	.45
c.		Block of 4, #2056a- 2058a, 2059b	11.50	11.50
2060a	A566	3p like #2054	2.00	.80
2071a	A566	5p like #2061	20.00	2.00
2076a	A566	6p dull rose	5.00	2.50
2077a	A566	6p pale yellow	5.00	2.50
2078a	A566	6p orange yel	5.00	2.50
2079b	A566	6p scarlet	5.00	2.50
c.		Block of 4, #2076a- 2078a, 2079b	40.00	40.00
2080a	A566	7p vermilion	8.50	4.00
2081a	A566	7p brt rose lil	8.50	4.00
2082a	A566	7p white	8.50	4.00
2083b	A566	7p dp lil rose	8.50	4.00
c.		Block of 4, #2080a- 2082a, 2083b	50.00	50.00
2084a	A566	8p red	8.50	4.00
2085a	A566	8p yellow	8.50	4.00
2086a	A566	8p white	8.50	4.00
2087b	A566	8p deep pink	8.50	4.00
c.		Block of 4, #2084a- 2086a, 2087b	50.00	50.00
2088a	A566	10p like #2070	13.50	3.00
		Nos. 2048a-2088a (26)	143.75	53.05

Issued: 2059c, 1/24/92. 2053d, 2060a, 2/10. #2079c, 2/12. No. 2083c, 2/27. No. 2048a, 3/4. No. 2071a, 3/24. No. 2087c, 3/25. No. 2088a, 9/22. No. 2053B, 1/23/93.
No. 2053B, although issued in 1993, is inscribed "1992."

Great Filipinos Type of 1989

Designs: a, Jorge B. Vargas (1890-1980). b, Ricardo M. Paras (1891-1984). c, Jose P. Laurel (1891-1959), politician. d, Vicente Fabella (1891-1959). e, Maximo M. Kalaw (1891-1954).

1991, June 3   Litho.   Perf. 14x13½
2089	A536	1p Strip of 5, #a.-e.	4.00	3.00

12th Asia-Pacific Boy Scout Jamboree A567

1p, Square knot. 4p, Sheepshank knot. 4.75p, Figure 8 knot.

1991, Apr. 22   Perf. 14x13½
2090	A567	1p multicolored	.50	.30
2091	A567	4p multicolored	1.25	.40
2092	A567	4.75p multicolored	1.50	.50
a.		Souv. sheet of 3, #2090-2092, imperf.	6.00	6.00
		Nos. 2090-2092 (3)	3.25	1.20

No. 2092a sold for 16.50p and has simulated perfs.

Antipolo by Carlos V. Francisco — A568

1991, June 23   Litho.   Perf. 14
Granite Paper
2093	A568	1p multicolored	.80	.30

Pithecophaga Jefferyi — A569

1p, Head. 4.75p, Perched on limb. 5.50p, In flight. 8p, Feeding young.

1991, July 31   Photo.
2094	A569	1p multi	1.00	.40
2095	A569	4.75p multi	2.10	.60
2096	A569	5.50p multi	3.50	1.00
2097	A569	8p multi	5.00	2.00
		Nos. 2094-2097 (4)	11.60	4.00

World Wildlife Fund.

Philippine Bar Association, Cent. — A570

Wmk. 391
1991, Aug. 20   Photo.   Perf. 14
2098	A570	1p multicolored	.60	.30

A571

1991, Aug. 29
2099	A571	1p multicolored	.75	.30

Size: 82x88mm
Imperf
2100	A571	16p like #2099	7.50	6.00

Induction of Filipinos into USAFFE (US Armed Forces in the Far East), 50th Anniv. For overprint see No. 2193.

A572

Independence Movement, cent.: a, Basil at graveside. b, Simon carrying lantern. c, Father Florentino, treasure chest. d, Sister Juli with rosary.

1991, Sept. 18
2101	A572	1p Block of 4, #a.-d.	4.00	4.00

A573

Wmk. 391
1991, Oct. 15   Photo.   Perf. 14
2102	A573	1p multicolored	.65	.30

Size: 60x60mm
Imperf
2103	A573	16p multicolored	6.00	5.00

St. John of the Cross, 400th death anniv.

United Nations Agencies — A574

Designs: 1p, UNICEF, children. 4p, High Commissioner for Refugees, hands supporting boat people. 5.50p, Postal Administration, 40th anniv., UN #29, #C3.

1991, Oct. 24   Perf. 14
2104	A574	1p multicolored	.35	.30
2105	A574	4p multicolored	1.00	.30
2106	A574	5.50p multicolored	1.50	.60
		Nos. 2104-2106 (3)	2.85	1.20

Philatelic Week — A575

Paintings: 2p, Bayanihan by Carlos Francisco. 7p, Sari-sari Vendor by Mauro Malang Santos. 8p, Give Us This Day by Vicente Manansala.

1991, Nov. 20

2107	A575	2p multicolored	.50	.30
2108	A575	7p multicolored	2.00	.50
2109	A575	8p multicolored	2.50	.70
	Nos. 2107-2109 (3)		5.00	1.50

16th Southeast Asian Games, Manila — A576

#2110, Gymnastics, games emblem at UR. #2111, Gymnastics, games emblem at LR. #2112, Martial arts, games emblem at LL, vert. #2113, Martial arts, games emblem at LR, vert.

Wmk. 391
1991, Nov. 22   **Photo.**   **Perf. 14**

2110	A576	2p multicolored	.40	.35
2111	A576	2p multicolored	.40	.35
a.	A576	Pair, #2110-2111	1.50	1.00
2112	A576	6p multicolored	1.00	.50
2113	A576	6p multicolored	1.00	.50
a.	A576	Pair, #2112-2113	3.00	2.00
b.		Souv. sheet of 2, #2112-2113, imperf.	4.00	3.50
c.		Souv. sheet of 4, #2110-2113	5.00	4.75
	Nos. 2110-2113 (4)		2.80	1.70

No. 2113b has simulated perforations.

No. 1585 Surcharged in Red
Souvenir Sheet
1991, Nov. 27   **Wmk. 372**   **Imperf.**

2114	A385	4p on 3.20p	3.50	3.50

First Philippine Philatelic Convention.

Children's Christmas Paintings — A577

1991, Dec. 4   **Wmk. 391**   **Perf. 14**

2115	A577	2p shown	.60	.30
2116	A577	6p Wrapped gift	2.00	.50
2117	A577	7p Santa, tree	2.40	.70
2118	A577	8p Tree, star	3.00	1.00
	Nos. 2115-2118 (4)		8.00	2.50

Insignias of Military Groups Inducted into USAFFE A578

White background: No. 2119a, 1st Regular Div. b, 2nd Regular Div. c, 11th Div. d, 21st Div. e, 31st Div. f, 41st Div. g, 51st Div. h, 61st Div. i, 71st Div. j, 81st Div. k, 91st Div. l, 101st Div. m, Bataan Force. n, Philippine Div. o, Philippine Army Air Corps. p, Offshore Patrol. Nos. 2120a-2120p, like #2119a-2119p with yellow background.

Perf. 14x13½
1991, Dec. 8   **Photo.**   **Wmk. 391**

2119	A578	2p Block of 16, #a.-p.	16.50	20.00
2120	A578	2p Block of 16, #a.-p.	16.50	20.00
q.		Block of 32, #2119-2120	50.00	70.00

Induction of Filipinos into USAFFE, 50th anniv.
Nos. 2119-2120 were printed in sheets of 200 containing 5 #2120q plus five blocks of 8.

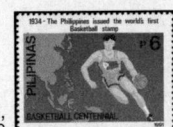

Basketball, Cent. — A579

Designs: 2p, PBA Games, vert. 6p, Map, player dribbling. 7p, Early players. 8p, Men shooting basketball, vert. 16p, Tip-off.

Wmk. 391
1991, Dec. 19   **Litho.**   **Perf. 14**

2121	A579	2p multicolored	.70	.30
2122	A579	6p multicolored	1.80	.50
2123	A579	7p multicolored	2.50	.80
2124	A579	8p multicolored	3.00	1.20
a.		Souv. sheet of 4, #2121-2124	8.50	7.25
	Nos. 2121-2124 (4)		8.00	2.80

Souvenir Sheet
Imperf

2125	A579	16p multicolored	6.50	6.50

No. 2125 has simulated perforations.

New Year 1992, Year of the Monkey — A580

Wmk. 391
1991, Dec. 27   **Litho.**   **Perf. 14**

2126	A580	2p violet & multi	1.50	.40
2127	A580	6p green & multi	3.50	1.00

See Nos. 2459a, 2460a.

Services and Products — A581

Wmk. 391
1992, Jan. 15   **Litho.**   **Perf. 14**

2128	A581	2p Mailing center	.50	.30
2129	A581	6p Housing project	1.25	.40
2130	A581	7p Livestock	1.75	.65
2131	A581	8p Handicraft	2.00	1.00
	Nos. 2128-2131 (4)		5.50	2.35

Medicinal Plants — A582

2p, Curcuma longa. 6p, Centella asiatica. 7p, Cassia alata. 8p, Ervatamia pandacaqui.

Wmk. 391
1992, Feb. 7   **Litho.**   **Perf. 14**

2132	A582	2p multi	.80	.30
2133	A582	6p multi	1.60	.50
2134	A582	7p multi	2.00	.60
2135	A582	8p multi	2.80	.80
	Nos. 2132-2135 (4)		7.20	2.20

Love — A583

"I Love You" in English on Nos. 2137a-2140a, in Filipino on Nos. 2137b-2140b with designs: No. 2137, Letters, map. No. 2138, Heart, doves. No. 2139, Bouquet of flowers. No. 2140, Map, Cupid with bow and arrow.

Wmk. 391
1992, Feb. 10   **Photo.**   **Perf. 14**

2137	A583	2p Pair, #a.-b.	1.00	1.00
2138	A583	6p Pair, #a.-b.	3.00	3.00
2139	A583	7p Pair, #a.-b.	4.00	4.00
2140	A583	8p Pair, #a.-b.	8.50	8.50
	Nos. 2137-2140 (4)		16.50	16.50

A584

Wmk. 391
1992, Apr. 12   **Litho.**   **Perf. 14**

2141	A584	2p blue & multi	.50	.30
2142	A584	8p red vio & multi	2.30	.60

Our Lady of Sorrows of Porta Vaga, 400th anniv.

A585

Expo '92, Seville: 2p, Man and woman celebrating. 8p, Philippine discovery scenes. 16p, Pavilion, horiz.

1992, Mar. 27

2143	A585	2p multicolored	.50	.30
2144	A585	8p multicolored	2.30	.70

Souvenir Sheet
Imperf

2145	A585	16p multicolored	7.50	6.00

Department of Agriculture, 75th Anniv. — A586

a, Man planting seed. b, Fish trap. c, Pigs.

1992, May 4

2146	A586	2p Strip of 3, #a.-c.	2.40	2.40

Manila Jockey Club, 125th Anniv. — A588

Wmk. 391
1992, May 14   **Litho.**   **Perf. 14**

2149	A588	2p multicolored	1.00	.40

Souvenir Sheet
Imperf

2150	A588	8p multicolored	4.00	3.00

No. 2150 has simulated perfs.

Great Filipinos Type of 1989

Designs: a, Pres. Manuel A. Roxas (1892-1948). b, Justice Natividad Almeda-Lopez (1892-1977). c, Justice Roman A. Ozaeta (b. 1892). d, Engracia Cruz-Reyes (1892-1975). e, Fernando Amorsolo (1892-1972).

Perf. 14x13½
1992, June 1   **Wmk. 391**

2151	A536	2p Strip of 5, #a.-e.	4.00	3.00

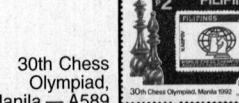

30th Chess Olympiad, Manila — A589

#2154: a, like #2152. b, like #2153.

1992, June 7   **Perf. 14**

2152	A589	2p No. 1352	.60	.30
2153	A589	6p No. B21	1.80	.50

Souvenir Sheet
Imperf

2154	A589	8p Sheet of 2, #a.-b.	6.00	5.25

No. 2154 has simulated perfs.

World War II, 50th Anniv. — A590

2p, Bataan, cross. 6p, Insignia of defenders of Bataan & Corregidor. 8p, Corregidor, Monument. #2158, Cross, map of Bataan. #2159, Monument, map of Corregidor.

Wmk. 391
1992, June 12   **Photo.**   **Perf. 14**

2155	A590	2p multicolored	.60	.30
2156	A590	6p multicolored	1.50	.40
2157	A590	8p multicolored	1.90	.60

Size: 63x76mm, 76x63mm
Imperf

2158	A590	16p multicolored	6.50	5.00
2159	A590	16p multicolored	6.50	5.00
	Nos. 2155-2159 (5)		17.00	11.30

Nos. 2158-2159 have simulated perforations.

President Corazon C. Aquino and President-Elect Fidel V. Ramos — A591

1992, June 30   **Perf. 14**

2160	A591	2p multicolored	.75	.40

Anniversary of Democracy.

Jose Rizal's Exile to Dapitan, Cent. — A592

1992, June 17

2161	A592	2p Dapitan shrine	1.20	.35
2162	A592	2p Portrait, vert.	1.20	.35

ASEAN, 25th Anniv. — A593

Contemporary paintings: Nos. 2163, 2165, Spirit of ASEAN. Nos. 2164, 2166, ASEAN Sea.

Wmk. 391
1992, July 18   **Litho.**   **Perf. 14**

2163	A593	2p multicolored	.60	.30
2164	A593	2p multicolored	.60	.30
2165	A593	6p multicolored	1.60	.50
2166	A593	6p multicolored	1.60	.50
	Nos. 2163-2166 (4)		4.40	1.60

Founding of Katipunan, Cent. — A594

Details or entire paintings of revolutionaries, by Carlos "Botong" Francisco: No. 2167a, Preparing for battle, vert. No. 2167b, Attack leader (detail), vert. No. 2168a, Attack. No. 2168b, Signing papers.

Wmk. 391
1992, July 27   **Photo.**   **Perf. 14**

2167	A594	2p Pair, #a.-b.	2.00	1.50
2168	A594	2p Pair, #a.-b.	2.00	1.50

Philippine
League,
Cent. — A595

Wmk. 391

1992, July 31		Photo.	*Perf. 14*
2169 A595	2p multicolored	1.00	.75

1992 Summer
Olympics,
Barcelona
A596

Wmk. 391

1992, Aug. 4		Litho.	*Perf. 14*
2170 A596	2p Swimming	.60	.40
2171 A596	7p Boxing	2.20	.60
2172 A596	8p Hurdling	2.50	.75
	Nos. 2170-2172 (3)	5.30	1.75

Souvenir Sheet

Imperf

2172A A596	Sheet of 3, #2171-2172, #2172Ab	6.00	6.00
b.	1p like #2170	.65	.65

No. 2172A has simulated perforations.

Religious of the
Assumption in
Philippines, Cent.
A597

Cathedral of
San
Sebastian,
Cent.
A597a

Wmk. 391

1992, Aug. 15		Photo.	*Perf. 14*
2173 A597	2p multicolored	.60	.30
2174 A597a	2p multicolored	.60	.30

Founding of Nilad
Masonic Lodge,
Cent. — A598

Various Masonic symbols and: 6p, A. Luna.
8p, M.H. Del Pilar.

Wmk. 391

1992, Aug. 15		Photo.	*Perf. 14*
2175 A598	2p green & black	1.20	.80
2176 A598	6p yellow, black & brown	2.75	1.20
2177 A598	8p blue, black & violet	3.50	2.00
	Nos. 2175-2177 (3)	7.45	4.00

Pres. Fidel V.
Ramos Taking
Oath of Office,
June 30,
1992 — A599

1992, July 30			
2178 A599	2p Ceremony, people	.75	.30
2179 A599	8p Ceremony, flag	2.00	.70

Freshwater Aquarium Fish — A600

Designs: No. 2180a, Red-tailed guppy, b, Tiger lacetail guppy. d, Flamingo guppy. e, Neon tuxedo guppy. e, King cobra guppy.
No. 2181a, Black moor. b, Bubble eye. c, Pearl scale goldfish. d, Red cap. e, Lionhead goldfish.
No. 2182, Golden arowana.
No. 2183a, Delta topsail variatus. b, Orange spotted hi-fin platy. c, Red lyretail swordtail. d, Bleeding heart hi-fin platy.
No. 2184a, 6p, Green discus. b, 6p, Brown discus. c, 7p, Red discus. d, 7p, Blue discus.

1992, Sept. 9		*Perf. 14*
2180 A600	1.50p Strip of 5, #a.-e.	4.00	4.00
2181 A600	2p Strip of 5, #a.-e.	4.00	4.00

Imperf

Size: 65x45mm

2182 A600	8p multicolored	5.00	3.50

Souvenir Sheets of 4

Perf. 14

2183 A600	4p #a.-d.	6.00	6.00
2184 A600	6p, 7p #a.-d.	11.00	11.00

Nos. 2182 and 2184 were overprinted "PHILIPPINE STAMP EXHIBITION 1992 — TAIPEI" in margins. Most of this overprinted issue was sold to the dealer to co-sponsored the exhibit. Value, $6 and $12, respectively.
See Nos. 2253-2257.

Birthday
Greetings — A601

1992, Sept 28		*Perf. 14*
2185 A601	2p Couple dancing	.60	.30
2186 A601	6p like #2185	1.50	.50
2187 A601	7p Cake, balloons	1.50	.50
2188 A601	8p like #2187	2.00	.75
	Nos. 2185-2188 (4)	5.60	2.05

Columbus'
Discovery of
America, 500th
Anniv. — A602

Various fruits and vegetables.

1992, Oct. 14		
2189 A602	2p multicolored	.60	.30
2190 A602	6p multi, diff.	1.60	.50
2191 A602	8p multi, diff.	2.30	.60
	Nos. 2189-2191 (3)	4.50	1.40

Intl. Conference
on Nutrition,
Rome — A603

1992, Oct. 27		
2192 A603	2p multicolored	.70	.30

No. 2100 Ovptd. in Blue "Second / National Philatelic Convention / Cebu, Philippines, Oct. 22-24, 1992"

Wmk. 391

1992, Oct. 15		Photo.	*Imperf.*
2193 A571	16p multicolored	6.50	6.00

Christmas — A604

Various pictures of mother and child.

Wmk. 391

1992, Nov. 5		Litho.	*Perf. 14*
2194 A604	2p multicolored	.75	.40
2195 A604	6p multicolored	2.00	.60
2196 A604	7p multicolored	2.00	.80
2197 A604	8p multicolored	2.50	1.20
	Nos. 2194-2197 (4)	7.25	3.00

No. 1452 Ovptd. "INAUGURATION OF THE PHILIPPINE POSTAL MUSEUM / AND PHILATELIC LIBRARY, NOVEMBER 10, 1992" in Red

Wmk. 372

1992, Nov. 10		Litho.	*Imperf.*

Souvenir Sheet

2198 A348	5p multicolored	3.50	3.50

Fight Against Drug
Abuse — A605

Wmk. 391

1992, Nov. 15		Litho.	*Perf. 14*
2199 A605	2p People, boat	.60	.30
2200 A605	8p People, boat, diff.	1.80	.60

A606

Paintings: 2p, Family, by Cesar Legaspi. 6p, Pounding Rice, by Nena Saguil. 7p, Fish Vendors, by Romeo V. Tabuena.

1992, Nov. 24		
2201 A606	2p multicolored	.60	.30
2202 A606	6p multicolored	1.60	.50
2203 A606	7p multicolored	1.80	.60
	Nos. 2201-2203 (3)	4.00	1.40

Philatelic Week.

Birds — A607

Designs: No. 2204a, Black shama. b, Philippine cockatoo. c, Sulu hornbill. d, Mindoro imperial pigeon. e, Blue-headed fantail.
No. 2205a, Philippine trogon, vert. b, Rufous hornbill, vert. c, White-bellied woodpecker, vert. d, Spotted wood kingfisher, vert.
No. 2206a, Brahminy kite. b, Philippine falconet. c, Pacific reef egret. d, Philippine mallard.

Wmk. 391

1992, Nov. 25		Litho.	*Perf. 14*
2204 A607	2p Strip of 5, #a.-e.	3.50	3.00

Souvenir Sheets

2205 A607	2p Sheet of 4, #a.-d.	4.00	4.00
2206 A607	2p Sheet of 4, #a.-d.	4.00	4.00

No. 2204 printed in sheets of 10 with designs in each row shifted one space to the right from the preceding row. Two rows in each sheet are tete-beche.
The 1st printing of this set was rejected. The unissued stamps do not have the frame around the birds. The denominations on the sheet stamps and the 2nd souvenir sheet are larger. On the 1st souvenir sheet they are smaller.
For overprint see No. 2405.

New Year 1993,
Year of the
Rooster — A608

2p, Native fighting cock. 6p, Legendary Maranao bird.

1992, Nov. 2		
2207 A608	2p multi	.60	.40
2208 A608	6p multi	2.00	.60
a.	Souvenir sheet of 2, #2207-2208 + 2 labels	3.50	3.00
b.	As "a," ovptd. in sheet margin	3.00	2.50

Nos. 2208a and 2208b exist imperf. Overprint on No. 2208b reads: "PHILIPPINE STAMP EXHIBIT / TAIPEI, DECEMBER 1-3, 1992" in English and Chinese.
Issued: Nos. 2207-2208, 2208a, 11/27; No. 2208b, 12/1.
See Nos. 2459b, 2460b.

Guerrilla
Units of
World
War II
A609

Units: a, Bulacan Military Area, Anderson's Command, Luzon Guerrilla Army Forces. b, Marking's Fil-American Guerrillas, Hunters ROTC Guerrillas, President Quezon's Own Guerrillas. c, 61st Division, 71st Division, Cebu Area Command. d, 48th Chinese Guerrilla Squadron, 101st Division, Vinzons Guerrillas.

1992, Dec. 7		
2209 A609	2p Block of 4, #a.-d.	4.00	4.00

National Symbols

A610c

Tree —
A610

Fish

Flower
A610a

A610b

Flag
A610d

A610e

Animal
A610f

A610g

Bird
A610h

A610i

Leaf
A610j

A610k

A610m
Costume

A610l

Fruit
A610n

A610o

A610p A610q
House Various

A610r A610s
José Rizal National
Dance

National Sport — A610t

Nos. 2210-2236 inscribed with year of issue unless noted otherwise
Wmk. 391, except #2212A, 2214, 2215, 2216A, 2218A, 2220, 2222 (Unwmk.)
Red (R) or Blue (B) "PILIPINAS" on bottom, except #2212 (Brown (Br) "PILIPINAS" on top)

1993-98	Litho.	Perf. 14x13½	
2210	A610	60s (R)	1.50	.70
2211	A610b	1p (R)	.50	.25
2211A	A610b	1p (R)	.35	.25
2212	A610a	1p (Br)	.35	.25
2212A	A610b	1p (R)	.35	.25
2213	A610c	1.50p (R)	.65	.25
a.		Dated "1995"	.40	.25
2214	A610c	1.50p (B)	.70	.25

Nos. 2212A and 2214 have blue security printing.
Issued: #2210, 6/12/93; #2211, 5/3/94; #2211A, 2/6/95; #2212, 4/29/93; #2212A, 2/12/96; #2213, 6/12/3; #2213a, 2/6/95; #2214, 2/12/6.
For surcharge see No. 2795.

Red "PILIPINAS" on bottom, except #2215a (Brown "PILIPINAS" on top)
Blue Security Printing

2215	2p Block of 14, #a.-n.	9.00	9.00
a.	A610d 2p multi	.40	.90
b.	A610r 2p multi	.40	.25
c.	A610p 2p multi	.40	.25
d.	A610m 2p multi	.40	.25
e.	A610s 2p multi	.40	.25
f.	A610t 2p multi	.40	.25
g.	A610i 2p multi	.40	.25
h.	A610e 2p multi	.40	.25
i.	A610d 2p multi	.40	.40
j.	A610b 2p multi	.40	.25
k.	A610 2p multi	.40	.25
l.	A610o 2p multi	.40	.25
m.	A610k 2p multi	.40	.25
n.	A610c 2p multi	.40	.25

Issued 11/2/95.

Red "PILIPINAS" on bottom, except #2216, 2217a (Brown "PILIPINAS" on top)
No Security Printing

2216	A610d 2p multi	.80	.25
2216A	A610e 2p multi	2.50	.30
2217	2p Block of 14, #a.-n.	9.00	9.00
a.	A610d 2p multi	.40	.90
b.	A610r 2p multi	.40	.25
c.	A610p 2p multi	.40	.25
d.	A610m 2p multi	.40	.25
e.	A610s 2p multi	.40	.25
f.	A610t 2p multi	.40	.25
g.	A610i 2p multi	.40	.25
h.	A610e 2p multi	.40	.40
i.	A610f 2p multi	.40	.25
j.	A610b 2p multi	.40	.25
k.	A610 2p multi	.40	.25
l.	A610o 2p multi	.40	.25
m.	A610k 2p multi	.40	.25
n.	A610c 2p multi	.40	.25

Issued: #2216, 4/29/93; #2216A (dated 1993), 2/10/94; #2217, 10/28/93.
#2217a is a later printing of #2216, in which the word "watawat" is much smaller. #2217h is a later printing of #2216A, in which the date is lowered near the middle of "PILIPINAS," rather than near the top of "PILIPINAS."

Red "PILIPINAS" on bottom

2218	A610f 3p multi	1.35	.35
a.	Dated "1994"	2.00	.35
b.	Dated "1995"	6.50	.35

Blue Security Printing at Top, Blue "PILIPINAS" on bottom

2218C	A610g 3p multi, dated "1996"	1.00	.35
d.	Dated "1997"	.40	.35

"PILIPINAS" red: Nos. 2218, 2218a, 2218c.
Blue security printing: Nos. 2218C, 2281d.

Issued: No. 2218, 6/12/93; No. 2218a, 4/19/94; No. 2218b, 2/1/95; No. 2218C, 3/1/96; No. 2218d, 4/18/97.

Blue "PILIPINAS" on bottom, except #2219n (Blue "PILIPINAS" on top)
Blue Security Printing

2219	4p Block of 14, #a.-		
n.		15.00	15.00
a.	A610d 4p multi	1.00	.30
b.	A610r 4p multi	1.00	.30
c.	A610p 4p multi	1.00	.30
d.	A610m 4p multi	1.00	.30
e.	A610s 4p multi	1.00	.30
f.	A610t 4p multi	1.00	.30
g.	A610i 4p multi	1.00	.30
h.	A610d 4p multi	1.00	.30
i.	A610f 4p multi	1.00	.30
j.	A610b 4p multi	1.00	.30
k.	A610 4p multi	1.00	.30
l.	A610o 4p multi	1.00	.30
m.	A610k 4p multi	1.00	.30
n.	A610c 4p multi	1.00	.30

Issued 1/8/96. Stamps are dated "1995."

Blue "PILIPINAS" on bottom, except #2220a (Blue "PILIPINAS" on top)
Blue Security Printing

2220	4p Block of 14, #a.-n.	17.00	17.00
a.	A610d 4p multi	1.00	.30
b.	A610r 4p multi	1.00	.30
c.	A610p 4p multi	1.00	.30
d.	A610m 4p multi	1.00	.30
e.	A610s 4p multi	1.00	.30
f.	A610t 4p multi	1.00	.30
g.	A610i 4p multi	1.00	.30
h.	A610e 4p multi	1.00	.30
i.	A610g 4p multi	1.00	.30
j.	A610b 4p multi	1.00	.30
k.	A610 4p multi	1.00	.30
l.	A610o 4p multi	1.00	.30
m.	A610k 4p multi	1.00	.30
n.	A610c 4p multi	1.00	.30

Issued 2/12/96.

Red "PILIPINAS" on bottom (R): #2221-2221b, 2223B, 2223c, 2224B, 2224c, 2226, 2226a, 2228-2228b. Blue "PILIPINAS" on bottom (B): #2222, 2223A, 2224A, 2227, 2229. Brown "PILIPINAS" on top (Br): #2223, 2224, 2225.

2221	A610h 5p (R)	2.00	.40
a.	Dated "1994"	2.40	.50
b.	Dated "1995"	2.20	.50
2222	A610i 5p (B)	1.70	.50
2223	A610j 6p (Br)	2.50	.40
2223A	A610k 6p (B)	2.50	1.00
2223B	A610k 6p (R)	2.50	.70
c.	Dated "1995"	2.50	.50
2224	A610l 7p (Br)	3.00	.40
2224A	A610m 7p (B)	3.00	.40
2224B	A610m 7p (R)	3.00	.80
c.	Dated "1995"	3.00	.80
2225	A610n 8p (Br)	3.50	.60
2226	A610o 8p (R)	7.50	1.00
a.	Dated "1995"	3.50	1.00
2227	A610o 8p (B)	3.50	1.00
2228	A610p 10p (R)	4.00	1.50
a.	Dated "1994"	4.50	1.50
b.	Dated "1995"	4.00	1.50
2229	A610p 10p (B)	4.00	1.50
	Nos. 2210-2229 (28)	102.75	63.65

Blue security printing: #2222, 2223A, 2224A, 2227, 2229.
Issued: #2221, 2228, 6/12/93; #2221a, 2228a, 4/19/94; #2221b, 2/1/95; #2222, 2/12/96; #2223, 2224, 2225, 4/29/93; #2223A, 11/21/96; #2223B, 12/1/94; #2223Bc, 2228b, 4/3/95; #2224A, 2227, 2229, 4/19/96; #2224Bc, 5/5/95; #2226, 10/4/93; #2226a, 3/14/95; #2224B, 7/6/94.
See Nos. 2463-2469A, 2544-2545.

Souvenir Sheets

Philippine Flag with National Symbols — A610u

	Unwmk.	Perf. 13½	
2231	A610u 1p, Sheet of 12, #a.-j.+2 labels	15.00	15.00
a.	A610e 1p multi	1.00	.80
b.	A610p 1p multi	1.00	.80
c.	A610m 1p multi	1.00	.80
d.	A610 1p multi	1.00	.80
e.	A610t 1p multi	1.00	.80
f.	A610o 1p multi	1.00	.80
g.	A610k 1p multi	1.00	.80
h.	A610c 1p multi	1.00	.80
i.	A610f 1p multi	1.00	.80
j.	A610h 1p multi	1.00	.80

No. 2231e does not have the blue security printing, present on No. 2212A.
Issued: 6/12/93.

Philippine Flag with National Landmarks — A610v

Designs: a, Aquinaldo Shrine; b, Rizal Shrine; c, Barasoian Shrine; d, Mabini Shrine.

2232	A610v 2p, 3p, #a.-d.	9.00	8.00
a.	A610q 2p multi	1.00	.80
b.	A610q 3p multi	1.00	.80
c.	A610q 3p multi	1.00	.80
d.	A610q 3p multi	1.00	.80

Issued 6/12/94.

1872 Cavite Mutiny A610w

Designs: a, Cavite Arsenal; b, La Fuerza de San Felipe-Cavite; c, Commemorative marker; d, Cristanto de Los Reyes y Mendoza.

2233	A610w 2p, 3p, Sheet of 4, #a.-d.	9.00	8.00
a.	A610q 3p multi	1.00	.80
b.	A610q 3p multi	1.00	.80
c.	A610q 3p multi	1.00	.80
d.	A610q 3p multi	1.00	.80

Issued 6/12/95.

1896 Philippine Revolution — A610x

Designs: a, Cry of Pudgadlawin; b, Battle of Pinaglabanan; c, Cry of Nueca Ecija; d, Battle of Binakayan.
Nos. 2234a-2234d have blue security printing.

2234	A610x 4p, Sheet of 4, #a.-d.	9.00	8.00
a.	A610q 4p multi	1.00	.80
b.	A610q 4p multi	1.00	.80
c.	A610q 4p multi	1.00	.80
d.	A610q 4p multi	1.00	.80

Issued 6/12/96.

Historical Events and Personages (1897) — A610y

Designs: a, Edilberto Evangelista; b, Vicente Alvarez; c, Francisco Del Castillo; d, Pantaleon Vallegas.
Nos. 2235a-2235d have blue security printing.

2235	A610y 4p, Sheet of 4, #a.-d.	9.00	8.00
a.	A610y 4p multi	1.00	.80
b.	A610q 4p multi	1.00	.80
c.	A610q 4p multi	1.00	.80
d.	A610q 4p multi	1.00	.80

Issued 6/12/97.

Historical Events of 1898 A610z

Designs: a, Tres de Abril Uprising in Cebu; b, Negros Uprising, 1898; c, Iligan Uprising, 1898; d, Philippine Centennial Logo, Kalayaan.
Nos. 2236a-2236d have blue security printing.

2236	A610z 4p, Sheet of 4, #a.-d.	9.00	8.00
a.	A610q 4p multi	1.00	.80
b.	A610q 4p multi	1.00	.80
c.	A610q 4p multi	1.00	.80
d.	A610q 4p multi	1.00	.80

Issued 6/12/98.

Butterflies A611

Designs: No. 2237a, Euploea mulciber. b, Cheritra orpheus. c, Delias henningia. d, Mycalesis ita. e, Delias diaphana.
No. 2238a, Papilio rumanzobia. b, Papilio palinurus. c, Trogonoptera trojana. d, Graphium agamemnon.
No. 2239, Papilio lowi, Valeria boebera, Delias themis.

Wmk. 391

1993, May 28	Litho.	Perf. 14	
2237	A611 2p Strip of 5, #a.-		
e.		4.50	4.50

Souvenir Sheets

2238	A611 2p Sheet of 4, #a.-d.	5.25	5.25
e.	Ovptd. in sheet margin	6.00	6.00
2239	A611 10p multicolored	7.50	7.50
a.	Ovptd. in sheet margin	6.00	6.00
b.	Ovptd. in blue in sheet margin	15.00	15.00

Issue dates: Nos. 2237-2239, May 28. Nos. 2238e, 2239a, May 29. No. 2239b, July 1.
Nos. 2238a-2238d are vert. No. 2239 contains one 116x28mm stamp.
Overprint on No. 2238e, 2239a reads "INDOPEX '93 / INDONESIA PHILATELIC EXHIBITION 1993" and "6th ASIAN INTERNATIONAL PHILATELIC EXHIBITION / 29th MAY-4th JUNE 1993 SURABAYA-INDONESIA." Issued June 29.
Overprint on No. 2239b reads "Towards the Year 2000 / 46th PAF Anniversary 1 July 1993" and includes Philippine Air Force emblem and jet. Issued July 1.

Great Filipinos Type of 1989

Designs: a, Nicanor Abelardo, composer. b, Pilar Hidalgo-Lim, mathematician, educator. c, Manuel Viola Gallego, lawyer, educator. d, Maria Ylagan Orosa (1893-1943), pharmacist, health advocate. e, Eulogio B. Rodriguez, historian.

1993, June 10		Perf. 13½	
2240	A536 2p Strip of 5, #a.-e.	3.00	3.00

17th South East Asia Games, Singapore A612

No. 2241: a, Weight lifting, archery, fencing, shooting. b, Boxing, judo. c, Track, cycling, gymnastics, golf.
No. 2242: a, Table tennis, soccer, volleyball, badminton. b, Billiards, bowling. c, Swimming, water polo, yachting, diving.
No. 2243, Basketball, vert.

1993, June 18		Perf. 13	
2241	A612 2p Strip of 3, #a.-c.	2.00	2.00
2242	A612 6p Strip of 3, #a.-c.	5.00	5.00

Souvenir Sheet

2243	A612 10p multicolored	6.00	6.00

#2241a, 2241c, 2242a, 2242c are 80x30mm. No. 2243 contains one 30x40mm stamp. No. 2242a exists inscribed "June 13-20, 1993." Value, strips of 3, $22.

Orchids — A613

No. 2244: a, Spathoglottis chrysantha. b, Arachnis longicaulis. c, Phalaenopsis mariae. d, Coelogyne marmorata. e, Dendrobium sanderae.

No. 2245: a, Dendrobium serratilabium. b, Phalaenopsis equestris. c, Vanda merrillii. d, Vanda luzonica. e, Grammatophyllum martae.

No. 2246, Aerides quinquevulnera. No. 2247, Vanda lamellata.

1993, Aug. 14   Unwmk.   Perf. 14
2244	A613	2p Block of 5, #a.-e.	3.50	3.50
2245	A613	3p Block of 5, #a.-e.	4.75	4.75

Souvenir Sheets
2246	A613	8p multicolored	3.50	3.50
a.		With additional inscription	3.25	3.25

Imperf
2247	A613	8p multicolored	3.50	3.00
a.		With additional inscription	3.25	3.00

No. 2246 contains one 27x78mm stamp.
Nos. 2246a, 2247a inscribed in sheet margin with Taipei '93 emblem in blue and yellow. Additional black inscription in English and Chinese reads: "ASIAN INTERNATIONAL INVITATION STAMP EXHIBITION / TAIPEI '93."

Greetings — A614

"Thinking of You" in English on Nos. 2248a-2251a, in Filipino on Nos. 2248b-2251b with designs: 2p, Flowers, dog at window. 6p, Dog looking at alarm clock. 7p, Dog looking at calendar. 8p, Dog with slippers.

Wmk. 391
1993, Aug. 20   Litho.   Perf. 14
2248	A614	2p Pair, #a.-b.	1.50	1.00
2249	A614	6p Pair, #a.-b.	4.25	3.25
2250	A614	7p Pair, #a.-b.	4.25	3.25
2251	A614	8p Pair, #a.-b.	5.50	4.00
		Nos. 2248-2251 (4)	15.50	11.50

Natl. Coconut Week — A615

1993, Aug. 24
2252	A615	2p multicolored	.80	.35

Fish Type of 1992

No. 2253: a, Paradise fish. b, Pearl gourami. c, Red-tailed black shark. d, Tiger barb. e, Cardinal tetra.

No. 2254: a, Albino ryukin goldfish. b, Black oranda goldfish. c, Lionhead goldfish. d, Celestial-eye goldfish. e, Pompon goldfish.

No. 2255: a, Pearl-scale angelfish. b, Zebra angelfish. c, Marble angelfish. d, Black angelfish.

No. 2256: a, Neon betta. b, Libby betta. c, Split-tailed betta. d, Butterfly betta.

No. 2257, Albino oscar.

1993, Sep. 9   Unwmk.   Perf. 14
2253	A600	2p Strip of 5, #a.-e.	4.00	4.00
2254	A600	2p Strip of 5, #a.-e.	4.00	4.00

Souvenir Sheets
Perf. 14
2255	A600	2p Sheet of 4, #a.-d.	5.25	5.25
2256	A600	3p Sheet of 4, #a.-d.	5.25	5.25
e.		Ovptd. in margin	5.25	5.25

Imperf
Stamp Size: 70x45mm
2257	A600	6p multicolored	4.50	4.00
a.		Ovptd. in margin	4.50	4.00

Nos. 2256e, 2257a overprinted in black "QUEEN SIRIKIT NATIONAL CONVENTION CENTER / 1-10 OCTOBER 1993," "BANGKOK WORLD PHILATELIC EXHIBITION 1993" with Bangkok '93 show emblem in purple in margin.
Nos. 2255a-2255d are vert.
Issued: #2256e, 2257a, 9/20; others, 9/9.

A616

Wmk. 391
1993, Sept. 20   Photo.   Perf. 14
2258	A616	2p multicolored	.60	.30

Basic Petroleum and Minerals, Inc., 25th anniv.

16th World Law Conference, Manila — A617

6p, Globe on scales, gavel, flag, vert. 7p, Justice holding scales, courthouse. 8p, Fisherman, vert.

Unwmk.
1993, Sept. 30   Litho.   Perf. 14
2259	A617	2p multicolored	.40	.30
2260	A617	6p multicolored	1.30	.40
2261	A617	7p multicolored	1.50	.50
2262	A617	8p multicolored	1.80	.50
		Nos. 2259-2262 (4)	5.00	1.70

Our Lady of the Rosary of la Naval, 400th Anniv. — A618

1993, Oct. 18   Wmk. 391
2263	A618	2p multicolored	.60	.30

Intl. Year of Indigenous People — A619

People wearing traditional costumes.

1993, Oct. 24   Unwmk.
2264	A619	2p multicolored	.50	.30
2265	A619	6p multicolored	1.75	.40
2266	A619	7p multicolored	1.75	.50
2267	A619	8p multicolored	2.25	.60
		Nos. 2264-2267 (4)	6.25	1.80

Environmental Protection — A620

Paintings: 2p, Trees. 6p, Marine life. 7p, Bird, trees. 8p, Man and nature.

1993, Nov. 22
2268	A620	2p multicolored	.50	.30
2269	A620	6p multicolored	1.75	.40
2270	A620	7p multicolored	1.75	.50
2271	A620	8p multicolored	2.25	.60
		Nos. 2268-2271 (4)	6.25	1.80

Philately Week.

A621

a, Lunar buggy. b, Floating power tiller.

Unwmk.
1993, Nov. 30   Litho.   Perf. 14
2272	A621	2p Pair, #a.-b.	1.40	1.40

Filipino Inventors Society, Inc., 50th Anniv.

A622

1993, Nov. 30
2273	A622	2p multicolored	.65	.30

Printing of Doctrina Christiana in Spanish and Tagalog, 400th anniv.

A623

Christmas: 2p, Nativity scene. 6p, Church, people. 7p, Water buffalo carrying fruits, vegetables, sea food. 8p, Christmas lantern, carolers.

1993, Dec. 1
2274	A623	2p multicolored	.60	.40
2275	A623	6p multicolored	1.75	.50
2276	A623	7p multicolored	2.00	.70
2277	A623	8p multicolored	2.60	.80
		Nos. 2274-2277 (4)	6.95	2.40

A624

Maps, Philippine guerrilla units of World War II: a, US Army Forces in the Philippines Northern Luzon. b, Bohol Area Command. c, Leyte Area Command. d, Palawan Special Battalion, Sulu Area Command.

1993, Dec. 10
2278	A624	2p Block or strip of 4, #a.-d.	4.00	4.00

Philippines 2000 — A625

Designs: 2p, Peace and Order. 6p, Transportation, communications. 7p, Infrastructure, industry. No. 2282, People empowerment. No. 2283, Transportation, communications, buildings, people.

Unwmk.
1993, Dec. 14   Litho.   Perf. 14
2279	A625	2p multicolored	.50	.35
2280	A625	6p multicolored	1.25	.45
2281	A625	7p multicolored	1.50	.50
2282	A625	8p multicolored	1.75	.60
		Nos. 2279-2282 (4)	5.00	1.90

Souvenir Sheet
Imperf
Size: 110x85mm
2283	A625	8p multicolored	4.00	4.00

New Year 1994 (Year of the Dog) — A626

2p, Manigong bagong taon. 6p, Happy new year.

Unwmk.
1993, Dec. 15   Litho.   Perf. 14
2284	A626	2p multi	.50	.40
2285	A626	6p multi	2.00	.60
a.		Souvenir sheet of 2, #2284-2285 + 2 labels	4.00	4.00

No. 2285a exists imperf.
See Nos. 2459c, 2460c.

First ASEAN Scout Jamboree, Mt. Makiling — A627

2p, Flags of ASEAN countries, Boy Scout emblem. 6p, Flags, Boy Scout, emblem.

1993, Dec. 28
2286	A627	2p multicolored	.50	.40
2287	A627	6p multicolored	1.50	.60
a.		Souv. sheet of 2, #2286-2287	4.00	4.00

Rotary Club of Manila, 75th Anniv. — A628

Unwmk.
1994, Jan. 19   Litho.   Perf. 14
2288	A628	2p multicolored	.60	.30

17th Asian Pacific Dental Congress, Manila — A629

2p, Healthy teeth. 6p, Globe, flags, teeth.

1994, Feb. 3
2289	A629	2p multicolored	.50	.30
2290	A629	6p multicolored	1.50	.50

Corals — A630

#2291: a, Acropora micropthalma. b, Seriatopora hystrix. c, Acropora latistella. d, Millepora tenella. e, Millepora tenella, up close. f, Pachyseris valenciennesi. g, Pavona decussata. h, Galaxea fascicularis. i, Acropora formosa. j, Acropora humilis.
#2292: a, Isis. b, Plexaura. c, Dendronepthya. d, Heteroxenia.
#2293: a, Xenia puertogalerae. b, Plexaura, diff. c, Dendrophyllia gracilis. d, Plerogyra sinuosa.

1994, Feb. 15   Litho.   Perf. 14
2291	A630	2p Block of 10, #a.-j.	9.00	9.00

Souvenir Sheets
2292	A630	2p Sheet of 4, #a.-d.	5.75	5.75
2293	A630	3p Sheet of 4, #a.-d.	5.75	5.75
e.		With added inscription	12.50	12.50

No. 2293e is inscribed in sheet margin "NAPHILCON '94 / 1ST NATIONAL / PHILATELIC CONGRESS / 21 FEBRUARY - 5 MARCH 1994 / PHILATELY 2000."
Issued: No. 2293e, 2/21.

Hong Kong '94 — A631

2p, Nos. 2126, 2207. 6p, Nos. 2284, 2285.

1994, Feb. 18
2294	A631	2p multicolored	.40	.30
2295	A631	6p multicolored	1.40	.45
a.		Souv. sheet of 2, #2294-2295, blue	3.00	3.00
b.		As "a," green	3.00	3.00

Backgrounds differ on Nos. 2295a, 2295b.

A632

1994, Feb. 20
2296 A632 2p multicolored   .60 .30

Philippine Military Academy Class of 1944, 50th Anniv.

A633

1994, Mar. 1
2297 A633 2p multicolored   .60 .30

Federation of Filipino-Chinese Chambers of Commerce and Industry, 40th Anniv.

A634

"Congratulations" in English on Nos. 2298a-2301a, in Tagalog on Nos. 2298b-2301b with designs: No. 2298, Books, diploma, mortarboard. No. 2299, Baby carried by stork. No. 2300, Valentine bouquet with portraits in heart. No. 2301, Bouquet.

1994, Apr. 15
2298 A634 2p Pair, #a.-b.   1.25 1.25
2299 A634 2p Pair, #a.-b.   1.25 1.25
2300 A634 2p Pair, #a.-b.   1.25 1.25
2301 A634 2p Pair, #a.-b.   1.25 1.25
   Nos. 2298-2301 (4)   5.00 5.00

A635

1994 Miss Universe Pageant, Manila: Nos. 2302a (2p), 2304a, Gloria Diaz, 1969 winner. No. 2302b (6p), Crown, Philippine jeepney. Nos. 2303a (2p), 2304b, Margie Moran, 1973 winner. No. 2303b (7p), Pageant participant, Kalesa horse-drawn cart.

1994, May 5   Litho.   Perf. 14
2302 A635 Pair, #a.-b.   2.00 1.00
2303 A635 Pair, #a.-b.   2.10 1.50
   Souvenir Sheet
2304 A635 8p Sheet of 2, #a.-b.   4.00 *4.00*

Great Filipinos Type of 1989

Designs: a, Antonio J. Molina, musician. b, Jose Yulo, politician. c, Josefa Jara-Martinez, social worker. d, Nicanor Reyes, Sr., accountant. e, Sabino B. Padilla, lawyer.

1994, June 10
2307 A536 2p Strip of 5, #a.-e.   2.50 2.50

Philippine Export Processing Zones — A637

No. 2308: a, Baguio City. b, Bataan. c, Mactan. d, Cavite.

No. 2309a, 7p, Map of Philippines, export products. b, 8p, Export products flowing around world map.

Unwmk.
1994, July 4   Litho.   Perf. 14
2308 A637 2p Block of 4, #a.-d.   2.00 2.00
2309 A637 Pair, #a.-b.   3.50 3.50

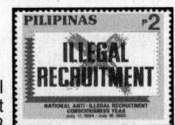

Fight Illegal Recruitment Year — A638

1994, July 15
2310 A638 2p multicolored   .60 .30

Wildlife A639

a, Palawan bearcat. b, Philippine tarsier. c, Scaly anteater. d, Palawan porcupine. 12p, Visayan spotted deer.

1994, Aug. 12   Litho.   Perf. 14
2311 A639 6p Block of 4, #a.-d.   5.75 5.75
   Souvenir Sheet
2312 A639 12p multicolored   7.00 7.00
   a. Ovptd. in margin   7.00 7.00

No. 2312a overprinted in white, black and red in sheet margin with "SINGPEX '94 / 31 August-3 September 1994" and show emblem.

PHILAKOREA '94 — A640

Shells: a, Conus gloriamaris. b, Conus striatus. c, Conus geographus. d, Conus textile.
No. 2314a, Conus marmoreus. No. 2314b, Conus geographus, diff. No. 2315a, Conus striatus, diff. No. 2315b, Conus marmoreus, diff.

1994, Aug. 16
2313 A640 2p Block of 4, #a.-d.   3.50 3.50
   Souvenir Sheets
2314 A640 6p Sheet of 2, #a.-b.   4.50 *4.50*
2315 A640 6p Sheet of 2, #a.-b.   4.50 *4.50*

Landings at Leyte Gulf, 50th Anniv. — A641

Designs: a, Pres. Sergio Osmena, Sr. b, Gen. MacArthur wading ashore. c, Dove of Peace. d, Carlos P. Romulo.

1994, Sept. 15
2316 A641 2p Block of 4, #a.-d.   3.00 2.50
   See Nos. 2391a-2391d.

Intl. Anniversaries & Events — A642

Unwmk.
1994, Oct. 24   Litho.   Perf. 14
2317 A642 2p Family   .50 .30
2318 A642 6p Labor workers   1.25 .40
2319 A642 7p Feather, clouds   1.50 .50
   Nos. 2317-2319 (3)   3.25 1.20

Intl. Year of the Family (#2317). ILO, 75th anniv. (#2318). ICAO, 50th anniv. (#2319).

Visit of US Pres. Bill Clinton — A643

1994, Nov. 12
2320 A643 2p green & multi   .60 .35
2321 A643 8p blue & multi   2.40 .65

East Asean Business Convention, Davao — A644

1994, Nov. 15
2322 A644 2p violet & multi   .40 .30
2323 A644 6p brown & multi   1.35 .50

Nos. 2322-2323 not issued without overprint "Nov. 15-20, 1994" and obliterator covering original date at lower left.

Philatelic Week — A645

Portraits by Philippine artists: 2p, Soteranna Puson Y Quintos de Ventenilla, by Dionisio de Castro. 6p, Quintina Castor de Sadie, by Simon Flores y de la Rosa. 7p, Artist's mother, by Felix Eduardo Resurreccion Hidalgo y Padilla. 8p, Una Bulaquena, by Juan Luna y Novicio.
12p, Cirilo and Severina Quiason Family, by Simon Flores y de la Rosa.

1994, Nov. 21
2324 A645 2p multicolored   .50 .30
2325 A645 6p multicolored   1.00 .45
2326 A645 7p multicolored   1.25 .55
2327 A645 8p multicolored   1.50 .65
   Nos. 2324-2327 (4)   4.25 1.95
   Souvenir Sheet
2328 A645 12p multicolored   3.00 *3.00*

No. 2328 contains one 29x80mm stamp.

Christmas — A646

1994, Nov. 25
2329 A646 2p Wreath   .60 .35
2330 A646 6p Angels   1.40 .65
2331 A646 7p Bells   2.00 .80
2332 A646 8p Basket   2.50 1.20
   Nos. 2329-2332 (4)   6.50 3.00

ASEANPEX '94 — A647

#2333: a, Blue-naped parrot. b, Bleeding heart pigeon. c, Palawan peacock pheasant. d, Koch's pitta.
No. 2334, Philippine eagle, vert.

1994, Nov. 8
2333 A647 2p Block of 4, #a.-d.   5.75 4.50
   Souvenir Sheet
2334 A647 12p multicolored   7.50 6.00

A648   Philippine Guerrilla Units in World War II — A649

No. 2335: a, Troops entering prison. b, Prisoners escaping.
Bombed building and — #2336: a, Emblem of East Central Luzon Guerrilla Area. b, Map, Mindoro Provincial Batallion, Marinduque Guerrilla Force. c, Map, Zambales Military District, Masbate Guerrilla Regiment. d, Map, Samar Area Command.

Unwmk.
1994, Dec. 8   Litho.   Perf. 14
2335 A648 2p Pair, #a.-b.   1.25 1.00
2336 A649 2p Block of 4, #a.-d.   2.50 2.00

No. 2335 is a continuous design. See Nos. 2392a-2392b.

New Year 1995 (Year of the Boar) — A650

1994, Dec. 5
2337 A650 2p shown   .50 .35
2338 A650 6p Boy, girl pigs   2.00 .50
   a. Souvenir sheet of 2, #2337-2338 + 2 labels   3.75 *3.75*

No. 2338 exists imperf. Value, unused $3.75. See Nos. 2459d, 2460d.

Kalayaan, Cent. (in 1998) — A651

a, Flag, 1898. b, Philippine flag. c, Cent. emblem.

1994, Dec. 15
2339 A651 2p Strip of 3, #a.-c.   2.00 1.50

AIDS Awareness — A652

1994, Dec. 12
2340 A652 2p multicolored   1.20 .40

Visit of Pope John Paul II — A653

Pope John Paul II and: #2342, Papal arms, globe showing Philippines. 6p, Emblem, map of Asia. #2344, Children.
#2341, a, Archdiocese of Manila. b, Diocese of Cebu. c, Diocese of Caceres. d, Diocese of Nueva Segovia.
#2345, Pres. Fidel V. Ramos, Pope John Paul II.

1995, Jan. 2
2341 A653 2p Block of 4, #a.-d.   2.00 1.50
2342 A653 2p multicolored   .50 .30
2343 A653 6p multicolored   1.00 .40
2344 A653 8p multicolored   1.50 .60
   Nos. 2341-2344 (4)   5.00 2.80

Souvenir Sheet

2345 A653 8p multicolored   3.50   3.00
  a.   Overprinted in margin   3.50   3.00

Federation of Asian Bishops' Conferences (#2343). 10th World Youth Day (#2344).
Overprint in margin of No. 2345a reads "CHRISTYPEX '95 / JANUARY 4-16, 1995 / University of Santo Tomas, Manila / PHILIPPINE PHILATELIC FEDERATION."

Lingayen Gulf Landings, 50th Anniv. — A654

a, Map of Lingayen Gulf, ships, troops. b, Map, emblems of 6th, 37th, 40th, 43rd Divisions.

1995, Jan. 9
2346 A654 2p Pair, #a.-b.   1.40   1.00

No. 2346 is a continuous design.
See Nos. 2391e-2391f.

Liberation of Manila, 50th Anniv. — A655

Statue honoring victims and: 2p, 8p, Various destroyed buildings.

1995, Feb. 3
2347 A655 2p magenta & multi   .60   .35
2348 A655 8p blue & multi   2.20   .65

See Nos. 2392m, 2392r.

Jose W. Diokno (1922-87), Politician — A656

1995, Feb. 26
2349 A656 2p multicolored   .50   .30

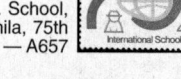

Intl. School, Manila, 75th Anniv. — A657

8p, Globe, cut out figures.

      Unwmk.
1995, Mar. 4   **Litho.**   **Perf. 14**
2350 A657 2p shown   .50   .30
2351 A657 8p multi   1.50   .50

Wildlife A658

No. 2352: a, Mousedeer. b, Tamaraw. c, Visayan warty pig. d, Palm civet.
No. 2353, vert: a, Flying lemur. b, Philippine deer.

1995, Mar. 20
2352 A658 2p Block of 4, #a.-d.   2.50   2.00

Souvenir Sheet

2353 A658 8p Sheet of 2, #a.-b.   4.00   3.25

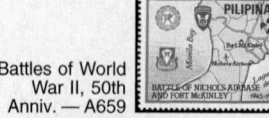

Battles of World War II, 50th Anniv. — A659

Unit emblems and and maps showing: No. 2354, Battle of Nichols Airbase and Ft. Mckinley. No. 2355: a, Nasugbu landings. b, Tagaytay landings.

1995, Apr. 9
2354 A659 2p multicolored   .75   .30
2355 A659 2p Pair, #a.-b.   1.50   1.25

See Nos. 2391g-2391h, 2392c.

Liberation of Baguio, 50th Anniv. — A660

1995, Apr. 27
2356 A660 2p multicolored   .80   .30

See No. 2392d.

Liberation of Internment Camps, 50th Anniv. — A661

1995, May 28
2357 A661 2p UST   .80   .30
2358 A661 2p Cabanatuan   .80   .30
2359 A661 2p Los Banos   .80   .30
   Nos. 2357-2359 (3)   2.40   .90

See Nos. 2392e-2392g.

Great Filipinos Type of 1989

Persons born in 1895: a, Victorio C. Edades. b, Jovita Fuentes. c, Candido M. Africa. d, Asuncion Arriola-Perez. e, Eduardo A. Quisumbing.

     Perf. 14x13½
1995, June 1   **Litho.**   **Unwmk.**
2360 A536 2p Strip of 5, #a.-e.   3.00   2.75

Catholic Bishops' Conference of the Philippines, 50th Anniv. — A662

1995, July 22   *Perf. 14*
2361 A662 2p multicolored   .60   .30

A663

1995, Aug. 2
2362 A663 2p multicolored   .75   .40

Jaime N. Ferrer (1916-87),

A664

Jars — #2363: a, Manunggul. b, Non-anthropomorphic. c, Anthropomorphic. d, Leta-leta yawning jarlet.
12p, Double spouted and legged vessel, presentation tray.

1995, Aug. 4
2363 A664 2p Block of 4, #a.-d.   2.40   2.00

Souvenir Sheet

2364 A664 12p multi, no show emblem in margin   3.50   3.00
  a.   Show emblem in margin   3.50   3.00

Archaeological finds. No. 2364 contains one 80x30mm stamp.
No. 2364a has Jakarta '95 show emblem in margin. Issued 8/19/95.

ASEAN Environment Year 1995 — A665

Designs: Nos. 2365a, 2366a, Left hand holding turtle, wildlife scene. Nos. 2365b, 2366b, Right hand below fish, bird, wildlife scene.

1995, Aug. 10
2365 A665 2p Pair, #a.-b.   1.75   1.50

Souvenir Sheet

2366 A665 6p Sheet of 2, #a.-b.   6.50   6.00

Nos. 2365-2366 are each continuous designs.

Souvenir Sheet

Philippine Eagle, New Natl. Bird — A666

1995, Aug. 11
2367 A666 16p multicolored   8.00   7.00

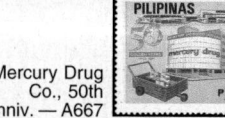

Mercury Drug Co., 50th Anniv. — A667

1995, Aug. 15
2368 A667 2p multicolored   .60   .30

Parish of St. Louis Bishop, 400th Anniv. — A668

1995, Aug. 18
2369 A668 2p multicolored   .50   .30

Asian-Pacific Postal Training Center, 25th Anniv. — A669

      Unwmk.
1995, Sept. 1   **Litho.**   **Perf. 14**
2370 A669 6p multicolored   1.20   .50

UN, 50th Anniv. A670

Filipinos serving in UN: No. 2371a, #2372, Carlos P. Romulo. b, Rafael M. Salas. c, Salvador P. Lopez. d, Jose D. Ingles.

1995, Sept. 25
2371 A670 2p Block of 4, #a.-d.   3.00   3.00
2371E A670 2p Cesar C. Bengson   125.00   125.00
  f.   Block of 4, #2371b-2731d, 2371E   175.00

Souvenir Sheet

2372 A670 16p multi   4.00   4.00

No. 2371E was issued with the wrong portrait and was withdrawn after two days.

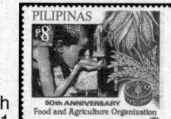

FAO, 50th Anniv. — A671

1995, Sept. 25
2373 A671 8p multicolored   2.00   .65

A671a

      Unwmk.
1995, Oct. 5   **Litho.**   **Perf. 14**
2373A A671a 2p multicolored   .50   .30

Manila Overseas Press Club, 50th anniv.

Total Eclipse of the Sun — A672

1995, Oct. 24
2374 A672 2p multicolored   1.00   .35

Natl. Stamp Collecting Month — A673

Paintings: 2p, Two Igorot Women, by Victorio Edades. 6p, Serenade, by Carlos "Botong" Francisco. 7p, Tuba Drinkers, by Vincente Manansala. 8p, Genesis, by Hernando Ocampo.
12p, The Builders, by Edades.

1995, Nov. 6
2375 A673 2p multicolored   .50   .30
2376 A673 6p multicolored   1.25   .45
2377 A673 7p multicolored   1.50   .60
2378 A673 8p multicolored   1.75   .70
   Nos. 2375-2378 (4)   5.00   2.05

Souvenir Sheet

2379 A673 12p multicolored   3.50   3.50

No. 2379 contains one 76x26mm stamp.

Christmas — A674

Musical instruments, Christmas carols.

1995, Nov. 22
2380 A674 2p Tambourine .60 .45
2381 A674 6p Maracas 2.00 .65
2382 A674 7p Guitar 2.00 .80
2383 A674 8p Drum 2.40 1.20
Nos. 2380-2383 (4) 7.00 3.10

Sycip Gorres
Velayo & Co.
Accounting Firm,
50th
Anniv. — A675

1995, Nov. 27
2384 A675 2p Abacus .50 .30

Souvenir Sheet

Pres. Fidel V. Ramos Proclaiming
November as Natl. Stamp Collecting
Month — A676

1995, Nov. 29
2385 A676 8p multicolored 6.00 5.00

New Year 1996
(Year of the
Rat) — A677

1995, Dec. 1
2386 A677 2p shown .50 .35
2387 A677 6p Outline of rat 1.50 .65
a. Souv. sheet, #2386-2387+2 labels 3.50 3.50
b. As "a," imperf 4.00

Printed in sheets of 20 stamps.
See Nos. 2459e, 2460e.

Philippine Guerrilla Units of World War
II — A678

Designs: a, Emblem, FIL-American Irregular Troops (FAIT). b, Emblem, BICOL Brigade. c, Map, FIL-American Guerrilla Forces (Cavite), Hukbalahap Unit (Pampanga). d, Map, South Tarlac, Northwest Pampanga Military Districts.

1995, Dec. 8   Litho.   Perf. 14
2388 A678 2p Block of 4, #a.-d. 3.50 3.50

Significant Events of World War II,
50th Anniv. — A679

Designs: a, Map, liberation of Panay and Romblon, 61st Division. b, Map, Liberation of Cebu, Americal Division. c, Battle of Ipo Dam,

43rd Division, FIL-American Guerrillas. d, Map, Battle of Bessang Pass, 37th Division. e, Sculpture, surrender of Gen. Yamashita.

1995, Dec. 15
2389 A679 2p Strip of 5, #a.-e. 6.00 6.00
See Nos. 2392h-2392 l.

Revolutionary Heroes — A680

a, Jose P. Rizal (1861-96) b, Andres Bonifacio, (1863-97). c, Apolinario Mabini (1864-1903).

1995, Dec. 27
2390 A680 2p Set of 3, #a.-c. 3.00 2.00

World War II Types of 1994-95 and

Map of Philippines — A681

Color of Pilipinas and denomination: Nos. 2391a-2391d, like #2316, red. Nos. 2391e-2391f, like #2346, red. Nos. 2391g-2391h, like #2355, red. Nos. 2391i-2391l, map of Philippines with blue background showing sites of Allied landings.
No. 2392: a-b, like #2335, white. c, like #2354, red. d, like #2356, white. e, like #2358, white. f, like #2357, white. g, like #2359, white. h.-l., like #2389a-2389e, purple. m, like #2347, red. n.-q., map of Philippines with green background showing location of prison camps. r, like #2348, red.

Miniature Sheets

1995, Dec. 27   Litho.   Perf. 14
2391 A681 2p Sheet of 12, #a.-l. 8.00 8.00
2392 A681 2p Sheet of 18, #a.-r. 12.00 12.00

23rd Intl. Congress of
Internal
Medicine — A682

1996, Jan. 10   Litho.   Perf. 14
2393 A682 2p multicolored .60 .30

Sun Life
Assurance
Company of
Canada in the
Philippines,
Cent. — A683

1996, Jan. 26
2394 A683 2p shown .50 .30
2395 A683 8p Sun over horizon 1.50 .60

Valentine's Day — A684

"I Love You" on Nos. 2396a-2399a, "Happy Valentine" on Nos. 2396b-2399b and: No. 2396, Pair of love birds. No. 2397, Cupid with bow and arrow. No. 2398, Box of chocolates. No. 2399, Bouquet of roses, butterfly.

1996, Feb. 9
2396 A684 2p Pair, #a.-b. 1.00 .75
2397 A684 2p Pair, #a.-b. 2.50 2.25
2398 A684 7p Pair, #a.-b. 3.25 2.50
2399 A684 8p Pair, #a.-b. 2.75 3.00
Nos. 2396-2399 (4) 9.50 8.50

St. Thomas
University
Hospital, 50th
Anniv. — A685

1996, Mar. 5
2400 A685 2p multicolored .60 .30

Gregorio Araneta
University Foundation,
50th Anniv. — A686

1996, Mar. 5
2401 A686 2p multicolored .60 .30

Fish — A687

No. 2402: a, Emperor fish. b, Mandarinfish. c, Regal angelfish. d, Clown triggerfish. e, Raccoon butterflyfish. g, Powder brown tang. h, Two-banded anemonefish. i, Moorish idol. j, Blue tang. k, Majestic angelfish.
No. 2403: a, like #2402d. b, like #2402k. c, like #2402c. d, like #2402h.

1996, Mar. 12
2402 A687 4p Strip of 5, #a.-e. 5.50 5.50
2402F A687 4p Strip of 5, #g.-k. 5.50 5.50

Miniature Sheet
2403 A687 4p Sheet of 4, #a.-d. 5.25 4.50
e. #2403 with new inscriptions 5.25 4.50

Souvenir Sheet
2404 A687 12p Lionfish 4.00 4.00
a. #2404 with new inscriptions 4.00 4.00

Nos. 2402, 2402F have blue compressed security printing at left, black denomination, white background, margin. Nos. 2403-2404 have blue background, violet denomination, continuous design.
ASEANPEX '96 (No. 2403-2404).
Nos. 2403e, 2404a inscribed in sheet margins with various INDONESIA '96 exhibition emblems. Issued: Nos. 2403e, 2404a, 3/21/96.
See Nos. 2410-2413.

No. 2206 Overprinted in Green

1996   Litho.   Wmk. 391   Perf. 14
2405 A607 2p Sheet of 4, #a.-d. 7.50 7.00
Ovpt. in sheet margin reads: "THE YOUNG PHILATELISTS' SOCIETY 10TH ANNIVERSARY."

Souvenir Sheet

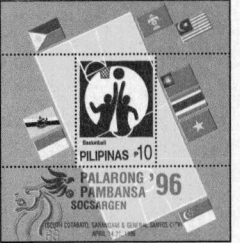

Basketball — A688

1996, Apr. 14
2406 A688 10p multicolored 12.50 12.50
PALARONG/PAMBANSA '96.

Francisco B. Ortigas,
Sr. — A689

1996, Apr. 30   Unwmk.
2407 A689 4p multicolored .75 .40

Discovery of
Radioactivity,
Cent. — A690

1996, Apr. 30
2408 A690 4p multicolored .60 .30

Congregation of
Dominican Sisters
of St. Catherine
of Siena, 300th
Anniv. — A691

1996, Apr. 30
2409 A691 4p multicolored .65 .40

Fish Type of 1996

No. 2410: a, Long-horned cowfish. b, Queen angelfish. c, Long-nosed butterflyfish. d, Yellow tang. e, Blue-faced angelfish.
No. 2411: a, Saddleback butterflyfish. b, Sailfin tang. c, Harlequin tuskfish. d, Clown wrasse. e, Spotted boxfish.
No. 2412: a, like #2410e. b, like #2410c. c, like #2410b. d, like #2411c.
No. 2413, vert: a, Purple firefish. b, Pacific seahorse. c, Red-faced batfish. d, Long-nosed hawksfish.

1996
2410 A687 4p Strip of 5, #a.-e. 5.50 5.50
2411 A687 4p Strip of 5, #a.-e. 5.50 5.50
2412 A687 4p Sheet of 4, #a.-d. 5.00 5.00
e. With added inscription 5.00 5.00
2413 A687 4p Sheet of 4, #a.-d. 5.00 5.00
e. With added inscription 5.00 5.00

Nos. 2412-2413 have white background. Nos. 2410-2411 have blue background.
ASEANPEX '96 (#2412-2413). Added inscription in sheet margin of #2412e, 2413e includes CHINA '96 emblem and "CHINA '96 - 9th Asian International Exhibition" in red.
Issued: #2410-2413, 5/10; #2412e, 2413e, 5/16.

Great Filipinos Type of 1989

Designs: a, Carlos P. Garcia (1896-1971), politician. b, Casimiro del Rosario (1896-1962), physicist. c, Geronima T. Pecson (1896-1989), politician. d, Cesar C. Bengson (1896-1992), lawyer. e, Jose Corazon de Jesus (1896-1932), writer.

Perf. 13½
1996, June 1   Litho.   Unwmk.
2414 A536 4p Strip of 5, #a.-e. 4.00 3.75

ABS CBN
(Broadcasting
Network), 50th
Anniv. — A692

8p, Rooster, world map.

1996, June 13   Perf. 14
2415 A692 4p shown .80 .40
2416 A692 8p multicolored 2.00 .80

Manila,
Convention
City — A693

1996, June 24
2417 A693 4p multicolored .80 .30

Jose Cojuangco, Sr.
(1896-1976),
Businessman, Public
Official — A694

1996, July 3
2418 A694 4p multicolored .80 .40

Philippine-American Friendship
Day — A695

Symbols of Philippines, U.S.: 4p, Hats. 8p,
National birds. 16p, Flags, vert.

1996, July 4
2419 A695 4p multicolored .80 .40
2420 A695 8p multicolored 2.25 .80
Souvenir Sheet
2421 A695 16p multicolored 3.50 3.50
See No. 2475.

Modern Olympic
Games,
Cent. — A696

4p, No. 2426a, Boxing. 6p, No. 2426b, Athletics. 7p, No. 2426c, Swimming. 8p, No.
2426d, Equestrian.

Unwmk.
1996, July 19   Litho.   Perf. 14
2422 A696 4p multicolored .80 .40
2423 A696 6p multicolored 1.25 .60
2424 A696 7p multicolored 1.75 .70
2425 A696 8p multicolored 1.90 .80
    Nos. 2422-2425 (4) 5.70 2.50
Miniature Sheet
2426 A696 4p Sheet of 4, #a.-d. 4.00 4.00

Nos. 2422-2425 have colored background,
blue security code at right, denominations at
LR. Nos. 2426a-2426d have colored circles on
white background, blue security code at top,
and denominations at UR, UL, LR, LL,
respectively.

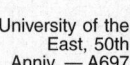

University of the
East, 50th
Anniv. — A697

1996, Aug. 15
2427 A697 4p multicolored .80 .40

Orchids
A698

No. 2428: a, Dendrobium anosmum. b,
Phalaenopsis. equestris-alba. c, Aerides
lawrenceae. d, Vanda javierii.
No. 2429: a, Renanthera philippinensis. b,
Dendrobium schuetzei. c, Dendrobium
taurinum. d, Vanda lamellata.
No. 2430: a, Coelogyne pandurata. b,
Vanda merrilli. c, Cymbidium aliciae. d, Den-
drobium topaziacum.

1996, Sept. 26
2428 A698 4p Block or strip of 4,
        #a.-d. 3.50 3.00
2429 A698 4p Block or strip of 4,
        #a.-d. 3.50 3.00
Miniature Sheet
2430 A698 4p Sheet of 4, #a.-d. 3.50 3.50

#2428-2429 were printed in sheets of 16
stamps.

ASEANPEX '96 (#2430). Complete sheets
of Nos. 2428-2429 have ASEANPEX emblem
in selvage.

6th Asia Pacific
Intl. Trade
Fair — A699

1996, Sept. 30
2431 A699 4p multicolored .80 .30

UNICEF,
50th
Anniv.
A700

Children in montage of scenes studying,
working, playing — #2432: a, Blue & multi. b,
Purple & multi. c, Green & multi. d, Red &
multi.
16p, Four children, horiz.

1996, Oct. 9
2432 A700 4p Block of 4, #a.-d. 3.25 2.50
Souvenir Sheet
2433 A700 16p multicolored 3.50 3.00

TAIPEX
'96
A701

Orchids: No. 2434: a, Fran's Fantasy "Alea."
b, Malvarosa Green Goddess "Nani." c, Ports
of Paradise "Emerald Isle." d, Mem. Conrada
Perez "Nani."
No. 2435: a, Pokai tangerine "Lea." b, Mem.
Roselyn Reisman "Diana." c, C. Moscombe x
Toshi Aoki. d, Mem. Benigno Aquino "Flying
Aces."
12p, Pamela Hetherington "Coronation," Liv-
ing Gold "Erin Treasure," Eleanor Spicer
"White Bouquet."

1996, Oct. 21   Litho.   Perf. 14
2434 A701 4p Block of 4, #a.-d. 3.25 2.50
2435 A701 4p Block of 4, #a.-d. 3.25 2.50
Souvenir Sheet
2436 A701 12p multicolored 4.50 3.50

Nos. 2434-2435 were issued in sheets of 16
stamps. No. 2436 contains one 80x30mm
stamp.

1996 Asia-Pacific
Economic
Cooperation
A702

Winning entries of stamp design competition: 4p, Sun behind mountains, airplane, skyscrapers, tower, ship, satellite dish, vert. 7p,
Skyscrapers. 8p, Flags of nations beside path,
globe, skyscrapers, sun, vert.

1996, Oct. 30
2437 A702 4p multicolored .80 .30
2438 A702 shown 1.25 .50
2439 A702 7p multicolored 1.35 .60
2440 A702 8p multicolored 1.50 .70
    Nos. 2437-2440 (4) 4.90 2.10

Christmas
A703

Designs: 4p, Philippine Nativity scene, vert.
6p, Midnight Mass. 7p, Carolers. 8p, Carolers
with Carabao, vert.

1996, Nov. 5
2441 A703 4p multicolored .75 .40
2442 A703 6p multicolored 1.50 .60
2443 A703 7p multicolored 1.75 .80
2444 A703 8p multicolored 2.00 1.00
    Nos. 2441-2444 (4) 6.00 2.80

Eugenio P. Perez
(1896-1957),
Politician — A704

1996, Nov. 11   Litho.   Perf. 14
2445 A704 4p multicolored .80 .40

New Year 1997
(Year of the
Ox) — A705

1996, Dec. 1
2446 A705 4p Carabao .75 .40
2447 A705 6p Tamaraw 1.25 .60
a.   Souv. sheet, #2446-2447 + 2
      labels 3.50 3.50

Printed in sheets of 20 stamps. No. 2447a
exists imperf. Value, $3.50.
See Nos. 2459f, 2460f.

ASEANPEX '96, Intl. Philatelic
Exhibition, Manila — A706

Jose P. Rizal (1861-96): No. 2448: a, At 14
years. b, At 18. c, At 25. d, At 31.
No. 2449: a, "Noli Me Tangere." b,
Gomburza to whom Rizal dedicated "El Filbus-
terismo." c, Oyang Dapitana, by Rizal. d,
Ricardo Camicero, by Rizal.
No. 2450, horiz: a, Rizal's house, Calamba.
b, University of St. Tomas, Manila, 1611. c,
Orient Hotel, Manila. d, Dapitan during Rizal's
time.
No. 2451, horiz: a, Central University,
Madrid. b, British Museum, London. c, Botani-
cal Garden, Madrid. d, Heidelberg, Germany.
No. 2452, Rizal at 14, horiz. No. 2453, Rizal
at 18, horiz. No. 2454, Rizal at 25, horiz. No.
2455, Rizal at 31, horiz.

1996
2448 A706 4p Block of 4, #a.-d. 3.00 2.75
2449 A706 4p Block of 4, #a.-d. 3.00 2.75
2450 A706 4p Block of 4, #a.-d. 3.00 2.75
2451 A706 4p Block of 4, #a.-d. 3.00 2.75
Souvenir Sheets
2452 A706 12p multicolored 2.50 2.00
2453 A706 12p multicolored 2.50 2.00
2454 A706 12p multicolored 2.50 2.00
2455 A706 12p multicolored 2.50 2.00

Issued: #2448, 2452, 12/14; #2449, 2453,
12/15; #2450, 2454, 12/16; #2451, 2455,
12/17. Nos. 2448-2451 were issued in sheets
of 16 stamps.

Independence, Cent. (in 1998) — A707

Revolutionary heroes: a, Fr. Mariano C.
Gomez (1799-1872). b, Fr. Jose A. Burgos
(1837-72). c, Fr. Jacinto Zamora (1835-72).

1996, Dec. 20
2456 A707 4p Strip of 3, #a.-c. 3.00 2.00

Jose Rizal — A709

1996, Dec. 30   Litho.   Perf. 14
2458 A709 4p multicolored .90 .45

New Year Types of 1991-96
Unwmk.
1997, Feb. 12   Litho.   Perf. 14
2459   Sheet of 6 5.00 7.00
 a.   A580 4p like #2126 .70 .60
 b.   A608 4p like #2208 .70 .60
 c.   A626 4p like #2284 .70 .60
 d.   A650 4p like #2337 .70 .60
 e.   A677 4p like #2386 .70 .60
 f.   A705 4p like #2446 .70 .60
2460   Sheet of 6 9.00 12.00
 a.   A580 6p like #2127 1.00 .85
 b.   A608 6p like #2207 1.00 .85
 c.   A626 6p like #2285 1.00 .85
 d.   A650 6p like #2338 1.00 .85
 e.   A677 6p like #2387 1.00 .85
 f.   A705 6p like #2447 1.00 .85

Hong Kong '97.

Nos. 2459a-2459b, 2460a-2460b have
white margins, color differences. Nos. 2459c-
2459d, 2459f, 2460c-2460d, 2460f have color
differences. Nos. 2459e, 2460e, do not have
blue security printing, and have color
differences.
Nos. 2459a-2459f, 2460a-2460f are all
dated "1997."

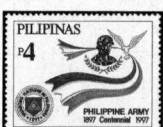

Holy Rosary
Seminary,
Bicent. — A710

1997, Feb. 18
2461 A710 4p multicolored .65 .30

Philippine Army,
Cent. — A711

1997, Feb. 18
2462 A711 4p multicolored .65 .30

Natl. Symbols Type of 1993-96 and

Gem — A711a

Blue "PILIPINAS" on bottom, except
#2464 (Black)

1997   Litho.   Unwmk.   Perf. 14x13½
2463 A610b 1p like #2212A .40 .25
2463A A610b 2p like #2212A .80 .30
2463B A610b 2p like #2212A .60 .60
2464 A711a 4p multicolored .90 .35
2465 A610i 5p like #2222 1.00 .70
2465A A610i 5p like #2222 1.75 .70
2466 A610m 6p like #2223A 2.25 .70
2466A A610m 6p like #2223A 2.25 .75
2467 A610m 7p like #2224A 3.50 1.00
2467A A610m 7p like #2224A 3.50 1.00
2468 A610o 8p like #2227 3.50 1.25
2468A A610o 8p like #2227 3.50 1.25
2469 A610p 10p like #2229 4.50 1.50
2469A A610p 10p like #2229 4.50 1.50
    Nos. 2463-2469A (14) 32.95 11.85

Nos. 2463, 2465, 2466, 2467, 2468 and
2469 do not have blue compressed security
printing at top and are dated "1997."

Nos. 2463A-2464, 2465A, 2466A, 2467A, 2468A and 2469A have blue compressed security printing at top and are dated "1997."
Issued: No. 2463, 2469, 2/27/97; 2463A, 4/15; 2463B, 2466A, 4/18; #2465A, 4/29; #2464, 6/10; #2465, 2/26; #2466, 3/10; #2467, 3/7; #2467A, 5/8; #2468, 3/6; #2468A, 5/8; #2469A, 4/22.

Dept. of Finance, Cent. — A712

1997, Apr. 8 Perf. 14
2471 A712 4p multicolored .80 .30

Philippine Red Cross, 50th Anniv. — A713

1997, Apr. 8
2472 A713 4p multicolored .80 .40

Philamlife Insurance Co., 50th Anniv. — A714

1997, Apr. 8
2473 A714 4p multicolored .80 .30

J. Walter Thompson Advertising, 50th Anniv. in Philippines A715

1997, Apr. 18
2474 A715 4p multicolored .80 .30

Souvenir Sheet

Philippine-American Friendship Day, Republic Day, 50th Anniv. — A716

1997, May 29
2475 A716 16p multicolored 4.25 3.75
PACIFIC 97.
See No. 2421.

Wild Animals A717

World Wildlife Fund: No. 2476, Visayan spotted deer. No. 2477, Visayan spotted deer (doe & fawn). No. 2478, Visayan warty pig. No. 2479, Visayan warty pig (adult, young).

1997, July 24
2476 4p multicolored 1.00 .70
a. Sheet of 8 8.50 8.50
2477 4p multicolored 1.00 .70
a. Sheet of 8 8.50 8.50
2478 4p multicolored 1.00 .70
a. Sheet of 8 8.50 8.50

2479 4p multicolored 1.00 .70
a. Sheet of 8 8.50 8.50
b. A717 Block or strip of 4, #2476-2479 4.25 3.50
Set of 4 sheets, #2476a-2479a 34.00 34.00
No. 2479b was issued in sheets of 16 stamps.

ASEAN, 30th Anniv. A718

Founding signatories: No. 2480, Adam Malik, Indonesia, Tun Abdul Razak, Malaysia, Narciso Ramos, Philippines, S. Rajaratnam, Singapore, Thanat Khoman, Thailand. No. 2481, Natl. flags of founding signatories. No. 2482, Flags of current ASEAN countries. No. 2483, Flags of ASEAN countries surrounding globe.

1997, Aug. 7 Perf. 14
2480 4p multicolored .80 .50
2481 4p multicolored .80 .50
a. A718 Pair, #2480-2481 2.00 1.25
2482 6p multicolored 1.00 .60
2483 6p multicolored 1.00 .60
a. A718 Pair, #2482-2483 3.00 2.00
Nos. 2480-2483 (4) 3.60 2.20

World Scout Parliamentary Union, 2nd General Assembly — A719

1997, Aug. 17
2484 A719 4p multicolored .80 .40

Manuel L. Quezon University, 50th Anniv. — A720

1997, Aug. 19
2485 A720 4p multicolored .80 .30

Great Filipinos Type of 1989
Famous people: a, Justice Roberto Regala (1897-1979). b, Doroteo Espiritu, dental surgeon, inventor (b. 1897). c, Elisa R. Ochoa (1897-1978), nurse, tennis champion. d, Mariano Marcos (1897-1945), lawyer, educator. e, Jose F. Romero (1897-1978), editor.

Perf. 14x13½
1997, June 1 Litho. Unwmk.
2486 A536 4p Strip of 5, #a.-e. 4.00 3.50

Battle of Candon, 1898 — A721

4p, Don Federico Isabelo Abaya, revolutionary leader against Spanish. 6p, Soldier on horseback.

1997, Sept. 24 Perf. 14
2487 A721 4p multi, vert. .80 .35
2488 A721 6p multi 1.00 .60

St. Therese of Lisieux (1873-97) — A722

1997, Oct. 16
2489 A722 6p multicolored 1.00 .50

Stamp and Philatelic Division, 50th Anniv. — A723

Abstract art: 4p, Homage to the Heroes of Bessang Pass, by Hernando Ruiz Ocampo. 6p, Jardin III, by Fernando Zobel. 7p, Abstraction, by Nena Saguil, vert. 8p, House of Life, by Jose Joya, vert.
16p, Dimension of Fear, by Jose Joya.

1997, Oct. 16
2490 A723 4p multicolored .80 .35
2491 A723 6p multicolored 1.00 .45
2492 A723 7p multicolored 1.50 .60
2493 A723 8p multicolored 1.75 .80
Nos. 2490-2493 (4) 5.05 2.20

Souvenir Sheet
2494 A723 16p multicolored 5.25 5.00
No. 2494 contains one 80x30mm stamp.

Heinrich von Stephan (1831-97) — A724

1997, Oct. 24 Litho. Perf. 14
2495 A724 4p multicolored 1.00 .40

Asian and Pacific Decade of Disabled Persons — A725

1997, Oct. 24 Litho. Perf. 14
2496 A725 6p multicolored 1.00 .45

Intl. Year of the Reef A726

1997, Oct. 24 Litho. Perf. 14
2497 A726 8p multicolored 1.75 1.20

Souvenir Sheet
2498 A726 16p multicolored 4.50 4.00
No. 2498 is a continuous design printed in sheets of 10 stamps.

Natl. Stamp Collecting Month — A726a

Paintings: 4p, Dalagang Bukid, by Fernando Amorsolo, vert. 6p, Bagong Taon, by Arturo Luz, vert. 7p, Jeepneys, by Vincente Manansala. 8p, encounter of the Nuestra Sra. de Cavadonga and the Centurion, by Alfredo Carmelo.
16p, Pista sa Nayon, by Carlos Francisco.

1997, Nov. 4 Litho. Perf. 14
2498A A726a 4p multicolored .80 .40
2498B A726a 6p multicolored 1.00 .60
2498C A726a 7p multicolored 1.50 .70
2498D A726a 8p multicolored 1.75 .80
Nos. 2498A-2498D (4) 5.05 2.50

Souvenir Sheet
2498E A726a 16p multicolored 4.00 3.50
No. 2498E contains one 80x30mm stamp.

Christmas — A727

Various stained glass windows.

1997, Nov. 7
2499 A727 4p multicolored .80 .40
2500 A727 6p multicolored 1.20 .60
2501 A727 7p multicolored 1.50 .80
2502 A727 8p multicolored 2.00 1.20
Nos. 2499-2502 (4) 5.50 3.00

Independence, Cent. — A728

Various monuments to Andres Bonifacio (1863-97), revolutionary, founder of the Katipunan: a, red & multi. b, yellow & multi. c, blue & multi.

1997, Nov. 30
2503 A728 4p Strip of 3, #a.-c. 3.00 2.00

New Year 1998 (Year of the Tiger) — A729

1997, Dec. 1
2504 A729 4p shown .90 .40
2505 A729 6p Tigers, diff. 1.60 .60
a. Souvenir sheet, #2504-2505 + 2 labels 4.00 3.50
Printed in sheets of 20.
No. 2505a exists imperf. Value, $4.

Philippine Eagle — A730

1997, Dec. 5
2506 A730 20p Looking right 5.00 1.80
2507 A730 30p Looking forward 5.00 2.20
2508 A730 50p On cliff 10.00 3.50
Nos. 2506-2508 (3) 20.00 7.50

Game Cocks A731

No. 2509: a, Hatch grey. b, Spangled roundhead. c, Racey mug. d, Silver grey.
No. 2510, vert: a, Grey. b, Kelso. c, Bruner roundhead. d, Democrat.
No. 2511, Cock fight, vert. No. 2512, Cocks facing each other ready to fight.

1997, Dec. 18
2509 A731 4p Block of 4, #a.-d. 3.50 2.25
2510 A731 4p Block of 4, #a.-d. 3.50 2.25

Souvenir Sheets
2511 A731 12p multicolored 3.00 2.50
2512 A731 16p multicolored 4.00 3.50
Nos. 2509-2510 printed in sheets of 16. Initial delivery has excess untrimmed margins. No. 2512 contains one 80x30mm stamp.

Art Association of the Philippines, 50th Anniv. — A732

Stylized designs: No. 2513, Colors of flag, sunburst. No. 2514, Association's initials, clenched fist holding artist's implements.

Unwmk.
1998, Feb. 14 Litho. Perf. 14
2513 A732 4p multicolored .80 .35
2514 A732 4p multicolored .90 .40
a. Pair, #2513-2514 2.25 1.50

Club Filipino Social Organization, Cent. — A733

1998, Feb. 25
2515 A733 4p multicolored .80 .30

Blessed Marie Eugenie (1817-98) — A734

1998, Feb. 25
2516 A734 4p multicolored .80 .30

Fulbright Educational Exchange Program in the Philippines, 50th Anniv. — A735

1998, Feb. 25
2517 A735 4p multicolored .80 .40

Heroes of the Revolution — A736

National flag and: 4p, Melchora Aquino (1812-1919). 11p, Andres Bonifacio (1863-97). 13p, Apolinario Mabini (1864-1903). 15p, Emilio Aguinaldo (1869-1964).

1998 Litho. Unwmk. Perf. 13½
Inscribed "1998"
2518 A736 4p multicolored .75 .25
2519 A736 11p multicolored 2.00 .50
  a. Inscribed "1999" 2.50 .65
2520 A736 13p multicolored 2.50 .60
  a. Inscribed "1999" 3.00 .70
2521 A736 15p multicolored 3.00 .75
  a. Inscribed "1999" 4.00 1.00
  Nos. 2518-2521 (4) 8.25 2.10

Issued: 4p, 3/3/98. 11p, 13p, 15p, 3/24/98.
See Nos. 2528, 2546-2550, 2578-2597, 2607.

Apo View Hotel, 50th Anniv. — A737

1998, Mar. 20 Perf. 14
2522 A737 4p multicolored 1.00 .35

Philippine Cultural High School, 75th Anniv. — A738

1998, May 5
2523 A738 4p multicolored .80 .40

Victorino Mapa High School, 75th Anniv. — A739

1998, May 5
2524 A739 4p multicolored .80 .30

Philippine Navy, Cent. — A740

1998, May 5
2525 A740 4p multicolored .80 .40

University of Baguio, 50th Anniv. — A741

1998, May 5
2526 A741 4p multicolored .80 .40

Philippine Maritime Institute, 50th Anniv. — A742

1998, May 5
2527 A742 4p multicolored .80 .40

Heroes of the Revolution Type of 1998

Design: Gen. Antonio Luna (1866-99).

Perf. 13½
1998, Apr. 30 Litho. Unwmk.
2528 A736 5p multicolored .90 .30

Expo '98, Lisbon — A743

4p, Boat on lake, vert. 15p, Vinta on water. 15p, Main lobby, Philippine Pavilion.

1998, May 22 Perf. 14
2529 A743 4p multicolored .80 .35
2530 A743 15p multicolored 2.50 1.00

Souvenir Sheet
2531 A743 15p multicolored 4.00 4.00
No. 2531 contains one 80x30mm stamp.

Clark Special Economic Zone — A744

1998, May 28
2532 A744 15p multicolored 3.00 2.50
Printed in sheets of 10 stamps.

Flowers A745

#2533: a, Artrabotrys hexapetalus. b, Hibiscus rosa-sinensis. c, Nerium oleander. d, Jasminum sambac.
#2534, vert: a, Gardenia jasminoides. b, Ixora coccinea. c, Erythrina indica. d, Abelmoschus moschatus.
#2535, Medinilla magnifica.

1998, May 29
2533 A745 4p Block of 4, #a.-d. 3.25 2.75
2534 A745 4p Block of 4, #a.-d. 3.25 2.75

Souvenir Sheet
2535 A745 15p multicolored 5.50 5.00

Nos. 2533-2534 were printed in sheets of 16. The initial delivery has untrimmed excess selvage.

Great Filipinos Type of 1989

Designs: a, Andres R. Soriano (1898-1964). b, Tomas Fonacier (1898-1991). c, Josefa L. Escoda (1898-1945). d, Lorenzo M. Tañada (1898-1992). e, Lazaro Francisco (1898-1980).

1998, June 1 Perf. 14x13½
2536 A536 4p Strip of 5, #a.-e. 3.50 3.50

Philippine Independence, Cent. — A746

No. 2537, Mexican flag, sailing ship. No. 2538, Woman holding Philippine flag, monument, sailing ship, map of Philippines. No. 2539, Spanish flag, Catholic Church, religious icon, Philippine flag.

1998, June 3 Perf. 14
2537 A746 15p multicolored 1.75 1.00
2538 A746 15p multicolored 1.75 1.00
2539 A746 15p multicolored 1.75 1.00
  a. Strip of 3, #2537-2539 5.00 4.50
  b. Souvenir sheet, #2537-2539 + 3 labels 7.00 6.00
  Printed in sheets of 15.
  See Mexico #2079-2080, Spain #2949. For overprint see #2629.

Philippine Independence, Cent. — A747

Patriots of the revolution: a, Melchora Aquino. b, Nazaria Lagos. c, Agueda Kahabagan.

Unwmk.
1998, June 9 Litho. Perf. 14
2540 A747 4p Strip of 3, #a.-c. 2.50 2.00

Pasig River Campaign for Waste Management A748

1998, June 19
2541 A748 4p multicolored .80 .30

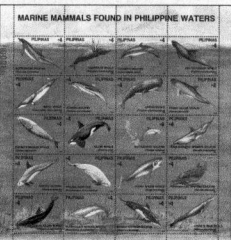

Marine Mammals — A749

No. 2542: a, Bottlenose dolphin. b, Humpback whale. c, Fraser's dolphin. d, Melon-headed whale. e, Minke whale. f, Striped dolphin. g, Sperm whale. h, Pygmy killer whale. i, Cuvier's beaked whale. j, Killer whale. k, Bottlenose dolphin. l, Long-snouted pinner dolphin. m, Risso's dolphin. n, Finless porpoise. o, Pygmy sperm whale. p, Pantropical spotted dolphin. q, False killer whale. r, Blainville's beaked whale. s, Rough-toothed dolphin. t, Bryde's whale.
15p, Dugong.

1998, June 19
2542 A749 4p Sheet of 20, #a.-t. 20.00 20.00

Souvenir Sheet
2543 A749 15p multicolored 4.50 5.00

Nos. 2218a, 2218b, 2220 Ovptd. in Gold with Philippine Independence Centennial Emblem

1998 Litho. Unwmk. Perf. 14x13½
2544 A610f 3p multi, dated "1995" (#2218b) .70 .25

2544A A610f 3p multi, dated "1994" (#2218a) 75.00 75.00
2545 A610g 4p Block of 14, #a.-n. 15.00 15.00
  a. A610d 4p multi .75 .40
  b. A610r 4p multi .75 .40
  c. A610p 4p multi .75 .40
  d. A610m 4p multi .75 .40
  e. A610s 4p multi .75 .40
  f. A610t 4p multi .75 .40
  g. A610i 4p multi .75 .40
  h. A610e 4p multi .75 .40
  i. A610a 4p multi .75 .40
  j. A610b 4p multi .75 .40
  k. A610 4p multi .75 .40
  l. A610o 4p multi .75 .40
  m. A610k 4p multi .75 .40
  n. A610c 4p multi .75 .40

Issued: No. 2544, 7/7/98; 2545, 6/12/98.
No. 2544A, dated "1994," was overprinted in error.

Heroes of the Revolution Type of 1998

2p, Emilio Jacinto. 4p, Jose P. Rizal. 8p, Marcelo H. del Pilar. 10p, Gregorio del Pilar. 18p, Juan Luna.

1998 Inscribed "1998" Perf. 13½
2546 A736 2p multicolored .70 .25
2547 A736 4p multicolored .80 .30
2548 A736 8p multicolored 1.50 .45
  a. Inscribed "1999" 2.00 .50
2549 A736 10p multicolored 2.00 .80
  a. Inscribed "1999" 3.00 .80
2550 A736 18p multicolored 4.00 1.50
  Nos. 2546-2550 (5) 9.00 3.30

Issued: 4p, 10p, 18p, 5/18/98. 2p, 8p, 7/20/98.
For surcharges, see Nos. 2879-2882.

Philippine Centennial A749a

No. 2550A: b, Spoliarium, by Juan Luna. c, 1st display of Philippine flag, 1898. d, Execution of Jose Rizal, 1896. e, Andres Bonifacio. f, Church, Malolos.

1998, July Perf. 14
2550A Souv. booklet 32.50 32.50
  b. A749a 4p multicolored 1.00 .80
  c. A749a 8p multicolored 2.00 1.50
  d.-e. A749a 16p multicolored 3.00 2.50
  f. A749a 20p multicolored 3.50 2.75

No. 2550A contains panes of 4 each of Nos. 2550Ab-2550Ac and one pane of 1 each of Nos. 2550Ad-2550Af. Sold for 150p.
For surcharges, see Nos. 2879-2882.

Philippine Coconut Industry, Cent. — A750

1998, Oct. 9 Perf. 14
2551 A750 4p multicolored 1.00 .60

Holy Spirit Adoration Sisters in Philippines, 75th Anniv. — A751

1998, Oct. 9
2552 A751 4p multicolored 1.25 .60

Universal Declaration of Human Rights, 50th Anniv. — A752

1998, Oct. 24
2553 A752 4p multicolored 1.00 .60

Intl. Year of the Ocean A753

1998, Oct. 24

2554	A753	15p multicolored	3.00	2.00
a.		Souvenir sheet, #2554	4.50	4.50

No. 2554a is a continuous design printed in sheets of 10.

A754

Philippine Postal Service, Cent. — #2555: a, Child placing envelope into mailbox, globe. b, Arms encircling globe, envelopes, Philippine flag as background. c, Airplane, globe, various stamps over building. d, Child holding up hands, natl. flag colors, envelopes.

15p, Child holding envelope as it crisscrosses globe.

1998, Nov. 4

2555	A754	6p Block of 4, #a.-d.	4.00	4.00

Souvenir Sheet

2556	A754	15p multicolored	4.50	4.50

No. 2555 was printed in sheets of 16. No. 2556 contains one 76x30mm stamp.

A755

Christmas: Various star lanterns.

1998, Nov. 5

2557	A755	6p multicolored	1.25	.50
2558	A755	11p multicolored	2.00	.80
2559	A755	13p multicolored	2.50	1.20
2560	A755	15p multicolored	2.75	1.50
	Nos. 2557-2560 (4)		8.50	4.00

Pasko '98.

Souvenir Sheets

Philippines '98, Philippine Cent. Invitational Intl. Philatelic Exhibition — A756

Revolutionary scenes, stamps of revolutionary govt.: No. 2561, Soldiers celebrating, #Y1-Y2. No. 2562, Signing treaty, telegraph stamps. No. 2563, Waving flag from balcony, #YF1, "Recibos" (Offical receipt) stamps. No. 2564, Procession, #Y3, perf. and imperf. examples of #YP1. No. 2565, New government convening, "Trans de Ganades" (cattle transfer) stamp, Libertad essay.

1998

2561	A756	15p multicolored	5.50	4.50
2562	A756	15p multicolored	5.50	4.50
2563	A756	15p multicolored	5.50	4.50
2564	A756	15p multicolored	5.50	4.50
2565	A756	15p multicolored	5.50	4.50
	Nos. 2561-2565 (5)		27.50	22.50

No. 2561 exists imperf. The first printing has varying amounts of black offset on the reverse. Value, $75. The second printing does not have the offset. Value, $12.50.

Nos. 2561-2565 were issued one each day from 11/5-11/9.

Pres. Joseph Ejercito Estrada — A757

1998, Nov. 10

2566	A757	6p Taking oath	1.00	.50
2567	A757	15p Giving speech	3.00	1.50

Shells A758

No. 2568: a, Mitra papalis. b, Vexillum citrinum. c, Vexillum rugosum. d, Volema carinifera.

No. 2569: a, Teramachia dalli. b, Nassarius vitiensis. c, Cymbiola imperialis. d, Cymbiola aulica.

No. 2570: a, Nassarius papillosus. b, Fasciolaria trapezium.

1998, Nov. 6   Unwmk.

			Litho.	Perf. 14
2568	A758	4p Block of 4, #a.-d.	3.50	3.50
2569	A758	4p Block of 4, #a.-d.	3.50	3.50

Souvenir Sheet

2570	A758	8p Sheet of 2, #a.-b.	6.50	5.00
c.		Souvenir sheet, Type II	10.00	10.00

Cloud in sheet margin touches "s" of Shells on #2570. On #2570c, cloud does not touch "s" of Shells. Colors are dark on #2570c, lighter on #2570.

Nos. 2568-2569 were printed in sheets of 16.

Natl. Stamp Collecting Month — A759

Motion picture, director: 6p, "Dyesebel," Gerardo de Leon. 11p, "Ang Sawa Sa Lumang Simboryo," Gerardo de Leon. 13p, "Prinsipe Amante," Lamberto V. Avellana. No. 2574, "Anak Dalita," Lamberto V. Avellana.

No. 2575, "Siete Infantes de Lara," costume design by Carlos "Botong" Francisco.

1998, Nov. 25

2571	A759	6p black & blue	1.00	.40
2572	A759	11p black & brown	1.75	.70
2573	A759	13p black & lilac	2.25	.80
2574	A759	15p black & green	3.00	1.00
	Nos. 2571-2574 (4)		8.00	2.90

Souvenir Sheet

2575	A759	15p black	3.50	3.25

No. 2575 contains one 26x76mm stamp.

Philippine Centennial — A759a

Pride, various women and: No. 2575A, Eagle (Resources). No. 2575B, Costume (Heritage). No. 2575C, Flag (Filipino People). No. 2575D, Artifacts with text (Literature). No. 2575E, Rice terraces (Engineering). No. 2575F, "Noli Me Tangere" (Citizenry).

1998, Nov. 20   Unwmk.

			Litho.	Imperf.
2575A	A759a	15p multi	3.50	3.00
2575B	A759a	15p multi	3.50	3.00
2575C	A759a	15p multi	3.50	3.00
2575D	A759a	15p multi	3.50	3.00
2575E	A759a	15p multi	3.50	3.00
2575F	A759a	15p multi	3.50	3.00
	Nos. 2575A-2575F (6)		21.00	18.00

Nos. 2575A-2575F have simulated perforations.

New Year 1999 (Year of the Rabbit) — A760

1998, Dec. 1

2576	A760	4p shown	.80	.40
2577	A760	11p Two rabbits	2.00	.80
a.		Souvenir sheet, #2576-2577	4.00	4.00

Printed in sheets of 20. No. 2577a exists imperf. Value, $4.

Heroes of the Revolution Type of 1998

1998, Dec. 15   Litho.   Perf. 13½

Booklet Stamps

Yellow Background

2578	A736	6p like #2518	1.00	.40
2579	A736	6p like #2519	1.00	.40
2580	A736	6p like #2520	1.00	.40
2581	A736	6p like #2521	1.00	.40
2582	A736	6p like #2528	1.00	.40
2583	A736	6p like #2549	1.00	.40
2584	A736	6p like #2547	1.00	.40
2585	A736	6p like #2550	1.00	.40
2586	A736	6p like #2546	1.00	.40
2587	A736	6p like #2548	1.00	.40
a.		Booklet pane, #2578-2587	14.00	12.00
		Complete booklet, #2587a	14.00	12.00

Green Background

2588	A736	15p like #2546	2.50	1.50
2589	A736	15p like #2518	2.50	1.50
2590	A736	15p like #2547	2.50	1.50
2591	A736	15p like #2528	2.50	1.50
2592	A736	15p like #2548	2.50	1.50
2593	A736	15p like #2549	2.50	1.50
2594	A736	15p like #2519	2.50	1.50
2595	A736	15p like #2520	2.50	1.50
2596	A736	15p like #2521	2.50	1.50
a.		Booklet pane, 2c #2546, 8c #2548, 2 each 11c, 13c, #2519-2520, 6c #2583, #2596	30.00	20.00
		Complete booklet, #2596a	30.00	20.00
2597	A736	15p like #2550	2.50	1.50
a.		Booklet pane, #2588-2597	30.00	25.00
		Complete booklet, #2597a	30.00	25.00

Nos. 2587a, 2596a, 2597a were made available to collectors unattached to the booklet cover.

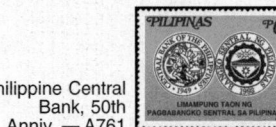

Philippine Central Bank, 50th Anniv. — A761

1999, Jan. 3   Litho.   Perf. 14

2598	A761	6p multicolored	1.00	.40

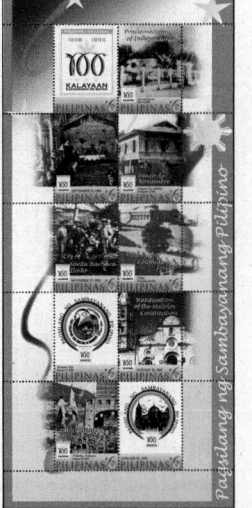

Philippine Centennial — A762

Designs: a, Centennial emblem. b, Proclamation of Independence. c, Malolos Congress. d, Nov. 5th uprising. e, Cry of Santa Barbara Iloilo. f, Victory over colonial forces. g, Flag raising, Butuan City. h, Ratification of Malolos Constitution. i, Philippine Republic formed. j, Barasoain Church.

1999, Jan. 11

2599	A762	6p Sheet of 10, #a.-j.	12.00	10.00

Scouting — A762a

Designs: No. 2599K, Girl Scout, boys planting tree. No. 2599L, Boy Scout, Girl Scout, flag, people representing various professions.

Perf. 13½

1999, Jan. 16   Litho.   Unwmk.

2599K	A762a	5p multicolored	2.10	.40
2599L	A762a	5p multicolored	2.50	.40

Nos. 2599K-2599L are dated 1995, are inscribed "THRIFT STAMP," and were valid for postage due to stamp shortage.

Dept. of Transportation and Communications, Cent. — A763

Emblem and: a, Ship. b, Jet. c, Control tower. d, Satellite dish, bus.

15p, Philpost Headquarters, truck, motorcycle on globe.

1999, Jan. 20

2600	A763	6p Block of 4, #a.-d.	4.50	4.00

Souvenir Sheet

2601	A763	15p multicolored	4.00	3.50

No. 2600 was printed in sheets of 16. No. 2601 contains one 80x30mm stamp.

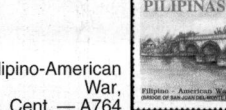

Filipino-American War, Cent. — A764

1999, Feb. 4

2602	A764	5p multicolored	.85	.35

Philippine Military Academy, Cent. — A765

1999-2001   Perf. 14

2603	A765	5p multicolored	1.25	.50
a.		Small "P" in denomination ('01)	2.50	1.75

"P" in denomination is 1¾mm tall on No. 2603, 1½mm tall on No. 2603a.

Issue dates: No. 2603, 2/4/99. No. 2063a, 2001.

Birds A766

#2604: a, Greater crested tern. b, Ruddy turnstone. c, Green-backed heron. d, Common tern.

#2605: a, Black-winged stilt. b, Asiatic dowitcher. c, Whimbrel. d, Reef heron.

#2606: a, Spotted greenshank. b, Tufted duck.

1999, Feb. 22   Litho.   Perf. 14
2604 A766 5p Block of 4, #a.-d.   3.50 3.50
2605 A766 5p Block of 4, #a.-d.   3.50 3.50

Souvenir Sheets
2606 A766 8p Sheet of 2, #a.-b.   6.00 6.00
  c. As #2606, diff. sheet margin,
    inscription   5.00 5.00

Issued: #2604-2606, 2/22; #2606c, 3/19.
Nos. 2604-2605 were printed in sheets of 16.
No. 2606c contains inscription, emblem for Australia '99 World Stamp Expo.

Heroes of the Revolution Type
Perf. 13½
1999, Mar. 12   Litho.   Unwmk.
Pink Background
2607 A736 5p like #2547   .80 .30

Manila Lions Club, 50th Anniv. — A767

Design: Emblem, Francisco "Paquito" Ortigas, Jr., first president.

1999, Mar. 20   Perf. 14
2608 A767 5p multicolored   1.00 .40

Philippine Orthopedic Assoc., 50th Anniv. — A768

1999, Mar. 20
2609 A768 5p multicolored   1.00 .40

La Union Botanical Garden, San Fernando — A769

Designs: No. 2610, Entrance sign, birdhouse. No. 2611, Ticket booth at entrance.

1999, Mar. 20
2610   5p multicolored   1.00 .70
2611   5p multicolored   1.00 .70
  a. A769 Pair, #2610-2611   2.50 2.00

Frogs A770

#2612: a, Woodworth's frog. b, Giant Philippine frog. c, Gliding tree frog. d, Common forest frog.
#2613: a, Spiny tree frog. b, Truncate-toed chorus frog. c, Variable-backed frog.

1999, Apr. 5
2612 A770 5p Block of 4, #a.-d.   3.50 3.00

Sheet of 3
2613 A770 5p #a.-c. + label   6.50 6.00
No. 2612 was printed in sheets of 16.

Marine Life A771

No. 2614: a, Sea squirt. b, Banded sea snake. c, Manta ray. d, Painted rock lobster.
No. 2615: a, Sea grapes. b, Branching coral. c, Sea urchin.

1999, May 11   Litho.   Perf. 14
2614 A771 5p Block of 4, #a.-d.   3.50 3.00

Sheet of 3
2615 A771 5p #a.-c. + label   8.00 7.50

Juan F. Nakpil, Architect, Birth Cent. — A772

1999, May 25
2616 A772 5p multicolored   .80 .40

UPU, 125th Anniv. — A773

Designs: 5p, Globe, boy writing letter. 15p, Globe, girl looking at stamp collection.

1999, May 26   Litho.   Perf. 14
2617 A773 5p multicolored   1.00 .40
2618 A773 15p multicolored   2.50 1.00

Philippines-Thailand Diplomatic Relations, 50th Anniv. — A774

Orchids: 5p, 11p, Euanthe sanderiana, cattleya Queen Sirikit.

1999, June 13   Litho.   Perf. 14
2619 A774 5p multicolored   1.00 .50
2620 A774 11p multicolored   2.00 1.00

Order of flowers from top is reversed on 11p value.
Issued in sheets of 20 (10 of each denomination in two rows of 5, separated by a central gutter). Most sheets of 20 were cut in half through the central gutter.
See #2623-2624, 2640-2641, 2664-2666, 2719-2721, 2729-2731.

Masonic Charities for Crippled Children, Inc., 75th Anniv. — A775

1999, July 5
2621 A775 5p multicolored   1.00 .50

Production of Eberhard Faber "Mongol" Pencils, 150th Anniv. — A776

1999, July 5
2622 A776 5p multicolored   .80 .40

Diplomatic Relations Type of 1999

Philippines-Korea diplomatic relations, 50th anniv., flowers: 5p, 11p, Jasminum sambac, hibiscus synacus.

1999, Aug. 9   Litho.   Perf. 14
2623 A774 5p multicolored   1.50 .60
2624 A774 11p multicolored   2.50 1.20

Order of flowers from top is reversed on 11p value.
issued in sheets of 20 (10 of each denomination in two rows of 5, separated by a central gutter). Most sheets of 20 were cut in half through central gutter.

Community Chest, 50th Anniv. — A777

1999, Aug. 30
2625 A777 5p multicolored   .80 .40

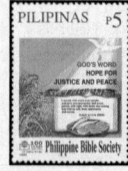

Philippine Bible Society, Cent. — A778

1999, Aug. 30
2626 A778 5p multicolored   .80 .40

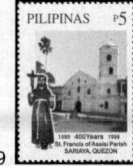

A779

1999, Sept. 3
2627 A779 5p multicolored   .80 .40
St. Francis of Assisi Parish, Sariaya, 400th anniv.

National Anthem, Cent. — A780

1999, Sept. 3
2628 A780 5p multicolored   1.00 .50

**No. 2539b Overprinted in Silver
"25th ANNIVERSARY IPPS"**
Souvenir Sheet
1999, Sept. 24   Litho.   Perf. 14
2629 A746 15p Sheet of 3, #a.-
    c., + 3 labels   8.00 6.00

Ovpt. in sheet margin has same inscription twice, "25th ANNIVERSARY INTERNATIONAL PHILIPPINE PHILATELIC SOCIETY 1974-99" and two society emblems.

Senate — A781

1999, Oct. 15
2630 A781 5p multicolored   .80 .40

A782

1999, Oct. 20
2631 A782 5p multicolored   .90 .45
New Building of Chiang Kai-shek College, Manila.

Issued in sheets of 10.

Tanza National Comprehensive High School, 50th Anniv. — A783

1999, Oct. 24
2632 A783 5p multicolored   .80 .40

San Agustin Church, Paoay, World Heritage Site — A784

Intl. Year of Older Persons — A785

World Teachers' Day — A786

1999, Oct. 24
2633 A784 5p multicolored   1.00 .50
2634 A785 11p multicolored   2.00 1.00
2635 A786 15p multicolored   3.00 2.00
    Nos. 2633-2635 (3)   6.00 3.50

United Nations Day.

Christmas — A787

1999, Oct. 27
Color of Angel's Gown
2636 A787 5p red violet   1.00 .40
2637 A787 11p yellow   2.00 .60
2638 A787 13p blue   2.50 1.00
2639 A787 15p green   3.00 1.50
  a. Sheet of 4, #2636-2639   10.00 8.00
    Nos. 2636-2639 (4)   8.50 3.50

Nos. 2636-2639 each issued in sheets of 10 stamps with two central labels.

Diplomatic Relations Type of 1999

Philippines-Canada diplomatic relations, 50th anniv., mammals: 5p, 15p, Tamaraw, polar bear.

1999, Nov. 15   Perf. 14
2640 A774 5p multi   1.25 .75
2641 A774 15p multi   3.00 1.50

Order of mammals from top is reversed on 15p value.
Issued in sheets of 20 (10 of each denomination in two rows of 5, separated by a central gutter). Most sheets of 20 were cut in half through central gutter.

Renovation of Araneta Coliseum — A788

1999, Nov. 19   Litho.
2642 A788 5p multicolored   1.00 .40

A789

1999, Nov. 19   **Color of Sky**
2643 A789 5p dark blue   1.00 .50
2644 A789 11p blue green   2.50 .80

3rd ASEAN Informal Summit.

A790

Sculptures: No. 2645, Kristo, by Arturo Luz. 11p, Homage to Dodgie Laurel, by J. Elizalde Navarro. 13p, Hilojan, by Napoleon Abueva. No. 2648, Mother and Child, by Abueva.

No. 2649: a, 5p, Mother's Revenge, by José Rizal, horiz. b, 15p, El Ermitano, by Rizal, horiz.

1999, Nov. 29
2645 A790 5p multi   1.00 .25
2646 A790 11p multi   2.00 .45
2647 A790 13p multi   2.25 .55
2648 A790 15p multi   2.75 .65
   Nos. 2645-2648 (4)   8.00 1.90

Souvenir Sheet
2649 A790   Sheet of 2, #a.-b. 6.00 5.00

Natl. Stamp Collecting Month.

New Year 2000 (Year of the Dragon) — A791

5p, Dragon in water. 11p, Dragon in sky.

1999, Dec. 1   **Perf. 14**
2650 A791 5p multicolored   1.25 .70
2651 A791 11p multicolored   2.75 1.30
   a.   Sheet of 2, #2650-2651   3.50 3.00
   b.   As "a," imperf.   3.50 3.00

Nos. 2650-2651 were normally printed in sheets of 20.

Battle of Tirad Pass, Cent. — A792

1999, Dec. 2   **Perf. 14**
2652 A792 5p multicolored   .80 .40

Orchids A793

No. 2653: a, Paphiopedilum urbanianum. b, Phalaenopsis schilleriana. c, Dendrobium amethystoglossum. d, Paphiopedilum barbatum.

No. 2654, horiz.: a, Paphiopedilum haynaldianum. b, Phalaenopsis stuartiana. c, Trichoglottis brachiata. d, Ceratostylis rubra.

1999, Dec. 3   **Litho.**
2653 A793 5p Block of 4, #a.-d. 4.50 4.00

Souvenir Sheet
2654 A793 5p Sheet of 4, #a.-d. 5.50 5.00

No. 2653 was printed in sheets of 16.

Battle of San Mateo, Cent. — A794

1999, Dec. 19
2655 A794 5p multicolored   .80 .40

People Power A795

People and: a, Tank. b, Tower. c, Crucifix.

1999, Dec. 31
2656 A795 5p Strip of 3, #a.-c. 3.50 3.50

Printed in sheets of 12.

Natl. Commission on the Role of Filipino Women — A796

2000, Jan. 7   **Litho.**   **Perf. 14**
2657 A796 5p multicolored   .80 .40

Printed in sheets of 10.

Manila Bulletin, Cent. — A797

2000, Feb. 2   **Litho.**   **Perf. 14**
2658 A797 5p multicolored   1.00 .50
   a.   Year at LR   1.50 .60

Issued: No. 2658a, 6/7.

La Union Province, 150th Anniv. A798

Arms of province and: a, Sailboat, golfer. b, Tractor, worker, building. c, Building, flagpole. d, Airplane, ship, telephone tower, people on telephone, computer.

2000, Mar. 2
2659 A798 5p Block of 4, #a.-d. 3.00 2.50

Civil Service Commission, Cent. — A799

2000, Mar. 20
2660 A799 5p multicolored   .80 .30

Millennium — A800

Designs: a, Golden Garuda of Palawan. b, First sunrise of the millennium, Pusan Point. c, Golden Tara of Agusan.

2000, Mar. 31
2661 A800 5p Strip of 3, #a.-c. 5.00 4.00

Printed in sheets of 12.

GMA Radio and Television Network, 50th Anniv. — A802

2000, Mar. 1   **Litho.**   **Perf. 14**
2662 A802 5p multicolored   .80 .40

Philippine Presidents A803

No. 2662A: b, Manuel Roxas. c, Elpidio Quirino. No. 2663: a, Presidential seal. b, Joseph Ejercito Estrada. c, Fidel V. Ramos. d, Corazon C. Aquino. e, Ferdinand E. Marcos. f, Diosdado Macapagal. g, Carlos P. Garcia. h, Ramon Magsaysay. i, Elpidio Quirino. j, Manuel Roxas.

2000   **Perf. 13½**
2662A A803 Pair   1.50 1.25
   b.-c.   5p Any single   .40 .30
2663   Block of 10   8.50 7.50
   a.-j.   A803 5p Any single   .60 .30

Nos. 2662b-2662c have presidential seal but lack blue lines at bottom. No. 2663a has denomination at left. Nos. 2663b-2663j have small Presidential seal at bottom.

Issued: No. 2662A, 2/6. No. 2663, 3/16.

See Type A828 for stamps showing Presidential seal with colored background.

See Nos. 2672-2676, 2786.

Diplomatic Relations Type of 1999

5p, Sarimanok, Great Wall of China. 11p, Phoenix, Banaue rice terraces.

No. 2666: a, 5p, Great Wall, horiz. b, 11p, Rice terraces, horiz.

2000, May 8   **Perf. 14**
2664-2665 A774 Set of 2   3.50 2.00

Souvenir Sheet
2666 A774   Sheet of 2, #a-b   4.00 3.50

Issued in sheets of 20 (10 of each denomination in two rows of 5, separated by a central gutter). Most sheets of 20 were cut in half through central gutter.

St. Thomas Aquinas Parish, Mangaldan, 400th Anniv. — A805

2000, June 1
2667 A805 5p multicolored   .80 .45

Battle Centenaries A806

Battles in Philippine Insurrection: #2668, Mabitac. #2669, Paye, vert. #2670, Makahambus Hill, vert. #2671, Pulang Lupa.

2000, June 19
2668-2671 A806 5p Set of 4   3.25 1.60

Presidents Type of 2000 Redrawn

No. 2672: a, Presidential seal. b, Joseph Ejercito Estrada. c, Fidel V. Ramos. d, Corazon C. Aquino. e, Ferdinand E. Marcos. f, Diosdado Macapagal. g, Carlos P. Garcia. h, Ramon Magsaysay. i, Elpidio Quirino. j, Manuel Roxas.

No. 2673: a, Magsaysay. b, Garcia.
No. 2674: a, Macapagal. b, Marcos.
No. 2675: a, Aquino. b, Ramos.
No. 2676: a, Estrada. b, Presidential seal.

2000   **Litho.**   **Perf. 13½**
     Blue Lines at Bottom
2672   Block of 10   12.00 10.00
   a.-j.   A803 5p Any single   .90 .50
2673   Pair   4.00 3.75
   a.-b.   A803 10p Any single   1.50 .60
2674   Pair   4.50 4.25
   a.-b.   A803 11p Any single   1.75 .70
2675   Pair   5.00 4.00
   a.-b.   A803 13p Any single   2.00 .80

2676   Pair   6.00 5.50
   a.-b.   A803 15p Any single   2.50 1.00
   Nos. 2672-2676 (5)   31.50 27.50

Issued: No. 2672, 7/3; Nos. 2673-2674, 8/4. Nos. 2675-2676, 6/19.

No. 2672a has denomination at R, while No. 2663a has denomination at L. Nos. 2672b-2672j have no presidential seal, while Nos. 2662Ab-2662Ac, 2663b-2663j have seal.

Insects A807

No. 2677: a, Ornate checkered beetle. b, Sharpshooter bug. c, Milkweed bug. d, Spotted cucumber beetle.

No. 2678: a, Green June beetle. b, Convergent ladybird. c, Eastern Hercules beetle. d, Harlequin cabbage bug.

2000, July 21   **Perf. 14**
2677 A807 5p Block of 4, #a-d   4.00 3.00
   e.   Souvenir sheet, #2677   6.00 6.00
2678 A807 5p Block of 4, #a-d   4.00 3.50
   e.   Souvenir sheet, #2678   6.00 6.00

Nos. 2677-2678 were printed in sheets of 16.

Occupational Health Nurses Association, 50th Anniv. — A808

2000, Aug. 30
2679 A808 5p multicolored   .85 .40

Diocese of Lucena, 50th Anniv. — A809

2000. Aug. 30
2680 A809 5p multicolored   .80 .40

Millennium — A810

Boats: a, Balanghai. b, Vinta. c, Caracoa.

2000, Sept. 21
2681 A810   Horiz. strip of 3   3.50 3.00
   a.-c.   5p Any single   .90 .60

Printed in sheets of 12.

Equitable PCI Bank, 50th Anniv. — A811

2000, Sept. 26
2682 A811 5p multicolored   .80 .40

Year of the Overseas Filipino Worker — A812

2000, Sept. 29   **Litho.**
2683 A812 5p multicolored   .80 .50

2000 Olympics, Sydney — A813

No. 2684: a, Running. b, Archery. c, Shooting. d, Diving.
No. 2685, horiz.: a, Boxing. b, Equestrian. c, Rowing. d, Taekwondo.

2000, Sept. 30
2684 A813 5p Block of 4, #a-d   4.00 3.50
Souvenir Sheet
2685 A813 5p Sheet of 4, #a-d   6.00 5.00
No. 2684 was printed in sheets of 16.

Teresian Association in the Philippines, 50th Anniv. — A814

2000, Oct. 10
2686 A814 5p multicolored   .80   .60
a.   Miniature sheet of 20   30.00
No. 2686 normally issued in sheets of 50.

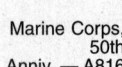

House of Representatives A815

2000, Oct. 15   Perf. 14
2687 A815 5p multicolored   .80   .45

Marine Corps, 50th Anniv. — A816

2000, Oct. 18
2688 A816 5p multicolored   .80   .40
Souvenir Sheet

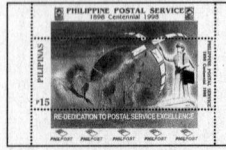

Postal Service, Cent. (in 1998) A817

2000, Nov. 6
2689 A817 15p multicolored   3.50 3.00

Clothing Exhibit at Metropolitan Museum of Manila — A818

No. 2690, 5p: a, Kalinga / Gaddang cotton loincloth. b, Portrait of Leticia Jimenez, by unknown artist.
No. 2691, 5p, horiz.: a, B'laan female upper garment. b, T'boli T'nalak abaca cloth.
No. 2692, a, 5p, Portrait of Teodora Devera Ygnacio, by Justiniano Asunción. b, 15p, Detail of Tawsug silk sash.

2000, Nov. 15   Pairs, #a-b
2690-2691 A818 Set of 2   4.00 3.00
#2690a-b, 2691a-b, any single   .60   .40
Souvenir Sheet
2692 A818 Sheet of 2, #a-b   4.50 4.50
Nos. 2690-2691 were printed in sheets of 16.

Natl. Stamp Collecting Month — A819

Designs: 5p, Portrait of an Unkown Lady, by Juan Luna, vert. 11p, Nude, by José Joya. 13p, Lotus Odalisque, by Rodolfo Paras-Perez. No. 2696, 15p, Untitled Nude, by Fernando Amorsolo. No. 2697, The Memorial, by Cesar Legaspi.

2000, Nov. 20   Perf. 14
2693-2696 A819 Set of 4   7.50 4.50
Souvenir Sheet
2697 A819 15p multi   4.50 4.00
No. 2697 contains one 80x29 stamp and label.

Christmas — A820

Angels: No. 2698, 5p, In pink robe, with bouquet of flowers. No. 2699, 5p, As #2698, with Holy Year 2000 emblem and inscription. 11p, In green robe. 13p, In orange robe. 15p, In red robe, with garland of flowers.

2000, Nov. 22   Litho.
2698-2702 A820 Set of 5   7.00 4.00
Nos. 2698-2702 were printed in sheets of 12.

APO Philatelic Society, 50th Anniv. — A821

Emblem and stamps: No. 2703, 5p, #620 (yellow background). No. 2704, 5p, #639 (light blue background), horiz. No. 2705, 5p, #850 (dull green background). No. 2706, 5p, #B21 (pink background), horiz.

2000, Nov. 23
2703-2706 A821 Set of 4   8.00 5.00
Printed in sheets of 16 in blocks of 4, each of the four designs on each corner, creating a se-tenant block of 4 in the center of each of the two types of sheets of 16 (horiz. or vert).

No. 1806 Handstamp Surcharged in Red

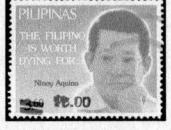

Perf. 13x13½
2000, Nov. 24   Litho.   Wmk.
2706A A469 5p on 3.60p multi   10.00 10.00
Nine varieties of the surcharge on No. 2706A exist.

New Year 2001 (Year of the Snake) — A822

Snakes with inscription in: 5p, Tagalog. 11p, English.

2000, Dec. 20   Unwmk.   Perf. 14
2707-2708 A822 Set of 2   3.50 2.00
2708a   Souvenir sheet, #2707-2708 + 2 labels   5.00 5.00
Nos. 2707-2708 were printed in sheets of 20. No. 2708a exists imperf. Value, $5.

Millennium A823

No. 2709: a, Trade and progress. b, Education and knowledge. c, Communication and information.

2000, Dec. 28
2709   Horiz. strip of 3   4.00 3.00
a.-c.   A823 5p Any single   .80   .50
No. 2709 was printed in sheets of 12.

Bank of the Philippine Islands, 150th Anniv. — A824

2001, Jan. 30   Litho.
2710 A824 5p multicolored   .80   .50
a.   Miniature sheet of 20   25.00
No. 2710 was normally issued in sheets of 50.

Hong Kong 2001 Stamp Exhibition — A825

Designs: No. 2711a, 5p, No. 2712, 11p, Tamaraw. No. 2711b, 5p, No. 2713, 11p, Agila. No. 2711c, 5p, No. 2714, 11p, Tarsier. No. 2711d, 5p, No. 2715, 11p, Talisman Cove orchid. No. 2711e, 5p, No. 2716, 11p, Pawikan.

2001, Feb. 1
2711   Horiz. strip of 5   5.00 4.00
a.-e.   A825 5p Any single   .80   .50
Souvenir Sheets
2712-2716 A825 Set of 5   20.00 15.00
2713a   Ovptd. in margin in red   6.50 5.00
2715a   Ovptd. in margin in red   6.50 5.00
No. 2711 was printed in sheets of 25. Nos. 2712-2716 have show emblem on sheet margin instead of on stamp.
Issued: Nos. 2713a, 2715a, 6/30/01. Overprint in margin on Nos. 2713a, 2715a has Chinese inscriptions and English text "PHILIPPINE-CHINESE PHILATELIC SOCIETY / 1951 GOLDEN JUBILEE 2001."

Gen. Paciano Rizal (1851-1930) — A826

2001, Mar. 7   Litho.   Perf. 14
2717 A826 5p multicolored   .90   .50

San Beda College, Cent. — A827

2001, Mar. 9
2718 A827 5p multicolored   .80   .40

Diplomatic Relations Type of 1999
Philippines-Vatican City diplomatic relations, 50th anniv., main altars at: 5p, St. Peter's Basilica, Vatican City. No. 2720, 15p, San Agustin Church, Manila.
No. 2721: a, Adam, from Creation of Adam, by Michelangelo. b, God, from Creation of Adam.

2001, Mar. 14
2719-2720 A774 Set of 2   4.00 3.00
Souvenir Sheet
2721 A774 15p Sheet of 2, #a-b   6.00 5.00
Nos. 2719-2720 issued in sheets of 20 (10 of each denomination in two rows of 5, separated by a central gutter). Most sheets of 20 were cut in half through central gutter.

Presidential Seal With Colored Background — A828

2001, Apr. 5   Perf. 13¾
Background Colors
2722 A828 5p yellow   .50   .30
2723 A828 15p blue   1.75   .50
Stamps of the same denomination showing the Presidential seal with white backgrounds are listed as Nos. 2663a, 2672a and 2676b. See Nos. 2746-2748. For surcharges, see Nos. 2834-2836. For overprints, see Nos. 2865-2866.

Tourist Spots — A829

No. 2724: a, El Nido, Palawan Province. b, Vigan House, Ilocos Sur Province. c, Boracay, Aklan Province. d, Chocolate Hills, Bohol Province.
15p, Banaue Rice Terraces, Ifugao Province.

2000, Apr. 14   Perf. 14
2724   Horiz. strip of 4   3.00 2.50
a.-d.   A829 5p Any single   .60   .40
Souvenir Sheet
2725 A829 15p multi   4.50 3.50
No. 2725 contains one 80x30mm stamp. No. 2725 exists with washed-out colors and a larger year date. Value, $25.

Canonical Coronation of Our Lady of Manaoag, 75th Anniv. — A830

2001, Apr. 22
2726 A830 5p multicolored   .75   .40

Pres. Gloria Macapagal-Arroyo A831

Pres. Macapagal-Arroyo: No. 2727, 5p, Waving. No. 2728, 5p, Taking oath of office.

2001, Apr. 29
2727-2728 A831 Set of 2   1.75 1.00

Diplomatic Relations Type of 1999
Philippines-Australia diplomatic relations, landmarks: 5p, Nos. 2730-2731, 13p, Sydney Opera House, Cultural Center of the Philippines. No. 2731 is horiz.

2001, May 21
2729-2730 A774 Set of 2   3.25 1.50
Souvenir Sheet
2731 A774 13p multi   4.50 3.50
Nos. 2729-2730 issued in sheets of 20 (10 of each denomination in two rows of 5, separated by a central gutter). Most sheets of 20 were cut in half through central gutter.
No. 2731 contains one 80x30mm stamp.

Supreme Court, Cent. — A832

2001, May 31
2732 A832 5p multicolored   .80 .40

Silliman University, Dumaguete City, Cent. — A833

2001, June 1
2733 A833 5p multicolored   .80 .40

Philippine Normal University, Cent. — A834

2001, June 1
2734 A834 5p multicolored   .80 .40

Joaquin J. Ortega (1870-1943), First Civil Governor of La Union Province — A835

2001, July 12
2735 A835 5p multicolored   .80 .50

Eugenio Lopez (1901-75), Businessman — A836

2001, July 12
2736 A836 5p multicolored   .80 .50

Illustrations from Boxer Codex, c. 1590 — A837

No. 2737: a, Visayan couple. b, Tagalog couple. c, Moros of Luzon (multicolored frame). d, Moros of Luzon (blue frame).
No. 2738: a, Pintados (denomination at left). b, Pintados (denomination at right). c, Cagayan female. d, Zambal.

2001, Aug. 1
2737 A837 5p Block of 4, #a-d   3.00 2.50
Souvenir Sheet
2738 A837 5p Sheet of 4, #a-d   3.75 3.00
e. Sheet of 4, #a-d, with Phila Nippon '01 margin   4.00 3.00
No. 2737 was printed in sheets of 16.

Arrival of American Educators (Thomasites), Cent. — A838

Designs: 5p, Thomasite teachers, US transport ship Thomas. 15p, Philippine students.

2001, Aug. 23
2739-2740 A838   Set of 2   3.00 1.60

Technological University of the Philippines, Cent. — A839

2001, Aug. 20   Litho.   Perf. 14
2741 A839 5p multicolored   .80 .40

National Museum of the Philippines, Cent. — A840

2001, Sept. 3
2742 A840 5p multicolored   .80 .40

Lands Management Bureau, Cent. — A841

2001, Sept. 17
2743 A841 5p multicolored   .80 .40

Colegio de San Jose and San Jose Seminary, 400th Anniv. — A842

2001, Oct. 1
2744 A842 5p multicolored   .80 .40

Makati City Financial District — A843

2001, Oct. 1
2745 A843 5p multicolored   .70 .40

Presidential Seal With Colored Background Type of 2001
2001, Oct. 5   Perf. 13¾
Background Colors
2746 A828 10p green   1.00 .35
2747 A828 11p pink   1.25 .40
2748 A828 13p gray   1.50 .45
Nos. 2746-2748 (3)   3.75 1.20

Musical Instruments — A844

No. 2749: a, Trumpet. b, Tuba. c, French horn. d, Trombone.
No. 2750, vert.: a, Bass drum. b, Clarinet, oboe. c, Xylophone. d, Sousaphone.

2001, Oct. 8   Perf. 14
2749 A844 5p Block of 4, #a-d   3.00 2.50
Souvenir Sheet
2750 A844 5p Sheet of 4, #a-d   5.00 4.00

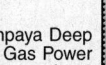

Malampaya Deep Water Gas Power Project — A845

Frame colors: 5p, Silver. 15p, Gold.

2001, Oct. 16
2751-2752 A845   Set of 2   4.00 2.00

Intl. Volunteers Year — A846

2001, Oct. 24
2753 A846 5p multicolored   1.00 .50

Year of Dialogue Among Civilizations — A847

2001, Oct. 24
2754 A847 15p multicolored   2.25 .80

Christmas — A848

Designs: 5p, Herald Angels. 11p, Kumukutikutitap. 13p, Pasko ni Bitoy. 15p, Pasko na naman.

2001, Oct. 30
2755-2758 A848   Set of 4   6.50 3.50

Philippines — Switzerland Relations, 150th Anniv. — A849

Monument statues by Richard Kissling: 5p, William Tell. No. 2760, 15p, Jose P. Rizal. No. 2761, 15p, Mayon Volcano, Philippines, and Matterhorn, Switzerland.

2001, Nov. 26
2759-2760 A849   Set of 2   3.75 2.00
Souvenir Sheet
2761 A849 15p multicolored   3.75 3.00
No. 2761 contains one 79x29mm stamp. Nos. 2759-2760 issued in sheets of 20 (10 of each denomination in two rows of 5, separated by a central gutter). Most sheets of 20 were cut in half through central gutter.

Drawings of Manila Inhabitants, c. 1840 — A850

Designs: 17p, Woman with hat, man with green pants. 21p, Woman with veil, man with brown pants. 22p, Man, woman at mortar and pestle.

2001, Dec. 1   Perf. 13¾
Inscribed "2001"
2762 A850 17p multicolored   2.00 .60
a. Inscribed "2002"   2.50 .70
b. Inscribed "2003"   5.00 2.00
2763 A850 21p multicolored   3.00 1.00
a. Inscribed "2002"   3.50 1.50
2764 A850 22p multicolored   3.00 1.00
a. Inscribed "2002"   3.00 1.00
Nos. 2762-2764 (3)   8.00 2.60
See No. 2779.

Solicitor General, Cent. — A851

2001, Dec. 7   Perf. 14
2765 A851 5p multicolored   .80 .40

Natl. Stamp Collecting Month — A852

Art: 5p, PUJ, by Antonio Austria. 17p, Hesus Nazareno, by Angelito Antonio. 21p, Three Women with Basket, by Anita Magsaysay-Ho, vert. No. 2769, 22p, Church with Yellow Background, by Mauro "Malang" Santos, vert. No. 2770, 22p, Komedya ng Pakil, by Danilo Dalena.

2001, Dec. 7   Litho.
2766-2769 A852   Set of 4   9.00 6.00
Souvenir Sheet
2770 A852 22p multicolored   4.50 3.50
No. 2770 contains one 79x29mm stamp.

New Year 2002 (Year of the Horse) — A853

Horse color: 5p, Red. 17p, White.

2001, Dec. 14   Perf. 14
2771-2772 A853   Set of 2   4.00 2.50
2772a   Souvenir sheet, #2771-2772, + 2 labels   6.00 5.00
Nos. 2771-2772 were printed in sheets of 20. No. 2772a exists imperf. Value $6.

Josemaria Escrivá (1902-75), Founder of Opus Dei — A854

2002, Jan. 9
2773 A854 5p multicolored   .80 .50
a. Miniature sheet of 20   35.00
No. 2773 was normally issued in sheets of 50.

World Heritage Sites — A855

Vigan City sites: 5p, St. Paul's Metropolitan Cathedral. 22p, Calle Crisologo.

2002, Jan. 22
2774-2775 A855   Set of 2   5.00 3.50
Nos. 2774-2775 were printed in sheets of 14 stamps plus one central label.

Salvador Z. Araneta, Statesman, Birth Cent. — A856

2002, Jan. 31
2776 A856 5p multicolored   .80 .40

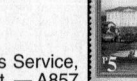

Customs Service,
Cent. — A857

2002, Feb. 1
2777 A857 5p multicolored   1.25   .60
   Printed in sheets of 20, with "fade away"
blue background, so each of the 20 stamps
has a different blue background.

Valentine's Day — A858

   No. 2778: a, Envelope. b, Man and woman.
c, Cat and dog. d, Balloon.

2002, Feb. 8
2778 A858 5p Block of 4, #a-d   3.75 3.00
   Printed in sheets of 16.

**Drawings of Manila Inhabitants Type
of 2001**

2002, Mar. 1   Litho.   Perf. 13¾
Inscribed "2002"
2779 A850 5p Man, woman on
              horses   .50   .25
   a.   Inscribed "2003"   .30   .25

Baguio General
Hospital and
Medical Center,
Cent. — A859

2002, Mar. 22   Perf. 14
2780 A859 5p multicolored   .75   .40

Beatification of Blessed
Pedro
Calungsod — A860

   Designs: 5p, Calungsod with palm frond.
22p, Map of Guam, ship, Calungsod with
cross.

2002, Apr. 2   Perf. 14
2781 A860 5p multicolored   1.00   .50
Size: 102x72mm
Imperf
2782 A860 22p multicolored   4.50 3.00

Negros Occidental
High School,
Cent. — A861

2002, Apr. 12   Perf. 14
2783 A861 5p multicolored   .75   .40

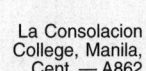

La Consolacion
College, Manila,
Cent. — A862

2002, Apr. 12
2784 A862 5p multicolored   .75   .40

Vesak Day — A863

2002, May 26
2785 A863 5p multicolored   1.25   .70
   a.   Miniature sheet of 20   47.50 47.50
   No. 2785 was normally issued in sheets of
50.

**Presidents Type of 2000 Redrawn
Without Years of Service**

   No. 2786: a, Gloria Macapagal-Arroyo. b,
Joseph Ejercito Estrada. c, Fidel V. Ramos. d,
Corazon C. Aquino. e, Ferdinand E. Marcos. f,
Diosdado Macapagal. g, Carlos P. Garcia. h,
Ramon Magsaysay. i, Elpidio Quirino. j,
Manuel Roxas.

2002, June 12   Perf. 13½
Without Presidential Seal
Blue Lines at Bottom
2786   Block of 10   7.50 8.00
   a.-j. A803 5p Any single   .55   .30

Cavite National
High School,
Cent. — A864

2002, June 19   Perf. 14
2787 A864 5p multicolored   .75   .40

Mangroves
A865

Fish — A866

Fish — A867

Hands and Small
Fish — A868

   No. 2792: a, Monitors in boats at marine
sanctuary. b, Mangrove reforestation. c,
Monitors checking reefs. d, Seaweed farming.

Unwmk.
2002, June 24   Litho.   Perf. 14
2788 A865 5p multicolored   1.20   .50
2789 A866 5p multicolored   1.20   .50
2790 A867 5p multicolored   1.20   .50
2791 A868 5p multicolored   1.20   .50
   Nos. 2788-2791 (4)   4.80 2.00
Souvenir Sheet
2792 A865 5p Sheet of 4, #a-d   4.00 3.00
   Coastal resources conservation.
   Nos. 2788-2791 were printed in sheets of
20.

Iglesia Filipina
Independiente,
Cent. — A869

2002, July 4
2793 A869 5p multicolored   .75   .40

Souvenir Sheet

Philakorea 2002 World Stamp
Exhibition, Seoul — A870

   No. 2794: a, 5p, Mangrove. b, 17p, Buddhist, temple and flower.

2002, Aug. 2   Unwmk.
2794 A870   Sheet of 2, #a-b   4.50 3.50
   No. 2794 exists imperf. with changed background color. Value $10.

No. 2210 Surcharged

Method & Perf. as Before
2002, Aug. 15   Wmk. 391
2795 A610 3p on 60s multi   .80   .40

Telecommunications
Officials Meetings,
Manila — A870a

2002, Aug. 22   Litho.   Perf. 14
2795A A870a 5p multicolored   .75   .40
   Second Telecommunications Ministerial
Meeting, Third ASEAN Telecommunications
Senior Officials Meeting, Eighth ASEAN Tele-
communications Regulators Council Meeting.

Marikina, Shoe
Capital of the
Philippines
A871

Unwmk.
2002, Oct. 15   Litho.   Perf. 14
2796 A871 5p multicolored   .75   .40

Souvenir Sheet

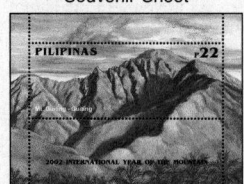

Intl. Year of Mountains — A872

2002, Oct. 28
2797 A872 22p multicolored   3.00 2.50

Christmas — A873

   Various holiday foods: 5p, 17p, 21p, 22p.

2002, Nov. 5
2798-2801 A873   Set of 4   9.00 5.00

Stamp Collecting
Month — A874

   Designs: 5p, Gerardo de Leon (1913-81),
movie director. 17p, Francisca Reyes Aquino
(1899-1983), founder of Philippine Folk Dance
Society. 21p, Pablo S. Antonio (1901-75),
architect. No. 2805, 22p, Jose Garcia Villa
(1912-97), writer.
   No. 2806, 22p, Honorata de la Rama (1902-
91), singer and actress.

2002, Nov. 2   Perf. 14
2802-2805 A874   Set of 4   8.00 5.00
Size: 99x74mm
Imperf
2806 A874 22p multicolored   3.25 2.50

First
Circumnavigation
of the World,
480th
Anniv. — A875

   No. 2807 — Ship and: a, Antonio Pigafetta.
b, Ferdinand Magellan. c, King Charles I of
Spain. d, Sebastian Elcano.
   22p, World Map and King Charles I of
Spain.

2002, Sep. 6   Perf. 14
2807 A875 5p Vert. strip of 4,
            #a-d   4.00 3.00
Size: 104x85mm
Imperf
2808 A875 22p multicolored   4.50 3.50

Fourth World Meeting
of Families — A876

   Designs: 5p, Sculpture of Holy Family. 11p,
Family, crucifix, Holy Spirit.

2002, Nov. 23   Perf. 14
2809-2810 A876   Set of 2   2.50 1.00

New Year 2003
(Year of the
Ram) — A877

Ram facing: 5p, Left. 17p, Right.

2002, Dec. 1
2811-2812 A877 Set of 2   4.00 2.50
a. Souvenir sheet, #2811-2812 + 2
    labels   6.00 5.00
Nos. 2811-2812 were printed in sheets of 20.
No. 2812a exists imperf. Value, $6.

Lyceum of the Philippines, 50th Anniv. — A878

2002, Dec. 5   *Perf. 14*
2813 A878 5p multicolored   .75   .40

Orchids A879

No. 2814: a, Luisia teretifolia. b, Dendrobium victoria-reginae, horiz. c, Gedorum densiflorum. d, Nervilia plicata, horiz. 22p, Grammatophyllum scriptum, horiz.

2002, Dec. 19   *Perf. 14*
2814 A879 5p Block of 4, #a-d 4.50 3.50
Souvenir Sheet
Imperf
2815 A879 22p multicolored   4.50 3.50
No. 2814 was printed in sheets of 16. No. 2815 contains one 69x40mm stamp.
No. 2814 was reprinted with a larger "2002" date. Value, block of 4, $11.

La Union National High School, Cent. — A880

2003, Jan. 22   *Perf. 14*
2816 A880 5p multicolored   .75   .40

St. Luke's Medical Center, Cathedral Heights, Cent. — A881

2003, Jan. 23
2817 A881 5p multicolored   .75   .40

Far Eastern University, 75th Anniv. — A882

2003, Jan. 28
2818 A882 5p multicolored   .75   .40

Manila Electric Railroad and Light Company, Cent. — A883

2003, Jan. 31
2819 A883 5p multicolored   .75   .40

St. Valentine's Day — A884

Mailman and: 5p, Heart-shaped strawberry. 17p, Hearts and mountains. 21p, Hearts and clouds. 22p, Butterflies and heart-shaped flowers.

2003, Feb. 11
2820-2823 A884 Set of 4   10.00 4.00
Nos. 2820-2823 were printed in sheets of 16.

Souvenir Sheets

Summer Institute of Linguistics, 50th Anniv. in Philippines — A885

No. 2824: a, 5p, Yakan weaving. b, 6p, Ifugao weaving. c, 5p, Kagayanen weaving. d, Bagobo Abaca weaving.
No. 2825, 11p: a, Ayta bow and arrows. b, Ibatan baskets. c, Palawano gong. d, Mindanao instruments.
No. 2826: a, 17p, Tboli cross-stitch. b, 5p, Aklanon Piña weaving. c, Kalinga weaving. d, Manobo beadwork.

2003, Feb. 28   *Litho.*
Sheets of 4, #a-d
2824-2826 A885 Set of 3   25.00 22.00
Intl. Decade of the World's Indigenous People.

Arrival of Japanese Workers for Construction of Kennon Road, Cent. — A886

2003, Feb. 20   *Perf. 14*
2827 A886 5p multi   .75   .40

National Heroes — A887

Designs: No. 2828, 6p, Apolinario Mabini (1864-1903), independence advocate. No. 2829, 6p, Luciano San Miguel (1875-1903), military leader.

2003, May 13   *Litho.* *Perf. 14*
2828-2829 A887 Set of 2   1.75 1.00

Orchids — A888

Designs (no flower names shown): 6p, Dendrobium uniflorum. 9p, Paphiopedilum urbanianum. 17p, Epigeneium lyonii. 21p, Thrixspermum subulatum.

2003, May 16   *Perf. 14½, 13¾ (9p)*
2830 A888 6p multi   .70   .25
2831 A888 9p multi   1.00   .35
2832 A888 17p multi   2.25   .90
2833 A888 21p multi   2.50 1.00
  Nos. 2830-2833 (4)   6.45 2.50
See Nos. 2849-2853, 2904-2912 for stamps with flower names.

No. 2722 Surcharged in Black or Red

2003   *Perf. 13¾*
2834 A828 1p on 5p multi   .70   .25
2835 A828 1p on 5p multi (R)   .60   .25
2836 A828 6p on 5p multi   .60   .25
  Nos. 2834-2836 (3)   1.90   .75
Issued: Nos. 2834-2835, 5/19; No. 2836, 6/4.

Philippine Medical Association, Cent. — A889

2003, May 21   *Perf. 14*
2837 A889 6p multi   .75   .40

Rural Banking, 50th Anniv. — A890

2003, May 22
2838 A890 6p multi   .75   .40

Mountains — A891

No. 2839: a, Mt. Makiling. b, Mt. Kanlaon. c, Mt. Kitanglad. d, Mt. Mating-oy.
No. 2840: a, Mt. Iraya. b, Mt. Hibok-Hibok. c, Mt. Apo. d, Mt. Santo Tomas.

2003, June 16
2839 A891 6p Block of 4, #a-d   3.75 3.00
Souvenir Sheet
2840 A891 6p Sheet of 4, #a-d   5.00 4.00
No. 2839 was printed in sheets of 16.

Chinese Roots of José Rizal — A892

Designs: 6p, Rizal Monument, Rizal Park, Jinjiang, People's Republic of China, vert. 17p, Rizal and Pagoda, Jinjiang.

2003, June 19
2841-2842 A892 Set of 2   3.25 2.50

Waterfalls — A893

No. 2843: a, Maria Cristina Falls. b, Katibawasan Falls. c, Bagongbong Falls. d, Pagsanjan Falls.

No. 2844: a, Casiawan Falls. b, Pangi Falls. c, Tinago Falls. d, Kipot Twin Falls.

2003, June 27
2843 A893 6p Block of 4, #a-d   3.75 3.00
Souvenir Sheet
2844 A893 6p Sheet of 4, #a-d   5.00 4.00
No. 2843 was printed in sheets of 16.

Philippine — Spanish Friendship Day — A894

Designs: 6p, Poster for Madoura Exhibit, by Pablo Picasso. 22p, Flashback, by José T. Joya.

2003, June 30
2845-2846 A894 Set of 2   3.75 2.25

Philippines Chamber of Commerce, Cent. — A895

2003, July 15
2847 A895 6p multi   .75   .40

Benguet Corporation, Cent. — A896

2003, Aug. 12
2848 A896 6p multi   .75   .40

Orchid Type of 2003 With Plant Names and

A897

Designs: 6p, Dendrobium uniflorum. 9p, Paphiopedilum urbanianum. 10p, Kingidium philippinense. 17p, Epigeneium lyonii. 21p, Thrixspermum subulatum. 22p, Trichoglottis philippinensis. 30p, Mariposa. 50p, Sanggumay. 75p, Lady's slipper. 100p, Waling-waling.

2003-04   *Perf. 14½*
2849 A888   6p multi   .65   .25
2849A A888   9p multi   .95   .35
2850 A888 10p multi   1.00   .40
  a. With space between "P"
      and "10," dated 2004
      ('04)   1.20   .50
2851 A888 17p multi   2.25   .70
  a. Base of "P" even with
      base of "17," dated
      2004 ('04)   2.00   .75
2852 A888 21p multi   2.40 1.00
  a. Base of "P" even with
      base of "21," dated
      2004 ('04)   2.25 1.00
2853 A888 22p multi   2.60 1.10
  a. Base of "P" even with
      base of "22," dated
      2004, plant name
      14mm long ('04)   2.50 1.00
  b. As "a," plant name
      12½mm long ('04)   3.25 1.50
            Perf. 14
2854 A897 30p multi   3.75 2.00
2855 A897 50p multi   6.00 3.50
2856 A897 75p multi   9.00 4.00
2857 A897 100p multi   12.00 5.50
  Nos. 2849-2857 (10)   40.60 18.80

Issued: 6p, 10p, 17p, 21p, 22p, 8/8; 30p, 100p, 8/21; 50p, 75p, 9/9. 9p, 11/4.
No. 2850a, 6/2/04; No. 2851a, 8/2/04; No. 2852a, 7/21/04; No. 2853a, 6/10/04. No, 2853b, 2004.
See Nos. 2904-2912.

Philippines — Mexico Diplomatic Relations, 50th Anniv. — A898

Designs: 5p, Our Lady of Guadalupe. No. 2859, 22p, Miraculous Image of the Black Nazarene. No. 2860, 22p, Crowd around church.

2003, Apr. 23 **Perf. 14**
2858-2859 A898 Set of 2 4.50 3.50
Souvenir Sheet
2860 A898 22p multi 4.50 4.00

Nos. 2858-2859 were issued in sheets of 20 (10 of each denomination in two rows of 5, separated by a central gutter). Most sheets of 20 were cut in half through central gutter. No. 2860 contains one 80x30mm stamp.

Our Lady of Caysasay, 400th Anniv. — A899

2003, Sept. 8
2861 A899 6p multi .75 .40

Cornelio T. Villareal, Sr., House Speaker, Birth Cent. — A900

2003, Sept. 11
2862 A900 6p multi .75 .40

National Teachers College, 75th Anniv. — A901

2003, Sept. 15
2863 A901 6p multi .75 .40

Sanctuary of San Antonio Parish, 50th Anniv. — A902

2003, Oct. 4 **Litho.**
2864 A902 6p multi .75 .40

Nos. 2722-2723 Overprinted in Red

2003, Oct. 17 **Perf. 13¾**
2865 A828 5p multi .70 .30
2866 A828 15p multi 1.75 1.00

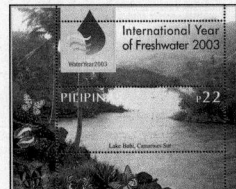

Souvenir Sheet

Intl. Year of Fresh Water A903

2003, Oct. 24 **Perf. 14**
2867 A903 22p multi + label 3.00 2.50

Federation of Free Farmers, 50th Anniv. — A904

2003, Oct. 25
2868 A904 6p multi .75 .40

Christmas — A905

Inscriptions: 6p, Mano po ninong ii. 17p, Himig at kulay ng Pasko, vert. 21p, Noche buena, vert. 22p, Karoling sa jeepney.

2003, Oct. 28
2869-2872 A905 Set of 4 9.00 6.00

National Stamp Collecting Month — A906

Cartoon art: 6p, Kenkoy, by Tony Velasquez, vert. 17p, Ikabod, by Nonoy Marcelo, vert. 21p, Sakay N'Moy, by Hugo C. Yonzon, Jr. No. 2876, 22p, Kalabong en Bosyo, by Larry Alcala. No. 2877, 22p, Hugo, the Sidewalk Vendor, by Rodolfo Y. Ragodon.

2003, Nov. 1
2873-2876 A906 Set of 4 8.00 5.00
Souvenir Sheet
2877 A906 22p multi 4.00 3.00

No. 2877 contains one 80x30mm stamp.

Winning Children's Art in National Anti-Drug Stamp Design Contest — A907

No. 2878: a, Globe, child with broom, by Nicole Fernan L. Caminian. b, Children, "No Drugs" symbol, by Jairus Cabajar. c, Children painting over "Drug Addiction" picture, by Genevieve V. Lazarte. d, Child chopping tree with hatchet, by Martin F. Rivera.

2003, Nov. 3
2878 A907 6p Block of 4, #a-d 4.00 3.00

Nos. 2550Ab, 2550Ac, 2550Ad and 2550Ae Surcharged

2003, Nov. 11 **Perf. 14**
2879 A749a 17p on 4p #2550Ab 3.00 1.75
2880 A749a 17p on 8p #2550Ac 3.00 1.75
2881 A749a 22p on 16p #2550Ad 4.00 2.50
2882 A749a 22p on 16p #2550Ae 4.00 2.50
Nos. 2879-2882 (4) 14.00 8.50

Nos. 2879-2882 were sold removed from the booklet the basic stamps were in.

Souvenir Sheet

First Philippine Stamps, 150th Anniv. — A908

2003, Nov. 14
2883 A908 22p Nos. 1, 2, 4 & 5, org to yellow background 3.00 2.50

Filipinas 2004 Stamp Exhibition, Mandaluyong City. See Nos. 2891-2897.

Camera Club of the Philippines, 75th Anniv. — A909

2003, Dec. 1 **Litho.**
2884 A909 6p multi .75 .40

New Year 2004 (Year of the Monkey) — A910

Monkey: 6p, Perched on branch. 17p, Hanging from branch.

2003, Dec. 1
2885-2886 A910 Set of 2 4.00 2.50
2886a Souvenir sheet, #2885-2886 + 2 labels 5.50 4.50

Nos. 2885-2886 were printed in sheets of 20. No. 2886a exists imperf. Value $5.50.

Succulent Plants — A911

No. 2887: a, Mammalaria spinosissima (yellow frame). b, Epithelantha bokei. c, Rebutia spinosissima. d, Turbinicarpus alonsoi.
No. 2888, horiz.: a, Aloe humilis. b, Euphorbia golisana. c, Gymnocalycium spinosissima. d, Mammalaria spinosissima (green frame).

2003, Dec. 5
2887 A911 6p Block of 4, #a-d 4.50 3.50
Souvenir Sheet
2888 A911 6p Sheet of 4, #a-d 5.00 4.00

No. 2887 was printed in sheets of 16 stamps.

Powered Flight, Cent. — A911a

No. 2888E — Do24TT: f, Green background. g, Yellow background.

2003, Dec. 17 **Litho.** **Perf. 14**
2888E A911a 6p Horiz. pair, #f-g 1.75 1.40

Printed in sheets of 8.

Architecture — A912

No. 2889: a, Luneta Hotel. b, Hong Kong Shanghai Bank. c, El Hogar. d, Regina Building.
No. 2890, horiz.: a, Pangasinan Capitol. b, Metropolitan Theater. c, Philtrust. d, University of Manila.

2003, Dec. 22
2889 A912 6p Block of 4, #a-d 4.50 3.50
Souvenir Sheet
2890 A912 6p Sheet of 4, #a-d 5.00 4.00

No. 2889 was printed in sheets of 16 stamps.

First Philpine Stamps, 150th Anniv. Type of 2003

No. 2891 (36x26mm each): a, Blue to lilac background, #1. b, Orange to yellow background, #2. c, Light to dark green background, #4. d, Dark to light pink background, #5.
Nos. 2892-2897: Like #2883.

2003-04 **Litho.** **Perf. 14**
2891 Horiz. strip of 4 4.50 3.50
a.-d. A908 6p Any single .85 .50
Souvenir Sheets
Background Colors
2892 A908 22p dk to lt rose 3.50 *3.00*
2893 A908 22p dk to lt blue 3.50 *3.00*
2894 A908 22p blue to lt grn 3.50 *3.00*
2895 A908 22p dk to lt pink 3.50 *3.00*
2896 A908 22p brn to yellow 3.50 *3.00*
2897 A908 22p white 3.50 *3.00*
a. With Postpex 2004 inscription added in red and black in sheet margin 4.00 *3.50*

Filipinas 2004 Stamp Exhibition, Mandaluyong City.
No. 2891 was printed in sheets of 16 stamps.
Issued: No. 2892, 12/15/03, No. 2893, 1/15/04; No. 2894, 1/30/04; No. 2895, 1/31/04; Nos. 2891, 2896, 2897, 2/1/04. No. 2897a, 4/19/04.
A sheet containing a block of four of perf. and imperf. examples of Nos. 2891a-2891d sold for 100p. Value, $20.

Arrival in Philippines of Sisters of St. Paul of Chartres, Cent. — A913

2004, Jan. 22 **Perf. 14**
2898 A913 6p multi .75 .35

Polytechnic University of the Philippines, Cent. — A914

2004, Jan. 22
2899 A914 6p multi .75 .35

Tanduay Distillers, Inc., 150th Anniv. — A915

2004, Jan. 22
2900 A915 6p multi .75 .35

Grepalife Life Insurance Co., 50th Anniv. — A916

2004, Jan. 22
2901 A916 6p multi .75 .35

2003 State Visit of U.S. Pres. George W. Bush — A917

Flags of U.S. and Philippines, George W. Bush and: 6p, Crowd. 22p, Philippines Pres. Gloria Macapagal-Arroyo, Malacañang Palace.

2004, Feb. 23 Litho. Perf. 13x13½
2902-2903 A917 Set of 2 3.00 2.00

Orchid Type of 2003 With Plant Names

Designs: 1p, Liparis latifolia. 2p, Cymbidium finlaysonianum. 3p, Phalaenopsis philippinensis. 4p, Phalaenopsis fasciata. 5p, Spathoglottis plicata.
No. 2909: a, Phalaenopsis fuscata. b, Phalaenopsis stuartiana. c, Renanthera monachia. d, Aerides quinquevulnera.
8p, Phalaenopsis schilleriana. 9p, Phalaenopsis pulchra. 20p, Phaius tankervilleae.
Two types of 1p and 5p:
I — Denomination and year date not touching edges of background color, digits of year date touching.
II — Denomination and year date touch edges of background color, digits of year date spaced.
Three types of 2p:
I — Plant name 13½mm long and 1mm from year date, denomination and year date not touching edges of background color.
II — Plant name 13½ mm long and 2mm from year date, denomination and year date touching edges of background color.
III — Plant name 14mm long and 1½mm from year date, denomination and year date touching edges of background color.

2004 Litho. Perf. 14½
2904 A888 1p multi, type I .50 .25
 a. Type II .60 .25
2905 A888 2p multi, type I .65 .30
 a. Type II .40 .25
 b. Type III 9.00 5.00
2906 A888 3p multi .45 .25
2907 A888 4p multi .50 .30
2908 A888 5p multi, type I .50 .25
 a. Type II .90 .35
2909 Block of 4 3.50 1.75
 a.-d. A888 6p Any single .75 .35
2910 A888 8p multi .80 .35
2911 A888 9p multi 1.00 .40
2912 A888 20p multi 2.25 .80
 Nos. 2904-2912 (9) 10.15 4.65

Issued: Nos. 2904, 2908, 3/9; Nos. 2904a, 2905, 2905b, 2910, 4/1; Nos. 2905a, 2908a, 4/28; Nos. 2906, 2907, 2911, 2912, 6/11; No. 2909, 12/20.

Pfizer Pharmaceuticals, 50th Anniv. in Philippines — A918

2004, Apr. 30 Perf. 14
2913 A918 6p multi .75 .35

Our Lady of Piat, 400th Anniv. — A919

2004, June 21
2914 A919 6p multi .75 .35
 a. Miniature sheet of 8 15.00 15.00
Normally issued in sheets of 50.

Bonsai — A920

No. 2915, vert. — Orange to yellow background: a, Bantigue. b, Kamuning Binangonan with thick trunk, dark brown pot. c, Balete. d, Mulawin aso. e, Kamuning Binangonan with root-like trunk, dark brown pot. f, Logwood. g, Kamuning Binangonan, orange clay pot. h, Bantolinao.
No. 2916 — Purple to white background: a, Bantigue with thick trunk, brown pot. b, Chinese elm. c, Bantigue with two trunks, brown pot. d, Bantigue, white pot. e, Balete with many green leaves, black and brown pot. f, Balete with few green leaves, brown pot. g, Bantigue, light brown rectangular pot. h, Mansanita.
Nos. 2917a, 2918a, Lomonsito. Nos. 2917b, 2918b, Bougainvillea, pot on table. Nos. 2917c, 2918c, Bougainvillea, orange brown pot. Nos. 2917d, 2918d, Kalyos.

2004 Perf. 14
2915 Block of 8 8.00 6.50
 a.-h. A920 6p Any single .80 .50
2916 Block of 8 8.00 6.50
 a.-h. A920 6p Any single .80 .50

Souvenir Sheets
Solid Blue Background
2917 Sheet of 4 5.00 4.00
 a.-d. A920 6p Any single 1.00 .75
Blue to White Background
2918 Sheet of 4 5.00 4.00
 a.-d. A920 6p Any single 1.00 .75

Nos. 2915-2916 were printed in sheets of 16. Issued: Nos. 2915-2917, 7/27; No. 2918, 8/28. 2004 World Stamp Championship, Singapore (No. 2918).

2004 Summer Olympics, Athens — A921

Designs: 6p, Shooting. 17p, Taekwondo. 21p, Swimming. No. 2922, 22p, Archery. No. 2923, 22p, Boxing.

2004, Aug. 13
2919-2922 A921 Set of 4 9.00 6.00
Souvenir Sheet
2923 A921 22p multi 3.50 2.75

Miguel Lopez de Legazpi (c. 1510-72), Founder of Manila — A922

2004, Aug. 20 Litho.
2924 A922 6p multi .75 .50

Admiral Tomas A. Cloma, Sr. (1904-96) A923

2004, Aug. 20
2925 A923 6p multi .75 .40

Animals of the Lunar New Year Cycle A924

Designs: Nos. 2926a, 2927a, Rat. Nos. 2926b, 2927b, Ox. Nos. 2926c, 2927c, Tiger. Nos. 2926d, 2927d, Rabbit. Nos. 2926e, 2927e, Dragon. Nos. 2926f, 2927f, Snake. Nos. 2926g, 2928a, Horse. Nos. 2926h, 2928b, Goat. Nos. 2926i, 2928c, Monkey. Nos. 2926j, 2928d, Cock. Nos. 2926k, 2928e, Dog. Nos. 2926l, 2928f, Pig.

2004, Sept. 9 Perf. 14
English Inscriptions at Left
2926 A924 6p Sheet of 12, #a-l, + 3 labels 15.00 15.00
Chinese Inscriptions at Left
2927 A924 6p Sheet of 6, #a-f, + 6 labels 20.00 20.00
2928 A924 6p Sheet of 6, #a-f, + 6 labels 20.00 20.00

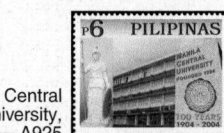

Manila Central University, Cent. — A925

2004, Sept. 21
2929 A925 6p multi .75 .35
 a. Miniature sheet of 8 12.50 12.50

Christmas — A926

Various Christmas trees: 6p, 17p, 21p, 22p.

2004, Oct. 1
2930-2933 A926 Set of 4 10.00 7.00

Filipino-Chinese General Chamber of Commerce, Cent. — A927

No. 2934: a, Intramuros, Philippines. b, Great Wall of China.

2004, Oct. 12
2934 A927 6p Horiz. pair, #a-b 2.00 1.50
 a. Miniature sheet of 8 12.50 12.50
Normally issued in sheets of 40.

Winning Designs in Rice Is Life National Stamp Design Contest A928

No. 2935, 6p: a, By Maria Enna T. Alegre. b, By Lady Fatima M. Velasco.
No. 2936, 6p: a, By Sean Y. Pajaron. b, By Ljian B. Delgado.
No. 2937, 6p: a, By Michael O. Villadolid. b, By Gary M. Manalo.

2004, Oct. 15 Litho.
Horiz. Pairs, #a-b
2935-2937 A928 Set of 3 6.00 5.00
2937c Miniature sheet, #2935a-2935b, 2936a-2936b, 2937a-2937b 9.00 9.00
Intl. Year of Rice.

Natl. Stamp Collecting Month — A929

Comic strip and comic book illustrations: No. 2938, 6p, Darna, by Nestor P. Redondo. No. 2939, 6p, Kulafu, by Francisco Reyes. No. 2940, 6p, El Vibora, by Federico C. Javinal, vert. No. 2941, 6p, Lapu-Lapu, by Francisco V. Coching, vert.
22p, Darna, by Mars Ravelo, vert

2004 Perf. 14
2938-2941 A929 Set of 4 4.00 3.00
Souvenir Sheet
2942 A929 22p multi 4.50 3.50
No. 2942 contains one 30x80mm stamp.

San Agustin Church, Manila, 400th Anniv. A930

No. 2943: a, Denomination at left. b, Denomination at right.

2004, Nov. 13
2943 A930 6p Horiz. pair, #a-b 1.75 1.40
 a. Miniature sheet of 8 12.50 12.50
Normally issued in sheets of 40.

New Year 2005 (Year of the Rooster) — A931

Designs: 6p, Rooster's head. 17p, Rooster.

2004, Dec. 1
2944-2945 A931 Set of 2 4.00 3.00
2945a Souvenir sheet, 2 each #2944-2945 8.00 8.00
Printed in sheets of 20 and in sheets of 10.

Worldwide Fund for Nature (WWF) — A932

Owls: No. 2946, 6p, Giant Scops owl. No. 2947, 6p, Philippine eagle owl. No. 2948, 6p, Negros Scops owl. No. 2949, 6p, West Visayan hawk owl.

2004, Dec. 22
2946-2949 A932 Set of 4 4.50 3.50
2949a Block of 4, #2946-2949 5.50 5.00
2949b Miniature sheet of 8 50.00 50.00
No. 2946-2949 were normally printed in sheets of 16.

Liceo de Cagayan University A933

2005, Feb. 5   Litho.   Perf. 14
2950 A933 6p multi   .75   .40
  a.   Miniature sheet of 8   12.50 12.50
    Normally printed in sheets of 50.

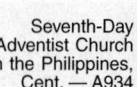

Seventh-Day
Adventist Church
in the Philippines,
Cent. — A934

2005, Feb. 18
2951 A934 6p multi   .75   .40
  a.   Miniature sheet of 8   12.50 12.50
    Normally issued in sheets of 50.

Baguio
Country
Club,
Cent.
A935

  No. 2952: a, Club in 1905. b, Club in 2005.

2005, Feb. 18
2952 A935 6p Horiz. pair, #a-b   2.00   1.75
  a.   Miniature sheet of 8   12.50 12.50
    Normally issued in sheets of 40.

Butterflies — A936

  Designs: 1p, Arisbe decolor stratos.
  No. 2954: a, Parantica noeli. b, Chilasa osmana osmana. c, Graphium sandawanum joreli. d, Papilio xuthus benguetanus.

2005   Litho.   Perf. 14½
2953 A936 1p multi   .50   .25
  a.   Butterfly redrawn with two an-
     tennae   .50   .30
2954   Block of 4   11.00   8.00
  a.-d.   A936 22p Any single   2.25   1.50
    Issued: 1p, 4/12; No. 2954, 3/3.
  See Nos. 2978-2981.

Shells
A937

  No. 2955: a, Chicoreus saulii. b, Spondylus varians. c, Spondylus linquaefelis. d, Melo broderipii.
  No. 2956: a, Chlamys senatoria. b, Siphonofusus vicdani. c, Epitonium scalare. d, Harpa harpa.
  No. 2957: a, Siliquaria armata. b, Argonauta argo. c, Perotrochus vicdani. d, Corculum cardisca.

2005, Apr. 15   Perf. 14
2955 A937 Block of 4   4.00   3.00
  a.-d.   6p Any single   .80   .65
2956 A937 Block of 4   4.00   3.00
  a.-d.   6p Any single   .80   .65
Souvenir Sheet
2957 A937 Sheet of 4 + 2 la-
    bels   7.50   7.50
  a.-d.   6p Any single   1.60   1.20
  Nos. 2955-2956 were normally issued in sheets of 16.

State Visit of Hu
Jintao, Pres. of
People's Republic
of China — A938

  Flags of Philippines and People's Republic of China, Philippines Pres. Gloria Macapagal-Arroyo and: 6p, Pres. Hu at right. 17p, Pres. Hu at left.

2005, Apr. 27
2958-2959 A938 Set of 2   4.00   2.50
  2959a   Souvenir sheet, #2958-2959   6.00   5.00

Architecture — A939

  No. 2960: a, Ernesto de la Cruz Ancestral House. b, Limjoco Residence. c, Pelaez Ancestral House. d, Vergara House.
  No. 2961: a, Gliceria Marella Villavicencio. b, Lasala-Guarin House. c, Claparols House. d, Ilagan Ancestral House.

2005, May 7
2960 A939 Block of 4   3.50   3.00
  a.-d.   6p Any single   .75   .65
Souvenir Sheet
2961 A939 Sheet of 4   5.00   4.00
  a.-d.   6p Any single   1.00   .80
  No. 2960 was printed in sheets of 16.

Central Philippine
University,
Cent. — A940

2005, May 13
2962 A939 6p multi   .75   .40
  a.   Miniature sheet of 8   12.50 12.50
    Normally issued in sheets of 50 stamps.

Rotary
International,
Cent. — A941

  Denomination: 6p, At left, in blue. 22p, At right, in red.

2005, May 31
2963-2964 A941 Set of 2   5.00   4.00
  2964a   Miniature sheet, 6 #2963, 2
    #2964   16.00 16.00

San Bartolome
Parish, 400th
Anniv. — A942

2005, July 25   Litho.   Perf. 14
2965 A942 6p multi   .75   .40

Senator Blas F. Ople
(1927-2003) — A943

2005, July 28
2966 A943 6p multi   .75   .40

Shells
A944

  No. 2967, 6p: a, Chrysallis fischeri. b, Helicostyla bicolorata. c, Helicostyla dobiosa. d, Helicostyla portei.
  No. 2968, 6p: a, Cochlostyla imperator. b, Helicostyla turbinoides. c, Helicostyla lignaria. d, Amphidromus dubius.
  No. 2969, horiz.: a, Calocochlia depressa. b, Cochlostyla sarcinosa. c, Calocochlia schadenbergi. d, Helicostyla pulcherrina.

2005   Blocks of 4, #a-d   Perf. 14
2967-2968 A944 Set of 2   10.00   8.00
Souvenir Sheets
2969 A944 6p Sheet of 4, #a-d, +
    2 labels   6.00   5.00
2970   Sheet, #2969a, 2969b,
    2970a, 2970b   6.00   5.00
  a.   A944 2p Like #2969c   1.00   .75
  b.   A944 3p Like #2969d   1.00   .75
  Nos. 2967-2968 issued in sheets of 16.
  Issued: Nos. 2967-2969, 8/8; No. 2970, 8/19. Upper left label on No. 2970 has Taipei 2005 Stamp Exhibition emblem, lower right label has "Greetings from the Philippines" inscription.

Intl. Year of the
Eucharist — A945

  Winning pictures in stamp design contest by: No. 2971, 6p, Carlos Vincent H. Ruiz. No. 2972, 6p, Rommer A. Fajardo. No. 2973, 6p, Telly Farolan-Somera. No. 2974, 6p, Allen A. Moran. No. 2975, 6p, Elouiza Athena Tentativa. No. 2976, 6p, Jianina Marishka C. Montealto.

2005, Sept. 8
2971-2976 A945 Set of 6   4.50   3.00
  2976a   Souvenir sheet, #2971-
    2976, + 6 labels   8.00   8.00

No. 1887 Surcharged in Red
Souvenir Sheet

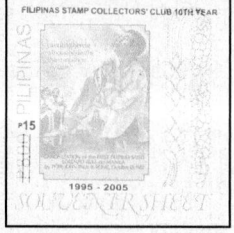

Wmk. 389
2005, Sept. 14   Litho.   Imperf.
2977 A493 15p on 8p multi   2.50   2.00

Butterflies Type of 2005 and

A946   A947

  Designs: 5p, Parantica danatti danatti.
  No. 2979: a, Hebemoia glaucippe philippinensis. b, Moduza urdaneta aynii. c, Lexias satrapes hiwaga. d, Cheritra orpheus orpheus. e, Achillides chikae chikae. f, Arisbe ideaoiedes ideaoiedes. g, Dellas schoenigi hermeli. h, Achillides palinurus daedalus. i, Dellas levicki justini. j, Troides magellanus magellanus.
  No. 2980: a, Idea electra electra. b, Charaxes bajula adoracion. c, Tanaecia calliphorus calliphorus. d, Trogonoptera trojana. e, Charaxes bajula adoracion, diff.
  No. 2981: a, Cethosia biblis barangingi. b, Menalaides polytes ledebouria. c, Appias nero palawanica. d, Udara tyotaroi.

2005   Unwmk.   Perf. 14½
2978 A946 5p multi   .60   .25
2979   Block of 10   10.00   9.00
  a.-j.   A946 6p Any single   .65   .30
2980   Block of 4, #a-d   8.00   7.00
  a.   A946 17p multi   1.60   1.00
  b.   A946 17p multi   1.60   1.00
  c.   A946 17p multi   1.60   1.00
  d.   A946 17p multi   1.60   1.00
  e.   A947 17p multi   25.00 25.00
  f.   Block of 4, #2980a, 2980c,
    2980d, 2980e   60.00 60.00

2981   Block of 4   9.00   8.00
  a.-d.   A946 21p Any single   2.00   1.50
  Nos. 2978-2981 (4)   27.60 24.25
  Issued: No. 2978, 11/22; No. 2979, 10/12; No. 2980, 12/9. No. 2981, 12/2.

Intl. Year of Sports and Physical
Education — A948

UN Millennium
Development
Goals — A949

  No. 2982: a, Dove, open book, Philippines flag, basketball, emblem at LL. b, Torch, sports equipment, people with joined hands, dove flying to right, emblem at LR. c, Torch, sports equipment, people with joined hands, dove flying to left, emblem at LL.

2005, Oct. 19   Perf. 14
2982 A948 6p Horiz. pair, #a-b   2.00   1.50
  c.   6p multi   .75   .50
  d.   Horiz. pair, #2982a, 2982c   2.50   1.75
2983 A949 6p multi   1.00   *1.00*
Souvenir Sheet
2984   Sheet, #2982a, 2982b,
    2984a   3.00   2.50
  a.   A949 10p multi   1.00   .80
  b.   Sheet, #2982a, 2982c, 2984a   4.00   3.50
    United Nations, 60th anniv.

Bureau of Corrections,
Cent. — A950

2005, Nov. 4
2985 A950 6p multi   .75   .40
  a.   Miniature sheet of 8   12.50 12.50
    Normally issued in sheets of 50.

Inauguration of Pres. Gloria
Macapagal-Arroyo — A951

  Pres. Macapagal-Arroyo: 6p, Taking oath. 22p, Giving inaugural speech.

2005, Nov. 9
2986-2987 A951 Set of 2   4.00   2.50

Christmas
A952

  Various department store window Christmas displays: 6p, 17p, 21p, 22p.

2005, Nov. 16
2988-2991 A952 Set of 4   9.00   6.50

23rd Southeast Asia
Games,
Philippines — A953

No. 2992: a, Boxing. b, Cycling. c, Wushu. d, Bowling. e, Badminton. f, Billiards. Eagle has black beak on all stamps.

No. 2993, horiz.: a, Track. b, Soccer. c, Taekwondo. d, Judo. e, Chess. f, Karate. g, Gymnastics. h, Pencaksilat. i, Dragon boat racing. j, Swimming.

No. 2994: a, Baseball. b, Shooting. c, Archery. d, Bowling (eagle with brown beak). e, Volleyball. f, Boxing (eagle with brown beak). g, Cycling (eagle with brown beak). h, Badminton (eagle with brown beak).

No. 2995: a, Archery. b, Shooting. c, Equestrian.

No. 2996, horiz.: a, Arnis. b, Chess. c, Dragon boat racing.

2005, Nov. 22   **Red Frames**

2992	Block of 6	7.50	6.50
a.-f.	A953 6p Any single	1.00	.75
2993	Sheet of 10 + 8 labels	20.00	20.00
a.-j.	A953 6p Any single	1.50	1.50
2994	Sheet of 10, #2992c, 2992f, 2994a-2994h, + 20 labels	20.00	20.00
a.-h.	A953 6p Any single	1.50	1.50

Blue Frames

2995	Sheet of 3	5.00	4.00
a.	A953 5p multi	1.20	.75
b.-c.	A953 6p Either single	1.20	.75
2996	Sheet of 3	5.00	4.00
a.	A953 5p multi	1.20	.75
b.-c.	A953 6p Either single	1.20	.75

No. 2992 was printed in sheets of 12 containing two blocks. Nos. 2993a-2993j lack perforations between the stamp and the adjacent labels that are the same size as the stamp. There are perforations between the stamps and labels on No. 2994. The labels to the right of the stamps could be personalized. Nos. 2993 and 2994 each sold for 99p with generic flag labels, and for 350p with personalized labels.

National Stamp Collecting Month — A954

Prints: No. 2997, 6p, Pinoy Worker Abr'd., by Ben Cab. No. 2998, 6p, Bulbs, by M. Parial. No. 2999, 6p, The Fourth Horseman, by Tequi. No. 3000, 6p, Breaking Ground, by R. Olazo. 22p, Form XV, by Brenda Fajardo, horiz.

2005, Nov. 28

2997-3000	A954 Set of 4	3.50	2.50

Souvenir Sheet

3001	A954 22p multi	4.00	3.00

No. 3001 contains one 80x30mm stamp.

New Year 2006 (Year of the Dog) — A955

Dog and inscription: a, 6p, "Manigong Bagong Taon." b, 17p, "Happy New Year."

2005, Dec. 1

3002-3003	A955 Set of 2	3.75	2.50
3003a	Souvenir sheet, 2 each #3002-3003	8.00	7.00

Nos. 2002-2003 were issued both in sheets of 20 and sheets of 10.

Third Asian Para Games — A956

Designs: 6p, Runner with amputated arm. 17p, Wheelchair racer.

2005, Dec. 6

3004-3005	A956 Set of 2	3.00	2.00

Pope John Paul II (1920-2005) — A957

Pope John Paul II, Vatican arms and text: 6p, "Mahal Namin Kayo!" 22p, "We Love You!"

2005, June 28   **Litho.**   **Perf. 14**

3006-3007	A957 Set of 2	4.00	2.50
3006a	Miniature sheet of 6 + 6 labels		25.00
3007a	Miniature sheet of 6 + 6 labels		25.00

Nos. 3006-3007 normally issued in sheets of 50 stamps.

Lighthouses — A958

No. 3008: a, Cape Santiago Lighthouse, Calatagan. b, Bacagay Lighthouse, Liloan. c, Malabrigo Lighthouse, Lobo. d, Capones Lighthouse, San Antonio.

No. 3009: a, Tubbataha Lighthouse, Cagayancillo. b, Cape Bojeador Lighthouse, Burgos. c, Cape Bolinao Lighthouse, Bolinao. d, San Fernando Point Lighthouse, San Fernando.

2005, Dec. 22

3008	A958 6p Block of 4, #a-d	4.00	3.00

Souvenir Sheet

3009	A958 6p Sheet of 4, #a-d	5.00	4.00

No. 3008 printed in sheets of 16 stamps.

St. Scholastica's College, Manila, Cent. — A959

2006, Jan. 3

3010	A959 6p multi	.70	.40
a.	Miniature sheet of 8	12.50	12.50

Normally printed in sheets of 50 stamps.

Filipinos in Hawaii, Cent. — A960

Contest-winning designs: 6p, Filipinos in Hawaii, by Allen A. Moran. 22p, Filipinos and flags, by Crisanto S. Umali.
No. 3013: a, Like 6p. b, Like 22p.

2006, Jan. 5

3011-3012	A960 Set of 2	3.50	2.50

Souvenir Sheet

3013	A960 11p Sheet of 2, #a-b	5.00	4.00

Mary Johnston Hospital, Manila, Cent. A961

No. 3014: a, Hospital building and founder Rebecca Parish. b, Surgeons, hospital building.

2006, Jan. 20

3014	A961 6p Horiz. pair, #a-b	2.00	1.50
a.	Miniature sheet of 8	14.50	14.50

Normally issued in sheet of 40 stamps.

Love A962

No. 3015 — Angel with: a, Letter. b, Flower.

2006, Feb. 8

3015	A962 7p Horiz. pair, #a-b	2.00	1.50

Jaime Cardinal Sin (1928-2005), Archbishop of Manila — A963

Sin and: 7p, Cathedral. 22p, Statue.

2006, Feb. 25

3016-3017	A963 Set of 2	3.00	2.00
3017a	Souvenir sheet, 2 each #3016-3017	8.00	7.00

Marine Turtles — A964

No. 3018: a, Olive Ridley turtle. b, Hawksbill turtle. c, Loggerhead turtle. d, Leatherback turtle.
26p, Green turtle.

2006, Mar. 31

3018	A964 Horiz. strip of 4	4.50	3.50
a.-d.	7p Any single	.75	.45

Souvenir Sheet

3019	A964 26p multi	5.00	4.00

No. 3018 normally issued in sheet of 16 stamps. No. 3019 contains one 80x30mm stamp.

Butterfly Type of 2005 and

Butterfly With Fully-colored Background A965

Butterfly With Blue Lines At Bottom A966

Butterfly With Partially-colored Background A967

Butterfly With Framed and Colored Background A968

Designs: 1p, Arisbe decolor stratos. 2p, Arhopala anthelus impar. 3p, Zophoessa dataensis nihrai. 4p, Liphyra brassolis justini. 5p, Parantica danatti danatti. 9p, Lexias satrapes amlana. 10p, Tanaecia aruna pallida. 30p, Appias nero domitia. 100p, Cepora aspasia olga.

Nos. 3030 and 3031: a, Hebemoia glaucippe philippensis. b, Moduza urdaneta aynii. c, Lexias satrapes hiwaga. d, Cheritra orpheus orpheus. e, Achillides chikae chikae. f, Arisbe ideaoiedes ideaoiedes. g, Delias schoenigi hermeli. h, Achillides palinurus daedalus. i, Delias levicki justini. j, Troides magellanus magellanus.

Nos. 3036 and 3037: a, Idea electra electra. b, Charaxes bajula adoracion. c, Tanaecia calliphorus calliphorus. d, Trogonoptera trojana.

Nos. 3038 and 3039: a, Cethosia biblis barangingi. b, Menalaides polytes ledebouria. c, Appias nero palawanica. d, Udara tyotaroi.

Nos. 3040 and 3041: a, Parantica noeli. b, Chilasa osmana osmana. c, Graphium sandawanum joreli. d, Papilio xuthus benguetanus.

Perf. 14½ (A936, A965), 13¾ (A966), 13x13¼ (A967), 14 (A968)

2006   **Inscribed "2006"**

3020	A965	1p multi	.50	.25
3021	A966	1p multi	.50	.25
a.		Inscribed "2007"	.50	.25
3022	A965	2p multi	.50	.25
3023	A966	2p multi	.50	.25
a.		Inscribed "2007"	.60	.25
3024	A936	3p multi	.60	.25
3025	A966	3p multi	.60	.30
a.		Inscribed "2007"	.70	.30
3026	A936	4p multi	.70	.30
3027	A966	4p multi	.70	.30
a.		Inscribed "2007"	.70	.30
3028	A965	5p multi	.70	.30
3029	A966	5p multi	.70	.30
a.		Inscribed "2007"	.70	.30
3030		Block of 10	8.00	7.50
a.-j.	A965 7p Any single		.70	.35
3031		Block of 10	9.00	8.00
a.-j.	A966 7p Any single		.75	.35
k.	Block of 10, inscr. "2007"		11.00	10.00
l.-u.	A966 7p Any single, inscr. "2007"		.80	.35
3032	A936	9p multi	1.10	.40
3033	A966	9p multi	1.20	.40
a.		Inscribed "2007"	1.20	.40
3034	A936	10p multi	1.20	.50
3035	A966	10p multi	1.20	.50
a.		Inscribed "2007"	1.50	.50
3036		Block of 4	10.00	8.00
a.-d.	A965 20p Any single		2.50	1.25
3037		Block of 4	11.00	9.00
a.-d.	A966 20p Any single		2.40	1.60
e.	Block of 4, inscr. "2007"		11.00	7.00
f.-i.	A966 20p Any single, inscr. "2007"		2.40	1.60
3038		Block of 4	12.50	10.50
a.-d.	A965 24p Any single		2.50	1.60
3039		Block of 4	12.50	10.50
a.-d.	A966 24p Any single		3.00	1.50
e.	Block of 4, inscr. "2007"		13.50	11.00
f.-i.	A966 24p Any single, inscr. "2007"		3.00	1.60
3040		Block of 4	12.50	11.00
a.-d.	A965 26p Any single		2.50	2.00
3041		Block of 4	12.50	11.00
a.-d.	A966 26p Any single		3.00	2.00
e.	Block of 4, inscr. "2007"		13.50	11.00
f.-i.	A966 26p Any single, inscr. "2007"		3.00	2.00
3042	A967	30p multi	3.00	2.25
3043	A968	30p multi	3.75	2.50
3044	A967	100p multi	11.50	6.00
3045	A968	100p multi	12.00	6.00
	Nos. 3020-3045 (26)		128.95	96.80

Issued: Nos. 3020, 3030, 4/28; Nos. 3021, 3029, 7/3; Nos. 3022, 3028, 5/10; No. 3023, 12/27; Nos. 3024, 3034, 11/10; Nos. 3025, 3027, 3033, 3035, 12/26; Nos. 3026, 3032, 9/9; No. 3031, 12/14; No. 3036, 6/7; Nos. 3037, 3039, 3041, 12/21; No. 3038, 6/15; No. 3040, 6/9; No. 3042, 9/18; Nos. 3043, 3045, 12/29; No. 3044, 9/26.
See Nos. 3101-3102.

No. 1511 Surcharged

2006, May 2   **Litho.**   **Perf. 13¾x13¼**

3046	A368 26p on 7.50p #1511	4.00	3.00

Lighthouses — A969

No. 3047: a, Punta Bugui Lighthouse, Aroroy. b, Capul Island Lighthouse, Samar del Norte. c, Corregidor Island Lighthouse, Cavite. d, Pasig River Lighthouse, Manila.

No. 3048: a, Cabo Engaño Lighthouse, Santa Ana. b, Punta Cabra Lighthouse, Lubang. c, Cabo Melville Lighthouse, Balabac Island. d, Gintotolo Island Lighthouse, Balud.

2006, May 17   **Perf. 14**
3047 A969 7p Block of 4, #a-d   4.50 3.50
         Souvenir Sheet
3048 A969 7p Sheet of 4, #a-d   6.00 5.00
No. 3047 issued in sheets of 16 stamps.

Xavier School, Manila, 50th Anniv. A970

No. 3049: a, Emblems. b, School building. c, Paul Hsu Kuang-ch'i, Chinese Christian convert. d, St. Francis Xavier (1506-52).

2006, June 6
3049 A970 7p Block of 4, #a-d   4.00 4.00
a.   Miniature sheet of 8   11.00 11.00
Normally issued in sheets of 16 stamps.

Air Materiel Wing Savings and Loan Association, Inc., 50th Anniv. — A971

No. 3050 — Emblem and: a, Soldier's family, piggy bank. b, Building.

2006, June 13
3050 A971 7p Horiz. pair, #a-b   1.75 1.50
a.   Miniature sheet of 8   15.00 15.00
Normally issued in sheet of 40 stamps.

No. 1721 Surcharged in Blue Violet

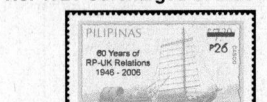

2006, July 4   **Litho.**   **Perf. 14**
3051 A436 26p on 7.20p multi   4.00 2.50

Knights of Columbus, 100th Anniv. in Philippines A972

2006, July 7
3052 A972 7p multi   .75   .40
a.   Miniature sheet of 8   12.50 12.50
Normally issued in sheets of 50.

Ortigas & Company, 75th Anniv. — A973

Anniversary emblem and: 7p, Map of Mandaloyon. 26p, Building.

2006, July 10
3053-3054 A973 Set of 2   4.50 2.50
3054a   Souvenir sheet, 2 each
            #3053-3054   11.00 10.00

Ozamiz Cotta Military Fort, 250th Anniv. — A974

2006, July 16
3055 A974 7p multi   .75   .40
a.   Miniature sheet of 8   12.50 12.50
Normally issued in sheets of 50.

Friendship Between Philippines and Japan, 50th Anniv. — A975

José P. Rizal and: 7p, Mt. Fuji and cherry blossoms. 20p, Mt. Mayon and flowers.

2006, July 23
3056-3057 A975 Set of 2   4.00 2.50
3057a   Miniature sheet of 8   12.50 12.50
3057b   Souvenir sheet, 2 each
            #3056-3057   9.00 8.00
Nos. 3056-3057 issued in sheets of 20 (10 of each denomination in two rows of 5, separated by a central gutter). Most sheets of 20 were cut in half through the central gutter.

Roque B. Ablan, (1906-43) Politician, Military Hero — A976

2006, Aug. 9
3058 A976 7p multi   .65   .40
a.   Miniature sheet of 8   12.50 12.50
Normally printed in sheets of 50.

No. 1809 Surcharged in Gold

         Perf. 13½x13
2006, Aug. 15   **Litho.**   **Wmk. 389**
3059 A470 7p on 1.20p multi   1.25   .90

Chan-Cu Association, Cent. — A977

No. 3060: a, Centennial emblem. b, Figurine of Chan-Tze, Chinese scholar.

2006, Aug. 28   **Unwmk.**   **Perf. 14**
3060 A977 7p Horiz. pair, #a-b   2.00 1.65
a.   Miniature sheet of 8   10.00 10.00
Issued in sheets of 20 with 5 central labels.

Cats A978

No. 3061: a, Himalayan cat. b, Maine Coon cat. c, Red point Siamese cat. d, Persian cat.

No. 3062: a, Japanese bobtail cat. b, Ragdoll cat. c, Egyptian mau cat. d, Abyssinian cat.

2006, Sept. 29
3061 A978 7p Block of 4, #a-d   5.00 4.00
         Souvenir Sheet
3062 A978 7p Sheet of 4, #a-d   5.00 4.00
No. 3061 printed in sheet of 16 stamps.

United Nations Month — A979

Text in: 7p, Tagalog and English. 26p, English.

2006, Oct. 19
3063-3064 A979 Set of 2   4.50 3.00
Issued in sheets of 20 with 5 central labels.

Philippines Postal Service, 108th Anniv. — A980

No. 3065: a, Ruins of Manila Post Office after Battle of Manila. b, Manila Central Post Office, 2006.

2006, Nov. 6   **Perf. 13¾**
3065 A980 Horiz. pair   2.50 2.00
a.-b.   7p Either single   1.00   .80
Printed in sheets of 10 stamps.

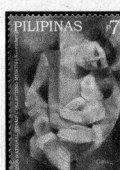

National Stamp Collecting Month — A981

Designs: No. 3066, 7p, Mother and child. No. 3067, 7p, Fish and fruit, horiz.. No. 3068, 7p, Oranges and grapes, horiz. No. 3069, 7p, Watermelon and coconut, horiz. 26p, Roses.

2006, Nov. 15
3066-3069 A981 Set of 4   4.00 3.00
         Souvenir Sheet
3070 A981 26p multi   3.50 3.00
No. 3070 contains one 30x80mm stamp.

Ascent of Mt. Everest by Filipino Climbers A982

Designs: No. 3071, 7p, Climbers ascending mountain. No. 3072, 20p, No. 3074a, 10p, Climbers ascending mountain and Philippines flag. No. 3073, 26p, No. 3074b, 7p, Climbers at summit with flag.

2006, Nov. 23   **Perf. 13¾**
3071-3073 A982 Set of 3   7.00 5.50
         Souvenir Sheet
3074 A982 Sheet of 3, #3071,
            3074a, 3074b   3.00 2.50

Christmas A983

Stars and: 7p, Manila Cathedral. 20p, Paoay Church. 24p, Miagao Church. 26p, Barasoain Church.

Litho. with Hologram Affixed
2006   **Perf. 14**
3075-3078 A983 Set of 4   10.00 8.50
Issued: 7p, 20p, 12/15; 24p, 26p, 12/19.

New Year 2007 (Year of the Pig) — A984

Designs: 7p, Head of pig. 20p, Pig.

2006, Dec. 27   **Litho.**
3079-3080 A984 Set of 2   4.50 3.50
3080a   Souvenir sheet, 2 each
            #3079-3080   9.00 8.00
Printed in sheets of 20 and in sheets of 10.

Fruit A985

No. 3081: a, Watermelons. b, Mangos. c, Custard apples. d, Pomelos.

No. 3082: a, Jackfruit. b, Lanzones. c, Coconuts. d, Bananas.

2006, Dec. 15
3081 A985 7p Block or strip of 4,
            #a-d   4.50 3.50
         Souvenir Sheet
3082 A985 7p Sheet of 4, #a-d   5.50 5.00
Printed in sheets of 15 stamps.

Graciano Lopez Jaena (1856-96), Journalist — A986

2006, Dec. 18
3083 A986 7p multi   .80   .40

Centro Escolar University, Cent. — A987

2007, Jan. 18   **Litho.**   **Perf. 14**
3084 A987 7p multi   .75   .40
a.   Miniature sheet of 8   12.50 12.50
Normally issued in sheets of 50.

Philippine School of the Deaf, Cent. — A988

2007, Jan. 19
3085 A988 7p multi   .75   .40

Rare Flowers A989

No. 3086: a, Medinilla magnifica. b, Strongylodon elmeri. c, Amyema incarnatiflora. d, Dillenia monantha. e, Xanthostemon fruticosus. f, Plumeria acuminata. g, Paphiopedilum adductum. h, Rafflesia manillana. 26p, Rafflesia manillana and man, horiz.

2007, Mar. 30
3086 A989 7p Sheet of 8, #a-h 8.00 *7.00*
Souvenir Sheet
3087 A989 26p multi 6.00 5.00

No. 3087 contains one 120x30mm stamp.

Manulife Philippines Insurance, Cent. — A990

2007, Apr. 26
3088 A990 7p multi 1.00 .60
  a. Souvenir sheet of 4 12.50 12.50

Colonial Era Bridges A991

No. 3089: a, Isabel II Bridge, Imus, Cavite. b, Dampol Bridge, Dupax, Nueva Viscaya. c, Barit Bridge, Laoad, Ilocos Norte. d, Blanco Bridge, Binondo, Manila.
No. 3090: a, Malagonlong Bridge, Tayabas, Quezon. b, Fort Santiago Bridge. c, Mahacao Bridge, Maragondon, Cavite. d, Busay Bridge, Guinobatan, Albay.

2007, May 16
3089 A991 7p Block of 4, #a-d 6.50 3.50
Souvenir Sheet
3090 A991 7p Sheet of 4, #a-d 5.00 4.00

No. 3089 printed in sheets of 16.

Diplomatic Relations Between Philippines and France, 60th Anniv. — A992

Symbols of France and Philippines including: 7p, Eiffel Tower. No. 3092, 26p, Castle.
No. 3093, 26p, Flags of France and Philippines, symbols of countries.

2007, June 26
3091-3092 A992 Set of 2 4.50 3.00
Souvenir Sheet
3093 A992 26p multi 4.50 3.50

No. 3093 contains one 30x80mm stamp.
Nos. 3091-3092 issued in sheets of 20 (10 of each denomination in two rows of 5, separated by a central gutter). Most sheets of 20 were cut in half through the central gutter.

Bureau of Fisheries and Aquatic Resources, 60th Anniv. — A993

No. 3094: a, Diana. b, Giant trevally. c, Skipjack tuna. d, Yellowfin tuna.
No. 3095: a, Cuttlefish. b, Bigfin reef squid and sacol (80x30mm).

2007, July 2
3094 A993 Horiz. strip of 4 5.00 4.00
  a.-d. 7p Any single .80 .50
Souvenir Sheet
3095 Sheet of 2 6.00 5.00
  a. A993 7p multi 1.25 .90
  b. A993 20p multi 3.00 2.40

No. 3094 printed in sheets of 16 stamps.

Scouting, Cent. — A994

Designs: No. 3096, 7p, Scouting flag, hand giving scout sign. No. 3097, 7p, Scouting and Scouting Centenary emblems.

2007, Aug. 1
3096-3097 A994 Set of 2 2.25 1.50
3097a Souvenir sheet, 2 each #3096-3097 + label 5.00 5.00

A995

Ducks and Geese A996

No. 3098: a, Mallards. b, Green-winged teal. c, Tufted ducks. d, Cotton pygmy geese.
Nos. 3099 and 3100: a, Northern pintails. b, Common shelducks. c, Northern shovelers. d, Greater scaups.

2007, Aug. 3
3098 A995 7p Block of 4, #a-d 5.00 4.00
Souvenir Sheets
3099 A996 7p Sheet of 4, #a-d 6.00 6.00
With Bangkok 2007 Emblem Added to Stamps
3100 A996 7p Sheet of 4, #a-d 9.00 9.00

No. 3100 sold for 50p.
No. 3098 printed in sheets of 16 stamps.

Butterfly Type of 2006
Designs: 8p, Troidaes magellanus magellanus. 17p, Achillides palinurus daedalus.

2007, Aug. 7   Perf. 13¾x13½
3101 A966 8p multi 1.20 .60
3102 A966 17p multi 2.25 .90

Association of South East Asian Nations (ASEAN), 40th Anniv. — A997

Designs: 7p, Malacañang Palace, Philippines.
No. 3104: a, Secretariat Building, Bandar Seri Begawan, Brunei. b, National Museum, Cambodia. c, Fatahillah Museum, Jakarta, Indonesia. d, Typical house, Laos. e, Malayan Railway Headquarters Building, Kuala Lumpur, Malaysia. f, Yangon Post Office, Myanmar (Burma). g, Malacañang Palace, Philippines. h, National Museum, Singapore. i, Vimanmek Mansion, Bangkok, Thailand. j, Presidential Palace, Hanoi, Viet Nam.
No. 3105, Malacañang Palace, Philippines (80x30mm).

2007, Aug. 8   Perf. 14
3103 A997 7p multi .90 .60
3104 A997 20p Sheet of 10, #a-j 30.00 30.00
Souvenir Sheet
3105 A997 20p multi 3.00 2.50

See Brunei No. 607, Burma No. 370, Cambodia No. 2339, Indonesia Nos. 2120-2121, Laos Nos. 1717-1718, Malaysia No. 1170, Singapore No. 1265, Thailand No. 2315, and Viet Nam Nos. 3302-3311.

Pres. Ramon F. Magsaysay (1907-57) A998

2007, Aug. 31   Litho.
3106 A998 7p multi .80 .40

Social Security System, 50th Anniv. A999

Nos. 3107 and 3108 — Anniversary emblem and: a, Family and building. b, Pres. Ramon Magsaysay. c, Pres. Magsaysay signing Social Security Act of 1954. d, Building.

2007, Sept. 1   Perf. 14
Stamps With White Margins
3107 A999 7p Block of 4, #a-d 4.50 3.50
Souvenir Sheet
Stamps With Gray Margins
3108 A999 7p Sheet of 4, #a-d 5.00 5.00

First Philippine Assembly, Cent. — A1000

Designs: No. 3109, 7p, People in front of Manila Opera House. No. 3110, 7p, Manila municipal building.

2007, Oct. 16
3109-3110 A1000 Set of 2 1.70 1.20

United Nations Month — A1001

Text in: 7p, Tagalog and English. 26p, English.

2007, Oct. 24
3111-3112 A1001 Set of 2 4.50 3.00

Nos. 3111-3112 were printed in a sheet of 20 stamps containing ten of each stamp separated by a central gutter of 5 different labels.

Paintings by Juan Luna (1857-99) — A1002

Designs: No. 3113, 7p, El Violinista. No. 3114, 7p, Indio Bravo. No. 3115, 7p, Old Man With a Pipe. No. 3116, 7p, La Bulakeña.
No. 3117a, Picnic in Normandy, horiz. (60x40mm).
No. 3118, horiz. — Parisian Life, with background color of: a, Light yellow and blue. b, Yellow orange and green. c, Yellow orange and red. d, Yellow orange and purple.

2007   Perf. 14
3113-3116 A1002 Set of 4 4.00 3.00
3117 Sheet of 4, #3113-3115, 3117a 5.00 5.00
  a. A1002 7p brown & multi, imperf. 1.20 1.00
3118 Sheet of 4 5.00 5.00
  a. A1002 7p Imperf. (73x48mm) 1.25 1.00
  b.-d. A1002 7p Any single 1.00 .80

Issued: Nos. 3113-3116, 10/24; No. 3117, 11/23; No. 3118, 12/21. No. 3116 was issued in sheets of 6.

Birds — A1003

Designs: 1p, Black-naped oriole. 2p, Asian fairy bluebird. 3p, Writhed hornbill. 4p, Crimson sunbird. 5p, Barn swallow. 8p, Hoopoe. 9p, Short-eared owl. 10p, Blue-winged pita. 50p, Head of Philippine eagle. 100p, Philippine eagle on tree branch.
No. 3124: a, Mindanao bleeding heart pigeon. b, Nicobar pigeon. c, Black-chinned fruit dove. d, Metallic pigeon. e, Pink-necked green

pigeon. f, Amethyst brown dove. g, Gray imperial pigeon. h, Red turtle dove. i, Pied imperial pigeon. j, Spotted imperial pigeon.
No. 3128: a, Dwarf kingfisher. b, Blue-capped wood kingfisher. c, White-throated kingfisher. d, White-collared kingfisher.
No. 3129: a, Green-faced parrotfinch. b, Java sparrow. c, Yellow-breasted bunting. d, White-cheeked bullfinch.
No. 3130: a, Great-billed parrot. b, Philippine cockatoo. c, Blue-naped parrot. d, Blue-backed parrot.

2007   Perf. 13¾x13½
Inscribed "2007"
3119 A1003 1p multi .50 .25
  a. Inscribed "2008" .50 .25
  b. Inscribed "2008A" .60 .25
  c. Inscribed "2008B" .60 .25
3120 A1003 2p multi .50 .25
  a. Inscribed "2008" .50 .25
  b. Inscribed "2008A" .60 .30
  c. Inscribed "2008B" .50 .25
3121 A1003 3p multi .65 .30
3122 A1003 4p multi .80 .35
  a. Inscribed "2008" .75 .30
3123 A1003 5p multi .65 .25
  a. Inscribed "2008" .60 .30
3124 Block of 10 12.00 12.00
  a.-j. A1003 7p Any single .75 .30
  k. Block of 10, inscr. "2008" 25.00 25.00
  l.-u. A1003 7p Any single, inscr. "2008" 1.25 .65
3125 A1003 8p multi .80 .50
3126 A1003 9p multi 1.20 .50
3127 A1003 10p multi 1.75 .65
  a. Inscribed "2008" 1.60 .45
  b. Inscribed "2008A" 1.75 .60
3128 Block of 4 10.00 9.00
  a.-d. A1003 20p Any single 1.75 1.20
3129 Block of 4 12.50 11.00
  a.-d. A1003 24p Any single 2.40 1.25
3130 Block of 4 12.50 11.00
  a.-d. A1003 26p Any single 2.60 1.50
  e. Block of 4, inscr. "2008" 17.00 14.00
  f.-i. A1003 26p Any single, inscr. "2008" 3.50 2.40
  j. Block of 4, inscr. "2008A" 20.00 18.00
  k.-n. A1003 26p Any single, inscr. "2008A" 2.75 1.75
Size: 30x40mm
Perf. 14
3131 A1003 50p multi 6.00 3.50
  a. Inscribed "2008" 12.00 10.50
  b. Inscribed "2008A" 6.00 4.50
3132 A1003 100p multi 12.50 7.00
  a. Inscribed "2008" 45.00 40.00
  b. Inscribed "2008A" 13.00 10.00
  Nos. 3119-3132 (14) 72.35 56.55

Issued: 1p, 100p, 10/30; 2p, 20p, 11/15; 3p, 4p, 8p, 26p, 12/12; 5p, 50p, 11/5; 7p, 12/10; 9p, 10p, 24p, 12/19.
For stamps without blue lines at bottom, see No. 3151.

Manila Central Post Office, 1926 — A1004

No. 3133: a, Shown. b, Manila Central Post Office and architect Juan Marcos Arellano (80x30mm).

2007, Nov. 5   Perf. 14
3133 Horiz. pair 4.50 3.50
  a. A1004 7p multi .80 .60
  b. A1004 20p multi 2.40 1.40

No. 3133 was printed in sheets of 10 stamps.

San Diego de Alcala Cathedral, Cumaca, 425th Anniv. — A1005

2007, Nov. 13   Perf. 13¾x13½
3134 A1005 7p multi 1.20 .80
  a. Miniature sheet of 5 7.50 7.50

Sacred Heart School, Cebu, 50th Anniv. A1006

No. 3135: a, School building and Philippines flag. b, School building and statue. c, Nun, school crest. d, Nun, school building.

2007, Nov. 16   *Perf. 14*
Stamps With White Margins
3135 A1006 7p Block of 4, #a-d   4.00 3.00
Souvenir Sheet
3136   Sheet of 4, #3135a,
   3135b, 3135d, 3136a   4.50 4.50
  a.   A1006 7p As #3135c, with greenish gray tint in margin at LL   1.00 .80
No. 3135 printed in sheets of 16 stamps.

Development Bank of the Philippines, 60th Anniv. — A1007

No. 3137: a, Ship emblem, blue back-ground. b, Bank building, brown background. c, Bank building at left, dark green back-ground. d, Bank building at right, olive green background.

2007, Nov. 26
3137 A1007 7p Block of 4, #a-d   4.00 3.00
  e.   Souvenir sheet, #3137a-3137d   4.50 4.50
No. 3137 printed in sheets of 16 stamps.

Christmas — A1008

Designs: 7p, Teddy bear. 20p, Toy train. 24p, Toy truck. 26p, Angel with candle decoration.

2007, Nov. 28
3138-3141 A1008   Set of 4   9.00 7.00

New Year 2008 (Year of the Rat) — A1009

Designs: 7p, Head of rat. 20p, Rat.

2007, Dec. 3
3142-3143 A1009   Set of 2   4.50 3.50
3143a   Souvenir sheet, 2 each
   #3142-3143   10.00 10.00
Nos. 3142-3143 printed in sheets of 10 stamps.

World Vision in Philippines, 50th Anniv. — A1010

Designs: 7p, Pres. Ramon F. Magsaysay and World Vision founder, Rev. Bob Pierce. 20p, World Vision anniversary emblem, horiz.

2007, Dec. 5
3144-3145 A1010   Set of 2   5.00 3.00

No. 1810 Surcharged in Silver

Methods, Perfs and Watermark As Before
2007, Dec. 14
3146 A470 7p on 2.40p #1810   1.00 .70

Dominican School, Manila, 50th Anniv. — A1011

No. 3147: a, St. Dominic de Guzman. b, St. Dominic, school, emblem. c, Two emblems. d, School, emblem.

Unwmk.
2008, Feb. 1   **Litho.**   *Perf. 14*
3147 A1011 7p Block of 4, #a-d   4.00 3.00

Valentine's Day — A1012

No. 3148: a, Roses in heart. b, Cupid, hearts.

2008, Feb. 6
3148 A1012 7p Pair, #a-b   2.40 1.60
  c.   Sheet of 10, 5 each
   #3148a-3148b   14.00 14.00
No. 3148c sold for 100p.

Missionary Catechists of St. Therese of the Infant Jesus, 50th Anniv. — A1013

Designs: No. 3149, 7p, Emblem and nuns. No. 3150, 7p, 50th anniv. emblem, St. Therese of the Infant Jesus, Bishop Alfredo Obviar.

2008, Feb. 23
3149-3150 A1013   Set of 2   1.75 1.20
3150a   Pair, #3149-3150   2.00 1.50
3150b   Miniature sheet of 8, 4
   each #3149-3150   12.50 12.50
No. 3149-3150 normally issued in sheets of 50.

Bird Type of 2007 Without Blue Lines at Bottom
Miniature Sheet
No. 3151: a, Mindanao bleeding heart pigeon. b, Nicobar pigeon. c, Black-chinned fruit dove. d, Metallic pigeon. e, Pink-necked green pigeon. f, Amethyst brown dove. g, Gray imperial pigeon. h, Red turtle dove. i, Pied imperial pigeon. j, Spotted imperial pigeon. k, Philippine eagle. l, Philippine cockatoo. m, Java sparrow. n, Blue-capped wood kingfisher.

2008, Mar. 7   *Perf. 13¾x13½*
3151 A1003 7p Sheet of 14,
   #a-n, + label   18.00 18.00
2008 Taipei Intl. Stamp Exhibition. No. 3151 sold for 125p.

Rodents of Luzon Island A1014

No. 3152: a, Luzon furry-tailed rat. b, Cordillera striped earth rat. c, Cordillera forest mouse. d, Cordillera shrew mouse.
No. 3153: a, 7p, Northern giant cloud rat. b, 7p, Lesser dwarf cloud rat. c, 20p, Bushy-tailed cloud rat, vert. (40x70mm).

2008, Mar. 7   *Perf. 14*
3152 A1014 7p Block of 4, #a-d   4.50 3.50
Souvenir Sheet
Perf. 14, Imperf. (20p)
3153 A1014   Sheet of 3, #a-c   5.00 4.00

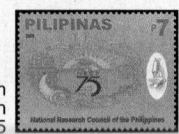

Natl. Research Council, 75th Anniv. — A1015

2008, Mar. 12   *Perf. 14*
3154 A1015 7p multi   .75 .40

Baguio Teachers Camp, Cent. A1016

No. 3155: a, Camp. b, Teachers, bridge.

2008, May 10
3155 A1016 7p Horiz. pair, #a-b   1.75 1.40

Bridges of the American Era — A1017

No. 3156: a, Gasan Bridge, Gasan, Marinduque. b, Hinigaran Bridge, Hinigaran, Negros Occidental. c, Wahig Bridge, Dagoboy, Bohol. d, Pan-ay Bridge, Pan-ay, Capiz.
No. 3157: a, Quezon Bridge, Quiapo, Manila. b, Governor Reynolds Bridge, Guinobatan, Albay. c, Mauca Railway Bridge, Ragay, Camarines Sur. d, Balucuan Bridge, Dao, Capiz.
Illustration reduced.

2008, May 16
3156 A1017 7p Block of 4, #a-d   4.50 3.50
Miniature Sheet
3157 A1017 7p Sheet of 4, #a-d   5.00 5.00
Issued in sheets of 16.

Miniature Sheet

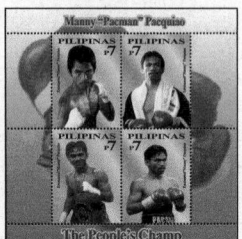

Manny Pacquiao, World Boxing Council Lightweight Champion — A1018

No. 3158 — Pacquiao: a, With hands taped. b, Wearing robe and gloves. c, Wearing championship belt. d, Wearing gloves.

2008, May 30
3158 A1018 7p Sheet of 4, #a-d   7.00 7.00

Dept. of Science and Technology, 50th Anniv. — A1019

Philippine Nuclear Research Institute, 50th Anniv. — A1020

2008, June 4
3159 A1019 7p multi   .75 .40
3160 A1020 7p multi   .75 .40

Liong Tek Go Family Association, Cent. — A1021

No. 3161: a, Association centenary emblem. b, Tai Bei Kong.

2008, June 11
3161 A1021 7p Pair, #a-b   1.50 1.50
  a.   Miniature sheet of 8   12.50 12.50
Normally printed in sheets of 20.

University of the Philippines, Cent. — A1022

Designs: Nos. 3162a, 3163c, 3164c, Emblem (with eagle). Nos. 3162b, 3163a, 3164a, Carillon. Nos. 3162c, 3163d, 3164d, Oblation sculpture. Nos. 3162d, 3163b, 3164b, Centenary emblem (with Oblation sculpture).

2008   *Perf. 13¾x13½*
3162 A1022 7p Block of 4, #a-d   3.50 3.00
Stamp Size: 40x30mm
Perf. 14
3163 A1022 7p Block of 4, #a-d   5.00 4.50
  e.   Souvenir sheet, #3163a-3163d   5.00 5.00
Litho. With Foil Application
3164 A1022 7p Block of 4, #a-d   6.00 6.00
  e.   Souvenir sheet, #3164a-3164d   8.00 8.00
No. 3164 was printed in sheets containing four blocks that sold for 160p. No. 3164e sold for 50p.

Friar Andres de Urdaneta (c. 1608-1568), Navigator — A1023

2008, June 26   *Perf. 14*
3165 A1023 7p multi   .80 .40
Philippine-Spanish Friendship Day.

Xavier University, Ateneo de Cagayan, 75th Anniv. — A1024

No. 3166: a, Immaculate Conception Chapel. b, Statue of St. Francis Xavier. c, Archbishop James T. G. Hayes. d, Science Center.

2008, June 26
3166 A1024 7p Block of 4, #a-d 3.25 3.00
a. Miniature sheet of 8 12.00 12.00
Normally issued in sheets of 40.

Ateneo de Davao University, 60th Anniv. — A1025

No. 3167: a, College building. b, High school building, statue. c, Grade school building, flags. d, Assumption (stained glass).

2008, July 31
3167 A1025 7p Block of 4, #a-d 3.50 3.00
e. Souvenir sheet, #3167a-3167d 5.00 5.00

2008 Summer Olympics, Beijing — A1026

Designs: 7p, Archery. 20p, Judo. 24p, Equestrian. 26p, Weight lifting.

2008, Aug. 11   Litho.
3168-3171 A1026 Set of 4 12.00 8.00

Se Jo Lim Family Association, Cent. — A1027

Designs: Nos. 3172a, 3173a, Pi Kan, Lim family ancestor. Nos. 3172b, 3173b, Senator Roselier T. Lim. Nos. 3172c, 3173c, Gen. Vicente P. Lim. Nos. 3172c, 3173c, Binondo Church, Chinese gate. Nos. 3172d, 3173d, Association centenary emblem, sun, stars and colors of Philippines flag.

2008, Aug. 22   Perf. 14
3172 A1027 7p Block of 4, #a-d 3.50 3.00
Souvenir Sheet
Perf. 14 on 3 Sides
3173 A1027 7p Sheet of 4, #a-d,
+ 2 labels 4.50 4.50
Printed in sheets of 16 with large horizontal central label.

Philippine Bonsai Society, 35th Anniv. — A1028

No. 3174: a, Pemphis acidula (on short-legged table), red background. b, Ficus microcarpa. c, Serissa foetida. d, Pemphis acidula, violet background. e, Pemphis acidula, blue background. f, Triphasia trifolia. g, Pemphis acidula (on piece of wood), cerise background. h, Bougainville sp.
No. 3175, vert.: a, Murraya sp. b, Pemphis acidula, tan background. c, Pemphis acidula,

gray blue background. d, Pemphis acidula, violet background. e, Pemphis acidula, blue background. f, Antidesma bunius. g, Maba buxifolia. h, Ficus concina.
No. 3176: a, Lagerstroemia indica. b, Pemphis acidula, yellow green background. c, Vitex sp. d, Ixora chinensis.

2008, Oct. 17   Perf. 14
3174 Block of 8 9.00 9.00
a.-h. A1028 7p Any single .80 .65
3175 Block of 8 9.00 9.00
a.-h. A1028 7p Any single .80 .65
Souvenir Sheet
3176 Sheet of 4 5.00 5.00
a.-d. A1028 7p Any single 1.10 .50
Printed in sheets of 16.

Miniature Sheet

Jakarta 2008 Intl. Stamp Exhibition — A1029

No. 3177 — Birds: a, Brahminy kite. b, Olive-backed sunbird. c, Purple-throated sunbird. d, Metallic-winged sunbird. e, Gray-headed fish eagle. f, Plain-throated sunbird. g, Lina's sunbird. h, Apo sunbird. i, Copper-throated sunbird. j, Flaming sunbird. k, Gray-hooded sunbird. l, Lovely sunbird. m, Crested serpent eagle. n, Philippine hawk eagle. o, Blue-crowned racquet-tail. p, Philippine eagle owl. q, Common flameback.

2008, Oct. 23   Perf. 13¾x13½
3177 A1029 7p Sheet of 17,
#a-q, + 13 labels 20.00 20.00
No. 3177 sold for 150p.

Visit of Ban Ki-moon, United Nations Secretary General — A1030

Ban Ki-moon and: 7p, UN emblem. 26p, Philippines President Gloria Macapagal-Arroyo.

2008, Oct. 29   Perf. 14
3178-3179 A1030 Set of 2 3.50 2.50

Tourism A1031

No. 3180: a, Boracay Beach, Aklan. b, Intramuros, Manila. c, Banaue Rice Terraces, Mountain Province. d, Mayon Volcano, Bicol. 20p, Puerto Princesa Underground River, Palawan. 24p, Chocolate Hills, Bohol. 26p, Tubbataha Reef, Palawan.

2008, Nov. 3   Perf. 13½x13¾
3180 Block of 4 4.00 3.00
a.-d. A1031 7p Any single .80 .65
3181 A1031 20p multi 2.25 1.50
3182 A1031 24p multi 3.00 1.75
3183 A1031 26p multi 3.25 1.75
Nos. 3180-3183 (4) 12.50 8.00
Philippine Postal Service, 110th anniv.

Christmas — A1032

Designs: 7p, Mother with brown hair, and child. 20p, Mother nursing child. 24p, Mother, child, dove. 26p, Mother with child in sling.
No. 3188: a, 7p, Madonna and Child. b, 26m, Mother with sleeping child.

2008, Nov. 10   Perf. 14
3184-3187 A1032 Set of 4 10.00 7.50
Souvenir Sheet
3188 A1032 Sheet of 2, #a-b 5.00 4.00

Comic Book Superheroes of Carlo J. Caparas — A1033

No. 3189, 7p: a, Joaquin Bordado. b, Totoy Bato. c, Gagambino. d, Pieta.
No. 3190: a, 7p, Ang Panday (with hammer). b, 20p, Ang Panday (holding sword).

2008, Nov. 17
3189 A1033 7p Block of 4, #a-d 3.50 3.00
Souvenir Sheet
3190 A1033 Sheet of 2, #a-b 4.50 3.50
Natl. Stamp Collecting Month.

Senator Benigno S. Aquino, Jr. (1932-83) — A1034

No. 3191: a, 7p, Photograph. b, 26p, Drawing.

2008, Nov. 27
3191 A1034 Horiz. pair, #a-b 4.50 3.50

Fernando G. Bautista (1908-2002), Founder of University of Baguio — A1035

2008, Dec. 8
3192 A1035 7p multi .75 .40

New Year 2009 (Year of the Ox) — A1036

Designs: 7p, Ox head. 20p, Ox.

2008, Dec. 10
3193-3194 A1036 Set of 2 4.50 3.50
3194a Souvenir sheet of 4, 2
each #3193-3194 11.00 11.00
Printed in sheets of 10.

Crabs A1037

No. 3195: a, Goneplacid crab. b, Largo's spider crab. c, Fuzzy sponge crab. d, Daniele's deepwater porter crab.
No. 3196: a, Stimpson's intricate spider crab. b, Spider crab.

2008, Dec. 19
3195 A1037 7p Block of 4, #a-d 4.00 3.00
Souvenir Sheet
3196 A1037 20p Sheet of 2, #a-b, + 2 labels 6.00 6.00
No. 3196 sold for 50p.
Printed in sheets of 16.

Dr. Manuel Sarmiento Enverga (1909-81), Educator and Politician — A1038

2009, Jan. 1   Litho.   Perf. 14
3197 A1038 7p multi .75 .40

Love A1039

No. 3198: a, Roses and heart. b, Hearts and envelope.

2009, Feb. 2
3198 A1039 7p Pair, #a-b 1.75 1.20

Philippine Intl. Arts Festival — A1040

Emblem and: a, Painting. b, Theater masks and book of poetry. c, Cymbal and dancers. d, Theater and movie poster.

2009, Feb. 16
3199 A1040 7p Block of 4, #a-d 3.50 3.00

Diplomatic Relations Between Philippines and Republic of Korea, 60th Anniv. — A1041

No. 3200: a, Panagbenga Flower Festival, Philippines. b, Cow Play, Hangawi, Republic of Korea.

2009, Mar. 3
3200 A1041 7p Horiz. pair, #a-b 2.00 1.50
See Republic of Korea Nos. 2304-2305. Printed in sheets of 10.

Birds — A1042

Designs: 1p, Mugimaki flycatcher. 2p, Narcissus flycatcher. 3p, Mountain verditer-flycatcher. 4p, Blue rock thrush. 5p, Brown shrike. 8p, Apo myna. 9p, Crested serpent-eagle. 10p, Blue-crowned racquet-tail. 17p, Common flameback. 50p, Gray-headed fish-eagle. 100p, Philippine hawk-eagle.
No. 3206: a, Olive-backed sunbird. b, Metallic-winged sunbird. c, Plain-throated sunbird. d, Lina's sunbird. e, Purple-throated sunbird. f, Apo sunbird. g, Copper-throated sunbird. h, Flaming sunbird. i, Gray-hooded sunbird. j, Lovely sunbird.
No. 3211: a, Palawan flowerpecker. b, Fire-breasted flowerpecker. c, Cebu flowerpecker. d, Red-keeled flowerpecker.

No. 3212: a, Philippine tailorbird. b, Mountain tailorbird. c, Black-headed tailorbird. d, Ashy tailorbird.

2009		Litho.	Perf. 13¾x13½	
3201	A1042	1p multi	.50	.25
3202	A1042	2p multi	.75	.30
3203	A1042	3p multi	.50	.30
3204	A1042	4p multi	.75	.30
3205	A1042	5p multi	1.50	.35
3206		Block of 10	35.00	35.00
a.-j.	A1042	7p Any single	1.50	.70
3207	A1042	8p multi	1.00	.35
3208	A1042	9p multi	1.20	.90
3209	A1042	10p multi	1.50	.45
3210	A1042	17p multi	2.00	.85
3211		Block of 4	12.50	10.00
a.-d.	A1042	20p Any single, dated "2009"	2.50	1.20
3212		Block of 4	15.00	13.00
a.-d.	A1042	26p Any single, dated "2009"	3.00	1.75

Size: 30x40mm
Perf. 14

3213	A1042	50p multi	6.00	2.00
3214	A1042	100p multi	12.50	9.00
	Nos. 3201-3214 (14)		90.70	73.05

Issued: 1p, 2p, No. 3206, 3/9; 3p, 4p, No. 3211, 6/2; 5p, 100p, 3/13; 8p, 9p, 10p, 17p, 50p, 3/23; No. 3212, 5/25.
See No. 3258.

2009-10		Litho.	Perf. 13¾x13½	
3201a	Dated "2009A"		.50	.25
3201b	Dated "2009B"		.50	.25
3201c	Dated "2009C"		.60	.25
3202a	Dated "2009A"		.60	.25
3202b	Dated "2009B"		.60	.25
3202c	Dated "2009C"		.50	.25
3203a	Dated "2009A"		.60	.25
3203b	Dated "2009B"		.70	.30
3203c	Dated "2009C"		.70	.30
3204a	Dated "2009A"		.70	.30
3204b	Dated "2009B"		.90	.35
3204c	Dated "2009C"		.80	.30
3205a	Dated "2009A"		1.00	.30
3205b	Dated "2009B"		.70	.30
3205c	Dated "2009C"		.70	.30
3206k	Block of 10, #3206l-3206u, dated "2009A"		15.00	15.00
3206l-3206u	Like Nos. 3206a-3206j, any single, dated "2009A"		1.20	.50
3207a	Dated "2009A"		1.20	.40
3207b	Dated "2009B"		1.00	.30
3207c	Dated "2009C"		1.00	.35
3208a	Dated "2009A"		1.50	.50
3208b	Dated "2009B"		1.20	.35
3208c	Dated "2009C"		1.50	.50
3208d	Dated "2009D"		1.10	.50
3209a	Dated "2009A"		1.25	.60
3209b	Dated "2009B"		1.25	.60
3210a	Dated "2009A"		2.50	1.00
3210b	Dated "2009B"		3.00	1.50
3210c	Dated "2009C"		2.25	1.20
3211e	Block of 4, #3211f-3211i, dated "2009A"		10.00	8.00
3211f-3211i	Like Nos. 3211a-3211d, any single, dated "2009A"		2.00	1.20
3212e	Block of 4, #3212f-3212i, dated "2009A"		13.00	11.00
3212f-3212i	Like Nos. 3212a-3212d, any single, dated "2009A"		2.50	1.25
3212j	Block of 4, #3212k-3212n, dated "2009B"		13.00	13.00
3212k-3212n	Like Nos. 3212a-3212d, any single, dated "2009B"		2.50	1.50

Size: 30x40mm
Perf. 14

3213a	Dated "2009A"		8.00	4.00
3213b	Dated "2009B"		6.00	3.50
3213c	Dated "2009C"		8.00	5.50
3213d	Dated "2009D"		6.00	3.50
3214a	Dated "2009A"		16.00	10.00
3214b	Dated "2009B"		13.00	8.00
3214c	Dated "2009C"		18.00	12.00
3214d	Dated "2009D"		13.00	7.00

Issued: No. 3206k, 5/13; Nos. 3205a, 5/25; Nos. 3201a, 3202a, 6/2; Nos. 3207a, 3208a, 3213a, 3214a, 6/8; Nos. 3201b, 3202b, 3205b, 8/6; No. 3208b, 8/10; Nos. 3203a, 3204a, 3210a, 8/13; Nos. 3207b, 3212e, 8/17; Nos. 3213b, 3214b, 9/1; Nos. 3209a, 3211e, 9/9; Nos. 3213c, 3214c, 11/24; No. 3205c, 12/11; Nos. 3209b, 3212j, 12/28; Nos. 3202c, 3204b, 3205c, 3210b, 1/11/10; Nos. 3203b, 3207c, 3208c, 1/12/10; Nos. 3213d, 3214d, 1/28/10; Nos. 3203c, 3204c, 3208d, 3210c, 2/5/10.

Minerals
A1043

No. 3215: a, Quartz. b, Rhodochrosite. c, Malachite. d, Nickel.
No. 3216: a, Cinnabar. b, Native gold. c, Native copper. d, Magnetite.

2009, Mar. 25			Perf. 14	
3215	A1043	7p Block of 4, #a-d	4.00	3.00

Souvenir Sheet

3216	A1043	7p Sheet of 4, #a-d	5.00	5.00

Mothers Dionisia (1691-1732) and Cecilia Rosa Talangpaz (1693-1731), Founders of Augustinian Recollect Sisters — A1044

2009, Apr. 28

3217	A1044	7p multi	.75	.40

Art Deco Theaters
A1045

No. 3218: a, King's Theater. b, Capitol Theater. c, Joy Theater. d, Scala Theater.
No. 3219, horiz.: a, Life Theater. b, Times Theater. c, Bellevue Theater. d, Pines Theater.

2009, May 8

3218	A1045	7p Block of 4, #a-d	4.00	3.50

Souvenir Sheet

3219	A1045	7p Sheet of 4, #a-d	5.00	4.00

Rodolfo S. Cornejo (1909-91), Composer — A1046

2009, May 15

3220	A1046	7p multi	.75	.30

Tourist Attractions in Taguig — A1047

No. 3221: a, City Hall. b, Global City. c, Santa Ana Church. d, Blue Mosque.

2009, June 5   Litho.

3221	A1047	7p Block of 4, #a-d	3.75	3.00

Diplomatic Relations Between Philippines and Thailand, 60th Anniv. — A1048

No. 3222 — Dances: a, Tinikling, Philippines. b, Ten Krathop Sark, Thailand.

2009, June 14			Perf. 14	
3222	A1048	7p Horiz. pair, #a-b	2.25	1.75

Printed in sheets of 10.
See Thailand No. 2429.

Ateneo de Manila University, 150th Anniv. — A1049

No. 3223: a, Sesquicentennial emblem. b, Blue eagle. c, St. Ignatius of Loyola. d, José Rizal.

2009, June 14

3223	A1049	7p Block of 4, #a-d	4.50	4.00
e.		Souvenir sheet, #3223a-3223d, + 2 labels	16.00	16.00

No. 3223e sold for 40p.

Baler, 400th Anniv. A1050

No, 3224: a, Old church. b, New church.

2009, June 30   Litho.

3224	A1050	7p Horiz. pair, #a-b	1.75	1.40

Che Yong Cua and Chua Family Association, Cent. — A1051

No. 3225: a, Chua Tiong. b, Chua Siok To.

2009, July 15			Perf. 14	
3225	A1051	7p Horiz. pair, #a-b	2.10	1.75

Souvenir Sheet

3226	A1051	Sheet of 4, #3225a-3225b, 3226a-3226b, + 2 labels	5.50	5.00
a.		7p Like #3225a, perf. 14 at left	1.25	1.00
b.		7p Like #3225b, perf. 14 at right	1.25	1.00

Printed in sheets of 12 stamps with 4 labels.
See Nos. 3239-3240.

Pheepoy, Mascot of Philippine Postal Corporation — A1052

2009, July 27			Perf. 13½x13¾	
3227	A1052	7p multi	.75	.40

See Nos. 3255, 3260, 3335, and 3336.

Knights of Columbus in Philippines, 50th Anniv. — A1053

Color of denomination outline: 7p, Red. 9p, Dark blue.

2009, July 31			Perf. 14	
3228-3229	A1053	Set of 2	2.10	1.50

Agricultural Cooperation Agreement Between Philippines and Brunei — A1054

2009, Aug. 3

3230	A1054	7p multi	.80	.50

Diplomatic Relations Between Philippines and Singapore, 40th Anniv. — A1055

No. 3231: a, Bamban Bridge, Philippines. b, Marcelo B. Fernan Bridge, Philippines. c, Cavenagh Bridge, Singapore. d, Henderson Waves and Alexandra Arch, Singapore.

2009, Aug. 29   Litho.

3231	A1055	7p Block of 4, #a-d	4.00	3.50
e.		Souvenir sheet, #3231a-3231d	5.00	5.00

Printed in sheets of 16.
See Singapore Nos. 1398-1401.

Baguio, Cent. A1056

No. 3232 — Butterfly on posters and Baguio landmarks: a, Mansion House. b, Mines View Park. c, Baguio Cathedral. d, Kennon Road.

2009, Sept. 1   Perf. 13¾x13½

3232	A1056	7p Horiz. strip of 4, #a-d	5.00	4.00
e.		Souvenir sheet, #3232a-3232d	7.50	7.50

Pres. Corazon Aquino (1933-2009) — A1057

No. 3233: a, With raised arm, denomination at UL. b, Head and signature, denomination at UR.
No. 3234: a, With raised arm, denomination at UR. b, Head and signature, denomination at UL.

2009   Litho.   Perf. 14

3233	A1057	7p Horiz. pair, #a-b	4.50	4.00
3234	A1057	7p Horiz. pair, #a-b	2.50	1.75

Issued: No. 3233, 9/8; No. 3234, 9/18.

Intl. Year of Natural Fibers — A1058

No. 3235: a, Ananas comosus, clothing made from pineaple fibers. b, Musa textilis, bags and hats made from abaca fibers. c, Musa textilis, Philippines bank notes made from abaca fibers. d, Musa textilis, abaca rope.

2009, Sept. 10

3235		Horiz. strip of 4	3.50	3.00
a.-d.	A1058	7p Any single	.75	.65

Lobsters
A1059

No. 3236: a, Locust lobster. b, Blind lobster. c, Northwest Reef lobster. d, Two-spot locust lobster.

No. 3237: a, Neptune Reef lobster. b, Fan lobster. c, Blue-back locust lobster. d, Banded whip lobster.

2009, Sept. 30
3236 A1059 7p Block of 4, #a-d   4.50 3.50
Souvenir Sheet
3237 A1059 7p Sheet of 4, #a-d   5.00 5.00
Printed in sheets of 16.

Quezon City, 70th Anniv. A1060

No. 3238: a, Statue of Pres. Manuel L. Quezon, Philippines flag. b, City Hall. c, Araneta Center. d, Eastwood City.

2009, Oct. 12
3238 A1060 7p Block of 4, #a-d   4.00 3.00
e.   Souvenir sheet, #3238a-3238d 4.50 4.50

Che Yong Cua and Chua Family Association, Cent. — A1061

No. 3239 — Philippines flag, emblem and: a, Cua Lo.

2009, Oct. 15   **Perf. 14**
3239 A1061 7p Horiz. pair,
      #3225a, 3239a.   2.00 1.75
Souvenir Sheet
3240 A1061   Sheet of 4,
      #3225a, 3226a,
      3239a, 3240a +
      2 labels   5.00 5.00
a.   7p Like #3239a, perf. 14 at
      right   1.00 1.00
Printed in sheets of 16.

Alpha Phi Beta Fraternity of the University of the Philippines, 70th Anniv. — A1062

No. 3241 — Fraternity emblem and: a, 70th anniv. emblem. b, Quezon Hall Oblation. c, Malcolm Hall. d, Founding fathers of fraternity.

2009, Oct. 17   **Perf. 14**
3241 A1062 7p Block of 4, #a-d   3.50 3.00

A1063

Children's Games and Activities — A1064

No. 3242: a, Tumbang preso. b, Luksong tinik. c, Holen (marbles). d, Sungka.
No. 3243: a, Taguan (hide-and seek) (30x40mm). b, Sipa (30x40mm). c, Saranggola (kite flying) (30x40mm). d, Bangkang papel (paper boat racing) (30x40mm). e, Paluan ng palayok (piñata) (48x38mm). f, Luksong lubid (rope jumping) (48x38mm). Illustrations reduced.

2009, Nov. 9   **Perf. 14**
3242 A1063 7p Block of 4, #a-d   4.50 4.00
Souvenir Sheet
Perf. 14, Imperf. (#3243e-3243f)
3243 A1064 7p Sheet of 6, #a-f   7.50 7.50
Natl. Stamp Collecting Month.
Printed in sheets of 16.

Christmas — A1065

No. 3244 — Lyrics from Christmas carol "Ang Pasko ay Sumapit" and: a, Four children caroling. b, Nativity. c, Magi on camels. d, Angels and baby Jesus. e, Christmas decorations.

2009, Nov. 18   **Perf. 14**
3244   Horiz. strip of 5   5.00 4.50
a.-e.   A1065 7p Any single   .85 .70

Cecilia Muñoz Palma (1913-2006), First Female Supreme Court Justice — A1066

2009, Nov. 22
3245 A1066 7p multi   .75 .50

Diplomatic Relations Between the Philippines and India, 60th Anniv. — A1067

Endangered marine mammals: Nos. 3246a, 3247a, Whale shark. No. 3246b, Gangetic dolphin.

2009, Nov. 27   **Litho.**
3246 A1067 7p Horiz. pair, #a-b   2.50 2.00
Souvenir Sheet
3247 A1067   Sheet of 2,
      #3246b, 3247a
      + 2 labels   6.00 6.00
a.   20p multi   4.50 3.50
See India No. 2374.

New Year 2010 (Year of the Tiger) — A1068

Designs: 7p, Tiger's head. 20p, Tiger.

2009, Dec. 1   **Perf. 14**
3248-3249 A1068   Set of 2   4.50 4.00
3249a   Souvenir sheet, 2 each
      #3248-3249   11.00 11.00
Printed in sheets of 10.

Nudibranchs — A1069

No. 3250: a, Hypselodoris apolegma. b, Glossodoris colemani. c, Chromodoris sp. d, Chromodoris elizabethina.
No. 3251: a, Jorunna funebris. b, Chromodoris lochi. c, Noumea alboannulata. d, Chromodoris hintuanesis. e, Risbechi tryoni. f, Chromodoris leopardus.

2009, Dec. 4
3250 A1069 7p Block of 4, #a-d   4.50 4.00
Souvenir Sheet
3251 A1069 7p Sheet of 6, #a-f,
      + 2 labels   7.50 7.50
Printed in sheets of 16.

Stamp Collage Depicting Daedalus — A1070

Designs: No. 3252, Entire collage.
No. 3253 — Quadrants of entire collage: a, UL. b, UR. c, LL. d, LR.

2009, Dec. 7
3252 A1070 7p multi   .75 .50
Souvenir Sheet
3253 A1070 7p Sheet of 4, #a-d   4.50 4.50
Intl. Civil Aviation Organization, 65th anniv.

Return of Olongapo to the Philippines, 50th Anniv. — A1071

No. 3254 — Official seals of the Philippines and US and: a, Turnover ceremony. b, Parade of flags of the Philippines and US.

2009, Dec. 7   **Perf. 14**
3254 A1071 7p Horz. pair, #a-b   1.75 1.40

Pheepoy Delivering Mail — A1072

2009, Dec. 10   **Perf. 13½x13¾**
3255 A1072 7p multi   .75 .40
See No. 3227, 3260, 3335-3336.

Philippine Charity Sweepstakes Office, 75th Anniv. — A1073

No. 3256 — 75th anniv. emblem and: a, Charity Sweepstakes Office Building, Presidents Manuel L. Quezon and Gloria Macapagal Arroyo. b, Building. c, Building and family. d, Building and employees.

2009, Dec. 18   **Perf. 14**
3256 A1073 7p Block of 4, #a-d   3.50 3.00
e.   Souvenir sheet, #3256a-3256d 4.50 4.50

Potter From San Nicolas — A1074

2009, Dec. 21
3257 A1074 7p multi   .75 .50
San Nicolas, Ilocos Norte Province, cent.

Birds Type of 2009

No. 3258: a, Philippine eagle owl. b, Luzon Scops owl. c, Philippine Scops owl. d, Spotted wood owl.

2010 **Litho.** **Perf. 13¾x13½**
3258   Block of 4   12.00 9.50
a.-d.   A1042 24p Any single   3.00 1.50
e.   Block of 4, #3258f-3258i, dated "2009A"   12.00 10.00
f.-i.   Like #3258a-3258d, any single, dated "2009A"   2.50 1.50
Nos. 3258a-3258d are dated "2009." Issued: No. 3258, 1/11; No. 3258e, 2/8.

St. Valentine's Day — A1075

No. 3259 — Cupid: a, With bow and arrow. b, Blowing flower petals.

2010, Jan. 25   **Perf. 14**
3259 A1075 7p Horiz. pair, #a-b   1.75 1.50

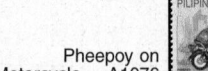

Pheepoy on Motorcycle — A1076

2010, Feb. 12   **Perf. 13½x13¾**
3260 A1076 7p multi   .75 .40
See No. 3227, 3255, 3335-3336.

Rotary International in the Philippines, 90th Anniv. — A1077

Nos. 3261 and 3262: a, Peace dove above people. b, Construction workers. c, Child receiving polio vaccine. d, Rizal Monument, map of the Philippines. No. 3262 has Rotary International emblem instead of "Service Above Self" slogan.

2010, Feb. 23   **Perf. 14**
3261 A1077 7p Block of 4, #a-d   4.50 4.00
Souvenir Sheet
Imperf
3262 A1077 7p Sheet of 4, #a-d   5.00 5.00

Beetles A1078

No. 3263: a, Agestra luconica. b, Glycyphana. c, Paraplectrone crassa. d, Astrea.
No. 3264: a, Agestra semperi. b, Heterorhina. c, Agestra antoinei. d, Clerota rodriguezi.

2010, Mar. 29   **Litho.**   **Perf. 14**
3263 A1078 7p Block of 4, #a-d   4.50   4.00

Souvenir Sheet
3264 A1078 7p Sheet of 4, #a-d   5.00   5.00
Printed in sheets of 16.

Marine Life — A1079

Designs: No. 3265, Christmas tree worm. No. 3266, Yellow seahorse. No. 3267, Manta ray. No. 3268, Sea slug. No. 3269, Pencil urchin. No. 3270, Daisy coral. No. 3271, Magnificent sea anemone. No. 3272, Striped surgeonfish. No. 3273, Sundial. No. 3274, Blue linkia sea star. No. 3275, Sea hare. No. 3276, Giant clam. No. 3277, Green sea turtle. No. 3278, Sacoglossan sea slug. No. 3279, Lionfish. No. 3280, True clownfish. 8p, Harlequin shrimp. No. 3282, Coral beauty. No. 3283, Blue-ringed angelfish. No. 3284, Mandarinfish. No. 3285, Ribbon eel. 15p, Bowmouth guitarfish. No. 3287, Bigfin reef squid. No. 3288, Blue-spotted fantail stingray. No. 3289, Blue sea squirts. No. 3290, Scarlet-fringed flatworm. 24p, Branching anemone. 25p, Boxer crab. 26p, Spotted porcelain crab. 30p, Chambered nautilus. No. 3295, Red grouper. No. 3296, Giant moray eel. 40p, Textile cone. No. 3298, Marble sea star. No. 3299, Upside-down jellyfish. No. 3300, Bottlenose dolphin. No. 3301, Blue-ringed octopus.

2010-11		**Litho.**	**Perf. 13½x13¾**	
3265	A1079	1p multi	.65	.25
3266	A1079	1p multi	.75	.25
3267	A1079	1p multi	.90	.25
3268	A1079	2p multi	.70	.25
3269	A1079	2p multi	.90	.25
3270	A1079	3p multi	.90	.25
3271	A1079	3p multi	.90	.25
3272	A1079	4p multi	.90	.30
3273	A1079	4p multi	.90	.30
3274	A1079	4p multi	.90	.30
3275	A1079	5p multi	1.25	.30
3276	A1079	5p multi	1.25	.30
3277	A1079	5p multi	.90	.30
3278	A1079	5p multi	1.25	.35
3279	A1079	7p multi	.90	.25
3280	A1079	7p multi	.90	.30
3281	A1079	8p multi	.90	.30
3282	A1079	9p multi	1.75	.50
3283	A1079	9p multi	1.60	.35
3284	A1079	10p multi	1.60	.40
3285	A1079	10p multi	1.60	.40
3286	A1079	15p multi	2.25	.65
3287	A1079	17p multi	3.50	1.40
3288	A1079	17p multi	1.40	1.70
3289	A1079	20p multi	2.75	1.40
3290	A1079	20p multi	3.00	1.70
3291	A1079	24p multi	3.25	2.50
3292	A1079	25p multi	3.25	1.80
3293	A1079	26p multi	3.45	1.70
3294	A1079	30p multi	4.00	2.25
3295	A1079	35p multi	5.00	2.40
3296	A1079	35p multi	4.50	2.40
3297	A1079	40p multi	5.50	3.00

Size: 40x30mm
Perf. 14

3298	A1079	50p multi	8.00	4.75
3299	A1079	50p multi	11.00	3.65
3300	A1079	100p multi	14.00	7.25
3301	A1079	100p multi	14.00	7.25
	Nos. 3265-3301 (36)		110.25	51.90

Nos. 3275 and 3278 have the same vignette; No. 3275 has an incorrect inscription and No. 3278 has the corrected inscription.

Issued: Nos. 3265, 3284, 3293, 3/29; Nos. 3266, 3290, 6/15; Nos. 3267, 3277, 3297, 11/18; No. 3268, 3275, 4/16; Nos. 3269, 3295, 7/15; No. 3270, 3273, 3298, 5/17; Nos. 3271, 3274, 3299, 12/3; No. 3278, 3292, 12/22; No. 3279, 3300, 5/13; No. 3280, 3296, 12/17; Nos. 3281, 3289, 4/21; Nos. 3282, 3287, 3291, 5/21; Nos. 3283, 3288, 12/13; Nos. 3285, 11/8; Nos. 3286, 3294, 7/23; No. 3301, 12/1; No. 3272, 1/20/11.

See Nos. 3357-3368, 3389-3403, 3447-3450, 3471-3481.

Intl. Rice Research Institute, 50th Anniv. — A1080

No. 3302: a, 50th anniversary emblem. b, Buildings. c, Rice field, water, mountains. d, Rice plants.

2010, Apr. 14   **Perf. 14**
3302 A1080 7p Block of 4, #a-d   3.50   3.00
   e.   Souvenir sheet of 4 #3302a-
        3302d   4.50   4.50

Eraño G. Manalo (1925-2009), Executive Minister of Iglesia ni Cristo — A1081

Manalo, church and: No. 3303, Country name in brown, "2010" at left under "P." No. 3304, Like #3303, "2010" under denomination. No. 3305, Like #3303, country name in black. No. 3306, Like #3305, "2010" under denomination.

2010
3303 A1081 7p multi   2.75   1.60
3304 A1081 7p multi   2.00   1.25
3305 A1081 7p multi   1.25   .80
3306 A1081 7p multi   1.25   .80
   Nos. 3303-3306 (4)   7.25   4.45

Issued: No. 3303, 4/23; No. 3304, 4/28; No. 3305, 5/11; No. 3306, 12/15.

Paintings by Vicente S. Manansala (1910-81) — A1082

Designs: No. 3307, 7p, Sabungero. No. 3308, 7p, Bayanihan, horiz. No. 3309, 7p, Fish Vendor, horiz. No. 3310, 7p, Nipa Hut, horiz. 20p, Planting of the First Cross, horiz. (80x30mm).
No. 3312: a, Rooster. b, Mamimintakasi. c, I Believe in God, horiz. d, Three Carabaos, horiz.

2010, May 20   **Perf. 14**
3307-3311 A1082   Set of 5   6.50   5.00
Perf. 14, Imperf. (#3312c-3312d)
3312 A1082 7p Sheet of 4, #a-d   5.00   5.00
Nos. 3307-3310 were printed in sheets of 8. No. 3311 was printed in sheets of 4.

Philippine Centennial Tree and Emblem of Municipality of Magallanes A1083

Tree at: 7p, Right. 9p, Left.

2010, May 28   **Perf. 14**
3313-3314 A1083   Set of 2   2.00   1.50

Bukidnon State University, 86th Anniv. — A1084

No. 3315 — University emblem and: a, Main building and sign. b, Education building and flagpole.

2010, June 18
3315 A1084 7p Horiz. pair, #a-b   2.00   1.50

Veterans Federation of the Philippines, 50th Anniv. — A1085

No. 3316 — Soldiers and: a, Emblem at left. b, Emblem at right.

2010, June 18
3316 A1085 7p Horiz. pair, #a-b   2.00   1.50

Light Rail Transit Authority, 30th Anniv. A1086

Nos. 3317 and 3318: a, Train on curved bridge. b, Train, domed building at right. c, Train, pink and blue buildings. d, Cars on road below train.

2010, July 12   **Perf. 14**
3317 A1086 7p Block of 4, #a-d   4.00   3.50
Souvenir Sheet
Imperf
3318 A1086 10p Sheet of 4, #a-d   6.00   6.00

Inauguration of Pres. Benigno S. Aquino III — A1087

Pres. Aquino: 7p, Taking oath. 40p, Giving inaugural speech, vert.

2010, July 26   **Perf. 14**
3319-3320 A1087   Set of 2   5.00   4.00

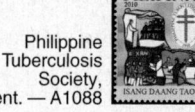

Philippine Tuberculosis Society, Cent. — A1088

Society emblem and health care workers with inscription at bottom in: 7p, Tagalog. 9p, English.
26p, Emblem and 1935 Manuel L. Quezon birthday seal.

2010, July 29   **Perf. 14**
3321-3322 A1088   Set of 2   2.00   1.60
Souvenir Sheet
3323 A1088 26p multi   5.00   5.00
No. 3323 contains one 120x30mm stamp.

Devotion to Our Lady of Peñafrancia, 300th Anniv. — A1089

No. 3324: a, Our Lady of Peñafrancia, red panel. b, Our Lady of Peñafrancia, green panel. c, Our Lady of Peñafrancia Shrine, blue panel. d, Our Lady of Peñafrancia Basilica, yellow panel.

20p, Our Lady of Peñafrancia Shrine, Naga City, horiz.

2010, Sept. 8   **Perf. 14**
3324 A1089 7p Block of 4, #a-d   3.50   3.00
Souvenir Sheet
3325 A1089 28p multi   3.50   3.00
No. 3325 contains one 80x30mm stamp.

Dogs A1090

No. 3326: a, Chow chow. b, Bull terrier. c, Labrador retriever. d, Beagle.
No. 3327: a, American Eskimo dog. b, Black and tan coonhound. c, Afghan hound. d, Mastiff.

2010, Sept. 9   **Perf. 14**
3326 A1090 7p Block of 4, #a-d   4.50   4.00
Souvenir Sheet
3327 A1090 7p Sheet of 4, #a-d   5.00   5.00
No. 3326 printed in sheets of 16.

Ozone Layer Protection — A1091

No. 3328: a, Hand over globe. b, Hands below globe.

2010, Sept. 16
3328 A1091 7p Horiz. pair, #a-b   1.75   1.50

Central Mindanao University, Cent. — A1092

No. 3329 — University emblem and: a, Administration Building and lamp poles. b, University building.

2010, Sept. 17
3329 A1092 7p Horiz. pair, #a-b   1.85   1.50

Pres. Diosdado Macapagal (1910-97) — A1093

2010, Sept. 28
3330 A1093 7p multi   .80   .50

Day of the Galleon A1094

No. 3331 — Galleon and map of: a, Pacific Ocean, East Asia, Western North America. b, Atlantic Ocean, Eastern North America, Western Europe and West Africa.
40p, Like #3331b.

2010, Oct. 8
3331 A1094 7p Horiz. pair, #a-b   2.50   2.00
   c.   Souvenir sheet of 2, #3331a-
        3331b   3.00   3.00
Souvenir Sheet
3332   Sheet of 2, #3331a,
       3332a   7.50   7.50
   a.   A1094 40p multi   5.00   5.00

Intl. Year of Biodiversity — A1095

No. 3333 — Children's art by: a, Krysten Alarice Tan. b. Justen Paul Tolentino.

2010, Oct. 26
3333 A1095 7p Horiz. pair, #a-b 2.50 2.00

Philippine Rice Research Institute, 25th Anniv. — A1096

No. 3334: a, Building. b, Plants in test tubes. c, Farmer in field. d, Farm workers and tractor.

2010, Nov. 5 Litho. Perf. 14
3334 A1096 7p Block of 4, #a-d 3.50 3.00

Pheepoy Types of 2009-10 Redrawn and

Pheepoy in Mail Van — A1097

2010, Nov. 8 Perf. 13½x13¾
3335 A1097 7p multi, "Pheepoy" 7mm wide .80 .40

Souvenir Sheet
3336 Sheet of 4 4.50 4.50
  a. A1052 7p multi, "Pheepoy" 6mm wide, dated "2010" .80 .65
  b. A1072 7p multi, dark blue sky, dated "2010" .80 .65
  c. A1076 7p multi, "Pheepoy" at bottom center .80 .65
  d. A1097 7p multi, "Pheepoy" 6mm wide .80 .65
  e. Sheet of 4, #3336f-3336i, imperf. 4.50 4.50
  f. As "a," imperf. .80 .65
  g. As "b," imperf. .80 .65
  h. As "c," imperf. .80 .65
  i. As "d," imperf. .80 .65

See Nos. 3227, 3255, 3260.

A1098

National Stamp Collecting Month — A1099

No. 3337: a, Levi Celerio (1910-2002), composer. b, Leonor Orosa Goquingco (1917-2005), dancer. c, Carlos L. Quirino (1910-99), historian. d, Nick Joaquin (1917-2004), writer.
No. 3338 — Fernando Poe, Jr. (1939-2004), actor: a, Scene from film *Ang Panday Ikatlong Yugto* (The Blacksmith, Part 3). b, Scene from film *Umpisahan Mo. . .Tatapusin Ko!* (You Start. . .I'll Finish). c, Scene from *Pepeng Kaliwete* (Pepe Lefty). d, Portrait.

2010 Perf. 14
3337 A1098 7p Block of 4, #a-d 4.50 4.00
3338 A1099 7p Block of 4, #a-d 5.00 4.50
  e. Souvenir sheet of 3, #3338a-3338c, + label 3.50 3.50

Issued: Nos. 3337, 3338e, 11/10; No. 3338, 11/25.
Nos. 3337 and 3338 printed in separate sheets of 16.

Inauguration of Vice-President Jejomar C. Binay — A1100

2010, Nov. 11 Litho. Perf. 14
3339 A1100 7p multi .80 .50

Printed in sheets of 15.

Christmas — A1101

No. 3340: a, Holy Family in Filipino clothing, St. Peter's Basilica. b, Holy Family. c, Holy Family on jar. d, Adoration of the Shepherds.

2010, Nov. 23
3340 A1101 7p Block of 4, #a-d 5.00 4.50

Ateneo de Manila Class of 1960, 50th Anniv. A1102

No. 3341: a, Ateneo de Manila emblems, "Fabilioh!" b, Eagle, cross on steeple, bell. c, Man, boy, statue of Virgin Mary. d, Bell.

2010, Dec. 2
3341 A1102 7p Block of 4, #a-d 3.75 3.25

New Year 2011 (Year of the Rabbit) — A1103

Designs: 7p, Head of rabbit. 30p, Rabbit.

2010, Dec. 6
3342-3343 A1103 Set of 2 5.00 4.00
  3343a Souvenir sheet of 4, 2 each #3342-3343 11.00 11.00

Printed in sheets of 10.

Senator Ambrosio B. Padilla (1910-90) — A1104

No. 3344 — Portrait of Padilla and: a, Padilla at microphone. b, Padilla playing basketball.

2010, Dec. 7
3344 A1104 7p Horiz. pair, #a-b 1.75 1.50

SyCip, Salazar, Hernandez & Gatmaitan Law Firm, 65th Anniv. — A1105

2010, Dec. 10
3345 A1105 7p multi .80 .50

Grace Christian College, Manila, 60th Anniv. A1106

No. 3346: a, Emblem and building. b, Emblem, "Grace at 60." c, Building, Chinese characters. d, Building, Chinese characters, founders Julia L. Tan, Dr. and Mrs. Edward Spahr.

2010, Dec. 16 Perf. 14
3346 A1106 7p Block of 4, #a-d 4.00 3.50
  e. Souvenir sheet of 4 #3346a-3346d 4.50 4.50
  f. Block of 4, #3346g-3346j 5.00 4.50
  g.-j. Like #3346a-3346d with "2010" date inside of frames, any single 1.00 .80
  k. Souvenir sheet, #3346g-3346j 6.00 6.00

The "2010" year dates on Nos. 3346a-3346d and 3346e are below the frame lines at the lower right of each stamp. Issued: Nos. 3346f, 3346k, 5/10/11.

Valentine's Day — A1107

No. 3347 — Earth, hearts and Philippine Postal Corporation mascot Pheepoy: a, Carrying flowers. b, Driving postal van.

2011, Jan. 14 Litho. Perf. 14
3347 A1107 7p Horiz. pair, #a-b 1.75 1.40

Kiwanis Club of Manila, 47th Anniv. — A1108

2011, Jan. 21
3348 A1108 7p multi .80 .35

University of Santo Tomas, Manila, 400th Anniv. — A1109

No. 3349: a, Main Building. b, Central Seminary. c, Arch of the Centuries. d, The foundation of the University of Santo Tomas by Archbishop Miguel de Benavides.
No. 3350, vert.: a, 7p, Statue of Archbishop Benavides. b, 30p, Quattro Mondial Monument.

2011, Jan. 25
3349 A1109 7p Block of 4, #a-d 4.00 3.50

Souvenir Sheet
3350 A1109 Sheet of 2, #a-b, + central label 6.00 5.00

Hoyas A1110

No. 3351: a, Mindoro hoya. b, Grandmother's wax plant. c, Summer hoya. d, Benito Tan's hoya.
No. 3352: a, Siar's hoya. b, Shooting star hoya. c, Imperial hoya. d, Buot's hoya.

2011, Mar. 8
3351 A1110 7p Block of 4, #a-d 4.50 4.00

Souvenir Sheet
3352 A1110 7p Sheet of 4, #a-d, + 2 labels 5.00 5.00

Printed in sheets of 16.

University of the Philippines College of Law, Cent. — A1111

No. 3353 — Building and emblem with: a, Scales. b, Lady Justice (centennial emblem).

2011, Apr. 11
3353 A1111 7p Horiz. pair, #a-b 1.75 1.40

Center for Agriculture and Rural Development Mutually Reinforcing Institutions, 25th Anniv. — A1112

2011, Apr. 25
3354 A1112 7p multi .80 .50

Department of Budget and Management, 75th Anniv. — A1113

2011, Apr. 25 Perf. 13½
3355 A1113 7p multi .80 .50

Wenceslao Q. Vinzons (1910-42), Leader of Resistance Forces in World War II — A1114

2011, May 3 Perf. 14
3356 A1114 7p multi .80 .50

Dated 2010.

Marine Life Type of 2010

Designs: 1p, Dendronephthya soft coral. 2p, Yellowstripe snapper. 4p, Branded vexillum. 5p, Sea apple. 7p, Spotted boxfish. 9p, Broadclub cuttlefish. 10p, Mushroom coral. 17p, Cowfish. 20p, Two-banded anemone fish. 30p, Lipstick tang. 40p, Yellow-backed damselfish. 100p, Pink tube sponge.

2011 Perf. 13½x13¾
3357 A1079 1p multi .65 .25
3358 A1079 2p multi .75 .25
3359 A1079 4p multi 1.00 .35
3360 A1079 5p multi 1.00 .35
3361 A1079 7p multi 1.00 .50
3362 A1079 9p multi 1.50 .60
3363 A1079 10p multi 1.75 .70
3364 A1079 17p multi 2.50 1.40
3365 A1079 20p multi 2.75 1.40

3366	A1079	30p multi	5.00	2.40
3367	A1079	40p multi	6.50	3.00

Size: 40x30mm
Perf. 14

3368	A1079	100p multi	16.00	9.00
		Nos. 3357-3368 (12)	40.40	20.20

Issued: 1p, 5p, 7p, 9p, 8/17; 2p, 20p, 30p, 40p, 5/5; 4p, 10p, 17p, 100p, 5/12.

Worldwide Fund for Nature (WWF) — A1115

Philippine crocodile: No. 3369, Hatchling and eggs (yellow and brown frame). No. 3370, Juvenile on log (olive green and yellow green frame). No. 3371, Adult on rock (blue green and blue frame). No. 3372, Adult with open mouth (orange and green frame).

2011, May 16　　　　　**Perf. 14**

3369	A1115	7p multi	1.20	1.00
a.		Miniature sheet of 8	12.50	12.50
3370	A1115	7p multi	1.20	1.00
a.		Miniature sheet of 8	12.50	12.50
3371	A1115	7p multi	1.20	1.00
a.		Miniature sheet of 8	12.50	12.50
3372	A1115	7p multi	1.20	1.00
a.		Block of 4, #3369-3372	6.00	6.00
b.		Miniature sheet of 8	12.50	12.50
		Nos. 3369-3372 (4)	4.80	4.00

Nos. 3369-3372 were printed in sheets of 16 containing four of each stamp.

Arnis A1116

No. 3373 — Arnis fighters wearing: a, Protective gear. b, White robes.

2011, May 23

3373	A1116	7p Horiz. pair, #a-b	1.75	1.50
c.		Sheet of 4, 2 each #a-b	4.50	4.50

Beatification of Pope John Paul II — A1117

No. 3374 — Pope John Paul II and: a, Grandstand, Rizal Park (denomination in green at UL). b, University of Santo Tomas (denomination in red at UR). c, Philippine International Convention Center (denomination in red at UL). d, Popemobile (denomination in green at UR).
40p, Pope with crucifix, vert.

2011, May 30

3374	A1117	7p Block of 4, #a-d	4.50	4.00

Souvenir Sheet

3375	A1117	40p multi + 2 labels	5.00	5.00

Printed in sheets of 16.

National Information and Communications Technology Month — A1118

No. 3376 — Inscriptions: a, Community eCenter. b, Creative content industries. c, Nationwide automated elections. d, Business process outsourcing.

2011, June 13

3376	A1118	7p Block of 4, #a-d	3.50	3.00

Security Bank Corporation, 60th Anniv. — A1119

No. 3377: a, Corporate Headquarters in 1951 and 2011. b, Company emblems.

2011, June 18

3377	A1119	10p Horiz. pair, #a-b	1.75	1.60

Goethe Institute in the Philippines, 50th Anniv. — A1120

No. 3378: a, José Rizal Statue, Wilhelmsfeld, Germany. b, Fountain from Wilhelmsfeld in Luneta Park. c, Residence of Rizal, Wilhelmsfeld. d, Anniversary emblem.

2011, June 19

3378	A1120	7p Block of 4, #a-d	4.00	3.50

A1121

A1122

José Rizal (1861-96), Patriot — A1123

No. 3379 — Rizal, anniversary emblem and: a, Dove, cover of *Noli Me Tangere*. b, Philippines flag elements.
No. 3380 — Annivesary emblem and Rizal in: a, Blue. b, Red.
No. 3381 — Philippines stamps depicting Rizal and monuments: a, 7p, #241, monument in Daet. b, 7p, #383, monument in Guinobatan. c, 7p, #461, monument in Santa Barbara. d, 7p, #497, monument in Biñan. e, 7p, #527, monument in Zamboanga. f, 12p, #813, monument in San Fernando. g, 13p, #857, monument in Lucban. h, 20p, #857A, monument in Romblon. i, 30p, #1313, monument in Jinjiang, China. j, 40p, #1198, monument in Illinois.

2011, June 19　　　　　**Perf. 14**

3379	A1121	7p Horiz. pair, #a-b	2.25	1.60
3380	A1122	7p Horiz. pair, #a-b	2.25	1.60

Perf. 13¾

3381	A1123	Sheet of 10, #a-j	20.00	20.00

Yuchengco Group of Companies, Cent. — A1124

2011, July 20　　　　　**Perf. 14**

3382	A1124	7p multi	.80	.60

People Power Revolution, 25th Anniv. — A1125

No. 3383: a, Pres. Corazon C. Aquino (1933-2009), with collar visible, person with raised arm at LL, small helicopter at UL. b, Jaime Cardinal Sin (1928-2005), wearing biretta, helicopter at UR. c, Sin, without biretta, wearing black vestments, people with raised arms at left, helicopter at UL. d, Aquino, nun at LR.
No. 3384: a, Aquino, without collar visible, background like #3383a. b, Aquino, backgrond like #3383b. c, Aquino, background like #3383c. d, Sin, without biretta like #3383c, crowds in background. e, Sin, wearing white vestments, people carrying crucifix at right. f, Sin, wearing rosary around neck, crowds in background. g, Sin, wearing biretta like #3383b, religious statue at left.

2011, Aug. 1　　　　　**Litho.**

3383	A1125	7p Block of 4, #a-d	4.50	4.00
3384	A1125	7p Sheet of 8, #3383d, 3384a-3384g	11.00	11.00

Holy Cross of Davao College, 60th Anniv. A1126

No. 3385: a, Bajada Campus facade. b, Grade school and high school buildings. c, Palma Gil and Mabutas Halls. d, Babak and Camudmud Campuses.

2011, Aug. 15　　　　　**Perf. 14**

3385	A1126	7p Block of 4, #a-d	3.50	3.00

Mother Francisca del Espiritu Santo de Fuentes (1647-1711), Founder of Dominican Sisters of St. Catherine of Siena — A1127

2011, Aug. 24

3386	A1127	7p multi	.80	.60

Lizards A1128

No. 3387: a, Luzon giant forest skink. b, Luzon karst gecko. c, Southern Philippines bent-toed gecko. d, Luzon white-spotted forest skink.

No. 3388: a, Philippine forest dragon. b, Philippine spiny stream skink. c, Philippine sailfin lizard. d, Cordilleras slender skink.

2011, Aug. 30　　　　　**Perf. 14**

3387	A1128	7p Block of 4, #a-d	4.50	4.00
3388	A1128	7p Sheet of 4, #a-d, + 2 labels	5.00	5.00

Printed in sheets of 16.

Marine Life Type of 2010 With Optical Code at Lower Right

Designs: 1p, Picasso triggerfish. 2p, Marmorated cone shell. 4p, Blue-faced angelfish. 5p, Copper-band butterflyfish. 7p, Murex shell. 9p, Polyclad flatworm. 10p, Triton trumpet shell. 13p, Valentine puffer. 17p, Polka-dot grouper. 20p, Bennett's feather star. 25p, Oriental sweetlips. 30p, Eibl's angelfish. 35p, Kunie's chromodoris. 40p, Royal empress angelfish. 100p, Regal tang.

2011　　**Litho.**　　　**Perf. 14½**

3389	A1079	1p multi	.65	.25
3390	A1079	2p multi	.75	.25
3391	A1079	4p multi	.75	.35
3392	A1079	5p multi	.90	.30
3393	A1079	7p multi	1.25	.30
3394	A1079	9p multi	1.60	.75
3395	A1079	10p multi	1.60	.60
3396	A1079	13p multi	2.25	1.75
3397	A1079	17p multi	2.25	1.75
3398	A1079	20p multi	4.25	1.75
3399	A1079	25p multi	4.25	2.40
3400	A1079	30p multi	5.75	3.00
3401	A1079	35p multi	6.50	3.50
3402	A1079	40p multi	6.50	3.50

Size: 40x30mm
Perf. 13x13½

3403	A1079	100p multi	21.00	15.00
		Nos. 3389-3403 (15)	60.25	35.45

Issued: 1p, 2p, 5p, 10p, 20p, 30p, 10/17; 4p, 7p, 100p, 10/25; 9p, 25p, 35p, 11/4; 13p, 17p, 40p, 11/11.

Intl. Year of Forests A1129

No. 3404: a, Batlag Falls, Tanay. b, Tree, Pansol.

2011, Oct. 24　　　　　**Perf. 13½x13**

3404	A1129	7p Horiz. pair, #a-b	1.75	1.50

Day of the Galleon — A1130

Nos. 3405 and 3406: a, Galleon at right, map of East Asia. b, Galleon at left, map of Central and North America. c, Galleon at center, map of Atlantic Ocean, Europe and Africa.

2011, Nov. 10　　　　　**Perf. 13x13½**

3405		Horiz. strip of 3	3.50	3.00
a.-c.	A1130	7p Any single	1.00	.75

Souvenir Sheet
Perf. 13x13½ on 2 or 3 Sides

3406		Sheet of 3 + label	3.50	3.50
a.-c.	A1130	7p Any single	1.00	.80

Printed in sheets of 12. Adjacent stamps in No. 3406 are separated by simulated perforations.

Paintings by Hernando R. Ocampo
(1911-78) — A1131

No. 3407: a, Homage to José Rizal. b,
Break of Day. c, Summer in September. d,
Mother and Child.
No. 3408, horiz.: a, Fiesta. b, Abstraction
#15, 17. c, Kasaysayan ng Lahi. d, Abstraction
#22, 26.

2011, Nov. 11   **Perf. 13½x13**
3407 A1131 7p Block of 4, #a-d   4.50 4.00
                          Perf. 13x13½
3408 A1131 7p Sheet of 4, #a-d   5.00 5.00
Stamp Collecting Month.

National Bureau of Investigation, 75th
Anniv. — A1132

No. 3409: a, Emblem of National Bureau of
Investigation. b, Justice José Yulo and Pres.
Manuel L. Quezon. c, Pres. Manuel A. Roxas
signing bill, J. Pardo de Tavera, first director of
National Bureau of Investigation. d, Fingerprint
under magnifying glass, laptop computer,
"Justice."

2011, Nov. 14   **Perf. 13½x13**
3409 A1132 7p Block of 4, #a-d   3.50 3.00

Christmas — A1133

No. 3410: a, Bells. b, Poinsettias. c, Toys
and gifts. d, Parol (Christmas star lantern).

2011, Nov. 26
3410 A1133 7p Block of 4, #a-d   4.00 3.50

New Year 2012
(Year of the
Dragon) — A1134

Designs: 7p, Head of dragon. 30p, Dragon.

2011, Dec. 5   **Perf. 13x13½**
3411-3412 A1134 Set of 2   7.50 6.00
3412a   Sheet of 4, 2 each
             #3411-3412   30.00 30.00
Printed in sheets of 10.
See Nos. 3435-3436.

Office of the Solicitor
General, 110th
Anniv. — A1135

2011, Dec. 15   **Perf. 13½x13**
3413 A1135 7p multi   .70   .50

Frogs
A1136

No. 3414: a, Philippine spiny cinnamon frog.
b, Philippine pygmy forest frog. c, Philippine
flat-headed frog. d, Luzon limestone forest
frog.
No. 3415: a, Gliding tree frog. b, Northern
Luzon tree-hole frog. c, Taylor's igorot frog. d,
Mary Inger's wart frog.

2011, Dec. 15   **Perf. 13x13½**
3414 A1136 7p Block of 4, #a-d   4.50 4.00
3415 A1136 7p Sheet of 4, #a-d
            + 2 labels   5.00 5.00
Printed in sheets of 16.

Lyceum of the
Philippines University,
60th Anniv. — A1137

2012, Jan. 2   **Litho.**   **Perf. 12**
3416 A1137 7p multi   .70   .40
Printed in sheets of 16.

Grand Lodge of Free and Accepted
Masons of the Philippines,
Cent. — A1138

No. 3417 — Centenary emblem and: a,
Grand Lodge, Pres. Manuel L. Quezon. b,
José Rizal, Marcelo H. del Pilar, Mariano
Ponce, Plaridel Masonic Temple.

2012, Jan. 19
3417 A1138 7p Horiz. pair, #a-b   2.50 2.00

Diocese of Malolos, 50th Anniv.
— A1139

No. 3418 — Centenary emblem and: a, Virgin of the Immaculate Conception of Malolos.
b, Immaculate Conception Cathedral and
Basilica.
40p, Virgin of the Immaculate Conception of
Malolos, vert.

2012, Jan. 25
3418 A1139 7p Horiz. pair, #a-b 1.75 1.50
             Souvenir Sheet
3419 A1139 40p multi + 2 labels 5.00 4.00

Davao,
75th
Anniv.
A1140

No. 3420: a, Davao City Hall. b, Kadayawan
Festival. c, Waling-waling orchids. d, Mt. Apo,
Philippine eagle.

2012, Mar. 16   **Litho.**   **Perf. 14**
3420 A1140 7p Block of 4, #a-d   4.50 3.50

Ateneo de Zamboanga University,
Cent. — A1141

No. 3421 — Centenary emblem and: a, Fort
Pilar Shrine. b, Father William H. Kreutz, S.J.
Campus. c, Ateneo Brebeuf Gymnasium. d,
St. Ignatius of Loyola.

2012, Mar. 19
3421 A1141 7p Block of 4, #a-d   4.50 3.50
   e.   Souvenir sheet of 4, #3421a-
        3421d   4.50 4.50

St. Agnes Academy, Legazpi City,
Cent. — A1142

No. 3422 — Centenary emblem and Main
Building: a, Facade (denomination at UR). b,
In ruins after World War II (denomination at
UL). c, Facade, with flag at right (denomina-
tion at UR). d, Facade, flowers and flagpole in
front (denomination at UL).

2012, Mar. 21
3422 A1142 7p Block of 4, #a-d   4.00 3.50

Maria Makiling, Mythical
Forest
Guardian — A1143

2012, Mar. 30   **Perf. 13½x13¾**
3423 A1143 7p multi   .70   .40

Asian-Pacific
Postal Union, 50th
Anniv. — A1144

Designs: 7p, Emblem and flags. 30p,
Emblem, flags, Philippines #1323 (80x30mm).

2012, Apr. 1   **Perf. 14**
3424-3425 A1144   Set of 2   4.00 3.00

Philippine Postal Corporation, 20th
Anniv. — A1145

No. 3426: a, Pres. Corazon Aquino, Postal
Service Act of 1992. b, Main Post Office,
Manila.

2012, Apr. 10
3426 A1145 7p Horiz. pair, #a-b 1.75 1.40

Felipe Padilla de
Leon (1912-92),
Composer
A1146

2012, May 1
3427 A1146 7p multi   .70   .40

Churches — A1147

No. 3428: a, La Immaculada Concepcion
Parish Church, Guiuan. b, San Joaquin Parish
Church, San Joaquin. c, Nuestra Señora de la
Porteria Parish Church, Daraga. d, San Isidro
Labrador Parish Church, Lazi.
No. 3429: a, Santiago Apostol Parish
Church, Betis. b, La Immaculada Concepcion
Parish Church, Jasaan. c, Our Lady of Light
Parish Church, Loon. d, San Gregorio Magno
Parish Church, Majayjay.

2012, May 1
3428 A1147 7p Block of 4, #a-d   3.00 2.50
             Souvenir Sheet
3429 A1147 7p Sheet of 4, #a-d   4.00 4.00

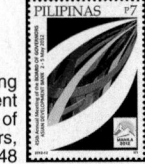

45th Annual Meeting
of Asian Development
Bank Board of
Governors,
Manila — A1148

2012, May 2   **Perf. 14**
3430 A1148 7p multi   .75   .50

Day of Valor, 70th
Anniv. — A1149

Designs: 7p, Soldiers in Bataan Death
March. 10p, Battery Hearn, Corregidor Island.
30p, Shrine of Valor, Mt. Samat, Bataan.

2012, May 6   **Litho.**
3431-3433 A1149   Set of 3   4.50 4.00

Government Service
Insurance System, 75th
Anniv. — A1150

No. 3434 — Emblem and: a, Head office in
Solano, 1937 (25x22mm). b, Head office in
Arroceros, 1957 (25x22mm). c, Financial
Center, Pasay City (50x22mm).

2012, May 28   **Perf. 13½x13¾**
3434   Horiz. strip of 3   6.00 5.00
   a. A1150 7p multi   .70   .50
   b. A1150 9p multi   .85   .60
   c. A1150 40p multi   3.25 2.50

Year of the Dragon Type of 2011
Redrawn Without Line To Right of
"Pilipinas" and Dated "2012"
Designs as before.

2012, June 8   **Perf. 14**
3435-3436 A1134   Set of 2   6.00 5.00
3436a   Souvenir sheet of 4, 2
             each #3435-3436   11.00 11.00
Printed in sheets of 10.

Whitewater Rafters, Cagayan de Oro — A1151

2012, June 15
3437 A1151 9p multi .80 .80

Winning Design in Intl. Year of Forests Children's Art Contest — A1152

2012, June 18
3438 A1152 9p multi .80 .80

Bonifacio Monument, Caloocan A1153

2012, June 25
3439 A1153 7p multi .70 .50

Habagat, God of Winds — A1154

2012, June 28 *Perf. 13½x13¾*
3440 A1154 7p multi .70 .40

2012 Summer Olympics, London — A1155

No. 3441: a, Athletics. b, Shooting. c, Swimming. d, Boxing.

2012, July 27 *Perf. 14*
3441 A1155 7p Block of 4, #a-d 4.50 4.00
Printed in sheets of 16.

Metrobank, 50th Anniv. — A1156

No. 3442: a, Binondo Branch, 1962. b, Metrobank Plaza, Makati City, 1977. c, GT International Tower, Makati City, 2004. d, Metrobank Plaza, Shanghai, People's Republic of China, 2001.

2012, Aug. 25 Litho.
3442 A1156 7p Block of 4, #a-d 3.50 3.00

José B. Laurel, Jr. (1912-98), Speaker of the House of Representatives A1157

2012, Aug. 27 *Perf. 14*
3443 A1157 9p multi .80 .50

Ramon O. Valera (1912-72), Fashion Designer A1158

2012, Aug. 31
3444 A1158 7p multi .70 .50

Amihan, Goddess of Monsoon Weather — A1159

2012, Sept. 28 *Perf. 13½x13¾*
3445 A1159 7p multi .70 .40

Manila Hotel, Cent. A1160

No. 3446: a, Facade. b, Maynila Ballroom. c, MacArthur Suite. d, Grand Lobby.

2012, Oct. 5 *Perf. 14*
3446 A1160 7p Block of 4, #a-d 3.00 2.50

Marine Life Type of 2010-11

Designs: 1p, Twin-spot wrasse. 5p, Pearlscale butterflyfish. 40p, Tassle filefish. 100p, Koran angelfish.

2012 *Perf. 13½x13¾*
3447 A1079 1p multi .75 .25
3448 A1079 5p multi .75 .40
3449 A1079 40p multi 5.50 3.50
Size: 40x30mm
Perf. 14
3450 A1079 100p multi 13.00 6.50
Nos. 3447-3450 (4) 20.00 10.65
Issued: 1p, 5p, 40p, 10/18; 100p, 11/16.

Canonization of Blessed Pedro Calungsod (1654-72) A1161

2012, Oct. 21 *Perf. 14*
3451 A1161 9p multi .90 .60
a. Miniature sheet of 20 24.00 24.00
No. 3451 was originally printed in sheet of 40, which sold out within a week. The additional printing was in sheets of 20, released on Nov. 28.

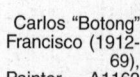

Carlos "Botong" Francisco (1912-69), Painter — A1162

2012, Nov. 4
3452 A1162 7p multi .70 .40

Christmas — A1163

No. 3453: a, Nativity. b, People arriving at church for dawn mass.

2012, Nov. 20 Litho.
3453 A1163 10p Horiz. pair,
#a-b 2.25 1.75
Printed in sheets of 16.

Bernardo Carpio, Mythical Cause of Earthquakes — A1164

2012, Nov. 28 *Perf. 13½x13¾*
3454 A1164 7p multi .70 .40

Lepanto Consolidated Mining Corporation, 75th Anniv. — A1165

No. 3455: a, Reforestation. b, Miners in mine entrance.

2012, Dec. 7 Litho. *Perf. 14*
3455 A1165 7p Horiz. pair, #a-b 1.75 1.40

New Year 2013 (Year of the Snake) — A1166

Designs: 10p, Head of snake. 30p, Coiled snake.

2012, Dec. 12 Litho. *Perf. 14*
3456-3457 A1166 Set of 2 7.00 5.00
3457a Souvenir sheet of 4, 2
each #3456-3457 12.50 12.50
Printed in sheets of 10.

Miniature Sheet

Paintings of People Holding Roses A1167

No. 3458 — Paintings by various artists numbered at LR: a, 1/10. b, 2/10. c, 3/10. d, 4/10. e, 5/10. f, 6/10. g, 7/10. h, 8/10. i, 9/10. j, 10/10.

2012, Dec. 14 *Perf. 14*
3458 A1167 10p Sheet of 10,
#a-j 14.00 14.00

Valentine's Day — A1168

2013, Jan. 14 Litho. *Perf. 14*
3459 A1168 10p multi .90 .50

Far Eastern University Save the Tamaraw Project — A1169

Designs: No. 3460, 10p, Tamaraw. No. 3461, 10p, Tamerarw, vert.

2013, Jan. 25 Litho. *Perf. 14*
3460-3461 A1169 Set of 2 2.00 1.50
Printed in sheets of 16.

Lucio D. San Pedro (1913-2002), Composer A1170

2013, Feb. 11 Litho. *Perf. 14*
3462 A1170 10p multi .80 .50

Teresita "Mama Sita" Reyes (1917-98), Restauranteur A1171

2013, Feb. 11 Litho. *Perf. 14*
Stamp With Pink Shading at Top and Bottom
3463 A1171 10p multi .80 .50
Souvenir Sheet
Stamp with White Frame at Top and Bottom
3464 A1171 10p multi + 2 labels 3.50 3.50
No. 3464 was sold at 30p.

Pitcher Plants A1172

No. 3465: a, Nepenthes peltata. b, Nepenthes truncata. c, Nepenthes burkei. d, Nepenthes attenboroughii.
No. 3466: a, Nepenthes mindanaoensis. b, Nepenthes sibuyanensis. c, Nepenthes mira. d, Nepenthes mantalingajanensis.

2013, Mar. 13 Litho. *Perf. 14*
3465 A1172 10p Block of 4, #a-d 4.00 3.50
Souvenir Sheet
Imperf
3466 A1172 10p Block of 4, #a-d 5.00 5.00
No. 3466 has simulated perforations.

University of the Philippines Alumni Association, Cent. — A1173

No. 3467: a, Emblem and Oblation, purple panel. b, Emblem and Carillon Tower, blue panel. c, Emblem and Ang Bahay Ng Building, green panel. d, Emblem, orange panel.

2013, Apr. 2 *Perf. 14*
3467 A1173 10p Block of 4, #a-d 3.50 3.00

Diplomatic Relations Between Italy and the Philippines, 65th Annv. — A1174

No. 3468 — Flags of the Philippines and Italy and: a, Cinque Terre National Park, Italy. b, Banaue Rice Terraces, Philippines.

2013, Apr. 4   Litho.   Perf. 14
3468   A1174   40p Pair, #a-b   8.00 7.00

Printed in sheets of 16.

Edible Nuts and Seeds A1175

No. 3469: a, Cashews. b, Pili nuts. c, Watermelon seeds. d, Peanuts.
No. 3470: a, Sunflower seeds. b, Mung beans. c, Coffee beans. d, Squash seeds.

2013, Apr. 15   Litho.   Perf. 14
3469   A1175   10p Block of 4, #a-d   4.00 3.50
Souvenir Sheet
3470   A1175   10p Sheet of 4, #a-d   4.00 4.00

Printed in sheets of 16.

Marine Life Type of 2010-11

Designs: 1p, Pinecone fish. 3p, Purple firefish. 5p, Pyjama cardinalfish. No. 3474, Long-nosed butterflyfish. No. 3475, Longnose filefish. 13p, Raccoon butterflyfish. 20p, Fire clown. 25p, Two-lined monocle bream. 30p, Green chromis. 40p, Common squirrelfish. 100p, Black-backed butterflyfish.

2013	Litho.		Perf. 13½x13¾
3471	A1079	1p multi	.65 .25
3472	A1079	3p multi	.65 .25
3473	A1079	5p multi	.80 .25
3474	A1079	10p multi	1.25 .60
3475	A1079	10p multi	1.25 .60
3476	A1079	13p multi	1.85 .80
3477	A1079	20p multi	2.60 1.20
3478	A1079	25p multi	3.25 1.50
3479	A1079	30p multi	4.00 1.75
3480	A1079	40p multi	5.00 2.40

Size: 40x30mm
Perf. 14
3481   A1079   100p multi   13.00 6.00
Nos. 3471-3481 (11)   34.30 15.60

Issued: 1p, 100p, 12/6; 3p, 5p, #3475, 13p, 12/10; #3474, 4/23; 20p, 40p, 12/13; 25p, 30p, 12/16.

Jesse M. Robredo (1958-2012), Interior Secretary — A1176

2013, May 27   Litho.   Perf. 14
3482   A1176   10p multi   .90 .50

Philpost Emblem and Manila Central Post Office A1177

Philpost Emblem A1178

2013, May 29   Litho.   Perf. 13½x13¼
Denomination Color

3483	A1177	1p brown	.50 .25
3484	A1177	7p blue gray	.75 .30
3485	A1177	9p org brn	1.00 .35
3486	A1177	12p yel org	1.25 .60
3487	A1177	30p orange	3.50 1.50
3488	A1177	35p violet	4.00 1.75
3489	A1177	40p green	4.50 2.25
3490	A1177	45p lilac	6.00 2.40

Perf. 14
3491   A1178   100p dull vio brn   13.00 6.00
Nos. 3483-3491 (9)   34.50 15.40

See Nos. 3593-3594, 3789-3790.

Malacañan Palace, Manila, 150th Anniv. A1179

Perf. 13½x13¾
2013, June 11   Litho.
3492   A1179   10p multi   1.00 .60

Miniature Sheet

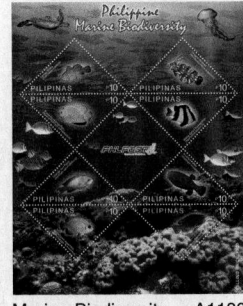

Marine Biodiversity — A1180

No. 3493: a, Lemon goby. b, Dragon wrasse. c, Three-spot angelfish. d, White-tailed damselfish. e, Orange sea perch. f, Spotted puffer. g, Lemonpeel angelfish. h, Electric blue damsel.

2013, Aug. 2   Litho.   Perf. 12
3493   A1180   10p Sheet of 8, #a-h, + central label   11.00 11.00
i. As #3493, with Thailand 2013 World Stamp Exhibition emblem on center label   13.00 13.00

Nos. 3493 and 3493i each sold for 100p.

Shrimp A1181

No. 3494: a, Banded deep-sea spiny shrimp. b, Deep-sea shrimp. c, Huxley's scissor-foot shrimp. d, Deep-sea armored shrimp.

2013, Aug. 8   Litho.   Perf. 14
3494   A1181   10p Block of 4, #a-d   4.50 4.00
e. Souvenir sheet of 4, #3494a-3494d   4.50 4.50

Printed in sheets of 16.

Mariano Ponce (1863-1918), Writer — A1182

2013, Sept. 5   Litho.   Perf. 14
3495   A1182   10p multi   1.00 .60

Printed in sheets of 10.

Boysen Paints, 60th Anniv. A1183

No. 3496: a, Tree, logo for Knoxout Air Cleaning Paint. b, Boysen logo, eagle with paint can, house. c, Houses, anniversary emblem. d, Map of Philippines, logo for Nation Quality Paint.
40p, Eagle with paint can, horiz.

2013, Sept. 9   Litho.   Perf. 14
3496   A1183   10p Block of 4, #a-d   5.00 4.50
Souvenir Sheet
3497   A1183   40p multi + 2 labels   6.00 6.00

No. 3497 contains one 80x30mm stamp.

Gerardo "Gerry" De León (1913-81), Film Actor and Director — A1184

2013, Sept. 12   Litho.   Perf. 14
3498   A1184   10p multi   1.00 .50

50th Fish Conservation Week — A1185

No. 3499 — Winning paintings of endangered species in Bureau of Fisheries and Aquatic Resources art contest: a, Green Sea Turtle with Giant Manta Ray and Hammerhead Sharks, by Jaylord G. Aligway. b, Tabios (dwarf pygmy goby), by Jon Carlos A. Tabios. c, Butanding (whale shark), by Bernardo V. Vergara, Jr.
40p, Tabios, by Tabios, diff.

2013, Oct. 14   Litho.   Perf. 14
3499   Horiz. strip of 3   3.50 3.00
a.-c. A1185 10p Any single   1.00 .70
Souvenir Sheet
3500   A1185   40p multi + label   5.00 4.50

Motorized Tricycles — A1186

No. 3501 — Tricycle from: a, Cabadbaran. b, Puerto Princesa. c, Ozamiz City. d, Bukidnon.

2013, Nov. 13   Litho.   Perf. 14
3501   A1186   10p Block of 4, #a-d   4.50 4.00
e. Souvenir sheet of 4, #3501a-3501d   5.00 5.00

Printed in sheets of 16.

Souvenir Sheet

Rodolfo "Dolphy" Vera Quizon (1928-2012), Comedian — A1187

Litho. With Foil Application
2013, Nov. 23   Perf. 14
3502   A1187   100p multi + label   13.00 13.00

A1188

Christmas — A1189

No. 3503 — Paintings by Filipino members of Association of Mouth and Foot Painting Artists: a, The Family, by Jovita Sasutona (1/4). b, The Nativity Star, by Sasutona (2/4). c, Christmas Lantern, by Amado Dulnuan (3/4). d, Christmas at the Lake, by Bernard Pesigan (4/4).
No. 3504: a, Fruit Stand, by Sasutona. b, Lantern Maker, by Sasutona. c, Season Delight, by Sasutona.

2013, Nov. 25   Litho.   Perf. 14
3503   A1188   10p Block of 4, #a-d   5.00 4.50
Souvenir Sheet
3504   A1189   10p Sheet of 3, #a-c   4.50 4.00

Andrés Bonifacio (1863-97), Founder of Katipunan Revolutionary Movement — A1190

No. 3505 — Winning designs in art contest: a, Dangal at Kabayanihan, by Roderick C. Macutay (1/4). b, Bonifacio Monument, by Marrion Dabalos (2/4). c, Dangal at Kabayanihan, by John Mark Nathaniel Trancales (3/4). d, Bonifacio, the Great Plebeian, by Julius R. Satparam (4/4).
No. 3506 — 150th anniversary emblem and vignette of: a, 30p, #3505a. b, 35p, #3505b. c, 40p, #3505d. d, 45p, #3505c.

2013, Nov. 30   Litho.   Perf. 14
3505   A1190   10p Block of 4, #a-d   4.50 4.00
Miniature Sheet
3506   A1190   Sheet of 4, #a-d   18.00 18.00

No. 3506 contains four 30x80mm stamps.

New Year 2014 (Year of the Horse) — A1191

Chinese characters and: 10p, Horse's head. 30p, Horse.

2013, Dec. 2   Litho.   Perf. 14
3507-3508   A1191   Set of 2   4.50 4.00
3508a   Souvenir sheet of 4, 2 each #3507-3508   11.00 11.00

Printed in sheets of 10.

Philippine Deposit Insurance Corporation, 50th Anniv. — A1192

2013, Dec. 5   Litho.   Perf. 14
3509   A1192   10p multi   1.00 .60

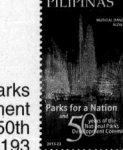

National Parks Development Committee, 50th Anniv. — A1193

2013, Dec. 5   Litho.   Perf. 14
3510 A1193 20p multi   2.25 1.50

Parts of the design are covered with ink that glows in the dark.

Diplomatic Relations Between Nigeria and the Philippines, 50th Anniv. — A1194

No. 3511 — Flags of Philippines and Nigeria and: a, 10p, Coat of arms of Nigeria, daisies. b, 45p, Coat of arms of the Philippines, sampaguita flowers.

2013, Dec. 20   Litho.   Perf. 14
3511 A1194 Horiz. pair, #a-b   6.50 5.00

Printed in sheets of 10.
See Nigeria Nos. 853-854.

Saint Louis College, San Fernando, 50th Anniv. — A1195

2014, Jan. 20   Litho.   Perf. 14
3512 A1195 10p multi   1.00 .60

Valentine's Day — A1196

2014, Jan. 27   Litho.   Perf. 14
3513 A1196 10p multi   1.00 .60

Souvenir Sheet

New Year 2014 (Year of the Horse) A1197

No. 3514: a, 50p, Snake (40x30mm). b, 50p, Goat (40x30mm). c, 100p, Horse (50x40mm).

Perf. 13¼x13x13¼x13¼ (#3514a), 13¼x13¼x13¼x13 (#3514b), 13 (#3514c)
Litho., Litho. & Embossed With Foil Application (100p)
2014, Jan. 31
3514 A1197 Sheet of 3, #a-c 25.00 25.00

Selection of Megan Lynne Young as Miss World 2013 A1198

No. 3515 — Young with: a, 30p, Arms not visible. b, 40p, Arms visible.
No. 3516: a, Like #3515a. b, Like #3515b.

2014, Feb. 24   Litho.   Perf. 14
3515 A1198 Horiz. pair, #a-b   8.50 7.50
Souvenir Sheet
Litho. & Embossed With Foil Application
3516 A1198 50p Sheet of 2,
#a-b   14.00 14.00
No. 3515 printed in sheets of 8.

Main Post Office, Manila A1199

2014, Feb. 24   Litho.   Perf. 14
3517 A1199 35p multi   8.00 8.00

No. 3517 was printed in sheets of six that sold for 250p. The right half of the stamp could be personalized. See Nos. 3703, 3763 and the footnotes below Nos. 3527 and 3550.

Alpha Phi Beta Fraternity at University of Philippines, 75th Anniv. — A1200

No. 3518: a, 75th anniv. emblem (1/4). b, 75th anniv. emblem, University of the Philippines emblem, statue (2/4). c, Statue, University building and emblem, fraternity members, 75th anniv. emblem (3/4). d, Silhouettes of statues, 75th anniv. emblem (4/4).

2014, Mar. 8   Litho.   Perf. 14
3518 A1200 10p Block of 4, #a-d 5.00 4.00

Election of Pope Francis, 1st Anniv. — A1201

2014, Mar. 21   Litho.   Perf. 14
3519 A1201 40p multi   5.00 3.00

Printed in sheets of 9.
See Vatican City Nos. 1553-1556.

Beach on Boracay Island A1202

2014, Mar. 28   Litho.   Perf. 14
3520 A1202 15p multi   8.00 8.00

No. 3520 was printed in sheets of six that sold for 250p. The right half of the stamp could be personalized.

Watchtowers — A1203

No. 3521 — Watchtower at: a, Luna, La Union Province. b, Panglao, Bohol Province. c, Oslob, Cebu Province. d, Narvacan, Ilocos Sur Province.

No. 3522, vert. — Watchtower at: a, Boljoon, Cebu Province. b, Bantay, Ilocos Sur Province. c, Samboan, Cebu Province. d, Tabaco, Albay Province.

Litho. & Silk-Screened
2014, Mar. 28   Perf. 14
3521 A1203 25p Block of 4,
#a-d   12.00 12.00
Miniature Sheet
3522 A1203 25p Sheet of 4,
#a-d   14.00 14.00

Central Luzon State University, 50th Anniv. — A1204

No. 3523 — 50th anniv. emblem and: a, Science and Technology Centrum. b, José Rizal.

2014, Apr. 4   Litho.   Perf. 14
3523 A1204 10p Horiz. pair, #a-b 2.00 1.60

Souvenir Sheets

2014 Canonization of Popes — A1205

Designs: No. 3524, 200p, Pope John XXIII. No. 3525, 200p, Pope John Paul II.

Litho. & Embossed
2014, Apr. 27   Perf.
3524-3525 A1205 Set of 2 48.00 45.00

Philippine Charity Sweepstakes Office, 80th Anniv. — A1206

No. 3526: a, People at Lotto office (1/2). b, Family, sweepstakes office vehicle (2/2).

2014, Apr. 28   Litho.   Perf. 14
3526 A1206 10p Horiz. pair, #a-b 2.00 1.60

Minister Felix Y. Manalo (1886-1963) and Iglesia ni Cristo Central Temple, Quezon City — A1207

2014, May 10   Litho.   Perf. 13½
3527 A1207 10p multi   1.20 .80

Printed in sheets of 10.
Three miniature sheets of 6 were issued on July 27, 2014, for the Iglesia ni Cristo centennial. The right half of each stamp could be personalized. One sheet bore design No. A1207 on the left half of each stamp. The other two bore images of the Iglesia ni Cristo Central Office Complex and the Philippine Arena. These sheets were only sold through the Iglesia ni Cristo and were not sold through any post office.

Teresita "Mama Sita" Reyes (1917-98), Restauranteur — A1208

No. 3528 — Reyes, various foods, with background colors of: a, Orange (1/4). b, Lilac (2/4). c, Blue green (3/4). d, Orange and red (4/4).

2014, May 11   Litho.   Perf. 14
3528 A1208 10p Block of 4, #a-d 4.50 4.00

San Bartolome Parish, 400th Anniv. — A1209

2014, May 17   Litho.   Perf. 14
3529 A1209 20p multi   2.00 1.50

Heritage Month A1210

No. 1210 — Various textile designs numbered: a, (1/4). b, (2/4). c, (3/4). d, (4/4). 100p, Weaver.

Litho. & Silk-Screened
2014, May 30   Perf. 14
3530 A1210 30p Block of 4,
#a-b   15.00 15.00
Souvenir Sheet
Perf. 13½x13¾
3531 A1210 100p multi   24.00 24.00

No. 3530 printed in sheets of 8.
No. 3531 contains one 50x35mm stamp.

Diplomatic Relations Between the Philippines and Germany, 60th Anniv. — A1211

No. 3532 — Flags of the Philippines and Germany and: a, 20p, Brandenburg Gate, Berlin. b, 40p, People Power Revolution Monument, Quezon City.

2014, June 25   Litho.   Perf. 14
3532 A1211 Horiz. pair, #a-b   7.00 6.00

Printed in sheets of 10.

Aquatic Flowers A1212

No. 3533: a, Lotus. b, Amazon lily. c, Water lily. d, Water hyacinth.
40p, Marsh marigold, horiz.

2014, June 27 Litho. Perf. 14
3533 A1212 10p Block of 4, #a-d 4.50 4.00
Souvenir Sheet
3534 A1212 40p multi 5.50 5.00
No. 3533 printed in sheets of 8.

Kapatagan Municipal Building, Seal of Kapatagan, Cathedral Falls — A1213

2014, July 5 Litho. Perf. 14
3535 A1213 10p multi 1.00 .60
Kapatagan, Lanao del Norte Province, 65th anniv.

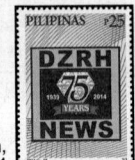
DZRH Radio Station, 75th Anniv. — A1214

2014, July 15 Litho. Perf. 14
3536 A1214 25p multi 2.50 1.50

Apolinario Mabini (1864-1903), Prime Minister — A1215

No. 3537 — 150th anniv. emblem and depiction of Mabini by: a, Pinky Ludovice. b, Kenneth V. Cantimbuhan. c, Julius R. Satparam.
40s, Mabini, by Dylan Ray A. Talon.

2014, July 23 Litho. Perf. 14
3537 Horiz. strip of 3 4.00 3.50
a.-c. A1215 10p Any single 1.00 .80
Souvenir Sheet
3538 A1215 40p multi + label 6.00 5.00
No. 3537 printed in sheets of 9.

ISO 9001: 2008 Certification of University of Mindanao — A1216

No. 3539: a, Bolton Campus. b, University emblem and check mark.

2014, July 27 Litho. Perf. 14
3539 A1216 10p Horiz. pair, #a-b 2.00 1.60

Paintings by Pres. Corazon C. Aquino (1933-2009) — A1217

No. 3540: a, Enchanting Blossoms. b, Overflowing with Good Wishes. c, Blooms of Unity. d, Fifth Painting.
100p, Rosary and Roses.

2014, Aug. 1 Litho. Perf. 14
3540 A1217 25p Block of 4, #a-d 12.00 10.00
Souvenir Sheet
Perf. 13½x13¾
3541 A1217 100p multi 14.00 12.00
Nos. 3540-3541 are impregnated with a rose scent. No. 3540 was printed in sheets of 8. No. 3541 contains one 50x35mm stamp.

Scouting in the Philippines, Cent. — A1218

No. 3542 — Centennial emblem and emblem of Philippines Scouting and: a, Boy Scout in Action Monument. b, Old and new Boy Scout National Headquarters.
30p, Emblems, Boy Scout in Action Monument, map of Philippines, vert.

2014, Aug. 30 Litho. Perf. 14
3542 A1218 10p Horiz. pair, #a-b 2.50 2.00
Souvenir Sheet
3543 A1218 30p multi 4.00 3.50
No. 3543 contains one 30x80mm stamp.

National Teachers' Month — A1219

2014, Sept. 5 Litho. Perf. 14
3544 A1219 10p multi 1.00 .60

University of San Carlos College of Engineering, 75th Anniv. — A1220

2014, Sept. 8 Litho. Perf. 14
3545 A1220 10p multi 1.00 .50

Waterfalls — A1221

No. 3546: a, Balagbag Falls. b, Merloquet Falls. c, Tinago Falls. d, Asik-asik Falls.
40p, Tinuy-an Falls.

Perf. 13½x13¾
2014, Sept. 22 Litho.
3546 A1221 10p Block of 4, #a-d 5.00 4.50
Souvenir Sheet
3547 A1221 40p multi 5.00 5.00
No. 3546 was printed in sheets of 16. No. 3547 contains one 100x35mm stamp.

National Family Week A1222

No. 3548 — Winning art in stamp design contest by: a, Leah Anne Rulloda. b, Maria Joannes R. Puno.

2014, Sept. 26 Litho. Perf. 14
3548 A1222 10p Horiz. pair, #a-b 2.00 1.60

Quezon City, 75th Anniv. A1223

No. 3549: a, Tandang Sora Shrine. b, Emilio Jacinto Shrine. c, North EDSA Shopping Mall. d, University of Philippines Ayala Techno Hub.
100p, Quezon Memorial Circle, horiz.

2014, Oct. 12 Litho. Perf. 13¾x13½
3549 A1223 10p Block of 4, #a-d 7.50 6.00
Litho. & Silk-Screened (Margin With Foil Application)
Souvenir Sheet
Perf. 13¾ Horiz.
3550 A1223 100p multi 14.00 14.00
No. 3549 was printed in sheets of 16.
No. 3550 contains one 86x50mm stamp.
A miniature sheet of 6 stamps showing a fountain on the left half, and being personalizable on the right of each stamp, was issued for the 75th anniversary of Quezon City. However, only 112 sheets were available at the post office. Each stamp has a face value of 10p. Sheets were sold for 250p.

Leyte Gulf Landing, 70th Anniv. — A1224

2014, Oct. 20 Litho. Perf. 14
3551 A1224 10p multi 1.20 .70

Christmas — A1225

No. 3552: a, Holy Family (1/4). b, Carolers (2/4). c, Respect for elders (3/4). d, Christmas Eve feast (4/4).

2014, Oct. 30 Litho. Perf. 14
3552 A1225 10p Block of 4, #a-d 5.00 4.50
Printed in sheets of 16.

Growing Plant — A1226

2014, Nov. 8 Litho. Perf. 14
3553 A1226 10p multi 1.00 .60
Philippine recovery after Typhoon Haiyan.

First Philippine Postage Stamps, 160th Anniv. — A1227

No. 3554 and 3555
Philippines #1-2, 4-5, with large illustration of: a, #1. b, #2. c, #4. d, #5.
Perf. 13½x13¾
2014, Nov. 10 Litho.
3554 A1227 10p Block of 4, #a-d 5.50 5.00
3555 A1227 20p Sheet of 4, #a-d 10.00 10.00
National Stamp Collecting Month. Printed in sheets of 16.

Filipino-Chinese General Chamber of Commerce, 110th Anniv. — A1228

No. 3556: a, Traders, ship, abacuses (1/2). b, People with computer, city skyline, airplane (2/2).

2014, Nov. 19 Litho. Perf. 14
3556 A1228 10p Horiz. pair, #a-b 1.75 1.75
a. Miniature sheet of 8 12.00 12.00

Festival Masks and Facial Decorations — A1229

No. 3557: a, Moriones Festival mask. b, Higantes Festival mask. c, Pintados Festival face decoration.
100p, Masskara Festival mask, horiz.

2014, Nov. 22 Litho. Perf. 14
3557 Horiz. strip of 3 3.50 3.00
a.-c. A1229 10p Any single 1.00 .80
Litho. & Silk-Screened
Souvenir Sheet
3558 A1229 100p multi 12.00 12.00
No. 3557 was printed in sheets of 12.
No. 3558 contains one 80x30mm stamp.

New Year 2015 (Year of the Goat) — A1229a

Designs: 10p, Head of goat. 30p, Goat.

2014, Nov. 24 Litho. Perf. 14
3558A-3558B A1229a Set of 2 5.00 4.00
3558Bc Souvenir sheet of 4, 2 each #3558A-3558B 11.00 11.00
Printed in sheets of 10.

Claudio Teehankee (1918-89), Chief Justice — A1230

2014, Nov. 27   Litho.   Perf. 14
3559 A1230 10p multi   1.00 .60

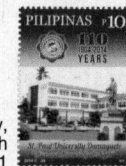

St. Paul University, Dumaguete City, 110th Anniv. — A1231

2014, Dec. 8   Litho.   Perf. 14
3560 A1231 10p multi   1.00 .60

National Anti-Corruption Day — A1232

2014, Dec. 9   Litho.   Perf. 14
3561 A1232 10p multi   1.00 .80

Shell Oil in the Philippines, Cent. — A1233

No. 3562: a. Shell Tabangao Refinery, 1960s (1/4). b, Shell Tabangao Refinery, 2014 (2/4). c, Shell retail station, 1930s (3/4). d, Shell retail station, 2014 (4/4).

Litho. With Foil Application
2014, Dec. 13   Perf. 13½x13¼
3562 A1233 25p Block of 4,
    #a-d   12.00 10.00
Printed in sheets of 8.

Severino Montano (1915-80), Playwright A1234

2015, Jan. 3   Litho.   Perf. 14
3563 A1234 10p multi   1.00 .60

A1235

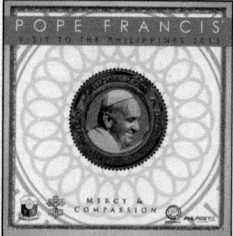

Visit of Pope Francis to the Philippines — A1236

No. 3564 — Winning art in Pope Francis stamp design contest by: a, Bryan Michael Bunag (1/4). b, Dave Arjay Tan (2/4). c, Salvador Banares, Jr. (3/4). d, Mark Leo Maac (4/4). 100p, Pope Francis.

2015   Litho.   Perf. 14
3564 A1235 10p Block of 4,
    #a-d   5.00 4.50

Litho. & Embossed With Foil Application
Souvenir Sheet
Perf.
3565 A1236 200p multi   25.00 22.00
Issued: No. 3564, 1/8; No. 3565, 1/12.

St. Valentine's Day — A1237

No. 3566 — Hearts and: a, Cupid (1/4). b, Boy and girl (2/4). c, Bride and groom (3/4). d, Elderly couple (4/4).

2015, Jan. 14   Litho.   Perf. 14
3566   Horiz. strip of 4   5.00 4.00
a.-d.   A1237 10p Any single   .80 .80
Printed in sheets of 16.

Open Doors Monument, Rishon LeZion, Israel, Flags of Philippines and Israel — A1238

2015, Jan. 27   Litho.   Perf. 14
3567 A1238 35p multi   4.00 3.00
See Israel No. 2048.

Laua-an, Cent. — A1239

2015, Jan. 31   Litho.   Perf. 14
3568 A1239 10p multi   1.00 .80

Fruit — A1240

Designs: No. 3569, Bananas. No. 3570, Black plums. 3p, Mangos. No. 3572, Papayas. No. 3573, Aratiles fruit. No. 3574, Pineapples. No. 3575, Rose apples. 13p, Lanzones. No. 3577, Santols. No. 3578, Strawberries. 25p, Custard apples. No. 3580, Soursops. No. 3581, Ramboutaniers. No. 3582, Avocados. No. 3583, Jocotes. No. 3584, Cashew fruit. No. 3585, Johey oaks.

Perf. 13½, 12¾ (#3570, 3573, 3575, 3578, 3581, 3583, 3585)
2015   Litho.

3569	A1240	1p multi	.60	.25
3570	A1240	1p multi	.60	.25
3571	A1240	3p multi	.80	.25
3572	A1240	5p multi	1.00	.25
3573	A1240	5p multi	1.00	.25
3574	A1240	10p multi	1.25	.40
3575	A1240	10p multi	1.50	.40
3576	A1240	13p multi	1.50	.70
3577	A1240	20p multi	2.00	1.00
3578	A1240	20p multi	2.00	1.00
3579	A1240	25p multi	2.50	1.25
3580	A1240	30p multi	3.00	1.50
3581	A1240	30p multi	3.00	1.50
3582	A1240	40p multi	4.00	2.00
3583	A1240	40p multi	4.00	2.00

Size: 43x43mm

3584	A1240	100p multi	10.00	5.00
3585	A1240	100p multi	10.00	5.00
Nos. 3569-3585 (17)			48.75	23.00

Issued: Nos. 3569, 3584, 3/12; Nos. 3570, 3585, 12/15; 3p, 13p, 25p, No. 3580, 2/10; Nos. 3572, 3577, 2/6; Nos. 3573, 3575, 3578, 12/10; Nos. 3574, 3582, 2/4; Nos. 3581, 3583, 12/11.
See Nos. 3651-3660, 3714-3718.

Salud S. Tesoro (1915-2000), Business Entrepreneur A1241

2015, Feb. 6   Litho.   Perf. 13¾x13½
3586 A1241 10p multi   1.00 .60

University of the Philippines College of Dentistry, Cent. — A1242

2015, Feb. 6   Litho.   Perf. 14
3587 A1242 10p multi   1.00 .50

University of Saint Louis, Baguio, 50th Anniv. — A1243

2015, Feb. 11   Litho.   Perf. 14
3588 A1243 10p multi   1.00 .50

Lamberto V. Avellana (1915-91), Film Director — A1244

2015, Feb. 12   Litho.   Perf. 14
3589 A1244 10p multi   1.00 .50

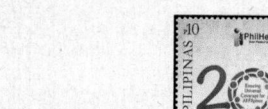

Philippine Health Insurance Corporation, 20th Anniv. — A1245

2015, Feb. 14   Litho.   Perf. 14
3590 A1245 10p multi   1.00 .50

Souvenir Sheet

New Year 2015 (Year of the Goat) A1246

No. 3514: a, 50p, Horse (40x30mm). b, 50p, Monkey (40x30mm). c, 100p, Goat (50x40mm).

Perf. 13¼x13x13¼x13¼ (#3591a), 13¼x13¼x13¼x13 (#3591b), 13 (#3591c)
Litho., Litho. & Embossed With Foil Application (100p)
2015, Feb. 19
3591 A1246   Sheet of 3, #a-c   38.00 38.00

Liceo de Cagayan University, Cagayan de Oro City, 60th Anniv. — A1247

2015, Feb. 24   Litho.   Perf. 14
3592 A1247 10p multi   1.00 .50

Philpost Type of 2013
Perf. 13½x13¼
2015, Mar. 20   Litho.
Denomination Color
3593 A1177 10p brown   1.00 .40
3594 A1177 15p gray olive   1.50 .60

Visit the Philippines Year — A1248

Perf. 13¾x13½
2015, Mar. 25   Litho.
3595 A1248 10p multi   1.00 .60

Dragonflies — A1249

No. 3596: a, Beautiful demoiselle. b, Small red damselfly. c, Golden-ringed dragonfly. d, Blue-tailed damselfly. e, White-legged damselfly. f, Emperor dragonfly. g, Club-tailed dragonfly. h, Ruddy darter. i, Halloween pennant.
40p, Broad-bodied chaser.

2015, Mar. 27   Litho.   Perf. 14
3596 A1249 10p Sheet of 9,
    #a-i   12.00 12.00

Souvenir Sheet
Perf. 13½x13¾
3597 A1249 40p multi + label   6.00 5.00
No. 3597 contains one 50x35mm stamp.

A1250

Discovery of Santo Niño Icon of Cebu, 450th Anniv. — A1251

2015, Apr. 20   Litho.   Perf. 14
3598 A1250 10p multi   1.00   .50

Souvenir Sheet

**Litho. & Embossed, Sheet Margin
Litho. & Embossed With Foil
Application
Perf. 13¼**

3599 A1251 200p gold & multi 28.00 28.00

Philippine Economic
Zone Authority, 20th
Anniv. — A1252

2015, Apr. 20   Litho.   Perf. 14
3600 A1252 10p multi   1.00   .50

Souvenir Sheet

**Litho. & Embossed With Foil
Application
Perf.**

3601 A1252 200p Emblem,
        diff.   22.00 22.00

No. 3601 contains one 38mm diameter
stamp.

Emmanuel
"Manny"
Pacquiao, Boxer
and
Politician — A1253

2015, Apr. 20   Litho.   Perf. 14
3602 A1253 10p multi   1.50   .80

Souvenir Sheet
Perf. 13½x13¾

3603 A1253 40p Pacquiao, diff. 6.00 5.00

No. 3603 contains one 50x35mm stamp.

Philippine Children's
Medical Center, 35th
Anniv. — A1254

2015, Apr. 20   Litho.   Perf. 14
3604 A1254 10p multi   1.00   .50

Miniature Sheet

Mythical Creatures — A1255

No. 3605: a, Nuno sa Punso. b, Sirena. c, Si
Malakas at Si Maganda. d, Diwata (Maria
Sinukuan).

2015, Apr. 24   Litho.   Perf. 14
3605 A1255 10p Sheet of 4,
                  #a-d   15.00 15.00

Taipei 2015 Intl. Stamp Exhibition. No. 3605
was sold for 150p at the date of issue.

City of San Pablo, 75th Anniv. of
Chartering — A1256

No. 3606: a, Municipal Building. b,
Sampaloc Lake.

2015, May 7   Litho.   Perf. 14
3606 A1256 10p Horiz. pair, #a-b 2.00 1.60

Hibiscus
Varieties
A1257

No. 3607 — Variety named: a, Goria. b, Nay
Isa. c, Tandang Sora. d, Nazaria.
No. 3608 — Variety named: a, Emerita V.
de Guzman. b, Helen L. Valmayor. c, Gelia T.
Castillo. d, Dolores A. Ramirez.

2015, May 12   Litho.   Perf. 14
3607 A1257 10p Block of 4, #a-d 4.50 4.00
3608 A1257 10p Sheet of 4, #a-
              d, + 2 labels   5.00 5.00

Romblon State
University,
Cent. — A1258

2015, May 22   Litho.   Perf. 14
3609 A1258 10p multi   1.00   .50

Archdiocese of Jaro, 150th
Anniv. — A1259

No. 3610: a, Jaro Cathedral. b, Nuestra
Señora de la Candelaria icon.

2015, May 27   Litho.   Perf. 14
3610 A1259 10p Horiz. pair, #a-b 2.00 1.60

Bilateral Relations Between the
Philippines and Finland, 60th
Anniv. — A1260

No. 3611 — Flags of the Philippines and
Finland and: a, 10p, Brown bear. b, 40p, Philippine tamaraw.

2015, June 3   Litho.   Perf. 14
3611 A1260 Horiz. pair, #a-b   6.00 5.00

Ateneo de Naga University, Naga City,
75th Anniv. — A1261

No. 3612: a, Emblem. b, University building.

2015, June 5   Litho.   Perf. 14
3612 A1261 10p Horiz. pair, #a-b 2.00 1.60

Diplomatic Relations Between
Philippines and People's Republic of
China, 40th Anniv. — A1262

2015, June 9   Litho.   Perf. 14
3613 A1262 30p multi   3.50 2.50

Kites
A1263

No. 3614 — Various kites numbered: a,
1/10. b, 2/10. c, 3/10. d, 4/10. e, 5/10. f, 6/10.
g, 7/10. h, 8/10. i, 9/10. j, 10/10.
40p, Kites.

2015, June 23   Litho.   Perf. 14
3614 A1263 10p Sheet of 10,
                  #a-j   12.00 12.00

Souvenir Sheet
Perf. 13¾x13½

3615 A1263 40p multi   6.00 5.00

No. 3615 contains one 35x50mm stamp.

City of San Carlos, 55th Anniv. of
Chartering — A1264

No. 3616: a, City Hall. b, Pinta Flores
Festival.

2015, July 1   Litho.   Perf. 14
3616 A1264 15p Horiz. pair, #a-b 3.00 2.40

Paintings of Flowers by Pres. Corazon
A. Aquino (1933-2009) — A1265

No. 3617: a, Harmony of Flowers (1/4). b,
Blue and Green Sea of Flowers (2/4). c, Valley
of Flowers (3/4). d, Flowers by Forest Hills
(4/4).
120p, Pink Flowers in a Vase, vert.

2015, July 28 Litho. Perf. 13½x13¾
3617 A1265 30p Block of 4,
                  #a-d   15.00 15.00

Souvenir Sheet
Perf. 13¾x13½

3618 A1265 120p multi + label 13.00 11.00

No. 3617 printed in sheets of 8.

Flags and Emblem of
Association of
Southeast Asian
Nations — A1266

2015, Aug. 8   Litho.   Perf. 13¼
3619 A1266 13p multi   1.50 1.20

See Brunei No. 656, Burma Nos. 417-418,
Cambodia No. 2428, Indonesia No. 2428,
Laos No. 1906, Malaysia No. 1562; Singapore
No. 1742, Thailand No. 2875, Viet Nam No.
3529.

Teresita "Mama Sita" Reyes (1917-98),
Restauranteur — A1267

No. 3620 — Reyes and: a, Fish, fruit and
vegetables (2/3). b, Basket and blue swirls
(3/3). c, Foods and stars (1/3).

Perf. 13¾x13½
2015, Aug. 24   Litho.
3620 A1267 10p Strip of 3, #a-c 3.00 2.50

Printed in sheets of 9.

Bureau of
Immigration,
75th Anniv.
A1268

2015, Sept. 4 Litho. Perf. 13½x13¾
3621 A1268 30p multi   3.00 2.50

Pres. Elpidio Quirino
(1890-1956)
A1269

2015, Sept. 5 Litho. Perf. 13¾x13½
3622 A1269 15p multi   1.50   .70

N. V. M.
Gonzales (1915-
99),
Writer — A1270

2015, Sept. 8   Litho.   Perf. 14
3623 A1270 10p multi   1.00   .60

Bandera Newspaper,
25th Anniv. — A1271

Perf. 13¾x13½
2015, Sept. 10   Litho.
3624 A1271 15p multi   1.50   .90

Manila
Observatory,
150th
Anniv. — A1272

2015, Sept. 25   Litho.   Perf. 14
3625 A1272 15p multi   1.50   .90

General Miguel
Malvar (1865-
1911)
A1273

2015, Sept. 27   Litho.   Perf. 14
3626 A1273 10p multi   1.00   .60

**San Miguel Brewery, 125th Anniv.
A1274**

No. 3627: a, Brewery building. b, 125th
anniversary emblem.
40p, 125th anniversary emblem, vert.

2015, Sept. 29　　Litho.　　Perf. 14
3627 A1274 15p Horiz. pair, #a-b　3.00 2.50
**Souvenir Sheet
Perf. 13¾x13½**
3628 A1274 40p multi　　　　　5.00 4.00
No. 3628 contains one 35x50mm stamp.

**Western Union in the Philippines, 25th
Anniv. — A1275**

No. 3629 — Western Union emblem and: a,
Various Filipinos. b, Text, "25 Years of Moving
the Filipino for Better."

Perf. 13½x13¾
2015, Sept. 30　　　　　　　Litho.
3629 A1275 25p Horiz. pair, #a-b　5.00 4.00

**Mahaguyog
Festival — A1276**

2015, Oct. 2　　Litho.　　Perf. 14
3630 A1276 10p multi　　　　　1.00 .60

**Manuel Conde
(1915-85), Film
Director — A1277**

2015, Oct. 15　　Litho.　　Perf. 14
3631 A1277 10p multi　　　　　1.00 .60

**2015 Asian-Pacific
Economic Cooperation
Summit, Manila — A1278**

Perf. 13¾x13½
2015, Nov. 10　　　　　　　Litho.
3632 A1278 30p multi　　　　　3.50 2.50

Miniature Sheet

**National Stamp Collecting
Month — A1279**

No. 3633: a, Boy holding stamp. b, Boy
holdind stamp album. c, Girl holding stamps.
d, Man holding stamps and magnifying glass.

2015, Nov. 10　　Litho.　　Perf. 14
Self-Adhesive
3633 A1279 15p Sheet of 4, #a-d　7.00 7.00

Miniature Sheet

Wildlife
A1280

No. 3634: a, Vizaysa flowerpecker. b, Philippine sail-fin lizard. c, Philippine pangolin anteater. d, Freshwater purple crab.

2015, Nov. 11　　Litho.　　Perf. 14
3634 A1280 15p Sheet of 4, #a-d　7.00 7.00

Christmas — A1281

No. 3635 — Children's art depicting Christmas tree by: a, Kobie Trambulo (2/4). b, Ver-
nice Prado (3/4). c, Lomi Capili (4/4). d, Javee
Fua (1/4).
No. 3636 — Children's art depicting Christmas lanterns by: a, Cedric Chua. b, Julius
Cabuang. c, Thridy Cabading.

2015, Nov. 25　　Litho.　　Perf. 14
3635 A1281 10p Block or strip of
　　　　　　　4, #a-d　　　　　9.00 8.00
Souvenir Sheet
3636 A1281 10p Sheet of 3, #a-c　4.00 3.00

**Office of the
Government
Corporate
Counsel,
80th Anniv.
A1282**

2015, Dec. 1　Litho.　Perf. 13½x13¾
3637 A1282 10p multi　　　　　1.00 .60

**New Year 2016
(Year of the
Monkey) — A1283**

Designs: 10p, Head of monkey. 30p,
Monkey.

2015, Dec. 1　　Litho.　　Perf. 14
3638-3639 A1283　Set of 2　　5.00 4.00
3639a　　　Souvenir sheet of 4, 2
　　　　　　each #3638-3639　11.00 11.00
Printed in sheets of 10.

**Philippine Daily
Inquirer Newspaper,
30th Anniv. — A1284**

**Litho. & Embossed With Foil
Application**
2015, Dec. 5　　　　　　　Perf. 13¼
3640 A1284 30p multi　　　　　3.50 3.00

**51st Intl. Eucharistic
Congress, Cebu
City — A1285**

Design: 15p, Emblem. 40p, Emblem and
dove's wing.

2015, Dec. 8　　Litho.　　Perf. 14
3641 A1285 15p multi　　　　　1.50 .80
**Souvenir Sheet
Perf. 13¾x13½**
3642 A1285 40p multi + label　4.50 3.50
No. 3642 contains one 35x50mm stamp.

**Cagayan
Economic Zone
Authority, 20th
Anniv. — A1286**

2015, Dec. 18　　Litho.　　Perf. 14
3643 A1286 15p multi　　　　　1.50 .80

**Commission on
Elections, 75th
Anniv. — A1287**

2015, Dec. 18　　Litho.　　Perf. 14
3644 A1287 15p multi　　　　　1.50 .80

**Liberty City
Center, 70th
Anniv. — A1288**

2015, Dec. 21　　Litho.　　Perf. 14
3645 A1288 15p multi　　　　　1.50 .80

**Pacita Madrigal
Gonzalez (1915-2008),
Senator — A1289**

2015, Dec. 22　　Litho.　　Perf. 14
3646 A1289 15p multi　　　　　1.50 .80

**Mabitac Church,
400th
Anniv. — A1290**

2016, Jan. 2　　Litho.　　Perf. 14
3647 A1290 15p multi　　　　　1.50 .80

**San Sebastian
College, Manila,
75th
Anniv. — A1291**

2016, Jan. 20　　Litho.　　Perf. 14
3648 A1291 15p multi　　　　　1.50 .80

**Court of Appeals, 80th
Anniv. — A1292**

2016, Feb. 1　　Litho.　　Perf. 14
3649 A1292 15p multi　　　　　1.50 .80

**Senate,
Cent. — A1293**

2016, Feb. 1　　Litho.　　Perf. 14
3650 A1293 15p multi　　　　　1.50 .80

Fruit Type of 2015

Designs: 1p, Egg fruit. 5p, Philippine wild
raspberry. No. 3653, Tangerine orange. No.
3654, Grapes. 13p, Star fruit. 14p, Pomelo.
15p, Star apple. 17p, Calamansi. 35p, Sweet
tamarind. 45p, Durian.

**Perf. 13½, 12¾ (#3653, 3655, 3657,
3659)**
2016　　　　　　　　　　　　Litho.
3651 A1240 1p multi　　　　　　.50　.25
　a.　Dated "2017"　　　　　　　.50　.25
3652 A1240 5p multi　　　　　　.50　.25
　a.　Dated "2017"　　　　　　　.50　.25
3653 A1240 12p multi　　　　　1.20　.50
3654 A1240 12p multi　　　　　1.20　.50
　a.　Dated "2017"　　　　　　　1.20　.50
3655 A1240 13p multi　　　　　1.40　.70
3656 A1240 14p multi　　　　　1.60　.80
　a.　Dated "2017"　　　　　　　1.40　.70
3657 A1240 15p multi　　　　　1.75　.80
3658 A1240 17p multi　　　　　1.75　.90
　a.　Dated "2017"　　　　　　　1.25 1.00
3659 A1240 35p multi　　　　　4.00 1.75
3660 A1240 45p multi　　　　　5.00 2.40
　a.　Dated "2017"　　　　　　　4.00 2.50
　Nos. 3651-3660 (10)　　　　18.90 8.85

Issued: 1p, 5p, No. 3654, 17p, 6/23; No.
3653, 13p, 15p, 35p, 2/2; 14p, 12/8; 45p, 6/30.
Nos. 3651a, 3652a, 3/14/17; No. 3654a,
3/29/17; Nos. 3656a, 3658a, 3/21/17; No.
3660a, 4/18/17.

**St. Valentine's
Day — A1294**

2016, Feb. 5　　Litho.　　Perf. 13½
3661 A1294 25p multi　　　　　2.50 2.00

**Tagkawayan, 75th
Anniv. — A1295**

2016, Feb. 10　　Litho.　　Perf. 14
3662 A1295 15p multi　　　　　1.50 .80

**Leprosy
Prevention and
Control
Week — A1296**

2016, Feb. 15　　Litho.　　Perf. 14
3663 A1296 15p multi　　　　　1.50 .80

Bago, 50th Anniv. — A1297

2016, Feb. 19   Litho.   *Perf. 14*
3664 A1297 15p multi   1.50 .80

Pia Alonzo Wurtzbach, 2015 Miss Universe — A1298

Wurtzbach with background color of: 15p, Gray. 40p, Pink.

2016, Apr. 17   Litho.   *Perf. 13½*
3665 A1298 15p multi   2.00 1.50

Souvenir Sheet
Litho. With Glitter Affixed
3666 A1298 40p multi   8.00 8.00

Festivals A1299

No. 3667: a, Sinulog Festival (1/4). b, Panagbenga Festival (2/4). c, Pahiyas Festival (3/4). d, Higantes Festival (4/4).

2016, Apr. 27   Litho.   *Perf. 14*
3667 A1299 15p Horiz. strip of 4,
#a-d   8.00 7.00

Printed in sheets of 16.

Heritage Month A1300

No. 3668 — Musical instruments: a, Kulintang. b, Kudyapi. c, Dabakan. d, Gangsa.
No. 3669 — Musical instruments: a, Kudlong. b, Libbit. c, Agung. d, Gabbang.

2016, May 5   Litho.   *Perf. 14*
3668 A1300 15p Block of 4, #a-d   6.00 5.00
3669 A1300 15p Sheet of 4, #a-d   6.00 6.00

No. 3668 printed in sheets of 16.

A1301

2016, May 6   Litho.   *Perf. 14*
3670 A1301 15p multi   1.50 .80

Intl. Organization for Standardization Certification of Office of the Regional Governor for Autonomous Region in Muslim Mindanao.

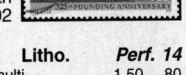

Tiaong, 325th Anniv. — A1302

2016, May 14   Litho.   *Perf. 14*
3671 A1302 15p multi   1.50 .80

A1303

Philippine National Bank, Cent. — A1304

No. 3672 — Winning art in stamp design contest by: a, Kenneth Olivar. b, Jean Christian Tormes. c, Jerico Martinez. d, Michael Montanez.
100p, Ferdinand Magellan from 100-peso banknote.

2016, June 12   Litho.   *Perf. 14*
3672 A1303 15p Block of 4,
#a-d   7.00 6.00

Souvenir Sheet
Perf. 13½
3673 A1304 100p multi   12.00 12.00

Knights of Rizal, Cent. — A1305

2016, June 19   Litho.   *Perf. 14*
3674 A1305 15p multi   2.00 1.00

Tagbilaran, 50th Anniv. — A1306

Designs: 15p, Tagbilaran City Hall. 100p, Saulog Festival.

2016, July 1   Litho.   *Perf. 14*
3675 A1306 15p multi   1.50 1.00

Souvenir Sheet
Litho. With Foil Application
3676 A1306 100p multi   20.00 20.00

Inauguration of Pres. Rodrigo Roa Duterte A1307

Size of photograph of ceremony: 17p, 43x26mm. 55p, 49x23mm.

2016, Aug. 1   Litho.   *Perf. 13½*
3677 A1307 17p multi   2.00 1.00

Souvenir Sheet
3678 A1307 55p multi   7.00 5.00

No. 3678 contains one 60x30mm stamp.

Lal-Lo, 435th Anniv. — A1308

2016, Aug. 4   Litho.   *Perf. 14*
3679 A1308 15p multi   1.50 .80

2016 Summer Olympics, Rio de Janeiro — A1309

No. 3680: a, Taekwondo. b, Boxing. c, Equestrian dressage. d, Archery. 55p, Basketball.

2016, Aug. 9   Litho.   *Perf. 14*
3680 A1309 12p Block of 4, #a-d   7.50 6.00

Souvenir Sheet
Perf. 13½
3681 A1309 55p multi + label   6.00 5.00

No. 3680 printed in sheets of 16.
No. 3681 contains one 35x50mm stamp.

Year of the Monkey Type of 2015
Miniature Sheet

No. 3682: a, Head of monkey. b, Monkey.

2016, Aug. 10   Litho.   *Perf. 14*
3682   Sheet of 4, 2 each
   #3682a-3682b   12.50 12.50
   a. A1283 12p multi   1.50 .70
   b. A1283 45p multi   3.00 2.25

Thailand 2016 Intl. Stamp Exhibition, Bangkok.

National Teacher's Month — A1310

2016, Sept. 5   Litho.   *Perf. 14*
3683 A1310 12p multi   1.20 .80

Orchids A1311

No. 3684: a, Mrs. Sander's dendrobium. b, Moth orchid (yellow background). c, Waling-waling. d, Dancing lady orchid.
No. 3685, horiz.: a, Deer antler moth orchid. b, Cattleya Hsiying rouge. c, Moth orchid (light blue background). d, Cattleya dark purple trichoglottis.

2016, Sept. 30   Litho.   *Perf. 14*
3684 A1311 12p Block of 4, #a-d   5.00 4.00

Souvenir Sheet
3685 A1311 12p Sheet of 4, #a-d   6.00 6.00

No. 3684 printed in sheets of 16.
No. 3685a "Deer" is spelled incorrectly on stamp.

Philippine Airlines, 75th Anniv. — A1312

2016, Oct. 19   Litho.   *Perf. 14*
3686 A1312 12p multi   1.20 .80

Philtrust Bank, Cent. — A1313

2016, Oct. 19   Litho.   *Perf. 14*
3687 A1313 12p multi   1.20 .80

National Stamp Collecting Month A1314

No. 3688: a, Philippines #502. b, Philippines #501. c, Philippines #500. 55p, Philippines #500-502.

2016, Oct. 21   Litho.   *Perf. 13½*
3688   Horiz. strip of 3   4.50 4.00
   a.-c. A1314 Any single   1.20 1.00

Souvenir Sheet
3689 A1314 55p multi   6.50 6.00

No. 3688 printed in sheets of 9.
No. 3689 contains one 100x35mm stamp.

Souvenir Sheet

New Year 2016 (Year of the Monkey) A1315

No. 3690: a, 75p, Goat (40x30mm). b, 75p, Rooster (40x30mm). c, 100p, Monkey (50x40mm).

Perf. 13¼x13x13¼x13¼ (#3690a), 13¼x13¼x13¼x13 (#3690b), 13 (#3690c)
Litho., Sheet Margin Litho. & Embossed With Foil Application
2016, Oct. 21
3690 A1315   Sheet of 3, #a-c 28.00 28.00

2016 Philatelpei World Stamp Exhibition, Taipei.

Diplomatic Relations Between Philippines and Portugal, 75th Anniv. — A1316

No. 3691 — Flags of Philippines and Portugal and: a, 12p, Lavender, national flower of Portugal. b, 55p, Sampaguita, national flower of Philippines.

2016, Oct. 24   Litho.   *Perf. 14*
3691 A1316   Horiz. pair, #a-b   7.50 6.00

Printed in sheets of 8.
See Portugal Nos. 3855-3856.

Philippines Securities and Exchange Commission, 80th Anniv. — A1317

2016, Nov. 11   Litho.   *Perf. 14*
3692 A1317 12p multi   1.20 .80

Dr. Sun Yat-sen (1866-1925), First President of the Republic of China — A1318

Designs: 18p, Drs. Sun Yat-sen and Mariano Ponce (1863-1918), Philippine physician and revolutionary hero. 45p, Drs. Sun Yat-sen and Ponce, diff.

2016, Nov. 12   Litho.   Perf. 14
3693 A1318 18p multi   2.00 1.50

Souvenir Sheet
Perf. 13¾x13½
3694 A1318 45p multi + label   5.50 5.00

No. 3694 contains one 35x50mm stamp.

Christmas — A1319

No. 3695 — Star lantern with "Pasko" in: a,
12p, White on red panel. b, 12p, Red on white
panel. c, 17p, White on green panel. d, 17p,
Green on white panel.

2016, Nov. 25   Litho.   Perf. 14
3695 A1319 Block of 4, #a-d   6.00 5.00

Printed in sheets of 16.

University of the
Philippines College of
Business
Administration Alumni
Association,
Cent. — A1320

2016, Dec. 4   Litho.   Perf. 14
3696 A1320 12p multi   1.20   .80

A1321

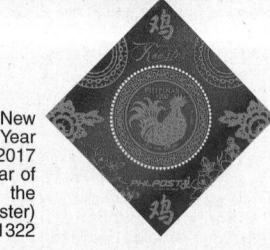

New
Year
2017
(Year of
the
Rooster)
A1322

No: 3697 — Rooster facing: a, 18p, Left. b,
45p, Right.

2016, Dec. 16   Litho.   Perf. 14
3697 A1321 Horiz. pair, #a-b   7.50 6.00

Souvenir Sheet
Litho. & Embossed With Foil
Application
Perf.
3698 A1322 200p multi   24.00 20.00

Printed in sheets of 16.

Catbalogan City,
400th
Anniv. — A1323

2016, Dec. 20   Litho.   Perf. 14
3699 A1323 18p multi   1.50   .80

Teresita "Mama Sita"
Reyes (1917-98),
Restauranteur
A1324

2016, Dec. 20   Litho.   Perf. 14
3700 A1324 18p multi   1.50   .80

10th-13th Century Items From Ayala
Museum "Gold of Ancestors"
Exhibition — A1325

No. 3701: a, Pectoral disc. b, Garuda-
shaped ear ornaments. c, Ear ornaments. d,
Kinnari.
No. 3702: a, Like #3701b. b, Like #3701c. c,
Like #3701a. d, Like #3701d.

2016, Dec. 21   Litho.   Perf. 14
3701 A1325 18p Block of 4,
             #a-d   8.00 7.00

Litho. & Embossed With Foil
Application
3702 A1325 50p Sheet of 4,
             #a-d, + 2 la-
             bels   22.00 22.00

No. 3701 printed in sheets of 16.

Main Post Office, Manila Type of
2014
2016, Dec. 23   Litho.   Perf. 14
3703 A1199 18p multi   10.00 10.00

No. 3703 was printed in sheets of six that
sold for 250p. The right half of the stamp could
be personalized.
Exists in a generic sheet of 6 with 6 different
printed labels. Value, $80.

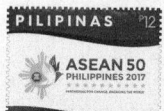

Association of
Southeast Asian
Nations, 50th
Anniv. — A1326

2017, Jan. 15   Litho.   Perf. 14
3704 A1326 12p multi   1.40   .80

In Nov. 2017, sheets of four 25p stamps of
type A1326 were printed in limited quantities
and sold only at the Philippine Postal Service
booth at ASEANPEX in Pasay City. Customers wanting to purchase these sheets could do
so only if they had purchased 500p worth of
stamps at the booth. A sheet containing four
stamps inscribed "S-27" was put on sale on
Nov. 4, a sheet containing four stamps inscribed "S-32" was put on sale on Nov. 5,
and another sheet of 4 stamps inscribed "S-
33" was put on sale on Nov. 6.

Bustos, 100th
Anniv. as
Municipality
A1327

2017, Jan. 15   Litho.   Perf. 14
3705 A1327 12p multi   1.20   .60

Santa Rosa,
225th
Anniv. — A1328

2017, Jan. 18   Litho.   Perf. 14
3706 A1328 12p multi   1.20   .60

Miss
Universe
Pageant,
Pasay
A1329

No. 3707 — Crown and: a, Philippines
#2304a. b, Philippines #2304b. c, Philippines
#3665.
100p, Philippines #2304a, 2304b, 3655.

2017, Jan. 24   Litho.   Perf. 13¾
3707   Horiz. strip of 3   10.00 8.00
  a. A1329 12p multi   1.20   .80
  b. A1329 17p multi   1.75 1.20
  c. A1329 55p multi   5.50 2.50

Souvenir Sheet
Perf. 13½
3708 A1329 100p multi   12.00 10.00

No. 3707 printed in sheets of 9.
No. 3708 contains one 60x30mm stamp.

Souvenir Sheet

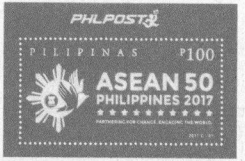

Association of Southeast Asian
Nations, 50th Anniv. — A1330

Litho. & Embossed With Foil
Application
2017, Jan. 30   Litho.   Perf. 13¼
3709 A1330 100p gold   12.00 10.00

National College
of Business and
Arts, 50th
Anniv. — A1331

2017, Feb. 2   Litho.   Perf. 14
3710 A1331 12p multi   1.20   .60

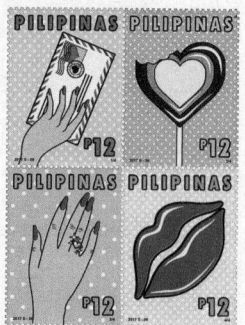

St. Valentine's Day — A1332

Designs: Nos. 3711a, 3712a, Hand holding
letter. Nos. 3711b, 3712b, Heart-shaped lolli-
pop. Nos. 3711c, 3712c, Ring on woman's
hand. Nos. 3711d, 3712d, Lips.

2017, Feb. 6   Litho.   Perf. 14
3711 A1332 12p Block of 4,
             #a-d   4.00 3.00
3712 A1332 17p Sheet of 4,
             #a-d, + 4 la-
             bels   25.00 25.00

No. 3711 printed in sheets of 8.
No. 3712 sold for 150p. Labels could be
personalized. No. 3712 was also printed with
generic labels showing Cupid, roses, heart-
shaped balloons and champagne flutes.

Cosmos Masonic
Lodge No. 8,
Manila,
Cent. — A1333

2017, Feb. 13   Litho.   Perf. 14
3713 A1333 12p multi   1.50 1.00

Fruit Type of 2015 and

Dragon
Fruit — A1334

Designs: 3p, Wild sweet sops. 23p, Bignays.
28p, Coconuts. 34p, Apples. 40p, Tamarinds.

2017   Litho.   Perf. 13½
3714 A1199 3p multi   .50   .25
3715 A1199 23p multi   2.00 1.00
3716 A1199 28p multi   2.75 1.25
3717 A1199 34p multi   3.50 1.75
3718 A1199 40p multi   4.00 2.00

Perf. 14
3719 A1334 100p multi   10.00 5.00
      Nos. 3714-3719 (6)   22.75 11.25

Issued: 3p, 100p, 3/14; 23p, 28p, 3/29; 34p,
4/18; 40p, 3/21.

Lizards
A1335

No. 3720: a, Luzon bicolored earth skink. b,
Philippine false gecko. c, Gigante limestone
gecko. d, Striped tree skink.
No. 3721: a, Emerald false gecko. b, Mar-
bled agamid lizard. c, Spotted forest dragon. d,
Mindanao water skink.

2017, Mar. 27   Litho.   Perf. 14
3720 A1335 12p Block of 4, #a-d   5.00 4.00
3721 A1335 12p Sheet of 4, #a-
             d, + 2 labels   5.00 5.00

No. 3720 printed in sheets of 16.

Philippine Postal
Corporation, 25th
Anniv. — A1336

Phipost emblem and: 12p, Main Post Office,
Manila. 55p, "25" and wreath.

2017, Apr. 3   Litho.   Perf. 14
3722 A1336 12p multi   1.20   .60

Souvenir Sheet
Litho. With Foil Application
Perf.
3723 A1336 55p dk blue & sil   6.00 5.00

No. 3723 contains one 38mm diameter
stamp.

Bataan Death March, 75th Anniv.
A1337

2017, Apr. 9   Litho.   Perf. 14
3724 A1337 17p multi   1.75 1.00

Silver Medalists at
2016 Summer
Olympics, Rio de
Janeiro — A1338

No. 3725: a, Anthony N. Villanueva, boxing. b, Mansueto B. Velasco, Jr., boxing. c, Hidilyn F. Diaz, weight lifting.
55p, Villanueva, Diaz and Velasco, horiz.

2017, Apr. 23   Litho.   Perf. 14
3725   Horiz. strip of 3   4.00 3.00
a.-c. A1338 12p Any single   1.00   .75

Souvenir Sheet
Perf. 13½
3726 A1338 55p multi   6.00 5.00

No. 3725 printed in sheets of 9. No. 3726 contains one 50x35mm stamp.

Sunsets A1339

No. 3727 — Sunset at: a, Ilocos Norte. b, Pangasinan. c, Batanes. d, Cebu.
No. 3728 — Sunset at: a, Manila. b, Camiguin. c, Zambales. d, Zamboanga.

2017, May 8   Litho.   Perf. 14
3727 A1339 12p Block or
            horiz. strip
            of 4, #a-d   5.00 4.00

Litho. With Foil Application
3728 A1339 25p Sheet of 4,
            #a-d   10.00 10.00

National Heritage Month.
No. 3727 printed in sheets of 16.

Diocese of Butuan, 50th Anniv. — A1340

2017, May 10   Litho.   Perf. 14
3729 A1340 12p multi   1.20   .60

Independence Day — A1341

No. 3730: a, Rizal Monument, Manila. b, Barasoain Church, Malolos. c, Emilio Aguinaldo Shrine, Kawit. d, Andres Bonifacio Monument, Caloocan.

Litho. With Foil Application
2017, June 12   Perf. 14
3730 A1341 12p Block of 4, #a-d 5.00 4.00
        Printed in sheets of 16.

St. Stephen's High School, Luzon, Cent. — A1342

No. 3731: a, Building and praying hands, denomination at UR. b, Building, denomination at UL.

2017, June 22   Litho.   Perf. 14
3731 A1342 12p Horiz. pair, #a-b 2.50 2.00
        Printed in sheets of 8.

Diplomatic Relations Between Philippines and France, 70th Anniv. — A1343

No. 3732 — Unnamed painting by: a, 12p, French painter Jacques Villon (1875-1963). b,

55p, Philippine painter Macario Vitalis (1898-1989).

2017, June 26   Litho.   Perf. 14
3732 A1343 Horiz. pair, #a-b 7.00 5.00
        Printed in sheets of 8.

        See France Nos. 5259-5260.

Davao del Norte Province, 50th Anniv. — A1344

2017, July 1   Litho.   Perf. 14
3733 A1344 12p multi   1.20   .60

Jasminum Sambac (National Flower) — A1345

Litho. With Foil Application
2017, Aug. 8   Perf. 14
3734 A1345 12p multi   1.50   .80
Association of Southeast Asian Nations, 50th anniv.

Snakes A1346

No. 3735: a, Philippine forest cat snake. b, Luzon forest cat snake. c, Yellow-spotted Philippine pit viper. d, Red-tailed blind snake.
No. 3736: a, Philippine variable paradise snake. b, Eastern Visayas wolf snake. c, Zig-zag-lined keelback. d, Philippine whip snake.

2017, Aug. 16   Litho.   Perf. 14
3735 A1346 12p Block of 4,
            #a-d   5.00 4.00

Litho. With Foil Application
3736 A1346 25p Sheet of 4,
            #a-d   12.00 12.00

No. 3735 printed in sheets of 16.

National Teachers Month — A1347

2017, Sept. 5   Litho.   Perf. 14
3737 A1347 12p multi   1.20   .80

Souvenir Sheet

New Year 2017 (Year of the Rooster) A1348

Litho., Sheet Margin Litho. With Foil Application
2017, Sept. 5   Perf. 13¼
3738 A1348 100p multi   12.00 12.00
2017 China International Collection Expo, Nanjing.

Pres. Ferdinand E. Marcos (1917-89) — A1349

2017, Sept. 11   Litho.   Perf. 14
3739 A1349 12p multi   1.50 1.00

Miniature Sheet

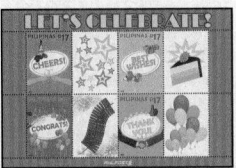

Greetings — A1350

No. 3740 — Inscriptions: a, "Cheers!" b, "Best Wishes!" c, "Congrats!" d, "Thank you!"

2017, Oct. 9   Litho.   Perf. 14
3740 A1350 17p Sheet of 4,
            #a-d, + 4 la-
            bels   15.00 15.00

No. 3740 sold for 150p, and was available with the generic labels shown or with labels that could be personalized.

Flowers A1351

No. 3741: a, Medinilla cordata. b, Begonia gutierrezii. c, Begonia cumingii. d, Hoya buotii.
No. 3742: a, Begonia oxysperma. b, Coelogyne candoonensis. c, Strongylodon macrobotrys. d, Plocoglottis lucbanensis.

2017, Oct. 16   Litho.   Perf. 14
3741 A1351 12p Block of 4, #a-d 5.00 4.00

Souvenir Sheet
3742 A1351 12p Sheet of 4, #a-
            d, + 2 labels 5.00 5.00

No. 3741 printed in sheets of 16.

Jeepneys A1352

No. 3743: a, 1943 Willys Jeep. b, 1945 Transformed Jeep. c, Decorated jeepney. d, Modern jumbo Jeep.

2017, Nov. 4   Litho.   Perf. 14
3743   Horiz. strip of 4   5.00 4.00
a.-d. A1352 12p Any single   1.00   .75

Miniature Sheet

National Flowers of Association of Southeast Asian Nations Members — A1353

No. 3744 — ASEANPEX emblem and: a, Sampauita (Philippines). b, Vanda "Miss Joaquim" (Singapore), Rumdul (Cambodia), Melati putih (Indonesia). c, Dok champa

(Laos), Ratchaphruek (Thailand), Lotus (Viet Nam). d, Padauk (Myanmar), Simpor (Brunei). Hibiscus (Malaysia).

2017, Nov. 4   Litho.   Perf. 14
3744 A1353 17p Sheet of 4,
            #a-d, + 4 la-
            bels   16.00 16.00

Association of Southeast Asian Nations, 50th anniv. No. 3744 sold for 150p, and was available with the generic labels shown or with labels that could be personalized.

Emblem of 2017 ASEANPEX, Pasay City — A1354

2017, Nov. 4   Litho.   Perf. 14
3745 A1354 17p multi + label 4.00 4.00

No. 3745 was printed in sheets of 4 + 4 labels, which sold for 150p. The sheets were available with the generic label shown or with labels that could be personalized.

Souvenir Sheet

New Year 2017 (Year of the Rooster) A1355

No. 3746: a, 75p, Monkey (40x30mm). b, 75p, Dog (40x30mm). c, 100p, Rooster (50x40mm).

Perf. 13¼x13x13¼x13¼ (#3746a), 13¼x13¼x13¼x13 (#746b), 13 (#3746c)
Litho. & Embossed With Foil Application
2017, Nov. 5
3746 A1355   Sheet of 3, #a-c 28.00 28.00
2017 ASEANPEX, Pasay City.

Postal Transportation — A1356

No. 3747: a, Galleon. b, Bagadero on horse. c, Train. d, Postman with bicycle.
55p, Two Philpost vans.

2017, Nov. 6   Litho.   Perf. 14
3747 A1356 12p Block of 4, #a-d 5.00 4.00

Souvenir Sheet
Perf. 13½x13¼
3748 A1356 55p multi   6.00 5.00

Philippine Postal Service, 250th anniv. No. 3748 contains one 60x30mm stamp.

Subic Bay Metropolitan Authority, 25th Anniv. — A1357

Designs: 12p, Family Monument. 100p, Subic Bay, 25th anniv. emblem, horiz.

2017, Nov. 24   Litho.   Perf. 14
3749 A1357 12p multi   1.00   .60

Souvenir Sheet
Perf. 13½
3750 A1357 100p multi　　　10.00 8.00
No. 3750 contains one 50x35mm stamp.

Christmas — A1358

No. 3751 — Children's art by: a, Roselyn Mahipas. b, Juan Dimata. c, Estella Benavidez. d, Jan Aton.
55p, Children's art by Rhey de Ocampo, horiz.

2017, Nov. 29　　Litho.　　Perf. 13¾
3751 A1358 12p Block or strip of
　　　4, #a-d　　　5.00 5.00

Souvenir Sheet
Perf. 13½
3752 A1358 55p multi　　　6.00 5.00
No. 3751 printed in sheets of 16. No. 3752 contains one 50x35mm stamp.

A1359

New Year 2018 (Year of the Dog) A1360

No: 3753 — Dog, with background color of: a, 12p, Light blue. b, 45p, Pink.

2017, Dec. 1　　Litho.　　Perf. 14
3753 A1359　Horiz. pair, #a-b　6.50 5.00

Souvenir Sheet
Litho. & Embossed With Foil Application
Perf.
3754 A1360 200p gold & red　20.00 20.00
No. 3753 printed in sheets of16.

A1361

Famous People — A1362

Designs: No. 3755, Nick Joaquin (1917-2004), writer. No. 3756, José Maceda (1917-2004), composer. No. 3757, Wilfrido Maria Guerrero (1911-95), playwright. No. 3758, Cesar Legaspi (1917-94), painter. No. 3759, Leonor Orosa Goquinco (1917-2005), dancer. No. 3760, Daisy Avellana (1917-2013), actress.

2017, Dec. 13　　Litho.　　Perf. 14
3755 A1361 12p multi　　　1.20 .75
3756 A1362 12p multi　　　1.20 .75
3757 A1362 12p multi　　　1.20 .75
3758 A1362 12p multi　　　1.20 .75
3759 A1362 12p multi　　　1.20 .75
3760 A1362 12p multi　　　1.20 .75
　　Nos. 3755-3760 (6)　　7.20 4.50

Apparition of the Virgin Mary at Fatima, Portugal, Cent. — A1363

No. 3761 — Inscription: a, The Apparition of Our Lady of Fatima. b, Our Lady of Fatima. c, The Miracle of the Sun. d, Lucia Dos Santos, Francisco Marto & Jacinta Marto.

2017, Dec. 14　　Litho.　　Perf. 14
3761 A1363 12p Block of 4, #a-d 5.00 5.00
　　Printed in sheets of 8.

Teresita "Mama Sita" Reyes (1917-98), Restauranteur — A1364

2017, Dec. 22　　Litho.　　Perf. 13½
3762 A1364 12p multi　　　1.00 .80

Main Post Office, Manila Type of 2014
2018, Jan. 29　　Litho.　　Perf. 14
3763 A1199 17p multi　　　10.00 10.00
No. 3763 was printed in sheets of six that sold for 250p. The right half of the stamp could be personalized. Some sheets were made available with generic images in the blank right half of the stamp. Value of sheet with generic images, \$80.

Ilocos Sur Province, 200th Anniv. A1365

No. 3764: a, Bantay Bell Tower. b, Potter. c, Pinsal Falls. d, Bessang Pass.
No. 3765: a, Calle Crisologo. b, Santa Maria Church.

2018, Feb. 8　　Litho.　　Perf. 13¾
3764 A1365 12p Block of 4, #a-
　　　d　　　4.00 3.00
Souvenir Sheet
Perf.
3765 A1365 75p Sheet of 2, #a-
　　　b　　　10.00 9.00
No. 3764 printed in sheets of 16.
No. 3765 sheet is in the shape of "200".

Miniature Sheet

Ilocos Sur Province, 200th Anniv. A1366

No. 3766: a, Bantay Bell Tower. b, Street in Vigan City at night. c, Pinsal Falls. d, Bessang Pass.

2018, Feb. 8　　Litho.　　Perf. 14
3766 A1366 17p Sheet of 4, #a-
　　　d, + 4 labels　　8.00 8.00
No. 3766 exists with blank labels that could be personalized and the printed labels shown, that could not be personalized, each of which sold for 150p.

Municipality of Mabini, Cent. — A1367

No. 3767: a, Centenary emblem. b, Underwater scene, Anilao Beach Resort.

2018, Feb. 10　　Litho.　　Perf. 14
3767 A1367 12p Horiz. pair, #a-b 1.50 1.50

St. Valentine's Day — A1368

2018, Feb. 14　　Litho.　　Perf. 14
3768 A1368 12p multi　　　.75 .55

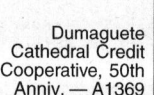

Dumaguete Cathedral Credit Cooperative, 50th Anniv. — A1369

2018, Feb. 17　　Litho.　　Perf. 14
3769 A1369 12p multi　　　.75 .55

La Castellana Municipality, Cent. — A1370

No. 3770 — Centenary emblem, municipality emblem and: a, Centennial Arch (denomination at UL). b, Municipal building (denomination at UR).

2018, Apr. 5　　Litho.　　Perf. 14
3770 A1370 12p Horiz. pair, #a-b 1.50 1.50

Miniature Sheet

Sports A1371

No. 3771: a, Boxing. b, Gymnastics. c, Volleyball. d, Basketball.

2018, Apr. 16　　Litho.　　Perf. 14
3771 A1371 17p Sheet of 4, #a-
　　　d, + 4 labels　　9.00 9.00
No. 3771 sold for 150p. Generic labels are shown, but labels could be personalized.

Flowers — A1372

Designs: 1p, Jasminum sambac. 5p, Hibiscus sp. 12p, Kopsia fruticosa. 17p, Strelitzia reginae. 35p, Pseuderanthemum reticulatum.

2018　　Litho.　　Perf. 13½
3772 A1372　1p multi　　　.30 .25
3773 A1372　5p multi　　　.30 .25
3774 A1372 12p multi　　　.75 .55
3775 A1372 17p multi　　　1.00 .75
3776 A1372 35p multi　　　2.10 1.60
　　Nos. 3772-3776 (5)　　4.45 3.40
Issued: 1p, 5p, 12p, 35p, 4/23; 17p, 10/9.
See Nos. 3813-3818.

Colonial Era Churches — A1373

No. 3777: a, Santa Monica Church, Minalin. b, Santa Catalina de Alejandria Church, Tayum. c, San Matias Church, Tumauini. d, Santa Monica Church, Pan-ay.
No. 3778: a, San Carlos Borromeo Church, Mahatao. b, Santa Catalina de Alejandria Church, Luna. c, Nuestra Señora del Patrocinio de Maria Church, Boljoon. d, Nuestra Señora de la Asuncion Church, Santa Maria. e, Nuestra Señora de la Asuncion Church, Dauis. f, Santo Tomas de Villanueva Church, Miagao.

2018, May 2　　Litho.　　Perf. 14
3777 A1373 12p Block or horiz.
　　　strip of 4, #a-d　3.00 3.00
Miniature Sheet
3778 A1373 12p Sheet of 6, #a-f 4.50 4.50
　　Heritage Month.
No. 3777 printed in sheets of 16.

Independence, 120th Anniv. — A1374

2018, June 12　　Litho.　　Perf. 14
3779 A1374 12p multi　　　.75 .55

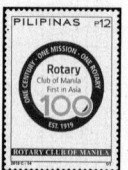

Rotary Club of Manila, Cent. — A1375

Designs: 12p, Centenary emblem. 55p, Two different centenary emblems, horiz.

2018, July 19　　Litho.　　Perf. 14
3780 A1375 12p multi　　　.75 .55
Souvenir Sheet
Perf. 13½ Horiz.
3781 A1375 55p multi　　　5.00 3.50
No. 3781 contains one 85x50mm stamp.

Miniature Sheets

Presidential Automobiles — A1376

No. 3782, 12p: a, 1924 Packard Single-6 Touring car of Pres. Emilio Aguinaldo. b, 1937 Chrysler Airflow Custom Imperial CW of Pres. Manuel L Quezon. c, 1942 Packard Custom Super Eight 180 Limousine of Pres. Jose P. Laurel. d, 1953 Chrysler Crown Imperial Limousine of Pres. Elpidio Quirino. e, 1955 Cadillac Series 75-23 of Pres. Ramon Magsaysay.

No. 3783, 12p: a, 1980 Lincoln Continental Mark VI Signature Series Limousine of Pres. Ferdinand E. Marcos. b, Mercedes-Benz 500SEL of Pres. Corazon C. Aquino. c, Mercedes-Benz 500SEL Guard of Pres. Fidel V. Ramos. d, Mercedes-Benz S600 of Pres. Joseph Ejercito Estrada. e, Mercedes-Benz S600 Limousine V140 of Pres. Gloria Macapagal-Arroyo.

2018, Aug. 10   Litho.   Perf. 14
Sheets of 5, #a-e
3782-3783 A1376   Set of 2   7.25 7.25

National Teacher's Month — A1377

2018, Aug. 30   Litho.   Perf. 14
3784 A1377 12p multi   .75   .55

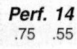

Lucrecia R. Kasilag (1918-2008), Composer — A1378

2018, Aug. 31   Litho.   Perf. 14
3785 A1378 12p multi   .75   .55

Christmas — A1379

No. 3786: a, Boy with Puto Bumbong and fruit (1/4). b, Father and daughter with Roast pig and fruit (2/4). c, Mother and son with Pancit noodles and fruit (3/4). d, Girl with Queso de Bola and fruit (4/4).

2018, Oct. 31   Litho.   Perf. 14
3786   Horiz. strip of 4   3.00 3.00
  a.-d. A1379 12p Any single   .75   .75
      Printed in sheets of 16.

Lakes
A1380

No. 3787: a, Lake Danum. b, Lake Balinsasayao. c, Mount Pinatubo Crater Lake. d, Gabawan Lake. e, Lake Apo. f, Lake Sebu.
No. 3788: a, 45p, Kabalin-An Lake. b, 55p, Lake Leonard.

2018   Litho.   Perf. 13½x13¾
3787 A1380 12p Sheet of 6, #a-f 4.50 4.50
Souvenir Sheet
Litho. With Foil Application
3788 A1380   Sheet of 2, #a-b   6.00 6.00
  c.   As #3788, with Thailand 2018
        World Stamp Exhibition emblem in sheet margin   6.00 6.00
    Issued: Nos. 3787-3788, 11/5; No. 3788c, 11/28. No. 3788 contains two 75x35mm stamps.

Philpost Type of 2013
2018, Nov. 8   Litho.   Perf. 13½x13¼
Denomination Color

3789 A1177 5p olive green   .30   .25
3790 A1177 17p red violet   .30   .25

Estancia Municipality, Cent. — A1381

No. 3791 — Centenary emblem and: a, Fishing village (denomination at UR). b, Fishing village, diff. (denomination at UL).

2018, Nov. 21   Litho.   Perf. 14
3791 A1381 12p Horiz. pair, #a-b 1.50 1.50

A1382

New Year 2019 (Year of the Pig)
A1383

No. 3792 — Pig with background color of: a, 12p, Blue green. b, 45p, Yellow green.

2018, Nov. 23   Litho.   Perf. 14
3792 A1382 Horiz. pair, #a-b   3.50 3.50
Souvenir Sheet
Litho. & Embossed With Foil Application
Perf.
3793 A1383 200p gold & multi   12.00 12.00
No. 3792 printed in sheets of 8.

Souvenir Sheet

Diplomatic Relations Between Philippines and Croatia, 25th Anniv. — A1384

No. 3794: a, 12p, St. Michael's Fortress, Sibenik, Croatia. b, 55p, Fort Santiago, Intramuros, Philippines.

2018, Dec. 5   Litho.   Perf. 14
3794 A1384   Sheet of 2, #a-b   4.00 4.00
      See Croatia No. 1099.

Dagupan Doctors Villaflor Memorial Hospital, Dagupan City, 50th Anniv. — A1385

Litho. With Foil Application
2018, Dec. 7   Perf. 14
3795 A1385 12p gold & multi   .75   .55

Pangasinan Province Capital Builiding, Cent. — A1386

No. 3796 — Capital Building with: a, Dark brown background. b, Sky in background.

2018, Dec. 17   Litho.   Perf. 14
3796 A1386 12p Horiz. pair, #a-b 1.50 1.50

General Santos City, 50th Anniv.
A1387

No. 3797: a, General Santos City Tuna Festival. b, Fresh tuna. c, Statue of General Paulino A. Santos. d, General Santos Plaza.

2018, Dec. 10   Litho.   Perf. 14
3797 A1387 12p Block or horiz.
              strip of 4, #a-d   3.00 3.00
      Printed in sheets of 16.

University of the Visayas, Cent. — A1388

2019, Jan. 12   Litho.   Perf. 14
3798 A1388 12p multi   .75   .55

St. Valentine's Day — A1389

No. 3799: a, King of Hearts. b, Queen of Hearts.

2019, Feb. 1   Litho.   Perf. 14
3799 A1389 12p Horiz. pair, #a-b 1.50 1.50
      Printed in sheets of 8.

A1390

Catriona Gray, 2018 Miss Universe
A1391

2019, Feb. 27   Litho.   Perf. 13¾
3800 A1390 12p multi   .75   .55
Souvenir Sheet
3801 A1391 55p multi   3.50 3.50

Manila Central Post Office
A1392

2019, Mar. 22   Litho.   Perf. 14
3802 A1392 17p multi + label   —   —

No. 3802 was printed in sheets of 4 + 4 labels that sold for 150p. Sheets were available with labels that could be personalized, which were first made available on Mar. 22, 2019, and with labels that had pre-printed images that could not be personalized, such as the label shown, which were produced in 2018 and later years.

No. 3802 exists dated "2022" from sheets of 4 + 4 labels issued that year that sold for 150p. It is not known if th labels on these sheets could be personalized.

A1393

Emilio Aguinaldo (1869-1964), First President of the Philippines — A1394

2019, Mar. 22   Litho.   Perf. 13¾
3803 A1393 12p multi   .75   .55
Souvenir Sheet
3804 A1394 55p multi   3.50 3.50

"100" and Map of Philippines — A1395

2019, Apr. 4   Litho.   Perf. 14
3805 A1395 12p multi   .75   .55

Tribute to Filipino centenarians. No. 3805 was printed in sheets of 40. Sheets containing four stamps and four labels were printed in limited quantities: 500 generic sheets with 4 blank labels printed, and 1,000 sheets with blank labels. The latter were given free to centenarians.

Claudio Teehankee (1918-89), Chief Justice — A1396

2019, Apr. 18   Litho.   *Perf. 14*
3806 A1396 12p multi   .75 .55

Francisco V. Coching (1919-98), Comic Book Illustrator A1397

2019, Apr. 19   Litho.   *Perf. 14*
3807 A1397 12p multi   .75 .55

Edith L. Tiempo (1919-2011), Writer — A1398

2019, Apr. 19   Litho.   *Perf. 14*
3808 A1398 12p multi   .75 .55

Women at Work A1399

No. 3809: a, Laguna rafters. b, Aurora hat weavers. c, Badjao mat weaver. d, Ilocos burnay potter. e, T'boli beadworker. f, Liliw coconut sap collector. g, Ifugao farmer. h, Tawi-Tawi seaweed farmer.

2019, May 9   Litho.   *Perf. 14*
3809 A1399 12p Block of 8, #a-h   6.00 6.00
     Heritage Month.
     Printed in sheets of 16.

Victorias Milling Company, Cent. — A1400

Centenary emblem and: 12p, Sugar mill. 55p, Sugar mill, diff.

2019, May 17   Litho.   *Perf. 14*
3810 A1400 12p multi   .75 .55
     Souvenir Sheet
     Perf. 14 Horiz.
3811 A1400 55p multi   3.50 3.50
No. 3811 contains one 85x50mm stamp.

Butterflies — A1401

No. 3812 — Flags of the Philippines and Singapore and: a, 12p, Common rose butterfly. b, 45p, Luzon lacewing butterfly.

Litho. With Foil Application
2019   *Perf. 14*
3812 A1401   Horiz. pair, #a-b   3.50 3.50
   c.   Sheet of 4, 2 each #3812a-
       3812b, with Singpex 2019
       emblem added in sheet
       margin   7.00 7.00
Diplomatic relations between Philippines and Singapore, 50th anniv. Issued: No. 3812, 5/16; No. 3812c, 7/31. No. 3812 was printed in sheets containing two pairs. See Singapore Nos. 1969-1970.

Flowers Type of 2018
Designs: 14p, Rafflesia. 45p, Everlasting. 50p, Blue plumbago. 55p, Lobster claws. 60p, Lantana. 100p, Bougainvillea.

2019   Litho.   *Perf. 13½*
3813 A1372 14p multi   .85 .65
3814 A1372 45p multi   2.75 2.10
3815 A1372 50p multi   3.00 2.25
3816 A1372 55p multi   3.50 2.60
3817 A1372 60p multi   3.75 2.75
     Size: 30x30mm
     Perf. 13¼
3818 A1372 100p multi   6.00 4.50
   Nos. 3813-3818 (6)   19.85 14.85
Issued: 14p, 45p, 8/28; 100p, 6/10; 50p, 55p, 60p, 9/21.

     Souvenir Sheet

New Year 2019 (Year of the Pig) A1402

Litho., Sheet Margin Litho. With Foil Application
2019, June 11   *Perf. 13½*
3819 A1402 100p gold & multi   6.00 6.00
   a.   As #3819, with China 2019
       World Stamp Exhibition em-
       blem added in sheet margin   6.00 6.00

Diplomatic Relations Between the Philippines and Thailand, 70th Anniv. — A1403

No. 3820 — Flags of the Philippines and Thailand and: a, 12p, Elephant. b, 45p, Carabao.

2019, June 14   Litho.   *Perf. 14*
3820 A1403   Horiz. pair, #a-b   3.50 3.50
     Printed in sheets of 8.
     See Thailand No. 3062.

     Souvenir Sheet

New Year 2018 (Year of the Dog) A1404

Litho., Sheet Margin Litho. With Foil Application
2019, July 11   *Perf. 13½*
3821 A1404 100p gold & multi   6.00 6.00

National Electrification Administration, 50th Anniv. — A1405

2019, Aug. 6   Litho.   *Perf. 14*
3822 A1405 12p multi   .75 .55

Man and Woman Wearing Traditional Filipino Clothing — A1406

2019, Aug. 8   Litho.   *Perf. 13¾*
3823 A1406 12p multi   .75 .55

National Teacher's Month — A1407

No. 3824: a, Student's raised hand. b, Stylized teacher and student reading.

2019, Sept. 5   Litho.   *Perf. 13¾*
3824 A1407 12p Horiz. pair, #a-b   1.50 1.50

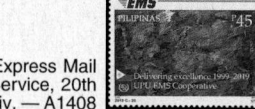

Express Mail Service, 20th Anniv. — A1408

2019, Sept. 10   Litho.   *Perf. 14*
3825 A1408 45p multi   2.75 2.10

Philippine Cinema, Cent. — A1409

José Nepomuceno (1893-1959), Film Director and Producer — A1410

2019, Sept. 12   Litho.   *Perf. 14*
3826 A1409 12p multi   .75 .55
     Souvenir Sheet
     Perf. 13¾
3827 A1410 55p multi   3.50 3.50

Cultural Center of the Philippines, Manila, 50th Anniv. — A1411

2019, Oct. 15   Litho.   *Perf. 14*
3828 A1411 12p multi   .75 .55

Sorsogon Province, 125th Anniv. — A1412

2019, Oct. 17   Litho.   *Perf. 14*
3829 A1412 12p multi   .75 .55

Leyte Gulf Landing, 75th Anniv. A1413

No. 3830: a, MacArthur's Landing, sculpture by Anastacio Caedo. b, Gen. Douglas MacArthur and others walking ashore at Leyte Gulf.

2019, Oct. 20   Litho.   *Perf. 14*
3830 A1413 12p Horiz. pair, #a-b   1.50 1.10

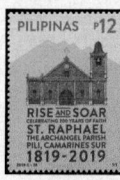

St. Raphael, the Archangel Parish, Pili, 200th Anniv. — A1414

Designs: 12p, Church and text. 55p, Church.

2019, Oct. 24   Litho.   *Perf. 14*
3831 A1414 12p multi   .75 .55
     Souvenir Sheet
     Perf. 13¾
3832 A1414 55p multi   3.50 3.50
No. 3832 contains one 35x50mm stamp.

Pinoy Rock Music Stars — A1415

No. 3833: a, Rene Garcia (1953-2018). b, Rico J. Puno (1953-2018). c, Pepe Smith (1947-2019).

Litho., Sheet Margin Litho. With Foil Application
2019, Nov. 11   *Perf.*
3833   Souvenir sheet of 3   8.25 8.25
   a.-c.   A1415 45p Any single   2.75 2.10

     Miniature Sheets

Birds A1416

Mushrooms — A1417

Rivers A1418

Shrimp A1419

No. 3834: a, Blue-tailed bee-eater. b, Visayan broadbill. c, Mountain white-eye. d, Firebreasted flowerpecker.
No. 3835: a, Brittle gill fungus. b, Earthstar. c, Circular bracket fungus. d, Parasol mushrooms.
No. 3836: a, Bayabas River. b, Baroro River. c, Cantingas River. d, Enchanted River.
No. 3837: a, Brilliant red carid. b, Domino shrimp. c, Mino nylon shrimp. d, Rock shrimp. e, Narwal soldier shrimp.

2019, Nov.   Litho.   *Perf. 14*
3834 A1416 25p Sheet of 4,
       #a-d, + label   6.00 6.00
3835 A1417 25p Sheet of 4,
       #a-d, + 3 la-
       bels   6.00 6.00
3836 A1418 25p Sheet of 4,
       #a-d, + label   6.00 6.00
3837 A1419 25p Sheet of 5,
       #a-e   7.50 7.50
   Nos. 3834-3837 (4)   25.50 25.50
     Issued: 3834, 3836, 11/20; 3835, 3837, 11/21.

Christmas — A1420

No. 3838 — Choir members and: a, Lyrist. b, Guitarist. c, Piper, drummer and tambourine player. d, Maracas player.

2019, Nov. 25   Litho.   *Perf.* 14
3838 A1420 12p Block of 4, #a-d   3.00 3.00
Printed in sheets of 16.

A1421

Southeast Asian Games, 30th Anniv. — A1422

No. 3839: a, Weight lifting. b, Badminton. c, Cycling. d, Billiards.
No. 3840: a, 12p, Clasped hands (30x30mm). b, 55p, Tennis player, handicapped runner, gymnast (60x30mm).

2019, Nov. 30   Litho.   *Perf.* 14
3839 A1421 12p Block of 4, #a-d   3.00 3.00
Souvenir Sheet
Perf. 13¼
3840 A1422 Sheet of 2, #a-b   4.00 4.00
Printed in sheets of 8.

International Civil Aviation Organization, 75th Anniv. — A1423

Designs: 12p, Emblems of ICAO and Civil Aviation Authority of the Philippines, map of Asia, airplanes, control tower.
55p, Airplanes and emblem of the ICAO and Civil Aviation Authority of the Philippines, horiz.

2019, Dec. 7   Litho.   *Perf.* 14
3841 A1423 12p multi   .75 .55
Souvenir Sheet
Perf. 13¾
3842 A1423 55p multi   3.50 3.50
No. 3832 contains one 50x35mm stamp.

Commission on Higher Education, 25th Anniv. — A1424

2019, Dec. 9   Litho.   *Perf.* 14
3843 A1424 12p multi   .75 .55

A1425

New Year 2020 (Year of the Rat) A1426

No. 3844 — Rat with background color of: a, 12p, Lemon. b, 45p, Pink.

2019, Dec. 13   Litho.   *Perf.* 14
3844 A1425 Horiz. pair, #a-b   2.75 2.10
Souvenir Sheet
Litho. & Embossed With Foil Application
Perf.
3845 A1426 200p gold & multi 12.00 12.00

Cebu Province, 450th Anniv. — A1427

2019, Dec. 16   Litho.   *Perf.* 14
3846 A1427 12p multi   .75 .55

Chartering of Mandaue City, 50th Anniv. — A1428

2019, Dec. 20   Litho.   *Perf.* 14
3847 A1428 12p multi   .75 .55

Miniature Sheet

International Year of Indigenous Languages — A1429

No. 3848: a, Calatagan pot. b, Gitgit. c, Monreal stones. d, Butuan ivory seal.

2019, Dec. 23   Litho.   *Perf.* 13¾
3848 A1429 17p Sheet of 4, #a-d 4.25 4.25

Municipality of Consolacion, Cent. — A1430

2020, Jan. 23   Litho.   *Perf.* 14
3849 A1430 12p multi   .75 .55

Valentine's Day — A1431

No. 3850 — Heart and inscription: a, Love Nature. b, Love for Country. c, Love Knows No Gender. d, Love Yourself.

2020, Feb. 6   Litho.   *Perf.* 14
3850 A1431 12p Block of 4, #a-d 3.00 2.25

Battle of Manila, 75th Anniv. — A1432

2020, Feb. 15   Litho.   *Perf.* 14
3851 A1432 12p multi   .75 .55

A1433

Aboitiz & Company, Cent. — A1434

2020, Apr. 27   Litho.   *Perf.* 14
3852 A1433 12p multi   .75 .55
Souvenir Sheet
Perf.
3853 A1434 55p multi   3.50 3.50

A1435

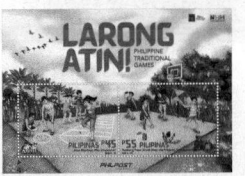

Traditional Games — A1436

No. 3854: a, 12p, Jack-en-Poy (Rock, Paper, Scissors). b, 14p, Bahay-bahayan (Playing house). c, 15p, Luksong Tinik (Jumping over thorns). d, 17p, Trumpo (Top spinning).
No. 3855: a, 45p, Jolen and Piko (Marbles and Hopscotch). b, 55p, Tumband Preso and Saranggola (Knock Down the Prisoner and Kite Flying).

2020, May 2   Litho.   *Perf.* 14
3854 A1435 Block of 4, #a-d   3.50 2.60
Souvenir Sheet
Perf. 13¾
3855 A1436 Sheet of 2, #a-b   6.00 6.00

A1437

Tribute to Workers During the COVID-19 Pandemic A1438

No. 3856 — Inscription: a, Nurses. b, Military personnel. c, Grocery personnel. d, Police officers. e, Doctors. f, Delivery personnel. g, Medical technicians. h, Chefs.

2020, July 13   Litho.   *Perf.* 13¾
3856 A1437 12p Block of 8, #a-h 5.75 4.50
Souvenir Sheet
3857 A1438 55p multi   3.50 3.50

National Teachers' Month — A1439

No. 3858 — Inscription: a, 12p, I am good. b, 14p, I am a star. c, 15p, I am bright. d, 17p, I am brave.

2020, Sept. 4   Litho.   *Perf.* 14
3858 A1439 Block of 4, #a-d   3.50 2.60

Camarines Norte Province, Cent. — A1440

2020, Sept. 14   Litho.   *Perf.* 14
3859 A1440 12p multi   .75 .55

Christmas — A1441

2020, Nov. 23   Litho.   *Perf.* 14
3860 A1441 12p multi   .75 .55

Salinta Monon (1920-2009), Textile Weaver — A1442

2020, Dec. 12   Litho.   *Perf.* 14
3861 A1442 12p multi   .75 .55

Shells — A1443

Designs: 1p, Hebrew cone. 5p, Black-striped or liver triton. 12p, Banded trochus snail. 14p, Asian moon scallop. 17p, Martini's

tibia. 35p, Pontifical mitre. 45p, Yoka star turban. 100p, Fluted giant clam, horiz.

2020-21		**Litho.**	**Perf. 13¾**
3862	A1443	1p multi	.25 .25
3863	A1443	5p multi	.30 .30
3864	A1443	12p multi	.75 .55
3865	A1443	14p multi	.85 .65
3866	A1443	17p multi	1.10 .85
3867	A1443	35p multi	2.10 1.10
3868	A1443	45p multi	2.75 2.10

Size: 40x30mm
Perf. 14

3869	A1443	100p multi	6.00 4.50
	Nos. 3862-3869 (8)		14.10 10.25

Issued: 1p, 5p, 12p, 35p, 12/21; 14p, 100p,
1/13/21; 17p, 45p, 1/6/21. 14p, 17p, 45p, 100p
are dated 2020.

Souvenir Sheet

New
Year
2020
(Year of
the Rat)
A1444

**Litho., Sheet Margin Litho With Foil
Application**

2020, Dec. 28			**Perf. 13½**
3870	A1444	100p gold & multi	6.00 6.00

A1445

New
Year
2021
(Year of
the Ox)
A1446

No. 3871: a, 12p, Ox in hay. b, 45p, Ox
standing.

2020, Dec. 28		**Litho.**	**Perf. 14**
3871	A1445	Horiz. pair #a-b	3.50 2.60

Souvenir Sheet
**Litho. & Embossed With Foil
Application**
Perf.

3872	A1446	200p gold & multi	12.00 12.00

China
Bank,
Cent. (in
2020)
A1447

No. 3873: a, Bank building, Binondo. b,
Centennial emblem.

2021, Jan. 26		**Litho.**	**Perf. 14**
3873	A1447	12p Horiz. pair, #a-b	1.50 1.10

Dated 2020.

Valentine's
Day — A1448

2021, Feb. 10		**Litho.**	**Perf. 14**
3874	A1448	12p multi	.75 .60

A1449

A1450

A1451

A1452

A1453

A1454

A1455

A1456

A1457

A1458

A1459

A1460

1734 Map and Illustrations, by Pedro
Murillo Velarde — A1461

2021, Mar. 16		**Litho.**	**Perf. 14x13¼**
3875		Sheet of 13	30.50 30.50
a.	A1449	12p multi	.75 .60
b.	A1450	12p multi	.75 .60
c.	A1451	12p multi	.75 .60
d.	A1452	14p multi	.85 .65
e.	A1453	14p multi	.85 .65
f.	A1454	14p multi	.85 .65
g.	A1455	17p multi	1.10 .85
h.	A1456	45p multi	2.75 2.10
i.	A1457	45p multi	2.75 2.10
j.	A1458	50p multi	3.00 2.25
k.	A1459	55p multi	3.25 2.50
l.	A1460	60p multi	3.75 3.00
m.	A1461	150p multi	9.00 6.75

Christianity in the Philippines, 500th
Anniv. — A1462

No. 3876: a, Limasawa Island, site of first
Easter Mass in the Philippines. b, Priest celebrating Mass.

2021, Mar. 22		**Litho.**	**Perf. 14**
3876	A1462	12p Horiz. pair, #a-b	1.50 1.50

Arrival of Santo Niño de Cebu Icon in
the Philippines, 500th Anniv. — A1463

No. 3877: a, Santo Niño de Cebu icon. b,
500th anniversary emblem.

2021, Apr. 14		**Litho.**	**Perf. 14**
3877	A1463	12p Horiz. pair, #a-b	1.50 1.50

Liberty Shrine,
Lapu-Lapu
City — A1464

2021, Apr. 21		**Litho.**	**Perf. 14**
3878	A1464	12p multi	.75 .60

Battle of Mactan and death of Ferdinand
Magellan, 500th anniv.

Boats
A1465

No. 3879: a, Vinta. b, Casco. c, Boanga. d,
Salisipan. e, Balangay. f, Paraw. g, Panco. h,
Guilalo. i, Parao Mangayaw. j, Caracoa.
55p, Bancas Filipinas.

2021, May 18		**Litho.**	**Perf. 14**
3879	A1465	12p Sheet of 10, #a-j	7.25 7.25

Souvenir Sheet
Perf. 13½

3880	A1465	55p multi	6.75 6.75

No. 3880 contains one 50x35mm stamp.

1971
Constitutional
Convention, 50th
Anniv. — A1466

2021, June 1		**Litho.**	**Perf. 14**
3881	A1466	12p multi	.75 .60

City of Manila, 450th Anniv.
A1467

No. 3882: a, Jones Bridge. b, City Hall
Clock Tower.

2021, Apr. 14		**Litho.**	**Perf. 14**
3882	A1467	12p Horiz. pair, #a-b	1.50 1.50

Two 17p stamps, depicting the Bonifacio
Shrine and Scyphiphora flowers were printed
in limited quantities in sheets of 4 stamps + 4
labels that could not be personalized that sold
for 150p.

Diplomatic Relations
Between the Philippines
and the United States,
75th Anniv. — A1468

2021, July 4		**Litho.**	**Perf. 13½**
3883	A1468	12p multi	.75 .60

Paulino Txanton
Aboitiz, Hemp Trader,
150th Anniv. of
Birth — A1469

Aboitiz and hemp rope coils at: 12p, Right.
55p, Left and right, horiz.

2021, July 27		**Litho.**	**Perf. 14**
3884	A1469	12p multi	.75 .60

Souvenir Sheet
Perf. 13½

3885	A1469	55p multi	3.25 3.25

No. 3885 contains one 50x35mm stamp.

Pres. Benigno S.
Aquino III (1960-
2021) — A1470

2021, Aug. 2		**Litho.**	**Perf. 14**
3886	A1470	12p multi	.75 .60

National Teachers'
Month — A1471

2021, Sept. 6		**Litho.**	**Perf. 14**
3887	A1471	12p multi	.75 .60

University of
Bohol, 75th
Anniv. — A1472

2021, Sept. 10   Litho.   Perf. 14
3888   A1472   12p multi   .75   .60

Miniature Sheet

Campaign for COVID-19
Vaccination — A1473

No. 3889 — Hypodermic needle, map of
Philippines and vaccinated: a, 12p, Man and
woman (dark red panels). b, 12p, Man (blue
panels). c, 14p, Man and woman (bister
panels). d, 14p, Woman (brown orange
panels). e, 15p, Man and woman (gray blue
panels). f, 15p, Man, (violet panels). g, 17p,
Woman (green panels). h, 17p, Man and
woman (rose panels).

2021, Sept. 16   Litho.   Perf. 13½
3889   A1473   Sheet of 8, #a-h   7.00   7.00

Philippine Medalists at 2020 Summer
Olympics — A1474

No. 3890: a, 12p, Hidilyn F. Diaz, weight
lifting gold medalist. b, 14p, Nesthy A. Petecio,
boxing silver medalist. c, 15p, Carlo C.
Paalam, boxing silver medalist. d, 17p, Eumer
D. S. Marcial, boxing bronze medalist.
55p, Diaz, Petecio, Paalam and Marcial.

2021, Sept. 18   Litho.   Perf. 14
3890   A1474   Block of 4, #a-d   3.50   3.50
Souvenir Sheet
Perf. 13¼
3891   A1474   55p multi   3.25   3.25
The 2020 Summer Olympics were postponed until 2021 because of the COVID-19
pandemic. No. 3891 contains one 30x60mm
stamp.

Hidilyn
F. Diaz,
First
Filipino
Olympic
Gold
Medalist
A1475

No. 3892 — Diaz: a, 12p, Preparing to lift
weights (green circle). b, 12p, Lifting weights
(blue circle). c, 12p, Wearing protective mask
and gold medal, holding flowers (green circle).
d, 14p, Lifting weights (black circle). e, 14p,
Celebrating (red circle). f, 14p, Holding gold
medal (black circle). g, 15p, Lifting weights
(blue circle). h, 15p, Celebrating (blue circle). i,
17p, Lifting weights (red circle). g, Wearing
protective mask and gold medal, holding flowers (red circle).
100p, Diaz lifting weights.

2021, Sept. 18   Litho.   Perf. 14
3892   A1475   Sheet of 10, #a-j   8.50   8.50
Souvenir Sheet
Litho., Sheet Margin Litho. With Foil
Application
Perf.
3893   A1475   100p multi   12.00 12.00
No. 3893 contains one 38mm diameter
stamp.

Grandparent's
Day — A1476

2021, Sept. 27   Litho.   Perf. 14
3894   A1476   12p multi   .75   .60

Robert Jaworski, Basketball
Player — A1477

No. 3895 — Jaworski: a, Holding ball for
free throw (stamp 1/8). b, Dribbling and pointing finger (stamp 2/8). c, Wearing Gordon's
Gin uniform (stamp 3/8). d, Making layup shot
(stamp 4/8). e, Holding basketball on palm
(stamp 5/8). f, Running, holding basketball
with both hands (stamp 6/8). g, Holding bas-
ketall in process of dribbling (stamp 7/8). h,
Running, holding basketball with one hand
(stamp 8/8).
60p, Jaworski dribbling basketball.

2021, Oct. 16   Litho.   Perf. 13¾
3895   A1477   17p Sheet of 8, #a-h 8.75 8.75
Souvenir Sheet
Perf. 13¼
3896   A1477   60p multi   3.75   3.75
No. 3896 contains one 30x60mm stamp.

Famous
People — A1478

No. 3897: a, Efren "Bata" Reyes, world
champion pool player (stamp 1/10). b, Josie
Natori, fashion designer (stamp 2/10). c, Jordan Clarkson, professional basketball player
(stamp 3/10). d, Lea Salonga, singer and
actress (stamp 4/10). e, Diosdado "Dado"
Banatao, computer engineer and entrepreneur
(stamp 5/10). f, Monique Lhuillier, fashion
designer (stamp 6/10). g, Kenneth Cobonpue,
industrial designer (stamp 7/10). h, Mascot for
Jollibee Restaurants (stamp 8/10). i, Eugene
Torre, chess grandmaster (stamp 9/10). j, Rafael "Paeng" Nepomuceno, world champion
bowler (stamp 10/10).

2021, Nov. 13   Litho.   Perf. 13¾
3897   Sheet of 10   10.00 10.00
a.-j.   A1478   16p Any single   1.00   .75

St. La Salle Hall
of De La Salle
University, Manila,
Cent. — A1479

2021, Nov. 22   Litho.   Perf. 14
3898   A1479   12p dp green   .75   .60

Christmas — A1480

No. 3899 — Various people celebrating
Christmas with inscription at bottom of: a,
"Narito na, Pasko ng Pag-asa" (Here it is, the
Christmas of Hope). b, "Sama-sama pa rin
tayo ngayong Pasko" (We are still together this
Christmas). c, "Taus-pusong pananalig sa
Paskong puno ng Pag-ibig" (Whole-hearted
faith in Christmas full of love). d, "Maniwala,
magtiwala, Pasko ng Himala" (Trust, believe,
Christmas of miracles).

2021, Dec. 3   Litho.   Perf. 14
3899   A1480   12p Block of 4, #a-d 3.00 3.00

City of
Bislig,
Cent.
A1481

No. 3900 — Philippine eagle and: a,
Centennial poster. b, Tinuy-an Falls. c, Kawa
Kawa Hills. d, Karawasan Festival.

2021, Dec. 15   Litho.   Perf. 14
3900   A1481   12p Block of 4, #a-d 3.00 3.00

Famous
People — A1482

No. 3901: a, Olivia "Bong" Coo, world champion bowler (stamp 1/10). b, Gloria Romero,
actress (stamp 2/10). c, Ramon Fernandez,
basketball player (stamp 3/10). d, Vilma Santos, actress and politician (stamp 4/10). e,
Romulo Galicano, painter (stamp 5/10). f,
Susan Roces (1941-2022), actress (stamp
6/10). g, Dr. Baldomero Olivera, chemist
(stamp 7/10). h, Rosa Rosal, actress (stamp
8/10). i, Dr. Ernesto Ochoa Domingo, physician (stamp 9/10). j, Nora Aunor, actress
(stamp 10/10).

2021, Dec. 28   Litho.   Perf. 13¾
3901   Sheet of 10   10.00 10.00
a.-j.   A1482   16p Any single   1.00   .75

José Rizal (1861-96), National
Hero — A1483

No. 3902 — Rizal: a, With hand over heart.
b, Holding book. c, Writing. d, Being executed.

2021, Dec. 30   Litho.   Perf. 14
3902   A1483   12p Block of 4, #a-d 3.00 3.00

A1484

New
Year
2022
(Year of
the
Tiger)
A1485

No. 3903 — Tiger: a, 12p, Raising paw. b,
45p, Roaring.

2022, Jan. 31   Litho.   Perf. 14
3903   A1484   Horiz. pair, #a-b   3.50   3.50
Souvenir Sheet
Litho. & Embossed With Foil
Application
Perf.
3904   A1485   200p gold & multi   12.00 12.00

Miniature Sheet

Valentine's Day — A1486

No. 3905 — Heart with inscription: a,
"Titibok pa rin." (stamp 1/8) b, "Magmamahal
pa rin." (stamp 2/8). c, "Lalaban pa rin." (stamp

3/8). d, "Nagmamalasakit pa rin." (stamp 4/8). e, "Nagmamahal pa rin." (stamp 5/8). f, "Titibok para rin sa bayan." (stamp 6/8). g, "Buo pa rin." (stamp 7/8). h, "Lumalaban pa rin." (stamp 8/8).

2022, Feb. 10   Litho.   Perf. 13¾
3905 A1486 12p Sheet of 8, #a-h 5.75 5.75

Yuka Saso, 2021 United States Women's Open Golf Champion — A1487

No. 3906 — Saso: a, 12p, Holding putter. b, 14p, Addressing ball. c, 15p, Finishing swing. d, 17p, Holding trophy.

2022, Feb. 22   Litho.   Perf. 14
3906 A1487   Block of 4, #a-d 3.50 3.50

Fall of Bataan, 80th Anniv. — A1488

2022, Apr. 9   Litho.   Perf. 14
3907 A1488 12p multi .75 .60

Map of Philippine Rise — A1489

2022, Apr. 25   Litho.   Perf. 14
3908 A1489 12p multi .75 .60
Territorial claim of Philippines government of Philippine Rise continental shelf, 10th anniv.

Asian-Pacific Postal Union, 60th Anniv. — A1490

2022, Apr. 28   Litho.   Perf. 14
3909 A1490 12p multi .75 .60

Miniature Sheets

A1491

National Heritage Month A1492

No. 3910 — Cartoons by Lauro "Larry" Alcala depicting: a, Batangas shellcraft makers (stamp 1/8). b, Cebu guitar makers (stamp 2/8). c, Bohol basket weavers (stamp 3/8). d, Bicol blacksmith (stamp 4/8). e, Bulacan mat weavers (stamp 5/8). f, Taal embroiderers (stamp 6/8). g, Ilocos potters (stamp 7/8). h, Iloilo rattan furniture makers (stamp 8/8).

No. 3911 — Details from "Cooking for a Fiesta" cartoon by Alcala, showing: a, House, tree, man with cart. b, People cooking food. c, House, men moving stove. d, House, horse cart, man chasing chickens.

2022, May 20   Litho.   Perf. 14
3910 A1491 12p Sheet of 8, #a-h 5.75 5.75
3911 A1492 17p Sheet of 4, #a-d 4.25 4.25

Miniature Sheet

Execution of Catholic Priests by Spanish Colonial Authorities, 150th Anniv. — A1493

No. 3912 — Inscriptions: a, "Kilusang Sekularisasyon." b, "Gomburza." c, "Pagmamalabis at Pag-aglahi." d, "1872 Pag-aaklas sa Kabite." e, "Paghatol, Pagbibintang." f, "Mga Taong nagmamahal sa 3 Pari." g, "Pebrero 17, 1872." h, "Pagsiklab ng Himagsikan."

2022, June 12   Litho.   Perf. 14
3912 A1493 12p Sheet of 8, #a-h 5.75 5.75

Independence Day.

Department of Finance, 125th Anniv. — A1494

2022, June 28   Litho.   Perf. 14
3913 A1494 12p multi .75 .60

Kidapawan City, 75th Anniv. — A1495

No. 3914: a, Lake Venado, Mount Apo Natural Park. b, Kidapawan Municipal Hall. c, Fruits at Fruit Festival. d, Paniki Falls, Eco-River Park.

2022, Aug. 18   Litho.   Perf. 14
3914   Block of 4 3.00 3.00
a.-d. A1495 12p Any single .75 .60

National Teacher's Month — A1496

2022, Oct. 5   Litho.   Perf. 14
3915 A1496 12p multi .75 .60

Ormoc City, 75th Anniv. — A1497

2022, Oct. 20   Litho.   Perf. 14
3916 A1497 12p multi .75 .60

Holy Name University, Tagbilaran City, 75th Anniv. — A1498

No. 3917 — University crest and crest of Holy Name College, and: a, Green building. b, Brown building. c, Brown, green and yellow green buildings.
55p, Father Alphonse Lesage (1905-77), founder, vert.

2022, Nov. 1   Litho.   Perf. 14
3917   Horiz. strip of 3 3.50 3.50
a. A1498 16p multi 1.00 .75
b. A1498 18p multi 1.10 .85
c. A1498 21p multi 1.30 1.00
Souvenir Sheet
Perf. 13¾
3918 A1498 55p multi 3.50 3.50
No. 3918 contains one 35x50mm stamp.

Inauguration of Pres. Ferdinand Marcos, Jr. — A1499

Pres. Marcos: 12p, Taking oath. 55p, Behind microphones, vert.

2022, Nov. 17   Litho.   Perf. 14
3919 A1499 12p multi .75 .60
Souvenir Sheet
Perf. 13¾
3920 A1499 55p multi 3.50 3.50
No. 3920 contains one 35x50mm stamp.

Inauguration of Vice President Sara Z. Duterte — A1500

Vice President Duterte: 12p, Taking oath. 55p, Behind microphones, vert.

2022, Nov. 17   Litho.   Perf. 14
3921 A1500 12p multi .75 .60
Souvenir Sheet
Perf. 13¾
3922 A1500 55p multi 3.50 3.50
No. 3922 contains one 35x50mm stamp.

Pres. Fidel V. Ramos (1928-2022) — A1501

Pres. Ramos: 12p, Wearing military cap. 55p, Standing next to flag.

2022, Nov. 17   Litho.   Perf. 14
3923 A1501 12p multi .75 .60
Souvenir Sheet
Perf. 13¾
3924 A1501 55p multi 3.50 3.50
National Stamp Collecting Month. No. 3924 contains one 35x50mm stamp.

Christmas — A1502

No. 3925 — People celebrating Christmas with stamps numbered: a, 1/4. b, 2/4. c, 3/4. d, 4/4.

2022, Dec. 7   Litho.   Perf. 13¾
3925 A1502 12p Block of 4, #a-d 3.00 3.00

Philippines Delegation to Third United Nations Conference on the Law of the Sea, 1973 — A1503

2022, Dec.   Litho.   Perf. 14
3926 A1503 12p multi .75 .60
Third United Nations Conference on the Law of the Sea, 40th anniv.

St. Mary's Academy, Pasay City, Cent. — A1504

2023, Jan. 20   Litho.   Perf. 14
3927 A1504 12p multi .75 .60
Dated 2022.

Miniature Sheet

First Circumnavigation of the Earth, 500th Anniv. (in 2021) — A1505

No. 3928 — Inscriptions: a, Humanity in Homonhon, 18 March 1521. b, Friendship with Rajah Calanao of Kipit, May 1521. c, Introduction of Christianity in Mazawa, 31 March 1521. d, Introduction of Christianity in Cebu, 14 April 1521. e, Crossing the Pacific, November 1520-March 1521. f, Victoria, the Ship that First Circumnavigated the World. h, Battle of Mactan, 27 April 1521. i, Mutiny Against Magellan, April 1520. j, Emperor Charles Approves Magellan's Expedition, 22 March 1518. k, Return to Spain, 6 September 1521. l, Arrival in Maluku, 8 November 1521.

2023, Jan. 20   Litho.   Perf. 14
3928 A1505 12p Sheet of 12, #a-l 8.75 8.75
Dated 2022.

A1506

New Year 2023 (Year of the Rabbit) A1507

No. 3929 — Rabbit: a, 12p, Facing left. b, 45p, Head.

2023, Jan. 20   Litho.   Perf. 14
3929 A1506   Horiz. pair, #a-b   3.50 3.50

Souvenir Sheet
Litho. & Embossed With Foil Application
Perf.
3930 A1507 200p gold & multi 12.00 12.00
Dated 2022.

Development Bank of the Philippines, 75th Anniv. (in 2022) — A1508

No. 3931 — 75th anniversary emblem and: a, Bank building (1/4). b, Various development projects (2/4). c, Bank building, diff. (3/4). d, Bank building, diff. (4/4).
100p, Bank building, vert.

2023, Feb.   Litho.   Perf. 14
3931 A1508   12p Block of 4, #a-
         d   3.00 3.00

Souvenir Sheet
Perf. 13¾
3932 A1508 100p multi   6.00 6.00
No. 3932 contains one 35x50mm stamp.

St. Valentine's Day — A1509

No. 3933 — Inscription: a, Pusong Nagmamahal (Loving heart) (1/4). b, Pusong para sa Iyo (Heart for you) (2/4). c, Itong Puso Ko (This is my heart) (3/4). d, Ikaw ang Puso Ko (You are my heart) (4/4).

2023, Feb.   Litho.   Perf. 14
3933 A1509   16p Block of 4, #a-
         d   4.00 4.00

SEMI-POSTAL STAMPS

Catalogue values for unused stamps in this section are for Never Hinged items.

Republic

Epifanio de los Santos, Trinidad H. Pardo and Teodoro M. Kalaw — SP1

Doctrina Christiana, Cover Page — SP2

"Noli Me Tangere," Cover Page — SP3

Unwmk.
1949, Apr. 1   Engr.   Perf. 12
B1 SP1 4c + 2c sepia   1.50 1.50
B2 SP2 6c + 4c violet   5.00 5.00
B3 SP3 18c + 7c blue   6.00 6.00
    Nos. B1-B3 (3)   12.50 12.50
The surtax was for restoration of war-damaged public libraries.

War Widow and Children SP4   Disabled Veteran SP5

1950, Nov. 30
B4 SP4 2c + 2c red   .40 .25
B5 SP5 4c + 4c violet .60 .30
The surtax was for war widows and children and disabled veterans of World War II.
For surcharges see Nos. 648-649.

Mrs. Manuel L. Quezon — SP6

1952, Aug. 19   Perf. 12
B6 SP6 5c + 1c dp bl   .40 .30
B7 SP6 6c + 2c car rose .60 .45
The surtax was used to encourage planting and care of fruit trees among Philippine children. For surcharge see No. 872.

Quezon Institute — SP7

1958, Aug. 19   Photo.   Perf. 13½
Cross in Red
B8   SP7 5c + 5c grn   .30 .25
  a.   Perf. 12   1.75 .90
B9   SP7 10c + 5c dp vio .45 .30
  a.   Perf. 12   7.50 1.75
These stamps were obligatory on all mail from Aug. 19-Sept. 30.
For surcharges see Nos. 849, B12-B13, B16.

The surtax on all semi-postals from Nos. B8-B9 onward was for the Philippine Tuberculosis Society unless otherwise stated.

Scout Cooking — SP8

1959   Engr.   Perf. 13
Yellow Paper
B10 SP8 6c + 4c shown   .40 1.00
B11 SP8 25c + 5c Archery   .60 1.50
  a. Nos. B10-B11 tête bêche, white 1.25 3.00
    Nos. B10-B11,CB1-CB3 (5) 4.50 6.00
10th Boy Scout World Jamboree, Makiling National Park, July 17-26. The surtax was to finance the Jamboree.
For souvenir sheet see No. CB3a. For surcharges see Nos. 832-833, C111.

Nos. B8-B9 Surcharged in Red

1959   Photo.   Perf. 13½
B12 SP7 3c + 5c on 5c + 5c   .30 .25
  a. "3 + 5" and bars omitted
  b. Perf. 12   5.00 3.00
B13 SP7 6c + 5c on 10c + 5c   .50 .25
  a. Perf. 12   3.50 1.75

Bohol Sanatorium SP9

1959, Aug. 19   Engr.   Perf. 12
Cross in Red
B14 SP9 6c + 5c yel grn   .30 .25
B15 SP9 25c + 5c vio bl   .50 .30

No. B8 Surcharged "Help Prevent TB" and New Value
1960, Aug. 19   Photo.   Perf. 13½
B16 SP7 6c + 5c on 5c + 5c   .50 .25

Roxas Memorial T.B. Pavilion — SP10

Perf. 11½
1961, Aug. 19   Unwmk.   Photo.
B17 SP10 6c + 5c brn & red   .50 .25

Emiliano J. Valdes T.B. Pavilion — SP11

1962, Aug. 19   Cross in Red
B18 SP11 6s + 5s dk vio   .30 .25
B19 SP11 30s + 5s ultra   .45 .25
B20 SP11 70s + 5s brt bl   .85 .50
    Nos. B18-B20 (3)   1.60 1.00

José Rizal Playing Chess — SP12

Design: 30s+5s, Rizal fencing.

1962, Dec. 30   Engr.   Perf. 13
B21 SP12 6s + 4s grn & rose lil   .50 1.00
B22 SP12 30s + 5s brt bl & cl   1.00 2.00
Surtax for Rizal Foundation.
For surcharges see Nos. 942-943.

Map of Philippines and Cross — SP13

1963, Aug. 19   Unwmk.   Perf. 13
B23 SP13 6s + 5s vio & red   .25 .25
B24 SP13 10s + 5s grn & red .40 .25
B25 SP13 50s + 5s brn & red .85 .35
    Nos. B23-B25 (3)   1.50 .85

Negros Oriental T.B. Pavilion SP14

1964, Aug. 19   Photo.   Perf. 13½
Cross in Red
B26 SP14 5s + 5s brt pur   .30 .25
B27 SP14 6s + 5s ultra   .30 .25
B28 SP14 30s + 5s brown   .45 .25
B29 SP14 70s + 5s green   .75 .50
    Nos. B26-B29 (4)   1.80 1.25
For surcharges see Nos. 986, 1586.

No. B27 Surcharged in Red with New Value and Two Bars
1965, Aug. 19   Cross in Red
B30 SP14 1s + 5s on 6s + 5s   .50 .25
B31 SP14 3s + 5s on 6s + 5s   .60 .25

Stork-billed Kingfisher — SP15

Birds: 5s+5s, Rufous hornbill. 10s+5s, Monkey-eating eagle. 30s+5s, Great-billed parrot.

1967, Aug. 19   Photo.   Perf. 13½
B32 SP15 1s + 5s multi   .40 .25
B33 SP15 5s + 5s multi   .40 .25
B34 SP15 10s + 5s multi   1.00 .25
B35 SP15 30s + 5s multi   3.25 .70
    Nos. B32-B35 (4)   5.05 1.45

1969, Aug. 15   Litho.   Perf. 13½
Birds: 1s+5s, Three-toed woodpecker. 5s+5s, Philippine trogon. 10s+5s, Mt. Apo lorikeet. 40s+5s, Scarlet minivet.
B36 SP15 1s + 5s multi   .50 .25
B37 SP15 5s + 5s multi   .80 .25
B38 SP15 10s + 5s multi   1.50 .30
B39 SP15 40s + 5s multi   2.75 .70
    Nos. B36-B39 (4)   5.55 1.50

Julia V. de Ortigas and Tuberculosis Society Building SP16

1970, Aug. 3   Photo.   Perf. 13½
B40 SP16 1s + 5s multi   .40 .25
B41 SP16 5s + 5s multi   .40 .25
B42 SP16 30s + 5s multi   1.20 .45
B43 SP16 70s + 5s multi   2.00 .55
    Nos. B40-B43 (4)   4.00 1.50
Mrs. Julia V. de Ortigas was president of the Philippine Tuberculosis Soc., 1932-69.
For surcharge see No. 1251.

Mabolo, Santol, Chico, Papaya SP17

Philippine Fruits: 10s+5s, Balimbing, atis, mangosteen, macupa, bananas. 40s+5s, Susong-kalabao, avocado, duhat, watermelon, guava, mango. 1p+5s, Lanzones, oranges, sirhuelas, pineapple.

1972, Aug. 1   Litho.   Perf. 13
B44 SP17 1s + 5s multi   .40 .25
B45 SP17 10s + 5s multi   .40 .25
B46 SP17 40s + 5s multi   .80 .25
B47 SP17 1p + 5s multi   2.40 .50
    Nos. B44-B47 (4)   4.00 1.35

Nos. B45-B46 Surcharged with New Value and 2 Bars
1973, June 15
B48 SP17 15s + 5s on 10s + 5s   .50 .25
B49 SP17 60s + 5s on 40s + 5s 1.50 .35

Dr. Basilio J. Valdes and Veterans Memorial Hospital SP18

1974, July 8   Litho.   *Perf. 12½*
Cross in Red
B50	SP18	15s + 5s blue grn	.40	.25
a.		Imperf.	.85	.70
B51	SP18	1.10p + 5s vio blue	1.50	1.00
a.		Imperf.	4.00	3.00

Dr. Valdes (1892-1970) was president of Philippine Tuberculosis Society. For surcharges see Nos. 1250, 1252.

AIR POST STAMPS

Madrid-Manila Flight Issue
Issued to commemorate the flight of Spanish aviators Gallarza and Loriga from Madrid to Manila.

Regular Issue of 1917-26 Overprinted in Red or Violet

Designs: Nos. C7-C8, Adm. William T. Sampson. No. C9, Adm. George Dewey.

1926, May 13   Unwmk.   *Perf. 11*
C1	A40	2c green (R)	20.00	25.00
		Never hinged	45.00	
C2	A40	4c carmine (V)	30.00	35.00
		Never hinged	55.00	
a.		Inverted overprint	2,600.	—
C3	A40	6c lilac (R)	60.00	90.00
		Never hinged	125.00	
C4	A40	8c org brn (V)	60.00	85.00
		Never hinged	125.00	
C5	A40	10c deep blue (R)	80.00	85.00
		Never hinged	140.00	
C6	A40	12c red org (V)	70.00	95.00
		Never hinged	150.00	
C7	A40	16c lt ol grn (V)	2,800.	3,250.
C8	A40	16c ol bister (V)	5,000.	5,000.
C9	A40	16c ol grn (V)	90.00	125.00
		Never hinged	160.00	
C10	A40	20c org ye (V)	90.00	125.00
		Never hinged	160.00	
C11	A40	26c blue grn (V)	90.00	125.00
		Never hinged	160.00	
C12	A40	30c gray (V)	90.00	125.00
		Never hinged	160.00	
C13	A41	2p vio brn (R)	500.00	600.00
		Never hinged	1,100.	
C14	A41	4p dk blue (R)	800.00	900.00
		Never hinged	1,300.	
C15	A41	10p dp grn (V)	1,000.	1,350.

Same Overprint on No. 269
Wmk. Single-lined PIPS (190)
Perf. 12
C16	A40	26c blue grn (V)	5,000.

Same Overprint on No. 284
Perf. 10
C17	A41	1p pale violet (V)	300.00	250.00
		Never hinged	450.00	

London-Orient Flight Issue
Issued Nov. 9, 1928, to celebrate the arrival of a British squadron of hydroplanes.

Regular Issue of 1917-25 Overprinted in Red

1928, Nov. 9   *Perf. 11*
C18	A40	2c green	1.00	1.00
		Never hinged	2.00	
C19	A40	4c carmine	1.25	1.50
		Never hinged	2.00	
C20	A40	6c violet	5.00	3.00
		Never hinged	10.00	
C21	A40	8c orange brown	5.00	3.00
		Never hinged	10.00	
C22	A40	10c deep blue	5.00	3.00
		Never hinged	10.00	
C23	A40	12c red orange	8.00	4.00
		Never hinged	12.00	
C24	A40	16c ol grn (No. 303a)	8.00	4.00
		Never hinged	12.00	
C25	A40	20c orange yellow	8.00	4.00
		Never hinged	12.00	
C26	A40	26c blue green	20.00	8.00
		Never hinged	35.00	
C27	A40	30c gray	20.00	8.00
		Never hinged	35.00	

Same Overprint on No. 271
Wmk. Single-lined PIPS (190)
Perf. 12
C28	A41	1p pale violet	55.00	30.00
		Never hinged	90.00	
		Nos. C18-C28 (11)	136.25	69.50
		Set, never hinged	230.00	

Von Gronau Issue
Commemorating the visit of Capt. Wolfgang von Gronau's airplane on its round-the-world flight.

Nos. 354-360 Overprinted

1932, Sept. 27   Unwmk.   *Perf. 11*
C29	A43	2c yellow green	.90	.60
		Never hinged	1.40	
C30	A44	4c rose carmine	.90	.40
		Never hinged	1.40	
C31	A45	12c orange	1.25	.65
		Never hinged	2.00	
C32	A46	18c red orange	5.00	5.00
		Never hinged	8.00	
C33	A47	20c yellow	3.50	3.50
		Never hinged	5.75	
C34	A48	24c deep violet	3.50	4.00
		Never hinged	5.75	
C35	A49	32c olive brown	3.50	3.00
		Never hinged	5.75	
		Nos. C29-C35 (7)	18.55	17.15
		Set, never hinged	31.55	

Rein Issue
Commemorating the flight from Madrid to Manila of the Spanish aviator Fernando Rein y Loring.

Regular Issue of 1917-25 Overprinted

1933, Apr. 11
C36	A40	2c green	.75	.45
		Never hinged	1.10	
C37	A40	4c carmine	.90	.45
		Never hinged	1.40	
C38	A40	6c deep violet	1.10	.80
		Never hinged	1.75	
C39	A40	8c orange brown	3.75	2.00
		Never hinged	5.75	
		P# block of 10, Impt.	120.00	
			150.00	
C40	A40	10c dark blue	3.75	2.25
		Never hinged	5.75	
		P# block of 10, Impt.	120.00	
			150.00	
C41	A40	12c orange	3.75	2.00
		Never hinged	5.75	
		P# block of 10, Impt.	120.00	
			150.00	
C42	A40	16c olive green	3.50	2.00
		Never hinged	5.25	
		P# block of 6	160.00	
			200.00	
C43	A40	20c yellow	3.75	2.00
		Never hinged	5.75	
		P# block of 10, Impt.	160.00	
			200.00	
C44	A40	26c green	3.75	2.75
		Never hinged	5.75	
a.		26c blue green	4.00	2.00
		Never hinged	6.00	
C45	A40	30c gray	4.00	3.00
		Never hinged	6.00	
		Nos. C36-C45 (10)	29.00	17.70
		Set, never hinged	44.25	

No. 290a Overprinted

Printed by the Philippine Bureau.
1933, May 26
C46	A40	2c green	.65	.40
		Never hinged	1.00	
		P# block of 6	12.00	
			15.00	

Regular Issue of 1932 Overprinted

C47	A44	4c rose carmine	.30	.25
		Never hinged	.45	
		P# block of 6	16.00	
			20.00	
C48	A45	12c orange	.60	.25
		Never hinged	.90	
		P# block of 6	20.00	
			25.00	
C49	A47	20c yellow	.60	.25
		Never hinged	.90	
		P# block of 6	20.00	
			25.00	
C50	A48	24c deep violet	.65	.25
		Never hinged	1.00	
		P# block of 6	24.00	
			30.00	
C51	A49	32c olive brown	.85	.50
		Never hinged	1.40	
		Nos. C46-C51 (6)	3.65	1.75
		Set, never hinged	5.65	

Transpacific Issue
Issued to commemorate the China Clipper flight from Manila to San Francisco, Dec. 2-5, 1935.

Nos. 387, 392 Overprinted in Gold

1935, Dec. 2
C52	A57	10c rose carmine	.40	.25
		Never hinged	.60	
C53	A62	30c orange red	.60	.35
		Never hinged	.90	

Manila-Madrid Flight Issue
Issued to commemorate the Manila-Madrid flight by aviators Antonio Arnaiz and Juan Calvo.

Regular Issue of 1917-25 Surcharged in Various Colors

1936, Sept. 6
C54	A40	2c on 4c carmine (Bl)	.25	.25
		Never hinged	.25	
C55	A40	6c on 12c red org (V)	.25	.25
		Never hinged	.30	
C56	A40	16c on 26c blue grn (Bk)	.25	.25
		Never hinged	.40	
a.		16c on 26c green	2.00	.70
		Never hinged	3.00	
		Nos. C54-C56 (3)	.75	.75
		Set, never hinged	.95	

Air Mail Exhibition Issue
Issued to commemorate the first Air Mail Exhibition, held Feb. 17-19, 1939.

Regular Issue of 1917-37 Surcharged in Black or Red

1939, Feb. 17
C57	A40	8c on 26c blue grn (Bk)	2.00	2.00
		Never hinged	4.00	
a.		8c on 26c green (Bk)	10.00	4.00
		Never hinged	16.00	
C58	A71	1p on 10p gray (R)	8.00	4.00
		Never hinged	12.00	

Moro Vinta and Clipper — AP1

1941, June 30
C59	AP1	8c carmine	2.00	.60
		Never hinged	2.75	
C60	AP1	20c ultramarine	3.00	.50
		Never hinged	4.00	
C61	AP1	60c blue green	3.00	1.00
		Never hinged	4.00	
C62	AP1	1p sepia	.70	.50
		Never hinged	1.00	
		Nos. C59-C62 (4)	8.70	2.60
		Set, never hinged	11.75	

For overprint see No. NO7. For surcharges see Nos. N10-N11, N35-N36.

No. C47 Hstmpd. in Violet

1944, Dec. 3
C63	A44	4c rose carmine	3,750.	2,750.

> Catalogue values for unused stamps in this section, from this point to the end of the section, are for Never Hinged items.

Republic

Manuel L. Quezon and Franklin D. Roosevelt — AP2

Unwmk.
1947, Aug. 19   Engr.   *Perf. 12*
C64	AP2	6c dark green	.60	.50
C65	AP2	40c red orange	1.40	1.00
C66	AP2	80c deep blue	5.00	2.75
		Nos. C64-C66 (3)	7.00	4.25

FAO Type
1948, Feb. 23   Typo.   *Perf. 12½*
C67	A89	40c dk car & pink	12.50	6.00

Junior Chamber Type
1950, Mar. 1   Engr.   *Perf. 12*
C68	A96	30c deep orange	1.50	.40
C69	A96	50c carmine rose	2.50	.70

F. D. Roosevelt Type
Souvenir Sheet
1950, May 22   *Imperf.*
C70	A98	80c deep green	4.00	2.50

Lions Club Type
1950, June 2   *Perf. 12*
C71	A99	30c emerald	2.00	.45
C72	A99	50c ultra	2.50	.60
a.		Souvenir sheet of 2, #C71-C72	5.00	4.00

Maria Clara Type
1952, Nov. 16   *Perf. 12½*
C73	A112	30c rose carmine	2.00	.75

Exists imperf. Value, $25.

Postage Stamp Cent. Type
1954, Apr. 25   *Perf. 13*
1854 Stamp in Orange
C74	A119	10c dark brown	3.00	1.00
C75	A119	20c dark green	5.00	1.60
C76	A119	50c carmine	10.00	3.25
		Nos. C74-C76 (3)	18.00	5.85

Rotary Intl. Type
1955, Feb. 23
C77	A123	50c blue green	2.50	1.00

Lt. José Gozar — AP10

20c, 50c, Lt. Gozar. 30c, 70c, Lt. Basa.

1955   Engr.   *Perf. 13*
C78	AP10	20c deep violet	1.50	.25
C79	AP10	30c red	1.00	.25
C80	AP10	50c bluish green	1.00	.25
C81	AP10	70c blue	1.50	.90
		Nos. C78-C81 (4)	5.00	1.65

Lt. José Gozar and Lt. Cesar Fernando Basa, Filipino aviators in World War II.

Constitution Type of Regular Issue
1960, Feb. 8   Photo.   *Perf. 12½x13½*
C82	A146	30c brt bl & silver	.75	.25

Air Force Plane of 1935 and Saber Jet — AP11

1960, May 2   Engr.   *Perf. 14x14½*
C83	AP11	10c carmine	.40	.25
C84	AP11	20c ultra	.60	.25

25th anniversary of Philippine Air Force. For surcharge see No. 847.

Olympic Type of Regular Issue
30c, Sharpshooter. 70c, Woman swimmer.

1960, Nov. 30   Photo.   *Perf. 13x13½*
C85	A150	30c orange & brn	.60	.35
C86	A150	70c grnsh bl & vio brn	1.40	.70

Postal Conference Type
1961, Feb. 23   *Perf. 13½x13*
C87	A152	30c multicolored	.70	.25

Freedom from Hunger Type
1963, Dec. 20   Photo.
C88	A168	30s lt grn & multi	.40	.25
C89	A168	50s multicolored	.75	.30

Land Reform Type

1964, Dec. 21   Wmk. 233   Perf. 14½
C90 A172 30s multicolored   .60   .25

Mass Baptism by Father Andres de Urdaneta, Cebu
AP12

70s, World map showing route of the Cross from Spain to Mexico to Cebu, and two galleons.

Unwmk.
1965, Oct. 4   Photo.   Perf. 13
C91 AP12 30s multicolored   .70   .25
C92 AP12 70s multicolored   1.50   .50
  a.   Souvenir sheet of 4   6.00 4.00

400th anniv. of the Christianization of the Philippines. No. C92a contains four imperf. stamps similar to Nos. 934-935 and C91-C92 with simulated perforation.
For surcharge see No. C108.

Souvenir Sheet

Family and Progress Symbols
AP13

1966, July 22   Photo.   Imperf.
C93 AP13 70s multicolored   6.00 4.25

50th anniv. of the Philippine Natl. Bank. No. C93 contains one stamp with simulated perforation superimposed on a facsimile of a 50p banknote of 1916.

Eruption of Taal Volcano and Refugees
AP14

1967, Oct. 1   Photo.   Perf. 13½x13
C94 AP14 70s multicolored   1.00   .50

Eruption of Taal Volcano, Sept. 28, 1965.

Eruption of Taal Volcano — AP15

1968, Oct. 1   Litho.   Perf. 13½
C95 AP15 70s multicolored   1.00   .55

Eruption of Taal Volcano, Sept. 28, 1965.

Rotary Type of 1969

1969, Jan. 29   Photo.   Perf. 12½
C96 A202 40s green & multi   .50   .25
C97 A202 75s red & multi   1.20   .50

Holy Child Type of Regular Issue

1969, June 30   Photo.   Perf. 13½
C98 A207 40s ultra & multi   1.20   .25

Pope Type of Regular Issue

1970, Nov. 27   Photo.   Perf. 13½x14
C99 A221 40s violet & multi   1.00   .30

Law College Type of Regular Issue

1971, June 15   Perf. 13
C100 A225 1p green & multi   1.20   .50

Manila Type of Regular Issue

1971, June 24
C101 A226 1p multi & blue   1.20   .50

Santo Tomas Type of Regular Issue

1971, July 8   Photo.   Perf. 13½
C102 A227 2p lt blue & multi   1.50   .80

Congress Type of Regular Issue

1972, Apr. 11   Photo.   Perf. 13½x13
C103 A232 40s green & multi   .90   .25

Tropical Fish Type of Regular Issue

1972, Aug. 14   Photo.   Perf. 13
C104 A235 50s Dusky angelfish   1.75   .60

Pope Paul VI Type of Regular Issue

1972, Sept. 26   Photo.   Perf. 14
C105 A237 60s lt blue & multi   1.00   .40

First Mass Type of Regular Issue

1972, Oct. 31   Photo.   Perf. 14
C106 A241 60s multicolored   .75   .40

Presidential Palace Type of Regular Issue

1973, Nov. 15   Litho.   Perf. 14
C107 A253 60s multicolored   1.20   .35

No. C92a Surcharged and Overprinted with US Bicentennial Emblems and: "U.S.A. BICENTENNIAL / 1776-1976" in Black or Red

Unwmk.
1976, Sept. 20   Photo.   Imperf.
C108   Sheet of 4 (B)   3.00 3.00
  a.   A179 5s on 3s multi   .25   .25
  b.   A179 5s on 6s multi   .25   .25
  c.   AP12 15s on 30s multi   .40   .30
  d.   AP12 50s on 70s multi   .75   .35
C108A   Sheet of 4 (R)   4.50 4.50

American Bicentennial. Nos. C108a-C108d are overprinted with Bicentennial emblem and 2 bars over old denomination. Inscription and 2 Bicentennial emblems overprinted in margin.

Souvenir Sheet

AMPHILEX '77, Intl. Stamp Exhibition — AP16

Netherlands No. 1 and Philippines No. 1 and Windmill

1977, May 26   Litho.   Perf. 14½
C109 AP16 Sheet of 3   10.00 10.00
  a.   7.50p multicolored   2.75 2.75

AMPHILEX '77, International Stamp Exhibition, Amsterdam, May 26-June 5.
Exists imperf. Value $20.

Souvenir Sheet

ESPAMER '77 — AP17

Philippines and Spain Nos. 1, Bull and Matador.

1977, Oct. 7   Litho.   Perf. 12½x13
C110 AP17 Sheet of 3   10.00 10.00
  a.   7.50p multicolored   2.75 2.75

ESPAMER '77 (Exposicion Filatelica de America y Europa), Barcelona, Spain, 10/7-13.
Exists imperf. Value $18.

Nos. B10 and CB3a Surcharged

1979, July 5   Engr.   Perf. 13
C111 SP8 90s on 6c + 4c car,
           yel   2.00 1.00

Souvenir Sheet
White Paper

C112   Sheet of 5   6.00 6.00
  a.   SP8 50s on 6c + 4c carmine   .75   .50
  b.   SP8 50s on 25c + 5c blue   .75   .50
  c.   SP8 50s on 30c + 10c green   .75   .50
  d.   SP8 50s on 70c + 20c red
           brown   .75   .50
  e.   SP8 50s on 80c + 20c violet   .75   .50

First Scout Philatelic Exhibition, Quezon City, July 4-14, commemorating 25th anniversary of First National Jamboree.
Surcharge on No. C111 includes "AIRMAIL." Violet marginal inscriptions on No. C112 overprinted with heavy bars; new commemorative inscriptions and Scout emblem added.

AIR POST SEMI-POSTAL STAMPS

Catalogue values for unused stamps in this section are for Never Hinged items.

Type of Semi-Postal Issue, 1959

Designs: 30c+10c, Bicycling. 70c+20c, Scout with plane model. 80c+20c, Pres. Carlos P. Garcia and scout shaking hands.

Unwmk.
1959, July 17   Engr.   Perf. 13
CB1 SP8 30c + 10c green   .75   .75
CB2 SP8 70c + 20c red brown   1.25 1.25
CB3 SP8 80c + 20c violet   1.50 1.50
  a.   Souvenir sheet of 5   7.00 7.00
       Nos. CB1-CB3 (3)   3.50 3.50

10th Boy Scout World Jamboree, Makiling Natl. Park, July 17-26. Surtax was for the Jamboree.
No. CB3a measures 171x89mm. and contains one each of Nos. CB1-CB3 and types of Nos. B10-B11 on white paper. Sold for 4p.
For surcharge see No. C112.

SPECIAL DELIVERY STAMPS

United States No. E5 Overprinted in Red

Wmk. Double-lined USPS (191)
1901, Oct. 15   Perf. 12
E1 SD3 10c dark blue   100.   80.
       Never hinged   185.
  a.   Dots in curved frame above mes-
       senger (Pl. 882)   175. 160.

Special Delivery Messenger
SD2

Wmk. Double-lined PIPS (191PI)
1906, Sept. 8
E2 SD2 20c deep ultra   45.00 8.00
       Never hinged   90.00
  b.   20c pale ultramarine   35.00 8.00
       Never hinged   70.00

See Nos. E3-E6. For overprints see Nos. E7-E10, EO1.

SPECIAL PRINTING

U.S. No. E6 Overprinted in Red

Wmk. Double-lined USPS (191)
1907
E2A SD4 10c ultramarine   3,250.

Wmk. Single-lined PIPS (190PI)
1911, Apr.
E3 SD2 20c deep ultra   22.00 1.75
       Never hinged   42.00

1916   Perf. 10
E4 SD2 20c deep ultra   175.00 150.00
       Never hinged   275.00

1919   Unwmk.   Perf. 11
E5 SD2 20c ultramarine   .60   .25
       Never hinged   .90
  a.   20c pale blue   .75   .25
       Never hinged   1.00
  b.   20c dull violet   .60   .25
       Never hinged   .90

Type of 1906 Issue
1925-31   Imperf.
E6 SD2 20c dull violet ('31)   27.50 75.00
       Never hinged   40.00
  a.   20c violet blue ('25)   50.00
       Never hinged   80.00

Type of 1919 Overprinted in Black

1939, Apr. 27   Perf. 11
E7 SD2 20c blue violet   .25   .25
       Never hinged   .40

Nos. E5b and E7, Hstmpd. in Violet

1944
E8 SD2 20c dull violet (On
           E5b)   1,400. 550.00
       On cover   —
       Block of 4   6,000.
E9 SD2 20c blue violet (On
           E7)   550.00 250.00

Type SD2 Overprinted

1945, May 1
E10 SD2 20c blue violet   .70   .55
       Never hinged   1.10
  a.   "IC" close together   3.25 2.75
       Never hinged   4.75

Catalogue values for unused stamps in this section, from this point to the end of the section, are for Never Hinged items.

Republic

Manila Post Office and Messenger — SD3

Unwmk.
1947, Dec. 22   Engr.   Perf. 12
E11 SD3 20c rose lilac   .60   .40

Post Office Building, Manila, and Hands with Letter — SD4

1962, Jan. 23   Perf. 13½x13
E12 SD4 20c lilac rose   .70   .30

SPECIAL DELIVERY OFFICIAL STAMP

Type of 1906
Issue Overprinted

1931	Unwmk.	Perf. 11	
EO1	SD2 20c dull violet	3.00	75.00
	Never hinged	4.50	
	P# block of 6	150.00	
	Never hinged	190.00	
a.	No period after "B"	50.00	250.00
	Never hinged	75.00	
b.	Double overprint		

It is strongly recommended that expert opinion be acquired for Nos. EO1 and EO1a used.

POSTAGE DUE STAMPS

U.S. Nos. J38-J44
Overprinted in Black

Wmk. Double-lined USPS (191)

1899, Aug. 16		Perf. 12	
J1	D2 1c deep claret	7.50	2.50
	Never hinged	15.00	
J2	D2 2c deep claret	7.50	2.50
	Never hinged	15.00	
J3	D2 5c deep claret	15.00	2.50
	Never hinged	30.00	
J4	D2 10c deep claret	19.00	5.50
	Never hinged	37.50	
J5	D2 50c deep claret	250.00	100.00
	Never hinged	425.00	

No. J1 was used to pay regular postage Sept. 5-19, 1902.

1901, Aug. 31			
J6	D2 3c deep claret	17.50	7.00
	Never hinged	35.00	
J7	D2 30c deep claret	250.00	110.00
	Never hinged	415.00	
	Nos. J1-J7 (7)	566.50	230.00
	Set, never hinged	882.50	

Post Office Clerk — D3

1928, Aug. 21	Unwmk.	Perf. 11	
J8	D3 4c brown red	.25	.25
	Never hinged	.25	
	P# block of 6	14.00	
	Never hinged	17.50	
J9	D3 6c brown red	.30	.75
	Never hinged	.45	
	P# block of 6	14.00	
	Never hinged	17.50	
J10	D3 8c brown red	.25	.75
	Never hinged	.35	
	P# block of 6	14.00	
	Never hinged	17.50	
J11	D3 10c brown red	.30	.75
	Never hinged	.45	
	P# block of 6	14.00	
	Never hinged	17.50	
J12	D3 12c brown red	.25	.75
	Never hinged	.35	
	P# block of 6	14.00	
	Never hinged	17.50	
J13	D3 16c brown red	.30	.75
	Never hinged	.45	
	P# block of 6	14.00	
	Never hinged	17.50	
J14	D3 20c brown red	.30	.75
	Never hinged	.45	
	P# block of 6	14.00	
	Never hinged	17.50	
	Nos. J8-J14 (7)	1.95	4.75
	Set, never hinged	2.75	

No. J8 Surcharged in Blue

1937, July 29	Unwmk.	Perf. 11	
J15	D3 3c on 4c brown red	.25	.25
	Never hinged	.35	

See note after No. NJ1.

Nos. J8 to J14
Handstamped in Violet

1944, Dec. 3			
J16	D3 4c brown red	150.00	—
J17	D3 6c brown red	100.00	—
J18	D3 8c brown red	110.00	350.00
J19	D3 10c brown red	100.00	—
J20	D3 12c brown red	100.00	—
J21	D3 16c brown red	100.00	350.00
a.	Pair, one without ovpt.		
J22	D3 20c brown red	110.00	—
	Nos. J16-J22 (7)	770.00	

> **Catalogue values for unused stamps in this section, from this point to the end of the section, are for Never Hinged items.**

Republic

D4

1947, Oct. 20	Unwmk. Engr.	Perf. 12	
J23	D4 3c rose carmine	.30	.25
J24	D4 4c brt violet blue	.55	.25
J25	D4 6c olive green	.75	.40
J26	D4 10c orange	.80	.50
	Nos. J23-J26 (4)	2.40	1.40

OFFICIAL STAMPS

Official Handstamped Overprints

"Officers purchasing stamps for government business may, if they so desire, surcharge them with the letters O.B. either in writing with black ink or by rubber stamps but in such a manner as not to obliterate the stamp that postmasters will be unable to determine whether the stamps have been previously used." C.M. Cotterman, Director of Posts, December 26, 1905.

Beginning January 1, 1906, all branches of the Insular Government used postage stamps to prepay postage instead of franking them as before. Some officials used manuscript, some utilized the typewriting machines but by far the larger number provided themselves with rubber stamps. The majority of these read "O.B." but other forms were: "OFFICIAL BUSINESS" or "OFFICIAL MAIL" in two lines, with variations on many of these.

These "O.B." overprints are known on U.S. 1899-1901 stamps; on 1903-06 stamps in red and blue; on 1906 stamps in red, blue, black, yellow and green.

"O.B." overprints were also made on the centavo and peso stamps of the Philippines, per order of May 25, 1907.

Beginning in 1926 the Bureau of Posts issued press-printed official stamps, but many government offices continued to handstamp ordinary postage stamps "O.B." The press-printed "O.B." overprints are listed below.

During the Japanese occupation period 1942-45, the same system of handstamped official overprints prevailed, but the handstamp usually consisted of "K.P.", initials of the Tagalog words, "Kagamitang Pampamahalaan" (Official Business), and the two Japanese characters used in the printed overprint on Nos. NO1 to NO4.

Regular Issue of 1926 Ovptd. in Red

1926, Dec. 20	Unwmk.	Perf. 12	
O1	A42 2c green & black	3.00	1.00
	Never hinged	4.50	
O2	A42 4c car & blk	3.00	1.25
	Never hinged	4.50	
a.	Vertical pair, imperf. between	550.00	
O3	A42 18c lt brn & blk	8.00	4.00
	Never hinged	12.00	
O4	A42 20c org & blk	7.75	1.75
	Never hinged	11.50	
	Nos. O1-O4 (4)	21.75	8.00
	Set, never hinged	32.50	

Opening of the Legislative Palace.

Regular Issue of 1917-26
Overprinted by the U.S.
Bureau of Engraving and Printing

 O.B.

1931		Perf. 11	
O5	A40 2c green	.40	.25
	Never hinged	.65	
	P# block of 6	20.00	
	Never hinged	25.00	
a.	No period after "B"	17.50	17.50
	Never hinged	27.50	
b.	No period after "O"	40.00	30.00
O6	A40 4c carmine	.45	.25
	Never hinged	.70	
	P# block of 6	20.00	
	Never hinged	25.00	
a.	No period after "B"	40.00	20.00
	Never hinged	60.00	
O7	A40 6c deep violet	.75	.25
	Never hinged	1.25	
	P# block of 6	40.00	
	Never hinged	50.00	
O8	A40 8c yellow brown	.75	.25
	Never hinged	1.25	
	P# block of 6	32.00	
	Never hinged	40.00	
	P# block of 10, Impt.	40.00	
	Never hinged	50.00	
O9	A40 10c deep blue	1.20	.25
	Never hinged	1.90	
	P# block of 10, Impt.	32.00	
	Never hinged	40.00	
O10	A40 12c red orange	2.00	.25
	Never hinged	3.00	
	P# block of 6	65.00	
	Never hinged	80.00	
	P# block of 10, Impt.	80.00	
	Never hinged	95.00	
a.	No period after "B"	80.00	80.00
	Never hinged	120.00	
O11	A40 16c lt ol grn	1.00	.25
	Never hinged	1.50	
	P# block of 6	24.00	
	Never hinged	30.00	
a.	16c olive bister	2.00	.25
	Never hinged	3.00	
	P# block of 6	20.00	
	Never hinged	25.00	
O12	A40 20c orange yellow	1.25	.25
	Never hinged	1.90	
	P# block of 10, Impt.	75.00	
	Never hinged	95.00	
a.	No period after "B"	80.00	80.00
	Never hinged	120.00	
O13	A40 26c green	2.00	1.00
	Never hinged	3.25	
	P# block of 6	120.00	
	Never hinged	150.00	
a.	26c blue green	2.50	1.50
	Never hinged	4.00	
	P# block of 6	130.00	
	Never hinged	165.00	
O14	A40 30c gray	2.00	.25
	Never hinged	3.25	
	P# block of 10, Impt.	80.00	
	Never hinged	100.00	
	Nos. O5-O14 (10)	11.80	3.25
	Set, never hinged	18.65	

Many collectors prefer to collect the plate blocks of 6 of Nos. O5-O6, O8, O10-O11a and O14 as blocks of 10 so they fit aesthetically with the other plate blocks of 10 with imprints.

 O.B.

Overprinted on Nos. 383-392

1935			
O15	A53 2c rose	.25	.25
	Never hinged	.30	
	P# block of 6	4.75	
	Never hinged	6.00	
a.	No period after "B"	15.00	10.00
	Never hinged	22.50	
b.	No period after "O"	—	—
O16	A54 4c yellow green	.25	.25
	Never hinged	.30	
	P# block of 6	4.00	
	Never hinged	5.00	
a.	No period after "B"	15.00	40.00
	Never hinged	22.50	
O17	A55 6c dark brown	.25	.25
	Never hinged	.40	
	P# block of 6	8.00	
	Never hinged	10.00	
a.	No period after "B"	35.00	35.00
	Never hinged	52.50	
O18	A56 8c violet	.30	.25
	Never hinged	.45	
	P# block of 6	9.50	
	Never hinged	12.00	
O19	A57 10c rose carmine	.30	.25
	Never hinged	.45	
	P# block of 6	8.00	
	Never hinged	10.00	
O20	A58 12c black	.75	.25
	Never hinged	1.10	
	P# block of 6	8.00	
	Never hinged	10.00	
O21	A59 16c dark blue	.55	.25
	Never hinged	.85	
	P# block of 6	8.00	
	Never hinged	10.00	
O22	A60 20c light olive green	.60	.25
	Never hinged	.90	
	P# block of 6	10.00	
	Never hinged	15.00	
O23	A61 26c indigo	.90	.25
	Never hinged	1.50	
	P# block of 6	20.00	
	Never hinged	25.00	

O24	A62 30c orange red	.80	.25
	Never hinged	1.20	
	P# block of 6	20.00	
	Never hinged	25.00	
	Nos. O15-O24 (10)	4.95	2.50
	Set, never hinged	7.40	

 O.B.

Nos. 411 and 418 with
Additional Overprint in Black

1937-38			
O25	A53 2c rose	.25	.25
	Never hinged	.30	
a.	No period after "B"	25.00	25.00
	Never hinged	45.00	
b.	Period after "B" raised (UL 4)	150.00	
O26	A60 20c lt ol grn ('38)	.70	.50
	Never hinged	1.10	
	P# block of 6	20.00	
	Never hinged	25.00	

Regular Issue of 1935 Overprinted In Black

a   b

1938-40			
O27	A53(a) 2c rose	.25	.25
	Never hinged	.30	
	P# block of 6	4.75	
	Never hinged	6.00	
a.	Hyphen omitted	10.00	10.00
	Never hinged	15.00	
b.	No period after "B"	20.00	30.00
	Never hinged	30.00	
O28	A54(b) 4c yellow green	.75	1.00
	Never hinged	1.10	
	P# block of 6	24.00	
	Never hinged	30.00	
O29	A55(b) 6c dark brown	.30	.25
	Never hinged	.45	
	P# block of 6	12.00	
	Never hinged	15.00	
O30	A56(b) 8c violet	.75	.85
	Never hinged	1.10	
	P# block of 6	9.50	
	Never hinged	12.00	
O31	A57(b) 10c rose carmine	.25	.25
	Never hinged	.30	
	P# block of 6	16.00	
	Never hinged	20.00	
a.	No period after "O"	50.00	40.00
	Never hinged	75.00	
O32	A58(b) 12c black	.30	.25
	Never hinged	.45	
	P# block of 6	12.00	
	Never hinged	15.00	
O33	A59(b) 16c dark blue	.30	.25
	Never hinged	.45	
	P# block of 6	16.00	
	Never hinged	20.00	
O34	A60(a) 20c lt ol grn ('40)	.55	.85
	Never hinged	.85	
	P# block of 6	16.00	
	Never hinged	20.00	
O35	A61(b) 26c indigo	1.50	2.00
	Never hinged	2.25	
	P# block of 6	12.00	
	Never hinged	15.00	
O36	A62(b) 30c orange red	.75	.85
	Never hinged	1.10	
	P# block of 6	16.00	
	Never hinged	20.00	
	Nos. O27-O36 (10)	5.70	6.80
	Set, never hinged	8.25	

 O.B.

No. 461 Overprinted in Black — c

1941, Apr. 14		Perf. 11x10½	
O37	A75(c) 2c apple green	.25	.40
	Never hinged	.30	

Official Stamps
Handstamped in Violet

1944		Perf. 11, 11x10½	
O38	A53 2c rose (On O27)	375.00	200.00
	Never hinged	750.00	
O39	A75 2c apple grn (On O37)	15.00	20.00
	Never hinged	20.00	
O40	A54 4c yel grn (On O16)	45.00	30.00
	Never hinged	80.00	
O40A	A55 6c dk brn (On O29)	8,000.	
O41	A57 10c rose car (On O31)	500.00	
a.	No period after "O"	4,000.	

O42	A60 20c lt ol grn (On O22)	8,000.	
O43	A60 20c lt ol grn (On O26)	1,750.	

No. 497 Overprinted Type "c" in Black

1946, June 19   Perf. 11x10½

O44	A76 2c sepia	.25	.25
	Never hinged	.25	
a.	Vertical pair, bottom stamp without ovpt.		

> Catalogue values for unused stamps in this section, from this point to the end of the section, are for Never Hinged items.

Republic

Nos. 504, 505 and 507 Overprinted in Black — d

1948, May   Unwmk.   Perf. 12

O50	A78 4c black brown	.60	.25
a.	Inverted overprint	25.00	
b.	Double overprint	25.00	
O51	A79 10c red orange	1.00	.25
O52	A81 16c slate gray	3.50	.55
	Nos. O50-O52 (3)	5.10	1.05

Issue dates: Nos. O50-O51, 5/1; No. O52, 5/28.
The overprint on No. O51 comes in two sizes: 13mm, applied in Manila, and 12½mm, applied in New York.

Nos. 527, 508 and 509 Overprinted in Black — e

Overprint Measures 14mm

O53	A91 2c bright green	.60	.25

1949, July 4

Overprint Measures 12mm

O54	A82 20c red brown	1.25	.25

1949, Jan. 23

O55	A83 50c dull green	1.75	.55

No. 550 Overprinted Type "e" in Black

1950, Sep. 20

Overprint Measures 14mm

O56	A91 1c on 2c brt green	.60	.25

Nos. 589, 592, 595 and 597 Overprinted in Black — f

1952-55

Overprint Measures 15mm

O57	A117 1c red brown ('53)	.60	.25
O58	A117 5c crim rose	.60	.25
O59	A117 10c ultra ('55)	.60	.25
O60	A117 20c car lake ('55)	1.75	.25
	Nos. O57-O60 (4)	3.55	1.00

No. 647 Overprinted — g

1959   Engr.   Perf. 12

O61	A117 1c on 5c crim rose	.50	.25

No. 813 Overprinted Type "f" Overprint measures 16½mm

1959

O62	A145 6c gray blue	.60	.25

Nos. 856-861 Overprinted

h

j

k

1962-64   Perf. 13½

O63	A158(j) 5s car rose ('63)	.60	.25

Perf. 13x12

O64	A158(h) 6s dk red brn	.60	.25

Perf. 13½

O65	A158(k) 6s pck blue ('64)	.60	.25
O66	A158(j) 10s brt purple ('63)	.60	.25
O67	A158(j) 20s Prus blue ('63)	.60	.25
O68	A158(j) 30s vermilion	1.00	.25
O69	A158(k) 50s violet ('63)	1.25	.25
	Nos. O63-O69 (7)	5.25	1.75

"G.O." stands for "Gawaing Opisyal," Tagalog for "Official Business."
On 6s overprint "k" is 10mm wide.
On No. O69, overprint "k" is 16mm wide.
For overprint see No. 1119.

No. 1082 Overprinted

l

1970, Dec. 30   Engr.   Perf. 14

O70	A222(l) 10s rose carmine	.60	.25

NEWSPAPER STAMPS

N1

1886-89   Unwmk.   Typo.   Perf. 14

P1	N1 ⅛c yellow green	.30	7.50
P2	N1 1m rose ('89)	.30	15.00
P3	N1 2m blue ('89)	.30	15.00
P4	N1 5m dk brown ('89)	.30	15.00
	Nos. P1-P4 (4)	1.20	52.50

N2

1890-96

P5	N2 ⅛c dark violet	.25	.25
P6	N2 ⅛c green ('92)	6.75	10.00
P7	N2 ⅛c org brn ('94)	.25	.25
P8	N2 ⅛c dull blue ('96)	.85	.60
P9	N2 1m dark violet	.25	.25
P10	N2 1m green ('92)	2.25	5.50
P11	N2 1m olive gray ('94)	.25	1.00
P12	N2 1m ultra ('96)	.35	.25
P13	N2 2m dark violet	.25	1.00
P14	N2 2m green ('92)	2.50	13.00
P15	N2 2m olive gray ('94)	.25	.45
P16	N2 2m brown ('96)	.30	.25
P17	N2 5m dark violet	.25	1.10
P18	N2 5m green ('92)	250.00	75.00
P19	N2 5m olive gray ('94)	.25	.45
P20	N2 5m dp blue grn ('96)	2.50	1.00
	Nos. P5-P20 (16)	267.50	110.35

Imperfs. exist of Nos. P8, P9, P11, P12, P16, P17 and P20.

POSTAL TAX STAMPS

Mt. Pinatubo Fund — PT1

25c, Lahar flow. #RA2, Erupting volcano. #RA3, Animals after eruption. #RA4, Village after eruption. #RA5, People clearing ash.

Wmk. 391

1992, Nov. 16   Litho.   Perf. 13¾

RA1	PT1 25c multi	.50	.25
RA2	PT1 1p multi	.70	.35
RA3	PT1 1p multi	.70	.35
RA4	PT1 1p multi	.70	.35
RA5	PT1 1p multi	.70	.35
a.	Block of 4, #RA2-RA5	3.50	2.00
	Nos. RA1-RA5 (5)	3.30	1.65

Use of Nos. RA1-RA5 as postal tax stamps was suspended on 2/1/93. These stamps became valid for postage on 6/14/93.

OCCUPATION STAMPS

Issued Under Japanese Occupation

No. 461 Overprinted in Black

No. 438 Overprinted in Black

No. 439 Overprinted in Black

1942-43   Unwmk.   Perf. 11x10½, 11

N1	A75 2c apple green	.25	1.00
	Never hinged	.30	
a.	Pair, one without overprint	—	
N2	A58 12c black ('43)	.25	2.00
	Never hinged	.40	
	P# block of 6	12.00	
	Never hinged	15.00	
N3	A59 16c dark blue	5.00	3.75
	Never hinged	7.50	
	P# block of 6	37.50	
	Never hinged	55.00	
	Nos. N1-N3 (3)	5.50	6.75
	Set, never hinged	8.20	

Nos. 435a, 435, 442, 443, and 423 Surcharged in Black

a

b

c

d

CENTAVOS

Type I

CENTAVOS

Type II

Two types of 50c surcharge

Type I: Center of "A" is a triangle.
Type II: Center of "A" is a pin hole.

1942-43   Perf. 11

N4	A55(a) 5(c) on 6c golden brown	.25	.75
	Never hinged	.35	
a.	Top bar shorter and thinner	.25	1.00
	Never hinged	.35	
	P# block of 6	50.00	
	Never hinged	60.00	
b.	5(c) on 6c dark brown	.25	.85
	Never hinged	.35	
c.	As "b," top bar shorter and thinner	.25	1.00
	Never hinged	.35	
d.	Double surcharge, on cover	—	
N5	A62(b) 16(c) on 30c org red ('43)	.25	.60
	Never hinged	.45	
N6	A63(c) 50c on 1p red org & blk ('43)	.75	1.25
	Never hinged	1.10	
	P# block of 4, 2 P#	16.00	
	Never hinged	20.00	
a.	Double surcharge		300.00
b.	Type I surcharge	100.00	90.00
	Never hinged	125.00	
	P# block of 4	500.00	
	Never hinged	600.00	
N7	A65(d) 1p on 4p bl & blk ('43)	100.00	150.00
	Never hinged	155.00	
	Nos. N4-N7 (4)	101.25	152.60
	Set, never hinged	156.90	

On Nos. N4 and N4b, the top bar measures 1½x22½mm. On Nos. N4a and N4c, the top bar measures 1x21mm and the "5" is smaller and thinner.
The used value for No. N7 is for postal cancellation. Used stamps exist with first day cancellations. They are worth somewhat less.

No. 384 Surcharged in Black

1942, May 18

N8	A54 2(c) on 4c yellow green	4.00	5.00
	Never hinged	8.75	

Issued to commemorate Japan's capture of Bataan and Corregidor. The American-Filipino forces finally surrendered May 7, 1942. No. N8 exists with "R" for "B" in BATAAN.

No. 384 Surcharged in Black

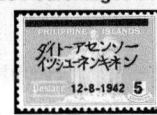

1942, Dec. 8

N9	A54 5(c) on 4c yellow green	.50	1.00
	Never hinged	.75	

1st anniversary of the "Greater East Asia War."

Nos. C59 and C62 Surcharged in Black

1943, Jan. 23

N10	AP1 2(c) on 8c carmine	.25	1.00
	Never hinged	.35	
	P# block of 6	20.00	
	Never hinged	25.00	
N11	AP1 5c on 1p sepia	.50	1.50
	Never hinged	.75	

1st anniv. of the Philippine Executive Commission.

Nipa Hut
OS1

Rice Planting
OS2

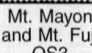

Mt. Mayon
and Mt. Fuji
OS3

Moro
Vinta
OS4

The "c" currency is indicated by four Japanese characters, "p" currency by two.

Engraved; Typographed (2c, 6c, 25c)

1943-44	Wmk. 257	Perf. 13	
N12 OS1 1c dp orange		.25	.40
Never hinged		.30	
Margin block of 6, inscription		2.40	
Never hinged		3.00	
N13 OS2 2c brt green		.25	.40
Never hinged		.30	
Margin block of 6, inscription		2.40	
Never hinged		3.00	
N14 OS1 4c slate green		.25	.40
Never hinged		.30	
Margin block of 6, inscription		2.40	
Never hinged		3.00	
N15 OS3 5c orange brown		.25	.40
Never hinged		.30	
Margin block of 6, inscription		2.40	
Never hinged		3.00	
N16 OS2 6c red		.25	.60
Never hinged		.30	
Margin block of 6, inscription		2.40	
Never hinged		3.00	
N17 OS3 10c blue green		.25	.40
Never hinged		.30	
Margin block of 6, inscription		2.40	
Never hinged		3.00	
N18 OS4 12c steel blue		1.00	1.50
Never hinged		1.50	
Margin block of 6, inscription		11.00	
Never hinged		14.00	
N19 OS4 16c dk brown		.25	.40
Never hinged		.30	
Margin block of 6, inscription		2.40	
Never hinged		3.00	
N20 OS1 20c rose violet		1.25	1.75
Never hinged		1.90	
Margin block of 6, inscription		15.00	
Never hinged		19.00	
N21 OS3 21c violet		.25	.40
Never hinged		.35	
Margin block of 6, inscription		2.40	
Never hinged		3.00	
N22 OS2 25c pale brown		.25	.40
Never hinged		.35	
Margin block of 6, inscription		2.40	
Never hinged		3.00	
N23 OS3 1p dp carmine		.75	1.25
Never hinged		1.15	
Margin block of 6, inscription		9.50	
Never hinged		12.00	
N24 OS4 2p dull violet		6.50	6.50
Never hinged		10.00	
N25 OS4 5p dark olive		16.00	18.00
Never hinged		25.00	
Nos. N12-N25 (14)		27.75	32.80
Set, never hinged		42.00	

Issued: Nos. N13, N15, 4/1; Nos. N12, N14, N23, 6/7; Nos. N16-N19, 7/14; Nos. N20-N22, 8/16; No. N24, 9/16; No. N25, 4/1/44.
For surcharges see Nos. NB5-NB7.

OS5

1943, May 7　Photo.　Unwmk.

N26 OS5 2c carmine red	.25	.75
Never hinged	.30	
Margin block of 6, inscription	4.00	
Never hinged	5.00	
N27 OS5 5c bright green	.25	1.00
Never hinged	.35	
Margin block of 6, inscription	6.50	
Never hinged	8.00	

1st anniversary of the fall of Bataan and Corregidor.

No. 440 Surcharged in Black

1943, June 20　Engr.　Perf. 11

N28 A60 12(c) on 20c light olive green	.25	.75
Never hinged	.35	
a. Double surcharge	—	

350th anniversary of the printing press in the Philippines. "Limbagan" is Tagalog for "printing press."

Rizal Monument, Filipina and Philippine Flag — OS6

1943, Oct. 14　Photo.　Perf. 12

N29 OS6 5c light blue	.25	.90
Never hinged	.30	
a. Imperf.	.25	.90
N30 OS6 12c orange	.25	.90
Never hinged	.30	
a. Imperf.	.25	.90
N31 OS6 17c rose pink	.25	.90
Never hinged	.30	
a. Imperf.	.25	.90
Nos. N29-N31 (3)	.75	2.70
Set, never hinged	.90	

"Independence of the Philippines." Japan granted "independence" Oct. 14, 1943, when the puppet republic was founded.

The imperforate stamps were issued without gum.

José Rizal
OS7

Rev. José Burgos
OS8

Apolinario Mabini — OS9

1944, Feb. 17　　Litho.

N32 OS7 5c blue	.25	1.00
Never hinged	.30	
a. Imperf.	.25	2.00
Never hinged	.35	
N33 OS8 12c carmine	.25	1.00
Never hinged	.30	
a. Imperf.	.25	2.00
Never hinged	.35	
N34 OS9 17c deep orange	.25	1.00
Never hinged	.30	
a. Imperf.	.25	2.00
Never hinged	.35	
Nos. N32-N34 (3)	.75	3.00
Set, never hinged	.90	

See No. NB8.

Nos. C60 and C61 Surcharged in Black

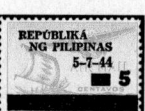

1944, May 7　　　Perf. 11

N35 AP1 5c on 20c ultra	.50	1.00
Never hinged	.75	
P# block of 6	32.50	
Never hinged	40.00	
N36 AP1 12c on 60c blue green	1.75	1.75
Never hinged	2.50	
P# block of 6	42.50	
Never hinged	52.50	

2nd anniversary of the fall of Bataan and Corregidor.

OS10

1945, Jan. 12　Litho.　Imperf.
Without Gum

N37 OS10 5c dull violet brown	.25	.50
Never hinged	.30	
N38 OS10 7c blue green	.25	.50
Never hinged	.30	

N39 OS10 20c chalky blue	.25	.50
Never hinged	.30	
Nos. N37-N39 (3)	.75	1.50
Set, never hinged	.90	

Issued belatedly on Jan. 12, 1945, to commemorate the first anniversary of the puppet Philippine Republic, Oct. 14, 1944. "S" stands for "sentimos."

OCCUPATION SEMI-POSTAL STAMPS

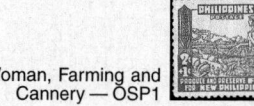

Woman, Farming and Cannery — OSP1

Unwmk.
1942, Nov. 12　Litho.　Perf. 12

NB1 OSP1 2c + 1c pale violet	.25	.60
Never hinged	.30	
NB2 OSP1 5c + 1c brt grn	.25	1.00
Never hinged	.30	
NB3 OSP1 16c + 2c orange	25.00	32.50
Never hinged	42.00	
Nos. NB1-NB3 (3)	25.50	34.10
Set, never hinged	42.60	

Issued to promote the campaign to produce and conserve food. The surtax aided the Red Cross.

Souvenir Sheet

OSP2

1943, Oct. 14　Without Gum　Imperf.

NB4 OSP2 Sheet of 3	60.00	17.50

"Independence of the Philippines." No. NB4 contains one each of Nos. N29a-N31a. Marginal inscription is from Rizal's "Last Farewell." Sold for 2.50p.

The value of No. NB4 used is for a sheet from a first day cover. Commercially used sheets are extremely scarce and worth much more.

Nos. N18, N20 and N21 Surcharged in Black

1943, Dec. 8　Wmk. 257　Perf. 13

NB5 OS4 12c + 21c steel blue	.25	1.50
Never hinged	.30	
Margin block of 6, inscription	4.00	
Never hinged	5.00	
NB6 OS1 20c + 36c rose violet	.25	1.50
Never hinged	.30	
Margin block of 6, inscription	4.00	
Never hinged	5.00	
NB7 OS3 21c + 40c violet	.25	2.00
Never hinged	.30	
Margin block of 6, inscription	4.75	
Never hinged	6.00	
Nos. NB5-NB7 (3)	.75	5.00
Set, never hinged	.90	

The surtax was for the benefit of victims of a Luzon flood. "Baha" is Tagalog for "flood."

Souvenir Sheet

REPUBLIKA NG PILIPINAS
MAYNILA

OSP3

Unwmk.
1944, Feb. 9　Litho.　Imperf.
Without Gum

NB8 OSP3 Sheet of 3	6.50	3.50

No. NB8 contains 1 each of Nos. N32a-N34a.

Sheet sold for 1p, surtax going to a fund for the care of heroes' monuments.

The value for No. NB8 used is for a stamp from a first day cover. Commercially used examples are worth much more.

OCCUPATION POSTAGE DUE STAMP

No. J15 Overprinted in Blue

1942, Oct. 14　Unwmk.　Perf. 11

NJ1 D3 3c on 4c brown red	25.00	35.00
Never hinged	37.50	

On examples of No. J15, two lines were drawn in India ink with a ruling pen across "United States of America" by employees of the Short Paid Section of the Manila Post Office to make a provisional 3c postage due stamp which was used from Sept. 1, 1942 (when the letter rate was raised from 2c to 5c) until Oct. 14 when No. NJ1 went on sale. Value on cover, $175.

Bottom plate blocks of 6 of No. NJ1 are much scarcer than the right side plate blocks. Value $325 hinged, $450 never hinged.

OCCUPATION OFFICIAL STAMPS

Nos. 461, 413, 435, 435a and 442 Ovptd. or Srchd. in Black with Bars and

1943-44　Unwmk.　Perf. 11x10½, 11

NO1 A75 2c apple green		.25	.75
Never hinged		.30	
a. Double overprint		400.00	
Never hinged		600.00	
NO2 A55 5(c) on 6c dk brn (On No. 413) ('44)		40.00	45.00
Never hinged		55.00	
NO3 A55 5(c) on 6c golden brn (On No. 435a)		.25	.90
Never hinged		.35	
P# block of 6		14.00	
Never hinged		17.50	
a. Narrower spacing between bars		.25	.90
Never hinged		.35	
b. 5(c) on 6c dark brown (On No. 435)		.25	.90
Never hinged		.35	
c. As "b," narrower spacing between bars		.25	.90
Never hinged		.35	
d. Double overprint			
NO4 A62 16(c) on 30c org red		.30	1.25
Never hinged		.45	
P# block of 6		20.00	
Never hinged		25.00	

a. Wider spacing between bars .30 *1.25*
Never hinged .45
Nos. NO1-NO4 (4) 40.80 *47.90*
Set, never hinged 56.10

On Nos. NO3 and NO3b the bar deleting "United States of America" is 9¾ to 10mm above the bar deleting "Common." On Nos. NO3a and NO3c, the spacing is 8 to 8½mm.

On No. NO4, the center bar is 19mm long, 3½mm below the top bar and 6mm above the Japanese characters. On No. NO4a, the center bar is 20½mm long, 9mm below the top bar and 1mm above the Japanese characters.

"K.P." stands for Kagamitang Pampamahalaan, "Official Business" in Tagalog.

Nos. 435 & 435a
Surcharged in Black

1944, Aug. 28   *Perf. 11*
NO5 A55 (5c) on 6c gldn brn .30 *.40*
Never hinged .45
P# block of 6 20.00
Never hinged 25.00
a. 5(c) on 6c dark brown .30 *.40*
Never hinged .45
P# block of 6 20.00
Never hinged 25.00

Nos. O34 and C62 Overprinted in Black

a   b

NO6 A60(a) 20c light olive
           green .40 *.50*
Never hinged .60
P# block of 6 12.00
Never hinged 15.00
NO7 AP1(b) 1p sepia .90 *1.00*
Never hinged 1.45
P# block of 6 20.00
Never hinged 25.00
Nos. NO5-NO7 (3) 1.60 *1.90*
Set, never hinged 2.05

FILIPINO REVOLUTIONARY GOVERNMENT

Following the defeat of the Spanish fleet by U.S. Commodore Dewey in Manila on May 1, 1898, which essentially ended the Spanish-American War in the Philippines, postal services were disrupted throughout the Philippines. Postal service was reestablished through U.S. Army military stations, beginning in June 1898 near Manila, continuing province by province until culminating at Zamboanga and other cities in the southern areas in late 1899.

Provisional stamps were prepared for use in the central part of the island of Luzon at Malolos in late 1898 under the leadership of General Emilio Aguinaldo, who had proclaimed the Philippine Republic on June 12, 1898. Later, other provisional stamps were prepared by local Filipino insurgents at Iloilo (Panay Island), Bohol, Cebu and Negros, and Spanish period stamps were overprinted and/or surcharged for use by postal officials at Zamboanga and La Union.

The most familiar of these provisionals were the "Aguinaldo" issues of the Filipino Revolutionary Government in central Luzon near Manila. The letters "KKK," the initials of the revolutionary society, "Kataas-taasang, Kagalang-galang Katipunan nang Mañga Anak nang Bayan," meaning "Sovereign Worshipful Association of the Sons of the Country," readily identify the Aguinaldo provisionals. Hostilities broke out between the Aguinaldo regime and the occupying American administration in February 1899, and the Filipino-American War continued until the American capture of Aguinaldo on March 23, 1901.

The Aguinaldo regular postage, registration, revenue, newspaper and telegraph stamps were in use in Luzon as early as November 10, 1898, and continued in use through early 1901. Although the postal regulations specified that these stamps be used for their inscribed purpose, they were commonly used interchangeably.

The Filipino Republic was instituted by Gen. Emilio Aguinaldo on June 23, 1899. At the same time he assumed the office of President. Aguinaldo dominated the greater part of the island of Luzon and some of the smaller islands until late in 1899. He was taken prisoner by United States troops on March 23, 1901.

The devices composing the National Arms, adopted by the Filipino Revolutionary Government, are emblems of the Katipunan political secret society or of Katipunan origin. The letters "K K K" on these stamps are the initials of this society whose complete name is "Kataas-taasang, Kagalang-galang Katipunan nang Mañga Anak nang Bayan," meaning "Sovereign Worshipful Association of the Sons of the Country."

The regular postage and telegraph stamps were in use on Luzon as early as Nov. 10, 1898. Owing to the fact that stamps for the different purposes were not always available together with a lack of proper instructions, any of the adhesives were permitted to be used in the place of the other. Hence telegraph and revenue stamps were accepted for postage and postage stamps for revenue or telegraph charges. In addition to the regular postal emission, there are a number of provisional stamps, issues of local governments of islands and towns.

POSTAGE ISSUES

A1   A2

Coat of Arms — A3

1898-99   **Unwmk.**   *Perf. 11½*
Y1 A1 2c red 250.00 *300.00*
a. Double impression *325.00*
Y2 A2 2c red .30 *4.00*
b. Double impression —
d. Horiz. pair, imperf. between —
e. Vert. pair, imperf. between *225.00*
Y3 A3 2c red 150.00 *300.00*

Imperf pairs and pairs, imperf horizontally, have been created from No. Y2e.

REGISTRATION STAMP

RS1

YF1 RS1 8c green 5.00 *30.00*
a. Imperf., pair 400.00
b. Imperf. vertically, pair —

NEWSPAPER STAMP

N1

YP1 N1 1m black 2.00 *20.00*
a. Imperf., pair 5.00 *20.00*

INDEX AND IDENTIFIER

All page numbers shown are
those in this Volume 5A.

Postage stamps that do not have
English words on them are shown in the
Scott *Stamp Illustrated Identifier*. To
purchase it visit AmosAdvantage.com or
call Amos Media at 800-572-6885.

INDEX TO ADVERTISERS
2024 VOLUME 5A

Appraisals

DR. ROBERT FRIEDMAN & SONS STAMP & COIN BUYING CENTER
2029 W. 75th St.
Woodridge, IL 60517
PH: 800-588-8100
FAX: 630-985-1588
stampcollections@drbobstamps.com
www.drbobfriedmanstamps.com

Asia

THE STAMP ACT
PO Box 1136
Belmont, CA 94002
PH: 650-703-2342
thestampact@sbcglobal.net

Auctions

DUTCH COUNTRY AUCTIONS
The Stamp Center
4115 Concord Pike
Wilmington, DE 19803
PH: 302-478-8740
FAX: 302-478-8779
auctions@dutchcountryauctions.com
www.dutchcountryauctions.com

British Commonwealth

ARON R. HALBERSTAM PHILATELISTS, LTD.
PO Box 150168
Van Brunt Station
Brooklyn, NY 11215-0168
PH: 718-788-3978
arh@arhstamps.com
www.arhstamps.com

ROY'S STAMPS
PO Box 28001
600 Ontario Street
St. Catharines, ON
CANADA L2N 7P8
Phone: 905-934-8377
Email: roystamp@cogeco.ca
www.roysstamps.com

THE STAMP ACT
PO Box 1136
Belmont, CA 94002
PH: 650-703-2342
thestampact@sbcglobal.net

Buying

DR. ROBERT FRIEDMAN & SONS STAMP & COIN BUYING CENTER
2029 W. 75th St.
Woodridge, IL 60517
PH: 800-588-8100
FAX: 630-985-1588
stampcollections@drbobstamps.com
www.drbobfriedmanstamps.com

Canada

CANADA STAMP FINDER LLC
2800 N 6th Street, Unit 1-708
St. Augustine, FL 32084
PH: 904-217-2166
Canadian Address:
PO Box 92591
Brampton, ON L6W 4R1
PH: 514-238-5751
Toll Free in North America:
877-412-3106
FAX: 323-315-2635
canadastampfinder@gmail.com
www.canadastampfinder.com

ROY'S STAMPS
PO Box 28001
600 Ontario Street
St. Catharines, ON
CANADA L2N 7P8
Phone: 905-934-8377
Email: roystamp@cogeco.ca
www.roysstamps.com

Collections

DR. ROBERT FRIEDMAN & SONS STAMP & COIN BUYING CENTER
2029 W. 75th St.
Woodridge, IL 60517
PH: 800-588-8100
FAX: 630-985-1588
stampcollections@drbobstamps.com
www.drbobfriedmanstamps.com

Ducks

MICHAEL JAFFE
PO Box 61484
Vancouver, WA 98666
PH: 360-695-6161
PH: 800-782-6770
FAX: 360-695-1616
mjaffe@brookmanstamps.com
www.brookmanstamps.com

German Colonies

COLONIAL STAMP COMPANY
5757 Wilshire Blvd. PH #8
Los Angeles, CA 90036
PH: 323-933-9435
FAX: 323-939-9930
info@colonialstamps.com
www.colonialstamps.com

Great Britain

COLONIAL STAMP COMPANY
5757 Wilshire Blvd. PH #8
Los Angeles, CA 90036
PH: 323-933-9435
FAX: 323-939-9930
info@colonialstamps.com
www.colonialstamps.com

New Issues

DAVIDSON'S STAMP SERVICE
Personalized Service since 1970
PO Box 36355
Indianapolis, IN 46236-0355
PH: 317-826-2620
ed-davidson@earthlink.net
www.newstampissues.com

Papua New Guinea

COLONIAL STAMP COMPANY
5757 Wilshire Blvd. PH #8
Los Angeles, CA 90036
PH: 323-933-9435
FAX: 323-939-9930
info@colonialstamps.com
www.colonialstamps.com

Proofs & Essays

HENRY GITNER PHILATELISTS, INC.
PO Box 3077-S
Middletown, NY 10940
PH: 845-343-5151
PH: 800-947-8267
FAX: 845-343-0068
hgitner@hgitner.com
www.hgitner.com

Rhodesia

COLONIAL STAMP COMPANY
5757 Wilshire Blvd. PH #8
Los Angeles, CA 90036
PH: 323-933-9435
FAX: 323-939-9930
info@colonialstamps.com
www.colonialstamps.com

St. Christopher

COLONIAL STAMP COMPANY
5757 Wilshire Blvd. PH #8
Los Angeles, CA 90036
PH: 323-933-9435
FAX: 323-939-9930
info@colonialstamps.com
www.colonialstamps.com

St. Helena

COLONIAL STAMP COMPANY
5757 Wilshire Blvd. PH #8
Los Angeles, CA 90036
PH: 323-933-9435
FAX: 323-939-9930
info@colonialstamps.com
www.colonialstamps.com

St. Kitts & Nevis

COLONIAL STAMP COMPANY
5757 Wilshire Blvd. PH #8
Los Angeles, CA 90036
PH: 323-933-9435
FAX: 323-939-9930
info@colonialstamps.com
www.colonialstamps.com

St. Lucia

COLONIAL STAMP COMPANY
5757 Wilshire Blvd. PH #8
Los Angeles, CA 90036
PH: 323-933-9435
FAX: 323-939-9930
info@colonialstamps.com
www.colonialstamps.com

St. Vincent

COLONIAL STAMP COMPANY
5757 Wilshire Blvd. PH #8
Los Angeles, CA 90036
PH: 323-933-9435
FAX: 323-939-9930
info@colonialstamps.com
www.colonialstamps.com

Samoa

COLONIAL STAMP COMPANY
5757 Wilshire Blvd. PH #8
Los Angeles, CA 90036
PH: 323-933-9435
FAX: 323-939-9930
info@colonialstamps.com
www.colonialstamps.com

Sarawak

COLONIAL STAMP COMPANY
5757 Wilshire Blvd. PH #8
Los Angeles, CA 90036
PH: 323-933-9435
FAX: 323-939-9930
info@colonialstamps.com
www.colonialstamps.com

Seychelles

COLONIAL STAMP COMPANY
5757 Wilshire Blvd. PH #8
Los Angeles, CA 90036
PH: 323-933-9435
FAX: 323-939-9930
info@colonialstamps.com
www.colonialstamps.com